KT-546-854

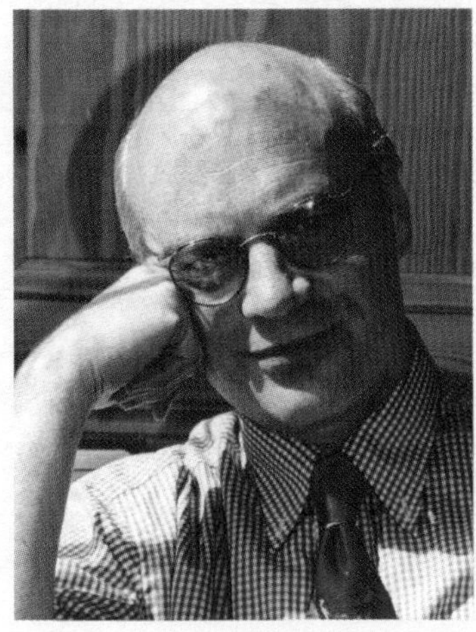

THE PUBLISHER'S PAGE

TO PREPARE this Guide, we conducted 6,552 interviews. Of these, 1,579 were with major purchasers of legal services, a substantial increase on last year. The interviews were conducted over the telephone, each call lasting on average 30 minutes. Telephone interviews have the advantage of eliminating self-selection – unlike postal questionnaires, for instance, which are completed and returned only by those people with the time and inclination to do so.

This year's audit by BMRB confirms the strength of our research. "We conclude," it says, "that the methodology employed is thorough and robust, from interviewer training and background research to sampling and data collection."

BMRB visited our offices for a spot check. They questioned our interviewers and examined our records. They also made random checks on the people our researchers had interviewed – both lawyers and clients – to find out how well the research had been done. They found "a very high degree of consensus that the research interviewers displayed thoroughness, objectivity and professionalism."

'Objectivity' is a real issue, of course, and the BMRB auditors commented that "there was a general acceptance that the information gathering process was a difficult one to get right, with some degree of subjectivity being inevitable." Nevertheless, the auditors found that "The Chambers Guide was generally felt to be 'as good as it could be'. A number of respondents commented that it was more reliable than its competitors. One respondent thought that this had a lot to do with the wide range of respondents that Chambers contacted."

On the key issue of sampling, the auditors commented that: "Chambers have continued to act on previous recommendations of BMRB to ensure that client perceptions are included...This is reflected in the number of interviews conducted in 2001, particularly among clients."

For further details of the BMRB audit, please see page 7.

Michael Chambers

CONTENTS

INTRODUCTION

The Chambers survey of best business lawyers

Solicitors' charges and remuneration

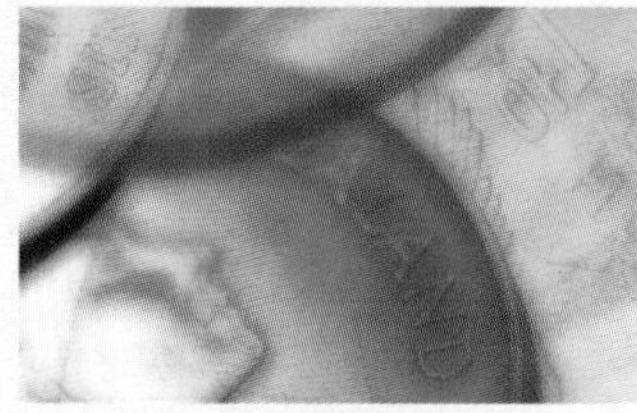

Reviews of the largest firms in the regions

THE LAW FIRMS

SOLICITORS: SPECIALIST AREAS

Chambers & Partners Legal Recruitment: (020) 7 606 8844

Published by **Chambers & Partners Publishing** (*a division of Orbach & Chambers Ltd*)
Saville House, 23 Long Lane, London EC1A 9HL
Tel: (020) 7 606 1300 **Fax:** (020) 7 600 3191

ISBN: 0-85514-111-5

Publisher: Michael Chambers
Editor: Rieta Ghosh
Head of Research: Juan Delgado-Moreira

Assistant Editor: Catherine Willberg
Consultant Editor: James Fairweather
Editorial Assistant: Jo Morgans
Profiles Editors: Richard Pettet, Laura Gladwin
Profiles Assistants: Alex Ballantine, Nicola Cowan, Christine Allen-Laird, Vicky Wood, Hayley Whiting, Marianne Fraser
Project Co-ordination: Fiona Boxall
Database Team: Derek Wright, Nigel Birch
Production Manager: John Buck

Production Team: Paul Cummings, Jasper John, Nicola Nicholson
Business Development Manager: Brad Sirott
Orders to: Chambers & Partners Publishing

Printed in England by Polestar Wheatons Limited

SOLICITORS: A- Z OF LAW FIRMS

IN-HOUSE LAWYERS & COMPANY SECRETARIES

SUPPORT SERVICES

THE BAR

THE BAR: SPECIALIST AREAS

LEADERS AT THE BAR

A-Z OF BARRISTERS' CHAMBERS

INDEXES

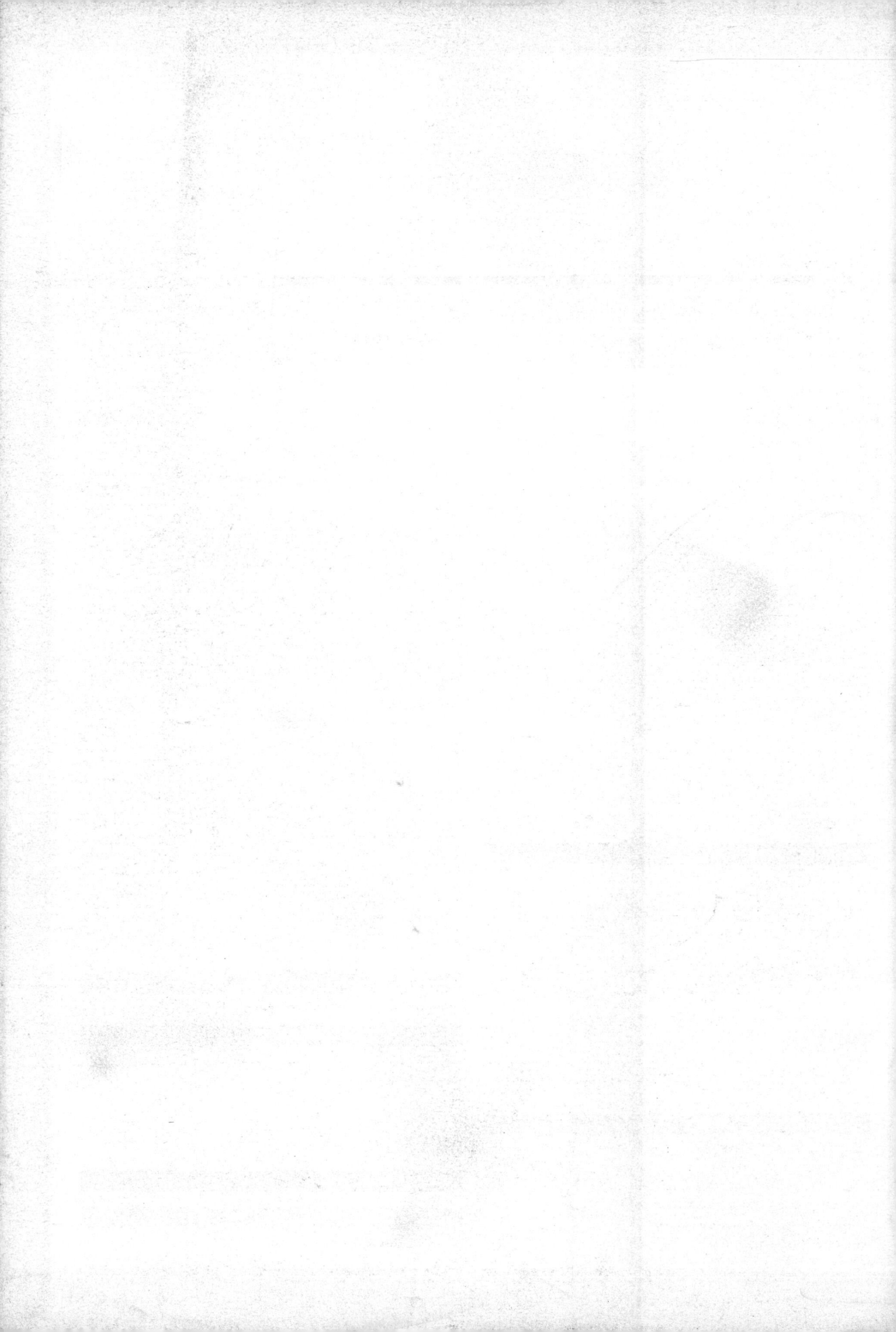

INTRODUCTION

CHAMBERS RESEARCH TEAM

Chambers researchers work full-time for six months researching the legal profession. They conduct thousands of telephone interviews discussing the strengths of leading specialists and their rankings. This research is audited by the British Market Research Bureau and provides an objective survey of the profession's leading practitioners.

- **Anna Williams**
Solicitor. Read Human Sciences at St Anne's College, Oxford. Practised commercial property and social housing at a top London firm for eight years. Also writes for Chambers Student Guide.

- **Sheena Lee**
Solicitor. Read Chemistry at University of York. Trained with leading niche City practice specialising in environmental law and personal injury. Qualified in 1997 and practised personal injury at a legal aid firm.

- **Lloyd Pearson**
Read Politics at University of Leeds. Worked as a political researcher for a government minister. Subsequently took up graduate scheme in publishing and worked as researcher for a travel organisation.

- **Paula Wasley**
Read English at Princeton University and took Diploma in French at the Sorbonne. Subsequently a bi-lingual assistant at a top Paris Hotel and a research assistant to a correspondent at the Paris office of a major news agency.

- **Ross Cogan**
Read Philosophy at Nottingham University. M.Phil at St John's College, Cambridge. PhD in Logic from Bristol in 1998. Has taught at several universities and previously worked in underwriting.

- **Angela Woodruff**
Solicitor. Read Psychology/Criminology at Melbourne University followed by Law at Monash University. Trained in Melbourne in general commercial law before joining the banking and finance practice of a leading Australian law firm.

- **Rob Wainwright**
Solicitor. Read Law and English at University of Queensland, Australia. Practised mainly litigation in Queensland and wrote for a national legal journal.

- **Caroline Murphy**
Graduated from Brasenose College, Oxford, with a First in Classics. Previously freelanced for The Independent newspaper.

- **Barbara Gruber**
Read Law at University of Munich, Germany. In-house lawyer at a German regional television station and then at an IT company. Last worked for a personal injury law firm in Miami, Florida.

- **Fleur Darkin**
Graduated from Bretton Hall with a First in Fine Art, and received a Masters with Distinction in Philosophy at Leeds. Has worked as a writer and an artist.

- **James Cowdell**
Barrister. Read Modern History at The Queen's College, Oxford. Practised at the Criminal Bar for five years and was a fee-earner in the family department of a leading London law firm.

- **Michael Leigh**
Gained a First in Philosophy from Bristol University, where he also completed a doctorate in modern social contract theory. Has taught ethics and political philosophy and undertaken freelance satire for local newspapers.

- **Sarah Thompson**
Read English Literature at University of Cambridge and travelled extensively before becoming a researcher.

- **Adele Caffrey**
Read English Literature at University of Sussex. Previously worked as a researcher for a criminologist at the University of Greenwich and as a paralegal for leading city law firms. Bilingual.

- **Timma McKean**
Read English Literature at the University of Edinburgh. Previously worked for a publishing company as a media sales executive.

- **Ben Tendler**
Graduated from the University of Bristol with a First in English Literature. Previously worked as a freelance market researcher.

- **Edward Bannell**
Read Law at London School of Economics. Worked as a Legal Executive for a leading Australian law firm. Has worked in legal publishing and most recently in legal recruitment.

- **Sophie Roberts-Powell**
Read French and German at the University of Bristol. Has recently worked in the techsolutions division of a leading American internet advertising solutions company.

- **Pippa Cunnah**
Solicitor. Read law at UCW Aberystwyth. LL.M in European and International Trade Law from Leicester University. Trained with a major law firm, subsequently qualifying into commercial property law. Previously worked as a translator and guide in Poitiers, France.

- **Tracey Sinclair**
First Class MA Hons in Philosophy and English Literature from Glasgow University. Worked as Publications Editor for a North East Enterprise Agency before becoming a freelance business writer and researcher. Also worked in the Correspondence Department of a national broadcaster.

- **Richard James**
Read English Literature at the University of Wales, Cardiff. Former paralegal and recently published author.

- **Daniel Freed**
Read Politics and Modern History at the University of Manchester. Gained experience in broadcasting, journalism and youth work before joining Chambers.

- **Ian McLachlan**
Read Classics at Brasenose College, Oxford. Worked in Italy for three years as an English teacher and as a writer and translator for a computer software company. Fluent in Italian.

- **John Doy**
Read English Literature and Language at Mansfield College, Oxford. Previous experience includes working for a local advertising publication and the National Opinion Poll.

BMRB AUDIT

We publish here in full the report from British Market Research Bureau on their audit of our research methods.

"

RESEARCH AUDIT

The research methodology employed in the compilation of *Chambers Guide to the Legal Profession* has been independently audited by market research firm BMRB International.

The audit covers all elements of the process from researcher training, questionnaire and data gathering through to analysis and reporting. BMRB also re-contacted a number of participants in the research programme to verify their contribution and to obtain their perspective on the research process.

In the audit we found the methodology employed for *Chambers Guide to the Legal Profession* to be thorough and robust. Chambers and Partners are committed to ongoing refinement and improvement of the methodology, indicated by a number of initiatives, including the following.

- The development of a formal researcher training programme and the appointment of a researcher training programme leader
- The appointment of a Head of research and expansion of the research team
- Further development of the database management team
- A further increase in the number of end-client interviews conducted
- Ongoing development of the data collection and analysis process to ensure that the research is validated and based on a robust methodology.

INDEPENDENT AUDIT OF THE RESEARCH METHODOLOGY

Trevor Wilkinson, Consultant, and Warren Linsdell, Project Director, BMRB International

August 2001

RESEARCH AUDIT

The research methodology employed in the compilation of *Chambers Guide to the Legal Profession* has been independently audited by market research firm BMRB International.

The audit covers all elements of the process from researcher training, questionnaire and data gathering through to analysis and reporting. BMRB also re-contacted a number of participants in the research programme to verify their contribution and to obtain their perspective on the research process.

In the audit we found the methodology employed for *Chambers Guide to the Legal Profession* to be thorough and robust. Chambers and Partners are committed to ongoing refinement and improvement of the methodology, indicated by a number of initiatives, including the following.

- The development of a formal researcher training programme and the appointment of a researcher training programme leader.
- The appointment of a Head of research and expansion of the research team.
- Further development of the database management team.
- A further increase in the number of end-client interviews conducted.
- Ongoing development of the data collection and analysis process to ensure that the research is validated and based on a robust methodology.

RESEARCH METHODOLOGY

The focus of *Chambers Guide to the Legal Profession* is to provide an objective list of recommended legal practitioners (law firms, sets of chambers and individual practitioners). This is based on a research programme conducted by a full-time research team in the first half of 2001. This research covered all key areas of law (for example Property, Corporate Finance, Environment, Advertising and Marketing).

RESEARCH METHODS

The focus of *Chambers Guide to the Legal Profession* is to provide an objective list of recommended legal practitioners (law firms, sets of chambers and individual practitioners). This is based on a research programme conducted by a full-time research team in the first half of 2001. This research covered all key areas of law (for example Property, Corporate Finance, Environment, Advertising and Marketing).

Chambers concentrates on corporate law, rather than high street practice, and this is reflected in the type of firms included in the universe for this study, coverage being of firms with 5 or more practitioners plus established individual practitioners in the commercial sector. The research therefore focuses on the estimated 1,900 firms with five or more partners (and approximately 22,500 partners working in those firms).

Chambers own database of client contacts includes 50,000 records and is subject to ongoing maintenance by a dedicated team.

In total 6,552 interviews were conducted during the first half of 2001. Of that total 4,419 were with solicitors and 554 with barristers. Those legal practitioners interviewed therefore represent a significant proportion of the target market. The practitioner interviews were conducted with senior personnel, usually heads of relevant departments and other key personnel in each area of law.

In 2001 Chambers conducted 1,579 interviews with major purchasers of legal services, which is an increase of 47% on 2000. Interviews with clients were usually conducted with the senior personnel in charge of selecting suppliers of legal services.

Interviews, lasting 30 minutes on average, were conducted by telephone. This form of data collection has the advantage of eliminating regional bias and avoids respondent self-selection, thereby enhancing objectivity of findings.

Within each area of law, the number of interviews varied according to the universe, but in all cases sample sizes were sufficient for the purpose. In some areas, particularly where there are relatively few practitioners, a full census was attempted. For other areas of law the interviews were conducted with a representative sample. The sample of client lists interviewed was derived largely from a combination of independent sources and practitioner client lists. In sampling for the research programme, Chambers and Partners have continued to act on previous recommendations by BMRB to ensure that client perceptions are included and representation of the universe is maximised as far as possible. These efforts are reflected in the number of interviews conducted in 2001, particularly among clients.

THE RESEARCH TEAM

Chambers' research programme utilises a team of full-time researchers, each dedicated to specific areas of law. Prior to commencement of the programme, all researchers undertake a comprehensive induction and spend time thoroughly investigating the background and current trends in the areas of specialism for which they are responsible.

For each area of law, a team member (or number of team members) has the responsibility for all data gathering, analysis, validation and reporting.

VALIDATION OF FINDINGS

A number of checks are implemented to validate the findings and ensure that they are not biased by individual responses. Quality is ensured by a number of means:

- Preparatory research before and during the interviewing period, with legal journals, press releases, professional reports (such as Corporate Finance Review), trade and business press and submissions from legal firms all referenced to alert the research team to possible changes in the market
- Weight of numbers, i.e. that there were sufficient respondents to form a representative sample
- Comparison of clients' views with those of practitioners to check for consistency
- Checks against former years to identify trends and variations over time
- Rigorous investigation of changes over time or inconsistencies within the findings through further research and discussion
- The interactive nature of the research process provides several opportunities to identify errors.

The research methods employed and quality control measures implemented serve to ensure that the findings can be reported with confidence.

Warren Linsdell, Project Director at BMRB
August 2001 "

The following report from BMRB contains a summary of the feedback they received while carrying out the audit.

" FEEDBACK ON METHODOLOGY

In previous audits we have expressed doubts about the objectivity of an analysis based on research predominantly among practitioners themselves. However this has been largely addressed by increasing the number of client-side interviews conducted. Indeed the number of interviews with clients has increased by almost 50% in the last year.

In addition the large sample sizes utilised and extensive internal validation and back checking ensure that information is as representative as possible within the practical constraints of the research programme.

As indicated in the separate audit report, it is clear that Chambers and Partners are committed to ongoing refinement and improvement of the methodology.

RESPONDENT FEEDBACK

As part of the audit we re-contacted a number of the participants in the research, both within legal firms and client-side. We confirmed that the participants were the most appropriate personnel to take part in the research. Reactions were positive and all respondents confirmed their willingness to participate in future research.

All respondents had a high regard for the publication and were happy to participate in the information gathering process. There was a general sense that the Chambers guide was the most reliable legal guide and that the research process was the most thorough. There was a high degree of satisfaction with the interviewers expressed by research respondents.

There is a very high degree of consensus that the research interviewers display thoroughness, objectivity and professionalism. No negative comments were made concerning the interviewers although some respondents commented that it was important to keep interviews as short as possible and one respondent mentioned the need for continuity due to the specialist nature of many areas. Some of the positive comments included *"The person who interviewed me was very amusing and professional." "I was given options on how I wanted to do things and the interviewer responded rather than prompting me to say things, she was very good."*

Although there was general satisfaction with the information gathering process some concerns were expressed. One respondent felt that there was always a question mark over how results are arrived at. He felt that there should be greater clarity about this issue and greater transparency in the information gathering and reporting process, although we believe that this concern has been addressed by the inclusion of comments within the Guide on the research methodology and number of interviews conducted.

Another respondent felt that the publication tended to be a little conservative and that it was a little slow to pick up on change. *"It takes a long time to get in there but once you are in there,"* he said, *"it takes a long time to get you out again."* The publication, he felt, could be a little self-confirming and didn't accurately reflect current conditions due to the time lag involved in changing entries.

There was general acceptance that the information gathering process was a difficult one to get right with some degree of subjectivity being inevitable. The Chambers Guide was generally felt to be *"as good as it could be."* A number of respondents commented that the Chambers Guide was more reliable than its competitors. "

BEST BUSINESS LAWYER 2001

The Best Business Lawyer survey is determined solely on the opinion of clients and this year the clients have spoken: Nigel Boardman's three-year reign as the Best Business Lawyer has come to an end. William Underhill, his esteemed colleague at Slaughter and May, has donned the mantle and moved into first place. This worthy successor "provides a first class service" and like his predecessor is praised for his "great commercial attitude." The title is in the hands of one who "has a sure touch."

And what of his predecessor? Nigel Boardman of Slaughter and May is still held in the utmost regard by clients as he slips by the smallest margin into second place. He remains "a truly brilliant individual" with the ability "to see his clients' interests" and "the knowledge to make the deal work."

William Underhill, Slaughter and May

Chris Ashworth of Ashurst Morris Crisp has leapt into joint third place this year after not even featuring in last year's table. This could be down to the fact that "if there's an off the wall solution to be found, he'll find it," or maybe it is simply his "extremely high quality legal advice" that impresses clients. Whatever the key to his success, the consensus is that he is fun to work with or, in other words, "passes the 'stuck-in-a-lift' test." Sharing third place is Will Lawes of Freshfields Bruckhaus Deringer. Described as "extremely pragmatic and a brilliant intellect," he continues to be the lawyer at his firm to whom the top clients turn.

As usual, corporate finance specialists abound at the top end of the table, but many practitioners were nominated from other specialisms for their all-round commerciality, breadth of legal knowledge and ability to provide solutions to business problems. The London-centric nature of the Best Business Lawyer table has also been breached by the arrival of Paul Devitt from Addleshaw Booth & Co's Manchester office.

Slaughter and May remains dominant at the top of the table for firm nominations. Linklaters has gained votes since last year, but has been unable to close the gap sufficiently to threaten the leaders. The top four positions in the Best Business Firms reflect the top ranks in our Corporate Finance table again this year, with only Ashurst Morris Crisp bucking the general trend. The firm has climbed from ninth to fourth. In contrast, a notable absence from the top echelons of the Best Business Lawyer table is Clifford Chance.

A small but vociferous minority of clients declined to nominate individuals. Some were unimpressed with the standard of service received this year, the main complaint being that leading individuals may be talented, but have been unable to devote enough time to each client. "They may have it," said one, "but they can't give it."

Continued overleaf

Nigel Boardman, Slaughter and May

Chris Ashworth, Ashurst Morris Crisp

Will Lawes, Freshfields Bruckhaus Deringer

➤ **James Davis,** Freshfields Bruckhaus Deringer

◄ **Paul Devitt,** Addleshaw Booth & Co

➤ **Richard Godden,** Linklaters

◄ **Helen Harrison-Hall,** Allen & Overy

➤ **Robert Stern,** Slaughter and May

◄ **Jeff Triggs,** Slaughter and May

LAW FIRMS WITH BEST BUSINESS LAWYERS

Showing number of individual recommendations.

Slaughter and May	30
Linklaters	20
Freshfields Bruckhaus Deringer	15
Allen & Overy	10
Ashurst Morris Crisp	10
Herbert Smith	10
Eversheds	7
Clifford Chance	6
DLA	6
Lovells	6
Garretts	4
Norton Rose	4
Simmons & Simmons	4
Addleshaw Booth & Co	3
CMS Cameron McKenna	3
Nabarro Nathanson	3
Pinsent Curtis Biddle	3
Wragge & Co	3
Baker & McKenzie	2
Denton Wilde Sapte	2
Dickson Minto WS	2
Morgan Cole	2
Hammond Suddards Edge	2
Macfarlanes	2
Rowe & Maw	2
Walker Morris	2

BEST BUSINESS LAWYERS

William Underhill *Slaughter and May*

Nigel Boardman *Slaughter and May*

Chris Ashworth *Ashurst Morris Crisp*
Will Lawes *Freshfields Bruckhaus Deringer*

James Davis *Freshfields Bruckhaus Deringer*
Paul Devitt *Addleshaw Booth & Co*
Richard Godden *Linklaters*
Helen Harrison-Hall *Allen & Overy*
Robert Stern *Slaughter and May*
Jeff Triggs *Slaughter and May*

SOLICITORS' CHARGES

THIS IS A REPRESENTATIVE selection of headline rates. These figures are only a general guide, as firms invariably consider a number of factors when setting fees. Increasingly, major clients are in a position to negotiate special rates based on the volume of business they bring. Furthermore, firms with branches located in geographically close areas (e.g. in Leeds and Manchester) tend to charge uniform fees rather than alter them from region to region.

A number of firms now no longer use hourly rates, preferring charges tailored to the specific requirements of the case, taking into consideration a matter's urgency, complexity and the level of resources and expertise required. The figures should nevertheless offer a useful guide to the differences between the levels of firms and how fees vary between major business centres. The lows and highs of our table are aboslute figures.

London is divided into three categories: the 'magic circle' (Allen & Overy, Clifford Chance, Freshfields Bruckhaus Deringer, Linklaters, Slaughter and May); second tier (those just outside the magic circle and usually having over 200 lawyers); and third tier (major city firms with over 50 lawyers). For other business centres we class as large those firms with over 50 lawyers, while medium sized firms are those with less than 50 lawyers.

Continued overleaf

PARTNERS

Area of Practice	Corporate			Commercial Litigation			Commercial Property		
	Low	Average	High	Low	Average	High	Low	Average	High
London – Magic Circle	380	450	550	375	430	550	380	430	550
London – 2nd Tier	250	350	425	250	350	425	250	350	400
London – 3rd Tier	220	300	400	210	300	400	200	310	385
Bristol – large	130	175	270	120	170	250	140	170	215
Bristol – medium	130	160	175	120	170	185	130	150	175
Birmingham – large	220	260	375	220	250	340	220	260	300
Birmingham – medium	195	210	220	195	210	220	195	210	220
Manchester – large	160	235	300	145	200	300	145	215	300
Manchester – medium	140	165	190	140	165	200	140	165	190
Leeds – large	160	220	260	150	220	260	150	220	260
Leeds – medium	125	150	165	125	150	200	125	150	165
Edinburgh – large	160	180	200	150	165	200	150	180	200
Edinburgh – medium	140	155	180	125	140	165	140	155	175
Glasgow – large	165	190	215	165	190	215	150	170	200
Glasgow – medium	130	155	200	150	160	200	150	165	200

ASSISTANT SOLICITORS									
Area of Practice	Corporate			Commercial Litigation			Commercial Property		
	Low	Average	High	Low	Average	High	Low	Average	High
London – Magic Circle	185	280	390	175	265	355	175	270	375
London – 2nd Tier	180	250	290	130	240	295	150	225	350
London – 3rd Tier	130	220	300	125	220	265	130	215	275
Bristol – large	100	135	185	100	135	175	95	140	170
Bristol – medium	75	110	150	75	100	120	75	105	140
Birmingham – large	160	200	250	150	195	200	150	170	200
Birmingham – medium	160	170	180	150	170	180	150	170	180
Manchester – large	110	160	240	110	150	240	110	155	240
Manchester – medium	100	120	140	100	120	140	100	120	140
Leeds – large	120	170	200	120	170	200	120	170	200
Leeds – medium	85	105	120	85	105	120	85	105	120
Edinburgh – large	120	145	165	120	135	150	120	140	155
Edinburgh – medium	100	110	145	100	110	145	100	110	145
Glasgow – large	120	145	165	120	135	150	120	140	155
Glasgow – medium	100	120	150	100	120	150	100	125	150

SOLICITORS' REMUNERATION

ONCE AGAIN WE INCLUDE a table indicating the range of annual salaries for both newly-qualified solicitors and assistants at the five year mark. The presence of the highest salaries at City-based US firms continues to exert upward pressure on the starting salaries at magic circle and other major London firms. Naturally, regional firms and primarily non-commercial practices will always struggle to follow suit. This table shows the broad range of salaries for 2001, varying across the regions and, within each region, varying depending on practice. The threefold distinction between London firms is the same as that in the solicitor hourly rates tables.

REMUNERATION		
	Newly Qualified	5 Years PQE
London – Magic Circle	£48-54,000	£73-95,000
London – 2nd Tier	£38-50,000	£52-88,000
London – 3rd Tier	£37-45,000	£52-80,000
South	£18-35,000	£30-45,000
Midlands	£20-34,000	£35-60,000
North	£18-30,000	£30-55,000
Scotland	£18-28,000	£25-50,000
US Firms (London Offices)	£55-80,000	£100-130,000

REGIONAL REVIEWS

NATIONWIDE FIRMS

Eversheds A year of peaks and troughs, inevitable perhaps for a firm of such national scale and international scale. National integration has been the maxim of the year, with the introduction of a single fiscal structure for all seven regions. This has been supported by the reorganisation of teams into national as opposed to regional departments. Efforts to streamline mark a plan to launch a greater advance into Europe, beyond the six Eversheds offices and allied offices already in existence on the continent. However, this "aggressive" stance is not without its problems. The loss of equity status for 10% of partners in January has been coupled with a push to increase profitability. Prime casualties of this drive have been the Bristol office, which recently closed.

The stars of this new regime have been the Leeds office, which has built upon its domination in the areas of environment, local government and telecommunications, the only regional firm appearing in the latter sector. The office has been dubbed pre-eminent for environment and "the Rolls Royce of local government work."

The attempt to throw off its public sector image and break into the corporate fold has been less successful in London than in the regions, but the firm can claim to act for 56 of the FTSE 100 companies.

The corporate finance team are perceived to be "*the top of the tree*" in the regions, advising the Peter Black management in the largest ever public to private in the North, valued at £300 million.

The pre-eminent firm for education nationwide, the firm fields the star practitioner, John Hall. An impressive 141 lawyers are endorsed as

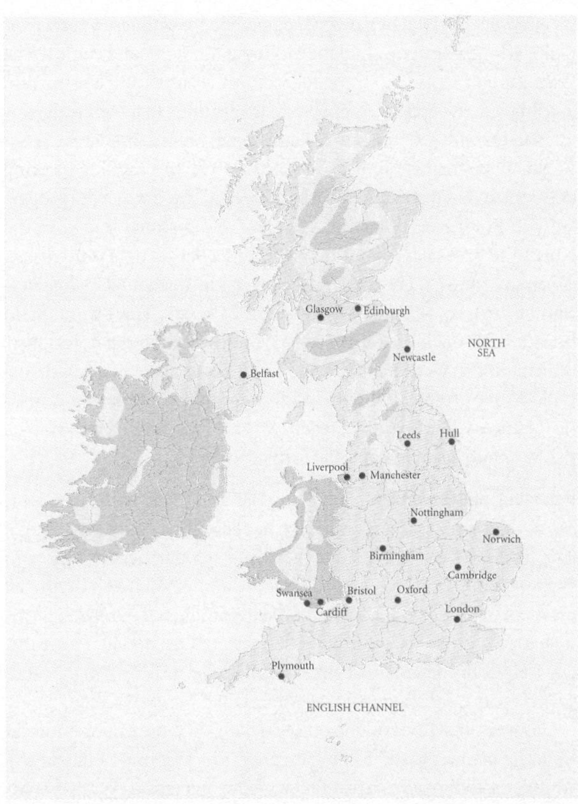

NATIONWIDE: the 50 Largest Firms

		Ptnrs	Asst Solrs	Other Fee Earners	Total Solrs
1	Clifford Chance	234	852	256	**1086**
2	Eversheds	339	739	592	**1078**
3	DLA	n/a	n/a	n/a	**n/a**
4	Linklaters	200	700	0	**900**
5	Allen & Overy	174	634	262	**808**
6	Freshfields Bruckhaus Deringer	161	538	394	**699**
7	Herbert Smith	138	394	194	**532**
8	Hammond Suddards Edge	180	348	262	**528**
9	CMS Cameron McKenna	158	356	138	**514**
10	Lovells	139	359	245	**498**
11	Denton Wilde Sapte	164	289	177	**453**
12	Norton Rose	122	330	173	**452**
13	Slaughter and May	102	340	128	**442**
14	Wragge & Co	109	297	186	**406**
15	Ashurst Morris Crisp	96	306	168	**402**
16	Pinsent Curtis Biddle	156	245	102	**401**
17	Beachcroft Wansbroughs	125	270	265	**395**
18	Simmons & Simmons	111	279	158	**390**
19	Addleshaw Booth & Co	128	244	273	**372**
20	Nabarro Nathanson	110	228	149	**338**
21	Berwin Leighton Paisner	130	183	117	**313**
22	Masons	79	227	52	**306**
23	Garretts	77	227	64	**304**
24	Osborne Clarke	92	208	88	**300**
25	SJ Berwin	86	193	69	**279**
26	Baker & McKenzie	67	208	82	**275**
27	Morgan Cole	94	155	139	**249**
28	Taylor Joynson Garrett	90	139	65	**229**
29	Rowe & Maw	80	148	70	**228**
30	Irwin Mitchell	77	148	444	**225**
31	Bevan Ashford	76	145	103	**221**
32	Dundas & Wilson CS	54	163	48	**217**
33	Bird & Bird	72	140	76	**212**
34	Barlow Lyde & Gilbert	68	144	80	**212**
35	Shoosmiths	78	130	314	**208**
36	Berrymans Lace Mawer	68	132	113	**200**
37	Bond Pearce	64	136	91	**200**
38	Lawrence Graham	88	107	71	**195**
39	Mills & Reeve	57	135	91	**192**
40	Clyde & Co	91	99	92	**190**
41	Maclay Murray & Spens	57	131	50	**188**
42	Thompsons	56	128	151	**184**
43	McGrigor Donald	58	125	62	**183**
44	Olswang	56	125	51	**181**
45	Field Fisher Waterhouse	71	107	70	**178**
46	Burges Salmon	50	125	48	**175**
47	Macfarlanes	56	116	61	**172**
48	Charles Russell	76	95	66	**171**
49	Stephenson Harwood	62	103	54	**165**
50	Richards Butler	72	92	95	**164**

The rankings in this table are determined by the number of solicitors working in the region. They are based on partner and assistant solicitor figures only: all other fee-earners are excluded.

leaders in their field. The firm continues to feature within 45 Chambers practice areas, a breadth to which its national competitors can only aspire.

DLA The third largest law firm in the UK and a strong regional player, its national overhaul of the banking practice continues to reap dividends with the firm consolidating its reputation. PFI and commercial litigation also remains a stronghold across the North and North West. The Manchester and Liverpool branches continue to attract the greatest plaudits with an impressive 22 individuals ranked in 17 areas, seven of which see the firm in the top position. The top ranking banking department has three individuals of note, as does commercial property, with Roy Beckett retaining his place as a regional leader. In the North the firm's concentration on commercial matters is proving a successful strategy. The corporate team was instrumental in the flotation of three companies in the space of 24 hours. The Birmingham branch is having more difficulty establishing itself in the notoriously difficult Midlands market. Banking continues to make progress up the ranks, while projects/PFI remains strong with the top ranked Anthony Randle, as does tax with Gregory Morris. In London, Peter Wayte's private equity team remains the firm's flagship.

Hammond Suddards Edge Following last year's whirlwind merger it seems this firm's period of transition has passed off smoothly enough. The firm now has 900 lawyers including 185 partners in offices in Birmingham, Brussels, Leeds, London and Manchester with the inevitable ambitions for pan-European expansion. Of its offices, Birmingham's future seems secure after the recruitment of 90 new fee-earners. Despite the departure of James Retallack in late Autumn, the office garners commendation in 24 sections of the *Chambers* Guide.

Unsurprisingly, the London office is taking on more importance and building up a reputation in the core areas of corporate finance and commercial litigation. Expanding its following among quoted companies, it can further point to niche successes such as its sports department which has a national reputation and acts for the Football League. This profile is set to continue in the light of the firm's merger with specialist outfit, Townleys. Securing a place in the top band in five areas in Leeds, it proves particularly adept at commercial litigation and debt recovery. In the latter area, the firm has now merged with niche London players Wilde & Partners. Manchester boasts particular strengths in corporate finance competition, IP and employment.

Beachcroft Wansbroughs For a firm whose bedrock is insurance and healthcare, Beachcroft suffered a blow this year as only the Bristol and Winchester branches retained their places on the NHLSA panel. This has led to the closure of the Sheffield branch, which dealt primarily with healthcare litigation, with the majority of the fee earners in Yorkshire now based in Leeds. Here the team's work for PCTs combined with the presence of healthcare supremo Diane Hallatt, ensures its prominence, although the loss of John Holmes to Hempsons has resulted in a lower profile in London. The firm demonstrates is strength in advisory work, and continues to carry out an impressive amount of NHS property, employment and projects work. This is the firm that advised on the first health sector public private partnership (PPP) deal to be funded by the European Investment Bank. Education also remains a strength for the London practice, with Julian Gizzi and his team being noted for funding work, winning the approval of such bodies as the Further Education Funding Council.

Dominating the regional insurance tables, acting for most of the leading insurance companies in the UK, it entered into a national partnership with Cornhill last year. Bristol, the second largest office, is famed for its personal injury work, another area of core expertise nationwide. The firm also tops the professional negligence tables, ranking highly in litigation and property, the latter where Michael Bothamley retains his individual crown.

Pinsent Curtis Biddle Keen to obtain a larger base from which to grow in the City, Pinsent Curtis joined forces with Biddle in February 2001. The union is deemed to have been a success, bringing together strengths in private equity and pensions. An ambitious operational plan has been instituted whereby the firm is concentrating on nine key areas, including projects, financial institutions, insurance and property. While it is a little early to say how far these aspirations have been realised, certain effects of the merger have become apparent. Turnover has increased by around 40%, partnership profits have risen by 25% and the firm now employs over 500 lawyers, including 150 in London alone. Across the regions, *Chambers'* findings indicate that the firm has maintained its healthy reputation.

In employee share schemes and employment in Leeds, top-flight status is undeniable, with John McMullen crafting an outstanding reputation as head of the national employment department, and David Pett enjoying similar status for share schemes work.

Expertise in a number of fields extends across the regions including tax, competition and banking in Birmingham and projects and property litigation in Leeds. These regional centres remain the lifeblood of the practice as the firm waits on its development as a true City player. Wider, international plans are afoot with a strategic alliance framework in place in order to improve European capability. Implementation of this has already resulted in an arrangement with a Swedish law firm.

Masons A year of steady expansion for a firm that boasts substantial expertise in four industry sectors; construction, energy, information technology and projects. With six offices in five different regions of the UK, two in Europe and three in the Asia Pacific region, the Masons formula has proved to be successful on a national and global level. The decision to run the UK practice as a single national operation, rather than as separate offices, has allowed the smaller practice areas to flourish through greater resources.

The new office opened in Edinburgh this year has already made an impact in the marketplace, becoming the only UK Masons office to be ranked in commercial property. The "highly commercial" PFI teams have been particularly successful, with five out of the six UK offices now achieving a place in the league tables, undertaking diverse projects from the privatisation and infrastructure development of the airports at Larnaka and Paphos in Cyprus to the financing of one of the London Underground PPP packages. However, the loss of Iain Fairbairn to Beachcroft Wansbroughs in Bristol office has had an impact on the profile of the team in the South West.

Construction remains the firm's raison d'être, with the firm acting for 18 of the top 20 UK contractors, and four offices attaining the leading position in the tables. The feedback from the marketplace consistently points to teams which are "all of a high calibre and focused." The cultivation of new sectors and outstanding expertise in the old favourites have proved a winning combination for the firm.

LONDON 1-10

Headquarters of the Greater London Authority

Clifford Chance The firm has consolidated its "credible global network" this year, and above all, remains a powerful force in banking. "More innovative" than its competitors, the London banking team handled seven jumbo loans worth £76 billion one two-month period. However, on the corporate front, although the firm is acknowledged to offer a "unified European product," only Adam Signy has a profile that can compare with the City market leaders. An "extremely cohesive" private equity team, by contrast, has advised on 16 of the 30 largest European buyouts.

On the equity side, Matthew Layton has led the team on several LBOs for Schroder Ventures, while on the debt side, James Johnson has a wonderful following among banks. The recent creation of a global communications, media and technology group, is set to focus on the international market, encouraging inter-office cooperation. In litigation, the group has had "an awesome year" according to peers, with the "smooth as silk" Jeremy Sandelson garnering the majority of plaudits. The lustre of the competition practice has dimmed with Chris Bright's departure to Shearman & Sterling. With a proposed move to Canary Wharf, the election of Peter Cornell as global head and the continued round of first year salary hikes, this is a firm that refuses to stand still.

Linklaters Already outstanding in corporate finance, the firm's banking practice has pulled ahead of rivals Freshfields, and it is now regarded as the firm which comes closest to matching equivalent expertise in these two sectors. The finance pairing of Hayden Puleston-Jones and John Tucker, attractive to so many clients, has attracted numerous plaudits.

The firm is still regarded as the class of the field for commercial property for its ability to handle the largest and most complex of transactions, both domestically and overseas. The team handled the disposal of MEPC's £1.1 billion shopping centre portfolio. The corporate finance practice has had a "wonderful transactional year," having "done well in getting its international strategy right" and advising on mammoth deals such as BT's rights issue, the UK's largest ever, to raise £5.9 billion. "Great brain" David Cheyne is "almost without peer in the country," having advised on Vodafone's £25 billion disposal of Orange to France Telecom. In litigation, generalist Christopher Style is much sought after for the common-sense attitude with which he imbues many a case, while the tax team has proved to be an innovative force within the transactional market.

Allen & Overy The jewel in its crown is undoubtedly its banking and finance practice, from which many of its other practice strengths derive and flourish. Insolvency, project finance, and capital markets all have their roots in the depth of expertise and client base emanating from this quarter. The judgement from clients and competitors alike is unequivocal: "I've never come across a bad lawyer at A&O." "Guru" Philip Wood is responsible for putting in place the finance teams 'know-how' system, while the "outstanding" David Morley, is acknowledged to be "a star and the public face of A&O's finance practice."

Employing some "fancy footwork" during the last recession has meant the insolvency team is a driving force in the market, drawing on a balanced and team for some of the largest cross-border restructurings. One robust practice area, not entwined with the firm's banking practice is its private client practice, where it is perceived to be impressive on the international front. A further feather in the firm's cap has been the highly successful combination of its project finance group, headed by the legendary Graham Vinter, and the the PFI team, led by the ubiquitous Anne Baldock.

Although still not thought to be the equal of the top three corporate finance practices, the team, led by the hardworking Alan Paul, continues to command respect, while the property practice has gained credibility over the past twelve months.

Freshfields Bruckhaus Deringer A law firm of choice for transactions throughout the global economy, it is built on a network of offices throughout Europe, Asia and the US. In keeping with development of its global culture, the firm's strategy of dispersing its UK partners abroad has resulted in successful inter-office "cross fertilization." Notable departures include securitisation specialist Ian Falconer to Paris and Philip Richards to Milan.

"A benchmark of quality in London," it pre-eminent in corporate finance, tax and competition. Anthony Salz and Will Lawes head the pack of "absolutely first rate" corporate finance heavy-hitters, whose league table-topping deals include the £18 billion Granada Compass merger. Teams of "talented" tax and competition players also play a vital role in the firm's accepted position as "a true one stop shop." The competition department scored a major coup in attracting Denton Wilde Sapte's star player David Aitman. Involved in London Underground's PPP, Nick Bliss retains his outstanding reputation, as does pensions heavyweight Ken Dierden. The firm sits just behind Herbert Smith in general litigation and, although it slips behind Linklaters in the banking tables, in its core areas, it remains "as good as it gets."

Herbert Smith A strong performance this year has seen the firm continue to develop its international network. Between January 2000 and January 2001, It opened an office in Tokyo, entered into an association with German firm Gleiss Lutz Hootz Hirsch, and formed associations in Indonesian and Singapore. The scope of its corporate transactions is indicative of the growth of its cross-border credentials. It represented Time Warner on the UK/European aspects of its $181 billion merger with AOL and on its $12 billion joint venture with EMI, deals that have led to high-profile work for the firm's top-rated competition department.

The commercial litigation practice has again proved to be the firm's powerhouse, boasting "brilliant litigators" of the ilk of David Gold and Ted Greeno. It continues to shake off its 'red meat' image with clients commenting on its "commerciality, quality and depth of resources." A strong recruitment drive has netted practitioners of the quality of IT specialist Christopher Rees from Bird & Bird, while departments such as energy are still held in the highest esteem.

Lovells Continuing to power its way through Europe, the firm has also had a better year at home, although in some areas it remains plagued by the perception that it is missing the influence of some key players. The securitisation and repackaging practice is thought to have been rebuilding after Peter Voisey's departure last year, although the loss of Nicholas Frome to Clifford Chance has been a setback to the insolvency team. A number of new partners have been created this year, many in the corporate finance department.

Obtaining rankings in 37 practice areas, with 59 notable practitioners, the firm has two star-rated players in Nicholas Cheffings (property litigation) and Greg Sinfield (tax). It holds onto its top ratings in civil fraud, pensions litigation and non-contentious insurance. Despite the departure of Gordon Innes, the firm also keeps its place at the top of the parliamentary and public affairs rankings. Under the leadership of the charismatic Bob Kidby, the property department is winning "new generation work" with its "utterly pragmatic" approach.

CMS Cameron McKenna Boasting 37 offices in 23 countries, the firm's move to push corporate to the forefront of its strategy has not yet received the desired market response. Its construction and property teams have had to weather the high profile losses of Ann Minogue and Jon Vivian respectively, although Tony Kitson has successfully continued to shoulder the weight of the planning practice.

In a number of areas, there is undoubted strength. "Dynamic" electricity guru Fiona Woolf and head of Aberdeen's O&G department, Penelope Warne are among several well-known personalities hailing from the firm's "silver service" energy department. The firm maintains pole positions in immigration, health and safety and product liability, in the latter of which Ian Dodds-Smith excels.

Norton Rose The firm continues to nurture its core businesses of corporate finance, banking and asset finance within its steadily expanding international network of offices, which now includes Milan, Warsaw and crucially, Germany. Retaining its unparalleled market position in shipping finance, the firm has achieved uniform expansion across its industry-focused offices in London, Greece, Paris and Singapore, while heavyweight leader John Shelton continues to shine. The asset finance and leasing practice headed by "top class" Peter Thorne, has regained its position alongside the leaders. Other areas of expertise include regulatory aviation and civil fraud work. The general litigation team's promotion this year confirms its healthy workload, highlighted by such instructions as the Thyssen case.

The firm preserves its reputation in banking, tax and energy, the latter despite the departure of star player Michael Taylor to Milan. Comfortably ensconced in the corporate finance big league, the firm has a growing profile on cross-border deals for clients such as Italian petroleum giant ENI and France Telecom.

Slaughter and May A name which is thought to embody "utterly first rate" quality, and where the "sheer intellectual capacity" of its lawyers has secured its iconic status as "the number one M&A firm in the UK." Content with its 'best friends' association, the firm stoically maintains relationships with the brightest and best of its global counterparts.

Claims for the "phenomenal M&A practice" are substantiated by recent mega-deals that include BHP's £20 billion merger with Billiton. The "ace" Nigel Boardman and "pre-eminent" William Underhill top the billing among the firm's constellation of corporate stars. The firm possesses a concomitant pedigree in competition and tax, boasting "towering strength" with big-ticket merger control work, and the presence of famed tax "genius" Steve Edge. Favouring a 'multi-specialist' approach, the firm's emphasis on transactional work has traditionally masked its 'stand alone' work. In reacting to its clients, the firm has created a TMT group where IT guru Nigel Swycher has directed a burgeoning workload. The firm has demonstrated renewed vigour in commercial property and litigation work, acting on high profile work such as the Punch Taverns securitisations and Barings liquidators' negligence claim. The 2002 incorporation of the firm's London operations under one roof in unique purpose-built premises will mark the beginning of a new era in the firm's history.

Denton Wilde Sapte More than a year after its merger, the firm is widely acknowledged to be a success story. The Media & Entertainment practice goes from strength to strength, attracting new banking clients. As tends to be the case in areas where the firm flourishes, such as sport and aviation, this top tier-publishing group earns praise for its "industry knowledge." That depth is certainly a powerful aspect of the firm's continued success in energy and natural resources, where clients adjudge its practitioners to wield "the greatest industry experience." The practice has been strengthened through the acquisition of Cameron McKenna's Almaty office, and the opening of an office in Tashkent. This expansion is typical of the past year and follows the trend of growth in the Denton International network.

Once again, the corporate finance team is perceived to be a force on transactions with a cross-border element, this year advising Royal Bank of Scotland on the £2.3 billion restructuring of its business in Tokyo. A rare setback this year was the departure of competition star David Aitman to Freshfields Bruckhaus Deringer.

LONDON: LARGER SIZED FIRMS

Ashurst Morris Crisp Thought to typify the progress of the firm, its energy practice is generally held to have acquired a better balance after the disruption of personnel changes during the last few years. The firm has consolidated vital relationships with banks, securing a following for its projects/PFI practice. Indeed, peers especially rate the firm's expertise in the Far East, as it wins "interesting IT and telecoms work."

Over the past year, the firm has accelerated the pace of development and integration of its European offices in the major business centres. Paris, Frankfurt and Milan offices have all grown, whilst the firm has opened an office in Madrid. Much of this expansion is thought to be as a result of the increasingly international profile of its private equity and corporate finance practice. Here the much-applauded Charlie Geffen advised on such transactions as the £230 million Gilde Investments acquisition of Armstrong Installation Products. The only sour note to the year has been star planning partner Michael Cunliffe's departure to West End property firm Forsters.

Simmons & Simmons With newly elected senior partner and employment star Janet Gaymer now at the helm, the firm is seen to be consolidating its strengths. The move to City Point means that all staff are finally under the same roof. Possessing 39 leaders in their fields, Simmons' strong points remain employment and IP.

The employment department remains at the top of its game, credited with the role of educator to industry in the UK. The IP team can lay claim to multi-jurisdictional litigation expertise in both patent and general IP. Head of department Kevin Mooney has advised on cases such as Bristol- Myers Squibb's appeal on the patent for cancer drug Taxol. The corporate team continues to advise a number of US corporates, most notably Wal-Mart, and enjoys a healthy following among quoted companies.

A ranking in 34 *Chambers* sections emphasizes the firm's breadth of service and continues to underline its status as one of those firms that can offer a credible alternative to the Magic Circle. Although not generally considered to be an international powerhouse, the opening of offices in Germany and Spain has at least demonstrated the firm's continuing overseas ambitions.

Berwin Leighton Paisner Early days for this newly merged firm, but the initial signs are promising. Berwin Leighton, with its core strengths in property, sought to beef up its corporate practice by merging with Paisner, a field where the latter had a strong reputation. Almost inevitably, there has been some fall out, with the departure of Anne Marie Piper to Farrer & Co hitting the charity rankings. Elsewhere the move has paid off, with the firm ranked in 21 areas of practice, and including 32 highlighted lawyers.

Property remains a key strength, in spite of the departure of David Taylor to Herbert Smith. The firm retains the top spot for planning, where it is "undoubtedly in pole position," servicing an enviable list of clients including Tesco and Blue Circle. The construction team also received a huge boost with the arrival of a team from Barlow Lyde & Gilbert. On the corporate front, the firm draws from its strength across various industry sectors, and is thought to be winning a good level of inward investment work.

SJ Berwin Under its dynamic management, the firm continues to score well across a broad base of disciplines. It is ranked in 19 separate areas of practice, with the spotlight shining on 34 of its practitioners. The commercial property practice continues to serve as the firm's backbone, while in planning, the "mighty presence" of star player Patricia Thomas garners plaudits from peers and clients alike. Property elements feed across industry sectors, and the firm also wins approval for its work in the hotels and leisure sector, acting on the sale and leaseback of Brannigans to First Leisure and on the acquisition of

LONDON: the 150 Largest Firms (continued overleaf)

		Ptnrs	Asst Solrs	Total No of Solrs '01	'00	'99	'98
1	Clifford Chance	234	852	**1086**	924	932	863
2	Linklaters	200	700	**900**	696	721	597
3	Allen & Overy	174	634	**808**	691	614	573
4	Freshfields Bruckhaus Deringer	161	538	**699**	781	577	516
5	Herbert Smith	138	394	**532**	470	456	409
6	Lovells	139	359	**498**	473	473	450
7	CMS Cameron McKenna	143	312	**455**	471	432	394
8	Norton Rose	122	330	**452**	424	380	344
9	Slaughter and May	102	340	**442**	513	400	361
10	Denton Wilde Sapte	160	278	**438**	448	n/a	n/a
11	Ashurst Morris Crisp	96	306	**402**	357	356	310
12	Simmons & Simmons	111	279	**390**	378	404	400
13	Berwin Leighton Paisner	130	183	**313**	n/a	n/a	n/a
14	SJ Berwin	86	193	**279**	264	198	193
15	Baker & McKenzie	67	208	**275**	234	177	165
16	Nabarro Nathanson	89	160	**249**	227	255	255
17	Taylor Joynson Garrett	90	139	**229**	203	186	166
18	Rowe & Maw	79	147	**226**	205	203	183
19	Bird & Bird	72	140	**212**	210	125	98
20	Barlow Lyde & Gilbert	67	141	**208**	219	190	184
21	Eversheds	73	129	**202**	196	184	187
22	DLA	n/a	n/a	n/a	210	194	203
23	Lawrence Graham	88	107	**195**	171	168	154
24	Masons	54	135	**189**	150	132	131
25	Olswang	56	125	**181**	141	109	85
26	Hammond Suddards Edge	69	111	**180**	180	n/a	n/a
27	Field Fisher Waterhouse	71	107	**178**	156	134	129
28	Macfarlanes	56	116	**172**	166	145	139
29	Stephenson Harwood	62	103	**165**	166	161	155
30	Richards Butler	72	92	**164**	160	149	146
31	Beachcroft Wansbroughs	61	103	**164**	195	187	n/a
32	Theodore Goddard	68	95	**163**	179	147	147
33	Travers Smith Braithwaite	49	105	**154**	128	125	120
34	Dechert	49	90	**139**	136	127	123
35	Reynolds Porter Chamberlain	50	83	**133**	118	117	110
36	Clyde & Co	66	65	**131**	130	128	133
37	Charles Russell	58	67	**125**	112	109	107
38	Sidley Austin Brown & Wood	41	84	**125**	n/a	n/a	n/a
39	Pinsent Curtis Biddle	48	73	**121**	n/a	n/a	n/a
40	D J Freeman	58	56	**114**	114	114	104
41	Weil, Gotshal & Manges	24	89	**113**	100	97	61
42	Withers	50	61	**111**	105	101	91
43	Osborne Clarke	40	67	**107**	76	45	45
44	Holman Fenwick & Willan	54	51	**105**	114	100	91
45	Shearman & Sterling	21	84	**105**	103	68	n/a
46	Trowers & Hamlins	48	56	**104**	96	96	92
47	Nicholson Graham & Jones	52	51	**103**	102	101	87
48	Davies Arnold Cooper	35	68	**103**	113	150	141
49	Gouldens	37	63	**100**	138	114	101
50	White & Case LLP	27	72	**99**	70	42	30
51	Kennedys	44	52	**96**	89	86	76
52	Watson, Farley & Williams	31	60	**91**	98	91	89
53	Garretts	30	61	**91**	64	58	57
54	Ince & Co	42	48	**90**	123	90	112
55	Farrer & Co	43	46	**89**	91	88	81
56	Edwards Duthie	13	75	**88**	n/a	n/a	n/a
57	Speechly Bircham	36	50	**86**	81	71	67
58	KLegal	17	66	**83**	46	n/a	n/a
59	Bristows	28	53	**81**	75	60	56
60	Howard Kennedy	41	39	**80**	72	64	48
61	Finers Stephens Innocent	39	40	**79**	77	n/a	n/a
62	Berrymans Lace Mawer	29	50	**79**	83	135	81
63	Mishcon de Reya	36	38	**74**	62	58	82
64	Lewis Silkin	34	40	**74**	59	58	57
65	Manches	30	40	**70**	79	79	73
66	Kingsley Napley	36	33	**69**	58	56	47
67	Latham & Watkins	18	50	**68**	41	22	16
68	Harbottle & Lewis	17	51	**68**	68	68	65
69	Sinclair Roche & Temperley	29	37	**66**	64	64	62
70	Davenport Lyons	28	38	**66**	51	41	30

The rankings in this table are determined by the number of solicitors working in the region. They are based on partner and assistant solicitor figures only: all other fee-earners are excluded.

the Malmaison Group for MWB.

The film finance team remains a major force in sale and leaseback work, and last year advised funders of Sky Pictures on four features. Much of its corporate offering relies on a high level of private equity expertise, where Jonathan Blake's good reputation is also endorsed in the US. The commercial litigation team is praised for its multi-jurisdictions skills, with peers believing that the firm is "going from strength to strength." Growing offices in Madrid, Paris and Munich have added to the impression of a firm unwilling to let the grass grow under its feet.

Baker & McKenzie Having pursued a global strategy for over 50 years, Baker & McKenzie now boasts more than 60 offices in 35 jurisdictions and an international client base. Focusing on the London office in isolation, therefore, is perhaps an unfair reflection of the firm's capabilities. Relatively lowly placed in corporate finance, the team is nevertheless acknowledged to do "incredibly well out of its international reputation and global reach," and to act as a centre for the firm's European work.

The same difficulty of categorisation is experienced in capital markets: equity. Here the London team is viewed as specialists in the Eastern European region, boosted by its expertise in international telecoms-related work. In London, IT remains a crucial strength, with the market agreeing it has come on strongly in e-commerce, to the point where it is now considered as a "fixture on large projects for established clients."

The commercial litigation team holds a strong position in the market, and is praised for its "strategic nous." As elsewhere with this firm, clients rely on it to "manage the co-ordination of cross-border issues."

Nabarro Nathanson Associated primarily with its public sector strength, the practice continues to dominate in the local government sector, where is it is considered "the largest and most experienced" team in the City. Among other impressive pieces of work, this year saw the team appointed to advise the London Borough of Southwark on the 10-year regeneration of the Elephant & Castle. "Ex local-authority bigwig" Malcolm Iley retains his top ranking in this sector. This expertise also spills over into administrative and public law work.

Traditionally a big name in property, some interviewees have this year queried the depth of the team. In related property litigation issues it holds onto the top rung, praised as a "real force" in the market. The strength of its retail work in particular helps the firm move up the planning tables. Staff losses – including the departure of both Peter Ford and Lesley Browning to Norton Rose – see the firm's ranking fall in both pensions and pensions litigation. Much of the firm's corporate work is derived from its strength in projects and property, with an extra niche in convergent new media. This year the team acted for Land Securities on its £165 million acquisition of Trillium. Altogether, the firm has 24 individuals featured in the Chambers Guide across 16 practice areas.

Taylor Joynson Garrett A good performance in information technology law has embellished a year when the firm also continued to expand on its core sectors of media and entertainment, advertising and intellectual property. Restored to top spot for general IP work, the firm is thought to have "talented people with great know-how," and niche strengths in pharmaceuticals and biotechnology. "Focused" Mark Hodgson led the firm's advice to Eli Lilly on multiple cases against Novo Nordisk concerning insulin technology. In the food law arena, the firm is recommended for defence work in relation to safety prosecutions. On the back of its technology company client base, the firm has developed a strong reputation for AIM and IPO activities. Across the IT field, its activities include large-scale IT supply and procurement and a great knowledge of the computer games market. Improvements in ranking for advertising and marketing, construction, e-commerce and general commercial litigation round off a sound year for the firm.

Rowe & Maw A steady performance with strong showings in pensions, partnerships, professional negligence, and mid tier corporate finance work. The "superb" pensions practice holds tight to its place at the peak of the tables, with an impressive roster of FTSE 100 clients and the formidable trio of partners securing its position. "Huge in the district audit field" the firm also remains at the head of the local government tables, with the presence of Tony Child gives the firm much of its following. Richard Linsell is once again considered the "guru on partnership law," while a first rate construction team is said to be "one of the best in the business." The practice is representing Laing in negotiating a contract to build the new £200 million Commonwealth Games stadium in Manchester. With 26 individuals ranked across ranked in 19 practice areas, this strongly commercial firm takes instructions from a multi-national client base.

Bird & Bird Leading the field in IT, e-commerce, telecommunications and intellectual property, the firm is applauded for its clear focus of strategy. In the IT field, the firm has expertise in advising on large-scale IT infrastructure projects, which are often global in nature. The depth of the team was proved this year by the unruffled way it handled the departure of leading light Chris Rees to Herbert Smith. In IP, the team of Morag Macdonald and Trevor Cook remains "unsurpassable." Acting on two of the most important patent matters of this year, the firm represented Oxford Gene Technology on a patent infringement case brought against Affymetrix, and acted for Pfizer on its revocation action concerning the Viagra field of use patent.

On the international front, the Paris and Stockholm offices continue to support the firm's private equity and venture capital activities. At the cutting edge of many developments in the market, the firm's strategy of focusing on biotechnology as an industry sector has seen it advise on seed financings and spinouts from educational establishments.

Barlow Lyde & Gilbert With the kind of performance that one has come to expect from the firm, it again claims sole top spot for insurance: general claims, although the firm and Colin Croly have to share the first place honours this year in the reinsurance table. The market awaits the effect of the firm's new Shanghai office, anticipated to strengthen its already successful cross border approach to insurance work.

2001 has seen an increase in professional negligence work, where the team of Stuart Hall and David Arthur is considered to be outstanding. Conversely, it has not been a good year in construction, with the departure of most of the team to Berwin Leighton Paisner. Now featuring in 15 Chambers sections, the firm continues to show up well in areas such as aviation and personal injury. Recent moves to strengthen the commercial litigation and IT departments have yet to be felt in our research.

Eversheds The London arm of this vast national and international enterprise is ranked in 18 sections of the Chambers Guide. It has continued to excel within its key areas of education and franchising. Both sectors benefit from expertise within the regions, and the stature of its leading lights. John Hall, enjoying nationwide commendation, is per-

LONDON: the 150 Largest Firms continued

		Ptnrs	Asst Solrs	Total No of Solrs '01	'00	'99	'98
71	Radcliffes	36	28	**64**	60	59	58
72	Bircham Dyson Bell	35	29	**64**	70	49	37
73	Fladgate Fielder	34	30	**64**	58	54	44
74	Landwell	16	47	**63**	56	n/a	n/a
75	Vizards, Staples & Bannisters	30	32	**62**	62	70	n/a
76	McDermott, Will & Emery	17	45	**62**	55	n/a	n/a
77	Tite & Lewis	10	52	**62**	n/a	n/a	n/a
78	Wedlake Bell	30	31	**61**	57	51	53
79	Penningtons	23	36	**59**	41	36	38
80	Russell Jones & Walker	26	32	**58**	58	48	46
81	Morgan Cole	25	30	**55**	56	25	n/a
82	Forsters	21	32	**53**	50	47	n/a
83	Hodge Jones & Allen	21	32	**53**	44	42	35
84	Russell-Cooke	21	32	**53**	47	40	41
85	Jones, Day, Reavis & Pogue	8	45	**53**	36	n/a	n/a
86	Boodle Hatfield	25	27	**52**	46	43	35
87	Capsticks	21	31	**52**	57	55	45
88	Tarlo Lyons	24	27	**51**	43	40	30
89	LeBoeuf, Lamb, Greene & MacRae, LLP	12	38	**50**	50	44	32
90	Fox Williams	16	32	**48**	41	37	33
91	Davis Polk & Wardwell	12	35	**47**	33	33	n/a
92	Brobeck Hale and Dorr	11	35	**46**	38	n/a	n/a
93	Reed Smith Warner Cranston	20	25	**45**	34	34	42
94	Winckworth Sherwood	18	27	**45**	40	43	33
95	Le Brasseur J Tickle	19	25	**44**	43	44	44
96	Hill Taylor Dickinson	22	21	**43**	43	23	54
97	Sullivan & Cromwell	13	29	**42**	33	33	n/a
98	Milbank, Tweed, Hadley & McCloy	7	35	**42**	29	20	16
99	Vizard Oldham	26	15	**41**	30	n/a	n/a
100	Jeffrey Green Russell	23	18	**41**	44	45	51
101	Cleary, Gottlieb, Steen & Hamilton	10	31	**41**	40	38	26
102	Beaumont and Son	19	21	**40**	42	37	37
103	Devonshires	14	26	**40**	37	19	26
104	Steptoe & Johnson Rakisons	17	22	**39**	44	37	27
105	Addleshaw Booth & Co	16	23	**39**	n/a	n/a	n/a
106	Payne Hicks Beach	22	16	**38**	29	20	28
107	Dewey Ballantine LLP	10	28	**38**	28	n/a	n/a
108	Collyer-Bristow	24	13	**37**	32	28	27
109	Salans Hertzfeld & Heilbronn	17	20	**37**	42	43	40
110	McGrigor Donald	13	24	**37**	26	26	21
111	Rosling King	9	28	**37**	37	50	39
112	Pritchard Englefield	25	11	**36**	40	39	34
113	Bates, Wells & Braithwaite	21	15	**36**	32	42	25
114	Pemberton Greenish	20	15	**35**	35	33	39
115	Sacker & Partners	17	18	**35**	33	31	30
116	Hobson Audley	13	22	**35**	33	37	35
117	Simpson Thacher & Bartlett	5	30	**35**	n/a	n/a	n/a
118	Constant & Constant	22	12	**34**	34	29	33
119	Dawson & Co	21	13	**34**	34	31	26
120	Kingsford Stacey Blackwell	20	14	**34**	36	35	35
121	Teacher Stern Selby	16	18	**34**	34	30	26
122	Rooks Rider	12	22	**34**	27	32	29
123	Skadden, Arps, Slate, Meagher & Flom LLP	11	23	**34**	43	32	25
124	Edwin Coe	22	11	**33**	32	33	30
125	Hempsons	12	21	**33**	32	29	28
126	Fisher Meredith	9	24	**33**	38	36	34
127	Debevoise & Plimpton	8	25	**33**	n/a	n/a	n/a
128	Amhurst Brown Colombotti	19	13	**32**	30	24	25
129	Campbell Hooper	18	14	**32**	32	35	37
130	Squire, Sanders & Dempsey LLP	11	21	**32**	n/a	n/a	n/a
131	Cadwalader, Wickersham & Taft	7	25	**32**	n/a	n/a	n/a
132	Clintons	17	14	**31**	27	22	19
133	Hextall Erskine	17	14	**31**	36	35	31
134	Thompsons	12	19	**31**	n/a	21	21
135	TV Edwards	8	23	**31**	34	34	30
136	Park Nelson	19	11	**30**	30	32	27
137	The Simkins Partnership	19	11	**30**	25	27	32
138	Hamlins	17	13	**30**	27	30	27
149	Thomas Cooper & Stibbard	16	14	**30**	26	25	23
140	Memery Crystal	14	16	**30**	26	25	25
141	Bindman & Partners	12	18	**30**	30	26	25
142	Mayer, Brown & Platt	10	20	**30**	29	31	20
143	Prince Evans	6	24	**30**	31	31	27
144	Goodman Derrick	20	9	**29**	29	25	27
145	William Sturges & Co	17	12	**29**	29	25	22
146	Fishburn Morgan Cole	10	19	**29**	30	30	n/a
147	Davies Lavery	9	20	**29**	n/a	n/a	n/a
148	Hickman & Rose	4	25	**29**	n/a	20	20
149	Tuckers	1	27	**28**	32	n/a	n/a
150	Leigh, Day & Co	13	14	**27**	n/a	22	23

The rankings in this table are determined by the number of solicitors working in the region. They are based on partner and assistant solicitor figures only: all other fee-earners are excluded.

ceived to be "the General of education law," while Martin Mendelsohn has been given the accolade of "the father figure of UK franchising." Litigation "star" Giles Orton has greatly strengthened the London pensions team with his move from the Derby office. Increased prominence within the patent side of intellectual property yet to be matched on the corporate side, although the team continues to draw solid market approval.

DLA DLA's commercial push in London is continuing, with the overhaul of the banking department paying particular dividends. The firm's client base has also been strengthened with appointments to the BNFL and Virgin panels. Peter Wayte and the corporate team continue to win market commendation, notably for private equity expertise.

Lawrence Graham The firm continues to improve on past performances with a strong showing in 17 sections of the Chambers Guide. A full-service firm, it is especially commended for its strength in commercial litigation. In corporate finance, the firm produces "good partners and a high standard of work," and is particularly recognised as a player in the AIM market, buoyed by its solid links with private equity houses and investment funds. To that extent, the corporate team's "front-line man" Michael Storar is one of the key figures at the firm. Another area of note lies in trusts and personal tax where the team's private banking client base applauds its "dynamism and responsiveness" combined with a strong commercial focus. Notably, the firm administers the estate of Diana, Princess of Wales.

Masons Clear water continues to separate the construction team from any pretenders to its throne. Non-contentious work has seen an increase, although it is still the domestic contentious scene where the department possesses "a stranglehold," representing Mowlem on various multi-million pound claims concerning the design construction of a major headquarters facility for a government body. This sector also provides the firm with its two practitioners who top the tables: "terrific lawyer" John Bishop and "obvious choice" Tony Bunch.

The London arm of this expanding international outfit is ranked in ten practice areas. Contentious IT work maintains its high profile, and the firm also enters the tables for its e-commerce and commercial litigation expertise. In the energy sector, an increasing volume of international work has led to market prediction of a "bright future" for the firm. Now perceived to be more than simply "construction giants," Masons is developing into a bright star in the London firmament.

Olswang The firm is perceived to be thriving, despite the turbulence of the market in which it operates, which has led to much publicised staff lay-offs. Still featured as leaders in 17 *Chambers* categories, the firm has turned in particularly strong performances in advertising, employment and tax. Ever present in the media law market, the firm recently launched Long Acre Partners, an independent corporate finance house designed to promote access to capital and strategic advice for the high-tech community. One of the first to use this service was Shine Entertainment, the new television production venture between Elisabeth Murdoch and Lord Alli. The film financing work carried out by the team has been commended this year, and it continues to enjoy an impressive client roster, featuring BBC Worldwide, Granada Media and Carphone Warehouse. 31 leaders are featured in the Guide, with "top class" defamation lawyer Geraldine Proudler retaining her stellar rank.

LONDON: MEDIUM SIZED FIRMS

Hammond Suddards Edge Following the excitement of last year's merger the London office's overall performance in this year's Chambers has been something of a curate's egg. Areas in which it had previously gained a foothold such as IT, IP:patent and buyouts are notable by their absence. However, the office has shown a strong performance in other areas. The recruitment of Caroline May, for example, has led to a newfound standing in environmental law, reflected by the firm's appointment to British Nuclear Fuels' external panel of legal advisors.

Unsurprisingly, considering Edge Ellison's historic position, the pensions team has developed its presence in the City, while the corporate finance team has also made strides, appearing in nationally renowned deals such as Hazelwood Foods acquisition by the Greencore Group. Here the firm is said to have "boosted its stock" in the public company market. A merger with Townleys has secured its standing in the sports law market, and a union with Wilde & Partners' debt recovery unit has confirmed its position as the number one choice for factoring companies.

Field Fisher Waterhouse The firm's corporate team has continued to be the main engine for generating business, bolstered by the increased publicity it received from the dot.com boom. The team has performed robustly once again, with successes for public companies allied to continued project finance growth in the French and German markets.

It has been a good year for the property team also, generally advising industrial property clients, hotels and brewing concerns. The firm's well-known 'new media' work has concentrated on 'bricks and clicks,' business-to-business clients such as Accenture and Thomas Cook. Furthermore, the firm's Brands, Technology, Media & Telecommunications super-department has made great strides this year, improving the firm's position in the e-commerce, IT and media & entertainment: broadcasting tables. Michael Chissick is often the name seen taking the honours on the biggest transactions. The firm also remains in the top band for franchising, licensing and travel.

Macfarlanes A highly focused and commercial offering, it maintains its lead in the fields of agriculture, advertising, and trusts and personal tax. In another eminently sound performance this year, the agriculture team focuses primarily on the institutional side, acting for pension funds as well as landed estates and wealthy foreign owners. In the advertising and marketing field, it has maintained an impressive corporate reputation, with a strong client list of top agencies and brand owners. Here, Jeremy Courtenay-Stamp is "a good operator with a great corporate reputation."

The private client team is thought to be the "quintessence of quality and expertise," and advises a notable stable of entrepreneurial clients on a range of big-ticket work.

Other notable achievements for the firm in a commendable year include promotion for its commercial litigation team. Despite its relatively small size, the firm has measured up well to the larger City corporate practices, securing its place in the larger sized deals corporate finance table. Robert Sutton is the leading figure in a "hard-working, commercially-minded" team.

Stephenson Harwood Despite personnel changes resulting from its restructuring programme, the firm holds its place in the rankings for most sectors, although it slips from banking and intellectual property. It remains strong in the shipping sectors, with Mark Russell proving his mettle in the shipping finance arena. Insurance insolvency is a niche area of expertise. The litigation team continues to garner market approval with the presence of "outstanding" John Fordham assisting it to top tier status for its size. Expansion of the business technology group has led helped the corporate finance team maintain its standing in a particularly tough market. All in all, the firm is ranked in ten practice areas, with 19 notable practitioners listed.

Richards Butler For a medium sized London firm, it has an impressive international practice with a network crossing from South America to Asia. Domestically, the firm has been steady this year. The firm features as leaders in 17 Chambers categories, and hold the top spot in commodities, licensing and film finance.

"Pre-eminent in soft commodities" according to its peers, the firm fields star practitioner David Pullen. Elizabeth Southorn advised on the licensing of the Great Eastern Hotel for Sir Terence Conran. In film finance, the respected team acted for the lenders to the British film Enigma and the producer of the £15 million feature 'Killing Me Softly.' Having acquired a number of heavyweight multi-nationals as clients, the "calm negotiators" of the corporate team have been active in inward investment work, often originating from the US.

Beachcroft Wansbroughs Subject to the twists of a turbulent healthcare market, the branch has been hit by the loss of a place on the

NHSLA panel and subsequent departure of key player John Holmes to Hempsons. This development caught the market by surprise and although the respected team continues to carry out work for NHS Estates, it has forced an element of restructuring. The London team led the largest ever property disposal by the NHS last year, in a project totalling £650 million, and advised on the first health sector PPP deal to be funded by the European Investment Bank. It continues to top the tables in personal injury, and this year scored well in legal professional negligence. The firm also remains strong in education, a field in which Julian Gizzi is a mainstay, involved in funding work and advising such bodies as the Further Education Funding Council. Respected for its following among local authorities, the corporate team has also secured increased instructions from industrial entities.

Theodore Goddard A year of proposed expansion, with the prospect of a merger with Franco-American firm, Salans Hertzfeld & Heilbronn. Such a move would aid growth areas such as PFI to gain an international presence. PFI work has taken a leap into the tables this year, growing as an offshoot of the firm's construction and banking expertise. "Impressive negotiator" James Ballingall continues to propel the practice. The defamation team has enjoyed an "annus mirabilis," as the "charming" Martin Kramer and his team offer "an expensive but Rolls Royce service."

Still a force in film and TV production, the firm has also scored well in the music and theatre sectors. "Genius" of the music scene James Harman has been involved in such cutting edge cases as Sade's attempt to recover her domain name from cyber squatters. Now ranked in 21 practice areas, it remains to be seen whether this gradually expanding firm will make its presence felt in the international arena.

Travers Smith Braithwaite Demonstrating a majority of home-grown lawyers, high retention rates and a strongly partner-led "collegiate" ethos, it is not surprising that this understated firm would countenance merger as being at variance with its internal culture. Although possessing an apparently cautious attitude towards overseas expansion, the firm is handling an increasing amount of cross-border work, fostering close working relationships with firms across Europe and the US.

The firm's key strength resides in its "amazing matrix" of "consistently superb lawyers" in corporate and private equity. Highlight deals have included advising on NTL's £8.2 billion acquisition of Cable & Wireless Communications. Christopher Bell and Spencer Summerfield are widely admired for their "substantial" corporate experience, while Chris Hale is thought to have "turned round" the private equity practice. The pensions team continues to challenge in terms of market share, while in financial services, CRESTCo's lawyer Margaret Chamberlain retains her popularity. Although slipping in the banking and litigation rankings, this year sees an impressive performances from the property team in high premium development work. The resurgence of the tax department's profile follows former MP Alistair Douglas' return to the fold.

Dechert Seeing the wider benefits of its trans-Atlantic merger, the firm has reported an increase both in profits and cross-border referrals. Although brand recognition for the new entity is taking time to filter through, the continuation of the firm's long-term approach – along lines that mirrors its US counterpart – is reaping benefits. It has maintained its position in customs & excise (where it is the sole name in band one), with Malachy Cornwell-Kelly again ruling the roost. Civil fraud and general litigation also remain strong.

There has been a renewed focus on investment management, with significant input from the firm's European offices, and the effect on such profitable niche areas is beginning to show. The firm has put in a strong showing in the investment funds table this year and is well regarded for corporate finance matters, where its strengths in retail and insurance have proved attractive. It has also had a good year in finance-related property work.

Reynolds Porter Chamberlain A strong showing in all aspects of professional negligence sees the firm rank second only to the far larger Barlow Lyde & Gilbert in this sphere. Paul Nicholas is a major force for the firm. Peers commend it as a "firm with strengths in most areas," but it is particularly strong in legal negligence, securing places on several panels including Zurich, Hiscox, and Bar Mutual. "Real rainmaker" Simon Greenley is in the top tier for insurance and continues his fine work in professional negligence. The defamation practice continues to do well, with last year's new arrivals from DAC now fully integrated into the team. Less impressive market feedback in commercial litigation and education, however, has seen the firm move down a spot in the Chambers tables.

Clyde & Co The firm has maintained its high profile for insurance work, this year joining Barlow Lyde & Gilbert at the top of the reinsurance table. It also continues to impress in commodities, energy and general litigation. Augmented by its work for international and overseas clients, the firm's shipping practice remains a solid foundation from which to expand. Like other firms well known for specific sector expertise, the firm is making a concerted effort to broaden – it features in 14 Chambers sections this year – using the corporate team as its engine for development. It is not yet clear what effect this will have on more traditional areas; at present its grip remains firm. Corporate finance saw the firm's Guildford office improving its standing, while overseas offices, notably in the UAE, have continued to bring in major corporate and IT clients.

Holman Fenwick & Wilan The firm goes from strength to strength in shipping, which is still the main string to the firm's bow and it is described as "extremely sharp and focused." The dry practice has expanded considerably, and despite the departure of Archie Bishop, the team fields a plethora of formidable individuals. Robert Wilson remains "amazingly diligent and intellectually rigorous." The firm has scored well with its focus on reinsurance work, where it is regarded as the "major firm," involved in areas as diverse as film financing, personal accident and international property. It also performs well in the general insurance sector. Links to European, Far Eastern and the Greek owner-markets have ensured interesting work for this "sharp and super confident" partnership.

DJ Freeman A mixed year for the firm, which has suffered a number of high profile departures, among them planning ace Richard Max. A focus on four core areas – property, insurance, media and communications, and commercial litigation – is designed to concentrate the firm's resources on its traditional strengths. Success in the insurance field, however, sees the firm move up the rankings for general claims and reinsurance, as well as entering the non-contentious listings. The firm also rises in the information technology tables, although it falls in general commercial litigation, insolvency and media and entertainment.

The defamation practice is still thriving, with the hugely praised Susan Aslan once again at the top of the listings, and her team commended for its "slickness, smoothness, good judgment and preparation." In property litigation, Vivien King is considered "a legend that doesn't stand still."

Charles Russell A successful year for this traditional player in the market. Bolstered by a number of relatively high profile new arrivals, the firm is ranked in 11 areas of practice, with 14 practitioners included in the Guide. It enters the defamation tables for the first time, where it is seen to be "getting stronger all the time," following the arrival of Duncan Lamont from Biddle. Proof of the hard work can be found in a client base that now includes names such as Hello! magazine. Along with a strong showing for the expanded team in family/matrimonial, the firm is also growing its presence in reinsurance and maintains its profile in clinical negligence. A slightly lower profile in the charities sector is balanced by continued success in trusts and personal tax, with the Guildford office offering additional support. Its work for the Jockey Club keeps the firm's flag flying in the sport: regulatory ratings.

Gouldens A highly focused and determined partnership that has clearly consolidated its existing strengths, most notably rising in our IP rankings. Managing partner Charters Macdonald-Brown heads this department, which peers acknowledge as "a good young team" able to offer a "one stop shop" for trademark filing and brand management advice. The team recently acted for Glaxo and Boehringer in a major action against parallel importers in the pharmaceutical sector.

The property team has solid foundations in retail and industrial parks, while the corporate lawyers are praised for their AIM market expertise and transactions with a cross-border element. In a year when several firms have been shedding lawyers, Gouldens bucked the trend with the addition of four new partners.

Ince & Co The firm has again excelled in its traditional strongholds of maritime law and insurance. In reinsurance, the firm has pushed back into the top band, and a strong year in general claims work has seen a steady flow of choice instructions. In shipping, the firm again features in the top tier of the *Chambers* tables, with Richard Sayer and Paul Herring at the helm. Now developing its international trade practice, much of the firm's corporate work has a cross-border element. In energy and commodities, the firm remains a respected force.

THE SOUTH

Blake Lapthorn This firm continues to enhance its stature, and is ranked in 20 areas of practice, leading the field in eight. It also has 13 lawyers featured in the Chambers Guide this year. Corporate finance, litigation (including clinical and professional negligence) and property once again figure highly as areas of expertise. The firm advised the management team in the £22.5 million MBI of Industrial Cooling Systems (ICS), the largest MBI on the South coast this year. The merger of the firm's investment management business with Ashcourt Asset Management has supplemented strategic associations and mergers (with Renouf & Co and Abbott King & Troen respectively).

DMH A full service offering that has carved its name into the fields of environment, IT and employment, the latter in which "impressive operator" Adrian Crawford moves into lead position. Competitors agree that the firm has a "big Brighton presence" in property litigation, which carries over into a solid showing in commercial litigation. This is boosted by the presence of Tim Aspinall who has "the right personality and character" to drive the department forward. Eight lawyers are featured in the Guide and the firm scores well in an impressive 20 sectors. The firm has formed four multi-disciplinary teams; innovation & media, land development, which incorporates the respected planning practice, dot.org and private client services. On March 2001 the firm acquired niche commercial property and litigation City firm Fairbairn Morris, which is expected to bolster its growing roster of clients based in the capital.

Lester Aldridge Still in its infancy, although evolving rapidly, the new Southampton office has so far been hailed as a success. Specialist units within broader practice areas offer consumer credit, employment and pensions advice, as well as insurance, housing and 'LA Gain', a consultancy and auditing service designed to grow business.

THE SOUTH: the 20 Largest Firms

	Firm	Ptnrs	Asst Solrs	Total Solrs '01	Total Solrs '00
1	**asb law** *Brighton, Chatham, Crawley, Croydon, Horsham, Maidstone, Mitcham*	42	72	**114**	82
2	**Blake Lapthorn** *Fareham, Portsmouth, Southampton*	41	61	**102**	120
3	**Thomas Eggar Church Adams** *Chichester, Horsham, Reigate, Worthing*	41	29	**70**	75
4	**Cripps Harries Hall** *Tunbridge Wells*	30	40	**70**	71
5	**Penningtons** *Basingstoke, Godalming, Newbury*	29	40	**69**	55
6	**Bond Pearce** *Southampton (3)*	22	43	**65**	59
7	**Shoosmiths** *Basingstoke, Fareham*	17	47	**64**	46
8	**Lester Aldridge** *Bournemouth, Southampton*	34	28	**62**	55
9	**Clyde & Co** *Guildford*	24	34	**58**	58
10	**Thomson Snell & Passmore** *Tonbridge, Tunbridge Wells*	34	21	**55**	55
11	**DMH** *Brighton, Crawley, Worthing*	25	28	**53**	52
12	**Hart Brown** *Cobham, Cranleigh, Godalming, Guildford (2), Woking*	15	33	**48**	51
13	**Stevens & Bolton** *Guildford*	19	28	**47**	46
14	**Brachers** *Maidstone*	19	25	**44**	39
15	**Moore & Blatch** *Lymington (2), Southampton (2)*	15	29	**44**	42
16	**Coffin Mew & Clover** *Cosham, Fareham, Gosport, Havant, Portsmouth, Southampton*	20	21	**41**	41
17	**Shadbolt & Co** *Reigate*	22	17	**39**	n/a
18	**Paris Smith & Randall** *Southampton*	14	25	**39**	36
19	**Barlows** *Chertsey, Godalming, Guildford*	14	24	**38**	34
20	**Warner Goodman & Streat** *Fareham, Parkgate, Portsmouth, Southampton, Waterlooville*	16	20	**36**	34

The rankings in this table are determined by the number of solicitors working in the region. They are based on partner and assistant solicitor figures only: all other fee-earners are excluded.

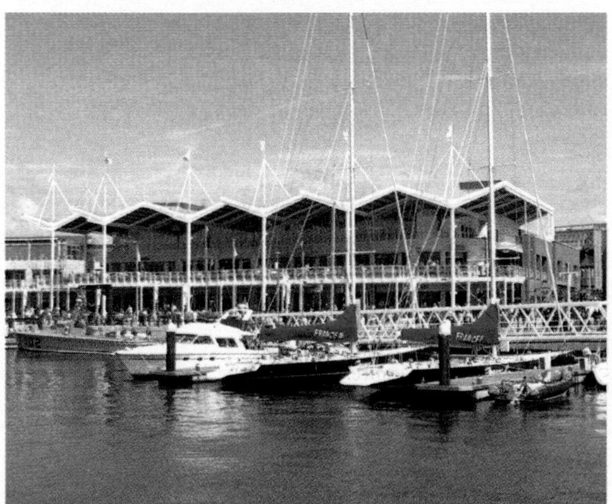

Gun Wharf, Portsmouth

Featured in 18 practice areas, the firm also has 12 lawyers highlighted by *Chambers* this year. Notable features are a steadily rising litigation team and an asset finance group that is felt to have risen to the challenge of the departure of Pip Giddins to DLA. Elsewhere, a concerted recruitment drive has netted new lawyers from Shoosmiths and Holmes Hardingham.

Cripps Harries Hall Renowned for its work in cutting-edge sectors of law such as high-tech and fund management, the firm also fields a robust commercial and property litigation team. Retaining its SIF work, the group has emerged as a leading light in professional negligence. Included in 14 practice areas, the firm boasts five ranked individuals. The jewel in its crown remains the private client practice, which sees competitors describe the firm as "in pole position" for trusts and personal tax.

Thomas Eggar Church Adams As with many firms in the region, the private client practice is the bedrock here. Both Amanda King-Jones and "excellent" Richard Thornely move up to leading position in *Chambers'* trusts and personal tax section. Although its rating has dropped in commercial property, this has been balanced by a strong showing for the commercial litigation team. Charities, church law and education are other areas of particular merit, and the firm has five practitioners ranked in the *Chambers* Guide.

Brachers Building from its Maidstone base, this respected firm has a sizeable influence on the South East market, most notably through its powerful agricultural practice, which is on the NFU panel for the region. This department is guided by the highly rated Douglas Horner who also leads the field in environment. The firm received positive feedback for its family law practice and scores well in the property litigation tables. Henry Abraham remains a leader in planning, while in clinical negligence, the "sensible and reasonable" John Sheath is a leading light of a team that has retained its presence on the NHSLA panel.

Bond Pearce The firm has had another vibrant year in the region, and is now ranked in thirteen areas. Top of the ladder for corporate finance, it also has individuals in the first tier for banking, IT and property work. The firm's presence in planning, environment, and energy and natural resources is secured by the presence of "acknowledged leader" Marcus Trinick who is "pre-eminent in his field" of wind energy and. Its involvement in the £1 billion port redevelopment of the Dibden Terminal remains a massive feather in the firm's local cap.

Thomson Snell & Passmore Balancing the needs of its wide ranging client base, offering a respected level of commercial awareness. Although the firm has lost its professional negligence ranking, this year has otherwise been overwhelmingly positive. Improvements were seen in both Property and General Commercial Litigation, while the firm secured a fresh ranking in employment. Its individuals also appear to be enjoying a higher profile this year, with six listings across a diverse range of specialisms.

Paris Smith & Randall Proud of its roots, the firm is described by one competitor as "the down to Earth Southampton practice you can refer cases to with absolute confidence." This rounded firm has particular expertise in commercial property, family/matrimonial and corporate finance, and overall, retains rankings in eight specialisms.

asb law Argles Stoneham and Burstows has re-branded after the successful tripartite merger that created the largest firm across the South. Now recognized in six areas, it leads in insolvency, an area in which it receives praise for covering "a range of work with a number of quality personnel." The key lawyers featured in Chambers are found in insolvency and commercial property, although there is a general feeling that the firm produces strong teams rather than propelling its individuals into the limelight. Strong in licensing, where the firm fields "a substantial department," it also wins market approval for its corporate finance and general litigation prowess.

THAMES VALLEY

Radcliffe Camera, Oxford

Morgan Cole The Oxford branch has this year been hit by number of high profile departures. Sue Ashtiany's move to Nabarro Nathanson is thought to have weakened the firm's employment law offering across the region, while Christopher Findlay, head of the agricultural practice, has also decamped to London, joining Bircham Dyson Bell. These moves, coupled with the loss of corporate partners, have resulted in an unsettled year. The Oxford and Reading branches of the firm are still rated in 15 areas, with both Iain Tenquist (personal injury) and Paddy Roche (licensing) holding the top spot in our tables. The firm has scored well in construction, commercial litigation and insolvency, but a poor showing in corporate finance has seen it lose its place in the *Chambers* rankings in this area.

Clarks Increasing its presence in the region's high-tech transactions, the firm is heavily endorsed by clients for its skill in advising owner-managed businesses. Now featuring in ten sections of the guide, Clarks outstrips its performance last year. The firm's growth appears to have been achieved without dilution of quality in the service it provides. Strong as ever in construction, commercial litigation, pensions and planning, it also reaches the top flight of our tables this year in employment, an area in which it is regarded by many as the firm of choice for referrals outside the City.

Henmans The firm is at its most impressive in professional negligence and agriculture, but offers consistency in a number of areas. From its Oxford base, the firm has witnessed an upward trend, with the agricultural team entirely fulfilling the potential identified last year. The family/matrimonial team is also proving an increasingly popular destination for work. The successful combination of commercial advice and expertise in the private client fields has won the support of peers, whose recommendations have secured a rating for the firm in eight sections of the *Chambers* Guide.

Manches Quadrupling turnover in the last eleven years, Manches continues to impress in both Oxford and London. Ranked in nine practice areas this year, it is known primarily for its high-end, high profile and occasionally international family work. The Oxford branch is driven by corporate finance, which accounts for just under half of its turnover. On the IP side, the team also has expertise in technology transfers for research councils. The social housing team enjoys a national reputation, while the education group leapfrogs into the first tier and acts, like the charities team, for many Oxford Colleges.

Boyes Turner A sterling performance pays dividends with a marked improvement in its focus and market profile. Now ranked in eight practice areas, clinical negligence and insolvency again prove the firm's key strengths, although it is in trusts and personal tax that a revolution has taken place. There, with the hiring of top-rated Ashley Wilkin, the practice leaps two bands. Of the six individuals ranked this year, four reside in the top tier, while the admired Adrian Desmond is now highly rated in personal injury as well as in clinical negligence.

THAMES VALLEY: the 20 Largest Firms

	Firm	Ptnrs	Asst Solrs	Total Solrs '01	Total Solrs '00
1	**Morgan Cole** *Oxford, Reading*	27	54	**81**	79
2	**Pitmans** *Reading*	16	44	**60**	39
3	**Pictons** *Bedford, Central Milton Keynes, Hemel Hempstead, Luton, St Albans, Stevenage, Watford*	31	27	**58**	69
4	**Iliffes Booth Bennett** *Chesham, Slough, Uxbridge (3)*	19	38	**57**	47
5	**Taylor Walton** *Harpenden, Hemel Hempstead, Luton, St Albans*	20	34	**54**	54
6	**Henmans** *Oxford, Woodstock*	19	30	**49**	42
7	**Shoosmiths** *Banbury, Milton Keynes, Reading*	20	22	**42**	44
8	**Clarks** *Reading*	15	26	**41**	49
9	**Manches** *Oxford*	17	20	**37**	31
10	**Bower & Bailey** *Banbury, Oxford, Witney*	22	14	**36**	56
11	**Blaser Mills Winter Taylors** *Aylesbury, Chesham, Harrow, High Wycombe (2), Rickmansworth*	11	25	**36**	46
12	**Darbys** *Oxford*	18	16	**34**	30
13	**Matthew Arnold & Baldwin** *Watford*	18	16	**34**	32
14	**Boyes Turner** *Reading*	17	17	**34**	32
15	**Osborne Clarke** *Reading*	7	26	**33**	n/a
16	**BP Collins** *Beaconsfield, Gerrards Cross*	16	15	**31**	30
17	**Linnells** *Bicester, Oxford*	17	13	**30**	34
18	**Turbervilles with Nelson Cuff** *Harrow, Hillingdon, Uxbridge*	15	15	**30**	n/a
19	**Winter-Taylors** *Aylesbury, Hazlemere, High Wycombe, Marlow, Princes Risborough*	19	8	**27**	41
20	**Blandy & Blandy** *Reading*	14	13	**27**	n/a

The rankings in this table are determined by the number of solicitors working in the region. They are based on partner and assistant solicitor figures only: all other fee-earners are excluded.

Boodle Hatfield A niche private client firm, which has now also built up its property, tax & financial planning, corporate and litigation services. The property litigation team is described as a "*small practice with some large clients*," an epithet which can be applied to the firm across the board. Originally a firm of estate managers and lawyers, property remains the cornerstone of the workload. The Oxford office is regarded as "*head and shoulders above the rest in the region*" for trusts and personal tax, while the expanding family & matrimonial practice has been bolstered by the arrival of "*local legal celebrity*" Barbara Simpson.

SOUTH WEST

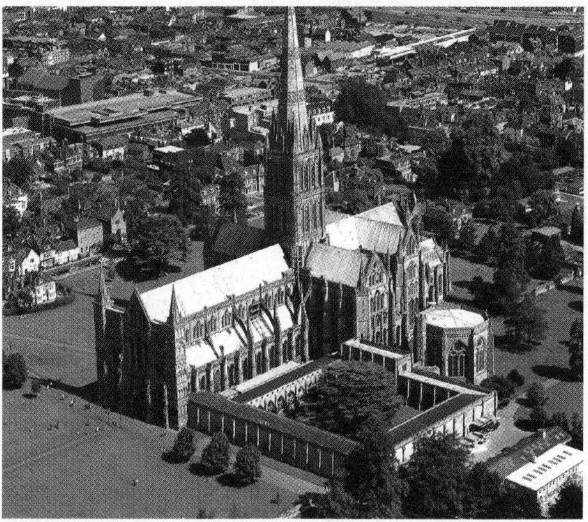

Salisbury Cathedral

Bevan Ashford Singled out by the market for its outstanding healthcare practice, the firm uses this as a springboard for its work elsewhere. Clients and peers alike comment on the commerciality and pragmatism of one of the largest regional firms in the country, which has recently opened a new office in Birmingham, where it has already established a strong reputation for clinical negligence.

The firm has been reappointed to the NHSLA panel across the UK, and has worked with the NHS in developing guidelines for future building that takes it into the fields of PFI, construction and commercial property. Our interviewees regard the group as "a key competitor" in these fields. In this edition of the Guide, the firm has 19 ranked individuals in Chambers Guide and has put in notably good showings in employment and local government.

Burges Salmon One of the country's leading regional commercial law firms, it has an impressive 38 individual lawyers rated across 29 practice areas. 16 of these areas see the firm placed in the top bracket. It continues to tussle with Osborne Clarke for corporate finance glory, sharing the honours this year. Interviewees commended the firm for its "a positive attitude and ability to reach solutions." Some 75% of this firm's clients are outside the region as it continues to score well with corporates disaffected by City rates and style, but who want advice on 'City-grade' deals. Railways are also an area of expertise, and the firm is newly ranked in health and safety. Still "unquestionably the national firm for agriculture," the firm has also had an excellent year in commercial property, powered by the respected John Dunn.

Osborne Clarke A dynamic firm with a deep well of commercial clients, which is rated in 28 practice areas this year. Broadly divided into three sectors (TMT, real estate/construction, and banking and finance), the Bristol office works with highly respected offices in London and Reading to advise on a range of big-ticket transactions.

Big name corporate partner Simon Beswick has headed to the firm's newly established San Francisco office, but the corporate team is this year considered to be broadly the equal of Burges Salmon.

SOUTH WEST: the 20 Largest Firms

		Ptnrs	Asst Solrs	Total No of Solrs '01	'00	'99	'98
1	**Bevan Ashford** *Bristol, Exeter, Plymouth, Taunton, Tiverton*	67	124	**191**	175	160	146
2	**Burges Salmon** *Bristol*	50	125	**175**	168	148	146
3	**Osborne Clarke** *Bristol*	45	115	**160**	123	137	117
4	**Bond Pearce** *Bristol (2), Exeter, Plymouth*	42	93	**135**	100	94	89
5	**Clarke Willmott & Clarke** *Bridgwater, Bristol, Taunton (2)*	41	54	**95**	91	93	96
6	**Beachcroft Wansbroughs** *Bristol*	23	61	**84**	70	63	n/a
7	**TLT Solicitors** *Bristol*	33	44	**77**	78	n/a	n/a
8	**Foot Anstey Sargent** *Budleigh Salterton, Exeter (2), Plymouth*	33	43	**76**	70	n/a	n/a
9	**Veale Wasbrough** *Bristol*	23	45	**68**	55	49	59
10	**Lyons Davidson** *Bristol (2), Plymouth*	19	40	**59**	54	47	50
11	**Stephens & Scown** *Exeter, Liskeard, Plymouth, St Austell, Truro*	35	23	**58**	61	64	59
12	**Thring Townsend** *Bath, Swindon*	36	21	**57**	n/a	n/a	n/a
13	**Michelmores** *Exeter, Sidmouth*	20	21	**41**	33	23	18
14	**Wolferstans** *Plymouth (2), Plymstock, Taunton*	21	19	**40**	48	42	42
15	**Burroughs Day** *Bristol, Portishead*	12	28	**40**	n/a	27	26
16	**Stones** *Exeter, Okehampton, Taunton, Tiverton, Torrington*	20	19	**39**	35	32	25
17	**Davies and Partners** *Bristol, Gloucester*	15	24	**39**	39	42	39
18	**Wilsons** *Salisbury*	18	18	**36**	36	29	26
19	**Woollcombe Beer Watts** *Bovey Tracey, Chagford, Exeter, Newton Abbot, Torquay*	24	11	**35**	35	36	35
20	**Hugh James Ford Simey** *Bristol, Exeter, Exmouth, Sidmouth, Southernhay Gdns*	22	13	**35**	36	29	n/a

The rankings in this table are determined by the number of solicitors working in the region. They are based on partner and assistant solicitor figures only: all other fee-earners are excluded.

Among the firm's 29 ranked individuals, Jeremy Phillips keeps his star status in the licensing ranks, while Sandra Brown moves into a leading position in Trusts and Personal Tax, as does Julian Hemming in Employment.

Bond Pearce The Bristol office has effectively doubled in size, creating the critical mass for the firm's expansion. Spurred on by its merger with niche firm Cartwrights, the firm has now added expertise in food and drink retailing, leisure and licensing to its burgeoning portfolio. In the Plymouth office, although the family department has been closed down, its shipping team has been developed with the addition of leading player Nick Horton. Professional negligence, debt recovery and employment are other areas which have seen an increase in a growth. Achieving first tier recognition in eight practice areas, the firm also boasts 10 top ranked individuals in the South West.

Clarke Willmott & Clarke Both the Taunton and Bristol offices are considered top-notch for planning work, and it comes as little surprise that firm fields an environment team nearly as strong. Taunton's particular strength is debt recovery work, whilst Bristol is the region's undisputed number one in sport. Six individuals rank as band one in their respective practice areas. The focus on commercial litigation has enjoyed some success, with that department moving up in our rankings this year. Peers and clients regularly commend the firm for its "proactive approach."

TLT Solicitors Post-merger the firm is performing strongly, with many practice areas showing an upward trend. One of the largest firms in the Bristol market, it is beginning to have a significant impact both inside and outside the region. A notable indication of the merger's strengthening effect is the "young and positive" corporate finance department's rise towards the premier league. The firm now boasts eight *Chambers*-listed individuals, of whom four are top rated. Remaining top-rated in family/matrimonial and partnership law, the firm's debt recovery team is thought by many to be "the best in the area." Philip May stands out at the firm for his top status in both partnership and commercial litigation.

Beachcroft Wansbroughs The Bristol branch of this national firm is ranked in 11 areas of practice and is in the top tier for professional negligence, insurance and personal injury. The latter boasts separate multi-track and fast track teams with Bob Beale holding his top ranking. Healthcare remains a strong sector for the Bristol branch, which retains its place on the NHSLA and has a strong health litigation department headed by Nigel Montgomery, highly rated in this year's Guide for clinical negligence. The firm moves up the construction and property litigation tables, as well as entering the South West corporate recovery/insolvency ranking. Altogether, the Bristol branch has eight ranked individual practitioners.

Foot Anstey Sargent At its best in shipping, family/matrimonial and defamation, the firm fields four band one rated players. Defamation especially sees the firm, which has an enviable clientele of regional newspapers, punching well above its weight. The firm's strong performance in the key commercial sectors has been complemented by its private client practice.

Stephens & Scown Equally balanced performances from both the Devon and Cornwall offices as the firm stakes its claim among the region's players. Ranked in eleven practice areas, it scores well in administrative and public law, crime and family/matrimonial. Crime is traditionally the firm's trump card and this year has seen the major appointment of top flight Michael Butler from Claude, Hornby & Cox.

Veale Wasbrough The firm retains a leading position in a wide number of disciplines, although education, energy, partnership and personal injury are the areas in which it clearly excels. This year, ten individuals are ranked, of whom six are considered top flight in their respective practice areas. With Tim Smithers at the helm, the firm moves up into the first band for energy, where it has won a national reputation for its pipeline expertise. Commercial litigation boasts two highly rated practitioners in Simon Pizzey and Nigel Puddicombe and in this sphere the firm is seen to have "strengthened its position." However, the property practice has suffered a setback with the departure of leading partner Nigel Somerville, though the department is felt to have enough strength to weather this loss.

WALES

Morgan Cole The firm continues to dominate the region by sheer force of size. Across its offices in Cardiff and Swansea, the firm scores a ranking in 30 areas and has 22 leading individuals highlighted. It is leading in ten areas and is particularly strong in professional negligence, described by many as "<u>the</u> team in Wales." "Analytical" Alan Wilson is on the leading commercial litigation team that acts for the NFU across Wales. Philip Howell Richardson retains his star rating in Alternative Dispute Resolution and the acquisition of "sensible, approachable" Julian Boswall from Clifford Chance has proved worthwhile for the planning department as it is now top-rated in *Chambers* Guide.

Eversheds A successful year for the Cardiff branch of this national giant, in spite of the firm's decision to move away from private client work in Wales. The firm enjoys leading status in 15 sections, with the education team representing one third of FE Colleges and one half of HE Colleges. Although it continues to stand out for employment,

Cardiff Bay

WALES: the 10 Largest Firms

	Firm	Ptnrs	Asst Solrs	Total No of Solrs '01	'00	'99	'98
1	**Morgan Cole** *Cardiff, Swansea*	38	65	**103**	105	112	n/a
2	**Hugh James Ford Simey** *Bargoed, Blackwood, Cardiff, Merthyr Tydfil, Pontlottyn, Talbot Green, Treharris*	37	46	**83**	78	66	n/a
3	**Eversheds** *Cardiff*	38	43	**81**	85	86	51
4	**Edwards Geldard** *Cardiff*	22	39	**61**	56	66	57
5	**Leo Abse & Cohen** *Cardiff, Swansea*	11	47	**58**	51	51	48
6	**John Collins & Partners with Edward Harris & Son** *Swansea (2)*	15	28	**43**	40	n/a	n/a
7	**Palser Grossman** *Cardiff Bay, Swansea*	15	18	**33**	33	27	25
8	**Dolmans** *Cardiff (2)*	12	20	**32**	32	26	26
9	**Douglas-Jones Mercer** *Swansea*	12	11	**23**	25	23	21
10	**Gamlins** *Colwyn Bay, Conwy, Flintshire, Llandudno, Rhos-on-Sea, Rhyl*	10	11	**21**	27	27	27

The rankings in this table are determined by the number of solicitors working in the region. They are based on partner and assistant solicitor figures only: all other fee-earners are excluded.

insolvency and commercial litigation, public sector advice remains the firm's real forte, with top rankings in administrative and public law and local government. Success in part is due to such "ubiquitous" experts as the "abrasive, purposeful" Eric Evans, who not only wins the leading position in both sections, but also is also included in planning. A year of improvement and consolidation has also seen additional numbers joining the office following the closure of the firm's Bristol office.

Hugh James Ford Simey A well-balanced practice that has refused to reduce its private client base. Huge effort has gone into successful claimant litigation, on behalf of miners with respiratory diseases, leading to the creation of a niche specialism in the area. Personal injury continues to be an area of strength, with consistent recognition of Andrew Harding and Mark Harvey as leaders in their field.

A good showing in insurance, which continues to form the mainstay of the commercial litigation practice, is supplemented by a flourishing property litigation practice, where Neil Morgan earns consistent market commendation. The commercial property has grown, although still does not typically act on the very largest deals, but the firm's education and family departments continue to set standards for others to match.

Edwards Geldard Fortified by its merger with Eking Manning, the firm continues to be best known for its corporate finance practice, where it has overseen high value M&A work for LG in its merger with Philips. The firm is also recognised for a broad range of commercial disciplines including IT and IP, where Ceri Delemore remains at the top of both rankings.

An established local name in commercial property, Rowland Davies continues to act for the Welsh Rugby Union. Property Litigation has also improved this year; with the department boasting clients such as Coats Viyella and Powergen. In commercial litigation, Paul Hopkins has helped to achieve success in overseeing commercial disputes before the House of Lords.

A major figure in local public law, Huw Williams is rated for administrative and public law, local government and planning. The firm works closely in these areas with the Welsh Development Agency and the National Assembly of Wales.

John Collins & Partners with Edward Harris & Son This merger of two strong Swansea firms has given the resulting practice a high profile within the saturated South Wales market. This firm is seen as "*clearly deserving its good reputation*" across practice areas – which include Clinical Negligence and Debt Recovery. However the firm only produced one ranked individual in this year's findings, that of Edward Harris, again seen as one of the leading practitioners in Agriculture.

MIDLANDS

Wragge & Co The firm can lay claim to the title of most successful regional firm in the land, reporting a record 40% increase in turnover this year. Its outstanding strategy of seeking second tier work from FTSE 100 corporates has paid dividends as the corporate team drives forwards, with much of its profile and workload being won in the London market. This team alone fields nine leading practitioners and the firm has won instruction from 39 of the FTSE 100.

Perhaps due to its success in securing these household name corporates and the conflict issues they bring with them, *Chambers* research this year has noticed that the banking team, although widely admired, has failed to hit the heights of its corporate counterpart. The London office remains confined to IP, in spite of rumours of a possible link with Tarlo Lyons, as the firm refuses to deviate from its 'one office' approach.

Birmingham

MIDLANDS: the 30 Largest Firms

		Ptnrs	Asst Solrs	Total No of Solrs '01	'00	'99	'98
1	**Wragge & Co** *Birmingham*	106	290	**396**	340	275	224
2	**Eversheds** *Birmingham, Derby, Nottingham*	63	196	**259**	245	167	160
3	**Pinsent Curtis Biddle** *Birmingham*	57	89	**146**	n/a	n/a	n/a
4	**Hammond Suddards Edge** *Birmingham*	46	81	**127**	127	n/a	n/a
5	**Browne Jacobson** *Birmingham, Nottingham*	41	72	**113**	102	95	88
6	**Nelsons** *Derby, Leicester, Nottingham*	55	53	**108**	72	72	61
7	**Freethcartwright** *Derby, Leicester, Nottingham*	49	55	**104**	100	104	104
8	**Shoosmiths** *Northampton (2), Nottingham*	41	61	**102**	95	108	101
9	**Martineau Johnson** *Birmingham*	40	60	**100**	94	64	79
10	**DLA** *Birmingham*	n/a	n/a	**n/a**	81	75	71
11	**Gateley Wareing** *Birmingham, Leicester, Nottingham*	15	53	**68**	49	36	40
12	**Lee Crowder** *Birmingham*	22	38	**60**	51	38	38
13	**The Smith Partnership** *Burton-on-Trent, Derby (2), Leicester (2), Longton, Newcastle-under-Lyme, Swadlincote*	21	36	**57**	45	39	39
14	**Harvey Ingram Owston** *Leicester*	23	27	**50**	52	54	50
15	**Anthony Collins Solicitors** *Birmingham*	17	33	**50**	45	41	11
16	**Thompsons** *Birmingham, Nottingham, Stoke-on-Trent*	9	40	**49**	42	41	41
17	**Irwin Mitchell** *Birmingham*	11	37	**48**	46	35	35
18	**Mills & Reeve** *Birmingham*	11	37	**48**	46	38	n/a
19	**Challinors Lyon Clark** *Birmingham, Edgbaston, West Bromwich*	28	18	**46**	45	44	43
20	**Shakespeares** *Birmingham*	22	23	**45**	50	52	49
21	**Edwards Geldard** *Derby, Nottingham*	20	24	**44**	n/a	n/a	n/a
22	**Higgs & Sons** *Brierley Hill, Dudley, Kingswinford, Stourbridge*	26	16	**42**	40	36	35
23	**The Wilkes Partnership** *Birmingham (2)*	17	25	**42**	42	41	38
24	**Wright Hassall** *Leamington Spa*	21	16	**37**	32	30	29
25	**Morton Fisher** *Bewdley, Bromsgrove, Kidderminster, Stourport-on-Severn, Worcester*	17	18	**35**	43	43	43
26	**Toller Hales & Collcutt** *Corby, Kettering, Northampton, Wellingborough*	22	11	**33**	37	35	33
27	**Garretts** *Birmingham*	8	25	**33**	31	27	27
28	**Hewitson Becke + Shaw** *Northampton*	17	15	**32**	32	33	34
29	**Knight & Sons** *Newcastle-under-Lyme*	19	12	**31**	n/a	34	37
30	**Weightmans** *Birmingham, Leicester*	17	14	**31**	34	34	6

The rankings in this table are determined by the number of solicitors working in the region. They are based on partner and assistant solicitor figures only: all other fee-earners are excluded.

Rated in 32 sections, it is a firm continuing to insist upon quality, rather than quantity of advice. In areas such as IP and construction, commended for is national spread of work, the firm continues to thrive. Currently investing heavily in its core areas of pensions, IT, commercial property and employment, these sectors also continue to perform well in the *Chambers* rankings.

Public sector work is far from suffering neglect: the firm swoops into the number one ranking spot in administrative & public law, and is seen to be "one of a very few firms to have a secure hold on local government work." With 53 solicitors from the firm featuring in the Guide, the firm is now almost out of sight of its local competitors.

Eversheds Although clearly behind Wragge & Co in the regional pecking order, the Birmingham office continues to excel in its key areas. The decision to reorganise teams into department-led rather than regionally-led practice areas has reaped benefits in such sectors as banking and debt-recovery, in which the firm has moved up to secure leading positions. Pat Johnstone has been lauded for "building up a stable banking team," aided by the ability to draw upon expertise from around the country. She acted on one of the year's headline deals, representing the Phoenix consortium on the financing of the acquisition of MG Rover from BMW.

Ranked in a respectable 26 different practice areas, with 31 leading individuals, a commercial edge becomes evident when looking at some of the nine sections with top rankings: banking; information technology; insolvency; and commercial property. Among individuals, Jeff Drew is seen as "still the regional market leader" for insolvency/corporate recovery. Only in environment and pensions, where Giles Orton's move to London has been keenly felt, is the firm considered to have performed below last year's standards.

Pinsent Curtis Biddle Again increasing its representation in *Chambers* both in terms of ranked departments and individuals, the Birmingham office has again proved to be one of the merged firm's jewels. Having laterally hired a team from Irwin Mitchell, the firm is top rated in administrative and public law, where it advises on major town centre redevelopment.

However, it is in the commercial areas that the firm's star shines brightest. Felt by our interviewees to have the "size, clients and economic muscle," its commercial litigation department has been involved in significant disputes in the water and power industries, while the banking team is noted for handling complex cross border transactions. In project finance, the team has also had a strong year, while the firm can justifiably point to tax and employee share schemes as areas of success. The tax department has been augmented by the recruitment of two new partners, while the share scheme operation, fronted by stellar David Pett, advises the choicest of clients and has been described as "by far the leading force in the regions." Construction and insolvency are two rare sectors of disappointment – the teams have been unable to progress up the tables in either area.

Hammond Suddards Edge Following merger, it had been suspected that the focus of the firm would be shifting South. While restructuring has clearly made some difference, with, for example, the debt recovery team largely relocating to Bradford, the change has not been seismic. Respected in the battleground areas of property, commercial litigation and corporate finance, the only sphere in which the firm appears to be on the retreat is IP, where the loss of Michael Luckman to Wragges is perceived as a blow. The firm can point to its media and sport departments as centres of excellence. Representing the Football League, the sports department led by Richard Alderson is particularly celebrated. One of the foremost in the country, it maintains a presence in the region, while having strong links with a London office that has been buttressed through the incorporation of niche firm Townleys.

Browne Jacobson An East Midlands firm with a foothold in London, although its reputation is primarily derived from the Nottingham office. Increasingly the firm is attracting work on the back of a national reputation in areas such as public authority, clinical negligence, PI and health-related issues. Work is split between the insurance & public sector division and the commercial division, with clients including local authorities, health and educational institutions, insurers and plcs.

The firm has consolidated its position in many areas, gaining impressive ground in healthcare in recognition of its "excellent understanding of the profession." The professional negligence team remains respected, with leading light Robert Ridgewell and his team thought to have "made big strides," while the personal injury team has expertise in fast track and high profile multi-party actions.

Featured in 18 areas, with 20 individuals taking the limelight, the firm continues to be a leading force in corporate finance, judged by competitors to be "the biggest player in the East Midlands, with the best resources."

Freethcartwright A substantial presence in the East Midlands market, which continues to flex its commercial muscle, rising in the *Chambers* rankings in corporate finance, employment, construction and commercial property. Over the last year, the firm has acted in numerous big deals across the region, including the £80 million share equity release of Travelesphere.

Key strength exists in the contentious areas of personal injury, clinical negligence and product liability, with much of this profile attributed to top performer Paul Balen. Only trusts and personal tax and intellectual property (where Helen Driscoll has departed) spoil an otherwise healthy year's achievement.

Shoosmiths A consistent year for the firm's Northampton and Nottingham offices, which are featured in ten practice areas this year, with the spotlight on five practitioners. The Northampton office, the firm's focal point, has held its ground. Food law continues to constitute an area in which the firm remains ahead of the pack; its "punchy and well-balanced" intellectual property team, headed up by Gary Assim, has also received a positive response from the market, as has the technically "excellent" commercial property team.

The office's entry into our tables for its "wide-ranging" and "respectable" debt recovery practice has, however, been balanced by a dip in banking, where the team has lost its foothold and been dropped. The Nottingham office has also had a steady rather than spectacular year, although its corporate finance team has moved up the rankings and Oliver Brookshaw is now recognised as a leading individual.

Martineau Johnson This long established player in the Birmingham market has seen progression in agriculture, corporate finance and property litigation. The IP department, under the aegis of William Barker, continues to gain recognition as the "one to watch," a position accentuated by the recent hires of Niall Head-Rapson and Helen Driscoll.

In its traditional fortes, the firm continues to excel, winning national recognition for its higher education practice, and offering a private client department that is regarded as "a classic old money practice with quality clients." Elsewhere, insolvency man Ian Baker is thought by competitors to be "among the best in Birmingham." A consistent firm, ranked in 16 areas, it secures top slot in Charities, Education; Energy and Trusts and Personal Tax. The opening of a new London office speaks volumes for the firm's confidence in its future.

DLA With nine individuals ranked in ten areas, the firm shows a slight downturn on last year's performance. The Birmingham office is respected for its strong PFI presence under the guidance of Anthony Randle, while the tax team benefits from the continued presence of Gregory Morris.

Lee Crowder Capitalising on its impressive growth and success in attracting big name lateral hires, this "*first class, personable*" firm is commended by clients for its clear focus and partner led approach. The construction team is being developed by Jeffrey Brown, whose individual profile continues to rise while the property team is praised by clients for its "sheer responsiveness." Much of this skill in residential development complements the activities of Andy Ballard and the admired social housing team. The firm remains one of the few in the regions to demonstrate an expertise in media and entertainment sphere.

EAST ANGLIA

King's College and chapel, Cambridge

Mills & Reeve A successful year once more for this particularly highly regarded firm. Demonstrating expertise in 27 practice areas, the firm is rated top in a prodigious 19 of these. With 34 ranked lawyers and 18 leading individuals, the firm's core areas of expertise include health, education and farming, as well as corporate finance, litigation and insolvency. Cambridge's reputation as a focal point for European high-tech and biotech work led to the firm's alliance with niche IP practice, Trask Britt (based in Salt Lake City) in January of 2001.

Development of the firm's property practice is increasingly pulling more work from London, with the Cambridge and Norwich offices ranked top again this year.

Eversheds The three East Anglian branches of this national powerhouse have immense presence within the region, snapping at the heels of leaders, Mills & Reeve. Ranked in 24 different practice areas, and fielding 21 leading individuals, the firm is the clear regional number two. The top-ranking sectors are similar to those in other Eversheds offices: administrative & public law; banking; employment, and cor-

EAST ANGLIA: the 10 Largest Firms

	Firm	Ptnrs	Asst Solrs	Total No of Solrs '01	'00	'99	'98
1	**Mills & Reeve** *Cambridge, Norwich*	44	93	**137**	139	129	127
2	**Eversheds** *Cambridge, Ipswich, Norwich*	44	84	**128**	123	99	89
3	**Taylor Vinters** *Cambridge*	22	48	**70**	55	47	43
4	**Hewitson Becke + Shaw** *Cambridge, Saffron Walden*	34	25	**59**	59	50	49
5	**Edwards Duthie** *Ilford*	14	42	**56**	n/a	n/a	n/a
6	**Ashton Graham** *Bury St Edmunds, Felixstowe, Ipswich*	22	15	**37**	37	43	37
7	**Prettys** *Ipswich*	16	20	**36**	36	34	31
8	**Greenwoods** *Peterborough*	16	17	**33**	31	33	31
9	**Fosters** *Bungay, Norwich*	14	13	**27**	n/a	20	23
10	**Birkett Long** *Colchester, Halstead*	16	9	**25**	n/a	n/a	n/a

The rankings in this table are determined by the number of solicitors working in the region. They are based on partner and assistant solicitor figures only: all other fee-earners are excluded.

porate recovery to name but a few. The firm's profile in construction has partially been attributed to the addition of Adrian Cole from Campbell Hooper, while the IP practice is also judged by peers to be making a push. The offices' decision to move away from private client work has underlined the regional emphasis on core areas of work.

Hewitson Becke & Shaw Featured in 15 sections with 13 ranked individuals this year, the firm remains a regional stalwart. Leading positions in the areas of employment, property litigation, and commercial property are backed by strong showings in information technology, environmental, general commercial litigation and planning law. At the time of writing, the firm was at an advanced stage of merger talks with Oxford based firm, Linnells.

However, the firm has had to cope with departures this year. Its corporate finance department suffered the loss of Bridget Kerle, who has left the profession, while the previously renowned IP department lost two key partners to US firm Dorsey & Whitney's London office.

Taylor Vinters A predominantly positive year for the firm, whose rankings both for practice areas and leading individuals number the same as last year (12 individuals in 11 areas), but whose position in several of these areas has strengthened. Evolving alongside the emerging high-tech businesses in Silicon Fen, the firm's IP practice advises both locally and internationally, and is sustaining its growth. Top-ranked John Short is seen as the driving force behind the insolvency team, which has also made headway this year. The commercial property and planning teams have both gone up a notch and the only area to take a knock in terms of rankings has been corporate finance.

Prettys This firm is ranked in a dozen areas in this year's edition. With strengths in road transport, agriculture (this is the NFU panel firm for the region), commercial property, the firm can be seen as tailoring its strengths to the needs of the geographic area. It has entered our rankings for shipping, a testament to the firm's involvement in overseas instructions. This year the firm has produced six ranked individuals, with Ian Waine recognised as one of the top regional practitioners in insolvency. The firm continues to be warmly rated by clients for its "team ethos and commerciality."

NORTH WEST

Liverpool Docks

DLA One of the strongest regions in the firm's national portfolio has managed to rack up 22 ranked individuals across 17 practice areas in Liverpool and Manchester. In eight sectors, the firm emerges in the top flight. An impressive banking department now has three leading individuals within the team. Commercial property also has three individuals ranked, with Roy Beckett rated as an outstanding performer. The environment, pensions, private equity, employment and commercial litigation departments all enjoy top status, although shipping and education have both lost ground.

Addleshaw Booth & Co Although 2001 saw the firm's London branch growing in strength, it remains overshadowed by its flagship offices in Manchester and Leeds. Top-ranked in ten sections of *Chambers* in Manchester, the firm's combination of judicious lateral hiring with the nurturing of home grown talent has led to the ranking of 35 individuals in the tables.

Corporate finance remains its bastion, where a team possessing "superb ability" services an enviable client base, including Airtours, Barclays Bank and Adidas. The commercial property department, which has involved itself in high profile regeneration work, has also enjoyed an outstanding year. The roll of honour extends to IP, employment, competition, pensions and projects, all of which are said to be staffed by individuals with "focus and drive."

Individual laurels go to Egan Brooks in the insolvency department, the only individual from the office to occupy the starred. Described by one competitor as "obviously on a different plane from the rest of us," he exhibited his skills to good effect in advising Arthur Andersen on the administration of Powernet Telecom.

Halliwell Landau Known for its impressive growth and increased turnover in recent years, this firm again features in a wide range of sections of Chambers. Although its market profile appears to have decreased in banking and employment, the firm has several areas of outstanding achievement. Richard Boardman's IP department is felt to have "real focus" and has represented Umbro on its sponsorship of Chelsea Football Club; the "brilliant" Roger Lancaster has a fine track record in advocacy on the planning front; the trusts department offers quality advice on estate planning and trust creation; the commercial property department is highly rated for development work.

Although not possessing quite such a high profile for commercial litigation, the firm remains a respected opponent, characterised by opponents as an "aggressive and commercially aware" team.

Berrymans Lace Mawer The focus of the firm is seen to have changed over the last year; with the eclipse of their Commercial Litigation and Commercial Property departments within the region, the firm's workload is now focused on insurance-related matters. With departments in the Manchester and Liverpool offices, the firm's presence in personal injury is felt across the region. Much of this work comes from its strength in insurance, which remains undiminished, despite the firm's failed bid to secure the services of the Cartwrights insurance team.

Hill Dickinson Another year in which this firm has been seen to play to its strengths, securing its profile across the region. It continues to lead the field nationally for road transport, with the "feisty and excellent" Julia Marshall coming in for particular praise. It also received warm endorsement from our interviewees in shipping, with five of the firm's nine ranked individuals rated in one of these two fields.

The firm remains strongest in its Liverpool base, where the teams are seen in the more contentious fields of insurance, personal injury, professional and clinical negligence. Anthony Gibbons and Allan Mowat remain top ranked for their work in clinical negligence. The Manchester office is seen to offer sound support. Although the firm slips a place in our commercial property section, Philip Woods' intellectual property department in Stockport continues to blossom.

Hammonds Suddards Edge Here in its traditional backyard, the firm enjoys recognised prowess across a range of disciplines. While having an effective presence in many important areas such as construction and property litigation, it is the employment department, the largest in the region, which reaches the heights of our tables. National head Sue Nickson enjoys a countrywide reputation.

Similarly lauded is the commercial litigation team, which has also joined the pack as one of the leading mainstream dispute resolution teams, having dispensed with its previous tigerish image, and gained a CEDR award. In corporate finance, the feeling persists that the firm has not regained the profile of two years ago, but it is at least perceived to have stabilised and even added powerful new clients. Elsewhere, the firm earns a ranking for IT. Here, the department has featured in several high value deals over the past year such as the US$100 million acquisition of Cyber Patrol.

Pannone & Partners Continuing to expand, the firm's annual turnover is now running at £16.5 million, a second consecutive 20% plus increase.

Core strength remains in personal injury, with Catherine Leech now joining Carol Jackson at the top of the leading individuals rankings. In addition no other firm in the region can approach the firm's level of success in clinical negligence and family, where the teams have gained national recognition. The Alder Hey theft of organs enquiry, in which Stephen Jones was the lead solicitor, and Re: A, (conjoined twins, Jodie and Mary), in which John Kitchingham represented the parents, are two major feathers in the firm's cap.

In the commercial arena, both the commercial property and corporate finance practices have prospered greatly this year. Now acting on such sizeable deals as the acquisition of Manchester Airport and the £500 million Phase III extension of Metrolink, the firm is showing a notably more balanced approach to its workload.

Cobbetts Overwhelming strength commercial property continues to be the foundation on which the firm's success is built. One recent highlight was the involvement of Stephen Benson and his team in the £1.6 billion sale of Whitbread's entire pub portfolio. Recognised in 13 areas of practice, the firm also continues to thrive in areas such as tax and contentious matters. Litigator Peter Stone is highly rated in both property litigation and defamation. A growing commercial litigation capacity has been widely noted, while the corporate team's profile has been assisted by such transactions as the merger between CRS and CWS.

The licensing team continues the good work, with Simon Jones taking the lead in developing expertise on the regulatory side, and Mike Gaskill reinforces the firm's pre-eminence in social housing, having recently completed a commission involving the transfer of nearly 10,000 council homes. Though trusts and personal tax is the only section in which the firm's profile falls, the recruitment of Catherine Graham from Eversheds' London office indicates its commitment to the area.

NORTH WEST: the 12 Largest Firms

	Firm	Ptnrs	Asst Solrs	Total No of Solrs '01	'00	'99	'98
1	**DLA** *Liverpool, Manchester*	n/a	n/a	**n/a**	170	145	144
2	**Addleshaw Booth & Co** *Manchester*	57	105	**162**	148	122	122
3	**Halliwell Landau** *Manchester*	48	98	**146**	126	132	103
4	**Eversheds** *Manchester*	30	93	**123**	77	114	74
5	**Pannone & Partners** *Manchester*	61	60	**121**	93	82	78
6	**Hill Dickinson** *Chester, Liverpool, Manchester, Stockport*	71	48	**119**	110	110	109
7	**Davies Wallis Foyster** *Liverpool, Manchester*	51	65	**116**	91	119	110
8	**Cobbetts** *Manchester*	50	54	**104**	87	87	69
9	**Hammond Suddards Edge** *Manchester*	26	68	**94**	94	n/a	n/a
10	**Weightmans** *Liverpool, Manchester*	41	50	**91**	93	93	93
11	**Berrymans Lace Mawer** *Liverpool, Manchester*	26	65	**91**	114	101	101
12	**Mace & Jones** *Huyton, Knutsford, Liverpool, Manchester*	27	42	**69**	69	60	42

The rankings in this table are determined by the number of solicitors working in the region. They are based on partner and assistant solicitor figures only: all other fee-earners are excluded.

Davies Wallis Foyster Emerging convincingly from a comparatively fallow period, the firm's status has grown in a number of areas, helped by the addition of 11 new partners this year and a doubling of the number of fee earners over the past three years. Its large insurance department gains recognition, both in Liverpool and Manchester, boosted by regular instruction from Royal & SunAlliance. The Manchester office also scores well in commercial litigation, an area perceived to be critical to the firm's resurgence. The insolvency team has gone from strength to strength, while work in commercial property is also expanding, the department having advised on several multi-million pound deals. Employment and licensing are other areas where the firm's influence has grown.

Eversheds Securing a ranking within 19 practice areas and fielding 22 leading individuals, the Manchester branch of the national firm continues to figure among the regional leaders. The corporate side has notched up another impressive set of rankings this year, with banking, competition, commercial litigation and commercial property all the subject of warm praise from our interviewees. Corporate finance ranks just below regional rivals Addleshaw Booth, with star individual and "doughty opponent," Edward Pysden considered as Manchester's number one.

The tax department also deserves recognition. Undertaking such complex deals as advising Telecity on a £550 million flotation, it has joined the biggest players of the region. Public sector work enjoys its usual high profile, with education moving up to the top spot, thanks to the "expert" John Boardman. Administrative & public law and employment also remain a strong focus for the firm's group of "talented lawyers."

YORKSHIRE

DLA An obvious regional contender, the firm in Yorkshire has 16 ranked individuals in 15 different areas of law. Commercial litigation and insolvency remain areas of particular expertise, while the corporate finance department, which includes the talents of Alistair da Costa and Andrew Darwin, gains widespread acclaim. The latter team advised on the floating of three companies within the space of 24 hours.

Addleshaw Booth & Co With 36 individual practitioners recognised across 27 practice areas, this office is a match for any in the region. Advising a host of blue-chip corporate clients, the Leeds office's corporate finance and commercial litigation departments, led by Sean Lippell and Simon Kamstra respectively, continue to receive warm endorsement in our research with the former team involved in headline cases such as 3i's £223 million takeover of Peter Black's.

The overall picture is one of sustained growth, with key areas such as tax, financial services and construction all buoyant, the last having impressed on a £130 million programme to restructure a portfolio of 120 primary and secondary schools. A competitor to leading City practices, its versatility is shown in the performance of its outstanding family department. Under the stewardship of David Salter, a nationally renowned expert, it continues to dominate the region. Only the departure of planning stalwart Steven Turnbull can cloud the firm's otherwise sunny year.

YORKSHIRE: the 30 Largest Firms

	Firm	Ptnrs	Asst Solrs	Total Solrs '01	Total Solrs '00
1	**DLA** *Bradford, Leeds (2), Sheffield*	n/a	n/a	**n/a**	188
2	**Addleshaw Booth & Co** *Leeds (2)*	55	116	**171**	159
3	**Irwin Mitchell** *Leeds, Sheffield*	56	94	**150**	141
4	**Eversheds** *Leeds*	39	110	**149**	139
5	**Pinsent Curtis Biddle** *Leeds*	51	83	**134**	n/a
6	**Hammond Suddards Edge** *Bradford, Leeds*	39	88	**127**	127
7	**Walker Morris** *Leeds*	37	86	**123**	121
8	**Nabarro Nathanson** *Sheffield*	15	47	**62**	62
9	**Ford & Warren** *Leeds*	16	44	**60**	47
10	**Beachcroft Wansbroughs** *Leeds*	18	40	**58**	77
11	**Ison Harrison & Co** *Chapeltown, Crossgates, Garforth, Goldthorpe, Leeds, York*	23	34	**57**	34
12	**Lupton Fawcett** *Leeds*	23	32	**55**	50
13	**Andrew M. Jackson & Co** *Hull*	23	31	**54**	53
14	**Gordons Cranswick Solicitors** *Bradford, Keighley, Leeds*	28	25	**53**	49
15	**Gosschalks** *Hull*	26	26	**52**	46
16	**Rollits** *Hull, York*	31	17	**48**	47
17	**Keeble Hawson** *Leeds (2), Sheffield*	26	19	**45**	46
18	**Hempsons** *Harrogate*	5	32	**37**	37
19	**Attey Dibb and Clegg** *Barnsley, Doncaster (2), Goldthorpe, Mexborough, Rotherham, Thorne, Wath*	24	10	**34**	32
20	**Howells** *Sheffield (3)*	12	22	**34**	27
21	**Masons** *Leeds*	6	26	**32**	n/a
22	**Praxis Partners** *Leeds*	7	22	**29**	n/a
23	**Harrowell Shaftoe** *Haxby, York (2)*	15	12	**27**	29
24	**Brooke North** *Leeds*	17	9	**26**	26
25	**Hamers** *Doncaster, Hull, Leeds, Sheffield*	5	21	**26**	34
26	**Read Hind Stewart** *Leeds*	17	8	**25**	26
27	**Denison Till** *Leeds, York*	14	10	**24**	24
28	**Last Cawthra Feather** *Bradford, Ilkley, Shipley*	12	12	**24**	23
29	**McCormicks** *Harrogate, Leeds*	11	13	**24**	n/a
30	**Wrigleys** *Leeds, Sheffield*	11	13	**24**	25

The rankings in this table are determined by the number of solicitors working in the region. They are based on partner and assistant solicitor figures only: all other fee-earners are excluded.

Civic Hall, Leeds

Irwin Mitchell A broad-based firm, ranked in 21 areas from corporate finance to travel, it fields ten leading individuals this year. Heralded for its ability in claimant clinical negligence, claimant personal injury and product liability, the firm is home to such noted practitioners as David Body, who is said to have "devoted his heart and soul" to the vCJD victims' families for whom he has acted.

"Innovation" is said to make the firm stand out from the crowd in areas such as human rights and civil liberties, where it lays claim to being "one of the few firms to have recently created a national team devoted to human rights." The introduction of a discrete financial services arm with fund management facilities for existing private and public clients, is evidence of a firm which is continuing to develop, while playing to its strengths.

Eversheds This flagship office of the nationwide firm continues to excel, with 27 practice areas and 21 individuals achieving recognition in our tables. It is the national centre of excellence for environment, local government and telecommunications.

The environment team has merited the accolade of the "leading firm in the regions," from several interviewees, with starred individual, the "astute and creative" Paul Smith receiving a stream of recommendations. Similarly in local government, the team retains the title of "the market leader" outside London. Leading light Stephen Cirell inspires massive confidence in peers and clients. One said: "If I were a local authority client in a difficult situation, I would want him on it." A "constant threat" in the key commercial areas, the firm's commercial litigation department is regarded with particular respect, while education and administrative and public law departments have also excelled. The corporate team continues to advise on major deals such as HSBC Private Equity's £496 million acquisition of Caradon's plumbing division.

Hammond Suddards Edge Continuing to hold its ground, the Yorkshire office remains a significant arm of this national operator. The firm has performed well in its keystone areas. The commercial litigation team is thriving, having appointed a barrister of 20 years' standing to form a specialist in-house advocacy unit, while debt recovery continues to be an area of distinct specialism, with the Bradford-based 'Debtline' team garnering national approval. Two areas of notable improvement have been private equity and construction, where the "first rate strategic thinker" Simon Palmer has exhibited skill in electrical and engineering disputes. The IT team has also come into its own, advising on a clutch of big deals including Halifax Estate Agencies on an online estate agency venture. The respected corporate team has advised on a host of public takeovers, while the property team has advised on the disposal of the Norfolk Park development site.

Walker Morris Operating a one-office policy, the firm continues to defy the sceptics and offer genuine competition to the national firms in Leeds. On the property and planning side, the firm shows up well, advising an imposing client base that now includes Starbucks, which the firm advises on its portfolio management. The corporate team also gains respect for its work on deals around the £100 million mark, while the insolvency department runs the gamut from complex corporate insolvencies to administrations, and houses a highly respected practitioner in Philip Mudd.

However, the firm's progress has been greatest in litigation, where, with lateral hires at partner level from Eversheds and Irwin Mitchell, it has become a real local force. Further strides have been made in construction, tax, trusts and local government while the only retrograde steps have occurred in debt recovery, pensions and projects work.

Pinsent Curtis Biddle Showing up strongly across a number of fields, the firm maintains its position among the regional elite, albeit unaffected in this area by the recent merger. Its strength in areas such as property litigation and tax continues. In the latter field, its "innovative team" has advised on the £225 million Whitbread/Punch Retail disposal of First Quench to Nomura. The projects team has also enjoyed "a cracking year," acting for funders, consortia and the public sector in a host of ventures including the Hull & East Yorkshire NHS Trust's £30 million maternity scheme. Last year's acclaimed ascent into the top bands for the core areas of IP and commercial litigation has, however, not been repeated. While both departments were praised for the weight and quality of their work the feeling persists that they have not quite the reach and visibility to claim regional superiority just yet. In one area at least, such a claim is justified. The employment department, led by the legendary John McMullen, has "the premier practice in the North," and advises an enviable array of heavyweight clients.

Nabarro Nathanson The Sheffield branch of this firm remains a robust contender in the region. Ranked in 11 areas once again, it has come top in energy and natural resources and proves to be a force in property litigation, personal injury, and projects/PFI. With the indomitable Mike Renger and top ranked Niall Logan at the helm of energy and natural resources, the firm is renowned for its strength in depth. Renger also merits a top rank in environment, contributing to its admirable reputation in that field. Six other individuals are also rated in a wide range of specialities, with Health and Safety practitioner Gareth Watkins also coming in the first tier.

Andrew M Jackson This Hull based firm maintains its national reputation for shipping, once again achieving a top tier ranking and boasting key lawyer Silas Taylor. Ranked in eight other areas, its strength in agriculture and trusts reflects a strong reputation for private client work. Five individuals are ranked, with Hugh Smith sustaining his reputation in the dual areas of food law and commercial litigation.

Lupton Fawcett This medium sized, Leeds firm capitalises on its position in the largest legal centre outside London. Though small compared to the national giants based in the city, it has grown by an impressive 40% in both turnover and staff numbers in the previous year. Its commercial departments have made a good showing in the tables this year, with commercial litigation and corporate finance being among seven rated practice areas for the firm. Licensing, debt recovery and trusts/personal tax are other high-achieving sectors.

NORTH EAST

Tyne Bridge, Newcastle

Dickinson Dees Another excellent year for the strongest firm in the region. Ranked in 24 practice areas, and taking a top band position in 13, the firm is described by some as "not London, but as good as." The opening of a new office in the Tees Valley is set to consolidate its domination of the North East.

The practice has shown great expertise in a range of disciplines. Corporate finance and banking remain particular strengths – holding the top band in each – with John Flynn and Chris Harker receiving particular praise in these disciplines. The construction and commercial litigation teams have emerged as the strongest in the region in this year's research. Yet in its diversification to a more national base, the firm has not relinquished its traditional interests. Agriculture, employment, family/matrimonial and social housing teams all retain their fine reputations. In all, the firm has 30 individuals ranked in this year's edition.

Eversheds A slightly unsettled year has seen the closure of the Middlesbrough office in September 2000, and the departure of four partners. However, feedback from clients has proved largely positive, with the number of top positions held by both departments and individuals both increased from last year. 18 practice areas have featured in the tables, with the number of top-flight ranks increasing by two to eight. The firm has seen an increase in profile in the shipping sector, where the team has demonstrated its ability to draw upon international resources and expertise. The department recently acted on a $14 million super yacht total loss case. It is perhaps best known in the region for its construction expertise, acting for the highest profile private and public contractors such as AMEC and Northumbrian Water. Ralph Wrighton is rated as one of the region's top litigators. 15 individuals are ranked this year, seven earning top rankings.

Ward Hadaway A year of great progress for Ward Hadaway, which has seen it achieve – if not the national prominence of Dickinson Dees or Eversheds – a strong position in its own backyard. The merger with Keenlyside & Forster is widely seen as a success, with the commercial litigation department again recognised as the best in the region. The firm is seen to have consolidated its position right across the board, rising this year in Clinical Negligence, Employment, Family/Matrimonial and Trusts & Personal Tax. Agriculture in particular provided a strong showing, with Christopher Hewitt recommended as "one of the key specialists in the North East." In all, the firm has nine individuals ranked in this year's edition (up three from last year), across 11 practice areas.

Watson Burton A focused firm that has "a clear idea of its key areas of strength and consistently plays to them." New managing partner Patrick Harwood presides over a firm whose reputation is strongest in construction, where Rob Langley is rated as a "*busy and aggressive*" operator. The corporate finance department has gained growing market respect, and the firm has five ranked individuals this year.

NORTH EAST: the 10 Largest Firms

	Firm	Ptnrs	Asst Solrs	Total Solrs '01	Total Solrs '00
1	**Dickinson Dees** *Newcastle upon Tyne, Stockton on Tees*	57	83	**140**	120
2	**Eversheds** *Newcastle upon Tyne*	41	67	**108**	110
3	**Ward Hadaway** *Newcastle upon Tyne, South Shields*	42	43	**85**	77
4	**Watson Burton** *Newcastle upon Tyne*	20	25	**45**	41
5	**Crutes** *Middlesbrough, Newcastle upon Tyne, Sunderland*	18	17	**35**	38
6	**Blackett Hart & Pratt** *Darlington (2), Durham (3), Newcastle upon Tyne (2), Newton Aycliffe*	23	11	**34**	n/a
7	**Hay & Kilner** *Gosforth, Newcastle upon Tyne, Wallsend*	22	11	**33**	32
8	**Robert Muckle** *Newcastle upon Tyne*	11	22	**33**	33
9	**Tilly Bailey & Irvine** *Barnard Castle, Darlington, Hartlepool, Stockton on Tees*	16	12	**28**	42
10	**Jacksons** *Gateshead, Stockton on Tees*	15	11	**26**	30

The rankings in this table are determined by the number of solicitors working in the region. They are based on partner and assistant solicitor figures only: all other fee-earners are excluded.

SCOTLAND

picture courtest www.scottish.parliament.uk

Foyer of the new Scottish Parliament, Edinburgh

Dundas & Wilson CS A firm that has gone from strength to strength in the past year. The Anderson Legal network and a stable of top rate lawyers continue to provide access to some of the biggest deals in Scotland. The quality of lawyers is high with 31 individuals ranked this year in 28 areas of practice.

Providing a comprehensive service to heavyweight corporates and blue-chip financial institutions, its real areas of strength are in the traditional spheres of corporate, banking & finance, investment funds and insolvency. The IP and IT departments have suffered the loss of Lorne Byatt to an in-house role, but any lasting effect is thought to be unlikely, due in part to the number of quality transactions which continue to roll through the door. These include a £1 billion IT outsourcing deal for Bank of Scotland with IBM and a £70 million internet joint venture for Royal Bank of Scotland. The firm makes no secret of its desire for a constant diet of large profitable corporate deals, and that is where *Chambers* has seen it focusing its energies. With profits up and the practice having doubled in size over the past four years, not to mention a long list of stellar clients, the firm is clearly making all the right moves.

McGrigor Donald Although Glasgow based, the firm has recently opened new high-tech offices in Edinburgh and has expanded its London and Belfast bases. Its turnover has increased by an impressive third. The firm is ranked top in nine areas of practice and has 25 ranked individuals, six with a band one position. Its enthusiastic banking practice complements a hard-hitting corporate finance team, which has enjoyed success in both Scotland and London. Head of technology Shonaig MacPherson continues to be a pioneer, while the top ranked IP team has all-round strength and a constant flow of highly technical, interesting work. The profile of a seasoned commercial litigation team has risen following involvement in the Lockerbie trial, and the commercial property team continues to be energetic and highly visible. The environment department has leapt ahead in the rankings, recovering from losses and continuing to build. Ian Gordon's sensible and pragmatic approach keeps the pensions and tax fires burning and Craig Connal is a litigation and planning expert whose profile is a boost to the firm.

MacRoberts Progressing with the appointment of a Chairman for the first time and the opening of a new office in Edinburgh. The firm has 20 notable practitioners across 18 sections including the ubiquitous David Flint, who is featured in IT, IP and Insolvency. The construction team retains its "strong pedigree" with three ranked individuals led by the queen of construction, Lindy Patterson. Employment and Employee Share Schemes stay at the top of the tree and corporate finance and banking provide solid foundations for the continued growth of the firm. Its skilled projects practice has recently scored a coup with its involvement in on the £100 million Edinburgh schools project. It has dropped down the rankings in IT as a result of the departure of Joanna Boag-Thompson, although many anticipate that the firm's commerciality and strong business links will continue to stand it in good stead even in this sector.

Maclay Murray & Spens With almost as many ranked individuals as market leader Dundas & Wilson, the firm is quietly and carefully on the rise. Comments across the board confirm that it is technically one of the best, and competitors and clients alike are impressed by "likeable and affable partners," who roll their sleeves up and "get the deals done with a minimum of fuss."

The firm has improved in commercial property and has a growing reputation in acquisition finance. On the employment front, it has joined forces with premier niche firm Mackay Simon and as a consequence has snatched the top spot in the market. The firm continues to have a solid reputation in banking and tax and has moved into shared first position in corporate finance after a stellar year, under the continued charismatic leadership of Magnus Swanson. The firm's competition practice continues to be top ranked and the commercial litigation team, despite its modest approach, has also moved into band one. Stunningly good IP and IT teams continue to be flagships of the firm. Valued clients of the firm include venture capital giant 3i.

Shepherd & Wedderburn WS Having appointed 12 new partners over the past two years, and now claiming half its partnership to be under the age of 40, the firm is cultivating a youthful, dynamic image. Under newly appointed CEO Paul Hale, the firm is charging full steam ahead. But how has this been reflected in the rankings? The firm is ranked in 28 areas and number one in seven areas. Areas of notable improvement include Admin & Public law where the firm has risen to band one on the back of its following among local authorities, and is led by seasoned campaigner Ian McLeod, who is ranked in the top tier for both admin and commercial litigation.

The aviation team continues to lead the market with some landmark cases, while the construction team has bounded ahead in the rankings owing in no small part to the tireless efforts of Kevin Taylor. Another area of improvement has been in planning where a broad client base and value for money ethos has overcome the competition. Electricty continues to be a strong point, with the team advising on the lion's share of Scottish Power work. The IT and e-commerce teams have been given a boost with the recruitment of Joanna Boag-Thompson from MacRoberts, adding further credibility and experience to an already successful group.

Brodies WS Maintaining its impressive level of performance of the past few years, the firm is ranked in 16 areas, and is home to 17 leading individuals, five of who are at the top of their disciplines. Strengths in many of the practice areas complement each other. The growth in the firm's corporate client base has been accompanied by a rapidly growing employment department. Added to this is the already formidable commercial litigation department, "studded with esteemed practitioners," where David Williamson successfully defends his title as "the best in Scotland." The dynamic duo of Neil Collar and Charles

Smith, covering planning and environment, both top their respective areas.

Tods Murray WS A strong showing is retained in the commercial areas has seen the firm's banking and corporate finance departments both move up a tier. This year finds the firm ranked in 15 areas with 14 notable individuals. The Investment Funds department's reputation remains intact as "the market leader" with top ranked Chris Athanas heading the team. The new Glasgow office has quadrupled in size since opening in 1999. It is home to the newly established T2M, the new e-commerce and new media grouping with Richard Finlay at the helm. He retains his position as "the leader in Scottish media." Although perceived by peers to be conservative, clients prefer to describe this as a "non-flashy, utterly professional firm."

Burness Continuing its improved run and snapping at the heels of the top five, the firm is ranked in an impressive 24 areas, more per fee earner than any other Scottish firm. Moving away from its historical Edinburgh focus, the firm's Glasgow office is developing in its own right.

The firm's concentration on commercial sectors, with an emphasis in PFI, capital projects and banking, is felt to be paying off. The banking, corporate finance and planning departments have all risen in our rankings, while the commercial property team has also made considerable progress. With the growth of the Glasgow office the department is seen to have "re-invented" itself. "A good all-round team" now has six lawyers ranked.

The pensions department has been bolstered with the appointment of Andrew Fleming from Richards Butler. The ubiquitous Andrew Sleigh is a leading light in the areas of insolvency/corporate recovery, corporate finance and sport, while Marsali Murray is still regarded as the supremo of product liability.

Paull & Williamsons Pre-eminent in its local market, the firm has proved itself capable of making its presence felt outside Aberdeen. Planning, in particular, has made an impact in the Central belt, due in part to the leadership of "excellent advocate" Bruce Smith. Retaining its place among the leaders in oil and gas energy work in Scotland, the firm has been dubbed "the Scottish firm to use," representing ARCO on its disposal of a number of interests in the North Sea to Tullow Exploration for a total of £200 million. It achieves rankings in seven other areas, the majority of which have gained a profile due to oil and gas-related work. However, securing commercial property clients such as BAA is proof positive that this expertise has not necessarily proved to be a handicap in developing a much broader practice.

Dickson Minto WS A niche corporate finance and private equity firm, which has had unprecedented success in London and punches far above its weight. High quality and clear focus characterise the firm, which was ranked this year in seven related areas of practice including private equity, banking, investment funds and tax. Success can in part be attributed to dynamic duo, Bruce Minto and Alistair Dickson, both great ambassadors for the firm, who inspire enviable client loyalty in both Scotland and London.

In Scotland, Colin McHale is again credited with the success of the top-ranked banking team, while the private equity team has improved its position in London with an aggressive and business-like approach.

SCOTLAND: the 30 Largest Firms

		Ptnrs	Asst Solrs	Total No of Solrs '01	'00	'99	'98
1	**Dundas & Wilson CS** *Edinburgh, Glasgow*	53	160	**213**	193	168	165
2	**Maclay Murray & Spens** *Edinburgh, Glasgow*	49	114	**163**	94	95	103
3	**McGrigor Donald** *Edinburgh, Glasgow*	43	97	**140**	129	129	112
4	**Shepherd & Wedderburn WS** *Edinburgh, Glasgow*	39	81	**120**	97	90	90
5	**MacRoberts** *Edinburgh, Glasgow*	30	81	**111**	102	87	72
6	**Tods Murray WS** *Edinburgh, Glasgow*	36	49	**85**	82	69	69
7	**Brodies WS** *Edinburgh*	32	53	**85**	82	73	72
8	**Burness** *Edinburgh, Glasgow*	33	38	**71**	65	67	57
9	**Anderson Strathern WS** *Edinburgh (2), Haddington*	25	43	**68**	52	53	53
10	**Paull & Williamsons** *Aberdeen (2), Edinburgh*	29	34	**63**	77	70	59
11	**Biggart Baillie** *Edinburgh, Glasgow*	25	38	**63**	60	53	52
12	**Ledingham Chalmers** *Aberdeen (3), Inverness*	29	30	**59**	62	51	57
13	**Morison Bishop** *Cumbernauld, Edinburgh (2), Glasgow, West Lothian*	28	30	**58**	65	65	n/a
14	**McClure Naismith** *Edinburgh, Glasgow*	21	34	**55**	54	52	58
15	**Henderson Boyd Jackson WS** *Edinburgh, Glasgow*	22	32	**54**	61	61	49
16	**Morton Fraser, Solicitors** *Edinburgh*	20	31	**51**	48	49	49
17	**Thorntons WS** *Arbroath, Dundee, Forfar, Perth*	25	23	**48**	42	41	40
18	**Semple Fraser** *Edinburgh, Glasgow*	16	28	**44**	45	32	27
19	**Simpson & Marwick WS** *Aberdeen, Dundee, Edinburgh, Glasgow*	14	28	**42**	41	39	38
20	**Turcan Connell** *Edinburgh*	14	25	**39**	35	37	n/a
21	**Balfour & Manson** *Edinburgh*	20	18	**38**	32	32	36
22	**Brechin Tindal Oatts** *Edinburgh, Glasgow*	15	23	**38**	33	31	29
23	**Stronachs** *Aberdeen (2), Inverness, Inverurie*	19	17	**36**	37	34	38
24	**DLA** *Edinburgh, Glasgow*	n/a	n/a	**n/a**	36	n/a	n/a
25	**Miller Hendry** *Crieff, Dundee (2), Perth*	14	20	**34**	28	24	23
26	**Harper Macleod** *Glasgow*	18	15	**33**	30	29	24
27	**Wright, Johnston & Mackenzie** *Edinburgh, Glasgow*	12	20	**32**	n/a	32	32
28	**Drummond Miller WS** *Bathgate, Dalkeith, Dunfermline, Edinburgh, Glasgow, Kirkcaldy, Musselburgh*	18	13	**31**	34	34	36
29	**Steedman Ramage** *Edinburgh, Glasgow*	15	16	**31**	33	27	28
30	**Golds** *Glasgow*	11	19	**30**	n/a	20	20

The rankings in this table are determined by the number of solicitors working in the region. They are based on partner and assistant solicitor figures only: all other fee-earners are excluded.

FIRMS AT A GLANCE – THE LIST OF LISTS

These lists show the key strengths of an individual firm. Please note: only the areas of practice for which a firm is ranked in bands 1-3 of the tables are listed. Bold type indicates the areas of law in which the firm is ranked in 'band one'.

A

ADAMS & REMERS
Trusts & Personal Tax

ADAMS WHYTE
Crime

ADDLESHAW BOOTH & CO
Administrative & Public Law: General, Agriculture, Asset Finance & Leasing: Consumer Finance, **Banking**, Charities, **Competition/Anti-trust**, **Construction**, **Corporate Finance**, E-commerce, Education: Institutions, Employee Share Schemes, **Employment**, Energy & Natural Resources, Environment, **Family/Matrimonial**, **Financial Services**, Health & Safety, Information Technology, **Insolvency/Corporate Recovery**, **Intellectual Property**, Licensing, **Litigation: General Commercial**, **Litigation: Property**, **Pensions**, Planning, **Private Equity**, Professional Negligence, **Projects/PFI**, **Property (Commercial)**, Social Housing: Advising Lenders, Sport, **Tax**, Trusts & Personal Tax

AE SMITH & SON
Education: Individuals

AE WYETH & CO
Personal Injury: Mainly Defendant

AGNEW, ANDRESS, HIGGINS
Personal Injury: Mainly Claimant, **Professional Negligence**

ALEXANDER HARRIS
Clinical Negligence: Mainly Claimant, Product Liability, Product Liability: Mainly Claimant

ALEXIOU FISHER PHILIPPS
Family/Matrimonial

ALISTAIR MELDRUM & CO
Crime

ALLAN JANES
Licensing

ALLEN & OVERY
Administrative & Public Law: Commercial, Arbitration (International), Asset Finance & Leasing, **Banking**, **Capital Markets: Derivatives**, **Capital Markets: International Debt & Equity**, **Capital Markets: Securitisation & Repackaging**, Competition/Anti-trust, Corporate Finance: Larger Deals, Employee Share Schemes, Employment: Mainly Respondent, Energy & Natural Resources, **Environment**, Financial Services, Information Technology, **Insolvency/Corporate Recovery**, **Litigation: Banking & Finance**, **Litigation: Civil Fraud**, Litigation: General Commercial (40+ Litigators), **Partnership**, **Partnership: Large International Mergers**, Pensions, **PFI**, Private Equity: Buyouts & Investment, **Private Equity: Debt**, **Project Finance**, Shipping: Finance, Social Housing: Advising Lenders, Tax, Telecommunications, **Trusts & Personal Tax**

ALLINGTON HUGHES
Church: Other Denominations

AMERY-PARKES
Personal Injury: Mainly Claimant

AMHURST BROWN COLOMBOTTI
Travel: Timeshare

ANDERSON STRATHERN WS
Agriculture, **Charities**, **Clinical Negligence: Mainly Claimant**, Education: Institutions, Litigation: General Commercial, Media & Entertainment, Personal Injury: Mainly Claimant, Personal Injury: Mainly Defendant, **Sport**, Trusts & Personal Tax

ANDREA & CO
Travel

ANDREW KEENAN & CO
Crime

ANDREW M JACKSON & CO
Agriculture, Family/Matrimonial, Food, **Shipping**, Trusts & Personal Tax

ANNE HALL DICK & CO
Family/Matrimonial

ANTHONY COLLINS SOLICITORS
Charities, **Church: Other Denominations**, Clinical Negligence: Mainly Claimant, Licensing, **Social Housing**

ANTHONY GOLD
Personal Injury: Mainly Claimant

ARCHIBALD CAMPBELL & HARLEY WS
Planning

ARNOLD THOMSON
Agriculture

ARTHUR COX
Banking, Property (Commercial)

AS LAW
Human Rights, Immigration

ASB LAW
Corporate Finance, **Insolvency/Corporate Recovery**, Licensing: Litigation: General Commercial, Litigation: Property

ASHOK PATEL & CO
Education: Individuals

ASHTON GRAHAM
Debt Recovery, Property (Commercial)

ASHURST MORRIS CRISP
Competition/Anti-trust, Corporate Finance: Larger Deals, Environment, Litigation: Civil Fraud, Litigation: Property, Local Government, Media & Entertainment: Broadcasting, PFI, **Private Equity: Buyouts & Investment**, Private Equity: Debt, Tax

B

BABBE LE PELLEY TOSTEVIN
Offshore: Corporate/Commercial

BABINGTON & CROASDAILE
Crime, **Family/Matrimonial**

BACKHOUSE JONES
Transport: Road - Regulatory

BADHAMS
Personal Injury: Mainly Defendant, Travel

BAKER & MCKENZIE
Customs & Excise, E-commerce, Employment: Mainly Respondent, Immigration: Business, **Information Technology**, Intellectual Property: General, Litigation: Civil Fraud, **Litigation: General Commercial (Fewer than 40 Litigators)**, Pensions, Telecommunications, Travel: Timeshare

BALFOUR & MANSON
Charities, **Clinical Negligence: Mainly Claimant**, Family/Matrimonial, Personal Injury: Mainly Claimant, Professional Negligence, Trusts & Personal Tax

BANNATYNE, KIRKWOOD, FRANCE & CO
Defamation, Media & Entertainment

BANNERS JONES MIDDLETON
Crime

BARCAN WOODWARD
Clinical Negligence: Mainly Claimant

BARKER GOTELEE
Agriculture, Transport: Road - Regulatory

BARLOW LYDE & GILBERT
Aviation: Insurance & Litigation, Aviation: Regulatory, Environment, Food, **Insurance: General Claims**, **Insurance: Reinsurance**, **Personal Injury: Mainly Defendant**, **Professional Negligence: Financial**, **Professional Negligence: Insurance**, **Professional Negligence: Legal**, Travel

BARLOWS
Charities

BARRATT GOFF & TOMLINSON
Personal Injury: Mainly Claimant

BARRIE WARD & JULIAN GRIFFITHS
Crime

BARTRAM & CO
Immigration: Personal

BATE EDMOND SNAPE
Crime

BATES, WELLS & BRAITHWAITE
Administrative & Public Law: Traditional, **Charities**, Immigration: Business, Partnership: Medical

BEACHCROFT WANSBROUGHS
Administrative & Public Law: General (Leeds), **Clinical Negligence: Mainly Defendant (Winchester)**, Clinical Negligence: Mainly Defendant (Bristol), Construction (Bristol), Education: Institutions (London), Healthcare (Bristol, Leeds, London, Winchester), Information Technology (Bristol), **Insurance (Birmingham, Bristol, Leeds, Manchester)**, Intellectual Property (Bristol), Litigation: General Commercial (Bristol), Litigation: Property (Bristol), **Personal Injury: Mainly Defendant (Birmingham, Bristol, Leeds, London, Winchester)**, Personal Injury: Mainly Defendant (Manchester), **Professional Negligence (Bristol, Leeds)**, Professional Negligence (Birmingham), Professional Negligence: Legal (London), Property (Commercial) (Bristol, Manchester)

BEALE AND COMPANY
Professional Negligence: Construction

BEAUMONT AND SON
Aviation: Insurance & Litigation, Aviation: Regulatory

BEDELL CRISTIN
Offshore: Corporate/Commercial

BELL & BUXTON
Church: Church of England

BELL & SCOTT WS
Partnership

BELMORES
Crime, Licensing

BELTRAMI & CO
Crime

BERMANS
Debt Recovery

BERRYMANS LACE MAWER
Insurance, **Personal Injury: Mainly Defendant**, Professional Negligence: Construction, Professional Negligence: Financial

BERRY SMITH
Property (Commercial)

BERWIN LEIGHTON PAISNER
Asset Finance & Leasing: Consumer Finance, Construction, Corporate Finance: Medium Deals, **Food**, **Licensing**, Litigation: Property, **Planning**, Property (Commercial): 50+ Solicitors, Travel: Hotels & Leisure

FIRMS AT A GLANCE

These lists show the key strengths of an individual firm. Please note: only the areas of practice for which a firm is ranked in bands 1-3 of the tables are listed. Bold type indicates the areas of law in which the firm is ranked in 'band one'.

BETESH FOX & CO
Crime, Fraud: Criminal

BEVAN ASHFORD
Administrative & Public Law: General, **Clinical Negligence: Mainly Defendant**, Construction, Corporate Finance, **Employment**, Environment, Food, Health & Safety, **Healthcare**, Information Technology, Intellectual Property, Litigation: General Commercial, **Local Government**, Personal Injury: Mainly Defendant, Planning, **Projects/PFI**, Property (Commercial), Social Housing

BHATT MURPHY
Human Rights

BIGGART BAILLIE
Administrative & Public Law: General, Charities, Competition/Anti-trust, Energy: Electricity, Insurance, Personal Injury: Mainly Defendant

BIGGER & STRAHAN
Debt Recovery

BINDMAN & PARTNERS
Administrative & Public Law: Traditional, Clinical Negligence: Mainly Claimant, **Crime**, Employment: Mainly Applicant, Family/Matrimonial, **Human Rights**, **Immigration: Personal**

BIRCHAM DYSON BELL
Parliamentary Agency, **Parliamentary: Public Affairs**

BIRCH CULLIMORE
Agriculture, **Charities**, Church: Church of England, Trusts & Personal Tax

BIRD & BIRD
E-commerce, Food, **Information Technology**, **Intellectual Property: General**, **Intellectual Property: Patent**, Sport: Commercial/Media, **Telecommunications**

BIRKETT LONG
Education: Institutions

BIRKETTS
Agriculture, Corporate Finance, **Debt Recovery**, Litigation: General Commercial, Property (Commercial), Shipping

BIRNBERG PEIRCE & PARTNERS
Crime, **Immigration: Personal**

BLACKETT HART & PRATT
Product Liability

BLAIR ALLISON & CO
Family/Matrimonial

BLAIR & BRYDEN
Crime

BLAKE LAPTHORN
Charities, **Clinical Negligence: Mainly Claimant**, Construction, **Corporate Finance**, Debt Recovery, **Education: Individuals**, Employment, **Environment**, Family/Matrimonial, Fraud: Criminal, **Insolvency/Corporate Recovery**, **Licensing**, **Litigation: General Commercial**, Pensions, Personal Injury: Mainly Claimant, **Professional Negligence**, **Property (Commercial)**, Tax, Trusts & Personal Tax

BLANDY & BLANDY
Family/Matrimonial, Licensing, Trusts & Personal Tax

BLYTHE LIGGINS
Family/Matrimonial

BOBBETTS MACKAN
Administrative & Public Law: General, **Crime**, **Fraud: Criminal**, **Immigration**

BOGUE AND MCNULTY
Crime

BOND PEARCE
Banking, Charities, Competition/Anti-trust, **Corporate Finance**, **Debt Recovery**, **Education: Institutions**, **Employment**, **Energy & Natural Resources**, **Environment**, Food, Health & Safety, Information Technology, Insolvency/Corporate Recovery, Insurance, Licensing, Litigation: General Commercial, Local Government, Partnership, **Personal Injury: Mainly Claimant**, **Personal Injury: Mainly Defendant**, **Planning**, **Professional Negligence**, Property (Commercial), Shipping, Trusts & Personal Tax

BOODLE HATFIELD
Agriculture, Family/Matrimonial, **Property (Commercial): Fewer than 25 Solicitors**, **Trusts & Personal Tax**

BOYES TURNER
Clinical Negligence: Mainly Claimant, Debt Recovery, **Insolvency/Corporate Recovery**, Litigation: General Commercial, Personal Injury: Mainly Claimant, Trusts & Personal Tax

BRABNERS
Charities, Defamation, Social Housing, **Trusts & Personal Tax**

BRABY & WALLER
Debt Recovery

BRACHERS
Agriculture, Clinical Negligence: Mainly Defendant, **Debt Recovery**, **Environment**, Family/Matrimonial, Litigation: General Commercial, Litigation: Property, Planning

BRECHIN TINDAL OATTS
Insurance, Social Housing

BRENDAN KEARNEY KELLY & CO
Crime

BRETHERTONS
Crime

BRIAN KOFFMAN & CO
Crime

BRISTOWS
Intellectual Property: General, **Intellectual Property: Patent**, Partnership

BRODIES WS
Administrative & Public Law: General, **Agriculture**, Employment, **Environment**, Family/Matrimonial, Franchising, **Litigation: General Commercial**, Litigation: Property, Local Government, **Planning**, Property (Commercial), Tax, Trusts & Personal Tax

BROOKE NORTH
Trusts & Personal Tax

BROOKSTREET DES ROCHES
Charities, Partnership: Medical, Property (Commercial)

BROWELL SMITH & CO
Personal Injury: Mainly Claimant

BROWNE JACOBSON
Administrative & Public Law: General, Clinical Negligence: Mainly Defendant, Corporate Finance, **Healthcare**, Insurance, Litigation: General Commercial, Litigation: Property, **Personal Injury: Mainly Defendant**, **Professional Negligence**, Social Housing, Trusts & Personal Tax

BRUNTON MILLER
Licensing

BRUTTON & CO
Church: Church of England

BUCKLE MELLOWS
Family/Matrimonial

BULLER JEFFRIES
Personal Injury: Mainly Defendant

BULLIVANT JONES
Property (Commercial)

BURGES SALMON
Agriculture, Asset Finance & Leasing, **Banking**, Charities, **Competition/Anti-trust**, **Corporate Finance**, **Debt Recovery**, **Employment**, **Environment**, **Family/Matrimonial**, **Financial Services**, Information Technology, Intellectual Property, **Investment Funds**, **Litigation: General Commercial**, **Litigation: Property**, **Partnership**, **Pensions**, Planning, Professional Negligence, Projects/PFI, **Property (Commercial)**, Social Housing, **Tax**, **Trusts & Personal Tax**

BURNESS
Administrative & Public Law: General, Banking, Charities, Competition/Anti-trust, Corporate Finance, Energy: Electricity, Insolvency/Corporate Recovery, Litigation: General Commercial, Litigation: Property, Local Government, Partnership, Pensions, Planning, **Product Liability**, Property (Commercial), Sport, Tax

BURNETT & REID
Agriculture, Family/Matrimonial

BURNSIDE KEMP FRASER
Employment, Personal Injury: Mainly Claimant

BURROUGHS DAY
Employment

BURTON COPELAND (LONDON)
Customs & Excise, **Fraud: Criminal**

BURTON COPELAND (NORTH)
Crime, Customs & Excise, **Fraud: Criminal**

CAINS
Offshore: Corporate/Commercial

CAMPBELL HOOPER
Media & Entertainment: Theatre

CAMPBELL SMITH WS
Education: Individuals

CAPSTICKS
Clinical Negligence: Mainly Defendant, **Healthcare**

CAREY LANGLOIS
Offshore: Corporate/Commercial

CARNSON MORROW GRAHAM
Family/Matrimonial

CARSON MCDOWELL
Construction, **Corporate Finance**, Employment, **Litigation: General Commercial**, **Professional Negligence**, Property (Commercial)

CARTER LEMON CAMERONS
Church: Other Denominations

CARTMELL SHEPHERD
Agriculture

CARTWRIGHT KING
Crime, **Fraud: Criminal**

CARTWRIGHTS ADAMS & BLACK
Licensing

CARTWRIGHTS INSURANCE PARTNERS
Insurance, Personal Injury: Mainly Defendant

CHAFFE STREET
Asset Finance & Leasing, Insolvency/Corporate Recovery

CHALLINORS LYON CLARK
Clinical Negligence: Mainly Claimant, **Family/Matrimonial**

CHARLES RUSSELL
Clinical Negligence: Mainly Claimant, Family/Matrimonial, Sport: Regulatory, Trusts & Personal Tax

CHRISTIAN FISHER
Crime, Human Rights

C & J BLACK
Trusts & Personal Tax

These lists show the key strengths of an individual firm. Please note: only the areas of practice for which a firm is ranked in bands 1-3 of the tables are listed. Bold type indicates the areas of law in which the firm is ranked in 'band one'.

CLARKE WILLMOTT & CLARKE
Administrative & Public Law: General, Agriculture, **Debt Recovery**, Environment, Family/Matrimonial, Licensing, Litigation: General Commercial, **Planning**, Property (Commercial), **Sport**, Trusts & Personal Tax

CLARK HOLT
Information Technology

CLARKS
Construction, Corporate Finance, Debt Recovery, **Employment**, Insolvency/Corporate Recovery, **Litigation: General Commercial**, **Pensions**, **Planning**, Property (Commercial)

CLARKSON WRIGHT & JAKES
Partnership: Medical

CLAUDE HORNBY & COX
Crime

CLAYTONS
Church: Church of England

CLEAVER FULTON RANKIN
Administrative & Public Law: General, Construction, Debt Recovery, Employment, **Environment**, Litigation: General Commercial, **Trusts & Personal Tax**

CLIFFORD CHANCE
Administrative & Public Law: Commercial, **Arbitration (International)**, **Asset Finance & Leasing**, **Banking**, Capital Markets: Derivatives, Capital Markets: International Debt & Equity, **Capital Markets: Securitisation & Repackaging**, **Commodities: Futures**, Corporate Finance: Larger Deals, E-commerce, Employee Share Schemes, Energy & Natural Resources, **Financial Services**, **Information Technology**, Insolvency/Corporate Recovery, Insurance: Non-contentious, Insurance: Reinsurance, Intellectual Property: General, **Investment Funds**, **Litigation: Banking & Finance**, **Litigation: Civil Fraud**, Litigation: General Commercial (40+ Litigators), Litigation: Property, Media & Entertainment: Broadcasting, **Parliamentary: Public Affairs**, Pensions, **PFI**, **Private Equity: Buyouts & Investment**, **Private Equity: Debt**, Private Equity: Fund Formation, Project Finance, Property (Commercial): 50+ Solicitors, **Social Housing: Advising Lenders**, Tax, **Telecommunications**, Transport: Rail, **Travel: Hotels & Leisure**

CLINTONS
Family/Matrimonial, Media & Entertainment: Music, **Media & Entertainment: Theatre**

CLYDE & CO
Corporate Finance, Information Technology, Insurance: General Claims, **Insurance: Reinsurance**, Litigation: General Commercial, Litigation: General Commercial (Fewer than 40 Litigators), Property (Commercial), Shipping, Transport: Road - Carriage/Commercial

CMS CAMERON MCKENNA
Administrative & Public Law: Commercial, Aviation: Insurance & Litigation, Banking, Construction, **Corporate Finance: Medium Deals**, Energy & Natural Resources, **Energy: Oil & Gas**, Environment, **Health & Safety**, **Immigration: Business**, Insolvency/Corporate Recovery, Insurance: General Claims, Insurance: Reinsurance, Litigation: Civil Fraud, Litigation: Pensions, PFI, Planning, **Product Liability: Mainly Defendant**, Professional Negligence, Professional Negligence: Construction, Professional Negligence: Financial, Professional Negligence: Insurance

COBBETTS
Debt Recovery, Defamation, Employment, Family/Matrimonial, **Licensing**, Litigation: General Commercial, **Litigation: Property**, Partnership, **Property (Commercial)**, **Social Housing**, Trusts & Personal Tax

COFFIN MEW & CLOVER
Family/Matrimonial, Litigation: Property, **Social Housing**

COKER VIS PARTNERSHIP
Immigration: Personal

COLE & CO
Crime

COLIN JONES
Crime

COLLAS DAY
Offshore: Corporate/Commercial

COLLYER-BRISTOW
Family/Matrimonial

COMERTON & HILL
Debt Recovery

CONDIES
Crime

CONINGSBYS
Education: Individuals

COPLEYS
Crime

COVINGTON & BURLING
Food

COZENS-HARDY & JEWSON
Charities

CRIPPS HARRIES HALL
Agriculture, Charities, Construction, Corporate Finance, Employment, Family/Matrimonial, Litigation: General Commercial, Litigation: Property, **Professional Negligence**, Property (Commercial), Social Housing, **Trusts & Personal Tax**

CROSSE & CROSSE
Crime, Licensing

CRUTES
Employment, Personal Injury: Mainly Defendant, **Professional Negligence**

CUFF ROBERTS
Family/Matrimonial, **Partnership**, Trusts & Personal Tax

CULBERT AND MARTIN
Employment

CUNNINGHAM JOHN
Clinical Negligence: Mainly Claimant, **Personal Injury: Mainly Claimant**

CUNNINGHAMS
Crime

CURREY & CO
Agriculture, Trusts & Personal Tax

DALE & CO
Shipping

DARBYS
Family/Matrimonial, **Immigration**, Insolvency/Corporate Recovery

DAVENPORT LYONS
Defamation, Licensing, Media & Entertainment: Film & TV Production, Media & Entertainment: Film Finance

DAVID CHARNLEY & CO
Crime

DAVID GIST SOLICITORS
Personal Injury: Mainly Claimant

DAVID GRAY SOLICITORS
Crime, Human Rights, **Immigration**

DAVID PRICE SOLICITORS & ADVOCATES
Defamation

DAVIES AND PARTNERS
Planning

DAVIES ARNOLD COOPER
Personal Injury: Mainly Defendant, Product Liability: Mainly Defendant, Professional Negligence: Construction, Transport: Road - Carriage/Commercial

DAVIES, JOHNSON & CO
Shipping

DAVIES LAVERY
Personal Injury: Mainly Defendant, Transport: Road - Carriage/Commercial

DAVIES WALLIS FOYSTER
Asset Finance & Leasing, Debt Recovery, Insolvency/Corporate Recovery, Property (Commercial), Trusts & Personal Tax

DAVIS BLANK FURNISS
Immigration

DAWSON & CO
Agriculture

DAWSON CORNWELL
Family/Matrimonial

DECHERT
Customs & Excise, Fraud: Criminal, Litigation: General Commercial (Fewer than 40 Litigators), Property (Commercial): 25-49 Solicitors

DEIGHTON GUEDALLA
Human Rights, **Immigration: Personal**

DENISON TILL
Church: Church of England

DENTON WILDE SAPTE
Asset Finance & Leasing, **Aviation: Regulatory**, Commodities: Futures, Competition/Anti-trust, Corporate Finance: Medium Deals, Debt Recovery, E-commerce, **Energy & Natural Resources**, Environment, Information Technology, Insolvency/Corporate Recovery, Litigation: Civil Fraud, Litigation: Property, **Media & Entertainment: Broadcasting**, Media & Entertainment: Film Finance, **Media & Entertainment: Publishing**, PFI, Planning, **Property (Commercial)**, Property (Commercial): 25-49 Solicitors, Social Housing: Advising Lenders, **Sport: Commercial/Media**, **Sport: Regulatory**, Telecommunications, Transport: Rail, Travel: Hotels & Leisure

DEVONSHIRES
Social Housing

DIAMOND HERON
Debt Recovery, Personal Injury: Mainly Claimant

DICKINSON CRUICKSHANK & CO
Offshore: Corporate/Commercial

DICKINSON DEES
Agriculture, **Banking**, Charities, Competition/Anti-trust, **Construction**, **Corporate Finance**, **Employment**, Energy & Natural Resources, **Family/Matrimonial**, **Financial Services**, **Insolvency/Corporate Recovery**, Licensing, **Litigation: General Commercial**, Litigation: Property, Pensions, **Planning**, Projects/PFI, **Property (Commercial)**, **Social Housing**, Tax, **Trusts & Personal Tax**

DICKSON MINTO WS
Banking, **Corporate Finance**, Financial Services, **Investment Funds**, **Private Equity**, Private Equity: Buyouts & Investment

DIGBY BROWN
Personal Injury: Mainly Claimant

DIXON, COLES & GILL
Church: Church of England

FIRMS AT A GLANCE

These lists show the key strengths of an individual firm. Please note: only the areas of practice for which a firm is ranked in bands 1-3 of the tables are listed. Bold type indicates the areas of law in which the firm is ranked in 'band one'.

DJ FREEMAN
Corporate Finance: Smaller Deals, Defamation, Insurance: Reinsurance, Litigation: General Commercial (Fewer than 40 Litigators), Litigation: Property, Property (Commercial): 25-49 Solicitors

DLA
Banking (Liverpool, Manchester), Banking (Birmingham, Leeds), Corporate Finance (Birmingham, Leeds, Liverpool, Manchester, Sheffield), Debt Recovery (Bradford), **Employment (Liverpool, Manchester)**, Employment (Birmingham, Leeds, Sheffield), **Environment (Manchester)**, Environment (Sheffield), **Food (Birmingham)**, Fraud: Criminal (Manchester), **Insolvency/Corporate Recovery (Leeds, Sheffield)**, Insolvency/Corporate Recovery (Glasgow, Liverpool), Intellectual Property (Leeds, Liverpool, Manchester, Sheffield), Licensing (Sheffield), **Litigation: General Commercial (Leeds, Liverpool, Manchester, Sheffield)**, Litigation: General Commercial (Birmingham), **Litigation: Property (Liverpool, Manchester)**, Litigation: Property (Leeds, Sheffield), Local Government (Birmingham), **Parliamentary: Public Affairs (London)**, **Pensions (Liverpool, Manchester)**, Pensions (Leeds, Sheffield), Personal Injury: Mainly Defendant (Bradford, Leeds, Sheffield), Planning (Manchester), **Private Equity (Manchester)**, Projects/PFI (Birmingham, Leeds, Manchester), **Property (Commercial) (Liverpool, Manchester)**, Property (Commercial) (Birmingham, Leeds, Sheffield), Shipping (Liverpool, Manchester), Tax (Birmingham), Transport: Road - Carriage/Commercial (Liverpool, London, Manchester)

DMH
Church: Other Denominations, **Education: Institutions**, **Employment**, **Environment**, Family/Matrimonial, Fraud: Criminal, **Information Technology**, Intellectual Property, Licensing, Litigation: General Commercial, **Litigation: Property**, Planning, Shipping, Social Housing

DOLMANS
Personal Injury: Mainly Defendant

DONNELLY & WALL
Crime

DONNS SOLICITORS
Personal Injury: Mainly Claimant

DOUGLAS & PARTNERS
Crime

DRAYCOTT BROWNE
Crime

DRUMMOND MILLER WS
Clinical Negligence: Mainly Claimant, Family/Matrimonial

DUNDAS & WILSON CS
Administrative & Public Law: General, **Banking**, Competition/Anti-trust, Construction, Corporate Finance, **Education: Institutions**, Employee Share Schemes, Employment, Energy: Electricity, Environment, **Financial Services**, Information Technology, **Insolvency/Corporate Recovery**, Insurance, Intellectual Property, **Investment Funds**, Licensing, **Litigation: General Commercial**, **Litigation: Property**, **Local Government**, **Media & Entertainment**, **Partnership**, **Planning**, Professional Negligence, **Projects/PFI**, **Property (Commercial)**, Sport

DUNDONS
Crime

EAMONN MCEVOY & CO
Personal Injury: Mainly Claimant

EDWARD FAIL BRADSHAW & WATERSON
Crime

EDWARDS & CO
Personal Injury: Mainly Claimant

EDWARDS DUTHIE
Crime, Personal Injury: Mainly Claimant, Personal Injury: Mainly Defendant

EDWARDS GELDARD
Administrative & Public Law: General, Banking, Church: Church of England, Clinical Negligence: Mainly Claimant, **Competition/Anti-trust**, Corporate Finance, Debt Recovery, Employment, Energy & Natural Resources, **Environment**, **Information Technology**, Insolvency/Corporate Recovery, **Intellectual Property**, **Litigation: General Commercial**, Litigation: Property, Local Government, **Planning**, Property (Commercial), Social Housing, **Trusts & Personal Tax**

ELAINE MAXWELL & CO
Education: Individuals

E & L KENNEDY
Licensing

ELLIOT MATHER
Crime

ELLIOTT DUFFY GARRETT
Construction, Defamation, Employment, Insolvency/Corporate Recovery, **Litigation: General Commercial**, Partnership, **Product Liability**, Property (Commercial)

ELLIOTTS
Food, Licensing, Professional Negligence

ELLISON & CO
Property (Commercial)

ELLIS WOOD
Church: Other Denominations

ENSOR BYFIELD
Personal Injury: Mainly Defendant

ERIC ROBINSON & CO
Immigration

ERSKINE MACASKILL & CO
Family/Matrimonial

EVERATT & COMPANY
Personal Injury: Mainly Defendant

EVERSHEDS
Administrative & Public Law: General (Cambridge, Cardiff, Leeds, Manchester, Norwich), Agriculture (Norwich), Asset Finance & Leasing: Consumer Finance (Cardiff, Leeds), **Banking (Birmingham, Cambridge, Cardiff, Ipswich, Manchester, Norwich, Nottingham)**, Banking (Newcastle upon Tyne), Charities (Cambridge, Norwich), **Clinical Negligence: Mainly Defendant (Newcastle upon Tyne)**, **Competition/Anti-trust (Cardiff, Leeds, Manchester, Newcastle upon Tyne)**, Competition/Anti-trust (Birmingham), **Construction (Newcastle upon Tyne)**, Construction (Cambridge, Cardiff, Ipswich, Norwich), **Corporate Finance (Ipswich, Norwich)**, Corporate Finance (Birmingham, Cardiff, Leeds, Manchester, Newcastle upon Tyne), **Corporate Finance: Smaller Deals (London)**, **Debt Recovery (Cardiff, Nottingham)**, Debt Recovery (Leeds, Norwich), **Education: Institutions (Cardiff, Leeds, London, Manchester, Newcastle upon Tyne)**, Education: Institutions (Derby, Ipswich, Norwich, Nottingham), Employee Share Schemes (Birmingham), **Employment (Birmingham, Cambridge, Cardiff, Ipswich, Manchester, Newcastle upon Tyne, Norwich, Nottingham)**, Employment: Mainly Respondent (London), Energy & Natural Resources (Birmingham), **Environment (Cardiff, Leeds, Manchester)**, Environment (Birmingham, Norwich), Family/Matrimonial (Cambridge), **Food (Birmingham, Norwich)**, **Franchising (Ipswich, London, Newcastle upon Tyne)**, **Health & Safety (Birmingham, Cardiff, Leeds, Manchester)**, Healthcare (Newcastle upon Tyne), Immigration: Business (London), **Information Technology (Birmingham, Nottingham)**, Information Technology (Cardiff, Leeds), **Insolvency/Corporate Recovery (Birmingham, Cambridge, Cardiff, Ipswich, Norwich)**, Insolvency/Corporate Recovery (Newcastle upon Tyne), Intellectual Property (Cambridge, Cardiff, Ipswich, Leeds, Manchester, Norwich), Intellectual Property: General (London), Investment Funds (London), Licensing (Cambridge, Ipswich, Norwich), **Litigation: General Commercial (Cambridge, Cardiff, Ipswich, Leeds, Manchester, Norwich)**, Litigation: General Commercial (Birmingham, Newcastle upon Tyne, Nottingham), Litigation: General Commercial (Fewer than 40 Litigators) (London), **Litigation: Pensions (London)**, **Litigation: Property (Ipswich, Norwich)**, Litigation: Property (Birmingham, Derby, Leeds, Manchester, Nottingham), **Local Government (Cardiff, Leeds)**, Local Government (Birmingham, Nottingham), Media & Entertainment (Leeds, Manchester), **Pensions (Cardiff, Norwich)**, Pensions (Birmingham, Leeds, Manchester), **Personal Injury: Mainly Defendant (Ipswich, Newcastle upon Tyne)**, **Planning (Cardiff)**, Planning (Birmingham, Leeds, Manchester), **Projects/PFI (Nottingham)**, Projects/PFI (Cardiff, Leeds, Manchester), **Property (Commercial) (Birmingham, Cambridge, Cardiff, Ipswich, Manchester, Norwich, Nottingham)**, Property (Commercial) (Leeds, Newcastle upon Tyne), **Shipping (Ipswich, Newcastle upon Tyne)**, **Social Housing (Cardiff)**, Social Housing (Manchester, Newcastle upon Tyne), Tax (Leeds, Manchester, Norwich, Nottingham), **Telecommunications (Leeds)**, Transport: Rail (Birmingham, Leeds, London), Travel (Newcastle upon Tyne)

EVILL AND COLEMAN
Clinical Negligence: Mainly Claimant, Personal Injury: Mainly Claimant

FARLEYS
Family/Matrimonial

FARRER & CO
Agriculture, Charities, Defamation, Sport: Regulatory

FENNEMORES
Personal Injury: Mainly Claimant

FENWICK ELLIOTT
Construction

FEW & KESTER
Property (Commercial)

FIELD CUNNINGHAM & CO
Property (Commercial)

FIELD FISHER WATERHOUSE
Clinical Negligence: Mainly Claimant, Corporate Finance: Smaller Deals, E-commerce, **Franchising**, Information Technology, **Licensing**, Partnership, Personal Injury: Mainly Claimant, **Travel**, Travel: Hotels & Leisure

FIELDINGS PORTER
Church: Other Denominations

FIELD SEYMOUR PARKES
Licensing

These lists show the key strengths of an individual firm. Please note: only the areas of practice for which a firm is ranked in bands 1-3 of the tables are listed. Bold type indicates the areas of law in which the firm is ranked in 'band one'.

FINERS STEPHENS INNOCENT
Media & Entertainment: Publishing, Partnership, Property (Commercial): Fewer than 25 Solicitors

FISHBURN MORGAN COLE
Professional Negligence: Construction

FISHER MEREDITH
Crime, Education: Individuals

FLEETWOOD & ROBB
Crime

FLETCHERS
Crime

FLYNN & MCGETTRICK
Crime, **Family/Matrimonial**

FOLLETT STOCK
Church: Church of England

FOOT ANSTEY SARGENT
Defamation, **Family/Matrimonial**, Information Technology, Insolvency/Corporate Recovery, Licensing, Litigation: General Commercial, **Shipping**, Trusts & Personal Tax

FORBES
Crime

FORD & WARREN
Transport: Road - Regulatory

FOX WILLIAMS
Employment: Mainly Respondent, **Partnership**

FRANCIS HANNA & CO
Personal Injury: Mainly Claimant

FREEMANS
Licensing

FREETHCARTWRIGHT
Clinical Negligence: Mainly Claimant, Debt Recovery, Family/Matrimonial, Partnership, Personal Injury: Mainly Claimant, Product Liability, Property (Commercial), Social Housing

FRESHFIELDS BRUCKHAUS DERINGER
Administrative & Public Law: Commercial, Arbitration (International), **Asset Finance & Leasing**, Banking, Capital Markets: Derivatives, Capital Markets: International Debt & Equity, Capital Markets: Securitisation & Repackaging, **Competition/Anti-trust**, **Corporate Finance: Larger Deals**, Employee Share Schemes, Energy & Natural Resources, **Environment**, **Financial Services**, Insolvency/Corporate Recovery, Insurance: Non-contentious, Insurance: Reinsurance, Litigation: Banking & Finance, Litigation: Civil Fraud, Litigation: General Commercial (40+ Litigators), **Pensions**, PFI, **Tax**, **Transport: Rail**

FYFE IRELAND WS
Partnership, Property (Commercial)

FYNN & PARTNERS
Environment, Licensing, Planning

GABB & CO
Agriculture

GADSBY WICKS
Clinical Negligence: Mainly Claimant

GALLEN & CO
Crime

GAMLINS
Crime

GAMON ARDEN & CO
Church: Church of England

GARRETTS
Corporate Finance, E-commerce, Information Technology, Intellectual Property, Litigation: General Commercial

GARSTANGS
Crime, Fraud: Criminal

GATELEY WAREING
Banking, Charities, Construction, Corporate Finance

GEORGE DAVIES
Clinical Negligence: Mainly Defendant, Sport

GEORGE IDE, PHILLIPS
Personal Injury: Mainly Claimant

GEORGE MATHERS & CO
Crime

GEPP & SONS
Crime

GILFEDDER & MCINNES
Crime

GILL AKASTER
Family/Matrimonial

GILL & CO
Immigration: Personal

GILLESPIE MACANDREW WS
Agriculture

GILLS
Education: Individuals

GLAISYERS
Crime, Fraud: Criminal

GLAZER DELMAR
Immigration: Personal

GOLDS
Debt Recovery

GOODMAN DERRICK
Media & Entertainment: Broadcasting

GOODMAN RAY
Family/Matrimonial

GORDON & SMYTH
Crime

GORDONS CRANSWICK SOLICITORS
Church: Church of England, Family/Matrimonial, Social Housing

GORNA & CO
Sport

GOSSCHALKS
Licensing

GOTELEE & GOLDSMITH
Crime

GOULDENS
Corporate Finance: Medium Deals, Litigation: General Commercial (Fewer than 40 Litigators)

GRAHAME STOWE, BATESON
Crime, Family/Matrimonial

GRAHAM EVANS & PARTNERS
Crime

GRANVILLE-WEST
Family/Matrimonial

GRAYS
Agriculture, Charities, **Church: Other Denominations**, Trusts & Personal Tax

GREEN & CO
Family/Matrimonial

GREENE & GREENE
Property (Commercial), Trusts & Personal Tax

GREENWOODS
Charities, Construction, Debt Recovery, Employment, Family/Matrimonial, Litigation: General Commercial, Personal Injury: Mainly Defendant, Property (Commercial)

GREGG GALBRAITH QUINN
Food, Licensing

GRIFFITH SMITH
Charities

GROSS & CO
Immigration

GROWER FREEMAN & GOLDBERG
Sport: Regulatory

H

H2O (HENRY HEPWORTH ORGANISATION)
Media & Entertainment: Publishing

HADENS
Family/Matrimonial

HALL & HAUGHEY
Crime

HALLINAN, BLACKBURN, GITTINGS & NOTT
Crime

HALLIWELL LANDAU
Banking, Charities, Corporate Finance, E-commerce, Information Technology, Insolvency/Corporate Recovery, **Intellectual Property**, Litigation: General Commercial, Personal Injury: Mainly Defendant, **Planning**, **Property (Commercial)**, **Trusts & Personal Tax**

HAMERS
Personal Injury: Mainly Claimant

HAMMOND SUDDARDS EDGE
Advertising & Marketing (London), Asset Finance & Leasing (Birmingham), Asset Finance & Leasing: Consumer Finance (Birmingham), Banking (Leeds), **Construction (Leeds)**, Construction (Birmingham, Manchester), Corporate Finance (Birmingham, Leeds), **Debt Recovery (Bradford, London)**, **Employment (Manchester)**, Employment (Birmingham, Leeds), Energy & Natural Resources (Birmingham), Environment (Birmingham, Manchester), Food (Birmingham), Franchising (Manchester), Fraud: Criminal (Birmingham), Health & Safety (Birmingham, Manchester), Insolvency/Corporate Recovery (Leeds, Manchester), Intellectual Property (Leeds, Manchester), Licensing (Birmingham), **Litigation: General Commercial (Leeds)**, Litigation: General Commercial (Birmingham, Manchester), Litigation: Property (Birmingham, Leeds, Manchester), **Media & Entertainment (Birmingham)**, Partnership (Birmingham), **Pensions (Leeds)**, Pensions (Birmingham, Manchester), Planning (Leeds), **Private Equity (Leeds)**, Professional Negligence (Leeds), Property (Commercial) (Birmingham, Leeds, Manchester), **Sport (Birmingham)**, Tax (Leeds, Manchester)

HARBOTTLE & LEWIS
Corporate Finance: Smaller Deals, Media & Entertainment: Film & TV Production, Media & Entertainment: Publishing

HARDING EVANS
Family/Matrimonial

HAROLD BENJAMIN LITTLEJOHN
Property (Commercial)

HARPER MACLEOD
Employment, Licensing, **Social Housing**, **Sport**

HARRIS & CARTWRIGHT
Clinical Negligence: Mainly Claimant, Personal Injury: Mainly Claimant

HARRIS & HARRIS
Church: Church of England

HARRISON BUNDEY & CO
Human Rights, Immigration

HARRISON CURTIS
Media & Entertainment: Theatre

HARRISON, LEITCH & LOGAN
Personal Injury: Mainly Defendant

FIRMS AT A GLANCE

These lists show the key strengths of an individual firm. Please note: only the areas of practice for which a firm is ranked in bands 1-3 of the tables are listed. Bold type indicates the areas of law in which the firm is ranked in 'band one'.

HARVEY INGRAM OWSTON
Church: Church of England

HATCH BRENNER
Crime

HAY & KILNER
Clinical Negligence: Mainly Claimant, Family/Matrimonial, Insolvency/Corporate Recovery, Personal Injury: Mainly Claimant, **Personal Injury: Mainly Defendant**, Professional Negligence

HBM SAYERS
Crime, Insurance, Personal Injury: Mainly Defendant

HEMPSONS
Clinical Negligence: Mainly Defendant, **Healthcare**, **Partnership: Medical**

HENDERSON BOYD JACKSON WS
Debt Recovery, **Shipping**, Social Housing, Sport

HENMANS
Agriculture, Charities, Employment, Family/Matrimonial, Personal Injury: Mainly Claimant, Personal Injury: Mainly Defendant, **Professional Negligence**, Trusts & Personal Tax

HENRY HYAMS & CO
Crime

HENRY MILNER & CO
Crime

HEPTONSTALLS
Clinical Negligence: Mainly Claimant

HERBERT SMITH
Administrative & Public Law: Commercial, Arbitration (International), **Competition/Anti-trust**, Construction, Corporate Finance: Larger Deals, Employee Share Schemes, **Energy & Natural Resources**, **Insurance: Non-contentious**, Insurance: Reinsurance, Intellectual Property: General, Intellectual Property: Patent, Investment Funds, **Litigation: Civil Fraud**, **Litigation: General Commercial (40+ Litigators)**, Litigation: Property, Partnership, **Partnership: Large International Mergers**, PFI, Planning, Professional Negligence: Financial, Property (Commercial): 50+ Solicitors, Tax

HEWITSON BECKE + SHAW
Agriculture, Charities, Construction, Corporate Finance, Debt Recovery, **Employment**, Environment, Information Technology, Intellectual Property, Litigation: General Commercial, **Litigation: Property**, Planning, **Property (Commercial)**, Trusts & Personal Tax

HEXTALL ERSKINE
Personal Injury: Mainly Defendant

HIBBERT DURRAD DAVIES
Agriculture

HICKMAN & ROSE
Crime

HIGGS & SONS
Employment, Trusts & Personal Tax

HILL DICKINSON
Church: Other Denominations, Clinical Negligence: Mainly Defendant, Healthcare, Intellectual Property, Personal Injury: Mainly Defendant, Professional Negligence, Shipping, **Transport: Road - Carriage/Commercial**

HILL TAYLOR DICKINSON
Commodities: Physicals, Shipping

HODGE JONES & ALLEN
Crime, Personal Injury: Mainly Claimant

HODKINSONS
Fraud: Criminal

HOLLINGWORTH BISSELL
Transport: Rail

HOLMAN FENWICK & WILLAN
Insurance: Reinsurance, **Shipping**

HOLMES HARDINGHAM
Transport: Road - Carriage/Commercial

HOOPER & WOLLEN
Family/Matrimonial, Trusts & Personal Tax

HORSEY LIGHTLY
Family/Matrimonial

HOWARTH GOODMAN
Social Housing

HOWELLS
Crime, **Human Rights**, **Immigration**

HOWES PERCIVAL
Licensing, Trusts & Personal Tax

HUGHES FOWLER CARRUTHERS
Family/Matrimonial

HUGH JAMES FORD SIMEY
Clinical Negligence: Mainly Claimant, Construction, **Education: Individuals**, Employment, **Family/Matrimonial**, Health & Safety, Insolvency/Corporate Recovery, **Litigation: General Commercial**, **Litigation: Property**, **Personal Injury: Mainly Claimant**, **Personal Injury: Mainly Defendant**, **Social Housing**, **Sport**, Trusts & Personal Tax

HUMPHREYS & CO
Insurance: Reinsurance, Intellectual Property

HUNT & MORGAN
Insolvency/Corporate Recovery

HUNT & COOMBS
Crime, Family/Matrimonial

HUTTONS
Clinical Negligence: Mainly Claimant, **Crime**, Fraud: Criminal

I

IAIN SMITH & COMPANY
Insolvency/Corporate Recovery

IAN DOWNING FAMILY LAW PRACTICE
Family/Matrimonial

ILIFFES BOOTH BENNETT
Charities, Crime, Trusts & Personal Tax

INCE & CO
Insurance: General Claims, **Insurance: Reinsurance**, Professional Negligence: Legal, **Shipping**

IRWIN MITCHELL
Administrative & Public Law: General, Charities, **Clinical Negligence: Mainly Claimant**, **Crime**, Family/Matrimonial, Fraud: Criminal, Human Rights, Litigation: General Commercial, **Personal Injury: Mainly Claimant**, Personal Injury: Mainly Defendant, **Product Liability**, Professional Negligence, Travel, Trusts & Personal Tax

JACKSON & CANTER
Immigration

JACKSONS
Employment, Personal Injury: Mainly Defendant

JAMES & CO
Immigration

JAMES CHAPMAN & CO
Personal Injury: Mainly Defendant, **Professional Negligence**, **Sport**

JAMESON & HILL
Planning

C & H JEFFERSON
Litigation: General Commercial, **Personal Injury: Mainly Defendant**

JEFFREY AITKEN SOLICITORS
Transport: Road - Regulatory

JEFFREY GREEN RUSSELL
Debt Recovery, **Licensing**

JENKINS & HAND
Social Housing

JJ RICE
Crime

JOELSON WILSON & CO
Licensing

JOHN BOYLE AND CO
Crime

JOHN COLLINS & PARTNERS WITH EDWARD HARRIS
Agriculture, Clinical Negligence: Mainly Claimant, Debt Recovery

JOHN FORD MORRISON
Education: Individuals

JOHN GAUNT & PARTNERS
Licensing

JOHN HODGE & CO
Clinical Negligence: Mainly Claimant

JOHN MCKEE & SON
Banking, Debt Recovery, Insolvency/Corporate Recovery

JOHN PICKERING & PARTNERS
Personal Injury: Mainly Claimant

JOHNS ELLIOT
Construction, Litigation: General Commercial, Property (Commercial), Trusts & Personal Tax

THE JOHNSON PARTNERSHIP
Crime

JOHNSONS
Defamation, Litigation: General Commercial, Personal Injury: Mainly Defendant

JOHN WESTON & CO
Shipping, Transport: Road - Carriage/Commercial

JONAS ROY BLOOM
Crime

JONES & CASSIDY
Employment

JONES MAIDMENT WILSON
Clinical Negligence: Mainly Claimant, Crime, Family/Matrimonial

JONES MYERS GORDON
Family/Matrimonial

JOY MERRIAM & CO
Crime

JULIAN HOLY
Property (Commercial): Fewer than 25 Solicitors

KEMP LITTLE LLP
E-commerce

KENNEDYS
Clinical Negligence: Mainly Defendant, Construction, Insurance: General Claims, Personal Injury: Mainly Defendant, Professional Negligence: Construction

KENNETH BUSH
Licensing

KENNETH CURTIS & CO
Licensing

KENT JONES AND DONE
Energy & Natural Resources, **Media & Entertainment**

These lists show the key strengths of an individual firm. Please note: only the areas of practice for which a firm is ranked in bands 1-3 of the tables are listed. Bold type indicates the areas of law in which the firm is ranked in 'band one'.

KEOGHS
Insurance, **Personal Injury: Mainly Defendant**

KERSHAW ABBOTT
Partnership

KIERAN & CO
Crime

KIMBELLS
Corporate Finance

KINGSFORD STACEY BLACKWELL
Licensing

KINGSLEY NAPLEY
Clinical Negligence: Mainly Claimant, **Crime**, Family/Matrimonial, **Fraud: Criminal**, **Immigration: Business**, Partnership

KIRK JACKSON
Construction

KNIGHTS
Administrative & Public Law: General

KNIGHT & SONS
Agriculture, Energy & Natural Resources

L

LAMPORT BASSITT
Personal Injury: Mainly Claimant

LANE & PARTNERS
Aviation: Regulatory

LANYON BOWDLER
Family/Matrimonial

LARBY WILLIAMS
Family/Matrimonial

LARCOMES
Church: Other Denominations

LATIMER HINKS
Agriculture

LAWFORD KIDD
Personal Injury: Mainly Claimant

THE LAW OFFICES OF MARCUS J O'LEARY
E-commerce, **Information Technology**, **Intellectual Property**

LAWRENCE GRAHAM
Corporate Finance: Smaller Deals, Litigation: Property, Local Government, Trusts & Personal Tax

LAYTONS
Construction, Family/Matrimonial, Information Technology, Insolvency/Corporate Recovery, Litigation: General Commercial

LEA & COMPANY
Media & Entertainment

LEATHES PRIOR
Charities, **Immigration**, Personal Injury: Mainly Claimant

LEDINGHAM CHALMERS
Energy: Oil & Gas, Social Housing

LEE BOLTON & LEE
Church: Church of England, Education: Institutions

LEE CROWDER
Charities, Property (Commercial), Social Housing, Trusts & Personal Tax

LEE & PEMBERTONS
Agriculture

LEES LLOYD WHITLEY
Debt Recovery

LEE & THOMPSON
Media & Entertainment: Film & TV Production, Media & Entertainment: Music

LEIGH, DAY & CO
Administrative & Public Law: Traditional, **Clinical Negligence: Mainly Claimant**, **Environment**, **Personal Injury: Mainly Claimant**, Product Liability, **Product Liability: Mainly Claimant**

LEO ABSE & COHEN
Family/Matrimonial, Personal Injury: Mainly Claimant

LÉONIE COWEN & ASSOCIATES
Local Government

LESTER ALDRIDGE
Asset Finance & Leasing, Asset Finance & Leasing: Consumer Finance, Charities, Debt Recovery, **Family/Matrimonial**, Health & Safety, Information Technology, Insolvency/Corporate Recovery, Intellectual Property, Licensing, **Partnership**, **Shipping**

L'ESTRANGE & BRETT
Banking, **Construction**, **Corporate Finance**, Employment, **Litigation: General Commercial**, **Partnership**, **Property (Commercial)**, **Trusts & Personal Tax**

LEVENES
Administrative & Public Law: Traditional, Education: Individuals

LEVI & CO
Crime

LEVISON MELTZER PIGOTT
Family/Matrimonial

LEVY & MCRAE
Crime, **Defamation**, Media & Entertainment

LEWIS SILKIN
Advertising & Marketing, Corporate Finance: Smaller Deals, Employment: Mainly Respondent, Social Housing

LINDER MYERS
Clinical Negligence: Mainly Claimant

LINDSAYS WS
Administrative & Public Law: General, Charities

LINKLATERS
Asset Finance & Leasing, Banking, Capital Markets: Derivatives, **Capital Markets: International Debt & Equity**, Capital Markets: Securitisation & Repackaging, Commodities: Futures, **Competition/Anti-trust**, Construction, **Corporate Finance: Larger Deals**, **Employee Share Schemes**, Energy & Natural Resources, Environment, **Financial Services**, Insolvency/Corporate Recovery, Insurance: Non-contentious, Intellectual Property: General, Intellectual Property: Patent, **Investment Funds**, Litigation: Banking & Finance, **Litigation: Civil Fraud**, Litigation: General Commercial (40+ Litigators), Litigation: Pensions, Litigation: Property, **Partnership: Large International Mergers**, **PFI**, Planning, Project Finance, **Property (Commercial): 50+ Solicitors**, **Tax**, Telecommunications, Transport: Rail, Travel: Hotels & Leisure

LINNELLS
Charities, **Construction**, **Partnership**, Property (Commercial)

LIVINGSTONE BROWNE
Crime

LOCHNERS TECHNOLOGY SOLICITORS
Intellectual Property

LODDERS
Trusts & Personal Tax

LOOSEMORES
Personal Injury: Mainly Claimant

LOVELLS
Administrative & Public Law: Commercial, Competition/Anti-trust, Employment: Mainly Respondent, Information Technology, Insolvency/Corporate Recovery, **Insurance: Non-contentious**, Insurance: Reinsurance, Intellectual Property: General, Intellectual Property: Patent, Litigation: Banking & Finance, **Litigation: Civil Fraud**, Litigation: General Commercial (40+ Litigators), **Litigation: Pensions**, Litigation: Property, Media & Entertainment: Publishing, **Parliamentary: Public Affairs**, Private Equity: Buyouts & Investment, Private Equity: Debt, Product Liability: Mainly Defendant, Professional Negligence: Financial, Professional Negligence: Legal, Property (Commercial): 50+ Solicitors, Travel: Hotels & Leisure

LUCAS & WYLLYS
Crime

LUPTON FAWCETT
Debt Recovery, Licensing, Litigation: General Commercial, Trusts & Personal Tax

LUQMANI THOMPSON
Immigration: Personal

LYONS DAVIDSON
Personal Injury: Mainly Claimant

M

MACE & JONES
Employment, Family/Matrimonial, Partnership, Partnership: Medical, Property (Commercial)

MACFARLANES
Advertising & Marketing, **Agriculture**, Private Equity: Buyouts & Investment, Private Equity: Fund Formation, Property (Commercial): 25-49 Solicitors, **Trusts & Personal Tax**

MACKAY SIMON
Employment

MACKINNONS
Shipping

MACKINTOSH DUNCAN
Administrative & Public Law: Traditional

MACLAY MURRAY & SPENS
Aviation, **Banking**, **Competition/Anti-trust**, **Corporate Finance**, E-commerce, Education: Institutions, Employee Share Schemes, **Employment**, Environment, Financial Services, **Information Technology**, **Intellectual Property**, Investment Funds, **Litigation: General Commercial**, **Litigation: Property**, **Partnership**, Pensions, Planning, Projects/PFI, Property (Commercial), Shipping, Tax, Trusts & Personal Tax

MACROBERTS
Banking, Charities, Competition/Anti-trust, **Construction**, Corporate Finance, **Employee Share Schemes**, **Employment**, Energy: Electricity, Environment, Insolvency/Corporate Recovery, Intellectual Property, Projects/PFI, Tax, Trusts & Personal Tax

MADDEN & FINUCANE
Administrative & Public Law: General, **Crime**

MADGE LLOYD & GIBSON
Church: Church of England

MAGRATH & CO
Immigration: Business

MAIDMENTS
Crime

MAITLAND & CO
Offshore: Corporate/Commercial

MANBY & STEWARD
Agriculture, Church: Church of England

MANCHES
Charities, Corporate Finance, **Education: Institutions**, **Family/Matrimonial**, Information Technology, Intellectual Property, **Media & Entertainment**, Property (Commercial): Fewer than 25 Solicitors, Social Housing

FIRMS AT A GLANCE

These lists show the key strengths of an individual firm. Please note: only the areas of practice for which a firm is ranked in bands 1-3 of the tables are listed. Bold type indicates the areas of law in which the firm is ranked in 'band one'.

MARGETTS & RITCHIE
Food

MARGRAVES
Agriculture, Trusts & Personal Tax

MARRONS
Personal Injury: Mainly Claimant, **Planning**

MARSONS SOLICITORS
Social Housing

MARTINEAU JOHNSON
Administrative & Public Law: General, Agriculture, Banking, **Charities**, Church: Church of England, Corporate Finance, **Education: Institutions**, Employment, **Energy & Natural Resources**, Insolvency/Corporate Recovery, Intellectual Property, Litigation: General Commercial, Litigation: Property, **Trusts & Personal Tax**

MARTYN PROWEL SOLICITORS
Crime, Family/Matrimonial, **Fraud: Criminal**

MASON BOND
Travel

MASON & MOORE DUTTON
Agriculture

MASONS
Construction (Bristol, Edinburgh, Glasgow, London, Manchester), Construction (Leeds), Environment (Manchester), Health & Safety (London), **Information Technology (Leeds, Manchester)**, Information Technology (London), Litigation: Property (Bristol), Pensions (Manchester), Projects/PFI (Glasgow)

MAX BARFORD & CO
Family/Matrimonial

MAX BITEL, GREENE
Sport: Regulatory

THE MAX GOLD PARTNERSHIP
Crime

MAXWELL BATLEY
Property (Commercial): Fewer than 25 Solicitors

MCCLENAHAN CROSSEY & CO
Crime

MCCLURE NAISMITH
Asset Finance & Leasing, Asset Finance & Leasing: Consumer Finance, **Debt Recovery**, Projects/PFI

MCCORMACKS
Crime

MCCORMICKS
Media & Entertainment, **Sport**

MCCOURTS
Crime

MC DARLINGTON
Church: Church of England

MCGRATH & CO
Human Rights

MCGRIGOR DONALD
Administrative & Public Law: General, **Banking**, Construction, **Corporate Finance**, E-commerce, Employment, Energy: Electricity, Environment, Financial Services, Information Technology, **Intellectual Property**, Investment Funds, Licensing, **Litigation: General Commercial**, Litigation: Property, Local Government, Media & Entertainment, **Partnership**, Pensions, Planning, **Product Liability**, Projects/PFI, **Property (Commercial)**, **Tax**

MCKAY & NORWELL WS
Crime

MCKENZIE BELL
Licensing

MCKINTY & WRIGHT
Defamation, Litigation: General Commercial, **Personal Injury: Mainly Defendant**, **Product Liability**, **Professional Negligence**, Property (Commercial)

MCLELLANS
Licensing

MCMANUS & KEARNEY
Insolvency/Corporate Recovery

MEMERY CRYSTAL
Corporate Finance: Smaller Deals

MERRICKS
Personal Injury: Mainly Defendant

MICHELMORES
Church: Church of England, Education: Institutions, Employment, Property (Commercial)

MIDDLETON POTTS
Commodities: Physicals

MILES PRESTON & CO
Family/Matrimonial

MILLAR SHEARER & BLACK
Crime

MILLER SANDS
Family/Matrimonial

MILLS & CO
Shipping

MILLS & REEVE
Administrative & Public Law: General, **Agriculture**, Banking, **Charities**, Church: Church of England, **Construction**, **Corporate Finance**, **Education: Institutions**, **Employment**, **Environment**, **Family/Matrimonial**, **Healthcare**, **Insolvency/Corporate Recovery**, **Intellectual Property**, Licensing, **Litigation: General Commercial**, **Litigation: Property**, **Personal Injury: Mainly Defendant**, **Planning**, **Professional Negligence**, Projects/PFI, **Property (Commercial)**, Tax, **Trusts & Personal Tax**

MILLS SELIG
Corporate Finance, **Defamation**, Litigation: General Commercial, **Product Liability**, Property (Commercial)

MINCOFFS
Family/Matrimonial, Licensing

MISHCON DE REYA
Family/Matrimonial, Litigation: Civil Fraud, Property (Commercial): Fewer than 25 Solicitors

MOORE & BLATCH
Personal Injury: Mainly Claimant, Trusts & Personal Tax

MORE & CO
Crime

MORGAN COLE
Administrative & Public Law: General, Agriculture, Banking, **Competition/Anti-trust**, **Construction**, **Corporate Finance**, Debt Recovery, **Education: Institutions**, Employment, **Environment**, Family/Matrimonial, Healthcare, Information Technology, Insolvency/Corporate Recovery, Intellectual Property, **Licensing**, **Litigation: General Commercial**, Litigation: Property, Local Government, **Media & Entertainment**, **Personal Injury: Mainly Defendant**, **Planning**, **Professional Negligence**, Projects/PFI, Property (Commercial), Social Housing

MORGAN JONES & PETT
Clinical Negligence: Mainly Claimant, Personal Injury: Mainly Claimant

MORISON BISHOP
Debt Recovery, Environment, Pensions, Professional Negligence, Sport

MORRISH & CO
Personal Injury: Mainly Claimant

MORTON FRASER, SOLICITORS
Asset Finance & Leasing, Charities, Debt Recovery, Environment, **Family/Matrimonial**, Trusts & Personal Tax

MOURANT DU FEU & JEUNE
Offshore: Corporate/Commercial

MOWAT DEAN & CO WS
Family/Matrimonial

MUNDAYS
Corporate Finance, Franchising, Partnership, Trusts & Personal Tax

MURRAY BEITH MURRAY WS
Trusts & Personal Tax

N

NABARRO NATHANSON
Administrative & Public Law: Traditional, **Charities**, Corporate Finance, E-commerce, **Energy & Natural Resources**, Environment, Health & Safety, **Information Technology**, Intellectual Property, Litigation: General Commercial, Litigation: General Commercial (Fewer than 40 Litigators), Litigation: Pensions, **Litigation: Property**, **Local Government**, Personal Injury: Mainly Defendant, Planning, Projects/PFI

NAPIER & SONS
Insolvency/Corporate Recovery

NAPTHEN HOUGHTON CRAVEN
Agriculture

NEEDHAM & JAMES
Social Housing

NELSONS
Crime, **Family/Matrimonial**, **Fraud: Criminal**, Immigration, Personal Injury: Mainly Claimant

NESS GALLAGHER
Crime

NICHOLSON GRAHAM & JONES
Corporate Finance: Smaller Deals, Litigation: General Commercial (Fewer than 40 Litigators), Property (Commercial): Fewer than 25 Solicitors, Sport: Commercial/Media, Travel

NICHOLSONS
Insolvency/Corporate Recovery

NICOL, DENVIR & PURNELL
Family/Matrimonial

NOLAN MACLEOD
Debt Recovery

NORTON ROSE
Asset Finance & Leasing, **Aviation: Regulatory**, Banking, Energy & Natural Resources, Investment Funds, **Litigation: Civil Fraud**, Private Equity: Debt, Project Finance, Property (Commercial): 25-49 Solicitors, **Shipping: Finance**, Tax, Travel

OGIER & LE MASURIER
Offshore: Corporate/Commercial

OGLETHORPE STURTON & GILLIBRAND
Agriculture

OLSENS
Offshore: Corporate/Commercial

OLSWANG
Corporate Finance: Medium Deals, **Defamation**, **E-commerce**, Information Technology, **Media & Entertainment: Broadcasting**, **Media & Entertainment:**

FIRMS AT A GLANCE

These lists show the key strengths of an individual firm. Please note: only the areas of practice for which a firm is ranked in bands 1-3 of the tables are listed. Bold type indicates the areas of law in which the firm is ranked in 'band one'.

Film & TV Production, Media & Entertainment: Film Finance, Sport: Commercial/Media, Telecommunications

O'REILLY STEWART
Licensing, Personal Injury: Mainly Defendant, **Product Liability**

OSBORNE CLARKE
Advertising & Marketing, Asset Finance & Leasing, **Banking**, Charities, **Corporate Finance**, **Debt Recovery**, **E-commerce**, Employee Share Schemes, **Employment**, **Environment**, **Health & Safety**, **Information Technology**, **Insolvency/Corporate Recovery**, **Intellectual Property**, Licensing, **Litigation: General Commercial**, Litigation: Property, Partnership, **Pensions**, Planning, **Private Equity**, **Property (Commercial)**, Sport, **Tax**, **Trusts & Personal Tax**

OSBORNE MORRIS & MORGAN
Clinical Negligence: Mainly Claimant, **Personal Injury: Mainly Claimant**

OSWALD GOODIER & CO
Charities, Church: Other Denominations

OVERBURY STEWARD EATON & WOOLSEY
Crime

OVER TAYLOR BIGGS
Clinical Negligence: Mainly Claimant

OWEN WHITE
Social Housing

OZANNES
Offshore: Corporate/Commercial

PALSER GROSSMAN
Litigation: General Commercial, **Personal Injury: Mainly Defendant**, Property (Commercial)

PANNONE & PARTNERS
Charities, **Clinical Negligence: Mainly Claimant**, Defamation, **Family/Matrimonial**, Fraud: Criminal, Litigation: Property, **Personal Injury: Mainly Claimant**, Property (Commercial), Trusts & Personal Tax

PARIS SMITH & RANDALL
Corporate Finance, Family/Matrimonial, Insolvency/Corporate Recovery, Property (Commercial), Trusts & Personal Tax

PARKER & GREGO
Crime

PARLBY CALDER
Crime

PARLETT KENT
Clinical Negligence: Mainly Claimant

PATTINSON & BREWER
Employment, **Employment: Mainly Applicant**, Personal Injury: Mainly Claimant

PAULL & WILLIAMSONS
Employment, **Energy: Oil & Gas**, Planning

PAYNE HICKS BEACH
Agriculture, Family/Matrimonial, Trusts & Personal Tax

PAYNE MARSH STILLWELL
Partnership: Medical

PEDEN & REID
Family/Matrimonial

PENNINGTONS
Clinical Negligence: Mainly Claimant, Social Housing, Trusts & Personal Tax

PETER CARTER-RUCK AND PARTNERS
Defamation

PETER MAUGHAN & CO
Clinical Negligence: Mainly Claimant

PETERS & PETERS
Customs & Excise, **Fraud: Criminal**

PHILIP CONN & CO
Intellectual Property

PINSENT CURTIS BIDDLE
Administrative & Public Law: General, **Banking**, **Competition/Anti-trust**, Corporate Finance, Education: Institutions, **Employee Share Schemes**, **Employment**, Energy & Natural Resources, **Environment**, **Financial Services**, Food, Franchising, Information Technology, Insolvency/Corporate Recovery, Intellectual Property, Licensing, **Litigation: General Commercial**, Litigation: Pensions, **Litigation: Property**, Local Government, **Partnership**, Planning, Professional Negligence, Professional Negligence: Legal, **Projects/PFI**, Property (Commercial), Social Housing, **Tax**, Trusts & Personal Tax

PITMANS
Corporate Finance, Employment, Insolvency/Corporate Recovery, Pensions, **Planning**, **Property (Commercial)**

POPPLESTON ALLEN
Licensing

POTHECARY & BARRATT
Church: Other Denominations

POWELL SPENCER & PARTNERS
Crime

PRESTON GOLDBURN
Clinical Negligence: Mainly Claimant

PRETTYS
Clinical Negligence: Mainly Claimant, Corporate Finance, Debt Recovery, Insolvency/Corporate Recovery, Litigation: General Commercial, Personal Injury: Mainly Defendant, Property (Commercial), Shipping

PRINCE EVANS
Social Housing

PRYCE COLLARD CHAMBERLAIN
Agriculture

PULLIG & CO
Licensing

PURCELL PARKER
Crime

R

R & JM HILL BROWN & CO
Licensing

RAMSBOTTOM & CO
Media & Entertainment

RAWLISON BUTLER
Corporate Finance, Employment, Partnership

RAYFIELD MILLS
Shipping

READ HIND STEWART
Property (Commercial)

REED SMITH WARNER CRANSTON
Corporate Finance: Smaller Deals, Debt Recovery, Immigration: Business

REES & FRERES
Parliamentary Agency

REYNOLDS DAWSON
Crime

REYNOLDS PORTER CHAMBERLAIN
Defamation, Insurance: General Claims, Partnership, Professional Negligence: Construction, Professional Negligence: Financial, Professional Negligence: Insurance, **Professional Negligence: Legal**

RICHARD BUXTON
Administrative & Public Law: General, **Environment**

RICHARD MONTEITH
Crime

RICHARDS BUTLER
Commodities: Physicals, Corporate Finance: Smaller Deals, **Licensing**, Litigation: Civil Fraud, Media & Entertainment: Broadcasting, **Media & Entertainment: Film Finance**, Shipping, Travel: Hotels & Leisure

RICKERBY WATTERSON
Education: Institutions

RM BROUDIE & CO
Crime

ROBERT LIZAR
Human Rights

ROBERT MUCKLE
Banking, Corporate Finance, Property (Commercial)

ROBERTSONS
Crime, Family/Matrimonial, Property (Commercial)

ROBSON MCLEAN WS
Partnership

ROEBUCKS
Church: Church of England

ROLLITS
Agriculture, Litigation: General Commercial, Social Housing, Trusts & Personal Tax

ROSS HARPER
Crime

ROWE & MAW
Administrative & Public Law: Traditional, Construction, Corporate Finance: Medium Deals, Employment: Mainly Respondent, Litigation: Pensions, Local Government, **Partnership**, **Professional Negligence: Construction**, Professional Negligence: Financial

ROWLEY ASHWORTH
Employment: Mainly Applicant, **Personal Injury: Mainly Claimant**

ROY MORGAN & CO
Fraud: Criminal

ROYTHORNE & CO
Agriculture, Trusts & Personal Tax

RUPERT BEAR MURRAY DAVIES
Family/Matrimonial

RUSSEL & AITKEN
Family/Matrimonial

RUSSELL-COOKE
Crime

RUSSELL JONES & WALKER
Clinical Negligence: Mainly Claimant, Crime, **Education: Individuals**, Employment: Mainly Applicant, **Personal Injury: Mainly Claimant**

RUSSELL & RUSSELL
Crime

RUSSELLS
Media & Entertainment: Music

RUSSELLS GIBSON MCCAFFREY
Family/Matrimonial

FIRMS AT A GLANCE

These lists show the key strengths of an individual firm. Please note: only the areas of practice for which a firm is ranked in bands 1-3 of the tables are listed. Bold type indicates the areas of law in which the firm is ranked in 'band one'.

SACKER & PARTNERS
Litigation: Pensions

SALANS HERTZFELD & HEILBRONN HRK
Asset Finance & Leasing: Consumer Finance, Debt Recovery

SAMUEL PHILLIPS & CO
Clinical Negligence: Mainly Claimant, Employment, Family/Matrimonial, Immigration

SAUNDERS & CO
Crime

SAVAGE CRANGLE
Social Housing

SCHILLING & LOM AND PARTNERS
Defamation

SCRIVENGER SEABROOK
Clinical Negligence: Mainly Claimant

SEARS TOOTH
Family/Matrimonial

SEMPLE FRASER
Litigation: Property, Planning, Property (Commercial)

SHADBOLT & CO
Construction, Corporate Finance

SHAKESPEARES
Charities, Debt Recovery, Education: Institutions

SHARPE PRITCHARD
Administrative & Public Law: Traditional, Local Government, Parliamentary Agency

SHEAN DICKSON MERRICK
Licensing

SHEPHERD & WEDDERBURN WS
Administrative & Public Law: General, **Aviation**, Banking, Charities, **Clinical Negligence: Mainly Defendant**, **Competition/Anti-trust**, Construction, Corporate Finance, E-commerce, Employment, **Energy: Electricity**, Financial Services, Information Technology, Insolvency/Corporate Recovery, Intellectual Property, Litigation: General Commercial, Litigation: Property, **Local Government**, **Pensions**, Planning, Projects/PFI, Property (Commercial)

SHERIDANS
Media & Entertainment: Music

SHERRARDS
Social Housing

SHERWIN OLIVER SOLICITORS
Insolvency/Corporate Recovery

SHOOSMITHS
Corporate Finance, **Debt Recovery**, **Food**, Litigation: General Commercial, **Personal Injury: Mainly Claimant**, Planning

SHORT RICHARDSON & FORTH
Employment

SIDLEY AUSTIN BROWN & WOOD
Capital Markets: Securitisation & Repackaging

SILVER FITZGERALD
Family/Matrimonial

THE SIMKINS PARTNERSHIP
Advertising & Marketing, Media & Entertainment: Film & TV Production, Media & Entertainment: Film Finance, Media & Entertainment: Publishing, Media & Entertainment: Theatre

SIMMONS & SIMMONS
Administrative & Public Law: Commercial, Capital Markets: Securitisation & Repackaging, Commodities: Futures, Competition/Anti-trust, **Employment: Mainly Respondent**, Environment, Food, Health & Safety, Intellectual Property: General, Intellectual Property: Patent, Litigation: Civil Fraud, Transport: Rail

SIMONS MUIRHEAD & BURTON
Crime, Fraud: Criminal

SIMPSON & MARWICK WS
Administrative & Public Law: General, **Aviation**, **Insurance**, Litigation: General Commercial, Local Government, **Personal Injury: Mainly Defendant**, **Product Liability**, **Professional Negligence**

SINCLAIRS
Education: Individuals

SINTON & CO
Family/Matrimonial, **Personal Injury: Mainly Defendant**

SJ BERWIN
Competition/Anti-trust, Corporate Finance: Medium Deals, Litigation: Civil Fraud, **Litigation: General Commercial (Fewer than 40 Litigators)**, Media & Entertainment: Film & TV Production, **Media & Entertainment: Film Finance**, **Parliamentary: Public Affairs**, Planning, **Private Equity: Fund Formation**, **Property (Commercial): 25-49 Solicitors**, Sport: Commercial/Media, Tax, **Travel: Hotels & Leisure**

SJ CORNISH
Professional Negligence

SLAUGHTER AND MAY
Asset Finance & Leasing, Aviation: Regulatory, Capital Markets: Securitisation & Repackaging, **Competition/Anti-trust**, **Corporate Finance: Larger Deals**, Employee Share Schemes, Environment, Financial Services, Insurance: Non-contentious, Litigation: Civil Fraud, **Partnership: Large International Mergers**, Pensions, **Tax**

SMITH LLEWELYN PARTNERSHIP
Personal Injury: Mainly Claimant

THE SMITH PARTNERSHIP
Crime

SPEECHLY BIRCHAM
Property (Commercial): Fewer than 25 Solicitors

SPIRO GRECH & HARDING-ROBERTS SOLICITORS
Crime

STAMP JACKSON AND PROCTER
Agriculture

STANLEY TEE
Agriculture

STEEDMAN RAMAGE
Litigation: Property

STEELE & CO
Employment, Licensing, **Local Government**

STEELE RAYMOND
Education: Institutions

STEPHENSON HARWOOD
Corporate Finance: Smaller Deals, Litigation: Civil Fraud, **Litigation: General Commercial (Fewer than 40 Litigators)**, Shipping: Finance

STEPHENSONS
Family/Matrimonial

STEPHENS & SCOWN
Administrative & Public Law: General, Agriculture, Crime, Employment, Environment, Family/Matrimonial, Planning

STEPIEN LAKE GILBERT & PALING
Property (Commercial): Fewer than 25 Solicitors

STEVENS & BOLTON
Corporate Finance, Environment, Litigation: General Commercial, Property (Commercial), Trusts & Personal Tax

STEWARTS
Personal Injury: Mainly Claimant

STONE KING
Charities, **Church: Other Denominations**, Education: Institutions

STONES
Crime, Social Housing, Travel, Travel: Timeshare

STURTIVANT & CO
Immigration: Business

SUGARÉ & CO
Crime

T

TARLO LYONS
Information Technology, **Media & Entertainment: Theatre**

TAYLOR JOYNSON GARRETT
E-commerce, Food, Information Technology, **Intellectual Property: General**, Intellectual Property: Patent, Media & Entertainment: Publishing

TAYLOR NICHOL
Crime

TAYLOR VINTERS
Agriculture, **Charities**, Corporate Finance, Employment, Insolvency/Corporate Recovery, Litigation: General Commercial, Personal Injury: Mainly Claimant, Planning, Property (Commercial), Trusts & Personal Tax

TC YOUNG & SON
Charities, **Social Housing**

TEACHER STERN SELBY
Administrative & Public Law: Traditional, **Education: Individuals**

THANKI NOVY TAUBE
Crime

THEODORE GODDARD
Advertising & Marketing, Defamation, Litigation: Civil Fraud, Media & Entertainment: Film & TV Production

THOMAS A HIGGINS & CO
Debt Recovery

THOMAS EGGAR CHURCH ADAMS
Agriculture, **Charities**, **Church: Church of England**, Corporate Finance, **Education: Institutions**, Litigation: General Commercial, **Trusts & Personal Tax**

THOMPSONS
Employment, Employment: Mainly Applicant, **Family/Matrimonial**, **Personal Injury: Mainly Claimant**

THOMSON SNELL & PASSMORE
Charities, Clinical Negligence: Mainly Claimant, Corporate Finance, Family/Matrimonial, Litigation: General Commercial, **Litigation: Property**, Personal Injury: Mainly Claimant, Property (Commercial), Trusts & Personal Tax

THOMSON WEBB CORFIELD
Crime

THORNHILL INCE
Immigration

THORNTONS WS
Agriculture

THRING TOWNSEND
Charities, Employment

FIRMS AT A GLANCE

These lists show the key strengths of an individual firm. Please note: only the areas of practice for which a firm is ranked in bands 1-3 of the tables are listed. Bold type indicates the areas of law in which the firm is ranked in 'band one'.

TLT SOLICITORS
Corporate Finance, **Debt Recovery**, Employment, **Family/Matrimonial**, Litigation: General Commercial, **Partnership**, Partnership: Medical, Planning, Property (Commercial)

TODS MURRAY WS
Administrative & Public Law: General, Agriculture, Banking, Charities, Financial Services, Investment Funds, Local Government, **Media & Entertainment**, Property (Commercial), **Travel: Timeshare**, Trusts & Personal Tax

TOWNLEYS
Sport: Commercial/Media, **Sport: Regulatory**

TOZERS
Charities, Church: Other Denominations, **Family/Matrimonial**

TRAVERS SMITH BRAITHWAITE
Corporate Finance: Medium Deals, Pensions, Property (Commercial): Fewer than 25 Solicitors

TRETHOWANS
Licensing

TREVOR SMYTH & CO
Crime

TROWERS & HAMLINS
Local Government, Property (Commercial): Fewer than 25 Solicitors, **Social Housing**, Social Housing: Advising Lenders

TUCKERS
Crime

TUGHAN & CO
Construction, Corporate Finance, Litigation: General Commercial, Personal Injury: Mainly Defendant, Property (Commercial)

TUNNARD CROSFIELD
Church: Church of England

TURBERVILLES WITH NELSON CUFF
Licensing

TURCAN CONNELL
Agriculture, **Charities**, **Family/Matrimonial**, **Trusts & Personal Tax**

TURNBULL, SIMSON & STURROCK WS
Agriculture

TV EDWARDS
Crime

TWITCHEN MUSTERS & KELLY
Crime

TYNDALLWOODS
Administrative & Public Law: General, Crime, **Family/Matrimonial**, **Human Rights**, **Immigration**

U

UNDERWOODS
Employment

VARLEY HADLEY SIDDALL
Crime, Fraud: Criminal

VARLEY HIBBS
Family/Matrimonial

VEALE WASBROUGH
Charities, **Education: Institutions**, Employment, **Energy & Natural Resources**, Environment, Litigation: General Commercial, Litigation: Property, **Partnership**, Partnership: Medical, **Personal Injury: Mainly Claimant**, Property (Commercial)

VEITCH PENNY
Personal Injury: Mainly Defendant

VENTERS & CO
Crime

VICTOR LISSACK & ROSCOE
Crime

VIZARD OLDHAM
Clinical Negligence: Mainly Defendant

VIZARDS, STAPLES & BANNISTERS
Personal Injury: Mainly Defendant

W

WACE MORGAN
Family/Matrimonial

WAKE DYNE LAWTON
Energy & Natural Resources, Environment, Planning, Transport: Road - Regulatory

WALKER CHARLESWORTH & FOSTER
Social Housing

WALKER MORRIS
Construction, Insolvency/Corporate Recovery, Intellectual Property, **Litigation: General Commercial**, Litigation: Property, Local Government, Planning, Property (Commercial), Sport, Tax

WALKER SMITH & WAY
Agriculture

WALTONS & MORSE
Transport: Road - Carriage/Commercial

WARD HADAWAY
Agriculture, Banking, Clinical Negligence: Mainly Defendant, Corporate Finance, Employment, Family/Matrimonial, **Litigation: General Commercial**, Planning, Property (Commercial), Trusts & Personal Tax

WARNER GOODMAN & STREAT
Personal Injury: Mainly Claimant

WATMORES
Personal Injury: Mainly Defendant

WATSON BURTON
Construction, Insolvency/Corporate Recovery, Litigation: General Commercial

WATSON, FARLEY & WILLIAMS
Asset Finance & Leasing, Shipping: Finance

WEIGHTMANS
Insurance, Licensing, **Personal Injury: Mainly Defendant**, **Professional Negligence**

WEIL, GOTSHAL & MANGES
Capital Markets: Securitisation & Repackaging, Corporate Finance: Medium Deals

WELLMAN & BROWN
Church: Church of England

WENDY HOPKINS & CO
Family/Matrimonial

WESLEY GRYK
Immigration: Personal

WHITE & BOWKER
Agriculture, **Church: Church of England**, Trusts & Personal Tax

WHITELOCK & STORR
Crime

WHITTLES
Employment, Personal Injury: Mainly Claimant

WIGGIN & CO
Defamation, **Media & Entertainment**, Media & Entertainment: Broadcasting, Tax, **Trusts & Personal Tax**

WILBRAHAM & CO
Planning

WILLIAMSONS SOLICITORS
Crime

LG WILLIAMS & PRICHARD
Church: Other Denominations

WILLOUGHBY & PARTNERS
Information Technology, **Intellectual Property**

WILSON NESBITT
Family/Matrimonial

WILSONS
Agriculture, Charities, **Trusts & Personal Tax**

WINCKWORTH SHERWOOD
Charities, **Church: Church of England**, **Education: Institutions**, **Parliamentary Agency**, Social Housing

WINSTANLEY-BURGESS
Immigration: Personal

WITHERS
Agriculture, Charities, **Family/Matrimonial**, **Trusts & Personal Tax**

WITHY KING
Clinical Negligence: Mainly Claimant

WOLFERSTANS
Clinical Negligence: Mainly Claimant, Crime, **Family/Matrimonial**, Personal Injury: Mainly Claimant

WOLLASTONS
Education: Institutions, **Immigration**, Property (Commercial)

WOODFORD-ROBINSON
Crime

WOOLLCOMBE BEER WATTS
Clinical Negligence: Mainly Claimant

WRAGGE & CO
Administrative & Public Law: General, Banking, **Charities**, **Competition/Anti-trust**, **Construction**, **Corporate Finance**, **Debt Recovery**, Defamation, E-commerce, Education: Institutions, Employee Share Schemes, **Employment**, **Energy & Natural Resources**, **Environment**, **Financial Services**, Franchising, **Information Technology**, Insolvency/Corporate Recovery, Insurance, **Intellectual Property**, Intellectual Property: General, Intellectual Property: Patent, **Litigation: General Commercial**, **Litigation: Property**, **Local Government**, **Pensions**, Planning, **Private Equity**, Professional Negligence, Projects/PFI, **Property (Commercial)**, **Tax**, Trusts & Personal Tax

WRIGHT HASSALL
Agriculture, Social Housing

WRIGHT, JOHNSTON & MACKENZIE
Media & Entertainment

WRIGLEYS
Agriculture, **Charities**, Energy & Natural Resources, Pensions, **Trusts & Personal Tax**

WYNNE BAXTER
Clinical Negligence: Mainly Claimant

YOUNG & LEE
Education: Individuals, Family/Matrimonial

YUILL & KYLE
Debt Recovery

Z

ZERMANSKY & PARTNERS
Family/Matrimonial

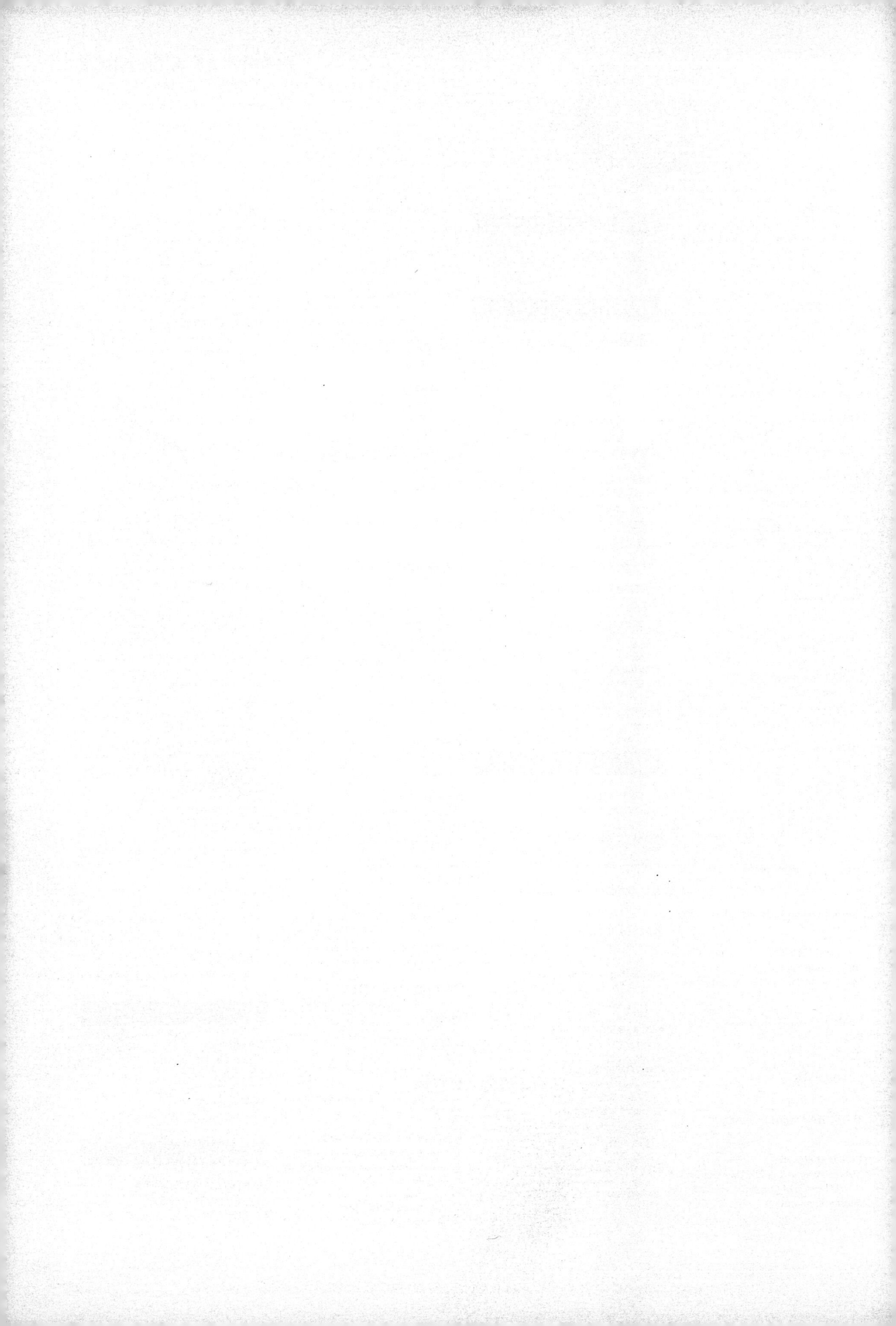

THE LAW FIRMS

ADMINISTRATIVE & PUBLIC LAW

RESEARCH APPROVED BY BMRB: *For this edition,* Chambers' *researchers conducted 6,552 interviews – 4,419 with law firms, 554 with barristers and 1,579 with clients.*

The validity of the research was scrutinised by BMRB International, who audited both the methodology and the results at our offices in July 2001. They interviewed Chambers' *researchers and cross-checked sample interviews. Details of the audit appear on page 7.*

LONDON

TRADITIONAL

ADMINISTRATIVE & PUBLIC LAW: TRADITIONAL • London	Ptnrs	Assts
1 Bindman & Partners	3	1
2 Leigh, Day & Co	3	4
Nabarro Nathanson	2	14
Rowe & Maw	2	9
3 Bates, Wells & Braithwaite	2	3
Levenes	1	3
Mackintosh Duncan	2	1
Sharpe Pritchard	6	2
Teacher Stern Selby	1	2
4 Bhatt Murphy	n/a	n/a
Winstanley-Burgess	3	2
5 Anthony Gold	1	4
Hickman & Rose	1	5
Winckworth Sherwood	n/a	n/a

LEADING INDIVIDUALS	
1 CHILD Tony Rowe & Maw	GROSZ Stephen Bindman & Partners
RABINOWICZ Jack Teacher Stern Selby	RUEBAIN David Levenes
STEIN Richard Leigh, Day & Co	
2 AMBROSE Ray Nabarro Nathanson	BURGESS David Winstanley-Burgess
DAY Martyn Leigh, Day & Co	MACKINTOSH Nicola Mackintosh Duncan
TROTTER John Bates, Wells & Braithwaite	
3 GRIFFITHS Trevor Sharpe Pritchard	ILEY Malcolm Nabarro Nathanson
SCHWEHR Belinda Rowe & Maw	
UP AND COMING	
SILAS Douglas Levenes	

This book is the product of 6,552 1/2 hour interviews. See p.7 for BMRB audit.
Within each band, firms are listed alphabetically. *See individuals' profiles p.58*

Bindman & Partners (see firm details p.882) Differentiated from its rivals through the sheer eclecticism of the practice. Handling generic public law with a human rights bent this is "*a significant firm of undoubted eminence.*" In the past year it has advised the Law Society on the Human Rights Act, made applications for de-proscription under the Terrorism Act, and initiated numerous judicial review applications against the Press Complaints Commission and in the fields of immigration and housing. Geoffrey Bindman, the father of this type of work, continues to attract quality work through the draw of his name. Day to day conduct falls, however, to **Stephen Grosz** (see p.425), who competitors feel brings his "*vast armoury of legal skills*" into play. He is expert on the subject of public law and its interface with human rights. **Clients:** Law Society of England & Wales; Amnesty International.

Leigh, Day & Co (see firm details p.1036) A diffuse practice with a pronounced environmental bias. Applicant led, its public law expertise reaches into the realms of clinical negligence, health, planning, social security, and community care. Notable recent judicial reviews have included an action by residents against the Borough of Camden's Swiss Cottage Leisure Development. The market discerns a political slant, illustrated by appearances for the Family Planning Association in a challenge on regulation of the morning after pill, and on behalf of Kenyans maimed by landmines manufactured in Britain. The team is led by "*two tireless campaigners:*" **Martyn Day** ("*the rainmaker*") and **Richard Stein** (see p.60), "*an excellent all round public lawyer.*" **Clients:** Individual applicants; human rights organisations.

Nabarro Nathanson (see firm details p.1078) The key strength of this nationally spread firm lies in its extensive public sector client base. Much of its activity relates to advising local authorities and other public bodies on judicial review prospects, public sector governance and procurement challenges. In addition it receives instructions from private sector clients wishing to work with public bodies, and is increasingly called upon to offer assistance on the implications of the Human Rights legislation. Commended nationwide as "*one of the forces in this field*" the team encompasses the "*immensely intelligent*" **Ray Ambrose** and **Malcolm Iley**, an "*ex-local authority bigwig*" who also devotes time to PFI matters. Highlights of the year include acting for Waste Recycling in respect of challenges on procurement matters against Norfolk County Council. **Clients:** Local authorities; further education colleges; London boroughs; health trusts.

Rowe & Maw (see firm details p.1113) Ex-district auditor **Tony Child** (see p.58) built the department's outstanding reputation through work on behalf of local government and health service external auditors. It has expanded significantly over the years and now services a diverse client base of public bodies, large corporations and individual applicants in the health, education and local authority sectors. Recent highlights include the first successful action against a private school for expulsion of a pupil, and the provision of advice to a member of the 'People's Lottery' consortium in its bid for the lottery licence. **Belinda Schwehr** (see p.59) is recommended by rivals as "*an able lieutenant,*" proactive in the community care sphere and known for her expertise in human rights compliance. **Clients:** Local authorities; Northern Ireland Audit Office; public and private community care and health service providers.

Bates, Wells & Braithwaite (see firm details p.871) Best known for its charity and immigration work, the practice is heavily applicant driven. Judicial review forms the bulk of the work undertaken although an interest in regulatory matters is maintained. **John Trotter** leads the team and is credited as being "*a good all rounder who exhibits industry and integrity.*"

Levenes (see firm details p.1039) Disability, community care and education are the principal generators of public law work in this niche practice. **David Ruebain** (see p.59) came to the firm after a successful career in local government, and is respected by barristers as an education specialist. His is a "*determined approach, ideal for those who wish to give no quarter,*" an ethos rapidly being instilled in his protégé **Douglas Silas** (see p.60). The firm emerged victorious in R v Secretary to the Employment Tribunal ex p.

Public Concern at Work in an application for rights of access to information concerning employment tribunal decisions. **Clients:** Public Concern at Work; Independent Panel for Special Educational Advice; Network 81.

Mackintosh Duncan Still a relative fledgling, this practice has garnered positive comment for its *"commitment and specialist knowledge."* Centred largely around community care JR work, further expertise is applied to employment and mental health issues. Noted for her *"tremendous work rate,"* **Nicola Mackintosh** is extremely active and has been witnessed in a number of recent high profile JRs.

Sharpe Pritchard (see firm details p.1123) The majority of work here is undertaken on behalf of local government and other public authorities. **Trevor Griffiths** (see p.592) conducts a vast array of judicial review cases and is commended for his *"sensible, practical and conciliatory stance."* The firm acted in the headline Alconbury case in which the Secretary of State's powers to call in and recover appeals were declared contrary to the Human Rights Act. Also appeared for the claimant in Birmingham City Council v Oakley, a leading case on the test for establishing whether a property is injurious to public health.

Teacher Stern Selby (see firm details p.1151) A practice spanning health, community care and social security concerns but weighted towards educational work. **Jack Rabinowicz** (see p.59), *"Mr Education and the leading solicitor in this field,"* is applauded by peers for his pioneering work on issues such as bullying. Recent highlights for the firm include the House of Lords case of Phelps, a decision on educational negligence. It also appeared in selected exclusion cases and in Persaud v University of Cambridge, assessing the question of whether universities should disclose reports to students over whom they had concerns. **Clients:** Individual applicants.

Bhatt Murphy *"No review of this area of law would be complete without mention of this firm,"* one barrister commented. Honing in on police law and prisoners' rights, a dedicated team tackles politically sensitive applications, often from a human rights standpoint. It has appeared in injunction proceedings on behalf of the Bulger killers and challenged the Metropolitan Police on its refusal to disclose a report on a murder, for which no charges have been brought but where the prime suspects are police officers.

Winstanley-Burgess (see firm details p.1186) Removed from the likes of Bindmans in terms of breadth, this firm secures its profile due to a vibrant immigration practice and the consistent stream of community based work which flows from it. It is recognised by rivals for its national security work and representation of Sikh groups looking for de-proscription under the Terrorism Act. A slice of the caseload has a political flavour, as illustrated by the firm's involvement with the group arrested for occupation of the London Eye. The team is led by **David Burgess**, *"never one to shy away from the difficult case."* **Clients:** Individual applicants; asylum seekers.

Anthony Gold (see firm details p.861) A diverse practice skewed towards applications in the housing sphere. These often incorporate a social welfare element, a side of the operation recently strengthened by the acquisition of a Legal Services Commission franchise for community care. The last year has witnessed a host of challenges against housing benefit decisions and applications to local authorities for housing for the homeless. Andrew Brooks is head of the group. **Clients:** Individual applicants.

Hickman & Rose (see firm details p.995) Instructions received by this firm broadly revolve around the theme of criminal justice. Particularly concerned with prisoners' rights it appeared in the Court of Appeal case of Hirst, scrutinising the procedural fairness of restrictions placed on those inmates wishing to make representations to the authorities. The group has also made submissions on the matter of when coroners should leave a question of neglect to a jury. Consistently active on mental health judicial review challenges, it is now targeting freedom of expression work. **Clients:** Individual applicants.

Winckworth Sherwood (see firm details p.1185) Perhaps best known for its work in the ecclesiastical field, the public law practice extends to education, health and housing. Amid a welter of judicial review applications, it was involved in the Bristol Royal Infirmary Inquiry and challenged Burntwood School over its exclusion policy.

COMMERCIAL

ADMINISTRATIVE & PUBLIC LAW: COMMERCIAL • London	Ptnrs	Assts
1 Clifford Chance	4	11
Herbert Smith	7	8
2 Lovells	13	7
3 Allen & Overy	4	9
CMS Cameron McKenna	6	9
Freshfields Bruckhaus Deringer	9	10
Simmons & Simmons	4	4
4 Beachcroft Wansbroughs	3	5
Denton Wilde Sapte	n/a	n/a
Slaughter and May	n/a	n/a
Theodore Goddard	3	3
Travers Smith Braithwaite	2	3
5 SJ Berwin	5	4

LEADING INDIVIDUALS	
1 LIDBETTER Andrew Herbert Smith	SMYTH Michael Clifford Chance
2 MCDERMOTT Jennifer Lovells	
3 BOWDEN Paul Freshfields Bruckhaus Deringer	
WATSON Peter Allen & Overy	

This book is the product of 6,552 1/2 hour interviews. See p.7 for BMRB audit.

Within each band, firms are listed alphabetically *See individuals' profiles p.58*

Clifford Chance (see firm details p.919) Successfully challenging Herbert Smith's previous hegemony in this field, this specialist department is considered *"highly visible and in possession of both strength and depth."* **Michael Smyth** (see p.60) is key to much of this profile and the group is peculiar in also having a designated partner to advise on public policy. Strong on regulatory and tribunal work, it is gaining a further reputation for political issues and assisted in the Northern Ireland peace process. Mainly acting for corporate clients and public bodies, it assisted GTECH Corporation in its successful JR of the decision of the National Lottery Commission, and acted for IBM on issues affecting the privatisation of the National Air Traffic Control Service. **Clients:** The Post Office; University of Cambridge; Public Health Laboratory Service; London Electricity.

Herbert Smith (see firm details p.993) This cross-departmental team has wide experience of acting for applicants, respondents and intervening third parties. Highly flexible, it advises the government, other public bodies and utilities on statutory powers, while representing individual clients in investigations by such bodies as the DTI and FSA. Skilled in regulatory matters, it has recently offered compliance advice to a number of bodies in light of the recent human rights legislation. Headline cases include acting for the Law Society concerning allegations of bullying by Kamlesh Bahl, and assisting the IMRO in successfully resisting a claim concerning the conduct of disciplinary proceedings. Originally a straight civil litigator, key figure **Andrew Lidbetter** (see p.59) has carved a name as *"the leading figure in the field, intellectually engaged in the work and immersed in its complexities."* **Clients:** Law Society; FSO; IMRO; Horserace Betting Levy Board; Severn Trent Water.

Lovells (see firm details p.1044) Having traditionally acted for companies who have been affected by government decisions, the firm is acquiring expertise in representing regulatory bodies. One key client acquired is the Radio-Communications Agency, which it advises on judicial review avoidance in respect of the granting of licences for radio frequencies. The thrust of the practice remains focused on challenges, usually conducted on behalf of manufacturing and retail concerns. The highlight of an impressive year has been the securing of a landmark judgment on behalf of tobacco companies, whereby an EC Directive on tobacco advertising as sponsorship was annulled. This represented the first time an annulment had occurred on the grounds that it was outside the powers of the EC. **Jennifer McDermott** (see p.59) is the mainstay, belonging to "*an exclusive club of pure public law specialists.*" With a media law background, she has successfully carved a niche and is on the Administrative Law Panel for Justice. **Clients:** Radio Communications Agency; Sport England; BAT; Rothmans.

Allen & Overy (see firm details p.856) Celebrated for the provision of advice to public bodies, the firm can boast the SFA, FSA, Radio Authority and Arts Council as standing clients. Last year it advised the Arts Council on the allocation of funds, and assisted the Radio Authority on drafts of new sponsorship and advertising codes. The practice extends to involvement in high level public inquiries where it has enjoyed a significant role in both the BSE and Burns inquiries. Representation of commercial interests in challenging public decisions is a growth area, and the firm has been active for Northern Electric in a threatened enforcement action by the regulator. Commercial litigator **Peter Watson** (see p.288) is a leading light; "*thoroughly competent in public law*" he is said to "*know his way around JR as well as the next man.*" **Clients:** Film Council; Radio Communications Agency; Countryside Alliance; Radio Authority; Treasury Solicitor.

CMS Cameron McKenna (see firm details p.922) Heartily recommended by peers for its pharmaceuticals work which is thought to feed the practice, rivals acknowledge that "*limited breadth or not, it has one hell of a depth.*" Often seen challenging the granting of licences to pharmaceutical industries, it has been at the forefront of the use of JR as a commercial tool. As illustrated by its presence in planning and environmental cases with a public law aspect, this group is extending its reach. It has also undertaken a number of challenges to regulated components in the financial services and electrical sectors. **Clients:** National Grid; pharmaceutical companies.

Freshfields Bruckhaus Deringer (see firm details p.964) Public law work exists here as an offshoot from other specialist departments across the firm. Energy, insurance, telecoms, sports law and energy practices all feature but by far the greatest contribution comes in the realm of financial services and environmental law. Regarding the latter, **Paul Bowden** (see p.58) impresses as "*energetic on the JR front.*" In acting for regulatory bodies and commercial clients, the firm is visible in front-line cases as exemplified by its advice to the National Lottery Commission on its procedures for selecting the next lottery operator. Other significant cases include the successful defence on behalf of One2One, of a challenge on health grounds brought by Mohammed Al Fayed against the grant of a mobile phone base station. **Clients:** Bank of England; Lloyd's of London; National Pharmaceutical Association; Football Association; One2One.

Simmons & Simmons (see firm details p.1132) Acts for both regulators and regulated industries in its core sectors of media, telecoms and energy. Major client, the ITC, continues to deliver some choice instructions such as the challenge brought by TV Danmark against the ITC's decision to refuse consent to the broadcast of Danish World Cup football matches. Traditionally strong in telecoms it acted for One2One in challenging the Secretary of State's payment timetable for third generation mobile phone licences. "*A regular combatant and nifty performer*" this practice is commended by our interviewees for its "*across the spectrum strength.*" **Clients:** ITC; Railtrack; One2One; MCI Worldcom; oil and gas industry.

Beachcroft Wansbroughs (see firm details p.872) The firm operates across the breadth of the sector placing its emphasis as much on advisory and preventative measures as on judicial review. It is best known for representing important bodies in the education and health sectors, and extends its activities into the territory of central government, local government, insurance and sport. It appeared for the National Institute for Clinical Negligence (NICE) in appeals against its guidance on the use of beta interferon in the treatment of multiple sclerosis. **Clients:** NICE; DETR; IDEA; English Cricket Board; Association of British Insurers; Further Education Funding Council; Chartered Institute of Public Finance & Accountancy.

Denton Wilde Sapte (see firm details p.939) Public law work emanates for the most part from this firm's famed energy practice. Accepting a substantial level of regulatory work, it acts for three of the ten water companies and has advised on the drafting of new electricity price mechanisms. It also acts for central and local government regulated industries and counts educational bodies amongst its clients. The group has secured its profile over the past year by virtue of having appeared in the Alconbury case. **Clients:** OFGEM; MoD; University College London.

Slaughter and May (see firm details p.1135) This firm's solicitors, judged by competitors as "*inhabiting the upper echelons in terms of quality,*" have expertise in commercial judicial review, and yet lack the visibility and range of some of their rivals. Generally providing a bespoke service for those of its corporate clients wishing to challenge administrative decisions, it further appears on behalf of the regulators. The group has advised the Office of the Rail Regulator in proceedings brought by Railtrack designed to challenge a penalty imposed for failing to achieve agreed performance targets. Also advised the Oxford Centre for Islamic Studies in relation to JR proceedings brought by individuals challenging planning decisions made by Oxford City Council. **Clients:** Office of the Rail Regulator; Deutsche Morgan Grenfell; Commonwealth Development Corporation.

Theodore Goddard (see firm details p.1152) Advises industry regulated bodies in areas as diverse as sports, media and education, while catering for an expanding roster of commercial clients seeking to contest decisions. Our interviewees invariably commented on its activity for linchpin client, the Advertising Standards Authority. Sample actions on behalf of this body have included resisting a JR brought by SmithKline Beecham and successfully defending a challenge by Matthias Rath BV & Anor which had sought to prevent publication of a report criticising their advertising. This group has also been active in advising a foreign government in relation to decisions of the UK government. **Clients:** Advertising Standards Authority; Airport Coordination Limited.

Travers Smith Braithwaite (see firm details p.1160) Strong in property, revenue and telecoms, this "*robustly constituted*" firm has a healthy history of commercial judicial review work. Applicant-led, its recent challenge on behalf of Ulster Bank to the Inland Revenue, concerning the latter's powers of investigation, is typical of the nature of the practice. Its acknowledged strength in the telecoms field has led many to expect an upturn in the volume of challenges mounted, as government licences of various kinds are granted and subsequently become the cause of objections. **Clients:** Ulster Bank; Channel 5 Broadcasting; Redland Aggregates.

SJ Berwin (see firm details p.879) A strong push in this area of work has been signalled by the recruitment of a specialist from Simmons & Simmons and the establishment of a Public Law and Human Rights Group. Particular footholds are found in the planning and environment, EU, media, and financial services fields, with most of the regulatory work being applicant driven. Many actions are the result of internal referrals, but the market anticipates that more will originate from a stand-alone base in the wake of involvement in high profile cases. One such example is the application on behalf of the musician Sting and others challenging the proposed development of Boscombe Down Airfield in Wiltshire. The team also acted on the widely reported case questioning Jamaica's Mercy Committee's procedures in deciding to implement the death penalty. **Clients:** British Land Company; Baltic Exchange; AES Electricity Act licence holders.

THE SOUTH

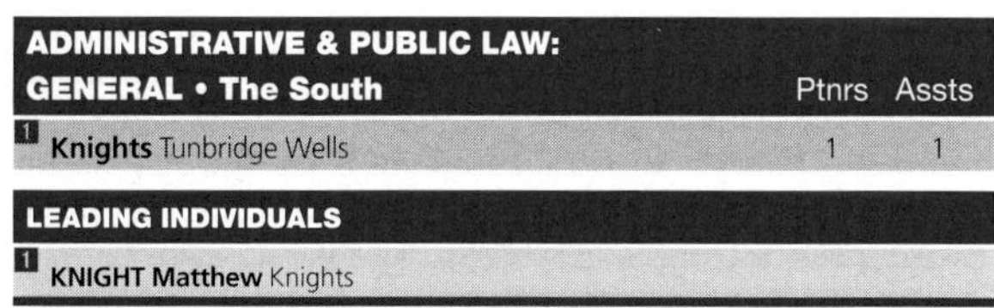

ADMINISTRATIVE & PUBLIC LAW: GENERAL • The South	Ptnrs	Assts
1 **Knights** Tunbridge Wells	1	1
LEADING INDIVIDUALS		
1 **KNIGHT Matthew** Knights		

This book is the product of 6,552 1/2 hour interviews. See p.7 for BMRB audit.
Within each band, firms are listed alphabetically. *See individuals' profiles p.58*

Knights Although narrow in its specialism, this firm has received glowing endorsement from leading figures in London. The focus is on advising countryside, farming and country sports clients on the implications of administrative decisions. Respected for his close and personal involvement with his cases, **Matthew Knight** (see p.59) counts the Countryside Alliance as a client and represented it in a successful bid to prevent a bogus spokesman claiming affiliation during the last election. Its interest in political affairs is witnessed in its presentation of detailed advice to clients on the Political Parties Elections & Referendums Act 2000. **Clients:** Countryside Alliance; National Smallbore Rifle Association; National Farmers Union.

SOUTH WEST

ADMINISTRATIVE & PUBLIC LAW: GENERAL • South West	Ptnrs	Assts
1 **Bevan Ashford** Bristol	3	2
2 **Bobbetts Mackan** Bristol	1	3
Clarke Willmott & Clarke Taunton	4	5
Stephens & Scown Exeter	2	1
LEADING INDIVIDUALS		
1 **JARMAN Christopher** Bevan Ashford		
PARKER Mike Wilsons		

This book is the product of 6,552 1/2 hour interviews. See p.7 for BMRB audit.
Within each band, firms are listed alphabetically. *See individuals' profiles p.58*

Bevan Ashford (see firm details p.880) The endeavours of the health and social care department of this thriving practice (now incorporating a branch in London) largely account for the firm's appearance at the head of our tables. Acting for a host of NHS bodies across southern England and Wales, its public law arm has risen in prominence in line with an increase in challenges to health authorities. Typically the firm finds itself acting for bodies such as the Gwent Health Authority, which it advised on objections to the closure of one of its institutions. Participation is not restricted to the health sector, with education, planning and local authority work also generating a substantial level of instructions. "*Highly versatile*" **Chris Jarman** (see p.59) is the lead individual here, more of a projects specialist but "*effective in a number of areas.*" **Clients:** NHS Trusts; health authorities.

Bobbetts Mackan (see firm details p.887) "*An applicants firm that crops up time and again*" according to our interviewees. New to the tables this year, its main focus is on mental health work, an area which the practice has been keen to promote. **Clients:** Individual applicants.

Clarke Willmott & Clarke (see firm details p.915) Acting for and against local authorities, this Taunton based practice offers a cross-departmental team. While acting in a number of areas such as planning and community care, it obtains a sizeable chunk of its work from the farming community. Recent matters have included advising on a potential JR in respect of MAFF's attempts to recover the allegedly overpaid Suckler Cow Premium. **Clients:** Local authorities; farmers and other individuals.

Stephens & Scown Historically viewed as acting for the farming community, it now finds education, community care and human rights issues are dominating the horizon. The last year has seen a clutch of JRs securing the correct levels of care and support for individual applicants in the community. Foremost among these has been a case against Liverpool City Council, which may have ramifications for assessment procedures in community care matters. It further advised on an application against the Home Office under Article 6 of the Human Rights Act, which may also yet prove to have legal implications in the public law field. **Clients:** Individual applicants.

Other Notable Practitioners Having moved from Clarke Willmott & Clarke to **Wilsons**, **Mike Parker** adds an extra dimension through his aptitude for highways and education work, mainly appearing on behalf of local authorities. He successfully resisted a JR relating to the closure of a footpath, sanctioned due to erosion caused by flooding.

WALES

ADMINISTRATIVE & PUBLIC LAW: GENERAL • Wales	Ptnrs	Assts
1 **Eversheds** Cardiff	6	9
2 **Edwards Geldard** Cardiff	1	2
Morgan Cole Cardiff	3	3
LEADING INDIVIDUALS		
1 **COLE Alun** Morgan Cole	**EVANS Eric** Eversheds	
WILLIAMS Huw Edwards Geldard		

This book is the product of 6,552 1/2 hour interviews. See p.7 for BMRB audit.
Within each band, firms are listed alphabetically. *See individuals' profiles p.58*

Eversheds (see firm details p.952) Acknowledged by its rivals to be "*way ahead due to its size and capabilities as a national practice.*" Providing governance and constitutional advice to a range of public sector bodies, the scope of the practice merits admiration. The group advises on issues such as procurement, statutory interpretation, JR, and rule changes, the key figure being **Eric Evans** (see p.58), a lawyer with "*an abrasive, purposeful stance,*" especially gifted on the property side. The team represented the Welsh Development Agency in establishing Finance Wales plc, and appeared for the Forestry Commission on various schemes and compliance matters relating to the Forestry Act. **Clients:** Estyn (Her Majesty's Inspectorate for Education and Training in Wales); Wales & West Housing Association; Elim Housing Association.

Edwards Geldard (see firm details p.948) A dedicated public law department which splits its time equally between acting for individual commercial applicants and public bodies. Once heavily dominated by planning and environmental concerns, it is increasingly looking to the local authority and 'best value' arenas for its instructions. Big name clients include the Welsh Development Agency, for which it acted on the Cardiff Bay Development Corporation. It has also advised on planning aspects for the Wales Millennium Centre Project. Head of the section, **Huw Williams** (see p.60) is a "*doughty old campaigner, familiar with the ebbs and flows of this partic-*

ular area of the law." **Clients:** Welsh Development Agency; Cardiff Bay Development Corporation; Arts Council of Wales; Silverlink Trains.

Morgan Cole (see firm details p.1074) A long-standing force in the health and local government sectors, advising both public bodies and private concerns in England and Wales. Marshalling a small team, **Alun Cole** is "*no pushover and firm in his grasp of the principles.*" Himself a veteran of the Governmental Legal Service he brings much experience to bear, advising on public authority powers and duties. His team is the exclusive legal adviser to the Human Fertilisation and Embryology Authority, assisting on policy and regulatory considerations. Much comment was elicited on the practice's involvement in urban regeneration on behalf of the likes of the Cardiff Bay Development Corporation. **Clients:** Local authorities; health authorities; NHS trusts; Cardiff Bay Development Corporation.

MIDLANDS

ADMINISTRATIVE & PUBLIC LAW: GENERAL • Midlands		Ptnrs	Assts
1	**Pinsent Curtis Biddle** Birmingham	6	6
	Tyndallwoods Birmingham	2	2
	Wragge & Co Birmingham	9	6
2	**Browne Jacobson** Nottingham	2	5
	Martineau Johnson Birmingham	2	2

LEADING INDIVIDUALS	
1	**GOULD Jean** Tyndallwoods
	KEITH-LUCAS Peter Wragge & Co
	SHINER Philip Public Interest Lawyers
	WALLACE Alastair Tyndallwoods
	WHITE Martin Pinsent Curtis Biddle

This book is the product of 6,552 1/2 hour interviews. See p.7 for BMRB audit.

Within each band, firms are listed alphabetically *See individuals' profiles p.58*

Pinsent Curtis Biddle (see firm details p.1098) "*Dominant enough to cherry pick the better work,*" this practice draws its lifeblood from its local authority, planning and housing capabilities. PFI, housing development, public procurement and urban regeneration are all to the fore, and the team has now significantly bolstered itself with the lateral hire of Irwin Mitchell's large scale voluntary transfer group. Leading figure **Martin White** (see p.60) "*has a good grasp of the pressures facing local authorities*" and proffers advice on planning and compulsory purchase matters. He has recently participated in a number of major town centre redevelopment projects, and advised the Commission for New Towns on aspects of planning and administrative law. **Clients:** County Councils; Health Trusts; Islington, Newham and Walsall LBCs.

Tyndallwoods (see firm details p.1165) Covering the spheres of health, education, planning, environmental and local authority JR, this firm is hailed as "*a leading force in public law.*" It is firmly applicant based and particularly noted for its community care work, for which it has been awarded a contract by the Legal Services Commission to deliver second tier advice to fellow practitioners. A discrete department within the firm is led by **Alastair Wallace** (see p.60), known for his efforts in immigration and asylum issues. His colleague **Jean Gould** (see p.58)is prominent on the scene, a recent highlight being her JR application to Coventry City Council regarding charging for community care services. **Clients:** Individual applicants.

Wragge & Co (see firm details p.1189) Nationally recognised as "*one of only a few firms to have a secure hold on local government work.*" Acting for both public bodies and their challengers, its client base incorporates local and central government entities such as the DETR and the Prison Service. There is a distinct property based flavour to the practice, while public law activity in education and housing abounds. The team handles all the housing law work for Croydon LA including nuisance actions, repossessions, and benefit applications. Team leader **Peter Keith-Lucas** adds an extra dimension as an expert on constitutions, having advised at length on the new structures for directly elected mayors. A former Chief Executive of Swansea City Council with 25 years of experience in local government, he is acknowledged nationwide to be "*a figure of importance.*" **Clients:** DETR; Prison Service; English Heritage; Maritime Agency; 75 local authorities; Guidance Accreditation Board.

Browne Jacobson (see firm details p.898) The firm brings to the table 30 years of experience in the field. Acting for a range of local government, health bodies and government agencies it undertakes JRs, public inquiries and prosecutions. The group is contracted to handle DTI work in relation to enforcement procedures. Successful tenders have seen it establish a deserved reputation in environmental protection with cases being conducted on behalf of English Nature and the Countryside Council of Wales. The team is headed by X and acted for Wolverhampton Health Authority dispensing advice on the legality of its funding arrangements for long term care. **Clients:** English Nature; Countryside Council for Wales; DTI; DETR; local authorities.

Martineau Johnson (see firm details p.1055) In the frame due to its "*excellent education capability,*" the firm acts in the main for those educational bodies seeking to resist challenges. Typical of its work is its recent appearance for Aston University in defending a JR by a student claiming wrongful exclusion. Health sector actions are also undertaken, and the team advises the General Osteopathic Council on its public law concerns. **Clients:** University of Birmingham; Aston University; other educational bodies.

Other Notable Practitioners **Phil Shiner** of **Public Interest Lawyers** has a national reputation as "*a highly successful and robust claimant JR solicitor*" who "*takes the case of the little man and advances it with energy.*" Much of his workload has an environmental and planning bias but a sizeable slice is taken up by peace issues. Instructed by the Nuclear Awareness Group he mounted a JR regarding the manufacture of nuclear weapons at Aldermaston, and in light of the Human Rights Act he advised on a challenge under Article 6 to the siting of an incinerator in Southampton.

EAST ANGLIA

ADMINISTRATIVE & PUBLIC LAW: GENERAL • East Anglia	Ptnrs	Assts
1 **Eversheds** Cambridge, Norwich	5	7
Mills & Reeve Cambridge, Norwich	8	8
Richard Buxton Cambridge	1	1

LEADING INDIVIDUALS
1 **BUXTON Richard** Richard Buxton

This book is the product of 6,552 1/2 hour interviews. See p.7 for BMRB audit.
Within each band, firms are listed alphabetically. *See individuals' profiles p.58*

Eversheds (see firm details p.952) Supported by a nationally renowned office network, the firm's East of England branches received plaudits from their peers. Commentators noted the close co-operation between the Cambridge and Norwich offices and applauded their efforts, particularly in the planning area. Accessing a generous client base, its instructions are a blend of central and local government, education and health work. The firm has been appointed to act for the Cabinet Office on the Civil Service Training College PFI and by East Kent Hospitals NHS Trust. **Clients:** Local authorities, police authorities, MAFF.

Mills & Reeve (see firm details p.1069) Despite having instituted a public law unit in Birmingham, a healthy proportion of cases are found in this region. The major areas of instruction are health, education and local government, in that order. The highlight of the year was the partnership with Leicester City Council for whom the firm conducts a large amount of litigation work. It has now obtained a contract in relation to the East of England Development Agency and assisted in the £60 million Norwich Millennium Library development. **Clients:** Local authorities; NHS trusts.

Richard Buxton Exhibiting a "*campaigning zeal,*" **Richard Buxton** is a lawyer who competitors see *as "snapping at the heels of decision making bodies."* Fundamentally an applicant and third party solicitor, many of his clients are residents and action groups with local grievances. He has intervened in a case of access rights over common land, and is awaiting judgment on the human rights implications of Heathrow night flights. **Clients:** Individual applicants; wildlife trusts; CPRE.

THE NORTH

ADMINISTRATIVE & PUBLIC LAW: GENERAL • The North	Ptnrs	Assts
1 **Eversheds** Leeds, Manchester	4	13
2 **Addleshaw Booth & Co** Manchester	n/a	n/a
Irwin Mitchell Sheffield	1	1
Pinsent Curtis Biddle Leeds	2	2
3 **Beachcroft Wansbroughs** Leeds	8	2
4 **Howells** Sheffield	1	3

LEADING INDIVIDUALS
1 **CIRELL Stephen** Eversheds

This book is the product of 6,552 1/2 hour interviews. See p.7 for BMRB audit.
Within each band, firms are listed alphabetically. *See individuals' profiles p.58*

Eversheds (see firm details p.952) The stated aim of this national leviathan is to nurture and minister to the needs of public authority bodies. Accordingly while support is given to private sector clients dealing with local authorities, direct challenges are not undertaken. The team concentrates on its hefty local government workload with interests in the education, health and central government sectors. Led by **Stephen Cirell** (see p.58), "*a figure on the larger stage and a 'best value' guru,*" the group has displayed nimbleness of foot in responding to market changes. Indicative of this is its present engagement with e-government, where it has established itself as something of a trendsetter. Recent highlights include acting for Greater Manchester Police in one of the largest Home Office PFI deals in the country concerning the provision of 18 new police stations. **Clients:** Local authorities; regional development agencies.

Addleshaw Booth & Co (see firm details p.853) Signalled as "*a major competitor,*" its nearest rivals admit to having, of late, lost out on a few major jobs to this rising force in the sector. Not so dominant on the local government side, it makes its main strides through its vibrant planning and projects practices. An illustration of its progress over the past year has been its entry into partnership with Cambridgeshire County Council.

Irwin Mitchell (see firm details p.1009) A firm with a national reach, which has consolidated its entire public law work into a specialist department, led by Andrew Lockley and based in Sheffield. Claimant work proliferates with individuals, businesses and institutions being provided instructions on JR and compliance issues. Medical claims, usually against the General Medical Council, are a speciality, as are actions on behalf of professionals before disciplinary bodies. The occasional institutional client such as the University of Sheffield is also part of this growing client roster. Having recruited a number of local authority solicitors the practice is seen by interviewees as "*a force to be reckoned with,*" supported by the existence of a dedicated human rights department. It acted in R v Chesterfield Justices & Chief Constable of Derbyshire ex P Bramley, a case that set limits on the powers of police officers in search and seizure raids. **Clients:** Individual applicants.

Pinsent Curtis Biddle (see firm details p.1098) Local government and health law forms the backdrop to this "*enterprising, go-ahead practice.*" Fronted by the former Chief Solicitor of Doncaster MBC (Nicholas Dobson), the team draws on expertise in local authority, NHS and education sectors in tending to a hybrid client base of public authorities and commercial clients. Testament to its progressive approach has been the launch of a strategic collaboration with PricewaterhouseCoopers (Rightsourcing), aiming to offer integrated legal, financial and consultancy advice. The firm continues to advise the DfEE on commercial contracting and training issues, and assists the DETR on PFI/PPP related issues. Acted for the NHS executive on the outsourcing of the entire NHS human resources and payroll system. The firm has also established a leading market position in PFI street lighting, having advised local authorities on three of the five projects so far. **Clients:** DfEE; MAFF; DETR; NHS trusts; universities; local authorities.

Beachcroft Wansbroughs (see firm details p.872) The Healthcare/Public Law team of this respected firm has now relocated to its Leeds office. A specialism in health is reinforced by local government work. Containing Melanie Print, a lawyer with ten years' experience in the NHS and public sector, (his name) the team advises on mental health law, purchasing policies, community care and corporate governance issues. Successful in its tender for JR work for the Durham & Darlington Health Authority, it also acts for over 200 NHS bodies. The group assisted the Shropshire & Staffordshire Education Consortium in the renegotiation of nursing and PAMS contracts. **Clients:** NHS bodies; GP practices; private health care providers.

Howells (see firm details p.1002) As one barrister noted, this practice has *"a rare enthusiasm for pursuing cases others might give up on."* Expert from a civil liberties perspective, the focus is firmly on the rights of the individual with the firm only acting for claimants challenging public bodies. The past year, for example, has seen a number of challenges against the police and the CPS. Seen as a practice with a growing reputation, it is one of a strictly limited number accredited by the Legal Services Commission as being a specialist provider of public law advice.

SCOTLAND

ADMINISTRATIVE & PUBLIC LAW: GENERAL • Scotland		Ptnrs	Assts
1	**Brodies WS** Edinburgh	5	4
	Dundas & Wilson CS Edinburgh	n/a	n/a
	McGrigor Donald Glasgow	n/a	n/a
	Shepherd & Wedderburn WS Edinburgh	3	1
2	**Biggart Baillie** Edinburgh	2	3
	Burness Edinburgh	6	5
	Lindsays WS Edinburgh	n/a	n/a
	Simpson & Marwick WS Edinburgh	2	2
	Tods Murray WS Edinburgh	4	4

LEADING INDIVIDUALS	
1	**HOLLIGAN William** Brodies WS
	MACLEOD Ian Shepherd & Wedderburn WS
	SHAW Kate Simpson & Marwick WS

This book is the product of 6,552 1/2 hour interviews. See p.7 for BMRB audit.

Within each band, firms are listed alphabetically. *See individuals' profiles p.58*

Brodies WS (see firm details p.896) The firm's efforts in this field are co-ordinated by the Public Affairs Group, which has the twin aims of servicing the legal requirements of public bodies and offering advice to clients on administrative and JR matters arising from the legislation of the Scottish Parliament and Europe. The driving force here is **William Holligan** (see p.59), an acknowledged expert on Scottish devolution and human rights. The group has conducted human rights audits for several public bodies and numerous JR hearings for local authorities. **Clients:** Local authorities and other government bodies.

Dundas & Wilson CS (see firm details p.947) *"A safe bet for larger scale work"* according to our interviewees; with the Andersen Legal connection it imposes itself through its sheer weight. Local authority, health and education are the major strands threaded through its public sector group, which also provides advice on the impact of the Human Rights Act. The group acted for Stirling Council on its £50 million Forthside development, and advised Glasgow City Council on its major schools project. **Clients:** Local authorities; University of Edinburgh; Stoke Mandeville Hospital Trust; Medical Defence Union.

McGrigor Donald (see firm details p.1062) *"A big fish"* with a cross-departmental approach providing advice to public bodies and local authorities on issues such as statutory powers, public procurement, state aid and statutory interpretation. Recent highlights include advising the Department for Regional Development (Northern Ireland) on a new legislative framework for NI ports. The group established a joint venture partnership with Mouchel Consulting Limited and a consortium of nine Scottish local authorities, to bid for a five year trunk roads management appointment and a maintenance contract outsourced by the Scottish Executive. **Clients:** Local authorities; Dept of Environment Northern Ireland; Aberdeenshire Housing Partnership; Tobacco Manufacturer's Association.

Shepherd & Wedderburn WS (see firm details p.1126) A *"highly competitive outfit"* with a pronounced degree of local government work. Perceived by its peers to be specialists on vires issues and the contracting out of services, it is spearheaded by **Ian MacLeod** (see p.575), *"a front ranker of thirty years standing who has seen it all."* A favourite of local authorities, the team further attracts a mass of planning, PFI and PPP work. It represented Aberdeenshire Council in a JR under Police Pensions Regulations, and advised Waterfront Edinburgh (a consortium including the local authority) on a major redevelopment of the Edinburgh waterfront. **Clients:** Councils including City of Edinburgh; Audit Scotland; Commissioner for Local Administration.

Biggart Baillie (see firm details p.882) Well-versed in local authority procedures, this firm enters the rankings due to its high visibility in JR challenges both for and against public bodies. The team acted for the Meat and Livestock Commission in a JR challenge to the MLC levy on OTMS, and for Caledonian Roads in proceedings against the Scottish Executive's tendering process regarding the award of contracts for the maintenance of trunk roads. Presently the group is advising British Railways Board on a JR relating to the extension of Eurostar services to Scotland. **Clients:** Meat and Livestock Commission; Highland Council; British Railways Board.

Burness (see firm details p.903) This specialist public sector practice offers a service tailored to the needs of public and quasi-public clients. Chiefly slanted toward local authority work its endeavours extend to the health and education sectors. *"Pre-eminent"* when it comes to urban regeneration, it acts for over 15 local economic development agencies and has also carved its name in the field of joint venture projects. In addition, it advised East Lothian Council in transferring its entire stock of secondary schools into the private sector. **Clients:** Glasgow Alliance; Highlands & Islands Partnership Programme; Area Tourist Boards, Scotland.

Lindsays WS (see firm details p.1041) Differing in nature wildly from the majority of firms in our table, this practice merits inclusion for its *"commitment to legal aid work."* Immigration and asylum challenges by way of JR predominate. **Clients:** Individual applicants; asylum seekers.

Simpson & Marwick WS (see firm details p.1133) Admired by our interviewees for its following among local authorities, this firm makes it its business to protect the same from JR challenges. Avoidance has as much a part to play as actual defence and team leader **Katherine Shaw** is kept occupied by a voluminous client list. Her *"profound understanding and widespread connections"* have won her much respect throughout the region. **Clients:** Several local authorities including East Ayrshire and West Lothian.

Tods Murray WS (see firm details p.1157) Noted for its stout defence of public bodies facing JR challenges, additional work is engineered through its interests in environmental, housing, planning and education law. In the past year, it successfully defended five JRs against the Local Government Property Commission concerning the allocation of disputed assets among local authorities following reorganisation. The group also acted for the RSPB in a JR on the decision of the Scottish Ministers to grant a licence to shoot Barnacle geese. **Clients:** Angus Council; Dundee City Council; Forestry Commission; Scottish Screen; educational institutions.

NORTHERN IRELAND

ADMINISTRATIVE & PUBLIC LAW: GENERAL • Northern Ireland	Ptnrs	Assts
1		
Cleaver Fulton Rankin Belfast	n/a	n/a
Madden & Finucane Belfast	n/a	n/a
LEADING INDIVIDUALS		
1		
FARIS Neil Cleaver Fulton Rankin		
RITCHIE Angela Madden & Finucane		

This book is the product of 6,552 1/2 hour interviews. See p.7 for BMRB audit.

Within each band, firms are listed alphabetically. *See individuals' profiles p.58*

Cleaver Fulton Rankin (see firm details p.918) This practice is sustained on a diet of planning and general public law in equal measure. On the planning side, it acted for the developer of Belfast City Airport in successfully resisting a challenge by a rival concern against the grant of planning permission. More generally, it has been retained by the Sentence Review Commission (an independent body supervising the post-Good Friday Agreement prisoner release programme). It was involved in the high profile case of Johnny Adair, who made a challenge under Article 6 of the Human Rights Act following the revocation of his licence after allegations of terrorist activity. The respected **Neil Faris** leads the team and is currently working on a JR by the Family Planning Association against the Department of Health alleging failure to issue guidelines. **Clients:** Sentence Review Commission; NIGEN; BT; Sports Council; local authorities.

Madden & Finucane (see firm details p.1049) Complementing its major rival well, this committed practice appears, often for the applicant, in politically charged cases. Best known for prisoner appeals, it further concerns itself with JRs against the Parades Commission and activity on behalf of the families in the Bloody Sunday Inquiry. Team leader **Angela Ritchie** is judged "*an avid challenger of government decisions*" by our interviewees, and is frequently seen acting for IRA prisoners against the Sentence Review Commission. **Clients:** Individual applicants.

LEADERS IN ADMINISTRATIVE & PUBLIC LAW

AMBROSE, Ray
Nabarro Nathanson, London (020) 7524 6000

BOWDEN, Paul
Freshfields Bruckhaus Deringer, London (020) 7936 4000
paul.bowden@freshfields.com
See under Litigation, p.566

BURGESS, David C.W.
Winstanley-Burgess, London (020) 7278 7911

BUXTON, Richard
Richard Buxton, Cambridge (01223) 328933

CHILD, Tony
Rowe & Maw, London (020) 7782 8686
tchild@roweandmaw.com
Specialisation: Practice covers the full range of public and administrative law. Specialist in local government and NHS law. Acts for public bodies and those who deal with them. Adviser to local government and NHS external auditors. Renowned expertise and experience in acting for both applicants and respondents in judicial review and public law proceedings. This includes the first successful challenge in any commonwealth jurisdiction to the adequacy of a government consultation exercise; bringing down the Rate Support Grant (RSG) and ratecapping regime in 1985; overcoming retrospective legislation on RSG; having interest rate swaps declared by the House of Lords to be ultra vires local authorities; 'Bookbinder v Tebbit (No. 2)' (1992); 'Allsop v North Tyneside MBC' (1992); 'Burgoine and Cooke v Waltham Forest LBC' (1996) Lasaethes v the Incorporated Froebell Institute (2000), the first successful challenge to the expulsion of a pupil from a private school.
Career: Articled Redbridge London Borough Council; qualified 1971. Assistant solicitor 1971-74. Senior solicitor 1974-76. Chief solicitor Greenwich LBC 1976-79. Assistant Chief Executive and solicitor 1979-83; Deputy Chief Executive 1983-87; solicitor to Audit Commission 1987-95; partner *Rowe & Maw* 1995. Education: Ilford County High School; University College, London (LLB First Class Hons).
Personal: Born 1947. Resides Chelmsford. Interests include football (player/manager Braintree and Bocking United FC), cricket (wicket-keeper, batsman, Redbridge Parks CC), sports generally, crosswords.

CIRELL, Stephen
Eversheds, Leeds (0113) 243 0391
stephencirell@eversheds.com
Specialisation: Partner in National Local Government Group. Principal area of practice covers governmnent, Best Value, major commercial transactions such as under the Private Finance Initiative, partnership outsourcing and public sector contracting generally. Lectures frequently on local government law and related matters for commercial course organisers, professional organisations, local authorities and in-house.
Prof. Memberships: Law Society.
Career: Qualified 1984 while with Stockport MBC. Assistant Solicitor, then Principal Solicitor with Dudley MBC 1984-88, then Head of Common Law/Assistant Director at Leeds City Council 1988-93. Joined *Eversheds Hepworth & Chadwick* as a Partner in the Local Government Group in October 1993.
Publications: Co-author of 'CCT- Law & Practice' (FT 1990), 'Municipal Trading' (FT 1992), 'Competitive Tendering for Professional Services' (FT 1994), 'Private Finance Initiative for Local Authorities' (FT 1997) 'Best Value: Law and Practice' (Sweet & Maxwell 1999), and 'E Government, Best Value and the Law' (SOCITM 2001). Specialist editor to 'Encyclopaedia of Local Government Law'. Specialist correspondent to the 'Local Government Chronicle' and author of numerous articles for professional publications.
Personal: Born 3rd July 1960. Attended University College of Wales Aberystwyth 1978-81. Leisure pursuits include motorcycling. Lives in Leeds.

COLE, Alun
Morgan Cole, Cardiff (029) 2038 5385

DAY, Martyn
Leigh, Day & Co, London (020) 7650 1200

EVANS, Eric
Eversheds, Cardiff (029) 2047 1147
Specialisation: Partner in commercial property department and head of both the planning and PFI units. Specialises in all aspects of property law including complex planning obligations, major town centre regeneration/shopping schemes, site assembly, agreements for the construction of major highways associated with developments, public/private sector joint ventures, planning gain, valuations, urban development/regeneration grants and land reclamation. 30 years public sector experience, dealing with all areas of local government. Extensive experience of PFI and led one of the first PFI/PPP deals in Wales, at University Hospital of Wales NHS Trust. Has since advised on numerous deals including Newport Southern Distributor Road, Chepstow Community Hospital, Wiltshire's grouped schools scheme and 'Waste to Energy' scheme at Neath.
Prof. Memberships: Member of Law Society's Planning Panel.
Career: Qualified in 1980. Town Clerk, Borough of Blaenau Gwent (1981-89). Deputy Chief Executive and Legal Adviser, Land Authority for Wales (1989-92). Partner *Eversheds* 1992.
Personal: Director of Silent Valley Waste Services. Lives in Abertillery.

FARIS, Neil
Cleaver Fulton Rankin, Belfast (028) 9024 3141

GOULD, Jean
Tyndallwoods, Birmingham (0121) 624 1111
jean_gould@tyndallwoods.co.uk
Specialisation: Particularly interested in social welfare and human rights applications of public law and in public interest litigation. Cases include R v Sefton MBC ex parte Help the Aged and others, and R v North Lancashire Health Authority ex parte A, D & G.
Career: Formerly project solicitor at the public law project and now a partner at *Tyndallwoods* and trainer in community care law for Carers National Association. Member of the Legal Services Commission Public Interest Advisory Panel.

Publications: Contributes articles to 'Legal Action' and other journals.
Personal: BA Hons. Taught in Inner London before qualifying in 1990.

GRIFFITHS, Trevor
Sharpe Pritchard, London (020) 7405 4600
See under Local Government, p.592

GROSZ, Stephen
Bindman & Partners, London (020) 7833 4433
s.grosz@bindmans.com
See under Human Rights, p.425

HOLLIGAN, William
Brodies WS, Edinburgh (0131) 228 3777
william.holligan@brodies.co.uk
Specialisation: Partner in *Brodies* litigation department dealing mainly with commercial and administrative law matters. Wide experience through involvement in judicial review matters involving councils and central government, and also European administrative law. Contributor to 'Scots Law Times' on litigation matters. Part-time lecturer at Edinburgh University on civil court practice; solicitor advocate; qualified to practice in Australia.
Prof. Memberships: Writer to the Signet, Law Society of Scotland.
Career: University of Edinburgh (LLB), Adelaide (LLM). Qualified 1981; assistant solicitor *Brodies* 1981-85; assistant solicitor and partner *Finlaysons*, Adelaide, Australia 1985-91; partner *Brodies* since 1992.
Personal: Married, lives in Edinburgh.

ILEY, Malcolm
Nabarro Nathanson, London (020) 7524 6000

JARMAN, Christopher
Bevan Ashford, Bristol (0117) 975 1621
c.jarman@bevanashford.co.uk
Specialisation: Project work. Member of the PFI and Projects Group. Deals with local authorities, NHS Trusts and M.O.D. work for the private sector. Recently: pathfinder local authorities PFI; closed largest NHS PFI in Wales; advising on largest (£9bn) PFI scheme to date.
Prof. Memberships: Law society.
Career: Sidcot School; University College, London (BA History). Articled, qualified 1987 and partner 1989 at *Sharpe Pritchard*; joined *Bevan Ashford* 1997 as associate partner, became partner, *Bevan Ashford*, 1998.
Publications: Editor and contibutor to 'Public Private Partnerships', Sweet & Maxwell. Contributor to 'TUPE and the Acquired Rights Directive', edited by Sharland and Isaacs Q.C.
Personal: Reading, walking, playing with my children, and Axbridge Saxons Football Club.

KEITH-LUCAS, Peter
Wragge & Co, Birmingham (0870) 903 1000

KNIGHT, Matthew
Knights, Tunbridge Wells (01892) 537311
knights@atlas.co.uk
Specialisation: Senior partner. Main area of practice is judicial review. Also handles defamation, crime, trespass, compulsory purchase compensation, commercial litigation and advising on and drafting legislation. Acted in Sawrij & Swalesmoor Mink Farm Ltd v Lynx & Others; in R v Somerset County Council ex parte Fewings, Leyland & Down and in British Field Sports Society ats Commissioners of HM Customs & Excise. Author of various articles.
Prof. Memberships: Law Society.
Career: Qualified in 1982 after joining *Farrer & Co* in 1980. Worked at *Sinclair Roche & Temperley* 1982-84, then at *Cripps Harries Hall* 1984-94, from 1986 as a partner. Established *Knights* in 1994.
Personal: Born 2nd April 1957. Attended Eltham College 1970-76, Newcastle University 1976-79 and College of Law 1979-80. Leisure interests include hunting and shooting.

LIDBETTER, Andrew
Herbert Smith, London (020) 7374 8000
andrew.lidbetter@herbertsmith.com
Specialisation: Commercial litigation partner specialising in public and administrative law and other contentious regulatory matters, particularly judicial review, statutory appeals, ECHR issues, DTI investigations, other inquiries, disciplinary proceedings, local government and environmental cases. Clients include both applicants and regulators. Member of the advisory board of 'JR' (Judicial Review) and frequently writes on public law. Author of 'Company Investigations and Public Law – A Practical Guide to Government Investigations' (Hart Publishing, 1999), and contributor of Judicial Review and Human Rights chapters to Blackstone's 'Civil Practice' (2001).
Prof. Memberships: Administrative Law Bar Association.
Career: Qualified 1990. Partner 1998.
Personal: Educated at Worcester College, Oxford (First class law degree and BCL).

MACKINTOSH, Nicola
Mackintosh Duncan, London (020) 7357 6464

MACLEOD, Ian
Shepherd & Wedderburn WS, Edinburgh (0131) 473 5245
ian.macleod@shepwedd.co.uk
See under Litigation, p.575

MCDERMOTT, Jennifer
Lovells, London (020) 7296 2000
jennifer.mcdermott@lovells.com
Specialisation: Commercial litigation with specialisation in media litigation, particularly including defamation, privacy, confidentiality and broadcasting regulatory matters. Advises many newspapers and corporate clients. Extensive expertise also in commercial judicial review having been involved in several high profile applications against and in conjunction with many regulatory authorities. On the editorial board of Communications Law; contributes to publications such as the Press Gazette and PLC and speaks at conferences and on radio and television on both judicial review and media law.
Prof. Memberships: Member of the Media Society, the Royal Television Society, Society of Editors, Executive Committee of JUSTICE; Amnesty International.
Career: Qualified 1981 with *Lovells;* partner 1989.

PARKER, Mike
Wilsons, Salisbury (01722) 412412

RABINOWICZ, Jack
Teacher Stern Selby, London (020) 7242 3191
j.rabinowicz@tsslaw.com
Specialisation: Partner in litigation department. Main areas of practice include education, medical negligence, and personal injury work.
Prof. Memberships: Director of Disability Law Service, Chair of Education Law Association (ELAS), Steering Committee of Whooping Cough Claims, Action for Victims of Medical Accidents (AVMA), American Trial Lawyers Association (ATLA), Medico-Legal Society, Association of Personal Injury Lawyers (APIL), Law Society's Group for the Welfare of People with a Mental Handicap, Council of Registration of Schools teaching Dyslexia (CresTeD).
Career: Qualified in 1977. Currently a partner with *Teacher Stern Selby.*

RITCHIE, Angela
Madden & Finucane, Belfast (028) 9023 8007

RUEBAIN, David
Levenes, London (020) 8881 7777
info@davidlevene.co.uk
Specialisation: The Department specialises in all aspects of education law, health law, community care law and disability discrimination. He has published and taught extensively on education and disability law and is co-author of 'Notes on the Disability Discrimination Act' (now in its 9th edition), co-author of 'Taking Action, a Guide for Parents of Children with Special Educational Needs', co-author of 'Education Law and Practice' and co-author of the forthcoming volume of Atkin's Court Forms volume on Education Law.
Prof. Memberships: Trustee of the Disability Discrimination Act Representation and Advice Project, Vice Chair of the Rights Now Campaign, a member of the Law Society's Mental Health and Disability Committee, a member of the editorial board of Disability and Society journal, Vice Chair of Disability Equality in Education, a member of the editorial board of Community Care Law Reports, a member of the Disability Rights Commission's Special Educational Needs and Disability Bill – Schools Duties Code of Practice Reference Group, and Honorary Legal Advisor to the Independent Panel for Special Education Advice.

SCHWEHR, Belinda
Rowe & Maw, London (020) 7782 8880
bschwehr@roweandmawe.co.uk
Specialisation: Conducts judicial review proceedings for applicants and respondents and advises on the interaction between public and private law principles for a wide range of clients. Practice ranges from adults' social services law to health, mental health and human rights. Recent work has involved the implementation of statutory functions in the context of scarce resources and the risk of tortious claims for breach of statutory duty given the implications of the Human Rights Act; the scope for public law challenge in actions for the recovery of debts arising from statutory charges; hospital discharge disputes; the extent of statutory powers of guardianship in respect of the mentally incapacitated and the implications of the Human Rights Act for the private and public sector, including collaboration with the LGA in the preparation of its booklet on the Act, for all local authorities. Advises both local authority and NHS auditors; currently acting for the proprietor of a clinic regarding his dealings with the Human Fertility and Embryology Authority. A solicitor-advocate. Offers annual advice packages to local authorities (in particular social services departments), involving preventative public law advice for departmental lawyers and Members, and training of care managers.
Prof. Memberships: Administrative Law Bar Association.

Career: Barrister 1985, private practice until 1990 in civil common law chambers; LLM in public law, UCL 1990; university lecturer in public law and a consultant 1990-97; legal consultant to author of Community Care Practice and the Law (Jessica Kingsley Ltd 1994); joined *Rowe & Maw* 1997; re-qualified as solicitor 1998; author of many articles on public law issues, regular speaker at national conferences, seminars and training sessions.
Personal: Born 1962.

SHAW, Kate
Simpson & Marwick WS, Edinburgh
(0131) 557 1545

SHINER, Philip
Public Interest Lawyers, Birmingham
(0121) 702 2110

SILAS, Douglas
Levenes, London (020) 8881 7777
info@davidlevene.co.uk
Specialisation: Education and disability law. In particular, special educational needs, community care and disability discrimination cases but also other public law areas. Developing human rights practice. Mainly claimant work for individuals and charities. Formerly a registered trainee British Sign Language Interpreter. Represented Jeff McWhinney, the first deaf Chief Executive of the British Deaf Association, in a test case challenge against the refusal of deaf people to serve as jurors.
Prof. Memberships: Trustee of the Disability Law Service. Member of Law Society, Education Law Association, Disability Discrimination Act Advisors Group, Deaf Legal Access Group, and British Deaf Association Advisory panel.
Career: Joined *Levenes Solicitors* in 1995 as trainee solicitor. Admitted 1997.
Personal: Born on 28 September 1966. Educated: John Lyons, Harrow; South Bank University (LL.B (Hons)); College of Law (LPC).

SMYTH, Michael
Clifford Chance, London (020) 7600 1000
michael.smyth@cliffordchance.com
Specialisation: Partner with extensive experience in all kinds of commercial disputes, including media litigation and public law cases. Clients include public authorities, newspapers, book publishers and news agencies. Heads pre-publication unit providing advice on 24-hour basis. Also ranked in the annual International Commercial Litigation survey. Author of 'Business and the Human Rights Act'. Runs firm's pro bono practice.
Prof. Memberships: Law Society, City of London Solicitors' Company, Administrative Law Bar Association. Member of the Law Society's Human Rights Act Task Force and of the Liason Group to the Home Office's Human Rights act Task Force. Member of the Law Society's Defamation Pre-action Protocol Committee.
Career: Royal Belfast Academical Institution; Clare College, Cambridge (MA Law). Qualified 1982; partner *Clifford Chance* 1990; also admitted in Hong Kong and Northern Ireland.

STEIN, Richard
Leigh, Day & Co, London (020) 7650 1200
Specialisation: Practice covers administrative and public law particularly with a human rights emphasis including environmental, town planning and community care matters. Acts principally for campaigning and community groups and individuals in judicial reviews of local authorities and public authorities. Acted in R v HFEA exp Diane Blood, forced caesarian re S and ex parte Belgium Pincohet case.
Prof. Memberships: United Kingdom Environmental Law Association and Environmental Law Foundation.
Career: Called to the Bar 1982. Admitted solicitor 1994. Joined *Leigh Day & Co* 1993.

TROTTER, John
Bates, Wells & Braithwaite, London
(020) 7551 7777

WALLACE, Alastair
Tyndallwoods, Birmingham (0121) 624 1111
Specialisation: Partner. Head of public law department. Specialises in administrative and public law on behalf of applicants in a range of, mainly, local government related issues, in particular community care, education, planning and health law. Considerable experience in judicial review on behalf of individuals and campaigning groups in public interest – type cases. Has particular interest in asylum support, village greens and care home closures. Has contributed articles to 'Legal Action' and 'Mineral Planning'.
Career: Joined *Tyndallwoods* in 1991
Personal: Film, music and cycling.

WATSON, Peter M
Allen & Overy, London (020) 7330 3000
peter.watson@allenovery.com
See under Defamation, p.288

WHITE, Martin
Pinsent Curtis Biddle, Birmingham
(0121) 200 1050
martin.white@pinsents.com
Specialisation: Handles planning and related areas, including highways and environmental issues, with emphasis on major projects, planning appeal work, development plans, issues of planning gain, Section 106 agreements and compulsory purchase. Has acted in appeals relating to major inward investment, airports and business parks, for local Planning Authorities and private sector clients. Also handles local government and public law generally. Author of articles, speaker at conferences and seminars on planning gain and general planning issues.
Prof. Memberships: Law Society (Member of Planning Panel), Legal Associate of Royal Town Planning Institute.
Career: Qualified in 1979. Articled at Solihull Council 1977-79. Joined *Pinsent & Co* in 1981. Partner in 1987.
Personal: Born 1953. Attended Cambridge University 1972-76; Newcastle Polytechnic 1976-77. Interests include drama and music.

WILLIAMS, Huw
Edwards Geldard, Cardiff (029) 2023 8239
huw.williams@geldards.co.uk
Specialisation: Partner, Public Law. Principal area of practice encompasses public, planning and environmental law. Has worked extensively since 1987 on major urban renewal projects for the Welsh Development Agency, Cardiff Bay Development Corporation and local authorities, including numerous compulsory purchase orders, Parliamentary procedures relating to the Cardiff Bay Barrage project and joint ventures. Advice to both public and private interests on planning law and related matters including highways and utilities. Environmental experience includes cases relating to water pollution and contaminated land. Retained on a number of Millennium projects including Wales Millennium Centre and National Botanic Garden of Wales. Other public bodies advised include Cardiff University, National Library of Wales and the Arts Council of Wales. Advising clients on the implications of the establishment of the National Assembly for Wales.
Prof. Memberships: Law Society.
Career: Qualified 1978. Assistant Solicitor, Mid Glamorgan County Council 1978-80, Senior Assistant Solicitor 1980-84 and Principal Assistant Solicitor (Environmental Services) 1984-87. Joined *Edwards Geldard* in 1987 and became Partner in charge of public law in 1988.
Personal: Born 4 January 1954. Attended Llanelli Grammar School 1965-72, then Jesus College, Oxford 1972-75 (MA). Member of Council and Chairman, South East Wales branch, The Oxford University Society; Treasurer, Wales Public Law and Human Rights Association; Member, Law Society Welsh Affairs Working Groups. Member of the Advisory Committee, Centre for Professional Legal Studies. Cardiff University; Trustee and Chairman of the De Cymru Regional Committee of Fairbridge (national youth charity). Leisure pursuits include scuba diving, skiing, occasional sailing, naval history, art and architecture.

ADVERTISING & MARKETING

London: 61; *Profiles*: 63

OVERVIEW: The advertising sector remains strong, and although the leading firms are no longer as pre-eminent as they once were, as yet there are no clear successors to the old guard of advertising lawyers. Unsurprisingly, internet advertising is an area that has become increasingly important, with the related data protection issues also rising on clients' agenda. The increase in comparative advertising and 'brand bashing' campaigns has matched a growing use of the ASA as a device for competitor complaints. The continued globalisation of advertising campaigns has favoured those firms which can offer an international service.

RESEARCH APPROVED BY BMRB: *For this edition,* Chambers' *researchers conducted 6,552 interviews – 4,419 with law firms, 554 with barristers and 1,579 with clients.*

The validity of the research was scrutinised by BMRB International, who audited both the methodology and the results at our offices in July 2001. They interviewed Chambers' *researchers and cross-checked sample interviews. Details of the audit appear on page 7.*

TOP IN-HOUSE LAWYERS

Giles CROWN, Head of Legal & Business Affairs, *TBWA*

Kate FULTON, Chief UK Counsel, *Young & Rubicam*

Larisa JOY, Vice-Chairman, *Ogilvy*

The *"clever and always agreeable"* **Giles Crown** is the barrister *"who swapped his wig for a pair of jeans."* Well-known for writing and speaking on advertising law topics, he has quickly established a high profile. **Kate Fulton** is recommended for her *"commercial understanding"* and wide range of experience. Heavily endorsed, **Larisa Joy**'s recent promotion to Vice-Chairman reflects her reputation for management work.

In-House lawyers profiles: p 1193

ADVERTISING & MARKETING • London	Ptnrs	Assts
1 Lewis Silkin	12	12
Macfarlanes	7	12
Osborne Clarke OWA	9	8
2 The Simkins Partnership	3	3
3 Hammond Suddards Edge	9	n/a
Theodore Goddard	5	9
4 Lawrence Graham	8	n/a
Rowe & Maw	2	1
Taylor Joynson Garrett	3	9
5 Baker & McKenzie	3	12
Clifford Chance	2	3
CMS Cameron McKenna	5	9
Field Fisher Waterhouse	2	5
Olswang	n/a	n/a
Townleys	n/a	4
6 Harrison Curtis	2	n/a
Lovells	n/a	n/a

LEADING INDIVIDUALS	
1 **ALEXANDER Roger** Lewis Silkin	**GROOM Stephen** Osborne Clarke OWA
HALL-SMITH Vanessa Harrison Curtis	**SWAN Charles** The Simkins Partnership
2 **BIRT Timothy** Osborne Clarke OWA	**COURTENAY-STAMP Jeremy** Macfarlanes
DRESDEN Brinsley Lewis Silkin	
3 **BRAFMAN Guilherme** Kaye Scholer LLP	**BYRT Sarah** Rowe & Maw
THOMAS Richard Clifford Chance	
4 **EARLE Rupert** Theodore Goddard	
UP AND COMING	
RAYMAN Alice The Simkins Partnership	
WEGENEK Robert Hammond Suddards Edge	

This book is the product of 6,552 1/2-hour interviews. See p.7 for BMRB audit.
Within each band, firms are listed alphabetically. *See individuals' profiles p.63*

LONDON

Lewis Silkin (see firm details p.1040) Holding its high profile in the sector, although some interviewees feel it is *"a main player but no longer pre-eminent on its own ."* Wide breadth of client coverage across agencies, promoters, industry bodies, headhunters and underwriters. *"Grand old man of advertising"* **Roger Alexander** (see p.63) commands enormous respect for his corporate and employment work, *"popular with clients, clever and jolly nice ."* **Brinsley Dresden's** (see p.63) reputation in pure advertising continues to grow, prompted by his *"relaxed manner, active interest"* and a *"good grounding working in-house."* Expertise in this area is exemplified by a commission to write the standard below-the-line client agency contract for sales promotion and direct marketing activities in conjunction with industry bodies. The team acts for Havas Advertising in relation to all its significant UK work. In corporate it advised in MBO of Delaney Lund Knox & Warren and acted for shareholders of The Partners Design Consultants in their sale to Young & Rubicam. Also represented Open Interactive TV on its Wedding Competition and agent HHCL on a planned Mercedes promotion for Texaco. **Clients:** Havas Advertising; Delaney Lund Knox Warren; Gateway; Abbott Mead Vickers Group.

Macfarlanes (see firm details p.1046) Remains in the top ranking due to its impressive corporate reputation, with a strong client list of agencies and brand owners. **Jeremy Courtenay-Stamp** (see p.63) is considered *"a good operator with a great corporate reputation,"* respected by clients for giving a *"fantastic service, understanding the business"* and always *"speaking plain English."* The team acts for top advertising agencies, PR agencies, below the line agencies, advertisers and brand owners. Successfully challenged adverse ITC and ASA rulings on behalf of Comet and Saatchi & Saatchi in a dispute with Currys over pricing claims and advised in the acquisition by Cordiant Communications of the Lighthouse Global Network. The firm continues to deal with the advertising and sponsorship arrangements for Jaguar Formula One. **Clients:** Interbrand Newell & Sorrell; Team Saatchi; Saatchi & Saatchi Advertising; BMP DDB Needham; Omnicon; Anhauseur Busch; Comet.

Osborne Clarke OWA (see firm details p.1086) Key to the firm's high profile remains the *"always impressive"* **Stephen Groom,** endorsed by clients as *"a good guy for a difficult campaign or cutting edge stuff."* Corporate lawyer **Tim Birt** (*"a really good guy and highly active"*) is also warmly praised. *"An excellent team"* heavily involved in new media, IT and telecoms work, it undertakes corporate work and offers content, compliance and commercial advice to a wide range of clients. Advised Young & Rubicam on the acquisition of Partners Design and Transart, a Canadian marketing services network. It carries out ongoing work for Times Newspapers on contracts relating to marketing, advertising and sponsored publications and provides content, compliance, employment and contractual work for TBWA London. **Clients:** Young & Rubicam; Times Newspapers; Envoy; Matthias Rath; Envoy Communications.

The Simkins Partnership (see firm details p.1131) Expert in 'pure' adverting work, the practice undertakes copy clearance, disputes and contract work for an envied client base including three of the largest agencies. Focused on media and entertainment-related issues with an overseas capability provided by the Advertising Law International network. "*Doyen*" **Charles Swan** ("*highly knowledgeable*") retains his high profile among fellow solicitors and clients for a "*tailored and specific service*" and "*consistently sound advice.*" He is joined in our rankings by the well-regarded **Alice Rayman**, although the departure of Vanessa Hall-Smith has raised concerns over "*the strength and depth*" of this somewhat "*traditional practice.*" Appointed sole legal advisors of Tribal DDB, major new media agency in the global DDB network, the firm continues to act for Fallon London and advises Institute of Practitioners in Advertising. **Clients:** Tribal DDB; Fallon London; Lowe Lintas; BMP DDB; J Walter Thompson; WWAV Rapp Collins.

Hammond Suddards Edge (see firm details p.984) Still best known for corporate advice for WPP Group, the practice provides clearance, contracts and corporate work for a number of agencies and advertisers. The practice also specialises in pharmaceuticals and healthcare and is increasingly active in digital media. Supreme client handler **Robert Wegenek** (see p.64) was rated by interviewees as "*pragmatic and understanding the business.*" The team advised Spafax on its joint venture with easyEverything to sell advertising and media space and assisted J Walter Thompson and MindShare on its client contracts with Boots. It also carries out regular advertising clearance work for Virgin Energy, Virgin Mobile, Levis, Boddingtons and Unilever. **Clients:** Ogilivy; Bartle Bogle Hegarty; One2One; Woolworths; B&Q; Futurebrand.

Theodore Goddard (see firm details p.1152) A high profile year, due in part to its role acting for Ryanair in the successful defence of British Airway's claim for damages over the former's comparative advertising campaign. Notable for its regulatory work for the Advertising Standards Agency, the practice also has a client portfolio of advertisers and agencies and is increasing its sports sponsorship work. Although thought to "*lack a heavy hitter on the advertising side,*" it is "*pushing hard*" while **Rupert Earle** (see p.63) is singled out for praise. Acted successfully for ASA in defence of judicial review proceedings brought by SmithKline Beecham regarding Ribena Toothkind, it also handled Firedup.com's sponsorship of a number of summer music festivals including Reading and V2. **Clients:** Advertising Standards Authority; Ryanair; Signet Group; British Horse Racing Board.

Lawrence Graham (see firm details p.1030) "*Experts*" in the field of direct marketing, selling and distribution, and also active in e-commerce, point of sale and sales promotion where Mike Smyth has a focus. The team is experienced in pan-European campaigns and both UK and EC inquiries on marketing practices, acting for agencies, brand owners and 'below the line' agencies. It advised Sony Computer Entertainment on the European launch of the Playstation II and Pure Entertainment on the European launch of an advertising model providing free computer games. Also advised on the sale of a below the line advertising agency to WPP. **Clients:** Sony Computer Entertainment; Pure Entertainment; Black Cat; Readers Digest; National Lottery Commission.

Rowe & Maw (see firm details p.1113) "*Good practice*" according to sources which advises leading agencies on copy clearance, client contracts, sales promotions, disputes with artists and web-based promotions. The team also advises a number of high profile advertisers and benefits from the profile of **Sarah Byrt** (see p.63) ("*a solid lawyer with an understanding of the creative process.*") Advised CDP on campaigns for advertisers including Hamlet and totaljobs.com. **Clients:** Camp Chipperfield Hill Murray; CDP; McCann-Erickson; St Luke's; Virgin Records; Monsanto.

Taylor Joynson Garrett (see firm details p.1150) Known primarily in the market for its IP and litigation work, the practice is also active on the corporate side, advising the Omnicon Group in the negotiation and documentation of its TBWA network acquisitions outside North America. Partner Richard Pertwee and the team handle litigation and corporate matters for both agencies and their clients and increasingly advise new media companies on e-marketing. **Clients:** Omnicon; TBWA Advertising Network; Visa; Wella; Saatchi & Saatchi; Zenith Media.

Baker & McKenzie (see firm details p.868) Based within the IP group, the practice specialises in internet advertising and licensing, franchising and data protection. Benefiting from an international network of offices supporting cross-border work, it advises both agency and advertiser clients on copy clearance, agency contracts and TV, print and internet advertisements. Ilana Saltzman and the team are respected by competitors for their "*quality advertising work for good brand clients.*" Advises a number of US IT and software firms with clients appreciating its "*understanding of how silicon valley firms work.*" **Clients:** Network Associates; Yahoo!; Agency.com; Camelot; Cisco.

Clifford Chance (see firm details p.919) The marketing and advertising group draws together lawyers from IP, commercial, media, IT and financial services rather than having a dedicated team. A strong reputation acting for advertisers, including leading global brands, is supported by an extensive international corporate client portfolio with less stand-alone work. Last year saw emphasis on pursuing and defending complaints involving competitors and comparative advertising issues as well as combating 'brand bashing' exercises (eg rogue websites.) **Richard Thomas** (see p.64) (former Director of Consumer Affairs at OFT) was typically considered "*able and bright though occasionally dry*" by our interviewees. The firm advised Safeway on legal issues arising out of the withdrawal of its loyalty card, Coca-Cola on its 'Cokeauction' promotion and redrafted the Advertising and Sponsorship Guide for the Radio Authority. **Clients:** Safeway; Coca-Cola; Hunters & Frankau; The Radio Authority.

CMS Cameron McKenna (see firm details p.922) Widely perceived to have suffered from the departure of Guilherme Brafman to Kaye Scholer, the remaining team is warmly rated by clients as "*friendly and responsive.*" Primarily involved with brand owners, the group led by Stephen Whybrow also undertakes work for brand owners and agencies, with a niche in pharmaceutical advertising. **Clients:** Consignia; Coca-Cola; Camelot Group; Grey Advertising.

Field Fisher Waterhouse (see firm details p.957) The firm's profile has suffered this year by the move in-house of key player Hayley Stallard, with many sources feeling it now "*lacks focus.*" Advises both agencies and advertisers, with a growing strength in internet advertising. Under the guidance of Shelley Nadler, the team advised British American Tobacco on the listings website for bars, clubs and pubs in a number of European countries and Thomascook.com on linking and banner advertisements with lastminute.com, Excite and Virgin. Continues to advise the Incorporated Society of British Advertisers (IBSA) on various legal issues. **Clients:** British American Tobacco; Accenture; BBC Worldwide; First Quench Retailing; The Post Office; Black Cat; The Lotteries Council; Thomascook.com.

Olswang (see firm details p.1084) "*Strong in new media,*" and respected in all aspects of above and below the line advertising, the practice provides advice to a range of agencies, advertisers, production companies and brand consultants. Jonathan Goldstein and the team advised Music Industry Chart Services on first sponsorship of the Official UK Top 40 Singles and Artists Charts, and the RSPCA on adverts relating to the fox hunting debate. Also advised Freeserve on its advertising sales terms and conditions, Carlton with regard to ITC issues and BBC Worldwide on cross-promotion of television channels and websites. **Clients:** Music Industry Chart

Services (MICS); Nike; Ladbrokes; Channel 4; Granada Media; MTV; M&C Saatchi.

Townleys (see firm details p.1159) "*Market leaders in sport,*" the firm maintains its ranking due to acknowledged expertise in sports sponsorship. Andy Korman undertakes all aspects of sponsorship, merchandising, licensing, endorsement and event organisation, as well as contracts between players and clubs or federations. The team handled npower's sponsorship of English domestic test match cricket, sponsorship of the rugby league Superleague by XXXX and Tetley's and the Skol sponsorship of the PDC World Darts Championships. **Clients:** Six Nations Committee; British Lions; Sport England; Everton FC; Carlsberg-Tetley.

Harrison Curtis (see firm details p.988) New to the rankings, this specialist niche firm is growing an impressive reputation since being joined by ex-Simkins partner **Vanessa Hall-Smith**. Acting for advertisers and agencies, the practice has expertise in television and film, and immigration and work permits issues surrounding the use of overseas talent. Clients agree that "*easy to get along with and accessible,*" Hall-Smith is "*a rising star.*" The group acted for BMP DDB in talent deals for major campaigns including Barclaycard and Vodafone, advised Circus on agency/client related matters and advised 4Learning on marketing, sponsorship and promotions of the new GridClub service. **Clients:** BMP DDB; Circus; WWAV Rapp Collins Scotland; Spaced UK; 4Learning.

Lovells (see firm details p.1044) Despite impressive clients on both the agency and advertiser sides, the firm has a surprisingly low profile in this sector. Peter Watts leads a team that acted for tobacco firms in successfully challenging the EU Directive banning advertising and sponsorship and advised Mars on its promotional campaigns connected to the Millennium Dome. The firm also advises Mars on its leading brands and pan-European advertising and marketing initiatives. Continues to act for Interpublic, McCann Erikson, Futurebrand, Lowe and Zentrophy agencies in both the corporate and commercial sphere and advises Estée Lauder on compliance issues. **Clients:** Interpublic; Mars; Trinity Mirror; Guardian Group.

Other Notable Practitioners **Guilherme Brafman** (see p.63) of **Kaye Scholer** (formerly with CMS Cameron McKenna) remains rated for his corporate work, although his new firm has yet to make an impact in the market.

LEADERS IN ADVERTISING & MARKETING

ALEXANDER, Roger
Lewis Silkin, London (020) 7074 8001
roger.alexander@lewissilkin.com
Specialisation: Partner in Corporate Department. Advising companies in the Marketing Services Industry in relation to corporate finance, mergers, acquisitions, flotations and high level employment issues including share incentivisation schemes. Acts for a raft of companies in the sector, both public and private, including some of the largest agency groups; also advises industry bodies. Lectures in the UK and overseas on issues and trends in the industry.
Prof. Memberships: Law Society, Solicitors European Group, Society of Share Scheme Practitioners.
Career: Qualified 1965. Partner at *Lewis Silkin* 1965. Head of Marketing Services Law Group. Lead Partner 1989-1998. Senior Partner 1999.

BIRT, Timothy D.
Osborne Clarke, London (020) 7809 1000

BRAFMAN, Guilherme
Kaye Scholer LLP, London (020) 8528 1400
gbrafman@kayescholer.com
Specialisation: Corporate, M&A, Advertising & Marketing, IT, e-commerce, media, copyright, Financial Services and sitting as arbitrator. All aspects of advertising, client contracts, artists' agreements, campaign clearance, and especially the buying and selling of agencies, P.R. companies and financial services businesses. Advertising disputes and high-level hiring and firing.
Prof. Memberships: M.C.I. Arb; City of London Solicitors Company; The Law Society.
Career: Qualified 1979 with *Slaughter and May*. 1983 founded *Brafmans* which (as *Brafman Morris)* merged in 1989 with *Cameron Markby Hewitt* (now *CMS Cameron McKenna*). Managing partner, London office of Kaye Schole LLP February 2001.
Publications: Various articles and chapter in an encyclopaedia of International Joint Ventures.
Personal: Educated at Downing College, Cambridge. Lives in London and Norfolk. Married, 2 sons. Interests: Family, tennis, swimming, food, etc. Fluent in Portuguese and French.

BYRT, Sarah
Rowe & Maw, London (020) 7248 4282
Specialisation: Intellectual property with a particular emphasis on advertising, publishing and media matters. Acts for several agencies including McCann-Erickson, CDP, Camp Chipperfield Hill Murray and Maher Bird Associates. UK contributor to a major French advertising law textbook.
Career: LLB (Law with French) Birmingham and Limoges Universities. Joined *Rowe & Maw* as trainee in 1986. Has specialised in IP since qualifying in 1988. Made partner in 1995.
Personal: Food, travel, friends.

COURTENAY-STAMP, Jeremy
Macfarlanes, London (020) 7831 9222
Specialisation: Head of commercial section. Specialises in advertising and marketing. Acting for five of the top 20 advertising agencies, as well as a number of other above, below and through the line agencies. Has written articles and lectured extensively on this subject. Also advises on all aspects of commercial and intellectual property.
Prof. Memberships: City of London Law Society. Member of Commercial Law sub-committee.
Career: Qualified in 1986 while with *Macfarlanes*. Became a partner in 1992.

DRESDEN, Brinsley
Lewis Silkin, London (020) 7074 8069
brinsley.dresden@lewissilkin.com
Specialisation: Head of Advertising Law and Partner in the Intellectual Property Unit specialising in non-contentious IP law. Advises a wide range of advertising agencies and advertisers, as well as clients seeking other IP advice. Frequently advises on clearance issues such as parodies of feature films, unauthorised references to living individuals, incorporation of third party IP rights; negotiating on contracts between advertisers and agencies, and for talent appearing in advertising campaigns; also advises on making and defending complaints to the ITC, the BACC and the ASA. Participated in negotiating and drafting standard form client/agency agreements for both the above-the-line and below-the-line sectors of the industry. Increasingly involved with new media advertising, including clearances for internet advertising and sales promotion and drafting web site design and hosting contracts. Regularly lectures on a wide range of legal issues concerning advertising and marketing.
Prof. Memberships: European Advertising Lawyers Association; Global Advertising Lawyers Alliance; Advertising Law Group.
Career: Born 25.2.66; Educated King's College School, Wimbledon; University of Bristol (LLB Hons 1987); College of Law, Guildford; King's College London (LLM 1999). Trained *Nabarro Nathanson* and qualified 1991. *BT Group Legal Services* 1993-1996; *Lewis Silkin* 1996; Partner 1999.
Personal: Interests include sailing, swimming and the arts.

EARLE, Rupert
Theodore Goddard, London (020) 7580 5806
rupertearle@theodoregoddard.co.uk
Specialisation: Media and public law with particular emphasis on advertising and marketing law. Has acted for the Advertising Standards Authority for many years (including, for example, in the defence of SmithKline Beecham's challenge in relation to their Ribena Toothkind advertising), and provides copy and trading standards advice to many commercial organisations, including the airline, high street retail and telecoms businesses.
Prof. Memberships: Law Society.
Career: Qualified at *Theodore Goddard* in 1988, partner 1997.
Personal: Educated at Winchester and Cambridge University. Interests include pots and strange places.

GROOM, Stephen
Osborne Clarke OWA, London (020) 7809 1000

HALL-SMITH, Vanessa
Harrison Curtis, London (020) 7611 1720

RAYMAN, Alice
The Simkins Partnership, London (020) 7907 3000

SWAN, Charles
The Simkins Partnership, London (020) 7907 3000

THOMAS, Richard
Clifford Chance, London (020) 7600 1000
richard.thomas@cliffordchance.com
Specialisation: Joined *Clifford Chance* in 1992 after six years as Director of Consumer Affairs at the Office of Fair Trading where (amongst other statutory functions) he implemented the Misleading Advertisements Regulations. Has an extensive network of contacts within governmental and regulatory bodies, self-regulatory organisations and trade associations. Holds the following positions: Member, Independent Television Commission Advertising Committee; Member, Direct Marketing Authority; Vice-President, Institute of Trading Standards; Member, Board of Financial Ombudsman Services. Richard Thomas is the author of 'Plain English for Lawyers'.
Prof. Memberships: Law Society; Royal Society of Arts.
Career: *Freshfields* (1971–1974); CAB Legal Service (1974–1979); National Consumer Council (1979–1986); Office of Fair Trading (1986–1992); *Clifford Chance* (1992–present).

WEGENEK, Robert
Hammond Suddards Edge, London
(020) 7655 1000
robert.wegenek@hammondse.com
Specialisation: London partner specialising in interactive media, advertising/marketing, retail and sports sectors. Has advised on the internet since 1994.
Prof. Memberships: Law Society, British Polish Legal Association.
Career: Qualified 1991. Partner *Edge Ellison* 1998. Partner *Hammond Suddards Edge* 2000.
Publications: 'E-commerce: A Guide to the Law of Electronic Business' (Butterworths).
Personal: Wolverhampton Grammar School; University of Durham, St Aidan's College 1985-88 (Hons) Law; College of Law, Chester 1988-89. Mountain biking, gym, cooking, real ale.

AGRICULTURE

OVERVIEW: In what has been acknowledged as a disastrous year for the agricultural sector, the onslaught of foot and mouth disease has meant that corporate work has been necessarily lax, while any resulting contentious work is only just emerging. Combined with the existing economic conditions, the crisis has forced farmers to concentrate on alternate forms of income and diversification. The replacement of MAFF with DEFRA, has yet to have a noticeable effect while the NFU's use of only nine panel firms has been met with mixed reviews. Burges Salmon remains the most nationally recognised firm, and with the farming industry moving into fewer and fewer hands, the market for legal services is also increasingly concentrated.

RESEARCH APPROVED BY BMRB: *For this edition,* Chambers' *researchers conducted 6,552 interviews – 4,419 with law firms, 554 with barristers and 1,579 with clients.*

The validity of the research was scrutinised by BMRB International, who audited both the methodology and the results at our offices in July 2001. They interviewed Chambers' *researchers and cross-checked sample interviews. Details of the audit appear on page 7.*

LONDON

AGRICULTURE • London	Ptnrs	Assts
1 Farrer & Co	5	4
Macfarlanes	4	5
Withers	3	2
2 Currey & Co	*	*
Dawson & Co	*	*
Lee & Pembertons	2	2
3 Boodle Hatfield	3	3
Payne Hicks Beach	3	n/a

LEADING INDIVIDUALS	
1 **JESSEL Christopher** Farrer & Co	**LANE Andrew** Withers
2 **MOORE John** Macfarlanes	
3 **FURBER James** Farrer & Co	**HORNBY John** Macfarlanes
PRING Simon Farrer & Co	
4 **ELLIOTT Penelope** Withers	**FINDLEY Christopher** Bircham Dyson Bell
JACKSON Andrew Macfarlanes	**KEDDIE Joanne** Dawson & Co

This book is the product of 6,552 1/2-hour interviews. See p.7 for BMRB audit.

Within each band, firms are listed alphabetically. *See Individuals' Profiles p.71*

**See editorial entries for explanation of team sizes.*

Farrer & Co (see firm details p.954) Three hundred years old, this firm retains its overwhelming reputation. Adjudged by peers "*an ideal*" to which traditional standards are set, the core of its work remains acquisitions and sales for large landed estates. Retains its expertise in matters such as commons rights and heritage law, while adding new skills in the field of farm business tenancies and the Agricultural Holdings Act. High profile **Christopher Jessel** (see p.74) continues to combine his work with writing and lecturing. He is supported by **Simon Pring** (see p.75), appreciated as one who "*rolls his sleeves up and gets things done.*" **James Furber** (see p.73), best known as solicitor to the Duchy of Cornwall, is also endorsed as "*a big name.*"

Macfarlanes (see firm details p.1046) Although seen as more commercial than the other two leading London firms, the practice continues to offer "*a Rolls-Royce service.*" With a focus in the more institutional side of agriculture, it represents pension funds as well as landed estates and wealthy foreign owners. The superb **John Hornby** (see p.74) heads the team and is endorsed by clients for being "*outstanding at giving rounded advice.*" He is assisted by the "*exceptional*" **John Moore** (see p.75) and newly-ranked **Andrew Jackson** (see p.74) ("*incredibly skilled*".) A highlight of the last year was the financial restructuring of an estate in the South West.

Withers (see firm details p.1187) Recognised for its expertise in the market of farm and estate conveyancing, this strong practice enjoys a client roster of over 130 landed estates. The core of the business remains transactional work, but the team is skilled in agricultural holdings issues and tax structuring. Former farmer **Andrew Lane** (see p.74) has "*a ferocious brain,*" according to competitors while the "*first class*" **Penny Elliott** (see p.72) joins him in the rankings this year. In the last year the firm has acted in the sales of a number of large estates nationwide.

Currey & Co (7 partners part-time) Rising up the ranks this year, the firm is typically praised by the market as "*a good intelligent firm*" with "*an excellent client base.*" The team, led by Nicholas Powell, retains its strength in conveyancing and is skilled in all aspects of agricultural land transfers.

Dawson & Co (see firm details p.936) (6 partners & 3 assistants part-time) Recommended contentious practice with expertise in landlord and tenant disputes, milk quota disputes and claims against DEFRA (formerly MAFF) and the EU. The market finds **Joanne Keddie** "*always in the thick of things,*" while her team is commended for its skills in employment and tax planning.

Lee & Pembertons (see firm details p.1035) A "*steady*" agricultural practice thought by rivals to have a "*specialist's focus.*" Fronted by Anita Symington, the group acts for estate owners and farmers across the country, with expertise in agricultural tenancy, conveyancing, diversification and estate management work.

Boodle Hatfield (see firm details p.889) This practice represents large rural estates and the rural holdings of urban estates and institutions. Along with acquisitions, sales and advising on farm re-organisations, the team is particularly praised for its taxation work under Kate Howe.

Payne Hicks Beach (see firm details p.1092) This firm has been less visible in the market place over the last year, but still boasts a good private client base. Acting mainly for large estates, the team including Alastair Murdie provides a full service, covering land transactions and tenancy work with an emphasis on diversification and tax structuring.

Other Notable Practitioners The former Morgan Cole (Oxford) man **Christopher Findley** (see p.73) has recently moved to Westminster firm **Bircham Dyson Bell.** He is rated for his "*experienced, practical approach.*"

THE SOUTH

AGRICULTURE • The South	Ptnrs	Assts
1 **Brachers** Maidstone	6	5
2 **White & Bowker** Winchester	3	3
3 **Cripps Harries Hall** Tunbridge Wells	2	1
Thomas Eggar Church Adams Chichester	2	1
4 **Knights** Tunbridge Wells	1	1
Penningtons Godalming	2	2

LEADING INDIVIDUALS	
1 **HORNER Douglas** Brachers	
2 **FELLINGHAM Michael** Penningtons	**KNIGHT Matthew** Knights
KYRKE Richard Thomas Eggar Church Adams	**STEEL John** White & Bowker

This book is the product of 6,552 1/2-hour interviews. See p.7 for BMRB audit.
Within each band, firms are listed alphabetically. *See individuals' profiles p.71*

Brachers (see firm details p.893) On the NFU panel for the region, the firm retains its strong position within the local market place. Pre-eminent in the field is "*thorough*" **Douglas Horner** whom fellow solicitors find "*a quality man to deal with.*" The firm deals with clients ranging from smallholders to large estates, and in the last year has acted in large value farm purchases, commercial disputes and succession claims. Also skilled in complex tenancies, milk quota disputes, and planning and environmental work.

White & Bowker (see firm details p.1178) "*Cutting edge*" firm, which maintains its balance between contentious and non-contentious work. **John Steel** has secured a high profile within the region among clients and competitors. Displays expertise on rights of way issues and has received instructions concerning the countryside bill. The group continues its work in milk quotas, mineral rights and diversification.

Cripps Harries Hall (see firm details p.927) Experienced in all areas of agricultural and countryside law, many of the firm's instructions lie in conveyancing, tenancies issues, planning and animal welfare proceedings. The warmly recommended team, which includes Michael Stevens, also specialises in equine law.

Thomas Eggar Church Adams (see firm details p.1153) The team, balancing non-contentious agricultural work with contentious, boasts a substantial private client base. It specialises in transactional and diversification work with a good profile in tax structuring. **Richard Kyrke** (see p.74) is the firm's standout individual.

Knights Praised by peers as an "*energetic team, it gets good results and comes highly recommended.*" A contentious practice with experience of judicial review, animal welfare and sporting disputes. Led by **Matthew Knight** (see p.59) ("*aggressive when he needs to be,*") the group has been active defending farmers from criminal prosecutions over alleged blocked rights of way and animal welfare.

Penningtons (see firm details p.1093) This "*active*" firm has been working to increase its profile in the last year. Acting for landed estates to corporate clients, it has recognised skills in tax planning, business restructuring, partnership disputes and environmental work. Also developing strengths in employment and diversification. New to this year's ranking, **Michael Fellingham** (see p.73) received market commendation for his "*clear communication and good advice.*"

THAMES VALLEY

AGRICULTURE • Thames Valley	Ptnrs	Assts
1 **Henmans** Oxford	2	1
2 **Pryce Collard Chamberlain** Abingdon	1	1
Stanley Tee Bishop's Stortford	2	1

This book is the product of 6,552 1/2-hour interviews. See p.7 for BMRB audit.
Within each band, firms are listed alphabetically.

Henmans (see firm details p.991) "*Acting for more farmers than anyone else in the Thames Valley,*" according to clients the firm has an excellent reputation. Led by Roger Henman, it acts for agricultural tenancies, offshore companies and landed estates nationwide. Instructed in development work, succession planning, partnership restructuring and landlord/tenant disputes. It continues to act for the Royal Agricultural Benevolent Institution. Highlights of the last year included the syndication of various fishing rights in Wales.

Pryce Collard Chamberlain (see firm details p.1102) Stuart Capel's team carries out a wide range of work across the agricultural marketplace. Acting for 40 firms across the region, it deals with acquisitions and disposals, tenancy disputes and employment. The practice also has an interest in quota advice and development work.

Stanley Tee (see firm details p.1139) The team, led by Richard Tee, represents large estates and owner-occupiers. Combines a strong private client side with expertise in agricultural, environmental and commercial litigation.

SOUTH WEST

Burges Salmon (see firm details p.902) Quite clearly the national leaders, it remains the most recognisable firm in the country, "*pre-eminent*" in the field. Within a group of "*exceptional individuals,*" **Andrew Densham** (see p.72) still stands out despite having reduced his workload to 20 hours a week. Also acclaimed by the market are **James Buxton** (see p.72) whose "*adversarial skills are excellent,*" while "*forceful*" **Peter Williams** (see p.76) continues to impress peers and clients with his drive and skill in banking disputes and farm receiverships. **William Neville** and "*impressive performer*" **Della Evans** (see p.72) (head of the unit) drew plaudits. "*Excellent, efficient*" **Alastair Morrison** (see p.75) focuses on sale and purchase issues and "*handy fighter*" **William Batstone** (see p.72) undertakes holdings disputes. "*Stylish*" **Miles Farren** (see p.73) makes up a team of nationally recognised names. In the last year the group has been working on restructuring the industry.

Wilsons (see firm details p.1185) An "*expert West Country firm with London professionalism*" is how this practice is perceived by interviewees. "*Excellent*" **Robert Swift** leads a team that has great expertise in the non-contentious side, with a client base that includes over 60 estates. Assisted by the respected **Peter Fitzgerald**, the group remains strong in tax planning and heritage law.

Clarke Willmott & Clarke (see firm details p.915) A firm endorsed as "*ahead of the game.*" Displaying expertise in planning and environmental law, judicial review and quota litigation. Leading partner, **Tim Russ** (see p.75) is noted by clients for having "*a speciality in agricultural litigation.*" The last year has seen instructions from various agricultural unions, and involvement in a large tenancy dispute in Dorset.

Stephens & Scown "*Fine traditional regional firm*" with a "*terrific client base.*" The practice acts for estates, working farmers and corporate clients.

AGRICULTURE • South West	Ptnrs	Assts
1 **Burges Salmon** Bristol	13	21
2 **Wilsons** Salisbury	6	8
3 **Clarke Willmott & Clarke** Taunton	2	4
Stephens & Scown Exeter	2	1
4 **Bevan Ashford** Bristol	3	2
Thring Townsend Bath	4	2
5 **Battens (with Poole & Co)** Yeovil	1	1
Bond Pearce Plymouth	1	3
Osborne Clarke Bristol	3	6
6 **Pardoes** Bridgwater	2	6
Porter Dodson Yeovil	2	n/a

LEADING INDIVIDUALS	
1 **BUXTON James** Burges Salmon	**DENSHAM Andrew** Burges Salmon
NEVILLE William Burges Salmon	**WILLIAMS Peter** Burges Salmon
2 **EVANS Della** Burges Salmon	**MORRISON Alastair** Burges Salmon
SWIFT Robert Wilsons	
3 **BATSTONE William** Burges Salmon	**CHEAL Jonathan** Thring Townsend
FARREN Miles Burges Salmon	**FITZGERALD Peter** Wilsons
RUSS Tim Clarke Willmott & Clarke	
4 **ADDY Alayne** Stephens & Scown	

This book is the product of 6,552 1/2-hour interviews. See p.7 for BMRB audit.
Within each band, firms are listed alphabetically. *See individuals' profiles p.71*

It specialises in tenancy, partnerships, share farming, pollution and planning advice, with an expertise in milk quotas. The client roll call includes Aggregate Industries and AMC. **Alayne Addy** joins our rankings this year, thanks to her recent work concerning foot and mouth disease.

Bevan Ashford (see firm details p.880) Large regional firm with an impressive client base and experience in partnership restructuring and contentious work including quota disputes, European court litigation and arbitrations. Tim Howells leads a "*highly approachable*" team.

Thring Townsend (see firm details p.1155) This recently merged firm retains its place on the NFU panel. The practice remains strong on both contentious and conveyancing work, with growing expertise in successions, diversification, public and private rights of way. "*Thoroughly able*" **Jonathan Cheal** leads a team which is described by commentators as "*geared up for action.*"

Battens (with Poole & Co) Strong regional presence acting for a number of estates, both freeholders and farmers. In the last year there has been a concentration on conveyances, diversification, successions and partnership arrangements. Robert Unwin leads a team which some feel has yet to realise its full potential.

Bond Pearce (see firm details p.888) Although the firm has secured a place on the NFU panel firm for Devon and Cornwall, it is felt to keep a low profile in this field. Andrew Tobey leads a team which specialises in employment and environmental disputes and diversification.

Osborne Clarke (see firm details p.1086) "*Cracking firm,*" according to competitors, with expertise in tenancy and environmental work, planning and diversification. Robert Drewett leads a team that has had experience in various land sales, purchases and reorganisations across the length of the country in the last year.

Pardoes Jeremy Orchard leads a team experienced in agricultural conveyancing and tenancy work. Representing large estates and small farmers, it has been particularly engaged with succession issues in the last year.

Porter Dodson (see firm details p.1099) Brian Maxwell leads this "*expanding*" local firm. Acting for individual farmers, the firm retains its strengths in property and tax planning.

WALES

AGRICULTURE • Wales	Ptnrs	Assts
1 **John Collins & Partners with Edward Harris & Son** Swansea	*	*
Margraves Llandrindod Wells	2	n/a
2 **Gabb & Co** Abergavenny	2	n/a
Morgan Cole Cardiff	*	*

LEADING INDIVIDUALS
1 **HARRIS Edward** John Collins & Partners with Edward Harris & Son
MARGRAVE-JONES Clive Margraves
2 **STEPHENS Jonathan** Jonathan Stephens & Co

This book is the product of 6,552 1/2-hour interviews. See p.7 for BMRB audit.
Within each band, firms are listed alphabetically. *See individuals' profiles p.71*
**See editorial entries for explanation of team sizes.*

John Collins & Partners with Edward Harris & Son (1 ptnr & 3 assts 25–35%) The recently merged practice has been elevated in our tables this year. Endorsed by competitors as "*strong players*" and instructed by clients in "*a number of high profile cases.*" Largely a contentious practice, it also has strengths in property and diversification. **Edward Harris** (see p.73) has "*an expertise in common land*" and recently took a case to the House Of Lords on rights of common.

Margraves A respected firm with strong interests in property and taxation. "*A definite presence in mid-Wales,*" according to industry sources, representing estates, large companies and working farmers. "*Leading light*" **Clive Margrave-Jones** heads a team that includes Professor Christopher Roberts.

Gabb & Co (see firm details p.967) Respected local firm displaying knowledge over "*a general range,*" which has experience in conveyancing, easements, overage, planning and quota work.

Morgan Cole (see firm details p.1074) (3 ptnrs & 3 assts part-time) NFU panel firm for Wales and Herefordshire. Phillip Howell-Richardson runs a team offering a range of services, from disputes and contentious work to advice on tax, planning and milk quotas.

Other Notable Practitioners **Jonathan Stephens** continues to hold his good reputation amongst peers for advice on non-contentious agricultural matters.

MIDLANDS

AGRICULTURE • Midlands	Ptnrs	Assts
1 Arnold Thomson Towcester	1	4
Wright Hassall Leamington Spa	1	2
2 Hewitson Becke + Shaw Northampton	2	2
Martineau Johnson Birmingham	2	2
3 Knight & Sons Newcastle-under-Lyme	2	3
Manby & Steward Wolverhampton	2	1
4 Gwynnes Wellington	2	1
Lanyon Bowdler Shrewsbury	1	1
Lodders Stratford-upon-Avon	1	2
Morton Fisher Worcester	6	n/a

LEADING INDIVIDUALS	
1 DAVIS Nigel Sole Practitioner	OGG Robin Wright Hassall
THOMSON Michael Arnold Thomson	
2 BARNETT Ian Hewitson Becke + Shaw	LODDER David Lodders
QUINN James Morton Fisher	
3 GWYNNE Michael Gwynnes	

This book is the product of 6,552 1/2-hour interviews. See p.7 for BMRB audit.
Within each band, firms are listed alphabetically. *See individuals' profiles p.71*

Arnold Thomson (see firm details p.65) "*Conscientious, industrious*" **Michael Thomson** (see p.76) leads this effective agricultural practice. Operating in a niche, with its client base almost exclusively consisting of owner-occupiers. Over the last year the firm has worked on partnership agreements, machine sharing and diversification. Enjoying a growing amount of tenancy work.

Wright Hassall (see firm details p.1190) Robust firm with "*a good depth of agricultural clients.*" Mainly acting for owner-occupiers, but also a number of agricultural and charitable institutions. Has expertise in transactional work and tax planning, and good knowledge of the Agricultural Holdings Act. **Robin Ogg** (see p.75) is typically praised by rivals as "*gentlemanly in dealings and highly respected for his knowledge.*" Clients include the Royal Agricultural Society.

Hewitson Becke + Shaw (see firm details p.994) Has a traditional reputation acting for large estates, for whom it provides taxation and property advice. It continues to broaden its client base to include smaller farmers, and has experience in tax planning and the establishment of ownership structures. **Ian Barnett** (see p.72) is according to market forces, an "*expert – he really knows what he is doing.*"

Martineau Johnson (see firm details p.1055) Has acted for 20 landed estates within the last year. The only firm in Birmingham with any presence in this work, Hugh Carslake's team offers advice on property, inheritance tax, employment and points of heritage law.

Knight & Sons (see firm details p.1025) Scoring a coup with its appointment to the NFU panel, the firm has, say interviewees, had some success with it. The work from this appointment has ranged from property and employment disputes to criminal matters. Bob Hoyle's team also acts for landed estates and tenants on commercial matters, with expertise on tax, strategic and succession planning. Further clients include Hepworth Minerals and Chemicals, and Josiah Wedgewood & Sons.

Manby & Steward (see firm details p.1050) A "*super firm with strong private client connections.*" It boasts a client roster leaning towards the landed estates, but with a large share of tenant farmers. Steve Corfield's team boasts across the board expertise, and has had a particularly busy year with diversification and successions.

Gwynnes Niche practice representing the landed estates and wealthier farmers. The main focus is property and tax planning, but the firm handles work from tenancy disputes to sporting and mineral rights. **Michael Gwynne** is new to the rankings this year on the back of strong local recommendation.

Lanyon Bowdler "*Thoroughly deserving their reputation,*" according to competitors, Andrew Evans' team has a strong focus on working farmers/owner-occupiers. Has expertise on milk quotas, tax planning, reconstructions and partnership disputes.

Lodders **David Lodder** (see p.74) remains "*one of the stars of the neighbourhood,*" a "*sensible, practical lawyer*" whose expertise is not doubted in the market. The team deals with the full range of agricultural law; within the last year it has handled a number of farm and farm company acquisitions.

Morton Fisher (see firm details p.1076) "*Cracking agricultural practice*" with a strong litigation slant and expertise on partnership disputes and arbitrations. Led by "*established name*" **James Quinn** (see p.75), the team acts for a number of large landowners in a range of non-contentious work.

Other Notable Practitioners Formerly with Roythornes, **Nigel Davis** (see p.72) has set up as a sole practitioner. Dealing with a number of partnership disputes and arbitrations, he continues to play an important role in the market.

EAST ANGLIA

Mills & Reeve (see firm details p.1069) The "*unsurpassed*" **William Barr** (see p.72) leads what is widely considered "*the strongest agricultural practice in East England.*" Acting for landowners, farm companies and institutions at the larger end of the market, it undertakes structural arrangements, successions and commercial work. The team is strengthened by **Michael Aubrey** (see p.71) ("*busy and clever*") and the "*smooth operator*" **Matthew Arrowsmith-Brown** (see p.71). Over the last year the firm has advised on the establishment of consortiums for the purchase of farmland.

Roythorne & Co Firmly entrenched within the Lincolnshire region, this large "*quality*" practice has clients ranging from 500 to 5,000 acres. A force in transactions, say rivals, the team has become increasingly involved in setting up joint ventures and machinery co-operatives. It also has expertise in business structuring and capital tax advice. The "*excellent*" **Graham Smith** (see p.75) heads the team, aided by **Alan Plummer** (see p.75) ("*certainly a key operator.*")

Barker Gotelee A practice with a strong European focus to its agricultural work, working closely with the European Commission and advising clients with regards to its policies. **Richard Barker** (see p.71) is recommended by clients as "*strong on Europe*" and benefits from the support of the "*highly knowledgeable*" **Geoff Whittaker** (see p.76). Maintains its high profile in agricultural and transportation fields, offering services from litigation to tax planning.

Birketts Acting for a national client base that includes landed estates to owner-occupiers, this firm deals with issues including acquisitions, tenancy and commons and milk quota advice. **Angela Sydenham** is judged by peers to be "*top dollar on access,*" while former Burges Salmon lawyer **James Harbottle** is appreciated by knowledgeable sources as "*excellent, he keeps his feet on the ground.*"

Taylor Vinters (see firm details p.1150) With a client roster that includes large estates, farms, food businesses and other institutions, peers value it as "*a good practice to deal with.*" It specialises in conveyancing, tenancy and tax advice, planning and environmental issues. The "*expert*" **Jeanette Dennis** (see p.72) and **Adrian Horwood-Smart** (see p.74) are the main prac-

	AGRICULTURE • East Anglia	Ptnrs	Assts
1	**Mills & Reeve** Norwich	8	8
	Roythorne & Co Spalding	6	4
2	**Barker Gotelee** Ipswich	2	5
	Birketts Ipswich	3	2
	Taylor Vinters Cambridge	5	3
3	**Eversheds** Norwich	2	2
	Hewitson Becke + Shaw Cambridge	3	2
4	**Ashton Graham** Bury St Edmunds, Ipswich	2	n/a
	Howes Percival Norwich	2	1
	Prettys Ipswich	3	3
5	**Wilkin Chapman** Louth	2	1

LEADING INDIVIDUALS

1	**BARR William** Mills & Reeve	**SMITH Graham** Roythorne & Co
2	**ARROWSMITH-BROWN Matthew** Mills & Reeve	
	BARKER Richard Barker Gotelee	**HEAL Jeremy** Howes Percival
	HORWOOD-SMART Adrian Taylor Vinters	**PLUMMER Alan** Roythorne & Co
3	**AUBREY Michael** Mills & Reeve	**DENNIS Jeanette** Taylor Vinters
	HARBOTTLE James Birketts	**POUND Toby** Prettys
	SYDENHAM Angela Birketts	**WHITTAKER Geoff** Barker Gotelee
	WYBAR David Ashton Graham	

This book is the product of 6,552 1/2-hour interviews. See p.7 for BMRB audit.

Within each band, firms are listed alphabetically. *See individuals' profiles p.71*

titioners in this busy team. Clients include the University of Cambridge and Jockey Club Estates.

Eversheds (see firm details p.952) Non-contentious practice with an interest in land and tenancies, and targeting a growing market in agri-business. Neil Sparrow's team handles a wide range of issues, from trusts and employment to milk quotas and diversification. Highlights of last year include a number of large deals covering property and mineral rights.

Hewitson Becke + Shaw (see firm details p.994) Robust firm with "*a good presence in the area.*" The team, including Denise Wilkinson, has seen an increase in sales and acquisitions over the last year. Also witnessed a rise in the number of diversifications and redevelopments. The firm represents large land owning charities alongside farmers and large estates.

Ashton Graham Led by the "*truly expert*" **David Wybar** (see p.76), the practice has had a lower profile of late. Its client base comprises larger farmers, estate owners and commercial owner-occupiers. The team specialises in tax and footpath work.

Howes Percival (see firm details p.1003) The "*talented*" **Jeremy Heal** (see p.73) is described as "*a good agricultural all rounder*" noted for his skills across the range of agricultural issues, from tenancies and trust work to mineral extraction. The firm boasts expertise in complex tax matters.

Prettys (see firm details p.1100) The NFU panel firm for the area is described by the market as "*impressive.*" The firm's profile is dominated by **Toby Pound** (see p.) who "*knows his stuff.*" Away from the NFU, it represents owner-occupiers and working farmers on a range of issues, from employment to diversification.

Wilkin Chapman "*A small firm, but expert,*" according to interviewees, it retains its North Lincolnshire foothold. Phillip Day's team acts for farms ranging from 100 to 5,000 acres, in both contentious and non-contentious matters.

NORTH WEST

	AGRICULTURE • North West	Ptnrs	Assts
1	**Cartmell Shepherd** Carlisle	1	2
2	**Oglethorpe Sturton & Gillibrand** Lancaster	1	2
	Walker Smith & Way Chester	2	1
3	**Birch Cullimore** Chester	1	1
	Hibbert Durrad Davies Nantwich	1	n/a
	Mason & Moore Dutton Chester	2	n/a
	Napthen Houghton Craven Preston	3	2

LEADING INDIVIDUALS

1	**CARTMELL Timothy** Cartmell Shepherd	
2	**COLLINS Peter** Walker Smith & Way	**GILLIBRAND Martin** Oglethorpe Sturton
3	**YOUNG David** Hibbert Durrad Davies	

This book is the product of 6,552 1/2-hour interviews. See p.7 for BMRB audit.

Within each band, firms are listed alphabetically. *See individuals' profiles p.71*

Cartmell Shepherd The most recognisable firm in the North West and carrying a strong reputation amongst clients and solicitors nationwide. Led by "*aggressive negotiator*" **Timothy Cartmell**, the team is experienced in conveyancing, quota and subsidy advice, tenancies and tax planning. The client roster includes English Nature and North West Water.

Oglethorpe Sturton & Gillibrand (see firm details p.1084) Rated practice which acts for owner/occupiers and landowners in a variety of agricultural issues, including milk and sheep quotas. It has a specialist interest in sporting and common land issues, rights of way and footpaths. Department head **Martin Gillibrand** (see p.73) is considered by peers to be "*enjoyable to deal with.*"

Walker Smith & Way Fronted by the respected **Peter Collins**, the firm is first choice for clients in Cheshire, acting for landowners and tenants advising on dairy farming matters, tenancies, diversification and business reorganisations. In the last year, it has had involvement in a contested land tribunal case.

Birch Cullimore "*Excellent firm*" with a predominantly landlord client base. David Mason's team represents large regional estates on such work as tenancy disputes, tax planning, diversification and conveyancing.

Hibbert Durrad Davies (see firm details p.995) A new firm to this year's rankings. Represents tenants and smaller owner-occupiers, offering advice on conveyancing, quotas and tax. According to market sources **David Young** is "*recommended as one of the biggest players in the country.*"

Mason & Moore Dutton Acting primarily for working farmers in the dairy sector. The team, led by Roy Lea, does work on conveyancing, tax planning, milk quotas and successions.

Napthen Houghton Craven (see firm details p.1079) Although the NFU panel firm for the region, the firm has a low profile in the market. Geoffrey Tomlinson's team has a client base that consists mainly of working farmers, and has expertise in retirement planning and partnership restructuring.

YORKSHIRE

AGRICULTURE • Yorkshire	Ptnrs	Assts
1 Rollits Hull	1	1
Wrigleys Leeds	*	*
2 Addleshaw Booth & Co Leeds	4	7
3 Andrew M Jackson & Co Hull	1	1
Grays York	2	n/a
Stamp Jackson and Procter Hull	*	*

LEADING INDIVIDUALS
1 STONE James Addleshaw Booth & Co
2 GITTINGS Simon Stamp Jackson and Procter

This book is the product of 6,552 1/2-hour interviews. See p.7 for BMRB audit.
Within each band, firms are listed alphabetically. *See individuals' profiles p.71*

Rollits (see firm details p.1110) Despite personnel changes over the last year, this firm is clearly still recognised in the market as "*the biggest player in the area.*" Neil Franklin's team acts for a number of large estates, as well as owner/occupiers, offering advice on property, tax and quotas. Conveyancing has provided the bulk of the work over the last year, and the firm has a flourishing contentious arm with particular focus on Europe.

Wrigleys (see firm details p.1191) (2 ptnrs 30%) This "*damn fine firm*" rises in the rankings, having drawn together private client expertise from around the region. Paul Nash's team has a client base that includes large estates and trusts, offering advice on successions and tenancy arrangements. Engaged in diversification and mineral rights, it is judged by peers "*a class outfit on tax.*"

Addleshaw Booth & Co (see firm details p.853) A dominant firm in the region, it continues its interest in agriculture. Acting for private clients and large estate owners, the bulk of the firm's instructions concern land holdings, undertaking issues such as succession, contract agreements and exploitation. **James Stone** (see p.76) remains well respected by rivals in the field.

Andrew M Jackson & Co (see firm details p.860) "*Long-standing*" non-contentious practice, led by Peter Rathbone, which is perceived by market sources to be insulated in the East Yorkshire area. Typical work includes purchase and disposal of land, tax and succession planning and tenancy work.

Grays (see firm details p.978) A robust if smaller team, a favourite for non-contentious landlord issues. Lyn Rickaston's team offers advice on conveyancing and tenancy work to quota matters. The firm has seen a recent rise in diversifications.

Stamp Jackson and Procter (3 ptnrs & 3 assts 30%) Has created a strong foothold in the market. **Simon Gittings** (see p.73) is praised by clients for "*dealing with matters practically and appropriately,*" while the firm runs the gambit of agricultural services for its clients.

NORTH EAST

AGRICULTURE • North East	Ptnrs	Assts
1 Dickinson Dees Newcastle upon Tyne	4	4
2 Ward Hadaway Newcastle upon Tyne	4	5
3 Latimer Hinks Darlington	3	n/a
4 Jacksons Stockton on Tees	4	2

LEADING INDIVIDUALS	
1 HARGREAVE Hume Dickinson Dees	HEWITT Christopher Ward Hadaway
2 KIRKUP Simon Dickinson Dees	

This book is the product of 6,552 1/2-hour interviews. See p.7 for BMRB audit.
Within each band, firms are listed alphabetically. *See individuals' profiles p.71*

Dickinson Dees (see firm details p.941) "*A massive, impressive team,*" by far the most recognised name in the region. **Simon Kirkup** (see p.74) now heads up the department and is judged by the market to do "*a great job.*" "*Legendary*" **Hume Hargreave** (see p.73) is considered to have set the standards for excellence in this area and continues to lend his expertise to the practice. Scoring well with its work in land transfers and partnership restructuring, the firm elicited recommendation in the fields of planning, quota and European issues. It draws warm endorsement for its tax advice. Recently involved in transfers of agricultural and sporting estates of around 35,000 acres.

Ward Hadaway (see firm details p.1173) This "*highly expert*" firm has a strong client base, which includes landed estates, farmers, public bodies and agri-businesses, for whom the practice provides a full range of agricultural services. "*Efficient*" **Christopher Hewitt** (see p.74) heads the team.

Latimer Hinks Anne Elliot leads the agricultural team, which is seen by peers as "*busy and always sound in its advice.*" Primarily advising tenant farms on a range of agricultural issues, the team has also been occupied with inheritance tax and trust issues.

Jacksons (see firm details p.1010) Since picking up the NFU contract, the firm has successfully developed a respected reputation in the market. "*Well organised*" and offering "*hard nosed advice,*" Phil Corbett's team mainly acts for smaller farmers on conveyancing, landlord and tenant and commercial disputes.

SCOTLAND

Anderson Strathern WS (see firm details p.859) "*The greatest expertise, always honourable deal-doers.*" **Alasdair Fox** (see p.73) heads up this "*incredibly fine*" agricultural team, and is himself regarded by clients and competitors as "*the main guy in Scotland.*" Experienced in transactional work, the practice also holds expertise in tax planning and landlord and tenant work. The "*first class*" **James Drysdale** is a "*bright operator,*" developing his profile. Clients include the Crown Estate, National Trust for Scotland and Tilhill Economic Forestry.

Brodies WS (see firm details p.896) Has successfully targeted offshore, mineral and forestry companies, farmers and landowners with interests across Scotland. Instructions in the area of land conveyancing flow as steadily as ever, but the firm has also been busy offering advise on foot and mouth and other pressing issues. **Hew Dalrymple** (see p.72) is applauded by the market as "*able to immediately start up a good working relationship.*" He is assisted by "*fantastic lawyer*" **David Houldsworth** (see p.74).

Turcan Connell (see firm details p.1164) This "*colossus*" of a firm represents a large number of landowners diversifying from its robust private client base. "*Wise*" **Malcolm Strang Steel** (see p.76) "*stands out from the crowd;*" he is assisted by "*extremely able*" **John Robertson** (see p.75) and **Robert Turcan** (see p.76), who is recognised by competitors as "*on the ball for tax.*" The practice has seen a rise in contentious matters in the last year, and recently completed a substantial purchase.

AGRICULTURE • Scotland	Ptnrs	Assts
1 **Anderson Strathern WS** Edinburgh	8	5
Brodies WS Edinburgh	8	14
Turcan Connell Edinburgh	5	10
2 **Thorntons WS** Dundee	5	2
3 **Burnett & Reid** Aberdeen	2	1
Gillespie Macandrew WS Edinburgh	3	2
Tods Murray WS Edinburgh	3	4
Turnbull, Simson & Sturrock WS Jedburgh	1	n/a
4 **Lindsays WS** Edinburgh	1	1
McLean & Stewart Dunblane	3	n/a
Murray Beith Murray WS Edinburgh	1	2
Paull & Williamsons Aberdeen	2	1

LEADING INDIVIDUALS	
1 **FOX Alasdair** Anderson Strathern WS	**RENNIE Donald** Donald Rennie WS
STRANG STEEL Malcolm Turcan Connell	
2 **DALRYMPLE Hew** Brodies WS	**ROBERTSON Jonathan** Turcan Connell
SHEARER Roy Lindsays WS	**STURROCK David** Turnbull, Simson & Sturrock
3 **BLAIR Michael** Thorntons WS	**DRYSDALE James** Anderson Strathern WS
HOULDSWORTH David Brodies WS	**TURCAN Robert** Turcan Connell
4 **ANDERSON Alastair** Anderson Beaton Lamond	

This book is the product of 6,552 1/2-hour interviews. See p.7 for BMRB audit.
Within each band, firms are listed alphabetically. *See individuals' profiles p.71*

Thorntons WS Major players in the Angus region, representing estates, working farmers and several forestry companies, and offering a "*quality*" service. Acted in a number of large purchases in the last year, as well as arbitration matters. Lead partner **Mike Blair** is described by some sources as "*the best agricultural lawyer in Scotland.*"

Burnett & Reid Strong in the Aberdeen market, acting for over 20 landed estates. Main areas of work include acquisitions and sales, quota work and the establishment of partnerships. The team, including John Sullivan, has a speciality in tax planning.

Gillespie Macandrew WS (see firm details p.972) Timothy Miles' team represents a range of agricultural clients, from large estates and farming plcs to smallholders. Displays expertise in tenancy disputes, quotas, sporting estates and crofting law. Clients include Moray Estates Development, Alcan Highland Estates and Lands Improvement Holdings.

Tods Murray WS (see firm details p.1157) This "*go ahead*" firm is seen by the market to have strengthened its position since it took over the forestry work. Its client roster includes 220 landowner clients, public bodies, charities and institutions, new and established landowners on a range of agricultural issues. In 2000 John Fulton's team acted on land transactions valued at £35 million.

Turnbull, Simson & Sturrock WS (see firm details p.1164) The "*experienced*" **David Sturrock** (see p.76) leads this department considered by peers an "*established force in the highlands.*" Strong local firm dealing with conveyancing, quotas, partnership arrangements and landlord and tenant work for a wide range of agricultural clients.

Lindsays WS (see firm details p.1041) "*Absolutely first class*" senior partner **Roy Shearer** (see p.75) is the key player at this traditionally strong firm. Acting for landed estates, the team does a full range of estate work, including tax planning, conveyancing, landlord/tenant disputes, sporting and mineral rights. It is felt to have specialist knowledge of the crofting market.

McLean & Stewart "*Has the local market stitched up,*" and is thought by interviewees to offer "*specialist expertise.*" Enjoys a strong reputation with its agricultural base among working farmers. James McIldowie's team handles all aspects of agricultural law, with noted strength in land conveyancing and tenancy work.

Murray Beith Murray WS (see firm details p.1078) "*Good traditional practice*" acting for over 100 landowners throughout Scotland. Instructions are primarily non-contentious and the team is particularly regarded for tax and investment expertise. Hugh Younger's team has skills in transactions involving sporting estates.

Paull & Williamsons (see firm details p.1091) A highly commercial "*knowledgeable*" operation acting for landed families, commercial farmers and a number of agri-businesses. Clive Phillips's team has seen an increase in activity in landlord/tenant work, successions, partnerships arrangements and tax advice.

Other Notable Practitioners **Donald Rennie** (see p.75) holds onto his place as the highest profile sole practitioner and "*a great asset to all agricultural practitioners in Scotland.*" **Alastair Anderson** of **Anderson Beaton Lamond** (formerly with Miller Hendry) carries a strong reputation across the industry.

LEADERS IN AGRICULTURE

ADDY, Alayne
Stephens & Scown, Exeter (01392) 210700

ANDERSON, Alastair
Anderson Beaton Lamond, Perth (01738) 639 999

ARROWSMITH-BROWN, Matthew R.
Mills & Reeve, Norwich (01603) 693 215
matthew.arrowsmith-brown@mills-reeve.com
Specialisation: Advising farming businesses and families. Examples of particular issues covered are BTs for diversification; cooperative arrangemens; irrigation schemes; family business disputes.
Prof. Memberships: Law Society; Agricultural Law Association; Royal Agricultural Society of England; Royal Norfolk Agricultural Association; Farmers' Club.
Career: Clifton College; University of York; articles and 2.5 years post qualification with *Slaughter and May* 1974-79; *Mills & Reeve* 1979 to date; partner since 1981.
Personal: Brought up on Dartmoor farm; married; two daughters (20 and 22); Driving fast cars.

AUBREY, Michael J.
Mills & Reeve, Cambridge (01223) 222 397
michael.aubrey@mills-reeve.com
Specialisation: Partner in Agriculture Department. Practice covers all areas of agricultural property work and in particular corporate and institutional agriculture. Main areas of work include acquisition and disposal of agricultural and development land and estates, the imposition of reserving future development value, agricultural tenancies, minerals, share farming, contract farming and partnerships.
Prof. Memberships: Royal Forestry Society; Law Society; Agricultural Law Association.
Career: BSc (Hons) in Agricultural Economics from University of Newcastle Upon Tyne. Joined *Mills & Reeve* in 1989 and became a partner in 1997.
Personal: Leisure interests include rugby, cricket and golf.

BARKER, Richard
Barker Gotelee, Ipswich (01473) 611211
Specialisation: Acting for landowners, farmers and the food industry throughout the UK. Head of Agricultural team dealing with all aspects of agricultural law both UK and EC Community legislation. His particular expertise is EC legislation and lobbying the EC Institutions on matters including state aids, competition, food quality standards and food health issues. Has an office in Brussels. Council member Suffolk Agricultural Association. Chairman Suffolk Professional European Committee. CLA branch member. Member of the EU Team Europe Panel of specialist speakers. Speaks nationally at seminars on agricultural and EU matters and writes regularly for specialist publications and newspapers and broadcasts on agricultural and EU matters.
Prof. Memberships: Qualified 1969. Now Senior Partner of *Barker Gotelee, Solicitors* and Managing Director of Stanyer Consulting Limited dealing with the non-legal aspects of lobbying and EU and UK policy.

LEADERS IN AGRICULTURE

BARNETT, Ian
Hewitson Becke + Shaw, Northampton (01604) 233233
ianbarnett@hewitsons.com
Specialisation: Senior Partner. Agricultural Property Division. Main area of practice is agriculture. Also deals with commercial property and charities.
Prof. Memberships: Northants Committee CLA.
Career: Qualified in 1965. Joined *Hewitson Becke + Shaw* in 1967, becoming a Partner in 1968 and Senior Partner in 1994.
Personal: Born in 1940. Educated at Repton School and Oxford University 1958-61 (MA). Undersheriff of Northamptonshire since 1973. Leisure interests include field sports, antiques, food and wine. Lives in East Haddon.

BARR, William D.W.
Mills & Reeve, Cambridge (01223) 222 480
william.barr@mills-reeve.com
Specialisation: Partner in Agriculture Department. Work covers farm tenancies and partnerships, share farming, quotas and farm taxation. Most recently he has been involved in food chain issues and reviewing the structures of farm businesses and co-operatives. Co-author of 'Farm Tenancies'. Lectures frequently and contributes the share farming section to 'Agricultural Law Tax & Finance' and agricultural articles to Solicitors' Journal.
Prof. Memberships: Law Society, Agricultural Law Association, USA Agricultural Law Association.

BATSTONE, William
Burges Salmon, Bristol (0117) 902 2716
william.batstone@burges-salmon.com
Specialisation: Acting for landowners and farmers he practises mainly in contentious agricultural holdings work. He undertakes advisory work and regularly appears as advocate before the Courts and Agricultural Land Tribunals, in particular presenting and responding to applications for succession, and Arbitrators, in particular dealing with rent review and notice to quit arbitrations. He also heads up the firm's growing bloodstock practice. He is a regular contributor to the Lawyer's Remembrancer and is a consultant to the RICS/CAAV joint 2000 Guidance Notes on Rent Review under the Agricultural Holdings Act 1986. He regularly addresses RICS and local Law Society meetings on agricultural topics.
Prof. Memberships: Law Society, Solicitors Association of Higher Court Advocates, Agricultural Law Association.
Career: University of York 1976-79, Philosophy. Called to the Bar in 1982, joined *Burges Salmon* and re-qualified as a solicitor in 1994, granted rights of audience in the Higher Courts in 1994 and became a partner in 1996.

BLAIR, J. Michael G.
Thorntons WS, Forfar (01307) 466886

BUXTON, James
Burges Salmon, Bristol (0117) 902 2758
james.buxton@burges-salmon.com
Specialisation: All aspects of the law relating to agricultural holdings including disputes relating to security of tenure, succession cases, rent reviews and end of tenancy compensation claims together with all aspects of milk and other commodity quotas.
Prof. Memberships: Agricultural Law Association, Law Society, Solicitors' Association of Higher Court Advocates.
Career: Called to the Bar in 1971, joined *Burges Salmon* in 1982 and became a partner in 1984. Granted rights of audience in the Higher Courts in 1997. Contributor to Halsbury's Laws of England (Agriculture Volume) and Butterworth's Encyclopaedia of Forms and Precedents.
Personal: Born 1948, read law and economics at Trinity College, Cambridge.

CARTMELL, Timothy H.
Cartmell Shepherd, Carlisle (01228) 516666

CHEAL, Jonathan
Thring Townsend, Bath (01225) 340 000

COLLINS, Peter
Walker Smith & Way, Chester (01244) 357 400

DALRYMPLE, Hew
Brodies WS, Edinburgh (0131) 228 3777
hew.dalrymple@brodies.co.uk
Specialisation: He specialises in all aspects of Rural Property Law, Country Estate work and Private Client practice. He has a special interest in farming, asset protection, and capital taxation and minerals and acts for a number of prominent landowners and their families and other high net worth individuals and commercial concerns with rural interests.
Prof. Memberships: Society of Her Majesty's Writers to the Signet.
Career: Edinburgh Academy; Edinburgh University; *Brodies WS* from 1975 to date.
Personal: Leisure interests include shooting, fishing, painting and sketching and travel.

DAVIS, Nigel R.
Nigel Davis – Sole Practitioner, Belper (01335) 372889
nigeldavis@talk21.com
Specialisation: Agricultural law. Particularly landlord and tenant disputes, arbitration and tribunal hearings, partnerships and EU interpretation – milk quota and livestock regimes. Accredited mediator; contributor to Legal Network Television; co-author of Agricultural Precedents Handbook (Jordans 2001) and numerous articles on agricultural law; considerable experience of lecturing and seminar presentations. Advisory work in Hungary (1993), consultancy on legal practice management in Lithuania via BESO (1996-1998), current Chairman of Agricultural Law Association.
Career: Qualified 1975. Set up own niche agricultural practice in October 2000.
Personal: Born 1949.

DENNIS, Jeanette
Taylor Vinters, Cambridge (01223) 423444
jad@taylorvinters.com
Specialisation: Partner in agriculture department. Principal area of practice is agriculture. Work includes sales and purchases of farms and land, tenancies (including Agricultural Holdings Act 1986, Agricultural Tenancies Act 1995 and short term business leases), crop loss claims and financial arrangements for farmers.
Prof. Memberships: Cambridge Young Solicitors, Cambridge Law Society. Agricultural Law Association, Committee member of the Game Conservancy Trust.
Career: Joined *Taylor Vinters* in 1988 and qualified in 1990. Has specialised in agricultural law since qualification. National AgriLaw Lecturer and BBC Radio contributor.
Personal: Graduated from Hull University in 1987(LL.B).

DENSHAM CBE, Andrew
Burges Salmon, Bristol (0117) 939 2000
andrew.densham@burges-salmon.com
Specialisation: An established expert in his practice area he has been involved in a substantial proportion of the leading agricultural holdings cases. Clients range from large landowners to substantial farming clients. A regular speaker all over the country for the CAAV, RICS and others.
Prof. Memberships: Law Society, Agricultural Law Association, Honorary Fellow of the CAAV.
Career: Articled with *Stanley Wasbrough* in Bristol 1962-65, joined *Burges Salmon* in 1969 and became a partner in 1970, senior partner 1992-98. Crown Court Assistant Recorder 1982-90.
Publications: Joint author of Scammell & Densham's 'Law of Agricultural Holdings' 8th edition (current) plus 6th and 7th editions. Contributor to Halsbury's Encyclopaedia of Forms and Precedents (title 'Agriculture') and principal contributor to the 5th (current) edition 1968 and1993 re-issue. Contributory editor to 'Agricultural Holdings' Halsbury's Laws of England 4th edition.
Personal: University of Bristol 1958-62. Freeman of the City of Bristol, Past President Antient Society of St Stephen's Ringers, member of the Society of Merchant Venturers. Leisure pursuits include skiing, golf and walking.

DRYSDALE, James
Anderson Strathern WS, Edinburgh (0131) 220 2345

ELLIOTT, Penelope
Withers, London (020) 7597 6000
penelope.elliott@withers.co.uk
Specialisation: Head of Withers' Landed Estate Group. Partner specialising in buying and selling of agricultural land and estates; advice on landlord and tenant issues; farming partnership; share farming and contract farming; agricultural insolvency; capital taxation; heritage property.
Prof. Memberships: Agricultural Law Association; Country Landowners Association (Cambridge and Bedfordshire branch committee); Legal and Parliamentary Committee.
Career: Trained at *Taylors*, Newmarket; qualified in 1985; partner at *Mills & Reeves* 1988-1998. Partner *Withers* 1998. Directorships – Fitzwilliam Museum Trust; Cambridge Festival Theatre Trust. Educated at Girton College, Cambridge.

EVANS, Della
Burges Salmon, Bristol (0117) 902 2781
della.evans@burges-salmon.com
Specialisation: Agriculture, primarily agricultural business advice; farming partnerships – advice and disputes; agricultural landlord and tenant – advice and disputes.
Prof. Memberships: Law Society, Agricultural Law Association.
Career: Qualified at *Burges Salmon* in 1991 and became a partner in 1995. Author of Sweet & Maxwell's 'Legislation Handbook on the Agricultural Tenancies Act 1995' and a contributor to Butterworths Encyclopaedia of Forms and Precedents on Agriculture. Also co-author of Scammell & Densham's 'Law of Agricultural Holdings'.
Personal: University of West of England and LLM at University of Bristol.

FARREN, Miles
Burges Salmon, Bristol (0117) 939 2000
Specialisation: Agricultural law particularly contentious landlord and tenant matters; claims for possession of land; milk and other agri-commodity quotas; tax trusts, wills and estate planning; contentious probate and inheritance claims; partnership creation and dissolution. Speaker at lectures and seminars on agricultural law.
Career: Former NFU Local Secretary in Shropshire; strong links with NFU. LLB (Hons) part time Staffordshire University; qualified 1994.
Personal: Shropshire born and bred; articled at *Lanyon Bowdler* in Shrewsbury. Born 12/1/56. Member of the Agricultural Law Association.

FELLINGHAM, Michael
Penningtons, Godalming (01483) 791800
fellinghammb@penningtons.co.uk
Specialisation: Tax planning strategies for rural businesses. Preserving the taxation benefits of farmers after diversification of farming businesses.
Prof. Memberships: STEP.
Career: Lecturer, College of Law, Guildford. Partner of *Penningtons*, formerly head of private client department, now finance partner.
Personal: St Catharine's College, Cambridge in mathematics and law. Married with one daughter. Golf, bridge.

FINDLEY, Christopher
Bircham Dyson Bell, London (020) 7222 8044
christopher.findley@bd-law.co.uk
Specialisation: All aspects of law including Agricultural Holdings and Arbitrations and Farm Business Tenancy legislation, advising Agricultural Estates on land and tax issues. Town & Country planning, experience includes Options and Sales of farm land and buildings for development, representation at Planning Appeals, Local Plan Inquiries and Judicial Review proceedings. Milk Quota and subsidy law CAP Reform. Extensive experience in creation and dissolution of Farming Partnerships and Companies. Advising on Mineral Extraction and Waste Disposal sites.
Prof. Memberships: Country Landowners Association (Oxfordshire Committee) and Legal & Parliamentary Sub-Committee member, Agricultural Law Association (Committee), National Farmers Union, Tenant Farmers Association.
Career: Qualified in 1979 Head of Agricultural Law Department at *Thomas Mallam* Oxford 1983-93. Joined *Cole & Cole* as Partner and Head of Agricultural Law Department 1994. Joined *Bircham Dyson Bell* as a partner in 2001.

FITZGERALD, Peter
Wilsons, Salisbury (01722) 412412

FOX, Alasdair
Anderson Strathern WS, Edinburgh
(0131) 220 2345
Specialisation: Head of Rural Department and Land Ventures Unit with over 30 years' experience of all aspects of rural property law. Particular expertise in the area of agricultural landlord and tenant law and agricultural arbitrations (acting principally for arbiters but also for parties). Practice also covers advice to major estate proprietors, purchase and sale of rural properties and land ventures including Diversification Agreements, opencast mining options and licences.
Prof. Memberships: Society of Writers to H.M. Signet; Law Society of Scotland's Rural Affairs Committee, Agricultural Law Association. Member of Scottish Office Consultative Panel on Land Reform (landlord and tenant).
Career: Qualified in 1969. Partner at *Anderson Strathern WS* since 1972. Accredited by the Law Society of Scotland as a specialist in agricultural law 1993. Renewed 1998.
Personal: Educated at Lime House School, Carlisle 1954-59, Fettes College, Edinburgh 1959-64 and at the University of Edinburgh 1964-67. Leisure pursuits include sailing, skiing, shooting and fishing. Born 1st January 1946. Lives in Edinburgh.

FURBER, James
Farrer & Co, London (020) 7242 2022
wjf@farrer.co.uk
Specialisation: Agricultural estates, property and institutional investment and most other aspects of property law. Solicitor to the Duchy of Cornwall. Partner in and head of estates and private property team.
Prof. Memberships: Law Society, Holborn Law Society (President 1996-97).
Career: Joined *Farrer & Co* in 1976. Qualified in 1979. Became an associate in 1981 and a partner in 1985.
Publications: 'Encyclopaedia of Forms & Precedents, Volume 36, Sale of Land – Trusts for Sale and Requisitions on Title.' Contributor to Television Education Network 1991-96.
Personal: Born 1 September 1954. Attended Westminster School and Gonville & Caius College, Cambridge. Married with three children. Lives in Blackheath. Leisure interests include golf.

GILLIBRAND, R. Martin
Oglethorpe Sturton & Gillibrand, Lancaster
(01524) 67171
Specialisation: Partner in Agriculture Department. Has over 25 years' experience in general agricultural work, including agricultural tax planning and conveyancing, quotas, and law relating to common land. Also handles tax, probate and industrial conveyancing. Clerk to the General Tax Commissioners. Has handled a number of Commons Enquiries and general upland negotiations. Has addressed numerous Moorland seminars.
Prof. Memberships: Agriculture Law Association, Secretary of Moorland Association.
Career: Qualified in 1972. Joined *Oglethorpe Sturton & Gillibrand* in 1972, becoming a Partner in 1973.
Personal: Born 9th October 1946. Attended Shrewsbury School 1960-65 and Pembroke College, Cambridge 1965-68. Leisure interests include gardening and shooting. Lives in Tatham, near Lancaster.

GITTINGS, Simon
Stamp Jackson and Procter, Hull (01482) 324591
srg@sjplaw.co.uk
Specialisation: Conservation and environmental issues (adviser to English Nature). Land management and development.

GWYNNE, Michael
Gwynnes, Wellington (01952) 641651

HARBOTTLE, James
Birketts, Ipswich (01473) 232300

HARGREAVE, R Hume M
Dickinson Dees, Newcastle upon Tyne
(0191) 279 9234
Specialisation: Partner in Agriculture Group. Main area of practice agriculture, encompassing all aspects of land ownership and management, partnerships, agricultural tenancies and European Law. Speaks frequently at RICS/ CAAV conferences and seminars; writes regularly for the press.
Prof. Memberships: Agricultural Law Association.
Career: Qualified in 1971. Partner in *Dickinson Dees* since 1974.
Personal: Born 24th September 1940. Shrewsbury School 1954-59, Merton College, Oxford 1959-63.

HARRIS, Edward
John Collins & Partners with Edward Harris & Son, Swansea (01792) 773773
Specialisation: Senior Partner specialising in the Law of Commons, the Manorial System and Lordship of Manors and appurtenant rights and interests, also agricultural law and tenancies. Other areas of law include rights of way, footpaths and other easements, copyholds, mineral rights, together with countryside law, town and country planning and other areas of agricultural law. Acted in the reported cases of 'Lewis and Others v Mid Glamorgan County Council' (1995) (House of Lords) 1ALL ER 760 and 'Re: Merthyr Mawr Common' (1989) 3 ALL ER 451 and 'Hancock v Brecon Water' etc. plus Commons Commissioners hearings etc. Acts for various Commoners Associations and Lords of the Manors. Appointed by the Countryside Commission to be Welsh Representative on the Common Land Forum. Co-author of Common Land Forum Report 1985. On Department of Environment list of Consultees in respect of Common Land legislation.
Prof. Memberships: Law Society, Agricultural Law Association, Country Land-Owners Association (Legal & Parliamentary Sub-Committee).
Career: Qualified in 1964 (Hons.). Partner at *Edward Harris & Son* since 1965. Senior Partner since 1988. Merged with *John Collins & Partners* in 2001.
Personal: Born 2nd April, 1941. Educated at St. Edwards, Oxford 1954-59. Lives in Swansea.

HEAL, Jeremy
Howes Percival, Norwich (01603) 762103
jpwh@howes-percival.co.uk
Specialisation: Partner, head of estates division. Acts for landowners and others in all areas of agricultural law, tax and land transactions, including agricultural tenancies and contracting agreements, minerals, farming partnerships, acquisition and disposal of farms and estates, town and country planning, landowners' consortia and joint ventures. Specialises in capital tax planning for landowners, and lectures regularly on inheritance tax and trusts, valuation and other tax-related topics. Work also includes charity law; and is a trustee of a substantial grant-making charity. Author of various articles in *Farmers Weekly*, *Taxation*, *Personal Tax Planning Review* and other periodicals.
Prof. Memberships: Agricultural Law Association; Chartered Institute of Arbitrators; Society of Trust and Estate Practitioners; Law Society; Country Landowners Association; Royal Norfolk Agricultural Association.
Personal: Born 1942. Educated Marlborough College and Queen's College, Cambridge. MA, LLM (Cantab), ACIArb, TEP.

LEADERS IN AGRICULTURE

HEWITT, Christopher
Ward Hadaway, Newcastle upon Tyne
(0191) 204 4000
Specialisation: Head of Countryside Law Group, specialising in agricultural holdings, quotas, partnerships, business and property law, land use, minerals and planning. Wide ranging cases for farmers, landowners and rural institutions. Spoken at CLA, RICS, CAAV and many other conferences on agricultural law. Regular contributor to local press.
Prof. Memberships: Law Society, Country Land and Business Association, Agricultural Law Association.
Career: Qualified in 1971, Partner in 1987 upon joining *Ward Hadaway*.
Personal: Born 16th September 1947. Attended Sedbergh School and the University of Newcastle upon Tyne.

HORNBY, John
Macfarlanes, London (020) 7831 9222
Specialisation: Partner in Property Department. Commercial work covering the leisure industry, agricultural law, housing and residential work. Acts for investors, private estate landlords and working farmers. Has acted on a significant number of transactions involving hotels, golf courses, caravan sites and other rural business ventures. Recent and current work includes the Millennium Commission funded £80 million development – The Renaissance of Portsmouth Harbour, a substantial flow of sales and purchases of prime landed estates and farms and advising a national firm of land agents on agricultural and housing landlord and tenant matters. Author of 'Leasehold Enfranchisement- The New Proposals Put in Context' (1993).
Prof. Memberships: Law Society.
Career: Qualified in 1980 while with *Macfarlanes*. Became a Partner in 1987.

HORNER, Douglas
Brachers, Maidstone (01622) 690691

HORWOOD-SMART, Adrian
Taylor Vinters, Cambridge (01223) 423444
ahs@taylorvinters.com
Specialisation: Partner in agriculture department. Principal area of practice is agriculture. Work includes landlord and tenant, contracting and management agreements, other joint farming operations, partnership arrangements, quota and set-aside transactions and the land law aspects of landed estates and farms. Regularly lectures at seminars and conferences.
Prof. Memberships: Law Society, Agricultural Law Association, Notaries Society.
Career: Qualified in 1977. At *Waltons & Morse* 1977-79 before joining *Taylor Vinters*. Became a partner in 1983.

HOULDSWORTH, David
Brodies WS, Edinburgh (0131) 228 3777
david.houldsworth@brodies.co.uk
Specialisation: David Houldsworth is a Private Client Department Partner specialising in agricultural and related matters, including landlord/tenant issues, farming contracts, acquisition of farms and estates, nature conservation and all other matters relating to rural businesses; he acts for a number of large estates and advises on every aspect of their business affairs; David has overall responsibility for the clients' tax and succession planning.
Prof. Memberships: Director: North Atlantic Salmon Fund (UK) Limited; Member of the Cairngorm Recreation Trust; Member Scottish Landowners Federation Law & Parliamentary Committee.
Personal: David received an LLB from the University of Edinburgh in 1974 and qualified in 1977. He has been a Partner with *Brodies* since 1981.He is married with one daughter and his interests include family farming and forestry businesses and the future of the countryside. When time allows he plays golf at Muirfield and Nairn, he fishes and shoots throughout Scotland; he is an avid gardener and enjoys contemporary art.

JACKSON, Andrew
Macfarlanes, London (020) 7831 9222
Specialisation: Planning and environmental law for a range of institutional and health authority clients, public and private companies and landed estates. Advice ranges from general planning strategy to drafting and negotiating highway and planning agreements as well as public inquiry work. Planning advice during the last year has been given to a Port Operator to protect its position in relation to the Isle of Wight Development Plan and a proposal to construct a Light Rapid Transport System under Portsmouth Harbour and to a major hotel operator in connection with planning issues arising in relation to a number of Central London hotel sites. A long running public planning inquiry was completed for the Health Authority on whether a substantial North London hospital site could be developed for housing, and work continues on whether an edge of centre site in Salisbury can be further developed for housing, retail and business use. Work is also beginning on securing a planning contract for an international client on a substantial site near High Wycombe through the Wycombe Local Plan Review process.
Prof. Memberships: Member of the Law Society Planning Panel. Member of the Planning and Environmental Law Sub-committee of the City of London Solicitors Company.
Career: Trinity College, Oxford. MA in Politics Philosophy and Economics. *Macfarlanes* 1975 to present.
Personal: Sport and family. Married with 2 children.

JESSEL, Christopher
Farrer & Co, London (020) 7242 2022
Specialisation: Partner in estates and private property team. Main area of practice covers rural estates, agriculture and manors. Acts on farms, common land and rural estate work generally including development sales with trust and personal advice. Also covers charity and constitutional work, establishing and advising charities on parliamentary and administrative law. Author of 'The Law of the Manor 1998, Farms and Estates – A Conveyancing Handbook', 1999, 'Development Land Overage and Clawback' (2001) and numerous articles in professional and investment magazines. Lectures extensively in London and elsewhere.
Prof. Memberships: Law Society.
Career: Joined *Farrer & Co* in 1967. Qualified in 1970. Became a partner in 1979.
Personal: Born 16 March 1945. Attended Bryanston School 1958-63, Balliol College, Oxford 1964-67. Leisure interests include archaeology. Lives in Guildford.

KEDDIE, Joanne
Dawson & Co, London (020) 7421 4800

KIRKUP, Simon
Dickinson Dees, Newcastle upon Tyne
(0191) 279 9374
Specialisation: Handles all aspects of agricultural law. Particular expertise in landlord and tenant issues, quotas and livestock premiums, agricultural land tribunal matters, arbitrations, farming partnerships and farm sales and purchases. Regularly lectures at seminars and conferences.
Prof. Memberships: Agricultural Law Association.
Career: Attended Sedbergh School 1979-84 and Exeter University 1985-88. Joined *Dickinson Dees* in 1990 and qualified in 1992. Is a partner in and head of the firm's agriculture group.
Personal: Born 31 August 1966. Leisure interests including fishing, shooting and golf.

KNIGHT, Matthew
Knights, Tunbridge Wells (01892) 537311
knights@atlas.co.uk
See under Administrative & Public Law, p.59

KYRKE, Richard
Thomas Eggar Church Adams, Horsham
(01403) 214500
richard.kyrke@teca.co.uk
Specialisation: Partner and head of agricultural law unit. Handles all aspects of agricultural law, particularly landlord and tenant issues, and advises on commercial property matters, including sales and purchases.
Prof. Memberships: Agricultural Law Association, CLA, NFU.
Career: 1951. Educated Marlborough College. Qualified 1976. Partner in *Thomas Eggar Church Adams* since 1979.

LANE, Andrew
Withers, London (020) 7597 6000
andrew.lane@withers.co.uk
Specialisation: Partner in Property Department. Practice covers all types of agricultural property work including agricultural holdings law, estate management and sales and acquisitions of farms and estates. Also advises on tax implications of property transactions; particularly Capital Gains Tax and VAT. Clients range from private individuals through family trusts and institutions to major plcs.
Prof. Memberships: Agricultural Law Association, Royal Agricultural Society of England.
Career: Was a full-time farmer between 1978 and 1987. Joined *Withers* in 1987 qualifying in 1992 and becoming a partner in 1994.
Personal: Born 22nd January 1957. Educated Malvern College 1970-74 Christ's College Cambridge 1975-78. Lives near Salisbury, Wiltshire.

LODDER, David
Lodders, Stratford-upon-Avon (01789) 293259
david.lodder@lodders.co.uk
Specialisation: Agricultural law in respect of Agricultural Holdings Act, farm successions, re-arranging the family farming partnership, diversification schemes. Major cases include: Succession case in Agricultural Land Tribunal, acquisition of farming estate, settling number of complicated partnership disputes.
Career: Educated at Uppingham School/Sheffield University. Articled in Sheffield. Joined family firm (then *G F Lodder & Sons*) 1974, became partner in 1978. Head of large commercial department.
Personal: Country Landowners Association. Legal

Parliamentary Committee Member. National Farmers Union. Agricultural Law Association.

MARGRAVE-JONES, Clive
Margraves, Llandrindod Wells (01597) 825565

MOORE, John
Macfarlanes, London (020) 7831 9222
Specialisation: Partner in Property Development. Has acted since qualification for Institutional Investors, including Insurance Companies and Pension Funds, in connection with the investment and development of land, and agricultural law. Represents tenants as well as landlords in relation to their agricultural holdings and Public Bodies (including NHS Trusts) in relation to agricultural tenancy rights on surplus land when considering developments and PFI proposals. Lectures on agricultural law.
Career: Joined *Macfarlanes* in 1970. Qualified 1973. Partner in 1979.

MORRISON, Alastair
Burges Salmon, Bristol (0117) 939 2258
alastair.morrison@burges-salmon.com
Specialisation: Is in the complexities of sale and purchase of farms and estates, and commercial farm investment and development. Also advises on agricultural tenancies and agricultural mortgages.
Prof. Memberships: Law Society; member of the Agricultural Law Association, member of Legal and Parliamentary sub-committee of the Country Land and Business Association.
Career: Trained and practised for five years with *Macfarlanes* before moving to practise in the North East for five years. Joined *Burges Salmon* as a partner in 1997.

NEVILLE, William
Burges Salmon, Bristol (0117) 939 2000

OGG, Robin
Wright Hassall, Leamington Spa (01926) 886 688
robino@wrighthassall.co.uk
Specialisation: All aspects of agricultural law.
Prof. Memberships: Law Society; Agricultural Law Association.
Career: Articled *Wright Hassall*; qualifed 1968; partner 1971; head of agricultural department; Chairman of *Wright Hassall* 1999.
Personal: Born 1944; Corpus Christi College, Cambridge (1966 BA Hons; MA); lives Warwick; leisure interests include farming, cricket and bridge.

PLUMMER, Alan J.
Roythorne & Co, Spalding (01775) 724141
alanplummer@roythorne.co.uk
Specialisation: Partner in litigation department. Main areas of practice are landlord and tenant litigation, particularly relating to agricultural holdings, contentious trust matters, employment law and professional indemnity litigation. Speaker at seminars and other professional conferences.
Prof. Memberships: ALA and Law Society Negligence Panel member.
Career: After gaining a degree in Bacteriology he joined *Roythorne & Co* in 1976 and qualified in 1979.

POUND, Toby
Prettys, Ipswich (01473) 232121
tpound@prettys.co.uk
Specialisation: Agricultural property and landlord and tenant law.
Prof. Memberships: Member of Agricultural Law Association.
Career: Articled at *Prettys* 1978-80; admitted 1980; became partner at *Prettys* 1982; managing partner 1992-95.
Personal: Educated Highgate School and University of Nottingham. Married with three children. Hon. Secretary of Suffolk County Cricket Club since 1991; member of Ipswich Golf Club.

PRING, Simon
Farrer & Co, London (020) 7242 2022
Specialisation: Partner in the estates and private property team. All aspects of property law with an emphasis on agricultural estates, charity land holding and VAT. Assistant solicitor to the Duchy of Lancaster.
Prof. Memberships: Holborn Law Society.
Career: Blundell's School, Devon, Robinson College, Cambridge. Joined *Farrer & Co* 1986, partner 1995.
Personal: Born 24 March 1964. Married. Lives in London. Leisure: country pursuits and golf.

QUINN, James
Morton Fisher, Worcester (01905) 610410
Specialisation: Partner in business division. Principal field of activity relates to agricultural matters, including landlord and tenant issues, agreements and disputes, tribunal and arbitration work, general estate advice and quota work. Also advises on commercial property matters, including sales and purchases and commercial and agricultural estate development. Acted in Williamson v Thompson.
Prof. Memberships: Member Law Society; Agricultural Law Association; LawNet Agriculture Unit.
Career: Qualified in 1964. Joined *Morton Fisher* and became a partner in 1964.
Personal: Born 11th July 1939. LL.B Birmingham University 1960. Leisure interests include golf, computing, caravanning and family. Is a Board Member of the Princes Youth Business Trust (Hereford & Worcester Region). Lives in Malvern.

RENNIE O.B.E., Donald G.
Donald Rennie WS, Edinburgh (0131) 476 7007
donald.rennie@cablenet.co.uk
Specialisation: Sole Practitioner. Specialist agricultural practice. Handles landlord and tenant, quotas, professional negligence claims, and partnerships. Author of articles on the valuation of agricultural leases and succession to agricultural tenancies. Has lectured extensively at seminars organised by the Law Society of Scotland, RICS and Agricultural Law Association. Editor, Connell on the Agricultural Holdings (Scotland) Acts.
Prof. Memberships: Agricultural Law Association, Scottish Lawyers' European Group, Society of Trust and Estate Practitioners.
Career: Qualified in 1972. Joined *Connell & Connell WS* in 1976, becoming a Partner in 1977-96. Secretary of the Scottish Agricultural Arbiters' Association 1989-1999; Member of the Panel of Arbiters, member the Agricultural Law Association.
Personal: Born 25th April 1947. Attended Aberdeen University (MA 1968, LLB 1970). Lives in Edinburgh.

ROBERTSON, Jonathan
Turcan Connell, Edinburgh (0131) 228 8111
jmr@turcanconnell.com
Specialisation: Partner in rural property section; specialist in agricultural law, crofting, forestry, aquaculture, conservation, diversification, rural finance, sporting and fishing, rural conveyancing, waste disposal, mining and development work, planning and environmental law. Considerable experience in hotel and leisure and general commercial property.
Prof. Memberships: Member Agricultural Law Association. Accredited as a specialist in agricultural law by the Law Society of Scotland. Writer to the Signet. Notary Public.
Career: Attended University of Aberdeen (LLB, DipLP). Articled *Dundas & Wilson CS* 1984-86; qualified 1986; assistant solicitor 1986-90; associate 1990; partner 1990-97. Partner *Turcan Connell* 1997.
Personal: Born 1960. Resides East Lothian. Leisure interests include walking.

RUSS, Tim
Clarke Willmott & Clarke, Taunton
(01823) 442 266
truss@cw-c.co.uk
Specialisation: Partner and head of the agriculture and environmental team. Tim's practice includes landlord and tenant work for both landowners and tenants, partnership disputes, agricultural land tribunal succession work, professional negligence and EU quotas. He regularly deals with judicial review and related administrative work. Often, particularly on partnership and tenancy cases, Tim works with the client's other advisors including accountants and land agents. He is a qualified mediator with both CEDR and ADR Group and has successfully mediated 25 cases to settlement, the greater part of which were related to agricultural issues. He is experienced in arbitration law and regularly acts as advocate or advisor in agricultural arbitrations. He has dealt with several high profile judicial reviews including those related to the IACS and Milk/Sheep quota schemes and represented the cheese producer in R v Minister of Health ex parte Eastside cheese company, the first case interpreting the powers of the state under ss 9 and 13 Food Safety Act. He is currently involved in several cases linked to the Swift v Dairywise litigation as to the nature of milk quota and is also advising on several disputes linked to FMD.
Prof. Memberships: Agricultural Law Association, Country Landowners Association, Fellow of the Chartered Institute of Arbitrators, The Food Law Group.
Career: Articled with *McFarlane Guy*; joined *CW&C* in October 1987, qualified November 1988 and made partner in 1994.
Personal: Attended Bristol Polytechnic (LLB); leisure interests include golf and rugby.

SHEARER, Roy
Lindsays WS, Edinburgh (0131) 229 1212
rgs@lindsays.co.uk
Specialisation: All aspects of landed estate work including; agricultural law, crofting law, minerals, salmon fishings, shootings, right of way.
Prof. Memberships: The Law Society of Scotland, The WS Society, Notary Public.
Career: Over 30 years' experience in landed estate work Partner at *Lindsays WS* since 1970.

SMITH, Graham C.H.
Roythorne & Co, Spalding (01775) 724141
grahamsmith@roythorne.co.uk
Specialisation: Partner in private client/agriculture department. Diverse workload includes tax planning and trusts, pensions, partnership and company affairs, succession planning, contracting and management agreements.
Career: Joined *Roythorne & Co* in 1972 and qualified in 1974. Author of practice texts such as 'Agricultural Law' and 'Agricultural Precedents Handbook' and

editor of EMIS Professional Publishing's newsletter on Agricultural Law. Speaker at seminars, various accountants' and surveyors' conferences and for Central Law Training on Agricultural Law.

STEEL, John
White & Bowker, Winchester (01962) 844440
Specialisation: Partner in agricultural and environmental law group. Main areas of practice are environmental and agricultural, including agricultural tenancy successions, farm partnership disputes, public rights of way, mineral abstraction and landfill, and water pollution cases. Also handles charity and education work, including formation of charities, advice to school governors and work for higher and further education colleges. Has written on pollution for the Agricultural Law Association Journal and the Royal Institution of Chartered Surveyors Technical Bulletin. Lectures on farm pollution, rights of way, independent schools. Holds Masters degree in Environmental Law from De Montfort University.
Prof. Memberships: Country Landowners Association, Agricultural Law Association.
Career: Qualified 1975, having joined *White & Bowker* in 1973. Became a partner in 1977. Member of the Country Landowners Association Legal and Parliamentary Committee 1988-92 and of its Hampshire Branch Committee 1981-86 and 1987-92. Agricultural Law Association Treasurer 1990-94.
Personal: Born 9 May 1949. School Governor. Leisure interests include woodland management. Lives in Winchester.

STEPHENS, Jonathan
Jonathan Stephens & Co, Usk (01291) 673344

STONE, James
Addleshaw Booth & Co, Leeds (0113) 209 2000
jfs@addleshaw-booth.co.uk
Specialisation: Partner in commercial property group. Main areas of practice are agriculture, commercial property and property tax. Work includes property investment, tenancy issues (including termination, compensation and succession rights), quotas, property finance, capital taxation and VAT.
Prof. Memberships: Law Society, Agricultural Law Association.
Career: Qualified in 1981. Joined the firm in 1981, becoming a partner in 1988.
Personal: Attended Bristol Grammar School 1964-75 and Exeter University 1975-78. Leisure interests include mountaineering, photography and travel. Lives in Harrogate.

STRANG STEEL, Malcolm
Turcan Connell, Edinburgh (0131) 228 8111
mgss@turcanconnell.com
Specialisation: Handles mainly rural property matters, including landlord and tenant, acting for proprietors of a number of landed estates with let farms and fishing interests; and purchase and sale of landed estates. Handles related taxation issues, and timeshare matters including fishings. Has lectured on numerous occasions to the Law Society of Scotland and other seminars on agricultural law and sporting law.
Prof. Memberships: Convener of Law Society of Scotland's Rural Affairs Committee; Convener of Legal and Parliamentary Committee of Scottish Landowners' Federation; Secretary of Scottish Agricultural Arbiters Association; Member, Agricultural Law Association; Member, Securities Institute.
Career: Partner *W & J Burness* 1973-97; partner *Turcan Connell* 1997-date.
Personal: Eton College; Trinity College, Cambridge; Edinburgh University.

STURROCK, David P.
Turnbull, Simson & Sturrock WS, Jedburgh (01835) 862391
dps@tssjed.co.uk
Specialisation: Managing partner. Main area of practice is agricultural law. Handles all aspects of land ownership, Agricultural Holdings (Scotland) Acts, quotas and arbitrations. Also handles wills, succession and inheritance tax planning. Has addressed a variety of Conferences and Seminars.
Prof. Memberships: Law Society of Scotland; Accredited by Law Society of Scotland as a Specialist in Agricultural Law; Writer to the Signet; Notary Public.
Career: Qualified in 1966. Joined *Turnbull, Simson & Sturrock* in 1966, becoming a partner in 1968 and managing partner in 1990.
Personal: Born 16th March 1943. Attended Rugby School 1956-61 and Edinburgh University 1961-65. Lives in Jedburgh.

SWIFT, Robert
Wilsons, Salisbury (01722) 412412

SYDENHAM, Angela
Birketts, Ipswich (01473) 232300

THOMSON, Michael
Arnold Thomson, Towcester (01327) 350266
miket@arnoldthomson.com
Specialisation: Partner specialising in agriculture. Main area of work covers agricultural property, development work, tenancies, quotas livestock premia and sporting rights. Regularly addresses farming and professional audiences.
Prof. Memberships: Agricultural Law Association, Country Land and Business Association, National Farms Union.
Career: Qualified 1981. Co-founder of *Arnold Thomson* in 1990.
Personal: Born July 1954. Attended Wrekin College 1967-71, then University College, London 1972-76. Leisure pursuits include shooting, golf and cricket. Lives in Blakesley, Northants.

TURCAN, Robert
Turcan Connell, Edinburgh (0131) 228 8111
rct@turcanconnell.com
Specialisation: Joint Senior Partner specialising in land law, trusts and tax planning, adviser to a substantial number of landowners and farmers.
Prof. Memberships: The Law Society of Scotland, Society of Writers to HM Signet.
Career: Trinity College, Oxford (MA) and University of Edinburgh (LLB). Articled *Shepherd & Wedderburn WS*; qualified 1972; Partner at *Dundas & Wilson CS* 1973-97. Member of Law and Parliamentary Taxation Committee, Scottish Landowners Federation; director of the Abercairny Estates Limited and others.
Personal: Born 1947. Resides Fife. Married with four children. Leisure interests include fox hunting, gardening, shooting and fishing.

WHITTAKER, Geoff
Barker Gotelee, Ipswich (01473) 611211
Specialisation: Specialist in land and estate sales, sales and purchases, agricultural holdings, farm business tenancies, IACS, milk and livestock quotas, specialist-crop contracting arrangements and land exploitation. Director of Stanyer Consulting Ltd, dealing with non-legal affairs, especially EU and national grant funding.
Prof. Memberships: Law Society, Agricultural Law Association (Committee Member 1997-).
Career: Qualified in 1980. Trained in native Liverpool before moving to Midlands, practised for 16 years.
Personal: Amateur musician (choral and small-group a capella singing) and computers. Confirmed cricket nut!

WILLIAMS, Peter Rhys
Burges Salmon, Bristol (0117) 939 2000
peter.williams@burges-salmon.com
Specialisation: All forms of dispute concerning the agricultural industry, primarily agricultural banking, the dissolution of farming partnerships and quota disputes.
Prof. Memberships: Fellow of the Chartered Institute of Arbitrators, member of Agricultural Law Association, Non-Administration Receivers Association and the British Institute of Agricultural Consultants.
Career: Joined *Burges Salmon* in 1980, qualified in 1982 and became a partner in 1987.
Publications: Joint author of the 'Encyclopaedia of Forms and Precedents on Agriculture'; 'Halsbury's Laws on Agriculture' and Sweet & Maxwell's 'Agricultural Law, Tax and Finance', the RICS publication 'Farm Receiverships' and (with Michael Johnston) the *Burges Salmon* publication 'Farm Cottages'. He is a contributor to 'Scammell & Densham's Law of Agricultural Holdings' and the CAAV publication 'Dispute Resolution'. Blundell Memorial lecturer in 1992.

WYBAR, David Kenneth
Ashton Graham, Ipswich (01473) 232425
david.wybar@ashtongraham.co.uk
Specialisation: Acts for farmers, landowners and farming businesses and related throughout East Anglia.
Prof. Memberships: Agricultural Law Association. Council Member of Suffolk Agricultural Association. Suffolk Farming and Wildlife Advisory Group, Country Landowners Association. Suffolk Professionals European Committee.
Career: Winchester College and St. Andrews University. Trained with *Macfarlanes* in London and worked for *Mills & Reeve* in Norwich immediately before joining *Bankes Ashton* in Bury St Edmunds in 1991. *Bankes Ashton* merged with *Graham & Oldham* in October 1998 to become *Ashton Graham.*
Personal: Married with three children. Member of Bury St. Edmunds Farmers' Club, Ipswich and Suffolk Club, Royal and Ancient Golf Club of St. Andrews, Aldeburgh Golf Club, Golf House Club, Elie, Gentlemen of Suffolk Cricket Club and Newmarket and Suffolk Real Tennis Club. Chairman of Earl Soham Parish Council.

YOUNG, David
Hibbert Durrad Davies, Nantwich (01270) 624225

ALTERNATIVE DISPUTE RESOLUTION

OVERVIEW: After the upsurge following the Woolf reforms, the number of cases brought to mediation has levelled off. Many neutral mediators note that as the market matures, parties are growing more sophisticated as to how to use the process to their advantage. This year we recognise mediators who do not hail from a legal background. We do so in order to avoid presenting a distorted picture of the marketplace and in acknowledgement that these individuals are significant players.

RESEARCH APPROVED BY BMRB: *For this edition,* Chambers' *researchers conducted 6,552 interviews – 4,419 with law firms, 554 with barristers and 1,579 with clients.*

The validity of the research was scrutinised by BMRB International, who audited both the methodology and the results at our offices in July 2001. They interviewed Chambers' *researchers and cross-checked sample interviews. Details of the audit appear on page 7.*

LONDON

LEADING INDIVIDUALS	
★ **WILLIS Tony** Sole Practitioner	
1 **ANDREWARTHA Jane** Clyde & Co	**BROWN Henry** Penningtons
PRYOR Nicholas Sole Practitioner	**SHAPIRO David** SJ Berwin
2 **CORNES David** Winward Fearon	**DODSON Charles** Sole Practitioner
MACKIE Karl CEDR Solve	**MARSH William** CEDR Solve
MILES David Glovers	**SIBLEY Edward** Sibley & Co
3 **ALLEN Anthony** CEDR Solve	**BISHOP John** Masons
CARROLL Eileen CEDR Solve	**CURTIS Tony** CEDR Solve
FINCHAM Anthony CMS Cameron McKenna	
NEWMARK Chris Baker & McKenzie	**TESTER Stephen** CMS Cameron McKenna
4 **HOLLOWAY Julian** Berwin Leighton Paisner	
MIDDLETON-SMITH Charles Hammond Suddards Edge	
RIVERS Elizabeth Sole Practitioner	
5 **ABRAMSON John** LeBoeuf, Lamb, Greene & MacRae	
NEILL Robert Herbert Smith	

See individuals' profiles p.79

Tony Willis (see p.83), **Sole Practitioner** Formerly of Clifford Chance, the "*hero and model*" of many mediators, Willis is now practising ADR full-time. An "*enormous case-load*" encompassing "*a breathtaking range of matters,*" is conducted in a "*calm, quiet, self-assured,*" manner. His "*impressive presence*" is said to be particularly effective with "*rowdy or emotional clients.*" Combining "*a great understanding of psychology,*" with "*sound commercial knowledge*" he is "*undoubtedly a star.*"

Jane Andrewartha, Clyde & Co "*Extraordinarily good,*" remains the typical description of Andrewartha's ability. Clients and peers alike are "*profoundly impressed*" by her "*articulate intelligence, warm personality, and tough-minded determination to move proceedings on at a fast pace.*" Has been involved with some 50 or more mediations as mediator or advocate. She has experience of a broad range of commercial mediations, but is particularly expert in the insurance and reinsurance sphere.

Henry Brown (see p.80), **Penningtons** A "*gentle, humane person with effective methods,*" Brown is still adjudged "*tremendously impressive – a first class mediator.*" Dual qualified as a South African attorney and a UK solicitor, he originally trained as a mediator in New York. Rated for his expertise in family and divorce mediation, his practice now concentrates on commercial areas, including professional negligence, partnership, family business and shareholder issues. Also active in publishing, passing off and other IP issues.

Nicholas Pryor (see p.82), **Sole Practitioner** This "*effective cracker of difficult issues and difficult people,*" is deemed such a "*smoothie*" that he "*could talk apples down from trees.*" A full-time mediator who "*can take on any case*" Pryor is endorsed by peers as "*one of the best – exceptionally good at the cathartic element.*" The "*classic sole practitioner,*" he conducted some 60 commercial mediations, some on a pro bono basis for the Central London County Court Scheme. His wide experience includes professional indemnity, finance and commercial contracts, defamation, shipping and aviation, environmental disputes and media.

David Shapiro (see p.82), **SJ Berwin** Although UK mediators express reservations about Shapiro's "*direct, evaluative, challenging, American style,*" they agree that he is "*hugely accomplished and experienced*" and that this style makes him "*particularly suited to difficult mediations when parties need to be told what to do.*" Clients add that his "*pure charisma*" and "*inventive solutions*" allow Shapiro to resolve problems that other, "*less tough*" mediators could not. He served as a mediator in 16 complex cases in 2000. With over 20 years of experience, he is commonly instructed on multi-party cases, pioneering deal mediations, and entrenched cases over a broad range of matters.

David Cornes (see p.80), **Winward Fearon** Boasting a "*stunningly good CV*" and "*huge experience in the field of construction mediation*" Cornes easily holds his position in the rankings. "*A delightful, gentle man,*" he is described by peers as "*quietly impressive*" and his qualifications as a chartered civil engineer with ten years experience in the construction industry are said to place him "*second to none.*" Has acted successfully in about 44 disputes, many high value involving multiple parties.

Charles Dodson (see p.80), **Sole Practitioner** Has conducted over 20 mediations in the past year for CEDR Sole and successfully mediated one of its largest cases. "*From the relaxed school of mediation,*" Dodson is said to be "*competent and informal, with a good keen mind.*" Most typically think him a "*strong performer.*" Has acted as mediator on matters ranging from cross border, high-value and multi-party cases, to no fee Central London County Court cases.

Karl Mackie (see p.81), **CEDR Solve** A name recognised across the UK and Europe, the "*excellent*" Karl Mackie has pioneered mediation in many new sectors. He has mediated and facilitated cases across in a variety of fields, and boasts experience of parties from over 20 different countries. Chief executive of CEDR, this non-practising barrister and trained psychologist has an "*intellectual approach that makes him suitable for complex cases and less emotional clients.*" He is considered by peers to command a "*subtle technique*" and to possess "*a way of steering a mediation.*"

William Marsh (see p.80), **CEDR Solve** Former solicitor and now director of CEDR, Marsh is held by clients to be "*facilitative and intuitive*" and able to "*adapt to a wide variety cases.*" He has successfully mediated a wide range of disputes both in the UK and internationally, including multi-million pound claims in banking, corporate acquisitions, insurance, professional negligence, partnership, passing off, communications, employment and sport. Successfully co-mediated the long-running multi-party dispute over board and shareholder control of Brighton & Hove Albion Football Club.

David Miles (see p.82), **Glovers** Another "*excellent*" mediator deemed, along with David Cornes, to be the "*leader*" for construction mediation. Although construction forms the bulk of the practice, his largest mediation of 2000 involved a sum of £2.5 million relating to a complex dispute in the energy field. Interviewees believe him "*eminent in promoting the area and active in CEDR and PIM,*" he is committed to encouraging the introduction of ADR in the Commonwealth, especially in Kenya, Nigeria and Uganda.

Edward Sibley (see p.82), **Sibley & Co** "*Established in the mediation field,*" Sibley has recently set up an eponymous firm where he is "*prodigiously busy.*" He is often described as "*skilled, subtle, and experienced, with a good feel for the realities of a dispute.*" A few consider his style "*a bit interventionist.*" Although still handling a number of banking and professional negligence mediations, his practice is increasingly focused on serious commercial contractual work. Consequently his mediations, though fewer in number than in previous years, have increased in value and complexity.

Anthony Allen (see p.79), **CEDR Solve** Formerly at Bunkers, now full-time with CEDR, Allen is universally considered to be "*clearly the best mediator in the UK for clinical negligence and personal injury.*" His "*avuncular, open-hearted and humorous*" approach is felt to "*count for a lot*" in cases "*with high emotional content.*" Industry sources continue to regard him as "*excellent*" on general commercial mediations.

John Bishop (see p.79), **Masons** Although much occupied as managing partner of Masons, Bishop maintains his profile for mediations relating to the construction and engineering industries. Noted for his skills in that arena, he is described by peers as a "*pleasant*" mediator who "*speaks the clients' language.*"

Eileen Carroll (see p.80), **CEDR Solve** Formerly of Howard Kennedy, now CEDR's Deputy Chief Executive, the "*experienced*" Carroll is felt to have "*the gift of the gab.*" Owing to ill-health, she is has had less visibility in the market but remains "*highly effective.*"

Tony Curtis (see p.80), **CEDR Solve** Erstwhile managing partner of Machins Solicitors in Luton, Curtis works full-time with CEDR as a mediator. "*Adored*" by clients, who appreciate his "*superb facilitative style*" as well as his "*wide experience,*" he has conducted over 20 mediations in the past year. Other mediators generally applaud his "*laid back*" approach to mediations, although some aver that "*he doesn't have teeth.*"

Anthony Fincham (see p.80), **CMS Cameron McKenna** A partner in CMS Cameron McKenna's employment department, Fincham is deemed a "*good listener*" by clients, described as a "*classic non-interventionist.*" He has mediated on ten occasions over the past two years, covering employment, partnership, construction and commercial contracts issues. These included one Court of Appeal matter and two Central Court matters. Relatively new to the field, his "*quiet style,*" combined with an ability to "*make people think by an incisive and timely comment*" has won him many admirers.

Christopher Newmark (see p.82), **Baker & MacKenzie** The "*bright, gentle and pleasant,*" Newmark is deemed to be "*building a real reputation.*" He has been involved in more than 20 mediations on a broad range of commercial matters and is a member of the ICC's working group on ADR, which is drafting the ICC ADR rules for publication. Mediators agree he "*always makes a helpful contribution.*"

Stephen Tester (see p.83), **CMS Cameron McKenna** Held by clients to be developing a sound practice, Tester is respected and used for his "*brain, ability and great effectiveness.*" A member of CMS Cameron McKenna's insurance group, it is in that sector that he has acted as mediator on ten matters.

Julian Holloway (see p.81), **Berwin Leighton Paisner** "*Devoted to the construction field,*" Holloway has a "*quiet and pleasant*" manner that renders him popular in construction and civil engineering cases.

Charles Middleton-Smith (see p.81), **Hammond Suddards Edge** With eleven mediations over the past year, Middleton-Smith is establishing a strong presence. Popular with clients and referral organisations, he is deemed "*marvellously thorough, understated and fair.*" His willingness to "*get involved in the discussion and make real efforts to bring parties together*" is applauded. Said to be "*suited to sophisticated clients*" and "*not afraid to challenge them.*" Recently acted on a claim conducted in Germany against a supplier arising from product recall of contaminated goods by an UK supermarket chain.

Elizabeth Rivers (see p.82), **Sole Practitioner** Conducted over 50 mediations in a number of areas, including employment, distribution, IP, professional indemnity and shareholder disputes. While specialising in commercial mediation, she also has experience of environmental, workplace and community mediation. Commercial clients praised this "*hard-working, patient and extremely competent*" practitioner. Mediated an $8 million contract for the design and installation of a telephone centre.

John Abramson, **LeBoeuf, Lamb, Greene & MacRae** Emerging into the spotlight, Abramson is seen by interviewees to focus on insurance and reinsurance related ADR.

Robert Neill (see p.82), **Herbert Smith** Considered "*a delightful mediator,*" Neill is dubbed by other mediators the "*nice face of Herbert Smith.*" CEDR accredited, he has mediated in areas such as share sale agreements, software agreements and professional negligence.

THE REGIONS

LEADING INDIVIDUALS	
★ HOWELL-RICHARDSON Phillip Morgan Cole	
PATON Andrew Pinsent Curtis Biddle	
1 LLOYD-JONES Jonathan Linnells	
2 BRADBEER Ronald Eversheds	GATENBY John Addleshaw Booth & Co
GOYDER Bill Sole Practitioner	WINKWORTH-SMITH John Sole Practitioner
3 DAVIES Mike Veale Wasbrough	GLAISTER Anthony Keeble Hawson
HOUGHTON Paul Lupton Fawcett	KENDALL John Sole Practitioner
SMITH Quentin Addleshaw Booth & Co	TEMPLE Euan Toller Hales & Collcutt

See individuals' profiles p.79

Phillip Howell-Richardson, **Morgan Cole** Dubbed by clients "*a star on any list,*" Howell-Richardson continues to develop a national reputation in this field. Undertaking around four mediations a month throughout the UK in the whole range of commercial disputes, he maintains a 97% success rate. Elected chairman of ADR Net and a member of the Advisory Committee on the Court of Appeal Mediation Scheme.

Andrew Paton (see p.82), **Pinsent Curtis Biddle** "*Just as good as if not better than any London based mediator*" Paton garners plaudits as a "*founding father of mediation.*" Mediated 48 cases, among which was a £10 million five-party construction dispute. Noted for his "*ability to establish rapport with clients of all varieties,*" he is reputed to be "*personable, feisty and highly skilled.*" Particularly experienced in personal injury disputes.

Jonathan Lloyd-Jones (see p.81), **Linnells** "*Talented and extremely sharp*" Lloyd-Jones gets most of his referrals through ADR Net, but is increasingly receiving direct referrals from other firms. "*An excellent player,*" he stands above many in the market place, according to our interviewees.

Ronald Bradbeer (see p.80), **Eversheds** Heading the Eversheds ADR department is "*formidable*" Ronald Bradbeer. He has conducted a substantial number of mediations in the past 12 months and has "*an excellent reputation in the field.*" "*Shrewd and sensible*" he is typically said to be "*well-known*" for his "*deep interest*" in the subject.

John Gatenby (see p.80), **Addleshaw Booth & Co** "*Definitely making a name for himself,*" the "*calm, thorough and sensible*" Gatenby is held by clients to be "*one to watch.*" Handles contractual disputes for major companies and is experienced at cross-border work. Averaging one appointment a month, he has mediated over 20 disputes across the commercial spectrum, including acquisitions, sale of goods, construction, IT and professional indemnity.

Bill Goyder (see p.81), **Sole Practitioner** Now retired from Jacksons, the "*avuncular and well-regarded*" Goyder continues his respected mediation practice. He is particularly noted for construction and clinical negligence mediations.

John Winkworth-Smith, **Sole Practitioner** A mediator who gains national recognition for his "*creative solutions.*" Attracting an increasing number of direct referrals, he is a mediator to whom others would "*go unhesitatingly.*" He has conducted CEDR mediations in the past 12 months and is praised for his "*calm, pleasant yet strong*" persona.

Mike Davies (see p.80), **Veale Wasborough** "*As capable as ever,*" Davies has been involved in mediation for 10 years and was a founder member of ADR Net. He is "*quietly effective*" and was highly praised during research for his "*soft, facilitative style*" and his "*enviable ability to listen.*" Experienced in professional negligence claims, he has recently handled a high value construction dispute involving major companies in the nuclear plant construction industry.

Anthony Glaister (see p.81), **Keeble Hawson** A "*mastermind*" behind the Association of Northern Mediators, "*strong, enthusiastic*" mediator, Glaister is endorsed by peers for his involvement in some "*notable initiatives*" such as the Leeds Combined Court Scheme. Offers expertise in construction, banking, partnership, professional negligence and landlord and tenant disputes.

Paul Houghton (see p.81), **Lupton Fawcett** A "*talented, strong intelligent chap*" who concentrates on commercial contract and professional negligence mediations, Houghton has notched up a large volume of CEDR mediations over the past year. A mediator "*in the Andrewartha mould*" he is much admired for "*moving the process forward from the beginning.*"

John Kendall (see p.81), **Sole Practitioner** Formerly at Allen & Overy, Kendall does some mediation work but wins most respect as "*the last word on expert determination.*" His "*quiet incisiveness*" is thought to be used to its best advantage in that role. He is author of the only textbook on expert determination.

Quentin Smith (see p.83), **Addleshaw Booth & Co** Recent entrant to the field, Smith wins plaudits from practitioners across the country. "*Young, earnest, and clearly one to watch,*" he has mediated over 20 disputes across the commercial, insurance and personal injury spheres. These included two of the first three defamation/mediation cases ever conducted in the UK, a subject in which he has developed "*a fund of information.*"

Euan Temple (see p.83), **Toller Hales & Collcutt** Clients speak highly of Temple, describing him as "*dogged but smooth.*" Specialises in mediations arising from patents, shareholder disputes and professional negligence matters.

NON-LEGALLY TRAINED PRACTITIONERS

LEADING INDIVIDUALS	
1 JACKSON-STOPS Mark	
RICHBELL David Sole Practitioner.	TABAKIN Roger Sole Practitioner

See individuals' profiles p.79

Mark Jackson-Stops (see p.81), **In Place Of Strife** "*A name to conjure with,*" Jackson-Stops has his own "*substantial practice*" with In Place Of Strife. A surveyor by training, he is applauded by fellow mediators for his "*competence in a wide variety of areas.*" Clients are equally emphatic: "*exceptionally good at getting to the nub of disputes; he's an impressively smooth operator.*"

David Richbell, **Sole Practitioner** "*Possibly the nicest person in mediation,*" and possessing a "*huge reputation,*" Richbell, a quantity surveyor by profession is a "*profoundly experienced*" mediator. He conducted close to 20 mediations for CEDR in the last year. His primary focus is construction where interviewees agree he is one of the "*best known names*" but he also mediates other legal disputes. Has conducted a number of international, multi-million pound disputes.

Roger Tabakin (see p.83), **Sole Practitioner** A former accountant, he is an "*eminent mediator,*" especially on financial disputes. An "*excellent negotiator*" who "*gets good results*" he has "*oodles of style.*" "*Approachable and understanding,*" fellow researchers assert that he is able to "*make even difficult clients relax.*"

LEADERS IN ALTERNATIVE DISPUTE RESOLUTION

ABRAMSON, John
LeBoeuf, Lamb, Greene & MacRae, London (020) 7459 5000

ALLEN, Anthony
CEDR Solve, London (020) 7645 1450
tallen@cedr-solve.com
Specialisation: Has mediated personal injury, clinical negligence, professional indemnity, contract, construction, housing and banking disputes. Particularly involved in developing mediation for personal injury and clinical negligence.
Prof. Memberships: *CEDR Solve* mediator; *CEDR* Director since 2000, responsible for personal injury and clinical negligence claims mediation; *CEDR* Training Faculty Member.
Career: MA Cambridge. Formerly partner with *Bunkers, Brighton & Hove* (from 1972), now consultant.

ANDREWARTHA, Jane
Clyde & Co, London (020) 7623 1244
See under Aviation, p.101

BISHOP, John
Masons, London (020) 7490 4000
john.bishop@masons.com
Specialisation: Specialised in UK and International Construction and Engineering matters since qualifying, more recently also in Professional Negligence disputes. Major matters include LTRS, MTR, SSDS and Second Harbour Crossing in Hong Kong, Falklands Airfield, Tiffany Oil Platform, Channel Tunnel, Eurostar, Cairo Plaza, Jubilee Line, Keadby Power Station, LNG facilities (Brunei), Lloyds Building, M25, A27, several arbitrations from Indonesian Geothermic programme; conducted disputes at all levels of the English Courts, domestic arbitrations and international arbitrations under ICC, UNCITRAL and Stockholm Chamber rules as well as ADR processes. Also acts as mediator, adjudicator and arbitrator.
Prof. Memberships: Dean of the Faculty of Mediation & ADR, Chairman of the Joint Consultative Committee of the London Court of International

Arbitration, Vice Chairman of the Academy of Experts, President of the Technology and Construction Solicitors Association (TeCSA), Chairman of TeCSA IT Committee. Past Chairman of TeCSA, Past Member of TCC (Technology and Construction Court) Users Committee, TCC's Rules Committee, IT Committee, ADR Committee, Law Society Civil Litigation Committee, ISE Committees on Expert Evidence and Woolf Reforms, Founder Member of CEDR, Chartered Institute of Arbitrators' Committees on new forms of arbitration and ADR, British Academy of Experts Sub Committee on Expert Evidence. Editorial board of Construction Law Journal. Lectures include Blundell Memorial lecture, Bar Conference, Judicial Studies Board, National Contractors Group annual lecture, Chartered Institute of Arbitrators, Kings College (Univ. of London).
Career: Qualified 1971, partner 1972, admitted Hong Kong 1983, managing partner 1986-90, senior partner 1990 to date. Qualified adjudicator (TeCSA), mediator (CEDR).
Personal: Sherborne School. LLB Hons Queen Mary College, University of London. Leisure interests include golf, fishing, cooking and tomatoes.

BRADBEER, Ronald
Eversheds, Newcastle upon Tyne (0191) 2611661
ronaldbradbeer@eversheds.com
Specialisation: Principal area of expertise is medical negligence. Principal legal advisor to area health authorities and trusts for many years. Specialised in medical negligence for over 25 years. Also handles commercial disputes specialising in commercial contracts, industrial tribunal cases and construction matters. Head of *Eversheds'* ADR Group.
Prof. Memberships: Accredited Mediator with Centre for Dispute Resolution (1993), a member of the CEDR Training Faculty. CEDR Lawyers' Role Faculty, Law Society.
Career: Joined *Wilkinson Maughan* in 1960. Qualified in 1963. Partner in 1967, managing partner in 1993 and senior partner in 1996.

BROWN, Henry
Penningtons, London (020) 7457 3000
HenryBrownADR@cs.com
Specialisation: Consultant in commercial department. Principal areas of practice are ADR (mediation), intellectual property, partnerships, shareholder disputes, professional negligence and contractual disputes. Author of 'Law Society's ADR Report' (1991), co-author of 'ADR Principles and Practice' (1993/1999). Commercial and family mediation trainer.
Prof. Memberships: Law Society, CEDR, panel of Independent Mediators, Chartered Institute of Arbitrators, Mediation UK, Society of Professionals in Dispute Resolution, SFLA, FMA. On CPR Institute's International panel of Distinguished Neutrals (New York).
Career: Qualified South Africa, 1962 and England & Wales 1975. Established *Simanowitz & Brown* 1975. Partner *Birkbeck Montagu's* 1980-91, *Penningtons* 1991-94. Consultant from 1994.
Personal: Born 29 May 1939. Educated at University of Cape Town and University of South Africa. Certificate in Fundamentals of Psychotherapy and Counselling (Regents College, 1994).

CARROLL, Eileen
CEDR Solve, London (020) 7645 1450
ecarroll@cedr-solve.com
Specialisation: She has a broad range of commercial mediation experience including banking; insurance; reinsurance; professional negligence; leasing; environmental; employment and partnership. One of a few mediators with experience of co-mediation in major projects.
Prof. Memberships: Law Society; CEDR Solve mediator; ABA; IBA.
Career: Moved from international business consultancy work to law. Qualified 1981. Partner *Turner Kenneth Brown* 1987. Management committee 1990 and International Strategy partner 1993. One of the lead lawyers who took initiative to found CEDR in 1989. Spent ten years working with North American clients and time working in San Francisco.
Publications: Co-author 'International Mediation – the Art of Business Diplomacy' – published by Kluwer.
Personal: Born 5 December 1953. Attended Kent University 1976-78 (LLB Hons). Leisure activities include horse-riding, water and snow skiing, writing poetry, dance, spending time with the family.

CORNES, David
Winward Fearon, London (020) 7420 2800
Specialisation: Founding partner. Gives advice to those involved in building, civil engineering and the construction professions (architects, engineers and quantity surveyors) and their insurers. Handles High Court and arbitration work, including abroad. Involved in major non-contentious projects including private finance. CEDR accredited Mediator (60 mediations completed). Arbitrator (UK and overseas). Regular speaker at conferences in the UK and occasionally abroad.
Prof. Memberships: Fellow of the Institution of Civil Engineers, Fellow of the Chartered Institute of Arbitrators, Law Society, Society of Construction Law, Technology and Construction Court Solicitors Association, International Bar Association.
Publications: Author of 'Design Liability in the Construction Industry', contributor to 'Construction Contract Policy'. Joint author of 'Collateral Warranties'.
Personal: Born 31 August 1944. Attended King's College, University of London. Member of Electoral Reform Society and Charter 88. Leisure interests include walking, traveling, opera. Lives Berkhamsted, Herts.

CURTIS, Tony
CEDR Solve, London (020) 7645 1450
tcurtis@cedr-solve.com
Specialisation: IT and telecom sectors; distribution, agency and franchise; aviation; multi-party disputes. Over the last nine years has mediated in almost all areas of commercial disputes, plus PI and professional negligence. Cases range in value from £100,000 to £60 million.
Prof. Memberships: *CEDR Solve* mediator – accredited in 1991; member of *CEDR* 's Training Faculty; Law Society; various other appointments over the years.
Career: Managing partner of a medium-sized firm of solicitors until left practice to concentrate on mediation. Now has a busy mediation practice (mediated 22 cases last year, with 77% settlement rate). Regularly leads and co-facilitates training courses in mediation and legal representation.
Personal: Married, two children. Keen private pilot. Amateur musician. Interests include theatre, languages and meeting people.

DAVIES, Mike
Veale Wasbrough, Bristol (0117) 925 2020
mdavies@vwl.co.uk
Specialisation: Founder member of ADR Group. Involved in ADR since 1991. Background in all aspects of litigation with particular mediation experience in employment issues, contract disputes, professional negligence claims, and financial services litigation. Currently specialising in employment related litigation.
Career: Qualified in 1978. MA, PhD. Partner *Veale Wasbrough*, since 1981. Head of employment law department. Two cases successfully taken to the Court of Appeal in 1999.
Personal: Born 1945. Educated at Hornchurch Grammar School.

DODSON, Charles
Charles Dodson – Sole Practitioner, Alresford (07802) 389 127
cadodson@candovermediation.com
Specialisation: Mediator, primarily of broad range of UK and international commercial disputes including professional negligence, insurance/reinsurance, pensions, rail industry, partnership/board disputes, commodity trading, government contracts. Became involved in ADR when resident partner in *Lovell White & King's* New York office in mid 80s. Subsequently involved in setting up CEDR (The Centre for Dispute Resolution), now one of the leading ADR bodies internationally. One of CEDR's original directors, five month secondment 1995, accredited mediator 1996, consultant from 1998, and a member of mediator and lawyer training faculties.
Career: Partner *Lovell White & King/Lovell White Durrant* 1981-98; managing partner 1991-95. Insead AMP 1991.

FINCHAM, Anthony
CMS Cameron McKenna, London (020) 7367 3000
Specialisation: Employment and Commercial Litigation.
Career: Degree in Modern History (Oriel College, Oxford). Qualified 1980. Partner *Cameron McKenna* from 1984.
Personal: Married with three children.

GATENBY, John
Addleshaw Booth & Co, Manchester (0161) 934 6548
jkg@addleshaw-booth.co.uk
Specialisation: Partner. Advises English and overseas private and public companies on international litigation, arbitration and alternative dispute resolution, including the enforcement of foreign judgements, and arbitral awards, commercial contract disputes and partnership law. Lectures regularly on civil procedure matters including international litigation, arbitration, ADR and documentary evidence.
Prof. Memberships: Law Society, Chartered Institute of Arbitrators (Fellow), Institute of Credit Management, IBA, SEG, LSLA, Commonwealth Lawyers Association, Association of Partnership Practitioners, Non-exec Director of CEDR. CEDR and ADR Group registered mediator.
Career: Qualified in 1975. Joined the firm in 1984;

Partner since 1985.
Personal: Educated at Trinity Hall, Cambridge 1968-72. Elder, Poynton Baptist Church.

GLAISTER, Anthony
Keeble Hawson, Leeds (0113) 244 3121
anthonyglaister@keeblehawson.co.uk
Specialisation: Anthony has a wide experience of resolving disputes including contractual, partnership, property and general commercial disputes and has acted as advocate and representative in all levels of courts and in arbitration and adjudications both here and abroad. Appointed as adjudicator in construction disputes, as an arbitrator in domestic disputes and as a mediator in a wide range of areas.
Prof. Memberships: A member of the Chartered Institute of Arbitrators and the International Bar Association as well as being Chairman of the Association of Northern Mediators and member of the Technolgy and Construction Solicitors Association. ORSA Adjudicator, CEDR Mediator.
Career: Qualified in 1980. Partner in *Fox & Gibbons*, London from 1985 to 1989, *Denison Till* Leeds from 1989 to 2001 and *Keeble Hawson* Leeds since.

GOYDER, Bill
Bill Goyder – Sole Practitioner, Darlington (01325) 730234
wgoyder@freeserve.co.uk
Specialisation: Experience in civil and mechanical engineering contractual disputes, construction, oil and gas, insolvency, partnership, professional negligence claims and mental health representation. Extensive mediation experience having mediated over thirty disputes and acted as a solicitor in a further fifteen cases.
Prof. Memberships: Director ADR Net Limited, former Member of Law Society's Mental Health Panel.
Career: International Paper Company, New York, USA, qualified 1968. Assistant Solicitor Berkshire County Council. Contracts Manager *Head Wrightson & Co*, 1970-73, partner *Hewitt Brown-Humes & Hare* 1973-83, partner *Jowett & Goyder* 1983-90, partner *Jacksons* 1990-2000.
Personal: Born 12.5.42. Educ Mill Hill, Trinity College Cambridge. Chairman of Governors, Polam Hall School, Darlington. Part time jazz musician.

HOLLOWAY, Julian
Berwin Leighton Paisner, London (020) 7427 1373
julian.holloway@berwinleightonpaisner.com
Specialisation: Partner. Construction and commercial litigation/arbitration and alternative dispute resolution. Former director of Centre for Dispute Resolution Limited ("CEDR") and Vice Chairman of CEDR's Construction Industry Working Party. Member of Drafting Committee of CEDR's Model Rules for Adjudication. Case Notes Editor of Construction Law Journal. CEDR accredited mediator (1993). Acts as mediator and for parties engaged in the mediation process. On CEDR's and RIBA's panel of adjudicators and is actively engaged in numerous adjudications. Member of the Construction Contacts Mediators Group. Has also been involved in setting up 'e-mediation' services.
Prof. Memberships: Law Society. Technology and Construction Court Solicitors Association.
Career: Articles with *Denton Hall & Burgin* 1979-81. Qualified solicitor since 1981. Assistant solicitor *Brecher & Co* 1981-83. Assistant solicitor with *McKenna & Co* 1984-88. Partner *McKenna & Co* 1988-92. Partner *Greenwoods* 1993 to 2000. Partner *Paisner & Co*, now *Berwin Leighton Paisner* 2001 to date.
Personal: Born 1954.

HOUGHTON, Paul
Lupton Fawcett, Leeds (0113) 282000
paul.houghton@luplaw.co.uk
Specialisation: Large complex litigation, arbitration and dispute resolution. CEDR mediator. Has been involved in over 60 mediations – 51 as a mediator up to a value of £9m. Cases mediated are mainly commercial contract and professional negligence matters. Co-author of Leeds Court Mediation Scheme.
Prof. Memberships: Registered and Accredited CEDR mediator. Law Society of England, Law Society of Scotland.
Career: Qualified in Scotland in 1984 and in England in 1990. Partner in charge of commercial litigation at *Lupton Fawcett* since 1997.
Personal: Classic rallying, sailing, fishing.

HOWELL-RICHARDSON, Phillip
Morgan Cole, Cardiff (029) 2038 5385

JACKSON-STOPS, Mark
In Place of Strife, London (020) 7917 9449
stops@mediate.co.uk
Specialisation: Professional negligence, insurance, commercial contract and property disputes among many others. Especially multi-party disputes working alone or with experts in specialist subject areas as co-mediators.
Prof. Memberships: Chartered surveyor (FRICS), CEDR-registered mediator.
Career: As a professional in property in 1970s and 1980s, now as full time mediator, having trained in UK and USA. Alumnus of the Program for the Instruction of Lawyers at Harvard Law School 2001 under Professor Roger Fisher. Founder in 1995 of mediation service provider, In Place of Strife, operating a panel of experienced mediators. Has mediated over 200 matters. On mediation panel of the Court of Appeal.
Personal: Born 1950. Educated Christ Church, Oxford (MA).

KENDALL, John
John Kendall, Presteigne (01544) 260019
jkendall@btinternet.com
Specialisation: Mediator, arbitrator, lecturer and trainer. CEDR consultant in expert determination. Author of 'Expert Determination', the only textbook on the subject, now in its third edition (Sweet and Maxwell 2001); co-author, 'Russell on Arbitration' (21st edition 1997). Registered mediator, CEDR; Fellow, Chartered Institute of Arbitrators and chartered arbitrator.
Prof. Memberships: Member the Law Society, the Society of Construction Law.
Career: Articled *Stephenson Harwood*, qualified 1976, partner *Allen & Overy* 1985-98; now freelance.
Personal: Oxford University (1972 BA, 1976 MA). Born 1950.

LLOYD-JONES, Jonathan
Linnells, Oxford (01865) 248607
jlj@linnells.co.uk
Specialisation: Senior partner – head of commercial dispute resolution. Construction and professional negligence litigation. Company, especially publishing, and general commercial disputes. Mediation.
Prof. Memberships: Law Society. Director of ADR Group Ltd.
Career: Qualified 1979. *Stephenson Harwood* 1977-80. *Claude Hornby & Cox* 1980-88 (Partner 1982-88). *Linnells* 1988 to date (partner 1990). Trained Mediator 1991.
Personal: Born 23rd November 1954. Educated at Sevenoaks School and Southampton University. Interests: Fly fishing, British water colours, family life. Lives in Oxford.

MACKIE, Karl
CEDR Solve, London (020) 7645 1450
kjmackie@cedr-solve.com
Specialisation: Major UK and international commercial, employment and public sector disputes. Mediated first substantial Court of Appeal case (NRG), facilitated resolution of British & Commonwealth Holdings and other major litigation cases.
Prof. Memberships: IBA; British Psychological Society; Chartered Institute of Arbitrators; Barrister (Gray's Inn); PhD and MBA.
Career: University of Nottingham; Honorary Professor in ADR – University of Birmingham; Partner in business strategy consultancy; Arbitrator and Mediator with ACAS; founding Chief Executive of *CEDR*; former director of studies, Management Programmes, Commerce and Industry Group and Law Society.
Publications: Co-author – 'International Mediation: the Art of Business Diplomacy'; co-author – 'The ADR Practice Guide'; Editor – 'The Handbook of Dispute Resolution'; co-author – 'Learning Lawyers Skills'; 'Lawyers in Business'.
Personal: Films, writing, skiing, Fellow of RSA.

MARSH, William
CEDR Solve, London (020) 7645 1450
wmarsh@cedr-solve.com
Specialisation: Mediates a broad range of cases (UK and internationally), particularly multi-party actions, including commercial contract, insurance/reinsurance, professional negligence, shareholder, medical negligence/PI, pensions, IT and others. An executive Director of CEDR since shortly after its launch. Currently advising UK and Russian governments on (unrelated) dispute resolution issues, as well as some major corporates. Recent cases include international energy case, multi-party pensions dispute, and shareholder group actions. Mediated the disputed takeover of Brighton & Hove FC at the request of the English Football Association.
Prof. Memberships: Member of UNCITRAL Experts Group on international commercial conciliation, Law Society, *CEDR Solve* Mediator, Mediator for the CMAP (Centre de Mediation et d'Arbitrage de Paris), Advisory Council Member of Coventry Centre for International Reconciliation.
Career: Solicitor in Paris (*Linklaters*)and UK (*Osborne Clarke*). Full time in mediation since 1991.
Publications: Co-author of 'The ADR Practice Guide: Commercial Dispute Resolution' (Butterworths, 1995 & 2000).
Personal: Educated at Durham University (1981-84). Married with three children. Lives in Sussex. Speaks French.

MIDDLETON-SMITH, Charles
Hammond Suddards Edge, London (020) 7655 1000
charles.middleton-smith@hammondse.com
Specialisation: Mediates regularly in general com-

mercial disputes and in many specific areas including IP, IT, competition, media and defamation. Litigation practice based in corporate disputes including joint ventures, acquisitions and disposals and shareholder agreements, often with an international element. Specialist sector areas include hotels, fine art and sport giving rise to general dispute resolution work.
Prof. Memberships: CEDR registered mediator. Also a member of the British Institute of International and Comparative Law in the Institute of Art and Law.
Career: Qualified in 1978. Partner since 1980.
Personal: Family, arts, sport, travel.

MILES, David
Glovers, London (020) 629 5121
dmiles@glovers.co.uk
Specialisation: Partner in Construction Department. Has specialised in construction since 1978. Deals with contract negotiations, joint venture agreements, claims involving both arbitration and litigation acting both for employers and contractors in the UK and overseas. Acted in the cases Rees Hough, Viking Grain and St Martins. Contributing Author 'Construction Conflict Management and Resolution.' Co-Author 'The ADR Practice Guide'. Director of CEDR and TECSA training faculty and lecturer on ADR. Mediator (CEDR/ CIA & B AE). Adjudicator TECSA and CEDR.
Prof. Memberships: F.C.I.Arb, Committee Member Technology and Construction Court Solicitors Association, Society of Construction Law.
Career: Commission Regular Army (1966-71). Joined *Alan Wilson & Co* in 1978, Partner 1979. Merged with *Glovers* in 1986.
Personal: Born 22nd June 1946. Haileybury 1960-64. Leisure interests: tennis, cricket, shooting, opera. Lives in North Moreton, Oxon.

NEILL, Robert
Herbert Smith, London (020) 7374 8000
Specialisation: Wide range of experience in commercial, corporate and banking-related litigation. He is an accredited mediator with CEDR (1996) and has acted as a mediator, or as an adviser, in a number of mediations covering a wide range of areas including Banking, Business Sale Agreements, Computer Software Agreements, Distribution Agreements, International Trade Agreements and Professional Negligence.
Career: Qualified with *Herbert Smith* in 1976; became a Partner in 1984; spent 3 years in the firm's Hong Kong office (1987-90).

NEWMARK, Chris
Baker & McKenzie, London (020) 7919 1000
chris.newmark@bakernet.com
Specialisation: Partner. Practices commercial international arbitration and litigation as well as alternative dispute resolution techniques (including mediation and expert determination). Has advised clients in mediation in both England and the United States and practices as mediator for commercial disputes. Has particular experience as both mediator and counsel in disputes related to the telecoms industry.
Prof. Memberships: The Law Society, LCIA, MClarb.
Career: Qualified 1990. At *Baker & McKenzie* since 1988. Elected partner in 1997. Spent 1993-94 working in the firm's Chicago office. Trained as mediator with CPR, New York in 1994. Accredited CEDR mediator since 1995. Member of the ICC Commission on International Arbitration and CPR International Panel of Distinguished Neutrals.
Personal: Born 16 January 1964. Educated at Abingdon School, Birmingham University and the University of Limoges, France. Interests include golf and photography. Lives in Greenwich.

PATON, Andrew
Pinsent Curtis Biddle, Birmingham
(0121) 200 1050
andrew.paton@pinsents.com
Specialisation: Partner and head of insurance litigation in Birmingham. Defending claims against professionals on instructions of their insurers. Uses mediation extensively to resolve claims. Acts as mediator in wide range of cases.
Prof. Memberships: Training faculty of CEDR. Director of ADR Net Limited. Member of the Panel of Independent Mediators. Chairman of the Association of Midlands Mediators. Member of Council of Birmingham Law Society – Chairman of the Civil Litigation Committee; member of the Policy Committee.
Career: Articled *Cripps Harries Hall & Co*, Tunbridge Wells. Qualified 1981. Joined *Pinsent & Co* (now *Pinsent Curtis Biddle*) September 1981. Partner 1985.
Personal: Born 1957. Educated at Bishop Vesey's Grammar School, Sutton Coldfield and Exeter University (LLB). Interests include yacht and dinghy racing, cycling and tennis.

PRYOR, Nicholas
Nicholas Pryor – Sole Practitioner, London
(020) 7359 2819
nicholaspryor@sotheby-road.co.uk
Specialisation: ADR and mediation. Have been mediating since 1986. Now acting full time as an independent mediator, and in representing parties at mediation and/or advising on the use of mediation. Specialises in large scale, multi-party commercial mediations, particularly insurance, reinsurance and professional indemnity matters.
Prof. Memberships: Founder member, Panel of Independent Mediators; Registered Mediator, CEDR; Accredited Mediator, ADR Group; Member, CPR Institute for Dispute Resolution (New York); Member, Mediation Panel, London Court of International Arbitration; Member, British Association of Lawyer Mediators; Member Chartered Institute of Arbitrators.
Career: Called to Bar (Middle Temple) 1970. Admitted solicitor 1980. Assistant *Rowe & Maw* (1980-82); assistant *Coward Chance / Clifford Chance* (1982-89); partner *Manches* (1990-95); company solicitor KWELM Management Services Ltd (1995-96).
Personal: Born 1946. Lives Highbury, London.

RICHBELL, David
David Richbell – Sole Practitioner, Melchbourne
(01234) 709 907

RIVERS, Elizabeth
Elizabeth Rivers – Sole Practitioner, London
(020) 8527 8654
mediate@elizabethrivers.co.uk
Specialisation: Commercial mediator dealing with a broad range of UK and international disputes. Recent mediations include an $8 million IT contract dispute and a conflict between a nuclear power station and a neighbouring landowner concerning alleged contamination. Other subject areas mediated include professional negligence, banking, contract, shareholder disputes, intellectual property and employment.
Prof. Memberships: CEDR Registered Mediator (1992), member of CEDR training faculty (1993), trustee of Mediation UK, Facilitator for The Environment Council.
Career: *Eversheds* (London) 1986-96: Litigator dealing with a broad range of commercial matters. Pioneered awareness and development of ADR across the firm. 1997-present: Independent mediator.
Personal: Educated at Loreto College, St Albans and Manchester University. Currently studying humanistic psychology. Interests: wilderness trekking, a capella singing, tango.

SHAPIRO, David
SJ Berwin, London (020) 7533 2421
d.shapiro@sjberwin.com
Specialisation: Alternative Dispute Resolution: accredited as a mediator by CEDR (Britain's Centre for Dispute Resolution), is on numerous mediation panels, was Director and Chief Mediator of JAMS Endispute Europe, and is currently Visiting Professor of Law, Nottingham Law School and Visiting Fellow, Department of Law, London School of Economics and Political Science, where he teaches mediation and mediation advocacy. Consultant to *SJ Berwin* where he serves as Director of that firm's ADR Services Unit.
Prof. Memberships: Centre for Dispute Resolution; CPR Institute for Dispute Resolution (Panel of Distinguished Mediators); British Assn. Of Lawyer Mediators; City Disputes Panel; Int. Bar Assn.; American Bar Assn.; The Chartered Inst. Of Arbitrators; Soc. of Professionals in Dispute Resolution (SPIDR); International Academy of Mediators (IAM).
Career: Formerly senior founding partner and Head of Litigation, *Dickstein, Shapiro & Morin*, New York and Washington DC. Since arriving in the UK in 1996, has successfully mediated more than eighty major disputes in this country and Europe. He was organiser of and lead-off speaker on 'Introduction to ADR', part of the Judicial Studies Board's Stage 1 seminars for UK judges and is a lecturer and writer on mediation issues.
Publications: Publications include 'Consumer Participation in Antitrust Class Actions,' 41 ABA Antitrust I.J. 257 (1972); 'Management of Consumer Class Actions after Eissen', 26 Mercer I.Rev. 851 (1975) (with James vanR. Springer); 'Trained Neutrals', New Law Journal (March 1997); 'Expert Mediators Not Experts as Mediators', 16 CEDR Resolutions (Spring 1997); 'ADR in the Commercial Court – One Year Later', 17 CEDR Resolutions (Summer 1997); 'ADR Under the New Civil Procedure Rules', Durham Univ. I.Rev. (Summer 1999); 'Pushing the Envelope – Selective Techniques in Tough Mediations', [2000] ADRLJ 89,117.

SIBLEY, LL.B., F.C.I. ARB., Edward
Sibley & Co, London (020) 7395 9790
Specialisation: Senior partner. Principal area of practice is international and domestic civil litigation, arbitration and mediation, including insurance and re-insurance disputes, professional negligence, product liability and civil fraud. Has acted as a mediator and advocate in over 100 commercial mediations. He has addressed conferences worldwide on issues relating to the conflict of laws and comparative law.
Prof. Memberships: Member of the Union Inter-

nationale des Avocats; American Bar Association; International Bar Association; The Law Society and the New York State Bar.
Career: Qualified in 1965. Articled with *Clifford Turner* 1961-64 and joined *Berwin & Co.* upon qualification. Became a partner in 1968. Thereafter became a founder partner *Berwin Leighton* in 1970 and managing partner 1984-86. Also admitted New York State Bar 1985 and founder member and director of the Centre for Dispute Resolution (CEDR) 1989; CEDR appointed mediator 1992; Solicitor Advocate Higher Courts (Civil) 1995; Fellow of the Chartered Institute of Arbitrators 1999.
Publications: Publications include 'The European Community 1992 and Beyond'.
Personal: Born 21st July 1935. Educated at Rhymney Grammar School and University of Wales, Aberystwyth 1958-61 (First Class Honours and Sir Samuel Evans Prize for the best student of the year). Member of Reform Club and MCC.

SMITH, Quentin
Addleshaw Booth & Co, Manchester
(0161) 934 6000
qps@addleshaw-booth.co.uk
Specialisation: Professional negligence; personal injury (employers liability; motor; public liability); health and safety; insurance. Extensive mediation experience with success rate in excess of 90% in wide range of disputes including professional negligence, personal injury, defamation, partnership, property, commercial, insurance and employment.
Career: Articled clerk, solicitor and partner at *James Chapman & Co* 1986-96; partner *Addleshaw Sons and Latham* 1996-97; partner *Addleshaw Booth & Co* 1997 to date. Frequent speaker at conferences and seminars.
Publications: Articles for various publications.
Personal: Arts; sports; travel.

TABAKIN, Roger
Roger Tabakin – Sole Practitioner, London
(020) 8374 2562
rogertabakin@compuserve.com
Specialisation: One of the first accountants to undertake commercial mediations in the UK, having mediated since 1991. Member CEDR Training Faculty since 1993. On number of specialist mediation panels. Mediated disputes involving professional negligence; acquisition and mergers; intellectual property; partnership, shareholder disagreements; consequential loss, of profit claims; insurance and pension; generally issues where professional accountancy background is of value to the process. Undertaken number of commercial mediations and achieved significant record of settled outcomes.
Prof. Memberships: Institute of Chartered Accountants of Scotland: Society of Chartered Accountants, South Africa: CEDR Accredited Mediator 1991.
Career: Provides consultancy service as facilitator, negotiator, mediator. Actively assists training commercial mediators; development of facilitative techniques for commercial dispute resolution; participating with establishment of social dispute resolution processes in Russian Federation. Possesses skills and awareness essential for multi-national and cross-cultural business disputes.
Personal: Married. Two children. Theatre; mountain walking; skiing; cooking; African tribal art; limited edition graphics; attempting to learn Japanese.

TEMPLE, Euan
Toller Hales & Collcutt, Northampton
(01604) 258558
euan.temple@tollers.co.uk
Specialisation: European law, M&A work, competition law, MBOs, joint ventures, e-commerce, partnerships, intellectual property licensing, R&D contracts, commercial mediation.
Prof. Memberships: Accredited mediator 1990 with ADR group; Law Society's European Group.
Career: Graduated Cambridge. Qualified 1970. Has lectured on mediation at home and abroad, and contributed articles on the subject. A regular speaker at conferences on e-commerce, competition and commercial law.
Personal: Western and central European history. Hockey (player and umpire).

TESTER, Stephen
CMS Cameron McKenna, London
(020) 7367 2894
skt@cmck.com
Specialisation: Practises in construction and surveyors' PI, Contractors All Risk Insurance, D&O and Transaction Support Insurance. Clients include insurance and reinsurance companies, Lloyds syndicates, insurance brokers and construction companies.
Prof. Memberships: Society of Construction Law. CEDR Accredited Mediator.
Career: KCS Wimbledon and St. John's College Cambridge. Qualified 1981. Partner since 1988.
Personal: Interests include family and friends, golf and squash.

WILLIS, Tony
Panel of Independent Mediators, London
(020) 7221 5893
tony.willis@cliffordchance.com
Specialisation: Independent mediator in business, financial and regulatory matters. Appointed direct and also by institutions such as CEDR, ADR Group, In Place of Strife, Chartered Institute of Arbitrators, InterMediation, CPR (NY) and others. Mediating since the early 1990s and full time mediator since 1998. More than 200 mediations conducted on a wide variety of subjects including oil and gas, insolvency, banking, construction and engineering, IT, insurance, shareholder disputes, partnership disputes, professional negligence, employment, pharmaceuticals, tax, charities and many others. Also instructed as settlement counsel.
Career: LLB (New Zealand) 1966, Barrister and Solicitor High Court of New Zealand, Solicitor England and Wales, 1971, partner *Clifford Chance* 1973, joint managing partner 1987-89, head of litigation practice 1989-96, consultant 1998-2001, CEDR accredited mediator, Fellow Chartered Institute of Arbitrators, Fellow International Academy of Mediators (US), International Panelist CPR Institute for Dispute Resolution (NY), Advanced Panel LEADR (Australia and New Zealand), founding member Panel of Independent Mediators (PIM).
Personal: Born 1941. Married with six children. Lives in central London.

WINKWORTH-SMITH, John
John Winkworth-Smith, Bakewell (01629) 640269

ARBITRATION (INTERNATIONAL)

London: 84; *Profiles*: 86

OVERVIEW: *Chambers* strongly emphasises that, once again, we have considered for research only the expertise of arbitration units based in the UK. Most of the firms included have strong overseas practices, which by the very nature of the specialist area act in tandem with London. For an overview of the strengths of these entities we refer you to *Chambers Global.*

RESEARCH APPROVED BY BMRB: *For this edition,* Chambers' *researchers conducted 6,552 interviews – 4,419 with law firms, 554 with barristers and 1,579 with clients.*

The validity of the research was scrutinised by BMRB International, who audited both the methodology and the results at our offices in July 2001. They interviewed Chambers' *researchers and cross-checked sample interviews. Details of the audit appear on page 7.*

LONDON

ARBITRATION (INTERNATIONAL) • London	Ptnrs	Assts
1 Clifford Chance	4	13
2 Freshfields Bruckhaus Deringer	5	16
Herbert Smith	6	12
3 Allen & Overy	5	18
4 Wilmer, Cutler & Pickering	2	10
5 Baker & McKenzie	5	19
Linklaters	5	10
Lovells	3	6
Masons	n/a	n/a
Norton Rose	3	7
Shearman & Sterling	n/a	6
Simmons & Simmons	3	8
6 Clyde & Co	4	10
CMS Cameron McKenna	7	n/a
Debevoise & Plimpton	1	3
Holman Fenwick & Willan	n/a	n/a
Ince & Co	*	*
Richards Butler	n/a	n/a

LEADING INDIVIDUALS	
1 **BEECHEY John** Clifford Chance	**BORN Gary** Wilmer, Cutler & Pickering
LEW Julian Herbert Smith	**MARRIOTT Arthur** Debevoise & Plimpton
2 **CAPPER Phillip** Lovells	**GILL Judith** Allen & Overy
RAWDING Nigel Freshfields Bruckhaus	**SHEPPARD Audley** Clifford Chance
3 **BRYNMOR THOMAS David** Herbert Smith	**COLBRIDGE Christopher** Shearman & Sterling
CROALL Philip Freshfields Bruckhaus	**LAMBERT Robert** Clifford Chance
MITCHARD Paul Wilmer, Cutler & Pickering	**STYLE Christopher** Linklaters
4 **DAVIS Michael** Herbert Smith	**FRASER David** Baker & McKenzie
NAIRN Karyl Simmons & Simmons	**SHACKLETON Stewart** Simmons & Simmons
WINTER Jeremy Baker & McKenzie	
UP AND COMING	
SHORE Larry Herbert Smith	

This book is the product of 6,552 1/2-hour interviews. See p.7 for BMRB audit.
Within each band, firms are listed alphabetically. *See individuals' profiles p.86*
** See editorial entries for explanation of team sizes*

Clifford Chance (see firm details p.919) Commands "*enormous admiration and respect*" from rival firms. Judged "*first port of call,*" the dedicated international arbitration group (as distinct from the teams conducting specialist shipping, commodity and insurance arbitrations) is felt to boast a greater "*depth and quality*" of work than its closest rivals. The team, which conducts its own advocacy, is "*cohesive and well-formed,*" and thought "*better integrated*" with its foreign offices than others. **John Beechey** (see p.86) is applauded by clients as its "*great strength*" for his "*exceptional dedication to the subject and the international outlook he brings.*" His "*energy and drive*" are appreciated by peers. The "*brilliant and dynamic*" **Audley Sheppard** (see p.88) is a "*rising star,*" while **Robert Lambert** (see p.87) is "*damn good and clearly knows his stuff.*" The group acted for the Czech Republic in defence of a claim brought by a Dutch company under the Netherlands-Czech Republic Bilateral Investment Treaty, which concerned investment in the Czech Republic's first private television company.

Freshfields Bruckhaus Deringer (see firm details p.964) A team respected by clients for its "*dynamic approach*" and which routinely conducts its own advocacy at procedural hearings. Although the London office is deemed less of a force than its "*huge powerhouse of an operation*" in Paris, and some see Nigel Blackaby's move to Paris as an "*indication of where the practice is developing,*" the "*cross-fertilisation*" between the two offices is undoubtedly a benefit to London. Attracts stand-alone clients, and offers all the multi-jurisdictional resources of its global network, boasting particular experience of bilateral investment treaties. "*Impressive*" **Nigel Rawding** (see p.87) is a "*first class operator*" with "*star quality*" while his colleague **Philip Croall** (see p.87) is thought to "*keep a low profile*" yet "*possesses unquestionable intellectual ability and stamina.*" The team has a mixed practice. Represented a major international food and drinks conglomerate in disputes arising out of an Indian joint venture which included ICC London arbitration proceedings and related Indian actions.

Herbert Smith (see firm details p.993) Although some peers opine that the team is mainly "*steeped in litigation,*" the clear majority judges the Herbert Smith arbitration outfit "*enormously strong.*" It is perceived to take on "*complex cases*" and to benefit from its strength on the Asian continent. Conducts its own advocacy. "*Stellar member of the international arbitration community,*" **Dr Julian Lew** (see p.87) may be "*learned and senior*" but "*has his finger on the international pulse.*" His status is complemented by the "*strong team*" beneath him. Clients typically believe that **David Brynmor Thomas** (see p.86) is "*formidably talented*" and "*definitely one to watch.*" "*Respected operator,*" **Michael Davis** (see p.202) is skilled in the construction and engineering fields, while the up-and-coming **Larry Shore** (see p.88) adds US advocacy skills and a "*great sense of organisation and focus*" to the group. Over 50% of the arbitrations currently being conducted have their seat in countries outside the UK. Acted for a Texan construction company in an ICC arbitration arising out of the refurbishment of a luxury hotel in Egypt (under Egyptian law, sited in Cairo). Also represented a Swiss pharmaceutical company in an ICC arbitration in Paris concerning approvals and distribution of a prescription drug in the PRC and Hong Kong.

Allen & Overy (see firm details p.856) Despite the departure of the charismatic David St John Sutton to the bar, the group is commended by peers for its efforts to "*improve*" an already "*admired*" practice. **Judith Gill** (see p.87) now leads the charge of a dedicated arbitration group: she is described as "*a quality act who knows her law, takes a common-sense approach and is prepared to roll up her sleeves.*" Benefitting from the resources of established arbitration practices within its network, international matters account for over 90% of the team's workload. The group is acting for a substantial private power company concerning some US$295 million of claims against Eastern European state entities, following investments made during the privatisation of the power industry.

Wilmer, Cutler & Pickering (see firm details p.1184) An "*international arbitration boutique*" that, though comparatively small, "*punches well above its weight*" and is "*immensely busy*" on international work. Clients and competitors comment on the group as "*truly innovative in its submissions,*" the "*genuinely international team*" conducts its own advocacy. The majority of clients are stand-alone, although the team's sectoral strengths in telecoms and oil and gas are driven by the firm's overall reputation. Acknowledged to get premium quality arbitrations, it obtained a favourable result in the largest arbitration in ICC history, representing Deutsche Telecom in a €30 billion case under ICC rules. Contemporaries aver that "*hard-working and energetic*" **Gary Born** (see p.86) is a "*real player and original thinker,*" while his colleague **Paul Mitchard** (see p.87) is "*tremendously effective.*"

Baker & McKenzie (see firm details p.868) A "*strong and numerous*" team, deemed by rivals "*increasingly impressive,*" handles a substantial level of international work and is said to do "*particularly well out of Eastern Europe.*" Integrated with its global network (which boasts specialist practitioners in 35 countries) it is notably strong in construction and engineering projects. "*Pleasant to work with and pragmatic,*" **Jeremy Winter** (see p.88) heads the department and is widely praised as producing "*tremendous work.*" "*Shrewd and dignified operator,*" **David Fraser** (see p.87) is judged to play a "*significant role.*" The group acted in an arbitration between a German equipment supplier and an American engineering company, which concerned the construction of three power plants in Latin America, valued at US$38 million.

Linklaters (see firm details p.1042) A mixed practice that is thought to rely heavily on commercial litigation. With the international expertise available across the alliance partners, it has developed a free web-based service offering access to clauses on dispute resolution, information on European jurisdictions and links to arbitration and mediation sites. **Christopher Style** (see p.582) is principally regarded as a litigator but is esteemed as a "*solid arbitrator who on the right case is up there with the best.*"

Lovells (see firm details p.1044) Possessing general international arbitration capability, the firm has consolidated its position through the expansion of its European network. In the past year it launched an internet based arbitration drafting aid. The team's greatest asset is still felt to be the presence of the "*tough and enormously busy*" **Phillip Capper** (see p.86), judged by peers as a "*serious contender*" on the construction side and "*a great, great catch for Lovells.*" Increasingly active as advocates in international arbitrations, the group acted for a US governmental agency in respect of a multi-million pound loan facility granted to a plant in Romania. Active on both the claimant and respondent side in UNCITRAL arbitrations. The firm is representing an international engineering and construction management company in two parallel ICC proceedings against a state-owned energy company concerning an infrastructure project in a former Eastern Block country. The seat of the arbitration is England.

Masons (see firm details p.1056) Despite the perception that it has yet to replace Phillip Capper, the group typically attracts comment that it is "*enormous on domestic and international construction disputes.*" It also offers experience in the energy, infrastructure and IT sectors. In the construction arena, the team consistently proves "*challenging to beat*" and demonstrates a "*unique style,*" fielding a "*large number of lawyers on each case.*" Typical clients are major contractors, state governments, parastatal organisations, airport owners, energy companies and operators of projects. Among a "*determined and experienced*" team is construction specialist Robert Knutson.

Norton Rose (see firm details p.1082) Weakened by the departure of Michael Lee for the bar, the team led by Juliet Blanch is yet to make the market aware of its individual stars. Nevertheless 2000 was a strong year for the team that advised on arbitrations across the fields of construction and engineering, oil and gas, shipping, intellectual property and insurance. Due to the international resources of the group, it has experience of arbitrations subject to a wide range of jurisdictions. The team conducts the whole of the arbitration, notably including oral and written submissions. Currently acting on the Solitaire arbitration, on its fourth hearing and one of the largest arbitrations ever seen in London. The team represented an Indian publishing company in an LCIA arbitration subject to English law against a Swiss corporation (value of $450 million).

Shearman & Sterling (see firm details p.1125) Although seen to be "*still in the process of establishing itself,*" the London international team is described as "*a classy operation.*" Viewed by rivals as in the shadow of a strong Paris practice led by Emmanuel Gaillard, they nonetheless insist that "*London is not to be underestimated.*" Clients talk of a young, international and "*expert*" team, fully dedicated to the area. The "*dynamic and charming*" **Christopher Colbridge** (see p.87) wins praise for his "*commercial understanding*" and is seen to work "*conscientiously*" for the interests of clients. Has experience of arbitrations under a variety of governing laws and arbitral rules around the world. Currently advising clients in two ICSID arbitrations against states. Power, pharmaceuticals and mining feature heavily in the group's portfolio of clients. Instructed in a dispute involving sums in excess of $1.6 billion by a multi-national corporation with mining interests in Australasia. The contract provided for ICC arbitration in London under the laws of the Australasian state. Also representing a South American bank in an LCIA arbitration held in London.

Simmons & Simmons (see firm details p.1132) Although many point to "*bright and personable*" **Karyl Nairn**'s (see p.87) "*other interests,*" she is nonetheless felt by many to be "*pushing hard and getting the practice on the map.*" **Stewart Shackleton** is deemed "*impressive if academic.*" The firm boasts some impressive clients of the ilk of Visa International and Railtrack, winning repeat work across the railway, telecoms, technology, international trade and finance sectors. A broad based practice, which can draw upon the international resources of the firm, the London team regularly conducts its own advocacy. Acted for VISA International in a court challenge to its arbitration processes in London. Advised a state entity in relation to an aircraft leasing dispute in an ICC arbitration in Paris.

Clyde & Co (see firm details p.921) A dominant player in arbitrations in the maritime sphere, it offers particular expertise of international trade and insurance (notably reinsurance and recoveries for political risk indemnities.) John Whittaker, Clive Thorpe and Jonathan Wood all play a significant part in the practice. Boasts familiarity with various foreign jurisdictions through its international offices in Asia, Europe and South America. Aside from certain categories of high volume arbitrations such as commodities, insurance and shipping in which it is recognised as "*a big hitter,*" the firm was involved in a significant number of international arbitrations mainly before the ICC, LCIA. Is involved in 14% of all current LCIA arbitrations. Handled a London arbitration for an overseas market concerning an alleged mass tort, and has been involved in arbitrations arising from the collapse of the Indonesian economy.

CMS Cameron McKenna (see firm details p.922) The international arbitration group is drawn from within the litigation, insurance, construction and banking groups. A "*good solid*" team led by Neil Aitken it is not seen to marshal "*quite the same depth of expertise*" as the firms ranked above it. Conducts arbitrations in a wide variety of countries, particularly those of Eastern Europe. Has carried out over 63 arbitrations this year. Acted on a patent licence dispute (with a value of approximately $1 billion) between English and Japanese parties, in an arbitration sited in London and conducted under ICC rules.

Debevoise & Plimpton (see firm details p.938) The "*knowledgeable, articulate and well-informed,*" **Arthur Marriott QC** enjoys a "*massive profile*" and is felt to "*generate much work on his own.*" As "*an incredibly responsive arbitrator,*" he has extensive experience as counsel in all forms of international commercial arbitration throughout the world, including oil and gas, civil engineering, construction and joint venture disputes. Currently representing a major US manufacturer in a dispute with a German company that has involved litigation both in American and English courts, as well as a simultaneous ICC arbitration in London.

Holman Fenwick & Willan (see firm details p.999) Perceived by many interviewees to be a force on domestic shipping and international commodities arbitrations, the firm is not thought to possess quite the range of the market leaders. Despite this it offers experience of a far wider range of areas of arbitration, including banking and financial disputes, engineering and construction claims, energy, professional negligence, corporate fraud, information technology, and Sovereign debt and asset recovery. The team led by **Noel Campbell,** has acted for a range of multi-national clients in institutional and ad hoc international arbitrations.

Ince & Co (see firm details p.1008) (Can draw upon 41 partners and 75 assistants.) Another maritime firm considered to be "*strong in its own niche.*" The team offers experience of arbitrations in London and New York with particular expertise in the commodities markets. These typically concern the international sale and purchase of oil, gas, agro-chemicals, grain, sugar, coffee and metals. Occasionally, UN sanctions lead to disputes. These may be in court or in specialised arbitration tribunals such as GAFTA, FOSFA, RSA and LME. Other disputes handled include marine, energy, and land-based disputes fought in a variety of arbitration tribunals such as the ICC and LCIA. Johnathan Lux heads the team.

Richards Butler (see firm details p.1107) Peers agree it handles a "*greater breadth of international arbitrations*" than many other traditional maritime and insurance firms. John Emmott heads the group. There are two distinct sides to its arbitration practice. The first comprises a broad raft of experience in ICC and UNCITRAL arbitrations in particular, relating to oil, construction, computer technology and defence. The second comprises shipping or commodities related arbitrations, which involve charterers, salvors, shipowners, cargo owners, pilots and crew members. Advised government entities in Uzbekistan on international arbitration.

LEADERS IN ARBITRATION (INTERNATIONAL)

BEECHEY, John
Clifford Chance, London (020) 7600 1000
john.beechey@cliffordchance.com
Specialisation: Partner and head of international commercial arbitration group dealing with all aspects of international arbitration and ADR.
Prof. Memberships: Fellow of the Chartered Institute of Arbitrators; Member of the Executive Committee of the Board of the American Arbitration Association; Chair, Corporate Counsel Committee of the AAA; appointed to the AAA Arbitrators' Panel in 1991; Member of the Board of the London Court of International Arbitration; Member of the ICC UK Arbitration Panel since March 1992 and a British representative on the ICC Commission. Member of the Council of the ICC Institute; appointed to the Arbitrator panel of the Regional Centre for International Arbitration in Cairo and of Korea Commercial Arbitration Board in 1995.
Career: MA (Oxon) French and German. Partner *Clifford Chance* 1983.

BORN, Gary
Wilmer, Cutler & Pickering, London
(020) 7872 1000
gborn@wilmer.com
Specialisation: Managing partner in international arbitration/litigation department. Principal area of practice is international arbitration. Represents European, US, Asian and other corporate clients in international commercial arbitration under all major institutional rules (ICC, LCIA, AAA, Stockholm, IACAC) and ad hoc (UNCITRAL) in all leading fora. Other main area of practice is international litigation (US) including advice on issues of jurisdiction, foreign sovereign immunity, international judicial assistance, conflict of laws. Particular expertise in joint ventures, telecommunications, M&A, construction, sales and agency disputes.
Prof. Memberships: American Law Institute, International Bar Association, American Bar Association, British Institute of International and Comparative Law, American Society of International Law.
Career: Joined *Wilmer, Cutler & Pickering* in 1984. Became a partner in 1988 and managing partner in London office in 1991.
Publications: Author of 'International Commercial Arbitration' (2nd edition, Kluwer 2000), 'International Civil Litigation in US Courts' (3rd edition, Kluwer 1996) and 'International Arbitration and Foreign Selection Agreements' (Kluwer 1999). Has undertaken numerous speaking engagements.
Personal: Educated at Haverford College, Haverford, Pennsylvania 1973-78 (BA, summa cum laude) and University of Pennsylvania Law School 1978-81 (J.D., summa cum laude); law clerk to Chief Justice William H. Rehnquist and Judge Henry J. Friendly. Proficient in German.

BRYNMOR THOMAS, David
Herbert Smith, London (020) 7374 8000
Specialisation: International arbitration and litigation, particularly in relation to major projects. Has acted in ad hoc arbitrations and arbitrations under the rules of the ICC, LCIA, SIAC and UNCITRAL involving parties and transactions from the UK, the US, Africa, India, the Gulf States and South-East Asia. Also has experience in project related expert determinations. Drafts and advises on dispute resolution provisions for projects.
Prof. Memberships: The Law Society, the City of London Solicitors' Company, London Court of International Arbitration, Institute of Arbitrators, including the Arbitration Practice sub-committee of the CIArb. CIArb representation to the UNCITRAL Working Group on arbitration. Member of the GCC Commercial Arbitration Centre Panel of Arbitrators.
Career: Articled at *Herbert Smith,* 1991 to 1993. Member of the *Herbert Smith* construction and engineering department since qualification in September 1993. Became a partner in 2000.
Personal: Born 1964. Originally qualified in and practised Medicine. Educated at the University of Edinburgh (MB, ChB 1987).

CAPPER, Phillip
Lovells, London (020) 7296 2000
phillip.capper@lovells.com
Specialisation: Partner, specialising in International Arbitration, Engineering and Construction. Recognised authority on engineering and construction risks and contracts. Substantial experience of international arbitration; as adviser, advocate and arbitrator. Worked on projects for highways, rail, power, defence, and process plant, building and construction in many countries worldwide. Lead counsel for TML, the Channel Tunnel contract consortium, under English and French law – keynote speaker on this at US AAA DART conference. Advised foreign state electricity generator/distributors, national gas distributors, high-speed rail authorities and suppliers, metro and light rail projects and privately financed infrastructure projects. Has sat as Arbitrator in ICC and LCIA arbitrations. Drafted the disputes clauses in standard forms NEC 2nd edition and ICE 7th. Engaged as expert by French Association of International Contractors (SEFI) to evaluate FIDIC's EPC Silver Book.
Prof. Memberships: UK member of the ICC Commission on International Arbitration in Paris. He directs the International Diploma of the Chartered Institute of Arbitrators.
Career: Formerly partner in construction and engineering and Head of International Arbitration at *Masons*. He is a visiting Professor in Construction Law and Arbitration at King's College London, and before moving to London in 1988 he was Chairman of the Faculty of Law at the University of Oxford. He has been a Fellow of Keble College Oxford for 23 years.
Publications: For CIRIA's 'Client's Guide to Risk in Construction' wrote legal risk management. Founding Editor of 'Construction Industry Law Letter' from 1983 to 1990. Recent publications include Construction Industry Arbitrations in Sweet & Maxwell's 'Handbook of Arbitration Practice' 3rd ed, and former General Editor of 'Emden's Construction Law'.
Personal: Born 1952. French language.

COLBRIDGE, Christopher
Shearman & Sterling, London (020) 7655 5000
CColbridge@shearman.com
Specialisation: Represents *Shearman & Sterling's* International Commercial Arbitration Group in London. Has acted as Counsel in international arbitrations, both institutional (ICC, LCIA, ICSID and other rules) and ad hoc around the world. Has represented multi-national corporations and governments in disputes involving international contracts, particularly investments, infrastructure and energy projects. Also specialises in law and practice of international litigation, conflict of laws and jurisdiction.
Prof. Memberships: London Court of International Arbitration. International Arbitration Institute. IBA.
Career: Qualified England & Wales, 1992. Admitted to Paris bar, 1999. *Clifford Chance* 1990-99.
Personal: Born 1967. Educated at Kings College, University of London (LLB Hons), 1987. University of Paris I Panthéon-Sorbonne (Licence and Maitrise in French private law), 1989.

CROALL, Philip
Freshfields Bruckhaus Deringer, London
(020) 7936 4000
philip.croall@freshfields.com
Specialisation: Partner specialising in arbitration, ADR and commercial litigation. Handles all aspects of international commercial arbitration work. Has appeared on Counsel in arbitrations under rules of the major arbitration institutions including the ICC, the LCIA as well as in ad hoc arbitration under the UNCITRAL Rules. Speaks regularly at seminars and writes articles on arbitration and international dispute resolution techniques. Also involved in all kinds of commercial litigation including cases relating to banking and financial services regulation.
Prof. Memberships: Associate of the Chartered Institute of Arbitrators.
Career: Qualified at *Freshfields* in 1985. Partner at *Freshfields* 1992.
Personal: Born 22 August 1959.

DAVIS, Michael
Herbert Smith, London (020) 7374 8000
See under Construction, p.202

FRASER, David
Baker & McKenzie, London (020) 7919 1000
david.fraser@bakernet.com
Specialisation: Business disputes with experience in the areas of insurance and reinsurance, trade finance, sovereign immunity, professional liability, carriage by sea, telecommunications and corporate joint ventures. Has acted as counsel in and managed several major commercial arbitrations in England and elsewhere and has brought a number of cases to trial in the Commercial Court and the Court of Appeal in London. Has recently represented the owners of the Kazakhstan metals industry in complex arbitration proceedings against former joint venture partners. Led the team acting for Geest in the banana wars with Fyffes. Acts for a number of professional consultancy firms including Tillinghast and LEK. Led the team acting for Camelot in proceedings for judicial review of a decision by the National Lottery Commission on granting a new licence. Adviser on crisis management and senior management responsibilities. Member of City Disputes Panel Users Committee and LCIA.
Prof. Memberships: The Law Society and New York Bar.
Career: Qualified in 1973. Joined *Baker & McKenzie* in 1975, becoming a partner in 1982.
Publications: 'Arbitration of International Commercial Disputes Under English Law -The American Review of International Arbitration' 1997/vol.8. no.1.
Personal: Education: University of Birmingham. Lives in London. Born 1948.

GILL, Judith A E
Allen & Overy, London (020) 7330 3779
judith.gill@allenovery.com
Specialisation: Specialises in arbitration and commercial litigation, both domestic and international, particularly arbitration under LCIA and ICC rules and handles general commercial litigation for a number of large quoted public limited companies on a range of matters including warranty claims, pensions litigation and insurance disputes.
Prof. Memberships: Law Society; City of London Solicitors' Company; Chartered Institute of Arbitrators; International Arbitration Club; Institute of Advanced Legal Studies.
Career: Articled *Allen & Overy* (1983). Qualified (1985). Partner (1992). Director of the London Court of International Arbitration.
Publications: Co-Author of the 21st Edition of 'Russell on Arbitration'.
Personal: Born 1959. Educated at Worcester College, Oxford University 1979-82. MA (Jurisprudence) 1988. Diploma in International Commercial Arbitration, University of London, 1990. Lives in Surrey.

LAMBERT, Robert
Clifford Chance, London (020) 7600 1000
robert.lambert@cliffordchance.com
Specialisation: Partner specialising in the law and practice of international arbitration, conflict of laws and jurisdiction. Particular experience in disputes involving international engineering, construction and infrastructure projects. Represents clients as counsel (advocate) before domestic and international arbitral tribunals. Regularly advises on the drafting of dispute resolution provisions for projects and other commercial contracts.
Career: Oxford University (St Edmund Hall), BA (Hons) Law (1st class). Trained *Clifford Chance*; qualified 1989.

LEW, Julian
Herbert Smith, London (020) 7374 8000
Specialisation: Head of international commercial arbitration practice group. Partner in litigation and arbitration division. 1970 (Bar) 1981 (Solicitor) 1985 (Attorney-at-Law, New York). Main area of practice is international commercial arbitration, acting as an adviser and representing clients in all the major forms of arbitrations. These arbitrations concern all kinds of international contracts, particularly engineering and infrastructure projects, investments, distribution, intellectual property licenses and joint ventures. Has also been appointed as an arbitrator in ICC, LCIA, AAA, Ad hoc and other arbitrations. Author of numerous publications including: 'Applicable Law in International Commercial Arbitration' (1978). Editor, 'Contemporary Problems in International Commercial Arbitration' (1985), 'The Immunity of Arbitrators' (1990) and 'Enforcement of Foreign Judgements' (1994). Visiting Professor and Head of the School of International Arbitration, Centre for Commercial Law Studies, Queen Mary, University of London. Director, London Court of International Arbitration; Member of Council of ICC Institute of World Business Law; Member, ICC Commission on International Commercial Arbitration.
Personal: Born 3rd February 1948. LLB (Hons) London, 1969; Academy of International Law 1970-71; and Doctorat special en droit international, Université Catholique de Louvain, Belgium, 1977.

MARRIOTT Q.C., Arthur
Debevoise & Plimpton, London
(020) 7786 9000

MITCHARD, Paul
Wilmer, Cutler & Pickering, London
(020) 7872 1000
Specialisation: Partner. Main areas of practice are international arbitration and commercial litigation, covering the conduct of ICC, LCIA, RSA, Lloyd's arbitrations, commercial, financial and administrative and public law disputes. Also handles dispute resolution and mediation. Accredited CEDR mediator, member of CPR's panel of distinguished neutrals and a Fellow of the Chartered Institute of Arbitrators. Has represented domestic and international companies and State organisations in many major disputes. Has given seminars in London, the USA and the Middle East on international arbitration.
Prof. Memberships: Law Society, American Bar Association, International Bar Association, City of London Solicitors' Company.
Career: Qualified in 1977. Worked at *Slaughter and May* 1977-84 in London and Hong Kong. Joined *Simmons & Simmons* in 1984, becoming a partner in 1985 and was head of litigation 1994-98 before joining the London office of *Wilmer, Cutler & Pickering* in January 1999.
Personal: Born 2nd January 1952. Attended Taunton School 1960-70 and Lincoln College, Oxford 1971-74. Leisure interests include travel, reading and walking. Lives in Chalfont St. Giles, Bucks.

NAIRN, Karyl
Simmons & Simmons, London (020) 7628 2020
karyl.nairn@simmons-simmons.com
Specialisation: Major cases in 2000-2001 include institutional and ad hoc arbitrations and mediations for various Western and Central European trading companies, an international sporting organisation, a worldwide banking consortium, an international technology company and a British railway company.
Prof. Memberships: Member LCIA. Fellow, CIA. Member for Australia (alternate), International Court of Arbitration of the ICC.
Career: Qualified as barrister and solicitor, Supreme Court of Western Australia, 1988; admitted as a solicitor in England and Wales in 1991. Joined *Simmons & Simmons* 1991; Partner in 1996; Head of International Arbitration Group.
Personal: University of Western Australia (B.Juris [Hons], LLB [Hons]) and LSE, University of London (LLM).

RAWDING, Nigel
Freshfields Bruckhaus Deringer, London
(020) 7936 4000
nigel.rawding@freshfields.com
Specialisation: Partner in litigation department and London head of *Freshfields'* London/Paris International Arbitration Group. International dispute resolution specialist representing clients in major commercial disputes involving litigation, international arbitration and ADR procedures. International arbitration experience includes ICC, LCIA, UNCI-

TRAL and ad hoc cases. Litigation experience comprises a wide variety of High Court commercial cases. Co-author of 'The *Freshfields* Guide to Arbitration and ADR' (Second revised edition Kluwer, 1999). Member of ICC Commission on International Arbitration and director of the LCIA. Regular contributor to arbitration journals and conference speaker on subjects relating to the resolution of international disputes.

SHACKLETON, Stewart
Simmons & Simmons, London (020) 7628 2020

SHEPPARD, Audley W
Clifford Chance, London (020) 7600 1000
audley.sheppard@cliffordchance.com
Specialisation: Partner specialising in the resolution of disputes, in particular arising out of infrastructure projects (including investment, energy and construction disputes).
Career: Lindisfarne College, Hastings, NZ; Victoria University of Wellington, NZ (LLB Hons 1983) (BCA 1984); Cambridge University, UK; (LLM 1986). Articled *Bell Gully Buddle Weir,* NZ; qualified New Zealand 1985, England 1990, made partner *Clifford Chance* 1995.
Personal: Sports, theatre. Born 1960; resides London.

SHORE, Larry
Herbert Smith, London (020) 7374 8000
laurence.shore@herbertsmith.com
Specialisation: Acting as counsel in international commercial arbitrations.
Prof. Memberships: London Court of International Arbitration; Research Advisory Committee of the Global Center for Dispute Resolution Research.
Career: Joined *Herbert Smith* in 1995. Became a partner in 1999. 1995: Attorney Adviser International, Office of the Legal Adviser, U.S. State Department. 1989-95: associate, *Williams & Connolly* (Washington, DC). 1983-86: Assistant Professor of History, Queen's University (Canada).
Publications: 'The Advantages of Arbitration for Banking Institutions', Journal of International Banking Law (Nov. 1999); 'Making Applicants Take Evidence Properly: Challenges to Letters of Request', International Commercial Litigation (July/August 1998); 'Southern Capitalists' (U. of N. Carolina Press 1986).
Personal: J.D. with distinction, Emory Univ. School of Law; PhD (History) The Johns Hopkins University; BA with highest honours, The University of North Carolina at Chapel Hill.

STYLE, Christopher
Linklaters, London (020) 7456 4286
christopher.style@linklaters.com
See under Litigation, p.582

WINTER, Jeremy
Baker & McKenzie, London (020) 7919 1000
jeremy.winter@bakernet.com
Specialisation: Arbitration of international construction and projects disputes. Particular expertise in civil engineering matters. Twenty years' experience in a total of 30 countries around the world (particularly Europe, Africa and the Middle East). Conducts own advocacy in arbitration and in High Court. Frequent speaker and writer on construction and arbitration topics.
Prof. Memberships: Hon Fellow of Institution of Civil Engineering Surveyors, Society of Construction Law, Technology and Construction Solicitors Association (Member of Committee). Member of Association for Project Management, Fellow of the Geological Society. Member of LCIA.
Career: Qualified 1979. Joined *Baker & McKenzie* London 1980. Worked in *Baker & McKenzie's* Sydney Office 1982-84. Partner 1987.
Personal: Born 26 December 1953. Warwick University (LLB Hons 1975). Lives in Toys Hill, Kent.

ASSET FINANCE & LEASING

RESEARCH APPROVED BY BMRB: *For this edition,* Chambers' *researchers conducted 6,552 interviews – 4,419 with law firms, 554 with barristers and 1,579 with clients.*

The validity of the research was scrutinised by BMRB International, who audited both the methodology and the results at our offices in July 2001. They interviewed Chambers' *researchers and cross-checked sample interviews. Details of the audit appear on page 7.*

TOP IN-HOUSE LAWYERS

Simon ELLIOT, *Barclays Mercantile*

Stephen GARRAT-FROST, *HSBC Holdings*

Janet GREGORY, *GE Capital Equipment*

Ian WOODCOCK, Group Legal, *Royal Bank of Scotland*

Mike KILBEE, *Lloyds TSB*

Mike McCLENAN, *Bank of Scotland Business Banking*

Robin ISACCS, *Lloyds TSB Financing*

"Technically competent – exceptionally good" **Simon Elliot** is rated alongside *"banking expert"* **Stephen Garrat-Frost**, who is *"well experienced"* in the field of asset finance. *"Able"* **Janet Gregory** is *"well suited to the in-house situation." "Excellent"* **Robin Isaccs** is seen as *"central to the operations"* at Lloyds TSB Leasing, and praised for his knowledge of the industry. Newcomers to the list are **Mike Kilbee** and **Mike McClenan** who are both warmly recommended. Still widely endorsed, **Ian Woodcock** now works with Royal Bank of Scotland.

In-House lawyers profiles: p 1193

LONDON

Clifford Chance (see firm details p.919) Considered up with the leaders despite the departure of key figures over recent years, a trend continued with Tom Budgett's move to ANZ. Promising young partners are driving the firm's profile, including **William Glaister** (see p.95) who has returned from the Hong Kong office. In his concentration on aircraft financing, he has been awarded the attribute of "*a star in the making.*" "*Defeasance lease expert*" **Simon Lew** (see p.96) is the up and coming team member who is "*undoubtedly top quality.*" The mainstays of the practice remain **Geoffrey White** (see p.98), "*the great white*" of cross border dealings, and the "*no nonsense*" **Clive Carpenter** (see p.94). Internationally focused, its broad asset finance and leasing work has an aircraft finance weighting. The group has been involved in several defeasance leases, acting for Barclays and ANZ as debt providers on a series of OFSC lease transactions for Cathay Pacific, Lufthansa, British Airways and other airlines. Its non-aircraft related transactions are equally high profile; acting for Deutsche Bank in relation to a $610,000,000 Euro/dollar financing multi-option facility for DHL. Its expertise in the rail sector runs deep; the firm acted for Dresdner Kleinwort Benson in the financing of the manufacture (by ALSTOM Transport) of 200 passenger rolling stock vehicles for the London commuter market. **Clients:** Cathay Pacific; City of Leipzig; Lan Chile; EADS; Barclays; Railtrack.

Freshfields Bruckhaus Deringer (see firm details p.964) No longer considered ahead of the pack despite the increased breadth of a warmly welcomed merger. Its large team is packed with quality. Approaching the sector from a corporate angle, it is at times perceived to be thinly spread. A broad range international asset finance practice, including both rail and the aircraft industry, is strongly supported by a top tax department.The "*highly commercial, but extremely busy*" **Bob Charlton** (see p.94) ("*the deal doer*") was a successful catch for the firm with a big impact on the market. Head of practice, "*effective*" **Tim Lintott's** (see p.96) work is heavily aircraft weighted and "*does his clients proud.*" He led the second European enhanced equipment trust certificate programme for the financing of a new aircraft on behalf of Iberia. "*With a brain the size of a planet*" **Simon Hall** (see p.95) spreads his time between a mixture of aircraft and rail finance and management issues, while "*elder statesman*" **Mark Freeman** (see p.95) handles the exotic products financing. "*Personable and enthusiastic*" **Andrew Littlejohns** (see p.96) has the "*ability to master the complex issues,*" and is joined in the rankings by aircraft specialist, the "*hard working and effective*" **Robert Murphy** (see p.96). The group advised Angel Train Ltd on a novel 'speculative' build contract for the new 'Desiro' trains manufactured by Siemens, and acted for the Post Office on the refinancing of parts of its Postal Sorting Equipment, valued at £241 million, featuring a cross-border QTE leasing arrangement. **Clients:** Bayerische Landesbank; Abbey National; Bank Austria Creditanstalt; BT Cellnet; Airbus Industrie Financial Services; debis Airfinance; Boeing; British Aerospace; Air Nostrum; Iberia.

Norton Rose (see firm details p.1082) Due to the sheer volume of its financing work, ranging from shipping to rail to aviation (with emphasis on the latter), the firm is thought to have caught up with the top ranks. The market commends its sound recruitment, while a respected tax practice and a strong Paris office provides added breadth. "*Top class*" team leader, the "*multi-disciplined*" **Peter Thorne** (see p.97), "*gets the job done without making a meal of it.*" He is supported by the "*confident*" **Jeremy Edwards** (see p.94), who "*works to tight time scales*" in his shipping and aviation finance practice. "*Sensible and able,*" **Giles Brand** (see p.94), and the "*technically astute*" **Jeremy Gibb** (see p.95) add depth to the team. **Gordon Hall's** (see p.95) speciality lies in the rail financing work and the "*commercially good*" **Philip Vallance** (see p.97) sways toward the aircraft work. **Simon Hartley** (see p.768) concentrates on shipping matters, mostly advising lessors while **Alan Crookes** (see p.94) led the team advising HSBC, CCF and Crédit Agricole Indosuez for the French tax lease financing of 18 High Speed Trains and 15 Electric Locomotives for Amtrak. Highlight deals include advice to ING Bank on a $135 million secured term loan and letter of credit facility for Netherlands based Petroplus International. It acted for DHL on the acquisition of 34 Boeing 757s, including their conversion from passenger to freight aircraft, with the financing arranged in a combination of operating finance and UK tax leases, and an umbrella debt facility organised by Deutsche Bank. Also advised P&O North Sea ferries in connection with the NorShip II CV, Dutch limited partnership based financing for the world's largest cruise ferry and the construction of another. **Clients:** ABN AMRO ; BMW; Crédit Lyonnais; SAS; Lloyds TSB Leasing; Abbey National; HSBC Rail; Den Norske Bank; debis Airfinance; Singapore Aircraft Leasing Enterprise; US Export Import Bank.

Allen & Overy (see firm details p.856) The international practice is perceived to have an aviation weighting, though transactions run across the whole spectrum of asset types with shipping work receiving considerable attention. Deals are debt or lease driven, with a diversity of risk. The "*brutally pragmatic*" **Julia Salt** (see p.97) is a leading light in aviation financing and together with "*seasoned practitioner*" **Graham Smith** (see p.97) noted for his attention to detail, forms a formidable double act heading the team. This "*easy to deal with team*" includes "*hard working*" **Mario Jacovides** (see p.95) who "*is making his way*" and "*gets on with things,*" "*the technically astute*" **David Smith** (see p.97) and **Andrew Joyce** (see p.96), who "*doesn't*

ASSET FINANCE & LEASING • London		Ptnrs	Assts
1	Clifford Chance	7	37
	Freshfields Bruckhaus Deringer	7	32
	Norton Rose	14	37
2	Allen & Overy	7	15
	Slaughter and May	4	12
3	Denton Wilde Sapte	7	15
	Linklaters	7	n/a
	Watson, Farley & Williams	9	n/a
4	Lovells	9	7
	White & Case	3	7
5	CMS Cameron McKenna	4	6
	Herbert Smith	6	12
	Simmons & Simmons	5	6
	Theodore Goddard	8	9
6	Beaumont and Son	2	5
	Berwin Leighton Paisner	4	5
	Clark Ricketts	2	n/a
	Harbottle & Lewis	2	3

LEADING INDIVIDUALS		
1	**CARPENTER Clive** Clifford Chance	**CHARLTON Bob** Freshfields Bruckhaus
	HALL Simon Freshfields Bruckhaus	**JOLLIFFE Peter** Slaughter and May
	KINNERSLEY Tom Slaughter and May	**LINTOTT Tim** Freshfields Bruckhaus
	THORNE Peter Norton Rose	**WHITE Geoffrey** Clifford Chance
2	**KAHN Gregory** Denton Wilde Sapte	**LITTLEJOHNS Andrew** Freshfields Bruckhaus
	MILES Adrian Denton Wilde Sapte	
3	**EDWARDS Jeremy** Norton Rose	**GIBBS Ronald** Linklaters
	HALLAM Robin Lovells	**JACOVIDES Mario** Allen & Overy
	OSBORNE David Watson, Farley & Williams	
	SALT Julia Allen & Overy	
4	**BRAND Giles** Norton Rose	**COLLINS Andrew** Denton Wilde Sapte
	GIBB Jeremy Norton Rose	**SMITH Graham** Allen & Overy
	THAINE Colin Denton Wilde Sapte	**TOTT Nicholas** Herbert Smith
	WALKLING Kim Simmons & Simmons	**WATTERS James** Watson, Farley & Williams
5	**FREEMAN Mark** Freshfields Bruckhaus	**GLAISTER William** Clifford Chance
	HALL Gordon Norton Rose	**JOYCE Andrew** Allen & Overy
	SMITH David Allen & Overy	**VALLANCE Philip** Norton Rose
6	**BENSON Justin** White & Case	**CHANDLER Nick** Denton Wilde Sapte
	CROOKES Alan Norton Rose	**MACCARTHY Rory** Theodore Goddard
	RICKETTS Robert Clark Ricketts	**WESTERN Mark** White & Case
UP AND COMING		
	HARTLEY Simon Norton Rose	**LEW Simon** Clifford Chance
	LIDDLE Guy Lovells	**MARKS Lisa** Denton Wilde Sapte
	MURPHY Robert Freshfields Bruckhaus	**WILSON Keith** Lovells

This book is the product of 6,552 1/2-hour interviews. See p.7 for BMRB audit.
Within each band, firms are listed alphabetically. *See individuals' profiles p.94*

make heavy weather." The Kreditanstalt für Wiederaufbau sought the firm's advice on a syndicated term loan financing for the purchase, by an Irish SPV in the Pembroke Group, of ten Boeing 717-200 aircraft, arranged on operating leases. Other aviation activity includes acting for Bouillion in transactions throughout Europe, including leases to Citijet, Tarom, Deutsche BA and Airtours and advising the EIB on the financing of three Airbus aircraft through a French GIE leased to TAP. The ship finance group has focused high value multi-jurisdictional financings, including a tax based operating lease of a luxury cruise ship. The team also acted for Nortel in connection with a large scale financing of €170.6 million worth of equipment (located in ten countries) leased by Dresdner Kleinwort Benson to Viatel. **Clients:** CIBC World Markets; DB Export Leasing; City of Düsseldorf; Citibank; GE Capital; Société Générale.

Slaughter and May (see firm details p.1135) Lacking the volume of its direct competitors yet "*what it does always reaches top quality standards.*" Aviation finance is the field of concentration, where "*a class act team*" matches the client base. The "*excellent*" **Tom Kinnersley** (see p.96) "*doesn't muck about and finds the solutions*" and the "*sensible and commercial*" **Peter Jolliffe** (see p.96) is a "*delight to work with.*" The team mainly acts for manufacturers and lessees, but advises a range of international banks, UK lessors and equipment manufacturers. Mainstay corporate clients provide the key to the team's success. It compiled facility agreements for the financing of Airbus aircraft for BA, supported the financing of aircraft for DHL and for Mobil, and was involved in the financing transactions of its tanker fleet. Once again, the formidable tax department is a great attraction to clients offering efficient and innovative structuring. **Clients:** British Airways; Boeing; Abbey National; BP; Bombardier; GE Capital; Mobil.

Denton Wilde Sapte (see firm details p.939) "*The team to keep an eye on,*" bolstered by its merger after partner loss, it has "*done a great job*" with "*hard working lawyers across the board.*" As "*a leading guru in the field,*" **Adrian Miles** holds the ground here and is experienced on the UK tax based lease front. The "*committed*" **Gregory Kahn** "*understands commercial reality.*" Arrived back from Paris, the head of aviation finance, **Colin Thaine** is "*well experienced and makes the contacts.*" The team advised Standard Chartered Bank on the acquisition of CIBC's aircraft finance portfolio, comprising transactions with aggregate value approximately $700 million. "*One hears nothing but good*" about the head of the general asset and leasing department, **Lisa Marks**, who specialises in rail financing. With a property finance focus, **Andrew Collins** has advised on several 'Landmark Millennium Projects' deals for Lombard North Central. A junior partner "*making his way*" in the aviation finance arena, is the "*pleasant and straight forward*" **Nick Chandler**. Although UK leveraged leases have been less prominent in the firm's workload, activity is spread across the sectors. The team acted for Lombard North Central in the refinancing of 50% of its £450 million acquisition of 352 train vehicles and the operating lease of those Cross Country Trains. Also advised ALSTOM on the purchase of £200 million of new trains by a syndicate of banks. On behalf of a Crédit Lyonnais led bank syndicate, the firm acted on the export credit supported financing of 27 new Airbus aircraft for Lan Chile, some combined with a Japanese operating lease structure. **Clients:** Lombard Corporate Finance; Bank of Scotland; Barclays Mercantile; Halifax; ABN AMRO; Lloyds TSB; Crédit Lyonnais; Standard Chartered Bank; Sabena; Deutsche Bank; Air Nostrum.

Linklaters (see firm details p.1042) Perceived to support the firm's corporate and projects strength, a long-standing focus on aviation finance is plateauing, allowing more room for rail-related work. Head of the department, the "*sensible and detail driven*" **Ron Gibbs** (see p.95) is responsible for the "*strength and depth*" of the team "*accounting for the high quality*" of advice offered. The firm is increasingly noted for its US activity. In the aviation sector, it advised Emirates in the financing of eight Airbus A330-200 aircraft (value $800 million) financed through Japanese operating lease, German leveraged lease, Export Credit Agency-backed and INTOL structures. Acted for debis AirFinance in the acquisition of Shannon-based AerFi Group, the team handled extensive due diligence work across a number of jurisdictions. On the rail front, the firm advised the Strategic Rail Authority on 13 rolling stock procurements, and acted on the proposed procurement of up to 1500 rolling stock vehicles on the South Eastern Network (value £1 billion.) **Clients:** Emirates; Lloyds TSB Leasing; First Asset Finance; SNCF; SSRA; Flightlease.

Watson, Farley & Williams (see firm details p.1174) "*With a high class client list*" the asset finance department can at times appear to be dominated by shipping finance, yet it is scoring well outside the sector, with an impressive track record in rail. The firm has an acknowledged position in the middle ticket leasing, active in advice to the lessees of ships. "*Commercially minded and sensible*" **David Osborne** (see p.96) has handled international transactions such as a series of leases for a Far Eastern container liner company in the UK lease of eight newbuilding container vessels. "*Astute and clever*" **James Watters** (see p.97) has built his reputation in medium ticket equipment leasing. Venturing into larger scale work, the team acted for R&B Falcon Group in a $245 million defeased lease of the semi-submersible drilling rig 'Deepwater Nautilus,' engaged on a service contract for Shell Deepwater Development in the Gulf of Mexico. It acted for Inmarsat in connection with the restructuring of its satellite leases. **Clients:** Bank of Nova Scotia; Barclays Capital; Citibank; Dresdner Kleinwort Benson; Norlease; PNC Bank; The CIT Group.

Lovells (see firm details p.1044) Key to the firm's profile is the "*respectable and sensible*" **Robin Hallam** (see p.95), who "*will not waste time on insignificant points.*" With aviation at its heart, the firm has a "*good client base,*" and strong reputation in the rail industry. Also on the asset team are "*good to deal with*" **Keith Wilson** (see p.98) and **Guy Liddle** (see p.96), "*who gets things done with his commercial approach.*" The team represented Bank of Nova Scotia on a multi-option revolving credit facility for Oasis International Leasing, and in a matter involving a defeased German leveraged lease of three Airbus A320/321 aircraft for AlItalia (using head lease/sub lease structure through Ireland) the team advised Banca Commerciale Italiana. Underlining its aviation specialism, the firm represented Lombard North Central, Naxtexis Banques Populaires and Banco Santander on the financing for the sale/leaseback of three A310-300 aircraft for TAP. **Clients:** Bank of Nova Scotia; Barclays Bank; Hamburgische Landesbank; Aircraft Lease Finance; Boeing Capital; Virgin Atlantic; Textron Financial; British Regional Airlines; Air Azurra.

White & Case (see firm details p.1178) Establishing itself in the asset finance world, the former Weil Gotshal & Manges team is considered to be "*dynamic and practical.*" "*Hard working,*" it has focused its attention on the aviation finance market. "*Troop leader*" **Mark Western** (see p.97) is "*effective and a smooth operator,*" whose work is complemented by **Justin Benson** (see p.94), "*more the details person, with quality standards.*" Together with the Paris office, the London team acted for the CIT Group on a $1.5 billion export credit loan facility for the purchase of up to 30 Airbus aircraft. The team advised the Bank of Tokyo Mitsubishi on the EEETC financing of two Airbus A320 aircraft and also advises Airtours on the full range of aircraft leasing transactions on an on-going basis. **Clients:** Air Belgium; GECAS; Airtours; Debis AirFinance Sweden; Hamburgische Landesbank; Babcock & Brown; Royal Bank of Canada.

CMS Cameron McKenna (see firm details p.922) With a low key presence, the firm covers a broad range of asset finance work, aviation to film finance. Chris St John-Smith has acted for various established oil and gas clients with regard to complex finance transactions involving security over and funding of marine assets. Aviation finance transactions have included the sub-lease of two Boeing 737 aircraft to Azzura Air for Lufttransport Unternehmen and acting for Flightlease as lessor of Boeing 737-400 aircraft from Euralair. The firm also acted for Royal Bank Leasing in connection with a £37 million structured leasing facility for the provision of a light rail maintenance depot in the West Midlands. **Clients:** National Australia Bank; BP Amoco; Angel Trains; Lloyds TSB; Westdeutsche Landesbank; GATX Capital; Flightlease; US Eximbank; Deutsche Bank.

Herbert Smith (see firm details p.993) Associated with a strong projects practice, **Nick Tott** (see p.97) is a high profile player who acted for Fasttrax (a Haliburton led consortium) in the provision of heavy equipment transporters on a PFI basis. The group is also active in the rail, water and aviation industries. It acted for EIB in relation to the financing of Airbus aircraft, and Philippine Airlines with regard to aircraft leasing. Growing its presence in rail financing, where leasing and procurement work for Stagecoach has kept the team busy. **Clients:** Eurotunnel; HSBC Rail; South West Trains; Fasttrax; EIB; Philippine Airlines.

Simmons & Simmons (see firm details p.1132) Led from the banking division, this cross-departmental, international grouping has a strong capital markets practice. A significant player with its work for the MoD, such as the lease financing by way of asset backed bond of four C-17A Globemaster aircraft, a deal valued at $860 million. The group is also involved in the UK and international regulatory regimes and potential finance structures for the MoD Future Strategic Tanker Aircraft Project. **Kim Walkling** (see p.97) ("*sensible and easy to deal with*") has a broad practice including cross-border aircraft, shipping and equipment leasing, the acquisition of equipment lease portfolios and the devising of tax-based structures. He acted for EIB on Project Wind, a telecom financing deal valued in excess of €4 billion. The firm continues to act for SEPI on the Iberia lease portfolio. **Clients:** Ministry of Defence; European Investment Bank; Iberia/SEPI; Barclays Capital.

Theodore Goddard (see firm details p.1152) Covering a wide range of asset finance from aviation and rolling stock, to general equipment. **Rory MacCarthy** (see p.96) is recognised for his aircraft expertise. In the past year his work involved acting for BA and its subsidiary, CitiFlyer Express, on the financing of five Avro RJ100 Aircraft. The firm advised Anglia Railways on the extension of numerous locomotive stock and coaching stock leases with Forward Trust. Also in the rail industry, the firm acted for Freightliner on numerous rolling stock leases with Porterbrook, along with other lease financings and haulage contracts. **Clients:** Bayerische Landesbank; Atlas Air; British Midland; Anglia Railways; Lan Chile; Lloyds TSB Leasing; Sumitomo.

Beaumont and Son Renowned as the long established aviation insurance firm, it also covers medium ticket financing with James Edmunds and the team recently advising a foreign start-up airline and acting in the creation of a new marketing company for Airbus Business Jets run by Hamlin Jets of Luton Airport. Reaching into non-aviation work, the firm acted for Western Industrial Finance in the creation of a finance programme for landmark millennium projects. Demonstrating its international endeavors, the firm was involved in the purchasing of a vendor programme leasing company with businesses throughout Europe. **Clients:** Western Industrial Finance; Whatrate.com; IIG; Hamlin Jets; Lombard North Central.

Berwin Leighton Paisner (see firm details p.878) Traditionally a strong player, the firm scored well with its shipping finance transactions. Nicola Davies and the team are a "*perfectly respectable operation,*" supported by the consulting work of Hugh Homan. The most significant instruction in the past year was the financing by a consortium of British shipping companies, headed by Andrew Weir, of six new Ro-Ro vessels for the MoD, with a capital value of £950 million. Combining the asset side with project finance, the firm has advised on the financing of floating production storage & off-loading systems (FPSOs,) such as Single Buoy Moorings. On non-shipping finance, the firm acts for DVI Financial Services and the Canadian Imperial Bank of Commerce. **Clients:** Angel Trains; Alcatel; Railtrack; Skanska; SBM; Houlder Marine Offshore; Transamerica Leasing; DSND Shipping; Barclays Bank.

Clark Ricketts A small niche firm that covers everything aviation related including complex financings. A specialist firm, it is considered a "*sensible, tight operation with good clients.*" Our researchers found its price/product ratio was particularly warmly received. "*Working his socks off,*" **Robert Ricketts** (see p.96) handles the financing side of the practice, having recently acted in the leasing of Boeing 737/767 aircraft for Excel Airways and in a number of leases for Babcock & Brown to various operators. **Clients:** Excel Airways; Air & General Finance; McAlpine Helicopters; Sloane Helicopters; Ghana Airways, Babcock & Brown.

Harbottle & Lewis (see firm details p.985) Renowned as "*Virgin's lawyers,*" the firm concentrates its asset finance work in the aviation field, also acting for other international airline clients. Dermott Scully is the firm's asset finance specialist and work over the past year has involved the representation of British Midland in the securitisation by AerFi of two Boeing 737 aircraft. For Virgin Atlantic Airways, the team negotiated agreements on the acquisition of B747 aircraft with Boeing. It also acted for UNI Airways in its leasing of aircraft to Vietnam Airlines. **Clients:** British Midland Airways; TNT; British World Airlines; Caribjet; Virgin Atlantic; World Courier; Sky Service Belgium; UNI Airways; TBJ Airways.

THE REGIONS

	ASSET FINANCE & LEASING • The Regions	Ptnrs	Assts
1	**Davies Wallis Foyster** Manchester	4	5
	Lester Aldridge Bournemouth	3	4
	Morton Fraser, Solicitors Edinburgh	3	4
2	**Hammond Suddards Edge** Birmingham	3	5
	McClure Naismith Glasgow	3	4
3	**Burges Salmon** Bristol	2	3
	Chaffe Street Manchester		
	Osborne Clarke Bristol	4	2

	LEADING INDIVIDUALS	
1	**WOOD Bruce** Morton Fraser, Solicitors	
2	**BOCHENSKI Tony** Davies Wallis Foyster	
	HOMAN Hugh Sole Practitioner	**MASKILL Andrew** Davies Wallis Foyster
3	**CAMPBELL Morag** McClure Naismith	**HEATH Kevin** Lester Aldridge
	LUMSDEN Christopher Chaffe Street	
UP AND COMING		
	DALY James Lester Aldridge	

This book is the product of 6,552 1/2-hour interviews. See p.7 for BMRB audit.
Within each band, firms are listed alphabetically. *See individuals' profiles p.94*

Davies Wallis Foyster (see firm details p.935) Having *"worked their way hard up the list"* the asset finance team has benefited with a new recruit from Capital Bank Financing,**Tony Bochenski** (see p.94), *"an experienced able guy, to be watched in private practice."* **Andrew Maskill** (see p.96) is the *"thoroughly astute, clear thinker"* who heads up the practice, which works on all aspects of middle and big ticket asset financing and leasing. In the past year the team has acted in a £100 million purchase of receivables, advised on the financing of a combined CH Power deal and a £12 million telecoms leasing tax structure.**Clients:** Bank of Ireland; Bank of Scotland Group; Cattles plc; Co-operative Bank; Sovereign Finance; Fleet Business Credit; ING Lease (UK); SLR.

Lester Aldridge (see firm details p.1038) Despite the loss of Pip Giddins, our researchers were told his well trained team retains a *"good client base and a fine operation."* Particular efficiency is attributed to the litigation practice of **Kevin Heath** (see p.95) and with the arrival of **James Daly** (see p.94) from VW Financing, its non-contentious work is in *"good hands."* The practice covers a wide range of financing and leasing, from motor to general equipment. Acted successfully for State Securities (v Gerson) before the Court of Appeal, the team also handles issues such as dual financing. Recent instructions include transactional advice for Daimler Crysler Financial Services (DEBIS). **Clients:** Automotive Financial Services; Bank of Ireland; BNP Paribas (HFGL); DaimlerCrysler Financial Services (DEBIS); Lloyds UDT Asset Finance; Pitney Bowes Finance.

Morton Fraser, Solicitors (see firm details p.1076) The *"well connected"* **Bruce Wood** is key to the success of the practice. *"Ask him a question and he'll know the answer"* not only on all Scottish issues related to the sector, but also cross-border. The bulk of the practice's work remains in the aircraft industry, yet shipping and equipment financing are also covered. More recently hire/purchase work has been arranged for Fokker and shorts and the team advised on the financing of the European distribution of lifting equipment for a US manufacturer through the IFSC in Dublin. **Clients:** Clydesdale Bank Asset Finance; Royal Bank Leasing; Dresdner Kleinwort Benson; National Astoria Group.

Hammond Suddards Edge (see firm details p.984) Predominantly known for the litigious side of asset finance, the firm also undertakes transactions in areas such as equipment and sales aid leasing, securitisations and receivables finance. Now that Angela Davis has retired from private practice, the non-contentious side will be an increasing focus and is headed up by Audrey Robertson. The firm boasts an on-line internet case management system for finance industry clients. Mainstay clients include GE and Barclays Mercantile. On the non-contentious side the firm acted for the Bank of Ireland in connection with the acquisition of a portfolio of Italian government debts and also for Riggs Bank Europe in the provision of wholesale funding to RDM Asset Finance. **Clients:** GE Capital Group; Barclays Mercantile Business Finance; Bank of Scotland; First National Bank; Bank of New York.

McClure Naismith (see firm details p.1059) Thought to *"punch above its weight"* and closing the gap on Morton Fraser. The firm benefits from its strong banking practice, recently boosted by the recruitment of a former Bank of Scotland specialist. The *"capable"* **Morag Campbell** (see p.94) concentrates on leasing and hire purchase agreements in the motor industry and in equipment such as plant machinery. The team acted for Lombard North Central in connection with invoice discounting by First National Bank and Singer & Friedlander Commercial Finance, and in marine mortgages by Bank of Scotland Business Direct. **Clients:** Capital Bank; General Guarantee; Singer & Friedlander Commercial Finance; RoyScot; Close Asset Finance; Wagon Finance; Credit Acceptance Corporation; Nissan Finance.

Burges Salmon (see firm details p.902) The asset finance team handles *"big ticket rail finance deals"* where Patrick Boumphrey spends most of his time. The team has acted on behalf of First Western and First Great Eastern in two transactions for the provision of automatic ticket barriers with a value in excess of £10 million. It also represented First Great Western, First North Western and First Great Eastern in relation to the acquisition of fleets of new trains with a total value in excess of £400 million. **Clients:** First Great Western; FirstGroup; First North Western; First Great Eastern; Standard Chartered Bank.

Chaffe Street (see firm details p.911) Always a *"recognised name"* in the market, working on small and medium ticket deals in the aircraft industry and machinery equipment. Often seen on the aircraft end of the financing deals, **Christopher Lumsden** (see p.402) is *"charismatic and professional."* The past year has brought supplier finance transactions for an aircraft components manufacturer, an £8 million cash flow finance secured on European patents and patent licenses and an aircraft operating lease to Germany. **Clients:** Jersey European Airways; mixture of financiers and end-users.

Osborne Clarke OWA (see firm details p.1086) Combining strengths in the tax, banking and commercial sector, the asset finance team is perceived to be low key. It has lately strengthened its connection to the FLA. The team covers equipment and lease financing and has acted in several telecoms leasing transactions. James Cross is the partner who concentrates on the asset finance practice. The firm acted in the conversion of John Deere Credit into a branch of John Deere Bank. It has drafted standard form leasing and security documentation and advised on leasing business for Deutsche Bank. **Clients:** Alexandra plc; BCH Vehicle Management; c2c rail; GATAX Capital; Newcourt; GE Capital Equipment Finance; John Deere Bank; turkerdirect.com.

Other Notable Practitioners Set up as sole practitioner in Salisbury, **Hugh Homan** (see p.95) has a *"long standing in the sector"* and remains active in small to medium ticket asset finance work. He continues to consult at Berwin Leighton Paisner once a week.

CONSUMER FINANCE – NATIONAL

CONSUMER FINANCE • National	Ptnrs	Assts
1 **Berwin Leighton Paisner** London	3	2
2 **Salans Hertzfeld & Heilbronn HRK** London	3	6
Eversheds Cardiff, Leeds	4	n/a
Lester Aldridge Bournemouth	4	6
McClure Naismith Glasgow	4	5
3 **Addleshaw Booth & Co** Leeds	n/a	n/a
Hammond Suddards Edge Birmingham	n/a	n/a

LEADING INDIVIDUALS
★ **ROSENTHAL Dennis** Berwin Leighton Paisner
1 **JOHNSTONE Frank** McClure Naismith
2 **FINCH Stephen** Salans Hertzfeld & Heilbronn HRK
GUEST Jonathan Eversheds
3 **GAINES Alison** Salans Hertzfeld & Heilbronn HRK
TOWERS Lennox Addleshaw Booth & Co
4 **COHEN Howard** Salans Hertzfeld & Heilbronn HRK
DALY James Lester Aldridge

This book is the product of 6,552 1/2-hour interviews. See p.7 for BMRB audit.
Within each band, firms are listed alphabetically. *See individuals' profiles p.94*

Berwin Leighton Paisner (see firm details p.878) "The stand out individual in the sector," **Dennis Rosenthal** (see p.97) has been described as *"top, lone fighter"* and key to the firm's success. The group has a strong connection to the Department of Trade and Industry and Office of Fair Trading, advising on consumer law matters, and counts the Consumer Credit Trade Association as one of its clients. The recent merger has increased the profile of the supporting team with its *"loyal client base."* Covering banking, asset and consumer finance and financial services law, it is in consumer credit that the firm has the highest profile. It developed a range of credit and leasing products for Electrolux Finance and advised on advertising material for Bradford & Bingley's campaign 'The Marketplace.' The group also acted for HFC Bank on new products and in consumer credit and consumer credit related litigation. **Clients:** Bradford & Bingley; Northern Rock; HFC Bank; CCTA; Hitachi Credit; FTYourMoney.com.

Eversheds (see firm details p.952) The firm concentrates on credit card and loan agreement design, structuring, advertising and sales, and purchase of debt. The impressive team is also devoting its energies on joint venture vehicles to promote and sell financial services products. *"Doing a string of things,"* standout individual here is Midlands based **Jonathan Guest** (see p.95). The past year has seen the firm winning the development work for the AMP Bank product launch and the firm handled the Bank of Scotland joint venture with Airtours for the provision of financial products. **Clients:** Bank of Scotland; Ventura; Leeds & Holbeck BS; Marks & Spencer Financial Services.

Lester Aldridge (see firm details p.1038) Suffered a loss through the departure of Pip Giddins to DLA, but was bolstered by the recruitment of **James Daly** (see p.94), *"a good, broader based lawyer"* from VW Financing. The team Giddins reared is considered strong, advising on and developing consumer credit products such as personal loans, credit cards and mortgage loans for consumer banks, building societies, finance houses and lending subsidiaries of retail groups. Since advising in the complex Dimond v Lovell case, the team has been active in motor financing. **Clients:** Automotive Financial Services; DaimlerCrysler Financial Services (DEBIS); Dixons Stores Group; Volkswagen Financial Services; Singer & Friedlander Finance.

McClure Naismith (see firm details p.1059) Not just *"adding the Scottish touch,"* the firm originates plenty of national consumer finance work. *"High profile"* **Frank Johnstone** (see p.96) *"keeps up-to-date with current trends,"* and has a *"particular specialty in data protection."* The team focuses on institutional creditor recovery work as well as commercial debt recovery. The personal banking division of a major Scottish bank has instructed the firm in connection with its litigation. Won a competitive tender to act for a major factoring company owned by a Scottish bank on a significant proportion of its debt recovery caseload in Scotland. Drafting and reviewing agreements regulated by the Consumer Credit Act, the firm also advises on title disputes, banking and regulatory compliance issues, and has had extensive experience in data protection matters. **Clients:** Capital Bank; Nationwide; British Credit Trust Finance; RoyScot Trust; Clydesdale Financial Services; Mercedes-Benz Finance; Ford Motor Credit Company; Barclays Mercantile Business Finance.

Salans Hertzfeld & Heilbronn HRK (see firm details p.1117) Covering the contentious and non-contentious sides of consumer finance, the firm covers a broad range from structuring procedures for start-up companies to being very active on the credit cards front. The *"likeable"* all-rounder **Stephen Finch** (see p.94) has *"built up a team"* here. Considered *"a good pedigree"* and a *"very alert, bright spark,"* **Alison Gaines** (see p.95) is a main part of this. Clients think well of **Howard Cohen** (see p.94), who has also been very active in this field. More recently the firm acted for Lloyds TSB Group on specialist consumer finance and motor dealer related due diligence in connection with the Group's acquisition of Chartered Bank for the sum of £627 million. Other general consumer finance advice was that for Bank of Ireland involving documentation work and data protection issues. **Clients:** FCE Bank; Nissan Finance (GB); Bank of Ireland; Barclays; Daewoo; Guinness Mahon; Saab Group; Jaguar Financial Services; Volkswagen Financial Services.

Addleshaw Booth & Co (see firm details p.853) With a greater profile in the North, the firm covers all aspects of consumer finance and is respected for its deep client roster. Active across the board, from preparing the standard form documentation for consumer credit transactions (credit cards, personal loans etc) to data protection, purchase/sale of receivables and advising its financial and retail clients on affinity products and joint ventures. In Manchester, **Lennox Towers** (see p.97), an experienced consumer finance lawyer, also covers asset finance. He advised Airtours on its credit card and loyalty scheme joint venture with Bank of Scotland. **Clients:** Woolwich; Skipton BS; Argos; National Australia Group.

Hammond Suddards Edge (see firm details p.984) The consumer finance side of the practice is noted for having a building society background having branched more into mortgage related issues. Work is undertaken on the CCA regulated hire purchase side as well as loan agreements. Head of the unit is Audrey Robertson since Angela Davis' retirement from private practice, who is backed in particular by a strong non-contentious team. In the past year the firm has acted for iGroup in connection with two mortgage backed securitisations, as well as advising a leading vehicle manufacturer's leasing subsidiary on all aspects of leasing and consumer credit law. **Clients:** iGroup; FCE Bank; Sensormatic; Volvo Contracts.

LEADERS IN ASSET FINANCE

BENSON, Justin
White & Case, London (020) 7397 3820
jbenson@whitecase.com
Specialisation: Partner in the bank finance department. Main area of practice is asset finance and leasing with particular experience in advising banks, financial institutions, lessors and arrangers in the aviation industry. Also has a broad background in international bank finance and has advised major financial institutions on a broad range of cross-border transactions.
Prof. Memberships: Law Society of England and Wales.
Career: Qualified 1992 at *Sinclair Roche & Temperley*; also worked at *Freshfields* and *Weil Gotshal & Manges.* Joined *White & Case* in 2000.
Personal: Born 1968. Educated at Dulwich College 1978-85, Southampton University 1986-89 (LLB) and College of Law, Guildford, 1989-90 (Solicitors Finals). Married with three children.

BOCHENSKI, Tony
Davies Wallis Foyster, Manchester
(0161) 228 3702
tjb@dwf-law.com
Specialisation: Asset finance and banking including structured finance, equipment leasing, acquisition finance, receivables funding. Acted for funder on MBO of Perrys Motor Sales from Perry Group plc.
Prof. Memberships: Manchester Law Society. Previously member of Law Society Commerce and Industry Group, North West Committee; ex-member of Finance and Leasing Association Legal Sub-Committee.
Career: Kenning Motor Group Plc 1974-76; admitted as solicitor 1976; solicitor BL (UK) Limited 1976-82; Group Solicitor TNT (UK) Limited 1982-84; Bank of Scotland Group 1984-2000; appointed Director and Group Solicitor Capital Bank Plc 1996; joined *Davies Wallis Foyster* as Head of Banking and Asset Finance Group 2000.
Personal: Marple Hall Grammar 1966-70; University of Sheffield 1970-73; College of Law, Chester 1973-74. Interests include home, family, skiing, bridge, rugby and cricket (as observer), travel and holidays (when time permits).

BRAND, Giles
Norton Rose, London (020) 7283 6000
brandg@nortonrose.com
Specialisation: Giles Brand specialises in UK tax-based leasing, cross-border leasing, operating leasing, aviation finance and ship finance.
Career: University College London, LLB.

CAMPBELL, Morag
McClure Naismith, Glasgow (0141) 204 2700
mcampbell@mcclurenaismith.com
Specialisation: Asset Finance: sale and leaseback; securing property and assets generally including heritable (real) property, vehicles, receivables, income streams; block and invoice discounting; tailoring English financial products for effective use in Scotland; advising on differences between English and Scots law in specialist area.
Prof. Memberships: Admitted as a solicitor in Scotland: 1981.
Career: Hillhead High School, Glasgow; University of Glasgow: LL.B (Hons) 1979; *Anderson & Gardiner*: Apprentice 1979-1981; Assistant Solicitor 1981-1983: Partner 1983-1984; *McClure Naismith* : Partner 1984-date.
Personal: Singing (choral); music; theatre.

CARPENTER, Clive
Clifford Chance, London (020) 7600 1000
clive.carpenter@cliffordchance.com
Specialisation: Partner. Asset finance and banking group. Principal areas of work involve acting for financiers and lessors on all aspects of asset and project finance, leasing and banking in relation to heavy transportation assets (aircraft, ships, rolling stock), satellites and plant and machinery, the securitisation of transportation assets, defeasance including tax driven structures employed in such financings and European and US ECA supported transactions.
Personal: BCL, MA (Oxon) in Jurisprudence.

CHANDLER, Nick
Denton Wilde Sapte, London (020) 7242 1212

CHARLTON, Bob
Freshfields Bruckhaus Deringer, London
(020) 7936 4000
bob.charlton@freshfields.com
Specialisation: Partner specialising in asset finance and leasing (in particular, aircraft and rolling stock), cross-border financings, structured finance, export credit finance and project finance.
Career: Educated Trinity Hall, Cambridge (1975-1978). Qualified England 1981; Hong Kong 1986; Brunei 1987; partner with *Freshfields* since November 1999; partner in another leading international law firm since 1987.
Personal: Born 1957.

COHEN, Howard
Salans Hertzfeld & Heilbronn HRK, London
(020) 7509 6000
hcohen@salans.com
Specialisation: Partner in the banking and finance department specialising in asset finance and leasing (notably consumer credit law) and retail banking. Advises finance houses, leasing companies and banks on all aspects of their activities, including procedures, documentation and marketing. Has particular expertise in motor vehicle financing, having spent a total of three years on secondment in the legal department of a leading motor manufacturer's captive finance company. Experience includes the securitisation of motor finance and other trade receivables. Lectures on consumer credit law and related issues.
Prof. Memberships: Law Society.
Career: Formerly a partner at *Harris Rosenblatt and Kramer*, London.
Personal: Education: London School of Economics (1983 LLB Hons). Interests include: opera and aviation.

COLLINS, Andrew
Denton Wilde Sapte, London (020) 7242 1212

CROOKES, Alan
Norton Rose, London (020) 7283 6000
crookesam@nortonrose.com
Specialisation: Partner whose practice ranges from asset finance (particularly equipment leasing) to corporate acquisitions and disposals (including private equity transactions). He has acted on two major acquistions of rail rolling stock companies: Angel Train Contracts (for Royal Bank of Scotland); Eversholt Leasing (for Forward Trust). He acted for AES on its acquisition of Drax Power Station and also for the Finalrealm Consortium on its bid for United Biscuits. He led the *Norton Rose* team which acted for The Airline Group on the NATS PPP.
Prof. Memberships: City of London Solicitors' Company.
Career: Qualified in 1981 while at *Norton Rose.* Became a partner in 1988.
Personal: Born 27 May 1957. Educated at Durham University 1975-78. Enjoys music (particularly opera). Lives in Shenfield.

DALY, James
Lester Aldridge, Bournemouth (01202) 786173
james.daly@lester-aldridge.co.uk
Specialisation: Asset finance, consumer finance, leasing; H.P; general contract matters; data protection; distance selling; consumer credit law. Moved to *LA* in December 2000 from head of legal and Member of Board at Volkswagen Financial Services.
Prof. Memberships: Law Society; Finance and Leasing Association.
Career: Business degree from Heriot-Watt University, followed by first career in marketing, switched to law and 13 years 'in house' before joining *LA* in December 2000 as head of non-contentious asset finance and banking.
Publications: Features from time to time in legal commentaries of legal magazines.
Personal: Educated in Scotland, qualified as an English lawyer. Interested in theatre, writing and horse racing.

EDWARDS, Jeremy
Norton Rose, London (020) 7283 6000
edwardsjp@nortonrose.com
Specialisation: Partner in banking department. Head of international aviation business group. Specialises in structured and asset finance, particularly of aircraft and rolling stock. Expertise includes all aspects of operating and finance leases, sales and purchases of aircraft and rolling stock, cross-border leases and export credit financing. Recent transactions include advising various airlines and banks on a number of Japanese operating leases, some export credit backed; advising on multi-option aircraft financing facilities; advising in connection with Brazilian export credit backed financing and leasing of Embraer aircraft; advising on the asset backed securitisation of six Boeing 747 aircraft; advising one of the UK's three rolling stock companies on its purchase and leasing of new and used rolling stock.
Career: Joined *Norton Rose* as a trainee in 1987. Qualified 1989. Spent three years in the firm's Paris office. Elected to partnership May 1997. Speaks fluent French.

FINCH, Stephen
Salans Hertzfeld & Heilbronn HRK, London
(020) 7509 6000
sfinch@salans.com
Specialisation: Partner and head of the banking and finance department. Advises lending institutions on all aspects of their activities, both consumer and commercial lending. Current work includes providing advice on asset finance and leasing arrangements,

including off-shore and tax-based leasing and securitisations, factoring project finance, repo facilities, syndicated loans, finance house management and service contracts as well as providing advice on retail banking law. Writes and lectures regularly on consumer finance and retail banking law.
Prof. Memberships: Law Society of England & Wales. Serves on E-banking and Non Prime Financial Committees of the Finance and Leasing Association.
Career: Qualified in 1975. Formerly a partner at *Harris Rosenblatt and Kramer*, London.
Personal: Education: University of London (1973 LLB Hons).

FREEMAN, Mark
Freshfields Bruckhaus Deringer, London (020) 7936 4000
mark.freeman@freshfields.com
Specialisation: Finance, in particular asset finance, leasing and structured finance. Main specialisation is aircraft financing.
Prof. Memberships: Law Society; admitted in UK and Hong Kong.
Career: Qualified 1969. Partner 1974.
Personal: Educated at Emmanuel College Cambridge. Leisure interests include motor racing, skiing, scuba.

GAINES, Alison
Salans Hertzfeld & Heilbronn HRK, London (020) 7509 6000
againes@salans.com
Specialisation: Partner in the banking and finance department specialising in asset finance, consumer finance and non-contentious insolvency. Alison has extensive experience advising clients in the finance industry on all aspects of loan finance, asset finance and consumer finance and on insolvency issues affecting her clients. Alison has particular knowledge of the motor finance industry and consumer credit law. She has written various articles on insolvency law and on consumer credit law.
Prof. Memberships: Law Society, International Bar Association.
Career: Qualified 1980. In-house counsel with Lloyds Bowmaker (now part of the Lloyds TSB group), London 1980-84. Community Law Centre, New York City 1984-86. Partner *Hill Bailey* London 1986-89. Formerly partner at *Harris Rosenblatt and Kramer*. Alison is also admitted to practice in New York.
Personal: Education: Birmingham University 1977 (LLB Hons). Leisure interests include hill walking, climbing and football.

GIBB, Jeremy
Norton Rose, London (020) 7283 6000
gibbsjsp@nortonrose.com
Specialisation: Partner in banking department. Principal area of practice is asset finance, especially for ships and aircraft. In particular has considerable expertise in domestic and cross-border leasing structures. In the shipping field has over 15 years experience in the City of London, acting for financiers and owners of all types of vessels, including cruise ships and offshore vessels, and has been involved in numerous FPSO financings. Also deals with acquisition finance, especially acquisition and disposal of leasing companies.
Prof. Memberships: Law Society, Connecticut Maritime Association.

GIBBS, Ronald
Linklaters, London (020) 7456 5984
ron.gibbs@linklaters.com
Specialisation: Project and asset finance department. Principal area of practice has been in the field of asset finance with emphasis on aviation, including finance, commercial and regulatory aspects of airlines, airports and air traffic control systems.
Career: 1989 to date: Partner, *Linklaters*; 1982-1989: Assistant solicitor, *Linklaters*; 1982: Admitted as a solicitor. 1982: University College, London, Diploma in Air and Space Law; 1980: College of Law, Guildford, Solicitors Finals; 1979: Leicester, BA (Hons) Law.

GLAISTER, William
Clifford Chance, London (020) 7600 1000
william.glaister@cliffordchance.com
Specialisation: Asset Finance: all areas of asset finance including leverage finance, operating leasing, securitisation and restructurings.
Career: *Clifford Chance* London (1991-96, 2001-). *Clifford Chance* Hong Kong (1997-2001).

GUEST, Jonathan
Eversheds, Leeds (0113) 243 0391
jonathanguest@eversheds.com
Specialisation: Consumer credit – acting for banks, building societies, finance houses and retailers in the provision of credit card products, fixed term loan documentation and compliance and advertising issues. Experience includes selling credit card receivable and debt transfer arrangements, data protection compliance, data warehousing arrangements and joint ventures in the credit sector. Lectures and provides seminars on the consumer credit legislation and provides input on proposals to deregulate the legislation.
Prof. Memberships: Consumer credit – trade association and data protection forum.
Career: Qualified 1982, partner 1986.
Personal: Interests include walking, trying to keep classic cars on the road and skiing.

HALL, Gordon
Norton Rose, London (020) 7283 6000
hallgcc@nortonrose.com
Specialisation: Partner specialising in asset finance: ships; aircraft; rolling stock. Emphasis on structured financing involving tax and operating leases.
Prof. Memberships: City of London Solicitor's Company; International Bar Association; Baltic Exchange.
Career: Admitted 1980. Partner at *Norton Rose* 1988. 1985-1988, resident in Singapore office. 1988-1989, resident in Bahrain office.

HALL, Simon
Freshfields Bruckhaus Deringer, London (020) 7936 4000
simon.hall@freshfields.com
Specialisation: Head of finance department. Main areas of practice are asset and aircraft finance, and banking and structured finance.
Prof. Memberships: Law Society; City of London Solicitors Company; American Bar Association.
Career: Qualified 1979 after joining *Freshfields* in 1977. Became a partner in 1985.
Publications: Co-author of 'Aircraft Financing' (Euromoney 3rd edition, 1998); co-author of 'Leasing Finance' (Euromoney 3rd edition, 1997).
Personal: Born 6th February 1955. Leisure interests include shooting and fishing.

HALLAM, Robin
Lovells, London (020) 7296 2000
robin.hallam@lovells.com
Specialisation: Aviation, rail and asset finance; secured lending, leveraged and operating leasing, tax based and defeased leases, securitisation, export credit and vendor sales finance, engine and equipment leasing principally in aviation but also in ships, containers, rolling stock and other forms of large assets. Substantial experience in aircraft securitisations and other aircraft finance transactions involving capital markets.
Prof. Memberships: City of London Law Society, Aviation Club – Associate Member, American Bar Association.
Career: Qualified 1980. Hong Kong 1981-82; Singapore 1982-83; partner *Lovells* 1995; various articles on aircraft finance.

HARTLEY, Simon
Norton Rose, London (020) 7283 6000
hartleys@nortonrose.com
See under Shipping, p.768

HEATH, Kevin
Lester Aldridge, Bournemouth (01202) 786134
kevin.heath@lester-aldridge.co.uk
Specialisation: Litigation and advisory work on asset finance and leasing (small to middle ticket), insolvency and commercial lending. Particular emphasis on fraud and injunctive work. In the last 12 months acted for the successful party on a number of claims arising out of a substantial motor finance fraud and, in a reported case, acted for the successful party in a fraud case which raised a novel point of jurisdictional law under the Brussels convention (Dexter v Harley).
Career: Qualified in 1988 with *Norton Rose*, joined *Lester Aldridge* in 1992 and became a partner in 1996 in the asset finance and banking team.
Personal: Education: Southampton University (1986). Leisure: sometime soccer player, lapsed supporter, born again follower. Family: Catherine (12), Jessica (12) and Elizabeth (8).

HOMAN, Hugh
Hugh Homan – Sole Practitioner, Salisbury (01722) 717960
hh@hugh-homan.com
Specialisation: Asset finance and equipment leasing.
Prof. Memberships: Law Society.
Career: Qualified in 1970. Partner at *Berwin Leighton Paisner* from 1975 to 1999. Established own practice in 1999 but remains a consultant with *Berwin Leighton Paisner*.
Personal: Born 26 June 1945. Educated at Worcester College, Oxford 1964-67. Lives in Salisbury.

JACOVIDES, Mario
Allen & Overy, London (020) 7330 2659
mario.jacovides@allenovery.com
Specialisation: Partner in the International Asset Finance Group specialising in asset finance and leasing, he particularly focuses on structured and large-scale tax-based and cross border lease financings, export credit supported transactions, Polish leveraged leases, Japanese leases and US leases. He represents financiers, operators, and manufacturers in aircraft, ship and satellite financings as well as financiers in the acquisition and disposal of portfolios of assets.

Career: Qualified *Wilde Sapte*, (1989), Partner (1996); Partner *Allen & Overy* 1998.
Personal: Interests include golf, squash and ornithology.

JOHNSTONE, Frank
McClure Naismith, Glasgow (0141) 204 2700
fjohnstone@McClureNaismith.com
Specialisation: Partner specialising in consumer credit law, asset recovery and data protection. Consumer credit law. Represents a number of finance houses, leasing companies, banks and credit card companies, with particular emphasis on litigation/debt recovery, sale and supply of goods and data protection. Convener of the Consumer Law committee of the Law Society of Scotland, convener of the Privacy committee of the Law Society of Scotland, member of the Legal Advisory group of the Scottish Consumer council, member of the Consumer Law committee of the International Bar association, chairman of Money Advice Liaison group (Scotland) and a frequent lecturer on consumer/credit law, data protection and debt recovery.
Career: Qualified 1982, joined present firm in 1985. Became a partner in 1988.
Personal: Born 12th October, 1957. Graduated M.A., LL.B., Glasgow University, British Universities Lightweight Boxing Champion 1979 – Runner up 1980.

JOLLIFFE, Peter
Slaughter and May, London (020) 7600 1200
peter.jolliffe@slaughterandmay.com
Specialisation: Aircraft and asset financing.
Prof. Memberships: The Law Society.
Career: Qualified in 1981 after joining *Slaughter and May* in 1979. Became a partner in 1989.
Personal: Born 6 June 1957. Educated Downing College, Cambridge. Lives in London.

JOYCE, Andrew
Allen & Overy, London (020) 7330 3000
Specialisation: Asset finance and leasing.
Career: Asset finance and leasing partner. His work has involved advising on a variety of secured and unsecured financings, including acting for financiers, lessors and manufacturers in the aircraft, rail and project finance areas. He spent nearly a year on secondment with GPA negotiating and documenting operating leases and aircraft acquisitions and disposals.

KAHN, Gregory
Denton Wilde Sapte, London (020) 7242 1212

KINNERSLEY, Tom
Slaughter and May, London (020) 7600 1200
tom.kinnersley@slaughterandmay.com
Specialisation: General banking, in particular structured finance and asset finance.
Prof. Memberships: The Law Society.
Career: Qualified 1972. Partner 1980.
Personal: Born 28 May 1947. Educated Hertford College, Oxford. Lives in London.

LEW, Simon
Clifford Chance, London (020) 7600 1000
Simon.Lew@cliffordchance.com
Specialisation: Partner in the Asset Finance Group since 1996.

LIDDLE, Guy
Lovells, London (020) 7296 2000
guy.liddle@lovells.com
Specialisation: Asset (principally aviation) finance.
Prof. Memberships: Law Society. City of London Solicitors' Company.
Career: Trained Inns of Court School of Law. Qualified: Barrister 1984, solicitor 1989, Lincoln's Inn 1984-85, *Sinclair Roche & Temperley* 1986-95; *Lovells* since 1995. Partner since 1998.
Publications: Sometime contributor to 'Airfinance Journal', 'Airfinance Annual', 'Aircraft Technology Engine Yearbook'.
Personal: Born 1962; resides London. Leisure interests include swimming, fitness training and travel.

LINTOTT, Tim
Freshfields Bruckhaus Deringer, London (020) 7936 4000
timothy.lintott@freshfields.com
Specialisation: Asset and project finance, including power stations and transmission, aviation, airports.
Prof. Memberships: Admitted in UK, Hong Kong.
Career: 1976-94 *Freshfields*, London and New York; 1984-92 *Baker & McKenzie*, Hong Kong; 1992 to date *Freshfields*, London.
Personal: Married, three daughters.

LITTLEJOHNS, Andrew
Freshfields Bruckhaus Deringer, London (020) 7936 4000
andrew.littlejohns@freshfields.com
Specialisation: Specialises in international banking, international finance, aviation finance, aircraft leasing, railway leasing and finance, and other equipment leasing. Involvement in aircraft financing includes a wide experience of cross-border tax leases, syndicated multi-option facilities, securitisations, asset value underwriting, joint ventures and operating leases.
Career: Education: Lincoln College, Oxford. Became partner in 1987.

LUMSDEN, Christopher
Chaffe Street, Manchester (0161) 236 5800
See under Financial Services, p.402

MACCARTHY, Rory
Theodore Goddard, London (020) 7606 8855
rorymaccarthy@theodoregoddard.co.uk
Specialisation: Head of *Theodore Goddard's* aviation group. Advises airlines, leasing companies and banks on a range of aviation matters, mainly involving aircraft financing.
Prof. Memberships: Member of the Law Faculty of the IATA Aviation Training and Development Institute, Law Society, International Bar Association.
Career: Solicitor. LLB (London). MA (Business Law). Diploma in Air and Space Law.
Publications: Contributing author to the 'Handbook of Airline Finance' (published by McGraw-Hill). Author of various articles on aviation law.
Personal: Pilot (UK and US licences).

MARKS, Lisa
Denton Wilde Sapte, London (020) 7242 1212

MASKILL, Andrew
Davies Wallis Foyster, Manchester (0161) 228 3702
asm@dwf-law.com
Specialisation: Middle and big ticket asset finance including receivables funding, tax based structures and equipment leasing.
Prof. Memberships: Law Society.
Career: Articled *Wilde Sapte*; qualified 1990; *Eversheds*; *Alsop Wilkinson*; partner *Davies Wallis Foyster* 1998.
Personal: Leeds Grammar School; Manchester University (LLB Hons); guitar (blues and rock); golf; running; languages (French and German); resides Manchester.

MILES, Adrian
Denton Wilde Sapte, London (020) 7242 1212

MURPHY, Robert
Freshfields Bruckhaus Deringer, London (020) 7936 4000
robert.murphy@freshfields.com
Specialisation: Partner in asset finance group, specialising in aviation finance, including the use of cross-border tax-based leasing structures, export credit agency supported financing and aircraft-based capital markets transactions. He advises a wide range of clients on aircraft financing transactions including banks, airlines, leasing companies, manufacturers and arrangers.
Career: Qualified Ireland, England and Wales. Joined *Freshfields* in 1993, having worked as an in-house lawyer with the Irish aircraft leasing company GPA. Partner 1998.
Personal: Educated Trinity College, Dublin; University College, Dublin. Born 1961.

OSBORNE, David
Watson, Farley & Williams, London (020) 7814 8000
dosborne@wfw.com
Specialisation: Partner in international finance group. Practice encompasses asset finance, leasing, secured lending, securitisation and structured finance; clients include lessors, lessees, originators, lenders and other credit providers.
Prof. Memberships: Law Society; New York Bar (admitted 1993).
Career: Ipswich School; Downing College, Cambridge; *Linklaters & Paines* 1979-82; *Watson, Farley & Williams* 1982 to date; *Watson, Farley & Williams* New York office 1990-95.
Personal: Married, three children.

RICKETTS, Robert
Clark Ricketts, London (020) 7404 1551
robertricketts@clarkricketts.com
Specialisation: Partner specialising in all aspects of aviation law, with particular emphasis on aircraft finance and leasing and regulatory work for airlines, leasing companies, aircraft operators, aircraft distributors, maintenance organisations and banks and who works closely with a wide network of law firms in many jurisdictions.
Prof. Memberships: The Royal Aeronautical Society and The Law Society.
Career: Qualified 1987, with *Norton Rose*, then went to *Frere Chomeley* in 1989 and set up *Clark Ricketts* in 1995. Partner since 1995.
Publications: Author of the 'Aircraft Financing and Leasing' section of the Butterworths 'Encyclopaedia of Forms and Precedents'.
Personal: Born 1962, educated at University College, London. Married with children and lives in London.

ROSENTHAL, Dennis
Berwin Leighton Paisner, London (020) 7427 113
dennis.rosenthal.berwinleightonpaisner.com
Specialisation: Partner in company and commercial department. Advises banks, finance and leasing companies, building societies and trade associations on all aspects of their commercial activities; deals with transactions; drafts agreements including standard form agreements; structures and advises on equipment and vehicle financing arrangements, retail credit schemes, sales and purchases of receivables, joint ventures and innovative products, including in relation to credit cards, personal loans, point of sale agreements, mortgages and bank savings products. Advises on commercial law, banking law, consumer credit law, advertising and marketing law, financial services law, insurance, fraud prevention, money laundering and data protection.
Prof. Memberships: Member of The Law Society, IBA, British South Africa Law Association.
Publications: Assistant editor of 'Goode: Consumer Credit Law and Practice' and 'Goode: Consumer Credit Reports'; author of 'Guide to Consumer Credit Law & Practice' (Butterworths) and 'Financial Advertising and Marketing Law' (Sweet & Maxwell); contributor to 'Consumer Credit' in Halsbury's Laws of England and to various legal journals.

SALT, Julia
Allen & Overy, London (020) 7330 2553
saltj@allenovery.com
Specialisation: Partner specialising in asset based finance. Has extensive experience in aircraft and other asset financing including finance and operating leasing, cross-border transactions, securitisations and structured loans. Experience also includes project financing, telecommunications financing and securitisation.
Career: Articled *Allen & Overy*, qualified 1980, partner 1985.
Personal: Oxford University (1977 MA). Born 1955. Enjoys sailing, golf, opera, literature.

SMITH, David
Allen & Overy, London (020) 7330 2555
david.smith@allenovery.com
Specialisation: Partner in the asset finance and leasing practice area, he represents all parties in domestic and cross-border structured transactions, both leasing and debt-based. Extensive experience of financing assets in many industries including telecoms and transportation (ships, aircraft, railways and containers). Experience includes export credit backed and government-guaranteed debt facilities, tax-based lease structures (including UK tax leases and US Lease-In-Lease-Outs and QTEs), off-balance sheet structures, vendor financing type structures and non tax-based leases including operating leases with and without residual value support, as well as combining these structures.
Career: Solicitor *Richards Butler*, 1984, Partner 1989; Partner *Wilde Sapte*, 1991; Partner *Allen & Overy*, 1999.
Personal: Born 1960, married with two children, enjoys family, motor cars, golf, cricket, eating out and theatre. BA Jurisprudence, Brasenose College, Oxford, 1981.

SMITH, Graham
Allen & Overy, London (020) 7330 3000
graham.smith@allenovery.com
Specialisation: Asset Finance & Leasing partner and global practice leader of the International Asset Finance Group. A specialist in asset finance for over 18 years, his experience included numerous large value lease financings of both fixed and movable assets in transport, power and telecommunications. He has advised at all levels of the industry from the purchase and sale of leasing companies and portfolios, to retail finance documentation, setting up cross-border sales aid schemes and the integration of lease finance into infrastructure projects.
Career: Royal Grammar School Guildford; Nottingham University (1979 BA Hons Law); Guildford College of Law (1980). Trained *Wilde Sapte*; qualified 1982; assistant solicitor 1982, partner asset finance group 1987, head of leasing 1993; partner *Allen & Overy* asset finance group,1999.
Personal: Born 1958; resides London. Enjoys modern art, golf, classic cars, food and wine.

THAINE, Colin
Denton Wilde Sapte, London (020) 7242 1212

THORNE, Peter
Norton Rose, London (020) 7283 6000
thornepg@nortonrose.com
Specialisation: Partner in banking department. Asset finance. Clients include airlines, manufacturers, banks, leasing companies and arrangers. Major transactions in 00/01 included advising banks and other financial institutions, on the remarketing and refinancing of aircraft (using Australian leases, note issues and asset value support) advising lessor on lease of equipment to Railtrack and advising lendors on JOL financing of 13 aircraft.
Prof. Memberships: International Bar Association, Royal Aeronautical Society.
Career: Qualified 1971. Joined *Norton Rose* that year. Partner since 1977.
Publications: Author of Aircraft Mortgages chapter in 'Interest in Goods' (2nd edn Lloyds of London Press 1998).
Personal: Born 2 June 1948. Attended Clifton College 1962-65.

TOTT, Nicholas
Herbert Smith, London (020) 7374 8000
nicholas.tott@herbertsmith.com
Specialisation: Principal areas of work include all forms of financing and banking work with particular emphasis on asset finance, leasing, project financing and PFI/PPP projects. Seconded to the Private Finance Panel Executive for fifteen months with responsibility for PFI Projects in Scotland, Northern Ireland and the Ministry of Defence.
Prof. Memberships: Law Society; City of London Solicitors' Company.
Career: Qualified Scotland (1985), England and Wales (1991). Partner 1992.
Publications: Publications include a chapter 'Public Finance in the UK' in Leasing Finance (Euromoney 1997, 3rd Edition). Co-author of 'The PFI Handbook' (Jordans, March 1999).
Personal: Born 8th May 1960. Educated at Edinburgh University. Leisure pursuits include golf and skiing.

TOWERS, Lennox
Addleshaw Booth & Co, Leeds (0113) 209 2000
Specialisation: Consumer finance – advises banks, building societies, finance companies and retailers on secured and unsecured lending, leasing and hiring, standard documentation, joint ventures, purchase and sale of receivables credit cards, regulatory and compliance matters data protection, advertising and sales promotion and general consumer credit issues.
Prof. Memberships: Finance and Leasing Association, Consumer Credit Trade Association, Building Societies Association, Council of Mortgage Lenders.
Career: Qualified in 1971. Partner 1974.
Personal: Graduate of Exeter University. Leisure activities include family pursuits, walking and sailing.

VALLANCE, Philip
Norton Rose, London (020) 7283 6000
vallancept@nortonrose.com
Specialisation: Principal area of work is structured asset finance transactions. Assets involved have been predominantly aircraft, but include offshore oil production vessels, locomotives, telecommunications and printing presses. Extensive experience in Japanese leveraged and operating leases, UK tax leases, export credit finance, operating leases, debt finance and residual value insurance.
Prof. Memberships: Law Society, City of London Solicitors Company.
Career: Qualified in NSW, Australia in 1982, after completing degrees in law and financial studies. Joined *Norton Rose* 1986. Spent two years with Japanese firm of *Nishimura & Partners* in Tokyo 1989-1991. Partner at *Norton Rose* 1993.

WALKLING, Kim
Simmons & Simmons, London (020) 7628 2020
kim.walkling@simmons-simmons.com
Specialisation: Big ticket asset finance and leasing, predominantly aviation; 2000/2001 Highlights: Acts for MOD on the Short Term Strategic Airlift Project (a Defence Procurement Authority prize winning project) and on the FSTA project, also a DPA winner; for SEPI on Iberia IPO.
Prof. Memberships: European Air Law Association.
Career: Qualified 1982. LLB (Hons) London (UCL).
Publications: Various contributions to magazines.
Personal: Married, two children.

WATTERS, James
Watson, Farley & Williams, London
(020) 7814 8000
jwatters@wfw.com
Specialisation: Partner in international finance group. Principal areas of practice are banking, asset and trade finance. Work includes the provision of asset finance in the UK and elsewhere by leasing, loan, receivable discounting and other facilities, and the sale and purchase of leasing companies and lease portfolios and conventional and structured trade finance facilities. Frequent lecturer and editor of section on Equipment Leasing in 'Asset and Project Finance: Law & Precedents' (Sweet & Maxwell).
Career: Qualified in September 1972. Partner at *Watson Farley & Williams* since May 1992.
Personal: Educated at KCS Wimbledon and Pembroke College, Oxford. Lives in London.

LEADERS IN ASSET FINANCE

WESTERN, Mark
White & Case, London (020) 7397 3709
mwestern@whitecase.com
Specialisation: Partner in banking department. Regularly represents major financial institutions on all aspects of banking law. Has particular expertise in the fields of asset and acquisition finance. Has worked extensively in the aircraft finance sector representing lessors, financial institutions, lessees and arrangers on operating leases, bank facilities and tax driven structures.
Prof. Memberships: Law Society of England and Wales.
Career: Qualified 1998. Partner at *Weil Gotshal & Manges* before joining *White & Case* in 2000.

WHITE, Geoffrey
Clifford Chance, London (020) 7600 1000
geoffrey.white@cliffordchance.com
Specialisation: Partner specialising in asset financing, banking and leasing and head of firm's international asset finance group.
Career: The Hutchins School, Hobart, Tasmania; University of Melbourne (LLB Hons and B Comm) 1966-71; Southern Methodist University, Dallas, Texas (LLM 1972-73). Articled *Freehill Hollingdale and Page*, Melbourne, Australia; qualified 1972 Melbourne Victoria, 1977 England, 1987 Japan; *Nakagawa Godo* Law Office, Tokyo 1977-80, 1986-87; partner *Clifford Chance* Tokyo office in 1987.
Personal: Born 1947.

WILSON, Keith
Lovells, London (020) 7296 2000
keith.wilson@lovells.com
Specialisation: Partner specialising in asset finance. Transactions include debt financings, tax leases, operating leases and defeasance arrangements. Major clients include Texaco, Granada, Xerox, Virgin, Bank of Nova Scotia, British Regional Airlines, BTM Capital Corporation, Erste Bank and Den Norske Bank.
Prof. Memberships: Law Society. Society of Scottish Lawyers in London.
Career: Trained *J & A Hastie SSC*; qualified Scotland 1986; Hong Kong 1989; England and Wales 1991; partner *Lovells* 1998.
Personal: Born 1963. Resides Harpenden. Married with one daughter. Interests include curling, running, supporting Scottish rugby and football. Member Rust Nail Curling Club; Hearts FC.

WOOD, R. Bruce
Morton Fraser, Solicitors, Edinburgh
(0131) 247 1000

AVIATION

Regulatory (London only): 99; Insurance & Litigation (London only): 100; Scotland: 101; *Profiles*: 101

OVERVIEW: London continues to dominate the aviation market with its expertise in regulatory and competition issues. As the larger airports and airlines have developed substantial in-house teams, the expertise within our leading firms rests on the shoulders of key individuals. Although many of the firms included do not have a Brussels office, this has not hindered their skill in managing EU compliance issues. Foreign ownership of airlines and international requirements on slot regulation issues remain hot topics and the Star Alliance has thrown up the need for cross-border competence. Consumer rights have dominated the media with DVT (deep-vein thrombosis) economy flight syndrome and air-rage (the control of passengers) filling column inches.

RESEARCH APPROVED BY BMRB: *For this edition,* Chambers' *researchers conducted 6,552 interviews – 4,419 with law firms, 554 with barristers and 1,579 with clients.*

The validity of the research was scrutinised by BMRB International, who audited both the methodology and the results at our offices in July 2001. They interviewed Chambers' *researchers and cross-checked sample interviews. Details of the audit appear on page 7.*

TOP IN-HOUSE LAWYERS

Regulatory:

Rupert BRITTON, Head of Legal, *Civil Aviation Authority*

Tim BYE, Legal Director & Copany Secretary, *British Midland*

Richard CHURCHILL-COLEMAN, Group General Counsel, *Thomsons Travel Group*

Owen HIGHLY, Commercial Lawyer, *British Airways*

Stephen WALSH, Head of Department, *British Airways*

Robert WEBB QC, General Counsel, *British Airways*

Rupert Britton is an *"impressive opponent"* and a sound legal advisor. *"Highly practical"* **Tim Bye** is praised for his *"grown up approach,"* while *"excellent"* **Richard Churchill-Coleman** is widely acclaimed. Owen Highly has been with BA for *"a long time developing a good knowledge of the industry." "Outstanding"* **Stephen Walsh** is rated by the market while the *"competent and well adjusted"* **Robert Webb** QC remains a leading light.

In-House lawyers profiles: p 1193

LONDON

REGULATORY

AVIATION: REGULATORY • London	Ptnrs	Assts
1 Denton Wilde Sapte	1	3
Lane & Partners	1	3
Norton Rose	2	n/a
2 Beaumont and Son	2	2
3 Barlow Lyde & Gilbert	2	7
Slaughter and May	n/a	n/a
4 Clark Ricketts	2	2
Harbottle & Lewis	2	3
Linklaters	2	2

LEADING INDIVIDUALS	
1 **BALFOUR John** Beaumont and Son	**O'DONOVAN Hugh** Denton Wilde Sapte
SOAMES Trevor Norton Rose	
2 **FARRELL Patrick** Norton Rose	**GIMBLETT Richard** Barlow Lyde & Gilbert
3 **CHAPPATTE Philippe** Slaughter and May	**HOWES Colin** Harbottle & Lewis
RICKETTS Robert Clark Ricketts	**SCULLY Dermot** Harbottle & Lewis

This book is the product of 6,552 1/2-hour interviews. See p.7 for BMRB audit.
Within each band, firms are listed alphabetically. *See individuals' profiles p.101*

Denton Wilde Sapte (see firm details p.939) Prominent for its work on behalf of easyJet, the firm covers all aspects of aviation regulatory issues, EC and competition law issues, and is endorsed as *"clearly the main player." "Energetic"* **Hugh O'Donovan** (see p.103) is acclaimed for his work in route licensing and has a specialism in operating licensing. The group represented easyJet in a High Court action against British Airways (alleged abuse of dominant position by GO), and has been engaged in the privatisation of National Air Traffic Services, acting for the CAA. United Airlines has continued to be a key client, with matters relating to regulatory and commercial issues, especially as the Star Alliance of airlines has developed. **Clients:** easyJet; United Airlines; National Jet Italia; Delta Airlines; TAG Aviation.

Lane & Partners (see firm details p.1027) A *"small outfit,"* which, in the wake of the retirement of the *"tough and exuberant"* Richard Venables, will be keenly scrutinised by the market this year. Known to *"put up a fight,"* the group covers regulatory issues such as ownership and control of airlines, and is involved in CAA hearings. The team acted for London Luton Airport in a dispute against easyJet over airport charges. Further highlights include acting for an airline in litigation on an aircraft leasing dispute and a major arbitration against a foreign airline involving significant regulatory issues. **Clients:** KLM (UK); Bristow Helicopters; Continental Airlines; London Luton Airport.

Norton Rose (see firm details p.1082)A strong regulatory presence in London and Brussels, the firm undertakes both EU competition matters and UK domestic regulatory issues. **Trevor Soames** (see p.103), often found in Brussels, is the *"driving force"* on competition cases, notably those relating to the Star Alliance. The UK regulatory work is managed by the *"versatile"* **Patrick Farrell** (see p.102), occupied with matters such as licensing by the CAA, start-up airlines and foreign airlines entering the UK market. Highlights include the firm's involvement in obtaining clearance from the EC of the proposed $4.3 billion acquisition by United Airlines of US Airways. It also advised British Midland, Lufthansa and SAS in securing clearance for its joint venture arrangements from the EC. It advises Britannia on all regulatory issues arising from the acquisition of its traffic rights on the Bilateral Air Service agreements in non-EU countries. **Clients:** United Airlines; Olympic Airways; British Midland; Britannia; orbitz.com; Lufthansa; SAS.

Beaumont and Son Traditionally known as aviation insurance specialist, the regulatory team's profile is carried by the *"academically astute and thoughtful"* **John Balfour** (see p.101), commended for his *"encyclopedic knowledge."* Ground handling, airport slots, competition and closedown of airline operations all feature in the caseload. The firm continues to represent BA on its case against ABTA, and advised a member state and its national carrier before the EU Commission on anti-competitive behaviour, a case concerning foreign ownership of airlines. The regulatory team advised IATA on whether the EC regulation on air carrier liability was in conflict with UK obligations under the Warsaw Convention/Hague Protocol. **Clients:** British Airways; Lufthansa; Virgin.

Barlow Lyde & Gilbert (see firm details p.870) Although the firm is best known for its outstanding aviation insurance practice, the regulatory team fields the *"excellent"* **Richard Gimblett** (see p.102) whose *"arguments are always to the point."* The group continues to act for IATA in the allocation of airport slots, terms and conditions of carriage and ticket conditions. On behalf of the FTO, it advised on the response to a Government Consultation Paper on corporate killing. **Clients:** IATA; FTO; CAA; Air New Zealand.

Slaughter and May (see firm details p.1135) Having won a great deal of BA's regulatory work over the last year, the firm is now considered a player in this field. Clients endorse the group, particularly on competition matters where the *"cool and experienced"* **Philippe Chappatte** (see p.181) is thought to have developed a genuine niche. The group acted for SAS on various regulatory and competition related issues and in the disposal of half of its stake in British Midland to Lufthansa. **Clients:** British Airways; National Air Traffic Services; Airtours; SAS; BAE Systems.

Clark Ricketts A small *"specialist unit,"* valued for its *"cost-effectiveness."* Acclaimed as one of the main regulatory players, **Robert Ricketts** (see p.96) has sound industry knowledge and *"good contacts."* The regulatory work is part of an all-encompassing aviation practice that is well-versed in airline start-up work and operational advice to foreign airlines entering the UK. More recently the firm has advised the shareholders in Excel Airways on a number of issues arising out of the aquisition of a majority interest in Sabre Airways. **Clients:** Excel Airways; Air & General Finance; McAlpine Helicopters; Sloane Helicopters; Ghana Airways.

Harbottle & Lewis (see firm details p.985)Lower profile this year, but maintaining its connection with Virgin Atlantic Airways, the group is overseen by *"effective operator"* **Colin Howes** (see p.102), while **Dermot Scully** (see p.103) (*"clever, one to watch"*) is making a name for himself in the regulatory field, alongside his aviation finance work. The firm is active in the frequency restrictions of airlines, slot exchange and transfers and advising airlines on the disposal of business parts. Highlights include acting for MOD's DERA on the harmonisation of European air traffic control systems. **Clients:** Virgin Express; Color Air; TNT.

Linklaters (see firm details p.1042) Competition specialists in this field, its profile has been weakened through its diminished representation of BA. Aviation-related work spans finance, corporate and to a lesser degree, regulatory work within the international market. **Clients:** KLM; Sabena; Sair Group.

INSURANCE & LITIGATION

AVIATION: INSURANCE & LITIGATION • London	Ptnrs	Assts
1 Beaumont and Son	12	16
2 Barlow Lyde & Gilbert	6	7
3 CMS Cameron McKenna	4	7
4 Clyde & Co	n/a	n/a
DLA	4	6
5 Clark Ricketts	2	2

LEADING INDIVIDUALS	
1 **GATES Sean** Beaumont and Son	
2 **AWFORD Ian** Barlow Lyde & Gilbert	**BRYMER Tim** CMS Cameron McKenna
FRANKLIN Mark DLA	**HUGHES Nicholas** Barlow Lyde & Gilbert
KAVANAGH Giles Barlow Lyde & Gilbert	**WILLCOX David** Beaumont and Son
3 **CLARK David** Beaumont and Son	**FARRELL Patrick** Norton Rose
GIMBLETT Richard Barlow Lyde & Gilbert	**McGILCHRIST Neil** Beaumont and Son
SCORER Tim DLA	
4 **ANDREWARTHA Jane** Clyde & Co	**CETTA Maria** Beaumont and Son
CLARK Ian Clark Ricketts	**FITZSIMMONS Anthony** Ince & Co
UP AND COMING	
SHEBSON Jeremy Barlow Lyde & Gilbert	

This book is the product of 6,552 1/2-hour interviews. See p.7 for BMRB audit.
Within each band, firms are listed alphabetically. *See individuals' profiles p.101*

TOP IN-HOUSE LAWYERS

Insurance & Litigation:

James HEALY-PRATT, Director of Claims and Legal Operations, *Amlin Aviation plc*

Ken WALDER, Director of Operations, *BAIG*

On the insurance and litigation side *"up and coming"* **James Healy-Pratt** has secured his high profile as *"experienced hand."* Also of note is "specialist" **Ken Walder**, thought to be *"involved in all major cases."*

In-House lawyers profiles: p 1193

Beaumont and Son Widely accepted as market leaders, the firm's resources and depth of client base receive unhesitating endorsement from all sections of the market. The *"shrewd, result-getting"* **Sean Gates** (see p.102), having recently returned from a one-year sabbatical, is the *"highest profile insurance aviation lawyer in London." "Extremely confident"* **David Willcox** (see p.104) and **David Clark** (see p.102) (*"a solid litigator with terrific client skills"*) also come warmly recommended. Another *"main player"* at the firm is **Neil McGilchrist** (see p.103) while **Maria Cetta** (see p.102) rejoins the team after a spell in-house at Amlin Aviation. The firm advised on the Matthew Harding accident and the interpretation of Article 25 of the Warsaw Convention/Hague Protocol. **Clients:** BAIG; ACE; Amlin; WAIG, AIG; IATA.

Barlow Lyde & Gilbert (see firm details p.870) *"The gap continues to narrow"* between the group and Beaumont and Son. *"Eminence grise"* **Ian Awford** (see p.101), a *"first class litigator,"* will be retiring from partnership to practice in Australia at the end of the year. Practice head **Nicholas Hughes** (see p.103) is also highly respected. *"Talented and confident"* former barrister **Giles Kavanagh** (see p.103) maintains his reputation in this field, as does the *"accomplished and personable"* **Richard Gimblett** (see p.102), who has a *"considerable pedigree"* in this area. Newly recruited from Clyde & Co, the *"impressive"* **Jeremy Shebson** (see p.103) has experience in cargo cases. The firm represented Western Digital in its successful case before the Court of Appeal, which clarified cargo owners' rights to sue in respect to their losses. **Clients:** Bombardier; Kingdom of Tonga; Qatar Airways; Rolls Royce; Gatwick Handling; SAAB; Air 2000.

CMS Cameron McKenna (see firm details p.922) *"Effective"* **Tim Brymer** (see p.102) is the key to the firm's success; *"he really gets on with things."* In the past year, the firm represented the Government of Malta in the Lockerbie Trial, which took place in the Netherlands. It is also acting for the insurers of airlines involved in losses while transporting UN personnel around war zones in Africa, and in relation to the loss in Kosovo of a carrier subcontracted to the UN. Other work includes advising an American airline in the defence of a personal injury claim concerning so-called economy class syndrome (DVT). **Clients:** Aerospace; Airbus; Lucas; Dunlop; BTR; UPS; Jet Airlines.

Clyde & Co (see firm details p.921) A general insurance and re-insurance practice supports expertise in the cargo market. Heading up the aviation department is **Jane Andrewartha** (see p.101), who is also active in mediations. Her team represented various interests in the accident investigation into crash of MD11 at Chek Lap Kok Airport in Hong Kong. It was also instructed by airline interests in the Rutaca crash in Venezuela, and advised the London underwriters in the case of a Thai Airways aircraft explosion at Bangkok airport. **Clients:** ACE; Amlin Aviation; Lloyds.

DLA **Tim Scorer** is best known for his work for the private pilot community, and is the leading figure at the team.

Clark Ricketts Often seen on the "*other side of the table*" representing the plaintiffs, the firm is again perceived to have laid claim to a strong niche in the market. The "*charming, but doggedly determined*" **Ian Clark** is the main litigator here. The firm has niche expertise in the helicopter industry. **Clients:** Excel Airways; McAlpine Helicopters; Sloane Helicopters.

Other Notable Practitioners Engaged in a great deal of repossession litigation, the "*user friendly, no nonsense*" **Patrick Farrell** (see p.102) at **Norton Rose** has carved a name for himself. "*Prolific*" **Anthony Fitzsimmons** (see p.102) at **Ince & Co** has been instructed by GAUM in relation to the Virgin Atlantic hard landing of an A340 airbus at Heathrow.

SCOTLAND

AVIATION • Scotland	Ptnrs	Assts
1		
Maclay Murray & Spens Glasgow	1	1
Shepherd & Wedderburn WS Edinburgh	1	1
Simpson & Marwick WS Edinburgh	1	2

LEADING INDIVIDUALS
1
ANDERSON Peter Simpson & Marwick WS
CLARK Richard Maclay Murray & Spens
DONALD Hugh Shepherd & Wedderburn WS

This book is the product of 6,552 1/2-hour interviews. See p.7 for BMRB audit.

Within each band, firms are listed alphabetically. *See individuals' profiles p.101*

Maclay Murray & Spens (see firm details p.1047) A leading light in Scotland and heavily instructed by London firms. On the plaintiff side, the firm advised on the SilkAir crash of 1997. The main litigator here is **Richard Clark** (see p.102), "*excellent, with a strong, sound technical background.*" The group represented Cessna Aircraft Corp in a fatal accident inquiry with regard to a crash at Glasgow in 1999. **Clients:** Insurers of BIH; Cessna Aircraft Corp; General Electric.

Shepherd & Wedderburn WS (see firm details p.1126) Handling all matters in relation to insurers' interests, the "*experienced and highly visible*" **Hugh Donald** (see p.102) is the firm's main player. Involved in a landmark appeal before the Inner House of the Court of Session, the firm also acted for Bristow Helicopters on aspects of the Warsaw Convention. Also advised Edinburgh Air Charter in the investigation and inquiry into a Cessna 404 crash. **Clients:** Bristow Helicopters; Edinburgh Air Charter; British Aviation Insurance Group.

Simpson & Marwick WS (see firm details p.1133) Active in the PI market, the aviation insurance sector is also catered for by a team of litigation specialists. **Peter Anderson** is a specialist with a "*safe pair of hands*" who "*presents his case well.*" **Clients:** Boeing; CAA; BA; Air UK.

LEADERS IN AVIATION

ANDERSON, Peter

Simpson & Marwick WS, Edinburgh
(0131) 557 1545

ANDREWARTHA, Jane

Clyde & Co, London (020) 7623 1244

Specialisation: Practice is rooted in major insurance and reinsurance litigation, claims and liability work. Is an accredited and experienced CEDR mediator. Acted in the Swazi Airline hijack, involved in personal injury aspect of Piper Alpha claims settlement and reinsurance aspects of Eastern European Newbuildings. Aviation practice consists of representing insurers and aviation interests in defence and policy matters including TAM and most major recent case being Rutaca Venezualan crash. Also involved in general aviation – light aircraft and helicopters. Clients include most major London and foreign market insurance and reinsurance companies and many Lloyd's syndicates. Is a regular conference speaker and contributor to insurance industry publications.
Prof. Memberships: Qualified in 1976, having joined *Clyde & Co* in 1974. Became a partner in 1980. London head of the firm's Latin American offices from 1989-97. Now head of aviation and sat on the Board of Management as finance partner from 1993.
Career: Law Society, CEDR accredited mediator, update author of the international publication 'Journal of Maritime Law & Commerce', Association of Average Adjusters (associate member), Lloyds (associate member), member of Air Law Group of the Royal Aeronautical Society.
Personal: Born 20th December 1952. Attended Exeter University 1970-73 (LLB Hons). Leisure activities include skiing, powerboat racing and swimming. Lives in London.

AWFORD, Ian

Barlow Lyde & Gilbert, London (020) 7247 2277
iawford@blg.co.uk

Specialisation: Partner in aviation department. Main area of practice is aviation law and the law relating to commercial uses of outer space. Also handles insurance law, litigation, arbitration and mediation. Has acted in many major air disaster cases.
Prof. Memberships: International Institute of Space Law of the International Astronautics Federation; International Society of Air Safety Investigators; European Society of Air Safety Investigators; Federation of Insurance and Corporate Counsel; International Associate of the American Bar Association; European Centre for Space Law; Air Law Working Party of the International Chamber of Commerce; Product Liability Advisory Council; International Association of Defense Counsel. European Air Law Association; Aviation Insurance Association; The Guild of Air Traffic Control Officers; International Court of Aviation and Space Arbitration.
Career: Qualified in 1967, in Hong Kong in 1988 and in Tasmania 1998. Joined *Barlow Lyde & Gilbert* in 1969, becoming a partner in 1973. Chairman of the Outer Space Committee of the International Bar Association: Section of Business Law 1987-90; Aerospace Law Committee, Inter Pacific Bar Association 1990-93; Elected fellow of the Royal Aeronautical Society 1988. Fellow of the Institute of Advanced Legal Studies 1998, CEDR Accredited Mediator 1998.
Publications: Author of various publications on legal issues concerning carriage by air, product liability and the law relating to outer space.
Personal: Born 15th April 1941. Sheffield University LLB (Hons). Leisure interests include skiing, theatre and music. Married. Five sons and one daughter. Lives in London.

BALFOUR, John

Beaumont and Son, London (020) 7709 5000
jbalfour@beaumont.co.uk

Specialisation: Partner in aviation department. Practice includes regulation, EC and CAA work; acci-

dents, liability and insurance; sale, purchase and leasing and other commercial arrangements; international issues. Author of 'European Community Air Law' and of many articles on aviation in the professional press. Lectures extremely widely; recent engagements include conferences and courses organised by the Royal Aeronautical Society, IFURTA Aix-en-Provence, ENAC Toulouse, Cranfield University, European Aviation Club and European Air Law Association.
Prof. Memberships: Royal Aeronautical Society (past chairman, Air Law Group); European Air Law Association (secretary); European Aviation Club (board member).
Career: Qualified 1979, having joined *Frere Cholmeley Bischoff* in 1977. Became a partner in 1986 and head of the aviation group in 1993. Joined *Beaumont and Son* as a partner in 1997.

BRYMER, Tim
CMS Cameron McKenna, London
(020) 7367 3000
trb@cmck.com
Specialisation: Partner – aviation group specialising in aviation and aerospace law and claims. Represents aviation insurers, airlines and manufacturers worldwide. Responsible for pioneering use of common law injunction in restraining forum shopping following aviation disasters.
Prof. Memberships: Founder member of Lawyers' Flying Association. Member of Guild of Pilots and Air Navigators. Elected member of Royal Aeronautical Society Air Law Discussion Group and Insurance Institute of London Aviation Committee. Holder of current pilot's licence.
Career: Dulwich College; College of Air Training, Hamble; College of Law, Lancaster Gate. Qualified 1977.
Personal: Art, music, tennis, cycling and flying.

CETTA, Maria
Beaumont and Son, London (020) 7709 5220
mcetta@beaumont.co.uk
Specialisation: Partner in aviation department. Practice includes all types of aviation liability and insurance law.
Prof. Memberships: Law Society; former member Lloyds of London Law Reform Committee, International Union of Aviation Insurers Legal and Claims Study Group.
Career: Qualified 1989; partner *Beaumont and Son* 1993; Lloyds of London 1995-2000; partner *Beaumont and Son* 2000.
Personal: Born 18 September 1960.

CHAPPATTE, Philippe
Slaughter and May, London (020) 7600 1200
philippe.chappatte@slaughterandmay.com
See under Competition/Anti-trust, p.181

CLARK, David
Beaumont and Son, London (020) 7709 5140
dclark@beaumont.co.uk
Specialisation: Partner in aviation department. Main areas of practice are all aspects of aviation liability work; also handles personal injury work for defendants. Extensive experience of dealing with claims in UK, France and Francophone countries, South America, India, European and Scandinavian countries. Matters handled include Swiss Bank Corporation v Brinks-MAT, Randolph Fields v Watts and others, Swissair-SR.111 Nova Scotia accident and securing awards for British Airways and their insurers from the United Nations Compensation Commission for Iraq/Kuwait war losses.
Prof. Memberships: Law Society; British, Brazilian and Portuguese Law Association; Anglo/Brazilian Society. Faculty member of IATA Learning Centre Management Development programme
Career: Qualified 1980. Partner 1986.
Personal: Born 8 March 1952. Attended University of Southampton and College of Law.

CLARK, Ian
Clark Ricketts, London (020) 7404 1551

CLARK, Richard
Maclay Murray & Spens, Glasgow
(0141) 248 5011
rafc@maclaymurrayspens.co.uk
Specialisation: Senior litigation partner specialising in aviation, fraud and financial services and shipping litigation. Recent cases include Silkair crash in Indonesia, Landcatch v The Braer Corporation and IOPCF. Co-author of the Scottish section of Butterworths 'Aircraft Finance'.
Career: Edinburgh University (LLB 1973).
Personal: Born 1949.

DONALD, Hugh
Shepherd & Wedderburn WS, Edinburgh
(0131) 473 5159
hugh.donald@shepwedd.co.uk
Specialisation: Partner. Specialist in clinical negligence, representing doctors and dentists in civil claims, inquiries and disciplinary proceedings. Also aviation representing airline and helicopter operators in both civil claims and accident inquiries. On the panel appointed to handle claims under Law society of Scotland Charter Policy.
Career: Qualified in 1975, having joined *Shepherd & Wedderburn WS* in 1973. Became a partner in 1977. Administrative head of litigation department 1990-94. Appointed managing partner in April 1994, and chief executive from April 1995 – April 1999.
Personal: Born 5th November 1951. Educated at Edinburgh University. Family Mediator. Chairman, Family Mediation Scotland. Leisure interests include gardening, walking and church. Lives in Edinburgh. Awarded OBE for services to family mediation in Scotland.

FARRELL, Patrick
Norton Rose, London (020) 7283 6000
farrellpa@nortonrose.com
Specialisation: (for aviation: insurance and litigation) Advises airlines, brokers, banks, financiers and underwriters on aviation insurance matters including liability claims world-wide, coverage disputes, advice on wordings and insurance claims generally. Acts for underwriters in political risk matters arising out of aircraft finance transactions and for airlines in regulatory matters.
Prof. Memberships: MRAeS; chairman of the Royal Aeronautical Society Air Law Group; chairman of the UK ICC Commission on Air Transport. Member of Institute of Travel and Tourism, IBA, LSLA, CLLS.

FITZSIMMONS, Anthony
Ince & Co, London (020) 7623 2011
anthony.fitzsimmons@ince.co.uk
Specialisation: Partner, leader of aviation team; specialises in handling aviation, insurance and reinsurance problems of all types, including investigations and political, brand, regulatory and competition problems; enjoys devising practical solutions to problems in these markets, including creating new insurance products.
Prof. Memberships: Royal Aeronautical Society and its Airlaw committee; associate member of the Institute of Electrical Engineers; secretary of pollution, products and new technologies, Insurance Working Party of International Insurance Law Association.
Career: Qualified as solicitor 1980; partner *Ince & Co.*
Publications: 'European Insurance Competition Law' (1994 Graham and Trotman); former editor of 'Journal of British Insurance Law Association'; editor of 'Pollution Law and Insurance' (1997 Klower International); associate editor of 'Geneva Papers on Risk and Insurance'.
Personal: Education: Cambridge (MA Engineering); requalified as a lawyer, Cambridge and London. Leisure: family, walking, gardens. Personal: resides London.

FRANKLIN, Mark
DLA, London (08700) 111 111

GATES, Sean
Beaumont and Son, London (020) 7709 5000
sgates@beaumont.co.uk
Specialisation: Joint senior partner and head of aviation claims department. Main area of practice is aviation insurance and liability. Represents insurers and airlines in respect of claims made against them, and insurers in respect of policy decisions with airlines and reinsurers. Also handles libel and slander work, representing both plaintiffs and defendants in defamation actions. Author of articles in numerous journals, frequent speaker on aviation issues. Legal adviser International Union of Aviation Insurers. Former Chairman Air Law Committee, Royal Aeronautical Society.
Career: Qualified in 1972. Joined *Beaumont and Son* in 1973, becoming a partner in 1978 and head of aviation claims department in 1991. Senior partner 1 November 1997. Arbitrator with Cour Internationale d'Arbitrage Aerien et Special.
Personal: Born 4 February 1949. Leisure pursuits include collecting 19th Century illustrated books. Lives in London.

GIMBLETT, Richard
Barlow Lyde & Gilbert, London (020) 7247 2277
rgimblett@blg.co.uk
Specialisation: Aviation and travel law; commercial litigation.
Prof. Memberships: Member of the IATA International Law Faculty; member of the European Centre for Space Law.
Career: Called to Bar 1982. Legal adviser, UK Civil Aviation Authority 1985-88. Admitted as a solicitor in 1990.
Personal: BA Hons (Oxon) (1981). Director of FTO Trust Fund Ltd; private pilot.

HOWES, Colin
Harbottle & Lewis, London (020) 7667 5000
colin.howes@harbottle.com
Specialisation: Partner. Handles regulatory, commercial, e-business and corporate work for a variety of clients, most of whom are in the entertainment, leisure and travel industries.

Prof. Memberships: Law Society; European Air Law Association.
Career: Qualified in 1981. Joined *Harbottle & Lewis* in 1979, became a partner in 1984.
Publications: Author of 'Slot Allocation at Heathrow Airport: The Legal Framework'.
Personal: Born 1956. Attended Ipswich School 1967-74; Oriel College, Oxford 1975-78. Lives in London.

HUGHES, Nicholas
Barlow Lyde & Gilbert, London (020) 7247 2277
nhughes@blg.co.uk
Specialisation: Head of aerospace department. Main area of practice is aviation law, covering aviation insurance and reinsurance, liability law, carriage of goods and aviation regulatory law.
Prof. Memberships: Royal Aeronautical Society, Law Society, International Bar Association, American Bar Association.
Career: Qualified in 1981. Joined *Barlow Lyde & Gilbert* in 1979, becoming a partner in 1984. Director of Association of Insurance and Risk Managers (AIRMIC) 1992 to date.
Publications: General editor (aviation) of 'Contracts for the Carriage of Goods by Land, Sea and Air' (LLP); editorial consultant of 'Transport Law and Policy'.
Personal: Born 10th October 1955. Attended Sheffield University, BA Law (Hons). Lives in London.

KAVANAGH, Giles
Barlow Lyde & Gilbert, London (020) 7247 2277
gkavanagh@blg.co.uk
Specialisation: Partner specialising in all aspects of aviation law. His practice includes insurance disputes (claims and coverage), product liability, regulatory and transactional advice. Giles also advises on the sale and leasing of aircraft and has appeared for lessors and lessees in disputes arising out of aircraft leases. Cases in the past twelve months include acting for insurers of landing gear manufacturer in very substantial multi-jurisdictional product liability dispute (ongoing); representing successful appellants in Western Digital v BA (CA) on whether an owner of goods who is neither consignor nor consignee has title to sue under the Amended Warsaw and Guadalajara Conventions; acting for insurers in relation to the Concorde disaster.
Prof. Memberships: Royal Aeronautical Society; the ICC's Air Transport Committee.
Career: Before joining *BLG* in 1999, Giles was recommended as a leading aviation barrister in the Chambers and Partners Directory. He appeared for the regulator in the reported cases of Philcox v CAA (CA) and in Perrett v Popular Flying Association (CA) and for insurers in mass disaster litigation, including the Kegworth crash. As a barrister he also appeared in a number of substantial arbitrations.
Publications: Regular contributor to aviation legal periodicals and conference speaker.
Personal: Education: St John's College, Cambridge; MA., LL.M. President of Cambridge Union Society, Michaelmas 1981. Recreation: swimming, golf, tennis, deep sleep. Lives Kingston Hill with wife, Anna and two children, Tierney and Conall.

McGILCHRIST, Neil
Beaumont and Son, London (020) 7709 5000
nmcgilchrist@beaumont.co.uk
Specialisation: Joint senior partner. Work includes reinsurance, aerospace and insurance litigation.
Prof. Memberships: Law Society.
Career: Qualified in 1969 as a barrister of the Middle Temple, becoming a partner in *Beaumont and Son* in 1981.
Personal: Born 8 December 1946. Attended Wadham College, Oxford, then Inns of Court School of Law. President of University of Oxford Law Society, 1966.

O'DONOVAN, Hugh
Denton Wilde Sapte, London (020) 7424 1212
hod@dentonwildesapte.com
Specialisation: Partner in Corporate Department and Aviation Industry Group. Main area of practice is aviation, covering air transport regulation, commercial agreements in aviation, EC and competition law, airline and airport operations, aircraft leasing and airport financing. Also covers travel agents and tour operators. Regular speaker at various conferences and seminars on aviation-related topics.
Prof. Memberships: Law Society, International Bar Association, Royal Aeronautical Society, Aviation Committee of the UK International Chambers of Commerce, member of Council of the Airport Operators' Association.
Career: Called to the Bar in 1975. Practised as a barrister before joining *Knapp Fishers* in 1985. Left for *Richards Butler* in 1987 (Partner 1989). Became a solicitor in 1988. Joined *Wilde Sapte* as a Partner in 1991.
Personal: Born 19th August 1952. Attended Royal Grammar School, Guildford 1963-69 then Balliol College, Oxford 1970-73. Leisure pursuits include golf, skiing, flying and rugby refereeing. Lives in Witley, Surrey.

RICKETTS, Robert
Clark Ricketts, London (020) 7404 1551
robertricketts@clarkricketts.com
See under Asset Finance & Leasing, p.96

SCORER, Tim
DLA, London (08700) 111111

SCULLY, Dermot
Harbottle & Lewis, London (020) 7667 5170
dermot.scully@harbottle.com
Specialisation: Dermot Scully is head of the aviation group at *Harbottle & Lewis.* He acts for airlines and other aviation businesses advising on all legal aspects of their operations, particularly aircraft acquisition and regulatory issues. Clients include Virgin Atlantic, TNT, Uni Airways and British Midland. Dermot holds an air law qualification from University College, London.
Prof. Memberships: Member of the Air Law Committee of the Royal Aeronautical Society.
Publications: Dermot has written articles for many industry publications and is a speaker at industry conferences.

SHEBSON, Jeremy
Barlow Lyde & Gilbert, London (020) 7247 2277
jshebson@blg.co.uk
Specialisation: Passenger and cargo legal liability; accident litigation. Has acted for aviation insurance market on claims in various jurisdictions, including providing advice on policy wordings; also involved in disputes arising out of aircraft leases; advises on standard terms and conditions in the aviation industry.
Prof. Memberships: Member of Royal Aeronautical Society.
Career: Joined *Clyde & Co* in 1989 and was made a partner in 1998. Joined as a partner in *BLG*'s aerospace department in January 2001. Aviation related cases of note include Thomas Cook v Air Malta (1997) and Malca Amit v British Airways and others (1999). Also represented the pilot and operator of the first commercial balloon to have incurred a fatality in the UK (1997).
Publications: Contributes articles in aviation/insurance press and has spoken on aviation related topics at conferences.
Personal: Graduated in law from London School of Economics in 1988. Is married to Ruth and has four sons. Enjoys football, being a keen Arsenal fan, and has also run three London marathons for charity.

SOAMES, Trevor
Norton Rose, London (00) 322 237 6111
soamest@nortonrose.com
Specialisation: Trevor Soames is a partner in Norton Rose's rapidly growing EU and competition group which presently numbers 9 partners and one consultant (John Bridgeman, former UK Director General of Fair Trading) plus 37 full time associates. Trevor's main area of practice is all aspects of EC and UK competition; trade and regulatory law in many economic sectors. Trevor is well known for his transportation expertise and aviation, in particular. He has regularly been identified by Euromoney as being one of the World's 20 Leading Aviation Lawyers and in 2000 was one of 15 Norton Rose partners to be named in the Euromoney Guide to the World's Leading Aviation Lawyers. In the field of aviation, Trevor's clients have included a wide range of Governments, regulatory agencies and multinational corporations from around the world. He has represented airlines, airports, Governments and national regulatory bodies. Most recent cases include representing United Airlines in successfully obtaining EU merger clearance for its proposed merger with US Airways as well as the European Commission's continuing Article 85 investigation of the alliance between United Airlines with its European partners, Lufthansa and SAS, as well as the concurrent investigation under Article 84 by the German FCO; United Airlines in opposing the hostile bid by Onex/AirCo for Air Canada and in its subsequent arrangements with Air Canada; British Midland, Lufthansa and SAS jointly in the notification of their intra-European alliance; the Greek Government and Olympic Airways regarding its proposed privatisation; British Midland (on a variety of major cases including the Aer Lingus Article 82 interlining case, the Brussels Airport Article 86 case which resulted in action being taken by the EC Commission against many EU airport authorities, the Aer Lingus and Air France state aid cases, the BA PRS and override case); Iberia in the Commission's investigation of the Spanish ground handling monopoly under Articles 82 and 86; Olympic Airways and the Greek Government in the Greek Article 82 and 86 ground handling case, successfully closed by a Commission Decision in 1997 dismissing the complaints, as well as in the Olympic Airways and Spata Airport state aid cases, most recently successfully securing a Commission decision of September 2000 regarding state guarantees; Ryanair in the Aer Lingus Article 82 predatory pricing and state aid cases including the

Ryanair v Commission case before the European Court. Trevor advises a number of leading scheduled and charter airlines and financial institutions on other key aviation regulatory issues including ownership and licensing requirements, environmental and consumer issues as well as representing clients before the UK CAA and EC Commission. He also has specific expertise in the field of UK aviation licensing and scarce capacity procedures, appearing as an advocate before the CAA and other authorities in a number of cases including Warsaw, Moscow I, Moscow II and Prague. Trevor has advised various Central and Eastern European Governments on air transport liberalisation related matters including those of the Czech Republic, Slovenia, Poland and Russia. In 1998, Trevor advised the rapporteur to the European Parliament's Transport Committee on important legislative proposals put forward by the Commission, the amendments suggested were subsequently adopted by the Parliament and the Commission.
Career: A graduate of Cambridge University. Called to the Bar of England & Wales in 1984 and enrolled as a Solicitor in 1989. Worked at UK Department of Trade and Industry before entering private practice. Trevor is Highly Recommended both as a leading EC competition lawyer and as an aviation lawyer, in 'Legal 500', 'Law Firms in Europe 2000', 'Chambers & Partners Guide to the Legal Profession' and 'Chambers Global - World's Leading Lawyers 2000-2001'. He is listed as a leading Brussels antitrust expert in 'Euromoney's Guide to the World's Leading Competition and Antitrust Lawyers' and in the 'International Who's Who of Competition Lawyers'. Trevor was recently selected by 'European Legal Business' as one of the leading Brussels state aid lawyers.
Publications: Author of many articles on competition and regulatory law as well as being editor of, or contributor to a number of books including: 'Corporate Mergers and Acquisitions', 'Air Transport and the European Community: Recent Developments', 'Airline Mergers and Co-operation', 'State Aids to Airlines', 'European Air Law Association' Volume 12 and Volume 13. Trevor is also an Associate Editor of 'Butterworths Competition Law Encyclopaedia'. Recent aviation-related articles include: 'Predatory Pricing and Air Transport' and 'State Aid and Air Transport, European Competition Law Review'; 'All bark and no bite', Airline Business; 'Ground Handling Liberalisation', Journal of Air Transport Management; 'European Commission: Great Expectations', Airline Business; 'Ground Handling Liberalisation', Royal Aeronautical Society; 'Essential facilities and Air Transport', European Air Law Association; 'The application of the EU competition rules to aviation and alliances' European Aviation Club; 'The differences in aeropolitical regimes and competition law' European Aviation Club; 'Airline mergers and alliances', European Air Law Association.

WILLCOX, David
Beaumont and Son, London (020) 7709 5314
dwillcox@beaumont.co.uk
Specialisation: Partner in aviation department. Main areas of practice are aerospace, commercial litigation and insurance litigation. His practice in aviation law covers handling of passenger and hull claims in respect of major accidents involving fixed and rotary wing operations including a large number of accidents in Africa, passenger cargo and baggage liability claims, advising on rights and liabilities of aviation engineering and maintenance organisations, and commercial litigation.
Prof. Memberships: Law Society.
Career: Qualified in 1981. Became a partner in 1987.
Personal: Born 25 March 1957. Attended Sheffield University. Past examiner aviation law and claims – Chartered Insurance Institute.

BANKING

OVERVIEW: As consolidation in the banking sector continues, and deals increasingly involve a cross border element, the market is putting work into fewer and fewer hands. Some industry figures predict that as few as ten firms could come to dominate this sector. Familiarity with innovative financial instruments, responsive service and a credible international network will become increasingly important.

At the lower end of the *Chambers* table, firms are looking to develop niche expertise. A number have strong property finance practices, and a few property finance lawyers make it into our rankings. Those City firms reliant on competing on costs in the mid-market may find this increasingly unprofitable as more of this work goes to the regions or is done in-house. Decreasing resistance to LMA documentation may hasten this process. In London, Linklaters is emerging as the most likely challenger to the hegemony of Allen & Overy and Clifford Chance. Although a "*changing of the guard*" has yet to occur in the most senior ranks, Mark Campbell and Stephen Gillespie rise in the rankings to join an exceptionally strong chasing pack.

RESEARCH APPROVED BY BMRB: *For this edition,* Chambers' *researchers conducted 6,552 interviews – 4,419 with law firms, 554 with barristers and 1,579 with clients.*

The validity of the research was scrutinised by BMRB International, who audited both the methodology and the results at our offices in July 2001. They interviewed Chambers' *researchers and cross-checked sample interviews. Details of the audit appear on page 7.*

TOP IN-HOUSE LAWYERS

Laurie ADAMS, Global General Counsel, *ABN AMRO*

Richard BENNETT, Group Legal Advisor, *HSBC*

Mitchell CALLER, Senior Vice President and Associate General Counsel, *JP Morgan Chase*

Alex CAMERON, Head of Legal for London & Europe, *Barclays Capital*

Paul CHELSOM, Director of Legal & Compliance, *Credit Suisse First Boston*

• **John COLLINS,** Global Legal Head, Corporate Finance, Clients, Loans, *ABN AMRO*

Simon DODDS, Head of Legal, *Deutsche Bank*

William ELLIOT, Executive Legal Director, *Goldman Sachs*

James GLEDHILL, First Vice President & Co-head of Corporate Finance Legal, *Citibank*

Clare JONES, First Vice President & Co-head of Corporate Finance Legal, Citibank

Ian JAMESON, European Corporate Counsel, *Lehman Brothers*

Geoffrey JOHNSON, General Counsel, *Lloyds TSB*

Howard TRUST, General Counsel, *Barclays*

Since moving from Citibank, the *"excellent"* **Laurie Adams** has taken on a *"mammoth job"* putting together ABN AMRO's legal department. **Simon Dodds** remains *"an influential figure"* if less transactional than some in our list. *"No-nonsense"* **Richard Bennett** *"has control and understanding of the whole operation."* **Mitch Caller** combines *"commercial understanding"* with *"logic."* **Alex Cameron** is regarded as a *"canny, impressive lawyer,"* while **Paul Chelsom** received warm commendation. The *"outstandingly good"* **John Collins** is applauded for his *"sensible and commercial approach." "Bright"* **William Elliot** is impressing the market, while *"pragmatic"* **James Gledhill** and *"ambitious and hard working"* **Clare Jones** form a prominent team at Citibank. *"Professional"* **Ian Jameson** often *"plays a larger role"* than that of in-house counsel. *"Outstanding"* **Geoffrey Johnson** is *"cerebral"* and **Howard Trust** is appreciated for his *"great personality and character."*

In-House lawyers profiles: p.1139

LONDON

Allen & Overy (see firm details p.856) "*I've never come across a bad lawyer at A&O.*" Although the two top firms are still too close to separate, our researchers discovered a consensus of opinion that "*across the board there's a slightly greater stamp of quality at A&O.*" This is due in part to the excellence of its documentation, "*everyone drafting documents is trying to emulate the standard set by A&O.*" Another reason is that "*the quality at A&O, especially of assistants, is better,*" the market agrees, "*the standard is consistently good – anyone you care to pull out will be excellent.*"

In both of these, the debt owed to "*guru*" **Philip Wood** (see p.123) is obvious. Considered by peers "*a legend in his own lifetime,*" although now not transactional, he is responsible for putting in place their 'know-how' system, involving training and documentation. Another ace in A&O's hand is the "*outstanding*" **David Morley** (see p.120). Acknowledged by the market to be "*a star and the public face of A&O's finance practice,*" he is highly visible on jumbo financings where "*his superb commercial negotiating ability makes him popular with clients.*"

Other bank lending experts include "*old school*" **Tony Humphrey** (see p.119), considered "*intelligent and knowledgeable,*" **Michael Duncan** (see p.117) who is "*a good forthright lawyer*" and "*technically excellent, user friendly bloke*" **Trevor Borthwick** (see p.116). "*Generalist*" **Peter Schulz** (see p.122) is considered by specialists to be "*an extremely strong lawyer who you can trust not to make mistakes*" while "*heroically senior*" Jonathan Horsfall Turner retains a profile in banking but is now acting as a consultant. **Stephen Kensell** (see p.119) ("*good fun, and the banks like him*") enters the rankings this year.

Much of this expertise has been on show in the field of telecoms financing where the firm advised on deals worth over €100 billion in 2000. This included the €8.4 billion financing to support Mobilcom Multimedia's successful bid for a German UMTS licence, and the €3.2 billion financing to support WIND Telecomunicazioni's successful bid for an Italian UMTS licence, in both of which it acted for the arrangers.

On the acquisition finance side, Allen & Overy has arguably led the way in offering banks a combined European acquisition finance facility with US and Euromarket high yield debt and securitisation advice. **Tony Keal** (see p.119) is a leader in this field – "*he's one of the most talented leveraged, structured finance lawyers around and arguably a father of some aspects of the area*" but "*the word irascible has been used, which is entirely fair.*" Both the "*quietly effective*" **Euan Gorrie** (see p.118) and the "*tenacious, no nonsense*" **Stephen Gillespie** (see p.118) rise in our rankings after substantial client commendation. "*Certainly one of the A&O quality operators,*" Gillespie is "*entirely comfortable in some of the biggest and most complicated deals.*" These include many of the year's highlight deals, such as advising

BANKING • London	Ptnrs	Assts
1 Allen & Overy	43	144
Clifford Chance	40	182
2 Linklaters	21	108
3 Freshfields Bruckhaus Deringer	10	30
Norton Rose	29	n/a
4 Ashurst Morris Crisp	7	18
Lovells	14	36
Slaughter and May	*	*
5 Denton Wilde Sapte	16	27
Herbert Smith	16	30
Shearman & Sterling	8	32
6 Baker & McKenzie	5	15
Berwin Leighton Paisner	7	12
CMS Cameron McKenna	n/a	n/a
DLA	n/a	n/a
Gouldens	3	5
Macfarlanes	3	4
Simmons & Simmons	6	n/a
SJ Berwin	5	8
Taylor Joynson Garrett	6	6
Theodore Goddard	6	7
Travers Smith Braithwaite	4	8
Watson, Farley & Williams	n/a	n/a
White & Case	8	15

Within each band, firms are listed alphabetically.

Barclays Capital on £680 million of senior and mezzanine financing to assist a consortium comprising Bourne Leisure, Candover and Legal & General to fund the acquisition of Rank Holidays. **Clients:** Barclays Capital; JP Morgan Chase; Morgan Stanley; KPN; UniCredito Italiano; ABN AMRO; Goldman Sachs; Citigroup; Dresdner; Deutsche; Salomon Smith Barney.

Clifford Chance (see firm details p.919) "*The strongest – far more innovative, the others tend to follow,*" according to one competitor. Where Clifford Chance really has the edge, though, is on size: "*worldwide it's considerably bigger,*" and, in particular, "*its international network is a more credible one.*" Some commentators perceived a more commercial approach: "*the firm was very keen to perform – I've never felt that it put barriers in front of you.*" In "*concentrating on its global network*" and its biggest clients, the CC strategy may yet pay dividends in the long run.

The extra US capability resulting from last year's merger is already beginning to bear fruit, as has the firm's ability to lead transactions from a number of global offices. A busy year has seen the team conduct an enormous quantity of deals – in one two month period acting in seven jumbo loans worth £76 billion. The €30 billion financing of France Telecom's acquisition of Orange was landed by "*great client getter*" **James Johnson** (see p.119), "*his strength is his personality and his ability to get on with clients.*" Although not fee-earning, "*gentlemanly and straightforward*" **Michael Bray** (see p.116) is "*one of the pillars of the city*" exerting enormous "*influence behind the scenes.*" "*Unflappable and client friendly*" **Stuart Popham** (see p.121) is "*still a smooth and effective operator.*" Other high quality partners include "*tough competitor*" **Mark Stewart** (see p.679), considered "*first rate, hands on, and highly commercial,*" and **Malcolm Sweeting** (see p.122), "*a clever man and a good operator, who can achieve what he sets his mind to,*" who is "*a big player in mainstream syndicated lending.*" "*Creative*" **Lee Cullinane** (see p.117) earned plaudits from peers as "*a nice guy to deal with and a good draftsman*" and **Robert Smith** (see p.122), "*a leading banking partner for some time,*" makes it into the tables this year. **Peter Kilner** (see p.119) ("*outstanding and a nice person as well*") joins our up and coming ranks as does the "*superb*" **Robert Lee** (see p.120) who impressed with his "*depth of experience and attention to detail.*"

Alan Inglis (see p.119) has a fairly low profile, yet is rated as "*first class, one of the best at Clifford Chance.*" He acted for Citibank in arranging the €3 billion senior credit facility and €800 million high yield bond issue with which Callahan Associates and others acquired part of the cable, telephone and internet business of Deutsche Telekom. The highest profile partner this year was undoubtedly **Mark Campbell** (see p.116); described by clients as "*a commercial operator with a fine mind,*" he is "*clearly at the peak of the practice*" and "*makes damn sure his team perform.*" He represented Candover, Legal & General and Bourne Leisure on the LBO of Rank Holidays, Warner and Oasis Holidays, a total transaction value of £1.1 billion. **Clients:** Citigroup; Barclays; JP Morgan; Deutsche; HSBC; ABN AMRO; Goldman Sachs; Morgan Stanley Dean Witter; BNP Paribas; Dresdner; CSFB; UBS Warburg; BankAmerica; RBS; West LB; ING Barings; Mediobanca; Lloyds TSB Capital Markets; LMA.

Linklaters (see firm details p.1042) Although not yet doing the same quantity as the top two, Linklaters has emerged from the pack this year as the clear number three. "*It's really woken up,*" according to competitors, and "*has had a successful year in improving profile and penetration.*" That focus has already led to "*a lot of work for medium syndication banks*" and is beginning to translate into mega-deals – "*the market is open for Linklaters to make an impact.*" One of these is the €3 billion worth of syndicated facilities that the firm assisted UBS Warburg and Morgan Stanley in arranging for Texas Utilities Group in its take-over of Hidroeléctrica del Cantábrico, a transaction in which an intricate understanding of credit support arrangements and Spanish regulatory issues was required.

That deal was led by "*brilliant draftsman*" **Haydn Puleston Jones** (see p.121), "*in technical terms one of the most accomplished lawyers in syndicated lending,*" often a popular pairing with the "*hugely forceful*" **John Tucker** (see p.122), who is "*much more business oriented and has built a good team.*" Clients rave, "*they're extremely strong, I've never been let down by either of them commercially or technically.*"

Robert Elliott (see p.118) maintains a strong reputation, though more on the insolvency side, and he is joined in the rankings by "*tough but fair*" **Giles White** (see p.123), considered by some "*the energy behind the banking practice,*" and "*rising star*" **Gideon Moore** (see p.120). The latter has led on impressive telecoms financings, including representing Chase Manhattan and Dresdner Luxembourg on the €2.1 billion syndicated facility with which TeleInvest acquired 10% of TPSA, the largest syndicated loan to a Polish company to date. **Clients:** Barclays Capital; Chase Manhattan; RBS; ABN AMRO; HSBC; Halifax; Dresdner; Morgan Stanley; Lehman Brothers; Commerzbank; Anglo-American; Billiton; Citibank.

Freshfields Bruckhaus Deringer (see firm details p.964) Clients have a high opinion of this firm: "*the partners understand your thinking, give a good client service and deliver on their promises.*" There is a perception that it hasn't broken into banking work to the same degree as Linklaters, although it "*does a huge amount of borrower work*" for its fantastic corporate client base. For example, the firm negotiated for Reed Elsevier on an $8.5 billion jumbo syndicated facility to finance its acquisition of Harcourt.

The team on that deal included group head **Edward Evans** (see p.118), considered by some "*the best banking lawyer at Freshfields by a long chalk.*" "*First class*" **David Ereira** (see p.118) is acknowledged to be "*pleasant, able, commercial and impressive,*" and "*effective*" **Sean Pierce** (see p.121) is "*an original thinker with a good perception of client needs.*" About 35% of the practice's work is for banks, especially in the leveraged finance side where there is less danger of conflicts. In this field it represented UBS Warburg and JP Morgan Chase on the co-financing of the acquisition of Wassall, at the time the largest public to private leveraged acquisition in the UK. **Clients:**JP Morgan Chase; CIBC World Markets; Deutsche; Barclays; Citigroup; CSFB; Goldman Sachs; HSBC; ING; Lehman Brothers; Morgan Stanley; UBS Warburg.

LEADING INDIVIDUALS	
★ MORLEY David Allen & Overy	
1 BRAY Michael Clifford Chance	EREIRA David Freshfields Bruckhaus
POPHAM Stuart Clifford Chance	PULESTON JONES Haydn Linklaters
WOOD Philip Allen & Overy	
2 ALLEN Maurice White & Case	CAMPBELL Mark Clifford Chance
GILLESPIE Stephen Allen & Overy	HUMPHREY Anthony Allen & Overy
JOHNSON James Clifford Chance	KEAL Tony Allen & Overy
SLATER Richard Slaughter and May	STEWART Mark Clifford Chance
SWEETING Malcolm Clifford Chance	
3 BALFOUR Andrew Slaughter and May	DUNCAN Michael Allen & Overy
EVANS Edward Freshfields Bruckhaus	PIERCE Sean Freshfields Bruckhaus
TUCKER John Linklaters	VICKERS Mark Ashurst Morris Crisp
4 COTTIS Matthew Lovells	CULLINANE Lee Clifford Chance
INGLIS Alan Clifford Chance	POLGLASE Timothy Norton Rose
SCHULZ Peter Allen & Overy	SPENDLOVE Justin Ashurst Morris Crisp
WARD Anthony Shearman & Sterling	WHITE Giles Linklaters
5 BORTHWICK Trevor Allen & Overy	CHESTERMAN James Latham & Watkins
ELLIOTT Robert Linklaters	FOX Ruth Slaughter and May
FURMAN Mark Macfarlanes	GORRIE Euan Allen & Overy
KENSELL Stephen Allen & Overy	MOORE Gideon Linklaters
WARD Nigel Ashurst Morris Crisp	
6 CARSLAW Debbie Denton Wilde Sapte	DISS Paul SJ Berwin
DUKES Rodney Taylor Joynson Garrett	LONG Peter Herbert Smith
MURRAY Neil Travers Smith Braithwaite	SHORT Stephen Ashurst Morris Crisp
SMITH Robert Clifford Chance	WAGHORN Mark Berwin Leighton Paisner
WILSON Dave Theodore Goddard	
UP AND COMING	
KILNER Peter Clifford Chance	LEE Robert Clifford Chance
ONES TO WATCH	
BATES Michael Clifford Chance	DE BASTO Richard Allen & Overy
ROBERTS Simon Allen & Overy	STEWART Suzy Clifford Chance

See individuals' profiles p.116

Norton Rose (see firm details p.1082) "*Active and well regarded,*" the practice retains a firm grip on the mid-market. As one competitor noted, "*the deals it is doing tend to be on the smaller side but the volume is there.*" The department's strength lies in a team of "*good, commercial deal-doing lawyers*" rather than in particular star individuals, although "*lawyer's lawyer*" **Tim Polglase** (see p.121) is considered by rivals an "*efficient and knowledgeable*" practitioner with technical expertise. In a year that has seen improvements in both the quantity and quality of deals, the firm has expanded its acquisition and telecoms finance practices. Strength in asset and project finance and an expanding international network complement a banking department that primarily represents lenders. Represented Deutsche and other arrangers on the $550 million financing for Global Telesystems Europe Holdings and Chase Manhattan on DM270 million of senior secured debt facilities to fund the LBO of Trevira GmbH by DB Investor. **Clients:** HSBC; ANZ Bank; Chase Manhattan; RBS; Toronto-Dominion Bank; Bank of New York; ABN AMRO; Société Générale; Deutsche; CIBC Wood Gundy.

Ashurst Morris Crisp (see firm details p.866) "*Ashursts have had a pretty good year. My perception is that the firm's hauled itself around.*" After its travails, the firm has recieved a high degree of market approval for the way the department has rebuilt itself into a top class acquisition finance outfit. Although **Justin Spendlove** (see p.122) has become managing partner, at present he spends around 10% of his time on client work. Into the breach has stepped "*first class*" **Mark Vickers** (see p.123). "*A well known name with a following,*" he is "*a strong operator, well liked in the mid market and very authoritative.*" He is joined by "*excellent acquisition finance guy*" **Nigel Ward** (see p.679) and **Stephen Short** (see p.122) who is "*personable and technically good.*" The department represented ING Bank and the Bank of Scotland in relation to the underwriting of the £560 million of senior and subordinated debt with which the Focus Do It All Group financed the public bid for Wickes and the acquisition of Great Mills DIY business. Also acted for SEB in relation to €1.1 billion of facilities to fund the MBO of the Alfa Laval group, one of the largest buy-outs in Europe. **Clients:** Merrill Lynch; Lehman Brothers; Deutsche; Bank of Scotland; RBS; West LB; Goldman Sachs; Dresdner Kleinwort Benson; ING Bank; SE Banken; BNP Paribas; UBS Warburg; Barclays; Bank of America; HypoVereinsbank.

Lovells (see firm details p.1044) Emerging from a turbulent period, although some believe it has yet to fully recover from the loss of John Penson and that it has "*fallen off the pace in the large deal syndication market.*" However there was praise from clients for the strength of its mid-market work, its historical connection to Barclays and its increased cross border capabilities in "*establishing good European connections.*" There was also praise for the way in which "*bright and common-sense*" **Matthew Cottis** (see p.117) ("*he's pragmatic, technically good and he rolls his sleeves up*") has "*inherited the mantle.*" He acted for Commerzbank in its £740 million financing of Vaillant's offer for Hepworth. He receives support from a capable team both at and below partner level. Strong in acquisition and structured trade finance, the firm has also been active in retail banking, often assisting new entrants to the market. Represented the Bank of Scotland on a £380 million facility for Pillar Properties' bid for Wates City of London Properties. **Clients:** Bank of Scotland; Banque Indosuez; Barclays; Creditanstalt; Crédit Lyonnais; EBRD; ING; Lloyds TSB; Standard Chartered.

Slaughter and May (see firm details p.1135) (32 partners part-time) Though less visible for banks, the firm is involved in some top class work for borrowers, such as the €16.3 billion 364 day loan arranged for Telecom Italia to back a tender offer for the outstanding share capital of SEAT Pagine Gialle. That deal was led by the "*fantastic*" **Andrew Balfour** (see p.116), praised as "*exceptionally intelligent, client friendly and without a hint of arrogance.*" Although not active for lenders in the volume syndications market, the firm does complex structured work and jumbo loans as well as acquisition and telecoms financing. It represented Société Générale and JP Morgan as arrangers of the $400 million debt financing for Havas Advertising to fund its bid for Snyder Communications. "*Excellent*" **Richard Slater** (see p.122), "*a lovely man, helpful and sensible,*" was responsible for that transaction and remains Slaughter's highest profile lawyer operating principally for banks. The firm also assists the corporate treasuries of blue chips and has a reputation for banking regulation where **Ruth Fox** (see p.118) is acknowledged as "*able, versatile, pleasant and commercial.*" **Clients:** JP Morgan; Société Générale; Telecom Italia; Blue Circle.

Denton Wilde Sapte (see firm details p.939) "*A good mainstream banking team,*" which remains as long-standing lawyers for a number of banks. Though young, the team is considered by clients to be "*competent pragmatic banking lawyers who want to get deals done,*" and that prospect could well improve shortly. At present its highest profile practitioner is "*focused, technically able and commercial*" property finance specialist **Debbie Carslaw**, considered "*approachable, accessible and willing to talk.*" Beyond its property finance strength, the firm is active on acquisition finance work for borrowers and lenders and specialised areas like trade finance and international structured facilities. It recently represented Morgan Stanley Dean Witter on a loan facility of £462 million to joint ventures between Westfield and MEPC in relation to the purchase of six shopping centres. **Clients:** RBS/NatWest; Citibank; GE Capital; Standard Chartered; ABN AMRO; Citibank; Deutsche; Dresdner Kleinwort Benson; Bank of Scotland; Barclays; Lloyds TSB.

Herbert Smith (see firm details p.993) "*A firm which is recognising that it wants to go places in this sector,*" and, according to one competitor, is "*strong* *and competent and probably does more than people realise and some top stuff for borrowers.*" Clients agree: "*the partners are creative, candid, good at delivering know how and prepared to put in a lot of work.*" "*Absolutely first rate*" **Peter Long** (see p.120) receives particular recommendation as "*a top lawyer, pragmatic, who always delivers what he says on time.*" He advised the Royal London Mutual Insurance society on its £1.5 billion bid, through a subsidiary, for the share capital of United Assurance Group. Currently increasing its proportion of banking clients, with first time instructions from several investment banks, the firm has been active in acquisition finance. It represented Eurotunnel on the innovative repackaging of its £1 billion junior debt. **Clients:** Barclays; Chase Manhattan; EIB; Greycoat; Norwich Union; Bank of Scotland; Royal London; Nomura International.

Shearman & Sterling (see firm details p.1125) "*Still the largest of the US firms,*" its overwhelming banking strength remains its "*established acquisition finance practice,*" which is amongst Europe's leaders. It offers expertise in complex structured products with a derivative or bond component and also conducts syndicated lending into the telecoms sector. With the loss this year of Stephen Mostyn-Williams, peers claim **Anthony Ward** (see p.123) ("*technically able, clients love him and big lenders turn to him*") is now "*the reason people go to Shearman & Sterling.*" US/UK and Europe-wide expertise are big selling points along with the power of the brand name. The firm represented Deutsche in providing senior, bridge and mezzanine facilities for the public to private bid for United Biscuits. Also advised Cinven and InvestCorp in the $2.11 billion leveraged acquisition of Zeneca Speciality Chemicals. **Clients:** Morgan Stanley; Merrill Lynch; Morgan Chase; Goldman Sachs; Deutsche; Barclays; RBS; UBS Warburg; Ericsson.

Baker & McKenzie (see firm details p.868) Low profile in the domestic market, this firm has a leading reputation for multi-jurisdictional transactions where its vast network comes into play; clients confirm that "*its global reach is an important consideration.*" The team led by Christopher Hogan acts for an equal mix of banks and borrowers, and has particular expertise in telecoms and acquisition financing, with private equity led acquisitions a growth area. It advised France Telecom on a €2.1 billion structured financing in connection with the purchase of a 35% stake in Polish telecoms operator TPSA, the largest syndicated financing in the Polish market to date. **Clients:** CSFB; Apax; Standard Bank; Nortel; Hewlett-Packard IB.

Berwin Leighton Paisner (see firm details p.878) Building from a strong base in property finance, market opinion acknowledges that the group "*has been working hard in bringing in new banks*" and as a result "*has moved on apace.*" Clients praise a "*good quality offering at a reasonable price.*" The banking department is active in a range of areas including acquisition finance, public to privates and corporate banking, and has developed niche expertise in tax based structured finance, some of it for film finance. Such is its strength in property, the highest profile finance lawyer is head of property finance **Mark Waghorn** (see p.123). The group acted for ABSA Bank on a $300 million syndicated facility. **Clients:** Barclays; Bank of Nova Scotia; Banca Nazionale del Lavoro; ABSA Bank; Helaba Landesbank.

CMS Cameron McKenna (see firm details p.922) According to competitors, banking is "*a product the firm concentrates on; it's got some decent clients*" though its strength is seen to rest with the team as a whole rather than stars. Banks agree that the firm is "*extremely professional and doesn't just throw in a junior person.*" Known for its long relationship with Lloyds, it has

Top Ten Loans (June 2000 to June 2001)

	Borrower	Lawyers to Borrower	Mandated Arranger	Lawyers to Lead Arrangers	Value (US$)	Loan Type
1	**British Telecommunications plc**	Linkaters & Alliance	ABN-AMRO Bank NV, Bank of Tokyo-Mitsubishi Ltd, Barclays, Bayerische Landesbank, Deutsche Bank AG, HSBC, Industrial Bank of Japan Ltd, Lloyds TSB Capital Markets, Royal Bank of Scotland plc, Salomon Brothers International Ltd, SG	Clifford Chance	24,469.820	Revolving Credit
2	**Vodafone Airtouch plc**	In-house team	ABN-AMRO Bank NV, Bank of America, Barclays, BNP Paribas, Deutsche Bank AG, HSBC, ING Barings, Lehman Brothers International, National Australia Bank Ltd, Salomon Brothers International Ltd, Royal Bank of Scotland plc, Toronto-Dominion Bank, UBS Warburg	Allen & Overy	14,550.000	Revolving Credit
3	**Vodafone Airtouch plc**	Linkaters & Alliance	UBS Warburg, ABN-AMRO Bank NV, Banca di Roma SpA, Bank of America, Bank of New York, Bank of Tokyo-Mitsubishi Ltd, Barclays, Bayerische Landesbank, BNP Paribas, Citibank NA, Commerzbank AG, Deutsche Bank AG, Fuji Bank Ltd, HSBC, ING Barings, IntesaBci, Le	Allen & Overy	13,275.000	Revolving Credit
4	**Reed International plc, Reed Elsevier plc**	Freshfields	Deutsche Bank AG, Morgan Stanley Dean Witter	White & Case	8,500.000	Revolving Credit
5	**One2One Ltd**	Clifford Chance	ABN-AMRO Bank NV, Chase Manhattan plc, Deutsche Bank AG, Dresdner Kleinwort Benson, HSBC, Salomon Brothers International Ltd	Allen & Overy	5,158.438	Revolving Credit
6	**Agip Investments plc, LASMO plc**	n/a	JP Morgan	n/a	4,387.248	Revolving Credit
7	**Hutchison 3G UK Holdings Lts**	Freshfields	JP Morgan plc, HSBC, WestLB, ABN-AMRO Bank NV, Citibank NA, Merrill Lynch International Ltd, Royal Bank of Scotland plc	Allen & Overy	4,066.200	Revolving Credit
8	**Brambles Industries plc** (signed but not sold into Syndication)	Clifford Chance	Deutsche Bank AG, HSBC, National Australia Bank Ltd, Commercial Bank of Australia Ltd, Commerzbank AG, ABN-AMRO Bank NV	Allen & Overy	3,400.000	Revolving Credit
9	**Telewest Communications Networks Ltd**	Weil Gotshal & Manges	Bank of America, Bank of New York, Barclays, CIBC World Markets, Citibank NA, Credit Suisse First Boston, Deutsche Bank AG, Fortis Bank NV/SA, Bayerische Hypo-und Vereinsbank-Hypovereinsbank, JP Morgan plc, Mizuho, Royal Bank of Scotland plc, Toronto-Domi	Norton Rose	3,254.714	Term Loan
10	**Gallaher Ltd**	Simmons & Simmons	Barclays, Dresdner Kleinwort Wasserstein, Goldman Sachs International Ltd, HSBC	Linklaters	2,966.122	Term Loan

Source: Syndicated Loans – Dealogic Capital Data Ware; Source: Law Firms – Chambers & Partners

developed links with a number of institutions across several areas and enjoys growth in property finance. John White leads a team that is strong in acquisition finance and regulatory work, and increasingly involved in cross-border transactions drawing upon its international network. Recently acted for the banks providing £460 million of senior and junior debt facilities for refinancing the Trafford Shopping Centre. **Clients:** Lloyds TSB; RBS; National Australia Bank; First Union.

DLA The firm has a presence on the debt side of private equity transactions and long-standing relationships with retail banks.

Gouldens (see firm details p.976) "*An intelligent firm,*" this small but high quality team, led by Tom Budd, is especially strong in property, structured finance and syndicated lending. Typically involved in complex work in the £75 to £100 million range, it represents a varied client base weighted towards borrowers. A growing property finance practice is undertaking some high quality work including acting for Pillar Property and the City of London Office Unit Trust on their £373.3 million recommended cash offer for Wates City of London Properties. This entailed establishing a £402 million acquisition finance facility (along with a medium term facility) and a loan facility offered in relation to part of the Wates portfolio. **Clients:** Standard Bank London; Standard Bank SA; HypoVereinsbank; Hanson; Pillar Property; Knight Group; ABN AMRO.

Macfarlanes (see firm details p.1046) "*A good firm with a lot of activity on the private equity front.*" Despite the department's small size, researchers received comment that "*it has a good quality banking group.*" Alongside acquisition finance, it has strength in property and trade finance, and has succeeded in growing its international practice through relationships with good quality firms in other jurisdictions. Busier this year on the lender side, the firm represented Pernod-Ricard in negotiating $5 billion facilities for its joint bid for Seagram's Wine and Spirits business. Head of department **Mark Furman** (see p.118) is considered sound and pleasant to deal with, and acted for Alchemy Partners on the financing of its public to private bids for Industrial Control Services, William Baird and Brooks Service Group. **Clients:** RBS; 3i Group; Alchemy Partners; Bank of Scotland; Pernod-Ricard; WestLB.

Simmons & Simmons (see firm details p.1132) "*Always strong in banking,*" the team's highlight deals include representing Pacific Century CyberWorks as borrower in a $12 billion syndicated facility, the largest ever in Asia. Harvey Chalmers heads a group that also represented Interbrew on financing its bids for Whitbread and Bass Brewers, including syndicated facilities of €6.5 billion. Marred by the lack of stars in the banking group, clients and competitors stress the overall consistency and quality. Strong in cross border acquisition finance, where its capital markets and structured finance expertise comes to the fore, it is growing its international practice and increasingly represents the banks. **Clients:** Barclays; Railtrack; Bank of Latvia; CSFB; Deutsche; Dresdner Kleinwort Benson; EIB; Interbrew; Pacific Century CyberWorks.

SJ Berwin (see firm details p.879) Making an entry into the rankings this year after impressive recommendations, the firm "*has an active banking group with some good focused people.*" Interviewees especially rate **Paul Diss** (see p.117) for his "*lateral thinking and ability to pick things up quickly.*" Expanding its representation of banks, in addition to its work for an impressive corporate client base, it is active in acquisition, trade and property finance, regulatory work and straight lending. Of particular interest is its niche in indirect property investment funds, allowing institutions to invest through advantageously structured mechanisms. The firm was involved in the £1.8 billion public to private of United Biscuits, advising NM Rothschild (one of the joint financial advisers). **Clients:** Banco Santander Central Hispano; Lloyds TSB; RBS; Dresdner Kleinwort Benson; Deutsche Hypothekenbank; British Land; BNP; Société Générale.

Taylor Joynson Garrett (see firm details p.1150) "*An impressive and unsung firm*" praised by clients as an outfit which "*ensures deals get done efficiently and quickly.*" Head of department **Rodney Dukes** (see p.117) is considered "*intuitive, commercial and one of the hardest working partners in the city.*" He recently represented BHF-Bank in negotiating £100 million of complex senior and mezzanine facilities in connection with the development of 90 High Holborn for Minerva plc. Noted for the strength of its property finance offering, the team operates a broad practice for banks and borrowers and is increasing its experience in public to privates and securitisation. **Clients:** BHF-Bank; Fortis; Citibank; Anglo-Irish; Halifax; Bank of Scotland; Chase Manhattan; Nomura.

Theodore Goddard (see firm details p.1152) Clients are full of praise for a department that has "*lots of young people with plenty of talent, energy and brains.*" In particular "*pragmatic and client friendly*" **Dave Wilson** (see p.123) is considered "*professional, bright and great to deal with.*" He represented NatWest on a £170 million syndicated facility for the Ashtenne Holdings Group. Strong on property and acquisition finance, the firm acts primarily for lenders and has niche expertise on receivables finance, film finance and the establishment of internet operations. **Clients:** NatWest; RBS; Anglo-Irish; Abbey National; DG Bank; Commerzbank; Scotiabank (Europe); NM Rothschild; Bank Austria; Burdale Financial.

Travers Smith Braithwaite (see firm details p.1160) Headed by **Neil Murray** (see p.121), "*intelligent, experienced and easy to get on with,*" clients praise a team which is "*commercially aware, efficient, crisp and knows what we want.*" Murray acted for NTL Holdings on £3.8 billion of credit and working capital facilities, in connection with NTL's £8.2 billion acquisition of Cable & Wireless' consumer division. Active in property finance, the department has increased its involvement in debt finance for corporate acquisitions. It has expertise in public to privates, representing, for example, Deutsche Bank in connection with the £1.8 billion public to private of United Biscuits. **Clients:** Bank of Scotland; Barclays; CCF Charterhouse Bank; HypoVereinsbank; RBS; Westdeutsche ImmobilienBank; Fortis; DG Bank; KBC Bank.

Watson, Farley & Williams (see firm details p.1174) Complementing its shipping and asset finance practices, the firm's banking strength is developing a broader outlook. Trade finance is a growing field, the team acted for ABN-AMRO on a $250 million L/C issuance facility. Undertaking securitisation work as part of its asset work, the firm also has sizeable banking transactions undertaken for its large banking client base. Michael Kenny and his team represented Crédit Lyonnais as lead arranger on a $420 million syndicated facility for a major French corporate. **Clients:** Chase Manhattan; Citibank; RBS; Vivendi; Bank of Scotland; Crédit Lyonnais; ABN-AMRO; Bank of Nova Scotia.

White & Case (see firm details p.1178) The recruitment of "*charismatic strategic thinker*" **Maurice Allen** (see p.116) in May 2000 was one of the year's most interesting developments. "*Definitely a superstar,*" he is considered "*not only a fantastic getter of work but an outstanding lawyer*" by his peers. Supported by a strong offering nationally and internationally, "*they are a great banking firm worldwide so they will undoubtedly pick up work.*" Although it's early to call the practice established, it is already playing a vital role in the network and feeding in work in its own right and its prospects are bright. Highlight deals include assisting Deutsche Bank and Morgan Stanley in the $8.5 billion jumbo syndicated facility extended to Reed Elsevier in connection with its purchase of Harcourt General. **Clients:** BNP Paribas; Dresdner Kleinwort Wasserstein; JP Morgan Chase; CIBC World Markets; Crédit Lyonnais; Morgan Stanley; Deutsche Bank.

Other Notable Practitioners **James Chesterman** (see p.116) of **Latham & Watkins** is "*excellent, hands on, popular with clients and very good at telecoms finance.*" Although it is still considered too early to rank the firm, "*his track record for deals is probably better than some whole departments.*"

THE SOUTH & SOUTH WEST

BANKING • The South & South West	Ptnrs	Assts
1 **Burges Salmon** Bristol	3	5
Osborne Clarke Bristol	2	5
2 **Bond Pearce** Bristol, Southampton	2	7
3 **CMS Cameron McKenna** Bristol	1	2
4 **Blake Lapthorn** Fareham	3	2

LEADING INDIVIDUALS	
1 **FORBES Sandra** Burges Salmon	**JEFFRIES Graham** Bond Pearce
KINSEY Julian Bond Pearce	
2 **LEEMING Richard** Burges Salmon	**WILTSHIRE Peter** CMS Cameron McKenna
UP AND COMING	
AL-NUAIMI Omar Osborne Clarke	

This book is the product of 6,552 1/2-hour interviews. See p.7 for BMRB audit.
Within each band, firms are listed alphabetically. *See individuals' profiles p.116*

Burges Salmon (see firm details p.902) "*A strong banking practice with good people,*" by common consent one of the leading teams in the region. Headed by "*top banking partner*" **Sandra Forbes,** (see p.118) rated for her technical expertise, who has the support of **Richard Leeming** (see p.120), "*a good lawyer who gets things done.*" Acting for a mix of lenders and large corporate borrowers, the firm is strong in general corporate banking and acquisition finance, where it advised the Bank of Scotland on the buyout of Bikes UK. Property finance has been an expanding area and the firm has experience in treasury advice, mezzanine lending and bespoke loan agreements for complex structured work. Represented Orange on the security and loan structures related to its pay as you go commercial agreements. **Clients:** Bank of Scotland; Lloyds TSB; RBS; Nationwide; Standard Chartered; AIB Capital Markets.

Osborne Clarke (see firm details p.1086) "*A big team doing a range of work,*" acquisition finance remains the core of its practice but it is beginning to develop general banking expertise on the back of a strong corporate department. As well as general syndicated lending, it is also expanding the property finance capacity and is active in treasury work and development finance. Seen in the market representing large venture capital funds, competitors regard the team as "*sensible and easy to deal with*" and single out associate **Omar Al-Nuaimi** as "*technically good, efficient and commercial.*" Represented Close Brothers on the £114.5 million acquisition financing of Yardbrace from Rentokil, and, on the borrower side, acted for the Vestey Group on the £35 million refinancing of its club facility. **Clients:** Bank of Scotland; RBS; NatWest; Barclays; HSBC; 3i group; Lloyds TSB; Ansbacher; Close Brothers; DePfa Bank.

Bond Pearce (see firm details p.888) "*An excellent firm,*" and "*a clued-up outfit,*" its regional network gives it a great deal of strength across the region as a whole. In the Southampton office, "*sane and sensible*" **Graham Jeffries** (see p.119) is "*highly rated, practical and good with clients,*" while in Bristol **Julian Kinsey** (see p.119) is considered "*a nice guy with a good reputation.*" Acting in a substantial amount of acquisition finance, the majority of it for banks, the firm has also been busy in refinancing, investment and development funding, and has a niche in finance in the motor trade. With the quality of its instructions this year, it is pressing the leaders hard, including representing the Bank of Scotland on a £40 million guarantee facility and a £60 million investment facility. **Clients:** Bank of Scotland; Fortis; Lloyds TSB; Nationwide; PSA Wholesale.

CMS Cameron McKenna (see firm details p.922) Known for its "*good relationship with Lloyds,*" the market feels that the firm is less visible in transactional banking and is better known for banking litigation and insolvency. The firm has been developing its relationship with a range of local lenders and is enjoying an increase in its transactional workload. **Peter Wiltshire** (see p.123) is "*certainly a good lawyer*" with a reputation that spans banking, restructuring and insolvency. Transactional work includes more esoteric activity like charity lending and non-recourse lends to pension funds, most of it sourced from Lloyds TSB. **Clients:** Lloyds TSB; RBS/NatWest.

Blake Lapthorn (see firm details p.886) "*As a firm it has proved that it can deliver what the bank wants*" according to one client and competitors agree that the team is good to have on the other side and "*knows what it's doing.*" Active in acquisition finance and general corporate lending, as well as regulatory work, it is witnessing a growth in deal size and volume across the board. Recently represented the Bank of Scotland on a £23 million MBO financing (involving partner Kathryn Shimmin) which included a fleet of helicopters located around the world. **Clients:** Bank of Scotland; HSBC; RBS/NatWest; Lloyds TSB; Capital Bank.

WALES

BANKING • Wales	Ptnrs	Assts
1 **Eversheds** Cardiff	1	4
2 **Edwards Geldard** Cardiff	*	*
Morgan Cole Cardiff	1	3

LEADING INDIVIDUALS
1 **VAUGHAN Philip** Eversheds
2 **MORGAN Meryl** Morgan Cole

This book is the product of 6,552 1/2-hour interviews. See p.7 for BMRB audit.
Within each band, firms are listed alphabetically. *See individuals' profiles p.116*

Eversheds (see firm details p.952) "*Great to deal with,*" without question the premier Welsh banking firm, and "*experienced technician*" **Philip Vaughan** (see p.123) is "*the leading banking lawyer in Wales.*" Focused on acquisition and structured finance, as well as retail finance, it has a niche in regulatory and compliance work, particularly in connection with consumer credit. With a substantial amount of non-local work, it acted for Investec Bank on a $105 million cross border financing that involved co-ordinating the legal advisors in Hong Kong and Guernsey. Appointed to ABN AMRO's legal panel, the group also acted for Deutsche Hypo Bank on a £52 million facility extended to a UK property investment company. **Clients:** Lloyds TSB; Citibank; ABN AMRO; Legal & General; Bank of Wales; Barclays; Investec Bank; Principality Building Society; Deutsche Hypo Bank.

Edwards Geldard (see firm details p.948) (5 partners part-time) Perceived by the market to be highly visible representing local clearing banks on property and smaller scale acquisition finance. Currently expanding its development and housing association finance practices, the department (headed by Karl Baranski) represented a large lender providing £5.95 million of facilities for the MBO of a South Wales manufacturer. **Clients:** Major local clearing banks and corporates.

Morgan Cole (see firm details p.1074) Researchers found the firm active on a range of banking work with strength in local acquisition and development finance; it is visible working for local clearing banks and supporting its corporate finance offering. Experienced ex-banker **Meryl Morgan** is "*the person working most exclusively on banking in Wales*" according to one competitor. Representing an even mix of lenders and borrowers, the firm has worked on syndicated facilities, invoice discounting, and debt restructuring. Recently represented the Bank of Scotland in providing £5 million of funding into the housing association sector and the RBS on £1.15 million second round funding for an MBO in the film production industry. **Clients:** HSBC; RBS; Barclays; Lloyds TSB; Bank of Wales; Bank of Ireland; Bank of Scotland; Wales Small Loan Fund; Swansea Building Society; Nationwide.

MIDLANDS

BANKING • Midlands	Ptnrs	Assts
1 **Eversheds** Birmingham, Nottingham	9	12
Pinsent Curtis Biddle Birmingham	8	10
2 **Wragge & Co** Birmingham	5	19
3 **DLA** Birmingham	1	5
Gateley Wareing Birmingham	4	4
Martineau Johnson Birmingham	4	6
4 **Browne Jacobson** Nottingham	2	8

LEADING INDIVIDUALS	
1 **BAKER Ian** Martineau Johnson	**JOHNSTONE Pat** Eversheds
MADDEN Andrew Gateley Wareing	**MILES Stephen** Pinsent Curtis Biddle
PALLETT Julian Wragge & Co	
2 **BRIERLEY Chris** Wragge & Co	**COOKE David** Pinsent Curtis Biddle
TWIST Patrick Pinsent Curtis Biddle	**WOOLCOCK Brian** DLA
3 **ALTON Philip** Garretts	**BROADFIELD Alice** Eversheds
HAGUE-HOLMES Rupert Eversheds	**KITTS Stephen** Eversheds
MURRAY Duncan Browne Jacobson	
UP AND COMING	
WALKER Gary Wragge & Co	

This book is the product of 6,552 1/2-hour interviews. See p.7 for BMRB audit.
Within each band, firms are listed alphabetically. *See individuals' profiles p.116*

Eversheds (see firm details p.952) "*Capable, practical, hands on and easy to get on with,*" the team's reputation has grown this year. "*Well known and experienced*" **Pat Johnstone** (see p.119) has "*built up a stable team and developed a good, practical reputation.*" Noted by rivals for its development of talented young lawyers, the "*sensible*" and highly regarded **Alice Broadfield** (see p.116) is joined by **Rupert Hague-Holmes,** (see p.118) "*a commercial operator with a good training behind him.*" In the East Midlands "*excellent, unflappable*" **Stephen Kitts'** (see p.120) intelligent approach and relaxed style makes him one of the region's market leaders. Strong on all aspects of acquisition finance and secured lending, the team has strength in tax efficient schemes involving debt instruments. In a headline deal, Johnstone represented the Phoenix consortium on the acquisition of MG Rover from BMW, including the negotiation of the £500 million loan note issued by the purchaser. **Clients:** RBS NatWest Group; Bank of Scotland; Fortis; HSBC; Lloyds TSB.

Pinsent Curtis Biddle (see firm details p.1098) "*Good commercial lawyers,*" according to competitors, "*they will stand their corner but not score points.*" Clients particularly rate the "*experienced and helpful*" **Stephen Miles** (see p.120), who "*can bring everything together, and knows all facets of a deal.*" He is supported by "*great all-rounder*" **David Cooke** (see p.117) ("*academic – if you have a problem, David is the man to cut through it*") and "*colourful*" **Patrick Twist** (see p.122), a "*highly professional*" finance lawyer also involved in projects and PFI. The team's representation of RBS and AIB Capital Markets on the £80 million institutional purchase of Chiller Rental Systems and SLD Pumps demonstrates its ability to handle both syndications and complex cross border transactions. **Clients:** RBS; Barclays; Bank of Scotland; Doncasters; IM Properties.

Wragge & Co (see firm details p.1189) "*Really successful in marketing themselves as a city firm in Birmingham;*" "*success tends to breed success.*" Ironically the overwhelming success of Wragge's corporate and private equity offerings has thrown its banking department into the shade. Competitors claim that it is less visible in the market, an observation borne out by the banks: "*it has such a strong presence that it tends to win the company mandate so it's always conflicted.*" Nonetheless, it has a large, powerful department headed by "*excellent*" **Julian Pallett** whose "*quick brain*" helps him "*assimilate complex points very quickly.*" He also has a profile in insolvency and restructuring and is increasingly involved in large project and development work. On the acquisition finance side he is supported by **Chris Brierley**, considered "*competent and easy to deal with.*" "*Promising*" associate **Gary Walker** has recently moved to the team from Pinsent Curtis Biddle and has a particular reputation for derivatives, but is also active on structured and acquisition finance. The firm represented Castlemore Securities in arranging development funding from HypoBank as senior lender of £78.5 million. **Clients:** Bank of Scotland; HSBC; Lloyds TSB.

DLA Brian Woolcock is the major name at a department which is known for structured finance, capital markets and work for invoice discounters.

Gateley Wareing (see firm details p.969) "*Moving onwards and upwards in terms of volume and quality,*" these are "*the people who have made the most progress this year.*" Particularly praised by clients is **Andrew Madden** who has a "*powerful combination*" of "*the qualities people aspire to: he's intellectually strong, commercially sensible and good at looking after his clients.*" Known for its mid-market volume work in acquisition finance, the team completed an impressive 94 transactions in 2000 including representing Barclays Acquisition finance on the £30 million MBO of GLS Educational Supplies. Already strong in the West of the region, the firm's Leicester and Nottingham offices are increasing its profile in the East Midlands. **Clients:** Dunbar Bank; Barclays; Lloyds TSB; Bank of Scotland; RBS; HSBC; Eurosales Finance.

Martineau Johnson (see firm details p.1055) Key to the firm's success, **Ian Baker** (see p.116) "*is possibly the best in Birmingham.*" "*Thorough*" but still "*commercial and proactive,*" Baker received strong recommendation from clients and competitors alike. He acted for Lloyds TSB on a £51 million MBO and for the Bank of Scotland on £35 million of acquisition facilities. The firm features in some high profile transactions without losing out on the smaller, volume work. Strong on property and acquisition finance, it has been involved in an increasing number of deals with international elements, while the opening of a London office increases its capability within the UK. **Clients:** Bank of Scotland; RBS; NatWest; HSBC; Lloyds TSB; AIB; Nationwide; Handelsbanken.

Browne Jacobson (see firm details p.898) "*Well established in the East Midlands,*" and alongside Eversheds, the firm is "*market leader*" in that area. "*Experienced*" **Duncan Murray** (see p.121) stands out in a team that clients praise for "*negotiating the nitty gritty and easing the deal process.*" Strong on property finance, acquisition finance and reconstructions, the firm represented RBS on the £12 million refinancing of the acquisition of Penn Pharmaceuticals, and the RBS and Bank of Ireland on the £26 million acquisition of Menzies Hotels. **Clients:** Bank of Scotland; RBS; NatWest.

Other Notable Practitioners With the demise of its Manchester banking department, "*fine banking lawyer*" **Philip Alton** (see p.116) is now responsible for much of **Garretts'** work in the North of England. As part of the Andersen Legal network he has a low profile in the local market but lenders confirm that they value his cross border expertise.

EAST ANGLIA

BANKING • East Anglia	Ptnrs	Assts
1 **Eversheds** Cambridge, Ipswich, Norwich	3	10
2 **Mills & Reeve** Cambridge, Norwich	*	2

LEADING INDIVIDUALS
1 **CROOME Andrew** Eversheds

This book is the product of 6,552 1/2-hour interviews. See p.7 for BMRB audit.
Within each band, firms are listed alphabetically. *See individuals' profiles p.116*

Eversheds (see firm details p.952) Competitors rate the region's largest banking group as *"Professional and easy to deal with."* In particular, **Andrew Croome** (see p.117), the leading specialist, is *"calm, mild mannered and sensible."* He recently led a team representing Care Homes No 3 Ltd on its £45 million release of a further drawings fund from the securitisation of a portfolio of leases. Acting from its Cambridge, Ipswich and Norwich offices, the firm attracts clients from outside of the region and is especially strong in securitisation, care home funding and the financing of sale and leasebacks. It acted for the Bank of Scotland on the £6 million refinancing of the Thompson and Morgan Group. **Clients:** Bank of Scotland; Barclays; Norwich and Peterborough Building Society; NHP; Nationwide; Ipswich Building Society.

Mills & Reeve (see firm details p.1069) (3 partners and 1 asst part-time) *"The other regional heavyweight,"* this generalist team headed by Claire Clarke operates from the corporate department. Perceived by the market to *"do a decent amount of good finance work,"* it is building on its links to higher education and the NHS. Major funding activity into those sectors includes representing Allied Irish Bank in a £4 million loan to the Pavilion House Association. **Clients:** Lloyds Bank; Nationwide; AIB; Bank of Scotland.

NORTH WEST

BANKING • North West	Ptnrs	Assts
1 **DLA** Liverpool, Manchester	n/a	n/a
Eversheds Manchester	2	9
2 **Halliwell Landau** Manchester	2	2
3 **Addleshaw Booth & Co** Manchester	2	5
4 **Chaffe Street** Manchester	2	2
Cobbetts Manchester	2	9
Davies Wallis Foyster Liverpool, Manchester	3	3
Hammond Suddards Edge Manchester	2	2
5 **Kuit Steinart Levy** Manchester	1	4

LEADING INDIVIDUALS	
1 **DALE Nigel** Eversheds	**WHATNALL John** Halliwell Landau
WOOLLEY Simon DLA	
2 **MOLLOY Susan** Halliwell Landau	**REARDEN Shaun** Chaffe Street
3 **EDWARDS Jonathan** Hammond Suddards	**SHEPHERD Claire** Hammond Suddards
ONES TO WATCH	
CHANDLER Richard Addleshaw Booth & Co	**CHRISTMAS Matthew** DLA
MORGAN Matthew DLA	

This book is the product of 6,552 1/2-hour interviews. See p.7 for BMRB audit.
Within each band, firms are listed alphabetically. *See individuals' profiles p.116*

DLA **Simon Woolley** is the leading light at a department which handles acquisition finance, syndicated lending, property finance and capital markets work.

Eversheds (see firm details p.952) The other firm with a claim on the top spot, *"our number one choice would be Eversheds"* said one client, *"because of the individuals and quality of service."* Chiefly responsible is *"aggressive negotiator"* **Nigel Dale** (see p.117) who *"knows his stuff and gets a good flow of work."* Strong on acquisition and property finance, it is increasingly involved in large syndicated deals for borrowers, notably the £80 million of syndicated facilities that the firm arranged for Holidaybreak plc. Amongst this year's crop of large deals, however, the £450 million IBO of Caradon Plumbing, where the firm represented HSBC Private Equity, stands out. **Clients:** HSBC Private Equity; Barclays; Co-operative Bank; BBA Group; Bank of Scotland.

Halliwell Landau (see firm details p.982) *"It's commercial, it has good relationships with the banks, and it does a first class job,"* according to one client. **John Whatnall** (see p.123) is particularly praised by competitors as *"superb to deal with, professional and bright – you can hammer out a deal in no time."* His broad practice includes expertise in performance bond transactions. Much of the department's work is acquisition finance for lenders and borrowers, though it is also experienced in property finance and is expanding its restructuring side. *"Highly competent"* **Sue Molloy** (see p.120) is strong on building society and regulatory work and has been involved in some high profile deals this year, including representing Barclays in an £89 million debt funding. **Clients:** Bank of Scotland; RBS; Co-operative Bank; Lloyds TSB; Anglo Irish Bank; Barclays; AIG; Zurich Insurance.

Addleshaw Booth & Co (see firm details p.853) Refocused and has *"rebuilt its team well,"* with Helen Corner at the helm. It has been involved in some high profile transactions, including the £55 million public to private of Joseph Holt Group, representing the borrower. Acting predominantly for banks, but with a significant borrower and private equity presence, the firm covers a wide range of areas, including property, acquisition, social housing and education finance. It has also redrafted the precedent lending documentation for a large number of banking clients. **Clients:** 3i; Barclays; HSBC; Co-operative Bank; National Australia Group; RBS; Britannia Building Society; NM Rothschild.

Chaffe Street (see firm details p.911) Strong in straight banking and with an increasing property finance presence, the firm has developed niche strength in consumer credit. Experience in asset finance also complements its banking expertise. Regularly representing large lenders on deals in the £5 to £60 million range, the team has seen an increase in instructions direct from clearing banks. Head of Department **Shaun Rearden** (see p.121) is *"bright and experienced"* and has a profile for large deals, he advised Barclays on the MBO of Sheet Piling UK and acted for Bank of Scotland on a term loan of over £16 million. **Clients:** RBS; Co-operative Bank; Bank of Scotland; NM Rothschild; JD Williams & Co; City Invoice Finance; Capital Bank.

Cobbetts (see firm details p.923) *"Competent lawyers and nice people,"* according to its clients, and for medium sized deals, particularly with a property element, this firm is acknowledged as *"the market leader."* With a typical deal range of £1-20 million and a strong bias towards lender work, it is prominent in property and development finance and active in the housing association sector. Its large building society client base also ensures a high degree of regulatory and compliance work. Paul Brown heads a team that has seen an increase in syndicated transactions. **Clients:** Lloyds TSB; Bank of Scotland; RBS; Britannia Building Society; AIB; Co-operative Bank; Northern Rock; Girobank; Singer & Friedlander; Manchester Building Society.

Davies Wallis Foyster (see firm details p.935) The group's dual focus on Liverpool and Manchester, and good connections with the regional banks, ensure it a regular flow of work. The appointment of Tony Bochenski this year from the Bank of Scotland Group to head the practice shows a commitment to the area. Well-established reputation in asset finance complements a banking group with experience in acquisition, structured and property finance. The department recently represented the Bank of Scotland on a £32 million acquisition finance facility. **Clients:** Bank of Scotland; Lloyds TSB; Co-operative Bank; Girobank.

Hammond Suddards Edge (see firm details p.984) Market opinion suggests it is the strongest firm in that banding. The department is headed by "*sound, professional*" **Jonathan Edwards** (see p.117) and has benefited from the recruitment of "*low key and pleasant*" **Claire Shepherd** (see p.122), a key attraction for the banks. Strong in acquisition finance, where it has been involved in high profile local deals, the firm also has experience of such diverse areas as film finance and Japanese bond work. Represented GMAC Commercial Credit on invoice discounting and facilities totalling £13.6 million to the Presspart Group. **Clients:** RBS; Barclays; Lloyds TSB; Co-operative Bank; GMAC Commercial Credit.

Kuit Steinart Levy (see firm details p.1025) "*It still retains strong links with Lloyds,*" according to competitors, but the firm has also been observed working for banks like AIB. Steve Eccleston's team operates mainly in the £1-10 million region. It is active in corporate lending and secured property finance. **Clients:** Lloyds TSB; RBS; AIB; Anglo-Irish Bank; Nationwide; Bank of Scotland.

YORKSHIRE

BANKING • Yorkshire	Ptnrs	Assts
1 **Addleshaw Booth & Co** Leeds	8	15
2 **Hammond Suddards Edge** Leeds	3	3
3 **DLA** Leeds	3	5
Pinsent Curtis Biddle Leeds	3	14
4 **Eversheds** Leeds	2	5
Walker Morris Leeds	n/a	n/a

LEADING INDIVIDUALS	
1 **MITCHELL Patrick** Hammond Suddards Edge	
PAPWORTH Richard Addleshaw Booth & Co	
2 **CHIDLEY Mark** Addleshaw Booth & Co	**CLELAND John** Pinsent Curtis Biddle
DAY Sarah DLA	**GOSNAY Andrew** Pinsent Curtis Biddle
3 **AKITT Ian** Walker Morris	**SMITH Mark** DLA
TAYLOR Michael Walker Morris	
UP AND COMING	
HANDY David Addleshaw Booth & Co	**OWEN Simon** Hammond Suddards Edge
WURZAL Jason Eversheds	

This book is the product of 6,552 1/2-hour interviews. See p.7 for BMRB audit.
Within each band, firms are listed alphabetically. *See individuals' profiles p.116*

Addleshaw Booth & Co (see firm details p.853) "*Overall Addleshaws are still the Leeds firm:*" competitors acknowledge that "*its connection with the Yorkshire Bank and the building society movement gives it the strongest practice*" and that "*it has more partners on the ground than anyone else.*" Group head **Mark Chidley** (see p.116) has "*built a great team*" but is perceived to be less visible this year, while "*pleasant and competent*" **Richard Papworth** (see p.783) has emerged with "*strong technical skills and a good following of banks.*" "*Sensible*" younger partner **David Handy** (see p.118) appears for the first time, having led in some impressive deals, including the negotiation of £624.5 million of syndicated guarantee facilities for a corporate client. Strong in capital markets, derivatives and structured work, with a superb reputation for social housing finance, the team conducts national transactions from its Leeds office. An example is the £240 million syndicated facilities it arranged for the Nationwide and NatWest/RBS housing finance to fund the transfer of Coventry's housing stock to the Whitefriars Housing Group, a commission it won against major city competition. **Clients:** Yorkshire Bank; Bank of Scotland; Bradford & Bingley; Britannia; Co-operative Bank; RBS; HSBC; Northern Rock; Skipton Building Society; 3i; NM Rothschild & Sons.

Hammond Suddards Edge (see firm details p.984) "*Clearly very strong in local acquisition finance,*" the reputation of "*excellent*" **Patrick Mitchell** (see p.120) sets the firm ahead of the chasing pack. "*Able, pleasant, and a skilled negotiator,*" he has the support of "*hard-working, competent and effective*" **Simon Owen** (see p.121), a recent recruit from Eversheds. Although acquisition finance remains the department's greatest strength, a broad practice includes general banking, property and development finance, restructuring, trade and treasury finance. Acted for Barclays in financing the acquisition by Tenet of Advisor Connect, Interdependence and the M&E Network. On the borrower side, it advised the management of Hydra Tools International on their buyout of the business. **Clients:** RBS; NatWest; Bank of Scotland; Barclays; Lloyds TSB; Co-operative Bank; GMac; HSBC.

DLA **Sarah Day** is the leading name for a team which handles acquisition and property finance work, as well as substantial asset backed lending and securitisation.

Pinsent Curtis Biddle (see firm details p.1098) A growing team with market approval for the pairing of "*technically extremely able*" **Andrew Gosnay** (see p.118) and "*easy going, relaxed*" **John Cleland** (see p.117). The department, according to one competitor, "*has strengthened with Cleland's promotion as team leader*" while he has also been involved in some large deals, such as a recent £200 million mortgage book acquisition for the Skipton Building Society. Evenly split between banks and borrowers, the department is strong on debt issues and mortgage book acquisitions and disposals, and has recently acted in a large number of public to privates, including Allied Textiles where Gosnay advised HSBC on £100 million of facilities. **Clients:** Bank of Scotland; Bradford & Bingley; RBS; Dunedin Capital Partners; Skipton Building Society; Northern Rock; Barclays; HSBC; Nationwide; West Bromwich Building Society; Fleet National Bank.

Eversheds (see firm details p.952) This department has undoubtedly been involved in some impressive work, notably the £223 million take-private of Peter Black Holdings. However, the loss of Simon Owen to Hammonds Suddards Edge and the refocusing of Stephen Hopkins on corporate work and management has reduced its profile. In addition to its projects strength, the firm is active in acquisition, property and development finance and represented NatWest in the £15 million development funding of Middlesborough City Centre. Peers consider **Jason Wurzal** (see p.124) "*a good technician*" and he enters the tables. **Clients:** Bank of Scotland; Fortis; NatWest; Heywood Williams Group; Peter Black Holdings.

Walker Morris (see firm details p.1171) "*Pretty active in bridging the gap between the smaller firms and the larger ones,*" this department is regarded by the market as having "*moved forward in the small to medium sized local market transactions.*" This does not preclude the firm from undertaking sizeable transactions, such as the £45 million senior debt facility it arranged for the Bank of Scotland. Acting primarily for banks, it has strength in property finance and funding buyouts and take privates. **Ian Akitt** (see p.116) is considered "*sensible, friendly and deal orientated,*" and **Michael Taylor** (see p.122) retains market approval, although he is more visible at the restructuring end of the field. **Clients:** RBS; Bank of Scotland; Lloyds TSB; Barclays; Halifax; Yorkshire Bank; Fortis.

NORTH EAST

BANKING • North East	Ptnrs	Assts
1 **Dickinson Dees** Newcastle upon Tyne	4	6
2 **Eversheds** Newcastle upon Tyne	1	4
Ward Hadaway Newcastle upon Tyne	3	3
3 **Robert Muckle** Newcastle upon Tyne	2	2

LEADING INDIVIDUALS	
1 **HARKER Chris** Dickinson Dees	
2 **HARRISON Julie** Ward Hadaway	**KIRTLEY Deborah** Dickinson Dees
ON Nicholas Eversheds	
3 **McNICOL Stephen** Robert Muckle	

Within each band, firms are listed alphabetically. *See individuals' profiles p.116*

Dickinson Dees (see firm details p.941) "*The main banking team in the North East*" according to competitors, undertaking a volume of lender work and highly visible on the borrower side "*with its high quality client base.*" Clients praise the department for being "*responsive and giving good advice and a good level of service,*" while peers enjoy working with "*competent, calm and commercial*" **Deborah Kirtley** (see p.119). "*Well organised*" **Chris Harker** (see p.118) is considered "*thorough and reasonable*" and acted for the Bank of Scotland in arranging a £19 million facility to fund the MBO of Waddington Jaycare. Property finance has been especially strong this year and the team has strengths in lending to both offshore registered companies and into the educational sector. Present in the high value end of the market, the firm negotiated a £150 million acquisition finance facility for Go-Ahead Group. **Clients:** Barclays; Bank of Scotland; Northern Rock; Newcastle Building Society; RBS; Allied Irish Bank; Clydesdale Bank.

Eversheds (see firm details p.952) Market opinion suggests that Eversheds is close on the heels of Dickinson Dees. Clients recommend its national and international network for cross-border work and are attracted by the "*well connected and well respected*" **Nick On** (see p.121). Rated as "*quite an intellect,*" according to peers the department "*has strengthened a lot since they recruited Nick.*" He acted for the Bank of Scotland as lead arranger on £40.5 million of syndicated facilities to the Matrix Tudor Street Limited Partnership, and advised NatWest on a £20 million refinancing. A rapidly expanding department with a large core of banking clients, it has particular strength in specialist, high value property finance. **Clients:** Barclays; RBS; NatWest; Dunbar Bank; Bank of Scotland.

Ward Hadaway (see firm details p.1173) Strong in acquisition, structured and development finance, clients praise this firm's "*strong team*" and the "*ease and experience*" with which it operates. A broad practice includes negotiating facilities for entities such as universities and housing associations, and assisting banks financing venture capital funds. Competitors acknowledge that "*highly competent*" **Julie Harrison** (see p.119) "*can't be faulted technically.*" She recently led on a £50 million funding for a speculative property development. **Clients:** Northern Rock; Barclays; Bank of Scotland; Co-operative Bank; Newcastle Building Society.

Robert Muckle Competitors concede that the firm's recruitment of **Stephen McNicol** (see p.120) "*certainly put it back in the frame*" for banking work. Although his practice contains a corporate recovery element, he is also "*making a name for himself in Newcastle*" for mainstream corporate lending and development funding. Clients say he has "*considerable strength to his armoury.*" The firm has enjoyed growth in a variety of areas, including property development. Advised the Newcastle Building Society in their first ever sell-down of lending, a transaction of around £5 million, involving redrafting standard documentation. **Clients:** Bank of Scotland; Newcastle Building Society; Lloyds TSB; HSBC; Co-operative Bank; Dunbar Bank; Yorkshire Bank.

SCOTLAND

BANKING • Scotland	Ptnrs	Assts
1 **Dickson Minto WS** Edinburgh	1	6
Dundas & Wilson CS Glasgow	5	n/a
Maclay Murray & Spens Edinburgh, Glasgow	6	8
McGrigor Donald Edinburgh, Glasgow	3	8
2 **Burness** Edinburgh	3	5
Shepherd & Wedderburn WS Edinburgh	4	4
Tods Murray WS Edinburgh	4	5
3 **MacRoberts** Glasgow	3	6
4 **McClure Naismith** Glasgow	1	2

LEADING INDIVIDUALS	
1 **McHALE Colin** Dickson Minto WS	
2 **KELLY Susan** Maclay Murray & Spens	**McKAY Colin** McGrigor Donald
STONEHAM Michael Dundas & Wilson CS	
3 **BURNSIDE Graham** Tods Murray WS	**LAING Robert** Maclay Murray & Spens
PATRICK Hamish Tods Murray WS	**SANDERS Shona** Shepherd & Wedderburn
WILSON Scott Burness	
4 **MACAULAY Iain** McGrigor Donald	**MORTON David** Dundas & Wilson CS
PHILLIPS Stephen Dundas & Wilson CS	**SCOTT Christopher** Burness

Within each band, firms are listed alphabetically. *See individuals' profiles p.116*

Dickson Minto WS (see firm details p.942) "*Absolutely superb,*" according to competitors, "*the leading practice for acquisition finance and no one comes close to them.*" The credit for this goes to "*excellent*" **Colin McHale** (see p.120) ("*commercial, reasonable and efficient – he knows the stuff and won't play silly games*"). The firm's acquisition finance strength has involved it in the largest and most complex work in the market such as advising the Bank of Scotland on the £160 million acquisition of the leisure division of the Littlewoods Organisation by Sportech. Also one of the most active firms in corporate banking, it advised Christian Salvesen on £300 million of facilities provided by a syndicate of banks led by Danske Bank. **Clients:** Bank of Scotland; RBS; Christian Salvesen.

Dundas & Wilson CS (see firm details p.947) "*A well set up organisation, still at the top of the tree.*" This is partly a function of size, quality ("*the best firm in terms of quality of work – I don't think anyone touches it*") and its range of work. "*Well positioned to get the larger deals the banks are sending out,*" its role in the Andersen network puts it in line for top class borrower work and international transactions. **Michael Stoneham**, considered for years the leading light of modern Scottish banking ("*before Michael there really were no proper banking departments in Scotland*"), is now principally involved in management and project finance although he continues to "*add that critical touch*" in transactions. His colleague **David Morton** is "*sound and sensible*" while head of department **Stephen Phillips** is rated for his derivatives and opinion work. He was involved recently for the Bank of Scotland in the £140 million syndicated facility for Technology and Income Trust. **Clients:** Abbey National; CGNU; Halifax; Lloyds TSB; National Australia Group; RBS; Bank of Scotland; Scottish Widows Bank.

Maclay Murray & Spens (see firm details p.1047) "*A well established firm with a good reputation, it handles complex work well.*" Chasing Dickson Minto as the best acquisition finance practice in Scotland, its full service offering includes bid and structured finance, securitisation, restructuring and treasury functions. Property finance has been growing this year. Head of department **Susan Kelly** (see p.119) is considered "*commercial, able and good to deal with*" and has "*a good following*" among the banks. She acted for the Bank of Scotland in the public to privates of Linden Homes and Furlong Homes. "*Gentlemanly*" **Robert Laing** (see p.120) is recommended for his "*clear, readable documents and totally fair approach.*" The firm also represented Wiseman Dairies in connection with its bid for the Unigate Dairy business. **Clients:** Lloyds TSB; Bank of Scotland; RBS; Bank of Ireland; Deutsche Bank; Den Norske Bank; Hypobank; Clydesdale Bank; Prudential.

McGrigor Donald (see firm details p.1062) "*Extremely enthusiastic and technically good,*" **Colin McKay** (see p.120) leads a strong team rated by clients for its top-flight property finance practice. Increasingly active in the telephone and internet banking sphere, it advised on the development by the Halifax of its 'Intelligent Finance' operation. The firm is also active in acquisition finance and represented the Bank of Scotland in the first ever transaction of its new 'integrated finance' all-debt funded leveraged finance product, the MBO of VI-Spring. This was undertaken by the "*bright*" **Iain Macaulay** (see p.712), who, though lower profile than McKay, "*in delivering a product is as good as anyone.*" **Clients:** Bank of Scotland; RBS; Halifax; Royal Bank of Canada.

Burness (see firm details p.903) Viewed by the market as "*building up its banking practice.*" The department is led by "*good, common-sense practitioner*" **Scott Wilson**, who acts in a wide variety of work including straight lending, structured and property finance, as well as project finance and PFI. **Chris Scott** (see p.122), most visible on structured finance, also retains a sound market reputation. Rapidly expanding, the department has consistently increased the size of its deals and represented the Bank of Scotland on a £145 million facility granted to the Pub Estate Company for the acquisition of a portfolio of licensed premises. **Clients:** Chase Manhattan; Bank of Scotland; RBS; Tesco Personal Finance; Royal Bank of Canada; Barclays.

Shepherd & Wedderburn WS (see firm details p.1126) The department is headed by "*competent, thorough and reliable*" **Shona Sanders** (see p.122) and has particular strength in property finance and securitisations. Active in borrower work, some of it on a referral basis, as well as for lenders, the firm's corporate and property strengths complement its banking expertise and clients appreciate the way these are seamlessly integrated. The group represented Northlink Orkney and Shetland Ferries in connection with loan facilities provided by RBS, and with £80 million of leased assets, a complex securitisation for a JV vehicle. The market also noted a strong focus towards project financing and PFI. **Clients:** HSBC; Bank of Scotland; Preferred Mortgages.

Tods Murray WS (see firm details p.1157) Strong in property and acquisition finance, the banking department also stands out for the quality of its securitisation practice, where **Graham Burnside** (see p.116) "*seems to have cornered the market completely.*" The group's profile is further enhanced by the quality of its referral work, with competitors seeing them on the Scottish aspects of some high profile work. Competitors praise lawyers who "*just go about their business in a non-flashy, professional way,*" such as "*pleasant academic practitioner*" **Hamish Patrick** (see p.121) who led on the Scottish side of the Clydesdale Financial Services buyout from Next, representing Bank of America and involving bank debt and a simultaneous securitisation. **Clients:** Bank of Scotland; Britannia Group; Barclays; Clydesdale Bank; Chase Manhattan; RBS; Deutsche; Bank of America; Skipton Building Society; First National Bank.

MacRoberts (see firm details p.1048) Less visible on mainstream banking work, competitors acknowledge that, as "*major players in PFI and projects,*" the banking department headed by Norman Martin is involved in some high quality deals particularly on the borrower side. It also leaves the firm well placed for development funding, where its practice is growing. Busy in acquisition finance and with a volume of refinancing work for banks, the group represented Bridgepoint Capital on the equity and debt refinancing of JDR Cable Systems, and Precision Technology on its MBO. **Clients:** Bank of Scotland; RBS; 3i Group; Halifax; Bank of Ireland; Railtrack; GE Capital.

McClure Naismith (see firm details p.1059) The firm's recruitment of John Blackwood from the Bank of Scotland to work full time on banking law has been interpreted as a sign of its commitment to the sector. Active in the consumer finance and business banking fields where it is developing partnering relationships with the banks, the firm has yet to take a hold on the high value transactional market. Represented the borrowers in two large transactions involving complex banking arrangements. Asset finance and PFI is felt to feed work into the banking department. **Clients:** Bank of Scotland; Lloyds TSB; Sainsburys Bank; Chase Manhattan.

NORTHERN IRELAND

BANKING • Northern Ireland	Ptnrs	Assts
1 Arthur Cox Belfast	1	2
L'Estrange & Brett Belfast	2	2
2 John McKee & Son Belfast	2	2

LEADING INDIVIDUALS	
1 CREED Angus Arthur Cox	HENDERSON Brian L'Estrange & Brett

This book is the product of 6,552 1/2-hour interviews. See p.7 for BMRB audit.
Within each band, firms are listed alphabetically. *See individuals' profiles p.116*

Arthur Cox (see firm details p.865) "*Professional*" outfit which has "*always had a strong tie to the Bank of Ireland,*" and benefits from the abilities of **Angus Creed**, a "*solid, professional, pragmatic banking lawyer.*" Active in property finance, the firm has experience of syndicated loans and MBOs, undertaken almost exclusively for the banks. Most deals are over £1 million with involvement in large transactions, including a £30 million syndicated facility and the Northern Irish aspects of a financing of over £600 million. **Clients:** Anglo Irish; Ulster Bank; Allied Irish; Bank of Ireland; Barclays; Bank of Scotland (Ireland); Irish Intercontinental.

L'Estrange & Brett (see firm details p.1038) "*An active firm with a great reputation in the market place,*" it acts for many of the leading banks on a range of secured lending, property and acquisition finance, securitisations and PFI. Linked in the market with Ulster Bank, it also has a strong borrower led practice. "*Competent and well reputed*" **Brian Henderson** (see p.119) is "*still as strong as he always was.*" He led the team acting for Ulster Bank and RBS in financing the acquisition of the Forestside Shopping Centre by a consortium of investors, one of the biggest single commercial property transactions in Northern Ireland. **Clients:** Ulster Bank; Bank of Scotland; RBS/NatWest; Bank of Ireland; Citibank; GE Capital; Merrill Lynch.

John McKee & Son (see firm details p.1014) Considered by competitors "*a fine department with work for local banks,*" it has been busy on secured lending, MBOs, acquisition finance and is developing a niche representing lenders in PFI deals. Lex Ross is the senior partner. Represented the Bank of Ireland on the banking side of a PFI transaction concerning the Vehicle Testing Agency in Northern Ireland, a deal with a value of £57 million. Also represented the Ulster Bank Group and another bank in a syndicated loan to Dunloe Ewart in connection with a site acquisition. **Clients:** Ulster Bank Group; Bank of Ireland.

LEADERS IN BANKING

AKITT, Ian
Walker Morris, Leeds (0113) 283 2500
iaa@walkermorris.co.uk
Specialisation: Acquisition finance, MBO/MBI finance, project finance and property development funding. Highlights this year include acting for banks and borrowers on over 12 leveraged buy-outs; £150 million bid finance for Homestyle Group plc; £120 million property financing; a number of PFI projects.
Career: Qualified 1988 – *Norton Rose*; *Pinsent Curtis* (Leeds) 1989-94; *Garretts* (Leeds) 1994-99; *Walker Morris* 1999.
Personal: Educated Wetherby High School and University of Sheffield. Leisure interests include golf, tennis, skiing. Married with four children. Resides Bardsey.

ALLEN, Maurice
White & Case, London (020) 7397 3690
mallen@whitecase.com
Specialisation: Leading international finance lawyer with particular expertise in banking and acquisition finance.
Prof. Memberships: Law Society of England & Wales.
Career: Head of banking, *White & Case*, London. Former head of *Weil, Gotshal & Manges'* London office. Former *Clifford Chance* banking partner.

AL-NUAIMI, Omar
Osborne Clarke, Bristol
(0117) 917 3000

ALTON, Philip
Garretts, Birmingham (0121) 644 2924
philip.alton@glegal.com
Specialisation: Banking, asset finance, acquisition finance, building societies, consumer credit. Recent highlights include acting for management in connection with the £550 million takeover private transaction of McKechnie plc and for Vislink in connection with a £14 million US dollar and sterling loan facility to assist in making a US acquisition.
Prof. Memberships: Law Society.
Career: Upon qualification joined Forward Trust Group Ltd as legal advisor. Joined *Edge & Ellison* in 1987 before becoming associate in 1989. Moved to *Hammond Suddards* in 1994 before joining *Garretts* in 1997.
Personal: Born 1959. Interests include classical music (member of the Warwickshire Symphony Orchestra), classic cars, motor racing and photography.

BAKER, Ian
Martineau Johnson, Birmingham (0121) 678 1575
ian.baker@martjohn.com
Specialisation: Advises on banking and debt finance of all kinds including acquisition and project finance, restructurings and security issues and all aspects of non-contentious insolvency.
Prof. Memberships: Associate member of the Securities Institute, member of R3.
Career: Qualified 1983; partner 1987.
Personal: Arts, cricket, rugby, soccer. Church – missionary and development work in Europe and Africa. Married, two children.

BALFOUR, Andrew
Slaughter and May, London (020) 7600 1200
andrew.balfour@slaughterandmay.com
Specialisation: Works mainly on banking and capital markets transactions. Particular experience in syndicated loans, structured finance, project finance, acquisition finance, international equity issues, bonds, commercial paper and medium term notes. Also advises banks and corporate clients on general banking and treasury matters.
Prof. Memberships: The Law Society; Honorary Fellow of The Association of Corporate Treasurers.
Career: Qualified 1981 and became a partner of *Slaughter and May* in 1988. Resident partner in New York office 1991-93.
Personal: Educated at Nailsea School (1968-75) and Manchester University (1975-78).

BATES, Michael
Clifford Chance, London
(020) 7600 1000

BORTHWICK, Trevor
Allen & Overy, London (020) 7330 3000
Specialisation: Trevor is a partner in the banking department with experience in all forms of bank finance. He specialises in particular in syndicated loans, securitisations and acquisitions, telecoms finance, project finance and workouts and reschedulings.
Career: Tonbridge School; Magdalene College, Cambridge. Trained *Allen & Overy*, qualified 1989; partner 1997.
Personal: Born 1962, resides Wimbledon, enjoys golf and rugby.

BRAY, Michael
Clifford Chance, London (020) 7600 1000
michael.bray@cliffordchance.com
Specialisation: Banking, project finance and debt restructuring.
Career: Liverpool University. Partner *Clifford Chance* 1976.

BRIERLEY, Chris
Wragge & Co, Birmingham
(0870) 903 1000

BROADFIELD, Alice
Eversheds, Birmingham (0121) 232 1000
alicebroadfield@eversheds.com
Specialisation: Corporate banking, acquisition finance, lending and security arrangements. Also acts for corporate borrowers.
Career: Trained at *Watson, Farley & Williams*. Qualified and joined *Eversheds* in 1997.
Personal: Born 1973. Educated Bablake School, Coventry; Selwyn College, Cambridge (MA Law). Interests include horse riding, theatre and reading. Lives in Leamington Spa, Warwickshire.

BURNSIDE, Graham
Tods Murray WS, Edinburgh (0131) 226 4771
graham.burnside@todsmurray.com
Specialisation: Partner in banking department. Asset and corporate finance, including securitisation, banking and refinancing. Developed, with partner Hamish Patrick, structures used in securitisation of Scottish assets. Has presented papers on securitisation of Scottish assets.
Prof. Memberships: Writer to the Signet.
Career: Qualified in 1978 *Dundas & Wilson CS*. Coal Industry Pension Fund 1979. Joined *Tods Murray WS* in 1983. Partner in 1984.
Personal: Born 1954. Educated at George Heriot's School, Edinburgh University (LLB Hons 1976). Governor of St. Columba's Hospice. Leisure: music, hill-walking.

CAMPBELL, Mark
Clifford Chance, London (020) 7600 1000
mark.campbell@cliffordchance.com
Specialisation: Partner dealing with all types of banking work including syndicated loans, public bid finance, leveraged transactions, insolvency, structured finance and corporate reconstruction.
Prof. Memberships: City of London Law Society Banking Law Sub-Committee.
Career: Oriel College, Oxford (BA 1981). Articled *Coward Chance*; qualified 1984; partner *Clifford Chance* since 1991; managing partner of finance practice 1998.

CARSLAW, Debbie
Denton Wilde Sapte, London
(020) 7242 1212

CHANDLER, Richard
Addleshaw Booth & Co, Manchester
(0161) 934 6000

CHESTERMAN, James
Latham & Watkins, London (020) 7710 1000
james.chesterman@lw.com
Specialisation: Partner with expertise in financial matters, including leveraged finance, media and telecommunications finance, workouts and restructurings. Experienced in all forms of senior and mezzanine finance, public to private transactions, leveraged buyouts and cross-border acquisition financing. Recent emphasis on deals which combine bank products such as senior debt high yield, bridge loans, mezzanine and securitisation in capital structure.
Career: Qualified as a solicitor in 1987, *Clifford Chance* 1985-94; *Freshfields* 1994-95; partner *Weil Gotshal & Manges* in London 1995-2000; partner *Latham & Watkins* 2000.
Personal: Born 1963. Resides London. Education: Sidney Sussex College, Cambridge University BA (1984).

CHIDLEY, Mark
Addleshaw Booth & Co, Leeds (0113) 209 2049
mac@addleshaw-booth.co.uk
Specialisation: Head of Banking and Finance Group. Specialises in acquisition finance and reconstructions of banking facilities and workouts. Also involved in private equity transactions and joint ventures.
Prof. Memberships: IBA.
Career: Qualified in 1979. Joined the firm in 1982, becoming a Partner in 1984.
Personal: Attended Ardingly College, Haywards Heath, Sussex 1968-73; then Southampton University 1973-76. Leisure interests include fishing, gardening and 60s/70s sports cars.

CHRISTMAS, Matthew
DLA, Manchester (08700) 111111

CLELAND, John
Pinsent Curtis Biddle, Leeds (0113) 244 5000
john.cleland@pinsents.com
Specialisation: Partner and head of banking, Leeds, with a particular expertise in Project Finance and PFI. Acted for RBS in £46 million facility for Bradford & Northern HA. Secured and unsecured funding, asset financing and mortgage book acquisitions and disposals.
Career: Qualified 1990. Solicitor *Simmons & Simmons* 1990-96; partner *Simmons & Simmons* 1996-97; partner *Pinsent Curtis Biddle* 1997 to date.
Publications: Various articles on legal implications of EMU.
Personal: Belmont Academy, Ayr; Cambridge University 1983-87; London University 1989-91. Principal interest – family; other interests reading and football.

COOKE, David J
Pinsent Curtis Biddle, Birmingham
(0121) 200 1050
david.j.cooke@pinsents.com
Specialisation: Partner specialising in banking and insolvency. Licensed insolvency practitioner. Main area of practice is non-contentious banking, professional indemnity and corporate insolvency. Work includes lending, security, restructurings, work outs, receiverships and administration. Also handles corporate finance, including mergers and acquisitions and professional indemnity and other litigation involving corporate, banking, security or insolvency issues.
Prof. Memberships: Appointed Deputy District Judge of the High Court and County Court in 1997. Law Society, Birmingham Law Society, Insolvency Lawyers Association.
Career: Qualified 1981. Joined *Pinsent & Co* in 1979, becoming a partner in 1983.
Publications: Contributing editor to the 'Encyclopaedia of Forms and Precedents' in relation to insolvency and corporate borrowing.
Personal: Born 1956. Educated at Cambridge University 1975-78. Leisure interests include golf, sailing and competitive swimming.

COTTIS, Matthew
Lovells, London (020) 7296 2000
matthew.cottis@lovells.com
Specialisation: Expertise in management buyouts/buy-ins, bids and takeovers and other types of acquisition finance, rescheduling, general banking work and syndicated loans.
Career: Articled *Lovells* 1985-87, partner 1993.

CREED, Angus
Arthur Cox – Northern Ireland, Belfast
(028) 9023 0007

CROOME, Andrew
Eversheds, Norwich (01603) 272727
andrewcroome@eversheds.com
Specialisation: Non-contentious company and banking work, handling a wide variety of matters for lenders and borrowers.
Career: Qualified in 1978 with *Allen & Overy*. Joined *Eversheds* in 1979 becoming a partner in 1982.
Personal: Born in Essex in 1954. Educated in Essex, Suffolk and at Trinity Hall, Cambridge. Lives in North Norfolk.

CULLINANE, Lee
Clifford Chance, London (020) 7600 1000
lee.cullinane@cliffordchance.com
Specialisation: General banking with emphasis on acquisition, cmt (communications, media and technology) and structured finance.
Career: London University (LLB 1985, SFC 1986). Qualified 1988; partner *Clifford Chance* 1995.
Personal: Born 1964; resides London and Winchester.

DALE, Nigel A
Eversheds, Manchester (0161) 831 8000
nigeldale@eversheds.com
Specialisation: Partner and head of banking department, *Eversheds* Manchester. Advises on all aspects of banking related matters, acting for banks and other financial institutions as well as borrowers. Main areas of practice include acquisition finance transactions, the full range of bilateral and syndicated facilities of all types, property finance, and advising on security. Regularly acts for a large number of banks and other financial institutions including Bank of Scotland, The Royal Bank of Scotland plc, Barclays Bank PLC, HSBC Bank PLC, The Co-operative Bank PLC, NM Rothschild & Sons Limited and Lloyds Bank Plc. Significant practice in advising large corporates on major banking transactions. Key deals in 2000 include advising the equity investors in the structure and negotiation of debt facilities on the £450 million IBO of Caradon Plumbing; acting for the syndicate of banks on the provision of debt finance on the £120 million secondary buyout of CRP Group Limited; advising Holidaybreak Plc on replacement £80 million syndicated facilities. During 2000 the team advised on over 25 further corporate and acquisition finance transactions. During 2000 significant property finance work was also undertaken acting both for banks and developers. Total debt deals for *Eversheds* Banking Manchester during 2000 exceeded £1.75 billion.
Career: Qualified in 1986 whilst at *Eversheds Hepworth & Chadwick*. Joined *Hammond Suddards* in 1990 and became partner at *Hammond Suddards* in 1993. Became partner at *Eversheds* in 1996.
Personal: Born 1962. Leisure pursuits include motor sports and cars generally, supporting Halifax Town, gardening and walking.

DAY, Sarah Jane
DLA, Leeds (08700) 111111

DE BASTO, Richard
Allen & Overy, London
(020) 7330 3000

DISS, Paul
SJ Berwin, London (020) 75332834
paul.diss@sjberwin.com
Specialisation: Partner advising banks, other financial institutions and corporate clients on a wide variety of financing issues. Specialises in (1) commercial lending (bilateral and syndicated) in the fields of acquisition, project, trade and property finance; (2) derivatives and other treasury products; (3) banking regulation and compliance; (4) payment transmission services and (5) debt restructuring and insolvencies. In the last year has advised banks and corporate clients on loan, derivatives and other finance transactions aggregating nearly £3 billion. A number of those transactions were in structured finance for borrowers in emerging jurisdictions. Is spending an increasing part of his time preparing and advising banks and corporate clients on derivative transactions including credit and equity derivatives and repurchase agreements. Recently been appointed external legal adviser to the Association for Payment Clearing Services (APACS).
Prof. Memberships: Hong Kong Society, City of London Solicitors Company, International Bar Association
Career: Trained *Linklaters & Paines*; qualified 1976; joined *Stephenson Harwood* 1977; partner 1982-99; *Stephenson Harwood* Hong Kong office 1980-84; partner *S J Berwin* since November 1999.
Personal: St Joseph's College, Stoke on Trent; St Mary's College, Toddington; St Catharine's College, Cambridge (1973 BA). Married to Jan (née Fletcher); 1 daughter (Nicola) and 2 sons (Jonathan and Matthew). Leisure: Cricket coaching, cycling, cinema, book collecting, fellow Royal Society of Arts.

DUKES, Rodney
Taylor Joynson Garrett, London (020) 7300 7000
rdukes@tjg.co.uk
Specialisation: Debt finance, particular specialisations include acquisition, telecom and property finance. In the last five/six years acting for BHF-Bank in relation to a variety of projects and property financing.
Prof. Memberships: Law Society
Career: *Taylor Garrett / Taylor Joynson Garrett* 1982-date.
Personal: Bryanston School, Keele University, Law and Economics. Reside – Northwood. Two children Max and Charlotte.

DUNCAN, Michael G
Allen & Overy, London (020) 7330 3000
michael.duncan@allenovery.com
Specialisation: Partner dealing in areas of practice comprising all types of banking and corporate finance, including in particular syndicated loans (acting for a variety of banks and borrowers), acquisition finance, asset financing, property finance, workouts/reschedulings.
Career: Articled *Allen & Overy*; qualified 1981; partner 1987.
Personal: Cambridge University (1978 BA). Born 1957.

EDWARDS, Jonathan
Hammond Suddards Edge, Manchester
(0161) 830 5113
jonathan.edwards@hammondse.com
Specialisation: Partner, banking. Specialises in acquisition finance, sales and asset finance, general secured lending and PFI/PPP. Deals in 2000/2001 include acting for the Royal Bank of Scotland plc in relation to its senior and mezzanine facilities to the ANC Group; acting for GMAC Commercial Credit Limited on its asset finance facilities to Presspart Group Limited, Oxford UK Limited and Northpoint Limited; acting for Queensborough Holdings plc in relation to its bank-funded public to private.
Career: Trained Simmons & Simmons; qualified 1991; solicitor *Simmons & Simmons*, 1991-96; solicitor *Davies Arnold Cooper*, 1996-99; partner *Hammond Suddards Edge* 1999.
Personal: Born 1965; resides Manchester. Enjoys cave-diving and climbing.

ELLIOTT, Robert
Linklaters, London (020) 7456 4478
robert.elliott@linklaters.com
Specialisation: Recent significant transactions include the £1.5billion acquisition financing of Southern Electric/Southern Water, GUS/Argos $1.6 billion takeover financing and the British Land Universal £300 million mortgage bond issue.
Career: Leeds Grammar School; London University. Qualified in 1976. *Wilde Sapte* 1976-90. Joined *Linklaters* 1990 as a partner in the banking department. Co-head corporate recovery and insolvency *Linklaters & Alliance.*

EREIRA, David
Freshfields Bruckhaus Deringer, London (020) 7936 4000
david.ereira@freshfields.com
Specialisation: Partner in finance department. Responsible for co-ordination of banking and property finance practices. Acts for banks, international institutions and borrowers on banking and finance related work. Acts for banks, property developers and investors on property related investments.
Prof. Memberships: Law Society, City of London Solicitors Company sub-committee on Banking Law; International Bar Association, sub-committees B and E; Justice Working Group of the Financial Law Panel.
Career: Qualified in 1981. Worked at *Wilde Sapte* 1981-90, from 1984 as a partner. Joined *Freshfields* in 1990, becoming a partner in 1991. Postgraduate student with the Open University studying for an MSc in mathematics. Lives in London.

EVANS, Edward
Freshfields Bruckhaus Deringer, London (020) 7936 4000
edward.evans@freshfields.com
Specialisation: Partner in finance department. Main areas of practice are banking and project and asset finance. Also handles energy law work. Has addressed numerous conferences and seminars on these subjects.
Career: Qualified 1980, having joined *Freshfields* in 1978. Became a partner in 1986.
Personal: Born 12th December 1954. Attended RGS High Wycombe 1964-72, then Trinity College Cambridge 1973-77. Leisure interests include rugby, fishing and racing. Lives in London.

FORBES, Sandra
Burges Salmon, Bristol (0117) 902 2707
sandra.forbes@burges-salmon.com
Specialisation: Head of the finance group specialising in corporate banking (including acquisition finance) and asset finance. Important transactions in the last 12 months have included: acting for FirstGroup plc on aggregate facilities in excess of £200 million; re-drafting standard loan and security documentation for Nationwide Building Society; advising Great Western Holdings on the financing of 27 new trains for First North Western and on the financing of 14 trains for First Great Western having on aggregate a contract value of £160 million.
Prof. Memberships: Law Society.
Career: Trained with *Frere Chomeley*, qualified in 1989, joined *Burges Salmon* in 1991, becoming a partner in 1996.
Personal: Manchester University 1983-86. 1st Class Honours in Law Society Finals.

FOX, Ruth
Slaughter and May, London (020) 7600 1200
ruth.fox@slaughterandmay.com
Specialisation: Practice covers a wide range of commercial work, with an emphasis on banking and capital markets, now focusing on financial regulation. Has acted extensively for banks and also for building societies, including in relation to conversions, and for corporate trustees.
Prof. Memberships: The Law Society.
Career: Qualified in 1979 with *Slaughter and May*. Became a partner in 1986.
Personal: Born 3 October 1954. Educated at St Helena School, Chesterfield and University College, London. Married with three sons. Lives in London and Hertfordshire.

FURMAN, Mark
Macfarlanes, London (020) 7831 9222
Specialisation: Specialises in acquisition finance and property finance and generally acting for lenders and borrowers in all aspects of debt finance.
Career: Dulwich College; St. John's College, Oxford (MA, 1980). Qualified as solicitor 1983.
Personal: Married with two children. Interests: guitar, wine, reading.

GILLESPIE, Stephen
Allen & Overy, London (020) 7330 3000
stephen.gillespie@allenovery.com
Specialisation: Steven Gillespie is a partner in the banking department, specialising in leveraged finance, telecoms/telemedia finance and project finance. Recent transactions include Cinven's purchase of Photo Service and Photo Station from GrandVision (for the arrangers); Drax I and II (for the arrangers and the senior lenders), the Rank Holidays/Bourne Leisure LBO (for Barclays Capital), the Wind Telecomunicazioni SpA 2G and 3G financings (for the arrangers and underwriters), the €10 billion 'jumbo' financing for ENEL SpA (for the arrangers) and the €100 million debut financing for Virgin Mobile (for the arrangers/underwriters), the Moyle Interconnector project financing (for RBS/Natwest) and various PFI financings for Edison Capital.
Prof. Memberships: Law Society. City of London Solicitors Company.
Career: Articled *Stephenson Harwood* 1985-87, Solicitor *Freshfields* 1987-91, Solicitor *Allen & Overy* 1991-95, Partner 1995.
Personal: Born 1962. Educated at Foyle and Londonderry College and Trinity College, Oxford (MA (Hons) Jurisprudence 1984). Interests include family, reading, outdoor pursuits and music. Lives in St. Albans.

GORRIE, Euan
Allen & Overy, London (020) 7330 3000
euan.gorrie@allenovery.com
Specialisation: He specialises in acting for banks, mezzanine lenders or borrowers in connection with acquisition finance, public bids and other leveraged or structured finance transactions, restructurings, syndicated loans and lending to investment funds. Recent transactions include advising the arranging banks on the RHM acquisition, the acquisition of Pubmaster, the acquisition of a portfolio of pubs from Bass plc and the refinancing of Impress.
Career: Glenalmond; New College Oxford; Articled *Allen & Overy*, Partner 1996.
Personal: Married; two children.

GOSNAY, Andrew
Pinsent Curtis Biddle, Leeds (0113) 244 5000
andrew.gosnay@pinsents.com
Specialisation: Banking partner. Mainstream banking, asset finance, leasing, property project finance and debt issues. Recent deals include acting for BPT plc on their £75 million Eurobond and HSBC on the £100 million public to private of Allied Textiles plc.
Career: Qualified 1985. *Cameron Markby Hewitt* 1983-86. Joined *Simpson Curtis* in 1986, becoming a partner in 1990.
Personal: Born 1961. Uppingham School 1974-79; Newcastle University 1979-82 and College of Law 1982-83. Interests include walking, skiing, travel and theatre.

HAGUE-HOLMES, Rupert
Eversheds, Birmingham (0121) 232 1000
ruperthague-holmes@eversheds.com
Specialisation: Acquisition finance, asset finance/receivables financing, corporate banking. Acts for both banks and borrowers.
Prof. Memberships: Law Society.
Career: Trained at *Titmuss Sainer & Webb*. Qualified 1990. *Investec Bank (UK) Limited* 1995-99. Joined *Eversheds* 1999.
Personal: Born 1965. The Oratory School, Durham University (BA). Leisure interests include cricket, rugby union and walking. Married with two children.

HANDY, David
Addleshaw Booth & Co, Leeds (0113) 209 2432
dah@addleshaw-booth.co.uk
Specialisation: In all aspects of banking and finance, with principal focus on acquisition finance and corporate treasury and capital markets. Highlights of the past year include advising 3i/Newco on the debt elements of the £100 million public to private of Allied Textiles Company plc, advising 3i on the debt aspects of the £300 million public to private of Peter Black Holdings plc, advising HSBC Bank plc on the senior debt funding for the institutionally led buy-out of Laybond Holdings Limited from Jarvis plc, advising Lloyds TSB Bank plc on the provision of debt facilities to Blazefield Holdings Limited to fund an acquisition; advising The Co-operative Bank plc in providing £16 million of funding to Merivale Moore plc to fund the acquisition of Dunsterville Allen plc; advising 3i and PPM Ventures on the provision of start-up funding to LiNK Financial Limited, advising The Royal Bank of Scotland Leveraged Finance on the provision of further facilities to The Intercare Group plc, advising 3i/Newco on the debt funding of the institutional buy-out of HPI Limited and advising The Royal Bank of Scotland and The Royal Bank of Scotland Commercial Services on the provision of facilities to Rockware Glass Limited.
Career: Qualified October 1993; joined *Addleshaw Booth & Co* January 1995. Became a partner at *Addleshaw Booth & Co* in February 2000.
Personal: Graduated from University of Sheffield in 1990 and spent 1990-91 at Chester College of Law. Married with two sons, living in Leeds. Leisure interests include rugby union, motoring and Everton FC.

HARKER, Chris
Dickinson Dees, Newcastle upon Tyne (0191) 279 9254
chris.harker@dickinson-dees.com
Specialisation: Main areas of practice are banking and commercial lending including acquisition, development and project finance. Works for banks and

building societies as well as quoted and unquoted companies as borrowers. Major transactions in the last year have been for Newcastle Building Society (12 facilities aggregating approx £110 million), Bank of Scotland (including funding for the 32m MBO of Waddington Jaycare Limited), Barclays and Co-operative Bank.

HARRISON, Julie
Ward Hadaway, Newcastle upon Tyne (0191) 204 4000
Specialisation: Head of banking unit. Acts for clearing banks, financial institutions and borrowers in relation to secured and unsecured loans, acquisition finance, property development and project finance, refinancing and security issues, debt restructuring and invoice discount.
Prof. Memberships: Law Society.
Career: Qualified January 1984; articled at *Norton Rose*; joined *Ward Hadaway* in 1997 as a partner having worked for *Middleton Potts* and *Robert Muckle*.

HENDERSON, Brian
L'Estrange & Brett, Belfast (028) 9023 0426
Specialisation: Partner and head of banking unit. All types of banking and finance work.
Prof. Memberships: The Law Society of Northern Ireland. Member of Non-Contentious Business committee; Solicitors European Group (NI)
Career: Qualified 1976. Administrative Trainee European Commission; Partner in *L'Estrange & Brett* since 1979.
Personal: Born 1951. Education: Trinity College Dublin, BA (Mod) LLB.

HUMPHREY, Tony
Allen & Overy, London (020) 7330 2711
tony.humphrey@allenovery.com
Specialisation: Partner specialising in structured finance with substantial experience in a wide range of corporate and financing transactions. Has extensive experience in all aspects of financing, particularly tiered or structured debt/equity financings including international project financings, acquisition financings and other complex multi-sourced financings. He has advised on transactions worldwide including the North Sea, North America, the Gulf, the Far East and Australia. He has given numerous public lectures on various aspects of financing, including 'The Bankability of Project Agreements', 'Project Finance – The Security Package', 'Sponsor Support' and 'Comparative Offtake Arrangements'.
Prof. Memberships: Member, Section on Energy and Natural Resources Law of the International Bar Association.
Career: Articled *Allen & Overy*, qualified 1975, Partner 1981.
Personal: Durham University (1972 BA). Born 1951.

INGLIS, Alan
Clifford Chance, London (020) 7600 1000
alan.inglis@cliffordchance.com
Specialisation: Partner specialising in banking, corporate finance, insolvency and corporate reconstruction.
Career: Exeter School; Birmingham University (LLB). Articled *Clifford Turner/Clifford Chance*; qualified 1985; partner *Clifford Chance* since 1992.

JEFFRIES, Graham
Bond Pearce, Southampton (023) 8033 2001
gjeffries@bondpearce.com
Specialisation: Partner in the specialist Banking and Insolvency Group and head of Southampton banking team. Specialises in banking and insolvency work. Advises clearing and secondary banks, finance houses, invoice discounters and other financial institutions specialising in structured and acquisition finance, regulatory matters, engineering of new products, restructuring, workouts, recovery and bank related insolvency matters.
Prof. Memberships: Member of the Association of Business Recovery Professionals (R3) and the Society of Computers and Law.
Career: Articled with *McKenna & Co*, qualified 1989. Joined *Lester Aldridge* 1992. Partner banking and finance department 1994. Joined *Bond Pearce* 1999 as partner in Banking and Insolvency Group.

JOHNSON, James
Clifford Chance, London (020) 7600 1000
james.johnson@cliffordchance.com
Specialisation: Advises on all forms of corporate banking but in particular is a leading specialist in acquisition finance, workouts, structured finance and housing association finance.
Career: Articled at *Wilde Sapte* and qualified in 1987. Partner at *Wilde Sapte* in 1991.
Personal: Born 1963. Educated: Roundhill College, Thurmaston, Leicester 1974-77, Wreake Valley College, Syston, Leicester 1977-81, Collingwood College, Durham University.

JOHNSTONE, Pat
Eversheds, Birmingham (0121) 232 1000
Specialisation: Corporate banking, lending and security arrangements.
Career: Qualified 1986. Joined *Evershed & Tomkinson* in 1984.
Personal: Born 1955. Educated Dumfries Academy, Glasgow University (MA), Grenoble University. Interests include ballet and horse riding. Lives near Stratford upon Avon.

KEAL, Tony
Allen & Overy, London (020) 7330 3000
tony.keal@allenovery.com
Specialisation: Tony Keal became a partner at Allen & Overy in 1982. He specialises in domestic and cross border acquisition finance (including LBOs, public bids and trade purchases) and other structured finance products. Recent transactions include advising the arrangers on the debt financing for the acquisitions of The Tetley Group; Italtel SpA and TFL GmbH, for the leveraged joint venture creating the Box Clever Group and for the public bids for Mid Kent Water and Wolverhampton and Dudley. Tony also acts frequently for investors on the debt side of LBOs where recent experience includes the acquisition of Wassall plc and the continental European Center Parcs companies. He leads the acquisition finance group.
Prof. Memberships: Law Society and City of London Solicitors Company.
Career: Articled *Allen & Overy*, qualified 1976; legal adviser/CoSec, Libra Bank plc 1976-78; Assistant Solicitor *Allen & Overy* 1979-81; Partner 1981.
Personal: Born 1951. Educated Stowe School and New College, Oxford (1973).

KELLY, Susan
Maclay Murray & Spens, Edinburgh (0131) 226 5196
smk@maclaymurrayspens.co.uk
Specialisation: Banking. Recent deals include acting for Bank of Scotland in the Linden Homes public to private; acting for Bank of Scotland in the Furlong public to private; acting for The Royal Bank in relation to the acquisition of Halliday Contract Catering; acting for Bank of Scotland in relation to the acquisition of the Heritage Hotel portfolio from Compass.
Career: Strathclyde University (1987-91); trainee, *Maclay Murray & Spens* (1991-93); assistant solicitor *Maclay Murray & Spens* (1993-96); Bank of Scotland secondment (1994); associate, *Maclay Murray & Spens* (1996-98); partner, *Maclay Murray & Spens* (1998-date).
Personal: Theatre, opera, antiques, travelling.

KENSELL, Stephen
Allen & Overy, London (020) 7330 3000
stephen.kensell@allenovery
Specialisation: He practises in all areas of banking and finance, including syndications, acquisition finance, telecommunications financing, collateralised lending, property finance and structured finance generally.
Career: Associate Blake Dawson Waldon, Sydney (1990-94); Associate Allen & Overy (1994-98), Partner (1998).
Personal: Macquarie University, Sydney (BA 1987, LLB 1990).

KILNER, Peter
Clifford Chance, London (020) 7600 1000
peter.kilner@cliffordchance.com
Specialisation: Banking and acquisition finance; structured finance.
Career: Trained *Clifford Chance* 1989-91; Assistant, *Clifford Chance* 1991-98; Partner, *Clifford Chance* May 1998.

KINSEY, Julian
Bond Pearce, Bristol (0117) 929 9197
jkinsey@bondpearce.com
Specialisation: Partner in the specialist Banking and Insolvency Group. Specialises in banking and asset finance work for banks, building societies and other financial institutions. Deals with all aspects of lending, refinancing and security issues particularly in connection with acquisition finance for clients based in Bristol, London and the South. Particular experience of issues relating to the financing of the motor sector.
Career: Qualified 1984, joined *Bond Pearce* 1988 having worked for City firm *Linklaters and Paines*, becoming partner 1993.
Publications: Regular contributor to 'Corporate Briefing' published by Monitor Press.

KIRTLEY, Deborah
Dickinson Dees, Newcastle upon Tyne (0191) 279 9000
law@dickinson-dees.com
Specialisation: Specialises in mainstream banking, corporate and acquisition finance work and in particular management buyout transactions. Acted for Barclays Bank plc in the £40 million redevelopment facility of Newcastle United Stadium, St. James Park and the £55 million securitisation. Other transactions include acting for MBO team on £38 million buy out, acting for bank in £35 million sterling and US dollar

acquisition facility and acting for bank in interest and foreign exchange transactions.
Career: Partner, banking group April 1999. Qualified 1991.
Personal: Travel and Sunderland AFC.

KITTS, Stephen
Eversheds, Nottingham (0115) 9507000
stephenkitts@eversheds.com
Specialisation: Corporate finance, private equity and acquisition finance for banks and mezzanine lenders and venture capitalists as well as general mergers and acquisitions.
Prof. Memberships: Law Society.
Career: Joined *Eversheds* in 1987 and became a partner in 1994. Qualified 1987. Head of corporate at *Eversheds* East Midlands.
Personal: Lives in Nottinghamshire with his wife and two children. Enjoys golf.

LAING, Robert
Maclay Murray & Spens, Edinburgh (0131) 226 5196
rjl@maclaymurrayspens.co.uk
Specialisation: Partner and member of banking and finance department. Acts for major clearing banks and other financial institutions as well as for borrowers in the provision of debt finance, including term loans, secured and unsecured lending, MBO/MBI finance and PFI finance. Also general corporate law.
Prof. Memberships: Law Society, Law Society of Scotland, International Bar Association.
Career: Qualified in 1977 (England) and 1985 (Scotland). University of Cambridge (MA 1974). At *Slaughter and May* 1975-83.
Personal: Born 1953.

LEE, Robert
Clifford Chance, London (020) 7600 1000
Robert.Lee@cliffordchance.com
Specialisation: Partner in the finance area specialising in structured finance (both domestic and cross border), syndicated loans, MBO's, acquisition financing and refinancings/restructurings; also specialises in advising Spanish banks and corporations on financing matters generally.
Career: Trained with *Clifford Chance*; 6 months in the New York office. Qualified in 1990. Seconded to *Clifford Chance* Madrid from 1993 to 1995. Returned to London in the autumn of 1995. Partner *Clifford Chance* 1997.
Personal: Exeter University, LLB Law Degree. Golf, rugby, cricket and squash, theatre and travelling – Born 1965, resides London.

LEEMING, Richard
Burges Salmon, Bristol (0117) 939 2216
richard.leeming@burges-salmon.com
Specialisation: Corporate banking partner – carrying out a range of corporate banking work in particular structured finance (including both acquisition finance and property finance). Special work includes advising Nationwide Business Finance on syndicated property finance transactions and preparing for them, new standard form loan and security documents, advising Bayerische Landesbank on various matters and advising Lloyds TSB, Royal Bank of Scotland and Bank of Scotland on acquisition finance and property finance transactions of up to £150 million.
Career: Trained at *Ashurst Morris Crisp* 1991-93, secondment to Bankers' Trust 1994. Joined *Burges Salmon* later that year. Partner from 1 May 2000

LONG, Peter
Herbert Smith, London (020) 7466 2321
peter.long@herbertsmith.com
Specialisation: Partner in finance division, dealing with a range of loan and security matters including property finance and acquisition finance.
Prof. Memberships: International Bar Association; City of London Law Society.
Career: Joined *Herbert Smith* as trainee in 1982; became partner in 1991.
Personal: The Perse School, St. Catherine College, Cambridge. Married, three daughters.

MACAULAY, Iain
McGrigor Donald, Glasgow (0141) 248 6677
See under Projects/PFI, p.712

MADDEN, Andrew
Gateley Wareing, Birmingham (0121) 234 0000

McHALE, Colin
Dickson Minto WS, Edinburgh (0131) 225 4455
colin.mchale@dmws.com
Specialisation: Partner 1997. Banking

McKAY, Colin
McGrigor Donald, Edinburgh (0131) 777 7000
Specialisation: Head of banking unit. Banking and debt finance generally; more particularly acquisition finance and property finance.
Prof. Memberships: Law Society of Scotland. The Law Society (England and Wales).
Career: *Biggart Baillie & Gifford* 1986-88; *Freshfields* (London & Tokyo) 1988-93; *Biggart Baillie & Gifford* (Glasgow) 1993 – March 1999; *McGrigor Donald* April 1999 to date.

McNICOL, Stephen
Robert Muckle, Newcastle upon Tyne (0191) 244 2904
SMcNicol@robertmuckle.co.uk
Specialisation: Partner and head of the banking and corporate recovery units. Specialises in corporate banking and commercial lending including all forms of acquisition and structured finance, business turnaround and all aspects of corporate insolvency. Clients include major clearing banks, buy in/buy out teams, insolvency practitioners and company directors.
Prof. Memberships: Law Society, Association of Business Recovery Professionals, Insolvency Lawyers Association.
Career: Qualified 1995 with *Robert Muckle*. Joined *Lovells* in 1997. Rejoined *Robert Muckle* as a partner in September 2000.
Personal: Born 1969. Educated at Buxton University and the University of Newcastle upon Tyne. Leisure interests include football, skiing, golf and classical guitar.

MILES, Stephen
Pinsent Curtis Biddle, Birmingham (0121) 626 5709
stephen.miles@pinsents.com
Specialisation: Non-contentious banking and finance work. Acts for both financial institutions and corporates – including, in particular, the national acquisition finance teams of the major clearing banks. Acted on the £80.5 million SmartStream institutional purchase and for Mettis Group on its £130 million HDA acquisition and refinancing.
Prof. Memberships: Law Society and Birmingham Law Society; ICC United Kingdom.
Career: Joined *Pinsent Curtis Biddle* (then *Pinsent & Co*) 1989. Qualified 1991; partner 1997.

MITCHELL, Patrick
Hammond Suddards Edge, Leeds (0113) 284 7000
patrick.mitchell@hammondse.com
Specialisation: Partner responsible for acquisition finance in the corporate finance and banking department. Acquisition finance, primarily for structured finance departments of banks, and related funding issues in the context of buy out/institutional purchase transactions. Also handles bank lending, venture capital and corporate finance generally.
Career: Qualified 1981 with *Cameron Markby*. Worked for Robert Holmes a Court's company Bell Group before joining *Hammond Suddards* in 1987. Became a partner in 1989.
Personal: Born 24 February 1957. Attended Ardingly College, Haywards Heath, and Magdalen College, Oxford. Leisure interests include running, riding, football and sport generally. Lives in Harrogate.

MOLLOY, Susan
Halliwell Landau, Manchester (0161) 835 3003
Specialisation: Practice covers loan and other credit/facilities letters/agreements, single bank, syndicated, single/multi-borrower, multi-option facilities, tender panel agreements and working capital facilities, acting for senior mezzanine lenders and borrowers. Dealing with property development and investment finance, leasing and hire purchase facilities, guarantees, loan notes, standstills, intercreditors, providing a full range of banking services. Acts for clearing banks, specialised finance banks, merchant and foreign banks as well as borrowers.
Career: Qualified in 1981 at *Addleshaw Sons & Latham*. Partner at *Alsop Wilkinson* 1989-95. Joined *Garretts* as a partner in June 1995. Joined *Halliwell Landau* January 2000.
Personal: Interests include theatre, walking, reading, cinema and wine.

MOORE, Gideon
Linklaters, London (020) 7456 2000
Specialisation: Syndicated and bilateral loans, acquisition finance, receivables finance, project finance PFI work-outs. Transactions of significance where substantial involvement can be disclosed have included: advised the banks in connection with the Dialog work-out/restructuring; advised the banks on the Elgin/Franklin limited recourse financing (including pre-completion risk); advised the banks refinancing a third generation UMTS licence; advising the banks re a debt for equity swap and corporate restructuring.
Career: 1999 to date: Partner, *Linklaters*; 1995-99: *Dibb Lupton Alsop*; 1987-95: *Clifford Chance*. 1990; University of London, LLM; 1981-84: University of London, LLB.

MORGAN, Matthew
DLA, Manchester (08700) 111111

MORGAN, Meryl
Morgan Cole, Cardiff (029) 2038 5385

MORLEY, David H.
Allen & Overy, London (020) 7330 2551
david.morley@allenovery.com
Specialisation: Banking and Corporate Finance:

Debt. Partner acting for banks and financial institutions, as well as borrowers, on all types of debt and structured finance transactions with particular emphasis on syndicated loans, project finance, telecommunications finance, public bid and other acquisition finance, property and asset finance.
Career: Articled *Allen & Overy,* qualified 1982, trainee solicitor Brussels 1981, assistant solicitor 1982-88. One year on secondment at Chase Investment Bank Limited 1985, partner 1988. Managing Partner, Banking Department 1998.
Personal: St John's College, Cambridge (1979 MA). Born 1956, enjoys cycling, sailing, skiing, family.

MORTON, David E
Dundas & Wilson CS, Glasgow
(0141) 222 2200

MURRAY, Duncan
Browne Jacobson, Nottingham (0115) 976 6538
dmurray@brownej.co.uk
Specialisation: Banking and insolvency. Advising banks and other institutional lenders, corporates and insolvency office holders on a wide range of lending and recovery solutions. Work areas include restructuring and workouts, acquisition and structured finance, property and development finance, security issues, participation issues. Particular experience of transactional work, particularly for MBO/MBI/IBO funding. Advisor to management and purchaser, Wirksworth on public to private of Utilitec plc (£13.2million).
Prof. Memberships: Law Society of England and Wales.
Career: Trained *Hammond Suddards.* Qualified 1988. Solicitor *Hammond Suddards* 1988-90. Solicitor *Simpson Curtis* starting 1990, associate 1992 and partner 1995. Deputy head of banking and finance – *Pinsent Curtis* 1997-99. Partner and head of banking and insolvency – *Browne Jacobson* 1999.
Personal: Education: Bexhill-on-Sea High School, Whitley Bay High School, University of Huddersfield (LLB Hons), Southampton University (LLM). Leisure: golf, photography, hill walking, films.

MURRAY, Neil
Travers Smith Braithwaite, London
(020) 7248 9133
neil.murray@traverssmith.com
Specialisation: Banking – principally acquisition finance and property finance. Also general banking, securitisation, project finance, structured finance. Principal transactions over the last year: NTL, Inc – £3.7 billion financing reacquisition of consumer division of Cable & Wireless; Mid-Kent Holdings – acting for bidder in £6 million acquisition of Mid-Kent Holdings plc; Cannonbridge, London EC4 – acting for bank resecured loan facilities to two borrowers investing by way of structured leasehold interests; Pinewood Studios – acquisition of Shepperton Studios; The Royal Bank of Scotland plc and Royal Bank of Scotland International – various transactions including leveraging of European property funds and limited partnerships (onshore and offshore).
Prof. Memberships: City of London Law Society; FIABCI; Investment Property Forum.
Publications: Various articles in the Estates Gazette and Law Society Gazette concerning property finance.
Personal: LLB (Soton), MA (Lond.).

ON, Nicholas
Eversheds, Newcastle upon Tyne (0191) 261 1661
nicholason@eversheds.com
Specialisation: Partner. All aspects of non-contentious banking and finance work including transactional lending and finance, regulatory work and restructuring. Regularly acts for a large number of banks and other financial institutions as well as large corporate borrowers. Particular expertise in property development finance on a national basis and acquisition finance.
Career: Qualified 1991 at *Robert Muckle.* Secondment with *Bank of Scotland Legal Services* in Edinburgh in 1993. Partner at *Robert Muckle* 1995. Joined *Eversheds* as partner August 1999.
Personal: Born 1963. Educated Cheltenham Grammar School, St. Catherine's College, Oxford (BA) and University of Northumbria. Married with two children. Plays the piano, golf and football.

OWEN, Simon
Hammond Suddards Edge, Leeds (0113) 243 0391
simon.owen@hammondse.com
Specialisation: Banking and commercial lending, all forms of acquisition and structured finance, general corporate banking and treasury, trade finance and derivatives documentation. Acting for the funders on the £320 million take private of Evans of Leeds plc; advising Peterhouse Group plc on its successful bid for Eve Group Plc; advising The Royal Bank of Scotland plc on the MBO of Anglo-Danish Fibre Industries Limited; advising Royal Bank Private Equity on their investment in the MBO of Darchen Engineering Limited; advising Barclays Bank plc on their £25, 000, 000 lend to E-Quisiter plc.
Prof. Memberships: Law Society.
Personal: Education: Maidstone Grammar School; Newcastle University; Chester Law School. Interests: most sports but particularly rugby, music and films. Resides: Harrogate. Family: married to Caroline, two children William and Oliver.

PALLETT, Julian
Wragge & Co, Birmingham
(0870) 903 1000

PAPWORTH, Richard
Addleshaw Booth & Co, Leeds (0113) 209 2310
rnp@addleshaw-booth.co.uk
See under Social Housing, p.783

PATRICK, Hamish
Tods Murray WS, Edinburgh (0131) 226 4771
hamish.patrick@todsmurray.com
Specialisation: Partner in banking department. Debt finance and recovery, including conventional banking, asset finance, PFI/project finance, innovative funding structures and funding reorganisation. Developed, with partner Graham Burnside, structures for securitisation of Scottish assets. Author, speaker and university examiner in field.
Career: Qualified 1989. Partner 1992.
Personal: Born 1962. Attended Dollar Academy, Edinburgh University (LLB 1st Class Hons 1984; DipLP 1985; PhD 1994: Cross-border securities and insolvency). Leisure: family, music, sports.

PHILLIPS, Stephen
Dundas & Wilson CS, Edinburgh
(0131) 228 8000

PIERCE, Sean
Freshfields Bruckhaus Deringer, London
(020) 7936 4000
sean.pierce@freshfields.com
Specialisation: Partner in the London office. Practice encompasses all aspects of banking work. Sean specialises in representing lenders but his clients also include corporates and other borrowers. In terms of products Sean has recently focused on cross-border leveraged buyouts and 'jumbo' acquisition financings. Sean has practised in New York and Hong Kong as well as London.

POLGLASE, Timothy
Norton Rose, London
(020) 7283 6000
polglaset@nortonrose.com
Specialisation: Principal area of practice is structured finance, including the financing of leveraged buy-outs and public bids, telecoms finance and project finance.
Career: Articled *Norton Rose;* qualified 1986; seconded to *Milbank, Tweed, Hadley & McCloy* (New York) 1988-89; seconded to banking supervision division, Bank of England 1990-91; partner *Norton Rose* 1994.
Personal: Born 1962. Educated at St John's College, Oxford.

POPHAM, Stuart
Clifford Chance, London (020) 7600 1000
stuart.popham@cliffordchance.com
Specialisation: Partner. Banking and finance, head of global finance practice. Principal area of work relates to finance for corporates including acquisition financing, work-outs, syndicated and capital market financing, structured and tax driven financing, acting for lenders and borrowers.
Career: Southampton University (LLB 1975). Qualified 1978; made partner 1984.

PULESTON JONES, Haydn
Linklaters, London (020) 7456 4454
haydn.pulestonjones@linklaters.com
Specialisation: Principal area of practice is in the field of banking. Areas of specialisation include syndicated, secured and structured financings and corporate rescues and recoveries. Has had extensive experience of advising banks, syndicates, steering committees and distressed companies on UK and international defaults and reschedulings.
Prof. Memberships: 1998 to date: Member of Loan Market Association Working Party on Primary Documentation for use in the syndicated loan market under English law (and member of LMA's Legal Forum, 1999 to date); 1996 to date: Member of the Single Currency Liaison Group of the Financial Law Panel; 1980-98: Member of the Banking Law Sub-Committee of the City of London Law Society (Chairman 1994-98).
Career: Qualified 1973, becoming a partner with *Linklaters* in 1979. Partner in international finance department, banking group. Head of *Linklaters & Alliance's* banking management team.

REARDEN, Shaun
Chaffe Street, Manchester (0161) 236 5800
Specialisation: Acquisition finance, property finance, restructuring, receivables finance and asset finance. Other area of work is consumer credit.
Prof. Memberships: Law Society.
Career: Qualified in 1979 while at *Rutherfords* in Liverpool. In-house solicitor at *Littlewoods* 1980-82, then

manager of legal department *North West Securities* to 1986. Legal Advisor *Co-operative Bank* to 1989 then partner and head of banking at *Addleshaw Sons & Latham*. Joined Chaffe Street in 1999.

ROBERTS, Simon C
Allen & Overy, London
(020) 7330 3000

SANDERS, Shona
Shepherd & Wedderburn WS, Edinburgh
(0131) 473 5260
shona.sanders@shepwedd.co.uk
Specialisation: Acquisition and Project Finance.
Prof. Memberships: Law Society of Scotland. Law Society (England and Wales).
Career: 1987-91 *Dundas & Wilson*; trainee (1987-89); assistant in banking group (1989-91). 1992 Sabbatical; including time at *Allen, Allen & Hemsley*, Sydney. 1993-98 *Dundas & Wilson*; Assistant to partner in banking group. 1998-99 *Mallesons Stephen Jaques*, Sydney; senior associate in project finance team. 1999 to date *Shepherd and Wedderburn*; partner in and head of banking group.
Personal: Born 1966. University of Edinburgh: LLB (1986), DIP LP (1987). Qualified in English Law 1998.

SCHULZ, Peter F
Allen & Overy, London (020) 7330 3000
peter.schulz@allenovery.com
Specialisation: Has a broad practice in banking and international finance, encompassing syndicated and structured lending, acquisition financing, the banking aspects of CDO issues and workouts and restructurings. Recent transactions he has led include multi-jurisdictional acquisition and bid financings including Sasol/Condea and Xstrata/Asturiana de Zinc, telecoms projects, sovereign loans and several jumbo corporate credits including those for Gucci, Michelin, Vivendi and Angelo American.
Career: Articled *Allen & Overy*, qualified 1983, partner 1989.
Personal: Educated at Haberdashers' Aske's School, Elstree; Downing College, Cambridge (MA Law).

SCOTT, Christopher
Burness, Edinburgh (0131) 473 6123
cs@burness.co.uk
Specialisation: Banking and corporate finance, including senior/mezzanine/equity funding packages in the context of acquisitions, development projects and joint ventures, reviewing and advising on the Scottish aspects of international financings involving Scottish borrowers, debt reorganisations/capitalisations. Also experience of private equity investment and listed/AIM corporate finance work. Recently acted for a Scottish bank in relation to the £107 million equity/subordinated/mezzanine funding of a UK hotel operator.
Prof. Memberships: Member of the Securities Institute; Writer to the Signet.
Career: Trainee at *Burness*; qualified 1985; assistant solicitor 1985-87; assistant solicitor *Travers Smith Braithwaite* 1987-88; assistant solicitor *Burness* 1988-89; partner 1989.
Personal: Edinburgh University (1982 LLB Hons 1st; 1983 Diploma in Legal Practice). Leisure interests include fly fishing, hill walking and motor cycling.

SHEPHERD, Claire
Hammond Suddards Edge, Manchester
(0161) 830 5000
claire.shepherd@hammondse.com
Specialisation: Acquisition finance, property and development finance, equipment leasing and other asset finance acting for both banks and borrowers.
Career: *Wilde Sapte* 1988-94. Solicitor – *Clifford Chance* 1994-95. *Halliwell Landau* 1996-2000 (partner 1998); partner *Hammond Suddards Edge*, 2000.
Personal: Cycling, squash and cinema. Married. Lives Hale, Cheshire.

SHORT, Stephen
Ashurst Morris Crisp, London (020) 7638 1111
stephen.short@ashurst.com
Specialisation: Partner specialising in domestic and cross-border structured finance (leveraged and other acquisition finance); recent transactions include (for Barclays Capital, Merrill Lynch International and UBS Warburg) finance for Ineos to refinance existing debt (including a tender offer for a bond), fund a cross-border corporate reorgansiation and an acquisition in Germany and the US; (for Lehman Brothers) finance for CFS International NV to refinance existing debt and fund and acquisition in Denmark, the Netherlands and the US; (for ING Bank NV and Bank of Scotland) finance for Focus Do It All to fund the public bid for Wickes plc and the acquisition of Great Mill DIY.
Career: Qualified 1989; partner 1998.
Personal: Education: LLB, LLM. Born 1964. Resides London.

SLATER, Richard
Slaughter and May, London (020) 7600 1200
richard.slater@slaughterandmay.com
Specialisation: Partner in financial/commercial department. Head of financing stream. Principal area of practice is debt financing of all types, including syndicated loan facilities, structured financings, securitisations, project financings and bond and note issues. Has also acted on international equity offerings, flotations, privatisations and corporate and commercial work of a general nature.
Prof. Memberships: The Law Society.
Career: With *Slaughter and May* throughout. Articles 1970; qualified 1972; partner 1979. Hong Kong office 1981-86.
Personal: Born 18 August 1948. Educated at University College School, Hampstead (1956-65), Lycée Michelet, Paris (1965-66) and Pembroke College, Cambridge (1966-69). Lives in London.

SMITH, Mark
DLA, Leeds (08700) 111111

SMITH, Robert
Clifford Chance, London (020) 7600 1000
robert.smith@cliffordchance.com
Specialisation: Specialises in all aspects of banking including acquisition finance, property finance, structured finance and debt restructuring.
Career: Qualified in 1976. Worked at *Slaughter and May* until 1981. Joined *Clifford Chance* in 1981. Opened and managed *Clifford Chance*'s office in Jeddah 1982-85. Returned to the London office in 1985 and became partner in 1987.
Personal: Interests include sailing, rugby, cricket, tennis and travel.

SPENDLOVE, Justin
Ashurst Morris Crisp, London (020) 7638 1111
justin.spendlove@ashursts.com
Specialisation: Head of *Ashursts*' banking and capital markets department until appointment (October 2000) as the firm's managing partner. Specialises in international structured finance transactions for mergers and acquisitions and corporate funding, generally acting for financial institutions and international corporations.

STEWART, Mark
Clifford Chance, London (020) 7600 1000
mark.stewart@cliffordchance.com
See under Private Equity, p.679

STEWART, Suzy
Clifford Chance, London
(020) 7600 1000

STONEHAM, Michael
Dundas & Wilson CS, Edinburgh
(0131) 228 8000

SWEETING, Malcolm
Clifford Chance, London (020) 7600 1000
malcolm.sweeting@cliffordchance.com
Specialisation: Partner in finance practice.

TAYLOR, Michael
Walker Morris, Leeds (0113) 283 2500
Specialisation: Work includes acquisition finance, MBO/MBI finance and general banking, lending and security advice, restructuring and work outs.
Career: Qualified 1986; partner *Walker Morris* 1991.
Personal: Attended King Edward VI School, Lichfield and University of Bristol 1980-83. Leisure interests include hockey and fly-fishing. Lives in Leeds.

TUCKER, John
Linklaters, London (020) 7456 4496
john.tucker@linklaters.com
Specialisation: Areas of specialisation include syndicated lending, secured and structured financings, acquisition and project finance and reorganisation work. Represents banks, bank syndicates and other creditors as well as borrowers in both UK and international financing transactions.
Career: 1999 to date: Head of Banking Department; 1990: Partner, *Linklaters*; 1989: Assistant solicitor, *Linklaters*; 1998: Admitted as a solicitor in England and Wales; 1984-89: Partner, *Finlaysons*, South Australia; 1980: Admitted as a barrister and solicitor in South Australia. 1982: South African Institute of Technology, BA (Accountancy); 1979: University of Adelaide, LLB (Hons).

TWIST, Patrick
Pinsent Curtis Biddle, Birmingham
(0121) 200 1050
patrick.twist@pinsents.com
Specialisation: Partner and national head of major projects. Specialises in the development and financing of major projects. Work includes railway infrastructure, energy from waste plants, oil and gas facilities, hospitals and schools. Also experienced in acquisition finance and banking generally.
Prof. Memberships: Chairman, Law Society Banking Law Committee.
Career: Finance and Leasing Association. Ford Credit Europe, Bank of Scotland. Joined *Pinsent & Co* (now *Pinsent Curtis Biddle*) 1987. Partner in 1988.

Personal: Born 1952. Educated Downside School and Keele University.

VAUGHAN, Philip
Eversheds, Cardiff (029) 2047 1147
Specialisation: Practice covers a wide-range of non-contentious banking and finance work and includes transactional work (including project and acquisition finance), regulatory advice and drafting of standard documentation for banks, building societies and finance companies. Has a particular expertise in consumer credit work. Also involved in a wide range of non-contentious insolvency work acting for receivers, administrators and liquidators and advising lenders on enforcement of security and restructuring/refinancings.
Career: Qualified 1984. Formerly with *Clifford Chance* and National Westminster Bank Legal Department. Joined current firm in 1987 and became partner in 1988.
Personal: Born 14th December 1958. Educated at Haverfordwest Grammar School, St. Edmund Hall, Oxford (M.A.) and Emmanuel College, Cambridge (LL.M.).

VICKERS, Mark
Ashurst Morris Crisp, London (020) 7638 1111
mark.vickers@ashursts.com
Specialisation: Corporate banking and international finance: specialising in UK and cross-border acquisition finance and leveraged acquisitions, particularly management buy-outs/buy-ins and institutional purchases; structured finance; global syndicated lending. He is one of the market's leading experts on the debt funding of public to private takeovers.
Career: Joined *Ashurst Morris Crisp* in 1999 having been head of European acquisition finance at a top-10 UK law firm (1980-99).
Publications: Author: 'Senior Debt Market for Management Buy-outs' and 'Public to Private Takeovers: The New Paradigms'.
Personal: Helicopter pilot. Owner of Saracen armoured personnel carrier.

WAGHORN, Mark
Berwin Leighton Paisner, London (020) 7760 1000
mark.waghorn@berwinleightonpaisner.com
Specialisation: Partner, and head of property finance group, specialising in property finance (including investment and development funding) and property related insolvency and turnaround work. Wide range of clients including banks, institutions, finance houses, senior and mezzanine funders and borrowers. Work includes lead partner for RBS/NatWest. Recent transactions include highly structured £1.9 billion hotels sale and leaseback with Nomura and Compass Hotels; advising on the financing of the redevelopment of Battersea Power Station; advising on the £144 million financing of the Nike Town/Top Shop (Arcadia Group) building at Oxford Street. Lead partner for KBC Bank NV acting most recently on the sale of a secured commercial property loan portfolio to First National Bank. Acting on the £100 million+ refinancing of the MWB Leisure Fund I limited liability partnership. Acting for Barclays Bank and Deutsche Hypo Bank on the syndicated £30 million development financing for a Regalian residential and commercial development in West London. Advising Marylebone Warwick Balfour on the £90 million syndicated financing to acquire Liberty's (including the flagship store). Advising Barclays Bank on more than £75 million of development finance for the construction of a prestigious landmark office development at Park Lane. A member of the team advising the Millennium Commission Capital Projects team having now dealt with more than £1.75billion of funding in relation to over £2.5billion of developments.
Prof. Memberships: Member of Law Society; Association of Business Recovery Professionals; Non Administrative Receivers Association; Society for Computers & Law.
Career: Trained at *Berwin Leighton*, qualified January 1992 and became a partner in 1997 and head of property finance in 1999.
Publications: Writes for Sweet & Maxwell Commercial Transaction Checklists on property development and insolvency and contributes occasional articles elsewhere.
Personal: Education: Bristol Grammar School, Exeter University, University of the West of England. Plays football. Car nut. Life member of CAMRA. Nearly married.

WALKER, Gary
Wragge & Co, Birmingham
(0870) 903 1000

WARD, Anthony
Shearman & Sterling, London (020) 7655 5000
award@shearman.com
Specialisation: Partner specialising in acquisition finance. Advises a variety of leading financial institutions and equity sponsors. Recent transactions include advising Investcorp in connection with the debt financing of the acquisition of Gerresheimer Glas AG. Advising Merrill Lynch in connection with debt financing of the acquisition of Center Parcs. Advising Morgan Stanley in connection with the debt financing of the acquisition of McKechnie Plc.
Career: Qualified in 1988. Partner *Ashurst Morris Crisp* in 1996. Partner *Shearman & Sterling* in 1998.
Personal: Education: School of Slavonic and East European Studies, London University, BA in Russian language and literature.

WARD, Nigel
Ashurst Morris Crisp, London (020) 7859 1236
nigel.ward@ashursts.com
See under Private Equity, p.679

WHATNALL, John
Halliwell Landau, Manchester (0161) 835 3003
Specialisation: Partner in corporate department. Main areas of practice are banking and corporate finance. He has been involved in several 'public to private' transactions such as Anglican Group and Sanderson Group.
Prof. Memberships: Law Society, Securities Institute.
Career: Qualified in 1981. Worked at *Herbert Oppenheimer Nathan & Vandyk* 1981-6. Joined *Halliwell Landau* in 1986, becoming a partner in 1987.
Personal: Born 22nd June 1957. Attended The Queen's College, Oxford 1975-78. Leisure interests include opera. Lives in Wilmslow.

WHITE, Giles
Linklaters, London (020) 7456 2000
giles.white@linklaters.com
Specialisation: Global finance – including banking/structured finance facilities and securities offerings. Main specialisms include syndicated lending, merger and acquisition finance, structured products (such as tax enhanced lending and high yield notes) and, in addition, South African based financings.
Career: 1996 to date: Partner, *Linklaters*, London; 1995-96: Head of international finance, Linklaters Hong Kong; 1992-96: Partner, *Linklaters*, Hong Kong; 1991-92: Partner in the international finance department of *Linklaters* London; 1988-91: Assistant solicitor, *Linklaters* London; 1985-88: *Credit Suisse First Boston Limited*, London; 1982-85: *Sonnenberg, Hoffman & Galombik* (attorneys), Cape Town, South Africa.
Personal: 1980-81: University of Cape Town, LLB; 1979: Admitted as barrister, Inner Temple, London; 1976-78: Oxford, MA (Law), Rhodes Scholar; 1972-75: University of Cape Town, BA.

WILSON, Dave
Theodore Goddard, London (020) 7880 5760
davewilson@theodoregoddard.co.uk
Specialisation: Partner in *Theodore Goddard's* banking and projects group acting for leading banks and financial institutions in a wide range of domestic and cross border structured finance transactions. These transactions have included large corporate restructurings (Brent Walker and National Home Loans among them) and sovereign and corporate syndicated financings with a recent focus on commercial and ground rent financings. Led the Theodore Goddard team for Bayerische Landesbank/Abbey National Treasury Services plc in relation to the £250 million plus financing of the Woolgate Exchange building in London completed in Spring 2001.
Prof. Memberships: Qualified as a solicitor in Scotland (1982) and England and Wales (1987).
Career: LLB (First Class Honours) Edinburgh University 1980. *Orr MacQueen* (Edinburgh) 1980-84, *Coward Chance* (thereafter *Clifford Chance*), London and New York 1984-91, *Theodore Goddard* from 1991 to date.
Personal: Married with four sons. Leisure pursuits include soccer (York City) and golf. Born 1958.

WILSON, Scott
Burness, Glasgow (0141) 248 4933

WILTSHIRE, Peter
CMS Cameron McKenna, Bristol (0117) 934 9300
prw@cmck.com
Specialisation: Non-contentious banking, including rescue and work-outs.
Career: Articled *Cameron Markby/Cameron Markby Hewitt* 1988-90. Qualified *Cameron Markby Hewitt*, London, 1990. Bristol *Cameron Markby Hewitt* 1991-date (now *CMS Cameron McKenna*). Partner 1999.
Personal: Church. Armchair sports critic. Singing. Married, five children.

WOOD, Philip
Allen & Overy, London (020) 7330 2552
woodp@allenovery.com
Specialisation: Head of Know How and Education. Specialist in international banking, including syndicated loans, project finance, title finance, trade finance, secured finance, payment and clearing systems, shipping and aircraft, insolvency and reconstructions, bank regulation, legal systems, and comparative financial law.
Prof. Memberships: City of London Law Society Banking Law Sub-Committee; Trust Law Committee;

Advisory Board of Cambridge's Centre for Corporate and Commercial Law; Honorary Fellow of The Society for Advanced Legal Studies; Visiting Professor, Queen Mary College; Yorke Distinguished Visiting Fellow, Cambridge University; UNIDROIT correspondent.
Career: Articled *Allen & Overy* (1970-73), Partner (1974).
Publications: Editorial Board of Butterworth's 'Journal of International Banking and Financial Law', 'Practical Law for Companies', 'European Financial Services Law and International Financial Law Review'. Advisory Board of 'Asia Business Law Review and Business Law International'. Author of ten books on international finance law.

WOOLCOCK, Brian
DLA, Birmingham (08700) 111111

WOOLLEY, R S
DLA, Manchester (08700) 111111

WURZAL, Jason
Eversheds, Leeds (0113) 243 0391
jasonwurzal@eversheds.com
Specialisation: Work covers all areas of banking related matters, including acquisition finance, property finance, project finance and PFI. Transactions include acting for Peter Black on £304 million take private funded by RBS.
Career: Qualified at *Lovell White Durrant* in 1994; joined *Ashurst Morris Crisp* in 1996 (including one years secondment to Bankers Trust); joined *Eversheds* in 1999, partner in 2000.
Personal: Leeds Grammar School and Nottingham University. Walking and gardening.

CAPITAL MARKETS

OVERVIEW: *"Pretty quiet"* sums up the level of activity in the equity capital markets. After last year's IPO wave, encouraged by the floating dot.com bubble, practitioners are now bemoaning *"difficult market conditions"* set by cautious dealings particularly in a foundering telecoms sector. Some detect regression towards the old economy companies, with activity related to spin offs created by oil sector privatisations. Clients looking beyond the depressed domestic market are homing in on firms offering a multi-jurisdictional capacity for global offerings and at the cutting edge of securitisations and derivatives. Additional firm resources such as tax and regulatory expertise are important requirements in supporting work that is *"global by its very nature."* In line with the aim of creating a single European capital market, the draft EU directive on European prospectuses should enhance work activity for these firms. There is some debate regarding whether IPOs can be transmuted into a commoditised business, as has become the case for some aspects of the debt market. Elements such as sensitive disclosure issues and the need for partner scrutiny dictate that it may be some time before the legal services market espouse this concept. For clients, the *"top criterion is quality."* They seek *"lateral thinking and the ability to negotiate rigorously."* Because *"bodies count on any securities issue or repackaging matter,"* clients stress the importance of consistent quality and stable teams of assistants.

TOP IN-HOUSE LAWYERS

Kate CRAVEN, Director of Law & Compliance, *Merrill Lynch International*

Tim GRACE, *Goldman Sachs*

Tracy KINGSLEY-DANIELLS, Director of Transaction Management, *Credit Suisse First Boston International*

Carol MOIR, Executive Director of Transactions Legal, *UBS Warburg*

Roger MUNGER, Global Head of Fixed Income Legal, *ABN AMRO Bank NV*

Roger SCOTTS, Executive Director, *Goldman Sachs International*

Kevin SOWERBUTTS, Head of Legal, *BNP Paribas*

Having recently taken over this post, **Kate Craven** is regarded as *"sensible and commercial with it."* Working on the debt side, the *"excellent"* **Tracy Kingsley-Daniells** is considered *"a bit of a star,"* strengthened by an *"excellent team"* working under her. **Carol Moir** is rated highly for her *"great all round experience,"* while **Roger Munger** is *"lively and commercial,"* able as he is to *"cut through to the issues."* The *"first class"* **Roger Scotts** works on the equity side, *"an impressive person who knows the business well."* **Kevin Sowerbutts** is considered to be *"fairly legendary, and highly personable."*

In-House lawyers profiles: p.1193

RESEARCH APPROVED BY BMRB: *For this edition,* Chambers' *researchers conducted 6,552 interviews – 4,419 with law firms, 554 with barristers and 1,579 with clients.*

The validity of the research was scrutinised by BMRB International, who audited both the methodology and the results at our offices in July 2001. They interviewed Chambers' *researchers and cross-checked sample interviews. Details of the audit appear on page 7.*

LONDON

INTERNATIONAL DEBT & EQUITY

Allen & Overy (see firm details p.856) Boasting an *"enormous history in this sector"* and considered by some to be *"streets ahead in the London markets,"* the team's *"strength across the board"* in its debt practice is well recognised. Dubbed the *"MTN kings,"* the firm also has a steady presence in high yield work. Clients value its input in complex transactions, opining that its lawyers are *"best for complicated structures and for creating a new product."* Last year, the group advised on 264 stand-alone debt issues, 740 individual issues under debt programmes and five Global CP programmes. MTN highlights include a €3 billion global programme for Deutsche Bank and a €3 billion EMTN programme for Warburg Dillon Read.With specialist partners based in the firm's network of 18 offices throughout Europe and New York, the group's cross-border capacity is adjudged *"first rate"* by peers, and includes particular strength in the telecoms sector. This year the firm advised on over 30 innovative tier 1 capital issues in ten jurisdictions such as Bank of Scotland's £300 million securities issue. *"Picking up great deals,"* the equity capital markets practice has kept pace with the globalising trend. In 2000 the team advised on over 35 equity offerings, while the US law group acted on over 30 transactions involving Rule 144A, also supporting on the US aspects of transactional work. *"A slick operator with a strong personality,"* **Boyan Wells** (see p.136) manages the team while still producing *"excellent work of his own."* He advised Syngenta on its debut €1.15 million eurobond issues and acted for Lehman Brothers on Clerical Medical Finance's €400 million bonds issue. *"Fast rising star"* **Stephen Miller** (see p.134) is *"making a name for himself."* *"Everyone in the world adores"* his *"professional, courteous, sensitive"* approach to deals – he *"keeps clients extremely happy."* His key high yield deals include Lloyds TSB's €430 million and £250 million securities issues, and Northern Rock's £200 million capital instruments issue. Primary contact for clients such as CSFB, Nomura and ABN AMRO, *"sensible, low key"* **Roger Wedderburn-Day** (see p.136) is *"committed and hardworking,"* while **Daniel Shurman** (see p.135) knows how to *"progress a transaction rather than point-score."* A major debt highlight for the team was advising Morgan Stanley on the €7.5 billion debt programme by Pfandbrief Bank International, the first programme issued under new legislation in Luxembourg. In repackagings, the team has advised on over 260 issues, including work for Barclays Capital on $600 million and £1 billion notes issues by Nerva and Corvus respectively. Further work includes advising Merrill Lynch on the establishment of the Euroschuldschein B.V programme and issues of Euro-convertible bonds. Equity highlights include advising Royal KPN on its €5.5 billion US SEC-registered Dutch equity offering, and acting as advisors to the Hong Kong office to Merrill Lynch as global co-ordinator on the Hutchison Whampoa $3 billion fund-raising under Rule 144A. **Clients:** ABN AMRO;

CAPITAL MARKETS: INTERNATIONAL DEBT & EQUITY •		Ptnrs	Assts
1	Allen & Overy	40*	149*
	Linklaters	35	116
2	Clifford Chance	29	125
3	Freshfields Bruckhaus Deringer	37	89
4	Slaughter and May	12	15
5	Baker & McKenzie	8	16
	Cleary, Gottlieb, Steen & Hamilton	7	30
	Shearman & Sterling	2	5
	Simmons & Simmons	7	20
	Weil, Gotshal & Manges	3	5
6	Ashurst Morris Crisp	6	9
	Herbert Smith	8	25
	Lovells	14	28
	Norton Rose	22	39

LEADING INDIVIDUALS		
1	BURN Lachlan Linklaters	CANBY Michael Linklaters
	EASTWELL Nick Linklaters	WELLS Boyan Allen & Overy
2	DUNNIGAN David Clifford Chance	EDLMANN Stephen Linklaters
	FRANK David Slaughter and May	MILLER Stephen Allen & Overy
3	BROWN Jane Linklaters	PITKIN Jeremy Freshfields Bruckhaus
	THOMSON Keith Linklaters	WEDDERBURN-DAY Roger Allen & Overy
4	BICKERTON David Clifford Chance	CLARK Charles Linklaters
	DUNLOP Stewart Clifford Chance	MACVICAR Robert Clifford Chance
5	EATOUGH David Clifford Chance	OVENDEN Simon Linklaters
	PRIDMORE Nigel Linklaters	SHURMAN Daniel Allen & Overy
UP AND COMING		
	MORRIS Tim Clifford Chance	

This book is the product of 6,552 1/2-hour interviews. See p.7 for BMRB audit.
Within each band, firms are listed alphabetically. *See individuals' profiles p.132*
**Figures denote total capital markets team sizes.*

Barclays Capital; Bear Stearns; CSFB; Deutsche Bank; Goldman Sachs; JP Morgan; Merrill Lynch International; Morgan Stanley Dean Witter; Nomura International.

Linklaters (see firm details p.1042) "*Clearly strong all round; a mature and established practice,*" it is consistently endorsed by clients and competitors for its balanced strength across the capital markets. With a strong focus on the Eurobonds markets, the group has a high profile in medium term loans, convertibles, exchangeables and project bonds. "*Cross-border by its very definition,*" the firm is "*clearly focused on Europe.*" Competitors readily acknowledge the firm's strong Nordic practice and burgeoning Eastern European network, which supports expertise in the emerging markets. In the past year, the team has advised on emerging markets issues throughout five continents. "*The best integrated US/UK proposition,*" the practice benefits from its 70-strong US securities law team on transactions involving sales of securities into the US.The group is a "*favourite*" with clients, who value "*stable, consistent*" teams packed with partners who "*act like glue on a transaction.*" Clients clamour for "*measured, considered, excellent*" **Lachlan Burn** (see p.132 for his "*wonderful judgement calls.*" Doing "*a fantastic job*" in a managerial role, he is endorsed as the "*guru for know-how.*" "*Thorough, diligent*" head of practice **Michael Canby** (see p.132) is "*a delight to deal with.*" He advised JP Morgan Securities on the groundbreaking Lithuanian note issue of Litas 100 million, the first internationally placed public debt issue denominated in that currency. "*Smooth and charming*" with clients, **Nick Eastwell** (see p.133) heads the Eastern European practice. An "*impressive all-round capital markets lawyer,*" he advised Robert Fleming and Nomura as global co-ordinators of the $70 million international equity offering of shares and global depository receipts by Turkish bank TEB. Clients appreciate **Stephen Edlmann** (see p.133); "*you can have absolute confidence that you are getting the best advice.*" He "*can advise at all levels without using jargon*" and "*has as much international experience as anyone in the business.*" "*Technically excellent*" **Jane Brown** (see p.132) specialises in international finance. "*Well respected*" on the debt side, **Keith Thomson** (see p.135) advised ABN AMRO Rothschild in a $150 million international equity offering by Turkish company Vestel Electronics, one of the largest manufacturers in Europe. "*Low key*" **Charles Clark** (see p.132) has "*an excellent reputation*" in structured products work. Formerly posted in the firm's Moscow office, **Simon Ovenden** (see p.134) "*works terribly hard.*" He advised on the $1 billion floating notes issue by Standard International Holdings. "*Proactive and accessible*" **Nigel Pridmore** (see p.134) is valued for his "*decision-making power and quick response.*" Other highlights for the group include acting for Zen Research on its global offer of shares, LSE listing and Rule 144A placement in the US, and advising lastminute.com on the US and UK aspects of its IPO. **Clients:** Barclays Capital; BNP-Paribas; JP Morgan Chase; CSFB; Lehman Brothers; Merrill Lynch; Nomura; UBS Warburg.

Clifford Chance (see firm details p.919) "*Marvellous in London and extremely strong on debt,*" the team is famed throughout the market for its "*huge*" capacity to undertake high volume MTN programmes and bulk Eurobonds. Clients comment that "*the team tends to mould precedent into form.*" Some also believe that the group is "*more rounded overall*" than its competitors, pointing to worldwide "*pockets of quality,*" most notably in the emerging markets. Continued growth in London's US securities law practice has resulted in completion of deals such as Gemini Genomics' US IPO (value $80 million) and the team's appointment as International Power's main corporate advisor, recently acting on a £250 million US placement of a convertible bond. A focus on domestic and European equity transactions and high yield bonds has seen the team completing deals such as Thomson Directories in the UK, Clondalkin Industries in Ireland and Concordia Bus in Sweden. Head of the practice, the "*genial*" **David Dunnigan** (see p.133) combines technical skill with managerial control; "*he can find the right guy for you.*" "*Leading*" specialist in debt financing and project bond work **David Bickerton** (see p.132) advised HSBC Holdings on its $3.2 billion equivalent multi-currency capital financing. He also advised the Nationwide Building Society on its $2 billion MTN programme establishment and its first drawdown of $750 million. "*Politic and sensible*" **David Eatough** (see p.133) acted for Goldman Sachs and Merrill Lynch on their commitment to place or purchase £1.4 billion tier 1 capital issues in RBS Group in the event that its bid for NatWest was successful. Clients "*hear good things*" about transactional lawyer **Stuart Dunlop** (see p.132), while "*diligent*" **Robert MacVicar** (see p.401) covers a range of work, including conduits, Nordic exchangeables and synthetic products. Focusing on hybrid capability and innovative financings, "*proficient*" **Tim Morris** (see p.134) acted for Lehman Brothers, Merrill Lynch International and Mediobanca in connection with the €2.5 billion issue by Technost International. A firm wide team of European and US lawyers advised the European Aeronautic Defence & Space Company on its simultaneous offering on three European exchanges. Other work includes advising the Government of Norway on the privatisation of Telenor ($1.7 billion). **Clients:** Bank of New York; BNP Paribas; Barclays Capital; CableEuropa; CSFB; Deutsche Bank; GE Capital Europe; Goldman Sachs International; HSBC Markets; JP Morgan Chase; Morgan Stanley Dean Witter.

Freshfields Bruckhaus Deringer (see firm details p.964) "*Coming up in the league,*" the firm is applauded by clients for "*always doing its best*" for them, and has a "*steadily increasing*" profile. Handled by partners within the corporate securities group, this "*quality*" practice benefits from strong links with key US investment banks and leverages successfully off the firm's first-rate corporate finance practice. The group boasts impressive capability in complex cross-border deals, backed by its integrated US securities capability and "*clear strength*" in securities work across 20 of the firm's 30 offices. The team was involved in 24 London flotations and other equity offerings last year. Major highlights include the IPO handled for Orange, one of the largest multi-jurisdictional European offerings, involving the firm's French, German and Italian teams. It also acted on the flotations of Granada Media (€2.462 million) and Arc International (€295 million), advised P&O on the £6 billion demerger of the Princess Cruises business, and recently completed the BT demerger (£20 billion). "*Switched on*" **Jeremy Pitkin** (see p.134) is a "*gentle and unassuming*" character and an "*experienced*" debt practitioner. He advised Rolls Royce on its £600 million MTN, and acted for the Lebanese Republic on its exchange offer of bonds. Other debt highlights for the team include advising Goldman Sachs on Allianz's exchangeable issue, and advising the joint lead managing banks on the Hellenic Republic's €3 billion notes issue. **Clients:** Warburg; Merrill Lynch; Morgan Stanley; Goldman Sachs; Pearson; Prudential; Royal Bank of Scotland.

Slaughter and May (see firm details p.1135) A "*can-do, analytical, creative style*" is the key feature of the team, which maintains a high profile in the Tier 1 arena. Examples of this work include issues of Tier 1 preference shares for the Standard Chartered Group ($1 billion and £300 million) and Abbey National (£300 million). "*Not wedded to precedent,*" the group bring "*extremely high levels of technical expertise*" into play when representing its exceptional corporate client base on matters such as complex bond issues, debenture stocks, tax-driven structures, exchangeables, convertibles and large-scale domestic floats. "*Gentlemanly and thoughtful*" **David Frank** (see p.133) "*covers all bases.*" He advised Technost on €2.5 billion exchangeables to shares of Telecom Italia, the largest ever convertible in Italy, and acted for Foster's Securities Corporation on $400 million exchangeable bonds guaranteed by Foster's Brewing Group.The team's moderate profile in international equity offerings is belied by its recent enviable transaction list. This includes Egg's international public offering, Vivendi Environnement's €2.5 billion flotation, and Cap Gemini's €1.9 billion international equity offering, the latter of which involved a public offering in France, a private placing with institutional investors outside France and a 144A in the US. Further highlights include MTR's global offering in Hong Kong and Regus' international public offering. **Clients:** Egg; Cap Gemini; Vivendi Environnement; AES Drax Holdings; Bradford & Bingley; Paragon; Abbey National.

Baker & McKenzie (see firm details p.868) Said by market sources to be "*specialists*" in the Eastern European region, the firm's equity-based emerging markets work is its central focus. The team's expertise has brought it into every telecom offering in this field, including Telecom Egypt's IPO and the prospective IPO of Croatia Telecom as the government's advisors, in addition to those in Lithuania, Poland and Hungary. Peter Magyar leads a "*flexible, commercial*" team that represented Numico on its €1.12 billion bonds and shares offering. The team also advised CA IB Investmentbank, Lehman Brothers and Dresdner Kleinwort Benson on the dual-listed international offerings by Polish oil company PK Orlen ($509 million) and Lithuania Telecom ($170 million). A major recent highlight was the firm's involvement in two billion-dollar UK IPOs led by investment banks Goldman Sachs, UBS Warburg and CSFB, a transaction which marks the first fruit of the team's endeavours to break into the UK IPO market at the top level. **Clients:** CSFB; Lehman Brothers; Dresdner Kleinwort Benson; Schroder Salomon Smith Barney.

Cleary, Gottlieb, Steen & Hamilton (see firm details p.918) Ashar Qureshi leads a "*commercial*" team with a "*great bench of smart securities partners,*" typically acting as issuers' counsel on high yield debt transactions. Key examples of recent work include acting for Deutsche Telekom on its $14.6 billion debut multi-currency global bond issue and acting as US counsel to Neste Chemicals International in its high yield debt offering worth €240 million. The group also represented the underwriters in connection with British Telecom's $10 billion multi-tranche note offering. A primarily US law-driven practice offers integrated international and US expertise in global equity offerings. London is often seen as the hub for the firm's global network on transactions such as representing Goldman Sachs on Egg's IPO and Autonomy Corporation's $336 million global shares offering. The team also advised Schroder Salomon Smith Barney, Chase Manhattan and Dresdner Kleinwort Benson on Billiton's £650 million share offering. **Clients:** Goldman Sachs; Schroder Salomon Smith Barney; Deutsche Telekom; Cable & Wireless; Morgan Stanley Dean Witter.

Shearman & Sterling (see firm details p.1125) Adrian Knight leads an "*international*" US/UK integrated team, whose reputation, claim competitors, resides in structured products and high yield senior debt work. The firm's established links with blue-chip investment banking clients ensure a steady stream of work. Last year, the team handled around a quarter of the 36 LPOs above $100 million in the London market. In UK equity capital markets work, the US/UK teams have jointly advised Morgan Stanley on the RyanAir rights issue, and Alsthom on Alcatel and Marconi's remaining shareholdings in Alsthom. Transactional highlights include acting as US and UK counsel to Novartis on Syngenta's global offering, and advising on the BT/Esat $2.5 billion US/Irish offer. The team acted for UBS Warburg on the placing of Matalan shares with institutional investors in Europe and the US. **Clients:** Merrill Lynch; Morgan Stanley; UBS Warburg.

Simmons & Simmons (see firm details p.1132) "*Performing extremely well,*" the team has yet to "*crank out international offerings*" at the pace of the market leaders, but remains rated by the market for its specialisms in structured finance, structured securities and derivative products. It is the client's choice for "*specialised, bespoke*" transactions. Ian Sideris leads the team, which this year was involved in the Vintage CBO for Bank of America, and established a Jersey multi-issue vehicle for Lehman Brothers as arrangers of the Quartz fund of funds. The firm also advised Deutsche Bank on the issue of a CBO under an SPV established in Ireland. The debt practice covers bond and high-yield debt issues, convertibles and MTN and ECP programmes. Highlights in this field include a $1 billion convertible bond issued by Pacific Century CyberWorks, part of the company's landmark merger with Cable & Wireless HKT. The firm also advised on Wal-Mart's £500 million notes issue, and acted for the Spanish government on the privatisation of Iberia, the Spanish national airline. **Clients:** Deutsche Bank AG London; UBS Warburg; Barclays Capital; Bank of America; CSFB.

Weil, Gotshal & Manges (see firm details p.1177) Following the departure of the UK team headed by Erica Handling to Ashurst Morris Crisp, equity-based transactions are now handled by an UK team headed by Paul Claydon from within the corporate department. A team headed by four US partners handles debt work with a primary focus on high yield, investment grade bond offerings, equity offerings and private placements. Clients are primarily UK and other European issuers. "*Working well in tandem*" with its Polish office, say knowledgeable sources, the team enjoys a good reputation in Eastern European equity capital markets, and advised on the privatisation and London listing of a Polish insurance company. Recent highlights include Pirelli's sale of shares in Cisco Systems through a £1 billion SEC registered offering and Telewest's £544 million high yield offering and £345 million convertible debt offering. The group also advised on Nomura's £45 million placement of Medisys shares and Enitel ASA's €250 million of high yield offering. **Clients:** Telewest; Hanson; Netia; United Biscuits; Premier International Foods; Yell Finance; Petroplus; Enitel.

Ashurst Morris Crisp (see firm details p.866) "*Good individuals,*" mostly seen on mid-cap domestic equity offerings and MTN programmes. The capital markets practice comprises European high yield, project bonds and plain vanilla products for corporate clients. Richard Kendall leads an "*impressive*" team that is widely expected to benefit from the addition of Weil Gotshal's key structured finance specialists. The team's major highlights include high yield note issues for Atlantic Telecom and Salter Weigh Tronix. For the project companies in bond financings, the firm advised on two major PFI deals (GCHQ at £450 million and HM Treasury Building, value £128 million). An issuer led practice, it leverages off the firm's strengths in corporate and private equity, advising issuers on equity-linked and straight eurobonds. A key transaction in this area was Swiss Re's $1 billion debt issuance programme, listed on the Luxembourg stock exchange, arranged by JP Morgan Securities. **Clients:** Banco Banif Primus; Bankers Trustee; Skandia; Swiss Re; N M Rothschild; Eco–Bat; Clubhaus.

Herbert Smith (see firm details p.993) "*Hungry for business,*" this highly regarded team of "*bright, proactive*" partners is jointly led by Martina Asma and Dina Albagli. Centred on leading underwriters in its equity capital markets practice, the team has garnered recognition across the industry for its technology IPO work, the majority handled for CSFB, Deutsche Bank and Goldman Sachs. The group advised CSFB on equity issues by QXL totalling £1 billion to fund its acquisitions of auctioneers Bidlet and Ricardo. Further work includes acting for CSFB as sponsor on the £245 million IPO of an internet personal financial service, and advising Deutsche Bank on its joint open offer on behalf of Cambridge Antibody Technology Group. Deal volume on the debt side is lower, in line with the group's focus on high value innovative work. It advised on the Bank of Scotland's £400 million issue of innovative tier 1 securities, and acted for Goldman Sachs and DLJ in connection with the structured financing of AES Corporation's acquisition of the Drax Power Station from National Power. **Clients:** CSFB; Deutsche Bank; Lazard Capital Markets; Bank of Scotland; Goldman Sachs.

Lovells (see firm details p.1044) Although maintaining a comparatively low profile, the team, led by David Hudd, is best known in the market for domestic issuer work for clients such as Barclays and Slough Estates. Key areas of focus are high yield and emerging markets and structured complex bond transactions and exchangeables. Major equity transactions include advising Goldman Sachs on the Egg IPO (value £1.3 billion) and acting for Granada Media on its £7.7 billion IPO. The firm was also involved in the €6.5 billion privatisation of Deutsche Post. On the debt side, it advised on Barclays Bank Reserve Capital Instruments' hybrid tier 1 securities offer, and acted for Kappa Beheer on its SEC-registered exchange offer for high yield bonds. **Clients:** Granada; Barclays; Ford Credit; Suez des Eaux; Kappa Beheer; BRE International Finance; BNP Paribas; Agricole Indosuez; Dresdner Kleinwort Benson.

Norton Rose (see firm details p.1082) "*Making some strides*" since the departure of its debt practice head, Gilles Thieffry, the group is now led by the head of the International Securities Group, Jonathan Walsh. Sources confirm that the team has retained its strong reputation in domestic securitisations, advising on the EBRD's issue of 26 notes under its Euro MTN Programme, and assisting Lehman Brothers and a syndicate of banks on the placement of a €100 million quasi-capital issue for French reinsurance company SCOR. Equity work is handled by the corporate department, accounting for the practice's profile in volume equity transactions. Boasting capability in dual UK/US law and locally, across its European office network, the firm also has strength in emerging markets. The team was one of the first to advise on a Russian GDR. It also advised easyJet on its high profile initial offering that involved a London listing and a global offering, including a Rule 144A placing in the US. Other highlights include advising JP Morgan on the initial global offering of Intertainment AG, a pan-European media company and advising HSBC Investment Bank on the £326 million flotation of Collins Stewart Holdings. **Clients:** Lehman Brothers International (Europe); Bank of Ireland; HSBC Holdings; HSBC Investment Bank; EBRD; TXU; AXA; easyJet; DLJ Securities; JP Morgan.

LONDON

SECURITISATION & REPACKAGING

Allen & Overy (see firm details p.856) Widely esteemed for its "*high profile transactions and quality of work,*" the firm is envied by peers for its ability to "*scoop major deals*" such as Madame Tussauds, Broadgate, Holmes and Mound. The group's domestic presence dominates its profile to the extent that its European coverage has a lower recognition factor. Pre-eminent in its work for ISDA, the team is known for its expertise in whole business, real estate and term securitisations, and has "*excellent understanding of the asset classes and related issues.*" "*Technically excellent,*" its lawyers are "*professional, always a pleasure to deal with.*" Clients comment "*they care so much about getting it right,*" approving the low turnover of associates, who successfully "*become a part of this mentality.*" **David Krischer** (see p.134) is a "*fantastic*" presence on creative, innovative deals. "*Not cuddly to deal with, but bloody bright,*" he is "*cool, calm and fun to work with.*" He acted for Deutsche Bank on the £610 million securitisation of the rental income generated by the 283 retail units in the Manchester Trafford Centre. "*Reserved, intelligent*" **Paul Bedford** (see p.132) has a "*quiet, consensual*" style that renders him an "*absolute pleasure to deal with.*" Repackaging expert **Geoff Fuller**'s (see p.133) profile in the field is increasing, following his copious work in building up the structured vehicle and investment practice. Clients report of his "*great analytical brain*" that "*he's the sort of lawyer an investment bank would want to employ.*" "*Larger than life*" **Julian Tucker** (see p.135) receives client recognition for his expertise in UK property-based transactions. He advised on the £975 million innovative lease rental securitisation for Canary Wharf. So flamboyant that he is "*something of an acquired taste,*" he is appreciated by others for his "*boundless energy and enormous enthusiasm.*" New partner **Angela Clist** (see p.132) has led on several deals for Schroder Salomon Smith Barney. Her highlights include the Holmes I-IV securitisations (over £7 billion in aggregate) as part of Abbey National's mortgage portfolio, the largest and first SEC-registered European mortgage-backed securitisation, and the Mound I and II deals, involving first use of master trusts for UK residential mortgages.

Clifford Chance (see firm details p.919) "*Size is on their side; they also have the longest deal list.*" Clients testify that "*with the 'A' Team, you're quids in – they are the best of the best.*" However, some have expressed concern that "*it can be difficult to get partner attention.*" With an undisputed global presence, clients agree it "*has the advantage of large overseas teams within a clearly defined securities field.*" This year has seen resource investment in the growing Italian market and improved capability in Germany. In cross-disciplinary matters, clients endorse its inter-departmental strengths, such as in US tax-related matters and 144A regulations. Possessors of a "*strong track record*" in whole business, real estate, CP conduits, master trust and structured credit card derivatives, the group is "*solid across the range of asset types.*" It has handled property financings for Sainsbury's including the Highbury Finance (secured bonds issue of £335.5 million) and the Dragon Finance floating rates notes, totalling over £200 million. Other highlights include the first securitisation of UK government receivables (lease payments) of military aircraft, acting for JP Morgan Securities and C17 Leading Company, and credit card securitisations for RBS, Arran 1 ($1.6 billion) and 2 ($700 million). The "*down to earth, consensus-driven*" team is headed by "*technically strong*" **Chris Oakley** (see p.134). His predecessor, former co-head with the legendary Robert Pillaci, **John Woodhall** (see p.136)("*extremely experienced*") now heads the international group. He is a "*great transactional lawyer,*" whom peers count "*among the top group of advisors.*" Voted by clients "*the best in London for master trust structures,*" **Kevin Ingram** (see p.134) has the potential to "*stand astride the whole market.*" His "*strong intellect and commercial approach*" is judged to "*go down well with clients,*" although some have noted his "*massive workload.*" Property finance specialist **Andrew Forryan** (see p.133) is "*a studious lawyer*"

CAPITAL MARKETS: SECURITISATION & REPACKAGING • London	Ptnrs	Assts
1 Allen & Overy	40*	149*
Clifford Chance	26	40
2 Freshfields Bruckhaus Deringer	5	60
Linklaters	12	28
3 Sidley Austin Brown & Wood	20	44
Simmons & Simmons	13	28
Slaughter and May	16	40
Weil, Gotshal & Manges	2	7
4 Ashurst Morris Crisp	4	8
Lovells	4	20
Norton Rose	5	14

LEADING INDIVIDUALS

★ **KRISCHER David** Allen & Overy

1 **INGRAM Kevin** Clifford Chance; **TROTT David** Freshfields Bruckhaus

2 **BEDFORD Paul** Allen & Overy; **MACKENZIE Marcus** Freshfields Bruckhaus Deringer; **OAKLEY Chris** Clifford Chance

3 **BRESSLAW James** Simmons & Simmons; **FORRYAN Andrew** Clifford Chance; **FULLER Geoff** Allen & Overy; **HANDLING Erica** Ashurst Morris Crisp; **HUGHES Richard** Linklaters; **KELLY Jacky** Weil, Gotshal & Manges; **PENN Graham** Sidley Austin Brown & Wood; **RAINES Marke** Shearman & Sterling; **SMITH Christopher** Slaughter and May; **SMITH Sarah** Sidley Austin Brown & Wood; **TUCKER Julian** Allen & Overy; **VOISEY Peter** Clifford Chance; **WOODHALL John** Clifford Chance

4 **HUDD David** Lovells; **RICE Jim** Linklaters; **RUSSELL John** Sidley Austin Brown & Wood; **VOISIN Michael** Linklaters; **WALKER John** Milbank, Tweed, Hadley & McCloy; **WALSH Jonathan** Norton Rose

UP AND COMING

CLIST Angela Allen & Overy

ONES TO WATCH

AXFORD Stuart Freshfields Bruckhaus Deringer; **LAMBIE Christian** Allen & Overy; **McKEAND James** Freshfields Bruckhaus Deringer

This book is the product of 6,552 1/2-hour interviews. See p.7 for BMRB audit.

Within each band, firms are listed alphabetically. *See individuals' profiles p.132*

**Figures denote total capital markets team sizes.*

who "*knows how to make a point.*" **Peter Voisey** (see p.135) "*talks a good story and gets results*" on mainstream UK consumer asset work such as mortgages and auto loans.The group advised ABN AMRO on the Amstel Corporate Loan offerings (combined value €8.5 billion), an innovative securitisation of Dutch corporate loans through a credit default swap structure.

Freshfields Bruckhaus Deringer (see firm details p.964) "*Consistently excellent, about as good as it gets,*" the firm's lawyers are said by clients to be "*of exceptionally high quality.*" The group's intrinsic strength is felt to lie in its "*serious, technical approach*" and "*proficiently managed resources,*" resulting in high levels of partner attention and "*superb documentation.*" Competitors acknowledge the Structured Finance Group's successful strategy in dedicating resource to support the firm's M&A work. The group has such "*tremendous strength*" that it can "*cherry-pick*" work, eschewing plain vanilla work beyond established client relationships. Securitisations and derivatives work are handled on a fully integrated basis, together with specialist support in tax, real estate and regulatory issues.Successful development of the firm's pan-European network has won widespread market approval. It advised on the CIBC World Markets deal, where teams from London, Milan, Paris, Madrid, Brussels and Amsterdam advised the financiers of a €350 million CP/conduit/bank financing for AAE, Europe's largest freight railcar fleet operator, a deal embracing 24 jurisdictions.Top-rated department head Ian Falconer has exchanged posts with his respected counterpart from the Paris office, Anthony Besse. Clients appreciate "*intelligent, energetic*" **David Trott** (see p.135) for his "*tactical commercial style*" and "*thorough commitment to deals.*" He has completed a series of demanding cross-border conduit transactions, including AAE and Craegmoor. "*Smart deal-doer*" **Marcus Mackenzie** (see p.134) advised Citibank as the arranger in Punch Funding II's £1.5 billion pub-backed securitisation, the largest of its type in the business sector to date, and on the establishment of the Siemens €10 billion programme. Other highlights from the firm's recent caseload include advising Glencore International on its Albis $1.2 billion securitisation of commodity trading receivables, located in 42 jurisdictions, the largest public market funding of this type in Europe.

Linklaters (see firm details p.1042) Clients believe that the firm is now "*nipping at the heels*" of the top three in the field. This relatively recent entrant to the market is said to "*put out a good product.*" Clients "*feel valued,*" opining that the firm's "*excellent infrastructure*" and "*great attitude, where everyone pitches in and nothing is too much trouble,*" puts it in a sound position to break into more sophisticated structuring work. Leveraging successfully off key contacts in debt and equity capital markets, the team has strengths in property-based transactions (non-conforming mortgage sector securitisations), repackaging and credit card receivables, handled within the full spectrum of structured finance. Completing over 350 repackaging deals for its top three structured and derivative clients alone, the team has consolidated its niche strengths in investment fund and convertible bond repackagings, credit-linked notes and warrants. "*Urbane*" **Richard Hughes** (see p.133) is "*tough to beat; he has such an effervescent personality.*" According to clients, "*he knows how to make things happen.*" Clients describe former Hong Kong-based **Michael Voisin** (see p.135) as "*smart and highly approachable.*" Key relationship partner for Goldman Sachs, he is "*skilled*" in structured finance. Peers rate **Jim Rice** (see p.135) as "*a real doer – he rolls his sleeves up and gets stuck in – a delight to deal with,*" while clients report that he "*makes things run sensibly.*" The firm acted for JP Morgan on Granite Mortgages and Northern Rock's securitisations of 2000 (Residential Mortgages Securities 7 and 8). It also advised AMBAC Assurance UK on its £630 million guarantee in the £1.48 billion asset-backed securitisation of the Punch Group, the first monoline insurance guarantee of a whole business securitisation.

Sidley Austin Brown & Wood (see firm details p.1130) The merger (May 2001) draws together the structured finance expertise of Sidley & Austin ("*a name you hear constantly in the market*") with the US backed repackaging practice of "*capital markets boutique*" Brown & Wood. Seen "*doing complex deals,*" the team's impressive clientele includes Morgan Stanley and JP Morgan. The market appears undecided on whether the merger will counter the team's perceived lack of resource in supporting areas such as tax, and the loss of Jane Borrows to Herbert Smith and Robert Plehn to ING Barings. However, the team covers the gamut of securitisation work, with niche strengths in inter-linking areas of commercial mortgage-backed deals, conduits and synthetic transactions. "*Incisive on treatment of bank capital,*" **Graham Penn** (see p.134) "*wears his academic background lightly;*" and has "*seen enough deals to know his onions.*" Clients describe him as "*extremely competent, responsive and creative.*" Known as the Fitch Rating Agency's advisor, **Sarah Smith** (see p.135) has a "*glowing reputation*" with clients, who find her to be "*constructive, helpful and commercial.*" Structured securities lawyer **John Russell** (see p.135) is also highly rated for his varied experience in the sector. The group acted for Morgan Stanley on the third and fourth European Loan Conduits, commercial mortgaged-backed securitisations involving floating rate notes (valued at £254 million and over £462 million respectively), structured under Rule 144A. Further highlights include acting for Barclays Capital in Interstar Millennium's $465 million cross-border mortgage-backed securities debut.

Simmons & Simmons (see firm details p.1132) Winning instructions on some "*interesting securitisations projects,*" the firm handles the key areas of structured finance and securities, alongside derivatives products work. The Financial Markets Group is appreciated by clients for its "*broad knowledge and cross-fertilisation with synthetic securities.*" Envied by rivals for its "*strong client base,*" the firm numbers corporates such as British Land and investment banks such as Deutsche Bank and UBS Warburg on the roster. **James Bresslaw** (see p.132) is "*not afraid to do his share of the heavy lifting.*" Clients like him because he "*makes himself available and produces the goods.*" He completed Paragon Mortgages No. 2, and acted for Barclay Capital as lead manager on Prospect 6, securitising £240 million of personal loans originated by HFC Bank. The team also advised ING Barings on the £300 million securitisation of Shipshape Residential Mortgages No. 1 by Bristol & West, and acted for Dresdner Kleinwort Benson on the €150 million G7 Payment Rights securitisation.

Slaughter and May (see firm details p.1135) A "*discrete, niche practice*" acknowledged by competitors for handling some "*chunky securitisations.*" It is seen to employ a multi-specialist approach to "*stylise the work for clients,*" who include a list of corporate originators and investment banks "*to die for.*" In the course of advising on the Holmes Funding Nos. 3 and 4 mortgage securitisations for key client Abbey National, the team pioneered trust structures to assist with repeat issuance. Peers rate **Christopher Smith** (see p.135) as "*methodical*" and "*extremely talented.*" The team advised Paragon Finance on a mixed asset (car finance and residential mortgage) securitisation, acting for Bradford & Bingley on its £1 billion buy-to-let mortgage portfolio, and advised Punch Group on a £1.484 billion acquisition refinancing securitisation, one of the largest ever made in sterling. Internationally it advised Skandinaviska Enskilda Banken on a €1 billion residential mortgage portfolio securitisation, and represented Thorn on the securitisation of rental agreements by its subsidiaries in Norway, Sweden and Denmark.

Weil, Gotshal & Manges (see firm details p.1177) An "*impressive, credible*" practice that "*does a great job*" according to clients on structured aspects, and has created a "*successful*" niche in synthetic securitisations and acquisition finance-related transactions. The firm has been hit by the loss of its CBO/CDO team to Ashurst Morris Crisp, and the market awaits the impact of this on the practice's overall profile. Now "*running the practice with a rod of iron,*" **Jacky Kelly** (see p.134) has strong banking contacts and "*a great rapport with clients.*" Key pieces of work this year include advising Merrill Lynch on the £385 million Monument transactions, and acting for Chase and Barclays on a $300 million cross-border receivables financing, part of the $1.2 billion financing by Schroders for the acquisition of VEBA Electronics. The firm was also instructed by the Royal Bank of Scotland and Barclays on the securitisation of music royalties by Chrysalis Music across the UK, US, Germany, Sweden and the Netherlands.

Ashurst Morris Crisp (see firm details p.866) A corporate-based practice, whose hitherto low profile is widely expected to blossom following the addition of "*constructive*" **Erica Handling** (see p.133) and her team from Weil, Gotshal & Manges. She brings with her a "*professional*" reputation in synthetic securitisations, and joins forces with the firm's established CDO/CLO practice. The team is also moving into whole business work, leveraging off the firm's core private equity practice. Key matters include instructions from Immediate Capital Group on the Euro credit CDO1, BV issue of €416 million asset-backed notes, the first Euro-denominated high-yield CDO transaction closed in the Euro Markets. The firm also acted for JZ Private Equity on its $169 million multi-tranche notes secured on a portfolio of bank loans, and advised NIB Capital on the US Power Projects IBV.

Lovells (see firm details p.1044) "*Active*" practice that "*does a good job*" from the secure foundation of its corporate client base. Its "*band of expertise*" encompasses real estate ("*they do a nice line in property-backed deals*"), CBOs and auto loan deals. **David Hudd** (see p.133) is credited.by competitors for "*building up the practice*" in the wake of the departure of Peter Voisey. He advised on an innovative £650 million whole business securitisation for RHM, the leading UK food group, and was instructed on a €85 million CDO by BNP-Paribas. The team advised Globaldrive (UK) and Ford Credit on the latter's third securitisation, and advised ALSTOM as originator in the securitisation of future receivables for Cruise Ship Finance.

Norton Rose (see firm details p.1082) "*Building a presence,*" the firm has "*won some good work*" within its niche in asset-backed conduit and contract work. "*Talented*" **Jonathan Walsh** (see p.136) brings valuable in-house expertise to the practice. Key matters for the firm include acting for Bristol & West on its first synthetic securitisation of £300 million buy-to-let mortgages, and in the £300 million mortgaged-backed securities issued by Shipshape Residential Mortgages, the first residential mortgage transaction of this type. The team also acted for HSBC/Regency on its asset-backed CP conduit, the first securitisation of £100 million UK mail order receiveables.

Other Notable Practitioners: "*Clever*" **Marke Raines** (see p.134) (formerly of Allen & Overy) is thought of by industry sources as "*a great acquisition*" for **Shearman & Sterling**. A "*talented*" individual, he handles mainly cross-border US-based deals, involving financial assets such as swaps and loans securitisations. According to clients, "*astute*" **John Walker** (see p.136) of **Milbank, Tweed, Hadley & McCloy** "*fosters an atmosphere of co-operation.*" The focus of his practice is on the project finance sector, CBO/CDO market, residential mortgages and public securitisations.

LONDON

DERIVATIVES

Allen & Overy (see firm details p.856) A "*class act,*" this "*pure*" derivatives group is felt by clients and competitors to have "*cornered the market*" in OTC derivatives work. Having successfully "*parlayed ISDA into the core of its practice,*" and now supported by ISDA specialist, Dan Cunningham in New York, the firm now has "*the inside track.*" Continuing to act as ISDA's European and South East Asian counsel, the group's European practice has expanded with the addition of derivatives experts to its Rome, Paris and Amsterdam offices. Clients appreciate that its "*excellent partners*" are "*supported by well-trained associates with expertise across the board.*" "*Big picture guy*" **Jeffrey Golden** enjoys a high industry profile from his work for ISDA. Clients claim he is "*a good diplomat and can marshal the right people for a transaction.*" He acted as an expert witness on behalf of Citigroup in a test case against Griffin. "*Responsive*" **David Benton** (see p.132) "*always has an answer for you; he gives practical advice because he understands where the banks are coming from.*" He is a "*master of ISDA concepts,*" and has been advising on several credit-linked note programmes. "*Colourful*" **Simon Haddock** (see p.133) is "*smart and well-versed*" in the field – he's "*seen it all.*" He led an international team advising Cygnifi Derivatives Services, an online derivatives services provider, in relation to Trinity, a new online service offering legal risk management for collateral. Endorsed for his OTC expertise, **Richard Tredgett** (see p.135) is a talented senior associate "*coming through the ranks.*" He led on two ISDA documentation projects, the EMU protocol in Greece and the 2000 ISDA definitions. The group has also worked with Lombard Risk Systems to develop e-commerce applications for risk management.

CAPITAL MARKETS: DERIVATIVES • London	Ptnrs	Assts
1 Allen & Overy	40*	149*
2 Clifford Chance	27	60
3 Freshfields Bruckhaus Deringer	5	32
Linklaters	11	35
4 Norton Rose	2	4
5 Baker & McKenzie	1	7
Slaughter and May	n/a	n/a

LEADING INDIVIDUALS	
1 **GOLDEN Jeffrey** Allen & Overy	**HENDERSON Schuyler** Norton Rose
MOTANI Habib Clifford Chance	
2 **BENTON David** Allen & Overy	**BROWN Claude** Clifford Chance
FIRTH Simon Linklaters	**HADDOCK Simon** Allen & Overy
WARNA-KULA-SURIYA Sanjev Slaughter and May	
3 **RUDIN Simeon** Freshfields Bruckhaus Deringer	
4 **BATES Chris** Clifford Chance	**BUSH Jane** Clifford Chance
UP AND COMING	
TREDGETT Richard Allen & Overy	

This book is the product of 6,552 1/2-hour interviews. See p.7 for BMRB audit.

Within each band, firms are listed alphabetically. *See individuals' profiles p.132*

**Figures denote total capital markets team sizes.*

TOP IN-HOUSE LAWYERS

Edmond CURTIN, Managing Director, *Credit Suisse First Boston International*

David GEEN, Executive Director and Senior Counsel, *Goldman Sachs*

David BLOOM, Senior Legal Adviser, *HSBC Holdings plc*

David LEWIS, Vice-President and Assistant General Counsel, *JPMorgan*

Joan Ma, Executive Director, *Morgan Stanley Dean Witter*

Jon ORMOND, Legal Adviser, *Deutsche Bank AG Ltd*

Charles ROSS-STEWART, Executive Director, *UBS Warburg*

Richard Atkinson received weighty recommendation while *"intelligent"* **Edmond Curtin** is regarded as an expert. In the field of credit derivatives, **David Geen** is *"experienced and friendly." "Extremely level headed,"* **David Lewis** is considered a *"star performer"* who possesses a *"wealth of experience." "Doing an excellent job,"* **Joan Ma** is widely respected as *"forthright and confident, always willing to challenge the status quo to improve processes."* Jon Ormond continues to build his good reputation. **Charles Ross-Stewart** has a *"good breadth of experience across a range of different derivatives"* and is *"focused on finding a solution."*

In-House lawyers profiles: p.1193

Clifford Chance (see firm details p.919) *"Expert in a wide range of products,"* the firm's range includes securities-based, credit and equity derivatives, e-commerce and documentation for ISDA. The team has combined resources with other specialists from within the firm's network, including key players in New York, Frankfurt and Hong Kong. Some clients comment that the partners appear *"in great demand,"* and that the team may need a deeper well of *"juniors who can run with things." "One of the first that clients call,"* **Habib Motani** (see p.134) runs the practice. *"A first-rate, versatile lawyer,"* he *"gets to see a lot of interesting transactions." "Hot on credit derivatives,"* **Claude Brown** uses his in-house experience to *"push deals through effectively."* Clients rave about the ability of **Jane Bush** (see p.132) to work with Motani as an *"impressive double act; they scoop up the ball so smoothly and provide a seamless service."* A leading OTC derivatives specialist, she is *"user-friendly and technically astute."* The respected **Chris Bates** (see p.401) is best known for his regulatory expertise.The team has handled the derivatives aspects of several key transactions, including the Chase acquisition of Fleming and the JP Morgan-Chase merger. It also advised on innovative synthetic CBOs, CLOs and structured credit derivatives, including Cygnus, Natix, Equinox Funding, and North Street I, II and III (Europe, New York and London).

Freshfields Bruckhaus Deringer (see firm details p.964) *"Excellent people who clearly know their stuff and have done some good deals,"* according to clients. The Structured Finance Group approaches derivatives as an integrated discipline within its transactional and securitisation work, *"intellectually difficult work which they do well."* It handles derivatives across a range of instruments ranging from trading (swaps, warrants and derivative-linked bonds), stock-lending, tax, insurance and capital arbitrage products. The team has been working on major CLO and other credit derivative based transactions for clients such as Citibank, Zurich Re and AIG FP.With a background in tax and securitisations, clients describe team leader **Simeon Rudin** (see p.135) as a *"bright, resourceful lateral thinker."* The team acted on a ground-breaking deal advising Citibank on a £900 million credit derivative transaction under which Prudential bought credit protection for a portfolio of residential mortgages. Further highlights include acting for the credit default swap provider in the Braveheart transaction, a £1 billion fully synthetic balance sheet securitisation by Royal Bank of Scotland.

Linklaters (see firm details p.1042) *"Extremely bright people."* Although the team has had a lower profile in the market than its competitors, it is thought to have the capability of pooling different parts of the firm to support its offering. *"Excellent"* on behalf of financial institutions, the team focuses on structured products, with niche strength in securitised derivatives and 'transformer' transactions, under which insurance companies write policies in lieu of entering into credit derivative transactions.The team has handled around 420 credit-linked note transactions over the past five years, as well as several synthetic CLOs and public CLOs, including the Bar CLO deal. Earlier in the year, the group launched Blue Flag Derivatives, an online data base advisory service relating to enforcement of derivatives transactions. *"First class lawyer"* **Simon Firth** (see p.133) is an *"excellent exponent of credit derivatives."* Clients describe him as *"highly intelligent"* and *"pleasant to deal with."* The group was instructed by Greenwich NatWest in the arrangement of a synthetic securitisation of Bristol & West's 'buy-to-let' residential mortgage portfolio, the first of its kind in the UK. It also acted for Brokertec in the establishment of an electronic inter-dealer broker system to facilitate transactions in bonds and futures, and advised the London Metal Exchange on its demutualisation.

Norton Rose (see firm details p.1082) Bolstered by the arrival of former Baker & McKenzie players, the firm has upped its profile with prospects appearing good for a resurgence. Boasting talented lawyers, the group has resources in supporting areas such as tax. Focused on its financial institution clients, the derivatives practice covers the full range of work, including transactional structures, enforcement of agreements, regulatory and tax issues, credit derivatives, and negotiation of standard (ISDA) and non-standard derivatives agreements. The industry respects *"SWAP veteran"* **Schuyler Henderson** (see p.133) for his impressive contribution. An *"awesome, brilliant lawyer,"* he has been at the forefront of the market for many years. Clients like to *"pick his brains"* because *"his analytical ability allows him to deal with the derivatives component in anything."* Enjoying *"fantastic product knowledge, he thinks around a matter for longer term application."* He has been advising financial institutions on various matters, including a €2.5 billion synthetic CDO offering, the synthetic securitisation of a £300 million innovative mortgage portfolio, and a series of regulatory-driven financings using SPVs.

Baker & McKenzie (see firm details p.868) A practice that has been *"a long time in the derivatives market,"* although it has a lower profile now that former head of practice Iona Levine has taken on a consultancy role. Capital markets lawyer Chris Hogan now spearheads work in this area. The team specialises in equity and credit derivatives, focusing on jurisdictions in which these products are newly developing. Clients include financial institutions and companies making strategic investments via derivatives. Key highlight this year was advising a major financial institution on entering into equity derivative transactions in a new market segment.

Slaughter and May (see firm details p.113) A "*respectable team, doing a good job on complex derivatives work.*" Although mostly handling the derivatives aspects of transactions within the context of structured finance, the team covers the spectrum from OTC derivatives, negotiating ISDA agreements for corporates, to ISDA master agreements, structured and credit-linked notes, credit and equity derivatives. "*Outstanding*" **Sanjev Warnakula-suriya** (see p.136) has a respected profile in litigation and has built "*a strong team.*" This year it received instructions from Enron on the Yosemite 2 transactions – an issue of Luxembourg notes backed by a series of credit, commodity and interest rate derivatives. The firm also advised on a synthetic securitisation by a UK bank of its portfolio of asset-backed securities using a credit default swap. The team acted on the High Court case Peregrine v Robinson, relating to the valuation and close-out mechanics of the 1992 ISDA Master Agreement.

LEADERS IN CAPITAL MARKETS

AXFORD, Stuart
Freshfields Bruckhaus Deringer, London (020) 7936 4000

BATES, Chris
Clifford Chance, London (020) 7600 1000
chris.bates@cliffordchance.com
See under Financial Services, p.401

BEDFORD, Paul
Allen & Overy, London (020) 7330 2881
paul.bedford@allenovery.com
Specialisation: Involved in securitisation since 1987 when the first rated UK residential mortgage-backed issue was completed. Advised on a large number of securitisations including issues for National Home Loans, Household Mortgage Corporation, NatWest, Sun Banking Corporation and CIBC (including their mortgage backed ECP programme); a number of Scandinavian issues including Fulmar, Osprey, St. Erik and Fennica; a securitisation rental income from an office block and the ALPS securitisation of aircraft leases for Porterbrook Leasing Company including their most recent securitisation to finance the purchase of new rolling stock. His clients have included originators, lead managers and trustees.
Career: Qualified *Allen & Overy* (1982); partner (1988).
Personal: Born 1956. Educated at Brighton College and Warwick University. Lives in Islington.

BENTON, David
Allen & Overy, London (020) 7330 3118
david.benton@allenovery.com
Specialisation: David has participated in ISDA documentation projects and was particularly involved in the development of the Bullion Definitions and the Credit Derivatives Definitions. He is a regular writer and speaker on the legal and documentation aspects of derivatives, including collateral, credit derivatives and the hedging aspects of structured financings.
Career: Articled *Allen & Overy* (1988); qualified (1990); partner (1997).
Publications: He is a regular writer and speaker on the legal and documentation aspects of derivatives, including collateral, credit derivatives and the hedging aspects of structured financings.
Personal: Born 1966. Educated Corpus Christi College, Cambridge.

BICKERTON, David
Clifford Chance, London (020) 7600 1000
david.bickerton@cliffordchance.com
Specialisation: Structured debt capital markets including: project bonds, acquisition finance, warrants and PFI/PPP. Recent transactions include: Glas Cymrn Bond Financing of acquisition of Welsh Water, Sutton and East Surrey Water Bonds, Nationwide Building Society PIBS Receipts, Hexham Hospital PFI/PPP and West Berkshire Hospital PFI/PPP.
Career: *Clifford Chance* 1987 to date. Seconded to Citibank (1992) and Bankers Trust (1993). Partner 1997.
Personal: Education: Downing College, Cambridge – MA. Family Details: three daughters.

BRESSLAW, James
Simmons & Simmons, London (020) 7628 2020
james.bresslaw@simmons-simmons.com
Specialisation: Securitisation and structured finance.
Prof. Memberships: Law Society.
Career: *Simmons & Simmons* 1984 to date.

BROWN, Claude
Clifford Chance, London (020) 7600 1000
claude.brown@cliffordchance.com

BROWN, Jane
Linklaters, London (020) 7456 4642
jane.brown@linklaters.com
Specialisation: Partner dealing with global securities, advises underwriters and issuers in connection with issues of debt, equity, derivative & structured products.
Career: Qualified 1986. Foreign lawyer programme, *Sullivan & Cromwell* 1986-87. Assistant solicitor *Linklaters* 1987-88 (New York). Assistant solicitor *Linklaters* 1988-92 (London). Partner *Linklaters* 1992-to date.

BURN, Lachlan
Linklaters, London (020) 7456 4614
lachlan.burn@linklaters.com
Specialisation: Specialises in banking and capital markets issues, with over 24 years' experience in the field. Typical matters handled include GDRs, convertible bonds and derivatives of all types.
Prof. Memberships: Legal advisor to the International Primary Market Association. External examiner to the University of London.
Career: Articled at *Linklaters* and qualified in 1976, becoming a partner in 1982. Seconded to the Paris office from 1982-87. Partner, international finance department.

BUSH, Jane
Clifford Chance, London (020) 7600 1000
jane.bush@cliffordchance.com
Specialisation: Derivatives, repackagings, structured finance.
Career: Joined *Clifford Chance* 1980. Qualified 1982. Partner 1988.

CANBY, Michael
Linklaters, London (020) 7456 4624
michael.canby@linklaters.com
Specialisation: Head of global securities group. Specialist in capital markets work advising on debt and equity financings, derivative products and documentation (having been involved for over nine years in the drafting of the various stages of industry standard documentation), and structured financings.
Career: Qualified 1980, seconded to New York 1982-84. Partner from 1986. Seconded to Paris 1988-95 (and managing partner of the Paris office 1992-95). Partner, international finance department and in charge of the securities group, 1995 to present.

CLARK, Charles
Linklaters, London (020) 7456 4630
charles.clark@linklaters.com
Specialisation: Extensive experience of international securities issues and derivatives transactions.
Career: 1989 to date, partner *Linklaters* in International Finance Department; 1986-89 assistant solicitor *Linklaters* London; 1983-86 assistant solicitor *Linklaters* Paris; 1982-83 assistant solicitor *Linklaters* London; 1980-82 trainee solicitor *Linklaters.*

CLIST, Angela H
Allen & Overy, London (020) 7330 2437
angela.clist@allenovery.com
Specialisation: Recent experience includes acting for Schroder Saloman Smith Barney on the award-winning Holmes Financing I & II transactions and the Mound Financing I & II. She also led the team on the recent Welsh Water securitisation acting for Western Power Limited. Other experience includes the €225m cross-border rolling stock securitisation for AAE, the £210m whole business securitisation for Rondchef and the £100m whole business securitisation for London City Airport.
Prof. Memberships: Registered Foreign Lawyers, English Law Society 2000.
Career: Solicitor in New Zealand before joining *Allen & Overy.*
Personal: Born 1967.

DUNLOP, Stewart
Clifford Chance, London (020) 7600 1000
stewart.dunlop@cliffordchance.com
Specialisation: Advising arrangers/borrowers in connection with EMTN Programmes and bond issues by developed and emerging market borrowers; regulatory capital issues; structured notes and equity related issues.
Career: Articled, *Allen & Overy.* Qualified 1991. Partner, *Clifford Chance* May 2000.

DUNNIGAN, David
Clifford Chance, London (020) 7600 1000
david.dunnigan@cliffordchance.com
Specialisation: Partner in international capital markets group specialising in Debt and Equity Capital Markets transactions.
Career: Nottingham University (LLB 2.1) 1980-83. Articled *Turner Kenneth Brown*; qualified 1986; *Coward Chance/Clifford Chance*; partner *Clifford Chance* since 1992.
Personal: Born 1961; resides Highgate.

EASTWELL, Nick
Linklaters, London (020) 7456 4660
nick.eastwell@linklaters.com
Specialisation: Specialises in capital markets transactions including issues of debt, equity related-debt, equity and depositary receipts in international markets, with a particular emphasis on emerging markets (in 1999/2000 in particular in South Africa, Egypt, Croatia, Romania, and Turkey). Areas of practice include repackagings of bonds, funds and other financial assets, debt issuance programmes and derivatives.
Career: Trinity Hall, University of Cambridge, BA Law, MA Law. Westcliff High School. Managing partner of Central and Eastern Europe; partner in international finance department and global securities group. 1990 to date partner *Linklaters* London, international finance department; 1989-90 partner *Linklaters* Hong Kong in charge of the international finance department; 1986-89 assistant solicitor *Linklaters* Hong Kong head of international finance department; 1982-83 assistant solicitor *Linklaters* London, corporate and international finance departments. Managing partner of *Linklaters'* practice in Central and Eastern Europe.

EATOUGH, David
Clifford Chance, London (020) 7600 1000
david.eatough@cliffordchance.com
Specialisation: Debt and equity capital markets, including preference shares and regulatory capital, medium-term note programmes, eurobonds and structured issues. Financing of NatWest acquisition by RBS and subsequent share issues by new group.
Career: Oxford University. Called to the English Bar 1986; Solicitor 1993. Joined *Clifford Chance* 1992 from NatWest Capital Markets. Partner since 1997.
Personal: Married with three children, lives near Henley-on-Thames.

EDLMANN, Stephen
Linklaters, London (020) 7456 4512
stephen.edlmann@linklaters.com
Specialisation: Specialist for over 20 years in debt, equity and equity-related issues in the international markets advising both issuers and investment banks. Areas covered include bonds, medium-term note and commercial paper programmes, convertible and exchangeable bonds, share and GDR issues and associated listing and regulatory rules and regulations.
Career: Partner. International finance department. 1973-76 Trinity Hall, Cambridge, Open Exhibitioner, MA Law. Member of Executive Committee and International Board of *Linklaters & Alliance* since formation. 1995 to date heads of international finance department; 1985 to date partner *Linklaters*; 1979-85 assistant solicitor, *Linklaters* London and New York; 1977-79 articled clerk *Linklaters*.

FIRTH, Simon
Linklaters, London (020) 7456 3764
simon.firth@linklaters.com
Specialisation: Financial Markets Group, Corporate Department. Specialises in the structuring and documentation of derivatives products, the structuring of financial services businesses and the regulatory capital treatment of financial products. He was part of the team which developed Blue Flag® Confirms, the system which enables ISDA-based derivatives confirmations to be generated electronically.
Career: 1998 to date; Head of *Linklaters'* derivatives practice; 1996-98: Partner, *Linklaters* London, financial markets group; 1993-96: Assistant solicitor, *Linklaters* London, financial markets group; 1992-93: Assistant solicitor, *Linklaters* New York; 1990-92: Assistant solicitor, *Linklaters* London, corporate department.

FORRYAN, Andrew
Clifford Chance, London (020) 7600 1000
andrew.forryan@cliffordchance.com
Specialisation: Securitisation of UK and European real estate; residential and commercial mortgages; whole businesses; sports rights; consumer finance assets; and Italian law governed assets.
Career: Associate with: *Slaughter and May*; *Sidley & Austin*. Joined *Clifford Chance* as a partner in 1997.

FRANK, David
Slaughter and May, London (020) 7600 1200
david.frank@slaughterandmay.com
Specialisation: Extensive eurobond and international equity experience with issuers in the UK and around the world. Also handles corporate and banking work with a number of listed plc clients and is active in the venture capital and project financing areas.
Prof. Memberships: The Law Society; International Bar Association.
Career: Qualified 1979. Assistant Solicitor, *Slaughter and May*, 1979-86. Partner *Slaughter and May*, 1986. Head of Capital Markets, 1993. Practice partner 2001.
Personal: Born 29 April 1954. Educated Shrewsbury School 1967-72. University of Bristol 1973-76. Interests include cars and lawn tennis. Lives in Surrey.

FULLER, Geoff
Allen & Overy, London (020) 7330 2806
geoff.fuller@allenovery.com
Specialisation: Partner specialising in international and domestic capital markets matters, with particular experience in repackagings and other structured finance transactions, debenture stocks and advising corporate trustees. Head of *Allen & Overy's* repackaging group.
Prof. Memberships: Fellow, Society for Advanced Legal Studies.
Career: Articled *Allen & Overy*, qualified (1986), partner (1994).
Publications: Author 'Corporate Borrowing, Law and Practice', (1st edition 1995, 2nd edition 1999). Contributor to 'Gore Browne on Companies.'
Personal: Educated Borden Grammar School and Mansfield College, Oxford (1983 MA).

GOLDEN, Jeffrey
Allen & Overy, London
(020) 7330 3000

HADDOCK, Simon A
Allen & Overy, London (020) 7330 2887
simon.haddock@allenovery.com
Specialisation: Over 15 years' experience of international capital markets. He was a founder member of the firm's derivative products group in London prior to spending five years in Hong Kong. Since returning to London in the summer of 1997, he has concentrated on developing the firm's structured products expertise and has been extensively involved in the whole range of derivative products. He is a regular speaker at conferences and seminars on swaps, derivatives and international securities offerings.
Prof. Memberships: Law Society.
Career: Articled *Allen & Overy*, qualified England and Wales 1986, Hong Kong 1992, assistant solicitor 1986-92, partner 1992, Hong Kong office (1992-97). London office since 1997.
Personal: Leeds University (1982 LLB). Born 1960. Resides in the UK.

HANDLING, Erica
Ashurst Morris Crisp, London (020) 7859 2485
erica.handling@ashursts.com
Specialisation: International finance partner with experience of a wide range of international financing transactions from syndicated loans to the raising of capital in the international debt and equity markets. She has particular experience of cross-border leveraged acquisitions and structured finance transactions. She has been involved in advising in connection with a variety of structured notes issues and programmes, collateralised bond and debt obligations and derivative instruments.

HENDERSON, Schuyler
Norton Rose, London (020) 7283 6000
hendersonsk@nortonrose.com
Specialisation: Practice covers the full range of lending, credit enhancement and securities transactions. Since moving to London in 1977, he has worked closely with many international financial institutions in creating, developing and documenting swaps and related derivatives, structured finance products and derivatives-driven financings, and advising with respect to enforcement, regulatory, tax and capacity issues.
Career: Obtained his undergraduate degree (BA) from Princeton University in 1967 and his law degree (JD) and business degree (MBA) from the University of Chicago in 1971 and is a member of the New York and Illinois bars.

HUDD, David
Lovells, London (020) 7296 2000
david.hudd@lovells.com
Specialisation: Head of *Lovells'* capital markets and securitisation practice. Extensive experience of securitisations and repackagings, debt issues (including high yield bonds), international equity and equity-linked offerings and derivatives.
Prof. Memberships: The City of London Solicitors' Company, The Law Society.
Career: Christ Church, Oxford University 1977-80 (MA Jurisprudence). Qualified 1983. *Linklaters* 1981-85; Paribas 1985-90; Sanwa International 1990-93; Indosuez 1993-94; joined *Lovells* as a partner in 1994.

HUGHES, Richard
Linklaters, London (020) 7456 4508
richard.hughes@linklaters.com
Specialisation: Partner, securitisation, asset finance, syndicated loans and property finance.

Career: 1998 to date; Partner, *Linklaters*. 1995-98; Partner, *Herbert Smith*. Qualified 1987.

INGRAM, Kevin
Clifford Chance, London (020) 7600 1000
kevin.ingram@cliffordchance.com
Specialisation: Debt securitisation, principle finance, asset backed commercial paper conduits, structured repackagings, secured lending and similar types of structured finance transactions.
Career: Trainee and Assistant *Clifford Chance* 1989-98. Made Partner May 1998.
Personal: Educated St Cyres Comprehensive School, Penorth and University College, Oxford University (BA, BCL). Married with two children. Resides Surrey.

KELLY, Jacky
Weil, Gotshal & Manges, London (020) 7903 1000
Specialisation: Heads up the firm's securitisation practice in London. She has been closely involved in the UK securitisation market since its inception in the mid-eighties. Her securitisation experience spans a number of asset types, including residential and commercial mortgages, commercial property, trade receivables, chargecards, equipment leases, autoloans and leases, corporate loans, aerospace assets and intellectual property assets in Europe, Asia and the US. Jacky has advised a number of clients in connection with the establishment of rated asset backed conduits, structured investment vehicles and CDO's. She is also active in the principal finance market, most recently completing a deal in the transport and infrastructure sector.
Career: *Clifford Chance* 1986-96; *Weil, Gotshal & Manges* 1996 to date.

KRISCHER, David S
Allen & Overy, London (020) 7330 2885
david.krischer@allenovery.com
Specialisation: Partner and head of the Securitisation Group. All forms of securitisation and asset backed transactions in the UK and a variety of European jurisdictions. Has advised on a wide range of asset-backed transactions for banks and originators in the UK and across Europe, including Broadgate, Madame Tussauds, Canary Wharf, the married service housing, commercial and consumer loans, future assets and infrastructure projects. Also advised on the establishment of leading structured programmes.
Prof. Memberships: Law Society's City of London Solicitors' Company American Bar Association.
Career: Associate *Hoffman & Davis* Chicago, U.S.A. (1982-85). Associate *Allen & Overy* (1985-92), Partner (1992).
Personal: Born 1956. BA Oberlin College (1978); JD Northwestern University, (1982); BCL Oxford University, (1986).

LAMBIE, Christian
Allen & Overy, London (020) 7330 3000

MACKENZIE, Marcus
Freshfields Bruckhaus Deringer, London (020) 7936 4000
marcus.mackenzie@freshfields.com
Specialisation: Partner in finance department specialising in whole business and other asset securitisations and other capital markets/derivatives and banking transactions acting for investment banks, originators and issuers.
Prof. Memberships: Law Society
Career: 1988: Joined *Freshfields*. 1993: Worked in *Freshfields* New York office. 1994: Seconded to *Salomon Brothers International* in London. 1998: Joined partnership.
Personal: Educated at Bristol University and Guildford Law School. Speaks French, German and Spanish.

MACVICAR, Robert
Clifford Chance, London (020) 7600 1000
robert.macvicar@cliffordchance.com
Specialisation: Debt capital markets, including commercial paper, certificates of deposit, medium term notes and Eurobonds. Also does some bank lending and asset backed work. Particularly active in Nordic and German work.
Career: Qualified 1979, became a partner at *Clifford Chance* in 1988.
Personal: Educated at Rugby School and Keble College, Oxford. Interests include motorsport (Aston Martin Owners' Club and others). Married with three children.

McKEAND, James
Freshfields Bruckhaus Deringer, London (020) 7936 4000

MILLER, Stephen M
Allen & Overy, London (020) 7330 2815
millers@allenovery.com
Specialisation: Debt capital markets. Has had over a decade of experience advising issuers and underwriters on new issuance in the international debt capital market. Work has been roughly split 90% acting for managers and underwriters and 10% acting for issuers. Engaged in new issues for sovereigns, supernationals, governmental agencies and entities, industrial companies and financial institutions.
Prof. Memberships: Law Society.
Career: Qualified 1992. Partner 1998.
Personal: Durham University – graduated 1988.

MORRIS, Tim
Clifford Chance, London (020) 7600 1000
tim.morris@cliffordchance.com
Specialisation: Capital Markets.
Prof. Memberships: Law Society.
Career: 1986-91: *Linklaters & Paines*. 1991: *Clifford Chance*.
Personal: 1977 MA Brasenose College, Oxford University.

MOTANI, Habib
Clifford Chance, London (020) 7600 1000
habib.motani@cliffordchance.com
Specialisation: Partner specialising in derivatives, capital markets and financial markets.
Career: Partner *Clifford Chance* 1986.

OAKLEY, Chris
Clifford Chance, London (020) 7600 1000
chris.oakley@cliffordchance.com
Specialisation: Partner specialising in international asset securitisation, structured repackagings and all types of structured finance transactions.
Career: Redborne School, Ampthill, Beds; Worcester College, Oxford (BA Hons Jurisprudence). Articled *Coward Chance*; qualified 1983; partner *Clifford Chance* since 1990.
Personal: Theatre, opera, travel. Born 1956; resides London.

OVENDEN, Simon
Linklaters, London (020) 7456 2000
simon.ovenden@linklaters.com
Specialisation: International capital markets including issues of debt and equity securities in both UK domestic and international markets including Russia, India, South East Asia and the Middle East. Recent experience includes advising on international equity offerings and private placements, and advising on restructurings of loans and other debt obligations in Russia.
Career: 2000 to date: Partner, *Linklaters* London, international finance department; 1997-00: Partner, *Linklaters* Moscow; 1993-96: Assistant solicitor, *Linklaters* London; 1991-93; Assistant solicitor, *Linklaters* Hong Kong; 1987-91: Assistant solicitor, *Linklaters* London. 1986-87; College of Law, Law Society Finals; 1983-86: Cambridge University, Faculty of Law.

PENN, Graham
Sidley Austin Brown & Wood, London (020) 7360 3600
gpenn@sidley.com
Specialisation: Securitisation, structured finance, banking and bank regulation.
Career: Partner *Cameron Markley Hewitt* 1988-94. Partner *Sidley & Austin* 1994. Following merger of *Sidley & Austin* and *Brown & Wood* on 1 May 2001, partner *Sidney Austin Brown & Wood*.

PITKIN, Jeremy
Freshfields Bruckhaus Deringer, London (020) 7936 4000
jeremy.pitkin@freshfields.com
Specialisation: Partner. Specialises in all aspects of international debt and equity capital markets offerings and privatisations. His work has included acting for the arrangers on the MTN programmes of the Hellenic Republic and Bank Austria, for issuers (such as the United Kingdom, the Republic of Lebanon, Rolls-Royce, Kingfisher, Repsol and Banco Espirito Santo), and for managers of international equity offers by BSkyB, Alpha Credit Banks, Elcoteq, Erste Bank, Gazprom and Mobistar. He has worked on privatisation transactions in Croatia, Greece, Latvia, Poland, Russia and the United Kingdom.
Career: Partner 1993.
Personal: Jeremy was born 1955 and educated at King's College, London.

PRIDMORE, Nigel
Linklaters, London (020) 7456 2000
nigel.pridmore@linklaters.com
Specialisation: Specialist in global securities, advising investment banks and issuers. Main areas of practice include UK corporate bond issues, convertible bond issues, Tier 1 capital issues, medium-term note programmes, emerging market debt and equity offerings and structured and derivative products.
Career: 1998 to date: Partner in the international finance department of *Linklaters* London; 1994-98: Assistant solicitor, *Linklaters* London; 1992-94: Assistant solicitor, *Linklaters* New York; 1990-92: Assistant solicitor, *Linklaters* London; 1988-90: Articled clerk, *Linklaters*. 1986-88: College of Law; 1983-86: Emmanuel College, Cambridge, MA History.

RAINES, Marke
Shearman & Sterling, London (020) 7655 5000
mraines@shearman.com
Specialisation: Partner in securitisation group securitisation and structured finance. Acts for investment banks and corporates in developing a wide

range of UK and international securitisation structures and top rated structured investment vehicles.
Prof. Memberships: ABA; IBA; City of London Solicitors' Company; Fellow of the Society for Advanced Legal Studies.
Career: Called to the Bar in Ontario (1982) and New York (1990). Admitted as a solicitor in England and Wales (1990). Practised with *Stikeman, Elliott* (1982-89) and *Clifford Chance* (1991-94). Joined *Allen & Overy* in 1994 (partner from 1996). Joined *Shearman & Sterling* as partner in 2000. Senior Visiting Fellow at Queen Mary and Westfield College, University of London (2000).
Personal: Born 17th June, 1953. Educated at Simon Fraser University (BA), University of British Columbia (LLB) and Trinity Hall, University of Cambridge (LLM). Interests include flying and skiing.

RICE, Jim
Linklaters, London (020) 7456 4525
jim.rice@linklaters.com
Specialisation: Experience in all aspects of capital markets work including equity and equity-related, straight debt and MTNs. Now specialises in structured finance and securitisations.
Career: Partner in the international finance department, securities group. 1999 to date: Partner, *Linklaters* London; 1997-98: Partner, *Linklaters* Hong Kong; 1989-97: Partner, *Linklaters* London; 1986-89: Assistant solicitor, *Linklaters* London; 1984-86: Assistant solicitor, *Linklaters*, New York; 1982-84: Assistant solicitor, *Linklaters* London; 1980-82: Articled clerk, *Linklaters*. 1979: Christ Church, Oxford University, Jurisprudence (First Class).

RUDIN, Simeon
Freshfields Bruckhaus Deringer, London
(020) 7936 4000
simeon.rudin@freshfields.com
Specialisation: Partner in the finance department advising on all aspects of capital markets work, including private and public debt, including equity, credit and commodity linked debt issues, tax structured financings, securitisations, CLOs, CBOs, CDOs, repackagings and all aspects of derivatives transactions (both exchange trade and over the counter), including repo and stocklending. Advises on alternative risk transfer and structured insurance products and transactions. Advises extensively on product development. Head of *Freshfields* Derivatives Unit.
Prof. Memberships: Law Society; City of London Solicitors Company.
Career: Qualified 1983. Partner 1995.
Personal: Born 1961. Attended St. Catharines College, Cambridge.

RUSSELL, John
Sidley Austin Brown & Wood, London
(020) 7778 1800
jrussell@sidley.com
Specialisation: International capital markets work, with particular emphasis on structured finance, securitisation, derivative issues and international equity offerings. Emerging markets experience, particularly in India. Transactions include a large number of structured securities programmes and trades and GDR issues.
Prof. Memberships: Member of the Securities Institute and member of Capital Markets Forum.
Career: Qualified in 1977 and in Hong Kong in 1981. Associate Director *Merrill Lynch* 1985-88. Partner *Simmons & Simmons* 1988-99. Partner *Brown & Wood* since 1999. Following merger of *Sidley & Austin* and *Brown & Wood* on 1 May 2001, partner *Sidley Austin Brown & Wood.*
Personal: Ski mountaineer.

SHURMAN, Daniel J
Allen & Overy, London (020) 7330 2855
daniel.shurman@allenovery.com
Specialisation: Partner in *Allen & Overy's* capital markets department since 1999. During 1994-95 worked in the capital markets group of a New York based law firm. Worked with many of the major international investment banks and has extensive world-wide experience of private and public offerings of debt and equity securities.
Career: Assistant solicitor, *Theodore Goddard* (1990 – 1996), Seconded to *Dewey Ballantine*, New York (1994 – 1995). Associate, *Allen & Overy* (1996 – 1999), Partner (1999).
Personal: Born 1965, Highgate School, Nottingham University. Leisure interests include sailing. Resides in London.

SMITH, Christopher
Slaughter and May, London (020) 7600 1200
christopher.smith@slaughterandmay.com
Specialisation: Main areas of practice include securitisations, structured financings and the full range of capital markets and banking transactions.
Career: Qualified 1980; partner 1987.

SMITH, Sarah
Sidley Austin Brown & Wood, London
(020) 7360 3600
sarah.smith@sidley.com
Specialisation: Securitisation; structured finance; banking and financial services regulation.
Career: Qualified 1990. Partner *Sidley & Austin* 1995. Following merger of *Sidley & Austin* and *Brown & Wood* on 1 May 2001, partner *Sidley Austin Brown & Wood.*

THOMSON, Keith
Linklaters, London (020) 7456 4584
keith.thomson@linklaters.com
Specialisation: Specialist in securities transactions; advising both lead managers and issuers in respect of issues of debt, equity-related debt, equity and depositary receipts in the international capital markets. Also advises clients in relation to medium-term note programmes, commercial paper programmes and derivative transactions. Has acted in relation to securities transactions in such jurisdictions as Australia, Scandinavia, Switzerland, Holland, Spain, South Africa and the UK and in such emerging markets as Turkey, Greece, Russia, Zimbabwe, Indonesia, India, Pakistan, Thailand and Kazakhstan.
Career: 1986 to date: Partner, Global Securities Group, *Linklaters*; 1983-86: Solicitor, International Finance Department, *Linklaters*; 1981-83 Assistant Solicitor, *Linklaters* Hong Kong; 1979-81 Assistant Solicitor, Corporate Department, *Linklaters*. 1975-76: Cambridge University, LLB (Law); 1972-75: Durham University, BA (Law).

TREDGETT, Richard P
Allen & Overy, London (020) 7330 3000
tregdetra@allenovery.com
Specialisation: Richard Tredgett is an associate who joined *Allen & Overy* in 1993. He has experience in advising on international transactions, and in particular OTC derivatives. He has worked on many documentation projects for the International Swaps and Derivatives Association, including the 1997 ISDA Government Bond Option Definitions, ISDA's EMU Protocol, the 1998 ISDA Euro Definitions and the 2000 ISDA Definitions. He was also extensively involved in ISDA's European economic and monetary union working groups and is a frequent speaker on derivatives documentation, collateral and the legal aspects of monetary union.

TROTT, David
Freshfields Bruckhaus Deringer, London
(020) 7936 4000
dtrott@freshfields.com
Specialisation: He has worked extensively in the banking and capital markets field acting for lenders, borrowers and arrangers on secured and unsecured transactions. He has particular experience of, and expertise in, asset-backed and structured transactions. He has been involved in securitisations since 1988, working on a number of the early mortgage backed deals to take place in the UK. He advised on the first residential and commercial mortgage securitisations by UK building societies.
Career: Qualified 1988; partner 1997.
Personal: Born 1963. Educated Durham University.

TUCKER, Julian A
Allen & Overy, London (020) 7330 2818
julian.tucker@allenovery.com
Specialisation: A partner in the international capital markets department, Julian has an extensive range of securitisation experience, encompassing numerous asset types and structures including commercial property based financings, building societies, nursing homes and sovereign originated assets. More recently he has worked on CLO transactions, receivables based financings and leisure assets. His clients include originators, banks, trustees and credit enhancers.
Prof. Memberships: Law Society.
Career: *Lovells* (1987-92). *Cameron Markby Hewett* (1993-July 1994), associate *Allen & Overy* (July 1994), partner (1998).
Publications: Articles published in ISR, IFR, IFLR.
Personal: University College London (LLB 1985). London University (LLM 1986). Food, wine, cooking, horse riding, music and travel. Married, two daughters.

VOISEY, Peter G
Clifford Chance, London (020) 7600 1000
peter.voisey@cliffordchance.com
Specialisation: Partner specialising in capital markets, securitisation and structured finance. Extensive experience of securitisations and repackagings, international securities issues (bonds and equities) and derivatives.
Prof. Memberships: City of London Solicitors' Company. Law Society.
Career: Joined *Clifford Chance* as a partner in 2000 from *Lovells*, where he had been a partner since 1994.
Personal: Education: Sir Anthony Browne's School, Brentwood. Trinity Hall, Cambridge University 1978-82 (MA Hons Modern and Medieval Languages).

VOISIN, Michael
Linklaters, London (020) 7456 4606
michael.voisin@linklaters.com
Specialisation: Specialises in capital markets securities work with particular emphasis on sophisticated financial products, note programmes and regulatory capital raising for financial institutions; responsible

for the development of *Linklaters*' medium-term note programme practice and one of core partners in *Linklaters*' derivatives practice.
Career: 1996 to date: Partner international finance department, global securities group; 1991-96: Assistant solicitor, *Linklaters*; 1991: Admitted as a solicitor of the Supreme Court of England and Wales; 1988-91: Legal assistant, *Linklaters*; 1987-88: Pupil barrister; 1987: Called to the Bar of England and Wales. 1986-87: Inns of Courts School of Law, London; 1983-86: Worcester College, Oxford University.

WALKER, John
Milbank, Tweed, Hadley & McCloy, London (020) 7448 3059
jwalker@milbank.com
Specialisation: John Walker is a partner in the firm's capital markets group. His practice encompasses the full range of capital markets instruments, including fixed and floating rate, convertible, exchangeable and capital bonds and bonds with warrants. He has significant experience in relation to securitisation and receivables financings in respect of a diverse range of domestic and overseas receivables and was instrumental in applying capital markets instruments and derivative products to meet the alternative risk transfer requirements of a major European re-insurer. He acted for HM government on the sale of a significant receivables portfolio. Having acted for issuers, arrangers and investors on numerous financing transactions, he is entirely familiar with customary and synthetic financing techniques to secure tax, balance sheet or regulatory capital advantage. He has extensive experience of customary swap, equity and credit-linked products, and related documentation, as well as more bespoke derivatives used for specific transactions. He has acted for a number of leading edge financial institutions in developing their product portfolios and executing related transactions. In relation to the nascent European CDO (collateralized debt obligation) market, John was transaction counsel on two landmark deals representing the lead underwriter and lead arranger in negotiating and structuring both transactions – the first balance sheet CDO in Portugal and the largest arbitrage CDO in Europe ever and also one of the most complex to date.
Career: Trained *Masons*; qualified 1987; solicitor *Freshfields* 1987-94; partner *Wilde Sapte* 1994-98; partner *Cadwalader, Wickersham & Taft* 1998; partner *Milbank, Tweed, Hadley & McCloy* 2000.
Personal: Born 1961. Desborough School; Southampton University (1984 LLB); Law School, Lancaster Gate. Resides London. Leisure interests include theatre, music and travel.

WALSH, Jonathan
Norton Rose, London (020) 7283 6000
walshjgf@nortonrose.com
Specialisation: Securitisation/repackaging. Acts for investment banks, corporates, arrangers and sponsors on a variety of UK and international securitisation and repackaging transactions, including synthetic structures, asset backed securities issues and asset-backed commercial paper conduits.
Prof. Memberships: Law Society. The Oriental Club.
Career: Kings College London, LLB, called to the bar 1984, requalified as a solicitor 1988. Secuitisation partner, *Norton Rose* international securities group 1997, head of international securities group 2000.
Publications: Editor of the 'International Securities Quarterly' and author of articles for other various publications.
Personal: Obscure rock music (pop trivia bore), cooking and mixing cocktails, swimming, skiing and surfing (very badly).

WARNA-KULA-SURIYA, Sanjev
Slaughter and May, London (020) 7600 1200
sanjevwks@slaughterandmay.com
Specialisation: Partner specialising in capital markets, derivatives, securitisation and structured finance.
Career: Articled *Slaughter and May*; qualified 1990; partner 1997.
Personal: Born 1964. Educated at King's College, London University (1986 LLB First Class Hons). Resides London. Leisure: cricket, theatre.

WEDDERBURN-DAY, Roger
Allen & Overy, London (020) 7330 2823
roger.wedderburn-day@allenovery
Specialisation: Partner, areas of practice include advising managers and issuers an all aspects of both debt and equity international capital markets work. Specialises in all aspects of the international debt and equity capital markets including eurobonds, medium term note programmes, privatisations and other international equity offerings and different types of equity linked debt, including convertible and exchangeable bonds. His practice involves working on transactions in countries throughout the world including India, Japan, the US, Scandinavia, Europe and the emerging markets of Eastern Europe, the Middle East and Africa
Prof. Memberships: Law Society
Career: Articled *Allen & Overy*, qualified (1987), associate (1987-95), partner (1995).
Personal: Born 1962. Bishop Wordsworth's school. University College London (LLB 1985). Resides Sevenoaks.

WELLS, Boyan S.
Allen & Overy, London (020) 7330 2886
boyan.wells@allenovery.com
Specialisation: Advises managers and issuers on all aspects of international capital markets work, high yield issues and derivative transactions; particular specialisations include medium term note programmes, listed and unlisted warrant issues and programmes and building societies. Spoken at conferences on derivatives and on the Euromarkets.
Prof. Memberships: Law Society.
Career: Articled *Allen & Overy*, qualified (1981), partner (1987).
Personal: Educated Colston's School and Wadham College, Oxford (1978 MA). Born 1956. Resides Dulwich.

WOODHALL, John
Clifford Chance, London (020) 7600 1000
john.woodhall@cliffordchance.com
Specialisation: Head of International Securitisation Practice.
Career: 1980 – present *Clifford Chance*. Partner 1988. Educated at Leicester University – LLB

CHARITIES

OVERVIEW: Charities are facing an increased pressure to conform to commerce with challenges in employment, property and regulatory matters. Lawyers in this sector are expected to offer full corporate support, as they would to any other business. Branding and marketing often come as high up the agenda as the more traditional trust matters. As times change, so too do the objectives of charities, and lawyers are liaising with the Charity Commission to secure constitutional amendments in order to meet these new needs.

RESEARCH APPROVED BY BMRB: *For this edition,* Chambers' *researchers conducted 6,552 interviews – 4,419 with law firms, 554 with barristers and 1,579 with clients.*

The validity of the research was scrutinised by BMRB International, who audited both the methodology and the results at our offices in July 2001. They interviewed Chambers' *researchers and cross-checked sample interviews. Details of the audit appear on page 7.*

LONDON

Bates, Wells & Braithwaite (see firm details p.871) The general consensus among our interviewees is that of a "*fantastic firm*" with "*huge commitment*" to the area enjoying "*a client list as long as your arm.*" Acts with an international remit, and establishes charities, transfers assets and offers ongoing commercial advice. Competitors claim that **Stephen Lloyd** is the "*best charities lawyer in the UK,*" because he couples "*strength at the law*" with "*understanding of charities' business needs.*" Constitutional specialist **Fiona Middleton** has "*gargantuan knowledge*" and founder member **Andrew Phillips** brings "*deep erudition*" to the practice. The firm advised on the establishment of Charity Bank for CAF and assisted over 15 major charities on complex overseas challenge event arrangements. It arranged a business and licence agreement between Charities Aid Foundation and the Directory of Social Change. Also prominent in the interface between charity law and frontline legislation such as the Human Rights Act and the protection of intellectual property rights, the firm has advised on issues arising from the internet, data protection and patents and trade marks. **Clients:** Charities Aid Foundation; Tate Gallery; British Red Cross Society; Resource; Football Foundation.

Farrer & Co (see firm details p.954) Adjudged a "*serious charities practice,*" it has been bolstered by the arrival of the "*doyenne*" **Anne-Marie Piper** (see p.148) from Paisner & Co. Coupled with the respected **Judith Hill** (see p.146), competitors feel this practice is "*clearly strengthened by two big hitters*" and now "*holds all the cards.*" Continues to work at the forefront of the market and acted in the establishment of the Charities Property Fund, the first ever common investment fund. Displays expertise in incorporating charities and independent schools, establishing trading companies and taxation matters. The firm advises charities and not for profit organisations on related issues such as IP, employment law and litigation. The firm acted for a children's charity concerning its proposed loan to a museum and advised on the sale of an important work of art to a national museum. It also advised a major US foundation on its establishment of a fellowship programme at a leading university, and acted for the Royal Literary Fund in the largest ever sale of literary copyrights. **Clients:** The Prince's Trust; National Heritage Memorial Fund; The National Endowment for Science, Technology and the Arts.

Withers (see firm details p.1187) "*Players with a commercial approach,*" this practice is considered by specialists to field "*a top quality team*" "*Known for its NHS work,*" it continues to advise several NHS charities on implications of the change in their status to trustees under section 11 of the NHS and Community Care Act (1990). The "*pre-eminent*" **Alison Paines** (see p.147) is deemed "*inspirational*" and garners plaudits for "*knowing her stuff.*" The firm continues to assist Guy's and St Thomas' Charitable Foundation on all its legal matters. It advised Macmillan Cancer Relief and the NSPCC on the structuring and taxation (corporation tax and VAT) implications of their innovative fundraising schemes. Has been involved with both Christian Aid and Royal Star & Garter on contentious charity issues, particularly disputed legacies. **Clients:** Cancer Research Campaign; British Heart foundation; Blenheim Foundation; NSPCC; Mencap.

Allen & Overy (see firm details p.856) "*A prominent charities department,*" so say competitors of this well-known city firm. The department is headed up by **Peter Mimpriss** (see p.147) whose "*commitment*" is exemplified by his cutting edge work in gift aid and the 'Institute for Philanthropy' initiative. The group advised the Royal Botanic Gardens, Kew on its Seedbank project at Wakehurst Place and assisted Wellcome Trust in the commercial exploitation of successful results from medical research. Heavily involved in the establishment of the Shell Foundation, a charity whose purpose is to help developing countries find economically sustainable sources of power and heat, the firm has also assisted in setting up a charity to improve medical care Africa-wide, especially in Zimbabwe. **Clients:** British Library; Arts Council of England; Royal Shakespeare Company; Wellcome Trust.

Berwin Leighton Paisner (see firm details p.878) This newly merged firm's charities practice is a highly "*visible*" force in the market. Competitors believe the loss of high profile Anne Marie Piper has had an impact, yet it retains the "*proactive*" **Moira Protani** (see p.148) as group head, exclusively focused on charities law. Respected **Martin Paisner** (see p.147) remains a key attraction for many clients. The firm is involved in Charity Commission matters and other regulatory work. Playing a heavyweight advisory role to charity trustees engaged in merger activity, it recently advised Jewish Care on its ongoing merger with the Otto Schiff Housing Association. Also acts for many private clients and assists in the establishment of trusts. **Clients:** National Family and Parenting Institute; University for Industry.

Bircham Dyson Bell (see firm details p.883) A "*tight team*" that specialises in the interface between the public law and charities sector, it is becoming "*stronger and stronger*" according to our interviewees. The "*active*" **Simon Weil** (see p.149) and "*calm*" **Paul Voller** (see p.149) are both deemed "*high profile charities players*" by peers. The group formed the Jill Dando Fund in record time, working with trustees including the Duchess of Westminster, Cliff Richard and Nick Ross. It undertook a comprehensive reorganisation of Epsom College and related charities, which involved the creation of a corporate charity. The firm acted for the Waterways Trust in connection with the acquisition of an inland waterway. **Clients:** Coalfields Regeneration Trust; Hospital Management Trust; Blue Cross.

Charles Russell (see firm details p.912) Offering specialist advice on IP, tax, employment and trusts issues the team is "*going great guns*" according to competitors. **Michael Scott** (see p.149) draws praise for his "*depth of experience*" and recently co-authored the book 'Guide to Charity Legislation'. Former barrister **Catriona Syed** (see p.847) is dubbed a "*quality prac-*

CHARITIES • London	Ptnrs	Assts
1 Bates, Wells & Braithwaite	7	7
2 Farrer & Co	3	7
3 Withers	5	8
4 Allen & Overy	1	4
Berwin Leighton Paisner	2	n/a
Bircham Dyson Bell	5	6
Charles Russell	4	5
Claricoat Phillips	2	n/a
Harbottle & Lewis	3	4
Nabarro Nathanson	1	3
Sinclair Taylor & Martin	5	5
Trowers & Hamlins	n/a	n/a
5 Lawrence Graham	3	3
Lee Bolton & Lee	2	1
Macfarlanes	n/a	n/a
Radcliffes	2	n/a
Winckworth Sherwood	2	4
6 Field Fisher Waterhouse	n/a	n/a
Herbert Smith	1	n/a
Linklaters	1	1
Vizard Oldham	1	1

LEADING INDIVIDUALS

1
- **HILL Judith** Farrer & Co
- **LLOYD Stephen** Bates, Wells & Braithwaite
- **PAINES Alison** Withers
- **PIPER Anne-Marie** Farrer & Co

2
- **BURCHFIELD Jonathan** Nabarro Nathanson
- **CLARICOAT John** Claricoat Phillips
- **DOLLIMORE Jean** Radcliffes
- **DRISCOLL Lindsay** Sinclair Taylor & Martin
- **MIDDLETON Fiona** Bates, Wells & Braithwaite
- **MIMPRISS Peter** Allen & Overy
- **PHILLIPS Andrew** Bates, Wells & Braithwaite
- **PHILLIPS Hilary** Claricoat Phillips
- **SINCLAIR TAYLOR James** Sinclair Taylor & Martin

3
- **PAISNER Martin** Berwin Leighton Paisner
- **PHILLIPS Ann** Stone King
- **PORTRAIT Judith** Portrait Solicitors
- **PROTANI Moira** Berwin Leighton Paisner
- **WEIL Simon** Bircham Dyson Bell

4
- **GREENHOUS Guy** Radcliffes
- **MEAKIN Robert** Stone King
- **SCOTT Michael** Charles Russell
- **SYED Catriona** Charles Russell
- **VOLLER Paul** Bircham Dyson Bell

This book is the product of 6,552 1/2 hour interviews. See p.7 for BMRB audit.

Within each band, firms are listed alphabetically. *See individuals' profiles p.146*

titioner," specialising in trusts and tax planning in the UK and overseas. The team advised on the complete review of all the constitutional documents for the Insolvency Practitioners Association. Helped establish internet-based training facilities for the London Chamber of Commerce and Industry Examinations Board. It also received instructions on a far-reaching amendment of the Royal Charter and laws of Royal College of Nursing (UK). **Clients:** Eton College; RAF Benevolent Fund; Marie Curie Cancer Care; Florence Nightingale International Foundation.

Claricoat Phillips A sui generis firm boasting a team of two "*first class*" ex-Charity Commissioners. "*Unbeatable for general advisory work,*" this boutique's strength lies in its "*pragmatic, high level advice.*" The "*amazingly experienced*" **John Claricoat** draws praise from leading practitioners for his "*encyclopaedic knowledge.*" The "*trenchant*" **Hilary Phillips** (see p.148) is "*efficacious*" and has an "*instinct for the work.*" The group advises charities on registration matters and dealings with the Charity Commission. Undertakes general advisory work for a number of bodies. **Clients:** Water Training International; Balliol College Oxford; School Councils UK.

Harbottle & Lewis (see firm details p.985) With a huge arts charity client base, the firm is best known as a force in media and cause-related marketing issues. Handled Richard Branson's bid for the National Lottery licence with his project 'People's Lottery,' which involved setting up a not-for-profit structure with guarantee companies, and negotiating conditions on operating agreements with key suppliers. It advised One2One and 'Time Bank' on a charitable project aimed at inspiring people to pledge their time to worthy causes. Advised Comic Relief on its arrangements for the Red Nose Day 2001, involving corporate governance issues, grants and commercial participator agreements. Procured two charity registrations for the Waterloo Millennium Green Project. **Clients:** Comic Relief; 1 Twenty; ICA; Contemporary Dance Trust; Wigmore Hall Trust.

Nabarro Nathanson (see firm details p.1078) With charity work equally spread between its London and Reading branches, the firm is considered "*a national name in charities.*" "*Good listener*" **Jonathan Burchfield** (see p.146) heads the practice and is highly esteemed as "*inspiring confidence*" in all matters. In general, the group has been busy with Charity Commission inquiries, dispute resolution and constitutional changes. It advised the RSPCA on a case in which the charity sought guidance from the court concerning its discretion to refuse membership to those recruiting for a pro-hunting campaign. Advised The National Trust on its merger with the Quarry Bank Mill Trust, and advised The Lowry Centre Trust on property matters. **Clients:** RSPCA; National trusts; RHLI; London Institute; Diabetes UK; Save The Children Fund.

Sinclair Taylor & Martin "*A dedicated charities practice,*" say competitors who rate this niche firm as "*producing the highest quality in every piece of advice.*" **Lindsay Driscoll** (see p.146) is a specialist in innovative charity registrations. "*Delightful entrepreneur*" **James Sinclair Taylor** (see p.149) garners respect for his "*commitment*" to the field. The group acts for service delivery charities, learned societies and has seen a recent growth in urban regeneration organisations. Advises Unicef on fundraising contracts. **Clients:** St. Christopher's Fellowship; BBC Children in Need; Unicef.

Trowers & Hamlins (see firm details p.1162) Renowned for its knowledge of housing association matters, charities work is handled cross-departmentally. The market awaits the effect of Jean Dollimore's departure to Radcliffes. The group advised on the defence to a judicial review application from a resident of a home due to be closed. Acted on the establishment of a group structure to facilitate the merger of two major disability charities. **Clients:** St. Dunstans; National Childbirth Trust; Leonard Cheshire Foundation.

Lawrence Graham (see firm details p.1030) The firm has a cross-departmental charities practice that is drawn from a strong private client base. Head of department Martin Gowar advised an educational charity on the regulatory aspects of its constitution. The group also advised a leading rural public body on the use of a trust to manage an area of outstanding natural beauty, and acted for a major arts charity on the regulatory aspects of its constitution. **Clients:** Action Against Hunger; Motability; Gardener's Royal Benevolent Society; Friends of the Earth.

Lee Bolton & Lee (see firm details p.1034) This Westminster firm is deemed "*a gentlemanly offering*" by one competitor. Rated as a "*top ecclesiastical practice*" and considered by peers to be "*long established in the field.*" With traditional strengths in ecclesiastical and educational charities work, the firm continues to service significant clients. **Clients:** Educational charities; ecclesiastical charities.

Macfarlanes (see firm details p.1046) Assisted by its property and corporate departments, the group continues to offer a broad range of charities advice. Typical work includes formation issues, advising on charitable status, trustee remuneration and tax. The firm has recently been involved in establishing charitable status for a non-UK body, whose financial affairs were in disarray, resulting in substantial corporation tax and ratings assessments being discharged. Garnered approval from the Charity Commission to establish a charity in the UK that provides branding services to the sector. Continues to advise on constitutional matters for large charity clients, including negotiations with government departments in updating a Royal Charter. **Clients:** Royal Academy; National Missing Persons Helpline; Trusthouse Forte Foundation; The Lister Institute.

Radcliffes (see firm details p.1103) This Westminster based firm acts for over 170 charities and specialises in education, animal welfare and medicine. The firm represented the trustees of the Dame Alice Owen Foundation in an action against the Treasury Solicitor and the Charity Commission. "*Down to earth*" **Guy Greenhous** (see p.146) acted for the Dame Alice Owen School at Potters Bar, at present the only beneficiary of the foundation. The arrival of "*first class*" **Jean Dollimore** (see p.146) has been eagerly anticipated by our interviewees, and she garners praise for her "*strength in trusts and probate law.*" The team has carried out consolidation exercises for the Children's Society. **Clients:** Children's Society; Animal Health Trust; Worshipful Company of Brewers; Combat Stress.

Winckworth Sherwood (see firm details p.1185) "*Cracking ecclesiastical firm*" with a "*strong education angle,*" according to competitors. Headed by Paul Morris, the firm acted on the establishment of the St. Pauls' Cathedral Foundation, its main fundraising arm, and established St. Ethelburga's Centre, a charity set up to rebuild the ancient city church for use as a centre for reconciliation and peace. The group also acted for the Krishnamurti Foundation, and continues to advise Marshall's Charity and St. Luke's Hospital for the Clergy, a private charitable hospital providing free treatment and surgery for the clergy and their families. **Clients:** Marshall's Charity; Greycoat Foundation; National Energy Action.

Field Fisher Waterhouse (see firm details p.957) A presence in the market place, the group that includes Heather Fuff acts for a full range of charity clients, with a particular strength in Royal Charter charities, medical institutes and ecclesiastical bodies. Successfully obtained charity status for its long-standing client, the General Medical Council. The firm is currently advising the Institute of Psychiatry on the use of funds, following its amalgamation with King's College, London. Also instructed by several US charities concerning registration in the UK as separate entities, and as branch offices. **Clients:** Aga Khan Foundation; Architectural Association; Handle Institute; British Psychological Society; Morley College.

Herbert Smith (see firm details p.993) Our researchers were informed that the trusts and charities department of this city firm holds a credible force in the marketplace. Acting for substantial asset-based charities, the department is able to offer advice on all areas of the law, including commercial, litigation and property issues. Headed up by John Wood, the team advised a London university college on the creation of a charity to run a library, acting on investment provisions in light of the Trustee Act 2000. Advised a leading children's charity in a dispute with an associated US charity and advised Friends Provident on the establishment of a charitable foundation as part of demutualisation. **Clients:** Wellcome Foundation; Weston Trust; Weinstock Trust.

Linklaters (see firm details p.1042) Headed by partner Nigel Reid, this team acted for a major institutional charity on an internet joint venture with a US not for profit organisation. Recent highlights have included updating a major charity's constitution and re-organising its associated subsidiaries. The group acted for an internet company on a novel 'affinity' scheme allowing web-site users to make donations to selected charities. Has an impressive following among large institutional charities, and a track record in advising charities on IP, property and funding issues. **Clients:** Royal Opera House; CAFOD; Tate Gallery; SANE.

Vizard Oldham (see firm details p.1169) Commended for its Royal Charter work, the firm has a specialist focus on public sector work including housing associations and NHS Trusts, eliciting praise for its "*good clients.*" The group is headed up by Ron Perry. Clients include grant-makers, training charities and long established charities. Formed the Brewing Guild Trust, a benevolent and training vehicle for the brewing industry, on behalf of the Brewers Guild. **Clients:** Dunhill Medical Trust; Royal British Legion; Training For Life.

Other Notable Practitioners "*Star*" **Ann Phillips** is rated for her depth of experience, and competitors say "*she's a great advantage to Stone King.*" Having also joined the new London office of **Stone King**, "*hardworker*" **Robert Meakin** has brought with him a track record won at Simmons & Simmons. The "*frighteningly competent*" **Judith Portrait** (see p.148), of **Portrait Solicitors in Association with Denton Wilde Sapte**, is known for her Sainsburys Charitable Trust work and is dubbed "*a skilled lawyer.*"

THE SOUTH

CHARITIES • The South	Ptnrs	Assts
1 **Blake Lapthorn** Portsmouth	1	1
Thomas Eggar Church Adams Chichester	1	1
Thomson Snell & Passmore Tunbridge Wells	2	2
2 **Barlows** Surrey	1	1
Cripps Harries Hall Tunbridge Wells	2	1
Griffith Smith Brighton	1	1
Lester Aldridge Bournemouth	1	1

LEADING INDIVIDUALS	
1 **CAIRNS Elizabeth** Sole Practitioner	
2 **DAVIS Elizabeth** Blake Lapthorn	**SMITH Tim** Griffith Smith

This book is the product of 6,552 1/2 hour interviews. See p.7 for BMRB audit.
Within each band, firms are listed alphabetically. *See **Profiles** on page 000*

Blake Lapthorn (see firm details p.886) Considered a one stop location for charities seeking specialist employment and commercial advice. "*A strong name,*" rated by competitors for its ability to "*just get on with things.*" The past year has seen a growth in its work for charitable registered social landlords. Newly made-up partner **Elizabeth Davis** is a specialist charity and voluntary sector lawyer, with substantial experience in company and commercial law. The group advised Cancer Care Society on constitutional, charity law and property issues, and advised the Portsmouth Area Hospice on fund-raising agreements and trading company issues. **Clients:** Cottage Homes; Hampshire Wildlife; Mary Rose Trust; Cancer Care Society; Pilgrim Homes.

Thomas Eggar Church Adams (see firm details p.1153) The firm advises several ecclesiastical bodies and guides the establishment of new charities. Operating from its private clients practice, charity work includes the administration of financial matters. Ecclesiastical specialist Christopher Butcher heads up the charities group. As well as church clients, the firm advises several charities ranging from educational trusts to elderly service providers. The group acted on the proposed merger of two substantial charities. **Clients:** Chichester Diocese; Dean and Chapter of Chichester Cathedral; The Aldingbourne Trust.

Thomson Snell & Passmore (see firm details p.1155) This respected charities department has an emphasis on formations, incorporations and drafting and reorganising charity constitutions. Jeremy Passmore heads up the department that acts for local arts charities, and charitable trusts. Recent work includes acting for several multi-million pound estates and probates. **Clients:** Arts charities; educational charities.

Barlows A cross-departmental offering undertakes a variety of commercial work for many charity clients, servicing their property, employment and contractual needs. Headed up by Christine Goodyear, the team offers legacy and constitutional work from its private client department. **Clients:** World Wild Life Fund for Nature; CHASE.

Cripps Harries Hall (see firm details p.927) This firm's charity office combines a private charity law practice with trust administration experience, investment management and tax expertise. Peter Scott and the team specialise in the applied use of charities and other not-for-profit structures. The group has extensive experience of Charity Commission negotiations, and marries its investment management and legal skills in enabling trustees to maximise growth for its charity clients. **Clients:** Great Britain Sasakawa Foundation; Royal Historic Society; Japan Festival Fund.

Griffith Smith (see firm details p.979) With the expressed mission of bringing charities closer to their communities, ex-voluntary sector manager **Tim Smith** (see p.149) acts for community education organisations, learning disability and community development charities. He undertakes structuring and constitutional changes, and Charity Commission investigations. **Clients:** Community organisations; public schools; service providers.

Lester Aldridge (see firm details p.1038) Specialists in formations, taxation and funding issues, the charities department is headed by Barry Glazier. It has acted for the Anti-Vivisection league on its international probate work and advised YMCA Bournemouth on its takeover of another local charity. **Clients:** Bournemouth Orchestras; Army Air Corps Fund; Western Association of Ballet Schools; YMCA Bournemouth.

Other Notable Practitioners Sole practitioner **Elizabeth Cairns** (see p.146) wins praise again this year for her specialism and experience.

THAMES VALLEY

	CHARITIES • Thames Valley	Ptnrs	Assts
1	**Manches** Oxford	1	2
	Nabarro Nathanson Reading	1	3
	Winckworth Sherwood Oxford	1	1
2	**BrookStreet Des Roches** Witney	1	n/a
3	**Henmans** Oxford	2	2
	Iliffes Booth Bennett Uxbridge	3	3
	Linnells Oxford	1	4

	LEADING INDIVIDUALS	
1	**BROOKS Ken** BrookStreet Des Roches	**POULTER Alan** Manches
	REES John Winckworth Sherwood	
2	**SAUNDERS Joss** Linnells	

This book is the product of 6,552 1/2 hour interviews. See p.7 for BMRB audit.

Within each band, firms are listed alphabetically. *See individuals' profiles p.146*

Manches (see firm details p.1051) Prominent for its Oxford College and other university institutions client base. The department, headed by the respected **Alan Poulter** (see p.148), also acts for museums, libraries and independent schools. It has witnessed growth in instructions from medical charities. Instructed by an American higher education institution on the formation of an educational charity in the UK, and by a New Zealand University on the formation of a charitable trust. **Clients:** Islamic Trust; National Trust; Oxford Colleges.

Nabarro Nathanson (see firm details p.1078) See London editorial.

Winckworth Sherwood (see firm details p.1185) "*Well known for its church work,*" and recommended by competitors for its activities in charities generally. **John Rees** (see p.148) is commended by peers, and has been involved in advising on all aspects of constitutional work. Continues to concentrate on the not-for-profit sector and acts for many ecclesiastical and housing charities. **Clients:** Ecclesiastical charities.

BrookStreet Des Roches (see firm details p.897) The "*brilliant*" **Kenneth Brooks**, who sits as a trustee on many charities, is recommended for his "*quality work and commitment.*" The group acts for a variety of national and international charities in the educational and religious sectors, and those arising from the disaster relief and grant making spheres. The firm has been engaged in establishing a number of grant making charitable trusts including the Peers Educational Trust. **Clients:** Educational charities.

Henmans (see firm details p.991) With a "*strong reputation in legacy work,*" this Oxford-based team is busy on commercial, property and employment matters. The group is headed up by Peter Jefferies and has been involved in defendant litigation in a probate case. Typical areas of instruction are mergers, restructuring, formations and advising on trading subsidiaries. **Clients:** RSPCA: RNIB; Oxfam; Guide Dogs for the Blind.

Iliffes Booth Bennett Backed by heavyweight commercial property, litigation and employment teams, this charities practice offers a cross-departmental approach to clients. Acted for the Institute of Our Lady of Mercy on the transfer of a private hospital in Sheffield to another registered charity. This involved the surrender of the existing lease and the grant of a new one, while ensuring the Institute's interests were protected at all times. **Clients:** Trinity College of Music; Institute of our Lady of Mercy; Musicians benevolent Fund; The PRS Members Fund; Ursuline Sisters.

Linnells (see firm details p.1043) With niche strengths in charity shops and trading issues, this Oxford practice continues to offer contract expertise, from lottery grants to social services. **Joss Saunders** (see p.149) continues his role as company secretary and in-house lawyer for Oxfam. The group advised NCVO on the launch of the NCVO stakeholder pension for the voluntary sector. Acted for BTCV, Earthwatch and On the Line in three multi-million pound lottery grants and assisted the University of Teeside and a consortium of North Eastern further education colleges on the University for Industry's 'LearnDirect' contract. **Clients:** Oxfam; Wateraid; several Oxford colleges.

SOUTH WEST & WALES

CHARITIES • South West & Wales	Ptnrs	Assts
1 Stone King Bath	3	1
2 Bond Pearce Exeter	1	n/a
Burges Salmon Bristol	1	1
Osborne Clarke Bristol	3	12
3 Thring Townsend Bath	2	1
Tozers Exeter	2	n/a
Veale Wasbrough Bristol	2	1
Wilsons Salisbury	2	2
4 Clarke Willmott & Clarke Taunton	1	1
Edwards Geldard Cardiff	1	1
Michelmores Exeter	3	1
Parker Bullen Salisbury	3	3
Rickerby Watterson Cheltenham	3	1

LEADING INDIVIDUALS	
1 KING Michael Stone King	
2 DE'ATH Gary Veale Wasbrough	KING Richard Tozers
WOODWARD Mark Osborne Clarke	WYLD Charles Burges Salmon

This book is the product of 6,552 1/2 hour interviews. See p.7 for BMRB audit.

Within each band, firms are listed alphabetically. *See individuals' profiles p.146*

Stone King (see firm details p.1145) With "*national standing*" and "*the number one name in charity law*," the newly opened London office has only bolstered this dominant practice which peers believe is going "*from strength to strength*." Ex-Chairman of the Charity Law Association **Michael King** is "*one of the country's leaders*" and many peers echo the sentiment that "*what he doesn't know, ain't worth knowing*." The group advised the trustees of the Somerset Care Trust and Redstone Trust on a wide-ranging section 8 inquiry, and the subsequent re-organisation of the charities' structure. Also advised the National Confederation of Parent Teacher Associations of England and Wales on trading and constitutional issues. **Clients**: Westminster Diocese; LSU College Trustees; Royal Photographic Society.

Bond Pearce (see firm details p.888) This respected practice has a cross-departmental base and is headed by Jonathan Nicholson. The team offers financial, general commercial and constitutional advice. The team acted for the National Trust on several major transactions throughout the UK, and advised on the use and occupation of its property. Also advised Village Hall Trustees on the complex sale of a site for development. **Clients:** Theatre Royal, Plymouth; The National Trust; Cluewin Trust; Robert Owen Foundation; Cornwall College.

Burges Salmon (see firm details p.902) An esteemed tax and trusts department advises charities on a wide range of issues. **Charles Wyld** (see p.848) is a "*terrific lawyer*" and has expertise on the formation of charities alongside general tax and estate planning. Active on a number of Charity Commission investigations, highlights include the representation of a large regional charity whose relationships with trading companies were seen as creating possible conflicts of interest. The group has also been involved in the re-structuring of schools, formation of trading subsidiaries and duties and liabilities of trustees or directors. **Clients:** @Bristol; Bath Spa Trust; National Trust.

Osborne Clarke (see firm details p.1086) Acting for over 100 charities, it garners plaudits from peers for its "*strong lawyers*." Increasingly active on section 8 inquiries, thanks to instructions from charity trustees and managers appointed by the Charity Commission. Headed by the esteemed **Mark Woodward**, the team advised on a fundraising campaign for the Professional Golfers' Association Benevolent Fund. Continues to advise a large national charity in connection with its proposed merger with one of the largest charities in a foreign jurisdiction. Advised trustees of the Bristol Woodland Memorial Trust on the successful registration of one of the few charitable woodland burial sites in the UK. **Clients:** Sue Ryder Foundation; Macmillan Cancer Relief; Bristol Old Vic Trust; Barton Hill Settllement.

Thring Townsend (see firm details p.1155) This recently merged firm can now boast three offices handling charity work. Typically, clients are long-standing charities in the land and grant-making sectors, but also include religious, educational and medical charities. The group advised on a successful grant application to central and local government to refurbish a Georgian property in an environmentally friendly manner and also papered a trust's ongoing partnership with its local authority. **Clients:** St. John's Hospital; Mr Willats' Charity; RJ Harris trust.

Tozers (see firm details p.1160) Still respected as "*a name in religious charities work*," this Exeter-based firm has expanded to encompass educational and community start-ups. Respected **Richard King** heads up the department and specialises in constitutional aspects of charity work, as well as mergers, and the establishment of trading subsidiaries. **Clients:** Plymouth Roman Catholic Diocese; Prior Park College; Forward Living.

Veale Wasbrough (see firm details p.1167) Ex-Wragges partner and multicultural initiatives specialist **Gary De'Ath** has joined this respected firm that advises many local charities. It closely works with lawyers across departments on employment and property issues for charities. Its main clients are service providers in health, arts and general social provision. Head of department Robert Boyd has a niche practice in education, advising over 600 independent schools. **Clients:** Arts (South West); Bristol Municipal Charities; Harry Crook Foundation.

Wilsons (see firm details p.1184) Busy expanding in the area of schools and educational charities, this Salisbury-based firm is commended by its peers. Arranged and advised on the structuring of lottery applications for charities. The firm is also involved in advisory work on incorporating companies and hiving off charitable trusts. **Clients:** Stanley Picker Trust; Salisbury Diocesan Board of Finance; Wiltshire Wildlife Trust.

Clarke Willmott & Clarke (see firm details p.915) Our researchers were informed that this practice is skilled in the field of establishing and structuring charities. Headed by tax planning specialist Stuart Thorne, the department advises a broad range of clients including several educational bodies. **Clients:** Countryside Agency; Community Forest Partnerships.

Edwards Geldard (see firm details p.948) With two people dedicated solely to charity work, this Cardiff-based practice is increasingly active on the Welsh charity scene. Public Law specialist Huw Williams heads up a department that offers formation and structural re-organisation advice to a wide range of clients. It acted for the National Botanic Garden of Wales in connection with land, corporate transactions and obtaining requisite Charity Commission consents. Also altered the Royal Charter of the Arts Council of Wales and created various new charities including The Dyscovery Trust and Cymured Cymru Communities Wales. **Clients:** National Botanic Garden of Wales; Princes Trust Bro; National Library of Wales; Kenfig Corporation Trust.

Michelmores (see firm details p.1066) Still busy with locally endowed, ecclesiastical and educational charity work, this firm is headed up by the all round charity specialist Richard Wheeler. Advises on pure charity law and related employment, contracts and property issues. The firm has acted in the establishment and dissolution of charities. **Clients:** University of Exeter; Diocese of Exeter; Exeter Hospice.

Parker Bullen This Salisbury firm offers experience and expertise in formation, administration and general advice to local and national charities. The firm has a growing schools department that generates instructions. Head of the private client department, Robert Sykes advises on a full range of related employment, litigation and other legal services. Offers a national will-making service for charities. **Clients**: South Wiltshire Mencap; Civil Service Benevolent Fund; Civil Service Pensioners Alliance: RNIB; Bryanston School.

Rickerby Watterson (see firm details p.1108) A force in educational charity work, the firm has been busy lecturing and advising on behalf of the Independent Schools Bursars Association. Much of its workload is concerned with the modernising of old charitable institutions through the examination of their constitutions. Head of department John Clarke acted for Gloucestershire College of Arts and Technology on the establishment of its new campus. The six-month negotiations with Gloucestershire County Council involved purchase and development agreements and successfully secured planning permission. **Clients:** National Meningitis Trust; Cheltenham Ladies College; Mines Advisory group; National Star centre for Disabled Youth.

MIDLANDS

	CHARITIES • Midlands	Ptnrs	Assts
1	**Anthony Collins Solicitors** Birmingham	1	2
	Martineau Johnson Birmingham	2	3
	Wragge & Co Birmingham	2	n/a
2	**Gateley Wareing** Birmingham	1	n/a
	Hewitson Becke + Shaw Northampton	2	2
	Lee Crowder Birmingham	1	1
	Shakespeares Birmingham	1	2

	LEADING INDIVIDUALS
1	**FEA Michael** Martineau Johnson
	THOMPSON Romaine Anthony Collins Solicitors
	WOODHEAD Louise Wragge & Co
2	**GATELEY Stephen** Gateley Wareing

This book is the product of 6,552 1/2 hour interviews. See p.7 for BMRB audit.

Within each band, firms are listed alphabetically. *See individuals' profiles p.146*

Anthony Collins Solicitors (see firm details p.860) Rated for its "*strength in church charities,*" the firm continues to dominate the region. The "*fastidious and effective*" **Romaine Thompson** (see p.149) has 12 years' experience of advising charities and churches. The team worked with a large city centre church in the course of a vast refurbishment programme, which involved advice on grant agreements and on the establishment of structures to manage the new facilities. The group also facilitated the merger of two multi-million pound turnover charities and assisted a charity under Royal Charter to restructure its governance system. **Clients:** Shaftesbury; Spring harvest; Parkinson's Disease; United Kingdom Evangelisation Trust.

Martineau Johnson (see firm details p.1055) With a full-service commercial offering at its disposal, this "*solid as a rock*" team fields the "*helpful and clever*" **Michael Fea** (see p.146). He advised De Montford University on its incorporation of trustees. The team advised a motor trading training organisation on a number of constitutional matters and assisted on the setting up of a charitable trust for the benefit of a specific geographic location. **Clients:** Foundation of Conductive Education; Christian Vision; The Sequel Trust; City of Birmingham Symphony Orchestra.

Wragge & Co (see firm details p.1189) The loss of Gary De'Ath to Bristol firm Veale Wasborough has taken the market by surprise and peers say it is too early to judge the outcome of his departure. **Louise Woodhead** continues to garner respect for her charities work. The group advised English Heritage on related charities matters and acted for The Discovery Centre, a major museum and visitor attraction opening at Birmingham's Millennium Point in 2001. Its client base includes significant grant-making charities including The Rowlands Trust. The team has developed the practice to now offer a clerking service as well as producing accounts and tax reclaim advice. **Clients:** Birmingham Foundation; English Heritage; Heart of England Care; R H Willis Charitable Trust.

Gateley Wareing (see firm details p.969) Commended to researchers for its expertise in religious charities work, this practice advises on constitutional, employment, property and corporate matters for ecclesiastical and smaller service providing clients. Respected **Stephen Gateley** remains a force in the field. **Clients:** RC Archdiocese of Birmingham; Oscott College; Fr. Hudsons Society.

Hewitson Becke + Shaw (see firm details p.994) This Northampton-based team specialises in advising substantial service-providing charities. Head of department Clare Colacicchi has advised on construction contracts for hospitals and schools and also gives employment advice to large charities. The group advised on the establishment of a private charitable trust securing a considerable capital gains tax relief. It has altered the constitutions of two independent schools, and acted on the merger and incorporation of a substantial property owning and service providing charity. **Clients:** St. Andrews Hospice; Harpur Trust; RSPB.

Lee Crowder (see firm details p.1035) Headed by Martin Woodward, the dedicated charities unit acts for over 100 charities and enjoys historic links with many of its clients. It has registered most of the local and regional bodies within the Townswomen's Guild with the Charity Commission. It handled the merger of institutions worth £7.5 million with the University of Birmingham, and continues to advise Selly Oak Colleges on the transfer of land and buildings. **Clients:** King Edward's School Foundation; United Reform West Midlands Province; National Townswomen's Guild.

Shakespeares (see firm details p.1122) This voluntary sector practice has niche strengths in registering new charities, reviewing and amending constitutions, administrating charities and funding agreements. Headed by Tony Jones, the firm also represents grant-making, religious and educational charities. The group registered the Care Partnership (Birmingham Community Home Support Federation) as a charity, and advised on the restructuring of the Institute of Welfare to enable the organisation to apply for registration as a charity. **Clients:** Muscular Dystrophy Group; Association of Child Psychologists and Psychiatrists; Newtown Cultural Project (The Drum).

EAST ANGLIA

Cozens-Hardy & Jewson A "*pre eminent Norwich firm*" according to its competitors, that acts for major local charities. Advises on a wide range of issues including the administration, establishment and guiding of trusts. **Matthew Martin** (see p.147), clerk to a number of charities, remains respected as "*a talented lawyer.*" **Clients:** Norwich Consolidated Charities; Norwich Town Close Estate Charity; Anguish's Educational Foundation; Memorial Trust of the Second Air Division.

Mills & Reeve (see firm details p.1069) Remaining "*a regional charities player,*" this firm retains its following among ecclesiastical and educational charity clients. It acts for charitable institutions on ongoing charity law issues and also in connection with their property matters. The "*top quality*" **John Herring** (see p.146) continues to advise church clients. Major clients of the group include Oxbridge colleges, other education institutions and public sector entities that hold charitable status. **Clients:** Major landowning charities; ecclesiastical bodies.

CHARITIES • East Anglia	Ptnrs	Assts
1 **Cozens-Hardy & Jewson** Norwich	2	n/a
Mills & Reeve Norwich	1	1
Taylor Vinters Cambridge	1	2
2 **Eversheds** Cambridge, Norwich	1	1
Greenwoods Peterborough	1	1
Hewitson Becke + Shaw Cambridge	2	1
Leathes Prior Norwich	n/a	1

LEADING INDIVIDUALS
1 **HERRING John** Mills & Reeve
MARTIN Matthew Cozens-Hardy & Jewson
WARREN Jennifer Taylor Vinters
2 **NORTON Philip** Eversheds
WOMACK Michael Taylor Vinters

This book is the product of 6,552 1/2 hour interviews. See p.7 for BMRB audit.
Within each band, firms are listed alphabetically. *See individuals' profiles p.146*

Taylor Vinters (see firm details p.1150) Busy working for the university of Cambridge Colleges, this firm's specialism lies with the acquisition, development and leasing of properties for charitable trusts. **Jennifer Warren** (see p.149) has a "*sophisticated knowledge*" of property work and **Michael Womack** (see p.150) is commended for his tax and investment advice. The firm helped effect the recent relaxation of rules relating to permanent endowment. Also obtained chartered corporation status for a college. **Clients:** Schools; universities; major grant-awarding charity.

Eversheds (see firm details p.952) The heart of this national firm's charities offering lies in the Norwich office. Headed up by the respected **Philip Norton** (see p.147), the department advises private charitable foundations and manages tax, trusts and financial matters. The group assisted several charities on their formation and trading activities. It also set up a trading company for the Norfolk & Norwich Healthcare NHS Trust's umbrella charity. Established the Norwich City Football Club in the Community Trust and advised on its charitable activities. **Clients:** Grenfell Association of Great Britain & Ireland; Norfolk & Norwich Benevolent Medical Society.

Greenwoods (see firm details p.978) The team continues to act for charities and professional institutes in the arts, education and environmental sectors. Head of department, Shelagh Smith specialises in incorporated charities and has been busy with restructurings and demergers by agreement. The group has advised on reorganisations and relationships with subsidiary trading companies, and increasingly handles related employment work. Involved in the reviewing of endowment funds for a national charity, which involved liaising with the Charity Commission. **Clients:** Institute of Credit Management, Wyggeston & Queen Elizabeth I College, Peterborough Environment City Trust.

Hewitson Becke + Shaw (see firm details p.994) Headed by Peter Ewart, the Cambridge team advises private and public charities. Their client list includes several research institutes, Cambridge colleges and arts charities. The team advise the RSPB and a number of major land-owning charities. The firm advised on the merger and incorporation of a substantial property-owning and service providing charity. Gives employment advice to large charities. **Clients:** Fund for Addenbrookes.

Leathes Prior A small Norwich firm best known for its activities in the local charity market, including advice to the RSPCA. Head of private client department William Riley holds the position of clerk for the Trustees of the Great Hospital in Norwich. **Clients:** The Great Hospital; Norfolk RSPCA.

NORTH WEST

CHARITIES • North West	Ptnrs	Assts
1 **Birch Cullimore** Chester	1	1
Brabners Liverpool	1	2
2 **Oswald Goodier & Co** Preston	1	n/a
3 **Halliwell Landau** Manchester	1	n/a
Pannone & Partners Manchester	1	n/a

LEADING INDIVIDUALS
1 **HOLDEN Lawrence** Brabners
2 **BELDERBOS Mark** Oswald Goodier & Co

This book is the product of 6,552 1/2 hour interviews. See p.7 for BMRB audit.
Within each band, firms are listed alphabetically. *See individuals' profiles p.146*

Birch Cullimore Respected charities practice which continues to administer and advise religious and educational charities, almshouses and service providers. The firm offers its charities clients particular expertise in formations, incorporation, employment and company services.

Brabners (see firm details p.892) Judged by peers to be "*serious players*" for its housing association and arts charities work, this year new clients in the regeneration sector exemplify the increasing breadth of the practice. **Lawrence Holden** (see p.147) draws praise from peers and clients. The group represented TCC, a broad-based Welsh organisation that combats social exclusion, on its successful application for charity status. **Clients:** Merseyside Youth Association; Furniture Resource Centre, Huyton Community Partnership; International Heart Centre; Liverpool Muslim Society.

Oswald Goodier & Co (see firm details p.1087) This long-established private client firm based in Preston drew respect from our interviewees. The "*effective operator*" **Mark Belderbos** (see p.146) leads the team and garners praise for his "*visibility in the more complex matters.*" Clients range from the religious to the educational sectors, as well as general welfare charitable trusts. **Clients:** RC Diocese of Lancaster; Montfort Missionary Society; Congregation of the Daughters of Wisdom.

Halliwell Landau (see firm details p.988) Working from within its trusts and estates department, the team acts for charities in the education, health and media sectors. The group, including Geoffrey Shindler, advises on formations, administration, accountancy and Charity Commission regulation. **Clients:** North West Media Charitable Trust; several university and medical bodies.

Pannone & Partners (see firm details p.1088) Operates with a significant volume of work for charities connected with public sector bodies. Dubbed a "*respectable and likeable*" firm, the charities work is led by Katherine Peterson. The group acted for a trust on the sale of its majority interest in a company providing residential care for the elderly. Continues to establish new charities, both trusts and companies, and assists its clients in applications for charitable status. **Clients:** Community Foundation for Greater Manchester, Sustainability North West; Tameside Sports Trust; The Brathay Hall Trust.

NORTH EAST

CHARITIES • North East	Ptnrs	Assts
1 **Wrigleys** Leeds	2	3
2 **Addleshaw Booth & Co** Leeds	1	3
Grays York	1	n/a
3 **Dickinson Dees** Newcastle upon Tyne	3	5
Irwin Mitchell Sheffield	1	2
4 **Eversheds** Newcastle upon Tyne	n/a	n/a
Keeble Hawson Sheffield	2	2
McCormicks Leeds	n/a	n/a

LEADING INDIVIDUALS	
1 **HARWOOD Ros** Rollits	**LAWTON Tony** Grays
LYNCH Malcolm Wrigleys	**WRIGLEY Matthew** Wrigleys

This book is the product of 6,552 1/2 hour interviews. See p.7 for BMRB audit.

Within each band, firms are listed alphabetically. *See individuals' profiles p.146*

Wrigleys (see firm details p.1191) Competitors agree this firm has been "*bolstered*" by the merger with Malcolm Lynch. The Wrigleys client base of mainly heritage, educational and religious charities adds to Malcolm Lynch's urban regeneration and environmental roster, producing a "*dynamic firm going places.*" The "*knowledgeable*" **Matthew Wrigley** and the "*committed*" **Malcolm Lynch** are the standout practitioners here. The group advised an educational charity on the hive down and subsequent sale of its trading activities into a subsidiary. Sole advisors to a major religious charity. **Clients:** Major heritage, educational and religious charities.

Addleshaw Booth & Co (see firm details p.853) Paul Howell heads this firm's private client department, of which the charities group forms a part. The group negotiated contracts for a major industrial heritage museum concerning funding provided by the National Lottery and a major national museum. It also advised a major clearing bank on its charitable foundations and acted for a well-known charity on commercial contracts with third parties and on the protection of its intellectual property rights. **Clients:** Major industrial heritage charity; local conservation charity.

Grays (see firm details p.978) Peers rate its "*enviable client list*" which, according to competitors, consists of "*a big slice of the landed estate charities sector.*" Respected ecclesiastical expert **Tony Lawton** (see p.147), who specialises in trusts and taxation as well as general charity work, heads the team. With a long tradition in this field, the firm acts for a range of clients including housing associations and arts charities. **Clients:** Roman Catholic Diocese of Middlesbrough; Dean and Chapter of York; Lady Elizabeth Hastings Charity.

Dickinson Dees (see firm details p.941) Contained in the private clients group, the team is led by ex-Charity Commissioner Claris D'Cruz. It advised Newcastle Grammar School on its successful application to become co-educational. Liaised with the Charity Commission to identify and provide solutions to the problems raised by NHS Trust mergers. The firm also advised Easington District Council on the formation of Community Leisure Partners, a charity set up to run the council's leisure services. Formed Bowes Museum, a new charitable company, and advised Durham County Council on its sole corporate trusteeship of the project. **Clients:** Newcastle Upon Tyne Grammar School; Newcastle University Development Trust; Age Concern North Tyneside; Northern Arts.

Irwin Mitchell (see firm details p.1009) Enjoying a recognised expertise in the fields of arts and educational charities, this firm has a growing emphasis on utilising charities law as a vehicle for former local authority services such as leisure, residential care and cultural facilities. Headed up by Andrew Uprichard, the team advised Sheffield City Trust on all aspects of its Eurobond issue on the Luxembourg Stock Exchange. The team conducted the demerger of the charity Sheffcare from the Sheffield City Trust Group, enabling it to pursue new service development opportunities. **Clients:** Sheffield City Trust; Sheffcare; Sheffield Galleries & Museums.

Eversheds (see firm details p.952) A multi-disciplinary team where expertise on tax, employment and IP issues is drawn from across departments. Clients include major medical, educational and local fundraising bodies. Education and health charity specialist Rowan Ferguson advised on a number of schemes involving Local Authorities working in partnership with commercial companies to establish new charities. The group established the new environmental charity Earth Balance 2000. **Clients:** Great North East Air Ambulance; International Centre for Life Trust; Stockton Arts Centre.

Keeble Hawson The charities section of this practice operates from within the private client department, and carries out constitutional, administration and some litigation matters. The practice draws praise from the market for its educational and ecclesiastical charities work.

McCormicks (see firm details p.1060) Respected Leeds practice that continues to advise a strong client base including sporting and outdoor charities. The celebrated Peter McCormick heads up a department that has won a substantial reputation in contentious and non-contentious taxation issues. The group acted for a substantial branch of the church in a multi-million pound tax matter involving the treatment of profits. It assisted Friends of War Memorials on property issues and on plans to receive substantial funding from English Heritage. **Clients:** The Duke of Edinburgh Award; The Order of the Holy Paraclete; The Harrogate Women's Centre.

Other Notable Practitioners Having left London-based Speechly Bircham, the highly respected **Ros Harwood** (see p.146) has joined **Rollits** in York. One commentator believes "*she brings a practice wherever she goes,*" and researchers were told that many anticipate the creation of a successful operation.

SCOTLAND

Anderson Strathern WS (see firm details p.859) Deemed "*well connected*" and "*strong on educational charities*" by our interviewees. The "*solid*" **George Russell** (see p.148) is experienced in the issues concerning the establishment of charities. Its broad client base includes organisations from the educational, heritage and religious sectors. The group advised the Iona Cathedral Trust and the Maggie Keswick Jencks Cancer caring centre. It acquired charitable status for the Scottish Council for National Parks, and provides ongoing advice to a substantial grant giving charitable trust. **Clients:** National Trust of Scotland; Iona Cathedral Trust; Fettes College; Edinburgh College of Art.

Turcan Connell (see firm details p.1164) Acting for over 850 charitable bodies, peers concede that this practice is "*alive and kicking.*" Researchers were told that **Douglas Connell** (see p.841) and **Simon Mackintosh** (see p.844) form a "*significant force*" in the market, acting for both privately established bodies and national institutions. On a pro bono basis, the firm established the Institute of Contemporary Scotland – a major new charity intended to be a focus of creative thinking. The group also advised on the re-incorporation of an English charity as a Scottish charity, which involved the transfer of substantial assets and winding-up of the English charity simultaneous to establishing the Scottish charity. **Clients:** National Gal-

CHARITIES • Scotland	Ptnrs	Assts
1 **Anderson Strathern WS** Edinburgh	2	1
Turcan Connell Edinburgh	n/a	1
2 **Biggart Baillie** Glasgow	1	2
Tods Murray WS Edinburgh	2	n/a
3 **Balfour & Manson** Edinburgh	3	1
Burness Glasgow	2	1
Lindsays WS Edinburgh	3	1
MacRoberts Glasgow	2	3
Morton Fraser, Solicitors Edinburgh	2	2
Shepherd & Wedderburn WS Edinburgh	2	2
TC Young & Son Glasgow	2	n/a
4 **Gillespie Macandrew WS** Edinburgh	2	2

LEADING INDIVIDUALS	
1 **CONNELL Douglas** Turcan Connell	**MACKINTOSH Simon** Turcan Connell
REITH David Lindsays WS	**RENNIE Brenda** Balfour & Manson
RUSSELL George Anderson Strathern WS	
WYLLIE Gordon Biggart Baillie	

This book is the product of 6,552 1/2 hour interviews. See p.7 for BMRB audit.

Within each band, firms are listed alphabetically. *See individuals' profiles p.146*

leries of Scotland; Scottish Hospital Endowments Research Trust; Bacher Trust; MacRoberts Trust; National Library of Scotland.

Biggart Baillie (see firm details p.882) "*Visible on the charity scene,*" this team offers constitutional, funding, property and tax advice to its charity clients. The team works cross-departmentally for a client roster that includes private and corporate charitable trusts, heritage and service provider charities. The "*vigorous*" **Gordon Wyllie** (see p.150) drew up a new constitution for The Scottish Grant Making Trust Foundation. The firm acted on the establishment of charitable trusts that channel benefits into the community from the use of power generators. Successfully challenged a local health authority to acquire a piece of scanning equipment at a local hospital and released significant funds on a matched funding basis. **Clients:** Deacon Convenor of the Trades of Glasgow; East Park; Lennoxlove Trust; The Trades House of Glasgow.

Tods Murray WS (see firm details p.1157) Boasts a client base of over 100 charities in a broad range of sectors, including national and community organisations. The firm assists in all matters including the formation of new charities, constitutional matters and charities' incorporation. Headed by formation expert Peter Ryden, the trusts, executives and tax department can draw commercial expertise from other areas of this "*serious firm.*" **Clients:** RSPCB; The Moredun Foundation; Royal Lyceum Theatre Company; Vetaid.

Balfour & Manson (see firm details p.869) Best known for its activities in medical and welfare charities work. Competitors single out the respected practitioner **Brenda Rennie** (see p.148) for praise. The practice is run from the private client department, with support across the firm's commercial and property lawyers. **Clients:** Age Concern Scotland.

Burness (see firm details p.903) This Glasgow based practice acts for over 250 charities. The firm's strength lies in the creation of innovative structures and charities working in partnership with the voluntary sector and public sector agencies. The charity group, that includes charities specialist Paul Pia, sits within the firm's corporate department, and is endorsed by peers for its high quality of commercial advice. It advised the Association of Chief Officers of Scottish Voluntary Organisations on securing charitable status and subsequent funding sources. Also instructed by the Scottish Arts Council in its role as distributor of lottery funding for artistic projects and bodies. **Clients:** Scottish Arts Council, The Big Issue in Scotland, Millennium Commission; Scottish Federation of Housing Associations.

Lindsays WS (see firm details p.1041) With a fine reputation for building preservation trust work, this firm is building up its roster of clients in the educational and service providing sector. The "*capable*" **David Reith** (see p.148) heads the practice, and advises on a wide range of charitable and trust matters. **Clients:** Scottish Historic Buildings Trust; Scottish Association of Citizens Advice Bureaux; Scottish Seabird Centre.

MacRoberts (see firm details p.1048) With a niche in charitable foundations, peers agree this firm has a real presence in the market. The group administers an ever-growing number of private charities, several of which control significant funds. Headed by David MacRobert, the team advises the Trustees of two of Paisley's largest and longest established charitable trusts. **Clients:** KIND (Scotland); SENSE (Scotland).

Morton Fraser, Solicitors (see firm details p.1076) Reputed for its representation of Edinburgh Trades, and its involvement with significant educational and grant-giving charities. Headed by Scott Ray and utilising a cross-departmental approach, the practice advises commercial operations and private clients on a range of issues including new charity formations. The firm has expertise in children's rights and has witnessed a growth in matters surrounding education and employment law. **Clients:** George Watsons College: RYA Scotland; Scottish Wildlife Trust; Scottish Agriculture College.

Shepherd & Wedderburn WS (see firm details p.1126) This Edinburgh firm's charities unit is part of a major tax and trust department. Private client and charity trust lawyers, including head of department Andrew Holehouse, work together developing ideas and trust concepts. Clients are typically found in the environmental, armed forces and medical sectors. Indicative of its strength in establishing charitable companies for its corporate clients, the group advised on the set up of the Power Partners Charitable Trust, in consultation with national charities to provide funds for projects to benefit the aged, infirm, and disabled. **Clients:** Dunblane Help Fund; Barnardo's; Scottish Power Green Energy Tariff Trust; Royal College of Surgeons.

TC Young & Son (see firm details p.1191) The group continues to act for service provider charities and private charitable trusts. Peers agree this firm has a respected reputation and remain "*stalwarts of the charities scene.*" Assists in constitutional issues, structuring, property and employment matters. **Clients:** Erskine Hospital; Princess Royal Trust for Carers; Turning Point Scotland.

Gillespie Macandrew WS (see firm details p.972) This Edinburgh-based firm is known for its strong private client base. The team, including Tom Murray, acted for a charity protecting the interests of a particular class of beneficiaries in a major charity re-organisation. The firm also advised on the establishment of a charity designed to promote crafts in Scotland, which created a collection of silver for the First Minister to use in an official capacity. It then papered the loan of that silver collection to the United States and UK institutions. **Clients:** Scottish Goldsmiths Trust; Royal British Legion of Scotland.

LEADERS IN CHARITIES

BELDERBOS, Mark
Oswald Goodier & Co, Preston (01772) 253841
OswGoodier@aol.com
Specialisation: All aspects of Charity Law, acting for many charitable organisations, both religious and secular. Ecclesiastical and Education. Commercial Property, particularly on behalf of charitable organisations. Substantial amounts of General Trust work.
Career: Qualified 1967. Partner 1968.
Personal: Born 09.11.1942. Educated at Stonyhurst College and University of Liverpool (LLB).

BROOKS, Ken
BrookStreet Des Roches, Witney
(01993) 771616

BURCHFIELD, Jonathan
Nabarro Nathanson, Reading (0118) 925 4606
j.burchfield@nabarro.com
Specialisation: Partner and head of charity group. Work includes constitutions of charities, the impact of charity law on all areas of charities' activities; and private client work, including trust and tax planning for individuals. Contributed to 'Charity Appeals: the Complete Guide to Success'.
Prof. Memberships: Deputy Chairman of the Charity Law Association, Chartered Institute of Taxation, Society of Trust and Estate Practitioners.
Career: Qualified in 1978, having joined *Turner Kenneth Brown* in 1976. Became a partner in 1983.
Personal: Born 22nd February 1954. Leisure interests include family and cricket. Lives in Guildford.

CAIRNS, Elizabeth
Elizabeth Cairns, Maidstone (01622) 858191
Specialisation: Specialist charity law practice established since 1990. Areas of particular interest include charitable status, constitutional issues, incorporation of charities and dispute resolution. She aims to give a high quality and sophisticated service to a wide range of charities and voluntary organisations.
Career: Charity Commission 1972-79; *Jaques & Lewis* 1979-90 (partner 1984).
Publications: 'Charities: Law & Practice' (Sweet & Maxwell) 3rd edn 1996; 'Fundraising for Charity' (Tolley) 1996.

CLARICOAT, John
Claricoat Phillips, London
(020) 7226 7000

CONNELL, Douglas
Turcan Connell, Edinburgh (0131) 228 8111
dac@turcanconnell.com
Specialisation: Joint senior partner. Specialist in trusts, tax planning, asset protection, charities and heritage property; acts as principal adviser to many chairmen and chief executives regarding their personal business and to the trustees of a number of major national charities, as well as private charitable foundations.
Prof. Memberships: President Scottish Young Lawyers Association 1975-76; member of Revenue Committee the Law Society of Scotland 1979-92; chairman Edinburgh Book Festival 1991-95; member Scottish Arts Council and chairman Lottery Committee, Scottish Arts Council 1994-97.
Career: Attended University of Edinburgh (LLB). Articled *Dundas & Wilson CS*; qualified 1976; partner 1979-97.
Personal: Born 1954. Resides Edinburgh. Leisure interests include books, travel and good food.

DAVIS, Elizabeth
Blake Lapthorn, Portsmouth (023) 9222 1122

DE'ATH, Gary
Veale Wasborough, Birmingham (0117) 925 2020

DOLLIMORE, Jean
Radcliffes, London (020) 7222 7040
jean.dollimore@radcliffes.com
Specialisation: Partner, private client. Head of Charity Group. All aspects of charity law with an emphasis on constitutional structures, the establishment of subsidiaries and trading companies, and the powers and duties of trustees. Also experienced in wills and trusts, estate planning, and the administration of estates. Experienced speaker and contributor to charity publications.
Prof. Memberships: Law Society; Member of the Executive Committee of the Charity Law Association; Charities Correspondent for Private Client Business.
Personal: Educated Hitchin Girls Grammar School and Lady Margaret Hall, Oxford.

DRISCOLL, Lindsay
Sinclair Taylor & Martin, London 0208 969 3667
ld@sinclairtaylor.co.uk
Specialisation: All aspects of charity law advising on a wide range of matters including constitutional reviews, establishment of charities, legal aspects of fund raising, trading companies, Charity Commission schemes, trustee issues. Experienced speaker and author of many articles in charity press and co-author of NCVO's 'Guide to Charities Acts'.
Prof. Memberships: Law Society. Charity Law Association. Executive Committee member.
Career: Qualified 1971. At *Biddle & Co.* 1969-73. Assistant Public Trustee Kenya 1974-78, Lecturer Kenya School of Law 1973-78, Charity Law Consultant 1981-87. Assistant Legal Adviser then Legal Adviser of NCVO 1987-95.
Personal: Born 17th April 1947. Educated St Hugh's College Oxford (MA). Trustee of several charities. As director of International Centre for Not for Profit Law participates in conferences on law and regulation of NGOs all over the world.

FEA, Michael
Martineau Johnson, Birmingham (0121) 678 1480
michael.fea@martjohn.com
Specialisation: Thirty years specialisation in estate planning, all aspects of charity law, wills, trusts, succession and probate. Trustee/clerk to a number of charities.
Prof. Memberships: Society of Trust and Estate Practitioners; Charity Law Association; Law Society.
Career: Partner 1971. Notary Public. Member West Midlands Mental Health Tribunal. Deputy Registrar Birmingham Diocese.
Personal: Born 1939. Attended Winchester College (1954-58). Recreations include: tennis, shooting, concerts, opera and gardening. Lives in Worcestershire.

GATELEY, Stephen
Gateley Wareing, Birmingham (0121) 234 0000

GREENHOUS, Guy
Radcliffes, London (020) 7222 7040
guy.greenhous@radcliffes.com
Specialisation: Charities and on-shore Private Clients Law.
Prof. Memberships: STEP, Charity Law Association and Law Society Probate Section.
Career: Articled *Radcliffes & Co*; qualified 1972; partner 1976; Joint head of charities group 1996-2001. Lay member of Berkshire Family Practitioner Committee 1985-91. Associate member of Berkshire FHSA and Berkshire Health Authority since 1991. Chairman of Berkshire Health Authority NHS Discipline Committee and Dispensing Services Committee since 1996. Chairman of the Radley Mariners Executive Committee 1996-99. Vice president of Marlow Rowing Club since 2000. Chairman of a Law Society monitoring of training contracts panel 1987-00. Trust of Guild of Aid for Gentlepeople since 1997. Director Greenhous Group, Shrewsbury 1972-90.
Publications: 'Caradoc's Last Stand' (1965) and 'Legal Aspects of NHS Trust Funds' (1984).
Personal: Born 6th September 1947. Educated at Radley College and College of Law. Married Sarah McFall 1972, one son and one daughter. Leisure pursuits include cycling, rowing, wine and three allotments. Club: Marlow Rowing Club.

HARWOOD, Ros J
Rollits, York (01904) 625 790
ros.harwood@rollits.com
Specialisation: Charity law exclusively. Acting for a wide range of charities on all aspects of charity law. Has written numerous articles for national newspapers and charity sector periodicals. Also frequent speaker at seminars.
Prof. Memberships: Secretary of the Charity Law Association. Law Society. ACEVO – Association of Chief Executives for Voluntary Organisations.
Career: Head of charity group at *Rollits*. First joined *Lee Bolton & Lee* as trainee in 1987. Partner at *Speechly Bircham* 1998-2000. Joined *Rollits* as partner in January 2001.
Personal: Educated at Bath High School for Girls, GDST and Churchers College, Petersfield; Birmingham University LLB. Enjoys hockey, cycling, walking, gardening. Lives in North Yorkshire.

HERRING, John
Mills & Reeve, Norwich (01603) 693 209
john.herring@mills-reeve.com
Specialisation: All aspects of charity law with particular emphasis on ecclesiastical charities and charity property. Also Registrar of Diocese of Norwich and legal secretary to the Bishop of Norwich.
Prof. Memberships: Law Society, Ecclesiastical Law Association (former Executive Committee Member), Ecclesiastical Law Society.

HILL, Judith
Farrer & Co, London (020) 7292 2022
Specialisation: Partner and head of the charity team, member of the Management Board. Main area of practice is charity law, including the establishment of charities, constitutional issues and trading companies. Also experienced in art and heritage law, general private client work, covering trusts, wills, capital taxation. Contributor to 'Trust Law International', 'The Charity Law and Practice Review', 'NGO Finance' and assistant editor of 'Art, Antiquity & Law', on advisory editorial board of 'The Charity Law & Practice Review' and the editorial board of 'Trust Law Interna-

tional'. Consultant editor of Peter Luxton's 'The Law of Charities' published by OUP. Regularly addresses conferences on charity law topics.
Prof. Memberships: Law Society, Holborn Law Society, International Bar Association (co-chairman committee 20), Charity Law Association (chairman).
Career: Joined *Farrer & Co* in 1973, qualifying in 1975. Moved to *Shoosmiths & Harrison* in Northampton in 1979, until 1981. Re-joined *Farrer & Co* in 1985. Partner 1986.
Personal: Born 8 October 1949. Attended Brighton & Hove High School 1956-69, Newnham College, Cambridge 1969-72. Appointed Lieutenant of the Victorian Order in 1995. Leisure pursuits include gardening and reading. Lives in London.

HOLDEN, Lawrence
Brabners, Liverpool (0151) 600 3000
lawrence.holden@brabners.com
Specialisation: Consultant. Principal area of practice involves advising a number of major housing associations and charities. Author of a number of articles on computers and the law and law practice management and legal education. Was a Panel Member of NFHA Independent Inquiry into Governance of Housing Associations 1994-5. Article on 'Charities and Governance' in Charity Law and Practice Review Vol. 4 Issue 4.
Prof. Memberships: Law Society, Charity Law Society, National Federation of Housing Association Solicitors' Group, Society for Computers and Law.
Career: Qualified in 1965 while with *Brabner Holden*, became a partner in 1966. Past President Liverpool Law Society, Pro Chancellor and former President of Council Liverpool University. Deputy Lieutenant of Merseyside.
Personal: Born 19th September 1940. Attended Liverpool College 1951-59, then Liverpool University 1959-62. Leisure pursuits include fell walking, gardening and wood sculpture. Lives in Birkenhead.

KING, Michael
Stone King, Bath (01225) 337599

KING, Richard
Tozers, Exeter (01392) 207020

LAWTON, F A (Tony)
Grays, York (01904) 634771
Specialisation: Partner in 1967. Main area of practice is charity law, conveyancing in relation to charity property, formation of charities and negotiating with Charity Commissioners. Also experienced in work relating to education (especially statutory interpretation of the Education Acts), unincorporated associations, non-Companies Act companies and housing associations.
Prof. Memberships: Law Society, Yorkshire Law Society, Charity Law Association, Education Law Association.
Career: Qualified 1966. Joined *Grays* in 1967. Partner 1967. Board member Trustee Savings Bank of Yorkshire & Lincoln 1976-89. Committee member Conference of Solicitors for Catholic Charities 1967-date. (Chairman 1998-date).
Personal: Born 9 July 1940. Attended Bordeaux University 1958-59, then Corpus Christi College, Cambridge 1959-62. Leisure pursuits include history, gardening and foreign travel. Lives in York.

LLOYD, Stephen
Bates, Wells & Braithwaite, London (020) 7551 7777

LYNCH, Malcolm
Wrigleys, Leeds (0113) 244 6100

MACKINTOSH, Simon
Turcan Connell, Edinburgh (0131) 228 8111
sam@turcanconnell.com
Specialisation: Main areas of practice are tax, trusts and charities. Work includes tax planning, heritage property, often with an international element, charity law and practice; and trust establishment, variation and practice. Lead partner for a number of the firm's major charity clients. Joint head of the firm's charity unit. Convenor of the Law Society of Scotland Tax Law Committee and of its panel on Trust Law Accreditation.
Prof. Memberships: Society of Trust and Estate Practitioners, International Academy of Estate and Trust Law.
Career: Partner *Turcan Connell* 1997; partner *W & J Burness WS* 1985-97; non-executive director of Macphie of Glenbervie Ltd and past board member of the Edinburgh International Book Festival. Member of the Scottish Executive Commission on reform of charity law.
Publications: Co-author of 'Revenue Law of Scotland', 1987.

MARTIN, Matthew T
Cozens-Hardy & Jewson, Norwich (01603) 625231
Specialisation: Consultant in private client department. Main areas of practice are charity law and administration. Solicitor and clerk to Trustees of a number of charities, including Norwich Consolidated Charities, Norwich Town Close Estate Charity, Anguish's Educational Foundation, The Memorial Trust of the 2nd Air Division USAAF and Laura Elizabeth Stuart Memorial Trust. Chairman of the Norfolk Archeological Trust.
Prof. Memberships: Law Society, Charity Law Association.
Career: Joined *Cozens-Hardy & Jewson* in 1962. Qualified in 1967. Became partner in 1969. Consultant in 1996.
Personal: Born 28 June 1943. Attended Bradfield College, Berkshire 1957-61. Under Sheriff of City of Norwich 1987-94. Leisure pursuits include golf and gardening.

MEAKIN, Robert
Stone King, London (020) 7796 1007

MIDDLETON, Fiona
Bates, Wells & Braithwaite, London (020) 7551 7777

MIMPRISS, Peter
Allen & Overy, London (020) 7330 3000
peter.mimpriss@allenovery.com
Specialisation: Partner in Private Client Department. Main areas of practice are private client and major national charities including universities, professional institutions, national museums and art centres.
Prof. Memberships: Law Society. Charity Law Association. Institute of Philanthropy and involved in many other trusts.
Career: Qualified 1967. Joined *Allen & Overy* in 1968, and became a Partner in 1972. Chairman of the Charity Law Association in 1992-97. Chairman of the Chariguard Group of Common Investment Funds in 1994-2000.
Personal: Born 22nd August 1943. Trustee or director of The Prince's Trust, Leeds Castle Foundation, The Edward Heath Charitable Trust, Michael Bishop Foundation, the Edwina Mountbatten Trust SolCare and The Institute of Philanthropy. Appointed University Solicitor, University of London in 1994. Interests include the development of charity law, maritime history, book collecting, contemporary art and driving vintage sports cars.

NORTON, Philip
Eversheds, Norwich (01603) 272638
philipnorton@eversheds.com
Specialisation: Creation and administration of charities; constitutional trading and governance issues. Honorary Solicitor for Age Concern Norwich, Norfolk and Norwich Benelovent Medical Society, Friends of Kelling Hospital and the Norfolk & Norwich University Hospital NHS Trust Hospital Arts Project. Also acts as solicitor for and trustee of a number of hospital based charities eg Norfolk Renal Fund, Norwich and Norfolk Diabetes Trust and NANIME Charitable Trust and private foundations. Advises commercial clients on charity issues. Lectures to charities, hospital management and retirement groups on charity law and personal affairs.
Prof. Memberships: Law Society, Charity Law Association, Norfolk & Norwich Medico-Legal Society, Society of Trust and Estate Practitioners.
Career: Qualified 1984 while with *Hill & Perks*, now *Eversheds*, and became a partner in 1990.
Personal: Born 17th September 1959. Attended Queen Elizabeth's School, Barnet 1972-78, then Sheffield University 1978-81. Leisure includes mountain walking. Lives near Wymondham, Norfolk.

PAINES, Alison
Withers, London (020) 7597 6000
Specialisation: Head of charities practice. Charity law and related tax and trust advice for not-for-profit organisations and their donors. Advises on structure, status, operations (including trading issues) and funding. Particular expertise in charitable issues relating to the NHS and government related charities. On editorial board and contributor to Kluwer's 'International Charitable Giving: Law and Taxation' and contributor to Tolley's 'Charities Manual' and FT Law and Tax's 'Practical Trust Precedents'.
Prof. Memberships: Charity Law Association (Executive Committee member); Society of Trusts and Estates Practitioners.
Career: Qualified 1981. Solicitor with *Crossman, Block & Keith* 1981-87; joined *Withers* 1988 and became a partner in 1991.
Personal: Educated Notting Hill and Ealing High School GPDST 1966-73; Girton College Cambridge 1974-78 (classics and law); trustee of two grant-making foundations.

PAISNER, Martin
Berwin Leighton Paisner, London (020) 7760 1000
martin.paisner@berwinleightonpaisner.com
Specialisation: Practice embraces tax and estate planning advice with particular emphasis on the high net worth entrepreneur, including trust structures both for the UK based (whether domiciled or not) and an international clientele. In addition, he advises widely on all aspects of charity law involving both grant-making and functional charities and serves as trustee of, and solicitor to numerous charitable bodies.
Prof. Memberships: Law Society, Society of Trust and Estate Practitioners, Charity Law Association.

Career: Born 1 September 1943. Attended St Paul's School, London 1956-61, Sorbonnne University, Paris 1961-62, Worcester College, Oxford 1962-65 and Ann Arbor, Michigan 1966-67. Honorary Fellow of Queen Mary and Westfield College, University of London. Qualified 1970. Partner at *Paisner & Co* (now *Berwin Leighton Paisner*) in 1972.
Personal: Leisure pursuits include antiquarian book-collecting (18th and 19th Century English and American literature), inter-war travel posters, music, reading, communal interests and learning from his children all the things he never knew! Currently Chairman of The Jerusalem Foundation (UK). Member of The Reform Club.

PHILLIPS, Andrew
Bates, Wells & Braithwaite, London (020) 7551 7777

PHILLIPS, Ann
Stone King, London (020) 7796 1007

PHILLIPS, Hilary
Claricoat Phillips, London (020) 7226 7000
philcoat@aol.com
Specialisation: Specialist in charity law. Fellow of the Society of Advanced Legal Studies. Consultant to several large national charities and city solicitors. Joint author with John Claricoat of numerous articles on charity law topics.
Career: In private practice before joining DES in 1970. Joined the Charity Commission in 1973. Served for 21 years reaching Grade 6.

PIPER, Anne-Marie
Farrer & Co, London (020) 7242 2022
amp@farrer.co.uk
Specialisation: Partner in the charity team. Practice encompasses charity law ranging from the formation and registration of new charities, advice to charity trustees on various matters including permissible activities, trading and commercial activities and tax-efficient fundraising through to the restructuring, variation and dissolution of charities. Acts for sponsors of new charities; directors, trustees and organisers of existing charities; and companies making charitable gifts or having dealings with charities. Frequent contributor of articles to professional publications on charity law subjects.
Prof. Memberships: Founder Charity Law Association.
Career: Called to the Bar in 1980. Noble Lowndes Personal Financial Services 1980-83. Joined private client department at *Richards Butler* in 1983. Admitted as a solicitor in 1988 and became a partner in 1989. Joined *Paisner & Co* as a partner in 1994. Joined *Farrer & Co* as a partner in 2001.
Personal: Born 27 January 1958. Attended North Walsham Secondary School 1969-74, then Norfolk College of Arts & Technology 1974-76. Went on to University College, London, 1976-79 and the Council of Legal Education 1979-80. Charity trustee. Leisure pursuits include family life and reading. Lives in London.

PORTRAIT, Judith
Portrait Solicitors in Association with Denton Wilde Sapte, London (020) 7320 3888
Specialisation: All aspects of charity law, advising both grant-making and service-providing charities. Also advising on private trusts, estate and tax planning for individuals and trustees.
Career: Treasurer of The Henry Smith Charity; Trustee and Legal Adviser to the Sainsbury Family Charitable Trusts.
Personal: Educated St Paul's Girls' School and St Hugh's College Oxford. Married; resides in Cambridge.

POULTER, Alan
Manches, Oxford (01865) 722106
alan.poulter@manches.co.uk
Specialisation: Principal areas of practice include advice to charitable and educational institutions, including universities and the colleges of Oxford University, formation of new charities, private trusts, tax-planning and related work for private clients.
Prof. Memberships: Charity Law Association; Society of Trust and Estate Practitioners.
Career: Qualified 1971 while at *Biddle & Co.* Joined *Morrell Peel & Gamlen* 1974 and became a partner in 1975. Became partner in *Manches* on the merger of *Morrell Peel & Gamlen* in 1997.
Personal: Born 4th November 1945. School Governor and Trustee of various charities.

PROTANI, Moira
Berwin Leighton Paisner, London (020) 7427 1198
moira.protani@berwinleightonpaisner.com
Specialisation: Head of the Charities Group. Advises on all aspects of the law as it affects charities, donors and businesses which deal with charities. Encompasses a whole range of matters including establishment of charities, trustee powers and duties, taxation, grant-making, fundraising, mergers, constitutional and good governance issues. Acted in a large scale charity merger and the incorporation of an unincorporated association. Frequently lectures on charity law issues.
Prof. Memberships: Charity Law Association, the Law Society and the Royal Society of Arts.
Career: Trained at and employed by *SJ Berwin & Co.* Qualified in 1990. Became a partner of *SJ Berwin & Co* in 1998. Became a partner of *Berwin Leighton Paisner* in September 2000.
Publications: Has written numerous articles on charity law. Most recently 'The Risk of Good Intentions – Should Charities Insure their Trustees?', NGO Finance September 1999; 'Incorporation – a Safer Bet?', Association Manager March 2000; 'Dealing with Founder Syndrome', NGO Finance April 2000.
Personal: Born 1 October 1957; interests include international travel, food and wine and tapestry. Sits on the board of four charities.

REES, John
Winckworth Sherwood, Oxford (01865) 297 200
jrees@ws-oxford.co.uk
Specialisation: Partner in ecclesiastical, education and charities department. Main area of practice is ecclesiastical law. Registrar, Province of Canterbury. Joint Registrar, Diocese of Oxford. Legal Adviser to the Anglican Consultative Council (the international liaison body for the Anglican Communion worldwide). Extensive experience in contested faculty cases, including Court of Arches Judgment in Re St. Luke, Maidstone: wide acquaintance with education law issues on behalf of governors and trustees.
Prof. Memberships: Ecclesiastical Law Association, Ecclesiastical Law Society (Treasurer).
Career: Qualified 1975. Joined *Winckworth Sherwood* 1986. Partner 1988.
Personal: Born 21 April 1951. Holds LLB (Southampton 1972), MA (Oxon 1984) and MPhil (Leeds 1984). Leisure interests include photography and cycling. Lives in Oxford.

REITH, David
Lindsays WS, Edinburgh (0131) 477 8708
Specialisation: Partner in commercial department. Main area of practice is commercial property, but specialises in charities, including building preservation and other conservation work. Acted for Lothian Building Preservation Trust in successful campaign to save Mavisbank House, near Edinburgh, from demolition. Legal adviser to the Scottish Seabird Centre millennium founded project and the Scottish Association of Citizens Advice Bureaux. Has spoken at various seminars on charity law.
Prof. Memberships: Law Society of Scotland, WS Society.
Career: Qualified in 1974, having joined *Lindsays WS* in 1972. Became a Partner in 1976. Director of Scottish Historic Buildings Trust, Cockburn Conservation Trust, Scottish Sculpture Trust, Boilerhouse Theatre Company and other charitable companies. Secretary of Scottish Seabird Centre and Queensberry House Trust. Treasurer of the Cockburn Association and Fet-Lor Youth Club.
Personal: Born 15th April 1951. Educated at Fettes College 1965-69 and Aberdeen University 1969-72. Leisure interests include winemaking, gardening and architectural heritage. Lives in East Lothian.

RENNIE, Brenda
Balfour & Manson, Edinburgh (0131) 2001275
brenda.rennie@balfour-manson.co.uk
Specialisation: Head of Private Client Department. As part of a general private client practice, has developed a particular interest in charities and in the elderly and disabled. Has considerable experience in setting up charities and giving ongoing advice. The administration of private charitable trusts is a specialty. Is the Solicitor to Age Concern Scotland.
Prof. Memberships: W.S.; Member of the W.S. Society Legal Education Committee; Member of Society of Trust and Estate Practitioners; Member of Board of EDINVAR Housing Association; Trustee and chairman – High Blood Pressure Foundation.
Career: Qualified in 1971, having joined *Balfour & Manson* in 1969. Became a Partner in 1976.
Publications: Editor of Butterworths 'Scottish Older Client Law Service'.
Personal: Born 21st December 1947. Educated in Aberdeen and graduated University of Aberdeen LLB Hons 1969. Enjoys reading, walking and looking at buildings. Lives in Edinburgh.

RUSSELL, George
Anderson Strathern WS, Edinburgh (0131) 220 2345
Specialisation: Main areas of practice are charities, trusts and tax planning and financial services. Charity work includes setting up charities and ongoing advice for a number of charitable trusts and large charities; clients include Napier University.
Career: Edinburgh University, qualified 1973, partner 1976; Chairman Scottish Solicitors' Staff Pension Fund; member Executive of Queen's Nurses Institute of Scotland; member Scottish Council for National Parks; Fiscal of W.S. Society; Council Member National Trust for Scotland 1991-96; awarded MBE in 1995.
Personal: Born 1946; resides Linlithgow, West Lothian. Enjoys hill walking, skiing, music and golf.

SAUNDERS, Joss
Linnells, Oxford (01865) 248 607
jss@linnells.co.uk
Specialisation: Partner and head of charity unit. Company secretary at Oxfam. Acts for educational, medical, development, children's and church charities, and grant-making trusts. Also active in e-business, intellectual property and publishing.
Prof. Memberships: Charity Law Association, Society for Computers and Law, Oxford Publishing Society.
Career: Qualified 1988. *Theodore Goddard* 1986-92. Eastern Europe 1992-95. Ran Polish branch of Prince of Wales Business Leaders' Forum. Lecturer, Warsaw University. Joined *Linnells* 1995.
Publications: NCVO's 'Guide to Contracts with Public Bodies' (1998); 'Business Law and Practice' (Cambridge Board of Continuing Education); contributor to 'Higher Education and the Law' (Open University).
Personal: Born 1962. Educated Trinity College, Oxford. LLM London. Trustee of charities working in education, in Africa, and a grant-making Trust. Also trustee of Helen House, the country's first children's hospice. Advisory Council Oxford University Law Foundation. Advisory board of Hugh Pilkington Charitable Trust.

SCOTT, Michael
Charles Russell, London (020) 7203 5069
mikes@cr-law.co.uk
Specialisation: Charity, company and commercial law. Incorporation of the Royal Air Force Benevolent Fund by Royal Charter. Constitutional and commercial advice to the Royal College of Nursing. Various transactions over the past year for other charities and institutions.
Prof. Memberships: The Charity Law Association, The Law Society.
Career: Joined *Charles Russell* as a trainee 1975. Qualified 1978 (and in Hong Kong 1979). Hong Kong Office 1979-85. Became a partner in 1985. Head of the Charities Group.
Publications: 'Butterworths Charity Law Handbook'. Various articles.
Personal: Wellington College, The Queen's College, Oxford. Married, three children. Leisure interests: Various outdoor sports.

SINCLAIR TAYLOR, James
Sinclair Taylor & Martin, London
(0208) 969 3667
jst@sinclairtaylor.co.uk
Specialisation: Partner specialising in charity law. Main area of practice is charity law. Work includes charity formation and mergers, company law, property transactions, internal structure and employment law, trading VAT and contracts with funders. Also deals with not for profit organisations, housing associations, schools and local authorities, advising on property, employment, corporate and charity law. Has substantial involvement in the urban regeneration development trust movement, learned societies, pressure groups, third world charities and housing and care. Author of numerous articles and of the 'Voluntary Sector Legal Handbook' and of the 'Company Handbook and Registers for Voluntary Organizations'. Involved in training for charities and Housing Associations with A.C.E.V.O. Directory for Social Change, Charity Finance Directors Group and other organisations.
Prof. Memberships: Charity Law Association.
Career: Qualified in 1975. Founded *Sinclair Taylor & Martin* in 1981.
Personal: Charity trustee of a wide variety of organisations.

SMITH, Tim
Griffith Smith, Brighton (01273) 324041
Specialisation: Specialises in all aspects of charity law (registration, constitutional issues, charity property, fundraising etc.) and provides an initial free 'legal audit' service as a way of identifying potential problems. He also draws on his experience of working full-time in charity management throughout the 1980s which gives him particular understanding of the practical issues facing charity managers and trustees.
Prof. Memberships: Charity Law Association.
Career: Qualified as Solicitor in 1979. Worked full time in charity management 1981-90. With *Griffith Smith* since 1990 (Partner 1991).
Personal: Married with two children. Interested in wide range of social and community issues – and jazz and hill-walking when time allows.

SYED, Catriona
Charles Russell, London (020) 7203 5000
catrions@cr-law.co.uk
See under Trusts & Personal Tax, p.847

THOMPSON, Romaine
Anthony Collins Solicitors, Birmingham
(0121) 200 3242
Specialisation: Heads up the constitution and charities department within the regeneration team providing specialist legal services to numerous charities, churches, RSLs, Community Associations and not for profit organisations throughout the UK. The department advises charities on all legal aspects of their activities such as formation and registration, compliance with the Charity Commission requirements, restructuring, fund-raising, trustee training, advice on employment law, copyright and property management issues. The department publishes a free newsletter to clients updating them on legal issues and also offers a fixed fee legal audit.
Prof. Memberships: Romaine is a member of the Charity Law Association, the Ecclesiastical Law Society.
Career: Educated at Trinity Hall, Cambridge. Qualified 1988. Romaine joined *Anthony Collins Solicitors* in 1989 and became a partner in 1993. She has written articles for professional journals and lectures on charity law issues.

VOLLER, Paul
Bircham Dyson Bell, London (020) 7222 8044
paulvoller@bdb-law.co.uk
Specialisation: Company commercial and charities group. Partner specialising in corporate services for larger charities, private companies and banks; represented a group of seven charities in projects to raise £50-£100m at the banks; negotiated ground-breaking agreement with the Charity Commission in the field of trustee remuneration; advised on transfers of car homes and school undertakings; amalgamation of professional institutes; equity and debt finance for private companies; lending and security arrangements for corporate commercial bank facilities.
Prof. Memberships: Charity Law Association; Institute of Directors; fellow of the Royal Society of Arts.
Career: Qualified 1981; partner 1988; partner *Bircham Dyson Bell* (*Bircham & Co*) 1999.
Publications: Regular contributor to Charity Legal Journals.
Personal: Sutton Grammar School; University of Keele. Born 1955; resides Sutton. Interests include: Theatre, music, gardening. Languages: French.

WARREN, Jennifer
Taylor Vinters, Cambridge (01223) 423444
Specialisation: Partner dealing with all property aspects of Charity Law. Acting for a wide range of charities and educational institutions, advising on the purchase, development, management and disposal of property holdings and investments, and the making and documentation of charitable grants. Recent transactions include acting for a disability charity on two joint ventures for Cambridge University on several developments and a major religious charity with substantial property holdings on compliance issues.
Career: Qualified 1981. With *Bischoff & Co* 1979-91. Associate partner from 1986. Joined *Bates Wells & Braithwaite* 1991 as head of property department. Partner 1992. Joined *Taylor Vinters* as Partner 1996.
Personal: Exeter University 1967-70. Arts administrator and Member of Tate Gallery Educational Committee 1971-77. Governor of Anglia Polytechnic University. Visual arts, reading, riding.

WEIL, Simon
Bircham Dyson Bell, London (020) 7222 8044
simonweil@bdb-law.co.uk
Specialisation: Specialist areas comprise charities, tax planning, commercial property for institutional investment clients (frequently with charitable status) and the resolution of potentially contentious issues for charities and others, arising out of wills, trusts and co-ownership of property. Important cases have included advising a substantial corporate charity with a turnover running into ten figures on governance and trustee duties; converting an educational trust from an unincorporated charity to a company limited by guarantee; arranging the reorganisation of a livery company's charitable trust with a view to protecting individual members of the company who had previously been personally liable to third parties; the disposal by legally binding tender to companies invited to bid, of a major commercial site in High Holborn; the establishment of a comprehensive divestment programme for a group of charities with a common trustee, involving the setting up of real property and securities investment pooling schemes; creating a corporate vehicle for the service provider aspects of a group of almshouse charities.
Prof. Memberships: CLA. EAPG. ACTAPS. Law Society.
Career: Served on the firm's Premises and General Purposes Committee and Staff Committee, becoming the partner responsible for the firm's practice development in 1988. Continued in the latter role until 1992 and was head of the Private Client Department between 1991 and 1995. Financial Services Act Compliance Officer between 1991 and 1997 and took a leading role in establishing Bircham Dyson Bell Investment Management. Head of the Charities Group since 1996.
Personal: Opera, singing and music generally; drawing; wine; reading history and novels (normally pre-00); member of Chatham House (RIIA) with a particular focus on central Europe; tennis; swimming; riding; member of Oxford and Cambridge Club. Also active within St. Mary's Church Islington.

WOMACK, Michael
Taylor Vinters, Cambridge (01223) 423444
Specialisation: Mainly educational and fundraising charities, universities, colleges, schools and grant

awarding bodies. The major tasks of this year have been to assist charities to use their assets as flexibly as possible by the use of constitutional changes approved by the Charity Commission or by schemes that the Charity Commission approves.
Prof. Memberships: Law Society; Anglo-German Lawyers; Law Society European Group; Licensing Executive's Society; Educational Law Association. Charity Law Association.
Career: Trinity Hall, Cambridge; LLM University College, London. Articled in City firm and joined *Taylors* as it then was in 1975. In November 2000 became a consultant to the firm.
Personal: Ornithology, hill-walking, photography, foreign languages and travel.

WOODHEAD, Louise
Wragge & Co, Birmingham (0870) 903 1000

WOODWARD, Mark
Osborne Clarke, Bristol (0117) 917 3000

WRIGLEY, Matthew
Wrigleys, Leeds (0113) 244 6100

WYLD, Charles
Burges Salmon, Bristol (0117) 902 2773
charles.wyld@burges-salmon.com
See under Trusts & Personal Tax, p.848

WYLLIE, Gordon
Biggart Baillie, Glasgow (0141) 228 8000
gwyllie@biggartbaillie.co.uk
Specialisation: Advises a range of public charitable bodies, including the Trades House of Glasgow and its related trusts, the Edinburgh Dog and Cat Home and several heritage bodies such as the Trades Hall Trust, The Clyde Maritime Trust and the Pollokshields Burgh Hall Trust. Founding Member of the Scottish Grant Making Trust Administrators' Forum and Clerk to the Commissioners of Income Tax for both Glasgow North and Glasgow South divisions. Also advises on succession matters and particularly enjoys problems with unusual or foreign elements.
Prof. Memberships: International Bar Association, Law Society of Scotland, Society of Trust and Estate Practitioners, Society of Writers To the Signet and Scottish Grant Making Trust Administrators' Forum.
Career: Head of Executry Department *Strathern and Blair WS*, Edinburgh 1975-77. Head of private client services and charities at *Biggart Baillie* (partner since 1980).
Publications: The Scottish contribution to the 'International Dictionary of Succession Terms'.
Personal: History, music and the arts, architecture and design, language (Italian, French, Spanish and Greek), country dancing, country walks and gardening.

CHURCH LAW

OVERVIEW: Divided into two parts, this section firstly covers firms with diocesan registrars who act for the Church of England and practice true ecclesiastical law. Secondly the research looks at firms acting for other denominations where work draws on diverse areas such as charity, education, employment, property and trusts. In the case of the Roman Catholic church, the work involves knowledge of the core area of canon law and its ramifications in relation to British law. The new faculty jurisdiction rules (January 2001) are designed to encourage more consultation between the clergy and the general public. This, together with other legislation such as the Human Rights Act and the Data Protection Act, is seeing the church under increasing pressure to change in line with other public bodies in becoming more regulated and accountable. Over the last few years a series of highly publicised incidents involving members of the clergy have highlighted issues of wide public concern such as child protection. A committee has been set up under Lord Nolan to investigate the church's procedures for dealing with sex abuse by clergy.

RESEARCH APPROVED BY BMRB: *For this edition,* Chambers' *researchers conducted 6,552 interviews – 4,419 with law firms, 554 with barristers and 1,579 with clients.*

The validity of the research was scrutinised by BMRB International, who audited both the methodology and the results at our offices in July 2001. They interviewed Chambers' *researchers and cross-checked sample interviews. Details of the audit appear on page 7.*

LONDON

CHURCH OF ENGLAND

CHURCH: CHURCH OF ENGLAND • London	
1	Lee Bolton & Lee
	Winckworth Sherwood

LEADING INDIVIDUALS		
1	**BEESLEY Peter** Lee Bolton & Lee	**MORRIS Paul** Winckworth Sherwood
	RICHENS Nicholas Lee Bolton & Lee	
2	**THATCHER Michael** Winckworth Sherwood	

This book is the product of 6,552 1/2-hour interviews. See p.7 for BMRB audit.
Within each band, firms are listed alphabetically. *See individuals' profiles p.154*

Lee Bolton & Lee (see firm details p.1034) A first-rate firm, with a dynamic approach, extensive experience and close involvement with the Ecclesiastical Law Association. **Peter Beesley** has many strings to his bow including expertise in marriage and charity law. "*Quiet-spoken, but knowledgeable,*" he is the current president of the Ecclesiastical Law Association and is said to be the "*most senior of all solicitors dealing with church law.*" "*Forceful*" **Nick Richens** is advisor to the national body that advises church schools and is warmly recommended.

Winckworth Sherwood (see firm details p.1185) The other prominent firm in London, Winckworth Sherwood is renowned for the breadth and scale of its practice. Somewhat unusually the recently expanded team advises both the Church of England and the Roman Catholic church, and has also undertaken the charity, trust and employment work for RC Diocese of Brentwood. "*Star*" **Paul Morris**, whose "*knowledge of law is second to none,*" is registrar to the London and Southwark dioceses and joint-registrar for the Leicester diocese. He is well known for his involvement in major curate employment issues. The "*unostentatious*" **Michael Thatcher** (see p.304) is an expert in education.

OTHER DENOMINATIONS

CHURCH: OTHER DENOMINATIONS • London	
1	Ellis Wood
2	Carter Lemon Camerons
	Pothecary & Barratt

This book is the product of 6,552 1/2-hour interviews. See p.7 for BMRB audit.
Within each band, firms are listed alphabetically.

Ellis Wood Although generally felt to have decreased in profile over the last year, Ellis Wood remains an active and respected firm in this area.

Carter Lemon Camerons Philip Ross Smith acts for Baptist deacons, church secretaries and church sub-committees in areas such as property and litigation, restructuring of church bodies and the maintenance of listed buildings belonging to the Church.

Pothecary & Barratt Retains its long standing reputation for advising the Methodist church central authority and the Baptist Union of Wales on matters relating to property, constitutional, trust, discipline and education issues.

THE SOUTH & SOUTH WEST

CHURCH OF ENGLAND

CHURCH: CHURCH OF ENGLAND • South & South West
Follett Stock Truro
Harris & Harris Wells
Michelmores Exeter
Thomas Eggar Church Adams Chichester
White & Bowker Winchester
Brutton & Co Fareham
Madge Lloyd & Gibson Gloucester

LEADING INDIVIDUALS	
BERRY Timothy Harris & Harris	**FOLLETT Martin** Follett Stock
WHITE Peter White & Bowker	
BUTCHER Christopher Thomas Eggar Church	**JOHNSON Andrew** Batt Broadbent
PEAK Chris Madge Lloyd & Gibson	**TYLER Hilary** Brutton & Co
WHEELER Richard Michelmores	

This book is the product of 6,552 1/2-hour interviews. See p.7 for BMRB audit.
Within each band, firms are listed alphabetically. *See individuals' profiles p.154*

Follett Stock Registrar to the Diocese of Truro, Martin Follett (see p.155) has a high profile in this area, commended by peers for his business nous and his "calming influence."

Harris & Harris (see firm details p.988) Responsible for the two dioceses of Bath & Wells and Bristol," Tim Berry (see p.154) leads an "energetic practice."

Michelmores (see firm details p.1066) The firm has a long-standing reputation in this field. Richard Wheeler is registrar for the Anglican Diocese of Exeter and continues to concentrate on the commercial redevelopment of property.

Thomas Eggar Church Adams (see firm details p.1153) Christopher Butcher (see p.154), registrar for the Diocese of Chichester, is a new addition following recognition of his increasing profile in this area.

White & Bowker (see firm details p.1178) Peter White (see p.155) has acted as registrar for the Diocese of Winchester for over 20 years. Described as "wise and gentle," he has also advised the Roman Catholic Diocese of Portsmouth and the Methodist Chapel and has worked on high profile cases.

Brutton & Co Hilary Tyler is registrar for the Diocese of Portsmouth. An unassuming figure, she is warmly recommended by her peers.

Madge Lloyd & Gibson Chris Peak acts as registrar for the Diocese of Gloucester and retains his reputation in this area.

Other Notable Practitioners A new addition this year, Andrew Johnson of Batt Broadbent is registrar to the Diocese of Salisbury and, despite being fairly new to the area, he is "pretty clued-up."

OTHER DENOMINATIONS

CHURCH: OTHER DENOMINATIONS • South & South West
Stone King Bath
DMH Brighton
Larcomes Portsmouth
Tozers Exeter

LEADING INDIVIDUALS	
KING Michael Stone King	
KING Richard Tozers	**TISDALL Miles** Larcomes

This book is the product of 6,552 1/2-hour interviews. See p.7 for BMRB audit.
Within each band, firms are listed alphabetically. *See individuals' profiles p.154*

Stone King (see firm details p.1145) Acts for the Roman Catholic Dioceses of Westminster and Clifton and various agencies of the Bishop's Conference of the Roman Catholic church, religious schools and religious charities. The firm also does work for the Jewish Community and advises the Representative Body of the Church of Wales. The firm is noted for its enthusiasm in this area and "live-wire" Michael King has achieved a high national profile. Stone King has recently opened an office in London.

DMH (see firm details p.944) The firm advises the RC Diocese of Arundel and Brighton and occasionally acts for the Anglican church in matters such as diocesan property work, providing advice on the structuring and management of church schools, constitutional and trust work. Over the last year DMH acted on a high-profile child abuse case.

Larcomes Acts for the Roman Catholic Diocese of Portsmouth. The team headed up by Miles Tisdall (see p.155) has concentrated to a large extent on property aspects.

Tozers (see firm details p.1160) Acts for the RC Diocese of Plymouth, as well as for a number of religious schools. Well-established in this field, Richard King "talks good sense."

WALES

OTHER DENOMINATIONS

CHURCH: OTHER DENOMINATIONS • Wales
Allington Hughes Wrexham
LG Williams & Prichard Cardiff

This book is the product of 6,552 1/2-hour interviews. See p.7 for BMRB audit.
Within each band, firms are listed alphabetically.

Allington Hughes Acts for Roman Catholic clients, including a diocese and a number of religious orders.

LG Williams & Prichard Acts for the RC Archdiocese of Cardiff as well as various religious charities and orders. Work is to a large extent property related, although also involves charity, employment and education law.

THAMES VALLEY / MIDLANDS / EAST ANGLIA

CHURCH OF ENGLAND

CHURCH: CHURCH OF ENGLAND • Midlands & East Anglia
1
Winckworth Sherwood Chelmsford
2
Claytons Luton
Manby & Steward Wolverhampton
Martineau Johnson Birmingham
Wellman & Brown Lincoln
3
Edwards Geldard Derby
Harvey Ingram Owston Leicester
Mills & Reeve Norwich

LEADING INDIVIDUALS	
1	
CHEETHAM David Claytons	**REES John** Winckworth Sherwood
2	
BLOOR Richard Harvey Ingram Owston	**CARSLAKE Hugh** Martineau Johnson
HOOD Brian Winckworth Sherwood	**THORNEYCROFT John** Manby & Steward
WELLMAN Derek Wellman & Brown	
3	
BATTIE James Edwards Geldard	**HALL James** Birketts

This book is the product of 6,552 1/2-hour interviews. See p.7 for BMRB audit.
Within each band, firms are listed alphabetically. *See individuals' profiles p.154*

Winckworth Sherwood (see firm details p.1185) Recognised unanimously to be the leading firm in the area. In Oxford, the registrar for the Southern Province of Canterbury is in the unusual position of being both a clergyman and a solicitor. Rev **John Rees** (see p.155), "*a man of considerable charm,*" is highly regarded for his knowledge of employment, human rights and data protection. In Chelmsford, **Brian Hood** (see p.155) has a lower profile, but is warmly recommended and Frank Robson retains his role as a consultant.

Claytons **David Cheetham** has displayed "*such a lot of experience, such a lot of wisdom*" that he is felt to be one of the most eminent ecclesiastical lawyers. Cited as a point of reference for other registrars, he is "*solid, reliable and sensible.*"

Manby & Steward (see firm details p.1050) Involved in high profile human rights work over the last year, **John Thorneycroft** is reputed to have "*a terrific amount of experience on a wide range of issues.*"

Martineau Johnson (see firm details p.1055) Continues to maintain a reputation in this area with **Hugh Carslake** (see p.155) commanding respect among his peers.

Wellman & Brown Registrar to the Diocese of Lincoln, **Derek Wellman** is warmly recommended for his knowledge in this area.

Edwards Geldard (see firm details p.948) Well established as registrar to the Diocese of Derby, **James Battie** (see p.154) is respected by his peers.

Harvey Ingram Owston (see firm details p.989) Joint registrar for the Diocese of Leicester, **Richard Bloor** maintains a strong reputation.

Mills & Reeve (see firm details p.1069) Registrar for the Diocese of Norwich, John Herring specialises in ecclesiastical property work and church charity law. The firm also advises the Roman Catholic Diocese of East Anglia.

Other Notable Practitioner Registrar to the Diocese of St. Edmondsbury, "*quiet*" **James Hall** of Birketts is recommended.

OTHER DENOMINATIONS

CHURCH: OTHER DENOMINATIONS • Midlands & East Anglia
1
Anthony Collins Solicitors Birmingham

This book is the product of 6,552 1/2-hour interviews. See p.7 for BMRB audit.
Within each band, firms are listed alphabetically.

Anthony Collins Solicitors (see firm details p.860) A respected team providing general advice on ecclesiastical matters to Roman Catholic, Anglican and Free Church clients.

THE NORTH

CHURCH OF ENGLAND

CHURCH: CHURCH OF ENGLAND • The North
1
Denison Till York
2
Dixon, Coles & Gill Wakefield
Gamon Arden & Co Liverpool
MC Darlington Manchester
3
Bell & Buxton Sheffield
Birch Cullimore Chester
Gordons Cranswick Solicitors Leeds
Roebucks Blackburn
Tunnard Crosfield Ripon

This book is the product of 6,552 1/2-hour interviews. See p.7 for BMRB audit.
Within each band, firms are listed alphabetically.

Denison Till (see firm details p.939) Now also undertaking work for the Diocesan Board of Finance (DFB) which includes church conveyancing and employment. As registrar for the Northern Province of York, **Lionel Lennox** (see p.155) is a "*serious-minded,*" approachable figure known for his breadth of experience. His work for the province includes keeping additional registers, dealing with overseas clergy and clergy discipline matters.

Dixon, Coles & Gill Registrar for the Diocese of Wakefield, **Linda Box** (see p.154) has a solid reputation.

Gamon Arden & Co "*Probably the longest-serving registrar in the northern region*" **Roger Arden** advises the Diocese of Liverpool. Vice-chairman of the Ecclesiastical Law Association, he is known to have "*vast experience.*"

CHURCH LAW • THE NORTH

LEADING INDIVIDUALS	
1 LENNOX Lionel Denison Till	
2 ARDEN Roger Gamon Arden & Co	BOX Linda Dixon, Coles & Gill
DARLINGTON Michael MC Darlington	MCALLESTER Alan Birch Cullimore
3 FAIRCLOUGH Neville Smith Roddam	HARDING Nicola Tunnard Crosfield
HOYLE Thomas Roebucks	LOWDON Jane Sinton & Co
MYERS Miranda Bell & Buxton	TUNNARD Chris Tunnard Crosfield

See individuals' profiles p.154

MC Darlington **Michael Darlington** is registrar to the Diocese of Manchester and acts for the Board of Education in Manchester. Praised for his innovative ideas, he is widely recommended.

Bell & Buxton **Miranda Myers** is registrar for Diocese of Sheffield. An "*interesting person,*" she is praised for her refreshing and dynamic approach.

Birch Cullimore **Alan McAllester** is registrar to the diocese of Chester and has particular experience in exhumations.

Gordons Cranswick Solicitors Acting as deputy registrar for Bradford, Stuart Robertson spends less time on this area than most. The firm has dealt with the transfer of property to church schools, and the legal work for the National Millennium Faith Experience exhibition financed by the National Lottery.

Roebucks Active in a number of high-profile cases, the firm has undertaken work in relation to church schools and telecommunications. **Tom Hoyle**, registrar to the Diocese of Blackburn, is litigation-oriented and is sometimes called into other dioceses for this type of work.

Tunnard Crosfield **Nicola Harding** and **Christopher Tunnard** are the joint registrars for Ripon and Leeds. The latter retains his impressive reputation for his conveyancing work. "*Hands-on*" Harding is widely regarded for her work in the controversial field of clergy discipline. Described as "*bright, sharp, well-informed,*" it is felt that "*we will hear much more of her.*"

Other Notable Practitioners **Jane Lowdon** (see p.155) of Sinton & Co (formerly with Crutes) has worked for administrative bodies for the Anglican Newcastle Diocese in areas such as finance, education and parsonages. A new addition this year following market recommendation, **Neville Fairclough** of Smith Roddam is registrar to the Diocese of Durham.

OTHER DENOMINATIONS

CHURCH: OTHER DENOMINATIONS • The North
1 Grays York
2 Fieldings Porter Bolton
Hill Dickinson Liverpool
Oswald Goodier & Co Preston

LEADING INDIVIDUALS
1 LAWTON Tony Grays
2 BELDERBOS Mark Oswald Goodier & Co
3 NALLY Edward Fieldings Porter

This book is the product of 6,552 1/2-hour interviews. See p.7 for BMRB audit.

Within each band, firms are listed alphabetically. *See individuals' profiles p.154*

Grays (see firm details p.978) Advised the Roman Catholic dioceses of Leeds and Middlesborough together with various other Catholic charities and religious orders. Generally agreed to be "*the leaders locally,*" **Tony Lawton** (see p.147) heads the department.

Fieldings Porter Acts for Roman Catholic clients and has represented various religious and educational charities. The "*high profile*" **Edward Nally** (see p.155) is recommended for his knowledge of charitable property matters.

Hill Dickinson (see firm details p.996) This firm acts for a big religious order in Liverpool.

Oswald Goodier & Co (see firm details p.1087) Acts for various Roman Catholic charities, religious orders, and the Diocese of Lancaster. "*Sensible*" **Mark Belberbos** is highly recommended.

LEADERS IN CHURCH LAW

ARDEN, Roger Hollins
Gamon Arden & Co, Liverpool
(0151) 709 2222

BATTIE, James
Edwards Geldard, Derby (01332) 331631
Specialisation: Solicitor to Derby Diocesan Board of Finance since 1972. Diocesan Registrar and Legal Secretary to the Bishop of Derby since 1986.
Prof. Memberships: Law Society. Ecclesiastical Law Association. Ecclesiastical Law Society.
Career: Ashby Boys Grammar School and Keble College Oxford. Partner *Hollis Briggs & Co* and *Edwards Geldard* 1966-96 (now consultant).
Personal: Gardening. Hill walking. Follows most sports (especially cricket). Trips overseas to sites of historic interest. Church of England lay reader.

BEESLEY, Peter
Lee Bolton & Lee, London (020) 7222 5381

BELDERBOS, Mark
Oswald Goodier & Co, Preston (01772) 253841
OswGoodier@aol.com
See under Charities, p.146

BERRY, Timothy
Harris & Harris, Wells (01749) 674747
Specialisation: Ecclesiastical and charity law. Registrar, Diocese of Bath and Wells and Diocese of Bristol. Has expertise in trust and inheritance tax law.
Prof. Memberships: Ecclesiastical Law Association, Ecclesiastical Law Society, member of STEP.
Career: Qualified in 1970. Joined *Harris & Harris* as a partner in 1970. Now senior partner.
Personal: Born 5th January 1945. Holds an LLB (Liverpool 1966). Leisure interests include gardening, walking and music. Lives at West Cranmore near Shepton Mallet, Somerset.

BLOOR, Richard
Harvey Ingram Owston, Leicester (0116) 254 5454

BOX, Linda
Dixon, Coles & Gill, Wakefield (01924) 373467
Specialisation: Eclesastical law, charity law.
Prof. Memberships: Law Society, Ecclesiastical Law Association, Ecclesiastical Law Society.
Career: LLB 1970; qualified solicitor December 1973; Deputy Diocesan Registrar 1979 – 1993; Diocesan Registrar 1994 to date.
Personal: Married with two sons. Interests include walking in the Lake District, theatre and the opera.

BUTCHER, Christopher
Thomas Eggar Church Adams, Chichester
(01243) 786 111
christopher.butcher@teca.co.uk
Specialisation: Partner and head of charities unit. Main area of work is probate, wills, powers of attorney and ecclesiastical law.
Prof. Memberships: Law Society, Chichester & District Law Society (President 1996/7), Society of Trust and Estate Practitioners, Ecclesiastical Law Association, Charity Law Association.
Career: Qualified as a solicitor 1973, partner in (now) *Thomas Eggar Church Adams* 1977, notary public 1995, Chichester Diocesan Registrar 1999.
Publications: Co-author of Probate Practice Manual (Sweet & Maxwell).
Personal: Mill Hill School 1961-7, Southampton University 1967-70. Married with three children. Involved in local community and family life.

CARSLAKE, Hugh
Martineau Johnson, Birmingham (0121) 678 1486
hugh.carslake@martjohn.com
Specialisation: Main area of practice covers tax planning, trusts and estate planning and ecclesiastical law. Acts for the owners of landed estates and private individuals in their personal and trustee capacities. Registrar for and legal adviser to the Diocese of Birmingham.
Prof. Memberships: Law Society, STEP. Ecclesiastical Law Association (ELA).
Career: Qualified in 1973, having joined *Martineau Johnson* in 1972. Became a Partner in 1974, Notary Public in 1981, Head of Private Client Department in 1991 and Diocesan Registrar in 1992.
Personal: Born 15th November 1946. Attended Rugby School, 1960-65, then Trinity College, Dublin, 1966-70. Chairman of the Barber Institute of Fine Arts (University of Birmingham); Member of the Council of the University of Birmingham; Trustee of the Worcester Cathedral Appeal Trust. Council Member of the Notaries Society. Leisure interests include family, music and gardening. Lives in Warwickshire.

CHEETHAM, David N.
Claytons, St Albans (01727) 865765/6

DARLINGTON, Michael C.
MC Darlington, Manchester (0161) 834 7545

FAIRCLOUGH, Arthur Neville
Smith Roddam, County Durham (01388) 603073

FOLLETT, Martin
Follett Stock, Truro (01872) 260744
martin.follett@follettstock.co.uk
Specialisation: Full range of ecclesiastical work including property, charity, education and contentious faculty work.
Career: Sidney Sussex College, Cambridge. Qualified 1977. Deputy Registrar 1983. Registrar of the Diocese of Truro 1987.

HALL, James S.
Birketts, Ipswich (01473) 232300

HARDING, Nicola
Tunnard Crosfield, Ripon (01765) 600 421

HOOD, Brian
Winckworth Sherwood, Chelmsford
(01245) 262212
bjhood@winckworths.co.uk
Specialisation: Partner in Ecclesiastical Department (Chelmsford). Specialises in ecclesiastical law. Deputy Registrar to Bishop of Chelmsford 1976-89. Registrar and Bishop's Legal Secretary since 1989. Also handles property and charities law, private and commercial matters.
Prof. Memberships: Ecclesiastical Law Association, Ecclesiastical Law Society.
Career: Qualified as a solicitor in New Zealand in 1966. Qualified in the UK in 1976. Joined *Winckworth Sherwood* as a partner in 1977.
Personal: Born 8th February 1943. Educated at Marlborough College, New Zealand 1956-62 and the University of Canterbury, New Zealand 1963-67 (LLM Hons). Leisure interests include golf, tennis, music and theatre. Lives in Terling, Essex.

HOYLE, Thomas
Roebucks, Blackburn (01254) 274000

JOHNSON, Andrew
Batt Broadbent, Salisbury (01722) 411 141

KING, Michael
Stone King, Bath (01225) 337599

KING, Richard
Tozers, Exeter (01392) 207020

LAWTON, F. A. (Tony)
Grays, York (01904) 634771
See under Charities, p.147

LENNOX, Lionel
Denison Till, York York (01904) 611411
Specialisation: Partner. Main area of practice is ecclesiastical law. Registrar of the Province and Diocese of York; Registrar of the Convocation of York; Legal Secretary to the Archbishop of York; Member of the Legal Advisory Commission of the General Synod. Expanding areas of practice are town and country planning and charity law. Advanced Professional Diploma in Planning and Environmental Law from Leeds Metropolitan University 1994. Legal advisor to various charities. Notary Public 1992.
Prof. Memberships: Yorkshire Law Society, Ecclesiastical Law Society.
Career: Qualified in 1973. Worked at *Denison Suddards* as a partner 1976-80; assistant legal advisor to the General Synod of the Church of England 1981-7. Joined *Denison Till* as a partner in 1987.
Personal: Attended St John's School Leatherhead 1962-67 and University of Birmingham 1967-70. Notary Public 1992. Lives in York. Trustee: St. Leonard's Hospice, York and Yorkshire Historic Churches Trust.

LOWDON, Jane
Sinton & Co, Newcastle upon Tyne
(0191) 212 7800
j.lowdon@sinton.co.uk
Specialisation: Diocesan Registrar and legal advisor to the Bishop. Day to day knowledge of ecclesiastical law. Commercial and residential property and conveyancing; charity law; conveyancing and commercial matters; wills.
Career: BA (Law) Trent Polytechnic. Qualified 1979. Twenty years in private practice. Joined *Sinton & Co* 2000.

MCALLESTER, Alan K.
Birch Cullimore, Chester (01244) 321066

MORRIS, Paul
Winckworth Sherwood, London (020) 7593 5000

MYERS, Miranda
Bell & Buxton, Sheffield (0114) 249 5969

NALLY, Edward
Fieldings Porter, Bolton (01204) 387742
Specialisation: Acts as diocesan solicitor for Salford Roman Catholic Diocese and has also represented various religious and educational charities.
Prof. Memberships: Council member of the Law Society for Central Lancashire and Northern Greater Manchester.
Career: De La Salle College, Salford and Nottingham University.
Personal: Married with two children.

PEAK, Chris
Madge Lloyd & Gibson, Gloucester
(01452) 520 224

REES, John
Winckworth Sherwood, Oxford (01865) 297 200
jrees@ws-oxford.co.uk
Specialisation: Partner in ecclesiastical, education and charities department. Main area of practice is ecclesiastical law. Registrar, Province of Canterbury. Joint Registrar, Diocese of Oxford. Legal Adviser to the Anglican Consultative Council (the international liaison body for the Anglican Communion worldwide). Extensive experience in contested faculty cases, including Court of Arches Judgment in Re St. Luke, Maidstone: wide acquaintance with education law issues on behalf of governors and trustees.
Prof. Memberships: Ecclesiastical Law Association, Ecclesiastical Law Society (Treasurer).
Career: Qualified 1975. Joined *Winckworth Sherwood* 1986. Partner 1988.
Personal: Born 21 April 1951. Holds LLB (Southampton 1972), MA (Oxon 1984) and MPhil (Leeds 1984). Leisure interests include photography and cycling. Lives in Oxford.

RICHENS, Nicholas
Lee Bolton & Lee, London (020) 7222 5381

THATCHER, Michael
Winckworth Sherwood, London (020) 7593 5000
mcthatcher@winckworths.co.uk
See under Education, p.304

THORNEYCROFT, John
Manby & Steward, Bridgnorth (01746) 761436

TISDALL, Miles
Larcomes, Portsmouth (023) 9266 1531
enquiries@larcomes.co.uk
Specialisation: Charity law. Acts for Roman Catholic Diocese of Portsmouth.
Prof. Memberships: Law Society.

TUNNARD, Chris
Tunnard Crosfield, Ripon (01765) 600 421

TYLER, Hilary A.G.
Brutton & Co, Fareham (01329) 236171

WELLMAN, Derek
Wellman & Brown, Lincoln (01522) 525463

WHEELER, Richard K.
Michelmores, Exeter (01392) 436244

WHITE, Peter
White & Bowker, Winchester (01962) 844440
peter.white@wandb.co.uk
Specialisation: Consultant in ecclesiastical and residential property department. Principal area of practice covers all aspects of ecclesiastical law. Appointed Diocesan Registrar for the Diocese of Winchester and Bishop's Legal Secretary 1981. Other main area of work is residential property.
Prof. Memberships: Current Secretary of Hampshire Law Society, member of Ecclesiastical Law Association, Ecclesiastical Law Society, Notaries Society, Law Society.
Career: Qualified in 1970 while at *White & Bowker* and became a partner in 1974.
Personal: Born 28th August 1945. Attended Winchester College 1958-63, then New College, Oxford 1964-67. Leisure pursuits include golf, cricket and fives. Lives in Romsey.

CLINICAL NEGLIGENCE

OVERVIEW: The continued institution of various regulatory panels has restricted the number of firms able to take on complex or high value clinical negligence claims. Many interviewees have described the recent round of NHSLA panel cuts as a sea change in the industry, with firms pulling out of defendant activities and either refocusing on claimant work or restructing their offering. This area of practice is in a state of flux with growing concerns over conditional fee structures and the volume of work available and *Chambers'* researchers expect further movement amongst the firms during the next year.

RESEARCH APPROVED BY BMRB: *For this edition,* Chambers' *researchers conducted 6,552 interviews – 4,419 with law firms, 554 with barristers and 1,579 with clients.*

The validity of the research was scrutinised by BMRB International, who audited both the methodology and the results at our offices in July 2001. They interviewed Chambers' *researchers and cross-checked sample interviews. Details of the audit appear on page 7.*

LONDON

MAINLY CLAIMANT

CLINICAL NEGLIGENCE: MAINLY CLAIMANT • London	Ptnrs	Assts
1 Leigh, Day & Co	9	6
2 Bindman & Partners	2	3
Kingsley Napley	3	6
Parlett Kent	4	n/a
3 Alexander Harris	1	1
Charles Russell	1	4
Evill and Coleman	4	4
Field Fisher Waterhouse	2	3

LEADING INDIVIDUALS	
1 **FAZAN Claire** Bindman & Partners	**LEIGH Sarah** Leigh, Day & Co
LEVY Russell Leigh, Day & Co	**McNEIL Paul** Field Fisher Waterhouse
VALLANCE Richard Charles Russell	**WINYARD Anne** Leigh, Day & Co
2 **BARTON Grainne** Alexander Harris	**CAHILL Julia** Kingsley Napley
LEE Terry Evill and Coleman	
3 **BATTEN Elizabeth** Parlett Kent	**DYSON Henry** Leigh, Day & Co
JENKINS Caroline Parlett Kent	**LEWIN Olive** Leigh, Day & Co
MARTINEZ Liz Evill and Coleman	**ROHDE Kate** Kingsley Napley

This book is the product of 6,552 1/2-hour interviews. See p.7 for BMRB audit.
Within each band, firms are listed alphabetically. *See individuals' profiles p.164*

Leigh, Day & Co (see firm details p.1036) "*In another league,*" the firm goes from strength to strength and is perceived by our interviewees to be the most serious practice in the field. It takes on a wide range of cases, from death of children to catastrophic injuries. The firm employs an accountant for quantum work. "*Far from being another PI add-on*" it fields an enviable array of specialised practitioners. **Sarah Leigh** (see p.168) is still considered a "*phenomenal*" practitioner and both peers and industry specialists agree that "*what she did for the Woolf reforms must be recognised.*" "*Respected and forward-looking*" **Russell Levy** "*works tremendously hard for clients*" while **Anne Winyard** (see p.170) is adjudged a "*brilliant lawyer, sound and experienced.*" Qualified as a nurse as well as a solicitor, **Olive Lewin** (see p.168) and her colleague **Henry Dyson** (see p.165) ("*extremely talented*") received heavy market endorsement.

Bindman & Partners (see firm details p.882) Researchers were told that this "*decent, straight-forward*" team is bolstered by the presence of "*thorough, pragmatic and talented*" **Claire Fazan** (see p.165). Maintains its profile for complex cases, including those for adults and children with profound disability, and claims arising from obstetrics, anaesthesia, orthopaedic, plastic and abdominal surgery, and failure to diagnose cancer and cardiac conditions. Matters challenging methods or the provision of treatment have been undertaken. The clinical negligence offering is supported by the firm's specialist mental health and care in the community team while some work is also undertaken by the specialist children's unit. Peers acknowledge that the firm is "*particularly able at assessing claims.*"

Kingsley Napley (see firm details p.1022) "*Immensely competent,*" the firm has a strong following in the market. It continues to handle the full range of cases and in the past 12 months has recovered in excess of £12 million in final settlements on behalf of claimants whose cases have included birth injury, delays in diagnosis or mismanagement of cancers, meningitis, and diabetes. It provides advice and assistance for inquests, GMC complaints and GP and hospital complaints procedures. **Julia Cahill** (see p.165) who replaces Christine Marsh as head of department, is deemed a "*strong player*" while sources thought **Kate Rohde** (see p.169) to be a "*talented lawyer.*" At contested hearings, the firm succeeded in obtaining high interim awards (£750,000 each) for two clients.

Parlett Kent (see firm details p.1090) "*First class outfit*" that delivers "*consistently high-quality cases.*" Competitors view **Caroline Jenkins** (see p.167) as "*hardworking*" and add that she "*gets the high value cases.*" **Elizabeth Batten** (see p.164) is a destination for many referrals since other practitioners "*think so highly of her and her ability with clients.*" The firm has a niche in psychiatric negligence, while it continues to handle the full range of claims.

Alexander Harris (see firm details p.854) A practice that is recommended to researchers for its wide-ranging expertise in all negligence matters, especially cerebral palsy, anaesthetic awareness, cancer, keyhole surgery and dental matters. "*Personable, committed and thorough,*" **Grainne Barton** (see p.164) is held largely responsible for the practice's strength. Cases of note include Tredgett v Bexley Health Authority and Smyth v Riverside Health Authority. Also secured an inquest at the Court of Appeal for the ongoing Laura Touche case.

Charles Russell (see firm details p.912) A "*superb*" practice that is "*exceedingly committed to its clients.*" The firm handles many claims, including those of maximum severity and complex medical issues. Foremost among the firm's specialist solicitors is the "*measured, modest and excellent*" **Richard Vallance** (see p.170). The team is active in claimant action groups for the improvement of procedures dealing with those let down by the medical profession. The group represented Monica Das against West Hertfordshire Health Authority concerning the birth injury she sustained as a result of the antenatal care provided to her mother, resulting in an award of £625,000.

Evill and Coleman (see firm details p.952) *"A strong and likeable bunch"* who remain popular with the barristers and solicitors interviewed by our researchers. **Terry Lee** (see p.168) is admired as *"committed to his clients"* while his colleague **Liz Martinez** (see p.168) is considered *"a favourite, she's fantastic with clients."* The group handles complex cases of catastrophic injury, anaesthetic mismanagement and paediatric cerebral palsy.

Field Fisher Waterhouse (see firm details p.957) In what has been the team's busiest year, the market recommends **Paul McNeil** (see p.169) as *"excellent and thorough,"* managing to secure some *"interesting wins."* The group saw three cases go to trial on liability (two won, one awaiting judgment) and acted on an increased number of high value claims on conditional fee arrangements, such as S v UCH NHS Trust and W v King's Healthcare NHS Trust. The group advised the Royal Brompton and Harefield families in relation to an inquiry set up to look at paediatric cardiac care. Handled a cerebral palsy case, which settled for £2.75 million on the day of trial, and in the case of F v Gardner (where previous solicitors had advised not to proceed) in which over £500,000 was recovered where an orthopaedic surgeon failed to obtain an MRI scan before operating.

MAINLY DEFENDANT

CLINICAL NEGLIGENCE: MAINLY DEFENDANT • London	Ptnrs	Assts
1 Capsticks	13	18
2 Hempsons	8	3
3 Vizard Oldham	7	12

LEADING INDIVIDUALS	
1 HOLMES John Hempsons	LEIGH Bertie Hempsons
MASON David Capsticks	
2 HAY Katie Capsticks	SMITH Janice Capsticks
3 DINGWALL Christian Bevan Ashford	FIELD Rena Vizard Oldham

This book is the product of 6,552 1/2-hour interviews. See p.7 for BMRB audit.
Within each band, firms are listed alphabetically. *See individuals' profiles p.164*

Capsticks (see firm details p.908) Our interviewees were impressed with the firm's *"professional and experienced approach,"* although some felt the firm had been *"strengthened by the cull around it."* Claimant firms testify to the *"uniform quality"* and method throughout the team. **David Mason** (see p.168) is *"committed and powerful on the other side – you have to watch your toes when he's around."* **Katie Hay** (see p.167) (*"practical"*) and **Janice Smith** (see p.170) attracted favourable comment. The firm offers a broad service including representation in specialist areas such as mental health and consent to treatment cases. About 90% of the firm's work consists of NHS work.

Hempsons (see firm details p.990) The firm has acted on thousands of cases in the past year for doctors and other healthcare practitioners. The London team handles applications to the High Court concerning issues of consent to treatment and has acted for seven health authorities and 17 NHS trusts. Acts for the MDU throughout England and Wales. *"Elder statesman"* **Bertie Leigh** (see p.168) is described by claimant firms as *"the face of the defendant"* and is judged to be a *"vociferous champion."* Formerly of Beachcroft Wansbroughs, **John Holmes** (see p.167) is *"a superb litigator who doesn't take silly points"* and his presence is expected to *"greatly strengthen the team."* In conjunction with the Manchester office, this team advised on the high profile conjoined twins case, Jodie and Mary. **Clients:** Lambeth Southwark & Lewisham HA; Buckinghamshire HA; Rampton Special Hospital Authority; Medical Defence Union; Dental Medical Council.

Vizard Oldham (see firm details p.1169) Although our researchers were told that it is too early to judge how this firm, newly appointed to the NHSLA panel, will perform, it is thought to have picked up many from the *"impressive"* Le Brasseur J Tickle team. **Rena Field** (see p.166) is one of these, and is described as *"vastly capable, knowledgeable and experienced."* A CEDR accredited mediator, she is felt to have a *"good grasp of the new order"* in the medico-legal field.

Other Notable Practitioners **Christian Dingwall** (see p.165) has moved from Le Brasseur J Tickle to **Bevan Ashford.** Operating in conjunction with the Bristol office, the market expects his presence to create a distinct impact in a short space of time, particularly with the firm's strong ties to the NHSLA.

THE SOUTH

MAINLY CLAIMANT

CLINICAL NEGLIGENCE: MAINLY CLAIMANT • The South	Ptnrs	Assts
1 Blake Lapthorn Portsmouth	4	2
2 Thomson Snell & Passmore Tunbridge Wells	2	3
3 Penningtons Godalming	1	n/a
Wynne Baxter Brighton	3	2

LEADING INDIVIDUALS	
1 HOOPER John Wynne Baxter	McCLURE Alison Blake Lapthorn
MINTER Melanie Wynne Baxter	WATSON Andrew Thomson Snell & Passmore

This book is the product of 6,552 1/2-hour interviews. See p.7 for BMRB audit.
Within each band, firms are listed alphabetically. *See individuals' profiles p.164*

Blake Lapthorn (see firm details p.886) Undertakes a range of cases, with particular experience of obstetric and gynaecology cases, urology, general surgery and oncology (notably breast cancer.) Honing its skills by the recruitment of medically qualified staff, interviewees agreed that it has strengthened its system for developing risk analysis. This enables it to take more cases on a conditional fee basis and it has consequently seen an increase in the number of referrals. *"Greatly respected"* **Alison McClure** settled a cerebral palsy case for £1.84 million.

Thomson Snell & Passmore (see firm details p.1155) Our researchers were told that **Andrew Watson** (see p.170) combines *"considerable skill"* as a litigator with *"in-depth"* clinical negligence knowledge. He leads a *"great team,"* assisted by two nurses. Handling the broad spectrum of cases, its fee earners possess particular areas of interest, including cerebral palsy, paediatric, gynaecology, cancer, orthopaedic and fatal accident cases.

Penningtons (see firm details p.1093) The Godalming practice is described as *"totally solid"* and deals exclusively with clinical negligence and personal injury matters outside London. On the claimant side, its *"conscientious and nice"* team offers experience of cerebral palsy cases and claims involving neurosurgery. Conducts an increasing amount of work on a conditional fee basis.

Wynne Baxter A practice that boasts some high profile and vociferous supporters who *"would always refer there."* **John Hooper** (see p.167) is *"a* *senior figure,*" while colleague and former nurse **Melanie Minter** (see p.169) is described by some interviewees as "*the best Sussex can offer.*" The firm takes on clients who have suffered injury in all clinical fields including obstetrics and gynaecology, orthopaedics, anaesthetics, general surgery and dentistry. It is considered expert in brain damage cases and the care and ongoing financial considerations that apply to a brain damaged child or young adult.

MAINLY DEFENDANT

CLINICAL NEGLIGENCE: MAINLY DEFENDANT • The South	Ptnrs	Assts
1 **Beachcroft Wansbroughs** Winchester	2	n/a
2 **Brachers** Maidstone	3	n/a

LEADING INDIVIDUALS
1 **McGRATH Matthew** Beachcroft Wansbroughs
SHEATH John Brachers

This book is the product of 6,552 1/2-hour interviews. See p.7 for BMRB audit.
Within each band, firms are listed alphabetically. *See individuals' profiles p.164*

Beachcroft Wansbroughs (see firm details p.872) Many sources are "*thrilled*" that this "*ever sensible*" defendant firm has strengthened its position in the region. Handles a range of cases, from the retention of swabs to more complex matters such as brain damaged baby claims that are valued at £2 million or more. Combines an in-depth knowledge of the NHS and medical negligence litigation with a commercial insurance approach. "*Fantastic practitioner*" **Matthew McGrath** (see p.169) is considered the region's "*key player.*" **Clients:** NHSLA.

Brachers (see firm details p.893) Reappointed to the NHSLA panel, the warmly endorsed **John Sheath** (see p.169) leads a "*proactive and responsible*" team. Active in the defence of local health authorities and GP practices, the firm is increasing its level of investigations and preliminary reporting and is judged to have strengths across the board. The team acted in the Kent and Canterbury cervical smear claims. **Clients:** Medway Health Authority; East Kent Hospitals NHS Trusts; Dartford & Gravesham NHS Trust.

THAMES VALLEY

MAINLY CLAIMANT

CLINICAL NEGLIGENCE: MAINLY CLAIMANT • Thames Valley	Ptnrs	Assts
1 **Boyes Turner** Reading	2	2
2 **Osborne Morris & Morgan** Leighton Buzzard	2	2
3 **Harris & Cartwright** Slough	1	1

LEADING INDIVIDUALS
1 **DESMOND Adrian** Boyes Turner
2 **OSBORNE Thomas** Osborne Morris & Morgan

This book is the product of 6,552 1/2-hour interviews. See p.7 for BMRB audit.
Within each band, firms are listed alphabetically. *See individuals' profiles p.164*

Boyes Turner (see firm details p.891) Interviewees informed our researchers that the "*dedicated*" **Adrian Desmond** (see p.165) has secured a strong profile in complex matters, particularly maximum severity cases, including brain injury. The cohesive and focused team secured a £3.3 million award for a nine-year old boy following mistakes at birth and negotiated a revised settlement following a House of Lords decision. Has a dedicated brain injury support group.

Osborne Morris & Morgan Thomas Osborne is described by peers as "*a national presence, respected for his forward thinking.*" This "*experienced team*" has a depth of knowledge across the board with strengths in brain injury and cerebral palsy cases.

Harris & Cartwright (see firm details p.987) An established presence in the field, this team led by Chris Gooderidge is respected for its wide ranging involvement which includes a substantial level of obstetrics claims. The team is supported by a registered nurse.

SOUTH WEST

MAINLY CLAIMANT

Barcan Woodward One of the region's "*main players – a serious, specialist practice*" which peers adjudge "*excellent, thorough and sensitive to its clients.*" "*Sensible and calm,*" **Richard Barcan** is universally acknowledged as a favourite for conflicts as he is "*so committed to patient care.*" The group is experienced in maximum severity cases, and committed to issues surrounding the development of funding. The firm places emphasis on the rehabilitation of clients and has recently displayed expertise in bowel-injury cases.

Preston Goldburn A small team that has moved away from the firm's main office in order to offer its clients disabled access and hearing loops. No surprise that interviewees described the team as "*extremely dedicated.*" **Tim Goldburn** (see p.166) is popular for referrals as he is "*an old stalwart, sensible and well-informed.*" It works closely with other claimant firms and undertakes almost all types of cases. Currently investing much time into exploring a local resolution for clinical compensation claims. The firm is recognised for seeking innovative solutions to conflicts.

John Hodge & Co A solid team led by **Richard England** who offers "*real experience*" in this area. He is a member of the Law Society Medical Negligence Panel. The firm covers a range of matters, including a significant number of gynaecological, cardiological and cerebral palsy cases. Offers a free initial interview and conducts some conditional fee cases. The firm continues its involvement in on-going Bristol baby cases.

Over Taylor Biggs Although some practitioners feel that the firm is "*not as specialist as it once was,*" it maintains a good reputation as a complement to its respected construction and transport practice. **Christopher Over** elicits warm commendation. The team has displayed expertise in failure to diagnose cancer, birth defects and catastrophic injury cases.

Russell Jones & Walker (see firm details p.1116) Part of a strong network, it can draw on the specialist experiences of leading figures nationwide.

CLINICAL NEGLIGENCE: MAINLY CLAIMANT • South West	Ptnrs	Assts
1 **Barcan Woodward** Bristol	2	2
Preston Goldburn Falmouth	1	n/a
2 **John Hodge & Co** Weston-super-Mare	2	1
Over Taylor Biggs Exeter	2	2
Russell Jones & Walker Bristol	1	2
Withy King Bath	n/a	n/a
Wolferstans Plymouth	2	1
3 **Woollcombe Beer Watts** Newton Abbot	n/a	n/a

LEADING INDIVIDUALS	
1 **BARCAN Richard** Barcan Woodward	
2 **ENGLAND Richard** John Hodge & Co	**FERGUSON Gerry** Withy King
GOLDBURN Tim Preston Goldburn	
3 **OVER Christopher** Over Taylor Biggs	**SOLLY Gillian** Russell Jones & Walker
VICK Laurence Michelmores	**YOUNG Magi** Parlett Kent

This book is the product of 6,552 1/2-hour interviews. See p.7 for BMRB audit.
Within each band, firms are listed alphabetically. *See individuals' profiles p.164*

Offers particular experience of group actions, breast cancer treatment and dental care among other areas. **Gillian Solly** (see p.650) is deemed a "*strong performer*" by our interviewees. The team obtained a settlement of £1.7 million on behalf of a client suffering from cerebral palsy due to a delayed delivery.

Withy King "*A strong clinical negligence outfit,*" according to our interviewees. The firm offers advice on the availability and suitability of rehabilitation and other support services, and covers the entire gamut of clinical negligence cases, including urology and psychiatric claims. "*Premier league player*" **Gerry Ferguson** (see p.166) specialises solely in clinical negligence and is particularly experienced in GP negligence, urology, gynaecology, psychiatry and claims for children.

Wolferstans (see firm details p.1188) Fields a team of specialist lawyers who offer experience of handling all types of clinical negligence claims against health authorities, NHS trusts, private hospitals, clinics and nursing homes. Also advises on matters arising from general medical practitioners and therapists providing alternative or complementary medicine. Simon Parford leads the team.

Woollcombe Beer Watts Led by Derek Reed, the practice continues to grow and to conduct a general range of clinical negligence work. Routinely advises on matters arising from obstetric, laporoscopic, psychiatric, negligence at birth and failure to recognise or diagnose cancer cases. Currently handling a number of cerebral palsy cases, one of which is settling for over £1 million.

Other Notable Practitioners Laurence Vick "*is a strong player*" at Michelmores while Parlett Kent's **Magi Young** (see p.170) offers "*enormous experience.*"

MAINLY DEFENDANT

CLINICAL NEGLIGENCE: MAINLY DEFENDANT • South West	Ptnrs	Assts
1 **Bevan Ashford** Bristol	7	34
2 **Beachcroft Wansbroughs** Bristol	1	2

LEADING INDIVIDUALS
1 **MONTGOMERY Nigel** Beachcroft Wansbroughs

This book is the product of 6,552 1/2-hour interviews. See p.7 for BMRB audit.
Within each band, firms are listed alphabetically. *See individuals' profiles p.164*

Bevan Ashford (see firm details p.880) Sources indicate that this is the principal team in the region, with Joanna Lloyd as its leading partner. Considered "*reasonable to deal with,*" its practitioners "*have a sensible approach.*" A number of well-known individuals have moved from the claims to the healthcare department. Together with the London office, it offers experience of group actions, high value and complex claims, and alternative dispute resolution. The group worked on Allingham v Northern Devon Healthcare Trust, Herd v Torbay Health Authority and Huggins v Avon Health Authority. **Clients:** NHSLA.

Beachcroft Wansbroughs (see firm details p.872) Some believe that the team here is "*more inquiring, more on the ball,*" than at its closest rival, providing a genuine alternative with claimant firms suggesting that it is "*as able, just smaller in size.*" **Nigel Montgomery** (see p.169) retains an "*impressive*" reputation bolstered by his 17 years of experience. Particularly expert in obstetric, renal and neurology claims, the team has been representing the United Bristol Healthcare NHS Trust and its staff in its inquiry into paediatric cardiac surgical services in Bristol. **Clients:** NHSLA; The BRI.

WALES

MAINLY CLAIMANT

CLINICAL NEGLIGENCE: MAINLY CLAIMANT • Wales	Ptnrs	Assts
1 **Huttons** Cardiff	1	2
2 **Edwards Geldard** Cardiff	1	3
Hugh James Ford Simey Cardiff	3	4
John Collins & Partners with Edward Harris Swansea	2	1
Russell Jones & Walker Cardiff	1	1

LEADING INDIVIDUALS
1 **MUSGRAVE Tim** Huttons
2 **DAVIES Andrew** Hugh James Ford Simey

This book is the product of 6,552 1/2-hour interviews. See p.7 for BMRB audit.
Within each band, firms are listed alphabetically. *See individuals' profiles p.164*

Huttons (see firm details p.1006) A practice "*greatly respected*" by our interviewees, that makes up "*in quality what it lacks in size.*" "*Strong performer,*" **Tim Musgrave** (see p.169) leads a team that covers clinical negligence cases from the routine to the complex, encompassing all fields from general surgery to obstetric work.

Edwards Geldard (see firm details p.948) Perceived to have been weakened by the departure of department head, Mari Rosser, to Hugh James Ford Simey. AVMA panel member Tom Beech is now the key contact. The firm covers the range of matters, and has received a number of instructions from claimants in the trilucent breast implant claim. Acted for a claimant who recovered £1 million damages to compensate him for a brain injury suffered as a result of Lithium Toxicity.

Hugh James Ford Simey (see firm details p.1004) "*Sound and admired*" **Andrew Davies** (see p.165) heads this "*rounded*" team, which fields a dedicated social worker and three nurses. Often seen on orthopaedic, oncology, gynaecology and obstetric matters, the firm has been strengthened by two new partners, recruited from the Smith Llewelyn Partnership and Edwards Geldard, respectively.

John Collins & Partners with Edward Harris Under the leadership of Keith Thomas, the merged group maintains a position as a respected force in the market. After a free initial interview, the group offers complex advice as well as assistance in complaints procedures. Expert in fatal medical accident claims and cerebral palsy cases, it counts medically trained personnel among its team.

Russell Jones & Walker (see firm details p.1116) Clients are eager in their praise of the "*dedicated, supportive and honest*" Cardiff team along with its head Sonya McGarigle. It also fields an in-house nurse. The group has experience in working for the Welsh Health Legal Service and is recommended by defendant firms as "*tenacious as an opponent*." It represented the family of Kieron Gregory in an alleged failure to diagnose meningococcal septicaemia leading to his death.

MIDLANDS

MAINLY CLAIMANT

CLINICAL NEGLIGENCE: MAINLY CLAIMANT • Midlands	Ptnrs	Assts
1 **Freethcartwright** Nottingham	3	5
Irwin Mitchell Birmingham	3	4
2 **Anthony Collins Solicitors** Birmingham	1	4
3 **Challinors Lyon Clark** Birmingham	2	5

LEADING INDIVIDUALS	
1 **BALEN Paul** Freethcartwright	**FOLLIS Richard** Irwin Mitchell
2 **BANNISTER Richard** Challinors Lyon Clark	**HALL Antony** Anthony Collins Solicitors

This book is the product of 6,552 1/2-hour interviews. See p.7 for BMRB audit.
Within each band, firms are listed alphabetically. *See individuals' profiles p.164*

Freethcartwright (see firm details p.964) This "*well-respected team*" settled a record number of claims last year with an increased workload after each office won its clinical negligence franchise. Able to offer a one-stop-shop and "*making a great job of it*" according to its peers, owing to the presence of an in-house counsel (also newly qualified as a solicitor). In addition it is supported by two full time nurses. The firm handled a £1 million settlement of a clinical negligence claim brought in South Africa. "*National superstar*" **Paul Balen** (see p.164) is applauded for his "*experience and forward-looking mind*" and has appeared in a number of inquests arising from errors by doctors.

Irwin Mitchell (see firm details p.1009) A "*tremendous*" team winning "*national recognition*," it maintains its retinue of supporters. Offers a great depth of trial experience and expertise in birth trauma and neonatal insult resulting in brain injury, oncology, wrongful birth and fatal accident cases. The team acted on a number of cerebral palsy cases including that of Adrian Simms arising out of events in 1982, in a case which had failed to progress with previous solicitors over a 15 year period. After winning the contested liability trial, damages were agreed at £2.3 million. "*Exceptional*" **Richard Follis** (see p.166) has been representing a group of more than 60 parents in relation to organ retention at Birmingham Children's hospital among others.

Anthony Collins Solicitors (see firm details p.860) **Tony Hall** (see p.166) has a reputation for being "*deeply committed*" to clients and is a notable advocate of mediation. The team acts for multi-parties and individuals, with niche strengths in cancer misdiagnosis, orthopaedic and brain damage claims. Also offers experience of medical ethics claims including those involving refusal of consent to medical treatment. The group is working on the £4.5 million Milloshas cancer misdiagnosis litigation in the High Court, multi-party actions where patients contracted Hepatitis C following blood transfusions, and a number of silicon implant and cerebral palsy cases.

Challinors Lyon Clark The team deals with all aspects of claimant clinical negligence from the most severe cases to the more moderate, including assistance at inquests and with NHS complaints. It has expanded once again with the recruitment of another partner on the Law Society specialist referral panel, and additionally fields an in-house nurse. **Richard Bannister** (see p.164) continues to win market approval.

MAINLY DEFENDANT

CLINICAL NEGLIGENCE: MAINLY DEFENDANT • Midlands	Ptnrs	Assts
1 **Bevan Ashford** Birmingham	2	8
2 **Browne Jacobson** Birmingham, Nottingham	3	n/a

LEADING INDIVIDUALS
1 **McCRORY Katrina** Bevan Ashford
UP AND COMING
SWANTON Vicki Browne Jacobson

This book is the product of 6,552 1/2-hour interviews. See p.7 for BMRB audit.
Within each band, firms are listed alphabetically. *See individuals' profiles p.164*

Bevan Ashford (see firm details p.880) The Birmingham office of the firm opened in April 2001 and the team here is led by former Bristol partner Paul Barber. It conducts a wide range of work, as do its teams in Bristol and London, and operates with them as a single unit. The practice offers experience of group actions, high value and complex claims. **Katrina McCrory** (see p.168) has won plaudits from practitioners for her work in this field. **Clients:** NHSLA.

Browne Jacobson (see firm details p.898) A growing team that exclusively handles defendant work, it has consolidated its position in the market place. Accustomed to managing high profile multi-party actions and the associated governance issues that affect public bodies. **Vicki Swanton** has a growing reputation in this "*effective*" team. **Clients:** NHSLA.

EAST ANGLIA

MAINLY CLAIMANT

CLINICAL NEGLIGENCE: MAINLY CLAIMANT • East Anglia	Ptnrs	Assts
1 **Cunningham John** Thetford	5	4
2 **Gadsby Wicks** Chelmsford	2	6
3 **Morgan Jones & Pett** Great Yarmouth	2	2
Prettys Ipswich	1	1
Scrivenger Seabrook St Neots	4	n/a

LEADING INDIVIDUALS	
1 **JOHN Simon** Cunningham John	
2 **GADSBY Gillian** Gadsby Wicks	**JONES David** Morgan Jones & Pett
WICKS Roger Gadsby Wicks	
3 **SCRIVENGER Mark** Scrivenger Seabrook	**SEABROOK Vicki** Scrivenger Seabrook

This book is the product of 6,552 1/2-hour interviews. See p.7 for BMRB audit.
Within each band, firms are listed alphabetically. *See individuals' profiles p.164*

Cunningham John (see firm details p.930) "*A serious, dedicated team,*" it has the unquestioned respect of claimant and defendant firms alike. Defendant firms add that when it "*issues a challenge you know it has a strong case.*" "*Respected for his experience,*" **Simon John** (see p.167) leads the team, which also boasts a number of medico-legal personnel. Handling a variety of cases including a substantial proportion of severe matters, the firm also has experience of handling cases in the US. Represented the victims of disgraced Canadian gynaecologist/obstetrician, Richard Neil.

Gadsby Wicks (see firm details p.967) Considered by defendant firms a "*very together*" team and possessed of an "*exceedingly professional*" reputation. **Gillian Gadsby** and **Roger Wicks** handle a range of claimants matters, including brain injury, general surgery, and misdiagnosis. The firm, which is on the Legal Services Multi-Party panel for group claims, places an emphasis on funding cases and now takes a third of its work on a conditional fee basis.

Morgan Jones & Pett Endorsed by interviewees as a small and "*specialised*" team led by the "*straight-taking and highly-rated*" **David Jones**. Extending its work nation-wide, with offices in Yarmouth and Norwich, it handles the range of clinical negligence matters. Settled a cerebral palsy case for £2.6 million.

Prettys (see firm details p.1100) Experienced in paediatric, gynaecology, orthopaedic and failure to diagnose cases. Steven Skinner leads the team, which screens potential cases in a free initial interview. Settled an infant cerebral palsy case at £800,000 and a retinopathy of prematurity case for £500,000.

Scrivenger Seabrook (see firm details p.1120) Formerly a well-respected defendant firm it has now become a claimant practice since falling off the NHSLA panel. Nevertheless the quality of its lawyers (including a former nurse) is such that most commentators agree that "*the change of sides will not affect it*" and consider it "*still a forceful team.*" Both **Mark Scrivenger** and **Vicki Seabrook** "*know their way around and are well suited to the work.*"

CLINICAL NEGLIGENCE: MAINLY DEFENDANT • East Anglia	Ptnrs	Assts
1 **Kennedys** Newmarket	2	9

LEADING INDIVIDUALS
1 **CHAPMAN John** Kennedys

This book is the product of 6,552 1/2-hour interviews. See p.7 for BMRB audit.
Within each band, firms are listed alphabetically. *See individuals' profiles p.164*

MAINLY DEFENDANT

Kennedys (see firm details p.1018) A dominant force in the market, now home to the former Mills & Reeve team which lost its NHSLA franchise. **John Chapman** and the team maintain their reputation of being "*capable and positive.*" Chapman himself is regarded as "*pleasant, practical, never dogmatic or unreasonable.*" **Clients:** NHSLA.

NORTH WEST

MAINLY CLAIMANT

CLINICAL NEGLIGENCE: MAINLY CLAIMANT • North West	Ptnrs	Assts
1 **Pannone & Partners** Manchester	4	7
2 **Alexander Harris** Altrincham	4	8
3 **Jones Maidment Wilson** Manchester	3	n/a
Leigh, Day & Co Manchester	1	2
Linder Myers Manchester	3	4

LEADING INDIVIDUALS	
1 **JONES Stephen** Pannone & Partners	**KITCHINGMAN John** Pannone & Partners
2 **ALEXANDER Ann** Alexander Harris	
SCATES Olivia Jones Maidment Wilson incorporating Hatton Scates Horton	
3 **JONES Eddie** Jones Maidment Wilson incorporating Hatton Scates Horton	
WARD Trevor Linder Myers	

This book is the product of 6,552 1/2-hour interviews. See p.7 for BMRB audit.
Within each band, firms are listed alphabetically. *See individuals' profiles p.164*

Pannone & Partners (see firm details p.1088) "*Absolutely top-notch*" the "*efficient*" team goes from strength to strength and is seen to "*hold a significant market share.*" The firm has handled some high-profile cases, including "*committed*" **John Kitchingman**'s (see p.168) representation of the parents in the conjoined twins case (Mary and Jodie.) "*Dazzlingly able*" **Stephen Jones** (see p.167) was appointed solicitor to the Royal Liverpool Children's Inquiry. The team has increased the number of assistant solicitors and nurses (three nurses plus a midwife) to deal with the greater workload this year. Obtained an award of £3.25 million for a 19 year old boy suffering from cerebral palsy.

Alexander Harris (see firm details p.854) The firm maintains its strong position in the marketplace and handles work beyond the confines of the region. Peers endorse managing partner **Ann Alexander** (see p.164) as a "*big personality*" with a practice that focuses on birth trauma, cerebral palsy, anaesthetic awareness, general surgery, dentistry and radiotherapy treatment. The firm is acting for the victims and alleged victims of Harold Shipman in their successful Judicial Review of the Secretary of State for Health's decision to hold a private inquiry.

Jones Maidment Wilson incorporating Hatton Scates Horton This smaller practice again wins plaudits for its "*specialist*" approach, while defendant firms applaud it as a "*pretty tough team, committed to its clients.*" Head of practice **Olivia Scates** (see p.169) is said to do "*a fantastic job*" while her colleague **Eddie Jones** (see p.167) is "*likewise strong.*" Deals with the entire range of work, and is experienced in handling cancer and orthopaedic cases.

Leigh, Day & Co (see firm details p.1036) Although considered an "*excellent team*" it is not seen as frequently as its immediate competitors. The London and Manchester teams play an active part in each other's cases. Acting exclusively on behalf of claimants, it specialises in complex high value compensation cases. It handles maximum severity cases with spinal and head injuries, and boasts a member of the Spinal Injuries Association among its number.

Linder Myers (see firm details p.1041) Known also for its personal injury work, the firm is respected for its commitment to this field. Handles the range of cases, including psychiatric. **Trevor Ward** (see p.170) is described by peers as "*hardworking, experienced and committed,*" he is typically said to "*play with a straight bat.*" The team is commended for the efforts it has put into the use of conditional fees and other varieties of funding.

MAINLY DEFENDANT

CLINICAL NEGLIGENCE: MAINLY DEFENDANT • North West	Ptnrs	Assts
1 **Hempsons** Manchester	n/a	n/a
2 **Hill Dickinson** Liverpool	8	8
3 **George Davies** Manchester	n/a	n/a

LEADING INDIVIDUALS	
1 **GIBBONS Anthony** Hill Dickinson	**HARRISON Frances** Hempsons

This book is the product of 6,552 1/2-hour interviews. See p.7 for BMRB audit.
Within each band, firms are listed alphabetically. *See individuals' profiles p.164*

Hempsons (see firm details p.990) During 2000, the Manchester office acted for 31 NHS trusts and 12 health authorities, plus the NHS Litigation Authority. In conjunction with London, it acted for the Central Manchester Healthcare NHS Trust on the conjoined twins case (Jodie and Mary.) The "*experienced and immensely humane*" **Frances Harrison** (see p.167) was the lead partner on that case. She is said to bring a "*great knowledge of medical law generally*" to every case. The team also incorporates three mental health specialists and several community care experts. It acted on Cannings v Manchester Health Authority where a structured settlement was reached, and it successfully defended a case involving a cardiac catheterisation. **Clients:** NHS trusts and health authorities; NHS Executive (NW region); NHS estates; Blood Transfusion Service; MDU.

Hill Dickinson (see firm details p.996 Described to our researchers as fielding "*experienced people,*" this firm is seen to take a "*pretty hard nosed*" approach to matters but always remains "*sensible.*" **Tony Gibbons** (see p.166) is respected by both claimant and defendant firms. The group acts for all NHS trusts and health authorities in Cheshire and Merseyside as well as a number in Lancashire and the North Midlands. Although specialising in medical negligence, the team is expert in all aspects of NHS law and ancillary matters and acted in the Benzodiazopine class action. **Clients:** NHSLA

George Davies (see firm details p.969) A "*solidly dependable*" team led by Claire Batchelor, which undertakes work for NHS trusts and health authorities across the broad spectrum of healthcare related issues, including extremely complex cases. Offers experience of high profile group actions and claims of maximum severity that have drawn considerable media scrutiny. **Clients:** NHSLA.

YORKSHIRE

MAINLY CLAIMANT

CLINICAL NEGLIGENCE: MAINLY CLAIMANT • Yorkshire	Ptnrs	Assts
1 **Irwin Mitchell** Sheffield	11	6
2 **Heptonstalls** Goole	2	1

LEADING INDIVIDUALS	
1 **BODY David** Irwin Mitchell	**PICKERING John** Irwin Mitchell

This book is the product of 6,552 1/2-hour interviews. See p.7 for BMRB audit.
Within each band, firms are listed alphabetically. *See individuals' profiles p.164*

Irwin Mitchell (see firm details p.1009) With the additional expertise of six in-house nurses, the team works as a single national unit. Head of department, "*incredibly thorough*" **David Body** (see p.164) has been mainly engaged in representing families of vCJD victims at the BSE Inquiry and in the BSE claims. This culminated in a comprehensive care package and no fault compensation for vCJD victims. "*Serious class act*" **John Pickering** (see p.169) is considered by his peers to be "*extremely bright and diplomatic*" and wins praise for his "*commitment to the reform process.*" He took the cases of Annabel and Warren to the Court of Appeal as landmark cases for the increase of the awards for general damages.

Heptonstalls (see firm details p.992) An "*enormously respected*" small practice which has strengths in cerebral palsy cases, brain and spinal injury, cancer misdiagnosis, gynaecological and orthopaedic cases. An exclusively claimant practice, it has this year expanded in response to the growth of its client base. The group settled a cerebral palsy case for £2 million, obtained £420,000 for an infant gastroschisis case, and was successful on a section 33 limitation case where the alleged negligence occurred over 21 years ago.

MAINLY DEFENDANT

CLINICAL NEGLIGENCE: MAINLY DEFENDANT • Yorkshire	Ptnrs	Assts
1 **Hempsons** Harrogate	4	n/a

LEADING INDIVIDUALS
1 **LOVEL John** Hempsons

This book is the product of 6,552 1/2-hour interviews. See p.7 for BMRB audit.
Within each band, firms are listed alphabetically. *See individuals' profiles p.164*

Hempsons (see firm details p.990) Strengthening its reputation amid an increasing caseload that comes from regular NHS clients as well as a volume of instructions from the NHS Litigation Authority. Peers consider **John Lovel** (see p.168) the "*lynch-pin*" of the practice. The group acted for the Hull & East Yorkshire Hospitals NHS Trust in the five week Christopher Alder Inquest that saw the Trust exonerated. Successfully defended the case of Winston-Whitely v Leeds Teaching Hospitals NHS Trust in the High Court.

NORTH EAST

MAINLY CLAIMANT

CLINICAL NEGLIGENCE: MAINLY CLAIMANT • North East	Ptnrs	Assts
1 **Peter Maughan & Co** Gateshead	2	1
2 **Hay & Kilner** Newcastle upon Tyne	3	1
3 **Samuel Phillips & Co** Newcastle upon Tyne	2	2

LEADING INDIVIDUALS
1 **MAUGHAN Peter** Peter Maughan & Co
2 **SPEKER Barry** Samuel Phillips & Co

This book is the product of 6,552 1/2 hour interviews. See p.7 for BMRB audit.

Within each band, firms are listed alphabetically. *See individuals' profiles p.164*

Peter Maughan & Co While "*extremely good with clients,*" our interviewees believe that **Peter Maughan** (see p.168) also makes a "*formidable opponent.*" He leads the team at this specialist firm that takes on any medico-legal matter including fatal accidents. Continues to offer a free women's clinic every week and is building a reputation in retinopathy of prematurity cases. The firm has recently had some notable successes on cerebral palsy cases.

Hay & Kilner The team now concentrates exclusively on claimant clinical negligence cases and has been appointed to the Legal Aid Multi-Party Action Panel. It offers experience of birth accident and breast cancer cases. One lawyer on the team is a former obstetrician. The group acted on a number of complex and substantial claims including a major anaesthetic claim in which the claimant suffered brain damage and was blinded following anaesthetic. A birth trauma claim valued in excess of £4 million will shortly go to trial.

Samuel Phillips & Co (see firm details p.1118) On the panel for Litigation Protection, the largest post event insurer for clinical negligence conditional fee arrangements, the firm is increasing its profile for claimant work. The group offers particular experience of NHS complaints procedure, the Human Rights Act, and matters arising from consent and access to records. "*Experienced*" **Barry Speker**'s (see p.395) profile remains strong.

MAINLY DEFENDANT

CLINICAL NEGLIGENCE: MAINLY DEFENDANT • North East	Ptnrs	Assts
1 **Eversheds** Newcastle upon Tyne	2	10
2 **Ward Hadaway** Newcastle upon Tyne	2	4

LEADING INDIVIDUALS	
1 **KEEBLE Jeffrey** Ward Hadaway	**SLACK Richard** Eversheds

This book is the product of 6,552 1/2-hour interviews. See p.7 for BMRB audit.

Within each band, firms are listed alphabetically. *See individuals' profiles p.164*

Eversheds (see firm details p.952) Now considered the region's "*only established*" defendant practice, its main asset remains the "*wonderful and dynamic*" **Richard Slack** (see p.170) who "*thinks hard and get masses achieved.*" He handled Caroline Smith v The NHS Litigation Authority. The team is particularly strong in birth injury and mental health matters, the latter for which the team has a dedicated sub unit. Its workload has increased due to its NHSLA panel membership. **Clients:** NHSLA; South Tees Acute Hospitals NHS Trust; North Tees & Hartlepool NHS Trust; South Durham Healthcare NHS Trust.

Ward Hadaway (see firm details p.1173) Now appointed to the NHSLA panel, although the firm carried out some defendant work prior to the changes. Claimant firms consider the growing team "*good to deal with.*" In the past year it has handled a large caseload of cerebral palsy claims. Also involved in a case arising out of a teenage girl's refusal to undergo a kidney transplant, and matters concerning cervical smear tests. **Jeffrey Keeble** (see p.167) is the standout practitioner here. **Clients:** Newcastle upon Tyne Hospitals NHS Trust; South Tyneside Healthcare NHS Trust; Northallerton Health Services NHS Trust; Gateshead Healthcare NHS Trust; North Durham Healthcare NHS Trust; South Durham Healthcare NHS Trust.

SCOTLAND

MAINLY PURSUER

CLINICAL NEGLIGENCE: MAINLY PURSUER • Scotland	Ptnrs	Assts
1 **Anderson Strathern WS** Edinburgh	3	9
Balfour & Manson Edinburgh	5	5
Drummond Miller WS Edinburgh	2	4

LEADING INDIVIDUALS	
1 **CARR Robert** Anderson Strathern WS	**TYLER Alfred** Balfour & Manson

This book is the product of 6,552 1/2-hour interviews. See p.7 for BMRB audit.

Within each band, firms are listed alphabetically. *See individuals' profiles p.164*

Anderson Strathern WS (see firm details p.859) Described by interviewees as a "*well-established*" team it boasts "*genuine specialist*" **Robert Carr** (see p.165), commended as "*diligent on behalf of his clients.*" He has a particular interest in anti-convulsive therapies given to pregnant women resulting in foetal valproate syndrome. The team has recovered damages for the victims of obstetrics negligence, failure to diagnose, and acted in relation to negligent treatment by GPs, orthopaedic surgeons, cardiologists, midwives and plastic surgeons. Unusually, in addition to pursuer work, it carries out defender work for The Royal College of Nursing.

Balfour & Manson (see firm details p.869) A "*leading*" practice with a significant share of the market. "*Exceptionally strong*" **Fred Tyler** (see p.650) is rated for his grasp of "*all the nuances of each claim*" and has much experience of multi-party claims. The group carries out the broad spectrum of work, including complex, high value matters and maintains its reputation for working at the cutting-edge of this field.

Drummond Miller WS (see firm details p.946) A "*dedicated*" practice that fields an "*impressive*" and growing team. It has been involved in an increasing number of cases against the MOD, and in complex obstetric and paediatric cases. Acted in the first claim in the Scottish Courts concerning the misuse of electro convulsive therapy, which successfully settled in favour of the pursuer.

MAINLY DEFENDER

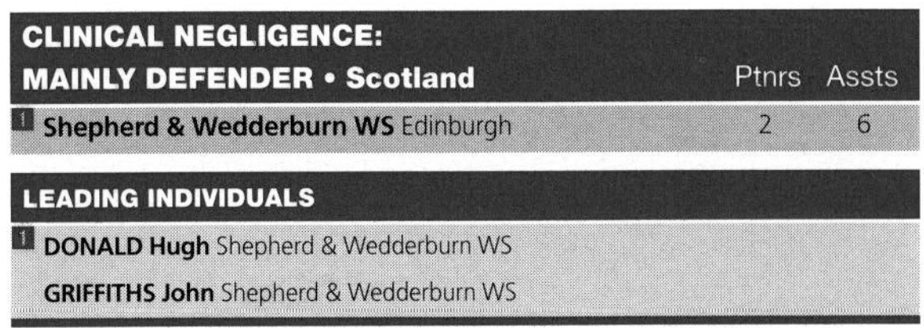

CLINICAL NEGLIGENCE: MAINLY DEFENDER • Scotland	Ptnrs	Assts
1 Shepherd & Wedderburn WS Edinburgh	2	6

LEADING INDIVIDUALS
1 DONALD Hugh Shepherd & Wedderburn WS
GRIFFITHS John Shepherd & Wedderburn WS

This book is the product of 6,552 1/2-hour interviews. See p.7 for BMRB audit.

See individuals' profiles p.164

Shepherd & Wedderburn WS (see firm details p.1126) The group brings together the combined skills of "*trustworthy*" players **John Griffiths** (see p.166) and **Hugh Donald** (see p.165), both described to researchers as "*hard but fair opponents*." They are supported by "*an extremely professional team*," forming the only significant private defender practice in Scotland. It has represented doctors and dentists at a number of high profile fatal accident inquiries over the last year. In particular, the team is acting for a consultant plastic surgeon in circumstances surrounding the death of a patient during an operation. **Clients:** Medical & Dental Defence Union of Scotland; Medical Protection Society; British Medical Association; Le Sou Medical; Royal College of Surgeons, Edinburgh; Scottish Ambulance Service.

LEADERS IN CLINICAL NEGLIGENCE

ALEXANDER, Ann
Alexander Harris, Altrincham (0161) 925 5555
ann@alexharris.co.uk
Specialisation: Managing partner and partner in charge of clinical negligence department. All areas of clinical negligence and concomitant issues of public and legal policy. The treatment of children has become a centre of excellence, with a long history of cerebral palsy and anaesthetics cases. To this expertise has been added work with criminal law aspects (representing families of Beverly Allitt's victims), and wider issues including the conduct of inquests (for example, into the death of Robert Benton) and inquiries (for example, into the death of Nicholas Geldard). More recently involved in representing over 180 relatives of victims and alleged victims of Harold Shipman. Successfully Judicially Reviewed the Secretary of State for Health, Alan Milburn's decision to hold the Inquiry into the Shipman matters in private. The practice represents families of victims of BSE/CJD, and is involved in a number of high profile multiparty actions including the MMR/MR vaccination. It also acts for patients suffering harmful consequences following their treatment with LSD. Ann contributes regularly to television news and current affairs programmes, is an expert frequently consulted by radio reporters and producers, and has been extensively quoted in the press. Lectures on medical negligence issues to legal and medical audiences, and is a visiting Fellow at the Department of Journalism Studies, University of Sheffield.
Prof. Memberships: Law Society, AVMA, ATLA (Member of Executive Committee Birth Trauma Litigation Group), assessor to Law Society Specialist Medical Negligence Panel. Member of Editorial Board of Health Care Risk Report.
Career: Qualified in 1978 and then became co-founder of *Alexander Harris* in May 1989. First practice in this country specialising exclusively in clinical negligence and pharmaceutical product liability. The practice also has a specialist personal injury department.
Personal: Born 5th November 1954. Attended University College, London (LL.B 1974), Nottingham Law School 1997 (MBA). Lives in Altrincham, Cheshire.

BALEN, Paul
Freethcartwright, Nottingham (0115) 936 9369
paul.balen@freethcartwright.co.uk
Specialisation: Offices also at Derby and Leicester. Head of personal litigation. Main areas of practice are clinical negligence and product liability. Acts in claims for compensation arising from accidents of all types, co-ordination of group actions and clinical negligence claims. Is co-ordinating the Trilucent soya breast implants; Leicester cervical smear; MMR, 3M hip and silicone breast implant claims. Editorial board member of Health Care Risk Bulletin. Lecturer on medico-legal matters to doctors and lawyers. Is a Radio Nottingham phone-in 'Legal Eagle'. Co-author of 'Multi-Party Actions' (LAG 1995).
Prof. Memberships: Law Society (Personal Injury Specialist Panel and Clinical Negligence Specialist Panel assessor) National Secretary of APIL 1998-00; Referral Solicitor for AVMA. Member of ATLA, APILA.
Career: Joined *Freeth Cartwright* in 1975. Qualified in 1977. Partner 1980.
Personal: Born 25 February 1952. Attended Nottingham High School 1960-71, then Cambridge University 1971-74.

BANNISTER, Richard
Challinors Lyon Clark, Birmingham (0121) 212 9393
rlb@challinors.co.uk
Specialisation: Handles all types of clinical negligence claims including obstetric, oncology, orthopaedic, neurosurgery, GP liability and general surgery. Legal Aid, CFA and privately funded cases. Representation at inquests.
Prof. Memberships: AVMA and Law Society specialist referral panels; APIL; Birmingham Medico Legal Society.
Career: Qualified 1990, became a partner in 1993.
Personal: Married, three sons. Leisure pursuits include football and cricket.

BARCAN, Richard
Barcan Woodward, Bristol (0117) 925 8080

BARTON, Grainne
Alexander Harris, London (020) 7430 5555
grainnebarton@alexharris.co.uk
Specialisation: Partner and head of clinical negligence department, London. Handles exclusively claimant clinical negligence matters and is renowned for her commitment, energy and enthusiasm in this area of the law. Main areas of practice are cerebral palsy, anaesthetic awareness, cancer, keyhole surgery and dental matters. Acted in R v H.M Coroner for Inner North London District, Ex parte Touche (successfully Judically Reviewed the decision by the Coroner not to hold an inquest into the death of the client's wife), Tredget v Bexley Health Authority (nervous shock) in 1994 and Smyth v Riverside Health Authority (malaria case) in 1993.
Prof. Memberships: APIL, AVMA, Law Society, Medical Negligence Panel.
Career: With *Boyes Turner & Burrows* 1987-90. Qualified in 1989. Joined *Pritchard Englefield* in 1990 and became a partner in 1993. Joined *Alexander Harris* as partner April 1999.
Personal: Born 8th October 1963. Educated at Brunel University 1982-86. Past Honorary Secretary of TSG. Lives in Epsom, Surrey.

BATTEN, Elizabeth
Parlett Kent, London (020) 7430 0712
Specialisation: Clinical negligence specialist since 1991. Particular interest in oncology, brain injury, accident and emergency cases and in psychiatric negligence, also negligence and abuse of people with learning disabilities. Reported case of 'Mahmood v Siggins'. Has lectured to lawyers and health professionals on clinical negligence and related topics.
Prof. Memberships: Law Society. Law Society Medical Negligence panel. AVMA referral panel member. APIL member.
Career: Admitted 1977. Partner in *Parlett Kent* from 1993. BA (Cantab) in Economics.

BODY, David
Irwin Mitchell, Sheffield (0114) 276 7777
Bodyd@irwinmitchel.co.uk
Specialisation: Partner in personal injury department. Head of clinical negligence team. Main area of practice is clinical negligence on behalf of plaintiffs. Acted in Maynard v West Midlands RHA, Davis v City and Hackney Health Authority, Aboul-Hosn v Governors of National Hospital for Nervous Diseases, Bolitho v City and Hackney Health Authority, Hopkins v McKenzie, Fisher v North Derbyshire Health Authority and the Creutzfeldt-Jacob Disease Litigation. Represented all the variant CJD victims' families at the BSE Inquiry 1998-00. 2000-1 presently negotiating No fault Compensation Scheme in Settlement of BSE Claims. Lectures regularly to both doctors and

lawyers. Chair of Medical Negligence Special Interest Group of APIL (1992-95).
Prof. Memberships: APIL, AVMA, ATLA (ATLA Birth Trauma Litigation Group).
Career: Qualified in 1981. Worked at *Halls* 1981-91, from 1984 as a partner. Joined *Irwin Mitchell* in 1991 as a partner.
Publications: Author of chapter on 'The Conduct of Proceedings' in Powers & Harris 'Medical Negligence' (all editions).
Personal: Born 1st August 1955. Attended Hereford High School and Corpus Christi College, Oxford (BA Hons, 1976). Leisure interests include despairing about the revival of the Welsh rugby team. Lives in Sheffield.

CAHILL, Julia
Kingsley Napley, London (020) 7814 1200
jcahill@kingsleynapley.co.uk
Specialisation: Partner and head of clinical negligence department. Specialist in clinical and professional negligence claims. Cases mainly involve serious disability or death. Advises on complaints procedures. Advises on inquests into death during medical care. Particular expertise in obstetric negligence claims on behalf of mother and child. Special interest in delayed diagnosis of meningitis in children and delayed diagnosis in adults of cervical cancer, bowel cancer, breast cancer and mismanagement of diabetes. Practice also covers legal negligence involving the pursuit of claims against legal advisers in medical negligence cases. Interesting recent cases include McAllister v Lewisham and North Southwark Health Authority, Davis v Jacobs, Camden & Islington Health Authority, Novartis Pharmaceuticals (UK) Ltd.
Prof. Memberships: Law Society Panel of Specialist Medical Negligence Solicitors; AVMA Lawyers Referral Panel; Member APIL, APLA, ATLA. Secretary to the APIL Medical Negligence Special Interest Group 1998-99. CEDR Accredited Mediator.
Career: DIP Physiotherapy 1976. Qualified LL.B 1980. Assistant Director, Action for Victims of Medical Accidents 1984-88. Partner *Parlett Kent & Co* 1992-94. Joined *Kingsley Napley* as partner in September 1994.
Personal: Two children. Lives in Islington, London.

CARR, Robert
Anderson Strathern WS, Edinburgh
(0131) 220 2345
robert.carr@andersonstrathern.co.uk
Specialisation: Partner in litigation department. Accredited by the Law Society of Scotland as a medical negligence specialist and admitted as a solicitor/advocate with extended rights of audience in the highest Scottish civil courts. Almost 20 years of practice in civil litigation covering all areas of court and tribunal work. One of a team involved in advising insurers, particularly in personal injuries and related actions, and in advising the Royal College of Nursing as their appointed Scottish agents. The RCN instructions cover the full spectrum of criminal and civil court work and employment law matters, including frequent advice on medical negligence issues and regular appearance at fatal accident enquiries. Also speaks and lectures to insurers, nurses and doctors on many aspects of civil law and court procedure and practice. Head of the firm's Parliamentary Unit; assisted the RCN in its evidence before the Scottish Parliament on the Adults with an Incapacity Bill. Represented the Denholm family at the much publicised recent fatal accident enquiry in relation to the death of Darren Denholm who died whilst undergoing dental surgery under general anaesthetic; the case resulted in a finding that dental surgery under general anaesthetic should no longer be conducted outside a hospital setting. *Anderson Strathern* also dealt with the case of Richard Adamson, one of the first medical negligence actions in Scotland to proceed before a jury for almost 50 years, which resulted in an award for pain and suffering of £100,000 for a young man whose only testicle was negligently removed by doctors at a hospital in West Lothian. Has also been pioneering in Scotland damages for children who have suffered disability as a consequence of their mothers undergoing anticonvulsant therapy whilst pregnant.

CHAPMAN, John
Kennedys, Newmarket

DAVIES, Andrew
Hugh James Ford Simey, Bargoed (01443) 822022
andrew.davies@hjfs.co.uk
Specialisation: Partner and head of clinical negligence group. His experience in medical negligence work includes obstetric negligence involving injuries of the utmost severity such as brain damage. His work has a broad spectrum however and involves a substantial number of orthopaedic medical negligence cases.
Prof. Memberships: One of only a handful of solicitors in Wales on the Law Society's Medical Negligence Panel, and is also a member of the Law Society's Personal Injury Panel and the AVMA Solicitors Referral Panel.
Career: Qualified 1988. Partner 1994.

DESMOND, Adrian
Boyes Turner, Reading (0118) 952 7219
adesmond@boyesturnerlegal.co.uk
Specialisation: Head of clinical negligence and personal injury. Acts for claimants in all types of clinical accident and personal injury cases with special interest in cases of maximum severity, brain, spinal, obstetric and paediatric injury. Has acted in many high profile and reported cases. AVMA referral solicitor since 1984. Assessor to and member of Law Society specialist medical negligence panel since formed in 1995 and personal injury panel. Secretary then co-ordinator of medical negligence special interest group of the Association of Personal Injury Lawyers. Member of Richard Grand Society. Author of legal and medical articles on issues related to medical negligence. Deputy Taxing Master Supreme Court Taxing Office 1994-98. Spinal Injuries Association and Headway Panel Solicitor.
Prof. Memberships: AVMA, APIL, SIA, Headway, ATLA, European Brain Injury Society, Richard Grand Society.
Career: Qualified and joined *Boyes Turner* in 1980.

DINGWALL, Christian
Bevan Ashford, London (020) 7421 4400
Specialisation: Partner handling defendant medical negligence dispute resolution. Head of the NHS Claimants Department at *Bevan Ashford.* Principal area of practice is medical negligence. Handles a wide range of medical negligence claims on behalf of defendants. Important cases include Poynter v Hillington HA and Jenkins v Lambeth Southwark & Lewisham HA. Other past cases include R v Managers of South Western Hospital ex p. M. R v NW London Mental Health Trust ex ps and R v Brent & Harrow HA ex p. LB of Harrow. Clients include the NHSLA. Has addressed conferences and seminars.
Prof. Memberships: Law Society.
Career: Qualified in 1986. Partner at *Le Brasseur J Tickle* 1988-00 and *Bevan Ashford from April 2000.*
Personal: Born 28th December 1959. Educated at Bristol University 1979-82 and the College of Law 1982-84. Leisure activities include gardening. Lives in Raynes Park, London.

DONALD OBE, Hugh
Shepherd & Wedderburn WS, Edinburgh
(0131) 473 5159
hugh.donald@shepwedd.co.uk
Specialisation: Partner. Specialist in clinical negligence, representing doctors and dentists in civil claims, inquiries and disciplinary proceedings. Also aviation representing airline and helicopter operators in both civil claims and accident inquiries. On the panel appointed to handle claims under Law society of Scotland Charter Policy.
Career: Qualified in 1975, having joined *Shepherd & Wedderburn WS* in 1973. Became a partner in 1977. Administrative head of litigation department 1990-94. Appointed managing partner in April 1994, and chief executive from April 1995 – April 1999.
Personal: Born 5th November 1951. Educated at Edinburgh University. Family Mediator. Chairman, Family Mediation Scotland. Leisure interests include gardening, walking and church. Lives in Edinburgh. Awarded OBE for services to family mediation in Scotland.

DYSON, Henry
Leigh, Day & Co, London (020) 7650 1200
Specialisation: Claimant Clinical Negligence. Particular interest in and experience of arranging presentation for families at inquests following deaths after medical intervention, for example, recently acted for the family of the young woman who died after taking Zyban, the anti-smoking drug. Neurological injury following either orthopaedic or neurosurgery. Complaints to the GMC and UKCC.
Prof. Memberships: APIL and the Medico-Legal Society. Law Society Clinical Negligence Panel Member. Legal Services Commission Funding Review Committee member.
Career: Joined *Leigh Day & Co* in 1991. Partner in 1998.
Personal: Born 1963. Degree in Biochemistry followed by CPE and LPC. Qualified 1989.

ENGLAND, Richard P.B.
John Hodge & Co, Bristol (0117) 929 2281

FAZAN, Claire
Bindman & Partners, London (020) 7833 4433
Specialisation: Partner in charge of personal injury and clinical negligence department. Clinical negligence litigation on behalf of claimants. Experienced in claims involving all types of injury. Extensive experience of claims on behalf of adults and children who have suffered brain and spinal cord injury and other permanent and severe disabilities including those arising from obstetric and anaesthetic care and failure to diagnose, for example, pulmonary embolism subarachnoid haemorrhage and cancer. Has regularly recovered awards in excess of £1 million. Major cases since 01.01.00 include Parkin & Parkin v Bromley Hospitals NHS Trust and Miles v Redbridge &

Waltham Forest Health Authority. Advises in relation to inquests into deaths during medical care. Experience in respect of provision and refusal of treatment. Co-author of 'Medical Negligence Litigation: A Practitioners Guide', by Irwin, Fazan & Allfrey. Frequently lectures on medico-legal issues.
Prof. Memberships: Law Society Medical Negligence Panel. Association of Personal Injury Lawyers, AVMA. Lawyers Referral Panel.
Career: Qualified in 1985. Joined *Bindman & Partners* in 1987 and became a partner in 1989.

FERGUSON, Gerry M.
Withy King, Bath (01225) 425731
gerry.ferguson@withyking.co.uk
Specialisation: Partner specialising in clinical negligence and product liability claims for claimants, including benzodiazepine/breast implant multi party litigation. Experience of high value claims, cerebral palsy, paraplegia, and psychiatric negligence cases.
Prof. Memberships: Law Society (Clinical Negligence Specialist Panel), APIL, ATLA, APLA and AVMA (panel member). Legal Services Commission Funding Review Committee. Bath and North East Somerset Racial Equality Council, Clinical Society of Bath, MIND Legal Network.
Career: Involved in medical negligence litigation since 1981. Joined *Withy King* in 1989 as the only fee-earner handling medical negligence work. Since then the clinical negligence department has grown to four part-time and five full-time fee-earners with a strong regional reputation.
Personal: Born 23.7.53. Education: Epsom College; Birmingham University. Married with two sons. Lives in Bath. Leisure interests: Motor sport photography.

FIELD, Rena
Vizard Oldham, London (020) 7663 2222
renafield@vizold.co.uk
Specialisation: Principal area of practice is clinical negligence, acting for defendant NHS Trusts, Health Authorities and NHSLA with particular emphasis on larger cases, especially birth injury cases. She has considerable experience of health service law, covering general advisory issues, consent, mental health and inquests. Leading cases include Re L (1996: use of force to carry out caesarean section on incompetent patient); Re MB (1997: Court of Appeal decision on capacity test for caesarean section).
Prof. Memberships: Law Societies of England, Wales and Ireland; CEDR accredited mediator.
Career: Qualified Ireland 1979; partner *Hughes & MacEuilly* until 1985; joined *Le Brasseur J. Tickle* 1989, partner 1990-2001; joined *Vizard Oldham* as a partner in April 2001.
Publications: Lectures regularly to health service bodies on topical medico-legal issues.
Personal: B.C.L National University of Ireland. Lives in Surrey, two children.

FOLLIS, Richard
Irwin Mitchell, Birmingham (0121) 212 1828
follisr@irwinmitchell.co.uk
Specialisation: Partner heading claimant clinical negligence team in Birmingham. Handles claimant only medical negligence litigation with legally aided, insurance funded and conditional fee work. Involved in medical negligence claims since 1979. Now heads a strong team dealing with all types of clinical negligence claims, including obstetric, orthopaedic, psychiatric, oncological, gynaecological, ophthalmological, general surgical and GP liability. Provides representation at inquests. Member of Medico-Legal Training Services Panel. Lectures regularly to both Doctors and Lawyers on medico-legal matters. Actively involved with issues relating from hospital organ retention.
Prof. Memberships: Law Society, Council Birmingham Law Society, Council Birmingham Medico-Legal Society, AVMA Lawyers Support Group. Chairman AVMA Midlands LSG. Hon. Part-time tutor Department of Bio-medical ethics, University of Birmingham. Member of Law Society and AVMA referral clinical negligence panels. Legal Services Commission Funding Review Committee.
Career: Qualified in 1981. Became a partner, Irwin Mitchell 1999.
Personal: Educated Halesowen Grammar School 1968-74. University College, Cardiff 1976-79.

GADSBY, Gillian
Gadsby Wicks, Chelmsford (01245) 494929

GIBBONS, Anthony
Hill Dickinson, Liverpool (0151) 236 5400
Specialisation: Partner in health department. Principal areas of practice are medical negligence, employment law and NHS advisory work. Handles a large volume of medical negligence cases, particularly brain damage cases of high value. Another significant element of work involves NHS property transactions acting on behalf of major NHS clients in the disposal of surplus property and in particular redundant hospitals. Important cases handled include Booth v Warrington Health Authority (disclosure of witness statements referred to in experts reports), Ashcroft v Mersey Regional Health Authority (standard of care of consultants in medical negligence cases) and O'Toole v Liverpool Health Authority (first self-funded structural settlement case in the medical negligence field). Major clients include North West Regional Health Authority and all NHS trusts in Cheshire and Merseyside. Has given lectures to various NHS clients. Participated as a presenter in Liverpool Law Society course on medical negligence.
Prof. Memberships: Law Society.
Career: Qualified in 1972. Former in-house legal adviser with Mersey RHA 1980-90. Joined *Hill Dickinson* as a partner in 1990. Presently a partner *Hill Dickinson.*
Personal: Born 10th October 1947. Educated at Xaverian College, Manchester 1959-66 and Nottingham University 1966-69 (Nottingham Co-operative Society Prize 1968, Hill Prize 1969). Leisure pursuits include food, wine and watching sport. Lives in Chester.

GOLDBURN, Tim
Preston Goldburn, Falmouth (01326) 318900
Tim.Goldburn@btinternet.com
Specialisation: Claimant's clinical negligence claims with particular emphasis on gynaecological and urological injuries. Based in the Falmouth Business Park, in an office with diabled access, facilities and equipment, and have a fully qualified nurse on the team.
Prof. Memberships: APIL, The Law Society Clinical Negligence panel, and also the Co-ordinator for the AVMA South west Lawyers Support Group.
Career: Admitted in 1977, articled at *Ince & Co*, post qualification experience at *Richards Butler* before joining *Stephens & Scown* in St Austell in 1979 leaving to set up in partnership in *Preston Goldburn* specialising in personal injury and clinical negligence claims in 1982.
Personal: Enjoys SCUBA diving and sailing.

GRIFFITHS, John
Shepherd & Wedderburn WS, Edinburgh
(0131) 473 5445
john.griffiths@shepwedd.co.uk
Specialisation: Partner. Main area of practice is medical negligence: previously Solicitor at the Central Legal Office for the Scottish Hospital Service, advising and acting for the fifteen Scottish Health Boards. With present firm, acts for a leading Medical Defence organisation. Chairman of Law Society Panel to certify solicitors with specialist experience in medical negligence work. Has been responsible for the conduct of litigation in the Scottish Supreme Court, the Court of Session, House of Lords and Sheriff Courts all over Scotland. Has specialist interest in representing parties at Fatal Accident Inquires and advising generally on all aspects of work relating to medical negligence and the National Health Service. Is engaged at any one time in an average of 300 claims, litigations or contentious matters relating to medical or dental negligence. Also advises on administrative and management structure of the NHS and on employment law with a particular emphasis on disciplinary cases against doctors and dentists with regular appearances before the GMC and GDC. Accredited specialist by the Law Society of Scotland. Has spoken and chaired conferences on medical negligence frequently. Author of a number of chapters in a textbook edited by Sir Michael Drury 'Clinical Negligence in General Practice' Radcliff Medical Press Ltd.
Prof. Memberships: Law Society of Scotland.
Career: Qualified in 1971. Trainee at *Shepherd & Wedderburn WS* and *MacAndrew Wright and Murray WS* 1969-71. Joined Central Legal Office for National Health Service in Scotland in 1972, becoming Chief Assistant Solicitor in 1984 and Acting Legal Adviser 1988-89. Joined *Simpson & Marwick WS* as Partner in 1989. *Shepherd & Wedderburn* May 2000.
Personal: Born 16th September 1944. Attended Edinburgh Academy; Wadham College, Oxford 1962-65 and Edinburgh University 1967-69. Lives in Edinburgh.

HALL, Antony
Anthony Collins Solicitors, Birmingham
(0121) 200 3242
Specialisation: Acts for both legally aided and privately funded claimants or under conditional fee agreements in all aspects of medical and personal injury litigation, but especially obstetric, GP, cancer misdiagnosis, orthopaedic and brain damage claims. Expertise in medical ethics claims including those involving refusal of consent to treatment.
Prof. Memberships: Law Society Medical Negligence panel, Referral panel solicitor for Action for Victims of Medical Accidents (AVMA), Law Society Personal Injury panel, member of Medical Negligence Special Interest Group of Association of Personal Injury Lawyers, Clinical Negligence Specialist Member of Legal Aid Board Committee, member of Birmingham Medico-Legal Society.
Career: Qualified 1986. Assistant solicitor with *Anthony Collins* 1986-89. Associate with a Worcestershire law firm 1989-90. West Midlands Regional Health Authority 1990-92. *Anthony Collins* 1992 onwards (partner since 1994).

HARRISON, Frances
Hempsons, Manchester (0161) 228 0011
fah@hempsons.co.uk
Specialisation: Partner in Medical & Healthcare Department and Senior Partner in the firm's Manchester office. Principal area of practice is the law relating to hospitals and general practice. Work includes medico-legal advice to and representation of Health Authorities, NHS Trusts and individual practitioners in medical negligence actions. Advises on ethics in relation to healthcare and also concerning the conduct of and representation at enquiries. Other main areas of practice are defamation and the law relating to children. Major cases include Re: A (Minor) Conjoined Twins: (separation) CA Sept 2000.
Prof. Memberships: Law Society.
Career: Qualified in 1978 and joined *Hempsons.* Became a Partner in 1982. Moved to Manchester in 1990 to lead the firm's Manchester office.

HAY, Katie
Capsticks, London (020) 8780 2211
Specialisation: Partner in clinical law department. Handles all types of medical negligence litigation for NHS clients. Has a particular interest in larger cases, especially birth injury baby cases. She is an authority on structured settlements having helped to pioneer structures in the health service. She has advised on the drafting of the NHS Executives Guidance on the subject and has had articles published on this and other medico-legal issues. She manages a team of lawyers and is responsible for business process systems in the department.
Prof. Memberships: Law Society, Association of Women Solicitors.
Career: Qualified in 1988 following articles at *Howard Kennedy.* With *Cole & Cole,* Oxford 1988-90. Joined *CAPSTICKS* in 1990. Became a partner in November 1992. Member of firm's Management Commitee.
Personal: Born 24th January 1964. Educated at Reading Abbey School 1976-82, Oxford Polytechnic (BA Hons in Law with History) 1982-85. Interests include running, reading and cinema. Lives in London.

HOLMES, John
Hempsons, London (020) 7839 0278
j.holmes@hempsons.co.uk
Specialisation: Partner in healthcare litigation department. Principal area of practice is medical negligence acting for health service bodies in defence claims. Also gives general advice in clinical issues and mental health (including human rights). Reported claims include Sion v Hampstead Health Authority, Clunis v Camden & Islington Health Authority, R v Bournewood NHS Trust and D v NHS Trust. The Firm is on the panel for the NHS Litigation Authority (NHSLA).
Prof. Memberships: Law Society.
Career: Qualified in 1984. Joined *Beachcroft Stanleys* in 1986 and became a Partner in 1992. Joined Hempsons in 2001.
Personal: Educated at Bristol University 1978-81.

HOOPER, John
Wynne Baxter, Brighton (01273) 775533
jhooper@wynnebaxter.com
Specialisation: Senior partner and leading member of Clinical Negligence Department at the firm's Head Office in Brighton. Wynne Baxter was among the first in the country to receive a Legal Aid Franchise in Clinical Negligence, recognition of their undoubted expertise and professionalism in the field. With more than 20 years' clinical negligence experience, he has recovered millions of pounds' compensation for clients who have suffered injury in all fields including obstetrics and gynaecology, having particular experience in brain damage cases. Represented the Claimant in the landmark case of Cassel v Riverside HA.
Prof. Memberships: Law Society Clinical Negligence and Children Panels; AVMA Referral Panel.
Career: Admitted 1962; Partner in *Selwood Leathes Hooper* 1963-97 merged with *Wynne Baxter in 1997.*
Personal: Educated Worthing High School; London University Law Degree.

JENKINS, Caroline
Parlett Kent, London (020) 7430 0712
Specialisation: Senior partner in personal injury/clinical negligence department. Principal area of practice is clinical negligence (claimant PI). Particular interest in gynaecological, oncological, obstetrics and professional negligence cases. Important cases handled include Gascoine v Sheridan & Co & Latham (MLR Dec 1994), Kirk v S.E. London Health Authority, Leech v Gloucester Health. Settlement of cerebral palsy case of £4.5m, Anderson v King's Healthcare NHS Trust, Costello v Epsom Healthcare NHS Trust. Member of Law Society's Medical Negligence Panel from 1995. Author of chapter on Quantum in AVMA Medical Accidents Handbook.
Prof. Memberships: AVMA, APIL, Law Society, ATLA.
Career: Qualified in 1980. Joined *Parlett Kent & Co* in 1982. Became a partner in 1983. Now senior partner.
Personal: King's College, London University (BA, 1975).

JOHN, Simon
Cunningham John, Thetford (01842) 752401
Specialisation: Main area of practice is catastrophic injuries. Leads a team of 19 PI/clinical negligence (CN) lawyers and paralegals. Has particular expertise in head, spinal injuries and CN. Notable and landmark cases: Farrant v Thanet DC (diving/tidal pool); Webb (a child) v Darbon (1st Judgement for identifying 30mph too fast); Edwards v Ogg (largest CN award for child £3.9 million); Mullings v Breckland DC (1st Judgement for Councils failure to grit); first NHS mediation; first structured settlement in East Anglia; first order for evidence by satellite link; largest award for amputee; many awards in excess of £1 million. Experience in litigation in Canada and many US states. Recent awards: $3.5 million CN and $2,040 million head injury. Lectures widely.
Prof. Memberships: AVMA, Headway and SIA Solicitor panels; Law Society CN and PI panels; sustaining member of ATLA; Brain and Birth Litigation groups; Richard Grand Society; APIL, Secretary; Clinical Negligence SIG; UKABIF, Treasurer. Fellow of the Society for Advanced Legal Studies; European Brain Injury Society.
Career: Qualified 1969, partner 1971, formed *Cunningham John* 1973.
Publications: Editor of BPILS chapter 'PI Litigation in the USA'. Author of papers; 'Plaintiff's Offer to Settle – resulting in PART 36 CPR; 'Split Trial'. Editor of 'ATLA Intnl Newsletter'

JONES, David
Morgan Jones & Pett, Great Yarmouth (01493) 334700

JONES, Eddie
Jones Maidment Wilson incorporating Hatton Scates Horton, Manchester (0161) 8281934
eddiej@jmw.co.uk
Specialisation: Partner in clinical negligence department specialising in claimant clinical negligence and mental health law. Deals with all aspects of clinical negligence litigation with a particular interest in psychiatric negligence. Co-ordinated the Maden litigation group action on behalf of patients indecently assaulted by their psychiatrist. In 1999-00 concluded two birth injury claims with combined damages of £4.15M.
Prof. Memberships: Defence Panel Solicitor for Action for Victims of Medical Accidents, Law Society's Mental Health Review Tribunal Panel Member. Member of Association of Personal Injury Lawyers. Member of a local NHS Trusts Clinical Ethics Committee.
Career: Qualified 1992. Previously with *Hempsons.* Joined *Jones Maidment Wilson* in 1998 as Partner.
Publications: Publications include 'Violence from Patients in the Community: Will the Courts Impose a Duty of Care on Mental Health Professionals,' with M Kennedy in 'Criminal Behaviour and Mental Health' 5 1995.

JONES, Stephen
Pannone & Partners, Manchester (0161) 909 4345
stephen.jones@pannone.co.uk
Specialisation: Partner in clinical negligence department. Specialised in clinical negligence work since qualification. Also covers mental health and has a specific interest in psychiatric negligence, represented patients at Ashworth Hospital in the Fallon Inquiry which reported in January 1999. In August 1999 represented VC, a 16 year old anorexic in proceedings brought by local trust to force feed. In February 2000 appointed solicitor to the Royal Liverpool Children's inquiry into the retention of organs following postmortems at Alderhey Hospital which was reported in January 2001. Previously a member of Birmingham Royal Orthopaedic Hospital Cancer Cases Co-ordinating Committee. Biggest settlement: £3.25m for 19 year old with cerebral palsy (1999).
Prof. Memberships: Member of Law Society Medical Negligence Panel, AVMA Solicitors Referral Panel, MIND Legal Network.
Career: Joined *Pannone & Partners* in 1984, qualified in 1986 and became a partner in 1992.
Personal: Educated at Manchester Grammar School and Queens College, Cambridge. Leisure interests include football.

KEEBLE, Jeffrey
Ward Hadaway, Newcastle upon Tyne (0191) 204 4312
jeffrey.keeble@wardhadaway.com
Specialisation: Head of litigation department and healthcare unit. Nominated partner to NHS Litigation Authority. Specialist in all aspects of health law including injuries of utmost severity. Regular lecturer in medico-legal topics and clinical risk management. Major clients include Newcastle upon Tyne Hospitals NHS Trust and North Durham Healthcare NHS Trust.
Prof. Memberships: Law Society; Medico-Legal Society.

Career: Qualified in London in 1978. Joined *Ward Hadaway* in 1991 and became partner specialising in health law in 1993.
Personal: Born 24 June 1954 in Hackney. Attended Hackney Downs Grammar School and Leeds University. Enjoys rugby union, cricket and exotic holidays. Lives in Tyne Valley.

KITCHINGMAN, John

Pannone & Partners, Manchester (0161) 909 4336
john.kitchingman@pannone.co.uk
Specialisation: Partner in Clinical Negligence department. Head of department dealing with all aspects of medical law and claims for Clinical Negligence with emphasis on cases of maximum severity.
Prof. Memberships: Law Society Medical Negligence panel, AVMA referral panel, APIL Medical Negligence Special Interest Group, ATLA, Justice.
Career: Qualified in 1975, became partner in *Pannone & Partners* 1978.
Personal: Fellow of RSA. Leisure pursuits include walking, birdwatching, and travel. Lives in Altrincham.

LEE, Terry

Evill and Coleman, London (020) 8789 9221
Terry.Lee@evillandcoleman.co.uk
Specialisation: Partner of personal injury/clinical negligence department. Main areas of practice are catastrophic injuries, clinical negligence, particularly brain damage at birth, head injuries, multiple injuries, fatal accident claims and Court of Protection work. Has been involved in a number of significant actions including Brown v Merton & Sutton Health Authority, Head v East Anglia Health Authority, Hall v Pirie and Lambert v Devon County Council. A further important case, Joyce v Wandsworth Health Authority, provided clarification of the judicial approach to causation in a clinical negligence case. Recently was involved in the well known sporting injury case which was the first of its kind brought against a rugby referee and which was successful. This was the case of Smoldon v Whitworth & Nolan. Further, the case of Dudley v East Dorset Health Authority is an important case relating to the removal of a litigation friend in an application that was contested. Has also been instrumental in dealing with a number of cases which involve the formation of a structured settlement. Is an assessor to the Personal Injury panel as well as a member of the Personal Injury panel of Solicitors. Is also a member of the Medical Negligence Specialist panel of Solicitors. Author of articles for legal magazines and a book on dealing with cases involving catastrophic injuries. Lectures extensively at conferences and seminars. Is also a referral solicitor to various organisations including AVMA, Spinal Injuries Association, Headway etc.
Prof. Memberships: Member of the Association of Personal Injury Lawyers, British Academy of Forensic Science and the Environmental Law Foundation.
Career: Qualified and joined *Evill and Coleman* in 1972. Became a partner in 1976.
Personal: Educated at Wimbledon College. Recreations include golf and tennis. Lives in Esher, Surrey.

LEIGH, Bertie

Hempsons, London (020) 7839 0278
mamsl@hempsons.co.uk
See under Healthcare, p.421

LEIGH, Sarah

Leigh, Day & Co, London (020) 7650 1200
Specialisation: Partner in medical negligence department. Handles primarily major medical negligence cases involving severe disability and death and cases involving mental handicap problems (e.g. Re F in 1989 – a leading case on consent in mental handicap). Has spoken at many conferences and seminars and written several articles.
Prof. Memberships: AVMA, Justice, APIL.
Career: Qualified in 1971. Founder partner (1974) of *Bindman & Partner*. Left to set up own firm in 1985 (renamed *Leigh Day & Co* in 1988).
Personal: Born 29th July 1942. Trustee of Immigrants Aid Trust. Campaigner for changes in medical negligence litigation system.

LEVY, Russell

Leigh, Day & Co, London (020) 7650 1200

LEWIN, Olive

Leigh, Day & Co, London (020) 7650 1200
Specialisation: Partner in the clinical negligence department. Handles mainly clinical negligence cases involving severe injury and death. Also handles a multi party product liability claim. Has advised the British Cardiology Society on Human Rights for the 5th UK cardiology review.
Prof. Memberships: AVMA, Liberty, APIL.
Career: Qualified as a registered General Nurse (RGN) in 1982. Qualified as a solicitor in 1990.
Personal: Enjoys travel, films, food, wine, and reading.

LOVEL, John

Hempsons, Harrogate (01423) 522331
wjml@hempsons.co.uk
Specialisation: Medical negligence. National Health Service law. Project leader (Northern and Yorkshire) Department of Health, clinical negligence mediation pilot.
Prof. Memberships: Law Society.
Career: Shrewsbury School; University College London – LLB Hons 1971; CEDR accredited mediator 1996. Trained at *Sintons*; qualified 1974; partner at *Maughan & Hall* 1975; solicitor with Yorkshire Regional Health Authority 1976; legal adviser to Yorkshire Regional Health Authority 1989; head of Yorkshire Health Legal Services 1990; partner *Hempsons* 1996.
Personal: Squash, cycling, skiing.

MARTINEZ, Liz

Evill and Coleman, London (020) 8789 9221
liz.martinez@evillandcoleman.co.uk
Specialisation: Partner. Specialist in clinical negligence. Mediator. Interests include anaesthetic brain damage, cerebral palsy and birth trauma, obstetrics, gynaecology, cardiology, general surgery and fatal cases.
Prof. Memberships: APIL, Law Society Personal Injury panel. CEDR Accredited Mediator.
Career: Qualified 1990. *Osborne Morris & Morgan* 1988-93 (partner from 1991). Yorkshire Health Legal Services 1993-94. *Evill and Coleman* 1994 (partner from 1995).

MASON, David

Capsticks, London (020) 8780 2211
Specialisation: Partner in clinical law department; defends clinical negligence claims, judicial reviews, especially involving issues arising from the reprovision of long stay services and resource allocation, consent to treatment cases and mental health law; major cases include: Buckingham-Smart v NHS Litigation Authority; Thomas and Alayan v Northwick Park NHS Trust; Joyce v Merton Sutton and Wandsworth HA; De Martell v Merton Sutton & Wandsworth HA; Waters v West Sussex HA; Corley v NW Herts HA; Knight v W Kent HA; Moore v Worthing HA; Muzio v NW Herts HA; handles many of the cases in Capsticks where court orders are required relating to future medical care, including Re R (adult), medical treatment, one of the leading cases on when care can be withheld. Co-author of 'Litigation – A Risk Management Guide for Midwives', published by the Royal College of Midwives, and articles on medical law for specialist publications. Regular lecturer on medical law and risk management topics, especially obstetrics-related. Honorary legal adviser to College of Health. Defence solicitor representative and executive Committee Member of the Clinical Disputes Forum until April 2001. Co-author of the Pre Action Protocol for the Resolution of Clinical Disputes, and the CDF 'Guidelines on Experts' Discussions in the Context of Clinical Disputes'.
Career: Called to Bar 1984. Employed Barrister with *Thomas Watts & Co* 1986-88. Joined *CAPSTICKS* in 1988 as employed Barrister. Requalified as Solicitor and became a Partner in 1990. Elected Fellow of the Society for Advanced Legal Studies 1998. Associate member of ATLA since 1998.
Personal: Born 16th October 1955. Attended Winchester College 1969-73, then Oriel College, Oxford 1974-77 (MA in Experimental Psychology). Dip L (City University) 1983. Lives in Wimbledon.

MAUGHAN, Peter J.

Peter Maughan & Co, Gateshead (0191) 477 9779
mailroom@gatlaw.demon.co.uk
Specialisation: Claimant medical negligence and personal injury claims. Visiting lecturer in nursing law to the University of Northumbria at Newcastle.
Prof. Memberships: FCIArb, FSALS, ADR Group, ATLA, APIL, APLA, AVMA.
Career: Principal and senior partner of *Peter Maughan & Co* since 1981. Arbitrator and Mediator.
Personal: Liberal Democrat Councillor and Parliamentary and Euro-Parliamentary Candidate. Rotarian. RSPCA Chairman Newcastle. Married, three sons. Highlands of Scotland – history and language.

McCLURE, Alison

Blake Lapthorn, Portsmouth (023) 9222 1122

McCRORY, Katrina

Bevan Ashford, Birmingham (0121) 634 5008
k.mccrory@bevanashford.co.uk
Specialisation: Associate in the claims department specialising in clinical dispute resolution. Handles a wide variety of clinical cases including complex birth injury and neurology claims. Runs seminars for healthcare professionals. Lectures in the Effective Claims Management Course run jointly by *Bevan Ashford* and the University of the West of England. Important cases in 2000/2001 include Scott v Northern Devon Healthcare (reported).
Prof. Memberships: Law Society.
Career: Qualified in 1995. Trained with *Bevan Ashford* Bristol and moved to *Bevan Ashford* Birmingham April 2001.
Personal: Educated at Newcastle University; read classics. Married with one daughter. Enjoys travel.

McGRATH, Matthew
Beachcroft Wansbroughs, Winchester (01962) 705 500 mmcgrath@bwlaw.co.uk
Specialisation: Partner specialising in all aspects of medical negligence and Health Service Law. Regularly advises clients on issues of consent, confidentiality and access to records. Lectures on risk management issues to clinicians as well as advising on clinical governance. Deals with high-value obstetric claims for the NHSLA. Has obtained Court orders for emergency treatment and is responsible for quality of service from the medical negligence department in the office. Sits on the Mediation Committee of the Clinical Disputes Forum. Previously had wide experience in insurance litigation before joining the firm.

McNEIL, Paul
Field Fisher Waterhouse, London (020) 7861 4000
Specialisation: Partner in the Medical Litigation Department of *Field Fisher Waterhouse* specialising in Clinical Negligence, Personal Injury and Product Liability, acting mainly for claimants. Has particular experience in cases involving head and other serious injuries. Publications include 'International Product Liability' (1993) co-author and 'The Medical Accidents Handbook' (1998) co-editor and contributor. Also lectures on various aspects of medical law.
Prof. Memberships: Law Society Medical Negligence Panel; Association of Personal Injury Lawyers; AVMA; Fellow Society for Advanced Legal Studies.
Career: Qualified 1983. *Field Fisher Waterhouse* 1992. Partner since 1994.
Personal: Educated at All Saints' Comprehensive, Huddersfield 1975-77 and Sheffield University 1977-80. Leisure pursuits include tennis, running and skiing. Born 26th July 1958. Lives in Putney, London.

MINTER, Melanie
Wynne Baxter, Brighton (01273) 775533 mminter@wynnebaxter.com
Specialisation: Clinical negligence claims on behalf of Claimants. Experience in claims involving all types of injury. Interests include cardiac, cardiology, brain damage arising from paediatric cardiac surgery; cerebral palsy claims, cervical cancer and breast cancer, obstetrics and gynaecology, fatal cases. Acts for publicly funded and private clients. Involved in Trilucent breast implant litigation.
Prof. Memberships: APIL, Law Society Clinical Negligence Panel.
Career: 1984 qualified as REN at St Bartholomew's Hospital. Qualified in 1990. Assistant Solicitor at *Norton Rose* 1990-92. Moved to *Capsticks* in 1992 and became a partner in 1994. Joined *Wynne Baxter* in 1999.
Personal: Born 3rd September 1962. LLB University of Wales 1987.

MONTGOMERY, Nigel
Beachcroft Wansbroughs, Bristol (0117) 918 2000 nmontgomery@bwlaw.co.uk
Specialisation: Partner and head of clinical negligence litigation in Bristol. Specialises in Defendant medical negligence and legal issues arising from the day provision of health care. Joined the Bristol office in May 1999 to lead its growing Health team. Has 17 years experience of medico-legal advisory and litigation work. In addition to dealing with medico legal claims of the utmost complexity, has substantial experience in defending group actions and specialises in obstetric, renal and neurology claims. Is a regular contributor to health publications and lectures widely at conferences on medico legal issues.
Career: Qualified 1985; partner, *Lyons Davidson* 1990-99, joined *Beachcroft Wansboroughs* May 1999.

MUSGRAVE, Tim
Huttons, Cardiff (029) 2037 8621
Specialisation: Partner. Clinical negligence and personal injury, acting for plaintiffs.
Prof. Memberships: AVMA, APIL, Member of Law Society Clinical Negligence and Personal Injury Panels and AVMA Panel.
Career: Qualified in 1987, with *Thomson Snell & Passmore*, Tunbridge Wells, then *Edwards Geldard* in Cardiff 1988-93. Joined *Huttons* in September 1993.
Personal: Born 1st September 1963. Bristol University 1981-84. Lives in Cardiff.

OSBORNE, Thomas R.
Osborne Morris & Morgan, Leighton Buzzard (01525) 378177

OVER, Christopher
Over Taylor Biggs, Exeter (01392) 823811

PICKERING, John
Irwin Mitchell, Sheffield (0114) 276 7777 pickeringj@irwinmitchell.co.uk
Specialisation: Partner and head of personal injury department; specialist interest in medical negligence, catastrophic injury cases and cases with an international content. Important cases include Hepworth v Kerr (medical negligence case in which a patient suffered paralysis after a routine middle ear operation); Bird v Hussain (a record award for chronic pain suffered as a result of a road traffic accident); Thomas v Charles (head injury sustained abroad, damages £750,000, then a record award for the Canary Islands); Ward v Newalls Insulations and Cape Contractors (the then highest damages award in this country of £750,000 for an asbestos disease case); Hodgson & Others v Imperial Tobacco Ltd and Gallagher & Hergall Ltd (acting on behalf of smoking related lung cancer victims against the major UK tobacco manufacturers case included a Court of Appeal decision on conditional fee agreements); Van Oudenhoven v Griffin Inns Ltd (£950,000 damages for head injury as a result of pub blackboard accident); dealt with the two cerebral palsy cases involved in the Heil v Ranking landmark judgment in the Court of Appeal, namely Warren (£3.1 million damages) and Annabel. Subsequent seperate Court of Appeal hearing on Warren dealt with the question of multiplier; other actions include acting in test cases for industrial deafness and Vibration White Finger, the latter leading to Irwin Mitchell's involvement in the VWF Solicitors Steering group and the subsequent £500 million settlement scheme with British Coal. Currently involved in the Hatfield and Selby train crash cases.
Prof. Memberships: Claimant Solicitors Representative on the Clinical Disputes Forum. Member of and Assessor for the Law Society's Personal Injury Panel. Member of The Law Society's Medical Negligence Panel and the AVMA Medical Negligence Panel. Former Executive Committee Member and a Secretary of APIL. Member of The Board of Governors of The Association of Trial Lawyers of America (ATLA). Past co-chair of International Practice Section and Member of the Board of the Birth Trauma Litigation Group, England and Wales Representative of the Pan European Organisation of Personal Injury Lawyers (PEOPIL).
Career: Articled *Irwin Mitchell*; qualified 1979; partner 1980; National Head of Personal Injury Department of *Irwin Mitchell* and member of the Management Board.
Publications: Co-author of the 'Clinical Negligence Pre-Litigation Protocol.' Regularly lectures in in the UK and abroad on the subjects of Medical Negligence amd Personal Injury. Co-author of 'Jordan's Civil Court Service' and contributor to 'Clinical Negligence in General Practice'.
Personal: Born 1955, resides Sheffield. Married with two children. Interests include theatre, squash, golf and motor racing.

ROHDE, Kate
Kingsley Napley, London (020) 7814 1200 krohde@kingsleynapley.co.uk
Specialisation: Majority of practice is medical negligence and clinical negligence litigation on behalf of plaintiffs. Experienced in claims involving all types of injury. Particular interest in obstetric claims and claims on behalf of children. Also handles education litigation.
Prof. Memberships: AVMA, APIL.
Career: Qualified in 1989. With *Compton Carr* 1987 to December 1995, as a partner from 1993. Joined *Teacher Stern Selby* as partner in 1996. Moved to *Kingsley Napley* as a partner in March 1997.
Personal: Born 3 November 1963, educated at University College London, lives in London.

SCATES, Olivia
Jones Maidment Wilson incorporating Hatton Scates Horton, Manchester (0161) 832 8087 olivias@jmw.co.uk
Specialisation: Partner and head of clinical negligence department.Firm has had a clinical negligence franchise since their introduction in February 1999. Wide experience of advising in all types of clinical negligence litigation for claimants, including cases of maximum severity. Recent settlements include cases of cerebral palsy, spinal injuries, anaesthetic awareness, orthopaedic injuries and several cases of delay in diagnosis of cancer as well as gynaecological cases.
Prof. Memberships: Referral Panel Solicitor for Action for Victims of Medical Accidents and The Spinal Injuries Association. Member of Law Society Medical Negligence Panel, Member of Association for Personal Injury Lawyers (Special interest groups: clinical negligence and spinal injuries). Legal Services Commission Funding Committee Member.
Career: Qualified 1989. Partner 1993.

SCRIVENGER, Mark John
Scrivenger Seabrook, St Neots (01480) 214900

SEABROOK, Vicki
Scrivenger Seabrook, St Neots (01480) 214900

SHEATH, John
Brachers, Maidstone (01622) 690691
Specialisation: Deals principally with clinical negligence and Health Service law. Has had the conduct of successful defence in many high profile decisions including Dobbie v Medway Health Authority, PVS and mental health consent cases.
Prof. Memberships: Chairman of the West Kent and East Kent GP Performance Review Panels.
Career: Educated at Sir Joseph Williamson's Mathematical School, Rochester. 1963-69. Southampton University 1970-73. *Norton, Rose, Botterell & Roche* 1974-81. Joined *Brachers* in 1981. Partner 1983. Formed 'clinical negligence' department which has

expanded since Crown indemnity in January 1990. Firm appointed to NHSLA panel in April 1998, re-appointed April 2001. Head of Litigation Department. Regularly lectures on selected health topics and tutor in Advanced Litigation Practice Diploma.

SLACK, Richard
Eversheds, Newcastle upon Tyne (0191) 2611661
richardslack@eversheds.com
Specialisation: Medical negligence; employment law; registration of nursing homes.
Prof. Memberships: Law Society.
Career: Upper Second Class Honours Law Degree; Law Society Finals.
Personal: Water sports.

SMITH, Janice
Capsticks, London (020) 8780 2211
Specialisation: Partner in clinical law department specialising in clinical negligence claims with a particular interest in cases involving obstetrics, orthopaedics and A&E, also deals with a variety of NHS advisory matters. Co-ordinates *Capsticks'* clinical governance programme including running training for Trust Boards. Advises Trusts on their risk management arrangements, particularly helping to identify high risk specialities and develop incident reporting schemes. Regular lecturer on *Capsticks'* Diploma in Risk Management and also lectures on various aspects of medical law.
Prof. Memberships: Law Society and its committees concerning issues of clinical negligence.
Career: Qualified in 1985. Assistant Solicitor with *Herbert Smith* 1985-86. Assistant solicitor at *Beckman & Beckman* 1987-90. Joined *Capsticks* in 1990 and became a partner in 1991, member of Firm's Management Committee.
Personal: Born 24th March 1960. Attended Tunbridge Wells Grammar School for Girls 1971-78, then Leeds University 1978-81 before taking a year out to work for the Boys Brigade. Vice President of London District Boys' Brigade and Director of Oasis Trust. Lives in Bicester.

SOLLY, Gillian
Russell Jones & Walker, Bristol (0117) 927 3098
g.c.solly@rjw.co.uk
See under Personal Injury, p.650

SPEKER, Barry
Samuel Phillips & Co, Newcastle upon Tyne (0191) 232 8451
admin@samuelphillips.co.uk
See under Family, p.395

SWANTON, Vicki
Browne Jacobson, Nottingham (0115) 976 6000

TYLER, Alfred
Balfour & Manson, Edinburgh (0131) 200 1210
fred.tyler@balfour-manson.co.uk
See under Personal Injury, p.650

VALLANCE, Richard
Charles Russell, London (020) 7203 5000
richardv@cr-law.co.uk
Specialisation: Partner in Litigation Department. Acted for claimants in the leading cases of Naylor v Preston Area Health Authority, 1987 2 All ER 353 and Thomas v Brighton HA 1998 3 All ER 481. Has lectured on medical negligence to lawyers, doctors and nurses since 1984. Contributed to Powers and Harris's 'Clinical Negligence' (Butterworths) and has written numerous articles.
Prof. Memberships: Assessor of Law Society Clinical Negligence Specialist Panel, Member of AVMA Specilialist Panel, Mediator in Court of Appeal, Chairman of APIL Medical Negligence Special Interest Group, Member of the Medico-Legal Society.
Career: Qualified in 1970. Partner in *Compton Carr* 1972 and, following merger, in *Charles Russell* 1996.
Personal: Born 1947. Secondary School Governor. Squash, gardening and theatre. Lives near Saffron Walden.

VICK, Laurence N.
Michelmores, Exeter (01392) 436244

WARD, Trevor
Linder Myers, Manchester (0161) 837 6806
trevor.ward@lindermyers.co.uk
Specialisation: Obstetrics; oncology; general surgery: Jones v Central Manchester HA: CP – 2.15M (190 PSL2A). Involved in MOD Group action cases re failure to diagnose and treat.
Prof. Memberships: AVMA, APIL, Law Society, ATLA, Greystoke.
Career: 1984 – *Linder Myers*, Manchester. Predominantly claimant clinical negligence and personal injury.
Publications: Book chapter – 'Funding of Claimant Injury Claims' – published 2000.
Personal: Manchester Metropolitan University 1981 (Maxwell Law Prize). Qualified October 1986. Married with two daughters. Interests include shooting. Lives in Glossop.

WATSON, Andrew
Thomson Snell & Passmore, Tunbridge Wells (01892) 510000
awatson@ts-p.co.uk
Specialisation: Partner and head of clinical negligence department. Deals exclusively with clinical negligence claims. Special areas of expertise are head and spinal injuries. Acted in Dobbie v Medway Health Authority, Bova v Spring, Harris v Bromley Health Authority and Taylor v West Kent Health Authority.
Prof. Memberships: A.P.I.L.
Career: Qualified in 1975, having joined *Thomson Snell & Passmore* in 1973. Became a partner in 1981. Panel solicitor for AVMA. Member of the Law Society's Clinical Negligence Panel.
Personal: Born 29 March 1950. Educated at Oxford (MA 1st Class Honours) 1968-71. Recreations include literature, music, running and cuisine. Lives in Tunbridge Wells.

WICKS, Roger
Gadsby Wicks, Chelmsford (01245) 494929

WINYARD, Anne
Leigh, Day & Co, London (020) 7650 1200
Specialisation: Partner and specialist in clinical negligence. Acts for plaintiffs. Cases mainly involve serious disabilities or death, including both adults and children who have suffered brain damage as a result of medical treatment. Publications include chapters in both 'Medical Negligence' (Powers & Harris) and 'Safe Practice in Obstetrics and Gynaecology' (Clements). Regular speaker at medico-legal conferences and seminars.
Prof. Memberships: AVMA, APIL, ATLA.
Career: Qualified 1977. Partner, *Fisher Meredith* 1983-92. Joined *Leigh Day & Co* as partner in 1992.
Personal: Born 1948.

YOUNG, Magi
Parlett Kent, Exeter (01392) 494 455
myoung@exeter.parlettkent.co.uk
Specialisation: Clinical Negligence Specialist with particular expertise in cases of maximum severity (e.g. recent awards in excess of £2 million). Specialises in acting for children injured at or around birth (eg cerebral palsy and Erbs Palsy), for people injured as a result of psychiatric negligence, handles brain injury and spinal injury cases and has particular expertise in obstetric and gynaecology cases and cancer cases. Acts for many people with learning difficulties and has an interest in education and community care provision. Has particular specialism in cases of sexual abuse of patients by health care workers. Also handles personal injury claims including claims against local authorities. Interested in issues of accountability and regularly trains nurses, social workers, doctors and clinical risk managers and lawyers. Also interested in psychological effects of litigation. Undertook research on 'Why patients sue doctors' (Lancet 1994) and has trained solicitors on dealing with distressed clients. Acts for clients nationwide particularly in the South East and South West of England and heads *Parlett Kent's* Exeter office.
Prof. Memberships: AVMA referral solicitor, member of and assessor for Law Society Medical Negligence Panel and Personal Injury Panel. ATLA.
Career: Qualified in 1987 with *Pannone Napier* and *Pannone Blackburn* from 1987-92. Partner from 1991. Joined *Parlett Kent* in 1992 and became a partner in 1993.
Personal: Born 08.12.60. Bristol University (B.Soc. Sci. 1982).

COMMODITIES

London – Physicals: 171; Futures: 172; *Profiles*: 173

OVERVIEW: Although Chambers' rankings continue to be led by the traditional soft commodities giants, the nature of the physicals market is changing. The market for legal services here is no longer buoyant. Casualties among some of the bigger commodities houses and a trend towards in-house teams taking the lion's share of work have led to restricted arbitration work. Many clients now require a wider offering, including advisory and trade financing services. The energy side of both commodities and futures is booming, encouraged by the liberalisation of the energy markets in both the UK and Europe.

RESEARCH APPROVED BY BMRB: *For this edition,* Chambers' *researchers conducted 6,552 interviews – 4,419 with law firms, 554 with barristers and 1,579 with clients.*

The validity of the research was scrutinised by BMRB International, who audited both the methodology and the results at our offices in July 2001. They interviewed Chambers' *researchers and cross-checked sample interviews. Details of the audit appear on page 7.*

LONDON

PHYSICALS

COMMODITIES: PHYSICALS • London
1 Richards Butler
2 Middleton Potts
3 Hill Taylor Dickinson
4 Clifford Chance
Clyde & Co
Holman Fenwick & Willan
5 Ince & Co
Lovells
RD Black & Co
Sinclair Roche & Temperley
6 Holmes Hardingham

LEADING INDIVIDUALS	
★ **PULLEN David** Richards Butler	
1 **GALLOWAY Diane** Richards Butler	**LUCAS David** Middleton Potts
SWINBURN Richard Richards Butler	
2 **ISAACS Jeffrey** Hill Taylor Dickinson	**MARTIN Patricia** Holman Fenwick & Willan
PARSON Robert Sinclair Roche & Temperley	
PATTON Ed Clifford Chance	**POTTS Christopher** Middleton Potts
3 **BLACK Richard** RD Black & Co	**TURNER Paul** Clyde & Co
4 **BEST David** Clyde & Co	**EMMOTT John** Richards Butler
LEACH Ben Sinclair Roche & Temperley	
5 **EVAGORA Kyri** Richards Butler	**HICKEY Denys** Ince & Co
SHEPHERD Stuart Ince & Co	**WALSER Nicholas** Holmes Hardingham
WILLIAMS Charles Thomas Cooper & Stibbard	
UP AND COMING	
PERROTT Brian Hill Taylor Dickinson	

This book is the product of 6,552 1/2-hour interviews. See p.7 for BMRB audit.
Within each band, firms are listed alphabetically. *See individuals' profiles p.173*

Richards Butler (see firm details p.1107) "*Still at the top,*" the team is widely considered to be pre-eminent for soft commodities. Elder statesman and "*the grandfather of the business*" **David Pullen** retains his position as the premier soft commodities lawyer in London. Clients agree he is "*immensely pleasant and affable,*" and still capable of "*a good fight.*" Supporting him is a high profile team, with **Richard Swinburn** (see p.174) "*going from strength to strength*" and widely considered "*first class*" and "*commercial.*" Grain specialist **Diane Galloway** (see p.173) is closely linked with Glencore, and is praised by clients as "*first rate*" and "*always ready with a quick answer.*" New partner **Kyri Evagora** (see p.173) moves up the tables in recognition of his increased profile, while **John Emmott** (see p.173) continues to draw client recommendation. Although still heavily involved in arbitration, the firm increasingly carries out advisory work. It regularly acts as advisor to a range of trade associations, acted on a £200 million metals pre-financing, and has been involved in commodity stock financing in a number of jurisdictions. Clients: Glencore International; Tradigrain; Louis Dreyfus.

Middleton Potts (see firm details p.1067) A year of change has been highlighted by the departure of "*heir apparent*" Robert Parson to Sinclair Roche & Temperley, a move that has affected the team's bid to close the gap on Richards Butler. "*Highly regarded*" **Christopher Potts** (see p.174) has stepped down as senior partner, with **David Lucas** (see p.174) ("*at the top of the tree*") moving into this role.The latter frequently acts as advisor to arbitrators, especially on the sugar trade. Adept at handling all physical commodities advice, the team is increasingly involved in trade finance matters on behalf of financial institutions. **Clients:** Major international trading houses; financial institutions.

Hill Taylor Dickinson (see firm details p.997) "*Pushing ahead*" again this year according to its rivals, the team continues to build its market profile. **Jeff Isaacs** (see p.173) is seen as "*a good opponent, not a pushover*" and a "*fine all-rounder,*" with strong GAFTA connections. He acts for both commodities houses and arbitrators. The team is strengthened by the recruitment of **Brian Perrott** (see p.174) from Cargill, a move which is considered to add depth to an already strong team. **Clients:** International commodity houses.

Clifford Chance (see firm details p.919) "*One of the main players in energy,*" the firm also retains its strong position for trade finance work, and remains an obvious choice for big-ticket disputes. Front man **Ed Patton** (see p.174) is heavily endorsed for his work in the oil sector, although he is felt to eclipse the profile of his junior colleagues. The group represented a major London-based sugar trader in a multi-million dollar arbitration with a Chinese counterparty, and continues to advise the Refined Sugar Association on a number of arbitrations. **Clients:** LIFFE; J. Aron; BP Amoco.

Clyde & Co (see firm details p.921) "*Upped their commodities strength,*" was a typical comment to our researchers. The firm's merger with Turner & Co has paid dividends, particularly boosting its sugar practice. **Paul Turner** (see p.175) has strong GAFTA connections, while **David Best** (see p.173) also remains respected, and has continued to work on the Metro case for Glencore. The group has been involved in substantial work in Eastern Europe, including Bosnia and Serbia, and acted for Glencore in a government led work-out of an Eastern European metals project. It also advised a leading trading bank in the development of new commodity derivative products. **Clients:** Glencore; Tate & Lyle; Gill & Duffus.

Holman Fenwick & Willan (see firm details p.999) Renowned shipping firm with a burgeoning commodities practice. High profile partner **Patricia Martin** (see p.174) has strong GAFTA connections and is endorsed by clients as "*straightforward and reliable.*" Increasingly involved in oil, gas and other energy-related areas, the group also acts for various Russian trading houses on multi-million dollar arbitrations before the Sugar Association of London, and continues to advise a major grain house in dealing with substantial defaults by Asian buyers in GAFTA arbitrations and appeals. **Clients:** Vitol; Continental Grain Company; Russian and Israeli trading houses.

Ince & Co (see firm details p.1008) Premier league shipping firm with a comparatively low-profile, but warmly endorsed commodities practice. The team is led by **Stuart Shepherd** (see p.174), with **Denys Hickey** (see p.173) also singled out for praise for his oil practice. The firm has particular strengths in oil and gas trading and acts across the board on commodity disputes, particularly those relating to coffee, grain and sugar. It acted on behalf of Man Alcohols in a joint venture dispute regarding the importation and distribution of pure alcohol in the European market. It also represented the Republic of Gambia in an arbitration under the auspices of the International Centre for Settlement of Investment Disputes (ICSID). **Clients:** Vitol; major international commodities houses.

Lovells (see firm details p.1044) Known for its IPE and LME-based practice, the firm has also established a reputation for trade financing work, and has increased its gas and electricity caseload. Advice on internet exchange proposals continues to be an important aspect of work. The departure of Philip Quenby from private practice leaves the group without a high-profile player, although David Moss and his team continue to work closely with the firm's Financial Services Group. The group has developed the documentation of an internet-based system for metals trading, and acted for trading companies on a variety of disputes relating to the trading of crude, refined products, metals, sugar and other soft commodities. **Clients:** Energy trading companies; major commodity trading houses.

RD Black & Co This small but respected practice continues to be "*highly active in the sector.*" **Richard Black** (see p.173) divides opinion, with some interviewees finding his approach "*confrontational,*" although all respect him for being "*diligent and extremely hard working – he doesn't spare himself in his efforts to get a good result for his clients.*" Involved in soft and hard commodities work, the firm's main markets are North and South America, the Far East and India. **Clients:** International trading houses.

Sinclair Roche & Temperley (see firm details p.1134) Moving more towards trade financing, the team is joined from Middleton Potts by **Robert Parson** (see p.174), who brings both clients and expertise in this field. Peers opine that "*someone with Parson's energy will move them forward,*" while the group also benefits from the presence of the respected **Ben Leach**. Although continuing to deal with contentious work, the firm has also established a client portfolio of trade finance banks . **Clients:** international commodity trading houses; trade finance banks.

Holmes Hardingham (see firm details p.1000) Known primarily as legal advisors to FOSFA and for its work in agricultural commodities, this respected shipping firm also acts for international oil traders. **Nicholas Walser** (see p.175) retains a good reputation. The group advised Indian soya bean meal exporters on a successful appeal to the GAFTA Board of Appeal, and also acted on a successful appeal to the Commercial Court in the Soules CAF v Louis Dreyfus Negoce case. **Clients:** FOSFA; international grain houses; foreign oil traders.

Other Notable Practitioners **Charles Williams** (see p.175), of shipping and international trade specialists **Thomas Cooper & Stibbard**, is recognised for his experience in this sector.

FUTURES

COMMODITIES: FUTURES • London
1 Clifford Chance
2 Denton Wilde Sapte
Simmons & Simmons
3 Linklaters
4 Richards Butler

LEADING INDIVIDUALS		
1	**FINNEY Robert** Denton Wilde Sapte	**JOHANSEN Lynn** Clifford Chance
	MELROSE Jonathan Simmons & Simmons	**PLEWS Tim** Clifford Chance
2	**BLACK Edward** Denton Wilde Sapte	**FIRTH Simon** Linklaters
	HARDING Mark Clifford Chance	

This book is the product of 6,552 1/2-hour interviews. See p.7 for BMRB audit.

Within each band, firms are listed alphabetically. *See individuals' profiles p.173*

Clifford Chance (see firm details p.919) Retaining its crown as the king of futures advice, the firm specialises in acting for exchanges and a number of leading investment banks. Although David Mayhew leaves the team for a move in-house, **Tim Plews** (see p.174) remains among the market leaders, while **Lynn Johansen** (see p.174) ("*good on regulatory stuff*") moves up the rankings in reflection of her increasing industry profile. **Mark Harding** (see p.173) also receives warm endorsement. The group acted for LIFFE on its venture capital financing by the Blackstone Group and Battery Ventures, and advised on its move into the field of b2b exchanges. It also represented LIFFE on the expansion of its electronic trading system across various countries, and acted for Spectron Group on its internet system for trading LME contracts. **Clients:** LIFFE; Spectron Group.

Denton Wilde Sapte (see firm details p.939) This broad futures and commodity derivatives practice capitalises on the firm's e-commerce and energy strengths. Energy trading specialist **Robert Finney** is "*trusted to give knowledgeable advice*" and forms a powerful double act with the respected **Ed Black**. The group advised Ofgem on settlement netting and other issues relating to the implementation of NETA (New Electricity Trading Arrangements). It also advised Man International and Stafford Trading on both contentious and non-contentious issues, including an SFA application for the latter. The firm also continues to win Islamic finance work. **Clients:** Ofgem; Man International; Stafford Trading.

Simmons & Simmons (see firm details p.1132) Now part of the firm's consolidated Financial Markets Group, the practice continues to command a reputation for its LME work. Acting for a number of exchanges including the Swiss Exchange and Eurex Zurich, the group also has a large energy practice. It undertakes commodities financing transactions and a range of regulatory and structural work, and has niche expertise in advising on the establishment of electronic trading venues for commodities and futures. **Jonathan Melrose** (see p.174) has extensive experience in the metals sector and can be relied upon to give a "*knowledgeable service,*" according to his clients. **Clients:** AIG Trading; Prudential-Bache International; Sempra Energy Trading Corp.

Linklaters (see firm details p.1042) Functioning as part of the firm's strong Derivatives Group, the futures team is headed by **Simon Firth** (see p.133), "*a derivatives expert*" who also commands respect in this market. Known for its long-standing representation of the London Metal Exchange, the firm advised on the LME's demutualisation, as well as its new Silver Contract and Index Contract rules. Last year the group launched Blue Flag Derivatives, an on-line database of legal advice. **Clients:** LME; international investment banks; commodity traders.

Richards Butler (see firm details p.1107) "*Making a concerted effort in this area,*" according to its rivals, the team is still better known for its contentious caseload. It acts for trading companies, banks, trade associations, commodities brokers and overseas Governments. Head of Financial Markets team Richard Parlour brings in-house experience to the table, and the team arranged the first remote membership of LIFFE for a client. **Clients:** Trading companies; trade associations.

LEADERS IN COMMODITIES

BEST, David
Clyde & Co, London (020) 7623 1244
David.Best@clyde.co.uk
Specialisation: Litigation disputes concerning oil and gas, metal, sugar and other international commodity contracts, both in arbitration and court, and related charterparty and bill of lading disputes. Client base is world wide with current disputes in the London High Court and arbitration and in foreign courts eg Dubai, Paris and Hong Kong, working with *Clyde & Co*'s regional offices. Acts principally for commodity traders and charterers. Part of the team acting for Glencore following the collapse of Metro Trading International Inc.

BLACK, Edward
Denton Wilde Sapte, London (020) 7242 1212

BLACK, Richard
RD Black & Co., London (020) 7600 8282
Specialisation: Partner specialising in shipping and commodities litigation and arbitration. Wide experience since 1978 of maritime and commodity arbitrations (both physical and futures) and Commercial Court hearings relating to shipping, trading, insurance and commercial litigation disputes and regulatory work with a particular emphasis on charterparty and cargo claims and commodity disputes including GAFTA, FOSFA, crude oil and petroleum and LME. Clients include international trading houses, commodity and derivatives traders, oil majors and traders, ship owners, charterers and marine insurers. Major cases include Deutsche Schachtbau v Raknoc & Shell International; Kloeckner v Gatoil; the M.V. 'P', The 'Taria', Comdel v Siporex.
Prof. Memberships: Law Society, GAFTA and FOSFA, supporting member LMAA.
Career: Qualified in 1977. Joined *Middleton Potts* from *Coward Chance* in 1984, becoming a partner in 1985. In December 1996, resigned from Middleton Potts to set up *R.D. Black & Co.*
Personal: Born 22nd March 1951. Holds an LLB from Manchester, 1969-72. Leisure interests include golf, tennis, chess and reading. Lives in Oxshott.

EMMOTT, John
Richards Butler, London (020) 7247 6555
jfe@richardsbutler.com
Specialisation: Partner in shipping unit. Specialises in international trade and commodities.
Career: Qualified in 1978 (Australia), 1985 (UK). Partner at *Richards Butler* since 1986.
Personal: Born 1953. Educated at the University of Sydney (BA, LLB).

EVAGORA, Kyri
Richards Butler, London (020) 7772 5896
ke@richardsbutler.com
Specialisation: International trade and commodities: his experience covers the related disciplines of international trade, trade finance, shipping and insurance. Recent high profile cases include 'Spiros C' (Court of Appeal); Agrocor AG v Tradigrain SA; Vinprom Rousse v Bulgarian Vinters (Court of Appeal). He has extensive experience of advising in a number of significant trade finance-related matters. Has lectured for GAFTA and the IGPA.
Prof. Memberships: Law Society.
Career: Articled with *Sinclair Roche & Temperley*; solicitor 1994-99; solicitor with *Richards Butler* 1997; partner at *Richards Butler* 2000.
Personal: Born 1 November 1968; educated at The Latymer School, Edmonton and Bristol University. Lives in London.

FINNEY, Robert
Denton Wilde Sapte, London (020) 7242 1212

FIRTH, Simon
Linklaters, London (020) 7456 3764
simon.firth@linklaters.com
See under Capital Markets, p.133

GALLOWAY, Diane
Richards Butler, London (020) 7247 6555
dg@richardsbutler.com
Specialisation: Principal areas of practice are commodities arbitrations and litigation, including in Grain and Feed Trade Association, Liverpool Cotton Association, Refined Sugar Association and FOSFA. Recent experience also includes Chinese Trade Arbitration (CIETAC). Has lectured for GAFTA and Sugar Association of London. Also specialises in sanctions related litigation.
Career: LL.B Trinity College, Cambridge, then Masters in International Law, Harvard Law School, USA. Joined *Richards Butler* in 1984 after internship with New York firm.

HARDING, Mark
Clifford Chance, London (020) 7600 1000
mark.harding@cliffordchance.com
Specialisation: Commodity and financial derivatives, including exchange traded and OTC, and in particular the regulatory regime applicable to them.
Prof. Memberships: 1997-2000 Board member of International Swaps and Derivatives Association (ISDA) (Chairman 1998-2000).
Career: 1980-96 *Clifford Chance* (partner 1987-96); 1996-2000 General Counsel, *UBS Warburg*; 2000-present partner, *Clifford Chance.*
Personal: MA Cantab. (French, German, Law). Married with three children.

HICKEY, Denys
Ince & Co, London (020) 7623 2011
Specialisation: Partner. A major part of his practice involves oil and gas trading disputes. Has acted in disputes involving many of the oil majors and independent oil traders in connection with contracts for the sale of crude, products and gas. Also involved in metals trading including LME disputes, tolling contracts, offtake agreements and other aspects of metals trading with particular reference to the FSU. Involved in disputes relating to time and voyage charters, long term contracts of affreightment, storage contracts, and shortage and contamination claims. Has advised on short and long term contracts and problems arising out of letters of credit and trade finance and the application of EU and UK competition law. Has spoken at numerous conferences on the legal aspects of transport, trading, letters of credit and EC competition law, and is a regular speaker at the Centre for Petroleum and Mineral Law at the University of Dundee.
Career: Post-graduate studies in Public International and EC Law, then qualified as a barrister. Joined *Ince & Co.*, requalified as a solicitor and became a partner in 1986.
Personal: Born 1952. Lives Saffron Walden. Leisure interests include golf, cycling and skiing.

ISAACS, Jeffrey
Hill Taylor Dickinson, London (020) 7283 9033
jeff.isaacs@htd-london.com
Specialisation: Partner. Practice covers the full range of maritime and Sale of Goods law, but with a specialisation in 'dry' shipping and Commodities disputes including both High Court litigation and arbitration at the various Trade Associations, including GAFTA, FOSFA, The Refined Sugar Association, The Sugar Association of London, LME and IGPA. Regularly sits as legal assessor to arbitration panels at the Sugar Associations and GAFTA. Author of articles on Shipping and Commodities matters. Speaks at seminars and on the GAFTA Trade Education Course. Shipping Editor of 'Law and Transport Policy'.
Prof. Memberships: Law Society, and through *Hill Taylor Dickinson* GAFTA, FOSFA and Refined Sugar Association.
Career: Qualified in 1983 having joined *Hill Taylor Dickinson* in 1981. Associate in 1987. Partner in 1989.
Personal: Born 11 April 1959. Attended Dulwich College then Christ's College, Cambridge (BA 1980). Leisure interests include tennis, badminton, horse riding, wine making and tasting and skiing. Lives in Putney.

JOHANSEN, Lynn
Clifford Chance, London (020) 7600 1000
lynn.johansen@cliffordchance.com
Specialisation: Principal area of work is advising on derivatives and financial regulation with a particular focus on exchange-traded derivatives issues for exchanges and clearing houses, banks and securities houses and other investment firms and commodity derivatives with a focus on energy products. Also specialises in establishing exchanges.
Career: MA (CANTAB) in History. Qualified 1985; partner 1995.

LEACH, Ben
Sinclair Roche & Temperley, London (020) 7452 4000

LUCAS, David
Middleton Potts, London (020) 7600 2333
Specialisation: Partner in commercial litigation department. Main area of practice is commodities, trade finance and shipping. Extensive experience of arbitration and litigation, acting for commodity trading houses (including the majors), oil companies and traders, shipowners, leading trade finance banks, insurers and P&I Clubs. Also acts extensively as legal adviser to Trade Association arbitrators. Major cases handled include Bremer v Vanden-Avenne, The Montone, The Caspian Sea, The Pegase, The Afovos, The Golden Bear, The Future Express, Czarnikow-Rionda v Standard Bank and The Elpa.
Prof. Memberships: Law Society.
Career: Qualified in 1972. Associate, *Crawley & de Reya* 1974-76. Founding partner at *Middleton Potts* in 1976. Senior partner since May 2001.
Personal: Born 15 December 1947. Attended St Paul's School 1960-65, then Bristol University 1966-69.

MARTIN (FORMERLY FRANCIES), Patricia
Holman Fenwick & Willan, London (020) 7488 2300
patricia.martin@hfw.co.uk
Specialisation: Partner in commercial litigation department. Litigation, soft and hard commodities, oil and gas trading disputes, international sale of goods. Has acted for Fiat's railway division in the Channel Tunnel disputes, the Santa Clara House of Lords Case for Vitol SA, Cargill SA, Continental Grain, Minermet SA and many others.
Prof. Memberships: Supporting member of LMAA, GAFTA, FOSFA, member of Law Society.
Career: LL.B Auckland 1978, LL.M London 1979, called to New Zealand Bar 1980, admitted as solicitor in England/Wales 1988. P&I Club 1979-1987. Claims Manager *Tindall Riley & Co.* (Director of the Management Co. 1983-1987). *Middleton Potts* 1988-1990. *Holman Fenwick and Willan* 1990-present. Partner 1993.

MELROSE, Jonathan
Simmons & Simmons, London (020) 7628 2020
jonathan.melrose@simmons-simmons.com
Specialisation: Partner in financial markets department. Handles all types of work relating to financial services and markets, including commodities/derivatives, securities, collective investment vehicles and asset management. Regular speaker at conferences and seminars.
Prof. Memberships: Union Internationale des Avocats, Law Society, The Securities Institute, Member of Commodities Committee of the Futures and Options Association.
Career: Qualified 1985, having joined *Simmons & Simmons* in 1983. Became a Partner in 1991.
Personal: Born 21st April 1959. Holds an MA (Hons) Oxon, 1981.

PARSON, Robert
Sinclair Roche & Temperley, London (020) 7452 4364
robert.parson@srtlaw.com
Specialisation: Partner in Commodity and Trade Finance Group. Specialises in trade, structured and transactional trade finance facilities and enforcing trade finance obligations in letters of credit and other instruments. He also advises on commodity contracts and disputes and Internet-based trading and finance.
Prof. Memberships: Law Society.
Career: Qualified 1986. Partner *Middleton Potts* 1995-01; Partner *Sinclair Roche & Temperley* 2001.
Personal: Born 7 February 1961. Sheffield University LLB 1979-82.

PATTON, Ed
Clifford Chance, London (020) 7600 1000
edwin.patton@cliffordchance.com
Specialisation: Partner specialising in maritime and international trading of commodities, energy, oil, gas, natural resources, and shipping litigation.
Career: Sullivan Upper School, Holywood, N Ireland 1953-1959; Queen's University, Belfast (LLB 1963) 1959-1963. Lectured in law at University of Bristol 1964-1967; articled *Coward Chance* 1968-1970; assistant solicitor 1970-1974; partner *Coward Chance/ Clifford Chance* since 1974.
Personal: Theatre, golf, bridge. Born 1942; resides London.

PERROTT, Brian
Hill Taylor Dickinson, London (020) 7280 9131
brian.perrott@htd-london.com
Specialisation: Specialist areas include: dispute resolution involving all forms of dry shipping work and all aspects of international physical commodity trading (grain, rice, oil, sugar, coffee, crude oil, rubber, metals) and paper trading (derivatives and exchange related disciplinary proceedings). Other specialist areas include environmental and protest group injunctive work, documentary credit problems, exchange proceedings and e-trading. Reported cases include: Cargill Investor Services v Monrovia; Ceval Alimentos SA v Agrimpex Trading Co Ltd; Ceval International Limited v Cefetra and Cefetra v Soules; Cargill Inc v Tate & Lyle; Evergos Naftiki Eteria v Cargill Plc; Sun Valley Foods v Fusion; Cargill France v Toepfer; Cargill International v Stone & Rolls; Cargill Plc v Greenpeace. Clients include: Cargill, Al Khaleej Sugar Co, Shell, Billiton, Enron, Sinochem, Swiss Marine.
Prof. Memberships: Law Society.
Career: Trained *Holman Fenwick Willan*; former head of litigation group at Cargill; partner *Hill Taylor Dickinson* 2000.
Publications: A regular contributor to 'Lloyd's List' and 'Public Ledger' and regular speaker at International Trade Seminars.
Personal: Born 1966. Resides Sevenoaks. Attended Mt St Jospeh's College, Ireland; University College Cardiff (LLB); College of Law, Guildford.

PLEWS, Tim
Clifford Chance, London (020) 7600 1000
tim.plews@cliffordchance.com
Specialisation: Specialises in law and regulation of international financial markets including technology and e-commerce developments.
Career: Trinity College, Cambridge (MA 1984). Articled *Coward Chance*; qualified 1988; partner 1994.
Personal: Born 1962; resides Surrey.

POTTS, Christopher
Middleton Potts, London (020) 7600 2333
Specialisation: Former senior partner of *Middleton Potts*. Over 35 years experience of law and practice relating to commodities, carriage of goods, insurance (marine and non-marine) and international trade. Many major cases handled are leading authorities. Clientele includes major trading houses, carriers, insurers and banks. Regularly lectures to trade audiences.
Prof. Memberships: Law Society.
Career: Qualified in 1965. Partner at *Crawley & de Reya* 1967-76. Founding partner of *Middleton Potts* in 1976.
Personal: Born 1 July 1939. Read law at University of London 1958-61. Lives in London.

PULLEN, David
Richards Butler, London (020) 7247 6555

SHEPHERD, Stuart
Ince & Co, London (020) 7623 2011
Specialisation: Main areas of practice are commodities and shipping. Is involved in advising those trading in various commodities, in particular oil, oil products and commodities traded on GAFTA terms, and handles all aspects of dry shipping work, with particular emphasis on carriage of goods by sea and charterparty disputes with particular emphasis on litigation. Leading reported cases have included ' 'Mathraki' (1989), 'Lefthero' (1992), 'Boucraa' (1993) and 'Kriti Rex' (1996). Author of articles on a number of commodity matters. Speaks at Lloyds of London shipping seminars and on the GAFTA's CPDP programme.
Prof. Memberships: Member of IBA, LMAA, and through *Ince & Co.*, GAFTA, FOSFA and Refined Sugar Association.
Career: Qualified in 1984, having joined *Ince & Co.* in 1982. Became a partner in 1990.
Personal: Born 17th October 1959. Attended Bexhill Grammar 1971-78, then University College, Cardiff 1978-81. Leisure interests include golf and skiing. Lives in Mayfield, East Sussex.

SWINBURN, Richard
Richards Butler, London (020) 7247 6555
rgs@richardsbutler.com
Specialisation: Advises trading companies, trade associations, banks and governments on all aspects of the buying, selling, financing and transporting of commodities.
Career: Qualified in 1988. Partner at *Richards Butler* 1994.
Personal: Born 1963. Educated at Sedbergh School, Cumbria and Robinson College, Cambridge.

TURNER, Paul
Clyde & Co, London (020) 7623 1244
Paul.Turner@clyde.co.uk
Specialisation: Partner handling commodities. Work includes trade arbitrations before the Sugar Associations, GAFTA, FOSFA, Cocoa Association, Coffee Trade Federation and Rice Association. Also handles oil disputes, bills of lading and charter party disputes, largely before commercial courts or the London Maritime Arbitrators Association.
Prof. Memberships: Law Society, Associate Member of the Sugar Association of London.
Career: Qualified 1973. Partner with *Thomas Cooper & Stibbard* from 1977-85. Founder partner of *Turner & Co.* in 1985. *Turner & Co* merged with *Clyde & Co* in January 2000.
Personal: Born 16 September 1948. Attended Skegness Grammar School 1960-67, then University College, London, 1967-70. Leisure interests include walking, travelling and eating. Lives in Esher, Surrey.

WALSER, Nicholas
Holmes Hardingham, London (020) 7283 0222
Nicholas.Walser@HHlaw.co.uk
Specialisation: Partner specialising in 'dry' shipping law, including commodity trade disputes. Work covers charterparty disputes, cargo loss/damage claims, and international sale contracts including agricultural commodities (GAFTA and FOSFA contracts) and oil trading. Major cases include the 'TFL Prosperity' (H.L.) (1984) Soules v Intertradex (1991) and Soules v P.T. Transap (1998). Associate member of French Maritime Law Association. Fluent French. Working knowledge of German.
Career: Qualified in 1977. Partner in *Ingledew Brown Bennison & Garrett* 1979-89. A founding partner of *Holmes Hardingham* in 1989.
Personal: Born 31st December 1952. Attended Cambridge University (MA 1975). Lives in London.

WILLIAMS, Charles
Thomas Cooper & Stibbard, London
(020) 7481 8851
charles.williams@tcssol.com
Specialisation: International trade: sale of goods, commodities, shipping; trade and commodity finance; credit and political risk insurance; counter trade; electronic trade. Major cases include Feedex v Warde; Argo Hellas; C Joyce; Dominique; Woodhouse Drake & Carey; Jeffrey S Levitt Limited (in receivership); Laconian Confidence; Metro. Lectures regularly on various subjects including electronic commerce, sale of goods, trade finance, charterparties and bills of lading.
Prof. Memberships: Chairman of the British Maritime Law Association Committee on Arbitration and ADR – 1993-99. Member of the Bolero Consortium and adviser on shipping law (1994-95); director of the Bolero Association (1998-99); member of the Legal Working Party of the Electronic Commerce Association (1995-96)
Career: Qualified at *Thomas Cooper & Stibbard* in 1979. Joined *Lovell White & King* in 1979 as an assistant, moved to *Richards Butler* in 1982 as an assistant. In 1988 Charles moved to *Wilde Sapte* as an assistant solicitor, becoming a partner the following year. He moved to *Thomas Cooper & Stibbard* in 1994 as a partner.
Publications: 'Bills of Lading in Trade Finance'.
Personal: University of Birmingham 1972-75, LLB (Hons). Rugby coach.

COMPETITION / ANTI-TRUST

London: 176; South West: 178; Wales: 178; Midlands: 178; The North: 180; Scotland: 180; *Profiles*: 181

OVERVIEW: Anti-trust and trade work involving merger control and behavioural work, continues to be the mainstay of practices featured in this section of the Guide. For issues relating to public procurement and state aid we refer you to the Administrative Law section. One key feature of the past year has been the development of sector specific expertise particularly in the telecoms, media and e-commerce spheres.

RESEARCH APPROVED BY BMRB: *For this edition,* Chambers' *researchers conducted 6,552 interviews – 4,419 with law firms, 554 with barristers and 1,579 with clients.*

The validity of the research was scrutinised by BMRB International, who audited both the methodology and the results at our offices in July 2001. They interviewed Chambers' *researchers and cross-checked sample interviews. Details of the audit appear on page 7.*

LONDON

COMPETITION/ANTI-TRUST • London	Ptnrs	Assts
1 Freshfields Bruckhaus Deringer	7	25
Herbert Smith	7	16
Linklaters	5	22
Slaughter and May	3	16
2 Allen & Overy	2	13
Lovells	10	25
3 Ashurst Morris Crisp	6	17
Denton Wilde Sapte	4	9
Simmons & Simmons	4	14
SJ Berwin	5	9
4 Baker & McKenzie	4	9
Clifford Chance	5	2
Norton Rose	4	n/a
5 Bristows	6	6
CMS Cameron McKenna	6	7
Eversheds	2	5
Richards Butler	2	2
Theodore Goddard	3	6

This book is the product of 6,552 1/2-hour interviews. See p.7 for BMRB audit.
Within each band, firms are listed alphabetically.

Freshfields Bruckhaus Deringer (see firm details p.964) "*A benchmark of quality in London,*" the firm is frequently applauded by rivals for its "*well-balanced practice and good technical skills that it's not irritatingly over-zealous about applying.*" The London office handles the full range of competition, regulatory and trade matters, including merger control, cartel investigations, horizontal and vertical restraints, EU and national abuse of dominance cases, state aids and public procurement work. It functions as part of the firm's much-vaunted pan-European competition group, and is perceived by clients to offer "*a true one-stop shop.*" Competitors acknowledge that the hiring of Denton Wilde Sapte's "*star player,*" the "*practical and down to earth*" **David Aitman** (see p.181), has "*considerably strengthened*" the team. His regulatory flair is expected to dovetail neatly with the firm's other established stars. Frequently lauded by opponents for her "*dynamism,*" **Deirdre Trapp** (see p.187) advised Tesco on the high profile supermarket investigation. Researchers received consistently positive client feedback for **Nick Spearing** (see p.187), "*a superbly co-operative practitioner.*" He was retained by AstraZeneca to advise on the competition aspects of the demerger of its agrochemicals business and subsequent merger with Novartis' agrochemicals business to form Syngenta. The team advised the UK government and London Transport on the EU and UK aspects of the proposed public private partnership for the London Underground. It also acted for Bass in connection with the disposal of its interests to Interbrew. **Clients:** ABN AMRO; Bass; English Welsh and Scottish Railways; Formula One Administration; London Stock Exchange; Manchester United; Nomura; PowerGen; Prudential; RJB Mining; Royal Bank of Scotland/NatWest; Scottish & Southern Energy; Scottish Media Group.

Herbert Smith (see firm details p.993) Although the verdict was not unanimous, researchers found that a clear majority of clients and competitors rate "*this clever and sensible team*" as "*definitely in the premier league.*" The firm advises on the spectrum of competition work, including monopoly references, merger control, trade law, state aids, public procurement and Article 81 and 82 cases. Opponents increasingly perceive the team to revolve around "*regulatory whizz*" **Elizabeth McKnight** (see p.185), who is said to be "*fantastically popular with clients.*" She represented Lloyds TSB on the Competition Commission investigation into the supply of banking services to SMEs. **Dorothy Livingston** (see p.184) has a huge reputation among her peers, and continues to act for BSkyB on matters such as the DM2.9 billion clearance of the concentration between BSkyB and Kirch Vermogensverwaltungs. The "*ruthlessly commercial*" **Jon Scott** (see p.186) is a huge favourite with clients, who acknowledge his "*marvellous knack of simplifying technical matters.*" He advised Chevron in relation to its proposed merger with Texaco. The "*aggressive*" **Richard Fleck** (see p.183) combines his managerial duties with work such as advising Time Warner on the European aspects of its proposed merger with AOL and its proposed merger with EMI. Some commentators see **Stephen Wisking** (see p.187) as a "*future star.*" He advised Freeserve on its proposed merger with Wanadoo. **Clients:** Time Warner; Pilkington; BAT; Robert Wiseman Dairies; Centrica Group; Lloyds TSB; London Electricity; Freeserve; Gannett UK; London Stock Exchange; Warner Bros UK.

Linklaters (see firm details p.1042) Rivals in London admire the team for its "*fantastic client base*" and "*technically brilliant team.*" In addition to its formidable merger control work, the group acts extensively on WTO and anti-dumping cases, Article 81 and 82 cases and public procurement. Said to be a team "*without weak links,*" its leading name remains **Bill Allan** (see p.181). Clients frequently acclaim his "*towering intellect, good practical judgement and feel for regulatory issues.*" He has regularly advised National Power on utility regulation and public procurement issues. **Gavin Robert** (see p.186) maintains his market standing through his work on deals such as SmithKline Beecham's £114 billion merger with Glaxo Wellcome. **Michael Cutting** (see p.182) is also a respected merger control specialist. The firm acted for Vodafone in obtaining EC clearance for Phase 1 of its takeover of Mannesmann. **Clients:** Allied Domecq; Anglo American; BT; Billiton; BP Amoco; British Aerospace; Goldman Sachs; IPC; Lattice; Microsoft; National Power; Scottish & Newcastle; GlaxoSmithKline; Vodafone Group.

Slaughter and May (see firm details p.1135) "*Rumbustious, aggressive and individualistic,*" the team divides market opinion more than any other. "*I hate to say it, but they're the best,*" is a typically reluctant concession by one

LEADING INDIVIDUALS		
★	**AITMAN David** Freshfields Bruckhaus	**BRIGHT Chris** Shearman & Sterling
	KON Stephen SJ Berwin	**NICHOLSON Malcolm** Slaughter and May
	WHISH Richard Sole Practitioner	
1	**ALLAN Bill** Linklaters	**CARSTENSEN Laura** Slaughter and May
	LIVINGSTON Dorothy Herbert Smith	**McKNIGHT Elizabeth** Herbert Smith
	POLITO Simon Lovells	**SPEARING Nicholas** Freshfields Bruckhaus
	TRAPP Deirdre Freshfields Bruckhaus	
2	**CHAPPATTE Philippe** Slaughter and May	**FREEMAN Peter** Simmons & Simmons
	FRIEND Mark Allen & Overy	**PARR Nigel** Ashurst Morris Crisp
	SCOTT Jonathan Herbert Smith	**SMITH Martin** Simmons & Simmons
3	**COOK John** Norton Rose	**FINBOW Roger** Ashurst Morris Crisp
	MARTIN ALEGI Lynda Baker & McKenzie	**PHEASANT John** Lovells
4	**HOLMES Katherine** Richards Butler	**LEIGH Guy** Theodore Goddard
	ROBERT Gavin Linklaters	**WEITZMAN Polly** Denton Wilde Sapte
	WHEATON Jim Clifford Chance	**WOTTON John** Allen & Overy
5	**AINSWORTH Lesley** Lovells	**COHEN Ralph** SJ Berwin
	COLEMAN Martin Norton Rose	**CUTTING Michael** Linklaters
	FLECK Richard Herbert Smith	**HOLMES Simon** SJ Berwin
	HUTCHINGS Michael Michael Hutchings	**KELLAWAY Rosalind** Eversheds
	OSBORNE John Clifford Chance	**ROSE Stephen** Eversheds
	SOAMES Trevor Norton Rose	
UP AND COMING		
	GIBSON-BOLTON Elaine SJ Berwin	**LINDSAY Alistair** Allen & Overy
	LOUVEAUX Bertrand Slaughter and May	**USHER Tom** SJ Berwin
	WISKING Stephen Herbert Smith	

See individuals' profiles p.181

rival to the team's "*towering strength.*" Although it is fed by an enviably strong corporate practice, the competition team would be "*an excellent stand-alone practice in any case,*" in the view of a number of clients. The team advises on big-ticket merger control work, Article 81 and 82 cases and high profile monopoly inquiries. Said to be "*the most forward thinking team,*" its aggressive attitude "*can irritate the regulators,*" according to some commentators. Nevertheless, the firm is home to a number of the country's leading competition lawyers. **Malcolm Nicholson** (see p.185) has huge experience of major cases, and is universally held to belong to the elite in this field. He acted on both the Glaxo Wellcome/SmithKline Beecham and the Unilever/Bestfoods mergers. **Laura Carstensen** (see p.181) possesses "*a nice, understated style,*" according to peers in London and Brussels, and is "*intellectually, second to none.*" **Philippe Chappatte** (see p.181) is noted for his forceful manner, and has substantially raised his profile with his advice to Carlton Communications on the referral to the Competition Commission of three proposed mergers. **Bertrand Louveaux** (see p.184) is regarded as a key name for the future. The firm acted for Asda on the Competition Commission supermarkets inquiry, and advised Blue Circle on its appeal against a commission decision in respect of a cement cartel. **Clients:** Carlton Communications; Unilever, Blue Circle; British Airways; BOC.

Allen & Overy (see firm details p.856) Advising on a broad range of competition work, including general issues of EU law, EU & UK competition rules, regulation of privatised utilities and public procurement, the team is praised by clients for its "*sound appreciation of technical matters.*" Fellow practitioners "*would be happy to refer work*" to **Mark Friend** (see p.183), whom they generally acclaim as a "*totally dedicated lawyer.*" He has particular expertise in the regulation of utilities, and acted for WPD on its successful hostile bid for Hyder and subsequent procurement litigation brought by Severn Trent. **John Wotton** (see p.187) is especially strong in broadcasting and advised the Radiocommunications Agency on the third generation mobile auction in the UK, which raised £22.5 billion for the government. New partner and former barrister **Alistair Lindsay** (see p.184) is newly rated this year, following substantial client commendation for his ability to "*master complex issues which he can then reduce to the salient points.*" **Clients:** Barclays; Deutsche Bank; Imperial Tobacco; Marconi; McDonald's; Nestlé; News Corp; Radio Authority; Twentieth Century Fox; West LB.

Lovells (see firm details p.1044) Often referred to as a "*well-rounded*" practice by competitors, the department's contentious practice continues to undertake work before the Commission, the European courts, and increasingly the UK courts. The merger with Boesebeck Droste is considered to have accelerated the firm's transactional workload, particularly at EC level, and the team has also been involved in a number of WTO dispute settlement and EU anti-dumping proceedings. Peers recommend **Simon Polito** (see p.185) for his "*decency and straightforwardness.*" He successfully advised Granada on three merger clearances within the space of three weeks. **John Pheasant** (see p.185), who divides his time between London and Brussels, is rated at the Bar for his work on contentious EC cases, while his experience in front of the Commission is widely acknowledged. **Lesley Ainsworth** (see p.181), who advised OM Gruppen on the competition aspects of its bid for the London Stock Exchange, also maintains her share of market approval. **Clients:** 3i; Mars; Avesta Sheffield; Credit Suisse First Boston; Guardian Media Group; Prudential; Tube Lines Group.

Ashurst Morris Crisp (see firm details p.866) Regarded by clients as "*practical and forthright,*" the competition practice encompasses merger control work, anti-cartel investigations, strategic business advice and compliance, regulatory advice to the energy, telecoms, broadcasting and media industries and trade law. The team includes three in-house economists, two of whom are ex-OFT. According to the Bar, head of the group **Nigel Parr** (see p.185) "*speaks with clarity, conviction and authority,*" while solicitors find him "*enjoyable to work with.*" **Roger Finbow** (see p.182) has also advised on a number of hefty cases. Both men advised Smith & Nephew on the formation of a joint venture with Beiersdorf-BDN. Other highlights for the firm include acting for Express Dairies and Claymore Dairies, the complainants, in relation to the Competition Commission inquiry into the supply of fresh processed milk to customers in Scotland. The team also advised P&O on a state aids case involving Brittany Ferries. **Clients:** Allied Domecq; BT; Ford Motor Company; Intel; Johnston Press; P&O; The Dairy Industry Federation.

Denton Wilde Sapte (see firm details p.939) The departure of practice head David Aitman to Freshfields Bruckhaus Deringer leaves what one commentator described as a "*black hole*" at the heart of the competition group. Despite the presence of the "*exceedingly competent*" **Polly Weitzman** (see p.187), most interviewees agreed that the department currently lacks an individual "*anywhere near Aitman's league.*" Weitzman received high praise for her work in structuring the auction rights for Premier League football on television. The team's merger control caseload has included a series of projects for Liberty in the media sector and for London Electricity and Electricité de France in the energy industry. Another team to be involved in the Competition Commission inquiry into supermarkets, it acted for J Sainsbury, and also advised three major water companies on regulatory and pricing issues. **Clients:** J Sainsbury; Premier League; Sumitomo Metal Industries; Liberty Media; Racecourse Association; London Electricity; Mastercard/Europay.

Simmons & Simmons (see firm details p.1132) Admired by clients for its "*ability to put competition law into a commercial context,*" the team's core expertise lies in merger and cartel law, combined with a strong position in litigation, regulation and broader European law. The telecoms industry remains a particularly fruitful source of instructions. **Peter Freeman** (see p.183) wins plaudits from the Bar, who regard him as one of the eminences grises of the sector. Peers consider **Martin Smith** (see p.186) to be an "*expert on merger control, with good judgement and technical skills.*" The firm represented Vivendi on the Competition Commission investigation into its BSkyB share acquisition. It continues to be involved in the European Commission's Seamless Steel Tubes, Newsprint and Vitamins investigations as well as a CFI appeal (cement) and two ECJ cases. **Clients:** Vivendi; GK; Railtrack; Ofgem; Ofreg; Independent Television Commission; Interbrew; Gallaher; Barclays; Bacardi-Martini.

SJ Berwin (see firm details p.879) The opening of offices in Madrid, Paris and Munich consolidates the firm's presence in Europe and boosts its multi-jurisdictional capability. The department has an active regulatory and trade competition practice, and boasts experience before both national and EU courts. Competitors still see **Stephen Kon** (see p.184) as "*an exceptional practitioner.*" A veteran of major cases, he acted for Universal in successfully opposing the Time Warner/EMI and Time Warner/AOL mergers. With 20 years experience behind him, **Simon Holmes** (see p.183) is seen as a "*safe pair of hands,*" and acted for Diageo on the competition aspects of the acquisition of the wine and spirits division of Seagram from Vivendi. **Ralph Cohen** (see p.181) is particularly admired for his trade law expertise. At a more junior level, clients are enthusiastic about **Elaine Gibson-Bolton** (see p.183), who has acted for AES Electricity Generators before the Competition Commission during an investigation into wholesale electricity generation pricing. **Tom Usher** (see p.187) is another newly ranked practitioner who is highly rated by both barristers and clients. **Clients:** Dixons Group; Marks & Spencer; Morgan Stanley Dean Witter; AES; Coca-Cola Enterprises; Diageo; Ladbroke Group; Universal Music Group.

Baker & McKenzie (see firm details p.868) Researchers were impressed by the depth of market recommendation for the firm's expertise in anti-cartel work. Clients pointed to the team's "*solid grasp of the technical side of things,*" and were especially enthusiastic about **Lynda Martin Alegi**'s (see p.184) "*commercial nous.*" She remains outstandingly the department's leading figure. In addition to merger control cases, the team has defended a number of clients against allegations of anti-competitive behaviour. The firm's global network is regarded as a key factor in the London team's multi-jurisdictional capacity. It achieved a notable success in a cement case, when it successfully persuaded the European Court of First Instance to annul the €5 million fine imposed on the Rugby Group. Other work includes advising Cisco Systems on the merger control implications of its proposed investment in Italtel, and representing Camelot on its successful challenge to the Lotteries Commission's decision to exclude the company from the second round of bidding for the new lottery licence. **Clients:** Mercedes; Fedex; ADM; Block Drug; Clear Channel; Cisco Systems; Clariant; HCA; Camelot; BG; Levi Strauss & Co.

Clifford Chance (see firm details p.919) The departure of the high profile Chris Bright after two years at the firm is considered by many to be a major blow to the competition department. However, he leaves behind him a team that clients describe as "*technically strong, highly experienced and solely focused on getting the job done.*" The team advises on merger filings, joint ventures and strategic alliances, multi-jurisdictional filings, anti-trust litigation and regulatory investigations. "*Knowledgeable*" **Jim Wheaton** (see p.187) was commended to researchers for his "*no-nonsense, sensible*" approach that "*really gets things moving.*" **John Osborne** (see p.185) also receives high marks from clients. The firm advised GE on its abortive merger with Honeywell. **Clients:** GE; Chase Manhattan; Pfizer; EADS; Sun Microsystems; Centrica; Citrix; Vivendi; General Healthcare; Accenture.

Norton Rose (see firm details p.1082) Covering a broad spectrum of work including merger and joint venture cases, Article 81 and 82 cases and state aids issues, the team has enjoyed a particularly strong year in banking-related matters advising clients such as HSBC, Switch and Visa International. The team's regulatory strength has been boosted by the arrival of the former Director General of Fair Trading. Clients believe that the "*eternally practical*" **John Cook** (see p.182) has "*the full range of skills.*" Peers applaud head of department **Martin Coleman** (see p.182) for his "*practical*" nature, while **Trevor Soames** (see p.186), who spends the majority of his time in Brussels, maintains a vast reputation for aviation-related cases. The team advised Mid Kent Water on its successful appeal to the Competition Commission against the determination of its price cap by OFWAT. This was the first case in which an English utility had succeeded in challenging the decision of a regulator on pricing. Another highlight was acting for France Télécom on its acquisition of Orange. **Clients:** Alcatel; AXA; France Télécom; Group4; HSBC; P&O Stena Line; Thomson Travel Group; TXU Europe.

Bristows (see firm details p.895) Working on the intersection between IP and competition law, the team, led by Pat Treacy, offers experience of 'eurodefences' in litigation, the application of the essential facilities doctrine to IP rights and the interpretation and application of technology transfer regulation to licences. The team acted for VIA Technologies on a complaint to the EU Commission against Intel, advised on the Competition Commission investigation into multiple retailers and acted on the OFT enquiry into the supply of veterinary medicines. Merger control work includes advising Eastman Kodak on the UK merger control aspects of a worldwide acquisition. **Clients:** Shering-Plough; Merck; Rambus; Via Technologies; Mitsubishi Electric; Mitsui Babcock; MTV Networks.

CMS Cameron McKenna (see firm details p.922) Relatively low profile team, led by Richard Taylor, with a sound reputation for regulatory utilities expertise. Pharmaceuticals and financial services are other areas of strength. The firm undertakes a range of EC and UK competition work, advising on issues including Articles 81 and 82, merger notifications and state aids submissions. A solid trade law practice has seen the firm advise on EC anti-dumping law, WTO law and EC customs law. The group represented Nestlé during the Competition Commission's ice cream and supermarket enquiries. **Clients:** National Grid Company; General Insurance Standards Council; Consignia (The Post Office); Nestlé; Halliburton.

Eversheds (see firm details p.952) Said by peers to be "*gathering momentum,*" the team has been widely commended to researchers as "*one to watch.*" Particularly experienced in advising the motor vehicle industry, utilities, and trade associations, the firm fields two highly regarded practitioners. Clients praise **Ros Kellaway** (see p.184) as an "*excellent lateral thinker.*" She advised Volkswagen Group (UK) on the Competition Commission's inquiry into the sale of new cars. Respected name **Stephen Rose** (see p.186) represented Solectron Corporation on the clearance of its $2.4 billion public bid for NatSteel Electronics. **Clients:** KPMG; DuPont; Volkswagen Group (UK); Envirologic; TXU; Seat; Audi; RollsRoyce; Bentley; PACT; Vallourec.

Richards Butler (see firm details p.1107) Claiming an impressive client base, including the BBC, the team acts on the full range of EU and Competition matters, offering particular expertise in the leisure and media sectors. Clients find **Katherine Holmes** (see p.183) to be "*reliable, skilled and friendly.*" The team has been closely involved in GNER's bid for the East Coast main line franchise, advising on regulatory aspects of the rail industry. It also advised McBride on the Competition Commission inquiry into supermarkets. **Clients:** DaimlerChrysler UK; GNER/Sea Containers; McBride; Fosters; Skanska; BBC; Galileo International; Rank.

Theodore Goddard (see firm details p.1152) Recommended to researchers as "*a strongly commercial team,*" it has particular experience of the media, telecoms and healthcare sectors. Trade work remains an area of niche expertise. Elder statesman **Guy Leigh** (see p.184) is the group's best-known name and is considered by peers to be "*central*" to the firm's reputation in this area. The firm advised Lanier Worldwide on its merger with Ricoh and acted for a group of telecommunications fixed network operators on a complaint to OFTEL about BT's conduct in the unmetered internet market. **Clients:** British Horse Racing Board; Lanier Worldwide; Napier Brown & Co; Colt Telecommunications; NatWest.

Other Notable Practitioners After his brief sojourn at Clifford Chance, **Chris Bright** (see p.181) is now charged with the task of building a competition department at **Shearman & Sterling**. He remains one of the best-known competition lawyers in the UK. Noted academic **Richard Whish** remains the choice of his peers as the obvious destination for those seeking an opinion on a point of law. **Michael Hutchings** (see p.183) is a sole practitioner who is respected for his knowledge of the workings of various competition authorities.

SOUTH WEST

COMPETITION/ANTI-TRUST • South West	Ptnrs	Assts
1 **Burges Salmon** Bristol	3	6
2 **Bond Pearce** Plymouth	2	2

LEADING INDIVIDUALS	
1 **CLAYDON Laura** Burges Salmon	**COPPEN Simon** Burges Salmon

This book is the product of 6,552 1/2-hour interviews. See p.7 for BMRB audit.
Within each band, firms are listed alphabetically. *See individuals' profiles p.181*

Burges Salmon (see firm details p.902) In addition to advice on mainstream competition matters, the firm deals with regulatory issues arising in industry sectors as diverse as aviation, rail, and sport. The team is headed by **Laura Claydon** (see p.181), who is commended by clients for her *"grasp of the technical detail."* **Simon Coppen** (see p.182) also remains a name to be reckoned with, especially on regulatory matters. The firm has advised transport clients on a consultation exercise to block exemption for public transport ticketing schemes. It also acted for CHC Helicopter Corp on the competition aspects of its acquisition of the Norwegian-quoted company, Helicopter Service Group. **Clients:** FirstGroup; The Racecourse Association; CHC Helicopter Corp; Great Western Trains.

Bond Pearce (see firm details p.888) Rob Murray's departure to K-Legal leaves the team, now fronted by Nick Page, with lower profile but an equally broad practice. Best known for its retail client base, the firm has advised a number of clients on dawn raids under both EC and UK regimes. The firm advised an independent wholesaler of Wall's ice cream on intended High Court proceedings against Birdseye Wall's, alleging breaches of EC competition law. **Clients:** B&Q; Safeway.

WALES

COMPETITION/ANTI-TRUST • Wales	Ptnrs	Assts
1 **Edwards Geldard** Cardiff	1	4
Eversheds Cardiff	2	1
Morgan Cole Cardiff	n/a	3

This book is the product of 6,552 1/2-hour interviews. See p.7 for BMRB audit.
Within each band, firms are listed alphabetically.

Edwards Geldard (see firm details p.948) EU and competition work is handled out of the IP/IT department by a team led by Ceri Delemore. For a client base largely made up of manufacturers, the team provides advice on matters from mergers and acquisitions to commercial agreements and risk management. It handles public procurement matters, traditionally for utilities and those in the energy and transport sector, and now advises an increasing number of potential service providers. **Clients:** Public bodies and private corporates.

Eversheds (see firm details p.952) The practice retains its reputation for state aid and public procurement work. Headed by Bridgette Wilcox, the team acts for a client base of public sector bodies, and advised a public agency on negotiations with the European Commission, concerning public sector grants for property developments. **Clients:** Welsh Development Agency.

Morgan Cole (see firm details p.1074) The firm's competition practice is integrated on a national basis and is led out of Oxford by David Whibley. Along with the Thames Valley and London offices, the Cardiff team handles a range of work, from mergers and compliance work to state aid and public procurement. The national group acted for Xerox in its recent acquisition of the worldwide colour printing division of Tektronix, a deal worth $950 million. **Clients:** Xerox; Clarins; Carlton International; TBI; Shimano; Mitel Corp; Addis Group; Integralis.

MIDLANDS

COMPETITION/ANTI-TRUST • Midlands	Ptnrs	Assts
1 **Pinsent Curtis Biddle** Birmingham	2	3
Wragge & Co Birmingham	2	8
2 **Eversheds** Birmingham	1	n/a

LEADING INDIVIDUALS	
1 **LOUGHER Guy** Wragge & Co	**REES Kate** Pinsent Curtis Biddle

This book is the product of 6,552 1/2-hour interviews. See p.7 for BMRB audit.
Within each band, firms are listed alphabetically. *See individuals' profiles p.181*

Pinsent Curtis Biddle (see firm details p.1098) The growing Birmingham team functions as part of a fully integrated national department, which includes teams in Leeds and London. Servicing a blue-chip client base, the firm is particularly strong on public procurement and the application of competition law to the regulated utilities. Peers agree that national practice leader **Kate Rees** (see p.186) *"obviously knows what she's talking about,"* and she is seen as a national leader for public procurement advice. The firm conducted an extensive lobbying exercise to secure changes to draft public procurement directives, involving representations to UK government departments, the EC Commission and the European Parliament. **Clients:** Arriva; Lattice; Glanbia; Iceland; BBC; Argos; Federal Mogul.

Wragge & Co (see firm details p.1189) The strength of the firm's corporate team is considered by many interviewees to be of enormous benefit to this stand-alone competition department. Recommended to researchers for the *"best"* merger control practice in the region, the firm also advises on public procurement issues and has a powerful clientele in the automotive, aviation, agrochemicals and financial services industries. Clients typically describe head of department **Guy Lougher** as *"easy to work with and technically competent."* The firm advised HJ Heinz on the competition aspects of its acquisition of certain consumer brands and businesses, and acted for DaimlerChrysler Rail Systems (UK) on its proposed acquisition of Railpart. **Clients:** DaimlerChrysler Rail Systems (UK); HJ Heinz; Preussag; 3i; British Airways.

Eversheds (see firm details p.952) The department, led in Birmingham by Richard Prowse, works alongside the London, Nottingham and Leeds offices, and caters for a range of blue-chip clients. Particularly experienced in motor manufacturing and airport cases, the team advises on merger clearance, distribution, agency and public procurement work. It represented Hagemeyer (UK) on its acquisition of WF Electrical and acted for Britax International on its sale of Rear Vision Systems. **Clients:** Birmingham International Airport; Granada Compass Group; Jessop Group; Volvo Truck & Bus.

THE NORTH

COMPETITION/ANTI-TRUST • The North	Ptnrs	Assts
1 **Addleshaw Booth & Co** Leeds, Manchester	3	10
Eversheds Leeds, Manchester, Newcastle upon Tyne	2	2
2 **Pinsent Curtis Biddle** Leeds	2	2
3 **Dickinson Dees** Newcastle upon Tyne	4	2

LEADING INDIVIDUALS	
1 **COLLINSON Adam** Eversheds	
2 **DAVEY Jonathan** Addleshaw Booth & Co	
JURKIW Andrij Pinsent Curtis Biddle	
LINDRUP Garth Addleshaw Booth & Co	
3 **McDONNELL Phil** Garretts	**SCHOLES Jeremy** Walker Morris
WARWICK Neil Dickinson Dees	

This book is the product of 6,552 1/2-hour interviews. See p.7 for BMRB audit.
Within each band, firms are listed alphabetically. *See individuals' profiles p.181*

Addleshaw Booth & Co (see firm details p.853) Said by rivals to field "*some extremely bright lawyers*," the firm is strong across the region and typically advises on EC and competition issues in the context of corporate transactions. **Garth Lindrup** (see p.184) and public procurement expert **Jonathan Davey** (see p.182) are both enthusiastically endorsed by clients for "*knowing their stuff inside out.*" The team has acted on seven deals involving multi-jurisdictional merger control filings, and has received more than a dozen instructions in relation to competition compliance training. **Clients:** Airtours; Asda; Adidas; Guardian Media Group; Jeyes Group; MOD; Regional Independent Media Group.

Eversheds (see firm details p.952) Considered by some commentators to be the firm's "*best for competition*," the Leeds office advises on a wide range of competition issues, and has seen a substantial rise in contentious cases. Other firms have "*no qualms*" about referring work to "*the personable and exceptionally able*" **Adam Collinson** (see p.182), whom clients describe as "*wonderful counsel; both thorough and prompt in his responses.*" The firm acted for HSBC Private Equity on multi-jurisdictional merger control filings relating to its £440 million acquisition of the plumbing division of Caradon. It also advised American Securities BD on competition issues arising from the Vivendi/Seagram/Canal+ merger. **Clients:** HSBC Private Equity; American Securities BD; English Welsh & Scottish Railway; Wolseley Centers; Huntsman (Europe).

Pinsent Curtis Biddle (see firm details p.1098) Versatile practice, dealing with merger clearance, public procurement, complaints/investigations, notifications, state aid, competition law litigation, compliance and parallel imports. The firm has particular expertise in the Competition Act, having been involved in some of the first dawn raids. Rivals concede that this is an "*area of enviable strength.*" Peers rate **Andrij Jurkiw** (see p.183) for his "*trustworthy judgement*" and "*proven client handling skills.*" The firm advised Arriva on the first dawn raids by the OFT, and acted for FCS/allpay.net in relation to its complaint to the OFT, alleging abuse of a dominant position by Girobank. **Clients:** Arla Foods; Arriva; Babcock International Group; IMI; Lattice; Pace Micro Technology; Schneider Electric; SIG; Smith & Nephew.

Dickinson Dees (see firm details p.941) Handling a range of both contentious and non-contentious competition matters, the firm advises on compliance programmes, state aid issues, anti-dumping and regulatory notifications. Competitors ascribe much of the credit for the firm's profile to the "*driven*" **Neil Warwick** (see p.187). On behalf of Govia/Go-Ahead, the firm applied for merger clearance at the European Commission for a deal valued at £1.5 billion. The team has also designed compliance programmes for Go-Ahead and Arriva. **Clients:** Arriva; The Go-Ahead Group; Nike UK; Stagecoach Busways.

Other Notable Practitioners **Phil McDonnell** (see p.185), who heads the **Garretts** national team from its Manchester office, continues to be a popular port of call for referrals. **Jeremy Scholes** (see p.186) of **Walker Morris** also retains a substantial body of market support.

SCOTLAND

COMPETITION/ANTI-TRUST • Scotland	Ptnrs	Assts
1 **Maclay Murray & Spens** Edinburgh, Glasgow	3	3
Shepherd & Wedderburn WS Edinburgh	5	6
2 **Biggart Baillie** Glasgow	1	n/a
Burness Edinburgh	3	2
Dundas & Wilson CS Edinburgh	1	3
MacRoberts Glasgow	1	3

LEADING INDIVIDUALS	
1 **DEAN Michael** Maclay Murray & Spens	
2 **DOWNIE Gordon** Shepherd & Wedderburn WS	
McLEAN James Burness	**MILLER Colin** Biggart Baillie

This book is the product of 6,552 1/2-hour interviews. See p.7 for BMRB audit.
Within each band, firms are listed alphabetically. *See individuals' profiles p.181*

Maclay Murray & Spens (see firm details p.1047) A dedicated EU and competition team advises on public procurement, distribution and agency, EC law, and regulation. Fed by a "*great commercial client base*," the team earns widespread acclaim from clients, who point to "*a firm that listens and offers incredibly good value for money.*" Leading light **Michael Dean** (see p.182) has "*vast experience*" in the sector. The firm advised a Scandinavian client on two major joint venture proposals, handled a distribution termination case before the Cour de Cassation and advised Ofgem in relation to various regulatory issues in the electricity field. **Clients:** Ofgem; Scottish Enterprise; Weir Group; British Polythene Industries; Grampian Holdings; Henry Technologies; Pringle of Scotland.

Shepherd & Wedderburn WS (see firm details p.1126) Handling the full range of UK and EU competition work, the firm regularly assists companies in establishing and maintaining compliance programmes. It also advises a variety of regulated industries on their dealings with sector regulators. Led by the respected **Gordon Downie** (see p.182), the firm defended Scottish Power from interim interdict proceedings raised by De La Rue over an alleged breach of EU procurement directives. The team also advised on UK and European competition law and regulatory aspects of the establishment of a B2B procurement consortium involving a group of European utilities. **Clients:** Bank of Scotland; Edinburgh Fund Managers; John Wood Group; Manweb; Scottish & Newcastle; Scottish Power; Stagecoach Holdings; Thus.

Biggart Baillie (see firm details p.882) "*Impressively sensible figure*" **Colin Miller** (see p.185) was consistently commended to researchers as the motor that is driving this team upwards. The bulk of the workload here involves public procurement, although the firm also advises extensively on distribution and compliance. The team advised The Drambuie Liqueur Co on the implications of a block exemption on vertical restraints, and acted for Original Shoe Co on issues affecting its distribution activities, including parallel imports and exhaustion of rights under EU competition rules. **Clients:** The Drambuie Liqueur Co; BSW Timber; Global Video; ScotRail Railways; Morrison Bowmore Distillers.

Burness (see firm details p.903) Although none of the team is fully dedicated to EU and competition work, the firm continues to advise a portfolio of major clients on acquisitions, disposals, supply and the conduct of business. The team also conducts risk assessments for corporate clients. **Jim McLean** (see p.185) is the firm's biggest hitting partner in this area. **Clients:** The Harris Tweed Authority; Diagnostic Instruments.

Dundas & Wilson CS (see firm details p.947) Acting for a broad range of clients on EU and UK competition issues and EU trade matters, the firm also provides advice on regulated utilities and public procurement. Christian Hook heads the department. Financial services are an area of niche expertise. The firm advised Macfarlane Group on its proposed acquisition of British Polythene Industries and acted for the Royal Bank of Scotland on the competition implications of two strategic joint ventures with CGUI. **Clients:** Macfarlane Group; Scottish Media Group; Scottish & Southern Energy; ITN; Rangers Football Club; Royal Bank of Scotland.

MacRoberts (see firm details p.1048) Although possessing a lower profile than the market leaders, the team has taken a leading role in lobbying on the new UK legislation. The versatile David Flint is the team's best-known figure. The firm handles merger notifications, compliance and third-party interventions, and advises British Energy on all competition issues. **Clients:** British Energy; Coca-Cola Schweppes; Johnston Press; Campbell Distillers.

LEADERS IN COMPETITION / ANTI-TRUST

AINSWORTH, Lesley
Lovells, London (020) 7296 2000
lesley.ainsworth@lovells.com
Specialisation: Specialist work includes UK and EC competition law (advisory work, investigations by the Office of Fair Trading, the Competition Commission and the EC Commission and proceedings before the European Court of Justice and national courts; state aids; free movement of goods and services; public procurement; advice on proposed EU legislation and the implementation of EU legislation in Member States.
Prof. Memberships: Member, Solicitors' European Group.
Career: Articled *Lovells*; qualified 1981; London 1979-83; Brussels office 1983-85; secondment to *LeBoeuf, Lamb, Leiby & McRae* 1985-86; London since 1986; partner 1988.

AITMAN, David
Freshfields Bruckhaus Deringer, London (020) 7936 4000
david.aitman@freshfields.com
Specialisation: Partner. Advising on all areas of EC and domestic competition law, particularly in the energy, transport, manufacturing, retail, communications and media sectors, and on regulation, in connection with privatised utilities.
Prof. Memberships: Competition Law Association; International Bar Association.
Career: Qualified 1982. Partner *Denton Hall* 1988. Joined *Freshfields Bruckhaus Deringer* 2001.
Publications: Editor of intellectual property licensing in Butterworths' 'Encyclopedia of Competition Law', of competition law in 'Practical Intellectual Property' and in the Yearbook of Media Law and author of telecoms chapter in 'Bellamy & Child'.
Personal: Born 1956. Educated at the Royal Academy of Music.

ALLAN, Bill
Linklaters, London (020) 7456 3574
bill.allan@linklaters.com
Specialisation: Specialises in EC and UK anti-trust law, mergers and acquisitions, and other competition and trade-related areas of the law. He has extensive experience in the UK and EC context, representing clients from diverse industries including utilities, food, transport, brewing, leisure, chemicals, construction materials and computers.
Career: Head of the EU and competition law group since 1999. Partner 1982 corporate department. Qualified 1976.

BRIGHT, Chris
Shearman & Sterling, London (020) 7655 5163
c.bright@shearman.com
Specialisation: Competition and regulatory law in the EU and the UK, including strategic anti-trust advice; merger control including global filings; cartels; abuse of dominance; economic regulation of utilites, particularly water, energy, rail and telecoms; state aid; public procurement; the Brussels process.
Prof. Memberships: Law Society of England and Wales, IBA, ABA.
Career: Partner, antitrust Sherman & Sterling 2001; head of *Clifford Chance* competition and regulatory practice 1999-2001; seconded to competition policy division DTI 1989-91; assistant solicitor and partner *Linklaters & Paines*; trainee 1983-89. Lecturer, Jesus College Oxford 1984-86.
Publications: 'Understanding the Brussels Process'; 'Public Procurement Handbook', numerous articles.

CARSTENSEN, Laura
Slaughter and May, London (020) 7710 4265
laura.carstensen@slaughterandmay.com
Specialisation: Partner, competition department. Practice in UK and EU competition law, predominantly in relation to strategic corporate events (M&A; key changes in business policy and practice) and contentious situations (cartel/abuse of dominance inquiries). Extensive experience before the European Commission, Office of Fair Trading, Competition Commission and European Courts.
Career: Qualified 1987 with *Slaughter and May* and became a partner in 1994.
Personal: Born 11 November 1960. Educated Withington Girls School, Manchester, then St. Hilda's College, Oxford (English Lang. & Lit.). Lives in Hampstead, London.

CHAPPATTE, Philippe
Slaughter and May, London (020) 7600 1200
philippe.chappatte@slaughterandmay.com
Specialisation: Provides a wide range of UK and EU competition law advice (including on state aid) in connection with transactions, litigation and regulatory investigations. Recent EU cases include the proposed dual listed company merger between BHP and Billiton, the proposed merger of British Airways and KLM, Monsanto/Pharmacia and Upjohn and Telia/Telenor. Involvement in European Court cases and Competition Commission investigations both in monopoly and in merger cases. Recent UK cases include acting for Punch in its contested acquisition of the Allied pub estate, the Carlton/United/Granada and Anglo/Tarmac mergers and British Airways' acquisition of British Regional Air Lines.
Prof. Memberships: Co-founder of European Competition Lawyers Forum.
Career: Bryanston School. Oxford University (BA Law, First Class). Université Libre de Bruxelles (Lic.Sp.Dr. Eur., Highest Distinction). Qualified *Slaughter and May* 1982. Partner 1989. Responsible for running and development of Brussels office between April 1991 and August 1996.
Personal: Three children.

CLAYDON, Laura
Burges Salmon, Bristol (0117) 939 2273
laura.claydon@burges-salmon.com
Specialisation: Main area of practice is competition and regulatory law; advised on and attended the first dawn raids in the UK under the 1998 Act; has conducted many merger cases and competition investigations before the OFT acting particularly for clients in the transport, food, sports and media and oil and gas industries. Recent cases include: the MMC inquiry into the acquisition by FirstBus plc (now FirstGroup plc) of SB Holdings Limited and subsequent review by the DTI/OFT which reduced divestment to behavioural undertakings; the Competition Commission inquiry into the acquisition by CHC Helicopter Corporation of Helicopter Services Group (referred September 1999); advised on and attended the first dawn raids in the UK under the 1998 Act; many cases involving allegations of price-fixing, market sharing, predatory behaviour, predatory pricing and refusal to supply. Advises on competition audits and compliance procedures in view of the new Competition Act 1998.
Prof. Memberships: Solicitors European Group, Law Society
Career: Joined *Burges Salmon* in 1988 and became a partner in 1996. Until 1990 she worked in the corporate service group gaining general experience in all types of company and commercial work dealing mostly with private companies.

COHEN, Ralph
SJ Berwin, London (020) 7533 2701
ralph.cohen@sjberwin.com
Specialisation: Partner specialising in EU and UK competition law and EC trade and customs law. Has extensive experience representing clients before the OFT, Competition Commission and European Commission across a wide range of industries. Practice areas include EU and UK merger clearances and coordinating multi-jurisdictional filings, advising on

compatibility of commercial agreements with competition law compliance, anti-dumping investigations, WTO and general customs related issues.
Prof. Memberships: Solicitors European Group.
Career: Qualified 1983. Partner at *SJ Berwin & Co* 1991.
Personal: Born 10 May 1959. Attended Clifton College, and University of Southampton. Married with three sons.

COLEMAN, Martin
Norton Rose, London 020 7444 3347
colemanmay@nortonrose.com
Specialisation: Martin Coleman is head of the competition and EC department at Norton Rose. He has led many cases before the European Commission, the Office of Fair Trading, The Competition Commission and UK sectoral regulators. Martin specialises in merger control (including contested bids), advising complainants and respondents in relation to investigations by competition authorities and advising businesses on antitrust compliance and competition law strategic planning. Martin has extensive experience in the application of UK and EC regulations in areas such as energy, transport, banking and financial services.
Career: Qualified 1978, Degree BA, BCL Oxford, languages – French.
Publications: Martin is a regular speaker at conferences on EC and competition law topics and has written a number of articles for both specialist and more general publications. He is also co-author (with Michael Grenfell) of 'The Competition Act 1998' (OUP, 1999).

COLLINSON, Adam G
Eversheds, Leeds (0113) 243 0391
adamcollinson@eversheds.com
Specialisation: Partner in commercial department and head of EU/competition practice for Leeds/Manchester. EU and UK competition and related commercial law. Significant exposure to automotive and chemical industries. Particular experience in advising on competition law compliance, merger control and pricing and distribution strategies. Advised Asda in its campaigns to end resale price maintenance for books and OTC medicines.
Prof. Memberships: Law Society's European Group (Committee member – Yorkshire Branch).
Career: Qualified in 1990 *(McKenna & Co)*. Joined *Eversheds* in 1994. Became a partner in 1998. Educated at Oundle School and Durham University (Hatfield College).
Publications: Co-authored 'CBI Business Guide to Competition Law' (July 1999).
Personal: Married with two daughters. Lives in Wetherby.

COOK, John
Norton Rose, London (020) 7444 3096
cookcj@nortonrose.com
Specialisation: Partner, competition and EC department. Competition law, EC law, (including international trade, public procurement and state aids) and transport and utilities regulation. A regular conference speaker and writer, he is the author, with CS Kerse, of 'EC Merger Control', the leading text book on EC merger control – published by Sweet & Maxwell – third edn December 1999.
Career: Called to the Bar of Grays Inn in 1975. Lectureship, Magdalen College, Oxford 1976-81. UK government legal service 1976-88. *Norton Rose* 1988-97 (headed competition and EC department). Rejoined *Norton Rose* in February 2000 after two years at *Macfarlanes*.

COPPEN, Simon
Burges Salmon, Bristol (0117) 939 2291
simon.coppen@burges-salmon.com
Specialisation: Simon has particular experience of the application of UK and EU competition law in the field of commercial transactions, including intellectual property, technology transfer, agency, distribution and joint ventures. His specialist areas include the application of competition law within the UK rail industry.
Prof. Memberships: Law Society.
Career: 1985-89, *Allen & Overy*; 1989 to date, *Burges Salmon*; 1993, partner. Head of commercial unit.
Personal: Brasenose College, Oxford 1981-84.

CUTTING, Michael
Linklaters, London (020) 7456 3514
michael.cutting@linklaters.com
Specialisation: Specialist in EU and competition and utility law and practice. Considerable experience of the application of competition law in the telecommunications, leisure and transport sectors. Recent merger control experience includes BP Amoco's acquisition of Burmah Castrol (phase I unconditional appearance), Coopers & Lybrand/Price Waterhouse (phase II unconditional appearance) and acting for Bass on its sale of Coral betting shops to Ladbroke plc. Utility experience includes advising British Gas plc and subsequently BG Group plc and Lattice plc on regulatory matters since 1992. In that context he has advised in relation to two MMC inquiries relating to BG and advised on the design and negotiation of the new regulatory framework for gas transportation and supply (1994-96) and various connected matters since then.
Career: 1984 Trinity Hall, Cambridge University, MA. 1995 to date partner competition and regulatory law group *Linklaters.* 1988-95 assistant solicitor *Linklaters.* 1986-88 articled clerk *Linklaters.*

DAVEY, Jonathan
Addleshaw Booth & Co, Manchester
(0161) 934 6349
jwd@addleshaw-booth.co.uk
Specialisation: Partner in Trade & Regulatory Department, Commercial Group. Main areas of work in this field are UK and EC competition law (including mergers and anti-competitive behaviour), public procurement law and state aids. Has been involved in the recent past in a number of significant notifications and complaints to the EC Commission and has considerable experience of UK Merger Control and of advising on UK competition law generally.
Prof. Memberships: Association Internationale des Jeunes Avocats, CBI National Consumer Law Advisory Panel, North West Law Society's European Group.
Career: Joined the firm in 1986 and qualified in 1988. Became an Associate in 1992 and a Partner in 1994.
Personal: Educated at Manchester University 1982-85 (LL.B Hons) and the College of Law, Chester 1985-86 (1st Class Hons in Law Society Final Examination). Enjoys hill walking, travel and good food.

DEAN, Michael
Maclay Murray & Spens, Glasgow
(0141) 248 5011
mjd@maclaymurrayspens.co.uk
Specialisation: Brussels +32 2 282 8415 Head of EU and competition law specialising in EU and UK competition matters. Practice covers agency, distribution, EC, UK and multi-state merger clearances, advising on general competition law issues; general European law issues; Competition Commission proceedings; public procurement issues, procedures and notices. Recent cases have involved advising on competition litigation under Chapter I and II of Competition Act 1998 in the sports sector; advising on compliance with ERDF rules; advising on termination of French distribution arrangements on behalf of a US/UK corporation utilising EU competition law arguments; advising on lodging a complaint under CA 1998; handling OFT dawn raid investigation under CA 1998; advising public sector bodies on European state aid obligations; retained by several multinationals for competition investigations; is on a panel of law firms advising the UK electricity and gas regulator. Frequently gives presentations to businesses on export issues and to lawyers on European law. Presented on distribution in Europe at ALI-ABA Conference. Recent presentations include 'European Distribution' at New Orleans and on 'Antitrust Aspects of B2bs' at LSEG Annual Conference.
Prof. Memberships: Law Society of Scotland; Scottish Lawyers European Group. Chairman German-British Chamber of Commerce in Scotland; Chair, Glasgow Export Club.
Career: Qualified 1986. Assistant solicitor, *Lovell White Durrant*, London 1988-1990. Assistant solicitor and partner *McGrigor Donald* 1991-1997. Recruited by *Maclays* as partner. Former external examiner, Europa Institute, Edinburgh.
Personal: Educated at St. Aloysius' College, Glasgow 1968-1978, University of Glasgow (LLB Hons and Diploma in Legal Practice) 1978-1983, and at the College of Europe, Bruges, (Diploma in Advanced European Studies) 1983-1984. Interests include local politics. Born 15th January 1960. Lives in Glasgow.

DOWNIE, Gordon
Shepherd & Wedderburn WS, Edinburgh (0131) 473 5162
gordon.downie@shepwedd.co.uk
Specialisation: Head of the firm's competition and regulation group, which deals with the full range of UK and EC competition law work, ranging from merger and anti-trust clearances, to contentious proceedings and complaints to the OFT and European Commission. Experienced in assisting clients in setting up and maintaining compliance programmes to minimise their exposure to the legal consequences of breach of competition laws. Also advises clients across a variety of regulated sectors in their dealings with sectoral regulators, such as OFGEM, OFWAT, and OFTEL, and on compliance with their regulatory obligations.
Prof. Memberships: Law Society of Scotland, WS Society, Scottish Lawyers European Group, member of LSS Competition Law Sub-Committee.
Career: Qualified 1992 with *Shepherd & Wedderburn WS.* Assumed as partner in 1998.
Personal: Born 7 May 1966. University of Edinburgh, graduated LLB (Hons) 1988. European University Institute, graduated LLM 1990. Lives in Edinburgh.

FINBOW, Roger
Ashurst Morris Crisp, London (020) 7638 1111
roger.finbow@ashursts.com
Specialisation: Partner in company department. Member of competition group. Head of sports law group. Handles all aspects of corporate and commercial law for principally public company clients; and competition law, especially mergers regulation. Recent matters include: Competition Commission inquiries into the acquisition by National Express of Scotrail and Central Trains; the merger of United News & Media and Carlton Communications; the acquisition by Air Canada of Canadian Airways; the joint venture between Pentre and Askern; the regulatory aspects of Imperial Tobacco Group's acquisition of Douwe Egberts Van Nelle; the merger between NFC and Ocean Group; the joint ventures between Smith & Nephew and Beiersdorf. Joint author of 'UK Merger Control: Law and Practice'.
Career: Qualified in 1977. Joined *Ashurst Morris Crisp* in 1975, becoming a partner in 1984.
Personal: Born 13 May 1952. Attended Woodbridge School 1963-70 and Mansfield College Oxford 1971-74 (MA 1977). Leisure interests include classic cars, collecting model cars, motor biking, keeping fit, ballet and gardening. Director of Ipswich Town Football Club Co. Limited; governor of The Seckford Foundation. Lives in the Suffolk/Essex borders.

FLECK, Richard
Herbert Smith, London (020) 7374 8000
richard.fleck@herbertsmith.com
Specialisation: Practice development partner. Handles EC and competition law, commercial disputes and accounting law. Has extensive experience of references of proposed merger and monopoly situations and on other competitive and regulatory matters such as investigations under the Competition Act. Also of European competition authorities, the Department of Trade and the Bank of England. Other areas of expertise include major commercial disputes and advising major accounting firms and the Institute of Chartered Accountants on technical and accounting matters. He is the only lawyer on the Auditing Practices Board.
Career: Qualified in 1973. Partner at *Herbert Smith* since 1979.
Personal: Educated at Southampton University.

FREEMAN, Peter
Simmons & Simmons, London 020 7628 2020
peter.freeman@simmons-simmons.com
Specialisation: Head of EC and competition law. Main area of practice is EC and UK competition and regulatory law, including mergers. Sector specialisations include broadcasting, energy and railways.
Prof. Memberships: IBA, UIA, Law Society, Competition Law Association. Chairman of the Regulatory Policy Institute, Oxford.
Career: Qualified 1972. Joined *Simmons & Simmons* in 1973.
Publications: Joint General Editor (with Richard Whish) of 'Butterworths Competition Law'. Author (with Richard Whish) of 'A Guide to the Competition Act 1998'. (Butterworths, 1999).
Personal: Born 2nd October 1948. Attended Kingswood School, Bath, 1961-66, Goethe Institut, Berlin, 1967, Trinity College, Cambridge 1967-71, and Université Libre de Bruxelles 1972-73. Leisure interests include naval history and music.

FRIEND, Mark
Allen & Overy, London (020) 7330 2440
mark.friend@allenovery.com
Specialisation: Partner specialising in EC and UK competition law and the economic regulation of utilities, state aids, public procurement and general issues of EC law.
Prof. Memberships: City of London Law Society Competition Law sub-committee; IBA; Solicitors European Group; Fellow of the Society for Advanced Legal Studies.
Career: Admitted as a solicitor (1982). Assistant *Allen & Overy* (1988-90); Partner (1990).
Publications: Numerous articles, case notes and book reviews in leading academic and professional journals.
Personal: Born 1957. Cambridge University (BA 1979); Universite Libre de Bruxelles (Lit.Sp.en Dr. Eur. 1983).

GIBSON-BOLTON, Elaine
SJ Berwin, London (020) 7533 2463
elaine.gibson-bolton@sjberwin.com
Specialisation: EU and competition law with a particular expertise in 'regulated industries' such as energy, transport and media. Regularly represents clients before the European Commission, Competition Commission, Office of Fair Trading, DTI and utility regulators. Current holder of 'Legal Business Competition Team of the Year' 2000, for successfully challenging Ofgem on behalf of US electricity generators AES before the Competition Commission in their wholesale electricity pricing investigation. She has extensive experience in EU and UK mergers and joint ventures. She has developed a particular expertise in the application of the EC Merger Regulation and domestic merger provisions to complex private equity transactions, advising a range of venture capital funds and investors in close conjunction with the firm's private equity group. She is also heavily involved with advising on the application of EU and UK competition law to regulated industries such as those in the energy and transport sectors. Her varied practice spans a broad range of industries and she has a particular specialisation in telecommunications and media, particularly all aspects of television. She continues to divide her working week between London and Brussels, generally spending two days every week in Brussels. Elaine writes and lectures widely on EU and competition law.
Prof. Memberships: Member of the Institute for Advanced Legal Studies; Law Society's European Group; Freeman of the City of London Solicitors' Livery Company; member European Aviation Association; founder Women in Media.
Career: University of Reading LLB (Hons) 1980-3; University of Amsterdam, Postgraduate Diploma in European Integration 1983-4; Trained *Clifford Harris & Co* 1985-7; qualified 1987; *Holman, Fenwick and Willan* 1987-1989; *Freshfields*, London and Brussels 1989-93; *SJ Berwin*, London and Brussels 1993 to date; partner 1997.
Publications: Co-writer of two volume looseleaf service 'Competition Law of the UK'; Subsidiarity, 'National Courts and EC Competition Matters'., 'GATT – The Perspective from Brussels', 'Kellog's Cornflakes as Loss Leaders' for News Brief plc; 'The Double Whammy' for Recording Artist Contracts; Water Bulletin 'Gas Lights the Way'; 'Parallel Imports' by WA Rothine Book Review.
Personal: Foreign travel; sports; film and music.

HOLMES, Katherine
Richards Butler, London (020) 7247 6555
kmh@richardsbutler.com
Specialisation: Partner in EU and competition group; specialises in EC and UK competition law and EC law generally. Advises clients from a wide variety of industries, including transport, media and entertainment, leisure, food and drink, construction, pharmaceuticals and computer software.
Prof. Memberships: Chairman of Joint Working Party of the UK Bars and Law Societies on Competition Law; Solicitors European Group; former Chairman and Vice-President of the Bar Association for Commerce, Finance and Industry (BACFI).
Career: Qualified as a barrister (1973). Joined *CBI* in 1976 becoming head of commercial law; from 1981 senior legal adviser to two major public companies; in 1989, joined *Richards Butler* and after admission as solicitor became partner in 1991.
Publications: Various topics in field including 'The EC White Paper on Modernisation', 'World Competition Law' and 'Economics Review', vol 23, no 4, December 2000.
Personal: Leisure pursuits include sailing, skiing, swimming, theatre and entertaining. Lives in London.

HOLMES, Simon
SJ Berwin, London (020) 7533 2222
simon.holmes@sjberwin.com
Specialisation: A wide range of work including extensive range of merger work acting for the parties, complainants or third parties; advising on dominance issues (pricing/discounts/parallel imports etc); a wide range of commercial arrangements both on and off-line.
Prof. Memberships: Recent chairman, Law Society's European group.
Career: 1st Class Hons, Law and Economics from Cambridge. Grande Distinction, Licence Spéciale en Droit Européen, Brussels University.
Personal: Married, two daughters. Walking, cycling, tennis, film.

HUTCHINGS, Michael
Michael Hutchings, Warminster (07768) 105777
mbh@dircon.co.uk
Specialisation: Advice on all aspects of EU law, especially internal market, competition and regulation; UK implementation of EU law; UK competition law.
Prof. Memberships: British Institute of International and Comparative Law (Chairman of Executive Committee). Solicitors European Group (Former Chairman). European Competition Law Review (Editorial Board).
Career: Qualified 1973; articled with *McKenna & Co* ; partner *Lovell White Durrant* 1981-96; established independent sole practice 1996.
Personal: Born 8 November 1948.

JURKIW, Andrij
Pinsent Curtis Biddle, Leeds (0113) 244 5000
andrij.jurkiw@pinsents.com
Specialisation: Head of competition, Leeds. Specialises in merger clearances, OFT & competition commission investigations; notifications and complaints to EC Commission; competition law litigation; competition law compliance programmes; parallel imports and public procurement. Important cases: advising Whitbread and Punch Retail on the merger implications of the £250m sale of First

Quench to Nomura; advising Arriva plc in relation to the first dawn raids by the OFT under the Competition Act 1998; acting in one of the few concluded Early Guidance Applications under the Competition Act and in what is believed to be the first interim measures application under the Competition Act; acting for Arla Foods plc in relation to the Competition Commission inquiry into supermarkets; currently acting in a major concurrent investigation by the EC Commission and US Department of Justice.

Prof. Memberships: Law Society. Solicitors' European Group.

Career: Articled *Slater Heelis* 1987-89; *Hammond Suddards* EC Unit 1989-91; *Eversheds* (Manchester) 1991-94, setting up EC Practice. *Pinsent Curtis Biddle* 1994 to date. Partner 1999. Law degree – Leeds Metropolitan University.

Personal: Travel, choral singing, fine wines, classic cars, photography.

KELLAWAY, Rosalind

Eversheds, London (020) 7919 4500
kellawr@eversheds.com

Specialisation: Rosalind Kellaway chairs the Eversheds national EU and Competition Group. Her practice covers all aspects of EU and competition law practice with particular expertise in motor industry, financial services and utilities work. She handles all types of related commercial work including distributive and licensing systems and complex contractual work generally.

Prof. Memberships: Solicitors European Group, CBI Competition Law Committee, Joint Bar Council and Law Society Working Party on Competition Law.

Career: Qualified in 1984. Joined *Jaques & Lewis* (now *Eversheds*) in 1981, becoming a partner in 1989.

Publications: Competition Act 1988: A Practical Guide (Tolleys).

Personal: Born 10th June 1957. Attended Lewes Priory School and the University of Sussex 1979 (BA Law with French). Leisure interests include riding. Lives in Lewes.

KON, Stephen

SJ Berwin, London (020) 7533 2237
stephen.kon@sjberwin.com

Specialisation: Head of the EU and competition department at *SJ Berwin*. Extensive experience in representing clients in contentious and non-contentious EU and domestic competition work, as well as general EU law. Regularly represents clients in proceedings before the Office of Fair Trading, the Monopolies and Mergers Commission, the European Commission and the Court of First Instance and the European Court of Justice in Luxembourg. Represented the European Commission in a number of competition cases before the CFI and the ECJ and has acted in a number of significant merger clearance enquiries; for example for Guinness in the EU clearance of its merger with Grand Metropolitan, for which the team won the Legal Business Competition Team of the Year award, and most recently for Diageo in the phase one clearance of its joint acquisition of the Seagram spirits and wines business with Pernod Ricard.

Prof. Memberships: 1986 Chairman of the Law Society's Solicitors' European Group; International Bar Association; Law Society's Solicitors' European Group.

Career: With *SJ Berwin* since formation in 1982, previously with a major City law firm; subsequently taught European Community and Competition Law at the Universities of Sussex and Reading. Most recently visiting lecturer at University of Oxford.

Publications: Has written and lectured extensively on various subjects relating to EU and competition law and numerous articles in most of the leading European law reviews, and most recently *SJ Berwin's* major looseleaf publication, 'The Competition Law of the UK'.

LEIGH, Guy

Theodore Goddard, London (020) 7606 8855
guyleigh@theodoregoddard.co.uk

Specialisation: Guy Leigh heads the firm's competition and regulation group, based in both London and Brussels. His practice focuses on EC and UK competition and regulatory work. He has extensive experience of mergers, joint venture, technology transfer, state aids and competition, regulatory and compliance issues, and has advised in relation to such issues particularly in the IT, media and communications, sports, pharmaceutical and healthcare, telecommunications, and transport sectors. Experience includes advising the British Horseracing Board on an ongoing basis, representing the Intellectual Property Owners Inc of the US before the European Court of Justice in the Magill TV Listings case and advising a leading software manufacturer with regard to a wide range of EC competition law issues. Guy also dealt successfully with the merger control aspects of the acquisition by MAID plc, now The Dialog Corporation plc, of Knight-Ridder Information Inc and Knight-Ridder AG.Guy's past experience includes having been involved with the TSB vesting and flotation, the acquisition by British Airways of British Caledonian, a major Monopolies and Mergers Commission reference concerning the bus industry and a number of newspaper merger references.

Prof. Memberships: Guy is Chairman of the English Competition Law Association, First Vice President and a past Reporter General and International Reporter of the International League for Competition Law. He is also a member of the Brussels-based European Competition Lawyers Forum and of the Law Society Bar Joint Working Party on Competition.

Publications: Guy is co-author with Diana Guy of 'The EEC and Intellectual Property', the author of various articles on EC law and a frequent speaker at the competition law conferences.

LINDRUP, Garth

Addleshaw Booth & Co, Manchester (0161) 934 6000

Specialisation: Partner in trade & regulatory department, commercial group. Work includes UK and EU competition law, especially merger control, articles 81 and 82, public procurement, joint ventures, distribution, agency and franchising, state aid. Editor, 'Butterworths Competition Law Handbook' and various other publications; Chairman, Law Society's European Group 1994/95.

Prof. Memberships: IBA, LIDC, CBI Competition Panel, ICC Competition Committee.

Career: Qualified 1975. Joined firm in 1979 and became Partner in 1984.

Personal: Holds BA, LLM (Cantab).

LINDSAY, Alistair

Allen & Overy, London (020) 7330 3273
alistair.lindsay@allenovery.com

Specialisation: Partner in the European Antitrust Group. Called to the Bar in 1993 and practised from Monckton Chambers for three years dealing extensively in EU, competition and public law. Whilst at the Bar, acted in the Factortame (Spanish fishermen) damages claim and taught EU law part-time at LSE. Since joining *Allen & Overy*, has requalified as a solicitor and has practised extensively in EU and competition law including mergers and restrictive agreements at both EU and UK level, utilities and litigation.

Career: Called to Bar (1993), Associate *Allen & Overy* (1997-2001), Partner (2001).

Publications: Widely published.

Personal: Born 1971. Cambridge University (BA 1992).

LIVINGSTON, Dorothy

Herbert Smith, London (020) 7374 8000
dorothy.livingston@herbertsmith.com

Specialisation: Partner, deputy head of European and competition law department and head of public sector and utilities procurement unit. Her areas of expertise cover the full range of EU and UK competition law, including restrictive agreements, monopolies, anti-competitive practices, abuse of dominant position, mergers, public procurement, state aids and utility regulation. Also contributes to the work of the firm's international finance and banking department with particular reference to EMU and state guarantees. Sits on the advisory board of the Centre for European Law at King's College, London.

Prof. Memberships: City of London Law Society (Chairman of Banking Law and Member of EC and Competition Law Sub-Committees), Financial Law Panel Working Party on State Aids.

Career: Qualified in 1972. With *Herbert Smith* since articles. Became a partner in 1980.

Publications: She is the joint author of 'Competition Law Sources' and author of 'Competition Law and Practice' (Sweet & Maxwell) and has contributed three chapters on competition and EC law to 'Finance Leasing' (Euromoney, 3rd ed), as well as being author of 'The Competition Act 1998: A Practical Guide' (Sweet & Maxwell, 2001).

Personal: Educated at St Hugh's College, Oxford, Central Newcastle High School GDST.

LOUGHER, Guy

Wragge & Co, Birmingham (0870) 903 1000

LOUVEAUX, Bertrand

Slaughter and May, London (020) 7600 1200
bertrand.louveaux@slaughterandmay.com

Specialisation: A broad range of UK and EC competition law. Has wide experience before the European Commission, the Office of Fair Trading and the Competition Commission (including both merger and monopoly enquiries). Recent merger cases have included Shell/Exxon (EC), British Steel/Hoogovens (EC), BAT/Rothmans (EC), Kodak/Imation (EC), Victoria Wine/Threshers (UK), Carlton/United/Granada (UK), Lincoln/Charter and Lloyds TSB/Abbey National (UK). On the contentious front, recently acted for Nomura/GPC in obtaining the landmark Article 81 'pubco' decision. He regularly advises clients on Articles 81 and 82 of

the EC Treaty and the 1998 Competition Act.
Career: Qualified 1994 with *Slaughter and May* and became a partner in 2001.
Personal: Born 28 April 1967. Educated London School of Economics (MSc Economics).

MARTIN ALEGI, Lynda
Baker & McKenzie, London (020) 7919 1000
lynda.martin.alegi@bakernet.com
Specialisation: Partner and head of department dealing with EC competition law – appeal against Article 85 decisions – lysine cartel (ADM), cement cartel (The Rugby Group plc); UK competition law – MMC Investigations – brown goods (Sony), photocopiers (Canon), fine fragrances (Guerlain), condoms (Mates); merger control – EC – de Havilland Case (for Aerospatiale/Alenia), Glaxo Smith Kline/Block Drug (for Block Drug), Gillette/Parker Pen (for Parker Pen), Shell IDEA (for Shell) – UK, Rockwool/Owens Corning (for Rockwool); advisory work (including Canon, Camelot, Levi Strauss, Sony, Tetra-Pak).
Prof. Memberships: CBI Competition Panel; ICC UK Committee on Law and Practices Relating to Competition.
Career: Articled *Baker & McKenzie*, qualified 1977, partner 1981.
Publications: Editor of Sweet & Maxwell's 'Encyclopaedia of Information Technology Law' (Competition Law chapter).
Personal: Woodford County High School; Newnham College, Cambridge (1973 MA); Institute of European Studies – Free University of Brussels (1975 Licence Speciale). Languages: French, Italian. Born 1952; resides London.

McDONNELL, Phil
Garretts, Manchester (0161) 200 0129
phil.mcdonnell@glegal.com
Specialisation: Advises on EC and UK competition law and merger control including all aspects of business practices, pricing, distribution and sales strategies, corporate acquisition, joint ventures and alliances. Deals with complaints, investigations and compliances matters. Also advises on public procurement (particularly relating to the utility sector) and data protection matters.
Prof. Memberships: Law Society, Solicitors European Group.
Career: Articled *Lovell White Durrant* (London and Hong Kong); *Lovell White Durrant* (London, New York and Brussels) 1988-93; commercial manager North West Water International Ltd 1994-5; *Garretts* 1995 (partner 1999) Head of EU & Competition.
Personal: Educated St Ambrose College Hale Barns; Wadham College Oxford.

McKNIGHT, Elizabeth
Herbert Smith, London (020) 7374 8000
elizabeth.mcknight@herbertsmith.com
Specialisation: Principal area of work covers UK and EC competition law, including cases relating to the exploitation of intellectual property rights and cases relating to regulated industries (electricity, water, gas, telecommunications, media).
Prof. Memberships: Law Society, International Bar Association.
Career: Qualified in 1988 and became a partner in 1994.
Personal: Born 3rd May 1961. Attended Jesus College, Oxford 1979-1983, then took an LLM at London School of Economics, 1989.

McLEAN, James
Burness, Edinburgh (0131) 473 6118
jmcl@burness.co.uk
Specialisation: Graduated in English and Scots Law at Cambridge and Edinburgh Universities. Competition practice covers national and European competition laws and their impact on the contracts and conduct of business undertakings and public authorities. Wider European Union practice involves other aspects of law affecting undertakings and authorities, as well as the interaction among the UK Parliament and executive, the Scottish Parliament and executive and the United Kingdom's European Community, European Union and European Human Rights Convention obligations.

MILLER, Colin
Biggart Baillie, Glasgow (0141) 228 8000
cmiller@biggertbaillie.co.uk
Specialisation: Acted for Miller & Bryce in the first ever successful action for interim interdict in the Court of Session under EU competition rules against the Keeper of the Registers of Scotland. Advised Drambuie on implications under the EU block exemption for vertical agreements. Recent advice includes advising a major UK retailer in a successful complaint to the OFT under the Competition Act 1998; various public procurement issues relating to ScotRail; advising a footwear manufacturer on parallel imports and international exhaustion of rights. Other clients include BSW Timber plc, the Highland Council, Scottish Power and the Original Shoe Company.
Prof. Memberships: Member of Society for Computers and the Law, Scottish Software Federation and the Intellectual Property Committee of the Law Society of Scotland.
Career: Qualified as a solicitor in Scotland and England. Assistant in two London City firms, *Linklaters and Eversheds*, before returning to Scotland in 1996.
Personal: Classical music, choral singing and hill walking. Married with two young children.

NICHOLSON, Malcolm
Slaughter and May, London (020) 7600 1200
malcolm.nicholson@slaughterandmay.com
Specialisation: EU, competition and regulatory law. Head of *Slaughter and May's* competition group. His practice covers the full range of UK and EU antitrust work for a number of blue chip clients (including RECs and other utilities), governments and regulatory authorities. On the UK competition front, he has extensive experience before the Competition Commission, including both merger and monopoly enquiries, and he deals regularly with the OFT. On the European front, he has been engaged in a number of competition cases before the Commission and the Court of Justice and in obtaining regulatory clearances from the Merger Task Force. He was heavily involved in the regulatory and competition aspects of the major UK privatisations and currently advises a number of electricity and water utilities with regard to price controls and other regulatory matters.
Career: Qualified in 1974 with *Slaughter and May* and became a partner in 1982.
Personal: Born March 1949. Educated Haileybury, Cambridge University, Brussels University. Married with six children.

OSBORNE, John
Clifford Chance, London (020) 7600 1000
john.osborne@cliffordchance.com
Specialisation: Partner in European Competition and Regulation Group. Full range of EC and UK competition law from merger control, strategic alliances, joint ventures and commercial agreements to monopoly and cartel investigations. Extensive experience in conducting cases and investigations before the EC Commission, the OFT, the CC and the CFI/ECJ for parties and complainants, and co-ordinating clearances in cross-border transactions. Acts for clients across a wide-range of business sectors including banking, financial services and broadcasting. Also advises on the EC law generally and utility regulation. Original contributing editor and author of 'Butterworths Competition Law' division on permitted horizontal agreements.
Prof. Memberships: IBA, Solicitors European Group, Committee Member of the Competition Law Association.
Career: Qualified 1973. Partner 1980.
Personal: Born 23 October 1947. LLB Bristol (1968); LLM London School of Economics (1969). Leisure interests include military history, cricket and horseracing. Lives in Richmond.

PARR, Nigel
Ashurst Morris Crisp, London (020) 7638 1111
nigel.parr@ashursts.com
Specialisation: Advises in relation to all aspects of UK and EC competition law and utilities regulation, particularly merger control. Has acted in relation to 28 UK Competition Commission inquiries including monopoly investigations, mergers and anti-competitive practices and in relation to a number of investigations under the Competition Act 1998. He regularly acts for clients in relation to notifications and investigations by the EC Commission, and has drafted many competition law compliance programmes.
Career: LLB, LLM, PhD. Partner, head of the competition group, co-author (with Roger Finbow) of 'UK Merger Control Law & Practice' (Sweet & Maxwell, 1995), and author of the competition section of PLC's 'Asset and Share Purchases' Manuals, as well as numerous articles on EC law and competition-related matters. Tutor in EC law and intellectual property law at Exeter University 1984-86.

PHEASANT, John
Lovells, London (020) 7296 2000
john.pheasant@lovells.com
Specialisation: EC and UK competition law in all its aspects, but particularly contentious proceedings and competition policy/regulation. Significant experience as an advocate before the Commission in administrative proceedings, and before the Court of First Instance and European Court of Justice on appeals (including interim measures). Co-author 'Competition Law' (Butterworths) and Editor of division on prohibited horizontal agreements.
Prof. Memberships: Member of the Advisory Board of the Regulatory Policy Institute, Oxford.
Career: Articled *Lovells*. Qualified 1979; partner since 1985. Brussels office: 1980-1983 and 1986 – present.

POLITO, Simon
Lovells, London (020) 7296 2000
simon.polito@lovells.com
Specialisation: Principally EC and UK competition law. Expertise acquired since late 1970s in numerous Commission cases under Articles 81 and 82 and the Merger Regulation as well as UK merger and monopoly inquiries. Advises UK, European and US multinationals on competition issues affecting manufacturing and service industries. Also advises on regulatory aspects of privatised industries, utilities and broadcasting.
Prof. Memberships: Member Joint Working Party on Competition Law of UK and Irish Bars and Law Societies; also of UK Committee of ICC on Competition Law and European Lawyers Forum.
Career: Called to Bar (Middle Temple) 1972. Qualified as solicitor with *Lovells* in 1976, partner 1982. Worked in Brussels 1977-81 (including 1990 "stage" with the Commission) and as a resident Brussels partner from 1988. Now based primarily in London.

REES, Kate
Pinsent Curtis Biddle, Birmingham
(0121) 200 1050
kate.rees@pinsents.com
Specialisation: EU and UK competition law including UK and EU merger clearances and OFT, Competition Commission and European Commission enquiries. Very extensive public procurement practice.
Career: LLB Hons 1st class. Qualified in 1988. Partner in *Pinsent Curtis Biddle.*

ROBERT, Gavin
Linklaters, London (020) 7456 3364
gavin.robert@linklaters.com
Specialisation: EU competition and regulatory department, with experience in all aspects of EU and competition law, public procurement and state aid. Particular focus on multimedia, healthcare, food and drink and energy. Recent major cases include state aid aspects of Channel Tunnel Rail Link and advising SmithKline Beecham on its proposed mergers with AHP and Glaxo.
Prof. Memberships: Legal consultant to the European Commission High Level working group on public-private partnership financing of trans-European transport projects (sub-group 4 on legal and administrative issues). Member of Liberalisation of Trade in Services (LOTIS) Committee of British Invisibles.
Career: 1999 to date: Partner, *Linklaters* London; 1994-1999: Assistant solicitor, *Linklaters* Brussels; 1993-1994: Assistant solicitor, *Linklaters* London (EC and anti-trust department); 1992-1993: Secondment to European Commission Legal Service; 1990-1992: Trainee solicitor, *Linklaters* London. 1989-1990: Licence Spéciale en Droit Européen, Université Libre de Bruxelles; 1988-1989: Law Society Finals, College of Law, Chancery Lane, London; 1985-1998: Emmanuel College, Cambridge, BA (Hons) in Law.

ROSE, Stephen
Eversheds, London (020) 7919 4785
roses@eversheds.com
Specialisation: All aspects of EC and UK competition law with a focus on the Competition Act 1998 and mergers, acquisitions and joint ventures.
Career: Qualified 1991; articled with *Slaughter and May*; partner at *Eversheds* 1997.
Personal: Born 27.5.65; educated at St Edmund Hall, Oxford (1984-87); lives in Great Chesterford Essex.

SCHOLES, Jeremy
Walker Morris, Leeds (0113) 283 2500
jas@walkermorris.co.uk
Specialisation: 20 years' experience of applying competition and EU law (the main areas of his practice) in a wide range of commercial contexts (transactions, litigation, dealing with regulatory authorities, compliance/advisory work). Recent work of note has included R v The Law Society, ex p Dalton (the 'test case' litigation against the former Solicitors' Indemnity Fund monopoly); representing one of the large grocery supermarket chains in the Competition Commission enquiry; advice to a district auditor on complaints against a local authority to the OPT under the Competition Act 1998.
Prof. Memberships: Law Society's European Group (former chairman of the East Midlands branch); Competition Law Association (convenor of the working group on the Competition Bill); LIDC (International Competition Law Association) (a national reporter for 1997/98).
Career: Law degrees from Cambridge and the Collège d'Europe, Brugge, Belgium. Qualified 1981. *Freshfields*; *Waltons & Morse*; *Wells & Hind/Eversheds*, Nottingham (partner till 1993; set up and led the *Eversheds* competition law practice group nationally); then several years a sole practitioner; now head of *Walker Morris* 's competition and EU law practice. Part-time law lecturer at Sheffield University and a visiting lecturer at the Université de Nancy II in eastern France.
Publications: Various, including the commercial agency chapter in the 'PLC Commercial Contracts' manual.
Personal: Works in French; also speaks good German and Dutch.

SCOTT, Jonathan
Herbert Smith, London 020 7466 2361
jonathan.scott@herbertsmith.com
Specialisation: Head of EC/competition department. Work includes mergers, joint ventures, anti-trust investigations and European Court of Justice work. Acted in major investigations involving the television industry, electricity industry, the food and drink industry; and most recently the travel, dairy and domestic appliance industries and EC merger investigations in the insurance, financial services, glass, spirits, titanium, petro-chemical and travel industries.
Prof. Memberships: IBA.
Career: Qualified in 1981. Worked at the Council of Europe Human Rights Directorate 1979. Joined *Herbert Smith* in 1979, becoming a partner in 1988.
Publications: Editor of 'EC Merger Reporter'. Editor merger chapters of Longman's 'Competition Law and Practice'.
Personal: Born 4th May 1956. Attended Shrewsbury School 1969-74, then St Catharine's College, Cambridge 1975-78. Lives in Cambridge.

SMITH, Martin
Simmons & Simmons, London 020 7628 2020
martin.smith@simmons-simmons.com
Specialisation: Partner. Main area of practice is competition and regulatory work (both EC and UK). Has experience of dealing with all the main EC and UK competition law authorities. He advises on EC and UK merger control and regularly coordinates multiple merger filings. His experience extends to a number of regulated industries, notably water, broadcasting and radio.
Prof. Memberships: Law Society, City of London Solicitors' Company Competition Law Sub-Committee, CBI Competition Panel, Solicitors European Group, International Bar Association, American Bar Association.
Career: Qualified in 1981. Joined *Simmons & Simmons* in 1977, becoming a partner in 1986, having worked at *Dechert Price & Rhoads* (Philadelphia) 1978 and *Linklaters & Paines* 1983-5.
Publications: Author of two major divisions of 'Butterworths Competition Law' and of 'Competition Law: Enforcement and Procedure' (2000). Frequently speaks at conferences and seminars.
Personal: Born 27th August 1955. Attended St Catharine's College, Cambridge 1974-77 (MA) and University of Pennsylvania (LLM) 1978-9. Leisure interests include sport, music and walking.

SOAMES, Trevor
Norton Rose, London (00) 32 2 237 6111
soamest@nortonrose.com
Specialisation: Trevor Soames is a partner in Norton Rose's rapidly growing EU and competition group which presently numbers 9 partners and one consultant (John Bridgeman, former UK Director General of Fair Trading) plus 37 full time associates. Recognised in all the key directories as one of the leading competition/regulatory lawyers in Brussels, Trevor's main areas of practice are all aspects of EU and national competition, trade and regulatory law. He has substantial experience in handling major merger and joint venture cases under the EC Merger Regulation (most recently successfully representing United Airlines before the EC Commission and securing a Phase I clearance of its merger with US Airways, opposing the hostile takeover of Air Canada by Onex/AirCo and the clearance of the acquisition of Sea-Land by Maersk) as well as under Article 81 (recent cases include P&O Stena Line and the joint venture between bmi british midland, Lufthansa and SAS). Trevor has handled a number of important recent multi-national cartel cases (such as Cement where the Norton Rose team was successful in quashing the fine imposed on Castle Cement and reducing the fines imposed on other clients). His many cases include major recent decisions of the European Commission under Articles 81, 82 and 86 in a number of economic sectors with a special emphasis on transportation. In addition, Trevor has handled a number of high-profile state aid cases before the European Commission and the European Court on behalf of complainants as well as for donor Governments and recipients. Trevor represents and advises a substantial number of major US and EU corporations in a wide variety of economic sectors on all matters relating to competition law, including Article 81 and 82 investigations as well as the implementation of compliance programmes. Recent clients include: Honeywell, Monsanto, bmi british midland, United Airlines, the Greek Government, Stena AB, Stena Line AB, Olympic Airways, Sea-Land, CSX, P&O Stena Line, Orbitz.com, Bombardier and Castle Cement. Trevor is an experienced litigator and proficient advocate, representing clients before the European Commission and European Court, as well as before the UK competition authorities.
Prof. Memberships: Member of IBA, ABA, EALA, EMLO and others.

Career: A graduate of Cambridge University. Called to the Bar of England & Wales in 1984 and enrolled as a Solicitor in 1989. Worked at UK Department of Trade and Industry before entering private practice. A graduate of Cambridge University. Called to the Bar of England & Wales in 1984 and enrolled as a Solicitor in 1989. Worked at UK Department of Trade and Industry before entering private practice. Highly Recommended both as a leading EC competition lawyer and as an aviation lawyer, in Legal 500, Law Firms in Europe 2000, Chambers & Partners Guide to the Legal Profession and Chambers World's Leading Lawyers 2000-2001. He is listed as a leading Brussels antitrust expert in Euromoney's Guide to the World's Leading Competition and Antitrust Lawyers and in the International Who's Who of Competition Lawyers. Trevor was selected in 1999 by European Legal Business as one of the leading Brussels state aid lawyers and was recently nominated by Euromoney as being one of the World's 20 leading aviation lawyers.
Publications: Author of many articles on competition and regulatory law as well as being editor of, or contributor to a number of books including: Corporate Mergers and Acquisitions, Air Transport and the European Community: Recent Developments, Airline Mergers and Co-operation and State Aids to Airlines. Trevor is also an Associate Editor of Butterworths Competition Law Encyclopaedia.

SPEARING, Nicholas
Freshfields Bruckhaus Deringer, London
(020) 7936 4000
nicholas.spearing@freshfields.com
Specialisation: Partner in Competition & Trade Group. Main area of practice is EC/Competition law. Extensive experience in monopolies, mergers and restrictive practices cases at both UK and EC levels. Acted for leading companies in MMC inquiries into car prices, perfumes, ice-cream, electrical goods and underwriting fees. Merger control work for a range of clients.
Prof. Memberships: Law Society, City of London Solicitors Company, Former Chairman Solicitors' European Group.
Career: Qualified 1978. Partner 1984.
Publications: Co-Author of 'Mergers' section of Butterworths' Competition law.
Personal: Born 1954. Educated Hertford College, Oxford 1972-75. Leisure pursuits include family, travel and golf.

TRAPP, Deirdre
Freshfields Bruckhaus Deringer, London
(020) 7936 4000
deidrie.trapp@freshfields.com
Specialisation: Joint head of Competition and Trade group. Main area of practice is competition and regulatory law. Has conducted monopolies, mergers and restrictive practices cases under both EU and UK jurisdictions. Extensive experience in utility, transport and media regulation.
Prof. Memberships: Law Society, City of London Solicitors' Company, Solicitors' European Group.
Career: Joined *Freshfields* in 1987. Partner 1995.
Personal: Born 1961. Attended St. Hilda's College Oxford 1980-1983 reading Philosophy, Politics and Economics.

USHER, Tom
SJ Berwin, London (020) 7533 2728
tom.usher@sjberwin.com
Specialisation: All aspects of EC law; expertise in competition/IP rights matters in music and pharmaceutical industries, also sports and broadcasting, collective selling and e-commerce. Litigation of EU issues in Europe and in the National Courts.
Prof. Memberships: Current chairman of the Law Society's European Group.
Career: Trained at SJ Berwin, qualified 1993, partner 1999.
Publications: 'This monopoly of music' (Ent Law Rev). 'The UK Competition Act 1998' (SJ Berwin).
Personal: Fettes College, Edinburgh; University of Saarbrucken, Germany; King's College London. Leisure: music, cricket, golf, rugby and cooking. Married with one child.

WARWICK, Neil
Dickinson Dees, Newcastle upon Tyne
(0191) 279 9375
neil.warwick@dickinson-dees.com
Specialisation: Competition law (both UK and EU) and EU law including European funding, anti-dumping and state aid. Major cases include Cowie/British MMC Inquiry, Merger Task Force reference (case IV/M.901), Polish Metals anti-dumping case. Highlights of the last 12 months include full compliance programmes for a number of clients (in particular Arriva and Go-Ahead), work with Nike, Stagecoach, Coca Cola and Transco. Successful ERDF regional funding application for the North East Investment Fund and a number of contentious cases (including defending cartels cases). Successful defence of C3D's bid for Go-Ahead.
Prof. Memberships: Law Society.
Career: Joined *Dickinson Dees* as a trainee in 1991, qualified in 1993, partner in 2001.
Publications: 'Croner Risk Management'.
Personal: Dame Allan's School, Newcastle University. Hobbies – football (five-a-side, eleven-a-side and Newcastle United), hockey, gym and running. Leisure – cooking, reading, DIY. Married with a young family.

WEITZMAN, Polly
Denton Wilde Sapte, London (020) 7246 7519
fmaw@dentonwildesapte.com
Specialisation: EU and UK competition law specialist advising on non-contentious (mergers, joint ventures, restrictive agreements) and contentious (cartel, restrictive practices, abuse of market power) issues with particular experience in the media and energy sectors. Extensive experience before the European Commission, Office of Fair Trading, Competition Commission and Restrictive Practices Court. Most recent major case is the successful defence of the collective and exclusive selling arrangements for the television rights to the Premier League Championship before the Restrictive Practices Court. Editor of section on gas in Butterworths 'Encyclopaedia of Competition Law'.
Prof. Memberships: Competition Law Society; The Law Society.
Career: Qualified in 1988 with *Denton Hall*. Became a partner in 1995.
Personal: Born 1961. Educated Godolphin & Latymer School, London; then Edinburgh University (Modern History).

WHEATON, Jim
Clifford Chance, London (020) 7600 1000
jim.wheaton@cliffordchance.com
Specialisation: Partner specialising in EU and competition law.
Career: Birmingham (LLB). Qualified 1973; partner *Clifford Chance* 1978.

WHISH, Richard P.
Richard Whish – Sole Practitioner, London
(020) 7848 2237

WISKING, Stephen
Herbert Smith, London 020 7466 2825
stephen.wisking@herbertsmith.com
Specialisation: Principal area of work involves all aspects of UK and European competition law and in particular, mergers, advisory work, investigations and litigation. Also undertakes broadcasting regulatory work. Advises clients in the areas of broadcasting, life sciences, the internet and IT.
Prof. Memberships: The Law Society.
Career: Qualified as barrister and solicitor (Australia) in 1988, as solicitor (England and Wales) in 1998 and as solicitor advocate in 1999. Joined *Herbert Smith* in 1997, becoming partner in 2000.
Personal: Born 9 September 1965, LLB (1988) and BEc (1987) at the University of Adelaide, then took an LLM (1991) at Jesus College, University of Cambridge. Married with one daughter. Lives in London.

WOTTON, John P
Allen & Overy, London (020) 7330 2444
john.wotton@allenovery.com
Specialisation: Partner specialising in UK, EU and international competition and trade law and in broadcasting and communications law. He has represented major public and private sector UK and international clients in numerous merger proceedings in the UK, EU and internationally, and on many other antitrust investigations and proceedings. He also advises on distribution and licensing, public procurement and government regulation in the utilities sector. He lectures on competition and broadcasting law and is an office holder in the Law Society's European Group.
Prof. Memberships: Treasurer, Law Society's European Group.
Career: Articled *Allen & Overy*; qualified 1978; partner 1984.
Personal: Born 1954. Jesus College, Cambridge 1975.

CONSTRUCTION

OVERVIEW: Our list remains eclectic in its mix of contentious and non-contentious firms but a deliberate decision has been made not to separate the two, following extensive market soundings. Construction clients are increasingly becoming interested in higher profit, longer term deals and are demanding a broader range of construction law advice. Firms that can provide a quality service on both fronts are faring the best. Masons, for example, has responded to this shift by building a non-contentious side to its practice, including an increasingly competitive projects team. The firm remains generally accepted as the number one in the sector.

RESEARCH APPROVED BY BMRB: *For this edition,* Chambers' *researchers conducted 6,552 interviews – 4,419 with law firms, 554 with barristers and 1,579 with clients.*

The validity of the research was scrutinised by BMRB International, who audited both the methodology and the results at our offices in July 2001. They interviewed Chambers' *researchers and cross-checked sample interviews. Details of the audit appear on page 7.*

TOP IN-HOUSE LAWYERS

Michael BLACKER, Head of Legal Services, *Amec Capital Projects*

Peter CHADWICK, Company Secretary, *Bovis Lend Lease Ltd*

Peter BRINLEY-CODD, Solicitor and Legal Services Manager, *Sir Robert McAlpine Ltd*

John FENWICK, Head of Group Legal Services, *Amec plc*

Dirk FITZHUGH, Company Secretary and Head of Legal Services, *Carillion plc*

Graham GIBSON, Head of Group Legal Services, *John Laing plc*

Martin LENIHAN, Legal Advisor, *Skanska Construction Ltd*

Frank McCORMACK, Head of Legal Services, *Balfour Beatty plc*

Phillip MORRIS, Solicitor, *Balfour Beatty plc*

Hilary WILSON, Legal Adviser, *Skanska Construction Ltd*

Valued as *"straightforward and down to earth – he understands his business,"* **Michael Blacker** and his team work on the UK and the Asia-Pacific sectors. With a wider brief, **John Fenwick** is thought to work well with panels of solicitors. With his *"extensive international experience,"* **Peter Chadwick** *"runs a good team,"* working mostly on the non-contentious side. **Peter Brinley-Codd** at Sir Robert McAlpine continues to be endorsed. **Dirk FitzHugh** is perceived as *"an outstanding commercial lawyer"* who is *"extremely incisive."* Working on the contentious side and therefore *"quite a street fighter,"* **Martin Lenihan** is highly regarded, while **Graham Gibson** is known for his *"considered approach."* Long-standing player **Frank McCormack** knows his business *"inside out." "A pleasure to work with,"* **Phillip Morris** is considered one of the best up and coming in-house lawyers in construction, rated for his *"good commercial grasp."* The "experienced" **Hilary Wilson** is appreciated as *"aggressive and fast thinking."*

In-House lawyers profiles: p.1193

LONDON

Masons (see firm details p.1056) Still rated number one by the majority of major players in the industry, its *"clear focus"* and length of construction experience keeps it ahead of the competition. Seen to have *"a stranglehold"* on the domestic contentious scene, the firm is packed with *"technically astute"* lawyers, who *"put a lot of energy into their clients." "Elder statesman"* **John Bishop** (see p.199) is considered to be a *"terrific lawyer,"* and although he is seen as a *"more managerial figure nowadays,"* no one is in any doubt about his status. **Tony Bunch** (see p.200) is another to be regarded as an *"obvious choice,"* and is held in high esteem for his *"fantastic knowledge of the law." "Top technician"* **Martin Harman** (see p.203) is endorsed as a *"calm and sensible"* practitioner, while clients respect **Mark Roe** (see p.199) for his *"unflappable competence."* **Mark Lane** (see p.205) and recognised litigator **Martin Roberts** (see p.207) also maintain their share of market approval. The firm acted for Mowlem on various multi-million pound claims concerning the design construction of a major headquarters facility for a government body. It also acted as legal advisors to the Arrow Consortium, comprising ADtranz, Carillion, Transdev and Nottingham City Transport, and represented Weldon Plant Ltd in Weldon Plant v The Commissioner for the New Towns, and on its successful appeal to the TCC. **Clients:** Mowlem; Net Line One; HBG Construction; Balfour Beatty; West Dorset District Council; Chiltern Railways.

CMS Cameron McKenna (see firm details p.922) In spite of the setback of the loss of property development expert Ann Minogue to Linklaters, most competitors still recognise that the firm possesses *"the essential quality and expertise"* of a market leader. **Trevor Butcher** (see p.200), who specialises in project-related construction, is widely regarded as a *"top quality"* lawyer. Head of the property construction group **Henry Sherman** retains a strong profile on the contentious side, while new partner **Marc Hanson** (see p.203), a protégé of Ann Minogue, has stepped into the limelight, and advises a range of institutional and employer clients. **Peter Long** (see p.205) received commendation for his work on major projects, and barristers have commended **Caroline Cummins** (see p.201) for her expertise in dispute resolution construction cases. On the property development side of the practice, the team has acted for Chelsfield in relation to a number of their major projects including the first phase of their £150 million office and residential development at Paddington Basin, and has advised Prudential Property Investment Managers on Atlantic House in Holborn. Construction projects include advising Metronet consortium on the construction contracts for the London Underground PPP and advising the underwriters on the construction contract for New England Patriots football stadium at Foxboro Massachusetts, USA. On the contentious front, the firm acted for Panatown in Alfred McAlpine Construction v Panatown, which has included a victory on a preliminary issue in the House of Lords. The firm also acted for Unex Investment Properties in a multi-party High Court action. **Clients:** BAA Lynton; Canary Wharf Group; Chelsfield; The Football Association; Lego; The Richard Rogers Partnership; Bowmeer & Kirkland; Drake & Scull Engineering; Chartered Institute of Building; Amey Ventures; John Laing; Kvaerner Skanska; Balfour Beatty; Carillion; Taylor Woodrow.

Rowe & Maw (see firm details p.1113) *"Thoroughly professional"* team, admired by rivals for its *"resilience,"* and which operates a balanced construction practice. Popular head of department **Michael Regan** (see p.207) specialises in insurance and is praised as *"an astute performer." "One of the best in the business,"* **John Rushton** (see p.208) acts for all parties in the construction industry and is regarded as a *"great lawyer, who richly deserves his reputation."* The *"hard-working"* **Gillian Birkby** (see p.199) also receives consistent market endorsement. On the contentious side, the firm acted for Ballast in High Court proceedings against R B Foundation Systems, which involved a claim for £4 million for alleged defect piling. International dispute work includes representing a Canadian contractor in arbitrations relating to the design and construction of a hydroelectric power station in

CONSTRUCTION • London	Ptnrs	Assts
1 Masons	18	40
2 CMS Cameron McKenna	8	15
Rowe & Maw	6	12
Shadbolt & Co	14	16
3 Berwin Leighton Paisner	9	22
Fenwick Elliott	6	7
Herbert Smith	4	12
Linklaters	8	26
4 Clifford Chance	11	n/a
Freshfields Bruckhaus Deringer	9	15
Lovells	7	n/a
Nicholson Graham & Jones	6	6
Norton Rose	5	20
Taylor Joynson Garrett	6	5
5 Allen & Overy	n/a	n/a
Ashurst Morris Crisp	4	12
Denton Wilde Sapte	8	11
Hammond Suddards Edge	7	14
Simmons & Simmons	2	9
Trowers & Hamlins	10	7
Winward Fearon	n/a	n/a
6 Baker & McKenzie	3	6
Beale and Company	n/a	n/a
Berrymans Lace Mawer	4	9
Campbell Hooper	4	2
Corbett & Co	n/a	n/a
Davies Arnold Cooper	n/a	n/a
Glovers	1	1
Kennedys	8	n/a
Macfarlanes	6	7
SJ Berwin	2	5
Wedlake Bell	1	2

This book is the product of 6,552 1/2-hour interviews. See p.7 for BMRB audit.
Within each band, firms are listed alphabetically.

Malaysia, and a claim for loss and expense following delays in the construction of a highway scheme in China. Elsewhere, the firm is representing Laing in negotiating a contract to build the new £200 million Commonwealth Games stadium in Manchester, and has acted for several high-tech companies in producing contract documents for their expanding office needs across Europe. **Clients:** Carillion; Mowlem; Laing; John Sisk & Son; Amey; Haden Young; Staveley; Sulzer; Matthew Hall; Bachy Soletanche; Van Oord ACZ; Guys and ST Thomas's NHS Trust; ICI; Brighton NHS Trust; Unilever; Southern Water; Aukett; DSSR; Gensler; Edward Cullinan; RJ Wallace & Others; The Chartwell Underwriting Group; QBE; AXA.

Shadbolt & Co (see firm details p.1121) "*Small and dynamic*" unit that continues to impress both clients and competitors. An acknowledged ability domestically, combined with substantial inroads into the Hong Kong market, see the firm climb in the rankings this year. Despite its size, the firm has been described as "*technically the equal of the top City players,*" and is praised by clients for its "*personal service – we really feel looked after.*" **Dick Shadbolt**'s (see p.209) "*charming manner and vast experience*" are considered to be "*indispensable to moving the practice forward,*" while **Dominic Helps** (see p.204) is said to be "*a great trail-blazer,*" who is highly rated in the contentious sphere. The firm represented the Government and the Roads Authority of an East African Country in an ICC arbitration worth around £40 million, and acted for a contractor on a multi-million pound dispute relating to a major development in Glasgow. Non-contentious matters include acting for Amey Asset Services on a successful bid for the design, construction and operation of an £80 million immigration detention centre, and advising the building contractor on a PFI project for the construction of new hospital facilities and associated refurbishment works in Birmingham. **Clients:** Amey Asset Services; Galliford Try.

Berwin Leighton Paisner (see firm details p.878) The merger between Paisner & Co and Berwin Leighton has resulted in a huge construction team, which also draws from the strength of the firm's property practice. Historically acclaimed for its advice on non-contentious matters, the team's contentious capacity was boosted by the arrival of a group from Barlow Lyde & Gilbert. **Terry Fleet** (see p.202) is seen as "*a good man and a real leader,*" whose work on a number of major projects has included advising Southern Water on its contractual procurement arrangements for a £750 million framework contract relating to the maintenance of water pumping station facilities in South East England. **Mike Gibson** (see p.202) is "*really rated*" by fellow practitioners, and has played a key role in developing the firm's PFI expertise. Recent work includes advising a client on the competition for the sale of the Millennium Dome, involving the review of 400 contracts. Former Greenwoods lawyer **Julian Holloway** (see p.204) joins the rankings this year following recommendation from competitors as "*a sound operator and a good chap.*" He advises contractors, sub-contractors and consultants in relation to domestic and international construction disputes. **John Wright** (see p.210) has a focus on arbitration and ADR, sits as an adjudicator and has recently acted for a US contractor in two adjudications brought by a sub-contractor in relation to loss and expense, delay and disruption. Recently arrived with her team from Barlow Lyde & Gilbert, **Caroline Pope** (see p.207) "*continues to show promise*" for dispute resolution work, and has advised Balfour Beatty Construction on its defence of a claim concerning allegations of breach of specification in the concrete supplied for a multi-storey car park. **Clients:** Akeler Developments; Balfour Beatty Major Projects; Ballast; Blue Circle; Cabinet Office; Constain Construction; Esporta; Highways Agency; Enco Engineering; Flack & Kurtz; Granada Group; Haslemere Estates; Legal and General; London Electricity; Millennium Commission; The New Millennium Experience Company; PACE; Railtrack; Royal Bank of Scotland; Tesco; Volund.

Fenwick Elliott (see firm details p.956) A "*true construction firm,*" which remains focused on the industry and is "*particularly impressive*" on the contentious side, having "*cornered the adjudication market.*" Clients describe the quality of work here as "*exceptional,*" with individual lawyers described as "*a delight to deal with.*" Peers "*have a lot of respect*" for the inimitable **Robert Fenwick Elliott** (see p.202), while the "*first-class*" **Julian Critchlow** (see p.201) is considered to be "*a real asset to the firm.*" **Victoria Russell** (see p.208) has proved herself to be "*a natural fit*" since her arrival from Berrymans Lace Mawer. The workload over the past year includes a steady stream of adjudications together with an increasing amount of non-contentious work, particularly in the energy and development fields. About 30% of work includes an international component. **Clients:** Contractors; insurers; financial institutions.

Herbert Smith (see firm details p.993) "*Substantial*" practice, which is respected for both its contentious and project-oriented non-contentious work. Active both domestically and overseas, the team is said to "*know its stuff, and generally hits the nail on the head.*" Head of Department **Michael Davis** (see p.202) is a "*seasoned performer and a shrewd tactician.*" Highlights of the past year include advising Government Communication Headquarters on their new building, acting for the ZRG consortium on its PFI bid to construct the Dutch High Speed Link, and representing BAT on its construction of factory installation in Turkey. On the contentious side, the team advised Bechtel on engineering disputes subject to ICC international arbitration in various parts of the world, and acted for Halliburton in a major engineering dispute in Eastern Europe. **Clients:** Astaldi; BHP; British Sugar; De La Rue; Ferrocemento Recchi; Hammerson; Kings College; Ministry of Defence; Siemens; Société Générale; Tate Gallery Projects; Vodafone; Westinghouse; Whitgift; Wiggins Gee Construction.

Linklaters (see firm details p.1042) Best known for its project-based non-contentious construction work, the firm benefits from outstanding property and finance support. The team received a massive fillip with the arrival of the "*stupendously good*" **Ann Minogue** (see p.206) from CMS Cameron McKenna, who is revered for her property-related construction work, and is thought to add "*genuine substance*" to the group. Head of department is the "*statesmanlike, charming and sensible*" **Marshall Levine** (see p.205), who recently advised the senior lenders for the £340 million Glasgow schools PPP deal, involving the construction of 12 new secondary schools and the refurbishment of 18 existing secondary schools. He also acted for the Tuberail consortium on its bid for the JNP contract. **Simon Burch** (see p.200) is a "*hard-nosed practitioner*," who is respected for his projects work. The firm advised Swiss Re on the construction of Lord Foster's 41-storey tower in EC3, and advised the BBC on its accommodation and services strategy project to outsource its property portfolio for 30 years. **Clients:** ABN AMRO; Amec; Barclays Capital; BP Amoco; BBC; Deutsche Bank; Enron; Goldman Sachs; Kajima; Lend Lease; MEPC; Merrill Lynch; Midland Bank; Reuters; SmithKline; Swis Re; University of Nottingham.

Clifford Chance (see firm details p.919) A "*large, high-profile*" outfit, noted for construction-related projects and international arbitration. The non-contentious side of the practice is felt to have "*flourished*" under the leadership of rising name **Tim Steadman** (see p.209), who is "*practical and great to deal with.*" The firm advised the project company, Modus Services, on the refurbishment of the one million square foot Ministry of Defence headquarters in Whitehall, and acted for International Power in relation to the engineering procurement and construction documentation for a \$100 million 290MW natural gas and distillate fuel oil-fired power station at Al Kamil in Oman. Other work includes a £1 billion revolving construction loan facility to enable The Canary Wharf Group to finance a number of office buildings, including a 40-storey tower pre-let to Citigroup. On the contentious side, the team acted for Eurostar (UK) on proceedings in the Technology and Construction Court in connection with defective glazing at Waterloo International Terminal. It also advised Bechtel in connection with disputes arising from the construction of an oil and gas facility and a petrochemical facility. **Clients:** ABB-Alstom; Amey; Bechtel; Bovis Lend Lease; Canary Wharf; Chase Manhattan; InterGen; John Laing; Mitsubishi; Multiplex; Post Office; Rotch Property Group; Skanska; Witkoff Group; Edison Mission Energy; Eurostar (UK); Grantchester; Siemens.

Freshfields Bruckhaus Deringer (see firm details p.964) Active on both contentious and non-contentious work, the firm is typically seen on large projects and some dispute resolution in the UK and overseas. The group is led by "*star performer*" **Sally Roe** (see p.208), who is "*so able and approachable, that she appears to have more hours in the day than anyone else.*" **Jane Jenkins** (see p.205) also continues to receive market recommendation. Recent matters include acting for Clifford Chance on its procurement of new business premises at Canary Wharf, and acting for ENEL, the Italian state-owned electricity supplier, in relation to the construction of two large wood-burning power stations in Italy. Contentious work includes advising the Arab Republic of Egypt on a pending ICSID arbitration against a British hotel management. This involved an \$80 million dispute arising from a lease, refurbishment and subsequent expropriation of two leading hotels in Egypt. **Clients:** BNFL; Scottish Widows; KEDO; HSBC Holdings; CSFB; Herzog & de Meuron; ENEL.

Lovells (see firm details p.1044) Renowned for its strong international capability, notably on the contentious side, this "*reliable*" team is led by former Masons "*guru*" **Phillip Capper** (see p.200). He is seen as the group's "*real strength,*" and has devoted much of his time to the rail industry in the past year. Specific matters include acting for two major rolling stock manufacturers in a complaint submitted to the Office of the Rail Regulator and acting on rail disputes in Spain, Portugal, Switzerland and Lithuania. Vastly experienced **Nicholas Gould** continues to have the respect of his peers as a "*heavy hitter.*" His workload this year has included advising a major Japanese trading house in disputes relating to a Saudi cement plant. The firm represented BT Management in the outsourcing of BT Facilities Management, and advised ALSTOM Automation in the BA New World Cargo Centre Case. **Clients:** ALSTOM Automation; BT Management.

LEADING INDIVIDUALS	
1	
BISHOP John Masons	**BLACKLER Tony** Macfarlanes
BUNCH Anthony Masons	**CAPPER Phillip** Lovells
MINOGUE Ann Linklaters	**RUSHTON John** Rowe & Maw
SHADBOLT Richard Shadbolt & Co	
2	
BUTCHER Trevor CMS Cameron McKenna	**CRITCHLOW Julian** Fenwick Elliott
DAVIS Michael Herbert Smith	**FENWICK ELLIOTT Robert** Fenwick Elliott
GOULD Nicholas Lovells	**HARMAN Martin** Masons
HUDSON James Nicholson Graham	**LEVINE Marshall** Linklaters
REGAN Michael Rowe & Maw	**ROE Mark** Masons
ROE Sally Freshfields Bruckhaus	**STEADMAN Tim** Clifford Chance
3	
BIRKBY Gillian Rowe & Maw	**BURCH Simon** Linklaters
CORBETT Edward Corbett & Co	**CORNES David** Winward Fearon
FLEET Terry Berwin Leighton Paisner	**GOWAN Daniel** Davies Arnold Cooper
HOSIE Jonathan Hammond Suddards	**JONES David** Hammond Suddards
REES Peter Norton Rose	**ROBERTS Martin** Masons
RUSSELL Victoria Fenwick Elliott	**WINTER Jeremy** Baker & McKenzie
4	
BRIDGEWATER Martin Norton Rose	**GIBSON Michael** Berwin Leighton Paisner
LANE Mark Masons	**LONG Peter** CMS Cameron McKenna
MOSEY David Trowers & Hamlins	**RACE David** Nicholson Graham & Jones
REEVES Suzanne Wedlake Bell	**SHAW Peter** Taylor Joynson Garrett
SHERMAN Henry CMS Cameron	**HELPS Dominic** Shadbolt & Co
5	
BOURGEOIS Christopher Taylor Joynson	**CANHAM Stephanie** Trowers & Hamlins
CUMMINS Caroline CMS Cameron	**GARTHWAITE Helen** Taylor Joynson
HOLLOWAY Julian Berwin Leighton Paisner	**WHITE Neil** Taylor Joynson Garrett
WRIGHT John Berwin Leighton Paisner	
UP AND COMING	
HANSON Marc CMS Cameron McKenna	**JENKINS Jane** Freshfields Bruckhaus
POPE Caroline Berwin Leighton Paisner	

See individuals' profiles p.199

Nicholson Graham & Jones (see firm details p.1081) Respected for its depth of "*strong senior players,*" the team is said to be "*up for a good fight*" on the contentious side, while the firm is also seen to be competing on PFI-related matters. Head of Department **David Race** (see p.207) is an ex-Blue Circle man with "*great industry experience,*" who has earned kudos for his work on the projects side of the practice. He acted for Blue Circle Industries on all contractual issues relating to the design and construction of a cement works in Kent, and advised Sharjah Cement & Industrial Development in drafting and completing a turnkey contract for the construction of a new cement works in Sharjah. "*Outstanding client man*" **James Hudson** (see p.204) is the firm's leading figure for contentious matters, and recently advised Phillips Petroleum on a claim for damages arising from alleged defective design of compression facilities on a gas platform in the North Sea. The team advised Regalian Properties on the construction aspects of the sale of Marble Arch Tower to MWB for £69 million. **Clients:** ABB Building Technologies; Allied Dunbar Assurance; Apcem Engineering; ASDA Properties; British Film Institute; Carillion Construction; Eurostar (UK); First London Estates; Heron International; HSBC; Omya UK; Thames Water Utilities; Wimpey Homes Holdings; Yanbu Cement Company.

Norton Rose (see firm details p.1082) A strong reputation for energy-related construction work and a "*quality client base*" keep the firm clearly among the front-runners in the sector. **Martin Bridgewater** (see p.200) and **Peter Rees** (see p.207) remain the most significant players at a department that advised the lead arrangers on the construction aspects of the \$1 billion debt financing of the Power Generation and Sea Water Desalination project in Abu Dhabi. Other work includes acting for Braehead on the successful defence of Bovis' Summary Judgment and Interim Payment Application. The firm advised Helical Bar on the development of new offices for Slaughter and May, and acted for Royal Bank of Scotland, Bank of America, Toronto Dominion Bank and Bayerische Landesbank on the £350 million replacement and refurbishment of London Underground's telecommunications system. **Clients:** Benchmark; Capital Shopping Centres; Helical Bar; Tate & Lyle; Kone Lifts; Mansell; Tarmac; Taylor Woodrow; ABB; Siemens; Thyssen; GMS Power; Norsk Hydro; Rolls Royce Power Ventures; Scottish Power; Compco Holdings; Nuovo Pignone.

Taylor Joynson Garrett (see firm details p.1150) Advising on both contentious and non-contentious matters, the team has featured on a variety of projects domestic work and dispute resolution cases. A raft of respected practitioners has recently been augmented by the arrival of **Helen Garthwaite** (see p.202) from Lewis Silkin. Clients recommend her for a "*communicative, responsive and astute*" manner. **Peter Shaw** is "*senior and sensible,*" and acted for MW Kellogg in connection with disputes arising from the construction of a liquefied natural gas project on Bonny Island, Nigeria. **Christopher Bourgeois** retains his share of market support, while **Neil White's** "*dynamism*" helps him to make his debut in this year's rankings. **Clients:** Metropolis Group; Buxton; ABB; MW Kellogg; Adtranz; Canada Life; MeesPierson; United Bank of Kuwait; Lidl UK; SAGE Engineering; Burford Group; Mitsubishi Heavy Industries.

Allen & Overy (see firm details p.856) Working closely with the firm's much-vaunted projects group, John Scriven and his team's reputation lies principally in infrastructure, energy and PFI deals on the international stage, typically acting for funders. These deals feature a number of telecoms projects, such as advising on the construction of a new fibre-optic network throughout the UK for Marconi and Fibreway. Energy projects have included advising the owner of a $1 billion integrated waste and power plant in the Middle East. On the contentious side, the firm acted for a sovereign state in a dispute with developers relating to the financing and construction of a major road project. **Clients:** KPNQwest; KPN; Vivendi; Schroders; Marconi; Fibreway; Edison Capital; The National Grid Company; Axone.

Ashurst Morris Crisp (see firm details p.866) A strong reputation for projects-related construction and international dispute resolution work highlights the construction practice, which is led by Chris Vigrass. The firm acted for an oil company joint venture on an $8 million dispute and mediation over contract compliance with an Asian contractor. This concerned an offshore construction project for a mooring system in Asia. Other work includes acting for Hydrocarbon Resources on its multi-million pound claim in the High Court for losses arising from design defects in an offshore platform. **Clients:** Amey; Babcock; Berkeley Group; Canary Wharf; Carillion; Docklands Light Railway; Hitachi; Marubeni; Mitsubishi; Mitsui & Co; Sumitomo; Tramtrack Croydon; United News and Media.

Denton Wilde Sapte (see firm details p.939) An "*adaptable, accessible and versatile*" department, handling a wide range of construction issues, and headed by Julian Pope. The firm draws praise from fellow practitioners and clients for its ability to provide "*constructive, practical*" solutions. The firm acted for the Home Office Immigration Service on drafting and negotiating contracts for the construction of three new immigration detention centres. It also represented the UK Government Highways Agency on the procurement procedure and novel contract terms for the high profile £130 million A303 Stonehenge Improvement Project. International matters include advising Icelandisbank in relation to a £43 million shopping centre project in Iceland, and acting for the Government of a South East Asian state in connection with the procurement of defence facilities from a UK contractor. **Clients:** Shell International; Highways Agency; Chicago Bridge International; Hutchison Whampoa; Skanska International; Project Management International.

Hammond Suddards Edge (see firm details p.984) Boasting a sizeable team, a nationwide presence and a sound reputation for non-contentious work, the London construction team is one of the jewels of the firm's crown in the capital. Peers hold head of department **David Jones** (see p.205) in "*high regard,*" while **Jonathan Hosie** (see p.204) is a "*decent, sensible operator*" on the non-contentious side. The team acted for London Underground in relation to problems arising from the Jubilee Line extension, and advised Dahl-Jensen on the first case to reach the High Court of Appeal on Construction Act adjudication. International work includes acting for shareholders in a multi-million pound restructuring of a JV project in Kuala Lumpur. **Clients:** Environment Agency; Canary Riverside; Citex; Building Information Warehouse; Tetra Pak; Wates Construction; Wilson Bowden Developments; London Underground; Ministry of Defence.

Simmons & Simmons (see firm details p.1132) An integral part of a cross-departmental projects group, Robert Bryan's team is best known for its infrastructure and PFI construction work. The firm advised the Province and the PPP Unit of the Dutch Government on the £80 million A59 Pathfinder PFI Road Contract, and acted for BP Amoco on the construction of a 400MW natural gas/liquid fuel combined cycle power facility near Dublin. Contentious matters include advising the Nationwide Building Society on multi-million pound claims against an architect and a nominated sub-contractor, as well as related remedial works issues. **Clients:** A&P Holdings; Abu Dhabi Investment Authority; Booker; Carillion; De Nationale Investerings Bank; Fitzpatrick; Flag International; Inter Ikea; Land Securities; Medway Power Station; Ministry of Defence; Railtrack; SEPI; Telewest; Symonds/Vivendi Group; Union Railways South; Viatel.

Trowers & Hamlins (see firm details p.1162) "*Developing well recently,*" the firm has enjoyed a higher profile since its release of the first Standard Form of Project Partnering Contract (PPC 2000) into the market. Head of department **David Mosey** (see p.206) retains a high profile among his peers, while **Stephanie Canham** (see p.200) is "*astute, pleasant and knows what she is talking about.*" Highlights of the past year include advising a consortium of 23 Housing Associations on a £400 million Amphion Timberframe Programme. The firm also acted on a £120 million regeneration programme for Whitefriars Housing Group, and advised the BBC on the £250 million redevelopment of White City and the £100 million redevelopment of Broadcasting House. **Clients:** Berkeley Group; BBC; Whitefriars Housing Group; University of Keele; Sir Robert McAlpine Ltd; Cyclerval; Amec Construction; Ryhurst; Castlemore; St George; London Borough of Hackney; Community Housing Association; Peabody Trust; Metropolitan Housing Trust; Amphion Consortium.

Winward Fearon (see firm details p.1186) Renowned for its contentious work both at home and overseas, this niche construction outfit is still highly respected by peers. **David Cornes** (see p.80) is "*still a name to conjure with,*" although mediation constitutes a sizeable chunk of his practice.

Baker & McKenzie (see firm details p.868) "*Serious competitors*" on the international front, the London team has been boosted by the arrival of a partner from the firm's highly rated Hong Kong project finance department. **Jeremy Winter** (see p.210) continues to receive warm commendation for his "*stellar*" international disputes practice. The firm advised a German equipment supplier on an ICC arbitration with an American engineering company, which involved a $38 million claim relating to the construction of three power plants in Latin America. It also acted for a Saudi company on the contract documentation for the $550 million, propane to polypropylene plant in Saudi Arabia. **Clients:** Autostrada Wielkopolska; Tycom.

Beale and Company (see firm details p.874) Especially highly regarded for construction-related insurance litigation work, the firm is praised by clients for its "*hands-on advice*" and "*superb personal service.*" The firm advised on matters arising from the London Millennium Bridge fiasco, and acted on a large claim against an engineer in connection with a highway in South East Asia. **Clients:** ACE; WREN; engineers.

Berrymans Lace Mawer (see firm details p.877) Despite suffering the loss of high-profile Victoria Russell to Fenwick Elliott, the firm still enjoys a solid reputation for its "*high quality*" insurance-based construction work. Significant cases include acting for Carillion in Co-op v Taylor Young Partnership and Others. Overseas, the firm acted for the design engineer in relation to a £10 million case brought by the government of Abu Dhabi for the failure of sewer pipes throughout Abu Dhabi. **Clients:** AXA Insurance; ACE Scheme; Norwich Union; Royal & Sun Alliance; Griffiths & Armour; Waterman Partnership; Whitby Bird & Partners; Maunsells.

Campbell Hooper (see firm details p.907) Newly ranked this year, the firm has added to an "*already significant*" practice with the recruitment of a three-strong in-house team from Taylor Woodrow. A well-rounded team, featuring Duncan Salmon, practises both contentious and non-contentious law, and has a strong contractor clientele. The firm advised Carillion Construction on a £200 million PFI deal to build a Light Rapid Transit System in Nottingham, and acted for Countryside Properties in relation to a subsidence claim brought by owners of a property developed by Countryside. The team also acted for Greenwich Millennium Village in relation to the £250 million scheme for 1377 new homes with community facilities on the Greenwich Peninsula. **Clients:** Countryside Properties; Carillion; Taylor Woodrow; Greenwich Millennium Village; Northacre; Crest Homes; David Wilson Homes; The Desalination Company of Trinidad and Tobago; Reading Borough Council; Cederholm & Voss Real Estate 1 BV; Geoconsult; The Conran Group.

Corbett & Co (see firm details p.925) Specialising in international contentious work, this niche team enjoys a reputation for "*quality work for high-profile clients.*" However, the group is felt to rely heavily on the skills of the "*delightful and capable*" **Ed Corbett** (see p.201), who specialises in FIDIC contracts. The firm successfully acted for Gibraltar Homes in suing Ferrovial Agroman in relation to a leaky high-rise housing estate in Gibraltar. Other work includes advising Hyundai on suing Prince Jefri of Brunei in relation to the construction of a marina in Brunei for housing his boat 'Tits'. **Clients:** Van Oord ACZ; SIETCO; Hinkins & Frewin; Hyundai; Gibraltar Homes.

Davies Arnold Cooper (see firm details p.934) Representing a range of different parties in the construction industry, the firm has noted insurance expertise and an international focus. "*Competent litigator*" **Daniel Gowan** (see p.203) has "*been around for years.*" Highlights over the past year include representing Victorian Channels Authority in an ICC Arbitration arising from a capital dredging contract in Melbourne Harbour, and advising United Utilities on insurance matters relating to a waste water project in Bangkok. **Clients:**Alfred McAlpine Construction; Balfour Beatty; John Mowlem; Walter Llewellyn & Sons; Victorian Channels Authority; John Laing; William Verry; Gibb Ltd; Independent; Royal & Sun Alliance; RJ Wallace; Allianz; Gerling.

Glovers (see firm details p.973) David Miles and his "*small but experienced*" team act for an enviable client base and have a particular reputation for dispute resolution. Recent matters include the defence of a major claim against Cardiff County Council by Dredging International in the Technology and Construction Court, and acting for Laserbore in the defence of a claim brought by The National Grid. The firm also advised Laserbore/Iseki Tunnelling Joint Venture on English arbitration matters in respect of the construction of a waste water treatment works in Bangkok. **Clients:** Sir Robert McAlpine; Abacus Developments; Hurley Robertson; Laserbore; Cardiff County Council.

Kennedys (see firm details p.1018) Another firm to be newly ranked this year, it has a burgeoning reputation for advising professionals and insurers on insurance-related construction matters. Nick Thomas and the team have also undertaken an increased number of international cases. The firm advised Allianz Cornhill and others as a consequence of a £9 million flood in railway tunnels, represented the insurers on a £35 million tunnel collapse case, and advised Railtrack on resolution of disputes concerning sums payable under major infrastructure contracts. **Clients:** Balfour Beatty; Alfred McAlpine; Royal and Sun Alliance Engineering; John Laing; Tarmac; Costain; Taylor Woodrow; Allianz; ABB; ACE Europe; Zurich; AIG; Gerling; ERC Frankona; Sampo; Limit; Admiral; Railtrack.

Macfarlanes (see firm details p.1046) Said to be "*reaping the rewards*" of its gradual growth policy, the firm boasts a number of heavyweight property development clients and is no longer felt to depend solely on the presence of the outstanding **Tony Blackler** (see p.200). He remains a hugely influential figure, and is described by rivals as a "*first-class man with great connections.*" The firm advised West End Quay Ltd, a joint venture between Rialto Homes, ING and Wates Construction, on the contract for the multi-million pound development of the Paddington Basin. Other work includes advising SPP Projects on a £16 million contract dispute against a contractor and sub-contractor, involving contract issues, bonds and insolvency procedures. **Clients:** Abbey Life; Associated British Ports; Akeler Developments; Allders; Edwards Project Management; Kohn Pedersen Fox; Michael Aukett Architects; P&O Developments; Gleeds; Huf Haus; Kier Construction; Universal Music; WS Atkins; Zaha Hadid.

SJ Berwin (see firm details p.879) A solid team, benefiting from the firm's excellent property capacity, which remains recognised by peers and clients. Significant matters of the past year include advising Broadgate Plaza on a successful 28-day adjudication and counterclaim against Miller Civil Engineering. It also acted for Delancey Estates on the acquisition and development of 1 New Fetter Lane, and advised Axa Sun Life on the construction aspects of the renovation of an old telephone exchange into a new headquarters building. **Clients:** Abbey Legal Protection; Axa Sun Life; Bouygues (UK); The British Land Company; Eve Group; Grant Thornton; Ladbroke Group; Marks & Spencer; Mowlem Southern Civil; National Audit Office; Pilkingto; Pinaci; Royal Academy of Music; Safestore; Urban Catalyst; Waterbridge Property Ventures.

Wedlake Bell (see firm details p.1175) A "*compact*" team doing both contentious and non-contentious work, which is felt to owe much to the presence of the "*experienced and pleasant*" **Suzanne Reeves** (see p.207). The firm represented Stent Foundation on a contentious matter, advised Fairbriar Homes in relation to documentation for various development projects and has provided contract advice for NSCC. **Clients:** Stent Foundation; Fairbriar Homes; Dairy Crest; Watts & Partners; NSCC; Scott Wilson.

THE SOUTH

CONSTRUCTION • The South	Ptnrs	Assts
1 **Shadbolt & Co** Reigate	14	16
2 **Cripps Harries Hall** Tunbridge Wells	2	1
3 **Blake Lapthorn** Portsmouth	2	4

LEADING INDIVIDUALS
1 **RYLAND Jane** Cripps Harries Hall

This book is the product of 6,552 1/2-hour interviews. See p.7 for BMRB audit.

Within each band, firms are listed alphabetically. *See individuals' profiles p.199*

Shadbolt & Co (see firm details p.1121) See London editorial.

Cripps Harries Hall (see firm details p.927) The arrival of **Jane Ryland** (see p.208) from Laytons as head of construction has bolstered the firm. Its expertise includes dispute resolution, contract conditions and collateral warranties. The firm acted for the developers of a £100 million major national sports stadium in Denmark. **Clients:** Persimmon Homes (South East); Berkeley Homes (Eastern); Wates Group.

Blake Lapthorn (see firm details p.886) Active for a mix of employers and contractors, sub-contractors, funds and consultants. Under the guidance of Peter Barber, the team handles adjudications, arbitrations and developments. Advised on the construction of several international submarine cable system supply and installation projects. Also endorsed for its strong contentious offering. **Clients:** Hampshire Wildlife Trust; Alcatel; Local Authorities.

THAMES VALLEY

CONSTRUCTION • Thames Valley	Ptnrs	Assts
1 **Clarks** Reading	1	2
Linnells Oxford	1	1
Morgan Cole Oxford	1	2

This book is the product of 6,552 1/2-hour interviews. See p.7 for BMRB audit.
Within each band, firms are listed alphabetically. *See individuals' profiles p.199*

Clarks (see firm details p.916) The team fields David Rintoul, an adjudicator who belongs to a team that "*gets the job done.*" The unit sits within the commercial litigation department and is engaged in contentious and non-contentious matters acting for contractors, sub-contractors and employers. Has handled a number of adjudications, bringing and defending claims for sub-contractors. Acted for a trust in successfully defending an adjudication claim of £1million. **Clients:** NHS Trusts; BOC; Thames Water.

Linnells (see firm details p.1043) Supporting the firm's large property client base, the department has been busy with party wall work, ADR, adjudications and mediations. Jonathan Lloyd-Jones heads a team which undertakes disputes for developer and contractor clients, including suppliers of high technology equipment with installation disputes. Highlights include acting on a construction case for suppliers of thermaplastics for roofing systems. **Clients:** Berkeley Homes (Oxford & Chiltern); JB Leadbitter & Co; Hinkins & Frewin.

Morgan Cole (see firm details p.1074) A practice balanced in its contentious and non-contentious workload. Its client base is much broader than its noted public sector relationships and includes not only NHS Trusts but also developers, occupiers, consultants, contractors and employers. Andrew Campbell leads a team that has experience in partnering and framework agreements for consultants as well as major arbitrations and adjudications. **Clients:** Amey; Oxford Brookes University; Bickerton.

SOUTH WEST

CONSTRUCTION • South West	Ptnrs	Assts
1 **Masons** Bristol	4	8
2 **Bevan Ashford** Bristol, Exeter	3	3
3 **Beachcroft Wansbroughs** Bristol	1	4
Laytons Bristol	2	3
4 **Burges Salmon** Bristol	1	5
Osborne Clarke Bristol	3	7
5 **Bond Pearce** Plymouth	1	2
Veale Wasbrough Bristol	1	4

LEADING INDIVIDUALS	
1 **COLLINGWOOD Mark** Masons	**HARLING Marcus** Burges Salmon
HARRIS Adam Masons	**REDMOND John** Osborne Clarke
2 **GUPPY Nicholas** Laytons	**HOWE Martin** Bevan Ashford
VASEY John Beachcroft Wansbroughs	
3 **HOYLE Roger** Veale Wasbrough	
4 **BIRCH John** Bevan Ashford	
UP AND COMING	
HANLEY Christine Bond Pearce	

This book is the product of 6,552 1/2-hour interviews. See p.7 for BMRB audit.
Within each band, firms are listed alphabetically. *See individuals' profiles p.199*

Masons (see firm details p.1056) "*Way out in front of the market.*" Operating as part of a national department, peers acknowledge that "*all the guys are talented.*" **Mark Collingwood** (see p.201) elicited heavy endorsement while **Adam Harris** (see p.203) is adjudged "*extremely competent.*" Richard Foley has relocated to Hong Kong. Highlights include acting for a contractor in claims of £80 million concerning the design and construction of a government headquarters. The caseload leans towards contractors on contentious matters, and the firm also acts for developers, employers and sub-contractors. **Clients:** Carillion Construction; Lorne Stewart; University of Bath.

Bevan Ashford (see firm details p.880) A group that has witnessed impressive growth and elicited national commendation. Praised by clients for adopting a "*practical approach,*" the team fields a "*fine performer*" in **Martin Howe** (see p.204) while **John Birch** (see p.199) was also recommended. The Exeter and Bristol offices compliment each others' strengths. Highlights include a £40 million waste energy incinerator project, and providing contract and frameworks on behalf of NHS Estates for publicly financed capital schemes. **Clients:** Lorne Stewart; Bovis Lend Lease; Isle of Man Department of Local Government.

Beachcroft Wansbroughs (see firm details p.872) "*Consistently proves himself capable of handling just about anything,*" is the verdict of one competitor on team leader **John Vasey** (see p.209). Best known as acting for insurance companies on professional indemnity matters, the firm also undertakes construction litigation for non-insurance clients, and non-contentious work for the property team. Recently appointed to the ACE scheme. **Clients:** Railtrack; Jarvis; Chase de Vere.

Laytons (see firm details p.1031) Successfully maintaining its strong following among contractor clients, this is "*a firm that knows what's what – it has a long history of dealing with construction issues.*" Both rivals and clients appreciate the commitment and focus of **Nick Guppy** (see p.203). The firm handled the construction of a new postal sorting office and a transport depot. **Clients:** London Underground; Cowlin Construction; Staveley Industries.

Burges Salmon (see firm details p.902) In a group acclaimed for its talented, commercial lawyers, **Marcus Harling** (see p.203) is the standout practitioner. "*Strong on the non-contentious front*" the firm is also rated in particular for its work in the public sector. Clients range from public authorities, developers and end-users of building and engineering services, to consultants and contractors. Acted on a £95 million Millennium Commission funded project and in the construction of a multi-million pound state of the art processing plant for United Milk plc. **Clients:** Bristol International Airport; First Group; London Fire and Emergency Planning Authority.

Osborne Clarke (see firm details p.1086) The "*well respected*" department has consolidated its position since the arrival of **John Redmond** at the helm last year. "*A good front man with a sound reputation,*" he has "*brought in good lawyers and encouraged some fine client wins.*" Highlights include advice on all the contractual aspects of Dublin Port Tunnel and involvement in a multi-million pound adjudication for a developer. **Clients:** Transco; RJB (Mining); Somerfield.

Bond Pearce (see firm details p.888) The "*competent and sensible*" **Christine Hanley** (see p.203) leads the growing profile of the team. Endorsed as an active force in the regional market, the firm has acted on a number of adjudications, and defended a £2.5 million arbitration claim. One recent highlight is the instructions from the Theatre Royal (Plymouth) concerning its new production and education centre. **Clients:** Rockeagle Land; Plymouth and South West Co-operative Society; National Marine Aquarium.

Veale Wasbrough (see firm details p.1167) "*Tremendously detailed and conscientious*," **Roger Hoyle** (see p.204) remains key to much of the firm's profile in this area. The whole team is applauded as "*skilled at the mechanics of a deal*." The firm acts for employers, contractors and professionals with a noted expertise in professional negligence cases. Advised on the Bath Spa Millenium Project, and represented contractors and sub-contractors in adjudication proceedings. **Clients:** BNFL; Parsons Brickerhoff; Jordan Engineering.

WALES

CONSTRUCTION • Wales	Ptnrs	Assts
1 **Morgan Cole** Cardiff, Swansea	1	7
2 **Eversheds** Cardiff	2	3
Hugh James Ford Simey Cardiff	2	1

LEADING INDIVIDUALS
1 **HERBERT Mary** Eversheds
2 **NEWMAN Paul** Hugh James Ford Simey

This book is the product of 6,552 1/2-hour interviews. See p.7 for BMRB audit.
Within each band, firms are listed alphabetically. *See individuals' profiles p.199*

Morgan Cole (see firm details p.1074) The leading light in the Welsh market due to its enviable client base and a raft of "*impressive*" lawyers. "*Good sensible litigators*" undertake a range of cases from adjudications to housing and insurance matters. The department acts for developers and employers. One non-contentious highlight for the firm is the establishment of a European freight rail terminal near Cardiff for the Welsh Development Agency. **Clients:** Welsh Development Agency; Amey; Bank of Wales.

Eversheds (see firm details p.952) **Mary Herbert** (see p.204) is endorsed by peers for her committed focus in cultivating a depth of resource within the team and establishing it as a force in the sector. The group completed the Neath waste-to-energy scheme in 2000, and carried out two adjudications, both in excess of £2 million. Clients commend Herbert; "*we received a quality result because we used a quality lawyer*." **Clients:** Tarmac; Sir Robert McAlpine; National Assembly of Wales.

Hugh James Ford Simey (see firm details p.1004) Recent highlights include advice on the construction of a new post office sorting facility and large-scale adjudications and arbitrations. Standout practitioner **Paul Newman** (see p.206) "*can be relied upon to get things going*." A non-practising barrister, he brings an envied depth of knowledge to the team. The firm handles claims for its "*gloriously mixed*" client base. **Clients:** Hyder; WRU (Millennium Stadium); contractors.

MIDLANDS

CONSTRUCTION • Midlands	Ptnrs	Assts
1 **Wragge & Co** Birmingham	9	22
2 **Hammond Suddards Edge** Birmingham	4	4
3 **Gateley Wareing** Birmingham	2	7
4 **Freethcartwright** Nottingham	4	3
5 **DLA** Birmingham	n/a	n/a
Eversheds Birmingham, Derby, Nottingham	3	10
Lee Crowder Birmingham	2	5
Merricks Birmingham	2	4
Pinsent Curtis Biddle Birmingham	1	3
6 **Browne Jacobson** Nottingham	2	4
Garretts Birmingham	1	2
Shoosmiths Northampton	1	2

LEADING INDIVIDUALS	
1 **BAYLIS Simon** Wragge & Co	**LLOYD JONES David** Hammond Suddards
2 **BARRETT Kevin** Wragge & Co	**BRADLEY Graeme** DLA
BROWN Jeffrey Lee Crowder	**DAVIES Peter** Gateley Wareing
3 **PIGOTT Ashley** Wragge & Co	**WILCOCK Christopher** Hammond Suddards
YULE Ian Wragge & Co	
ONES TO WATCH	
GREEN Richard Wragge & Co	

This book is the product of 6,552 1/2-hour interviews. See p.7 for BMRB audit.
Within each band, firms are listed alphabetically. *See individuals' profiles p.199*

Wragge & Co (see firm details p.1189) Universally praised as "*a robust team*" that can be relied upon "*to give sensible and pragmatic advice*." The merger with specialist construction outfit Neil F Jones has produced a rounded practice, who act for contractors, developers and utility clients. Led by **Simon Baylis** who "*deserves every accolade*," the team has gone from strength to strength. **Ian Yule** is "*steady, efficient – he doesn't mess around*," while **Kevin Barrett** is a technically accomplished lawyer who brings a "*practical*" approach to the deal table. Clients endorsed **Ashley Pigott** "*he comes across well to specialists and speaks their language*." This display of talent is thought to extend to its younger members, who have developed "*a real eye for detail*." The firm acted on the Balfour Beatty AMEC (Jubilee) joint venture in connection with the Waterloo to Westminster section of the Jubilee Line extension, and advised on the contracts and sub contracts for the Birmingham Northern Relief Road. **Clients:** AMEC; Miller Group; Carillion.

Hammond Suddards Edge (see firm details p.984) The "*clever and respected*" **David Lloyd Jones** (see p.205) is acclaimed as "*the best non-contentious lawyer outside London – I like his style*." **Christopher Wilcock** (see p.209) continues to elicit strong commendation from the market. The firm enjoys a respected developer client base. It handled the construction issues surrounding the building of a new stadium for Leicester City Football Club and advised Aston Villa Football Club on the Trinity Road Stand. On contentious matters, the firm secured judgement in a dispute regarding 41 trains. Continues to draw recommendation for its work on M&E/process engineering litigation. **Clients:** Wates Construction; Galliford Try; Shimizu Europe.

Gateley Wareing (see firm details p.969) "*Ones to watch*," the firm's strength lies in its house builder client base. Also engaged in a heavy workload for developers, contractors, and sub-contractors, contentious matters dominate the firm's output. **Peter Davies** remains the standout practitioner. Adjudications and mediations have flooded in over the past 12 months. **Clients:** Wimpey; Alfred McAlpine; Wrekin.

Freethcartwright (see firm details p.964) The firm has focused on delivering a "*huge boost on contentious construction matters*," successful in part due to the arrival of Chris Hollwell. The team has a heavy client base of developers and also acts for employers, contractors and consultants. Highlights include instructions on a multi-million pound distribution facility, and advice on the reclamation and redevelopment of a 22 acre landfill site for onward development. **Clients:** Mansell Construction Services; Brydon Developments; Monk Estates.

DLA **Graeme Bradley** heads the department, which is best known for its local re-development work.

Eversheds (see firm details p.952) Endorsed by clients as "*helpful, responsive and a calming influence in any complex deal.*" Its powerful development and contractor client base provides the quality instructions which secure the firm its profile. Highlights include acting on the acquisition of a Cable Liner Shuttle from Birmingham International Railway Station to the airport terminal. Instructed on a number of town centre redevelopments. The firm's contentious highlights include advising on the first successful challenge to the enforcement of an adjudicator's award. **Clients:** AMEC; Birmingham Mailbox.

Lee Crowder (see firm details p.1035) A growing department moving out of the shadows of its Neil F Jones connections. "*An impressive bunch*" handles contentious and non-contentious matters for main and sub-contractors, employers, funding institutions and local authorities. **Jeffrey Brown** (see p.200) is perceived to have strengthened the group which has displayed expertise in dispute resolution and the defence of professional negligence claims for underwriters.

Merricks (see firm details p.1065) Led by Philip Harris, the firm is agreed to have developed "*a name in construction,*" handling adjudications, mediations, disputes and partnering facilitation for employers, contractors and sub-contractors. Said by clients to provide "*a good personal service*." Focusing on the water industry, the group acted on the Hopwas Canal Project. One further highlight was its involvement in a PFI project for the construction of nine new Birmingham Schools. **Clients:** Lorne Stewart; Adonis Construction; University of Birmingham.

Pinsent Curtis Biddle (see firm details p.1098) Nick Goddard is the figurehead at this firm, which has consolidated its position. The team has experience in advising funding institutions in relation to PFI projects, encouraging instructions from developers, contractors and facility managers. Also undertakes adjudications. Contentious highlights include the case of ABB Power Construction v Norwest Holst Engineering. **Clients:** ABB Construction; Stannifer Developments.

Browne Jacobson (see firm details p.898) The team has proved its worth with its following of construction and professional indemnity insurers. Heavily involved in risk management and dispute work, highlights of the year include acting for contractors in the negotiation of contracts for the construction of a food processing factory, and advising professional indemnity insurers of an architect on a claim for £2.5 million. **Clients:** Wheatley Construction; The Clegg Group; Shepherd Construction.

Garretts (see firm details p.968) Led by Raymond Joyce, the group undertakes PFI construction matters, arbitrations, and office and retail developments. Significant instructions over the last year include acting on the construction of a new UK head office and national distribution centre valued at £30 million. **Clients:** Galliford Try; Lyreco UK; Finning.

Shoosmiths (see firm details p.1129) Led by Christopher Cox and servicing the property client base of the firm, the department is strongly developer-led. Dealing with mediation, adjudication, arbitration and non-contentious matters, highlights include acting on behalf of a main contractor against its sub-contractor under the Partnering Scheme with the Highways Agency. **Clients:** Developers; home-builders.

EAST ANGLIA

CONSTRUCTION • East Anglia	Ptnrs	Assts
1 **Mills & Reeve** Cambridge	3	6
2 **Eversheds** Cambridge Ipswich, Norwich	1	4
Hewitson Becke + Shaw Cambridge	2	2
3 **Greenwoods** Peterborough	1	3

LEADING INDIVIDUALS	
1 **PICKUP Raith** Mills & Reeve	**PLASCOW Ronald** Mills & Reeve
2 **OATS Simon** Eversheds	**WOOD Martin** Greenwoods

This book is the product of 6,552 1/2-hour interviews. See p.7 for BMRB audit.
Within each band, firms are listed alphabetically. *See individuals' profiles p.199*

Mills & Reeve (see firm details p.1069) Enjoying a "*strong reputation,*" the firm acts for a number of Cambridge Colleges and Universities. Here **Ron Plascow** (see p.207) is praised as "*dominant on non-contentious matters – he is the leading person in the area,*" while PFI specialist **Raith Pickup** (see p.207) is "*commercial and deal driven.*" The group has been instructed on a number of lottery-funded projects as well as conducting contentious matters; recent cases include Harbour and General Works v Environment Agency. Acts for contractors, employers and consultants. **Clients:** Colleges and Universities.

Eversheds (see firm details p.592) Bolstered by the addition of Adrian Cole (from Campbell Hooper), the team has expanded and re-structured. Spread across three offices, much of the work is sourced on a national basis. Ipswich based **Simon Oats** (see p.206) continues to elicit commendation, clients praised his plain language: "*we feel comfortable with his advice.*" Highlights for the team include acting on a PFI project for the provision of serviced office accommodation at a value of £15 million. **Clients:** Jackson Group; TXV Europe; Wilcon Homes.

Hewitson Becke + Shaw (see firm details p.994) Rated by the market for its work on a West Cambridge site, including the Microsoft Research Building, and on the S&N retail headquarters. Tim Richards' group is also busy with contentious matters. The firm acts for a range of employers, contractors, specialist sub-contractors and professionals. **Clients:** Turnstone Estates; VKR Holdings A/S (formerly VELUX).

Greenwoods (see firm details p.978) Successfully consolidated, this team is perceived to have re-established its presence in the market. Acting for a mix of employers and contractors, the department, led by the "*knowledgeable*" **Martin Wood**, has been busy with adjudications and arbitrations. Highlights of the year include involvement in the Millennium Project in Norwich. **Clients:** RG Carter Holdings; RMC Group Services.

NORTH WEST

Masons (see firm details p.1056) "*Able and robust,*" this team is packed with "*tough opponents.*" Considered one of the star offices in a respected national network with its envied following of contractor clients. **Huw Baker** (see p.199) is a "*dominant personality*" within the group who epitomises Masons' powerful style. "*Talented*" **Peter Wood** (see p.210) and **Edward Davies** (see p.202) ("*there is no doubt as to his pre-eminence*") also elicited warm commendations. Successfully represented Alfred McAlpine Construction in a decision of the House of Lords on recovery of damages. Also instructed by a national contractor on disputes to the value of £50 million relating to the design, management and construction of a £300 million shopping centre. **Clients:** Alfred McAlpine Group; Bovis Lend Lease; Carillion Group.

Hammond Suddards Edge (see firm details p.984) "*Worthy opponents,*" the firm is particularly rated for its contentious workload. Led by the "*typically robust litigator*" **David Moss** (see p.206), it is valued as "*a good operation producing quality work.*" With a strong employer bias, the firm has seen

CONSTRUCTION • North West	Ptnrs	Assts
1 **Masons** Manchester	6	23
2 **Hammond Suddards Edge** Manchester	3	15
3 **Kirk Jackson** Manchester	2	n/a
4 **Addleshaw Booth & Co** Manchester	1	5
DLA Liverpool, Manchester	n/a	n/a
Halliwell Landau Manchester	4	6
Hill Dickinson Liverpool	2	2
5 **Elliotts** Manchester	3	3
Pannone & Partners Manchester	3	3

LEADING INDIVIDUALS	
1 **DAVIES Edward** Masons	**WOOD Peter** Masons
2 **MOSS David** Hammond Suddards Edge	
3 **BAKER Huw** Masons	**CHINN David** Hill Dickinson
PINSENT Jim DLA	**ROUT Peter** DLA
SALMON Kenneth Kirk Jackson	

This book is the product of 6,552 1/2-hour interviews. See p.7 for BMRB audit.
Within each band, firms are listed alphabetically. *See individuals' profiles p.199*

growth in PFI schemes acting for the public and private sectors and including success in the field of power. The firm is also acting on a number of substantial contentious matters for Manchester Airport, Manchester City Council and BNFL. **Clients:** AMEC; BNFL; Birse Construction.

Kirk Jackson Heading the team, **Ken Salmon** (see p.208) is "*a good chap who knows his stuff – extremely practical.*" Peers agree that in opposing him "*you have to be on your toes.*" The bulk of the firm's workload lies in contentious matters for contractors including adjudications, enforcement and arbitrations. It is witnessing a growth in pre-contract advice, while a fine roster of suppliers and insurers rounds out its client base. **Clients:** Mainly contractors; employers.

Addleshaw Booth & Co (see firm details p.853) "*Its strength lies on the non-contentious side.*" Nancy McGuire's team has acted on construction documentation for office and industrial developments. Recent highlights for the firm include the development of a new Asda WalMart at Sportcity in Manchester. The team also deals with contentious matters, led by Paul Donnelly. Clients said "*they will put their neck on the line for you – they give good commercial advice and have done some cracking stuff in a short space of time.*" **Clients:** AMEC Developments; Birchwood Park Estates; North West Development Agency.

DLA Jim Pinsent is the best-known figure at a team which acted on the construction of Manchester's first five star hotel.

Halliwell Landau (see firm details p.982) Applauded by clients for its work under performance bonds and surety work ("*if they weren't excellent, we would not use them*"), while rivals acknowledge that "*they certainly fight their client's corner.*" Respected for its project related construction work, the firm is also heavily engaged in insurance-related litigation. The firm is also licensed by the nuclear installation inspectorate. Acted in connection with a performance bond of £102 million. **Clients:** NUKEM Nuclear; AIG Europe (UK).

Hill Dickinson (see firm details p.996) On the contentious side, the firm fields the "*positive and commercial*" **David Chinn** (see p.201), "*he will look to see what the issues are and focuses on them constructively.*" Servicing a client base that ranges from public authorities to subcontractors. Highlights include drafting and advising on the construction of a multi-million pound concrete plant and on the remediation contract of a brownfield site. **Clients:** DJ Construction; Metropolitan Borough of Wirrall; AIG Consultants.

Elliotts (see firm details p.950) Headed by Michael Woolley, the group is thought to be "*often aggressive but always straight in its approach.*" Reputed for its work in the commercial insurance sector, the firm acts for insurers, contractors and employers. It represented Henry Boot in the Henry Boot Construction (UK) v Malmaison Hotel (Manchester) dispute. **Clients:** Birse; Henry Boot; Norwest Holst.

Pannone & Partners (see firm details p.1088) Gareth Jessop leads a team which is presently involved in Phase 3 of the Metrolink Tram system on behalf of the Greater Manchester Passenger Transport Executive. The group has also advised one of its respected developer client base on the construction of office developments and a football stadium. Niche strengths lie in the light rail industry, infrastructure projects and public sector. **Clients:** Public sector clients.

YORKSHIRE

CONSTRUCTION • Yorkshire	Ptnrs	Assts
1 **Addleshaw Booth & Co** Leeds	2	3
Hammond Suddards Edge Leeds	3	12
2 **Masons** Leeds	2	12
3 **Walker Morris** Leeds	3	4
4 **DLA** Leeds, Sheffield	n/a	n/a
Nabarro Nathanson Sheffield	1	4
Pinsent Curtis Biddle Leeds	2	3
5 **Eversheds** Leeds	3	7
Irwin Mitchell Leeds	1	2

This book is the product of 6,552 1/2-hour interviews. See p.7 for BMRB audit.
Within each band, firms are listed alphabetically.

Addleshaw Booth & Co (see firm details p.853) Highly respected in Leeds for its non-contentious work (*"there is no doubt they are absolutely superb"*), the group is led by the "*technically strong*" **Richard Cockram** (see p.201). Rated for its development finance work, and active in large scale projects, the firm also has strength in professional indemnity matters arising from construction projects. **Jane Stubbs** (see p.209)continues to grow her profile in this market. Highlights for the group include acting on a £130 million programme to restructure a portfolio of 120 primary and secondary schools. **Clients:** Halifax; Stadium Group; Met Office.

Hammond Suddards Edge (see firm details p.984) Boasting the "*first rate strategic thinker,*" **Simon Palmer** (see p.206) and the "*reputable*" **Mark Hilton** (see p.204), the team is heavily endorsed for its contentious work. Peers agree, "*its lawyers are aggressive when they have to be, but more often than not co-operative.*" It is judged to have focused its efforts on building on the foundations of a powerful litigation department. Contractors feature heavily on the client roster alongside a strong employer base. The firm has displayed strength in electrical and engineering disputes, and acts for Mitsubishi in relation to a substantial dispute in Singapore. It acted for Whites Properties on a £15 million contract claim. **Clients:** Whites Properties; Birse Construction; AMEC.

Masons (see firm details p.1056) Respected across the region, its lawyers are acclaimed as "*all of a high calibre and focused.*" **Keith Hartley** (see p.203) provides an "*excellent strategic overview*" and operates with a "*consistently commercial approach.*" The firm acted on the re-roofing of Leeds railway station and dealt with a dispute concerning a £2 million loss and expense claim. It is currently advising on local disputes with a combined value in excess of £60 million. **Clients:** AMEC Process & Energy; Galliford Northern; Roberts Construction.

LEADING INDIVIDUALS	
1	
BENTLEY Bruce DLA	
2	
COCKRAM Richard Addleshaw Booth	**HILTON Mark** Hammond Suddards Edge
PALMER Simon Hammond Suddards	**ROBSON Nigel** Eversheds
3	
HARTLEY Keith Masons	**SCOTT Martin** Walker Morris
STANIFORTH Alison Eversheds	
UP AND COMING	
STUBBS Jane Addleshaw Booth & Co	

This book is the product of 6,552 1/2-hour interviews. See p.7 for BMRB audit.
Within each band, firms are listed alphabetically. *See individuals' profiles p.199*

Walker Morris (see firm details p.1171) "*Undoubtedly a presence.*" **Martin Scott** (see p.208) remains the key player at this expanding firm. The group is instructed by employers and banks on contentious and non-contentious matters. It was involved in the Kenburgh Investments (Northern) Ltd v David Yablon Minton & Others dispute and advised a multi-national conglomerate in the relocation of its pharmaceutical plant to a brownfield site. **Clients:** Dew Pitchmastic; Medlock Group; MAG Hansen.

DLA The department's reputation rests on **Bruce Bentley**. It has acted on various re-developments, and drafted a number of construction agreements.

Nabarro Nathanson (see firm details p.1078) Praised by clients as "*proactive,*" Mark Rocca and the team act for both developers and contractors. The firm scores well with its projects work such as its involvement in a processing plant in Egypt. On the PFI front, the group has advised on schools and accommodation schemes including Sheffield Grouped Schools and Humberside Magistrates Court. Advised the Coal Authority on extensive ground remediation works. **Clients:** RJB Mining; Ballast; Wates Construction.

Pinsent Curtis Biddle (see firm details p.1098) Building on the foundations of a strong PFI practice, the firm is also noted for its contentious caseload. Led by Jonathan Hawkswell and renowned for arbitration, conciliation and adjudication work, peers endorse the team as packed with "*good operators who are easy to deal with.*" Enjoys a substantial base of employer clients, while recent highlights include acting on the Kirklees school project. **Clients:** ABB Power Construction; Stannifer Developments; Carillion.

Eversheds (see firm details p.952) Thought to be "*solid and strengthening*" since the arrival of the "*leading light*" **Nigel Robson** (see p.208). The outflow of personnel to other firms has eased and the department is now run between the Leeds and Manchester offices. Acts for main contractors and developers on PFI support and other non-contentious and contentious matters, including a large number of adjudications. Bolstered by the presence of **Alison Staniforth** (see p.209), highlights include the development of a third generation mobile phone network. **Clients:** NG Bailey; Mill Group; Yorkshire Electricity.

Irwin Mitchell (see firm details p.1009) Bolstered by the addition of a team from Berrymans, the construction unit deals with contentious and non-contentious matters for employers, contractors, specialist sub-contractors and funders. Dealing with arbitrations and adjudications, town centre developments and PFIs also feature for this growing department. **Clients:** Employers; contractors; funders.

NORTH EAST

CONSTRUCTION • North East	Ptnrs	Assts
1		
Dickinson Dees Newcastle upon Tyne	2	7
Eversheds Newcastle upon Tyne	3	7
2		
Watson Burton Newcastle upon Tyne	5	6

LEADING INDIVIDUALS	
1	
LANGLEY Robert Watson Burton	**LEWIS Simon** Dickinson Dees
WRIGHTON Ralph Eversheds	
2	
GORDON Roderick Watson Burton	**ROWLAND Simon** Dickinson Dees
UP AND COMING	
HENDERSON Nick Dickinson Dees	

This book is the product of 6,552 1/2-hour interviews. See p.7 for BMRB audit.
Within each band, firms are listed alphabetically. *See individuals' profiles p.199*

Dickinson Dees (see firm details p.941) The depth in this "*first class*" firm has been bolstered by the addition of "*super*" **Simon Rowland** from Watson Burton. He joins the "*sensible, practical and hard-working*" **Nick Henderson** (see p.204). The "*focused*" **Simon Lewis** (see p.205) provides the firm with much of its high profile, his drive having secured an envied client base. Engaged in PFI matters, property development spin-off work, energy and professional negligence work. Highlights include activities on the £1.5 billion infrastructure project of the South Central Railway network. **Clients:** Focus; Miller; Robertsons.

Eversheds (see firm details p.952) "*Practical and personable*" **Ralph Wrighton** (see p.210) remains the office's best known practitioner; "*unassuming, you can't pull the wool over his eyes.*" Unanimously endorsed, he is perceived as one of the region's leading litigators. The team receives a regular flow of instructions from its envied client base of employers, main contractors and some sub-contractors. The department has been busy in the public sector and an impressive engineering strength continues to push through quality work. Currently advising on a multi-million pound mediation. **Clients:** AMEC; Lorne Stewart; Northumbrian Water.

Watson Burton The highly visible **Rob Langley** has secured a fine reputation for the firm on the contentious side, as peers applaud him as "*quite a character.*" "*Only aggressive when he needs to be,*" Langley has set the direction and style of the firm: "*they like a challenge.*" The unit has also expanded with the addition of **Roddy Gordon** (see p.203) from Robert Muckle. It enjoys a deep well of developer clients with support from some employers and contractors. Currently busy with major disputes and adjudications. **Clients:** Bellway; Bowey Group; Carillion.

SCOTLAND

MacRoberts (see firm details p.1048) Led by the universally respected **Lindy Patterson** (see p.206) ("*her profile is untouchable*"). Thought to fight her client's corner with gusto, interviewees claim, "*if I were a contractor with a juicy dispute, she is the only person I would go to.*" "*Hard to knock*" a team that has such "*a strong pedigree.*" **Craig Turnbull** (see p.209) "*speaks well, knows the law, and clients like him*" while **Neil Kelly** (see p.205) is "*an easy chap to deal with, he will not take unnecessary risks.*" The group is currently involved in two judicial review actions in connection with a trunk road repair and the maintenance contracts put to tender for all trunk roads in Scotland. It has also advised on contracts for Eurocentral Mossend and Tay Rail Bridge. **Clients:** Ballast; Kvaerner Oil and Gas; Laing.

Masons (see firm details p.1056) **Alastair Morrison** (see p.206) and **Vincent Connor** (see p.201) are judged to be "*a good combination, approachable, personable and down to earth.*" Well established and respected individuals before Masons entered the Scottish market, this successful pairing is judged to have "*achieved an awful lot*" in creating "*an effective, efficient operation.*" Recent significant instructions include advising the National Museum of Scotland on the construction of the Museum of Scot-

CONSTRUCTION • Scotland	Ptnrs	Assts
1 **MacRoberts** Edinburgh, Glasgow	7	18
Masons Edinburgh, Glasgow	3	13
2 **McGrigor Donald** Edinburgh, Glasgow	3	9
3 **Dundas & Wilson CS** Edinburgh	3	9
Shepherd & Wedderburn WS Edinburgh	3	4
4 **Maclay Murray & Spens** Glasgow	2	11
5 **Biggart Baillie** Glasgow	3	3
Burness Edinburgh, Glasgow	1	4
Ledingham Chalmers Aberdeen	2	1
Morison Bishop Glasgow	2	4

LEADING INDIVIDUALS	
1 **CONNOR Vincent** Masons	**MORRISON Alastair** Masons
NOLAN Brandon McGrigor Donald	**PATTERSON Lindy** MacRoberts
2 **KELLY Neil** MacRoberts	**McLEAN Alistair** Dundas & Wilson CS
SHAW Murray Biggart Baillie	**WELSH John** Morison Bishop
3 **MASON Fenella** DLA	**TURNBULL Craig** MacRoberts
UP AND COMING	
TAYLOR Kevin Shepherd & Wedderburn WS	

This book is the product of 6,552 1/2-hour interviews. See p.7 for BMRB audit.
Within each band, firms are listed alphabetically. *See individuals' profiles p.199*

tish Country Life, conducting over 50 adjudications, and advising on a dispute from the development of the Braehead Shopping Centre. **Clients:** Ballast; Melville Dundas; Ondeo Degremont.

McGrigor Donald (see firm details p.1062) Led by the "*cerebral*" and "*personable*" **Brandon Nolan** (see p.206) *("he is intimidating in that he is on a different level from everyone else intellectually")*. The firm is rated for its "*excellent practice through and through,*" attracting commendation in construction procurement, projects and energy work. Much of its non-contentious work stems from the high quality property department. Acting for blue chip contractors and developers, its key highlights include acting for the tenant and developer on a new call centre facility in Dundee, and instructions on a multi-million pound professional negligence action. **Clients:** Sir Robert McAlpine; Morrison Developments; Kvaerner Construction.

Dundas & Wilson CS (see firm details p.947) "*Well known and respected,*" **Alistair McLean** is valued by peers and clients alike; "*you can sit down with him and get a deal done.*" Although considered a low key participant in the market, its specialisms include waste water and alternative power projects supporting a respected PFI group. Also skilled in contract structuring and professional indemnity matters. The firm is at present advising on construction issues surrounding three waste power projects; clients range from institutional investors to main and sub-contractors. **Clients:** The Miller Group; Bank of Scotland; West of Scotland Water.

Shepherd & Wedderburn WS (see firm details p.1126) With "*an excellent client base*" the team moves up the table this year on the back of heavy endorsement. "*A talented construction procurement lawyer,*" **Kevin Taylor** (see p.209) is said to "*work around the clock,*" although some feel he may be "*spread too thinly*" as a consequence. Significant deals for the firm include construction matters relating to a major office and leisure retail development for the largest gap site in Edinburgh. **Clients:** Scottish Power; Amey Asset Services; Teesland Management Services.

Maclay Murray & Spens (see firm details p.1047) A "*sound*" department, said by clients to be "*really excellent.*" Led by Mark Macaulay, the group acts for developers and contractors with much of its profile drawn from its advice on the firm's high quality PFI instructions. On the contentious front highlights include acting for the successful claiming party in Strathmore Building Services v Colin Scott Greig t/a Hestia Fireside Design, and advising and drafting contracts for the City Science Project. **Clients:** Wilson Bowden Developments; Stannifer; Robertson Group.

Biggart Baillie (see firm details p.882) **Murray Shaw** (see p.581) is key to much of the firm's profile in this area; "*a quality operator,*" he is judged to bring a "*sensible approach to a fair body of work.*" The group is active in adjudications, disputes and general development work, with a noted expertise in the energy sector. Highlights include undertaking all the construction aspects of a multi-million pound gas storage project. **Clients:** Link Housing Association; Lilley Construction; Scottish Power.

Burness (see firm details p.903) The "*efficient*" team has been busy building on the firm's banking, PFI and property success. Head of Construction, Christopher Mackay is active on both contentious and non-contentious matters. Highlights for the team include reviewing all the construction documentation for the Scottish Football Association with a view to it taking over and operating the national stadium, and advising Royal Bank of Scotland on the construction of an office development at St James House, Edinburgh. Also instructed by Jarvis on the Balfron and East Renfrewshire Schools project. **Clients:** Ballast; Jarvis; BBC.

Ledingham Chalmers (see firm details p.1034) A "*healthy practice*" with a strong reputation in power work, the firm remains the dominant player in the North East of Scotland from its base in Aberdeen. The team led by Jennifer Howitt has a healthy following among contractors and developers. Recent highlights include acting on one of the most high profile and high value adjudications in Scotland. **Clients:** Medical Centres (Scotland); Rigblast Energy Services; MacDonald Hotels.

Morison Bishop (see firm details p.1075) "*Experienced litigator*" **John Welsh** (see p.209) is the standout individual at this practice, famed for its expertise in professional indemnity. The cohesive group receives instructions from its respected base of insurance clients in connection with claims against engineers, architects and surveyors. **Clients:** Insurers and their professional clients; contractors and sub-contractors.

Other Notable Practitioners **Fenella Mason** of **DLA** received market approval.

NORTHERN IRELAND

Carson McDowell (see firm details p.909) "*Well established and highly commercial*" full service practice fielding talented lawyers. **Peter Davison** (see p.202) leads this respected group that services contractors, architects and surveyors and numbers three of the major construction companies in Northern Ireland among its clients. Acted on the developments at Foyleside and Castle Court, the firm has also been occupied in the contentious sphere. Advised the Department of the Environment for Northern Ireland on an arbitration arising from a civil engineering project.

Elliott Duffy Garrett (see firm details p.949) Michael Lynch and his team deal primarily with contentious matters for contractors. The firm also undertakes judicial reviews relating to planning issues and housing disputes.

Johns Elliot (see firm details p.1014) "*Senior figure*" **Maurice Butler** (see p.200) operates within a team that is perceived to be "*well respected*" for its work on behalf of the Northern Ireland Housing Executive. Mainly involved in the contentious sphere, it deals with the defence of contract claims, building contract disputes and arbitrations.

L'Estrange & Brett (see firm details p.1038) **Sam Beckett** (see p.565) approaches the deal table with a "*realistic view of things.*" Involved in adjudications, PFI work and planning enquiries, the firm acted on the first 'bundled' PFI project in Northern Ireland (Wellington College/Balmoral High School) and on the town centre redevelopment of Lisburn. It numbers developers, insurers and contractors among its client base and con-

CONSTRUCTION • Northern Ireland	Ptnrs	Assts
1 **Carson McDowell** Belfast	1	2
Elliott Duffy Garrett Belfast	4	4
Johns Elliot Belfast	1	1
L'Estrange & Brett Belfast	2	1
2 **Cleaver Fulton Rankin** Belfast	2	5
Kennedys Belfast	1	1
Tughan & Co Belfast	2	1

LEADING INDIVIDUALS	
1 **BECKETT Sam** L'Estrange & Brett	**BUTLER Maurice** Johns Elliot
CRAIG Seán Kennedys	
2 **DAVISON Peter** Carson McDowell	
3 **FOX Brendan** Cleaver Fulton Rankin	

This book is the product of 6,552 1/2-hour interviews. See p.7 for BMRB audit.
Within each band, firms are listed alphabetically. *See individuals' profiles p.199*

tinues to advise Morrison Homes on issues arising from its residential development work. **Clients:** Cusp; Morrison; Braidwater.

Cleaver Fulton Rankin (see firm details p.918) **Brendan Fox** (see p.202) has a solid profile on the contentious side of the market. The firm acts for developers, building contractors and councils, with its client base mixture of claimant and defendant. The unit also undertakes non-contentious work for, among others, local councils. Skilled in the defence of loss and expense claims, it also conducts professional negligence claims, and matters arising out of arbitration. **Clients:** Stothers (M&E), Lisburn Borough Council; Fin Engineering Group.

Kennedys (see firm details p.1018) Dealing mainly with contentious matters, acting for an outstanding insurance client base on professional indemnity matters, the firm also acts for those insured on the application of policies. **Seán Craig** (see p.201), a "*sound and thorough lawyer*," leads this team. **Clients:** Chartwell; Norwich Union; Countrywide and Nationwide.

Tughan & Co (see firm details p.1163) Led by Michael Gibson this "*efficient*" firm deals with both contentious and non-contentious construction matters, active with building contracts, arbitration and ADR. The group has acted for Northern Ireland Housing Executive on a recent arbitration and advised Sperrin Lakeland Trust on a telecoms PFI project. The client roster includes developers, construction companies, specialist sub-contractors and suppliers. **Clients:** Northern Ireland Housing Executive; Sperrin Lakeland Trust; Mivan.

LEADERS IN CONSTRUCTION

BAKER, Huw
Masons, Manchester (0161) 234 8357
huw.baker@masons.com
Specialisation: Partner in charge of PFI and major project work in *Masons'* Manchester office. Experienced in all aspects of PFI and major project work including project agreements, finance, building contracts and FM contracts.
Prof. Memberships: Society of Construction Lawyers. Member of TECSA. TECSA accredited adjudicator.
Career: Qualified in 1987. In September 1998 moved from *Addleshaw Booth & Co* where he had been partner in charge of the Manchester construction team to head up PFI and major project work in *Masons'* Manchester office.
Personal: Born 22 September 1962. Graduated from Cambridge University in 1984 with 1st Class Honours in Law. Leisure pursuits include gardening, walking and reading. Lives in Hebden Bridge, West Yorkshire.

BARRETT, Kevin
Wragge & Co, Birmingham (0870) 903 1000

BAYLIS, Simon
Wragge & Co, Birmingham (0870) 903 1000

BECKETT, Sam
L'Estrange & Brett, Belfast (028) 9023 0426
sam.beckett@lestrangeandbrett.com
See under Litigation, p.565

BENTLEY, Bruce
DLA, Sheffield (08700) 111111

BIRCH, John
Bevan Ashford, Exeter (01392) 663388
j.birch@bevan-ashford.com
Specialisation: Specialist construction lawyer having extensive experience of dispute resolution in the construction industry. Acts for and advises international and national contractors in mediations, adjudications, arbitrations and litigation. Recent reported cases – Midland Veneers Ltd v Unilock, Hescorp Italia Spa v Morrison. Heads up the *Bevan Ashford* construction law team based in Exeter. Recently spoke at conferences on adjudication, non-concluded contracts and current construction issues. Former quantity surveyor having wide and varied experience of construction industry. For more details please see www.bevanashford.com/construction
Prof. Memberships: Society of Construction Law, Law Society.
Career: Quantity surveyor for 17 years prior to entering legal profession. Chief Quantity Surveyor for international contractor in Middle East. Qualified 1986, *Townsends* 1984 – 1999. Joined *Bevan Ashford* as partner 1999.
Personal: Resides South Hams, Devon. Leisure interests include, walking and reading.

BIRKBY, Gillian
Rowe & Maw, London (020) 7782 8772
gbirkby@roweandmaw.com
Specialisation: Construction and engineering law, both contentious and non-contentious. Involved in innovative forms of contracting leading to reduced confrontation. Expert in the application of the CDM Regulations (Health and Safety).
Prof. Memberships: ACIArb. Honorary Member of the Association of Planning Supervisors. Chairman of the Construction Industry Council's Task Force on Health and Safety.
Career: Joined the construction and engineering group of *Rowe & Maw.*
Personal: Walking and archaeology.

BISHOP, John
Masons, London (020) 7490 4000
john.bishop@masons.com
Specialisation: Specialised in UK and international construction and engineering matters since qualifying, more recently also in professional negligence disputes. Major matters include LTRS, MTR, SSDS and Second Harbour Crossing in Hong Kong, Falklands Airfield, Tiffany Oil Platform, Channel Tunnel, Eurostar, Cairo Plaza, Jubilee Line, Keadby Power Station, LNG facilities (Brunei), Lloyds Building, M25, A27, several arbitrations from Indonesian Geothermic programme; conducted disputes at all levels of the English Courts, domestic arbitrations and international arbitrations under ICC, UNCITRAL and Stockholm Chamber rules as well as ADR processes. Also acts as mediator, adjudicator and arbitrator.
Prof. Memberships: Dean of the Faculty of Mediation & ADR, Chairman of the Joint Consultative Committee of the London Court of International Arbitration, Vice Chairman of the Academy of Experts, President of the Technology and Construction Solicitors Association (TeCSA), Chairman of TeCSA IT Committee. Past Chairman of TeCSA, Past Member of TCC (Technology and Construction Court) Users Committee, TCC's Rules Committee, IT Committee, ADR Committee, Law Society Civil Litigation Committee, ISE Committees on Expert Evidence and Woolf Reforms, Founder Member of CEDR, Chartered Institute of Arbitrators' Committees on new forms of arbitration and ADR, British Academy of Experts Sub Committee on Expert Evidence. Editorial board of Construction Law Journal. Lectures include Blundell Memorial lecture, Bar Conference, Judicial Studies Board, National Contractors Group annual lecture, Chartered Institute of Arbitrators, Kings College (Univ. of London).
Career: Qualified 1971, partner 1972, admitted Hong Kong 1983, managing partner 1986-1990, senior partner 1990 to date. Qualified adjudicator (TeCSA), mediator (CEDR).
Personal: Sherborne School. LLB Hons Queen Mary College, University of London. Leisure interests include golf, fishing, cooking and tomatoes.

BLACKLER, Tony
Macfarlanes, London (020) 7831 9222

Specialisation: Partner, Property Department. Tony Blackler graduated from Downing College, Cambridge, as a Harris Scholar in law, and qualified as a solicitor in 1967. He has since specialised in construction law, initially on the contentious side, where he has been involved over the years in major disputes before the courts and in arbitration. More recently he has become involved in front-end work, negotiating contract documentation and advising on procurement generally. Until recently Tony chaired a sub-committee of the International Bar Association's Committee T (International Construction Projects). He is a lecturer, and currently writes a column for 'Building' magazine. He was the principal author of a book published by Sweet & Maxwell on the JCT Management Contract. Tony is a trained and accredited mediator, and undertakes mediations when he is available to do so. He has advised a number of industry bodies about the legislation affecting construction contracts which is now embodied in the Housing Grants, Construction & Regeneration Act 1996, and more recently upon the likely effect of the Contracts (Rights of Third Parties) Bill upon the construction industry.

BOURGEOIS, Christopher
Taylor Joynson Garrett, London (020) 7300 7000

BRADLEY, Graeme
DLA, Birmingham (08700) 111111

BRIDGEWATER, Martin
Norton Rose, London (020) 7444 2834
bridgewaterm@nortonrose.com
Specialisation: Partner in construction and engineering group. Main area of practice covers non-contentious construction and engineering contracts, both UK and international and PFI/PPP projects. Generally advises developers or contractors on major UK building projects and banks or sponsors on PFI infrastructure, process plant and independent power projects.
Prof. Memberships: International Bar Association, Society of Construction Lawyers.
Career: Qualified in England and Wales in 1976, and in Hong Kong in 1978. Joined *Nabarro Nathanson* in 1980, became a partner in 1984 and headed their construction department from 1986-1997. Joined *Norton Rose* in 1997.

BROWN, Jeffrey
Lee Crowder, Birmingham (0121) 236 4477
Specialisation: Contentious and non-contentious work on behalf of developers, main contractors, subcontractors and their insurers.
Prof. Memberships: Technology and Construction Solicitors Association, Chartered Institute of Arbitrators, Chartered Insurance Institute.
Career: Assistant solicitor *Pinsent & Co* 1981-82 (now *Pinsent Curtis Biddle*); assistant solicitor *Johnson & Co* 1982-1984 (now *Martineau Johnson*); *Neil F Jones* 1984-1999 (partner 1986, senior partner 1993-1999); partner and head of construction and engineering department *Lee Crowder* 1999 to date.
Publications: Co-author 'Professional Negligence in the Construction Industry' (published in 1998 by LLP).
Personal: Resident Nant-Y-Deri, Gwent. Married with one son. Interests – sailing, windsurfing, swimming.

BUNCH, Anthony
Masons, London (020) 7490 6216
anthony.bunch@masons.com
Specialisation: Worldwide Managing Partner, Head of Energy Group. Has experience in all aspects of contentious and non-contentious matters relating to construction and energy law. Has drafted a full range of contracts for major projects in the UK and the Far East on behalf of employers, major contractors and international consultants. Has conducted proceedings to all levels, including the House of Lords, and in other countries including Hong Kong, Singapore and China. His primary experience concerns all forms of arbitration proceedings and in particular proceedings which concern the energy sector. The majority of his dispute resolution work during recent years relates to major disputes concerning the oil and gas industry. Author of numerous articles on dispute resolution and in particular ADR. Joint author on the chapter on Hong Kong in the International Handbook on Commercial Arbitration and the specialist chapter on construction in the Handbook of Arbitration Practice. Speaks widely on construction and energy issues.
Prof. Memberships: Member of the Chartered Institute of Arbitrators, Former Council Member of Chartered Institute of Arbitrators, Member of TECSA, Member of the Departmental Advisory Committee responsible for the Arbitration Act 1996, Member of the International Advisory Board to the Arbitration Institute of the Stockholm Chamber of Commerce; CEDR Accredited Mediator.
Career: Qualified in 1978, having joined *Masons* in 1976. Became a Salaried Partner in 1980 and Equity Partner in 1982. Admitted as a Solicitor in Hong Kong in 1985; Senior resident Partner in Hong Kong office 1985-90. Became Managing Partner in 1991.
Personal: Born 8th February 1953. Holds a BA (Hons) from Nottingham. Leisure interests include cycling, music and theatre. Lives in Radlett, Herts. 4 children.

BURCH, Simon
Linklaters, London (020) 7456 3582
simon.burch@linklaters.com
Specialisation: Construction and engineering group, commercial property department. Specialist in construction and engineering law and contracts providing primarily non-contentious advice in connection with major construction projects in the UK and overseas. Particular specialisation in drafting construction contracts and ancillary documents in connection with project financing with emphasis on power, energy and infrastructure projects. Also experience in concession agreements, operation and maintenance agreements, fuel supply agreements and facilities management agreements. Project experience includes major buildings, civil engineering works, power stations, petrochemical plants, industrial plants and offshore projects.
Prof. Memberships: ACI Arb; Society for Construction Law.
Career: Qualified 1974 (New Zealand), 1991 (UK). Partner at *Linklaters* since 1994.

BUTCHER, Trevor
CMS Cameron McKenna, London (020) 7363 3000
Specialisation: Partner in projects group. Main area of practice is in major infrastructure projects, particularly private finance work in the UK and internationally including central and eastern Europe. Particular specialisation in transport infrastructure projects, especially roads, light rail and heavy rail. Acted for DETR on the BNRR project and part of team on CTRL. Also acted on numerous DBFO road projects leading teams on the M40, A55 and A130 deals and acting on similar projects overseas including road and rail projects in Poland. Author of various articles and speaker at a number of conferences on PFI and PPP projects. Drafted the Association for Project Management standard form appointment.
Career: Qualified in 1986, having joined *McKenna & Co.* in 1984. Became a partner in 1992.
Personal: Born 10th February 1960. Graduated from Leicester University in 1983.

BUTLER, Maurice
Johns Elliot, Belfast (028) 9032 6881
Specialisation: All aspects of company and commercial work including corporate finance and mergers and acquisitions. Construction Claims/Arbitrations. Involved in two recent landmark appeals by way of Cases Stated to High Court from an arbitrator.
Prof. Memberships: Law Society of Northern Ireland.
Career: Graduated QUB 1965. Qualified 1968. Partner 1972, Senior/Managing Partner 1997. Appointed to Solicitor's Disciplinary Tribunal in 1986. Appointed President of Solicitors' Disciplinary Tribunal in 1999. Appointed Deputy County Court Judge in 1990.
Personal: Sailing (National Judge) and Bridge. Abbeyfield Society – Member of Regional Council and of Executive Committee of Abbeyfield NI Development Society Limited. Married with two daughters.

CANHAM, Stephanie
Trowers & Hamlins, London (020) 7423 8000
scanham@trowers.com
Specialisation: Partner, projects and construction group. Has specialised in construction law for the past 14 years and is well known and respected, particularly among developers, as a commercial construction specialist. Has considerable experience in construction related matters, having advised in negotiations on major projects across the private and public sectors with substantial involvement in PFI, joint ventures, partnering, Egan compliant procurement and major commercial developments.
Prof. Memberships: Member of the Chartered Institute of Arbitrators; the Construction Law Practice Sub-Committee of the City of London Solicitors' Company and the Society of Construction Law.
Career: Member of the Construction Clients Forum/JCT Working Party and a regular contributor of articles to journals. Lectures widely on construction and development issues and is a well known IBC/SBIM speaker by invitation for developers.
Publications: Has contributed to several construction-based publications including Butterworths' 'Encyclopaedia of Construction Forms and Precedents'; co-authoring a guide to design and build.
Personal: Two children and a house husband (previously a lawyer).

CAPPER, Phillip
Lovells, London (020) 7296 2000
phillip.capper@lovells.com
Specialisation: Partner, specialising in International Arbitration, Engineering and Construction. Recognised authority on engineering and construction risks

and contracts. Substantial experience of international arbitration; as adviser, advocate and arbitrator. Worked on projects for highways, rail, power, defence, and process plant, building and construction in many countries worldwide. Lead counsel for TML, the Channel Tunnel contract consortium, under English and French law – keynote speaker on this at US AAA DART conference. Advised foreign state electricity generator/distributors, national gas distributors, high-speed rail authorities and suppliers, metro and light rail projects and privately financed infrastructure projects. Has sat as Arbitrator in ICC and LCIA arbitrations. Drafted the disputes clauses in standard forms NEC 2nd edition and ICE 7th. Engaged as expert by French Association of International Contractors (SEFI) to evaluate FIDIC's EPC Silver Book.
Prof. Memberships: UK member of the ICC Commission on International Arbitration in Paris. He directs the International Diploma of the Chartered Institute of Arbitrators.
Career: Formerly partner in construction and engineering and Head of International Arbitration at *Masons*. He is a visiting Professor in Construction Law and Arbitration at King's College London, and before moving to London in 1988 he was Chairman of the Faculty of Law at the University of Oxford. He has been a Fellow of Keble College Oxford for 23 years.
Publications: For CIRIA's 'Client's Guide to Risk in Construction' wrote legal risk management. Founding Editor of 'Construction Industry Law Letter' from 1983 to 1990. Recent publications include 'Construction Industry Arbitrations' in Sweet & Maxwell's 'Handbook of Arbitration Practice' 3rd ed, and former General Editor of 'Emden's Construction Law'.
Personal: Born 1952. French language.

CHINN, David
Hill Dickinson, Liverpool (0151) 236 5400
Specialisation: All types of construction and engineering matters. Acts for insurers, developers, employers, local authority, NHS trusts, main contractors, sub contractors, specialist sub-contractors and the professional team.
Prof. Memberships: Member of TeCSA, Society of Construction Law, Secretary of the Liverpool Technology and Construction Users' Committee, Law Society, secretary of the Liverpool Branch of the Society for Computers and Law.
Career: 1982-1987 *Mace & Jones* (incorporating Latin & Masheder); 1988- to date *Hill Dickinson* (became partner in 1992). Fellow of Chartered Institute of Arbitrators (January 1996); TeCSA Adjudicator (September 1996); Accredited Mediator (June 1997).
Publications: Various articles on arbitration, ADR and adjudication.
Personal: Lives in Southport, loves include family, Liverpool F.C., squash and vintage fountain pen collection.

COCKRAM, Richard
Addleshaw Booth & Co, Leeds (0113) 209 2000
rac@addleshaw-booth.co.uk
Specialisation: Partner, Head of Non-Contentious Construction Unit. Construction drafting and PFI projects.
Prof. Memberships: Fellow, Chartered Institute of Arbitrators. Member, Society of Construction Lawyers.
Career: Qualified 1973. Partner, *McKenna & Co.*, 1986-89. Joined the firm in 1989.
Publications: 'Manual of Construction Agreements' (Jordans, 1998, 2nd edition 2001).
Personal: Educated: Cambridge University 1967-70: MA in law. Interests include books and walking.

COLLINGWOOD, Mark
Masons, Bristol (0117) 924 5678
mark.collingwood@masons.com
Specialisation: Partner in Construction and Engineering Group. Heads *Masons'* thirty lawyer Bristol office and the firm's Construction and Engineering team in Bristol office. Specialist construction lawyer since qualification. Particular specialisms include litigation, arbitration, adjudication and dispute resolution generally, contract and project documentation negotiation and drafting. Has acted in many 'heavyweight' construction cases — civil engineering and building in the UK and abroad. Drafted project documentation for £350m Devonport dockyard redevelopment scheme. Lectures frequently on the law relating to the construction industry.
Prof. Memberships: Law Society, Faculty of Building.
Career: Qualified in 1980. Articled at *Crossman Block and Keith* 1978-80, before joining *Masons*. Became a Partner in 1985.
Personal: Born 19th December 1954. Attended Durham University, taking a BA in law and politics. Leisure interests include tennis. Has four young children.

CONNOR, Vincent
Masons, Glasgow 0141 248 4858
Edinburgh 0131 718 6006
vincent.connor@masons.com
Specialisation: Partner specialising in contentious construction law, including tactical and strategic advice and the pursuit and defence of claims in a variety of forms of dispute resolution.
Prof. Memberships: Law Society of Scotland, Society of Construction Law & Technology and Construction Solicitors Association.
Career: Educated at Glasgow University 1982-87 (LLB 1st class honours. 1986, DipLP 1987). Assistant Solicitor *Hughes Dowdall* 1987-90. Qualified as Notary Public in 1989. Joined *McGrigor Donald* in 1990, became an Associate in 1993 and assumed as a Partner in 1995. Accredited as a Solicitor Mediator in 1994. Jointly established *Masons'* Scottish practice in 1998.
Personal: Born 1964. Leisure interests include music, cinema and running. Married. Resides in Glasgow.

CORBETT, Edward
Corbett & Co, Teddington (020) 8943 9885
ecorbett@corbett.co.uk
Specialisation: Active in the UK and all over the world advising contractors, clients, consultants and others on building and civil engineering procurement, contract preparation and negotiation, on dispute avoidance, management and resolution including mediation, adjudication and, if unavoidable, arbitration. Author of 'FIDIC 4th – A Practical Legal Guide'. Regular seminar speaker.
Prof. Memberships: FCIArb, SCL, IBA Committee T – Chair, FIDIC Sub-committee, TeCSA, Affiliate Member of FIDIC, FIDIC Mediator and Adjudicator, AAA Panellist. Former partner at *Masons*.
Personal: Born 10 September 1957. MSc in Construction Law and Arbitration, King's College. MA Jurisprudence, Oxford; Accredited Adjudicator and Mediator. Keen sailor and windsurfer.

CORNES, David
Winward Fearon, London (020) 7420 2800
See under Alternative Dispute Resolution, p.80

CRAIG, Seán
Kennedys, Belfast (028) 90 240067
s.craig@kennedys-law.com
Specialisation: Construction related litigation. Disputes against professionals: architects, engineers, surveyors, geophysicists etc. Also claims against brokers and financial advisers. Acted for Lewis and Tucker on the BBL case. Acting for the engineer on DED v Kennedys & Co, Loughrey Agnew etc.
Prof. Memberships: English Bar 1985; Law Society (England) 1988; Law Society (Northern Ireland) 1994; Law Society (Republic of Ireland) 1998.
Career: Joined *Kennedys'* City office in June 1987, becoming a partner in January 1993. Helped establish *Kennedys'* Belfast office which opened in March 1996.

CRITCHLOW, Julian
Fenwick Elliott, London (020) 7956 9354
jcritchlow@fenickelliott.co.uk
Specialisation: Partner specialising in both non-contentious and contentious construction matters and arbitration.
Prof. Memberships: Fellow of the Chartered Institute of Arbitrators; CEDR accredited mediator; TeCSA registered adjudicator; Associate Fellow of the Society for Advanced Legal Studies; member of TeCSA; member of the Construction Contracts Mediators Group; member of the Arbitration Club, member of the American Judicature Society; member of King's College Construction Law Association; Commissioner of the Foundation for International Commercial Arbitration; Liveryman of the Worshipful Company of Arbitrators.
Career: Qualified 1984. University College London (LL.B. 1981). King's College London (M.Sc. 1993). King's College London (Ph.D. 2000). Articled *Field Fisher and Martineau.*
Publications: Author of Making Partnering Work in the Construction Industry (Chandos 1998), joint author of Arbitration Forms and Precedents (LLP 2000), contributor to the Construction Law Handbook (Thomas Telford 2000), Arbitration Editor of Amicus Curiae, Construction Law Editor of the Journal of ADR, Mediation and Negotiation.
Personal: Born 1958. Married, two children. Leisure interests include shooting and English poetry.

CUMMINS, Caroline
CMS Cameron McKenna, London
(020) 7367 2914
cxc.cmck.com
Specialisation: Concentrates on disputes resolution work for the construction industry. Clients are generally main contractors and employers. Cases have involved a wide range of issues and projects. Acted for Panatown in McAlpine v Panatown. Has also advised on non-contentious matters including PFI projects. CEDR accredited mediator and TeCSA accredited adjudicator.
Prof. Memberships: Law Society; Society of Construction Law; TeCSA (committee member).
Personal: Attended St George's School, Ascot 1972-78 then Jesus College Oxford 1979-82. Qualified in 1989 after spending some years working for United Biscuits plc. Joined *CMS Cameron McKenna* in 1992

and became a partner in the construction group in 1996.

DAVIES, Edward
Masons, Manchester (0161) 234 8234
edward.davies@mason.com
Specialisation: Head of *Masons* construction and engineering, energy and infrastructure groups in Manchester office. Construction and engineering work, together with technology expertise. Litigation, arbitration and ADR (trained as mediator by American Arbitration Association in San Francisco) and CEDR accredited mediator. Contract drafting and procurement advice for major projects – especially energy and infrastructure. Joint editor – 'Dispute Resolution and Conflict Management in Construction (An International Review).'
Prof. Memberships: Law Society, Manchester Law Society, Society of Construction Law, American Arbitration Association. Joint co-ordinator of CIB International Research Group on conflict management. Visiting research fellow UMIST (University of Manchester Institute of Science and Technology).
Career: Qualified 1982. Joined *Masons* 1986 in London. Became partner and established Manchester office in 1989.
Personal: Born 1958. Manchester University (LLB); College of Law Guildford then Kings College London MSc. Lives in Manchester.

DAVIES, Peter
Gateley Wareing, Birmingham (0121) 234 0000

DAVIS, Michael
Herbert Smith, London (020) 7374 8000
Specialisation: Head of construction and engineering department. Has specialised in major national and international construction and civil engineering projects since qualification, advising UK and overseas clients and conducting construction and civil engineering disputes both within the English jurisdiction and in international arbitrations, both ad hoc and subject to ICC, LCIA and UNCITRAL rules worldwide. He is also responsible for the preparation and negotiation of contracts for all aspects of process, construction and civil engineering projects acting on behalf of all sectors of the industry, project companies and banks and has advised in numerous projects both nationally and internationally including a number of major infrastructure projects.
Prof. Memberships: Law Society, City Solicitors Company, International Bar Association, LCIA, Society of Construction Law, United Kingdom Energy Lawyers Group, British Academy of Experts, Founder Member of the Centre for Dispute Resolution (Alternative Dispute Resolution), Founder Member of the City Disputes Panel.
Career: Qualified in 1977, became a partner in 1986, head of construction and civil engineering law 1986. Lectured widely in respect of construction, civil engineering and arbitration, including the International Bar Association, ICC, LCIA and the Law Society Commerce and Industry Group Center for International Legal Studies and most recently published a paper in the Sweet Lectures 'Comparative Studies in Construction Law' entitled 'Choice of Law Rules in International Construction Contracts'.
Personal: Born 14th August 1951, educated BA (London).

DAVISON, Peter William
Carson McDowell, Belfast (01232) 244 951
peter.davison@carson-mcdowell.com
Specialisation: Over 20 years of practical experience in general commercial litigation, with particular reference to construction matters, working for both private and public sector under ICE/JCT/GC and other forms of contract. Established links with leading construction counsel in Belfast and London and experienced expert witnesses if required. Law Society ADR training course completed.
Prof. Memberships: Law Society of Northern Ireland. Society of Construction Law.
Career: 1974 MA Trinity College, Dublin (Legal Science), joined *Carson & McDowell* and admitted solicitor 1977. Partner 1979.

FENWICK ELLIOTT, Robert J.
Fenwick Elliott, London (020) 7956 9354
rjfe@fenwickelliott.co.uk
Specialisation: Senior partner of firm, specialising in construction law. Emphasis on resolution of disputes in the area of building and civil engineering contracts. Also advises on the drafting of building contracts. Has handled many large cases in adjudication, litigation, arbitration and mediation. Accredited TeCSA, CIC, CIOB Adjudicator. Qualified CEDR mediator.
Prof. Memberships: Vice President of TeCSA. Chairman of ICLA. Society of Construction Law Member.
Career: Qualified 1977. Founded *Fenwick Elliott* in 1980.
Publications: Author of 'Building Contract Litigation' and 'Building Contract Disputes: Practice and Precedents.'
Personal: Born 17th March 1952. Attended Eastbourne College 1965-69, then the University of Kent 1969-72. Lives in London.

FLEET, Terry
Berwin Leighton Paisner, London (020) 7760 1000
terry.fleet@berwinleightonpaisner.com
Specialisation: Partner and Head of Construction and Engineering Department. Principal area of practice is construction law advising on building and civil engineering projects in the UK and internationally, including procurement strategy, contract drafting and negotiation, bonds, warranties, insurance, contract advice and dispute resolution. Has advised in connection with major projects in the UK, the Caribbean, Europe (including Eastern Europe), Africa, the Middle East and the Far East. Currently involved in major office, retail, road, power, leisure and PFI projects in the UK, and overseas most recently in Bahrain, the Congo, Hungary, Norway, Poland, and Russia. Clients include institutions, government departments, funders, developers, major construction and engineering companies and professional architectural and civil engineering consultants. Has written articles in 'Construction Law', 'Building', 'Property Week', 'Estates Gazette' and 'Chartered Surveyor Weekly'. Co-Author of 'Tolleys Guide to Construction Contracts'. Speaks at conferences on construction law matters.
Prof. Memberships: The Law Society, International Bar Association and Society of Construction Law.
Career: Qualified in 1980. Articled at *Heald & Nickinson* 1977-79 and moved to *Speechly Bircham* 1979-80. Legal Advisor to Costain Group 1980-82, Babcock International 1982-84 and Cementation International, (Trafalgar House) 1984-87. Joined *Berwin Leighton* in 1987 before becoming a Partner in 1988, now *Berwin Leighton Paisner.*
Personal: Born 1954. Attended Southampton University (graduated 1976 LLB Hons.). Leisure interests include flying, travel and family. Lives in Twickenham.

FOX, Brendan
Cleaver Fulton Rankin, Belfast (028) 9027 1325
b.fox@cfrlaw.co.uk
Specialisation: Construction and property litigation, intellectual property and competition law.
Prof. Memberships: The Law Society of Northern Ireland.
Career: Educated at St Patrick's College, Knock, Belfast and The Queen's University of Belfast (LLB). Qualified in 1991. Became a partner in *Cleaver Fulton Rankin* 1 April 1998.
Personal: Born 7 December 1966. Hobbies include music and sport.

GARTHWAITE, Helen
Taylor Joynson Garrett, London (020) 7300 7000
Specialisation: Provides construction advice and documentation for a wide range of corporations and institutions owning, occupying, financing, investing in and designing development projects in the office, retail, industrial and leisure sectors as well as for significant civil engineering and infrastructure projects. Experienced in public and privately funded schemes, including partnering and PFI arrangements; due diligence and development support for corporate and property deals; construction e-procurement and health and safety. Writes and lectures regularly and is often asked for comment by the construction industry media, recently featuring in 'Building' magazine's "40 under Forty" interviewed as one of the top 40 personalities in the construction industry under 40 years of age.
Prof. Memberships: Secretary and Member of Council of the Society of Construction Law and a Member of the Chartered Institute of Arbitrators.
Career: Qualified 1990, Solicitor *Nabarro Nathanson* 1990-1996. Partner and Head of Construction and Engineering, *Lewis Silkin* 1996-2001. Partner, Construction and Engineering Group, *Taylor Joynson Garrett* 2001.
Personal: M.Sc. Construction Law and Arbitration (1992). Interests include yachting. Resides in Westminster.MSc Construction Law and Arbitration (1992). Interests include yachting and woodland management. Resides in Westminster.

GIBSON, Michael
Berwin Leighton Paisner, London (020) 7760 1000
mike.gibson@berwinleightopaisner.com
Specialisation: Partner. All aspects of law and practice relating to construction and engineering procurement in the UK and internationally, advising authorities, developers, funds, Government agencies, Health Trusts, contractors and designers on contracts for design, construction, financing and facilities management of major building and engineering projects and resolution of disputes arising from them. Principally involved with projects assembled under the Government's Private Finance Initiative.
Prof. Memberships: Society of Construction Law.
Career: Admitted in 1977. Legal department of Costain Group 1975-78. Head of Legal Department, Construction Division, Trafalgar House plc, 1981-87. Joined *Berwin Leighton* (now *Berwin Leighton*

Paisner) in 1987 as co-founder of its Construction and Engineering Group. Head of Construction and Engineering Group until 1998.
Personal: Born 1952. Educated at St. Edward's School, Oxford 1965-70 and Southampton University 1970-74. Lives in Oxshott, Surrey.

GORDON, Roderick
Watson Burton, Newcastle upon Tyne
(0191) 244 4444
roddy.gordon@watsonburton.co.uk
Specialisation: Partner and Head of Non-contentious Construction Division. Practices as a specialist in construction and engineering law, including all forms of contracts, works for developers, property owners, lenders and contractors. Also handles construction & engineering diputes. Strong interest/commitment to ADR.
Career: Qualified 1988. Moved from *Masons*, where he was a partner, to *Robert Muckle* in Newcastle in 1993. Moved onto *Watson Burton* as a partner and head of Non-contentious Construction in 2001. Member of the Chartered Institute of Arbitrators; adjudicator approved by TeCSA, CEDR accredited mediator.

GOULD, Nicholas
Lovells, London (020) 7296 2000

GOWAN, Daniel
Davies Arnold Cooper, London (020) 7936 2222
dgowan@dac.co.uk
Specialisation: Executive Partner in Construction Department. Handles all aspects of contentious and non-contentious construction work, contract drafting and reviewing, joint ventures, arbitration and litigation. Experienced in mechanical and civil engineering and building. Also handles construction insurance, including professional indemnity, contractors all risks and public liability claims. Acted for Petrotrin (Trinidad) in dispute with SNC Lavalin; PI insurers in Heathrow Tunnel collapse and Eurotunnel disputes; Project Insurer on Hong Kong Airport; Victorian Channels Authority in dredging dispute with Van Oord. Has spoken on many publicly-paid-for seminars for Hawkesmere, and for a number of in-house seminars and presentations to the construction industry.
Prof. Memberships: Fellow, Chartered Institute of Arbitrators;
Career: Qualified in New Zealand in 1976, and in England in 1983. Worked at *Meredith Connell & Co.*, New Zealand, 1975-78, then *Freedman & Co.*, London, 1980-83. Joined *Davies Arnold Cooper* in 1983, becoming a Partner in 1987.
Personal: Born 2nd October 1951. Leisure interests include cricket, tennis, golf, theatre, opera, music and reading. Lives in Rotherwick, Hampshire.

GREEN, Richard
Wragge & Co, Birmingham (0870) 903 1000

GUPPY, W Nicholas
Laytons, Bristol (0117) 930 9530
nick.guppy@laytons.com
Specialisation: Head of Construction Law and Editor of quarterly publication, 'Laytons Building'. Qualified in 1976 and worked in London until 1990 with ever increasing specialisation in construction law. Acts for a wide range of employers, contractors and sub-contractors on both contentious matters (now mainly adjudication, but litigation and arbitration not dead yet!) and non-contentious. Regularly speaks at seminars.
Prof. Memberships: Law Society.
Career: Qualified in 1976. Joined *Laytons* in 1990 and became a Partner in 1992.
Personal: Born in 1951. Leisure interests include family life, squash and golf. Lives in London.

HANLEY, Christine
Bond Pearce, Plymouth (01752) 266633
chanley@bondpearce.com
Specialisation: Partner & head of the Construction and Engineering Group. Specialises in funded project work, waste to energy projects, construction dispute avoidance and resolution including adjudication, TCC litigation and arbitration.
Prof. Memberships: Fellow of the Chartered Institute of Arbitrators and member of the Society of Construction Lawyers. Committee member of the South West Construction Network.
Career: Qualified 1989, becoming Associate 1997 and Partner 1998.
Publications: A contributor to 'The Construction Act-Time for Review', published by Kings College London, and regularly invited to lecture on construction law and project work. Paper presented at Kings College University of London. Speaker at CIOB/CIC Objective One Conferences and CIOB seminars on partnering in various countries.

HANSON, Marc
CMS Cameron McKenna, London
(020) 7367 2366
mch@cmck.com
Specialisation: Principally provides construction procurement advice and drafts construction and facilities management contracts for major construction and outsourcing projects. Recent projects include the redevelopment of Paddington Basin for Chelsfield, Prudential's development of Green Park, the development of Legoland 4, Munich, and the construction of the National Football Centre for the Football Association.
Prof. Memberships: The Society of Construction Law; Editorial Board of Facilities Management Legal Update.
Career: Joined *McKenna & Co* as articled clerk 1992; qualified 1994 and became a partner in *CMS Cameron McKenna* in 2001.
Publications: Author of The Chartered Institute of Building Standard Form of Facilities Management Contract, The PACE GC/Works/10 Standard Form of Facilities Management Contract and 'Guide to Facilities Management Contracts' published 1999.
Personal: Born 1968, read Politics at the University of East Anglia (1986-1989). Leisure interests: Participating in motorsport and Arsenal FC. Married with a daughter and residing in Wimbledon.

HARLING, Marcus
Burges Salmon, Bristol (0117) 939 2206
marcus.harling@burges-salmon.com
Specialisation: Head of construction unit advising on all aspects of construction and engineering projects, insurance and risk and related liability and claim issues. Specialises in PPP, PFI and project structures procurement and implementation. Current projects include a series of waste to energy projects, chp projects, a £40m process plant and advising London Fire Brigade on its Corporate Property Project.
Prof. Memberships: Society of Construction Law, Committee of the Technology and Construction Solicitors' Association (TeCSA). Specialist practice consultant to RIBA.
Career: Qualified in 1985, joined *Burges Salmon* in 1986 and became a partner in 1992.
Publications: Author, 'TeCSA Protocol on Expert Evidence', Contributing Editor to Tolley's 'Knights Best Value and Public Procurement', RICS training video, 'Copyright in the Construction Industry'.

HARMAN, Martin
Masons, London (020) 7490 4000
martin.harman@masons.com
Specialisation: Partner and Head of Infrastructure Group worldwide. Main area of practice major infrastructure projects covering both contentious and transactional work. Advising various international entities, both governmental and private, upon the procurement of major infrastructure projects in collaboration with the private sector, and in that capacity, advising upon contract procurement strategy and drafting of project documentation. Substantial experiance of Light Rail Transit Systems and Airport Projects Worldwide. Has undertaken international arbitrations in Hong Kong, Lebanon, Singapore, Egypt, Kuwait, Yemen, Pakistan and India. Lectures widely for various international conference organisers.
Prof. Memberships: Faculty of Building, International Bar Association, Law Society of Hong Kong. Member of editorial team of the International Arbitration Law Review; member of Chartered Institute of Logistics and Transport; Chairman British Consultants Bureau's East Asia and Pacific Group, committee member of British Trade International's Asia Pacific Advisory Group.
Career: Qualified in 1971. Joined *Masons* in 1975, becoming a Partner in 1976. Admitted in Hong Kong 1983; first resident Partner at *Masons* in Hong Kong 1983. Head of Infrastructure Group of *Masons* worldwide.
Personal: Born 24th December 1946. Attended Brighton College, Brighton 1960-65, then Bristol University 1966-69. Leisure interests include wooden toy making, walking, reading and music. Lives in London.

HARRIS, Adam
Masons, Bristol (0117) 924 5678
adam.harris@masons.com
Specialisation: Partner in Infrastructure Group. Contentious and non-contentious work with a particular interest in PFI. A specialist in the building, civil engineering, process plant and electricity industries. Acts for both contractors and employers.
Career: Qualified 1981. *Lovell White Durrant* 1982-1988 (Hong Kong 1983-1987). Admitted Hong Kong 1984. Partner at *Masons* 1990.
Personal: Born 3rd January 1956. Educated Wellington School and Birmingham University (LLB).

HARTLEY, Keith
Masons, Leeds (0113) 233 8905
keith.hartley@masons.com
Specialisation: Partner in Construction & Engineering group. Leads 17-lawyer Construction & Engineering team in Leeds. Dispute resolution including High Court, arbitration and ADR and major project work, including many PFI and BOT schemes. Particular interests are transport systems and infrastructure and off shore process installations. Worked in UK and several Asian countries.
Prof. Memberships: Law Society, Chartered Institute of Arbitrators, Pacific Lawyers Association.

Career: Joined *Masons* in1980. Admitted as solicitor in England (1982) and in Hong Kong (1984) and became a partner in 1986. Resident in Hong Kong for 10 years before becoming Managing Partner of Leeds office in 1995.
Personal: Born 11 October 1957. Educated at King's College, London. Lives at Adel near Leeds.

HELPS, Dominic
Shadbolt & Co, Reigate (01737) 226 277
dominic_helps@shadboltlaw.co.uk
Specialisation: Specialises in the handling of all sorts of building and civil engineering disputes, both domestic and international. Cases on which he has worked include the Tsing Ma Bridge, Heathrow Tunnel Collapse, the Broadgate development and MEPAS tunnel dispute. Also acted for a major German contractor on a number of substantial ICC arbitrations. Acted for parties involved in adjudication and in enforcement of adjudicators' decisions. Involved in many of the reported enforcement decisions. Non-contentious experience includes drafting documentation for a major project finance project and acting for funds, developers, contractors and consultants on a wide variety of drafting work. Regular contributor to the construction and legal press and speaker on construction law. Accredited adjudicator (TeCSA).
Prof. Memberships: Technology and Construction Solicitors Association (Secretary); Society of Construction Law; Law Society; Arbitration Club (Chairman, Law Courts Branch).
Career: Articled and qualified with *Linklaters & Paines* 1983. Joined *Lovell White & King* (later *Lovell White Durrant*) in Hong Kong in 1985, returning to London office in 1986. Became a partner with *Shadbolt & Co* in 1996.
Personal: Born 8th July 1956. Attended Radley College, Oxon, then Cambridge University 1975-1978 and 1979-1980. In between was staff writer for Management Today. Leisure interests include playing cricket, Arsenal FC, scuba-diving, reading novels/history and cinema. Lives in Reigate.

HENDERSON, Nick
Dickinson Dees, Newcastle upon Tyne
(0191) 279 9281
nick.henderson@dickinson-dees.com
Specialisation: Partner in the construction and engineering group, specialising in dispute resolution. Has had experience in all forms of dispute resolution including arbitration and High Court litigation. Increasingly involved in adjudication having acted for employers, contractors, sub-contractors and professionals in the adjudication process. Has experience of enforcing adjudicator's decisions in the courts, both in London and the regions. Has also extensive experience of mediations. Has most recently become increasingly involved in the prosecution of professional negligence claims.
Prof. Memberships: Member of Chartered Institute of Arbitrators, ADR net.
Career: Qualified while at *Dickinson Dees* in 1993. Partner 2000.
Personal: Nottingham University 1986-89 LLB Hons. Interests include cricket; golf; football; rugby; reading; history.

HERBERT, Mary
Eversheds, Cardiff (029) 2047 1147
maryherbert@eversheds.com
Specialisation: Contractual claims, both defects claims and loss and expense claims. Extensive experience in arbitration, mediation, and adjudication in the health, energy, offshore and process plant sectors as well as in general building and engineering. Also very experienced in PFI, contract drafting, amending and professional appointments and warranties.
Prof. Memberships: Law Society.
Career: Qualified in 1988 and joined *Eversheds*, becoming a partner in 1993.
Personal: Theatre, art and gardening. Lives in Cardiff.

HILTON, Mark W
Hammond Suddards Edge, Leeds (0113) 284 7137
mark.hilton@hammondse.com
Specialisation: Partner in construction and engineering unit. Main area of practice is construction law. Acts on behalf of contractors, sub-contractors and employers in relation to non-contentious and contentious matters and contractual and other disputes in all areas of construction, in arbitration, litigation, adjudication and increasingly mediation. Acted in Duquemin v Slater, Preston v Torfaen, Yorkshire RHA v Fairclough and Percy Thomas, Strachan and Henshaw v Stein Industrie.
Prof. Memberships: Law Society, TeSCA, Fellow of the Chartered Institute of Arbitrators, CEDR Accredited Mediator.
Career: Qualified in 1982. Worked at *Last Suddards* in Bradford 1980-82, *Barlow Lyde & Gilbert* 1982-84 and rejoined *Last Suddards* (later *Hammond Suddards*) in 1984, becoming a partner in 1985.
Personal: Born 15th July 1958. Attended Wrekin College 1972-76 and University of Leeds 1976-79. Leisure interests include swimming, scuba diving, skiing and tennis. Lives in Harrogate.

HOLLOWAY, Julian
Berwin Leighton Paisner, London (020) 7427 1373
julian.holloway@berwinleightonpaisner.com
Specialisation: Partner. Construction and commercial litigation/arbitration and alternative dispute resolution. Former director of Centre for Dispute Resolution Limited ("CEDR") and Vice Chairman of CEDR's Construction Industry Working Party. Member of Drafting Committee of CEDR's Model Rules for Adjudication. Case Notes Editor of Construction Law Journal. CEDR accredited mediator (1993). Acts as mediator and for parties engaged in the mediation process. On CEDR's and RIBA's panel of adjudicators and is actively engaged in numerous adjudications. Member of the Construction Contacts Mediators Group. Has also been involved in setting up 'e-mediation' services.
Prof. Memberships: Law Society. Technology and Construction Court Solicitors Association.
Career: Articles with *Denton Hall & Burgin* 1979-1981. Qualified solicitor since 1981. Assistant solicitor *Brecher & Co* 1981-1983. Assistant solicitor with *McKenna & Co* 1984-1988. Partner *McKenna & Co* 1988-1992. Partner *Greenwoods* 1993 to 2000. Partner *Paisner & Co*, now *Berwin Leighton Paisner* 2001 to date.
Personal: Born 1954.

HOSIE, Jonathan
Hammond Suddards Edge, London
(020) 7655 1000
jonathan.hosie@hammondse.com
Specialisation: Partner in the construction and engineering unit of *Hammond Suddards Edge* in London. Handling drafting of documentation for construction and major projects and the resolution of complex construction disputes. Has published over 50 papers and articles and regularly addresses conferences and seminars on the legal aspects of construction projects.
Prof. Memberships: Society of Construction Law (Council member); Technology & Construction Court Solicitors Association (TECSA accredited adjudicator); Chartered Institute of Arbitrators; Arbitration Club, King's College Branch (Chairman); Chairman of Working Group 3 of the Design Build Foundation. Tutor at the Centre for Construction Law, Kings College.
Career: Qualified 1984. Associate with *Baker & McKenzie*'s construction and engineering law department 1989-95 before joining *Edge Ellison.*
Personal: Educated at the University of Wales (LL.B Hons) and at King's College, London (MSc Construction Law and Arbitration) 1989-91. Winner of the Alfred Hudson Prize awarded by Society of Construction Law 1993. Interests include family and Manchester United FC. Born 5th December 1958. Lives in London.

HOWE, Martin
Bevan Ashford, Bristol (0117) 918 8975
m.howe@bevanashford.com
Specialisation: Partner. Construction law with particular experience of drafting and interpretation of construction related documentation. Also experienced in the resolution of construction disputes.
Prof. Memberships: Regional co-ordinator for the Society of Construction Law in Bristol. Member of the Reading Construction Forum. Fellow Member of the Faculty of Building. Member of 'Teamwork 2001'.
Career: Qualified 1983. Joined *Bevan Ashford* as a partner in May 2000. Previously partner and head of construction at *Veale Wasbrough.*
Personal: Born 1958. Educated King's College, London.

HOYLE, Roger
Veale Wasbrough, Bristol (0117) 925 2020
rhoyle@vwl.co.uk
Specialisation: Head of construction team. Construction law. Has extensive experience of dispute resolution in the construction industry, involving claims concerning defective design and construction, the liability of professionals and their insurers, and the interpretation and enforcement of contracts, including claims for loss and expense.
Prof. Memberships: Committee Member of the Technology and Construction Solicitors Association, Law Society (London and Bristol).
Career: Qualified 1971. Became a partner of *Veale Wasbrough* in 1973.
Personal: Born 1947. Educated at Sedbergh School.

HUDSON, James
Nicholson Graham & Jones, London
(020) 7360 8150
james.hudson@ngj.co.uk
Specialisation: Partner in Construction and Engi-

neering Department. Principal area of practice is construction and engineering law. Has extensive experience of litigation, arbitration and other forms of ADR including mediation and adjudication. Important cases have included 'Minter v. WHTSO' and 'ICI v. Bovis' and others.
Prof. Memberships: Past Chairman (now Vice President) of Technology and Construction Solicitors Association (TeCSA), Chairman TeCSA Civil Litigation Committee, Member of TCC Users Committee, Society of Construction Law, International Bar Association and was a member of the Official Referees Working Group to the Woolf Enquiry.
Career: Called to the Bar in 1972. Qualified as a Solicitor in 1977. Joined *Bristows Cooke & Carpmael* in 1979 and became a Partner in 1984. Joined *Nicholson Graham & Jones* as a Partner in 1998. Accredited TeCSA adjudicator. Accredited CEDR adjudicator.
Personal: Born 13th May 1949. Educated at Winchester College 1962-66 and King's College, London (LL.B Hons, 1971). Leisure activities include golf, tennis and cricket.

JENKINS, Jane
Freshfields Bruckhaus Deringer, London
(020) 7936 4000
jane.jenkins@freshfields.com
Specialisation: Has broad experience of dispute resolution on and the drafting and negotiation of major construction and engineering projects. Contentious work covers ADR, arbitration and litigation in construction and energy sectors including public procurement bid challenge advice. Non-contentious work covers PFI (including road, rail and prisons projects,) process plant and power projects and institutional development.
Prof. Memberships: City of London Solicitors Company; CEDR accredited mediator.
Career: Qualified 1988, partner with *Freshfields* 1996.
Publications: Contributor to Sweet & Maxwell's 'Construction Law: Themes and Practice' and LLP's 'Privity of Contracts: Impact of the Contract: (Rights of Third Parties) Act 1999.'
Personal: Born 20 March 1963, educated at Lincoln College, Oxford (1981-1985). Married with two children.

JONES, David
Hammond Suddards Edge, London
(020) 7655 1000
david.jones@hammondse.com
Specialisation: Large scale construction and civil engineering disputes both national and international. Experienced in ADR and has successfully concluded a number of mediation/conciliations for clients as well as more traditional forms of dispute resolution such as arbitration, expert determination and litigation (including a year long trial in the Caribbean). He has been involved in non-contentious infrastructure work and more recently with the MoD as its legal adviser in the development of prime contracting. He also has extensive knowledge in particular of tunnelling, water and railway contracts and contracts relating to the maintenance of assets.
Prof. Memberships: TeCSA; London Court of International Arbitration; Society of Construction Law; Court Member of the Company of Water Conservators.
Career: Articles at *Lovell White Durrant*; qualified 1976; *Masons* (equity partner 1982-94) 1980-94; *Hammond Suddards* (equity partner) 1995 to date.
Personal: Married with two student daughters. Interests: football, films and golf.

KELLY, Neil J.
MacRoberts, Edinburgh (0131) 229 5046
neil.kelly@macroberts.co.uk
Specialisation: Practice covers full range of advice to commercial clients in connection with dispute avoidance and resolution (Arbitration, Court, ADR) with particular reference to the construction and civil engineering industries acting for related professions, contractors, sub-contractors and suppliers.
Prof. Memberships: Notary Public, Associate of the Chartered Institute of Arbitrators, Commissioner of the Scottish Council for International Arbitration, Member of International Bar Association.
Career: Aberdeen University (LLB with Distinction and Dip. L.P.). Trainee *MacRoberts*; qualified 1984; partner 1990.
Personal: Born 28th June 1961. Interests include opera and classical music. Lives in Edinburgh.

LANE, Mark
Masons, London (020) 7490 6214
mark.lane@masons.com
Specialisation: Principally contract drafting and dispute resolution. Includes ICC arbitrations, domestic litigation and contract drafting for international and UK infrastructure projects. Also handles EU public procurement advising contracting authorities (including government departments, agencies and utilities) on tendering procedures and structuring tendering procedures under PFI schemes. Acted for Eric Cumine Associates on Harbour City litigation in Hong Kong. Member of the firm's team on Channel Tunnel and Canary Wharf projects and on a number of PFI projects including hospitals (procurement issues) and water and waste water treatment works (project agreements and construction issues). Contract drafting on other water related projects in the recent past includes projects in India, the Philippines, Australasia, and Scotland. Editor-in-chief of *Masons*' 'Water Yearbook'. Has extensive African experience (much of it FIDIC related) including matters in Nigeria, Gambia, Ghana, Mozambique, Kenya and Mali. Has recently worked on projects in Maldives (airport) and Belgium. In March of 1998, led *Masons*' team acting for the Government of Ukraine in negotiations to establish the Project Management Unit to manage the project to render the Chernobyl Nuclear Reactor No4 safe. (The project is ongoing.) Experienced conference speaker nationally and internationally.
Prof. Memberships: Society of Construction Law; IBA (Committee T) Chairman of sub-committee on International Procurement in Construction Projects; European Construction Institute (Member of Executive Committee) (Chairman of European Legislation Task Force).
Career: Qualified in 1975. Partner at *Masons* since 1988.
Personal: Born 18th March 1950. Educated at Cranleigh School 1962-67 and Trinity College, Cambridge 1968-72. Lives in London.

LANGLEY, Robert L.
Watson Burton, Newcastle upon Tyne
(0191) 244 4444

LEVINE, Marshall
Linklaters, London (020) 7456 3580
marshall.levine@linklaters.com
Specialisation: Involved in a wide range of construction and engineering matters, including advice in relation to many construction and engineering projects and major real estate joint ventures, property developments and construction financing. Highly experienced in drafting construction contracts, and in advising on dispute resolution over a wide variety of projects including process plants, civil engineering, substantial headquarter office redevelopment, relocations and refurbishments as well as PFI transactions in the health, property, transportation and waste water sectors. Was involved in the BR privatisation.
Prof. Memberships: 1995 to date: Member of British Consultants Bureau.
Career: Partner and head of the construction and engineering group. 1989 to date: Partner, *Linklaters*; 1982-1989: Assistant solicitor, *Linklaters*. 1987-1989: Reading University, MSc (Construction Management); 1985: ACIArb Institute of Chartered Arbitrators; 1980-1984: Reading University, BSc (Estate Management); 1975-1978: UCL University, LLB.

LEWIS, Simon
Dickinson Dees, Newcastle upon Tyne
(0191) 279 9552
simon.lewis@dickinson-dees.com
Specialisation: Covers full range of Construction Law, including offshore and minerals industries. In particular deals with dispute resolution, including litigation, arbitration, ADR and Adjudication. Also extensively involved in PFI work. Acts for all sectors of the Construction industry. Writes and lectures extensively on construction law and PFI issues. Has a regular column in Building magazine. General Editor of and contributor to 'Tolley's Guide to Construction Contracts.'
Prof. Memberships: Member of the Chartered Institute of Arbitrators, member of TECSA (accredited adjudicator) and ARCOM.
Career: Qualified 1986. Joined *Lovell White Durrant* 1988. Joined *Dickinson Dees* 1992 (Partner from 1995).
Personal: Born 20 November 1960. Bristol University 1979-83 : LL.B, LL.M. Interests include: cinema, hillwalking and American Football. Lives in Newcastle upon Tyne.

LLOYD JONES, David
Hammond Suddards Edge, Birmingham
(0121) 222 3000
david.lloydjones@hammondse.com
Specialisation: Extensive experience in contentious and non-contentious construction. Principal areas of work involve drafting and negotiation of construction and engineering contracts and development agreements covering all aspects of property development, rail, road and engineering projects whether acting for developers, owners, funders, contractors or consultants.
Prof. Memberships: Fellow, Chartered Institute of Arbitrators, Technology and Construction Solicitors Association (Committee Member), CEDR accredited mediator, Society of Construction Law.
Career: Joined *Edge Ellison* in 1989 (partner from 1991).

LONG, Peter
CMS Cameron McKenna, London
(020) 7367 2507
pjl@cmck.com
Specialisation: Partner in Construction Group.

Specialist in construction law with over 20 years experience advising contractors, consultants and employers in the construction industry. Includes advice on construction aspects of major projects and PFI schemes, procurement advice, drafting and negotiation of construction contracts, consultancy agreements, collateral warranties, concession agreements and operating and maintenance agreements. Also advising on contractual claims against and by contractors and consultants, dispute resolution procedures and conduct of litigation, arbitration and ADR procedures. Experienced in all kinds of construction projects including large-scale commercial buildings, civil engineering projects and process plant and heavy engineering. Contributor of articles to the construction press. Speaker at construction law seminars. Accredited mediator with CEDR (Centre for Dispute Resolution).
Prof. Memberships: Law Society, Society of Construction Law, Technology and Construction Solicitors Association.
Career: Qualified in 1978, having joined *McKenna & Co.* in 1975. Became a Partner in 1984. Worked in Hong Kong office 1981-1985, having qualified as a solicitor in Hong Kong in 1981. Partner in *Cameron McKenna* 1997.
Personal: Born 18th October 1950. Attended Balliol College, Oxford 1969-1973 (1st Class Honours in Classics).

MASON, Fenella
DLA, Edinburgh (08700) 111111

McLEAN, Alistair
Dundas & Wilson CS, Edinburgh (0131) 228 8000

MINOGUE, Ann
Linklaters, London (020) 7367 2505
ann.minogue@linklaters.com
Specialisation: Construction law specialist with 20 years' experience in drafting and disputes work on building and construction related contracts for a number of major developments and projects. She has advised developers, occupiers, lenders and government and industry bodies.
Prof. Memberships: University of Reading, Construction Management Forum, and Design-Build Foundation, BPF Construction Committee, 'Justice' Committee (legal remedies for home-owners), Latham Working Group 10, JCT Drafting Sub-Committee.
Career: 2001 to date: Partner, *Linklaters*; 1997-2001: Partner, *CMS Cameron McKenna*; 1985-1997: Partner, *McKenna & Co*; 1980-1985: Assistant, *McKenna & Co*; 1978-1980: Articles, *McKenna & Co*. 1974-1977: Clare College, Cambridge, Law Tripos Parts I and II; 1966-1973: Aylesbury Girls' High School.

MORRISON, Alastair
Masons, Glasgow (0141) 248 4858
alastair.morrison@masons.com
Specialisation: Partner providing legal and strategic advice on all aspect of construction projects, drafting of bespoke contracts and construction arbitration and litigation. Specialising in construction and engineering law and has a depth of experience in major projects.
Prof. Memberships: Law Society of Scotland, International Bar Association Construction Division and Technology and Construction Solicitors Association.
Career: Attended University of Cape Town, University of Glasgow (LLB Hons, DipLP). Assistant solicitor *Digby Brown* 1986-1989; assistant solicitor *McGrigor Donald* 1989-1993; associate partner *Dundas & Wilson CS* 1993-1994; Partner and Head of Construction and Engineering Group 1994-1998; Jointly established *Masons'* Scottish practice in 1998.
Personal: Born 1962. Resides Glasgow. Leisure interests include running and rugby.

MOSEY, David
Trowers & Hamlins, London (020) 7423 8000
dmosey@trowers.com
Specialisation: Partner, Commercial. Head of Projects and Construction Group. Has advised for more than 20 years on UK and international construction law, including major projects in the commercial, industrial, housing, urban regeneration, health and education sectors. Substantial involvement in PFI and leading adviser on partnering and Egan-compliant procurement. Particular expertise in procurement strategies, risk analysis, standard and bespoke contracts and professional appointments. Author of 'PPC2000' (the first standard form of Project Partnering Contract) and of 'Design and Build in Action' (Chandos 1998).
Prof. Memberships: Member of working groups of CIC, Local Government Task Force and Housing Forum and member of the Society of Construction Law, also a highly experienced conference/seminar speaker.

MOSS, David J
Hammond Suddards Edge, Manchester (0161) 830 5000
david.moss@hammondse.com
Specialisation: Partner in construction and engineering unit, head of Manchester unit. Principal area of practice is contentious construction and engineering industry claims. Wide experience of the standard form of building and engineering contract (including JCT, ICE, RMR '80, MF/I, IMechEE, FIDIC).
Prof. Memberships: O.R.S.A., ACIAArb, Society of Construction Law, O.R.S.A. Accredited Adjudicator. CEDR Mediator.
Career: Qualified in 1986. Joined *Hammond Suddards* in 1990.
Personal: Born November 1961. University of Sheffield 1980-83. The College of Law Guildford.

NEWMAN, Paul
Hugh James Ford Simey, Cardiff (029) 2039 1171
paul.newman@hjfs.co.uk
Specialisation: Barrister and senior associate in construction and civil engineering department. (Bar) Has a full practising certificate and rights of audience in all the courts of England and Wales. Deals with contentious and non-contentious construction law. Regularly appears as advocate in arbitration and court hearings and sits as an adjudicator. Has provided seminars on construction law to many organisations, including the College of Law and professional bodies. Author and/or co-author of 10 books as well as papers on construction law.
Prof. Memberships: Called to the Bar by Gray's Inn November 1982, Fellow of the Chartered Institute of Arbitrators, accredited Adjudicator for the Royal Institute of British Architects and the Construction Industry Council.
Career: Called to the Bar in November 1982 and joined *Hugh James Ford Simey* in August 1999.
Personal: Born 5 March 1958. Educated at Clare College, Cambridge (1976-1980), City University, London (1980-81) and the Inns of Court School of Law (1981-82).

NOLAN, Brandon
McGrigor Donald, Glasgow (0141) 248 6677
Specialisation: Head of construction unit. All aspects of construction law including contract drafting, appointment documentation, contract advice, disputes and mediation work. Currently involved in procurement and dispute work in all parts of the UK as well as internationally. Has conducted the advocacy in a number of substantial arbitrations. Sits from time to time as an arbitrator. A frequent speaker at commercially organised seminars.
Prof. Memberships: Member of the Chartered Institute of Arbitrators; Society of Construction Law; International Bar Association; Technology and Construction Solicitors Association.
Career: Qualified 1980 with *McGrigor Donald & Co* (as it was then). Became a partner in 1987. Head of the construction and engineering unit at *McGrigor Donald*.
Personal: Born 4th November 1955. Educated at Glasgow University 1974-1978. Leisure interests include visiting a gym and films.

OATS, Simon
Eversheds, Ipswich (01473) 284546
simonoats@eversheds.com
Specialisation: Construction and engineering related law encompassing contractual advice and disputes resolution. Acts for a number of substantial construction clients including employers, developers, contractors and professionals. Particular experience in engineering contracts, arbitration, adjudication and projects.
Prof. Memberships: Law society, Society of Construction Law, Interact.

PALMER, Simon
Hammond Suddards Edge, Leeds (0113) 284 7000
simon.palmer@hammondse.com
Specialisation: Construction and engineering. Adjudication; technology and construction court litigation; domestic and international arbitration; forms of alternative dispute resolution; advising on construction and engineering contracts, consultants' appointments and collateral warranties. Visiting Lecturer on arbitration and construction law MSc at Leeds Metropolitan University. Speaker on a wide range of construction issues to other forums.
Prof. Memberships: Member of the Chartered Institute of Arbitrators; Honorary Secretary of the North East Branch of the CIArb; member and regional Coordinator of the Society of Construction Law; member of the Yorkshire Construction Association; visiting lecturer.
Career: Qualified 1987. Partner *Eversheds*, 1994-1999. Partner *Hammond Suddards*, 2000.
Personal: Born May 1963. BA in law at Durham University. Interests include music, rugby, walking, socialising. Lives near York.

PATTERSON, Lindy A.
MacRoberts, Edinburgh (0131) 229 5046
lindy.patterson@macroberts.co.uk
Specialisation: Specialises in contentious building and civil engineering matters. Lindy is widely regarded as one of Scotland's leading construction and civil engineering law experts. She acts for a number of the UK's leading construction and engineering companies, regularly handling disputes in arbitration and

litigation covering all aspects of building and civil engineering disputes. She represents clients in the Commercial Court and the Court of Session, as one of Scotland's first Solicitor-Advocates and the first female Solicitor Advocate. She speaks regularly at industry seminars and contributes to building and civil engineering publications.
Prof. Memberships: Obligations Committee of the Law Society; Industrial and Professional Liaison Body of Napier University in connection with the Department of Building and Surveying; Writer to the Signet; Commercial Court Consultative Committee set up to monitor the workings of the Commercial Court; Law Commission Contract Law Advisory Group; laymember of RICS Chairman's Advisory Group; associate, Chartered Institute of Arbitrators.
Career: Trainee Solicitor *W & J Burness* 1980-1982. Solicitor *Biggart Billie & Gifford* and *Menzies Dougal* 1982-1985. Joined *Bird Semple* 1985, became partner 1988; Solicitor-Advocate 1993. Head of construction group at *MacRoberts* (partner 1997). Contributes regularly to publications and seminars.
Personal: Graduated LLB (Hons) Edinburgh University 1980. Skiing, hillwalking and watersports.

PICKUP, Raith
Mills & Reeve, Cambridge (01223) 222283
raith.pickup@mills-reeve.com
Specialisation: Has extremely wide experience of drafting and negotiating the documentation for many substantial projects. These include business parks, retail developments, university campuses, hospitals and large infrastructure projects such as power stations. He heads the *Mills & Reeve* Private Finance Initiative (PFI) team and has advised on more than 30 PFI projects in the health, education, defence and local authority sectors.
Prof. Memberships: Leads the Lectures regularly on the legal aspects of the building and engineering industries as well as PFI and is a member of the Society of Construction Law.

PIGOTT, Ashley
Wragge & Co, Birmingham (0870) 903 1000

PINSENT, Jim
DLA, Liverpool (08700) 111111

PLASCOW, Ronald H.
Mills & Reeve, Cambridge (01223) 222 261
ron.plascow@mills-reeve.com
Specialisation: Partner in Construction and Projects Department. Has practised exclusively in construction and civil engineering since 1982 beginning in industry at Trafalgar House plc and subsequently at *Lovell White Durrant* in London. Regularly advises on the JCT, ICE, ECC and most other forms of standard contracts including partnering forms, used in the UK and on FIDIC Contracts used abroad. Prepares and drafts construction contracts, consultants' appointments and bonds and warranties. Represents employers and contractors involved in litigation in the Courts, or in arbitration. A trained mediator familiar with the use of other ADR techniques to resolve disputes and has represented clients in mediations and concilliations. Editor of Arbitration Practice and Procedure, Interlocutory and Hearing Problems (Lloyd's of London Press Ltd) first edition, contributing author to Tolleys Guide to Construction Contracts, regular speaker at conferences arranged by the RICS, RIBA, ICE and CIArb. Past Secretary to the East Anglia Branch of the CIArb.

POPE, Caroline
Berwin Leighton Paisner, London (020) 760 1000
carolinepope@berwinleightonpaisner.com
Specialisation: Partner specialising in contentious and non-contentious construction and civil engineering. Represents clients from all sides of the construction and engineering industry in project advice and a wide range of dispute resolution. Has particular experience of tunnelling and power projects, defects claims in prestigious office buildings and shopping centres. Has been involved in expert determinations under the IChemE form of contract.
Prof. Memberships: Society of Construction Law; The Law Society of England and Wales; the British Tunnelling Society and the Technology and Construction Solicitors' Association.
Career: Articled *Stilgoes*; qualified 1985; solicitor *Rowe & Maw* 1985-93; solicitor *Barlow Lyde & Gilbert* 1993, partner 1997. Partner, *Berwin Leighton Pasiner* 2001.
Personal: Born 1958; Sherborne School for Girls; London School of Economics (BSc Economics). Resides in Berkshire.

RACE, David
Nicholson Graham & Jones, London
(020) 7360 8106
david.race@ngj.co.uk
Specialisation: Head of Construction and Engineering Department. Main areas of practice are construction and engineering law. Handles major infrastructure projects, particularly in transport and international project work in process engineering and related fields. Also undertakes general commercial work including project finance, joint ventures, procurement, tendering and contracting in the private and public sectors. Major clients include Blue Circle Industries PLC, West African Portland Cement plc, YANBU Cement Company, Essex County Council, and Eurostar (UK) Limited. Author of various articles for professional journals. Visiting lecturer to Crown Agents on international procurement and engineering law. Honarary Solicitor to the Samaritans.
Prof. Memberships: Institute of Arbitrators, Society of Construction Law. Technology and Commercial Construction Solicitors Association, Accredited TeCSA Adjudicator.
Career: Qualified in 1974. Joined *Nicholson Graham & Jones* as Partner in 1987. Before qualifying worked in overseas banking 1969-71. Legal adviser to Mass Transit Railway Corp., Hong Kong 1978-82 and Chief Solicitor to Blue Circle Industries PLC 1985-87.

REDMOND, John V.
Osborne Clarke, Bristol (0117) 917 3000

REES, Peter
Norton Rose, London (020) 7283 6000
reespj@nortonrose.com
Specialisation: Head of *Norton Rose* Litigation Department and Senior Partner in the Construction and Engineering Law Group. All aspects of contentious and non-contentious construction and engineering law. Particular expertise in international arbitration (especially ICC and LCIA). Has advised government departments, multilateral agencies, international organisations and international contractors. Sits as an arbitrator.
Prof. Memberships: Chairman International Construction Projects Committee of IBA; Chairman Technology and Construction Solicitors Association; solicitor representative on Technology and Construction Court User's Committee; Fellow Chartered Institute of Arbitrators; accredited TECSA adjudicator; Board of Advisers, Centre for International Legal Studies, Member Institute of Petroleum.
Career: Qualified 1981 with *Norton Rose.* Partner 1987.
Personal: Born 21st April 1957. MA from Downing College, Cambridge University. MBA from Nottingham Trent University. Leisure interests include football (still crazy enough to be playing), golf and scuba diving.

REEVES, Suzanne
Wedlake Bell, London (020) 7395 3000
Specialisation: Partner and head of the Construction and Engineering team. Acts for all sectors of the industry. Non-contentious work focuses on developers, financial institutions and consultants. Contributor to industry publications. Speaks at industry seminars and conferences. Has close association with major subcontractor organisations. Places emphasis on finding cost-effective solutions in both contentious and non-contentious matters.
Prof. Memberships: Accredited adjudicator, CEDR accredited mediator, Law Society, Technology and Construction Solicitors Association.
Career: Qualified in 1979. Joined *Wedlake Bell* the same year, becoming a Partner in 1986. Head of Construction and Engineering Team.
Personal: Born 13th August 1955. LLB (Exon) 1976. Lives in London.

REGAN, Michael
Rowe & Maw, London (020) 7248 4282
Specialisation: Partner in and Head of Construction and Engineering Department. Advises contractors, employers and professionals, and also insurers, particularly in relation to professional indemnity matters.
Prof. Memberships: Law Society, Chartered Institute of Arbitrators, Society of Construction Law.
Career: Qualified in 1980, having joined *Rowe & Maw* in 1978. Became a Partner in 1985.
Personal: Born 4th October 1955. Attended Westcliff High School 1969-74, then Pembroke College, Oxford 1974-77. Leisure interests include watching cricket, talking about football and playing tennis. Lives in London and Gloucestershire.

ROBERTS, Martin
Masons, London (020) 7490 4000
martin.roberts@masons.com
Specialisation: Partner and Manager of Construction & Engineering Group. Specialises in dispute resolution and non-contentious advice on construction and engineering matters. Leads team of lawyers advising contractors, employers, professionals and insurers on wide range of issues and projects. Recently involved in advising on Croydon Tramlink, Peterborough and Corby CCGT Power Stations, Navotas Power Station where advised successful Plaintiff in Hopewell Project Management Ltd v Ewbank Preece Ltd 1998 1 LLR, major refurbishment of holiday centres for UK leisure group, CHP Plant in UK and major road project in South East. Currently advising on various issues relating to HGCR Act, Arbitration Act and on several adjudications and mediations. Accredited CEDR Mediator and Adjudicator.
Prof. Memberships: Law Society, elected committee member of City of London Law Society, member of Litigation Sub-Committee of City of London Law

Society, Society of Construction Law, ORSA, CEDR.
Career: Qualified 1979, partner with *Masons* 1983, member of *Masons'* Partnership Strategy Board 1992 to 1997.
Personal: Born 11th April 1955. Attended City of London Freeman's School, Kingston University (BA Hons) Law. Leisure interests include theatre, cinema, pop music, tennis, swimming and two children. Lives in Sussex.

ROBSON, Nigel R
Eversheds, Leeds (0113) 243 0391
nigelrobson@eversheds.com
Specialisation: Partner in Construction and Engineering Unit. Principal area of practice involves handling contractual disputes arising from construction or engineering projects on JCT, ICE, GC Works and FIDIC forms of contract or bespoke contracts with particular emphasis on loss and expense claims and defects claims. Has considerable experience in relation to hospitals, process engineering, power stations, off-shore, waste incinerators, major civil engineering and defence related projects. Other main area of work involves drafting and amending commercial agreements for construction and engineering projects.
Prof. Memberships: Law Society; Fellow, Chartered Institute of Arbitrators.
Career: Qualified in 1977 and went on to join *Eversheds*, becoming a Partner in 1980. Managing Partner of *Eversheds* North East since 1992-2000. Head of Construction North 2000.
Personal: Born 23rd May 1951.

ROE, Mark
Masons, London (020) 7490 6545
mark.roe@masons.com
Specialisation: Partner specialising in major projects and international dispute resolution in the Construction Industry. Expert in advising on major projects in the engineering construction and related industries. Has advised and acted extensively in the resolution of disputes by mediation and mini-trial/structured settlement procedures, adjudication arbitration (both UK and international), expert determination and litigation. Sits as a mediator. Drafted several construction specific sets of mediation rules. Advises on transactional matters, partnering and PFI. Has advised on a number of major PFI deals. Currently advising on a major partnering initiative. Lectures on ADR, partnering, project management and construction law matters. Described previously in Chambers as a "flamboyant streetfighter with a good grasp of the issues" – a description which his clients seemed to recognise.
Prof. Memberships: TECSA Committee Member, Former Director of CEDR 1989-1999, Accredited Mediator.
Career: Qualified in 1981. Joined *Masons* in 1981. Partner of *Masons* since 1985.
Personal: Born 30th May 1955. Attended the John Fisher School 1965-73, educated at Balliol College, Oxford 1974-77. Leisure interests include rugby, tennis, cycling, skiing, theatre and the arts and crafts movement. Lives in Central London.

ROE, Sally
Freshfields Bruckhaus Deringer, London (020) 7936 4000
sallyroe@freshfields.com
Specialisation: Partner in Litigation Department. Authorised to exercise rights of audience in the Higher Courts (Civil Proceedings), July '95. Head of Construction and Engineering Group. Extensive experience of litigation and arbitration in these fields, acting for employers and contractors. Also handles non-contentious projects including property developments and infrastructure projects. Other areas of practice include advising on the application of the EC Procurement Regime.
Prof. Memberships: City of London Solicitors Company.
Career: Qualified in 1981. Joined *Freshfields* in 1988, becoming a Partner in 1990.
Personal: Born 1956. Attended Wakefield Girls' High School 1965-74 and St Hilda's College, Oxford 1974-77.

ROUT, Peter
DLA, Manchester (08700) 111111

ROWLAND, Simon J.
Dickinson Dees, Newcastle upon Tyne (0191) 279 9000

RUSHTON, John Michael
Rowe & Maw, London (020) 7248 4282
Specialisation: Partner in construction department. Acts or has acted for all sides of the construction industry: developers, building owners, consultants, main contractors, sub-contractors trade associations, adjudicators and arbitrators regarding building and civil engineering projects. Handles litigation, arbitration and adjudication. Cases have involved dredging, ground conditions, mechanical and electrical disputes, decontamination contracts and defects claims, fee claims and claims of loss and expense and extensions of time. Drafts and advises on terms of construction contracts. Accredited adjudicator of the Technology and Construction Court Solicitors Association. Lectures both for private and for public organisations. Accredited mediator with the Centre for Dispute Resolution. Has some advocacy experience in the High Court and before arbitrators and adjudicators.
Prof. Memberships: Chartered Institute of Arbitrators (Fellow), Institution of Civil Engineering Surveyors (Fellow), Society of Construction Law, Worshipful Company of Arbitration (Liveryman) and Member of the Advisory Panel of the Institution of Civil Engineers. Regular contributor to construction press. Firm has corporate or associate membership of British Academy of Experts and Confederation of Construction Specialists.
Career: Qualified 1975. Joined *Rowe & Maw* in 1980, becoming a partner in 1981.
Personal: Born 22nd March 1950. Attended Uppingham 1963-68, then Sidney Sussex College, Cambridge, 1969-72. Liveryman of the Worshipful Company of Arbitrators. Leisure interests include MCC and family life: he has two children. Lives in Loughton.

RUSSELL, Victoria E.
Fenwick Elliott, London (020) 7956 9354
v.russell@fenwickelliott.co.uk
Specialisation: Partner. Handles contentious and non contentious construction and engineering matters with a special emphasis on litigation, adjudication, arbitration and ADR. Advises employers, main contractors, specialist subcontractors and members of the professional team on a variety of points of law, practice and procedure. Has dealt with a number of complex construction disputes, some arising from the various JCT and ICE standard forms of contract and others from bespoke contractual arrangements. German speaker. Experienced arbitrator, CEDR accredited mediator and TECSA adjudicator.
Prof. Memberships: TECSA, IBA (Business Section), LCIA, Society of Construction Law (Council Member since 1990, Chairman 2000-), European Society of Construction Law (Vice-President 2000-); Chartered Institute of Arbitrators – Fellow (1991). Member of the Diploma in Arbitration Advisory Board of the College of Estate Management in Reading (1991-97). Freeman of the Worshipful Company of Constructors. Member of the Court of Assistants and Master-elect of the Worshipful Company of Arbitrators and Chairman of its Charitable Trust. Fellow of the Chartered Institute of Building (2001).
Career: Qualified and joined *Freedmans* in 1981. Became a partner in 1985. Joined *Berrymans* in 1996. Joined *Fenwick Elliot* 2000.
Personal: Born 12th October 1956. Educated at Benenden School, Kent 1968-73 and Exeter University 1974-77 (LL.B Hons). Member of Benenden School Trust and Alumni Board of Exeter University. Lives in West London. Sons aged eight and ten.

RYLAND, Jane
Cripps Harries Hall, Tunbridge Wells (01892) 506354
hjr@crippslaw.com
Specialisation: Construction law, both contentious and non-contentious. Represented many claimants in adjudication, all with success. Qualified adjudicator.
Prof. Memberships: Member of the Chartered Institute of Arbitrators – MCI Arb. Association of Women in Property; The Society of Construction Law; Interact, TeCSA and The Adjudication Society.
Career: *Laytons* solicitors (assistant 1991-97, associate 1997, partner 1999). Qualified as construction adjudicator 2001. *Cripps Harries Hall*, partner and head of construction, 2001.
Personal: Queens' College, Cambridge. Enjoys sport, gardening, walking and travel.

SALMON, Kenneth T.
Kirk Jackson, Manchester (0161) 794 0431
law@kirk_jackson.com
Specialisation: Partner construction law department. Main area of work is building and civil engineering disputes, in court adjudication and arbitration, and advising on contract documentation. Conducts in-house seminars for clients.
Prof. Memberships: Law Society, TECSA, Northern Arbitration Association, Manchester Law Society, A.C.I. Arb.
Career: Qualified 1973 while at *Kirk Jackson* and became a partner in 1975.
Personal: Born 16 April 1946. Leisure pursuits include cycling, five-a-side soccer, hill-walking, music and reading. Lives in Warrington.

SCOTT, Martin
Walker Morris, Leeds (0113) 283 2500
mls@walkermorris.co.uk
Specialisation: Partner and Head of Construction Group. Practice covers the full rage of construction and engineering law, both contentious and non-contentious. Particularly active in the field of disputes where defects whether by design or in construction are the central issue. Acts mainly for Employers/Developers and specialist sub-contractors but also undertakes work for main contractors within the region.

Career: Qualified 1985. At *Scott Turnbull & Kendall*, now *Walker Morris*, since 1984. Became a Partner in 1992.
Personal: Born 13th August 1959. Educated at Ashville College, Harrogate and Leicester Polytechnic BA Law. Interests include flying, farming and family. Lives in Harrogate.

SHADBOLT, Richard
Shadbolt & Co, London (020) 7332 5750
Dick_Shadbolt@shadboltlaw.co.uk
Specialisation: Senior partner. Main area of practice is construction law, including work on engineering and major projects, with experience in UK and internationally since 1967. Particular experience of structuring and drafting of contracts for major projects and construction. Litigation and arbitration work covered as well as environmental, trade and other commercial matters. Involved with the drafting of the widely praised Association of Consultant Architects standard contract form. Author of articles in professional and other periodicals and occasional lecturer on International Construction Contracts. Regular speaker at professional conventions and international conferences on construction contract and other legal topics.
Prof. Memberships: Law Society, Law Society of Hong Kong, American Bar Association (Associate Member), International Bar Association, Inter-Pacific Bar Association, British Consultants Bureau.
Personal: Born 18th December 1942. Attended Okehampton Grammar School 1954-60; King's College, London 1961-64 then College of Law, Guildford 1967. Leisure pursuits include family life.

SHAW, Murray
Biggart Baillie, Glasgow (0141) 228 8000
mshaw@biggartbaillie.co.uk
See under Litigation, p.581

SHAW, Peter
Taylor Joynson Garrett, London (020) 7300 7000

SHERMAN, Henry
CMS Cameron McKenna, London (020) 7367 3000

STANIFORTH, Alison J
Eversheds, Leeds (0113) 243 0391
alisonstaniforth@eversheds.com
Specialisation: Partner, construction and engineering. Principal area of practice is construction/engineering. Drafting and negotiating standard and bespoke contracts and professional appointments and ancilliary documents. Also focus of dispute resolution, important matters handled include facilities management agreements; power generation projects; PFI/PPP; projects in China, mainland Europe and Poland; railway track and maintenance. Clients include Yorkshire Electricity, British Waterways Board, Weir Pumps Ltd, Morrison Construction. Visiting Lecturer at Leeds Metropolitan University (MSc in Arbitration and Construction Law). Conference speaker for RICS, CIOB, the Institute of Structural Engineers and IRR.
Prof. Memberships: CIArb, TeCSA, Common Purpose Graduate, Network.
Career: Qualified 1985. With *Herbert Smith* 1983-86. Joined *Hepworth & Chadwick* 1986; became a partner at *Eversheds Hepworth & Chadwick* in 1991.
Personal: Born 13 December 1957. Leeds University 1976-79 (LL.B), Trinity Hall, Cambridge 1980-83 (MLitt), Nottingham Trent 1999 (MBA). Interests include golf, malt whiskey and gardening.

STEADMAN, Tim
Clifford Chance, London (020) 7600 1000
tim.steadman@cliffordchance.com
Specialisation: Partner and Head of Construction Group, specialising in the drafting of construction contracts and related documents. Particular experience in connection with privately financed projects, such as those arising from the UK Public Private Partnerships programme and PPP schemes elsewhere, and with the construction aspects of private sector project financings.
Prof. Memberships: European Construction Institute; IBA committee "T"; CBI Modernising Government Committee; UN/ECE PPP Forum.
Career: Hertford College; Oxford University. Trainee and assistant *Lovell White & King* 1976-1982; associate *Baker & McKenzie* 1982-1985; partner *Baker & McKenzie* 1985-1997; partner *Clifford Chance* since March 1997.
Personal: Born 1955; resides London.

STUBBS, Jane
Addleshaw Booth & Co, Leeds (0113) 209 2362
jlts@addleshaw-booth.co.uk
Specialisation: Non-contentious construction and PFI work. Acts for a variety of clients including developers, funding institutions, the public sector, consultants and contractors. Extensive experience in drafting of development and funding agreements, partnering contracts, construction contracts, consultancy agreements and warranties.
Career: Articles with *Lovells*, qualifying in 1993. Joined *Booth & Co* on qualification and became a partner of *Addleshaw Booth and Co* in February 2000.
Personal: Born 1967. Educated at Nottingham University. Leisure interests include golf, travel and cinema. Lives in Leeds.

TAYLOR, Kevin
Shepherd & Wedderburn WS, Edinburgh (0131) 228 9900
kevin.taylor@shepwedd.co.uk
Specialisation: Non-contentious construction, projects and PFI/PPP across all sectors including property development; engineering, infrastructure, process plant, energy, outsourcing/facilities management; corporate PFI.
Prof. Memberships: Law Society of Scotland, Writer to the Signet.
Career: Articled *Steedman Ramage*; *Shepherd & Wedderburn* 1994 to date; secondment The Scottish Office M6 DBF0 Project (1997-98); partner and head of construction and special projects group 1998 to date.
Personal: Perth High School; Edinburgh University. Sport, travel, reading and music.

TURNBULL, Craig
MacRoberts, Glasgow (0141) 332 9988
craig.turnbull@macroberts.co.uk
Specialisation: Partner in construction group representing employers, contractors, sub-contractors and consultants in litigation, adjudication and arbitration. Regularly acts as arbiter's clerk and as legal advisor to adjudicators. In addition represents construction clients in health and safety and environmental prosecutions and advises generally on those matters. Acted in the first Scottish case seeking enforcement of an adjudicators award. Acts for AMEC, Safeway, Carillion, Railtrack, Henry Boot, Smith Kline Beecham and Scottish Power amongst others.
Prof. Memberships: Society of Construction Law, Associate of the Chartered Institute of Arbitrators.
Publications: Co-author of 'MacRoberts on Scottish Building Contracts'.
Personal: Born 1966. Lives Glasgow. Married, one son. Leisure interests include golf and football.

VASEY, John
Beachcroft Wansbroughs, Bristol (0117) 918 2000
jvasey@bwlaw.co.uk
Specialisation: Well known for construction-related claims for insurers but increasingly acting also on contentious and non-contentious issues for developers and contractors. Has detailed knowledge and experience of the insurance provisions of construction and development contracts. Typically handles the contract aspects of major property damage and contractors' 'all risks' claims. Also deals with professional indemnity claims on behalf of architects and engineers and is involved in defending construction-related health and safety precautions. In addition to work for insurers, acts for major contractors, public authorities and developers. A keen exponent of cheaper and quicker methods of resolving disputes. Team works closely with the firms expanding property group on a range of major developments across the country. Major new clients include Rail Track and the ACE Engineering Insurance scheme.
Career: Qualified in 1980. *McKenna & Co* 1984-87. Joined *Beachcroft Wansbroughs* in 1988. Partner in 1993.

WELSH, John
Morison Bishop, Glasgow (0141) 248 4672
Specialisation: Chairman of Morison Bishop and Partner in the Litigation Division. Main area of practice is construction law, including professional negligence claims against engineers, architects and surveyors, arbitrations, drafting and advising on construction law contracts, appointments and warranties. John Welsh speaks frequently at conferences and seminars on construction law and related topics including mediation. He has also advised arbiters and clerks in arbitrations and more recently this practice has developed into advising generally on professional negligence and claims against solicitors and accountants.
Prof. Memberships: Law Society of Scotland, Royal Faculty of Procurators in Glasgow.
Career: Qualified in 1968. Assistant Solicitor and Partner at *Robertson Chalmers & Auld* 1969-86. Partner with *Bishop and Robertson Chalmers* (now known as *Morison Bishop*) from 1986. Accredited by the Law Society of Scotland as a Specialist in Construction Law in 1993 and as a Solicitor-Mediator in 1994.
Personal: Born 12th September 1945. Educated at Glasgow University 1963-66. Enjoys golf and fishing. Lives in Bearsden.

WHITE, Neil
Taylor Joynson Garrett, London (020) 7300 7000

WILCOCK, Christopher
Hammond Suddards Edge, Birmingham (0121) 222 3286
chris.wilcock@hammondse.com
Specialisation: Main practice areas are construction and engineering. Contentious and non-contentious work. Lectured on dispute resolution techniques. Acts as adjudicator and is an accredited adjudicator and

mediator. Acts for diverse clients involved in the construction/engineering sectors.
Prof. Memberships: Associate Chartered Institute of Arbitrators, Member Pipeline Industries Guild.
Career: Qualified 1987. Specialised in construction/engineering since then.
Personal: Leisure interests – Manchester United FC, walking, golf.

WINTER, Jeremy
Baker & McKenzie, London (020) 7919 1000
jeremy.winter@bakernet.com
Specialisation: Resolution of construction and projects disputes by arbitration, litigation and ADR. Particular expertise in civil engineering matters. Twenty years' experience of construction law in a total of 30 countries around the world (particularly Europe, Africa and the Middle East). Conducts own advocacy in arbitration and in High Court. Frequent speaker and writer on construction and arbitration topics. Chairman of Society of Construction Law Working Group on delay analysis.
Prof. Memberships: Hon Fellow of Institution of Civil Engineering Surveyors, Society of Construction Law, Technology and Construction Solicitors Association (Member of Committee). Member of Association for Project Management, Fellow of the Geological Society, Member of LCIA.
Career: Qualified 1979. Joined *Baker & McKenzie* London 1980. Worked in *Baker & McKenzie's* Sydney Office 1982-84. Partner 1987.
Personal: Born 26 December 1953. Warwick University (LLB Hons 1975). Lives in Toys Hill, Kent.

WOOD, Martin
Greenwoods, Peterborough (01733) 887700

WOOD, Peter
Masons, Manchester (0161) 877 3777
peter.wood@masons.com
Specialisation: Called to Bar 1979 (Solicitor 1985) Partner in Construction & Engineering Group. Handles all aspects of contentious and non-contentious construction and engineering law. Also deals with all aspects of energy law. Has handled numerous reported cases including Lorne Stewart v. William Sindall, Walter Lawrence v. Commercial Union Props, Emson v. Protea, AMEC v. Crown House and Davy v. Tate & Lyle. Former editor of *Construction Law Journal*; currently editorial board member. Lectures extensively on construction and engineering law.
Prof. Memberships: Law Society, Northern Arbitration Association, Energy Industries Council.
Career: Qualified for the Bar in 1979 and as a solicitor in 1985. Joined *Masons* in 1982, becoming a Partner in 1985, Senior Partner in Manchester office in 1989 and UK Managing Partner in 1997. Editor of *Construction Law Journal* in 1988 and editorial board member in 1991. Council Member Northern Arbitration Association in 1992.
Personal: Born 17th August 1956. Attended Altrincham Grammar School to 1975, and King's College London to 1978. Leisure interests include gardening and family. Lives in Prestbury, Cheshire.

WRIGHT, John
Berwin Leighton Paisner, London (020) 7760 1000
john.wright@berwinleightonpaisner.com
Specialisation: John Wright is a member of *BLP's* construction and engineering Group. He acts for contractors, sub-contractors, professional indemnity insurers and employers and has particular expertise in arbitration and alternative dispute resolution (ADR). Recent work includes a substantial international arbitration relating to a design and build hi-tech contract; a series of disputes on a construction project in Central London; and acting as mediator and adjudicator in several significant disputes. John lectures on a variety of construction issues and ADR to clients and outside organisations. He is an Accredited Mediator with CEDR (Centre for Dispute Resolution) and an Accredited Adjudicator with TeCSA (Technology and Construction Solicitors' Association). He is a TeCSA committee member, a Fellow of the Chartered Institute of Arbitrators and a Past Chairman of the London Branch. He is also a member of the Society of Construction Arbitrators.
Career: Qualified in 1976. Head of the *Warner Cranston* Construction Department from 1984-1998. Joined *Paisner & Co* in 1999.
Personal: Born 2nd May 1952. Educated Hereford Cathedral School 1963-69 and St John's College, Cambridge 1970-73 (BA 1973, MA 1977). Leisure interests include golf, cricket, wine tasting and theatre. Lives in Richmond, Surrey.

WRIGHTON, Ralph
Eversheds, Newcastle upon Tyne (0191) 2611661
ralphwrighton@eversheds.com
Specialisation: Partner. Head of construction and engineering group in North East. Specialising exclusively in construction law since 1979 in connection with civil engineering, power generation, offshore engineering, environmental and process engineering and building projects in the public and private sectors both in the UK and overseas. Over 10 years' involvement in international arbitration conducted in the main European arbitration centres. Regularly advising on major infrastructure contracts including education, health and local government projects and major dispute management and resolution.
Prof. Memberships: Law Society. The Society of Construction Law. Northern Dispute Resolutions.
Career: Articled *Berwin Leighton*. Qualified 1976. Trafalgar House Plc 1979. *Herbert Oppenheimer* 1986. *Church & Church* 1987. *Eversheds* 1990.
Personal: Born 1951. Educated at University College London. Interests include music, theatre and history.

YULE, Ian
Wragge & Co, Birmingham (0870) 903 1000

CORPORATE FINANCE

OVERVIEW: The general downturn in domestic public M&A work has left even the most esteemed corporate departments barely ticking over in comparison with last year's business boom – "*there are only a few remaining on the floor by early evening*". While the landscape has been peppered with a few key highlights, such as Vodafone's disposal of Orange to France Telecom, the investment banks predict resurgence in market conditions, possibly by the end of the year. Further afield, European corporate consolidation continues to generate demand for cross-border work, while many firms continue to gear up their global operations. A word of explanation on this year's new league table format is in order. For pragmatic reasons (ie format) and in order to facilitate accurate comparison of 'like with like', the corporate finance league tables in previous editions were split on the basis of core team size. However in the interest of addressing firms which truly "punch above their weight", the criteria for grouping firms have been re-assessed. While accepting that a team's critical mass is relevant to its dealing capacity, the new tables reflect a (truer) correlation between firms, which demonstrate comparable levels of typical deal size and flow. Factors such as deal complexity, quality of client base and consistency of transactional encounter with peers were taken as indicators of these considerations. The rankings within each table strongly reflect market opinion of firm performance within the sector.

TOP CORPORATE FINANCE FIRMS NATIONWIDE

TOP TWELVE (ranked by clients)

	FIRMS	OVERALL SCORE	NO. OF TIMES RANKED 1st	POSITION LAST YEAR
1	Slaughter and May	198	21	2
2	Linklaters	160	12	1
3	Allen & Overy	134	8	5
4	Freshfields Bruckhaus Deringer	133	11	3
5	Clifford Chance	124	14	4
6	Herbert Smith	64	8	6
7	Ashurst Morris Crisp	55	1	7
8	Lovells	30	2	11
9	CMS Cameron Mckenna	25	4	n/a
10	Addleshaw Booth & Co	17	1	n/a
10	Macfarlanes	17	3	10
11	Eversheds	15	3	n/a

THE SURVEY

Each year we conduct a client-only survey among the FTSE All Share companies. All respondents are key buyers of legal services. We ask them which corporate finance teams they rate in the Top Twelve. The results published here are based on the first 100 replies and should be used in conjunction with our main tables.

RESEARCH APPROVED BY BMRB: *For this edition,* Chambers' *researchers conducted 6,552 interviews – 4,419 with law firms, 554 with barristers and 1,579 with clients.*

The validity of the research was scrutinised by BMRB International, who audited both the methodology and the results at our offices in July 2001. They interviewed Chambers' *researchers and cross-checked sample interviews. Details of the audit appear on page 7.*

LONDON

LARGER DEALS

Freshfields Bruckhaus Deringer (see firm details p.964) "*A classy firm*" whose well-developed relationships with investment banks are seen to be "*paying dividends on M&A.*" Rated by clients for the "*true quality*" of its "*absolutely first rate*" individuals, the style of this "*immensely experienced*" team is described as "*commercial, focused on the client's objective, and able to do deals quickly and to deadlines.*" The firm's merger with Bruckhaus Westrick Heller Löber in August last year has seamlessly reinforced its outstanding pan-European coverage. "*Sharp, quick*" **Barry O'Brien** (see p.254) is a "*potent operator with old school quality.*" A "*first class advisor,*" he has been involved in a number of high profile cross-border takeover bids, including SKW's £1.36 billion cash offer for Laporte, Telewest's £2.3 billion takeover of Flextech, and Schlumberger's £3.6 billion takeover of Sema Group. Researchers were told that the "*red hot*" **Will Lawes** (see p.250)is "*highly intelligent and efficient, with a super manner.*" His presence is "*no surprise on big deals*" such as advising Pearson on the £12 billion-plus agreement for the merger of one of its subsidiaries, and on its $2.5 billion acquisition of National Computer Systems. He also advised PowerGen on the £5.1 billion recommended takeover by E.ON and BT's agreement with Vodafone AirTouch to acquire £7.2 billion of additional shares in Airtel. Well known in the banking community, **Mark Rawlinson** (see p.255) is "*great with clients and a good all-rounder.*" He is "*commercial, knows the law and has fantastic experience.*" He advised Ineos Capital on the purchase of various businesses from ICI, and represented EMI on its proposed mergers with Warner Music and Bertelsmann. Concentrating more on running the firm, senior partner **Anthony Salz** (see p.256) is seen these days "*more at the top end of deals.*" Said to be "*charm personified,*" he "*uses the power of silence well.*" Although he "*visits the front line less often,*" he is admired for "*generating the instinctive trust of his clients.*" He advised Prudential on its proposed merger with American General Corporation. "*Investment banks absolutely adore*" **Tim Emmerson** (see p.245), who has "*built up an excellent following.*" Seen advising the joint global co-ordinators on the IPO of Orange, and advising on Bass' £2.3 billion sale of its brewing arm to Interbrew, he is a "*first class lawyer's lawyer*" who "*extracts knowledge brilliantly*" and "*knows his way round all the corporate finance issues.*" "Confident, rigorous" **Edward Braham** (see p.242) has "*a constructive approach to deal-doing.*" He uses his "*incisive mind*" to "*get the best out of everybody.*" His highlights include acting for Hewlett-Packard on demergers, the possible acquisition of PwC's consulting division and the Kingfisher bid for an Irish telephone company. **Julian Long** (see p.251) has an "*unstuffy, intelligent approach*" that "*instantly gets respect from everyone.*" He advised TI on

CORPORATE FINANCE: LARGER DEALS • London	Ptnrs	Assts
1 Freshfields Bruckhaus Deringer	50	150
Linklaters	50	167
Slaughter and May	n/a	n/a
2 Allen & Overy	38	n/a
Clifford Chance	27	40
Herbert Smith	37	n/a
3 Ashurst Morris Crisp	49	n/a
4 Lovells	19	75
Norton Rose	34	80
5 Macfarlanes	13	23
Simmons & Simmons	26	55

LEADING INDIVIDUALS	
★ **BOARDMAN Nigel** Slaughter and May	**CHEYNE David** Linklaters
1 **CANN Anthony** Linklaters	
LAWES William Freshfields Bruckhaus	**O'BRIEN Barry** Freshfields Bruckhaus
PAUL Alan Allen & Overy	**RAWLINSON Mark** Freshfields Bruckhaus
SALZ Anthony Freshfields Bruckhaus	**UNDERHILL William** Slaughter and May
2 **CLARKE Tim** Linklaters	**COOKE Stephen** Slaughter and May
EMMERSON Tim Freshfields Bruckhaus	**GODDEN Richard** Linklaters
HATTRELL Martin Slaughter and May	**MACAULAY Anthony** Herbert Smith
MIDDLEDITCH Matthew Linklaters	**PALMER James** Herbert Smith
PECK Andrew Linklaters	**SIGNY Adam** Clifford Chance
3 **ASHWORTH Chris** Ashurst Morris Crisp	**BARNARD Stephen** Herbert Smith
BOND Richard Herbert Smith	**BRAHAM Edward** Freshfields Bruckhaus
CLARK Adrian Ashurst Morris Crisp	
HATCHARD Michael Skadden, Arps, Slate, Meagher & Flom LLP	
LEWIS David Norton Rose	**LONG Julian** Freshfields Bruckhaus
RANDELL Charles Slaughter and May	**SACKMAN Simon** Norton Rose
WOOTTON David Allen & Overy	
4 **ALLEN-JONES Charles** Linklaters	**AP SIMON Charles** Freshfields Bruckhaus
BERINGER Guy Allen & Overy	**CHILDS David** Clifford Chance
CLARK Tim Slaughter and May	**CRANFIELD Richard** Allen & Overy
EVANS Stuart Simmons & Simmons	**JAMES Glen** Slaughter and May
MURPHY Frances Slaughter and May	**PEARSON Christopher** Norton Rose
PEARSON David Clifford Chance	**PELL Marian** Herbert Smith
RYDE Andy Slaughter and May	**SUTTON Robert** Macfarlanes
WIPPELL Mark Allen & Overy	
5 **BELLIS Tim** Herbert Smith	**COPPIN Jonathan** Norton Rose
DAVIDSON John Lovells	**DAVIS James** Freshfields Bruckhaus
ELDER Ian Allen & Overy	**ELLARD John** Linklaters
GOODALL Caroline Herbert Smith	**KING Peter** Linklaters
KNAPP Vanessa Freshfields Bruckhaus	**KNIGHT Adrian** Shearman & Sterling
LETH Mary Macfarlanes	**MACFARLANE David** Ashurst Morris Crisp
MARCHANT Simon Freshfields Bruckhaus	
STEPHENSON Barbara Norton Rose	**STERN Robert** Slaughter and May
SULLIVAN Michael Linklaters	**TWENTYMAN Jeff** Slaughter and May
UP AND COMING	
NICHOLSON Graham Freshfields Bruckhaus	
NORMAN Guy Clifford Chance	**VON BISMARCK Nilufer** Slaughter and May
ONES TO WATCH	
BEASTALL Jonathan Clifford Chance	

This book is the product of 6,552 1/2 hour interviews. See p.7 for BMRB audit.
Within each band, firms are listed alphabetically. *See individuals' profiles p.239*

its £4.5 billion merger with Smiths Industries and the Royal Bank of Scotland on the financing of Mellon Financial Corporation's regional banking business. "*Gentlemanly*" **Charles ap Simon** (see p.239) is a "*traditional lawyer*" with a "*mild but effective*" manner, while in a similar mould, "*charming*" **James Davis** (see p.244)can also be a "*formidable opponent.*" The latter advised Compass on its £18 billion merger with Granada to form Granada Compass, and on the £1.3 billion demerger of hotels. **Vanessa Knapp** (see p.250)is "*extremely impressive*" on technical matters, while clients find "*commercial*" **Simon Marchant** (see p.252) a "*responsive*" lawyer who "*talks the same language and works like a Trojan.*" "*Effective operator*" **Graham Nicholson** (see p.253)has been impressing peers on work such the merger of Allied Zurich and Zurich Financial Services. The team advised RBS on its £26.5 billion bid for NatWest, and acted for CSFB, financial advisors to Barclays, on the proposed £5.5 billion acquisition of Woolwich. **Clients:** Corporates: AstraZeneca; Bass; Marconi; Pearson Group; Powergen; Prudential; Reed Elsevier; Rolls Royce; Telewest; Tesco Group; ICI; Kingfisher Group; Hewlett-Packard; EMI; DaimlerChrysler; British Telecom. Financials: CSFB; Deutsche; Dresdner Kleinwort Benson; Goldman Sachs; Merrill Lynch; Morgan Stanley Dean Witter; UBS Warburg; Royal Bank of Scotland.

Linklaters (see firm details p.1042) "*Top of the tree,*" this "*consistently impressive*" team has had a "*wonderful transactional year.*" As reflected in European league table surveys, the practice has "*done well in getting its international strategy right,*" while clients report of its "*first rate service on inter-European cross border transactions,*" some opining that it is "*stronger because of the Alliance.*" The team's "*proactive, high quality*" lawyers are "*strong deal-doers*" who operate with "*quiet business efficiency.*" Competitors concede that the firm's focus on its overseas empire has done nothing to impair its capacity for capturing big-ticket work. "*Great brain*" **David Cheyne** (see p.242) is a "*highly skilled advisor*" and "*formidable opponent.*" "*Proactive, bright and outgoing,*" he has "*an incredible client list*" and is "*almost without peer in the country,*" according to clients. He advised on Vodafone's £25 billion disposal of Orange to France Telecom, and the NatWest/Bank of Scotland/Royal Bank of Scotland mergers. New senior partner, the "*patrician*" **Anthony Cann** (see p.242), is "*extremely personable.*" An "*outstanding lawyer,*" he "*thinks around all aspects of a deal, and gets things done in a practical manner.*" His highlights include advising BG on its £13 billion restructuring and on the subsequent £15 billion demerger of Lattice from the group, as well as Scottish & Newcastle's £670 million disposal of CenterParcs. Known for his strong links with key corporates and investment banks, "*pragmatic*" **Richard Godden** (see p.246) is a "*loyal and highly skilled individual,*" although he can be "*a little dry*" for some tastes. He advised on Ernst & Young's £7.2 billion merger with Cap Gemini. Peers regard **Matthew Middleditch** (see p.517) as a "*real pleasure to do business with on tricky deals.*" A lawyer of "*fine intellect,*" he is "*impossible to rattle and unfailingly pleasant*" and wins client respect for "*getting it right without melodrama.*" He advised on Unigate's demerger and merger of its dairy business with Dairy Crest. "*Modest and calm,*" **Tim Clarke**'s (see p.243) star is rising fast. He is commended for his "*lucid and clear*" advice and is an "*outstanding draftsman.*" He has advised on the privatisations of Telecom Italia, Telkom Kenya and South African Airways. Acting for clients such as Halifax and Commercial Union, building society work forms a significant part of **Andrew Peck**'s (see p.254) practice. Managing "*complex deals in highly regulated sectors,*" he is "*a man of broad-ranging talents, who will develop a fair way to deal with a matter on its merits.*" He advised Halifax on its acquisition of up to 60% of Prudential Holdings in St James's Place Capital. "*Devoted to his clients,*" former senior partner **Charles Allen-Jones** (see p.239) has a strong track record which includes SmithKline Beecham's £115 billion merger with Glaxo Wellcome. **John Ellard** (see p.244) is known for his privatisations expertise, notably in the transport sector, while "*true generalist*" **Peter King** (see p.250) "*keeps his name high in a variety of fields.*" He advised on Dresdner Bank's $1.37 billion acquisition of Wasserstein Perella. "*Bright as a button,*" **Michael Sullivan** (see p.258) is "*fun to deal with.*" He advised on National Power's demerger of its UK generation and supply business to form Innogy and International Power. Further cross-border highlights for the firm include Vodafone AirTouch's acquisition of a 43.5% stake in Airtel (£7 billion,) BP Amoco's recommended cash offer for Burmah Castrol (£3 billion) and Scottish & Newcastle's acquisition of Kronenbourg Brewing Assets from Danone (£2.4 billion). **Clients:** Corporates: Anglo American; BAE Systems; BG Group; BP Amoco; Bass; Billiton; BT; Centrica; Halifax; Lattice Group; MEPC; Scottish & Newcastle; SmithKline Beecham; Vodafone. Financials: CSFB; Deutsche Bank; Dresdner Kleinwort Wasserstein; Goldman Sachs; JP Morgan Chase; Lazards; Lehman Brothers; Merrill Lynch; Morgan Stanley; RBS NatWest; Schroder Salomon Smith Barney; Warburg Dillon Read.

Slaughter and May (see firm details p.1135) (62 ptrs undertake corporate work)"*Utterly first rate,*" say commentators of what many of them consider "*the best corporate finance firm in the world in terms of sheer intellectual capacity.*" The firm's market reputation for its "*phenomenal M&A practice*" on behalf of an "*unbelievable client list*" continues to be unsurpassed. Adhering to its "*best friends*" policy, the firm's focus on high-end transactions has been aided by its liaisons with some of the world's finest corporate exponents, including German firm Hengeler Mueller, Spain's Uría & Menéndez, Bredin Prat in France and US firms Cravath Swaine & Moore and Davis Polk & Wardell. The team is reported to "*espouse excellence in achieving the firm brand,*" with its practitioners displaying "*a uniformly outstanding quality.*" Clients report: "*If you can't get your first choice, you can be sure your next will be a bloody good second.*" The team's multi-specialist lawyers are said to be "*extremely on the ball, nothing fazes them.*" They distinguish themselves by their ability to "*provide more than just technical legal support – they advise on commercial aspects as well.*" "*The ace in the pack,*" **Nigel Boardman** (see p.241) maintains his reputation as "*just about the best corporate lawyer in London.*" His "*considerable insight into bigger pictures*" ensures his status as "*a trusted advisor*" to more than 800 of the world's leading corporates ("*no one has figured out how he does it!*"). He advised Orange on its £25.1 billion sale by Vodafone AirTouch to France Telecom, and Hyder on bids for the company by St David Capital Group and WPD. This year has seen significant changes at senior level, with Michael Pescod's high profile retirement and Senior Partner Giles Henderson's appointment as Master of Pembroke College, Oxford. His newly appointed successor, **Tim Clark** (see p.242), advised Abbey National on Lloyd's TSB's £19.8 billion pre-conditional offer for the company, and also on its £1.6 billion acquisition of Scottish Provident and £773 million purchase of Stagecoach Porterbrook from Stagecoach Holdings. Thought by peers to be "*simply great,*" he also advised on Old Mutual's £525 million bid for Gerrard Group. "*Pre-eminent performer*" **William Underhill** (see p.259) is "*one of the most hands-on partners one could wish to see.*" "*Extremely gifted intellectually,*" one of his key strengths is his ability to "*make an independent analysis, not merely regurgitate received wisdom.*" He advised Colt Telecom Group on English law aspects of its acquisition of Fitec for £17.7 million, and together with Clark, advised on Norwich Union's £26 billion merger with CGU. Also on this transaction was the "*likeable*" **Andy Ryde** (see p.256), "*a clever hard worker*" with a "*down to earth style.*" "*Charming and efficient*" **Stephen Cooke** (see p.243) is "*committed to doing a good job.*" He advised on Scottish Media Group's £225 million acquisition of Ginger Media Group, and the $10.5 billion Diageo combination of Pillsbury Company and General Mills. "*Everyone likes working with*" **Martin Hattrell** (see p.248), who is "*even handed and open.*" An "*extremely accomplished lawyer,*" he "*bears the Slaughter and May hallmarks,*" being "*calm, relaxed and focused*" with a "*pukka, straight-down-the-middle*" style. He acted for Bentalls on Fenwick's £70.8 million recommended cash offer for the company. Known for his "*fundamental, intimate*" knowledge of the financial institutional industry, **Glen James** (see p.488) is "*always good,*" although sometimes "*a little too tenacious.*" He and Hattrell advised on Schroder's £1.35 billion sale of its worldwide investment banking business to Salomon Smith Barney. "*Unflappable and bright*" **Charles Randell** (see p.255)advised E.ON on its £5.1 billion recommended takeover of PowerGen, and acted for Goldman Sachs and UBS Warburg on Vodafone's new shares placing to part finance the acquisition of BT's interest in Japan Telecom, The J-Phone Group and Airtel. "*Impressive and pleasant to work with,*" **Frances Murphy** (see p.253) advised on the £825 million Williams sale of Yale to Assa Abloy, and acted for the Marconi Group on outsourcing of manufacturing operations. "*Good operator*" **Robert Stern** (see p.258) advised on Glaxo Wellcome's £115 million merger with SmithKline Beecham and RWE's £4.3 billion bid for Thames Water. **Jeff Twentyman** (see p.259) has displayed his "*real can-do mentality*" on a number of deals, including DelGro's £373.8 million bid for Metroline and Ipsaris' £357 million merger with Easynet. "*Academic and measured*" **Nilufer von Bismarck** (see p.259) advised on EVOTEC Biosystems' £316 million bid for Oxford Asymmetry and Chase Manhattan's £4.88 billion bid for Robert Fleming. Among numerous major transactions, the team acted for Meyer International on Compagnie de Saint-Gobain's £1.04 billion bid for the company, advised on Ocean Group's £2.75 billion bid for NFC and was instructed on Unilever's $20.3 billion merger with Bestfoods. **Clients:** Corporates: Abbey National; Old Mutual; Orange; Unilever; BUPA; Whitbread; British Airways; Diageo; Marks & Spencer; Shell; Hilton Group; Carlton Communications; Emap; Colt Telecom. Financials: Goldman Sachs; UBS Warburg; Schroder Salomon Smith Barney; Cazenove; Standard Chartered; Dresdner Kleinwort Wasserstein; 3i.

Allen & Overy (see firm details p.856) Some regard this as "*essentially a finance-driven practice with a jolly good corporate team.*" Shored up by its "*fantastic*" banking and capital markets practices, and "*broad-ranging*" expertise in ancilliary areas such as tax, competition and telecoms, this "*interesting*" practice has "*come on like mad,*" in some competitors' eyes. One of its recent developments is the launch of its newchange dealroom client intranet site, an online service tailored to streamline and expedite cross-border transactions. Despite the active expansion of its European resource by more than 60 partners in Frankfurt and Belgium the majority of the market do not see the firm to have "*broken into continental Europe in a big way*". However, it receives endorsement for the integration of its US practice to give it leading status as advisor to US acquirers of European targets. Noted for its "*consistent quality,*" clients approve the team's "*tremendously well trained*" individuals. **Alan Paul**'s (see p.254) name "*is always mentioned in the same breath as the firm's.*" A "*real problem solver,*" who "*finds his way around big points and cuts through to the commercial issues,*" he is "*recommended for difficult deals*" such as GE Capital and Leconport Estates' £1.9 billion acquisition of MEPC, and the €12.5 billion acquisition of World Online by Tiscali. Viewed by clients as "*a great relationship partner,*" "*smooth and sophisticated*" **Richard Cranfield** (see p.243) advised the Government's Radiocommunications Agency on its £22.5 billion 3G mobile licence auction. He also advised Cable & Wireless on the $38 billion disposal of its Hong Kong Telecom operations to Pacific Century CyberWorks. Senior partner **Guy Beringer** (see p.241) is "*a consummate City corporate practitioner,*" whose management duties have taken him away from an active role on deals. Known for his securities work with clients such as UBS Warburg, "*easy-going, no-nonsense deal-maker*" **David Wootton** (see p.260) is said to be "*keen to do whatever is necessary to get a deal done.*" He has displayed "*sound judgement*" on deals such as the £1.77 billion merger of Smiths Industries with TI Group and Singapore Airline's £600 million acquisition of a minority interest in Virgin Airlines. "*Clever*" ex Ashursts' **Mark Wippell** (see p.260) "*gets it right*" and has been seen on major matters such as The Hartford International Financial Services Group's disposal of its Zwolsche insurance businesses to Assurances Générales de France. "*Decisive*" **Ian Elder** (see p.354) has "*a good client manner*" and "*sees the bigger picture.*" He recently acted on the £421 million sale of BT Group's storage assets to Dynergy, as part of the company's restructuring programme.The team also advised Chase Manhattan Bank on the $1.3 billion disposal of its Hong Kong retail banking and credit card subsidiaries to Standard Chartered Bank. **Clients:** Corporates: Cable &

Wireless; ICI; BAE Systems; GE Capital; Royal & SunAlliance; Smiths Industries. Financials: ABN AMRO; Deutsche Bank; Barclays Bank; Goldman Sachs; Merrill Lynch; UBS Warburg.

Clifford Chance (see firm details p.919) The team "*continues to have a good corporate practice*," although the market perception that it has "*not yet broken into the first rank of corporate work*" has not altered. However, competitors "*increasingly see its name on the big deals*," while its presence in "*volume deals involving private companies*" is ubiquitous. Now numbering over 900 lawyers, the firm's global corporate practice is thought to be "*getting good work*" and "*achieving a unified Euro product*," with the completion of the merger with Grimaldi e Associati at the beginning of the year emphasising its trans-European integration. Multi-jurisdictional expertise is demonstrated by deals such as advising Schroder Ventures on the $2.3 billion purchase of VEBA Electronics from E.ON. Transatlantic highlights include advising Citigroup on its £368 million acquisition of the People's Bank UK credit card operations by its subsidiary Citibank International and advising Sema Group on its $4.7 billion merger with LHS Group and its subsequent $5.3 billion sale to Schlumberger. Although some raise concerns over the consistency of lawyer quality, a "*business-minded*" team is said to have "*fantastic experience across a lot of areas*." The group's "*rolled up sleeves*" approach is considered to be "*more likely to see a deal through to a commercial result*." A "*strong presence in meetings*," **Adam Signy** (see p.256) is a "*bright spark*" with a "*strong client portfolio*." He advised CGU on its £19 billion merger with Norwich Union. "*Steady, sensible*" **David Pearson** (see p.254) advised Nomura on its £625 million acquisition of 988 pubs from Bass Taverns. He also acted for Merrill Lynch in its capacity as financial advisor to Eircom on its €4.5 billion disposal to Vodafone Group, and to Ocean Group on its £2.75 billion merger with Excel. "*Clients have confidence*" in **David Childs** as "*a good deal manager*." He advised Merrill Lynch on its joint venture with HSBC to form the world's first global internet bank. **Guy Norman** (see p.253) utilises his experience at the Takeover Panel to do "*an excellent job*" on deals such as advising Morgan Stanley on the £8.2 billion acquisition by NTL of the cable television division of Cable & Wireless Communications. Headline deals for the firm have also included acting for Lloyds TSB on its £20 billion offer for Abbey National, and advising Chase Manhattan, both on its $4.8 billion takeover of Robert Fleming, and on the European aspects of its £36 billion merger with JP Morgan. **Clients:** Corporates: CGNU; EADs; Energis; NTT DoCoMo; International Power; HJ Heinz; Kimberley-Clark; Intel; Siemens; Volvo; British Energy; Air Products; Reuters; Philip Morris; Lend Lease; Carrefour; Lagardere. Financials: CSFB; GE; Goldman Sachs; JP Morgan Chase; Lloyds TSB; Kohlberg Kravis Roberts; Merrill Lynch; Morgan Stanley Dean Witter; Schroder Salomon Smith Barney; UBS Warburg.

Herbert Smith (see firm details p.993) The practice earns "*tremendous admiration*" from its competitors, having "*come on a enormous amount, making greater inroads into major deals*" such as the Bank of Scotland's bid for NatWest and £28 billion merger with the Halifax. Credited with an "*entrepreneurial*" approach, the team is perceived to have "*achieved a balance in what it does*." It has succeeded in making the transition from industry focus sectors such as insurance and utilities into mainstream work that "*people would drool over*." In addition, the team receives market commendation for its cross-border capacity, which is acknowledged to have been reinforced by the firm's relationship with German firm Gleiss Lutz Hootz Hirsch. Top-class work includes advising De Beers on the $19.6 billion recommended offer by a consortium comprising Central Holdings, Anglo American and the Debswana Diamond Company. Although the team's lawyers generally lack the profile of the leading triumvirate of firms, there are a number of "*strong, doughty performers*." **Anthony Macaulay** (see p.252) is "*commercial and sensible*" on deals such as advising BT Pension Scheme on its £1.9 billion recommended cash offer (jointly with GE Capital) for MEPC through joint venture company Leconport Estates. "*Organised*" **James Palmer** (see p.254) is an "*imaginative, clear, creative thinker*" with "*a lot of deal experience*" which includes advising Time Warner on the proposed $20 billion combination of its music division with that of EMI in a 50:50 joint venture, Warner EMI Music. Senior partner **Richard Bond** (see p.241) is seen less on transactions, shifting his role within the practice towards management responsibilities. **Stephen Barnard** (see p.240) is "*associated with some of the practice's success stories*," and with his strong investment banking contacts, "*he has been instrumental in raising the team's profile*." He advised The London Stock Exchange in connection with the planned merger with Deutsche Börse and the defence of the c.£800 million hostile offer by OM Gruppen. Head of corporate **Caroline Goodall**

UK M&A Top Ten Deals (Jan 1st to Aug 6th 2001)

Target	Lawyers to Target	Bidder	Lawyers to Bidder	Value of Deal ($m)
Bank of Scotland	Herbert Smith; Tods Murray	Halifax Group plc	Linklaters	**16,067.222**
Billiton plc	Linklaters; Freehills	BHP Ltd	Slaughter and May; Allen Allen & Hemsley; Sullivan & Cromwell	**11,891.680**
Powergen plc	Freshfields Bruckhaus Deringer; Jones Day Reavis & Pogue; Sullivan & Cromwell	E.ON AG	Slaughter and May; Steptoe & Johnson; LeBoeuf, Lamb, Greene & MacRae	**7,339.186**
Japan Telecom Co Ltd, J-Phone Group (20% each)	Freshfields Bruckhaus Deringer	Vodafone Group plc	Linklaters	**6,449.849**
Veba Oel AG	Freshfields Bruckhaus Deringer	BP plc	Linklaters	**5,552.234**
Sema plc	Clifford Chance	Schlumberger plc	Freshfields Bruckhaus Deringer	**5,200.058**
Brambles Industries plc	Clifford Chance; Malleson Stephens Jacques	Bramble Industries Ltd	Freshfields Bruckhaus Deringer; Allen Allen & Hemsley; Sullivan & Cromwell	**4,266.457**
Blue Circle Industries plc	Slaughter and May	Lafarge SA	Linklaters	**3.635.880**
BT plc (UK Property Portfolio)	Ashurst Morris Crisp	Telereal Holdings plc	Freshfields Bruckhaus Deringer	**3,152.844**
Yell Group Ltd	Allen & Overy; Clifford Chance	Apax Partners & Co Ltd; Hicks, Muse, Tate & Furst Inc.	Weil Gotshal & Manges; Travers Smith Braithwaite	**3,043.231**

Source: Source: Dealogic M&A Global (database);

* Excludes withdrawn deals and share buybacks, based on deals announced where target or bidder nationality is UK.

(see p.247) offers "*a wealth of experience*," while **Marian Pell** (see p.490) "*represents clients with great energy*" in insurance, building societies and mutual funds-related matters. Responsible for the firm's reputation for having "*carved up the insurance field*," she has been advising GE Capital on its £570 million acquisition of National Mutual and acting on the £4.2 billion demutualisation and flotation of Friends Provident. "*Solid*" **Tim Bellis** (see p.241)gets "*so focused on a transaction that nothing disturbs his concentration.*" A "*decisive*" individual, "*he can always see the main objective of exercise.*" He advised Deutsche Bank, acting on behalf of PPL Therapeutics, as sponsor and manager of a £45 million share offer to American and European institutional investors. Although now departed to the firm's Singapore office, Chris Parsons advised Banco Bilbao Vizcaya Argentaria and Terra Networks in conjunction with Uría & Menéndez on the €2.4 billion merger between Uno-e and first-e group to create the first global online bank and financial services provider.Other core deals for the group have encompassed advice to Royal London on its £1.1 billion acquisition of the business from Scottish Life. IPO highlights include flotations of Michael Page (£650 million), Real Estate Opportunities Limited (£800 million) and LiDCO (£100 million). **Clients:** Corporates: Royal London; BAT; ABF; Chevron; Eurotunnel; Securicor; De Beers; Time Warner; Stagecoach. Financials: Goldman Sachs; CSFB; JP Morgan Chase; Merrill Lynch; Bank of Scotland; Zurich Financial Services; Lazard.

Ashurst Morris Crisp (see firm details p.866) Felt to be "*consolidating*" its position this year, the firm continues to win a vast volume of work, powered by its "*excellent corporate client base*" with "*a good little niche in the mid cap market.*" Endorsing the firm's leading reputation for private equity, some competitors consider it "*less usual*" to see the team on deals outside this context. Although still perceived as "*predominantly UK- focused*," the team is continuing to develop its pan-European network. Paris is the template for the development of other continental European offices in Frankfurt, Brussels and Milan, while a further office in Madrid opened at the beginning of the year. The recent addition of a capital markets team from Weil, Gotshal & Manges is expected to consolidate the firm's relationships with key investment banks, while bolstering the finance and investment banking practice. Clients see the team's approach as "*sharp and nippy. This is a big player which is competitive on price.*" Peers comment that "*it is rare to come across a weak lawyer there; they have a strong culture of reaching a successful conclusion, and being innovative when obstacles arise.*" "*Ambitious, driven*" **Chris Ashworth** (see p.240) has "*a good client following*" as a result of his "*extreme dedication.*" He has advised on several key deals, including AMVESCAP's £1.25 billion recommended cash offer for Perpetual and Deutsche Morgan Grenfell's $3.4 billion disposal of its interest in Formula One. He also acted for United News & Media on its £7.4 billion proposed merger with Carlton Communications. "*Diplomatic*" **Adrian Clark** (see p.242) is an "*amiable and experienced*" advisor to longstanding clients such as NFC, which he advised on its £2.75 billion merger with Ocean Group. "*Professional*" **David Macfarlane** is "*practical and sensible.*" A "*good knock-about corporate lawyer*," he acted for National Express Group on its recommended takeover bid for Prism Rail and its sale of Bournemouth and East Midlands airports.The team also advised the Carphone Warehouse on its £1.6 billion flotation and NM Rothschild on the £1.04 billion recommended cash offer made by Saint-Gobain for Meyer International. **Clients:** Corporates: AMVESCAP; Amey; United Business Media (formerly United News & Media); BT; Chelsfield; Laird Group; Smith & Nephew; Virgin. Financials: Rothschilds; Merrill Lynch; Close Brothers; Royal & SunAlliance.

Lovells (see firm details p.1044) The small team maintains its historical client base of manufacturing and 'old economy' sector companies such as Ford, Exxon and Texaco, while representing 169 FTSE 500, 8 FTSE 250 and 6 FTSE 100 companies. However, some comment that the group "*is not packing the appropriate punch*" for its pedigree. Perceived to be "*a bit overstretched*," the team is not considered to have adequately replaced the "*talismanic*" Dan Mace. Such doubts are at odds with the firm's well-received forays abroad. Mergers with Dutch firm Ekelmans Den Hollander and French outfit Siméon & Associés, the formalisation of a joint venture with Lee & Lee in Singapore, and the maturing of the firm's merger in Germany have generated market approval and genuine cross-border clout. The team advised on 13 public takeovers with an aggregate value of almost £12 billion last year, and is acknowledged by competitors as a "*good place for referrals.*" Major deals have included advising Barclays on its £5.6 billion bid for the Woolwich, and Granada on its £18.2 billion merger and subsequent demerger from the Compass Group. The firm also advised on Granada Media's £7.7 billion IPO, and its links with key investment banks Goldman Sachs and Lazard Brothers have generated work such as Preussag's £1.8 billion bid for the Thomson Travel Group and OM Gruppen's c.£800 million offer for London Stock Exchange. Endorsed by peers as "*extremely intelligent*," **John Davidson** (see p.243) is now the firm's top-rated corporate practitioner, and advised Goldman Sachs International on the £1.3 billion IPO of Egg. **Clients:** Corporates: Granada; South African Breweries; Ford; ExxonMobil; GCNU; BT Cellnet. Financials: Barclays; Prudential; Wellington Underwriting; Goldman Sachs; JP Morgan Chase; Lazard; WestLB Panmure.

Norton Rose (see firm details p.1082) "*They've had a good run with some substantial work*," say competitors, who point to the team's track record in big-ticket deals such as the Daimler Benz/British Aerospace deal, and more recently, acting for France Telecom in Mannesman's divestiture of Orange and advising BMW on its £1.85 billion sale of Land Rover to Ford. Strength across the firm's other industry groups such as shipping, asset finance and competition are said to "*complement the team's M&A business.*" Although said to be "*taking longer to develop its international strategy*" than some of its competitors, the firm's acquisition of part of the former Gaedertz firm in Germany will help its cross-border profile. A top name for more than 20 years, "*star*" Senior Partner **David Lewis** (see p.251) is an "*impressive, skilled, smooth operator*," whose influence now comes more from his managerial role. **Simon Sackman** (see p.256) is the "*strong leader*" of an "*extremely effective, good quality*" corporate finance team. Although some find him "*a touch pedantic*," most concede that he "*never leaves loose ends*" on a transaction. He advised Wanadoo and France Telecom on Wanadoo's £1.6 billion all share offer for Freeserve. "*Always entertaining to deal with*," **Barbara Stephenson**'s (see p.257) "*force of personality gets her a long way*" in deals such as advising Citigroup on UK aspects of the £1.4 billion acquisition of the investment banking division of Schroders. "*Great operator*" **Jonathan Coppin** (see p.243) can "*lead a team effectively to handle big work*," such as advising AXA on the recommended offer for the £2.37 billion minority shares interest in its UK subsidiary, Sun Life and Provincial Holdings. He also advised Eni on the £2.7 billion recommended cash offer by Lazard and JP Morgan on behalf of Agip for LASMO. "*Solid practitioner*" **Chris Pearson** (see p.254) has had a lower profile this year but receives endorsement for his "*decent*" bid work last year. The firm advised Caisse National de Crédit Agricole on its business partnership with Commercial Bank of Greece, and acted for HSBC on its $1 billion joint venture with Merrill Lynch to create a worldwide online banking and investment services company, Merrill Lynch HSBC. **Clients:** Corporates: Taylor Woodrow; Eni; Citigroup; BMW; France Telecom; Siemens. Financials: AXA; HSBC.

Macfarlanes (see firm details p.1046) A "*class act for its size*" and an established presence on big-ticket deals, the firm continues to "*punch far above its weight*," in spite of the lack of an international network comparable to its major rivals. With a non-institutional approach, the team is said by clients to have "*a superb ethic: strive for excellence and never compromise quality.*" Interviewees spoke of "*individual, consistently high standards of service*" and "*excellent continuity of staff.*" Senior partner **Robert Sutton** (see p.258) is credited with imbuing this culture into this "*hard-working outfit.*" "*Refreshingly willing to roll his sleeves up*," he is esteemed as "*the man for a really tough takeover.*" Clients report that "*he weighs his words precisely*" and is "*capable of getting precisely what he wants.*" He advised Pernod Ricard on its

£5.5 billion acquisition of the wine and spirits business of The Seagram Company, and acted for Compagnie Saint-Gobain on its £1.04 billion public offer for Meyer International. Sutton is ably assisted by the "*superb*," if occasionally "*overly technical*," **Mary Leth** (see p.251), who advised Warner Chilcott on its £260 million acquisition by Galan Holdings.The team acted for Virgin Investments on the £1.2 billion sale of a 49% interest in Virgin Atlantic Airways to Singapore International Airlines. **Clients:** Corporates: Pernod Ricard; Rentokil Initial; Compagnie de Saint-Gobain; Cordiant Communications Group; John Mowlem & Company; Carlton Communications; Kingspan Group; Retail Decisions; Vivendi. Financials: Cazenove; JP Morgan; Hawkpoint Partners; ING Barings; Cinven; 3i; Candover; Royal Bank of Scotland; Barclays.

Simmons & Simmons (see firm details p.1132) Now a department with specialist sector focuses covering employment, TMT, energy, biotechnology, financial institutions and rail, the corporate team has "*had a pretty good year*." The firm is felt by the market to have "*steadied the ship*" following the departures of a number of big names over the preceding two or three years. Credited as "*the main conduit*" for high-end deals, "*studious*" **Stuart Evans** (see p.245) has extensive experience in public takeovers and London Stock Exchange listings. He advised Interbrew on its acquisitions of Bass (£2.3 billion) and Whitbread Beer Company (£400 million). The team also advised fund managers Perpetual on Schroder's £1.05 billion recommended cash and share offer on behalf of AMVESCAP, and Gencorp on its €243 million acquisition of the worldwide car body interests of Laird Group. On the international side, the firm's European network has seen the addition of further offices in Dusseldorf and Madrid, while its Italian offices have been active on deals such as ENEL's £7.5 billion acquisition of Infostrada from Vodafone. Further afield, the London team demonstrated its integrated service capacity as joint advisers with its Hong Kong counterpart on Pacific Century Cyberworks' $35.9 billion acquisition of Cable & Wireless HKT and $3.5 billion strategic alliance with Telstra Corporation. **Clients:** Corporates: Cadbury Schweppes; Gallaher Group; Interbrew; Pacific Century Cyberworks; SFI Group; Railtrack. Financials: Barclays; Cazenove; Deutsche Bank (London); Nomura International.

Other Notable Practitioners **Adrian Knight** (see p.250) of **Shearman & Sterling** is "*a strong performer*" who continues to be "*a major force in corporate deals*," such as acting for Novartis on the global offering by Syngenta and Fiat on the auction of part of Magnetti Marelli. "*Punchy performer*" **Michael Hatchard** (see p.248)of **Skadden, Arps, Slate, Meagher & Flom** is "*incredibly bright*" and has an enviable client roster, including Cendant, Datamonitor and Easynet. He advised Salomon Smith Barney on its recommended $1.35 billion offer for Schroders and acted for Morgan Stanley as financial advisers to Degussa SKW on its £1.4 billion recommended offer for Laporte.

MEDIUM DEALS

CMS Cameron McKenna (see firm details p.922) "*Particularly good in certain areas*," the team is typically seen acting for small corporates on volume transactions in specialist sectors such as construction, hi-tech, biotech, electricity and leisure. A large international network gives the team cross-border strength, enabling it to advise on deals such as the £35.5 million acquisition of Sweden's leading vaccination company, SBL, by PowderJect. On flotations, the team acted on the first London/Singapore dual listing for biogeneric pharmaceutical company, GeneMedix (£260 million), the largest company traded on OFEX. It also acted on the £100 million flotation of Big Yellow Group, raising £45 million, and the £80 million flotation of IQ Quorum.Team leader **Sean Watson** (see p.259) "*inspires confidence in clients*." He advised the National Grid Company on its £3.2 billion purchase of New England Electric System and its acquisition of Niagara Mohawk Holdings for £2.1 billion. Endorsed as "*helpful and constructive to deal with*," the team advised on Lloyds TSB Group's £627 million cash acquisition of Chartered Trust Group and ACL Holdings, and UK leisure group Luminar's £585 million acquisition of Northern Leisure. **Clients:** Corporates: Energis; National Grid Group; NSB Retail Systems; Post Office; Roland Berger; Warner Brothers; Blockbuster Entertainment; Camelot; Warner Lambert; George Wimpey; Black & Decker; Vivendi. Financials: NatWest Equity Partners; Lloyds TSB; HSBC; Banque Nationale de Paris; Hawkpoint Partners.

Travers Smith Braithwaite (see firm details p.1160) Widely acclaimed in the market, this "*outstanding corporate-driven*" firm boasts "*an impressive spread of older line corporate finance clients*," as well as "*consistently superb lawyers*" and a "*splendid private equity arm*," from which the team has leveraged successfully. Although its domestic profile dominates, the team has demonstrated its ability to handle an increasing amount of cross-border transactional work. It advised on the establishment of a global joint venture between Beiersdorf and Smith & Nephew, involving multi-jurisdictional due diligence expertise. Best known for its work on behalf of funders, researchers were given a picture of a "*cohesive, thorough, responsive*" team that "*always gives a quality performance*" on deals. "*Urbane and sophisticated*," with "*the experience of ages*," **Christopher Bell** (see p.240) remains "*at the heart of the industry*." Having "*weathered lots of storms*" in regulatory structuring matters, he "*shoulders clients' cases*" well. He advised on Deutsche Bank's £1.27 billion offer on behalf of Finalrealm for United Biscuits. "*Successful operator*" **Spencer Summerfield** (see p.258) is the firm's relationship partner for NTL, and is said to display "*excellent judgement*" on deals such as NTL's investment in the €1.2 billion Hessen franchise owned by Deutsche Telekom, involving a complex limited partnership investment vehicle. Acting for Beeson Gregory on its £195 million internet flotation, "*courteous and quietly effective*" **Oliver Barnes** (see p.240) has a "*serious*" approach to his work. Over the past year, the team has advised on a number of public to private transactions, such as General London Constructors' £370 million takeover of Fairview Holdings. **Clients:** Corporates: NTL; Intec Telecoms Systems; Peel Holdings; Wilshaw; Charles Baynes; Harvey Nash Group; Channel 5; Intec Telecom Systems. Financials: Hawkpoint; HSBC.

Denton Wilde Sapte (see firm details p.939) Interviewees perceive the team's activity within the domestic arena to be "*sporadic*" by comparison with its increasing focus on cross-border transactional work in conjunction with its respected overseas offices. The team's corporate finance work derives from enormous expertise in industries such as energy, transport, media and telecoms. Key examples of such work include advising Crédit Agricole Indosuez on the French Government's restructuring of the French nuclear industry, and acting for Gazprom on the issuance and public offering of £310 million fixed rate notes. The team also advised Royal Bank of Scotland on the £2.3 billion restructuring of its business in Tokyo following its merger with NatWest. Steven Goodman leads a team of "*good people*" whose key deals include acting for Liberty Media in Telewest's £10 billion offer for Flextech. Further highlights include Rentokil Initial's disposal programme and £1.5 billion acquisition of Ratin, and London Electricity's £466 million purchase of Sutton Bridge Power Station from Enron. **Clients:** Corporates: Dixons; Tadpole Technology; easyJet; Freeserve; Rentokil; London Electricity; J Sainsbury. Financials: Royal Bank of Scotland; Bank of Scotland; CSFB; Salomon Smith Barney; Société Générale.

Gouldens (see firm details p.976) A "*top quality operator*," which "*makes regular and impressive appearances on interesting deals*." Competitors acknowledge that the team has built up an "*excellent client base*." Focusing mostly on domestic transactions, the team's focus on smaller investment banks such as Close Brothers has enabled it to "*generate good deal flow*." Renowned for its AIM work, the firm has appeared on flotations such as the £153 million float for Brainspark, and acted for WestLB Panmure on

CORPORATE FINANCE: MEDIUM DEALS • London		Ptnrs	Assts
1	CMS Cameron McKenna	29	42
	Travers Smith Braithwaite	11	32
2	Denton Wilde Sapte	22	51
	Gouldens	6	12
	Rowe & Maw	20	n/a
	SJ Berwin	12	30
	Weil, Gotshal & Manges	10	30
3	Berwin Leighton Paisner	22	35
	Olswang	18	n/a
4	Baker & McKenzie	15	32
	Hammond Suddards Edge	16	34
	Nabarro Nathanson	n/a	n/a
	Taylor Joynson Garrett	19	38
	Theodore Goddard	16	18
5	Bird & Bird	10	26
	Dechert	11	16
	DLA	n/a	n/a
	Osborne Clarke	9	18
	Pinsent Curtis Biddle	19	24

LEADING INDIVIDUALS		
1	**BELL Christopher** Travers Smith Braithwaite	
	FRANCIES Michael Weil, Gotshal & Manges	
2	**SUMMERFIELD Spencer** Travers Smith Braithwaite	
3	**BARNES Oliver** Travers Smith Braithwaite	
	BENNETT John Berwin Leighton Paisner	**BIRT Timothy** Osborne Clarke
	BOTT Adrian Olswang	**BURROW Robert** SJ Berwin
	CHESTER Martin Theodore Goddard	**GREAVES Adam** Gouldens
	MAHER Paul Rowe & Maw	**STEINFELD Michael** Dechert
	STELLA Keith Berwin Leighton Paisner	**WATSON Sean** CMS Cameron McKenna
4	**GEE Tim** Baker & McKenzie	**LEVY Graeme** Olswang
	MORGAN Simon Olswang	
	ROSEFIELD Stephen Berwin Leighton Paisner	
	ROSENBERG Daniel Taylor Joynson Garrett	**THORNEYCROFT Max** Gouldens
	WAYTE Peter DLA	
	WEBSTER Martin Pinsent Curtis Biddle	**WINTER Martin** Taylor Joynson Garrett
UP AND COMING		
	NEWMAN Iain Nabarro Nathanson	

This book is the product of 6,552 1/2 hour interviews. See p.7 for BMRB audit.

Within each band, firms are listed alphabetically. *See individuals' profiles p.239*

the £162 million Official List flotation of XTL Biopharmaceuticals, an Israeli biotechnology company. Work with a cross-border element has included acting for BancBoston Capital in connection with its investment in three companies in Continental Europe, and for Gyrus on its US acquisitions. Property deals are another area of niche strength, exemplified by the firm's advice on Hanson's £185 million disposal of its waste management businesses to Waste Recycling Group. The team gains client plaudits for its "*reliable and practical service*" and "*uniformly high quality at partner level.*" Endorsed as "*technically superb,*" the lawyers here "*really focus on issues and don't take too legalistic a view.*" Well known in mainstream M&A and corporate finance work, **Max Thorneycroft** (see p.259) has "*a good rapport with clients*" and "*delivers his opinions without resorting to jargon.*" In addition to the Hanson deal, he acted for Send Group on its purchase and subsequent AIM float of four companies from TT Group. Equally well regarded for his work spearheading the firm's private equity caseload, "*practical*" corporate lawyer **Adam Greaves** (see p.247) was commended to our researchers for his "*on the ball*" approach. He acted for the management team and Nednil on the 'take-private' of Linden for £73 million. Other recent team highlights include advice to Investec Henderson Crosthwaite on TechMARK flotations for Patsystems (£134.66 million) and The Innovation Group (£124.1 million) and on the £172 million acquisition by Intec Telecom Systems of Computer Generation. The firm also advised on Apax Partners' £150 million merger with Deutsche Börse-listed GoldZack to form Altium Capital. **Clients:** Corporates: Hanson; Ennstone; Unite Group; Sibir Energy; Deanes Holdings; Energizer UK; UK Plant; Cargill; Outburst; Delancey Estates; Thomson Intermedia; Spring Group. Financials: Altium Capital; Collins Stewart; Teather & Greenwood Holdings; West LB Panmure; Investec Henderson Crosthwaite; Standard Bank Investment Corporation; Close Brothers; Durlacher.

Rowe & Maw (see firm details p.1113) "*Solid, heavily tax-driven*" practice, which is said to benefit from its "*key industry client base*" of multinationals, conglomerates and corporates such as EMI, ICI and Huntsman. The team acts for an established FTSE 200 client base, while increasing its representation among FTSE 100 clients, private equity and VC companies. Telecoms are a sector of particular expertise. Active on flotations and IPOs, the team is growing its traditional practice acting for issuers towards advising sponsors and financial advisors. Highlights include Independent News & Media's £198 million Official List admission and £49 million admission of its subsidiary iTouch to TechMARK. "*Aggressive team leader*" **Paul Maher** (see p.252) is described by clients as an "*energetic and dogged*" presence on deals such as advising ICI on the sale of its three commodity chemical businesses to Ineos Group for £600 million. The group advised Waste Recycling Group on its £185 million acquisition of Hanson Waste Management and Persimmon on its £537.5 million offer for Beazer Group. **Clients:** Corporates: Cable & Wireless; Reuters Greenhouse Fund; Syngenta; Unilever; EMI Group; ICI; Marconi; The Smiths Group. Financials: GE Capital.

SJ Berwin (see firm details p.879) Leveraging successfully off its "*incredibly strong*" private equity practice, the team has been "*putting itself about on a lot of deals.*" Said to be "*built on VC clients,*" the practice is not generally a fixture on the largest deals, but still appears on a range of high profile transactions such as acting for The British Land Company in its proposed acquisition of a 29.9% stake in Liberty International. In flotations work, the team has been active on behalf of VC investors and AIM/NASDAQ companies within the IT, technology, media and communications sectors. Major flotations on the London Stock Exchange include Collins Stewart (£326 million) and Dechra Pharmaceuticals, while on AIM, the firm advised on Delyn Group's £188 million reverse takeover of Ingenta. Clients endorse the team's "*bright people with bags of experience*" who "*find a way through to solving issues.*" Ex-merchant banker **Robert Burrow** (see p.242) displays "*a good marriage of skills*" between his "*commercial and technical grasp*" of matters such as the Musgrave Group's £89 million acquisition of 28% of Budgens. Further team highlights include the Neuer Markt €960 million flotation of IM International media and acting for Guardian iT on various deals including its £170 million acquisition and related rights issue of SafetyNet. **Clients:** Corporates: Guardian iT; The British Land Company; Gullane Entertainment; Hilton Group; Vector Industries; ITG Group; Princedale Group. Financials: Apax Partners; Phildrew Ventures; Atlas Venture; Candover; Barclays Private Equity; Brewin Dolphin Holdings.

Weil, Gotshal & Manges (see firm details p.1177) Possessing Anglo-US integrated capability, the firm is perceived by the market to have successfully "*reinvented itself*" to achieve a "*huge deal flow this year,*" despite suffering defections from its financing team. The group offers expertise in securitisations, project finance, and specialist finance sectors including leveraged, telecoms and (other than high yield) principal finance. "*Superb leader of the orchestra*" **Mike Francies** is "*a strong workhorse.*" Peers hail his "*fantastic achievement in building up the office.*" A "*fanatical worker*" with a "*rapid turnaround time,*" he is said to provide "*a tremendous service*" to a loyal clientele. His team is "*hard-nosed, sensible and pragmatic*," and handled the biggest leveraged transaction in Europe for United Biscuits (£1.6 billion) on behalf of Burlington Biscuits, the takeover vehicle formed by Hicks Muse and Nabisco. **Clients:** Corporates: MediaOne; Flextech; Pirelli; SUN Brewing; Simply Internet; Burford Group; Sara Lee; Burlington Biscuits/ British Associated Foods; Oxford BioMedica. Financials: GE Capital; Hicks Muse Tate & Furst; Nomura International.

Berwin Leighton Paisner (see firm details p.878) The merger (1 May 2001) is expected by competitors to result in "*good synergy*" between the "*solid*" Paisners team and "*rounded practice*" of Berwin Leighton, while compensating for recent defections to other firms such as Taylor Joynson Garrett and Olswang. Drawing on the firm's combined strengths in financing, banking, securitisation and property, the team focuses on mid-tier work for larger corporates in the growth sector industries. On the international front, the team handles a good proportion of inward investment work, such as acting for Dutch company Petroplus International on the $42 million acquisition of Phillips Imperial Petroleum. Head of Corporate **John Bennett** (see p.241) "*drives deals through pretty aggressively.*" His recent work includes AIM-listed Shore Capital's £260 million recommended bid for Jellyworks and Official List admission. Clients find that "*knowledgeable, experienced, diligent*" practitioner **Keith Stella** (see p.257) is "*an intelligent, tough negotiator*" on deals such as the public to private bid for Goodhead Group and Esporta's Official List flotation. He also advised on Albas' joint venture with Virgin to create Bush Internet TV. **Stephen Rosefield** (see p.255) is also praised for his ability to "*reach a deal sensibly and commercially.*" The team acted on the merger of CLS Holdings and Citadel Holdings and subsequent £250 million re-listing on the London Stock Exchange. **Clients:** Corporates: Tesco; Lex Service; RAC; Burberry; CSS Stellar; AON; Del Monte; LA Fitness; Esporta; Great Universal Stores; Gap; Courts; Medisys; First Leisure; Transamerica; Lombard Medical; Tullet & Tokyo; Petroplus; Welcome Trust; Chorion; PNC Tele.com and Oasis Stores. Financials: Legal and General; Durlacher; Shore Capital; Ermgassen; Deutsche Bank; Apax Partners; Granville Baird; Insinger Townsley; Investec Bank; EO; Dawney Day; Old Mutual; Clerical Medical; LaSalle Investment Management; Scottish Widows.

Olswang (see firm details p.1084) The team receives endorsement from peers and clients: "*You've got to hand it to them, they're in their own market which they've got sewn up.*" Strongly associated with the TMT sector, and possessing an acknowledged private equity niche, the group is said to be "*an entrepreneurial outfit of gutsy players.*" However, it is not yet perceived as a force in mainstream corporate finance. Effective lateral hiring has resulted in an "*effective, stable*" team of "*gifted individuals with great brain power, who have moulded together extremely well*". With his "*knowledgeable, hard-working*" attitude, department head **Adrian Bott** (see p.241) "*always gets a good write-up*" from clients for his skill in deals such as BBC Worldwide's creation of the £240 million beeb Ventures in conjunction with its internet business and a major US VC. "*Clients come back*" to **Simon Morgan** (see p.253) on account of his "*thorough, technical drafting*" and strong negotiation skills. He can "*hold his own*" on major Official List IPOs such as those for Jupiter Investment Trust (£110 million by way of retail offer and placing with Jupiter Group employees). Known for his insolvency expertise, **Graeme Levy** (see p.251) displays a combination of "*tremendous brain power without losing his temper or getting aggressive.*" The team advised on HIT Entertainment's £280 million acquisition of Lyrick Corporation. **Clients:** Corporates: Anite Group; BBC Worldwide; Carphone Warehouse Group; Genetix; HIT Entertainment; ITE Group; Netstore; Sportal International; Warner Bros/Warner Music. Financials: Mainly VC and investment funds such as Jupiter Dividend & Growth Trust.

Baker & McKenzie (see firm details p.868) Competitors admire the team for "*doing incredibly well out of its international reputation and global reach.*" Although the team is not a feature on the domestic front, the London office is the hub for European work, acting predominantly for inwardly investing US corporates. Niche industry sectors of excellence include TMT, chemicals and pharmaceuticals and oil and gas. The firm acted for BT on its $6.6 billion partnership with Japan Telecom and Vodafone AirTouch to develop high-speed mobile services in Japan, and advised France Telecom on its $4.3 billion acquisition of a stake in Polish national provider, TPSA. Clients describe the "*technically strong*" team as "*pleasant to deal with,*" although the firm does incur some criticism for "*over-lawyering*" on deals. Global head of M&A **Tim Gee**'s (see p.246) name stands out at the practice. Characterised to researchers as "*cool as a cucumber,*" he is "*extremely commercial*" and "*never flinches*" on deals. He advised on PepsiCo's £100 million cross-border takeover of Chipsy International in Egypt. The team has acted for BP Amoco on several large cross-border deals, including its $2 billion strategic alliance with Solvay in Europe and the US to create a petrochemical joint venture. **Clients:** Corporates: BP Amoco; Cisco; Compaq; Hutchison Whampoa; United Business Media; PepsiCo; Nortel; France Telecom; British Telecommunications. Financials: Apax Partners; CSFB; Dresdner Kleinwort Wasserstein; Schroder Salomon Smith Barney.

Hammond Suddards Edge (see firm details p.984) "*Seen frequently*" by some of the country's corporate leaders, the firm is said to be a "*dominant presence*" in the small to mid-cap sector and "*well tapped in*" to the public company market. The firm advised on 18 AIM flotations in the past year, including Ideal Shopping Direct (£31.05 million), Focus Solutions Group (£48.9 million) and RMR (£63.6 million). Happy to use the London team, clients acknowledge that the firm's "*regional presence makes deals cheaper.*" The team has demonstrated its national reach in deals such as advising Hazlewood Foods on its £257.9 million acquisition by Greencore Group. National head of corporate Richard Burns leads a team that peers credit for its "*extreme competence and practicality.*" Clients also note a "*can-do attitude that says 'let's get the deal done'.*" The firm advised J Walter Thompson, Ogilvy & Mather and WPP Group on an acquisition programme totalling $251 million. **Clients:** Corporates: WPP; Hazelwood Foods; ITW; Chloride Group; Findel; Macro 4; Lambert Howarth. Financials: Altium Capital; Beeson Gregory; Peel Hunt; Seymour Pierce; Williams de Broe.

Nabarro Nathanson (see firm details p.1078) Prominent on corporate work derived from the firm's strengths in property, project finance, IT and convergent new media, the team advises a wide range of clients from major institutions to significant individuals. It advised Investec Henderson Crosthwaite on the £200 million Official List IPO of Music Choice Europe, and has expanded its institutional VC private equity client base to act on over 50 investments in the new technologies sector. Complex property finance transactions have included acting for Land Securities on its £165 million acquisition of Trillium. The team is acknowledged by competitors to be "*doing well with increasing international work*" such as advising Australian company Westfield on its inward investment of over £1 billion into the UK. Clients report that the team's "*individual partners make business worthwhile.*" "*Conscientious*" **Iain Newman** (see p.253) is "*impressive on delivery*". A "*commercial*" lawyer, he "*knows his stuff and doesn't flap*". He advised Investec Henderson Crosthwaite in connection with the £118 million Official List flotation of IFX Power. **Clients:** Corporates: Alphameric; City Reach International; NewMedia SPARK. Financials: Investec Henderson Crosthwaite.

Taylor Joynson Garrett (see firm details p.1150) Our research confirms that the group's strategic focus on the TMT sector is considered to have brought dividends to its AIM IPO practice. High profile work includes advising Altium Capital (as nominated advisor and broker) on the £220 million AIM flotation of ITIS Holdings.US inward investing companies now account for a sixth of the firm's raft of corporate and institutional clients. The team advises across a range of other sectors including sport, advertising, manufacturing, energy, leisure and education. The group has received a boost to its strength in depth with the addition from Berwin Leighton of the respected **Daniel Rosenberg**, while **Martin Winter**, formerly of Biddle, is another recent acquisition. Described to researchers as an "*energetic,* *enthusiastic negotiator,*" he is said to "*get the deal done with the minimum of fuss.*" The team acted for Bidco, a special purpose vehicle backed by the Rutland Recovery Fund, on a takeover offer for Woltenhome Rink worth £48.7 million. It also advised on Generics Group's £226 million official listing. **Clients:** Corporates: TBWA; Huon Holdings; Sun Microsystems; Macmillan; Eidos. Financials: Rutland Recovery Fund; Digital Ventures; Amadeus Capital Partners; Electra Investment Trust; Altium Capital.

Theodore Goddard (see firm details p.1152) After last year's upheavals in the corporate department, the firm is perceived by competitors to be "*making great efforts to reclaim lost ground.*" The team continues to have acknowledged areas of strength such as media, communications, IT and food, while its stock exchange related work has also received recognition in the market. The team advised on the £140 million flotation of Motion Media. Peers rate **Martin Chester** (see p.242) as "*a strong operator*" who "*could easily have built a profile for himself at one of the larger M&A practices.*" He's "*your man if you want to know about disclosure rules.*" His team is described as "*knowledgeable and responsive.*" Clients say that it can be "*trusted to work hard to deliver the right result.*" Team highlights include Anglogold's $335 million agreed joint venture investment in Tanzania's Geita gold mine, including the acquisition of a 50% interest from Ashanti Goldfields. The group also advised Landswell Properties on its £51 million recommended cash takeover of Raglan Properties. **Clients:** Corporates: Ambassador Theatre Group; Diageo; Signet Group; Blagden; Freightliners; Stavely Industries; Polygram Film Entertainment. Financials: Peel Hunt; Deutsche Bank; Beeson Gregory; Bridgewell.

Bird & Bird (see firm details p.884) "*Going places on the back of its IT practice,*" this is "*a team worth watching,*" according to clients. Competitors acknowledge that its strategy of pursuing an industry sector focus model is generating a "*sound corporate practice.*" Over 80% of the team's corporate work derives from clients in telecommunications, IT, e-commerce and pharmaceuticals. Advice on the £182 million IPO of Pharmagene, a human tissue-based research service, typifies increased activity within the biotech and pharmaceutical sectors. The firm also acted on Orchid Biosciences' acquisition of Cellmark Diagnostics from AstraZeneca. In spite of the departure of Charles Crosthwaite, Chris Barratt leads a "*tight team*" which is said by clients to be "*responsive, efficient and good value.*" The group advised Ingenta on its reverse take-over of Delyn Group for £118 million, and acted for Expocentric, a leading provider of virtual exhibitions, on its £31.5 million admission to TechMARK. **Clients:** Corporates: Carlton Communications; Expocentric; Global Crossing (UK) Telecommunications; Imperial College Innovations; Lastminute; Orchestream Group. Financials: GE Capital; Global Retail Partners; Amadeus Capital.

Dechert (see firm details p.938) Bolstered by the firm's "*extremely successful*" private equity and funds practice, and possessing integrated US/European capability, the corporate team continues to act for a traditional client base of owner-managed businesses. Niches exist in retail, property, engineering, insurance and IT. The team continues to be active in public takeovers and IPOs, and also provides M&A and regulatory advice to the Lloyd's market. Following its full merger with Dechert Price & Rhoads in July last year, the team has been developing international cross-border expertise, acting extensively for US buyers in UK and Europe in conjunction with offices in Brussels, Paris and across the US. Researchers had their attention drawn to the team's "*excellence*" at partner level. A "*delight to deal with,*" **Michael Steinfeld** demonstrates "*the right balance of legal and commercial input*" on deals such as Travelex's £440 million acquisition of the worldwide Thomas Cook foreign currency and travellers' cheques operations. The team also advised on Philip Green's £200 million acquisition of British Home Stores. **Clients:** Corporates: Fairview New Homes; Frogmore Estates; BRIT Insurance Holdings; Marylebone Warwick Balfour Group; CDI Corporation; Travelex. Financials: Beeson Gregory; Internet Capital Group; Mellon Bank Corporation; Lehman Brothers.

DLA **Peter Wayte** is the leading figure here. The department has advised on a number of communications-related M&A deals.

Osborne Clarke (see firm details p.1086) Researchers found that the firm's "*well-founded corporate reputation*" has been consolidated by "*an extremely successful year.*" It is seen by market leaders to be growing its London operation noticeably, with some commentators judging that it "*may have the fire-power to make it into the next league.*" Competitors comment on the firm's ability *to "offer good service at a good price,*" and point to the firm's Bristol office as the firm's mainstay, with Reading leading the drive for hi-tech work. A well-known name in PE and VC matters, "*ferocious advisor*" **Tim Birt** "*drives hard on his client's behalf.*" Described by peers as "*a sensible opponent,*" he "*gets the deal done without posturing.*" He acted for Stepstone on its £160 million dual listing on the London and Oslo Stock Exchanges, one of the largest internet company flotations, and the first to include an internet-only retail offer.Other team highlights include seven acquisitions for Redstone Telecom totalling over £100 million in aggregate, and Torex's £41 million acquisition of the Laufenberg Group. **Clients:** Corporates: Diagonal; Infobank Holdings; Majestic Wine; Redstone Telecom; Torex; XKO Group. Financials: Beeson Gregory; Williams de Broe.

Pinsent Curtis Biddle (see firm details p.1098) Market opinion is divided as to how this "*interesting merger*" will affect this "*understated but effective*" team. The team's combined strength sees it acting for 31 FTSE 100 companies, 11 Fortune 500 companies and 28 AIM listed companies. Said by competitors to "*know its business,*" the team has been active in a number of high value transactions, including acting for the management of Cannons Group on a £260 million take-private buyout. Major flotations include the Parkman Group's £43.8 million flotation on the London Stock Exchange. "*Energetic, enthusiastic*" **Martin Webster** (see p.259) is an experienced MBO specialist. With a "*workmanlike understanding of the position,*" he "*tries to find the right answer without missing any technical points.*" He advised on the £1.5 million AIM flotation of Internet Direct. The team acted for Barclays Private Equity on the £270 million MBO of Preferred Mortgages from Rotch Property Group, and the £89.4 million BIMBO of Clydesdale Financial Services from Next. **Clients:** Corporates: Abbot Group; Arlington; Bank Restaurant Group; Baxi Group; Cedar Group; City North Group; cybIT Holdings; e-xentric; Fulcrum Pharma; Intrinsic Value; J2C; Transacsys; Louisiana Pacific Corporation. Financials: Barclays Bank; Barclays Private Equity; Bridgepoint Capital; Brown Shipley & Co; Gresham Trust; Old Mutual Securities.

SMALLER DEALS

CORPORATE FINANCE: SMALLER DEALS • London	Ptnrs	Assts
1 DJ Freeman	8	14
Eversheds	13	20
Lawrence Graham	11	13
Stephenson Harwood	3	17
2 Field Fisher Waterhouse	9	18
Memery Crystal	4	6
Reed Smith Warner Cranston	11	8
Richards Butler	7	19
3 Harbottle & Lewis	5	12
Lewis Silkin	8	6
Nicholson Graham & Jones	13	15
4 Coudert Brothers	2	10
Hobson Audley	5	8
Sinclair Roche & Temperley	5	15
Watson, Farley & Williams	7	20
Wedlake Bell	5	6
5 Fox Williams	5	10
Howard Kennedy	7	6
Manches	4	4
Marriott Harrison	4	4
6 Beachcroft Wansbroughs	8	9
Charles Russell	6	13
Laytons	5	6
Middleton Potts	4	4
Steptoe & Johnson Rakisons	3	7

LEADING INDIVIDUALS	
1 **AUDLEY Max** Hobson Audley	**STORAR Michael** Lawrence Graham
2 **BEHARRELL Steven** Coudert Brothers	**GRAYSTON Clare** Lewis Silkin
GREGORY Lesley Memery Crystal	**JOHNS Michael** Nicholson Graham & Jones
SWEET Jon Marriott Harrison	
3 **BAKER Andrew** Wedlake Bell	**DEAN Kevin** Sinclair Roche & Temperley
FAGELSON Ian Reed Smith Warner Cranston	
WILLIAMS Christine Fox Williams	

This book is the product of 6,552 1/2 hour interviews. See p.7 for BMRB audit.
Within each band, firms are listed alphabetically. *See individuals' profiles p.239*

DJ Freeman (see firm details p.943) Led by Richard Spiller, the team primarily handles corporate finance work within the context of three main sector focuses; media and communications, insurance and property. The team advises on corporate transactions ranging between £50-200 million and on structured insurance and property financing up to £2.5 billion. Among its market successes within the property sector, the team advised the Benchmark Group and JER Partners Joint Venture on their acquisition of a £250 million property portfolio from MEPC. The team's development of expertise in e-commerce matters has resulted in a number of key deals, including the £100 million reverse takeover by Glenchewton of I-spire, an AIM-listed internet operating company. **Clients:** Capital & Regional; Carillion; H-G Holdings; SOC Group; Domestic & General Insurance; Shell.

Eversheds (see firm details p.952) Martin Issit leads a "*hungry, active*" team that handles a substantial number of deals for companies outside London. Clients comment that the firm's "*national reputation*" leads to a number of instructions for the London office. In addition to the main corporate and M&A thrusts of the team's work, it continues to develop private equity-related expertise, working closely with the Financial Services and Corporate Insurance teams. Recent deals include acting for the equity funders in the £110 million MBO of Admiral, while the team has also handled such IPOs as IQE's £557 million offering, with further offerings on EASDAQ and in the US, and the £260 million dual listing of GeneMedix on the London and Singapore Stock Exchanges. Other highlights include advising IRG in its £100 million sale to The Capital Group and acting for a shareholder of Rafael Hotels on the £89 million sale of the business to Mandarin Oriental Hotels. **Clients:** Corporates: Jarvis; Invensys; DuPont; Capital Radio; Dow Chemical; Thales (formerly Thomson CSF). Financials: Legal & General; M&G; Threadneedle; Gartmore Joint Ventures; Royal Bank Private Equity.

Lawrence Graham (see firm details p.1030) Respected by competitors for its "*good partners and high standard of work,*" the team advises on a high proportion of AIM work, as well as private equity and M&A work in areas such as brewing, leisure, hotels and e-commerce. Clients comprise a mix of active AIM companies and nominated advisors/brokers, as well as larger listed corporates, while the team also benefits from strong connections with the corporate finance divisions of stockbrokers and other City intermediaries. **Michael Storar** (see p.258) "*doesn't take points unnecessarily.*" Described by peers as "*cool, efficient and helpful,*" he led on Radio Trust's £158 million placing and capital reorganisation and Fibrenet Group's £76.96 million rights issue. The team also acted on Tullow Oil's £201 million acquisition of North Sea gas fields and infrastructure, and London & Regional Property Group's £410 million acquisition of a controlling interest in 60 Victoria Embankment. **Clients:** Corporates: Scottish & Newcastle; Strategic Hotel Capital Group; Fibrenet Group; Fulcrum Investment Trust; Gartmore High Income Trust/ Securities; Premier Asset Management; Radio Trust; St David's Investment Trust. Financials: Investec Henderson Crosthwaite; Old Mutual Securities; Teather & Greenwood.

Stephenson Harwood (see firm details p.1141) Andrew Sutch leads a practice that is perceived by some interviewees to have had "*a tough time*" in maintaining its corporate profile. However, the scope of the team's corporate offering has increased through the recent expansion of the business technology team, together with a renewed focus on key market sectors of financial industry, property and maritime services. The team has been acting on a major joint venture created by two global banking groups to launch an internet financial services operation. Among the highlights of the year, the firm advised Bristol City Council on the sale of its shareholding in Bristol International Airport. Other work includes acting for Kuwait Investment Office on the £100 million sale of the London Bridge, Lister and Devonshire Hospitals to American company HCA, and acting for Heytesbury Property on its £87.5 million share sale of Stoll Moss Theatres to the Stoll Moss Group Holdings. **Clients:** Corporates: Accor; Andrew Weir & Company; Christie's International; Hepworth; Kuwait Investment Office; Macdonald Hotels; Financials: Collins Stewart; HSBC; Framlington Group.

Field Fisher Waterhouse (see firm details p.957) Seen by clients as an "*upwardly mobile and energetic team,*" it handles M&A, joint ventures, AIM, capital raisings and private equity work. Clients include public sector and government departments, companies and institutions and wealthy individuals. Competitors perceive that Tim Davies and his team are "*doing well*" on the back of their reputation in the hi-tech and telecoms sector, while energy-related projects, OFEX and AIM sector work are other areas of new focus. The team advised on Future Internet Technologies' reverse takeover of Griff-Tech.com, its £3 million placing and £8 million acquisition of Hubbard Communications. Other work includes advising London Regional Transport on its internal reorganisation and transfer of operation to Transport for London, and acting for Thomas Cook Holdings on its joint venture with BA, involving a merger with the latter's tour-operating business. **Clients:** Corporates: CallServe; Investec; Henderson Crosthwaite; LRT; TFL; Future Internet Technologies; RSL Communications; Web Angel.

Memery Crystal (see firm details p.1064) Researchers were impressed by the warmth of client recommendation for a "*big specialist boutique with a degree of professionality which belies its size.*" Enjoying a high profile for AIM flotations, the team acts for well-known brokers in the field, handling a broader spread of corporate finance work than some of its competitors. AIM-listed companies account for roughly half of the client base; the rest are mainly private and fully listed FTSE 500 companies and entrepreneurs. In addition to secondary issuings, the team handles new and secondary capital raisings and M&A work, with an increasing focus on sports, leisure and digital technology sectors. "*Effective and practical,*" **Lesley Gregory** (see p.247) is reported by peers to have "*developed a fan club*" for her AIM and smaller capital markets work. Clients respect her for "*not over-lawyering deals and just getting them done.*" The team represented Seymour Pierce, the nominated advisor and broker on the AIM listing of World Life Sciences (c. £4.6 million). It also advised Propan Homes on its AIM listing. **Clients:** Wembley; QuadraNet; Adval Group; Radio First; Osprey Communications; Hansard Group; Digital Sport Group; Tamaris.

Reed Smith Warner Cranston Acknowledged by rivals as a "*trendy, commercial niche player*" which is "*beginning to make a name for itself,*" the firm has taken advantage of its US merger to increase the scope of its corporate transactional work through transatlantic client referrals. **Ian Fagelson** leads an "*intelligent, committed*" team that is "*easy to work with*" and "*only makes points that matter.*" He advised Virgin Trains on a 12-year £20 million agreement with Rail Gourmet, and advised McDonald's on the purchase of a 33% stake in Pret A Manger. The team has also handled several transactions for Swiss Re Newmarkets, including two securities placements of £400 million and $100 million. **Clients:** France Telecom; Rexel; Sara Lee Courtaulds; Akzo Nobel; Swiss Re Newmarkets.

Richards Butler (see firm details p.1107) David Boucher leads a team of "*calm negotiators*" which clients rate for its "*excellent attention to our needs.*" Within its strong sector focuses of media, leisure, transport and increasingly, telecoms work, the team acts for overseas (often US) inwardly investing clients, such as Frontier Europe. It has also demonstrated a capacity for handling international joint ventures and other cross-border work, such as Skanska Europe's £237 million acquisition of Kvaerner's worldwide construction business, a deal spanning 13 jurisdictions. The team also acted for Rank Group on the sales of Odeon Cinemas to Cinven (£280 million), Tom Cobleigh to Electra (£95 million) and Pinewood Studios to a consortium led by Michael Grade (£62 million). **Clients:** The Rank Group; Skanska Europe; MTV; BBC Worldwide; Blooms of Bressingham Holdings; Cordiant Communications Group; Sea Containers.

Harbottle & Lewis (see firm details p.985) A "*friendly, young and efficient*" team, primarily recommended to researchers for handling work leveraged from the firm's well-established IP/telecoms and entertainment practice. Mark Bertram leads a "*business-oriented*" team that "*takes the trouble to familiarise itself with clients.*" The team's caseload ranges from start-up and financing tiers, to IPOs for AIM and Stock Exchange-listed companies. It has particular expertise in new media consolidation strategic advice, handling deals such as the sale of Talkback Productions to Pearson Television for £62 million. Other highlights include SCi's £21 million shares placings, its subsequent listing on the London Stock Exchange and recent investment in music3w.com, and Attenda's £5 million financing through DLJ European Private Equity. **Clients:** Attenda; Richard Branson/The Virgin Group of Companies; Rivals Europe; SCi Entertainment Group; Take 2 Interactive Software; Chrysalis.

Lewis Silkin (see firm details p.1040) An "*entrepreneurial*" team that is thought to have "*cornered the market*" in small companies' flotations. Clients comment that it "*gets through deals quickly*" because of its "*speedy, accurate, commercial*" response. Acting for both issuer and sponsor, the team has expanded its traditional entrepreneurial corporate client base, now acting for FTSE 250, AIM and foreign companies from a wide range of sectors. Niche strength exists in internet private equity funding work, as demonstrated by the team's seed investment work for Net Partners, a pioneer internet-only VC company. "*Incredibly efficient team manager*" **Clare Grayston** (see p.247) has "*a jolly good practice*" and "*knows her stuff on regulatory matters,*" according to peers. She acted for John East & Partners on the AIM flotation of Totally, which runs the community website, Totallyjewish.com. The team also advised Integrated Dental Holdings in its acquisition of the Whitecross Dental Care Group, the largest dental group in Europe. **Clients:** John East & Partners; ClaraNET (the ISP); Haymarket Publishing Group; Integrated Dental Holdings; Havas Advertising Group; Net Partners.

Nicholson Graham & Jones (see firm details p.1081) A "*traditional*" firm with a team of corporate lawyers that is commended by clients for "*getting on with things.*" The team handles a broad spread of corporate work in SME and growing company markets, with particular strength in areas such as leisure, gaming and media. Competitors speak of a team "*doing well for its size,*" and advising on high profile deals such as GWR Group's £146 million acquisition of DMG Radio Group from Daily Mail and General Trust. "*Effective*" managing partner, **Michael Johns** (see p.249) "*has real gravitas.*" A "*client-charmer,*" he can "*occupy space without being overbearing.*" He advised Eurodis Electron on its £28.7 million acquisition of Ericsson's electronic component distribution business. The team also advised Sportech on its £161 million acquisition of Littlewoods Leisure from the Littlewoods Organisation. **Clients:** GWR Group; Henderson Ventures; Kleeneze; Union; Singer & Friedlander Group; Sportech.

Coudert Brothers (see firm details p.925) Despite its low profile in the London market, peers acknowledge that the team "*gets through a lot of deals.*" Acting for a foreign, largely multinational client base, the majority of the team's work relates to cross-border transactions handled in the UK or with a UK element. One such example was Vivendi's acquisition of a Hong Kong business. Although the team continues to benefit from US referrals, it handles an increasing amount of work for European clients, following the firm's recent merger with Frankfurt firm Schurmann & Partners. "*Commercial, aggressive and energetic*" **Steven Beharrell** (see p.353) has a solid reputation for his energy-related transactional work, such as acting for Telenor in a series of major transactions in Russia. **Clients:** Telenor; Vivendi.

Hobson Audley (see firm details p.997) *Chambers'* researchers were left in no doubt that the firm occupies an "*excellent corporate niche.*" Providing a "*solid M&A and IPO practice,*" the firm's strengths lie in corporate finance, innovation and technology, where it continues to act for its traditional client base of medium and smaller public companies and leading US entities. While its association with Minneapolis firm Faegre & Benson continues to provide a steady stream of work from significant clients such as Wells Fargo and Halliwell, the team now has the added benefit of German law capability following a merger between its US ally and Frankfurt-based Brendel Ekkenga Daniel. The energy market is an area of increasing focus. "*Respected individual*" **Max Audley** has "*always had a good name.*" Clients report that "*he goes straight to the point and doesn't mess about.*" He acted for the German food distributor REWE on its £89.4 million disposal of its shareholding in Budgens to the Musgrave Group. The team also acted for Paladin Resources on its £79 million acquisition of the Norwegian oil and gas assets owned by Petro-Canada. **Clients:** Investec Henderson Crosthwaite; Nabarro Wells & Co; Paladin Resources; Quintiles Transnational Corp; The Hearst Corporation; Halliburton Company; Havas/Groupe de la Cité.

Sinclair Roche & Temperley (see firm details p.1134) Well-regarded practice that handles a range of corporate work leveraged off the firm's established key sectors in shipping, aviation, energy, trade and financial institutions. The team acts for funds taking stakes in publicly listed and shareholder-valued companies, and on financial restructuring matters such as the Daewoo Group's reconstruction of its heavy industry divisions in Korea. The practice has also expanded into work for incubator funds, exemplified by the reverse takeover of The Multimedia Corporation for the incubator company, Illuminator. Head of Corporate, **Kevin Dean** (see p.244) leads the team. An "*able, knowledgeable, straightforward*" dealer, according to peers, he has gained profile in his work for international shipping companies such as Cunard, Carnival and Harland & Wolff. His team has acted for Active Value Funds on several of its investments. **Clients:** Daewoo; Carnival Corporation; Cunard; Illuminator; Securiplan; Active Value Funds.

Watson, Farley & Williams (see firm details p.1174) Jan Mellmann leads a team endorsed by peers as "*extremely easy to work with.*" Although shipping work is the firm's core area of focus, the team is perceived as "*more broadly based*" in general corporate work, covering telecoms, e-commerce and media. It handles cross-border M&A work requiring advice on US, French and Russian law, in addition to UK law. Other work includes domestic flotations, including OFEX, AIM and stock exchange-related work. A highlight was the team's work for Vivendi Universal on several matters relating to the $35 billion merger with The Seagram Company, involving advice on tender offers, financing arrangements and securities placings. The team has also handled several significant deals for Charles Stanley, including the BV Group's AIM admission and £2.3 million placing, and General Industries' £25 million acquisition of The Celltalk Group. **Clients:** Vivendi; ECS Avaya; French Property Trust; Hellas Can; ICB Shipping; Charles Stanley & Company; Anglo St James; Citadel Holdings; Beaumont Cornish; Matrix Corporate Finance.

Wedlake Bell (see firm details p.1175) Approvingly described by competitors as "*an active firm with a long history, which is comfortable with its identity,*" it acts for a wide range of clients. These include start-ups, serial entrepreneurs, brokers, small listed companies and international corporates. Focusing on cross-border M&A and collective investment schemes, satisfied clients report that the team "*works hard to understand our approach and understand our position in negotiations.*" "*Good rainmaker*" **Andrew Baker** (see p.240) (formerly of Slaughter and May) has a profile from his role as Chair of the Smaller Companies Alliance and is well known for his work in the junior markets. The team has advised on nine new issues for Hoodless Brennan, as well as flotations and acquisitions for Auto Indemnity Group and takeovers and acquisitions for Global Group. **Clients:** Global Group; Hoodless Brennan & Partners; Bell Microproducts (San Jose); Nestor Healthcare; Intrepid Energy.

Fox Williams (see firm details p.963) Clients choose this "*extremely capable, cohesive*" team for its "*personable service*" and ability to "*get the job done within tight time-frames.*" Acting for large corporations and start-ups with an entrepreneurial flavour, the team handles joint venture and shares options work, with cross-border transactional capacity via its international corporate law network. A key specialism is M&A capital-raising work (up to £250 million), such as offers for subscription to raise up to £5 million for Midas Films and £5 million for Epoch Software Holdings. **Tina Williams**' (see p.617) reputation goes before her. Peers describe her negotiating style as "*firm but pleasant.*" She advised Xchanging on a $50 million investment by General Atlantic Partners, and VTech on its $29.17 million aggregate acquisition of Sensei. Team highlights include acting for the vendors of Bankhall Investment Management on its £114 million sale to Lynx Group. **Clients:** Cinram International/ Cinram UK; Dione; Earls Court & Olympia Group; Epoch Software Holdings; EU Smart; Grant Thornton; Simply Hub; VTech Holdings; Xchanging.

Howard Kennedy (see firm details p.1001) The team's reputation lies principally in listing work for VCTs and EIFs, and stems from its historic work on tax-related finance products and business expansion schemes during the 1980s. Led by Michael Harris, the group handles public offer work for an entrepreneurial-led client base that includes partnerships, companies and sponsors and virtual start-ups. The team has recently launched Kennedy Gee Corporate Finance, a new joint venture with Levy Gee, acting as a nominal adviser to AIM. This year's highlights include advising Beeson Gregory on the £20 million listing on the TechMARK of Service Power, a provider of resource management software. **Clients:** Friendly Hotels; Comprehensive Business Services; Zevco; Next Generation Clubs Holdings; Longbridge; Downing Corporate Finance.

Manches (see firm details p.1051) Melvin Pedro leads a team which competitors endorse for "*handling its work well.*" Focused on mid-market transactions ranging between £5 and £100 million, the team acts for management and entrepreneurial clients with sector focus in technology and property. It acted for management on the £452 million MBO and MBI of Caradon and the £134 million private purchase of Allied London Properties. Further key matters include WILink.com's £55 million reverse takeover of Knutsford Group and the AIM flotation of Musicunsigned Holdings. **Clients:** Jigsaw; Bouyzes/ Saur; WI Link; Durlacher; Munrow K; Ultasis; Syngenta; Lloyds TSB; Kingfisher Property Division; Sport First.

Marriott Harrison (see firm details p.1053) Characterised as "*a neat corporate practice,*" it has established a media specialisation that earns the respect of its peers. Representing an established client base of media-based corporates, private equity and VC institutions, the firm is perceived to be "*heavily into film finance, and jolly good at it too.*" Having "*made its name within the VC field,*" the team has expanded its focus from film and television work into the IT and music sectors. "*Tremendously professional and diligent*" **Jon Sweet** (see p.258) is seen as a "*real asset to the firm,*" although it is widely asserted that "*he could do with more back-up.*" Known for his representation of the Eccleston family interests, he acted for shareholders of the Formula One Group in relation to the acquisition of an interest in SLEC by Hellman & Friedman and EM.TV & Merchandising. The team also acted for Online Travel Corporation on its AIM flotation and for Octagon Holdings in relation to the acquisition of a schools division. **Clients:** LICA Development Capital; Durlacher Corporation; Eagle Rock Entertainment; Online Travel Corporation; GLE Development Capital.

Beachcroft Wansbroughs (see firm details p.872) In addition to its well-established insurance company client base, the team, led by Simon Hodson, acts for borrowers within a range of mid-cap industrial companies, demonstrating notable expertise in water and other utilities. Key matters handled by the team include acting for Vivendi Water (UK) in the merger of North Surrey Water and Three Valleys Water, and acting for East Surrey Holdings in the purchase of a quarter of Northern Ireland's Phoenix Natural Gas from BG Energy Holding for around £50 million. **Clients:** Association of British Insurers; Charante Steam Ship Company; Cornhilll Insurance; Dee Valley Group; East Surrey Water; Vivendi Water UK; Dalkia.

Charles Russell (see firm details p.912) Simon Gilbert leads an "*aggressive*" team that handles a range of corporate finance work, and has a strong focus on recruitment, insurance and communications. The team does attract criticism from some quarters for its style, which "*can sometimes make a meal of things.*" It advised Inquam on the acquisition of RDT (Holdings) and SIH's subscription of €100 million for bearer depository receipts in Vedior, the Amsterdam listed recruitment company. Another highlight involved acting for Scoot.com in the acquisition of Loot's £180 million issued share capital. **Clients:** Cable & Wireless; Ericsson Enterprises; Vedior; Morgan Sindall; Scoot.com; BV Group; JM Finn & Co; Trifast.

Laytons (see firm details p.1031) Richard Kennett leads a low-profile team that handles a range of general corporate finance work ranging between £5 million and £50 million. In addition to its established client base of smaller listed corporates and hi-tech start-ups, the team acts for companies in raising equity capital from existing or new investors in the US or UK. Recent work in this field includes raisings of £3.7 million for Fresh & Wild, a chain of organic food stores, and £3 million for Family Genetix, a medical software company. Growing its multi-jurisdictional capability, the team advised Newport Technology Group, a UK electronics company with US and Chinese subsidiaries, on its reconstruction and £35 million sale to a US company. The firm also acted for Westvaco on its acquisition of a Dutch printing subsidiary of Sony Corporation. **Clients:** Newport Technology Group; Westvaco Corporation (including IMPAC Group); Goodhead Group; Lexington Group; J&M Entertainments; WestLB Panmure; Po Na Na; Priory Investments; Red Bull; Compel Group; Oxford Instruments.

Middleton Potts (see firm details p.1067) Although best known for its shipping expertise, the team's corporate finance capability is integrated with non-marine commercial work, such as asset and project finance, construction, PFI, IP and energy. David Godfrey leads a close-knit team that acts for a predominantly international client base. A major recent highlight was acting on Belgrave Properties' £31 million disposal of a company and underlying portfolio of companies to Dorrington Investment. **Clients:** Assicurazioni Generali; Hamburgische Landesbank; Altram Consortium; Ansaldo Energia; Ansaldo Signal; Union Switch & Signal; Alitalia; The Phoenix Home Life Mutual Insurance Group.

Steptoe & Johnson Rakisons (see firm details p.1142) The market appears undecided about the effect of the firm's merger with Washington firm Steptoe & Johnson on its practice. Jonathan Polin leads a team that handles a range of corporate M&A work, specialising in hi-tech start-ups and acquisitions within the telecoms industry, and acting for vendors on exit.The team advised Dynergy on its $155 million acquisition of iaxis (in administration), and advised Stratos Global Corporation on UK regulatory and corporate aspects of the $340 million acquisition of BT's worldwide aeronautical and marine satellite business. Other work includes advising Redbus Group on its £76 million reverse takeover of Horace Small Apparel. **Clients:** London Securities; Stanley Leisure; Causeway Technology; Playboy; Funmail; Chiltern; Stratos Global Corporation; Dynergy; Redbus Group; Andrews Sykes Group.

THE SOUTH

CORPORATE FINANCE • The South	Ptnrs	Assts
1 **Blake Lapthorn** Fareham, Portsmouth, Southampton	6	26
Bond Pearce Southampton	4	13
2 **Shadbolt & Co** Reigate	6	2
Stevens & Bolton Guildford	5	11
3 **asb law** Crawley	4	4
Clyde & Co Guildford	6	13
Cripps Harries Hall Tunbridge Wells	4	9
Mundays Esher	6	3
Paris Smith & Randall Southampton	4	2
Rawlison Butler Crawley	2	2
Shoosmiths Fareham	2	5
Thomas Eggar Church Adams Chichester, Horsham, Reigate, Worthing	7	5
Thomson Snell & Passmore Tunbridge Wells	2	3
4 **Brachers** Maidstone	3	3
DMH Brighton, Crawley	2	2
Lester Aldridge Bournemouth, Southampton	5	9

LEADING INDIVIDUALS	
1 **BAXTER Richard** Stevens & Bolton	**TROTTER Andrew** Shadbolt & Co
2 **BUTLER-GALLIE Stuart** Brachers	**CHATFIELD James** Rawlison Butler
NORCROSS WEBB Sally Shoosmiths	
PARTRIDGE James Thomson Snell & Passmore	
WRIGHT Sean Blake Lapthorn	
3 **HEATHCOCK Andrew** Paris Smith & Randall	
4 **HART Neil** Thomas Eggar Church Adams	**JEFFRIES Graham** Bond Pearce
MUNDAY Peter Mundays	**SADKA Tim** Rawlison Butler
SHIMMIN Kathryn Blake Lapthorn	
UP AND COMING	
SYSON Keith Stevens & Bolton	

This book is the product of 6,552 1/2 hour interviews. See p.7 for BMRB audit.
Within each band, firms are listed alphabetically. *See individuals' profiles p.239*

Blake Lapthorn (see firm details p.886) "*They're all good lawyers there,*" so claim the firm's rivals. Considered "*impressive to deal with,*" the majority of its solicitors come from city firms. Handles the full range of corporate finance work with strength in MBOs, MBIs, and the acquisition of shares. "*Good guy*" **Sean Wright** is judged "*a practical player*" and acted for the vendors in the sale of KJC mobile phone company for a consideration of more than £60 million. **Kathryn Shimmin** also stands out of the pack, and acted for the Bank of Scotland on a £23 million franchising of the acquisition of certain business and assets of British International Ltd. **Clients:** Bank of Scotland; HSBC; Lloyds TSB; National Westminster Bank; Royal Bank of Scotland; Pratt & Whitney.

Bond Pearce (see firm details p.888) The strength of the overall team is attested to by a number of big ticket transactions, yet the departure of Moray Macpherson to KLegal combined with the movement of Simon Hewes to the Bristol office is perceived to have weakened the Southampton team. Clients comment that the team is "*relatively young with a number of interesting prospects,*" agreeing that it has "*performed well.*" **Graham Jeffries** (see p.119), working at the intersection of banking and corporate finance, is considered "*excellent*" by his peers. The group handles the range of matters, with an emphasis on buy-outs, for a clientele encompassing large plcs. Average deal size lies in the region of £10 million. Particularly strong in media, e-commerce, retail, aviation, financial services and the food sector. The firm acted on the MBO of SP Systems, valued at £50 million. **Clients:** Chilworth Manor Ltd; Computer Associates.

Shadbolt & Co (see firm details p.1121) The "*great success*" of this growing team is widely attributed to the presence of **Andrew Trotter** (see p.259) who has secured the "*admiration of the market*" through his "*competence and focus.*" He "*fights for his clients on all fronts*" and they "*adore him.*" M&A accounts for the bulk of the work with a client roster which includes large quoted construction companies and smaller regional companies. The group acted on the sale of Membertrak to Gladstone for £7.67 million and advised on the investment of venture capital in Microscience, a biotech company, by Merlin Partners and APAX funds. It also conducted capital reductions by Mitsui Babcock Engineering and MESCO (UK), involving the cancellation of share capital with an aggregate value of £76 million. **Clients:** Membertrak; Microscience; Schoolsnet; Edmund Nuttall.

Stevens & Bolton (see firm details p.1143) Our interviewees endorsed this "*strong team*" led by the "*wise and commercial*" **Richard Baxter** (see p.240). Seen to have "*good recruits at the younger levels,*" among whom **Keith Syson** (see p.258) stands out as "*immensely and impressively able.*" In the main it receives instructions from quoted and foreign corporates, with owner-managed clients accounting for the balance. M&A forms the thrust of the practice, but it is carrying out an increasing amount of fund-raising work. The group acted for Gladedale Holdings on its £24 million recommended offer for AIM-listed Furlong Holmes Group, including a group refinancing. Also advised Hays on its acquisition of legal recruitment company ZMB. **Clients:** BOC Distribution Services; Berkeley Morgan Group; British Association of Pharmaceutical Wholesalers; ENER.G; Mobile Telecom; Novartis Pharmaceuticals.

asb law (see firm details p.865) Servicing M&A, private equity and restructuring work this firm is one of the largest corporate teams in the region. It acts for owner-managed businesses and quoted companies and over the past year has acted on more than 50 transactions, with deal values mainly in excess of £2 million. Don Burstow is the group's leader. It acted for the shareholders on the sale of Awarenet to a German listed company for £32 million. Represented the shareholders of Trident Microsystems during its sale to component distributors Abacus Polar; the purchase was for £10 million plus a potential £8 million contingent on performances. **Clients:** Mailcom; Olympian Consultancy; Awarenet; Trident Microsystems; Prismo/Jarvis Group; AirMiles Travel Promotions; First Choice Holidays.

Clyde & Co (see firm details p.921) Peers congratulate a "*well-known and powerful team*" that "*doesn't raise petty problems.*" Seen to have invested heavily in its Guildford office, its "*impressive*" city-trained lawyers are carving out their own names. Andrew Holderness leads the team, which can call on the resources of City and international offices. Strengths include Stock Exchange transactions, M&A, and buyouts in the distribution and logistics, insurance, publishing, and support services sector. Advised Securicor on all aspects of its successful project for the rollout of ATM cash machines in retail outlets across the UK, and in its admission to the Link organisation. It launched ecapitalstart.com in conjunction with BDO Stoy Hayward and Euro Sales Finance, designed to provide a single source of online advice to entrepreneurs wanting to raise finance. **Clients:** Johnson & Johnson; Ion Energy Resources; Cathedral Capital; BRIT Insurance Holdings; Bass; William Reed Holdings.

Cripps Harries Hall (see firm details p.927) Many of our interviewees described this firm as "*on the rise.*" It offers a comprehensive service for an impressive client-base including advice on MBOs, MBIs, M&A, joint venture companies and shareholder agreements. Now particularly focusing on the new technology sector. Trevor Carney is the team's senior figure. The group acted on the establishment of two websites for an international insurer with an investment in excess of £40 million. Also acted on behalf of the management in the £14 million MBO of Blaze Neon Group. **Clients:** British Airways Pension Investment Management; Dencare Management Group; JSC Ispat Karmet; Paydens; Swiss Life.

Mundays (see firm details p.1077) "*Strong players,*" led by the "*able and experienced*" **Peter Munday** (see p.253), the firm is commended for its quality advice and relationships with clients such as E Moss (part of Unichem). It has developed expertise in the retail and IT sectors which form a facet of a much wider base. Instructions often arise from M&A, public to private transactions, joint ventures, reorganisations, IPOs, and venture capital funding. **Clients:** E Moss; Kewell Systems; Octagon Developments.

Paris Smith & Randall (see firm details p.1089) "*Coming on strong recently*" the firm benefits from the presence of "*assertive*" **Andrew Heathcock** (see p.248). It handles mainstream corporate finance work for finance houses, large plcs, and owner-managed businesses. Particularly strong in the manufacturing sector, with which it has long-standing ties. The group acted for Southampton Leisure Holdings in the refinancing of the new St Mary's Stadium, involving a corporate bond structure of more than £25 million. Also represented Vosper Thornycroft (UK) in its acquisition of Hospitality Plus (UK) for £10.5 million. **Clients:** Southampton Institute; Hampshire County Cricket Club; Vosper Thornycroft; Bank of Scotland.

Rawlison Butler (see firm details p.1104) The team handles the gamut of work, encompassing traditional M&A, private equity, and corporate restructuring. Considered by some peers to be only limited by its size, its two dedicated partners both enjoy a high profile. **James Chatfield** is deemed "*a pretty switched on individual,*" while **Tim Sadka** also elicits praise. A broad client base encompasses owner-managed businesses and an increasing number of plcs. It has notable experience in the hi-tech and pharmaceutical sectors and its portfolio includes drinks distributors and pubs. The group acted on the acquisition of a division of British Airways on behalf of Amadeus Global Travel Distribution, and represented the shareholders (including 3i) on the disposal of The Alan Group to Carclo for £6.9 million. **Clients:** Suzuki GB; Dragon Health Clubs; California Software Corp; TBC Group.

Shoosmiths (see firm details p.1129) Plaudits flood in for "*great breath of fresh air*" **Sally Norcross Webb** (see p.253) who is thought "*commercial and pleasant to deal with.*" Clients find the team "*sound and responsive*" and add that the City-trained staff "*bring a sensible, commercial view.*" Undertakes the full range of work and is able to draw on the resources of offices across the region. The group acted for HJ Heinz on the acquisition, development and leasing of National Distribution Centre by way of the UK's first synthetic lease. It also acted on the sale of Deacon Insurance Group to Hercules Property Services for £14.25 million. **Clients:** HJ Heinz; Tandberg Television; Sourceree; The Royal Bank of Scotland; Industrial Rubber.

Thomas Eggar Church Adams (see firm details p.1153) Peers acknowledge this firm's "*significant presence,*" while clients note that it is "*aware of the commercial realities,*" with one commenting "*we appreciate the full service that we can get from this one firm.*" Although there is "*always someone there to talk to,*" **Neil Hart** (see p.248) stands out as "*approachable and responsive.*" Expert in acting for mortgage lenders, and on ATM work, e-commerce and pension trusteeship. The firm acted for Wyndeham Press Group in its £17.5 million acquisition of Print Direct. **Clients:** Club Direct Insurance Services; Lec Refrigeration; H+H International AS; NCH Marketing Services; C&C Marshall.

Thomson Snell & Passmore (see firm details p.1155) Respected by peers as a "*robust but small team*" blessed with the "*profound ability*" of **James Partridge** (see p.254) who is said to be "*affable and easy to deal with.*" The turnover of the department has grown by 150% in the last year. It acted for an investee company on its $5.5 million venture capital funding into the internet access technology sector. The firm also advised in connection with an offer of £9.3 million for an AIM listed company, and was involved on a major outsourcing contract for road maintenance in Scotland. **Clients:** Colas Ltd; Dean & Wood; William Ransom & Son.

Brachers (see firm details p.893) Many competing lawyers refer to this firm "*with complete confidence,*" agreeing that **Stuart Butler-Gallie** (see p.242) is a "*talented guy doing good things.*" The value of individual transactions commonly lies in the £5 to £20 million range. The firm offers considerable expertise in the waste disposal and recycling industry. It acted on the £11.8 million MBO of Cyborg Systems, and acted for the vendors in the £14 million sale of Media Merchants Television Company. **Clients:** Charlton Athletic Football Club; Eurotunnel; Towergate Underwriting Group; Poggo Group.

DMH (see firm details p.944) Handles the full range of work including reorganisations, MBOs, and structured fundings with experience of AIM and stock exchange works. The firm conducts deals that tend to fall in the £3-10 million range for a number of plcs. Strengths include start-up and shareholder investment work for the technology media and telecoms sectors. It acted for the majority shareholders on the sale of Colour Processing Laboratories and advised on a public company refinancing of £12.5 million. Mike Long leads the team. **Clients:** HSBC Enterprise Fund; Bank of Scotland; National Westminster Bank; Venture Finance.

Lester Aldridge (see firm details p.1038) Seen to have successfully picked up "*some interesting people*" in its recent expansion, the firm is commended for its advice in the field of M&A, buyouts, joint ventures and restructurings. Continues to advise the Federal Republic of Yugoslavia in respect of the Federal Air Traffic Control Authority. The firm also conducted an MBO for the management team of Widney Aish Ltd. **Clients:** CDI Anders Elite; Daler-Rowney; ITW; Newday Group; Bath Travel.

THAMES VALLEY

CORPORATE FINANCE • Thames Valley	Ptnrs	Assts
1 **Osborne Clarke** Reading	4	15
2 **Manches** Oxford	4	4
3 **Clarks** Reading	3	6
Kimbells Milton Keynes	2	3
Nabarro Nathanson Reading	2	6
Pitmans Reading	4	5
4 **Brobeck Hale and Dorr** Oxford	3	3
5 **BP Collins** Gerrards Cross	n/a	n/a
Garretts Reading	2	6
Shoosmiths Reading	5	n/a

LEADING INDIVIDUALS	
1 **ANGEL Peter** Manches	**GOWANS Andrew** Osborne Clarke
PILLMAN Joe Brobeck Hale and Dorr	
2 **HUTCHINSON John** Pitmans	**LEE Richard** Clarks
SMERDON Richard Osborne Clarke	
3 **DREW Dean** Shoosmiths	**JONES Hugh** Osborne Clarke
KIMBELL Stephen Kimbells	**LEYSHON Greg** Osborne Clarke
LOAKE Jonathan Brobeck Hale and Dorr	**TAYLOR Glyn** Nabarro Nathanson

This book is the product of 6,552 1/2 hour interviews. See p.7 for BMRB audit.
Within each band, firms are listed alphabetically. *See individuals' profiles p.239*

Osborne Clarke (see firm details p.1086) An "*outstanding*" team that clients value for its national network. "*Trusted*" regional panel lawyers for major clients such as 3i, the team distinguishes itself by its "*commercial, relevant and robust approach.*" Private equity is a key focus within the team's scope of corporate and M&A work. Peers endorse "*solid, city-trained*" Head of Department **Andrew Gowans**, active on deals such as advising British Airways on the disposal of Speedwing worldwide software applications business. "*Class act*" **Richard Smerdon** is "*extremely highly regarded*" in the market. Clients on banking matters esteem "*business-like*" **Hugh Jones**, formerly of Morgan Cole. He has been advising Tribal Group on a series of acquisitions across a range of sectors ranging between £2-10 million. Clients favour "*extremely competent*" private equity specialist **Greg Leyshon** who enters the tables this year. He advised on the $180 million disposal of Microcosm Communications. The team acted for ECI and Newco on a £13 million IBO of Sedgemore College and the management shareholders in Woods of Windsor's £5.9 million MBO. **Clients:** Innogy; Torex; Trader Media Group; Tribal Group; 3i Group; Lloyds Development Capital.

Manches (see firm details p.1051) Researchers were told that the team has "*done well in targeting technology related work within the Oxford science park community,*" having acted on the formation or financing of about half the technology 'spin-out' companies from Oxford University since 1990. Peers hail "*excellent practitioner*" **Peter Angel** (see p.239) as "*a mentor – exemplary for his superb client management skills.*" He advised the shareholders of M&J (including Lloyds TSB Development Capital) on the £48 million sale of the company to Brake Brothers. The team advised on the £370 million London Stock Exchange listing of Staffware, and on genomics company Oxagen's £31.75 million fund-raising, one of the largest in Europe at the time. **Clients:** Mayflower Corporation; Xenova Group; Blackwell's; Oxford Asymmetry International; Oxagen; Oxford Gene Technology; Leyland DAF Trucks; Staffware; Avidex; Achilles Group.

Clarks (see firm details p.916) Clients endorse the team's "*excellent local reputation*" in private equity and owner-managed businesses transactions. The integrated practice incorporates technology and employee share schemes work. It represents a number of FTSE 250 and equivalent international clients and is attracting an increasing number of technology start ups, financing and cross border transactions. Peers continue to regard Head of Corporate **Richard Lee** (see p.251) as "*an excellent practitioner.*" The team advised on Dynex Corporation's acquisition of Mitel, the reorganisation of Connectivity Plus, and spin out and $18.5 million financing of Axiom Systems. A key private equity highlight was the £32.2 million MBO of Auto Sleepers Group. **Clients:** Norsk Hydro; Bunzl; Fazer Group; CFBT Education Services; Dynes Semiconductor; Axiom Systems; Auto-Sleepers; Highcroft Investment Trusts.

Kimbells (see firm details p.1021) This compact practice handles a mixture of corporate finance, company sales and acquisitions, public to private and high value MBO/ MBI transactions. Best known in the market is the "*excellent, impressive*" **Stephen Kimbell** who is said to have a "*pragmatic approach.*" The team advised on the £50 million MBO of the ICL's logistics division, and Kingswell's £10.5 million sale to Guardian IT. Further team highlights include the reorganisation of Dawsongroup and sale of Spillers division. **Clients:** Dawsongroup; Minolta UK; Nationwide Access.

Nabarro Nathanson (see firm details p.1078) Researchers were told that the local profile of this integrated corporate and commercial practice is obscured, given the nature of its work, which is perceived as being predominantly based outside the region. The team indeed works in tandem with the London office. Niche areas are IT/ technology and e-commerce, as exemplified by the team's investment related work for MTI Partners and ET Capital, and its instructions in the sale of Bayton Thompson Networks to Cable & Wireless. Specialist in AIM flotations, "*tremendous*" **Glyn Taylor** (see p.258) is said to be doing "*a great job*" acting on six new prospective floats this year in addition to handling TransEDA's float. The team advised on Whatman's £42 million sale, Costco's £150 million reorganisation and £35 million purchase of Littlewood's shareholding in the company. **Clients:** Bank of Scotland; Costco; ET Capital; HSBC; London Scottish Bank; MTI Partners; Ninth Floor Group; Oracle; Really Useful Group; Siemens; Sondex; Sun; The Met Office.

Pitmans (see firm details p.1099) **John Hutchinson** (see p.249) leads an integrated team of corporate and commercial specialists, which services a mixed client base of listed companies and owner-managed businesses. Handling an increasing amount of IT and internet related investment, including funding for start-ups. The team acted for Sensor Highway in an £8.25 million venture capital investment involving 3i and others, and in its acquisition of York Sensors from GN Nettest (UK). Further team highlights include the Mabey Group's £6 million sale of its London underground maintenance division to MJ Gleeson, and GSD Field Marketing's sale to US company McCann-Erikson Group. **Clients:** Crown Resources AG; Dura Automotive; Mabey Group; Porsche Cars Great Britain; Biocompatibles International; Bank of Scotland.

Brobeck Hale and Dorr (see firm details p.895) Recently established by former partners of Morgan Cole, this is the second of the US law firm's UK offices. In keeping with its parent's global technology sector focus, the team's client base comprises emerging European technology companies, such as established client, Bookham Technology. Researchers were told "*grafter*" **Joe Pillman** (see p.255) "*commands the confidence of his clients,*" while "*well-regarded and lucid*" **Jonathan Loake** handles the commercial side of transactions. The team advised on the VC capital funding of Searchspace by HSBC Private Equity and the acquisition of MarketingNet by Day Interactive. **Clients:** Searchspace; Day Interactive Holding AG.

BP Collins Described by competitors as a "*small scale, respectable outfit,*" the team is visible on smaller ticket mergers, acquisitions and investment management for its local client base.

Garretts (see firm details p.968) Perceived by market commentators as a "*uniquely focused*" practice on account of its international work and support role to Andersen Legal's accountancy network. The team specialises in complex tax driven reorganisations for clients such as Cardinal, ITW and Red Brigade. Technology related transactions are another area of focus, as exemplified by fundraising for Peramon Technology and Cardionetics. This year's highlight was the Bikes-UK transaction, in which the team advised on a £25 million MBI/MBO to establish one of the UK's largest motorbike sales networks. The team also advised on a £20 million sale of the privately owned Zeuros to AIM listed Harrier Group. Andrew Watson has taken up an in-house post. **Clients:** Bikes-UK; Zeuros; Peramon Technology; MAPA Spontex (Total Fina Elf Oil subsidiary); Fat Face; Cardinal Healthcare.

Shoosmiths (see firm details p.1129) Said to "*offer the backup and resources of a large firm,*" the team's southern network of offices is located in Reading, Banbury and most recently, Milton Keynes. Active on general corporate finance and major transactional work, the team also handles VC funding and start-up work. For clients, **Dean Drew** (see p.244) "*is the main attraction.*" Vouching that he "*never lets us down and is extremely reliable,*" clients rate him " for his diligence, attention to detail, responsiveness, and willingness to understand the commercial objectives." National Unit Head Nigel Thorne leads a "*good, solid*" team, which advised on the MBO of Woods of Windsor, acted in EM Warburg Pincus' £8 million investment in Translogica, and Donantonio's acquisition of F&S businesses and Olga Catering. **Clients:** ComponentSource; SageMaker; Donantonio; Black Box; SGI; The Open University; PWA Group; Fired Earth; Karcher UK.

SOUTH WEST

CORPORATE FINANCE • South West	Ptnrs	Assts
1 **Burges Salmon** Bristol	6	16
Osborne Clarke Bristol	10	26
2 **TLT Solicitors** Bristol	3	13
3 **Bevan Ashford** Bristol, Exeter	6	6
Bond Pearce Exeter, Plymouth	5	6
4 **Bretherton Price Elgoods** Cheltenham	3	3
Charles Russell Cheltenham	2	1
CMS Cameron McKenna Bristol	1	3
Foot Anstey Sargent Exeter, Plymouth	4	5
Laytons Bristol	4	8
Lyons Davidson Bristol	n/a	n/a
Michelmores Exeter	2	4
Stephens & Scown Exeter, St Austell, Truro	3	3
Veale Wasbrough Bristol	3	4
5 **Clark Holt** Swindon	2	n/a

LEADING INDIVIDUALS	
1 **COOPER Paul** Osborne Clarke	**GODFREY Christopher** Burges Salmon
2 **BARR Alan** Burges Salmon	**GRAVES Patrick** Osborne Clarke
PESTER David TLT Solicitors	**ROUS Simon** Bevan Ashford
ROXBURGH Bruce Osborne Clarke	
3 **HAWES Roger** Burges Salmon	**RUNDALL Francis** Charles Russell
4 **ACOCK Roger** Lyons Davidson	**BELLEW Derek** Veale Wasbrough
COOMBS Richard Foot Anstey Sargent	**JONES Michael** CMS Cameron McKenna
LEWIS Mark Foot Anstey Sargent	**LIVINGSTONE Alisdair** Osborne Clarke
MORSE Stephen Michelmores	**WATTS Clive** Osborne Clarke
5 **HEWES Simon** Bond Pearce	**KELIHER James** Stephens & Scown
MARSH David Burges Salmon	**NORTON Richard** Charles Russell
SPINK Richard Burges Salmon	

This book is the product of 6,552 1/2 hour interviews. See p.7 for BMRB audit.
Within each band, firms are listed alphabetically. *See individuals' profiles p.239*

Burges Salmon (see firm details p.902) Described by peers and clients as a "*conservative, pin-striped*" outfit, this team's strength and depth remains beyond question. Its "*excellent, constructive*" team of "*scholarly*" individuals services a "*blue-chip*" plc client base across the full range of corporate finance work. "*Charismatic*" head of the corporate finance unit **Christopher Godfrey** (see p.247) is recommended for his "*macro views and ability to reach a conclusion.*" Described as "*an extremely smooth operator*" he is said to have "*a good niche in investment trust work.*" His recent deals include Bristol & West's £26 million acquisition of the b2c business of Moneyextra and a £31 million share placing for AMIC. Heading the company commercial department, **Alan Barr** (see p.240) has displayed a "*strong technical ability*" on transactions such as the £234 million disposal of Bristol Airport for FirstGroup and Surface Technology System's £50 million AIM flotation. Popular with his peers, "*pleasant*" **Roger Hawes** (see p.248) is credited with a "*no-nonsense, sensible, pragmatic*" approach on deals such as the public takeovers of ARAM Resources, Oneview.net (value £135 million) and Pegasus Group. Co-heading the firm's private equity unit with Hawes, "*competent*" **Richard Spink**'s (see p.257) recent deals include the ECI Ventures £10.5 million MBO of MM Group and Motion Media's £141 million official listing. Having maintained his corporate practice as senior partner (term completed) **David Marsh** (see p.616) is involved in transactions such as the £28.5 million public to private of Lumination. In addition, the team advised on the £95 million acquisitions of Annova for Orange and the $50 million cross-border acquisition of CODA worldwide business for Science Systems. **Clients:** Science Systems; Systems Union Group; Orange; Bristol & West; Gooch & Housego; Exeter Investment Group; Motion Media; Surface Technology Systems.

Osborne Clarke (see firm details p.1086) Hailed by leading players as a "*go ahead, aggressive*" team, thought to "*have shown great initiative in its strategy*" which is gradually extending beyond the UK with streams of work from Germany and the US, such as Bowman Capital's $25 million development investment in Sendo. Technology, media, telecoms and biotech sectors from IPOs to e-commerce start-ups continue to be burgeoning areas of growth. Noted for its "*positive, commercial, in your face*" approach, clients endorse the team as being "*great advisors on deal and bid tactics*". Expressing satisfaction at the way they are kept informed, clients esteem the team's "*fabulous delivery and ability to get deals done with minimum fuss.*" Among the team's "*talented and conscientious partners,*" **Paul Cooper** "*cuts through mire quickly and is fair to deal with.*" Admired for "*stepping into the breach in crises,*" ex-Ashursts **Patrick Graves** ("*urbane, presentable, sharp*") is commended for combining technical acumen with commerciality. Peers describe "*eminently sensible*" **Bruce Roxburgh** as a "*steady, well-organised guy who gets the job done.*" Clients rate "*great negotiator,*" **Alisdair Livingstone** as a "*competent, personable*" operator while many have praise for "*canny*" **Clive Watts** because he is "*such great fun to work with.*" Having left for Silicon Valley, Simon Beswick's unsurpassed reputation throughout the market lingers on as a contribution to the team's strength. The team advised the 3i Group on the £20 million MBO of Autocue Group, the public to private of Fairview Holdings and the combined £76 million funding in Kymata. Further international highlights include Invensys Group's £65 million sale of Westinghouse Brakes business in the UK, Germany, Australia and South Africa. **Clients:** 3i Group; Alterian; Bank of Scotland; Dresdner Kleinwort Benson Private Equity; Invensys; Pubmaster Group; Western Power Distribution Group.

TLT Solicitors (see firm details p.1157) The word among leading players is that this "*young, positive*" team has been "*making a big noise in the market*" bolstered by the merger. A "*cohesive*" team of "*good individuals*" is endorsed for its raft of "*strong*" clients. Niche strengths exist in OFEX, AIM and partnership work, with increasing focus in technology and media sectors. Well known in the market, "*impressive, driven*" Head of Department **David Pester** (see p.255) is described as "*a sharp chap*" who is "*a breath of fresh air*" to the group. Team highlights include Advanced Technology's £13 million acquisition of RAMAR Technology, Brooks Service Group's public to private backed by Alchemy and the £27.5 million sale of British Self Storage to Mentmore Abbey. The team also acted for Fowlers Motorcycles in the £25 million BIMBO to Bikes-uk.com, and advised on the £6.2 million VC investment for BlazePhototonics, a 'spin out company' of the University of Bath. **Clients:** Aardman Animations; Parragon; Brooks Service Group; AP Aerospace; University of Bath; Advanced Technology (UK); Fowlers Motorcycles; Avon Rubber.

Bevan Ashford (see firm details p.880) Competitors perceive the majority of the team's corporate finance work to arise out of a public sector context, endorsing its "*outstanding*" profile in PFI work and niche in the health sector. Specialist areas include VC equity capital raisings, MBOs and AIM/ OFEX offerings. "*A strong name,*" peers hail **Simon Rous** (see p.255) as "*the force behind the offering.*" Bringing a "*commercial approach*" to the deal table, he advised on Schlumberger Industries' multi-million share purchase of Data Marine Systems, and Global Investment House of Kuwait's subscription for a strategic holding in Savoy Asset Management (over £5 million). A further team highlight was Grey Matter Holdings' MBO (over £1 million). **Clients:** Schlumberger Industries; Grey Matter Holdings; Global Investment House of Kuwait; ABS Hovercraft, Germany; Bank of Scotland; HSBC; Medical Industrial Equipment.

Bond Pearce (see firm details p.888) Competitors hold this team "*in high regard*" as having successfully "*made a measured entry and carefully built up*" its presence. Working on an integrated office basis, the team represents a "*loyal*" client base in a range of MBO/MBI, private and public company work, backed by specialist resource in supporting areas such as banking, tax and property. Niche strengths exist in the media, e-commerce, retail, logistics, financial services, food and aviation sectors. Last year, the team acted in roughly 50 deals of £375 million in aggregate. Peers find "*competent*" **Simon Hewes** (see p.248) "*a nice chap to deal with, who gets on with the work.*" Heading corporate finance across the firm's offices in the South and South West, he advised on the £35.5 million BIMBO of British International. Highlights for the team include advice on the £13 million MBO of Momentum Financial Services and Redcliffe Associates' £15 million merger with Thomsons. Further highlights include Teachers Assurance Group's £12 million acquisition of CIM Group, and a £6 million sale of Capital Credit. **Clients:** Computer Associates; Plymouth & South West Co-operative Society; Two Four Productions; Momentum Financial Services; Friends Provident Life Office.

Bretherton Price Elgoods (see firm details p.894) A "*flamboyant*" firm, whose clients give the warmest endorsement that they "*wouldn't go anywhere else outside London for corporate finance work.*" The team boasts established relationships with local, regional and national corporate finance departments of two 'top ten' accountancy firms and Bristol-based stockbrokers. Head of Department John Workman leads a "*pragmatic, competent and personable*" team, which is said to handle its work "*with ease.*" The team advised on company sales of Sedgemoor College (£13 million) and Synamic (£13 million), as well as a £10 million AIM float for JAB Holdings and a £7.5 million VC funding for Ultronics. **Clients:** Mears Group; DCS Europe; Ultronics Holdings; Barclays Bank; Nabarro Wells.

Charles Russell (see firm details p.912) A "*capable*" team led by former 'magic circle' partners enjoys a good profile among its peers. In addition to advising on nine takeovers, the team has been acting on acquisitions in the USA, Mexico, Hungary, Hong Kong, Taiwan and France. Competitors endorse "*damn fine lawyer*" **Francis Rundall** (see p.256) as "*reasonable, civil and easy to deal with,*" while **Richard Norton** (see p.253) is known for his expertise in yellow book work. They acted for Britannia Group on its £12 million recommended bid from YJL, and for Browallia International on its successful hostile takeover bid for British Mohair Holdings (£22 million). The team acted for Healthcare Services Group on its joint venture with Sovereign Computers and others, to provide a new computer based ordering and pharmacy service for the NHS. **Clients:** Trifast; Howle Holdings; Eagle Star; YJL; Pennant International; Healthcare Service Group; Recall Recruitment; Matcon; Travail Group.

CMS Cameron McKenna (see firm details p.922) This "*competent*" outfit receives strong market endorsement for its Lloyds work, while recognised as a "*city player picking up good work*" in the region. Competitors perceive the team's London back-up in banking and litigation expertise as a distinct advantage. Carrying a "*great reputation*" **Michael Jones** (see p.250) is judged by peers to be "*well-organised, collaborative and sensible.*" The team acted for Relyon Group in the demerger and £30 million AIM admission of its subsidiary, Photo-Scan. Further highlights include advising the UK-1 Group in the £25 million BIMBO to Bikes-uk.com and Walker Greenbank's £10 million acquisition of Standfast and Weavestyle from Courtaulds Textiles. **Clients:** Matthew Clark; Relyon Group; Photo-Scan; WH Breakspear & Sons; Walker Greenbank; Pegasus Retirement Homes; Primetime Petfoods; Systems Engineering & Assessment; Swift Computing; In2Focus Contract Sales; Photonetics SA.

Foot Anstey Sargent (see firm details p.961) Well-received by the market, this "*active*" team is said to be "*committed*" to the region, commanding an envied dual presence in Exeter and Plymouth. Niche strengths exist in e-commerce, hi-tech, media and financial services sectors. **Richard Coombs** (see p.243) and **Mark Lewis** (see p.251) are the team's best known personalities. This year's highlights were the £32 million sale of distribution business to a listed company, and the MBO of Shephards Insurance Group from a Canadian parent. The team also acted for British Airways on the sale of Plymouth City Airport, and for Northcliffe Newspaper Group on the Fish4 on-line advertising joint venture. **Clients:** UKRD Group; Northcliffe Newspapers Group; Bank of Scotland; David & Charles.

Laytons (see firm details p.1031) A "*small, well established*" team which competitors consider "*punches above its weight*" within the construction and property sectors. Head of Department Richard Brown leads a "*respected*" team noted by rivals for its "*impressive*" Bristol client base. The team advised major UK coal distributor EH Bennett on various acquisitions, commercial transactions and joint ventures, including one in the Isle of Man. Advised the Anglo Welsh Group on the sale of its holiday management business. **Clients:** Somerfield Stores; David S Smith Group; Anglo-Welsh Group; EH Bennett Group; Zuken Group; World Kitchens Group; National Packaging Council.

Lyons Davidson (see firm details p.1045) Competitors deem this respected if smaller unit to be "*producing quality work*" on behalf of its "*extremely loyal and active*" client base. The recent arrival of senior corporate finance lawyer **Roger Acock** (see p.239) from Bond Pearce is thought to "*boost the team's presence.*" He consolidates its existing expertise with his experience in high value corporate finance and M&A transactions. Among several key matters, the team advised on Knapp New Homes' sale to Galliford Try, and was involved in several acquisitions for the Grafton Group. The firm also acted in a VC transaction for Exor Corporation and advised a major computer virus software company on an investment by Amadeus. **Clients:** Grafton Group; Momentum Financial Services (formerly Aon Financial Services); Knapp New Homes; SITA Environmental Trust.

Michelmores (see firm details p.1066) Peers endorse this locally focused practice headed by Malcolm Dickinson who is said to be "*good to work with.*" The company and commercial team provides strategic business advice covering European legislation, M&A and disposals, buyouts, corporate reconstruction and capital reductions. Our researchers were told that **Stephen Morse** is "*friendly, efficient and sensible*" on M&A and private equity matters. The team advised on TJ Brent's buy-out from the Pennon Group. **Clients:** Rockeagle Ltd (now ROC plc); TJ Brent; Clarement Capital; Interlube Ltd.

Stephens & Scown A well regarded locally focused firm, which handles a mixture of corporate finance and property work out of its commerce department. Deal values go up to £20 million. Peers endorse *"good chap"* **James Keliher** who is said to *"get on well with clients and handle matters efficiently."* A highlight of the year was the $29.5 million sale of a South West software telecommunications company to a Delaware corporation. The team also advised on IMERYS Minerals' purchase of a china clay heat and power plant, the refinancing of Pendennis Shipyard Holdings, and the capital reorganisation of F Davey & Sons (Tresillian). **Clients:** IMERYS Minerals; Pendennis Shipyard Holdings; F Davey & Sons (Tresillian).

Veale Wasbrough (see firm details p.1167) *"A sensible"* outfit which competitors perceive as *"a team to watch"* while it is *"making a push"* with lateral hires. It receives instruction from a client base comprising mainly SMEs and owner-managed businesses. Deal sizes range up to £20 million. Peers recommend *"good client relations man"* **Derek Bellew** (see p.240). The highlight of this year was acting for the MoD in its Whitefleet PPP involving the £500 million outsourcing of its tri-service non-combatant vehicles to the private sector. The team also advised IOP Publishing on purchases of shares and a business from American entities, and acted for the University of Bristol on various matters including a euro-linked financing facility. **Clients:** Ministry of Defence; Ironside Technologies Europe; Fire Service College; UK Hydrographic Office; IOP Publishing; University of Bristol; Hobbs Properties.

Clark Holt (see firm details p.916) This *"commercial"* team enjoys a *"good reputation"* in its niche areas of IT, technology and private equity, representing significant AIM-listed companies. Richard Clark leads the team, which is said to be *"excellent and easy to live with."* It acted for the UK's largest independent planning consultancy, Chapman Warren in its £9 million sale of business to RPS Group, a listed company. Further highlights include the £2.3 million equity financing of computer security company Advisor Technologies, and the £9.8 million sale of MCA Holdings to AIM-listed e-xentric. **Clients:** Advisor Technologies; AIT Group; Blick; DICA Technologies; e-xentric (UK); genetix gx ltd; Isotron; Transense Technologies.

WALES

CORPORATE FINANCE • Wales	Ptnrs	Assts
1 **Morgan Cole** Cardiff	3	8
2 **Edwards Geldard** Cardiff	4	4
3 **Eversheds** Cardiff	2	5
4 **Berry Smith** Cardiff	1	3
M and A Solicitors Cardiff	3	2
5 **MLM** Cardiff	n/a	n/a

LEADING INDIVIDUALS	
1 **MACINTOSH Duncan** Morgan Cole	
2 **BOUND Andrew** Berry Smith	**MORRIS Andrew** Edwards Geldard
PEARSON Jeffrey Edwards Geldard	
3 **BERRY Stephen** M and A Solicitors	**LOWE Paul** Eversheds
4 **CHERRY Robert** Morgan Cole	**FERNANDEZ LEWIS Jon** MLM
UP AND COMING	
THOMAS Michelle Eversheds	

This book is the product of 6,552 1/2 hour interviews. See p.7 for BMRB audit.
Within each band, firms are listed alphabetically. *See individuals' profiles p.239*

Morgan Cole (see firm details p.1074) Competitors perceive the team as leveraging work comfortably from *"big"* entities within the firm's established client base of private and public sector clients. Peers and clients hold **Duncan Macintosh** in high regard for his dominant local reputation, although he is perceived to be increasingly involved in spearheading the firm's work in the Thames Valley region. He recently advised on several high value MBOs and MBIs, including Pure Wafer's £34 million investment and ace-quote.com's £28 million sale to Deutsche Börse-listed DCI (Database for Commerce and Industry AG). Also recommended, **Robert Cherry** advised on ten acquisitions for the PHS Group aggregating £40 million, and two AIM listed reverse-takeovers of Celltalk Group (£23 million) and Mazaran Leisure (£19 million). The team also advised on three disposals for Mitel Corp, including sale of Mitel Telecom to March Networks as part of a C$350 million disposal. **Clients:** BP Amoco; HSBC; Mitel Corporation; PHS Group; Focus Do It All.

Edwards Geldard (see firm details p.948) A team operating with *"the highest level of local experience,"* that services a blue chip client list as well as an increasing number of SMEs. Head of Department **Jeffrey Pearson**'s (see p.254) reputation goes before him on account of his *"cracking practice"* in Welsh water related work for prestigious clients such as Hyder. *"Likeable"* **Andrew Morris** (see p.253) commands *"the highest respect"* among his peers. The team's highlights include acting for Hicking Pentecost on its takeover by Coats Viyella, and advising Windward Capital Partners $1 billion private equity fund in its acquisition of a business of Aracomp, a South Wales manufacturing company. **Clients:** Hyder plc; S4C; Pendragon; Barclays Bank; KCS Management Systems; Hicking Pentecost.

Eversheds (see firm details p.952) Competitors acknowledge the team is *"building its corporate practice nicely,"* focusing beyond the local market towards overseas clients operating in UK and Europe, with niche strengths in technology related transactions and life sciences. With a background in litigation, *"civilised"* **Paul Lowe** (see p.251) manages a skilled corporate team. He has been involved on a number of major local MBOs including Sherman Cooper's acquisition of the Ben Sherman business. He also acted for US based Sun Valley Foods on a large disposal of business to Brandons Poultry. Peers see **Michelle Thomas**'s (see p.258) *"name on a lot of the firm's national work."* A *"capable operator,"* she advised on US based Solectron Corporation's $900 million acquisition of Nortel Networks' European operations, and acted on the cross border joint venture for Festival Parks. The team acted for Molins on the £12 million acquisition of Filtrona from Bunzl. **Clients:** Caledonia Investments; Hawtin; IQE; Solectron (California); Ben Sherman; Molins.

Berry Smith A smaller outfit judged to have a *"moderate presence"* limited by its size. Peers and clients alike respect the *"excellent"* **Andrew Bound** (see p.241) for his expertise in small to mid-sized MBOs and property-based work. The *"technically skilled"* team acted for Redizenith's MBO of British Biocell, and acted in a multi-million pound reorganisation of Invacare in the UK, US and Denmark. A further highlight was the restructuring and reorganisation of Stilo International and its subsequent £20 million AIM flotation. **Clients:** Redizenith; JW & E Morris & Sons; CBL Ceramics; Invacare; Bayswater Tubes & Sections.

M and A Solicitors (see firm details p.1051) *"A fine team"* handling *"high value work"* as part of its niche corporate and commercial practice. The *"extremely close"* links between this Eversheds splinter and corporate finance company Gambit remain. Peers rate **Stephen Berry** (see p.241) as *"a good lawyer who conducts himself well."* He advised on the £33.5 million acquisition of Glasgow Prestwick Airport from Stagecoach. The team advised on the £41.5 million acquisition of Wafer Technology by IQE, and on the MBO of British Biocell. In addition it acted in the merger of Aerosonic with the German company ContTec GmbH and in its subsequent public listing. **Clients:** IQE; ActionLeisure; Omniport; Aerosonic; Dr JD Hull & Associates; Tomos Watkin; Riley Leisure.

MLM Well regarded by his peers, **Jon Fernandez Lewis** (see p.245) leads the original team from Bevan Ashford, which competitors perceive to have *"a good practice,"* benefiting from a *"good influx of work."*

MIDLANDS

CORPORATE FINANCE • Midlands		Ptnrs	Assts
1	**Wragge & Co** Birmingham	19	60
2	**Eversheds** Birmingham	18	48
	Pinsent Curtis Biddle Birmingham	9	16
3	**Browne Jacobson** Nottingham	10	24
	DLA Birmingham	n/a	n/a
	Gateley Wareing Birmingham, Nottingham	13	n/a
	Hammond Suddards Edge Birmingham	4	14
	Martineau Johnson Birmingham	7	12
4	**Freethcartwright** Nottingham	7	5
	Lee Crowder Birmingham	5	6
	Shoosmiths Northampton, Nottingham	3	5
5	**Edwards Geldard** Nottingham	4	6
	Garretts Birmingham	4	5
	George Green Cradley Heath	3	2
	Harvey Ingram Owston Leicester	3	7
	Hewitson Becke + Shaw Northampton	n/a	n/a
	Howes Percival Northampton	5	5

LEADING INDIVIDUALS		
1	**DWYER Maurice** Wragge & Co	**METCALFE Ian** Wragge & Co
	METCALFE Rob Browne Jacobson	**PSYLLIDES Milton** Eversheds
2	**EASTGATE Andrew** Pinsent Curtis Biddle	**GREEN Guy** Eversheds
	GRONOW Simon Pinsent Curtis Biddle	**HAYWARD Paul** Gateley Wareing
	HULL David Hammond Suddards Edge	**KITTS Stephen** Eversheds
	LEWIS Susan Eversheds	**McHUGH Peter** Eversheds
	MILLINGTON Jeremy Wragge & Co	**MOORE Austin** Gateley Wareing
	RAWSTRON Chris DLA	**WILD David** Eversheds
3	**BIRCHALL Roger** Hammond Suddards Edge	
	BRAITHWAITE Stephen Wragge & Co	**CRABTREE John** Wragge & Co
	HAYWOOD Richard Wragge & Co	**HUGHES David** Pinsent Curtis Biddle
	SEABROOK Michael Eversheds	**STILTON Andrew** Martineau Johnson
	VAUGHAN David Wragge & Co	**WARD Michael** Gateley Wareing
4	**ALLEN Amanda** Pinsent Curtis Biddle	**BROOKSHAW Oliver** Shoosmiths
	CHOHAN Baljit Wragge & Co	**CUMMINGS Gavin** Browne Jacobson
	GARNETT Chris Eversheds	**JANSEN Karl** Freethcartwright
	LAVERY James Pinsent Curtis Biddle	**LAWTON SMITH Andrew** Wragge & Co
	WRIGLEY Richard Martineau Johnson	
UP AND COMING		
	DAWES Edward Wragge & Co	**JOHNSON Ben** Eversheds

This book is the product of 6,552 1/2 hour interviews. See p.7 for BMRB audit.

Within each band, firms are listed alphabetically. *See individuals' profiles p.239*

Wragge & Co (see firm details p.1189) "*The clear market leader,*" this "*major national player*" is widely endorsed as "*head and shoulders above the rest.*" The "*potent*" team predominates by force of its client base, strength in depth, quality and size, being the single largest unit outside the Capital. Its stated strategy of being a City firm based in Birmingham, and taking an ever increasing level of FTSE instructions, has set it on different plane, as one commentator claimed, "*it's a different beast to any in the region.*" A "*great deal junkie*" noted for his private equity expertise, clients appreciate **Maurice Dwyer**'s "*practical*" approach and absence of "*airs and graces.*" Recommended for plc related work, **Ian Metcalfe** advised on the £162 million LSE flotation of XTL Biopharmaceuticals. Heading the plc team, **Jeremy Millington** advised on Preussag AG's £1.8 billion recommended bid for Thomson Travel Group. **Stephen Braithwaite**'s practice revolves around property related transactions, while Corporate Group leader **David Vaughan** is client partner for AT&T and PowerGen. "*Thoroughly excellent,*" Senior Partner **John Crabtree** is seen less on the deal floor, while new recruit from Hammonds, "*commercial, street-fighting lawyer*" **Baljit Chohan** is thought to be "*exceedingly good*" for private equity related work on the IT/ e-commerce side. Peers endorse **Andrew Lawton Smith** as having a long-established track record in the field. Together with major client-winner **Richard Haywood**, he advised on the £1.4 billion institutional buyout by Doughty Hanson of Ranks Hovis MacDougall from Tomkins. Clients "*sing the praises of*" **Ed Dawes**, a "*nice guy with a very sensible approach,*" described as "*practical without being overly technical.*" The team advised on City Waste's sale of business to SITA Wastecare, the leading operator of waste disposal and collection, and acted for Pressac in its £24 million acquisition of WH Smith (Scotland). **Clients:** Ranks Hovis MacDougall Group; PowerGen; Severn Trent; Cadbury Schweppes; McDonald's; AT&T.

Eversheds (see firm details p.952) A "*robust corporate finance practice*" which competitors perceive as having "*sewn up a lot of the large local listed clients*" on account of its national brand. The teams of "*sensible individuals*" based in Nottingham and Birmingham are seen to work closely together on deals. Head of department **Peter McHugh** (see p.252) receives high ratings throughout the market, while popular with his peers **Milton Psyllides** (see p.255) is endorsed as an "*excellent plc transactional lawyer.*" Credited for having "*made a mark*" at the firm by spearheading its "*great inroads into the SME market,*" **Guy Green** (see p.247) is said to "*combine the practicality of a small operation with the experience of big firm transactions.*" Clients endorse his "*excellent combination of technical and commercial*" skills. "*Shrewd operator*" with banking expertise, **Stephen Kitts** (see p.250) is "*one of the accountants' favourites for his technical and commercial ability.*" A "*safe pair of hands,*" he handled Rolls-Royce Power Engineering's sale of Cochrane Boilers, and Motorworld's MBO. **Sue Lewis** (see p.251) has been seen on high profile transactions such as the £10 million purchase of MG Rover from BMW AG, in which she acted for the Phoenix Consortium, and Bourne Leisure's £700 million acquisition of Rank Group UK's holding business. Entrepreneurial client specialist **David Wild** (see p.260) is credited by peers as a "*good quality operator*" on deals such as uDate.com's $68 million flotation on NASDAQ and Birch's sale to The Miller Group. Leading corporate partner **Michael Seabrook** (see p.256) advised on Sanderson's £130 million public to private. Also recommended by our interviewees, **Chris Garnett** (see p.246) advised Workplace Systems on Telework Group's £250 million flotation, while **Ben Johnson** (see p.249) receives strong endorsement for his private equity skills on MBOs such as Utilitec's public to private and Royal Crown Derby (£16.5 million). In addition the team also advised on Project Telecom's £152 million admission to the Official List. **Clients:** Breedon; Britax International; Jessops; Rolls-Royce; Weetabix.

Pinsent Curtis Biddle (see firm details p.1098) Seen to be "*gathering pace in developing its network*" although still relatively London-centric, it fields a team of "*practical and technically astute lawyers.*" The firm displays expertise for its across the board skills including M&A, private equity and flotations on the London Stock Exchange. It has had some success in assisting hi-tech start-ups through the course of their development. Head of Department **Andrew Eastgate** (see p.244) acted for iSOFT Group on its £120 million flotation on the London Stock Exchange, and for Old Mutual Securities in relation to its £69 million takeover of Ash & Lacy. **Simon Gronow** (see p.247) is said to be "*handy to have on the complex*" deals. **David Hughes** (see p.248) acted for Babcock International Group on the return of £30 million to shareholders, while both **Amanda Allen** (see p.239) and **James Lavery** (see p.250) continue to elicit commendations for their commercial awareness. **Clients:** IMI; Johnson Controls; Glanbia; iSOFT Group; Babcock International Group.

Browne Jacobson (see firm details p.898) Perceived as "*the biggest local player with the best resources,*" researchers were impressed by the market's endorsement of the team's "*strong individuals,*" of whom peers claim "*there's no fussing, they just get on with it.*" In addition to its domestic profile, the team is increasingly involved in cross-border work such as LDC's investment in Magnet Applications Group and the acquisition of US, French and UK targets. Clients commend "*leading light*" **Rob Metcalfe** (see p.253) for being "*great to deal with.*" An "*experienced*" practitioner, he is described *as "excellent, pragmatic and commercial.*" Interviewees pointed to **Gavin Cummings**' (see p.243) ever increasing workload, packed with "*quality instructions.*" Liked by his peers, Nigel Blackwell is a "*no-nonsense*" individual who "*doesn't play games.*" The team advised on Utilitec's public to private, and acted for Stanton on its acquisition of Biwater Claycross. **Clients:** Utilitec; Saint Gobain/Stanton; Securitas UK.

DLA Leveraging work from its national network, this respected team, which fields **Chris Rawstron**, is endorsed for its work across private equity, flotations and public company M&A.

Gateley Wareing (see firm details p.969) Researchers were impressed by the body of endorsement for this "*small, high quality and interesting*" outfit with a dominant local profile. Respected as "*prominent for its private equity work,*" particularly buyouts. Leading competitors have "*no qualms*" about referring work to the well-resourced team which is said to be "*hands on and effective to deal with.*" Former leading light of the Eking Manning corporate practice, **Austin Moore** receives lavish recommendations. Described as "*a generalist with a strongly individual style,*" he is said to be "*well-liked by the accountants*" and considered "*ahead of the game for pure MBO & private equity work.*" Peers report that he is "*good fun to deal with and always relaxed.*" Commanding "*immense respect*" for his leadership, **Paul Hayward** is described by peers as a "*practical and commercial chap*" who "*gets the deal done,*" while **Michael Ward** gains admiration for his "*fine laid back*" approach.

Hammond Suddards Edge (see firm details p.984) Felt to have "*boosted its stock*" following the merger, the firm's "*revitalisation is kicking in and starting to gel.*" In addition to the range of corporate work, the team participates in the national firm's sector initiatives, covering engineering, automotive, IT & technology, chemicals, utilities, sport, media and entertainment. Peers believe that **David Hull** (see p.248) has an "*established reputation for major transactions*" such as advising Jabil Circuit on its acquisition of Marconi manufacturing operations across four jurisdictions (in excess of £4 billion). Also eliciting support from the market, **Roger Birchall** (see p.241) specialises in MBOs and MBIs in the venture/development capital sector. The team advised on NTL's media partnerships with Aston Villa (£26 million) and Leicester City Football Club (£12.5 million). **Clients:** Jabil Circuit; Focus Solutions Group; Aston Villa; Leicester City Football Club; T&S Stores; Galliford Try.

Martineau Johnson (see firm details p.1055) Widely regarded as a niche player in the local market, the team is endorsed for its institutional client base and ability to handle quality referral work. The best known personalities here are **Andrew Stilton** (see p.258) ("*a safe pair of hands*") and **Richard Wrigley** (see p.260), who advised on several high profile MBOs including Alstom Handling Services (£55 million) and Aktrion (£22 million). The team acted for Ash & Lacy on its takeover by Hill & Smith and advised on the £7 million MBO of Silvertown. A further highlight was the acquisition of a $35 million investment in a Cambridge technology company by a major US corporation. **Clients:** South Staffordshire Group; Foresight Technology VCT; Enterprise VCT; Trivest VCT; Matrix e-Ventures Fund VCT; Bullough; Claverley Group.

Freethcartwright (see firm details p.964) This "*sizeable*" team has a strong focus on private equity related buyout work. Despite having completed several high value transactions over the past year and handling an increasing amount of work for overseas companies principally based in America and Germany, the team is felt by competitors to have not secured a high profile. "*Likeable*" **Karl Jansen** (see p.249) is rated among peers as "*a good practical operator who doesn't waste time.*" He acted on the sale of Database Group of Companies to Ramesys Holdings. The team acted on the £10 million MBO of Paul Fabrications from Tyco, and advised on Fresenius Medical Care AG's $161 million acquisition of Total Renal Care Holdings. **Clients:** Travelsphere Group; The Database Group; Fresenius Medical Care AG; Paul Fabrications; Flow Industries.

Lee Crowder (see firm details p.1035) Described by competitors as "*experienced and sensible,*" the team handles a range of corporate finance work for listed companies and SMEs. Although still suffering loss of profile following key client 3i's defection to Wragges, the team maintains credit for fielding "*good lawyers.*" Our interviewees have proclaimed the Nottingham office as "*a corporate finance centre of excellence,*" while strong individuals have been redistributed among the firm's other offices, most notably Reading. Led by Graham Muth, the team acted on the £47 million sale of ML Group, and advised on the acquisition of Lowton Glass & Glazing from Laird Group for £6.75 million. **Clients:** Myratech.net; 10 Group.

Shoosmiths (see firm details p.1129) A well-regarded team spread between Nottingham and Northampton, handling a range of corporate finance work both in and outside the Midlands market. "*Quality lawyer*" **Oliver Brookshaw** (see p.242) is said to bear the "*hallmark of city training.*" He advised on the acquisition by British Land of a 50% interest in London and Henley Holdings, including re-financing, valued at £152 million. He also acted for Tomkins on the UK aspects of the combined sale of Murray Inc and Hayter Ltd to the Chicago based Summersong Investment for £151.3 million, and advised on the Northampton Saints' £2.5 million flotation. The team advised on several acquisitions for the Casella Group totalling around £20 million, and on the disposal of Associated British Foods. **Clients:** Games Workshop Group; British Gypsum; Gala Leisure; Schroder Property Investment Management; Tomkins; Northampton Saints.

Edwards Geldard (see firm details p.948) Our researchers were told that this firm dominates the Derby market, with an office perceived by competitors to be handling "*quality work,*" which "*has developed well*" following the demerger of key client Williams. The Nottingham team boasts new capability in owner managed business related work following its acquisition of Eking Manning, despite losing out to Gateley Wareing on the firm's corporate finance star, Austin Moore. Andrew Borkowski leads the team, which acted in the acquisition by the MBO team of Wade Furniture Group, and the £12 million sale of Compress Cleaning. **Clients:** Chubb; Kidde; Pendragon; Norcross; Newell Rubbermaid; Yale.

Garretts (see firm details p.968) The team's local profile is somewhat obscured by its membership of the Andersen Legal international network, a connection that draws it into the sphere of multi-jurisdictional transactional work. Niche strengths include project management of overseas transactions and cross border M&A work such as Vislink's acquisitions of Advent Communications (£16 million) and US based microwave communications business Adaptive Broadband Corporation ($20.75 million), which included an associated placing. Paul Finlan leads a team which advised McKechnie on its £580 million public to private takeover, and Oneview.net on its £345 million merger with freecom.net. **Clients:** Capital Bars; McKechnie; Vislink; Wagon; Wealth Management Software.

George Green (see firm details p.970) Clients endorse this "*practical, commercial*" team whose "*positive*" attitude "*helps to bridge gaps and make things happen.*" Focused on the local market, the team, led by Richard Cliff, acted on Crisp Computing's £50 million disposal to Moneyextra and advised on the merger between Axis Milk and Scottish Milk. A further highlight for the team was its involvement in the National Design Consultancy's first MBO out of the Post Office. **Clients:** Caparo Engineering;

Helix Ltd; Axis Milk; Venture Finance; Barclays Bank Acquisition Finance Unit; Cradley Print.

Harvey Ingram Owston (see firm details p.989) Long established in Leicester, the team is felt to have a stronghold on the local market. Servicing clients ranging from family-based enterprises to household name plcs, the full service practice is seen to be thriving within the Leicester market despite the recent departures of financial institutions and accountants. Martin Smith leads the team, which advised on Benson Shoe's successful recommended cash offer for Oliver Group. The group was also involved in the sales of Rigid Group to VPK and Hill Osborne to Brewin Dolphin. On the international side, the team advised on acquisitions for Texon International and Bland Bankart. **Clients:** Shoe Zone; Bland Bankart; De Montfort Housing Society; FOL Networks; Midlands Co-operative Society; Walkers Midshires Foods (a division of Samworth Brothers).

Hewitson Becke + Shaw (see firm details p.994) Judged by peers to be a "*competent*" team yet lower in profile than its sister office, acting for a broad client base comprising SMEs, listed plcs and multinational corporates. Led by Richard Ingram, the team advised on the sale of Power Innovations to the US corporate Bourns Inc, and on the buy-in MBO from the Concentric Group of Yorkshire Moulds. **Clients:** Vartech Telecommunications; Pittway International; Power Innovations.

Howes Percival (see firm details p.1003) Jit Singh leads a "*competent*" outfit said to have a "*strong reputation,*" typically seen acting for local owner-managed businesses. With niche strengths in motor trade, event management and insolvency, the team handles work from clients such as Silverstone Circuits and the British Racing Drivers Club. It advised on the £12 million disposal of 49% of Eurofleet to Inchcape. Further team highlights include acting for the new management team in the £80 million plus equity release/MBI of Travelsphere. In conjunction with the Milton Keynes office, the team advised Dimension Data Holdings on its £200 million acquisition of 50.1% of Chernikeef Networks. **Clients:** Groupe Norbert Dentressangle; Ricardo Group; Shanks Group; Renault.

EAST ANGLIA

CORPORATE FINANCE • East Anglia		Ptnrs	Assts
1	**Eversheds** Ipswich, Norwich	8	16
	Mills & Reeve Cambridge, Norwich	7	10
2	**Garretts** Cambridge	2	4
	Hewitson Becke + Shaw Cambridge	6	7
	Taylor Vinters Cambridge	3	5
3	**Birketts** Ipswich	3	2
	Prettys Ipswich	4	1
4	**Greene & Greene** Bury St Edmunds	n/a	n/a
	Greenwoods Peterborough	3	1
	Steele & Co Norwich	3	3

LEADING INDIVIDUALS		
1	**FISCHL Nicolas** Mills & Reeve	**FITZSIMONS Gerry** Garretts
	GOULD Terry Eversheds	**SHORT John** Taylor Vinters
2	**DIX John** Hewitson Becke + Shaw	**MARDLE David** Garretts
	STANFIELD Glynne Mills & Reeve	**WAINE Ian** Prettys
3	**CROOME Andrew** Eversheds	**EVANS Michael** Greenwoods
	FALKUS Bryony Mills & Reeve	**HUNTER James** Mills & Reeve
	LUBBOCK Nigel Steele & Co	**THOMSON Christopher** Greene & Greene
UP AND COMING		
	AUSTIN James Birketts	**WHYBROW Annette** Birketts

This book is the product of 6,552 1/2 hour interviews. See p.7 for BMRB audit.

Within each band, firms are listed alphabetically. *See individuals' profiles p.239*

Eversheds (see firm details p.952) Known for "*aggressive marketing*" and for having "*deep development resources,*" the firm is in the process of building up the Cambridge office. Peers consider that **Terry Gould** (see p.247) runs an "*effective operation*" in Norwich, while the versatile **Andrew Croome** (see p.243) also gains strong client feedback for his "*commercial acumen.*" Healthcare and hi-tech are areas of niche strength. The firm advised on the Bernard Matthews public to private for £232million, and acted on the establishment of Cyan Technology, raising £1.5million from First Cambridge Gateway Fund. **Clients:** Southern Cross Healthcare; Celsis International; NHP.

Mills & Reeve (see firm details p.1069) Although Ian Alexander-Sinclair has been indisposed for much of the past year, clients continue to recommend the corporate team to researchers for "*making things much more straightforward than most.*" It specialises in higher education, NHS Trusts, life sciences and IT-related work. **Nicolas Fischl** (see p.245) is acknowledged by peers as "*an excellent performer,*" and together with the respected **Bryony Falkus** (see p.245), has been involved in local, national and cross-border work, drawing on the skills of a dedicated tax, pensions and IT department. Researchers found sustained support for **James Hunter** (see p.249) this year, with clients often describing him as "*approachable and user friendly.*" The "*quick, although sometimes abrasive*" **Glynne Stanfield** (see p.257) heads the Cambridge office. The team advised the University of Cambridge on its $100 million joint venture with MIT, and acted for Virgin Wine Online on funding, infrastructure and commercial agreements relating to the launch of Virginwines.com. **Clients:** Stafford Group; Porex Corporation; University of Cambridge.

Garretts (see firm details p.968) Researchers found a corporate team full of lawyers who "*stand out as individual characters rather than being moulded by the firm,*" according to clients. The group often advises young, fast-growing companies in the life sciences industry. Clients praise the "*non-confrontational, but still tough*" **Gerry Fitzsimons** (see p.245) and the "*extremely responsive*" **David Mardle** (see p.245) for "*creating a high level of confidence*" in negotiations. The firm advised on the £542 million IPO of TTP Communications, following its demerger from the TTP Group, and acted for The Astron Group on the merger with e-doc for £92 million. **Clients:** TTP Group; Cambridge Gateway Fund; The Astron Group.

Hewitson Becke + Shaw (see firm details p.994) The loss of the esteemed Bridget Kerle to an in-house position at a dot.com has removed what some clients considered to be the firm's principal asset. However, **John Dix** (see p.244) remains renowned among peers for his "*pragmatic view on life.*" His strengths lie in venture capital work for early stage technology companies, while the remainder of the team shoulders the MBO and M&A workload, which involves a substantial international element. The firm acted on the funding rounds for Plastic Logic, a technology start-up company, backed by three venture capital funds. **Clients:** Plastic Logic; Kamelian; Cambridge Research and Innovation.

Taylor Vinters (see firm details p.1150) Acknowledged by competitors to "*deserve its sound reputation,*" the team is headed by **John Short** (see p.256), who is said to "*know his law precisely.*" Steve Sharratt is now working part-time as a consultant. Acting predominantly for domestic entities and the subsidiaries of overseas companies, the team has particular expertise in the technological field, and also boasts high profile clients in manufacturing, consultancy and engineering. The firm advised on placing three investments for the Dutch-based venture capital company, MB Venture Capital Fund. It also acted for the management on the MBO of East Central Distribution, involving a total consideration of around £8 million. **Clients:** Artisan (UK); MB Venture Capital Fund INV; Analysys.

Birketts Acting for companies, shareholders, and some institutional investors, the firm has profited from the surge in technological commerce in the region. It has also acted on acquisitions and disposals in the farming/food processing business. Two rising names were consistently recommended to researchers. "*Absolutely first-class*" and "*quick to respond,*" **Annette Whybrow** is joined in the table this year by **James Austin**, who "*can see the wood for the trees.*" **Clients:** Local and international corporates.

Prettys (see firm details p.1100) "*Refreshingly down to earth,*" **Ian Waine** (see p.259) is renowned for his corporate practice at a firm that clients commend for "*not having the pompousness of some City firms.*" Acting mainly for companies and owner-managed businesses, the firm is notably strong on transport, agri-business and IT. The team has been active in M&A and private equity work, both regionally and nationally. **Clients:** Owner-managed businesses.

Greene & Greene "*Practical*" **Christopher Thomson** is noted for having "*one or two good loyal clients,*" and his team is often associated with its work for key client Western Medical Group. The firm acts for a range of private companies on sales, funding and acquisition work nationwide. **Clients:** Western Medical Group; private clients.

Greenwoods (see firm details p.978) The respected **Michael Evans** continues to lead this traditional firm's corporate finance department. The firm acts in sales and acquisitions, franchising and contract work for an eclectic domestic clientele. It has acted for a high profile media group on M&A matters, as well as advising a newspaper on buy-ins and buy-outs. Overseas work has included advising a US computer damage assessment firm on its expansion. **Clients:** Media groups; aviation and transport companies.

Steele & Co (see firm details p.1140) Popular with clients for "*choosing the shortest route to a solution,*" the "*practical*" **Nigel Lubbock** (see p.252)heads this recently expanded corporate team. Possessing niche expertise in the automotive industry, the firm has a substantial US client base. Re-organisations and transactional work comprise a substantial proportion of the team's workload. **Clients:** Pi Group; Ionics (UK); Tulip International (UK).

NORTH WEST

Band	CORPORATE FINANCE • North West	Ptnrs	Assts
1	**Addleshaw Booth & Co** Manchester	24	55
2	**DLA** Liverpool, Manchester	n/a	n/a
	Eversheds Manchester	11	31
3	**Halliwell Landau** Manchester	11	35
4	**Brabners** Liverpool	5	7
	Chaffe Street Manchester	8	7
	Hammond Suddards Edge Manchester	4	11
5	**Cobbetts** Manchester	7	6
	Davies Wallis Foyster Liverpool, Manchester	n/a	n/a
6	**Kuit Steinart Levy** Manchester	2	2
	Pannone & Partners Manchester	4	2
	Wacks Caller Manchester	n/a	n/a

Band	LEADING INDIVIDUALS	
★	**PYSDEN Edward** Eversheds	
1	**HOLT Andrew** DLA	**PRINCE Michael** DLA
2	**COOKE Darryl** Addleshaw Booth & Co	**CRAIG Alexander** Halliwell Landau
	DEVITT Paul Addleshaw Booth & Co	**HALL Daniel** Eversheds
	JOHNSTON Keith Addleshaw Booth & Co	
	LEE Richard Addleshaw Booth & Co	**STREET Robert** Chaffe Street
3	**BLOWER Geoffrey** Eversheds	**BRABNER Michael** Brabners
	DOWNS William Hammond Suddards Edge	**GARSTON Clive** Halliwell Landau
	GRISEWOOD Rebecca Halliwell Landau	**HALPIN Peter** Eversheds
	LEE Paul Addleshaw Booth & Co	**O'CONNOR Mark** Davies Wallis Foyster
	TURNBULL Robert Cobbetts	**WARBURTON Mark** Addleshaw Booth & Co
	WHATNALL John Halliwell Landau	
4	**CADWALLADER David** DLA	**FITZGERALD Sean** Chaffe Street
	HARPER Tony Brabners	**LEVY Robert** Kuit Steinart Levy
UP AND COMING	**BOWCOCK David** Eversheds	

This book is the product of 6,552 1/2 hour interviews. See p.7 for BMRB audit.
Within each band, firms are listed alphabetically. *See individuals' profiles p.239*

Addleshaw Booth & Co (see firm details p.853) Sheer weight of market opinion has convinced our researchers that the firm should retain sole top spot in Manchester. Competitors point to the team's "*superb ability*" at partner level, while clients approve of its capacity to "*get through so much work.*" Acting for entities well beyond its Manchester base, the firm includes notable financial institutions and corporates on its client roster. "*Big local cheese*" **Darryl Cooke** and client favourite, the "*thoroughly congenial*" **Paul Devitt** (see p.244), rank highly among a battery of well-known individuals here. "*Commercial heavyweight*" **Keith Johnston** (see p.249) also features, alongside "*sensitive, responsive*" **Richard Lee** (see p.250), whom peers applaud as a "*strong deal lawyer.*" **Paul Lee**'s (see p.250) "*good name as a regional mover and shaker*" ensures his continued presence in the rankings, and **Mark Warburton** (see p.259) also maintains his share of client support. The firm acted for the shareholders on the sale of Auto Windscreens, and continues to advise 3i on a number of substantial venture capital deals. **Clients:** 3i; Barclays Bank; Auto Windscreens; Airtours.

DLA **Andrew Holt** and **Michael Prince** are the leading names at a firm that undertakes M&A work for public and private clients in addition to regulatory compliance work. **David Cadwallader** is also recommended.

Eversheds (see firm details p.952) Recommended by clients as "*commercially-minded and practical,*" the corporate team is felt to be "*getting closer to the top.*" Strong in the high-tech industry, the firm advises on high value cross-border work for a clientele that includes a number of US names. **Edward Pysden** gains universal acclaim. Said to be a "*doughty opponent*" and a "*tough negotiator,*" he is renowned among his peers for handling problems "*creatively.*" He advised on the £496 million IBO of Caradon Plumbing, which involved nine jurisdictions. Known to be extremely self-confident, **Daniel Hall** also acted on this deal. Clients regard him as "*unquestionably, a top class lawyer.*" "*Commercial and sensible*" **Geoffrey Blower** (see p.241) and the understated **Peter Halpin** also receive strong market approval. **David Bowcock** (see p.242) continues to be regarded as one to watch. The firm has advised Anglo American on disposals and acquisitions worth £100 million, and acted for Telecity on its full list IPO, with a market cap of £500 million. **Clients:** HSBC Private Equity; Telecity; Anglo American; Coats Viyella.

Halliwell Landau (see firm details p.982) Generally perceived by competitors as "*a broad church,*" the corporate team is not felt to have the uniformity of quality of some of its leading rivals. Working autonomously from each other, the partners act for medium sized public companies on M&A work, often with a technology focus. An "*effective rainmaker and manager,*" **Alexander Craig** (see p.243) has particular experience in the high-tech/bio-tech sector. Researchers unearthed substantial recommendation for **Clive Garston** (see p.246) and **Rebecca Grisewood** while newly ranked **John Whatnall** (see p.123), best known for his banking work, has developed his corporate profile substantially, and is viewed by peers as "*an* *exceptionally gifted lawyer.*" The firm acted for Knowledge Support Systems on its £55 million placing and admission to the Official List, and advised the original owner on the acquisition of Pontins from Scottish & Newcastle. **Clients:** Acorn Corporate Finance; Knowledge Support Systems; The Intercare Group; UMBRO.

Brabners (see firm details p.892 Having taken three new partners and four lawyers from Berrymans Lace Mawer, the firm now has respected critical mass in its corporate finance department. It acts on acquisitions and disposals for its core client base of owner managed businesses, as well as advising on substantial MBOs and MBIs. Renowned for his niche expertise in computer games, **Michael Brabner** (see p.242) is said by clients to "*know what we want.*" Peers and clients also warmly endorse **Tony Harper** (see p.248). The team has acted for Rage Software on a number of recent deals, and advised Booth Dispensers on its MBO. **Clients:** Baumann Hinde & Co; Booth Dispensers; Rage Software.

Chaffe Street (see firm details p.911) Highly regarded by its clients, the corporate team is led by **Robert Street** (see p.258), "*a senior figure, but still very much into the detail,*" and also contains the respected **Sean FitzGerald** (see p.245). The firm advises a number of professionals including accountants, solicitors and architects, in addition to acting for several owner-managed businesses. The team advised on the MBO of Coats Viyella Clothing and acted on the sale of Alec Finch Professional Indemnity Business to Tower Gate. **Clients:** Jungheinrich; Granville Baird Capital Partners; Danzas.

Hammond Suddards Edge (see firm details p.984) Although the firm is not perceived by commentators to have regained its profile of two years ago, it continues to win major new clients, including BNFL and Ineos Fluor. With a focus on utilities, chemical bio-industry, engineering and IT/telecoms, it acts locally, nationally and on cross-border transactions. **William Downs** (see p.244) remains the team's leading figure. The team acted for the Co-operative Wholesale Society on its merger with Co-operative Retail Services to create a company with a combined turnover in excess of £4.7 billion. **Clients:** Co-operative Wholesale Society; Bradford City AFC; British Aluminium/Luxfer.

Cobbetts (see firm details p.923) Described to researchers as a "*really steady, establishment type*" team, it is led by the warmly recommended **Robert Turnbull** (see p.259), praised by clients for his ability to "*strike up constructive, positive relationships.*" The firm acts for owner managed businesses, major plcs and UK subsidiaries of multi-national companies. It recently advised CRS on its merger with CWS and acted for The Milk Group on its £7.5 million acquisition of Lubborn Cheese. **Clients:** CRS; The Milk Group; The Roberts Group; Essex Golf & Country Club.

Davies Wallis Foyster (see firm details p.935) The Liverpool based firm has a reputation among its peers for being "*successful in acquiring clients, and good at retaining them.*" "*Quiet, careful, and sensible,*" **Mark O'Connor** (see p.254) continues to enjoy the respect of his contemporaries. The firm acted for Inventive Leisure on its AIM flotation, and advised The Hamilton Syndicate on the funding of Orbital Software Group and its subsequent flotation. **Clients:** Princes; Edward Billington Group; Inter Link Foods.

Kuit Steinart Levy (see firm details p.1025) Peers view the "*positive and highly competent*" **Robert Levy** (see p.251) as the team's major asset. Advising a broad client base, the firm has represented a number of leading companies and private investors from the region. Flotations of leisure industry companies continue to be an area of niche expertise. The firm advised on the AIM flotation of Poptones record label, and acted for SSL International on its acquisition of worldwide (excluding Japan) brand rights to the 'Hibi' antiseptic product range. **Clients:** Manchester City Football Club; SSL International; Poptones; Park Royal Hotel.

Pannone & Partners (see firm details p.1088) Although the firm is better known for litigation and private client work, it also has a sizeable coporate team that brings in a good percentage of cross-border deals. Søren Tattam heads the department that acts on acquisitions, disposals, MBOs, leveraged transactions and PFI work in the public sector. The firm advised Manchester Airport on the acquisition of Bournemouth International Airport and East Midlands Airport, a deal valued at £241 million. **Clients:** Manchester Airport; Chevin Software; Ellis Hayward.

Wacks Caller (see firm details p.1170) Acting mostly for large entrepreneurial companies, the firm is a regular regional performer on local corporate transactions in the healthcare, biotechnology and IT sectors. Its institutional lender client base arouses particular market endorsement. Martin Caller is the leader of the department, which takes on major M&A deals, disposals, MBOs and IPOs. **Clients:** Dot.coms; biotech companies.

YORKSHIRE

Addleshaw Booth & Co (see firm details p.853) Still the leader in the field owing to the "*volume and size of deals*" and remarkable "*strength and depth*" at partner level. **Sean Lippell** (see p.251) specialises in public issues, MBO/MBIs and private equity, mergers and acquisitions. According to his rivals, his "*charismatic personality*" serves him well in "*winning new clients.*" **Tim Wheldon** (see p.260) focuses on transactional and project work with a following of institutional, public and owner-managed businesses. He is known for being "*practical and commercial.*" **Ian McIntosh** (see p.252) regularly structures and manages major transactions in the domestic and international marketplace and is judged "*extremely competent.*" Highlights of the past year include acting for Atlas/Axis Asset Management group on its merger with Soditic Asset Management, forming a new international asset management group with $1.5 billion of funds under management. The team also acted for Airtours on a cash tender offer by its subsidiary for Travel Services International, valued at £250 million, and acted for 3i on the £223 million take private of Peter Black Holdings. **Clients:** 3i Group; Airtours; Amtrak; APU Group; Barlows; Borden Inc; CGNU; Darby Group; Enterprise; Flowserve Corporation; Granville Private Equity; Interior Services Group; J Sainsbury; Lancashire Dairies; The Miller Group Limited; Novar; Riva Group; Seddon Group; University of Leeds; Yorkshire Group.

Eversheds (see firm details p.952) Researchers were told that this highly active group has had a "*successful year,*" despite its high-profile individuals, Robert Pitcher and Ian Richardson, now operating out of the London office. **Robin Johnson** (see p.249), who focuses on e-commerce, international and mainstream corporate work, is seen as "*the backbone*" of the practice while new Head of Department **Stephen Hopkins** (see p.248) also received market commendation. Recent deals include advising the Peter Black management in the largest ever public to private in the North, valued at £300 million, and advising HSBC Private Equity in its £496 million acquisition of Caradon's plumbing division. The team advised Holf Technology in the £200 million reverse takeover of InTechnology. **Clients:** Communisis (formerly Waddingtons); SPX Corporation; Keor; ASDA; BBA.

Hammond Suddards Edge (see firm details p.984) A team of "*strong operators*" whose highlights of a busy year include six public takeovers. Clients typically commend Head of Department **Ian Greenfield** (see p.247) as an "*able lawyer who gives sensible advice.*" Fellow partners include the respected **David Armitage** (see p.240) and new partner and "*bright young spark*" **Jonathan Jones** (see p.249). The group advised Allied Textile Companies in the recommended bid by management valued at £99.4 million and acted for Authoriszor Inc on a private placing valued at $30 million. In the hostile field, the group received instructions from Findest SRL in its contested bid for Bray Technologies valued at £15.7 million. In addition it advised Sports Internet Group in the £20 million recommended offer for Surrey Group. **Clients:** Allied Textile Companies Limited; Austin Reed; Bank of

CORPORATE FINANCE • Yorkshire	Ptnrs	Assts
1 **Addleshaw Booth & Co** Leeds	10	55
2 **Eversheds** Leeds	8	28
Hammond Suddards Edge Leeds	7	8
3 **DLA** Leeds, Sheffield	n/a	n/a
4 **Pinsent Curtis Biddle** Leeds	15	28
Walker Morris Leeds	4	12
5 **Irwin Mitchell** Leeds, Sheffield	5	13
Lupton Fawcett Leeds	3	2
Read Hind Stewart Leeds	n/a	n/a
Rollits Hull, York	n/a	n/a
6 **Andrew M Jackson & Co** Hull	3	5
Gordons Cranswick Solicitors Bradford, Leeds	3	4
Gosschalks Hull	n/a	n/a

LEADING INDIVIDUALS	
1 **DA COSTA Alastair** DLA	**DARWIN Andrew** DLA
EMMETT Paul Walker Morris	**GILBERT Ian** Walker Morris
LIPPELL Sean Addleshaw Booth & Co	**SHAW Martin** Pinsent Curtis Biddle
WHELDON Tim Addleshaw Booth & Co	
2 **ARMITAGE David** Hammond Suddards Edge	
CUNNINGHAM Kevin Irwin Mitchell	**JOHNSON Robin** Eversheds
McINTOSH Ian Addleshaw Booth & Co	**SMART Peter** Walker Morris
3 **GREENFIELD Ian** Hammond Suddards Edge	
HARRISON Wendy DLA	**HOPKINS Stephen** Eversheds
JONES Jonathan Hammond Suddards Edge	
ROBINSON Michael Pinsent Curtis Biddle	

This book is the product of 6,552 1/2 hour interviews. See p.7 for BMRB audit.
Within each band, firms are listed alphabetically. *See individuals' profiles p.239*

Scotland; Barclays Private Equity; Brand Holdings; DBS Management; Europower; Findel; FKI; Halifax; Jewson Limited; Quantica; Torotrak; Venture Capitalists; VHE Holdings.

DLA The group undertakes a mix of private equity and M&A. Much of its profile lies with the respected **Alastair Da Costa** and **Andrew Darwin**, while **Wendy Harrison** continues to elicit market approval.

Pinsent Curtis Biddle (see firm details p.1098) Interviewees consistently endorsed this "*high profile and proactive team*" thought to have unquestionable strength at the top end. The firm has bolstered its junior ranks with the recruitment of six new fee-earners over the past year. The stand-out practitioners here are **Martin Shaw** (see p.256) ("*hugely experienced*") and **Michael Robinson** (see p.255), who has a lower profile but boasts a "*quality list of clients.*" Highlights of the past year include advising Baxi UK in a £750 million acquisition by Newmond plc, and advising BPT during a bid by Deutsche Bank/Grainger Trust. The team also advised 4imprint Group on two disposals to MBO teams and in a strategic alliance with US Corporation (£92 million). Also instructed by Brown Shipley & Co in its acquisition of Cawood Smithie. **Clients:** Abbeycrest; American Greetings; Arla Foods; Baxi UK; Case Corporation; Encon Ltd; Northern Spirit; Sema; Smith & Nephew; Sutherland; Thistle Hotels; Weir Technology; various venture capitalists.

Walker Morris (see firm details p.1171) Adjudged a "*pleasant team to work with*" by clients, smaller than some of its competitors but nonetheless filled with top-rated lawyers who pick up significant public company work. Head of Department **Peter Smart** (see p.257) is "*larger than life*" and a "*client relations man.*" **Ian Gilbert** (see p.246) is rated for his venture capital work, and **Paul Emmett** (see p.245) is seen as "*understated, an excellent technician.*" The firm is involved in complex transactions such as its advice to Homestyle Group in its £135 million recommended takeover of Harveys Furnishing, where the offer included a £60 million term loan facility and a £35 million revolving credit facility. The team also acted for Bradford Particle Design in a $200 million recommended offer by California based Inhale Therapeutic Systems, and acted for Kelda Group in its sale of the leading analytical testing laboratory business, A1control, to Bridgepoint Capital for £72 million. **Clients:** Aquarius Group; Bradford Cith Holdings; BUPA; Caterpillar; ECI Ventures; Homestyle Group; Jarvis Facilities; London Securities; Persimmon; Stylo; Surgical Innovations; Vymura; Wilton Investments; Waste Recycling Group.

Irwin Mitchell (see firm details p.1009) Acts for a number of institutional clients out of Leeds and Sheffield. Head of Department in Leeds, **Kevin Cunningham** (see p.243) elicits warm market approval and in the past year acted for Zoo Media Corporation in the reverse takeover of Kazoo 3D, valuing Zoo at £7 million. The firm has also been instructed by the MBO team in the acquisition of the Redhead Freight Group, and is acting for the shareholders in the disposal of PolyBiomed to Lombard Medical for £6 million, satisfied by the issue of AIM listed shares. **Clients:** Adfil; AES Engineering; Cooper Cameron Corporation; Granville Development Capital; JDA group; New World Computer Systems; Severfield Rowen; Wheatley Packaging; Wilton Investments; United Industries; Gripple Group; J&J Dyson; Hattersley & Davidson.

Lupton Fawcett Lower in profile than its closest rivals, the firm, under the guidance of Bob Harrap, continues to be respected by peers and clients alike for its work with local listed companies and substantial owner managed entities. In the past year the firm has advised on a range of transactions including the £23 million sale of Sunway Travel to Airtours and the £4 million sale of Airbath to Aquarius. It also acted in the £4 million acquisition of Cochran Boilers from Rolls Royce and the £2.5 million acquisition of Altor by ICM Computer Group. **Clients:** Listed companies; owner managed companies.

Read Hind Stewart (see firm details p.1104) Providing quality advice to local companies and family owned businesses, the firm is gaining ground in the mid-tier market. Interviewees praised a consistently solid performance from a team that has strength in the hi-tech market. **Clients:** Owner-managed businesses.

Rollits (see firm details p.1110) Richard Field is the lead partner in this group, which is now focused in York and Hull and described by its peers as "*Hull's premier firm.*" It is busy advising local companies with a telecoms, e-commerce and retail bent. Significant matters over the past year include advising Kingston Communications (Hull) in the disposal of its 25% shareholding in KSCL to Telesense. It is also advising Anglia Oils in the acquisition of Allied Foods and represented Fenner in the disposal of its Polymer Engineering Division. **Clients:** American Standard Plumbing (UK); ABP; Cranswick; Danka UK; EMIH; Horncastle Group; Ideal Standard/Armitage Shanks; JR Rix & Sons; Joseph Rowntree Foundation; Kingston Communications (Hull); Marr Foods; Slumberland; University of Hull; William Jackson & Son.

Andrew M Jackson & Co (see firm details p.860) Competitors commended this practice to our researchers for its "*consistently decent quality.*" It specialises in shipping, fish processing and food manufacturing. As example of the latter, it acted for Northern Foods in its £16 million acquisition of 40% of Solway Foods Holdings, and advised Express Dairies in the merger of its liquid milk business in Northern Ireland with that of Golden Vale by way of an 80/20 joint venture. The team, which includes Martin Whitehead, was also involved in the £6 million Hull Fish Auction capital project, acting for the founding consortium and dealing with all corporate finance aspects. **Clients:** ARCO; Burndene Investments; Coldwater Seafood (UK); De Smet Rosedowns; Eimskip; Express Dairies; EYMS Group; Icelandic Freezing Plants Corporation; Image Data Group; Northern Foods; Oughtred & Harrison; Seven Seas.

Gordons Cranswick Solicitors A solid firm originating from Bradford, a region where it is particularly successful. The practice has picked up a number of new lawyers over the past year, bolstering its offering across Leeds and Bradford. The group, led by John Holden, advised Acertec Engineering in the sale of Norlec Engineering and acted for Peter Black Footwear & Accessories in the acquisition of the M&S Division of Littlestone and Goodwin for £2 million. Further highlights include advising the board of British Mohair Holdings on a £21.6 million acquisition bid. **Clients:** Bradford & District Training & Enterprise Council; Bradford Chamber of Commerce; British Mohair Holdings; Peter Black Holdings; Carrington Wire Limited.

Gosschalks A respected Hull practice that is bolstered by its licensing operation, which has attracted many leisure clients to the firm. Interviewees admired the firm's work with its entrepreneurial client base and its involvement in the smaller range of MBO transactions.

NORTH EAST

CORPORATE FINANCE • North East		Ptnrs	Assts
1	**Dickinson Dees** Newcastle upon Tyne	13	25
2	**Eversheds** Newcastle upon Tyne	8	8
	Ward Hadaway Newcastle upon Tyne	5	5
3	**Robert Muckle** Newcastle upon Tyne	5	6
4	**Watson Burton** Newcastle upon Tyne	5	4

LEADING INDIVIDUALS		
1	**BELLIS Nigel** Dickinson Dees	**DAVISON Andrew** Eversheds
	FLYNN John Dickinson Dees	**HULLS Martin** Ward Hadaway
	SPRIGGS Michael Eversheds	
2	**GILTHORPE Ian** Robert Muckle	**PASS Jamie** Dickinson Dees
	PHILLIPS Robert Robert Muckle	
3	**HARKER Chris** Dickinson Dees	**HOYLE Andrew** Watson Burton
	ON Nicholas Eversheds	**SPETCH Michael** Eversheds
	WILLIAMS Nigel Dickinson Dees	

This book is the product of 6,552 1/2 hour interviews. See p.7 for BMRB audit.

Within each band, firms are listed alphabetically. *See individuals' profiles p.239*

Dickinson Dees (see firm details p.941) *"Pre-eminent"* firm in Newcastle according to its is rivals, due to the *"strength and breadth"* of service it offers. **John Flynn** (see p.245 specialises in M&A work and as a *"good marketer"* is commended as the driving force behind the team. He was kept busy last year by the defence of Go-Ahead from a hostile bid by French government-owned transport operator Caisse Des Depots – Development (C3D) and Rhone Capital. Younger partner **Nigel Williams** (see p.260) is regarded as *"sensible to deal with"* and **Jamie Pass** (see p.254), who focuses on corporate finance and MBOs, has seen some *"high-profile"* deals of late. Head of Department **Nigel Bellis** (see p.241) is considered *"technically the best,"* with a strong all-round practice. **Chris Harker** (see p.248) is also recommended. Highlights of the year include advising Grainger Trust on a joint venture with Deutsche Bank to bid for BPT plc, valued at £477 million. Acted for Gona in relation to its acquisition of the South Central rail franchise, and acted for CN Group in its acquisition of local radio franchises. **Clients:** Go Ahead; Arriva; Grainger Trust; Bellway; Northern Electric & Gas; CN Group; Northern Rock; James Cropper; Northern Recruitment Group; Northgate Motor Holdings.

Eversheds (see firm details p.952) An impressive force both in terms of its national coverage and involvement in cross border transactions, yet national practice requirements and restructuring have raised questions over this office's direction. A shift of focus towards public company work has yet to gain the team profile of Dickinson Dees. The office has also seen losses at partner level. **Michael Spetch** (see p.257) specialises in corporate finance and private equity transactions and receives heavy market commendation. **Nick On** (see p.121) is *"strong on the finance side"* while clients agree that **Andrew Davison** (see p.244) *"has the technical skills."* **Michael Spriggs** (see p.257) combines fee earning with his role as managing partner. Highlights of the past year include advising Tarmac/Anglo American on the sale of 44 concrete plants and advising Synpac Pharmaceuticals on a multi-million asset disposal. The team also represented Invensys on its disposal of businesses in the UK and US. **Clients:** Newcastle International Airport; Jennings Brothers; Northern Enterprise; Invensys; Tarmac; UK Land Estates; Jennings Bros.

Ward Hadaway (see firm details p.1173) A respected practice which focuses on the private equity and technology side of the market. Head of department **Martin Hulls** (see p.249) is a private equity specialist and the standout practitioner in this *"quality team."* Significant deals over the past year include advising Bede in the £55 million Techmark flotation and assisting E-comeleon in its £21 million AIM flotation. Institutional buy-outs include advising Motherwell Information Systems in its £78 million IBO and Waddington Jaycare in its £28 million IBO. **Clients:** Bede; e-comeleon; Leighton Management.

Robert Muckle Peers feel that this *"well-run"* team *"markets itself aggressively,"* securing a strong hold over its respected client base. The past year has seen a number of internal promotions, while the group focuses on large owner-managed businesses and listed company work. Head of the corporate group **Robert Phillips** (see p.255) is key to much of the firm's profile and managing partner **Ian Gilthorpe** (see p.246) wins heavy approval for his *"rainmaker"* role. Hallmark deals include advising Brulines in its reverse takeover of CBS Business Services and acting for Metal Spinners in its purchase of part of T&D Industries. Also instructed by QSP Group in its acquisition of Inform Software Systems. **Clients:** C&D Insulation; Hays Travel; Labelling Dynamics; Voyager Foods.

Watson Burton Competitors rate this solid team, which includes good technical lawyers and a strong mix of corporate and commercial work. Led by the respected **Andrew Hoyle**, who combines his work with the role of managing partner, the team is active in AIM listings and mid-market transactions.

SCOTLAND

CORPORATE FINANCE • Scotland	Ptnrs	Assts
1 **Dickson Minto WS** Edinburgh	n/a	n/a
Maclay Murray & Spens Edinburgh, Glasgow	11	n/a
McGrigor Donald Edinburgh, Glasgow	13	37
2 **Dundas & Wilson CS** Edinburgh	13	39
Shepherd & Wedderburn WS Edinburgh	16	29
3 **Burness** Edinburgh	5	5
MacRoberts Glasgow	6	17
4 **Biggart Baillie** Glasgow	8	11
Brodies WS Edinburgh	6	7
Ledingham Chalmers Aberdeen	7	9
McClure Naismith Glasgow	6	5
Paull & Williamsons Aberdeen	11	12
Tods Murray WS Edinburgh	7	9
5 **Fyfe Ireland WS** Edinburgh	4	2
Henderson Boyd Jackson WS Edinburgh	5	6
Iain Smith & Company Aberdeen	n/a	n/a
Semple Fraser Glasgow	5	6
Thorntons WS Dundee	3	3

LEADING INDIVIDUALS	
1 **BRUCE Roderick** Dickson Minto WS	**McNEILL Morag** McGrigor Donald
MINTO Bruce Dickson Minto WS	
SWANSON Magnus Maclay Murray & Spens	
WILL James Shepherd & Wedderburn WS	
2 **ANDERSON Keith** Dickson Minto WS	**CUNNINGHAM Neil** MacRoberts
DICKSON Ian MacRoberts	**GRAY Colin** McGrigor Donald
HARDIE David Dundas & Wilson CS	**LUMSDEN Ian** Maclay Murray & Spens
McDONALD Kevan Dickson Minto WS	**PATRICK Bruce** Maclay Murray & Spens
RAFFERTY John Burness	**SLEIGH Andrew** Burness
3 **ALLAN David** Biggart Baillie	**BARRIE Sidney** Paull & Williamsons
FRIER George McClure Naismith	**GIBB Stephen** Shepherd & Wedderburn WS
GLEN Marian Shepherd & Wedderburn WS	
MEIKLEJOHN Iain Shepherd & Wedderburn WS	
SIMMONS William Tods Murray WS	**SLOAN Graeme** Maclay Murray & Spens
SMITH Campbell Biggart Baillie	
4 **BUCHAN Gordon** Paull & Williamsons	**DEANE David** Semple Fraser
FEECHAN Catherine Biggart Baillie	**KANE Hilary** Maclay Murray & Spens
LINDGREN David Fyfe Ireland WS	**MASTERS Richard** McGrigor Donald
McGINN James MacRoberts	**ROSE Kenneth** Dundas & Wilson CS
SHAND Kenneth Maclay Murray & Spens	

This book is the product of 6,552 1/2 hour interviews. See p.7 for BMRB audit.

Within each band, firms are listed alphabetically. *See individuals' profiles p.239*

Dickson Minto WS (see firm details p.942) A team thought by peers to be "*so specialist*" that it "*really makes an impression.*" Continually involved in "*high quality work*" to the extent that it makes a dent in the London market. **Bruce Minto** (see p.253) is typically described as "*an exceptionally gifted individual – a real ambassador*" for the firm, and retains an enviable following of blue-chip clients. **Roderick Bruce** (see p.242) and **Kevan McDonald** (see p.252) are seen "*leading the transactions,*" both described by clients as "*focused and commercial with tremendous technical ability.*" **Keith Anderson** (see p.239) heads up the Glasgow office and enjoys a high profile. Recent transactions include advising 3i, RBDC and other sellers in the sale of KSCL to Telesens AG for approximately £130 million. The group also acted for MIS Holdings in its acquisition of the information systems division of Motherwell Bridge for £85 million, and was instructed by the Bank of Scotland on the £65 million merger of the oil companies, AFOS International and Specialised Petroleum Services. **Clients:** 3i; Dunedin Capital Partners; Bridgepoint Capital Partners; Penta Capital Partners; BC Partners; Cinven; Investcorp; Charterhouse Development Capital; Mercury Asset Management; Apax Partners; Royal Bank Private Equity; Aberdeen Development Capital.

Maclay Murray & Spens (see firm details p.1047) A practice that peers feel has "*re-awakened*" itself on the corporate front. Kept busy by stellar client 3i, the team is prominent on the venture capital front. "*Charismatic and smooth*" **Magnus Swanson** (see p.258) is judged to be the partner who "*brings the firm along.*" In contrast, **Ian Lumsden** (see p.252) is a "*capable and personable*" lawyer who "*quietly gets on with things.*" **Bruce Patrick** (see p.254) is "*top-quality*" in both his legal knowledge and highly commercial manner, while **Graeme Sloan** (see p.257) is commended for his involvement on significant deals including the demutualisation of Scottish Widows. At the more junior end, **Hilary Kane** (see p.250) has "*performed well on deals*" over the past year and **Kenneth Shand** (see p.256) is a "*man about town*" in Glasgow, where he has been working on the £600 million public to private of Highland Distilleries. Venture capital continues to provide highlight transactions with the representation of 3i, Scottish Equity partners and twenty other venture capital houses. A growth in financial sector work has seen the firm representing Scottish Widows, Bank of Scotland and Bell Lawrie Wise Speke. Other notable instructions have been the restructuring and refinancing of Semple Cochrance, with a value of £7.4 billion, and the defence of BPI against the £200 million hostile bid by MacFarlance. **Clients:** 3i; Scottish Widows; Hewden Stewart; Grampian Holdings; Scottish Enterprise; Motherwell Bridge; Weir Group; Novartis; Stagecoach; John Menzies; Stiell Group; Clyde Marine; Clyde Bowers; BPI; Private & Commercial Finance Group.

McGrigor Donald (see firm details p.1062) Active particularly in the technology market, the firm continues to enjoy a steady degree of success with support from a growing London office. Originating from its base in Glasgow, the firm is increasingly UK-wide focused with a new presence in Belfast and the taking of new offices in Edinburgh. Peers acknowledge that Head of Department **Colin Gray** "*gets the job done*" and "*knows what the clients want,*" while "*high achieving*" **Morag McNeill** can be "*tough to deal with*" but is thought "*never to let her clients down.*" The past year has seen her acting for Morrison in its recommended takeover offer by Anglian Waters, valued at £280 million, and acting for Indigo Group in its £135 million flotation. Judged by interviewees to be "*immensely able,*" **Richard Masters** has been busy over the past year acting for web solutions company Reality Group in its sale by Great Universal Stores, and acting for internet service provider Iomart Group in its AIM listing and £20 million fundraising. Other significant transactions for the team include acting for Channel Health in its £5 million placing and admission to AIM, and acting for Orbital Software Holdings in its flotation on Techmark raising £25 million. **Clients:** Aberdeen Murray Johnstone; Penta Capital; Bank of Scotland; BDL Hotels; Noble & Co; Beeson Gregory; Seymour Pierce Group; Blue Software Inc; BCO Technologies; All-Hotels.com; Bell Lawrie Investment Management; Legendary Investments.

Dundas & Wilson CS (see firm details p.947) A practice which capitalises on its Andersen Legal connection to partake in increasingly complex and international deals. The firm may not be as visible in local matters, but a quality list of transactions confirms that this connection is taking them in the right direction. Head of the Corporate Group **David Hardie** excels at management and transactional work, while **Kenneth Rose** continues to win market approval. Highlight deals include advising Rangers Football Club on a rights issue to raise up to £53.1 million on OFEX and advising Scottish Radio Holdings in a placing and open offer to raise £75 million.

The group also advised Digital Animations in a placing for £12 million. In the M&A sphere it represented Scottish Radio Holdings on its £21.5 million acquisition of the Kilkenny People Newspaper Group. Hi-tech projects included instructions from the Digital Animations Group on the negotiation of licensing arrangements following the acquisition of Ananova by Orange, and on its £12 million placing of shares. **Clients:** Abbey National; Bank of Scotland; Dig Media; Digital Animations Group; Franklin Templeton; Kymata; Macfarlane Group; Martin Currie Investment Management; Murray International Holdings; National Australia Group; SMG; Scottish Radio Holdings; Scottish Value Management; The Royal Bank of Scotland Group; Torridon; University of Glasgow.

Shepherd & Wedderburn WS (see firm details p.1126) A strong year has seen this practice busy acting for public companies with strong exposure to the technology sector. Head of Department **James Will** (see p.260) is endorsed by clients as a "*smart guy*" who is thought to "*spearhead the public company work.*" **Iain Meiklejohn** (see p.253) has a lower profile but is "*a steady hand and a real thinker.*" **Marian Glen** (see p.246) has a financial bent to her practice and "*gets the deals done in an efficient and commercial manner.*" **Stephen Gibb** (see p.246) has really stepped into the limelight this year with his involvement in some major transactions, and a reputation for "*really knowing what he is talking about.*" He led a team advising Telesens AG in its £129 million acquisition of KSCL (Holdings) Limited. The firm has also acted for Melville Craig Group on its sale to TMP Worldwide, and was instructed by City of Edinburgh Council in its £150 million ICT partnering agreement with BT to remove ICT inhibitors, progressing and delivering new IT projects. In addition the firm represented Scottish Power UK in the establishment of Selectusonline to administer competitive tendering processes for the procurement of certain projects. **Clients:** Scottish Power; Cairn Energy; Stagecoach Holdings; Bank of Scotland; Scottish Enterprise; Thus; Axis-Shield; Scottish & Newcastle; Shell UK; Edinburgh Fund Managers; Friends Ivory & Sime; Scottish Life; European Investment Bank; Miller Group.

Burness (see firm details p.903) A traditional corporate practice with solid lawyers; interviewees acknowledge the firm's involvement in quality public company transactions. In Edinburgh, **John Rafferty** is judged to have an "*excellent reputation in the Scottish finance community,*" while Glasgow-based **Andrew Sleigh** (see p.257) is respected for being a "*generalist who can turn his hand to a range of matters.*" Highlights for the group include acting for the vendor shareholders in the £33.75 million sale of Beat 106, and advising The Royal Bank of Scotland on all corporate aspects of its acquisition from Scottish & Newcastle of a licensed premises portfolio worth £170 million. In the hi-tech market it advised Spider Software in the £28 million sale of a new economy business to Artesyn Technologies. **Clients:** Bank of Scotland; Big Beat Group; Bonnier Media; Fairbriar; Idesta Group; Jarvis Porter; Millennium Commission; Royal Bank Private Equity; Royal Bank of Scotland Investment Limited; SEET; Standard Life Bank Limited; Transatlantic Software Company; UA Group.

MacRoberts (see firm details p.1048) Considered an "*energetic*" team by clients, it has a strong market profile for acquisitions and disposals including MBOs and MBIs and private equity. Head of Department **Neil Cunningham** (see p.243) is said to be "*highly active, he understands numbers.*" **Ian Dickson** (see p.244) is a "*senior player, one of the clear leaders*" in the field. **James McGinn** (see p.252) also receives a good share of market commendation. The firm recently advised the ISI Group in the MBO of McLaren Consulting and acted for Omnia Books on the MBO of Calendonian International Book Manufacturing. **Clients:** AMEC Group; Bank of Ireland; Chiltern Scotland Limited; Clydesdale Bank; Ford Motor Company; Initiative Software; ISI Group; Omnia Books; Railtrack; Royal Bank Private Equity; Smith & McLaurin; University of Strathclyde; 21 Colour; 3i Group.

Biggart Baillie (see firm details p.882) Public deals over the past year include advising AorTech International in its listing on the Stock Exchange and related fundraising of approximately £74 million, and acting for Bell Lawrie White in the AIM flotation of Blavod Vodka valued at £14 million. Venture capital matters have included acting for ADC (Glasgow) Limited, part of Aberdeen Asset Management, in connection with several investments. Strength in private company work is demonstrated by the firm's work for the shareholders of Atlantech Technologies in its sale to Cisco Systems for $200 million. **David Allan** (see p.239), whose public company work occupies most of his time, is said to "*know what he is doing and doesn't mess around.*" Interviewees also judge the "*popular*" **Catherine Feechan** (see p.245) to be "*good news*" for the firm by taking the lead in both private and public company transactions. **Campbell Smith** (see p.257) also continues to have a strong reputation among fellow lawyers for the quality of work, which this year included activities for Scottish Amicable Life. **Clients:** ADC (Glasgow); Brewin Dolphin Securities; AorTech International; Scottish Power; Thus; Global Video UK; Scottish Tanning Industries; Scottish Legal Life; Loganair; Thorburn Colquhoun; The Scottish Investment Trust; Inch Kenneth Kajang Rubber; BSW Timber; The Highland Council.

Brodies WS (see firm details p.896) A "*niche*" corporate practice, which acts alongside an outstanding private client team, has some long experienced practitioners, including Julian Voge. The firm is committed to building the team. It has seen an increase in government advisory work and highlight deals have included the disposal of 90% of Martyn Scott Ltd to Witzenmann GmbH. Also acted in the acquisition of DMB Inc's shareholding in Loch Lomond Golf Club by the Lyle Anderson Companies, and in the acquisition of share capital in Caledonian Exchange Ltd. **Clients:** Sykes Enterprises; VF Northern Europe; The Royal Bank of Scotland; Enterprise Rent-a-Car UK; Shetland Leasing and Property Developments Limited; Loch Lomond Golf Club; United Bank of Kuwait; FMC Corporation; European Commission; Lithuanian Government; Nestlé UK; The Co-operative Group (CWS).

Ledingham Chalmers (see firm details p.1034) A "*big Aberdeen firm*" which peers perceive houses some "*first-class*" lawyers and valued clients, particularly in the oil and gas industry. An Edinburgh presence is beginning to take hold. Highlights of Malcolm Laing's team include acting for Newco and 3i in the £40 million institutionally led merger of Specialised Petroleum Services and AFOS to create the SPS-AFOS Group. The team advised Macdonald Hotels on a £100 million fund established by Bank of Scotland and Royal Bank of Scotland for hotel acquisitions, and acted for Bank of Scotland in the £1.3 million MBO of Norcom in Inverness. **Clients:** George Craig Group; 3i; Macdonald Hotels; Ramco Energy; University of Aberdeen; John Wood Group; Aberdeen Development Capital; Highland Energy Holdings.

McClure Naismith (see firm details p.1059) A "*real strength*" in Glasgow according to clients, this practice acts for a range of owner-managed businesses and a number of companies in the drinks, manufacturing, engineering and leisure sectors. **George Frier** (see p.246) retains his strong market reputation as a "*commercial operator.*" The group acted for the management in the £20 million IBO of McLaren Consulting and represented Plexus Corp (USA) in the £17.5 million acquisition of Keltek Electronics Group. Also received instructions from Altnamara Shipping concerning its £6 million prospectus and placing. **Clients:** Unicorn Leisure Group; Fortis Leisure; JBB (Greater Europe); Celtic plc; Compaq Computer Manufacturing; Lithgows; First Engineering; Eastern Group; GAP Holdings; BOC Group; Blick; Strathclyde Investment Fund.

Paull & Williamsons (see firm details p.1091) "*Top of the tree*" in the Aberdeen market where it is well placed to take advantage of the increase in corporate oil and gas instructions, resulting from a higher level of activity in the North Sea. **Sidney Barrie** (see p.240) is endorsed by interviewees as one of the most experienced practitioners in the field. **Gordon Buchan** (see p.242) also received recommendation. Highlights of the past year include advising the vendor shareholders of the Orwell Group in its sale to

Weatherford International. The team was also active in the sale of Marine Systems to Schlumberger Industries and involved in the purchase by the PSL Group of the AGR Group of Norway. Further cross border activity came when the group advised ASCO in its proposed IPO on the New York Stock Exchange. **Clients:** FirstGroup; ASCO; Orwell Group; PSL.

Tods Murray WS (see firm details p.1157) A robust showing on the finance side, the firm also maintains its quality clients. Originating from Edinburgh, the firm has increased its Glasgow presence since opening an office there two years ago. **William Simmons** (see p.715) combines his practice with a strong PFI focus, and is seen by some interviewees as the "*mainstay of the practice, one immensely smart lawyer.*" Significant instructions over the past year include acting for the Bank of Scotland on the constitutional and Scots law aspects of its takeover bid for National Westminster Bank and related funding arrangements. The firm also represented Pan European Seafood Holdings in two acquisitions, namely the Macrae Group and the Strathaird Group and related funding valued at €50 million. The team also acted for Dobbies Garden Centres in an AIM placing and open offer of £2.4 million of ordinary shares. **Clients:** Bank of Scotland; Dobbies Garden centres; Melrose Resources; Pan European Seafoods; Clark Pub Company; Kenmore Group; Nevis Range Development Company.

Fyfe Ireland WS (see firm details p.967) A "*personable*" practice bolstered by the appointment of three new partners, it remains in the eyes of our interviewees a "*strong and capable*" practice. Working from a strong commercial property base, the team handles a wide spectrum of corporate transactions including advice to start-ups, and private and public investment. Highlights of the past year include the £21 million Quadstone cross-border fundraising and acting for the management team in a buyout from its Canadian parent company in the field of computer software. The group, which is led by **David Lindgren** (see p.251), also acted for Axis-Shield in the £1.5 million disposal of its TTP diagnostic products portfolio. **Clients:** Quadstone; Pentland Business Management; Optos; Queen Margaret University College; Kingsbarns Golf Links; Axis-Shield.

Henderson Boyd Jackson WS Considered by peers to be a "*sensible and well-led business,*" instructed in a broad range of corporate work over the past year. Highlight deals for the group, which is headed by Hugh Macmaster, include advising Bell Lawrie White on the AIM placing of Aberdeen FC, and advising Peel Hunt on the introduction to AIM and subsequent open offer by e-quisitor. Also advised Sadusky in the acquisition of Beloit Walmsley of Bolton. **Clients:** BUE Marine Limited; Highfield; Heriot Watt University; Eurobenefits; Peel Hunt.

Iain Smith & Company (see firm details p.1007) A "*well-respected*" team in Aberdeen, assisting companies in all aspects of start-up, together with providing business advice to private clients.

Semple Fraser (see firm details p.1121) A firm with a strong corporate property base and a robust attitude to building up corporate finance as a core practice area. Peers acclaim **David Deane** (see p.244) for his "*level-headed and commercial manner;*" this year he acted for Ronald Higg in the £5 million sale of interests in SPH (Scotland) Limited and advised on the sale of Oakwood Foods to MacPhie of Glenbervie for £14 million. Further highlights for the team include acting for Off-ExPress.com in securing first-round funding for development of its internet-based investor information website. Also acting for the management team in the $12.3 million MBO of Cleveland Bridge from Kvaerner ASA. **Clients:** The Miller Group; The Laird Group; SMG; National Express Group; Value & Income Trust; William Morton; First Press Publishing; Georgeson Office Interiors; Anderson Precision Gears; GDX Technologies; The Falkirk Football and Athletic Club; The Best of Health (Scotland); Thomson Pettie Tube Products.

Thorntons WS A firm which handles the corporate needs of the Dundee market and represents the University and technology-type companies. The team advises on all aspects of company law, contracts, terms of trading, mergers, acquisitions and MBOs/MBIs.

NORTHERN IRELAND

Band	CORPORATE FINANCE • Northern Ireland	Ptnrs	Assts
1	**Carson McDowell** Belfast	2	4
	L'Estrange & Brett Belfast	3	3
2	**Mills Selig** Belfast	3	1
3	**Tughan & Co** Belfast	2	5
4	**Arthur Cox** Belfast	2	2
5	**Cleaver Fulton Rankin** Belfast	4	n/a
	Elliott Duffy Garrett Belfast	3	4
	Johns Elliot Belfast	2	1
	Johnsons Belfast	n/a	n/a
	McKinty & Wright Belfast	2	5

Band	LEADING INDIVIDUALS	
1	**IRVINE John** L'Estrange & Brett	**JOHNSTON Michael** Carson McDowell
2	**FULTON Richard** Mills Selig	**GRAY Richard** L'Estrange & Brett
	JAMISON David Carson McDowell	
3	**McBRIDE Paul** L'Estrange & Brett	
4	**BUTLER Maurice** Johns Elliot	**CANAVAN Kerry** Arthur Cox
	MARSHALL John Johnsons	**WILLIS John-George** Tughan & Co
UP AND COMING		
	McVEIGH Kevin Elliott Duffy Garrett	**STAFFORD Peter** Arthur Cox

This book is the product of 6,552 1/2 hour interviews. See p.7 for BMRB audit.
Within each band, firms are listed alphabetically. *See individuals' profiles p.239*

Carson McDowell (see firm details p.909) "*Always good to have them on the other side,*" say rivals of a firm that boasts two especially highly regarded practitioners. "*Pragmatic, business-like*" and "*not difficult for the sake of it,*" **Michael Johnston** (see p.249) and his colleague **David Jamison** (see p.249) were commended to researchers for their "*excellence in getting a deal done.*" The firm's clients span the range of industry areas, with a focus on utility companies, and a particular emphasis on US firms establishing themselves in Northern Ireland. The firm advised Avalanche Technologies on its $8.5 million investment by 3i and IDB, and has also advised Open+Direct (a Viridian subsidiary) on various acquisitions. **Clients:** Nigen; Open+Direct; Avalanche; Translink.

L'Estrange & Brett (see firm details p.1038) Regarded as "*among leaders in the field*" by their peers, the team includes a number of the leading individuals in the region. "*Sensible*" **John Irvine** (see p.249) leads a team that includes the "*affable*" **Richard Gray** (see p.247) and the "*cautious, thorough*" **Paul McBride** (see p.252). Communications and hi-tech are areas of core expertise. Recently appointed to advise Sx3, the team has completed a number of acquisitions for them with a combined value of over £65 million. It acted for a global e-mail company on a private placing of shares, raising more than £7 million. **Clients:** UTV; Galen; Viridian; Sx3.

Mills Selig (see firm details p.1070) "*Leading player*" **Richard Fulton** (see p.246) is known universally for his pragmatic and commercial approach. Acting for blue-chip private local companies and plcs, the firm advises on M&A work, reconstructions and venture capital transactions. Expanding into hi-tech industry, the firm also retains its base of leisure and agri-chemical industry clients. It carried out a recent acquisition for DCC Energy NI, and also advised on the disposal of high street retailer, Options. **Clients:** DCC Energy NI; Options.

Tughan & Co (see firm details p.1163) Though described as "*reasonably aggressive*" by his peers, clients see **John-George Willis** (see p.260) as a "*practical*" man, who is able to "*convert the legal stuff into plain language.*" The firm has been active on M&A work for food, fuel and telecoms businesses. It acted for Glenfarm Holdings on its acquisition of Fats and Proteins, and advised Lamont Holdings on the disposal of five businesses in Northern Ireland. **Clients:** Amacis; Kainos; Glenfarm Holdings; Lamont Holdings.

Arthur Cox (see firm details p.865) Highly rated by clients for her technical proficiency, **Kerry Canavan** (see p.242) and her team have a broad range of clients, including technology companies, builder's merchants and supermarkets. Rising name **Peter Stafford** (see p.257) also received substantial peer endorsement. The firm acted on the fund raising for a property consortium that raised £7 million from private investors, and also acted for a government department setting up an investment fund through a limited partnership structure. **Clients:** Technology companies; supermarkets.

Cleaver Fulton Rankin (see firm details p.918) Still carving out its reputation as a corporate firm, the team has developed a large client base with an international focus. Led by Jennifer Ebbage, the group also acts on banking regulatory work, including transactional work and lending terms and conditions. The team advised on the sale of Synthetic Packaging Ltd. **Clients:** William Dowling; Lindsay Cars; Synthetic Packaging.

Elliott Duffy Garrett (see firm details p.949) Newly made partner **Kevin McVeigh** (see p.252) has been strongly recommended to researchers over the past year. He is now the brightest star of a team that acts on acquisitions and disposals locally and advises on the Northern Irish aspects of European transactions. **Clients:** Local corporates.

Johns Elliot (see firm details p.1014) Respected by peers as "*an extremely intelligent man,*" **Maurice Butler** (see p.200) is the leading figure at a firm that advises small to medium sized companies on their corporate transactions. The team recently handled an MBO in the public relations sector and a joint venture in the textiles industry. **Clients:** Local medium sized companies.

Johnsons (see firm details p.1015) **John Marshall** (see p.252), noted for his M&A work and "*pragmatic*" approach, is said by clients to "*fight our corner.*" The firm continues to advise primarily on local M&A activity. **Clients:** Local corporates.

McKinty & Wright (see firm details p.1063) Although better known as a property firm, the corporate team, headed by Frederick Boyd, continues to undertake M&A and private equity advice for a clientele that includes 3i. **Clients:** 3i; Manufacturing companies; animal feed companies; insurance brokers.

LEADERS IN CORPORATE FINANCE

ACOCK, Roger
Lyons Davidson, Bristol (0117) 904 5887
racock@lyonsdavidson.co.uk
Specialisation: Recently moved from *Bond Pearce* to *Lyons Davidson* to continue corporate work, specialising in corporate finance. Whilst at *Bond Pearce* led teams on many high profile MBO, MIB, IBO and other corporate finance transactions across the Southern region, including £35million buy-out of British International from CHC Helicopter Corporation, £150million merger of Flagship Foods, MBO of financial services division of Aon Corporation to form Momentum Financial Services and 2 major acquisitions for Flagship Foods. Since joining *Lyons Davidson* in May 2001 has completed a £97million refinancing for a listed plc and disposal of a South West based housebuilding company. Special interest and experience in waste mangement and aviation law.
Prof. Memberships: Member of the International Bar Association and Solicitors European Group. Chairman of the Devon and Cornwall Branch of the Institute of Directors. Director of SITA Environmental Trust and plc Employee Share Trust.
Career: Qualified 1980. Partner at *Bond Pearce* 1985. Previous firm *Durrant Piesse* (now *Lovells*); *Bond Pearce.*

ALLAN, David
Biggart Baillie, Glasgow (0141) 228 8000
dallan@biggartbaillie.co.uk
Specialisation: Specialist in corporate finance. ATM/listed company work. Equity investments acquisitions and disposals. Major deals in 2000 – sale of Atlantech Technologies Ltd to Cisco Systems Inc for US$180 million, placing and open offer for Aortech International plc to raise £18 million.
Prof. Memberships: Law Society of Scotland.
Career: Glasgow University LLB. Trained at *Wright Johnston & Mackenzie*, assistant at *Maclay Murray & Spens*, Group Legal Adviser at Allenwest Group. *Biggart Baillie* since 1982. Head of corporate department 2000.
Personal: Married with two children. Interests golf and sailing. Lives in Troon.

ALLEN, Amanda
Pinsent Curtis Biddle, Birmingham
(0121) 200 1050
amanda.allen@pinsents.com
Specialisation: Partner in Corporate Finance Department and Head of Automotive Team. Handles all types of corporate finance work including mergers and acquisitions, disposals, joint ventures, take overs, business and corporate reorganisation etc.
Career: Qualified in 1986. Partner at *Pinsent Curtis Biddle* since 1992.
Personal: Born 1960. Leisure interests include golf, skiing and travel.

ALLEN-JONES, Charles
Linklaters, London (020) 7456 3720
charles.allen-jones@linklaters.com
Specialisation: Specialist in corporate matters, particularly equity issues, public and private acquisitions, privatisations and projects. Responsible for managing the firm's relationships with several key clients.
Career: Partner in charge of *Linklater's* International Finance Department 1981-83; Partner in charge of Corporate Department 1985-91; Senior partner 1996-2001. Qualified 1963.

ANDERSON, Keith T
Dickson Minto WS, Glasgow (0141) 229 4455
keith.anderson@dmws.com
Specialisation: Partner in corporate department, based in Glasgow. Corporate and commercial; mergers and acquisitions, management buy-ins and outs, institutional buy-outs, sale and purchase of companies and businesses, refinancings. Recent deals include the £14 million IBO of McLaren Consulting Limited for Penta Capital Partners and £7 million subsequent acquisition of Empace Limited and the £130 million sale of KSCL (Holdings) Limited to Telesens AG for the vendors.
Prof. Memberships: Law Society of Scotland; Society of Writers to the Signet.
Career: Qualified in 1981. Joined *Dickson Minto W.S.* as senior assistant in 1989 and assumed as a partner in 1994.
Personal: Born 24th January 1957. Attended George Watson's College 1962-75; University of Edinburgh 1975-79 (LLB(Hons)). Leisure interests include rugby, golf, football and music.

ANGEL, Peter
Manches, Oxford (01865) 722106
peter.angel@manches.co.uk
Specialisation: Partner in the Company & Commercial Department. General corporate finance and venture capital work, with particular interest in corporate and regulatory aspects of the Lloyd's insurance market. Regular speaker at seminars on corporate finance topics.
Career: Qualified 1970.
Personal: Born 27th July, 1946. Attended Maidstone Grammar School 1959-64 and then University College London. Board member of The College of Estate Management. Lives in Oxford.

AP SIMON, Charles
Freshfields Bruckhaus Deringer, London
(020) 7936 4000
charles.apsimon@freshfields.com
Specialisation: Partner in corporate department. Main area of practice is corporate and corporate finance. Advises corporate and merchant banking

clients on corporate, stock exchange and take-over related issues, including securities issues, joint ventures and private acquisitions and disposals.
Prof. Memberships: Law Society and City Solicitors' Company. Listing Authority Listing Rules Committee member.
Career: Qualified in 1977. Joined *Freshfields* in 1977, becoming a partner in 1982.
Personal: Born 28th June 1947. Attended Epsom College 1960-65 and Christ's College Cambridge 1966-69 (MA, LLB).

ARMITAGE, David W.K.
Hammond Suddards Edge, Leeds (0113) 284 7000
david.armitage@hammondse.com
Specialisation: Corporate finance partner for the firm operating out of its Leeds and London offices and specialising in national and international merger and acquisition work, MBOs and MBIs, joint ventures, competition issues, commercial and sports sponsorship and endorsement work; corporate restructuring; capital issues and Yellow Book and Blue Book work for plc clients. Leads *Hammond Suddards Edge's* engineering sector group and sports group. Recent highlights include: acting for Halifax plc in its multiple estate agency disposal programme and its rightmove.co.uk joint venture; acting for FKI plc on its £131 million recommended bid for Bridon plc; acting for Umbro International in its £90 million disposal of Umbro to Doughty Hanson.
Prof. Memberships: Law Society.
Career: Rydal School, Colwyn Bay; Queens' College, Cambridge (1980 BA, 1983 MA). Articled *Alexander Tatham*, Manchester; qualified 1983; Ferranti plc 1985-86; joined *Hammond Suddards Edge* 1986; partner since 1988.
Personal: Born 1958; resides Harrogate; married with three children. Leisure interests include golf, rugby, motor sports.

ASHWORTH, Chris
Ashurst Morris Crisp, London (020) 7638 1111
Specialisation: Mergers and acquisitions, corporate finance, insolvency, transactional work and finance. Clients include investment banks and corporates such as United News & Media, Thuraya, Deutsche Telekom, British Telecom, AMVESCAP, Northern Foods plc and Henlys.
Career: LLB graduate of Southampton University. Lectured at Manchester University. Joined *Ashurst Morris Crisp* in 1982 and became a partner in 1986, head of company in 2001.

AUDLEY, Max
Hobson Audley, London (020) 7450 4500

AUSTIN, James
Birketts, Ipswich (01473) 232300

BAKER, Andrew
Wedlake Bell, London (020) 7395 3000
Specialisation: Partner. Head of corporate finance. Corporate. Acts for a wide range of listed companies, brokers and venture capitalists with regard to mergers and acquisitions, equity issues and flotations. Speaker at seminars and conferences with regard to corporate governance and buying and selling companies.
Career: Articled with *Slaughter and May* in 1970. Qualified 1972 joining the commercial department of *Slaughter and May.* Joined *Wedlake Bell* 1979 becoming a partner in 1982. Head of corporate finance 1985 to date. President of the international alliance of independent commercial law firms, TELFA (Trans European Law Firms Alliance). Member of legal and tax and corporate governance committees of European Association of Securities Dealers.
Personal: Born 12th October 1946. LLB(Hons) Birmingham 1969. Lives in Surrey. Also a Director of The Global Group plc, The Egyptian-British Chamber of Commerce and Lambeth Building Society.

BARNARD, Stephen
Herbert Smith, London (020) 7466 2069
stephen.barnard@herbertsmith.com
Specialisation: Corporate finance, mergers and acquisitions, private equity and leveraged transactions, privatisations, major projects and major reorganisations. His work involves acting for a number of listed clients as well as financial intermediaries, institutions and government. Deals include the establishment of global arrangements for the governance of *PricewaterhouseCoopers* and local *PwC* mergers in Europe and Africa, the London Stock Exchange demutualisation and the defence of hostile bid by OM Gruppen, the reorganisation and sale of the Married Quarters Estates of the Armed Forces and the reorganisation of the renewables energy structure in the UK.
Career: Qualified in 1974. Partner at *Herbert Smith* since 1983. Head of one of the firm's corporate groups.
Personal: Educated at Southampton University.

BARNES, Oliver
Travers Smith Braithwaite, London
(020) 7295 3000
Oliver.Barnes@TraversSmith.com
Specialisation: Head of *Travers Smith Braithwaite's* company department. Corporate and corporate finance. Public takeovers, mergers and acquisitions, flotations and secondary issues. Corporate governance.
Prof. Memberships: Member of Law Society's Company Law Committee; International Bar Association.
Career: Articled at *Travers Smith Braithwaite.* Qualified 1976. Partner 1980.
Personal: Born 1950. Educated at Eton College and Trinity Hall, Cambridge.

BARR, Alan
Burges Salmon, Bristol (0117) 939 2255
alan.barr@burges-salmon.com
Specialisation: Company law and corporate finance including business and company acquisitions and disposals, public company flotations and reversals, equity financing and takeovers, corporate restructuring and management buy-outs and buy-ins for clients such as Brandon Hire plc FirstGroup plc, Milk Link, Orange Personal Communications, Rotork plc, Science Systems plc, Surface Technology Systems, Synstar plc. Alan acts for and is company secretary of Bristol City Football Club.
Prof. Memberships: Law Society's Standing Committee on Company Law.
Career: Trained with *Slaughter and May*, joined *Clifford Chance* for four years, joined *Burges Salmon* in 1986 and became a partner in 1988.
Personal: Brought up in Northern Ireland, graduated in law from University of Wales. Keen hill walker, cyclist and swimmer.

BARRIE, Sidney
Paull & Williamsons, Aberdeen (01224) 621621
sbarrie@paull-williamsons.co.uk
Specialisation: Partner in the Corporate Department specialising in MBOs and acquisitions and disposals. Also advises on general corporate law, including reconstructions, investment documentation and contractual work.
Prof. Memberships: Law Society of Scotland; Society of Advocates in Aberdeen.
Career: *James & George Collie* 1971-73. Joined *Paul & Williamsons* 1973, partner 1978.
Personal: Educated at Robert Gordon's College, Aberdeen 1962-68 and at Aberdeen University 1968-71. Leisure pursuits include golf and watching football. Lives in Aberdeen. Born 14th June 1950.

BAXTER, Richard
Stevens & Bolton, Guildford (01483) 734 213
Specialisation: All aspects of company law, including acquisitions, disposals, MBOs and other venture capital transactions, reorganisations, joint ventures and new issues. Recent transactions include the sale of Delphis Consulting plc to Morse plc for up to £40 million and the purchase by Hays Personnel Services Limited of leading legal recruitment consultants ZMB Limited for a substantial undisclosed sum.
Career: St Paul's School; Exeter University (LLB Hons). 1985 *Clifford-Turner* (now *Clifford Chance*). Specialised in corporate finance before joining *Stevens & Bolton*, becoming partner in 1990. Head of company/commercial department.
Publications: Contributor to 'Tolley's Company Law'.
Personal: Born 5 May 1962. Married with two children. Leisure interests include golf (Hankley Common Golf Club), fishing, horse riding, other sport, cinema, gardening and family.

BEASTALL, Jonathan
Clifford Chance, London (020) 7600 1000

BEHARRELL, Steven
Coudert Brothers, London (020) 7248 3000
beharrells@london.coudert.com
See under Energy & Natural Resources, p.353

BELL, Christopher
Travers Smith Braithwaite, London
(020) 7295 3000
Specialisation: Corporate and corporate finance – mergers and acquisitions, equity financings, MBO's and MBI's. Corporate governance issues.
Prof. Memberships: Member of the City of London Solicitors Company.
Career: Articled at *Crossman Bloch & Keith* 1969; he became an assistant at *Travers Smith Braithwaite* in 1971 and was elected a partner in 1976. He is now the senior partner.

BELLEW, Derek
Veale Wasbrough, Bristol (0117) 925 2020
dbellew@vwl.co.uk
Specialisation: Partner in company commercial department. Chairman. Work covers company sales and purchases, MBOs, corporate finance and professional partnerships. Specialist practice in medical partnerships.
Career: Qualified 1967. Managing partner of *Veale Wasbrough* 1993-98. Chairman since 1998.
Personal: Born 1942. St John's College, Oxford 1961-64. Chairman St George's Music Trust.

BELLIS, Nigel
Dickinson Dees, Newcastle upon Tyne
(0191) 279 9250
Specialisation: Partner in Company and Commercial Department. Handles flotations, share issues, mergers and acquisitions, IT contracts, e-commerce advice and complex commercial agreements. Clients include public companies, utilities and substantial private companies, as well as public sector organisations.
Prof. Memberships: Law Society.
Career: Qualified in 1977. Joined *Dickinson Dees* in 1980 and became a Partner in 1982.
Personal: Born 1953. Educated at Cambridge University 1971-74. Lives in Newcastle upon Tyne.

BELLIS, Tim
Herbert Smith, London (020) 7374 8000
Specialisation: Partner in corporate division. Has concentrated particularly in the areas of mergers and acquisitions, corporate finance, securities offerings and capital markets transactions on international stock exchanges (London, Hong Kong and Luxembourg) and investment and joint venture work.
Career: Qualified in 1981 and became partner in 1987.

BENNETT, John
Berwin Leighton Paisner, London (020) 7760 1000
john.bennett@berwinleightonpaisner.com
Specialisation: Mergers and Acquisitions, corporate finance, private equity and general company and securities law specialist.
Prof. Memberships: City of London Law Society Company Laws Sub-Committee.
Career: Qualified in 1983 with *Berwin Leighton.* Became a partner in 1987. Head of Corporate.

BERINGER, Guy Gibson
Allen & Overy, London (020) 7330 3000
guy.beringer@allenovery.com
Specialisation: He has a wide experience of advising major corporations and financial institutions in relation to their commercial affairs. He has been closely involved in major cross-border M&A work arising from public take-over bids as well as purchases and sales of privately-owned companies and businesses. He has also been involved in the establishment of joint ventures and strategic alliances and has broad experience of commercial negotiations involving many industrial sectors.
Career: Associate, *Allen & Overy* 1980-85. Partner, *Allen & Overy* since 1985. Managing Partner, Corporate Department 1994-98. Head of the Corporate Department 1998-99. Senior Partner 2000.
Personal: Born 1955. MA Cambridge University, admitted as Solicitor 1980.

BERRY, Stephen
M and A Solicitors, Cardiff (029) 2066 5793
Specialisation: Corporate and commercial work. Transactions in the last twelve months include advising a consortium of United Kingdom and New Zealand investors on the acquisition of Glasgow Prestwick Airport from Stagecoach Group plc, advising the selling shareholders of Mono Equipment Limited on its sale to Glynwed International plc, a major fundraising by JDH Holdings Limited and various investments by the Wales Innovation Fund.
Career: 1991-93 *Herbert Smith*; 1993-99 *Eversheds*, appointed partner in 1998; 1999 present *M and A Solicitors*, one of the founding partners.
Personal: Married with two daughters. Lives in Cardiff and is a keen sportsman. He enjoys sailing, skiing, windsurfing, rugby and football.

BIRCHALL, Roger
Hammond Suddards Edge, Birmingham
(0121) 222 3000
roger.birchall@hammondse.com
Specialisation: Partner with *Hammonds Suddards Edge* and a member of the company/commercial department. From a background of general acquisition and disposal work, has particular expertise in management buy-out/buy-in transactions and the venture/development capital sector generally. Whilst he is well known for acting for management teams, he has substantial experience in acting for vendors and a number of the major providers of equity finance. Roger's experience ranges from small local, to large cross-border transactions.
Career: Hull University LLB (Hons). College of Law, Chester.

BIRT, Timothy D.
Osborne Clarke, London (020) 7809 1000

BLOWER, Geoffrey
Eversheds, Manchester (0161) 831 8000
geoffreyblower@eversheds.com
Specialisation: Partner in Corporate Department, *Eversheds*, Manchester. Main area of practice is Corporate Finance including mergers and acquisitions, flotations, management buy-outs, disposals, stock exchange and "Blue Book" work and non-contentious corporate work. Sector experience includes dairy industry, pharmaceuticals, leisure, automotive and engineering. Principal transactions include the Co-operative Wholesale Society's £111 million disposal of its Food Manufacturing Group; again for the Co-operative Wholesale Society spearheaded the team which dealt with the complex exchange of assets and businesses with Dale Farm Dairy Group where the total assets involved were £30m; Stanley Leisure plc in its £15 million recommended take-over of Gus Carter plc and its subsequent casino and betting shop acquisitions; for Kingspan Group in the acquisition of Kooltherm Holdings Limited and for United Northwest Co-operatives Limited in its acquisition of Hanburys Limited and its chain of 30 convenience stores and in the Society's acquisition of Nevins Limited and its 12 convenience store chain and a chain of 26 'Dawn til Dusk' convenience stores. He acted for Quicks Group plc in its acquisition of the Motor Retail Division of Caverdale Group plc (comprising some 30 companies) for £45.5 million with its attendant Rights Issue and Placing and for Granville Private Equity in its £20 million MBI of Ora Electronics UK Limited. His more recent deals include acting for Holidaybreak plc (formerly Eurocamp plc) in its £37.5 million recommended take-over of Baldwins plc and the subsequent disposal of Baldwins restaurant division; for the United Northwest Co-operatives and West Midlands Co-operative Society in the joint venture with First Choice plc in relation to the development 'Holiday Hypermarkets'; for Stanley Leisure plc in its attempted £350 million acquisition of the Coral betting business and the subsequent disposal of this interest for E4SM; and in its successful £86.4 million recommended take-over of Capital Corporation plc, and the acquisition of two internet casinos; for Holidaybreak in its £30 million acquisition of Explore Worldwide Limited and for United Norwest Co-operatives in its acquisition of SCI's Funeral Business in Northern Ireland.
Prof. Memberships: Law Society, Securities Institute.
Career: Qualified in 1972 and became a Partner in 1974.
Personal: Born 14th March 1948. Leisure pursuits include walking, cricket and theatre.

BOARDMAN, Nigel
Slaughter and May, London (020) 7600 1200
nigel.boardman@slaughterandmay.com
Specialisation: M&A, corporate finance, corporate and commercial. Advises UK and overseas companies and investment banks on the full range of corporate transactions, including acquisitions, disposals, takeovers, joint ventures, financings, flotations, MBOs and general corporate advice.
Career: Qualified in 1975 while with *Slaughter and May.* Joined the corporate finance department of *Kleinwort Benson Limited* before returning to *Slaughter and May*, becoming partner in 1982 and head of corporate in 1996.

BOND, Richard
Herbert Smith, London (020) 7374 8000
richard.bond@herbertsmith.com
Specialisation: Senior partner. Wide ranging experience of corporate transactions, particularly in the fields of energy and natural resources, utilities and privatisations.
Career: Qualified in 1969. Partner with *Herbert Smith* since 1977.

BOTT, Adrian
Olswang, London (020) 7208 8888
ajb@olswang.com
Specialisation: Partner in corporate group. Main area of practice is corporate finance. Since 1980, has been consistently involved in activities ranging from M&A, MBOs and MBIs, through flotations (including many on AIM), rights issues, placings and other means of financing, to private equity (acting for both providers and consumers), both in domestic and international transactions. Clients are predominantly quoted or subsidiaries of multinationals. Most have a technology, communications or media bias. Also active in significant corporate joint ventures (such as BBC Worldwide/Flextech and Carphone Warehouse/AOL) and a broad spectrum of commercial contracts and employee share schemes. Has handled numerous consortium arrangements, leading a variety of consortia in bids for various TV and radio broadcasting licences.
Prof. Memberships: Law Society, British Venture Capital Association.
Career: Qualified in 1980. *Rooks Rider* 1978-87, from 1984 as a partner. Partner at *Olswang* from 1988.
Personal: Born 9th June 1956. Charterhouse School 1969-73, Manchester University 1974-77 and Guildford Law School 1977.

BOUND, Andrew
Berry Smith, Cardiff (02920) 345511
abound@berrysmith.com
Specialisation: Full range of corporate and commercial work including acquisitions, MBOs, refinancing and joint venture arrangements.
Prof. Memberships: Law Society.
Career: Qualified in 1989. Articled at *Eversheds*, Cardiff. Joined *Berry Smith* in 1984 as a partner.
Personal: Born 25 March 1965. Educated at Reading University and Guildford College of Law. Interests include traveling and motor sports.

BOWCOCK, David
Eversheds, Manchester (0161) 831 8000
davidnbowcock@eversheds.com
Specialisation: IPO's, acquisitions, takeovers and fund raising.
Prof. Memberships: Law Society, Institute of Directors.
Career: 1990-94 *Eversheds*, Birmingham. 1994-97 *Bowcock Cuerden*, Chester. 1998-2001 *Eversheds*, Manchester.
Personal: Education: Birmingham University, Chester College of Law. Interests: cricket, golf, public speaking, scuba diving.

BRABNER, Michael
Brabners, Liverpool (0151) 600 3000
michael.brabner@brabners.com
Specialisation: Corporate/corporate finance.
Prof. Memberships: Law Society.
Career: Shrewsbury School; Liverpool University; qualified 1974. Worked in corporate department of *Herbert Oppenheimer Nathan & Van Dyke* 1974-76. Partner *Brabner Holden Banks Wilson* 1976 to date.

BRAHAM, Edward
Freshfields Bruckhaus Deringer, London (020) 7936 4000
edward.braham@freshfields.com
Specialisation: Partner in corporate department specialising in major cross-border mergers and acquisitions and corporate finance matters. In addition to the UK and USA, he has worked on transactions in many European countries and on various multi-jurisdictional acquisitions and disposals.
Prof. Memberships: Law Society.
Career: Qualified 1987, Partner 1995.
Personal: Born 1961. Educated at Worcester College, Oxford 1980-84 (BA, BCL).

BRAITHWAITE, Stephen
Wragge & Co, Birmingham (0870) 903 1000

BROOKSHAW, Oliver
Shoosmiths, Nottingham (0115) 906 5000
Specialisation: M&A/Corporate finance. Flotation of Northampton Saints plc (Rugby club); sale of 50%, and re-financing of London residential property company, London & Henley at £153million; Rawplug acquisition for BPB plc.
Prof. Memberships: Law Society, IoD. The City of London Solicitor Company (livery company).
Career: Trained with *Linklaters & Paines* (now *Linklaters & Alliance*). Qualified 1983. 1983 to 1989: solicitor in corporate department of *Linklaters & Paines*. Joined *Shoosmiths* in 1989, partner 1991. Head of Corporate Department.
Personal: Education: Uppingham School, Oriel College, Oxford. Member of the Honourable Artillery Company.

BRUCE, Roderick
Dickson Minto WS, Edinburgh (0131) 225 4455
roderick.bruce@dmws.com
Specialisation: General corporate, mergers and acquisitions, venture capital, re-organisation.
Prof. Memberships: Law Society of Scotland; Writer to the Signet.
Career: Boroughmuir Secondary School; Edinburgh University (LLB (Hons 2.1)).
Personal: Wife: Jane; Four children: 3 girls, 1 boy. Squash, skiing, golf, rugby (spectating), theatre.

BUCHAN, Gordon
Paull & Williamsons, Aberdeen (01224) 621621
gabuchan@paull-williamsons.co.uk
Specialisation: General corporate law, (particularly acquisitions and disposals) and oil and gas law.
Career: Qualified 1976; Partner in corporate department at *Paull and Williamsons* since 1981. Non-executive director of Aberdeen Football Club plc.
Personal: Born 1952.

BURROW, Robert
SJ Berwin, London (020) 7533 2777
robert.burrow@sjberwin.com
Specialisation: Partner in corporate finance department. Main area of practice is domestic and international merger and acquisition work.
Prof. Memberships: Law Society.
Career: Qualified in 1975. Joined *SJ Berwin* as a partner in 1985. Managing Director of J Rothschild & Co Ltd 1982-85.
Personal: Born 24th March 1951. Educated at Fitzwilliam College, Cambridge 1969-72. Leisure interests include cars, tennis, and skiing. Lives in Surrey.

BUTLER, Maurice
Johns Elliot, Belfast (028) 9032 6881
See under Construction, p.200

BUTLER-GALLIE, Stuart
Brachers, Maidstone (01622) 690691
Specialisation: Focuses entirely on M&A work, debt and equity funding, private equity transactions, AIM company work, joint ventures (UK and international), corporate reorganisations and reconstructions and general corporate work. Non-executive Director of AIM listed company.
Career: Articled *Denton Hall* 1988-90. Qualified *Denton Hall* 1990. Joined *Brachers* Jan 96. Partner May 97.
Personal: Born 1.3.64. St. Dunstan's College Catford. Sheffield University (LLB). Law School Chester. SSVC in Regular Army 1PWO (Prince of Wales's Own Regiment of Yorkshire). Married, five children. Local Borough Councillor. Cross country running, military history.

CADWALLADER, David
DLA, Liverpool (08700) 111111

CANAVAN, Kerry
Arthur Cox – Northern Ireland, Belfast (028) 9023 0007
kcanavan@arthurcox.ie
Specialisation: Company commercial including M&A's, fundraisings, commercial agreements.
Prof. Memberships: Law Society of Northern Ireland.
Career: Trained with *Slaughter and May*, post-qualification experience in a general company and commercial department; joined *Norman Wilson & Company* in Belfast 1993, which merged with *Arthur Cox* Northern Ireland in 1996.
Personal: Educated: Coleraine High School and St Catharine's College Cambridge.

CANN, Anthony
Linklaters, London (020) 7456 3592
anthony.cann@linklaters.com
Specialisation: Specialist in UK corporate finance and company law, advising both corporate clients and investment and merchant banks; main areas of practice include public and private mergers and acquisitions, issues, joint ventures and general corporate advice.
Career: Educated Shewsbury School; Southampton University (1969 LLB Hons). Articled *Linklaters* 1970-72; qualified 1972; *Linklaters* New York 1975-82; partner since 1978. Head of corporate department 1995-2000 and co-head of the M&A and corporate practice area of *Linklaters & Alliance* since 1998. Senior partner of *Linklaters* from October 2001.

CHATFIELD, James H.T.
Rawlison Butler, Crawley (01293) 527744

CHERRY, Robert
Morgan Cole, Swansea (01792) 634634

CHESTER, Martin
Theodore Goddard, London (020) 7606 8855
martinchester@theodoregoddard.co.uk
Specialisation: Corporate finance, including mergers and acquisitions, public offerings, flotations, share capital and debt restructuring, investment trusts, corporate governance and general corporate advice. Major transactions include the Lloyds TSB merger, reorganisation of the 5 classes of share capital of the Signet Group plc into a single class, the disposals by Blagden plc of its packaging division, chemical manufacturing and distribution businesses and its winding up and the acquisition by Nedbank of Fleming (Jersey) Limited.
Career: Qualified 1967. Partner in *Theodore Goddard* since 1972. Chairman of the Company Law Sub-Committee of the City of London Law Society 1990-93 and of the Law Society's Company Law Committee 1993-96 (remains a member of each and leads a number of their working parties). Outside expert on the working party on corporate capital maintenance of the UK Company Law Review. Educated at St. Albans School and Exeter University.
Personal: Leisure interests include swimming, scuba diving and enjoying good food and wine.

CHEYNE, David
Linklaters, London (020) 7456 3164
david.cheyne@linklaters.com
Specialisation: Involved in a wide range of corporate transactions including M&A work, flotations, general corporate finance work and Stock Exchange related matters.
Career: Qualified 1974. Became a partner in 1980. Partner *Linklaters* Hong Kong office 1981-86. Head of *Linklaters* corporate department.

CHILDS, David
Clifford Chance, London (020) 7600 1000

CHOHAN, Baljit
Wragge & Co, Birmingham (0870) 903 1000

CLARK, Adrian
Ashurst Morris Crisp, London (020) 7638 1111
adrian.clark@ashursts.com
Specialisation: Company Department.
Career: Educated – Peterhouse, Cambridge (MA). Qualified 1983. *Slaughter and May* 1981-86; *Ashurst Morris Crisp* 1986 onwards. Partner 1990. Seconded to Take-over Panel 1988-90.

CLARK, Tim
Slaughter and May, London (020) 7600 1200
tim.clark@slaughterand may.com
Specialisation: Senior Partner. Principal area of practice is UK and international corporate work, cor-

porate finance and mergers and acquisitions (including public takeovers, flotations, international equity offerings), advising corporate and investment bank clients. Practice also involves demutualisations (building societies and insurance companies).
Prof. Memberships: The Law Society.
Career: Qualified 1976 with *Slaughter and May.* Became partner in 1983; senior partner 2001.
Personal: Born 9 January 1951. Educated at Sherborne School and Pembroke College, Cambridge. Interests include theatre, sport, Italy and flying. Lives in London.

CLARKE, Tim
Linklaters, London (020) 7456 3304
tim.clarke@linklaters.com
Specialisation: Specialist in UK corporate finance and company law, with a particular experience of privatisations internationally. Main areas of practice include public and private mergers and acquisitions, issues, joint ventures, general corporate advice and privatisations.
Career: 1971-72: College of Law, Law Society Part 2; 1968-71: Cambridge University BA, Law. 1982 to date: partner and head of international privatisations *Linklaters*; 1974-82: assistant solicitor *Linklaters*; 1972-74 articled clerk, *Linklaters.*

COOKE, Darryl
Addleshaw Booth & Co, Manchester (0161) 934 6000

COOKE, Stephen
Slaughter and May, London (020) 7600 1200
stephen.cooke@slaughterandmay.com
Specialisation: Partner in company/commercial department. Principal area of practice is company and commercial work with a particular emphasis on M&A.
Prof. Memberships: The Law Society.
Career: Qualified in 1984 while with *Slaughter and May.* Worked in the New York office 1989-90; became a partner in 1991 and head of M&A in 2001. Publications include 'Takeovers' (Legal & Commercial Publishing, 1997).
Personal: Born 7 March 1959. Educated Lincoln College, Oxford (1978-81). Lives in London.

COOMBS, Richard
Foot Anstey Sargent, Exeter (01392) 411221
richard.coombs@foot-ansteys.co.uk
Specialisation: Partner in charge of company commercial team. Corporate finance, mergers, acquisitions, MBOs, MBIs, share schemes, FSA compliance, friendly societies.
Prof. Memberships: IOD, Chamber of Commerce.
Career: Qualified 1979. *Clifford Chance* 1977-80, *Turner Kenneth Brown* 1980-81, *British Coal* 1981-85, *Bond Pearce* 1985-94 (partner from 1988). Joined *Foot Anstey Sargent* as partner in 1994.
Personal: Born 16 March 1954. Attended Kings School Chester, Cardiff High School, Downing College, Cambridge (First in Law). Interests: walking and music. Lives in Ivybridge.

COOPER, Paul
Osborne Clarke, Bristol (0117) 917 3000

COPPIN, Jonathan
Norton Rose, London (020) 7283 6000
coppinjds@nortonrose.com
Specialisation: Main area of practice is corporate finance in particular mergers and acquisitions, flotations and international securities offerings.
Prof. Memberships: Member of the Law Society's Company Law Committee.
Career: Articled at *Norton Rose* 1987-89, Partner Corporate Finance Department *Norton Rose* 1996.
Publications: Author of numerous articles in professional publications.
Personal: Married (Lucy). Hobbies include sailing and running.

CRABTREE, John
Wragge & Co, Birmingham (0870) 903 1000

CRAIG, Alexander
Halliwell Landau, Manchester (0161) 835 3003
Specialisation: Senior Partner. Specialises in all corporate finance work. Work includes MBOs and MBIs, and flotations, mergers, sales and acquisitions. Specialist in institutional fundraising in the technology area. Has spoken at numerous seminars and conferences.
Prof. Memberships: Law Society, Institute of Management, Securities Institute.
Career: Qualified in 1985, joining *Halliwell Landau* in the same year. Became a Partner in 1989. Senior Partner 2000.
Personal: Born 28th September 1957. Attended Sheffield University 1979-82 then College of Law, London 1983. Public Company non executive director. Leisure interests include football, squash and fell walking. Lives in Alderley Edge.

CRANFIELD, Richard
Allen & Overy, London (020) 7330 3200
richard.cranfield@allenovery.com
Specialisation: Head of Corporate Department. Has a wide range of corporate finance experience including domestic and cross-border mergers and acquisitions, privatisations and buy-outs and capital markets work for equity and debt financings. He lead the *Allen & Overy* team which advised the DTI on the privatisation of British Energy, the team which advised Cable & Wireless on the formation of Cable & Wireless Communications in 1996 and its division into two in 1999/2000, the sale of their interests in One2One to Deutsche Telekom and the sale of Hong Kong Telecom to PCCW. He is currently advising DFID on the public/private partnership for Commonwealth Development Corporation.
Career: Articled (Allen & Overy) 1978, qualified 1980, Partner 1985, Head of Corporate Department 1999, *(Allen & Overy).*
Personal: Born 1956. Educated at Winchester College and Fitzwilliam College, Cambridge. Married with four children.

CROOME, Andrew
Eversheds, Norwich (01603) 272727
andrewcroome@eversheds.com
Specialisation: Non-contentious company and banking work, handling a wide variety of matters for lenders and borrowers.
Career: Qualified in 1978 with *Allen & Overy.* Joined *Eversheds* in 1979 becoming a partner in 1982.
Personal: Born in Essex in 1954. Educated in Essex, Suffolk and at Trinity Hall, Cambridge. Lives in North Norfolk.

CUMMINGS, Gavin
Browne Jacobson, Nottingham (0115) 976 6000
gcummings@brownej.co.uk
Specialisation: Corporate finance specialising in MBIs, MBOs, IBOs, disposals, mergers and acquisitions and private equity. Recent transactions include the MBO of Staffline Recruitment and disposal of the Stancliffe Group.
Prof. Memberships: Law Society.
Career: Articled *Browne Jacobson.* Qualified 1994. Partner 2000.
Personal: Born 1970, Stamford; educated at Stamford School and Nottingham University (BA Hons Law) Interests: football, cricket, golf.

CUNNINGHAM, Kevin
Irwin Mitchell, Leeds (0113) 234 3333
cunningham@irwinmitchell.co.uk
Specialisation: Corporate finance, mergers and acquisitions, buy outs and venture capital.
Prof. Memberships: The Law Society.
Career: Qualified 1979. Joined *Irwin Mitchell* 1983. Partner 1985 and appointed to Management Board in 1989.
Personal: Born 1956. Interests include tennis and skiing.

CUNNINGHAM, Neil
MacRoberts, Glasgow (0141) 332 9988
neil.cunningham@macroberts.co.uk
Specialisation: Corporate finance, mergers and acquisitions, reconstructions and partnership law. Recent deals include acting for Keydata UK Ltd in connection with its equity fund raising; acting for Wylies (1989) Ltd in its merger with Eleander Ltd; acting for Glenvarigill Company Limited in connection with several acquisitions.
Prof. Memberships: Law Society of Scotland, Institute of Chartered Accountants in England & Wales, Institute of Chartered Accountants of Scotland.
Career: Price Waterhouse, Chartered Accountants, London and Glasgow 1984-88; *Ledingham Chalmers,* Solicitors, Aberdeen 1989-91; *MacRoberts,* Solicitors, Glasgow 1991 – to date (became a partner in 1995), head of corporate group.
Personal: Born August 6, 1964. Married with three daughters. Leisure interests include golf, football and squash.

DA COSTA, Alastair
DLA, Leeds (08700) 111111

DARWIN, Andrew
DLA, Sheffield (08700) 111111

DAVIDSON, John
Lovells, London (020) 7296 2000
john.davidson@lovells.com
Specialisation: Is a member of Lovells' corporate finance group, specialising in public and private UK and cross-border mergers and acquisitions and joint ventures, international equity offerings and private equity investments, and is a member of the firm's market-leading corporate insurance practice. Recent major transactions have included advising South African Breweries plc on its £4 billion listing on the London Stock Exchange and its admission to the FTSE 100 Index in March 1999 and its US $500 million convertible bond offering in July 2001, AEGON UK plc on its £759 million acquisition of Guardian Life in September 1999, and Goldman Sachs International as sponsor of the £1.4 billion IPO of Egg plc in June 2000.
Career: Articled *Lovells,* qualified 1985; partner 1991; resident partner New York office 1991-95.

DAVIS, James
Freshfields Bruckhaus Deringer, London
(020) 7936 4000
james.davis@freshfields.com
Specialisation: Corporate finance, acting for companies and investment bank on M&A and equity issues. Clients include Cinven, Compass, Hays, Logica, Scottish and Southern Energy and Wolseley.
Career: Balliol College, Oxford. Partner since 1976.
Personal: Wife (Sally) and four children. Interests include golf and fishing.

DAVISON, Andrew J
Eversheds, Newcastle upon Tyne (0191) 261 1661
andrewdavison@eversheds.com
Specialisation: Partner in corporate department. General company law with particular reference to public company, corporate finance, and mergers and acquisitions work.
Prof. Memberships: Chairman of Law Society Standing Committee on Company Law. Member of DTI Company Law Review Consultative Committee. Member of London Stock Exchange Primary Markets Group.
Career: Qualified in 1985, becoming a partner in 1986.

DAWES, Edward
Wragge & Co, Birmingham (0870) 903 1000

DEAN, Kevin
Sinclair Roche & Temperley, London
(020) 7452 4149
kjdean@srtlaw.com
Specialisation: Head of Company/Commercial Department. General Practice consists principally of acting for corporate clients, investment institutions and government and international bodies. Has considerable experience of UK and international merger and acquisition work, corporate finance, joint ventures and privatisations. In recent years he has concentrated on contentious UK M&A, advising active fund management groups and clients in the international transportation and leisure sectors. He has also been widely involved in international restructurings, recently including Daewoo and Harland & Wolff. Is also very involved in shareholder democracy matters and has extensive knowledge of the SME and private equity worlds.
Prof. Memberships: Law Society, IBA.
Career: Qualified in 1979. Joined *Sinclair Roche & Temperley* in 1984, becoming a partner in 1985. Previously worked at *Nabarro Nathanson* and *Clifford-Turner.*
Personal: Born in 1954. Educated at High Wycombe RGS and Lincoln College, Oxford University (MA, Jurisprudence). Lives in Islington. Leisure interests include defending his castle in Umbria and, cricket and rugby.

DEANE, David
Semple Fraser, Glasgow (0141) 221 3771
david.deane@semplefraser.co.uk
Specialisation: Corporate finance, venture capital, acquisitions, joint ventures. He has also gained extensive experience in a wide range of corporate transactions including business start-ups, company formations, partnerships and management buy-outs.
Prof. Memberships: Law Society of Scotland.
Career: Articled *Bird Semple Fyfe Ireland* 1986-88; legal assistant *Bird Semple Fyfe Ireland* 1988-90; legal assistant *McGrigor Donald* 1990-94; partner *Henderson Boyd Jackson* 1994-98; partner *Semple Fraser WS* 1998.
Personal: Born 26 August 1964. Educated at Kelvinside Academy and Aberdeen University. Interests include golf, rugby and Partick Thistle Football Club. Married with three children. Lives in Glasgow.

DEVITT, Paul
Addleshaw Booth & Co, Manchester
(0161) 934 6000
pyd@addleshaw-booth.co.uk
Specialisation: Partner in corporate finance group. Company and corporate finance, with particular specialisation in public company and public issue work: flotations; public issues; takeovers; other public company/stock exchange-related advice; acquisitions and disposals of companies and businesses.
Prof. Memberships: Law Society; London Stock Exchange Regional Advisory Group – North West.
Career: Qualified 1988. Joined the firm in 1993. Partner from 1995.
Personal: Educated at University of Bristol (LL.B). Lives in Wilmslow. Trustee of the Lowry Centre.

DICKSON, Ian
MacRoberts, Glasgow (0141) 332 9988
ian.dickson@macroberts.co.uk
Specialisation: Partner in corporate group. Although principal area of practice is corporate law and corporate finance, also practises in electricity (and in particular) nuclear energy law. Acts for British Energy.
Prof. Memberships: Law Society of Scotland, International Bar Association, American Bar Association, Institute of Directors.
Career: Qualified 1971. Joined *MacRoberts* in 1973. Partner in 1977, now its chairman. Non-executive director of Johnston Press plc (1987-2000).
Personal: Born 10 April 1950. Attended Hillhead High School, Glasgow 1962-68; then Strathclyde University 1968-71. Chairman of Friends of the Beatson Oncology Centre. Leisure interests include music, golf and football. Lives in Glasgow.

DIX, John
Hewitson Becke + Shaw, Cambridge
(01223) 461155
johndix@hewitsons.com
Specialisation: Main area of practice is corporate finance work: acquisitions, disposals, MBOs/MBIs and venture capital funding. Acts for two venture capital providers and many high technology and biotech companies.
Prof. Memberships: Law Society.
Career: University of Sydney BA(Hons) and LLB. Solicitor New South Wales 1986. Qualified in UK 1991. *Hewitson Becke + Shaw* since 1988. Partner 1996.
Personal: Born 1961. Resides Cambridge.

DOWNS, William N
Hammond Suddards Edge, Manchester
(0161) 830 5000
william.downs@hammondse.com
Specialisation: Merger and acquisition work, flotations and listed company work generally. Head of firm's utilities group. Recent transactions include acting for Innogy Holdings plc on M&A work, acting for Co-operative Wholesale Society Limited on the merger with CRS, acting for Torotrak plc on its demerger from BTG plc.
Prof. Memberships: Law Society, RSA.
Career: Bradford Grammar School; Downing College, Cambridge.
Personal: Golf, tennis, gardening. Married with three children.

DREW, Dean
Shoosmiths, Reading (0118) 965 8765
dean.drew@shoosmiths.co.uk
Specialisation: Mergers and acquisitions, venture and development capital, MBO's and joint ventures, particularly in the technology sector. Clients include major US corporates, technology start-ups and other emerging companies. Acts for Thames Water and for the sellers of a software company to Great Plains Software, Inc for $38million in cash and shares, closing the deal in under a week.
Prof. Memberships: Law Society.
Career: Trained in London, qualified in 1990 and joined *Shoosmiths* in 1995 becoming a partner in 1997 and head of the Thames Valley corporate team in 1998.
Personal: Educated at Leeds University. Leisure interests include music, swimming and gardening. Married with three children. Lives in Newbury.

DWYER, Maurice
Wragge & Co, Birmingham (0870) 903 1000

EASTGATE, Andrew
Pinsent Curtis Biddle, Birmingham
(0121) 200 1050
andrew.eastgate@pinsents.com
Specialisation: Partner and Head of Corporate in Birmingham. Acts predominantly for quoted companies including Glanbia, Severn Trent, Castings, Booker, Misys and Fountain Forestry. Recent deals include acting for iSOFT Group plc on its flotation on the London Stock Exchange which valued the company at £123 million and for Deloitte & Touche on the AIM flotation of Compass Software.
Prof. Memberships: Law Society.
Career: Qualified in 1980. Assistant Solicitor with *Stephenson Harwood* 1980-83. *Pinsent & Co.* from 1983. Partner in 1985 and Head of Corporate, Birmingham in 1997.
Personal: Born 1956. Attended Uppingham School and Mansfield College, Oxford.

ELDER, Ian
Allen & Overy, London (020) 7330 3044
ian.elder@allenovery.com
See under Energy & Natural Resources, p.354

ELLARD, John
Linklaters, London (020) 7456 3324
john.ellard@linklaters.com
Specialisation: Significant experience in corporate finance, international equity issues and privatisations. Transactions of significance where substantial involvement can be disclosed have included advising the UK government on all three stages of the privatisation of British Telecommunications plc (1982-84, 1991, 1993 (team leader); advising the UK government on the privatisation of the UK passenger rail industry and European Passenger Services 1992-97 (team leader 1996 onwards); advising the UK government on the Thameslink 2000 and West Coast Main Line rail infrastructure projects 1996 to date; advising the global co-ordinators of the Wellcome (1992) and Elf (1994) global share offers, the government of the Netherlands on the privatisation of KPN (1994(, the Republic of Italy on the privatisation of Telecom Italia

(1997) and the global co-ordinators on the privatisation of Telecom Eireann (1998 to date); advising Coca-Cola beverages on its demerger from Coca-Cola Amatil and listing on the London Stock Exchange, the second largest equity offer of 1998, and on its proposed acquisition by Hellenic Bottling SA; advising the Tube Rail Consortium on its bid for the London Underground public/private partnership and advising a consortium bidding for the Dutch High Speed Link Infrastructure project; advising the Shadow Strategic Rail Authority on the rail franchise renegotiation programme. Also advised on the privatisations of Associated British Ports, BP, British Airways, Jaguar, Wessex Water, the UK Regional Electricity Companies, National Power plc and PowerGen plc and Forth Ports.
Career: 1971-74 Trinity Hall Cambridge M.A. Law (First Class Honours). 1989 to date partner *Linklaters* London, corporate department; 1986-89 partner *Linklaters* New York; 1983-86 partner *Linklaters* London tax department; 1977-83 assistant solicitor *Linklaters* tax department; 1975-77 articled clerk *Linklaters.*

EMMERSON, Tim
Freshfields Bruckhaus Deringer, London (020) 7936 4000
tim.emmerson@freshfields.com
Specialisation: Mergers and acquisitions, IPOs, securities and derivatives law. Legal adviser to the Takeover Panel (on Takeover Code issues) and to numerous investment banks and companies on a wide range of commercial matters including numerous takeovers and IPOs.
Career: BA (Hons) Law (First), Sussex University; MA EC Law (First), College of Europe, Bruges.

EMMETT, Paul
Walker Morris, Leeds (0113) 283 2500
pde@walkermorris.co.uk
Specialisation: Partner in Corporate Department. Principal area of practice is corporate finance, mergers and acquisitions. Work includes flotations, rights issues, other forms of equity financing, acquisitions and disposals. Other main area of practice is general corporate advice. Important transactions have included the £30 million demergers of Collins and Hayes Group plc and Airbath Group plc from Aquarius Group plc, the £300 million demerger of TeamTalk.com from IMS Group plc, £190 million flotation of Newcastle United plc, £150 million offer by TOTAL for the minority shareholdings in Kalon Group plc, £35 million acquisition of Sheffield Forgemasters Group Limited, £41 million acquisition of The Decorative Holding Company Limited by Roseby's plc, £23 million acquisition of North Shoe Limited by Brown & Jackson plc and £75 million offer by BUPA for Goldsborough Healthcare plc. Author of several articles in the *Yorkshire Post* and legal journals. Has spoken at seminars on Stock Exchange listing rules and director's duties.
Prof. Memberships: Law Society.
Career: Qualified in 1987. With *Slaughter and May* 1985-91. Joined *Walker Morris* in 1991 and became a Partner in 1993.
Personal: Born 7th November 1961. Educated at Cheadle Hulme School, Cheshire 1974-80 and King's College, London University 1981-84. Lives in Leeds.

EVANS, Michael
Greenwoods, Peterborough (01733) 887700

EVANS, Stuart
Simmons & Simmons, London (020) 7628 2020
stuart.evans@simmons-simmons.com
Specialisation: Head of Corporate Finance at *Simmons & Simmons.* Led teams advising: Interbrew on its £2.7 billion acquisition of the beer businesses of Whitbread and Bass; Pacific Century CyberWorks on its US$27 billion acquisition of Cable and Wireless HKT; Wal-Mart on its £6.8 billion acquisition of Asda.
Career: Qualified in 1972. With *Slaughter and May* 1972-79. Joined *Simmons & Simmons* in 1979, Partner since 1981.
Publications: Chapter on Transactions in 'A Practitioner's Guide to the FSA Listing Rules' 2000/2001 edition. Former Chairman Patrons of New Art Tate Gallery; director of HBV Enterprise; trustee start 2000; Chair Islington International Festival and Reader St Stephen's, Canonbury.
Personal: Born 31st December 1947. Educated Royal Grammar School, Newcastle-upon-Tyne 1956-66, Leeds University 1966-69.

FAGELSON, Ian B.
Reed Smith Warner Cranston, London (020) 7403 2900

FALKUS, Bryony
Mills & Reeve, Norwich (01603) 693225
bryony.falkus@mills-reeve.com
Specialisation: Partner in corporate department. Work covers acquisitions and sales, MBOs, MBIs, reconstructions, offers of securities and UKLA work. Also handles corporate insolvency generally and in particular receiverships and administrations, acting for banks, specialised lending institutions and insolvency practitioners.
Prof. Memberships: Law Society.
Career: Qualified 1976; partner *Pickering Kenyon* 1980; partner *Mills & Reeve* 1992.

FEECHAN, Catherine
Biggart Baillie, Glasgow (0141) 228 8000
cfeechan@biggartballie.co.uk
Specialisation: Specialist in corporate finance placing, aim/listed company work, equity investments, acquisition and disposals. Major deals in 2000/2001: sale of Atlantech Technologies Ltd to Cisco Systems Inc for US $180m. Admission to Official List, Planning & Open Offer for AorTech International plc to raise £20m.
Prof. Memberships: Law Society of Scotland, Law Society of England & Wales.
Career: Glasgow University LLB (Hons) 1991. Trained at *Dickson Minto* 1991-93. Assistant at *Dundas & Wilson* 1993-95. *Biggart Ballie* 1995 to date.
Personal: Born 12/4/68, attended Wellington School, Ayr and Glasgow University. Married in 1996, interests include cinema, food and travel.

FERNANDEZ LEWIS, Jon
MLM, Cardiff (029) 2046 2562
jfl@mlmsolicitors.com
Specialisation: Corporate finance including venture capital and loan funding, both for providers and recipients of such funding, company and business acquisitions and disposals, corporate reorganisation and refinanceing. Acts for Wesley Clover Corporation and Celtic House, subtantial private equity funds providing seed and development capital to telecoms technology companies.
Prof. Memberships: Law Society and local Law Society.
Career: Articled at *Morgan Bruce*, qualified 1984. Partner in *Eversheds Phillips & Buck* 1988 to 1993. Partner in *Rubin Lewis O'Brien* 1993-98. Partner in *Bevan Ashford* 1998 to 2001. Partner in *MLM* since April 2001.
Personal: Born 1958. Educated at Bushey Meads School, Hertfordshire and University College, Cardiff. Lives in Cardiff. Married with a daughter. Leisure interests include playing golf and tennis, watching football and rugby.

FISCHL, Nicolas
Mills & Reeve, Norwich (01603) 693223
nick.fischl@mills-reeve.com
Specialisation: MBOs, MBIs, private equity, joint ventures. Also facilities management and other computer/IT agreements.
Prof. Memberships: Law Society, Norfolk and Norwich Law Society.
Career: Qualified with *Clifford Turner* 1979. Joined *Mills & Reeve* in 1984. Partner *Mills & Reeve* 1986.
Personal: MA (Cantab)

FITZGERALD, Sean
Chaffe Street, Manchester (0161) 211 9231
dsf@chaffestreet.co.uk
Specialisation: Corporate finance including mergers and acquisitions, venture and development capital and management buy-outs and buy-ins.
Prof. Memberships: Law Society.
Career: Articled at *James Chapman & Co.* Qualified in 1984. Joined *Chaffe Street* in 1988. Became a partner in 1991.
Personal: Born 22nd January 1960. Attended St Bede's College, Manchester and Hull University. Leisure interests include golf, cricket and football. Lives in Greenmount, Lancashire.

FITZSIMONS, Gerry
Garretts, Cambridge (01223) 535225
gerry.fitzsimons@glegal.com
Specialisation: Corporate transactions with particular specialism in private equity. Has led a number of substantial transactions in 2000 including, in particular, the £542 million IPO of TTP Communications plc and £92 million merger of The Astron Group and e-doc Group plc. Acts for a number of technology funds including Amadeus, TTP Ventures, First Cambridge Gateway Fund and Technomark/Lloyds TSB Development Capital. Has wide experience of private equity transactions in the technology sector in which these funds specialise. Also acts for investee companies such as Metris Therapeutics Limited in its recent £11 million financing led by Schroder Ventures.
Prof. Memberships: The Law Society.
Career: 1982-84, trainee, *Coward Chance*; 1984-85, *Shearman & Sterling*, New York; 1986-87, *Clifford Chance*; 1987-96, *Taylor Vinters*; 1996-present, Senior Partner, *Garretts*, Cambridge.
Personal: Born 28 October 1959. Educated Cranbrook School, Kent; Oxford University.

FLYNN, John
Dickinson Dees, Newcastle upon Tyne (0191) 279 9252
john.flynn@dickinson-dees.com
Specialisation: Partner in corporate finance department. Work includes mergers and acquisitions, flotations, rights issues and similar related Stock Exchange work, as well as joint ventures. Acted in the acquisition of Thameslink and Thames Trains rail

franchises, the £300 million acquisition by Arriva of British Bus and the £513 million sale by Arriva of AAS. Led the team voted UK Regional Corporate Team of the Year by Legal Business Magazine. Recently led the team which successfully defended the hostile bid by C3D for long-standing client Go-Ahead, believed to be the most comprehensive defeat of a hostile bid.
Prof. Memberships: Law Society.
Career: Qualified in 1979. Joined *Dickinson Dees* in 1981, becoming a partner in 1986.

FRANCIES, Michael
Weil, Gotshal & Manges, London (020) 7903 1000

FRIER, George
McClure Naismith, Glasgow (0141) 204 2700
gfrier@McClureNaismith.com
Specialisation: Partner, corporate finance and commercial/tax/VAT. Handles complex negotiations for commercial contracts specialising in MBOs/MBIs, mergers, banking, trade acquisitions and sales, insolvency and shareholder disputes. Recent deals include acting for management in the £20 million IBO of McLaren Consulting Limited from ISI Group plc; acting for a vendor shareholder in the £19.5 million sale of Anchor International Limited to an IBO led by 3i Group plc; acting for Plexus Corp (USA) in its £17.5 million acquisition of Keltek (Holdings) Limited; MBI of GOALS Soccer Centres Ltd.
Career: Trained *Dorman Jeffrey*, qualified 1987, assistant *Maclay Murray & Spens* 1987-93, associate *McClure Naismith* 1993-94, partner 1994.
Personal: Born 1962, resides Glasgow. Educated at Morrison's Acadamy, Glasgow University (1984 LLB Hons Private Law). Leisure pursuits include hill walking, family, theatre, cycling and bad golf.

FULTON, Richard
Mills Selig, Belfast (028) 9024 3878
richard.fulton@nilaw.com
Specialisation: Main areas of practice are mergers, acquisitions and disposals, joint ventures, corporate finance generally and distribution and agency agreements. Represents three major venture capital houses. Has extensive experience in mergers and acquisitions and joint ventures both locally and internationally.
Prof. Memberships: Law Society of Northern Ireland.
Career: Queens University, Belfast LLB 1976. Qualified England and Wales 1980. Qualified Northern Ireland 1990. Formerly Senior Company/Commercial Partner with *Blaser Mills*. Joined *Mills Selig* 1991.
Personal: Windsurfing, countryside, literature. Lives outside Belfast.

GARNETT, Chris J
Eversheds, Birmingham (0121) 232 1000
Specialisation: Mergers and acquisitions, flotations public company share issues and takeovers, corporate reconstructions and joint ventures.
Prof. Memberships: Law Society.
Career: Birmingham University. Articled to *Eversheds* (formerly *Evershed & Tomkinson*) 1983-85, associate 1989, partner 1992.
Personal: Married to Kathryn; with 2 children, Daniel (aged 8) and Anna (aged 6). A keen interest in natural history, particularly ornithology, and enjoys playing tennis and watching football and cricket.

GARSTON, Clive
Halliwell Landau, Manchester (0161) 835 3003
Specialisation: Specialises in all aspects of corporate finance and general corporate work, particularly mergers and acquisitions and flotations.
Prof. Memberships: Law Society, International Bar Association, American Bar Association, Institute of Directors.
Career: Articled at *Hall Brydon* qualified 1968, partner 1971, partner *Halliwell Landau* 1978. Senior Partner (1989-95).
Personal: Education: Manchester Grammar School, Leeds University (1965 LL.B). Born 1945, resides Hale, Cheshire, enjoys cricket & football.

GEE, Tim
Baker & McKenzie, London (020) 7919 1000
timothy.gee@bakernet.com
Specialisation: Public and private company M&A, privatisation and equity capital markets transactions, acting for underwriters and issuers. Extensive cross-border and emerging markets experience. Identified as one of the UK's leading privatisation lawyers in Euromoney's 'Guide to the World's Leading Privatisation Lawyers' and as one of the UK's leading M&A lawyers in Euromoney's 'Guide to the World's Leading Mergers and Acquisitions Lawyers'. Head of *Baker & McKenzie*'s Global M&A Practice Group.
Prof. Memberships: The Law Society; City of London Solicitors Company.
Career: Educated at Worcester College, Oxford. Qualified in 1986 with *Baker & McKenzie*. 1989-90 *Baker & McKenzie*, Hong Kong. 1991 *Baker & McKenzie*, Budapest. Partner in 1992.
Personal: Married with two sons. Interests include rugby and fly fishing.

GIBB, Stephen
Shepherd & Wedderburn WS, Edinburgh (0131) 228 9900
stephen.gibb@shepwedd.co.uk
Specialisation: Partner in the corporate department.
Prof. Memberships: Institute of Directors, Writer to the Signet.
Career: Trained *Bird Fyfe Ireland*, qualified 1988 (Scotland), 1993 (England and Wales), 1995 (WS); assistant *Bird Semple Fyfe Ireland* 1988-91; associate *Bird Semple Fyfe Ireland* 1991-93; associate *Fyfe Ireland* 1994; partner 1994-99; partner *Shepherd & Wedderburn* 1999.
Personal: Education: King's Park; Glasgow University (1985 LLB Hons). Born: 1964. Resides: Edinburgh. Leisure: Football, guitar, music, children (own).

GILBERT, Ian
Walker Morris, Leeds (0113) 283 2500
img@walkermorris.co.uk
Specialisation: Partner in Corporate Department. Main area of practice is corporate finance, management buy-outs and venture capital. Has been involved in venture capital and development capital for 17 years, acting on both sides. Involved in numerous MBOs of varying size and complexity, including take privates, as well as public and private company acquisitions and disposals, flotations, joint ventures, and share issues.
Career: Qualified in 1981. With 3i Group plc 1979-85. Joined *Walker Morris* in 1985 and became a Partner in 1986.
Personal: Born 22nd July 1957. Educated at Sheffield University 1975-78. Recreations include tennis, walking, golf and unpaid taxi driver for children. Lives in Follifoot.

GILTHORPE, Ian
Robert Muckle, Newcastle upon Tyne (0191) 232 4402
Specialisation: Partner in commercial department. Managing Partner. Main area of practice is corporate finance, including MBOs, acquisitions, disposals, sources of finance, debt re-structuring and flotation.
Career: Qualified in 1978. Partner 1979. Current non-executive directorships: QSP Group plc; Vald Birn (UK) Ltd, Mercantile Building Society.

GLEN, Marian
Shepherd & Wedderburn WS, Edinburgh (0131) 228 9900
marian.glen@shepwedd.co.uk
Specialisation: Partner in corporate finance, specialising in mergers and acquisitions and joint ventures; recent deals include acting for Friends Ivory & Sime plc in the £128.9 million acquisition from Friends Provident of their retail investment business (Friends' Provident Unit Trust Managers Limited), their managed pension fund business (Friends Ivory & Sime Managed Pensions Funds Limited) and as a company engaged in the marketing of investment trusts and other retail investment products (Ivory & Sime TrustLink Limited); and acting for Scottish Power UK plc in setting up of a joint venture company with United Utilities plc, Northern Electric plc and The Electricity Supply Board to administer competitive tendering processes for the procurement of certain products.
Prof. Memberships: Institute of Directors; British/German Jurists Association.
Career: Trained at *Dundas & Wilson*, Edinburgh; qualified 1989; solicitor *Linklaters & Paines*, London, 1989-94; joined *Shepherd & Wedderburn* 1994; partner 1996.
Personal: Education: Notre Dame High School, Glasgow/Glasgow University (1983 MA Hons French and German); Edinburgh University (1987 LLB). Born 1960; resides Edinburgh. Leisure: hill walking, golf and travel. Languages: French and German.

GODDEN, Richard
Linklaters, London (020) 7456 3610
richard.godden@linklaters.com
Specialisation: Has wide experience both in general corporate advisory work and corporate transactions. Advises a wide range of corporate clients and merchant and investment banks in connection with public mergers and takeovers, the establishment of joint ventures, private merger and acquisition transactions, flotations, other corporate equity fund raising, and advises corporations of various sizes in relation to their on-going affairs (e.g. issues connected with general meetings, scrip dividend schemes, removal of directors, etc).
Career: 1990 to date: Partner, corporate department, *Linklaters*; 1988-90: Secretary to takeover panel; 1987-88: Assistant solicitor, corporate department, *Linklaters* London; 1985-87: Assistant solicitor, *Linklaters* Hong Kong; 1982-85: Assistant solicitor, commercial department, *Linklaters* London; 1980-82: Trainee solicitor, *Linklaters* London. 1979-80: College of Law; 1976-79: Trinity Hall, Cambridge University, MA First Class.

GODFREY, Christopher
Burges Salmon, Bristol (0117) 939 2219
chris.godfrey@burges-salmon.com
Specialisation: Corporate finance. Chris also heads *Burges Salmon's* practice in the field of investment funds, where the firm has a specialism, unique among English regional firms, in the area of collective investment schemes. In recent months Chris has advised on deals including: schemes of arrangement to merge two co-operatives with, together, 12 000 members; flotation of SignCorp plc; flotation of IFTE plc; hostile bid for Newport Holdings plc; investment in Insignia Technologies by 3i.
Prof. Memberships: Law Society.
Career: Trained with *Linklaters*, qualifying in 1986, and joining *Burges Salmon* later that year, becoming a partner in 1990.
Personal: Jurisprudence, Hertford College, Oxford 1980-83.

GOODALL, Caroline
Herbert Smith, London (020) 7374 8000
Specialisation: Specialises in corporate work in particular corporate finance and mergers and acquisitions. She has been involved, as an adviser to both companies and to investment banks, in numerous takeovers (hostile and agreed), international mergers and acquisitions, international share issues, IPOs, rights issues and placings. She has also advised on a number of cross border transactions and complicated international joint ventures. Most recently she has acted for the Department of Trade and Industry in relation to the commercialisation of the post office; for Koninklijke Hoogovens N.V. in relation to its merger with British Steel. She has acted for Lazard Brothers, financial advisers to Electra Investment Trust plc, on the hostile £1.2bn bid by 3i Group plc and the alternative proposals by Electra for a share buy back and related restructuring, for BSkyB in relation to its £623 million offer for Manchester United plc and for Friends Provident in relation to its £744 million offer for the London and Manchester Group.
Prof. Memberships: City of London Solicitors' Company.
Career: Admitted in 1980 and became a partner in 1987. Head of the Corporate Division.

GOULD, Terry
Eversheds, Norwich (01603) 272727
terrygould@eversheds.com
Specialisation: Head of corporate finance with particular experience in M&A and private equity. Within last 12 months worked on the acquisitions and disposals for ECNG and CGNU. Has worked increasingly on developing business in North America. Addresses seminars.
Prof. Memberships: Law Society.
Career: Qualified 1977 with *Freshfields*. Joined present firm in 1978 and became a partner in 1981.
Personal: Born 7th March 1952. Attended Downing College, Cambridge 1971-74. Governor Norwich School. Lives in Norwich.

GOWANS, Andrew
Osborne Clarke, Reading (0118) 925 2000

GRAVES, Patrick
Osborne Clarke, Bristol (0117) 917 3000

GRAY, Colin
McGrigor Donald, Glasgow (0141) 248 6677

GRAY, Richard
L'Estrange & Brett, Belfast (028) 9023 0426
richard.gray@lestrangeandbrett.com
Specialisation: Partner, corporate department. Main areas of practice are corporate, corporate finance and banking work. Also active in project finance and PFI work.
Prof. Memberships: Law Society of Northern Ireland; Law Society of England and Wales.
Career: Called to the Northern Ireland Bar in 1989. Admitted as a solicitor in England and Wales in 1992 and in Northern Ireland in 1992. Assistant solicitor with *Cameron Markby Hewitt* (now *Cameron McKenna)* 1989-92. Partner in *L'Estrange & Brett* since 1996.
Personal: Born 1966. Education: Queen's University of Belfast (LLB). Course adviser (company law): Institute of Professional Legal Studies, Belfast.

GRAYSTON, Clare
Lewis Silkin, London (020) 7074 8004
clare.grayston@lewissilkin.com
Specialisation: Head of Corporate Department. Practice area covering mergers and acquisitions and corporate finance. Practice is predominantly in mergers and acquisitions, public and private, acting for both buyers and sellers and in IPOs and secondary issues on the main market and AIM, frequently representing the sponsor/NOMAD and broker.
Prof. Memberships: Active in l'Association Internationale des Jeunes Avocats.
Career: Qualified in 1985. Other interests: Director (Chair of Finance Committee) of Women in Film and Television (UK) Limited (1992-98), Director of Living Earth Foundation (environmental charity) (1995-96). Published author on a number of comparative law texts. French speaker.
Personal: Born 1960. Lives in central London.

GREAVES, Adam
Gouldens, London (020) 7842 6188
acg@gouldens.com
Specialisation: Partner in company/commercial department and head of the private equity team. Very diversified practice covers private equity, mergers and acquisitions (private and public), flotations, corporate finance, corporate reconstructions and commercial agreements and joint ventures.
Career: Qualified in 1982. Joined *Nabarro Nathanson* in 1980, joining and becoming a Partner of *Gouldens* in 1986.
Personal: Born 9 July 1958. Attended Bradfield College 1972-76, Selwyn College, Cambridge 1976-79 and Guildford College of Law 1979-80. Leisure interests include fly fishing (member of the Red Sea Casters), bridge, hockey, walking and cooking. Lives in London.

GREEN, Guy
Eversheds, Birmingham (0121) 232 1000
Specialisation: Corporate finance with a private equity bias, mergers and acquisitions for both private and public companies advising buyers, sellers and funders.
Career: Qualified at *Bird & Bird* in 1982. Partner at *George Green & Co* 1989 to 1999. Became partner at *Eversheds* in January 2000 heading up *Eversheds* private equity team.
Personal: Leisure interests include sailing, hockey, skiing and golf.

GREENFIELD, G N Ian
Hammond Suddards Edge, Leeds (0113) 284 7000
ian.greenfield@hammondse.com
Specialisation: Head of corporate finance in Leeds. Specialises in merger and acquisition work, flotations and secondary issues, stock exchange and take-over code work for plc and substantial private companies. Significant transactions have included the £750 million FKI/Babcock demerger, £68 million acquisition of Hero Drinks Group (UK) Limited by Cott Corporation of Canada, the flotation of DBS Management plc on the Official List, acting for Great Lakes Chemical Corporation on the $300 million demerger of Octel Corp on the New York Stock Exchange and the £99 million public to private bid for Allied Textile Companies plc and the £310 million bid by Vopak N.V. for Ellis & Everard plc.
Prof. Memberships: Law Society.
Career: Educated at Hymers College, Hull and Emmanuel College Cambridge (MA Cantab). Articled *Coward Chance* London; qualified 1978. Solicitor *Coward Chance* 1978-80; solicitor and associate, *Brooke North & Goodwin* Leeds 1980-83; solicitor and partner *A V Hammond & Co.* 1984-88; partner *Hammond Suddards* 1988 to date.
Personal: Born 1953; resides Ikley; married with two children. Leisure interests include golf, tennis and rugby.

GREGORY, Lesley
Memery Crystal, London (020) 7242 5905
lgregory@memerycrystal.com
Specialisation: Corporate and commercial matters including corporate finance, acquisitions and disposals, Official List and AIM, capital raising and joint ventures. Included in The Hot 100 lawyers shaping the Legal Profession in 2001 and has been involved in over 80 AIM transactions since its start in 1995. Her work in corporate finance has resulted in the firm being recognised as niche firm of the year for 2001.
Prof. Memberships: The Law Society, Women in Management, CISCO and the British Association for Sport and Law.
Career: Articled *Courts & Co.* Qualified 1983; solicitor *Memery Crystal* 1983-88; partner since 1988.
Personal: Born 1960; resides London.

GRISEWOOD, Rebecca
Halliwell Landau, Manchester (0161) 835 3003

GRONOW, Simon
Pinsent Curtis Biddle, Birmingham (0121) 625 3072
simon.gronow@pinsents.com
Specialisation: Partner in Corporate Finance Department. Principally engaged in general corporate work for UK and International public companies and investment banks/brokers, including flotations, rights issues, takeover offers, capital reconstructions, acquisitions and disposals.
Prof. Memberships: Law Society.
Career: Qualified 1986. Joined *Pinsent & Co* (now *Pinsent Curtis Biddle*) in 1984, partner in 1991.
Personal: Born 1961. Educated at King's College Cambridge 1979-83.

HALL, Daniel
Eversheds, Manchester (0161) 831 8000

HALPIN, Peter
Eversheds, Manchester (0161) 831 8000

HARDIE, David
Dundas & Wilson CS, Edinburgh (0131) 228 8000

HARKER, Chris
Dickinson Dees, Newcastle upon Tyne
(0191) 279 9254
chris.harker@dickinson-dees.com
Specialisation: Main areas of expertise are venture capital and mergers and acquisitions. Has acted for Northern Venture Managers Limited in some 20 venture capital investments and disposals over the last year with a value of approx £55 milion. Also handled a £15 million placing and related acquisition for an AIM company and a £10 million placing and open offer.
Prof. Memberships: Law Society.
Career: Qualified in 1978, having joined *Dickinson Dees* in 1976. Became a partner in 1981.
Personal: Born 25th January 1954. Attended Rossall School, Fleetwood 1962-71, then The Queen's College, Oxford 1972-75. Leisure interests include cricket, golf, skiing and other sports. Lives in Ponteland. Married with two children.

HARPER, Tony
Brabners, Liverpool (0151) 600 3000
Specialisation: Partner in corporate department. Work includes corporate finance, MBOs, MBIs, venture and development capital, mergers, acquisitions and disposals, housing association funding.
Prof. Memberships: Law Society, Liverpool Law Society.
Career: Educated at St. Ambrose College, Altrincham; University of Liverpool. Articled at *Brabner Holden* 1981-83 becoming partner in 1986.
Personal: Born 1959. Interests include golf, fell walking, Round Table. Married with three children. Lives in Stockton Heath.

HARRISON, Wendy
DLA, Leeds (08700) 111111

HART, Neil
Thomas Eggar Church Adams, Chichester
(01403) 214500
neil.hart@teca.co.uk
Specialisation: Neil Hart specialises in corporate finance, mergers and acquisitions, joint ventures, and corporate insolvency. During the past 12 months Neil has dealt with several companies raising venture capital, a management buyout of a major construction company, several rounds of funding in relation to a dot.com company followed by its successful disposal and has also acted for a US company completing a complicated joint venture in the United Kingdom.
Prof. Memberships: Neil is past Chairman of the Sussex Chamber of Commerce and Industry and a past member of the Board of Sussex Business Link. He is currently a Director of the Weald & Downland Open Air Museum.
Career: Neil is 48 and has been a partner of the firm since 1986. He is currently Chairman of the partnership. He trained with *Norton Rose* in the City and after two years post qualification experience, joined *Johnson Stokes & Master* in Hong Kong, specialising in banking and corporate recovery. In 1986 he joined what is now *Thomas Eggar Church Adams* and has specialised in corporate law and corporate finance ever since.
Personal: Neil was educated at Oundle and Exeter University. He is married with two children and his main outside interests are sailing and military history.

HATCHARD, Michael E.
Skadden, Arps, Slate, Meagher & Flom LLP, London (020) 7519 7020
mhatchard@skadden.com
Specialisation: Partner specialising in corporate finance and M&A. Principally mergers, acquisitions and joint ventures and the full range of securities distribution transactions, particularly where significant UK/US implications arise.
Career: Qualified 1980 with *Theodore Goddard*, partner 1985. Joined *Skadden, Arps* as a partner in 1994 with responsibility for the English legal and regulatory aspects of global securities offerings and cross-border transactions.
Personal: Born 21st November 1955.

HATTRELL, Martin
Slaughter and May, London (020) 7600 1200
martin.hattrell@slaughterandmay.com
Specialisation: Corporate department. Principal area of practice is corporate and commercial law, in particular mergers and acquisitions.
Prof. Memberships: The Law Society.
Career: Qualified in 1987 with *Slaughter and May* and became a partner in 1994.
Personal: Born 9 August 1961. Educated at Ampleforth College, Yorkshire and The Queen's College, Oxford.

HAWES, Roger
Burges Salmon, Bristol (0117) 939 2243
roger.hawes@burges-salmon.com
Specialisation: Corporate finance and private equity. Recent deals include the £45 million fundraising for United Milk plc, advising on the takeover of Aram Resources plc, MBOs of Rapid Racting (£15m) and Colleagues Direct Marketing (N/d) and implementation of a disposal program by Systems Union Group plc.
Prof. Memberships: Law Society.
Career: Qualified in 1984, joined *Burges Salmon* in 1988 from *Linklaters*, became a partner in 1990 and head of *Burges Salmon's* company/commercial department in 2001.

HAYWARD, Paul
Gateley Wareing, Birmingham (0121) 234 0000

HAYWOOD, Richard
Wragge & Co, Birmingham (0870) 903 1000

HEATHCOCK, Andrew
Paris Smith & Randall, Southampton
(02380) 482482
andrew.heathcock@parissmith.co.uk
Specialisation: Partner in charge of Company and Commercial Department. Main area of practice includes over 25 years experience in company and corporate finance work in the private sector.
Prof. Memberships: Law Society.
Career: Qualified with *Bird & Bird* 1977; *Lovell White & King* 1979-81. Partner in charge of Commercial Department of *Boodle Hatfield* in Southampton 1981-90. Joined *Paris Smith & Randall* as a Partner in October 1990.

HEWES, Simon
Bond Pearce, Bristol (0117) 929 9197
shewes@bondpearce.com
Specialisation: Partner in the Corporate Group. Specialises in corporate finance, particularly acquisitions, disposals and mergers, private equity, including MBO's, MBI's and IBO's and shareholder arrangements. Recent deals include the management buyout of Allen & Heath Limited and the acquisition for Newsquest of the Dimbleby Newspaper Group.
Prof. Memberships: Member of the British Venture Capital Association.
Career: Qualified in 1987 with *Pinsent & Co.*, Birmingham (now *Pinsent Curtis Biddle*). Joined *Hepherd Winstanley & Pugh* in 1992, becoming a Partner in 1994. Joined *Bond Pearce* in 1998 on merger.

HOLT, Andrew
DLA, Manchester (08700) 111111

HOPKINS, Stephen Martyn
Eversheds, Leeds (0113) 243 0391
stephenhopkins@eversheds.com
Specialisation: Vastly experienced corporate finance partner acting for clients such as Anglo American, Tarmac, Hazelwood Foods, EWS and WRG. Has edited the financial assistance chapter of Tolley's 'Company Law'. Corporate finance practice continues to develop. Became overall head of the corporate group in Leeds and Manchester in 2000.
Prof. Memberships: Law Society.
Career: Qualified in 1984. Joined *Eversheds* in 1988. Became a partner in 1991.
Personal: Born 17 March 1960. Attended Sheffield University 1978-81. Leisure interests include golf, cricket and rugby. Lives near Wetherby.

HOYLE, Andrew C.
Watson Burton, Newcastle upon Tyne
(0191) 244 4444

HUGHES, David
Pinsent Curtis Biddle, Birmingham
(0121) 625 3066
david.hughes@pinsents.com
Specialisation: Partner in Corporate Finance Dept. Corporate finance, including mergers and aquisitions, takeovers and primary and secondary equity issues. He is a senior corporate partner for a number of the firm's major listed clients and also acts for a number of US, German and other multinational companies on UK transactions. Recent transactions include acting for DONCASTERS plc on its US $260 million takeover bid by RCG Holdings.
Career: Qualified in 1980. Partner in 1987. Worked at *Nabarro Nathanson* 1978-82, then *Slaughter and May* 1982-85, before joining *Pinsent & Co* in 1985.
Personal: Born 1955. Attended Wolverhampton Grammar School 1966-73, then Jesus College, Oxford 1973-77.

HULL, David
Hammond Suddards Edge, Birmingham
(0131) 222 3000
david.hull@hammondse.com
Specialisation: Partner in the corporate department and liaison partner for the firm in North America, *Hammond Suddards Edge*. Specialises in corporate finance and company commercial work. Primary expertise is mergers and acquisitions, IPOs, Stock Exchange work, international cross-border transactions, media, entertainment and leisure, PFI and facilities and management arrangements and theatre and sports law.
Prof. Memberships: LL.B (Hons) (Sheff'd). Is responsible for many of the firm's large corporate clients. Regular writer of legal articles and occasional visiting lecturer at the Universities of Wolverhampton and Aston. Non executive director of the Midland

Arts Centre and Birmingham Repertory Theatre. Named as one of the 'Top 30 regional corporate heavyweights' by Legal Business.
Career: Qualified 1986. *Dibb Lupton Broomhead* 1984-86, *Hammond Suddards* 1986-87, *Edge Ellison* 1987-00 (partner from 1990), *Hammond Suddards Edge* 2000 to date.
Personal: Born 18th October 1961. Educated at Banbury School and Sheffield University. Interests include theatre and West Bromwich Albion FC. Lives in Knowle, Solihull.

HULLS, Martin
Ward Hadaway, Newcastle upon Tyne (0191) 204 4000
Specialisation: Corporate finance; private equity transactions; MBOs/MBIs.
Prof. Memberships: Law Society.
Career: LLB from Birmingham University. Practised in Birmingham and Nottingham before moving to the North East in 1993. Became Head of Commercial Department in 1994.
Personal: Keeping fit, mountain biking, fast cars, motor racing. Married with three young daughters.

HUNTER, James
Mills & Reeve, Norwich (01603) 693267
james.hunter@mills-reeve.com
Specialisation: Company sales and acquisitions and general corporate finance matters. Acted on acquisitions worth £45 million over two years for one US client. Also advises on start ups, fund raising and joint ventures/commercial agreements.
Prof. Memberships: Law Society.
Career: Trainee at *Mills & Reeve* (1993-95). Solicitor at *Mills & Reeve* (1995-2000). Associate at *Mills & Reeve* 2000-2001. Partner 2001 to date.
Personal: Married. Cycling, sailing, fishing. LLB (UEA) – College of Law, York.

HUTCHINSON, John
Pitmans, Reading (0118) 958 0224
jhutchinson@pitmans.com
Specialisation: Company/commercial specialist whose main areas of work include MBO/MBIs, acquisitions, disposals, private equity and bank funding.
Career: Qualified 1990. Partner 1994.
Personal: Born 7th December 1961. Lives in Oxford. Interests include golf, football and opera.

IRVINE, John
L'Estrange & Brett, Belfast (028) 9023 0426
john.irvine@lestrangeandbrett.com
Specialisation: Partner and head of corporate department. Main area of work: Corporate and commercial law.
Prof. Memberships: Law Society of Northern Ireland.
Career: Lecturer in law: Queen's University, Kingston, Ontario; University of Central Lancashire. Tutor in law, University of Exeter; course tutor, Institute of Professional Legal Studies, Belfast. Qualified 1986. Partner in *L'Estrange & Brett* since 1988.
Personal: Born 1957. Education: Queen's University, Belfast (LLB), Queen's University, Kingston, Ontario (LLM.)

JAMES, Glen
Slaughter and May, London (020) 7600 1200
glen.james@slaughterandmay.com
See under Insurance, p.488

JAMISON, David
Carson McDowell, Belfast (028) 9024 4951
david.jamison@carson-mcdowell.com
Specialisation: Emphasis on mergers, acquisitions and disposals, intellectual property and insolvency.
Prof. Memberships: Law Society of Northern Ireland and Law Society of England and Wales.
Career: Born 1964. Qualified 1989. University of Manchester. Articled and practised in London and latterly in North of England prior to returning to Northern Ireland in 1995. Partner 1998.

JANSEN, Karl
Freethcartwright, Nottingham (0115) 936 9369
karl.jansen@freethcartwright.co.uk
Specialisation: Corporate transactional work including mergers and acquisitions, management buyouts/buyins, private equity and refinancing, acting for buyers, sellers and equity/debt funders. Highlights of last year include the sale of the Data Base Group of Companies to the Ramesys Group and acting for management on the MBO of Freshtime UK and the MBI of The Burlington Press (Cambridge).
Career: Articles with *Davies Arnold Cooper*, London. Joined present firm on qualification in 1990. Appointed partner in 1994. Appointed head of corporate in 1999.
Personal: Educated at Loughbrough Grammar School and the London School of Economics. Season ticket holder at Leicester City FC. Married with two children.

JEFFRIES, Graham
Bond Pearce, Southampton (023) 8033 2001
gjeffries@bondpearce.com
See under Banking, p.119

JOHNS, Michael
Nicholson Graham & Jones, London (020) 7648 9000
michael.johns@ngj.co.uk
Specialisation: Managing Partner and Partner in the Company and Commercial Department. Main area of practice is corporate finance. Work includes acquisitions, mergers, venture capital, buy-outs, equity issues, yellow book work and general corporate work for public listed companies. Member of sports group; acts for organisations and individuals in the sports field including sponsors and sports organisers. Has spoken at seminars both in the UK and USA on subjects such as buy-outs, international strategic activities, law firm management and sports sponsorship.Non-Executive Director of Merchant Retail Group plc since 1979.
Prof. Memberships: Institute of Directors, Law Society. Chairman of Globalex.

JOHNSON, Ben
Eversheds, Nottingham (0115) 950 7000
benjohnson@eversheds.com
Specialisation: Corporate finance, predominantly private equity, mergers and acquisitions. Deals in 2001 include the MBO of CTEX Seat Comfort and acquisitions for Host Europe plc and Project Telecom plc.
Prof. Memberships: Law Society.
Career: Qualified 1988; *Burges Salmon* 1986 to 1998 (seconded to *Wragge & Co* 1988/89) a partner from 1996. Partner at *Eversheds* 1998 to date.

JOHNSON, Robin
Eversheds, Leeds (0113) 243 0391
robinjohnson@eversheds.com
Specialisation: A corporate finance and commercial partner specialising in M&A, purple book and joint venture work with a strong emphasis on technology. Member of the Regional Advisory Group for the Stock Exchange. Robin is client partner for a number of US corporates including Parker Hannifin Corporation, Waters Corporation, SPX Corporation and Geon Corporation as well as leading advisor to UK listed companies such as AEA Technology plc, CD Bramall plc, Chapelthorpe plc Trans LPA plc, Richmond Foods plc and K3 Technology plc. Extensive experience on public takeover bids, having been involved in 21 since March 1998. Voted one of "40 under 40" to watch by the Yorkshire Business Insider in 1999.
Career: Qualified 1987, partner 1994.
Publications: A number of articles on corporate governance have been published in publications such as International Financial Law Review and Corporate Society.
Personal: Born 1963, resides Leeds, married with two children.

JOHNSTON, Keith
Addleshaw Booth & Co, Manchester (0161) 934 6000
byj@addleshaw-booth.co.uk
Specialisation: Partner in corporate finance group. Principal area of practice is corporate finance mainly for listed companies including mergers and acquisitions, takeovers and general transaction and corporate advice. Other main areas of work include public/private sector partnerships and project work (see separate entry).
Prof. Memberships: Law Society. Chairman: North West Company Secretaries' Forum. Head of Projects Group at the firm.
Career: Qualified in 1976. Became a partner in 1981. 1991-94 member of board of *Norton Rose* M5 Group. Board member of *Addleshaw Booth & Co.*
Personal: Educated at London University 1970-73 (External). Governor of The Grange School, Hartford, Cheshire. Company Secretary API Group plc. Leisure pursuits include Liverpool FC, skiing, chess and tennis. Lives in Hale, Cheshire.

JOHNSTON, Michael
Carson McDowell, Belfast (028) 9024 4951
michael.johnston@carson-mcdowell.com
Specialisation: Mergers and acquisitions, subscription and shareholders agreements, PFI/PPP, MBO's and MBI's and JV's. Advised Avalanche Technologies with regard to its recent $8.5 million investment by 3i and IDB, advised Open & Direct Limited in various acquisitions, advising University of Ulster in Springvale Project.
Prof. Memberships: Law Society of Northern Ireland.
Career: Joined *Carson & McDowell* 1983; admitted as a solicitor in Northern Ireland 1984; became a partner at Carson & McDowell 1993.

JONES, Hugh
Osborne Clarke, Reading (0118) 925 2000

JONES, Jonathan
Hammond Suddards Edge, Leeds (0113) 284 7000
jonathan.jones@hammondse.com
Specialisation: Based in the Leeds office. Specialises in venture capital, MBOs, MBIs and IBOs, mergers

and acquisitions and corporate finance.
Prof. Memberships: Law Society; British Venture Capital Association.
Career: Articled *Simpson Curtis* (now *Pinsent Curtis Biddle*) 1990; qualified 1992; solicitor *Pinsent Curtis Biddle* (formerly *Pinsent Curtis*) 1992-98 (associate 1996-98); assistant solicitor *Hammond Suddards Edge* (formerly *Hammond Suddards*) 1998-2000, became a partner in 2000.
Personal: Newcastle-under-Lyme School 1981-86; Sheffield University (LLB Hons 2:1) 1986-89; York Law School 1989-90. Married to Ruth, two sons. Lives in Burley-in-Wharfedale, Yorkshire. Enjoys watching rugby, football and cricket and playing golf. Stoke City supporter.

JONES, Michael
CMS Cameron McKenna, Bristol (0117) 930 0200
mgj@cmck.com
Specialisation: Partner in charge of the Bristol corporate practice. The practice covers all company and corporate finance work with particular emphasis on mergers and acquisitions, private equity and venture capital, flotations, takeovers, financings, joint ventures and general corporate advice.
Career: Qualified with *McKenna & Co* in 1987; *McKenna & Co* 1987-89; Investment Banking Division of Samuel Montagu & Co. Ltd 1989-92; and HSBC Investment Bank (Asia) Limited 1992-97, becoming a Director; Partner *CMS Cameron McKenna* 1997.
Personal: Born 23 November 1960. Educated at Haberdashers' Aske's School, Elstree; Durham University and College of Law, Guildford. Married with three children, lives in Bath.

KANE, Hilary
Maclay Murray & Spens, Glasgow
(0141) 248 5011
hak@maclaymurrayspens.co.uk
Specialisation: Partner specialising in mergers and acquisitions (including cross-border) and corporate finance. Recent transactions include lead partner advising on the demerger of the non power operations of the Clyde Blowers Group and the sale of its power operations for c £60m; advising Stagecoach Holdings plc in its £33.4 million sale of Glasgow Prestwick International Airport, advising British Polythene Industries plc in its successful defence of Macfarlane Group's hostile takeover bid and its tender offer to buy back c 30% of its shares
Prof. Memberships: Mergers and Acquisitions Committee of AIJA (International Lawyers Association).
Career: Articled *Maclay Murray & Spens*; qualified 1985; partner, *Maclay Murray & Spens,* since 1991; established London office where partner in charge before returning to Glasgow office in 1997.
Personal: Craigholme School; Glasgow University (LLB 2(1) Hons, Dip LP). Born 1962; resides Glasgow. Enjoys good food and wine, spinning, watching football, skiing.

KELIHER, James
Stephens & Scown, Exeter (01392) 210700

KIMBELL, Stephen
Kimbells, Milton Keynes (01908) 668 555

KING, Peter
Linklaters, London (020) 7456 3448
peter.king@linklaters.com
Specialisation: Corporate department. Co-head of *Linklaters'* international equities practice. Experienced in all aspects of corporate finance, including, in particular, international equity offers, privatisations, mergers and acquisitions and advice to financial institutions on regulatory matters.
Career: Co-head international equity practice. 1990 to date: Partner, *Linklaters.* 1977-80: St John's College, Cambridge.

KITTS, Stephen
Eversheds, Nottingham (0115) 9507000
stephenkitts@eversheds.com
Specialisation: Corporate finance, private equity and acquisition finance for banks and mezzanine lenders and venture capitalists as well as general mergers and acquisitions.
Prof. Memberships: Law Society.
Career: Joined *Eversheds* in 1987 and became a partner in 1994. Qualified 1987. Head of corporate at *Eversheds* East Midlands.
Personal: Lives in Nottinghamshire with his wife and two children. Enjoys golf.

KNAPP, Vanessa
Freshfields Bruckhaus Deringer, London
(020) 7936 4000
vanessa.knapp@freshfields.com
Specialisation: Partner in corporate department. Main area of practice is company/ commercial, covering corporate finance and general corporate work. Also handles financial services. Chairman of the City of London Law Society Company Law Sub-Committee and Member of Law Society, Company Law Committee.
Prof. Memberships: Law Society.
Career: Qualified in 1981. Joined *Freshfields* in 1979, becoming a Partner in 1988.
Personal: Born 3rd November 1956. Attended Exeter University (LLB) 1975-78. Member of the London Symphony Chorus. Lives in London.

KNIGHT, Adrian
Shearman & Sterling, London (020) 7655 5000
aknight@shearman.com
Specialisation: Partner in M&A and Equity Capital Markets.
Career: Qualified in March 1984. Became a Partner at *Ashurst Morris Crisp* in 1992. Resigned from *Ashurst Morris Crisp* becoming a partner at *Shearman & Sterling* in June 1999.
Personal: Graduated from Cambridge University in 1980.

LAVERY, James
Pinsent Curtis Biddle, Birmingham
(0121) 200 1050
james.lavery@pinsents.com
Specialisation: Partner. Head of private equity, Birmingham. Main practice areas are private equity principally acting for venture capital funders and management, and M&A work for private and public companies. Recent deals include the £441 million RBPE backed bid for Britax International plc, the Friends Ivory & Sime backed MBI of Thomas Sanderson Blinds and the 3i backed secondary buy-out of the Hymatie Group.
Prof. Memberships: Law Society.
Career: Educated at King Edward's School, Birmingham and Exeter University. Qualified 1990. Joined *Pinsent Curtis* in 1994. Partner 1996.
Personal: Born 1964. Leisure interests include golf and music.

LAWES, William
Freshfields Bruckhaus Deringer, London
(020) 7936 4000
Specialisation: Main practice areas are mergers and acquisitions, demergers, joint ventures, restructurings, international offerings and UK domestic issues of all types. Acts for a range of corporate clients (with a media bias) and investment banks. His major transactions include the mergers of BP and Amoco, SmithKline and Beechon and Lloyds Bank and TSB.
Prof. Memberships: Law Society, City of London Solicitors Company.
Career: Qualified as barrister and solicitor in New Zealand in 1986. Judges' Clerk at New Zealand Court of Appeal 1985. Joined *Freshfields* in 1986. Partner in corporate department 1994.
Personal: Born 1964. Educated in England and New Zealand. Victoria University, Wellington N.Z. 1981-85. Gonville and Caius College, Cambridge 1985-86. Leisure pursuits include golf and family.

LAWTON SMITH, Andrew
Wragge & Co, Birmingham (0870) 903 1000

LEE, Paul
Addleshaw Booth & Co, Manchester
(0161) 934 6000
pal@addleshaw-booth.co.uk
Specialisation: Senior partner and chairman of the board of *Addleshaw Booth & Co,* partner in the corporate finance group. Work covers acquisitions and disposals for both listed and non-listed companies. MBOs and venture capital specialising in strategic advice and business planning. Addresses conferences and seminars.
Career: Qualified 1970. Joined the firm in 1970, becoming a partner in 1973, managing partner in 1991 and senior partner in 1997.
Personal: Attended Clare College, Cambridge. Director of several companies, both public and private, including banking and property. Vice-Chairman of the CBI -North West. Chairman of the Royal Exchange Theatre; Chairman of the Board of Governors of Chetham's School of Music and a member of the board of governors of Royal Northern College of Music. Director of Northern Ballet Theatre. Leisure interests include the arts, sport and wine. Lives in Manchester.

LEE, Richard
Addleshaw Booth & Co, Manchester
(0161) 934 6000
rnl@addleshaw-booth.co.uk
Specialisation: Partner in corporate finance group. Work covers mergers and acquisitions, City Code takeovers (in particular public to private transactions), flotations and secondary issues. Also deals with general corporate work including Stock Exchange compliance.
Prof. Memberships: Law Society, Manchester Law Society.
Career: Qualified in 1983 before joining the firm in 1986. Became a partner in 1988.
Personal: Educated at Trinity College, Cambridge 1977-80. Leisure interests include sport and family. Lives in Wilmslow.

LEE, Richard
Clarks, Reading (0118) 960 4638
richardlee@clarks-solicitors.co.ok
Specialisation: Head of Corporate. Work covers company law, corporate finance and private equity, public issues, company acquisitions and transaction finance. Advises large corporates, owner/managers, buy-in and buy-out teams and debt and equity funders. Richard also has a significant practice in employee share schemes.
Prof. Memberships: Thames Valley Commercial Lawyers Association (Co-founder 1987, Chairman 1991-93).
Career: Qualified in 1976. Held various marketing positions with Shell International 1969-72; trained with *Norton Rose* specialising in corporate finance until 1980. A partner at *Simpson Curtis* 1981-86. Head of corporate at *Clarks* since 1986.
Personal: Born 16th June 1947. BSc (Economics and Politics) from Bristol University 1969. Leisure interests include golf, music and theatre. Lives in Reading.

LETH, Mary
Macfarlanes, London (020) 7831 9222
Specialisation: Partner company, commercial and banking department. Deals with corporate finance including acquisitions, mergers, demergers and corporate reconstructions.
Career: Educated in United States: University of Colorado. Attorney, *Holland and Hart*, Denver Colorado, USA (1978-84). Articled at *Macfarlanes*; qualified 1988; partner 1995. Admitted States of Colorado 1977; New York 1984.
Personal: Born 1952. Resides London. Interests include music, opera, walking, cycling.

LEVY, Graeme
Olswang, London (020) 7208 8754
gdl@olswang.com
Specialisation: Partner and Head of Finance Unit. Specialises in corporate, finance and insolvency matters, acting for corporates, institutions, insolvency practitioners and banks. Work includes mergers and acquisitions, joint ventures and public issues, as well as all aspects of funding and insolvency. Co-author of 'Practical Insolvency Precedents' (Sweet & Maxwell) and consulting editor to Butterworths Encyclopedia of Forms and Precedents.
Career: Qualified 1985. Previously at *Herbert Oppenheimer, Nathan & Vandyk, Richards Butler* and *SJ Berwin & Co* (partner there from 1990). Joined *Olswang* as a partner in 1995.
Personal: Born April 1959. Educated at Trinity Hall, Cambridge. Interests include tennis, theatre (musicals) and playing the guitar.

LEVY, Robert
Kuit Steinart Levy, Manchester (0161) 832 3434
robertlevy@kuits.com
Specialisation: Corporate finance; corporate and commercial; tax investigation.
Prof. Memberships: Manchester Law Society.
Career: Articled *Kuit Steinart Levy*; qualified 1984; partner *Kuit Steinart Levy* 1988. Made Executive Partner 2000.
Personal: Born 1959. Manchester Grammar School & University College London – 1981 LLB Hon. Resides Manchester. Interests – tennis, theatre, amateur dramatics, member Royal Exchange Theatre special events committee, active involvement in the Starlight Foundation.

LEWIS, David T.R.
Norton Rose, London (020) 7283 6000
lewisdtr@nortonrose.com
Specialisation: Partner in corporate finance department; senior partner. Main area of practice is corporate finance, including take-overs (public and private), flotations, stock exchange work of all types, MBOs, schemes of arrangement, international global offerings, all types of commercial agreements, and debt restructurings. Has handled over 100 listings and numerous take-overs including HSBC Holdings/ Midland, GEC Siemens/Plessey, Imperial Group/ Hanson/UB, BA/B-Cal, BMW/Rover, Redland/Steetley, Ladbroke/Hilton, Dixons/Currys, Guinness/Grandmet, Ciba/Allied Colloids, BMW/Rolls Royce. Has chaired and spoken at numerous conferences.
Prof. Memberships: Member of the Law Society of London Company Law Committee 1982-97. Hon. Fellow Jesus College Oxford.
Publications: Author of articles in Gazette and plc; also the Norton Rose Guide to Take-overs.

LEWIS, Mark
Foot Anstey Sargent, Exeter (01392) 411221
mark.lewis@foot-ansteys.co.uk
Specialisation: Partner. Leader of commercial services division. Practice covers a wide range of corporate finance activities including mergers and acquisitions and public and private fund raisings. Also handles company and commercial work, including joint ventures and other strategic commercial agreements and has very substantial experience of public takeovers, floatations and secondary issues on the London Stock Exchange as well as privatisations.
Prof. Memberships: Law Society.
Career: Qualified in 1978. Joined *Foot Anstey Sargent* as a partner in 1995.
Personal: Born 1953. Attended Millfield School 1965-71 and Exeter College, Oxford 1972-75 (Exhibitioner). Lives near Exeter.

LEWIS, Susan
Eversheds, Birmingham (0121) 232 1063
susanlewis@eversheds.com
Specialisation: Transactional work (including multi-jurisdictional). Used to heading a large team of lawyers (where the job demands) on substantial matters. Acted for the Phoenix Consortium in the acquisition of Rover Group from BMW.
Career: Oxford University 1976-79. Articled at *Evershed & Tomkinson*, became a partner in 1988. Has been with *Eversheds* throughout career.
Personal: Married with 2 children. The time for non-work related external interests is almost non-existent, and limited to children and Aston Villa!

LEYSHON, Greg
Osborne Clarke, Reading (0118) 925 2000

LINDGREN, David
Fyfe Ireland WS, Edinburgh (0131) 343 2500
dlindgren@fyfeireland.com
Specialisation: Head of the corporate department, specialising in mainstream corporate finance law with a particular interest in banking, public and private project funding, M&As and internet law. Most recent deals include a £21 million fundraising for Quadstone Limited, acting for the project manager of an internet bank and on a £100 million structured refinancing.
Prof. Memberships: Law Society of Scotland.
Career: *Dundas & Wilson* (Edinburgh and Glasgow); *Cameron Markby Hewitt* (London); *McGrigor Donald* (Edinburgh). Joined *Fyfe Ireland* as head of corporate department in February 2000.
Publications: Banking law section of 'Greens Practice Styles'.
Personal: Born in 1961. Educated at Daniel Stewarts and Melville College, Pembroke College, Cambridge (MA in Law) and Edinburgh University (LLB and Dip. LP). Leisure interests include golf, skiing and supporting lost causes.

LIPPELL, Sean
Addleshaw Booth & Co, Leeds (0113) 209 2081
csl@addleshaw-booth.co.uk
Specialisation: Partner and head of corporate finance group. Principal area of practice is corporate finance. Work includes public issues, takeovers, MBO/MBIs and private equity, mergers and acquisitions (including cross-border/international transactions), demergers and corporate reconstructions and corporate joint ventures.
Prof. Memberships: Law Society.
Career: Qualified in 1979. Joined June 1999.
Personal: Educated at Kelly College, Tavistock and Durham University. Leisure interests include keeping fit, walking, reading, wine and films.

LIVINGSTONE, Alisdair
Osborne Clarke, Bristol (0117) 917 3000

LOAKE, Jonathan
Brobeck Hale and Dorr, Oxford (01235) 823000
loake@bhd.com
Specialisation: Partner. Company mergers and acquisitions, group reorganisations, MBOs, venture capital subscriptions, corporate transactions in the music industry. Clients include a wide range of technology companies, publishers and record companies.
Prof. Memberships:IBA; Thames Valley Commercial Lawyers' Association (former Chairman).
Career: Editor with *Hodder & Stoughton*. Qualified with *Denton Hall* in 1979; left after four years to co-found *Dallas Brett*. Partner at *Dallas Brett* from 1983-97. Partner at *Morgan Cole* from 1997-2000.
Personal: Born 21 March 1951. Educated at Rugby School and Trinity College, Oxford. Married with three children. Leisure pursuits include sport, reading and music.

LONG, Julian
Freshfields Bruckhaus Deringer, London (020) 7936 4000
julian.long@freshfields.com
Specialisation: Is a corporate partner based in London and is a member of *Freshfield's* European M&A Group. Sector experience includes pharmaceuticals, food, publishing and water.
Career: Partner at *Freshfields* since 1995.

LOWE, Paul
Eversheds, Cardiff (029) 2047 1147
paullowe@eversheds.com
Specialisation: UK and international corporate finance including flotations, public and private company mergers, acquisitions and disposals; joint ventures; MBOs, MBIs, venture capital funds, etc, together with general corporate advice.
Prof. Memberships: The Law Society, Institute of Bankers, Cardiff Business Club, Institute of Directors.
Career: Solicitor qualified in Hong Kong. *Phillips & Buck* 1982-87. *Richards Butler* Hong Kong 1988-91. *Eversheds* 1991 to date.
Personal: Interested in golf, running and water sports.

LUBBOCK, Nigel
Steele & Co, Norwich (01603) 274 700
commercial@steele.co.uk
Specialisation: Corporate and commercial work for both national and international businesses specialising particularly in sales and acquisitions, merger and company restructuring. Domestic clients include Pi Group Ltd, Tulip Int. (UK). Ltd and Ionics (UK) Ltd. The team also deal with tendering, procurement and PFI contracts for their local authority clients and draft a wide variety of commercial agreements for use by the authorities.
Career: Trained Bristol, London and Norwich, qualified 1975, partner *Steele & Co* 1979.
Personal: Married, has a son and daughter; enjoys opera and cricket.

LUMSDEN, Ian G.
Maclay Murray & Spens, Edinburgh (0131) 226 5196
igl@maclaymurrayspens.co.uk
Specialisation: Partner in corporate department specialising in corporate finance and mergers and acquisitions. Work includes flotations, rights issues and other fund raising activity for plcs as well as acquisitions and disposals for listed and unlisted companies and investment trust reconstructions. Advised Motherwell Bridge Holdings Limited in the £75 million disposal of its Information Systems Division; John Menzies plc in its £79 million acquisition of Ogden Ground Services and Grapian Holdings plc in its £49 million disposal of Edinburgh Woollen Mill.
Career: Qualified in 1976. University of Cambridge (BA 1972), University of Edinburgh (LLB 1974). Spent two years working with *Slaughter and May* in London 1978-80.
Personal: Born 1951.

MACAULAY, Anthony
Herbert Smith, London (020) 7374 8000
anthony.macaulay@herbertsmith.com
Specialisation: Partner in corporate division. Experienced in company and commercial matters, especially corporate finance work, including takeovers and flotations. Has particular expertise in relation to the Takeover Code (having spent two years as Secretary of the Takeover Panel) and insider dealing.
Career: Qualified in 1974. Became a partner at *Herbert Smith* in 1983.
Personal: Educated Keble College, Oxford.

MACFARLANE, David
Ashurst Morris Crisp, London (020) 7638 1111

MACINTOSH, Duncan
Morgan Cole, Cardiff (029) 2038 5385

MAHER, Paul
Rowe & Maw, London (020) 7782 8815
pmaher@roweandmaw.com
Specialisation: Head of corporate group. Expertise in mergers and acquisitions, flotations and private equity. Main focus in recent years has been transactional and private equity work in both the telecoms and chemicals sectors.
Prof. Memberships: Law Society.
Career: Articled to *Boodle Hatfield* 1982-84; solicitor ICI Group Legal Department, 1984-90; solicitor at *Rowe & Maw* 1990. Partner 1992.
Personal: Born 30th July 1959. London Law Degree, LLB Bristol. Interested mainly in books, politics and travel. Other leisure pursuits include running, football and squash. Lives in Wandsworth Common.

MARCHANT, Simon
Freshfields Bruckhaus Deringer, London (020) 936 4000
simon.marchant@freshfields.com
Specialisation: Partner specialising in mergers and acquisitions, securities and corporate work. Co-heads the firm's global telecoms, media and technology group.
Career: Articled *Stephenson Harwood*; qualified 1989. Joined *Freshfields* 1989. Spent 1993 on secondment to the New York firm of *Cravath, Swaine & Moore*. Partner *Freshfields* 1997.
Personal: Born 1964. Educated Southampton University.

MARDLE, David
Garretts, Cambridge (01223) 535326
david.x.mardle@glegal.com
Specialisation: Partner, Cambridge office (Corporate Department). Advises on a wide range of corporate transactions, including private equity transactions and mergers and acquisitions. In 1999, he advised the shareholders in the Dalehead Group on the £50 million merger with Roach Foods. Notable transactions in 2000 include advising TTP Communications plc on its IPO on the London Stock Exchange (valuing the company at £542 million) and Astron Group on its £92 million merger with e-doc Group plc.
Prof. Memberships: Law Society.
Career: *Denton Hall* 1990-94; *Allen & Overy* 1994-99; *Garretts* 1999.
Personal: Worcester College, Oxford (1985-88) (BA) and Guildford College of Law. Interests include all sports. Married with two children.

MARSH, David
Burges Salmon, Bristol (0117) 939 2288
david.marsh@burges-salmon.com
See under Partnership, p.616

MARSHALL, John
Johnsons, Belfast (02890) 240183
jm@johnsonslaw.co.uk
Specialisation: Corporate and commercial work including mergers and acquisitions.
Prof. Memberships: Law Society of Northern Ireland.
Career: Queens University, Belfast, LLB (1977). Qualified Northern Ireland 1978.

MASTERS, Richard
McGrigor Donald, Glasgow (0141) 248 6677

McBRIDE, Paul
L'Estrange & Brett, Belfast (028) 9023 0426
paul.mcbride@lestrangeandbrett.com
Specialisation: Corporate and commercial including mergers and acquisitions, management buy-outs, venture capital and project finance.
Prof. Memberships: Law Society of Northern Ireland.
Career: Queens University, Belfast (LLB), Cambridge University (LLM). Called to the Northern Ireland Bar in 1990. Admitted as a solicitor in Northern Ireland in 1993. Partner in *L'Estrange & Brett* since 1998.

McDONALD, Kevan
Dickson Minto WS, Edinburgh (0131) 225 4455
kevan.mcdonald@dmws.com
Specialisation: Partner in corporate department. Main areas of practice are corporate and commercial: mergers and acquisitions, management buy-ins and outs, sales and purchases of companies and businesses, refinancings and corporate finance. Recent deals include AONIC purchase of RGIT's occupational health interests, the buyout of Charles Letts, the purchases of Aquascot, Shetland Salmon and Mainland Salmon for EWOS and the £85 million institutional buy-out of the information systems division of Motherwell Bridge.
Prof. Memberships: Law Society of Scotland, IBA.
Career: Qualified in 1982. Joined *Dickson Minto WS* as senior assistant in 1985 and assumed as a partner in 1987.
Personal: Born 7th July 1958. Attended Aberdeen University 1976-79 (LLB) and Dundee University 1979-80 (Diploma in Petroleum Law). Leisure interests include fishing, swimming and squash. Lives in Edinburgh.

McGINN, James
MacRoberts, Glasgow (0141) 332 9988
james.mcginn@macroberts.co.uk
Specialisation: Corporate finance including mergers and acquisitions and private equity. Recent deals include acting for RBDC in further funding of Alpha Telecom; acting for Bridgepoint Capital Partners Ltd in further funding to PSL Group to fund £20 million acquisition of AGR Group.
Prof. Memberships: Law Society of Scotland. Law Society (England and Wales).
Career: University of Glasgow 1980-85 (LLB Hons; Dip LP). Qualified 1986 Scotland; 1994 England. Assistant *Levy & McRae*, Glasgow 1987; assistant *Taylor Vinters*, Cambridge 1988-89; assistant *Dickson Minto WS*, London 1990-96, Edinburgh 1997; *MacRoberts* 1997; partner 1988.

McHUGH, Peter
Eversheds, Birmingham (0121) 232 1000
petermchugh@eversheds.com
Specialisation: Head of corporate services, Birmingham. Handles mainly public company work, share acquisitions and disposals and general corporate advice.
Prof. Memberships: Birmingham Law Society.
Career: Qualified in 1982. Became a partner in *Eversheds Wells & Hind* in 1989.
Personal: Born 23 July 1958. Lives in Hartlebury, Worcestershire. Fellow of the RSA.

McINTOSH, Ian
Addleshaw Booth & Co, Leeds (0113) 209 2000
iwm@addleshaw-booth.co.uk
Specialisation: Partner in corporate finance group. Corporate finance and company law including mergers and acquisitions, joint ventures, MBOs and private and public capital raisings. Acts for a range of public and private companies, banks and venture capitalists.
Prof. Memberships: Law Society.
Career: Qualified 1983. Joined the firm in 1988, becoming a partner in 1989.
Personal: Leisure interests include golf, cinema and playing the drums badly.

McNEILL, Morag
McGrigor Donald, Glasgow (0141) 248 6677

McVEIGH, Kevin
Elliott Duffy Garrett, Belfast (028) 9024 5034
kevin.mcveigh@edgsolicitors.co.uk
Specialisation: Banking and turnaround finance; mergers and acquisitions.
Prof. Memberships: Law Society of N Ireland; Law Society England and Wales.

MEIKLEJOHN, Iain
Shepherd & Wedderburn WS, Edinburgh (0131) 228 9900
Specialisation: Partner in Corporate Department. Main areas of practice are corporate finance, mergers and acquisitions, banking, company law, small and medium businesses and insolvency law. Scottish Editor of 'International Bank Secrecy'.
Prof. Memberships: Law Society of Scotland.
Career: Apprenticed to *Allan Dawson Simpson & Hampton* 1976-78. Qualified in 1976 and joined *Shepherd & Wedderburn WS.* Became a Partner in 1982.
Personal: Born 3rd November 1954. Educated at Edinburgh Academy 1961-72 and Edinburgh University 1972-76. Director of The Scottish Trust for Underwater Archaeology, Stagecoach ESOP Trust Limited and Aggreko QUEST Trustee Limited.

METCALFE, Ian
Wragge & Co, Birmingham (0870) 903 1000

METCALFE, Rob
Browne Jacobson, Nottingham (0115) 976 6000 rmetcalfe@brownej.co.uk
Specialisation: Corporate/corporate finance. Wide experience of transaction oriented work heading unit which advises buyers, sellers and funders (equity and debt).
Prof. Memberships: Law Society.
Career: Articled *Eking Manning.* Qualified 1980. Partner *Browne Jacobson* 1985.
Personal: Born 1956; Educated Barnard Castle School, Co. Durham and Nottingham University (LLB Hons). Resides Nottingham. Interests: football, cricket, squash, watersports, climbing and trekking, travel and music.

MIDDLEDITCH, Matthew
Linklaters, London (020) 7456 3144 matthew.middleditch@linklaters.com
See under Investment Funds, p.517

MILLINGTON, Jeremy
Wragge & Co, Birmingham (0870) 903 1000

MINTO, Bruce
Dickson Minto WS, Edinburgh (0131) 225 4455 bruce.minto@dmws.com
Specialisation: Work includes Stock Exchange listings, Yellow Book work generally, mergers and acquisitions and institutional finance.
Prof. Memberships: Law Society of Scotland.
Career: Qualified in 1981. Formed *Dickson Minto WS* in 1985.
Personal: Born 30th October 1957. Attended Edinburgh University 1975-79. Leisure interests include golf, shooting and music.

MOORE, Austin
Gateley Wareing, Birmingham (0121) 234 0000

MORGAN, Simon
Olswang, London (020) 7208 8606 sdm@olswang.com
Specialisation: Partner, corporate. Corporate finance. Advises businesses and professional advisers on business start-ups, joint ventures, equity issues, acquisitions, disposals and take-overs. Recent transactions have included the flotations of Tuus plc, Jupiter Dividend & Growth Trust plc, New Star Investment Trust plc, Paradigm Media Investments plc and WMRC plc and various private equity financings for Two Way TV, Moneybox Corporation and New Star Asset Management Group.
Career: Qualified in 1987. Joined *Frere Cholmeley Bischoff* in 1985, becoming a Partner in 1994. Joined *Olswang* in August 1998.
Personal: Born 25th June 1963. Attended Oakwood Comprehensive School 1974-79, Thomas Rotherham College 1979-81 and Pembroke College, Cambridge 1981-84. Married with three children.

MORRIS, Andrew
Edwards Geldard, Cardiff (029) 2023 8239 andrew.morris@geldards.co.uk
Specialisation: Corporate finance, company and business acquisitions and disposals, management buy-outs and buy-ins, joint ventures and reorganisations, acts for clients receiving venture capital and bank funding and for banks and venture capital organisations providing funding.
Prof. Memberships: Law Society.
Career: Assistant Solicitor at *Edwards Geldard* between 1989 and 1995. Partner in *Edwards Geldard* since 1995.
Personal: Born 1965. Educated at Lady Mary High School, Cardiff and University of Glamorgan. Lives in Cardiff.

MORSE, Stephen
Michelmores, Exeter (01392) 436244

MUNDAY, Peter
Mundays, Esher (01372) 809000 peter.munday@mundays.co.uk
Specialisation: Head of corporate department and senior partner. Mergers, acquisitions and disposals. Clients include Alliance UniChem plc, The BOC Group plc. Photo-Me International plc, Corporate Express Inc, Air Express International (UK) Ltd, E. Moss Ltd, Fine Frangrances & Cosmetics Ltd, Morgan Elliott Group Ltd, Granger Telecom (Holdings) plc, Kewill Systems plc. Has undertaken lecture tours of USA under the title "Building a Bridge To The United States of Europe".
Personal: Born 31.10.1938. Educated: College of Law Guildford. Leisure interests include playing hockey, squash and cricket – member of the MCC. Lives in Oxshott, Surrey.

MURPHY, Frances
Slaughter and May, London (020) 7600 1200 frances.murphy@slaughterandmay.com
Specialisation: General practice consists principally of acting for corporate clients and investment banks on corporate finance and M&A transactions, both in England and overseas, and generally on corporate matters. Wide experience of acquisitions and disposals (both public and private), joint ventures and of equity and debt financing structures. Also has a significant practice in relation to demutualisation of building societies.
Prof. Memberships: The Law Society.
Career: Qualified in 1983 after articles with *Slaughter and May.* Became a partner in 1990, after a year in the Hong Kong office.
Personal: Born 24 September 1957.

NEWMAN, Iain
Nabarro Nathanson, London (020) 7524 6423 i.newman@nabarro.com
Specialisation: Head of public equity group. Diversified practice including flotations, fundraisings, private equity transactions and mergers and acquisitions. Significant recent transactions include a number of transactions for New Media SPARK plc and Investec Henderson Croswaithe and WSP Group; takeover of Jacussa & Widsmith and associated fundraising.
Prof. Memberships: BVCA.
Career: Qualified in 1990 with *Nabarro Nathanson.* Became a partner in 1997.
Personal: Born 1966. Attended St. Bees School and Mansfield College, Oxford. Principal leisure interest is spending time with my wife (Vicki) and two children (Anna and Peter).

NICHOLSON, Graham
Freshfields Bruckhaus Deringer, London (020) 7936 4000 graham.nicholson@freshfields.com
Specialisation: Partner dealing with corporate law, international finance, joint ventures, mergers and acquisitions, securities offerings with particular reference to the insurance and telecommunications industries.
Career: Qualified 1974. Partner 1980.
Personal: Born 1949. Educated at Trinity Hall, Cambridge.

NORCROSS WEBB, Sally
Shoosmiths, Fareham (01489) 881 010 sally.norcrosswebb@shoosmiths.co.uk
Specialisation: Company and corporate finance work, especially acquisitions and disposals of companies, MBOs, MBIs, banking, joint ventures, corporate transactions generally, commercial work and business strategy; recent transactions include sale of Ede's Group and structured framework for banks. Head of corporate at Solent office.
Prof. Memberships: Past Chairman Hampshire CBI. Governor of Portsmouth University.
Career: MA LLM (Cantab). Articled *Allen & Overy*; one year *Allen, Allen & Hemsley,* Sydney Australia; *Slaughter and May*; partner in small firm *Norcross Hill* which merged with *Shoosmiths* in 1992.
Personal: Sailing, gardening. Two sons. Lives Chichester.

NORMAN, Guy T D
Clifford Chance, London (020) 7600 1000 guy.norman@cliffordchance.com
Specialisation: Principal area of practice is corporate and corporate finance. Advises corporate and investment banking clients on takeovers and mergers, capital raising, stock exchange issues, joint ventures, private acquisitions and disposals. Has particular expertise in relation to the Takeover Code and related matters.
Prof. Memberships: Law Society.
Career: Articled with *Clifford Chance* 1989-91, qualified in September 1991 and became a Partner in 1998. *Schroders* corporate finance (on secondment) 1994. Secretary of Takeover Panel (on secondment) 1997-99.
Personal: Born 1966. Educated Sevenoaks School and Downing College Cambridge. Interests include cars, tennis and golf. Lives in London.

NORTON, Richard
Charles Russell, Cheltenham (01242) 221122 richardn@ce-law.co.uk
Specialisation: Corporate finance/banking. Acted for: Trifast plc on acquisition of Special Fasteners Engineering Company Limited in Taiwan for a consideration of £15 million; shareholders of Recall

Recruitment plc on its sale to the Capita Group plc for a consideration of up to £15 million; Collins Stewart, the bankers to the Character Group plc, on the Character Group's 1 for 1 rights issue.
Prof. Memberships: Law Society.
Career: *Linklaters & Paines*: 1982-87; *Charles Russell*: 1987-date.
Publications: Corporate finance/Financial Services Act sections on Legal Education Network videos.
Personal: Golf and shooting. Two children.

O'BRIEN, Barry
Freshfields Bruckhaus Deringer, London
(020) 7936 4000
barry.obrien@freshfields.com
Specialisation: Partner in corporate department: head of corporate department. Specialises in mergers and acqusitions and securities work, much of which has an international element. Acts for a number of the firm's key investment banking clients as well as a wide range of corporate clients. In 1996 led a team of 200 lawyers on the implementation of the Reconstruction and Renewal plan and reinsurance into Equitas.
Prof. Memberships: Law Society.
Career: Qualified in 1978. Joined *Freshfields* in 1983 and became a partner in 1986.
Personal: Born 1952. Educated at University College, London. Enjoys sport. Lives in London.

O'CONNOR, Mark
Davies Wallis Foyster, Liverpool (0151) 236 6226
moc@dwf-law.com
Specialisation: Corporate finance transactions, business structuring, commercial advice, corporate governance, public company work and the establishment of regional investment funds.
Prof. Memberships: Law Society.
Career: Articled *Cuff Roberts North Kirk*; qualified 1980; Partner *Davies Wallis Foyster* 1984; Head of Corporate.

ON, Nicholas
Eversheds, Newcastle upon Tyne (0191) 261 1661
nicholason@eversheds.com
See under Banking, p.121

PALMER, James
Herbert Smith, London (020) 7374 8000
Specialisation: Principal areas of work are mergers and acquisitions, equity capital markets and general corporate, including takeovers, UK and international securities offerings, demergers, schemes of arrangement and joint ventures. Experience in many sectors including financial institutions and media/technology.
Prof. Memberships: City of London Solicitors Company, Company Law Sub-Committee.
Career: Joined 1986, qualified 1988, Partner 1994.
Personal: Born 10.9.1963. Educated at Winchester College and Queens' College Cambridge 1982-85.

PARTRIDGE, James
Thomson Snell & Passmore, Tunbridge Wells
(01892) 510000
jpartridge@ts-p.co.uk
Specialisation: Head of company/commercial department. Deals with all company and commercial matters but specialises in the sale and purchase of companies and businesses, management buy-outs, the establishment of joint ventures and corporate finance.
Career: Qualified in 1983. Trained and practised in London before joining *Thomson Snell & Passmore* in 1986. Became a partner in 1987.
Personal: Born 14 March 1958. Educated at Lancing College and Trinity College, Cambridge BA (CANTAB) 1977-80. Other interests: member of the Territorial Army, walking, sailing. Lives near Tunbridge Wells.

PASS, Jamie
Dickinson Dees, Newcastle upon Tyne
(0191) 279 9285
jamie.pass@dickinson-dees.com
Specialisation: Mainstream corporate finance, mergers & acquisitions, new issues and private equity work.
Prof. Memberships: Law Society.
Career: Educated Doncaster Grammar School & Jesus College, Cambridge. *Clifford Chance* 1986-92. Joined *Dickinson Dees* in 1992. Partner 1995.
Personal: Born Doncaster, resides Newcastle upon Tyne.

PATRICK, Bruce R.
Maclay Murray & Spens, Edinburgh
(0131) 226 5196
brp@maclaymurrayspens.co.uk
Specialisation: Senior partner experienced in all areas of corporate law but most notably in venture capital, MBO's/MBI's, receiverships and ship finance. Vice-Convenor of the Company Law Committee of the Law Society of Scotland. Has been a panel solicitor for 3i plc for over 25 years. Head of the firm's Scottish Parliamentary Group.
Career: Qualified 1973. University of Oxford (BA 1967) and University of Edinburgh (LLB 1971). Former managing partner of *Maclay Murray & Spens* (1991-94). Senior partner (2000-).
Personal: Born 1945.

PAUL, Alan D.
Allen & Overy, London (020) 7330 3000
alan.paul@allenovery.com
Specialisation: Partner in the Corporate Department. Principal area of work is corporate finance, particularly corporate acquisitions with a specialisation in public takeovers and transactions for financial buyers. Other main area of work is equity-linked financings, including flotations. Author of 'Corporate Governance in the Context of Takeovers of UK Public Companies' in 'Contemporary Issues in Corporate Governance' (1993) and has written numerous articles for various legal journals.
Prof. Memberships: Law Society.
Career: Articled with *Allen & Overy* 1978-80, qualified in March 1980 and became a Partner in 1985. Secretary of Takeover Panel (on secondment) 1985-88.
Personal: Born 19th July 1954. Attended St. Paul's School 1966-72, then University College, Oxford 1973-77. Lives in London.

PEARSON, Christopher
Norton Rose, London (020) 7283 6000
pearsoncc@nortonrose.com
Specialisation: Main area of practice is public company and stock exchange transactions, including public company takeovers, other mergers and acquisitions, flotations, securities offerings, and company reconstructions and institutional investments. Also international transactions, including cross-border mergers and acquisitions and joint ventures. Important public company transactions include Guinness/Grand Metropolitan (£22 billion); Texas Utilties/The Energy Group (£4.45 billion); Ciba Specialty Chemicals/Allied Colloids (£1.42 billion); Trinity/Mirror Group (£2.1 billion); Mannesmann/Orange (£20 billion) and Airtours/Carnival, a subscription and partial offer involving Carnival acquiring 29.5% of Airtours for some £200 million. Securities transactions include the flotation of Beeson Gregory and the "trombone" rights issue by Trinity International Holdings to raise £182 million in connection with the acquisition of regional newspaper interests of The Thomson Corporation and the HSBC Holdings Enhanced Scrip Dividend Scheme. Other mergers and acquisitions include the linked disposal by Siemens of its shareholding in GPT Holdings to GEC and acquisition of GEC's shareholding in Siemens GEC Communication Systems (£700 million). International transactions include the formation of a cross border joint venture between Redland and Koramic in respect of brick products in Belgium and Holland (to create the largest facing brick manufacturer in continental Europe) and the establishment of a joint venture, Sun International Investments (owned by Royale Resorts, Caledonia Investments and World Leisure Group) to invest over US$100 million in the billion dollar Paradise Island resort project in the Bahamas.
Prof. Memberships: Member of the Law Society, the City of London Solicitors Company and the Royal Automobile Club; also the firm's representative on the City of London Law Society Company Law Sub-Committee.
Personal: Family status: married. Hobbies/interests: squash, tennis, rugby, theatre and cinema.

PEARSON, David
Clifford Chance, London (020) 7600 1000
david.pearson@cliffordchance.com
Specialisation: Partner specialising in corporate finance, takeovers, flotations, mergers and acquisitions and secondary issues, also venture capital, management buy-outs and buy-ins.
Career: Ashville College, Harrogate; Downing College, Cambridge (MA Law). Articled *Clifford Chance*; qualified 1989; made partner 1996.
Personal: Golf, skiing, running. Born 1964; resides London.

PEARSON, Jeffrey
Edwards Geldard, Cardiff (029) 2023 8239
jeff.pearson@geldards.co.uk
Specialisation: Corporate finance, public takeovers, mergers and acquisitions and multi-jurisdictional joint ventures. Recent work includes a number of transactions for Barclays Bank plc, Hyder plc, WPD Inc, Pendragon plc, Chevron in the quoted company sector and a number of MBO's and acquisition and disposal work in the private company sector.
Prof. Memberships: Law Society.
Career: *Slaughter and May* London between 1984 and 1991. Partner in *Edwards Geldard* since 1991.
Personal: Born 1961. Educated at Bishop Gore SC, Swansea and University College of Wales, Aberystwyth. Married with two children. Lives in Cardiff.

PECK, Andrew
Linklaters, London (020) 7456 3454
andrew.peck@linklaters.com
Specialisation: Deals with a wide range of company law matters, including new issues, takeovers and mergers, sales and purchases of private companies and company reorganisations, with extensive experience in the financial services sector, for example, insurance companies and building societies.

Career: Group leader in the corporate practice. 1984: Seconded to the Council for the Securities Industry to assist in drafting a City response to the Gower Report; 1983 to date: Partner, *Linklaters*; 1981-83: Assistant solicitor, corporate department, *Linklaters*; 1976-81: Corporate finance department, NM Rothschild & Sons Limited (assistant director 1980); 1971-73: Articled clerk, *Linklaters*. 1967-71: Cambridge University, MA, LLB.

PELL, Marian
Herbert Smith, London (020) 7374 8000
marian.pell@herbertsmith.com
See under Insurance, p.490

PESTER, David
TLT Solicitors, Bristol (0117) 917 7777
dpester@TLTsolicitors.com
Specialisation: Head of Corporate Finance Team. Mergers, acquisitions and disposals, other corporate finance and company law. Particular experience of OFEX, AIM and other listings. Led the disposal of Bakers Dolphin to First Choice Holdings for £16million; disposal of the retail operation of Fowlers Bristol for £8million; admission of Advanced Technology plc to AIM (£50million initial market cap).
Prof. Memberships: Company Secretary of Bristol Tourism and Conference Bureau. Bristol Chamber of Commerce and Initiative.
Career: Manchester University, BA (1st), Bristol University, LLM (Employment and Corporate Law); articled at *Lawrence Tucketts* (now *TLT Solicitors*, the merged firm of *Trumps* and *Lawrence Tucketts*), admitted 1989.
Personal: Sailing and football.

PHILLIPS, Robert
Robert Muckle, Newcastle upon Tyne (0191) 232 4402
Specialisation: General Corporate Finance. Partner and head of commercial group- quality commercial work for both public and private companies. Specialisation in corporate sales and acquisitions and investment venture capital.
Career: Articled *Denton Hall*; work in corporate finance sector; 2 years with *Memery Crystal*. Qualified 1990. Joined *Robert Muckle* as an associate in 1994; became a partner in 1997 and group head in 2000.

PILLMAN, Joe
Brobeck Hale and Dorr, Oxford (01235) 823000
pillman@bhd.com
Specialisation: Partner. Handles general company law for technology companies including flotations, mergers and acquisitions, MBOs, MBIs and reconstructions. Important matters handled include several acquisitions by Screen and CRC, various investments in Bookham Technology, including private placements by Intel and CISCO, the sales of Carfax Publishing to Routledge and Supergas to Centrica, the dual listings of QXL and Bookham Technology on the LSE and NASDAQ and the listings of Screen and Tricorder Technology on AIM.
Career: Qualified in 1977. Partner with *Cole & Cole* from 1983-2000. Partner with *Brobeck Hale and Dorr* 2000 to date.
Personal: Born 7th July 1952. Educated at Rugby School 1965-69 and Cambridge University 1970-74. Lives in Northumberland.

PRINCE, Michael
DLA, Liverpool (08700) 111111

PSYLLIDES, Milton
Eversheds, Birmingham (0121) 232 1067
miltonpsyllides@eversheds.com
Specialisation: Partner. Public company transactions, including flotations, mergers and acquisitions, new issues and funding transactions.
Prof. Memberships: Chairman of the Midlands & North Wales Stock Exchange Regional Advisory Group. Member of the Law Society and the Birmingham Law Society. Treasurer of the Birmingham Law Society. Member of the Birmingham Law Society Company and Commercial Law sub-committee. Council Member West Midlands CBI.
Career: Qualified March 1978 with *Evershed & Tomkinson*. Partner May 1984 with *Evershed & Tomkinson*. *Eversheds* national firm created May 1989.
Personal: Born 30th October 1953. Brockley County Grammar School and Liverpool University. Married with one daughter and one son.

PYSDEN, Edward
Eversheds, Manchester (0161) 831 8000

RAFFERTY, John
Burness, Edinburgh (0131) 473 6000

RANDELL, Charles
Slaughter and May, London (020) 7600 1200
charles.randell@slaughterandmay.com
Specialisation: Company/commercial.
Career: Articled *Slaughter and May*; qualified 1982; partner 1989.
Personal: Educated at Trinity College, Oxford.

RAWLINSON, Mark
Freshfields Bruckhaus Deringer, London (020) 7936 4000
markrawlinson@freshfields.com
Specialisation: Partner in the corporate department specialising in mergers and acquisitions, particularly international and cross border. Also covers general corporate finance (including IPOs, rights issues and other issues) and joint ventures. Publications include 'A Practitioners Guide to Corporate Finance and the Financial Services Act 1986' (contributor) and 'Rights Issues Practice Manual' (contributor and editor).
Career: Qualified 1984. Assistant solicitor, *Freshfields* 1984-90. Partner since 1990. Listed as one of the top fifteen 'Best Business Lawyers' in Chambers' 1998 survey.
Personal: Educated at Haberdashers' Aske's School, Elstree and Sidney Sussex College, Cambridge 1976-80. Interests include family and sport. Born 1957. Lives in London.

RAWSTRON, Chris
DLA, Birmingham (08700) 111111

ROBINSON, Michael
Pinsent Curtis Biddle, Leeds (0113) 244 5000
michael.robinson@pinsents.com
Specialisation: Specialises in corporate finance and company law with a particular emphasis on public company work including primary and secondary issues. Major transaction include: the £300 million bid for Polypipe plc by IMI plc; the acquisition of Henry Cooke Group by Brown, Shipley & Co. Various AIM and full listings.
Prof. Memberships: Institutute of Directors
Career: Articles: *Linklaters & Paines* 1983-85. Assistant solicitor, *Linklaters & Paines* 1985-87. Assistant solicitor, *Simpson Curtis* (now *Pinsent Curtis Biddle*) 1987-90. Partner *Pinsent Curtis Biddle* 1990 to date.
Personal: Education: Northallerton Grammar School, St Edmund Hall Oxford University (1st class honours Jurisprudence).Leisure: Football (watching Middlesbrough!) all kinds of music and family.

ROSE, Kenneth
Dundas & Wilson CS, Edinburgh (0131) 228 8000

ROSEFIELD, Stephen
Berwin Leighton Paisner, London (020) 7760 1000
stephen.rosefield@berwinleightonpaisner.com
Specialisation: Co-Chairman with responsibility for merger integration and partner in corporate department. Main area of practice is mergers and acquisitions and corporate finance including takeovers (both public and private), purchase and sale of businesses, MBO's, joint ventures and reconstructions. Acts for a wide range of listed property, trading and investment companies. Writes and speaks widely on the purchase and sale of companies and businesses, and joint ventures including having contributed to Butterworths Encyclopaedia of Forms & Precedents Vol. 11.
Prof. Memberships: Law Society.
Career: Qualified in 1977, having joined *Paisner & Co* in 1975. Became a Partner in 1980. Appointed as the first Managing Partner in 1999. Co-Chairman *Berwin Leighton Paisner* 2001.
Personal: Born 19th December 1952. Educated at St. Paul's School 1965-70 and St. Edmund Hall, Oxford 1971-74. Recreations include theatre, music, tennis and soccer. Lives in London.

ROSENBERG, Daniel
Taylor Joynson Garrett, London (020) 7300 7000

ROUS, Simon
Bevan Ashford, Exeter (01392) 663 333
s.rous@bevan-ashford.com
Specialisation: Heads *Bevan Ashford's* Corporate & Banking Team. Simon is active in corporate finance, MBO's, mergers and acquisitions and new issue work. Simon has spent 25 years specialising on corporate transactions. Much of his work is London based or international, especially from Germany, the USA and the Middle East. *Bevan Ashford's* London Office at No 1 Chancery Lane, enables him to deliver on London based and international transactions at regional charge-out rates. Simon regularly lectures both in the UK and abroad, most recently on 'Acquisitions & Divestitures in the UK' (delivered in Paris), 'Developments in Minority Shareholder Issues' and 'EBT Financed Investor Exits'. His seminars have quite a reputation, commanding fee-paying audiences of over 200. His home ISDN link enables him to stay in contact with his clients' affairs even while notionally off duty. For more details see www.bevan-ashford.com/corporate.
Prof. Memberships: He keeps his memberships to a few influential bodies, such as the CBI (Southwest) and Exeter University Business Forum, so as to be able to concentrate on his clients.
Career: Simon read Law at Trinity College Cambridge and then spent 11 years with *Clifford Chance* in London, Paris, Brussels, the Middle East and New York before joining *Bevan Ashford* in 1985.

ROXBURGH, Bruce O.
Osborne Clarke, Bristol (0117) 917 3000

RUNDALL, Francis R S
Charles Russell, Cheltenham (01242) 221122
francisr@cr-law.co.uk
Specialisation: Corporate finance, acquisitions and disposals, public and private. Also advises on flotations and other capital raising projects. Recent work includes acting for Browalia International BV on the takeover of British Mohair Holdings plc; acting for the Montpellier Group plc on the acquisition of the building construction division of Allen plc; acting for Browalia plc on the takeover of Union plc. Additionally advises on charity law. Acted for the Countryside Animal Welfare Group in their attempt to prevent the RSPCA excluding pro-hunting people from membership.
Career: Marlborough College; University College, Durham. Qualified 1975; Assistant Solicitor at *Slaughter & May* 1975-78; joined *Charles Russell* 1978, becoming a partner in 1981.
Personal: Secretary to Network Gloucestershire Limited. Leisure interests include hunting and shooting, opera and church music.

RYDE, Andy
Slaughter and May, London (020) 7600 1200
andy.ryde@slaughterandmay.com
Specialisation: Partner specialising in general corporate and corporate finance; acts for a number of listed companies and investment banks in connection with mergers and acquisitions and corporate finance transactions.
Career: Articled *Slaughter and May*; qualified 1989; partner 1996.
Publications: Author of 'Share Dealings – Restrictions and Disclosure Requirements', a chapter in the 'Practitioner's Guide to the City Code on Takeovers and Mergers'.
Personal: Born 1964. Educated at the Minster School, Southwell, Nottinghamshire, and Wadham College, Oxford (1986 MA Hons Jurisprudence). Resides Northwood. Interests: sports.

SACKMAN, Simon
Norton Rose, London (020) 7283 6000
Specialisation: Partner and head of corporate finance. Main practice area is mergers and acquisitions, IPOs and other equity issues, demergers and other restructurings. Also experienced in investment trusts, the property/hotel sector and regulatory investigations. Recent transactions include the proposed merger of Deutsche Börse with the London Stock Exchange, Finalrealm's offer for United Biscuits, the purchase of EM.TV of 50 percent of Formula One and the subsequent restructuring of EM.TV, the sale by Benchmark of a portfolio of West End properties to The West End of London Property Unit Trust, the enquiry into Lanica's bid for CWS and numerous hotel acquisitions, including the Caledonian in Edinburgh and the Landmark in London.
Prof. Memberships: Law Society, City of London Solicitors Company, International Bar Association.

SADKA, Tim
Rawlison Butler, Crawley (01293) 527744

SALZ, Anthony
Freshfields Bruckhaus Deringer, London
(020) 7936 4000
anthony.salz@freshfields.com
Specialisation: Senior partner and partner in corporate department. Main area of practice is mergers and acquisitions and all aspects of corporate finance work, both in the UK and internationally.
Prof. Memberships: Law Society.
Career: Qualified 1974. Joined *Freshfields* in 1975. 1977/8 *Davis Polk & Wardwell*, New York. Partner in corporate department 1980. Senior partner 1996. Chair, Tate Gallery Corporate Advisory Group.
Personal: Born 1950. Attended Summerfields 1958-63, Radley College 1964-67. Exeter University 1968-71. Leisure pursuits include golf, family and fishing and supporting Southampton FC.

SEABROOK, Michael
Eversheds, Birmingham (0121) 232 1084
michaelseabrook@eversheds.com
Specialisation: Partner in corporate services department specialising in private equity. Work includes IBOs, MBOs and MBIs and mergers and acquisitions (both domestic and international).
Prof. Memberships: Law Society, Securities Institute.
Career: Qualified in 1976 with *Lovell White & King*. Assistant solicitor at *Clifford Turner* 1977-79. With *Needham & James* 1980-86 (partner from 1981). Joined *Evershed & Tomkinson* as a partner in 1986. Now deputy senior partner (Birmingham).
Personal: Born 24 March 1952. Educated at King Edward's School, Birmingham 1963-70 and Exeter University (LL.B) 1970-73. Recreations include cricket, golf, soccer, rugby, and horse racing. Lives in Dorridge, Solihull.

SHAND, Kenneth
Maclay Murray & Spens, Glasgow
(0141) 248 5011
kds@maclaymurrayspens.co.uk
Specialisation: Head of corporate department. Kenneth handles a range of mainstream corporate transactions, principally for private companies both large and small; his practice covers mergers and acquisitions, MBOs/MBIs/IBOs and institutional finance. Following completion in late 1999 of its successful £600 million bid (through a joint venture with William Grant & Sons Limited) for Highland Distillers plc, advised The Edrington Group Limited on a significant restructuring to simplify and streamline group arrangements. Spent much of 2000 advising the new board of directors of Semple Cochrane plc on issues arising from the board's discovery of accounting discrepancies at the group and on the reconstruction of its finances. His group advised on a number of 3i investments, particularly in Ireland, and several investments by the Scottish Enterprise Network. Other deals have included Scottish disposals for the Kvaerner Group and the investment by MCR Holdings Limited in new start hi-technology printing company, FST and its contract with IF.com. Worked closely throughout 2001 with innovative time ownership operator Residence International Limited on its acquisition of the high profile One Devonshire Gardens Hotel in Glasgow and on several deals in New York, South Carolina, Florida, Italy, Portugal and England as the group's portfolio develops, and related financing exercises. Leads the firm's inward investment team which advises a number of foreign headquartered businesses including Compaq, Mack Technologies, MSA and Sally Beauty.
Prof. Memberships: Law Society of Scotland.
Career:*Maclay Murray & Spens* 1982-84 (trainee); *Maclay Murray & Spens* 1984-88 (assistant solicitor); *McKenna & Co* 1988-89 (assistant solicitor); *Maclay Murray & Spens* 1989-date (partner).
Personal: Education: Glasgow Academy (1969-77); University of Glasgow (1981 LLB Hons); University of Glasgow (1982 Diploma in Legal Practice). Leisure interests: most sports, especially golf, rugby, tennis and football. Family: married with one son and one daughter.

SHAW, Martin
Pinsent Curtis Biddle, Leeds (0113) 244 5000
martin.shaw@pinsents.com
Specialisation: Head of Corporate Department, Leeds. Specialises in corporate finance and company law including M&A, stock exchange primary and secondary issues and company re-organisations primarily for public listed companies. Recent transactions include: The SIG plc bid for Roskel plc (£26 million), the bid by Baan Company NV for the CODA Group plc (£11.1 million), the BPT £75 million London Stock Exchange listing of Eurobonds, the Sunderland plc strategic media alliance with the BskyB Group plc (£13 million), the OFEX flotation of SquareSum plc, the disposal by Yule Catto & Co plc of its William Cox Plastics subsidiary (£14.5 million), the refinancing of Youngs Bluecrest Seafood Holdings (£53 million), an auction sale and recommended takeover bid for BPT plc by Deutsche Bank/Grainger Trust (£477 million) and the Cosalt plc bid for SEET plc and associated debt facilities (£29 million).
Prof. Memberships: Member of the Solicitors European Group; the American Bar Association and the International Bar Association.
Career: Articled *Simpson Curtis* (now *Pinsent Curtis Biddle*) 1966-69. Qualified 1969. Lecturer in law (part-time) Leeds Metropolitan University. Partner 1971. Former managing partner at *Simpson Curtis*.
Personal: Member of Headingley Rotary Club (past council member and Chairman of International Services Committee); Chairman of Governors of Gateways School. Hon. Secretary of Yorkshire Regional Committee of the Variety Club of Great Britain.

SHIMMIN, Kathryn
Blake Lapthorn, Southampton (023) 8063 1823

SHORT, John
Taylor Vinters, Cambridge (01223) 423444
Specialisation: Partner in company/commercial department. Work covers acquisitions and sales, reconstructions, venture capital, investment, and MBO/MBIs. Also handles insolvency and banking, advising receivers and liquidators. Advises on taking and enforcing security.
Prof. Memberships: Law Society, Committee Member of Eastern Region Branch of R3.
Career: Qualified 1974. Trainee and solicitor at *Pretty*s, Ipswich, 1972-75; assistant solicitor at *Coward Chance*, London, 1976-78. Joined *Taylor Vinters* in 1979, became a partner in 1982. Secretary of Cambridgeshire and District Law Society, 1983-87; Vice President 1999-2000; President 2000-2001.
Personal: Born 28th December 1949. Attended Sheffield University 1968-71. Leisure interests include walking, music and photography.

SIGNY, Adam
Clifford Chance, London (020) 7600 1000
adam.signy@cliffordchance.com
Specialisation: Partner specialising in corporate finance, public and private M&A, private equity.
Career: City of London School; Sussex University (Economics). Articled *Clifford Chance*; qualified

1982; partner *Clifford Chance* since 1987.
Personal: Born 1955; married, three children; resides Suffolk and London.

SIMMONS, William
Tods Murray WS, Edinburgh (0131) 226 4771
william.simmons@todsmurray.com
See under Projects/PFI, p.715

SLEIGH, Andrew
Burness, Glasgow (0141) 248 4933
afs@burness.co.uk
Specialisation: Andrew has significant experience in all aspects of private company corporate finance, including acting for management, venture capital houses and vendors involved in MBO and MBI transactions. Notable recent deals include acting for consortium which acquired Bruichladdich Distillery, Islay; Ladbrokes in acquisition of John Smith Bookmakers; vendor of the Malcolm family companies in sale to Grampian Holdings plc; acting in the acquisition of a significant regional soft drinks manufacturer; acting in the sale of Beat 106 to Capital Radio plc; representing interests of SFA in rescue of Hampden Stadium, Glasgow.

SLOAN, Graeme
Maclay Murray & Spens, Edinburgh (0131) 479 2867
gecs@maclaymurrayspens.co.uk
Specialisation: Partner specialising in corporate finance, mergers and acquisitions and private equity. Has extensive experience in public company work, advising both companies and financial advisers. Principal clients include Bank of Scotland, Candover, John Menzies, McDermott International and Scottish Widows.
Career: *Balfour & Manson*, trainee solicitor 1985-87; *Arthur Young*, tax senior 1987-88; *Maclay Murray & Spens*, assistant solicitor 1998-89; *Freshfields*, manager 1990-92; *Maclay Murray & Spens*, partner 1992 to date.

SMART, Peter
Walker Morris, Leeds (0113) 283 2500
pcs@walkermorris.co.uk
Specialisation: Head of Corporate. Main areas of practice are corporate finance, M&A work, venture capital and (because they're interesting) the resolution of shareholder disputes. Recent deals include the £72 million multijurisdictional disposal of Alcontrol by Kelda Group plc to Bridgepoint Capital.
Prof. Memberships: Law Society.
Career: Qualified in 1979, having joined *Walker Morris* in 1977. Became a Partner in 1981, Managing Partner 1993-98 and Chairman in 2001. A director of several public and private companies.

SMERDON, Richard W.
Osborne Clarke, Reading (0118) 925 2000

SMITH, Campbell
Biggart Baillie, Glasgow (0141) 228 8000
csmith@biggartbaillie.co.uk
Specialisation: Managing partner and partner in corporate department. Main area of practice is corporate transactions. Work includes acquisitions and disposals of private companies and assets. Also insurance companies and friendly societies. Former Director of the Joint Insolvency Examination Board; member of several Law Society Committees.
Prof. Memberships: Law Society of Scotland, International Bar Association.
Career: Qualified in 1972. Assistant at *Herbert Smith & Co.* 1972-73 and *Biggart Baillie & Gifford* (now *Biggart Baillie*) 1973-74. Became partner there in 1974.
Personal: Born 17th May 1946. Attended Glasgow Academy 1951-65, St Catharine's College, Cambridge 1965-68 and the University of Glasgow 1968-70. Ex-Deacon Incorporation of Barbers, Glasgow. Leisure interests include golf, croquet, barbershop and choral singing. Lives in Glasgow.

SPETCH, Michael
Eversheds, Newcastle upon Tyne (0191) 261 1661
mikespetch@eversheds.com
Specialisation: Corporate finance, mergers and acquisitions.
Prof. Memberships: Law Society.
Career: Qualified Oct 1988. Three years in corporate department of *Hammond Suddards*. Then (1991) joined *Wilkinson Maughan* and then *Eversheds* in 1997. Head of corporate, *Eversheds* North East.
Personal: University of Leicester – LLB (Hons). Married, two children.

SPINK, Richard
Burges Salmon, Bristol (0117) 939 2218
richard.spink@burges-salmon.com
Specialisation: Venture capital and corporate finance. Numerous venture capital transactions include acting for Scottish and Southern Energy plc on its £10 million e-commerce investment in Simple2, the first web based company to offer virtual employee financial services; Orange Ventures on its £16 million investment in Digital Rum; and ECI Ventures on three transactions including the £10.5 million buy out of MM Group. Other transactions include acting for Motion Media on its admission to the Official List, various acquisitions by Transport Development Group plc and acting for Gooch & Housego plc on its £4.75 million acquisition of US corporation Neo Technologies.
Prof. Memberships: Law Society.
Career: Trained and worked with *Freshfields* including a 6 month secondment in New York. Qualified in 1989. Joined *Burges Salmon* in 1994 becoming a partner in 1999. Has had two secondments – one with *Steele Hector & Davis* in Florida and the other with Transport Development Group plc as in-house counsel. Downing College, Cambridge 1984-88, Masters in Public International Law.
Personal: Cricket, golf and rowing.

SPRIGGS, Michael
Eversheds, Newcastle upon Tyne (0191) 2611661
michaelspriggs@eversheds.com
Specialisation: Senior partner *Eversheds* North East. Head of North East corporate group. Corporate finance, covering venture capital, mergers and acquisitions, joint ventures and shareholder disputes.
Prof. Memberships: Law Society.
Career: Banker with Standard Chartered Bank, Hong Kong 1979-81. Trained at *Frere Cholmeley*, London. Qualified as a solicitor in 1985. Joined *Wilkinson Maughan*, becoming partner in 1987. Senior partner 2000.

STAFFORD, Peter
Arthur Cox – Northern Ireland, Belfast (028) 9023 0007
pstafford@arthurcox.ie
Specialisation: General corporate finance including M&A , takeovers, fundraisings, buyouts and shareholders agreements. Also financial services work.
Prof. Memberships: Law Society of Northern Ireland; Law Society of England and Wales.
Career: Qualified 1995. Assistant solicitor *Herbert Smith*, London 1995-97. Corporate finance executive IBI Corporate Finance, Belfast 1997-99. Assistant solicitor with *Arthur Cox* Northern Ireland since 1999.
Personal: Educated at Royal Belfast Academical Institution and Jesus College, Cambridge. Interested in most sports.

STANFIELD, Glynne
Mills & Reeve, Cambridge (01223) 222250
glynne.stanfield@mills-reeve.com
Specialisation: Advises on wide range of corporate and commercial matters for higher education clients. This year he has advised on the merger between Imperial and Wye Colleges and the joint venture between the University of Cambridge and MIT. He also advises extensively on commercialisation of technology and this year has been involved in, for example, the spin outs of Ilotron for the University of Essex (£6 million start up), Gendel from the University of Ulster (£5 million start up) and the establishment of three University Challenge funds. He has a particular interest in the funding of higher education by conventional and unconventional/innovative financing methods including tax based schemes.

STEINFELD, Michael
Dechert, London (020) 7583 5353

STELLA, Keith G.
Berwin Leighton Paisner, London (020) 7760 1000
keith.stella@berwinleightonpaisner.com
Specialisation: Partner and head of Corporate Finance. Practice covers the full range of corporate finance activities, including flotations, secondary offerings, bids and takeovers (both public and private). Acts for wide range of listed and private companies, as well as for banks, brokers and other intermediaries.
Career: Qualified 1978. Partner from 1980. Educated at City of London School and University College, London (LL.B 1st Class Hons). First Class Hons in Law Society Finals.
Personal: Living in Hertfordshire. Interests include classical music, antiques and wine.

STEPHENSON, Barbara
Norton Rose, London (020) 7283 6000
stephensonb@nortonrose.com
Specialisation: Main area of practice is corporate finance, including public company takeovers, other mergers and acquisitions, initial public offerings, securities offerings and company reconstructions and institutional investments. Also international transactions, including cross-border, mergers and acquisitions and joint ventures. Important transactions handled include the £2.5 billion takeover of Eastern Group by Hanson, the £1.4 billion acquisition of the investment banking business of Schroders by Citigroup by way of scheme of arrangement and non Code offer and the flotation of Fox Kids Europe on the Amsterdam Stock Exchange. Corporate clients include Taylor Woodrow, Pillar Property, Fox Kids Europe, Old Mutual, QBE, Blacks Leisure Group, Matsushita Electric Europe and TBI. Investment banks include Schroders Salomon Smith Barney, Credit Agricole Indosuez, HSBC, SG Hambros, Credit Lyonnais, West LB and ABN Amro.
Prof. Memberships: Member of the Law Society.
Personal: Married with three daughters.

STERN, Robert
Slaughter and May, London (020) 7600 1200
robert.stern@slaughterandmay.com
Specialisation: General practice consists principally of acting for corporate and investment bank clients on corporate finance and M&A transactions, both in England and overseas and generally on corporate matters. Wide experience of acquisitions and disposals (both public and private), joint ventures and of equity and debt financing structures.
Career: BA in French and German at The Queen's College, Oxford. Qualified as a solicitor in 1986. Became a partner in 1993.

STILTON, Andrew
Martineau Johnson, Birmingham (0121) 678 1556
andrew.stilton@martjohn.com
Specialisation: Corporate finance: buy-outs, buy-ins and general merger and acquisition work as well as venture capital and flotation work. Also some banking work.
Prof. Memberships: Law Society, Securities Institute, member of the Law Society's Company Law Committee.
Career: Qualified in 1981. Partner in *Ryland Martineau* in 1985. Partner in *Martineau Johnson* on merger in 1987.
Personal: Born 31st October 1957. Educated at Trinity Hall, Cambridge. Leisure interests include cricket, football, music and travel until parenthood intervened.

STORAR, Michael
Lawrence Graham, London (020) 737 9000
michael.storar@lawgram.com
Specialisation: Head of company/commercial department. Main area of practice is corporate finance, covering mergers and acquisitions, flotations, listings and venture capital. Also handles advertising and marketing. Advised the government and the Director General of the National Lottery on its structure and start up.
Career: Qualified in 1981. Worked at *Ashurst Morris Crisp* 1978-83. Joined *Blyth Dutton* in 1983, which merged to become *Lawrence Graham.*
Personal: Born 25th October 1955. Attended Cranleigh School 1963-73, Camberwell 1973-4 and Birmingham 1974-7. Lives in Suffolk.

STREET, Robert
Chaffe Street, Manchester (0161) 211 9218
rhs@chaffestreet.co.uk
Specialisation: Partner in company/commercial department. Handles all areas of company commercial work including corporate finance, company and business acquisitions and disposals, intellectual property and commercial contracts.
Prof. Memberships: Law Society.
Career: Qualified in 1975. Articles at *Coward Chance.* Became a partner at *Harold Chaffe & Co* in 1978. Partner at *Chaffe Street* since 1983.
Personal: Born 25th May 1951. Involved with North West Kidney Research. Leisure interests include golf, cricket, fell walking and skiing. Lives in Pott Shrigley, Cheshire.

SULLIVAN, Michael
Linklaters, London (020) 7456 3166
michael.sullivan@linklaters.com
Specialisation: Corporate department. Specialist in corporate law including mergers and acquisitions, initial and secondary public offerings, corporate reorganisations and demergers and privatisations.
Career: 1994 to date: Partner, *Linklaters*, corporate department; 1991-94: Assistant solicitor, *Linklaters*; 1990-91: Foreign temporary associate, *Davis Polk & Wardwell* New York; 1987-90: Assistant solicitor, *Linklaters*; 1985-87: Articled clerk, *Linklaters.* 1984: King's College, University of London, LLB (Hons).

SUMMERFIELD, Spencer
Travers Smith Braithwaite, London
(020) 7295 3000
Spencer.Summerfield@TraversSmith.com
Specialisation: Corporate finance; company.
Prof. Memberships: Law Society.
Career: Chigwell School; Cambridge University, Gonville & Caius College; College of Law, London; Joined *Travers Smith Braithwaite* as a trainee solicitor in 1987; made a partner in 1997.
Personal: Interests include cinema/theatre, aerobics, rugby. Married to Karen.

SUTTON, Robert
Macfarlanes, London (020) 7831 9222
rhs@macfarlanes.com
Specialisation: Senior partner. Work covers mergers and acquisitions, corporate finance, securities law, take-overs (private and public, friendly and hostile), flotations and corporate reconstructions, representing corporate and investment banking clients.
Prof. Memberships: Law Society.
Career: Qualified in 1979 while with *Macfarlanes.* Spent a year on secondment to *White & Case*, New York 1980-81. Became partner in *Macfarlanes* in 1983 and senior partner in 1999.

SWANSON, Magnus
Maclay Murray & Spens, Glasgow
(0141) 248 5011
mps@maclaymurrayspens.co.uk
Specialisation: Partner in corporate department. Principal areas of work are MBOs/MBIs, mergers and acquisitions and joint ventures. Led the team on the £30 million MBI of Phillips International Auctioneers and its subsequent sale to LVMH group; acted for Stagecoach Holdings plc in its acquisition of Prestwick Airport; led the team acting for Redwood Group in the taking private of Clyde Blowers plc, the first significant take private completed in Scotland and in recent times with £61 million of funding provided by 3i and the subsequent secondary buyout and reoganisation of the group financed by Sawmill Capital and the Bank of Scotland, and the MBO of Peliran Hardcopy – a multinational business bought from NuCote, which was then in Chapter II insolvency proceedings. Winner of 1998 Legal Dealmaker of the Year Award.
Career: Qualified in 1982. University of Edinburgh (LLB 1980). Spent 18 months working in New York with *Paul Weiss Rifkind Wharton & Garrison* (1986-87).
Personal: Born 1958.

SWEET, Jon
Marriott Harrison, London (020) 7209 2020
jonsweet@marriotharrison.co.uk
Specialisation: Partner in Corporate Department. Main area of practice is corporate and commercial, principally venture capital, mergers and acquisitions and general corporate finance. Handles a mix of private and public company work, but primarily private company. Has a broad range of experience in company/business sales and purchases, complex company and group restructurings, financings (debt and equity) and joint ventures as well as more general commercial advice such as agency and distribution. Past experience has included the full range of stock exchange and take over code work. Also handles banking and insolvency.
Prof. Memberships: Law Society, Associate Member of BVCA.
Career: Qualified in 1982. Worked at *Slaughter and May* 1980-90 (including 1986-88 in the Hong Kong office). Partner at *Iliffes* 1990-93, and at *Marriott Harrison* since 1993.
Personal: Born 7th March 1956. Attended Trinity College Glenalmond 1969-74, Brunel University 1975-79 and Guildford Law College 1979-80. Leisure interests include target rifle shooting, motor sport and classic cars. Lives in Hertfordshire.

SYSON, Keith
Stevens & Bolton, Guildford (01483) 734 215
keith.syson@stevens-bolton.co.uk
Specialisation: All aspects of company and corporate finance work including acquisitions, disposals, MBOs/MBIs and other venture capital work. Recent deals include the sale of Mobile Telecom Group plc to Vodafone Group plc, and a number of acquisitions for Hays plc.
Prof. Memberships: All aspects of company and corporate finance work including acquisitions, disposals, MBOs/MBIs and other venture capital work. Recent deals include the sale of Mobile Telecom Group plc to Vodafone Group plc, and a number of acquisitions for Hays plc.
Career: Southampton University; articled *Boodle Hatfield*; qualified 1991; joined *Stevens & Bolton* 1991, becoming partner 1999.
Publications: Southampton University; articled *Boodle Hatfield*; qualified 1991; joined *Stevens & Bolton* 1991, becoming partner 1999.
Personal: Born 29 June 1967. Married. Leisure interests include golf and motorsport.

TAYLOR, Glyn
Nabarro Nathanson, Reading (0118) 925 4637
g.taylor@nabarro.com
Specialisation: Corporate finance particularly flotations, venture capital, fundraisings, and mergers and acquisitions.
Prof. Memberships: Law Society; Oxford University Business Alumni.
Career: *Nabarro Nathanson* trainee 1985-87, assistant solicitor 1987-94, equity partner 1994 to date.
Publications: Numerous magazine articles.
Personal: Dartford Grammar School pre 1979. Oxford University (Hertford College) 197901982. M.A. (English). College of Law 1983-85. Cricket, tennis, football (supports Arsenal F.C.). Theatre and music concerts.

THOMAS, Michelle
Eversheds, Cardiff (029) 2047 1147
michellethomas@eversheds.com
Specialisation: Partner specialising in corporate and corporate finance. Advises UK and international clients on corporate transactions including mergers and acquisitions, private equity, joint ventures, corporate funding and restructurings. In addition to the UK and United States, she has worked on transactions in South Africa, France, Spain, Austria, Sweden and The Netherlands.
Prof. Memberships: The Law Society; Member of New York Bar.
Career: Joined *Eversheds* as a partner in 1999 following eight years practice in London with *Freshfields*

and *Baker & McKenzie*.
Personal: Born 3 November 1966. LLB, University College Eversheds. LLM – University College Berkeley. Fulbright and John Rankin Scholar. Admitted to NewYork State Bar 1994.

THOMSON, Christopher
Greene & Greene, Bury St Edmunds (01284) 762211

THORNEYCROFT, Max
Gouldens, London (020) 7842 6111
mbt@gouldens.com
Specialisation: Advises a range of public and private companies, banks and brokers on mergers and acquisition transactions and equity and debt financings. Throughout the 1980s and 90s, he has been involved in all of Hanson plc's major acquisitions and disposals including its four way demerger in the mid 90s and its more recent concentration on the building materials sector. In addition, he advises Tomkins, TT Group, Mid Kent Holdings, Sibir Energy and Severn Trent Water plc as well as a number of private companies and entrepreneures from the United Kingdom and abroad such as Kingston Metals Limited, which acquired the stainless steel and aliminium distribution business of Glynwed International plc for £100 million, UK Plant Limited, which disposed of its plant hire business to Ashtead Group plc for £20 million, the shareholders of Eurotel Telecom Holdings Limited which was sold to a 3i backed MBO for £30 million and Integralis Limited which reversed into Neuer Markt quoted Articon Information Systems AG for £171 million. On the financing side, he led the corporate aspects of the firm's advice to Bankers Trust on its loan of $2.1 billion to Huntsman to fund the acquisition of part of the business of ICI as well as advising houses such as Investec Henderson Crosthwaite, Campbell Lutyens, Strand Partners and Bulldog Partners.
Prof. Memberships: The Law Society and the CBI Corporate Law Committee.
Career: After reading law at Oxford, he qualified at *Macfarlanes* in 1975 and then spent six years in the Corporate Finance Department of *Norton Rose* before joining *Gouldens* in1981 and becoming a partner in 1983. Managing Partner 1987-97. Head of the company department 1997 to date.
Personal: Educated King's School Macclesfield, Cheshire. Member of the Fund Raising Committee of Lincoln College, Oxford. Leisure pursuits include skiing, rugby, opera and gardening. Lives Holland Park and Gloucestershire.

TROTTER, Andrew
Shadbolt & Co, Reigate (01737) 226277
andrew_trotter@shadboltlaw.co.uk
Specialisation: Partner and head of corporate department. Main area of practice is company sales and purchases and corporate finance, including MBOs, MBIs, venture capital, joint ventures and cross-border transactions. Leads a team which also handles general company commercial work, including franchising, IT contracts and intellectual property. Regular lectures on his subject, including a series of seminars 'Buying and Selling Unquoted Companies' and an address to US lawyers on UK and EU competition law.
Career: Qualified in 1981. At *Withers* 1977-83, *Norton Rose* 1983-85, *Donne Mileham & Haddock* 1985-97 and *Shadbolt & Co* from May 1997.
Personal: Born 5th August 1954. Educated at Lancing College and Oxford. Lives in Cuckfield in Sussex. Interests include football and golf.

TURNBULL, Robert
Cobbetts, Manchester (0161) 833 3333
robert.turnbull@cobbetts.co.uk
Specialisation: Mergers & acquisitions, MBOs & MBIs, venture capital, joint ventures, corporate finance.
Career: Partner with *Cobbetts* since 1992.
Personal: Educated at King Edward VII School, Lytham and Cambridge University.

TWENTYMAN, Jeff
Slaughter and May, London (020) 7710 3476
jeffrey.twentyman@slaughterandmay.com
Specialisation: Mergers and acquisitions, corporate finance, public and private equity finance, joint ventures and commercial contracts, acting for listed and unlisted companies and investment banks; partner in technology, media and telecoms practice group, acts extensively for companies and investors in the telecommunications and technology sectors, but represents clients in all sectors.
Career: Articled *Slaughter and May*; qualified 1991; *Morgan Grenfell & Co. Limited* (1993-94); *Slaughter and May* 1994; partner 1998.
Personal: Born 1965. Educated at Sackville School, East Grinstead and the University of Newcastle-upon-Tyne (1987 LL.B). Resides London; two daughters.

UNDERHILL, William
Slaughter and May, London (020) 7600 1200
william.underhill@slaughterandmay.com
Specialisation: Specialises in corporate finance, including acting for underwriters and issuers of securities, M&A, London Stock Exchange rules and regulations and FSA compliance. Also experienced in mortgage and other asset securitisation, and other mortgage-backed financing. Editor of 'Weinberg and Blank on Takeovers and Mergers'.
Career: Qualified 1983 with *Slaughter and May*. Partner 1990.

VAUGHAN, David
Wragge & Co, Birmingham (0870) 903 1000

VON BISMARCK, Nilufer
Slaughter and May, London (020) 7600 1200
nilufer.vonbismarck@slaughterandmay.com
Specialisation: Partner specialising in corporate finance, general company and commercial work and some banking.
Career: Articled *Norton Rose* 1986-90; qualified 1988; *Slaughter and May* 1990 to date; partner 1994.
Personal: Born 1961. Educated at James Allen's Girls' School and Trinity College, Cambridge (1983 BA Law 2 (1)). Resides London.

WAINE, Ian
Prettys, Ipswich (01473) 232 121
iwaine@prettys.co.uk
Specialisation: Main areas of work include company law, mergers, acquisitions and reorganisations, corporate finance MBOs, insolvency and advice on directors' responsibilities. Works with both private and public companies.
Prof. Memberships: A Member of the IP City Initiative, and active with the rapidly growing Ipswich Cambridge Hi Tech sector.
Career: Qualified 1986. Partner at *Prettys* since 1989.

WARBURTON, Mark
Addleshaw Booth & Co, Manchester (0161) 934 6000
mww@addleshaw-booth.co.uk
Specialisation: Expert in all aspects of corporate transactions involving SMEs and owner-managed businesses in particular. This is complemented by his experience in funding and security matters.
Career: Qualified 1975. Joined firm as partner 1998.
Personal: Education: Kings School, Chester and Selwyn College, Cambridge. Resides Wilmslow. Leisure: golf, walking and reading.

WARD, Michael
Gateley Wareing, Birmingham (0121) 234 0000

WATSON, Sean
CMS Cameron McKenna, London (020) 7367 2802
smw@cmck.com
Specialisation: Partner in corporate department. Advises corporate, investment banking and venture capital clients on all areas of corporate finance including corporate reconstructions, take-overs, mergers and acquisitions, flotations, international equity offerings, placings, secondary equity offerings and venture capital transactions.
Prof. Memberships: Law Society, City of London Solicitors Company.
Career: Qualified in 1972. Joined *McKenna & Co* in 1979, becoming a partner in the same year.
Personal: Born 5 April 1948. Attended The Leys School, Cambridge, 1961-66 and Manchester University 1966-69. Leisure interests include tennis, golf, skiing, gardening and family. Lives in Weybridge, Surrey.

WATTS, Clive
Osborne Clarke, Bristol (0117) 917 3000

WAYTE, Peter
DLA, London (08700) 111111

WEBSTER, Martin
Pinsent Curtis Biddle, London (020) 7418 9598
martinwebster@pinsents.com
Specialisation: Partner in Corporate Finance Department. Main areas of practice are corporate finance and mergers and acquisitions work generally. In recent years, has particularly specialised in MBOs/MBIs and other deals involving employee share interests. Also specialises in media related corporate transactions. Is secretary of Parliamentary Broadcasting Unit Ltd, the vehicle for the dissemination of Parliamentary broadcasting, which is owned by the major broadcasters but ultimately controlled by Parliament.
Prof. Memberships: Chartered Institute of Taxation, Law Society.
Career: Qualified in 1983. ATII 1986. Joined *Biddle* in 1981, becoming a Partner in 1987 and in *Pinsent Curtis Biddl* e in 2001.
Personal: Born 1st July 1958. Attended Christ's College, Cambridge, 1976-79. Leisure interests include music, theatre and gardening. Lives in London SE11 and Norfolk.

WHATNALL, John
Halliwell Landau, Manchester (0161) 835 3003
See under Banking, p.123

WHELDON, Tim
Addleshaw Booth & Co, Leeds (0113) 209 2000
tjw@addleshaw-booth.co.uk
Specialisation: Partner in corporate finance group. Corporate/commercial; venture capital.
Prof. Memberships: Law Society.
Career: Qualified 1983. Joined the firm as partner in 1990.
Personal: Educated at Hymers College, Hull; Manchester Polytechnic BA(Hons) Law and French. Leisure interests include sailing and skiing.

WHYBROW, J. Annette
Birketts, Ipswich (01473) 232300

WILD, David
Eversheds, Derby (01332) 542428
davidwild@eversheds.com
Specialisation: Corporate finance and MBOs.
Prof. Memberships: Council Member, Derby Law Society.
Career: Articled Wells & Hind, Nottingham. Qualified 1981. Partner Eversheds, 1985.
Personal: Born 1956. Educated Nottingham High School and Jesus College, Cambridge.

WILL, James
Shepherd & Wedderburn WS, Edinburgh (0131) 228 9900
james.will@shepwedd.co.uk
Specialisation: Partner in corporate department. Main areas of practice are Stock Exchange work, company law, mergers and acquisitions, major start-ups and development capital, with emphasis on the technology sector.
Prof. Memberships: Law Society of Scotland, Society of Writers to Her Majesty's Signet.
Career: Qualified in 1978. With Tods Murray WS 1978-79 and Clifford Chance 1980-81. Joined Shepherd & Wedderburn in 1981 and became a partner in 1982.
Personal: Born 30th April 1955. Educated at Merchiston Castle and Aberdeen University.

WILLIAMS, Christine
Fox Williams, London (020) 7628 2000
See under Partnership, p.617

WILLIAMS, Nigel
Dickinson Dees, Newcastle upon Tyne (0191) 279 9000
Specialisation: M&A work, particularly owner managed business sales and disposals for corporate clients. Tasked with spearheading Dickinson Dees' new Tees Valley Office.
Prof. Memberships: Newcastle upon Tyne Law Society, Durham & North Yorkshire Law Society.
Career: Trained with Cameron Markby Hewitt (now CMS Cameron McKenna), qualifying in 1991. Spent five years with Eversheds before moving to Dickinson Dees.
Personal: Newcastle University and Chester College of Law. One psychiatrist wife and two cats. Leisure interests include any form of sport and frequent trips to Ibiza.

WILLIS, John-George
Tughan & Co, Belfast (028) 9055 3344
j-g.willis@tughan.co.uk
Specialisation: Handles all types of company and commercial work including mergers and acquisitions. MBOs/MBAs, joint ventures and public and private share issues. Represents several of Northern Ireland's leading technology companies.
Career: Qualified 1984. Assistant solicitor at Tughan & Co 1987-92. Partner since 1992.
Personal: Educated at The Royal School, Dungannon and Queen's University Belfast. Interests include family and sport.

WINTER, Martin
Taylor Joynson Garrett, London (020) 7300 7000

WIPPELL, Mark
Allen & Overy, London (020) 7330 3000
mark.wippell@allenovery.com
Specialisation: Specialises in corporate finance, mergers and acquisitions and securities offerings, advising investment banks and major international quoted companies. Has particular expertise in transactions involving US companies and transactions in the financial sector.
Career: Educated at Oxford University (MA) 1979; LLM Tulane University, USA (1980); admitted as Solicitor (1983); admitted attorney in New York (1987); became Allen & Overy partner in 1999. Previously a partner in Ashurst Morris Crisp (1990-98).
Personal: Born 1958.

WOOTTON, David
Allen & Overy, London (020) 7330 3000
david.wootton@allenovery.com
Specialisation: Partner in corporate department since 1979, handling all areas of corporate work, public and private mergers and acquisitions, IPOs flotations and joint ventures. He specialises in flotations and led the Allen & Overy teams advising the sponsor and underwriters on the IPOs of Billiton (1997), Canary Wharf Group (1999), The eXchange Holdings (1999), The Carphone Warehouse Group (2000), and on the attempted flotation of William Hill (1999), and the issuer and selling shareholder of Thomson Travel Group (1998). All of these involved 144A placings in the US and four involved retail offers in the UK. He is particularly interested in developing the use of the Internet as a medium for selling shares on IPOs. In public M&A, he led the A&O teams for Whitbread on its acquisition of Swallow Group, Bristol United Press on the agreed bid by DMGT, Admiral on the recommended offer by CMG, Thomson Travel Group on the agreed bid by Preussag and Smiths Industries on its merger with TI Group.
Career: Associate Allen & Overy 1975-79; Partner Allen & Overy since 1979.
Personal: BA Cambridge University 1972. MA Cambridge University.

WRIGHT, Sean
Blake Lapthorn, Southampton (023) 8063 1823

WRIGLEY, Richard
Martineau Johnson, Birmingham (0121) 678 1586
richard.wrigley@marjohn.com
Specialisation: Corporate finance, particularly private equity, acquisitions, disposals and joint ventures. Recent deals include £53 million Alstec IBO, £22 million Aktrion BIMBO and seven acquisitions and joint ventures for South Staffordshire Group plc.
Prof. Memberships: Securities Institute.
Career: Partner Martineau Johnson 1996; Norwich (King Edward VI) School; Leeds University.
Personal: Golf, wine, family. Lives in Harborne.

CRIME

OVERVIEW: Firms listed in our tables cover a wide variety of criminal practice ranging from road traffic and shoplifting to murder and professional or white collar crime. Many top band London firms specialise in certain areas of criminal law and have therefore acquired national reputations for excellence in particular niches. In the regions, firms tend to be more generalist, acting in any criminal matter that comes through the door. Many such firms report feeling pressurised by the low legal aid remuneration rates. Legal aid block contracting has now been instituted and whilst this is a boon in easing cash flow problems it brings its own difficulties. The widespread view is that the greater administrative challenges it poses are likely to impact particularly heavily on the small high street firms. Amalgamation is predicted as the minnows band together to mitigate the effect of high overheads.

RESEARCH APPROVED BY BMRB: *For this edition,* Chambers' *researchers conducted 6,552 interviews – 4,419 with law firms, 554 with barristers and 1,579 with clients.*

The validity of the research was scrutinised by BMRB International, who audited both the methodology and the results at our offices in July 2001. They interviewed Chambers' *researchers and cross-checked sample interviews. Details of the audit appear on page 7.*

LONDON

CRIME • London	
1	Bindman & Partners
	Birnberg Peirce & Partners
	Edward Fail Bradshaw & Waterson
	Hodge Jones & Allen
	Kingsley Napley
	Saunders & Co
	Simons Muirhead & Burton
	Taylor Nichol
2	Edwards Duthie
	Fisher Meredith
	Hallinan, Blackburn, Gittings & Nott
	Henry Milner & Co
	Hickman & Rose
	Powell Spencer & Partners
	Russell Jones & Walker
	Russell-Cooke
	Thanki Novy Taube
	TV Edwards
	Whitelock & Storr
3	Alistair Meldrum & Co
	Andrew Keenan & Co
	Christian Fisher
	Claude Hornby & Cox
	Dundons
	Iliffes Booth Bennett
	Joy Merriam & Co
	McCormacks
	Reynolds Dawson
	Tuckers & Co
	Venters & Co
	Victor Lissack & Roscoe

This book is the product of 6,552 1/2-hour interviews. See p.7 for BMRB audit.
Within each band, firms are listed alphabetically.

Bindman & Partners (see firm details p.882) A "*thoroughbred practice*" dealing with weighty criminal defence cases including homicide, firearms, sexual abuse and internet crime. A political slant manifests itself through involvement in human rights, race, police misconduct, extradition and terrorist issues. The department, created and managed by **Neil O'May** (see p.269), acted for high profile child killer Edward Crowley and the bookmaker implicated in the cricket match rigging scandal.

Birnberg Peirce & Partners "*Niche firm with a political edge*" boasting a specialism in terrorism cases. **Gareth Peirce** is a "*headline practitioner utterly dedicated to her clients*" who "*treats injustice as her motivating force.*"

Edward Fail Bradshaw & Waterson (see firm details p.947) "*Classic blaggers' firm*" traditionally handling volume armed robbery cases although broadening its scope, to include murder and drug cases. Deploying "*considerable skill,*" **Edward Preston** has had a significant involvement in the corruption inquiry into the activities of the Flying Squad.

Hodge Jones & Allen (see firm details p.998) A large enterprise with resources to take on volume legal aid work. The dedicated, energetic department has "*a fantastic internal system which ensures that the client always gets the right lawyer.*" Acted for the alleged leader of a Turkish heroin cartel and the defence of a senior civil servant charged with murder. The respected **Mark Studdert** (see p.270) has a particular interest in computer misuse.

Kingsley Napley (see firm details p.1022) Although pre-eminent fraud specialists the firm also acts for private clients in high profile, complex prosecutions. Acted for David Jones, ex Southampton football manger, over child abuse charges and represented the Captain of the Bow Belle in the Marchioness Inquiry.

Saunders & Co (see firm details p.119) Led by "*long standing heavyweight operator*" **James Saunders** the firm is "*seen in and around a number of the biggest cases*" including murder, sex and drugs matters.

Simons Muirhead & Burton (see firm details p.1133) Blending top end private client and legal aid work the firm rises in the rankings in recognition of its "*no fuss, quality approach.*" Much of the caseload involves serious matters such as the recent triad conspiracy to murder case of Hui. Having closed its offices in Wandsworth, the practice is now based round its original central London location, led by the widely commended **Anthony Burton** (see p.267).

Taylor Nichol Famed for its appeal work and committed stance "*giving the humblest case a qualified solicitor's attention.*" **James Nichol** is "*formidable in miscarriage of justice cases*" while **Mark Ashford** "*can't be touched as an expert on youth crime.*" Completing *a "high-flying team,"* **Carolyn Taylor** has a noted specialism in defending those with mental disorders. Acted in the appeal of Peter Fell and in Rowe, Davis and Johnson, the M25 case.

Other Notable Firms and Practitioners Newly merged **Edwards Duthie** is a "*serious player*" enjoying strong links with the medical profession. One

LEADING INDIVIDUALS

1	**HASLAM Mark** Burton Copeland	**NICHOL James** Taylor Nichol
	PEIRCE Gareth Birnberg Peirce & Partners	
2	**ASHFORD Mark** Taylor Nichol	**EDWARDS Anthony** TV Edwards
	FISHER Michael Christian Fisher	**HICKMAN Jane** Hickman & Rose
	MILNER Henry Henry Milner & Co	**NOTT Colin** Hallinan, Blackburn, Gittings
	O'MAY Neil Bindman & Partners	**PRESTON Edward** Edward Fail Bradshaw
	SAUNDERS James Saunders & Co	
3	**BURTON Anthony** Simons Muirhead & Burton	**CADMAN Peter** Russell-Cooke
	HALLAM Richard Claude Hornby & Cox	**HEWITT Stephen** Fisher Meredith
	HUBER Bernard Edwards Duthie	**KEENAN Andrew** Andrew Keenan & Co
	MERRIAM Joy Joy Merriam & Co	**MURPHY Shaun** Edwards Duthie
	NOVY Rod Thanki Novy Taube	**POWELL Greg** Powell Spencer & Partners
	ROSCOE Robert Victor Lissack & Roscoe	**RYAN Ian** Russell-Cooke
	SPENCER Richard Powell Spencer & Ptnrs	**STUDDERT Mark** Hodge Jones & Allen
	TAYLOR Carolyn Taylor Nichol	**THANKI Girish** Thanki Novy Taube
	VENTERS June Venters & Co.	

See individuals' profiles p.265

of the larger practices, it has in **Bernard Huber** a "*lawyer that can't be faulted*" and in **Shaun Murphy** "*a bullish fighter with heaps of experience.*" At **Fisher Meredith, Stephen Hewitt** (see p.268) "*handles a substantial practice with measured control.*" **Colin Nott** (see p.269) of **Hallinan, Blackburn, Gittings & Nott** is a "*definite face*" approaching heavyweight cases in a "*cool and competent*" fashion. **Henry Milner** of **Henry Milner & Co** is "*in a category of his own*" concentrating on high profile, serious villains such as Kenneth Noye. **Hickman & Rose** is a general practice with an emphasis on human rights where the "*committed and passionate*" **Jane Hickman** (see p.268) is noted for her work on behalf of prisoners. Also possessing a "*radical energy*" **Greg Powell** (see p.269) and **Richard Spencer** (see p.270) of **Powell Spencer & Partners** service a community client base. **Russell-Cooke** has a "*strong presence in south west London*" handling routine crime and the occasional weightier matter, its lead practitioners **Ian Ryan** (see p.269) and **Peter Cadman** were commended for their "*level-headed attitude.*" **Russell Jones & Walker**, "*the bobby's friend,*" combines a general practice with work on behalf of the police federation. "*Battler for the underdog*" **Thanki Novy Taube** is known for its prison law and extradition work handled by **Girish Thanki** (see p.270) and **Rod Novy**, both seen as "*intense and dogged.*" **T.V. Edwards** possesses a network of offices handling volume legal aid work. Architect of the practice, **Anthony Edwards** (see p.267) is "*a towering presence and an excellent lawyer.*" With connections in the Italian community and a specialism in extradition work, **Whitelock & Storr** retains its prominence despite the recent departure to the bench of figurehead John Zani. Via a connection with the Dutch Embassy, **Alistair Meldrum & Co** receives a number of Dutch clients and a sizeable proportion of police work. It is due to represent the mastermind of the Dome diamond heist. **Andrew Keenan & Co** is "*a smallish but seasoned outfit*" led by name partner **Andrew Keenan**, noted in the field of professional crime. **Claude Hornby & Cox**, "*traditionally expert in this area,*" covers the full spectrum of crime and has in **Richard Hallam** (see p.267) "*a vivacious and gritty*" practitioner. **Michael Fisher**, in common with his firm **Christian Fisher**, is rated for handling actions against the police within a general practice. **Joy Merriam** of **Joy Merriam & Co** stewards "*a young team infused with vitality.*" **McCormacks** is "*a coming firm with a rapidly expanding team*" which has recently opened a branch office in Basildon. **Tuckers** is noted for its large number of fee earners and the sheer volume of cases it undertakes while **Iliffes Booth Bennett** can make similar claims as to workload, being the eleventh largest legal aid practice in the country **Robert Roscoe** (see p.269) of **Victor Lissack & Roscoe** has a recognised specialism in extradition within his general practice. At the time of going to press, Venters Reynolds announced its demerger, producing **Reynolds Dawson**, (a member of the serious fraud panel and well-known for its work on behalf of the police) and **Venters & Co**, the latter being home to **June Venters** (see p.270) who practices in a "*thoroughly business like*" fashion. **Dundons** continues to run "*a thriving practice in South London.*" Operating from within Burton Copeland, a firm celebrated for its fraud work, **Mark Haslam** (see p.267) was widely held up as "*a top end general criminal practitioner, with expert all round knowledge.*"

SOUTH WEST

CRIME • South West

1	**Bobbetts Mackan** Bristol
	Douglas & Partners Bristol
2	**John Boyle and Co** Redruth
	Stephens & Scown Exeter
	Stones Exeter
3	**Crosse & Crosse** Exeter
	Parlby Calder Plymouth
	Wolferstans Plymouth

LEADING INDIVIDUALS

1	**BOYLE John** John Boyle and Co	**BUTLER Michael** Stephens & Scown
	FANSON David Douglas & Partners	**MILES Anthony** Bobbetts Mackan
	NUNN Stephen Stephens & Scown	**ROSE Timothy** Douglas & Partners
2	**SVENSSON Zara** Stones	

This book is the product of 6,552 1/2-hour interviews. See p.7 for BMRB audit.

Within each band, firms are listed alphabetically. *See individuals' profiles p.265*

Two Bristol firms dominate in terms of size and quality. **Bobbetts Mackan** has a "*youngish but highly experienced*" team including two in-house advocates and an ex-barrister. Led by **Anthony Miles** (see p.268) it has a specialism in court martial cases. **Douglas & Partners** handles all manner of criminal defence work. **David Fanson** excels at fraud while **Tim Rose** has higher rights of audience and "*impresses in court.*" A youth court department is in place and mental health tribunal work is undertaken. **John Boyle** of **John Boyle & Co** "*has been synonymous with the law in Cornwall for many years.*" Working on behalf of the Police Federation he also has a respected appellate and drugs importation practice. Possessing a historically large client base **Stephens & Scown** has "*a couple of legal big hitters.*" **Stephen Nunn**, "*an excellent advocate*" with higher rights of audience, has been joined by **Michael Butler** (formerly of Claude, Hornby & Cox in London.) Seen as "*a major appointment*" it further enhances the reputation of a firm with the biggest practice south of Bristol. A sizeable practice in the region, **Stones** is known to provide"*good competition to the other firms*" and has in **Zara Svensson** (see p.270) "*a lawyer respected by clients and court staff alike.*" Despite the loss of a partner to personal injury work, **Crosse & Crosse** continues to be recommended for its youth court work and defence of DTI and DSS prosecutions. It concentrates on pharmaceutical cases and those with a mental health aspect. New to the rankings, **Parlby Calder** has "*risen to prominence over the last two years*" and has "*two able solicitors serving one of the largest police stations in the country.*" **Wolferstans** received commendation for its full range criminal practice.

Recent High Profile Criminal Cases

Case	Parties	Significance
Jill Dando murder trial	Michael Mansfield QC and Marilyn Etienne of Kean Etienne (London) acted for defendant Barry George, who was found guilty of murdering the TV presenter.	High profile murder case. Controversial verdict due to prosecution's heavy reliance on circumstantial evidence.
David Jones child abuse case	Stephen Pollard of Kingsley Napley and Henry Globe QC acted for defendant.	David Jones, ex-footballer and Southampton football club manager, was acquitted when principal witness refused to testify. Part of controversial 'Operation Care'. Acquittal has serious implications for how future cases of suspected child abuse are investigated.
Peter Fell appeal	James Nichol of Taylor Nichol and Patrick O'Connor QC acted for appellant. David Perry acted for the Crown.	"Serial fantasist" Peter Fell had his conviction for the murder of Ann Lee and Margaret "Peggy" Johnson quashed at the Court of Appeal after serving 17 years in prison. Significant ruling casting doubt on reliability of confessions as basis of conviction.
M25 Three appeal	James Nichol of Taylor Nichol and Patrick O'Connor QC represented Raphael Rowe; Trevor Linn (Linn & Associates), Courtenay Griffiths QC and Henry Blaxland acted for Randolph Johnson; the firm JB Wheatley & Co and Michael Mansfield QC acted for Michael Davis.	Conviction for murder quashed after Rowe, Davis and Johnson spent 12 years in prison. Appeal raised issues such as police's duty of disclosure and public interest immunity.
Edward Alex Crowley murder case	Neil O'May of Bindman & Partners and Edward Fitzgerald QC acted for Crowley.	Edward Crowley found guilty of stabbing Diego Pineiro-Villar, a young boy he had become obsessed with. Verdict has important mental health ramifications.
R v Tony Martin	Original legal team having been sacked, James Saunders of Saunders & Co and Michael Wolkind QC acting for appellant. Appeal ongoing.	Tony Martin appeal against conviction of murder. High profile case raising issue of how far householders can go in defence of their property.
David Copeland, the London nail bomber	Peter Silver of Silver, Spencer & Co and Michael Wolkind QC acted for defendant.	David Copeland found guilty of murder despite pleas of guilty of manslaughter due to diminished responsibility. Mental health ramifications.
R v Michael O'Connor & ors	James Saunders of Saunders & Co represented Michael O'Connor. Robert Banks & Tyrone Smith acted for defendant.	Client acquitted of involvement in massive cocaine importation trial. 14 month trial was the longest in English criminal history.
Perry Wacker	Oliver Kirk of Kirk, Jackson and Waitt (Dover) and Michael Lawson QC acted for defendant, Victor Temple QC prosecuting.	Lorry driver jailed over death of 58 Chinese immigrants.
Jeffery Archer	Nicholas Purnell QC and Tony Morton-Hooper of Mishcon de Reya acting for defendant.	The peer was convicted for perjury and perverting the course of justice.
Greenpeace crop case	Michael Schwarz of Bindman & Partners acted for defendants.	Lord Melchett and fellow protesters acquitted at retrial of causing criminal damage to a field of GM crops.

WALES

CRIME • Wales	
1	**Graham Evans & Partners** Swansea
	Huttons Cardiff
	Martyn Prowel Solicitors Cardiff
	Spiro Grech & Co Cardiff
2	**Colin Jones** Barry
	Gamlins Rhyl
	Robertsons Cardiff

LEADING INDIVIDUALS		
1	**HUTTON Stuart** Huttons	**PROWEL Martyn** Martyn Prowel Solicitors
2	**JONES Gwyn** Gamlins	**WILLIAMS Ian** Robertsons
3	**BIRD Jeremy** Marchant Harries & Co	**PENNINGTON John** Savery Pennington
	RICHARDS Geraint Martyn Prowel Solicitors	

This book is the product of 6,552 1/2-hour interviews. See p.7 for BMRB audit.

Within each band, firms are listed alphabetically. *See individuals' profiles p.265*

Unsurprisingly Cardiff practices continue to dominate our tables. **Martyn Prowel Solicitors** is "*an established first class practice peopled by sincere individuals.*" **Martyn Prowel** (see p.269) is "*quiet, persuasive and exceptionally good,*" described as "*the number one choice*" in violent and white-collar cases. He is assisted by the "*humorous and sensible*" **Geraint Richards** (see p.269). **Huttons** has a hefty caseload and is involved in miscarriage of justice and weighty matters such as the Cardiff Newsagent Three. **Stuart Hutton** (see p.268) "*brings the work in through his name*" and is "*a calm, methodical and above all determined individual.*" **Spiro Grech & Co** is a specialist with "*an awful lot of work at the volume end.*" Having a number of solicitor advocates it handles representation for the young. **Graham Evans & Partners** is generally acknowledged to "*have got Swansea sewn up*" handling a high proportion of the serious cases in the area. Ex-Cardiff lawyer **Gwyn Jones** of **Gamlins** is seen as "*earnest and hard working*" and is perceived to be doing well with a practice encompassing licensing, magistrate court and environmental protection work. Colin Jones of the eponymous **Colin Jones** is a "*bright individual, both competent and sensible*" with a growing practice. Amongst a clutch of talented individuals **Ian Williams** is respected at **Robertsons**, "*a small firm with some high profile clients*" whilst both **John Pennington** and **Jeremy Bird** garnered approval.

MIDLANDS

CRIME • Midlands	
1	**Fletchers** Nottingham
	Glaisyers Birmingham
	Nelsons Nottingham
	The Johnson Partnership Nottingham
	The Smith Partnership Derby
2	**Banners Jones Middleton** Chesterfield
	Barrie Ward & Julian Griffiths Nottingham
	Bate Edmond Snape Coventry
	Brethertons Rugby
	Elliot Mather Chesterfield
	Jonas Roy Bloom Birmingham
	Kieran & Co Worcester
	Parker & Grego Birmingham
	Purcell Parker Birmingham
	Tyndallwoods Birmingham
	Varley Hadley Siddall Nottingham
	Woodford-Robinson Northampton

LEADING INDIVIDUALS	
GOULBORN Caroline Fletchers	**GREGO Kevin** Parker & Grego
MATHER Bertie Elliot Mather	**PURCELL Michael** Purcell Parker
TOMLINSON Kevin Kieran & Co	

This book is the product of 6,552 1/2-hour interviews. See p.7 for BMRB audit.

Within each band, firms are listed alphabetically. *See individuals' profiles p.265*

With the exception of a few noteworthy local practices, Birmingham and Nottingham once again provide the lion's share of our ranked firms. **Fletchers** is renowned for the quality of its advocates such as **Caroline Goulbourn** who *"regularly demonstrates her mental agility in the courtroom."* **Nelsons** has a large practice divided into general crime and business defence units, the latter boasting a fine reputation in white-collar crime. **The Johnson Partnership** and **Glaisyers** are respected for the breadth and quality of their caseloads while **The Smith Partnership** *"always does a good job."* Between them **Banners Jones Middleton** and *"capable"* **Elliot Mather** has *"carved up the work in Chesterfield"* with **Bertie Mather** being *"extremely well known in the area."* The retirement of Barrie Ward from **Barrie Ward & Julian Griffiths** has been a blow, but the firm continues to impress with its work on behalf of minorities and members of the gay community. **Purcell Parker** *"has been around for a long time"* and has grown through the absorption of smaller firms while **Michael Purcell** remains *"a familiar figure in the magistrates court."* **Tyndallwoods** and **Woodford-Robinson** are both said to *"offer a consistently good service"* while **Varley Hadley Siddall** offers a specialist service and prosecutes for the Health and Safety Executive. The latter was involved in the first solo prosecution by the Prescription Pricing Authority. **Kevin Tomlinson** of **Kieran & Co** *"runs a small but adept practice"* while **Kevin Grego** (see p.267) of **Parker & Grego** *"marshals a solid group of lawyers."* **Bate Edmond Snape**, **Jonas Roy Bloom** and **Brethertons** were also commended for the quality of their service.

EAST ANGLIA

CRIME • East Anglia	
1	**Belmores** Norwich
	Cole & Co Norwich
	Copleys Huntingdon
	Hunt & Coombs Peterborough
	Overbury Steward Eaton & Woolsey Norwich
2	**David Charnley & Co** Romford
	Gepp & Sons Chelmsford, Colchester
	Gotelee & Goldsmith Ipswich
	Hatch Brenner Norwich
	Lucas & Wyllys Great Yarmouth
	Thomson Webb Corfield Cambridge
	Twitchen Musters & Kelly Southend-on-Sea

LEADING INDIVIDUALS		
1	**BECKFORD Trevor** Beckford & Co	**FISHER Ian** Overbury Steward Eaton
	MASTERS Peter Thomson Webb Corfield	**NICHOLLS Simon** Belmores
2	**CARR Ken** David Charnley & Co	**COLE Michael** Cole's
	KELLY Philip Twitchen Musters	**MUSTERS Patrick** Twitchen Musters
	WARBOYS Kevin Copleys	

This book is the product of 6,552 1/2-hour interviews. See p.7 for BMRB audit.

Within each band, firms are listed alphabetically. *See individuals' profiles p.265*

Fronted by *"go-ahead"* **Simon Nicholls** and *"applying an innovative approach,"* **Belmores** is one of the foremost teams, large enough to contain five solicitor advocates. It is rivalled by the relatively embryonic **Cole & Co**, said to be *"doing brilliantly"* under the leadership of *"superb businessman and technological enthusiast"* **Michael Cole**. **Hunt & Coombs**, more expert in white-collar crime, deals with serious matters and has a resident mental health law expert. In Norwich, **Overbury Steward Eaton & Woolsey** is *"a professional and able outfit"* seen in high profile murders. Its leading light **Ian Fisher** is *"a talented, maverick character with a good engine room behind him."* Covering a smaller locality and led by **Kevin Warboys**, **Copleys** is *"a highly competent firm with good back up."* Preparation and advocacy skills are the keynotes of **Gotelee & Goldsmith's** practice, benefiting from regular referral work. **Hatch Brenner** is the nominated solicitor for the Norfolk Probation Service and has handled its prosecution work since 1993. **Lucas & Wyllys** retains its position in the tables due to the perceived quality of its advocates. In Essex, **Twitchen Musters & Kelly** recently opened an additional Chelmsford branch and is seen in serious drug cases including a recent ten month cocaine importation. The respected team includes **Philip Kelly** and **Patrick Musters** (see p.269), both solicitor advocates. **David Charnley & Co** is *"a substantial firm doing a lot of high value work"* and represented eight defendants in the Stansted hijacking case. Lead practitioner **Ken Carr** is *"heavily involved in serious criminal cases, often travelling worldwide."* Also in this area **Gepp & Sons** is active and has a sound reputation. **Thomson Webb Corfield** is similarly rated in the Cambridge area where **Peter Masters** *"has a following due to his reassuring presence and judgement."* Ranked individual **Trevor Beckford** (see p.266), having broken away from Leathes Prior, remains in the table through consolidation of his new practice that now employs three advocates.

NORTH WEST

CRIME • North West	
1	**Burton Copeland** Manchester, Liverpool
2	**Betesh Fox & Co** Manchester
	Jones Maidment Wilson, Manchester
	Maidments Manchester
	Tuckers Manchester
3	**Brian Koffman & Co** Manchester
	Cunninghams Manchester
	Draycott Browne Manchester
	Forbes Blackburn
	Garstangs Bolton
	RM Broudie & Co Liverpool
	Russell & Russell Bolton
4	**Cobleys** Salford
	Farleys Blackburn
	Jackson & Canter Liverpool
	Kristina Harrison Solicitors Salford
	Linskills Solicitors Liverpool
	The Berkson Globe Partnership Liverpool

LEADING INDIVIDUALS		
1	**GROGAN Peter** Jones Maidment Wilson incorporating Hatton Scates Horton	
	MAIDMENT Allan Maidments	**SINCLAIR Franklin** Tuckers
2	**BROUDIE Robert** RM Broudie & Co	**CUNNINGHAM Martin** Cunninghams
	CUTTLE Barry Cuttle & Co	**DRAYCOTT Shaun** Draycott Browne
	FREEMAN Nicholas Freeman & Co	**MACKEY Michael** Burton Copeland
3	**KOFFMAN Brian** Brian Koffman & Co	**PETER Charles** The Berkson Globe Partners

This book is the product of 6,552 1/2-hour interviews. See p.7 for BMRB audit.

Within each band, firms are listed alphabetically. *See individuals' profiles p.265*

The leader in terms of size and ubiquity, **Burton Copeland** has cast its shadow across the region through the opening of a branch in Liverpool. Practising crime exclusively, with an emphasis on fraud, it has in **Michael Mackey** (see p.268) *"a gifted all rounder comfortable at all levels."* Dominating the Salford area, **Betesh Fox & Co** also shines in commercial fraud and undertakes a substantial amount of general crime work. Much lauded by barristers, **Jones Maidment Wilson** is *"a fine established firm that runs as a tight ship"* where department head **Peter Grogan** is *"justifiably revered"* for his general practice. Growing nationally, **Maidments** has offices in Manchester, London, Liverpool and Birmingham and **Allan Maidment** (see p.268) *"covers everything in some depth"* and is an *"excellent advocate."* **Tuckers** handles the full spectrum and is recognised for its *"fine internal organisation"* managed by *"sparkling advocate"* **Franklin Sinclair.** (see p.269) **Martin Cunningham** (see p.267) heads a four partner firm at **Cunninghams** that has recently opened a prison law department and successfully defended a double execution killing in Leeds. Born originally from Maidments, **Draycott Browne** has *"an excellent team"* led by **Shaun Draycott**, *"a young, eager lawyer who has known what he's been doing since day one."* On a smaller scale, **Brian Koffman** (see p.268)of **Brian Koffman & Co** *"knows the ropes and always gives his full attention to every case."* **RM Broudie & Co** is *"huge in Liverpool in terms of volume of work,"* much of it brought in by the reputation of the respected **Robert Broudie**. Other recommended firms in Liverpool include **Jackson & Canter, Linskills Solicitors**, **Cobleys** and **The Berkson Globe Partnership** whose **Charles Peter** was complimented on *"crafting a fine practice."* Bolton, meanwhile, is largely the dominion of **Garstangs** and **Russell & Russell** while neighbouring Blackburn is well serviced by **Forbes** and **Farleys**. New to the tables this year is **Kristina Harrison Solicitors** who picked up plaudits for *"engaging in serious criminal cases often for high profile clients."* Other prominent individuals once again featured include *"outstanding road lawyer"* **Nicholas Freeman** who has a niche practice in privately funded road traffic cases and appears for Manchester United members and regional celebrities. Also recommended, **Barry Cuttle** (see p.267) *"has been around for ages and is loved by his clients."*

NORTH EAST

CRIME • North East	
1	**David Gray & Company** Newcastle upon Tyne
	Grahame Stowe, Bateson Leeds
	Henry Hyams & Co Leeds
	Irwin Mitchell Sheffield
	Sugaré & Co Leeds
	The Max Gold Partnership Hull
2	**Howells** Sheffield
	Levi & Co Leeds
	Williamsons Hull

LEADING INDIVIDUALS	
1	**SUGARÉ Anthony** Sugaré & Co

This book is the product of 6,552 1/2-hour interviews. See p.7 for BMRB audit.

Within each band, firms are listed alphabetically. *See individuals' profiles p.265*

Anthony Sugaré of **Sugaré & Co** is our only recommended individual on the basis of his specialist road traffic and drink driving work within a general practice. **Henry Hyams & Co** rises in the rankings as *"one of the best in Leeds,"* involved in large scale money laundering and murder cases over the past year. **Grahame Stowe, Bateson** is *"prominent"* in terms of volume of cases while **Levi & Co** *"continues to have a good name."* **David Gray & Company** has four full-time practitioners devoted to crime, noted in sexual offences, drug related matters and charges brought against foreign nationals. In Sheffield, **Irwin Mitchell** is a city firm best known for fraud but recognised as having *"an effective general crime arm."* Many firms outside Hull stated **The Max Gold Partnership** to be their first port of call in that vicinity. Expert in serious crime, it has been involved in one of the biggest cannabis importations this country has seen. Gosschalks' criminal department has now joined **Williamsons**' forming *"one of the serious players in their locality."* **Howells** is recommended for its *"commitment to defence work"* and advice on behalf of youths and prisoners.

SCOTLAND

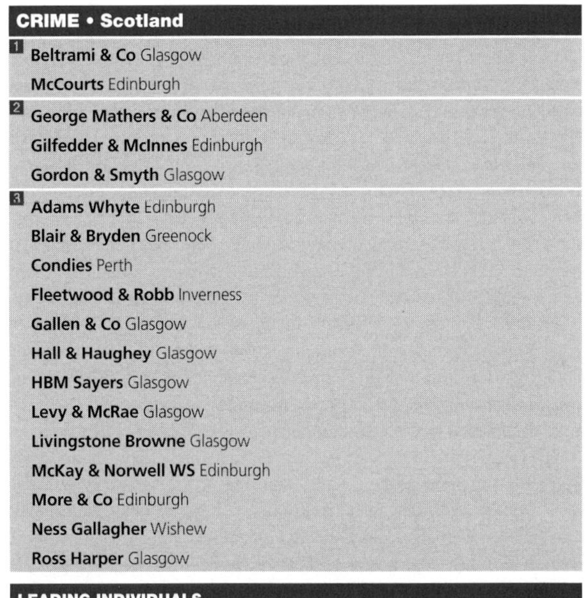

CRIME • Scotland	
1	**Beltrami & Co** Glasgow
	McCourts Edinburgh
2	**George Mathers & Co** Aberdeen
	Gilfedder & McInnes Edinburgh
	Gordon & Smyth Glasgow
3	**Adams Whyte** Edinburgh
	Blair & Bryden Greenock
	Condies Perth
	Fleetwood & Robb Inverness
	Gallen & Co Glasgow
	Hall & Haughey Glasgow
	HBM Sayers Glasgow
	Levy & McRae Glasgow
	Livingstone Browne Glasgow
	McKay & Norwell WS Edinburgh
	More & Co Edinburgh
	Ness Gallagher Wishew
	Ross Harper Glasgow

LEADING INDIVIDUALS		
1	**BELTRAMI Joseph** Beltrami & Co	**DUFF Alistair** McCourts
	GILFEDDER Brian Gilfedder & McInnes	**MACARA Murray** Beltrami & Co
	MAIN Douglas McCourts	**McINNES John** Gilfedder & McInnes
	MORE George More & Co	**PRENTICE Alexander** McCourts
	SMYTH Maurice Gordon & Smyth	

This book is the product of 6,552 1/2-hour interviews. See p.7 for BMRB audit.
Within each band, firms are listed alphabetically. *See individuals' profiles p.265*

"*Perennial achiever*" **Beltrami & Co** is known for its "*recognised quality of service*" and "*the ability to secure the best advocates.*" **Joseph Beltrami's** (see p.266) "*status is legendary*" while "*switched-on*" **Murray Macara** (see p.268) is raising his profile. Joining the firm at the top of the rankings is **McCourts**, "*well respected by all, from the client to the high court judge.*" Its position has been boosted by the return of the "*careful and thorough*" **Alec Prentice**, **Douglas Main** and **Alistair Duff**, fresh from the Lockerbie defence team. **Gilfedder & McInnes** is increasingly seen in the High Court and has four solicitor advocates including the highly rated **Brian Gilfedder** and **John McInnes**. **Gordon & Smyth** is following this trend away from lower end work, allowing **Maurice Smyth** to display his "*undoubted skill in the larger arena.*" In Aberdeen **George Mathers** "*handles the meatier cases*" including the recent abuse case of Sister Alphonso. Other ranked Glasgow firms include **Gallen & Co**, which is active in Scottish Review Commission cases, and **Levy & McRae**, often seen acting in police federation matters. **Hall & Haughey**, **HBM Sayers**, **Ross Harper** and **Livingston Browne** are all further recommended here. In the capital, **Adams Whyte** is "*incredibly busy*" following its merger, as is **McKay & Norwell**. **More & Co** has lost a slice of its practice in Fife with the departure of two solicitors but continues to be applauded for the efforts of "*very able*" **George More**. Other commended firms, active in more outlying areas, include **Ness Gallagher**, **Fleetwood & Robb**, **Blair & Bryden** and **Condies**.

NORTHERN IRELAND

CRIME • Northern Ireland	
1	**Bogue and McNulty** Belfast
	Brendan Kearney Kelly & Co Derry
	Donnelly & Wall Belfast
	Flynn & McGettrick Belfast
	Madden & Finucane Belfast
2	**Babington & Croasdaile** Londonderry
	JJ Rice Belfast
	McClenahan Crossey & Co Coleraine
	Millar Shearer & Black Cookstown
	Richard Monteith Portadown
	Trevor Smyth & Co Belfast

This book is the product of 6,552 1/2-hour interviews. See p.7 for BMRB audit.
Within each band, firms are listed alphabetically.

The nature of the jurisdiction and the relatively small population it covers dictate that the majority of firms have broad based practices. **Madden & Finucane**, prominent in the Saville Inquiry, has a further renown for judicial review and miscarriage of justice cases. Other Belfast firms include **Bogue & McNulty**, **Flynn & McGettrick**, **Donnelly & Wall** and **Trevor Smyth & Co**, all of which have substantial magistrates court practices. In Derry, **Brendan Kearney Kelly & Co** also acts in the Saville Inquiry and has "*a fine all round practice.*" **Babington & Croasdaile**, **JJ Rice**, **McClenahan Crossey & Co**, **Richard Monteith** and **Millar Shearer & Black** are also featured for their respected general practices.

LEADERS IN CRIME

ASHFORD, Mark
Taylor Nichol, London (020) 7272 8336

BECKFORD, Trevor
Beckford & Co, Norwich (01603) 660 000

BELTRAMI, Joseph
Beltrami & Co, Glasgow (0141) 221 0981
Specialisation: Consultant and solicitor advocate specialising in criminal law. Instructed in more than 350 murder and manslaughter cases. Acted in the only two Scottish Royal Pardons this century on matters of substantive crime – Maurice Swanson in 1975 and Pat Meehan in 1976; in each case compensation was awarded. Also acted in the cases of WS Ellis, Howard Wilson, Johnny Ramensky, James Boyle and Alan Hasson. First solicitor advocate to appear before the Criminal Appeal Court (1993) and the first to lead in a successful murder acquittal (June 1994).
Prof. Memberships: Solicitor advocate, solicitor to the Supreme Court.
Career: Qualified in 1953. Founding partner of *Beltrami & Co*, established in 1958.
Publications: Author of 'The Defender' (1980), 'Beltrami's Tales of the Suspected' (1988) and 'A

Deadly Innocence' (1989). Has written numerous articles for 'New Law Journal' and 'Scottish Law Journal'.
Personal: Born 15 May 1932. Educated at St Aloysius's College, Glasgow and Glasgow University. Recreations include bowls, soccer, snooker and writing. Lives in Bothwell.

BIRD, Jeremy
Marchant Harries, Aberdare (01685) 885 500

BOYLE, John
John Boyle and Co, Redruth (01209) 213507

BROUDIE, Robert
RM Broudie & Co, Liverpool (0151) 227 1429

BURTON, Anthony
Simons Muirhead & Burton, London (020) 7734 4499
anthony@smab.co.uk
Specialisation: Senior partner. Main area of practice is white collar crime and enquiries by DTI, SFO, Customs & Excise and Inland Revenue. Also handles other criminal defence work and libel. Has written for law journals and national newspapers, and lectured on criminal law. Is also a regular broadcaster.
Prof. Memberships: Law Society, LCCSA, IBA. Member of the Council of Justice, Recorder of the Crown Court, Higher Courts (Crime) Advocate.
Personal: Vice chairman of the Board of the Royal Court Theatre. Groucho Club.

BUTLER, Michael
Stephens & Scown, Exeter (01392) 210700

CADMAN, Peter
Russell-Cooke, London (020) 7405 6566

CARR, Ken
David Charnley & Co, Romford (01708) 766155

COLE, Michael
Cole's, Norwich (01603) 441 111

CUNNINGHAM, Martin
Cunninghams, Manchester (0161) 833 1600
Specialisation: Purely criminal defence work, specialising in the defence of people charged with serious crime. He is regularly instructed by defendants in high profile cases in the North West, Lancashire and the Midlands, involving gangland shootings and related crime. He also specialises in white collar crime involving Inland Revenue investigations, VAT fraud and has recently successfully defended in what has been described by the Crown Prosecution Service as one of Manchester's largest serious fraud cases. He is currently instructed to act in relation to a fraud squad investigation of corruption involved in the allocation of building contracts for the Millennium Dome.
Prof. Memberships: Law Society, Manchester Law Society, Criminal Law Solicitors Association, Manchester Duty Solicitor Scheme.
Career: Educated as an external student from London University obtaining an LLB Honours in 1979. Admitted 15 July 1982. Set up in practice in August 1985 as *Martin Cunningham & Co Solicitors* in Moss Side, Manchester, where he practised until the firm moved to Central Manchester in 1995. The firm expanded rapidly, changing its name to *Cunninghams Solicitors* where he is senior partner. His career aim is to continue to provide a much needed service in the field in which he practices.
Personal: Aged 45. Married with three children. Leisure interests include classical music, walking, fine wines and Manchester United. Lives between homes in Cheshire and Derbyshire. Ambitions: to walk the Cuillins, the Knoydart, and the Monroe Mountain Ranges.

CUTTLE, M Barry
Cuttle & Co, Manchester (0161) 835 2050
jerry_cuttles@lineone.net
Specialisation: Criminal Law. Appointed as solicitor in the Strangeways prison riots to negotiate between prisoners and officers towards ending of individual personal disputes in 1990.
Prof. Memberships: Law Society.
Career: Qualified in January 1963. Worked with the Crown Prosecution Service in Manchester. Promoted to new CPS Department in charge of Bolton Borough, thereafter in Lanchashire County Prosecutions. Formed *MB Cuttle & Co* 1972. Deals with crime of all levels, and many fraud conspiracy murders. Now senior partner of *MB Cuttle & Co.*
Personal: Educated at Worksop College in Nottinghamshire. Married with two children and upon leaving school at Worksop, became heavily involved in swimming, particularly long distance and raising money for good causes. Interested in all sports. Officer in the Cheshire RGT. Shena (wife) teacher and past president of Soroptimist International Manchester Club; Louise (daughter) bar clerk; Fraser (son) has joined the practice and is an officer with the Cheshire RGT.

DRAYCOTT, Shaun
Draycott Browne, Manchester (0161) 833 1333

DUFF, Alistair
McCourts, Edinburgh (0131) 225 6555

EDWARDS, Anthony
TV Edwards, London (020) 7726 0776
Specialisation: Senior partner. Criminal and licensing department. Lecturer on all aspects of criminal practice, and specialist in criminal costs and professional conduct.
Prof. Memberships: Law Society; London Criminal Courts Solicitors Association; CLSA; LAPG; member of Legal Services Commission; editorial board of Criminal Law Review and Executive Board of Justice
Career: Qualified in 1974, having joined *TV Edwards* in 1972. Became senior partner in 1993.
Publications: 'Advising the suspect in the police station' and 'Criminal Defence A guide to good practice'. Regular contributor to 'Law Society Gazette'.
Personal: Born 6 December 1949. Attended Bristol University, taking a first class LLB in 1971. Leisure interests include walking, reading, and theatre.

FANSON, David
Douglas & Partners, Bristol (0117) 955 2663

FISHER, Ian
Overbury Steward Eaton & Woolsey, Norwich (01603) 610481

FISHER, Michael
Christian Fisher, London (020) 7831 1750

FREEMAN, Nicholas
Freeman & Co, Manchester 0161 236 7007

GILFEDDER, Brian
Gilfedder & McInnes, Edinburgh (0131) 553 4333

GOULBORN, Caroline
Fletchers, Nottingham (0115) 959 9550

GREGO, Kevin
Parker & Grego, Birmingham (0121) 633 3031
Specialisation: Serious crime and childcare. Successfully disposing of serious cases by ensuring the prosecution observes the rules upon proper disclosure.
Prof. Memberships: Law Society, Childcare panel member.
Career: Qualified 1980, founding partner present firm. Specialising in crime and children's matters – public law.

GROGAN, Peter
Jones Maidment Wilson incorporating Hatton Scates Horton, Manchester (0161) 832 8087

HALLAM, Richard
Claude Hornby & Cox, London (020) 7437 8873
Specialisation: Partner in criminal litigation department since 1989. Has substantial experience of conducting cases in the Magistrates Courts, Higher Criminal Courts and before Courts Martial in UK and Germany. Normally instructed as a defence advocate, but has experience of prosecuting for the CPS and will prosecute privately for individuals or organisations. Nationwide experience of prosecuting video piracy cases. Defends in professional disciplinary proceedings. Has successfully represented defendants facing allegations of murder, terrorism, large-scale drugs importation and fraud, but equally interested in defending clients charged with less serious offences.
Prof. Memberships: City of Westminster Law Society, London Criminal Courts Solicitors Association, Legal Aid Practitioners Group.
Personal: Born 24 April 1948. Educated at the King's School, Canterbury and Oxford University. Lives in London.

HASLAM, Mark
Burton Copeland (London), London (020) 7430 2277
mhaslam@burtoncopeland.co.uk
Specialisation: Partner in Criminal Litigation Department. Practice covers all areas of criminal defence work including white collar, large scale drugs cases, serious public order offences and murder and manslaughter cases. Acted successfully in a number of substantial prosecutions brought by Customs & Excise including Charington and Others. Has experience of Court Martial Proceedings and defended Christine Dryland, the wife of Major Dryland, in a highly publicised murder trial in Germany. Recently represented Sgt. Jason Arder and Lance Bombardrer Heidi Cochrane in a case of AWOL which attracted a considerable amount of public interest. Also specialises in motoring cases including excess alcohol, careless driving and speeding. Regular broadcaster and lecturer on criminal legal affairs on radio, television and at seminars and conferences.
Prof. Memberships: President of the London Criminal Court Solicitors Association from November 2000. Member of Forces Law, The Criminal Law Committee of the Law Society and the National Duty Solicitor Committee. Sits as a solicitor assessor in the High Court in taxation matters.
Career: Qualified in 1981, worked at *Claude Hornby & Cox* from 1979-1993 and *Magrath & Co* from 1993-1997. Partner at *Burton Copeland* from January 1998.
Personal: Born 16 June 1957. Attended Wellington College, Berkshire 1971-1976 and Pembroke College,

Cambridge, 1976 to 1979 (MA). Leisure interests include cricket, horse racing and the theatre. Married and lives in Cobham in Surrey.

HEWITT, Stephen
Fisher Meredith, London (020) 7622 4468
stephenh@fishermeredith.co.uk
Specialisation: Managing partner and department head of one of the largest and most successful criminal defence teams in London. Wide experience of criminal defence and associated civil liberties work with lengthy history of major homicide, sex offences, drug trafficking and business crime cases. Particular experience of acting for mentally disturbed defendants and undertaking complex appeals to the Court of Appeal. Lectured on aspects of criminal practice, legal aid franchising, contracting and law firm practice management. Member of national committee of LAPG; Fellow of Institute of Advanced Legal Studies. Currently undertaking a part time MBA in 'Law Firm Management' at Nottingham University.
Prof. Memberships: Law Society, London Criminal Courts Solicitors Association, Criminal Law Solicitors Association, Liberty, Justice.
Career: Qualified 1980. Joined *Fisher Meredith* as partner in 1986.
Publications: 'Legal Aid Practice' Sweet & Maxwell (co-author)
Personal: Born 14 November 1953. Lives in Hove.

HICKMAN, Jane
Hickman & Rose, London (020) 7700 2211
Specialisation: Heads one of Britain's leading criminal law firms. Vast experience in handling criminal defence work nationwide, particularly murder and serious crime. Creative strategist who fights hard for clients and who 'takes no prisoners'. Has specialist skill in managing complex scientific and medical issues. Particularly capable with cases where lawyer negligence contributes to a miscarriage of justice. Writes and lectures on quality issues in criminal defence firms.
Prof. Memberships: Law Society, LCCSA, Legal Action Group (committee member).
Career: MA (First Class Hons) Edinburgh 1972. Qualified 1977. Founded *Hickman & Rose* in 1991. MBA in law firm management from Nottingham Law School 2000. Special adviser to Lord Justice Auld in his Criminal Courts Review, 2000-01.

HUBER, Bernard
Edwards Duthie, London (020) 8472 0138

HUTTON, Stuart
Huttons, Cardiff (029) 2037 8621
smch@huttons-solicitors.co.uk
Specialisation: Senior partner. Criminal department. Has been primarily involved in criminal work for over 20 years. Also deals with childcare, adoption and fostering. Has been on the Childcare panel for over 10 years. Has handled some notable murder cases, including the high profile Tooze double Farmhouse murder and the acquittal of Jonathan Jones, another the subject of the Bloody Valentine book, and 'vigilante' killing Penrhys, Rhondda, Mid Glamorgan. Has had continuing success in taking miscarriages of justice to the Court of Appeal. Former part-time chairman of Social Security Appeals tribunals. Has special interest in entertainment and media law.
Career: Qualified in 1975. With *Edwards Geldard* 1973-86 (as a partner from 1976). Established own practice, *Huttons*, in August 1986. The practice has a reputation for specialist litigation.
Personal: Born 21 October 1946. Lives in Cardiff.

JONES, Gwyn
Gamlins, Rhyl (01745) 343500

KEENAN, Andrew
Andrew Keenan & Co, London (020) 8659 0332

KELLY, Philip
Twitchen Musters & Kelly, Southend-on-Sea (01702) 339222

KOFFMAN, Brian
Brian Koffman & Co, Manchester (0161) 832 3852
Mobile (07880) 588624
brian.koffman@briankoffman.co.uk
Specialisation: Very experienced and highly regarded advocate in cases involving serious crime. Has acted in numerous fraud, murder, armed robbery, firearms, sex, drugs and conspiracy cases. Has recently been instructed in NCIS investigations into organised crime in Salford; the 'Good Samaritan Murder' (complicated by an additional attempted murder charge the day before); a highly complicated nationwide multi-million pound business fraud which was successfully prepared for the Court of Appeal; innumerable gangland shooting cases in Manchester; a murder case in Sunderland involving organised crime in the North East; a London based chartered accountant charged with Incitement to Murder after a nationwide undercover surveillance and many other similar matters throughout the country.
Prof. Memberships: Law Society, Manchester Law Society Criminal Law Solicitors Association.
Career: Qualified in 1973. Established *Brian Koffman and Co* in 1977.
Personal: Born 1948. Educated Salford Grammar School and Liverpool Polytechnic. Married with two children. Interests include modern political history, reading, current affairs, snooker and Manchester United.

MACARA, JD Murray
Beltrami & Co, Glasgow (0141) 221 0981
Specialisation: Solicitor advocate specialising in criminal law. Has appeared in all courts throughout Scotland. Has appeared in numerous cases in the High Court. In 1999 defended Harvey Good in cellular therapy trial.
Prof. Memberships: Society of Solicitors in the Supreme Court; Law Society Criminal Law committee; committee of Society of Solicitor Advocates.
Career: Qualified in 1973. Partner in *Beltrami & Co* since 1975. Solicitor advocate 1993
Personal: Born 22 July 1949. Educated at Loretto School Musselburgh and Glasgow University. Interests include most sports, travel and dining out. Lives in Glasgow.

MACKEY, Michael
Burton Copeland (North), Manchester (0161) 834 7374
Specialisation: Criminal practitioner with experience in all aspects of criminal prosecutions, including road traffic and prosecutions by HSE and Trading Standards. For the past two decades has primarily been involved in the defence of the most serious criminal cases, including numerous murders, serial robbery and sexual offences. Substantial experience of major drug trafficking cases and criminal confiscation proceedings generally. Particular expertise in forensic aspects of investigations, including challenge of DNA evidence and scrutiny of medical expert statements, especially with reference to 'shaken baby' and child abuse prosecutions. Has been involved in many leading Appeal cases including McGarry (adverse inference) and lately, the case of Sally Clark.
Career: Admitted 1974; West Yorkshire County Prosecuting Solicitors' Office 1976; *Glaisyers*, Manchester 1976-80; *Crossley Mackey*, Manchester 1980-87; *Burton Copeland* 1987 to present.
Personal: De La Salle College, Leeds University. Aged 50, married and lives in Altrincham. Interests include music, astronomy and computers.

MAIDMENT, Allan
Maidments, Manchester (0161) 834 0008
alm@amaidment.fsnet.co.uk
Specialisation: Senior partner of *Maidments*. Works exclusively in crime and commercial fraud. Founded *Maidments* in 1993 as a specialist criminal law practice with particular emphasis on serious crime and commercial fraud. Developed the firm into one of the country's leading criminal law practices with three offices in Manchester and offices in Birmingham, Liverpool, London, Bolton, Leeds and Sale.
Prof. Memberships: A member of the Law Society and Local Societies in Manchester and Birmingham. Former member of the Manchester Duty Solicitor Committee. Member of the Criminal Law Solicitors Association. Member of the Serious Fraud Panel. Chairman of Serious Fraud Association.
Career: Educated in Scotland, LLB Leeds University. Qualified in 1976.

MAIN, Douglas
McCourts, Edinburgh (0131) 225 6555

MASTERS, Peter
Thomson Webb Corfield, Cambridge (01223) 578070

MATHER, Bertie JM
Elliot Mather, Matlock (01629) 584885

McINNES, John
Gilfedder & McInnes, Edinburgh (0131) 553 4333

MERRIAM, Joy
Joy Merriam & Co, London (020) 8980 7171

MILES, Anthony
Bobbetts Mackan, Bristol (0117) 929 9001
tmiles@bobbettsmackan.co.uk
Specialisation: Partner responsible for criminal defence team. 24-hour Criminal Defence helpline (0117) 929 8987 Main area of practice is criminal defence and advocacy. Engaged in the conduct of all cases before the Criminal Courts and at Courts Martial. Has developed an expertise in the defence of cases before Courts Martial, District and General. Has handled serious fraud cases; offences involving serious dishonesty and violence and complex murder and drugs cases. Higher Court Advocate (Crime).
Prof. Memberships: Law Society, Bristol Law Society (Former President), CLSA, LAPG.
Career: Qualified in 1972. Joined *Bobbetts Mackan* in 1972, becoming a partner in 1974.
Personal: Born 12th February 1947. Leisure interests include sailing, walking, skiing and reading.

MILNER, Henry
Henry Milner & Co, London (020) 7831 9944

MORE, George M
More & Co, Edinburgh (0131) 557 1110

MURPHY, Shaun
Edwards Duthie, London (020) 8472 0138

MUSTERS, Patrick
Twitchen Musters & Kelly, Southend-on-Sea (01702) 339222
pmusters@tmksols.co.uk
Specialisation: Solicitor advocate specialising in all areas of criminal litigation especially serious crime (murder, armed robbery and sexual offences), prison mutiny and escape, large drug importations, serious white collar fraud and international terrorism. Cases have attracted national and international notoriety. Substantial experience on advice on appeal against conviction.
Prof. Memberships: Law Society, Criminal Law Solicitors Association, Association of Higher Court Advocates, London Criminal Courts Solicitors Association, Serious Fraud Panel, British Academy of Forensic Scientists. Member of Legal Services Commission Funding Committee and Regional Duty Solicitor Committee.
Career: Admitted June 1978. Higher Court advocate April 1994
Personal: Born 20 July 1952. Educated Allhallows School, Lyme Regis. Interests include Law Society Golf Club, running and skiing. Consultant to both BBC Radio Essex and Essex Radio on criminal law matters.

NICHOL, James
Taylor Nichol, London (020) 7272 8336

NICHOLLS, Simon J.
Belmores, Norwich (01603) 617947

NOTT, Colin
Hallinan, Blackburn, Gittings & Nott, London (020) 7233 3999
Specialisation: Specialist in criminal defence work, extradition and judicial review.
Career: Qualified 1978. Sole practitioner 1979-82. Joined *Hallinan Blackburn Gittings & Nott* as a partner – 1982.
Personal: Born 27 June 1952. Educated Weymouth Grammar School, London University. LLB (Hons). Interests: sport, rugby and football in particular, theatre and travel.

NOVY, Rod
Thanki Novy Taube, London (020) 7833 5800

NUNN, Stephen
Stephens & Scown, Exeter (01392) 210700

O'MAY, Neil
Bindman & Partners, London (020) 7833 4433
info@bindmans.com
Specialisation: Wide range of criminal defence work from murder and terrorist cases to more general crime. All types of serious fraud (including SFO cases). Supervisor status for the Legal Services Commission Serious Fraud Panel of approved solicitors for large-scale fraud cases, particularly those involving professionals (solicitors and accountants) as defendants. Particular expertise in large scale public order arrests and multi-defendant trials (from Poll Tax demonstrators to the recent May Day events). Specialist in cases involving complex scientific and expert evidence including computer and internet crime. Extensive experience in defending journalists' civil liberties issues (the 'AVP' trial in Manchester) and other 'professionals in trouble' (including professional body disciplinary proceedings). Defending against top prosecution teams, including the Anti-Terrorist Squad (in the Israeli Embassy bombing case and IRA mortar attack on Heathrow Airport) and Special Branch on Official Secrets Act cases. Experience in the defence of complex drugs cases and sexual abuse cases including recovered memory cases (R v Reeves). Fresh evidence appeals in the Court of Appeal and the investigations of miscarriages of justice (including R v Siôn Jenkins). Inquests including deaths in police custody and judicial review. Ground-breaking cases in the House of Lords (R v Doody & Others; R v Aziz & Others; R v English). Recent involvement on behalf of Amnesty in the Pinochet case. Human Rights Act specialist (R v Offen & Others). Writer, lecturer and broadcaster on legal issues.
Prof. Memberships: Law Society; London Criminal Courts Solicitors Association; Criminal Law Solicitors Association.
Career: Qualified 1985. Joined *Bindman & Partners* as head of criminal department in 1990.
Personal: Degree in Biochemistry; BSc (Hons); Londoner.

PEIRCE, Gareth
Birnberg Peirce & Partners, London (020) 7284 4620

PENNINGTON, John
Savery Pennington, Cardiff 02920 457 222

PETER, Charles
The Berkson Globe Partnership, Liverpool (0151) 236 1234

POWELL, Greg
Powell Spencer & Partners, London (020) 7624 8888
Specialisation: Criminal defence, especially murder, conspiracies to import and supply drugs, armed robbery. Magistrates Court advocacy. Acting for an increasing number of professional clients such as accountants, doctors, estate agents and solicitors.
Prof. Memberships: Law Society, Haldane Society, Liberty.
Career: Qualified 1973. Degrees in Law (LSE) and Psychology (Birkbeck).
Publications: Co-author of a 'Practical Guide to the Police and Criminal Evidence Act'.

PRENTICE, Alexander
McCourts, Edinburgh (0131) 225 6555

PRESTON, Edward
Edward Fail Bradshaw & Waterson, London (020) 7790 4032

PROWEL, Martyn
Martyn Prowel Solicitors, Cardiff (02920) 470909
mprowel@mped.globalnet.co.uk
Specialisation: Complex fraud trials, commercial and VAT/revenue fraud and other serious crime trial defences. Prosecutions undertaken for RSPCA. General crime, magistrates and crown court defence.
Prof. Memberships: Law Society. South Wales Duty Solicitors Regional committee member. Serious Fraud panel.
Career: LLB (Hons) Wales 1962-1965. European Law Studies 1965-1966 Nancy Univ. France. Qualified 1970. Former senior partner Hallinans solicitors and South Wales Duty Solicitors' Regional committee member.
Personal: Married with two children.

PURCELL, Michael
Purcell Parker, Birmingham (0121) 236 9781

RICHARDS, Geraint
Martyn Prowel Solicitors, Cardiff (02920) 470909
grichards@mped.globalnet.co.uk
Specialisation: General crime, Magistrates and Crown Court advocacy.
Prof. Memberships: Law Society.
Career: LLB Wales 1977-1980. Qualified 1984.
Personal: Married with three children

ROSCOE, Robert
Victor Lissack & Roscoe, London (020) 7240 2010
robertroscoe@victorlissack.co.uk
Specialisation: Partner in crime department. Main areas of practice are white-collar fraud, serious criminal offences, extradition and general criminal practice.
Prof. Memberships: Law Society; City of Westminster Law Society; London Criminal Courts Solicitors' Association; Criminal Law Solicitors' Association.
Career: Qualified in 1976. Higher Courts (Criminal Proceedings) Qualification 1994. Joined *Victor Lissack & Roscoe* in 1969, becoming a partner in 1978. Law Society council member 1992-98; chairman of Criminal Law Committee 1995-98; LCCSA: president 1996-97, committee member and advocacy training officer 1983-93; chairman of no 14 Regional Duty Solicitor Committee (1991-97); Legal Aid Board Costs Appeals Committee (1993-94).

ROSE, Timothy
Douglas & Partners, Bristol (0117) 955 2663

RYAN, Ian
Russell-Cooke, London (020) 8788 0005
ryani@russell-cooke.co.uk
Specialisation: Head of the criminal department leading a team of five fee earners; deals with the full range of criminal defence work but specialises in larger and more complex cases including murder, armed robbery, sexual offences, drugs cases, extradition, and all types of fraud including VAT fraud and diversion frauds. Has a particular interest in cases involving forensic or medical issues. Successfully defended Colin Stagg and has been involved in a number of other high profile cases that have attracted national attention. More recently has specialised in representing professional people (particularly solicitors) in criminal and disciplinary proceedings. Solicitor Advocate in the Crown Court and regular appearances as an advocate at professional disciplinary tribunals.
Prof. Memberships: Member of the LCCSA.
Career: Qualified 1987. Partner from 1995. Head of department 2000.

SAUNDERS, James
Saunders & Co, London (020) 7404 2828

SINCLAIR, Franklin
Tuckers, Manchester (0161) 233 4321
Specialisation: In overall control of large criminal practice dealing in all aspects of criminal defence work. Particular specialisation as an advocate defending the rights of clients in a robust manner and dealing with many serious cases, including extensive involvement in preparation from the outset of a case to its conclusion. Has dealt with numerous murder cases and specialises in large scale drugs importation and armed robbery cases. Has previously dealt with the first case involving challenge to DNA evidence

which was initially successful in the Court of Appeal.
Prof. Memberships: Manchester Law Society. Solicitor Member of Criminal Justice Liason Committee for the North-West. Chairman of Criminal Law Solicitors' Association (C.L.S.A.).
Career: Qualified 1982. Partner with Barry Tucker in *Tuckers Solicitors* since 1984.
Personal: Manchester Grammar School; Manchester University; College of Law, Chester. Married with three children. Interests include golf, environmental issues, gardening. Born 28 June 1958. Lives in Cheshire.

SMYTH, Maurice T
Gordon & Smyth, Glasgow (0141) 275 4875

SPENCER, Richard
Powell Spencer & Partners, London (020) 7624 8888
Specialisation: A criminal law specialist for over 20 years covering the whole range of defence work, but particularly murder and possession of cannabis offences. Excellent Magistrates Court defence advocate practising throughout the London area.

STUDDERT, Mark
Hodge Jones & Allen, London (020) 7482 1974
Specialisation: Partner in large franchised criminal department dealing with wide range of offences. Own specialisation – homicide, drug importation, fraud.
Prof. Memberships: Member Liberty; Haldane Society; Prisoners Advice Service. Organiser and administrator of Highbury and Old Street Duty Solicitor scheme. Committee member London Criminal Courts Solicitors' Association for whom he lectures.
Career: Qualified 1979. Joined *Hodge Jones & Allen* 1985, partner 1987.
Personal: Lives in Stoke Newington with partner and young son. Interests: film, popular culture, food.

SUGARÉ, Anthony
Sugaré & Co, Leeds (0113) 244 6978

SVENSSON, Zara
Stones, Exeter (01392) 666777
zarasvensson@stones-solicitors.co.uk
Specialisation: Criminal law.
Prof. Memberships: Criminal Law Solicitors Association.
Career: Degree 1984-88 Nottingham Trent University; Law Society Finals 1988-89 Chester College of Law; Articles 1989-91 Slee Blackwell, Barnstaple, North Devon; Admitted 16 September 1991; 1995 – present *Stones*, Exeter.

TAYLOR, Carolyn S.
Taylor Nichol, London (020) 7272 8336

THANKI, Girish
Thanki Novy Taube, London (020) 7833 5800
girishthanki@tntlaw.co.uk
Specialisation: Acting for Battered Women who Kill, mainly at appellant and CCRC stages; two recent Third Party interventions at House of Lords on provocation (R v Morgan James Smith) and rape (R v A). Wide range of criminal defence and civil liberties work including murder, armed robberies and white collar crime with considerable experience of handling complex and weighty cases. Specialist knowledge of forensics and scientific issues. Active extradition practice with particular emphasis on the USA. Recent case involved arguing fairness of trial for black defendants in the State of Missouri. Judicial reviews and appellate work including the House of Lords and the Privy Council.
Prof. Memberships: Member Law Society Task Force on implementation of the Human Rights Act; LCCSA; BAFS; Medico-Legal Society; IBA; Liberty; Justice (Criminal Justice Panel member); Prisoners' Advisory Service; Inquest; Law Society.
Career: Worked as an independent film-maker primarily in the community video sector, prior to training as a lawyer. Joined *Thanki Novy Taube* in 1997 and made a partner in 2000.
Publications: Articles in Legal Action (LAG); Liberty and Rights of Women newsletters.
Personal: Lives in London. Leisure interests confined to food, wine, travelling, armchair politics, cricket and family life.

TOMLINSON, Kevin
Kieran & Co, Worcester (01905) 28635

VENTERS, June
Venters & Co, London (020) 7277 0110
j.venters@ventersreynolds.co.uk
Specialisation: The two main areas of specialisation are general crime and public law childcare. CRIME: Representation in all areas of criminal law. Most notable cases include sexual offences cases involving a referral from the Home Secretary resulting in an eventual re-trial and acquittal; large scale vat fraud; large scale conspiracy to rob which was a well publicised 'yardie' case and conspiracy to defraud involving a large-scale national football scam. CHILDCARE: Serious and complex cases involving High Court advocacy; one such case forming a Court of Appeal Law Report on the rules of disclosure and another case forming a Practice Direction.
Prof. Memberships: Solicitor Advocate Higher Courts (all proceedings); vice president of the London Criminal Courts Solicitors Association; regional chairman of the South East London Legal Aid Committee; Law Society accredited trainer; Gray's Inn advocacy trainer; Assessor of the Children's panel; member of the Children's panel; criminal duty solicitor
Career: June Venters is an equity partner in the firm of Venters Reynolds. In 1998 June Venters was appointed Assistant Recorder. In 2000 she was appointed Recorder.
Publications: Various published articles. Author of *Standard Letters and Forms for the Criminal Practitioner.*
Personal: In 1996 June Venters featured in a BBC1 prime time documentary entitled *Law Women* which focused on the life of a criminal lawyer. Since then she has continued to make various television and radio appearances. In addition she has presented various lectures including a lecture which was video-linked to America and which concerned legal aid block contracting.

WARBOYS, Kevin
Copleys, St Ives (01480) 464515

WILLIAMS, Ian
Robertsons, Cardiff (029) 20237777

CUSTOMS & EXCISE

OVERVIEW: Customs and Excise has been cited as an area of gradual growth, especially with the introduction of legal aid, which will come into force on 2nd April 2001.

RESEARCH APPROVED BY BMRB: *For this edition,* Chambers' *researchers conducted 6,552 interviews – 4,419 with law firms, 554 with barristers and 1,579 with clients.*

The validity of the research was scrutinised by BMRB International, who audited both the methodology and the results at our offices in July 2001. They interviewed Chambers' *researchers and cross-checked sample interviews. Details of the audit appear on page 7.*

NATIONWIDE

	CUSTOMS & EXCISE • Nationwide	Ptnrs	Assts
1	**Dechert** London	2	n/a
2	**Baker & McKenzie** London	2	1
3	**Burton Copeland** London, Manchester	n/a	n/a
	Peters & Peters London	n/a	n/a
4	**Berwin Leighton Paisner** London	1	2
	DLA London	3	4
	Kingsley Napley London	2	2
	Lovells London	1	1
	Russell Jones & Walker London	4	5
5	**Irwin Mitchell** Sheffield	1	3
	Pannone & Partners Manchester	3	2
	Tarlo Lyons London	2	3
	Watson, Farley & Williams London	n/a	n/a

	LEADING INDIVIDUALS	
1	**CORNWELL-KELLY Malachy** Dechert	
2	**GERRARD Neil** DLA	**HANMAN David** Russell Jones & Walker
3	**DUNCAN Susan** Baker & McKenzie	
	HODGKINSON Milly Berwin Leighton Paisner	
4	**KENYON Michael** Burton Copeland	**MARTIN Maurice** Tarlo Lyons
	PRESTON Christopher Watson, Farley	**RAPHAEL Monty** Peters & Peters
	SALTISSI Sally Dechert	**TRAVERS Harry** Burton Copeland

This book is the product of 6,552 1/2-hour interviews. See p.7 for BMRB audit.
Within each band, firms are listed alphabetically. *See individuals' profiles p.272*

Dechert (see firm details p.938) An "*outstanding*" reputation upheld by an ability to offer clients advisory and litigation expertise in all areas of customs and excise law. **Malachy Cornwell-Kelly** (see p.272) is cited by peers as the "*senior, most able player*" in the market. He is flanked by lawyers with a great depth of knowledge, many of whom join the team from HM Customs & Excise including the highly rated **Sally Saltissi.** (see p.273) Continuing to attract high profile clients, most notably in contentious work, it successfully acted for PricewaterhouseCoopers in an anti-dumping appeal, and has demonstrated an expertise in duties work by successfully acting for SmithKline Beecham in a customs duty appeal.

Baker & McKenzie (see firm details p.868) Although Andrew Hart has retired from full time practice he maintains a consultancy role specialising in valuation disputes involving sizeable companies. A significant new presence in the team is that of **Susan Duncan** (see p.272) (formerly HM Customs & Excise,) described by peers as "*strong, hardworking and conscientious.*" A formidable team advises importers and exporters on both contentious and pre-emptive classification and valuation disputes. Active for hi-tech clients, the team obtained the withdrawal of a substantial post-importation duty and VAT demand over the classification of hi-tech goods.

Burton Copeland (see firm details p.904) This association of two partnerships in London and Manchester operates a "*formidable team*" with the "*exceptionally bright*" **Harry Travers** (see p.273) in London and **Michael Kenyon** (see p.272), "*an important player*" in the Manchester market. Selected to work on such high profile investigations as the under-declaration of VAT by Frank Warren in his pay-per-view boxing enterprise. The core of the team's work consists of advocacy for those prosecuted by Customs, and the aversion of prosecution by civil settlement. The work undertaken ranges from fraud in the international computer chips trade to the largest diversion frauds such as gold smuggling.

Peters & Peters (see firm details p.1095) "*Pre-eminent in crime work,*" the team is led by the "*experienced figurehead*" **Monty Raphael.** (see p.412) Defending individuals prosecuted by the inland revenue forms the core of the team's work with a solid reputation for its civil settlement work.

Berwin Leighton Paisner (see firm details p.878) The firm continues to specialise in e-commerce and has experienced growth in cross-border VAT issues. It offers advice in litigation, consultancy and compliance issues. **Milly Hodgkinson** (see p.272), knowledgeable on the subject of indirect tax, provides expertise gained from a former career in HM Customs & Excise. The team has recently advised on the controls placed by the DTI upon the import and export of agricultural machinery, and has been involved in the negotiations surrounding the manufacturing industry and UN sanctions.

DLA **Neil Gerrard** heads a team that advises on white collar crime, acting for a range of large US multinationals.

Kingsley Napley (see firm details p.1022) The firm, regarded as "*notoriously good*" continues to be an important player in the market. Active both within civil fraud and white collar crime, the team, headed by Christopher Murray, represents various bodies and individuals who have had charges brought against them by the SFO, Customs & Excise and Inland Revenue.

Lovells (see firm details p.1044) "*Experts in civil litigation*", according to its peers the team headed by Greg Sinfield has been engaged in a number of high profile contentious VAT and indirect tax cases. They recently undertook the appeal of the Mirror Group concerning the ability of fully taxable companies to recover VAT incurred on the issue of shares. A substantial part of the practice also comprises VAT advice in non-contentious matters to clients such as Ford Motor Company and British American Tobacco.

Russell Jones & Walker (see firm details p.1116) The firm undertakes a variety of fraud and commercial crime work. "*An important presence,*" **David Hanman** (see p.272) has increased the stature of the firm. His expertise in Inland Revenue and Customs & Excise investigations is increasingly deployed in regulatory issues, such as landfill VAT tax.

Irwin Mitchell (see firm details p.1009) This well regarded practice is given an expertise by its strength in the area of judicial review on the civil side of customs work. Fraud specialist, Kevin Robinson, heads the team that is highly recommended for its client relations. The group specialises in contentious white collar criminal matters, including VAT and diversion fraud.

Pannone & Partners (see firm details p.1088) Although not perceived to have a high profile this year, the team undertakes a substantial amount of fraud work, including VAT and diversion fraud cases. Paul Taylor leads a group that also provides expertise in regulatory indirect tax issues.

Tarlo Lyons (see firm details p.1149) Unusual in acting both for taxpayers against customs and the SFO and also for receivers in restraint and confiscation work where the claimants are these departments. The "*experienced*" **Maurice Martin** (see p.272) leads the team, the majority of whose work lies in major customs investigations, often with Inland Revenue or SFO connections, and general white-collar crime.

Watson, Farley & Williams (see firm details p.1174) Best known for its VAT and indirect tax advice within the customs remit, the"*whiz*" **Christopher Preston** (see p.807) has impressed his peers with his expert knowledge within the field. It continues to advise Inmarsat on VAT and customs issues arising from its effective privatisation. Clients include Dresdner Kleinwort Benson and, increasingly, new technology and internet companies.

LEADERS IN CUSTOMS & EXCISE

CORNWELL-KELLY, Malachy

Dechert, London (020) 7775 7577
malachy.cornwellkelly@dechertEU.com

Specialisation: Consultant to international trade and customs practise in London which negotiates and handles disputes with Customs and Excise and IBEA on all VAT, customs and excise duty matters. Work covers investigation cases, tariff classification, valuation and transfer pricing issues, origin, duty preference, export rebates, CAP questions, import and export licensing, anti-dumping duties, and appeals to and appearances before the VAT and Duties Tribunal and the European Court. Cases have included agricultural levy disputes and CAP export refunds, tariff classification, origin disputes, customs duty panel, VAT liability, Single Market excise liabilities, collateral insurance rights, judicial review of Customs & Excise and United Nations trade sanctions.

Prof. Memberships: Law Society Revenue Law Committee, Customs Practitioners Group, Institute of Indirect Taxation, Law Society representative on Joint Customs Consultative Committee, UKWA representative on the Joint Alcohol and Tobacco Consultation Group.

Career: Qualified in 1971. Worked at Customs and Excise Solicitor's Office 1972-77, then *Richards Butler* 1977-83. Joined the Law Society as Revenue Law Committee Secretary in 1983 before becoming Director of Tax Investigations for the Parliamentary Ombudsman in 1988. Joined *Titmuss Sainer & Webb* (now *Dechert*) in 1993.

Publications: Author of 'European Community Law', 2nd edition, a regular column in CCH Indirect Tax News and articles in Taxation, The Law Society's Gazette and Exporting Today. Frequent conference speaker.

Personal: Born 11th May 1947. Attended King's College, London, 1965-68 (LLB), then College of Law, London, 1968-69, Ecole Nationale d'Administration, Paris, 1975, secretary of the Tax Law Review Committee at the Institute for Fiscal Studies 1993-95. Leisure interests include cider and beer making and collecting Customs memorabilia. Lives in Sevenoaks, Kent.

DUNCAN, Susan

Baker & McKenzie, London (020) 7919 1000
susan.duncan@bakernet.com

Specialisation: Customs matters covering a variety of issues and procedures, e.g. valuation, inter-company pricing, classification, reliefs and warehousing. She also deals with VAT and Climate Change Levy. During the past year Susan has dealt with some contentious work. Disputes with Customs & Excise concerning classification of computer and telecoms equipment have been successfully resolved. In relation to the former, although litigation had been commenced in the Tribunal, the matter was still resolved before a full hearing.

Prof. Memberships: Customs Practitioners' Group member.

Career: Called to the Bar (1987); HM Customs & Excise (1989-00) – Susan spent four and half years in VAT Tribunal litigation section, one and half in VAT advisory work and a further fifteen months in Customs litigation and advisory work; joined *Baker & McKenzie's* tax department (March 2000).

Publications: Susan has recently published an article entitled 'Changes to the Community Customs Code' in Croner's 'Trading in Europe' as well as an article in 'VAT Intelligence' regarding Electronic Invoicing and proposed amendments to the Sixth Directive. She has also contributed the section on Community Transit to 'Croner's Europe'.

Personal: BA(Hons) Spanish & Latin American Studies from University of Newcastle upon Tyne (1982). Susan is married with three step-children. Her husband is a barrister and sits part time as a Recorder. Leisure interests include collecting antique silver and glass, playing the piano, travel, going to the theatre.

GERRARD, Neil

DLA, London (08700) 111 111

HANMAN, David

Russell Jones & Walker, Manchester
(0161) 832 8877
d.i.hanman@rjw.co.uk

Specialisation: Partner in the tax investigations department of *Russell Jones & Walker*. Represents clients involved in criminal tax investigations conducted by National Investigation Service of HM Custom & Excise, Special Compliance Office of HM Inland Revenue, Serious Fraud Office and also investigations by the Department of Trade and Industry and Trading Standards.

Prof. Memberships: Member of the Chartered Institute of Taxation (CIOT). Also a member of the Institute of Direct Taxation, (AIIT), VAT Practitioners Group (VPG) and Customs Practitioners Group (CPG).

Career: Qualified in 1992.

HODGKINSON, Milly

Berwin Leighton Paisner, London (020) 776 1000
milly.hodgkinson@berwinleightonpaisner.com

Specialisation: E-commerce, VAT, Customs & Excise duties. *Berwin Leighton Paisner* specialises in e-commerce for both start-up and major international retailing clients.Has developed a particular specialisation in advising on cross-border VAT and Customs duties issues and Customs & Excise warehousing in Europe.

Prof. Memberships: The International Bar Association, The American Bar Association, World Trade Law Association, British Importers Association, United Kingdom Association for European Law, The CBI, The Enterprising Women Network.

Career: Qualified at *Kingsley Napley* in 1991, joined the Solicitors' Office of Customs & Excise in 1992 specialising in European law, customs duties, VAT and international advisory work. Seconded to MAFF in 1998 before joining City law firm *Berwin Leighton Paisner* as head of indirect tax at the beginning of 1999.

Publications: A regular contributor to journals including the 'Tax Journal', 'Tornado-Insider.com', 'Legal Week', 'The Institute of Indirect Taxation', 'The Evening Standard' and 'The Financial News'.

Personal: Educated at SOAS London University. Leisure interests include gardening and opera.

KENYON, Michael

Burton Copeland (North), Manchester
(0161) 834 7374

Specialisation: Acts on behalf of numerous corporate clients under investigation by Customs for VAT & Excise duty irregularities and also defends individuals subject to prosecution. Wider practise includes commercial fraud investigation and defence including prospectus fraud, loan and leasing fraud, insider dealing, fraudulent tradings, frauds on investors, property and mortgage fraud, corruption and tax investigations.

Prof. Memberships: Law Society, Criminal Law Solicitors Association.

Career: Qualified in 1980. Partner at *Chafes*, Stockport 1985-86. Senior Crown Prosecutor in Manchester 1987-89. Partner at *Burton Copeland* from 1990.

Personal: Born 1956. Attended Manchester Grammar School and University of Kent. Leisure interests include salmon fishing, game shooting, military and political history and opera. Lives in Cheshire and Scotland.

MARTIN, Maurice

Tarlo Lyons, London (020) 7405 2000

Specialisation: Senior partner (1999) and former head of civil and criminal litigation (1989-99). Investigations by HM Customs & Excise and/or Inland Revenue, whether civil, criminal or both; negotiation of settlements wherever possible and the defence of proceedings where unavoidable; financial crime in general. Cases include Richmond Rendezvous Chinese Restaurant Group, Le Rififi (Court of Appeal), Westminster Cemetaries 15p sale, BT plc share application; Maxwell/Bishopsgate Investments;

Hambros/CWS Enquiry and Morgan Grenfell. Usually acts for defendants, often in cases with international aspects, eg Europe-wide VAT carousels; works closely with *Tarlo Lyons* restraint and forfeiture team when instructed by CJA Receivers for HM Customs & Excise and other prosecution authorities, thereby involving negotiation on 'both sides of the fence', written articled for 'Taxation Practitioner' and 'Construction News'.
Prof. Memberships: Law Society; London Criminal Courts Solicitors' Association; International Bar Association (Committee W). Speaker on tax investigations for Business Crime Committee of IBA in Vancouver (1998) and Barcelona (1999).
Career: Qualified in 1973. Entire career thereafter spent with *Tarlo Lyons.*
Personal: Born 1949. Read law at University College London. Enjoys time with family, supporting Watford FC and lunch.

PRESTON, Christopher
Watson, Farley & Williams, London
(020) 7814 8000
cpreston@wfw.com
See under Tax, p.807

RAPHAEL, Monty
Peters & Peters, London (020) 7629 7991
See under Fraud, p.412

SALTISSI, Sally
Dechert, London (020) 7775 7321
sally.saltissi@dechertEU.com
Specialisation: Director of the international trade and customs practise in London. Negotiates and handles disputes with Customs and Excise and IBEA on all VAT, customs and excise duty matters. Work covers investigations cases, tariff classification, valuation and transfer pricing issues, origin, duty preference, export rebates, CAP questions, import and export licensing, anti-dumping duties, and appeals to and appearances before VAT and Duties Tribunal and the European Court. Cases have included agricultural levy dispute and CAP export refunds, tariff classification, origin disputes, customs duty panel, VAT liability and Single Market excise liabilities. Experienced Advocate intending to exercise full rights of audience in the Higher Courts.
Prof. Memberships: Law Society Revenue Law Committee, Customs Practitioners Group, Law Society representative on Joint Customs Consultative Committee, Honorary Legal Adviser to UKWA.
Career: Called to the Bar (Inner Temple) in July 1985 having studied law in London 1981-84. Worked for Crown Prosecution Service 1986-88 and the Solicitors Office of HM Customs & Excise from 1988 to 2000. Joined *Dechert* July 2000.
Personal: Qualified as a radiographer in 1970 and practised as such until qualifying in law. Lives in South London.

TRAVERS, Harry
Burton Copeland (London), London
(020) 7430 2277
Specialisation: Acts on behalf of numerous clients under investigation by HM Customs & Excise for VAT and Excise duty irregularities, and also defends individuals subject to prosecution. Has substantial expertise in securing negotiated financial settlements with HM Customs & Excise and/or bringing judicial review proceedings in respect of their actions, particularly in relation to the conduct of raids under powers conferred by warrants obtained by Schedule 11 of the Value Added Tax Act 1994. Wider practice includes white-collar crime, often with an international element, including tax fraud, corruption, insolvency/banking/insurance fraud/insider dealing and money laundering and regulatory and disciplinary work (eg Lloyds, FSA).
Prof. Memberships: LCCSA (sub-committees relating to fraud), BISLA.
Career: Qualified as a barrister in 1986, a solicitor in 1990. 1987-91, *Berwin Leighton* tax and trusts department specialising in tax investigations, trusts and tax avoidance litigation including Craven v White up to the House of Lords. 1991 joined *Burton Copeland* commercial fraud department. Partner February 1995.
Personal: Educated at Manchester Grammar School and St Edmund Hall, Oxford (BCL MA). Leisure interests include Manchester United, golf, languages and music.

DEBT RECOVERY

OVERVIEW: The area of debt recovery continues its polarisation between high volume computerised debt recovery and the strong commercial litigation teams who handle complex cases for existing clients. Developments and growing investment in IT packages and web based systems are key to providing an efficient service in the volume market.

RESEARCH APPROVED BY BMRB: *For this edition,* Chambers' *researchers conducted 6,552 interviews – 4,419 with law firms, 554 with barristers and 1,579 with clients.*

The validity of the research was scrutinised by BMRB International, who audited both the methodology and the results at our offices in July 2001. They interviewed Chambers' *researchers and cross-checked sample interviews. Details of the audit appear on page 7.*

LONDON

DEBT RECOVERY • London
1 Braby & Waller
Hammond Suddards Edge
2 Jeffrey Green Russell
3 Salans Hertzfeld & Heilbronn HRK

This book is the product of 6,552 1/2-hour interviews. See p.7 for BMRB audit.
Within each band, firms are listed alphabetically.

Braby & Waller (see firm details p.892) Typically described as the "*major player in the debt field.*" Although part of Irwin Mitchell, Braby & Waller has retained its own strong "*highly respected*" brand and identity. An experienced team of 31 in the London office (which can draw on the support of the Sheffield office) services large commercial clients including utilities, financial institutions, accountants and trade retail. Offers a bespoke service, fixed fees, internet access and credit management training for clients. **Clients:** EuroFactor (UK); Paypoint Network; Lafarge Aggregates

Hammond Suddards Edge (see firm details p.984) Although most of the debt recovery work is based in Bradford, the takeover of the Wilde & Partners debt recovery unit has strengthened its London presence. Described by peers as the "*most professional in London*" and acclaimed as "*the name in factoring,*" it acts for factoring companies and finance houses nationwide. **Clients:** Factoring Industry.

Jeffrey Green Russell (see firm details p.1012) This debt recovery team of 20 is split into three sections, which handle debt recovery across the board, with particular focus on the hire industry and credit card debt. With a "*reputation for being aggressive,*" the firm acts for banks, plant hire, electrical and construction companies. The focus is on high volume debt recovery including a mix of commercial and consumer debt. **Clients:** Citibank; Diners Club; American Express.

Salans Hertzfeld & Heilbronn HRK (see firm details p.1117) This debt recovery team includes eight qualified assistants and 18 paralegals. The main undefended work is undertaken in Bromley, which increases the firm's capacity for single contested cases. Has strength in consumer credit recovery in the motor finance industry, and also acts for banks and building societies. The firm conducts mortgage repossession, recovery of vehicles and recovery of outstanding loans for banks. **Clients:** Barclays; Britannia; Bank of Scotland.

THE SOUTH

DEBT RECOVERY • The South
1 Brachers Maidstone
2 Blake Lapthorn Portsmouth
3 Lester Aldridge Bournemouth
4 Cripps Harries Hall Tunbridge Wells
5 DMH Brighton
Trethowans Southampton
6 Moore & Blatch Southampton

This book is the product of 6,552 1/2-hour interviews. See p.7 for BMRB audit.
Within each band, firms are listed alphabetically.

Brachers (see firm details p.893) "*Top quality firm*" which is endorsed by interviewees as having been "*successful in building up a debt practice over a long period.*" This joint debt recovery and insolvency practice has a team of 28 focusing on bulk debt recovery and post invoice credit management. Its wide ranging client base includes utilities, hauliers, building suppliers, employment agencies, IT, credit card and transport companies. The firm has a subsidiary company based in Milton Keynes, which is outsourced as a credit management operation for a single, large commercial client.

Blake Lapthorn (see firm details p.886) Respected firm, with a team of nine - including the attentions of one partner - acting for large multi-nationals and smaller companies on commercial and consumer debt recovery. Having invested in its computer system, the firm offers a personalised bespoke service to its clients. **Clients:** SGB Services; Key Industrial Equipment.

Lester Aldridge (see firm details p.1038) 20 fee earners and two partners operate at this firm, which is perceived to be a "*major player*" in debt recovery. With a focus on the volume market, the firm services collection agencies, utilities, accountants, retailers, manufacturers, IT and credit insurance companies. It is noted by the market for its success in transport and financial services. The firm has developed 'Lester Aldridge Fast Track' as its computerised debt recovery system.

Cripps Harries Hall (see firm details p.927) This team of five (including two partners) services a strong commercial client base targeting high net worth recoveries. It has developed a bespoke service tailored to individual debts. A wide client base includes manufacturing companies, insurance commissions and the service industry. The firm recently received instructions from insolvency experts. **Clients:** National Provident Institution; Duncan Web Offset.

DMH (see firm details p.944) This team of six acts mainly for commercial and institutional clients, including retail, road haulage, construction companies and local authorities. With a hi-tech computer system, factoring and automated debt recovery are growth areas. The firm also undertakes tracing and status enquiries, and operates credit control seminars for its clients. **Clients:** Credit Acceptance; Atalink; London Borough Of Croydon.

Trethowans (see firm details p.1161) Perceived by peers to be "*keen*" this debt recovery practice of five paralegals in Southampton is supported by a team of five in Andover. Acts for a range of clients including large multinationals, finance houses, smaller local companies and local councils (in the north of England.) The team conducts disputed actions, judgements and enforcements.

Moore & Blatch (see firm details p.1072) Acting for a range of clients from large retailers to individuals. With a team of three, it is perceived in the industry as a small, robust presence in the field. Engaged in all levels of debt recovery, including bespoke packages for individuals.

THAMES VALLEY

DEBT RECOVERY • Thames Valley
1 **Shoosmiths** Reading
2 **Boyes Turner** Reading
Morgan Cole Reading
3 **Clarks** Reading
Denton Wilde Sapte Milton Keynes
4 **Fennemores** Milton Keynes
Matthew Arnold & Baldwin Watford

This book is the product of 6,552 1/2-hour interviews. See p.7 for BMRB audit.
Within each band, firms are listed alphabetically.

Shoosmiths (see firm details p.1129) Enjoys "*the biggest reputation in the market,*" the firm "*remains undoubtedly the leaders*" in the eyes of our interviewees. Operates with a "*heavily dedicated, large team*" of 23 debt recovery specialists undertaking high volume undefended trade debt recovery. The team refers contested cases to a large commercial litigation department where each client has a pre-allocated solicitor. Acts for commercial debtors, with a strong focus on recruitment agencies, computer and construction companies. Equipped to take instructions electronically.

Boyes Turner (see firm details p.891) A team of four assistants and one active partner is devoted to servicing the debt recovery needs of a large insolvency and commercial client base. Represents recruitment agencies, goods manufacturers, spread betting, freight forwarding firms and insurance companies. **Clients:** Kelly Services UK; IG Index.

Morgan Cole (see firm details p.1074) With a debt recovery team of 12, the firm is thought by peers to be building a strong reputation in this area. Primary instructions come from finance and factoring companies, but it also acts for firms involved in telecommunications, manufacturing and education.

Clarks (see firm details p.916) Although traditionally a factoring firm, its focus continues to target a more specialist invoice debt recovery client base. Within the litigation department, this "*respected*" team of four associate solicitors and five fee-earners acts for academic institutions, recruitment agencies, IT companies, consumer finance companies and building contractors. **Clients:** BMW Financial Services Group.

Denton Wilde Sapte (see firm details p.939) Based within the commercial litigation department, this "*respected, efficient*" team of four serves commercial organisations and banking entities with growing strength in property related debt recovery work. Retains a strong interest in overseas debt recovery work, acting for NCM - the large trade debt insurer based in Holland, recovering its UK debt. **Clients:** CNT English Partnerships; NCM.

Fennemores Winning market recognition for its experience in debt recovery, this firm services its substantial commercial client base with niche strength in invoice discounting. The practice offers pre-legal telephone and written collections, with specialist litigators taking up defended cases. **Clients:** The factoring industry.

Matthew Arnold & Baldwin (see firm details p.1057) This debt recovery team of one assistant and three paralegals is based within commercial litigation and acts for accountants, manufacturers, publishers and letting agents. Undertakes the full range of debt recovery, including defended actions and negotiations to settlement. **Clients:** Barclays.

SOUTH WEST

DEBT RECOVERY • South West
1 **Bond Pearce** Plymouth
Burges Salmon Bristol
Clarke Willmott & Clarke Taunton
Osborne Clarke Bristol
TLT Solicitors Bristol

This book is the product of 6,552 1/2-hour interviews. See p.7 for BMRB audit.
Within each band, firms are listed alphabetically.

Bond Pearce (see firm details p.888) An "*excellent firm*" felt by commentators to have "*good processes in place,*" the firm retains its respected reputation. The team of nine boasts niche strength in retail and education. It also acts for smaller plcs and limited companies. Its focus is fixed on the institutional side of debt recovery. **Clients:** B&Q; University of Southampton; Friends Provident.

Burges Salmon (see firm details p.902) Based within the litigation department, the team of two dedicated legal executives handles all aspects of debt recovery including pre-legal work. Manages large caseloads for existing clients, and displays skills in commercial and trade debt. Advises its clients on the establishment of internal procedures for debt management.

Clarke Willmott & Clarke (see firm details p.915) This unit of 12 fee earners and one partner is seen by rivals as "*one of the top*" for debt recovery. With a focus on banks, building societies and factoring companies, the volume side of the practice continues to increase due in part to the offer of conditional fee arrangements. Clients include small businesses, large motoring organisations and financial institutions. **Clients:** BOCM Pauls; Amtrak Express Parcels; NatWest.

Osborne Clarke (see firm details p.1086) A small team of five including one partner is approved of by interviewees as "*a handy operation.*" Its client base includes a mixture of professional, industrial and commercial plcs and smaller limited companies. The firm receives instructions from German firms collecting debts from UK companies, as well as servicing Danish companies through a dedicated London based Danish team. **Clients:** Danish Bacon; Bristol & West.

TLT Solicitors (see firm details p.1157) Described as "*the best firm in the area*" and the one with "*the best set up for this type of work,*" the successfully merged firm rises in our tables. With a dedicated team of five, specialising in volume-repeat recoveries, the firm boasts clients within agriculture, factoring, hire firms, banks and building societies. Offers a comprehensive service, from tracing debtors to handling complex contested cases. **Clients:** Brandon Hire; Barclays Sales Financing; Lloyds TSB.

WALES

DEBT RECOVERY • Wales
1 **Eversheds** Cardiff
2 **Edwards Geldard** Cardiff
John Collins & Partners with Edward Harris & Son Swansea

This book is the product of 6,552 1/2-hour interviews. See p.7 for BMRB audit.
Within each band, firms are listed alphabetically.

Eversheds (see firm details p.952) With a team of five partners and a sizeable group of fee earners, the firm is by far the pre-eminent debt recovery unit in Wales. Judged by sources "*a safe pair of hands,*" the group handles debt recovery for financial houses right across the Eversheds network. The closure of the Bristol office has added extra staff, and the team specialises in mortgage enforcements, shortfall recoveries and personal loan/overdraft collections. **Clients:** Abbey National; Cheltenham & Gloucester; Bank of Scotland; Legal & General.

Edwards Geldard (see firm details p.948) With a team of 12 fee earners, the firm acts on behalf of its large commercial client base. Has recently established a limited liability company branded 'Go Debt Ltd', which handles collection of debt prior to proceedings. **Clients:** Thames Water; Halifax.

John Collins & Partners with Edward Harris & Son Recommended by its peers, this team of 18 fee earners and one partner is seen as "*deserving its good reputation.*" The firm has a client base focusing on banks, building societies and smaller local companies, and has acted for Lloyds TSB since 1983, servicing substantial volume debt recovery to high court and county court enforcements. **Clients:** Lloyds TSB.

MIDLANDS

DEBT RECOVERY • Midlands
1 **Eversheds** Nottingham
Wragge & Co Birmingham
2 **Freethcartwright** Nottingham
Hewitson Becke + Shaw Northampton
3 **Reed Smith Warner Cranston** Coventry
Shakespeares Birmingham
Shoosmiths Northampton
4 **Browne Jacobson** Nottingham
Howes Percival Northampton

This book is the product of 6,552 1/2-hour interviews. See p.7 for BMRB audit.
Within each band, firms are listed alphabetically.

Eversheds (see firm details p.952) A broad range of consumer and commercial work is undertaken by a team of 22 "*sensible people.*" The team based in Nottingham is best known for its "*superb internet service*" (real time case management) which is recognised across the country for its quality. Its client base includes manufacturing and service companies, as well as local authorities. **Clients:** Credit Acceptances Corp; Pirelli; Powergen.

Wragge & Co (see firm details p.1189) "*An excellent firm*" operating nine full time debt recovery staff. Operates an across the board service - but with a fast track team that has seen a dramatic rise in work over the last year. Clients include entities in construction, banking, the service industry, and local authorities. **Clients:** Croydon Council; Solaglas; Bank of Scotland.

Freethcartwright (see firm details p.964) Debt recovery forms part of the commercial litigation offering and includes one legal executive and three fee earners recovering both commercial and consumer debt. The firm also provides a High Court and County Court information service on all UK business. Its client roster draws from the firm's wider commercial base, including credit reference agencies, large national and smaller local companies. **Clients:** Bass Brewers; Top Service; Nottingham Trent University.

Hewitson Becke + Shaw (see firm details p.994) Enjoys a team of "*fine, reputable performers,*" which covers a sizeable client base in the steel, gas, water and insurance industry sectors. Its coverage also includes financial institutions, haulage and educational establishments. Defended actions are conducted by litigation specialists in each relevant section of the firm, with associates in the Cambridge office ready to assist.

Reed Smith Warner Cranston Peers believe this an "*effective, proactive*" firm which targets high volume debt recovery. A team of eight looks after trade and credit insurance agencies, and manufacturing and financial institutions. Credit management advice is offered, as well as the full range of debt recovery services, from pre-litigation to enforcement proceedings, and High Court and County Court actions. **Clients:** Courtaulds Textiles; Anchor Homes.

Shakespeares (see firm details p.1122) Working within the commercial litigation department, this team of nine, including one partner, runs a full debt recovery service - handling pre-letters to litigation. Advising a broad range of clients, including high street banks, computer companies, manufacturers and small local businesses, the firm has experience of overseas debt recovery in Northern Ireland and mainland Europe.

Shoosmiths (see firm details p.1129) The Northampton based unit of this firm is typically seen by our interviewees as "*a respectable, growing outfit,*" that merits inclusion in the tables. This team of four partners, four solicitors and 20 support staff handle volume debts and contested large value debt recoveries. With an impressive client list that includes banks, building societies and leading financial houses, the firm is acknowledged as "*a wide ranging competitor.*"

Browne Jacobson (see firm details p.898) The team of five offers a full debt recovery service, with a focus on high volume. Its client base mirrors the firm as a whole, and includes major IT companies, publishing and local businesses. Able to receive instructions over the web. **Clients:** Parceline.

Howes Percival (see firm details p.1003) A small team of two operating full-time out of commercial litigation, servicing the firm's existing client base with tailored solutions to debt recovery. Acts for universities, a small bank and has a focus on medium sized businesses. Adjudged by peers "*a handy practice in the South Midlands.*"

EAST ANGLIA

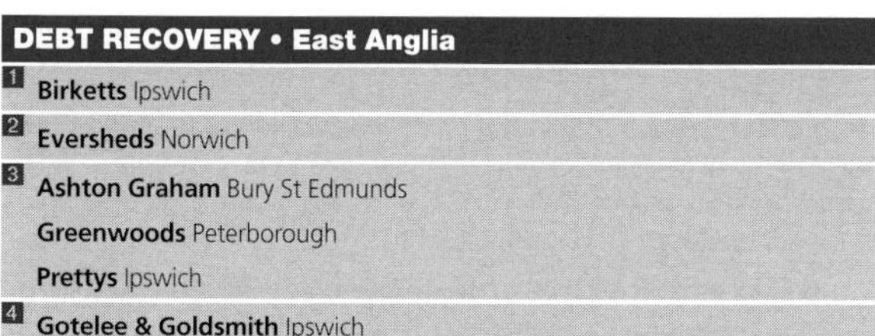

DEBT RECOVERY • East Anglia	
1	**Birketts** Ipswich
2	**Eversheds** Norwich
3	**Ashton Graham** Bury St Edmunds
	Greenwoods Peterborough
	Prettys Ipswich
4	**Gotelee & Goldsmith** Ipswich

This book is the product of 6,552 1/2-hour interviews. See p.7 for BMRB audit.
Within each band, firms are listed alphabetically.

Birketts Described by rivals as "*the biggest local firm*" and perceived to be "*the specialists.*" This dedicated team of two handles high volume debt recovery for small commercial companies. Representing building merchants, a major regional newspaper group and a commercial vehicle parts supplier, recovering debts on a national scale.

Eversheds (see firm details p.952) Acting for its East Anglian client base, this branch of Eversheds keeps up its national reputation. With a team of three operating within the litigation department, the unit acts for a whole raft of commercial clients - from local businesses to plcs. Operates a full letters to litigation debt recovery service. **Clients:** Dairy Crest Ltd/Unigate; Premier Holidays.

Ashton Graham This practice has a team of two, and is seen "*more and more as worthy competitors.*" Its clients are based largely in Suffolk, and the firm focuses on medium sized, owner managed businesses. Housed in the litigation department, the team offers a bespoke service.

Greenwoods (see firm details p.978) The steady team of eight is endorsed by competitors as employing "*the personal touch.*" Largely focused on business to business debt, it services local businesses, national and international companies, including building societies, insurance companies and foreign banks. Operates a volume recovery IT system and has created bespoke packages for referrals from the Electrical Contractors Association. **Clients:** Electrical Contractors Association; Thomas Cook.

Prettys (see firm details p.1100) This team of three works closely with a commercial litigation team that handles any contested cases. The firm has some volume debt recovery, but concentrates on higher value commercial debt. The client base is reflective of the local economy, with the firm witnessing growth in shipping, transport and freight. Also receives instructions from hospitals, insolvency practitioners and insurance brokers.

Gotelee & Goldsmith A team of five handles a variety of work for its existing client base, representing haulage companies and local authorities. Issues letters before action, and undertakes high court and county court actions. The firm also offers advice on credit control and debt management procedures.

NORTH WEST

DEBT RECOVERY • North West	
1	**Thomas A Higgins & Co** Wallasey
2	**Bermans** Liverpool
3	**Cobbetts** Manchester
	Davies Wallis Foyster Liverpool
	Lees Lloyd Whitley Liverpool
4	**Cuff Roberts** Liverpool
	Halliwell Landau Manchester

This book is the product of 6,552 1/2-hour interviews. See p.7 for BMRB audit.
Within each band, firms are listed alphabetically.

Thomas A Higgins & Co The most prominent debt recovery firm in the country, this large team has a national reputation that rests with its pure focus on uncontested, high volume debt collection. Perceived as a specialist niche practice in the market, it is acclaimed by peers as "*a true debt recovery operation,*" but is criticised for lacking the personal touch.

Bermans Impressing our researchers this team of twelve offers a complete package from pre-litigation to advance proceedings, and is appreciated as "*strong on volume.*" The client roll-call includes banks, building societies, factoring companies, advertising agencies and government bodies. Part of its success may be to do with its highly cost effective letter before action service.

Cobbetts (see firm details p.923) Small team of two paralegals (with four litigators dedicated to contested cases) offers a complete package to clients. Undertakes general trade debt recovery for the motor retail, finance and construction sectors. Recently instructed to act nationwide for The Insolvency Service.

Davies Wallis Foyster (see firm details p.935) A respected stand-alone unit that operates with a team of ten across Liverpool and Manchester. Its range of clients includes finance, factoring and leasing companies, large plcs and a variety of smaller local clients.

Lees Lloyd Whitley This practice has a good profile within debt recovery and is praised by competitors as being "*up to date on IT.*" A team of paralegals undertakes bulk debt recovery work and services a range of local businesses including those with only occasional requirements.

Cuff Roberts A team of 15 operates in a department where trade debt is the main focus. The bulk of the workload comes from medium sized businesses and sole traders. Increased instructions have come from the IT, agriculture and consumer credit sectors, and from within insolvency related book debt.

Halliwell Landau (see firm details p.982) Stand alone commercial debt team practice, with a varied client base including large cosmetic companies, hire firms and computer wholesale companies. Also wins bulk instructions from banks and building societies, with mortgage repossession and shortfall still seen as growth areas.

NORTH EAST

DEBT RECOVERY • North East
1 Hammond Suddards Edge Bradford
2 DLA Bradford
Eversheds Leeds
3 Lupton Fawcett Leeds
4 Ford & Warren Leeds
Walker Morris Leeds

This book is the product of 6,552 1/2-hour interviews. See p.7 for BMRB audit.
Within each band, firms are listed alphabetically.

Hammond Suddards Edge (see firm details p.984) A "*large presence*" with a national reputation, which is seen by our interviewees as a "*massive competitor*" across the country. The branded commercial 'Debtline' team provides a service to over 600 commercial clients, including financial houses, builders' merchants and recruitment agencies. Operates as part of a separate business unit. **Clients:** BSS; Abbey National.

DLA The team is involved in volume work, as well as offering pre-legal collection and a comprehensive litigation service. Noted for its recovery of secured debts from the financial sector, including the sale and realisation of assets.

Eversheds (see firm details p.952) A team of 70 undertakes high volume, consumer debt work as part of a branded operation across the country. Acting for banks and credit card companies, it runs a collections call centre for bulk recovery.

Lupton Fawcett Proving itself to the market as a "*competent*" team, it has a significant client base and is driving forward with bulk debt recovery. A group of 40 acts for large plcs, insurance entities, hi-tech companies, trade associations and owner-managed businesses.

Ford & Warren (see firm details p.961) A small team, which offers an across the board debt recovery service to a client base that includes transport companies, estate/recruitment agencies and some consumer finance work.

Walker Morris (see firm details p.1171) A large team specialising across institutional and corporate clients, representing banks, petroleum and healthcare companies. The firm has recently merged its secured and unsecured recovery teams, and has developed a specialist online facility. **Clients:** Bank of Scotland.

SCOTLAND

DEBT RECOVERY • Scotland
1 McClure Naismith Glasgow
2 Morton Fraser, Solicitors Edinburgh
Nolan Macleod Glasgow
Yuill & Kyle Glasgow
3 Golds Glasgow
Henderson Boyd Jackson WS Edinburgh
Morison Bishop Glasgow
4 Blacklock Thorley Edinburgh
Macdonalds Glasgow
5 Bonar Mackenzie WS Edinburgh
Brodies WS Edinburgh
Shepherd & Wedderburn WS Edinburgh

This book is the product of 6,552 1/2-hour interviews. See p.7 for BMRB audit.
Within each band, firms are listed alphabetically.

McClure Naismith (see firm details p.1059) A "*well established*" firm, seen to give "*good commitment to its clients.*" A team of two partners and 14 paralegals work in volume debt recovery, acting for finance houses, leasing and credit card companies. Active from the initial letter to contested cases. The firm has invested heavily to provide internet access to case files for its clients. **Clients:** Birmingham Midshires Mortgage Services; Capital Bank; Bank of Scotland; Royscot Trusts.

Morton Fraser, Solicitors (see firm details p.1076) A strong practice in debt factoring, acting for banks, building societies, academic institutions and small businesses. The firm has a "*reputation for quality*" among its peers in debt factoring, while Interlaw membership provides access to clients on a global basis.

Nolan Macleod Two partners and a team of 20 undertake the spectrum of legal service, with a focus on volume collections including tracing. Active for blue chip clients including major banks, factoring companies, leasing and hire purchase companies, the firm also wins additional instructions from English solicitors.

Yuill & Kyle This practice of three qualified solicitors and two paralegals acts for a range of clients including multi-nationals and smaller companies. Receives instructions from financial institutions, debt collectors and English practitioners venturing north of the border. The unit offers a full service, including factoring, and is seen by the market as "*top of the league, a big confident firm.*" Clients; B&Q; MFI; Scottish Widows.

Golds A specialist in commercial debt recovery, known throughout Scotland for its "*expertise in IT.*" Handles work on behalf of retailers, manufacturers, financial institutions, motor finance companies and IT companies. A broad-based practice, it has witnessed a growth in the factoring sector.

Henderson Boyd Jackson WS A "*high profile*" team, acting as part of a well regarded commercial litigation department. With three account handlers engaged with financial institutions and English solicitors, it also targets high volume recovery work.

Morison Bishop (see firm details p.1075) A team of five provides a full debt recovery service to its commercial client base. Handles volume work for firms ranging from plcs to smaller businesses. The market perceives that the firm is consolidating after merger, only held back by personnel changes.

Blacklock Thorley A recognised name in the market place, this team of four handles high volume debt recovery. Instructed by debt collection agencies in England and Scotland, as well as English solicitors. The unit is perceived to be a small firm committed to providing a quality service.

Macdonalds Based within the commercial litigation department, the team of five is judged by interviewees to be "*pretty aggressive,*" enjoying a strong reputation in factoring. Busy acting for large factoring companies in Scotland, it provides a volume service to a variety of commercial clients. Considered to benefit from an association with factoring specialists, Bermans (based in Liverpool,) the firm also acts for Glasgow Sheriff's Court.

Bonar Mackenzie WS (see firm details p.888) This team of two paralegals (with a supporting partner) offers a full letters to litigation service. Its client base includes banks, building societies, manufacturing and supply companies, as well as some factoring entities.

Brodies WS (see firm details p.896) Described by sources as a "*slick*" firm with a strong traditional client base and an established reputation for commercial litigation. Undertakes cases for individuals and commercial companies, most often existing clients of the firm.

Shepherd & Wedderburn WS (see firm details p.1126) A new entrant to the tables thanks to its strength in work for government agencies and financial institutions. Adjudged "*major players,*" its focus is mainly on high value debts for blue chip companies. A team of five is thought to offer a "*good quality*" full-service debt recovery operation. **Clients:** HM Customs & Excise; DTI; HSBC; Shell Direct (UK).

NORTHERN IRELAND

DEBT RECOVERY • Northern Ireland	
1	**Comerton & Hill** Belfast
2	**Bigger & Strahan** Belfast
	Diamond Heron Belfast
3	**Cleaver Fulton Rankin** Belfast
	John McKee & Son Belfast

This book is the product of 6,552 1/2-hour interviews. See p.7 for BMRB audit.
Within each band, firms are listed alphabetically.

Comerton & Hill The practice contains three solicitors and three paralegals. It has maintained its strong reputation for debt recovery. Concentrating on volume recoveries, the firm has a client base that ranges from large finance houses to small local businesses, with additional skills in factoring. **Clients:** HSBC; NIIB.

Bigger & Strahan This team of four paralegals, supported by a strong commercial litigation and insolvency department, has a good reputation in factoring. Offers a full range service to banks, English and Irish finance companies and factoring companies, as well as winning referrals from English solicitors. Receives instructions for European debt recovery.

Diamond Heron This recently merged firm keeps its reputation in debt recovery. Mainly known by peers as "*the Ulster Bank firm*," the practice carries out repossession orders, judgement enforcements and bankruptcy proceedings. The firm recovers advertising debts for major newspapers and acts for hire companies as part of a large commercial base. **Clients:** Ulster Bank; Halifax.

Cleaver Fulton Rankin (see firm details p.918) Although not thought to focus on this area, a team of three paralegals and one solicitor services an envied client base including financial institutions, schools and construction companies. Much of the caseload comes from England, thanks to the firm's membership of the LawNet scheme. **Clients:** Bank of Scotland.

John McKee & Son (see firm details p.1014) Portrayed as a "*canny firm*" by peers, it services a range of commercial and financial companies. The team of two solicitors and one paralegal handles high volume work for financial institutions, credit agencies, construction companies and debt recovery agencies. It also receives instructions from English solicitors and clients in Denmark.

DEFAMATION

OVERVIEW: This section of the guide is devoted to pure libel work, although libel lawyers now find themselves instructed on broader issues of reputation management. With the advent of the Human Rights Act and an increasing appreciation of the right to privacy, libel specialists will doubtless lead the way in bringing forward the case law on privacy.

RESEARCH APPROVED BY BMRB: *For this edition,* Chambers' *researchers conducted 6,552 interviews – 4,419 with law firms, 554 with barristers and 1,579 with clients.*

The validity of the research was scrutinised by BMRB International, who audited both the methodology and the results at our offices in July 2001. They interviewed Chambers' *researchers and cross-checked sample interviews. Details of the audit appear on page 7.*

TOP IN-HOUSE LAWYERS

John BATTLE, Head of Compliance, *ITN*
Alistair BRETT, Legal Manager, *The Times*
Patricia BURGE, Company Solicitor, *The Times*
Siobhan BUTTERWORTH, Head of Legal Affairs, *Guardian Newspapers Ltd.*
Charles COLLIER-WORTH, Group Legal Manager, *Trinity Mirror plc*
Tom CRONE, Legal Manager, *News International*
Martin CRUDDACE, Solicitor, *Trinity Mirror plc*
Marcus PARTINGTON, Solicitor, *Trinity Mirror plc*
Justin WALFORD, Legal Advisor, *Express Newspapers*
Arthur WYN-DAVIES, Legal Manager, *The Telegraph*
Eddie YOUNG, Group Legal Advisor, *Associated Press*

John Battle continues to attract heavy endorsement. *"Determined"* **Alistair Brett** *"enjoys a tussle and gets results"* while **Patricia Burge** *"has her feet firmly on the ground."* **Siobhan Butterworth** is *"down to earth, practical and a tough fighter."* **Charles Collier-Worth** is a well-known player in the market. *"Calm and collected,"* **Tom Crone** is *"without a doubt superb"* standing *"head and shoulders above the market." "Great"* **Matin Cruddace** is *"clear about what he wants,"* while **Marcus Partington** is widely recommended. **Arthur Wyn-Davies** is perceived to *"successfully stave off writs." "Courteous and charming,"* **Justin Walford** has *"been there and done it all." "Pragmatic and ocassionally hard-nosed"* **Eddie Young** *"really knows his stuff."*

In-House lawyers profiles: p 1193

LONDON

Olswang (see firm details p.1084) A *"phenomenal"* team which carries a *"helluva reputation"* and is seen to be bursting with popular, busy and media-savvy practitioners. Lawyers of choice for newspapers, book publishers, ISPs and an array of celebrity and corporate claimants, they are noted for their ability to alternate between tenacity and a softer approach, whilst always *"putting clients first."* Feedback for the team was without criticism throughout our research. *"Experienced"* and now almost legendary **Geraldine Proudler** (see p.287) is *"smart," "talented"* and operates in a *"thoroughly organised"* manner. **Julia Palca**, (see p.338) a former in-house newspaper lawyer, with a combined practice in employment work, and newly ranked **Debbie Ashenhurst** (see p.284) also gain widespread plaudits from both barristers and clients. Best known for its defendant work, the team was instructed on one of the first internet libel cases by Demon Internet (now Thus plc) in its defence of proceedings brought by Laurence Godfrey. On the claimant side, the firm recovered £150,000 in damages for Peter Gadsby, Vice-Chairman of Derby County FC, in his action against club director Stuart Webb. **Clients:** Guardian Newspapers Ltd; Associated Newspapers Ltd; Mirror Group plc; Grigori Loutchansky; Random House Group Ltd.

DJ Freeman (see firm details p.943) Said to *"make a barrister's life easy,"* the firm is commended for its *"slickness, smoothness, good judgement and preparation."* **Susan Aslan** (see p.284) is the recipient of a huge volume of praise, and sets the tone for her team. She *"gets to sensible and amicable solutions quite quickly,"* while her team *"knows that rottweilers don't get anywhere."* The last year has been characterised by the pre-publication and pre-transmission advice given to the team's many clients in TV and in film and publishing. Following success for its client Mohammed Al Fayed in the libel action brought by Neil Hamilton, the team has fended off various appeals brought to the Court of Appeal and House of Lords and is currently involved in action against the maintainers of the claimant in the original libel action. **Clients:** Channel 4; Carlton; Channel 5; Reed Business Information; Working Title Films; Company Television.

Davenport Lyons (see firm details p.931) Carrying out the lion's share of work for Express Newspapers, in addition to advising MGN, smaller publishers and some TV clients, the firm's defamation team is frequently referred to as a *"delightful,"* group which is *"lovely to deal with,"* but *"must be taken seriously."* **Kevin Bays** (see p.284) is said by peers to be *"well-disposed to the concept of settlement,"* but he also knows how to conduct a high profile, protracted fight. He continues to act for Penguin Books in the attempt by David Irving to appeal last year's decision. **Philip Conway** (see p.285) is also highly rated and has a close relationship with his clients, such as Express Newspapers. The firm is acting on Hamilton v Private Eye, in connection with entry to Tiny Rowland's safety deposit box at Harrods. **Clients:** Private Eye; Ginger Media/Virgin Radio; Centaur Communications; Fran Cotton.

Farrer & Co (see firm details p.954) *"Old style firm,"* with a long-established reputation and a high-profile clientele, which recently boosted its defamation team through the merger with Crockers Oswald Hickson. **Robert Clinton** (see p.285) still holds court at the top of our rankings. As an opponent, he is *"sensible and experienced,"* and ensures a *"businesslike"* approach from his team. His colleague Penelope Gorman has now moved into a consultancy role at the firm. Covering a volume of defence work for regional newspapers, magazines and insurers, the former Crockers Oswald Hickson includes a pair of lawyers with established reputations. **Rupert Grey** (see p.285) maintains his name for *"solid achievement,"* while **Richard Shillito** (see p.287) has a *"sensible and academic approach."* He is seen as a *"classical"* lawyer with *"good technical ability."* The Farrer's team has undertaken a broad caseload of reputation management and confidence infrigement for an ecclectic clientele, ranging from Royals to tabloids. It is acting for The Sunday Telegraph in the libel action brought by Saif Al Gaddafi. The Crockers team handled appeals on behalf of Neil Hamilton in his libel action against Mohammed Al Fayed. **Clients:** NewsGroup; The Daily Telegraph; Haymarket; regional newspapers; insurers; The Law Society.

Peter Carter-Ruck and Partners (see firm details p.1094) A predominantly claimant firm, which although not perceived by the market to retain

DEFAMATION • London		Ptnrs	Assts
1	Olswang	3	4
2	DJ Freeman	3	7
	Davenport Lyons	3	5
	Farrer & Co	6	7
	Peter Carter-Ruck and Partners	7	4
	Schilling & Lom and Partners	3	5
	Theodore Goddard	3	3
3	David Price Solicitors & Advocates	1	2
	Reynolds Porter Chamberlain	4	5
4	Goodman Derrick	3	2
	H2O (Henry Hepworth Organisation)	2	3
	Lovells	2	3
	Pinsent Curtis Biddle	n/a	n/a
	Russell Jones & Walker	3	3
	Simons Muirhead & Burton	2	2
	Wiggin & Co	1	3
5	Bindman & Partners	n/a	n/a
	Charles Russell	2	2
	Clifford Chance	*	*
	Swepstone Walsh	n/a	n/a
6	Finers Stephens Innocent	2	2
	Harbottle & Lewis	1	3
	Lewis Silkin	1	n/a
	Mishcon de Reya	*	*

LEADING INDIVIDUALS

★
CLINTON Robert Farrer & Co
PROUDLER Geraldine Olswang

1
ASLAN Susan DJ Freeman
HOOPER David Pinsent Curtis Biddle
PRICE David David Price Solicitors & Advocates
SCHILLING Keith Schilling & Lom and Partners

2
BAYS Kevin Davenport Lyons
KRAMER Martin Theodore Goddard
SHILLITO Richard Farrer & Co
TAIT Nigel Peter Carter-Ruck and Partners

3
CONWAY Philip Davenport Lyons
GREY Rupert Farrer & Co
HARTLEY Liz Reynolds Porter Chamberlain
MIRESKANDARI Razi Simons Muirhead & Burton
PEPPER Alasdair Peter Carter-Ruck and Partners
STEPHENSON Andrew Peter Carter-Ruck and Partners

4
BINDMAN Geoffrey Bindman & Partners
MATHIESON Keith Reynolds Porter Chamberlain
MCCUE Jason H2O (Henry Hepworth Organisation)
ROBERTSON Rhory Swepstone Walsh
SMYTH Michael Clifford Chance

5
ARMSTRONG Nicholas Goodman Derrick
DADAK Roderick Lewis Silkin
FOX Paul H2O (Henry Hepworth Organisation)
LAMONT Duncan Charles Russell
MCDERMOTT Jennifer Lovells
PALCA Julia Olswang
RIMELL Katherine Theodore Goddard
SKREIN Michael Richards Butler
THOMSON Mark Schilling & Lom and Partners
WEBB Sarah Russell Jones & Walker

UP AND COMING
ASHENHURST Debbie Olswang
DOLEY Cameron Peter Carter-Ruck and Partners
MELVILLE-BROWN Amber Finers Stephens Innocent

This book is the product of 6,552 1/2 hour interviews. See p.7 for BMRB audit.

Within each band, firms are listed alphabetically. *See individuals' profiles p.284*

quite the sparkle of the days of Peter Carter-Ruck himself, nevertheless continues to score a number of notable successes. Always "*ferocious litigators,*" the team "*pursues actions vigorously and takes no prisoners,*" although some have winced at the firm's high costs. The firm has embraced CFA, and runs a substantial proportion of claims on this basis. Possessor of a "*flexible mind,*" **Nigel Tait** (see p.288) has emerged as the key name here. Acting for regular client Victor Kiam last year, Tait achieved a £105,000 award following a claim against the Daily Mail. **Alasdair Pepper** (see p.287) is said to be "*reliable*" and "*constructive*" in his approach. A notable coup saw him advise Kevin Keegan on his successful action against News of The World, winning £150,000 damages. With "*long term experience of developments in the law,*" **Andrew Stephenson** (see p.288) is known for his "*persistence,*" and has been acting for Russian businessman Boris Berezovsky on his case against Forbes Magazine. "*Accessible and comprehensible*" **Cameron Doley** (see p.285) has caught the eye of seasoned observers at the Bar, and is new to the rankings this year. **Clients:** Express Newspapers; Harper Collins; National Magazine Company; Penguin Books; Egon Ronay.

Schilling & Lom and Partners (see firm details p.1119) Although also maintaining a defendant practice, the firm is better known for its claimant work. Our research found them to be "*good opponents who are bright and tough, but good at recognising the merits of cases.*" **Keith Schilling** (see p.287) is a "*fair and vigorous*" lawyer, who "*doesn't start a claim that he won't finish.*" He can write "*volcanic letters,*" and when he starts a case, lawyers report that they have to be prepared to "*fight it all the way.*" "*One man nuclear reactor*" **Mark Thomson** (see p.288) handles much of the firm's work, and although some have commented that "*he can take cases too personally,*" clients attest to the "*reassurance*" that they receive from his "*good advice.*" The firm handled Philip Green v Sunday Times, concerning allegations arising from a proposed take over of M&S, and appeared on Marco Pierre White v The Times. **Clients:** Chris Evans; Naomi Campbell; London Weekend Television; Carlton Television; Monty Norman.

Theodore Goddard (see firm details p.1152) Favoured by The Times and Sunday Times, and hitting the headlines for privacy and cyber-libel cases, this is considered to have been an "*annus mirabilis*" for Theodore Goddard. One of our interviewees went so far as to suggest that this was the "*top libel firm in London this year.*" "*Sensible*" **Martin Kramer** (see p.286) has "*a lot of charm,*" and runs a team which has now "*flowered*" and which offers "*an expensive but Rolls Royce service.*" Fellow partner **Katherine Rimell** (see p.287) has been "*extremely busy on leading cases.*" It acted for Times Newspapers on appeal to the House of Lords in the libel action brought by Northern Irish solicitors McCartan Turkington Breen, a case which concerned whether a press conference was a public meeting under the Defamation Act. It also acted for Takenaka and its Deputy MD in an internet libel action against an anonymous e-mailer. **Clients:** The Sunday Times; The Times and Times Supplements; Western Provident Association; Northern & Shell.

David Price Solicitors & Advocates **David Price** (see p.287) runs "*a boutique practice to die for.*" One client confirmed admiringly that "*Price sees what the client wants and he provides it – sooner rather than later.*" A former barrister, he handles all aspects of a case, including the advocacy, and is often felt to out-perform opposing counsel. Inevitably, such a high profile individual overshadows the rest of the team, and leads to Price being labelled as "*a one man wonder.*" In fact, he is assisted by a barrister, an assistant solicitor, a trainee and three paralegals. Cases in the last year have included Sally Farmiloe v Associated Newspapers Ltd, Keith Burstein v Times Newspapers Ltd and actions for nine members of The Cook Report production team against News of The World. **Clients:** Maria Fernandez (wife of Keith Vaz); Punch; Versace; Charlie George; John McVicar.

Reynolds Porter Chamberlain (see firm details p.1106) This team shot into the limelight when joined by a contingent of media litigators from DAC in May 2000. Now fully integrated, the group is seen as a "*good and sensible*" player, with a loyal clientele of newspapers. "*Tough*" **Elizabeth Hartley** (see p.285) heads the team and is supported by the "*wily*" **Keith Mathieson** (see p.286), who impresses peers as a "*calm and effective*" practitioner. The firm advised on Loutchansky v Times Newspapers Ltd and represented Tom Bower in connection with proceedings brought by Richard Branson. **Clients:** Associated Newspapers; Independent Newspapers; Telegraph Group; Times Newspapers; HTV.

Goodman Derrick (see firm details p.974) A team with "*some experienced people who have done some interesting work.*" Seen to be acting more in the broadcast rather than publishing area, but also attracting interesting claimant instructions from producers and cast members of TV shows, including Coronation Street, Eastenders and Tonight with Trevor McDonald. **Nicholas Armstrong** (see p.284) is recommended but Jeffrey Maunsell has now retired. It has been acting for investigative reporter Donal MacIntyre in his libel action against Kent Police. **Clients:** Granada TV; ITV; Chrysalis Group; Scottish Media Group.

H2O (Henry Hepworth Organisation) (see firm details p.981) "*Refreshingly youthful,*" the team has had another active year, and is "*beginning to make some waves.*" Northern Ireland specialist **Jason McCue** (see p.286) ("*bright and exceptionally able*") has recently worked for the victims of the Omagh bombing and for Martin McGartland. His colleague **Paul Fox** (see p.285) is noted for his connections with IPC and Punch. In addition to advising on issues arising from Sean McPhilemy's book 'The Committee,' the firm has been involved in notable cases such as David Trimble v Amazon and Ruth Dudley Edwards v Random House. **Clients:** Times Newspapers, Express Newspapers; News International; Guardian Newspapers.

Lovells (see firm details p.1044) Broadcast and newspaper clients sit side by side with the firm's existing commercial clients at this "*well balanced*" claimant/defendant libel practice. The team is led by "*tough cookie*" and new entrant to the defamation tables, **Jennifer McDermott,** (see p.286) who is seen as a "*formidable*" opponent. The team also includes an experienced barrister and ex in-house lawyer from the BBC. Continuing to advise the Daily Star on its ongoing battle with Lord Archer, the firm also acted on a pro bono basis for Albert Tate in his action against Safeway Stores Ltd, in which a CA decision on summary judgment was handed down. Also instructed by The Observer in its defence of a libel action brought by solicitor David Kershaw. **Clients:** Guardian Newspapers; Express Newspapers; Trinity Mirror; Granada.

Pinsent Curtis Biddle (see firm details p.1098) The old Biddle defamation team is felt by many to have received a dent, following the departure of three partners prior to the firm's merger with Pinsent Curtis. However, leading name **David Hooper** (see p.285) ("*an old fox*") continues to impress peers and clients and has some "*clients to die for.*" Libel work is now done within the Media and IP group, with a number of lawyers handling instructions as a part of a wider caseload. Last year, Biddle acted for Lord Ashcroft in his action against The Times and for Forbes Magazine in the House of Lords on a jurisdiction issue in the libel action brought by Russian billionaire Boris Berezovsky. **Clients:** Tom Bower; Robert Loftus; Simon & Schuster; Little, Brown.

Russell Jones & Walker (see firm details p.1116) Said to be involved in "*a lot of interesting cases,*" the firm is respected for its work on behalf of a claimant client base that is heavily oriented towards institutions, unions and The Police Federation, but also includes a number of individuals. The well-known **Sarah Webb** (see p.289) has been instructed by Lord Harris of High Cross and other supporters of Neil Hamilton concerning the funding of his libel action against Mohammed Al Fayed. The team was also instructed by a young female teacher, wrongly accused of having an affair with a pupil, and by Diana, Princess of Wales' former chef Mervyn Wycherley in his claim against The Mail on Sunday. **Clients:** The Police Federation; David Gregson; National Autistic Society.

Simons Muirhead & Burton (see firm details p.1133) The team's leading figure, **Razi Mireskandari** (see p.287), is viewed as "*pragmatic and a good tactician*" by those who have faced him. It acts for some impressive names in publishing, especially magazines and in the last couple of years has broken into TV, acting for independent production companies and broadcasters. A number of celebrity clients have instructed the firm on claimant work, while trade libel also features in the caseload. **Clients:** Channel 4; Dennis Publishing; Random House; Time Out.

Wiggin & Co (see firm details p.1180) Previously only ranked in *Chambers*' regional tables, the firm's defamation practice is considered to operate "*more and more like a London practice.*" **Caroline Kean** (see p.286) ("*experienced and well-liked by clients*") works from the firm's offices in both Cheltenham and London, acting for a mixed clientele. The team concentrates on defendant work, occasionally acts for claimants and also does some pre-publication libel reading. **Clients:** Magazines; regional newspapers; book publishers; insurers; broadcasting companies.

Bindman & Partners (see firm details p.882) Such is **Geoffrey Bindman**'s (see p.425) profile as a "*fiercely motivated lawyer,*" that other colleagues are sometimes overlooked. However, market opinion points to a number of talented libel lawyers here, typically advising on cases "*with a campaigning element.*" The team is particularly recognised for its work in championing journalists' rights. Geoffrey Bindman acted on Tsikata v The Independent and represented Makhboul Javaid in actions against Associated Newspapers and The Daily Telegraph. The team had success on cyber-libel case Godfrey v Demon Internet and famously acted on McPhilemy v Sunday Times. **Clients:** New Statesman; MPs; Gay Times; TV producers and journalists.

Charles Russell (see firm details p.912) Widely considered to be "*getting stronger all the time,*" the firm appears in the defamation tables this year following consistent market recommendation. The arrival of broadcasting expert **Duncan Lamont** (see p.286) from Biddle and the acquisition of enviable new clients such as Hello! magazine have helped to raise the group's profile substantially. The firm has acted for celebrities, institutions and internet/telecoms clients on libel issues. **Clients:** Hello!; ITN; ntl; celebrities; Conquest Business Media.

Clifford Chance (see firm details p.919) Libel work at the firm is handled by two partners, who are assisted by a number of solicitors with a media litigation pedigree. A varied caseload has included cyber-libel and pre-publication advice for foreign (especially US) media companies, as well as substantial work for corporate plaintiffs. Whenever the versatile **Michael Smyth** (see p.288) appears on a case, he is rated by peers as an "*excellent lawyer.*" The firm acted for GTECH Corporation in a claim against BskyB and advised JVC on an action against News Group Newspapers. **Clients:** Reuters; American Law Media; The Conservative Party.

Swepstone Walsh A niche firm which continues to retain the respect of its peers, thanks in large part to the esteemed **Rhory Robertson**. **Clients:** Newspapers.

Finers Stephens Innocent (see firm details p.958) Renowned for advising a high-profile stable of thoroughbred US publishers, the team has also received instructions from a number of UK newspapers. Up and coming associate **Amber Melville-Brown** (see p.286) handles much of the defamation work for the firm, and makes her debut in the *Chambers* tables. She particularly impressed interviewees with her advice on the Marco Pierre White v International Herald Tribune case. **Clients:** Dow Jones; Wall Street Journal; CNN; Time Magazine; New York Times; Washington Post.

Harbottle & Lewis (see firm details p.985) Operating from the media litigation department, the defamation team, in which Gerald Tyrrell is the best-known name, handles a variety of claimant work for an extensive list of media figures and celebrities. The group advised Richard Branson on his case against Tom Bower, the author of his unauthorised biography. Other matters include giving clearance and content advice to recently launched celebrity lifestyle portal Peoplenews.com and Kate Moss' action against Associated Newspapers. **Clients:** Celebrities; music industry; companies and organisations.

Lewis Silkin A mixed claimant and defendant practice headed by **Roderick Dadak** (see p.285). Clients range from newspaper and book publishers, through to websites and individual claimants. Cases of note in the last year include the claim brought by Lords Dixon, Cox and Bragg against The Independent on Sunday in connection with an article wrongly attacking the peers for poor attendance in the House of Lords. It is representing Express Newspapers in the action brought by Roger Windsor, a former finance officer of the NUM. **Clients:** Express Newspapers; Newsquest; Bass Brewers.

Mishcon de Reya (see firm details p.1071) With the traditional big libel names at the firm now operating as consultants, there are two contentious media lawyers at partner level and four at assistant level handling defamation. Team head Karen Sanig also works on art, IP and contempt cases. The firm is now acting on Skrine & Co & Ors v Euromoney Institutional Investor plc & Ors, and also carries out pre-publication and clearance advice for press and publishing clients. **Clients:** Alfonso Fanjul; book publishers; IT companies; business newspapers.

Other Notable Practitioners At **Richards Butler**, **Michael Skrein** (see p.287) has been applauded as "*a quality litigator,*" and is regularly instructed by a variety of press and individual clients.

THE REGIONS

DEFAMATION • The Regions	Ptnrs	Assts
1 **Foot Anstey Sargent** Exeter	2	2
Wiggin & Co Cheltenham	1	3
2 **Cobbetts** Manchester	1	0
3 **Brabners** Liverpool	1	2
Pannone & Partners Manchester	*	*
Wragge & Co Birmingham	*	*

LEADING INDIVIDUALS	
1 **JAFFA Tony** Foot Anstey Sargent	**KEAN Caroline** Wiggin & Co
2 **MANLEY Mark** Brabners	**STONE Peter** Cobbetts

This book is the product of 6,552 1/2 hour interviews. See p.7 for BMRB audit.
Within each band, firms are listed alphabetically. *See individuals' profiles p.284*

Foot Anstey Sargent (see firm details p.961) A particularly strong regional newspaper clientele enables this Exeter firm to "*pack a big punch.*" **Tony Jaffa**'s (see p.286) team (which also includes a barrister) is seen as "*helpful and business-like.*" As well as producing highly rated client work, Jaffa is "*an assiduous and respected author.*" In addition to its core newspaper work, the team also handles online defamation matters. **Clients:** Northcliffe Newspapers Group Ltd.

Wiggin & Co (see firm details p.1180) See London editorial.

Cobbetts (see firm details p.923) **Peter Stone** (see p.288) has a well established reputation and has an established relationship with the Manchester Evening News. The group also advises the firm's corporate clients and occasional individual claimants, while internet libel is a newer source of instructions. **Clients:** Manchester Evening News.

Brabners (see firm details p.892) Mediation-inclined **Mark Manley** has a name for "*always acting in the best interests of his clients.*" He leads a team of media lawyers with sound defamation experience, and has built up his own reputation through his work in radio broadcasting. The practice has seen a rise in claimant work over the past year, and recently acted for Tommy James in his action against The Sunday People. **Clients:** All 20 EMAP plc radio stations; Insider Publications (part of Regional Independent Media); celebrities; sports personalities.

Pannone & Partners (see firm details p.1088) Two partners handle defamation matters. The firm has acted for a variety of high-profile individuals on complex actions, as well as advising a number of companies which have been the subject of BBC Watchdog programmes. **Clients:** Local authorities; politicians; small journals; The Big Issue.

Wragge & Co (see firm details p.1189) A small number of lawyers (including one ex-Carlton TV in-house adviser) from within the IP group handle defamation work for insurers and corporate clients. Internet libel is another area of niche expertise, while the team also advised on the claim against the Daily Mail in connection with the paper's 'brawling barristers' story. **Clients:** St Paul Insurance Co; ITNet; AT&T; British Airways.

SCOTLAND

DEFAMATION • Scotland	Ptnrs	Assts
1 **Bannatyne, Kirkwood, France & Co** Glasgow	2	1
Levy & McRae Glasgow	3	1

LEADING INDIVIDUALS
1 **SMITH Martin** Bannatyne, Kirkwood, France & Co
WATSON Peter Levy & McRae
2 **SCOTT Niall** McGrigor Donald

This book is the product of 6,552 1/2 hour interviews. See p.7 for BMRB audit.
Within each band, firms are listed alphabetically. *See individuals' profiles p.284*

Bannatyne, Kirkwood, France & Co (see firm details p.869) **Martin Smith** is regarded by many in the market as "*the man*" for defamation in Scotland. "*Self-assured and thorough,*" he is said to have "*real insight,*" and to provide "*detailed advice.*" The majority of work is for newspaper clients, but the firm also handles cyber libel enquiries and does some pursuer work for celebrities and politicians. **Clients:** Independent Newspapers; Scottish & Universal Newspapers; business a.m.; Oban Times Group.

Levy & McRae (see firm details p.1039) **Peter Watson** (see p.288) has a great reputation both north and south of the border. Newspaper clients are the firm's staple diet but as recent cases show, the firm also handles some interesting claimant matters. It has recently been representing Irene Adams MP and Brian Souter, chairman of Stagecoach, in their claims against The Guardian. It represented SMG newspapers in an action by Greenpeace and Lord Melchett against The Herald. Clients: Scottish Media Group; ITV; Daily Record; Sunday Mail.

Other Notable Practitioners The "*courteous but determined*" **Niall Scott** (see p.287) of McGrigor Donald is "*knowledgeable about his subject*" and remains highly rated by the market.

NORTHERN IRELAND

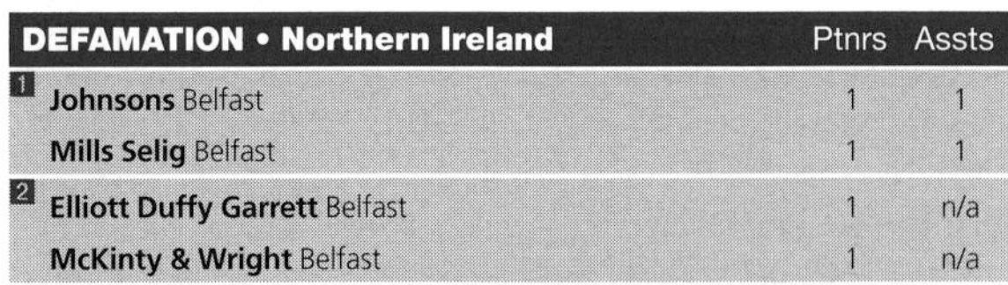

DEFAMATION • Northern Ireland	Ptnrs	Assts
1 **Johnsons** Belfast	1	1
Mills Selig Belfast	1	1
2 **Elliott Duffy Garrett** Belfast	1	n/a
McKinty & Wright Belfast	1	n/a

LEADING INDIVIDUALS	
1 **SPRING Paul** Mills Selig	**TWEED Paul** Johnsons
2 **DEENY Brian** Elliott Duffy Garrett	
UP AND COMING	
MCDONNELL Paul McKinty & Wright	

This book is the product of 6,552 1/2 hour interviews. See p.7 for BMRB audit.

Within each band, firms are listed alphabetically. *See individuals' profiles p.284*

Johnsons (see firm details p.1015) Primarily a claimant practice, the team also takes on defence work for the Belfast and Dublin editions of the Sunday Times. "*Tenacious*" **Paul Tweed** (see p.288) is "*a top rank lawyer*" whose "*style is to fight hard.*" Whilst some felt that "*every letter is a declaration of war,*" others acknowledge that even in a hard fight "*you can have a good relationship with him and can resolve cases.*" The group has advised on around 50 claims arising from Sean McPhilemy's book 'The Committee'. **Clients:** Liam Neeson; Natasha Richardson; The Corrs; Tom Tracy; BJ Eastwood.

Mills Selig (see firm details p.1070) **Paul Spring** (see p.582) "*is the only one in Belfast we'd instruct,*" said a leading London newspaper group. His reputation is strong across the UK for defending newspapers, broadcasters, magazines and book publishers in libel matters, and he also carries out pre-publication advice and trade libel. Other lawyers who have encountered him talk of his willingness to "*make an attempt to negotiate matters.*" **Clients:** Associated Newspapers; News Group; RTE; WH Smith.

Elliott Duffy Garrett (see firm details p.949) **Brian Deeny** (see p.285) is respected as "*a safe pair of hands*" at a firm which advises primarily defendant clients, but has acted for a number of claimants, including senior civil servants. The work in the last year has included the defence of actions involving employers' references and actions brought against US online book seller Powells Books, arising out of the sale of 'The Committee'. It acted for McCartan Turkington Breen in the House of Lords case with Times Newspapers. **Clients:** Mirror Group Newspapers; Little, Brown.

McKinty & Wright (see firm details p.1063) **Paul McDonnell** (see p.286) has taken on the libel work at the firm, and is busy "*earning his stripes.*" Typically, he advises defendants, among which newspapers and professionals with indemnity insurance figure prominently. **Clients:** Belfast Telegraph, Sunday Life, Telegraph Group; Times Newspaper Group.

LEADERS IN DEFAMATION

ARMSTRONG, Nicholas

Goodman Derrick, London (020) 7404 0606
narmstrong@goodmanderrick.co.uk

Specialisation: Partner in media group specialising in media litigation for clients in UK and France, especially defamation: defending media organisations against action (including pre-broadcast/publication clearance), securing remedies for claimants (especially against tabloid press). Also contempt, confidentiality, copyright and passing off, harassment protection, obscenity, public and human rights law, judicial review, French-related litigation and company matters. Recent activity: advising Granada Television (eg libel action v News of the World over Lawrence suspects), advising makers and cast members of television programmes including Coronation Street, Emmerdale, EastEnders, Tonight with Trevor McDonald.

Prof. Memberships: Royal Television Society; Law Society.

Career: Qualified 1986. Trained and qualified with *Theodore Goddard* (London and Paris). Joined *Goodman Derrick* media group 1994.

Publications: Numerous in-house seminars and related paperwork for clients and contacts on media law issues.

Personal: Educated Nottingham High School and Jesus College Cambridge. Hobbies include music, cars, French and English literature, cinema, food and drink.

ASHENHURST, Debbie

Olswang, London (020) 7208 8797
dja@olswang.com

Specialisation: Specialises in media litigation including breach of contract, breach of confidence, malicious falsehood and passing off but with particular emphasis on defamation which makes up 85% of her practice. Also provides pre-publication advice in relation to newspapers, films and advertisements and helps companies and individuals respond to media attention and allegations of trade rivals. Acted for 'The Guardian' in its libel victory over Jonathan Aitken and continues to advise it in relation to Mr Aitken's bankruptcy. Acted for Tom Cruise and Nicole Kidman in their libel action against 'The Express' and for Grigori Loutchansky in his recent libel victory against 'The Times' in the first full jury trial of a Teynolds qualified privilege defence.

Career: Trained *Denton Hall*, qualified 1992; *Biddle & Co*, 1992-95; *Olswang*, 1995-date; made partner, 1998.

Personal: Clayesmore School, Dorset; Jesus College, Cambridge (1988 MA 1st Class Hons); Chester College of Law (1989 Law Society finals 2nd Class Hons). Interests: swimming, tennis, surfing.

ASLAN, Susan

D J Freeman, London (020) 7583 4055
saa@djfreeman.co.uk

Specialisation: Partner in media and communications department. Principal area of practice is advising terrestrial and satellite broadcasting companies in relation to libel, contempt of court, breach of copyright and other programme content issues. Also undertakes a smaller amount of claimant work and covers breach of confidence and contractual disputes including claims in relation to programme format rights. Important cases handled include Channel 4 v Jani Allan (libel trial); Press Alliance v Sherill (libel jurisdiction case before the European Court of Justice); Channel 4 v Dr Nixon (libel trial), Hamilton v Al Fayed (libel trial). Clients include Channel 4, Channel 5 Thames and Carlton. Has appeared on ITV, radio, etc on libel matters.

Prof. Memberships: Media Society.

Career: Qualified in 1985. Partner at *D J Freeman* since 1991.

Publications: Co-author of 'A Short Guide to Small Screen Law'.

BAYS, Kevin

Davenport Lyons, London (020) 7468 2600
kbays@davenportlyons.com

Specialisation: Partner in 1982. Defamation, publishing and media law. Principal solicitor for Private Eye for over 13 years. Other publisher clients include Mirror Group Newspapers, Express Newspapers, John Brown Publishing, Centaur Communications, Northern Shell, Penguin Books, Media Ventures together with several large independent producers, literary agents, television and film clients. Also acts for plaintiffs in defamation cases and media related disputes such as breach of confidence. Handles general commercial litigation with an entertainment bias. Recently acted for Penguin Books in a major libel action brought by revisionist historian David Irving arising out of a book entitled 'Denying the Holocaust'.

Prof. Memberships: Law Society.

Career: Qualified 1979, having joined *Wright Webb Syrett* in 1977. Became a partner in 1982.

Personal: Born 24 April 1955. Leisure interests include skiing, golf, cricket, football and travelling. Member of The Media Society and The Groucho Club.

BINDMAN, Geoffrey

Bindman & Partners, London (020) 7833 4433
info@bindmans.com
See under Human Rights, p.425

CLINTON, Robert
Farrer & Co, London (020) 7242 2022
rgc@farrer.co.uk
Specialisation: Partner. Head of media. Main areas of practice are defamation and publishing related litigation. Involves extensive range of claimant and defendant work for prominent individuals, institutions and companies, including newspaper and publishing companies. Pre and post-publication advice involving privacy, breach of confidence, contempt etc. Intellectual property work, covering general trademark and passing off work for commercial clients.
Prof. Memberships: Media Society. International Bar Association.
Career: Qualified in 1975. Joined *Farrer & Co* in 1972. Became partner in 1979.
Personal: Born 1948. Attended Brasenose College, Oxford 1967-71. Lives in London.

CONWAY, Philip
Davenport Lyons, London (020) 7468 2600
pconway@davenportlyons.com
Specialisation: Partner in litigation department. Main area of practice is defamation, especially with regard to the newspaper and entertainment industries and undertakes a growing amount of pre-publication work. Acts for Private Eye, Mirror Group Newspapers, Express Newspapers, Centaur Communications, Bloomsbury Publishing and Omnibus Press.
Prof. Memberships: Law Society (Member of Privacy and Defamation Working Committees).
Career: Qualified in 1984. Joined *Wright Webb Syrett* in February 1986. Became partner in August 1988. Joined *Davenport Lyons* as a partner on merger with *Wright Webb Syrett* in March 1995.
Personal: Born 15 April 1959. Attended Aldenham School 1972-77. Former director Southend United Football Club. Member of The Media Society, Groucho Club and a barker of The Variety Club of Great Britain.

DADAK, Roderick
Lewis Silkin, London (020) 7074 8080
rod.dadak@lewissilkin.com
Specialisation: Partner and head of defamation. Main areas of practice are defamation (libel and slander) and malicious falsehood, privacy, confidentiality and contempt. Also deals with regulatory bodies including the Press Complaints Commission, Broadcasting Standards Commission and Advertising Standards Authority. Wide experience acting for the media and, in particular, newspapers and publishers. Undertakes both plaintiff and defendant work, and pre-publication libel reading and clearance. New business includes advising companies and ISP's on defamation on the internet. Also lectures at seminars and appears on television and radio on defamation and related matters. Has represented Associated Newspapers in leading actions.
Prof. Memberships: Law Society.
Career: Qualified in 1972. Articled *Theodore Goddard*. Partner at *Swepstone Walsh* in 1983, becoming senior partner in 1991. The *Simkins Partnership* 1996-98. Joined *Lewis Silkin* in 1998 as head of defamation.
Personal: Attended Lancing College and King's College, London. LLB (Hons). Leisure pursuits include tennis, cinema, theatre and holidaying in Provence. Lives in Farnham. Married with three sons.

DEENY, Brian
Elliott Duffy Garrett, Belfast (028) 9024 5034
brian.deeny@edgsolicitors.co.uk
Specialisation: Defamation, commercial litigation and professional negligence. Acts for six national newspapers in defence of claims in N Ireland. Also extensive experience acting for plaintiffs in libel actions.
Prof. Memberships: Law Society of N Ireland.
Career: Graduated University College, Dublin 1982. Admitted solicitor 1985. Admitted partner 1990.

DOLEY, Cameron
Peter Carter-Ruck and Partners, London (020) 7353 5005
cameron.doley@carter-ruck.com
Specialisation: Claimant and defendant defamation, privacy and breach of confidence work; broad range of publishing and broadcasting clients including three of the ITV companies and the National Magazine Company (the publishers of Esquire, Cosmopolitan and Good Housekeeping); claimant clients include a strong Arab and Middle Eastern component as well as plcs, sportsmen and politicians; important cases include Esquire ats Reichmann, Skuse v Granada, Condliffe v Pressdram, HTV ats Welsh Rugby Union, Awwad v Geraghty; now undertakes a substantial proportion of claimant work on a 'no win, no fee' basis; recent CFA cases include Horgan v News of the World (libel arising out of newspaper's 'naming and shaming' campaign) and Windsor v Express (claim brought by former NUM Chief Executive following allegations that he worked as an MI5 mole during the miners' strike).
Career: Graduate of The Queen's College, Oxford (MA Hons 1st Class) and The College of Law (CPE Distinction; Law Society Finals Hons); joined Peter Carter-Ruck and Partners as trainee solicitor in 1990; qualified 1992; partner 1995; managing partner 2001.

FOX, Paul
H2O (Henry Hepworth Organisation), London (020) 7539 7200
paul.fox@H20-law.com
Specialisation: Media Law: defamation; confidentiality; intellectual property, including pre-publication advice and High Court advocacy; privacy; copyright (including music); publishing; trade mark; advertising; contempt. Acted and advised on all aspects of media law (pre-publication/broadcast clearance, injunctions and litigation) for broadcasters, national newspapers and magazines, journalists, authors, public figures and corporations.
Career: Qualified 1986. Also qualified to practice in Hong Kong. Joined *Henry Hepworth (H2O)* in 1999.
Personal: Cycling, football (QPR supporter) and modern history.

GREY, Rupert
Farrer & Co, London (020) 7242 2022
rcg@farrer.co.uk
Specialisation: Partner in media team. Principal area of practice is defamation and copyright. Retained by leading magazine and newspaper publishers and their insurers to advise on libel and allied matters prior to publication and post publication complaints. Also by leading photographic/syndication agencies to handle matters connected with literary and artistic copyright. Lectures, writes and gives seminars. Also retained by high profile individuals in advisory, pre-emptive and plaintiff work. Clients include: The Financial Times, Telegraph Group, Emap, Hello! Limited, Royal Geographical Society, The Liverpool Institute for Performing Arts and Members of Parliament.
Prof. Memberships: Fellow of Royal Geographical Society.
Career: Qualified in 1975, served articles with *Farrer & Co.* Joined *Crockers* in 1981, partner in 1983, head of department in 1989, senior partner in 1997. Joined *Farrer & Co* in 2001 when merged with *Crockers Oswald Hickson.* Previous lives include prospecting for copper in the Fiji Islands, for nickel in Australia, as a roughneck in the Yukon and freelance photo-journalism.
Personal: Born 8th September 1946. Educated Wellington College and UCL. Principal leisure activities are expeditions to wild places and building barns. Married to Jan Sinclair, three daughters; lives in the South Downs.

HARTLEY, Liz
Reynolds Porter Chamberlain, London (020) 7242 2877
ebh@rpc.co.uk
Specialisation: Partner and head of media and technology group. A very experienced litigation practitioner with wide knowledge of the media, in particular the newspaper industry. Principal areas of practice are defamation and media related litigation, including contempt of court, breach of confidence, privacy, malicious falsehood, reporting restrictions, content issues, PCC and BSC complaints and copyright infringement. Also provides pre-publication clearance and advice. Acts for several national newspaper groups as well as magazines and insurers. Also experienced in information technology disputes and has represented both users and suppliers of IT products and services. Has advised on IT disputes in banking, manufacturing, publishing, health, aviation and in privatisations.
Prof. Memberships: The Media Society; honorary fellow of the American Bar Association; The Society for Computers and the Law.
Career: Qualified 1982. Chairman of London Young Solicitors Group 1987-88. Partner, *DJ Freeman* 1987, head of commercial litigation from 1996. Joined *RPC* as a partner 1997.
Personal: Born 1957. Education: Royal Masonic School for Girls; University of Sheffield (LLB Hons). Resides Surrey. Leisure: music, reading and walking.

HOOPER, David
Pinsent Curtis Biddle, London (020) 7418 7000
david.hooper@pinsents.com
Specialisation: Partner in Media Department. Main area of practice is media and defamation. Also handles entertainment, copyright matters, publishing and broadcasting and all issues relating to new media. Acted for Peter Wright and the publishers in the Spycatcher case. Successfully involved in defending libel actions brought by Robert Maxwell. Acted for John Major in his libel action and for the Sunday Times against Derbyshire County Council and Forbes magazine against Berezovsky in the House of Lords. Has contributed many articles on defamation and media matters in periodicals and the national press and regularly addresses conferences.
Prof. Memberships: Law Society, American Bar Association, International Bar Association, Libel Defense Resource Center.

Career: Qualified in 1971 as a Barrister and in 1977 as a Solicitor. Joined *Biddle* as a Partner in 1986.
Publications: Publications include 'Public Scandal Odium and Contempt', 'Official Secrets: The Use and Abuse of the Act' and 'Reputations Under Fire', (Little, Brown 2001) a survey of the law of libel in the last 10 years.
Personal: MA (Oxon). Leisure pursuits include cricket, theatre and country activities. Lives in London and Wales.

JAFFA, Tony
Foot Anstey Sargent, Exeter (01392) 203992
arj@foot-ansteys.co.uk
Specialisation: Partner. Head of media team and commercial litigation division. Handles libel, contempt of court, court secrecy orders and related law for media clients. Author of articles and reviews on all aspects of media law. Speaker at conferences for the Newspaper Industry.
Prof. Memberships: Law Society; Society of Notaries.
Career: Qualified in 1980. Articled at *Boyce Hatton & Co.* 1978-80. Worked at *Wilde Sapte* 1980-83, before joining *Foot Anstey Sargent* in 1983. Became a partner in 1987. Chairman of the Devon Young Solicitors Group 1989-90; member of National Committee of Young Solicitors Group 1988-89. Notary Public 1989.
Personal: Born 6 August 1956. Attended St Boniface's College, Plymouth 1967-74 and Oxford University 1974-77. Leisure interests include windsurfing, sailing and cycling. Married with two children. Lives in Torquay.

KEAN, Caroline
Wiggin & Co, Cheltenham (01242) 224114
caroline.kean@wiggin.co.uk
Specialisation: Partner, head of litigation department. Main areas of practice are defamation and media related commercial litigation. Includes contentious work for plaintiffs, defendants and insurers, advising on copy pre-publication and broadcast, confidence, copyright and passing off. Specialises in private seminars to companies and organisations on issues which include media handling/damage limitation and systems.
Prof. Memberships: Law Society; The Media Society (Council Member). Legal adviser to Women in Journalism.
Career: Articled *Rubinstein Callingham.* Qualified 1985. Partner 1987. Partner *Olswang* 1989-95. Joined *Wiggin & Co* 1995 as a partner and head of litigation.
Personal: Born 1960. Burford School 1971-78, Newnham College, Cambridge 1978-81. College of Law, Lancaster Gate 1981-82.

KRAMER, Martin
Theodore Goddard, London (020) 7606 8855
martinkramer@theodoregoddard.co.uk
Specialisation: Media-related litigation for corporate and individual clients, both plaintiffs and defendants. Main newspaper clients are The Sunday Times and The Times. Areas of expertise include libel and slander; malicious falsehood; contempt of court; human rights cases relating to freedom of expression; confidentiality and official secrets; copyright and passing off. Recent and current cases include acting for The Times in its appeal to the House of Lords arising out of the libel action brought by Irish solicitors McCartan Turkington Breen which widened the defence of qualified privilege, defending 'The Times' and book publishers Hurst & Company in a libel action brought by President Charles Taylor of Liberia, acting for 'The Sunday Times' in Court of Appeal which resulted in publication of extracts from Richard Tomlinson's book 'The Big Breach' and acting for Michael Douglas, Catherine Zeta-Jones and 'OK!' magazine against 'Hello!' in a case in which the Court of Appeal has recognised the right to privacy in English law. Main areas of practice are media-related litigation and administrative and public law.
Prof. Memberships: The Law Society.
Career: Qualified 1969. Partner 1978.

LAMONT, Duncan
Charles Russell, London (020) 7203 5000
duncanl@CR-law.co.uk
Specialisation: Media law. Representing Broadcasters, including before the Broadcasting Standards Commission, providing election coverage, prepublication advice and protection of Intellectual Property. Also advising individuals and publishers on media issues.
Career: Barrister 1985-87, in-house media lawyer 'Sunday Mirror' 1987-89, qualified as solicitor 1990. Partner at *Biddle* now at *Charles Russell* (since February 2001).
Publications: Articles in 'Press Gazette', 'The Times', 'Society of Authors'. Television media pundit.
Personal: MA in law from Cambridge, Diploma in copyright law from King's College, University of London. West Ham fan and opera lover!

MANLEY, Mark
Brabners, Liverpool (0151) 600 3000

MATHIESON, Keith
Reynolds Porter Chamberlain, London (020) 7242 2877
kam@rpc.co.uk
Specialisation: Partner in IP and media department. Main area of practice is media law, particularly defamation, but including contempt of court, reporting restrictions, copyright and passing off. Has acted for and against numerous national and regional newspaper and magazine groups and their insurers. As well as litigation, advises on copy clearance and pre-broadcast issues, including compliance. Clients include national newspapers, business and consumer magazine publishers to companies and media insurers.
Career: Qualified 1983 with *Lovell White & King.* Joined *Oswald Hickson Collier* 1990. Partner 1992. Partner *Davies Arnold Cooper* 1997-00. Joined *Reynolds Porter Chamberlain* May 2000.
Personal: Born 1959. Caius College, Cambridge 1977-80. Postgraduate diploma in UK and European law of copyright, King's College, London 1997.

MCCUE, Jason
H2O (Henry Hepworth Organisation), London (020) 7539 7200
jason.mccue@h2o-law.com
Specialisation: Partner in media department. Legal campaigns/PR: advising groups (eg Omagh Victims Legal Actions, corporations, industry bodies) or individuals (eg politicians). Media law/reputation management: defamation, human rights, confidentiality, privacy, copyright, publishing, trade mark, advertising, contempt. Acted and advised (on all aspects of media law (pre-publication/broadcast clearance, injunctions and litigation)) for national broadcasters (eg Carlton Television), national newspapers (eg The Sunday Times), publishers (eg IPC), journalists, authors, public figures (eg politicians, businessmen, celebrities) and corporations. Speciality: complex case investigation, politics, investigative journalism, security forces, organised crime and international terrorism; internet libel/'cyber policing'; reputation risk management; managing Irish and Northern Ireland litigation; managing media litigation on behalf of insurers; cross-border libel. Acted in many leading cases.
Personal: Interested in writing, driving, terrorism, countryside, folk music, politics and travel.

MCDERMOTT, Jennifer
Lovells, London (020) 7296 2000
jennifer.mcdermott@lovells.com
Specialisation: Commercial litigation with specialisation in media litigation, particularly including defamation, privacy, confidentiality and broadcasting regulatory matters. Advises many newspapers and corporate clients. Extensive expertise also in commercial judicial review having been involved in several high profile applications against and in conjunction with many regulatory authorities. On the editorial board of Communications Law; contributes to publications such as the Press Gazette and plc and speaks at conferences and on radio and television on both judicial review and media law.
Prof. Memberships: Member of the Media Society, the Royal Television Society, Society of Editors, Executive Committee of JUSTICE; Amnesty International.
Career: Qualified 1981 with *Lovells;* partner 1989.

MCDONNELL, Paul
McKinty & Wright, Belfast (028) 9024 6751
post@mckinty-wright.co.uk
Specialisation: Extensive defamation practice both advisory and litigation for local and national media. Also acts for corporate and individual clients in this area. Other main areas of practice are commercial litigation, professional negligence and general insurance defence litigation.
Prof. Memberships: Law Society of Northern Ireland, Society of Editors.
Career: Qualified 1993. Partner in *McKinty & Wright* since 2000.

MELVILLE-BROWN, Amber
Finers Stephens Innocent, London (020) 7323 4000
amelville-brown@fsilaw.co.uk
Specialisation: Head of defamation at *Finers Stephens Innocent.* Practice exclusively defamation, free speech, privacy, data protection and related media work. Pre-publication and broadcast advice, forum advice and litigation for US clients, including CNN, Time Inc, New York Times, International Herald Tribune, and UK media clients. Also media management advice to UK clients.
Career: Admitted in 1995. Training contract at *Simons Muirhead & Burton.* Moved to *Stephens Innocent* 1 April 1996, and with *Finers Stephens Innocent* post merger December 1999.
Publications: Media columnist for the 'Law Society Gazette'. Writes regularly on legal and other matters for 'The Independent' newspaper. Contributes legal articles to 'The Times' and various US publications. Also non legal journalism and some freelance photography for other publications including 'CNN Traveller Magazine'.

MIRESKANDARI, Razi
Simons Muirhead & Burton, London
(020) 7734 4499
razi@smab.co.uk
Specialisation: Partner 1988. Head of civil litigation department. Main areas of practice are media-related. Particularly noted for defamation. Acts for book/newspaper/magazine/internet publishers, broadcasters, authors' agents, writers, journalists and a wide variety of clients in the media and entertainment world, ranging from rock bands to restaurants.
Career: Qualified in 1986. Member Groucho club. Century Club.

PALCA, Julia
Olswang, London (020) 7208 8888
jcp@olswang.com
See under Employment, p.338

PEPPER, Alasdair
Peter Carter-Ruck and Partners, London
(020) 7353 5005
alasdair.pepper@carter-ruck.com
Specialisation: One of the most experienced media lawyers in the business. He is viewed as having 'a no nonsense style, gets things done and clients like him'. Alasdair has a busy media practice. His highlight for 2000/2001 was achieving a settlement for Kevin Keegan against News of the World which included the payment of £150,000 damages. He also acted successfully for many other prominent and well known individuals, companies and organisations. In addition, Alasdair has a thriving defendant practice acting for the Scotsman and HarperCollins among other publishers. Alasdair is the architect behind Carter-Ruck's groundbreaking and very successful Conditional Fee Agreement ('No win No fee') scheme and also its MediaAlert service through which it helps clients to deal with hostile media interest.
Prof. Memberships: Law Society, IBA.
Career: Qualified in 1984. Has remained with *Peter Carter-Ruck and Partners* since qualification. Became a partner in 1986.

PRICE, David
David Price Solicitors & Advocates, London
(020) 7916 9911
enquiries@lawyers-media.com
Specialisation: A solicitor advocate who offers a 'one-stop' service, including representation at trial. Principal area of practice is defamation and media litigation, representing both claimants and a wide range of publishers. Has acted in many high profile and landmark cases.
Career: Qualified as a solicitor (1990). Barrister (1991). Principal of *David Price Solicitors & Advocates* since 1993.
Publications: Author of 'Defamation: Law, Procedure and Practice' published by Sweet & Maxwell 2000.
Personal: Born 16 October 1963. Educated at Haberdashers' Aske School (1970-82), Harvard High School, Los Angeles (1982-83) and Manchester University (1983-86).

PROUDLER, Geraldine
Olswang, London (020) 7208 8888
gap@olswang.com
Specialisation: Head of Defamation. Main area of practice is media law including defamation, contempt of court, breach of confidence, broadcasting complaints and associated matters. Acts for both claimants and defendants. She acts for national and regional newspapers, magazine publishers, advertising agencies, media and other companies, as well as acting for plaintiffs. Geraldine has led the teams in cases that include: acting for the Guardian in its successful defences against former cabinet minister Jonathan Aitken and Neil Hamilton MP; acting for Demon Internet (now Thus plc) in its defence of libel proceedings brought by Laurence Godfrey. The case produced one of the first High Court judgements in relation to alleged internet libel; acting for Marks & Spencer plc in its successful action against Granada Television; acting for Mr George Carman QC (just before his death) against Punch magazine and obtained for him a half page apology in Punch together with damages paid to a cancer charity plus his legal costs; acting for Mr Peter Gadsby, vice-chairman of Derby County FC and chairman of Birch plc in a libel action against Mr Stuart Webb, a former director of Derby County FC. Olswang recovered a total of £350,000 for Mr Gadsby in damages and costs, including £150,000 damages, which is one of the largest damages figures of the last few years; acting for Associated Newspapers in defending proceedings brought by Lord Foster and his company over Evening Standard articles about the British Museum; acting for The Daily Mirror in proceedings brought by Victor Kiam, chairman of Ronson plc. Mr Kiam recovered £105,000 damages, but the defendant has been given permission by the Court of Appeal to appeal against his award; also acting for The Sunday Mirror in defending contempt of Court proceedings over the stoppage of a criminal trial in Leeds against Leeds footballers.
Prof. Memberships: Law Society, Media Society.
Career: Qualified 1980. Became a partner with *Lovell White & King* (now *Lovell White Durrant*) in 1987. Joined *Olswang* as a partner 1995.
Personal: Born 2 July 1956. BA Law at Nottingham University 1974-77. Lives in London.

RIMELL, Katherine
Theodore Goddard, London (020) 7606 8855
katherinerimell@theodoregoddard.co.uk
Specialisation: Main practice areas are media related litigation, particularly defamation, malicious falsehood, confidence, official secrets, rights of free expression and privacy under the Human Rights Act and public law. Acts for a variety of corporate and individual clients, both plaintiffs and defendants. Has acted on behalf of 'The Times' and 'The Sunday Times' in many cases including the Reynolds action which extended the defence of qualified privilege to the media. Most recently involved in the first privacy action on behalf of Michael Douglas, Catherine Zeta Jones and 'OK!' magazine.
Prof. Memberships: The Law Society.
Career: Qualified in 1985. Partner of *Theodore Goddard* in 1997.

ROBERTSON, Rhory
Swepstone Walsh, London (020) 7404 1499

SCHILLING, Keith
Schilling & Lom and Partners, London
(020) 7453 2500
Specialisation: Senior partner. Main area of practice is media and internet litigation especially libel. Represents insurers, broadcasters, publishers, film producers, film distributors, sportsmen, internet users and many leading celebrities. Other areas of practice in media litigation include copyright, breach of confidence, passing off and divorce.
Prof. Memberships: Law Society, City of Westminster Law Society.
Career: Articled at *Wright Webb Syrett* before setting up *Schilling & Lom* which he founded with Nicholas Lom and one other in 1984.
Publications: Contributor on libel, breach of confidence and copyright in the 'Entertainment Law Review'.
Personal: Born 25 July 1956. Has an MA in European Business Law. Leisure interests include reading and mountaineering. Member of Grouchos and Chelsea Arts Club.

SCOTT, Niall
McGrigor Donald, Glasgow (0141) 248 6677
Specialisation: Head of commercial litigation unit. Pre and post publication editorial advice in relation to contempt of court and defamation. Advised the BBC in relation to the Zircon Affair and the raid by Special Branch on the headquarters of BBC Scotland. Has acted for most of the the main newspaper publishers in Scotland in a career spanning 1979 to 2001. Now also acts for individuals and corporations in defamation claims.
Prof. Memberships: Law Society of Scotland. Royal Faculty of Procurators, Glasgow.
Career: Jordanhill College School, Glasgow. LLB University of Aberdeen. Qualified as a solicitor in 1975. 1991-93 External examiner for diploma in legal practice, University of Glasgow. Managing Partner, *McGrigor Donald* from April 1994 to August 1997.
Personal: Married to Judith with four children Edward, Antonia, Virginia and Nicholas. Hill walking, golf, tennis, skiing and swimming.

SHILLITO, Richard
Farrer & Co, London (020) 7242 2022
ras@farrer.co.uk
Specialisation: Partner in media team. Main area of practice is defamation. Acts for a large number of national, regional and trade press clients and their insurers. Other areas of expertise are contempt, reporting restrictions and copyright. Contributor to the 'Yearbook of Copyright and Media Law' (OUP, 2000).
Career: Qualified in 1976, having joined *Oswald Hickson, Collier & Co* in 1973. Became a partner in 1984. Joined *Farrer & Co* in 2001 when merged with *Crockers Oswald Hickson*. Previously a trainee journalist at Yorkshire Weekly Newspaper Group Limited, 1970-72.
Personal: Born 13th March 1948. Attended Westminster School, then Magdalen College, Oxford (1970, PPE (Hons)). Leisure interests include music and sailing. Lives in London. Married, with three daughters.

SKREIN, Michael
Richards Butler, London (020) 772 5720
spms@richardsbutler.com
Specialisation: Partner. A leading lawyer in intellectual property and media. Work is mainly litigation, but also advisory, particularly in relation to insurance and advertising and media clearance work. Specialist areas of work include administrative law, aviation, competition, contempt of court, defamation, insurance, intellectual property (the law of confidence, copyright, patents and trade marks), international law and judicial review. Has years of experience in the aviation, food and drink, insurance, leisure, (including sports) and media industries as well as many

other areas of litigation after over 20 years as a litigation partner in a firm with very broad and notably international scope of practice. His team's media work won 'The Lawyer 2001 Litigation Team of the Year' Award.
Prof. Memberships: Fellow of the Society for Advanced Legal Studies; Law Society; The City of London Solicitors' Company; Copinger Society, the Baltic Exchange.
Career: Articled *Richards, Butler & Co* 1971; qualified 1973; partner since 1976; head of litigation department 1990 to 1996; lectured on advertising law, copyright infringement, intellectual property and defamation implications of the Internet, libel and trade marks; chair of the Protecting the Media series of conferences, the market leader.
Personal: Born 1947. Educated at Oxford University (MA, Modern History) and the University of Southern California (AM *magna cum laude* International Relations). Honor Society of *Phi Kappa Phi*.

SMITH, Martin B.
Bannatyne, Kirkwood, France & Co, Glasgow (0141) 221 6020

SMYTH, Michael
Clifford Chance, London (020) 7600 1000
michael.smyth@cliffordchance.com
Specialisation: Partner with extensive experience in all kinds of commercial disputes, including media litigation and public law cases. Clients include public authorities, newspapers, book publishers and news agencies. Heads pre-publication unit providing advice on 24-hour basis. Also ranked in the annual International Commercial Litigation survey. Author of 'Business and the Human Rights Act'. Runs firm's pro bono practice.
Prof. Memberships: Law Society, City of London Solicitors' Company, Administrative Law Bar Association. Member of the Law Society's Human Rights Act Task Force and of the Liaison Group to the Home Office's Human Rights act Task Force. Member of the Law Society's Defamation Pre-action Protocol Committee.
Career: Royal Belfast Academical Institution; Clare College, Cambridge (MA Law). Qualified 1982; partner *Clifford Chance* 1990; also admitted in Hong Kong and Northern Ireland.

SPRING, Paul
Mills Selig, Belfast (028) 9024 3878
paul.spring@nilaw.com
See under Litigation, p.582

STEPHENSON, Andrew
Peter Carter-Ruck and Partners, London (020) 7353 5005
andrew.stephenson@carter-ruck.com
Specialisation: Partner in litigation department. Early in his career, conducted the successful defence of criminal proceedings brought under the Official Secrets Act. Acted for Martin Packard, who was in awarded £450,000 damages for libel in 1987, a record at the time. Main area of practice since 1982 is defamation, acting for claimants, including government ministers, MPs of all the main political parties and sports and music personalities. Also acted for defendants including book, magazine and newspaper publishers and television companies. Also experienced in media law generally, including the law of contempt, copyright and passing off. Has handled a number of leading defamation cases where jurisdiction has been an issue, including: Papendreou v Time magazine; Bachchan v Dagens Nyheter (Swedish publication); Schapira v Ha'aretz (Israeli publication); Berezovsky v Forbes.
Prof. Memberships: Law Society, Media Society.
Career: Graduate of University College London 1975-78. Council of Stock Exchange 1979-81. Joined *Peter Carter-Ruck and Partners* in 1982; qualified 1983; became partner in 1986.

STONE, Peter
Cobbetts, Manchester (0161) 833 5246
peter.stone@cobbetts.co.uk
Specialisation: Over 20 years experience in litigation for national and regional blue-chip clients. Particular expertise in commercial property litigation (forfeiture, dilapidations, covenants, contested lease renewals, brewery/licensed retailer work) and in defamation (plaintiff and defendant) for individual and media clients.
Prof. Memberships: Law Society. Notaries Society.
Career: Articled at *Cobbetts*, 1974. Qualified 1976, partner 1979.
Personal: Born 1951. Educated at Rossall School and Liverpool University (LLB Hons 1st class). Leisure interests include fell walking, climbing and mountain biking.

TAIT, Nigel
Peter Carter-Ruck and Partners, London (020) 7353 5005
nigel.tait@carter-ruck.com
Specialisation: Partner in media department. Main area of practice is media law, acting for claimants and defendants and giving pre-publication advice. Cases of interest include Beta Construction v Channel 4 (award of £568,000 – highest ever libel award paid to a company); Telnikoff v Matusevitch (first libel case to go to the House of Lords for over a decade – award of £240,000); Jack Slipper v BBC (£50,000 damages – leading case on liability for republication); Jonathan Hunt (aged 6) v The Sun (settlement of £35,000 plus costs to mother and son – youngest ever libel plaintiff); Faraggay v Al Hayat (award of £170,000 plus costs); Scholar v Mail (award of £100,000 plus costs); Gorman v Mudd (award £150,000 plus costs); Morelli v Sunday Times (award of £45,000 plus costs – first conditional fee libel action to go to trial); Kirby Harris v Baxter (leading case on trial by jury); Victor Kiam v Sunday Times (£45,000 plus costs); Shah v Standard Chartered Bank (leading case on resonable grounds to suspect); Kiam v The Mirror (award of £105,000 plus costs); Walker v Newcastle Chronicle (settlement of £100,000 plus costs); Rahamim v Channel 4 and ors (settlement of £175,000 plus costs and broadcast apology on Channel 4 news); X v Sunday Sport (injuction to restrain publication obtained within 2 hours of receiving instructions); Y v Sunday Sport and anor (the first injunction ever obtained in the new tort of privacy resulting in the pulping of 40,000 copies of a magazine). Has won over 90% of his cases. Conducts wrongful and unfair dismissal actions (including claims for slander and libel). Head of firm's employment group. Also conducts personal injury work (highest award £755,000). Has spoken at the Oxford Union Debating Society on three occasions on law reform.
Prof. Memberships: Law Society; International Bar Association; Member of Law Society Privacy, Defamation and Pre-Action Protocol Working committees.
Career: Qualified in 1988, having joined *Peter Carter-Ruck and Partners* in 1986. Appointed partner in 1990, managing partner 1997-01, and now marketing partner.
Publications: Contributor to 'Carter-Ruck on Libel and Slander 4th and 5th editions'; contributor to 'McNae's Essential Law for Journalists'; has presented numerous papers to conferences on media law, defamation and conditional fees.

THOMSON, Mark
Schilling & Lom and Partners, London (020) 7453 2500
Specialisation: Head of defamation and media litigation department. He specialises in all aspects of media law, including defamation, confidence, human rights and privacy and acts for both claimants and defendants. His other areas of practice in media litigation include copyright and passing off, and his expertise also covers media regulatory work involving BSC, PCC and ITC. He acts for a wide variety of high profile clients and companies.
Prof. Memberships: Law Society.
Career: MA (Hons), Cambridge. Qualified 1988; articled at *McKenna & Co* before joining *Schilling & Lom*. He became a partner in 1992.
Publications: 'Privacy and prior restraint after the Human Rights Act' – communications law. 'A new respect for the right to privacy' – Legal Week.
Personal: Born 22 October 1959. Epsom College, 1972-78; Cambridge University, 1978-81. Leisure interests include films, reading and tennis.

TWEED, Paul
Johnsons, Belfast (02890) 240183
pt@johnsonslaw.co.uk
Specialisation: Defamation – the most well known case being for B J Eastwood against the boxer Barry McGuigan, resulting in an award of £450,000. More recently has acted for Robert McCartney QC, the MP for North Down, who was awarded £80,000 in a high profile case against The Irish Times on the eve of the 1997 General Election, and for the actors Liam Neeson and Natasha Richardson against a number of Irish newspapers in relation to false reports regarding the state of their marriage. Has represented the Irish band The Corrs and is currently involved in multiple defamation actions against UK and US based internet book distributors, requiring the issue of what is believed to be the largest number of writs in respect of the publication of one book. Acts for a number of other media, political, public, business and legal personalities and also on the defence side for several newspapers (including The Sunday Times) and other publications. Other areas of media practice include copyright and related entertainment work.
Prof. Memberships: Incorporated Law Society of Northern Ireland (1978); Law Society of England and Wales (1993); Law Society of Ireland (1999).

WATSON, Peter
Levy & McRae, Glasgow (0141) 307 2311
peterwatson@lemac.co.uk
Specialisation: Media; defamation; libel; aviation; international claims and litigation; personal injury litigation; public and fatal accident inquiries; civil and criminal litigation; Inland Revenue and Customs & Excise investigation; employment law; partnership law; secretary of the Lockerbie Air Disaster Group; secretary of Braer Disaster Group; member of the Steering committee of the Piper Alpha Disaster Group; Gecas v Scottish Television plc; Cavendish v

The Scotsman Publications & Others; representing the Dunblane Families at the Dunblane public inquiry; involved in litigation in more than 12 countries other than the UK.
Prof. Memberships: Law Society of Scotland; SSC Society; APIL; ATLA; past president of the Society of Solicitor Advocates; chairman of the Scottish Mediation Bureau; member of the IBA.
Career: BA in Economics, University of Strathclyde; Bachelor of Law, University of Edinburgh; research at Scandinavian Maritime Institute and thereafter at Dundee University, Centre for Petroleum and Mineral Law Studies; visiting scholar in International Law, Nova University, Florida, USA; on the board of Anglia Sports Law Research Centre.
Publications: Author of 'In Pursuit of Pan Am' and 'The Search for Justice – A Case for Reform to the Civil Justice System in Britain'.
Personal: Horseracing; travel; married with two daughters, Anna and Sophie.

WEBB, Sarah
Russell Jones & Walker, London (020) 7837 2808
s.l.webb@rjw.co.uk
Specialisation: Head of the litigation business and private client group specialising in defamation and commercial litigation. Has acted for a number of lawyers and members of the judiciary in libel claims including recently a solicitor who was also a local councillor in his claim against the 'South London Press'. Also acting for a number of charitable organisations involved in libel actions including the National Autistic Society. Currently advising contributors to the costs of Neil Hamilton libel action being pursued by Mr Al Fayed for maintenance.
Prof. Memberships: Law Society, Equine Lawyers Association.
Career: Articled to *McDonald Stacey*; qualified in 1983; joined *Russell Jones & Walker* in 1983, partner since 1990.
Publications: Published a number of articles in 'Solicitors Journal', 'The Lawyer' and the 'Law Society Gazette' and has a regular column in an equestrian magazine.
Personal: Educated at Malvern Girls College of Law. Resides in Kent. Interests include family and horse riding.

E-COMMERCE

OVERVIEW: The field of e-commerce encompasses a wide range of traditional practice areas, including corporate finance, competition, intellectual property, tax and telecoms, as well as e-law itself. Over the past year, the crash and subsequent slowdown in the dot.com market has had continuing ramifications for e-commerce practices throughout the country. Many firms are increasingly following the lead of the major players in shifting their focus away from start-ups and emerging companies, towards larger technology companies and traditional old economy corporates looking to invest in the technology sector.

TOP IN-HOUSE LAWYERS

Clare GILBERT, Vice President & General Counsel, *AOL Europe*

Chris HEATHER, Group Legal Counsel, *Vizzavi*

Jonathan KEMBERY, Director of Legal & Business Affairs, *Open Interactive*

Marijke REED, Legal/Compliance Manager, *Open Interactive*

Clare Gilbert is known as *"big news"* in e-commerce although occupied with *"an awful lot of policy work."* Heading up new internet company, Vizzavi, is ex-boo.com *"survivor"* the *"top-notch and commercial"* **Chris Heather**. **Jonathan Kembery** has *"a good eye for detail"* while low profile but *"talented"* **Marijke Reed** continues to elicit recommendations.

In-House lawyers profiles: p 1193

RESEARCH APPROVED BY BMRB: *For this edition,* Chambers' *researchers conducted 6,552 interviews – 4,419 with law firms, 554 with barristers and 1,579 with clients.*

The validity of the research was scrutinised by BMRB International, who audited both the methodology and the results at our offices in July 2001. They interviewed Chambers' *researchers and cross-checked sample interviews. Details of the audit appear on page 7.*

LONDON

E-COMMERCE • London
1 Bird & Bird
Olswang
2 Baker & McKenzie
Clifford Chance
Denton Wilde Sapte
Field Fisher Waterhouse
3 Kemp Little LLP
Osborne Clarke
Taylor Joynson Garrett
4 Harbottle & Lewis
5 Brobeck Hale and Dorr
Herbert Smith
Masons
Tarlo Lyons
6 Allen & Overy
Ashurst Morris Crisp
Berwin Leighton Paisner
Bristows
Linklaters
Lovells
SJ Berwin
The Simkins Partnership
Theodore Goddard

This book is the product of 6,552 1/2 hour interviews. See p.7 for BMRB audit.
Within each band, firms are listed alphabetically.

Bird & Bird (see firm details p.884) The firm's knowledge of the e-commerce sector and strengths in related areas such as telecoms, IT and IP set it apart from most of its rivals. It is widely seen to remain *"pre-eminent for its understanding of complex technology transactions and its ability to manage large-scale global projects."* Although the firm suffered the departure of Chris Rees to Herbert Smith, market perception is that it has *"more than enough strength in depth to weather the loss."* **Graham Smith** (see p.296) is said to be *"bright, punchy and to the point,"* while head of the firm's e-commerce group **Graham Defries** (see p.295) has *"broad knowledge of the technology sector,"* and is *"one of the more active and commercial lawyers around."* The firm advised iVillage on a joint venture with Tesco.com to create iVillage.co.uk, a dedicated portal for women, valued at US$70 million. Other work includes acting for MP3.com on the rollout of its service across Europe, involving contract liability, distance selling and copyright infringement. The team also advised on all aspects of the establishment of Orchestream, as well as acting as co-counsel on the company's IPO, which raised over £50 million. **Clients:** American Express Bank; Associated Newspapers; B2Build.com; BT; Carlton Communications; Digital Media Corporation; Dresdner Kleinwort Benson; EMAP; The Football Association; GE Capital; iWEB.com; MP3.com; QVC; Telegraph Group; Video Networks.

Olswang (see firm details p.1084) The e-commerce department is a cross-departmental affair, drawing in partners from IP, IT, litigation, media and corporate finance. Peers admit that the firm is *"difficult to get away from in this area,"* pointing to its overall focus on technology and *"an excellent client base"* which includes infrastructure providers, search companies, ASP companies, pure content players and online retailers. The *"technically brilliant"* **John Enser** (see p.295) is seen as one of the firm's *"major talents,"* while versatile TMT lawyer **Kim Nicholson** (see p.449 & 814) is *"sharp"* and *"in tune with market developments." "Rising rapidly through the ranks,"* **Victor Timon** (see p.296) is *"sound on commercial matters,"* and **Matthew Cowan** (see p.295) also retains his share of market support. The firm advised DaimlerChrysler on the launch of its groundbreaking e-commerce initiative for the sale and delivery of smart cars, and acted for Music Choice on its £50 million flotation on the London Stock Exchange. Other matters include representing The Carphone Warehouse Group on a WAP venture with America Online and its affiliate, AOL Europe S.A. **Clients:** BBC Worldwide; Channel 4; CNET Networks; DaimlerChrysler; eBay; e-comsport; E* Trade; First Tuesday; Granada Media Group; Kingfisher; peoplesound.com; Kingfisher; Ladbrokes; Moreover.com; Music Choice; Netstore; Shell; Sportal; WRMC.

Baker & McKenzie (see firm details p.868) A fixture on large projects for established clients, the firm also advises on internet liability issues and

LEADING INDIVIDUALS	
1 **ENSER John** Olswang	**KEMP Richard** Kemp Little LLP
MCNEIVE Liam McNeive Solicitors	**MILLARD Christopher** Clifford Chance
SMITH Graham Bird & Bird	
2 **CHISSICK Michael** Field Fisher Waterhouse	**HAFTKE Mark** KLegal
SMALL Harry Baker & McKenzie	
3 **CALOW Duncan** Denton Wilde Sapte	**KAYE Laurence** Garretts
NICHOLSON Kim Olswang	**PHILLIPS Mark** Harbottle & Lewis
REES Chris Herbert Smith	
4 **AZIM-KHAN Rafi** McDermott, Will & Emery	**COWAN Matthew** Olswang
DOWNING Robbie Baker & McKenzie	**GRIFFITHS David** Clifford Chance
HENRY Michael Buchanan Ingersoll	**RENDELL Simon** Osborne Clarke OWA
TURNER Mark Herbert Smith	**WILLIAMS Alan** Denton Wilde Sapte
UP AND COMING	
DEFRIES Graham Bird & Bird	**GREW Chris** Brobeck Hale and Dorr
MULLOCK James Osborne Clarke OWA	**SANDELSON Daniel** Clifford Chance
TIMON Victor Olswang	

See individuals' profiles p.294

online venture agreements for new names such as agency.com and espotting.com, an internet search engine. Commended for its "*strength in depth*," the firm is said to have the "*all-round expertise that you would expect of them.*" Leading light **Harry Small** (see p.451) is praised as "*an excellent commercial lawyer who can turn his hand to most things.*" "*First-class*" **Robbie Downing** (see p.295) draws on "*a wealth of experience in IT and telecoms,*" and is most closely associated with the firm's b2b exchange work. The highlight of the past year was the firm's work for Global Freight Exchange, a new b2b exchange in the air transport field, involving advice on patent strategy, technology agreements and standard terms for access to the exchange. **Clients:** Agency.com; AOL; Apple; Arts Council; Canon; Cisco Systems; COLT; Global Freight Exchange; Hewlett-Packard; Levi-Strauss; Oracle; Overnet Data; Research Summary; Sony; Telstra; Yahoo!

Clifford Chance (see firm details p.919) Drawn from a number of departments, the firm is recognised for its "*strong corporate technology practice*" and its niche strength in data protection work. "*Developing nicely*" on a European level, the team acts for large service providers and a variety of leading corporates, rather than emerging companies from the dot.com market. The "*ubiquitous*" **Chris Millard** (see p.296) is widely accepted as "*the number one port of call for data protection work.*" **David Griffiths** (see p.447) is regarded as an "*underrated*" corporate technology lawyer, while **Daniel Sandelson** (see p.606) does "*excellent work in the broadcasting industry,*" and is "*one of a number of high quality assistants at the firm*" in this sector. The firm advised Carrefour on the creation of GlobalNetXchange, a b2b online exchange, enabling retailers and suppliers to transact business in real time. In addition, it represented Merrill Lynch on an equal partnership with HSBC Holdings, to create the first global online banking and investment services company. **Clients:** Accenture; Agency.com; ABN AMRO; Boots; Handbag.com; Citigroup; Crédit Suisse; Deutsche Bank AG; Energis; HSBC; Lehman Brothers; LevelSeas; Metro AG; Standard Chartered; UBS AG; Volbroker.com.

Denton Wilde Sapte (see firm details p.939) Advising a mixture of old and new economy clients, both at home and abroad, the team has seen substantial growth on the corporate side of e-commerce. M&A, joint ventures and IPOs sit alongside financial services and contentious work as growth areas for the practice. Rivals acknowledge that the firm "*got into e-commerce early on,*" and provides "*the full range of related work.*" **Duncan Calow** (see p.294), who has a "*rock-solid reputation for corporate work,*" and "*client-pleasing*" content expert **Alan Williams** (see p.607) are the team's best-known names. The firm advised London Electricity on its Virgin Energy joint venture for the internet-based sale of gas and electricity, and acted for Achilles Information on the launch of its e-procurement marketplace for utilities. Other instructions have come from bol.com on a dispute with a major internet service provider, and Robert Fleming on the launch of its online private banking account facilities. **Clients:** Abbey National; AIG Computer Services; Bond Digital; British Aviation Insurance Group; Classic FM; Compaq; ESB International; GE Equity Capital; Harper Collins; Marks & Spencer; Net Online; Shell Capital; Telewest.

Field Fisher Waterhouse (see firm details p.957) Renowned for advising entrepreneurs and SMEs on their start-up ventures, the firm also acts for FTSE-listed companies on their global e-commerce strategies, and banks on website compliance with financial services law. Accepted as a "*pre-eminent force for start-up work,*" the firm is still felt to lack the corporate muscle of its nearest rivals. Nevertheless, a "*quality client base*" is still served by the team, whose guiding star remains the "*trail-blazing*" **Michael Chissick** (see p.294). "*A serious individual with a serious practice,*" he co-authored the standard industry text 'Electronic Commerce Law and Practice'. Over the past year, the firm has handled increased b2b work, advising on a range of e-commerce issues for its clients. **Clients:** Accenture; BATP; Globix; Thomas Cook.

Kemp Little LLP (see firm details p.1018) Dedicated to IT, e-commerce and telecoms, the team has added substantial work for major corporates to its advice on behalf of established IT clients. Microsoft remains a key client, and the team now also works with the company's internet and e-commerce properties, bCentral and Carview, in the UK. Regarded as "*an excellent niche firm, doing a healthy mix of work,*" it owes much to the "*visionary*" **Richard Kemp** (see p.296), who "*deserves a lot of credit for going his own way.*" The team advised Volkswagen Group UK on a large dealer services enhancement project, represented Volkswagen Financial Services on a range of e-commerce enabling projects, and acted for Wembley on a number of e-commerce infrastructure projects to support its sports, leisure and gaming businesses. **Clients:** Expedia; FTSE International; Marsh and McLennan; Microsoft; QBE Insurance; The St Paul Insurance Company; T-Motion; Wembley.

Osborne Clarke (see firm details p.1086) The firm's focus on technology continues to bear fruit in London, as it advises IT suppliers, users and retailers on the gamut of e-commerce issues. Said to be "*a quality outfit,*" the team performs a sizeable proportion of Yahoo!'s UK work, and advises on both large corporate transactions and smaller start-up work. Closely identified with the dot.com boom, the firm has extended its international practice since the downturn in the domestic market. "*Ambitious*" head of department **Simon Rendell** is said by clients to have "*a good, organised head on his shoulders,*" while data protection expert **James Mullock** is felt to be "*developing nicely,*" and often advises Virgin Mobile. Ashley Winton has moved to the firm's Reading office. The firm acted on the £20 million funding package from Chase Capital Partners, 3i and Flatiron Partners to Breathe, negotiated a joint venture between the Professional Golfers' Association and World Online to offer a golf portal called Golfserve, and advised Investia on a US$20 million joint venture with Chase Manhattan. **Clients:** Broadstone Telecommunications; Scenera; Station 12; Viatel; Virgin Mobile; Yahoo!

Taylor Joynson Garrett (see firm details p.1150) Utilising the firm's intellectual property and corporate finance departments for added expertise, the e-commerce department is best known for its strong technology IPO practice, acting either for venture capitalists or for the companies themselves. Peers admire the firm's "*top-rank US client base,*" and acknowledge its efforts in building itself into "*a funding and joint venture leader in the technology field.*" The firm advised on the listing of the shares of Generic Groups, with a market capitalisation of £226 million, and acted for Digital Ventures and ePartners on their investments in Eyestorm.com. **Clients:** Accenture; Arriba; Callfire; eBay; Infospace; Interworld; Priceline.

Harbottle & Lewis (see firm details p.985) Known for its advice on behalf of new media clients, the firm also advises traditional economy clients moving into the technology sector. Particularly knowledgeable in music, film and television, the firm is recognised for its "*outstanding*" expertise in its niche of computer games. Clients rate **Mark Phillips** (see p.296) as "*a force to be reckoned with*" on multi-media work, while peers agree that he is "*an accomplished business getter.*" The firm advised Attenda on its first £5 million external round of financing through DLJ European Private Equity (now part of CSFB) and Texas Pacific Group, as well as advising on three subsequent sources of finance through the original investors and UBS Capital. The team also acted for Chrysalis Group on its formation of a joint venture, Rivals Europe, responsible for building the largest online network of sports team sites in Europe. Other work includes representing Mongrel Channels on the building of three multi-media portals. **Clients:** Amazon.com; Chrysalis Group; Click Music; Comic Relief; Digital Arts; Easy Group; Lifestylesonline; Ministry of Sound; MSN; Peermusic; The Really Useful Group; Recordstore; Sportsicon.com; World Rally Championships.

Brobeck Hale and Dorr (see firm details p.895) This US law firm has an increasingly respected position in the London market, and is known for its work on the corporate finance aspects of e-commerce, from venture capital financing to IPOs. "*A fantastic US client base*" commends the team for its "*performance of European transactions to an American standard.*" **Chris Grew** (see p.295) is seen to have "*made a big impact since his arrival - he's a star of the future.*" Highlights from the past year include the €6.1 billion IPO of Infineon Technologies, where the firm advised the underwriters, Goldman Sachs and Deutsche Bank. The firm also represented Geneva Technology on the US aspects of its US$700 million merger with Convergys, and acted for Autonomy on its US$363.4 million secondary offering on the London Stock Exchange, Nasdaq and Easdaq. **Clients:** Bookham Technology; Brainpower; Cipher; Eyretel; letsbuyit.com; Parthus; Sports.com; Trintech; Wavecom.

Herbert Smith (see firm details p.993) Generally associated with its work for merchant banks and blue-chip corporates, the team has particular experience in internet IPO and public company work. A historic market accusation of the firm's "*lack of pure industry awareness*" was countered this year with the arrival of **Chris Rees** (see p.450) from Bird & Bird. "*A top-class IT lawyer with real e-commerce experience,*" his move is viewed by clients and rivals as "*a major acquisition*" and "*a serious signal of intent.*" **Mark Turner** (see p.296) is recognised as "*the practice's busiest bee,*" and is singled out for his "*excellent work for Freeserve*" over the past year. The firm advised Freeserve on its clearlybusiness joint venture with Barclays to create an internet portal aimed at UK small businesses. It also acted for Freeserve on its disposal to Wanadoo, and performed the commercial work for FT in connection with its new web site FTMarketwatch.com, which involved drafting content acquisition and distribution agreements. **Clients:** BAT; BSkyB; clearlybusiness.com; CSFB; Freeserve; Goldman Sachs; John Charcoal; Macromedia; QXL; Royal & Sun Alliance; Selftrade; Swiss Reinsurance; Viglen.

Masons (see firm details p.1056) Particularly active in the supplier and dot.com market, the firm also advises traditional businesses on developing e-commerce strategies. A fine reputation for pure IT, notably in data protection, is teamed with a superb client base to produce what one rival acknowledged as "*a team which we see more and more.*" The firm advised Realise Ltd on e-commerce development agreements for contracts with a number of major financial organisations, including Standard Life Bank, and dot.coms. It also advised Dreamticket on a £3 million web development agreement. **Clients:** Bank of Ireland; BlackID; CGNU; Enfomedia; Equifax; Infobank International Holdings; ISI Dentso; MCI Worldcom; Platima; Realise; Tekscion.

Tarlo Lyons (see firm details p.1149) Said to have "*gathered momentum*" recently, this newly ranked team "*generates some impressive internet-related work*" for a highly rated clientele, including banks, insurance companies, retailers and internet service providers, as well as start-ups and e-commerce ventures. It advises on issues including online terms and conditions, internet access and use, domain name protection, data protection compliance, and EDI/encryption. **Clients:** Internet start-ups; service providers; financial institutions.

Allen & Overy (see firm details p.856) Focusing on international projects, the firm is also respected for its advice on the development of the e-commerce offerings and joint ventures of its larger corporate clients. The team has acted on complex b2b exchanges, domain disputes, and a number of internet and e-commerce start-ups over the past year. Specific matters handled include advising Barclays on its joint venture with Nomura in relation to IndigoSquare, an internet shopping portal to be run in association with Barclaycard. In addition, the firm acted for KPN Mobile on its joint venture with NTT Docomo to establish an internet-based portal for mobile telephones, and advised Royal Bank of Scotland on its involvement in a number of internet-based trading platforms, including Volbroker, FX Alliance and SwapsWire. **Clients:** Adidas; ADT College; CIMA; EDS; Lloyds TSB; Thomson Financial; The Sage Group.

Ashurst Morris Crisp (see firm details p.866) "*Well run*" practice, which is said to have been "*appreciably more active lately.*" The firm advises established businesses setting up online, new media and technology businesses online and start-ups, and has niche strength in the areas of insurance, financial services, data protection and the pharmaceutical industry. The team acted for Superdrug on the establishment of superdrug.com, the first e-pharmacist site in Europe offered by a major market incumbent. It also advised ShopSmart on its alliances with AOL and Asda/Walmart, and acted for Royal & Sun Alliance on setting up the usecolor.com business and web site. **Clients:** AltaVista; Carlyle; Chase Capital Partners; Nomura; The Ritz Casino; Trader.com; Virgin.net; West LB Panmure; Yahoo!

Berwin Leighton Paisner (see firm details p.878) Drawn from a wide range of departments, the firm's e-commerce team advises on fundings, joint ventures, flotations, acquisitions and disposals, data protection and privacy issues, encryption and web advertising and linking. The merger is considered to give the department "*a nice balance of skills.*" Acknowledged as an active force in the start-up market, the firm also advises the e-commerce divisions of major organisations. The former Berwin Leighton team acted for Tesco.com on a US$70 million joint venture with iVillage to launch iVillage UK. The erstwhile Paisner team, recognised for its work on e-commerce acquisitions and joint ventures, advised The Great Universal Stores on its acquisition of jungle.com. **Clients:** Tesco.com; Ove Arup; Lex/RAC; Investec Bank; Line One/United News and Media; Gaming Internet; EO.

Bristows (see firm details p.895) The firm's superb reputation in IP is perceived to have led to "*a healthy spin-off e-commerce practice.*" The firm's e-business practice advises on structuring internet start-ups, negotiating joint ventures, domain name disputes, IP agreements and legal health-checks for web sites. The team advised Airmiles Travel Promotions on competition issues relating to patents for its e-commerce system. It has also acted on various e-commerce matters for a web-based company selling financial products over the internet, including drafting terms and conditions for the site and negotiating the purchase of a number of URLs. **Clients:** British Airways; Digimask; Finsoft; Fleet Street Publications; Hotgen Studios; Know How Systems; Misys Interactive; Revolution Software; Sara Lee; Sony Computer Entertainment Europe.

Linklaters (see firm details p.1042) An outstanding corporate practice and vast client base has translated into substantial work on dot.com flotations, including that of last minute dot.com. Since the recent decline in that area of business, the firm has advised a number of banks and venture capitalists on e-commerce issues. The team acted for Goldman Sachs on the IPO of TeleCity and its admission to trading on the London Stock Exchange, and advised Dixons on Wanadoo's all-share offer for Freeserve, which involved class 1 disposal by Dixons of its 79% stake in Freeserve. **Clients:** CSFB; CWC; Halifax Group; Lehman Brothers; Vivendi SA; World Online.

Lovells (see firm details p.1044) Acting for a respected corporate client base on e-commerce issues, the firm is particularly noted in the areas of disputed domain names and electronic banking. Said to be "*more focused than some City practices*" in the field, the team's clients include both established companies using new electronic methods, and companies whose business is exclusively derived from e-commerce. The firm acted for Baltimore Technologies on its US$1 billion acquisition of Content Technologies and advised Barclays, NatWest and HSBC on their participation in Identrus, the global trust organisation for secure electronic commerce. **Clients:** Active Booking Company; Barclays Bank; Cable & Wireless; Mars; Mattel; The Post Office; Trinity Mirror; Waitrose.

SJ Berwin (see firm details p.879) Renowned for its expertise in fund establishment, the firm's work in the e-commerce field is generally on behalf of venture capitalist clients. Now "*clearly on the radar screen*" in this field, the team acted for BT on the licensing of content for inclusion in its mobile internet and WAP portal, Genie. The firm also advised virginmoney.com on all aspects of the establishment, launch and operation of its financial services portal, virginmoney.com. **Clients:** Advent Venture Partners; Atlas Venture; BT Broadcast Services; Interactive Investor International; iXL London; Liquid Audio; Monitor Ventures; UBF Capital.

The Simkins Partnership (see firm details p.1131) The firm's e-commerce group deals with all regulatory and contractual matters relating to the establishment of a web presence (both conventional and wireless) and the distribution of product, services and content. It specialises in advising clients from the media and high-tech industries, and has particular expertise in the streaming and downloading of all types of audio and audio-visual material. The firm advised NMTV (silicon.com) on the £14 million second round of venture capital investment in the company, and continues to act for WAP Forum on all aspects of their business in the UK and Europe. **Clients:** Launch; Sony UK; Improveline; The Really Useful Group; Theatre Now; Post2Post; IFG; ISM; Epic; Matrix Group.

Theodore Goddard (see firm details p.1152) The firm's e-commerce team operates from its Media and Communications Group, and advises online businesses from start-up through launch to general trading. General commercial, regulatory and content licensing advice is prominent in the caseload. Niche strengths exist in domain name strategy and recovery work, online advertising and contracting and data protection. The firm has been involved in substantial domain name recovery work, most notably the recovery of Sade.com, Nationalgeographic.tv and Sponsorship-brasserie.co.uk. It also advised on IchooseTV, one of the first television portals to be launched on the internet, and represented News International on the online activities of its subsidiary, News Network. **Clients:** Advertising Standards Authority; Leisure Link; National Information Consortium; Small Rockets; Tower Hill Estates; Universal Music.

Other Notable Practitioners A number of rated individuals thrive elsewhere in London. **Liam McNeive** (see p.296), acclaimed by peers as "*a genuine specialist*," is best known for his work on behalf of AOL, where he was formerly in-house counsel. At K-Legal, **Mark Haftke** (see p.295) remains a name to conjure with, although his profile is considered to have dipped since his move from Bird & Bird. **Laurence Kaye** (see p.295) is a "*thoroughly able*" lawyer, who has specific expertise in the publishing aspects of e-commerce, notably on the contentious side. He recently joined Garretts from Paisner & Co. American firm McDermott, Will & Emery is home to the much-travelled **Rafi Azim-Khan** (see p.294). Said to have "*obvious potential*," he has advised on a number of major ISP start-ups and b2b and b2c exchanges and auctions. **Michael Henry** has now switched to Buchanan Ingersoll from H2O. A "*sound technician*," he has wide experience of all aspects of the high-tech sector.

THE REGIONS

E-COMMERCE • The Regions	
1	**Osborne Clarke** Reading
2	**Addleshaw Booth & Co** Manchester
	Garretts Reading
	Maclay Murray & Spens Edinburgh
	Nabarro Nathanson Reading
	Shepherd & Wedderburn WS Edinburgh
	Wragge & Co Birmingham
3	**Halliwell Landau** Manchester
	McGrigor Donald Edinburgh
	The Law Offices of Marcus J O'Leary Bracknell

LEADING INDIVIDUALS	
1	**WINTON Ashley** Osborne Clarke OWA
2	**BAILES Tony** Nabarro Nathanson
	BOAG-THOMSON Joanna Shepherd & Wedderburn WS
	HARRINGTON Alison Garretts
	O'LEARY Marcus The Law Offices of Marcus J O'Leary

This book is the product of 6,552 1/2 hour interviews. See p.7 for BMRB audit.
Within each band, firms are listed alphabetically. *See individuals' profiles p.294*

Osborne Clarke (see firm details p.1086) "*Thriving*" practice, acting for infrastructure providers and leading companies in the Thames Valley region. Considered to have "*the M4 corridor sewn up*," the team has acquired the services of **Ashley Winton** from the London office. "*Colourful and mildly eccentric, he has a first-class brain and is maturing into a first-class lawyer.*" The firm advised Sonera Zed on the launch of an internet and mobile e-commerce service, and acted for Bass Brewers on the creation of a business-to-business marketplace. **Clients:** 2c.com; Amazon.com; Netline.com; Onyx; Kompass.com; Classic Freenet; Digital Village; Porsche AG; Dixon; Tumbleweed; VCI.

Addleshaw Booth & Co (see firm details p.853) Feeding off its IP/IT strength, and advising a huge corporate client base, the e-commerce team has particular strengths in the retail sector and in data protection issues. The firm advised Reckitt Benckiser on its global e-commerce policy, which encompassed advice on e-mail, internet policies, customer profiling and domain name disputes. It also advised Pentland on an e-commerce project for leading brands such as Ellesse, involving advice on web site content, terms of business, data protection and internal e-mail. **Clients:** Argos; DebiTech AB; DebiTech Ltd; GUS; Pentland Group; Phoenix Datacom; Reckitt Benckiser; TradeDoubler.

Garretts (see firm details p.968) The firm's Reading office is commended for its high-tech versatility, and is "*poised to take advantage of the technology boom in the area*," according to some London commentators. The respected **Alison Harrington** (see p.295) is the team's leading figure here, and comes from a non-contentious IP background. Niche strengths include contracts, data protection, regulatory advice and distribution channel advice. The firm advised Peramon Technology on the creation of standard licensing terms for various products relating to wireless web applications. **Clients:** Motorola; Network Appliance UK; Axxia Systems; eCredit.com; Microsoft Europe; SciQuest.com.

Maclay Murray & Spens (see firm details p.1047) Advising on data protection, domain name protection, trademark protection, secure extranets and web site development, the firm acts largely for existing businesses procuring e-commerce services, and is rated as one of the strongest in Scotland. The team advised TSN Sport.com on its £10 million first round investment from Warburg Pincus to create a sports portal site focusing on snooker. It also acted for Sun, Oracle, Cisco and The Royal Bank of Scotland on their e-business incubator and their e-development engine. **Clients:** Cisco; Oracle; The Royal Bank of Scotland; Sun; TSN Sport.com.

Nabarro Nathanson (see firm details p.1048) Seen as a "*major player in the Thames Valley*," the e-commerce group has been active in the e-charity market, as well as representing internet enablers and venture capitalists investing in new media companies. The team has developed a specialist niche in advising many of its large property clients (such as Hammerson) on their e-commerce activities, particularly trade mark, domain name and copyright matters. **Tony Bailes** (see p.445) is recognised for his "*general spread of technology knowledge.*" The firm advised Fashionmall.com on its purchase of trademark and other IP rights from insolvent online retailer Boo.com. It also acted for New Media Spark on its £80 million recommended share exchange with Internet Indirect. **Clients:** Ask Jeeves; Commerce One; ETF; Land Securities; web-angel.

Shepherd & Wedderburn WS (see firm details p.1126) The firm's Technology and IP Group has advised many technology companies through all stages of funding from start-up to flotation or trade sale. It also advises clients in relation to issues such as the drafting of website contracts, preparation of e-mail policies, advertisements and services on the internet and copyright and trademark infringement. A major coup was the lateral hire of **Joanna Boag-Thompson** (see p.294) from MacRoberts. Rivals believe that "*her arrival gives their team real credibility.*" The firm advised Friends Ivory & Sime on an agreement with FTYourMoney.com concerning the selling of the 'ZeroCharge ISA' product. **Clients:** Scottish & Newcastle; Cairn Energy; Colonial First Investment.

Wragge & Co (see firm details p.1189) Advising on joint ventures, fund-raising, domain name protection and data protection, the firm is considered to be doing "*some tremendous stuff*" in the field. Rivals and clients applaud the team for its "*rare focus*" on the e-commerce sector. The firm advised Specialist Computer Holdings on its £18.5 million acquisition of Compelsource, and its £115 million purchase of Buhrmann NV. It is also the leading adviser to Cap Gemini Ernst & Young, one of the world's leading suppliers of IT and consultancy services. **Clients:** BT; Cap Gemini Ernst & Young; Interplan; Specialist Computer Holdings.

Halliwell Landau (see firm details p.982) Perceived to have a "*thoroughly respectable technology practice in Manchester,*" the firm advises a mix of old and new economy clients on a variety of commercial and corporate issues relating to e-commerce. Particularly known for its contentious work, the firm is a familiar figure on domain name disputes. The firm advised Edison Mission Energy on a multi-million pound software procurement deal. **Clients:** Dedicated Microcomputers Group; Knowledge Management Software; Time Group; Voxsurf International.

McGrigor Donald (see firm details p.1062) Originally known for its "*substantial dot.com work,*" the firm also advises on content acquisition, advertising endorsements, name disputes and joint ventures. Financial institutions comprise a core element of the client base. The team acted for Intelligent Finance on the establishment of an online telephone and internet bank for Halifax. It also advised on the establishment of Channelhealth.com, a new portal for health-related issues, and the establishment, fund-raising and operation of Globalfarmers.com. **Clients:** Channel Health; globalfarmers.com; goodpractice.net; Intelligent Finance; Unipharma.com; the vcx.com.

The Law Offices of Marcus J O'Leary (see firm details p.1030) The firm offers a range of advice to hi-tech companies, as well as acting for leading international companies on various IT and e-commerce matters. Described as "*one of the industry's true specialists,*" **Marcus O'Leary** (see p.449) and his team are said to perform "*cutting edge work in the Thames Valley.*" **Clients:** Leading national and international clients.

LEADERS IN E-COMMERCE

AZIM-KHAN, Rafi

McDermott, Will & Emery, London
(020) 7577 6900
razimkhan@europe.mwe.com

Specialisation: Partner heading *McDermott, Will & Emery's* e-business and marketing groups in Europe and a member of the firm's international e-business group. Specialises in advertising/marketing, entertainment, intellectual property, internet/e-commerce and commercial law. Has considerable experience of advising media, marketing and leading brand clients on wide range of advertising, sales promotions, sponsorships (e.g. France '98 World Cup), lotteries, newspaper and television promotions (e.g. UK's first £1 million prize promotions on TFI Friday and Virgin Radio) and on all aspects of e-commerce, including, full 'e-audits' of sites, e-enablement projects and B2B/B2C operations for multinationals, major ISPs, B2B exchanges. Experience also of data protection, distance selling, Pan-EU online contracting, PKI, digital TV and interactive media, net shopping, gaming and portals. Lectures regularly and is author of sections in 'e-Commerce from Cradle to Grave' and 'A Practitioner's Guide to Regulation of the Internet'. Rafi is the firm's representative to the Advertising Law Group and the e-Commerce Law Group.
Career: Qualified 1993. Previously at *Lewis Silkin* 1993-95, *Cameron McKenna* 1995-97, *Theodore Goddard* 1997-00.
Personal: Educated at Cranbrook College and at Queen Mary College, University of London (LLB Hons). Keen sportsman and enjoys travel, music and motor racing. Resides London.

BAILES, Tony

Nabarro Nathanson, Reading (0118) 925 4602
a.bailes@nabarro.com
See under Information Technology, p.445

BOAG-THOMSON, Joanna

Shepherd & Wedderburn WS, Glasgow
(0141) 566 8570
joanna.bt@shepwedd.co.uk

Specialisation: Accredited by Law Society of Scotland as a specialist in intellectual property law. Principal areas of practice are e-commerce and IP/IT, with a focus on B2B e-commerce. Was part of Scottish Enterprise's E-commerce Strategy Committee for Scotland.
Prof. Memberships: Law Society of Scotland; Licensing Executives Society; TIPLO; Society for Computers and Law.
Career: Trained *Wright Johnston & Mackenzie*, Glasgow and Edinburgh 1988-90. Assistant *Wright Johnston & Mackenzie Callander* 1990-91. Assistant *Bird Semple Fyfe Ireland* 1991-93. Assistant, associate then partner *MacRoberts* 1993-00. Partner in IP and technology at *Shepherd & Wedderburn* 2000 to date.
Publications: Numerous magazine and newspaper articles. Co-edited Greens 'Scottish E-commerce Handbook'.
Personal: Educated Craighome School, Glasgow, then LLB and Dip LP at Edinburgh University. Interests – theatre, travel, reading and writing.

CALOW, Duncan

Denton Wilde Sapte, London (020) 7320 3794
dcc@dentonwildesapte.com

Specialisation: Senior solicitor specialising in publishing and digital media work. Advises content owner, producer and distributor clients on a wide range of projects including Internet, on-line and e-commerce services; print, CD-Rom, DVD and video games publishing; broadband, interactive television and mobile services.
Prof. Memberships: International Association of Entertainment Lawyers and Publishers Association Legal Committee.
Publications: Written and spoken widely on the legal issues of digital media including contributions to specialist and legal press, national newspapers, radio and television. Contributor (with Alan Williams) to 'Halsburys Laws on Internet Publishing', (Butterworths, 1999); author (with Alan Williams and Nicholas Higham) of 'Digital Media: Contracts, Rights and Licensing', (2nd edn, Sweet & Maxwell, 1998).

CHISSICK, Michael

Field Fisher Waterhouse, London (020) 7861 4000
mpc@ffwlaw.com

Specialisation: Head of IT and e-commerce law group which comprises a team of seven partners and 18 specialist lawyers. Main areas of practice include outsourcing projects, data protection, digital mixed media, electronic commerce and m-commerce contracts, linking agreements, software contracts and internet law. In the past year has advised on several major outsourcing projects, including advising Lewisham Council on a major outsourcing of all its IT and communication infrastructures and Thomas Cook on its e-commerce projects.
Prof. Memberships: Law Society; Solicitors European Group; FAST Legal Advisory Group; Computer Law Association.
Career: 1st Class Degree in Law (LLB); Law Society Finals 1st Class; Masters Degree in IT and Telecommunications.
Publications: Author of 'Internet Law' published in October 1997 by FT Publications and co-author of 'Electronic Commerce Law and Practice' published in 1999 and 2000 by Sweet & Maxwell.

COWAN, Matthew
Olswang, London (020) 7208 8713
mac@olswang.com
Specialisation: Commercial and corporate work in the Internet and telecommunications fields. Acted on the establishment of Worldpop.com and flotation of Netstore plc. Practice includes venture capital funding and acquisitions in the Internet and telecommunications fields.
Career: Joined *Olswang* in 1993 upon qualification and became a partner in 1999. Attended Bristol Grammar School 1979-86, then Exeter University 1986-90.
Personal: Born 31 March 1967. Lives in Surrey.

DEFRIES, Graham
Bird & Bird, London (020) 7415 6000
Specialisation: Partner and head of e-commerce department. Telecommunications, corporate/commercial matters. Major transactions include acting for Wall Street Systems, Inc. on the establishment of a joint venture with Deutsche Bank AG to provide back office outsourcing services to the European and Asian banking sector; representing 360networks, Inc. in a dark fibre swap valued at $180 million involving the provision of US fibres in exchange for the provision by Telia AB of European fibres; representing Barclays Bank plc on a £250 million data telecoms network outsourcing agreement with BT; advising Last-minute.com on its Australian and South African joint ventures with local partners to develop a travel portal.
Prof. Memberships: Law Society.
Career: *Bird & Bird* 1992; qualified 1994. Partner 1999.
Publications: Contributor to 'Internet Law and Regulation' (Sweet and Maxwell, 2nd edition, edited by Graham Smith).
Personal: Married with three children. BA (Law & Politics) Oxford Brookes University. Interests include tennis, bridge, cartoons, music.

DOWNING, Robbie
Baker & McKenzie, London (020) 7919 1000
robbie.downing@bakernet.com
Specialisation: Partner specialising in IT and telecoms with a particular focus on e-commerce and antitrust. Key clients include AOL, Bolero Association, Cisco Systems, COLT, Global Freight Exchange, ntl and UUNet.
Prof. Memberships: Society of Computers & Law; Computer Law Association.
Career: Articled *Baker & McKenzie*; qualified 1988; associate 1988-90; legal advisor IBM (UK) Limited 1990-92; lecturer in law King's College, London 1992-95; *Baker & McKenzie*, London 1995; partner 1998 to date.
Publications: 'EC Information Technology Law' (John Wiley 1995); competition law chapter and section on IPRs and the Internet in Sweet & Maxwell 'Encyclopedia of Information Technology Law'; 'Magill and the Software Directive: are they interoperable?' (Web Journal of Current Legal Issues 1995); 'On-line Services and the EU Database Directive' (International Review of Law Computers and Technology 1996); 'Article 30 of the EC Treaty vs patent rights: Merck exhausted again' (King's College Law Journal 1997); edited 'Baker & McKenzie Guide to IP in the IT Industry' (Sweet & Maxwell 1998); UK section of 'Doing E-Commerce in Europe' (Baker & McKenzie 2001); editor of monthly e-commerce alerts in 'plc' magazine.
Personal: King Edwards VI School, Birmingham; Exeter College, Oxford (1984 BA Jurisprudence [1st Class] Martin Wronker Prize); Law Society Finals (1985); Univ Libre de Bruxelles (1986 Licence Spéciale en Droit Européen; la plus grande distinction).

ENSER, John
Olswang, London (020) 7208 8716
jxe@olswang.com
Specialisation: Principal area of practice: commercial and regulatory advice for Internet, interactive TV, television and music industries. Specialises in all aspects of digital media solutions in business to business and consumer markets. Clients include ISPs, leading websites, broadcasters, digital TV platform operators, internet technology providers, major film and record companies, retailers and insurers.
Prof. Memberships: ICC.
Career: Qualified: 1989. *Frere Cholmeley* 1987-94 (Brussels 1993-94). *Olswang* 1994 to date. Partner since 1996. School: Queen Elizabeth's Hospital, Bristol 1975-82. Pembroke College, Oxford 1982-85.
Personal: Born 21 October 1964. Married (one son). Lives in London.

GREW, Chris
Brobeck Hale and Dorr, London (020) 7645 2400
grew@bhd.com
Specialisation: Principally advises technology companies on venture capital investments, US securities law issues (particularly initial public offerings for non-US companies on Nasdaq and the European new markets), cross-border mergers and acquisitions and general corporate transactions. Advises a wide range of high technology (particularly software and Internet) companies as well as the investment banks, venture capitalists and other financial intermediaries that serve technology companies. Recent transactions include representing ARC International plc in its initial public offering, BuildOnline in the recent investment by ETF; Memscap SA in its initial public offering and Global Freight Exchange in the investments by Deutsche Post, Lufthansa, Panalpina and SwissAir. Selected as a Top Deal Maker by the 'Wall Street Journal European Edition'. Also named as one of The Digital Dozen – Top Individual Lawyers by 'The Insider's Guide to Legal Services – Digital Media & E-commerce'.
Prof. Memberships: Registered foreign lawyer; Bar of England and Wales (Honourable Society of Middle Temple); American Bar Association; New York State Bar Association.
Career: Partner, registered foreign lawyer, *BHD*, 1997 to present; associate *BHD* 1992-97; associate *Hughes Hubbard & Reed*, 1989-92; barrister, Chambers of Michael West QC (Gray's Inn), 1987-88.

GRIFFITHS, David
Clifford Chance, London (020) 7600 1000
david.griffiths@cliffordchance.com
See under Information Technology, p.447

HAFTKE, Mark
KLegal, London (020) 7694 2655
mark.haftke@kpmg.co.uk
Specialisation: Partner, head of eBusiness and Digital Media practice. Internet specialist since 1995. Specialist areas: digital media, interactive television, internet radio, e-commerce, m-commerce, data protection, PKI, EU regulation, joint ventures, B2B exchanges, P2P networking, B2C fulfillment, domain names.
Prof. Memberships: IAEL; SCL.
Career: Joined *KLegal* as partner June 2000. *Bird & Bird* 1995-00 (made partner 1997); *Russells* 1988-95 (made partner 1992). Qualified as barrister 1986; re-qualified as solicitor 1992.
Publications: Consultant editor of and contributing author to CFI's 'Practitioner's Guide to the Internet' (2nd edition); author of Internet chapter in 'Copyright & Designs Law' by Merkin & Black (Sweet & Maxwell).
Personal: BA Jurisprudence St Edmund Hall (1982-85) MA (Oxon).

HARRINGTON, Alison
Garretts, Reading (0118) 949 0000
alison.harrington@glegal.com
Specialisation: Practice covers all aspects of computer and technology law including media and communications. Areas of practice include electronic commerce, computer software development, systems integration, network maintenance, information provision, IT distribution, outsourcing, data protection, internet and new media related work. Work also includes the protection and exploitation of copyright, trademarks, designs, patents and confidential information.
Prof. Memberships: Law Society; Committee Member Thames Valley branch of the Society for Computers and Law; Federation Against Software Theft.
Career: Qualified in 1989 – *Denton Hall* (1987-94), *Garretts* (1994-date) (Head of Technology Group – *Garretts*, Reading). Partner from September 1997.
Personal: Born 13 July 1963. Educated at Harrogate College/Harrogate Grammar School and St Edmund Hall, Oxford University. Lives in Henley-on-Thames. Leisure interests include sailing and hill walking.

HENRY, Michael
Buchanan Ingersoll, London (020) 7920 3700

KAYE, Laurence
Garretts, London (020) 7304 8255
laurence.kaye@glegal.com
Specialisation: Partner in technology, media and communications group. Advises a wide range of clients in the publishing, digital media and e-commerce industries. Clients range from internet start-ups to multinationals. Recent work has included e-commerce, joint ventures and partnership agreements in the publishing, financial services, and entertainment sectors, media joint ventures, co-publishing agreements, agreements for interactive television and mobile phone services and 'due diligence' advice on copyright ownership issues. In addition to transaction based work, also advised a number of media industry bodies on digital media and e-commerce legal issues, including the European Publishers Council, the Directory Publishers Association and the Periodical Publishers Association. Advised the Cross Industry Working Group which made representations to the UK government on behalf of the publishers on the implementation of the Database Directive into UK law. Also legal adviser to the European Publishers Council – a member of the Brussels-based Rightsholders Alliance which is actively involved in representing media owners' interests on proposed new copyright and regulatory laws, particularly the forthcoming EU Copyright Directive.
Prof. Memberships: Law Society, Society for Computers & the Law.
Career: Qualified in 1975. *Brecher & Co* 1975-80. *Saunders Sobell Leigh & Dobin* partner 1980-94. *Simkins* partnership in 1994-98. *Paisner & Co* partner 1998-00. Partner, Head of Technology Media Communications, *Andersen Legal* (*Garretts*) 2000.
Personal: Born 1st September 1949. Attended Hab-

erdashers' Askes School, Elstree, then the Sorbonne, and then Sidney Sussex College, Cambridge. Leisure interests include tennis, jogging, yoga, playing the saxophone, cinema, theatre and family life.

KEMP, Richard
Kemp Little LLP, London (020) 7710 1610
richardk@comlegal.com
Specialisation: Practice covers intellectual property, competition/EU regulatory and general business law for the full range of IT, e-commerce and telecoms sectors, acting for both suppliers and acquirers.
Prof. Memberships: Law Society; Chartered Institute of Patent Agents; Computer Law and Security Reports – editorial board member. Guide to the World's Leading IT Lawyers (1999); one of top 20 global IT lawyers ('Best of the Best') (2000); board member, Computer Law Association (2001).
Career: *Clifford-Turner* (1978-84); *Hopkins & Wood* 1984-91 (partner 1985); *(Hammond Suddards* (1991-95 (head of IT group; founder partner London office)); *Garrett & Co* (partner 1995, IP/IT London office group head 1996; IP/IT European Service Line head, 1997). Set up *Kemp & Co* in November 1997 to specialise in IT, e-commerce and telecoms work – firm now has 20 lawyers and 30 staff.
Personal: Born 8 July 1956. Educated Oakham School, St. Catharine's College Cambridge, Université Libre de Bruxelles.

MCNEIVE, Liam
McNeive Solicitors, London (020) 7253 0535
liam@mcneive.com
Specialisation: Liam McNeive established *mcneive solicitors* in March 1998 to provide an informal, responsive service to businesses operating in the media, communications and technology sectors. He has since been joined by lawyers Natasha Doman (ex *Masons*) and Rupesh Chandrani (ex *Theodore Goddard*). Clients include QXL ricardo plc (www.qxl.com), AOL UK and AOL Europe (www.aol.co.uk), Real Media UK (www.realmedia.com), Sonnet Internet (www.sonnet.co.uk), e-xentric plc (www.e-xentric.com), The National Trust (www.national trust.org.uk) and Good Technology (www.goodtech.co.uk). The firm also acts for a major multinational media corporation in respect of its interactive offerings. As well as addressing the myriad e-commerce law requirements of its clients, the firm has discrete specialisms in advertising, betting/gaming/lotteries, auction, music/video/multimedia, information technology and telecommunications law. The firm is focused on assisting enterprises - ranging from web developers to interactive service providers; from casinos to auctioneers; from software houses to interactive game producers - having interests in any or all of these areas. Liam was one of three co-founding directors of ICrunch (www.icrunch.com), the online music service, which was acquired in April 2001 by Music Choice Europe.

MILLARD, Christopher
Clifford Chance, London (020) 7600 1000
christopher.millard@cliffordchance.com
Specialisation: Partner in the Media, Computer and Communications Group, specialises in online services and the Internet, telecommunications regulation and contracts, data protection, outsourcing, computer procurement and distribution arrangements, software development and licensing, intellectual property rights in software and data.
Prof. Memberships: Senior visiting fellow University of London teaching LLM courses in IT Law and Telecommunications Law; joint chairman Society for Computers and Law, president International Federation of Computer Law Associations; general editor OUP 'International Journal of Law and Information Technology'; board member Computer Security Research Centre LSE; board member 'Cyberspace Lawyer' and many other IT and telecoms journals.
Career: Manchester Grammar School; University of Sheffield (LLB Hons 1980); University of Toronto (MA 1982, LLM 1983). Articled *Clifford Turner*, qualified 1986, partner *Clifford Chance* since 1992.
Personal: Music. Born 1959; married with two children; resides London.

MULLOCK, James
Osborne Clarke, London (020) 7809 1000

NICHOLSON, Kim
Olswang, London (020) 7208 8731
kan@olswang.com
See under Information Technology, p.449, Telecommunications, p.814

O'LEARY, Marcus
The Law Offices of Marcus J. O'Leary, Bracknell (01344) 303044
See under Information Technology, p.449

PHILLIPS, Mark
Harbottle & Lewis, London (020) 7667 5000
mark.phillips@harbottle.com
Specialisation: Partner and head of both the Interactive and New Media Group and the Publishing Group specialising in commercial and corporate work for media, leisure and arts industries.
Prof. Memberships: Law Society, Society for Computers and Law.
Career: Qualified in 1986. Worked at *Clifford Chance* 1984-88. Joined *Harbottle & Lewis* in 1988, became a partner in 1990.
Personal: Born 1961. Attended Manchester Grammar School 1972-78, University College, London 1979-82. Trustee of Performing Arts Lab and School Governor.

REES, Chris
Herbert Smith, London 020 7374 8000
christopher.rees@herbertsmith.com
See under Information Technology, p.450

RENDELL, Simon
Osborne Clarke, London (020) 7809 1000

SANDELSON, Daniel
Clifford Chance, London (020) 7600 1000
daniel.sandelson@cliffordchance.com
See under Media & Entertainment, p.606

SMALL, Harry
Baker & McKenzie, London (020) 7919 1000
harry.small@bakernet.com
See under Information Technology, p.451

SMITH, Graham
Bird & Bird, London (020) 7415 6000
Specialisation: Computer project disputes, commercial litigation in computer and telecommunications industries. Evidence, document imaging and computer records. Internet law including domain name disputes, website advice, internet/e-mail use policies and regulatory issues. Intellectual property disputes. Gave evidence to the House of Lords Science and Technology Select Committee on Digital Images as Evidence. Advised Guernsey on its electronic transaction legislation.
Prof. Memberships: American Intellectual Property Law Association; Council Member, Society for Computers and Law; Computer Law Association; eCentreUK Legal Advisory Group; Fellow of the Society for Advanced Legal Studies.
Career: Qualified 1978. Joined *Bird & Bird* 1983. Partner 1985.
Publications: Contributes a section on Non-Contractual Liability to the loose-leaf 'Encyclopedia of Information Technology Law' (Sweet & Maxwell). Editor and a co-author of the book 'Internet Law and Regulation' (Sweet & Maxwell, 2nd edition December 1997). Speaks and writes regularly in the UK and abroad mainly on IT and internet legal issues.
Personal: Born 1953. Educated Bristol University (LLB, 1975). Lives London.

TIMON, Victor
Olswang, London (020) 7208 8744
vwt@olswang.com
Specialisation: Victor Timon is a partner in Olswang's e-commerce group and head of its IT unit. The group's clients span the whole spectrum of those engaged in e-commerce. These include ISPs, ASPs, telcos, online auction houses, providers of content to the Internet, mobile portals and interactive television as well as major retail outlets involved in the business of selling their goods and services through the medium of online. Highlights of the last year have included the application of the Distance Selling Regulations to clients in this sector and the growth of the ASP/outsourcing model.
Career: Qualified in Ireland in 1982 and re-qualified in the UK in 1991. IBM, Ireland/UK 1984 to 1987; Unisys UK Limited 1987-89; *Clifford Chance* 1989-94; *Olswang* 1994 to date, partner since 1995. Law degree and diploma in European Law from University College Dublin.
Personal: Born 7 February 1958. Lives in London.

TURNER, Mark
Herbert Smith, London (020) 7466 3602
mark.turner@herbertsmith.com
Specialisation: Partner specialising in transactional and advisory work in IT and e-business. Regularly advises major corporations, government agencies and leading edge technology companies. Most of his work has a strong international element. At the forefront of developments in e-business, advising on online exchanges, regulation of business online, contracts and payment on the internet. Work includes acting for BSkyB on new technologies; Freeserve on a range of internet issues; Credit Suisse First Boston, Goldman Sachs, Bear Stearns and Schroders on IT and e-commerce issues arising from IPOs, listings and other transactions by their clients.
Prof. Memberships: International Chamber of Commerce; International Bar Association; Society for Computers and Law; Computer Law Association; City of London Law Society.
Career: Qualified in 1983. *Macfarlanes* 1981-85. Denton Hall 1985-95 (Partner 1988). *Garretts* 1995-97. *Herbert Smith* 1998.
Personal: Born 1956. Educated Latymer Upper School and University College, Oxford (Exhibitioner).

WILLIAMS, Alan
Denton Wilde Sapte, London (020) 7320 6249
apw@dentonwildesapte.com
See under Media & Entertainment, p.607

WINTON, Ashley
Osborne Clarke, Reading (0118) 925 2000

EDUCATION

OVERVIEW: Ranked firms in this sector are divided between those acting for individuals and those acting for institutions. The former is largely litigation work for individual pupils or parents on matters such as special educational needs, exclusions and bullying. The incorporation of the Human Rights Act and the newly introduced tort of educational negligence has led to increased activity in this field - with most of the listed firms now offering advice on it. On the institutional side, clients include Higher Education (HE), Further Education (FE), or schools (usually in the private or voluntarily aided sectors). Services offered range from governance, student and constitutional issues to broader employment and commercial work. Although the Education section is separated into regions, it is important to remember that institutional firms in particular tend to have a catchment area that stretches beyond their geographic locality.

RESEARCH APPROVED BY BMRB: *For this edition,* Chambers' *researchers conducted 6,552 interviews – 4,419 with law firms, 554 with barristers and 1,579 with clients.*

The validity of the research was scrutinised by BMRB International, who audited both the methodology and the results at our offices in July 2001. They interviewed Chambers' *researchers and cross-checked sample interviews. Details of the audit appear on page 7.*

LONDON

FIRMS ACTING FOR INSTITUTIONS

EDUCATION: INSTITUTIONS • London		Ptnrs	Assts
1	Eversheds	3	4
2	Beachcroft Wansbroughs	4	7
3	Lee Bolton & Lee	2	1
	Winckworth Sherwood	3	5
4	Lawfords	4	2
	Reynolds Porter Chamberlain	3	4
5	Farrer & Co	4	2

LEADING INDIVIDUALS		
★	HALL John Eversheds	
1	BEESLEY Peter Lee Bolton & Lee	GIZZI Julian Beachcroft Wansbroughs
	THATCHER Michael Winckworth Sherwood	
2	BOYD-CARPENTER Henry Farrer & Co	RICHENS Nicholas Lee Bolton & Lee
UP AND COMING		
	CAREW-JONES Owen Winckworth	

This book is the product of 6,552 1/2-hour interviews. See p.7 for BMRB audit.
Within each band, firms are listed alphabetically. *See individuals' profiles p.302*

Eversheds (see firm details p.952) The largest education practice in the country, with a huge interest in FE colleges and a growing roster of HE institutions and representative bodies. Able to draw on expertise from across the country, yet keeping "*a strong dedicated education department*" within the capital. The firm covers the full needs of an educational body, from general issues such as property and commercialisation, through to governance (including mergers and alliances), student issues and PFI/PPP. It is particularly recommended in education employment. **John Hall** (see p.303), judged by peers to be "*the General on education law,*" heads the department. **Clients:** Royal Institute of Chartered Surveyors; NAHT; New York University.

Beachcroft Wansbroughs (see firm details p.872) Well-regarded education firm combining representations for public bodies with work for higher education institutions. One of the busiest firms within London, the respected **Julian Gizzi** (see p.303) heads up an expert team. Its main strength remains funding work and advice for such bodies as the Further Education Funding Council, while the growing HE practice now stretches worldwide. One of the highlights of the last year was the continued legal support given to a new e-university.

Lee Bolton & Lee (see firm details p.1034) Highly rated team led by **Peter Beesley**, which is seen by interviewers as "*good on voluntary schools work*" and known for the "*depth*" of its client base. Although regarded as mainly a church schools practice, increasingly its presence is in the independent school sector and it has picked up HE clients. Work includes charity and governance issues and student matters, with particular strengths in employment and property. **Nicholas Richens** remains well respected in the field. **Clients:** Independent and church schools.

Winckworth Sherwood (see firm details p.1185) Retains a high profile in the church and foundation schools sector. Competitors agree that the "*respected*" **Michael Thatcher** (see p.304) is "*practically a legend in the education field,*" heading a team that includes the well-regarded **Owen Carew-Jones** (see p.302). The firm provides a wide spectrum of education services, including employment, property, student discipline and contract work. It acted for 3Es in the first contracted out state school, King's College, Guilford. **Clients:** Oxford Diocesan Board of Education; 3Es; Kingshurst City Technology College.

Lawfords (see firm details p.1029) Sizeable education practice that deals mainly with HEs, but keeps a strong interest in the FE sector. Works across the board on services to institutions; from commercial aspects to property to employment to student related issues. With "*the human touch,*" the team, led by Clive Robertson, is helping clients develop the skills needed to survive within the financial restraints of the sector. **Clients:** Loughborough University; HE and FE colleges.

Reynolds Porter Chamberlain (see firm details p.1106) Known for its work with unions and schools, but also adding more HE and FE clients to its roster. Geraldine Elliot heads a team well versed in employment law for this field, it also boasts expertise in commercial, contractual and liability matters. Through its insurance practice, it also has experience of litigation and educational negligence. **Clients:** ATL; NASUWT.

Farrer & Co (see firm details p.954) Keeps its strong reputation in the independent schools sector. Perceived by sources to be "*a good quality firm with good quality clients,*" the education range now extends from schools to FEs to universities. The "*excellent team*" is headed by the respected **Henry Boyd-Carpenter** (see p.302) and its expertise includes employment, governance issues and student matters. Also involved in advice on human rights and information technology. **Clients:** Eton College; Westminster School; Independent School's Council.

FIRMS ACTING FOR INDIVIDUALS

EDUCATION: INDIVIDUALS • London	Ptnrs	Assts
1 Teacher Stern Selby	1	2
2 Gills	1	1
Levenes	1	3
3 Ashok Patel & Co	2	1
Coningsbys	1	1
Fisher Meredith	1	1
John Ford Morrison	1	1

LEADING INDIVIDUALS	
1 **RABINOWICZ Jack** Teacher Stern Selby	
2 **RUEBAIN David** Levenes	**GILL Jaswinder** Gills
3 **CONRATHE Paul** Coningsbys	**FORD John** John Ford Morrison
WILKINS Patricia Fisher Meredith	

This book is the product of 6,552 1/2-hour interviews. See p.7 for BMRB audit.

Within each band, firms are listed alphabetically. *See individuals' profiles p.302*

Teacher Stern Selby (see firm details p.1151) "*The first players in the field.*" Clearly the most respected firm, with a tremendous local and national reputation. Known for representing pupils and parents in such matters as bullying, admissions and special educational needs. **Jack Rabinowicz** (see p.59) is acknowledged by the market as the "*driving force in the sector*" and the firm is regarded as "*the leading education law practice.*" It also has specialist knowledge of educational negligence, thanks to its involvement in the landmark House of Lords ruling on the Phelps case.

Gills (see firm details p.972) Carved itself a niche thanks to the large amount of work it does in the HE sector, although it does have a client roster that includes FE students. Active in issues across the sector, from expulsions to re-marking. **Jaswinder Gill** (see p.303) "*has a good name on the student front,*" according to our interviewees with expertise on educational negligence and judicial reviews. Currently working on cases dealing with human rights issues and universities.

Levenes (see firm details p.1039) A strong practice with a "*particular interest in disability law,*" the majority of its work relates to special education needs, capitalising on the interest in educational negligence since the Phelps judgment. All aspects of educational litigation are represented, from bullying and exclusions to curriculum issues. **David Ruebain** (see p.304) heads the team and is judged to have "*a good approach to education law.*"

Ashok Patel & Co A new firm to this year's guide, recommended for its strength in exclusions and special educational needs. The firm, under the guidance of Anjan Patel, also carries out work in bullying, educational negligence and race discrimination.

Coningsbys (see firm details p.924) High profile **Paul Conrathe** leads a team that has a growing reputation in the market. Primarily focused on special education cases, with particular attention paid to autism and ADHD. Active right across the education field – including bullying, student grants, disciplinary matters and educational negligence.

Fisher Meredith (see firm details p.959) Maintains its profile in the education sector, with a team that primarily handles special needs and disability. There has been a growth in cases of access to schools, exclusions and educational negligence. The team is headed by **Patricia Wilkins** (see p.304), who is seen to have a common sense approach.

John Ford Morrison Primarily acting for parents and children in special needs, in which it has instigated a number of judicial reviews. The "*professional*" **John Ford**, heads a team that also deals with exclusion, dyslexia and educational negligence work.

THE SOUTH

FIRMS ACTING FOR INSTITUTIONS

EDUCATION: INSTITUTIONS • The South	Ptnrs	Assts
1 **Bond Pearce** Southampton	2	3
DMH Brighton	3	3
Steele Raymond Bournemouth	2	n/a
Thomas Eggar Church Adams Chichester	2	2

This book is the product of 6,552 1/2-hour interviews. See p.7 for BMRB audit.

Within each band, firms are listed alphabetically.

Bond Pearce (see firm details p.888) Providing a full range of legal services to a wide selection of FE and HE colleges, it is recognised for its expertise in employment. The team, led by Nick Barwood, has a reputation for being able to "*cut through the Byzantine.*" Recent highlights include the restructuring of Isle of Wight College. **Clients:** University of Southampton; Farnborough College; Isle of Wight College.

DMH (see firm details p.944) Established firm, which acts in the HE and schools sector. Able to offer support in areas from property to student disputes, the team including Martin Allen has "*developed a great expertise in IT law.*" Strong in the local area, it is regarded by peers as having an understanding of "*the complexity of education law.*" **Clients:** University of Sussex; Diocese of Arundel and Brighton; Windlesham School.

Steele Raymond (see firm details p.1141) Has a strong local presence, with interests in representing both individuals and institutions. Peter Rolfe heads a group that handles a range of contentious and non-contentious matters, including employment, property and contract work. **Clients:** Bournemouth University.

Thomas Eggar Church Adams (see firm details p.1153) The firm retains its reputation in the HE and independent schools sector, but also has a growing amount of FE work. Peter Stevens and his team cover all aspects of education law, including employment, commercial, property and student work. Its advice is described by interviewees as "*a thousand percent accurate.*" **Clients:** University College, Chichester; Hastings College; Christ's Hospital.

FIRMS ACTING FOR INDIVIDUALS

EDUCATION: INDIVIDUALS • The South	Ptnrs	Assts
1 **Blake Lapthorn** Fareham	1	n/a

See individuals' profiles p.302

Blake Lapthorn (see firm details p.886) A new firm to this section, but one which has carved a niche for itself and is seen to have "*a fine education practice.*" Sarah Palmer and her team deal with all issues for parents and pupils, from exclusion and educational negligence, to failure to provide school transport.

THAMES VALLEY

FIRMS ACTING FOR INSTITUTIONS

EDUCATION: INSTITUTIONS • Thames Valley	Ptnrs	Assts
1 Manches Oxford	2	1
Morgan Cole Oxford	1	4
Winckworth Sherwood Oxford	1	1

This book is the product of 6,552 1/2-hour interviews. See p.7 for BMRB audit.
Within each band, firms are listed alphabetically.

Manches (see firm details p.1051) A strong reputation within the HE sector, known for its work with the Oxford colleges. Clients include universities, FEs and independent schools. Under the guidance of Daff Richardson, the team provides advice on constitutional issues, student and staff discipline matters, risk assessment, employment and property work. The firm's commercial practice is active in joint ventures, research contracts, IT/IP and spin-off companies in this sector. Clients: 24 Oxford Colleges.

Morgan Cole (see firm details p.1074) A large practice led by Robert Breedon, which acts for a range of universities, FE colleges and private schools. Experienced in college take-overs and hi-tech companies, while developing an interest in project work, including PFI/PPPs. **Clients:** Oxford Brooks University; Weymouth College; Dragon School.

Winckworth Sherwood (see firm details p.1185) Continues its focus within the religious schools sector, advising trustees and governors of over 300 church schools and several private schools. The team, led by John Rees, has a growing secular school practise. Active across the board, from admissions and exclusions to employment issues, the firm is also developing an expertise in privatisation matters. **Clients:** Oxford Diocesan Board of Education; 3Es.

SOUTH WEST

FIRMS ACTING FOR INSTITUTIONS

EDUCATION: INSTITUTIONS • South West	Ptnrs	Assts
1 Veale Wasbrough Bristol	4	10
2 Stone King Bath	2	2
3 Michelmores Exeter	n/a	n/a
Rickerby Watterson Cheltenham	3	1
4 Tozers Exeter	1	1
5 Bevan Ashford Bristol	2	3
Bond Pearce Plymouth	3	1
Osbourne Clarke	1	1

LEADING INDIVIDUALS	
1 BOYD Robert Veale Wasbrough	GOLD Richard Stone King
2 DICKINSON Malcolm Michelmores	KING Michael Stone King

This book is the product of 6,552 1/2-hour interviews. See p.7 for BMRB audit.
Within each band, firms are listed alphabetically. *See individuals' profiles p.302*

Veale Wasbrough (see firm details p.1167) A national reputation through its work with independent schools, it is able to offer "*specialist cover in all areas.*" Active on employment, property, charity, IP and various student issues, the firm has started to offer advice on the international stage. Headed by the "*charismatic*" **Robert Boyd** (see p.302), the "*expert*" team continues to consolidate its high profile. **Clients:** Independent schools; FE colleges.

Stone King (see firm details p.1145) Well established, thanks to its strength in the schools sector and the national reputation of its leading partners; **Richard Gold** is perceived as "*outstanding*" while **Michael King** maintains his high profile. Clients include state and maintained schools and the firm's workload ranges from admissions and staff discipline to mergers and redevelopments. Although primarily seen as a religious schools practice, it represents the whole FE and independent Schools sector. **Clients:** Independent Schools; Maintained Schools; FE colleges.

Michelmores (see firm details p.1066) Respected team, headed by the "*clear thinking*" **Malcolm Dickinson**, looking after a broad range of clients including FE and private and Anglican schools, sources agree it has "*a good expertise in HE areas.*" It has experience in property matters, fund-raising, JVs, commercial spin off arrangements, employment and student complaints. **Clients:** HE institutions; FE institutions.

Rickerby Watterson (see firm details p.1108) Impressive practice with a good reputation in independent schools, and a growing portfolio of HE and FE clients. John Clarke's team is involved in employment, governance, restructuring, IT and parent's rights, and was instructed in a large land deal for a leading local college. **Clients:** Cheltenham College; Edgbaston High School.

Tozers (see firm details p.1160) A schools practice which counts foundation, independent and voluntary-aided schools as clients, offering advice on restructuring, charity and child protection. It is recommended by competitors as having a particular expertise in employment. The team, guided by Richard King, acts in special education needs cases. **Clients:** The Diocese Of Plymouth.

Bevan Ashford (see firm details p.880) A strong interest in property and PFI sectors, this established practice is praised by clients for its "*jargon free*" expertise in employment and commercial work. Although known for its work in the FE sector, the team, which includes Sarah Billington, now receives instruction from HEs and schools across the country. **Clients:** Newbury College; Canterbury College; Falmouth College of Arts.

Bond Pearce (see firm details p.888) "*Responsive*" educational department which includes Nikki Duncan, acts for a mainly FE client base and a growing HE roster. Wide range of work including outsourcing and procurement, employment, tax advice, charity issues and property matters. **Clients:** University College of St Mark & St John; St Austel College; Cornwall College.

Osborne Clarke (see firm details p.1086) An active firm in the HE sector, the team including Joachim Steinbach delivers a speciality in tax matters for the local institutions. Has experience of giving broadly based commercial and compliance advice to universities. **Clients:** University of Bath; University of Bristol; University of Plymouth.

EDUCATION: INDIVIDUALS • South West	Ptnrs	Assts
1 **AE Smith & Son** Stroud	1	2
LEADING INDIVIDUALS		
1 **LOVE Robert** AE Smith & Son		

This book is the product of 6,552 1/2-hour interviews. See p.7 for BMRB audit.
Within each band, firms are listed alphabetically. *See individuals' profiles p.302*

FIRMS ACTING FOR INDIVIDUALS

AE Smith & Son (see firm details p.1135) A nationally rated practice led by **Robert Love**, "*the foremost authority in the country.*" The team has an interest in special education needs, particularly advising dyslexic children. Other areas include exclusion/admission appeals and educational negligence.

WALES

FIRMS ACTING FOR INSTITUTIONS

EDUCATION: INSTITUTIONS • Wales	Ptnrs	Assts
1 **Eversheds** Cardiff	2	–
2 **Morgan Cole** Cardiff	n/a	n/a

This book is the product of 6,552 1/2-hour interviews. See p.7 for BMRB audit.
Within each band, firms are listed alphabetically.

Eversheds (see firm details p.952) "*A large firm able to draw on a range of expertise rapidly,*" Eversheds maintains its domination of the Welsh market, representing one third of FEs and one half of HEs. The department, including Kim Howell, undertake traditional issues such as property, employment and student matters, as well as an increased amount of IT/IP and PFI work. Recently appointed to act for the General Teaching Council of Wales. **Clients:** University of Glamorgan; Cardiff University; GTCW.

Morgan Cole (see firm details p.1074) Long established education group covers a wide range of work, from constitutional/governance issues to commercial and IP work and PFI/PPP. **Clients:** Swansea University, St Michael's college, Bridgend College.

FIRMS ACTING FOR INDIVIDUALS

EDUCATION: INDIVIDUALS • Wales	Ptnrs	Assts
1 **Hugh James Ford Simey** Cardiff	1	n/a
Russell Jones & Walker Cardiff	1	n/a
Sinclairs Penarth	1	n/a
LEADING INDIVIDUALS		
1 **IMPERATO Michael** Russell Jones & Walker		

This book is the product of 6,552 1/2-hour interviews. See p.7 for BMRB audit.
Within each band, firms are listed alphabetically. *See individuals' profiles p.302*

Hugh James Ford Simey (see firm details p.1004) Recommended practice for special education needs, representing pupils and parents. Michael Jones' group handles cases in admissions, exclusions, educational negligence, ADHD and has a particular focus on dyslexia issues.

Russell Jones & Walker (see firm details p.1116) Headed by the "*able*" **Michael Imperato** (see p.303), who sources agree holds "*a good reputation outside of Wales,*" the established team acts for pupils in cases of special needs, admissions and educational negligence.

Sinclairs "*Busy*" education practice led by Michael Charles, it handles a full range of work for pupils and parents, from special education needs, to bullying and transport matters.

MIDLANDS

FIRMS ACTING FOR INSTITUTIONS

EDUCATION: INSTITUTIONS • Midlands	Ptnrs	Assts
1 **Martineau Johnson** Birmingham	2	2
2 **Eversheds** Derby, Nottingham	1	8
3 **Shakespeares** Birmingham	2	1
Wragge & Co Birmingham	n/a	n/a
LEADING INDIVIDUALS		
1 **PHARAOH Paul** Martineau Johnson		
2 **HART Nicola** Martineau Johnson		

This book is the product of 6,552 1/2-hour interviews. See p.7 for BMRB audit.
Within each band, firms are listed alphabetically. *See individuals' profiles p.302*

Martineau Johnson (see firm details p.1055) "*The prime firm in the Midlands,*" it continues to be a national force in the HE sector, with a growing roster of FE clients. The "*exceptional*" **Nicola Hart** (see p.303) rises in the rankings this year, thanks to her profile in HE work. Respected **Paul Pharoah** (see p.303) continues his work in the FE field. A comprehensive service offered includes property, employment, litigation, finance and IP. **Clients:** Aston & Birmingham Universities; Coventry Universities.

Eversheds (see firm details p.952) A large FE practice recommended for offering "*expertise across the board,*" with particular strengths in employment, student matters, PFI and hi-tech spin-off ventures. Nigel Sternberg's team has seen a growth in the number of HEs and schools it now represents. **Clients:** Sandwell College; Nottingham Trent University; University of Derby.

Shakespeares (see firm details p.1122) Acts for a mix of FEs, HEs and foundation schools, offering a wide range of support, from employment and contract matters to student discipline. The team led by Anthony Jones has recently increased its interest in the commerciality issues in education. **Clients:** University of Central England; Technology and Information Centre; Great Barr Foundation School.

Wragge & Co (see firm details p.1189) Endorsed by peers as a "*no nonsense*" education practice acting in the FE sector. Offering across-the-board service, with expertise in property, education and IT/IP. Phillip Clisset's team is supported by the firm's strong commercial base which provides advice in trading subsidiaries, EU law implications and mergers. **Clients:** Walsall College; Tameside College; Sutton Coldfield College.

FIRMS ACTING FOR INDIVIDUALS

EDUCATION: INDIVIDUALS • Midlands	Ptnrs	Assts
1 **Young & Lee** Birmingham	1	n/a

See individuals' profiles p.302

Young & Lee Respected local firm that handles special education, admission, bullying and educational negligence. Phil Storey has undertaken a number of judicial reviews and high court appeals handled for pupils and parents in the last year.

EAST ANGLIA

EDUCATION: INSTITUTIONS • East Anglia	Ptnrs	Assts
1 **Mills & Reeve** Cambridge, Norwich	5	10
2 **Eversheds** Ipswich, Norwich	3	8
3 **Birkett Long** Colchester	2	n/a
Wollastons Chelmsford	2	n/a

LEADING INDIVIDUALS
1 **STANFIELD Glynne** Mills & Reeve
2 **GEORGE Philip** Birkett Long
UP AND COMING
ATTLE Gary Mills & Reeve

This book is the product of 6,552 1/2-hour interviews. See p.7 for BMRB audit.
Within each band, firms are listed alphabetically. *See individuals' profiles p.302*

Mills & Reeve (see firm details p.1069) Top rated HE firm, with a national reputation and a large amount of work drawn from outside the region. **Glynne Stanfield** (see p.304), "*one of the prime experts in the field*" is supported by an able team which includes "*up and coming name*" **Gary Attle** (see p.302). A full range of legal services is available, including property, employment, student disputes and tax schemes. Recently the team has had high profile cases in mergers and educational spin-outs. **Clients:** Imperial College; UEA; University of Portsmouth.

Eversheds (see firm details p.952) The leading FE practice in the region, which acts for 20 out of 28 FE colleges, as well as a number of independent schools and HEs. Alongside mainstream employment, property, governance and commercial contract work, the team with David Woods at the helm has experience in advising on mitigation of VAT and IT matters. It also enjoys a good reputation for "*local offices with access to national expertise.*" **Clients:** Downing College; University College Suffolk; Association of Colleges in the Eastern Region.

Birkett Long (see firm details p.885) Maintains its reputation within the local independent schools sector, and has an added focus on HEs and FEs. Exclusions, admissions and appeals are undertaken with expertise in governance and commercial issues. Headed by the well regarded **Phillip George** (see p.303), the team also does exclusions work for pupils and parents. **Clients:** University of Essex; Colchester Institute; Thurrock College.

Wollastons (see firm details p.1188) A local education practice with a client roster that includes FEs and independent schools. Alongside Nicholas Cook, the team provides services in property, commercial and financing contracts with a particular experience in employment. **Clients:** FEs; schools.

THE NORTH

FIRMS ACTING FOR INSTITUTIONS

EDUCATION: INSTITUTIONS • The North	Ptnrs	Assts
1 **Eversheds** Leeds, Manchester, Newcastle upon Tyne	6	15
2 **Addleshaw Booth & Co** Manchester	4	7
Pinsent Curtis Biddle Leeds	5	8

LEADING INDIVIDUALS
1 **BOARDMAN John** Eversheds

This book is the product of 6,552 1/2-hour interviews. See p.7 for BMRB audit.
Within each band, firms are listed alphabetically. *See individuals' profiles p.302*

Eversheds (see firm details p.952) Boasts a substantial HE and FE practice, and a strong reputation within schools work. Handles a range of employment, student matters, governance and commercial issues (such as spin-off companies and IP exploitation.) "*Expert*" **John Boardman** (see p.302) heads a team that has established "*a great name in this area.*" Highlights of the past year include advising the Government's LearnDirect initiative. **Clients:** University of Manchester; University of York; University of Newcastle upon Tyne.

Addleshaw Booth & Co (see firm details p.853) Retains an active presence in education with a national reputation. A strong profile in HEs, FEs and independent schools, the firm also acts for a selection of public bodies. The team, including Michael O'Connor, advises on matters including governance, finance, employment, commercial contracts and grant funding, although the focus remains on PFI/PPP. **Clients:** University of Lancaster; Royal Northern College of Music; Victoria University of Manchester.

Pinsent Curtis Biddle (see firm details p.1098) Known within the field for its expertise on employment matters, the firm has a client base of FE colleges and HE institutions, with experience of PFI for both. The team, led by Dr John McMullen, is an advisor for the Department of Education and Employment. Highlights include the successful defence of a number of significant employment tribunal cases. **Clients:** University of Birmingham; University of Leeds; University of Keele.

EDUCATION: INDIVIDUALS • The North	Ptnrs	Assts
1 **Elaine Maxwell & Co** Lancaster	1	2

LEADING INDIVIDUALS
1 **MAXWELL Elaine** Elaine Maxwell & Co

This book is the product of 6,552 1/2-hour interviews. See p.7 for BMRB audit.
Within each band, firms are listed alphabetically. *See individuals' profiles p.302*

FIRMS ACTING FOR INDIVIDUALS

Elaine Maxwell & Co Nationally recognised practice with expertise in special education needs, it also handles exclusion and disciplinary matters for HE/FE students. Former barrister, **Elaine Maxwell**, "*talks business*" and has developed a great reputation in this field.

SCOTLAND

FIRMS ACTING FOR INSTITUTIONS

EDUCATION: INSTITUTIONS • Scotland	Ptnrs	Assts
1 **Dundas & Wilson CS** Edinburgh	n/a	n/a
2 **Anderson Strathern WS** Edinburgh	3	1
Maclay Murray & Spens Glasgow	3	7

This book is the product of 6,552 1/2-hour interviews. See p.7 for BMRB audit.
Within each band, firms are listed alphabetically.

Dundas & Wilson CS (see firm details p.947) "*Still the top firm in Scotland,*" according to our interviewees boasting a range of important clients in HE, FE and school sectors. Brian Leggat's team is boosted by its experience of representing a number of professional bodies. Experienced in funding, employment, commerciality issues, PFI/PPP schemes and human resources matters. **Clients:** University of Glasgow; University of Stirling; Dollar Academy.

Anderson Strathern WS (see firm details p.859) An established presence in the schools market, the department, headed by Alasdair Fox, is perceived to be expert on employment issues, with an added focus on disciplinary and constitutional issues. Represents a number of HEs, operating a full range of advice on property and commercial issues and undertakes pupil claims against education authorities. One highlight was the drafting of an amendment to the Standards in Scottish Schools Bill, which was accepted by the Scottish Executive. **Clients:** Napier University; Fettes College; Mary Erskine School Edinburgh.

Maclay Murray & Spens (see firm details p.1047) Under the guidance of Fiona Nicholson, the firm represents HE institutions and FE colleges, with focus on commercialisation matters. Examples include PFI, exploitation of IP rights in high-tech projects, university spin-out companies, outsourcing, joint ventures and employment issues. **Clients:** Paisley University; Robert Gordon University; Higher Education Quality Council.

FIRMS ACTING FOR INDIVIDUALS

EDUCATION: INDIVIDUALS • Scotland	Ptnrs	Assts
1 **Campbell Smith WS** Edinburgh	n/a	1

See individuals' profiles p.302

Campbell Smith WS Special educational needs practice which acts for pupils and parents in record of needs appeals and refusal of placement appeals. The team, which includes Matthew Clark, also has expertise in judicial reviews, exclusions and bullying work.

LEADERS IN EDUCATION

ATTLE, Gary
Mills & Reeve, Cambridge 01223 222 394
gary.attle@mills-reeve.com
Specialisation: Acts for universities and colleges in contentious matters; appeals to the Visitor; discrimination claims; judicial review proceedings; defamation actions; injunctions. Advises on governance and liability issues. Clients include University of Cambridge; Imperial College; LSE; Quality Assurance Agency; Association of Colleges.
Prof. Memberships: Education Law Association; Universities and Colleges Education Law Network.
Career: Trained *Mills and Reeve*, qualified 1992, partner 1999, trained as mediator 1996.
Personal: Born 1968; resides Cambridge. Education: Westbourne High School Ipswich; Lincoln College, Oxford (1st class in law). Leisure: young family, church, sport.

BEESLEY, Peter
Lee Bolton & Lee, London (020) 7222 5381

BOARDMAN, John
Eversheds, Manchester (0161) 831 8000 / (0113) 243 0391 (Leeds)
johnboardman@eversheds.com
Specialisation: Partner in education law department. Principal area of work is education law advising higher education, further education and schools. Also advises other non-profit making bodies.
Prof. Memberships: ELAS, Charity Law Association, Justice, Affiliate of Institute of Risk Management.
Career: Qualified 1979 while at *Alexander Tatham*, now *Eversheds* and became a partner in 1986.
Publications: Contributes articles to various specialist education law journals and gives numerous lectures and seminars on these areas.
Personal: Born 26th July 1955. Attended Manchester Grammar School 1966-73 and Downing College, Cambridge 1973-76. Former Governor of a further education college. Forum Member of an EAZ. Leisure pursuits include pottery, bats, films, books, music and guinea pigs. Lives in Mellor, Derbyshire.

BOYD, Robert
Veale Wasbrough, Bristol (0117) 925 2020
rboyd@vwl.co.uk
Specialisation: Partner and head of schools team. Partner in charge of the education department which has advised more than 600 independent schools in the UK and abroad and some special and grant maintained schools in the last decade. Author of textbook 'Independent Schools: Law, Custom and Practice' (Jordans, 1988) and 'Running a School Boarding House' (BSA, 2000) and of the Parent Contract and numerous other education templates and articles on education issues. Advises schools in matters of governance, management, structural change, incorporation, charity and trust issues, the parent contract and many other concerns. An invited speaker at seminars all over the country for HMC, GBA, IAPS, GSA, and SHMIS.
Prof. Memberships: Bristol Law Society; Bristol Medico-Legal Society; Education Law Association.
Career: Qualified 1972. Joined *Veale Wasbrough* as a partner in 1988. Council of Bristol Law Society 1986-88; Council Member of Academy of Experts 1989; Co-opted to Judicial committee 1992.
Personal: Born 1946. Stonyhurst College 1960-65 and Birmingham University 1966-69.

BOYD-CARPENTER, Henry
Farrer & Co, London (020) 7242 2022
hbc@farrer.co.uk
Specialisation: Acts for educational institutions in the secondary and tertiary sectors.
Prof. Memberships: Law Society, Holborn Law Society.
Career: Joined *Farrer & Co* in 1962. Qualified in 1966, became a partner in 1968. Private solicitor to the Queen since 1995. Solicitor to the Duchy of Cornwall 1976-94.
Personal: Born 11 October 1939. Educated at Charterhouse 1953-58 and Balliol College, Oxford 1959-62. School governor and charity trustee. Member of the board of the British Library since 1999 and chairman of the governing body of Charterhouse. Trustee and council member of many charities: the Merlin Trust, Sutton's Hospital, the Chelsea Physic Garden, the Institute of Cancer Research among several others. Enjoys reading, music, hill walking and gardening. Lives in Ascot, Berkshire.

CAREW-JONES, Owen
Winckworth Sherwood, London (020) 7593 5034
ocarew-jones@winckworths.co.uk
Specialisation: Education and employment, mainly acting for institutions eg Governing Bodies and Diocesan Boards. Acted for Governors in Court of Appeal cases ex p C and ex parte L on the meaning of reinstatement after a permanent exclusion.
Prof. Memberships: Law Society, Education Law Association.
Career: Qualified teacher. Trainee, then solicitor, now partner with *Winckworth Sherwood*.
Publications: Various articles eg 'Infant Class Size

Prejudice in Education', 'Public Law and the Individual'.
Personal: MA (Cantab). Married with three children.

CONRATHE, Paul
Coningsbys, Croydon (020) 8680 5575

DICKINSON, Malcolm K
Michelmores, Exeter (01392) 436244

FORD, John
John Ford Morrison, London (020) 8800 6464

GEORGE, Philip
Birkett Long, Colchester (01206) 217300
philipg@birkettlong.co.uk
Specialisation: Partner in company commercial department. Advises a university, further education and sixth form colleges and a wide range of foundation and independent schools on contractual and constitutional issues, and upon the interpretation of statutes.
Prof. Memberships: Education Law Association. Fellow of the Society for Advanced Legal Studies.
Career: Qualified April 1975. Partner since 1976. Heads the firm's education unit.

GILL, Jaswinder
Gills, Southall (020) 8893 6869
jgill@gills-solicitors.co.uk
Specialisation: Offers expert legal advice in protecting and promoting students' legal rights in the law of higher education. Has gained a nation-wide reputation as the leading lawyer in the country in this area in challenging local authorities and universities, previously being unfamiliar territory. Set up his own firm to offer specialist guidance and advice for students aggrieved by decisions made by the above bodies. Also involved in bringing about a greater sense of awareness of legal remedies available to students within a complex framework of education law. Many cases involve novel issues and will have a strong element of wider public importance issues for all students. Specialises in challenging (a) local authorities' decisions refusing discretionary and mandatory awards in the area of student funding and (b) decisions made by universities/colleges regarding examination results, by way of judicial review proceedings. In respect of the latter, also handles cases involving damages for breach of contract and/or negligence. Also focuses on judicial review proceedings within the education field embracing statements of special educational needs and appeals, exclusion appeals and admissions.
Publications: Co-author of the recent publication 'Universities and Students' (2001) specifically dealing with the growing number of legal actions by students against universities. This book contains live case studies handled by Jaswinder Gill as well as providing an up to date and authoritative guide to student's rights and remedies with regard to the law and procedure in higher education.

GIZZI, Julian
Beachcroft Wansbroughs, London (020) 7242 1011
jgizzi@bwlaw.co.uk
Specialisation: Partner, head of public law department. All aspects of education law including funding matters, incorporations, mergers, learning difficulties, enquiries, judicial reviews and e-learning.
Prof. Memberships: Law Society.
Career: Qualified in 1981, having joined *Beachcroft Stanleys* in 1979. Became a partner in 1986. Member of the Structure and Governance Working Group of the National Committee of Inquiry into Higher Education. Fellow of the Royal Society of Arts. Member of the Admissions and Exclusions Appeals panel of the Schools' Commission.
Publications: Butterworth's 'Education Law Manual' (General Editor).
Personal: Born 13 February 1957. Educated at Downside School and Cambridge University. Lives in Little Chart, Kent.

GOLD, Richard
Stone King, Bath (01225) 337599

HALL, John
Eversheds, London (020) 7919 4500
hallj@eversheds.com
Specialisation: Partner and chairman of *Eversheds* education group. Work includes governance, the Education Acts, employment law, industrial relations, judicial review, the student relationships, commercial law, funding and asset management. Clients include in excess of 200 education institutions, mainly universities and colleges of higher and further education. Also handles company/commercial and employment and constitutional advice for professional and other bodies.
Prof. Memberships: Law Society, Chair of the Further and Higher Education Group of Education Law Association, Fellow of the Royal Society of Arts. Fellow of the Institute of Continuing Professional Development.
Career: Qualified in 1975. Partner at *Wedlake Saint* 1978-93. Chair, London Young Solicitors' Group, 1985; Company Secretary, Polytechnics and Colleges Employers' Forum, 1988; Governor, Barnet College of Further Education, 1992; Company Secretary, Colleges' Employers' Forum, 1992; Council Member of the Royal College of Music (1999) and governor of Lochinver House School (1999). Joined *Eversheds* in 1994 as a partner.
Publications: General Editor 'Purposive Governance - an annotated guidance for further education colleges' (Sweet & Maxwell). Contributor to 'Education and the Law', the 'Times Education Supplement' and education press. Author of further and higher education module in University of Buckingham Postgraduate Diploma in Education Law and contributor on 'Higher Education and the Law' (Open University Press) and The Journal of College and University Law (the National Association of College and University Attorneys).
Personal: Born 23rd December 1948. College Governor. Leisure interests include walking, music, history, art and Spain. Lives in Hadley Wood, Barnet, Herts.

HART, Nicola
Martineau Johnson, Birmingham (0121) 678 1311
nicola.hart@martjohn.com
Specialisation: Partner and head of *Martineau Johnson*'s education practice. Leads specialist education team and the firm's full service to university and college clients. Practice covers a wide range of work, from institutional mergers, joint ventures and international work, to disputes with students and academic staff and judicial review. A regular speaker at education sector conferences and seminars, and contributes articles to education law and trade publications.
Career: Qualified 1988, *Le Brasseurs*; joined *Martineau Johnson* 1989; partner since 1995; head of education since 1997.
Publications: Introduction and chapters on student issues in 'Higher Education and the Law: A Guide for Managers', Open University Press, 1998. 'Teacher Stress: the consequences of harassment and bullying', Monitor Press, 2000.
Personal: Born 1962. Educated Worcester Girls Grammar School and Jesus College, Oxford. Director, Midlands Arts Centre.

IMPERATO, Michael
Russell Jones & Walker, Cardiff (029) 20262 800
Specialisation: Education law and claimant personal injury. Acts particularly for children with special educational needs. Receives referrals from several charities. Recently represented parents group challenging Cardiff Council's Welsh medium schools admissions policy. Also instructed in exclusion cases and education negligence. Undertakes legal aid work with education law franchise. Written articles, presented seminars and lectured on education law at University of Glamorgan. Member of Law Society Personal Injury panel, LSE appeals committee and National Education Forum..
Prof. Memberships: ELAS - Convenor for Wales & West, APIL, PEOPIL, ATLA, Law Society.
Career: Qualified 1990 with *Hugh James*, Cardiff. 1994-97 *Gabb & Co*, Abergavenny. Joined *RJW* 1997. Partner from 1999.
Personal: Born 24 May 1962. Education at Whitchurch High School, Cardiff and Reading University 1980-84. Taught history for two years. School governor. Interests include sport, politics and young family. Lives in Cardiff.

KING, Michael
Stone King, Bath (01225) 337599

LOVE, Robert
AE Smith & Son, Stroud (01453) 757444

MAXWELL, Elaine
Elaine Maxwell & Co, Lancaster (01524) 840810

PHARAOH, Paul
Martineau Johnson, Birmingham (0121) 678 1314
paul.pharaoh@martjohn.com
Specialisation: Partner in education department. Handles contractual, property-related and constitutional issues for higher and further education institutions and schools. Speaker on education law and judicial review at various conferences and seminars.
Prof. Memberships: Law Society, ELAS.
Career: Qualified in 1971. Joined *Bettinsons* in 1969, becoming partner in 1973. Partner in *Shakespeares* on merger 1990. Partner in *Martineau Johnson* 1996. Law Society council member since 1990. Midlands convenor for Education Law Association. Member of West Cumbria College Corporation.
Publications: Author of articles in various legal journals, chapters on judicial review in 'Higher Education and the Law' and on due diligence in 'Managing Mergers', and module on law affecting pupils in school for University of Buckingham Diploma in Education Law. Member of editorial advisory board, 'Education Law Journal'.
Personal: Born 1947. Attended Manchester University 1965-68 and Liverpool College of Commerce 1968-69. FRSA.

RABINOWICZ, Jack
Teacher Stern Selby, London (020) 7242 3191
j.rabinowicz@tsslaw.com
See under Administrative & Public Law, p.59

RICHENS, Nicholas
Lee Bolton & Lee, London (020) 7222 5381

RUEBAIN, David
Levenes, London (020) 8881 7777
info@davidlevene.co.uk
Specialisation: The Department specialises in all aspects of education law, health law, community care law and disability discrimination. He has published and taught extensively on education and disability law and is co-author of 'Notes on the Disability Discrimination Act' (now in its 9th edition), co-author of 'Taking Action, a Guide for Parents of Children with Special Educational Needs', co-author of 'Education Law and Practice' and co-author of the forthcoming volume of Atkin's Court Forms volume on Education Law.
Prof. Memberships: Trustee of the Disability Discrimination Act Representation and Advice Project, Vice Chair of the Rights Now Campaign, a member of the Law Society's Mental Health and Disability Committee, a member of the editorial board of Disability and Society journal, Vice Chair of Disability Equality in Education, a member of the editorial board of Community Care Law Reports, a member of the Disability Rights Commission's Special Educational Needs and Disability Bill - Schools Duties Code of Practice Reference Group, and Honorary Legal Advisor to the Independent Panel for Special Education Advice.

STANFIELD, Glynne
Mills & Reeve, Cambridge (01223) 222250
glynne.stanfield@mills-reeve.com
Specialisation: Advises on wide range of corporate and commercial matters for higher education clients. This year he has advised on the merger between Imperial and Wye Colleges and the joint venture between the University of Cambridge and MIT. He also advises extensively on commercialisation of technology and this year has been involved in, for example, the spin outs of Ilotron for the University of Essex (£6 million start up), Gendel from the University of Ulster (£5 million start up) and the establishment of three University Challenge funds. He has a particular interest in the funding of higher education by conventional and unconventional/innovative financing methods including tax based schemes.

THATCHER, Michael
Winckworth Sherwood, London (020) 7593 5000
mcthatcher@winckworths.co.uk
Specialisation: Partner in education, ecclesiastical and charities department. Acts for voluntary aided schools, foundation schools, voluntary controlled schools, Church of England and Roman Catholic boards of education and finance, further education colleges and local education authorities. Also acts for charities, airlines, and in general commercial and property law. Has acted in Judicial Review of Appeal Committee decisions, all types of disciplinary and appeal hearings, and Commission for Racial Equality proceedings against Governors. Author of various editorials in the specialist press. Has spoken at a wide range of conferences and seminars on various aspects of education and employment law.
Prof. Memberships: Law Society; Ecclesiastical Law Association; Ecclesiastical Law Society; Education Law Association.
Career: Qualified in 1968. From 1969 to 1989 was clerk to the Governors of St Clement Danes School, to St Clement Danes Parochial Charities and to Isaac Ducketts Trustees. Registrar to the Diocese of Rochester, Joint Registrar to the Diocese of London, Chapter Clerk St Paul's Cathedral.
Personal: Born 19th May 1943. Attended Ardingly College 1956-60, then King's College, London 1961-64, and College of Law 1964-65. Clerk to the Worshipful Company of Cooks, Secretary to the Reunion des Gastronomes, Parish Councillor. Leisure interests include running, shooting, fishing and gardening. Lives outside Guildford.

WILKINS, Patricia
Fisher Meredith, London (020) 7622 4468
patw@fishermeredith.co.uk
Specialisation: Head of education and community care department. Department specialises in education law, health law and all aspects of community care. She has a particular specialisation in special educational needs. Recent cases include R v Lambeth LBC ex p N, inadequate consultation on the closure of a special school; R v EFC and Bradford MBC ex p. Parkinson on overlapping responsibilities of LEAs and FEFCs; R (on the application of C) v Governors of B, school reinstatement of an excluded pupil. Founder member of Education Law Practitioners Group for practitioners acting on behalf of applicants/claimants.
Prof. Memberships: Education Law Association; Community Care Practitioners group, Legal Action.
Career: Admitted 1992. Developed specialism in education and community care before joining *Fisher Meredith* in 1997.
Personal: School governor.

EMPLOYEE SHARE SCHEMES

OVERVIEW: The ESS sector has increased in prominence, boosted by the introduction of the All Employee Share Ownership Plan and Enterprise Management Incentive Schemes. While the latter has proved extremely popular, particularly with hi-tech and start up entities, the former has been slower to take off. This specialist practice has benefited from the increased interest in all types of share options, although most firms still operate from within an integrated Tax, Pensions and Employment department. Once again Linklaters, guided by Janet Cooper, leads the table, closely followed by a tightly packed group. Competing with the best of them, Pinsent Curtis Biddle continues to dominate our regional table, building on their impressive national reputation and client base, with David Pett increasingly active in London. The increasing trend towards the globalisation of share scheme plans, supported by the development of the software that makes international schemes viable, has seen a sharp rise in the amount of international work available to London firms. Firms continue to work with and compete against accountancy firms and remuneration consultants, although the complexity of the sector and the perceived high prices charged, works in the law firms' favour.

RESEARCH APPROVED BY BMRB: *For this edition,* Chambers' *researchers conducted 6,552 interviews – 4,419 with law firms, 554 with barristers and 1,579 with clients.*

The validity of the research was scrutinised by BMRB International, who audited both the methodology and the results at our offices in July 2001. They interviewed Chambers' *researchers and cross-checked sample interviews. Details of the audit appear on page 7.*

LONDON

EMPLOYEE SHARE SCHEMES • London	Ptnrs	Assts
1 Linklaters	3	25
2 Freshfields Bruckhaus Deringer	3	7
Herbert Smith	2	4
Slaughter and May	2	5
3 Allen & Overy	4	12
Clifford Chance	3	9
4 Ashurst Morris Crisp	2	5
Field Fisher Waterhouse	1	2
Lovells	1	5
Norton Rose	1	5
5 Baker & McKenzie	1	2
Nicholson Graham & Jones	1	1
Travers Smith Braithwaite	1	4

LEADING INDIVIDUALS	
1 **CHAMBERLAIN Colin** Herbert Smith	**COHEN David** Norton Rose
COOPER Janet Linklaters	**EVANS Simon** Freshfields Bruckhaus
2 **CODRINGTON Eddie** Slaughter and May	**FENN Jonathan** Slaughter and May
MITCHELL Jocelyn Freshfields Bruckhaus	**TREMAINE Robin** Clifford Chance
3 **CROFT Anne** Linklaters	
4 **CHATER Stephen** Allen & Overy	**NICHOLL Victoria** Travers Smith
RANDALL Paul Ashurst Morris Crisp	**ROWLANDS-HEMPEL Graham** Linklaters
WHITEWRIGHT Louise Lovells	
5 **ALLEN Barbara** Ashurst Morris Crisp	**ELLERMAN Paul** Herbert Smith
INGLE Michael Baker & McKenzie	**JACOBS Michael** Nicholson Graham & Jones
MCCARTHY Paul Allen & Overy	**NUTTALL Graeme** Field Fisher Waterhouse
THOMPSON Kevin Clifford Chance	
UP AND COMING	
WATTS Sylvie Allen & Overy	

This book is the product of 6,552 1/2-hour interviews. See p.7 for BMRB audit.
Within each band, firms are listed alphabetically. *See individuals' profiles p.308*

Linklaters (see firm details p.1042) "*Undoubtedly the leader*" in the ESS market, building on its corporate client base with increasing amounts of standalone share work. "*Ambassador for the firm*" **Janet Cooper** (see p.308) continues to raise the "*strong team's*," commanding international profile, although some have expressed concern over the high assistant/partner ratio. Key players endorsed by interviewees include "*capable*" **Graham Rowlands-Hempel** (see p.310) and "*technical guru*" and tax specialist **Anne Croft** (see p.308) ("excellent and enthusiastic but occasionally terrifying.") Retaining its FTSE 250, Euro 300 and Fortune 500 client base, the group has a strong profile in the e-commerce market with blue-chips seeking to establish their own e-businesses. The roster includes Freeserve, Computacenter, Biomni, e.bookers and lastminute.com, as well as a number of foreign multi-national internet companies. The firm has developed its online service for international share plans, Blue Flag ESP, covering over 100 countries. Last year saw the practice involved in the implementation of international share plans for BP Amoco, Invensys and Allied Domecq. **Clients:** Invensys; SmithKline Beecham; Riversoft.

Freshfields Bruckhaus Deringer (see firm details p.964) Operating from the integrated employment, pensions and benefits team, it advises on the structure and design of share schemes and also in managing the impact of complex corporate transactions on share schemes in the UK and overseas. Supported by expertise throughout Europe and the Far East, the practice carries out work for a number of FTSE 100 clients and produces "*cutting edge*" work. The group advised Scottish Power on the implementation of an AESOP. **Simon Evans** (see p.309) *("knows his stuff inside out")* and the "*fearsomely good*" **Jocelyn Mitchell** (see p.309) operate a powerful double act. Both have strong tax backgrounds and are regarded by clients as leading lights in the share schemes field. **Clients:** Scottish Power; Prudential.

Herbert Smith (see firm details p.993) An impressive team home to the "*old man of the business*" **Colin Chamberlain** (see p.308) and recently bolstered by **Paul Ellerman** (see p.308) (ex-Clifford Chance) who "*knows his onions.*" The latter brings his international expertise to a team that handles both transactional and advisory work, defusing criticism from peers that the practice is "*a one man band.*" The group advised on the flotation of Bradford & Bingley and the demutualisation of the London Stock Exchange. It devised a new share option scheme for Associated British Foods, arranged a long term incentive plan for Hammerson and advised on share schemes during the Iceland Group's take-over of Booker and the reorganisation of Allied Zurich. **Clients:** Bradford & Bingley; London Stock Exchange; Iceland Group; Allied Zurich; BskyB; Associated British Foods; Dorling Kindersley; BG Group.

Slaughter and May (see firm details p.1135) Its corporate client base remains the firm's major strength, although it also has a broad range stand-alone practice. Operating from within the pensions and employment Department, both partners are also heavily involved in pension work and this generalist approach has led to concerns over resourcing in this field, but the calibre of the work remains unequivocally high. Clients agree that "*exceptional practitioner*" **Eddie Codrington** (see p.308) commands "*enormous respect*" and **Jonathan Fenn** (see p.309) ("*knows his stuff*") now spends the bulk of his time on share scheme work. The group advised on the Glaxo Wellcome/SmithKline Beecham merger, the flotation of Egg and the demerger of Williams plc. It also set up new employee benefits schemes for clients including Colt Telecom, Saatchi & Saatchi and Schroders plc. **Clients:** GlaxoSmithKline; Egg; Williams; Colt Telecom; Saatchi & Saatchi; Schroders.

Allen & Overy (see firm details p.856) Part of the integrated employee, pensions and incentives practice, the employee benefits group has recently added two partners and two assistants to the existing team led by the "*effective operator*" **Stephen Chater** (see p.308). **Paul McCarthy** (see p.309) and **Sylvie Watts** (see p.310) both come highly regarded from Garretts, and peers view their addition as "*beefing up*" a practice that some felt was "*not punching at its proper weight.*" Benefiting from its international network, the team has acted for UK and overseas, public and private companies on the development of employee share schemes as well as advising on service contracts and remuneration packages. The group provided transactional support to United News & Media (now United Business Media) on the sale of its TV assets (valued at £1.75 billion) to Granada Media and Burmah Castrol on its take-over by BP Amoco. **Clients:** United Business Media; Burmah Castrol; WPP Group; The Sage Group; Celltech.

Clifford Chance (see firm details p.919) The team led by the "*excellent*" **Robin Tremaine** (see p.310) offers a "*responsive and client focused, quality service.*" Supported by **Kevin Thompson** (see p.310) ("*technically superb*") it deals with all aspects of ESS benefiting from a network of global offices and its close association with the New Bridge Street Consultants. The group advised companies such as Standard Chartered, Energis and Sema on executive share schemes, major listed companies (including WS Atkins and Canary Wharf Group) on AESOPs and Woolwich on the share scheme aspects of its merger with Barclays. Internationally the group advised Getronics (Netherlands based global ICT services provider) on web-based stock employee share purchase plans in 16 countries and Diageo on granting all-employee savings-related share options to employees in 13 countries. **Clients:** Debenhams; Standard Chartered; Sema; Cookson; Energis; Whitbread; Unilever; WS Atkins; United News & Media; GKN; Reuters; British Energy; Arcadia; Diageo.

Ashurst Morris Crisp (see firm details p.866) In addition to its involvement in transactional work for Ashurst's corporate clients and others, the employee benefits practice continues to have significant stand-alone non-transactional work and advises on all aspects of share schemes and benefits. International share scheme plans account for a substantial proportion of the workload, with launches and rollouts taking place in over 40 countries. The team has also developed its hi-tech clientele during the year. Clients commend both the "*Jolly nice chap and technically good,*" **Paul Randall** (see p.310) and "*excellent*" new partner **Barbara Allen** (see p.308) but the practice retains a comparatively low profile in ESS work. The team advised on the acquisition by Atlantic Telecom of First Telecom, the merger of Exel with Ocean Group and on the £1.6 billion flotation of Carphone Warehouse. **Clients:** Exel; National Express; Imperial Tobacco; Royal & Sun Alliance Insurance Group.

Field Fisher Waterhouse (see firm details p.957) Originally a niche practice involved in associate worker ventures and employee ownership of private companies, the group has expanded due to the "*focus and hard work*" of head of employee benefits **Graeme Nuttall** (see p.309). The practice has built on its profile with technology firms and is building up global reward plan work. Nuttall "*knows his stuff*" and manages a core team of two assistants dealing exclusively with share schemes and related matters. The team continues to develop work for established private UK companies, advising various US Stock Exchange and NASDAQ companies on applying UK PAYE on option exercises following changes in UK law. **Clients:** Wilkin & Sons; Donald Insall Associates; Parc Technologies; Digex.

Lovells (see firm details p.1044) Dedicated share scheme unit with strong links to the tax team. **Louise Whitewright** (see p.310) is viewed by peers as "*focused and determined,*" and retains a high profile due in part due to her continuing role as secretary to the Share Scheme Lawyers Group. The "*strong*" practice does a mixture of transactional work and new scheme design for wide range of clients. It acted for Barclays in its acquisition of Woolwich, Baltimore Technologies on its acquisition of GTE Cyber Trust Solutions and Arjo Wiggins in sale to Worms. The group also advised Granada Group on the merger of Granada and Compass. **Clients:** Barclays; Baltimore Technologies; Arjo Wiggins; Appleton; Granada Group.

Norton Rose (see firm details p.1082) With "*leading light*" **David Cohen** (see p.308) at the helm, this practice continues to work on take-overs and flotations as well as setting up stand-alone schemes for both FTSE 100 and private companies. "*Excellent and popular*" Cohen continues as chairman of the Share Scheme Lawyers Group and assisted the Government and Inland Revenue advisory committee on the development of new tax-favoured employee share schemes. Despite being "*surprisingly small,*" the team advised on the share scheme aspects of Wanadoo's acquisition of Freeserve, the easyJet flotation and AXA's take-over of Sun Life. The group also acted for The Great Universal Stores on the launch of its savings related share option scheme for its UK and Irish employees. The firm has also developed an extranet service for clients. **Clients:** Airline Group; easyJet; Wanadoo; Great Universal Stores; AXA.

Baker & McKenzie (see firm details p.868) Operating as part of "*a truly global firm,*" the employee benefits practice acts for a number of multinational corporations, drawing on a network of overseas offices. The group advises on the employment, tax/national insurance implications of moving employees from one country to another and on the implementation in the UK of foreign share schemes or extending UK schemes to other countries. Two assistants support the "*charming*" but low profile **Michael Ingle** (see p.309). The firm advised Clariant on benefits issues arising from its acquisition of BTP and Bobst in its take-over of Fairfield Enterprises. **Clients:** Bobst; Staples International; Clariant; Nortel Networks; Towers Perrin Share Plan Services.

Nicholson Graham & Jones (see firm details p.1081) Known for its association with smaller quoted companies, the practice continues to strengthen its corporate finance capabilities, with a focus on e-commerce, new technology and sport. Head of share schemes, **Michael Jacobs** (see p.309) is "*very good at what he does*" and is well known as a founder member of the Share Scheme Lawyers Group and through his work on the Executive Committee of the Quoted Companies Alliance. The group advised Union on the disposal of WorldInvest Holdings, Arena Leisure on extensive revisions to its share schemes and Peel Hunt and Finelot on share schemes pre-AIM flotation. **Clients:** Arena Leisure; Peel Hunt; Finelot; Fastfill; Union; PWS Holdings; Sportech.

Travers Smith Braithwaite (see firm details p.1160) Building on a reputation in the area of private equity transactions, including MBOs and reconstructions, the practice has attracted a wide range of new client work, such as international employee share offers for larger private international groups whose shares are not traded. Continuing to advise corporate clients such as ntl and Beeson Gregory on innovative structures, the group was centrally involved in the sale of TDLi.com and Thomson Directories and the public-to-private bid for Fairview Holdings. Located within the tax department, the team works closely with the employment and pensions department. "*Particularly impressive*" **Victoria Nicholl** (see p.309) leads a small but respected team and has "*practicality and speaks in a language everyone can understand.*" **Clients:** Beeson Gregory; ntl; Universe Group; Kier Group.

THE REGIONS

EMPLOYEE SHARE SCHEMES • The Regions	Ptnrs	Assts
1 **Pinsent Curtis Biddle** Birmingham, Leeds	2	7
2 **Addleshaw Booth & Co** Leeds, Manchester	1	1
Eversheds Birmingham	1	6
Wragge & Co Birmingham	1	3
3 **Osborne Clarke OWA** Bristol	2	4
4 **Walker Morris** Leeds	1	3

LEADING INDIVIDUALS	
★ **PETT David** Pinsent Curtis Biddle	
1 **GREAVES Judith** Pinsent Curtis Biddle	
2 **GREEN Lawrence** Eversheds	**HAYES Richard** Addleshaw Booth & Co
3 **POOLE Kevin** Wragge & Co	**WOMERSLEY Mark** Osborne Clarke

This book is the product of 6,552 1/2-hour interviews. See p.7 for BMRB audit.
Within each band, firms are listed alphabetically. *See individuals' profiles p.308*

Pinsent Curtis Biddle (see firm details p.1098) By far the leading firm in the regions and, with the Biddle merger, an increasing presence in London. The team advises a broad range of clients, from multinationals and FTSE 100 to SMEs. "*Leading light, doyen*" **David Pett** (see p.310) is based in Birmingham although spends much of his time in London and is active in the Government Advisory Committee on Share Schemes. Both he and the highly respected **Judith Greaves** (see p.309) ("*intelligent and gives good advice*") are active on the Share Scheme Lawyers Group. "*High quality people*" with a strong tax background, the firm is considered by competitors across the UK as "*the one to aim at.*" It has seen an increase in private equity work and instructions from overseas multi-nationals. It advised Pace Micro Technology on share incentive issues including maturity of SAYE share option schemes and proposed US SAYE schemes, and Misys and ITNET on AESOPs. **Clients:** Misys; ITNET; Smith & Nephew; ScS Upholstery; Filtronic.

Addleshaw Booth & Co (see firm details p.853) Operating from the commercial services department, partner **Richard Hayes** (see p.309) is "*well known across the country,*" working closely with the firm's tax department and Avantages Consultancy. "*A good outfit,*" the team is dedicated to share scheme work and heavily involved in advising on the consequences for option holders of take-overs and mergers. Take-privates have formed a significant element of the practice including those of Joseph Holt and Peter Black Holdings. The group advised L Gardner Group and Direct Message on the demerger of Direct Message. **Clients:** 3i; Airtours; De Vere Group; N Brown Group.

Eversheds (see firm details p.952) Acting for over 60 listed companies from the FTSE 100, FTSE 350 and overseas, the team has built a substantial practice advising fledgling e-commerce businesses, and the technology and telecoms sectors. **Lawrence Green** (see p.309) ("*skilled and extremely good to deal with*") leads a team which is part of the firm's business tax group and draws on its Leeds, Manchester and Norwich offices. The group advised on introduction of share schemes at MG Rover under which 60% of the company is held on behalf of MG Rover employees and dealers. It also advised on the introduction of new schemes on the flotation of Actinic and ESS aspects of the proposed flotation of Jungle.com. **Clients:** MG Rover; Capital One; Britax International.

Wragge & Co (see firm details p.1189) The employee benefits team, which operates as part of a wider human resources team, (includes tax, employment and pensions) has doubled in size over the last year. Leading an "*impressive practice,*" **Kevin Poole** devotes most of his time to share scheme work with three assistants experienced in tailoring schemes for specific companies, divisions of businesses or individual employees. The group advised on the Thomson Travel agreed take-over by Pressuag AG and the Hill & Smith Holdings agreed take-over of Ash & Lacy. **Clients:** 3i Group; UBC Media Group; Recognition Systems Group.

Osborne Clarke (see firm details p.1086) The pensions and employee benefits unit is headed by the "*highly recommended*" **Mark Womersley** who, combines ESS with his pensions practice. The firm has an increased level of telecoms and new media clients and has seen a significant flow of work for the 3i Group. The firm has been active with new instructions from larger listed companies and in the use of offshore trustees on share scheme projects. It advised independent radio company GWR Group on share schemes, HP Bulmer Holdings on AESOP scheme and Malborough Stirling on the firm's flotation. **Clients:** 3i Group; HP Bulmer Holdings; GWR Group; Malborough Stirling; Redstone Telecoms; Prism Rail.

Walker Morris (see firm details p.1171) Working out of the firm's tax group, the team led by Peter Smart can also draw on corporate lawyers bringing in ESS work from an existing client base. It carried out a number of cross-border deals last year and set up approved and unapproved schemes for Tay Homes, and advised Homestyle and Cattles on share schemes. **Clients:** Tay Homes; Homestyle; Cattles.

SCOTLAND

EMPLOYEE SHARE SCHEMES • Scotland	Ptnrs	Assts
1 **MacRoberts** Glasgow	1	1
2 **Dundas & Wilson CS** Edinburgh	n/a	1
Maclay Murray & Spens Glasgow	1	2

LEADING INDIVIDUALS
1 **TROTTER Peter** MacRoberts
UP AND COMING
TURLEY Brendan Dundas & Wilson CS

This book is the product of 6,552 1/2-hour interviews. See p.7 for BMRB audit.
Within each band, firms are listed alphabetically. *See individuals' profiles p.308*

MacRoberts (see firm details p.1048) The pensions and employment team, led by the highly respected **Peter Trotter** (see p.632), operates from within a large employment department and can draw on a strong tax capacity within the group. It has put many EMIs and unapproved share schemes in place, expanding its customer base from smaller plcs and private companies. It advised on the corporate restructuring of Weir & McQuiston (Scotland) and Sigtronics to put in place EMI options, unapproved share options and employee trusts and on the winding up of Strathclyde Buses Employment Trust. **Clients:** Sigtronics; Weir & McQuiston.

Dundas & Wilson CS (see firm details p.947) As part of Arthur Andersen's worldwide network it has acted for companies listed on NASDAQ and NYSE, alongside its AIM, LSE and EASDAQ clients. Researchers were impressed that the practice has successfully targeted the technology field. **Brendan Turley** is said to be dedicated to ESS work. The group undertakes transactional work and designs, implements and gives ongoing advice in respect of all share scheme issues. It arranged a Dutch stock option plan for the Dutch employees in a subsidiary of a fast growing Scottish technology client and did SAYE scheme work for Scottish & Southern Energy. **Clients:** Scottish & Southern Energy; Digital Animations; Kymata; Martin Currie.

Maclay Murray & Spens (see firm details p.1047) Operating an integrated employment pensions and benefits department, the practice led by Maureen Burnside advises on all aspects of employee share and benefit schemes for quoted and private companies. Judged to be "*proactive, good at coming up with solutions,*" it has strengthened its tax team and has been boosted by the recent merger with employment specialists Mackay Simon. Advised Claims Direct on share option issues at the time of its listing and Clyde Marine Place on new SAYE scheme. **Clients:** Claims Direct; LTG Technologies; British Polythene Industries; Stiell.

LEADERS IN EMPLOYEE SHARE SCHEMES

ALLEN, Barbara

Ashurst Morris Crisp, London (020) 7859 1312
barbara.allen@ashursts.com

Specialisation: Partner in employee benefits and incentives. Advises on all aspects of the design and implementation of employee share schemes, long-term incentive plans and bonus arrangements, including the use of employee benefit trusts. Also has considerable experience of the implications of flotations, mergers and acquisitions, management buy-outs and demergers on such arrangements. Major clients include The Body Shop International plc, Dynacast International Ltd, Garban-Intercapital plc, Imperial Tobacco Group plc, The Laird Group plc, Redbus Interhouse plc and Xansa plc.
Prof. Memberships: Share Schemes Lawyers Group.
Career: Qualified in 1983. Joined *Ashursts* 1988 and became a partner in 2001.
Publications: Directors as Trustees chapter in 'Company Directors: Law and Liability' (Sweet & Maxwell).

CHAMBERLAIN, Colin

Herbert Smith, London (020) 7466 2281
colin.chamberlain.@herbertsmith.com

Specialisation: Partner in employment department. Specialises in employee share schemes and employee benefit arrangements in the UK and overseas including employee cash incentives and ESOPs.
Career: Qualified in 1977. Between 1985 and 1989 he worked as a director of the former CC&P, now part of Bacon & Woodrow. Became a partner at *Herbert Smith* in 1989.
Publications: He is author of Tolley's 'Practical Guide to Employees' Share Schemes' and a regular speaker at conferences.
Personal: Educated at Sussex University. ATII.

CHATER, Stephen

Allen & Overy, London (020) 7330 3000
slephen.chater@allenovery.com

Specialisation: Specialises in employee tax and share incentives in an international context. Deals with flotations, privatisations, mergers and acquisitions and management buy-outs and advises on the establishment, operation, variation and termination of employees' share schemes. Advises UK listed companies on the UKLA Listing Rules, Institutional Investor Protection Committee Guidelines, the City Code on Takeovers and Mergers and corporate governance issues. Also advises senior executives and companies in relation to service contracts and remuneration packages.
Prof. Memberships: Law Society; Share Scheme Lawyers Group; Society of Share Scheme Practitioners.
Career: Joined *Allen & Overy* 1979; qualified 1981; partner 1989.
Personal: Educated at Hartlepool Grammar School and Christ Church, Oxford. Lives in Surrey.

CODRINGTON, Eddie

Slaughter and May, London (020) 7600 1200
eddie.codrington@slaughterandmay.com

Specialisation: Main areas of practice are employee benefits, pensions and employment. Deals with the establishment of all types of employee benefit plans, both cash and share based, ESOPs and AESOPs. Also handles pensions work including setting up, merger and termination of pension schemes.
Prof. Memberships: The Law Society, Association of Pensions Lawyers, Share Scheme Lawyer Group.
Career: Joined 1974, qualified 1976, partner 1985.
Personal: Born 12 April 1951. St Benedict's School, Ealing 1957-70. Birmingham University 1970-73. Interests include family and sport (watching).

COHEN, David

Norton Rose, London (020) 7283 6000
cohendhj@nortonrose.com

Specialisation: Employee share ownership in all its various forms.
Prof. Memberships: Fellow of the Chartered Institute of Taxation; chairman of the Share Scheme Lawyers Group. Member of the advisory group set up by the government in March 1999 to work with the Inland Revenue on the development of the new employee share schemes.
Career: Qualified in 1980. Joined *Norton Rose* as a partner in May 1998. Visiting fellow in Employee Share Ownership Law at London University's Centre for Commercial Law Studies since 1995.
Publications: Author of 'Employee Participation in Flotations' annually since 1987. Contributor to the 'Encyclopaedia of Forms and Precedents'. Regular contributor to the 'Financial Times'. Member of editorial board of Palmer's 'Company Law'. Joint author of 'The New Employee Share Incentives: AESOPs and EMI' published by Sweet & Maxwell.
Personal: Born Cardiff 15 December 1955. Educated Jesus College, Oxford. Governor of Independent Jewish Day School. Vice-president, Glamorgan County Cricket Club. Lives in London.

COOPER, Janet

Linklaters, London (020) 7456 3662
janet.cooper@linklaters.com

Specialisation: Employment and employee benefits group, head of the employee share plans team. Specialises in employee share plans, executive incentives and corporate governance. On qualification was a general corporate lawyer before specialising in employee and executive plans and therefore familiar with how corporate transactions affect employee share plans. Her work includes advising on, designing and drafting documentation for a variety of employee and executive plans, advising on corporate governance implications for executive plans and generally on codes of conduct.
Prof. Memberships: Director of Employee Share Ownership Centre; firm's representative with ProShare; founder member of Share Schemes Advanced Studies Group; Committee member of Share Scheme Lawyers Group; Director of Global Equity Organisation (GEO); member of Recruitment Society.
Career: Leeds University, LLB. Head of the employee incentives group. 1991 to date, partner *Linklaters.* 1984-91 assistant solicitor *Linklaters.*

CROFT, Anne

Linklaters, London (020) 7456 3706
anne.croft@linklaters.com

Specialisation: Specialises in tax, in particular employee-related tax and national insurance contributions. Practice areas include employee share schemes, ESOPs (including ESOP financing techniques), new venture structuring (including EMI options and forfeitable shares) unapproved pension arrangements, employment contracts and flexible remuneration packages, termination of employment and international employment contracts. Transactional work involves complex corporate reconstruction, including the recent arrangements to eliminate the Anglo-American De Beers cross holdings. Active in consultation with the Inland Revenue and the Accounting Standards Board in relation to share scheme policy matters.
Prof. Memberships: Fellow of the Chartered Institute of Taxation, Share Scheme Lawyers Group.
Career: Called to the Bar 1975; LLM, tax and company law (University of London) 1976. Requalified as a solicitor 1990; Consultant 1998.

ELLERMAN, Paul

Herbert Smith, London (020) 7446 2728
paul.ellerman@herbertsmith.com

Specialisation: Specialises in employee share schemes including transactional aspects (takeovers, mergers/schemes of arrangement and flotations) and all aspects of UK and international share incentive arrangements.
Prof. Memberships: Share Scheme Lawyers Group; The Global Equity Organisation.
Career: *Ashurst Morris Crisp* 1990-94; *Clifford Chance* 1994-2000. Joined *Herbert Smith* as a partner in November 2000.

Personal: Born 11 June 1968. Educated at the City of London School and Girton College, Cambridge.

EVANS, Simon
Freshfields Bruckhaus Deringer, London (020) 7936 4000 simon.evans@freshfields.com
Specialisation: Partner in employment pensions and benefits department. Specialises in share option, restricted share plan and ESOP arrangements, relating both to establishment of schemes and advice on the impact of corporate transactions on schemes. Also handles employment law, notably executive appointments and dismissals. Devised numerous long term incentive plans and other tailor-made incentive schemes. Regularly lectures on share scheme topics.
Prof. Memberships: Share Scheme Lawyers Group.
Career: Qualified in 1983. Joined *Freshfields* in 1981, becoming a partner in 1991.
Personal: Born 16th June 1957. Attended Rugby School 1970-75; MA from Sidney Sussex College, Cambridge, 1976-79. Lives in Staplehurst, Kent.

FENN, Jonathan
Slaughter and May, London (020) 7600 1200 jonathan.fenn@slaughterandmay.com
Specialisation: Principal area of practice is employee share schemes, both Inland Revenue approved and unapproved, including deferred bonus and long-term incentive schemes and ESOPs. Also advises on pensions, including in particular the pensions aspects of M&A and corporate transactions, as well as general pensions advice.
Prof. Memberships: The Law Society; Share Scheme Lawyers Group (member of Committee); Society of Share Scheme Practitioners; Association of Pensions Lawyers (member of Legislative and Parliamentary Sub-Committee).
Career: Qualified 1986. At *Slaughter and May* 1984 to date. Became a partner in 1995.
Personal: Born 30 May 1961. Educated at Maidstone Grammar School and King's College, London. Lives in Kent.

GREAVES, Judith
Pinsent Curtis Biddle, Leeds (0113) 244 5000 judith.greaves@pinsents.com
Specialisation: National practice head of tax. Main areas of practice are employee share schemes: approved and unapproved schemes (including Enterprise Management Incentives and AESOPS), long term incentive plans, employee trusts, employee buy outs and international schemes; and corporate tax, covering acquisitions and disposals, group reorganisations and MBOs.
Prof. Memberships: Share Schemes Lawyers Group; the Global Equity Organistaion.
Career: Qualified 1986 with *Linklaters & Paines.* Joined *Pinsent Curtis Biddle* in 1988, becoming partner in 1991.

GREEN, Lawrence
Eversheds, Birmingham (0121) 232 1042 lawrencegreen@eversheds.com
Specialisation: Advises on planning and implementation of all types of employee share incentive arrangements. Acts for a range of quoted and private companies on UK and overseas implications and for overseas companies implementing share schemes in the UK. Charge-out rate is £265 per hour.
Career: Trained with *Evershed & Tomkinson* and qualified in 1988. Originally practised as a corporate tax lawyer before specialising exclusively in employee share incentives. Partner and head of *Eversheds'* National Share Incentives group.
Personal: Born 8 March 1964. Educated at Queen Elizabeth Grammar School, Trinity Hall, Cambridge and Chester Law School. Leisure interests include cycling and mountain walking.

HAYES, Richard
Addleshaw Booth & Co, Manchester (0161) 934 6419 vwh@addleshaw-booth.co.uk
Specialisation: Partner in commercial tax department, commercial group. Specialises in employee share schemes including ESOPs, option schemes and long term incentive schemes for both public and private companies.
Prof. Memberships: Law Society, Society of Share Scheme Practitioners.
Career: Qualified in 1972. Joined the firm in 1973, becoming a partner in 1975.
Personal: Trinity Hall, Cambridge (MA 1969, LLB 1970). Leisure interests include railways, opera, classical music and sheep.

INGLE, Michael
Baker & McKenzie, London (020) 7919 1000 michael.ingle@bakernet.com
Specialisation: Practice covers the full range of employee benefits and employment taxation. Coordinates the firm's practice in the area of share schemes and incentive plans, including the related transactional issues. Works closely with share schemes colleagues in other *Baker & McKenzie* offices around the world in designing and implementing cross-border schemes. Clients include banks, software and other hi-tech companies and numerous multinational companies. Is a contributing editor of the Gee publication 'Practical Tax Planning'.
Prof. Memberships: Share Schemes Lawyers Group; Employee Share Ownership Centre.
Career: Qualified 1981. At *Dunham Brindley & Linn* 1979-84, Engineering Employers Federation 1984-85; *Baker & McKenzie* from 1985 (Partner from 1990).
Personal: Born 27 April 1951. Lives in London and Sheringham, Norfolk. Educated in Canada and obtained LLB degree from the University of Western Ontario in 1974.

JACOBS, Michael
Nicholson Graham & Jones, London (020) 7648 9000 michael.jacobs@ngj.co.uk
Specialisation: Tax; employee share schemes; international tax, trusts, charities, and public sector bodies. Author of 'Tax on Take-overs' (7 editions) and 'Rewarding Leadership' (published by CISCO, now Quoted Companies Alliance, February 1998); contributor to 'Tolley's Tax Planning' and 'Tolley's VAT Planning'. Consultant editor of Tolley's 'Trust Law International'.
Prof. Memberships: Trust Law Committee (Founder Member and Secretary, 1994-97, Executive Committee Member); Share Scheme Lawyers Group (Founder Member and Vice-Chairman); Executive Committee (Member) and Employee Share Schemes Committee (Chairman) Quoted Companies Alliance; STEP; IFA; IFS; Charity Law Association; FRSA; Academician of the Academy of the Learned Societies for the Social Sciences; Fellow of The Society for Advanced Legal Studies.
Career: Articled at *Nicholson Graham & Jones* (1970). Partner 1976. Head of Private Client Department 1981.

MCCARTHY, Paul
Allen & Overy, London (020) 7330 4889 paul.mccarthy@allenovery.com
Specialisation: Advises on full range of employee share schemes (discretionary and all employee) issues for listed and unlisted companies, both UK and international; also specialises in employees share schemes issues in mergers, acquisitions and flotations. Specialises in designing and implementing share incentive arrangements/remuneration packages for senior executives and dealing with employment law issues on executive appointments and dismissals. Regularly lectures on share schemes.
Prof. Memberships: Share Scheme Lawyers Group; Society of Share Scheme Practitioners.
Career: Educated at Bancroft's School and St Edmund Hall, Oxford. *Freshfields* 1985-93; *Garretts* 1993, Partner 1994. *Allen & Overy*, Partner 2001.
Personal: Born 1961. Married, four children. Lives in Kent.

MITCHELL, Jocelyn
Freshfields Bruckhaus Deringer, London (020) 7936 4000 jocelyn.mitchell@freshfields.com
Specialisation: Main areas of practice are share schemes and employee benefits. Deals with the establishment and ongoing advisory work relating to share option schemes, long term incentive plans, ESOPs, QUESTs and international share schemes. Has extensive experience of share schemes and employment issues on mergers and acquisitions and flotations. Also advises on senior executive terminations, employment tax and the law relating to directors and corporate governance.
Prof. Memberships: Share Scheme Lawyers Group.
Career: Qualified in 1985. *Freshfields* 1995 (partner 1997).

NICHOLL, Victoria
Travers Smith Braithwaite, London (020) 7295 3000 Victoria.Nicholl@TraversSmith.com
Specialisation: Advises on design and operation of UK and international employee incentives and employee taxation. Specialises in employee share schemes, employee benefit trusts and QUESTs (including financing), corporate governance and employee benefits both generally and in relation to MBOs, flotations and other corporate transactions.
Prof. Memberships: Share Scheme Lawyers Group; Society of Share Scheme Practitioners; ESOP Centre.
Career: Qualified 1987. Joined *Travers Smith Braithwaite* 1989. Partner 1995.

NUTTALL, Graeme
Field Fisher Waterhouse, London (020) 7861 4000 gjn@ffwlaw.com
Specialisation: Partner in the tax department. Particular interest in employee share schemes. Has advised on the employee ownership aspects of privatisations both in the UK and overseas in Bulgaria, Macedonia, Romania and Slovenia. Regularly addresses conferences both in the UK and internationally on tax and employee share schemes. Frequently called on to assist in lobbying government for tax and other changes to encourage employee ownership and now a member of the HM Treasury

advisory group involved in helping the Inland Revenue develop new share schemes. European regional coordinator of Global Reward Plan Group.
Prof. Memberships: Associate of the Institute of Taxation since 1985; member of the Share Schemes Lawyers Group since 1989; member of the Taxation committee of the Intellectual Property Institute; member of HM Treasury employee ownership advisory group (1999).
Career: Qualified 1984. Assistant solicitor, *Field Fisher Martineau* 1984-88. Partner since 1988. Spent six months on secondment to *Touche Ross & Co* in 1987. Non-executive director of Job Ownership Ltd. Director *Field Fisher Waterhouse Limited.* Managing Director Equity Incentives Limited.
Publications: Publications include 'Employee Ownership – Legal and Tax Aspects' (co-author) 1987; 'Share Incentives for Employees' (co-author) 1990; 'Butterworths Tax Planning' (looseleaf service) (contributor); 'Butterworths UK Corporate Finance' (2nd edn 1992) (contributor); 'Nelson-Jones and Nuttall's Tax Tables' (5 editions) (co-author); 'Nuttall's Tax Tables 1994-95'; 'Sponsorship Endorsement and Merchandising' (co-author) (2nd edn 1998); 'Electronic commerce-law and practice' (co-author) 1998; 'Essential law for the tax practitioner' (contributor) (3rd edn 2001).
Personal: Educated at Price's Grammar School, Fareham, Hants. and Peterhouse, Cambridge (MA law) 1978-81. Lives in Blackheath, London.

PETT, David
Pinsent Curtis Biddle, Birmingham
(0121) 200 1050
david.pett@pinsents.com
Specialisation: Tax partner and head of the employee share schemes team in Birmingham. Acknowledged specialist in all aspects of employee share schemes and employee trusts. Responsible for devising many of the more innovative share schemes for public and private companies including long-term incentive plans; the use of QUESTs, with SAYE option schemes, the tax efficient buyout of companies using employee trusts; and international schemes. As a member of the Government's Advisory committee on Employee Share Schemes, he took part in the consultation for the development of the new AESOP and the EMI.
Prof. Memberships: The Share Scheme Lawyers Group, the Global Equity Organisation and the Society of Share Scheme Practitioners.
Career: Qualified 1980, became a partner in 1985.
Publications: Author of 'Employee Share Schemes' Gee Publishing – two volume updated looseleaf) and with David Cohen 'The New Employee Share Incentives: AESOPS and EMI' (Sweet & Maxwell 2000).
Personal: Educated at Lincoln College, Oxford.

POOLE, Kevin
Wragge & Co, Birmingham (0870) 903 1000

RANDALL, Paul
Ashurst Morris Crisp, London (020) 7859 1298
paul.randall@ashursts.com
Specialisation: Partner and head of employee benefits and incentives. Advises on the design, implementation and operation of domestic and international employee share option and acquisition schemes, incentives and employee trusts. Transactional experience covers MBOs, flotations, bids, mergers and privatisations. Advises on tax, corporate, stock exchange and governance aspects. Major clients include Albert Fisher, Amvescap, Coca-Cola HBC, Exel, The Laird Group plc, National Express, Royal & Sun Alliance and Taylor Nelson Sofres.
Prof. Memberships: Share Scheme Lawyers Group (member Corporate Governance Committee).
Career: Qualified 1984. Joined *Ashurst Morris Crisp* 1987, partner 1995.

ROWLANDS-HEMPEL, Graham
Linklaters, London (020) 7456 3680
graham.rowlands-hempel@linklaters.com
Specialisation: Specialises in employee share plans and executive incentives. On qualification was a corporate tax lawyer. Work includes advising on the design and operation of many international share plans including supervising and co-ordinating the overseas legal advice for companies like BP Amoco, British Airways and Blue Circle, and dealing with employee share plans on various major corporate reorganisations and transactions. Recently returned from secondment to the Inland Revenue as policy advisor on the Government's new share scheme.
Prof. Memberships: Member of Society of Share Scheme Practitioners and the Share Schemes Lawyers' Group.
Career: 1998 to date: Partner, *Linklaters*; 1994-98: Senior assistant, *Linklaters*; 1987-94: Assistant solicitor, *Simmons & Simmons.* Spent six months with the Inland Revenue as technical adviser advising on the government's new share plan.

THOMPSON, Kevin
Clifford Chance, London (020) 7006 8930
kevin.thompson@cliffordchance.com
Specialisation: Advises UK and non-UK companies (listed and unlisted, MBOs etc) on all aspects of employee incentive arrangements, with an emphasis on employee share schemes in both the UK and elsewhere. Recent matters include advising on a web-based all-employee share plan in 20 countries for Getronics (Dutch based global IT company) and currently advising a major US organisation on share schemes in 49 countries as part of July 2001 IPO.
Prof. Memberships: Member of the Society of Share Scheme Practitioners. Also member of the Share Scheme Lawyers Group and sits on its Company Law and Accounts Committee.
Career: Joined *Clifford Chance* in 1988 and has worked in the employee benefits group throughout.
Publications: Has edited the two main *Clifford Chance* brochures on employee share schemes – 'Employee Share Participation Schemes in the UK' and 'Employee Share Participation in the European Union'.
Personal: Educated at St John's College, Cambridge (MA (Cantab)). Called to the Bar in 1988 and requalified as a solicitor in 1992. Partner since 1999.

TREMAINE, Robin
Clifford Chance, London (020) 7600 1000
robin.tremaine@cliffordchance.com
Specialisation: Partner, head of the employee share schemes unit in UK and on global basis. Has more than 20 years experience of devising and implementing employee share incentive arrangements for quoted and private companies.
Prof. Memberships: Member Share Schemes Lawyers Group; Society of Share Scheme Practioners; Share Scheme Advanced Studies Group.
Career: Plymouth College; Trinity Hall, Cambridge (MA (Cantab) 1978). Qualified as barrister in 1979; requalified as a solicitor in 1986; partner 1989.
Publications: 'Employee Share Ownership in the UK' (Butterworths).

TROTTER, Peter
MacRoberts, Glasgow (0141) 332 9988
peter.trotter@macroberts.co.uk
See under Pensions, p.632

TURLEY, Brendan
Dundas & Wilson CS, Glasgow (0141) 222 2200

WATTS, Sylvie
Allen & Overy, London (020) 7330 4874
sylvie.watts@allenovery.com
Specialisation: Advises on the full range of employee share schemes issues, discretion and all employment issues for both listed and unlisted companies. She has considerable experience of the share scheme aspects of corporate transactions as well as working with companies on the design and implementation of their share schemes, particularly for senior associates.
Prof. Memberships: Share Schemes Lawyers Group; Society of Share Scheme Practitioners.
Career: *Theodore Goddard* 1986-90; *Linklaters* 1990-94; BT legal department 1994-96; *Garretts* 1996-2001 (partner in 1997); *Allen & Overy*, partner 2001.
Publications: Has published articles on employee share schemes and is a regular speaker at conferences about this area. Articles in 'PLC Magazine'.
Personal: Born 1961. Married, one daughter. Lives in London. Leisure interests: spending time with family and friends. Educated at St Paul's Girls' School and Cambridge.

WHITEWRIGHT, Louise
Lovells, London (020) 7296 2000
louise.whitewright@lovells.com
Specialisation: Principal area of practice is employee share schemes and employee benefits advising on all aspects of the design, structure, establishment and operation of approved and unapproved employee share schemes (including ESOPS, restricted share schemes and international share schemes) for private and public companies. Deals with all aspects of these schemes on flotations, takeovers, privatisations etc. Contributor to a chapter in CCH Editions Employment Manual and joint editor of a chapter of Tolley's 'Tax Planning'.
Prof. Memberships: Law Society; Share Scheme Lawyers Group (Secretary and member of Executive Committee). ESOP Centre; City of London Lawyers and Global Equity Organisations.
Career: Articled *Rakisons* 1984-86; qualified 1986 with *Lovells* as an assistant solicitor in the tax group. Specialised in employee share schemes from 1987 and became a partner in 1996.

WOMERSLEY, Mark
Osborne Clarke, Bristol (0117) 917 3000

EMPLOYMENT

RESEARCH APPROVED BY BMRB: *For this edition,* Chambers' *researchers conducted 6,552 interviews – 4,419 with law firms, 554 with barristers and 1,579 with clients.*

The validity of the research was scrutinised by BMRB International, who audited both the methodology and the results at our offices in July 2001. They interviewed Chambers' *researchers and cross-checked sample interviews. Details of the audit appear on page 7.*

LONDON

RESPONDENT FIRMS

Simmons & Simmons (see firm details p.1132) The firm that "*has got to be top on anyone's list.*" Dominant for a long time and certainly still there, this firm is well known to employers of all types, whether or not they are clients of the firm. The department is perceived to have taken on a role as educator to industry in the UK. The country's best known and seemingly most admired employment lawyer, **Janet Gaymer** (see p.333), has now taken on the role of senior partner at the firm. Described as "*a good lateral thinker,*" she "*looks at the big picture and puts the clients' interests first.*" Control of the employment team has passed to "*positive*" **William Dawson** (see p.331), who "*deals with things constructively.*" Partner **Simon Watson** (see p.343) also attracts his own fans above the stature of other partners in the team. Similarly, the rest of the team is seen to have "*a momentum of its own.*" Last year the team advised Bob Ayling on his departure from British Airways, and more recently it has seen Court of Appeal action in Beedell v West Ferry Printers over the reasonableness test in cases of unfair dismissals. Redundancy advice included an instruction relating to the Dome. **Clients:** Railtrack; Deutsche Bank; BASF; Ministry of Defence; Bank One; Mizuho International.

Baker & McKenzie (see firm details p.868) Clients report on the department's ability to communicate with clarity, appreciating lawyers who are "*solution finders with commercial nous and strategy.*" **Christine O'Brien** (see p.338) ("*just great*") provides a steady influence on a team in which younger partners are developing respect and trust throughout the market. Acting only for employers, the work ranges across the board, from discrimination to collective rights, including European Works Councils. The advantages of a network of offices, particularly those in the US and Europe, are in evidence. One of last year's highlights was the advice given to Camelot in its second successful lottery bid. The team also acted for United Business Media in connection with employment matters arising concerning its potential merger with Carlton Communications. **Clients:** WR Grace; Halifax; Morgan McKinley; Old Mutual; Pfizer; Phone.com.

Allen & Overy (see firm details p.856) Patently "*prospering – really pushing it,*" clients talk of the lawyers being able to "*play the game up or down as required.*" A&O's apparent break to the top of the market comes at a time when the team has expanded quite dramatically, "*hoovering up good practitioners.*" At the top of the pyramid come inspired ideas man **Mark Mansell** (see p.337) ("*a joy to deal with*") and **Karen Seward** (see p.341), who one client described as "*the most organised person I have come across in my life.*" Younger partners proving their worth include **Stefan Martin** (see p.337), who offers "*clear advice and a pragmatic approach.*" The roster of new clients is impressive and covers a multitude of sectors, with three distinct groupings (Lifestyle & Equality/Workplace Surveillance/ Representation & Consultation) created within the team to deal with the range of instructions. Last year it handled a multi-million pound claim

TOP IN-HOUSE LAWYERS

Sally BOYLE, Executive Director and Counsel, *Goldman Sachs International*

Mark COOPER, Senior Legal Counsel, *Nortel*

Julia HARRISON, Employment Lawyer, *British Airways*

Melanie JONES, Director of Legal & Business Affairs, *Warner Bros.*

Hilary SCHRADER, Solicitor, *Nestlé*

Jane STABLES, Legal & Personnel Director, *United Business Media*

Soulla TSIOUPRA-LEWIS, *United Business Media*

The "*superb*" **Sally Boyle** "*manages a difficult business*" and is rated for her technical understanding. **Mark Cooper** is "*an impressive guy*" who "*does an enormous job*" while **Julia Harrison** is held in high regard despite a low profile this year. **Melanie Jones** is experienced and "*extremely good,*" and **Hilary Schrader** is endorsed as "*excellent.*" "*Well-worthy of note*" is the "*knowledgeable*" **Jane Stables** and the equally capable **Soulla Tsioupra-Lewis**.

In-House lawyers profiles: p 1193

(Clarke against Nomura International) by a former employee for unpaid bonuses and advised on the employment aspects of the merger between Paine Webber and UBS. It has recently been acting for Mobil in the Exxon/Mobil merger and, prior to that, on the cessation of the joint venture with BP concerning the company's fuels and lubricant business. Clients continue to remark on the importance of the firm's European network of offices. **Clients:** Morgan Stanley; Cable & Wireless; Nikko; EDS; GE Capital; ICI.

Eversheds (see firm details p.952) A "*formidable*" style is delivered by the London office of this leading national employment group. Ably led by **Elaine Aarons** (see p.327), who puts up a good fight, the team is felt to take employment law seriously fielding strong lawyers. This year, **Helga Breen** (see p.329) is ranked, having been warmly recommended by peers who have worked with her. The team includes two HR professionals and a German employment lawyer. It is currently co-ordinating the response to over 600 equal pay tribunal claims against the Electricity Association arising out of the Preston case. The firm continues to handle interesting work in the education sector, such as whistle-blowing, high profile disputes and issues arising out of the restructuring of educational establishments. **Clients:** HSBC Investment Bank; FSA; GAP; Deloitte & Touche; NM Rothschild.

Fox Williams (see firm details p.963) A thoroughbred employment practice within a firm which has put in "*a large amount of dedication to employment work.*" One interviewee likened this "*collection of feisty individuals*" to barristers' chambers; "*city oriented and successful,*" it remains a favourite for referral work. There is particular experience with partnership matters. "*High powered*" **Ronnie Fox** (see p.332) and Chairman of ELA **Jane Mann** (see p.337) ("*Jane is dedication*") are the key players and attract business on the strength of their personal reputations, while the team as a whole also attracted commendation. On the agenda during 2000 was the well publicised Kamlesh Bahl inquiry and subsequent resignation and discrimination claims. The group acted for the five complainants in the inquiry and later for three individuals named as respondents in the tribunal claims. High profile claims for individuals have included Isabelle Terrillon's sex discrimination claim against Nomura and Michael Bourgeois' £1.1 million race discrimination claim against Saga Petrolium. **Clients:** Hasbro International; Heron Corporation; The Law Society; Billiton; The London Stock Exchange; Oftel.

EMPLOYMENT: MAINLY RESPONDENT • London	Ptnrs	Assts
1 Simmons & Simmons	4	23
2 Baker & McKenzie	4	22
3 Allen & Overy	4	32
Eversheds	4	15
Fox Williams	4	14
Lewis Silkin	5	19
Lovells	4	12
Rowe & Maw	2	12
4 Herbert Smith	3	13
5 Beachcroft Wansbroughs	n/a	n/a
Charles Russell	2	17
Clifford Chance	4	19
CMS Cameron McKenna	2	9
Dechert	2	5
Denton Wilde Sapte	4	12
Linklaters	2	23
McDermott, Will & Emery	3	8
Olswang	3	13
Slaughter and May	1	6
Stephenson Harwood	2	7
6 Archon	3	4
Berwin Leighton Paisner	4	10
Boodle Hatfield	2	3
Doyle Clayton	3	2
Farrer & Co	4	3
Freshfields Bruckhaus Deringer	2	15
Hammond Suddards Edge	2	12
Macfarlanes	3	9
Nabarro Nathanson	2	7
Norton Rose	2	15
Osborne Clarke OWA	3	15
Salans Hertzfeld & Heilbronn HRK	2	4
Speechly Bircham	2	4
Theodore Goddard	2	5
Travers Smith Braithwaite	2	7

This book is the product of 6,552 1/2-hour interviews. See p.7 for BMRB audit.
Within each band, firms are listed alphabetically.

Lewis Silkin (see firm details p.1040) The Lewis Silkin lawyer is "*not a softie but essentially pragmatic,*" proffering a firm but fair approach to work and fees. The firm is widely known to be "*more cost effective than other top firms, but the quality is no less.*" The team, that has just undergone another phase of expansion, is said to have more good juniors than ever before and to have "*caught the public mood.*" Well known figure **James Davies** (see p.331) "*gives practical and sensible advice,*" and his style is seen to be complementary to that of **Michael Burd** (see p.329), who is viewed as "*vigorous within the box*" and "*deals well with demanding clients.*" The firm acts for a number of large law firms in connection with their employment problems, including those experienced by CMS Cameron McKenna in relation to its CIS practice. It advised former ONdigital director John Egan in his successful tribunal complaint for unfair and wrongful dismissal and unpaid bonuses. It also gave employment advice to The Millennium Commission in connection with the Dome. **Clients:** Chubb; Lloyd's Register of Shipping; The House of Lords Establishment Office; Dell Computer Corporation; BAA; Greater London Authority.

Lovells (see firm details p.1044) A respected team with "*good judgement,*" undeniable "*technical ability*" and real consistency in "*quality standards.*" "*Not blasé, it inspires confidence*" although some interviewees looked for a more dynamic profile. Dealing with **David Harper** (see p.334) is "*always a good experience,*" while **Naomi Feinstein** (see p.332) ("*always informative*") is endorsed for her discrimination work. **Andrew Williamson** (see p.344) defended Tomkins in its dispute with its former chief executive. Successful mergers with Boesebeck Droste and Siméon et Associés open the way for an increased cross border capability. The Lovells team advised on the sale of The Equitable Life to Halifax, on the proposed privatisation of National Air Traffic Services and on Granada's merger and demerger with Compass. **Clients:** Barclays; Esso; Ford; IKEA; Merrill Lynch; Texaco.

Rowe & Maw (see firm details p.1113) A long-standing name in employment work, the firm has plenty of experience acting for both employer and employee, the latter often as a result of referrals from other leading firms. Leading figure **Julian Roskill** (see p.340) is "*self assured and more than competent,*" while "*supremely bright*" **Nicholas Robertson** (see p.340) is "*to the point and very able.*" All round experience is demonstrated in the range of work handled recently, including a collective bargaining unit case referred to the CAC, in which the firm successfully represented the Union Bank of Nigeria. It also acted on the Court of Appeal case of ADI v Willer & Others on the application of TUPE to outsourcing and the issue of motive. **Clients:** Cable & Wireless; DHL; EMI Group; M&G; Kingfisher; Independent News & Media.

Herbert Smith (see firm details p.993) "*Doing interesting work but underestimated,*" according to certain interviewees. Attracting first rate, non-contentious and often "*interesting commercial matters,*" the team is still best known for its contentious work. The duo of partners dominates the reputation of the team. The "*ever youthful*" and "*always positive*" **John Farr** (see p.332) provides "*a calm influence*" and, while attempting to keep a low profile, manages to impress many. **Peter Frost** (see p.332) has equal stature, described as "*sensible, decent and sound on a conflict.*" One of the firm's most publicised recent instructions was advice to the Law Society on the Kamlesh Bahl matter. Its lawyers also successfully represented Securicor in two applications brought by trade unions under statutory recognition procedure, including the first application for de-recognition. **Clients:** Chevron UK; Crédit Lyonnais; CSFB; Iceland Group; St Ives; Nomura.

Beachcroft Wansbroughs (see firm details p.872) The firm offers a clutch of focused and active employment lawyers, amongst the best known being national head of department, "*switched on*" **Elizabeth Adams** (see p.327) and London head **Rachel Dineley** (see p.331) ("*punchy and energetic but level headed*"). Last year saw the team advising on the amalgamation of all London probation services, involving complicated TUPE aspects, and advising an employee from a financial institution in relation to a £17 million termination package. McCormick instructed the firm on its restructuring of the Haddenaham (principal UK office) operations. **Clients:** Tate & Lyle; Unilever; Kvaerner Oil & Gas; DARCY; Associated Press Television News.

Charles Russell (see firm details p.912) "*A good team quietly built up over the years*" is matched by the attraction of a good client base and the recruitment of a partner from Biddle. "*Delightful*" **David Green** is not only well liked but "*extremely competent.*" In addition to several discrimination claims against law firms and two of 2000's largest pay offs to senior executives, the team has numerous large employer clients which form the bulk of its roster. It was successful last year in a claim brought by pensioners against its client Heinz. The group has also had two recent successes in the Court of Appeal and the House of Lords in separate racial discrimination claims against the University of Oxford and South Bank Student Union and the University. **Clients:** JO Hambros; Ntl Group; Pharmacia & Upjohn; London and Royal Philharmonic Orchestras; The Royal College of Nursing; KLM.

Clifford Chance (see firm details p.919) The whole team is "*all up to scratch and excellent technically.*" Add in some popular partners and the market anticipates great things from a group that has traditionally felt to be fed by

LEADING INDIVIDUALS		
★	**GAYMER Janet** Simmons & Simmons	
1	**AARONS Elaine** Eversheds	**AUERBACH Simon** Pattinson & Brewer
	COCKBURN David Pattinson & Brewer	**DAVIES James** Lewis Silkin
	JACOBS Howard Slaughter and May	**JEFFREYS Simon** CMS Cameron McKenna
	MANSELL Mark Allen & Overy	
2	**ADAMS Elizabeth** Beachcroft Wansbroughs	**BURD Michael** Lewis Silkin
	DAWSON William Simmons & Simmons	**FARR John** Herbert Smith
	FROST Peter Herbert Smith	**OSMAN Chris** Clifford Chance
	ROBERTSON Nicholas Rowe & Maw	**ROSKILL Julian** Rowe & Maw
	YOUNSON Fraser McDermott, Will & Emery	
3	**BREARLEY Kate** Stephenson Harwood	**DALE Stephanie** Denton Wilde Sapte
	FLANAGAN Tom Stephenson Harwood	**GREEN David** Charles Russell
	HARPER David Lovells	**JEFFERS Raymond** Linklaters
	JULYAN Alan Speechly Bircham	**MANN Jane** Fox Williams
	O'BRIEN Christine Baker & McKenzie	**SEWARD Karen** Allen & Overy
	WATSON Simon Simmons & Simmons	**WHINCUP David** Hammond Suddards Edge
	WYNN-EVANS Charles Dechert	
4	**FEINSTEIN Naomi** Lovells	**FOX Ronnie** Fox Williams
	MORDSLEY Barry Salans Hertzfeld & Heilbronn	**THOMPSON Tony** Macfarlanes
	WILLIAMSON Andrew Lovells	
5	**ASHTIANY Sue** Nabarro Nathanson	**CAVALIER Stephen** Thompsons
	COOPER Edward Russell Jones & Walker	
	DALGARNO David McDermott, Will & Emery	
	DINELEY Rachel Beachcroft Wansbroughs	
6	**ANDREW Jill** Archon	**DANIELS Paul** Russell Jones & Walker
	HOWARD Clive Russell Jones & Walker	**LANGLEY Dale** Dale Langley & Co
	LILLEY Andrew Travers Smith Braithwaite	**RALPH Nick** Archon
	RUSSELL Timothy Norton Rose	**SMELLIE David** Farrer & Co
UP AND COMING		
	BREEN Helga Eversheds	**GALLAGHER Yvonne** Lawrence Graham
	GOODWILL Christopher Clifford Chance	**HUNTER Ian** Bird & Bird
	KEEBLE Sarah Olswang	**MARTIN Stefan** Allen & Overy
	NESBITT Sean Garretts	**PALCA Julia** Olswang
	TAYLOR Catherine Olswang	
ONES TO WATCH		
	TWIGGER Elizabeth Slaughter and May	
	WETHERFIELD Alison McDermott, Will & Emery	

See individuals' profiles p.327

the mass of transaction support work delivered by the brand name practice. The reality is that this team is doing a much smaller proportion of transaction work than the market assumes. "*Mr Integrity*" **Chris Osman** (see p.338) "*doesn't shout about it and he's extremely considered*" – he is said to "*treat everyone with ultimate respect.*" Newly ranked **Chris Goodwill** (see p.333) also adds a personal touch and increases the group's top level strength. Recent high profile transactional matters include Chase Manhattan's acquisition of the business of Flemings and its subsequent merger with JP Morgan. On the contentious side it advised Commerzbank and Jupiter International on the departure of John Duffield. **Clients:** Coca-Cola; ICL/Fujitsu; Whitbread; Manpower; Yardley; Honda.

CMS Cameron McKenna (see firm details p.922) The verdict in the market is that the team remains "*modest, down to earth and sensible.*" "*Superb*" **Simon Jeffreys** (see p.335) is "*clear, precise and commercial*" and widely felt to be "*one of the best lawyers around.*" Last year the firm undertook an equal opportunities training programme for the Home Office and the Post Office and obtained judgement in the House of Lords on the maternity leave case Halfpenny v GE. Another highlight was the injunction obtained for a client against an ex-employee under the Prevention of Harassment Act. **Clients:** Bayer; Benetton Group; Commerzbank; Eli Lilly; Nestlé; Lloyds TSB.

Dechert (see firm details p.938) A much smaller team which is winning work away from the larger players on the strength of its big personality, charm, client care and quality of work. Clients value its approach as "*extremely practical*" and a match "*philosophically*" with their own. Others referred to **Charles Wynn-Evans** (see p.344) as "*warm*" and "*our sort of lawyer.*" The team benefits from the firm's notable strength in retail and insurance. It has been acting for Advantage Business Systems in the successful defence of an £800,000 wrongful dismissal, bonus and shareholding dispute, for JC Decaux in relation to the harmonisation of terms of employment of 800 employees and handled the employment aspects of Travelex's acquisition of Thomas Cook Global & Financial Services business. **Clients:** Saatchi & Saatchi; Amlin; Saga Group; Etam; Hitachi Home Electronics; Badenoch & Clark.

Denton Wilde Sapte (see firm details p.939) A good team which is "*fair and to the point*" in its dealings. It has some good names despite recent defections to Bird & Bird. Best known of the partners, **Stephanie Dale** is described as "*a smooth operator – a classic swan.*" Last year the team was instructed by Jennie Page in connection with her departure from the Dome and gave advice on the merger of DLJ with CSFB and Old Mutual's acquisition of Gerrard Group. **Clients:** British Airways; Ford; Equitable Life Assurance Society; Universal Group of Companies; Société Générale; Delta Airlines.

Linklaters (see firm details p.1042) Felt to be so closely tied in with the firm's high profile transactional work that the reputation for stand alone work is stifled. Bolstered by a raft of capable assistants there has been growth on the contentious side with many quality examples of pure employment instructions, both contentious and non contentious. Lead partner in the team is the "*well-informed*" **Raymond Jeffers** (see p.335), much respected for his "*cerebral and careful approach.*" The dissolution of BP Amoco's fuels and lubricants joint venture with Mobil provided one of last year's highlights for the employment team. Another came in the form of a case for Scottish & Newcastle concerning the issue of the application of TUPE to outsourcing contracts. The firm also advised BP Amoco on the employment aspects of the dissolution of the fuels and lubricants European joint venture with Mobil Corporation, which covered 25 countries, and the Lattice demerger from BG Group. For Scottish & Newcastle Group, it acted on a complex tribunal claim arising out of the application of TUPE to the termination of an outsourcing contract. **Clients:** ABN AMRO; AstraZeneca; Inogy; Lazard; Vodafone; WestLB.

McDermott, Will & Emery (see firm details p.1061) The market is still watching this relatively new team with interest. **Fraser Younson** (see p.344), as charismatic as ever, provides a highly visible front to a team which also includes **David Dalgarno** (see p.330), best known for his work in the financial sector. Clear team structure and a growing client base make the group a significant player in the market. Last year's work included advice to a multinational on a 27-country pan-European redundancy exercise, a series of garden leave injunctions for a leading investment bank and a pan-European contract review for a hi-tech company covering 12 jurisdictions. **Clients:** BAE Systems; British American Tobacco; Dow Jones; Oracle Corporation; Levi Strauss & Co; EMI.

Olswang (see firm details p.1084) A triumvirate at partner level: "*to the point and efficient*" **Catherine Taylor** (see p.342), **Sarah Keeble** (see p.335) and **Julia Palca** (see p.338) (also specialising in defamation and drawing from her newspaper background). The team as a whole is viewed as "*supremely competent and lively people*" doing some "*exciting work*" for "*excellent clients.*" Among the key pieces of work recently was the successful defence of a major manufacturing client in a tribunal claim by 923 claimants. It also had two Court of Appeal cases for Cantor Fitzgerald. On the non contentious side, it advised on the floats of Carphone Warehouse and Music Choice. **Clients:** General Motors; Thus plc; Bloomberg; BBC Worldwide; Warner Music; Granada.

Slaughter and May (see firm details p.1135) The approach is simple: the employment team serves an outstanding corporate client base with a high level of transactional skill. This is a team of high calibre lawyers who can advise on any employment or pensions related issue. **Howard Jacobs** (see p.335) *"plays things close to his chest, he's a good negotiator"* and completely focused *on "getting things done."* A smart choice for board restructuring or high level executive issues on takeovers. The firm acted for Symbian in the restraint case Symbian v Christiansen. **Clients:** Senior executives; large corporates.

Stephenson Harwood (see firm details p.1141) Its reputation revolves around two leading names: restrictive covenants and confidentiality injunctions specialist **Kate Brearley** (see p.328) and *"practical"* **Tom Flanagan** (see p.332), who is best known for his work in the field of TUPE and employee consultation. A *"pleasant, delightful"* manner belies the tenacity of these two lawyers. Works Councils are an important focus area. A high proportion of clients come from the financial services sector and the firm also attracts instructions from high-value individuals. The team has recently handled large scale redundancy issues, acting for 4,000 Rover managers. Part-timers' pensions claims have also been prominent through the cases of Preson v Wolverhampton BC and Fletcher v Midland Bank. The group advised on issues arising from the internet bank venture between Merrill Lynch and HSBC. **Clients:** Crédit Agricole Indosuez; Kuwait Investment Office; McGraw-Hill International (UK); Thorn Lighting Group.

Archon (see firm details p.862) This is the new name for the larger part of a practice formerly known as Langley & Co before it split last year. Two partners are recommended by the market: **Jill Andrew** (see p.327) acted for Kamlesh Bahl and also advised claimants against CMS Cameron McKenna in the much publicised but unsuccessful discrimination claims. *"Switched on"* **Nick Ralph** (see p.339) is thought to have proved his worth of late. City practices commonly refer individuals to the Archon team. Typical work includes employment tribunal cases and high court claims. **Clients:** Financial services; construction; hotels; newspapers; airlines.

Berwin Leighton Paisner (see firm details p.878) The merger is judged to have been of benefit to the employment group, adding quality Berwin Leighton lawyers to an already established Paisner & Co team. To Paisner's mixed corporate/private client base, Berwin Leighton supplies further employer clients, notably in the financial sector. The experienced team is led by Robert Eldridge. In 2000 the Paisners group acted for Air Canada on the discrimination claim brought by Basra, which eventually went to the Court of Appeal. Berwin Leighton highlights included advice to Schroder Securities in the equal pay, sex discrimination case brought by Julie Bower, and acting for David Robins, Malcolm Le May and other senior executives in connection with their departures from ING-Barings. **Clients:** Granada; GUS; Whitbread; Tullett & Tokyo Liberty; UBS; National Air Traffic Service.

Boodle Hatfield (see firm details p.889) A small quality team holding its own among much larger operations. Its hallmark is an absence of aggression with a personable approach from the partners. Russell Brimelow is ranked in the Thames Valley section of *Chambers* as much of his time is spent working from that office, although this has not impacted on the strength of the London team. Acted for Computacenter in the sex discrimination claim brought by Caroline Olds, it also represented Gerry Hodes, a former Marks & Spencer executive, in his unfair dismissal claim against the retailer. **Clients:** Blockbuster; Grosvenor Estate; MTV; Viacom Group; Allied Dunbar; Zurich Insurance; UK Life.

Doyle Clayton This newly ranked niche practice (set up in 1997) was recommended to our researchers by a number of City practitioners. Peter Doyle is one of the founding partners and, along with his colleagues, is seen as an effective recipient of City executive referrals. The firm is by no means reliant on this type of work and has a larger proportion of employer clients. The emphasis lies in contentious work. It has advised on large scale redundancies and alterations in contract terms, and handled cases involving solicitors and doctors. **Clients:** Dixons Group; Sara Lee; Zurich London; Shanks Group.

Farrer & Co (see firm details p.954) New head of department **David Smellie** (see p.341) leads this compact unit which has won instructions on interesting cases. Last year it attained considerable media coverage as a result of involvement in the case of the gender reassignment of a schoolteacher at Charterhouse. Active in 'City' cases, it advised a team moving to Lehman Brothers, which resulted in the successful defence of a garden leave injunction in the High Court. **Clients:** Victoria & Albert Museum; Amerada Hess; London Business School; Science Museum; UK Athletics; RHM Foods.

Freshfields Bruckhaus Deringer (see firm details p.964) Perceived to target large scale strategic and transaction-led work, the department offers pensions and employee benefits advice. Working closely in conjunction with its European counterparts, the team, led by Nicholas Squire and Peter Jeffcote, is international in its outlook. Recent key advice includes that given on the disposal of Bass's brewing arm to Interbrew, Ford's acquisition of Land Rover from BMW and Hewlett Packard's proposed acquisition of the management consulting business of PricewaterhouseCoopers. **Clients:** Agilent Techologies; British Nuclear Fuels; ICI; Tyco; Goldman Sachs; New Look.

Hammond Suddards Edge (see firm details p.984) *"Clients adore"* **David Whincup** (see p.343), a *"worldly wise and straight to the point"* lawyer who demonstrates *"flair."* Operating as part of a respected national network, a good proportion of the group's clients are attracted to the firm solely for employment law. Advised on the business transfer of Renault UK's parts distribution centre. **Clients:** ABN AMRO; Best Foods; Granada Compass; Cornhill Insurance.

Macfarlanes (see firm details p.1046) Acting for both employers and senior executives, the team is thoroughly respected in the market. Central to the operation is *"smooth"* and *"well informed"* **Tony Thompson** (see p.342). A freshly combined contentious/non contentious entity now stands alone. Notable work has included the employment and pensions advice given in relation to the Alchemy/Rover deal and advice to Pernod-Ricard in the acquisition with Diageo of Seagram's spirit business. It also acted for a client on a whistle-blowing claim. **Clients:** Legal & General; KFC; Carlton Communications; Saatchi & Saatchi; Anheuser Busch; Allders.

Nabarro Nathanson (see firm details p.1078) A player following its success in attracting **Sue Ashtiany** from Morgan Cole's Oxford office, her presence will undoubtedly give leverage to the team. Last year the firm acted for the Legal Services Commission in six separate trade union victimisation claims and advised the Met Office in Edgar v The Met Office, a whistle-blowing case concerning the BBC weathermen. **Clients:** HSBC; Oxford University; OUP; Unipart; BAA McArthurGlen UK; AA.

Norton Rose (see firm details p.1082) In the last two years the balance of this team's work has moved markedly from corporate support to stand alone. **Tim Russell** (see p.340) (one time head of the Hammond Suddards employment group) leads. Following on from last year's advice to BMW on the Rover disposal, it advised on the easyJet flotation and acted for France Telecom and Wanadoo on the purchase of Freeserve. **Clients:** BMW; Norsk Hydro; HSBC; Burberry; AXA; Mobil Shipping Company.

Osborne Clarke (see firm details p.1086) A *"well run team with good people,"* which works in tandem with a strong Bristol operation and serves an *"eminent client base."* Ralph Nathan leads the London team which has attracted several lawyers from other leading practices in the last year. Its lawyers successfully defended a high profile email abuse, unfair dismissal claim for British Airways. It recently acted for four of the outgoing executives of both Taylor Woodrow and Bryant Homes following the recent merger and advised on 1500 potential redundancies at Prudential Assurance following its decision to reduce its Direct Sales Force. **Clients:** Egg; Zurich Insurance; Danish Bacon; Unipart Eberspacher; 3i; Cosworth Racing.

Salans Hertzfeld & Heilbronn HRK (see firm details p.1117) Clients tell us that they "*value the advice and support*" given by **Barry Mordsley** (see p.338). Peers talk of the trust they feel towards him, appreciating that "*you get a very personal service.*" Last year the group advised William Baird on a major redundancy programme involving over 4,000 employees and was instructed by Rotary Watches in connection with its restructuring. The firm has begun the first stages of merger discussions with Theodore Goddard. **Clients:** Parity Group; Pfizer Group; Rotch Property Group; State Street Bank; National Grid Group; Essex & Suffolk Water.

Speechly Bircham (see firm details p.1136) A variety of work from this small team which has attracted lawyers from magic circle firms in the last year. This is the "*quality not volume*" end of the market. **Alan Julyan** (see p.335) is "*understated, paternal*" and "*offers good practical solutions.*" The team gave wide ranging assistance on the integration of The Royal Bank of Scotland and National Westminster Bank and acted on team poaching issues in the Lloyds market. **Clients:** Baring Asset Management; Surrey County Council; Thomas Cook Group; Commissioner for the rights of Independent Trade Union Members; MORI; Scottish Life Assurance Company.

Theodore Goddard (see firm details p.1152) As the department head is the firm's managing partner, day to day control rests in the hands of Jane Bullen. A third partner focuses on pensions and employee benefits. Last year successes included the defence of a race discrimination claim brought against Glaxo Wellcome and an injunction by Freeport Leisure against a former manager planning to join a competitor. **Clients:** Chrysalis Group; Oracle Corporation UK; SBJ Group; Diageo; Kelly Services; USAA.

Travers Smith Braithwaite (see firm details p.1160) A good year for a team that leaves clients "*impressed over all.*" The approach is "*sound and practical,* " while "*thorough*" **Andrew Lilley** (see p.336) continues to draw recommendations. The team advised Harland & Wolff Holdings on a redundancy programme affecting around 600 employees. It also acted for Guinness on the reorganisation of its brewing operation at Park Royal in London. **Clients:** Association of British Insurers; Bank of England; Cadbury Schweppes; Channel 5; Geest; 3i.

Other Notable Practitioners Following the fragmentation of Langely & Co, **Dale Langley** (see p.336) has formed **Dale Langley & Co. Lawrence Graham's** head of department **Yvonne Gallagher** (see p.332) is gaining profile while **Garretts** head **Sean Nesbitt** (see p.338) is "*a good bloke – making headway.*" "*Charming*" **Ian Hunter** (see p.334) of **Bird & Bird** is rated for his work in the technology and finance sectors.

APPLICANT FIRMS

EMPLOYMENT: MAINLY APPLICANT • London	Ptnrs	Assts
1 Pattinson & Brewer	6	8
2 Russell Jones & Walker	6	14
Thompsons	4	9
3 Bindman & Partners	4	2
Rowley Ashworth	3	9
4 Lawfords	2	2
5 Irwin Mitchell	4	2

This book is the product of 6,552 1/2-hour interviews. See p.7 for BMRB audit.
Within each band, firms are listed alphabetically.

Pattinson & Brewer (see firm details p.1091) Union-endorsed and widely admired amongst employment lawyers of all types. "*First class intellect*" **Simon Auerbach** (see p.328) and "*always fair*" **David Cockburn** (see p.330) are both "*prominent*" and "*good to deal with.*" One employer indicated that the firm is known to produce "*fierce litigators.*" The group has a depth of experience in executive severance, discrimination cases and human rights issues. Recent cases include Jones v Post Office, a Court of Appeal case concerning the defence of justification in disability discrimination, and another involving London Underground concerning the complex legal requirements relating to notices of industrial action. **Clients:** Trade Unions.

Russell Jones & Walker (see firm details p.1116) "*Highly rated*" by unions and employers' lawyers, many of whom were enthusiastic in referring private clients to the firm. The effective team has grown in size as its profile runs high. Top names **Edward Cooper** (see p.330) and **Clive Howard** (see p.334) are joined this year in *Chambers'* rankings by **Paul Daniels** (see p.331). Referring lawyers confirm that they "*always get good reports back on him,*" opposing lawyers are impressed by his ability to "*hector employers.*" Cases have included the American Airlines maternity claims and the team recently defended NASUWT in a Court of Appeal claim brought by a student who challenged the right of the union to progress industrial action. **Clients:** Police Federation; FDA; TUC; Connect (formerly STE); UNIFI; building society staff unions.

Thompsons "*Tacticians who give as little as possible up front*" according to some, "*reasonable and sensible*" according to others. There is unanimous praise for "*inspiring*" **Stephen Cavalier**, acknowledged to be only one of a talented team that has "*geared up in a major way*" and now competes for senior executive work as well as its more traditional union work. Recently involved in a case in the European Court relating to paid annual leave and working time regulations against the British government and a case for the TUC about parental leave and regulations. **Clients:** UNISON; GMB; MSF; PCS; GPMU

Bindman & Partners (see firm details p.882) Best known for its discrimination claims, the employment practice sits well within the broader civil liberties context of the rest of the firm. A significant amount of its work is in the not-for-profit sector acting for charities, London Bouroughs, the Law Society, Birkbeck College and the Labour Party. Cases often have a bias towards sex discrimination and maternity rights. **Clients:** Law Society; Labour Party.

Rowley Ashworth Known to "*fight its corner*" on cases, the team no longer includes Michael Short, who has retired. Lufthansa case. The group enjoys a following among leading industrial trade unions, offering a high level of quality advice. It advised AEEU, MSF and GMB in relation to the Rover rescue and was involved in the Security and facility division vs Hayes case defending employess rights to subsistence allowance success. Successfully argued before the CAC in the AEEU and VIA Systems case that a maintenance department is an appropriate bargaining unit. **Clients:** AEEU; MSF; GMB.

Lawfords (see firm details p.1029) The firm is popular with union clients because of the "*clear and thorough advice*" given, speedy response to urgent matters and clarity of its communication with lay representatives. Increasingly the team is acting for employers following its move to central London. The lead lawyer is Joy Drummond who has received plaudits for the firm's work on Fletcher v HSBC (part of the Preston case). Other topics on the agenda of late are whistle-blowing, references and the interrelation of employment law with issues of ill health. **Clients:** UNIFI; other trade unions and professional organsations; employers.

Irwin Mitchell (see firm details p.1009) Focusing largely on trade union sponsored employment claims, particularly discrimination claims, equal opportunities and human rights issues. It also advises on constitutional matters for unions and assists on TUPE and other questions arising out of mergers and business reorganisations. Sara Leslie heads the team which is growing its profile with the Enderby Speech Therapists case, now into its 14th year. The group also received endorsement for its work on the part time pension action Stirzaker & Others v North Birmingham Mental Health Trust & Others. **Clients:** UNIFI; RCM; AUT; MSF; NATFHE; LMA.

THE SOUTH

EMPLOYMENT • The South	Ptnrs	Assts
1 **DMH** Crawley	3	3
2 **Blake Lapthorn** Portsmouth	2	3
3 **Cripps Harries Hall** Tunbridge Wells	1	3
Rawlison Butler Crawley	1	2
4 **asb law** Crawley	3	6
Bond Pearce Southampton	3	5
Brachers Maidstone	2	2
Paris Smith & Randall Southampton	1	2
Thomson Snell & Passmore Tunbridge Wells	3	1
5 **Clarkson Wright & Jakes** Orpington	1	2
Pattinson & Brewer Chatham	5	4
Stevens & Bolton Guildford	1	2

LEADING INDIVIDUALS	
1 **CRAWFORD Adrian** DMH	**DABBS Louise** Rawlison Butler
KELLY Jill Thomson Snell & Passmore	
2 **ARCHER Catherine** Bond Pearce	**SHERRARD Harry** Sherrards
TATA Rustom DMH	**WHITEMORE Sarah** Warner Goodman

This book is the product of 6,552 1/2-hour interviews. See p.7 for BMRB audit.
Within each band, firms are listed alphabetically. *See individuals' profiles p.327*

DMH (see firm details p.944) After a move to Crawley, this "*good, solid decent firm*" is still holding the top band in the South, boasting some "*impressive operators*" at the senior end of the team. With a public sector bias to the client roster, the work is balanced between the contentious and the non contentious. Quintin Barry is now a consultant. **Rustom Tata** (see p.342) ably heads the group and **Adrian Crawford** (see p.330), who handles most of the private sector work, has impressed our interviewees, being someone "*you can get things done with.*" In the last year the team has undertaken high profile work for LB Croydon. **Clients:** City individuals; Thistle Hotels; NHS trusts; Forbouys; HFC Bank; FIMAT.

Blake Lapthorn (see firm details p.886) Advising employers in the leisure, charities, retail and manufacturing sector, and applicants from the City and the high street, the firm offers an across the board service. One of the key contacts in the team is Gillian Leach. The team has proven its skills to clients, its advice and training courses being "*detailed, impressive and pragmatic.*" It acted on the TUPE case of Kerry Foods v Creber in the EAT (Court of Appeal case now pending). **Clients:** Lockheed Martin; De La Rue; Twinings Tea; Medicaid; Johnson Controls; Amey.

Cripps Harries Hall (see firm details p.927) A smaller team than previously, but continuing its good reputation acting for a majority of employer clients. At the controls is partner Roger Byard. Last year the group advised a major client on the restructuring of its business, which entailed the redundancies of some 40% of the workforce in one sector of the business. **Clients:** Hidden Hearing International; Swiss Life (UK); Hoverspeed; Dencare Management Group.

Rawlison Butler (see firm details p.1104) Newly ranked this year, the small team is headed by "*no nonsense practical lawyer*" **Louise Dabbs** (see p.330), who "*chooses carefully what points to fight.*" A number of City practitioners mentioned their "*healthy respect for her.*" The firm advised on the outsourcing transaction between British Airways and Amadeus, involving some 200 staff. On the contentious side it is advising in a disability discrimination case against a public utility. **Clients:** Suzuki GB; LeadingSide; West Pharmaceutical Services; Wartsila NSD (UK); Centacom; Amadeus.

asb law (see firm details p.865) The loss of a senior figure in the employment group is thought to be a disappointment for the team but it continues to keep a good name in the region. Headed by Rebecca Thornley-Gibson, the team includes a barrister. With clients in both the public and private sectors, work in the last year has included a Court of Appeal hearing on time limits for a large Surrey educational establishment and the defence of sex discrimination allegations for a local authority client. It has handled numerous tribunal matters for insured and uninsured corporate clients, particularly in insurance, travel and transport and recruitment. **Clients:** Direct Line Group Services; Virgin group companies; Marley; Whirlpool; Tomy; QS Group.

Bond Pearce (see firm details p.888) The Southampton branch of the firm enters the employment rankings this year with positive feedback for both **Catherine Archer** (see p.328) and the team. Clients speak of "*good quality and a good relationship with them.*" The team has grown noticeably in the last year and advised Isle of Wight College in connection with a major reorganisation. It is currently handling a case concerning the employment status of agency workers. **Clients:** B&Q; University of Southampton; Post Office; New Look; British American Tobacco; Safeway.

Brachers (see firm details p.893) Acting principally for employers and for applicants through insurers, the lead partner here is Alan Hannah. The Maidstone team works with further lawyers in the firm's London office. Clients include a number of NHS trusts and large regional employers. It has acted repeatedly in unfair dismissal cases for City fund managers and last year advised a port operator in a strike dispute. **Clients:** Eurotunnel; Kimberly Clark; Link Insurance; The Tate Gallery; NHS trusts.

Paris Smith & Randall (see firm details p.1089) Following the retirement of Malcolm Ross, the team is felt to have successfully maintained its profile. It acts for small to large local employers and a wide range of individuals in the South. Mary Siddall now heads the department. Recently the firm was selected by Mondial Assistance UK (the legal expenses insurers) to be one of two providers of employment services in the UK. It also received instructions from the Equal Opportunities Commission in the case of Sawyer v Robson Cottrell. **Clients:** Portsmouth FC; Southampton Institute; Millbrook Furnishing Industries; Skandia Life Assurance.

Thomson Snell & Passmore (see firm details p.1155) "*Building up a practice of good quality work.*" **Jill Kelly** (see p.335) received special praise for her "*straightforward*" and "*excellent*" approach. Work has ranged from City executive terminations through to union recognition issues. In a recent case, it brought a claim against the Amalgamated Engineering and Electrical Union concerning the duties of trade union officials to their members. **Clients:** East Sussex County Council; Floplast; Boots; Advanced Healthcare; Colas; Friendly Hotels.

Clarkson Wright & Jakes (see firm details p.917) An Orpington firm headed by Claire Singleton, handling employment matters for a range of clients from individual applicants through to multinationals. In the last year it has advised a worldwide executive search company on the dismissal of a senior consultant and a multinational hi-tech company on a nationality discrimination claim. **Clients:** Heidrick & Struggles; Panalpina World Transport; Global Home Loans.

Pattinson & Brewer (see firm details p.1091) An applicant/union based practice which is judged to "*get the job done.*" It is known to work well with instructed counsel and has strength in discrimination, human rights and executive severances. The majority of work comes from the transport and general workers union and is mainly handled by Paul Meehan. Typical cases involve sex discrimination, unfair dismissal and harrassment. **Clients:** RMT; Communication workers union; transport and general workers union.

Stevens & Bolton (see firm details p.1143) Instructed by large multinationals and their subsidiaries on contentious and non contentious matters and also by employees. The group, under the guidance of Paul Lambdin, has recently seen court action on issues including unfair constructive dismissal following allegations of harassment and bullying, and breach of confidence, copyright and covenants issues. **Clients:** BOC; Guildford College; Hays and subsidiaries; Novartis Pharmaceuticals; Procter & Gamble; Computeraid Services.

Other Notable Practitioners **Harry Sherrard** (see p.341) of **Sherrards** continues to attract recommendations, while "*sensible*" **Sarah Whitemore** of **Warner Goodman & Streat** is endorsed by the market for her applicant work.

THAMES VALLEY

EMPLOYMENT • Thames Valley	Ptnrs	Assts
1 **Clarks** Reading	2	12
2 **Henmans** Oxford	1	2
Morgan Cole Oxford, Reading	2	8
Underwoods Hemel Hempstead	2	4
3 **Osborne Clarke** Reading	2	7
Pitmans Reading	2	2

LEADING INDIVIDUALS	
1 **BRIMELOW Russell** Boodle Hatfield	**HENNEY Colin** Henmans
SIPPITT Michael Clarks	**UNDERWOOD Kerry** Underwoods
2 **KINGDON Danielle** Osborne Clarke	

This book is the product of 6,552 1/2-hour interviews. See p.7 for BMRB audit.

Within each band, firms are listed alphabetically. *See individuals' profiles p.327*

Clarks (see firm details p.916) A large respondent dominated practice, which is actively encouraging more applicant work. The team has grown rapidly in recent years and is cited by a number of quality London practitioners as the firm of choice for referrals outside the City. Much of the success is due to the fine reputation of "*top class*" **Michael Sippett** (see p.341). The group, which also includes two HR professionals, has recently been acting in Haddock v Sema Group for the applicant, which involved a £20,000 award for injury to feelings, and was the first award for psychiatric injury in a claim of this type. **Clients:** Global Crossing; Sun Microsystems; Thames Water; News International; Blue Circle Industries; BMW Financial services (GB).

Henmans (see firm details p.991) A tight team working for all types of employees, with a slight majority of employer clients, in areas such as healthcare, pharmaceuticals, agriculture and IT. The recommended name is **Colin Henney** (see p.334), whose long experience places him amongst the region's leading lawyers. **Clients:** EDS; Baxter Healthcare; British BioTech.

Morgan Cole (see firm details p.1074) A much changed team which is felt to undoubtedly miss the leadership of Sue Ashtiany (moved to Nabarro Nathanson in London) and other experienced lawyers from the Oxford office. The new lead employment lawyer in the Thames Valley is Wendy Leydon. In the last year the firm advised BP on employment aspects arising out of a multi jurisdictional outsourcing of BP's telecommunications function to MCI WorldCom. It also advised Oxford Radcliffe Hospital on the employment aspects of a major internal enquiry and other health authorities on employment issues, including TUPE and consultation, arising out of the development of Primary Care Trusts. **Clients:** Amey Group; HSBC Bank; Oxford Instruments; Unipart Group; John Wyeth & Brother; Berkshire Health Authority.

Underwoods (see firm details p.1166) Recently moved to Hemel Hempstead and with a strong following in the local area amongst employers and employees. The partners deal with a number of high level executive terminations and the juniors with a broader range of applicant work. **Kerry Underwood** (see p.343) receives referrals from a number of leading employment practices. The group acted for many of the departing executives following Whitbread's takeover of Swallow Hotels. Issues of note in the last year have included sex discrimination based on gender and sexuality, less favourable treatment for part-time workers, public interest disclosure and human rights issues. In one case, the firm negotiated a settlement of £30,000 for unfair dismissal and sex discrimination arising out of the claimant's gender re-assignment. **Clients:** De La Rue; Atlanco; J&M Insurance Services (UK); HR Owen; JW Russell Group; Friedman Corporation.

Osborne Clarke (see firm details p.1086) Newly ranked this year, the Osborne Clarke team is felt to have done well at establishing a good reputation in the Reading area. **Danielle Kingdon** (see p.336) leads a team working in concert with the London and Bristol offices. A number of the firm's employers fall within the financial and IT sectors. On the contentious side, the team was successful in its defence of SITA Holding in a tribunal claim turning on whether the claimant was an employee or an agency worker. This primarily non-contentious team has handled the employment aspects of the Bournemouth Library PFI for Allied Worldwide and negotiated termination agreements for directors of a number of companies including Black & Decker and National Power. **Clients:** Cunningham Lindsey; Willis National; William Sutton Trust; Prudential; BG; Anite IT Personnel.

Pitmans (see firm details p.1099) A balanced group bolstered by the arrival of a partner from Morgan Cole's Oxford office. Under the guidance of Mark Symons, the group covers primarily respondent work with some board-level applicant instructions. Shareholder issues are a regularly feature of the practice and tribunal claims are handled alongside a range of advice to the firm's corporate clients. **Clients:** Berkeley Homes; De Beers Industrial Diamond; Porsche Great Britain; Norton Healthcare; NHBC; AFN.

Other Notable Practitioners **Russell Brimelow** (see p.329) of **Boodle Hatfield** is building a practice in the Oxford office; at present his profile is greater than that of the group.

SOUTH WEST

Bevan Ashford (see firm details p.880) Dominating the public sector, particularly in healthcare, with a "*credible corporate client base*," the team has "*marked strength.*" It operates out of Bristol and its other west country offices. Clients appreciate "*consistency across the team*" and are "*happy to talk to any of them.*" High profile lawyers include **Sarah Lamont** (see p.336) ("*as good as her reputation*") and **Julian Hoskins** (see p.334), who brings advocacy skills from his time at the bar. Union recognition cases have been on the agenda recently, as have high value High Court and employment tribunal matters. The team was instructed by Orange PS Ltd in connection with a group action following dismissals for email abuse. **Clients:** Rolls-Royce; Allied Domecq; HSBC; University Hospital Birmingham; St George's NHS Trust.

Bond Pearce (see firm details p.888) A "*sensible and pragmatic*," team that displays "*no ego-trips*" and works flexibly between offices in Bristol, Exeter and Plymouth. Lead name **Nikki Duncan** (see p.331) operates primarily out of Plymouth but is known nationally (in part as the current secretary of ELA). The reputation of its Bristol partner is growing and that office has

EMPLOYMENT • South West	Ptnrs	Assts
1 **Bevan Ashford** Bristol	6	12
Bond Pearce Plymouth	3	9
Burges Salmon Bristol	1	7
Osborne Clarke Bristol	3	12
2 **Pattinson & Brewer** Bristol	1	1
Thompsons Bristol	1	2
Thring Townsend Bath	1	2
3 **Burroughs Day** Bristol	1	3
Michelmores Exeter	*	*
Stephens & Scown Exeter	2	n/a
TLT Solicitors Bristol	n/a	n/a
Veale Wasbrough Bristol	1	6

LEADING INDIVIDUALS	
1 **DUNCAN Nikki** Bond Pearce	**HEMMING Julian** Osborne Clarke
SOUTHAM Chris Osborne Clarke	
2 **LAMONT Sarah** Bevan Ashford	**SEATON Christopher** Burges Salmon
3 **BENSON Nick** Michelmores	**MOORE Nigel** Stephens & Scown
UP AND COMING	
HOSKINS Julian Bevan Ashford	**ROBERTS Stephen** Thring Townsend

This book is the product of 6,552 1/2-hour interviews. See p.7 for BMRB audit.
Within each band, firms are listed alphabetically. *See individuals' profiles p.327*

now taken on the team of employment lawyers from the now disbanded Cartwrights. Last year it advised two international and a number of national clients on strategic issues, including European Works Councils, union recognition bids and employee consultation. An HR professional now heads the training schemes offered to clients. **Clients:** Post Office; The National Trust; B&Q; British European Airways; Newscom; Tibbett & Britten; Safeway; FirstGroup; Greene King; Dunlop Slazenger.

Burges Salmon (see firm details p.902) "*A marvellous client list*" which includes expertise in education, the voluntary sector, hotels, security and transport. The team sees an increasing amount of European clients. Although not the biggest team on offer, other lawyers "*feel comfortable referring work to them.*" Partner **Chris Seaton** (see p.340) will "*crack on and sort things out*" and his team has been supplemented at senior level in the last year. Advised Standard Chartered Bank on a national basis on issues including Working Time Regulations and assisted Airsprung Furniture Group on its major restructuring. **Clients:** Bristol Water; Forte Hotel Group; Group 4 Securitas; Chase de Vere; Hunting Aviation.

Osborne Clarke (see firm details p.1086) Fresh from the firm's London office, **Chris Southam** (see p.342) has added further profile to an already strong and stable Bristol team that inspires "*confidence.*" Handling much of the sizeable volume of corporate support work, busy **Julian Hemming** "*works his socks off.*" From the Adviceline service to the one-off Employment Tribunal instructions, corporate clients come primarily from the firm's impressive client base. Last year, it had a Court of Appeal outing concerning an equal pay claim against Innology Holdings (formerly National Power) and handled employment aspects of a series of significant M&A transactions. **Clients:** The Royal Mint; EMI; P&O group companies; 24Seven Utility Services; Hanson; Telewest; StepStone.

Pattinson & Brewer (see firm details p.1091) "*If I was a trade union it would be the only place I'd go*" one interviewee reported. The group is noted for its skill in health and safety issues and equal pay issues. A recent case was Michele Chew v Avon & Somerset Constabulary and involved a single mother police officer who worked rotating shift patterns and won a claim of indirect sex discrimintation in the Employment Appeal Tribunal. The firm successfully sued UNISON under the sex discrimination act on behalf of 11 regional women's offices and won a test case against the DSS relating to time off for health and safety training on behalf of a member of the PCS. **Clients:** Public and Commercial Services Union; Police Federation; Transport and General Workers Union.

Thompsons Another strong union oriented practice packed with experience and "*efficient*" lawyers who "*know their stuff.*" Typical cases involve sex, disability and race discrimination claims. Also involved in collective issues and successfully claimed unfair dismissal on behalf of a discharged factory work-force.**Clients:** Unison; MSF; GPMU; AEU; GMB.

Thring Townsend (see firm details p.1155) Formerly Thrings & Long, a small post-merger team continues to receive recommendations for "*quite a mixed bag of work.*" **Stephen Roberts** (see p.339) is known as a good lawyer and attracts referrals from other practices.

Burroughs Day Newly ranked and highly recommended for applicant referral work by leading Bristol practices. The team also acts for employers, particularly within the care homes sector (40 in the region), engineering and manufacturing. Has handled a number of multi-party claims in the last year, including 44 employees of Strachan & Henshaw Machinery (in liquidation) in respect of protective award, breach of contract and unfair dismissal. Also advised 32 employees of an accountancy practice in respect of redundancy, unfair dismissal and protective award claims, and 36 employees of Richmond Frozen Foods/Allied Foods in relation to unfair dismissal and protective awards for failure to consult on a TUPE transfer. **Clients:** Employees; 24seven Vending; nursing/residential care homes; owner-managed engineering and manufacturing business.

Michelmores (see firm details p.1066) **Nick Benson** and a small team within the company and commercial department has experience acting for a variety of employer clients, particularly in the hi-tech sector. The group also acts for applicants from farm labourers to senior executives. Local companies and public sector organisations.

Stephens & Scown Acting primarily for west country based employers and particularly experienced in advocacy nationwide. The leading name within this contentious led practice is **Nigel Moore**, who works from the Exeter office. Last year it handled a range of discrimination trials including some disability claims involving depression and ME. **Clients:** Essillor; Somerset Probation Service; Torbay County Council.

TLT Solicitors (see firm details p.1157) Growth has been quite rapid in recent years and consequently the firm's reputation may not yet have caught up with the pace of activity. Tied into the insurance and financial services sectors, the employment team has been working on a succession of reorganisations and related redundancy programmes. The team, led by Alana Weeks, also serves clients from the public sector and household names in several other sectors. Senior executive work also features. **Clients:** Allied Dunbar; Eagle Star; The St Paul Insurance Company; Zurich Financial Services; Helphire; United Parcel Service.

Veale Wasbrough (see firm details p.1167) With a heavy preponderance of local authority and independent schools clients, this practice is employer led. The team, which is run by Mike Davies, also serves a number of large regional employers on both contentious and non contentious issues. Last year for client BNFL, it was successful in defending a high profile discrimination case. It advised on the Barton Hill urban regeneration scheme, which involved the transfer of local authority employees, and also on the employment issues of the restructuring of Avon Rubber. **Clients:** Countrywide Farmers; Direct Line; Great Mills; Wessex Water; several city and district councils; Universities of Bath and Bristol.

WALES

EMPLOYMENT • Wales	Ptnrs	Assts
1 **Eversheds** Cardiff	3	16
2 **Morgan Cole** Cardiff, Swansea	4	6
3 **Edwards Geldard** Cardiff	1	4
Hugh James Ford Simey Cardiff	1	2
4 **Palser Grossman** Cardiff Bay	2	3

LEADING INDIVIDUALS	
1 **DU-FEU Vivian** Eversheds	**WARREN Martin** Eversheds
WILLIAMS Audrey Eversheds	
2 **REES Anthony** Morgan Cole	
3 **CLARKE Michael** Morgan Cole	**NOTT Christopher** Palser Grossman
UP AND COMING	
DAVIES Joanne Morgan Cole	**LOVE Alison** Hugh James Ford Simey

This book is the product of 6,552 1/2-hour interviews. See p.7 for BMRB audit.
Within each band, firms are listed alphabetically. *See individuals' profiles p.327*

Eversheds (see firm details p.952) Since the closure of the firm's Bristol office, this star team has been supplemented by colleagues from the South West. It also includes HR professionals. "*Biggest in size and the best in Wales,*" the firm and its three ranked partners seem virtually unassailable. **Viv Du-Feu** (see p.331) "*has really got the machinery working there.*" Discrimination expert **Audrey Williams** (see p.343) is "*outstanding*" and **Martin Warren** (see p.343) received endorsement for his work on industrial relations. The client list is superb, for Corus and Sun Life of Canada it successfully defended tribunal claims following dismissals. On the non contentious side, it advised Krupp Camford and Thyssen Krupp in respect of restructuring and redundancy issues. **Clients:** Guernsey Board of Trade and Industry; Hitachi; Panasonic; Sony; Bank of Ireland Asset Management; Stena Line.

Morgan Cole (see firm details p.1074) From Cardiff and Swansea the firm's well established reputation continues and it represents the closest competition to Eversheds in Wales. A number of oil and energy companies are to be found on the client roster, which is also dominated by public sector employers. National head **Anthony Rees** "*is a good advocate and sensible on the other side of matters.*" **Michael Clarke** is "*personable and gets on well with clients,*" and **Joanne Davies** is also recommended. **Clients:** BP Amoco; British Energy; Scottish and Southern Power, University of Wales Swansea; Cardiff and Vale NHS Trust; HSBC.

Edwards Geldard (see firm details p.948) Stephen Jenkins leads this dedicated team that has seen a couple of high profile cases of late. The firm went head to head with Rowe & Maw on the case of ADI v Willer & Others, heard in the Court of Appeal in July 2001, concerning the application of TUPE to outsourcing contracts. It saw further action in the defence of a multi-party claim relating to the alteration of terms and conditions following a TUPE transfer. **Clients:** Williams; Citibank; Chubb; Admiral Insurance Services; NCM Credit Insurance; Arts Council of Wales.

Hugh James Ford Simey (see firm details p.1004) **Alison Love** (see p.336) has raised the profile of the team over the last couple of years. It still handles applicant work but now primarily services large employers within and outside of the region. It successfully brought an unfair dismissal claim against IBM for an employee who had worked for the company for 22 years. It also saw success in its defence of an employer in an unfair dismissal claim in which evidence caught on CCTV was suggested to have been in breach of the applicant's human rights. Successfully defended client Maxibrite in a claim pertaining to dismissal following a water pollution incident. **Clients:** WRU/Millennium Stadium; GE Capital Equipment Services; Leekes of Llantrisant; Sekisui; Yu Sung; Christ College Brecon.

Palser Grossman **Chris Nott** (see p.338) is "*a top choice*" and has an enhanced profile through his work for ELA in Wales. Most of the clients are Welsh businesses but the team also acts for a number of national clients and deals with higher value applicant/senior executive instructions. The case brought against client TRW by various unions (TNG, AEU, MSF) continues and is now in the EAT. It also acted for South East Wales TECH on employment issues arising from its demise. **Clients:** Dyson; International Greetings.

MIDLANDS

EMPLOYMENT • Midlands	Ptnrs	Assts
1 **Eversheds** Birmingham, Nottingham	5	28
Wragge & Co Birmingham	5	20
2 **Hammond Suddards Edge** Birmingham	4	5
Pinsent Curtis Biddle Birmingham	3	6
3 **DLA** Birmingham	n/a	n/a
Higgs & Sons Brierley Hill	2	1
Martineau Johnson Birmingham	1	5
4 **Browne Jacobson** Nottingham	1	3
Freethcartwright Nottingham	4	4
Shakespeares Birmingham	1	2
Shoosmiths Nottingham	1	3
5 **Mills & Reeve** Birmingham	2	n/a

This book is the product of 6,552 1/2-hour interviews. See p.7 for BMRB audit.
Within each band, firms are listed alphabetically.

Eversheds (see firm details p.952) "*An extremely capable team*" operating from Birmingham and Nottingham with a small presence in Derby. "*It has the brand and the resources*" to keep it at the top and competitors feel that its approach ensures "*a clean and quick fight.*" **David Beswick** (see p.328) ("*we habitually refer clients to him*") and **Martin Hopkins** (see p.334) (who is developing the US technology client business) are the big guns in a substantial Birmingham team. They are joined by the "*outstanding*" **Julia Edwards** (see p.331) who has recently moved from Hammond Suddards Edge. In Nottingham, the work is led by newly ranked **Hilary Campion** (see p.329), who "*plays with a straight bat.*" The firm advised on employment issues in the MG Rover (Phoenix) sale and on Guinness' integration with UDV. **Clients:** Alliance & Leicester; Boots; Cap Gemini Ernst & Young; Hewlett Packard; IBM; Post Office; WH Smith.

Wragge & Co (see firm details p.1189) "*Top class and switched on.*" **Martin Chitty** heads a "*strong*" department acting for a wide range of clients including those in financial services, retail and utilities. Non contentious support is drawn from the rest of the firm, but this does not detract from the stand alone activities of this large team. Competitors report that they are "*impressed by the quality of the work.*" **Jonathan Chamberlain** is viewed as "*a typical London lawyer transported to Birmingham and thriving.*" Of "*switched on*" **Andrew Hodge**, one client said "*he's on my wavelength,*" while **Jane Ellis** has also attracted positive recommendation. Last year saw injunctive action in Sun Valley Foods v Vincent and advice to a large industrial concern in relation to industrial action, redundancies and business reorganisation. **Clients:** AT&T; British Airways; BT; BUPA; Lloyds TSB Group; PowerGen.

LEADING INDIVIDUALS		
1	**BESWICK David** Eversheds	**FIELD Roger** Higgs & Sons
	GOODIER Colin Pinsent Curtis Biddle	
2	**CHITTY Martin** Wragge & Co	**DEAN Veronica** Hammond Suddards Edge
3	**BENSON Edward** Browne Jacobson	**CHAMBERLAIN Jonathan** Wragge & Co
	HOPKINS Martin Eversheds	**JONES Alan** DLA
	MARSHALL Ian Martineau Johnson	**POTTER David** Freethcartwright
	RETALLACK James Hammond Suddards Edge	
	WOFFENDEN Sara Shoosmiths	
4	**CAMPION Hilary** Eversheds	**EDWARDS Julia** Eversheds
	GILLESPIE Michael Lee Crowder	**HIBBS Michael** Shakespeares
	HODGE Andrew Wragge & Co	**JAMIESON Andrew** Nelsons
5	**ARMSTRONG Ruth** Gateley Wareing	**ELLIS Jane** Wragge & Co
	JONES Linda Pinsent Curtis Biddle	**MASON Helen** Mason and Co

See individuals' profiles p.327

Hammond Suddards Edge (see firm details p.984) Top of the range of the smaller Midlands teams, the Birmingham branch of this national practice is now operating without the Leicester lawyers that departed following the merger last year. Head of department **Veronica Dean** (see p.331) received warm endorsement, as did former managing partner and "*businessman's lawyer*" **James Retallack** (see p.339) who at time of press announced his intention to move to an in-house role. Julia Edwards has joined the Eversheds team. The group advised Jabil Circuit on the employment aspects in its acquisition of the manufacturing business of Marconi across four jurisdictions. On the contentious side, it was instructed by FA Premier League in the defence of a claim of race discrimination brought by a referee. **Clients:** Boots; Securicor Management Services; Autoglass; Cornhill Insurance; ABN AMRO; Dixons Group.

Pinsent Curtis Biddle (see firm details p.1098) A team which is seen to be stronger and more visible at the senior end than the more junior. There is "*enormous respect*" for "*fabulous*" **Colin Goodier** (see p.333), who is unanimously felt to be a "*gifted technical lawyer.*" **Linda Jones** (see p.335) has returned to the firm from Wragge & Co and has now taken up the reins as head of the department. Last year the firm advised the board of a major plc on the departure of its chief executive and chairman, and advised another major client on the investigation of 50 employees following pornographic email abuse and the subsequent disciplinary action. **Clients:** Crown Prosecution Service; West Bromwich BS; Maersk International; 3i; Smith & Nephew; GKN.

DLA Birmingham is felt by the market not to be the strongest of this national firm's employment teams, but it is headed by "*capable advocate*" **Alan Jones** who continues to attract recommendation.

Higgs & Sons (see firm details p.995) Known to have a good reputation and to "*punch above their weight*" in the Midlands. **Roger Field** (see p.332) is on the referral lists of many of the larger commercial practices in Birmingham "*because he's such a safe pair of hands,*" and although "*he's not quite the grand old man, he's pretty close to it.*" One recent highlight was an instruction from an NHS trust to defend a claim brought by a consultant. **Clients:** Allied Carpets Group; Magnet; Wolverhampton & Dudley Breweries; Wyko Group; Nelson Hind Catering Management.

Martineau Johnson (see firm details p.1055) Has developed a "*competent and capable team*" handling some interesting matters in the last year, including advice on industrial action and union recognition. **Ian Marshall** (see p.337) has a fine reputation in the region and is felt to lead the team well. Strong in the education sector, it defended a race discrimination claim by a lecturer and advised on a disciplinary investigation into allegations of sexual harassment by a senior post holder. In the private sector, the team has defended high value claims from former senior executives. **Clients:** De Montfort University; Warwick University; Birmingham University; Shipley Europe; Bullough.

Browne Jacobson (see firm details p.898) Acting for some large East Midlands employers in both the public and private sectors, **Edward Benson** (see p.328) runs a "*reasonable team.*" He is a "*delightful man*" with the ability and reputation to attract high profile cases. Successful defences last year included sex discrimination claims against Nottingham Fire and Rescue Service, and against Eric Potter Clarkson, and a race discrimination claim against Wilkinson Hardware Stores. **Clients:** Derbyshire Police; Hardy & Hansons; Nottinghamshire Police; Leicestershire Police; Kingdom of Leather; Nottingham City Hospital.

Freethcartwright (see firm details p.964) The firm has proved that its employment lawyers can offer "*immense experience, intelligence and charm.*" Most warmly recommended is **David Potter** (see p.339) in the Nottingham office. Clients speak favourably of the "*incredibly good service*" that they get from this "*focused, no frills and impressive*" lawyer and his team. In addition to a high volume of tribunal claims, the firm has also devoted time to working with clients' HR teams. Its focus on the textiles industry has seen it advise a number of manufacturers on the employment aspects of the Marks & Spencer decision to source fewer of its goods within the UK. **Clients:** Experian; Coats Viyella Clothing; Powergen UK; Speedo (Europe); Welbeck UK; Polestar Group.

Shakespeares (see firm details p.1122) In addition to the team size shown, two further partners undertake employment work. The firm is seen as a "*safe bet*" and although some commentators feel that the team could be "*taken up a gear,*" there is no question as to the skills possessed by **Mike Hibbs** (see p.334), who is visiting professor of employment law at the University of Central England. Last year it saved £0.5 million for an insured client company on a claim by employees for enhanced redundancy pay. **Clients:** Pertemps Group; Assicurazioni Generale SpA; Brintons; UCE; Paxar UK; Ansell UK.

Shoosmiths (see firm details p.1129) "*You only ever hear positive things about them,*" our interviewees reported. **Sara Woffenden** (see p.344) inspires "*total confidence*" and is "*a lawyer to be reckoned with.*" Clients include substantial corporates. Recently the firm has been asked to advise employers on statutory trade union recognition, and it handled one of the first cases that involved a contested application to the CAC. It also advised a major manufacturer with disability discrimination claims and gave employment advice to a manufacturer contracting out a process to another company. **Clients:** DHL Aviation; Universal Salvage; Nike Retail; RMD Kwikform.

Mills & Reeve (see firm details p.1069) The health sector focus of the Birmingham office gives the firm a stack of large employer clients. Others include local authorities, police and higher education establishments while the private sector client base is being enhanced. The head of department is Kate Levy. Work covers all aspects of employment advice and combines the particular knowledge required in relation to GMC and NHS enquiries, and ethics committees. **Clients:** Public and private sector employers and senior executives.

Other Notable Practitioners **Ruth Armstrong** at **Gateley Wareing** "*has a well deserved reputation.*" **Michael Gillespie** (see p.333) of **Lee Crowder** continues to pull in favourable comment, as does **Andrew Jamieson** (see p.335), known for his advocacy skills at **Nelsons**. In Derbyshire, **Helen Mason** of **Mason & Co**, who acts for applicants and large employers, received commendations.

EAST ANGLIA

EMPLOYMENT • East Anglia	Ptnrs	Assts
1 **Eversheds** Cambridge, Ipswich, Norwich	5	9
Hewitson Becke + Shaw Cambridge	4	5
Mills & Reeve Cambridge, Norwich	3	10
2 **Steele & Co** Norwich	2	2
3 **Greenwoods** Peterborough	2	5
Taylor Vinters Cambridge	1	6
4 **Prettys** Ipswich	1	2

LEADING INDIVIDUALS	
1 **LAMB Norman** Steele & Co	**SAYER Nicholas** Hewitson Becke + Shaw
WARNOCK Owen Eversheds	
2 **HEMMINGS Richard** The Law Offices of Richard Hemmings LLM Solicitor	
3 **BROWN Nicola** Mills & Reeve	**DILLARSTONE Robert** Greenwoods
TYNDALL Timothy Hewitson Becke + Shaw	
4 **BLOOM Martin** Hegarty & Co	**CASSEL Richard** Hatch Brenner
LYNE Amanda Taylor Vinters	**MATHER Ian** Eversheds
PRYKE Oliver Taylor Vinters	**SCOULAR Gillie** Mills & Reeve
YATES Tracy Eversheds	
ONES TO WATCH	
ROY Judy Mills & Reeve	

This book is the product of 6,552 1/2-hour interviews. See p.7 for BMRB audit.
Within each band, firms are listed alphabetically. *See individuals' profiles p.327*

Eversheds (see firm details p.952) The powerhouse operation is the Norwich office where more than half of the team's lawyers are based. In control is national voice **Owen Warnock** (see p.343), acknowledged "*top dog*" and "*always impressive*," particularly on discrimination. **Tracy Yates** (see p.344) is ranked for her executive severance work and equal pay expertise and in Cambridge, established race discrimination expert **Ian Mather** (see p.337) has attracted endorsement. As in other parts of the country, the Norwich office now has an in-house HR consultant. The majority of work is for employers and the practice has a good niche in health, education and food manufacturing. The team has won instructions from BT Brightstar spin-out companies. For the Archbishops' Council it resolved a complex race discrimination case by mediation, and has now been appointed to provide general employment advice. It has recently been appointed to the new Virgin Group legal panel. **Clients:** Dairy Crest; Eastern Counties Newspapers Group; Centrica; TXU Europe; Elan Pharma; Cambridgeshire Constabulary.

Hewitson Becke + Shaw (see firm details p.994) The Cambridge and Northampton offices are both known for quality advice serving local and national clients, in hi-tech, manufacturing, engineering and brewing. **Nick Sayer** (see p.340) is known as "*a strong and learned player*" and fellow Cambridge partner **Tim Tyndall** (see p.343) "*handles matters extremely ably.*" Both partners have advised on trade secrets and restrictive covenants and also produced instructions concerning industrial disputes. The team successfully defended a plc client in a lengthy Employment Tribunal claim by a senior former employee. **Clients:** TNT International; Johnson Mathey; Booker Cash and Carry; Travis Perkins; Scottish & Newcastle Retail.

Mills & Reeve (see firm details p.1069) **Nicola Brown** (see p.329) in the Cambridge office runs a team which has a focus on the higher education sector. Newly ranked this year, **Gillie Scoular** (see p.340) in Norwich is "*high calibre, with loads of drive and energy.*" Despite the loss of NHSLA work, employment instructions from NHS clients continue. The firm acts for clients nationally but also wins substantial work from the region's hi-tech industries. It was successful in its defence of a sex discrimination claim made against a large local employer and also advised a higher education institution in a sex discrimination claim involving allegations against a member of the academic staff. On the subject of internet abuse, it advised a client on disciplinary procedures and the subsequent dismissal of the offending employee. **Clients:** Education and health sector; agricultural concerns.

Steele & Co (see firm details p.1140) Small but high quality team which achieved its profile through pregnancy in the military class action cases, the firm continues to be instructed on equal pay claims brought against the MOD by recruitment officers. **Norman Lamb** (see p.336) is valued by the market as "*pragmatic and experienced.*" In the last year, there has been an increase in instructions from local authorities. Other clients include those in food manufacturing and local industry. **Clients:** The Stationery Office; Campbell Soups; Kerry Foods; Jeyes; London Boroughs of Croydon, Lambeth and Westminster.

Greenwoods (see firm details p.978) A decent Peterborough based firm that is attracting work from impressive larger clients. This is undoubtedly down to the efforts of **Robert Dillarstone** ("*good and knows what he's talking about.*") Much of the work is contentious tribunal matters for which the team provides most of the advocacy. Pensions and share options advice is also on hand. The team is presently handling a case in the EAT concerning post-termination discrimination under the DDA. It has been acting for a client in the food sector, defending a £1 million claim for unfair dismissal and breach of contract brought by its former Managing Director. Further work includes the defence of eleven separate Tribunal applications brought by four applicants against a client in the pharmaceutical sector. **Clients:** Emap; Railtrack; Enterprise Oil; Barnardos; Willmott Dixon.

Taylor Vinters (see firm details p.1150) Last year saw an influx of tribunal claims and issues concerning whistle blowing. University, hi-tech and bio-informatics clients call upon the firm for contract draftng and advice relating to restrictive covenants. **Mandy Lyne** (see p.336) is "*able, a safe pair of hands*" and the team also offers younger lawyer **Oliver Pryke** (see p.339) who has had a big impact on the firm's operational profile. High value employee work is undertaken. Dick Hemmings continues to act as a consultant to the firm. It has recently been involved on behalf of the employee in a number of cases arising from the laying off of a work-force in Cambridge and two large scale redundancy cases on the side of the employer. Currently acting for a school in relation to the dismissal of a teacher for inappropriate conduct and two tribunals pertaining to sex discrimination. **Clients:** English Nature; Cambridge University; Sanger Centre; Phillips.

Prettys (see firm details p.1100) Acting principally for owner managed businesses in Suffolk and Essex and seeing an increase in instructions from the NFU. The partner in charge of the team is Richard Stace. Last year it advised a client relocating business from France to England, assisted in the closure of the Wolsey Theatre in Ipswich and was instructed in connection with the transfer of 250 drivers from a petrochemical company to a fuel haulier. **Clients:** A local port; IP-City; NFU.

Other Notable Practitioners Dick Hemmings (see p.334) remains a consultant to Taylor Vinters and also runs his own practice, **The Law Offices of Richard Hemmings**. Well known, he is much admired for his "*all round expertise.*" **At Hatch Brenner**, deceptively "*laid back and relaxed*" **Richard Cassel** (see p.330) has come in for widespread praise. **Martin Bloom** (see p.328) at **Hegarty & Co** is known locally to be an able practitioner.

NORTH WEST

EMPLOYMENT • North West	Ptnrs	Assts
1 **Addleshaw Booth & Co** Manchester	2	11
DLA Liverpool, Manchester	n/a	n/a
Eversheds Manchester	2	13
Hammond Suddards Edge Manchester	4	15
2 **Mace & Jones** Liverpool, Manchester	6	9
Whittles Manchester	2	4
3 **Cobbetts** Manchester	4	6
Thompsons Liverpool, Manchester	2	3
4 **Davies Wallis Foyster** Liverpool, Manchester	3	8
Pannone & Partners Manchester	3	3
5 **Halliwell Landau** Manchester	2	5
Weightmans Liverpool, Manchester	2	7

LEADING INDIVIDUALS	
1 **CHAMBERLAIN Andrew** Addleshaw Booth & Co	
HANTOM Charles Whittles	
NICKSON Sue Hammond Suddards Edge	**NORBURY Peter** Eversheds
PIKE Malcolm Addleshaw Booth & Co	
2 **CLARKE Mary** DLA	**WATSON Judith** Cobbetts
3 **EDWARDS Martin** Mace & Jones	**MALONE Michael** Mace & Jones
4 **JACKS David** Weightmans	**PARKINSON Helen** Whittles
RESTON Vincent DLA	**THOMPSON Michael** Eversheds
TRANTER Ian Hammond Suddards Edge	

This book is the product of 6,552 1/2-hour interviews. See p.7 for BMRB audit.
Within each band, firms are listed alphabetically. *See individuals' profiles p.327*

Addleshaw Booth & Co (see firm details p.853) No end of high value employment advice from the large team in Manchester. It acts almost exclusively for employers in all sectors on both contentious and a considerable amount of non-contentious instructions. Peers consider "*impressive*" and "*on the ball*" **Andrew Chamberlain** (see p.330) for referrals: "*I would call him in the vain hope he'd be available.*" He is known to have a great manner with clients. "*Affable*" **Malcolm Pike** (see p.339) is also well known across the UK, regarded as "*proficient and a good all-rounder.*" Last year the group defended 63 employment tribunal claims from former employees of North West Water who retired as a result of ill health from VWF. Also advised on employment matters relating to the PFI project involving Manchester hospitals. **Clients:** Airtours; AstraZeneca; United Utilities; American Airlines; Rolls-Royce Motor Cars; Trinity Mirror; Co-operative Bank.

DLA Felt by the competition to be stronger in Manchester than Liverpool. **Mary Clarke** is said to produce "*world class paperwork*" and **Vincent Reston** is described as "*a charming man, he'll look after you, he's a good technician and a gentleman.*"

Eversheds (see firm details p.952) The employment group has now been joined by a small team of HR consultants and includes a barrister. Its lawyers are judged to be "*hard working and practical in their advice.*" Last year saw increased activity in trade union-related advice for a wide and impressive client base. This office of the national practice also has a strong foothold in the education sector. For some, **Peter Norbury** (see p.338) is "*the best in the table,*" for others the younger name, **Michael Thompson** (see p.342), is equally impressive. The group advised on the reorganisation of United Utilities, and also acted for the Football Association in a number of matters. It was recently successful on appeal for an employer client on a complex and acrimonious DDA claim. **Clients:** Asda; Sharp Electronics; The Corporate Services Group; BNFL; Express Dairies; Princes Soft Drinks.

Hammond Suddards Edge (see firm details p.984) "*Successful in raising its profile*" this employment team, not only the largest in the North West, is also home to the firm's national head **Sue Nickson** (see p.338). A substantial player in the North West, the group also offers newly ranked **Ian Tranter** (see p.342), latterly of Chase Street. The team has close links with the Chartered Institute of Personnel and Development, running their legal advisory helpline. Last year it was instructed by Dewsbury Civil Engineering on a case involving more than 150 applicants. It has also seen some significant trade union recognition instructions. **Clients:** Crédit Lyonnais; Air 2000; Laporte; Niceday Ltd; First Choice Holidays; Matalan Retail.

Mace & Jones (see firm details p.1046) A value for money firm which takes its employment practice seriously and pays particular attention to related areas of health and safety, pensions and benefits and HR training. Its two leading lawyers are **Martin Edwards** (see p.332) and **Michael Malone** (see p.336), both of whom received recommendations from outside of the region. Handling work for a high proportion of public sector clients, it also has a Premier League football club and high claim value applicants amongst its clients. The larger of the two teams is in the Liverpool office. The group has acted recently for three NHS trusts in a multi-party sex discrimination and in equal pay actions. **Clients:** Shell; Merseyside Police; Merseyside Tec; Emerald Airways Group; South Lakeland DC; The Mersey Docks and Harbour Company.

Whittles (see firm details p.1179) Of the firm's four offices, Manchester has the most recognised name for employment work, in no small part due to the superb reputation of "*star personality*" **Charles Hantom** (see p.333). For many the Whittles team is "*the best there is for union issues*" and defendant lawyers speak of it as the most visible player in the market. **Helen Parkinson** (see p.339) is growing her profile in this area. Work spans the whole range of union issues from injunctive proceedings, ballots, collective bargaining and recognition to individual tribunal claims. The firm also acts for non-union claimants.

Cobbetts (see firm details p.923) A partner-heavy team with established names in the area including **Judith Watson** (see p.343), whose practice has a senior executive flavour to it. Other partners handle TUPE, industrial relations, discrimination and public sector clients. Additionally, it is recognised that "*the younger lawyers are committed.*" The respondent orientation of the firm is becoming less dominant, with a more balanced practice emerging. The corporate client roster includes the brewing and licensed trades, communications and IT, manufacturing, trade associations and unions. **Clients:** Royal Ordnance; Sonoco Products; Loot; John Kennedy (Civil Engineering); North British HA.

Thompsons Highly visible in its activities for Unison and GMB, this remains a group of strong practitioners which dominates employee work throughout the region. Enjoys noted strength in equal opportunities and TUPE-related work. **Clients:** UNISON; GMB; The Fire Brigade's Union.

Davies Wallis Foyster (see firm details p.935) Split between Liverpool and Manchester and under the guidance of Andrew Leaitherland this "*growing*" team received warm recommendations from the market. Focusing on corporate clients, last year it advised on the employment aspects of the MBO of Capital Incentives from Bank of Scotland. It handles contentious work as well as non-contentious and subscribes to a broader HR perspective on employment law issues. It recently gave advice to a major cable company on redundancies.**Clients:** Alta Gas; Castrol UK; DSS; EWS Freight Railways; Sega Amusements (Europe); Phillips Components.

Pannone & Partners (see firm details p.1088) Traditionally "*a great breeding ground*" for high calibre employment lawyers, the team has seen significant growth off the back of an increase in its corporate client base and high profile senior executive departures (acting for both individuals and employers). Also found on the agenda is union recognition, employment tribunals and a smaller but increasing amount of corporate support work. Last year the group (which includes Jim Lester) acted for Milliken Industrials in a union recognition dispute which involved an application to the Central Arbitration Committee. **Clients:** Bank of England; Greater Manchester Passenger Transport Executive; KPMG; Reebok UK; Kellogg Management Services (Europe).

Halliwell Landau (see firm details p.982) After a period of cross-selling, the employment department has seen a rise in the volume of business, particularly in terms of corporate support, insolvency-related advice, TUPE and senior exec work. The team head is Stephen Hills. It advised KTH on the employment issues arising out of the acquisition and restructuring of the automotive division of Transtec. **Clients:** AIG Europe (UK); Betterware; Emap Performance; Kwik Fit; Pontins; Umbro International.

Weightmans (see firm details p.1176) The firm has "*a small but good team*" handling employment law, which is split between its Liverpool and Manchester offices. Its core of activity lies in the retail and leisure sectors. **David Jacks** (see p.335) has been singled out as the most recognised lawyer and not only for his niche in education. The team benefits increasingly from the firm's experience in personal injury. **Clients:** Whitbread; Post Office; Triumph Motorcycles; Telewest.

YORKSHIRE

EMPLOYMENT • Yorkshire	Ptnrs	Assts
1 **Pinsent Curtis Biddle** Leeds	3	10
2 **Hammond Suddards Edge** Leeds	3	14
3 **Addleshaw Booth & Co** Leeds	1	4
DLA Leeds, Sheffield	n/a	n/a
4 **Eversheds** Leeds	1	10
Ford & Warren Leeds	2	5
Read Hind Stewart Leeds	2	1
Rollits Hull	2	1
Walker Morris Leeds	1	6
5 **Irwin Mitchell** Sheffield	1	2
Nabarro Nathanson Sheffield	2	3

LEADING INDIVIDUALS	
★ **MCMULLEN John** Pinsent Curtis Biddle	
1 **BOOTH Christopher** Pinsent Curtis Biddle	
2 **MOLYNEUX Pauline** Rollits	**PREST Catherine** Hammond Suddards Edge
SHRIVES Mark Hammond Suddards Edge	
3 **BRADLEY David** DLA	**BREWER Martin** Hammond Suddards Edge
4 **DRAKE Ronald** Read Hind Stewart	**EMMOTT Jeremy** DLA
HILL David DLA	**TWEEDIE Colin** Addleshaw Booth & Co
5 **HEARN Keith** Ford & Warren	**PUGH Keith** Nabarro Nathanson
ROBERTSON Stuart Gordons Cranswick Solicitors	

This book is the product of 6,552 1/2-hour interviews. See p.7 for BMRB audit.

Within each band, firms are listed alphabetically. *See individuals' profiles p.327*

Pinsent Curtis Biddle (see firm details p.1098) Deserving of its "*notch above*" status: "*quite rightly the premier practice in the North.*" Leading lawyer and head of the firm's national practice, encyclopaedic **John McMullen** (see p.337) has a "*stellar*" reputation. He is "*terribly good and has a tremendous academic mind.*" If McMullen is known for the lofty thinking then partner **Christopher Booth** (see p.328) ("*bright and practical*" and "*good with clients*") exemplifies the highly commercial approach of the team. Martin Brewer has recently moved to Hammond Suddards Edge. The client roster is breathtaking and impressive new names are continually added. McMullen advised the Universities and Colleges Employers Association on industrial action involving five unions. On the transactional side, the team advised a US company on employment issues arising out of a disposal of businesses in several countries. **Clients:** Marconi; HSBC; Marks & Spencer; numerous universities; BBC; KPMG.

Hammond Suddards Edge (see firm details p.984) A firm that has put a considerable effort into developing the profile of its Leeds employment team. It has an impressive list of large regional employer clients across a wide spectrum of business sectors. This large team offers three big names at partner level. "*Respected*" and "*pleasant*" **Catherine Prest** (see p.339) is now splitting her time between Leeds and London. Eventually this will leave **Mark Shrives** (see p.341) ("*reasonable to deal with, doesn't get taken for a ride*") as the most established partner in the office. The team has enticed "*sound and straight talking*" **Martin Brewer** (see p.329) from rival Pinsent Curtis Biddle. In the last year, high profile cases included the Huddersfeld Giants RL High Court defence of claims arising out of the termination of the last three former coach/managers, including England coach John Kear and a TUPE claim made against client ICI by 400 former employees. **Clients:** The Post Office; The Building Societies Association; Bradford & Bingley BS; Conoco UK; Kelda Group; Newcastle and Tyneside Health Authority.

Addleshaw Booth & Co (see firm details p.853) A smaller team but acting for big name clients on contentious issues and significant business restructurings, TUPE and redundancies. Head of department, "*experienced*" **Colin Tweedie** (see p.342) "*lives and breathes employment law.*" In the last year he acted for HSBC in its successful Court of Appeal application to overturn the previous decision on reasonableness in unfair dismissal in the case of HSBC v Madden. The firm also advised the major investor in the MBO of Peter Black Holdings, involving service agreements for the three main board directors and 27 other members of management. **Clients:** Yorkshire Electricity Group; The Rugby Football League; Oxford Molecular Group; Leeds Metropolitan University; J Sainsbury; Invensys Group.

DLA "*A sound reputation*" in the region, it operates out of Leeds and Sheffield. It has three well known names at partner level, **David Bradley** ("*the driver*"), **David Hill** and **Jeremy Emmott**.

Eversheds (see firm details p.952) "*A generalist firm with a good broad client base*" and a superb brand name in employment law, although the Leeds office is not felt to be the brightest star in Eversheds' galaxy of employment teams. This is put down to the relative youth of the team. Its partner is Jayne Corr. In the last year it gave advice concerning SpectraSite's joint venture with Transco, handled a racial harassment case for N G Bailey and defended a multi-party TUPE action for Richmond plc.

Ford & Warren (see firm details p.961) A firm getting good press and with a "*strong local client base.*" Knowledgeable **Keith Hearn** leads the team that has expertise in equal pay issues, discrimination claims and directors' dismissal cases. Enjoys a noted niche in the transport industry and successfully obtained injunctions against the RMT in the 2001 rail dispute. Acts for a number of hospital trusts and represented Pinderfield and Pontefract NHS Trust in the Ingoldby Inquiry. **Clients:** Firstgroup; National Express; Danka UK; Hoyer UK; Norbert Dentressangle.

Read Hind Stewart (see firm details p.1104) An admirable showing in the rankings by this small Leeds team, which offers partner attention to local SMEs and owner managed businesses. It also acts for European concerns and is building a reputation with professional firms and education establishments. **Ron Drake** (see p.331) ("*straightforward and talks sense*") is warmly recommended. **Clients:** Solicitors; accountants; a local authority; contract cleaners; national blue collar contracting company; manufacturers.

Rollits (see firm details p.1110) A team that acts in conjunction with lawyers in the litigation department and is felt to be doing "*a good job*" receiving referrals from leading regional employment practices. **Pauline Molyneux** (see p.337) is "*excellent*" and serves clients well. In addition to impressive employer client names, the team advises senior executives and lower paid employees. The firm is currently focusing on hotels and higher education clients. **Clients:** Two universities and higher education clients; Accenture; Kingston Communications; GB Agencies.

Walker Morris (see firm details p.1171) Seen around a lot on the local circuit maintaining its good profile under the guidance of leading partner David Smedley. Endorsed by the market for its contentious employment work on behalf of an envied corporate client base, the group has been active in retail of late acting for Homestyle Group and Redcats plc. It has advised on implementing several large scale redundancy programmes as well as severance arrangements for a number of senior executives. It is currently acting on a DDA claim for the Housing Association in Bradford and acted on a consultancy basis in relation to a number of site closures. **Clients:** Homestyle Group; Redcats; Caterpillar; Damart; Poundstretcher.

Irwin Mitchell (see firm details p.1009) "*Good to deal with and focused on satisfying its clients.*" Operating from Sheffield, the focus is clearly on contentious work. Barry Warne and the team are rated for their skills in TUPE and executive severances, especially in transport, steel and education. Last year the group set up a nationwide employment law helpline for franchised motor dealers and provided wide ranging advice to Sheffield TEC concerning the reorganisation of post 16 education and training. **Clients:** CBR Group; Thorntons; Sheffield Wednesday FC; Henry Boot; Sheffield Centre for Sports Medicine.

Nabarro Nathanson (see firm details p.1078) A team which offers two partners with long experience in industrial relations and large scale employment issues. Drawing on the firm's strengths in London, PFI and outsourcing are growth areas. Department head **Keith Pugh** (see p.339) is well known and liked. Clients come from far beyond the industrial and manufacturing base of the office and include local authorities and property companies. The team acted in Smith & Ors v British Coal Corporation, an equal value claim brought by 1300 claimants, and continues to act in national minimum wage case Bellfield & Ors v Aviation and Airport Services. **Clients:** Capital Shopping Centres; Conoco; Costco Wholesale UK; HSBC; DTI; Siemens.

Other Notable Practitioners "*Sound*" **Stuart Robertson** (see p.340) of **Gordons Cranswick Solicitors** retains his "*good profile.*"

NORTH EAST

EMPLOYMENT • North East	Ptnrs	Assts
1 **Dickinson Dees** Newcastle upon Tyne	3	6
Eversheds Newcastle upon Tyne	2	5
Short Richardson & Forth Newcastle upon Tyne	2	3
Thompsons Newcastle upon Tyne	1	1
2 **Crutes** Newcastle upon Tyne	1	2
Jacksons Stockton on Tees	2	2
Samuel Phillips & Co Newcastle upon Tyne	2	1
Ward Hadaway Newcastle upon Tyne	3	1

LEADING INDIVIDUALS	
1 **CROSS Stefan** Thompsons	**SHORT Michael** Short Richardson & Forth
2 **BLOOM Robin** Dickinson Dees	**GIBSON Robert** Samuel Phillips & Co
LOY Simon Eversheds	**SMITH Tim** Crutes
3 **FLETCHER Kevin** Jacksons	**HESSELBERTH David** Ward Hadaway
UP AND COMING	
TWINEHAM Andrew Jacksons	

This book is the product of 6,552 1/2-hour interviews. See p.7 for BMRB audit.

Within each band, firms are listed alphabetically. *See individuals' profiles p.327*

Dickinson Dees (see firm details p.941) True to form, the firm offers an "*efficient and sensible*" team and one which the market expects to continue to increase its stand alone work. The firm's "*fantastic client base*" provides a heavy flow of instructions while a fine contentious practice remains active. "*Good catch*" **Robin Bloom** (see p.328) is having a positive effect on the team's reputation. Last year it advised Newcastle Hospital NHS Trust on the HR issues arising out of its PFI project, and Formica on its acquisition of Perstorp Warerite. On the contentious side, it was instructed by Rothmans on unfair dismissal claims following a factory closure. **Clients:** ARRIVA; Go-Ahead; Northern Electric; Environment Agency; Reg Vardy; NHS trusts.

Eversheds (see firm details p.952) Working with two HR consultants in the team, this is "*a good bunch of lawyers*" and thought to be the "*most straightforward*" employer firm in the region. "*You know where you stand with them, they don't make a fuss of things.*" Clients report feeling "*at ease*" with the style of service. The standout player here is **Simon Loy** (see p.336), whose work is focused on public sector clients, particularly in health and education. In a matter for the Commissioner for Rights of Trade Union Members, it was involved in an action against AEEU for six lay officials. For one public sector client, it assisted in a major investigation into e-mail and internet abuse. Instructed by a private sector multi-site client, the firm managed a major redundancy programme involving over 100 employees. **Clients:** Invensys; Walkers Snack Foods; Newcastle City Health NHS Trust; North East Chamber of Commerce; University of Newcastle upon Tyne.

Short Richardson & Forth (see firm details p.1130) Employment law is the firm's main specialisation and accordingly it has a well deserved reputation. **Michael Short** (see p.341) is nothing short of an "*employment guru*" according to our interviewees and his profile is by far the strongest in this team. Although acting primarily for employers across the board, from small businesses to plcs, the team also handles some applicant work. **Clients:** Local Authorities; Northern Rock; Peterhouse Group; Nissan Motor Manufacturing (UK).

Thompsons **Stefan Cross** is "*bright and creative in his use of the law;*" as evidence of his success he is perceived to be "*simply deluged with work.*" Union clients know his value and are seen to use him to push forward important issues and agendas. Almost all work is for trade unions and their members; private client work is tangential. On the increase is work arising out of employers' failure to consult with workers, such as the case brought by 200 employees against a BP subsidiary and another brought against Pride Valley Foods. CAC application advice has been popular in the last year. Acted on Morris v AG, a Francovich claim on Working Time. **Clients:** UNISON; GMB; GPMU.

Crutes (see firm details p.928) "*Experienced advocate*" **Tim Smith** (see p.342) is "*totally excellent*" and praised for being well prepared and always on top of things. "*He demonstrates a sound understanding of the law and he confines what he's doing to the relevant areas.*" The team has been appointed to act for the Treasury Solicitor in employment matters and has picked up a number of local authority clients. All advocacy is undertaken in-house. Last year's notable case was the successful defence of a local authority client against a claim of sexual harassment. **Clients:** Mainly public sector.

Jacksons (see firm details p.1010) Busy **Kevin Fletcher** (see p.332) is well known in the area and the profile of younger lawyer **Andrew Twineham** (see p.342) ("*excellent grasp of detail*") is rising. Last year the firm successfully defended British Bakeries in a multi-applicant case concerning changes to terms and conditions of employment. It advised Corus in a demanning exercise and is now representing it in a multi-applicant case arising from consequential redundancies. It also acted for a multinational engineering company in an injunction application following the defection of its MD to a competitor. **Clients:** National Farmers' Union; Black & Decker; Electrolux; Samsung.

Samuel Phillips & Co (see firm details p.1118) The firm is known primarily for its applicant work and much of the praise received by *Chambers'* researchers was for head of team and managing partner **Robert Gibson** (see p.333). He is identified by peers as "*a tenacious fighter*" but has also proved his worth in other arenas, such that he is a newly appointed ACAS Arbitrator. The group is defending a multi-party equal pay claim for an NHS Trust client and has handled some interesting applicant work including a claim by a senior female police officer against Northumbria Police. **Clients:** NHS Trusts; Nestlé; Ultimate Leisure; Alfas Group.

Ward Hadaway (see firm details p.1173) A team that will "*fight a hard match but in an approachable manner.*" **David Hesselberth** (see p.334) is the key name here. The firm acts for an employer led client base and is split evenly between contentious and non-contentious matters. The team advised on the employment aspects of the restructuring of Ken Bell International and handled an eight week race discrimination claim against South Tyneside Healthcare NHS Trust. **Clients:** Wilkinson Sword; Northumbrian Environmental Management; Warner Lambert; Northumberland County Council; Barratts; Philips Components Limited.

SCOTLAND

EMPLOYMENT • Scotland	Ptnrs	Assts
1		
Mackay Simon Glasgow, Edinburgh	9	16
MacRoberts Edinburgh, Glasgow	4	5
2		
Burnside Kemp Fraser Aberdeen	2	3
Dundas & Wilson CS Edinburgh	3	11
McGrigor Donald Glasgow	3	6
3		
Brodies WS Edinburgh	3	5
Harper Macleod Glasgow	2	2
Paull & Williamsons Aberdeen	2	3
Shepherd & Wedderburn WS Edinburgh	3	7
4		
Kidstons & Co Glasgow	2	1
McClure Naismith Edinburgh, Glasgow	2	4
Raeburn Christie & Co Aberdeen	1	1
Thompsons Edinburgh	2	1
5		
Biggart Baillie Glasgow	1	1
Blackadders Dundee	2	n/a
Brechin Tindal Oatts Glasgow	2	2
Maxwell MacLaurin Glasgow	n/a	2
Morton Fraser, Solicitors Edinburgh	n/a	n/a

LEADING INDIVIDUALS	
1	
MACKAY Malcolm Maclay Murray & Spens	**MILLER Stephen** Harper Macleod
SIMON Shona Maclay Murray & Spens	**WILLIAMSON Raymond** MacRoberts
2	
BURNSIDE David Burnside Kemp Fraser	**CULLEN Joyce** Brodies WS
KEMP Sandy Burnside Kemp Fraser	**MACLEOD Euan** Dundas & Wilson CS
NICOL Diane McGrigor Donald	**SALUJA Sean** Paull & Williamsons
YOUNG James McGrigor Donald	
3	
ATACK Iain Kidstons & Co	**BELL Emma** MacRoberts
CHRISTIE Reg Raeburn Christie & Co	**COCKBURN Alistair** Maxwell MacLaurin
GRIFFITHS John Shepherd & Wedderburn WS	**GUNN Sheila** Shepherd & Wedderburn
MACLEOD Ian Shepherd & Wedderburn WS	**MCKENZIE Rod** Harper Macleod
SPEIRS William Brechin Tindal Oatts	**THOMSON Alan** McClure Naismith
WALKER David Dundas & Wilson CS	

This book is the product of 6,552 1/2-hour interviews. See p.7 for BMRB audit.
Within each band, firms are listed alphabetically. *See individuals' profiles p.327*

Mackay Simon (**the employment division of Mackay Murray & Spens**) (see firm details p.1047) Retaining its name, Scotland's premier niche employment practice has joined forces with one of the country's leading commercial practices, Maclay Murray and Spens. It now holds top ranking with an even bigger team located in Glasgow and Edinburgh. The enhanced client base offers a seemingly unlimited supply of good work for this heavily endorsed employment group "*containing a number of very good people who are seen as key players in the field.*" At the head is **Malcom Mackay** (see p.336) who has a broad guru-like vision of employment issues. **Shona Simon** (see p.341) is an adviser to the Scottish Parliament and also a part time tribunal chair. **Clients:** Allied Distillers; British Airways; Compaq.

MacRoberts (see firm details p.1048) A respondent practice handling some higher value applicant matters. Several clients in the power and education sectors sit with many other corporates from the firm's general client base. **Raymond Williamson** (see p.344) ("*an employment lawyer even before employment law started*") is "*exceptionally good and always measured.*" Peers are coming across **Emma Bell** (see p.328) more often and "*have a high opinion of her.*" Last year the group advised on TUPE and other issues in relation to the PPP projects of the Direct Labour Organisation of North Lannarkshire Council, and also on the building and refurbishment of 33 schools for Glasgow City Council. **Clients:** Scottish Power; GlaxoSmithKline; Safeway; Railtrack; Scottish and Southern Energy.

Burnside Kemp Fraser (see firm details p.904) A niche practice in Aberdeen with a distinct leaning towards oil industry clients. It covers primarily contentious tribunal work. "*Bright*" **David Burnside** (see p.329) is valued highly by the market while **Sandy Kemp** (see p.335) blends "*good client presence and good preparation – he is thoroughly good on his feet.*" He is praised for the quality of his pleadings. The team has received some interesting TUPE and disability discrimination instructions relating to employees offshore. **Clients:** Oil and gas companies; educational establishments.

Dundas & Wilson CS (see firm details p.947) Handling its fair proportion of corporate support work, which is only to be expected in this leading commercial practice. Its employer clients also seek strategic and policy advice, with around half of the team's work being contentious. A raft of nearly 700 part time pensions cases is being handled at present. Leading names include **Euan MacLeod** (see p.575) ("*all round skills, brilliant in tribunal and meticulous preparation*") and **David Walker**. The Arthur Andersen link is paying dividends in the number of relocation instructions from the organisation. Last year's highlights included advice on terms and conditions for Bank of Scotland's 22,000 employees and the transfer of 505 staff by the bank to its outsourcing of computer operations to IBM. **Clients:** Bank of Scotland; The Standard Life Assurance Company; Scottish Daily Record and Sunday Mail; Scottish Widows Group; Lloyds TSB Scotland.

McGrigor Donald (see firm details p.1062) Employer-based with some senior executive work, the team is split between Edinburgh, which handles a number of technology companies and start up businesses, and Glasgow, which serves more traditional industries and professional clients. "*Fantastically laid back*" **James Young** (see p.344) "*knows more than he lets on*" and has the approach that attracts other employment lawyers. **Diane Nicol** (see p.338) continues to receive plaudits. The firm advised Scottish Amicable on the re-organisation and transfer of its sales force and acted on the contractual arrangements relating to Martin O'Neil's move from Leicester City to Celtic. Appeared in a PFI deal relating to West Lothian Schools advising on related employment issues. **Clients:** Scottish Amicable; McDonald's Association of Head Teachers of Scotland; Consignia; Forth Ports; Ladbrokes.

Brodies WS (see firm details p.896) A team with "*good people, common sense style and practicality.*" "*Sound and sensible*" **Joyce Cullen** (see p.330) is well known for her work and her speaking engagements. The team has provided key advice to a number of clients, especially in the financial sector, including support for the HR function in the Royal Bank of Scotland concerning the integration of its business with NatWest. For Scottish Amicable, it assisted the HR department during a restructuring exercise relating to its customer service arrangements, which involved widespread change to job functions for over 200 staff. It successfully defended at the EAT, a protective award for 120 former employees of Scotch Premier Meat. **Clients:** BAE Systems; Royal Ordinance; The Melville Craig Group; Royal Scottish Assurance; Scottish Higher Education and Further Education Funding Councils; Dumfries and Galloway Council.

Harper Macleod (see firm details p.987) A respected practice serving mainly employers with some applicant work. **Stephen Miller**, who rises into the top band this year, has "*a good balance between knowing the law and presenting it in a sound and not overstated way.*" **Rod McKenzie** is also recommended. High profile but confidential work has touched on issues of workplace monitoring, pay negotiations and trade union issues. Last year it acted for a former police constable dismissed by Strathclyde Police, who wished to bring a claim for unfair dismissal. It also acted for Douglas King in the compensation case King v Tunnock. **Clients:** Aberdeen City Council; Thus; Box Clever; Direct Line; Excell Multimedia; First Ford.

Paull & Williamsons (see firm details p.1091) Described as "*a strong team,*" it remains a great name on the employment law scene in Aberdeen. Leading light **Sean Saluja** (see p.340), although still young, is already well known as "*a bright guy and a good lawyer.*" Advised Elf Exploration in connection with the sale of its fourth round assets in the North Sea, involving redundancy, TUPE and over 150 compromise agreements. The group advised again on the merger between Elf and Total Fina. **Clients:** Oil and gas industry; educational establishments; healthcare trusts.

Shepherd & Wedderburn WS (see firm details p.1126) A "*pretty strong team*" that is definitely felt to be "*moving onwards.*" Its best known partner, **Sheila Gunn** (see p.333), is "*getting more and more profile.*" **Ian MacLeod** (see p.575) is also solicitor in Scotland to the DfES, the Health and Safety Executive and HM Customs & Excise. **John Griffiths** (see p.333) ("*always charming and able*") has a combined personal injury and employment practice. The team has conducted a high profile TUPE dispute involving employees who transferred from Edinburgh Council and have been claiming pay from collective bargaining still continuing with the Council. Further highlights include advice to Scottish Power in connection with the company's outsourcing and restructuring, and the restructuring of the Scottish Tourist Board. **Clients:** Scottish Life; Mitsubishi Electronic UK; Stagecoach Holdings; Scottish Ambulance Service; Scottish Rugby Union; Allied Distillers/Allied Domecq.

Kidstons & Co (see firm details p.1021) A smaller unit that has a respected presence in the market for small to medium enterprises. Key to much of that profile remains the respected **Iain Atack** (see p.328), head of the department.

McClure Naismith (see firm details p.1059) A team that has earned "*respect*" and can "*work well together*" with other lawyers. The real strength in this team is thought to be **Alan Thomson** (see p.342), who has long experience in all aspects of employment law and industrial relations. Recent work includes employment tribunal cases involving unfair dismissal, redundancy and sex discrimination, the drafting and revising of terms and conditions of employment and advising on industrial relations. **Clients:** BOC Distribution Services; Stagecoach Scotland; First Engineering; Unigate; The Post Office; Chubb.

Raeburn Christie & Co **Reg Christie** (see p.330) ("*extremely good*") and an associate handle work for a number of employer clients in the Aberdeen area, notably those in the oil industry. Instructions are also received from employees at all levels, including some high value severance packages. **Clients:** Employers and employees.

Thompsons The Edinburgh office of this nationally respected firm retains its profile for producing quality work. The group has strong ties to Unison and continues to dominate the union focused market. Works solely for Trade Unions and Employment Trade Unions. **Clients:** Trade Unions.

Biggart Baillie (see firm details p.882) Paul Brown leads the employment work at the newly ranked firm. The team has grown considerably in the last year and services high quality employer clients. Advised Thus in connection with contracts for its call centre staff and Aberdeen Asset Management on the employment aspects of its acquisition of Murray Johnstone. Scottish Power instructed the firm concerning the outsourcing of the workforce at the Longannet Power Station. **Clients:** Belhaven Brewery; ScotRail; Scottish Legal Life; Bargain Books; Loganair; Freightliner.

Blackadders (see firm details p.885) Sandy Meiklejohn leads this Dundee employment practice. In addition to the numbers shown, a further two partners also handle employment work. For Day International, it advised on employment aspects of its business reorganisation, including union consultation. Similarly, it was instructed by Douglas Group in its reorganisation, which involved employee relocation issues. On the contentious side, it handled an eleven day tribunal on race discrimination for NCR Financial Solutions. **Clients:** Madison Cable; Travel Dundee; Day International; Douglas Group; NCR Financial Solutions.

Brechin Tindal Oatts (see firm details p.893) "*Talented*" **Bill Speirs** (see p.342) is "*an able civil practitioner who can turn his hand to anything.*" In the last year the firm has been involved in major redundancy exercises in the textiles industry and the further education sector, and issues concerning email abuse and the management and defence of stress-related illness claims. **Clients:** Employers and employees.

Maxwell MacLaurin A team spearheaded by "*down to earth*" employment lawyer **Alistair Cockburn**.

Morton Fraser, Solicitors (see firm details p.1076) David Stewart leads the employment work, acting mainly for employers in a broad range of business sectors. The last year has seen the team instructed by several senior executives concerning departures in the financial services industry. Also on the agenda have been issues pertaining to TUPE and downsizing in the engineering and manufacturing sectors, and an interesting case of the re-recognition of a previously de-recognised union. **Clients:** Employers and employees.

NORTHERN IRELAND

EMPLOYMENT • Northern Ireland	Ptnrs	Assts
1		
Jones & Cassidy Belfast	3	2
2		
Elliott Duffy Garrett Belfast	2	2
L'Estrange & Brett Belfast	1	1
3		
Carson McDowell Belfast	1	2
Cleaver Fulton Rankin Belfast	2	n/a
Culbert and Martin Belfast	1	2
4		
Napier & Sons Belfast	2	1

LEADING INDIVIDUALS	
1	
JONES Beverley Jones & Cassidy	
2	
BRETT Adam L'Estrange & Brett	**BROCK Adrienne** Elliott Duffy Garrett
CASSIDY Fiona Jones & Cassidy	**COLL Harry** Elliott Duffy Garrett
3	
GRAY David Culbert and Martin	
PRYTHERCH Rosalie Cleaver Fulton Rankin	
TURTLE Brian Carson McDowell	

This book is the product of 6,552 1/2-hour interviews. See p.7 for BMRB audit.

Within each band, firms are listed alphabetically. *See individuals' profiles p.327*

Jones & Cassidy "*Real specialists,*" who may have started out as applicant lawyers but have now crossed over and handle work for employers too. It still has "*the freshness of a new practice set up specifically for employment work.*" It is reported that "*star*" **Beverley Jones** is such a "*hard hitting lawyer*" that employers are "*wary of getting claims from her.*" Less fiery, **Fiona Cassidy** is "*more academic.*" You'll "*get a pragmatic solution from her.*" Both have solid connections with the Equality Commission.

Elliott Duffy Garrett (see firm details p.949) **Adrienne Brock** delivers "*cool and sound advice,*" and is felt to have "*come through from the shadow*" cast by high profile **Harry Coll** (see p.330). His reputation has helped the firm achieve its status as one of NI's leading employment teams, handling the employment aspects of the firm's corporate transactional caseload. The last year has seen a number of significant TUPE matters for employers, which form the bulk of the team's clients. Additionally, work is undertaken for senior execs and managers. **Clients:** Queens University; Goldendale; Seagate; public sector clients.

L'Estrange & Brett (see firm details p.1038) A well respected firm offering advice to companies investing into Northern Ireland and defending tribunal claims on behalf of employers in retail, manufacturing, IT and education. The group has extensive experience in the enforcement and defence of claims concerning restrictive covenants. "*Specialist*" **Adam Brett** (see p.329) is the key lawyer in the unit. **Clients:** RMC; Visteon; Coca-Cola; Galen; Sainsbury's; the Legal Aid Department.

Carson McDowell (see firm details p.909) The firm's large commercial practice provides a wealth of clients, with a substantial number in health and education. General litigator **Brian Turtle** (see p.791) has acquired a fine reputation in employment matters. He "*acts with authority and takes decisions without having to rely on counsel the whole time.*" **Clients:** University of Ulster; Down Lisburn Trust; Avalanche Technology; Shell Direct.

Cleaver Fulton Rankin (see firm details p.918) **Rosalie Prytherch** (see p.339) continues to elicit warm recommendations, while the group is rated for its depth of resources and quality output. **Clients:** Open University, Ireland; Presbyterian Church, Ireland; Clinton Cards; Local authorities.

Culbert and Martin **David Gray** received high praise for his approach: he is "*excellent in his discipline,*" mainly discrimination cases, and is well known for his Law Society disciplinary work. Typically works for semi-government bodies. **Clients:** Equality Commission.

Napier & Sons "*Good, small and well respected.*" The firm is new in the tables this year, with an increased profile as a result of the work of Orlagh O'Neill. It acts for some of the province's largest employers. **Clients:** Post Office; Equality Commission; BT; Fujitsu Telecom; The Council for Catholic Maintained Schools.

LEADERS IN EMPLOYMENT

AARONS, Elaine

Eversheds, London (020) 7919 4500
aaronse@eversheds.com

Specialisation: Partner in employment and pensions group dealing with the full range of contentious and non-contentious employment law matters. Advises employers and senior executives. Specialises in all aspects of employment law, including high level strategic advice, business reorganisations, international projects, service agreements, bonus schemes, restrictive covenants, senior executive severances, board room disputes and high profile discrimination cases. Well known conference speaker, regularly appearing on radio and television.
Prof. Memberships: Employer's Forum on Statute and Practice (Chair), London Law Society (Employment Law Sub-Committee), Employment Lawyers Association (member, having been an officer 1997-00, Management Committee Member 1992-00).
Career: Qualified in 1982 with *Norton Rose* specialising in employment law since then. Head of employment at *Eversheds* London (and its predecessor firms) since 1989.
Publications: General editor of Tolley's 'Termination of Employment'.

ADAMS, Elizabeth

Beachcroft Wansbroughs, London (020) 7242 1011
eadams@bwlaw.co.uk

Specialisation: Partner and departmental leader of employment; practice covers contentious and non-contentious employment work undertaken for both public and private sector clients including discrimination claims on the grounds of sex, race, disability and trade union activities including harassment claims. Has in-depth knowledge of the Transfer of Undertakings (Protection of Employment) regulations 1982 (TUPE). Particular interest in EU social policy aspects and working time. Lectures extensively on all aspects of expertise; regular contributor to the firm's Employment Focus and contributor to 'Strategic Procurement for the NHS' (The NHS Confederation).
Prof. Memberships: Member of the City of London Solicitors Employment sub-committee; CBI Competing for Quality Advisory Group; member of the Employer Lawyers Association and its International Committee.
Career: LLB (Hons) Law 1977. Admitted 1980 at *Beachcroft Hyman Isaacs* (now *Beachcroft Wansbroughs*) from 1981. Partner 1986 to date.
Personal: Born 15 April 1955. Interests include reading and travel. Lives in Horsley.

ANDREW, Jill

Archon (formerly Langley & Co), London (020) 7397 9650

Specialisation: Partner. Handles all aspects of contentious and non-contentious employment law. Acted in Payne & others v Port of London Authority (then the longest ever Industrial tribunal). Frequent contributor to legal and personnel publications. Regular lecturer. Media contributions have included Newsnight, Panorama, Business Breakfast and Kilroy.

Prof. Memberships: Employment Lawyers Association

Personal: Born 8 March 1956. Attended Exeter University, LLB(Hons); London School of Economics, MSc in Industrial Relations and Personnel Management. Lives in Chislehurst.

ARCHER, Catherine

Bond Pearce, Southampton (023) 8063 2211
carcher@bondpearce.com

Specialisation: Solicitor advising on all aspects of employment work, especially contentious matters, including advocacy at Employment Tribunals. Advises public and private companies in particular on matters relating to sex, race and disability discrimination, contested dismissals, major redundancies and large-scale reorganisations. Particular importance is placed on preventative advice to avoid disputes. Provides in-house training to clients and other HR professionals.

Prof. Memberships: Member of the Employment Lawyers Association.

Career: Articled with *Higgs & Sons*; qualified 1997; joined *Bond Pearce* 2000.

ARMSTRONG, Ruth

Gateley Wareing, Birmingham (0121) 234 0000

ASHTIANY, Sue

Nabarro Nathanson, London (020) 7524 6000

ATACK, Iain F.

Kidstons & Co, Glasgow (0141) 221 6551
mail@kidstons.co.uk

Specialisation: Senior partner. Main area of practice is employment law: accredited as a specialist by the Law Society of Scotland. Advises mainly employers on all aspects of employment law. Represents at tribunals in Scotland and England. Also handles general civil litigation and factoring law. Advises invoice factors on all commercial matters. Major clients include several large plcs operating both in England and Scotland, banks, financial institutions and many medium sized companies. Lectures at conferences. Formerly tutor in Advocacy & Pleading at Glasgow University.

Prof. Memberships: Law Society of Scotland, Royal Faculty of Procurators in Glasgow, Employment Law Group. Member Law Society of Scotland Employment Law Committee.

Career: Qualified in 1971. Joined *Kidstons & Company* in 1972, becoming a partner in 1975 and senior partner in 1993. Council member of Royal Faculty of Procurators 1989-92. Committee member of Employment Law Group since 1984. Chairman of NHBC Appeal Tribunal since 1990.

Personal: Born 22 November 1947. Attended Kelvinside Academy, Glasgow, then St Andrew's University. Leisure interests include walking, skiing and sailing.

AUERBACH, Simon

Pattinson & Brewer, London (020) 7400 5100

Specialisation: Partner in Employment Department. Practises in all areas of labour, employment and discrimination law. Particular interest in transfers of undertakings, industrial conflict and trade union law. Has addressed meetings of the Industrial Law Society, Employment Lawyers' Association and the Institute of Employment Rights. Occasional media commentator.

Prof. Memberships: Industrial Law Society, Institute of Employment Rights, Employment Lawyers' Association.

Career: Qualified in 1985. Partner with *Pattinson & Brewer.*

Publications: Co-author of 'A Guide to The Employment Act 1988' and author of 'Legislating for Conflict' (OUP, 1990) and 'Derecognition and Personal Contracts' (IER, 1993). Has had articles published in the Industrial Law Journal and Political Quarterly. Regular writer in specialist publications and conference speaker.

Personal: Born in 1961. Educated at Oxford University (BA in Jurisprudence, 1st Class Hons, 1982 and D.Phil, 1988). Lives in London.

BELL, Emma

MacRoberts, Glasgow (0141) 332 9988
emma.bell@macroberts.co.uk

Specialisation: Partner in employment law group. Significant experience in conducting Employment Tribunal and Employment Appeal Tribunal hearings and in negotiating exit and entrance packages at senior executive level. Advises on disability, sex and race discrimination issues and the implications of collective redundancies, business transfers and business re-organisations.

Prof. Memberships: Law Society of Scotland.

Career: Trained with *John Wilson & Co.* Qualified 1993. Assistant, associate and partner (2000) with *MacRoberts* in employment law group.

Personal: St Josephs College, Dumfries; University of Strathclyde LLB (Hons), Dip LP, NP. Leisure interests include walking, skiing, hockey. Lives in Glasgow.

BENSON, Edward

Browne Jacobson, Nottingham (0115) 976 6000
ebenson@brownej.co.uk

Specialisation: Practice covers full range of employment law services including drafting contracts of employment, general employment advice, representation at employment tribunals, unfair dismissal, redundancy pay, discrimination, equal pay, minimum wage, working time, union recognition etc.

Prof. Memberships: Member of Industrial Law Society.

Career: Admitted 1980. *Slaughter and May* 1978-82. Joined *Browne Jacobson* 1989, partner since 1993.

Publications: Contributor and general editor of 'Employment Law Service for IPD', published by Jordans. Assistant editor of handbooks and supplements at IDS (1982-84). Editor of 'Industrial Relations Legal Information Bulletin (1985-89)'.

BENSON, Nick

Michelmores, Exeter (01392) 436244

BESWICK, David

Eversheds, Birmingham (0121) 232 1000

Specialisation: Contentious and non-contentious employment law, advising mainly employers, including education institutions, with strengths in executive severance packages, TUPE issues, mergers and acquisitions, restructuring and restrictive covenants. David is also an accredited mediator.

Prof. Memberships: Law Society. Employment Lawyers' Association. Education Lawyers' Association; CEDR Mediator.

Career: Joined *Eversheds* in 1985. Partner 1996.

Personal: Born 18.2.63. Attended Newcastle University 1981-84. Leisure interests include badminton and tennis.

BLOOM, Martin

Hegarty & Co, Peterborough (01733) 346333

Specialisation: Partner and head of employment law department. Undertakes a wide range of contentious and non-contentious employment work primarily for business clients, but also for individuals. Undertakes advocacy at Employment Tribunals and regularly presents seminars across the UK to clients and fellow professionals.

Prof. Memberships: Law Society; Employment Lawyers Association; Industrial Law Society.

Career: Joined *Hegarty & Co* in 1979, qualified in 1981 and became partner in 1983. Appointed part-time Employment tribunal chairman in 1995.

Personal: Born 23 May 1956, educated at King's School Peterborough and Leicester University (LLB). College of Law, Chester. Leisure activities include squash and fly-fishing.

BLOOM, Robin

Dickinson Dees, Stockton on Tees (01642) 631700
law@dickinson-dees.com

Specialisation: Employment law and employment litigation (including use of alternative dispute resolution).

Prof. Memberships: Law Society. Founder Member Newcastle Industrial Tribunal User Group.

Career: Educated: Rugby School, Durham University and Chester College of Law. Career: Articled *Cohen Jackson* and *Addleshaw Sons and Latham.* Admitted October 1982, worked for and subsequently partner in *Cohen Jackson*, now *Jacksons.* Trained as mediator by ADR Net Ltd.

Personal: Married with two children. Main leisure interests are sport (mainly watching but still play the occasional game of cricket); foreign travel; gardening.

BOOTH, Christopher

Pinsent Curtis Biddle, Leeds (0113) 244 5000
chris.booth@pinsents.com

Specialisation: Specialises in employment law dealing with high-profile executive terminations, trade union recognition, TUPE, restrictive covenants and discrimination cases.

Prof. Memberships: Management committee of Employment Lawyers Association (ELA) as North East representative (including membership of ELA International committee). Leeds Law Society.

Career: Educated at Hull University (LLB 1984). Joined former *Simpson Curtis* (now *Pinsent Curtis Biddle*) in 1987 on qualification. Partner 1993.

Personal: Born 1963. Leisure interests: golf, skiing, cooking, family and personal computer.

BRADLEY, David

DLA, Sheffield (08700) 111111

BREARLEY, Kate

Stephenson Harwood, London (020) 7809 2107
kate.brearley@shlegal.com

Specialisation: Partner, head of employment and pensions practice group. Handles all aspects of contentious and non-contentious employment law acting for public and private sector clients, high profile senior executives/directors and teams of employees seeking to join competitors. Leading expert and co-author of the lay textbook on competition in the employment field. Advises on all aspects of employee competition including drafting and enforcement of restrictive covenants. Work includes drafting/negotiating service agreements, and termination packages; Employment Tribunal; County and

High Court claims; stress and discrimination claims; boardroom disputes; employment aspects of corporate transactions; TUPE transfers. Cases of note include representing Charing Cross and Westminster Medical School (now Imperial College School of Medicine) in the fixed term contract case Bhatt v Charing Cross and Westminster Medical School and Another. Chairs conferences and lectures for IBC, EuroForum, CLT and TQPC on employment related topics.
Prof. Memberships: City of London Solicitors Company (Member of the Employment Law Sub-Committee); Employment Lawyers Association; Industrial Law Society; United Kingdom Environmental Law Association.
Career: Called to the Bar 1979. Joined *Stephenson Harwood* in 1986; qualified as a solicitor in 1989; partner 1989.
Publications: Brearley and Bloch, 'Employment Covenants and Confidential Information; Law Practice and Technique' (Butterworths).
Personal: Born 1957. Educated Harrogate Ladies College and Exeter University 1975-78, LLB Hons.

BREEN, Helga
Eversheds, London (0207) 919 4824
breenh@eversheds.com
Specialisation: Partner in employment, pensions and immigration group. Specialises in all aspects of law for corporates and senior executives in both the private and public sector. Her particular interests are project management, business transfers, mergers and acquisitions, directors, executive recruitment and severances. Has developed high level expertise in the banking and financial sectors, particularly financial services regulation and the employment law aspects of outsourcing. Major clients include the Financial Services Authority, Deloitte & Touche/Deloitte Consulting, Cazenove & Co. Responsible for Evershed's Corporate Immigration Services and director/co founder of the Employers' Forum on Statute & Practice. Runs *Eversheds* London client seminar programme and conducts training sessions for clients and external providers. Writes and lectures regularly on employment and HR issues.
Prof. Memberships: Employment Lawyers' Association. Employers' Forum on Statute & Practice (director and co-founder).
Career: BA (Hons) Classics 1981. Qualified 1986 employee benefits group, *Linklaters & Alliance* (then *Linklaters & Paines*). 1991 *PricewaterhouseCoopers* (then *Coopers & Lybrand*). Joined *Eversheds* in 1992 and became a partner in 1994.
Personal: Born 1959. Married with two children. Lives Reigate in Surrey.

BRETT, Adam
L'Estrange & Brett, Belfast (028) 9023 0426
adam.brett@lestrangeandbrett.com
Specialisation: Partner. Main area of work: employment law, discrimination law and commercial litigation.
Prof. Memberships: Law Society of Northern Ireland.
Career: Qualified 1981. Partner in *L'Estrange & Brett* since 1985.
Personal: Born 1957. Education: Oxford University (MA). Committee member Employment Lawyers group in Northern Ireland and member Employment Lawyers Association. Contributor to two Sweet & Maxwell publications on employment law.

BREWER, Martin
Hammond Suddards Edge, Leeds (0113) 284 7000
martin.brewer@hammondse.com
Specialisation: All aspects of employment law including advocacy in large multi-party disputes, non-contentious employment law including advice on TUPE and PFI.
Prof. Memberships: Employment Lawyers' Association; IPD; Industrial Law Society.
Career: Nottingham University (BA) Politics. Studied law at Nottingham Trent University. Qualified 1991. Joined *Pinsent Curtis* in 1993. Partner 1997. Joined *Hammond Suddards Edge* in 2001.
Publications: Co-author of 'Redundancy: The Law and Practice' (2001), Sweet & Maxwell, second edition; Co-author and joint editor of 'Working Time: Law & Practice' 2001, Sweet & Maxwell.
Personal: Photography, guitar, books and horse riding.

BRIMELOW, Russell
Boodle Hatfield, Oxford (020) 7318 8135
rbrimelow@boodlehatfield.com
Specialisation: Partner and head of employment group. Covers all aspects of employment law for companies of all sizes, with some work for senior individuals. Areas of expertise include business transfers (TUPE), working time, executive terminations and discrimination law.
Prof. Memberships: Employment Lawyers Association, Industrial Law Society, Law Society. On editorial board of Croner's 'Questions and Answers', 'Bulletin and European Newsletters'. Writes a weekly column on employment matters in 'Personnel Today'. Regular lecturer at many employment law conferences.
Career: Qualified 1991. With *Denton Hall* 1988-94. Joined *Boodle Hatfield* in 1994, becoming an associate in 1996 and a partner in 1997.
Publications: A range of articles in 'Personnel Today', 'Employers Law', 'Employment Law Journal', 'The Independent', 'Croner's Employment Law Journal' and others. Co-wrote Tolley's 'Working Time' looseleaf.
Personal: Born 1963. Oxford graduate. Father of three. Keen traveller, cyclist, piano, guitar and tennis player.

BROCK, Adrienne
Elliott Duffy Garrett, Belfast (028) 9024 5034

BROWN, Nicola
Mills & Reeve, Cambridge (01223) 222 282
nicola.brown@mills-reeve.com
Specialisation: Specialises in all aspects of employment law acting mainly for employers both in the public and private sector. Deals with contract drafting, advice on dismissals and industrial tribunal claims. Increasing emphasis on discrimination claims and advice on the Transfer of Undertaking Regulations.
Career: 1983 – LLB University of Southampton; 1987 – qualified as a solicitor; 1987-90 – assistant solicitor *Kennedys*, Chiswell Street, London; 1990-95 – senior solicitor *Mills & Reeve*, Cambridge; 1995 to date – partner *Mills & Reeve*, Cambridge.

BURD, Michael
Lewis Silkin, London (020) 7074 8000
michael.burd@lewissilkin.com
Specialisation: Partner and joint head of employment team. Advises in all aspects of employment law. Particular areas of interest include contested dismissals and redundancy, business transfers, Employment Tribunal claims and advice aimed at preventing employment disputes and ensuring compliance with statutory regulations.
Prof. Memberships: Employment Lawyers Association. Committee Member, London Solicitors Litigation Association. President of City of Westminster Law Society (1995/96).
Career: Qualified 1986. Partner at *Lewis Silkin* 1988.
Publications: Consultant Editor, Croner's 'Managing Termination of Employment'. Section Editor, Employment Section, 'Gee Practical Tax Planning and Precedents.'
Personal: Born 07/02/58. BA Columbia University 1980. MPhil Cambridge University 1982.

BURNSIDE, David
Burnside Kemp Fraser, Aberdeen (01224) 327500
Specialisation: Senior partner in court department. Main area of practice is employment. Has handled employment tribunal cases since 1967 in the fields of redundancy, unfair dismissal, sexual and racial discrimination and transfer of undertakings. Acts for a number of major clients in these matters. Accredited by the Law Society of Scotland as an Employment Law Specialist since 1990. Also handles personal injury work. (Member of Personal Injury panel.) Since 1970 has worked predominantly for claimants. Has substantial experience of offshore cases, although also deals with many cases involving injury at work or in road traffic accidents and medical negligence. Joint lead negotiator in Piper Alpha for claimants. Group spokesman for steering committees involving major helicopter crashes. Gives occasional lectures for Aberdeen University, the Law Society, IPM and other outside bodies. Has considerable media experience arising from matters of local and national interest.
Prof. Memberships: Law Society of Scotland, Society of Advocates in Aberdeen, Association of Personal Injury Lawyers, Aberdeen Bar Association, Employment Law Group, ATLA.
Career: Qualified in 1966. Established *Messrs Burnside Advocates* as senior partner in 1989; firm became *Burnside Kemp Fraser* in 1994. President of Junior Chamber of Commerce, Aberdeen, 1978-79; president of Aberdeen Bar Association 1987-89; board member of Legal Defence Union since 1990; Scottish convenor and member of National Executive Committee of APIL 1990-96. Treasurer of Employment Law Group. Treasurer of Society of Advocates in Aberdeen 1990-00.
Personal: Born 5 March 1943.

CAMPION, Hilary
Eversheds, Nottingham (0115) 950 7000
Specialisation: All areas of employment law, contentious and non-contentious. Acts principally for employers but also executive severances.
Prof. Memberships: Employment Lawyers' Association; Nottinghamshire Law Society.
Career: Articled at *Ashton Hill and Co*, Nottingham 1976-78; Lecturer, College of Law, Chester 1978-80; *Eversheds*, Nottingham (formerly *Wells & Hind*) 1980-date. Partner since 1983.
Publications: Various articles in professional and local journals. Contributor to 'Workplace Survival Guide'.
Personal: Emmanuel College, Cambridge MA. CAMRA Member. Derby County Football Club supporter. Enjoys skiing and windsurfing.

CASSEL, Richard
Hatch Brenner, Norwich (01603) 660811
richardcassel@hatchbrenner.co.uk
Specialisation: All aspects of employment and discrimination law. Wide experience of advocacy and tribunal practice and procedure. Advises a substantial number of large and small employers in relation to Employment Law issues both individual and collective.
Career: Qualified as a solicitor in 1980. Partner at *Crotch Brenner and Dunkley* in Norwich. Since 1992 partner and head of employment law department of *Hatch Brenner*. Part-time chairman of the Employment Tribunal from 1993.
Personal: Born 1950, educated at Stationers' Company's School, London and University of Warwick. Lives in Norwich, married with three daughters.

CASSIDY, Fiona
Jones & Cassidy, Belfast (028) 9064 2290

CAVALIER, Stephen
Thompsons, London (020) 7290 0000

CHAMBERLAIN, Andrew
Addleshaw Booth & Co, Manchester (0161) 934 6000
ajc@addleshaw-booth.co.uk
Specialisation: Partner in Employment Department, member of firm's Partnership Board. All aspects of employment law including the drafting of service agreements, Transfer of Undertakings Regulations, restrictive covenant injunctions, executive terminations and all contentious employment matters (including advocacy at the Industrial Tribunals), employment aspects of M & A work, and immigration matters.
Prof. Memberships: Employment Lawyers Association, Manchester Industrial Relations Society.
Career: Joined the firm in September 1995.
Personal: Educated at the University of Nottingham. Interests: golf, rugby, cricket and squash.

CHAMBERLAIN, Jonathan
Wragge & Co, Birmingham (0870) 903 1000

CHITTY, Martin
Wragge & Co, Birmingham (0870) 903 1000

CHRISTIE, Reg
Raeburn Christie & Co, Aberdeen (01224) 640 101
rgc@raeburnchristie.com
Specialisation: Partner specialising in employment law. Full range of issues relating to all aspects of employment law.
Prof. Memberships: Law Society of Scotland, Employment Law Group of Scotland.
Career: Qualified in 1971. Partner in *Raeburn Christie & Co.* 1975.

CLARKE, Mary
DLA, Manchester (08700) 111 111

CLARKE, Michael
Morgan Cole, Cardiff (029) 2038 5385

COCKBURN, Alistair
Maxwell MacLaurin, Glasgow (0141) 332 5666

COCKBURN, David
Pattinson & Brewer, London (020) 7400 5100
Specialisation: Partner in Employment & Trade Union Law Department. Advises in all areas of trade union, employment and discrimination law.
Prof. Memberships: Immediate past Chair of Employment Law Committee of the Law Society. Former Chair and Vice-President of the Employment Lawyers Association. Vice-President of the Industrial Law Society. Chair of EAT Users Group. Treasurer of the Institute of Employment Rights.
Career: Joined *Pattinson & Brewer* in 1972. Qualified 1975; partner 1978.
Publications: Co-author of 'Know-How for Employment Lawyers'.
Personal: Born 30 November 1948. Educated at Kings School, Pontefract, and at LSE for LLB and MSc (Econ) Industrial Relations (distinction).

COLL, Harry
Elliott Duffy Garrett, Belfast (028) 9024 5034
harry.coll@edgsolicitors.co.uk
Specialisation: Partner and head of employment and education law unit. Practice covers all aspects of employment and discrimination law including advising on contractual arrangements for senior employees, dispute resolution and representation at tribunals and elsewhere. Clients include public authorities, third level educational institutes and commercial sectors.
Prof. Memberships: Employment Lawyers Association, American Bar Association.
Career: Qualified 1973. Partner in *Elliott Duffy Garrett* since 1975.
Personal: Born 1946. Educated at Queen's University, Belfast. Awarded OBE in 1994 for services to employment.

COOPER, Edward
Russell Jones & Walker, London (020) 7339 6435
Specialisation: Partner and head of national employment department. Principal area of practice is trade union and employment law. Advises on a wide range of industrial employment and constitutional issues. Also covers administrative and public law. Advises on police terms and conditions of service; acts on union mergers, major privatisations, terms and conditions reviews, new legislation, health and safety, pensions, disputes, discrimination and other employment cases. Clients include the TUC, Police Federation and trade unions in the public and private sectors. The department (now of over 20 executives and with a national presence) has growing employee private client practice.
Prof. Memberships: Industrial Law Society.
Career: Qualified in 1984. With *Simmons & Simmons* 1982-85. Joined *Russell Jones & Walker* in 1985 and became a partner in 1988.
Publications: Author of the trade union section of 'CCH Employment Law Service' and trade union section 'Butterworths Encyclopaedia of Forms and Precedent'.
Personal: Born 12 June 1959. Educated at Bristol University 1977-80. Leisure interests include family, jazz, saxophone, cricket, theatre and tennis. Lives in London SW15.

CRAWFORD, Adrian
DMH, Brighton (01293) 605 072
adrian.crawford@dmh.co.uk
Specialisation: Partner dealing in all aspects of employment law. He has particular interest in the Transfer of Undertaking (Protection of Employment) Regulations 1981 and his recent work includes advising a number of public sector bodies on the legal implications of restructuring under the regulations and statutory transfers orders. He also regularly advises senior executives and appears in employment tribunals and the Employment Appeal Tribunal.
Prof. Memberships: Member of the Employment Lawyers Association.
Career: Trained at *Simmons and Simmons*, qualifying in 1988, made partner in 1995; joined *Donne Mileham and Haddock* (now *DMH*) as partner 1998.
Personal: Leisure interests include family, walking, cycling, avoiding the gym and waiting for his children to be old enough to sail.

CROSS, Stefan
Thompsons, Newcastle upon Tyne (0191) 269 0400

CULLEN, Joyce
Brodies WS, Edinburgh (0131) 228 3777
joyce.cullen@brodies.co.uk
Specialisation: Partner within litigation department's employment law group providing a full range of advice to companies, institutions, partnerships and individuals, including a major Scottish Bank, national retailers, colleges, professional firms and clients in the industrial and manufacturing sectors. Specialises in employment contracts, change management policies, business transfers and redundancies. Extensive experience as an advocate in Employment tribunals, EAT and the Court of Session.
Prof. Memberships: Member of the Management Committee of the Employment Lawyers Association, Industrial Law Group, Institute of Directors.
Career: Qualified in 1981. With *Brodies*, initially as an assistant solicitor and as a partner since 1986. Accredited specialist in employment law and solicitor advocate with extended rights of audience in the Civil Courts.
Personal: Born in 1958. Educated Leith Academy, Edinburgh and Dundee University. Married with three children. Interests include travel and politics.

DABBS, Louise
Rawlison Butler, Crawley (01293) 527744
ldabbs@rawlisonbutler.com
Specialisation: Partner specialising in all aspects of employment law including contractual matters and contract, statutory claims, non-contentious advice and corporate support. Major matters in 2000: advised on all aspects relating to a major outsourcing – providing detailed information and consultation advice in a unionised environment; advised on large-scale redundancy programmes, major employment tribunal matters.
Prof. Memberships: Employment Lawyers Association; associate member of the Institute of Personnel and Development.
Career: Trained *Hunters*, Lincoln's Inn; qualified 1992; solicitor employment department, *Simmons & Simmons* 1995-98; secondment during time at *Simmons & Simmons* to major plc; joined *Rawlison Butler* in 1998; partner and head of employment unit 2000.
Publications: Regular contributor to Croner Publications.
Personal: Education – Jesus College, Oxford (exhibitioner) (BA Jurisprudence). Leisure interests include swimming, walking, cinema.

DALE, Stephanie
Denton Wilde Sapte, London (020) 7242 1212

DALGARNO, David
McDermott, Will & Emery, London (020) 7577 6945
DDalgarno@europe.mwe.com

Specialisation: Partner in Employment group of nine specialist lawyers. Undertakes all types of advisory employment work, contractual and statutory, contentious and non-contentious; primarily for employers, but also acts for senior executives: principal interests include management of integration, employee consultation and organisational change programmes, collective and trade union issues, discrimination, trial advocacy. He also advises on employee benefits and share scheme issues. He frequently speaks on employment law issues; the author of the CCH Employment Contracts manual. Clients include UK and global financial institutions, major industrial concerns, airlines, major retail businesses, inward investors and 'Fortune 500' companies.
Prof. Memberships: Employment Lawyers Association, City of London Law Society Employment Law Sub Committee, Industrial Law Society.
Career: Called to the Bar at Inner Temple 1978; in-house lawyer specialising in employment and labour law at Courtaulds plc 1979-87; Head of Employment *Warner Cranston* 1987-99. Joined *McDermott, Will & Emery* 1999.
Personal: Born in 1955. Educated at Hatfield School 1969-74 and Warwick University 1974-77. ICSL 1977-78.

DANIELS, Paul
Russell Jones & Walker, London (020) 7339 6409
p.a.daniels@rjw.co.uk
Specialisation: Specialises in advising employees and trade unions on all aspects of employment law. Particular expertise in complex discrimination cases (particularly disability), whistleblowers, trade union victimisation and senior executive terminations. Recent cases include Goodwin V Patent Office and Wilding V British Telecom.
Career: Joined *Linklaters* in 1991, qualified in 1993. Joined *Russell Jones and Walker* in 1995, became a partner in 2000.
Personal: Educated in Swansea and Oxford University (Wadham College). Leisure interests include climbing, travelling, acting, pretentious films and the Welsh rugby team.

DAVIES, James
Lewis Silkin, London (020) 7074 8035
james.davies@lewissilkin.com
Specialisation: Partner and joint head of employment team. Advises in all areas of employment law and business immigration. Particular interests include EC employment law, discrimination law, TUPE and sports law.
Prof. Memberships: Employment Lawyers Association (Treasurer, Management Committee for seven years, Chair of Working Groups on TUPE and Age Discrimination); European Employment Lawyers Association; ILS; IPD; ILPA; and BASL. Management Committee of the AIRE Centre. Member Advisory Group of the Employers Forum on Age.
Career: Qualified in 1988. At *Denton Hall* 1986-90. Joined *Lewis Silkin* in 1992.
Personal: Born 26th February 1962. Educated at Ysgol Gyfun, David Hughes, Menai Bridge; Leicester University (LLB and LLM); and Strasbourg University (Dip Ed Jr Fr). Long-suffering supporter of Glamorgan Cricket and Welsh rugby; most sports and travel.

DAVIES, Joanne
Morgan Cole, Cardiff (029) 2038 5385

DAWSON, William
Simmons & Simmons, London (020) 7628 2020
william.dawson@simmons-simmons.com
Specialisation: Has advised on numerous acquisitions, disposals and mergers and transfers of undertakings, both UK and internationally, for major corporations and institutions. He has a strong City-based practice acting for insurance, banking and financial services institutions covering a wide range of complex issues associated with 'high flyers' and has a strong focus on cases involving 'reputational risk'. Has handled many interlocutory matters. Has been voted a 'leading expert' in employment law for several years.
Prof. Memberships: Law Society.
Career: He joined the employment law department at *Simmons & Simmons* in 1981 and became a partner in 1986. He is an employment law practitioner and the department's managing partner. He gained his MA (Hons) law degree from Cambridge University in 1977 and admitted as a solicitor in England and Wales in 1980.

DEAN, Veronica
Hammond Suddards Edge, Birmingham (0121) 222 3000
veronica.dean@hammondse.com
Specialisation: Head of Midlands employment unit. All areas of contentious and non-contentious employment law with a particular interest in Trade Union and labour relations, TUPE and discrimination issues. A regular tribunal advocate.
Prof. Memberships: Law Society, Employment Lawyers Association, Birmingham Employment Tribunal Users Group.
Career: Qualified 1984, Joined *Edge Ellison* 1986, partner 1993.
Personal: Born 1959, Graduate of University of Wales, Cardiff. Interests include art, gardening and entertaining. Lives in Worcestershire.

DILLARSTONE, Robert
Greenwoods, Peterborough (01733) 887700

DINELEY, Rachel
Beachcroft Wansbroughs, London (020) 7242 1011
rdineley@bwlaw.co.uk
Specialisation: Practice in both contentious and non-contentious employment work on behalf of employers and individuals in the public and private sectors. Regularly deals with commercial transactions and preparation/negotiation of executive service agreements as well as board room disputes, dismissals and executive termination packages. Has developed a particular expertise in the protection of data, confidential information and enforcement of restrictive covenants. Has an in-depth knowledge of discrimination law and is a member of the editorial board of Croner's 'Discrimination Law Briefing' in addition to writing the chapter on race discrimination and contributing to two other chapters of Croner's book 'Discrimination Law'. Regularly lectures on these and other topics and devises and delivers training to corporate clients.
Prof. Memberships: Member of the Employment Law Association; Chartered Institute of Personnel and Development; Industrial Law Society.
Career: University of Exeter Scholar LLB (Hons) 1979. Admitted in 1983. Solicitor and then partner at *Denton Hall* before joining *Beachcroft Stanleys* in December 1994.
Personal: Married and lives in the Chiltern Hills. Interests include theatre, extensive travel, photography, skiing and walking.

DRAKE, Ronald
Read Hind Stewart, Leeds (0113) 246 8123
rdrake@rhs-law.co.uk
Specialisation: Unfair/wrongful dismissal, redundancy, equal pay, discrimination and harassment industrial action, TUPE transfer and contracting out. Involved as lead solicitor in Tanks & Drums v T & GWU, Kelman v Care, Janciuk v Winerite, and the Staffordshire Legionnaires' Disease Public Inquiry.
Prof. Memberships: Associate of the Chartered Institute of Arbitrators; affiliate of the Institute of Personnel & Development; member of the Employment Lawyers Association; Industrial Law Society; Competition Law Association; British-Nordic Lawyers Association.
Career: Bradford GS, Manchester University and Chester College of Law. Articles to J Aucott at *Edge & Ellison*, Birmingham. Partner *Last Suddards* (later *Hammond Suddards*) 1981-90. Partner *Read Hind Stewart* 1990 to date. Part-time chairman of Employment Tribunals (Newcastle Region) 1997.
Personal: Married to ex-solicitor teacher, two children. Interests are choral singing, classical music, Scandinavian culture and music. Director of Arts & Business Yorkshire, Kirklees Media Centre Ltd.

DU-FEU, Vivian
Eversheds, Cardiff (029) 2047 1147
vivdufeu@eversheds.com
Specialisation: Partner. Head of the *Eversheds* national employment and pensions group of over 180 lawyers. Has wide experience in providing advice on all aspects of contentious and non-contentious employment law. Lectures and writes regularly on various employment issues and is a member of the editorial advisory board for Croners.
Prof. Memberships: A Fellow of the Chartered Institute of Personnel and Development (CIPD); Director of Principle Training Limited.
Career: Graduate of University of Wales College of Cardiff. Qualified in 1979. Became a partner in 1984.
Personal: Married and resides in Cardiff.

DUNCAN, Nikki
Bond Pearce, Plymouth (01752) 266 633
nduncan@bondpearce.com
Specialisation: Partner and Head of Employment Law Group. Considerable experience in employment law litigation, advocacy and the employment aspects of corporate transactions and discrimination law issues. Regularly speaks at, or chairs, both regional and national employment law seminars and conferences. Has had published numerous articles and given radio and television interviews on topical employment law issues.
Prof. Memberships: Elected Secretary of the Employment Lawyers Association (the first time anyone outside London has been appointed to this key role), previously their UK Training Co-ordinator. Member of the European Employment Lawyers Association and the Regional IT Users Consultative Committee.
Career: Qualified in 1979. Joined *Bond Pearce* in 1982, becoming partner 1985. Previous firm *McKenna & Co.*

EDWARDS, Julia
Eversheds, Birmingham (0121) 232 1000
juliaedwards@eversheds.com
Specialisation: All aspects of employment law including unfair, wrongful and constructive dismissal, sex, race and disability discrimination, corporate reorganisation and executive severance.

Prof. Memberships: Employment Lawyers Association. Association of Women Solicitors.
Career: Articled *Edge & Ellison* (latterly *Edge Ellison* then *Hammond Suddards Edge)*. Admitted 1992; associate 1996; partner 1998.
Personal: Born 1968. Alice Ottley School, Worcester, 1973-86 and Bournemouth University 1986-89. Lives in Worcestershire.

EDWARDS, Martin
Mace & Jones, Liverpool (0151) 236 8989
Specialisation: Head of employment law department. Employment law specialist with extensive advocacy experience. Advises on all aspects of industrial relations law and acts for major clients in the public and private sectors throughout the UK. Also expert in relation to computer contracts. Major cases include Lavery v Plessey Telecommunications (maternity leave).
Prof. Memberships: Law Society, Liverpool Law Society, Employment Lawyers Association, Society for Computers and Law, Society of Authors, Crime Writers Association.
Career: Qualified in 1980 while at *Mace & Jones.* Became a partner in 1984.
Publications: Advised on film 'Letter to Brezhnev'. Author of 'Dismissal Law', 'Managing Redundancies', 'Careers in Law', 'How to get the Best Deal from your Employer', 'Understanding Computer Contracts', 'Know-How for Employment Lawyers', 'Tolley's Equal Opportunities Handbook' and numerous articles.
Personal: Born 7 July 1955. Attended Balliol College, Oxford 1974-77. 1st Class Honours Degree in Law. Leisure pursuits include writing crime novels about Liverpool solicitor Harry Devlin, the first of which was nominated for the award for best first crime novel of 1991. Lives in Lymm, Cheshire.

ELLIS, Jane
Wragge & Co, Birmingham (0870) 903 1000

EMMOTT, Jeremy
DLA, Leeds (08700) 111 111

FARR, John
Herbert Smith, London (020) 7374 8000
Specialisation: Partner in employment and trusts department. Well known for his representation of companies and senior individuals in contentious matters, including High Court applications in connection with restrictive covenants, confidential information and group defections. He deals with corporate governance and boardroom disputes; bonus issues; dismissals and redundancies; pension disputes; discrimination and harassment claims. He also advises on partnership disputes. Non-contentious work covers, inter alia, business transfers and reorganisations, the devising and introduction of new terms of employment and the implementation of new UK and European employment and trade union legislation. He covers immigration and work permit matters.
Career: Qualified in 1974. Became a Partner at *Herbert Smith* in 1982. Member of the City of London Solicitors' Company Employment Law Committee.
Personal: LL.B. (London).

FEINSTEIN, Naomi
Lovells, London (020) 7296 2000
naomi.feinstein@lovells.com
Specialisation: Deals with all aspects of employment law, both contentious and non contentious, including advice on employment contracts, termination packages, employment tribunal claims, redundancies and reorganisations, general day to day employment advice and the employment aspects of corporate transactions.
Career: Articled *Osborne Clarke* and *Lovell White & King.* Qualified 1987. Partner *Lovell White Durrant* (now *Lovells*) 1997.

FIELD, Roger
Higgs & Sons, Dudley (01384) 342 100
Specialisation: All aspects of employment law, 80% employer – 20% employee. Emphasis on national retailer clients. Contentious and non-contentious. Part-time chairman of Employment Tribunals.
Prof. Memberships: Law Society, Birmingham Law Society, Employment Lawyers Association.
Career: Qualified in 1970. Joined *Higgs & Sons* in 1968, becoming a partner in 1974.
Personal: Born 13 January 1946. Educated at Dudley Grammar School and the London School of Economics. Interests include crosswords, railways and cricket. Lives in Stourbridge.

FLANAGAN, Tom
Stephenson Harwood, London (020) 7809 2148
tom.flanagan@shlegal.com
Specialisation: Managing partner, employment and pensions practice group. Employment law, providing a full range of advice to individuals, partnerships, companies and institutions, with particular experience in the banking and finance sector. Also has strong experience in acting for high profile individuals, negotiating both employment and termination packages. Tom is one of the country's leading experts on the application of TUPE to corporate transactions and outsourcing, and has taken an early lead in advising on the changing law of employee consultation. Cases to note include representing the UK banking sector, through HSBC, in the part-time pensions cases in the European Court of Justice and House of Lords in Fletcher v Midland Bank, Preston v Wolverhampton Borough Council; representing the managers of the Rover Group in its sale to Phoenix.
Prof. Memberships: Employment Lawyers Association (Management Committee); Industrial Law Society; Institute of Personnel and Development; Institute of Directors.
Career: Qualified 1979. *Brian Thompson & Partners,* Manchester 1980-84; *Barlow Lyde & Gilbert* 1984-85; *Speechly Bircham* 1985-92 (partner 1988); partner in *Booth & Co* (then *Addleshaw Booth & Co)* 1992-98; joined *Stephenson Harwood* as partner in July 1998.
Publications: Chapters on Transfer of Undertakings Regulations and Employment and Self-employment in 'Tolley's Employment Law'.
Personal: Born 16 January 1954. Educated at Ushaw College, Durham; St Mary's College Middlesborough; University College London. Interests include playing guitar, theatre, blues and jazz. Resides in London.

FLETCHER, Kevin
Jacksons, Stockton on Tees (01642) 643643
genquiry@jacksons.law.co.uk
Specialisation: Senior partner and head of employment law team. Exclusive area of practice is employment law advising and representing mainly employers in all aspects, both contentious and non-contentious. Advocates in tribunals throughout the country and the EAT. Major clients include Corus plc, British Bakeries Ltd, Black & Decker and the National Farmers Union. Part-time chairman of Industrial tribunals in 1991. Regularly gives seminars to clients, professional bodies and employers' associations.
Prof. Memberships: Law Society and Employment Lawyers' Association.
Career: Qualified in 1971. Appointed a partner at *Jacksons* in 1972. Became senior partner in 1995.
Personal: Born 6 March 1947. Educated at Hull Grammar School 1958-65; St Catharine's College, Cambridge 1965-68; The College of Law, Guildford 1968-69. Leisure interests include music, sport, art, reading and travel. Lives in Middlesbrough.

FOX, Ronnie
Fox Williams, London (020) 7614 2501
rdfox@foxwilliams.com
Specialisation: Main areas of practice are employment law and partnership law. Specialises in advising on the calculation and taxation of payments on termination of employment. Frequently negotiates on behalf of the boards of listed companies on the departure of senior executives. Past Master of the City of London Solicitors' Company, Past Chairman of the Practice Management Sub-Committee of the IBA; Past Member of the Law Society Law Management Section Advisory Group. Frequently broadcasts and is the author of numerous articles in the professional and national press on employment, partnership and management topics.
Prof. Memberships: European Employment Lawyers Association, IBA, Law Society, City of London Law Society, Employment Lawyers' Association.
Career: Qualified 1972. Senior partner at *Fox Williams.*
Publications: Author of 'Payments on Termination of Employment' (now in its 3rd edition).

FROST, Peter
Herbert Smith, London (020) 7374 8000
Specialisation: Partner in employment section. Deals with both contentious and non-contentious employment matters with expertise in TUPE issues, executive severances, team defections, the drafting and enforcement of special arrangements for executives (including incentive arrangements and restrictive covenants), proceedings in the Employment Tribunal (particularly discrimination) and the High Court (including injunctive relief), collective matters (including works councils, union recognition and industrial action), and transactional work, including cross-border matters.
Prof. Memberships: Member of the ELA Legislation and Policy Sub-Committee.
Career: Emmanuel College, Cambridge. Qualified in 1985. Became a partner at *Herbert Smith* in 1994.

GALLAGHER, Yvonne
Lawrence Graham, London (020) 7759 6537
yvonne.gallagher@lawgram.com
Specialisation: Specialises in employment issues generally with particular interest in TUPE and dismissals of directors.
Prof. Memberships: ELA, APL.
Career: Trainee at *Copley Clark & Bennett* 1985-87. *Howletts* 1987-89. *Lawrence Graham* 1989-date. Partner since 1996.
Publications: TUPE section of 'Knights Guide to CCT' and Best Value Employment section of Tolleys 'Construction Law'. Numerous articles in professional and trade journals.
Personal: Lives in London. Married.

GAYMER, Janet
Simmons & Simmons, London (020) 7628 2020
janet.gaymer@simmons-simmons.com
Specialisation: Head of employment law department. Employment. Work covers collective and individual, contentious and non-contentious matters and occupational health and safety. Acted for the Ministry of Defence on the contractorisation of the Royal Dockyards and for Railtrack on the British Rail privatisation. Founder chairman of the Employment Lawyers Association and (in 1998) of the European Employment Lawyers Association. Given 'The Times' Woman of Achievement in the Law Award in 1997 and in 1998 'The Lawyer/HIFAL Partner of the Year Award'.
Prof. Memberships: UIA, IBA, Institute of Advanced Legal Studies (Honorary Fellow). Visiting Law Fellow, St Hilda's College, Oxford (1998). Member of the Chartered Institute of Arbitrators, Member of the Council of ACAS until April 2001 and the Executive Board of 'Justice'. Member of the Board of the Royal Shakespeare Company. Patron of the Association of Women Solicitors.
Career: Articled with *Simmons & Simmons* in 1971, qualified in 1973 and became a partner in 1977. Currently head of employment law department and senior partner elect.
Publications: Written numerous articles on employment law and is a frequent lecturer on employment law topics. 'The Employment Relationship', Sweet and Maxwell (2001).
Personal: Born 11th July 1947. Attended Nuneaton High School for Girls 1958-65, then St Hilda's College, Oxford 1966-70. Read LLM at London School of Economics 1976-78. Leisure pursuits include watercolour painting, theatre, music and learning to play the flute. Lives in Effingham.

GIBSON, Robert
Samuel Phillips & Co, Newcastle upon Tyne (0191) 232 8451
Specialisation: Applicant and respondent work in unfair dismissal, race, sex and disability claims. Special interest cases this year being claims under the National Minimum Wage, Working Time Regulations, Whistleblowing and Equal Pay. Advice on policies and procedures. In-house training and employment audits.
Prof. Memberships: ELA; ACAS appointed arbitrator; Deputy District Judge.
Career: Qualified as assistant solicitor 1984; Partner *Samuel Phillips* 1990; Managing Partner 2000.
Personal: Royal Grammar School, Newcastle University, Trustee Talbot House Independent School. Married with two children. Sports: Golf and rugby.

GILLESPIE, Michael
Lee Crowder, Birmingham (0121) 236 4477
michael.gillespie@leecrowder.co.uk
Specialisation: Acting for employees (especially senior executives) and employers in employment disputes. Acted for major French group in connection with the departure of its chief executive and the closure of one of its facilities.
Prof. Memberships: Midlands representative of Employment Lawyers Association.
Career: Admitted in 1971.
Publications: Occasional articles.
Personal: Educated in Birmingham and went to Birmingham University. Married with two children. Interested in the theatre and photography.

GOODIER, Colin
Pinsent Curtis Biddle, Birmingham (0121) 200 1050
colin.goodier@pinsents.com
Specialisation: Partner in employment department, Birmingham. Employment law including contentious and non-contentious work, advice on individual and collective rights and heavy involvement in TUPE, employee consultation and employment aspects of mergers and acquisitions.
Prof. Memberships: Chairman of employment tribunals (England and Wales). Founder member of managing committee of Employment Lawyers' Association. Member of Birmingham Industrial Tribunal Users' group and of Employment Law committee of Birmingham Law Society.
Career: Admitted 1972. Specialist in employment law throughout career. Partner *Bettinsons* Birmingham 1976. Partner *Pinsent & Co* (now *Pinsent Curtis Biddle*) 1987. Head of litigation (Birmingham) 1995. Head of employment (Birmingham) 1996-01.
Personal: Born 1947. Educated Hertford College, Oxford. Interests include renovation of timber-framed cottage; walking; old prints. Elected FRSA 1996.

GOODWILL, Christopher Paul
Clifford Chance, London (020) 7600 1000
christopher.goodwill@cliffordchance.com
Specialisation: All areas of contentious, transactional and advisory employment law.
Prof. Memberships: Employment Lawyers Association. Law Society.
Career: *Clifford Chance*: trainee (1986-88), associate (1988-95), partner (1995 to date).
Publications: Various articles.
Personal: Married to Jane, three children, Sam, Jake and Zac. Interests: Leeds United, cinema and opera.

GRAY, David J.
Culbert and Martin, Belfast (028) 9032 5508

GREEN, David
Charles Russell, London (020) 7203 5000

GRIFFITHS, John
Shepherd & Wedderburn WS, Edinburgh (0131) 473 5445
john.griffiths@shepwedd.co.uk
Specialisation: Partner. Main area of practice is medical negligence: previously Solicitor at the Central Legal Office for the Scottish Hospital Service, advising and acting for the fifteen Scottish Health Boards. With present firm, acts for a leading Medical Defence organisation. Chairman of Law Society Panel to certify solicitors with specialist experience in medical negligence work. Has been responsible for the conduct of litigation in the Scottish Supreme Court, the Court of Session, House of Lords and Sheriff Courts all over Scotland. Has specialist interest in representing parties at Fatal Accident Inquires and advising generally on all aspects of work relating to medical negligence and the National Health Service. Is engaged at any one time in an average of 300 claims, litigations or contentious matters relating to medical or dental negligence. Also advises on administrative and management structure of the NHS and on employment law with a particular emphasis on disciplinary cases against doctors and dentists with regular appearances before the GMC and GDC. Accredited specialist by the Law Society of Scotland. Has spoken and chaired conferences on medical negligence frequently. Author of a number of chapters in a textbook edited by Sir Michael Drury 'Clinical Negligence in General Practice' Radcliff Medical Press Ltd.
Prof. Memberships: Law Society of Scotland.
Career: Qualified in 1971. Trainee at *Shepherd & Wedderburn WS* and *MacAndrew Wright and Murray WS* 1969-71. Joined Central Legal Office for National Health Service in Scotland in 1972, becoming Chief Assistant Solicitor in 1984 and Acting Legal Adviser 1988-89. Joined *Simpson & Marwick WS* as Partner in 1989. *Shepherd & Wedderburn* May 2000.
Personal: Born 16th September 1944. Attended Edinburgh Academy; Wadham College, Oxford 1962-65 and Edinburgh University 1967-69. Lives in Edinburgh.

GUNN, Sheila
Shepherd & Wedderburn WS, Edinburgh (0131) 473 5181
sheila.gunn@shepwedd.co.uk
Specialisation: Head of employment unit at Shepherd & Wedderburn. Accredited as an employment specialist by the Law Society. Advising on (i) the outsourcing for ScottishPower on its £420 million outsourcing and joint venture relating to its IS Division; (ii) advising ScottishPower UK plc on the full range of employment issues in the group restructure of ScottishPower; (iii) advising ScottishPower UK plc on a range of matters including ongoing tribunal cases; (iv) advising on all employment issues and employee integration issues in relation to Scotland's biggest technology acquisition of KSCL (Holdings) Limited by a German company, Telesens AG; (v) advising Northlink Orkney and Shetlands Ferries Limited (a joint venture between The Royal Bank of Scotland plc and Caledonian MacBrayne Limited) on the full range of employment issues (including complex TUPE issues) likely to arise following the company's successful tender to provide ferry services to Orkney and Shetland; (vi) appointed as employment advisor to Britannic Asset Management Limited, a subsidiary of Britannic plc and one of Scotland's fastest growing asset management companies; (vii) appointed as employment advisor to Thus plc throughout the UK; (viii) advising on a wide range of new technology companies, preparing contractual documentation for incentivisation, renumeration and retention of their key executives; (ix) advising on the City of Edinburgh's recent IT PPP outsourcing of the entire IT division to achieve the 'Smart City' vision; (x) the drafting and implementation of The Bank of Scotland's policy under the Public Interest Disclosure Act and other corporate activities of Bank of Scotland. Also engaged in delivering management training for managers of many Scottish companies, including TelesensKSCL, Scottish Ambulance Service, Ballie Gifford, NMT plc, Marriot Hotels, Edinburgh Fund Managers and Britannic Asset Management Limited.
Career: Governor of Hutchesons' Grammar School; Glasgow University (1985 LLB Hons; 1986 Dip. LP).
Personal: Born in 1963; resides in Strathaven. Leisure interests include skiing and walking.

HANTOM, Charles
Whittles, Manchester (0161) 228 2061
Specialisation: Senior partner. Main areas of practice are employment, trade union and industrial. Handles Employment tribunal and EAT work. Undertakes advocacy for employment tribunals. Also handles High Court Injunctive proceedings. Predom-

inantly Trade Union practice. Gives occasional seminars for Trade Union clients.
Prof. Memberships: Employment Lawyers Association.
Personal: Born 24 January 1942. Attended Windermere Grammar School 1954-60, Nottingham University 1960-63, and College of Law 1966. Leisure interests include walking, classic boats and outdoor pursuits. Lives in Bowdon.

HARPER, David
Lovells, London (020) 7296 2000
david.harper@lovells.com
Specialisation: Deals with all aspects of employment law both collective and individual, including executive contracts and severance packages (plus tax, pension and employee benefits aspects), all tribunal litigation, redundancies, discrimination, restrictive covenants, union recognition claims, works councils and employment policies and practices. Handles all employment aspects of transactional work, particularly in relation to PPP/PFI transactions. Regularly appears as an advocate in Employment Tribunals. Substantial experience of collective labour law issues including the new statutory recognition procedure, recently union recognition claims and injunction proceedings.
Prof. Memberships: Employment Lawyers' Association, City of London Solicitors Employment Law Sub-committee.
Career: Articled with *Lovell White & King* (now *Lovells*); qualified 1978; partner 1986.
Publications: Principal editor of CCH Employment Manual, member of editorial board of Employment Lawyer and regular writer on employment matters.
Personal: Born 1954. Educated Stowe School and Keble College, Oxford. Lives in Richmond. Married with four children.

HEARN, Keith
Ford & Warren, Leeds (0113) 243 6601

HEMMING, Julian
Osborne Clarke, Bristol (0117) 917 3000

HEMMINGS, Richard
The Law Offices of Richard Hemmings LLM Solicitor, Ipswich (01473) 833844
Hemmings@dial.pipex.com
Specialisation: Employment law – predominantly for corporate, NHS and local authority clients. Particularly contentious employment law and TUPE. Management training on all employment law issues.
Prof. Memberships: Member of the Council of Employment Chairmen.
Career: LLB (London), LLM (London). Qualified 1974. Partner, 1976-97. Established specialist sole practice employment law, May 1997. Employment tribunal chairman (part-time), 1997. Practising in Ipswich, Cambridge and London Docklands. Consultant with Cambridge solicitors, *Taylor Vinters.*
Publications: Author of the Stationery Office 'Point of Law' series on Employment Law Acts.

HENNEY, Colin
Henmans, Oxford (01865) 722181
Specialisation: Partner and head of employment team. Sole area of practice is employment. Handles the full range of employee and employer work, both contentious and non-contentious. Undertakes advocacy in EAT and Employment tribunals. Member of ELAAS advice and representation scheme at EAT Involved in ACAS training, giving seminars at individual conciliation workshops since 1990. Also provides training to major employer clients and insurers.
Prof. Memberships: Employment Lawyers' Association, Industrial Law Society.
Career: Qualified in 1982. Articled with *Rickerby Watterson* 1980-82; joined *Henmans* in 1983, becoming a partner in 1987; managing partner 1991-3.
Personal: Born 25 November 1957. Attended Daniel Stewart's and Melville College, Edinburgh 1962-75, and Oxford University 1976-79 (Law, BA). Leisure interests include music, golf and Partick Thistle FC. Lives in Eynsham, Oxfordshire.

HESSELBERTH, David
Ward Hadaway, Newcastle upon Tyne (0191) 204 4322
david.hesselberth@wardhadaway.co.uk
Specialisation: Head of employment unit. Dealing with all aspects of employment law. Conducts own advocacy in Employment tribunals. Part-time chairman of Employment tribunals.
Career: Attended RGS Newcastle then Leeds University. Qualified 1976. Trained at *Ward Hadaway* and became a partner in 1987.
Personal: Golf and sailing.

HIBBS, Michael
Shakespeares, Birmingham (0121) 632 4199
Specialisation: Employment law both contentious and non-contentious. Advises mainly employers but also senior employees. Undertakes advocacy in the tribunals. Author of numerous articles. Provides training for a variety of organisations and clients. Speaker at seminars and conferences.
Prof. Memberships: Law Society; Birmingham Law Society; Employment Lawyers Association.
Career: Articled with *Ryland Martineau & Co.* Qualified 1983. Solicitor with *Maurice Putsman & Co* 1983-85; *Bettisons* 1985 (became *Shakespeares* 1990). Partner from 1987. Head of employment law from 1998. Visiting professor of employment law at the University of Central England in Birmingham.
Personal: Born 1958. Leisure pursuits include gardening, walking, watching cricket and rugby.

HILL, David
DLA, Leeds (08700) 111111

HODGE, Andrew
Wragge & Co, Birmingham (0870) 903 1000

HOPKINS, Martin
Eversheds, Birmingham (0121) 232 1000
Specialisation: Partner and head of employment. Main area of practice is employment and industrial relations law. Has wide experience of handling all types of contentious and non-contentious employment work in both the public and private sector. Has an international practice and advises many US businesses on UK start up issues. Leads team of 32 specialist employment lawyers, trainers and HR professionals.
Prof. Memberships: Member of Institute of Personnel and Development and Employment Lawyers Association.
Career: Joined *Eversheds* 1980, qualified in 1982, and made partner and head of employment in 1989.
Publications: Co-author of 'Health and Safety: Are You at Risk?' (1993), 'The Maternity Manual' (1994), 'The Law of Harassment' (1998) and 'EU and International Employment Law' (2000). Speaks frequently on employment issues and regularly delivers in-house tailored training courses for clients.
Personal: Born 28th October 1957. Attended Warwick School 1971-76 and Coventry University 1976-79. Leisure interests include family and travel. Lives in Lighthorne, near Warwick.

HOSKINS, Julian
Bevan Ashford, Bristol (0117) 975 1608
j.hoskins@bevanashford.co.uk
Specialisation: Acts primarily for employers in the private sector, advising on all aspects of employment and discrimination law, both contentious and non-contentious. Has extensive advocacy experience in the higher courts and appears regularly in the EAT and Employment tribunals as advocate for clients of the firm's various offices. Frequent speaker at seminars, both internal and external, and provides tailored training for clients.
Prof. Memberships: Employment Lawyers Association.
Career: Called to the Bar in 1987; practised at 1 Serjeants Inn, Fleet Street, 1987-95. Joined *Bevan Ashford* 1995. Re-qualified as a solicitor and became a partner in 1998.
Personal: Born 1962.

HOWARD, Clive
Russell Jones & Walker, London (020) 7339 6432
c.p.howard@rjw.co.uk
Specialisation: Specialises in employment law. From employees' perspective, with particular emphasis on executive, disputes and terminations, discrimination and data protection. Recent cases include Turner v Grovit (injunction preventing employer from legal action overseas) and Edgar v Met Office (whistleblowing).
Prof. Memberships: ELA
Career: Articled *Gordon Dadds*; qualified 1988. Assistant solicitor *Russell Jones & Walker* 1989-94; partner 1994.
Personal: Kingston Grammar School, Worcester College, Oxford. Interests: family, tennis, golf, skiing, QPR.

HUNTER, Ian
Bird & Bird, London (020) 7415 6000
Specialisation: Partner in the Employment and Immigration section of the Company Commercial Department. Main area of practice is employment law. Specialises in negotiation of payments on termination of employment, the Transfer of Undertakings Regulations, employment aspects of acquisitions and disputes, immigration and sex, race and disability discrimination. Has handled departures from the boards of listed companies and advised on major outsourcing projects.
Prof. Memberships: Law Society, Employment Lawyers' Association.
Career: Qualified in 1989. Joined *Bird & Bird* in 1996.
Publications: Co-author of 'Britain's Invisible Earnings'. Regular contributor to The Financial Times and professional press. Author of 'The WHICH? Guide to Employment Law'. Appears regularly on Channel 5's 'Serious Money' and BBC radio.
Personal: Born 1961. Educated Bristol University. Writing, current affairs. Lives in London.

JACKS, David
Weightmans, Liverpool (0151) 242 7997
david.jacks@weightmans.com
Specialisation: Practice in both contentious and non-contentious employment work and industrial relations law. Principally acts for employers but also for senior executives to negotiate severance packages. Experienced advocate in the employment tribunals. Strengths also in advising companies on contracts of employment/service agreements, re-structuring/redundancy strategies, TUPE and discrimination matters.

JACOBS, Howard
Slaughter and May, London (020) 7600 1200
howard.jacobs@slaughterandmay.com
Specialisation: Executive engagements and dismissals. TUPE.
Prof. Memberships: City of London Solicitors' Company Employment Law Sub-committee.
Career: *Slaughter and May* since 1975.
Personal: Winchester College. Pembroke College, Cambridge. Married, three children. Interests: family and gardening.

JAMIESON, Andrew P
Nelsons, Nottingham (0115) 989 5217
andy.jamieson@nelsons-solicitors.co.uk
Specialisation: Employment law with particular emphasis on disability discrimination and TUPE issues. Involved in major case Kirker v British Sugar, which remains the highest disability discrimination award to date. Highlight of last year has been the introduction of the 'Emplus' scheme providing an all-encompassing service for employer clients.
Prof. Memberships: Law Society. Member of the Employment Lawyers Association.
Career: Articled with Notts. County Council 1980-82. Chief Prosecuting Solicitors Office 1982-85. Joined *Nelsons* 1985. Admitted as partner 1988.
Publications: Regular contributor to legal and business journals on employment related subjects.
Personal: Educated: Punahov School USA, Keele University and Chester College of Law. Leisure interests include military history and music; plays guitar in a band comprising three other lawyers. Married with three children.

JEFFERS, Raymond
Linklaters, London (020) 7456 3702
raymond.jeffers@linklaters.com
Specialisation: Has specialised in the field of employment law since 1978; while covering all aspects of this area, principle roles have been advising public sector and private sector clients of the firm (national, multinational and foreign) an all aspects of employment law.
Prof. Memberships: Chairman UK Employment Lawyers Association. Legislative and Policy Committee since 1999. Vice Chair International Bar Association. Employment and Industrial relations Committee since 2000.
Career: 1998 to date: Co-chair of labour practice group of *Linklaters & Alliance*; 1997 to date: Leader of employment and benefits group; 1986 to date: Partner, *Linklaters*; 1980-85: Assistant solicitor, *Linklaters*; 1978-79: Trainee solicitor, *Linklaters*. 1975-77: Oxford University BCL.

JEFFREYS, Simon
CMS Cameron McKenna, London
(020) 7367 3000
sbj@cmck.com
Specialisation: Partner employment group. Has specialised in employment and labour relations law since qualifying, advising predominantly employer clients in the public and private sectors on all aspects of their legal relationship with employees and trade unions. Work includes contractual documentation, corporate policies towards employees, workforce reductions, negotiations with trade unions, anti-discrimination law, employee and trade union aspects of acquisitions, disposals and PFI deals together with general advice on all aspects of the day to day employment relationship and the resolution of disputes with employees and trade unions. Has appeared as an advocate in the Employment Tribunal and has conducted litigation for clients in the Employment Appeal Tribunal, County Court, High Court and Court of Appeal. Frequently advises clients on interpretation of legislation and the impact of proposed legislation. Has spoken at numerous conferences and seminars. Contributor of employment precedents to Sweet & Maxwell's 'Practical Commercial Precedents' and 'Commercial Checklists', joint editor of 'Employment Precedents and Company Policy Documents' and 'Transfer of Undertakings' and author of 'Hiring and Firing Senior Executives'. Also legal editor for FT Management's 'HR Expert' on-line service.
Prof. Memberships: Employment Lawyers Association; Industrial Law Society; City of London Law Society; Member Law Society of England and Wales Employment Law Committee.
Career: Joined *CMS Cameron McKenna* in 1980 and qualified in 1982. Became a partner in 1988.

JONES, Alan
DLA, Birmingham (08700) 111 111

JONES, Beverley
Jones & Cassidy, Belfast (028) 9064 2290

JONES, Linda
Pinsent Curtis Biddle, Birmingham
(0121) 623 8655
linda.jones@pinsents.com
Specialisation: Head of employment department, Birmingham. Specialises in all areas of employment law with particular experience of large scale redundancies, outsourcing and TUPE in the public and private sectors, executive termination agreements.
Prof. Memberships: Law Society; Employment Lawyers Association.
Career: Educated at Nottingham University 1982-85. Articled to *Pinsent & Co.* Qualified in 1994 and remained with *Pinsent & Co/Pinsent Curtis* until 1999. Joined *Wragge & Co* in 1999 as associate and in 2001 rejoined *Pinsent Curtis Biddle* as partner and subsequently head of department. Previously worked in Human Resources for subsidiary of Mobil Oil Company Limited.
Personal: Married with one son. Leisure interests include food, wine, art, jazz music and supporting Newcastle United Football Club.

JULYAN, Alan
Speechly Bircham, London (020) 7427 6407
alan.julyan@speechlys.com
Specialisation: Practice covers full range of employment and labour law specialising in the employment and corporate governance issues arising on the recruitment, retention and termination of senior executives, TUPE and the management of organisational change.
Prof. Memberships: Law Society. Committee member of the Employment Law Subcommittee of the City of London Law Society. Member of the Industrial Law Society, and the Employment Lawyers Association.
Career: Qualified 1974. Joined *Speechly Bircham* and became partner in 1977.
Publications: Author 'Key Employees-Drafting Service Agreements' published by Sweet & Maxwell and joint Editor of 'Employment Precedents and Employment Policies' published by Gee Publishing Ltd.
Personal: Born 14th October 1949. Educated at Bristol Grammar School and Lanchester Polytechnic. Interests include tennis, painting and jazz.

KEEBLE, Sarah
Olswang, London (020) 7208 8669
sxk@olswang.com
Specialisation: Sarah specialises in all aspects of employment law, both contentious and non-contentious. She is an acknowledged expert on the recently introduced family friendly laws and discrimination issues. In addition, she is very experienced on union law and is an established speaker at seminars on employment issues.
Prof. Memberships: Law Society.
Career: Articles – *Lovell White Durrant* (1987-89); solicitor – *Warner Cranston* (1989-94); solicitor – *Manches* (1994-99, becoming a partner in 1997); joined *Olswang* as a partner, September 1999.
Personal: Education: Nottingham University – 2:1 BA (Hons); Guildford School of Law (All Heads Past First Attempt). Leisure: young daughter.

KELLY, Jill
Thomson Snell & Passmore, Tunbridge Wells
(01892) 510000
jkelly@ts-p.co.uk
Specialisation: Head of employment law department which acts for a substantial commercial client base and senior executives of UK and international businesses, advising on all aspects of employment law.
Prof. Memberships: Employment Lawyers Association; Employment Lawyers Association Training committee; committee of the Weald of Kent CIPD; committee of the St Hilda's College Law network; treasurer of the Tonbridge, Tunbridge Wells & District Law Society 1998-01.
Career: Trained at *Baileys Shaw & Gillett*, London; qualified in 1995; joined *Thomson Snell & Passmore* in 1996.
Publications: Regular contributor to Personnel Today Magazine and the Employment Lawyers Association Briefing.
Personal: University St Hilda's College, Oxford. Enjoys running, gardening and Cornwall.

KEMP, Sandy
Burnside Kemp Fraser, Aberdeen (01224) 327500
Specialisation: Has specialised in employment law and personal injury claims throughout career. Accredited as an Employment Law Specialist by the Law Society of Scotland and member of Assessment Committee for Personal Injury panel. Advises employers and individuals on all aspects of employment law, particularly in relation to offshore oil industry. Has lectured for Law Society and others on employment law, negotiation and on personal injury claims, both generally and arising from offshore industry.

Prof. Memberships: Law Society of Scotland, Society of Advocates in Aberdeen, Employment Law Group, European Employment Lawyers Association, Association of Personal Injury Lawyers, Association of Trial Lawyers of America, Pan European Organisation of Personal Injury Lawyers.
Career: Qualified 1983. Partner at *Philip and Kemp* 1986. Joined *Burnside* 1994 and established *Burnside Kemp Fraser.*
Personal: Born 8 February 1959.

KINGDON, Danielle
Osborne Clarke, Reading (0118) 925 2000

LAMB, Norman
Steele & Co, Norwich (01603) 274 700
noremp@steele.co.uk
Specialisation: Main areas of practice are employment and discrimination. Tribunal advocacy, drafting and advising on terms and conditions, and reorganisations of companies, trade unions recognition issues, collective redundancy consultation, works councils, working time, minimum wage, commercial agents regulations. Regularly lectures and presents training sessions on employment law.
Prof. Memberships: Employment Lawyers Association, Discrimination Law Association.
Career: Qualified in 1984.
Publications: 'Remedies in the Employment Tribunal' (Sweet & Maxwell, 1998).
Personal: Born 16.9.1957.

LAMONT, Sarah
Bevan Ashford, Bristol (0117) 918 8943
s.lamont@bevanashford.co.uk
Specialisation: Partner in employment law department dealing with all aspects of contentious and non-contentious employment law including employment aspects of corporate transactions and PFI; TUPE; service agreements; sex, race, disability discrimination; equal pay; restrictive covenants; trade unions/industrial action; and employment litigation including tribunals and advocacy.
Prof. Memberships: Law Society; Institute of Personnel and Development; Employment Lawyers Association; Industrial Law Society; Bristol Law Society Equal Opportunities Committee; National Employment Tribunal Users Consultative Committee.
Career: MA Cambridge University, trained *Macfarlanes*, London. Qualified 1992, *Veale Wasbrough*, Bristol 1994-99. Joined *Bevan Ashford* as partner 1999.
Publications: Co-author of Jordan's 'Secretarial Administration', Jordan's/IPD 'Employment Service' and Sweet & Maxwell's 'Public and Private Partnerships'. Regularly publishes articles and speaks at employment seminars/courses, including tailored training for clients, and lectures on the Legal Practice Course.
Personal: Astronomy, painting and sketching.

LANGLEY, Dale
Dale Langley & Co, London (020) 7464 8433
dale.lan@btinernet.com
Specialisation: Handles all aspects of contentious and non-contentious employment law, for both individual and corporate clients, with particular knowledge of company law, tax and stock exchange requirements. Often acts for senior city brokers, analysts and traders, and for top executives, including the main board of FTSE 100 companies.
Prof. Memberships: Employment Lawyers Association, Law Society.
Career: Downer Grammar School. Southampton University LLB 2:1 in 1976 (Maxwell Prizewinner 1977). Articled at *Stephenson Harwood*, qualifying in 1981; in 1986 joined *Ashurst Morris Crisp*, establishing their employment law group in 1988. Left in 1993 to set up *Langley & Co*. His firm (now *Dale Langley & Co*) specialises only in employment law, with particular emphasis on acting for the individual.
Personal: Cycling and tennis. Four children.

LILLEY, Andrew
Travers Smith Braithwaite, London
(020) 7295 3253
Andrew.Lilley@TraversSmith.com
Specialisation: Advises on UK/EC employment law and employee relations. Experience includes executive employment contracts; severance arrangements; corporate issues (Transfer of Undertakings Regulations, managing integration etc.); employee consultation (including European works councils), trade union issues, restrictive covenants, redundancy programmes and all aspects of employment litigation and industrial disputes.
Prof. Memberships: Employment Lawyers Association; Industrial Law Society; Law Society.
Career: Qualified at *Freshfields*. Joined *Travers Smith Braithwaite* in 1995, partner from 1997.
Publications: 'Tolley's Employment Law' (contributing author). Other current year publications include articles in 'The European Lawyer' and 'Employment Law Journal'.

LOVE, Alison
Hugh James Ford Simey, Cardiff (029) 2022 4871
alison.love@hjfs.co.uk
Specialisation: Employment law, including both contentious and non-contentious work. Particular interest and experience in discrimination claims. Recently defended a lengthy and high profile racial discrimination claim. Regularly conducts training seminars for a variety of organisations including the Chamber of Commerce and the Law Society as well as in house and external seminars for clients. Regularly speaks at employment law and HR conferences and is currently lecturing on the PGD/MSC human resources management course at the University of Glamorgan.
Prof. Memberships: Employment Lawyers Association. Member of the Chartered Institute of Personnel and Development.
Career: Prior to qualifying as a solicitor, worked for a number of years in personnel within the public and private sector. Since qualifying in 1992, specialised in employment work acting for a broad range of clients. Joined *Hugh James Ford Simey* in April 1999 as a partner and head of the employment law group.
Publications: Regular contributor to national newspapers and business HR journals including 'Croners', 'Employee Benefits', 'Personnel in Practice' and 'Personnel Management'. BBC Wales Radio commentator.
Personal: Ex-county swimmer. Any spare time now spent with her two young sons.

LOY, Simon
Eversheds, Newcastle upon Tyne (0191) 261 1661
Specialisation: All aspects of European and domestic employment law including discrimination, TUPE, equal pay and trade union law. Involved in several reported cases on equal pay, collective consultation and trade union discrimination.
Prof. Memberships: Industrial Law Society; Employment Law Association.
Career: Research Assistant, University College, London. Joined *Eversheds* 1992; partner 1996; Head of employment team at Newcastle office.

LYNE, Amanda
Taylor Vinters, Cambridge (01223) 423444
aml@taylorvinters.com
Specialisation: Partner and head of employment department. Work involves all aspects of employment law, national and European, contentious and non-contentious for companies, institutions and individuals. Contracts and benefits, reorganisations and redundancies, dismissals, transfers of undertakings, equal opportunity and human rights, restrictive covenants. In-house training. Tribunal advocacy. Clients include major high tech, biotechnology, telecoms, printing, pharmaceutical, education (including Cambridge University, other Colleges and schools) and national public sector bodies.
Prof. Memberships: Law Society, Employment Lawyers Association, Industrial Law Society.
Career: Called to the bar in 1969. Qualified as a solicitor in 1981. Joined *Vinters* in 1986 (becoming *Taylor Vinters* after merger in 1988). Became partner in 1989.
Personal: Educated in Adelaide, Australia and Cambridge (MA, LLB). Keen sailor, tennis player, theatre, film and concert goer.

MACKAY, Malcolm
Maclay Murray & Spens, Edinburgh
(0131) 226 5196
mrm@mclaymurrayspens.co.uk
Specialisation: Partner. Practises only in the field of employment law. Lectures in employment law at various universities. Particular interests – industrial relations, transfer of undertakings.
Prof. Memberships: Society to Writers of HM Signet. Member of Institute of Personnel and Development. Law Society of Scotland Employment Law Committee.
Career: Qualified in 1975. Founded *Mackay WS* now *Mackay Simon WS* in 1988 (now the employment law division of *Maclay Murray & Spens*).
Publications: Co-author of Employment Law Update in the 'Journal of the Law Society of Scotland' co-editor of 'Greens Employment Law Bulletin'; co-author of 'Employment Law' published by Greens 1998.
Personal: Born 24 January 1953. Attended Edinburgh University. Lives in Edinburgh.

MACLEOD, Euan
Dundas & Wilson CS, Edinburgh (0131) 228 8000

MACLEOD, Ian
Shepherd & Wedderburn WS, Edinburgh
(0131) 473 5245
ian.macleod@shepwedd.co.uk
See under Litigation, p.575

MALONE, Michael
Mace & Jones, Manchester (0161) 236 2244
michael.malone@maceandjones.co.uk
Specialisation: Partner in employment department. Extensive advocacy experience notably in complex sex discrimination and equal pay cases. Deals with the whole range of employment work acting mainly for employers.

Prof. Memberships: Law Society; International Bar Association.
Career: Admitted in 1968; partner at *Henry Fallows & Co* in Bolton from 1968-91; partner in *Mace & Jones* since 1991.
Publications: Recent publications include 'Your Employment Rights', 'Discrimination Law – A Practical Guide' and the Employment Law section of 'Butterworths Guide on Law for Accountants'. Has also spoken regularly at conferences and seminars.
Personal: Born Bury 1943, educated at Brasenose College, Oxford. Leisure pursuits include tennis, bridge, golf, walking, theatre. Lives in Bolton.

MANN, Jane
Fox Williams, London (020) 7628 2000
jemann@foxwilliams.co.uk
Specialisation: Advises a number of large employers in relation to employment law issues and business immigration. Works closely with in-house legal and personnel departments to provide an integrated service to line management. Has handled a number of difficult and high profile cases. Also acts for senior executives in relation to the termination of employment. Discrimination law and employment litigation are particular interests. Jane has a particular interest in the relationship between good management practice and the successful defence of employment claims. Member of several editorial boards.
Prof. Memberships: Co-founder of Employment Lawyers Association and currently its Chairman. Former Treasurer of the Immigration Law Practitioners Association. Member of the International Bar Association, Member of the Industrial Law Society, the Employment Law Sub-Committee of the City of London Law Society and The American Immigration Lawyers Association. Associate Member of the Institute of Personnel and Development.
Career: Qualified 1981. Worked at *McKenna & Co* 1979-86, then at *Denton Hall* until 1994, where became a partner. Joined *Fox Williams* in 1994 as a partner.
Publications: Legal contributor to 'ExeComp', software to calculate executive compensation. Devised and reported on a survey of women's rights at work for the International Bar Association.
Personal: Born 1957. Attended Cambridge University 1975-78.

MANSELL, Mark
Allen & Overy, London (020) 7330 3663
mark.mansell@allenovery.com
Specialisation: Partner specialising in contentious and non-contentious employment law. Has extensive experience of dealing with all types of employee representative bodies and devising contracts, policies and procedures. Advises on the full range of contentious matters and High Court and tribunal. Has substantial experience in dealing with multi-jurisdictional employment issues – from mergers and acquisitions to outsourcing and individual and collective dismissals. Is an accredited CEDR mediator and heads the department's Lifestyle and Equality Group (LEG).
Prof. Memberships: Employment Law Sub-Committee of the City of London Solicitors Company; European Employment Lawyers Association.
Career: LLB (Hons) London University. Admitted as Solicitor 1985. Legal Advisor, CBI Employment Affairs Directorate (1985-87). Assistant Solicitor *Allen & Overy* 1987-91, Partner (1992).

MARSHALL, Ian
Martineau Johnson, Birmingham (0121) 678 1377
ian.marshall@martjohn.com
Specialisation: All aspects of employment law, contentious and non-contentious, largely for employers. Trial experience includes actions against trade unions, injunctions, contempt of court, and wrongful dismissal. Advice on TUPE, severance agreements, restrictive covenants and equality issues in the private and educational sectors.
Prof. Memberships: Employment Lawyers Association, Birmingham Law Society, Birmingham Employment Tribunal Users Group.
Career: Articled Ry*land Martineau & Co*; partner in *Ryland Martineau & Co.* 1976; *Martineau Johnson* 1987; head of employment department 1994.
Personal: Born 1947. Rugby School and Magdalene College, Cambridge. Married, four children. Lives in Edgbaston, Birmingham. Chairman of council, Edgbaston High School for Girls, Birmingham and Edgbaston Debating Society. St Paul's Club, Birmingham. Fell Walking.

MARTIN, Stefan
Allen & Overy, London (020) 7330 3000
stefan.martin@allenovery.com
Specialisation: Stefan became a partner in the employment, pensions and incentives department in 2000. He advises on the full range of employment law matters, both contentious and non-contentious. Increasingly, his work involves providing and co-ordinating advice in relation to Europe as well as the UK. He regularly advises in relation to high level terminations, discrimination issues, drafting executive contracts of employment, drafting and commenting on employment policies and advising in relation to the employment issues which arise in relation to business transfers. His contentious work involves conducting both high court and tribunal proceedings concerning contractual and statutory claims. Stefan is a regular speaker at client seminars and is head of the department's Workplace Representation and Consultation Group (WoRC).
Prof. Memberships: Employment Lawyers' Association; European Employment Lawyers' Association.
Career: Articled *Allen & Overy* 1990; partner since 2000.
Publications: Contributor to various employment law journals.
Personal: Born 1965. Educated University of Hull (LLB 1988).

MASON, Helen
Mason and Co, Bakewell (01629) 815 175

MATHER, Ian Philip
Eversheds, Cambridge (01223) 224218
ianmather@eversheds.com
Specialisation: Partner in employment department. Heads the employment team in Cambridge. Represents a wide range of employers in various industry sectors including high technology, pharmaceuticals, education, health and the police. His work includes advocacy in the Employment Tribunals dealing with sex, race and disability discrimination as well as unfair dismissal. Ian speaks regularly on employment law topics.
Prof. Memberships: Law Society.
Career: York University (BA Hons Economics, 1979) and Newcastle Polytechnic 1981-82 (CPE and LSF). President of Cambridge Chamber of Commerce and Industry.

MCKENZIE, Rod
Harper Macleod, Glasgow (0141) 221 8888
See under Sport, p.791

MCMULLEN, John
Pinsent Curtis Biddle, Leeds (0113) 244 5000
john.mcmullen@pinsents.com
Specialisation: Partner and national head of employment group. Acts for a wide range of household name plcs, national and multinational, universities and public sector organisations. Leading authority on transfer of undertakings. Expert on European Works Councils. Part-time Professor of Labour Law at University of Leeds.
Prof. Memberships: FCIPD. FRSA. Founder member Law Society's Employment Law Committee. Industrial Law Society Executive Committee; International Bar Association, Member; fellow, Society for Advanced Legal Studies; executive committee member Involvement and Participation Association.
Career: Qualified in 1978. With *Rotheras*, 1978-80. Fellow in Law at Girton College, Cambridge, 1980-86. Bye Fellow 1986-00. Partner, *Rotheras* 1986-91. Partner and head of employment, *Simpson Curtis*, 1991. National head of employment, *Pinsent Curtis Biddle*, 1995.
Publications: Author 'Business Transfers and Employee Rights', 'Butterworths Employment Law Guide', 'Aspects of Employment Law', 'Acquired Rights of Employees', 'Tolley's Employment Law' (Joint), 'Redundancy: The Law and Practice', 'Jordans/IPD Employment Law Service', 'Working Time: Law and Practice'. Contributes widely to legal, human resources and business journals. Member, editorial board Sweet & Maxwell's 'Encyclopaedia of Employment Law'.
Personal: Born 1954. Educated Emmanuel College, Cambridge (BA 1975, double 1st Class (Hons), MA 1979, PhD 1993).

MILLER, Stephen
Harper Macleod, Glasgow (0141) 221 8888
stephen.miller@harpermacleod.co.uk
Specialisation: Law Society of Scotland accredited specialist in employment law and acts as adviser to some of Scotland's largest businesses and local authorities. In addition to his commercial client base he has a large public sector practice providing employment advice to a number of Scottish FE Colleges, tourist boards and local authority clients. Stephen also specialises in sports law. He has been listed in Chambers Guide to the Legal Profession since 1996-97 as one of Scotland's leading practitioners in sports law and he acts for the Scottish Premier League and a number of leading sportsmen in this country.
Publications: He is the author of the chapter 'Judicial Review of Sporting Bodies' in 'Sport and the Law – The Scots Perspective', a Butterworths publication.

MOLYNEUX, Pauline
Rollits, Hull (01842) 323 239
pauline.molyneux@rollits.com
Specialisation: Partner in commercial department. Covers all aspects, contentious and non-contentious, including Working Time Regulations, boardroom disputes and negotiation of severance arrangements, review and drafting of documentation, the conduct of High Court cases and advising on employment consequences of commercial sales, specialising in matters involving TUPE. Has been involved in a variety of Tribunal cases including sex, race and disability discrimination claims and equal pay claims; cases

involving the application of the Transfer of Undertakings Regulations and cases involving injunctions to enforce post-termination employment restrictions. Author of articles in local press and various law journals. Speaker at external and internal seminars for clients and employers' organisations.
Prof. Memberships: Employment Lawyers Association, Industrial Law Society, Law Society.
Career: Qualified in 1977. *Clifford Turner* 1977-79, *Field Fisher and Martineau* 1979-84. Senior lecturer at the College of Law, Lancaster Gate, 1984-86; *Clifford Chance* 1986-89. Joined *Rollit Farrell & Bladon* as a partner in 1989. Part-time Chairman of Employment Tribunals (appointed 1995).

MOORE, Nigel
Stephens & Scown, Exeter (01392) 210700

MORDSLEY, Barry
Salans Hertzfeld & Heilbronn HRK, London (020) 7509 6000
bmordsley@salans.com
Specialisation: Partner and head of the employment department. Deals with all employment law issues, contentious and non-contentious, including contracts and handbooks, restrictive covenants, discrimination, transfer of undertakings, executive terminations and collective representation issues. Advocate in the Employment tribunal. Lectures frequently on employment law and has lectured at Queen Mary and Westfield College University of London and London Guildhall University, and is a visiting professor at Cornell University, USA.
Prof. Memberships: Founder member of the management committee of the Employment Lawyers' Association and a member of numerous sub-committees. Formerly on the Law Society's Employment Law committee for many years and made major contributions on disability and age discrimination reports. Fellow of the Chartered Institute of Personnel and Development and a fellow of the Institute of Continuing Professional Development.
Career: Qualified in 1972. Formerly a partner at *Harris Rosenblatt and Kramer*, London. Part-time chairman of Employment tribunals (England and Wales) since 1984.
Publications: Editorial board member of Croners 'Discrimination Law Briefing' and co-author of 'Butterworth's Employment Law Guide' as well as of 'Butterworth's Older Clients' Service'. A regular contributor to various major HR publications such as 'People Management' and 'Personnel Today'.
Personal: Interests include theatre, music, travel, squash, cricket and football.

NESBITT, Sean
Garretts, London (020) 7438 5698
sean.nesbitt@glegal.com
Specialisation: Head of *Garretts* employment and immigration practice in London.
Prof. Memberships: Employment Lawyers' Association, Industrial Law Society, Association of Pension Lawyers, Immigration Law Practitioners' Association.
Career: Qualified 1991; *Slaughter & May* 1991-97, *Garretts* 1997.
Publications: Chapter on TUPE in Sweet & Maxwell's 'Encyclopedia of Employment Law'.
Personal: Educated at Hertford College, Oxford.

NICKSON, Sue
Hammond Suddards Edge, Manchester (0161) 830 5000
susan.nickson@hammondse.com
Specialisation: Head of national employment unit with a team of more than 50 specialist employment lawyers working from the firm's four main offices in Manchester, Leeds, Birmingham and London. Handles the full range of contentious and non-contentious employment law issues acting for companies within the public and private sectors including retail, manufacturing and construction companies. Her particular speciality is advice in relation to the Transfer of Undertakings Regulations. Regularly contributes to journals and lectures frequently. Also runs the employment unit's training company 'In-Tuition' which provides in-house training on a wide variety of employment law topics. Appointed national marketing partner for the firm in May 2000.
Career: Qualified in 1988. Worked at *Pannone & Partners* 1986-94 as a partner from 1991 and as head of employment department from 1992. Joined *Hammond Suddards Edge* as a partner in 1994 and became head of national employment unit in 1998.
Personal: Born 1 January 1964. Holds a 1st Class Honours Degree from Gonville and Caius College, Cambridge (1982-85) with a TAPP postgraduate scholarship. Associate member of Institute of Linguists. Interests include motorbike riding, ball room dancing, theatre and Manchester United. Lives in Hale, Cheshire.

NICOL, Diane
McGrigor Donald, Glasgow (0141) 248 6677
www.mcgrigors.com
Specialisation: Partner in the firm's employment law unit. Advises on all aspects of employment law and has considerable experience in appearing at Employment Tribunal. Activities in the recent past have included providing high level strategic advice to major (Scottish) financial institutions, tailored training for major multi-nationals and as ever dealing with severance packages, problems associated with large outsourcing contracts and dealing with a range of discrimination issues.
Prof. Memberships: Associate Member of the Institute of Personnel and Development; Law Society of Scotland.
Career: Qualified in 1989. Spent one year with Australian law firm *Blake Dawson Waldron* and two years at *Maclay Murray & Spens* before joining *McGrigor Donald* in 1992. Became a partner in 1997.
Publications: Contributor to the 'Employment Law Journal' and other publications.
Personal: Born 2nd September 1965; Educated Shawlands Academy, Glasgow and Glasgow University (LLB (Hons) (First Class)). Married. Interests include running, hillwalking and travel.

NORBURY, Peter
Eversheds, Manchester (0161) 831 8000
peternorbury@eversheds.com
Specialisation: Head of employment for Leeds and Manchester. Experienced advocate before Employment Tribunals throughout the UK and Employment Appeal Tribunal, together with representation at Joint Industries Board hearings. Particular expertise in trade unions executive terminations, TUPE and discrimination. Key work on collective issues including recognition agreements. Regular speaker at seminars and conferences and contributor to publications. Reported cases include Stoker v Lancashire County Council, Monsanto v TGWU, Roevin BP v Gillick, Akzo Coatings v Thompson and others, Rock Refrigeration v Seward, Merchant Ferries v Brown and Atlas Wright v Wright.
Prof. Memberships: Employment Lawyers Association, Industrial Law Society, RSA, EFSP.
Career: Qualified in 1978 and stayed with the firm before being made partner in 1984.
Personal: Born 12.1.53. Educated at Manchester Grammar School and Sheffield University. Interests include rugby and golf. Lives in Saddleworth.

NOTT, Christopher
Palser Grossman, Cardiff Bay (029) 2045 2770

O'BRIEN, Christine
Baker & McKenzie, London (020) 7919 1000
christine.oibrien@bakernet.com
Specialisation: Partner and head of the London Employment Law Department, and co-chair of the *Baker & McKenzie* European Employment Group. Specialises in contentious and non-contentious employment law, including corporate re-organisations, transnational mergers and acquisitions, advice on European Works Councils and collective issues and EU employment law. Has acted in high profile discrimination cases for public and private sector clients, including investment banks and other financial institutions.
Prof. Memberships: Law Society, Employment Lawyers Association (management committee member), Industrial Law Society.
Career: Qualified 1987 with *Simmons & Simmons*. Joined *Baker & McKenzie* in 1989 and became a partner in 1995.
Publications: Frequent speaker at external conferences, contributor to various publications including the new Sweet & Maxwell publication 'European Employment Law and The UK' and television appearances commenting on employment law issues.
Personal: Born 6 September 1959.

OSMAN, Chris
Clifford Chance, London (020) 7600 1000
chris.osman@cliffordchance.com
Specialisation: Partner and head of employment unit specialising in all aspects of employment law.
Prof. Memberships: Editor of 'Harvey on Industrial Relations and Employment Law'; advisory editor 'Butterworths Employment Law Guide'; and an editor of Butterworths PFI manual.
Career: Ramsden School; Southampton University (LLB 1973). Articled *Coward Chance*; qualified 1976; partner *Clifford Chance* since 1981.
Personal: Hot air ballooning. Born 1951; resides Westerham.

PALCA, Julia
Olswang, London (020) 7208 8888
jcp@olswang.com
Specialisation: Main areas of practice are media and employment litigation. Represents both print and broadcast defendants, and some plaintiffs, in defamation, breaches of copyright and other media and entertainment-related disputes including judicial review of decisions of media regulatory and quasi-regulatory bodies. Also advises mainly employers on all aspects of employment law, including unfair and wrongful dismissal, discrimination and the application of restrictive covenants. Acted as an in-house

libel litigator to a major newspaper group 1985-86. Speaks on both media and employment law issues.
Career: Qualified in 1980. Joined *Olswang* in 1986, becoming partner in 1987. Appointed part-time Employment Tribunal Chairman.
Publications: Author of 'Employment Law Checklists' and numerous articles on media and employment issues.

PARKINSON, Helen
Whittles, Manchester (0161) 228 2061
helenparkinson@whittles.com
Specialisation: Specialises in all aspects of contentious employment law including advocacy at employment tribunals and the Employment Appeal Tribunal, acting mainly for trade unions and employees.
Career: Qualified 1989. Joined *Whittles* in 1990, became a partner in 1996 and manager of the firm's employment department in April 2000.

PIKE, Malcolm
Addleshaw Booth & Co, Manchester
(0161) 934 6000
mjp@addleshaw-booth.co.uk
Specialisation: Partner. Main areas of practice are employment and industrial relations. Includes drafting and advising on terms and conditions of employment, personnel policies and collective agreements, industrial relations and other trade union matters, discrimination and equal pay, board room disputes, defending and prosecuting High Court and Employment Tribunal proceedings and advising on employment aspects of the sale and reorganisation of companies and businesses. Various publications include 'The Lawyers Factbook', 'Essential Facts Employment,' Butterworths' 'Encyclopaedia of Forms and Precedents,' 'Workplace Discrimination' and Jordan's 'IPD Employment Law Service.' Regular speaker at seminars and conferences.
Prof. Memberships: Law Society, Employment Lawyers Association, Industrial Law Society, Manchester Industrial Relations Society, IBA, ABA.
Career: Qualified in 1984. Joined the firm as a Partner in 1992.
Personal: Attended Leicester University 1978-81.

POTTER, David
Freethcartwright, Nottingham (0115) 936 9369
david.potter@freethcartwright.co.uk
Specialisation: Advises on all aspects of employment law, predominantly on instructions from employers, in-house legal teams and senior director/employees. Has recently handled a number of sensitive race, sex and disability discrimination claims as well as providing strategic employment advice on a wide range of issues including TUPE, human rights and employee consultation. Regularly speaks at seminars and provides in-house training.
Prof. Memberships: Employment Lawyers Association.
Career: Articled at *Freeth Cartwright* (now *freethcartwright*); qualified in 1989; partner in 1994. Current head of employment.
Personal: Born 1964. Educated at Rossall School and Reading University (LLB). LLM (Advanced Litigation) with distinction at Nottingham Trent University 1996. Resides in Nottingham. Interests include hockey and golf.

PREST, Catherine
Hammond Suddards Edge, Leeds (0113) 284 7000
catherine.prest@hammondse.com
Specialisation: Advises on all areas of contentious and non-contentious employment work. Particular experience in discrimination law, strategic employment advice and transfer of undertakings. Experienced Tribunal advocate. Speaks regularly on a wide range of employment law issues. Acted on a number of high profile terminations, mergers and business transfers. Advised on introduction of new contracts and family friendly policies.
Prof. Memberships: Employment Lawyers Association, Secretary West Riding Oxford and Cambridge Club.
Career: Qualified as a Barrister in 1988. Tenant 8, King Street Chambers, Manchester 1988-90. In-House Lawyer with Alliance & Leicester Building Society. Joined *Eversheds* in Leeds in 1993, became a partner and head of Leeds employment team in May 1997. Joined *Hammond Suddards* as partner in April 1999.
Personal: Born 22nd May 1966. Educated Notre Dame High School, Leeds, St Hilda's College Oxford University BA Law 1987, Hardwicke Scholar Lincoln's Inn 1988. Married Charles Prest. Resides in Ilkley and London.

PRYKE, Oliver
Taylor Vinters, Cambridge (01223) 423444
ocpp@taylorvinters.com
Specialisation: Specialises in all aspects of employment law, both contentious and non-contentious. Acts for private and public sector organisations and senior employees with a particular emphasis on clients in high-tech, bio-technology and pharmaceutical industries. Provides in-house training to clients and other HR professionals.
Prof. Memberships: Employment Lawyers Association.
Career: Qualified as a solicitor in 1996. Joined *Taylor Vinters* in January 1998.
Personal: Born 30 July 1971. Educated at The Judd School, Tonbridge and Oxford University (BA Hons in Law 1989-92). A keen tennis player and pianist. Lives in Suffolk.

PRYTHERCH, Rosalie
Cleaver Fulton Rankin, Belfast (028) 9027 1322
r.prytherch@cfrlaw.co.uk
Specialisation: Acts for employers in the retail, manufacturing, financial, education and IT sectors and for local councils and public bodies. Rosalie Prytherch deals with the broad spectrum of contentious work and provides corporate support and advice. She has gained an impressive reputation in the area of restrictive covenant disputes where her clients have enjoyed considerable success and she is also recognised for her expertise in dealing with TUPE issues
Prof. Memberships: Employment Lawyers' Group (NI). Law Society of Northern Ireland.
Career: Qualified 1987. Partner in *Cleaver Fulton Rankin* 1996.

PUGH, Keith
Nabarro Nathanson, Sheffield (0114) 279 4000
k.pugh@nabarro.com
Specialisation: Employment law specialist for 18 years dealing with both contentious and non-contentious issues ranging from drafting employment contracts policies and procedures; tribunal claims; restrictive covenants and garden leave; trade union recognition and collective issues; industrial action and transfer of undertakings. Instructed by BFL in BFL v Meade (House of Lords).
Prof. Memberships: Law Society. Employment Lawyers Association. Industrial Law Society.
Career: Admitted 1980. British Coal Legal Department 1980-90. Joined *Nabarro Nathanson* as a partner in 1990. Head of employment department.
Personal: Music, food, wine and gardening.

RALPH, Nick
Archon (formerly Langley & Co), London
020) 7397 9650
n.ralph@archonlaw.co.uk
Specialisation: Partner. Handles contentious and non-contentious employment matters for both employers and employees.
Prof. Memberships: Employment Lawyers Association.
Career: Qualified as a solicitor at *Ashurst Morris Crisp* in 1988. Moved to *Archon* (formerly *Langley & Co*) in 1997. Partner from 1998.
Publications: Contributor to Sweet & Maxwell's 'Company Directors: Law and Liability'. Editor of Sweet & Maxwell's 'Practical Commercial Precedents'.
Personal: Born 9 December 1963. Attended Exeter University, LLB (Hons). Lives in Hammersmith.

REES, Anthony
Morgan Cole, Swansea (01792) 634634

RESTON, Vincent
DLA, Liverpool (08700) 111111

RETALLACK, James
Hammond Suddards Edge, Birmingham
(0121) 222 3224
james.retallack@hammondse.com
Specialisation: Partner in charge of the Birmingham office of *Hammond Suddards Edge*. All aspects of employment, human resource and industrial relations law and employment and personnel training.
Prof. Memberships: Law Society, Employment Lawyers Association, Birmingham Industrial Tribunal Users Committee.
Career: Qualified in 1981. Joined *Edge & Ellison* in 1981, becoming a partner in 1988 and senior partner in 1998.
Personal: Born 8 July 1957. Attended Malvern College 1970-74 and Manchester University 1975-78. Leisure interests include reading, skiing, gardening and American Football. Lives in Worcester.

ROBERTS, Stephen
Thring Townsend, Bath (01225) 340000
sroberts@thringtownsend.co.uk
Specialisation: Deals with all areas of contentious and non-contentious employment law including dismissals, discrimination, transfers of undertakings and redundancies. Particular experience in education, sport and agriculture sectors.
Prof. Memberships: Employment Lawyers Association; Justice: British Association for Sport and Law.
Career: Qualified 1980. Became a partner with *Thrings and Long* 1988. Head of employment law at *Thring Townsend.*
Personal: BA Law, University of Kent 1977. LLM (Employment and European Law), University of Bristol 2000. Married with two sons. Lives near Bath.

ROBERTSON, Nicholas
Rowe & Maw, London (020) 7782 8919
nrobertson@roweandmaw.co.uk
Specialisation: Nicholas has advised on employment matters since he qualified. This covers the full range of employment matters, both on a collective basis and advising employers in relation to individual employees. Recent examples of collective work have included advice in connection with outsourcing arrangements, advice on the conduct of consultation meetings with unions and employee representatives, and advice on large-scale corporate reorganisations, from the employment perspective. He is currently handling one of the furthest advanced cases before the Central Arbitration Committee on compulsory union recognition. Recent examples of individual work have covered advice on discrimination claims, executive recruitment and termination of executives, as well as advising on policy issues. He has represented employers before the Employment Tribunal and EAT.
Prof. Memberships: Employment Lawyers Association, Industrial Law Society. Sits on the Editorial Committee of Croner's Discrimination Law Briefing and the Employment Lawyers Association Working Party on the Transfer Regulations.
Career: Qualified 1998. Joined *Rowe & Maw* 1991 and became partner 1995.

ROBERTSON, Stuart
Gordons Cranswick Solicitors, Bradford (01274) 202202
stuart.robertson@gordonscranswick.co.uk
Specialisation: All aspects of employment law. Extensive experience of Employment tribunal advocacy. Particular knowledge of sex and race discrimination, restrictive covenants and major redundancy/ reorganisation exercises. Regular presenter of seminars to clients and to outside bodies including Chamber of Commerce and ACAS.
Prof. Memberships: Employment Lawyers Association.
Career: Bradford Grammar School. Trinity Hall, Cambridge. Articled: *Durrant Piesse.* Qualified: October 1982. *Hepworth & Chadwick,* Leeds 1982-86. *Dibb Lupton* 1986-92. Joined *Gordons Wright & Wright* as partner in 1992. Part-time Employment tribunal chairman 1994. Deputy Registrar, Bradford Diocese (Church of England) 1997.
Personal: Born 1 May 1957. Married with two children. Church activities, hill walking, rugby league.

ROSKILL, Julian
Rowe & Maw, London (020) 7248 4282
jroskill@roweandmaw.co.uk
Specialisation: Julian is acknowledged as being one of the leading employment lawyers in the UK. He heads Rowe & Maw's employment group, which is consistently ranked in the top tier in all the major legal directories. The group has been described as "commercial, practical and friendly, it is pound for pound amongst the best in the City". Recently, the group joined Ius Laboris International Employment Law, Pensions and Employment Alliance, an international alliance offering Pan European advice to its clients on employment, pensions and employee benefits. Julian is the UK board member of this prestigious alliance which consists of 400 European advisors. Julian advises employers on the full range of employment and industrial relations law and practice. Clients are drawn from a broad range of industrial and financial sectors, particularly major corporates to owner-managed business and partnerships. He also represents senior executives. Julian's special interests are European employment law, discrimination, collective issues, garden leave and restrictive covenants, moves of key employees and team moves, outsourcing and business transfers. Apart from client work, he is also a sought after speaker and writes on a variety of employment topics for business publications.
Prof. Memberships: Advisory board of Croner's Industrial Relations Briefing since 1991; Chairman Employment Sub-Committee City of London Solicitors' Company since 1996. Member of the Law Society and Industrial Law Society.
Career: Qualified in 1974; joined *Rowe & Maw* 1986; became partner in 1988.
Personal: Born 1950. Leisure interests include tennis, photography and music, theatre and opera.

ROY, Judy
Mills & Reeve, Cambridge (01223) 364422

RUSSELL, Timothy
Norton Rose, London (020) 7444 2468
russellt@nortonrose.com
Specialisation: Partner and head of employment unit of 18 solicitors. Specialising purely in employment law. Has handled many major transfer of undertakings, wrongful dismissal and sex discrimination cases. Part time employment tribunal chairman. Practical approach based on in-house commercial experience.
Prof. Memberships: Law Society, Employment Lawyers Association, CBI Employee Relations Panel, Industrial Law Society, London Chamber of Commerce.
Career: Worked at *Wilde Sapte* 1982-86. Qualified in 1985 and was Ciba Geigy's legal adviser 1986-87. Senior legal adviser at Lloyds Bank 1987-91. Joined *Hammond Suddards* in 1991 and became a Partner in 1992. Joined *Norton Rose* 1999.
Personal: Born 17th June 1960. Educated at Pocklington School and Cambridge University. Enjoys all sports. Lives in West London.

SALUJA, Sean
Paull & Williamsons, Aberdeen (01224) 621621
sasaluja@paull-williamsons.co.uk
Specialisation: Almost exclusive area of practice is employment. Advises mainly employers on all aspects of employment and collective relations matters both contentious and non-contentious. Appears regularly in tribunals in both Scotland and England. Has dealt with a number cases involving transfer of undertakings and contracting issues in the offshore oil industry. Lectured on employment law from 1991-95 at Aberdeen University. Regularly presents seminars and training programmes for clients.
Prof. Memberships: Law Society of Scotland, Employment Law Group. Accredited by the Law Society of Scotland as a specialist in employment law.
Career: Graduated in 1989, LLB Hons (1st Class); diploma in Legal Practice, 1989. Qualified 1991.
Personal: Born 1967. Interests include golf, walking and travel.

SAYER, Nicholas
Hewitson Becke + Shaw, Cambridge (01223) 461155
nicksayer@hewitsons.com
Specialisation: Partner and Head of Employment Law Department. Principal area of practice is contentious employment matters, particularly injunctive relief (trade secret and confidential information matters, non-competition, non-solicitation and non-dealing covenants, search orders, orders for delivery up, etc.). Also deals with all other contentious and non-contentious employment matters, including wrongful dismissal, unfair dismissal, redundancy, discrimination, trade disputes and other collective employment matters, transfers of undertakings, drafting contracts of employment. Has presented seminars to other professionals and clients and written numerous articles.
Prof. Memberships: The Employment Lawyers Association; The Industrial Law Society; the Institute of Employment Rights; Fellow of the Society for Advanced Legal Studies.
Career: Joined *Hewitson Becke + Shaw* in 1985. Qualified in 1987. Became a partner and Head of Employment Law in 1993.
Personal: Born 26 September 1961. Educated at the Cambridgeshire High School for Boys 1973-80 and Leicester University 1981-84. Awarded an LLM in Law and Industrial Relations from Leicester University in 1993. Leisure pursuits include cricket, photography and gardening. Lives in Cambridgeshire.

SCOULAR, Gillie
Mills & Reeve, Norwich (01603) 693 265
gillie.scoular@mills-reeve.com
Specialisation: Has specialised in employment law for 20 years, 13 of which were in London. Deals with all aspects of contentious and non-contentious employment law, acting mainly for employers but also for senior executives within the public and private sectors. Work includes service agreements; restrictive covenants; review and drafting of documentation (contracts, handbooks, policies); business reorganisations; TUPE; the employment aspects of corporate transactions (mergers, acquisitions, disposals); board room disputes; senior executive severances; redundancies (collective and individual); discrimination; Employment Tribunal claims; collective; trade union issues. Conducts external and internal seminars for clients.
Prof. Memberships: Law Society, Employment Lawyers Association.
Career: Qualified in 1980; articled clerk, solicitor and then partner at *Jacques and Co/Jacques and Lewis,* London (1978-89) before joining a major publishing, multi-media, printing and newspaper group based in London as in-house group commercial lawyer (1989-92); with *Mills and Reeve* since 1992.
Personal: Educated at Sherborne School for Girls, then Cambridge University (Girton College) graduating in law 1977; married with three young daughters (triplets); leisure interests currently limited but would include theatre, choral singing, music, travel and entertaining; lives in Norfolk.

SEATON, Christopher
Burges Salmon, Bristol (0117) 939 2000
chris.seaton@burges-salmon.com
Specialisation: Head of employment group dealing with full range of contentious and non-contentious employment work. Experienced tribunal advocate and frequent user of Bristol Mercantile Court for wrongful dismissal and other contractual claims as well as employment related injunctions. Adviser to a number of multinational companies based in USA and Europe.

Prof. Memberships: Employment Lawyers Association, European Employment Lawyers Association, Bristol Employment Tribunal Users Committee, policy advice on the Regional Committee of IPD.
Career: Royal Navy Officer 1979-90. Trainee at *Burges Salmon* 1991-93. Specialised in employment law beginning in 1993; associate in 1997; partner in 1999. Appointed head of employment group in July 1999. One of three partners on the firm's International Steering Committee.
Publications: Regular contributor to the 'Employment Law Journal'. Author of a chapter on European Works Councils for 'International Employment Law' published by the Centre for International Legal Studies.
Personal: Married with two daughters. Interests include sailing, skiing, music and squash.

SEWARD, Karen
Allen & Overy, London (020) 7330 3936
karen.seward@allenovery.com
Specialisation: Specialises in contentious and non-contentious employment law and is highly regarded for her expertise in the areas of dignity at work and privacy. She advises a broad client base – primarily financial institutions and global corporates – on a variety of strategic matters and deals with mergers, acquisitions and outsourcing and collective and individual dismissals. She is head of the Workplace Surveillance Group (vision@allenovery.com).
Prof. Memberships: Employment Lawyers Association: European Employment Lawyers Association.
Career: 1988-94 *Simmons & Simmons.* 1994-97 *Stephenson Harwood* (Partner 1996). 1997-00 *Pinsent Curtis. Allen & Overy,* Partner (2000).
Publications: Writes for both Tolley's and Croner's and sits on several editorial boards.
Personal: LLB (Hons) Bristol 1987. LSF College of Law 1988.

SHERRARD, Harry
Sherrards, Haywards Heath (01444) 473344
advice@harrysherrard.com
Specialisation: Employment law. Acting for many well-known employers in the South East, with a particular emphasis on aviation and travel related businesses. Clients include KLM, Emirates and Aer Lingus. Advised Korean car giant Daewoo through its recent extensive redundancy programme. New clients include the National Trust and Cancer Research Campaign. Active in employment law training with training clients which include GlaxoSmithKline and Novartis.
Prof. Memberships: CIPD, IoD, CBI, ELA.
Career: Previously head of employment law at large regional practice, established *Sherrards* in 1999. The practice is multi-disciplinary, and as well as providing core employment law services, the firm offers a range of Human Resource consultancy skills, as well as its own branded employment/legal expenses insurance policy. Recent expansion has seen recruitment of a solicitor and an employment law paralegal.
Personal: Currently learning to fly. Heavily involved in the motor racing world, a qualified RAC Motor Sports Association instructor, active racer and proprietor of a small motor racing team.

SHORT, Michael
Short Richardson & Forth, Newcastle upon Tyne (0191) 232 0283
mcs@short-richardson-forth.co.uk
Specialisation: Founder partner in employment law department. Has 25 years' experience in employment law, acting on both sides of industry and dealing with the full range of employment law matters including appearing before employment tribunals regularly throughout the country and lecturing regularly on employment law matters to Companies. Extensive experience in senior executive terminations.
Prof. Memberships: Member of the Law Society's Employment Law Committee, Employment Lawyers Association, Industrial Law Society and is the Secretary of the Newcastle Employment Tribunal Users Group.
Career: Senior partner and founding partner of *Short Richardson & Forth* since 1978.
Personal: Leisure interests include theatre. Lives in Newcastle-upon-Tyne.

SHRIVES, Mark
Hammond Suddards Edge, Leeds (0113) 284 7000
mark.shrives@hammondse.com
Specialisation: Partner – employment unit. Specialising in all aspects of contentious and non-contentious employment and discrimination law acting predominately for multi-national and large corporate clients and senior executives. Conducts all own advocacy before employment and employment appeal tribunals. Also handles work permit and other employment-related immigration issues. Speaks regularly on a wide-range of employment issues for clients and external organisations such as CIPD and ACAS.
Prof. Memberships: Law Society; fellow of the Society for Advanced Legal Studies; European Employment Lawyers Association; Employment Lawyers Association; Industrial Law Society.
Career: Articled at *Cameron McKenna.* Qualified 1990. *Eversheds* (Manchester) 1990-92. *Hammond Suddards Edge* 1992 onwards. Partner 1995.
Personal: Born 13 April 1964. Educated Downing College, Cambridge, BA (Hons) 1986. LLM (1st Class honours) 1987. Law Society Finals (1st Class honours) 1988. Interests include gardening, music and cinema.

SIMON, Shona
Maclay Murray & Spens, Edinburgh (0131) 226 5196
smws@maclaymurrayspens.co.uk
Specialisation: Practises only in the field of employment law. Accredited by the Law Society of Scotland as an employment law specialist. Appointed as a part-time Chairman of Employment tribunals in 2000. Particular interest and experience in discrimination, maternity law and in police discipline cases. Has acted in a number of EOC funded cases. Acted for the successful appellant in Brown v Rentokil which was referred by the House of Lords to the European Court of Justice. Lectures widely in discrimination law at various universities and for a range of other organisations. Currently equal opportunities development adviser at the Scottish Parliament.
Prof. Memberships: Member of Institute of the Careers Guidance, Member of Employment Law Group Committee, Notary Public, Writer to the Signet.
Career: MA (Hons) English Literature and English Language – 1983; diploma in Careers Guidance – 1984. LLB (Dist) – 1990; diploma in Legal Practice – 1991. Qualified 1993; worked for a number of years as careers adviser with special responsibility for advising on equal opportunities issues; traineeship with *Mackay WS* (now *Mackay Simon WS*).
Publications: Co-author of 'Employment Law' (Greens Concise Scots Law series); co-editor of 'Green's Employment Law Bulletin'; update editor of 'Employment Tribunal Practice in Scotland'; update editor of employment law chapters in 'Scottish Business Administration Manual' and 'Scots Law Factbook'; regular contributor to 'Journal of the Law Society of Scotland'.
Personal: Born 1960, resides Edinburgh.

SIPPITT, Michael
Clarks, Reading (0118) 958 5321
michael.sippitt@clarks-solicitors.co.uk
Specialisation: *Clarks Solicitors*' managing partner and head of the firm's employment services team. Specialises in employment work, handling both contentious and non-contentious business and appearing as an advocate in tribunals. Deals with all areas of employment and discrimination law. Leads a specialist team which acts for a wide range of corporate and institutional clients including: News International, Sun Microsystems, Blue Circle Industries, Transport Development Group, University of Reading and Thames Water. Has also been much involved in providing in-house management training for corporate clients on employment and discrimination issues. He has a particular interest in collective employment law issues and employment relations, on which he has addressed meetings of the Employment Lawyers' Association, a client international HR conference in the United States and the CBI. Member of the CBI's Employment Relations Panel and Southern Region Human Resources Forum. Formerly a part-time university lecturer in Labour Law. Also a member of the Advisory Board of the TAGLaw International Legal Network and of the Network Employment Speciality Group.
Prof. Memberships: Employment Lawyers Association.
Career: Trained at Clarks Solicitors, became a partner in 1978 and managing partner in 1997.
Personal: Graduated from Southampton University with a 1st class LLB honours degree and obtained honours in the Law Society Finals. Active in Church membership. Other interests include chairmanship of a charitable trust and golf.

SMELLIE, David
Farrer & Co, London (020) 9242 2022
dcs@farrer.co.uk
Specialisation: Main area of practice is employment law. Experience with commercial and institutional clients including newspapers, magazines, banks and academic establishments, as well as an increasing proportion of high-profile individual work. Has been involved in advising many such clients on restructuring and redundancy programmes and on the transfer of undertakings regulations, as well as handling industrial disputes, team moves and individual cases.
Prof. Memberships: Employment Lawyers Association.
Career: Joined *Farrer & Co* in 1987 as a trainee. Qualified in 1989, became a partner in 1996. David heads *Farrer & Co's* employment and pension team. Given a four star ranking in the 'Insiders Guide to Employment Law 2000' and runner-up in Employment Lawyer of the Year.
Publications: Published a considerable amount, in

various Croners publications, in Butterworths' 'Company Service' (the employment chapter) and in Tolley's 'Employment Policies and Precedents'. Also regularly asked to contribute to various employment law magazines including 'Employment Lawyer'.
Personal: Born 1964. Educated at Glenalmond College and St John's College, Cambridge (MA). Lives in London.

SMITH, Tim
Crutes, Newcastle upon Tyne (0191) 212 5600
tim.smith@crutes.co.uk
Specialisation: Head of Employment Law acting predominantly for NHS, Local Authority and company clients. Particular interest in contentious employment law and TUPE.
Prof. Memberships: Member of The Employment Lawyers Association. Member of The Employment Tribunals User Group.
Personal: Born 4th April 1959. Educated at Whitby Grammar School. Masters degree in Employment Law.

SOUTHAM, Chris
Osborne Clarke, Bristol (0117) 917 3000

SPEIRS, William
Brechin Tindal Oatts, Glasgow (0141) 221 8012
wscs@bto.co.uk
Specialisation: Advises mainly employers – from a number of spheres including retail, insurance, leisure, financial, charity and the further education sector – on all areas of industrial relations and employment law. Specialist areas: transfer of undertakings; redundancy schemes; race and sex discrimination and directors' service contracts. Seminar speaker on topical employment issues.
Prof. Memberships: Law Society of Scotland; The Society of Solicitors to the Supreme Court; The Royal Faculty of Procurators in Glasgow.
Career: Graduated in 1972, LLB (Hons) Public Law, Glasgow University, Notary Public. Practised Employment Law since 1978. Partner 1984.
Publications: Author of the employment law section of W Green's 'Scottish Human Rights Service' (published by Sweet & Maxwell).
Personal: Golf and travel.

TATA, Rustom
DMH, Brighton (01293) 605 068
rustom.tata@dmh.co.uk
Specialisation: Partner and head of employment group, deals with all aspects of employment law and specialises in the European influence on UK employment law, education employment contracts and corporate re-organisations; appears regularly as an advocate in the Employment Tribunal and Employment Appeal Tribunal.
Career: University of Sussex, BA Law and French; King's College, London, LLM. Articled *Donne Mileham and Haddock* (now *DMH*); qualified 1992; associate 1994; partner 1996. Lectures extensively on employment issues, often at the invitation of local business organisations, such as Business Link and the Institute of Chartered Secretaries.
Personal: Born 1965.

TAYLOR, Catherine
Olswang, London (020) 7208 8711
cjt@olswang.com
Specialisation: Employment law, specialising in both contentious and non-contentious. Recent cases/matters include advising on all the employment aspects of the dissolution of a major investment fund and several successful applications to enforce restrictive covenants.
Prof. Memberships: ELA; ILS; IPD
Career: Trained at *Norton Rose*, qualifying in 1993. Moved to *Olswang*, in 1995 and became a partner in 1998.
Publications: 'Employment Law Checklists' – joint author with Julia Palca.

THOMPSON, Michael
Eversheds, Manchester (0161) 831 8000
michaelthompson@eversheds.co.uk
Specialisation: Deals with all aspects of employment law work both contentious and non-contentious acting mainly for employers. Extensive experience both in the public and private sectors. Experienced advocate before the Employment Tribunal and the Employment Appeal Tribunal. Particular expertise in executive terminations, TUPE and injunctive relief. Regularly provides training to clients both in-house and on external courses. Reported cases include Atlas Wright v Wright.
Prof. Memberships: Employment Lawyers Association, The Law Society and the Industrial Society.
Career: Qualified with the firm in 1992, became senior solicitor in 1997 and was promoted to partner in May 2000.
Personal: Born 8.10.65. Educated at Leeds University. Interests, all sports, particularly football and golf. Lives in Rochdale.

THOMPSON, Tony
Macfarlanes, London (020) 7831 9222
tony.thompson@macfarlanes.com
Specialisation: Contentious and non-contentious employment law. Drafting and advising on employment contracts, service agreements, secondments and consultancies. Employment policies and procedures. Transfers of undertakings. Drafting and enforcement of restrictive covenants. Negotiation of severance packages.
Prof. Memberships: Law Society. Employment Lawyers Association. City of London Solicitors Company Employment Law Sub-Committee. Currently secretary of the Committee.
Career: Oundle School. MA Cantab (St Catharine's College). Articled at *Markbys* (now part of *Cameron McKenna*). Admitted as a solicitor June 1976. Joined *Macfarlanes* 1980; partner 1986, head of litigation 1989-99. Head of employment group.

THOMSON, Alan
McClure Naismith, Glasgow (0141) 204 2700
athomson@mcclurenaismith.com
Specialisation: Lead partner in employment unit. Almost exclusively engaged in employment law practice. Principally advising employers but has a growing practice in pursuing claims for senior executives and negotiating severance arrangements. Regularly appears before employment tribunals. Heads a growing team of lawyers in the firm's Glasgow and Edinburgh offices focusing on employment law matters.
Prof. Memberships: Law Society of Scotland, Employment Law group (Scotland) and Employment Lawyers association.
Career: Trained at McGrigor Donald, qualifying in 1976. Joined *McClure Naismith* in 1976 and became a partner in 1979.
Personal: Born in 1952 and lives in Glasgow. Educated at The High School of Glasgow (1957-70) and Edinburgh University (1970-74), LLB (Hons). Enjoys skiing, and escaping from employment law to remote croft on west coast of Scotland.

TRANTER, Ian
Hammond Suddards Edge, Manchester
(0161) 830 5000
ian.tranter@hammondse.com
Specialisation: Partner in employment department. Handles contentious and non-contentious employment issues. Acted in Hungarian International Bank v First Energy (ostensible authority), Parkinson v March Consulting Limited (establishment of reason for dismissal). Clients include multi-national, public and private companies, and private clients.
Prof. Memberships: Law Society.
Career: Qualified 1982. Partner at *Chaffe Street* 1989-01. Partner at *Hammond Suddards Edge* 2001.
Personal: Born 1955. Educated at Chetham's Hospital School, Manchester and St Catharine's College, Cambridge. Interests include skiing, horse racing, art history and antiques. Lives in Henbury, Cheshire.

TURTLE, Brian
Carson McDowell, Belfast (028) 9024 4951
See under Litigation, p.791

TWEEDIE, Colin
Addleshaw Booth & Co, Leeds (0113) 209 2032
cqt@addleshaw-booth.co.uk
Specialisation: Partner in Employment Law Department. Has specialised exclusively in employment law and industrial relations since qualification. Deals with all aspects, mainly for employers, including employment contracts, procedures and policies, restrictive covenants, discrimination, the employment aspects of the sale and reorganisation of companies and businesses and contentious matters including appearing before employment tribunals throughout the country. Conducts seminars for clients, lectures and has appeared on local radio. Author of occasional articles.
Prof. Memberships: Employment Lawyers Association.
Career: Qualified in 1978. Joined firm as Partner in 1998.
Personal: Educated at Fitzwilliam College, Cambridge 1972-75. Leisure interests include sports, railways and Scottish history.

TWIGGER, Elizabeth
Slaughter and May, London (020) 7600 1200

TWINEHAM, Andrew
Jacksons, Stockton on Tees (01642) 643643
Specialisation: All aspects of employment law with particular emphasis on Employment Tribunal Advocacy (including Employment Appeal Tribunal). Acts principally for respondents nationally together with quality base of North East clients. Regularly gives seminars to clients and employers generally.
Prof. Memberships: Employment Lawyers Association, Newcastle Employment Tribunal Users' Group, governor on Employment Law Committee of a sixth form college.
Career: Graduated University of Birmingham 1991; Law School York 1992; trained in Birmingham before joining *Jacksons* on qualification in October 1994. Appointed partner January 2000.
Personal: Born in Selby 1966, educated at Selby High School. Interests include travel, walking and sport. Lives on Teesside.

TYNDALL, Timothy
Hewitson Becke + Shaw, Cambridge
(01223) 461155
timtyndall@hewitsons.com
Specialisation: Practices exclusively in employment and industrial relations law, both contentious and non-contentious. Regularly appears as an advocate in employment tribunals and has substantial experience in the area of injunctions. Deals with personnel aspects of the firm's merger and acquisition work. Presents seminars to other professionals and clients.
Prof. Memberships: Employment Lawyers' Association.
Career: Educated at Liverpool College and Hull University. Qualified in 1988 and became a partner at *Hewitson Becke + Shaw* in 1998 having practiced in Liverpool and Leeds.
Personal: Interests include Liverpool FC's squad rotation system, family life and three children. Lives in Trumpington, Cambridge.

UNDERWOOD, Kerry
Underwoods, Hemel Hempstead (01442) 430900
Specialisation: Senior partner of *Underwoods.* Practice covers full range of employment law acting for employers and employees. Well known for advocacy in employment tribunals and the EAT where he is a member of the Employment Law Advisors Appeal Scheme. Clients include plcs and a number of Directors of plcs. Lectures regularly for University of Cambridge, Law Society and others. Appears regularly on radio, television and in the national press in relation to legal topics. Conducts in-house training for government departments, local authorities and major companies. Was successful appellant's advocate, pro bono, in leading pregnancy rights case of Day v T Pickles Farms Ltd (1999) IRLR 217. Advocate in other reported cases.
Prof. Memberships: Fellow Chartered Institute of Arbitrators, Association of Trial Lawyers of America, Law Society, Employment Tribunal Chairman 1993-00, Employment Law Advisors Appeal Scheme, Transport and General Workers Union, Equal Opportunities Commission Panel.
Career: Qualified in 1981. Set up *Underwoods* in 1991. Pioneered Contingency Fees, Fixed Fees and menu-pricing in employment tribunals. Pioneered television advertising. Pioneered 'Community Law Club' concept. Author of Best Seller 'No Win No Fee No Worries'. Author of 'Advertising Litigation'. Editor of 'Employment Litigation'. Editorial Board Member of 'Litigation Funding'. Editor, Costs Production Section of Butterworths 'Personal Injury Law Service'. Part-time Employment Tribunal Chairman 1993-00. London Borough Councillor 1978-82. Parliamentary Candidate 1979. Only UK employment lawyer listed in Association of Trial Lawyers of America Directory.
Personal: Born in 1956. Leisure interests include cricket, football and literature, especially the poetry of T S Eliot. Has travelled extensively around the world

WALKER, David James
Dundas & Wilson CS, Glasgow (0141) 222 2200

WARNOCK, Owen
Eversheds, Norwich (01603) 272727
owenwarnock@eversheds.com
Specialisation: Has specialised in employment law for 19 years and heads the *Eversheds* East of England employment department, consisting of 17 lawyers, one human resources consultant and one employment law trainer. He has considerable Employment Tribunal advocacy experience and has particular strength in discrimination law and health service employment law. He is a regular speaker on employment law issues at events ranging from local IPD groups to CBI and similar national conferences. Employment law is main area of practice, but also advises on food and drink law.
Prof. Memberships: Employment Lawyers Association, Industrial Law Society, The Food Law Group.
Career: Qualified 1982 with *Daynes Hill & Perks* (partner 1985).
Publications: Consultant Legal Editor to the CCH Disability Manual and co-author of 'Employment Law in the NHS' (Cavendish 1995).
Personal: Born 5 April 1957. Graduated in Law from Cambridge University in 1979. Lives in Norwich.

WARREN, Martin
Eversheds, Cardiff (029) 2047 1147
martinwarren@eversheds.com
Specialisation: Partner and head of the employment department at *Eversheds* Cardiff office. An experienced employment lawyer with particular expertise in strategic and reorganisational issues, trade union recognition, redundancies and business transfers, industrial action, balloting, and in the area of collective labour law generally. Acted successfully for employer clients in reported cases including O'Dea v ISC Chemicals (Court of Appeal 1995) and Alcan Extrusions v Yates (EAT 1996). Advises multinational companies, in particular in the US, on the implications of developments in UK labour and employment law.
Prof. Memberships: Member of the Employment Lawyers Association; member of the Cardiff Employment Tribunal User Group; Fellow of the Royal Society of Arts; member of the Reform Club; member of the American Employment Law Council; member of the American Bar Association.
Career: Qualified in 1985. Joined *Phillips & Buck* in 1986 (now *Eversheds*). Became a partner in 1989.
Personal: Resides in Magor, Gwent.

WATSON, Judith
Cobbetts, Manchester (0161) 833 5205
judith.watson@cobbetts.co.uk
Specialisation: Partner and head of *Cobbetts'* 10-strong employment law team. Handles the whole spectrum of employment law and industrial relations issues. Specialist interest in discrimination and regularly advises on negotiation of senior executive recruitment contracts and severance packages. A regular media spokesperson for the firm who manages training for clients on all issues concerning human resources and employment.
Prof. Memberships: Firm's representative of Eurolegal, a network of 30 European law firms. North West representative and a management committee member of the Employment Lawyers Association.
Career: Educated at Sheffield High School for Girls and Sheffield University (1981-84). Articled with *Leak Almond & Parkinson* which subsequently became *Cobbett Leak Almond* and then *Cobbetts.* Qualified in 1987. Became a partner in January 1997.

WATSON, Simon
Simmons & Simmons, London (020) 7628 2020
simon.watson@simmons-simmons.com
Specialisation: Employment Law. Simon has a strong City-based employment law practice acting for insurance and major corporations and regularly advises on the employment aspects of acquisitions, disposals and mergers including the Transfer of Undertakings Regulations. In addition, Simon has extensive experience of handling litigation both in the industrial tribunal and the High Court, including applying for interlocutory relief, injunctions and Anton Piller orders.
Prof. Memberships: Law Society.
Career: St. Catherines's College, Oxford, College of Law, *Simmons & Simmons.*
Personal: Bridge, Opera.

WETHERFIELD, Alison
McDermott, Will & Emery, London
(020) 7577 6900

WHINCUP, David
Hammond Suddards Edge, London
(020) 7655 1000
david.whincup@hammondse.com
Specialisation: Partner and head of employment unit, London. Dealing with a wide variety of employment-related issues, including recruitment issues; policy documents and contracts of employment at all levels; disciplinary and grievance procedures; the defence of employee discrimination claims and other litigation, particularly for Square Mile clients; non-contentious experience includes advising on TUPE, warranties and indemnities and union-related matters. Speaks and writes regularly on employment matters. Chapter author of FT Law and Tax 'Guide to Pensions'; HS/Jordans 'Pensions Disputes'; CILS 'Guide to International Employment Law'; and Jordans/IPD 'Employment Law Services'. Member of editorial board and chapter author of Croners 'Managing Termination of Employment'. Member of editorial board of Croners ''Diversity and Discrimination in Practice', monthly legal columnist for 'Education Law' briefing. Reported cases include 'Clark v BET', 'Wallace v Cantor Fitzgerald' and 'Wakeman v Quick Corporation'.
Prof. Memberships: Law Society.
Career: *Clifford Chance* 1984-94, *Hammond Suddards* 1994-95; partner *Hammond Suddards Edge* 1995 to date.
Personal: Born 1962. Oriel College, Oxford 1980-83. Chester Law School 1983-84. Lives in Blackheath, SE London.

WHITEMORE, Sarah
Warner Goodman & Streat, Fareham
(01329) 288121

WILLIAMS, Audrey
Eversheds, Cardiff (029) 2047 1147
audreywilliams@eversheds.com
Specialisation: Partner in the employment law department at Eversheds Cardiff office. Specialises in employment law. Particular experience of sex discrimination, race discrimination and disability discrimination. Advises on equal opportunities, maternity, parental leave, harassment and bullying policies; providing advice and training for establishing such policies; grievance procedures and counselling. Author of a number of publications.
Prof. Memberships: Member of the Chartered Institute of Personnel and Development.
Career: Graduate of Southampton University; qualified in 1989, joined *Eversheds Phillips and Buck* in 1989 (now *Eversheds* Cardiff); became a partner in 1993.
Personal: Married and resides in Cardiff.

WILLIAMSON, Andrew
Lovells, London (020) 7296 2000
andrew.williamson@lovells.com
Specialisation: Employment and labour law, and head of Employment Group.
Prof. Memberships: Past chairman and current member of City of London Law Society Employment Law Sub-Committee.
Career: Partner *Bowman Gilfillan & Blacklock* Johannesburg 1971-78 practising in insurance and general commercial litigation and political criminal cases; articled *Lovells* 1978; qualified England 1980, Partner 1982.

WILLIAMSON, Raymond
MacRoberts, Glasgow (0141) 332 9988
raymond.williamson@macroberts.co.uk
Specialisation: Partner in employment group. Specialist in employment law since the early 1970's. Advises on the drafting of contracts of employment, on management of staff, on redundancies and disciplinary matters. Also experienced in representing clients' interests before employment and other tribunals. Holder of specialist authorisation from the Law Society of Scotland in employment law. Convener of the Law Society's Employment Law Committee and chairman of the Employment Law Specialisation Committee. Lectures extensively on employment matters for various course giving bodies and has been an external examiner on employment law at Glasgow University. Author of the chapter on employment law in Greene & Fletcher's 'The Law and Practice of Receivership in Scotland'.
Prof. Memberships: Law Society of Scotland, Royal Faculty of Procurators in Glasgow.
Career: Joined *MacRoberts* solicitors in 1966 and qualified in 1968. Became a partner in 1972.
Personal: Born 24 December 1942. Educated at the High School of Glasgow 1949-60 and the University of Glasgow 1960-66. Vice-chairman of the Royal Scottish Academy of Music and Drama; governor of The High School of Glasgow; chairman of the John Currie Singers Ltd; chairman National Youth Choir of Scotland; chairman Scottish International Piano Competition. Leisure interests include music and gardening. Lives in Glasgow.

WOFFENDEN, Sara
Shoosmiths, Nottingham (0115) 906 5000
Specialisation: Head of employment team – Nottingham. All aspects of employment law but mainly business transfers, re-organisations, trade union recognition and severance agreements.
Prof. Memberships: Part time Chairman of Employment Tribunals (England and Wales); Midlands representative on Management Committee of Employment Lawyers Association 1995-00; Member of Training Committee of Employment Lawyers Association.
Career: Educated Leeds University. Admitted 1985. 1985-89 *Bettinsons*, Birmingham; 1989-94 *Pinsent & Co*; 1994-98 *Wragge & Co*; 1998 *Shoosmiths* – Partner.
Personal: Born 1959. Leisure interests currently limited to chauffeuring children (eight and four).

WYNN-EVANS, Charles
Dechert, London (020) 7583 5353
charles.wynnevans@dechertEU.com
Specialisation: Partner and head of the employment unit. Deals with all aspects of contentious and non-contentious employment law, including discrimination, transfers of undertakings, share option and incentive schemes, senior executive appointments and departures and restrictive covenant matters. Regularly writes on employment law for a variety of journals.
Prof. Memberships: Industrial Law Society, Employment Lawyers' Association, Law Society.
Career: Joined *Titmuss Sainer & Webb* (now *Dechert*) in 1990. Qualified 1992. Appointed partner 1997.
Personal: Born 1967. Educated at King Henry VIII School Coventry; Bristol University (LLB 1988) and Merton College Oxford (BCL 1990). Interests include cricket, rugby and current affairs. Married with one daughter. Lives in Kennington, London.

YATES, Tracy
Eversheds, Norwich (01603) 272727
traceyyates@eversheds.com
Specialisation: Employment, handling unfair dismissal and a wide range of other Tribunals claims, including sex race and disability discrimination, and breach of contract claims for commercial clients, including undertaking advocacy in the Employment Tribunals. Also handles wrongful dismissal claims in the courts. Advises commercial clients and senior employees in respect of compromise agreement/severage packages; and on all aspects of employment law (TUPE, redundancy, dismissals etc). Drafting, and advising on service agreements and statements of main terms and conditions of employment. Immigration: Advises on applications for entry clearance, work permits and naturalisation.
Prof. Memberships: Law Society and Employment Lawyers Association.
Career: Qualified October 1986. Trainee solicitor, *Daynes, Chittock & Back* 1984-86; partner *Eversheds* 1992 to date.
Personal: Two daughters – Helena and Sophia.

YOUNG, James
McGrigor Donald, Edinburgh (0131) 777 7000
Specialisation: Head of Employment Unit. Has been involved in Employment Law since the initiating UK legislation in the 1970's. Head of *McGrigor Donald*'s Employment Law Unit and provides advice on a full range of Employment Law issues. Particular concerns of clients in the past year have included human rights; issues arising out of e-mail use/abuse; trade union issues; the increase in discrimination claims; post-termination restrictions and the impact of new legislation. Has represented and continues to represent a large number of clients at Employment Tribunals. Member of the Law Society Committee of Employment Law; member of Institute of Personnel and Management; speaker at conferences on various aspects of employment law; Scottish contributor to Employment Precedents and Company Policy documents.
Prof. Memberships: Law Society of Scotland; Institute of Personnel and Management.
Career: Qualified in 1975 at *McGrigor Donald & Co.* After two years as Legal Officer West Lothian District Council and two years as Assistant Solicitor at *Moncrieff Warren Patterson & Co.*, became partner in 1979 and joined *McGrigor Donald* as partner in 1985.
Personal: Born 26 February 1950. Educated at Hutchesons' Boys Grammar School and the University of Glasgow. Leisure interests include watching and participating in sport (now mainly golf), Contemporary Scottish Art and Theatre. Lives in Edinburgh.

YOUNSON, Fraser
McDermott, Will & Emery, London
(020) 7577 6992
FYounson@europe.mwe.com
Specialisation: (Bar 1975) Partner and Head of Employment Group. Main area of practice is employment law, covering executive termination, employment aspects of mergers and acquisitions, sex, race and disability discrimination, employee fraud, breach of fiduciary duties, restrictive covenants, unfair dismissal and redundancy, wrongful dismissal, union recognition claims law, industrial disputes, worker representation and European Work Councils, EC labour law, Employment Tribunal advocacy and compensation claims, transnational reorganisation and collective redundancies.
Prof. Memberships: Law Society, Industrial Law Society, Former Chairman and now life Vice-president of Employment Lawyers Association.
Career: Qualified for the Bar in 1975, and as a Solicitor in 1987. Previously Employment Law Adviser to British Aerospace Group HQ, and previously Editor of IDS Brief. Joined *Baker & McKenzie* in 1983-99, becoming a Partner in 1990. Joined *McDermott, Will & Emery* 1999.
Publications: Author of 'Employment Law Handbook', 'Employment Law and Business Transfers – A Practical Guide', 'Croner's Industrial Relations Law', and contributor to plc and the Law Society Gazette on employment law issues. Lectures extensively on labour law; 'Transfers of Undertakings' (Sweet & Maxwell).
Personal: Born 11th November 1952. Attended Oxford University. Lives in Houghton, Cambs.

ENERGY & NATURAL RESOURCES

London: 345; The South 350; Midlands: 350; The North: 351; Scotland: 351; *Profiles*: 353

RESEARCH APPROVED BY BMRB: *For this edition,* Chambers' *researchers conducted 6,552 interviews – 4,419 with law firms, 554 with barristers and 1,579 with clients.*

The validity of the research was scrutinised by BMRB International, who audited both the methodology and the results at our offices in July 2001. They interviewed Chambers' *researchers and cross-checked sample interviews. Details of the audit appear on page 7.*

LONDON

ENERGY & NATURAL RESOURCES • London	Ptnrs	Assts
1 Denton Wilde Sapte	16	30
Herbert Smith	27	n/a
2 CMS Cameron McKenna	n/a	n/a
3 Allen & Overy	25	n/a
Clifford Chance	28	n/a
Freshfields Bruckhaus Deringer	n/a	n/a
Linklaters	15	n/a
Norton Rose	6	n/a
4 Ashurst Morris Crisp	13	11
Lovells	9	17
Slaughter and May	8	n/a
Vinson & Elkins LLP	8	16
5 Lawrence Graham	2	2
Nabarro Nathanson	8	16
Simmons & Simmons	7	n/a
6 Baker & McKenzie	n/a	n/a
Baker Botts	6	6
Beachcroft Wansbroughs	6	6
Clyde & Co	8	11
Coudert Brothers	3	n/a
Field Fisher Waterhouse	n/a	n/a
Ince & Co	n/a	n/a
Masons	n/a	n/a
Morgan Cole	4	4
Shearman & Sterling	n/a	n/a
Watson, Farley & Williams	8	12

This book is the product of 6,552 1/2-hour interviews. See p.7 for BMRB audit.
Within each band, firms are listed alphabetically.

Denton Wilde Sapte (see firm details p.939) Regarded by clients as *"the team with the greatest industry experience,"* the firm continues to go from strength to strength. Advising on pure energy work, as well as financing, rivals view the oil and gas team as *"pre-eminent in terms of volume of business and quality."* **Myles Cave-Browne-Cave** is *"a charming and delightful adversary,"* who *"stands out from a strong team"* for upstream and downstream oil and gas work. He advised TotalFinaElf Exploration UK on the arrangements relating to its upstream assets and its gas sales agreements. An impressive client base includes BG International and EDF, and his caseload is largely international. *"Urbane and sensible"* **James Dallas** *"is a commercial negotiator with real gravitas."* He advised ENH on the US$1.18 million deal to develop Mozambique's Pande and Temane natural gas fields. In the power sector, the firm's involvement with NETA has placed it firmly at the heart of the domestic industry, particularly on the regulatory side. *"Clear thinker"* **Charles Wood** (also *"highly respected"* for his knowledge of the gas industry) is praised by industry majors for having *"drafted the Balancing and Settlement Code to a supreme level."* The firm's overseas practice has grown, notably through the strengthening of its Middle Eastern, Asian and African client base. It closed two IPPs for the Government of Oman and advised Arab Bank on the first IPP in the Palestinian Autonomous Territories. *"Clients love"* recent hire and *"serious contender"* **David Birchall**, while international managing partner **David Moroney** retains his profile in the sector, despite devoting much of his time to his

TOP IN-HOUSE LAWYERS

Electricity

Yehuda COHEN, Head of Legal, *Dynergy UK Ltd*
Nigel FOWKES, Solicitor, *Innogy Holdings Plc*
Robert HIGSON, Group Solicitor & Company Secretary, *London Electricity plc*
Eldon PETHYBRIDGE, Director of Legal and Regulatory Affairs, *Centrica*
Paul SIMONS, Assistant General Counsel, *Enron*

"Very much hands on and highly competent," **Yehuda Cohen** is recommended as one of a new generation of lawyers working in a liberalised industry; his specialism is downstream electricity and gas. **Nigel Fowkes** is respected for his *"sensible perspective"* and *"good sound knowledge."* **Robert Higson** remains heavily endorsed. Rated for his gas knowledge, **Eldon Pethybridge** is also included within electricity this year in recognition of extensive work under NETA. Renowned for his *"all encompassing knowledge"* of the market, **Paul Simons** continues to attract praise.

Oil & Gas

David BATE, Legal Manager, *Enterprise Energy Ireland Ltd*
Justin BOYD, Senior Legal Adviser, *Enron*
Ian CHITTY, Solicitor, *BG Group*
Alan DUNLOP, Head of Legal and Public Affairs, *Amerada Hess*
Mark EVANS, General Counsel, *Enron*

Considered *"a safe pair of hands,"* **David Bate** continues to be recognised as a leader. A *"first class lawyer,"* **Ian Chitty** is seen as *"commercial – he's good to have working alongside you,"* and recognised for his upstream oil and gas background. **Alan Dunlop** is perceived by some as "one of the most experienced and most highly thought of in-house lawyers." With the industry currently changing at pace, it is also noteworthy that **Mark Evans** is thought to be *"a very, very quick learner,"* while **Justin Boyd** is considered *"extremely able."*

Water

Keith DONALD, General Counsel, *International Water*
David HOSKER, Head of Legal Services, *United Utilities*
Michael KNIGHT, Company Solicitor, *Severn Trent Water*
Victoria RIGBY, International Counsel, *Vivendi Water*

Keith Donald operates with a global outlook and remains well renowned for his *"wide-ranging commercial experience."* *"Professional"* **David Hosker** continues to be recognised as a *"leader in the field."* An *"excellent lawyer,"* **Michael Knight** is *"commercially minded"* and enjoys a *"detailed knowledge of the industry."* **Victoria Rigby** continues to *"command respect."*

In-House lawyers profiles: p 1193

LEADING INDIVIDUALS: Oil and Gas

Band		
1	**CAVE-BROWNE-CAVE Myles** Denton Wilde Sapte	**GRIFFIN Paul** Herbert Smith
	SALT Stuart Linklaters	
2	**BOND Richard** Herbert Smith	**DALLAS James** Denton Wilde Sapte
	DAVIES Roger Allen & Overy	**KHAN Rafique** CMS Cameron McKenna
	PICTON-TURBERVILL Geoffrey Ashurst Morris Crisp	
	REES Jonathan Freshfields	**ROBERTS Martin** Slaughter and May
	ROBERTS Martin Slaughter and May	**STANGER Michael** Lovells
	WOOD Charles Denton Wilde Sapte	
3	**BEHARRELL Steven** Coudert Brothers	**BLAKE Peter** Clifford Chance
	DAVEY Henry Herbert Smith	**HIGGINSON Tony** Baker Botts
	JONES Gareth Nabarro Nathanson	**PUGH Chris** Freshfields Bruckhaus
	SAUNDERS Mark Dewey Ballantine	**TYNE Sally** CMS Cameron McKenna
4	**BRETTON Linda** Lawrence Graham	**CARVER Jeremy** Clifford Chance
	COFFELL Howard Field Fisher Waterhouse	**GREENO Ted** Herbert Smith
	KING Ronnie Ashurst Morris Crisp	**MACGIBBON Sam** Vinson & Elkins LLP
	RANDELL Charles Slaughter and May	**VERRILL John** Lawrence Graham

LEADING INDIVIDUALS: Electricity

Band		
★	**WOOLF Fiona** CMS Cameron McKenna	
1	**SALT Stuart** Linklaters	
2	**BLAKE Peter** Clifford Chance	**ELDER Ian** Allen & Overy
	LANE Robert CMS Cameron McKenna	
	PICTON-TURBERVILL Geoffrey Ashurst Morris Crisp	
	STACEY Paul Slaughter and May	
3	**BIRCHALL David** Denton Wilde Sapte	**CLOUGH Adrian** Herbert Smith
	DAVEY Henry Herbert Smith	**GRIFFIN Paul** Herbert Smith
	MORONEY David Denton Wilde Sapte	**ROWEY Kent** Freshfields Bruckhaus
	TUDWAY Robert Nabarro Nathanson	**WALLACE Patrick** Freshfields Bruckhaus

LEADING INDIVIDUALS: Mining

Band	
1	**HURST Philip** Ashurst Morris Crisp
2	**CUTHBERT Michael** Clifford Chance
UP AND COMING	
	KELLY Christopher Linklater

LEADING INDIVIDUALS: Water

Band	
1	**TURTLE Trevor** Herbert Smith
2	**TEMPLE Richard** CMS Cameron McKenna
3	**LANE Mark** Masons
	McGEE-OSBORNE Christopher Denton Wilde Sapte
	SCRIVEN John Allen & Overy

See individuals' profiles p.353

managerial role. Water work includes the continuing involvement for the MOD on Project Aquitrine, as well as advising the Government of Oman (in conjunction with the electricity team) on its water and electricity restructuring and privatisation programme. Head of practice, **Christopher McGee-Osborne** is highly rated for his "*pragmatic approach.*" The firm's mining practice has been significantly strengthened through the acquisition of Cameron McKenna's Almaty office, and the opening of an office in Tashkent. **Clients:** TotalFinaElf; BG International; EDF; Korea National Oil Company; OFGEM: London Electricity; Arab Bank; MOD; Government of Oman; ENH; DEPA.

Herbert Smith (see firm details p.993) Recognised by peers for a "*genuine predilection for energy work,*" the firm wins plaudits as "*a superb mixed practice with a strong profile for energy litigation.*" Universally respected for its regulatory work, the firm is regarded by some as "*even stronger on the power side,*" although high level oil and gas lateral hires have given the team "*a genuinely balanced ticket.*" "*Electricity is their traditional bread and butter and they're among the leaders there,*" pronounce peers. The team's expertise in the industry includes restructuring, project finance, supply, distribution, transmission and generation, fuel supply and retail sales. Acknowledged for its "*strong work*" on behalf of RECs, the firm also advises major European players Electricité de France and financing giants such as Goldman Sachs. **Henry Davey** (see p.353), also recognised for his oil and gas regulatory expertise, acts extensively for Goldman Sachs, and is considered to be "*an amiable, relaxed guy to deal with.*" **Adrian Clough** (see p.353) is also recommended for his "*dogged, determined manner.*" The hiring of **Paul Griffin** (see p.354) ("*as good a lawyer as you'll find*") is considered by the market to have brought "*added credibility*" to the firm's oil and gas offering, as well as bolstering its power projects expertise. He advised IVO Fortum on the renegotiation and restructuring of the Humber Power Project, and advised SSB Hong Kong/ Bank of China International, financial advisers to China National Offshore Oil Co, on its postponed US$2 billion listing on the stock exchanges of Hong Kong and New York. **Richard Bond** (see p.241), although much less high profile since his election as senior partner, has "*a brain that you'd pay good money for,*" and is rated for his "*high degree of industry knowledge.*" Peers maintain that this is "*the only big corporate firm with real water expertise.*" The "*superb*" **Trevor Turtle** (see p.356) is "*admired by the industry,*" and oversaw the firm's appointment to act for British Waterways Board on the proposed PPP Water Grid project. The team also represented Anglian Water on its corporate restructuring by scheme of arrangement, involving the introduction of a new holding company, awg plc. A strong energy litigation practice is masterminded by "*clever and thoughtful litigator*" **Ted Greeno** (see p.571). He represented Amerada Hess and Enterprise in proceedings relating to the cancellation of a drilling contract. **Clients:** Electricité de France; TXU Europe/Eastern; London Electricity; awg plc; British Waterways Board; Amerada Hess; Chase Manhattan; British Borneo Oil & Gas; IVO Fortum.

CMS Cameron McKenna (see firm details p.922) Heralded by the industry as "*a silver service department,*" the firm maintains its advantage in power over most of the field, although its oil and gas practice is felt by some to generate "*more work out of Aberdeen than you would expect from a City firm.*" Nevertheless, the London oil and gas team has also increased its volume of corporate and international work, and runs the full gamut of upstream and downstream advice. "*Good all-round operator*" **Sally Tyne** (see p.356) is esteemed by peers as "*always excellent: sensible, energetic and a good laugh,*" while **Rafique Khan** (see p.354) is a "*meticulous and pragmatic*" lawyer, whose star has risen this year. The firm advised Cairn Energy in relation to long-term gas sales agreements from its recently discovered Lakshmi field off India. The power group, seen as a "*regulatory kingpin,*" is still pre-eminent for privatisations and retains the services of the "*tremendously dynamic*" **Fiona Woolf** (see p.357) at the helm. The team advised the South African Department of Minerals and Energy on the restructuring of the country's electricity market. "*Reliable and well-informed*" **Robert Lane** (see p.354) has represented The National Grid Company on a number of design and implementation issues, as well as advising on the codification of the connection and use of systems arrangements into a new regulatory-based document (CUSC). Peers recognise the firm's water practice for its blend of "*good local coverage and international presence.*" Projects in Eastern Europe have been a particularly fruitful source of instruction. **Richard Temple** (see p.356) is said to "*know the industry inside out.*" The firm advised on the Sofia water and sewerage project, the first major municipal infrastructure concession in Bulgaria, and the Bucharest water and sewerage privatisation, the first municipal infrastructure project under the new Romanian concession law. **Clients:** Municipality of Sofia; International Finance Corporation; Municipality of Bucharest; The National Grid Company; Northern Ireland Electricity; Cairn Energy; Sullom Voe Terminal Owners.

Allen & Overy (see firm details p.856) Best known for its work on energy projects, and possessing universally admired financing clout, the group is held to display "*impressive industry knowledge.*" The oil and gas practice is led by "*good man and great lawyer*" **Roger Davies** (see p.354). Combining specialist expertise with international reach, it has a substantial presence in the key oil and gas markets in Europe, Asia, and the Middle East. The European capability has been formalised with the recent establishment of a European energy group. The firm advised TXU on its acquisition of interests in various North Sea oil fields, notably the Johnston Field. Other work includes advising the Government of Oman on the privatisation of the Omani Gas System and the financing of new pipelines. **Ian Elder** (see p.354), who leads the international electricity, nuclear power and renewables team, maintains his status as an "*effective negotiator.*" His team, "*always there or thereabouts,*" acted for The National Grid Company on the development of an HVDC 1000MW interconnector between the UK and Norway. It has also advised a number of IPPs and sponsors on the implications of NETA in the UK. Energy financing continues to thrive; the firm acted for Deutsche Bank on the innovative financing for the 3960MW Drax coal-fired station. "*A fine client man,*" **John Scriven** (see p.356) leads the water team. The group's eclectic clientele includes water companies, governments, export credit agencies and banks. It advised the City of Tallinn on the privatisation of its water system and acted for the City of Zagreb on a BOT waste water treatment plant. At home, the firm acted for the arrangers in relation to the proposed splitting of Kelda's assets and operations. **Clients:** Biwater; Vivendi UK; Severn Trent; Yorkshire Electricity; TXU; ExxonMobil.

Clifford Chance (see firm details p.919) "*You ignore them at your peril,*" say rivals of the firm's respected all-round energy group. Primarily recognised for its expertise in power projects and energy financing, the group is considered to owe much to the "*industrious*" **Peter Blake** (see p.709), head of electricity. "*A tremendously client-friendly practitioner,*" according to competitors he leads a team which advises on M&A, privatisations, trading and marketing, regulation and market reform and power projects, advising sponsors, developers, governments and lenders. The group has represented UK portfolio generators, several IPPs, and two of the proposed new electricity exchanges on the introduction of NETA. It also advised British Energy on its US$1.5 billion acquisition of the Eggborough coal-fired power station from National Power. Peter Blake is also admired for his gas work: "*gas lawyers don't come much better than him.*" Downstream oil and gas has an international flavour, highlighted by the firm's work for the joint arrangers and overall co-ordinators of the Blue Stream Pipeline Project, a $2.6 billion multi-source financing to construct a gas pipeline to the Russian coast and then under the Black Sea from Russia to Turkey. Contentious work constitutes a significant element of the practice. In this sphere, **Jeremy Carver** (see p.353) is said to be able to handle "*even the most difficult clients.*" The firm represented Ocean Rig and Transocean in disputes relating to the construction, repair and upgrading of semi-submersible oil rigs. Upstream work includes gas sale and purchase agreements, primarily in the context of fuel supply for power stations. The team advised the PSCs on the proposed South Sumatra Pipeline Project in Indonesia, which will supply gas to Singapore. Mining and minerals work encompasses advice on mining finance, projects, refining contracts and metals trading. **Michael Cuthbert** (see p.353) is the name in this area, and led the team that advised the Government of the Republic of Zambia on the privatisation of Zambia Consolidated Copper Mines. **Clients:** Chiyoda/Foster Wheeler; Bechtel; Petrobras; Bord Gais; ZCCM; British Energy Group.

Freshfields Bruckhaus Deringer (see firm details p.964) "*Impressive, rising*" energy team, which advises on oil and gas, electricity, regulatory work and energy disputes. Although the firm is perceived by the market to "*come at it from a corporate angle,*" they are nevertheless felt to field individuals with genuine industry knowledge. The "*acute*" **Jon Rees** (see p.355), for example, is considered by peers to have "*a sympathetic negotiating style.*" The emphasis in the upstream oil and gas caseload is still on big-ticket M&A, but commercial contract, PSA and negotiation work also figure prominently. The firm advised Amerada Hess on its takeover bid for LASMO and represented the Government of Bahrain in the development of a new exploration and production-sharing contract. London is central to the firm's international downstream gas practice, advising on the industry's liberalisation in Europe. The team has also acted on a steady flow of oil and gas project work of an international nature. It advised Shell and Chevron inter alia on the development of the West African gas pipeline system connecting Nigeria and Ghana. The litigation group is headed by "*excellent tactician,*" **Chris Pugh** (see p.355), described by one leading client as "*our favourite: not only commercial but superb in support of the settlement process.*" The firm acted for British American Offshore in a drilling rig dispute with Amoco UK and a number of other oil companies. In the power sector, the "*astute*" **Kent Rowey** (see p.355) and the "*versatile*" **Patrick Wallace** (see p.357) oversee the group's focus on projects and regulatory work. Seen to possess a "*great client portfolio,*" the firm has played a key role in the restructuring of the electricity sector in Europe. **Clients:** Amerada Hess; Government of Bahrain; Shell; Chevron Corp; Powergen; NGC; ScottishPower; Distrigas; Electrabel; BAOL.

Linklaters (see firm details p.1042) Principally noted for power projects, M&A and financings, the firm's strong all-round practice is built around the figure of the universally admired **Stuart Salt** (see p.356). "*Down to earth, but a hard negotiator,*" he is also praised by rivals as "*pragmatic and superbly easy to deal with.*" He is the only practitioner to be band one rated in both oil and gas and power. In the power sector the UK practice enjoyed a memorable transactional year, acting for National Power on its £5 billion reorganisation and demerger, and for London Electricity on its purchase of Cottam Power Station (2000MW) from PowerGen. A highlight power project involved advice to the lenders on the US$1.2 billion refinancing for the 512MW ISAB Energy integrated gasification combined cycle power station in Sicily. The established upstream oil and gas practice has been involved in projects worldwide and some notable M&A deals, such as acting for BP Amoco on its US$26 billion takeover of ARCO. The expanding downstream practice has been active in the structuring and financing of a range of global projects. Mining and minerals expertise is offered to a range of financiers and industry players. **Christopher Kelly** (see p.354), recently made partner, retains his reputation as one of the "*best of the new wave of lawyers.*" The firm represented Deutsche Bank AG as the lead arranger for the project financing of the US$248 million Olympias gold, silver, lead and zinc mine in Halkidiki, Greece. **Clients:** Citibank/SSSB; Duke Energy; NRG; Royal Bank of Scotland; BG; BP; Dresdner Bank; Shell; EBRD; Hyder; Anglo American; Billiton; De Beers.

Norton Rose (see firm details p.1082) The departure of "*driving force*" Michael Taylor to Milan (from where he is heading the firm's Energy International Group) has deprived the London office of its outstanding figure by far. However, clients still commend the "*uniform quality*" of the rest of the team, although, to date, no single individual has emerged to fill Taylor's shoes. During the past year, the firm has performed strongly on the corporate side of oil and gas, advising Agip Ventures on its £788 million takeover of British Borneo Oil & Gas and on its subsequent takeover of LASMO. The team also represented SACE, JBIC, MITI/EID and ECGD on the US$1.76 billion ECA-supported financing of the Blue Stream gas pipeline. The firm's electricity practice remains at the forefront of IPP work internationally, acting for governments, developers and banks. It advised Singapore Power on the liberalisation and restructuring of Singapore's electricity industry, and acted for the Public Power Corporation of Greece on licensing and regulatory issues and the drafting of the country's new Operating Code and Power Exchange Code. **Clients:** ABN AMRO; Bank of Scotland; Bank of Tokyo Mitsubishi; BNP Paribas; ExxonMobil; Intergen; Norsk Hydro; Ranger Oil; Singapore Power; Texaco.

Ashurst Morris Crisp (see firm details p.866) Perceived to have "*steadied*" this year, the energy team has not quite regained its profile of two years ago. However, a "*friendly and supportive team*" is now felt by the market to have a "*better balanced*" practice, active in energy projects, litigation, acquisitions and disposals. **Geoffrey Picton-Turbervill** (see p.355) remains the "*great presence*" at the firm, acknowledged by peers as "*a true industry specialist with broad UK and overseas knowledge*" on the corporate/commercial side of both oil and gas and power. The firm was lead advisor to Kuwait Petroleum Corporation on its proposed project to import gas from the Enhanced Gas Utilisation project in Qatar's North Field. It also advised ONEPM (UK) on its acquisition from Shell UK of interests in the Elgin/Franklin development in the North Sea. **Philip Hurst** (see p.354), "*an expert on mining matters overseas,*" retains his status as a luminary of the sector. Focusing on exploration and development, the team advised Noranda on its base metals exploration and development program in Iran, and represented CDC Capital Partners on its acquisition of a minority interest in Konkola Mines plc. The litigation and arbitration practice, led by the "*tenacious*" **Ronnie King** (see p.575), is another important string to the group's bow. It acted for BG Trading in securing settlement of an £11 million claim brought by the owners of a UK offshore gas field. It also successfully settled a £20 million claim against Unocal Corporation, brought by DNO ASA. **Clients:** BG; BP Amoco; Repsol YPF; Unocal Corp; Cinergy Global Power; Marubeni Corp; NRG Energy; PowerGen UK; Anglo American; Barclays; Rio Tinto.

Lovells (see firm details p.1044) Felt to have weathered the departure of Tony Higginson, the firm is admired by competitors for its "*operational nous*" and a "*classy client base.*" "*Thorough and bright*" **Michael Stanger** (see p.356) remains the leading figure here. The firm holds a strong position in the European gas trading market, the competition aspects of that market and the competition aspects of downstream oil and gas. The merger with Boesebeck Droste has enabled it to develop its workload in Central and Eastern Europe and Russia. Downstream matters have included corporate work and litigation, while the team also advises extensively on LNG, production sharing agreements, joint operating agreements, oil trading and FPSOs. Gas trading is an area of niche strength, highlighted by the team's advice on the sub-letting of capacity in the Belgian transmission system. Elsewhere, the firm represented Hamburgische Elektrizitäts Werke (HEW) on the acquisition of VEAG, the main utility company in the former East Germany, and LAUBAG, the largest lignite mining company in the former East Germany. **Clients:** Statoil; HEW; Exxon; Texaco; Gaz de France.

Slaughter and May (see firm details p.1135) Although the firm does not have a dedicated energy department, its cross-departmental team of experts continues to win market plaudits. Clients describe **Martin Roberts** (see p.714), who handles upstream and downstream oil and gas work, as "*an astute lawyer with commercial savvy.*" Peers admire his "*shrewd appreciation of the industry and his professional common sense.*" The firm acted on the sale of United Utilities' retail energy supply business, Norweb Energi, to TXU Europe for £310 million. New to the rankings this year is "*excellent lawyer*" **Charles Randell** (see p.255), a corporate man with "*real expertise*" in oil and gas M&A work. In the power sector, **Paul Stacey** (see p.356) is regarded as a "*pragmatic and sensible*" practitioner. The team is felt to be "*technically strong on the regulatory side,*" with rivals acknowledging its "*sound work*" on behalf of the Electricity Pool. The group advised the Electricity Pool/Elexon on the introduction of NETA in England and Wales, and acted for ESB National Grid on the electricity trading and settlement code for Ireland. In other areas, the firm's renowned corporate strength has enabled it to advise on big-ticket transactions, such as Shell's sale of its international coal business to Anglo American for US$900 million. **Clients:**Electricity Pool/Elexon; Corus; Blue Circle; Shell; Anglo American; Thames Water.

Vinson & Elkins LLP Impressing clients and rivals alike, the energy giant's London office continues to rise in public estimation. "*Clearly first-class industry specialists,*" the firm combines oil and gas and power regulatory expertise with a regular diet of corporate work. The contentious side of the practice has also grown substantially. A long-standing relationship with Enron stands out from an impressive clientele of major industry players. The "*versatile*" **Sam MacGibbon** (see p.355), who focuses on gas and electricity work, is acclaimed by market sources as an "*able and well-informed lawyer.*" The firm represented one of the parties in the ongoing Project Dolphin, and has advised on NETA issues, North Sea pipeline work and a number of power projects in Africa. It also acted for Fortum on Project Matrix, the divestiture of electricity power projects in England, Ireland, Scotland and Hungary.**Clients:** Enron; Duke Energy; Shell; Devon; Fortum.

Lawrence Graham (see firm details p.1030) Led by the "*assertive*" **John Verrill** (see p.356), and also including LASMO favourite **Linda Bretton** (see p.353), the team polarises views. Client opinion ranges from "*aggressive and abrasive*" to "*sound and easy to deal with,*" in assessing the team's style. The majority of interviewees accept that "*ultimately, they do provide a good service.*" This includes large scale package acquisitions and disposals, as well as the handling of routine work and overflow from in-house teams, an area of work for which the team is particularly noted.The firm acted for Tullow Oil on the £201 million acquisition of Southern Gas Basin assets from ARCO and Britoil. It also advised Intrepid Energy on the acquisition of a package of oil and gas interests in the Moray Firth area of the North Sea. **Clients:** Tullow Oil; Intrepid Energy; Veba Oil; LASMO.

Nabarro Nathanson (see firm details p.1078) A national energy group, based in London and Sheffield, is renowned within the industry for its focus on domestic projects. In London, the team's leading figure is the "*formidable*" **Robert Tudway** (see p.356). He remains a leading figure in regulatory power circles. **Gareth Jones** is respected for his regulatory and transactional experience, and has a focus on UK gas law. A panel member to the Office of Gas and Electricity Markets, the firm is currently preparing the licensing schemes required under the Utilities Act for all the gas and electricity companies in the UK. Substantial strength in environmentally compatible energy schemes encompasses CHP, energy from waste and embedded generation. The firm has advised on three major recent CHP schemes, acted for embedded generators such as Slough Heat & Power on regulatory matters, and represented Southampton City Council on a district heating scheme. **Clients:** London Electricity; Ofgem; Southampton City Council; EniChem.

Simmons & Simmons (see firm details p.1132) Acknowledged by competitors to have "*deep resources in this area,*" the firm is especially respected for its contentious expertise. Oil and gas, power and water all feature prominently in a broad caseload. Led by Jerry Walter, the team is praised by clients for its "*vigorous defence of our interests*" and its "*commercial attitude.*" Strong on overseas pipeline projects, the firm advises on project structure, intergovernmental arrangements, shareholding arrangements and commercial issues. It acted on Project Dolphin in the Middle East, advising on the structuring, gas purchase and sales arrangements, as well as on the joint venture between Offsets Group, TotalFinaElf and Enron. Specialists in oil projects work in Iran, the team has worked widely with representatives of the National Iranian Oil Company and local Iranian lawyers. It also advised on the CPC project, the first private oil pipeline in Russia. **Clients:** Offsets Group; TotalFinaElf; Enron.

Baker & McKenzie (see firm details p.868) Led by Neil Donoghue, the energy team's workload encompasses oil and gas, electricity and water. The oil and gas practice focuses on international transactional work, utilising the firm's global network. The London office is generally seen on the financing side of transactions, and was described by one investment bank as "*a strong team, always available.*" Acting for IBJ and ABN AMRO, the arrangers, the firm was involved in the US$125 million non-recourse borrowing facility to finance the acquisition of North Sea oil and gas assets by Marubeni Oil & Gas (UK) from Verba Oil & Gas (UK). In the power sector, the group acted for AES Corporation and JSC AES Talasi in relation to the US$60 million financing by the EBRD and IFC of privatised electricity distribution assets in the Republic of Georgia. The water practice has had a domestic focus, and includes advice to Southern Water on construction and procurement issues relating to a number of UK projects.

Clients: BP Amoco; BNP Paribas; EBRD/KfW; European Investment Bank; KazTransOil; Lonrho; Shell UK.

Baker Botts (see firm details p.867) Ex-Lovells man **Tony Higginson** is admired by market commentators for his "*immense knowledge of the industry,*" allied with "*a tremendous appetite for work.*" Under his guidance, and with the assistance of the firm's powerful international influence, the energy team makes its debut in this year's rankings. The firm's reputation lies chiefly with its upstream and midstream oil and gas practices, advising a clientele which includes oil companies, foreign governments, investment banks and drilling companies. In addition to work in the UK, the firm has advised on projects in the Middle East, Africa, South America and Russia. On the power side, the firm acts for a number of generators, advising on co-generation projects and representing Dynergy and Entergy on NETA-related issues. **Clients:** BHP; Lukoil; Sasol; Reliant Energy; Gaz de France; Oderbrecht; Pan-Canadian; Morgan Stanley.

Beachcroft Wansbroughs (see firm details p.872) Still best known for its "*respectable water practice,*" the team, under the guidance of Jim Beshoff, concentrates on the domestic market, where it provides a full service to water companies on both transactional and regulatory matters. The caseload includes large acquisitions, selling surplus land and water prosecutions. Involved in the reorganisation of funding for the water industry and in substantial acquisitions of non-core industries, the firm represented East Surrey Water on the first successful challenge of the regulator's price determination. The team also represented Cambridge Water on its acquisition by Ufacex Holdings for over £50 million. **Clients:** East Surrey Water; Cambridge Water.

Clyde & Co (see firm details p.921) "*A decent operation,*" according to rivals which advises on all aspects of the energy industry, but has particular expertise in acting for exploration, production and operation companies. Headed by Andrew Wells, a traditional oil and gas practice also profits from the firm's shipping focus, and advises on all marine-related issues. These encompass offshore construction and operations (including FPSO and LNG), transportation and insurance, including political risk. The team acted for Brovig on a development agreement with Premier Oil for the Chestnut Field. Recognised by peers for its "*solid knowledge*" of the mining and minerals industries, the firm acted for Glencore in relation to the international purchase of a metal smelting complex in Scandinavia. Power and electricity work has focused on energy trading, derivatives and regulatory advice. The group acted for Woking Borough Council on a public/private partnership to construct and operate an energy-efficient CHP plant. **Clients:**Glencore; Navan Mining; Woking Borough Council; Amerada Hess.

Coudert Brothers (see firm details p.925) "*An experienced energy lawyer who would be an asset to any team,*" **Steven Beharrell** (see p.353) wins widespread plaudits from fellow practitioners. He is considered to dominate a team that focuses on oil and gas and power, typically for offshore investors. The firm advised the Greater Johannesburg Metropolitan Municipality on a public/private agreement in relation to coal-fire plant. Other work includes acting for the Electricity Supply Board on the UK-Ireland Gas Interconnector, and representing the sponsor on a 100MW project in Mombasa, the first project in Kenya to be funded by the IFC. **Clients:** ESB; Electricité de France; Greater Johannesburg Metropolitan Municipality.

Field Fisher Waterhouse (see firm details p.957) Our research uncovered a national reputation as "*unquestioned leaders*" for advice on gas pipeline projects that shows no sign of diminishing. In addition, the team has been visible on a number of power projects, most notably the Great Yarmouth project. Peers admire **Howard Coffell** (see p.353) for his qualities of leadership. The team advises new client Transco on complex pipeline matters, as well as maintaining established relationships with other leading domestic entities.**Clients:** Transco; Interconnector (UK); Enfield Energy; British Pipeline Agency.

Ince & Co (see firm details p.1008) Traditionally powerful in offshore exploration and production, the group, led by Chris Sprague and David Steward, specialises in energy litigation and arbitration, which is combined with offshore marine and insurance expertise. The last year saw the return of over US$100 million to one client through the resolution of two separate disputes. The firm also represented Global Marine on its successfully resolved drilling rig dispute with Maersk Vinlander, and advised Vintage Petroleum on a dispute involving gas concessions in Argentina. Non-contentious work includes joint ventures, drilling contracts, FPSOs, project, asset, and trade finance, oil and gas contracts, decommissioning offshore installations, and the design, construction and operation of rigs. **Clients:** Global Marine; Transocean Sedco Forex; Tidewater; Saipem SpA, Milan; Horizon Offshore Contractors; Pride Foramer; Marathon; Occidental/LASMO; British Gas.

Masons (see firm details p.1056) Organised on a national basis, the firm's energy practice embraces upstream and downstream oil and gas, power and water. While contractors form the core client base, there has been an increase in work on behalf of owners and operators, both within the UK and overseas. There has also been a rise in non-contentious international projects work, advising on issues such as acquisitions, consultancy agreements, flotations, procurement strategies, EPC and EPIC contracts. The firm acted on contractual and claim issues for Mexican contractor Empresas ICA Sociedad Controladora, relating to a natural gas pipeline between Bolivia and Brazil, and advised the Pakistan Water and Power Development Authority on arbitration over a disputed electricity tariff. Interviewees claim that the firm's reputation in the water sector owes much to the "*effective*" **Mark Lane** (see p.354). Much of the work is project-related, but the team also advised the South African Department of Water Affairs and Forestry on a regulatory framework for PPPs in the sector. **Clients:** Independent Power; Oderbrecht Oil & Gas Services; Statoil; Government of Sri Lanka.

Morgan Cole (see firm details p.1074) After a year of high profile activity, the firm enters the rankings having impressed both barristers and leading competitors in the oil and gas and power sectors. The team is thought to have had "*more success than anyone in getting their hands on outsourced in-house work.*" The firm represented Kerr-McGee on its purchase of the UK assets of Repsol, a deal worth US$555 million. **Clients:** BP; International Power; TotalFinaElf.

Shearman & Sterling (see firm details p.1125) Said by market sources to be "*making an impact in power projects,*" the firm's London energy practice is recognised to have "*bulked up noticeably,*" and consequently is ranked in this area for the first time. Although not possessing the depth of some of the leaders, the team advises a number of heavyweight financial institutions. It advised the banks on the financing of the Tawleelah A2 power and water generation facility in Abu Dhabi. Nick Buckworth and Ken MacRitchie are the leading figures here. **Clients:** ABN AMRO; BG.

Watson, Farley & Williams (see firm details p.1174) Cross-departmental practice, with its principal focus on power generation projects. Douglas Wardle is the main contact partner. Acting mainly for sponsors, but also occasionally advising contractors, the team has been involved in power projects in Hungary, Romania, Bulgaria and Slovakia. Niche expertise exists in the area of coal-fired power plants. Oil and gas work includes advising contractors for North Sea oil projects on their production and development contracts, in addition to financing. Approximately 75% of the workload has an international element. The firm advised Mitsubishi Heavy Industries and FLS Miljo on the supply of new power plants in Spain and the UK and on the provision of equipment for reducing emissions from a UK coal-fired plant. **Clients:** AES Horizons; Vivendi Universal; Mitsubishi Heavy Industries.

Other Notable Practitioners **Mark Saunders** of **Dewey Ballantine** has a "*fine track record in the oil and gas industry,*" dating back to his time in-house at Elf. "*A fine technician,*" he has worked on a variety of projects for some of the leading names in the sector.

THE SOUTH

ENERGY & NATURAL RESOURCES • The South	Ptnrs	Assts
1 **Bond Pearce** Plymouth	5	4
Veale Wasbrough Bristol	1	3

LEADING INDIVIDUALS	
1 **SMITHERS Tim** Veale Wasbrough	**TRINICK Marcus** Bond Pearce

This book is the product of 6,552 1/2-hour interviews. See p.7 for BMRB audit.
Within each band, firms are listed alphabetically. *See individuals' profiles p.353*

Bond Pearce (see firm details p.888) Recognised nationwide for his long-term commitment to renewable sources of energy, **Marcus Trinick** (see p.670) is an "*acknowledged leader,*" in areas such as wind farms. His team has advised on site acquisition, planning and corporate finance on numerous renewables projects, both on and offshore. The firm acted for Scottish Power UK on its renewable energy portfolio in Scotland, and continues to advise a predominantly domestic clientele on a variety of energy projects. **Clients:** DTI; Enron; Scottish Power; Renewable Energy Systems; National Windpower; British Wind Energy Association.

Veale Wasbrough (see firm details p.1167) Possessing a national profile for pipeline work, headed by the "*thoroughly capable*" **Tim Smithers** (see p.754), the team is said by competitors to have an "*enviable client list.*" It advised TotalFinaElf on its national fuel oil pipeline network and acted for Transco on compulsory purchase of rights for gas pipelines. The team also represented Esso Petroleum Company on the replacement of its jetline aviation fuel pipeline. **Clients:** Esso Petroleum Company; TotalFinaElf; Transco; Huntsman.

MIDLANDS

ENERGY & NATURAL RESOURCES • Midlands	Ptnrs	Assts
1 **Martineau Johnson** Birmingham	2	4
Wragge & Co Birmingham	2	9
2 **Eversheds** Birmingham	1	2
Kent Jones and Done Stoke-on-Trent	1	1
Knight & Sons Newcastle-under-Lyme	2	4
3 **Edwards Geldard** Derby	2	2
Hammond Suddards Edge Birmingham		

LEADING INDIVIDUALS	
1 **HAMLETT David** Wragge & Co	**UPTON Neil** Wragge & Co
WHITEHEAD Andrew Martineau Johnson	
2 **BELL Anthony** Knight & Sons	**BRENNAN Paul** Martineau Johnson
REEVES Tony Kent Jones and Done	**WILLIAMS Gwyn** Hammond Suddards Edge

This book is the product of 6,552 1/2-hour interviews. See p.7 for BMRB audit.
Within each band, firms are listed alphabetically. *See individuals' profiles p.353*

Martineau Johnson (see firm details p.1055) Hailed by law firms throughout the country as a "*sophisticated practice,*" the energy team continues to enjoy a high profile for power, oil and gas and water. The firm is heavily involved in the contractual arrangements governing the energy sector, through its work for the National Grid Company. **Andrew Whitehead** (see p.357) earns the respect of competitors for his "*detailed, technical knowledge of the electricity business.*" He leads the team advising NGC on the adoption of system balancing contracts for NETA and its Connection and Use of System Code. The respected **Paul Brennan** (see p.353) advised Hyder on its successful application for a public gas transportation licence. In the water sector, the firm advised South Staffordshire Water on the introduction of competition regulations into the industry. **Clients:** Hyder Gas Networks; EnMO; The National Grid Company; East Midlands Pipelines; South Staffordshire Group.

Wragge & Co (see firm details p.1189) Recognised in the industry for its "*national profile,*" the team, one of the largest outside London, has increased its turnover by 70% in the last year and includes former in-house and OFGEM lawyers. Areas of expertise include electricity generation, combined heat and power, outsourcing, energy regulation and trading. Head of department **David Hamlett** is considered by peers to be a "*vital cog*" in the team's wheel. He advised PowerGen on four major combined heat and power projects. **Neil Upton** moves up the rankings in recognition of commendation from competitors and clients, who value his "*experience and understanding of electricity and gas.*" He advised the Macedonian Government in relation to the privatisation of its electricity industry. **Clients:** British Energy; British Telecom; Electricity Association; Kemira Chemie GMBH; Milk Marque; PowerGen; Severn Trent; Shell International; South Staffordshire Water; Transco.

Eversheds (see firm details p.952) With the reorganisation of the firm's national energy practice, the Birmingham team has been boosted both in size and importance. National head of energy Malcolm Titcomb is based in the city. Although the team is not yet considered to threaten the dominance of the leading duo, clients are "*more than satisfied with their resources and skills, their ability to deal with instructions quickly and their sheer expertise.*" The firm is recognised for its knowledge of renewable energy, energy infrastructure and CHP schemes. Highlight of the year was advising on the purchase of a share of an offshore gas field in Papua New Guinea. **Clients:** Energy Power Resources; GPU Power UK (Midlands Electricity); Ridgewood Power Corporation.

Kent Jones and Done (see firm details p.1020) Larger firms comment on the firm's "*respected*" niche minerals practice and envy its "*committed portfolio of clients.*" **Tony Reeves**, an expert on coal mining subsidence, is admired as a "great client man." The client base includes landed estates, mineral operators, plcs and the Crown Estate. The firm represented a mineral operator on the grant of a mining lease for a new quarry, and advised on the grant of a lease for the extraction of peat. **Clients:** Laporte; The Crown Estate.

Knight & Sons (see firm details p.1025) Possessing a strong reputation in the minerals sector, the firm is said by interviewees to maintain a "*loyal following of clients based between Manchester and Birmingham.*" **Tony Bell** has an acknowledged regional name, and is singled out for his work on behalf of Hanson. Typically, the firm handles the acquisition and disposal of mineral interests, prospecting licences and leasing of mineral and surface interests. It acted on ownership rights issues arising from a greenfield mineral development. **Clients:** Hanson Quarry Products Europe.

Edwards Geldard (see firm details p.948) Led by Roman Surma, the team concentrates on utilities work. It advises on supply and distribution in all areas of energy, acts on generation projects (CHP and peak conversions) and renewables, and offers a niche in gas metering. NETA-related issues have been a recurrent theme of the past year's caseload. **Clients:** Alkane Energy.

Hammond Suddards Edge (see firm details p.984) **Gwyn Williams** (see p.357) is noted in the market for his "*particular expertise*" in natural resources, notably mining and quarrying. The firm has also expanded its capacity in the water sector, where it often acts for potential new entrants. Advising trade associations on various agreements with the Government relating to the Climate Change Levy, the team was also instructed to prepare a model form of agreement to be entered into by trade associations. Elsewhere, the firm advised Agrigate Industries on its acquisition of quarries and plants from Anglo-American. **Clients:** Lafarge Redland; Agrigate Industries.

THE NORTH

ENERGY & NATURAL RESOURCES • The North	Ptnrs	Assts
1 **Nabarro Nathanson** Sheffield	1	4
2 **Dickinson Dees** Newcastle upon Tyne	n/a	n/a
Wake Dyne Lawton Chester	n/a	n/a
Wrigleys Leeds	1	2
3 **Addleshaw Booth & Co** Leeds	4	5
Pinsent Curtis Biddle Leeds	3	n/a

LEADING INDIVIDUALS
1 **LOGAN Niall** Nabarro Nathanson
RENGER Mike Nabarro Nathanson
WAKE Brian Wake Dyne Lawton
2 **WHITAKER Neil** Pinsent Curtis Biddle

This book is the product of 6,552 1/2-hour interviews. See p.7 for BMRB audit.
Within each band, firms are listed alphabetically. *See individuals' profiles p.353*

Nabarro Nathanson (see firm details p.1078) "*Market leaders for minerals work,*" the Sheffield energy team boasts the pre-eminent coal practice in England and Wales. It is retained by the Coal Authority, by several privatised coal operators, and by a number of coal-fired power stations. Working as a single national unit with the London office, the team also handles downstream oil work, and has diversified into the regional electricity market. Environmentally compatible energy schemes, including combined heat and power, energy from waste and embedded generation, are also important elements of the practice. The esteemed **Mike Renger** brings widely recognised environmental expertise to energy work, while **Niall Logan** (see p.355) is commended by competitors for his experience of mineral rights issues. The firm acted on the sale of four disused and contaminated former colliery sites to English Partnerships. **Clients:** The Coal Authority; Hanson Brick; RJB Mining; Celtic Energy; Pioneer Aggregates.

Dickinson Dees (see firm details p.941) Seen by the market to possess a "*naturally loyal local clientele,*" the firm handles a range of downstream oil and gas work, as well as substantial power transactions. Jonathan Hewitt heads the energy and utilities group. The firm continues to advise Northern Electric on regulatory matters and supply and purchase agreements. The minerals practice, led by Barney Corrigan, has experience of planning applications and waste licensing issues, and has advised on the negotiation of options and working rights agreements for operators and owners. **Clients:** Northern Electricity; HJ Banks; W&M Thompson.

Wake Dyne Lawton (see firm details p.1170) Headed by the experienced **Brian Wake** (see p.357), the firm is said to have "*a focused minerals practice and specialist knowledge.*" Larger firms applaud Wake's "*hands-on*" approach, and maintain that he has "*developed a fantastic practice.*" The firm has acted for landowners and operators on options to lease and purchase sites, and advised a major landowner in the Northern Home Counties on an option agreement for a new mineral extraction prospect with a value of more than £10 million. **Clients:** The Grosvenor Estate; Tarmac; Parkhill Group; HJ Banks.

Wrigleys (see firm details p.1191) Known in the market for its mining expertise and its niche in renewables, the team is led by Malcolm Lynch. It advised Dulas on a solar heating project, and acted for Ogwr Groundwork Trust on a biomass project. **Clients:** Ogwr Groundwork Trust; Wind Prospect.

Addleshaw Booth & Co (see firm details p.853) Said by one client to be "*strong in all areas and good at juggling its workload,*" the firm is especially rated for its "*good grasp of the commercial point of a deal.*" Headed by Sandra Humphrey, the group's expertise covers the whole utilities sector, and includes a respected renewables practice. The firm advised First Renewables on its investment in a company that has built three power stations, fuelled by chicken litter, under NFFO. It also acted for Kelda Group on its involvement in an £80 million Waste Water Treatment facility in Aberdeen and represented the BREY consortium on its bid for the MOD PPP, the £800 million Project Aquatrine. **Clients:** Kelda Group; British Gas Group; Invensys; Railtrack; Waterways Board.

Pinsent Curtis Biddle (see firm details p.1098) "*Thorough*" team that "*doesn't hide behind legal jargon,*" and is best known for its expertise in the minerals sector. Led by the "*trusted and excellent*" **Neil Whitaker** (see p.357), the Mines, Minerals and Landfill unit also offers planning and environmental expertise, and worked on the £32.9 million acquisition by Hanson of 12 quarries and associated businesses from Anglo American. **Clients:** Hanson; Marshalls.

SCOTLAND

OIL & GAS

ENERGY: OIL & GAS • Scotland	Ptnrs	Assts
1 **CMS Cameron McKenna** Aberdeen	3	n/a
Ledingham Chalmers Aberdeen, Edinburgh	2	n/a
Paull & Williamsons Aberdeen	2	5

LEADING INDIVIDUALS
1 **RUDDIMAN Robert** Ledingham Chalmers
WARNE Penelope CMS Cameron McKenna
UP AND COMING
MILLAR Stephen Paull & Williamsons

This book is the product of 6,552 1/2-hour interviews. See p.7 for BMRB audit.
Within each band, firms are listed alphabetically. *See individuals' profiles p.353*

CMS Cameron McKenna (see firm details p.922) Competitors describe **Penelope Warne** (see p.357), who heads the entire firm's oil and gas team from Aberdeen, as "*high-profile, enthusiastic and committed.*" Her team focuses on upstream work, covering licensing and regulatory matters, operational and services contracts and asset sales and purchase. It also possesses a respected litigation capacity. The firm advised BP on the gas sale agreement for the Magnus Enhanced Oil Recovery Project, a project worth £320 million. It continues to advise Shell and Halliburton on mutual hold harmless agreements for offshore operations in the UK, and drafted the mutual hold harmless standard industry document for CRINE. **Clients:** BP; CRINE; Shell; Halliburton.

Ledingham Chalmers (see firm details p.1034) **Bob Ruddiman** (see p.356), characterised by one London lawyer as "*straightforward and a joy to deal with,*" marshals a "*great technical*" team, which is especially noted for its work on complex allocation agreements. The team has been strengthened by the hire of a former in-house lawyer at ExxonMobil. Handling the spectrum of upstream work for contractors and operators, the firm has offices in Istanbul and Baku, and offers expertise in project and development work domestically and overseas. The team acted for Ramco Energy on the $150 million sale of its interest in the Azeri Chirag Gunlashi fields, and advised Highland Energy on its acquisition of Statoil's interests in the Anglia and Victor oil fields. **Clients:** Highland Energy; Ramco Energy; TotalFinaElf; Exploration UK.

Paull & Williamsons (see firm details p.1091) Described by one leading industry player as "*the Scottish firm to use*," the firm's position in the non-contentious market continues to strengthen. Rising star **Stephen Millar** (see p.355), recently made partner, is said by clients to be "*a persuasive lawyer who knows his business.*" The firm acted for Talisman Energy (UK) in acquiring the interests of Elf Exploration UK, ARCO British and Texaco Britain in the 'Fourth Round Assets' for a total consideration of C$583 million. It also represented ARCO on its disposal of a number of interests in the North Sea to Tullow Exploration for a total of £200 million. **Clients:** BP Exploration Operating Company; Dana Petroleum; Kerr-McGee Oil (UK); Talisman Energy (UK).

ELECTRICITY

ENERGY: ELECTRICITY • Scotland	Ptnrs	Assts
1 **Shepherd & Wedderburn WS** Edinburgh, Glasgow	4	10
2 **Biggart Baillie** Glasgow	7	6
Dundas & Wilson CS Edinburgh, Glasgow	5	6
MacRoberts Glasgow	1	2
3 **Burness** Edinburgh	5	4
McGrigor Donald Glasgow	4	3
4 **Harper Macleod** Glasgow	n/a	n/a

LEADING INDIVIDUALS	
1 **CUMMING Donald** Dundas & Wilson CS	**DICKSON Ian** MacRoberts
ROSS David Biggart Baillie	**SAUNDERS James** Shepherd & Wedderburn WS

This book is the product of 6,552 1/2-hour interviews. See p.7 for BMRB audit.

Within each band, firms are listed alphabetically. *See individuals' profiles p.353*

Shepherd & Wedderburn WS (see firm details p.1126) Best known for advising on "*the lion's share of recent Scottish Power work*," this large department is now rated by many as the number one power firm in Scotland. "*Impressive and knowledgeable*" **James Saunders** (see p.356) is regarded by the market as the group's outstanding practitioner. Active both domestically and overseas, the firm advised on the regulatory and commercial structure of the German electricity market, and represented Scottish Power in connection with trading on the Amsterdam Power Exchange. **Clients:** Cairn Energy; Scottish Power; Scottish Electricity Settlements; Shell Renewables UK.

Biggart Baillie (see firm details p.882) The firm's electricity practice encompasses retail and wholesale work, including sales or connection agreements, renewables and regulatory work. The "*technically able*" **David Ross** (see p.355) is said by clients to have "*bags of experience and good commercial sense.*" The firm advised Scottish Power on the refurbishment of the Cruachan Pumped Water Storage Generating Station in Argyll, and on a £60 million salt cavern underground gas storage project in Cheshire. **Clients:** Scottish Power; Shell.

Dundas & Wilson CS (see firm details p.947) A broadly based practice that offers experience in power station projects, long-term energy supply contracts, NETA in the UK, energy project funding and regulatory work. Peers note that the firm's workload is "*by no means confined to Scotland*," and commend its work for Scottish & Southern Energy. **Donald Cumming** is considered to be the team's "*driving force.*" The firm advised Scottish & Southern Energy on the restructuring of regulated electricity businesses, and on the renegotiation of various long-term power contracts in response to NETA. Other work includes representing Alstom on the acquisition of Scottish Power's utility contracting services division. **Clients:** Alstom UK, Bank of Scotland, East of Scotland Water; North of Scotland Water; Scottish & Southern Energy; Yorkshire Electricity; West of Scotland Water.

MacRoberts (see firm details p.1048) A national force for nuclear energy, the practice is recognised in the industry for its "*prestigious*" British Energy work. With around a third of Scottish energy produced by nuclear power stations, the firm is considered to be "*punching way above its weight.*" The "*reliable*" **Ian Dickson** (see p.244) has advised the cream of the British nuclear energy industry on a wide range of matters. **Clients:** British Energy; Scottish Nuclear; Nuclear Energy.

Burness (see firm details p.903) Generally seen operating on power projects, the team, headed by Martin Sales, also advises extensively on local waste to energy work and planning issues. The firm acted for The Renewable Development Company on its acquisitions of wind power sites, and advised J Fenton & Sons on obtaining planning permissions in central Scotland. **Clients:** J Fenton & Sons; The Renewable Development Company.

McGrigor Donald (see firm details p.1062) The firm's energy department is split between Scotland and London, and is headed from London by Murdo Maclean. However, its "*technically accurate work*," notably on power projects, sees it retain its status. The group advised BP on the construction of a 500MW Combined Cycle Gas Turbine power plant and a smaller combined heat and power generating facility in Baglan Bay, South Wales. **Clients:** BP; Northern Ireland Electricity.

Harper Macleod (see firm details p.987) Regarded by market sources as "*leaders in mining*," the team, headed by Pamela Todd, continues to provide a full complement of legal services to Scottish Coal Company, Scotland's largest mineral supplier. It also represents landowners in their negotiations with mineral operators and waste management developers. The firm acted for Mining (Scotland) on the sale of more than 60% of its issued share capital to Parkburn and for The Scottish Coal Company in the acquisition of the Scottish mining interests of CP Holdings. **Clients:** Scottish Coal Company; Mining (Scotland).

LEADERS IN ENERGY

BEHARRELL, Steven
Coudert Brothers, London (020) 7248 3000
beharrells@london.coudert.com
Specialisation: Senior partner, *Coudert Brothers*, London. Specialises in energy, oil, gas and power and natural resources, infrastructure investment, project finance, transportation and privatisation. Has over 30 years experience advising on oil and gas law in the Middle East, Asia, North Sea and Russia. Also involved in electricity and other privatisations since the late 1980s. Regularly addresses conferences and seminars on the subject of energy and privatisation law.
Prof. Memberships: International Bar Association; Institute of Directors; The Law Society (of England and Wales).
Career: Assistant solicitor, *Denton Hall* 1966-72 and partner 1972-90. Partner, *Coudert Brothers* since 1990.
Personal: Educated at Sorbonne University, Paris 1961-62 and the College of Law, London 1964-66. Lives in London. Born 22 December 1944.

BELL, Anthony
Knight & Sons, Newcastle-under-Lyme (01782) 619225

BIRCHALL, David
Denton Wilde Sapte, London (020) 7242 1212

BLAKE, Peter
Clifford Chance, London (020) 7600 1000
peter.blake@cliffordchance.com
See under Projects/PFI, p.709

BOND, Richard
Herbert Smith, London (020) 7374 8000
richard.bond@herbertsmith.com
See under Corporate Finance, p.241

BRENNAN, Paul
Martineau Johnson, Birmingham (0121) 678 1527
paul.brennan@martjohn.com
Specialisation: Advises energy companies and major users on energy trading, transportation and generation, also advises on competitive water supply. Career highlights include international litigation involving production assets in Kazakhstan, de-merger of British Gas plc and associated gas purchase and transportation arrangements, drafted Network Codes for Phoenix Natural Gas and East Midlands Pipelines Ltd, advised on the establishment of EnMo, an online energy market.
Prof. Memberships: Law Society, UK Energy Lawyers Association, Society for Computers & Law.
Career: Stonyhurst College, Durham University; Leeds University College of Law; articled *TV Edwards & Co.* Various positions BG plc. Partner, *Martineau Johnson Solicitors* 1997.
Publications: Editor: 'Code Update'.
Personal: Born 1961, resides Warwick with wife and two children. Interests – cricket, football and the other arts.

BRETTON, Linda
Lawrence Graham, London (020) 7759 6696
linda.bretton@lawgram.com
Specialisation: Partner in company commercial department. Specialises in energy law, mainly upstream oil and gas with particular emphasis on asset and share sales and purchases, swaps, farm-ins and farm-outs, and reorganisations. Has worked in-house through placements with clients and has therefore advised on a range of oil industry contracts and upstream petroleum issues.
Prof. Memberships: UK Energy Lawyers' Group (International Bar Association), The Law Society.
Career: Reading University (BA Psychology). Qualified as a solicitor in 1991.
Personal: Enjoys the gym, dancing, wine, interior design and family.

CARVER CBE, Jeremy
Clifford Chance, London (020) 7600 1000
jeremy.carver@cliffordchance.com
Specialisation: Head of international law group, representing states, government agencies and international organisations in relation to proceedings in England and elsewhere. Representing Kuwait and its Oil Sector companies in claims to the United Nations Compensation Commission. Areas of expertise include state and diplomatic immunity; status, privileges and immunities of international organisations; upstream oil and gas operations; international economic sanctions; maritime and territorial boundary issues; world trade law, jurisdiction, conflicts of laws, extraterritoriality.
Prof. Memberships: International Law Association, British Branch, Hon Treasurer 1981-98, Vice-President since 1998; Executive Council, International Law Association since 1991; ILA International Trade Law Committee since 1996; Executive Committee, British Institute of International and Comparative Law since 1996; Council of Management since 1998; American Society of International Law since 1977; Fellow Royal Geographical Society since 1971; Advisory Council, RefAid (UNHCR-UK) since 1997; Board Member, International Rescue Committee; Chairman, British Invisibles CIS Panel 1993-95; Kazakh-British Trade and Industry Council since 1994; Uzbek-British Trade and Industry Council since 1994; British Export Promotion Forum since1996; City Promotion Panel since 1995.
Career: Trinity College, Cambridge (MA Engineering). Qualified 1969; made partner 1974; *Coward Chance* 1969-87; *Clifford Chance* since 1987; resident manager Brussels 1973-74; resident partner Singapore 1982-83; contributions to numerous books and professional publications.
Personal: Born 1943; resides London.

CAVE-BROWNE-CAVE, Myles
Denton Wilde Sapte, London (020) 7242 1212

CLOUGH, Adrian
Herbert Smith, London (020) 7374 8000
adrian.clough@herbertsmith.com
Specialisation: Partner in *Herbert Smith*'s energy and infrastructure group, specialising in privatisation, public private partnerships, major restructurings, infrastructure projects and complex commercial contracts, particularly in the electricity and transport sectors. Involvement with the electricity sector began when part of the team advised the Area Boards of England and Wales on the 1990 restructuring and their subsequent privatisation. Continues to advise various members of the industry on contractual and regulatory issues. Had day to day responsibility for the Herbert Smith team advising the 14 Public Electricity Suppliers in Great Britain on the major revisions to the industry's contractual and regulatory structure which were necessary to enable full supply competition to be introduced. Has also advised British Gas in relation to the Northern Ireland electricity privatisation and the Magnox division of Nuclear Electric on the restructuring that preceded the privatisation of British Energy. Advised a group of RECs on implementation of the New Electricity Trading Arrangements, a new entrant generator in relation to the restructuring of the electricity sector in the Republic of Ireland and two RECs on the disposals of their metering and data services businesses.
Career: Educated at Christ Church, Oxford (MA); qualified as a solicitor 1988; partner of *Herbert Smith* 1995. Seconded for two years as an Assistant Director of the Office of Passenger Rail Franchising, leading the development of the new contractual and regulatory structure of the railway industry as it developed.

COFFELL, Howard
Field Fisher Waterhouse, London (020) 7861 4000
Specialisation: Partner commercial property department. Head of Pipeline Services Unit. Practice covers acquisition, disposal and development of commercial property including industrial sites, oil and gas terminals and facilities and the construction of cross-country pipelines. Acts for a number of major UK oil and gas companies, pipeline operators and other industrial concerns.
Prof. Memberships: Law Society.
Career: Qualified 1974, having joined *Field Fisher Waterhouse* in 1972. Became a partner in 1978.
Personal: Born 23 November 1948. Attended King Henry VIII School, Coventry and Magdalen College, Oxford.

CUMMING, Donald
Dundas & Wilson CS, Edinburgh (0131) 228 8000

CUTHBERT, Michael
Clifford Chance, London (020) 7600 1000
michael.cuthbert@cliffordchance.com
Specialisation: Corporate and capital markets; specialist in energy and natural resources matters with particular emphasis on mining and oil and gas. Advised Government of Republic of Zambia on privatisation of copper industry. Advisor to other mining houses.
Prof. Memberships: Solicitor of the Supreme Court of England and Wales; solicitor of the Supreme Court of Hong Kong; licensed legal consultant, State of New York. Member of Law Society, City of London Solicitors Company, International Bar Association.
Career: Partner *Clifford-Turner* 1986; *Clifford Chance LLP* 1986 to date (managing partner New York 1990-93).
Personal: Enjoys opera, food and wine. Married with one child.

DALLAS, James
Denton Wilde Sapte, London (020) 7242 1212

DAVEY, Henry
Herbert Smith, London (020) 7374 8000
henry.davey@herbertsmith.com
Specialisation: Electricity: Involved in the privatisation and restructuring of the UK electricity industry in 1990, acting on behalf of the 12 Regional Electricity

Companies and in the restructuring of the electricity industry in Northern Ireland. Continues to advise on the UK electricity industry, including UK power projects (for example Humber Power, Teesside, Sutton Bridge, Kingsnorth, Salt End, South Denes), and advises on innovative electricity and gas trading contracts. Advises on international power projects and on electricity transmission projects including in Europe, India and the Middle East.
Prof. Memberships: Member of IBA. Member of the United Kingdom Energy Lawyers Group. Representative on the SERL Oil Committee.
Career: Partner in *Herbert Smith*. Joined *Herbert Smith* as a trainee in September 1986; qualified in 1988. MA Cantab (Queens' College), Law; Nottingham High School.

DAVIES, Roger
Allen & Overy, London (020) 7330 3239
roger.davies@allenovery.com
Specialisation: Heavily involved in oil and gas work since the initial development of BP's Forties Field in the UKCS in the early 1970s, Roger has represented a number of oil companies ranging from US majors to small UK independents, as well as governments, advising on licensing and concession matters, farm-ins and carries, acquisitions and disposals, asset auctions, joint venture documentation and financings, both corporate and project related.
Prof. Memberships: City of London Solicitors Company, United Kingdom Energy Lawyers' Group.
Career: Associate *Allen & Overy* (1972-75), partner (1976), head of Dubai office (1980-83).
Personal: Cambridge University (MA 1969).

DICKSON, Ian
MacRoberts, Glasgow (0141) 332 9988
ian.dickson@macroberts.co.uk
See under Corporate Finance, p.244

ELDER, Ian
Allen & Overy, London (020) 7330 3044
ian.elder@allenovery.com
Specialisation: Head of *Allen & Overy's* European Energy Group, has extensive experience of mergers, acquisitions and joint ventures, as well as a large number of energy transactions, both in the UK and internationally. Companies he has acted for include ICI, BG, Enron, Mobil, Zeneca, Courtaulds and SWEB, as well as a number of UK IPPs, including Teeside Power, Barking Power, Derwent Power, Humber Power and Seabank Power. He co-led the A&O team on the UK nuclear privatisation (British Energy). He is advising a number of clients on the implications of the de-regulation of the European Energy Markets and on the new electricity trading arrangements in the UK.
Prof. Memberships: Law Society (England and Scotland), IBA, City of London Solicitors Company.
Career: Articled *Dundas & Wilson*; qualified Scotland (1977), England (1984); Solicitor ICI legal department (1977-87); Associate, *Allen & Overy* (1987-89), Partner (1989).
Personal: St Andrew's University (1972 MA); Edinburgh University (1974 LLB). Born 1951.

GREENO, Ted
Herbert Smith, London (020) 7374 8000
See under Litigation, p.571

GRIFFIN, Paul
Herbert Smith, London (020) 7466 2261
paul.griffin@herbertsmith.com
Specialisation: Partner in energy and project finance. Wide experience in energy and project finance, in particular the oil, gas and power sectors, both in the UK and overseas. Deals with a variety of projects and transactions in both the energy and infrastructure fields, together with privatisations. Involved in the re-negotiation of long term contracts in liberalised gas and electricity markets and has also been much involved in energy related disputes in court and before experts and arbitrators. Experience in the related areas of competition and regulation. Writes and lectures widely.

HAMLETT, David
Wragge & Co, Birmingham (0870) 903 1000

HIGGINSON, Tony
Baker Botts, London (020) 7778 1400

HURST, Philip
Ashurst Morris Crisp, London (020) 7638 1111
philip.hurst@ashursts.com
Specialisation: Partner in projects group and energy and natural resources group. Heads mining team and electricity team. Leading practitioner in natural resources law, especially in Africa, Middle East and South Asia. Extensive experience in advising sponsors of independent power projects, particularly in India and Pakistan. Currently advising on major greenfield mining projects in Iran and India, and on power projects in Tanzania and Uganda. Visiting lecturer in natural resources law, Imperial College, London.
Career: BA, LLB (ANU), MA, LLM (Virginia) FRGS. 1981-85 associate *White & Case*, New York; 1985-87, Counsel, The World Bank, Washington DC; 1988-92, solicitor *Linklaters & Paines*, London.

JONES, Gareth
Nabarro Nathanson, London (020) 7524 6000

KELLY, Christopher
Linklaters, London (020) 7456 3600
christopher.kelly@linklaters.com
Specialisation: Specialist in corporate law, including M&A, takeovers, privatisations, joint ventures, securitisations and corporate reorganisations. Key focus on the technology sector. Also specialist in mining-related corporate and projects work.
Career: Co-head of the e-commerce business group. 2000 to date: partner, *Linklaters*; 1997-00: Senior assistant solicitor, *Linklaters*; 1999: Admitted as a solicitor of the Supreme Court of England and Wales; 1995-97: Assistant solicitor, *Linklaters* London; 1992-95: Solicitor with *Allen, Allen & Hemsley*, including a 12-month secondment to MIM Holdings Limited; 1992: Admitted as a solicitor to the Supreme Court of Queensland (Australia); 1990: Commenced Articles of Clerkship with *Feez Ruthning* (now *Allen, Allen & Hemsley*) in Australia. 1987-92: University of Queensland, LLB (Hons); 1987: University of Queensland, Bachelor of Commerce (Accounting and Business Finance).

KHAN, Rafique
CMS Cameron McKenna, London
(020) 7367 2469
rzk@cmck.com
Specialisation: Specialises in oil and gas particularly in the areas of natural gas production, transportation and supply with an additional emphasis on project-financed CCGT Power Projects. He has extensive experience of the European natural gas industries both in the commercial and regulatory field. Speaker on legislative, regulatory and commercial issues facing the gas industries in the UK, elsewhere in the European Union and Central and Eastern Europe.
Prof. Memberships: Law Society of England and Wales; The Institute of Petroleum.
Career: Graduated in 1982 from the University of Leeds; articled clerk and senior legal adviser at British Gas 1984-92. In 1992 joined the firm as assistant solicitor and became a partner in 1994 in the Energy, Projects and Construction Group. Became a consultant in the group in 2001.
Personal: Cinema, opera, eating, walking and motorsport.

KING, Ronnie
Ashurst Morris Crisp, London (020) 7638 1111
ronnie.king@ashursts.com
See under Litigation, p.575

LANE, Mark
Masons, London (020) 7490 6214
mark.lane@masons.com
Specialisation: Principally contract drafting (much of it on a PPP/BOT basis) and dispute resolution both nationally and internationally. Also advises employers on tendering procedures under PPP schemes. Acted for Eric Cumine Associates on Harbour City litigation in Hong Kong. Member of the firm's team on Channel Tunnel and Canary Wharf projects and on a number of PFI projects including hospitals (procurement issues) and water and waste water treatment works (concession agreements and construction issues). Contract drafting on water related projects in the recent past includes projects in India, the Philippines, Australasia and Scotland. Led the legal team for the preferred bidder on the Levenmouth PPP waste water project in Scotland in a £63 million financial project. Currently leading the team which is advising the Sri Lankan government on the Negombo water privatisation project. Editor-in-chief of Mason's 'Water Yearbook'. Has extensive African experience (much of it FIDIC related) including matters in Nigeria, Gambia, Ghana, Mozambique, Kenya, Mali, the Maldives and Ethiopia. In March of 1998, led Masons' team acting for the Government of Ukraine in negotiations to establish the Project Management Unit to manage the project to render the Chernobyl Nuclear Reactor No 4 safe. (The project is ongoing.) Experienced conference speaker nationally and internationally.
Prof. Memberships: Society of Construction Law; IBA (Committee T) chairman of sub-committee on International Procurement in Construction Projects; European Construction Institute (member of Executive Committee) (chairman of European Legislation Task Force).
Career: Qualified in 1975. Partner at *Masons* since 1988.
Personal: Born 18th March 1950. Educated at Cranleigh School 1962-67 and Trinity College, Cambridge 1968-72. Lives in London.

LANE, Robert
CMS Cameron McKenna, London
(020) 7367 3000
rcl@cmck.com
Specialisation: Partner specialising in utilities law and regulation. Extensive experience of electricity projects and restructurings in the UK and overseas

with over 13 years experience. Adviser to The National Grid Company plc. From 1988 to 1990 advised on the restructuring of the England and Wales electricity industry, including drafting the Grid Code for the England and Wales system, with extensive involvement in the design of the regulatory regime and pooling arrangements and in drafting and advising on many of the documents (eg: those dealing with connection to and use of the system). Continues to advise on these topics and on the development and reform of the market structure. Was heavily involved in the introduction of the New Electricity Trading Arrangements and the CUSC (the Connection and Use of System Code). Also adviser to Northern Ireland Electricity plc on its re-structuring and privatisation and on the further recent restructuring in the Northern Ireland markets to introduce the requirements of the European IME Directive, which introduced bi-lateral trading and balancing mechanisms. Further afield he advised the ESI Reform Unit of the State Government of Victoria on the restructuring of the electricity market there, which involved consideration of and scoping of the regulatory, contractual and code structures and critiquing the licences, codes and contracts. Has also advised on power purchase agreements for Electricidade de Portugal and the Public Power Corporation of Greece and advised on all aspects of the restructuring of the electricity supply industry in Orissa, India. Advised Electricity Supply Board in Eire and Ontario Hydro in Canada. Advising in a number of jurisdictions on the implementation of the European IME Directive, including drafting of legislation for Greece and drafting transitional regimes for stranded costs, which has also involved advising a major Western European integrated utility on its compliance with the Directive including advising on Grid Code, connection and use/access agreements, legislation, licensing and ancillary services. Regular speaker at conferences throughout the world.
Prof. Memberships: International Bar Association (member of Section on Energy and Natural Resources Law and co-chairman of Utilities Law Committee). Member of UK government's Power Sector Working Group
Career: Qualified in 1982. Joined *McKenna & Co*, now *CMS Cameron McKenna*, in 1988.
Personal: Educated at University College, London.

LOGAN, Niall
Nabarro Nathanson, Sheffield (0114) 279 4000
n.logan@nabarro.co.uk
Specialisation: Mineral development and extraction, royalty agreements, post extraction landfill schemes, coalbed methane gas exploitation. From 1992 to 1995 worked on the restructuring and privatisation of the UK coal industry. Recent projects include advising mineral owners on large scale extension to workings at Boulby Potash Mine in North Yorkshire, advising the Coal Authority in relation to colliery closures and advising on the acquisition of copper mines in Zambia.
Career: Qualified 1981. British Coal Legal Dept, 1982-90; partner, *Nabarro Nathanson* 1990.

MACGIBBON, Sam
Vinson & Elkins LLP, London (020) 7618 6000
smacgibbon@velaw.com
Specialisation: Project finance and development; mergers and acquisitions. Recent transactions include renegotiation of PPA for 1875 MW Teesside power project, bids for UK power stations, private equity investment in UK oil and gas start-up.
Prof. Memberships: Law Society.
Career: Qualified in New Zealand in 1985. Moved to London in 1988. *Vinson & Elkins*, London since 1992; partner since 1997.
Personal: Educated Christ's College, NZ and University of Otago, NZ. Resides London since 1988. Married with three children.

McGEE-OSBORNE, Christopher
Denton Wilde Sapte, London (020) 7242 1212

MILLAR, Stephen
Paull & Williamsons, Aberdeen (01224) 621621
samillar@paull-williamsons.co.uk
Specialisation: All areas of oil and gas law and in particular: offshore developments whether in the form of new projects or revised commercial and contractual arrangements for existing developments; acquisition and sale of interests in oil and gas acreage and related infrastructure, including platforms, pipelines and terminals.
Prof. Memberships: Law Society of Scotland.
Career: Joined *Paull & Williamsons* as trainee in 1994. Became an associate in 1999 and a partner in 2000.
Personal: Born 22 November 1972. Studied at University of Dundee from 1989-94 and graduated with LLB (Hons)/DipLP. Thereafter, part-time post graduate study (whilst working at *Paull & Williamsons*) at Centre for Petroleum Mineral Law & Policy, Dundee and graduated with LLM (Natural Resources & Mineral Law).

MORONEY, David
Denton Wilde Sapte, London (020) 7242 1212

PICTON-TURBERVILL, Geoffrey
Ashurst Morris Crisp, London (020) 7638 1111
geoffrey.picton-turbervill@ashursts.com
Specialisation: Partner in energy and projects groups. Commercial lawyer specialising in energy and natural resources law, in particular upstream and downstream oil and gas and power both in the UK and overseas. His work covers all aspects of oil and gas and electricity industries, and he has particular expertise in mergers and acquisitions and project work. Represents many UK and international energy clients on corporate, project and regulatory matters.
Prof. Memberships: Association of International Petroleum Negotiators; UK Energy Lawyers' Group; Institute of Petroleum; IBA Section on Energy and Resources Law (member of Gas Committee).
Publications: India editor of 'Oil & Gas Law & Taxation Review', and the author of the chapter on 'Oil and Gas Acquisition Agreements' for Sweet & Maxwell.

PUGH, Chris
Freshfields Bruckhaus Deringer, London
020 7936 4000
christopher.pugh@freshfields.com
Specialisation: Partner specialising in commercial litigation including all aspects of oil and gas disputes, banking and financial services and fraud. His energy work covers litigation, arbitration and mediation and includes acting for the J Block owners in their proceedings with Enron Europe in London and Houston and a major US energy company in a series of insurance arbitration proceedings. He has also represented various parties in arbitrations under Production Sharing Agreements. He has acted for a variety of securities firms in connection with the collapse of Barings & BCCI.
Career: Qualified 1983; Partner 1991.
Personal: Educated University College, London.

RANDELL, Charles
Slaughter and May, London (020) 7600 1200
charles.randell@slaughterandmay.com
See under Corporate Finance, p.255

REES, Jonathan
Freshfields Bruckhaus Deringer, London (020) 7936 4000
jonathan.rees@freshfields.com
Specialisation: Head of the Freshfields Energy Group; specialises in M&A, commercial and regulatory work in the oil and gas, electricity and natural resource sectors. Clients include oil companies, government, utilities and investment banks.
Prof. Memberships: International Bar Association (Section on Energy and Natural Resources Law), Member Institute of Petroleum, Vice Chair of the American Bar Association, Section on International Energy and Resources.
Career: *Freshfields* 1982, qualified in 1984 and became a partner in 1992.
Personal: Educated at Wadham College, Oxford (MA).

REEVES, Tony
Kent Jones and Done, Stoke-on-Trent (01782) 202 020

RENGER, Mike
Nabarro Nathanson, Sheffield (0114) 279 4000

ROBERTS, Martin
Slaughter and May, London (020) 7710 3481
martin.roberts@slaughterandmay.com
See under Projects/PFI, p.714

ROSS, David
Biggart Baillie, Glasgow (0141) 228 8000
dross@biggartbaillie.co.uk
Specialisation: Chairman and senior partner. Leads team working extensively in electricity and gas fields. Widely involved in the drafting/negotiation of a range of contracts relating to the electricity industry, including Connection, Use of System Supply and Sales Agreement throughout Great Britain. Advised on the review of the Nuclear Energy agreement (supplies 50% of Scotland's electricity), adviser on Scottish aspects of the contract required for all the Public Electricity Suppliers in Great Britain post-88, first Energy PFI projects throughout Great Britain. Extensively involved in gas matters. Drafting/negotiating contracts for the purchase/sale of gas from field to domestic customers throughout Great Britain. Separately advises those holding Transporters, Shippers and Suppliers licences on porous and non-porous gas storage in the UK.
Publications: Author of texts for internal circulation in the firm on energy matters; lectures on energy and PFI topics. 'Deputy President Chamber of Commerce 2001'.

ROWEY, Kent
Freshfields Bruckhaus Deringer, London
(020) 7936 4000
kent.rowey@freshfields/com
Specialisation: Head of *Freshfields'* international project finance group, with over fourteen years expe-

rience representing lenders, sponsors and suppliers in independent power projects and other project financing throughout Europe, Asia and the Americas. Currently involved in projects in Israel, Croatia, Australia, Russia and the Indian Sub-continent.
Prof. Memberships: State Bar of California, American Bar Association, International Bar Association.
Career: B.A. Philospohy, University of California, Los Angeles, (Magna cum laude) J.D. New York University. Partner, *Perkins Coie*, London. Associate *Milbank, Tweed, Hadley & McCloy*, Los Angeles, London.
Personal: Lives in Oxfordshire with wife Rosalie and two children, Allison and Austin. Avid (but average) golfer.

RUDDIMAN, Robert
Ledingham Chalmers, Aberdeen (01224) 408515
bob.ruddiman@ledinghamchalmers.com
Specialisation: Oil and gas exploration and production. Bidding agreements; licence applications; joint operating agreements; production sharing agreements; unitisation; pipeline and transportation agreements; trading in field and licence interests; onshore/offshore construction agreements; drilling contracts; integrated services agreements; logistics agreements; all aspects of contracting and operational philosophy.
Prof. Memberships: Law Society of Scotland, The Law Society.
Career: Qualified in Scots law 1989, English law 1994. Articled and assistant with *Shepherd & Wedderburn WS* 1987-91. Legal counsel Elf Exploration 1991-93. *Cameron Markby Hewitt* 1993-97. Partner *Ledingham Chalmers* 1997.

SALT, Stuart
Linklaters, London (020) 7456 5912
stuart.salt@linklaters.com
Specialisation: Main area of practice has been international projects. Extensive experience of acting for governments, sponsors and lenders on major projects in the power, energy and transport sectors.
Career: Partner in the project and asset finance group. 1992 to date: Partner, *Linklaters*; 1986-92: Solicitor, *Linklaters*; 1985: Admitted as a solicitor. 1983: Law Society Qualifying Examinations; 1982: Southampton University LLB (Hons).

SAUNDERS, James
Shepherd & Wedderburn WS, Edinburgh
(0131) 473 5288
james.saunders@shepwedd.co.uk
Specialisation: Partner in corporate department. Main areas of practice are energy law and I.P. (including computer law). Advises on electricity agreements and on I.P. agreements including licensing and turnkey.
Career: Qualified in 1984. Trainee with *McClure Naismith*, Glasgow 1983-85. Worked for ICI plc 1986-87 and *Freshfields* 1987-93. Joined *Shepherd & Wedderburn WS* in 1993.

SAUNDERS, Mark
Dewey Ballantine, London (020) 7456 6000

SCRIVEN, John
Allen & Overy, London (020) 7330 3360
john.scriven@allenovery.com
Specialisation: The head of *Allen & Overy* Water Project Practice, he has advised public authorities project companies and lenders on concessions, BOT schemes and management arrangements. He has recently advised on the Nelsprint concession, the Tallin privatisation and the privatisation of the Athens Thessaloniki water companies. He is also advising on the Muscat concession and the MOD Aquatrine project in the UK.
Career: Associate *Allen & Overy* (1979-88), Partner (1988).
Publications: Editor and co-author of 'A Constuctional Guide to Major Construction Projects' (1999) and regular contributor to Construction Land Review and other publications.
Personal: MA Trinity College Cambridge (1979).

SMITHERS, Tim
Veale Wasbrough, Bristol (0117) 925 2020
tsmithers@vwl.co.uk
See under Property (Commercial), p.754

STACEY, Paul
Slaughter and May, London (020) 7600 1200
paul.stacey@slaughterandmay.com
Specialisation: Main areas of practice include electricity-related work, banking and project finance.
Prof. Memberships: The Law Society.
Career: Qualified with *Slaughter and May* 1983. Partner 1990.
Personal: Born 1959.

STANGER, Michael
Lovells, London (020) 7296 2000
michael.stanger@lovells.com
Specialisation: Practice covers a wide range of energy and projects work; energy work related primarily to the gas industry; heavily involved in the structural changes in the UK, acting on behalf of gas shippers in relation to the drafting of the Network Code and the 'Claims Validation' agreements; and acting for the Bacton Agent's Group in relation to gas flows through the Interconnector to Belgium. Practice covers gas trading, gas supply, gas storage and independent gas pipeline systems, with frequent involvement in transactions in Continental Europe.
Prof. Memberships: Law Society, City of London Solicitors Company, Institute of Petroleum, UK Energy Lawyers Group.
Career: Field Engineer in the oil industry for SPE Schlumberger, mainly in Africa, 1975 to 1978; articled *Lovells*; qualified 1981; partner 1986.

TEMPLE, Richard
CMS Cameron McKenna, London
(020) 7367 3000
richard.temple@cmck.com
Specialisation: Richard Temple is head of water in the energy projects and construction group at *CMS Cameron McKenna*. Richard specialises in infrastructure projects and advised the World Bank on the water and sanitation toolkit: a manual on how to implement water and sewerage projects worldwide. He has advised on water projects in Romania, Bulgaria, India, the Czech Republic, Panama, Oman, Bolivia, Poland, Peru, Ghana, Kazakhstan, Hungary, England and Scotland.
Prof. Memberships: Vice-president Europe, Africa and Middle East of the International Private Water Association; the Water Sector Group of the Department of Trade and Industry; committee member of the Overseas Forum of British Water; International Bar Association; Project Finance Law sub-committee of the IBC; Law Society of England and Wales.
Career: Partner, *CMS Cameron McKenna* 1997. Articled clerk 1987-89 *Lovell White Durrant*, Solicitor 1989-95 *Lovell White Durrant*, 1996-97 *Ashurst Morris Crisp*.
Personal: Tennis and squash.

TRINICK, Marcus
Bond Pearce, Southampton (023) 8063 2211
mtrinick@bondpearce.com
See under Planning, p.670

TUDWAY, Robert
Nabarro Nathanson, London (020) 7524 6421
r.tudway@nabbarro.com
Specialisation: Head of energy group *Nabarro Nathanson* energy law. Advises developers and other parties on electricity distribution and generation contracts, electricity and environmentally compatible forms of energy production; notably, combined heat and power in industry, distant heating schemes and renewables.
Career: International Bar Association. Statute Law Society managing the developer's forum of the combined heat and power association and policy committee, 'Cogen Farope'. General editor, energy law and regulation in the European Union, 'Sweet & Maxwell'. Qualified in 1973. Joined *Nabarro Smith* as a partner 1995.

TURTLE, Trevor
Herbert Smith, London (020) 7374 8000
trevor.turtle@herbertsmith.com
Specialisation: Partner since 1987 in company department, with general corporate and commercial practice. Head of firm's water practice. Specialisations include regulatory, privatisation, project and corporate work in water sector. One of two core partners on team acting for water companies on water privatisation in England and Wales. Since then increasingly involved in water project work in UK and overseas. Member of IBA Water Law Committee, member of management board of British Water.

TYNE, Sally
CMS Cameron McKenna, London
(020) 7367 2693
smt@cmck.com
Specialisation: Specialises in oil and gas, with particular emphasis on acquisitions and disposals of UKCS and international petroleum interests via share or asset deals. Extensive experience of oil industry contracts and joint venture issues. Speaker on licensing, unitisation, JOAs and oil and gas acquisition agreements.
Prof. Memberships: United Kingdom Energy Lawyers Group (IBA); Law Society.
Career: Educated Trinity College, Oxford. Joined the firm as an oil and gas partner in London, reinforcing its strong existing energy practices in London and Aberdeen. Previously specialised in oil and gas for ten years at *Norton Rose*.
Publications: Co-author of second edition of 'Taylor & Winsor on Joint Operating Agreements' (standard industry textbook).
Personal: Married with three children.

UPTON, Neil
Wragge & Co, Birmingham (0870) 903 1000

VERRILL, John
Lawrence Graham, London (020) 7379 0000
john.verrill@lawgram.com
Specialisation: Significant area of practice is oil and gas law. Head of oil and gas team. Work covers all

aspects of upstream asset management, including sales and purchases, farm-ins and earn-ins, transportation and joint ventures. Recent work has included advice on decommissioning of installations and pipelines and security therefore, and also advice on public procurement issues in abandonment. Has worked in the UK, Netherlands and Norwegian sectors of the North Sea and on first major offshore gas development in Bangladesh in the summer of 1996, a project structured around the industry's 'alliancing' concept. Also has an insolvency practice.
Prof. Memberships: UK Energy Lawyers Group, International Bar Association Section on Energy and Resources Law; Insolvency Practitioners Association; Insolvency Lawyers Association (council member R3).
Career: Qualified in 1981. Licensed insolvency practitioner 1990. Joined *Lawrence Graham* in 1983, becoming a partner in 1986.
Personal: Born 25th March 1954. Attended University College School Hampstead, then University College, London (LLB Hons.). Leisure interests include shooting, rowing and gardening. Lives in South Oxfordshire.

WAKE, Brian
Wake Dyne Lawton, Chester (01829) 773101
bdw@wdl.co.uk
See under Environment, p.376

WALLACE, Patrick
Freshfields Bruckhaus Deringer, London
(020) 7936 4000
patrick.wallace@freshfields.com
Specialisation: Advised on establishing the UK electricity market structure at privatisation. Acted on a wide range of electricity projects in the UK and internationally. Advises on energy and natural resources, project financing, regulatory issues, privatisation, commercial contracts and corporate transactions. Speaks English, German and French.
Career: Holds degrees from London, Paris and Harvard Universities. Qualified in 1986. Partner since 1992.
Personal: Born 1959. Educated King's College, London. University of Paris and Harvard Law School.

WARNE, Penelope
CMS Cameron McKenna, Aberdeen (01224) 622002 ex 4412/4437
spw@cmck.com
Specialisation: Practice covers commercial agreements and advice of all types associated with oil and gas exploration and production; dealings in oil and gas interests, farm-ins and farm-outs; unitisation and joint operating agreements; partnering, alliances and joint ventures; and service contracts including pipeline, construction and drilling contracts.
Prof. Memberships: Honorary fellow of Centre for Energy, Petroleum and Mineral Law and Policy, University of Dundee.
Career: Qualified in English law in 1981. Articled and assistant solicitor with *Slaughter and May* 1976-83. Thereafter in-house legal adviser to Marks & Spencer plc before establishing own practice in Aberdeen. 1993 joined *CMS Cameron McKenna* to establish the Aberdeen office. Became a partner in 1994. Also qualified in Scots law.

WHITAKER, Neil
Pinsent Curtis Biddle, Leeds (0113) 244 5000
neil.whitaker@pinsents.com
Specialisation: Partner in commercial property department. Head of mines, minerals and landfill unit, specialising in transactions involving minerals extraction and utilisation of airspace. Acts for nationally known clients in this field including Hanson plc.
Career: University of Leeds; qualified 1987; partner *Pinsent Curtis Biddle* 1996.

WHITEHEAD, Andrew
Martineau Johnson, Birmingham (0121) 678 1528
andrew.whitehead@martjohn.com
Specialisation: Head of utilities department acting for a broad client base of electricity, gas and water companies. Heavily involved in ongoing reviews of electricity and gas trading arrangements for several major utilities. Leads a team advising The National Grid Company plc on contractual, regulatory and pool issues affecting its transmission services business, in particular the procurement of balancing services. Also leads a team advising on a variety of CHP projects. Advised on creation of the world's first reactive power market.
Prof. Memberships: Law Society.
Career: South Hunsley School, Birmingham University (1985 LLB). College of Law, Chester (1986). Articled *Ryland Martineau* (now *Martineau Johnson*). Qualified 1988; partner 1994.
Personal: Born 1963, resides Warwick with wife and daughter. Music (plays piano and oboe). Member UK Energy Lawyers Association. Associate London College of Music, piano, curries.

WILLIAMS, Gwyn
Hammond Suddards Edge, Birmingham
(0121) 222 3000
gwyn.williams@hammondse.com
Specialisation: Consultant. Main areas of practice are in energy and natural resources law including the environmental and financing aspects of mineral exploration and development, power generation, waste to energy and utilities regulation. Also has experience of rail privatisation and the development of large rail freight terminals and railway infrastructure projects.
Prof. Memberships: Law Society.
Career: Qualified in 1970, Tarmac Group legal department 1972. Company secretary and solicitor Tarmac Quarry Products 1981-89. Partner with *Edge Ellison* since 1990.
Personal: Educated at Liverpool University. Leisure interests include industrial archaeology.

WOOD, Charles
Denton Wilde Sapte, London (020) 7242 1212

WOOLF, Fiona
CMS Cameron McKenna, London
(020) 7367 3000
cfw@cmck.com
Specialisation: Energy projects and construction group. Main areas of practice are electricity restructurings and privatisations, regulation and the introduction of wholesale and retail competitive markets in the power sector, power station and transmission projects and financings. Worked exclusively on banking and project finance transactions in Bahrain, 1982-85. Acted in the Channel Tunnel project as one of the lead negotiators on the Concession Agreement and the Treaty with British and French Governments. Led a team of 40 lawyers acting for The National Grid Company plc on the privatisation of the Electricity Supply Industry in England and Wales and advised on the Northern Ireland Electricity restructuring and privatisation. Advised Electricidade de Portugal on the Tapada do Outeiro and Pego power projects and the project to bring natural gas to Portugal. Worked on independent transmission projects in Pakistan and Malaysia and the privatisation of the transmission system of Argentina. Has worked on power sector restructurings, utility regulation and privatisations in Australia, Canada, India, California, South Africa, the Republic of Ireland, Central America and Russia. Contributor to 'Utilities Law Review' and the Electricity Journal; regular speaker at conferences.
Prof. Memberships: Council Member of the Law Society.
Career: Qualified in 1973. Worked at *Coward Chance* 1973-78 before joining *McKenna & Co* (now *CMS Cameron McKenna*) in 1978. Became a partner in 1981.
Personal: Born 11 May 1948. Attended Keele University 1966-70. Leisure interests include wine and opera. Lives in Esher, Surrey.

ENVIRONMENT

OVERVIEW: A stable market for environmental practice is reflected in *Chambers'* relatively static rankings. Specialised practitioners and dedicated environmental departments are largely restricted to London firms. With a few exceptions, environmental teams in the regions tend to be composites of planning, commercial or litigation solicitors, assembled as needed. The 2000 contaminated land regime is still in the initial stages of implementation and has yet to make a noticeable impact on the legal market. Within environmental practices, the greatest scope for growth appears to be in pro-active advisory work for corporate clients on risk avoidance and potential implications of EU regulation as companies gear up for anticipated climate change levies and other projected environmental initiatives.

TOP IN-HOUSE LAWYERS

Simon BOYLE, Environment Lawyer, *Marconi*

Peter KELLETT, *Environment Agency*

Elizabeth LOWE, *AstraZeneca*

Stephen SYKES, Legal Director, *Certa*

"Leading environmental lawyer in the UK," **Simon Boyle** is rated for his varied, multinational work. Both *"excellent"* **Peter Kellett** and the respected **Elizabeth Lowe** attracted endorsement. Working for an insurance underwriting agency, **Stephen Sykes** is commended for his *"knowledge of environmental law"* and his *"highly commercial approach."*

In-House lawyers profiles: p 1193

RESEARCH APPROVED BY BMRB: *For this edition,* Chambers' *researchers conducted 6,552 interviews – 4,419 with law firms, 554 with barristers and 1,579 with clients.*

The validity of the research was scrutinised by BMRB International, who audited both the methodology and the results at our offices in July 2001. They interviewed Chambers' *researchers and cross-checked sample interviews. Details of the audit appear on page 7.*

LONDON

Allen & Overy (see firm details p.856) The firm retains its top band position, following widespread recommendation of the practice's "*good focus and excellent array of assistants.*" Noted corporate and banking strength allow the group to advise major UK and international plcs on transactional environmental issues. In addition, the 2000 launch of the firm's Integrated European Environmental Law Services team has led to widespread acknowledgement that the group is "*making a strong drive to develop a pan-European capability.*" Although the workload is heavily weighted towards transactional due diligence, the group receives a substantial amount of stand-alone advisory work, benefiting from the common perception that "*they have plenty of people to step in and do a good job.*" "*Quality operator*" **Owen Lomas** (see p.373) heads the group. Experienced in regulatory compliance, waste management and contaminated land liability, he is especially noted for his knowledge of packaging law. Peers report that his academic background makes him an ideal choice for clients seeking "*excellent analysis and technical precision.*" He recently acted for both ASW and Valpak on judicial review proceedings brought by Mayer Parry against the EA, relating to accreditation to sell packaging recovery notes. "*Young and approachable*" **Ross Fairley** (see p.371) has recently been promoted to the partnership. Reported to be more experienced on deal work than regulatory issues, many consider him "*Lomas' right hand man.*" An environmental auditor, much of his practice relates to infrastructure, power and energy from waste projects. Up and coming practitioner **Matthew Townsend** (see p.375) is "*making a name for himself*" in the field of environmental litigation. Both Fairley and Townsend advised United Waste on strategic acquisitions and waste contracts. **Clients:** Valpak; ICI; HSBC; United Waste Services; Celltech; Balfour Beatty; UK Steel; GE Capital; Cable & Wireless; Pennon Group; Hyder; Laporte; Glynwed; Marconi; Nestlé; Vivendi.

Freshfields Bruckhaus Deringer (see firm details p.964) "*A truly all-round practice*" with a "*staggering volume of both transactional and stand-alone work.*" The firm has integrated environmental, regulatory and planning work into one international practice group, and its recent merger is considered to have been a substantial boost to the practice. Clients have noted that in the "*breadth and quality of their cross-Europe service,*" the firm is "*five years ahead of the rest.*" The group's reputation is greatest for contentious work, where "*commercially-minded*" **Paul Bowden** (see p.566) has carved out a niche as a "*leading light*" in environmental defence litigation. Handling all matters from toxic tort to judicial review, he is felt to be "*pre-eminent in nuclear work,*" and numbers BNFL and UK Atomic Energy Authority among his clients. He often works in tandem with young partner **Jonathan Isted** (see p.372), recommended by clients as "*resourceful and informative.*" The firm recently represented a major biotechnology company in relation to direct action by UK protesters campaigning against genetically modified crops, and has acted on numerous pollution/ breach of discharge permit prosecutions and regulatory investigations in the automotive, engineering, shipbuilding and mining sectors. An "*old school gentleman,*" **Malcom Forster** (see p.371) maintains a mixed litigious, regulatory and transactional practice. Said to have "*a brain the size of a planet,*" his "*academic*" style serves him well in warranty and indemnity disputes, as well as environmental impact assessments. **Paul Watchman** (see p.376) is the practice's deal maker. "*Great fun in negotiations,*" he is rated highly for his client care. With a background in planning, he is "*good at crystallising issues*" relating to infrastructure projects, water law and contaminated land. Notable recent work includes acting for INEOS on its acquisition of Klea, Chlor-Chemicals and the Crosfield companies and advising PowerGen on the acquisition and disposal of a number of power stations. **Clients:** AstraZeneca; British Nuclear Fuels; Marconi; PowerGen; Conoco; Enron; Tyco International; Ministry of Defence; UK Atomic Energy Authority; One2One; Lafarge.

CMS Cameron McKenna (see firm details p.922) "*Knocking on the door of the premier league,*" the firm is particularly noted for the strength of its stand-alone environmental practice. A large percentage of the group's work originates within the department, although the team also advises on transactions led by the firm's banking, corporate, property, insurance and tax departments. Clients report that the team "*considers all the angles*" on matters including climate change levy, waste and water regulation, risk management, landfill tax and packaging law. UKELA Chairman Pamela Castle

ENVIRONMENT • London		Ptnrs	Assts
1	Allen & Overy	2	8
	Freshfields Bruckhaus Deringer	4	12
2	CMS Cameron McKenna	2	5
	Simmons & Simmons	1	6
3	Ashurst Morris Crisp	1	4
	Barlow Lyde & Gilbert	4	3
	Denton Wilde Sapte	1	3
	Leigh, Day & Co	3	5
	Linklaters	2	9
	Slaughter and May	1	3
4	Berwin Leighton Paisner	1	4
	Clifford Chance	2	4
	Herbert Smith	n/a	n/a
	Lawrence Graham	2	2
	Lovells	1	4
	Nabarro Nathanson	1	2
	Norton Rose	1	7
	Rowe & Maw	1	3
	SJ Berwin	2	4
5	Gouldens	2	2
	Hammond Suddards Edge	3	3
	Nicholson Graham & Jones	1	2
	Stephenson Harwood	1	1
	Theodore Goddard	2	2
	Trowers & Hamlins	2	2

LEADING INDIVIDUALS		
1	**BOWDEN Paul** Freshfields Bruckhaus	**DAY Martyn** Leigh, Day & Co
	FORSTER Malcolm Freshfields Bruckhaus	**LOMAS Owen** Allen & Overy
	MYLREA Kathy Simmons & Simmons	**WATCHMAN Paul** Freshfields Bruckhaus
2	**FAIRLEY Ross** Allen & Overy	**FOGLEMAN Valerie** Barlow Lyde & Gilbert
	HAVARD-WILLIAMS Vanessa Linklaters	**KEEBLE Ed** Slaughter and May
	LOOSE Helen Ashurst Morris Crisp	**MAY Caroline** Hammond Suddards Edge
	O'KEEFFE Jacqui Denton Wilde Sapte	**RICE Paul** Lawrence Graham
	SHERIDAN Paul CMS Cameron McKenna	**WAITE Andrew** Berwin Leighton Paisner
3	**CUCKSON David** Stephenson Harwood	**DEANESLY Clare** Gouldens
	GARBUTT John Nicholson Graham & Jones	**NASH Mike** Simmons & Simmons
	SHEPPARD Claire Theodore Goddard	**WISEMAN Andrew** Towers & Hamlins
4	**BRUMWELL Mark** SJ Berwin	**DOOLITTLE Ian** Towers & Hamlins
	GREENWOOD Brian Norton Rose	**HOBLEY Anthony** CMS Cameron McKenna
	ISTED Jonathan Freshfields Bruckhaus	**LLOYD Deborah** Herbert Smith
	MOORE Louise Lovells	**REDMAN Michael** Clifford Chance
	SHARP Cate Rowe & Maw	
UP AND COMING		
	HUTCHINSON Michael Rowe & Maw	**MARSHALL Anna** Nabarro Nathanson
	TOWNSEND Matthew Allen & Overy	
ONES TO WATCH		
	KEELE Helen Travers Smith Braithwaite	

This book is the product of 6,552 1/2-hour interviews. See p.7 for BMRB audit.

Within each band, firms are listed alphabetically. *See individuals' profiles p.369*

has now become a consultant and "*creative and commercial*" partner **Paul Sheridan** (see p.375) is seen by peers "*at the coal face*" of the group's operations. Part of the "*next generation of environmental lawyers*," he has particular experience of environmental impairment liability insurance matters and is considered to be the "*principal force*" in the group's contentious practice. He and his team have worked on a number of appellate cases, and are equally active on civil contentious matters, involving the migration of contaminants, waste, water and IPPC compliance and regulatory enforcement matters, environment permits, and noise and nuisance claims. The group recently acted for the Atomic Weapons Establishment on a judicial review threatening the continued production and maintenance of the UK's independent nuclear deterrent, and represented Hanson Waste Management and Hanson Quarry Products Europe on waste law prosecutions. "*Master of detail*" **Anthony Hobley** (see p.372) has a largely transactional practice. This "*solid performer*" has been especially occupied with emissions and climate change matters. He has advised clients such as British Ceramics Confederation, Hunting Engineering and Kimberly-Clark on economic instruments relating to climate change levy, emissions trading and packaging recovery notes. The firm was also instructed by Lattice and Aventis Crop Science on contaminated land and remediation issues, and advised Delphi Automotive Systems on its multi-million pound acquisition of businesses and subsidiaries of AP Group. **Clients:** Aventis; Lattice; Atomic Weapons Establishment; Environmental Industries Commission; Heathrow Airport; British Ceramic Confederation; Northumbrian Water; Eastman Chemicals.

Simmons & Simmons (see firm details p.1132) Although the department is felt to have a lower profile since the loss of Stephen Tromans to the Bar over a year ago, it is "*still turning stuff around well*" for a "*multitude of clients*" in the chemicals, energy and waste sectors. Felt to be "*less transactionally oriented*" than its principal competitors, the group earns market plaudits for its stand-alone regulatory and advisory ability. Said by clients to be "*up to date on laws as they emerge,*" the team has been instructed on matters as diverse as GM crop issues, proposed new Oil Storage Regulations, liability under the Radioactive Substances Act and landfill tax credits. With "*good contacts at UK and European government level,*" the group is said to provide a "*damn good briefing*" on the commercial implications of new European and UK legislation. Contentious and non-contentious matters have been combined into one pure environmental group located within the litigation department. This is headed by "*smashing*" **Kathy Mylrea** (see p.373), who garners high praise for her "*tough negotiating style*" and work in building up the team. Active in contaminated land and water pollution issues as well as transactional support, she is valued for her "*realistic advice*" and "*forthright*" approach. Her reputation is greatest for litigation, where she commands a "*detailed knowledge of defence prosecution.*" She is currently defending an individual director against prosecution by the Environment Agency, as well as advising on a nuisance case involving contaminated land and pollution of a major drinking water source."*Understated*" senior associate **Mike Nash** (see p.373) offers "*personalised service*" relating to contaminated land and nature conservation. Clients note that "*he comes to our sites to see things for himself and then whizzes documents back to us.*" He acted for the New Millennium Experience Company on environmental matters in relation to the sale of the Dome site, and continues to provide advice to The European Commission's DG Environment in connection with the White Paper on Environmental Liability. **Clients:** Aventis; BAA; British Sugar; Motorola; Cleanaway; Ministry of Defence; Railtrack; Shell UK; Vivendi UK; Scotch Whisky Association; PowerGen; Invensys; British Alcan Aluminium.

Ashurst Morris Crisp (see firm details p.866) A "*good steady team,*" involved principally in advising on environmental aspects of corporate, banking and property transactions. The group works closely with the firm's property and PFI/projects departments in acting for a range of construction, engineering, chemical and energy clients. "*Young and dynamic,*" the Environmental Risk Management Group is commended for its "*technical excellence.*" At its head is **Helen Loose** (see p.373), an expert on environmental insurance, emissions trading and energy and waste matters. Described by clients as an "*articulate and gritty*" performer, she has "*energy to spare,*" and maintains a high profile through her role at UKELA. She led the team in acting for Enviros on the sale of the landfill gas company Thomas Graveson, and advised AMS NV and Finmeccanica on their joint venture arrangements with BAE and EADS. Although the workload is weighted towards transactional matters, the group also undertakes its share of stand-alone regulatory matters, such as advising BTP and Polestar on environmental permitting requirements, and counselling Lattice Property Holdings on contaminated land issues prior to property disposals and acquisitions. Litigation is another cornerstone of the workload. Lawyers from both the litigation and environment departments deal with claims of breach of environmental warranties, and advise clients on workplace exposure litigation, including chemical, asbestos and radiation exposure. **Clients:** BAE Systems; Carillion Group; NRG Energy Group; JP Morgan; Northern Foods; United News and Media; the Laird Group; BT Property; Automotive Products; Enviros.

Barlow Lyde & Gilbert (see firm details p.870) Focused on environmental insurance and liability matters, the firm has established itself as "*the only firm to go to for insurance advice.*" A varied workload includes devising specialist environmental policies for insurers and reinsurers, advising on the environmental implications of public liability and indemnity policies, and environmental insurance litigation. Commended by peers for its "*appreciation of UK regulatory structures*" and "*user friendly products,*" the firm is further endorsed by its clients who appreciate the team's "*interest in our long-term strategy.*" Much of the group's reputation springs from the achievements of "*superstar*" **Valerie Fogleman** (see p.371), who is said to "*know more about insurance law than anybody.*" Both US and UK qualified, she "*knows where the law is going,*" and offers "*valuable global expertise.*" She and her team recently advised an international reinsurer on coverage disputes arising from inward asbestos, pollution and health hazard claims, and acted for a Lloyd's syndicate and an international insurance company on pollution exclusions and other environmental aspects of insurance policies. Although perceived to lack the corporate back-up of the market leaders, the team has undertaken an increased volume of corporate support work, and has handled a number of Environment Agency prosecutions in the past year. The team offered transactional support to Trelleborg on its £102 million acquisition of the Laird Group's automotive division, and acted for Qual-Effic Services during its merger with Keddy Services. **Clients:** Reliance National Insurance Company; Trelleborg; Zurich London Specialities; Qual-Effic Services.

Denton Wilde Sapte (see firm details p.939) A small practice, combining health and safety and environmental law specialists within the energy and infrastructure department. Strong ties to leading energy clients see the group especially active in petroleum, chemical and waste sectors on both contentious and non-contentious issues, and it frequently advises on PFI/PPP matters. Although the recent departure of Paul Rice to Lawrence Graham is thought to represent a setback for the team, **Jacqui O'Keeffe** remains at its head and continues to be seen as a "*significant commercial player.*" Over 60% of her practice involves stand-alone regulatory advice, and peers and clients alike appreciate her "*sensible*" approach - "*she knows what she's doing and gets it done.*" She acted on the decommissioning, decontamination and redevelopment of the Lots Road Power Station Site on behalf of Hutchinson Whampoa. On the contentious side, the firm has been involved in a number of prosecutions under the Water Resources Act, and most notably acted on behalf of Mayer Parry Recycling in a judicial review against a decision of the Environment Agency. The team also advised Wastepack on potential judicial review proceedings, successfully lobbying the Department of Environment in Northern Ireland in relation to the fee structure for compliance schemes. **Clients:** Mayer Environmental; Wastepack; English Partnerships.

Leigh, Day & Co (see firm details p.1036) "*A different piece of the puzzle,*" this niche claimant litigation firm is at the "*cutting edge of public law prosecutions.*" Generally representing individuals or groups of claimants in class action proceedings, the team's work ranges from toxic tort to judicial review. The "*outstanding*" **Martyn Day** leads an "*excellent crusade on behalf of those less able to act for themselves,*" and receives top marks from solicitors who come up against him in litigation. The firm is noted for its continued work on the South African Cape asbestos cases in the House of Lords. It has also advised on a number of landfill site cases, representing individuals damaged as a result of landfill gases, and successfully acted on a multi-party claim against Monsanto. Other areas of expertise include carbon monoxide leakages and water pollution. **Clients:** Individual and group claimants.

Linklaters (see firm details p.1042) An expanding team "*has the opportunity to work on great deals for a fabulous client base,*" and consequently has its greatest reputation for its transactional capacity. However, the caseload also includes substantial litigation and environmental planning components. A perennial presence on big-ticket cross-border transactions, the combined planning and environment group has become increasingly involved in real estate deals and structured financing work, as well as the management of contaminated land problems, parent company liability for the acts and omissions of subsidiaries, and environmental aspects of insolvency matters. **Vanessa Havard-Williams** (see p.372) is a "*down to earth*" practitioner with sound experience of energy and chemicals-related transactions. Respected by clients for her "*good, balanced judgement*" and "*no frills*" attitude, she is often personally credited with the team's growth both in size and stature. She has a developing practice in environmental impairment liability insurance, and recently led the team in advising National Power on environmental and health and safety issues arising from the demerger of its UK business Innogy. The group also provided environmental assessments and risk analysis for Sainsbury's disposal of Homebase. Interviewees have praised the firm's environmental litigation achievements, which have included representing corporations on multi-party toxic tort claims. **Clients:** Amec; Cargill; AstraZeneca; Trelleborg AG; Honeywell; J Sainsbury; Balfour Beatty; Deutsche Bank; National Power; Railtrack; BP Amoco; Barclays Capital; London Electricity.

Slaughter and May (see firm details p.1135) The lion's share of the practice is transactionally driven, in support of the firm's huge flow of corporate work. An unparalleled clientele of blue-chip plcs is backed by the first-class personal reputation of the "*brilliant*" **Ed Keeble** (see p.372). Although sometimes characterised as a "*tough cookie,*" he combines "*constructive advice with a laid back approach.*" Considered the practice's "*jewel*" by peers and clients alike, "*somehow he manages to do it all.*" The team acted for Huntsman Corporation on the acquisition of the European surfactants business of Albright & Wilson, and advised Laporte on the sale of all its businesses apart from Speciality Organics to K-L Holdings for approximately US $1.1 billion. A small proportion of non-transactional work includes acting on contaminated land site clean-ups and advising on operating authorisations, packaging laws, climate change levy and corporate environmental policy. **Clients:** BBA; Laporte; Marconi; Blue Circle; Tomkins; Shell Oil Company/ Shell Petroleum NV; Croda International; Huntsman Corporation.

Berwin Leighton Paisner (see firm details p.878) A combined planning and environment practice, focused on property-based transactions, is headed by **Andrew Waite** (see p.375), said to be a "*genuine environmental lawyer of great depth.*" His experience of lecturing and writing underlines an "*academic*" approach, which he applies to areas such as contaminated land, waste management and noise law. Other members of the team focus on environmental insurance claims and liability. Non-contentious work includes advising Petroplus on environmental aspects of its acquisition of an oil refinery from ICI, and acting for English Partnerships on the proposed sale of the Dome site at Greenwich. The team has also acted for Lattice Properties (formerly BG) on environmental issues relating to management, remediation and sale of property holdings, including advice on radioactive waste, landfill tax and contaminated land issues. On the contentious side, the group represented Tesco on a claim for compensation brought under Packaging Waste Regulations. **Clients:** English Partnerships; ICI; Lex; Mercury Asset Management; Newcastle Estates;

Petroplus; National Power; Blue Circle; Prudential; Tesco; Waste Facilities Audit Association.

Clifford Chance (see firm details p.919) Although the firm's environment group does not have a high stand-alone profile, it is able to work on the environmental aspects of the firm's huge turnover of corporate and banking transactions, notably in the telecoms, energy and utilities sectors. Contentious and non-contentious work is handled from within a specialist Environmental and Planning unit, and the group has seen a marked increase in cross-border instructions. "*Diligent and conscientious*" **Michael Redman** (see p.374) focuses on regulatory issues, particularly those relating to the power and nuclear industries. Clients report that "*his research into obscure areas of the law is first-class,*" and that he "*gives priority to our needs.*" A former barrister, Redman is also known for his expertise in environmental assessment litigation. The team advised Acordis on entry into the climate change levy scheme and acted for KKR on the acquisition of approximately 55% of Laporte for £810 million. **Clients:** Emerson Electric; Volkswagen; Coca-Cola; British Energy; Daimler Chrysler; Kohlberg Kravis Roberts & Co; CVC Capital Partners; European Aeronautic Defence and Space Co.

Herbert Smith (see firm details p.993) Six partners work on a part-time basis on both contentious and non-contentious matters for an environment team which has a solid reputation for transactional support. The team works closely with the firm's Energy and Corporate groups in handling a range of matters for water, waste, power and utility companies. Niche expertise exists in advising on water projects. Australian-trained senior assistant **Deborah Lloyd** (see p.372) works full-time on non-contentious environmental matters, including US and European acquisitions, public-private partnership projects, refinancing deals and real estate or redevelopment transactions. Said to have a "*good future ahead of her,*" she recently acted for United Utilities on its acquisition of Hyder Industrial Services, and negotiated environmental warranties and indemnities for Tikkurila in connection with the disposal of a coatings and distribution business. Elsewhere, the firm's outstanding litigation capacity has been turned to environmental matters such as complex liability claims for insurers. The group acted for Anglian Water in a High Court trial arising from the rupture of gas and water mains in Northamptonshire. **Clients:** EMI; British Energy; Royal & SunAlliance; British Sugar; Severn Trent; ICI; CGNU; St Paul International Insurance; EMI; Johnson Matthey; South West Water.

Lawrence Graham (see firm details p.1030) A year of swings and roundabouts has seen the departure of notable specialist Caroline May to Hammond Suddards Edge, and her immediate replacement with former Denton Wilde Sapte man **Paul Rice** (see p.374). Considered to be a "*rising star,*" the latter is reported to be both "*charming and switched on.*" While at his former firm, Rice acted on a comprehensive range of environmental matters, and is recognised for his experience from the Mayer Parry judicial review proceedings. During the past year, Lawrence Graham has advised a metropolitan council on a major LSVT, and acted for a developer client on purchase, redevelopment and insurance issues connected to a redevelopment site in South London. On the contentious side, the practice negotiated with a national charity on a threatened prosecution by the Environment Agency concerning breach of water discharge consent. **Clients:** BT; GATX Terminals; Crest Nicholson; J Sainsbury; Mining & Chemicals Products.

Lovells (see firm details p.1044) A small team, combining a stand-alone environmental capacity with health and safety compliance, which liaises closely with the firm's planning and litigation practices. "*Pragmatic*" partner **Louise Moore** heads a "*well-rounded*" team, which is described as "*commercial and alive to environmental issues.*" She acts on both contentious and advisory work, and has experience of Water Resources Act prosecutions, asbestos and toxic chemical contamination claims. The group acted for Cory Environmental on an appeal relating to Cory's proposal to extend its landfill operations. Transactional work includes advising Ikea on environmental aspects of a planning application for the regeneration of two disused sites in Edmonton, and acting for Prudential on its proposed redevelopment of the Manchester Arndale Centre. **Clients:** Cory Environmental; Ikea; Prudential.

Nabarro Nathanson (see firm details p.1078) Part of a national environmental practice, the firm's London office focuses on transactional and cross-border advisory work while regulatory expertise is the remit of the team in Sheffield. In London, the stand-out performer is the "*steady*" **Anna Marshall** (see p.373), who has played a key role in advising a number of US-based clients on environmental due diligence for international transactions. In the property sector, the firm has liaised with insurers on the negotiation of bespoke insurance policies to cover risks on portfolio acquisition, development sites and operating landfill sites. The team acted for the prospective purchaser of a large portfolio of petrol stations, which included co-ordinating all due diligence, drafting and negotiation of documentation. It also prepared a report for an international bank on contaminated land liability regimes in eight European jurisdictions. **Clients:** DigiPlex SA; Merrill Lynch Investment Managers; Coats Viyella; Balfour Beatty; Access Storage Group; Biffa; Syngenta; Prologis Developments; Deutsche Bank.

Norton Rose (see firm details p.1082) Although better known for planning, the firm's integrated planning and environmental unit has a name for advising on environmental due diligence for banking and corporate transactions. The group was especially recommended for mining and property-related expertise, and advises a solid clientele of developer and house-building clients on contaminated land issues. Planning guru **Brian Greenwood** (see p.371) also maintains his standing in the market for environmental advice. The team recently acted for Castle Cement on a public inquiry arising from the company's intention to enlarge its cement works in North Wales. Other matters include advising BMW on environmental warranties and indemnity in connection with the sale of both Rover and Land Rover. **Clients:** BMW; Castle Cement; Scottish Power; Siemens; Taylor Woodrow; Legacy; ABN-Amro; Stena; Anheuser-Busch; Yorkshire Water; Kelda.

Rowe & Maw (see firm details p.1113) Seen to be "*making real efforts in this area,*" the environment team is considered to be "*on the up.*" Situated within the firm's corporate practice, the group is instructed on environmental aspects of large transactions both independently and in conjunction with the firm's property, banking and projects teams. The team is expert in the chemicals sector, and served as the sole environmental advisors to ICI on the sale of its worldwide Chlor-Chemicals, Klea and Crosfield businesses to INEOS for approximately £325 million. Expertise extends into regulatory matters, where the team has advised on the application of the contaminated land regime, Packaging Waste Regulations, EU eco-labelling schemes and statutory nuisance abatement notices. The firm's Litigation and Dispute Resolution Group also has experience of acting for insurers on contamination and health and safety claims. "*Lively*" new partner **Cate Sharp** (see p.374) enters the rankings as a "*proactive transactional player,*" while her "*bright*" colleague **Michael Hutchinson** (see p.372) also maintains a heavy workload. They advised Syngenta AC on environmental matters associated with its creation through the demerger of Novartis agribusiness from Novartis and the demerger of the Zeneca agrochemicals business from AstraZeneca. **Clients:** Imperial Chemical Industries; Syngenta; Hunstman Tioxide; Unilever; Cable & Wireless; Waste Recycling; Marley; Aquila Energy; Chemical Industries Association; DHL International (UK); IP Powerhouse.

SJ Berwin (see firm details p.879) Felt to be "*doing excellent work*" in property-related environmental matters, the firm has a caseload which encompasses compulsory purchases, waste management licensing, landfill tax, environmental audits and nature conservation controls. **Mark Brumwell** (see p.370) focuses on corporate and water related work, notably concerning flood defence schemes, and is said to offer "*pragmatic advice.*" He recently advised the EA on flood alleviation schemes in north-west London. The firm also handles contentious work relating to water pollution, land contamination and planning/environmental judicial review, and advised the EU on a research project for nuclear waste storage. Other highlights include representing J Sainsbury Developments on the acquisition of a redevelopment site in Farnborough for a Homebase store, which included advice on contamination issues for site purchase and redevelopment. **Clients:** Southern Water; ASDA Properties; Chelsfield; Environment Agency; British Land; London City Airport; Marylebone Warwick Balfour; Crown Estate.

Gouldens (see firm details p.976) Based within the property department, this compact group "*doesn't shout about itself,*" but continues to advise a growing body of high-profile clients. Approximately 75% of the practice deals with stand-alone matters, with support work on property and corporate transactions making up the balance. The group is headed by "*deal-focused*" **Clare Deanesly** (see p.371), who specialises in minerals, waste management and contaminated land matters. Highlights include advising Hanson plc on the sale of its waste management businesses, including 30 landfill and mineral sites, to Waste Recycling Group for a consideration of £185 million. Individual practitioners are brought in from the litigation department for contentious issues, and the firm recently acted for Mid Kent Water on a long-running prosecution by the Government concerning water unfit for human consumption. **Clients:** Hanson; Biffa Waste Services; Mid Kent Water; Decco; Mayr-Melnhof Karton AG; Thames Waste Management; Pillar Property.

Hammond Suddards Edge (see firm details p.984) The firm's recent recruitment of **Caroline May** (see p.373) from Lawrence Graham has catapulted it to prominence in this area of practice. The group operates as part of a national safety, health and environmental team, servicing clients such as ICI and BNFL across the London, Leeds, Birmingham and Manchester offices. "*Dynamic and ambitious,*" the "*multi-skilled*" May is heavily involved in transactional work, and is reputed to be a "*tough negotiator.*" Other practitioners at the firm specialise in European environmental regulatory work and construction-related environmental warranties and indemnity. The group also assists London corporate finance and commercial property teams, offering environmental support on urban regeneration and development projects. The firm has recently been appointed to the new external panel of legal advisors set up by British Nuclear Fuels, for whom the team is undertaking a health and safety audit and compliance programme. Additionally, the team is advising a local authority on a special site identified under the new contaminated land regime, with remediation costs between £10 -20 million. **Clients:** British Energy; British Nuclear Fuels; Cleanaway; Ellis Everard; Environment Agency; OECD; Transco; Imperial Chemical Industries; Texas Utilities.

Nicholson Graham & Jones (see firm details p.1081) "*One of the originals,*" **John Garbutt** (see p.371) commands widespread respect for his enormous experience of waste management and minerals work. An author of numerous text books and articles on waste law, he is actively involved in the market and is considered "*one of the most knowledgeable lawyers around.*" Interviewees note that "*if you want to build an incinerator, talk to John.*" He leads an integrated planning and environmental unit which provides advice to a core of cement, concrete and minerals clients. The firm retains long-standing ties with key client Blue Circle Industries, and represented the company on a public inquiry over a new cement works and quarry. Other work includes acting for London Waste on the eviction of Greenpeace protesters from a waste disposal site in Edmonton, offering advice on the Pollution Prevention and Control Act to soap and detergent industry clients, and acting on a judicial review challenge for the UK Renderers Association against the Secretary of State for the Environment, Transport and Regions under the Environmental Protection Act 1990. **Clients:** London Waste; Blue Circle Industries; UK Renderers Association; Strong & Fisher Holdings.

Stephenson Harwood (see firm details p.1141) Former UKELA chairman **David Cuckson** (see p.370) heads the firm's environment team, and is highly regarded by peers as someone who "*knows his stuff.*" He maintains a varied practice, focusing on property-related matters, corporate support and waste management regulation. The group also draws upon the strengths of practitioners from other departments to deal with planning, criminal and regulatory offences, marine pollution and insurance matters. The firm was chosen to assist US lawyers Arnold & Porter in acting for Asahi Chemical Industry on the multi-national corporate acquisition of NS&N. Other highlights include acting on behalf of Petrochem UK on the acquisition of Carless Refining and Marketing from its Spanish parent company Repsol. **Clients:** AEA Technology; Cenargo; Petrochem UK; Peel Holdings; Kuwait Investment Office; Sorin Biomedica; Caird Group; Elementis.

Theodore Goddard (see firm details p.1152) A varied practice involved in both corporate support and stand-alone environmental matters. Considered to be stronger on the contentious side, the group undertakes much of its own advocacy in litigation relating to contaminated land and packaging waste regulations. Individual practitioners possess niche strength in energy to waste matters. "*Technically superb*" **Claire Sheppard** (see p.375) is said to have "*done extremely well in launching the practice,*" but is sometimes perceived to lack support of similar quality. Trained in commercial litigation, she was commended by barristers for her "*attention to detail*" and experience advising on environmental liabilities within the power, gas, nuclear, chemical and pharmaceutical industries. The team acted for Staveley Industries on the disposal of its salt business to US Salt and advised Hampshire Waste Services on three EfW projects. **Clients:** Hogonas; Becker Acroma; Hampshire Waste Services; Staveley; Burdale Financial; Edmund Nuttall/Halcrow Consortium.

Towers & Hamlins (see firm details p.1162) With an unrivalled base of housing association and local authority clients, the team concentrates on contaminated land issues in the context of brownfield redevelopment projects. Acting on the side of the local authority, the group has long experience of advising on the issuance of remediation and enforcement notices. The team also undertakes a substantial volume of waste cases, typically for trade associations within the secondary metals sector. "*Incredibly bright*" **Ian Doolittle** (see p.371) heads the group, and spends much of his time on the planning and environment aspects of housing work. Full time environment specialist **Andrew Wiseman** (see p.376) was recommended for his "*well-rounded skills,*" and has specific expertise in waste management matters. Both individuals advised Wellingborough Borough Council on the serving of a remediation notice under contaminated land regulations. **Clients:** Wellingborough Council; local authorities; housing associations.

THE SOUTH

Blake Lapthorn (see firm details p.886) Seen to be "*consolidating its position*" within the region, the team is split between the firm's Southampton and Portsmouth offices. Locally, the group is well known for packaging and waste regulation seminars and publications, and was recommended for its ability to "*translate complicated legalese.*" Pollution cases resulting from planning and property transactions have been notable features of the team's caseload. Commended for his "*all-round expertise,*" commercial property partner **David Rayner** heads the firm's environmental law group and is particularly knowledgeable on contaminated land issues. He has acted for Chelton on business and property acquisitions with environmental implications. Other work includes the successful defence of Hillier Nurseries and the Horticulatural Trades Association from litigation under the Producer Responsibility Obligations. **Clients:** Hillier Nurseries; Planned Maintenance Engineering; Webb Country Foods; Chelton.

ENVIRONMENT • The South	Ptnrs	Assts
1 Blake Lapthorn Portsmouth, Southampton	2	4
Bond Pearce Southampton	1	1
Brachers Maidstone	2	1
DMH Brighton	1	1
2 Fynn & Partners Bournemouth	2	2
Stevens & Bolton Guildford	1	n/a

LEADING INDIVIDUALS	
1 **ABRAHAM Henry** Brachers	**ALLEN Tony** DMH
DAVEY Catherine Stevens & Bolton	**HORNER Douglas** Brachers
RAYNER David Blake Lapthorn	**TRINICK Marcus** Bond Pearce

This book is the product of 6,552 1/2-hour interviews. See p.7 for BMRB audit.
Within each band, firms are listed alphabetically. *See individuals' profiles p.369*

Bond Pearce (see firm details p.888) A small Southampton contingent offers environmental advice in conjunction with the firm's Plymouth-based environment team. Continuing to act for Associated British Ports in connection with the Dibden Terminal project to extend the Port of Southampton, the team has expertise in environmental and public law issues relating to large infrastructure projects. Other strengths include waste management issues, renewable energy, urban development and nature conservation. On the contentious side, the team has defended prosecutions under the Environmental Protection Act 1990 and Water Resources Act 1991 for waste management agencies Sid Knowles Waste, Devon Waste Management, and Devonport Management. **Marcus Trinick** (see p.670), who possesses vast experience of wind and alternative energy projects, has now arrived from the firm's Plymouth office. "*Pre-eminent in his field*," he advises on environmental impact assessments in connection with renewable energy developments in Scotland, England and Wales. **Clients:** Associated British Ports; Devonport Management; Sid Knowles Waste; Scottish Power.

Brachers (see firm details p.893) Operating as an adjunct to the firm's town and country planning department, environmental practitioners carry out contentious and corporate support work for clients in manufacturing, waste management and agriculture. Department head **Henry Abraham** advises on environmental aspects of the sale and purchase of assets in conjunction with his planning practice, while **Douglas Horner** remains heavily involved in agriculture-related work. The group has been acting on soil erosion issues resulting from flooding, and provides planning and waste regulation advice concerning land-raising proposals on agricultural land. Particularly strong on regulatory matters, the team has been involved in a number of contentious matters, including defence work in criminal proceedings concerning water course pollution in Kent and the Isle of Wight. **Clients:** Manufacturing and waste companies; landowners.

DMH (see firm details p.944) **Tony Allen** (see p.662) heads the firm's Planning and Environmental group and has handled a number of contaminated land cases, as well as the environmental aspects of planning applications and corporate acquisitions. The team includes environmental litigation specialists, who advise on statutory nuisance appeals, defence against environmental prosecutions, noise and odour complaints and judicial reviews. In addition to the House of Lords Reprotech case, the firm acts for a number of NHS Trusts, housing associations and local authorities, and recently advised on the environmental aspects of a planning application for Brighton public library. Expertise in waste and incinerator matters was highlighted by advice to Crawley Abattoir on a planning inquiry relating to an animal remains incinerator. **Clients:** Cory Environmental; Reprotech; Crawley Abattoir; Friends Provident Life Office; Brighton Healthcare NHS Trust.

Fynn & Partners (see firm details p.967) Headed by Lionel Fynn, the environment group frequently advises landowners or interested parties against local authorities in litigation relating to noise abatement, waste disposal and village green matters. His team handles all aspects of advocacy for environmental work including statutory nuisance notice appeals and defence against criminal environmental prosecutions. The team successfully represented Murco Petroleum Group in an appeal relating to the redevelopment of a petrol forecourt, and has advised on several planning applications in sensitive areas, such as those covered by the EC Birds Directive, Coastal SSSI and protected lowland. **Clients:** SFI Group; Hall & Woodhouse; Bowlplex; Murco Petroleum Group.

Stevens & Bolton (see firm details p.1143) Dividing her time between planning and environmental matters, **Catherine Davey** (see p.370) is recognised as one of the few environmental specialists in Surrey. Much of the firm's caseload involves transactional support for a clientele of commercial and residential developers, private investment companies and multi-nationals. Davey herself has particular expertise in contaminated land issues and environmental assessment, and advises ENER-G on waste licensing and contamination issues in relation to new sites. Other notable work includes advice on emissions trading legislation, land drainage, and flood and sea defence issues. **Clients:** Hays; ENER-G.

SOUTH WEST

ENVIRONMENT • South West	Ptnrs	Assts
1 Bond Pearce Plymouth	3	3
Burges Salmon Bristol	1	4
Osborne Clarke OWA Bristol	2	4
2 Bevan Ashford Bristol	1	3
Clarke Willmott & Clarke Bristol, Taunton	2	2
3 Stephens & Scown Exeter	n/a	1
Veale Wasbrough Bristol	1	2

LEADING INDIVIDUALS	
1 **BAKER Neil** Clarke Willmott & Clarke	**GIBBS Kevin** Osborne Clarke
HOLMES Sarah Bond Pearce	**JOHN Alan** Osborne Clarke
SALTER Ian Burges Salmon	
2 **HAYDEN Tim** Clarke Willmott & Clarke	**SCOTT Peter** Toller Beattie

This book is the product of 6,552 1/2-hour interviews. See p.7 for BMRB audit.
Within each band, firms are listed alphabetically. *See individuals' profiles p.369*

Bond Pearce (see firm details p.888) The firm's environmental team is largely based in Plymouth, although some work is undertaken by the Bristol office. The team is best known for its "*fantastic niche in renewable energy*," although its leading figure in this area, Marcus Trinick, has recently moved to the firm's Southampton office. **Sarah Holmes** (see p.372) maintains a broad practice. Praised by interviewees for her "*sharp intellect*" and "*commercial edge*," she deals with environmental judicial reviews and declarations, environmental impact assessment and risk management. The group provides environmental support on corporate acquisitions across the food, waste, construction, and motor sectors, and has advised extensively on the introduction of Pollution Prevention and Control, notably in relation to climate change levy exemption agreements. **Clients:** Renewable Energy Systems; Enron Corporation; Aggregate Industries; National Windpower; Pennon Group; Taylor Woodrow.

Burges Salmon (see firm details p.902) A stand-alone environmental regulation practice headed by **Ian Salter,** (see p.374) who has a nationally recognised niche in nuclear law and radioactive licensing. The firm is retained by the Ministry of Defence for advice on the Aldermaston and Burghfield nuclear establishments, and also acts for a number of clients in the waste, energy, and transport industries. Beyond pure environment advice, the team also undertakes transactional support and contaminated land work for the corporate and property departments. The firm recently advised Atlanta-based Sevalco on the climate change levy and construction of a new combined heat and power plant in Avonmouth. It has also advised Nirex on radioactive waste disposal. **Clients:** United Kingdom Nirex; Ministry of Defence; FirstGroup; Sevalco; Brightstar Environmental; Aram Resources.

Osborne Clarke (see firm details p.1086) A "*commercially oriented team,*" operating out of the firm's corporate department, which also draws on the experience of two scientists. The group is heavily involved in waste management work and contaminated land issues, and has advised Hygiene at Work on waste management licensing issues concerning the treatment of clinical waste. Department head **Alan John** is in the field of waste and renewable energy and is respected for his corporate experience, while the firm's 2000 recruitment of partner **Kevin Gibbs** from Lyons Davidson is considered to have reinforced the firm's position in the region. Recent highlights include advising on the environmental aspects of Hanson's sale of a portfolio of businesses, and negotiating complex indemnities on the sale of a town centre contaminated site. **Clients:** Churngold Waste Management; Hanson; Recycling Services Group; SITA Holding UK; St Regis Paper.

Bevan Ashford (see firm details p.880) A public authority-based firm with environmental work linked to its health & safety, planning and PFI practices. Led by partner David Wood, the group includes trained engineers, scientists and a former Environment Agency employee. Acting for a clientele of NHS trusts, energy and waste management companies, the group has wide experience of renewable energy issues, brownfield development, clinical waste, municipal waste disposal and collection contracts. The firm has advised on investigations against clients by Radiological Protection Officers. **Clients:** Energy Power Resources; Border Biofuels; National Health Service; Isle of Man Government; Wessex Incineration; Merck; Gloucester Health Authority.

Clarke Willmott & Clarke (see firm details p.915) A planning-based environmental team split between the firm's Taunton and Bristol offices, it is renowned for the quality of its individual lawyers. **Tim Hayden** (see p.369) has traditionally had a high profile for his environmental prosecution practice. As a solicitor advocate, he undertakes both prosecution and defence work relating to waste disposal, contaminated land, statutory nuisance, air and water pollution. He has conducted proceedings relating to BSE litigation, County Council applications, agricultural accidents and fraud subsidy claims. **Neil Baker** (see p.369) advises on planning appeals into industrial, mineral and waste installations, and is perceived to be devoting a greater part of his practice to pure environmental matters. "*Extremely clued-up about the relevant legislation,*" he is considered by rivals to be particularly knowledgeable about European environmental directives, and has acted on EPA Part I hearings under Integrated Pollution Control and Local Authority Air Pollution Control. The firm has advised Pfizer on the interpretation of waste management licensing regulations, special waste regulations, and the transfrontier shipment of waste regulations. **Clients:** The Scotts Company (UK); Pfizer; Classic Mouldings (UK); Countryside Residential (South West); Hydraulic Lias Limes.

Stephens & Scown Drawing on the experience of two non-specialist partners, the firm is active throughout Devon and Cornwall and is primarily recognised for local work on behalf of English China Clay and Aggregate Industries. The remainder of the team's clientele comprises local companies from the farming and tourism industries, with particular emphasis on mining and quarry concerns. Ian Lamond heads the joint planning and environmental practice from the firm's St. Austell office, and the group also utilises the expertise of a High Court advocate in the litigation department for contentious environment cases. **Clients:** Aggregate Industries; ECC International.

Veale Wasbrough (see firm details p.1167) Headed by Tim Smithers, and handling environment work within the context of planning and property transactions, the firm is particularly active in advising local authorities on environmental liabilities and contaminated land remediation schemes in conjunction with a busy property development practice. Other strengths lie in waste management planning and landfill development and acquisition. The group recently acted for the landowners of the British Harbourside regeneration development on the remediation scheme for a 65-acre development site which includes an old gas works. It also advised Esso in relation to its jetline pipeline replacement project to provide aviation fuel to Heathrow airport, and represented Bath and North East Somerset on a judicial review challenge arising from the Bath Spa Millennium Project. **Clients:** Esso Petroleum Co; Total-Fina; Hemmings Waste Management; Bristol City Council; Crest Nicholson Properties.

Other Notable Practitioners **Peter Scott** (see p.374) of **Toller Beattie** in Barnstaple is "*deeply committed*" to the fields of water and sewerage law. Active in wildlife conservation issues, he also has an unusual niche in fishery law and acts for health authorities, fishery and shellfish interests throughout the UK and Republic of Ireland.

WALES

ENVIRONMENT • Wales	Ptnrs	Assts
1 **Edwards Geldard** Cardiff	1	2
Eversheds Cardiff	1	1
Morgan Cole Cardiff	2	2

LEADING INDIVIDUALS
1 **BOSWALL Julian** Morgan Cole

This book is the product of 6,552 1/2-hour interviews. See p.7 for BMRB audit.

Within each band, firms are listed alphabetically. *See individuals' profiles p.369*

Edwards Geldard (see firm details p.948) Environmental practitioners at the firm focus mainly on contaminated land and water pollution matters, and are generally drawn from within the planning and public law departments. The group advises a number of local authorities on environmental aspects of public law, continues to advise the Welsh Development Agency in relation to the reclamation of a derelict former steelworks site in Wrexham and represented a major contractor in a water pollution case. Huw Williams heads the practice. **Clients:** Welsh Development Agency.

Eversheds (see firm details p.952) A mixed environment and health and safety team in Cardiff is best known for advising on the environmental aspects of property, corporate and planning transactions. The group recently represented Celtic Energy in a prosecution brought by the Environment Agency following a pollution incident. During the past year, Dale Collins' team has also advised Hatwin on contaminated land issues. **Clients:** Allied Bakeries; Celtic Energy; British Aluminium Plate; Jewson; Solutia UK.

Morgan Cole (see firm details p.1074) "*Highly reputable firm*" heavily involved in the energy, mining and waste industries. The group handles a mixture of public and private sector cases, as well as substantial commercial property environmental spin-off work. The forte here, however, is litigation in which the group has handled a volume of cases relating to waste licensing, packaging waste, water pollution and health and safety matters. Recent activity in this area includes defending a major dust nuisance class action. Practice head **Julian Boswall** (see p.370) is commended by peers for his "*commercial*" attitude and "*all-round knowledge*" of contaminated land issues. The team recently advised on the disposal of a former oil refinery site, involving liability allocation and remediation of the site. **Clients:** Cardiff & Vale NHS Trust; HSBC Trust Company; NFU Services; PHS Group; Welsh Development Agency; Elf Oil UK; Corus; LAS Waste; Liberty Properties.

MIDLANDS

ENVIRONMENT • Midlands	Ptnrs	Assts
1 **Pinsent Curtis Biddle** Birmingham	n/a	1
Wragge & Co Birmingham	2	1
2 **Eversheds** Birmingham	3	6
3 **Hammond Suddards Edge** Birmingham	n/a	2
4 **Kent Jones and Done** Stoke-on-Trent	1	2

LEADING INDIVIDUALS	
1 **SHINER Philip** Public Interest Lawyers	
2 **MACKINLAY Hannah** Pinsent Curtis Biddle	**TURNER John** Wragge & Co
3 **WILLIAMS Gwyn** Hammond Suddards Edge	

This book is the product of 6,552 1/2-hour interviews. See p.7 for BMRB audit.
Within each band, firms are listed alphabetically. *See individuals' profiles p.369*

Pinsent Curtis Biddle (see firm details p.1098) The group's central figure is "*impressive*" associate **Hannah MacKinlay** (see p.373), who is said to be "*an independent and original thinker on contaminated land matters.*" The bulk of the practice consists of providing corporate support, handling warranties and indemnities and advising on environmental aspects of property transactions. However, the group also advises on environmental assessment, IPC, IPPC, and APC and can draw upon solicitor advocates to undertake defence work in EA prosecutions. The firm has a stable base of waste industry clients such as Onyx and Severn Waste Services, and continues to advise the environmental health department of Daventry District Council. **Clients:** Onyx; Severn Waste Services; Daventry District Council; Johnson Controls; Glanbia.

Wragge & Co (see firm details p.1189) Maintaining its high ranking this year, the group is felt to owe much to the profile of **John Turner,** a "*well connected*" environmental specialist, who "*keeps up to date on policy matters.*" He is involved in a range of general advisory, waste management, packaging and regulatory matters. While a substantial proportion of the caseload is non-contentious due diligence, his reputation is greatest in contentious matters, where he has acted on a number of prosecutions relating to noise abatement, water pollution and health and safety breaches. He recently advised Cadbury and Burmah Castrol in nuisance and waste management actions against adjoining land owners. The team has specific expertise in air pollution, waste management, contaminated land and utilities, and advised on the institutional buy-out of the Vickers turbine component business from Vickers Engineers. **Clients:** HSBC; PowerGen; Cadbury; Burmah Castrol; Royal & Sun Alliance; PwC; British Energy.

Eversheds (see firm details p.952) A large team, spread across the firm's Birmingham and Nottingham offices, handles a range of contentious and non-contentious work, under the guidance of planning supremo Rod Bull. The group works closely with the corporate and property departments, and is noted for its work on the environmental aspects of brownfield site developments and city regeneration projects. A steady volume of advisory work for manufacturing, mining, construction, engineering and retail clients is supplemented by a strong contentious capacity. Noise, nuisance and pollution cases have all featured recently, and the team has specialised knowledge of water pollution regulations. The firm acted for Stonecross East Sussex on the pollution of a watercourse with foul drainage, represented Sims Metal UK in a noise nuisance matter and counselled MG Rover on environmental due diligence for a corporate transaction. **Clients:** Bass Leisure Retail; Bellway Homes; EMDA; McDonald's Restaurants; TRW.

Hammond Suddards Edge (see firm details p.984) A combined environment and health and safety practice is led by **Gwyn Williams** (see p.357), who has an established reputation within the waste and mining industries. The team, active in both contentious and non-contentious matters, focuses on waste management and contaminated land issues and has substantial experience of regulatory work relating to water pollution. Recent work includes providing climate change levy advice to trade associations. **Clients:** companies in waste and mining sector.

Kent Jones and Done (see firm details p.1020) A mixed planning and environment group, led by Grant Anderson, that benefits from the firm's established base of minerals and quarrying clients. The practice therefore has a considerable niche in extraction related environmental matters, and advises local ceramic manufacturers on environmental planning. The group is also active in the waste management sector. The firm recently advised two national plcs in conjunction with a waste transfer station development, and acted for a landfill operator in relation to disputed rights to tip under the planning and waste management system. **Clients:** Laporte; Shraff Tip; Bliss Sand & Gravel.

Other Notable Practitioners Interviewees believe that **Phil Shiner** of **Public Interest Lawyers** "*deserves applause for pushing back the frontiers of public law.*" Assisted by a trainee solicitor, he maintains a widely respected niche practice acting for plaintiffs and third party objectors in a variety of environmental, planning and human rights cases. Much of the work is legally aided, although Shiner also regularly represents organisations such as Friends of the Earth and the Nuclear Awareness Group. Said to "*know more than anyone about judicial review,*" he acted on the judicial review of the Aldermaston nuclear submarine case and the House of Lords Alconbury case.

EAST ANGLIA

Mills & Reeve (see firm details p.1069) Receiving general commendation for its "*experience, depth and resources,*" the environmental team is distributed between Cambridge and Norwich and is felt to have grown in stature since the recruitment of **David Brock** (see p.370) from Herbert Smith. Although better known as a planning lawyer, Brock has long experience of handling environmental aspects of transactions within minerals and waste sectors. Recommended by clients for his "*winning manner,*" he is said to be "*vigorous in his approach to negotiation.*" "*Extremely thorough*" associate **Rebecca Carriage** (see p.370) maintains a broader stand-alone practice, with particular emphasis on waste management, statutory nuisance, Water Resources Act cases and contaminated land remediation. In addition to advising on environmental impact assessment in planning projects, the team defends companies and institutions in prosecutions and third party claims, and has both health and safety and food law capacities. Representative work includes acting for a national waste operator bidding for waste management contracts and advising a food manufacturer on environmental liability. **Clients:** Norfolk Environmental Waste Services; Ugbrooke Environmental; Jarrold; UEA; NHS trusts; landowners.

Richard Buxton Litigator **Richard Buxton** is "*a name that crops up all the time.*" Acting on the side of local residents and individual objectors, he has a "*one of a kind practice,*" focusing entirely on claimant litigation and judicial review. Considered a "*leading light in environmental assessment,*" Bux-

ENVIRONMENT • East Anglia	Ptnrs	Assts
1 **Mills & Reeve** Cambridge, Norwich	1	1
Richard Buxton Cambridge	1	1
2 **Eversheds** Norwich	1	1
Hewitson Becke + Shaw Cambridge	1	2

LEADING INDIVIDUALS	
1 **BRYCE Andrew** Andrew Bryce & Co	**BUXTON Richard** Richard Buxton
2 **BROCK David** Mills & Reeve	**CARRIAGE Rebecca** Mills & Reeve
JEWKES Penny Eversheds	

This book is the product of 6,552 1/2-hour interviews. See p.7 for BMRB audit.
Within each band, firms are listed alphabetically. *See individuals' profiles p.369*

ton has extensive expertise in nature conservation, water and nuisance cases. Recent work includes acting in the Heathrow Night Flight cases, and environmental impact assessment cases R v Durham County Council and others, ex parte Huddleston and Berkeley v Secretary of State for the Environment. **Clients:** Resident groups; individual applicants.

Eversheds (see firm details p.952) The firm's environmental unit provides a comprehensive transactional support service to property, commercial and corporate departments. Barrister **Penny Jewkes** (see p.372) is the department's full time environmental specialist, acting on a range of non-contentious matters. The main areas of the caseload are environmental impact assessment, contaminated land and packaging issues. The group has advised Lancaster on environmental issues arising from the ownership of brown field sites, and acted for the Borough Council of King's Lynn and West Norfolk on developments in the Nar-Ouse regeneration areas. **Clients:** Electricity Supply Nominees; Lancaster; Borough Council of King's Lynn and West Norfolk.

Hewitson Becke + Shaw (see firm details p.994) Planning-oriented practice, based in Cambridge, which works closely with the firm's Northampton office in undertaking contaminated land and environmental liability instructions. The group has been active in advising waste disposal client Shanks Waste Services on management of landfill sites, potential water pollution, renewable resource issues and noise complaints. Practitioners also represent clients in civil and criminal proceedings, and recently defended clients in litigation involving waste management licensing rules. Peter Brady heads the Cambridge planning and environmental team. **Clients:** Shanks Waste Services; Cambridge University; Norfolk Homes; Medical Research Council; RSPB.

Other Notable Practitioners "*An environmental lawyer through and through,*" sole practitioner **Andrew Bryce** maintains an unusual niche practice advising a range of UK and international plcs on environmental matters. Widely admired for his defence of corporates in civil and criminal prosecutions, he is regarded by peers as "*an authority on waste matters,*" and is well known for his writing on environmental assessment. His clientele includes construction contractors, waste management agencies, oil companies and a large environmental consultancy.

NORTH WEST

ENVIRONMENT • North West	Ptnrs	Assts
1 **DLA** Manchester	n/a	n/a
Eversheds Manchester	1	3
Leigh, Day & Co Manchester	1	1
2 **Addleshaw Booth & Co** Manchester	1	1
Hammond Suddards Edge Manchester	2	3
Masons Manchester	1	2
Wake Dyne Lawton Chester	3	1

LEADING INDIVIDUALS	
1 **DAWSON Andrew** DLA	**SHEPHERD Elizabeth** Eversheds
SHEPHERD Michael Hammond Suddards Edge	**WAKE Brian** Wake Dyne Lawton

This book is the product of 6,552 1/2-hour interviews. See p.7 for BMRB audit.
Within each band, firms are listed alphabetically. *See individuals' profiles p.369*

DLA A largely contentious practice, it is most noted for defending manufacturing and industrial clients in Environment Agency prosecutions. Litigator **Andrew Dawson** is the team's leading practitioner.

Eversheds (see firm details p.952) Recommended by specialists for "*a good spread of work deriving from major M&A transactions,*" the group is also occasionally called upon to defend clients in environmental prosecutions. Partner **Elizabeth Shepherd** (see p.375) has the "*commercial nous*" to "*run an excellent regional practice.*" A stable client base includes a number of American companies, who are advised on the investment implications of new legislation, environmental accounting and environmental management systems. Development of brown field sites is an area of niche expertise. The firm advised HSBC Private Equity on environmental issues connected with the £496 million acquisition of the Caradon Plumbing Division, and acted for SpectraSite Holdings on the environmental aspects of its joint venture with Transco and transfer of over 3000 sites to the joint venture company. **Clients:** DuPont (UK); AstraZeneca; Waste Recycling Group; BF Goodrich; Solectron; Ineos Acrylics UK; Anglo American; Renold.

Leigh, Day & Co (see firm details p.1036) Less well known than its London headquarters, the firm's Manchester office continues to focus on environmental plaintiff work under the leadership of partner Gisele Bakkenist. The group's work is entirely contentious, representing individuals in civil suits and multi-party claims for environmental damages. Particularly recommended for its toxic tort expertise, the team has a specialism in carbon monoxide poisoning cases. In the past year the Manchester group achieved settlements on carbon monoxide cases against a landlord and against a company responsible for servicing gas equipment. **Clients:** Individual applicants.

Addleshaw Booth & Co (see firm details p.853) A "*traditional Manchester firm*" with a solid reputation for corporate work. Led by planning name Michael Kenworthy, the team advises on a range of contentious, corporate support and stand-alone matters. The utilities sector and environmental aspects of insolvency and corporate transactions are key elements of the workload. Recent work includes advising English Partnerships on its colliery portfolio and the national Land Stabilisation Programme, acting for Borden Chemical UK on the sale of a chemical works, and a number of noise nuisance cases. **Clients:** Barclays Private Equity; Borden Chemical UK; English Partnerships; North West Development Agency; GeoDelft Environmental.

Hammond Suddards Edge (see firm details p.984) **Michael Shepherd** (see p.375) heads the firm's national Safety, Health and Environment Group. Recommended as a "*well known commercial litigator*" he has long experience of defending corporate clients against claims of land contamination, statutory nuisance and regulatory breach in criminal and civil prosecutions. He recently acted for Meristem over a contravention of the Environmental Protection Act 1990, relating to waste disposal. Other practitioners are involved in corporate and property support, as well as substantial advisory work. Clients are drawn from the chemical, utilities and nuclear industries, and the group advised Kelda on the disposal of clinical waste incineration company White Rose Environmental. **Clients:** Cleanaway; Chemfuel; AES Drax Power; ICI Chemicals & Polymers; British Nuclear Fuels; Kelda; CIBA Speciality Chemicals; Aventis CropScience.

Masons (see firm details p.1056) Although the environment practice has continued to suffer departures, it is recognised for its substantial environmental caseload, which derives mainly from a well-established construction department. The combined planning and environment department operates in both Manchester and London, with Stephen Chalcraft heading the former practice. With a particular focus on city centre regeneration, compulsory purchase work, contaminated land and liability transfer, the group acts for a range of developers, contractors, engineers, and housebuilding clients. It advised a high profile industrial client on statutory and common law liabilities in relation to contaminated land at a power station. **Clients:** Trafford Borough Council; Roland Bardsley; Morris Homes; Peel Holdings.

Wake Dyne Lawton (see firm details p.1170) Benefiting from the firm's broad base of clients within extraction industries, the practice rates highly for environmental work relating to minerals, planning and road haulage. **Brian Wake** (see p.376) receives commendation for his expertise in waste disposal work within a planning context. Although the bulk of the work is non-contentious, the team recently represented a group of objectors to a proposal for a new cement plant in Wales. The firm is also handling an increasing amount of work on behalf of landowners, involving rights to extract minerals, run electricity supplies, and dispose of waste. Renewable energy sources is another growth area for the practice. **Clients:** RTZ.

NORTH EAST

	ENVIRONMENT • North East	Ptnrs	Assts
1	**Eversheds** Leeds	1	6
2	**Nabarro Nathanson** Sheffield	2	3
3	**Addleshaw Booth & Co** Leeds	2	2
	DLA Sheffield	n/a	n/a
4	**Dickinson Dees** Newcastle upon Tyne	1	2
	Hammond Suddards Edge Leeds	2	3
	Pinsent Curtis Biddle Leeds	1	2

	LEADING INDIVIDUALS	
★	**SMITH Paul** Eversheds	
1	**CLARKE Ray** Nabarro Nathanson	**HITCHCOCK Teresa** DLA
	RENGER Mike Nabarro Nathanson	
2	**BELL Stuart** Eversheds	**BERESFORD Amanda** Addleshaw Booth & Co
	DOWEN Denise Dickinson Dees	**PIKE John** Addleshaw Booth & Co

This book is the product of 6,552 1/2-hour interviews. See p.7 for BMRB audit.
Within each band, firms are listed alphabetically. *See individuals' profiles p.369*

Eversheds (see firm details p.952) Frequently recommended as the "*leading firm in the regions,*" Eversheds' Leeds office is, by general consensus, "*the best of the lot,*" and benefits from the outstanding reputation of "*astute businessman*" **Paul Smith** (see p.375). A "*prominent litigator,*" Smith represents industrial companies in civil and criminal proceedings and is praised by peers and clients alike for his "*creative service*" and "*straightforward style*". As the firm's "*centre of excellence*" for contentious matters, the group has acted in a variety of toxic tort, insurance, water pollution, noise and nuisance cases and judicial reviews. The group recently represented British Waterways Board in the court of appeal on a test case on pollution of canals and acted for English, Welsh and Scottish Railway in an Environment Agency and Health & Safety investigation following a derailment in London. Beyond contentious work, the group undertakes a general range of transactional support and compliance work for the firm's chemicals, utilities and manufacturing clients. Particular strengths include waste and water law and crisis management. The team draws upon the "*academic*" strengths of consultant **Stuart Bell** (see p.369), also a professor of environmental law at the Nottingham Law School. He has expertise in both commercial and regulatory matters, and can be seen advising public organisations such as the EPA and World Health Organisation, as well as private companies, on environmental liability. **Clients:** British Waterways Board; Harewood House; McCain Foods; English, Welsh and Scottish Railway; DuPont; Mothercare; Waste Recycling Group.

Nabarro Nathanson (see firm details p.1078) The Sheffield team is widely recognised for its important ties to the Coal Authority and its group of dedicated environmental specialists. The group is led by the "*exceptionally knowledgeable*" **Mike Renger**, who is known for his long experience in mining, energy, and construction sectors. As contact partner for UK Nirex, he is active in offering policy advice on long-term solutions for radioactive waste. His colleague **Ray Clarke**'s (see p.370) strength is felt to lie in regulatory advice and environmental litigation. The firm advised Biffa Waste Services in defending civil and criminal proceedings, successfully represented Balfour Beatty Major Projects in the Crown Court in resisting alleged infringements of waste regulation, and acted for the Environment Agency on a chemical leak prosecution. Non-contentious work has seen the group act for landowner Brown & Sharpe Group on the drafting and negotiation of an agreement with a major waste company for the extraction of gravel and subsequent filling with waste. The firm has also been involved in assisting public sector clients such as Trafford MBC in devising strategies under the new statutory contaminated land regime. **Clients:** Balfour Beatty; Biffa Waste Services; Coal Authority; UK Nirex; Suffolk Waste Disposal Company; Waste Recycling Group; Leicester City Council.

Addleshaw Booth & Co (see firm details p.853) As the hub of the firm's environmental unit, the Leeds office provides non-contentious support to a base of chemical, minerals, and property development clients. Department head **Amanda Beresford** (see p.370) has a "*well-rounded practice,*" advising clients in both public and private sectors on contaminated land liability and minimising environmental risk. She has been active in planning and highway issues arising from urban regeneration and development, and is retained as adviser to the MOD on environmental issues relating to a number of sites. **John Pike** (see p.374) heads the firm's commercial property group and advises on contaminated land and waste issues connected with property transactions. The team also benefits from an in-house environmental consultant with particular expertise in brownfield sites and environmental rehabilitation. The firm advised Sainsbury's Supermarkets on the implications of the new contaminated land regime on its non-operational property portfolio. It also acted for the Health & Safety Executive on its first prosecution under the Protection of the Ozone Layer Regulations. **Clients:** Sainsbury's Supermarkets; MOD; Health & Safety Executive.

DLA **Teresa Hitchcock** is best known for regulatory compliance, while the department advises on environmental issues resulting from corporate finance transactions.

Dickinson Dees (see firm details p.941) An expanding practice considered by many competitors to be "*head and shoulders above everyone else in Newcastle,*" which absorbs most of the environmental work in the region. The team has particular strength in litigation and has seen an increase in environmental criminal work. Practice head **Denise Dowen** (see p.371) concentrates on contentious work, and has defended a number of waste and water prosecutions in the Crown Court. Other areas of expertise for the department include defence of noise abatement notices and food safety prosecutions and acting on civil claims. Recent recruits are also expected to boost the firm's environmental risk assessment capacities. The team advises a stable base of chemical and waste management companies on acquisition and disposal due diligence, and provides support on property transactions, particularly those attached to regeneration projects. **Clients:** Chemical company; food manufacturer; local authority; waste management company.

Hammond Suddards Edge (see firm details p.984) The firm's Leeds office retains a slight bias towards litigation and environmentally sensitive planning projects, under the aegis of partners David Williams and David Goodman. Praised as a team which "*thinks things through from start to finish,*" the group acts for a range of waste management, engineering, energy, oil and nuclear clients. Recent highlights include advising National Grid on environmental issues arising from a proposed power line in North Yorkshire, and acting for Scottish Power on the negotiation of easements for a pipeline to the gas storage caverns currently being developed at Hatfield Moor. On the contentious side, the group is representing an oil company in relation to contaminated land claims brought against it as a result of oil spillages. **Clients:** ICI; BASF; Royal Bank of Scotland; Rank Group; Kelda; KPMG; Horizon; Scottish Power; National Grid Company; BNFL; John Mowlem & Co.

Pinsent Curtis Biddle (see firm details p.1098) The firm's national environment team is spread across the Leeds and Birmingham offices and is felt to have been largely unaffected by the recent merger. Headed by Peter Atkinson, the team covers the range of contentious and non-contentious work, including corporate and property support and stand-alone matters. Work includes advising clients on prosecution by regulatory bodies, environmental assessments, accident management and negotiating warranties on corporate deals. The group is particularly recommended for its skill in negotiating with the Environment Agency to avoid prosecutions, and recently advised a client who had been raided by 14 Environment Agency officers. It also advised on due diligence in the sale of Airfresh UK by Armour Trust, and the acquisition of quarries by Hanson. **Clients:** Abbott Laboratories; Hanson; Tesco; Premdor; Case Corporation; Schneider Electric; OSS Group; Viridor Waste Management; Powell Duffryn; IMI; SIG.

SCOTLAND

	ENVIRONMENT • Scotland	Ptnrs	Assts
1	**Brodies WS** Edinburgh	1	1
2	**Maclay Murray & Spens** Glasgow	1	2
	McGrigor Donald Glasgow	1	3
	Morison Bishop Glasgow	1	1
3	**Dundas & Wilson CS** Edinburgh	1	3
	MacRoberts Glasgow	1	1
	Morton Fraser, Solicitors Edinburgh	n/a	n/a
4	**Burness** Edinburgh	1	1
	Tods Murray WS Edinburgh	n/a	n/a

	LEADING INDIVIDUALS	
1	**SMITH Charles** Brodies WS	
2	**ROSS Kenneth** Morison Bishop	
3	**BROWN Vincent** Semple Fraser	**GRANT James** MacRoberts
	PRIMROSE Andrew Maclay Murray & Spens	
4	**McPAKE Ian** Tods Murray WS	**SALES Martin** Burness
	ONES TO WATCH	
	SPENCE Michael McGrigor Donald	

This book is the product of 6,552 1/2-hour interviews. See p.7 for BMRB audit.
Within each band, firms are listed alphabetically. *See individuals' profiles p.369*

Brodies WS (see firm details p.896) This mid-sized Edinburgh firm has "*produced a lot of environmental experts over the years,*" most notably the "*outstanding*" **Charles Smith** (see p.375). Said to be the "*standard-bearer for environment lawyers in Scotland,*" he has lectured and written extensively on the sector. A substantial proportion of the workload is stand-alone, with heavy emphasis on contaminated land, environmental liability insurance policies, applications for licensees and consents under the IPPC regime. The firm continues to advise Corus UK on all environmental matters relating to the redevelopment of the former Ravenscraig Steelworks Site, and has acted for Dalgleish Associates on the interpretation of the Pollution Prevention and Control (Scotland) Regulations 2000, in connection with the first application in Scotland for a waste management licence. **Clients:** Corus UK; Dalgleish Associates; Dumfries & Galloway Council; Tarmac Quarry Products; Dames & Moore; Crop Chemicals.

Maclay Murray & Spens (see firm details p.1047) Since the 2000 creation of a separate planning and environment division, the firm is felt to have been successful in attracting stand-alone environmental work under UK, Scottish and EU law. The firm is frequently associated with the British Waterways Board, whom it advised on the remediation of the Union Canal. Peers acclaim the experience of **Andrew Primrose** (see p.374), who is described as "*charming, but no pushover.*" With a background in commercial property, he is especially highly recommended for his contaminated land expertise. However, he and his associates also handle matters such as environmental insurance contracts, waste management licensing, clinical waste incineration, the proposed WEEE Directive, climate change levy and IPC/IPPC regimes. The group recently acted for Kvaerner Govan on environmental issues relating to the sale of Kvaerner Govan Shipyard, and advised whisky manufacturers on whether whisky casks are classified as packaging. **Clients:** British Waterways Board; Allied Distillers; Bank of Scotland; DuPont Teijin Films; National Semiconductor (UK); Compaq Computer Manufacturing.

McGrigor Donald (see firm details p.1062) Although still considered to be rebuilding in the wake of the departure of Patricia Hawthorn over a year ago, the firm is not felt to have lost significant ground to its rivals. The practice is now closely allied with the litigation department, but handles all aspects of land contamination, waste matters, water treatment and waste to energy schemes. Interviewees particularly recommended the team for its experience in handling a number of complex projects relating to the outsourcing of waste management by local authorities. The firm continues to advise MoD on Project Aquatrine, the outsourcing of water and sewerage sites for the MoD in the UK. Steven Scates heads the environment practice from the London office. **Clients:** MoD; BP; Lattice; Clyde Port; Forth Port Authority; Dexter Corp.

Morison Bishop (see firm details p.1075) "*One of the outstanding players in Scotland,*" **Kenneth Ross** (see p.374) is the practice's key environmental figure. Considered to be "*technically knowledgeable,*" he rates highly for his work in contaminated land issues, which he handles from within his wider commercial property practice. The group also undertakes some regulatory advice, much of which consists of advising and redrafting contracts for UK clients in compliance with Scottish law. Other work includes due diligence on property acquisitions and disposals, negotiations of sewerage rights and discharge consents, and advising on IPC/IPPC matters. **Clients:** ICI; Greenpeace; Transorganic; Motorola.

Dundas & Wilson CS (see firm details p.947) The environmental practice benefits from the firm's volume of commercial work. Much of the work is transactional support for an extensive list of institutional clients within the chemicals, water, technology and engineering sectors. The group undertakes a significant amount of cross-border work with over half of its assignments based in England. However, the loss of Vincent Brown to Semple Fraser has been regarded as an unexpected setback. The firm advises a number of clearing banks, including Lloyds Bank and Abbey National Treasury Services, on environmental due diligence and the reporting and structuring of funds relating to investment in industrial projects and property redevelopment. Highlights of the year include representing East of Scotland Water Authority in respect of its European and UK legal obligations under the Urban Waste Water Treatment Directive. This was the result of a major PFI sewage treatment/purification scheme, affecting the River Forth estuary. Iain Doran heads the practice. **Clients:** Bank of Scotland; West of Scotland Water Authority; Tilbury Douglas; Abbey National Treasury Services; Scottish Environment Protection Agency; Micron Technologies.

MacRoberts (see firm details p.1048) A combined planning and environmental unit is headed by "*details man*" **Jamie Grant** (see p.371), who "*knows the ropes*" of environmental law. The group is highly rated for its work on a number of Scottish waste water PFI projects, and services a base of energy, engineering and landfill clients, as well as public bodies and NHS trusts. Landfill tax, environmental liability, integrated pollution control, packaging regulations and noise, odour and vibration nuisance are additional areas of expertise. The unit is frequently called upon to advise on the impact of new EU directives and recently acted for an NHS trust on contaminated land issues. **Clients:** Yorkshire Environmental Solutions; B&S Visual Technologies; Scottish Nuclear; Beechams; AMEC Construction; Edinburgh Royal Infirmary NHS Trust; Texaco.

Morton Fraser, Solicitors (see firm details p.1076) The team is considered to have a reduced profile since widely regarded practitioner Donald Reid changed his status from partner to consultant. He still maintains his position as head of the practice, however, and undertakes work on an ad hoc basis, although the bulk of his time is absorbed by redrafting EU law for Eastern European countries from within his own environmental consultancy company. Routine environmental work now falls to practitioners in the firm's commercial property or litigation departments. The group still maintains a specialisation in nuclear energy, and receives regular instructions from British Nuclear Fuels. **Clients:** British Nuclear Fuels; United Distilleries and Vintners; BP Chemicals; Royal Society for the Conservation of Nature.

Burness (see firm details p.903) Strong ties with mining clients and local quarries provides a lot of associated environmental work. Approaching environment from a planning perspective, the group concentrates largely on minerals, waste, PFI and planning applications. Head of the environment group **Martin Sales** (see p.374) has a background in litigation and planning, and his team has extensive experience in environmental assessment procedures, including those relating to nuclear contamination and sensitive site disposal. The firm advised Shanks Group in relation to its bids for waste management PFI/PPP projects in Scotland. **Clients:** Brown Brothers (Rolls Royce); The Royal Bank of Scotland; Lothian Hospital Trust; DERA; Caledonian Paper; Shanks Group; Lafarge Redland Aggregates.

Tods Murray WS (see firm details p.1157) An "*old-fashioned Edinburgh law firm*" with a "*nice mix of private and public body clients needing advice on environmental considerations.*" This integrated planning and environmental team is led by highly regarded **Ian McPake** (see p.373). The bulk of the work is transactional support, relating to PFI and planning. The group advises Aberdeen Environmental Services on planning and environmental issues, including UK and EC water quality requirements and sludge disposal considerations in relation to two wastewater treatment PFI projects. Individuals within the firm's litigation department also undertake environmental judicial reviews. The team acted for the RSPB in a judicial review of the decision of Scottish Ministers to grant a licence to shoot Barnacle geese. **Clients:** Aberdeen Environmental Services; Dundee Energy Recycling; Forestry Commission; Nevis Range Development; RSPB; WWF; Woodland Trust.

Other Notable Practitioners **Vincent Brown** (see p.370), recently moved from Dundas & Wilson to **Semple Fraser**, is an experienced commercial property lawyer who rates highly for his transactional advice. He is charged with building up the brownfield site development practice at Semple Fraser.

NORTHERN IRELAND

ENVIRONMENT • Northern Ireland	Ptnrs	Assts
1 Cleaver Fulton Rankin Belfast	2	n/a

LEADING INDIVIDUALS
1 FARIS Neil Cleaver Fulton Rankin

This book is the product of 6,552 1/2-hour interviews. See p.7 for BMRB audit.
Within each band, firms are listed alphabetically. *See individuals' profiles p.369*

Cleaver Fulton Rankin (see firm details p.918) Maintains its status as the only firm in Northern Ireland with a notable environmental law capacity. Commercial property lawyer **Neil Faris** advises on environmental impact assessment, waste licensing appeals and environmental concerns resulting from planning applications. The firm advised on the environmental aspects of the planning application for a new terminal building at Belfast City Airport. **Clients:** Water Service; Belfast City Airport; Antrim Borough Council.

LEADERS IN ENVIRONMENT

ABRAHAM, Henry
Brachers, Maidstone (01622) 690691

ALLEN, Tony
DMH, Brighton (01273) 744451
See under Planning, p.662

BAKER, Neil
Clarke Willmott & Clarke, Bristol (0117) 941 6658
nbaker@cw-c.co.uk
Specialisation: Specialises in environmental and planning law including planning and other development applications, agreements, appeals, public inquiries, High Court proceedings such as judicial review, pollution control under the Environment Acts and related legislation, defending environmental prosecutions and advice on minerals, waste and contaminated land. Recent experience has included advising Pfizer Limited on the interpretation of waste regulations, acting for a major horticultural company in connection with environmental issues surrounding peat harvesting activities and advising a national housebuilder on the law relating to contaminated land, nature conservation and effluent discharge in connection with a proposed residential development in the Cotswolds.
Prof. Memberships: Law Society. Committee Member, UKELA, South West branch.
Career: Articled with *Nicholson Graham & Jones*; qualified in 1994. Joined *Clarke Willmott & Clarke* in 1999 as Senior Associate.
Personal: Born 19 September 1967. Attended Queen Elizabeth's School and Bristol University (BSc Hons Biochemistry). Leisure interests include golf; squash, and the theatre. Lives in Bristol.

BELL, Stuart
Eversheds, Leeds (0113) 243 0391
stuartbell@eversheds.com
Specialisation: Consultant. Main area of practice is environmental law. Advises on the whole range of environmental issues with particular emphasis on commercial and regulatory matters. Institutional clients include the Environment Agency, the Australian Commonwealth Environmental Protection Agency, the World Health Organisation and the Euro-

pean Commission. Commercial clients include chemical companies, utilities and retailers. Editor of the 'Environmental Law Reports' and 'Water Law'. Editorial board member of the 'Journal of Planning and Environment Law'. *Eversheds* Professor of Environment Law at Nottingham Law School.

BERESFORD, Amanda
Addleshaw Booth & Co, Leeds (0113) 209 2325
aqb@addleshaw-booth.co.uk
Specialisation: All planning work including retail, leisure, industrial, residential and advocacy at Public Inquiries. Comprehensive environmental advice including pollution control, energy, waste, transport, contaminated land and due diligence. Clients advised include major development and manufacturing companies, utilities, banks and local authorities. Particular expertise in environmental and planning issues in urban regeneration projects. Recognised authoress and speaker at conferences.
Prof. Memberships: Qualified planner. Member U.K.E.L.A.
Career: Qualified in 1985, joined *Addleshaw Booth & Co* in 1997.

BOSWALL, Julian
Morgan Cole, Cardiff (029) 2038 5385
julian.boswall@morgan-cole.com
Specialisation: Head of planning and environment group. Specialises in planning, environmental and local government law.
Career: Qualified 1992. Became a partner 1999.

BOWDEN, Paul
Freshfields Bruckhaus Deringer, London (020) 7936 4000
paul.bowden@freshfields.com
See under Litigation, p.566

BROCK, David
Mills & Reeve, Cambridge (01223) 222 438
david.brock@mills-reeve.com
Specialisation: Has a wide ranging environmental, planning and minerals law practice. Work includes judicial review, integrated pollution control, contaminated land, defence, waste, power generation and oil and gas. Advises on all aspects of planning law. Contributor to 'Commercial Environmental Law and Liability' 1993-98.
Career: Qualified in 1980. Partner at *Herbert Smith* 1989-2000, *Mills & Reeve* 2000 to date.
Personal: Born in 1954. Educated at Dame Allan's Boys School, Newcastle, Marylebone Grammar School and University College, London (LL.B). Practising Christian. Enjoys opera, skiing, modern art and architecture. Lives near Saffron Walden.

BROWN, Vincent
Semple Fraser, Glasgow (0141) 221 3771
vincent.brown@semplefraser.co.uk
Specialisation: Environmental indemnities, contracts; contaminated land; IPPC; waste; landfill tax; environmental aspects of construction law and commercial property development. Assignments include two Scottish Water Authorities, advising on contaminated land and EU urban waste water compliance; ICI, advising on chemicals/explosives, contamination issues; Bank of Scotland, advising on lender liability and contracts in respect of power station developments.
Prof. Memberships: Law Society of Scotland, British Urban Regeneration Agency (BURA), Lanarkshire Environmental Business Club.
Career: *Shepherd and Wedderburn*, Edinburgh (2 years); *Dorman Jeffrey and Co*, Glasgow (10 years, 6 as Partner); *Dundas and Wilson/Anderson Legal* (4 years as partner), *Semple Fraser WS*, partner, June 2001.
Personal: University of Glasgow: M.A. LL.B. Married with two children (11and 5).

BRUMWELL, Mark
SJ Berwin, London (020) 7533 2222
mark.brumwell@sjberwin.com
Specialisation: All areas of environmental law with particular emphasis on environmental aspects of corporate transactions, due diligence, contaminated land, land use planning, water and nature conservation. Recent work has included advice on contaminated land on development for a supermarket and a DIY store, restructuring a multinational environmental consultancy and compliance issues for a pharmaceutcal plant. Has also advised on other environmental and health and safety issues for the property, banking, private equity, engineering, construction, pharmaceutical, plastics and automotive sectors. Has particular expertise of infrastructure projects, especially flood alleviation schemes and railways.
Prof. Memberships: Member of the Law Society's Planning Panel. Legal Associate of the Royal Town Planning Institute Council. Member of the United Kingdom Environmental Law Association, Co-ordinator of all UKELA's Working Groups and Convenor of its Water Working Group. Associate of the Institute of Environmental Science.
Career: University of Bristol - LLB (Hons). Law Society's Finals. Articled with *Simmons & Simmons*. With *Ashurst Morris Crisp* for seven years including a period of secondment to the London Docklands Development Corporation. Environment Group at *SJ Berwin & Co* since March 1996. Partner since May 1998.
Personal: Married and lives in Hertfordshire. Leisure interests include motorsport, photography, hill walking, golf and badminton.

BRYCE, Andrew John
Andrew Bryce & Co, Coggeshall (01376) 563123

BUXTON, Richard
Richard Buxton, Cambridge (01223) 328933

CARRIAGE, Rebecca
Mills & Reeve, Norwich (01603) 693 228
rebecca.carriage@mills-reeve.com
Specialisation: Environmental (including health and safety and food safety), town and country planning (including compulsory purchase). Recent work includes major mineral and waste planning appeals and development plan work; defence of a number of statutory nuisance and health and safety prosecutions; referrals to the Lands tribunal involving questions of law and valuation; enrolment of environmental bodies under the Landfill Tax Regulations 1996.
Prof. Memberships: Member of Steering Group of East Anglian Business Environment Club. Associate member of Environmental Services Association. Panel list on BBC Radio Norfolk's monthly legal slot.
Career: Articled *Hill & Perks* (now *Eversheds*, Norwich). Moved to *Mills & Reeve* 1988. Associate 2000.

CLARKE, Ray
Nabarro Nathanson, Sheffield (0114) 279 4028
r.clarke@nabarro.com
Specialisation: Civil and criminal environmental litigation including advocacy; waste and other enforcement appeals, industrial nuisances, water, air pollution, PPC and WML issues, environmental and health and safety prosecutions. Defending high profile multi-party actions. Lead adviser to waste and chemical internationals (COMAH). Acquisitions and disposals. Privatisation - mines and chemicals. Urban regeneration with particular emphasis on brownfield sites. Human Rights issues. Management of large development schemes including town centres, sub-regional shopping centre (Trafford centre). Judicial review and public inquiries. Crisis and awareness training for directors and managers.
Prof. Memberships: Former member of UKELA Council. Fellow of the Institute of Quarrying. Visiting tutor on environmental, planning and Regeneration, International Development Law Institute, Rome.

CUCKSON, David
Stephenson Harwood, London (020) 7809 2505
david.cuckson@shlegal.com
Specialisation: Partner, property department and head of environmental law group. He covers most aspects of environmental law. Specific work includes issues relating to contaminated land, corporate mergers and acquisitions and waste management. He also handles property law work relating to education, local government and other public bodies, including PFI projects. Has written articles and lectured extensively on environmental law topics.
Prof. Memberships: Chairman of UK Environmental Law Association 1999-2001, also member of Contaminated Land and Waste Working Parties.
Career: Qualified October 1978. Held various posts in different local government authorities, most recently as Borough Secretary and Solicitor for Test Valley Borough Council 1988-89. Joined *Stephenson Harwood* in 1989 and became partner in 1992.

DAVEY, Catherine
Stevens & Bolton, Guildford (01483) 734 234
Specialisation: All aspects of environmental law including contaminated land, statutory nuisances, waste disposal, corporate support. Highways and commons law. Town and country planning.
Prof. Memberships: Law Society; council member United Kingdom Environmental Law Association; executive committee Environment Law Foundation; FRGS.
Career: Woking County Grammar School for Girls, University of Exeter (BA Hons). Joined *Stevens & Bolton* 1988 from local government, becoming a partner in 1989.
Publications: Contributor to 'Sustainable Architecture, European Directives & Building Design' (Butterworths). Joint-editor: 'E-law' - e-journal of United Kingdom Environmental Law Association.
Personal: Leisure interests are foreign travel, photography, sailing, film, theatre, the arts and virtual reality gardening.

DAWSON, Andrew
DLA, Manchester (08700) 111111

DAY, Martyn
Leigh, Day & Co, London (020) 7650 1200

DEANESLY, Clare
Gouldens, London (020) 7842 6144
chd@gouldens.com
Specialisation: Partner and head of environmental law group. Principal area of practice is environmental law, dealing with minerals, waste management, landfill and contaminated land cases. Also handles general commercial property work including landlord and tenant matters and retail and development work. Major transactions include: 1986 acted on sale of London Brick Landfill to Shanks & McEwan; 1993 acted for the Landfill Division of ARC (Greenways) in their acquisition of Econowaste from Tarmac plc; 1993 and 1996 acted for London Brick Property Limited on sale of substantial landfill void to Shanks & McEwan; 1996 acted for minerals division of ARC in Midlands joint venture with Tarmac plc; 1998 acted on landfill and minerals sites in connection with sale of Hanson Properties; 1999 acted on sale of Hughes Waste Management Limited; 2000 acted on sale of Hanson Waste Management to Waste Recycling Group plc. Other major clients include Hanson Brick Limited, SITA, Biffa Waste Management and Thames Waste Management. Advised on landfill tax and environmental bodies. Contributor to ESA training seminar on Duty of Care and on Transfer Stations and MRF's; speaker on waste management issues at conferences and seminars.
Prof. Memberships: Law Society, UKELA, ESA. Member of UKELA Waste Working Party. Member of ICC Committee on Environment, ESA Public Affairs Committee and ESA General Planning Committee.
Career: Qualified in 1977 while at *Field Fisher Martineau.* Joined *Gouldens* in 1978 and became a partner in 1980.
Publications: Author of Badlands 'Essential Environmental Law for Property Professionals' (1993) and author of various articles on waste management property issues for professional publications.
Personal: Born 30 May 1953. Attended Edgbaston C of E College for Girls, Brimingham 1957-71, then Southampton University 1971-74 (LLB Hons). Leisure pursuits include family, skiing, walking, tennis, travel, theatre and opera. Lives in London.

DOOLITTLE, Ian
Trowers & Hamlins, London (020) 7423 8000
idoolittle@trowers.com
Specialisation: Specialist in environmental law, especially transactional and regulatory work (including contaminated land and waste management). Former vice-chairman of the International Bar Association's sub-committee on European Environmental Law. Also specialist in public sector law.
Publications: Editor of 'Garner's Environmental Law'. Author of 'Butterworths Environmental Regulation'.

DOWEN, Denise
Dickinson Dees, Newcastle upon Tyne
(0191) 279 9215
law@dickinson-dees.com
Specialisation: Practice covers all aspects of environmental law in relation to company and property transactions including EIAs, waste management, water pollution, process authorisations and contaminated land. Acts for developers, lending institutions and waste management companies.
Prof. Memberships: Law Society. Member of CBI Environment Committee.
Career: Qualified in 1990. Trained with Avon County Council before moving to private practice. Joined *Dickinson Dees* in 1994.
Personal: Born July 1965. Read Law at the University of Leeds.

FAIRLEY, Ross
Allen & Overy, London (020) 7330 3087
ross.fairley@allenovery.com
Specialisation: Involved in all aspects of UK and EU environmental law particularly in areas such as policy, management and audit, contaminated land, power and renewables projects and lender liability. Writes and speaks regularly on environmental matters.
Prof. Memberships: Law Society, United Kingdom Environmental Law Association, Institute of Environmental Management and Assesment.
Publications: Legal Editor of Gee's 'Environmental Risk Manager' and 'Premises, Health and Safety' and Tolley's 'Environmental Law and Procedures Management'.
Personal: Interests include all sports, particularly hockey, cricket and driving an old Austin Healey 'Frogeye' Sprite. Born 1968. Leicester University (LLB 1990).

FARIS, Neil
Cleaver Fulton Rankin, Belfast
(028) 9024 3141

FOGLEMAN, Valerie
Barlow Lyde & Gilbert, London (020) 7247 2277
vfogleman@blg.co.uk
Specialisation: All aspects of environmental law including environmental liability matters, particularly contaminated land and water pollution, specialist environmental insurance policies, environmental insurance coverage claims, due diligence, criminal and civil environmental litigation, lender liability.
Prof. Memberships: Convenor, United Kingdom Environmental Law Association (UKELA) Insurance and Liability Working Party; Chair, Construction Industry Research and Information Association Contaminated Land and Urban Regeneration Working Party. Memberships include Lloyd's European Environment Working Group; UKELA Council; City of London Law Society Planning and Environmental Law Subcommittee.
Career: Solicitor and member of Texas State Bar; practised environmental and insurance law in Texas before joining *Barlow Lyde & Gilbert* in 1992; became a partner in 1998. University of Illinois (1992 LLM); Texas Tech University (1989 MSc, 1989 JD, 1983 BLA).
Publications: Numerous books and articles on environmental liabilities and environmental insurance in UK and US publications including regular articles in Insurance Day; frequent speaker in UK and overseas.

FORSTER, Malcolm
Freshfields Bruckhaus Deringer,
London 020 7936 4000
malcom.forster@freshfields.com
Specialisation: Partner dealing with environmental aspects of corporate transactions and financings, handling environmental indemnity and warranty disputes, negotiating with regulatory agencies over environmental remediation requirements for contaminated land and groundwater, production and management of environmental impact assessments.
Prof. Memberships: International Bar Association, Selden Society. Professor of International Environmental Law, University of Kent.
Career: Qualified 1992. Partner 1995. Director of the Centre for Environmental Law at the University of Southampton 1973-84 and 1987-91. General Counsel for the Commission on Environmental Law at the International Union for Conservation of Nature and Natural Resources, Bonn, Germany, 1984-87.
Publications: Editor of 'Environmental Law & Management'.
Personal: Born 1948. Attended University of Southampton 1967-70.

GARBUTT, John
Nicholson Graham & Jones, London
020 7360 8208
john.garbutt@ngj.co.uk
Specialisation: Head of Planning and Environment Unit. Planning and environmental law, including appeals, development plans, environment disputes, audits and policy, compulsory purchase, rating, Lands Tribunal, major planning inquiries concerning minerals, waste management, leisure developments, and judicial reviews.
Prof. Memberships: UKELA, CBI Minerals Committee and Environment Protection Panel, Mining & Mineral Law Group. The firm is a member of the Land Pollution Consortium.
Career: Qualified in 1963. Local government 1965-69. Blue Circle Industries (1978-85), Chief Executive, Blue Circle Industrial Minerals (1986-88) and Blue Circle Waste Management (1989). *Nicholson Graham & Jones*, Partner 1991.
Publications: 'Environmental Law - A Practical Handbook'; 'Waste Management Law: A Manager's Handbook'. Contributor, 'Commercial Environmental Law and Liability'.

GIBBS, Kevin
Osborne Clarke, Bristol
(0117) 917 3000

GRANT, James
MacRoberts, Glasgow (0141) 332 9988
jamie.grant@macroberts.co.uk
Specialisation: Main areas of practice are planning and environmental law, although he also does some commercial property work (especially licensed trade).
Prof. Memberships: Law Society of Scotland.
Career: Edinburgh University 1979-84. *Mitchells Roberton* 1984-88 (trainee/assistant). *Maclay Murray & Spens* 1988-91 (assistant/associate). *MacRoberts* 1991 - present (assistant/associate/partner -1993).
Personal: Born 29 June 1961. Lives Glasgow. Leisure interests include sailing, music and gardening.

GREENWOOD, Brian
Norton Rose, London (020) 7283 6000
greenwoodbj@nortonrose.com
Specialisation: Corporate acquisitions, disposals and funding; environmental due diligence (including BMW sale of Rover and Land Rover), project finance, waste, water and IPC including appeals and advocacy (acted for Castle Cement in North Water cement works inquiry and use of alternative fuels); international practice with considerable experience in Eastern Europe.
Prof. Memberships: Former chairman Law Society's Planning and Environmental Law committee, CBI Environmental Protection panel; UKELA.
Career: Qualified in local government, with posts at Westminster, South Yorkshire and Kent before being appointed chief solicitor at Bedfordshire County Council. Joined *Norton Rose* in 1985, partner in 1988.

Publications: Author 'Butterworths Planning Law Service'. Co-author 'Environment Regulation and Economic Growth'. Editor 'Butterworths Planning Law Handbook'.

HAVARD-WILLIAMS, Vanessa
Linklaters, London (020) 7456 4280
vanessa.havard-williams@linklaters.com
Specialisation: Member of the firm's environmental unit since 1990 and founding partner of the Environmental Law Group. Specialist in all aspects of environmental and health and safety work, (including corporate and property transactions, projects, advisory and EHS litigation).
Career: 1999 to date: Partner, *Linklaters* London (environmental law group); 1994-99: Assistant solicitor, *Linklaters* London (litigation department); 1991-93: Assistant solicitor, *Linklaters* Brussels; 1990-91: Assistant solicitor, *Linklaters* London (litigation department); 1998-90: Trainee solicitor, *Linklaters*. 1987-88: College of Law, Law Society Final Examinations; 1984-87: Oxford University, BA (Hons).

HAYDEN, Tim
Clarke Willmott & Clarke, Taunton
(01823) 442 266
thayden@cw-c.co.uk
Specialisation: Partner specialising in environmental prosecutory work. Wide range of prosecution experience relating to waste disposal, contaminated land, air and water pollution and statutory nuisance including noise and odour abatement. Regularly conducts proceedings relating to BSE regulation, county council applications and agricultural accidents. Tim is a Solicitor Advocate with rights in the Magistrates and Crown Courts.
Prof. Memberships: UKELA.
Career: Qualified in 1981. Joined *Clarke Willmott & Clarke* in 1979, becoming a partner in 1985. Qualified as a Higher Courts Advocate in 1995.
Personal: Born 10th December 1956. Attended Bristol Grammar School 1968-74, University College Cardiff 1974-78 and College of Law Guildford 1978-79. Leisure interests include golf and cricket.

HITCHCOCK, Teresa
DLA, Sheffield (08700) 111111

HOBLEY, Anthony
CMS Cameron McKenna, London
(020) 7367 2759
arh@cmck.com
Specialisation: Senior solicitor in the environmental law group. Handles a wide range of environment law matters with particular emphasis on the environment aspects of national and international corporate, banking and property transactions. Advises regularly in relation to contaminated land and its redevelopment; regulatory and enforcement issues and major infrastructure projects; waste; trading of economic environment instruments; lender liability issues; environmental liability in the context of insolvency; landfill tax, the terms and coverage of environment insurance products. Increasingly advising on climate change issues, permit trading, climate change levy energy efficiency agreements and related matters. He is regularly invited to speak at public conferences on a range of issues and has had a number of articles published on issues such as contaminated land and greenhouse gas emissions. He is currently the coordinator for his firm's central European environment law group and travels regularly to central Europe in this capacity.
Prof. Memberships: Law Society, UK Environmental Law Association, graduate of the Royal Society of Chemistry.
Career: 1st Class Honours Degree in Chemistry with Physics. Qualified as a solicitor in 1994. Joined CMS *Cameron McKenna* (formerly *McKenna & Co*) in 1996.
Personal: Born 24 November 1966.

HOLMES, Sarah
Bond Pearce, Plymouth (01752) 266633
sholmes@bondpearce.com
Specialisation: Associate specialising in environmental and planning law with MA (Oxon) and Master of Arts in Environmental Law (1997). National reputation for work in renewable energy having been at the forefront of the industry since 1991. Advises on all stages of the planning process, including environmental impact assessment, with clients in public and private sector. Extensive environmental practice includes contaminated land remediation, risk minimisation and allocation, environmental insurance, complex landfill tax issues, European Sites (nature conservation) and consents/permits. Active involvement in major waste, minerals, food and motor deals with due diligence on many further transactions.
Prof. Memberships: Council Member of UK Environmental Law Association; Secretary of UKELA South West and member of British Wind Energy Association.
Career: Qualified 1991 with *Bond Pearce*, becoming Associate 1997.

HORNER, Douglas
Brachers, Maidstone (01622) 690691

HUTCHINSON, Michael
Rowe & Maw, London (020) 7782 8164
michael.hutchinson@roweandmaw.co.uk
Specialisation: Environmental aspects of corporate, property and finance transactions, as well as stand-alone UK and EU advisory work. Recent clients from a variety of sectors including waste, energy, chemicals, pharmaceuticals and banking.
Prof. Memberships: United Kingdom Environmental Law Association.
Career: Qualified and practised for three years at *Linklaters & Paines*. Assistant solicitor, *Freshfields* (1996-2000). Joined *Rowe & Maw*, 2000.

ISTED, Jonathan
Freshfields Bruckhaus Deringer, London
020 7936 4000
jonathan.isted@freshfields.com
Specialisation: Defence of multi-party toxic tort claims, including Sellafield childhood leukaemia cases, electromagnetic field cases, judicial review and product liability actions, disaster litigation and contaminated land liability claims. Also general commercial litigation. Member of Lord Woolf's Advisory Group on Multi-Party actions.
Prof. Memberships: Law Society, UKELA.
Career: Qualified 1989. LLM (with Distinction) in Advanced Litigation from Nottingham Trent University in 1996. Partner in *Freshfields* 1998. CEDR Accredited Mediator in 2000.
Personal: Born 5 May 1964. Educated at Newport Free Grammar School and Durham University, College of Law (Chester) 1987. Leisure activities include golf, squash, running and travel. Reform Club.

JEWKES, Penny
Eversheds, Norwich (01603) 272727
pennyjewkes@eversheds.com
Specialisation: Handles a broad range of environmental matters including property support and due diligence audits arising in the course of major property and commercial transactions, regulatory compliance (advisory and defence), civil liability, waste management and packaging issues. Also practices on the planning/environment interface. Major clients include machinery manufacturers, food producers, government bodies, charities and premier car dealerships. Regular speaker at conferences and seminars.
Prof. Memberships: Barrister (non-practising). United Kingdom Environmental Law Association (UKELA), Chair, East Anglian Branch.
Career: Called to the English Bar in 1974 and the Hong Kong Bar in 1976. Crown Counsel in Hong Kong. Lecturer in law at Hong Kong University and from 1990 at the University of East Anglia specialising in planning and environmental law. Returned to practice in 1997.
Publications: Has published in the 'Journal of Occupational Safety and Health' on Corporate Killing. Article published in the 'Journal of Planning and Environment Law' on Light Pollution frequently referred to in planning and committee meetings.

JOHN, Alan
Osborne Clarke, Bristol
(0117) 917 3000

KEEBLE, Ed
Slaughter and May, London (020) 7600 1200
edward.keeble@slaughterandmay.com
Specialisation: Wide range of environmental matters, including major transactions, due diligence, contaminated site issues and general environmental law advice.
Prof. Memberships: United Kingdom Environmental Law Association.
Career: Qualified in 1988 and became a partner at *Slaughter and May* in 1995.
Personal: Ipswich School; Cambridge University.

KEELE, Helen
Travers Smith Braithwaite, London
(020) 7295 3000

LLOYD, Deborah
Herbert Smith, London (020) 7374 8000
Specialisation: Advising on the full range of environmental and health and safety issues arising in corporate, banking, investment and real estate transactions, public private projects and providing specialist advice on litigious matters. Areas of specialty include contaminated land, waste, IPPC, water law and energy related matters from a compliance, risk management or the allocation of liabilities perspective.
Prof. Memberships: Law Society, United Kingdom of Environmental Law.
Career: Admitted as a barrister and solicitor of the Supreme Court of Victoria and High Court, Australia 1995 practising in environmental law. Commenced work in the UK in 1997 (admitted UK 1998) and has continued to specialise in environmental law.

LOMAS, Owen
Allen & Overy, London (020) 7330 3067
owen.lomas@allenovery.com
Specialisation: Specialist in the strategic management of environmental and health and safety issues arising in day to day business and in the context of mergers, acquisition, divestitures and corporate finance, property transactions and energy/infrastructure projects. Particular areas of expertise include new forms of environmental regulation involving use of economic and fiscal instruments - notably in relation to climate change and emission trading; project responsibility and recycling in areas such as packaging and electrical goods; waste management and liability for land contamination - focusing, in particular, on managing legacy properties.
Prof. Memberships: Founding council member of UK Environmental Law Association; Director and Trustee of the Environmental Law Foundation and Chair of the Law and Policy Working Party of the Environmental Industries Commission.
Career: Lecturer in Law University of Birmingham (1979-88), University of Warwick (1988-91), Professor in Law University of Trier Germany (1991-91); Senior Associate *Allen & Overy* (1992-95), Partner (1995).
Publications: Consulting Editor, 'Commercial Environmental Law & Liability'; Author, 'Frontiers of Environmental Law and Packaging Waste Recycling Obligations: a business guide to British regulations'; and member of the Editorial Boards of 'Water Law', 'the Utilities Law Review' and 'Environmental Law and Management'.
Personal: London University (LLB 1976), Solicitor (1980), University of Birmingham (LLM 1987).

LOOSE, Helen
Ashurst Morris Crisp, London (020) 7638 1111
helen.loose@ashursts.com
Specialisation: Head of the environmental risk management group which specialises in both transactional and advisory environmental and health and safety matters both on a standalone basis and in relation to corporate, major projects, banking and property transactions.
Prof. Memberships: Council member of United Kingdom Environmental Law Association; member of the air pollution Working Group of the Sustainability Unit of London First; chair of the Local Government Working Group of the Energy from Waste Association; UK representative of the Environmental Law Association; member of the editorial board, Asbestos Risk Management (Croners.CCH); chair of the UKELA Climate Change Working Group.
Career: Trained at *Freshfields*; qualified in 1992; partner in 2000.
Personal: Resides in London.

MACKINLAY, Hannah
Pinsent Curtis Biddle, Birmingham
(0121) 200 1050
hannah.mackinlay@pinsents.com
Specialisation: Advising in relation to the environmental issues involved in: corporate mergers and acquisitions, handling UK and multinational matters, negotiating warranties and indemnities, often in transactions involving many properties and various jurisdictions, advising on risks and compliance issues. Recent significant deals for GTRM, Lex Service Group, Corus, 3i and Onyx. Property transactions, including English Partnerships work, contaminated land issues and advising waste industry companies on issues such as licensing and landfill developments.
Prof. Memberships: Graduate member of Institute of Wastes Management. Member National Council of the UK Environmental Law Association.
Career: LLB (Hons) Sheffield. Qualified 1981. MA (Environmental Law) Distinction, De Montfort University. Partner *Shoosmiths & Harrison*, Northampton 1986-95. Associate, *Pinsent Curtis Biddle* 1995.
Publications: Author of UKELA Internet website and joint-author of its e-journal. Co-author of 'What Every Manager Needs to Know about Environmental Law'.
Personal: All aspects of new technology, skating, piano. Director of Birmingham Art Trust.

MARSHALL, Anna
Nabarro Nathanson, London (020) 7524 6000
a.marshall@nabarro.com
Specialisation: Non-contentious environmental work with particular emphasis on risk assessment and apportionment in context of corporate and property transactions; advice on contaminated land issues in context of developments, property portfolio management and landlord and tenant issues; advice on environmental policy and management systems. Clients include a wide range of UK property investment companies seeking advice on environmental risk on cross-border transactions.
Prof. Memberships: CBI Environmental Protection Panel, UKELA.
Career: 1983-87 *Freshfields* (qualified 1985); 1988-92 *Hay Management Consultants* (working as a management consultant specialising in strategy and organisation); 1992-94 *Norton Rose*; 1994 President, *Nabarro Nathason.*
Personal: Education: Girton College, Cambridge (MA(Hons)); University of Bath (MBA). Interests include tennis, skiing, football, ballet, opera and gardening.

MAY, Caroline
Hammond Suddards Edge, London
(020) 7655 1613
caroline.may@hammondse.com
Specialisation: Caroline is a partner in the firm's safety, health and environment group based in London. She specialises in all aspects of environmental law and liability. She is involved in regulatory and compliance work as well as transactional work including acquisitions and disposals, financings, planning and property development issues. Her work has an international flavour with multinational and transatlantic corporations with varied environmental concerns. She has specialist knowledge of dioxin and methane emission problems, chemical waste management issues and contaminated land. On the development side, she has become increasingly involved in the liability issues arising from brownfield site remediation on behalf of commercial property developers, institutional investors and banks. She is experienced in environmental insurance issues. Caroline is a regular speaker at public seminars and trade association events.
Prof. Memberships: Member of the National Council of the United Kingdom Environmental Association and member of its Noise and Finance Working Parties. Freeman of the City of London and winner of the Institute of Energy Roscoe Prize 1995.
Career: Articled *Beachcroft Stanley* 1985-87; qualified October 1987; solicitor *Clifford Chance* 1988-94; joined *Lawrence Graham* 1994; partner *Lawrence Graham* 1995-2001; partner *Hammond Suddards Edge* March 2001.
Personal: Trevelyan College, Durham University BA Hons. Married. Lives in Hertfordshire. Leisure interests: tennis, golf, eating out, theatre. Speaks German.

McPAKE, Ian
Tods Murray WS, Edinburgh (0131) 226 4771
ian.mcpake@todsmurray.com
Specialisation: Partner in Capital Projects department. Work includes PFI, property and environmental law.
Prof. Memberships: Member of United Kingdom Environmental Law Association; convenor of UKELA Scottish Law Working Party.
Career: Qualified in 1971. Articled *J & W Buchan*, Peebles, 1969-72. *Ranken & Reid SSC* 1972-90, partner 1973. Joined *Tods Murray WS* as a partner in 1990.
Personal: Born 1948. Attended George Watson's College, Edinburgh and St Andrew's University (LLB 1969). Married with three daughters. Leisure: golf, walking, skiing, reading. Lives in Edinburgh.

MOORE, Louise
Lovells, London (020) 7296 2000

MYLREA, Kathy
Simmons & Simmons, London (020) 7628 2020
kathy.mylrea@simmons-simmons.com
Specialisation: Head of environmental law group. Advises on all aspects of UK and EU environmental law including transaction work involving allocation of environmental liabilities and co-ordination of due diligence, advice on authorisations and permits, criminal and civil litigation, in particular defence of criminal prosecutions. Particular expertise in contaminated land, water pollution, IPPC and waste management issues. Organises and conducts training seminars on the application of environmental law to individual businesses and business sectors. Major clients include Rohm & Haas, Owens Corning, Vivendi Water UK, Associated British Ports and Railtrack.
Prof. Memberships: Law Society, International Bar Association, UK Environmental Law Association.
Career: Qualified in Ontario, Canada in 1986 and in England and Wales in 1992. With *McKenna & Co* 1988-92. Joined *Simmons & Simmons* in May 1992.
Personal: Born 6th November 1958. Educated at Brown University, Providence, Rhode Island, USA (BA 1980) and the University of Toronto (LLB, 1984). Outside interests include skiing, scuba diving and ballet. Lives in London. Married with one son.

NASH, Mike
Simmons & Simmons, London (020) 7628 2020
mike.nash@simmons-simmons.com
Specialisation: Practises in all areas of UK, EU and international environmental law with particular emphasis on waste, contaminated land, chemicals and water law and its application to commercial transactions and contracts and in litigation. Significant recent matters include advising on settling third party claims and site remediation/disposal of an explosive contaminated site; advising on the acquisition of a water and sewerage undertaker; advising OFGEM on its new renewable energy functions (Climate Change Levy, Renewables Obligation). Clients over the last year include OFGEM AKZO Nobel, British Sugar, Railtrack, Invensys, CLA, NFU, Owens

Corning, Wimpey Homes, English Nature.
Prof. Memberships: Law Society of England and Wales.
Career: BA (First Class Honours) New College, Oxford University. Joined *Booth & Co*, 1991. Joined *Simmons & Simmons* 1994.
Publications: Editor of the 'Encyclopaedia of Environmental Law' and co-author of 'The Environment Acts 1990-95' (annotated).

O'KEEFFE, Jacqui
Denton Wilde Sapte, London
(020) 7242 1212

PIKE, John
Addleshaw Booth & Co, Leeds (0113) 209 2000
jdp@@addleshaw-booth.co.uk
Specialisation: Main area of practice is commercial property work, in particular development, banking, investment and private sectors. A particular specialism is land pollution and he frequently advises on land contamination and remediation, waste and lender risk.
Career: Qualified 1972. Partner 1976.
Personal: Jesus College Cambridge (MA: Hons). De Montfort University (MA: Environmental Law). Chairman of Governors Moorlands School, Leeds and Governor of St Peters School, York. Director of Urban Mines Limited and heavily involved in the Brownfields project as a member of the Advisory Group. Interests include sports and family.

PRIMROSE, Andrew
Maclay Murray & Spens, Glasgow
(0141) 248 5011
ahp@maclaymurrayspens.co.uk
Specialisation: Senior commercial property and environmental law partner. Qualified to practise in both Scotland and England. In-depth experience of all property and environmental issues, including those relating to acquisitions, waste management, risk assessment and climate change agreements. Currently advising on acquisition of fuel depots and environmental bodies. Author of numerous publications. Chairman of IBA's Section on Legal Practice.
Prof. Memberships: UK Environmental Law Association, Scotland Europa Environmental Group, Scottish Environmental Industries Association.
Career: Oxford University (BA 1961) and Glasgow University (LLB 1964).
Personal: Married with two children.

RAYNER, David
Blake Lapthorn, Southampton
(023) 8063 1823

REDMAN, Michael
Clifford Chance, London (020) 7600 1000
michael.redman@cliffordchance.com
Specialisation: Solicitor advocate (qualified in criminal and civil jurisdiction). He has experience in dealing with the environmental aspects of corporate, banking and property transactions and infrastructure projects. Appears in judicial review and criminal proceedings. A considerable depth of expertise in energy sector going back to his time at the bar, he has been involved in British Coal and Nuclear Electric privatisation as well as recently a number of independent power projects.
Prof. Memberships: UKELA.
Career: Barrister (1975); solicitor (1986).

RENGER, Mike
Nabarro Nathanson, Sheffield
(0114) 279 4000

RICE, Paul
Lawrence Graham, London (020) 7379 0000
paul.rice@lawgram.com
Specialisation: Specialises solely in environment and health and safety law. Recent work includes redevelopment of former heavy industrial sites, including gasworks, ordnance sites and power stations, advising on Environment Agency water prosecutions, contaminated land, flytipping, LAAPC authorisations and an asbestos related warranty claim in the context of an LSVT. Clients include Homebase Limited, JS Developments, Legal and General, Rover Group and Local Authorities.
Prof. Memberships: UKELA Waste and Liability Working Groups, ICC Wastes Committee, member of Institute of Wastes Management.
Career: LLB (Hons) Queen's University Belfast with DJ Hill Memorial Prize (1992). University of London LLM (Environmental Laws). King's College (1993). *Denton Hall* (1994). *Lawrence Graham* (2001).
Publications: Contributing author of 'A-Z Guide to Environmental Practice'.
Personal: Interests include food, travel, performing arts, mountain biking and running. Was warded the first UKELA Andrew Lees Prize in 1997.

ROSS, Kenneth
Morison Bishop, Glasgow (0141) 248 4672
kenneth.ross@morisonbishop.co.uk
Specialisation: Partner in charge of commercial property division. Head of environmental law group. All aspects of environmental law, with particular emphasis on contaminated land and waste. Frequent lecturer to conferences.
Prof. Memberships: Convenor of Law Society of Scotland Environmental Law Committee; member of the National Council of UK Environmental Law Association (UKELA); Chair of the Scottish Committee of UKELA.
Career: Qualified in1982, partner since 1984.
Publications: Author of chapter on Contaminated Land in Second Edition of 'Greens Guide to Environmental Law in Scotland'. Author of articles regarding a variety of environmental law topics, particularly contaminated land and its connection with commercial property transactions, waste management licences and other waste issues.
Personal: Born 30th September 1958. Graduate of Glasgow University (LLB 1st Class Hons 1980). Spare time interests include archaeology. Lives in Glasgow.

SALES, Martin
Burness, Edinburgh (0131) 473 6130
mas@burness.co.uk
Specialisation: Martin Sales has for many years acted for a wide range of environmental interests, particularly in relation to the legal aspects of environmental assessment, the disposal of non-waste and waste materials using available exemptions from UK Licensing requirements, waste water and sewerage projects, the scope and conditions attaching to environmental consents including planning permissions, discharge consents, license transfer and modification and the registration of waste carriers. For corporate acquisition work, Martin is well placed to advise on the need for and scope of environmental warranties especially in the context of corporate recovery.

SALTER, Ian
Burges Salmon, Bristol (0117) 939 2225
ian.salter@burges-salmon.com
Specialisation: Environmental and Energy. Particular expertise in the waste, PFI and projects, transport, chemical, nuclear and food/agricultural sectors. Advises on all aspects of waste law; radioactive waste and nuclear licensing; IPPC; IPC; LAAPC; water law and abstraction licensing; contaminated land and remediation notices; packaging waste; related criminal prosecutions; corporate due diligence.
Prof. Memberships: Legal Associateship Royal Town Planning Institute; Law Society's Planning panel; UKELA; International Nuclear Law Association.
Career: Joined *Burges Salmon* 1990, partner 1999.
Publications: Joint author Tolley's 'Environmental Law and Procedures Management' and Butterworths 'Forms and Precedents' (agriculture and the environment).
Personal: Ian enjoys golf and spending time with his family.

SCOTT, Peter
Toller Beattie, Devon (012) 717 5821
solicitors@tollerbeattie.co.uk
Specialisation: Water law, drainage, fisheries. Involved in various cases including Bowden v South West Water; R v Falmouth & Triro Port Health Authority ex parte SNU; Moase & Lomas v SSETR.
Prof. Memberships: Member of Water and Mature Conservation Working Groups of United Kingdom and Environmental Law Association.
Career: Admitted 1971, assistant with *Stephens & Scoun St Austell* 1975-82 in between two periods in local government practice; assistant/associate with *Toller Beattie* since 1985.
Publications: Reports to European Commission on shellfish waters and freshwater fishwaters directives as implemented in the UK. Articles in 'Water Law', 'Property Law Journal', 'Urela Journal'.
Personal: Educated Truro School, Keble College Oxford. Married with four children. Interests include walking, ecology, chess and music.

SHARP, Cate
Rowe & Maw, London (020) 7782 8891
csharp@roweandmaw.co.uk
Specialisation: Extensive experience in a wide range of environment related work, particularly in the chemicals and manufacturing fields. Has a particular expertise in transactional support as well as stand-alone regulatory advice on a broad variety of environmental issues such as waste management, the climate change levy and contaminated land. Recently advised ICI plc on all the environmental aspects of the sale of its worldwide Chlor-Chemicals, Klea and Crosfield businesses to Ineos. This involved drafting and negotiating complex environmental documentation covering many jurisdictions and advising on permit transfer issues and property documentation. She also lectures regularly on a wide range of environmental topics and most recently on the contaminated land regime and the PPC Regulations.
Prof. Memberships: United Kingdom Environmental Law Association.
Career: Graduated from London University with an environmental BSc (Biology & Geography combined Hons). Articled to *Rowe & Maw* in 1991. Qualified and has been a member of the Environment Group since 1993. Partner in 2000.

SHEPHERD, Elizabeth
Eversheds, Manchester (0161) 831 8000
elizabethshepherd@eversheds.com
Specialisation: Environmental and Health and Safety. Head of Manchester Environmental, Health and Safety Team advising on corporate and property transaction related environmental issues and general environmental compliance, carrying out legal environmental audits and formulating on behalf of clients corporate environmental policies and management systems.
Prof. Memberships: UKELA (United Kingdom Environmental Law Association). CBI North West Environment Business Forum, GMEA (Greater Manchester Environmental Association) and Law Society Environmental Law Sub-Committee.
Career: Cambridge University, Churchill College M.A. First Class Honours. Admitted as a Solicitor in October 1984. Articled with *Eversheds Alexander Tatham* in Manchester and appointed partner of *Eversheds* in 1988.
Personal: Elizabeth lives near Knutsford, Cheshire. Her interests include classical music, skiing and gardening.

SHEPHERD, Michael
Hammond Suddards Edge, Manchester
(0161) 860 5023
michael.shepherd@hammondse.com
Specialisation: Partner in commercial dispute resolution unit. National head of safety health and environment group. Main areas of practice are environment, health and safety, food safety and trading standards. Clients include ICI, BNFL, One 2 One, Mowlem, Rank, Norwest Holst, Bradford City AFC.
Prof. Memberships: Law Society. Member of UKELA, CBI Environment Committee, Construction Industry Safety Group and European Food Law Association.
Career: MA (Oxon); articled to Sir George Ogden; qualified in 1969. Worked in Town Clerk's office, Manchester 1966-72. Joined *Hammond Suddards Edge* in 1972, becoming a partner in 1974.
Personal: Born 26 September 1944. Attended Bradford Grammar School 1954-63, then The Queen's College, Oxford 1963-66. Leisure interests include cricket, football, golf and foreign languages (Portuguese, French and Spanish).

SHEPPARD, Claire
Theodore Goddard, London (020) 7606 8855
clairesheppard@theodoregoddard.co.uk
Specialisation: All areas of environmental law with particular emphasis on the environmental aspects of corporate, banking, PFI and property transactions, toxic tort and contaminated land litigation, contaminated land insurance and regulatory and compliance advice.
Prof. Memberships: Land and Water Committee of the Society of Chemical Industry.
Career: Articled *Linklaters & Alliance* (1989-91), assistant in the environmental unit and litigation department of *Linklaters & Alliance* (1991-98), joined *Theodore Goddard* 1999 and made a partner in November 1999.

SHERIDAN, Paul
CMS Cameron McKenna, London
(020) 7367 2186
pfs@cmck.com
Specialisation: Partner and Head of the environment law group. The environment law group is dedicated to providing a full environment law service. He advises numerous national and international clients on a wide range of domestic and international non-contentious and contentious matters. Non-contentious matters include transactional services in share and asset transactions, joint ventures, PFI/PPPs, major infrastructure projects, contaminated land transfers and developments, lenders transactions and business recoveries; advice on the insurance of environment risks; climate change regulatory compliance advice; environment, economic and fiscal instruments; packaging and producer responsibilities; and the compilation of databases on both domestic and international environment laws. He is very active in contentious environment matters both civil and criminal. He has, for instance, acted for parties in many high-profile test cases. He is regularly involved in water, waste and licence/permit related prosecutions. He is particularly involved with environment issues relating to waste, water, contaminated land, IPPC and APC energy, climate change, nuclear installations, hazardous substances, transport and construction. He is a regular speaker at UK and overseas conferences, has contributed to several environment law textbooks and is the author of several articles.

SHINER, Philip
Public Interest Lawyers, Birmingham
(0121) 702 2110

SMITH, Charles
Brodies WS, Edinburgh (0131) 228 3777
charles.smith@brodies.co.uk
Specialisation: Partner in corporate department. Advises on environmental law and liability generally and in respect of land, water and air pollution, sales and purchases of land, assets and shares, leases and security/banking transactions. Also handles major commercial contracts (including PFI and privatisations) and banking transactions. Advises companies on environmental compliance, housebuilders on environmental liability, contractors on waste management licensing and the landfill tax, and numerous clients on contaminated land. Continues to advise on Ravenscraig Steelworks Site. Co-author of 'Pollution Control: The Law in Scotland', published in November 1997.
Prof. Memberships: Law Society of Scotland; United Kingdom Environmental Law Association; Royal Society of Arts, Manufactures and Commerce; National Society for Clean Air & Environmental Protection; Scottish Environmental Industries.
Career: Qualified in 1987 having joined *Brodies* in 1985. Became a partner in 1990.
Personal: Born in 1960. Attended Perth Academy 1972-78, Exeter College, Oxford 1978-82, then University of Edinburgh 1982-85. Lives in Edinburgh.

SMITH, Paul
Eversheds, Leeds (0113) 243 0391
paulsmith@eversheds.com
Specialisation: Partner in commercial litigation department. Main area of practice is environment and health and safety law. Heads *Eversheds'* national environmental law group, having established the unit in 1988. Acts principally for major industrial companies in the UK, US and Europe in civil and criminal proceedings. Successfully took the River Derwent test case to the House of Lords. In the crisis management field he acted in the Hickson & Welch Castleford incident, the Hickson International Cork incident and the Associated Octel fire at Ellesmere Port. *Eversheds* client partner for Du Pont in the UK. Visiting Professor in Environment Law at the Nottingham Law School.
Prof. Memberships: UKELA, Law Society, ABA, IBA.
Career: Qualified in 1982, having joined *Freshfields* in 1980. Joined *Eversheds Hepworth & Chadwick* in 1984 and became a Partner in 1987.
Publications: Co-author of 'College of Law Environment Law' and 'Environmental Manual' published by CCH Publications. Regular contributor to BBC radio programmes.
Personal: Born 14th November 1956. Attended Warwick University 1975-79, winner Sweet and Maxwell prize. Governor of Richmond House School. Director Nottingham Law School Limited. Member Reform Club. Professional Puppeteer. Lives in Menston, West Yorks.

SPENCE, Michael
McGrigor Donald, Edinburgh
(0131) 777 7000

TOWNSEND, Matthew
Allen & Overy, London (020) 7330 3000
matthew.townsend@allenovery.com
Specialisation: Specialises in all aspects of UK and EU environmental law. Advises regularly in relation to waste, IPPC, contaminated land and producer responsibility. He has particular experience in environmental, health and safety litigation (both civil and criminal) including high profile prosecutions arising from the release of radioactive contamination.
Prof. Memberships: Law Society. Chairman of UKELA's Contaminated Land Working Group. Member of a number of the EIC's working groups.
Career: Qualified in 1996 with *Morgan Cole.* Between 1996 and 2000 practised with *Cameron McKenna.* Joined *Allen & Overy* in early 2000.
Publications: Contributor to and reviewer of 'Environmental Law and Procedures Management Handbook', contributor to 'Health, Safety and Environment Cases' and 'Environmental Assessment'. Regular speaker on environmental matters and has published a number of articles including providing the environmental law update section of the Law Society Gazette.
Personal: Born 18 February, 1971 in Sheffield. Interests include theatre, history and most sports.

TRINICK, Marcus
Bond Pearce, Southampton (023) 8063 2211
mtrinick@bondpearce.com
See under Planning, p.670

TURNER, John
Wragge & Co, Birmingham
(0870) 903 1000

WAITE, Andrew
Berwin Leighton Paisner, London (020) 7760 1000
andrew.waite@berwinleighton.com
Specialisation: Partner planning and environment department and coordinator of the environment group. Specialist in environmental liability and pollution controls, dealing principally with contaminated land, waste management, noise, water resources issues, integrated pollution controls, air pollution and nature conservation. Advises on environmental liabilities in corporate and property transactions, lender liability issues, environmental litigation and legal

issues involved in establishing and operating environmental management systems. Clients advised include English Partnerships, Blue Circle, Lattice Property Holdings (formerly BG plc), Tesco, Royal Bank of Scotland, Girobank, Prudential Property Management, Philips and Drew Fund management, Legal & General, Kronospan, WH Smith, Harnischfeger Industries, Transamerica, Schenectady inc and Petroplus. Advises Waste Facilities Audit Association on waste management issues and the Brownlands Group on law and policy developments relating to contaminated land. Has advised the Bulgarian and Ukrainian governments with regard to their proposed environmental legislation and has drafted forestry legislation for Sierra Leone as well as contributing to the Environmental Protection Act 1990 and the Environment Act 1995. Co-author of 'Environmental Law in Property Transactions' (2nd edn Butterworths' 2001); Editor of Butterworths' 'Environmental Handbook' (3rd edn 2001) and author of numerous articles on environmental law. Frequent speaker at national and international conferences on environmental law, with TV and radio experience.
Prof. Memberships: President of the European Environmental Law Association; co-founder and former secretary of the UK Environmental Law Association; vice-chairman (western Europe) of the IUCN Commission on Environmental Law; member of the International Court of Environment Arbitration and Conciliation; chairman of CBI ad hoc working party on environmental liability; former chairman of the UKELA working party on contaminated land.
Career: Qualified 1975. Lecturer in law at Southampton University from 1980-88; acting director of the Centre for Environmental Law at Southampton University 1984-87; visiting professor in Environmental Law at the University of Georgia 1987. Head of environmental law group at *Masons* 1988-90 and coordinator of the environment group at *Linklaters & Paines* 1990-93. Joined *Berwin Leighton* in 1993, partner 1996.
Personal: Born 25 February 1950. Attended Lincoln College, Oxford, 1969-72, BA (Hons) 1972, MA 1977. Leisure interests include history, archaeology, wildlife, theatre, cinema and walking in the countryside. Lives in Chandlers Ford, Hampshire.

WAKE, Brian
Wake Dyne Lawton, Chester (01829) 773101
bdw@wdl.co.uk
Specialisation: Mineral extraction, waste management, land reclamation and environmental law. Acts for major mineral companies and landowners, and advises regularly on contaminated land and pollution control matters.
Prof. Memberships: Fellow of the Institute of Quarrying. United Kingdom Environmental Law Association.
Career: Qualified 1978 with *Linklaters & Paines.* Tarmac Quarry Products 1981-86.
Personal: Born 1953 in Hong Kong. Speaks Cantonese. LLB Liverpool 1975.

WATCHMAN, Paul
Freshfields Bruckhaus Deringer, London
(020) 7936 4000
paul.watchman@freshfields.com
Specialisation: Property department: environment group. Principal area of work is environmental law, including contaminated land, water pollution, waste management, energy and minerals. Other main area of work is planning law, covering mineral developments (including coal mining and coastal superquarries), planning inquiries and retail office and business developments. Author or co-author of books and articles on environmental planning and public law. Lectures regularly on planning and environmental law.
Prof. Memberships: Law Society, Law Society of Scotland.
Career: Qualified as a Scottish Solicitor in 1977 and as an English Solicitor in 1994, partner *Freshfields,* 1995.
Personal: Born 1952. Lives in Surrey.

WILLIAMS, Gwyn
Hammond Suddards Edge, Birmingham
(0121) 222 3000
gwyn.williams@hammondse.com
See under Energy & Natural Resources, p.357

WISEMAN, Andrew
Trowers & Hamlins, London (020) 7423 8000
awiseman@trowers.com
Specialisation: Practice covers the full range including waste, contaminated land, noise, pollution and planning. Former member of London Waste Regulation Authority. Visiting lecturer at Brunel University. Has addressed numerous conferences and been interviewed on TV and radio.
Prof. Memberships: Vice-chairman UK Environmental Law Association; City of London Law Society (Planning and Environmental Law Sub-Committee); Member Institute of Waste Management.
Career: Qualified in 1989. Former partner at *Shindler & Co, Finers and Wiseman Solicitors.*
Publications: Joint editor 'Butterworths Environmental Law Bulletin'.
Personal: Fellow of the Royal Society of Arts.

FAMILY / MATRIMONIAL

RESEARCH APPROVED BY BMRB: *For this edition,* Chambers' *researchers conducted 6,552 interviews – 4,419 with law firms, 554 with barristers and 1,579 with clients.*

The validity of the research was scrutinised by BMRB International, who audited both the methodology and the results at our offices in July 2001. They interviewed Chambers' *researchers and cross-checked sample interviews. Details of the audit appear on page 7.*

LONDON

FAMILY/MATRIMONIAL • London	Ptnrs	Assts
1 Manches	8	10
Withers	6	10
2 Alexiou Fisher Philipps	4	2
Charles Russell	9	7
Hughes Fowler Carruthers	3	5
Levison Meltzer Pigott	3	2
Miles Preston & Co	4	2
Sears Tooth	3	3
3 Bindman & Partners	2	2
Clintons	3	2
Collyer-Bristow	5	3
Dawson Cornwell	7	3
Goodman Ray	3	6
Kingsley Napley	5	3
Mishcon de Reya	2	5
Payne Hicks Beach	4	6
4 Cawdery Kaye Fireman & Taylor	3	4
Farrer & Co	3	4
Gordon Dadds	5	2
Hodge Jones & Allen	4	5
International Family Law Chambers	3	1
Reynolds Porter Chamberlain	2	5
The Family Law Consortium	6	4
5 Anthony Gold	2	2
Barnett Sampson	2	4
Dawson & Co	2	1
Fisher Meredith	2	8
Forsters	1	1
Russell-Cooke	3	4
Stephenson Harwood	1	2

This book is the product of 6,552 1/2-hour interviews. See p.7 for BMRB audit.
Within each band, firms are listed alphabetically.

Manches (see firm details p.1051) Consistently in the spotlight on high-profile cases, this heavyweight practice tackles ancillary relief matters with "*a high quality, no-nonsense approach.*" The firm's clientele of professionals, businessmen and celebrities is advised by a distinguished team that boasts enviable strength in depth. "*Star performer*" **Helen Ward** (see p.396) "*stalks the larger stage with intent*" in company with the "*sober and assured*" **Richard Sax** (see p.394) and **Jane Simpson** (see p.394), who melds "*compassion with acuteness of mind.*" **William Massey** (see p.392), up and coming only two years ago, continues to impress, and rises again in the main rankings. Often visible in the big money cases, the firm undertakes the full spectrum of private children, abduction and cohabitation work.

Withers (see firm details p.1187) Revered for "*combining thoroughbred partners with truly excellent assistants,*" this team is renowned for the quality and complexity of its work. Supported by the largest private client department in Europe, with specialisms in trusts, tax and trust litigation, it is handily placed to advise on high value cases, many of which have an international flavour. Supplementary specialisms include cohabitation, a particular interest of the "*level-headed and intelligent*" **Mark Harper** (see p.390), and surrogacy, where newcomer to the rankings **Marcus Dearle** (see p.389) lends his expertise. Other prominent practitioners include managing partner **Diana Parker** (see p.392), whose "*quality of work and client pulling*" remain excellent, the "*redoubtable*" **Gill Doran** (see p.389), and **James Harcus** (see p.390), whose aplomb as a draftsman was widely commended. Up and coming **James Copson** (see p.388) is "*increasingly carving out a name out for himself,*" and epitomises the team's recognised ability to nurture talent. Highlights of the past year include acting in Re W, the leading authority on procedure in the Family Division on Writs of Sequestration.

Alexiou Fisher Philipps (see firm details p.855) Formed from the cream of a celebrated team at Gordon Dadds, this recently established, exclusively family law firm seems "*set fair to enjoy the sort of success that the quality of its lawyers merits.*" Pre-eminent amongst these is **Douglas Alexiou** (see p.386), "*a suave ambassador for the law,*" whose presence ensures a portfolio of high profile clients and participation in complicated international ancillary relief matters. The other named partners, **Susan Philipps** (see p.393) and the "*experienced and bright*" **Jeremy Fisher** (see p.389), receive strong recommendation for providing expertise in the firm's other specialist areas, such as forum shopping, abduction and trusts.

Charles Russell (see firm details p.912) Historically one of the first ports of call for divorce law, the department has recently expanded with the recruitment of six new lawyers from Campbell Hooper and Rooks Rider. "*Impressive in terms of size and quality of work,*" the team generally acts for the wealthier individual, offering particular expertise in ancillary relief, private children work and abduction. Although perhaps lacking a star name, in **David Davidson** (see p.388) the department possesses "*a lawyer whose knowledge of pensions is rarely surpassed,*" while **Maryly La Follette** (see p.391) and **Erica Shelton** (see p.394) have acted for notable society clients (Countess Spencer and Lady Conran respectively). Completing the team is **William Longrigg** (see p.391), who is noted for his "*assiduous approach and commitment to the SFLA.*"

Hughes Fowler Carruthers (see firm details p.1004) Newly formed niche firm, which shocked the market when splitting away from City firm Bates Wells & Braithwaite. Handling all types of family law work, but with a strong bias toward those cases with complex financial and international issues, the team "*displays particular excellence in heavily contested matters.*" Moving spirit **Frances Hughes** (see p.390) is "*a highly intelligent, practical lawyer, who goes out of her way to avoid unnecessary unpleasantness.*" A well-drilled team also includes **Pauline Fowler** (see p.389)who is "*up with the best in the children field*" and the up and coming **Alex Carruthers** (see p.388), referred to by one commentator as "*the zoo-keeper*" for his "*ability*

LEADING INDIVIDUALS		
★	**PRESTON Miles** Miles Preston & Co	**SHACKLETON Fiona** Payne Hicks Beach
	TOOTH Ray Sears Tooth	**WARD Helen** Manches
1	**ALEXIOU Douglas** Alexiou Fisher Philipps	**DORAN Gill** Withers
	HUGHES Frances Hughes Fowler Carruthers	**LEVISON Jeremy** Levison Meltzer Pigott
	PARKER Diana Withers	**SAX Richard** Manches
	SIMPSON Jane Manches	
2	**COLLIS Pamela** Cawdery Kaye Fireman & Taylor	
	CORNWELL John Dawson Cornwell	**DAVIDSON David** Charles Russell
	DAVIS Sandra Mishcon de Reya	**DEARLE Marcus** Withers
	FISHER Jeremy Alexiou Fisher Philipps	**FOWLER Pauline** Hughes Fowler Carruthers
	GIEVE Katherine Bindman & Partners	**HARPER Mark** Withers
	HUTCHINSON Anne-Marie Dawson Cornwell	
	MASSEY William Manches	**PARRY Richard** Farrer & Co
	PIGOTT Simon Levison Meltzer Pigott	**RAE Maggie** Clintons
	RAY Peggy Goodman Ray	**RUTTER Geoffrey** Collyer-Bristow
3	**BAKER Miranda** Kingsley Napley	**CHAPMAN Ellie** Barnett Sampson
	DRAKE Michael Collyer-Bristow	**HARCUS James** Withers
	KEIR Jane Kingsley Napley	**LA FOLLETTE Maryly** Charles Russell
	LEVERTON David Payne Hicks Beach	**LONGRIGG William** Charles Russell
	MARCO Alan Collyer-Bristow	**MONRO Pat** Darlington & Parkinson
	PEARSON Philippa The Family Law Consortium	
	PEMBRIDGE Eileen Fisher Meredith	**PHILIPPS Susan** Alexiou Fisher Philipps
	PIRRIE James The Family Law Consortium	
	READHEAD Siobhan Miles Preston & Co	**RODGERS Hilary** Forsters
	SHELTON Erica Charles Russell	**STANCZYK Julia** Miles Preston & Co
	TRUEX David International Family Law Chambers	
UP AND COMING		
	BROWN Fiona Payne Hicks Beach	
	CARRUTHERS Alex Hughes Fowler Carruthers	
	COPSON James Withers	
	NICE Anna Miles Preston & Co	

See individuals' profiles p.386

to handle the more histrionic client when the fur starts to fly." An increase in international referrals has been highlighted by the case of Mubarak v M, a landmark decision that is likely to lead to an overhaul of the Judgment Summons Procedure.

Levison Meltzer Pigott (see firm details p.1039) "*A smaller niche practice, prizing quality over quantity in all it does.*" High net worth financial settlements form the core of the caseload, with attendant specialisms in pure divorce and private children work. At the firm's heart lie **Jeremy Levison**, "*a dogged battler who knows his own mind,*" and the "*reliable and highly experienced*" **Simon Pigott**. An impressive client base includes prominent figures from the professional and business worlds plus a smattering of personalities from the arts and media.

Miles Preston & Co (see firm details p.1068) One of the first totally specialist family law practices, this is a "*small but perfectly formed operation.*" Acting for UK and foreign business people, professionals, landowners and media and entertainment personalities, it has built up a strong reputation, domestically and internationally, for finance and private children work. **Miles Preston** (see p.393) "*provides a steady hand on the tiller*" in combination with the respected **Julia Stanczyk** (see p.395) and **Siobhan Readhead** (see p.393), who possesses "*a fine balance of experience and sympathy.*" Recently appointed to the partnership, the promising **Anna Nice** (see p.392) makes her debut in the rankings this year.

Sears Tooth (see firm details p.1120) Specialist practice, which is built around the luminous presence of **Ray Tooth** (see p.395), "*a lawyer who doesn't practise like any other.*" Adopting a "*tenacious, sometimes confrontational approach,*" he is "*an effective opponent,*" who is particularly adept at tracing hidden assets. Although the firm does undertake some private children work, its forte lies in contentious ancillary relief cases, where Ray Tooth's reputation is such that "*the mere mention of his name is enough to ensure his opponents get their houses in order.*"

Bindman & Partners (see firm details p.882) Although also a player in ancillary relief cases, this department's real strength lies in its children work, both private and publicly funded, where it is hailed as "*possibly the market leader.*" The highlights of a distinguished year include acting for one of the infants in the conjoined twins case, and in Re C, a landmark case concerning the treatment of minors infected by HIV. Heading the team, **Katherine Gieve** (see p.390) is "*both committed and first class*" in all child-related areas, including care proceedings, abduction, private law conflicts and medical treatment questions.

Clintons (see firm details p.920) "*A strong all-round practice,*" it encompasses the full range of family work. Much of the caseload has an international aspect, with expertise offered in areas such as forum shopping, jurisdictional disputes and the investigation of offshore assets. While efforts have been made to consolidate its financial practice the firm's real strength lies in private children work and abduction. Here, **Maggie Rae** impresses with her "*excellent legal knowledge, tough personality and business acumen.*"

Collyer-Bristow (see firm details p.924) Concentrating on high value ancillary relief, jurisdiction disputes, child abduction and cases involving an international element, this firm has risen in the rankings this year in recognition of its "*excellent, high-powered team.*" Supported by proficient trust, tax and property departments, the team offers a full service to a predominantly professional and business clientele. **Geoffrey Rutter** (see p.393) is "*a popular old stager, much seen on the circuit,*" while **Michael Drake** (see p.389) is "*conciliatory and easy to deal with without being a pushover.*" The aura of maturity and experience throughout the firm is epitomised by **Alan Marco** (see p.392), who has been active in the field for over thirty years, and sits as a DDJ in the Principal Registry. The team has acted on a number of contested ancillary relief hearings in the High Court, including the reported case of AvA (2001) 1FLR 377.

Dawson Cornwell (see firm details p.937) A renowned practice, which fuses high value ancillary relief work with an esteemed designated children's department. On the money side, **John Cornwell** (see p.388), instrumental in introducing mediation to this country, is noted for his "*imaginative negotiation style.*" Heading the children team, **Anne-Marie Hutchinson** (see p.391) is acknowledged by peers to be "*the queen of child abduction.*" Also shining in the areas of international custody disputes and adoption, she was seen to good effect in Re H (Abduction: Conflict of Jurisdiction).

Goodman Ray (see firm details p.975) The firm rises in the ranks this year following fulsome praise for its work in the children field. Fêted for her role in childcare work, **Peggy Ray** (see p.393) is "*a tireless battler with an encyclopaedic knowledge of public law,*" and is seen to be "*one of the doyennes in this area.*"

Kingsley Napley (see firm details p.1022) Relatively young team, which enjoys a well-established reputation for child abduction work. Involvement in cases with an international element has grown to the extent that matters have been undertaken over the last year in countries as diverse as Spain, Iceland, New Zealand, France and Greece. "*Effectively led*" by the "*assured*" **Jane Keir** (see p.391), the team's workload also includes high value ancillary relief cases and specialist surrogacy work. **Miranda Baker** (see p.387) maintains her share of market support, and is rated for her "*sound judgement.*" The firm advised on a groundbreaking case looking at the quantum of a maintenance award for the children of unmarried parents.

Mishcon de Reya (see firm details p.1071) Typically acting for high net worth individuals, the firm is often associated with divorce cases of particular interest to the media. In the wake of her work for Jerry Hall, a number of wealthy women have made the pilgrimage to be advised by **Sandra Davis** (see p.388), who is said to have "*a feisty, take no prisoners approach.*" The firm acts on a substantial number of international matters, focusing inter alia on jurisdictional issues, forum shopping and enforcement.

Payne Hicks Beach (see firm details p.1092) Strongly fortified by the much-heralded arrival of **Fiona Shackleton** (see p.394) from Farrer & Co, the firm strides forcefully up the rankings. Most notably the lawyer for the Prince of Wales, she is seen as "*a front page news practitioner with extraordinary intuition and negotiation skills.*" **David Leverton** continues to impress the market as the firm's managing partner, while the rising **Fiona Brown** (see p.387) is seen as "*a worthy member of the team.*" Acting for professionals, businessmen, landowners and the aristocracy in big money financial settlements, the firm earned further recognition through its involvement in one of the highest profile cases of the year. This was White v White, a landmark judgment where the House of Lords laid down guidelines for dealing with financial claims on divorce.

Other Notable Firms Despite the loss of Fiona Shackleton, **Farrer & Co**, led by the "*excellent and industrious*" **Richard Parry** (see p.392), remains "*a sound department with a bedrock of high earning private clients.*" Similarly, the team at **Gordon Dadds**, although suffering from the departure of a distinguished group of partners, continues to function as "*a talented and diligent group.*" **The Family Law Consortium** is known for its "*conciliatory approach*" and embrace of mediation and therapy. **James Pirrie** and **Philippa Pearson** "*embody the SFLA spirit*" of this department. **Hodge Jones & Allen** is said to display a similar "*committed approach*" to the high volume of legal aid work that comes its way. **Cawdery Kaye Fireman & Taylor** enters the tables this year under the stewardship of the "*experienced, talented and popular*" **Pamela Collis** (see p.388), who has "*stacks of experience of dealing with the moneyed client.*" **International Family Law Chambers** receives many overseas referrals and is especially versed in contracting Irish, Australian and German disputes. Organised as a set of independently practising solicitors, it is headed by **David Truex** (see p.395), whose specialist knowledge continues to earn him personal recognition. On the children side, **Reynolds Porter Chamberlain** receives praise for its expertise in child abduction, while **Pat Monro**, celebrated for her efforts in the public law sphere, has left Wilford Monro for **Darlington & Parkinson**. **Eileen Pembridge** (see p.392) of **Fisher Meredith**, **Hilary Rodgers** (see p.393) of **Forsters**, and **Elspeth Chapman** (see p.388) of **Barnett Sampson** all receive backing as "*talented individuals in quality firms.*" **Anthony Gold**, **Dawson & Co**, **Russell-Cooke** and **Stephenson Harwood** were also commended for their broadly based family practices.

THE SOUTH

Band	FAMILY/MATRIMONIAL • The South	Ptnrs	Assts
1	**Lester Aldridge** Bournemouth	2	4
2	**Brachers** Maidstone	1	1
	Paris Smith & Randall Southampton	2	3
	Thomson Snell & Passmore Tunbridge Wells	2	2
3	**Blake Lapthorn** Portsmouth	2	4
	Coffin Mew & Clover Portsmouth	6	4
	Cripps Harries Hall Tunbridge Wells	1	1
	DMH Brighton	2	1
	Horsey Lightly Newbury	2	2
	Max Barford & Co Tunbridge Wells	2	3

Band	LEADING INDIVIDUALS
1	**FOSTER Stephen** Lester Aldridge
2	**WRIGHT Barbara** Thomson Snell & Passmore

This book is the product of 6,552 1/2-hour interviews. See p.7 for BMRB audit.
Within each band, firms are listed alphabetically. *See individuals' profiles p.386*

Lester Aldridge (see firm details p.1038) Boasting a stronger caseload than many London firms, this Bournemouth team stands as the clear leader across the south of England. Receiving referrals from many of the larger City firms, such as Slaughter and May, it handles high value cases up to and beyond the £20 million mark. Active in international cases, the firm has a niche Tokyo practice, crafted through close links with Herbert Smith, and recently acted on a £40 million asset case. 60% of lead partner **Stephen Foster**'s (see p.389) workload involves international or London-based cases, making this "*ambitious and dedicated lawyer*" the key player in the region.

Brachers (see firm details p.893) Despite an accent on high value divorce work for the agricultural and business communities, the firm also advises on cohabitation and children's public law. Admired by rivals for its "*grown up approach to litigation,*" the firm recently advised on two divorce cases where the assets amounted to £6 million. "*Sensible and easy to deal with,*" the team also operates a mediation practice.

Paris Smith & Randall (see firm details p.1089) A full service firm which acts for high net worth individuals from the professions, industry and the local media. "*Down to earth and firmly established locally,*" it has negotiated multi-million pound mediation and pre-nuptial settlements over the last year. Instructions from overseas sources are on the rise, and the practice is unique in the area in having instituted a dedicated mediation suite. Other elements of the caseload include public law childcare and work for guardians ad litem.

Thomson Snell & Passmore (see firm details p.1155) Ancillary relief dominates a practice known for complex agricultural divorce work and a substantial local client base. **Barbara Wright** (see p.396) is "*a high calibre performer,*" and is known for her "*forensic*" accounting skills. Having recently recruited a new partner with expertise in child law work, the firm's family department seems set to prosper.

Horsey Lightly Complex money matters and private children cases form the main elements of this respected local firm's workload, with many of the cases having an international element. The team makes its debut in the rankings in recognition of its "*established consistency over the years.*"

Other Notable Firms **Coffin Mew & Clover** has a sizeable department, concentrating on high value cases and containing two full-time childcare lawyers. **Blake Lapthorn** has discrete family and children's teams with particular expertise in pensions and public law proceedings. **DMH** handles a full range of matters, including national and international adoption and childcare cases. **Cripps Harries Hall** and **Max Barford & Co** were both commended for their general family law practices.

THAMES VALLEY

FAMILY/MATRIMONIAL • Thames Valley	Ptnrs	Assts
1 **Blandy & Blandy** Reading	4	3
Manches Oxford	1	1
2 **Darbys** Oxford	3	1
Henmans Oxford	1	1
Morgan Cole Oxford	2	3
3 **Boodle Hatfield** Oxford	3	2
4 **Iliffes Booth Bennett** Uxbridge	2	7
Linnells Oxford	1	3

LEADING INDIVIDUALS	
1 **DON Andrew** Blandy & Blandy	**EDDY Catherine** Darbys
MITCHELL Jane Manches	**SIMPSON Barbara** Boodle Hatfield
2 **BLORE Sian** Blandy & Blandy	**GOSS Helen** Morgan Cole
HOWARD Jenni Morgan Cole	

This book is the product of 6,552 1/2-hour interviews. See p.7 for BMRB audit.
Within each band, firms are listed alphabetically. *See individuals' profiles p.386*

Blandy & Blandy (see firm details p.886) Despite maintaining a legal aid franchise, this firm's emphasis lies on higher end private client work. Harvesting clients from an area extending through the Thames Valley, London and beyond, the firm boasts a fine reputation for advice on both financial and public/private children matters. Counselling and mediation are also provided through its STEPahead scheme. **Andrew Don** (see p.389) has "*a positive, sensible, settlement-oriented approach*" and receives able support from the "*well- organised*" **Sian Blore** (see p.387).

Manches (see firm details p.1051) Close links with the firm's London office lead to a high profile in big-ticket cases for the Oxford team. Some have described the firm as "*the king of decent private client work.*" Although leaning more towards ancillary relief the firm covers all aspects of family law bar local authority care work. Marshalling a clientele of doctors, academics and other professionals is the "*informed and resolute*" **Jane Mitchell** (see p.392).

Darbys (see firm details p.931) Split evenly between ancillary relief and public care children work, the team concentrates on work in Oxford and its immediate environs. At least 50% of cases are publicly funded, and the firm has a particularly strong reputation for acting on behalf of guardians and parents. Ancillary relief expert **Catherine Eddy** is said to be "*safe and sensitive to her clients' needs.*"

Henmans (see firm details p.991) "*A reliable, tried and tested*" department, catering for high net worth individuals from professional, business and academic backgrounds. Ancillary relief forms the backbone of the caseload, although private children work is also undertaken.

Morgan Cole (see firm details p.1074) Following the departure of Barbara Simpson to Boodle Hatfield and the outsourcing of all legal aid work, the team is felt to have successfully reinvented itself as a private client practice. Ancillary relief (often with an international angle) predominates here, with children work only featuring in the context of divorce proceedings. Credit for the group's continued success has been ascribed to **Helen Goss** and **Jenni Howard** (see p.390), both of whom received warm recommendation from their peers.

Boodle Hatfield (see firm details p.889) Covering all areas including divorce, children, forum shopping and co-habitation, the practice is known as a "*thoroughly seasoned*" handler of heavyweight disputes. "*Local legal celebrity*" **Barbara Simpson** (see p.394) is the focal point, and is acclaimed for her "*penetrating insight and determined approach.*" Her arrival in December 1999 from Morgan Cole has heralded an increase in the firm's caseload, reflected by the recruitment of two assistants over the past year.

Iliffes Booth Bennett (see firm details p.1007) A "*solid outfit,*" best known for dealing with high net worth clients, domestic violence issues and children's matters. Located in both Chesham and Uxbridge, the department comprises of two distinct matrimonial and children teams. The firm has two representatives on the Lawyers Relate Panel and two lawyers on the Child Care Panel.

Linnells (see firm details p.1043) Once known for its legal aid practice, the firm has now relinquished all publicly funded work. High net ancillary relief is the order of the day on behalf of a client base that extends as far as West London.

SOUTH WEST

Burges Salmon (see firm details p.902) Focused on the resolution of complex financial disputes, the team offers specialist advice on dealing with business, company and partnership assets. "*Pillar of the establishment*" **Catherine Hallam** (see p.390) is a Fellow of the International Academy of Matrimonial Lawyers (one of only two outside London) and has expertise on the implications of pension sharing on divorce. Acting for a range of professional, business and landed clients, the team also has niche expertise in cohabitation issues.

Foot Anstey Sargent (see firm details p.961) The wholesale recruitment of the family department of local rivals Bond Pearce has added to the lustre of this already respected team. A specialist family finance team now exists in Plymouth, while the department's renowned childcare team continues to impress peers in complex adoption, childcare and surrogacy cases. **Margaret Bonner** (see p.387), "*a doughty and worthy opponent,*" maintains her strong reputation for childcare, acting for guardian ad litems and advising on the more abstruse aspects of this area of law.

Gill Akaster (see firm details p.972) Despite some involvement in midrange and legally aided financial cases, it is the public law children work of the practice that catches the eye. **Jacqueline Ashley** (see p.386), "*a dedicated and purposeful lawyer,*" leads the team, assisted by a specialist mental health practitioner.

TLT Solicitors (see firm details p.1157) "*A strong and sizeable presence in the area,*" the team, led by the "*thorough and charming*" **David Woodward** (see p.396), busies itself with high value financial cases for the region's professionals, gentry and celebrities. Much of the work involves international issues, and the department is further bolstered by the presence of a specialist in public and private child law.

Tozers (see firm details p.1160) A "*distinguished child care and public law department*" is renowned for the quality of its individual practitioners. **Philip Kidd** is respected as "*a highly knowledgeable legal dynamo,*" and marshals an effective supporting cast, which includes **Tracy Lambert**, **Andrew Dodd** and **Julie Shrimpton**. Specialities include international adoption and acting across the board for local authorities.

Wolferstans (see firm details p.1188) Covering the full spectrum of family work, the team is divided into specialist departments. High value ancillary relief cases in the £1-6 million range are handled by the "*impeccably fair*" **Paul Woods** (see p.396). **Susan Jury** (see p.391) and team leader **Philip Thorneycroft** (see p.395) blend children law with their financial practices, while legal executives assist with volume legal aid matters. The group can also call on the services of a trained mediator and a unit for dealing with emergency injunctions in instances of domestic violence.

FAMILY/MATRIMONIAL • South West	Ptnrs	Assts
1 **Burges Salmon** Bristol	1	2
Foot Anstey Sargent Plymouth	3	6
Gill Akaster Plymouth	1	2
TLT Solicitors Bristol	3	2
Tozers Exeter, Plymouth, Torquay	5	5
Wolferstans Plymouth	4	5
2 **Clarke Willmott & Clarke** Bristol, Taunton	3	1
Stephens & Scown Exeter	5	4
3 **Hooper & Wollen** Torquay	3	2
Ian Downing Family Law Practice Plymouth	1	1
4 **Stone King** Bath	3	4
Stones Exeter	2	6
Woollcombe Beer Watts Newton Abbot	1	3
5 **E David Brain & Co** St Austell	2	4
Hartnell & Co Exeter	3	3
Hugh James Ford Simey Exeter	3	n/a
Veale Wasbrough Bristol	n/a	2
Withy King Bath	3	6

LEADING INDIVIDUALS	
1 **ASHLEY Jacqueline** Gill Akaster	**BONNER Margaret** Foot Anstey Sargent
HALLAM Catherine Burges Salmon	**SHAKESPEAR Felicity** Clarke Willmott & Clarke
THORNEYCROFT Phil Wolferstans	**WOODWARD David** TLT Solicitors
2 **DOWNING Ian** Ian Downing	**KIDD Philip** Tozers
LAMBERT Tracy Tozers	**SCOFIELD Ian** Hooper & Wollen
WOODS Paul Wolferstans	
3 **ALLEN Elizabeth** Stephens & Scown	**DODD Andrew** Tozers
JURY Susan Wolferstans	**PAYNE Peter** Stephens & Scown
SHRIMPTON Julie Tozers	

This book is the product of 6,552 1/2-hour interviews. See p.7 for BMRB audit.

Within each band, firms are listed alphabetically. *See individuals' profiles p.386*

Clarke Willmott & Clarke (see firm details p.915) Respected in most areas of the sector, the firm has particular expertise in farming partnerships, pensions and care proceedings. **Felicity Shakespear** (see p.394), a recognised authority on the implications of marriage and partnership agreements within the farming sector, benefits from the firm's strong links with the agricultural community. The undoubted highlight of the year was appearing for the husband in the headline-making case of White v White.

Stephens & Scown Dotted across the whole region, this firm's offices provide a complete family law service. Complex financial matters, often involving foreign assets and intricate pension issues, are handled, with the Exeter and St Austell offices having a high profile with the local farming community. Both private and public law children work is also undertaken, including adoption, abduction and surrogacy matters. **Peter Payne** is a member of the Children Panel, while the "*increasingly impressive*" **Elizabeth Allen** is a trained mediator.

Hooper & Wollen (see firm details p.1001) Although the firm possesses a legal aid franchise, its workload is weighted towards high value ancillary relief and public care work. On the financial side, **Ian Scofield** (see p.394) is "*always willing to talk*" and "*takes the heat out of contentious situations.*"

Ian Downing Family Law Practice A specialist practice, which is built around the "*approachable and level-headed*" **Ian Downing.** Privately paid ancillary relief is the firm's bread and butter, where expertise in pension, insurance, and Inheritance Act issues is brought to bear. Private children work and mediation round out the caseload.

Other Notable Firms **Woollcombe Beer Watts**' "*young, fresh and enthusiastic team*" is viewed as "*a band of lawyers with great potential.*" **Stone King** and **Stones** are both said to have created "*attractive, broad-based practices,*" while **E David Brain & Co, Hartnell & Co, Hugh James Ford Simey, Veale Wasbrough** and **Withy King** also inspire positive local sentiment.

WALES

FAMILY/MATRIMONIAL • Wales	Ptnrs	Assts
1 **Hugh James Ford Simey** Cardiff	5	4
Larby Williams Cardiff	2	1
Nicol, Denvir & Purnell Cardiff	3	3
2 **Martyn Prowel Solicitors** Cardiff	1	1
3 **Granville-West** Newbridge	4	4
Harding Evans Newport	1	2
Leo Abse & Cohen Cardiff	n/a	4
Robertsons Cardiff	2	1
Wendy Hopkins & Co Cardiff	3	2

LEADING INDIVIDUALS	
1 **NICOL Frazer** Nicol, Denvir & Purnell	**POWELL Mark** Hugh James Ford Simey
WILLIAMS Frances Larby Williams	**WILLIAMS Jane** Larby Williams
2 **EDWARDS Robert** Martyn Prowel	**GREGORY-JONES Rosemary** Leo Abse & Cohen
WILLIAMS Gail Robertsons	**WILLIAMS Ian** Robertsons
3 **FORD Lindsay** Lindsay Ford Solicitors	**HAMER Melanie** Wendy Hopkins & Co
HOPKINS Wendy Wendy Hopkins & Co	

This book is the product of 6,552 1/2-hour interviews. See p.7 for BMRB audit.

Within each band, firms are listed alphabetically. *See individuals' profiles p.386*

Hugh James Ford Simey (see firm details p.1004) The largest family department in Wales undertakes substantial legal aid work, but is considered to have its real forte in public children law. **Mark Powell** (see p.393) is "*a superb public law practitioner,*" whose "*penetrating analysis*" is crucial in the firm's niche strengths of childcare, domestic and international adoption, incapacity, and abduction. He also sits on the mental health tribunal. The firm maintains a domestic violence hotline, and acts regularly on behalf of women's aid refuges.

Larby Williams Increasingly focusing on ancillary relief at the £1million plus mark, the firm also has a deserved reputation for private adoption work. Both the "*pleasant and hard-working*" **Frances Williams** and the "*judicious*" **Jane Williams** sit on the Children Panel, and the firm also provides a mediation service.

Nicol, Denvir & Purnell "*Excellent in the legal aid market,*" and celebrated for public childcare work, the team is considered to owe much to "*bastion of the practice*" **Frazer Nicol.** He devotes his time to representing guardians ad litem, parents and local authorities, and is praised for approaching his cases with "*great sensitivity.*" Ancillary relief work and mediation are other key elements of the caseload.

Martyn Prowel Solicitors (see firm details p.1055) The focus of this practice has shifted perceptibly towards the financial side, although a proportion of care work is still dealt with. Shouldering the burden is **Robert Edwards** (see p.389), seen as "*a stalwart of the local legal community*" and "*proficient in all aspects of ancillary relief.*"

Other Notable Practitioners Granville-West received commendation for its largely publicly funded practice and commitment to public law. **Ian Williams** and **Gail Williams** from **Robertsons** are both experienced child-care practitioners, as is sole practitioner **Lindsay Ford**. **Leo Abse & Cohen** has a substantial client base of professionals and business people, which allows highly rated **Rosemary Gregory-Jones** (see p.390) to shine in ancillary relief and private children work. **Wendy Hopkins** and the "*sensible*" **Melanie Hamer** are said by peers to "*combine to good effect*" at **Wendy Hopkins & Co**, while **Harding Evans** leans towards ancillary relief work, but "*displays a sureness of touch in all areas.*"

MIDLANDS

	FAMILY/MATRIMONIAL • Midlands	Ptnrs	Assts
1	**Blair Allison & Co** Birmingham	3	3
	Challinors Lyon Clark West Bromwich	3	5
	Nelsons Nottingham	4	2
	Rupert Bear Murray Davies Nottingham	3	4
	Tyndallwoods Birmingham	1	2
2	**Freethcartwright** Nottingham	4	2
	Hadens Walsall	2	2
	Lanyon Bowdler Shrewsbury	1	n/a
	Wace Morgan Shrewsbury	1	2
	Young & Lee Birmingham	1	n/a
3	**Blythe Liggins** Leamington Spa	2	1
	Varley Hibbs Coventry	2	1

	LEADING INDIVIDUALS	
1	**CARTER Barbara** Sole Practitioner	
	DAVIES Murray Rupert Bear Murray Davies	
2	**APPLEBY John** Nelsons	**FLINT Peter** Lanyon Bowdler
	McDONALD Roberta Sole Practitioner	**MEISEL Mari** Blair Allison & Co
	MESSENGER Mercy Sole Practitioner	**YOUNG Ian** Young & Lee

This book is the product of 6,552 1/2-hour interviews. See p.7 for BMRB audit.
Within each band, firms are listed alphabetically. *See individuals' profiles p.386*

Blair Allison & Co (see firm details p.885) High value ancillary relief and public/private childcare work constitute the main planks of this practice. Two partners are on the Child Care Panel and act for children, parents and guardians. In matrimonial matters, **Mari Meisel** exercises "*strong negotiating skills*" and is visible in an increasing number of cohabitation cases. SFLA-accredited, she is heavily involved in family mediation.

Challinors Lyon Clark This youthful team runs the full gamut of family law cases, both in terms of range and value. A sizeable team "*allows the client to get the correct lawyer for each case*" and encourages a wide variety of specialisation. Such specialisms include adoption, abduction and Hague Convention cases, while advice is also offered to domestic violence victims at the local women's refuge.

Nelsons (see firm details p.1080) Now with offices in many of the major conurbations in the Midlands, this firm has one of the largest legal aid practices around. High value ancillary relief also abounds, however, as a result of its considerable private client base. Many of these cases involve acting for British nationals abroad, and specialist advice is also provided on pension regulations. A complementary care practice exists with four lawyers on the Child Care Panel, including the respected **John Appleby** (see p.386).

Rupert Bear Murray Davies (see firm details p.1115) "*Well-organised*" niche family practice led by **Murray Davies** (see p.388), "*an excellent, individualistic lawyer*" with long experience of big money divorce settlements. Professionals and the business and farming communities provide the majority of instructions here, with an in-house conveyancer available for cases relating to wills. The full range of children matters is also handled.

Tyndallwoods (see firm details p.1165) Skewed towards legal aid work, the practice is also involved in a proportion of high value ancillary relief. Private children and care matters form much of the caseload, with two lawyers being members of the Child Care Panel. 24 hour emergency advice is available.

Freethcartwright (see firm details p.964) Personal recommendation, a large private client base and an expanding commercial practice ensure plenty of referrals for this busy department. Many of the financial settlements weigh in over the £1 million mark, and the practice deals with company directors, professionals and figures from the world of sport. Acting for local authorities, guardians and parents, the children's team also has a healthy workload. The departure of respected Hugh Young late last year is seen as a blow, but market perception is still of "*a highly credible firm.*"

Hadens Six offices across the region cover the whole gamut of work, both in terms of variety and value. Divorce, ancillary relief and care proceedings form the staple diet for a client base of business and professional people, and the firm is also franchised to do legal aid work.

Lanyon Bowdler A small mixed practice with a bias towards high value ancillary relief. **Peter Flint** (see p.389) heads the team, bringing "*a shrewd but open mind to more involved cases,*" and doubles up as an effective part-time mediator.

Wace Morgan The largest legal aid practice in Shrewsbury covers all aspects of the sector, including the financial implications of divorce, separation and co-habitation. Children work and domestic violence are particular specialities, with two practitioners being on the Child Care Panel. The firm also boasts a 24-hour TraumaLine.

Young & Lee This niche practice rises in the tables this year due to the "*continuing excellence*" of **Ian Young** (see p.396), who "*combines excellent technical knowledge with a lightness of touch.*" The practice offers a full service, but is primarily celebrated for its work in the field of childcare.

Other Notable Firms **Blythe Liggins** possesses "*a good all-round team of committed professionals,*" whilst **Varley Hibbs** is respected for its public law and middle to high value ancillary relief work. Among a clutch of renowned sole practitioners in the region are **Barbara Carter** and **Roberta McDonald**, recognised for their work in private and public children work, and **Mercy Messenger** (see p.392) who "*runs high value financial cases with efficiency.*"

EAST ANGLIA

Mills & Reeve (see firm details p.1069) A team with "*distinct cachet,*" well known for farming divorces and those involving family run businesses. Experienced in dealing with trusts, pensions and the tax implications of divorce, the firm is also in the vanguard of developing mediation services in the area. **Bruce Wilson** (see p.396), operating out of Norwich, is highly rated by the local bar as "*a technical lawyer of great standing,*" who is "*one of the foremost practitioners outside London.*" His academic prowess is complemented by Cambridge-based **Roger Bamber**'s (see p.387) "*superb showmanship and personable nature.*"

Greenwoods (see firm details p.978) A "*small but laudable*" department inside a predominantly commercial firm. Despite a continuing reputation for quality public law work, the emphasis is shifting towards private client

FAMILY/MATRIMONIAL • East Anglia	Ptnrs	Assts
1 **Mills & Reeve** Cambridge, Norwich	2	4
2 **Greenwoods** Peterborough	2	1
Hunt & Coombs Peterborough	2	3
Silver Fitzgerald Cambridge	2	5
3 **Buckle Mellows** Peterborough	3	3
Eversheds Cambridge	1	1
Miller Sands Cambridge	3	2
4 **Cozens-Hardy & Jewson** Norwich	2	2
Fosters Norwich	2	2
Hatch Brenner Norwich	3	1
Leonard Gray Chelmsford	2	1
Rudlings & Wakelam Thetford	1	3
Ward Gethin King's Lynn	2	2

LEADING INDIVIDUALS	
1 **CARMICHAEL Graeme** Graeme Carmichael	
WILSON Bruce Mills & Reeve	
2 **BAMBER Roger** Mills & Reeve	**HENSON John** Hunt & Coombs
O'REGAN Timothy Rudlings & Wakelam	**PROCTOR Jane** Greenwoods
SANDS Rosemary Miller Sands	**SILVER Raphael** Silver Fitzgerald
SISSON David Eversheds	
3 **FIFE Peter** Ward Gethin	**ILIFF Catherine** Fosters
O'DONNELL Caroline Miller Sands	**RANDALL Richard** Leonard Gray
WHITE Denis Hunt & Coombs	**WHITE Iain** Cozens-Hardy & Jewson

This book is the product of 6,552 1/2-hour interviews. See p.7 for BMRB audit.
Within each band, firms are listed alphabetically. *See individuals' profiles p.386*

ancillary relief and private law children disputes. **Jane Proctor** is the team's anchor, and is noted for her "*highly professional SFLA approach*" and "*clarity of thought.*"

Hunt & Coombs Split evenly between public law and ancillary relief, the practice performs substantial legal aid work in addition to advising a client base of high net worth individuals. Typically advising guardians and local authorities, **John Henson** is "*a committed advocate of some stature,*" with long experience of complex high court matters. **Denis White** "*handles financial matters with skill,*" and is a member of the Child Care Panel. The firm played a leading role in D v D, a contested nullity case involving assets of around £1million.

Silver Fitzgerald (see firm details p.1131) An "*outstanding name for child care*" keeps the firm among the leaders in the region. Regularly instructed by guardians, local authorities and parents, the team has particular experience of adoption issues and care proceedings. The firm can also call on the services of an in-house social worker. At the team's heart lies **Raphael Silver** (see p.394), "*a gifted advocate with a skilful adversarial style.*"

Other Notable Firms Sole practitioner **Graeme Carmichael** (see p.387) enjoys a strong reputation for his work in the children field. Instructed heavily by guardians, he is "*much sought after for complex care proceedings,*" and brings "*geniality and warmth to the more sensitive matters.*" A "*well-run department*" at **Buckle Mellows** continues to be seen to good effect in farming cases, while **Hatch Brenner** is said to run a legal aid franchised department in a "*straightforward and sensible*" manner. **David Sisson** (see p.394) maintains **Eversheds**' presence in this area, handling the high value divorce cases associated with the firm. **Miller Sands** boasts two admired individuals in the "*competent and careful*" **Rosemary Sands** (see p.394) and the emerging **Caroline O'Donnell** (see p.392). In childcare work, **Timothy O'Regan** of **Rudlings & Wakelam** shines as "*a larger than life, highly talented performer,*" while **Iain White** (see p.396) of **Cozens-Hardy & Jewson** has a "*wealth of experience*" in this area. The "*sensible and purposeful*" **Catherine Iliff** of **Fosters** and the "*approachable*" **Peter Fife** of **Ward Gethin** also maintain their share of market support. In Essex, **Richard Randall** (see p.393) of **Leonard Gray** is a favourite of guardians ad litem, and is active in mediation.

NORTH WEST

FAMILY/MATRIMONIAL • North West	Ptnrs	Assts
1 **Pannone & Partners** Manchester	7	6
2 **Cuff Roberts** Liverpool	1	3
Farleys Blackburn	3	7
Laytons Manchester	2	1
3 **Cobbetts** Manchester	2	1
Green & Co Manchester	1	5
Jones Maidment Wilson Manchester	1	2
Mace & Jones Knutsford	1	7
Stephensons Leigh	1	4
4 **Addleshaw Booth & Co** Manchester	2	3
Burnetts Carlisle	3	2
Morecroft Urquhart Liverpool	4	5
Rowlands Manchester	2	1

LEADING INDIVIDUALS	
1 **DEVLIN Michael** Stephensons	**JONES Catherine** Pannone & Partners
WILKINS Beth Pannone & Partners	
2 **BARKER Christine** Laytons	**COTTRELL Patricia** Cuff Roberts
GREEN Michael Green & Co	**HUGHES Kathryn** Farleys
MILBURN Paula Jones Maidment Wilson	
3 **ATKINSON Carol** Mace & Jones	

This book is the product of 6,552 1/2-hour interviews. See p.7 for BMRB audit.
Within each band, firms are listed alphabetically. *See individuals' profiles p.386*

Pannone & Partners (see firm details p.1088) The largest department in the region is also regarded as "*a team of proven substance, streets ahead in terms of both volume and quality of work.*" Now eschewing publicly funded matters, the focus is on complex, high net worth settlements and private children cases, where adoption of those in care is a speciality. The clientele comprises senior professionals, business and sporting personalities, with many cases involving business assets and domestic and offshore trusts. Prominent in "*a uniformly impressive set-up*" are the "*trustworthy and eminently fair*" **Beth Wilkins** (see p.396) and "*straight to the point*" **Catherine Jones** (see p.391).

Cuff Roberts Considered to be the leading light in Liverpool, the department is known for its private children work and excellence in the field of child abduction. **Patricia Cottrell** (see p.388) heads the unit and is characterised as "*a lawyer one can do business with.*" Ancillary relief provides a substantial element of the team's workload.

Farleys (see firm details p.954) A practice that attracts clients from across the region and is especially active in ancillary relief, cohabitation and children law. A significant quantity of public law work is undertaken for guardians ad litem. Handling the higher value financial claims is **Kathryn Hughes** (see p.391), who "*lends common sense and focus to all she does.*"

Laytons (see firm details p.1031) Having recently relinquished its franchise, the firm no longer undertakes legally aided work in this area. Noted specialisms now exist in key children areas such as abduction. Referrals from the firm's London office and a business-heavy client base lead to involvement in higher value cases, where the "*pragmatic*" **Christine Barker** (see p.387) is known for her "*ability to see the wider picture.*"

Cobbetts (see firm details p.923) Operating from a commercially dominated firm, the department is characterised by "*a tough and aggressive attitude.*" Most visible in big-ticket money cases, the firm also advises on the full range of private work.

Green & Co "*One of only a couple of firms in the region to have top quality children work sewn up.*" **Michael Green**'s name acts as a magnet for a variety of referrals. Representing children instructed by guardians in care proceedings, he is "*absolutely top-drawer in his approach to the legal and human side of his cases.*" A sizeable team is also on hand to assist in all other areas of the sector.

Jones Maidment Wilson incorporating Hatton Scates Horton Covering all facets of family law, including domestic violence, the firm's reputation largely derives from its expertise in public and private children law cases. **Paula Milburn**, who also deals with financial matters, "*really impresses on the children side,*" where adoption is felt by peers to be one of her strong suits.

Mace & Jones (see firm details p.1046) New to the tables this year, this substantial practice has offices across the region and "*really knows its law.*" Regularly instructed on high value complex ancillary relief cases, it represents individuals from industry, politics and the entertainment world. A regular recipient of referrals, **Carole Atkinson** (see p.386) is said to be a "*polished big money case practitioner.*"

Stephensons One of the region's largest family groups handles the gamut of family work. Childcare specialist **Michael Devlin** is lauded for his "*excellent client-handling skills,*" and has niche expertise in adoption work.

Other Notable Firms **Addleshaw Booth & Co** is commended for its divorce and ancillary relief ability on behalf of its high net worth professional clientele. **Burnetts**, **Morecroft Urquhart** and **Rowlands** received praise for their broad-based practices and recognised commitment to children law.

YORKSHIRE

FAMILY/MATRIMONIAL • Yorkshire	Ptnrs	Assts
1 **Addleshaw Booth & Co** Leeds	1	4
2 **Grahame Stowe, Bateson** Leeds	3	6
Irwin Mitchell Sheffield	3	2
Jones Myers Gordon Leeds	4	2
3 **Andrew M Jackson & Co** Hull	2	4
Gordons Cranswick Solicitors Bradford	3	3
Zermansky & Partners Leeds	4	3
4 **Chivers Walsh Smith & Irvine & Co** Bradford	2	1
Crombie Wilkinson York	3	3
Kirbys Harrogate	1	2

LEADING INDIVIDUALS	
1 **SALTER David** Addleshaw Booth & Co	
2 **JONES Peter** Jones Myers Gordon	**LOXLEY Martin** Irwin Mitchell
STAKES John Anthony Gordons Cranswick	**STOWE Marilyn** Grahame Stowe, Bateson
TAYLOR Norman Zermansky & Partners	**WAY Philip** Addleshaw Booth & Co
3 **AYRTON Lyn** Gordons Cranswick Solicitors	
BRAITHWAITE Anne Lupton Fawcett	**MANNING Richard** Walker Morris
WALSH Terry Chivers Walsh Smith & Irvine & Co	

This book is the product of 6,552 1/2-hour interviews. See p.7 for BMRB audit.
Within each band, firms are listed alphabetically. *See individuals' profiles p.386*

Addleshaw Booth & Co (see firm details p.853) A small practice within a much larger commercial firm, but one which "*commands enormous respect.*" Focusing largely on ancillary relief and private children work for high net worth individuals, it represents leading professionals, business people and media. Referrals from the London office have seen an increase in international work. "*In a league of his own,*" **David Salter** (see p.393) is "*superb on ancillary relief*" and a renowned expert on pension implications, where "*nobody disputes his top status.*" One of only two fellows of the International Academy of Matrimonial Lawyers outside London, he is supported by his deputy, the "*technically sound*" **Philip Way** (see p.396).

Grahame Stowe, Bateson Spread across six branch offices, the firm advises on the spectrum of family work and maintains a legal aid franchise. However, it is increasingly instructed on cases involving substantial assets and an international dimension. The firm's "*hard-edged philosophy,*" embodied in team powerhouse **Marilyn Stowe** (see p.395), does not meet with universal admiration, but even the most grudging accept that she has "*built up a matrimonial practice of some prominence.*"

Irwin Mitchell (see firm details p.1009) Unusually for a commercially biased firm, its family practice engages in both public and private work. At the Sheffield office, **Martin Loxley** (see p.392) enjoys the status of "*one of the stars of the area.*" Inroads have also been made in Leeds, where across the board ancillary relief is tackled, much of it the result of referrals from the corporate department.

Jones Myers Gordon (see firm details p.1017) Full service firm with the capacity to deal with high value ancillary relief claims. Senior professionals, directors of plcs and members of landed families are among the clientele handled by "*seasoned, able communicator*" **Peter Jones** (see p.391). Two Child Care Panel members handle public and private children work, and legal aid cases are also conducted.

Andrew M Jackson & Co (see firm details p.860) Covering all areas of the sector, the firm has niche strengths in ancillary relief, children matters and domestic violence. Clients are drawn from across the North of England, with a high representation from the professional, business and farming communities. The firm's mediation unit Family Solution employs a probation officer, counsellor and specialist family mediator.

Gordons Cranswick Solicitors Dealing exclusively with privately funded work, the firm often advises on cases involving assets in excess of £1million. The team is "*uniformly impressive,*" and is fronted by head of department **Lyn Ayrton** (see p.387), who is "*good-humoured and brings a certain style to her cases.*" **John Stakes** (see p.395) also stands out for his breadth of experience and specialist knowledge of international child abduction.

Zermansky & Partners (see firm details p.1192) A broad family law practice that scores particularly well for the performance of its specialist childcare unit. The majority of the caseload is legally aided ancillary relief, although medium and high value work is also undertaken, notably by **Norman Taylor** (see p.395), "*a capable and honourable lawyer who brings clarity of thought to his cases.*"

Other Notable Practitioners **Richard Manning** (see p.392) of **Walker Morris** is "*an experienced and formidable operator*" in high value ancillary relief cases, while **Anne Braithwaite** (see p.387) of **Lupton Fawcett** is "*feisty and proactive,*" and is particularly known for her mediation skills. At the higher volume end of the market, **Terry Walsh** of **Chivers Walsh Smith & Irvine & Co**, known as "*one of the best advocates in the area,*" is rated for his child care work and "*solid connections with guardians.*" In North Yorkshire, **Crombie Wilkinson** in York and **Kirbys** in Harrogate have "*niche practices one can admire.*"

NORTH EAST

FAMILY/MATRIMONIAL • North East	Ptnrs	Assts
1 **Dickinson Dees** Newcastle upon Tyne	2	3
2 **Sinton & Co** Newcastle upon Tyne	3	n/a
3 **Hay & Kilner** Newcastle upon Tyne	5	3
Mincoffs Newcastle upon Tyne	1	1
Samuel Phillips & Co Newcastle upon Tyne	2	2
Ward Hadaway Newcastle upon Tyne	3	2
4 **Askews** Redcar	n/a	3
Jacksons Stockton on Tees	n/a	2

LEADING INDIVIDUALS	
1 **GRAY Tim** Sinton & Co	**RUTHERFORD Lyn** Dickinson Dees
SMITH Michael Mincoffs	
2 **CARLISLE Kenneth** Hay & Kilner	**GLENDINNING David** Ward Hadaway
SPEKER Barry Samuel Phillips & Co	

This book is the product of 6,552 1/2-hour interviews. See p.7 for BMRB audit.
Within each band, firms are listed alphabetically. *See individuals' profiles p.386*

Dickinson Dees (see firm details p.941) Easily the highest profile family practice in the area, it concentrates on high value ancillary relief for professionals, business people, landed gentry and media personalities. Team leader **Lyn Rutherford** (see p.393) is regularly involved in cases involving assets up to the £70m mark. He adopts a "*tendentious but effective style,*" and is supported by experts in the field of children law.

Sinton & Co (see firm details p.1134) "*Present in a significant amount of the quality cases,*" the team handles all the financial and children-related aspects of divorce and separation, and retains a legal aid practice. **Tim Gray** (see p.390), a specialist in high value and company-oriented divorce, is "*a name in Newcastle with good commercial connections.*"

Hay & Kilner A sizeable team, spread across three offices, covers all aspects of family law. Niche strength exists in childcare, mental health and mediation, with five lawyers sitting on the Family Law Panel. Active in high net worth matrimonial matters, **Kenneth Carlisle** (see p.387) is commended as an "*utterly reliable lawyer.*" Over the past year, the team has dealt with a number of Inheritance Act claims on behalf of minors and cohabitees.

Mincoffs (see firm details p.1070) Small team with a catholic approach and clients spanning the income divide. **Michael Smith** (see p.395) is noted for his "*approachability and impeccable eye for detail,*" and spearheads a practice that is "*limited in size, but doing a thoroughly decent job.*"

Samuel Phillips & Co (see firm details p.1118) Especially strong in private and public children law work, the firm has three members on the Children Panel and specialist knowledge in child abduction and adoption. **Barry Speker** (see p.395), legal adviser to Barnardo's adoption agency, "*has many strings to his bow,*" but is best known for conducting contested adoption hearings. High value, complex matrimonial cases also feature strongly here.

Ward Hadaway (see firm details p.1173) Discrete department within a largely commercial firm, and the beneficiary of a number of referrals. The Newcastle team's clientele includes names from the agricultural and business worlds, while the South Shields office concentrates on public law work. **David Glendinning** (see p.390) acts on numerous £1 million plus cases "*in a realistic and conciliatory style.*" An established children law practice has been highlighted by work on a number of contact, residence and adoption matters.

Other Notable Firms Cleveland firms **Askews** and **Jacksons** were both commended for "*wide-ranging practices offering a quality service.*"

SCOTLAND

FAMILY/MATRIMONIAL • Scotland	Ptnrs	Assts
1 **Anne Hall Dick & Co** Glasgow	2	1
Morton Fraser, Solicitors Edinburgh	1	3
Turcan Connell Edinburgh	1	2
2 **Balfour & Manson** Edinburgh	1	4
Brodies WS Edinburgh	1	3
Erskine MacAskill & Co Edinburgh	2	2
Mowat Dean & Co WS Edinburgh	2	2
3 **Burnett & Reid** Aberdeen	1	1
Drummond Miller WS Edinburgh	n/a	n/a
Russel & Aitken Edinburgh	2	3
Russells Gibson McCaffrey Glasgow	1	1

LEADING INDIVIDUALS	
1 **DICK Anne** Anne Hall Dick & Co	**LOUDON Alasdair** Turcan Connell
SMITH Caroline Russel & Aitken	
2 **BALLANTINE Tom** Mowat Dean & Co WS	**BRUCE LOCKHART Karen** Brodies WS
CATTO Joan Burnett & Reid	**ERSKINE Sarah** Erskine MacAskill & Co
FOTHERINGHAM John Ross & Connel	**GIBB Andrew** Balfour & Manson
GRAHAM Caroline Macleod & MacCallum	
MAIR Leonard Morton Fraser, Solicitors	**PATIENCE Iain** Patience & Buchan
SCANLAN Margaret Russells Gibson McCaffrey	
SHEEHAN Wendy Mowat Dean & Co WS	**TAIT Fiona** Drummond Miller WS
3 **JAMIESON George** Walker Laird	**SMITH Shona** Balfour & Manson

This book is the product of 6,552 1/2-hour interviews. See p.7 for BMRB audit.
Within each band, firms are listed alphabetically. *See individuals' profiles p.386*

Anne Hall Dick & Co Now based solely in Glasgow, the firm handles financial and property arrangements following separation and contingent child related matters. Respected leader **Anne Dick** is "*no pushover,*" and is praised for being "*switched on to the major issues.*" Her acknowledged skills in child law extend to producing reports for the local court welfare officers.

Morton Fraser, Solicitors (see firm details p.1076) Rising to the top tier of the rankings this year, this is "*a firm on an upward curve,*" renowned for its enviable local clientele. **Leonard Mair** deals with a number of high value family cases in the capital and is "*always ready to pick up the phone and show commitment to a case.*" All major sectors of children work are also undertaken, including residence, contact, adoption and care.

Turcan Connell (see firm details p.1164) Following the implosion of perennial market leaders Loudons, this firm has come to the fore with the recruitment of **Alasdair Loudon** (see p.391). Known for his "*quickness of mind and creativity,*" his arrival is considered to represent a major coup for the firm. Although children work is handled, the accent lies heavily on the resolution of financial disputes for a variety of clients.

Balfour & Manson (see firm details p.869) The departure of the respected Wendy Sheehan to Mowat Dean is widely recognised to have been a setback to the team. However, the practice is still felt to provide a "*consistently good service,*" covering high value ancillary relief and public and private children work. Benefiting from the firm's traditionally healthy private client base, "*colourful character*" **Andrew Gibb** (see p.390) is "*a top all-rounder,*" who often appears in major cases with an international dimension. He receives solid support from the respected **Shona Smith.** (see p.395)

Brodies WS (see firm details p.896) The team is often seen in the Court of Session, contracting big money cases for affluent clients from the landed classes. At the helm is **Karen Bruce Lockhart** (see p.387), *"a formidable opponent who doesn't stand any nonsense."* Her talent is unquestioned, although she is sometimes felt to overshadow the rest of her colleagues. Also prominent in private children work, the practice has been involved in a leading child abduction case involving a US national.

Erskine MacAskill & Co (see firm details p.951) Well-regarded practice, noted for its work with children and the victims of domestic violence. Seen mostly in the Sheriff's Court doing legal aid work, *"its commitment to, and real concern for, the young"* is widely admired. Epitomising this spirit is the *"indefatigable"* **Sarah Erskine**, who *"demonstrates real conviction in all she does."*

Mowat Dean & Co WS A firm *"on the rise,"* which is especially visible in the Sheriff Court and Court of Session, covering Child Law and financial provision cases. The acquisition from Balfour & Manson of **Wendy Sheehan**, *"a practical opponent always ready to move things along,"* is seen as a fillip to the practice. Operating in tandem with the *"considered"* **Tom Ballantine**, she and the practice have gained increased market recognition this year. The group has advised on around twenty mediation cases in the past year.

Other Notable Practitioners From its seven offices, **Drummond Miller WS** tackles the full spectrum of work, including high value ancillary relief, where the respected **Fiona Tait** (see p.395) takes the lead. **Russells Gibson McCaffrey** is known for its children and financial work and possesses in **Margaret Scanlan** (see p.394) *"a real street-fighter,"* who is also a member of the International Academy of Family Lawyers. **Burnett & Reid** has *"a fine general practice,"* led by *"the matriarch of family law in Aberdeen,"* **Joan Catto** (see p.388). **Russel & Aitken** enters the tables this year, having recruited the *"bright, precise and energetic"* **Caroline Smith** (see p.394), formerly of Loudons. **George Jamieson** of **Walker Laird** receives recommendation for his acknowledged prowess in children law, while three other individuals also retain high standing among their peers: **John Fotheringham** of **Ross & Connel**, **Iain Patience** (see p.392), who has left Iain Smith & Co to co-found **Patience & Buchan**, and *"rising force"* **Caroline Graham** of **Macleod & MacCallum**.

NORTHERN IRELAND

FAMILY/MATRIMONIAL • Northern Ireland		Ptnrs	Assts
1	**Babington & Croasdaile** Londonderry	2	1
	Flynn & McGettrick Belfast	1	1
	Peden & Reid Belfast	1	2
	Thompsons Newtownards	1	2
2	**Carnson Morrow Graham** Bangor	2	1
	Wilson Nesbitt Belfast	1	2

LEADING INDIVIDUALS		
1	**CALDWELL Anne** Flynn & McGettrick	**PALMER George** Peden & Reid

This book is the product of 6,552 1/2-hour interviews. See p.7 for BMRB audit.

Within each band, firms are listed alphabetically. *See individuals' profiles p.386*

George Palmer at **Peden & Reid** is adept at handling cases involving substantial assets, while **Anne Caldwell** at **Flynn & McGettrick** handles all areas in an *"astute and sympathetic manner."* Also in Belfast, **Wilson Nesbitt** maintains a reputation for its *"sensitive handling of cases."* Outside the capital, **Babington & Croasdaile** in Derry and **Thompsons** in Newtownards are regarded as *"among the best you can get,"* while **Carnson Morrow Graham** in Bangor also retains substantial local support.

LEADERS IN FAMILY / MATRIMONIAL

ALEXIOU, Douglas

Alexiou Fisher Philipps, London (020) 7409 1222
dalexiou@afp-law.co.uk

Specialisation: Covers all areas including divorce, judicial separation, financial disputes, co-habitation, children and international aspects (including recognition and enforcement). Lectures, gives TV, radio, magazine and newspaper interviews.

Prof. Memberships: Law Society; Solicitors Family Law Association (chairman of London Regional Group 1992-96); founding fellow and current president International Academy of Matrimonial Lawyers (president, European Chapter 1998-00); member of the Family Mediators Association; member of the International Bar Association.

Career: Qualified in 1970. Joined *Gordon Dadds* in February 1971, and was made a partner later that year. Became senior partner in 1986. Founding partner *Alexiou Fisher Philipps* 2001. Director of Tottenham Hotspur Football Club from 1980-98. Chairman 1982-84. Director of Tottenham Hotspur plc 1983-91 and 1993-98. Member of 1996 British Olympic Appeal Council.

Personal: Born 24 May 1942. Attended St Paul's School 1955-59, Kings College, London (LLB Hons) 1965 and College of Law. Leisure interests include golf, tennis, association football and collecting old fountain pens. Lives in Kingston-upon-Thames.

ALLEN, Elizabeth

Stephens & Scown, Exeter (01392) 210700

APPLEBY, John

Nelsons, Nottingham (0115) 989 5327
john.appleby@nelsons-solicitors.co.uk

Specialisation: Family law with emphasis on high value financial and pension related matters.

Prof. Memberships: SFLA, Law Society (Children Panel).

Career: Admitted 1970. Formerly managing partner of *Trumans* in Nottingham (prior to its merger with *Nelsons* in 1999). Solicitor High Court Advocate. Recorder on Midland Circuit.

Publications: Contribution to Organisation and management of a solicitor's practice.

Personal: Leisure interests include theatre, cinema, travel and wine.

ASHLEY, Jacqueline

Gill Akaster, Plymouth (01752) 203500

Specialisation: Partner and head of family department. Main areas of practice are public law, childcare and ancillary relief. Member of Law Society's Children panel since March 1986. Accredited SFLA specialist. Member of Law Society Family panel. Experienced practitioner for children, guardians and parents. Handles all aspects of marriage and cohabitation breakdown, both private and Legal Aid. Lecturer from 1983-88 on Legal Executive Course. Committed member of Children Act Business and Services committees for Plymouth. Currently chair of SFLA Children committee.

Prof. Memberships: Law Society, Children panel, committee member of local SFLA.

Career: Qualified in 1984. Previous training as legal executive. Joined *Gill Akaster* in 1975, becoming a partner in 1985.

Personal: Born 28 April 1950. Attended College of Law, Guildford 1982-83. Leisure interests include walking, theatre and amateur theatre. Lives in Plymouth.

ATKINSON, Carol

Mace & Jones, Liverpool (0151) 236 8989

Specialisation: Family – high value ancillary relief claims. Acted for national know figures. Many very high asset cases.

Prof. Memberships: Law Society, Solicitors Family Law Association.

Career: Nottingham University, Chester College of Law. Joined *Mace & Jones* upon qualifying in 1979.

Partner since 1982. Appointed Deputy District Judge in 2000.
Publications: Magazine articles, newspaper editorial.
Personal: Fell walking, reading, music. Married with children.

AYRTON, Lyn
Gordons Cranswick Solicitors, Bradford (01274) 202202
lyn.ayrton@gordonscranswick.co.uk
Specialisation: Complex/high value financial settlements, in particular those involving owner managed businesses and pension issues.
Prof. Memberships: Solicitors Family Law Association; member of SFLA Procedure Committee and Press Officer for North and West Yorkshire; Law Society's Family Law Panel.
Career: Qualified at *Booth and Co* (now *Addleshaw Booth and Co*), Leeds; joined *Gordons Wright and Wright* (now *Gordons Cranswick*) as a partner in 1997; head of department since April 2000.
Publications: Contributor to 'Humphreys Family Proceedings' and 'Debt and Insolvency on Family Breakdown'; joint author of 'Residence and Contact: A Practical Guide'.
Personal: Married; lives near Harrogate; enjoys fast cars and good wine but not together!

BAKER, Miranda
Kingsley Napley, London (020) 7814 1200
mbaker@kingsleynapley.co.uk
Specialisation: All aspects of family law, including complex children and ancillary relief applications. Advice in relation to the legal implications of surrogacy arrangements. Occasional writer and lecturer on family law. SFLA trained mediator. Law Society Family Law Panel member.
Prof. Memberships: SFLA (member of the editorial team for the Review) member of Children Committee since 1989 and chair of its Surrogacy subcommittee), National Council for Family Proceedings.
Career: Qualified 1981. With *Collyer-Bristow* 1983-86, *Rubinstein Callingham* 1986-94 (partner from 1989) and *Manches & Co* (following the merger with *Rubinstein Callingham*) 1994-95. Joined *Kingsley Napley* as a partner in 1995.
Personal: Born 16/05/56. Attended Wimbledon High School, then New Hall, Cambridge (1974-77). Leisure interests include travel, opera, football and swimming. Lives in London.

BALLANTINE, Tom
Mowat Dean & Co WS, Edinburgh (0131) 555 0616

BAMBER, Roger
Mills & Reeve, Cambridge (01223) 222203
roger.bamber@mills-reeve.com
Specialisation: Partner in family department. With partner Bruce Wilson and associate Nick Stone, leads the largest and most specialist team in the region. He has lectured extensively within the legal profession in particular to District Judges for the Judicial Studies board. Work includes mainly financial provision, in particular complex financial cases involving businesses, trusts and pensions. He is a member of the SFLA and the UK College of Family Mediators.
Career: Qualified in 1981. Joined *Mills & Reeve* as a partner in 1989.
Publications: Co-author of 'Pensions and Insurance on Matrimonial Breakdown'. Editor of 'The Family Through Divorce', which is a comprehensive guide to the personal, financial and legal aspects of family breakdown. He is author of divorce.co.uk – a leading website dealing with all aspects of family breakdown.
Personal: Born 5 February 1955. MA Cantab. Leisure interests include music, art and rowing.

BARKER, Christine
Laytons, Manchester (0161) 834 2100
Specialisation: Divorce, ancillary relief (high value cases), contact and residence disputes; Fournier v Fournier.
Prof. Memberships: SFLA member.
Career: Family lawyer for past 20 years. Qualified October 1978. Law degree, Nottingham University. Moved to *Laytons* 1992, set up department.
Personal: Married to hotelier and restauranteur. Two children aged 11 and 13. Hobbies; travel, food and wine.

BLORE, Sian
Blandy & Blandy, Reading (0118) 951 6804
sian_blore@blandy.co.uk
Specialisation: Advice on all areas of family law with particular emphasis on complex and substantial financial issues (including those with an international element) arising from matrimonial and relationship breakdown.
Prof. Memberships: SFLA, Law Society Family Law Panel.
Career: Qualified 1985. Specialised in family law at *Theodore Goddard*; joined *Farrer & Co* in 1989 and became partner in 1993; joined *Blandy & Blandy* as partner in 1996 having decided to leave London to work nearer home and family.
Personal: Born 1961. Attended University College of Wales, Aberystwyth. Lives in Henley-on-Thames with husband and three small sons.

BONNER, Margaret
Foot Anstey Sargent, Plymouth (01752) 675000
margaret.bonner@foot-ansteys.co.uk
Specialisation: Partner; head of legal aid division. Acts in cases involving children, in both public and private law. Work includes adoption and child abduction.
Prof. Memberships: Member of SFLA, Law Society's Children Panel; Association of Lawyers for Children; Association of Women Solicitors, Plymouth Child Care Support Group; past National Secretary SFLA 1994-00; Conference Chairman at the SFLA fifth National Conference in 1993.
Career: Qualified in 1985. Joined *Foot Anstey Sargent* in 1986, becoming a partner in 1987. Previously Nursing Auxiliary in geriatric hospital, trainee assistant editor of cookery magazine and personal assistant to clinical psychologist.
Personal: Born 31st August 1946. Attended University of Sussex 1965-68. Leisure interests include opera, gardening, yoga, walking, food, wine and visiting Italy.

BRAITHWAITE, Anne
Lupton Fawcett, Leeds (0113) 280 2100
anne.braithwaite@lupfaw.co.uk
Specialisation: Family/matrimonial work with the main focus on ancillary relief and All Issues family mediation.
Prof. Memberships: Law Society Children panel; Solicitors Family Law Association (regional treasurer); recognised All Issues mediator.
Career: Trained with *AV Hammond*, moved one year after admission to Bradford where she was a partner with *Last & Co.* Anne joined *Lupton Fawcett* where she heads the family department (since 1995).

BROWN, Fiona
Payne Hicks Beach, London (020) 7465 4300
jbrown@paynehicksbeach.co.uk
Specialisation: All aspects of high net worth ancillary relief cases; many cases contain an international element with potential and actual forum disputes; prenuptial contracts; cohabitation issues; children disputes; experience of many high profile cases, since 1994.
Prof. Memberships: SFLA.
Career: Articled at *Herbert Smith* 1992-94; assistant solicitor at *Farrer & Co* 1994-00; associate – *Payne Hicks Beach* 2001.
Personal: Education: Hirworth Comprehensive School and Queen Elizabeth Sixth Form College 1979-86; Magdalen College, Oxford 1986-89 (1st class Hons, Mod. Hist). Leisure: running (triple blue – Oxon). Family: married with two daughters.

BRUCE LOCKHART, Karen
Brodies WS, Edinburgh (0131) 228 3777
karen.brucelockhart@brodies.co.uk
Specialisation: Partner in litigation department and heads the family law team. A family law practitioner for 30 years. Deals herself mostly with high value or complicated divorces in the Court of Session. Her team acts both in the Court of Session and the Sheriff Court and handles Legal Aid. Proud of settling most cases and seldom getting involved in fought divorces. The team also specialises in international child abduction
Prof. Memberships: International Academy of Matrimonial Lawyers; Scottish Family Law Association; Writer to the Signet; APIL; Law Society of Scotland Personal Injuries Panel; accredited for medical negligence.
Career: School in Canada and New Zealand. Edinburgh University 1966-70 (LLB and MSc in Forensic medicine 1998-00). Partner *Courtney Crawford & Co* 1974-77. Partner *Brodies WS* since 1978.
Personal: Born in 1942. Leisure interests: walking, reading and skiing. Lives in Edinburgh and Cumbria.

CALDWELL, Anne I.M.
Flynn & McGettrick, Belfast (028) 90244212

CARLISLE, Kenneth
Hay & Kilner, Gosforth (0191) 284 2818
Specialisation: Partner and head of family law department, leads a team of eight. Specialises in dealing with substantial financial and property matters within divorce and cohabitee proceedings including inheritance claims and contact/residence applications. Also a trained mediator.
Prof. Memberships: Founder and Chairman of Solicitors Family Law Association (N.E. Region). Member of the Law Society Family Law Panel.
Career: Qualified 1972. Partner 1975.
Personal: Born 28/1/44. Married with two children. Interests include cycling, walking, reading and travel.

CARMICHAEL, Graeme
Graeme Carmichael, Ipswich (01473) 252159
Specialisation: Principally work concerning children in public and private law, including advocacy. Balance of caseload divorce and related issues.
Prof. Memberships: Law Society Children panel;

Law Society Family Law panel, SFLA (Regional Chairman); Association of Lawyers for Children.
Career: Qualified 1976. Previously family law partner at *Eversheds* (Norwich) and *Prettys* (Ipswich).
Personal: Born 1950. Educated Fettes College and Newcastle University.

CARRUTHERS, Alex
Hughes Fowler Carruthers, London (020) 7421 8383
mail@hfclaw.com
Specialisation: Partner in niche family law practice. Work includes complex international financial cases; private children's law including child abduction.
Prof. Memberships: SFLA; previously founder member of YSFLA (London); IBA.
Career: Articled *Bates, Wells & Braithwaite*; qualified 1994; partner 1999; co-founder of *Hughes Fowler Carruthers* 2001.
Personal: Born 1967. Resides London and Cambridge. Interests include bridge.

CARTER, Barbara
Barbara Carter, Birmingham (0121) 441 3238

CATTO, Joan
Burnett & Reid, Aberdeen (01224) 644333
Specialisation: Partner in court department. Main area of practice is family law. Deals with numerous divorce cases including ancillary issues such as financial arrangements and residence and contact orders. Also handles child law: acts as curator ad litem and reporter in adoptions, residence and contact disputes. Was for 10 years safe guarder to the Children's panel and to the Sheriff Court. Acted as safe guarder in W which went to the Inner House of the Court of Session. Acted on behalf of the petitioners in K Petitioners, for child in Cameron v Cameron, and in 2001, CICA case of K (award £1.4 million). Has participated in and organised numerous family law seminars in Aberdeen and elsewhere.
Prof. Memberships: Member of Family Law Association, member of Family Mediation (Grampian).
Career: Qualified in 1968. Joined *Burnett & Reid* in 1988, becoming a partner in 1991.
Personal: Born 30 April 1946. Attended Aberdeen High School for Girls and Aberdeen University. Member of Business Committee, General Council, Aberdeen University; committee member, Aberdeen Civic Society. Leisure interests include needlework, walking and foreign travel. Lives in Aberdeen, and Glenbuchat.

CHAPMAN, Ellie
Barnett Sampson, London (020) 7831 7181
Specialisation: Partner in the expanding family department. Specialises in substantial ancillary relief applications, often with an international, trust or offshore aspect for both married and cohabiting clients. Also undertakes private children's applications. Has written a number of articles and book reviews.
Prof. Memberships: Founder member and immediate past Treasurer of the Solicitors Family Law Association.
Personal: Educated at Howells School, Denbigh 1957-63 and University College, London (LLB 1968). Leisure pursuits include travel, horse riding, cooking, reading, gardening and practice management.

COLLIS, Pamela
Cawdery Kaye Fireman & Taylor, London (020) 7431 7262
Specialisation: Head of family department. International and domestic family law work, particularly financial aspects of marriage and cohabitation breakdown, pre-nuptial contracts and Children Act work. Contributor to legal journals and speaker on matters relating to family law.
Prof. Memberships: Fellow of the International Academy of Matrimonial lawyers and member of the SFLA and of the Family Law panel of the Law Society.
Career: Qualified 1981. Partner and head of family law at *Kingsley Napley* 1984-99. Joined *Cawdery Kaye Fireman & Taylor* in 1999 as partner and head of family.
Personal: Born 9 March 1957. Attended Rosemead School for Girls, then Bristol University (LLB 1978). Leisure pursuits include sailing, books and family life. Lives in London.

COPSON, James
Withers, London (020) 7597 6044
james.copson@withers.co.uk
Specialisation: Family law with emphasis on the resolution of substantial money and international cases. Represented the successful appellant in Wick v Wicks [1998] 1 FLR 470 confirming the law on interim capital arrangements in divorce and the successful respondent in Re A (Specific Issue Order: Parental Dispute) [2001] 1 FLR 121, both in the Court of Appeal.
Prof. Memberships: Solicitors Family Law Association, SFLA Pensions Committee, American Bar Association (associate member).
Career: Qualified at Withers 1991. Partner at Withers since 1998.
Publications: Born 20 May 1966. Educated at Wellingborough School and the Univserity of Birmingham. Interests Chelsea Football Club, sport and travel. Lives in Fulham, SouthWest London and the South of France.

CORNWELL, John
Dawson Cornwell, London (020) 7242 2556
cornwellj@dawsoncornwell.co.uk
Specialisation: Has practised in family law as a specialist since 1970; particular specialism in ancillary relief and pensions on divorce. Has practised as a mediator in family law since 1985. Practises as a mediator under the auspices of the SFLA. Spent the summer term of 1999 at Wolfson College, Oxford as visiting fellow at the Institute for Socio-Legal Studies. Lectures on pension in divorce.
Prof. Memberships: Solicitors' Family Law Association, founder, chairman 1982-87; Family Mediators Association, co-founder 1988; has chaired the SFLA Children committee and the SFLA Mediation committee; member of the Law Society Family Law committee 1993-99; Deputy District Judge at the Principal Registry of the Family Division, 1986 to date.
Career: Qualified in 1969. Founding partner of *Dawson Cornwell* in 1972. Founder of the SFLA, chairman 1982-87 and returned to the committee in 1994. Co-founder of FMA, vice chairman 1992-93 and board member from inception until 1994. Deputy District Judge since 1987.
Personal: Born 21 September 1943. Educated at St. Paul's School 1957-62 and Bristol University 1962-65. Leisure interests include theatre, cricket and Georgian architecture. Lives in London.

COTTRELL, Patricia
Cuff Roberts, Liverpool (0151) 237 7777
Specialisation: Partner in family department. Patricia deals with high-profile matrimonial work principally for clients in the corporate and professional sectors, invariably involving complex high value pension and share valuation issues. The practice deals with all aspects of family law, particularly divorce, separation, ancillary relief, co-habitation and private law children cases, including child abduction.
Prof. Memberships: Member of Law Society Family panel; Solicitors Family Law Association (SFLA); Merseyside Legal Services Commission Appeals committee; former chair of Merseyside SFLA; appointed Deputy District Judge in 1997.
Career: Qualified 1983; joined *Cuff Roberts* in 1981, now franchise partner and head of family department.
Personal: Leisure interests include walking, theatre, gardening, reading and travel. Lives on the Wirral Peninsula.

DAVIDSON, David
Charles Russell, London (020) 7203 5114
davidd@cr-law.co.uk.
Specialisation: Partner in family law department. Handles all areas of family law with emphasis on substantial financial applications, frequently with an international aspect. Author of 'A Guide to Pensions and Marriage Breakdown'. Contributor of chapters on pensions to 'Essential Family Practice' and 'Encyclopaedia of Financial Provision in Family Matters'. Joint author 'Precedents for Pre-Marital Agreements'. Featured regularly in national and legal press.
Prof. Memberships: International Academy of Matrimonial Lawyers. Solicitors Family Law Association.

DAVIES, Murray
Rupert Bear Murray Davies, Nottingham (0115) 924 3333
Specialisation: Murray Davies has over 20 years experience of matrimonial and family law, with a particular specialisation in the financial aspects of divorce and separation.
Prof. Memberships: Member of SFLA.
Career: Admitted in 1978, Murray has gained experience within prominent firms in Nottingham before joining *Rupert Bear* in partnership, in the firm of *Rupert Bear Murray Davies.*
Personal: Born in 1951, Murray is married with four children. Interests include walking, bird watching and bricklaying.

DAVIS, Sandra
Mishcon de Reya, London (020) 7440 7000
Specialisation: Head of Family Department with over 20 years experience in the field. Work includes international and domestic 'big money' cases with a specialisation in high profile and high net worth individuals attracting media attention, international child abduction, divorce and separation, cohabitation disputes and contact and residency disputes. Author of 'International Child Abduction' and numerous articles. Frequently lectures at various national and international events. Lord Chancellor's Department panel solicitor.
Prof. Memberships: Solicitors Family Law Association; Law Society; fellow of the International Academy of Matrimonial Lawyers.
Career: Qualified with *Mishcon de Reya* in 1981, becoming a partner in 1984.

Personal: Born 3 July 1956. Attended University of Sussex 1974-78 and Universite Aix-en-Provence, France, reading European Studies/Law. Languages: French and German. Leisure interests include travel, painting and photography. Lives in London. Married with two children.

DEARLE, Marcus
Withers, London (020) 7597 6000
marcus.dearle@withers.co.uk
Specialisation: Exclusively family law and, in particular, substantial financial and children cases including those with an international element. Also deals with surrogacy and medico-legal issues. Has broadcast on TV and radio and regularly written articles for the national press.
Prof. Memberships: Law Society. SFLA 1990 to date. SFLA International Committee 1992 to date.
Career: Articled *Eversheds Daynes Hill & Perk*. Qualified January 1990. Joined *Withers'* family law department in September 1990. Partner at *Withers* 1995.
Publications: Contributor to family section Practical Civil Court Precedents (Sweet & Maxwell). Co-contributor to SFLA International Committee's 'Guide to Family Law in Europe' (1992) and 'International Aspects of Family Law, A Guide to Good Practice and Procedure' (2000).
Personal: Born 6 May 1964. Educated at Bryanston School and University of East Anglia. Interests include modern history, theatre, cinema and Dad's Army. Married and lives in Windlesham, Surrey.

DEVLIN, Michael
Stephensons, Leigh (01942) 777777

DICK, Anne
Anne Hall Dick & Co., Glasgow (0141) 636 0003

DODD, Andrew
Tozers, Plymouth (01752) 206460

DON, Andrew
Blandy & Blandy, Reading (0118) 958 7111
Andrew_Don@blandy.co.uk
Specialisation: Head of one of the largest family departments in the Thames Valley region consisting of seven specialist lawyers. Involved with substantial financial/property matters and children issues arising from divorce and separation. An experienced mediator having trained with the FMA in 1990. In the past has trained other solicitors to be mediators. Member of the UK College of Mediators.
Prof. Memberships: Solicitors Family Law Association. Family Mediators Association.
Career: Parachute regiment 1976-79. Qualified with *Blandy & Blandy* in 1981 and became a partner in 1984. Deputy District Judge.
Personal: Born 1 December 1952. Educated at Malvern College and Liverpool University. Lives in Hampshire. Married with four sons. Enjoys outdoor and sporting activities which include playing rackets and rough gardening.

DORAN, Gill
Withers, London (020) 7597 6000
Specialisation: Partner in and head of the family law department. Has specialised in family and matrimonial work for 20 years. Has written articles about family matters, addressed conferences and done committee work for the Solicitors Family Law Association (SFLA).
Prof. Memberships: International Academy of Matrimonial Lawyers (IAML), Family Mediators Association (FMA).
Career: Qualified in 1974. Joined *Gordon Dadds* (1979-96). Joined the family law department at *Withers* in 1996.
Personal: Born 28th September 1949. Educated at The Abbey School 1960-68 and Manchester University 1968-71. Leisure interests include music, opera and horses. Lives in London.

DOWNING, Ian
Ian Downing Family Law Practice, Plymouth (01752) 226224

DRAKE, Michael
Collyer-Bristow, London (020) 7242 7363
michael.drake@collyerbristow.com
Specialisation: Head of Matrimonial Department. Handles all areas of matrimonial and family law, particularly where there is a commercial, financial or international element. Also advises on business law, including contract and commercial advice.
Prof. Memberships: SFLA (National Committee 1987 to 1994).
Career: Qualified in 1971. Joined *Collyer-Bristow* as a partner in 1984.
Publications: Author of various textbooks, SFLA publications, articles. Co-author of 'Divorce and the Family Business', published in 1997 by Jordans – second edition imminent. Has lectured and broadcast on radio and television, and featured in a series of family law videos for TEN.
Personal: Born 14 August 1947. Educated at Haberdasher's Askes's Elstree (to 1965) and Selwyn College, Cambridge (to 1968). Recreations include travel, arts reading and tennis. Lives in London.

EDDY, Catherine
Darbys, Oxford (01865) 811700

EDWARDS, Robert
Martyn Prowel Solicitors, Cardiff (02920) 470909
Specialisation: Partner in family department. Principal area of practice is matrimonial and care work, dealing with personal representation from the Magistrates Court through to the High Court. Specialises in complicated financial and property issues and representing both guardians and parents in care proceedings. Chairman of Bro Taff Health Authority Disciplinary committee. Former vice-chairman of the South Wales Family Law Association.
Prof. Memberships: Law Society, Family Law Association, Childcare panel.
Career: Qualified in 1975.
Personal: Born 26 February 1948. Educated at Penarth Grammar School 1960-67 and the University of Wales, Aberystwyth 1967-70 (LLB). Past captain of Glamorganshire Golf Club and member of Welsh Solicitors' Golf Team. Also enjoys gardening, reading and travel. Lives in Penarth, Vale of Glamorgan.

ERSKINE, Sarah
Erskine MacAskill & Co, Edinburgh (0131) 622 6062

FIFE, Peter R.G.
Ward Gethin, King's Lynn (01553) 660033

FISHER, Jeremy
Alexiou Fisher Philipps, London (020) 7409 1222
jfisher@afp-law.co.uk
Specialisation: Partner. Specialises in the problems arising out of the breakdown of family relationships. Particular expertise in complex financial and trust structures both domestic and international.
Prof. Memberships: International Academy of Matrimonial Lawyers; International Bar Association.

FLINT, Peter
Lanyon Bowdler, Shrewsbury (01952) 291222
shrewsbury@lblaw.co.uk
Specialisation: Head of family law department, *Lanyon Bowdler*. Based in firm's Shrewsbury office, specialising in all aspects of family law.
Prof. Memberships: Member of Legal Aid Area (No 12) Committee. Member of SFLA, Family Mediators Association, SALM (Shropshire Associated Lawyer Mediators) and Law Society Family Law Panel.
Career: Articled to *J.C.H. Bowdler & Sons*, Shrewsbury, in 1967. Qualified in 1971. Admitted into partnership with *J.C.H Bowdler & Sons* in 1972.
Personal: Educated at St Martin's Preparatory School, Northwood, Haileybury and I.S.C, Hertford and College of Law. Passed Law Society Pt II exams with 2nd class honours. Married, with 3 daughters. Lives in Bayston Hill, near Shrewsbury. Interests include golf and tennis.

FORD, Lindsay
Lindsay Ford Solicitors, Caerphilly (029) 2088 2441

FOSTER, Stephen
Lester Aldridge, Bournemouth (01202) 786161
Specialisation: Head of family law unit, leading a team of six specialist lawyers dealing with all areas of family law work, financial and children. Specialises in dealing with substantial financial and property matters within divorce and cohabitee proceedings, including related shareholding and other company disputes. Cases often involve an international element. Team includes two SFLA qualified mediators. Also specialises in solicitors' negligence covering all areas of family law.
Prof. Memberships: Solicitors Family Law Association (Good Practice committee member).
Career: Qualified 1986. *Bircham & Co Westminster* 1986-92 as lead family lawyer and member of the commercial litigation team. Joined *Lester Aldridge* in 1993 as a partner to head up large family law unit. Qualified SFLA mediator 1998.
Personal: Born 1959. Educated at Newport High School and University of Wales, University College Swansea (1980 BA History). Lives near Dorchester, Dorset. Interests include his two young daughters, English and American literature, swimming and tennis.

FOTHERINGHAM, John M.
Ross & Connel, Inverkeithing

FOWLER, Pauline
Hughes Fowler Carruthers, London (020) 7421 8383
mail@hfclaw.com
Specialisation: Partner in niche family law practice. Work includes complex financial matters, often where consideration of commercial implications is necessary and regularly with off-shore assets and an international dimension; private children's law including international adoption; mediation, particularly in complex financial matters.
Prof. Memberships: SFLA; IBA; FMA (Vice Chair).

Career: *Bates, Wells & Braithwaite* 1985 (partner 1990); co-founded niche practice of *Hughes Fowler Carruthers* in 2001. Trained as accredited FMA mediator. Lectures and writes on family law.
Personal: Born 1955; lives in London; leisure interests include chamber music.

GIBB, Andrew
Balfour & Manson, Edinburgh (0131) 200 1250
andrew.gibb@balfour-manson.co.uk
Specialisation: Partner in litigation department. Accredited family law specialist. Has a substantial practice in family law in both the Court of Session and Sheriff Court, also involving drafting of separation agreements with particular regard to financial provision. Is involved in all aspects of education law including contract disputes, disciplinary matters, criminal prosecutions and accident cases. Provides employment law advice to both employers and employees. Solicitor to The Educational Institute of Scotland, the main teaching union in Scotland. Joint editor of 'The Family Law Bulletin' and regular contributor to 'Update' (Education Department of Law Society of Scotland) on family law matters.
Prof. Memberships: Law Society of Scotland; Family Law Association; member International Academy of Matrimonial Lawyers; chair, Family Law Accreditation Panel of Law Society of Scotland.
Career: Qualified in 1971. Became a partner in *Balfour & Manson* in 1975. Member of Council of Law Society of Scotland 1981-93 and president of Law Society of Scotland 1990-91.
Personal: Born 17 August 1947. Educated at Perth Academy 1959-65 and Edinburgh University 1965-69. Chairman, Management Committee Lothian Allelon (probation hostel). Leisure interests include golf and music. Lives in Edinburgh.

GIEVE, Katherine
Bindman & Partners, London (020) 7833 4433
info@bindmans.com
Specialisation: All aspects of work concerning children, both private and public law cases; adoption; abduction; consent to treatment. On Law Society Children panel. Member of Nuffield Child Protection and Family Law and Justice committee.
Prof. Memberships: Solicitors Family Law Association (on Children Sub-committee); Association of Lawyers for Children; National Council for Family Proceedings.
Career: Qualified 1978, *Bindman & Partners* 1988, partner 1991.
Publications: Co-author, 'Co-habitation Handbook'.
Personal: Born 1949, attended Merchant Taylor's School and Oxford University.

GLENDINNING, David
Ward Hadaway, Newcastle upon Tyne
(0191) 204 4000
Specialisation: Head of family law specialising in high value ancillary relief cases, many involving a foreign trust element.
Prof. Memberships: Law Society; Solicitors Family Law Association.
Career: LLB London. Qualified 1974. Appointed partner with *Ward Hadaway* 1986.
Personal: Married with three children. Golf and fell walking in Lake District.

GOSS, Helen
Morgan Cole, Oxford (01865) 262 600

GRAHAM, Caroline J.M.
Macleod & MacCallum, Inverness (01463) 239393

GRAY, Tim
Sinton & Co, Newcastle upon Tyne
(0191) 212 7800
t.gray@sinton.co.uk
Specialisation: Substantial ancillary relief work especially involving participators in limited companies, professional partnerships etc. Has handled a large number of cases involving assets in excess of £1 million and settlements of similar size particularly in the last two years. Considerable work load in dealing with cases under the Inheritance (Provision for Family & Dependants) Act 1975.
Prof. Memberships: Member of SFLA. Member of the Law Society Family Law panel.
Career: MA (Cantab). Qualified 1978. Articled clerk, assistant solicitor and then partner in the firm of *Sinton & Co* (1980). Specialist in family law work and especially ancillary relief throughout that time.
Personal: Devotee of Newcastle United Football Club and 'The Times' crossword puzzle.

GREEN, Michael
Green & Co, Manchester (0161) 834 8980

GREGORY-JONES, Rosemary
Leo Abse & Cohen, Cardiff (02920) 383252
rosemaryg@leoabse.co.uk
Specialisation: Family law, particularly practising in the areas of divorce, complex ancillary relief cases and private law children matters.
Prof. Memberships: Member of the Law Society's Family Law panel. Member of the SFLA.
Career: Degree in Economic History from Leicester University. Thereafter qualified as a solicitor in 1994 and has practised in family law throughout her career.

HALLAM, Catherine
Burges Salmon, Bristol (0117) 939 2245
catherine.hallam@burges-salmon.com
Specialisation: Advice about separation, divorce and related financial/children issues. Particular specialist knowledge of high asset value and complex financial settlements, restructuring of family businesses and pensions on marriage breakdown. Also settlements with an international element.
Prof. Memberships: Fellow, International Academy of Matrimonial Lawyers; SFLA; accredited specialist (pensions and substantial asset cases); member of Law Society Family Panel; Solicitors Family Law Association Pensions Committee.
Career: Qualified 1984. Worked in London until 1988. Partner at *Burges Salmon* since 1990. Regular contributor to legal journals and lecturer on family law issues. Co-author of 'Pensions and Insurance on Family Breakdown'. (Jordans 1999).
Personal: Jesus College, Oxford 1977-80. Married with two children.

HAMER, Melanie
Wendy Hopkins & Co, Cardiff (029) 20342233

HARCUS, James
Withers, London (020) 7597 6000
Specialisation: Partner in family law department. Specialises in divorce, matrimonial finance and taxation, children and cohabitation (including international cases) and pre-marital contracts. Acted in Robinson v Robinson 1982 (case involving setting aside for material non-disclosure) and Cornick v Cornick 1994 (Barder principles).
Prof. Memberships: Fellow of the International Academy of Matrimonial Lawyers (IAML). Treasurer of the Solicitors Family Law Association (SFLA) 1982-87.
Career: Qualified in 1974. Partner of *Gordon Dadds* (1981-96). Joined family law department at *Withers* in 1996.
Publications: Author of articles in Family Law (Pre-Nuptials/Term Maintenance). Has lectured for the Solicitors Family Law Association and the Institute of Financial Planning.
Personal: Born 15th April 1949. Educated at Exeter University 1968-71. Leisure interests include riding, skiing, sailing and gardening. Lives in London.

HARPER, Mark
Withers, London (020) 7597 6000
Specialisation: Partner in family law department. Exclusively family law and in particular, substantial financial cases including those with an international element and cohabitation disputes.
Prof. Memberships: SFLA National Committee 1992-98, SFLA Family Law Bill team, SFLA Cohabitation Working Group Chairperson 1995-97, SFLA Press Officer 1997-98, Law Society, Family Law Committee 1998 to date.
Career: Qualified in 1988. Became a partner in 1990 at *Anthony Gold* after articles with the firm. Head of family law department 1991-99. Joined *Withers* February 1999.
Publications: Author of articles in Family Law and SFLA Newsletter. Author of Model Letters for Family Lawyers (Jordans). Has broadcast on TV and radio and been quoted regularly in national press.
Personal: Born 2 February 1962. Educated at Malvern College and Pembroke College, Oxford. Enjoys travel, architecture and classic cars. Lives in Balham, South London.

HENSON, John S.
Hunt & Coombs, Peterborough (01733) 565312

HOPKINS, Wendy
Wendy Hopkins & Co, Cardiff (029) 20342233

HOWARD, Jenni
Morgan Cole, Oxford (01865) 262600
jenni.howard@morgan-cole.com
Specialisation: Partner and head of family law practice, specialising in complex financial divorce cases but handles all aspects of family law including cohabitation.
Prof. Memberships: Solicitors Family Law Association.
Career: Qualified in 1985. Joined *Cole & Cole* (now *Morgan & Cole*) in 1988. Became partner in 1996 and head of family law in 1999.
Personal: LLB (Hons), University of Birmingham. Leisure interests include sport (mainly hockey, running and golf) and adventure holidays abroad.

HUGHES, Frances
Hughes Fowler Carruthers, London
(020) 7421 8383
mail@hfclaw.com
Specialisation: Senior partner of family law niche practice. Practice covers the full range of family law, especially international cases and cases involving trust law or complex offshore corporate entities, as well as complex children's work. Clients include City professionals, entertainment clients and other lawyers.
Prof. Memberships: International Academy of

Matrimonial Lawyers; vice-president of the European Chapter of IAML; SFLA; coordinator of SFLA Mediation Training (1996-99). Accredited SFLA and FMA Mediator.
Career: Qualified in 1981. Assistant at *Theodore Goddard.* Joined *Bates Wells & Braithwaite* to establish the family department in 1983 and became a partner in 1984. Set up *Hughes Fowler Carruthers* in 2001.
Publications: Former contributing editor 'Butterworths Family Law Service'. Writes, lectures and broadcasts on family law, nationally and internationally.
Personal: Born 15 June 1954. Oxford 1973-76. School governor. Enjoys opera and gardening. Lives in London and Wiltshire. Sits on the Board of the Poetry Society.

HUGHES, Kathryn
Farleys, Blackburn (01254) 606060
klh@farleys.com
Specialisation: Partner in family law department. Main areas of practice are childcare and ancillary relief in divorce together with the law relating to cohabitants. Handles all aspects, privately paid and publicly funded, and public and private law cases. Children Panel member, Law Society Family Law Panel member, SFLA Accredited Specialist (advocacy-ancillary relief and children law – private). Ancillary relief – substantial assets cases and high volume of such work; Children – care work in particular, but also adoption. Past contributing author to Butterworth's 'Family Law Service'.
Prof. Memberships: Law Society Family Law Committee member and member of the Children Sub-committee, SFLA, Child Concern.
Career: Qualified in 1985; past member of the Bar (called 1977); joined *Farleys* in 1983, becoming a partner in 1985; Recorder, sitting on crime, civil and family.
Personal: Born 5 June 1954. Leisure interests include walking, swimming and reading. Lives in Hale, Cheshire.

HUTCHINSON, Anne-Marie
Dawson Cornwell, London (020) 7242 2556
mail@dawsoncornwell.co.uk
Specialisation: Practises exclusively in family law, with particular specialism in international family law, international custody disputes and child abduction. SFLA accredited specialist. Is currently engaged in extensive research into forced marriage and has represented many victims of forced marriage. Awarded the inaugural UNICEF Child Rights Lawyer Award, 1999.
Prof. Memberships: Chair of Reunite International Child Abduction Centre; Solicitors' Family Law Association; International Society of Family Law; International Bar Association; Association of Lawyers for Children; National Council for Family Proceedings; The Society for Advanced Legal Studies; management committee member of the AIRE Centre (Advice on Individual Rights in Europe), member of New Scotland Yard's child protection steering group; member of Metropolitan Police forced marriage project board; member of steering group of the International Centre for Missing and Exploited Children; member of the Adoption Forum.
Publications: Consultant editor Hershman and McFarlane 'Children Law and Practice' and co-author 'International Parental Child Abduction'. International correspondent: 'International Family Law'.

ILIFF, Catherine
Fosters, Norwich (01603) 620508

JAMIESON, George
Walker Laird, Paisley (0141) 887 5271

JONES, Catherine
Pannone & Partners, Manchester (0161) 909 3000
catherine.jones@pannone.co.uk
Specialisation: Partner and Joint Head of Family Department. Work includes divorce, separation, financial provision and children including contested adoption and cohabitation, with special emphasis on the settlement of complex financial matters for corporate, other business, professional and high net worth clients.
Prof. Memberships: Law Society, Manchester Law Society, SFLA.
Career: Qualified 1977. Joined *Pannone & Partners* in 1982. North West SFLA secretary and Regional Representative on the National Liason Committee and solicitor representative to Greater Manchester Adoption Committee.
Personal: Leisure interests include walking, sailing, theatre and travel. Lives in Altrincham.

JONES, Peter
Jones Myers Gordon, Leeds (0113) 246 0055
Specialisation: Main areas of practice divorce and high value ancillary relief together with cohabitation disputes and mediation.
Prof. Memberships: Former national chairman of the Solicitors Family Law Association; lecturer and member of the UK College of Family Mediators.
Career: Qualified 1980. Founded a specialist family law practice nine years ago.
Personal: Born 4 June 1948. Married with two daughters. Lives in Harrogate.

JURY, Susan
Wolferstans, Plymouth (01752) 663 295
sjury@wolferstans.com
Specialisation: Family/matrimonial. Family law – all areas of divorce work; ancillary relief; children, private and public law; cohabitee and domestic violence.
Prof. Memberships: Member of SFLA and special accredited member – children's matters; member Law Society, Children Panel, trained SFLA family mediator.
Career: Tavistock School; Huddersfield University; Chester College of Law; LLB. Articled *Wolferstans* 1987, qualified 1990, became a partner 1995.
Personal: Year of birth: 1964; town of residence: Christow. Main leisure activities: skiing, aerobics, reading and caring for two small children.

KEIR, Jane
Kingsley Napley, London Mobile: 07887 571050
jkeir@kingsleynapley.co.uk
Specialisation: Partner since 1999 and head of the Department of Family Law. Specialises in all aspects of family law work particularly dealing with the complexities which can arise in negotiating financial settlements and upon the arrangements that divorcing or separating couples may need to work out in relation to their children and their property. The department is highly regarded for its work in the field of child abduction and receives instructions from the Lord Chancellor's department in this area.
Prof. Memberships: Member of the Law Society and the Solicitors Family Law Association and former chair of its International Committee. Fellow of the Society for Advanced Legal Studies and member of its previous working party looking at the issues arising from the cross border movement of children. Member of its current working party looking at the issues arising in the medical treatment of persons under a disability.
Career: Qualified in December 1987. Joined *Kingsley Napley* in 1989 and became a partner in the Department of Family Law in November 1992.
Publications: Contributing author to 'Evidence in Family Proceedings' published by Jordan Publishing Limited and 'International Aspects of Family Law – A Guide to Good Practice and Procedure' published by the SFLA in 2000 has also been published recently in the Family Law Journal. Was much in demand for comment from the media in relation to the recent Internet twins story.
Personal: Born 4 March 1962. Lives in London and enjoys horses and National Hunt racing, fine wines, running and travel.

KIDD, Philip
Tozers, Newton Abbot (01626) 207020

LA FOLLETTE, Maryly
Charles Russell, London (020) 7203 5000
marylyl@cr-law.co.uk
Specialisation: Partner in the family department. International divorce, ancillary relief and child related work (private law).
Prof. Memberships: Solicitors Family Law Association; Family Mediators Association.

LAMBERT, Tracy
Tozers, Torquay (01803) 407020

LEVERTON, David
Payne Hicks Beach, London (020) 7465 4300

LEVISON, Jeremy I.
Levison Meltzer Pigott, London (020) 7556 2400

LONGRIGG, William
Charles Russell, London (020) 7203 5096
williaml@cr-law.co.uk
Specialisation: Partner in family department. Main areas of practice are divorce, ancillary relief and child-related work (private law).
Prof. Memberships: Solicitors Family Law Association; chairman SFLA London Regional Group since 1996.

LOUDON, Alasdair
Turcan Connell, Edinburgh (0131) 228 8111
ajl@turcanconnell.com
Specialisation: Sole area of practice is family law, including divorce cases, particularly those involving claims for capital payments or property transfer orders. Also handles substantial number of cases involving the negotiation of separation agreements. Acts in Court of Session and Sheriff Court. Former tutor in criminal advocacy at Edinburgh University. Accredited by the Law Society of Scotland as a specialist in family law.
Prof. Memberships: WS Society, Edinburgh Bar Association (past president), Family Law Association. Member of Sheriff Court Rules Council for Scotland.
Career: Qualified in 1978. Apprentice at *Tods, Murray & Jamieson WS* 1978-80. Qualified assistant at *Warner & Co* 1980-82 and partner 1982-92. Founded *Loudons WS* in 1992. Joined *Turcan Connell* as a partner, 2001.
Personal: Born 7 April 1956. Attended Dundee Uni-

versity 1974-78. Leisure interests include golf (member of Bruntsfield Links and Luffness New) and football (Hearts season ticket holder). Lives in Edinburgh.

LOXLEY, Martin
Irwin Mitchell, Sheffield (0114) 276 7777
loxleym@irwinmitchell.co.uk
Specialisation: High value ancillary relief including pension cases, cohabitation disputes, private Children Act cases.
Prof. Memberships: Law Society, National Committee of SFLA.
Career: Articled at *Irwin Mitchell* 1978-80; partner at *Irwin Mitchell* 1981 to date; head of family law at *Irwin Mitchell* since 1986.
Publications: Editor of SFLA Consent Order Precedents 1998, editor of SFLA Separation and Pre-Marital Agreements 2001.
Personal: Educated at High Storrs, Sheffield and Trent Polytechnic, Nottingham. Leisure interests include sport, music and family. Keen interest in the fortunes of Sheffield Wednesday FC. Married with two daughters.

MAIR, Leonard
Morton Fraser, Solicitors, Edinburgh (0131) 247 1000

MANNING, Richard
Walker Morris, Leeds (0113) 283 2500
Prof. Memberships: Deputy District Judge (Magistrates Court).

MARCO, Alan
Collyer-Bristow, London (020) 7242 7363
alan.marco@collyerbristow.com
Specialisation: Partner, matrimonial department. Handles all areas of family and matrimonial law with emphasis on financial provision applications. Deputy District Judge at Principal Registry of the Family Division.
Prof. Memberships: Solicitors Family Law Association.
Career: Qualified in 1965. Partner at *Baileys Shaw & Gillett* 1972-96. Partner *Collyer-Bristow* 1996.
Personal: Born in Devon. Married with three children.

MASSEY, William
Manches, London (020) 7404 4433
william.massey@manches.co.uk
Specialisation: Practises exclusively in family and matrimonial law.
Prof. Memberships: Solictor's Family Law Association, SFLA London Regional Committee (Treasurer), SFLA Accredited Specialist (Big Money and International Cases), London Guildhall University LPC Advisory Panel.
Career: Qualified in 1990 at *Freshfields. Penningtons* 1991-94. Joined *Manches* in 1994, became partner 1999.
Personal: Born 3rd May 1964. Educated at Oundle School and Exeter University. Married with three young children. Enjoys sports, outdoors and constructive solutions.

McDONALD, Roberta
Roberta McDonald – Sole Practitioner, Birmingham (0121) 449 6821

MEISEL, Mari
Blair Allison & Co, Birmingham (0121) 233 2904

MESSENGER, Mercy
Mercy Messenger – Sole Practitioner, Solihull (01564) 779427
family@mercymessenger.co.uk
Specialisation: High value ancillary relief; strong focus on companies and pensions aspects; handles the cases personally. Xydhias v Xydhias Court of Appeal (winning side) and now in the textbooks.
Prof. Memberships: SFLA.
Career: Qualified 1996. Founded present firm 1983.
Personal: Family – two grown up sons; husband is company law specialist and consultant to the practice. Leisure interests – gardening and renovating old houses.

MILBURN, Paula
Jones Maidment Wilson incorporating Hatton Scates Horton, Manchester (0161) 832 8087

MITCHELL, Jane
Manches, Oxford (01865) 722 106
jane.mitchell@manches.co.uk
Specialisation: Advises on all areas of family law, particulary complex financial and children issues arising from matrimonial and relationship breakdown.
Prof. Memberships: Solicitors Family Law Association, Law Society.
Career: Qualified in 1988. Has practised at *Manches* since then, first in London and then, in 1995, moving to their Oxford office to set up its family law department. Partner since 1997.
Publications: Contributing editor to 'Current Law Weekly'.
Personal: Born 17th May 1963. B.A. Hons (English and Related Literature). Married with three children. Leisure interests include theatre and gardening.

MONRO, Pat
Darlington & Parkinson, London (020) 8998 4343

NICE, Anna
Miles Preston & Co, London (020) 7583 0583
anna.nice@milespreston.co.uk
Specialisation: All aspects of family law, particularly cases involving substantial assets and/or disputes relating to children, including those with an international element.
Prof. Memberships: Solicitor's Family Law Association.
Career: *Manches* 1994-97; *Miles Preston & Co* 1997; partner 2000; SFLA Accredited Specialist (Substantial Assets and Advocacy: Ancillary Relief); accredited member of Law Society's Family Law Panel.
Personal: Born 1968. Educated University College, London.

NICOL, Frazer
Nicol, Denvir & Purnell, Cardiff (029) 20796311

O'DONNELL, Caroline
Miller Sands, Cambridge (01223) 366 741
cod@millersands.com
Specialisation: Children (private and public law), divorce and ancilliary relief. SFLA Mediator.
Prof. Memberships: SFLA member. Legal Aid Committee member (SFLA). Association of Lawyers for Children, National Committee member. Member of the Law Society's Children Panel.

O'REGAN, Timothy
Rudlings & Wakelam, Thetford (01842) 754 151

PALMER, George
Peden & Reid, Belfast (028) 9032 5617

PARKER, Diana
Withers, London (020) 7597 6000
Specialisation: Partner in family law department. Exclusively family law. The senior partner of *Withers* but still handling heavy caseload of complex cases.
Prof. Memberships: Solicitors Family Law Association (SFLA); Family Mediators Association (FMA); International Academy of Matrimonial Lawyers (IAML).
Publications: Co-author of 'Longman's Practical Matrimonial Precedents' and 'Know How for Family Lawyers'. Author of articles in professional journals and elsewhere. Occasional lecturer, speaker at conferences and contributor to the media.
Personal: MA (Cantab); MPhil (Cantab). Lives in London and Oxford.

PARRY, Richard
Farrer & Co, London (020) 7242 2022
rwp@farrer.co.uk
Specialisation: Partner in family team. Main area of practice is family law.
Prof. Memberships: Solicitors Family Law Association.
Career: Qualified in 1976. Joined *Farrer & Co* in 1974, becoming a partner in 1983.
Personal: Born 6 December 1951. Educated at Eton College (1964-69) and Balliol College, Oxford (1970-73). Governor of Downe House. Leisure interests include golf, bridge and music. Lives in London.

PATIENCE, Iain
Patience & Buchan, Aberdeen (01224) 588333
iain@patienceandbuchan.com
Specialisation: Partner. Law Society accredited specialist in Family Law and Family Mediation.
Career: Admitted December 1979. Previously one of the senior partners at *Iain Smith & Company*. Set up the only Aberdeen partnership specialising in family law in August 2000. A member of the Law Society of Scotland and Family Law Association. Qualified mediator – member of CALM.

PAYNE, Peter
Stephens & Scown, Exeter (01392) 210700

PEARSON, Philippa
The Family Law Consortium, London (020) 7420 5000

PEMBRIDGE, Eileen
Fisher Meredith, London (020) 7622 4468
eileenp@fishermeredith.co.uk
Specialisation: Senior partner and head of family department. Deals with all aspects of family law, but especially complex ancillary relief on divorce and other financial matters. Has always taken on Legal Aid work. Has written various opinion pieces on family law and the legal profession, lectured and addressed sessions on family law at the Solicitors Annual Conference.
Prof. Memberships: Law Society; council member for London South since 1990; Family Law committee 1990 to date (chair 1990-94); Courts and Legal Services committee from 1987; now Vice-Chair Access to Justice Working Party. International Human Rights Working Party for five years from 1993 and Equal Opportunities Committee since 1994, (Chair from 1999). LAPG (Committee Member since 1982 and Chair 1987-88); SFLA; International Family Law Association; Chair of Law Society Reputation Working Party; 1999-01, Member Institute of Advanced Legal Studies.

Career: Worked as a freelance interpreter for the UN 1967-73 and casually thereafter until 1983. Qualified in 1975. Co-founder of *Fisher Meredith* in 1975, now 100 strong. Challenged Law Society convention by standing for election as President, July 1995.
Publications: General Editor and now Consulting Editor, Sweet and Maxwell 'Legal Aid Practice Manual'.
Personal: Born 15 March 1944. Educated at Worcester Girls' Grammar School; Newnham College, Cambridge (Natural Sciences degree and postgraduate French and Russian), and Bath University (postgraduate language studies). FRSA. Interests include sailing, animal welfare, children's activities, hill-walking, vegetable-growing and reading novels in French, Russian and Spanish. Lives in Dulwich Village, London with her two young children and husband (a judge).

PHILIPPS, Susan
Alexiou Fisher Philipps, London (020) 7409 1222
sphilipps@afp-law.co.uk
Specialisation: Partner. Covers all areas of family and matrimonial law. SFLA trained mediator.
Prof. Memberships: Solicitors Family Law Association. Serves on Education committee of the SFLA.
Career: Qualified in 1984. Joined *Ward Bowie* in 1982 and became a partner in 1986 on merger with *Penningtons*. Head of family law department since 1994 until joined *Gordon Dadds* in 1999. Founding partner *Alexiou Fisher Philipps* 2001.
Personal: Born 9 April 1957. Lives in London.

PIGOTT, Simon
Levison Meltzer Pigott, London (020) 7556 2400

PIRRIE, James
The Family Law Consortium, London (020) 7420 5000

POWELL, Mark
Hugh James Ford Simey, Bargoed (01443) 822022
mark.powell@hjfs.co.uk
Specialisation: Partner and head of family group. Public childrens law, mental health.
Prof. Memberships: Association of Lawyers for Children (Past Chair).
Career: Rugby School. University College, London. Admitted as solicitor 1977. Barrister and Solicitor of the High Court of New Zealand (admitted 1990). Assistant Recorder 1995. Made Recorder in the year 2000.

PRESTON, Miles
Miles Preston & Co, London (020) 7583 0583
miles.preston@milespreston.co.uk
Specialisation: Practises exclusively in matrimonial and family law.
Prof. Memberships: Solicitors Family Law Association, International Academy of Matrimonial Lawyers.
Career: Qualified in 1974. Partner with *Radcliffes & Co* (1979-94). Founding partner *Miles Preston & Co* (1994). Served on Sir Gervaise Sheldon's Family Law Liaison Committee 1982; founder member SFLA 1982; served on Main Committee of SFLA 1982-88; chaired working party on procedure 1982-88; founder member of IAML 1986; Governor IAML 1986-89; Parliamentarian to Main Committee 1989; president of English Chapter 1989; president of European Chapter 1989-92; president Elect of Main Academy 1992-94. President of Main Academy 1994-96. Member of the President's International Family Law Committee (chaired by Lord Justice Thorpe) since 1994.
Personal: Born 1950. Educated Shrewsbury School 1963-68. Leisure interests include food, travel and classic cars. Lives in Chelsea, London.

PROCTOR, Jane
Greenwoods, Peterborough (01733) 887700

RAE, Maggie
Clintons, London (020) 7379 6080

RANDALL, Richard
Leonard Gray, Chelmsford (01245) 504904
Specialisation: All aspects of family law including complex cases involving substantial financial assets or children. Particular specialisation in contact cases involving hostile parents and the representation of teenage children in legal proceedings. Broadcasts, lectures and writes on family law and related issues.
Prof. Memberships: Solicitors Family Law Association. Founder member British Association of Lawyer Mediators.
Career: Qualified 1972. Partner *Leonard Gray* 1975. Head of family law department 1984. Senior partner 1991. Sole family mediator 1996.
Personal: Born 17 May 1948. Educated at Brentwood School, LLB London. Lives and works in Chelmsford. Enjoys performing choral music and opera, cricket, cycling.

RAY, Peggy
Goodman Ray, London (020) 7254 8855
peggyray@goodmanray.com
Specialisation: Practice covers all areas of child care work including both public and private law cases, adoption and associated areas such as judicial review and administrative law. Speaker and trainer in childcare. Former member of the Law Society Family Law Committee, current member of Solicitors Family Law Association children committee, member of the Expert Witness Group, former member of the Inner London Children Act Business committee. Member of the Law Society Children panel since 1985. Member of Funding Review committee, member of President's Interdisciplinary committee, member of Family Appeals Review Group.
Prof. Memberships: Solicitors Family Law Association, Association of Lawyers for Children, NaGALRO, BAAF.
Career: Qualified 1980. Established own practice with Judith Goodman in Hackney in 1985.

READHEAD, Siobhan
Miles Preston & Co, London (020) 7583 0583
siobhan.readhead@milespreston.co.uk
Specialisation: All areas of matrimonial and family law, including resolution of financial issues on divorce and separation; all issues relating to children; pre-marriage and cohabitation contracts.
Prof. Memberships: Solicitors Family Law Association; International Academy of Matrimonial Lawyers.
Career: *Radcliffes* 1982-94; partner 1989; founding partner *Miles Preston & Co* 1994; SFLA Accredited Specialist (Advocacy: Ancillary Relief and Substantial Assets; Trustee of Mediation in Divorce).
Personal: Born 1957. Educated Southampton University; married, two children; resides Richmond.

RODGERS, Hilary
Forsters, London (020) 7863 8333
hrodgers@forsters.co.uk
Specialisation: Head of family law practice, specialising in complex financial divorce settlements and children matters. Also experienced in issues of jurisdiction, taxation, trusts and pensions in relation to matrimonial matters.
Prof. Memberships: Solicitors Family Law Association treasurer; SFLA; chair of the Cohabitation committee; International Bar Association; International Academy of Matrimonial Lawyers.
Career: Admitted 1987. Assistant at *Theodore Goddard*. Joined *Frere Cholmeley Bischoff* 1991. Partner 1994. Founder partner of *Forsters*, August 1998.
Personal: Born 1962. Married with two children. Lives in North London.

RUTHERFORD, Lyn
Dickinson Dees, Newcastle upon Tyne (0191) 279 9229
law@dickinson-dees.com
Specialisation: Partner and head of family law department. The practice covers a full range of family law matters. In particular specialisation in high net worth private clients and major ancillary matters.
Career: Qualified 1972. Thereafter one year at *Clayton Mott* in Nottingham. Joined *Dickinson Dees* in January 1974. Became a partner in 1976.
Personal: Born 20 January 1948. Educated at Hookergate Grammar School and Liverpool University – LLB Degree. Interests include sports, particularly horse racing, football and reading. Lives in Newcastle upon Tyne.

RUTTER, Geoffrey
Collyer-Bristow, London (020) 7242 7363
geoffrey.rutter@collyerbristow.com
Specialisation: Many years experience in family law, principally involving substantial financial issues resulting from marriage breakdown, including forum issues. Considerable knowledge of and experience in the investigative elements of domestic and international work including offshore trusts and structures. Regularly advises on the commercial and tax considerations involved in financial negotiations and settlements.
Prof. Memberships: Solicitors Family Law Association (accredited specialist and assessor), International Academy of Matrimonial Lawyers. Committee member of the London Regional Committee of the Solicitors Family Law Association.

SALTER, David
Addleshaw Booth & Co, Leeds (0113) 203 2454
das@addleshaw-booth.co.uk
Specialisation: Partner and head of family law department. Handles all aspects of family law, but principally financial relief with an emphasis on pensions. Author or joint author of 'Humphreys Family Proceedings', 'Matrimonial Consent Orders and Agreements', 'Family Finance and Tax' and 'Family Courts: Emergency Remedies and Procedures'. Editor of 'Pensions and Insurance on Family Breakdown' and 'Longman Litigation Practice'. Contributor to 'Insolvency on Family Breakdown' and 'Butterworths Family Law Service'. Frequent lecturer on family law topics.
Prof. Memberships: SFLA (Chairman 1997-99). Chairman of SFLA Accreditation and Pensions Committees. International Academy of Matrimonial Lawyers (Fellow; Member, Management Committee, European Chapter).
Career: Qualified in 1972. Joined the firm in 1975, becoming a Partner in 1978. Recorder (North Eastern Circuit); Member of the Family Committee of the Judicial Studies Board.
Personal: Educated Pembroke College, Cambridge.

SANDS, Rosemary
Miller Sands, Cambridge (01223) 366 741
rs@millersands.com
Specialisation: Head of family law department. Work includes divorce (especially for other lawyers), ancillary relief, adoption and children (public and private law). FMA mediator. Hon Adviser for local CAB.
Prof. Memberships: Law Society; SFLA; FMA; ALC; BAAF; chair of Cambridgeshire Guardian ad litem advisory panel; member Children panel; Law Society Family Law panel; member UK College of Family Mediators.
Personal: LLB 1954. Barrister (Middle Temple) 1956-64.

SAX, Richard
Manches, London (020) 7404 4433
richard.sax@manches.co.uk
Specialisation: Partner in family department. Advises on all areas of family law, particularly complex financial and children issues arising from matrimonial and relationship breakdown including international, trust and tax aspects.
Prof. Memberships: Solicitors Family Law Association, International Academy of Matrimonial Lawyers, Law Society, Family Law Committee.
Career: Qualified in 1967. 1968 Partner and subsequently Managing Partner at *Rubinstein Callingham* (which merged with *Manches* in 1994). Since 1990 has sat as a Deputy District Judge at the Principal Registry. Past Chairman of the Solicitors Family Law Association. Governor and Vice-President International Academy of Matrimonial Lawyers European Chapter. Member of the DSS Consultation Panel on Pension Sharing.
Publications: Co-Author 'Know how for Family Lawyers', published by Longmans. Joint General Editor Butterworth's 'Family Law Service'.

SCANLAN, Margaret
Russells Gibson McCaffrey, Glasgow
(0141) 332 4176
info@russellsgm.co.uk
Specialisation: Family law and child law, including negotiating settlements and court work. Law Society of Scotland accredited specialist in family law.
Prof. Memberships: Family Law Association, Sheriff Court Rules Council, Scottish Legal Aid Board.
Career: Qualified 1972 after apprenticeship with *Flowers & Co.* Thereafter wide general practice, specialising in family law for last 10 years. Founder member and past chair of Family Law Association.
Personal: Bad golf, good food.

SCOFIELD, Ian
Hooper & Wollen, Torquay (01803) 213251
Specialisation: Senior partner and head of department advising on all aspects of family law and child care. Specialises in financial and property issues and has a substantial case load of high value divorces involving complex negotiation. Accredited mediator with the Family Mediators Association and one of the few mediators in the South West with a regular case load. Member of the Solicitors Family Law Association and a member of the Law Society's Childcare panel.

SHACKLETON, Fiona
Payne Hicks Beach, London (020) 7465 4300
Specialisation: Partner in family team. Principal area of practice is family law. Solicitor to HRH The Prince of Wales and TRH Princes William and Harry since 1996.
Prof. Memberships: SFLA, IAML.
Career: Qualified in 1980. Became a partner with *Brecher & Co* in 1982. Joined *Farrer & Co* in 1984; became a partner in 1987. Joined *PHB* in 2001 as a partner.
Publications: Co-author of 'The Divorce Handbook'.
Personal: Born 26th May 1956. Attended Benenden School and Exeter University. Governor of Benenden School since 1985. Leisure pursuits include calligraphy, cooking, opera and bridge. Lives in London.

SHAKESPEAR, Felicity
Clarke Willmott & Clarke, Taunton
(01823) 329 845
fshakespear@cw-c.co.uk
Specialisation: Partner, head of family department. Has specialised in family law since qualification and is now Leader of eight specialist lawyers. All areas of family law are covered, in particular, high asset ancillary relief claims involving companies, pensions and farmers, and also public law child care. Acted for Mr White in the House of Lords regarding the interest of spouses on dissolution of marriage which has become the leading authority in this field.
Prof. Memberships: Member of Children Panel. SFLA Regional Committee Member, Family Law Panel Assessor, Law Society.
Career: Qualified in 1973. Partner with *Darlington & Parkinson* (Ealing, London) 1985/1986. President of Central and South Middlesex Law Society. Joined *Clarke Willmott & Clarke* in 1986, becoming a partner in 1989.
Personal: Born 1948. LLB Southampton. Married. Leisure interests include gardening, bridge and running a large apple orchard.

SHEEHAN, Wendy
Mowat Dean & Co WS, Edinburgh
(0131) 555 0616

SHELTON, Erica
Charles Russell, London (020) 7203 5000
ericas@cr-law.co.uk
Specialisation: Family law, ancillary relief, particularly experienced in dealing with cases where there are trusts involved, and children. Acted for wife in Conran v Conran.
Prof. Memberships: Law Society, SFLA, Association of Contentions Trust and probate practitioners.

SHRIMPTON, Julie
Tozers, Plymouth (01752) 206460

SILVER, Raphael
Silver Fitzgerald, Cambridge (01223) 562001
Specialisation: Senior litigation partner. Childcare, crime.
Prof. Memberships: Law Society Children Panel. SFLA. Associate Member NAGALRO and BAAF.
Personal: Born 1960, Liverpool. Graduated Durham University. Married. Lives in Saffron Walden. Interests include cricket, gardening and wine.

SIMPSON, Barbara
Boodle Hatfield, Oxford (01865) 265128
bsimpson@boodlehatfield.co.uk
Specialisation: Highly experienced in handling substantial financial cases, including those with an international element or complex commercial issues. Practice also includes dealing with all types of privately funded children law and ancillary relief issues. Experienced in emergency work including injunctions and strong contacts with London office.
Prof. Memberships: SFLA (was the first chair of the Solicitors Family Law Association in Oxford); Deputy District Judge in the Principal Registry of Family Division since 1995.
Career: Qualified 1974. Assistant at *Herbert & Gowers* from 1975-76. Head of the *Cole & Cole* (now *Morgan & Cole*) family law department from 1984. Joined *Boodle Hatfield* as a partner in 1999.
Personal: Born 1948. Educated at Durham University. Enjoys squash, cinema, chess and singing.

SIMPSON, Jane
Manches, London (020) 7753 7519
jane.simpson@manches.co.uk
Specialisation: Partner and head of family law department. Deals in particular with divorce and complex financial issues, children, tax, and the commercial implications of divorce and separation; international aspects of divorce and separation and forum shopping. Has lectured extensively.
Prof. Memberships: Founder member of International Academy of Matrimonial Lawyers. Non-executive Director and Vice-Chairman of the Tavistock Portman NHS Trust.
Career: Qualified in 1967. Marriage Guidance Counsellor 1972-77. Founded *Manches* family law department in 1977. Co-founder of Solicitors Family Law Association in 1982 and chairman 1993-95. Member of Ancilliary Relief Advisory Group 1991-00. Member of Lord Chancellor's Advisory Board on Family Law 1996-01.
Personal: Born 15 July 1942. Educated at Channing School, Highgate and University College, London. Enjoys music, reading, travel. Has two adult daughters and one son.

SISSON, David
Eversheds, Norwich (01603) 272727
davidsisson@eversheds.com
Specialisation: Exclusively family law, with emphasis on finance.
Prof. Memberships: SFLA; SFLA International Committee.
Career: Qualified 1977. Partner *Eversheds* 1985. Head of *Eversheds* family law department since 1991.
Personal: Born 5th May 1951. Leisure interests include bridge and golf.

SMITH, Caroline
Russel & Aitken, Edinburgh (0131) 228 5500
caroline.smith@russelaitken.com
Specialisation: Associate dealing with family law. Sixteen years experience dealing exclusively with family law. Accredited by Law Society of Scotland as specialist in family law and as a family mediator. Member of local panel of reporting officers/curators ad litem for adoption proceedings. Prepares child welfare reports for Sheriff Court.
Prof. Memberships: Family Law Association, Edinburgh Bar Association. W.S. Society, Comprehensive Accredited Lawyer Mediators.
Career: Qualified MB.Ch.B 1979 and worked as hospital doctor 1979-82. Assistant *Warner & Co* 1985-88. Qualified LLB 1986. Assistant (Litigation) *Morton Fraser Milligan WS* 1988-93. Partner *Loudens WS* July 1994 to February 2001. Associate *Russel & Aitken* March 2001.
Personal: Born 23 June 1955. Educated St. Denis School, Edinburgh 1960-73 and Edinburgh University 1973-79 and 1982-85. Leisure interests include walking, swimming, reading. Lives in Edinburgh.

SMITH, Michael
Mincoffs, Newcastle upon Tyne (0191) 281 6151
Specialisation: Family Law.
Prof. Memberships: Secretary of the North East Region SFFA, member of Family Law Panel.
Career: Qualified in 1974.
Personal: Jogging, keeping fit and speedway racing. Together with Mary Smith probably representing the only husband and wife family law team in the country.

SMITH, Shona
Balfour & Manson, Edinburgh (0131) 200 1238
shona.smith@balfour-manson.co.uk
Specialisation: Practises exclusively in the family law field both in the Sheriff Court and the Court of Session. Accredited by the Law Society of Scotland as a family law specialist. Author for Butterworths 'Family Law Service'.
Prof. Memberships: Law Society of Scotland; Family Law Association (committee member 1997-99, chair 1999-date); Child Law Centre (member of board of trustees 1997-00).
Career: Qualified in 1991. Specialised in family law since 1993. Joined the family law team at *Balfour & Manson* in 1996. Also appointed regularly by the Sheriff Court to report on child welfare issues.
Personal: Born 17 November 1996. Educated at Edinburgh University 1984-89. Leisure interests include travel and theatre. Lives in Edinburgh.

SPEKER, Barry
Samuel Phillips & Co, Newcastle upon Tyne (0191) 232 8451
admin@samuelphillips.co.uk
Specialisation: Medical negligence, personal injury, family (including child care and adoption) and employment law. Legal adviser for Newcastle Health Authority and various NHS trusts, NSPCC and Barnardo's North East. Regular lecturer on child care law, medical negligence and employment law. Affiliate of Institute of Risk Management.
Prof. Memberships: Law Society (Medical Negligence and Children Panels). President Newcastle Law Society 2000.
Career: Qualified 1971 while with *Leigh Gold & Co*, then joined *Samuel Phillips & Co.* Partner 1973, senior partner 1987. Part time Employment Tribunal Chairman.
Personal: Born 28th June 1947. Heaton Grammar School, London University. Member of Mensa. Leisure pursuits include golf, debating and the Times Crossword.

STAKES, John Anthony
Gordons Cranswick Solicitors, Leeds (0113) 245 2450
john.stakes@gordonscranswick.co.uk
Specialisation: Family Law: Divorce, Finance, Cohabitation and Abduction.
Prof. Memberships: Former National SFLA Regional Press Officer and chairman of West and North Yorkshire SFLA. Currently ex-officio committee member.
Career: Qualified 1971. Partner 1975.
Personal: Married with two children and three stepchildren. Leisure interests include walking, amateur dramatics and cricket.

STANCZYK, Julia
Miles Preston & Co, London (020) 7583 0583
julia.stanczyk@milespreston.co.uk
Specialisation: Financial cases, often involving complex and international issues; pre-marriage contracts; cohabitation cases and private Children Act cases. Instructed in the leading case on reciprocal enforcement of maintenance orders: K v M, M and L (Financial Relief: Foreign Orders) 1998 2 FLR 59.
Prof. Memberships: SFLA.
Career: Articled *Radcliffes*; partner 1990; partner *Miles Preston & Co* 1994. One of the first SFLA accredited specialists (substantial assets/emergency relief) 1999.
Personal: Educated Haberdashers' Aske's Girls' School, Elstree and Southampton University.

STOWE, Marilyn J.
Grahame Stowe, Bateson, Leeds (0113) 260 6191
famlaw@grahame-stowe-bateson.co.uk
Specialisation: Deals in particular with divorce and complex financial issues, children, tax, commercial implications of divorce and separation.
Prof. Memberships: The Law Society, The Law Society Family Law Panel.
Career: Qualified in 1980. Former lecturer in English Law at University of Le Mans, France. Partner in *Grahame Stowe Bateson* 1982. Chair Child Support Appeals Tribunal 1993 to date. Chair Social Security Appeals Tribunal 1994 to date. Chief assessor and chief examiner of the Law Society's Family Law Panel 1998 to date – appointment renewed 2001.
Publications: Author; 'Divorce – A New Beginning' published 1993.
Personal: Born 30 April 1954. Attended Leeds Girls High School 1965 -72 and University of Leeds 1973-76. Leisure interests include distance running. Married with one son. Lives in Leeds.

TAIT, Fiona
Drummond Miller WS, Edinburgh (0131) 226 5151
ft@drumil.demon.co.uk
Specialisation: Partner. Head of Drummond Miller's family law team which deals with divorce, financial provision, child law, child abductions and children's hearings. Accredited specialist in family law. Tutor at the University of Edinburgh LLB course in Commercial Law (1990-97).
Prof. Memberships: Law Society of Scotland, Edinburgh Bar Association Council Member (1993-96).
Career: Qualified in 1991. Joined *Drummond Miller* in 1989, becoming a partner in 1996.
Personal: Born 9 January 1966. Attended University of Edinburgh: LLB (Hons) 1988, DipLP 1989. Lives in Edinburgh.

TAYLOR, Norman
Zermansky & Partners, Leeds (0113) 245 9766
norman@zermansky-solicitors.com
Specialisation: Ancillary relief in divorce and cohabitation disputes.
Prof. Memberships: West and North Yorkshire SFLA committee.
Career: Qualified July 1975. With *Zermansky & Partners* since February 1974. Head of family department.
Personal: Born 14 January 1951. Educated at University of Newcastle upon Tyne (LLB). Married with three children. 1st Dan Black Belt Japan Karate Association (retired). Lead guitarist in charity rock band.

THORNEYCROFT, Phil
Wolferstans, Plymouth (01752) 663295
pthorneycroft@wolferstans.com
Specialisation: Partner 1990. Head of family office. Main areas of practice are childcare and ancillary relief. Acts on behalf of parents and children, and Children's Guardians, in care proceedings and related matters. Acts for private and legally aided clients in divorce and ancillary relief. Head of the firm's mediation unit. Has made a number of appearances on local radio dealing with such issues as sexual abuse, cohabitation contracts and the effect of pensions on divorce.
Prof. Memberships: Chair of the Devon & Cornwall Solicitors Family Law Association committee; a member of the Children panel; founder member of the Plymouth Childcare Support group. Associate member of the National Association of Guardians ad Litem and reporting officers. SFLA trained family mediator. SFLA accredited specialist (advocacy, ancillary relief and children's law).
Career: Qualified in 1982. Joined *Wolferstans* in 1982, becoming a partner in 1990.
Personal: Born 2 December 1957. Attended Chesterfield Grammar School 1970-76, Hull University 1976-79 and Chester Law College 1979-80. Leisure interests include hockey, skiing, music and Sheffield Wednesday. Lives in Plymouth.

TOOTH, Ray
Sears Tooth, London (020) 7499 5599
Specialisation: All aspects of matrimonial matters with particular emphasis on financial cases, often of an international nature. Has habitually been involved in difficult cases.
Prof. Memberships: The Law Society.
Career: Dragon School. Oxford. Kings School, Canterbury. University College Oxford.
Personal: Extensive horse racing interests, including breeding. Carlton Television produced a half-hour documentary about Mr Tooth, 'Tooth and Nail' in August 1997 demonstrating the practice of matrimonial law.

TRUEX, David
International Family Law Chambers, London (020) 7583 5040
truex@internationalfamilylaw.com
Specialisation: SFLA accredited specialist family lawyer (1999). Particular expertise in multi-jurisdictional disputes involving forum, recognition, enforcement and analysis of foreign laws.
Prof. Memberships: Chair, SFLA International Committee; Chair, UK Host committee 2001 World Congress on Family Law and the Rights of Children and Youth. Member: SFLA; Law Society; ABA; AFCC; Law Council of Australia Family Law Section; Law Institute of Victoria.
Career: Qualified Australia 1974; England and Wales 1990. Founded *David Truex and Company* (now *International Family Law Chambers) 1990.*
Personal: Born 7 March 1949 Washington, DC. Educated USA and Australia. Enjoys creative thinking, problem solving and fracturing French and German grammaticals.

WALSH, Terry
Chivers Walsh Smith & Irvine & Co, Bradford (01274) 740 077

WARD, Helen
Manches, London (020) 7404 4433
helen.ward@manches.co.uk
Specialisation: Partner in family law department. Handles all areas of family law, particularly complex financial aspects of matrimonial and relationship breakdown involving an international element.
Prof. Memberships: Solicitors Family Law Association, International Academy of Matrimonial Lawyers, Law Society.
Career: Qualified in 1978. Partner at *Ward Bowie* from 1978, which subsequently became *Penningtons.* Joined *Manches* as a partner in July 1994. Deputy District Judge in the Principal Registry and Recorder.
Personal: Born 28th May 1951. Attended King Alfred School, London 1955-69 and Birmingham University 1970-73. Family come first but leisure interests include music, theatre, tennis and gardening.

WAY, Philip
Addleshaw Booth & Co, Leeds (0113) 209 2000
Specialisation: Partner in the firm's family law department. Deals with all aspects of marriage and relationship breakdown. Wide experience of the financial issues arising on divorce including those surrounding the family business and pensions. Typically represents successful business and professional people where the family assets exceed £1m. SFLA trained mediator.
Prof. Memberships: Chairman of the West & North Yorkshire SFLA and member of the SFLA Good Practice Committee. Accredited SFLA specialist family lawyer with particular expertise in dealing with substantial assets on divorce and emergency financial procedures on divorce. Associate of UK College of Family Mediators.
Career: Joined the firm in 1990 as a trainee, qualified into the firm's family law department in 1992 and became a partner in 2001.
Publications: Contributor to 'Humphreys Family Proceedings', 'Pensions on Family Breakdown', 'Insolvency on Family Breakdown' and 'Family Finance and Tax'. Regular author of articles for legal journals.
Personal: Educated at Durham University. Married. Lives in Wakefield.

WHITE, Denis
Hunt & Coombs, Peterborough (01733) 565312

WHITE, Iain
Cozens-Hardy & Jewson, Norwich (01603) 625231
Specialisation: Family department. Specialises in child-related work, divorce and matrimonial finance.
Prof. Memberships: Original member of the Children panel. Member of the Family Law panel and Solicitors Family Law Association. Representative on the Norwich Family Court Business committee.
Career: Qualified 1977. Partner 1986.

WILKINS, Beth
Pannone & Partners, Manchester (0161) 909 3000
beth.wilkins@pannone.co.uk
Specialisation: Partner and joint head of family department. Handles all aspects of marriage breakdown, matrimonial finance and private law relating to children. Advises on co-habitation and pre-nuptial agreements. A large percentage of work comprises acting for professionals and high net-worth individuals, and in cases with a corporate/business element.
Prof. Memberships: Member of SFLA National Committee and Chair of Good Practice Committee; SFLA North West Branch press officer.
Career: Qualified in 1981. Formerly partner and head of family department at *Maurice Rubin Clare* (now *DAC*); partner *Pannone & Partners* 1995. Regular speaker, lecturer and broadcaster on family law topics.
Personal: Leisure interests include gluttony, theatre, cinema, the arts and travel. Lives in Greater Manchester.

WILLIAMS, Frances
Larby Williams, Cardiff (029) 20472100

WILLIAMS, Gail
Robertsons, Cardiff (029) 20237777

WILLIAMS, Ian
Robertsons, Cardiff (029) 20237777

WILLIAMS, Jane R.
Larby Williams, Cardiff (029) 20472100

WILSON, Bruce
Mills & Reeve, Norwich (01603) 693207
bruce.wilson@mills-reeve.com
Specialisation: High value and complex applications for ancillary relief with emphasis on landed estates. Partner deals with high net worth individuals seeking advice on divorce and family matters; has vast experience in large landed estates and farming cases supported by the private client, tax and agricultural departments. Has written and lectured on pensions and divorce.
Prof. Memberships: Solicitors' Family Law Association.

WOODS, Paul
Wolferstans, Plymouth (01752) 663295
pwoods@wolferstans.com
Specialisation: Family/matrimonial specialising in divorce clients, including ancillary relief and advocacy. SFLA accreditation for 'Big money cases' and 'cohabitation'.
Career: Qualified in 1975. Senior partner *Wolferstans.* Part-time chairman Social Security Appeal tribunal 1988 to date; president Plymouth Law Society 1996-97; founder member and past committee member of Devon and Cornwall SFLA.
Personal: Wellford Grammar School, Durham; Liverpool University; LL.B. 1972. Year of birth: 1949. Town of residence: Plymouth. Main leisure activities golf, rugby and theatre. Clubs: past chairman, Plymouth Albion Rugby FC; member St Mellion and Yelverton Golf Clubs.

WOODWARD, David
TLT Solicitors, Bristol (0117) 917 7501
dwoodward@tltsolicitors.com
Specialisation: Partner in family law team. Main areas of practice are divorce, ancillary relief and children. Acted in Richardson 1994 1FLR 188, B v B 1995 IFLR 9 and Richardson (No2) 1996 2 FLR 617. Contributor to Western Daily Press. Experience includes cable television work, LNTV and occasional lecturing.
Prof. Memberships: SFLA, Law Society, Chairman Bristol SFLA. Member of Family Law panel. Accredited member of SFLA. Director Bristol Family Mediators Association.
Career: Qualified in 1975. Joined *Trumps* in 1979, becoming a partner in 1981. *Trumps* merged with Bristol law firm *Lawrence Tucketts* to become *TLT Solicitors* on 1 May 2000. Heads up family law team of 12.
Personal: Born 10 January 1950. Holds an LLB from Bristol. Leisure interests include cycling, badminton and cricket. Lives in Bristol.

WRIGHT, Barbara
Thomson Snell & Passmore, Tunbridge Wells (01892) 510000
bwright@ts-p.co.uk
Specialisation: Partner and head of family department. Deals with all areas of family breakdown. Particular interest in financial aspects.
Prof. Memberships: Member of Solicitors Family Law Association. Founding chair of Kent Solicitors Family Law Association and member of National Committee of SFLA from March 1997 to 1998. Deputy vice-president Tonbridge, Tunbridge Wells & District Law Society January 2001.
Career: Qualified 1979. Joined *Thomson Snell & Passmore* in 1987. Equity partner from 1995. Honorary legal adviser to West Kent Relate. Accredited mediator and supervisor trained by the Family Mediators Association.
Personal: Born 16 March 1955. Honours Law degree Sheffield University. 2nd Class (Hons) in Part II Law Society's examinations. Interests include English and French history, current affairs, cuisine. Lives in the Tunbridge Wells area.

YOUNG, Ian
Young & Lee, Birmingham (0121) 633 3233
Specialisation: Childrens Law including care proceedings, adoptions, human fertilisation and embryology matters. Training to local authorities and health service trusts in these areas..
Prof. Memberships: Law Society's Children panel; former member Law Society, Family Law committee; SFLA; Birmingham Childcare Support Group.
Career: Qualified 1975; formed *Young & Lee* 1979; provided training to solicitors who wished to become members of Children panel for many years through independent training agency.
Publications: 'The Child as Client' a handbook for solicitors who represent children. Contributor, 'Open Adoptions Research Law Policy and Practice'. Contributor to various legal and health journals.
Personal: Saltash Grammar School – Cornwall. University of Birmingham 1969-71. Articles *Pinsent & Co* Birmingham. Married with four children.

FINANCIAL SERVICES

London: 397; South West: 399; Midlands: 399; The North 399; Scotland: 400; *Profiles*: 401

OVERVIEW: The magic circle firms continue to hold sway over the rest as the first choice of global investment houses. This scenario is reinforced by the cross border nature of cutting edge work. Commentators speculate that the perceived downturn in mainstream M&A work is likely to be offset by consolidations and rationalisations occurring Europe-wide. The development of new trading platforms in the financial markets will undoubtedly boost infrastructure related advisory work, with wider implications in litigation.Notwithstanding the e-commerce downturn, there is ongoing work among established financial institutions with appetite to grow their businesses via the internet. With implementation of the Financial Services & Markets Act looming in November 2001, compliance issues within the new market abuse regime will continue to be an important part of these firms' workload in the forthcoming year.

TOP IN-HOUSE LAWYERS

Mitchell CALLER, Senior Vice President and Associate General Counsel, *The Chase Manhattan Bank*

Therese MILLER, Managing Director and General Counsel, *Goldman Sachs International*

Richard ROSENTHAL, Managing Director and European Counsel, *Morgan Stanley Dean Witter*

Howard TRUST, General Council, Barclays Group, and Company Secretary, *Barclays*

Andrew WHITTAKER, Deputy General Counsel, *Financial Services Authority*

Mitch Caller continues to be highly regarded. The *"extremely good"* **Therese Miller** is secure in her *"all-round strength." "An excellent manager,"* **Richard Rosenthal** *"leads a very good team"* and is widely recognised in this area. Howard Trust is *"experienced"* and *"forward thinking – he considers the serious issues before they arise."* **Andrew Whittaker** is deemed to have *"become an outstanding general counsel."*

In-House lawyers profiles: p.1193

RESEARCH APPROVED BY BMRB: *For this edition,* Chambers' *researchers conducted 6,552 interviews – 4,419 with law firms, 554 with barristers and 1,579 with clients.*

The validity of the research was scrutinised by BMRB International, who audited both the methodology and the results at our offices in July 2001. They interviewed Chambers' *researchers and cross-checked sample interviews. Details of the audit appear on page 7.*

LONDON

FINANCIAL SERVICES • London	Ptnrs	Assts
1 Clifford Chance	n/a	n/a
Freshfields Bruckhaus Deringer	n/a	n/a
Linklaters	4	25
2 Allen & Overy	8	12
3 Slaughter and May	9	10
4 CMS Cameron McKenna	3	8
Lovells	5	13
Norton Rose	5	14
Simmons & Simmons	6	18
SJ Berwin	7	5
Travers Smith Braithwaite	4	6
5 Herbert Smith	4	12
Macfarlanes	2	4

LEADING INDIVIDUALS	
1 **ABRAMS Charles** SJ Berwin	**HERRINGTON Tim** Clifford Chance
MORTON Guy Freshfields Bruckhaus	**NELSON Paul** Linklaters
2 **BATES Chris** Clifford Chance	
CHAMBERLAIN Margaret Travers Smith Braithwaite	
MORRIS Simon CMS Cameron McKenna	
3 **BAGGE James** Norton Rose	**SYKES Annabel** Freshfields Bruckhaus
4 **FINKLER Deborah** Slaughter and May	**FOX Ruth** Slaughter and May
LITTLE Tamasin SJ Berwin	**STONES Richard** Lovells
5 **PHILLIPS Paul** Allen & Overy	**SLATER Richard** Simmons & Simmons
UP AND COMING	
FLETCHER Stephen Linklaters	

This book is the product of 6,552 1/2-hour interviews. See p.7 for BMRB audit.
Within each band, firms are listed alphabetically. *See individuals' profiles p.401*

Clifford Chance (see firm details p.919) *"Deeply resourced – they have the widest, deepest spread of work."* The sheer size of the London team alone reflects the firm's dedication to this core area of practice. *"A long time in the sector, that huge experience has paid off"* to the extent that some market sources consider them pre-eminent in wholesale to large securities houses and in acting for major exchanges such as IPE and LIFFE. Integral to the practice is its in-depth coverage across overlapping areas of specialisation, ranging from investment and commercial banking, asset management, insurance and retail financial services to investigations and disputes. A key player for global investment banks, mergers in the US, Germany and Luxembourg have further enhanced its integrated capability. *"The grand old man of financial regulatory services"* **Tim Herrington** (see p.402) is esteemed by clients as *"a terrific all-rounder who can see all angles and tries to get a sensible solution."* He advised Chase Manhattan (now JP Morgan Chase) on the financial services aspects of its acquisition of Robert Fleming, a deal co-ordinating regulatory consents in 79 jurisdictions. *"Extremely talented and imaginative,"* **Chris Bates** (see p.401) has according to peers *"done a super job this year"* with his involvement in the FSMA consultative process. He advised ISDA on European regulatory matters and jointly led the London team advising JP Morgan and Chase Manhattan on the UK aspects of the merger to form JP Morgan Chase. **Clients:** International Swaps and Derivatives Association; Financial Services Authority; Jiway; JP Morgan Chase; Morgan Stanley Dean Witter.

Freshfields Bruckhaus Deringer (see firm details p.964) *"A top-ranking, high quality team."* Lawyers within the Financial Services Group are valued by clients as having a *"wide but mature vision in dealing with matters."* It offers expertise in a broad spectrum of regulatory, contentious and transactional work to its core client base of investment banks, banks and insurance companies. *"Terribly polished"* Group Head **Guy Morton** (see p.402) is favoured by clients who find him *"extremely user-friendly with sound judgement."* He has been advising Deutsche Bank on a multi-jurisdictional range of projects relating to the delivery of financial services over the internet. "*Impressive*" **Annabel Sykes** (see p.402) has developed an "*excellent*" reputation in regulatory matters including advising on Eureko's acquisition of Foreign & Colonial and on various matters for Charles Schwab including its Self Invested Personal Pension Scheme (SIPPS). **Clients:** AMP; ABN AMRO; ISMA; NM Rothschild & Sons; UBS; Zurich Financial Services; Royal Bank of Scotland; Deutsche Bank; Morgan Stanley; Charles Schwab.

Linklaters (see firm details p.1042) "*A focused practice with a clear, successful strategy.*" The Financial Markets Group ('FMG') has maintained a "*fantastic reputation*" among its core client base of leading commercial, retail and global investment banks for its "*up to date and innovative*" approach and "*enormous in-house and general experience.*" The practice provides expertise in structuring, product design, documentation and marketing, working closely with the firm's litigation department in relation to regulatory representations and investigations. Its envied expansion is attributed to its twin industry-dedicated services: the on-line Blue Flag regulatory advisory service and the Breakfast Briefing series. For cross border M&A and other multi-jurisdictional work, the London office can call upon six specialist Alliance partners stationed throughout Europe, America and the Far East. "*Leading figure in regulatory advice and the brains behind Blue Flag,*" **Paul Nelson** (see p.402) is endorsed by clients and rivals as a "*stunningly good draftsman*". He led the team advising on all cross border regulatory and financial services aspects of the HSBC, Merrill Lynch joint venture (£500 million) to deal with retail customers on Internet. Other recent highlights include Next Access, acting for consortium and Atriax advising on OTC derivatives. Up and coming partner **Stephen Fletcher** (see p.401) received warm recommendations from his peers. **Clients:** Lehmann; JP Morgan; Chase; Solomon Smith Barney; Goldman Sachs; Toronto Dominion; CSFB; Merrill-HSBC.

Allen & Overy (see firm details p.856) A "*first class*" practice fed by "*meaty work*" generated by the firm's "*enormously successful banking practice.*" Accordingly, the team boasts expertise in custodianship, investment management, exchanges and website structuring including retail offers, and bank capital adequacy in restructuring and securitisation. "*All round commercial advisor*" **Paul Phillips** (see p.402) heads the Financial Services Group which provides cross disciplinary expertise from the firm's banking, capital markets, tax and litigation departments. Highlights include acting for Robert Fleming on its merger with Chase, advising Nomura, Merrill Lynch and GE Capital on group restructuring and advising RBS on regulatory capital issues. The group has also been active advising on major internet projects for established market participants and start-ups. **Clients:** HSBC; ING Barings; CSFB; Morgan Stanley; Deutsche Bank; RBS NatWest.

Slaughter and May (see firm details p.1135) An "*excellent*" group whose increasingly focused activities in the financial services arena are said by sources to be "*bearing fruit.*" Its "*outstanding*" reputation in providing regulatory support for the firm's transactional work in M&A and financing, dominates its profile in 'free-standing' advisory work for major regulators, blue chip corporates and financial institutions. The team continues to act for a range of global investment banks with a substantial presence on a number of regulatory investigations and enforcement proceedings. "*Extremely able and effective operator*" **Ruth Fox** (see p.401 is a prime partner on regulatory aspects while **Deborah Finkler** (see p.401) (a "*punchy client individual with good judgement*") is a leader on the contentious side. Among the "*big deals*" handled, the group has advised Abbey National in all financial regulatory aspects of its proposed deal with the Bank of Scotland, and on Lloyds TSB's bid for the company. It also acted for Schroders in the financial regulatory aspects of its internal reorganisation following the sale of its bank business to Salomon Smith Barney. **Clients:** Abbey National; JP Morgan; Prudential; Standard Chartered.

CMS Cameron McKenna (see firm details p.922) "*An interesting composite*" characterised by competitors as "*retail in the city*" on account of its niche strength the insurance sector. The financial services team provides "*good overall coverage*" across corporate acquisitions and reorganisations, start-ups, commercial projects, product development and regulatory work. Well known for his expertise on regulatory and contentious aspects, **Simon Morris** (see p.402) receives praise from clients and peers alike as "*extremely well-versed and thorough with a pragmatic approach.*" While the team has been heavily involved advising financial institution clients on the impact of FSMA, he has been providing advice to the opposition during the passage of the bill. Other highlights include advising the General Insurance Standards Council on all areas of its establishment and ongoing operation, and setting up a high street bank's Internet banking operation, advising on its website, terms of business, deposit taking and offering regulated and unregulated products. **Clients:** Co-operative Insurance Society; Legal & General; Lloyds TSB; M&G; Royal Bank of Scotland.

Lovells (see firm details p.1044) "*A good widespread practice*" with institutional and retail investment funds and fund managers comprising a substantial proportion of its client base. "*Always pleasant to deal with,*" the team specialises in retail regulatory project work, spanning investment business, banking, consumer credit and investment based insurance products. It supports the securities litigation group on money laundering and cross border dealing matters by assessing implications of regulatory impact. "*Low key*" **Richard Stones** (see p.518) is perceived by specialists as an "*extremely bright all-rounder*" with a background in funds related work. "*Sensible and constructive to work with,*" he advised Lloyds TSB on the launch of Create. The group also advised on the integration of Barclays and Woolwich (together with drafting the necessary Act of Parliament) and the launch of Britannic Money. **Clients:** Barclays; Britannic Money; Invesco; Thomas Cook; Lloyds TSB; Bank of Scotland; Merrill Lynch Asset Management; Abbey National; Egg.

Norton Rose (see firm details p.1082) A "*well structured, well resourced*" department with key strengths in transactional investment management and regulatory enforcement work. Reputed by clients to be "*the best around in his specialism,*" **James Bagge** (see p.401) heads the litigation and enforcement practice. A "*level headed, commonsensical*" investigatory lawyer, his long established reputation dates back to the Barings and Hambros investigations. He has been advising the FSA in its enquiry into the supervision of Equitable Life. In regulatory matters, a key highlight for the team was acting for HSBC on its $1 billion 50/50 joint venture with Merrill Lynch to create a worldwide on-line banking and investment services company. **Clients:** AXA; HSBC; JP Morgan Chase; ABN AMRO; Bank of Ireland; Crédit Lyonnais; Merrill Lynch; Royal Bank of Scotland.

Simmons & Simmons (see firm details p.1132) Funds-related work, particularly hedge funds and derivatives, is still perceived as the main thrust of the firm's financial services practice. It remains to be seen whether the group's profile will broaden following its recent absorption into the financial markets department which brings together areas such as banking, capital markets, corporate recovery, insurance, disciplinary and litigation. Clients are primarily financial institutions, including investment banks, stockbrokers, unit trust managers and commodities traders. Peers rate "*extremely experienced*" funds specialist **Richard Slater** (see p.402) as a "*knowledgeable and intelligent operator.*" He advised Barclays on its strategic alliance with Legal & General to promote the latter's insurance, pensions and funds products. Other highlights for the group include advising Swiss Exchange on its joint venture with Tradepont to create virt-x, and advising the opposition treasury team on FSMA drafting proposals during a twelve-month project. **Clients:** AIG; Barclays Bank; Barclays Global Investors; Enron; Prudential-Bache International Bank; Swiss Exchange.

SJ Berwin (see firm details p.879) The "*serious reputation*" of this practice derives from its expertise in the establishment of fund structures for VC and equity providers, which comprise a significant proportion of its client base. Its "*well respected team of specialists*" has recently expanded with the addition of a team from Hammond Suddards Edge. "*Fiercely dedicated to* *financial services regulations,*" prominent commentator and lobbyist **Charles Abrams** (see p.401)' "*enthusiasm and passion are at the root of their profile.*" Returning to practice following extended leave, he will be moving towards a more consultative role and maintaining his lobbying pursuits. Deemed "*helpful, professional and knowledgeable*" by clients, **Tamasin Little** (see p.402) led the team acting for Mercury Private Equity in its buyout from Merrill Lynch Investment Management. The group is active advising on all UK/European regulatory aspects of acquisition deals. It acted for SLK Global Markets on the $6.5 billion acquisition of its parent Spear, Leeds & Kellogg by Goldman Sachs, and advised Herzog Heine Geduld International on the $450 million acquisition of its parent by Merrill Lynch. **Clients:** Bridgepoint Capital; Dresdner Kleinwort Wasserstein; Electra Managers; Mercury Private Equity.

Travers Smith Braithwaite (see firm details p.1160) A "*focused*" practice in the areas of products, advisory and service related work. Its core specialisms remain within trading and (electronic) settlement systems, custody, management and corporate finance services. Universally endorsed for her expertise, Group Head **Margaret Chamberlain** (see p.401) is popular with clients for her "*ability to sit down with business people and explain in a pretty snappy way what they're after.*" Key matters handled include advising Western Union Financial Services and First Data Corporation on the UK regulatory aspects of their businesses. The group continues to advise key clients CRESTCo on its business development, and Bloomberg LP and its subsidiary on UK regulatory issues relevant to their provision of order routing services, investment bulletin boards and electronic trading systems. **Clients:** Bloomberg LP; Bloomberg Tradebook Europe; Western Union Financial Services; Abbey National.

Herbert Smith (see firm details p.993) The profile of the firm's financial services expertise is somewhat obscured by its organisational approach. Spread widely across departments including litigation, corporate, funds and insurance its practitioners are acknowledged in the market as a "*savvy*" team of "*good technicians.*" Highlights include advising the Bank of Scotland on its ongoing merger negotiations and advising Goldman Sachs on a dispute arising out of the contested takeover of Mannesman. The group (headed by Dominic Clarke) also provided regulatory advice to Bradford & Bingley on its demutualisation and conversion to a bank, and on joint venture arrangements with Freeserve, including establishing a funds supermarket. **Clients:** Bank of Scotland; Goldman Sachs; Bradford & Bingley; Lazard Brothers; HM Treasury; Creditex.

Macfarlanes (see firm details p.1046) Built around the firm's "*big name*" in funds related work, this discreet practice, guided by Bridget Barker, has a "*strong*" reputation among clients in its niche specialist areas of private equity and investment management, and private offshore banking. Its "*closely linked*" contentious and non-contentious teams handle the scope of FSA related advisory work for entities seeking authorisation, co-ordination of cross border project work and retail products. Clients include IMRO members, Lloyds' entities and the SFA. The group advised Fidelity on several regulatory matters including its supermarket funds internet project, retailing ISA products. **Clients:** Deutsche Asset Management; Fidelity; Abbey Life.

SOUTH WEST

FINANCIAL SERVICES • South West	Ptnrs	Assts
1 **Burges Salmon** Bristol	2	8

This book is the product of 6,552 1/2-hour interviews. See p.7 for BMRB audit.
Within each band, firms are listed alphabetically.

Burges Salmon (see firm details p.902) An "*excellent, modern, go-ahead, committed*" practice centred on UK based unit trust and OEIC related work. Additional expertise is provided in pensions related work and regulatory dispute matters. Christopher Godfrey and the team are seen by key advisors as "*attracting good quality work outside London*" due to its cost effectiveness and "*hands on*" partner attention. Clients include a substantial proportion of the ISA sector, unit trusts, regionally based stockbrokers and corporate clients of the firm. **Clients:** Exeter Investment; St James's Place Capital; Bristol & West; Nationwide; Premier Fund Managers; Sarasin Investment Managers.

MIDLANDS

FINANCIAL SERVICES • Midlands	Ptnrs	Assts
1 **Pinsent Curtis Biddle** Birmingham	2	3
Wragge & Co Birmingham	2	4

This book is the product of 6,552 1/2-hour interviews. See p.7 for BMRB audit.
Within each band, firms are listed alphabetically.

Pinsent Curtis Biddle (see firm details p.1098) The core strength of this cross-disciplinary team is its expertise in contentious work. Seen by peers to be handling a volume of pensions and endowment mis-selling claims, the team is deeply committed to this area as its key focus. Clients range over corporate, insurance, broking and intermediary sectors. Andrew Long and the group were recently involved in the recovery of a multi-million pound award in international litigation for New York Life. **Clients:** New York Life (UK); DBS; Britannic Assurance; Point & York Vosse (PYV).

Wragge & Co (see firm details p.1189) Recommended by key advisors as a "*strong*" non-contentious advisory financial services practice, particularly in acting for banks and building societies. The team, led by Jonathan Denton aims to provide risk management support to wholesale and retail financial services businesses. A key feature of the practice is the compliance consultation service, training programmes for Board and senior management, which are run in conjunction with the Institute of Directors. Major highlights include advising the Chelsea Building Society on the establishment of £750 million Euro MTN programme and acting on the sale of Advanced Mortgage Funding to Skipton Building Society. **Clients:** Abbey National; Bank of Scotland; Britannic Assurance; Cambridge Building Society; Derbyshire Building Society.

THE NORTH

Addleshaw Booth & Co (see firm details p.853) Clients testify to its "*sound, solid*" regulatory advisory practice. The banking and financial services group boasts major financial services institutional clients including building societies, banks and insurance companies, for which it advises on regulatory compliance across the range of contentious and non-contentious work. Specialist sector expertise includes building society and mortgage law, data protection legislation and finance leasing litigation. Adam Bennett and the team have advised on eleven mortgage portfolio transfers, including advising Norwich Union on the sale of a substantial residential portfolio. On the contentious side, it acted for Scottish Equitable on recovery of a payment by mistake which proceeded to the Court of Appeal. **Clients:** HSBC; Bradford & Bingley; Royal Bank of Scotland; Nationwide; Britannia; CGNU; Royal & Sun Alliance.

FINANCIAL SERVICES • The North	Ptnrs	Assts
1 **Addleshaw Booth & Co** Leeds	n/a	n/a
Dickinson Dees Newcastle upon Tyne	2	1
LEADING INDIVIDUALS		
1 **GERVASIO James** Keeble Hawson		
LUMSDEN Christopher Chaffe Street		
LYNCH Malcolm Wrigleys		

This book is the product of 6,552 1/2-hour interviews. See p.7 for BMRB audit.
Within each band, firms are listed alphabetically. *See individuals' profiles p.401*

Dickinson Dees (see firm details p.941) "*Doing well*" in its "*ring-fenced*" market. The firm's core client base of VCs and regionally based plcs provides a stream of work to the financial services team. Working in tandem with the firm's private client financial planning team, the group, under the guidance of David Rewcastle, advises on the range of regulatory and compliance matters. Highlights include fundraisings of £10 million in Euro commission in Northern Rock and £60 million for Applied Optical Technologies. **Clients:** NE Regional Investment Fund; NE Seed Capital Fund; NE Regional VC Capital Fund; Northern Enterprise.

Other Notable Practitioners Peers rate **James Gervasio** (see p.401) of **Keeble Hawson** for his expertise in VC trusts related matters. A "*thorough and competent*" IMRO regulations compliance officer, he provides advice to institutional investors and fund managers regarding schemes, funds, marketing rules and investment advertising. Known among banks and other financial houses, **Christopher Lumsden** (see p.402) of **Chaffe Street** provides advisory support to his IFA dominated client base on regulatory compliance matters. "*Technically sound*" **Malcolm Lynch** of **Wrigleys** handles financial services work in the context of ethical and charitable institutions such as Shared Interest, an investment society in the developing economy.

SCOTLAND

FINANCIAL SERVICES • Scotland	Ptnrs	Assts
1 **Dundas & Wilson CS** Edinburgh	3	11
2 **Dickson Minto WS** Edinburgh	3	4
Maclay Murray & Spens Glasgow	n/a	n/a
McGrigor Donald Glasgow	2	3
Shepherd & Wedderburn WS Edinburgh	3	6
Tods Murray WS Edinburgh	2	1

LEADING INDIVIDUALS	
1 **ATHANAS Chris** Tods Murray WS	**MACKAY Philip** Dundas & Wilson CS
2 **DORAN Frank** McGrigor Donald	**LIVINGSTON Michael** Maclay Murray & Spens
MINTO Bruce Dickson Minto WS	**THURSTON SMITH Martin** Tods Murray WS

This book is the product of 6,552 1/2-hour interviews. See p.7 for BMRB audit.
Within each band, firms are listed alphabetically. *See individuals' profiles p.401*

Dundas & Wilson CS (see firm details p.947) "*The big grandparent*" of the select firms that represent the Edinburgh fund management community. Leading advisors dub them "*the Slaughter and May of the Scottish legal establishment,*" a reflection of its "*high quality*" expertise and comprehensive service approach to heavy weight corporates and blue chip financial institutions. **Philip Mackay** has "*served a long apprenticeship,*" he acted for Abbey National in the Scottish aspects of its acquisition of the Scottish Provident Institution including advice on its demutualisation. The team has handled various matters for the Royal Bank of Scotland Group relating to its acquisition of NatWest and on its outsourcing of the Bank's Personal and Trustee Services to Mazars Neville Russell (£30 million). **Clients:** Abbey National; Bank of Scotland; National Australia Group Europe; Royal Bank of Scotland Group; Scottish Widows.

Dickson Minto WS (see firm details p.942) The primary focus of the firm's financial services expertise is concentrated around its leading investment funds practice. Perceived by the market as "*becoming more active and increasingly involved*" in the area, the team is judged to be "*extremely competent.*" "*Great lawyer*" **Bruce Minto** (see p.517) led the team on an innovative fund-raising for Aberforth Partnership to invest in small cap listed companies, involving £150 million in assets. **Clients:** Aberforth Partners; Artemis; Edinburgh Fund Managers; Friends Ivory & Sime.

Maclay Murray & Spens (see firm details p.1047) Noted by the market for its involvement in "*some interesting deals.*" Approaching financial services from a corporate perspective, the group is endorsed for its focus in banking regulatory and compliance work. With expertise in insurance company demutualisations, key partner **Michael Livingston** (see p.402) can "*work through any problem and come to a solution on it.*" Recent highlights include the Scottish Widows demutualisation and transfer to Lloyds TSB and the £1.1 billion demutualisation and transfer of Scottish Life to Royal London. **Clients:** Edinburgh Investment Trust; BPI; Scottish Widows; Lloyds TSB; Scottish Amicable; Brewin Dolphin Bell Lawrie; Colonial; Robertson & Baxter.

McGrigor Donald (see firm details p.1062) A team with a "*growing reputation*" believed by key advisors to have successfully built a practice outside the traditional Scottish investment trusts and institutions market, focusing instead on life companies, fund managers and banks. The team advises on a range of investment issues, website matters, regulatory compliance, management and custody agreements. "*Technically competent*" **Frank Doran** (see p.401) commands "*huge respect*" among his peers. The team's highlight this year was advising on the sale of Murray Johnstone to Aberdeen Asset Managers (value £150 million). **Clients:** Direct Line; Gartmore Investment Trusts; Britannic Asset Managers.

Shepherd & Wedderburn WS (see firm details p.1126) Suffering "*a bit of a battle to maintain their strong reputation*" following the loss of a highly respected partner. Strong historical links with key investment trust Ivory & Sime have granted the firm a significant advantage in the investment and unit trust market. Long standing relationships subsequently forged with clients such as Edinburgh Fund Managers, Baillie Gifford and Bank of Scotland provide a steady flow of work for a team headed by Malcolm Gillies. Key matters handled included acting for Ivory & Sime ISIS Trust in its reorganisation, issue of capital and renewing the taking of share buyback authority. The group also advised Orbitex Investments on the launch of the exempt unauthorised unit trust, Orbitex Exempt UK Equity Fund. **Clients:** Friends Ivory & Sime; Edinburgh Fund Managers; Baillie Gifford; Colonial First State Investments; McInroy & Wood.

Tods Murray WS (see firm details p.1157) Recognised in the market for its financial services expertise in collective investments, including OEICs and unit trusts. Commanding "*huge respect*" in the market, the team's well-known individuals are "*colourful*" **Chris Athanas** (see p.516) who has "*been around the block many times*" and "*quietly careful and thoughtful*" **Martin Thurston Smith** (see p.632). A highlight this year was acting for Britannic Asset Management in the financial services aspects of a possible acquisition of Murray Johnstone. **Clients:** Bank of Scotland; Baillie Gifford; Britannic Fund/Asset Managers/Britannic Investment Managers; Edinburgh Unit Trust Managers/Edinburgh Fund Managers.

LEADERS IN FINANCIAL SERVICES

ABRAMS, Charles

SJ Berwin, London (020) 7533 2222
charles.abrams@sjberwin.com
Specialisation: Advises almost exclusively on securities law and regulatory issues including EU directives, the marketing of investment funds, insider dealing, market abuse and the disclosure of interests in shares, primarily to investment and private banks, venture capital fund managers, stockbrokers, and corporate finance houses. Has developed a niche specialisation in advising clients on how to reorganise group structures or activities to minimise regulation and financial resources requirements, often as a result of persuading regulators to agree with helpful interpretations of EU and UK rules. Co-author of a leading text book on the Financial Services Act, 'Guide to Financial Services Regulation' (CCH, 3rd edn 1997). Author of 'A Short Guide to the Financial Services and Markets Act 2000' and contributor to 'Bond Market Compliance' (IFR), for which he wrote an analysis of the FS Act's money market exemption, 'Futures Trading Law and Regulation' (Longmans), for which he wrote an analysis of SFA's customer categorisation rules, and 'International Survey of Investment Advisor Regulation' (Kluwer, 2nd edn 1999), for which he wrote an analysis of UK regulatory law relevant to investment and fund managers. Was a legal adviser to the Conservative Party's Shadow Treasury team in relation to the Financial Services and Markets Bill from June 1999 to June 2000, especially in relation to the provisions relating to financial promotion (including on the internet), cross-border issues including the use of the single European passports and market abuse. Member of the editorial advisory board of 'European Financial Services Law' (Kluwer Law International). Writes and lectures frequently on regulatory issues. Is chairman of the CBI's Financial Services Group and the APCIMS' FSA committee, member of the City of London Law Society's Regulatory sub-committee and was formerly an arbitrator for SFA's Consumer Arbitration Scheme and a special adviser to IMRO on Venture Capital.
Prof. Memberships: Chartered Institute of Arbitrators.
Career: Qualified in 1976 with *Linklaters & Paines* and moved to *SJ Berwin* in 1985. Became a partner in *SJ Berwin* in 1988.

ATHANAS, Chris

Tods Murray WS, Edinburgh (0131) 226 4771
chris.athanas@todsmurray.com
See under Investment Funds, p.516

BAGGE, James

Norton Rose, London (020) 7283 6000
baggeajs@nortonrose.com
Specialisation: Partner in commercial litigation department. Practice focuses on fraud and the regulation of investment and banking business, in particular advising on all forms of investigations, statutory or private, and associated legal proceedings involving the SFO, DTI, SRO and Revenue authorities. Advised the Board of Banking Supervision on the Barings inquiry. Has acted for LIFFE in relation to market investigations and enforcement actions. Conducted the Banking Act inquiry into Hambros involvement with the aborted bid for the Co-operative Wholesale Society. Is representing the trustees of the Thyssen Bornemisza Trust in action commenced by Baron Thyssen in Bermuda. Acts for three global investment banks in relation to ongoing regulatory investigations. Is currently assisting with the enquiry with the FSA's supervision of the Equitable Life.
Prof. Memberships: International Bar Association.
Career: Qualified 1979. Spent eight years at the Criminal Bar and two years on secondment to the Serious Fraud Office. Joined *Norton Rose* in 1990 and became a partner in 1993.

BATES, Chris

Clifford Chance, London (020) 7600 1000
chris.bates@cliffordchance.com
Specialisation: Advice to financial institutions on e-business, financial regulation, regulatory capital issues, the EU single market programme, financial institution M&A and clearing and settlement systems, as well as advising on derivatives transactions and securities offerings.
Career: Foreign associate, *Sullivan & Cromwell*, New York 1980. Joined *Clifford Chance* 1980. Based in Hong Kong office 1983-88. Became a partner in 1987. Based in London 1988 to date.

CHAMBERLAIN, Margaret

Travers Smith Braithwaite, London
(020) 7295 3000
margaret.chamberlain@traverssmith.com
Specialisation: Specialist in trading, clearance, settlement, investment management and custody issues. Part of team at *Travers Smith Braithwaite* which advised The Bank of England and CREST Co Limited on the legal arrangements for the introduction of CREST and continues to advise CREST Co, including on links to overseas settlement systems, central counter party development, dematerialisation of money-market instruments and central bank money. Advises on custody relationships; on the legal and regulatory requirements relevant to the establishment and management of funds; on a wide range of general regulatory and legal issues arising from the conduct of financial services business.
Prof. Memberships: Chairman regulatory committee of the British Venture Capital Association and member of BVCA Council. Member of City of London Law Society Regulatory Working Party. Contributor to Tolley's 'Company Law'. International Bar Association; chairman of sub-committee on regulation of markets and exchanges.
Career: Qualified September 1985. Partner *Travers Smith Braithwaite* 1991.
Personal: Educated at University College, Oxford. Married.

DORAN, Frank

McGrigor Donald, Glasgow (0141) 248 6677
Specialisation: Partner in Corporate Unit. Advises on securities law and regulatory issues generally including compliance with FSA Rule books, insider dealing legislation, global custody and insurance law. Also involved in the development and marketing of retail financial products and establishment and management of investment funds.
Prof. Memberships: Member of the Law Society of Scotland Investor Protection Committee.
Career: Qualified in 1985 with *Maclay Murray & Spens* and then moved to *McGrigor Donald*. Became a partner in *McGrigor Donald* in 1991.

FINKLER, Deborah

Slaughter and May, London (020) 7600 1200
deborah.finkler@slaughterandmay.com
Specialisation: Broad range of commercial litigation including advising Unilever Superannuation Fund in its negligence claim against Mercury Asset Management, as well as a wide range of financial regulatory matters for a number of global financial institutions.
Career: Partner 1991.

FLETCHER, Stephen

Linklaters, London (020) 7456 2000
stephen.fletcher@linklaters.com
Specialisation: Advises investment banks and securities houses on a wide range of financial markets, regulatory and securities law issues in the UK, Europe and internationally. Particular experience in: e-commerce platforms in the international fixed income, equity and derivatives markets; European and international restructurings to minimise compliance and regulatory capital burdens; design and distribution of new investment products; and in relation to regulatory investigations for compliance breaches, insider dealing and market abuse.
Career: 1994 to date: Associate solicitor, financial markets group, *Linklaters & Alliance*; 1992-94: Trainee solicitor, *Linklaters*. Undergraduate degree: 1988-92 – Jurisprudence, Bachelor of Arts, Oxford University – First Class Honours. Postgraduate degree: 1992-93 – Bachelor of Civil Law, Oxford University.

FOX, Ruth

Slaughter and May, London (020) 7600 1200
ruth.fox@slaughterandmay.com
Specialisation: Practice covers a wide range of commercial work, with an emphasis on banking and capital markets, now focusing on financial regulation. Has acted extensively for banks and also for building societies, including in relation to conversions, and for corporate trustees.
Prof. Memberships: The Law Society.
Career: Qualified in 1979 with *Slaughter and May*. Became a partner in 1986.
Personal: Born 3 October 1954. Educated at St Helena School, Chesterfield and University College, London. Married with three sons. Lives in London and Hertfordshire.

GERVASIO, James

Keeble Hawson, Leeds (0113) 294 5059
jimgervasio@keeblehawson.co.uk
Specialisation: Jim specialises in regulatory compliance, with particular reference to IMRO. He graduated first in economics and then in law before qualifying as a solicitor. He has a particular interest in all aspects of private equity work and venture capital deals, structuring investment funds and financial services regulation. He is company secretary to a number of companies including three venture capital trusts.
Prof. Memberships: Member of the Securities Institute.
Career: BSc Econ (Hons); LLB; IMRO Compliance Officer.
Personal: Married with two adult daughters. Enjoys walking and the theatre.

HERRINGTON, Tim
Clifford Chance, London (020) 7600 1000
tim.herrington@cliffordchance.com
Specialisation: Partner specialising in financial services including mutual funds, asset management and investment trust work, securities and derivatives trading and regulatory issues, insurance, mergers and acquisitions, Stock Exchange and other corporate work for the financial services industry. Head of the firm's Global Asset Management Group.
Prof. Memberships: Member Law Society's Company Law Committee (past chairman); Vice Chairman, Investment Funds Committee; International Bar Association.
Career: Queen Mary's Grammar School, Basingstoke; Bristol University (LLB). Articled *Clifford Chance*; qualified 1978; partner *Clifford Chance* since 1985.
Personal: Cricket, travel, walking, gardening and wine. Born 1954; resides London and the Isle of Wight.

LITTLE, Tamasin
SJ Berwin, London (020) 7533 2222
tamasin.little@sjberwin.com
Specialisation: Specialises in financial markets and regulatory matters including structuring, funds, derivatives and other investment products and advising investment managers, banks, financial services groups, brokers, venture capitalists, insurance companies and other investment firms on regulatory and related matters.
Prof. Memberships: City of London Law Society, International Bar Association, EASD Legal and Regulatory committee, Futures and Options Association Legal Scrutiny committee, Financial Services Authority Advisory panel on Authorisation Manual.
Career: 1st class BA Jurisprudence, Oxford; LLM London School of Economics. Legal associate seconded to the Bank of England's Legal Risk Review committee 1991/2. Partner *Stephenson Harwood* 1992-96. Partner *SJ Berwin & Co* financial services group 1996-date.
Publications: Editor of 'Bond Markets: Law & Regulation' (Sweet & Maxwell 1999). Articles on marketing funds and an overview of the regulation of OTC derivatives in 'Swaps and Off-Exchange Derivatives Trading' (FT Law and Tax) and contributor to 'Issues in Derivative Instruments' (Kluwer).

LIVINGSTON, Michael
Maclay Murray & Spens, Glasgow
(0141) 248 5011
mbl@maclaymurrayspens.co.uk
Specialisation: Partner specialising in corporate finance and financial services. Particular experience working with public companies and in the insurance sector. Advises on listings, rights issues and takeovers and financial services regulatory matters. Has also advised on insurance demutualisations.
Career: After qualifying, spent 10 years in industry. Joined *Maclay Murray & Spens* in 1992.
Personal: Born 1958.

LUMSDEN, Christopher
Chaffe Street, Manchester (0161) 236 5800
Specialisation: Partner in banking department. Main area of practice is banking, including debt/equity swaps, documentary credits, management buy-ins and buy-outs, invoice discounting, reconstructions, refinancings and ship and aircraft financing. Also experienced in corporate acquisitions and disposals.
Prof. Memberships: Law Society.
Career: *Chaffe Street*, partner 1990.

LYNCH, Malcolm
Wrigleys, Leeds (0113) 244 6100

MACKAY, Philip
Dundas & Wilson CS, Edinburgh
(0131) 228 8000

MINTO, Bruce
Dickson Minto WS, Edinburgh (0131) 225 4455
bruce.minto@dmws.com
See under Corporate Finance, p.253, Investment Funds, p.517

MORRIS, Simon
CMS Cameron McKenna, London
(020) 7367 2702
sm@cmck.com
Specialisation: Partner in financial services group. Establishing financial institutions in the United Kingdom and advising on financial sector acquisitions and disposals; handling corporate reorganisations of onshore and offshore fund managers and insurers; advising on internet projects for banks, brokers and insurers; working on novel products and distribution structures such as a wholesale tracker fund for pension investment, a retail timeshare bond and converting an insurer's salesforce into a franchise; representing brokers, managers and insurers in over 40 FSA disciplinary cases and in a further 60 enforcement and investigation actions. An advisor to HM Opposition on FSM Bill.
Career: Qualified in 1982, having joined *Cameron Markby (now CMS Cameron McKenna)* in 1980. Became a partner in 1988.
Publications: Author of 'Financial Services: Regulating Investment Business' (3rd edn forthcoming)
Personal: Born 24 January 1958. Attended Cambridge University. Member of Council, London Topographical Society. Leisure interests include travel and cartography. Lives in Islington.

MORTON, Guy
Freshfields Bruckhaus Deringer, London
(020) 7936 4000
guy.morton@freshfields.com
Specialisation: Head of the financial services group. Practice covers a wide range of financial services, regulatory and banking work. Specialises in banking and securities regulation, payment systems and trading law, repos and securities lending. Is particularly experienced within the banking, securities dealing, investment trading and insurance sectors. Has given evidence to the Joint Committee on Financial Services and Markets on the Financial Services and Markets Bill.
Prof. Memberships: Chairman of the City of London Law Society Regulatory Sub-Committee, which is reviewing and commenting on the Financial Services and Markets Bill and the associated regulatory reforms in the UK.
Career: Became partner in *Freshfields* in 1986. Corpus Christi College, Oxford.

NELSON, Paul
Linklaters, London (020) 7456 3766
paul.nelson@linklaters.com
Specialisation: Specialises in markets and financial institutions including investment banks, securities houses and their affiliates in the UK and internationally.
Career: 1996 to date: Head of financial markets group; 1987 to date: Partner in *Linklaters*; 1981-87: Assistant solicitor, *Linklaters*; 1979-81: Articled clerk, *Linklaters*. 1978: Law Society Final Examination; 1978: Corpus Christi College, Cambridge, BA in Law (First Class), George Long Prize for Jurisprudence.

PHILLIPS, Paul
Allen & Overy, London (020) 7330 2510
paul.phillips@allenovery.com
Specialisation: Experience is in financial services and the regulatory field, including the Financial Services Markets Act 2000, Banking Act, SRO Rules – restrictions on marketing investments, prospectuses, advertisements, collective investments, regulatory aspects of acquisitions, reorganisations, drafting and negotiating terms of business for investment activities, investment management, custody arrangements, capital adequacy requirements, conduct of investment business, cross-border regulatory practice, bank-customer duties.
Career: Barrister (1983-87); Assistant *Allen & Overy* (1987-94), Partner (1991).
Publications: Co-author of 'Encyclopedia of Banking Law'.
Personal: BA Cambridge (1982).

SLATER, Richard
Simmons & Simmons, London 020 7628 2020
richard.slater@simmons-simmons.com
Specialisation: Partner in financial markets department. Corporate and regulatory work with a particular emphasis on the financial services industry. Work covers regulatory advice on the formation and promotion of investment vehicles of all types, the acquisition and disposal of financial services businesses and the reconstruction and merger of investment trust companies, unit trusts and other investment entities. Transactional advice includes public and private company take-overs and acquisitions, joint ventures, initial share offerings and flotations.
Career: Qualified in 1977, after joining *Simmons & Simmons* as an articled clerk in 1975. Became a partner in the corporate department in 1981.
Personal: Born 9th November 1950. Attended City University 1979-82, then Cambridge University 1982-84. Lives in London.

STONES, Richard
Lovells, London (020) 7296 2000
richard.stones@lovells.com
See under Investment Funds, p.518

SYKES, Annabel
Freshfields Bruckhaus Deringer, London
(020) 7936 4000
annabel.sykes@freshfields.com
Specialisation: Partner dealing with regulatory and other issues for asset managers, custodians, broker-dealers and other institutions in the financial services and insurance sectors. Has advised Lloyd's on various regulatory matters including the admission of corporate capital and the market's reconstruction and renewal and the 1998 premiums trust deeds revision.
Prof. Memberships: Law Society; Member of the Financial Services Working Party of the Law Society Company Law Committee; Member of the Financial Services Authority's advisory group on its rules and guidance handbook.
Career: Trinity College, Cambridge; University of Auckland.
Personal: Born 1961.

THURSTON SMITH, Martin
Tods Murray WS, Edinburgh (0131) 226 4771
martin.thurston.smith@todsmurray.com
See under Pensions, p.632

FRANCHISING

Nationwide: 403; *Profiles*: 404

OVERVIEW: This year we continue to reflect the inherent, nationwide nature of most franchising work with a single, national table. This table focuses on those that advise both franchisors and franchisees and is limited to those considered to have specialist franchising expertise.

RESEARCH APPROVED BY BMRB: *For this edition,* Chambers' *researchers conducted 6,552 interviews – 4,419 with law firms, 554 with barristers and 1,579 with clients.*

The validity of the research was scrutinised by BMRB International, who audited both the methodology and the results at our offices in July 2001. They interviewed Chambers' *researchers and cross-checked sample interviews. Details of the audit appear on page 7.*

NATIONWIDE

FRANCHISING • Nationwide	Ptnrs	Assts
1 **Eversheds** London, Ipswich, Newcastle upon Tyne	3	11
Field Fisher Waterhouse	9	8
2 **Mundays** Esher	3	4
Wragge & Co Birmingham	4	6
3 **Brodies WS** Edinburgh	1	3
Hammond Suddards Edge Manchester	1	4
Pinsent Curtis Biddle Birmingham	2	4
4 **Dundas & Wilson CS** Edinburgh	1	2
Leathes Prior Norwich	3	1
Owen White Slough	7	2

LEADING INDIVIDUALS	
1 **ABELL Mark** Field Fisher Waterhouse	**MENDELSOHN Martin** Eversheds
2 **BATES Anton** Owen White	**ISHANI Manzoor** Mundays
PRATT John Pinsent Curtis Biddle	
3 **CHADD Jonathan** Leathes Prior	**CHAMBERS John** Chambers & Co
COWIE Pauline Hammond Suddards Edge	**HARRIS Gordon** Wragge & Co
VOGE Julian Brodies WS	**WORMALD Chris** Eversheds
UP AND COMING	
BROWN Victoria Wragge & Co	

This book is the product of 6,552 1/2-hour interviews. See p.7 for BMRB audit.
Within each band, firms are listed alphabetically. *See individuals' profiles p.404*

Eversheds (see firm details p.952) Consistently rated by the market as leading lights, the team, which includes a significant presence in the Newcastle and Ipswich offices, has impressed with its involvement in multi-jurisdictional instructions. It advised US-based franchisor Miss Universe on its contract revision process in 29 countries. Head of the national practice **Martin Mendelsohn** (see p.404) is lauded by peers as "*the father figure of UK franchising,*" who "*knows franchising lore – as well as law – backwards.*" The technically expert **Chris Wormald** (see p.405) heads the London office. The group has advised on new media distribution methods for existing clients' networks and seen growth in the restaurant and leisure sectors. **Clients:** Berry Palmer & Lyle; COSTA; McDonald's; Mothercare; Prontaprint; Robin Harper; Thorntons.

Field Fisher Waterhouse (see firm details p.957) According to peers, this strong team continues to press hard on Eversheds' heels under **Mark Abell**'s (see p.404) "*experienced*" leadership. Although an "*acquired taste*" for some, he is rated for his commercial approach and one competitor noted that "*his experience is second to none.*" The team has assisted the expansion of major franchisor clients such as The Body Shop and Regus into new markets and has pursued franchisee buy-ins for a number of major UK companies. **Clients:** The Body Shop; Caterpiller; Dublcheck; Fatty Arbuckles; First Quench; Land Rover; MFI; National Rent A Car; Pret A Manger; Regus; Securicor.

Mundays (see firm details p.1077) Heavily involved in aiding UK companies, such as Southern Fried Chicken, expand their franchises overseas, the group has also advised non-domestic companies in their transactions abroad. The practice group is helmed by the high profile **Manzoor Ishani** (see p.404), who has "*been there since before franchising was fashionable – he has seen everything before.*" **Clients:** Mailboxes, etc; Pronuptia; Sevenoaks Sound & Vision; Stagecoach Theatre Arts; Southern Fried Chicken; Young's Formal Wear; Cash Converters; KFC.

Wragge & Co (see firm details p.1189) "*A cracking firm*" with a structured, team-based approach. Clients recommend the "*attention and effort, they are always prepared and willing.*" Recently appointed to the BFA Legal Committee, **Gordon Harris** is the figurehead of the group. Noted for its advice to both franchisees and franchisors. "*Extremely helpful and efficient*" team leader **Victoria Brown** is viewed by many in the industry as a rising star. **Clients:** British Franchise Association; Rosemary Conley.

Brodies WS (see firm details p.896) Continues to offer one of the best services north of the border under the steady steering hand of **Julian Voge** (see p.405), described by one competitor as "*a mentor in the field.*" The team acts for both franchisors such as Mailboxes, etc and the Strategic Rail Authority and start-up franchisees. Perceived to be the natural choice for national referral, the group contains "*the premier franchising lawyers in Scotland.*" **Clients:** Mailboxes, etc; Strategic Rail Authority; hoteliers.

Hammond Suddards Edge (see firm details p.984) The group has advised Bradford & Bingley on several matters, including the franchise of their estate agency network, and has seen a growth in the area of financial services. It also acted on the national franchising of the Churches National Housing Coalition. The practice is headed by enterprise and technology head **Pauline Cowie** (see p.404), commended by clients for "*always looking for the win/win situation*" and offering "*a more personable, accessible, direct service.*" **Clients:** Bradford & Bingley; Churches National Housing Coalition.

Pinsent Curtis Biddle (see firm details p.1098) A consistently strong performance under the leadership of the "*talented and charming*" **John Pratt** (see p.405), taking on 50 new franchise clients. With "*tremendous industry experience*" he has secured the preparation franchise documents for Initial Rentokil, and advised Decorating Den in the termination of its master franchise agreement. The team devotes full-time litigators to franchising work and the recruitment of a banking figure has underlined its commerciality. **Clients:** Amtrak; Cash Generator; Dolland & Aitchison; Forte; Initial City Link; Minster Cleaning; Select Appointments; ServiceMaster.

Dundas & Wilson CS (see firm details p.947) Working out of the corporate group, the firm has been involved with Scotwork International's expanding network of management training franchises to global brand names worldwide. The firm has established franchises in most corners of the world over the last year. Headed up by Glasgow partner Eric Galbraith, the firm has also made inroads into the hospitality and leisure sector. **Clients:** Scotwork International; Airtec International; Toni & Guy (Scotland.)

Leathes Prior Active in the selling on of franchising businesses, the team is also heavily involved in e-commerce and telecoms business franchising. "*Approachable and professional*," **Jonathan Chadd** leads the practice, offering "*experience on both sides of the franchising fence.*" Membership of the EU-Lex group has supported its cross-border work. The firm acts for both franchisors and is said by the market to "*never fail*" its franchisee client base. **Clients:** Belvoir Property Management; Restaurant Systems International; Bridgewater Pottery Café; Ceroc.

Owen White Led by the well-known, "*absolute stalwart*" **Anton Bates** (see p.404), legal advisor to the British Franchising Association, the firm has been particularly active in the fast food and printing sectors as well as staff recruitment and other service markets. The team has acted for a US master franchisor and is active in internet-based publishing. **Clients:** Dynarod; Janekin; Rymans.

Other Notable Practitioners Sole practitioner **John Chambers** continues to undertake national franchises for clients such as Texaco and international work for French Connection. Described by peers as "*a client's lawyer*," he has a particular focus on small business franchisors with "*a personal approach.*"

LEADERS IN FRANCHISING

ABELL, Mark
Field Fisher Waterhouse, London (020) 7861 4000
Specialisation: Partner heading the brands technology, media and telecommunications department. Main areas of practice are franchising and licensing of intellectual property. Work covers negotiating, drafting and advising generally on international and domestic matters, area and unit franchises, development agreements, concessions, subordinated equity arrangements, technology transfers, merchandising, endorsement and sponsorship. Expert to the United Nations WIPO advising on the appropriate legal regime for franchising and trademark licensing and evaluation of IP in developing countries. Credited as the originator of the FBI (franchise buy-in) and FBO (franchise buy-out). Acted in the Moosehead decision of the EC Commission, an important trademarks and anti-trust case. Clients include Bodyshop, National Car Rental and Regus plc. Visiting lecturer and external examiner at University of London. Lectures regularly in the USA, Japan, PRC and Europe. Editorial board member of 'Trade Mark World' and 'Franchise Law and Business Review', 'IP World' and 'IP Business'. Creator of europeanfranchising.com
Prof. Memberships: IFA, IBA, INTA, UIA, LES, Society of Franchising, British Franchise Association (BFA).
Career: Worked for Japanese company in Japan 1980-81. Qualified in 1984.
Publications: Author of 'The Franchise Option', 'The International Franchise Option', 'European Franchising-Law and Practice in the European Community Vol I & II', 'International Technology Transfer for Profit', 'Franchising in India', chapters in ten textbooks and over 300 articles on franchising, licensing and I.P.
Personal: BFA Legal committee member. Leisure interests include Japanese, Chinese and Thai culture (Japanese speaker), scuba diving, opera, and his family.

BATES, Anton
Owen White, Slough (01753) 876818
antonbates@owenwhite.com
Specialisation: Partner leading the commercial department. Main area of practice is franchising. Legal advisor to British Franchise Association since advising founder members and drafting constitution in 1977. Chairman of BFA legal committee and BFA representative on European Franchise Federation legal committee. Has advised scores of franchisors and franchisees including companies engaged in international franchising. Acts for many household names in the franchising industry. Author of many articles in various specialist magazines and newspapers. Organiser and speaker at numerous seminars in the UK (for the BFA) and abroad.
Prof. Memberships: Law Society, Chartered Institute of Arbitrators, ADR Mediator.
Career: Qualified in 1967. After 5 years as a Partner in a large city firm, joined *Owen White* as a Partner in 1973.

BROWN, Victoria
Wragge & Co, Birmingham (0870) 903 1000

CHADD, R. Jonathan
Leathes Prior, Norwich (01603) 610911

CHAMBERS, John
Chambers & Co, Norwich (01603) 616 155

COWIE, Pauline
Hammond Suddards Edge, Manchester (0161) 830 5000
pauline.cowie@hammondse.com
Specialisation: Partner in enterprise and technology unit providing advice on franchising, significant commercial contracts, outsourcing, information technology and e-commerce. Leads the national franchise team and specialises in franchising on a national and international basis for listed PLC's and large corporates. Has personally advised clients on over 150 franchised systems and developed a substantial computerised franchising database. Contributes articles on franchising and speaker at seminars on how to franchise, its benefits and legal structures. Affiliate member of the British Franchise Association, Solicitors European Group, Institute of Directors, Institute of Logistics and Transport, Institute of Purchasing and Supply, Computers and the Law.
Career: Qualified in 1985 joining *Janet Scowcroft & Co* on qualification. Became a partner in 1988 and remained a partner on merging the practice with *Coleman & Co* to form *Colemans* solicitors in 1991. Joined *Hammond Suddards* as a partner in 1998.
Personal: Born 1961, resides Wilmslow. Married, two children.

HARRIS, Gordon
Wragge & Co, Birmingham (0870) 903 1000

ISHANI, Manzoor
Mundays, Esher (01372) 809000
Manzoor.ishani@mundays.co.uk
Specialisation: Partner and head of franchise department. Principal area of practice (for over 20 years) UK and international franchising, including franchise dispute resolution and joint ventures with overseas companies. Over the past four years has assisted UK companies franchise into more than 25 countries. Has advised: Clarks International, TDK, London International Group Plc, Prèt á Manger, Redland Roofing Systems, Stagecoach Theatre Arts, Securicor Pony Express, Early Learning Centres, (John Menzies), New Covent Garden Soup Company, Claims Direct.
Prof. Memberships: British Franchise Association (Legal Committee), International Bar Association (Franchise Committee – Section of Business Law), American Bar Association (Forum Committee on Franchising), fellow of the Centre for International Legal Studies, fellow of the Society for Advanced Legal Studies, Association of Swiss Arbitrators, fellow Royal Society of Arts.
Career: Qualified 1976. Joined *Mundays* as a partner in 1992. Previously a partner with a City practice.
Personal: Born 6 October 1949. Attended St Edmund's School, Canterbury 1963-68, then the University of St Andrews 1969-72. Leisure pursuits include classic cars, reading and jazz. Lives in Oxshott.

MENDELSOHN, Martin
Eversheds, London (020) 7919 4500
mendelm@eversheds.com
Specialisation: Has 40 years experience of handling a wide range of commercial, corporate and international transactions. Has particular expertise in franchising, distribution, agency and licensing transactions, both domestic and international, as well as UK and EC competition law. Obtained a Doctorate from Middlesex University in 1999 on Effective Business and Professional practice in Franchising. Has been active in many parts of the world in providing support and assistance to franchise associations. Has advised Governments. Visiting Professor of Franchise Management, Middlesex University Business School where he introduced an undergraduate course and a

Masters Degree course in Franchising. Member of the UNIDROIT study group on franchising, by whom he was appointed a correspondent in 2000. Legal consultant to the British Franchise Association. Assisted in the introduction of a franchising law course by Queen Mary & Westfield College, London University as a subject for the University's Master of Law Degree. Was first chairman of the International Franchising Committee of the International Bar Association.
Prof. Memberships: Fellow of the Chartered Institute of Arbitrators, Law Society, International Bar Association, American Bar Association (and Forum on Franchising).
Career: Qualified in 1959. Joined *Jaques & Lewis* (now *Eversheds)* as a partner in 1992.
Publications: Current publications include 'The Guide to Franchising' (6th edition), and 'How to evaluate a Franchise' (7th edition) and 'The Ethics of Franchising' (2nd edition), 'How to Franchise Internationally' (3rd edition). He is also co-author of several publications, including 'How to Franchise your Business' (4th edition) 'Franchising and the Block Exemption Regulation' and 'Franchising', as well as 'A Guide to the EC Block Exemption for Vertical Agreements' and 'Negotiating an International Master Franchise Agreement' both due to be published in 2001. Editor of the 'International Journal of Franchising and Distribution Law' and editor of and contributor to 'Franchising in Europe' and the Canadian Franchise Guide; Co-editor of the International Encyclopaedia of Franchising. His works have been published in ten languages. Frequent lecturer at conferences and seminars world-wide. Regular contributor to journals and publications.
Personal: Born 6th November 1935. Lives in Stanmore, Middlesex.

PRATT, John

Pinsent Curtis Biddle, Birmingham
(0121) 200 1050
john.pratt@pinsents.com
Specialisation: Managing partner, Birmingham office. Main area of practice is franchising. Drafts franchise agreements, advises on international franchising and prepares documentation. Expertise also in competition law including anti-trust compliance programmes, notifications and general advice. Acts for 100 UK franchisors including FTSE 100 companies.
Prof. Memberships: Law Society; Birmingham Law Society.
Career: Qualified in 1976. Worked at *Lovell White Durrant* from 1974-83, then *Needham & James* 1983-93. Joined *Pinsent Curtis Biddle* as a partner in 1993. Previously chairman of Young Solicitors of England and Wales.
Publications: Author of 'Franchising Law & Practice', and 'Franchising'. Contributor to 'New Frontiers in Competition Law' and 'Il Franchising Internazionale'. Lectures in the UK and overseas.
Personal: Born 1951. Attended Dulwich College 1960-69; Oxford University 1969-72; Universite D'Aix-Marseille 1972-73. Interests include theatre, wine, food and sport.

VOGE, Julian

Brodies WS, Edinburgh (0131) 228 3777
julian.voge@brodies.co.uk
Specialisation: Main areas of practice are corporate and contract law, including franchising and licensing. Author of chapters on Scots law for 'Franchising Law and Practice' and 'International Franchising Law'.
Prof. Memberships: Law Society of Scotland, Writer to the Signet. Also admitted as a solicitor in England and Wales.
Career: Qualified in 1982. Articled at *Tods Murray.* Then worked at *Brodies* and *Berwin Leighton* before re-joining *Brodies* as a partner in 1987.
Personal: Born in 1958. Attended Daniel Stewarts & Melville College 1964-76, then University of Edinburgh 1976-80. Lives in Edinburgh.

WORMALD, Chris

Eversheds, London (020) 7919 4862
wormaldc@eversheds.com
Specialisation: Main areas of practice for over 19 years – franchising and other variants of business system expansion; substantial volume of international work in addition to domestic UK practice; related EC competition law; acts primarily for franchisors, master franchisees and franchisee associations. Joined McDonald's European headquarters in 1984 as their first European General Counsel and became a Vice-President of McDonald's Europe two years later. During ten years with McDonald's played a key role in developing the local teams as the system grew to 2000 restaurants in Europe. Hired and managed outside lawyers; negotiated master, development and joint venture franchise arrangements throughout Europe, North Africa and the Middle East; and designed and implemented franchise arrangements for new jurisdictions. Trained European real estate and franchising teams and was responsible for the legal side of the property acquisition programme. General Counsel role also involved him in trouble-shooting, litigation, lobbying and multinational group restructuring in view of his international tax origins. In 1996 joined Martin Mendelsohn to strengthen Eversheds' experienced franchising group as it began its international joint venture with Horwath International to form a global franchise consultancy. Today he leads the firm's London team. Specialises in strategic advice to businesses ranging from start ups to the largest multinationals, reviewing their expansion options and considering re-engineering and international expansion, and to government organisations. Works across commercial sectors – from hotels, restaurants and retail to IT, insurance and financial services, manufacturing, distribution and the public sector. He speaks French and German and has lived and worked in Brussels and Frankfurt.
Prof. Memberships: IBA, American Bar Association, International Franchise Association, British Franchise Association, Law Society.
Career: Qualified with *Simmons & Simmons* 1979 – international tax and commercial structuring for six years. McDonald's Europe – European General Counsel and vice-president; partner *Eversheds* London 1996.
Publications: Writes and speaks frequently worldwide on legal and business aspects of system expansion, most recently co-authoring for specialist UK publishers 'The Guide to Franchising in UK Pubs and Restaurants'.
Personal: Born 1954. Law degree from Sidney Sussex College, Cambridge University. Leisure interests include IT, sailing, fishing, travel and family.

FRAUD (CRIMINAL)

London: 406; The South & South West: 407; Wales: 407; Midlands: 408; North: 408; *Profiles*: 409

RESEARCH APPROVED BY BMRB: *For this edition,* Chambers' *researchers conducted 6,552 interviews – 4,419 with law firms, 554 with barristers and 1,579 with clients.*

The validity of the research was scrutinised by BMRB International, who audited both the methodology and the results at our offices in July 2001. They interviewed Chambers' *researchers and cross-checked sample interviews. Details of the audit appear on page 7.*

LONDON

FRAUD: CRIMINAL • London	Ptnrs	Assts
1		
Burton Copeland	10	5
Kingsley Napley	5	5
Peters & Peters	9	6
2		
Dechert	2	10
Irwin Mitchell	2	5
3		
Simons Muirhead & Burton	5	3
4		
Garstangs	1	3
Russell Jones & Walker	4	6
5		
Claude Hornby & Cox	2	3
Victor Lissack & Roscoe	3	3

LEADING INDIVIDUALS		
★	**BURTON Ian** Burton Copeland	**RAPHAEL Monty** Peters & Peters
1	**BYRNE David** Dechert	**CORKER David** David Corker Solicitors
	MURRAY Christopher Kingsley Napley	**OLIVER Keith** Peters & Peters
	POLLARD Stephen Kingsley Napley	**TRAVERS Harry** Burton Copeland
2	**CAPLAN Michael** Kingsley Napley	**COWELL Adam** Irwin Mitchell
	DELAHUNTY Louise Peters & Peters	**FLETCHER Rod** Russell Jones & Walker
	KIRK David Simons Muirhead & Burton	**SPIRO Brian** Burton Copeland
3	**CARNELL Bernard** Simons Muirhead	**FRANKLAND Matthew** Dechert
	HARDING John Kingsley Napley	**HUME John** Kingsley Napley
4	**BINNING Peter** Peters & Peters	**CORNTHWAITE Richard** Garstangs
	MATHER Catherine Burton Copeland	**PEACOCK Karen** Burton Copeland
	ROBINSON Kevin Irwin Mitchell	**WOOLLEY Linda** Kingsley Napley
	COLHOUN Aileen Ormerods	

This book is the product of 6,552 1/2 hour interviews. See p.7 for BMRB audit.
Within each band, firms are listed alphabetically. *See individuals' profiles p.409*

Burton Copeland (see firm details p.904) Pure fraud specialists consistently at the forefront and possessing in **Ian Burton** (see p.409) "*one of the great trailblazers.*" Involved in CPS, SFO, DTI and Revenue prosecutions, this "*powerhouse team*" includes the "*boundlessly energetic*" **Harry Travers** (see p.413), "*seasoned*" **Catherine Mather** (see p.411) and **Karen Peacock** (see p.411) who is "*young and coming through.*" It has recently been bolstered by the arrival of **Brian Spiro** (see p.412) from Simons Muirhead & Burton in what peers have judged to be a "*signal appointment.*"

Kingsley Napley (see firm details p.1022) "*Top quality outfit with a thoroughly justified reputation for excellence.*" Regularly seen defending the larger SFO cases, such as the high profile Deutsche Morgan Grenfell prosecution, its "*talented individuals*" figure heavily in our tables. **Stephen Pollard** (see p.411), ("*assured and exuding gravitas*") leads alongside **Christopher Murray** (see p.411) who is "*steeped in experience.*" **Michael Caplan** (see p.409) "*thinks things through both laterally and directly*" while **John Harding** (see p.410), **John Hume** (see p.410) and the "*self-effacing but first class*" **Linda Woolley** (see p.413) lend further assistance.

Peters & Peters (see firm details p.1095) "*A strong band of respected practitioners*" fronted by **Monty Raphael** (see p.412) "*the godfather of this field*" and "*a gifted rainmaker.*" Practitioners feel that his reputation attracts a substantial level of work, which is harvested by the "*highly regarded*" **Keith Oliver** (see p.411) and the "*assiduous*" **Peter Binning** (see p.409). **Louise Delahunty** (see p.410) possesses "*vim and vigour in abundance*" and is seen as emblematic of the forthright approach of the department as a whole.

Dechert (see firm details p.938) "*A big name with a fund of work*" covering SFO, DTI, and CPS prosecutions including revenue and substantial money laundering cases. Unusual for a city firm in its commitment to Legal Aid work, it has acted in four major SFO prosecutions in the last year alone. "*Larger than life*" **David Byrne** (see p.409) is an "*imposing presence,*" celebrated by competitors for his work in the revenue field. Working alongside him is the "*thorough and capable*" **Matthew Frankland** (see p.410), a member of the London Business Crime Group.

Irwin Mitchell (see firm details p.1009) In London for only three years, the Business Crime unit of this large, commercially orientated firm "*has come on leaps and bounds*" with rivals believing it is "*knocking on the door of the big three.*" "*Extremely proactive*" it handles inter alia, SFO, DTI, health and safety and revenue prosecutions for clients both nationally and internationally. **Adam Cowell** (see p.410), "*a bright chap with a strong crime background*" has now been joined from the firm's Sheffield office by the "*extensively experienced*" **Kevin Robinson** (see p.412) in what is seen as an attempt to further advance in the market.

Simons Muirhead & Burton (see firm details p.1133) Handles the whole gamut of criminal fraud advice including customs, VAT frauds, sanctions busting and revenue cases. Often seen in the weightier cases it has, in the past year, been active on the Deutsche Morgan Grenfell case and the UK side of the Christie's anti-trust affair. The departure of Brian Spiro to Burton Copeland is seen as a blow. This has been offset by the arrival of émigrés from the now defunct Offenbach & Co including the "*highly regarded and well connected*" **Bernard Carnell** (see p.409). He joins department supremo **David Kirk** (see p.411) who is "*academically strong and has a wealth of experience.*"

Garstangs (see firm details p.968) Having sprung to fame through the Guinness case, this department continues to enjoy high market recognition. SFO cases and general company frauds occupy much of the portfolio. A distinct emphasis lies on customs and excise work, with diversion frauds over the £10 million mark regularly undertaken. Stewarding matters is **Richard Cornthwaite** (see p.410) who is valued by peers for "*shouldering a heavy workload with aplomb.*"

Russell Jones & Walker (see firm details p.1116) Part of a national network of offices, a respected London department covers SFO, Customs, DTI and Inland Revenue investigations and prosecutions. Recent matters include major corruption prosecutions arising out of the privatisation of British Rail, and corruption allegations against Metropolitan Police officers, the latter of which is felt to be a specialism of the firm. The team is headed by **Rod Fletcher** (see p.410), "*a good talker, both pleasant and persuasive.*"

Claude Hornby & Cox (see firm details p.917) Middle ranking fraud cases are undertaken as part of a wider specialist criminal practice. Not generally seen on the complex SFO cases, the firm's bread and butter comes from Customs, VAT and DTI prosecuted matters. Recently acted for a surveyor charged with colluding with others to defraud ETAM through the submission of inflated invoices.

Victor Lissack & Roscoe (see firm details p.1168) A traditional practice, which has expanded its fraud capability of late and now counts two solicitor advocates amongst its number. Although not prominent on SFO prosecutions, it devotes itself to general fraud cases to good effect. Robert Roscoe's team acted on a substantial, three month case concerning a fraud perpetrated on the Training and Enterprise Council.

Other Notable Practitioners Having broken away from Peters & Peters, **David Corker** has established **David Corker & Co**, and continues to handle the big ticket cases he is synonymous with. "*A fine academic lawyer, highly intelligent and gifted,*" he has recently conducted a £12 million customs diversion fraud. **Aileen Colhoun** (see p.409) has left Oury Clark to join **Omerods**. While peers continue to commend her skills as a lawyer, they await future developments with interest.

SOUTH & SOUTH WEST

FRAUD: CRIMINAL • South & South West	Ptnrs	Assts
1 **Bobbetts Mackan** Bristol	1	6
2 **Blake Lapthorn** Fareham	2	2
DMH Brighton	2	1
Hodkinsons Locks Heath	3	1

LEADING INDIVIDUALS
1 **MITCHELL John** Blake Lapthorn

This book is the product of 6,552 1/2 hour interviews. See p.7 for BMRB audit.
Within each band, firms are listed alphabetically. *See individuals' profiles p.409*

Bobbetts Mackan (see firm details p.887) Criminal specialists who undertake fraud cases in the context of an "*excellent general practice.*" Whilst not participating in the larger SFO cases, the firm is on the fraud panel and handles regulatory and large scale investigatory matters, many of which concern sums in the millions. Represented one of the defendants in the highly publicised case of Robinson, an alleged fraud on the legal aid board by solicitors.

Blake Lapthorn (see firm details p.886) A commercial firm judged by peers to have a substantial level of fraud activity. Acting mainly for companies and individuals, much of the work involves defending against regulatory bodies and recovering peculated funds through civil litigation. Here **John Mitchell** is recommended. The firm is also endorsed for its work prosecuting for professional bodies and others, such as the RSPCA. Recently involved in a £1 million fraudulent trading case relating to the importation of furniture from Indonesia.

DMH (see firm details p.944) A commercial fraud and business defence practice with some white collar crime thrown into the mix. The team mainly acts for companies in complex international actions often involving freezing and search orders. It has recently acted for the defrauded former President of an African country, and in a 17 handed oil company fraud. Active on the regulatory side, it advises public bodies, including the London Borough of Croydon on issues such as trading standards and health and safety.

Hodkinsons Another specialist criminal practice picking up a sound reputation for handling medium to large frauds. It enters our tables this year due to warm praise from its peers. Appeared in a major horse doping trial and on a £50-70 million drug smuggling and money laundering case.

WALES

FRAUD: CRIMINAL • Wales	Ptnrs	Assts
1 **Martyn Prowel Solicitors** Cardiff	2	2
2 **Huttons** Cardiff	4	8
Roy Morgan & Co Cardiff	1	3

LEADING INDIVIDUALS
1 **PROWEL Martyn** Martyn Prowel Solicitors
2 **MORGAN Roy** Roy Morgan & Co

This book is the product of 6,552 1/2 hour interviews. See p.7 for BMRB audit.
Within each band, firms are listed alphabetically. *See individuals' profiles p.409*

Martyn Prowel Solicitors (see firm details p.1055) A unique entity, being a Welsh firm with fraud panel status. **Martyn Prowel** (see p.269) is "*a veritable bastion of the law*" benefiting from years of experience in criminal matters. The practice revolves around white collar crime and cigarette, VAT and liquor duty evasions with a further noted specialism in mortgage fraud.

Huttons (see firm details p.1006) The practice is an amalgamation of civil and criminal work with the stress being on the latter. VAT fraud is a particular feature, and cases over the £1 million mark are not unusual. The team acts mainly for individuals and companies, while a specialism in computer fraud and database theft is becoming readily apparent.

Roy Morgan & Co A solid criminal practice, which has attacked the fraud market with impressive results. Having established a designated investigation unit, under the leadership of **Roy Morgan**, it has captured some of the more interesting cases such as Robinson, the legal aid solicitors' fraud, while maintaining a healthy portfolio of VAT and customs fraud. Also seen increasingly in local authority and NHS related matters.

MIDLANDS

FRAUD: CRIMINAL • Midlands	Ptnrs	Assts
1 **Cartwright King** Nottingham	2	n/a
Nelsons Nottingham	2	10
2 **Glaisyers** Birmingham	4	4
3 **Hammond Suddards Edge** Birmingham	1	1
Varley Hadley Siddall Nottingham	1	n/a

LEADING INDIVIDUALS
1 **NELSON Richard** Nelsons
THURSTON Michael Cartwright King
WILSON Mark Cartwright King
2 **ROYLE Charles** Glaisyers

This book is the product of 6,552 1/2 hour interviews. See p.7 for BMRB audit.
Within each band, firms are listed alphabetically. *See individuals' profiles p.409*

Cartwright King "*Serious players*" who act for national companies and heavyweight commercial individuals. Acclaimed for its defence of commercial and professional fraud, it has a further specialism in Customs & Excise, Inland Revenue and DTI investigations. A substantial proportion of the practice is regulatory (including health and safety, environmental and trading standards matters). Committed to dealing with serious fraud cases at partner level, "*two thrusting and positive individuals,*" **Michael Thurston** (see p.412) and **Mark Wilson** (see p.413), shoulder the burden.

Nelsons (see firm details p.1080) Professional fraud, business crime and investigatory matters form the crux of this "*polished and well run department.*" **Richard Nelson's** (see p.411) group is enjoying something of a boom in regulatory and money laundering matters while the firm has four offices spread across the region to handle the volume. Recent cases include a major ostrich farming fraud and involvement in the Robinson legal aid case.

Glaisyers (see firm details p.973) Rising in the tables this year as a result of hearty approbation from the bigger names in the field. White collar crime is the order of the day, including serious fraud, Inland Revenue and Customs & Excise cases all practised under the supervision of the highly rated **Charles Royle** (see p.412).

Hammond Suddards Edge (see firm details p.984) A commercial firm with a discrete capacity for handling white collar crime and regulatory work. It generally defends companies or individuals who have fallen foul of the regulator. The unit is active in health and safety, environmental and trading standards related regulatory matters.

Varley Hadley Siddall (see firm details p.1167) The group handles fraud within a general crime practice. Current cases include customs prosecutions and prescription frauds. Also prosecutes for the Health and Safety Executive.

THE NORTH

FRAUD: CRIMINAL • The North	Ptnrs	Assts
1 **Burton Copeland** Manchester	4	3
2 **Betesh Fox & Co** Manchester	3	2
Irwin Mitchell Sheffield	n/a	n/a
Pannone & Partners Manchester	2	2
3 **DLA** Manchester	n/a	n/a
Garstangs Bolton	1	n/a
4 **McCormicks** Leeds	4	4
Russell Jones & Walker Manchester	1	3

LEADING INDIVIDUALS	
1 **BURROWS Lesley** Burton Copeland	**KENYON Michael** Burton Copeland
SMYTH Richard DLA	
2 **BARNFATHER Anthony** Pannone & Partners	**COOPER Ian** Burton Copeland
FOX Stephen Betesh Fox & Co	**TAYLOR Paul** Pannone & Partners
3 **HANMAN David** Russell Jones & Walker	**KENYON Andrew** Betesh Fox & Co
4 **MCCORMICK Peter** McCormicks	

This book is the product of 6,552 1/2 hour interviews. See p.7 for BMRB audit.
Within each band, firms are listed alphabetically *See individuals' profiles p.409*

Burton Copeland (see firm details p.904) Following a formal parting of the ways with its London office, this team of dedicated fraud specialists maintains its pre-eminent position. Staffed by "*lawyers who have been immersed in fraud for most of their professional lives,*" both barristers and fellow solicitors agree it has a "*top notch pedigree.*" Acting largely for corporates in difficulties, it receives significant amounts of customs, VAT, money laundering and SFO cases. The "*highly experienced*" **Michael Kenyon** (see p.410) works alongside **Lesley Burrows** (see p.409), who is a "*formidable, confident practitioner*" and **Ian Cooper** (see p.409) who "*receives his fair share of quality work.*" Presently engaged on an £80 million carousel fraud.

Betesh Fox & Co (see firm details p.880) Covering both the criminal and civil sphere, from small cheque fraud to top end SFO work, this is "*a fine firm with personable individuals.*" Its two dedicated partners **Stephen Fox** and **Andrew Kenyon** have "*bags of experience*" and have been seen to good effect in the Smith Robinson case.

Irwin Mitchell (see firm details p.1009) Despite the transfer of the respected Kevin Robinson to its London office, this group continues to receive plaudits for its "*professional approach to commercial crime.*" Adept at following complicated paper trails, it has been extensively involved in the intensive Doncaster Council corruption inquiry. The team is familiar with the heftier SFO cases, and is presently handling the Anglo American Ventures worldwide advanced fee fraud.

Pannone & Partners (see firm details p.1088) Handling complex fraud this firm is active in tax and customs investigations. On the regulatory side it acts for large private companies and plcs in response to OFT, DTI and Environment Agency prosecutions. Head of the Business Crime Unit **Paul Taylor** (see p.412) is felt by peers to have established a forceful presence, and is currently working on a multi-million pound SCO investigation. His colleague **Tony Barnfather** (see p.409) elicited much praise for his acknowledged skill in health and safety investigations.

DLA Eschewing legal aid work in favour of advising its corporate clients, the firm acts on SFO, investigatory and regulatory matters. **Richard Smyth** remains the department's leading name.

Garstangs (see firm details p.968) Focusing on criminal fraud, this practice with its sister office in London, "*straddles the country, picking up some of the juicier morsels.*" The northern side of operations, is typically described by peers as "*a significant presence in the region.*"

McCormicks (see firm details p.1060) One of a select handful of firms in Yorkshire capable of handling complex fraud matters. The firm has been involved in the Doncaster Council corruption and fraud inquiry, and a nationally publicised matter arising from alleged conspiracy to disseminate food unfit for human consumption. **Peter McCormick** (see p.411) impresses in his more strategic role.

Russell Jones & Walker (see firm details p.1116) Renowned as an excellent practice for revenue and customs investigations, this department has successfully branched out into more general fraud work. **David Hanman** (see p.272) brings to bear his "*vast technical knowledge in the revenue arena*" and is tipped to broaden the variety of his practice further in the next year.

LEADERS IN FRAUD

BARNFATHER, Anthony

Pannone & Partners, Manchester (0161) 909 4523
anthony.barnfather@pannone.co.uk

Specialisation: Main area of specialisation encompasses all aspects of business crime. Prime areas of expertise include representation of corporations and individuals subject to investigation by regulatory agencies. Present/recent case load includes Customs & Excise, F.S.A., Inland Revenue, Office of Fair Trading and SFO work. Also assists a number of corporations including multinationals regarding quasi-criminal investigations brought by such agencies as the Environment Agency and Health and Safety Executive. (Presently advising on a number of fatal accidents). Acts for professional clients in respect of allegations of serious/complex crime.
Prof. Memberships: The Law Society.
Career: Anthony Barnfather's initial involvement with criminal litigation was in his role as a police officer. He served with the West Yorkshire Police and thereafter continued this investigative role in the tax haven of Bermuda. He gained his law degree in Leeds, later becoming a partner in a Leeds practice. He joined *Pannone & Partners* in 1998 and is now a partner in their business crime unit.
Personal: Interests include Rugby League, motorcycling and hillwalking.

BINNING, Peter

Peters & Peters, London (020) 7629 7991
pbinning@petersandpeters.co.uk

Specialisation: All aspects of business crime and other complex criminal cases, including extradition, tax and customs fraud, money laundering and data protection. Regulatory inquiries involving the DTI and FSA as well as other regulatory bodies such as the Health and Safety Executives. Current cases include first ever extradition request from the UAE.
Prof. Memberships: JUSTICE Executive Board, Treasurer, London Criminal Courts Solicitors Association and IBA.
Career: Called to the Bar: 1985. Crown Prosecution Service: 1989-94. Serious Fraud Office: 1994-96. Joined *Peters & Peters*: 1996 – partner 1998.
Publications: Articles in legal journals and responses to consultation papers. Numerous broadcasting appearances.
Personal: Resides London. Sailing, ski mountaineering. Member of Royal Ocean Racing Club, Royal Geographical Society.

BURROWS, Lesley

Burton Copeland (North), Manchester
(0161) 834 7374

Specialisation: Commercial fraud defence work including liquidation, banking, stock market, loan and leasing and mortgage and property fraud. Considerable experience of SFO investigations and prosecutions having acted for the first defendants in the Arrows and Butte Mining prosecutions.
Prof. Memberships: Law Society and Criminal Law Solicitors Association.
Career: Qualified 1980. Partner at *Burton Coplend* from 1990.
Personal: Attended Arnold School in Blackpool and the University of Sheffield.

BURTON, Ian

Burton Copeland (London), London
(020) 7430 2277

Specialisation: Commercial fraud, tax investigations, company investigations, problem solving.
Prof. Memberships: International Bar Association; London Criminal Courts Solicitors Association.
Career: Qualified 1971. Founded *Burton Copeland* 1982.
Personal: Lives London and Cheshire.

BYRNE, David

Dechert, London (020) 7775 7415
david.byrne@dechertEU.com

Specialisation: Partner and head of litigation and investigations, London. Responsible for all aspects of investigation work including disciplinary hearings, insurance disputes, financial services matters and serious fraud. He specialises in civil and criminal fraud for both claimants and defendants. In particular, he has dealt with cases brought by the SFO, city regulators, Inland Revenue and Customs & Excise. He has acted for clients involved directly and indirectly in many of the biggest fraud prosecutions of the last 15 years and also acted for the only successful defendant in the recent Jyske Bank case. David also co-ordinates the firm's growing practice in corporate manslaughter.
Prof. Memberships: Law Society; Society Practitioners of Insolvency.
Career: Qualified in 1978. Articled at *Norton Rose.* Solicitor *Norton Rose* 1978-83. *Clifford Turner* (now *Clifford Chance)* 1983-85. Partner *Titmuss Sainer & Webb* (now *Dechert*) since 1987.
Personal: Born 1951. Attended Kings College London, Masters degree in insurance law, Sweet & Maxwell prize for company law. Interests include golf and fell walking.

CAPLAN, Michael

Kingsley Napley, London (020) 7814 1200
mcaplan@kingsleynapley.co.uk

Specialisation: Partner in Criminal Litigation Department. Work includes criminal law, advocacy, extradition, casino applications, gaming and licensing, and prosecuting for and advising professional and regulatory bodies. Sits as a Recorder. Rights of audience in the Crown Court. Chairman of the Solicitors Association of Higher Court Advocates.
Career: Qualified in 1977. Joined *Kingsley Napley* in 1978 and became a partner in 1982.
Personal: Born 3rd May 1953. Attended Kings College, London: LLB (Hons), AKC. Leisure interests include family, sport and reading. Lives in London.

CARNELL, Bernard

Simons Muirhead & Burton, London
(020) 7734 4499
bernard.carnell@smab.co.uk

Specialisation: Senior Partner in Criminal Department. Work includes commercial fraud, insider dealing, drug related crime, obscene publications and all areas of general crime. Particular experience of legal aid regulations and international and financial investigations. Acted in R v Kellard and Others (Britannia Park Fraud trial, the longest in English history); BCCI Investigation; R v Fisher (the first insider dealing trial); R v Adelaja and Others (the first trial using computers); R v Howard Marks and others (one of the largest and well-publicised drug cases); the inquest of Cynthia Jarrett (Tottenham riots); and R v Gay News Ltd and Lemon (Blasphemy trial) and numerous Divisional Court, Court of Appeal and House of Lords proceedings. Individual charge-out rate is usually £150-£220 per hour, depending on nature and seriousness of case.
Prof. Memberships: Law Society.
Career: Qualified in 1972. Joined *Offenbach & Co* in 1976, becoming a Partner in 1982.
Personal: Born 1947. Attended LSE (1966-69) and Law College. Lives in London. Former Board Director of Release.

COLHOUN, Aileen

Ormerods, Croydon (020) 8686 5000

Specialisation: Specialist in criminal litigation. Practice covers all areas of criminal work, particularly large scale white collar criminal defence work. Advises in investigations conducted by other regulatory bodies.
Prof. Memberships: Law Society, London Criminal Courts Solicitors Association, International Bar Association, British Academy of Forensic Sciences, Chairman of Criminal Law Sub-Committee, City of Westminster Law Society, Justice.
Career: Qualified in 1983. Worked at *Kingsley Napley* 1981-87, then *Powell Magrath & Spencer* 1987-90. Partner at *Magrath & Co.* 1990-97. Founding partner of *Oury Colhoun and Co* 1997 (now *Oury Clark*).
Personal: Born 14 September 1957. Attended University of Bristol 1976-79 (LLB), then University of Cambridge (MPhil in Criminology 1979-80). Leisure interests include reading and live music. Lives in London.

COOPER, Ian

Burton Copeland (North), Manchester
(0161) 834 7374

Specialisation: Partner specialising in business and corporate fraud, investment, offshore and tax fraud, mortgage and property fraud, professional misconduct matters, share and securities fraud.
Career: Articled *Copeland Glickman*; qualified 1987; assistant solicitor *Hugh Pond & Co* 1987-89; assistant solicitor *Burton Copeland* 1989-91, partner 1991. King Edward VII School. Liverpool University (1973 BA Hons).

CORKER, David
David Corker Solicitors, London 0207 353 6007

CORNTHWAITE, Richard
Garstangs, London (020) 7242 4324
r.cornthwaite@garstangs.co.uk
Specialisation: Specialises in the defence of fraud cases, including SFO, Inland Revenue, HM Customs and Excise and D.T.I. prosecutions. Also handles ancillary commercial litigation, particularly in relation to fraud and asset recovery in the Chancery Division. Acted in the Guinness, Eagle Trust, Thermastor and Brent Walker cases. Also secured the acquittal of Kevin Taylor in the 'Stalker Affair'. Recently represented a principal defendant in Chancery proceedings brought by Jyske Bank (Gibraltar) Limited. Currently acting for defendant in Hungarian International Bank (SFO prosecution) and three major HM Customs and Excise investigations.
Prof. Memberships: Law Society.
Career: Qualified in 1977. Joined *Garstangs* as a partner in 1990.
Personal: Born 12 November, 1951. Keele University 1970-74. Lives in London and Manchester.

COWELL, Adam
Irwin Mitchell, London (020) 7404 3600
cowella@irwinmitchell.co.uk
Specialisation: Partner in Company Regulation Group, specialises in SFO and DTI investigations and advises on regulatory matters including S447 enquires, CDDA proceedings and FSA and Inland Revenue investigations. Currently instructed in Jubilee Line Extention Fraud and SFO prosecution of internet company, BCCI related litigation (Gokal-v-UK) and numerous DTI, FSA and tax investigations and related civil cases.
Prof. Memberships: Hon. Secretary of International Criminal Law Association; Committee member LCCSA; Law Society.
Career: Qualified 1989. Solicitor *Bindman & Partners*, then partner at *Moss & Co.* 1993 to 1998. Partner *Irwin Mitchell* 1998.
Publications: Regular lecturer and writer on Company Investigations (including White Collar Crime Conferences 1999 & 2000), FSA powers (Eurolegal 2001), Business Crime and Internet (ICLA Conference 2000) and Business Crime and Human Rights, Tax Investigations (Butterworths Annual Lecture 2001) and Asset Recovery (ICLA 2001).
Personal: Lives in London. Enjoys golf.

DELAHUNTY, Louise
Peters & Peters, London (020) 7629 7991
ldelahunty@petersandpeters.co.uk
Specialisation: Partner in Business Crime. Her principal area of practice is white collar crime, dealing with prosecutions and enquiries by the SFO, DTI, Customs & Excise and Inland Revenue. She also deals with regulatory and disciplinary proceedings. Extensive experience in acting for professionals, including solicitors. In 1998 she defended Judge Richard Gee. She currently represents Peter Young.
Prof. Memberships: Law Society, The City of Westminister Law Society, London Criminal Courts Solicitors Association (LCCSA), International Bar Association, Hong Kong Law Society. She is a member of the Law Society Criminal Law Committee and Chairman of the Law Society Money Laundering and Serious Fraud Task Force.
Career: Joined *Peters & Peters* in 1982 and qualified in 1984. Spent 4 years in Hong Kong between 1986 and 1990, practising in both criminal and commercial litigation. Returned to *Peters & Peters* in 1990 and became a Partner in 1991. Lectures on mortgage fraud, money laundering and human rights. In 1998 & 2001 lectured on behalf of the Law Society to lawyers in the Middle East.

FLETCHER, Rod
Russell Jones & Walker, London (020) 7837 2808
Specialisation: Partner and Head of Criminal and Business Investigations Department. Main area of practice is criminal defence. Has particular involvement with white collar/ business crime and major miscarriage of justice cases. Also regularly instructed in disciplinary cases. Represents individuals attending a number of government and other public inquiries: examples include the Scott Inquiry, the Stephen Lawrence Inquiry, the Marchioness Inquiry and the Bloody Sunday Inquiry. Acted in many miscarriage of justice cases, including the representation of the police officers prosecuted following the Birmingham Six, Guildford Four and Broadwater Farm investigations. Acted in the Maxwell, Barings and Bute Mining cases. Currently acting in a series of major corruption cases.
Prof. Memberships: Law Society, LCCSA, IBA
Career: Qualified in 1981. Worked with *Kingsley Napley*, 1979-83. Left to join *Russell Jones & Walker* in 1983, becoming a Partner in 1985.
Personal: Born 21st April 1957. Attended Berkhamstead School, then Birmingham University 1975-8. Leisure interests include sailing, golf, cricket and music. Lives in London.

FOX, Stephen
Betesh Fox & Co, Manchester (0161) 832 6131

FRANKLAND, Matthew
Dechert, London (020) 7583 5353
matthew.frankland@dechertEU.com
Specialisation: Partner in the investigations department. Specialises in the defence of national and international fraud/white collar crime cases, including those brought by the SFO, DTI, CPS, Inland Revenue and Customs & Excise. He has particular experience of Crown Court confiscation and High Court restraint proceedings. He also jointly heads a team that specialises in financial services regulatory investigations including those by the FSA and lectures on this topic. He advises on investigations by professional institutes including fraud enquiries at the General Medical Council and the General Dental Council. He has conducted litigation arising from criminal law in the House of Lords and European Court of Human Rights. He also advises on transatlantic investigations and prosecutions, an area of work which has increased following the merger of *Titmuss Sainer Dechert* with US practice, *Dechert Price & Rhoads.*
Prof. Memberships: Law Society; Criminal Law Solicitors' Association; Association of Business Recovery Professionals.
Career: Qualified in September 1991. Joined *Titmuss Sainer Dechert* (now *Dechert*) in 1995.
Personal: Born 1964, attended University of Wales, resides London and Sussex. Leisure interests include sport, travel and art.

HANMAN, David
Russell Jones & Walker, Manchester
(0161) 832 8877 d.i.hanman@rjw.co.uk
See under Customs & Excise, p.272

HARDING, John
Kingsley Napley, London (020) 7814 1200
jharding@kingsleynapley.co.uk
Specialisation: Partner in Criminal Litigation Department dealing with white collar and general crime. Recent cases include SFO and Inland Revenue Investigations, and International case work involving sanctions legislation and fraud and mutual legal assistance. Currently involved in the Jubilee Line Extension case and the criminal prosecutions of the staff and partners of *Robinson's*, solicitors.
Prof. Memberships: Law Society; LCCSA; CLSA; BAFS.
Career: Qualified in October 1988. Joined *Kingsley Napley* in 1990 and became a partner in 1994.
Personal: Born 9th April 1963. Educated at Derby School and Brunel University.

HUME, John
Kingsley Napley, London (020) 7814 1200
jhume@kingsleynapley.co.uk
Specialisation: Partner specialising in corporate litigation civil and criminal with an emphasis on fraud related shareholder and partnership disputes. Experience encompasses international fraud actions, large white collar crime trials, takeover battles, post company acquisition claims, directors disqualification applications and Commonwealth capital appeals. Represents professionals in all disciplinary regulatory inquiries, tribunals and criminal matters.
Prof. Memberships: Liveryman and member of the Court of the City of London Solicitors' Company, past committee member of the London Litigation Solicitors' Association and member of London Criminal Courts Solicitors Association. Solicitor Advocate All Higher Courts.
Career: Qualified in 1970. Articled at *Titmuss Sainer & Webb.* Partner in 1973. Partner *Ralph Hume Garry* August 1997. Partner *Kingsley Napley* 2001.
Personal: Born 1945. Educated at Cranleigh School and College of Law, Lancaster Gate. Interests include shooting, scuba diving, watching cricket, rugby, motor racing and rallying classic cars.

KENYON, Andrew
Betesh Fox & Co, Manchester (0161) 832 6131

KENYON, Michael
Burton Copeland (North), Manchester
(0161) 834 7374
Specialisation: Commercial fraud investigation and defence including prospectus fraud, loan and leasing fraud, insider dealing, fraudulent trading, frauds on investors, property and mortgage fraud, corruption and tax investigations. Considerable recent experience of advising and defending in customs, duty and VAT cases. Defends numerous solicitors charged with mortgage and other frauds.
Prof. Memberships: Law Society, Criminal Law Solicitors Association.
Career: Qualified in 1980. Partner at *Chafes* Stockport 1985-86. Senior Crown Prosecutor in Manchester 1987-89. Partner at *Burton Copeland* from 1990.
Personal: Born 1956. Attended Manchester Grammar School and University of Kent. Leisure interests include salmon fishing, game shooting, military and political history and opera. Lives in Cheshire and Scotland.

KIRK, David
Simons Muirhead & Burton, London
(020) 7734 4499
david.kirk@smab.co.uk
Specialisation: Head. Fraud Department. Commercial Fraud (including SFO, DTI, Inland Revenue and Customs & Excise investigations), Regulation, Investigations. Co-author of 'Serious Fraud – Investigation and Trial' (2nd Edition, Butterworths 1997).
Prof. Memberships: Law Society, LCCSA, IBA.

MATHER, Catherine
Burton Copeland (London), London
(020) 7430 2277
Specialisation: White collar and general crime. Regulatory proceedings; Involvement in following trials: Guinness, Blue Arrow, Nissan UK, Levitt, Maxwell. Finch Bossino and others, Jane Andrews.
Career: Assistant Solicitor at Metropolitan Police Solicitors Department; Senior Crown Prosecutor Inner London; Associate – Fraud and Regulation Unit, *Stephenson Harwood.* Joined *Burton Copeland* in 1994 and made Partner December 1995. Appointed part time Immigration Adjudicator, May 2001.

MCCORMICK OBE, Peter
McCormicks, Leeds (0113) 246 0622
p.mccormick@mccormicks-solicitors.com
Specialisation: Over 20 years experience of complex fraud cases of all types – defending white collar fraud; DTI investigations, prosecutions and applications to disqualify Directors; Inland Revenue, VAT, back duty and other Customs and Excise prosecutions and inquiries on an international basis including appearing in the High Court on Mareva and other restraining order hearings; conducts cases before the VAT Tribunals and Commissioners of Inland Revenue. Holds the Higher Courts (Criminal Proceedings) Qualification, conducting cases in the Magistrates and Crown Courts and the Court of Appeal. Has conducted a number of substantial and high profile cases internationally including the first case of extradition from Uruguay (the bullion dealer Harvey Michael Ross – alleged £20m fraud), the first G.P. to be prosecuted for conspiracy to defraud the Health Service, the largest fraud case ever prosecuted by the West Yorkshire Fraud Squad and taxation cases where the tax involved has exceeded £25m; founder member of the Complex Case Practitioners Group; Supervisor for Serious Fraud Panel Work, Criminal Defence Service. Other areas of practice include: Sports Law and Media and Entertainment Law (Leader in the Field in both – see elsewhere) and Commercial. Lectures widely. Resident legal expert on Radio Leeds, Yorkshire Television and the Yorkshire Post. Also writes for the Gazette, the Lawyer and other legal and business journals. Author of 'Sport, Business and the Law' published by Jordans.
Prof. Memberships: Associate Director and Legal Counsel Leeds United F.C. Chairman of the Yorkshire Young Achievers Awards. Member of the Advisory Board, Sports Law Centre, Anglia University; Vice-President of The Outward Bound Trust; Solicitor to The Duke of Edinburgh's Award; Member of the Legal Working Party of The F.A. Premier League; Patron of the Harrogate Junior Chamber of Commerce; Trustee, Friends of War Memorials.

MITCHELL, John
Blake Lapthorn, Fareham (01489) 579 990

MORGAN, Roy
Roy Morgan & Co, Cardiff (029) 20398511

MURRAY, Christopher
Kingsley Napley, London (020) 7814 1200
cmurray@kingsleynapley.co.uk
Specialisation: Partner and head of the Criminal Litigation Department. Specialises in both white collar and general crime with a strong emphasis on the international aspects and pre-inquiry stages of this area. Particular expertise in money laundering, corruption, fraud and mutual assistance cases. Involved in many highly publicised cases including Maxwell, Polly Peck, Guinness, Banco Ambrosiano. Curently acting for Henry Sweetbaum in the SFO prosecution against Wickes and the Nigerian Government in its mutual assistance proceedings to recover the ABACHA funds. Speaks regularly at national and international conferences and writes on money laundering, lawyer confidentiality and international cooperation in white collar crime. Regular contributor to TV and radio on criminal law matters. Vice Patron Missing Persons Helpline.
Prof. Memberships: Member of Criminal Justice Consultative Council; London Criminal Courts Solicitors Association (LCCSA) (President 1997/8); LCCSA Committee on Disclosure (Chairman); Law Society Criminal Law Committee; Law Society Criminal Law Sub Committee on Juries in Serious Fraud Trials; Law Society Evidence to House of Lords on EU Corpus Iuris Anti-fraud proposals; City of London Solicitor's Society (sub-committee on Judicial Appointments for City Solicitors) CLSA, IBA, British Academy of Forensic Sciences; Justice (Sub Committee on Serious Fraud).
Career: Qualified 1972. Partner at *Kingsley Napley* since 1974. Recorder of the Crown Court.
Publications: Numerous, including jointly with Lorna Harris 'Mutual Assistance in Criminal Matters,' Sweet & Maxwell, 2000.
Personal: Educated at Kings College, Taunton 1961-65, and University College, London (LLB) 1966-69. Member of the Athenaeum and 2 Brydges Place. Leisure pursuits include music, theatre, modern art and design, 20th Century English literature. Born 6 November 1947.

NELSON, Richard
Nelsons, Nottingham (0115) 958 6262
richard.nelson@nelsons-solicitors.co.uk
Specialisation: Leads substantial business crime department comprising in-house solicitors and barristers covering full range of business related investigation and prosecution, acting for companies and individuals. Practice involves cases over wide geographical area throughout England and Wales often with international element. Current case work of fraud (including computer fraud), revenue and customs & excise investigations (including tax and duty evasion), trading standards (including for nationwide retail chain), HSE, environmental, Companies Act, DTI and insolvency offences, regulatory and environmental, professional disciplinary conduct and management issues, corporate and other individual crime and SFO prosecutions (this year including Ostrich Farming case and instructed by Tim Robinson before Bristol Crown Court). Casework often involves pursuit and consideration of large volumes of evidence in various forms (several million documents in one case) and liaison with technical and forensic experts. The firm also has a separate department dealing with civil law implications and further department dealing with general and other serious crime.
Prof. Memberships: Notts Crim Justice Strategy Committee. Notts Law Society Criminal Business Committee (former chairman). Former Council Member Notts Law Society. Solicitors advisory Scheme.
Career: Qualified 1975. *J A Bright Richards & Flewitt* 1972-77. *Freeth Cartwright & Sketchley* 1977-83 (partner from 1980). Formed *Nelson, Johnson & Hastings* (now *Nelsons*) with two partners and no staff in 1983. *Nelsons* is now one of the largest firms in the region, based in several cities.
Personal: Born 14.06.50. Educated Nottingham High School and Bristol University. Interests include sport and comedy.

OLIVER, Keith
Peters & Peters, London (020) 7629 7991
Specialisation: Partner in Commercial & Regulatory/Commercial Fraud Litigation. Main areas of expertise are commercial, regulatory and business crime litigation, both domestically and internationally. Has extensive experience in this area and acted for Kevin Maxwell following the collapse of the Maxwell Group of Companies and for Anthony Parnes in the Guinness proceedings. Has done considerable work involving the powers of the SFO and the privilege against self-incrimination both at Common Law and under insolvency legislation. Wide experience of DTI Companies Act and various regulatory enquiries. President of AIJA Business Crime Sub-commission. Lectures, and has delivered papers on regulatory, jurisdictional and human rights issues.
Prof. Memberships: Association Internationale de Jeunes Avocats (AIJA), International Bar Association, Law Society, British Italian Law Association.
Career: Qualified in 1980, having joined *Peters & Peters* in 1978. Became a Partner in 1983.
Personal: Lives in London.

PEACOCK, Karen
Burton Copeland (London), London
(020) 7430 2277
Specialisation: Partner in Commercial Fraud Department. All types of commercial fraud and white collar crime. City background in commercial litigation particularly banking. Extensive experience in SFO investigations and prosecutions including George Walker, BCCI and Morgan Grenfell.
Prof. Memberships: Law Society, LCCSA.
Career: Qualified 1990. At *Slaughter and May* 1988-92; *McKenna & Co* 1992-93; *Harkavys* 1993-94; *Burton Copeland* 1995, partner December 1995.
Personal: Educated at Longsands College and London University.

POLLARD, Stephen
Kingsley Napley, London (020) 7814 1200
spollard@kingsleynapley.co.uk
Specialisation: Partner in criminal and regulatory department. Practice covers all criminal work, but particularly white collar fraud and 'city crime'. Also handles regulatory work including disciplinary proceedings before the SFA and the FSA. Acted for Lou Macari in the revenue prosecution of Swindon Town FC, and in the SFO prosecution of the directors of DPR Futures. Recently represented the football manager David Jones, acquitted of child abuse allegations. Currently represents Nick Leeson, the ex-Barings trader, a defendant in the Deutsche Morgan Grenfell SFP prosecution, and is part of the team representing 450 former soldiers in Lord Saville's Inquiry into 'Bloody Sunday'. Has various clients involved in cur-

rent SFA proceedings. Appears regularly on TV and radio on criminal law matters.
Prof. Memberships: AIJA, London Criminal Courts Solicitors' Association.
Career: Qualified 1985. Worked at *Payne Hicks Beach* 1982-87, including 1984-85 as a Member of Secretariat of the European Commission of Human Rights, Strasbourg. One year with the Crown Prosecution Service 1987-88. Joined *Kingsley Napley* in 1989, becoming a partner in 1990.
Personal: Born 5th September 1958. Attended Manchester Grammar School 1972-77, and Pembroke College, Oxford 1977-80. Leisure interests include reading, sport, theatre and family. Lives in Putney, London. Married with four children.

PROWEL, Martyn
Martyn Prowel Solicitors, Cardiff (02920) 470909
mprowel@mped.globalnet.co.uk
See under Crime, p.269

RAPHAEL, Monty
Peters & Peters, London (020) 7629 7991
Specialisation: Senior partner. Main area of practice is business crime and associated litigation. Handles major cases involving fraud, tax and securities offences, customs infractions and general financial regulatory problems. Has specialised in commercial fraud for 30 years. Author of numerous articles and publications on the subject. Has spoken widely at conferences held by, among many others, the American Bar Association, American Bankers Association, American Society of Criminology, The Crown Agents, Commonwealth Secretariat, Jesus College, Cambridge, British-German Jurists Association, the Anglo-French Law Society and the Bank of England and many others.
Prof. Memberships: Law Society; Westminster Law Society; International Bar Association; International Association of Penal Law; Transparency International; ALPFIEC (Association of Lawyers for the Protection of the Financial Interests of the European Community); British-German Jurists Association; American Bar Association.
Career: Qualified 1962; senior partner of *Peters & Peters*. In 1979 became the first advocacy training officer appointed by the London Criminal Courts Solicitors' Association (president 1982-84). Provided detailed written and oral evidence on the prosecution and trial of commercial fraud to the Roskill Committee and to the Royal Commission on Criminal Justice. Founder and past chairman of the Business Crime Committee of the section on business law of the International Bar Association. Served as a member of the Home Office Working Party advising on the proposed alterations to 'right to silence' in 1988-89. Chairman of the White Collar Crime Unit at the Liverpool Business School. Assisted the Council of Europe in its programme to help the emergent economies of Eastern Europe in their transition to a market economy. Has advised a number of offshore jurisdictions on money laundering measures. Honorary solicitor to the Howard League for Penal Reform. Member ICAEW Fraud Advisory Panel. Chair IBA Anti-Corruption Working Group.
Publications: Latest publications include 'Fraud and Solutions for Fraud Prevention, Detection and Investigation' (Unisys, France, October 1996; introduction to D Corker, 'Disclosure in Criminal Proceedings' (Sweet & Maxwell 1997); 'Sentencing and Fraud' (Central Law Training, January 1997); 'Representation of Foreign Clients in US Investigations' (ABA White Collar Crime Conference March 1997); 'The Role of Lawyers in the Fight Against Corruption' (IBA Global Law in Practice Anniversary Book 1997); 'UK Anti-Money Laundering Legislation' (IBC Cayman Islands April 1997); Bank Confidentiality and the Constructive Trustee Dilemma (Bank of England April 1997); 'Transnational Crime and Human Rights (University of Edinburgh May 1997); 'Criminal Proceedings Arising from Fraud' (EuroForum Asset Recovery June 1997); Fraud: A Crisis for Commerce and Criminal Justice (Institute of Chartered Accountants Annual Conference 1997); The Case for the Retention of a Jury in Cases of Serious or Complex Fraud ('International Journal of Risk Security and Crime Prevention' vol 3, no 1, 1998); What is wrong with the idea of a "Super-SFO"? ('The Lawyer' October 1997); introduction to the 'Euromoney Publication' (September 1998); 'City Regulation into the 21st Century – Insider Dealing as a Limb of Market Abuse' (IBC December 1998); 'The SFO – Ten Years On' (SFO December 1998); Justice for Dictators? The Pinochet Case ('Human Rights Institute News – May 1999'); with Professor M Levi – Anti-corruption – A Signpost for Transactional Lawyers ('Business Law International' September 1999); Proposals for Procedural Reform in Cases of Serious Fraud Pre-trial procedures ('New Law Journal' March 2000); 'Money Laundering and the Law: Progression all Fronts in Europe' (The Anti-laundering and Fraud Alert' January 2000).
Personal: Lives in London.

ROBINSON, Kevin
Irwin Mitchell, London (020) 7404 3600
Specialisation: Partner heading Business Crime Unit. Based in London. Acted in the major Iraqi arms export cases and also Astra/BMARC disqualification proceedings. Involved in arms export prosecutions in this country and the US. Represents company directors, managers and professionals subject to investigation or charged with fraud, particularly SFO prosecutions, fraudulent trading, VAT Inland Revenue and like offences. Also represents corporations including multi-nationals and Plc's in criminal proceedings arising out of their commercial activities. Additionally acts in local authority corruption cases.
Prof. Memberships: Member International Bar Association. Legal Reds. Committee member Solicitors Associates of Higher Court Advocates, London criminal Courts Solicitors Association.
Career: Qualified in 1973. Joined *Irwin Mitchell* in 1974 became a partner in 1975. Former Treasurer of Criminal Law Solicitors Association. Higher Courts Rights of Audience 1995.

ROYLE, Charles
Glaisyers, Birmingham (0121) 233 2971
charlesroyale@glaisyers.co.uk
Specialisation: Crime, all areas including Youth & Motoring, Licensing – liquor & gaming.
Prof. Memberships: Law Society, Birmingham Law Society, Duty Solicitor.
Career: Palmers School Grays, George Dixon Grammar School Birmingham, Sheffield University. Articled *George Jonas*, Partner with *Jonas Grove & Co*, Partner with *Glaisyers* since 1979, now Senior Partner.
Personal: Keen Sportsman & Fan; Cricket, Tennis, Golf, Soccer, Rugby. Married with 3 children; President of Edgbaston Nursery School.

SMYTH, Richard
DLA, Manchester (08700) 111111

SPIRO, Brian
Burton Copeland (London), London
(020) 7430 2277
bspiro@burtoncopeland.co.uk
Specialisation: Partner. Criminal defence litigation, specialising in business crime, drugs law and serious offences against the person. Also fraud investigation and international consultancy work. Regular contributor to legal journals and broadcaster.
Prof. Memberships: Law Society, LCCSA, I.B.A, A.I.J.A, Lawyers for Liberty.
Career: Qualified in 1984, Partner of *Simons Muirhead & Burton* (1986-01). Partner of *Burton Copeland* (London) from April 2001.
Publications: Author of 'Police Station Advisers' Index' (Sweet & Maxwell).

TAYLOR, Paul
Pannone & Partners, Manchester (0161) 909 4556
paul.taylor@pannone.co.uk
Specialisation: All aspects of business crime, fraud and related proceedings. Advising and representing individuals and corporations at all stages of investigation and litigation by the SFO, Customs & Excise, DTI, Fraud Investigation Group, Trading Standards, Health and Safety Executive, and other regulatory authorities. Significant experience in representing solicitors and accountants in a wide range of fraud cases, including those with an international dimension, money laundering and in serious/complex criminal cases generally. Successfully acted in a number of recent major cases for a solicitor charged with perverting the course of justice; a chartered accountant charged with a VAT cash accounting fraud; a solicitor in connection with a SFO investigation; a solicitor in connection with a Customs & Excise investigation and other substantial work.
Prof. Memberships: Law Society of England & Wales and Hong Kong; former member of the Criminal Law Sub-committee Hong Kong; Complex Case Practitioners Group; Serious Fraud Panel Supervisor.
Career: Admitted in England & Wales 1980; admitted in Hong Kong 1985: Head of business crime *Alsop Wilkinson* Hong Kong 1989-93; Head of business crime *Pannone & Partners* 1995 to date.
Personal: Born 1955. Graduated University College of Wales 1977. Keen sportsman and enjoys traveling.

THURSTON, Michael
Cartwright King, Nottingham (0115) 958 7444
mthurston@cartwrightking.co.uk
Specialisation: All types of fraud, defending businesses, companies, directors and professionals. SFO, Fraud Squad, DTI, Customs & Excise, Inland Revenue cases and regulatory investigations and prosecutions by the HSE, Environment Agency, Trading Standards, etc. Consultancy advice to commerce to prevent and detect and deal with the aftermath of fraud, L.S.C. Serious Fraud Panel Supervisor. *Cartwright King* is a specialist corporate crime (and general criminal defence) practice, and is a member of the LSC Serious Fraud Panel.
Career: Engineering graduate and worked in industry prior to qualification. Criminal Litigation partner in *freethcarthwright* 1974-99. De-merged to set up *Cartwright* 2000. Remains consultant to *freethcartwright*.
Personal: Born 1948. Leisure: tennis, golf, skiing.

TRAVERS, Harry
Burton Copeland (London), London (020) 7430 2277
Specialisation: Partner specialising in white-collar crime, often with an international element, including tax fraud, corruption, insolvency/banking/insurance fraud/insider dealing and money laundering. Also specialises in regulatory and disciplinary work (e.g. Lloyds, FSA), Inland Revenue and Customs & Excise investigations, directors' disqualifications, and prosecutions for breach of environmental protection/health and safety legislation. Has substantial experience in securing negotiated financial settlements with the Inland Revenue and/or bringing Judicial Review proceedings in respect of their actions, particularly in relation to the conduct of raids under Section 20C TMA 1970. Acted for Darius Guppy, Dieter Abt, George Hendry (the European Leisure case), Hisham Alwan (R v Allcock & Others) and Victoria Aitken. Disciplinary work has included acting for Derek Walker (Lloyd's Disciplinary Proceedings relating to Gooda Walker). Fluent French speaker.
Prof. Memberships: LCCSA (sub-committees relating to fraud), BISLA.
Career: Qualified as a barrister in 1986, a solicitor in 1990. 1987-91: *Berwin Leighton* Tax & Trusts Dept specialising in tax investigations, trusts and tax avoidance litigation including Craven v White up to House of Lords. 1991 joined *Burton Copeland* Commercial Fraud Dept. Partner February 1995. Educated at Manchester Grammar School and St Edmund Hall, Oxford (BCL MA).
Personal: Leisure interests include Manchester United, golf, languages and music.

WILSON, Mark
Cartwright King, Nottingham (0115) 958 7444 mwilson@cartwrightking.co.uk
Specialisation: Commercial and professional fraud and regulatory crime. LSC Serious Fraud Panel Supervisor. Recent experience of investigations and prosecutions by all fraud investigation agencies, DTI, Revenue, HMC&E, Trading Standards, HSE, Environment Agency, for corporations and individuals. Mainly defence representation but also prosecutions for regulatory bodies and advice to commerce on the subject of fraud. *Cartwright King* is a niche commercial crime (and general criminal defence) practice, and is a member of the LSC Serious Fraud Panel.
Career: Partner in *freethcartwright* White Collar Crime department 1990 to 1999. De-merged to set up *Cartwright King* on 1 January 2000. Remains a consultant to *freethcartwright.*
Personal: Born 1961. Leisure: Family, motor racing, mountain biking.

WOOLLEY, Linda
Kingsley Napley, London (020) 7814 1224 lwoolley@kingsleynapley.co.uk
Specialisation: Practice includes all areas of criminal work, but particularly serious fraud and business crime, extradition, international crime and mutual legal assistance. Also handles public inquiries, tax investigations and professional disciplinary matters.
Prof. Memberships: Committee member, London Criminal Courts Solicitors Association; International Bar Association; Criminal Law Solicitors Association; City of London Solicitors Company; Amnesty International.
Career: Joined *Kingsley Napley* 1990; qualified 1992; partner 1998.
Publications: Articles on extradition and international law, 'Solicitors' Journal', IBA publications.
Personal: University of Warwick (1983); College of Law (1990). Leisure – arts, reading, travel.

HEALTH & SAFETY

OVERVIEW: In response to the growing number of prosecutions pursued by the HSE and Environment Agency, firms are increasingly developing specialist health and safety practices. For others, health and safety remains a part of employment, environmental, personal injury and insurance claim practices. Interviewees identified the rising pressure on businesses to improve their health and safety conduct, particularly in light of future legislation such as the Corporate Killing Policy and new working time regulations.

RESEARCH APPROVED BY BMRB: *For this edition,* Chambers' *researchers conducted 6,552 interviews – 4,419 with law firms, 554 with barristers and 1,579 with clients.*

The validity of the research was scrutinised by BMRB International, who audited both the methodology and the results at our offices in July 2001. They interviewed Chambers' *researchers and cross-checked sample interviews. Details of the audit appear on page 7.*

LONDON

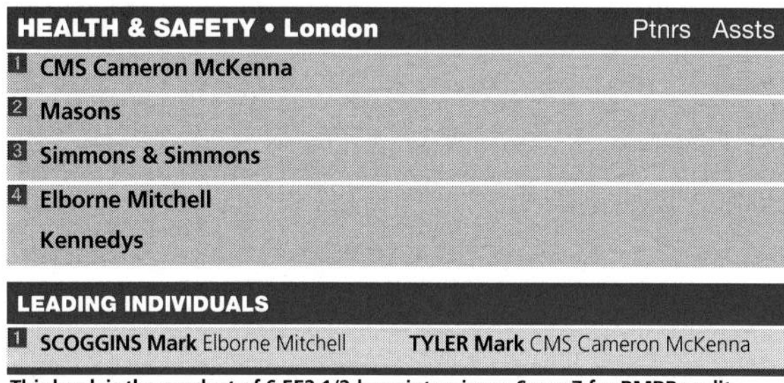

HEALTH & SAFETY • London	Ptnrs	Assts
1 CMS Cameron McKenna		
2 Masons		
3 Simmons & Simmons		
4 Elborne Mitchell		
Kennedys		

LEADING INDIVIDUALS	
1 SCOGGINS Mark Elborne Mitchell	TYLER Mark CMS Cameron McKenna

This book is the product of 6,552 1/2-hour interviews. See p.7 for BMRB audit.
Within each band, firms are listed alphabetically. *See individuals' profiles p.416*

CMS Cameron McKenna (see firm details p.922) High profile **Mark Tyler** (see p.416) continues to be seen as a leading health and safety lawyer who "*knows his stuff.*" He leads an expanding team described by barristers as "*pre-eminent due to the quality of its people*" and renowned for "*the best and biggest clients.*" It is actively involved in regulatory issues, defending organizations in enforcement and prosecution situations and legal audits of health and safety management arrangements. The team represented Angel Trains in the Southall and Ladbroke Grove inquiries, has advised clients in the organophosphate sheep dip multi-party litigation and provided advice in corporate manslaughter investigations. **Clients:** Rail companies; construction and sports sector.

Masons (see firm details p.1056) Operating from London and Leeds offices, the team has seen significant growth including advice to clients on the Corporate Killing legislation, risk allocation and fatalities. Karen Cooksley leads a team rated by clients rate for its "*commonsense*" and "*practical advice.*" The group has a strong construction and manufacturing client base and has worked for rail companies including Nottingham Light Rail. **Clients:** Wates Construction; Bovis Lend Lease; Railcare; LEM; Water Lilly.

Simmons & Simmons (see firm details p.1132) Rated by peers for its cross–skilled group, which combines expertise in employment, construction and environmental law. The team, assisted by construction partner Richard Dyton, advised Railtrack on the repositioning of the Safety and Standards Directorate and the Royal Shakespeare Company on the health and safety aspects of new working time regulations. It also provides advice on bullying and stress in the workplace. **Clients:** Railtrack; Department of Public Enterprise (Ireland); Province Noord-Brabent (Netherlands); RSC; Viatel.

Elborne Mitchell (see firm details p.949) **Mark Scoggins** (see p.416)heads this "*small and tight*" team judged by peers to be experienced in the rail, water and chemicals sector. Described by clients as "*the quickest, sharpest brain I've ever met,*" he has been heavily involved in the Ladbroke Grove and Hatfield derailment inquiries. The team is also involved in construction management for Balfour Beatty Group. **Clients:** Balfour Beatty Group; Severn Trent; Thames Trains; St Pauls Insurance.

Kennedys (see firm details p.1018) Perceived by peers as "*making inroads into the field,*" this team led by Andrew Gilbert is newly ranked in Chambers. Recommended for its growing workload and expertise in the rail and transport industries. The team advised Railtrack in the Southall, Ladbroke Grove and Hatfield rail crash inquiries. **Clients:** Railtrack; Balfour Beatty.

SOUTH & SOUTH WEST

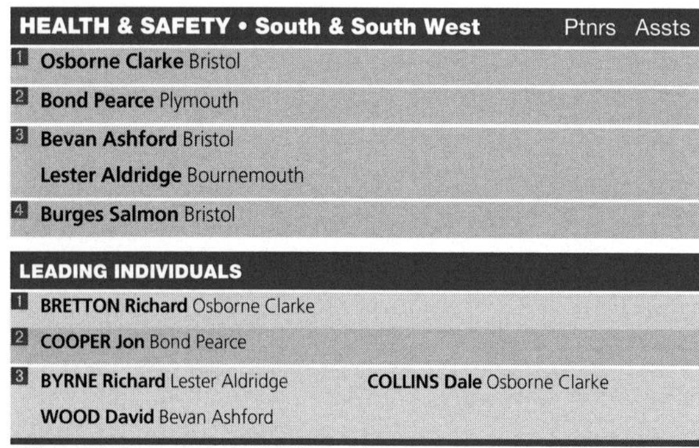

HEALTH & SAFETY • South & South West	Ptnrs	Assts
1 Osborne Clarke Bristol		
2 Bond Pearce Plymouth		
3 Bevan Ashford Bristol		
Lester Aldridge Bournemouth		
4 Burges Salmon Bristol		

LEADING INDIVIDUALS	
1 BRETTON Richard Osborne Clarke	
2 COOPER Jon Bond Pearce	
3 BYRNE Richard Lester Aldridge	COLLINS Dale Osborne Clarke
WOOD David Bevan Ashford	

This book is the product of 6,552 1/2-hour interviews. See p.7 for BMRB audit.
Within each band, firms are listed alphabetically. *See individuals' profiles p.416*

Osborne Clarke (see firm details p.1086) "*Wise and efficient,*" **Richard Bretton** is rated by peers and clients for his ability to "*communicate at all levels.*" He leads a team of specialists with a national client base, active in enforcement proceedings, criminal defence and proactive health and safety advice. Alongside noted growth in the construction sector, the team also assisted regional county councils and the Association of Police Health and Safety advisors with a training programme. Well regarded **Dale Collins** has joined the team from the Eversheds' Cardiff office. **Clients:** Hanson Group; Transco; Nishimatsu Construction Co.

Bond Pearce (see firm details p.888) "*Switched on*" **Jon Cooper** is regularly instructed by the HSE. The team, rated for its strength across the board, handles risk management, due diligence and general advisory work. It has acted in prosecutions arising from the collapse of the M5 Avonmouth Bridge gantry and successfully challenged a local authority's policy on swimming pools. **Clients:** Post Office; Woolworths; HSE; Virgin Vie; NEG (UK.)

Bevan Ashford (see firm details p.880) **David Wood** (see p.416) leads a well-regarded team that acts with the support of the firm's regulatory department. It prosecutes for the HSE nationally and frequently acts for the NHS. The team acted for Kent & Sussex Weald NHS Trust in a prosecution involving blood transfusion procedures and advised Jewson on general health and safety matters. **Clients:** St Gobain; Plymouth Hospitals NHS Trust; Jewson.

Lester Aldridge (see firm details p.1038) A "*highly competent*" team with a noted focus on the construction sector also has expertise in care home cases. It has been active in prosecutions arising from fatalities and injuries. Highly rated by his peers for his prosecution work, **Richard Byrne** (see p.416) has acted for HSE Dorset and Wiltshire. He also advises corporate clients on the health and safety aspects of employment contracts and on the ramifications of the new Corporate Killing act. **Clients:** Construction companies; care homes; HSE; corporate clients.

Burges Salmon (see firm details p.902) "*Quick, thorough and tenacious*" Chris Jackson "*fights his client's corner with no stone unturned.*" He leads a well-regarded team that undertakes contentious and non-contentious work with a focus on the rail industry. Its commercial litigation disaster response group was involved in the Ladbroke Grove and Southall rail disasters. The team provides documentation reviews for Nationwide Building Society and New Zealand Milk and continues to be active in the construction and chemical sectors. **Clients:** FirstGroup; Great Western Trains Company; St Paul International Insurance Co.

WALES

HEALTH & SAFETY • Wales	Ptnrs	Assts
1 **Eversheds** Cardiff		
2 **Hugh James Ford Simey** Cardiff		

LEADING INDIVIDUALS
1 **HAVARD Robin** Morgan Cole

This book is the product of 6,552 1/2-hour interviews. See p.7 for BMRB audit.
Within each band, firms are listed alphabetically. *See individuals' profiles p.416*

Eversheds (see firm details p.952) This "*practical and well-informed*" unit headed by Vivien Du-Feu is rated rated by peers for its experience in prosecution and regulatory law. Noted for its defence work, it advises on the risk assessment of health and safety matters. It advised Hartwin on contaminated land issues and represented Allied Bakeries in a prosecution under the Food Safety Act resulting in the withdrawal of charges. **Clients:** British Aluminium Plate; Jewson; Hawtin.

Hugh James Ford Simey (see firm details p.1004) Largely an insurance driven practice working for Norwich Union, Royal Sun Alliance and AIG amongst others. Described by competitors as "*good pragmatic lawyers,*" the team, which includes Gareth Williams, has been active in prosecutions under the Health and Safety at Work act. It advised on the Cleveland bridge accident and is involved in a nursing home fatality and the prosecution of a catering company. **Clients:** Hoover; Barratts; Hyder Welsh Water.

Other Notable Practitioners With a focus on construction, **Robin Havard** of **Morgan Cole** is a recognised specialist. He represented a company involved in an HSE investigation into an outbreak of Legionnaires disease and acted on double fatality caused by the escape of chemicals.

MIDLANDS & THE NORTH

HEALTH & SAFETY • Midlands & The North	Ptnrs	Assts
1 **Eversheds** Birmingham, Leeds, Manchester	n/a	n/a
2 **Hammond Suddards Edge** Birmingham, Manchester		
3 **Addleshaw Booth & Co** Leeds		
Nabarro Nathanson Sheffield		
4 **Weightmans** Liverpool		

LEADING INDIVIDUALS	
1 **BURNLEY Paul** Eversheds	**ELLIKER Michael** Addleshaw Booth & Co
SHEPHERD Michael Hammond Suddards	**WATKINS Gareth** Nabarro Nathanson
2 **PARRINGTON Simon** Hill Dickinson	

This book is the product of 6,552 1/2-hour interviews. See p.7 for BMRB audit.
Within each band, firms are listed alphabetically. *See individuals' profiles p.416*

Eversheds (see firm details p.952) Its corporate defence lawyers have earned a national reputation as leaders in health and safety – they are "*collectively, very much in the swing of health and safety.*" The Birmingham office is included for the first time as a result of its increasing caseload, which includes both Bass and McDonalds. A barrister commented "*I haven't come across a case in Birmingham that hasn't involved them.*" The team was involved in the Ladbroke rail inquiry on behalf of Dupont and has advised the Midlands Electricity board. "*Expert*" **Paul Burnley** (see p.416) is perceived to be "*go-ahead, always looking and thinking.*" **Clients:** Midlands Electricity Board; Railway companies; Estate Director for University of Wales; Bass; McDonalds.

Hammond Suddards Edge (see firm details p.984) Perceived by rivals to be "*committed to having a specialist team,*" this "*impressive*" practice has expanded with an increased caseload. The team is active in electricity, nuclear and renewable resources, oil and gas, waste management, engineering and property sectors. Operating a nationwide emergency service, the team advises on crisis management. Skilled **Michael Shepherd** (see p.416) is rated as "*the best defendant solicitor around*" and has been active in fatality cases. **Clients:** ICI; BNF.

Addleshaw Booth & Co (see firm details p.853) A committed team recently bolstered to focus on construction. It has been active in investigations arising from derailments, fatal accidents on building sites, breaches of airport regulations and factory accidents. **Michael Elliker** (see p.416) is widely respected by rivals as "*thorough, he leaves nothing to chance.*" The team advised on the prosecution of a rail company in connection with two derailments and provided advice to a principal company involved in the Hatfield Rail Inquiry. **Clients:** Construction and transport industry.

Nabarro Nathanson (see firm details p.1078) This stand alone team is acknowledged to provide "*a professional, first class service.*" Focused on defence work, "*impressive*" **Gareth Watkins** is widely regarded as a leading light. The team advised Hays Chemicals on enforcement issues and acted for Friskies Petcare (UK) on a fatality prosecution in the Court of Appeal. **Clients:** Amey Group; Cradle Runways International; Hanson Brick.

Weightmans (see firm details p.1176) Perceived to act from its strong base in insurance litigation, the team, which includes John Williams, is well regarded by peers. **Clients:** Mainly insurance sector.

Other Notable Practitioners **Simon Parrington** (see p.416) of **Hill Dickinson** undertakes "*substantial*" cases for the HSE. He has prosecuted Imperial College London, Birmingham University and a chain of dry cleaners in a case involving twenty-seven summonses.

LEADERS IN HEALTH & SAFETY

BRETTON, Richard
Osborne Clarke, Bristol (0117) 917 3000

BURNLEY, Paul
Eversheds, Leeds (0113) 243 0391
paulburnley@eversheds.com
Specialisation: Principal area of practice is acting for corporate/commercial clients and other directors in complex civil and criminal, health and safety litigation. Known for his extensive experience of crisis management, having represented clients in major incidents, large scale disasters and product recall. He and his team undertake all their own advocacy where possible. Experienced in all aspects of health and safety issues including Coronor's Court. A "no-nonsense" advocate! Invited to many venues as a guest speaker on corporate and individual director liability.
Prof. Memberships: UKELA.
Career: Qualified April 1980. Nine years as a prosecuting solicitor, he joined *Eversheds* in 1989 becoming a partner in May 1996. A gamekeeper turned poacher!
Personal: Born 31 August 1955.

BYRNE, Richard
Lester Aldridge, Bournemouth (01202) 786121
richard.byrne@lester-aldridge.co.uk
Specialisation: Advises on all aspects of health and safety legislation, company health and safety policies and their management. Provides representation in connection with Health and Safety at Work Act and associated regulatory prosecutions. Advises and represents the health and safety executive in prosecutions. Part time employment tribunal chairman. Lectures nationwide, and a visiting lecturer at Bournemouth University in health and safety law.
Career: Qualified in 1978. Joined *Lester Aldridge* 1983, becoming a partner in 1984.
Publications: Regular contributor to the 'Employment Lawyer' covering health and safety issues in the employment context.
Personal: Born 1955. Lives near Romsey, Hampshire. Fellow of the Royal Geographic Society.

COLLINS, Dale
Osborne Clarke, Bristol (0117) 917 3000

COOPER, Jon
Bond Pearce, Plymouth (01752) 266633
jcooper@bondpearce.com
Specialisation: Partner and head of the Health and Safety Group. Specialises in all aspects of health and safety including prosecutions in all Courts, and advisory work in relation to health and safety policies and risk management and increasingly health and safety due diligence issues in corporate transactions. The work arises from all sectors of industry and commerce ranging from the nuclear industry to agriculture.
Prof. Memberships: Member of the Law Society Personal Injury Panel; member of the Editorial Advisory Board for 'Tolley's Health and Safety at Work' publication.
Career: Qualified in 1984 with *Bond Pearce,* becoming a partner in 1989.

ELLIKER, Michael
Addleshaw Booth & Co, Leeds (0113) 209 2000
Specialisation: Senior solicitor in litigation and dispute resolution group. Specialises in health and safety matters but also deals with trading standards and environmental cases. An experienced advocate who frequently conducts prosecutions on behalf of the Health and Safety Executive.
Prof. Memberships: Law Society and Leeds Law Society.
Career: Articled at *Booth and Co.* and qualified in 1974; with *R.C. Moorhouse and Co.* from 1977 to 1984; rejoined *Booth & Co.* in 1984. Deputy District Judge from 1988 to 1998.
Publications: Contributor to 'Litigation Practice' (Sweet and Maxwell).
Personal: Born 11 December 1949. Educated at St. Michael's College Leeds and University of London (Queen Mary College). Lives in Leeds.

HAVARD, Robin
Morgan Cole, Cardiff (029) 2038 5385

PARRINGTON, Simon
Hill Dickinson, Chester (01244) 896600
Specialisation: Personal injury specialist with an interest in health and safety. Much of his work is handling employers' liability and public liability for insurers but a significant portion of his work is in the handling of prosecutions brought by the Health and Safety Executive. He has been involved in a number of high profile prosecutions of major industrial companies including the Associated Octel case which settled law in relation to sections 2 and 3 of the Health & Safety at Work Act 1974 and other major cases concerning hazardous installations, construction, dangerous pathogens and GM crops.
Prof. Memberships: Law Society.
Career: Law Society's Civil Litigation committee member. Formerly member of Lord Woolf's working group on the fast track. Deputy District Judge. Admitted 1975. Partner *Hill Dickinson.*
Personal: Gardening, country sports, skiing, music, theatre.

SCOGGINS, Mark
Elborne Mitchell, London (020) 7320 9000
scoggins@elbornes.com
Specialisation: Commercial dispute resolution: health and safety and environmental regulation; defence of civil and criminal proceedings. Acted (1998-99) for Balfour Beatty in prosecution over collapse of the Heathrow Express tunnels and for Albright & Wilson in the HSE proceedings following explosion of their Avonmouth works. Represents Thames Trains in the aftermath of the Ladbroke Grove collision of 5 October 1999. Acts for a number of UK water companies in regulatory and environmental claims. Experienced advocate in public inquiries, inquests and court. Insurance: coverage, claims and industry regulation. Product liability and personal injury defence, principally mass tort. International (mainly EEA): commercial litigation and arbitration. Firearms law.
Career: Nottingham High School; Cambridge University (MA 1984); Inns of Court School of Law 1981-82. Barrister of Gray's Inn 1983-93; qualified as solicitor 1993; *Davies Arnold Cooper* 1989-99 (partner 1993-99); joined *Elborne Mitchell* 1999. Visiting lectureships at the Police Staff College Bramshill and Fire Service College Moreton-in-Marsh. Regular conference speaker and contributor to professional journals.
Personal: Leisure interests include target shooting, DIY and family. Born 1957. Resides in Dulwich, London. Member of Hawks Club, Cambridge.

SHEPHERD, Michael
Hammond Suddards Edge, Manchester
(0161) 860 5023
michael.shepherd@hammondse.com
Specialisation: Partner in commercial dispute resolution unit. National head of safety health and environment group. Main areas of practice are environment, health and safety, food safety and trading standards. Clients include ICI, BNFL, One 2 One, Mowlem, Rank, Norwest Holst, Bradford City AFC.
Prof. Memberships: Law Society. Member of UKELA, CBI Environment Committee, Construction Industry Safety Group and European Food Law Association.
Career: MA (Oxon); articled to Sir George Ogden; qualified in 1969. Worked in Town Clerk's office, Manchester 1966-72. Joined *Hammond Suddards Edge* in 1972, becoming a partner in 1974.
Personal: Born 26 September 1944. Attended Bradford Grammar School 1954-1963, then The Queen's College, Oxford 1963-66. Leisure interests include cricket, football, golf and foreign languages (Portuguese, French and Spanish).

TYLER, Mark
CMS Cameron McKenna, London
(020) 7367 3000
mlt@cmck.com
Specialisation: Main areas of practice are product liability and health and safety. Co-author of 'Product Safety' and 'Safer by Design'; consultant editor of 'Health and Safety Liability and Litigation'; legal reviewer for Croner's 'Management of Construction Safety'. Contributor to 'Buildings and Health: The Rosehaugh Guide to the Design Construction and Management of Buildings', 'A New Balance: A Guide for Property Owners and Developers', 'Environmental Issues in Construction' - CIRIA Special Report, CIOB Handbook Facilities Management and 'Medicines, Medical Devices and the Law', 'PLC Legal Risk Management Manual'.
Prof. Memberships: Law Society, Institution of Occupational Safety and Health (IOSH), CBI Health and Safety Panel, CBI Consumer Affairs Panel, Forum of Insurance Lawyers, International Association of Defense Counsel.
Career: Joined *McKenna & Co* in 1984 and qualified in 1986. Became a partner in 1992.
Personal: Born 10 October 1960. Educated at Sir William Borlase's Grammar School, Marlow, Worcester College, Oxford and Kings College, London.

WATKINS, Gareth
Nabarro Nathanson, Sheffield (0114) 279 4000

WOOD, David
Bevan Ashford, Bristol (0117) 975 1635
d.wood@bevanashford.co.uk
Specialisation: Partner and head of planning and energy department. Main area of practice is planning and environmental. Handled local authority planning work in Essex 1972-76; specialised in planning and advocacy at Public Inquiries while a partner in Bristol. Lead partner on privatisation of Port of Bristol including the environmental issues and parliamentary procedures arising. Lectured for NHS Training Authority, University of the West of England, CBI and others.
Prof. Memberships: Law Society, UK Environmental Law Association.
Career: Qualified in 1969. Worked at *Hatten, Jewers & Mephan* in Basildon, Essex 1969-76. Partner at *Harris & Harris,* Bristol 1976-88, then partner *at Bevan Ashford* since 1988.
Publications: Author of an article in 'Urban Regeneration'. Wrote planning law section for NHS Estates 'Estate Code' guidance to land transactions by Health Authorities and Trusts.
Personal: Born 7 January 1946. Attended Taunton School, Somerset 1957-62.

HEALTHCARE

OVERVIEW: Dramatic cuts to the NHSLA panel have seen certain firms lose their place in the tables, with others gaining a substantial share of the market. Certain firms maintain a presence owing to significant property expertise. The introduction of Primary Care Groups in April 1999 has elicited a plethora of legal issues this year, as many Groups evolve into Primary Care Trusts. The Human Rights Act has impacted on all areas of healthcare, most significantly within mental health, where issues such as patient confidentiality and the right to refuse treatment have been brought to the fore.

RESEARCH APPROVED BY BMRB: *For this edition,* Chambers' *researchers conducted 6,552 interviews – 4,419 with law firms, 554 with barristers and 1,579 with clients.*

The validity of the research was scrutinised by BMRB International, who audited both the methodology and the results at our offices in July 2001. They interviewed Chambers' *researchers and cross-checked sample interviews. Details of the audit appear on page 7.*

LONDON

HEALTHCARE • London		Ptnrs	Assts
1	Capsticks	18	19
2	Bevan Ashford	n/a	n/a
	Hempsons	8	16
3	Beachcroft Wansbroughs	14	n/a
4	Le Brasseur J Tickle	n/a	n/a
5	Trowers & Hamlins	11	15

LEADING INDIVIDUALS		
1	DINGWALL Christian Bevan Ashford	HOLMES John Hempsons
	MASON David Capsticks	
2	BARBER Janice Hempsons	BROADHURST Marisa Beachcroft
	FRANCIS Barry Pinsent Curtis Biddle	LEIGH Bertie Hempsons
	SMITH Janice Capsticks	
3	BLACKWELL Hilary Capsticks	SUMERLING Robert Le Brasseur J Tickle

This book is the product of 6,552 1/2-hour interviews. See p.7 for BMRB audit.

Within each band, firms are listed alphabetically. *See individuals' profiles p.219*

Capsticks (see firm details p.908) A firm "*almost entirely geared towards servicing the NHS*" which, according to competitors, is "*going from strength to strength.*" Clients enjoy "*a 24 hour service with experts in all areas,*" maintaining Capsticks' position within"*a league of their own.*" **Janice Smith** not only "*runs a strong team*" specialising in advice on clinical governance within trusts and claims management, but also possesses a strong "*empathy with the clients.*" She is joined by the "*talented, impressive character*" of **David Mason**, perceived by one client to be the "*star of healthcare,*" and the "*knowledgeable*" **Hilary Blackwell** (see p.420), who is currently "*building up a profile.*" The team is involved in the cutting edge of the legal basis of the new Primary Care Trusts, developing a new model Personal Medical Services contract between health authorities and GPs. **Clients:** Over 100 NHS trusts, health authorities and primary care trusts.

Bevan Ashford (see firm details p.880) Retaining its place on the NHSLA panel last year has greatly increased the profile of this "*thriving, expanding team*" which, although small, draws upon a strong Bristol practice. Viewed as "*focused, strategic and on top of the field*" by its clients, its is "*leaping ahead*" according to competitors. The head of the claims department and "*leading light*" **Christian Dingwall** (see p.165) is perceived by clients to be an"*asset to the firm*" in its expanding litigation capacity. Litigation work aside, the team has been advising health authorities on partnerships agreements with local authorities on long term care issues such as the integrated management of services for those with learning disabilities and the mentally ill. **Clients:** 76 healthcare bodies.

Hempsons (see firm details p.990) This practice has also been a "*net gainer from the NHSLA panel.*" "*The NHSLA rate them,*" not simply due to the fact that they are "*all-round specialists,*" but that they are "*excellent opponents for claimant solicitors*" according to their clients. "*One of the best legal opinions around,*" **John Holmes** (see p.167), has recently been acquired from Beachcroft Wansbroughs. The well known "*character*" and "*leader*" in the field, **Bertie Leigh** (see p.421), is supported by **Janice Barber** (see p.419), whose factual knowledge within clinical disciplinary work is reputed to be the best in the field. They have seen a growth in advisory work, formulating policies for claims handling, regulatory and disciplinary issues to 118 healthcare bodies in the past year. Offering the full range of health services to a select and increasing number of NHS bodies, their specialism is clinical disciplinary cases. **Clients:** 17 NHS trusts; 7 health authorities.

Beachcroft Wansbroughs (see firm details p.872) Although healthcare litigation work has been much reduced due to the loss of a place on the NHSLA panel, the firm nevertheless retains "*a large share of the market,*" most notably in their work for NHS Estates. The London team led the largest ever property disposal by the NHS last year, in a project totalling £650 million. *The "established and feisty*" player, **Marisa Broadhurst** (see p.420), has been particularly recommended for her work in this field. The team has been particularly active in commercial and advisory roles for healthcare bodies, who believe the practice has "*a firm handle on complex matters, coming out ahead compared to other firms.*" **Clients:** 100 trusts; 19 health authorities.

Le Brasseur J Tickle (see firm details p.1033) While this firm does not have a place on the NHSLA panel, it is nevertheless principal advisor to two out of the three medical defence organisations, and comes highly recommended in this field. The team is perceived by competitors to be "*finding their feet after some departures.*" Active this year in the partnership formation of PCTs and clinical negligence work, they are also instructed by many firms within the private sector. **Robert Sumerling** has been noted for his experience and presence in the field.

Trowers & Hamlins (see firm details p.1162) Another firm which has lost its place on the NHSLA panel, while nevertheless "*retaining big name healthcare bodies,*" who view its commitment as "*second to none; they are client-focused, not point-scorers.*" Predominantly renowned for its corporate healthcare advice, the firm is recommended for its work in hospital accommodation schemes. Joanne Easterbrook has been a pioneering awareness of the Human Rights Act and its influence upon mental health law, producing a paper on the subject. **Clients:** 27 healthcare bodies

Other Notable Practitioners Although focussing more upon PFI work than general representation of healthcare bodies, **Barry Francis** (see p.420) is set to join the London office of **Pinsent Curtis Biddle**, leaving the now disbanded Buchanan Ingersoll unit. He retains an "*excellent reputation*" and is currently advising the NHS upon the restructuring of various PFI deals.

THE SOUTH, SOUTH WEST, WALES & THAMES VALLEY

	HEALTHCARE • South, South West, Wales & Thames Valley	Ptnrs	Assts
1	**Bevan Ashford** Bristol	9	12
2	**Beachcroft Wansbroughs** Bristol, Winchester	8	n/a
3	**Morgan Cole** Cardiff, Oxford, Reading	7	11
4	**Brachers** Maidstone	5	7

	LEADING INDIVIDUALS
1	**ANNANDALE Richard** Bevan Ashford **BARBER Paul** Bevan Ashford
2	**BROADHEAD Jill** Bevan Ashford

This book is the product of 6,552 1/2-hour interviews. See p.7 for BMRB audit.

Within each band, firms are listed alphabetically. *See individuals' profiles p.219*

Bevan Ashford (see firm details p.880) This "*great presence in the South*" is the "*undisputed leader*" again this year. The "*well respected*" **Richard Annandale** (see p.419) enjoys an "*excellent reputation*" in high profile clinical governance issues this year, such as the retention of children's organs after post-mortem in Birmingham Children's Hospital. Alongside him is the "*outstanding*" **Paul Barber** (see p.420), who has received nation-wide recommendations this year for his work in mental health and human rights issues. Also on the team is the "*determined*" **Jill Broadhead** (see p.420). The team has "*cornered the market in PFI this year,*" with other niche strengths in registered homes and partnerships in action. **Clients:** Over 100 NHS trusts and health authorities.

Beachcroft Wansbroughs (see firm details p.872) The two branches have retained their place on the NHSLA, continuing their full service for numerous healthcare bodies, which, according to their clients, "*gets to the heart of the matter.*" The strong health litigation department headed by Nigel Montgomery has a niche in neurological and renal claims, particularly in claims relating to cerebral palsy. The team has also been particularly active in IT procurement for healthcare bodies this year and advising on large PFI schemes. **Clients:** 54 NHS trusts, and health authorities.

Morgan Cole (see firm details p.1074) The "*leaders*" in Wales with a strong healthcare presence, although the firm's Reading and Oxford branches do not enjoy the same profile. Clients, however, perceive an "*improved flexibility, scale and technical expertise,*" while solicitors view the firm as "*exceptionally professional.*" The team, headed by Graham Miles, is perhaps best known for judicial reviews on human fertilisation issues. It also provides a full service for Welsh healthcare bodies (excluding clinical negligence) and has been particularly active in providing training for clients in the areas of human rights, mental health and children. **Clients:** 30 NHS trusts, 11 health authorities.

Brachers (see firm details p.893) "*In tune with the new culture within the NHSLA,*" the firm is, according to its clients, "*proactive; experienced and knowledgeable.*" The team is headed by John Sheath, and has experienced an increasing workload due to its reappointment to the NHSLA panel, not simply in litigation but also in other non-contentious areas such as employment and PFI. Commercial property work last year included the disposal of healthcare sites amounting to £12 million and the planning of the development of housing estates from redundant hospital sites. **Clients:** 12 NHS trusts, 3 health authorities.

MIDLANDS & EAST ANGLIA

	HEALTHCARE • Midlands & East Anglia	Ptnrs	Assts
1	**Browne Jacobson** Birmingham, Nottingham	5	21
	Mills & Reeve Birmingham, Cambridge, Norwich	9	35

	LEADING INDIVIDUALS
1	**KING Stephen** Mills & Reeve
2	**PICKUP Raith** Mills & Reeve

This book is the product of 6,552 1/2-hour interviews. See p.7 for BMRB audit.

Within each band, firms are listed alphabetically. *See individuals' profiles p.219*

Browne Jacobson (see firm details p.898) An expanding clinical negligence team, due to the securement of NHSLA panel work, with "*an excellent understanding of the healthcare profession.*" "*Client-orientated and on the ball,*" the practice deals with a wide range of healthcare issues. Brian Smith led the team responsible for advising Nottingham City Hospital on a PFI scheme for on-site residential accommodation. **Clients:** 64 NHS trusts and 31 health authorities.

Mills & Reeve (see firm details p.1069) Although the firm has been dropped from the NHSLA panel, it is nevertheless viewed as "*experienced*" by peers and responsive and knowledgeable by clients. "*Top dog*" **Stephen King** (see p.421) is not simply "*high profile*" but also "*charismatic and personable.*" **Raith Pickup** (see p.421), best known for his PFI work, retains a high profile within this sector. Still offering the full range of services outside NHSLA panel work, the team has been particularly active this year in dealing with the ramifications of the health and social care act; joint working between care trusts and local authorities. **Clients:** Over 150 NHS clients across the country.

THE NORTH

Hempsons (see firm details p.990) Viewed by peers as "*a formidable outfit, excellent at marshalling evidence,*" the firm has risen to the top of the table on the strength of their NHSLA panel work, and the perception from clients that "*other solicitors have their hands held by Hempsons.*" They undertook perhaps the highest profile case within the healthcare sector last year, the separation of the conjoined twins, Jodie and Mary. The team, led by the "*excellent*" **Frances Harrison** (see p.167), acted on the successful application for the twins' separation by the Central Manchester Healthcare NHS Trust. The team has also been particularly active this year in acting for primary care groups and the legal ramifications of their transformation into trusts. **Clients:** 73 NHS trusts; 26 health authorities.

Beachcroft Wansbroughs (see firm details p.872) Still "*a significant player in the field,*" despite being dropped from the NHSLA panel. Highly rated by its clients, the "*expert*" **Diane Hallatt** (see p.421) leads a "*good team with a range of skills.*" The team has been instructed this year by the majority of PCTs that went live in the Trent region in April 2001. Inroads have been made this year in the areas of projects and employment, in particular in the renegotiation of nursing and PAMS contracts for the Shropshire and Staffordshire Education Consortium. **Clients:** Over 70 NHS trusts and PCTs.

Eversheds (see firm details p.952) A place on the NHSLA panel has secured Eversheds' reputation as a significant player in the healthcare market, rather than being seen as simply a PFI specialist. **Richard Slack** (see p.421) has been described by a peer in London to be "*steeped in the NHS, developing with it as it has evolved.*" He is joined by the "*excellent*" **Ronald Bradbeer** (see p.420). Innovative in acting on phase II of the PFI for Wansbeck

HEALTHCARE • The North	Ptnrs	Assts
1 **Hempsons** Harrogate, Manchester	13	49
2 **Beachcroft Wansbroughs** Leeds	8	10
Eversheds Newcastle upon Tyne	4	20
Hill Dickinson Liverpool, Manchester	10	22

LEADING INDIVIDUALS	
1 **HALLATT Diane** Beachcroft Wansbroughs	**SLACK Richard** Eversheds
2 **BRADBEER Ronald** Eversheds	**HARRISON Frances** Hempsons

This book is the product of 6,552 1/2-hour interviews. See p.7 for BMRB audit.

Within each band, firms are listed alphabetically. *See individuals' profiles p.219*

General Hospital, partly powered by windmills, the team has also acted for a consortium of health authority and social services departments providing aftercare to discharged mentally ill patients. **Clients:** 16 NHS trusts; 5 PCTs and 4 health authorities.

Hill Dickinson (see firm details p.996) "*A strong team,*" "*known for recruiting from within the NHS,*" which provides specialist advice in all aspects of NHS representation. Particularly reputed for litigation, thus retaining their position on the NHSLA panel. Head of department, Allan Mowat recently acted for Alderhay Children's Hospital in the Redfern Inquiry into the retention of organs. **Clients:** Over 60 NHS trusts and health authorities.

MENTAL HEALTH: REPRESENTING PATIENTS

LEADING INDIVIDUALS
1 **SCOTT-MONCRIEFF Lucy** Scott-Moncrieff, Harbour & Sinclair
2 **MACKINTOSH Nicola** Mackintosh Duncan
EDWARDS Peter Charles Peter Edwards & Co

See individuals' profiles p.219

Lucy Scott-Moncrieff "*An excellent street-fighter*" who is "*blazing a path through case-law.*" Indubitably the "top of the field," her ability to apply "*thorough up-to-date knowledge*" in review tribunals and judicial reviews for patients detained in Broadmoor is second to none.

Peter Edwards This "*energetic*" character is not only "*the leader in the North*" but also "*popular with clients.*" He has worked on high profile cases such as the defence of the attacker of George Harrison, Michael Abram. He is also well-regarded for his human rights work and training in connection with mental health law.

Nicola Mackintosh "*Stunningly competent*" within the field of the right to community care services, she is "*someone who knows legislative law incredibly well and can anticipate where it is likely to go wrong in practice.*" Recently won a case against Brighton and Hove Council, thus preventing the closure of a children's home for autistic children with high level needs.

MENTAL HEALTH: REPRESENTING HOSPITALS

LEADING INDIVIDUALS
1 **ELDERGILL Anselm** Anselm Eldergill
2 **IRONS Ashley** Reid Minty
PARSONS Andrew Radcliffes

See individuals' profiles p.219

Anselm Eldergill (see p.420) "*Academically brilliant,*" whilst able to "*link up law and practice,*" he has chaired six NHS inquiries for mental health patients who have committed serious crimes. In addition to this, his "*authoritative, thoughtful and reliable*" textbook, 'Mental Health Review Tribunals' has been nominated for a Nobel Prize, eliciting praise for its "*empathy for the plight of those suffering from mental health disorders.*"

Ashley Irons According to one client, "*no other lawyer in the land is as knowledgeable about patients in forensic psychiatric services.*" He recently acted on the Ashworth Health Authority v MGM Limited, successfully obtaining a Court of Appeal Order for the Daily Mirror to disclose the source of the leak of confidential patient records from Ian Brady. This decision created new laws to enforce the confidentiality of patient records.

Andrew Parsons (see p.421) "*Excellent*" according to his peers - "*value for money and responsive*" according to his clients. Acted on many cases relating to the legality of detention under the Mental Health Act, such as the groundbreaking ex parte Huzzey v Brent Kensington Chelsea and Westminster Trust. The team have provided several seminars and advice on the implementation of the Human Rights Act and its impact upon mental health.

LEADERS IN HEALTHCARE

ANNANDALE, Richard

Bevan Ashford, Bristol (0117) 975 1656
r.annandale@bevanashford.co.uk

Specialisation: Head of the Health and Social Care Group specialising in clinical governance, medical law and risk management, particularly for hospitals with acute services. Richard is now involved in a high profile series of claims arising from the breast screening programme and with nationally sensitive issues relating to the retention of childrens' organs.

Career: Qualified 1977. Partner since 1993. Director of QRM Healthcare Limited (*Bevan Ashford's* healthcare risk management company) since 1993.

Personal: Educated at Manchester University (LL.B) 1968-71.

BARBER, Janice

Hempsons, London (020) 7839 0278
jcb@hempsons.co.uk

Specialisation: Managing Partner. Has wide experience of all areas of Healthcare Law, though she specialises in disciplinary and employment law. Has undertaken variously: medico-legal advice to and representation of defendant Health Authorities, NHS Trusts and individual practitioners covering all areas of hospital and general practice; professional disciplinary and other Tribunals and statutory Inquiries; defence of serious criminal charges and employment law, particularly in relation to hospital practice. Leading cases include R v Cox 1992: manslaughter, euthanasia, acting for the defendant; Howard v E Dorset Health Authority 1993: hospital, negligence, applicability of res ispa loquitur principle in medical negligence cases, for the defendant; Thomson v Blake-James CA 1997: re. forseeability; WG Dick v Brookmount Estates Limited & Ford Sellar Morris Developments Limited CA 1992: successful recovery of fees, under Order 14, acting for Plaintiff, a quantity surveyor; The Orkney Child Abuse Inquiry, Stanley Royd Hospital Inquiry: Salmonella Inquiry, led to the

lifting of Crown Immunity for hospital kitchens and the BSE Inquiry; United Leeds Hospital v Duncan Walker 1997: Disciplinary Inquiry under HSG(95)25 and subsequent appeal to the Secretary of State.
Career: Graduated with a 1st Class Hons BA at the University of Reading. Was articled at *Hempsons* and admitted in 1983. Has been a partner since 1984. Often conducts seminars and lectures in all the specialist areas of practice set out above.

BARBER, Paul
Bevan Ashford, Bristol (0117) 923 0111
Specialisation: Head of the firm's health and social care group. Is widely experienced in all areas of hospital litigation, in particular major obstetric cases. Pre-eminent area of work in recent years has been the handling of multi-party medical negligence actions (such as the haemophiliac HIV, Debedox and Benzodiazipine claims and the Myodil litigation on which he was the lead solicitor for Health Authorities nationally). In addition, has specialist experience of mental health law.
Prof. Memberships: Law Society.
Career: Trained with *Bevan Ashford.* Admitted 1976; Partner 1979.

BLACKWELL, Hilary
Capsticks, London (020) 8780 2211
h.blackwell@capsticks.co.uk
Specialisation: Partner specialising in commercial, property and administrative law cases on behalf of the NHS, including acute hospital PFI and community care schemes (pioneered the Lewisham Partnership approach to joint commissioning and recent work on the Health Act flexibilities). Recent projects include working with the Department of Health on developing local authority contracts for residential care placements, the £24 million refinancing of staff accommodation schemes for three NHS Trusts and the reprovision of Queens Mary's Hospital, Roehampton.
Prof. Memberships: Law Society.
Career: LL.B (Hons) University of Bristol, College of Law, Guildford. Articles *Veale Benson* (now *Veale Wasborough*). 1992 joined *Capsticks* to head property and commercial department, 1993 partner. Member of firm's management committee.
Personal: Lives Wimbledon.

BRADBEER, Ronald
Eversheds, Newcastle upon Tyne (0191) 261 1661
ronaldbradbeer@eversheds.com
See under Alternative Dispute Resolution, p.xxx

BROADHEAD, Jill
Bevan Ashford, Bristol (0117) 975 1603
j.broadhead@bevanashford.co.uk
Specialisation: Partner in the health and social care group. Has over 25 years experience in the medical negligence and medical law fields dealing with a wide variety of matters for the NHS. Was admitted in 1978, becoming a partner at *Bevan Ashford* in 1986. Specialises in healthcare, clinical and organisational issues and regulated care legislation. Is advising Avon Health Authority regarding the Bristol Royal Infirmary Inquiry into the management of care of children receiving complex heart surgery at the Bristol Royal Infirmary. The Inquiry is considering the adequacy of the management and delivery of service. As the largest Inquiry ever set up to look into the NHS it is also looking at its organisation and culture, as well as the action taken both within and outside the hospital to deal with the concerns raised about the surgery. It is to make recommendations to secure high quality care across the NHS. Lectures widely to managers and clinicians on a wide range of medico-legal issues affecting the NHS and provides consultancy advice and services to NHS Trusts.

BROADHURST, Marisa
Beachcroft Wansbroughs, London (020) 7242 1011
mbroadhurst@bwlaw.co.uk
Specialisation: All aspects of estates and commercial property transactions, with particular emphasis on development. Currently lead partner acting for the Secretary of State for Health on the public private partnership involving the disposal of £400 million worth of NHS properties and the Trading Group.
Prof. Memberships: Law Society.
Career: Admitted 1970, articles at *Max Bitel Greene & Co*, a Partner from 1970-71, the Greater London Council from 1971-76, the London Residuary Body from 1988-89 and *Beachcroft Stanleys* from 1989 to present, a Partner from 1991.
Personal: Born in Spain. Educated in Spain, France and at The Convent of Our Lady of Sion London. Interests include cinema and theatre, travelling and reading. Lives in Wimbledon, London.

DINGWALL, Christian
Bevan Ashford, London (020) 7421 4400
See under Clinical Negligence, p.165

EDWARDS, Peter Charles
Peter Edwards & Co, Hoylake (0151) 632 6699

ELDERGILL, Anselm
Anselm Eldergill, London (020) 7284 1006
medicolegal@hotmail.com
Specialisation: Specialist in mental health law. Practice includes NHS and social services inquiries, legislative drafting, conferences, lecturing, policy development, drafting, representation and training for NHS trusts and local authorities, agency and consultancy work. Chairman, Mental Health Act Commission Legal & Ethical Committee, 1997-98. Discussant, XXIIIrd International Congress on Law and Mental Health, Sorbonne (1998). Chairman, IBC Conference, Mental Health Law, Regents Park (1998). Keynote speaker, 1st National Conference on Risk Management in Mental Health, Royal College of Physicians (1998). Keynote speaker, Institute of Mental Health Law Conference on Mental Health Review Tribunals, Law Society's Hall (1998). Speaker, Institute of Mental Health Act Practitioners Conference on the Code of Practice, Royal College of Physicians (1999). Speaker, Infolog Conference, Mental Health 2000 and Beyond, Barbican Centre (2000). Speaker, Institute of Mental Health Act Practitioners' Mental Health Act Green Paper Conference, Royal College of Physicians (2000). Speaker, Ad Idem Conference, The Human Rights Act 1998 and Mental Health Law, Royal College of Physicians (2000). Speaker, Institute of Mental Health Conference, Lessons from recent homicide inquiries, King's Fund Centre (2000). Speaker, Institute of Mental Health Act Practitioners' Annual Conference, Legal remedies for patients, Royal College of Physicians (2000). Keynote address, IBC Conference, Mental Health Law: The Implications of the Review Explained, London (2000). Speaker, Capital Conference, Mental Health Services and the Law, London (2000). Keynote address, Mental Health Lawyers Association Annual Conference, Regent's Park (2000). Keynote speaker, Laing-Buisson Conference, The Review of Mental Health Legislation, London (2000). Consultant, Department of Health – Legislation Branch, Reform of the Mental Health Act 1983 (2001). Visiting Professor in Mental Health Law, University of Northumbria (2001). Keynote speaker, Reforming the Mental Health Act 1983, Institute of Mental Health Act Practitioners' Annual Conference, Royal College of Physicians (2001). Speaker, Institute of Mental Health Conference, Reforming the Mental Health Act 1983, King's Fund Centre (2001). Speaker, European Convention on Human Rights and Mental Health, Institute of Mental Health Act Practitioners, London (2001). External Confidential Review of the X Eating Disorders Unit (2001). Law Society video, Human Rights and Mental Health (2001). Legal chairman of eight independent NHS and social services inquiries into homicides committed by psychiatric patients (1999-2001). Advising foreign states on the reform of their mental health legislation (1999-2001).
Career: London School of Economics, Oxford University, The College of Law. Mental Health Act Commissioner, 1992- 2000. Alexander Maxwell Law Trust Scholar. David Hallett Prize for Government. Visiting Professor in Mental Health Law, University of Northumbria.
Publications: *Mental Health Review Tribunals – Law & Practice* (Sweet & Maxwell, 1998, lxxvii, 1333pp., nominated for a Nobel Prize). "The Falling Shadow and the Deteriorating Patient" 'Mental Health Act Commission Discussion Paper, 1998'. "Psychopathy, the law and individual rights" 'Princeton University Law Journal', Volume III, Issue 2, Spring 1999. "The legal logistics of independent inquiries: Common steps and principles for navigating through tragedy" 'British Journal of Health Care Management', May 1998. "A greater evil" 'The Guardian', 20 July 1999. "Reforming Inquiries following Homicides" 'Journal of Mental Health Law', October 1999. "The law and individual rights" in 'The treatment of the personality disordered offender' (ed. R Blackburn, et al., Butterworth-Heinemann, 2000). "The European Convention and Mental Health Review Tribunals" 'Journal of Mental Health Law', June 2001. "White Paper: Reform of the Mental Health Act" (Editorial) 'Journal of Forensic Psychiatry', August 2001.

FRANCIS, Barry
Buchanan Ingersoll, London (020) 7920 3800
francisb@buchananingersoll.com
Specialisation: Public/private interface transactions including PPP, PFI projects and other commercial transactions in the health and other public sectors including public sector/private sector joint ventures outsourcing contracts and procurement and administrative law advice. Current projects include major hospital building and services projects (PFI). Managing Partner *Buchanan Ingersoll*. Regular speaker at conferences and seminars. Contributor to a range of specialist publications including Butterworths 'PFI Manual'. A member of the Editorial Board of 'The PFI Report'.
Prof. Memberships: Law Society.
Career: Admitted 1977, at *Beachcroft Hyman Isaacs* (now *Beachcroft Wansbroughs*). Associate 1979-80, Partner 1980-1999, Managing Partner *Buchanan Ingersoll* 2000.
Personal: Born 14th March 1953. Educated at Enfield Grammar School and University of Bristol. Interests include travel, history and food. Lives in North London.

HALLATT, Diane
Beachcroft Wansbroughs, Leeds (0113) 251 4700
dhallatt@bwlaw.co.uk
Specialisation: Partner specialising in medical negligence inquests, major untoward incidents and all aspects of medical and health service law. Has 20 years experience in the public sector, 14 years for the NHS and has a wide range of experience in public administrative law/corporate and clinical governance issues. Has defended several Judicial Reviews, health and safety prosecutions and has advised in several major untoward incidents, including Hillsborough, Allitt, Kiberu and Jenkinson. Was on the Law Society's Working Party considering Lord Woolf's proposed civil litigation reforms.
Career: Qualified 1980. Trent Regional Health Authority 1986-89. Partner at *Oxley & Coward* 1989-95 and at *Wansbroughs Willey Hargrave* from February 1995. 1999 Partner in *Beachcroft Wansbroughs*.

HARRISON, Frances
Hempsons, Manchester (0161) 228 0011
fah@hempsons.co.uk
See under Clinical Negligence, p.167

HOLMES, John
Hempsons, London (020) 7839 0278
j.holmes@hempsons.co.uk
See under Clinical Negligence, p.167

IRONS, Ashley
Reid Minty, London (020) 7318 4444

KING, Stephen
Mills & Reeve, Norwich (01603) 693257
stephen.king@mills-reeve.com
Specialisation: Partner in health care team. Specialises in professional negligence, including medical negligence. Acts for specialist Lloyds underwriters and also acts for NHS Trusts and Health Authorities, including the NHS Litigation Authority, advising on claims made against them for damages. Also covers mental health law, coroners' inquests, drug trials, and acts as client partner for health care clients. Has acted in many self-funded structured settlements financing the payment of substantial damages in brain damage cases. Regular lecturer to hospitals on health care law, negligence, risk management and awareness and claims management. Editorial Board Member of 'Health Care Risk Report' (Eclipse Publications), 'Personal Injury Journal' (John Wiley Publications).

LEIGH, Bertie
Hempsons, London (020) 7839 0278
mamsl@hempsons.co.uk
Specialisation: Senior Partner. Principal area of practice is medical law, with particular interest in cases involving obstetrics, anaesthesia, paediatrics, orthopaedics, neurosurgery and general practice. Other main area of expertise is National Health Service Acts and associated Regulations. Has dealt with a number of Court of Appeal cases including Gregory v Pembrokeshire (1989), Forest (1991), and Bull & Wakeham v Devon Health Authority (1989), DeFreitas v O'Brien (1994), R v Nottingham HA (1996), Re MB (1997) and Thomas v Brighton HA in the House of Lords (1998). Major clients include the Association of Anaesthetists and the Royal College of Paediatrics and Child Health of which he is an Hon. Fellow. Author of chapters in 'Ethics & Obstetrics & Gynaecology' (RCOG 1994) and 'Safe Practice in Obstetrics & Gynaecology' (1994), Dewhursts 'Obstetrics' 1999 and 'Neonatology' (Ed Roberton & Rennie) 1997. Lectures regularly to lawyers and doctors. Delivered the John Snow Lecture to the Association of Anaesthetists in 1999
Prof. Memberships: Medico-Legal Society.
Career: Qualified in 1976, having joined *Hempsons* in 1973. Became a Partner in 1977.
Personal: Born 30th August 1946. Educated at St. Christopher School, Letchworth 1960-65 and the University of East Anglia 1966-69. Lives in Clapham.

MACKINTOSH, Nicola
Mackintosh Duncan, London (020) 7357 6464

MASON, David
Capsticks, London (020) 8780 2211
See under Clinical Negligence, p.168

PARSONS, Andrew
Radcliffes, London (020) 7222 7282
andrew.parsons@radcliffes.com
Specialisation: Partner in Litigation Department (Head of Health Group). Principal area of practice is Healthcare Law. Specialises in mental health law and human rights. Advises extensively on the administration and powers of the NHS. Extensive experience of psychiatric related issues and advocacy at inquests. Advises on relationships with local authorities and other healthcare contracts. Has wide experience in drug related fatal cases and drug testing protocols. Acts for Health Authorities and NHS Trusts, Teaching Hospitals, private clinics and health insurers. Also acts for institutional, property investment funds and NHS clients in connection with property and general commercial litigation matters. Author of 'Tenant Default Under Commercial Leases' (1993, 3rd edition published 1999). 'Labour Ward Manual' (legal chapter), 'Mental Health Law Compendium' (2000), and 'Health Service Law' (mental health chapter, Butterworths 2001). Lectures widely to doctors, nurses and other NHS staff.
Prof. Memberships: Law Society, City of Westminster Law Society and Royal Society of Medicine.
Career: Qualified in 1987 having been at *Radcliffes* since 1985. Became a Partner in 1992.
Personal: Born 5th February 1963. Educated at Norwich School 1971-80 and the University of Reading 1981-84. Leisure pursuits include music, sports and handicrafts. Member of Mensa and RAC. Lives in London.

PICKUP, Raith
Mills & Reeve, Cambridge (01223) 222283
raith.pickup@mills-reeve.com
Specialisation: Head of PFI at *Mills & Reeve*. Considerable experience of advising on capital projects in the NHS. Completed PFI schemes for several NHS trusts and the NHS Executive with projects including acute facilities, mental health schemes, staff accommodation, nurse training facilities and car parks. Work includes joint ventures between NHS trusts and other public sector bodies or the private sector; EC procurement and tendering; CIM and Concode compliance, income generation schemes. Is a regular speaker at NHS seminars.

SCOTT-MONCRIEFF, Lucy
Scott-Moncrieff, Harbour & Sinclair, London (020) 7485 5588

SLACK, Richard
Eversheds, Newcastle upon Tyne (0191) 2611661
richardslack@eversheds.com
Specialisation: Medical negligence; employment law; registration of nursing homes.
Prof. Memberships: Law Society.
Career: Upper Second Class Honours Law Degree; Law Society Finals.
Personal: Water sports.

SMITH, Janice
Capsticks, London (020) 8780 2211
See under Clinical Negligence, p.170

SUMERLING, Robert
Le Brasseur J Tickle, London (020) 7836 0099

HUMAN RIGHTS

London: 422; Midlands: 424; The North: 424; *Profiles*: 425

OVERVIEW: While not causing dramatic change in any one area of law, the impact of the Human Rights Act has been far wider than this section of the *Chambers* Guide could possibly reflect. The traditional civil liberties firms display a depth of experience built up by individuals, particularly on prisoners' rights, deaths in custody and actions against the police. Such work often runs alongside rights based work under administrative law, involving *inter alia* employment, discrimination and mental health. Currently, human rights concerns are felt to be ancillary to commercial cases, with companies or individuals continuing to instruct the specialists. Larger commercial firms are responding to the challenge. The impact of Article 6 on commercial judicial review has been significant and readers should refer to the Administrative & Public Law section of the Guide (p.xx) for the leading practitioners, of whom Andrew Lidbetter (Herbert Smith) and Michael Smyth (Clifford Chance) have a special interest in the HRA.

RESEARCH APPROVED BY BMRB: *For this edition,* Chambers' *researchers conducted 6,552 interviews – 4,419 with law firms, 554 with barristers and 1,579 with clients.*

The validity of the research was scrutinised by BMRB International, who audited both the methodology and the results at our offices in July 2001. They interviewed Chambers' *researchers and cross-checked sample interviews. Details of the audit appear on page 7.*

LONDON

HUMAN RIGHTS • London		Ptnrs	Assts
1	Bindman & Partners	4	4
2	Bhatt Murphy	4	1
3	Christian Fisher	3	12
	Deighton Guedalla	2	1
4	Birnberg Peirce & Partners	n/a	n/a
	Hickman & Rose	1	6
5	Simons Muirhead & Burton	3	2
	Winstanley-Burgess	2	n/a
6	Irwin Mitchell	7	4
	Taylor Nichol	4	2
	Thanki Novy Taube	6	6

LEADING INDIVIDUALS		
1	**BHATT Raju** Bhatt Murphy	**BINDMAN Geoffrey** Bindman & Partners
	GROSZ Stephen Bindman & Partners	
2	**CHRISTIAN Louise** Christian Fisher	**DEIGHTON Jane** Deighton Guedalla
	KHAN Sadiq Christian Fisher	**MURPHY Fiona** Bhatt Murphy
	PEIRCE Gareth Birnberg Peirce & Partners	
3	**CHARALAMBOUS Louis** CCL	**CONRATHE PAUL** Coningsbys
	CREIGHTON Simon Bhatt Murphy	**LESKIN Nigel** Birnberg Peirce & Partners
	LESLIE Sara Irwin Mitchell	**MACHOVER Daniel** Hickman & Rose
	NICHOL James Taylor Nichol	**SCHWARZ Michael** Bindman & Partners
	WISTRICH Harriet Thanki Novy Taube	

This book is the product of 6,552 1/2-hour interviews. See p.7 for BMRB audit.
Within each band, firms are listed alphabetically. *See individuals' profiles p.425*

Bindman & Partners (see firm details p.882) Though not unreachable in every sphere of civil liberties work, the practice retains its gold standard breadth. A first rate operation across mental health, judicial review, animal rights, discrimination and freedom of speech, it is judged by peers as "*number one on any view.*" "*A legend*" in his own right, **Geoffrey Bindman** (see p.425) not only secured high profile work, such as the Pinochet and Hanratty cases, but also represented a torture victim at the ECHR and advised organisations affected by the 2000 terrorism act. "*A skilled technician,*" **Stephen Grosz**'s (see p.425) strength lies in judicial reviews and he continues to "*break ground in human rights jurisprudence.*" **Michael Schwarz** (see p.426) has a focus on public order issues with an environmental and animal rights slant, acting for Greenpeace campaigners across the country. "*Extremely good with his clients,*" he is also involved in cases involving race issues.

Bhatt Murphy With "*excellent solicitors, all of them highly respected,*" it has been another good year for a relatively small firm that consistently appears in high profile cases. Hailed by interviewees for his involvement in claims against the police **Raju Bhatt**'s status as a leader in his field "*cannot be disputed.*" Having won a review of the death of Alton Manning, he also continues to work on public law remedies with an emphasis on the right to a fair trial and prisoners rights. **Fiona Murphy** is rated for the breadth of her work. She is representing escapee prisoners from Whitemoor and working on a high level case that impacts on the future of mandatory life sentences. "*Extraordinarily bright and extremely dedicated,*" **Simon Creighton** is a leading prison law practitioner. He acted on one of the first cases brought under the Human Rights Act (for Mr John Quaquah) against the home secretary, and he also advised on the Daly case, regarding the lines of authority in administrative decisions involving Convention rights.

Christian Fisher (see firm details p.914) Having expanded to cover mental health, family and medical negligence, peers regard the firm as an "*extremely serious*" component of the market. While remaining intimately involved with the Ladbrook Grove enquiry, **Louise Christian** continues her work at the level of the ECHR (including a recent death in custody case) as well as specialising in medical negligence cases. Judged by interviewees at the bar to be "*the best solicitor going,*" she is "*phenomenal at getting her teeth into her clients' interests.*" **Sadiq Khan** wins "*valuable work,*" including cases at ECHR level such as that of a police shooting. He also advised Kamlesh Bahl in a discrimination case brought against the Law Society and acted on the successful challenge to the bar on the Brothers of Islam leader, Farrakhan entering the UK.

Deighton Guedalla Valued for its work in discrimination, immigration, police protection and criminal issues, its involvement in the Stephen Lawrence case has won plaudits. With a lasting reputation for her part challenging the Lord Chancellor's selection of special advisor, **Jane Deighton** is perceived by some as "*in a class of her own.*" This year she won a case that resulted in the highest award (over £1 million) in a sex discrimination case involving breach of contract by the police. The firm is also representing a number of May Day protestors.

Birnberg Peirce & Partners Although criminal cases substantially outweigh the firm's human rights oriented work, it remains endorsed by peers as an exceptional force. "*Courageous fighter for people*," **Gareth Peirce** who advises on the Ocalan and Shayler cases, continues to work on high profile cases including the representation of Irish prisoners who claim to have been beaten by prison officers. "*Absolutely excellent*" according to barristers **Nigel Leskin**'s involvement in criminal defence warrants his inclusion here for his coverage of important issues.

Hickman & Rose (see firm details p.995) Strongly endorsed for its work dealing with judicial reviews in every element of the criminal justice system, and particularly prisoners rights work. "*Energetic and well organised*," peers believe it has shown "*initiative in moving the debate forward*" in the civil liberties field. There are two cases in point, both at the Court of Appeal: the representation of a woman prisoner seeking to retain access to her child; and the challenge that prisoners should have voting rights. "*Top human rights specialist*," **Daniel Machover** continues to work on the cases brought against violent prison officers, both at Wormwood Scrubs and Brixton prisons. Further ongoing cases include the deaths of Harry Stanley (shot dead by the police) and Roger Sylvester, who died in detention. The firm has an established mental health practice, and continues to offer advice to protesters on the Prevention of Terrorism Act. Advises the Close Supervision Centre in Woodhill Prison.

Simons Muirhead & Burton (see firm details p.1133) Dedicated practice for death row prisoners in the Caribbean, it is the largest in the UK for appeals to the Privy Council. Involved in appeals against convictions as well as challenges to the duration of a prisoner's stay on death row. The firm continues to command enormous respect for its envied client base. The crime department continues to act for organisations such as Friends of the Earth and Greenpeace. Anthony Burton overseas all general human rights works, while Saul Lehrfreund is director of the death penalty project.

Winstanley-Burgess (see firm details p.1186) Despite a heavy immigration workload, the firm has an established reputation for police action work, on top of refugee and asylum cases. The firm is representing organisations identified by a prescription issued in February under the 2000 Terrorism act. Julie Holden is well known for work on police actions.

Irwin Mitchell (see firm details p.1009) One of the few firms to have recently created a national team devoted to human rights. A wide ranging caseload includes representing individuals such as hunt saboteurs against the police, and also the rights of employees in multi-applicant challenges. Highlights include a harassment case the firm is bringing against the Metropolitan Police on behalf of Mr Lindo. Though the practice has yet to make the same impact as the classic civil liberties firms, there is no doubt about the quality of its service. **Sara Leslie** (see p.425) is respected as "*an impressive individual*" heavily recommended for her multi-applicant employment cases against public authorities.

Taylor Nichol "*Hard to beat*" in the field of miscarriages of justice work, the firm has a special focus on youth crime, and also continue to act for Myra Hindley. **James Nichol**, having won his case for a mentally impaired man accused of the murder of women on Aldershot Common, is thought to be a leading light. He is now representing a man known as Pemberton, convicted of murder in 1985, who has never had a trial or appeal by jury. This case will go to the House of Lords to determine whether, in the event of fresh evidence, a jury should be allowed to consider the case.

Thanki Novy Taube (see firm details p.1151) "*Strengthened this year*," report our interviewees, the niche Prison Law Department has acted on cases central to the defining of prisoners' rights. Its public law dominance has enabled it to bring a case challenging the procedure of intimate body searches in prisons to the criminal court. The firm has also been involved in representing a prisoner in determining access rights to her child. **Harriet Wistrich** (see p.426) gained recognition for her involvement with an intervention on behalf of Justice for Women, among others, in the House of Lords. The case challenges whether the complainant in a rape case can be cross-examined on past sexual relations. Work on a volume of judicial reviews into coroners' inquests continues.

Other Notable Practitioners The "*dedicated*" **Louis Charalambous** (see p.425) of **CCL** is working on a ground-breaking international human

Recent High Profile Human Rights Cases

Case	Lawyers	Significance
Offen	Edward Fitzgerald QC, Phillippa Kaufmann, Danny Friedman, Andrew Katzen and Michael Grewcock (Moss & Co)	The first case brought under the HRA; caused "three strikes and you're out" legislation (re: mandatory life sentences) to be rewritten by Lord Woolf.
Daly	Tim Owen QC, Phillippa Kaufmann Simon Creighton (Bhatt Murphy)	Landmark decision on the proper role of the court when reviewing administrative decisions which engage Convention rights.
P & Q	Richard Gordon QC Hickman & Rose; Thanki Novy Taube	Challenge to the policy of removing babies from their imprisoned mothers when they reach the age of 18 months.
R v Mental Health Review Tribunal ex parte H	Richard Gordon QC, Paul Bowen Scott-Moncrieff Harbour & Sinclair	The first incompatibility case granted under the HRA; Court of Appeal declared s.72 of the Mental Health Act to be incompatible with the HRA in so far as it placed the burden of proof on the patient to disprove the existence of criteria justifying detention.
Lambert	Tim Owen QC, Keir Starmer, Rebecca Trowler	Successful challenge to compatibility of Misuse of Drugs Act with Article 6 (2) as well as ruling on retrospective effect of the HRA.
Alconbury (planning)	Rabinder Singh (responsible for human rights aspects of case)	First pure human rights case to go before the House of Lords.
Shayler	Edward Fitzgerald QC, Michael Mansfield QC, Keir Starmer John Wadham (Liberty), Gareth Peirce (Birnberg Peirce & Partners)	Challenge to the Official Secrets Act under article 10 of the HRA.
Farrakhan	Nicholas Blake QC, Sadiq Khan (Christian Fisher)	Successful challenge, under the Human Rights Act, to the ban on the Brothers of Islam leader entering the UK.
Ocalan v Turkey	Sydney Kentridge QC, Tim Otty, Mark Muller, Gareth Peirce (Birnberg Peirce & Partners), Louis Charalambous (CCL)	At the time of going to press, gained admissibility to ECHR; challenge to the death penalty as inhuman and degrading; test of consequences of unlawful kidnapping for subsequent proceedings.
Newton Spence; Peter Hughes, prisoners on death row in the Eastern Caribbean	Edward Fitzgerald QC; James Guthrie QC; Keir Starmer Saul Lehrfreund (Simons Muirhead & Burton)	A landmark decision made in April 2001 could lead to eventual abolition of the death penalty in the Eastern Caribbean.

rights case, as well as continuing with freedom of expression work. **Paul Conrathe** at **Coningsbys** has gained wide-ranging recognition for working on a plethora of issues including hospital closures, education and abortion.

MIDLANDS

HUMAN RIGHTS • Midlands	Ptnrs	Assts
1 **Tyndallwoods** Birmingham	3	3
2 **McGrath & Co** Birmingham	1	2
LEADING INDIVIDUALS		
1 **PHILLIPS Mark** Tyndallwoods		

This book is the product of 6,552 1/2-hour interviews. See p.7 for BMRB audit.
Within each band, firms are listed alphabetically. *See individuals' profiles p.425*

Tyndallwoods (see firm details p.1165) Moving the debate on human rights forward, the firm is active in advising less experienced firms wishing to take up legal aid work. It is one of the few organisations to have been awarded this advisory capacity by the Legal Services Commission. Having recently recruited at partner level, it complements a strong reputation in immigration issues with rights based cases in the community, especially in mental health. **Mark Phillips** (see p.434) continues to draw recommendation.

McGrath & Co Though primarily perceived as a criminal and immigration practice, the firm also focuses on public law actions against the police, police complaints, and deaths in custody. The small team is led by Emma Guilfoy Lecary.

THE NORTH

HUMAN RIGHTS • The North	Ptnrs	Assts
1 **AS Law** Liverpool	2	4
Harrison Bundey & Co Leeds	3	1
Howells Sheffield	2	8
2 **David Gray Solicitors** Newcastle upon Tyne	n/a	n/a
Irwin Mitchell Sheffield	2	4
Robert Lizar Manchester	n/a	n/a
LEADING INDIVIDUALS		
1 **BUNDEY Ruth** Harrison Bundey & Co		
2 **ABRAHAMSON Elkan** AS Law		
SIMPSON Danny Howells		
UP AND COMING		
PURCHAS Simon Harrison Bundey & Co		
ONES TO WATCH		
PRICE Richard Howells		

This book is the product of 6,552 1/2-hour interviews. See p.7 for BMRB audit.
Within each band, firms are listed alphabetically. *See individuals' profiles p.425*

AS Law Recognised for its work on prisoners' rights first and foremost, notably teaming up with Hickman & Rose this year in a case concerning voting rights. In a case currently at the Court of Appeal, the firm is representing a prisoner attempting to secure his right to artificially inseminate his wife. Under the guidance of **Elkan Abrahamson** it also advises on access to condoms issues at the ECHR. As founders of the Association of Prisoners, it is negotiating with the prison service (Home Secretary level).

Harrison Bundey & Co (see firm details p.988) Covering civil liberties, mostly against a criminal background, the firm has a focus on youth crime and education work involving the rights of the individual. For this range of work it attracts commendation from players in both the regions and London. **Ruth Bundey** (see p.425) "*a real dynamo outside London,*" and a "*true civil rights campaigner,*" is well regarded nationally for inquest work. **Simon Purchas** (see p.426) is "*approachable and knows his subject well*" particularly with regard to civil liberties with a criminal slant.

Howells (see firm details p.1002) Considered by some interviewees "*the best firm in the North*" due to the breadth and scope of its work. Judicial reviews are undertaken and the firm represents individuals against public bodies. Continues to be well regarded for its immigration and criminal expertise. Successful in its Court of Appeal challenge, prisoners undergoing mandatory drug tests in custody are now uniformly provided with representation before governors. The firm also affected procedural changes through a challenge against the Criminal Injuries Compensation Board, so that a decision not to award damages has to be backed up by reasons. "*Fantastic*" **Danny Simpson** (see p.426) remains key to the firm's profile.

David Gray Solicitors Recognised for representing individuals against institutions and sometimes the State. Mike Bishop leads this Newcastle-based group that has a long established human rights expertise.

Irwin Mitchell (see firm details p.1009) Acknowledged by peers as "*one of the best*" with regard to civil litigation, covering a range of human rights work. A successful case, which was handled by Andrew Lockley, involved a judicial review challenge to the Lord Chancellor and DTI against legal aid for directors' disqualification proceedings. The group also advised on a case that set limits on the powers of the police in search and seizure raids on business premises. Continues to represent the hunt saboteurs against Cheshire Police for unlawful arrest, false imprisonment and assault and battery. Also acted on behalf of a businessman who was assaulted by police officers at the World Cup final in Rome with a case against the Italian government currently being taken forward to the ECHR.

Robert Lizar Well regarded for actions against the police, a notable example being the successful representation of the 'Bolton Seven,' involving the rights of seven gay men to privacy following a police house-raid.The firm's reputation extends beyond the regions, with Robert Lizar's "*humane approach to work*" winning plaudits in London.

LEADERS IN HUMAN RIGHTS

ABRAHAMSON, Elkan
A S Law, Liverpool (0151) 707 1212

BHATT, Raju
Bhatt Murphy, London (020) 7253 7744

BINDMAN, Geoffrey
Bindman & Partners, London (020) 7833 4433
info@bindmans.com
Specialisation: Senior partner. Specialises in civil liberties and human rights, media law, defamation, anti-discrimination and general litigation. Author of numerous articles in the professional and national press on these subjects, and has broadcast frequently. Has represented the ICJ, IBA, Amnesty International, and other bodies in human rights missions in many countries.
Prof. Memberships: Law Society; president, Discrimination Law Association; president, Client Interviewing Competition of England and Wales.
Career: Established *Bindman & Partners* in 1974. From 1966 to 1976 was legal adviser to the Race Relations Board and thereafter until 1983 to the Commission for Racial Equality. Visiting professor, UCLA (1982); currently visiting professor of law at University College London; honorary fellow Society of Advanced Legal Studies; Hon LLD (De Montfort University); Liberty and Law Society Gazette Award for Lifetime Human Rights Achievement 1999.
Personal: Born 3 January 1933. Attended Newcastle RGS and Oriel College, Oxford.

BUNDEY, Ruth
Harrison Bundey & Co., Leeds (0113) 200 7400
Specialisation: Partner specialising in crime and immigration. Main areas of practice since 1980: crime, immigration and inquests. Acted in the Helen Smith inquest, the case of the Bradford 12 and of Anwar Ditta, and various Yorkshire drug operations, and involving women and violence. Contributor to the Liberty Guide 'Know Your Rights' and member of the Liverpool 8 Inquiry which published 'Loosen the Shackles'. Involved more and more with inquests into deaths and custody and currently instructed by the sister of Christopher Adler who died on video in Hull Police Station on 1 April 1999.
Prof. Memberships: Law Society, Leeds Law Society, Liberty. Chairs Law Society Immigration Sub-Committee.
Career: Qualified in 1980. Formed *Ruth Bundey & Co* in 1986. Merged in 1993 to form *Harrison Bundey & Co*.
Personal: Educated at the University of Kent (BA Hons in English & American Literature). Awarded Honorary Master of Arts Degree for services to law in November 1995: University of Kent. Management member of Chapeltown CAB and of Umoja House (hostel) and a member of West Yorkshire Justice for Women. Lives in Chapeltown, Leeds.

CHARALAMBOUS, Louis
CCL, London (020) 7253 2277
louis@cclsolicitors.com
Specialisation: Main areas of practice are criminal, media and public law, with a particular interest in free expression. Clients include National Union of Journalists, Channel 5, Medya TV, Savoy Books and National Union of Teachers. Special expertise in representing professionals in high profile cases. Clients include photographers, journalists, artists, teachers, and solicitors. Current cases include Abdullah Ocalan v Turkey (death penalty case); Michael Kyprianou v Cyprus (advocate's contempt of court), London Oratory Church, and Adeniji v London Borough of Newham (breach of confidence), Jo Smith (Battered Woman Syndrome murder appeal).
Prof. Memberships: London Criminal Courts Solicitors Association and Serious Fraud Panel, Association of Personal Injury Lawyers. Frequently asked to comment on human rights matters on radio and TV.
Career: University of Bradford (BA Hons) and University of Leeds (MA). Qualified in 1987. Practised with *Ruth Bundey* 1986-1990 and with *John Pickering & Partners* 1990-1993 and joined *Stephens Innocent* in 1994 as head of crime and civil liberties, becoming a partner in 1998. Founded *CCL* in January 2001 in partnership with Sarah Culshaw. Honorary Legal Officer of National Civil Rights Movement since its inception.
Personal: Born 1957. Educated at St. Marylebone Grammar School (1968-1975).

CHRISTIAN, Louise
Christian Fisher, London (020) 7831 1750

CONRATHE, Paul
Coningsbys, Croydon (020) 8680 5575

CREIGHTON, Simon
Bhatt Murphy, London (020) 7253 7744

DEIGHTON, Jane
Deighton Guedalla, London (020) 7359 5700

GROSZ, Stephen
Bindman & Partners, London (020) 7833 4433
s.grosz@bindmans.com
Specialisation: Partner in public law and litigation department. Specialises in public and administrative law and human rights handling applicant work on behalf of pressure groups and individuals in civil liberties and environmental cases including European Community law. Also handles respondent work on behalf of the Law Society and the Office for the Supervision of Solicitors. Major clients have included Friends of the Earth, the World Development Movement War on Want, Campaign Against Arms Trade, Tapol, Mencap and Amnesty International. Frequently writes articles on public law and human rights. Co-author, with Jack Beatson QC and Peter Duffy QC, of 'Human Rights: the 1998 Act & the European Convention'.
Prof. Memberships: Administrative Law Bar Association, United Kingdom Environmental Law Association, Solicitors European Group, Executive Committee of Public Law Project and Governor of British Institute of Human Rights, Member of the Council of JUSTICE. Member of the Advisory Board of Judicial Review quarterly; Member of the Advisory Board of Education, Public Law & the Individual; Member of the Council of Liberty.
Career: Qualified in 1978. Entire career spent at *Bindman & Partners*. Partner since 1981.
Personal: Born April 1953. Graduate in Law of Cambridge University and in European Law of Université Libre de Bruxelles.

KHAN, Sadiq
Christian Fisher, London (020) 7831 1750
sadiqk@christianf.co.uk
Specialisation: Partner in Civil Litigation Department. Main area of practice is actions against the police, employment and discrimination law, judicial reviews, inquests. Involved in all areas of civil liberties work. Sadiq has given oral evidence to the Home Affairs Select Committee. Won landmark cases including: in police damages (HSU v Met Police), negligence (Reeves v Met Police), discriminations (Bahl v Law Society), inquests (Bentley v HM Coroner District of Avon). Human Rights Act (Farrakhan V S of S of Home Dept), Chairman of Liberty (NCCL).
Prof. Memberships: Police Action Lawyers Group, Executive Committee of Legal Action Group, Inquest Lawyers Group, Society of Labour Lawyer. APIL. Member of The Law Society's Equal Opportunities Committee. Panel member of EOC Solicitors. Member of Discrimination Law Association and Employment Practitioners Group Executive Committee.
Career: Trainee Solicitor with *Christian Fisher & Co* where he is now a partner. He is a visiting lecturer in Employment Law at the University of North London.
Publications: Has authored various articles on legal reform and writes extensively on civil liberties issues.
Personal: Awarded Sweet & Maxwell Law Prize, Governors Award, Windsor Fellowship, Esso Law Bursary and Awarded Society of Black Lawyers bursary. Councillor in Wandsworth since 1994. Representative on Police Consultative Committee and Racial Incidents Panel. Involved in human rights visits to Turkey and has lectured in Poland on the ECHR on behalf of Justice. Member of Institute of Advanced Legal Studies Advisory Committee examining civil legal aid and Advisory Committee of Liberty examining independent police complaints system. Member of Steering Group Camden Community Legal Services Partnership and Member of Working Party looking into Pre Action Protocol for Police actions.

LESKIN, Nigel
Birnberg Peirce & Partners, London
(020) 7284 4620

LESLIE, Sara
Irwin Mitchell, London (020) 7250 1749
Specialisation: Head of *Irwin Mitchell*'s human rights unit and discrimination law units. Specialises in human rights and discrimination law. Last year in particular was involved in two notable cases - Hone v Hansell and Stirzaker and Others v Northern Birmingham Mental Heath Trust and others. She received the Wainwright Trust Breakthrough award and was runner up in The Lawyer Employment Team of the Year award 2001 for her conduct of Enderby v Frenchay Health Authority and the Secretary of State for Health and the speech therapists' equal value litigation.
Prof. Memberships: The Employment Lawyers Association; Industrial Law Society; TUC's Equal Value Working Party.
Career: Articled clerk, assistant solicitor, partner *Robin Thompson and Partners* 1979-95; Partner *Irwin Mitchell* 1995 (opened London office).
Personal: Born 1956, resides London. Education:

Ursuline Convent, Westgate on Sea; Brunel University (1980, BSc Law and S ociology). Leisure: Opera, skiing.

MACHOVER, Daniel
Hickman & Rose, London (020) 7700 2211
dmachover@hickmanandrose.co.uk
Specialisation: Civil remedies to all problems experienced by people within the criminal justice system, including actions against the police, judicial review of chief officers of police, magistrates, prison governors and the Home Secretary, inquests and claims arising out of assaults by prison officers. Represents over fifty alleged victims of assaults at HMP Wormwood Scrubs.
Prof. Memberships: Founder of Lawyers for Palestinian Human Rights, convenor of the Working Group of Lawyers for Liberty, member of Council of Liberty, Inquest Lawyers Group, Prisoners' Rights Legal Group and APIL.
Career: Qualified 1988, worked at North Kensington Law Centre, Liberty's legal department (locum) and *Christian Fisher* before joining *Hickman and Rose* in January 1997 as head of the civil litigation department. Partner since March 1998.
Personal: LLB, LLM. in International Human Rights Law.

MURPHY, Fiona
Bhatt Murphy, London (020) 7253 7744

NICHOL, James
Taylor Nichol, London (020) 7272 8336

PEIRCE, Gareth
Birnberg Peirce & Partners, London (020) 7284 4620

PHILLIPS, Mark
Tyndallwoods, Birmingham (0121) 624 1111
Mark_Phillips@tyndallwoods.co.uk
See under Immigration, p.434

PRICE, Richard
Howells, Sheffield (0114) 249 6666

PURCHAS, Simon
Harrison Bundey & Co., Leeds (0113) 200 7400
Specialisation: Experienced criminal defence practitioner now specialising in related civil law aspects of criminal defence work, principally actions against police, prisoners' rights, judicial review and a range of civil liberties work.
Prof. Memberships: Law Society.
Career: BA (Hons) History and Philosophy, Leeds University. Qualified as a solicitor in 1985. Joined *Ruth Bundey & Co* as a partner in 1988 and since 1993 a partner in the merged practice of *Harrison Bundey & Co.*

SCHWARZ, Michael
Bindman & Partners, London (020) 7833 4433
Specialisation: Specialist in criminal defence work, including fresh evidence appeals to the Court of Appeal. Acts often for political activists and campaigners on environmental, animal rights, peace/disarmament, race, social justice issues. Particular experience of public order arrests and multi-defendant trials. Has represented anti-roads protestors at Twyford Down, the M11 and Newbury. Represents Greenpeace campaigners against GMOs and destruction of rainforests. Represented campaigners facing serious public order charges at London demonstrations on June 18th 1999, November 30th 1999 and 1st May 2000. Represents family of Michael Menson, the black musician set alight by racists in North London, at inquest, Old Bailey Prosecution and police complaint. Represented Animal Defenders in successful prosecution of Chipperfields for animal cruelty. Also inquests, extradition, police complaints, complaints to the European Court of Human Rights.
Career: Qualified in 1992. Partner at Bindmans since 1995.
Personal: Degree in law (Oxford) and postgraduate degree in European Law (College of Europe, Brugge, Belgium).

SIMPSON, Danny
Howells, Sheffield (0114) 249 6666
Specialisation: Partner and head of criminal law department. All aspects of criminal law, including miscarriage of justice cases and a range of civil liberties issues.
Prof. Memberships: Law Society.
Career: BA (Hons) Degree, Exeter College, Oxford, Politics, Philosophy and Economics, qualified as a solicitor in 1984 and employed at *Bindman & Partners* solicitors. Became a partner in 1989 before moving to Sheffield in 1990 as a partner. Head of department at *Howells* solicitors.
Personal: Lives in Sheffield, married to GP practising locally, with three children. Member of Labour Party.

WISTRICH, Harriet
Thanki Novy Taube, London (020) 7833 5800
harrietwistrich@tntlaw.co.uk
Specialisation: Actions against the police and the prison service; inquests especially deaths in custody; advising rape/child abuse victims re police investigations; 'Battered Women Who Kill', mainly at appellant/CLRC stage; two recent third party interventions in House of Lords cases on rape and provocation - women's rights as human rights.
Prof. Memberships: Founder member of Justice For Women and the Emma Humphreys Memorial Prize Trust; Police Action Lawyers Group; Lawyers For Liberty; Justice Association of Child Abuse Lawyers.
Career: Was a film maker working in community video before training to be a lawyer. Trainee at *Winstanley-Burgess* prior to moving to *Thanki Novy Taube*, made partner 2000.
Publications: Article in 'Lace and Liberty' newsletter.

IMMIGRATION

OVERVIEW: Most prominent this year has been the launch of the Innovator scheme after leading business immigration lawyers consulted with government ministers and successfully lobbied for the two year pilot-scheme to go ahead. Introduced in September 2000, the scheme is designed to address a gap in the market and allow entry to individuals who are neither employees nor business investors, but innovative entrepreneurs. Initially designed to attract dot.com pioneers, the category has been successfully adapted by creative thinking London lawyers to accommodate other sectors. The category has been utilised by over 60 applicants so far, and lawyers feel it has been a success. This year has also seen the government agency that administers work permits relocated from the DfEE to the rigorous Home Office Immigration and Nationality Directorate. Lawyers await the effect of this on the work permit application process. On the personal immigration side, changes to the legal aid system have meant a dramatic drop in the number of firms active in the area.

RESEARCH APPROVED BY BMRB: *For this edition,* Chambers' *researchers conducted 6,552 interviews – 4,419 with law firms, 554 with barristers and 1,579 with clients.*

The validity of the research was scrutinised by BMRB International, who audited both the methodology and the results at our offices in July 2001. They interviewed Chambers' *researchers and cross-checked sample interviews. Details of the audit appear on page 7.*

LONDON

BUSINESS

CMS Cameron McKenna (see firm details p.922) Reigns supreme again as, according to our interviewees, "*for size and profile, it takes some beating.*" The "*entrepreneur*" **Julia Onslow-Cole** (see p.432) is responsible for this success. According to some competitors "*she has single-handedly developed the best London immigration team.*" The group continues to advise multinationals, financial institutions, entrepreneurs and high net worth individuals. The recently established Hong Kong immigration practice has won new clients and, thanks to the tripartite offices incorporating New York, the firm can offer a seamless service to corporate clients wishing to rotate their staff. The only UK immigration team to be shortlisted by the World Bank to advise a developing country on the re-writing of its immigration laws. The firm is sole immigration advisor for European banking group BNP Paribas, and was also consulted in meetings with the Home Office and Ministers from the DfEE and DTI about possible amendments to immigration categories. **Clients:** Corporate multi-nationals; investment banks; IT/Software houses; football clubs.

Kingsley Napley (see firm details p.1022) "*On expertise alone, it's top.*" Competitors concede this is a "*stable team*" with "*tremendous strength in depth.*" The "*shrewd and knowledgeable*" **Hilary Belchak** (see p.432) works with "*leading light*" **Elspeth Guild,** (see p.433) who is "*ahead of every lawyer on EC law,*" and the respected **Nicolas Rollason** (see p.435). Active across the board for large corporations through to newly established companies. The team has been involved in discussions with the Home Office and DfEE over formulating new policies and regulations, such as the Innovator category. Has been busy processing work permit applications from the US to London's West End on the transfer of a play. The group acts for several artists, including a group of classical musicians given leave to remain under the EC association agreements. **Clients:** Pharmaceutical multi-nationals; banks and financial service companies; technology and internet sites.

Bates, Wells & Braithwaite (see firm details p.871) Researchers were informed that this "*small but dedicated team*" remains a steady force due to its "*expertise and thorough service.*" The "*excellent*" **Philip Trott** is "*a hard worker*" who has consulted with the government on reforms to immigration law. "*Knowledgeable*" **Peter Moss** has niche strength in in-house appeal advocacy and has lobbied to change European Union law on matters of permanent residence. The team advises corporate and commercial individual clients on a wide range of work including work permits, business applications and the Innovator scheme. Peers believe that the team offers creative solutions on unusual immigration cases, often incorporating human rights issues. Currently advising an astronaut on his immigration status. **Clients:** Shell; BP; EMI; Agip.

Magrath & Co (see firm details p.1049) Still a "*large, professional team*" which services a prestigious, global client list. The "*charismatic*" **Chris Magrath** is credited by our interviewees with "*building up this impressive practice*" and garners plaudits for his "*underrated US practice.*" The firm has been servicing American companies who are bringing people in and hiring British individuals in the US. Also acts for UK companies on the transfer of subsidiaries. **Clients:** International banks; media organisations; retailers; oil companies; record companies; management consultants.

Reed Smith Warner Cranston This "*boosted practice*" works on a range of commercial work including work permit and investor application services for a mainly corporate client base. The sum of "*sound*" **Peter Alfandary** (see p.432) and "*capable*" **Lesley Kemp** (see p.433) is "*a strong team who are definitely building a forceful presence.*" The department works for major US, Japanese and Middle Eastern corporations and financial institutions. Thanks to the merger with US firm Reed Smith, the London office now has recourse to immigration-capable offices in Philadelphia and Pittsburgh. Busily engaged in applications in the Innovator category, as well as work permits and business applications for investors. **Clients:** Hitachi; TI Group; Saudi International Bank; Ogilvy & Mather.

Baker & McKenzie (see firm details p.868) A consistent presence in the field of immigration, industry specialists believe this firm is enjoying "*a higher profile*" this year. Many single out **Tony Haque**'s (see p.433) "*fine job of running that practice*" as the driving factor in the firm's success. Services a multi-national client base drawn from countries including the US, Japan and Asia. The team boasts the services of a Japanese speaking case-worker who has brought in a host of Japanese corporate clients. It assisted Honda Racing Development to transfer over 100 technical specialists and members of senior management to the UK for work on the joint project with British American Racing establishing a Formula One racing team. Also advised a leading UK telecoms company on a substantial number of work permits on an expedited basis. **Clients:** Toyota Manufacturing UK; Elsevier Science; Towers Perrin; Forster & Crosby Inc; Novell UK; Storage Networks.

IMMIGRATION: BUSINESS • London	Ptnrs	Assts
1 CMS Cameron McKenna	1	7
Kingsley Napley	2	4
2 Bates, Wells & Braithwaite	2	2
Magrath & Co	4	10
Reed Smith Warner Cranston	2	3
3 Baker & McKenzie	1	2
Eversheds	1	5
Sturtivant & Co	1	1
4 Gherson & Co	1	2
Mishcon de Reya	2	2
Norton Rose	1	3
5 DJ Webb & Co	2	3
Fox Williams	1	1
Gulbenkian Harris Andonian	3	n/a
Harbottle & Lewis	1	1
Pullig & Co	1	4
6 Campbell Hooper	n/a	1
Penningtons	n/a	1

LEADING INDIVIDUALS	
1 **BELCHAK Hilary** Kingsley Napley	**GUILD Elspeth** Kingsley Napley
ONSLOW-COLE Julia CMS Cameron McKenna	
STURTIVANT Karen Sturtivant & Co	**TROTT Philip** Bates, Wells & Braithwaite
2 **ALFANDARY Peter** Reed Smith Warner Cranston	
BARTH Philip Mishcon de Reya	**DEVINE Laura** Eversheds
KEMP Lesley Reed Smith Warner Cranston	**MAGRATH Chris** Magrath & Co
3 **HAQUE Tony** Baker & McKenzie	**MANN Jane** Fox Williams
MEHMET Gülay Penningtons	**MOSS Peter** Bates, Wells & Braithwaite
ROLLASON Nicolas Kingsley Napley	**WEBB David** DJ Webb & Co
4 **ANDONIAN Bernard** Gulbenkian Harris Andonian	
BALCOMB Anne Harbottle & Lewis	
DIXON Marion Lovells	**GHERSON Roger** Gherson & Co
POPE Caron Norton Rose	**RIVIERE Susanna** Harbottle & Lewis

This book is the product of 6,552 1/2-hour interviews. See p.7 for BMRB audit.

Within each band, firms are listed alphabetically. *See individuals' profiles p.432*

Eversheds (see firm details p.952) Clients and peers alike agree that the London office has "*its own identity.*" It is known for "*handling a large volume*" of corporate clients' immigration work. The "*dynamic*" **Laura Devine** (see p.432) leads the team and is rated as a "*capable practitioner*" who "*cuts the mustard on any matter.*" The client base is drawn from the manufacturing, financial and management consultancy sectors. The team specialises in project management of work permit and immigration requirements for global organisations. Successfully handled the first ever Innovator category permit application, prior to the Home Office concession coming into force, and has since processed more. Increasingly active on US visa work and advising several new airline clients. **Clients:** Fidelity Group; Boston Consulting Group; Deloitte & Touche; Cable & Wireless.

Sturtivant & Co (see firm details p.1148) This stand-alone practice is considered to offer "*a high quality service.*" Head of the team **Karen Sturtivant** (see p.435) is unanimously thought of as "*honourable and knowledgeable,*" but peers believe that firm's size "*limits the practice.*" Handles a considerable volume of corporate and private client work for a wide range of clients including sole representatives and commercial companies. Active on work permits, business residence and investor status. **Clients:** Commercial companies; multi-nationals; private clients.

Gherson & Co (see firm details p.971) This mixed niche practice is respected for its immigration expertise. **Roger Gherson** (see p.433) heads up the practice and is commended for his "*entrepreneurial skills.*" Avoiding the high volume work permit business, this practice services an eclectic mix of smaller enterprises and private clients requiring complex immigration issues resolved. **Clients:** Banks; film companies; internet/e-commerce businesses.

Mishcon de Reya (see firm details p.1071) This firm garners plaudits for its "*pure corporate immigration practice*" which operates with a healthy level of "*good commercial sense.*" The "*lateral thinker*" **Philip Barth** (see p.432) is rated by competitors for his depth of experience and is credited with "*developing Mischon's practice single-handed.*" The team provides visas and work permits for 'propeller,' an on-line administrative service for all aspects of the expatriation process. Also acted on a number of sensitive cases involving expedition of the grant of British citizenship. The firm continues to expand its profile assisting the inward investment by Indian IT companies to establish operations in the UK. **Clients:** Architects; designers; hi-tech companies; new media clients.

Norton Rose (see firm details p.1082) "*A pure business immigration practice*" that peers believe is "*underrated*" by the market. Led by the "*experienced*" **Caron Pope** (see p.434), the team is based within the firm's employment unit. Its client base is drawn from the firm's existing commercial base, as well as attracting a significant share of stand-alone work. Has advised start-ups, IT companies and individuals entering under the Innovator scheme. The team also advises on the application of European law. **Clients:** Financial companies; software/dot.com companies; major international manufacturers.

DJ Webb & Co (see firm details p.943) This "*small but high quality*" firm is commended for its all-encompassing immigration coverage. The firm's direction toward commercial and business related work continues apace. The "*knowledgeable*" **David Webb** heads up the practice and was recently joined by ex-Powell & Co partner Belayeth Hussain who features in our personal immigration section. The firm has been busy with Japanese and Middle Eastern activities, and caters for many US writers and artists wanting to exhibit or reside in the UK. It has witnessed its biggest growth in work from Eastern Europe and recently acted for a Yugoslavian rock star. **Clients:** IT/Software companies; Rolls-Royce; M&C Saatchi; BEA Systems.

Fox Williams (see firm details p.963) Researchers were told that this firm "*has a lot to offer*" in its widely recognised speciality: the interface between employment and immigration. The "*bright*" **Jane Mann** (see p.434) is a known employment specialist, credited with developing this side of the practice. The group has been advising US law firms and other professional practices on bringing employees into the UK. Also active for IT companies setting up UK offices and busy with compliance checks on resident employees under Section 8 of the Asylum and Immigration Act. **Clients:** Professional practices; IT/technology companies; financial advisors.

Gulbenkian Harris Andonian (see firm details p.980) With three partners dealing with corporate immigration on a full time basis, this "*long established practice*" is deemed a constant presence in the market. The team includes the esteemed practitioner **Bernard Andonian** (see p.432) who has written extensively about immigration issues, and is active on a mixture of corporate matters, permit applications and private client work. The firm recently acted on the controversial Rolet and Baumbat case at the ECJ, representing an individual who applied to regularise their status for continued residence in the UK. **Clients:** Anna Dako; BAT; Coca-Cola; L'Oréal.

Harbottle & Lewis (see firm details p.985) Still "*a huge force with its media clients,*" the market commends the firm for building on its expertise. The "*specialist*" **Susanna Riviere** (see p.435) is joined by respected ex-Pullig & Co partner **Anne Balcomb** (see p.432) in a move deemed "*a positive recipe for success*" by peers. As well as its established media client base, the firm is taking a strong hold on new industry clients, including software publishers, internet and biotechnology companies. Has worked on urgent work permits for high profile individuals. **Clients:** Attenda; Carlton Television; Untitled management; Rapido Television; Simon Fuller/19 Management.

Pullig & Co The departure of respected partner Anne Balcomb to Harbottle & Lewis is seen as "*a far-reaching loss*" by our interviewees. This broad-based immigration practice continues its business and commercial private client focus, and services clients in the media, technology and educational sectors. Has recently opened a second London office specifically for immigration and human rights work. The firm is busy with activities concerning family reunions, citizenship and business agreement type work. Gooch Heer heads the team. **Clients:** Media companies; educational institutions; software companies.

Campbell Hooper (see firm details p.907) The team, which includes William Granger, is typically judged by its peers as "*having the capability,*" yet it remains better known for its strong entertainment work. Continues to offer a range of immigration services to clients in the media and entertainment industries. **Clients:** PR companies; advertising agencies.

Penningtons (see firm details p.1093) Competitors suggest this "*competent but small*" practice is limited only by its size. "*All-rounder*" **Gülay Mehmet** (see p.434) is rated for her work and "*visibility on cases.*" The group advises a wide range of IT clients from the US and India. Handles referrals from US, Canadian and South African firms. **Clients:** IT/Software companies; private clients; international businesses.

Other Notable Practitioners Ex-immigration officer **Marion Dixon** of **Lovells** also received market recommendation for her "*unique expertise*" and "*steady, reasonable*" approach.

PERSONAL

Band	IMMIGRATION: PERSONAL • London	Ptnrs	Assts
1	Bindman & Partners	1	2
	Birnberg Peirce & Partners	2	1
	Deighton Guedalla	1	n/a
	Wesley Gryk	1	5
	Winstanley-Burgess	4	1
2	Coker Vis Partnership	1	n/a
3	Bartram & Co Hounslow	1	n/a
	Gill & Co	1	6
	Glazer Delmar	1	2
	Luqmani Thompson	2	2
4	Powell & Co	1	5
	Wilson & Co	3	4

Band	LEADING INDIVIDUALS	
1	**BURGESS David** Winstanley-Burgess	**COKER Jane** Coker Vis Partnership
	GRYK Wesley Wesley Gryk	**GUEDALLA Vicky** Deighton Guedalla
	LINDSLEY Fiona Birnberg Peirce & Ptnrs	**RANDALL Christopher** Winstanley-Burgess
	STANLEY Alison Bindman & Partners	
2	**DAVIES Matthew** Wilson & Co	**HANLEY Michael** Wilson & Co
	LUQMANI Jawaid Luqmani Thompson	**RIPLEY Fiona** Winstanley-Burgess
3	**BARTRAM Peter** Bartram & Co	**HUSSAIN Belayeth** DJ Webb & Co
	LESKIN Nigel Birnberg Peirce & Ptnrs	**PENROSE Martin** Winstanley-Burgess
	THOMPSON Sally Luqmani Thompson	

This book is the product of 6,552 1/2 hour interviews. See p.7 for BMRB audit.

Within each band, firms are listed alphabetically. *See individuals' profiles p.432*

Bindman & Partners (see firm details p.882) This firm of "*serious immigration players*" is "*rated across the board*" by peers and clients. The firm was founded in 1974 with the aim of providing legal services predominantly to the disadvantaged and is perceived by the market to be "*heavily committed.*" The "*excellent*" **Alison Stanley** (see p.434)is rated for her "*enormous intelligence*" and "*depth of knowledge in a whole range of immigration issues.*" The group is active in matters arising from asylum, refugee, nationality and family work. Its highlight success this year was the European Court of Justice case of Yiadom, where a decision to refuse leave to a Dutch national on public policy grounds was quashed.

Birnberg Peirce & Partners Adjudged a "*long established, high quality practice,*" known for its work in crime and immigration. The "*excellent*" **Fiona Lindsley** draws praise from peers for her "*knowledge and commitment*" and has recently specialised in applications for falsely imprisoned asylum seekers under the ex gratia compensation scheme. Her colleague **Nigel Leskin** has acted on the quashing of these false imprisonments and specialises in immigration work on behalf of, inter alia, Africans and Orthodox Jews. Oriented toward 'political crime' work, the firm has represented alleged Islamic fundamentalists and Irish clients on immigration cases. Also involved in a judicial review that centred on definitions of 'illegal entrant' and advised on a judicial review to preserve the confidentiality of an asylum seeker's case. Involved in the high profile Sepet and Bulbul matter, representing the latter appellant on his claim for asylum. The case centred around issues of whether refusing to perform military service was a ground for seeking asylum abroad.

Deighton Guedalla With a reputation for "*pulling out all the stops*" this smaller niche immigration practice is commended by fellow solicitors for its "*high standards of work.*" The "*assertive*" **Vicky Guedalla** draws unanimous praise for her "*hard work and commitment to the field.*" The firm is active on a wide range of immigration matters from asylum to children's issues.

Wesley Gryk (see firm details p.1178) Rated by peers as a "*strong practice run by strong professionals,*" this firm is a substantial player in the field. The "*efficacious*" **Wesley Gryk** (see p.433) is endorsed for his "*huge amount of political work.*" The practice has six lawyers working full time on the wide spectrum of issues from private client and legal services to commission work. With acknowledged strength in gay rights cases, Gryk also represents individuals who are challenging, under the Human Rights Act, decisions taken to remove them from the UK to a country where they will no longer be able to receive life-saving medical treatment. Also worked on the case of Sepet and Bulbul, a Court of Appeal hearing concerning asylum seekers who are conscientious objectors.

Winstanley-Burgess (see firm details p.1186) This large personal immigration practice continues to draw endorsement for its asylum and human rights work. A "*busy and high profile team*" includes "*top notch*" **David Burgess** who recently acted on a judicial review concerning individuals' confinement to sovereign bases in Cyprus, and their asylum rights in the UK. **Christopher Randall** garners praise for his "*thorough, committed and intelligent attitude*" while **Fiona Ripley** is respected for her activities in asylum cases from Kosovo, Turkey, Iraq and Afghanistan. **Martin Penrose** has a lower profile, yet interviewees continue to vouch for the quality of his output.

Coker Vis Partnership A small firm driven by the founder member of the Refugee Womens Legal Group, **Jane Coker**. Dubbed an "*influential practitioner*" Coker draws praise for her "*fighting spirit.*" The practice has niche strength in family cases, acting for children in local authority care whose parents face deportation. Also involved in critical asylum work.

Bartram & Co A specialist immigration practice working mainly on asylum and human rights cases, but also wining instruction in the private client field. Respected **Peter Bartram** (see p.432) leads the work for clients coming from Iran, Colombia and Congo. The firm is pursuing an Iranian appeal to establish whether persecution by corrupt officials can be regarded as a 'political' issue. On the private client side, the firm has been involved in applications and appeals for entry from clients in the Indian sub-continent, the Philippines, Algeria, Morocco and Jamaica.

Gill & Co This firm is "*capable of producing some high quality work,*" according to one competitor. Busy with asylum matters, judicial reviews and human rights related work. The firm has processed applications for same-sex relationships, as well handling matters arising from a range of nationalities including African, Columbian and Algerian entrants.

Glazer Delmar A "*terrific firm*" according to competitors, its strength is judged to lie in the "*high quality work*" it produces. With a long-standing reputation in detention and asylum cases, the firm is applauded for an approach that encourages the "*exchanging of ideas.*" The departure of David Rhys-Jones to an NGO is felt to affect the firm's profile this year. Jackie Pierce now heads up the practice and concentrates on Latin American human rights cases.

Luqmani Thompson This firm of "*hard workers*" includes "*knowledgeable*" **Jawaid Luqmani** (see p.434)who specialises in education and human rights issues. The "*thorough*" **Sally Thompson** (see p.435) has an exclusively immigration related practice, which includes a focus in advising women and minors. The asylum work of the firm encompasses worldwide clients including many Iranian and Turkish nationals.

Powell & Co Still busy on its community and legal aid focused practice, conducting the full range of personal immigration services. The departure of respected Belayeth Hussain to DJ Webb is viewed by the market as "*a blow.*" The firm, led by Franck Kiangala, services asylum applications involving Central African nationals, among others.

Wilson & Co (see firm details p.1184) Adjudged by interviewees to be "*a quality offering,*" it advises on a range of immigration matters. **Matthew Davies** specialises in asylum and has a niche in advising on gay rights and HIV issues. Respected head of department **Michael Hanley** is a dominant player in asylum and refugee law, advising clients from Somalia, Turkey and Kosovo. He acted in a recent House of Lords case on safety of return to third countries, representing an asylum seeker from Somalia. The team was recently to be found in the Court of Appeal on a military service case, acting on the issue of persecution by non-State agents.

Other Notable Practitioners **Belayeth Hussain** of **DJ Webb** (formerly with Powell & Co) draws praise for his "*commitment to the field*" and "*hard-working attitude.*" The market awaits his success in developing this side of the respected immigration practice.

THE SOUTH & SOUTH WEST

IMMIGRATION • The South, Thames Valley & South West	Ptnrs	Assts
1 **Bobbetts Mackan** Bristol	n/a	2
Darbys Oxford	1	2
Eric Robinson & Co Southampton	1	1

LEADING INDIVIDUALS	
1 **HARVEY Jenny** Darbys	**TURPIN Philip** Dukes Arnold Du Feu

This book is the product of 6,552 1/2-hour interviews. See p.7 for BMRB audit.
Within each band, firms are listed alphabetically. *See individuals' profiles p.432*

Bobbetts Mackan (see firm details p.887) This Bristol firm has opened a second part-time office that offers drop-in sessions. Headed by Derek McConnell, the team has seen a client-based expansion in cases from Iraq, Afghanistan and the Sudan. The group continues to act for a predominantly local client base on asylum, family reunion and dependent relatives type matters.

Darbys (see firm details p.931) This Oxford firm has a respected and established immigration department. The team of three, lead by "*solid*" **Jenny Harvey** (see p.433), specialise in work permits and corporate immigration, with an emphasis on Formula One racing teams. In the field of asylum, the firm has seen an increase in Sudanese, Algerian and Afghan applications.

Eric Robinson & Co This small immigration practice has recently given up its legal aid franchise to concentrate on private immigration. The team, lead by Astrid Grafton, advises on entry clearance, marriage and student applications and EC Association agreements. The firm receives instructions on asylum issues from many areas including Iran, Iraq and Eastern Europe. Processes work permit applications for a wide range of businesses in the South, including restaurants and construction companies. The firm recently went to the High Court on a judicial review of a domestic violence concession.

Other Notable Practitioners **Philip Turpin**, who left Linnells for **Dukes Arnold Du Feu**, continues to garner plaudits for his immigration work.

MIDLANDS

IMMIGRATION • Midlands	Ptnrs	Assts
1 **Tyndallwoods** Birmingham	2	3
2 **Nelsons** Nottingham	1	1

LEADING INDIVIDUALS	
1 **PHILLIPS Mark** Tyndallwoods	**SMITH David** Nelsons

This book is the product of 6,552 1/2-hour interviews. See p.7 for BMRB audit.
Within each band, firms are listed alphabetically. *See individuals' profiles p.432*

Tyndallwoods (see firm details p.1165) Considered by peers to be "*the Midlands' number one immigration practice,*" this firm's strength lies in its "*good bunch of lawyers.*" Head of department **Mark Phillips** (see p.434) is deemed "*an impressive performer*" advising on the immigration rights of children and HIV cases using the European Convention on Human Rights. The practice takes instructions from Eastern Europe, Libya and other Islamic countries, and also advises on business immigration. The team recently acted on the high profile Muchai case, concerned with the background and expert evidence of an East African asylum-seeker; the case forced the Court to re-evaluate the political situation from which the appellant was fleeing. This case succeeded at the Court of Appeal.

Nelsons (see firm details p.1080) A leading force in personal immigration, the team, led by the respected **David Smith** (see p.435), acts on judicial reviews, typically representing smaller employers. Has had involvement in several cases of prisoners facing deportation and, with the organisation Stonewall, has acted on immigration problems faced by couples in same-sex relationships.

EAST ANGLIA

IMMIGRATION • East Anglia		Ptnrs	Assts
1	**Gross & Co** Bury St Edmunds	1	n/a
	Leathes Prior Norwich	1	n/a
	Wollastons Chelmsford	n/a	1

LEADING INDIVIDUALS		
1	**CARY Tim** Leathes Prior	**KIRK Graeme** Gross & Co

This book is the product of 6,552 1/2-hour interviews. See p.7 for BMRB audit.
Within each band, firms are listed alphabetically. *See individuals' profiles p.432*

Gross & Co (see firm details p.979) **Graeme Kirk** (see p.433) heads up a practice known for its first-rate business immigration services. Acts for a wide range of clients including international firms such as the South African Investec banking group and ING Barings. Also advises private clients seeking investor applications.

Leathes Prior This Norwich-based practice recently unveiled a website designed especially to assist clients' asylum and immigration enquiries. **Tim Cary** leads a team of paralegals doing full time corporate work permit and personal immigration work. The firm has seen a rise in its Eastern European refugee cases.

Wollastons (see firm details p.1188) Headed up by Nicholas Burnett, this Essex-based commercial practice offers a specialist international employment service for UK employers and their overseas staff. Covering all aspects of business immigration, the team has a niche in handling short-term work permits for film and TV projects. Also handles applications by writers and artists settling in the UK with permit-free employment.

THE NORTH

IMMIGRATION • The North		Ptnrs	Assts
1	**David Gray Solicitors** Newcastle upon Tyne	1	2
	Howells Sheffield	n/a	5
2	**AS Law** Liverpool	1	1
	Harrison Bundey & Co Leeds	1	1
	Jackson & Canter Liverpool	1	4
	James & Co Bradford	1	1
3	**Davis Blank Furniss** Manchester	1	1
	Samuel Phillips & Co Newcastle upon Tyne	1	n/a
	Thornhill Ince Manchester	2	n/a

LEADING INDIVIDUALS		
1	**GRAY David** David Gray Solicitors	**JAMES Charles** James & Co
	SIMM Peter AS Law	
2	**BUNDEY Ruth** Harrison Bundey & Co	**DONKERSLEY John** Howells
	HOLROYD Andrew Jackson & Canter	**INCE Robin** Thornhill Ince

This book is the product of 6,552 1/2-hour interviews. See p.7 for BMRB audit.
Within each band, firms are listed alphabetically. *See individuals' profiles p.432*

David Gray Solicitors Competitors agree that the firm is a definite presence in the market place. Busy on a substantial number of Iraqi and Iranian asylum cases. Head of department **David Gray** is dubbed "*a serious and committed player,*" commended for his control of complex non-asylum cases. The team has been involved in family settlements, marriage nationality applications and advice to students.

Howells (see firm details p.1002) Recently expanded with the absorption of the immigration practice of another local firm. Led by the "*experienced*" **John Donkersley** (see p.433), the team has a broad expertise in civil, family and housing law. It handles a large volume of asylum cases and represents individuals from countries including Somalia, Yemen and the former Yugoslavia.

AS Law Interviewees continue to regard the firm as fielding "*quality practitioners*" securing its name in this field. Unaffected by the changes to legal aid, the firm advises on a range of asylum and immigration cases. "*Quality operator*" **Peter Simm** is known for having "*a presence on leading cases,*" and he continues to advise on refugee and judicial review matters.

Harrison Bundey & Co (see firm details p.988) Based in Leeds, the firm's immigration department has been busy on Albanian, Croat and Serbian asylum cases this year. Former chair of the Law Society immigration committee **Ruth Bundey** is nationally renowned as "*informed and committed.*" As well as asylum cases, the team has undertaken same-sex work, and continues its established practice in crime and human rights. The group has overseen applications from people with HIV for stay under Provision 3 of the Human Rights Act.

Jackson & Canter (see firm details p.1010) Our interviewees were told that this firm of "*serious operators*" offers a broad depth of knowledge in immigration law. Respected practitioner **Andrew Holroyd** (see p.433)oversees a team that is active in advising on work permits and small business applications. On the asylum side, it assists with applications from Yugoslavian, Iraqi, Iranian and Afghan clients.

James & Co (see firm details p.1011) This Bradford-based firm has been exclusively focused on immigration since 1997. The "*professional*" **Charles James** is on the Law Society Immigration panel and is endorsed for his advice on family, marriage, business, and dependent relatives immigration issues. The firm also advises on political asylum cases.

Davis Blank Furniss This respected Manchester practice has ceased to conduct legal aid work, and now concentrates on corporate and private cases including marriage immigration advice for clients from Poland and Russia. Led by Guy Robson, the team advises local IT firms on applications to bring specialist staff from the Far East and India.

Samuel Phillips & Co (see firm details p.1118) Engaged in a range of work including business immigration services and asylum cases. Barry Speker and the team have been advising several doctors on applications to bring their Indian sub-continent based patients to the UK. The team has strong links to the local Chinese community in part due to the presence of a full-time, Cantonese-speaking member of staff. The group has advised a North East based electronics company on immigration applications.

Thornhill Ince Operating a respected practice in immigration and crime, **Robin Ince** continues to garner plaudits from his peers. He sits as a part-time adjudicator. The firm undertakes all aspects of immigration work including asylum matters.

LEADERS IN IMMIGRATION

ALFANDARY, Peter
Reed Smith Warner Cranston, London
(020) 7403 2900
palfandary@reedsmith.co.uk
Specialisation: Partner and head of corporate immigration department. Corporate immigration. 17 years of experience advising national and multinational corporations on work permits and related immigration issues with the Home Office and Department of Education and Employment. Advice on nationality law, overseas investor rules and business related immigration for individuals. Author of chapter on immigration in 'CCH Employment Contracts Manual.'
Prof. Memberships: Law Society; Immigration Law Practitioners Association.
Career: Articled *Lovell White & King*; qualified 1979 followed by a year in industry and a year with a leading firm of French avocats. Joined *Warner Cranston* as a partner in 1982. Managing partner 1991-93.
Personal: Born 10 January 1953, resides in London. Educated at Lycée Francais de Londres, University of Kent and London School of Economics. Interests include Theatre, Music and Anglo-French relations. Deputy-President French Chamber of Commerce; decorated by the French Government as a *Chevalier dans L'Ordre Nationale du Mérite* in 1991.

ANDONIAN, Bernard
Gulbenkian Harris Andonian, London
(020) 7937 1542
Specialisation: Partner in immigration department. Principal areas of practice are UK and US business immigration for multi national companies and foreign business executives. Deals with work permit applications and business insolvency inter applications; preparation, submission of business and investor plans; independent means. Contributor to numerous business immigration articles. Lectures on business immigration. Has recently reviewed 'Law and Practice' by Michael Supperstone QC and Declan O'Dempsey; appointed by the Lord Chancellor as part-time Immigration Adjudicator and Special Adjudicator.
Prof. Memberships: Member of Immigration Law Practitioners Association, and former Executive Committee Member, the International Bar Association, Law Society, Holborn Law Society.
Career: Qualified 1985 while at *Gulbenkian Harris Andonian*, and became a partner in 1986.
Personal: Born 11 September 1949. Attended City of London and Thames Valley Universities. Obtained Distinction in Intellectual Property for MA Degree. Leisure pursuits include reading, rambling, table tennis, snooker, swimming. Lives in Osterley, Middlesex.

BALCOMB, Anne
Harbottle & Lewis, London (020) 7667 5000
Specialisation: All aspects of immigration and nationality law; advising corporate and private clients, in particular on employment and business-related matters. Joint head of the immigration group.
Prof. Memberships: Law Society; Immigration Law Practitioners' Association.
Career: Worked as a teacher from 1964 to 1978; qualified as a solicitor in 1982; practised in immigration and nationality law since 1986; worked for *Simmons and Simmons* from 1990 to 1993 and for *Pullig & Co* from 1993 to 2000. Joined *Harbottle & Lewis* 2001.
Publications: Various articles in professional journals.
Personal: St Anne's College Oxford 1960-63; BA Hons Modern Languages 1963. College of Law 1978-79. Fluent in French. Lives in London and Devon.

BARTH, Philip
Mishcon de Reya, London (020) 7440 7000
philip.barth@mishcon.co.uk
Specialisation: Specialises in all aspects of immigration and nationality law other than asylum. Having a background as an experienced company/commercial lawyer, his combination of expertise is of particular benefit for all businesses, corporates and persons who wish to move to the UK to pursue economic activities. He is regulary involved in cases at the cutting-edge of business immigration practice and has many years experience in providing practical immigration advice within the wider commercial context to meet the needs of business. Writes and speaks regularly on business immigration topics. Philip was responsible for the recent selection of *Mishcon de Reya* as the sole UK alliance partner providing work permit and visa services for a web enabled service (www.propelleronline.com), which provides a first of its kind consolidated expatriation service to assist HR professionals.
Prof. Memberships: Immigration Law Practitioners Association; co-chair of the Employment & Business Sub-committee. Law Society.
Career: Rugby School; Magdalene College, Cambridge University. 1980-82 articles with *Malkin Cullis & Sumption*; 1983-86 Assistant solicitor at *Clintons*; 1986-88 assistant solicitor at *Walters Fladgate*; 1988-98 partner in successor firm, *Fladgate Fielder*; 1998-present: partner *Mishcon de Reya.*

BARTRAM, Peter
Bartram & Co, Hounslow (020) 8814 1414
Specialisation: Head of Practice near Heathrow Airport devoted to all aspects of UK immigration and asylum law with Community Legal Service contract in immigration law.
Prof. Memberships: Law Society Immigration Law Panel; Immigration Law Practioners Association.
Career: Qualified 1981. Immigration specialist since 1984. Has worked in law centres, advice centres and in private practice. Established own firm, *Bartram & Co*, in 1994.
Personal: Born 21 August 1957. Bristol University (LLB, 1978) and Brunel University (MA, 1988). Spanish and French speaker.

BELCHAK, Hilary
Kingsley Napley, London (020) 7814 1200
hbelchak@kingsleynapley.co.uk
Specialisation: Partner and head of immigration department. Main areas of practice are UK immigration and nationality law. Has seventeen years experience in this field. Presently covering corporate immigration such as work permits, immigration advice to entrepreneurs and high net worth individuals wishing to invest and settle in the UK, and nationality issues. Numerous articles including in the 'International Quarterly', 'Offshore Investment', the new quarterly publication 'Immigration and Employment Law', as well as being deputy editor of that journal. Has spoken at ILPA and the immigration committees of AILA, IBA and IPBA annual conferences as well as conferences of CBI Employee Relocation Council, IBC UK, Employment Lawyers Association, the Japan Institute for Overseas Investment and In-house Seminars. Recently prepared contribution for the Croner's publication 'Managing Internationally Mobile Employees', as well as articles for its monthly bulletin.
Prof. Memberships: ILPA, IPBA, AILA, ABA. Chair IPBA's Immigration Committee 1997-9. Secretary of ILPA 1995-97.
Career: Qualified in 1984. Senior lecturer at North London Polytechnic 1971-81; worked at *Winstanley Burgess* 1982-84 and *Clinton Davis & Co.* 1984-88. Joined *Simmons & Simmons* in 1988, becoming a partner in 1994. Joined *Kingsley Napley* February 1999.
Personal: Born 17th March 1949. Holds an LLB (1970) and LLM (1971). Leisure interests include opera and cinema. Lives in London and Suffolk.

BUNDEY, Ruth
Harrison Bundey & Co., Leeds (0113) 200 7400
See under Human Rights, p.425

BURGESS, David C.W.
Winstanley-Burgess, London (020) 7278 7911

CARY, Tim
Leathes Prior, Norwich (01603) 610911

COKER, Jane
Coker Vis Partnership, London (020) 8885 1415

DAVIES, Matthew
Wilson & Co, London (020) 8808 7535

DEVINE, Laura
Eversheds, London (020) 7919 4856
devinel@eversheds.com
Specialisation: Laura heads the immigration and nationality team at *Eversheds.* Laura qualified as a solicitor at *Cameron Markby Hewitt* (now *CMS Cameron McKenna*). She established the immigration unit at *Coopers & Lybrand* (now *PricewaterhouseCoopers*). She has an LLM from the London School of Economics, where she specialised in immigration law. Laura advises clients on immigration to the UK for work and business including work permits, sole representatives, business persons and innovators. Additionally, Laura advises on family reunion, settlement and nationality. She has a growing practise in US immigration law. She lectures on immigration and is author of 'Key Techniques in Employing Overseas Nationals Under the Work Permit Scheme, Immigration for Employment – Practical Guidance to the Law' published by Palladian in 2000. Laura contributes to 'Croners'. She is a visiting lecturer at Hull University. She is featured in 'An International Who's Who of Corporate Immigration Lawyers' and the 'Legal Experts Directory' as being one of the top ten executive immigration solicitors in the UK.

DIXON, Marion
Lovells, London (020) 7296 2000

DONKERSLEY, John
Howells, Sheffield (0114) 249 6666
Specialisation: All aspects of immigration, in particular Kosovan, Yemeni and Somali asylum cases, family reunion cases and judicial review. Teaches immigration courses for NACAB, local authorities etc. The team he heads has now grown to five (soon to be six) solicitors, six caseworkers and six support staff and he is an external supervisor for another firm's immigration work.
Prof. Memberships: Law Society, ILPA, Stonewall.
Career: Welfare Rights worker and freelance trainer 1985-88. Articled, and qualified 1991 at current firm where cut teeth representing detained Iraqis during Gulf War.
Personal: Born 1st December 1961. Attended London School of Economics (University of London), LLB (Hons) 1985. Leisure interests include building computers and Linux.

GHERSON, Roger
Gherson & Co, London (020) 7724 4488
Specialisation: Principal of firm. Practices exclusively in immigration and nationality. Work includes work permits, business investors, sole representations, writers and artists visas, appeals before the Special Immigration Appeals Commission, adjudicators and the Tribunal, as well as judicial review matters in the High Court.
Prof. Memberships: Law Society, Immigration Law Practitioners' Association.
Career: Qualified in 1981. Established *Gherson & Co.* in 1988.
Personal: Born 24th August 1954. Attended University College, London 1975-78.

GRAY, David
David Gray Solicitors, Newcastle upon Tyne (0191) 232 9547

GRYK, Wesley
Wesley Gryk, London (020) 7401 6887
Specialisation: All areas of UK immigration and nationality law.
Prof. Memberships: Law Society, Immigration Law Practitioners Association, Association of the Bar of the City of New York.
Career: Qualified in 1990, admitted to the Bar of New York in 1976. Federal Judicial Clerk to Judge Constance Baker Motley, Southern District of New York, 1975-76; associate, *Shearman & Sterling*, New York and Hong Kong, 1976-80; Deputy Representative and Legal Advisor, UN High Commissioner for Refugees, 1980-81; Deputy Head of Research Department, Amnesty International, 1981-86; *B.M. Birnberg & Co*, London, 1988-94; established own firm 1995.
Personal: Born 12th May 1949; attended East Catholic High School, 1963-67; Harvard College, 1967-71, BA; Warsaw University, 1971-72, Fulbright Scholar; Harvard Law School 1972-75, JD. Active in the work of Stonewall. Has travelled widely on human rights missions for Amnesty International, Human Rights Watch, and Article 19.

GUEDALLA, Vicky
Deighton Guedalla, London (020) 7359 5700

GUILD, Elspeth
Kingsley Napley, London (020) 7814 1200
eguild@kingsleynapley.co.uk
Specialisation: Partner, immigration department. Primarily specialises in European Community law relating to free movement of persons including the transfer of staff from companies in one Member State to another Member State, the right of self-employment and provision of services. Wide expertise in UK immigration and nationality issues. Author of numerous books including, 'Immigration Law in the European Community', 'Free Movement of Persons in the European Union,' and 'Developing Immigration and Asylum Policy of the European Union.' She is also Professor of European Immigration Law at the University of Nijmegen, and Visiting Fellow at the London School of Economics, where she also lectures.
Prof. Memberships: Chair of the Immigration Law Practitioners' Association European Group; Member of the Council of Justice; British representative of the European Sections of the International Commission of Jurists; Member of the Executive Committee, Centre of European Law, Kings College London.
Career: 1989-97 *Baileys Shaw & Gillett*: Head of immigration department. Joined *Kingsley Napley* as a partner in March 1997.

HANLEY, Michael
Wilson & Co, London (020) 8808 7535

HAQUE, Tony
Baker & McKenzie, London (020) 7919 1000
tony.haque@bakernet.com
Specialisation: Solicitor, immigration department. Specialising in all areas of UK immigration and nationality work and related European Community law with emphasis on employment and business related applications. Acts principally for multinational companies and other corporate clients, entrepreneurs and high net worth individuals offering creative solutions to effect international transfers as expediently and cost-effectively as possible. Client base is particularly strong in the information technology sector. Also extensively involved with the firm's leading Japanese practice. Works closely with *Baker & McKenzie's* worldwide network of offices, particularly in the North America and Asia Pacific regions, to assist clients who require advice upon relocation issues outside of the UK. Member of the firm's International Executive Transfer Practice Group which provides advice on a broad range of related corporate, tax and labour law issues. Has published articles and spoken at seminars on a wide number of immigration issues.
Prof. Memberships: Law Society, Immigration Law Practitioners' Association.
Career: 1994-97 *Baileys Shaw & Gillett*; qualified at *Kingsley Napley*; joined *Baker & McKenzie* as an associate in November 1997.

HARVEY, Jenny
Darbys, Oxford (01685) 811719
jharvey@darbys.co.uk
Specialisation: All aspects of immigration work including family reunion, work permit applications and other business/employment matters including increasing involvement in the field of Formula One motor racing. Extensive experience in the field of asylum law, with large caseload of Kosovan, Sudanese and Algerian asylum seekers. Has developed close links with Asylum Welcome, a local charity set up to help asylum seekers, and has worked with a large number of detainees at Campsfield Detention Centre.
Prof. Memberships: Law Society, Immigration Law Practitioners Association, Joint Council for Welfare of Immigrants.
Career: Degree in Modern History at Lady Margaret Hall, Oxford (2:1), worked in Sydney Legal Centre, Australia upon completion of law finals. Completed articles at *Darbys* and qualified in October 1994.
Personal: Has travelled extensively throughout Australia, Africa and Asia and enjoys sport including sailing and waterskiing.

HOLROYD, Andrew
Jackson & Canter, Liverpool (0151) 282 1732
Specialisation: Partner in immigration department. Covers all aspects of immigration law including business immigration matters.
Prof. Memberships: Law Society Council Member and member of Law Society Immigration Sub-Committee. Past President of Liverpool Law Society. ILPA. Immigration Law Panel member.
Career: Qualified 1974 in Liverpool, joined *Jackson & Canter*. Became a partner in 1977.
Personal: Born 13th April 1948. Attended Nottingham University.

HUSSAIN, Belayeth
DJ Webb & Co, London (020) 7253 2400

INCE, Robin
Thornhill Ince, Manchester (0161) 839 2550

JAMES, Charles
James & Co, Bradford (01274) 729900

KEMP, Lesley
Reed Smith Warner Cranston, London (020) 7403 2900
lkemp@reedsmith.co.uk
Specialisation: Partner, business immigration department. Primarily specialises in business/employment related immigration. Advises both small and large scale global organistions in the relocation process for expatriates transferring to the UK; individual entrepreneurs and overseas firms seeking to establish a business in the UK; professionals in the entertainment, arts and media fields. Expertise in all aspects of UK immigration and nationality law including personal applications for investors; retired persons of independent means; spouse and family applications.
Prof. Memberships: Lectures and has published articles on immigration issues. Member of Immigration Law Practioners' Association (ILPA) (past treasurer and member of the Executive Committee of ILPA 1995-97).
Career: Qualified February 1989. Assistant solicitor 1989-93, *Kingsley Napley*; assistant solicitor and partner 1993-95, *Magrath & Co*; returned to *Kingsley Napley* as a partner, 1995-2000, to establish the firm's immigration department. Joined *Warner Cranston* as a partner in March 2000.
Personal: Born 1960. Tiverton Grammar School; University of Kent at Canterbury (BA Hons); College of Law, Chancery Lane.

KIRK, G
Gross & Co., Bury St Edmunds (01284) 763333 and (020) 7935 5541
gdk@gross.co.uk
Specialisation: Senior partner and head of immigration. Principal area of practice is immigration and nationality law. Also deals with company/commercial work for private companies and businesses, including foreign businesses seeking to establish a UK presence. Handles work permit, self-employment, investor, business sole representative independent means innovator and all other immigration cases. Addressed IBA conferences regularly since 1991 and has given semi-

nars throughout the world. Acts as consultant in immigration law to solicitors firms throughout the UK. Has lectured on business immigration for CLT. Client base includes international banks, major foreign and UK corporations, IT and high tech companies, entrepreneurs and high net-worth individuals.
Prof. Memberships: Law Society, IBA, ILPA.
Career: Qualified in 1981. Assistant solicitor with *Radcliffes & Co.* 1981-84, then joined *Gross & Co.* in 1984 becoming a partner in 1986. Currently chair man of the Immigration & Nationality Committee of the International Bar Association, and member of the Law Society Immigration Law Panel.
Personal: Educated at Westminster School and University of East Anglia. A member of Bury St. Edmunds Rotary Club. Lives in Bury St. Edmunds.

LESKIN, Nigel
Birnberg Peirce & Partners, London (020) 7284 4620

LINDSLEY, Fiona
Birnberg Peirce & Partners, London (020) 7284 4620

LUQMANI, Jawaid
Luqmani Thompson, London (020) 8365 7800
jawaid@luqmanithompson.com
Specialisation: Partner specialising in immigration. Work includes Administrative Court and Court of Appeal litigation in immigration law and related fields of education, crime and civil actions against the immigration service. Cases include interrelations between asylum and terrorism, asylum and crime and free movement entitlements for non EU nationals in particular rights of Eastern European nationals.
Prof. Memberships: Executive Committee Member for ILPA since 1992, current Treasurer of ILPA, appointed by the Law Society as Immigration Assessor since 1999, member of the Law Society.
Publications: Co-author of 'Recent Developments in Immigration' for Legal Action Group and author of immigration sections in 'Defending Suspects at Police Stations'. Lecturer for ILPA, LAG, UKCOSA and CAB. Numerous TV and radio interviews in respect of topical immigration issues.

MAGRATH, Chris
Magrath & Co, London (020) 7495 3003

MANN, Jane
Fox Williams, London (020) 7628 2000
jemann@foxwilliams.co.uk
Specialisation: Specialises in immigration related to business and employment. Advises multi-national companies relocating employees to the UK, overseas companies establishing an office in the UK for the first time and overseas nationals wishing to establish a UK business. Handles problems with both immigration and employment law aspects.
Prof. Memberships: Founder Member of Employment Lawyers Association and currently its Chairman. Former Treasurer of the Immigration Law Practitioners Association. Member of The International Bar Association and The American Immigration Lawyers Association. Associate Member of the Institute of Personnel and Development.
Career: Qualified 1981. Worked at *McKenna & Co.* 1979-86, then at *Denton Hall* until 1994, where became a Partner. Joined *Fox Williams* in 1994 as a Partner.
Personal: Born 1957. Attended Cambridge University 1975-78.

MEHMET, Gülay
Penningtons, London (020) 7457 3000
mehmetg@penningtons.co.uk
Specialisation: All aspects of Immigration, nationally and related European Community law. Corporate/business and private client work. Clients include international companies, including three of India's top 10 companies; investors; sole representatives, work permits for international firm of accounts; and leading Japanese company.
Prof. Memberships: Law Society Immigration Committee, ILPA European Group, Trustee to the Immigration & Nationality Research and Infomation Charity, International Bar Association.
Career: Liverpool University, College of Law. 1991-94 Assistant Director, Joint Counsel for Welfare of Immigrants. Consulted with Home Office, House of Commons Home Affairs Committee and House of Lords Select Committee on immigration law issues.
Personal: Bilingual Turkish. Trustee of Refugee Legal.

MOSS, Peter
Bates, Wells & Braithwaite, London (020) 7551 7777

ONSLOW-COLE, Julia
CMS Cameron McKenna, London (020) 7367 3000
Specialisation: Partner and head of immigration and nationality group. Partner responsible for the firm's global immigration and nationality group, the largest in the UK and ranked number one by all the legal directories. *CMS Cameron McKenna* is the only City firm to offer a US immigration law service. The group deals with all the aspects of immigration and nationality law (except asylum and refugee) and advises principally on applications for work permits, business persons, sole representatives, investors, retired persons of independent means and applications for British citizenship; on the US side specialising in international transfers, professionals and investors. The group also provides advice on immigration to China, Singapore and Hong Kong through its Hong Kong Office. Offices in Germany and Poland cater for clients moving individuals to Central and Eastern Europe. The group has an extensive international client base, principal clients being multinational businesses and financial institutions whose employees need to be able to move rapidly. In 1999, the group launched a dedicated UK immigration sports and entertainment practice – advising football clubs and sports associations and individual entertainers and artists. In addition the group has a specialised practice for high net worth individuals and entrepreneurs, particularly in the field of e-commerce, from all parts of the world. The group makes several applications at the cutting edge of European immigration law. The Group has an impressive track record, taking an innovative approach to solve client problems and offers tailored in-house training to corporate clients on immigration issues.
Prof. Memberships: Chairman of International Bar Association, Immigration & Nationality Committee, Member of Immigration Law Sub-Committee of Law Society, convenor of Immigration Law Practitioners Association's Business and Employment Sub-Committee, Member and Assessor of the Law Society's Immigration Law Panel, Member of the UK Association for European Law, Fellow of the Society for Advanced Legal Studies, member of Home Office User Panel, member of American Immigration Lawyers Association.
Career: Qualified 1984. Worked for British Coal 1982-86, then *Simmons & Simmons* as head of UK immigration and nationality department 1986-90. Joined *Cameron Markby Hewitt* in 1990 as head of immigration and nationality group, partner from 1991.
Personal: Born 30th September 1959. Took an LLB(Hons) in 1981, Law Society exams in 1982.

PENROSE, Martin
Winstanley-Burgess, London (020) 7278 7911

PHILLIPS, Mark
Tyndallwoods, Birmingham (0121) 624 1111
Mark_Phillips@tyndallwoods.co.uk
Specialisation: Partner and head of immigration department. Area of practice is immigration and public law, mainly refugee, marriage and family reunion cases. Undertakes advocacy and judicial review work. Author of 'Tenants Control' (Council Housing Co-operatives). Has lectured for LIBERTY on civil liberties issues (especially policing and Human Rights Act) and for ILPA and IISA on judicial review and immigration appeals advocacy. Member of Amnesty International and Joint Council for the Welfare of Immigrants. Member of the Law Society Immigration Law Committee, Chairperson Midland Immigration Practitioners (MIP). Member of Region 6 Legal Services Commission Review Committee.
Prof. Memberships: Law Society, Birmingham Law Society, Immigration Law Practitioners Association, Assessor and Member Law Society Immigration Law Panel.
Career: Paralegal advisor at Stepney Green Law Centre 1973-75. Action/research project on tenant's co-operatives 1975-77. Articled clerk at *T.V. Edwards* 1978-81. Assistant solicitor at *Geffens* 1981-83. Senior solicitor at Handsworth Law Centre, Birmingham, 1983-85. Joined *Tyndallwoods* in 1985, becoming a partner in 1988.
Personal: Born 10th May 1947. Educated at Lymm Grammar School, Cheshire, 1958-64; Dame Allen's School, Newcastle-on-Tyne, 1964-66, Hull University 1967-70; then London School of Economics 1970-71. Married with two children. Leisure interests include mountain biking. Lives in Walsall.

POPE, Caron
Norton Rose, London (020) 7444 3359
popeccp@nortonrose.com
Specialisation: Caron has specialised in UK business immigration law since qualification in 1990 and has extensive experience in the full range of business immigration applications. Particular areas of expertise include work permit applications, particularly obtaining permits for outside hires which have not been advertised or which do not fully meet the requirements of the work permit scheme and her team has maintained a 100% success rate for work permit applications over the last five years. In addition, Caron has made numerous applications for sole representatives and other permit free employment categories, applications for businessmen, applications under Home Office concessions and settlement and naturalisation applications. She has also made a number of applications for investors and the innovator

category which was introduced in September 2000. She also advises on the application of European Law.
Prof. Memberships: Immigration Law Practitioners Association. Associate member – Canada/UK Chamber of Commerce; Member Inter Pacific Bar Association (IPBA).
Career: Croydon High School for Girls 1977-84. University of East Anglia, Norwich 1984-87 (LLB Hons). Guilford College of Law. *Cameron Markby Hewitt* 1988-96. Articled Clerk (1988-90). Solicitor, Immigration & Nationality Law Group (1990-96). *Norton Rose* Head of Business Immigration Team August 1996 to date. Caron has lectured and written on UK immigration issues in the UK and overseas and is recognised in all the leading legal directories.

RANDALL, Christopher W.
Winstanley-Burgess, London (020) 7278 7911

RIPLEY, Fiona
Winstanley-Burgess, London (020) 7278 7911

RIVIERE, Susanna
Harbottle & Lewis, London (020) 7667 5000
sriviere@harbottle.co.uk
Specialisation: Joint head of the immigration group. Practices exclusively in immigration and nationality work covering the full spectrum of business/employment related immigration and most personal immigration. Particular expertise in corporate and personal immigration work for clients in *Harbottle & Lewis'* key industry areas of media, entertainment, travel and leisure.
Prof. Memberships: Law Society; Immigration Law Practitioners Association; British Institute of Human Rights; Stonewall.
Career: Attended Churchill College, Cambridge. Joined *Harbottle & Lewis* in 1977. Qualified in 1979. Head of immigration group 1996.
Personal: Married with three children. Leisure interests include sailing.

ROLLASON, Nicolas
Kingsley Napley, London (020) 7814 1200
nrollason@kingsleynapley.co.uk
Specialisation: All areas of business and personal immigration and nationality law with particular emphasis on EU free movement law and the rights of establishment under the EC Asssociation Agreements with central and eastern Europe. Substantial experience of immigration appeals, judicial review and proceedings before the ECJ and Court of First Instance in Luxembourg. Reported cases before the ECJ include Case C-356/98 Kaba v SSHD and C-416/96 El Yassini v SSHD. Frequent lecturer on EU free movement and related human rights issues. Rapporteur to the European Commission on free movement 1996-2000.
Prof. Memberships: Member of the ILPA European Subcommittee since 1996, Law Society.
Career: Qualified in 1996. Assistant in immigration department *Baileys Shaw and Gillet* 1996-97. Joined *Kingsley Napley* in March 1997.
Personal: Born 1968. Attended Oxford University 1986-89. Lives in London.

SIMM, Peter
A S Law, Liverpool (0151) 707 1212

SMITH, David
Nelsons, Nottingham (0115) 958 6262
david.smith@nelsons-solicitors.co.uk
Specialisation: Partner, head of immigration unit. Developed immigration work from scratch at *Nelsons* since 1989. Works across full range of individual and corporate immigration cases.
Prof. Memberships: Law Society, Immigration Law Practitioners Association. Panel solicitor for Stonewall and Refugee Legal Centre. Member of and Assessor for Law Society Immigration Panel.
Career: After ten years in social work qualified as a solicitor in 1989. Partner at *Nelsons* since 1995.
Personal: Born 5/3/54. BA Philosophy 1976, Master in Social Work 1978.

STANLEY, Alison
Bindman & Partners, London (020) 7833 4433
Specialisation: Practice covers all aspects of immigration, asylum and nationality law.
Prof. Memberships: Deputy Chair of the Law Society's Immigration Law Sub-Committee, member of Immigration Law Practitioner's Association, the JUSTICE administrative law panel and the Refugee Women's Legal Group.
Career: Articled at *Winstanley-Burgess*. Subsequently worked for 4.5 years as the solicitor to the Joint Council for the Welfare of Immigrants. Joined *Bindman & Partners* in July 1994. Became partner and head of immigration department in May 1995.

STURTIVANT, Karen
Sturtivant & Co, London (020) 7486 9524
visas@sturtivant.co.uk
Specialisation: Principal. Runs a practice devoted entirely to UK Immigration and Nationality law. Emphasis on business clients, but covers the full range of private client immigration work, although legal aid not undertaken. Author of numerous articles and has spoken widely at seminars in the UK and abroad.
Prof. Memberships: Immigration Law Practitioners Association, American Immigration Lawyers Association, International Bar Association, Law Society Immigration Law Sub-Committee, Deputy Assessor Immigration Law Panel.
Career: Qualified in 1980. Founded *Sturtivant & Co.* in 1985.

THOMPSON, Sally
Luqmani Thompson, London (020) 8365 7800
sally@luqmanithompson.com
Specialisation: Partner specialising in immigration work with emphasis on human rights issues. Work includes administrative court litigation. Main client base includes unaccompanied children and clients assessed as particularly vulnerable.
Prof. Memberships: ILPA, Law Society.
Career: Articled in London and Reading, qualified in 1991. Working exclusively in immigration since qualifying. Founding partner of *Luqmani Thompson & Partners* from December 1998.

TROTT, Philip
Bates, Wells & Braithwaite, London (020) 7551 7777

TURPIN, Philip
Dukes Arnold Du Feu, High Wycombe (01494) 511900

WEBB, David J.
DJ Webb & Co, London (020) 7253 2400

INFORMATION TECHNOLOGY

OVERVIEW: Our leading IT firms display an expertise that cuts across a number of areas such as outsourcing, systems integration and other contracts. Data protection and privacy alongside regulatory and IP rights issues underlying IT systems have proved to be a strong source of instructions recently.

RESEARCH APPROVED BY BMRB: *For this edition,* Chambers' *researchers conducted 6,552 interviews – 4,419 with law firms, 554 with barristers and 1,579 with clients.*

The validity of the research was scrutinised by BMRB International, who audited both the methodology and the results at our offices in July 2001. They interviewed Chambers' *researchers and cross-checked sample interviews. Details of the audit appear on page 7.*

LONDON

Baker & McKenzie (see firm details p.868) Described by our interviewees as "*the top practice with a great IT product – they have been at the pinnacle for years.*" Competitors respect its slant towards major US investors and its success in attracting some of the biggest names in the IT industry, both on the supplier side and the user side. It has acted on a number of major outsourcing matters in the past year and witnessed a substantial increase in the level of contentious work, particularly domain name disputes. Famed litigator **Harry Small** (see p.451) is said to be "*a smart man who loves computers,*" and "*leads a pretty powerful team.*" One client claimed that in the IT world, "*he is the business.*" The "*outstanding*" **Michael Hart** (see p.447) is also endorsed for his work, which crosses over into IP. Don Jerrard is now a consultant at the firm. Highlights for the team include acting for Hewlett-Packard on the European rollout of the easyEverything chain of internet cafes, which involved complex procurement of hardware, software and internet connectivity. It also advised Yahoo! UK on numerous commercial ventures and on contentious matters relating to its liability for content listed on its website. The firm is currently acting for ntl on its outsourcing of IT services to IBM. **Clients:** Apple Computer; Cisco Systems; Compaq Computers; Hewlett-Packard; Lotus; Mitsubishi Electric; NCR; Nortel Networks; Oracle; Orange; PeopleSoft; Sony; Viasoft.

Bird & Bird (see firm details p.884) Competitors view it as "*one of the classic firms in the IT sphere,*" fielding "*top quality people*" and enjoying a niche in public sector activities with government-backed PFI IT projects providing interesting instructions. The firm has particular expertise in advising on large-scale IT infrastructure projects which are often of a global nature. Its IT contract work ranges from leasing, facility management and service outsourcing to ASP arrangements. The recent loss of Chris Rees to Herbert Smith is not considered to be a major setback for the firm, despite his standing in the field, as the team is considered to be buoyed by an "*impressively deep client base and talented lawyers.*" Peers describe **Hamish Sandison** (see p.450) as "*eminent in the field,*" although his managerial commitments have lowered his visibility at the coalface. **Roger Bickerstaff** (see p.445) is respected for his relationships in the public sector, which are thought to provide the firm with complex PFI projects. **Hilary Pearson** (see p.450) is rated as a "*super litigator,*" while "*commercial*" **Graham Smith** (see p.451) is said to be "*excellent at dealing with major, complicated cases.*" The firm acted for the Employment Service on the award of a major (£800 million) PFI scheme to introduce a new e-commerce infrastructure into the Employment Service and to all Job Centres in England and Wales. It

TOP IN-HOUSE LAWYERS

Tanya BLAKE, Legal Director, *Capita Group*

Robert MARCUS, Senior Counsel, *IBM*

Jane MCELHATTON, Senior Legal Advisor, *Cable & Wireless*

Jeremy NEWTON, Assistant General Counsel, *Sun Microsystems*

Jane REEVES, Company Lawyer, *Thomson Financial (Primark Financial Data)*

David WITT, Senior Counsel, Europe Middle East and Africa, Litigation and Intellectual Property, *IBM*

Endorsed heavily, **Tanya Blake** is *"practical and switched on."* **Robert Marcus** is *"intellectually strong"* one of a group of *"good negotiators"* within the market. *"Experienced and extremely well organised,"* **Jane McElhatton** covers IT work connected with the telecoms industry. *"Excellent at communicating,"* **Jeremy Newton** is widely respected, particularly as a speaker on IT subjects while **Jane Reeves** continues to draw recommendation. Renowned as one of the main players *"running the big transactions,"* **David Witt** also picks up strong recommendations.

In-House lawyers profiles: p.1193

	INFORMATION TECHNOLOGY • London	Ptnrs	Assts
1	Baker & McKenzie	7	27
	Bird & Bird	14	45
	Clifford Chance	8	27
2	Allen & Overy	5	21
	Lovells	7	16
	Masons	11	24
	Olswang	7	14
	Osborne Clarke	13	32
	Taylor Joynson Garrett	24	45
3	Denton Wilde Sapte	16	35
	Field Fisher Waterhouse	3	9
	Tarlo Lyons	n/a	n/a
4	Bristows	12	22
	Freshfields Bruckhaus Deringer	3	24
	Herbert Smith	6	15
	Kemp Little LLP	3	7
	Linklaters	4	18
	Rowe & Maw	6	15
	Slaughter and May	6	23
5	Ashurst Morris Crisp	7	22
	Berwin Leighton Paisner	19	40
	Brobeck Hale and Dorr	n/a	n/a
	CMS Cameron McKenna	4	18
	DJ Freeman	3	5
	Nabarro Nathanson	5	16
	Shaw Pittman	4	15
	Simmons & Simmons	7	6
	Theodore Goddard	n/a	n/a

This book is the product of 6,552 1/2 hour interviews. See p.7 for BMRB audit.
Within each band, firms are listed alphabetically.

also acted on an international outsourcing project for Sema Group's client Standard Chartered Bank, with systems and services rolled out across the bank's operations in England, Malaysia, Singapore and Hong Kong. In addition it advised The Woolwich on its 'Open Plan' internet-based home banking service, including innovative WAP-enabled website banking applications. **Clients:** AXA Sun Life; BBC World Service; BP Amoco; British Telecom; European Commission; Health & Safety Executive; Lend Lease Project Limited; OFSTED; SEGA Europe Limited; UBS Warburg; United Kingdom Passport Agency.

Clifford Chance (see firm details p.919) The firm undertakes IT work out of its communications, media and technology group and has witnessed an increasing amount of business process outsourcing over the last year. Market commentators believe that *"you can't fault the advice they give"* and it remains one of the leading lights in this sphere. The firm enjoys *"a sensible, stable and mature practice,"* which both clients and peers agree is the result of *"its long-standing and dedicated focus."* Practice head **Christopher Millard** (see p.296) is *"one of the best around"* for his data protection work in particular, while some acknowledge that *"talented lawyer"* **David Griffiths** (see p.447) is possibly *"underrated."*

Allen & Overy (see firm details p.856) Thought by some commentators to *"rightly have a claim to the tag of specialists,"* particularly on corporate related matters. The firm has been involved in a range of technology and outsourcing projects advising leading suppliers, corporates and international finance houses. **Laurence Jacobs** (see p.448) consistently provides a *"truly quality service"* and is considered *"definitely one of the cleverest people in the City."* Newly ranked **Colleen Keck** (see p.448) has a *"keen eye for detail"* and interviewees acknowledged her advice to *"an impressive array of clients."* Key transactions from the past year include acting for Accenture on a £1.8 billion outsourcing project with Sainsburys, the largest international deal by the former in Europe. The firm also advised Unisys, Lloyds TSB and Barclays on an outsourcing joint venture for cheque clearance services valued at over £1 billion, and KPN Mobile on access to NTT DoCoMo's cutting edge 3G technology (I-Mode) for use outside Japan. **Clients:** Accenture; Barclays; Equant; HSBC; JP Morgan Chase; Lloyds TSB; Marconi Communications; Mobil Corporation; News Group; Unisys; Virgin.

Lovells (see firm details p.1044) Our researchers were told that this firm demonstrates *"a high level of all-round expertise"* with a robust client roster. It acts for clients in the financial services sector and large industrial organisations in relation to their IT systems and the introduction of new services. This *"collection of talented lawyers,"* includes *"experienced"* head of team **Quentin Archer,** who *"knows his stuff"* and benefits the team with skills developed in-house at Acorn. **Heather Rowe** (see p.450) is endorsed for her data protection work, and is thought to handle *"an enormous amount of publishing-related IT work"* while **Conor Ward** (see p.451) is *"highly proficient,"* particularly on encryption, public key infrastructure and digital signatures. Key matters over the past year include acting for Kingfisher in concluding a contract for the implementation of new EPOS systems at Woolworths, B&Q, Superdrug and other stores around the country. The firm also advised the Willis Group on the establishment of WISe, a worldwide system of communication and risk placement for members of the insurance industry. Instructed by the BBC on arrangements for the development of the TIVO agreement (involving the implementation of ASP systems) for the UK market. **Clients:** BBC; Cable & Wireless; Deutsche Bank; Guardian Media; Kingfisher; Mars; Nintendo; Reuters; Standard Chartered Bank; UnionAmerica; Willis Group.

Masons (see firm details p.1056) Commentators in the market agree that the firm *"certainly knows what it's doing in the litigation sphere,"* and is thought to win a number of public sector instructions. The workload for this practice is divided between commercial IT work and contentious matters. Niche strengths for the practice include PFI-related IT procurement work, outsourcing and data protection. Peers praise **Rob McCallough** (see p.449) as *"a tough street-fighter"* best known for his two leading exclusion

LEADING INDIVIDUALS		
1	**KEMP Richard** Kemp Little LLP	**MILLARD Christopher** Clifford Chance
	SMALL Harry Baker & McKenzie	
2	**CHISSICK Michael** Field Fisher Waterhouse	**GRIFFITHS David** Clifford Chance
	MAUGHAN Alistair Shaw Pittman	**REES Chris** Herbert Smith
	SANDISON Hamish Bird & Bird	**SMITH Graham** Bird & Bird
3	**ARCHER Quentin** Lovells	**BARRETT David** Simmons & Simmons
	BICKERSTAFF Roger Bird & Bird	**GRAHAM Rory** Osborne Clarke
	JACOBS Laurence Allen & Overy	**MCCALLOUGH Rob** Masons
	PEARSON Hilary Bird & Bird	**RENDELL Simon** Osborne Clarke
	ROWE Heather Lovells	**SWYCHER Nigel** Slaughter and May
	WARD Conor Lovells	**WESTMACOTT Philip** Bristows
4	**DAVIES Clive** DJ Freeman	**GARDNER Nick** Herbert Smith
	GARDNER Paul Osborne Clarke	**HART Michael** Baker & McKenzie
	HIGHAM Nicholas Denton Wilde Sapte	**LISTER Richard** Freshfields Bruckhaus
	NICHOLSON Kim Olswang	**SINGLETON Susan** Singletons
	TURNER Mark Herbert Smith	
	WEBSTER Michael Nicholson Graham & Jones	
	WILDISH Nigel Field Fisher Waterhouse	
5	**BREWARD Alastair** Taylor Joynson Garrett	
	BURNETT Rachel Salans Hertzfeld & Heilbronn HRK	
	CAROLINA Robert Tarlo Lyons	**LUBBOCK Mark** Ashurst Morris Crisp
	MARTINDALE Avril Freshfields Bruckhaus	**MONAGHAN Iain** Masons
	MORGAN Glyn Taylor Joynson Garrett	**PRINSLEY Mark** Rowe & Maw
	ROBERTSON Ranald Robertson & Co	**WORTHY John** Denton Wilde Sapte
UP AND COMING		
	CARBONI Anna Linklaters	**DINSDALE Danelle** DLA
	KECK Colleen Allen & Overy	

See individuals' profiles p.445

litigation cases for ICL. **Iain Monaghan** (see p.449) is rated for his involvement in corporate-related matter, and is active on the IT service provision side, especially in relation to demergers. Rachel Burnett has recently left to join US firm Salans Hertzfeld & Heilbronn. The firm was sole legal adviser to leading IT and e-solutions consultancy Charteris on its £30 million AIM flotation. It also advised STS Systems on the disposal of its Canadian and US assets and STS Systems Europe for a total consideration of in excess of CAN$600 million. It is currently advising United Assurance Group on a substantial High Court claim against Unisys. **Clients:** Bank of Ireland; Charteris; Equifax; Freedom Group of Companies; ICL; Metropolitan Police; Standard Chartered Bank; STS Systems; United Assurance.

Olswang (see firm details p.1084) Competitors view the firm as having *"aggressively and successfully expanded into the IT and e-commerce field"* from its media base. Felt to be content-led and *"entrepreneurial in spirit,"* it fields *"impressive general TMT lawyers."* Work undertaken in the last year includes procurement contracts, software distribution agreements, licences and development agreements, in addition to its litigation work for clients across the IT industry. **Kim Nicholson** (see p.449) is said to be *"the crossover queen"* for her work in telecoms, e-commerce and general IT, with an increasing profile in corporate transactions. The firm advised Whitbread on the outsourcing of its data centre and desktop issues to CSC, and acted for United News & Media in the outsourcing of certain data services to BT. For Davy Stockbrokers (Dublin), it advised on a major contractual dispute with TCA Synergo and the subsequent acquisition of an alternative settlement system. **Clients:** Anite Networks; Daiwa Bank; Financial Network Services (Europe); Grant Thornton; Moneybox Corporation; Robert Fleming & Co; RSPCA; UUNet Technologies; Ziff Davis.

Osborne Clarke (see firm details p.1086) The core business of this firm's IT practice tends to flow from US suppliers, and the firm has won an increasing amount of work for large-scale users from both the US and Europe in the past year. Respected for its involvement in the start-up arena it has "*a fine corporate offering in the technology field.*" **Simon Rendell** uses his "*bloody good manner*" to great effect in winning clients and at the deal table, although much of his profile relates to e-commerce activities. **Rory Graham** is a "*real hard hitter*" and **Paul Gardner** leads the firm's distinct expertise in computer games. Significant matters for the firm include acting for KPMG in the preparation of terms of trade for its e-commerce consultancy. Also advised Edotech on an MBO from Barclays Bank and on three £30 million plus outsourcing deals to provide statement printing and electronic document delivery services to MBNA, Chase Manhattan Bank and Legal & General. Acted for Carlton Screen Advertising on the procurement of a business critical campaign management system from Cap Gemini. **Clients:** ADS Associates; Bass Brewers; British Airways; Data Access Corporation; Equitas; FirstMark; IDX; KPMG; LeasePlan UK; Omega International SA; Prudential Corporation; Salmon; Tuskerdirect; UBS Warburg.

Taylor Joynson Garrett (see firm details p.1150) The prevailing market view is that this firm has "*developed a strong reputation for corporate work on behalf of technology companies,*" bolstered by the presence of a "*team of pure specialists who do this and nothing but.*" Niche strengths include outsourcing, large-scale IT supply and procurement and activities in computer games. **Glyn Morgan** drew comment on "*his commercial attitude – he is highly knowledgeable and he has back-up.*" **Alastair Breward** is particularly rated for his internet and website activities. The firm recently advised Novalogic on the exclusive arrangements for the UK distribution of computer games. It also advised Tornado Group on its European partnership with EMI to test the infrastructure for music downloads, and Sun Microsystems on its acquisition of Trustbase. **Clients:** Ariba Technologies; Britannia Airways; CoWare; Eidos; Genesys; Guardian Royal Exchange; Internet Travel Network; MCPS; NCR; Onyx Software; Rank Group; Touchstone; Unisys; Visa.

Denton Wilde Sapte (see firm details p.939) The firm has seen a growth in public sector IT projects, in addition to corporate transactions, outsourcing and projects involving the exploitation of personal data. Judged by the market to have a "*serious IT and telecoms group,*" the firm is strong on content, cashing in on its entertainment and media practice. Clients agree that these lawyers "*understand the industry and realise how the technology works.*" Competitors view **Nick Higham** (see p.813) as "*a serious player, well established and knowledgeable,*" while **John Worthy** (see p.452) continues to elicit support for his sensible and thorough approach. Major matters from the past year include advising the British Library on the Digital Library Project arrangement with IBM, and acting for Property Golf and Finance on its deal with the English Golf Union for a national computerised handicap and booking system for amateur golfers. The firm also advised the Highways Agency on the Traffic Control Centres Project. **Clients:** IT suppliers, public sector organisations.

Field Fisher Waterhouse (see firm details p.957) Expert in undertaking outsourcing and IT procurement work for technology companies. Competitors agree that the practice remains bolstered by an envied client base that includes Accenture, despite the possible effects of the dot.com bubble burst. Success on the corporate level ensures this firm's continued profile. Prolific writer and speaker **Michael Chissick** (see p.446) is perceived by interviewees to be "*a real name in the industry – definitely a specialist*" while "*experienced*" **Nigel Wildish** (see p.452) also received market commendation. Highlights for the firm include advising Autodesk, a major US CAD base software developer, on licensing distribution issues, and COLT Telecom Group on all aspects of its IT and technology procurement. Instructed by Empower Interactive Group on its establishment and the drafting of reseller and distribution agreements for the provision of WAP enabling services. **Clients:** Accenture; BondClick; CRIF; Dexterus; First Quench Retailing; Konami; London Borough of Lewisham; London Regional Transport; New Deal; RSL Communications; Thomas Cook Holdings.

Tarlo Lyons (see firm details p.1149) Perceived to be "*visible if smaller*" and "*genuinely IT-driven.*" Active in the convergence between new media and IT, the firm is commended for its "*pure focus.*" **Robert Carolina** (see p.446) elicited comment that he "*knows his way around IT projects.*" The firm is active in procurement and outsourcing matters.

Bristows (see firm details p.895) The firm acts for a range of clients including household names in the IT sector as well as global companies dependent on state-of-the-art IT systems. An increasingly significant area of instruction is advising clients in relation to the network of data protection and privacy laws regulating the use of personal data. Bolstered by its IP practice, the firm remains a powerhouse in heavyweight litigation. Clients and competitors alike commend the firm's "*cracking people*" who many feel are unduly under-rated in this IP heavy atmosphere. **Philip Westmacott** (see p.452) is described as "*an electronics expert*" who is rated for both litigation and his transactional work. The group acted for VIA Technologies in two disputes concerning computer chip sets, and advised Rambus in two disputes concerning semiconductor memory. The firm also advised Matsushita on the corporate, tax and competition aspects of a major transaction with BSkyB, BT and HSBC that will rewrite the parties' ownership of Open. **Clients:** Aerotel; British Airways; Dolby; Finsoft; IBM; Marconi; MTV Networks; Philips; Symbian; Texas Instruments; Thomson; Viatel UK.

Freshfields Bruckhaus Deringer (see firm details p.965) Although best known for its high quality corporate support, in the last year the firm has been active on a number of stand-alone outsourcing projects and has seen a growth in advising on data protection issues. Interviewees claim that "*the sheer volume and quality of its corporate client base*" ensures interesting instructions. Respected **Richard Lister** (see p.448) and **Avril Martindale** (see p.507) continue to draw market plaudits. Recent transactions include advising Aon on a £400 million IT outsourcing, one of the largest projects in the UK. It has also been advising various clients (including Seagate Software, PowerGen and P&O) on issues arising from the Data Protection Act. **Clients:** Aon; AstraZeneca; Financial Times; Ford; ICI; London Regional Transport; Marconi; Morgan Stanley; PowerGen; Tyco; Video Networks.

Herbert Smith (see firm details p.993) "*Investing heavily,*" interviewees believe that this firm has made a strategic decision to accelerate the growth of its commercial IT practice, building on its traditional strengths in big ticket IT litigation and PFI. "*Prominent*" **Chris Rees** (see p.450) has joined from Bird & Bird and is applauded as a "*major asset*" whose energy and dedication will assist **Mark Turner** (see p.451) in driving the practice forward. One rival commented "*I expect good things of them in terms of the larger specialist transactions.*" Turner is rated for his public sector relationships and is said to demonstrate a "*track record in systems procurement and software development.*" **Nick Gardner** (see p.447) is "*expert in internet domain name disputes.*" Major matters for the firm include advising Abbey National on a software development and outsourcing contract with Capita for the administration of all its consumer insurance policies, valued in excess of £300 million. The firm also acted for WH Smith in a High Court action against Siemens and Fujitsu Siemens Computers in relation to IT hardware, and advised BSkyB on its acquisition of Open, the TV shopping and interactive services company. **Clients:** Abbey National; Anglian Water; BAA; British Gas; Cisco; Centrica; IBM; Jigsaw; London Electricity; NATS; SAP; Vodafone; WH Smith.

Kemp Little LLP (see firm details p.1018) Dedicated to IT, e-commerce and telecoms through its commercial, corporate and employment practices. Competitors were of the view that **Richard Kemp** (see p.296) was "*one of the very first genuine IT lawyers*" whose "*brilliant mind*" and cutting edge work "*commands a fantastic client following.*" A niche player, smaller in size, it continues to win significant instructions. Recent transactions include acting for Microsoft on a wide range of commercial and operational issues arising from its core software distribution business in Europe. The firm is continuing its work with the AFR Consortium of 34 UK police authorities in relation to its automatic fingerprint recognition operations, and is also acting for QBE International Insurance on its project 2002, a comprehensive upgrade of IT and e-commerce systems. **Clients:** AFR Consortium; Microsoft; QBE Insurance; Thomson Financial.

Linklaters (see firm details p.1042) Felt by peers to act from a heavily corporate-led base with quality instructions derived from its existing roster of clients. Known for her mixed IP/IT practice, **Anna Carboni** (see p.502) is endorsed as "*sharp, bright and always effective*" with one barrister moved to comment that "*I was very impressed at her thorough preparation and good grasp of the issues.*" The group advised J Sainsbury on the outsourcing of its IT systems, and acted for CGEY in a joint venture with BAT for the development and supply of CRM systems and related services. The firm also advised Merrill Lynch HSBC on its IT systems and issues arising from the establishment of its consumer internet banking site in the UK, US, Canada, France, Germany and Australia. **Clients:** BBC; BP; CMG; Dixons; Ernst & Young; KPMG; London Metal Exchange; PwC; Reuters; World Online.

Rowe & Maw (see firm details p.1113) "*A vibrant practice.*" Outsourcing is the area in which this firm excels, with competitors acknowledging "*some interesting and complex deals.*" In addition to the firm's growth in the financial services sector, it also wins instructions from internet technology suppliers and communication companies on new media issues and procurement. **Mark Prinsley** (see p.450) has gained recognition at the head of the firm's IT department. Highlight of the year was advice to Cable & Wireless in its agreement with IBM for the outsourcing of its IT infrastructure on a global basis. Instructed by IXNet UK (now known as Global Crossing Financial Markets) on the outsourcing of Garban Intercapital's telecommunications network, and acted for Fleming Asset Management on an agreement with GlobalNet for the provision of online access to Fleming's funds. **Clients:** AMP (UK); BNP Paribas; Bull Information Systems; Cable & Wireless; CNBC; Global Crossing Financial Markets; HMV Media; Intershop; Magic Software; Morgan Stanley; PCTV; Syngenta; Vignette.

Slaughter and May (see firm details p.1135) Development, procurement and licensing remain the core of the firm's IT practice, although it continues to see growth in outsourcing and services work. Competitors acknowledge that "*they have made a successful play for the technology market.*" While some comment on the generalist nature of the firm, most typically agreed with one solicitor; "*I wouldn't pick a fight with them – these lawyers are without doubt thoroughly excellent.*" One such figure remains the "*always on the ball,*" **Nigel Swycher** (see p.451)who "*covers the whole waterfront*" including licensing transactions as well as competition work. Recent significant transactions for the firm include undertaking IT licensing work for Alcatel in relation to its pan European telecom network. Also advised Schroders on the outsourcing of its custody business to Chase, and successfully mediated a major IT dispute with Bull for Kwik-Fit. **Clients:** Abbey National; Alcatel; Fidelity; Open Interactive; Psion; Symbian.

Ashurst Morris Crisp (see firm details p.866) Perceived to field a talented cross-departmental team acting for both users and suppliers. The firm is endorsed for its "*decent client base and interesting projects,*" while **Mark Lubbock** (see p.448)has a "*good head on his shoulders.*" On the user side, the firm acted for the global e-ventures unit of Royal & SunAlliance on a number of projects, including the set-up and launch of the SME online service usecolour. On the supplier side, the firm advised Omega Logic (a start-up) on the exploitation of its middleware technology which enables pre-pay mobile phone users to top up their talk time at various retail outlets. The firm also acted for AltaVista in a £200 million dispute against Free Internet Group relating to an alleged breach of contract. **Clients:** AltaVista; Computer Associates; CyberLife Technology; Express Newspapers; Motorola; Royal & SunAlliance; Virgin Net.

Berwin Leighton Paisner (see firm details p.878) Perceived to be a "*stronger force*" after the merger with "*a powerful combined team.*" Berwin Leighton's respected e-commerce activities now link with Paisner's data protection capability, although the market awaits the impact it will have on a 'pure' IT capacity. "*Interesting work for a strong client roster*" includes acting for OnCue Telecommunications in connection with the initial £80 million investment into the company by Soros Private Equity, Madison Dearborn Partners and TD Capital. The firm also acted for Tullett & Tokyo Liberty on a wide range of IT matters including developing financial systems, software licence disputes and the establishment of a global electronic trading system. In addition, it assisted software developer Demica on a £5 million investment by Friends Ivory & Sime Private Equity. **Clients:** Capita Group; Demica; Internet Incubator; OnCue Telecommunications.

Brobeck Hale and Dorr (see firm details p.895) The firm is seen to be "*extremely active on the corporate side,*" buoyed by its presence in IPOs and fundings. Thought to field "*good lawyers with corporate backgrounds and a focus on emerging companies.*" Highlights for the firm include acting for Element 14, a Cambridge-based developer of digital subscriber line chipsets, software and processor technology, in its $594 million acquisition by Broadcom. The firm also acted for Southampton Photonics in a $55.2 million venture capital investment, and advised Chordiant Software in a $24 million technology licensing deal with Lloyds TSB. **Clients:** ARC International; Bookham Technology; Cisco Systems; Deutsche Bank; Goldman Sachs; Lehman Brothers; Parthus Technologies; Robertson Stephens.

CMS Cameron McKenna (see firm details p.922) The firm advises IT companies and users across a broad range of industry sectors, including energy, retail and financial services. It attracted commendations for "*its bright people,*" who bring a "*sensible approach to the deal table.*" The group assisted Camelot as its sole external adviser in relation to its lottery IT systems and advised the Home Office on IT2000, its flagship £350 million PFI IT/telecoms project. Also instructed by Nuffield Hospitals on the procurement of hospital management IT systems for the entire network of hospitals. **Clients:** Alcatel; Amazon.co.uk; Benetton; Camelot; J Sainsbury; Omron; The Post Office; Radio Advertising Bureau; Silverline Technologies.

DJ Freeman (see firm details p.943) The firm acts for computer, telecoms and media clients on a variety of commercial matters, including procurement contracts. It has seen a growth in contentious matters and has won a place on the Hiscox panel for insurance disputes. Competitors value the firm's media related work. Much of the firm's profile lies with **Clive Davies** (see p.446) whose in-house experience at ICL has gained him a reputation for "*commercial nous.*" Significant matters from the last year include acting for The Post Office on two major automation systems contracts, each with a value in excess of £100 million. In addition, the firm has acted for the UK software house Pilat on the licensing of broadcast management software (originally developed for BSkyB) to broadcasters in the UK including Channel Five and FoxKids, and to the US, Australia, New Zealand and Israel. Also provided litigation advice to Envision Licensing with reference to its £700 million service contract to collect and administer the licence fee revenue of the BBC. **Clients:** ASP Industry Consortium; Energis; Envision Licensing; Hiscox; Pilat; The Post Office; Reed Exhibition Companies.

Nabarro Nathanson (see firm details p.1078) The firm represents multinationals, corporate finance institutions and many UK and US fast growth technology companies. It has a focus on acting for service providers, while the Reading office continues to provide strong foundations. The firm advised the Post Office on the restructuring of its business and the acquisition of IT systems. It also acted for Mapeley, a company set up to undertake property outsourcing, in relation to negotiating a contract with EDS, and advised the Bournemouth Bourough Council on its Pathfinder PFI library project. **Clients:** Ask Jeeves; Benchmark Capital; CMG; Deutsche Bank Ventures; ETF Group; Gateway; Oracle; Siemens; Sun; Synstar Computer Services.

Shaw Pittman (see firm details p.1124) A niche technology practice, this US firm is best known for outsourcing and systems integration – "*that's* *their big selling point.*" Peers commend the team for attracting "*big ticket IT acquisition work,*" agreeing that "*by any measure they've been successful.*" **Alistair Maughan** (see p.448 has acted on major technology transactions, particularly in the outsourcing side. The group advised AstraZeneca on its $2.2 billion outsourcing contract to IBM and represented the UK Home Office on its £1.5 billion Airwave project to replace the UK emergency police mobile phone radio network. Instructed by Cable & Wireless on its landmark agreement with Nortel Networks to provide a 'voice over internet protocol' network worth £950 million. **Clients:** Abbey Life Assurance Company; AC Nielsen; Deutsche Bank; Home Office; IPC Media Ltd; Lloyds TSB; Prudential Assurance.

Simmons & Simmons (see firm details p.1132) The bulk of this firm's IT work is in commercial advice and the drafting and negotiating of contracts with strength in the corporate and data protection fields. **David Barrett**'s (see p.445) arrival from Arnold & Porter is thought to have given the practice a major boost. Commentators acknowledge that his long experience is an attraction for new clients. The firm recently advised Riyad Bank on its continuing program of banking systems expansion, and assisted the Department of Health on its information management services and procurement. It also advised Dot Com Holdings Inc on its licensing and development contracts in the UK. **Clients:** IT suppliers and users.

Theodore Goddard (see firm details p.1152) Mixing both contractual and advisory work, much of its load is stand-alone although corporate finance transactions continue to flow from its existing client base. Competitors acknowledge that the firm's IT practice is built on solid foundations, although the departure of former head of department Arnold Segal is a blow, with "*no-one of quite the same calibre*" to step into his shoes. Key transactions for the group include advising STA Travel on its contract with Unisys for the worldwide roll-out of a new booking system. Renegotiated major outsourcing arrangements between CRESTCo and Cap Gemini, and advised Sporting Index in its negotiations for the provision of spread betting software. **Clients:** Beiersdorf UK; CRESTCo; Premium TV; SimNet; STA.

Other Notable Practitioners **Susan Singleton** (see p.451) of **Singleton's** is said to be "*level-headed*" and "*always on the ball.*" **Ranald Robertson** (see p.450) of **Robertson & Co** is said to be "*one of the first lawyers who got into technology pretty early on.*" The "*tremendous*" **Rachel Burnett** (see p.446) recently moved to **Salans Hertzfeld & Heilbronn** from Masons, which prompted the comment from one practitioner that "*Masons will miss her outsourcing skills.*" **Michael Webster** (see p.451) of **Nicholson Graham & Jones** received warm endorsement for his depth of experience and **Danelle Dinsdale** from **DLA** drew plaudits from her peers.

THE SOUTH

INFORMATION TECHNOLOGY • The South	Ptnrs	Assts
1 **DMH** Brighton	5	4
2 **Bond Pearce** Southampton	2	3
Clyde & Co Guildford	5	6
Lester Aldridge Bournemouth	3	3

LEADING INDIVIDUALS
1 **HAMBLIN Julian** Bond Pearce

This book is the product of 6,552 1/2 hour interviews. See p.7 for BMRB audit.
Within each band, firms are listed alphabetically.

DMH (see firm details p.944) IT contract and regulatory work remains the mainstay of this practice, in both the contentious and non-contentious spheres. Its niche strengths include internet/e-commerce matters as well as trade mark and domain name disputes. The firm has acted on a large number of EIS implementations for technology companies. It has also undertaken a number of website portability disputes and is currently handling ongoing IT contract and dispute advice for Eyretel. In addition, the firm has been involved in defective IT system disputes, including advice on the supply of a defective server for a well known ISP. **Clients:** Crane Telecommunications Group; Diarymanager.com; getfrank.com; Globalink Telecommunications; Herculez; HFC Bank; InsurE-com; Norwood Adam Distribution.

Bond Pearce (see firm details p.888) Having been open in Southampton since February, the firm has demonstrated its strength in non-contentious IT work, particularly in the retail, leisure and financial services sectors. Head of department **Julian Hamblin** (see p.447) is described by his competitors as "*someone with big plans*" for the practice. Highlights for the firm include advising a household name media company on its new internet-related venture, and advising a major insurer on an IT indemnity policy. It was also instructed on contentious IT issues for a major regional airline. **Clients:** COR Systems; Datacard; elata; English Heritage; Kier Project Investment; Safeway Stores; TRIAGE.

Clyde & Co (see firm details p.921) In addition to assisting the firm's telecoms clients in the IT sphere, it has developed a focus on advice to insurance companies and dotcom start-ups. Over the past year, the firm has been undertaking due diligence on the sale and acquisitions of IT businesses, and a range of e-commerce-related IT agreements, including website development. It has also established a new internet auction site for Electio Ltd. **Clients:** Catalyst Solutions; Ericsson; FutureSoft; Microgen; NCM; Nokia; Psion; Skandia; Winterthur; WS Atkins.

Lester Aldridge (see firm details p.1038) Winning a variety of instructions including advice on software development agreements, the acquisition of IT systems and acting on infringement actions. The firm advised Wam!Net on new pan-European products for the entertainment industry. The firm now acts for Voice Integrated Products, a leading voice telephony software company, and has also been advising Printrak International on a multi-million pound system supplied to the London Fire and Civil Defence Authority. **Clients:** Communications Consultants Worldwide; Hugh Symons; Ibcos; Printrak International; Voice Integrated Products; Wam!Net (UK).

THAMES VALLEY

Nabarro Nathanson (see firm details p.1078) The firm's Reading office acts for over 50 Thames Valley-based IT suppliers, including major international names such as Sun Microsystems, Oracle and Siemens. The practice is skilled in IT projects, both in contract creation and disputes, and matters involving EU competition law. Though to have established its base in Reading "*with a view to becoming the specialists.*" Practice head **Tony Bailes** (see p.445) is described as "*top class*" and "*seriously driven,*" while **Sara Ellacott** (see p.446) combines a "*personable approach*" with her "*talents for efficiency and tremendous organisation.*" Highlights from the past year include advising a UK IT services company in ongoing UK High Court proceedings against a multinational IT services company for breach of European and UK competition rules. The firm also provided an 'IT audit' to Mapeley, the preferred bidder in a strategic estates and property services outsourcing project for major government departments (including the

INFORMATION TECHNOLOGY • Thames Valley	Ptnrs	Assts
1		
Nabarro Nathanson Reading	2	7
The Law Offices of Marcus J O'Leary Bracknell	5	3
2		
Garretts Reading	2	5
Manches Oxford	4	4
Osborne Clarke Reading	2	8
3		
Clark Holt Swindon	1	1
Willoughby & Partners Oxford	6	9
4		
Boyes Turner Reading	1	3

LEADING INDIVIDUALS
1
BAILES Tony Nabarro Nathanson
O'LEARY Marcus The Law Offices of Marcus J O'Leary
TIGHE David Manches
2
ELLACOTT Sara Nabarro Nathanson
HARRINGTON Alison Garretts
HOLT Jeremy Clark Holt
3
GOODGER Ben Willoughby & Partners
GORNALL-KING William Boyes Turner

This book is the product of 6,552 1/2 hour interviews. See p.7 for BMRB audit.
Within each band, firms are listed alphabetically. *See individuals' profiles p.445*

Treasury). In addition it acted for venture capitalists MTI Partners and ET Capital in twelve development capital and MBO deals. **Clients:** Benchmark Capital; CMG; Deutsche Bank Ventures; ETF Group; Oracle; Siemens; Sun Microsystems.

The Law Offices of Marcus J O'Leary (see firm details p.1030) This specialist practice acts for some of the world's leading hi-tech companies. Its client base lies mainly on the supplier side and the team is active in outsourcing and convergence issues. Interviewees regard the firm as enjoying a "*tremendous focus*" on the technology field with a "*treasure trove of clients*" and practitioners who "*really know what they're talking about.*" **Marcus J O'Leary** (see p.446) himself is said to be a "*bit of a guru in the area*" and is "*forward-thinking*" in his approach. **Clients:** IT suppliers and users.

Garretts (see firm details p.968) One of the niche strengths for this firm is e-business, which encompasses data protection, privacy and distribution channel advice. The firm has recently been advising the UK subsidiary of Network Appliance on its distribution channel activities in Europe, including drafting reseller agreements and associated licence and support arrangements. It has a track record for converting US IT agreements for use in Europe and advising US entrants to Europe. Competitors view the firm as "*reaping the rewards of the Andersen Legal connection.*" "*Ambitious*" head of department **Alison Harrington** (see p.295) is endorsed by her peers. The firm has been instructed by Motorola on its e-business strategies, including regulatory and pan-European advice, drafting its e-contracts. In addition, the firm has been establishing charitable foundations and structures to house Microsoft's existing 'anywhere anytime learning initiative' aimed at providing lap top computers for every child in the UK. **Clients:** Axxia Systems; BEA Systems; eCredit.com; Futureproof; Microsoft Europe; Motorola; Network Appliance UK; Optimal Communications; SeraNova.

Manches (see firm details p.1051) Much of the firm's work load is found in systems procurement and development in the financial services and banking sector. Clients spring from Europe, Asia, the Middle East and the US. **David Tighe** (see p.451) is commended by his peers and is felt to have a greater involvement in corporate matters. The firm negotiated contracts for the implementation of financial services systems in London, New York, Singapore, Japan and the Channel Islands. Engaged in outsourcing and facilities management agreements, it has recently acted in connection with multi-million pound outsourcing projects in the education and travel sectors. **Clients:** Blackwells; Deutsche Bank; Numerical Algorithms Group; OAG; Plant Consulting; Q Associates; Rebus; Thomson Financial.

Osborne Clarke (see firm details p.1086) Building on its foundation as a leading light in the dot.com market, the firm's Reading office is increasingly undertaking specialist work for technology companies and their customers in the region. A "*sizeable presence,*" particularly for corporate and capital raising matters, the firm is praised by our interviewees for its "*good resources and a strategy.*" The group advised Splash Plastic, an innovative secure payment system, on its commercial and contractual issues, including network agreements for the collection of monies. Instructed by Kompass International Neuenschwander on its e-commerce and internet offerings, the firm was also involved in arranging contracts for the sale of computer-generated financial information. Also advised Isotrak on its joint venture and supply arrangements with Tesco, JRL and IBM concerning its proprietary computerised vehicle tracking system. **Clients:** Allied Worldwide; Bass Brewers; Compuserve; General Motors; Network Commerce; Phones International; SAS Design; Tribal Group.

Clark Holt (see firm details p.916) The firm acts primarily for smaller software houses, handling licensing, data protection and internet-related advice. One practitioner noted that the firm's location has it on the doorstep for a "*surprising number of high-tech entities such as Intel.*" Seen to be "*thorough*" **Jeremy Holt** (see p.448) enjoys "*good contacts*" and is said to "*share information with the local lawyers' community.*" **Clients:** Advisor Technologies; AIT Group; ARVAL Phh; British Computer Society; CQ Systems; Langdale Systems; Phoneme; Star Internet.

Willoughby & Partners (see firm details p.1183) Viewed by leading practitioners as demonstrating "*genuine expertise,*" both in and outside of the region, the firm is strengthened by its respected IP practice. **Ben Goodger** (see p.447) is described as "*leading player in the field,.*" Recent instructions include advising Telecommunikacja Polska on the establishment of a B2B platform in Poland. Handling all its IT and e-commerce work, the firm has advised The Stationery Office on its transformation into a digital information business and provided EU legal and regulatory advice for Kodak in connection with its transactional e-commerce website. **Clients:** IT users; corporates.

Boyes Turner (see firm details p.891) Peers see it as "*making a big effort to bulk up on the IT side,*" while practice head **Bill Gornall-King** (see p.447)is credited with the firm's success. Its client base includes suppliers, outsourcing companies, ASPs and ISPs. Highlights of the year include advising IKON Office Solutions on its provision of facilities management services to Manchester Airport. The firm also negotiated procurement agreement terms with IBM for Kyocera-Mita, concerning warranty support of the latter's printers. Also acted for Diamond Consulting in relation to a worldwide agreement for the licensing of software technology, including a patent issue. **Clients:** CommVault Systems; Geac Computer Systems; IKON Office Solutions; Information Resources; Pink Elephant (UK) Prophecy International.

SOUTH WEST

INFORMATION TECHNOLOGY • South West	Ptnrs	Assts
1 **Osborne Clarke** Bristol	3	7
2 **Bevan Ashford** Bristol	3	4
Burges Salmon Bristol	6	13
3 **Beachcroft Wansbroughs** Bristol	4	4
Foot Anstey Sargent Plymouth	1	1
Laytons Bristol	3	8

This book is the product of 6,552 1/2 hour interviews. See p.7 for BMRB audit.
Within each band, firms are listed alphabetically.

Osborne Clarke (see firm details p.1086) "*Still pre-eminent in the market,*" the firm's client base ranges from owner-managed business suppliers through to large FTSE companies seeking procurement advice. Over the past year it has handled work for over 50 start-ups including advice on competition law issues and disputes between purchasers and suppliers. The group acted for BlueU.com in its launch of an online learning website, and negotiated content reseller agreements. Also advised the new e-commerce division of Lloyds Bank on a series of web-linking agreements, and assisted Speedwing, the IT consultancy division of British Airways, on the disposal of its airline management software business to Kale Consultants of India. **Clients:** 3i Group; Alterian; Bristol & West; Elateral; European Telecom; Knowledge Group; Marlborough Stirling; Nano Magnetics; Saitek; Strategys Group; Web Weekends.

Bevan Ashford (see firm details p.880) Viewed by its peers as undertaking "*a number of major IT PFI projects*" for a client roster that includes public sector organisations. The group has recently been advising on a procurement matter for all the NHS Trusts in Wales, concerning a financial management system. It advised on content and testing arrangements for a WAP technology provider and acted for a manufacturing company in an action regarding the supply of a defective accounts system. **Clients:** Biotrace International; Digital Mobility; Information Leverage; Orange PCS; Welsh Health Supplies; public sector bodies.

Burges Salmon (see firm details p.902) Our interviewees viewed the group as being active in the end-user market for its outstanding corporate client base, while some discerned an increased focus on winning instructions from the supplier market. The firm recently acted for Science Systems following its acquisition and subsequent distribution of CODA's international software. It also advised on the contractual matters for Bristol & West's procurement of a new mortgage administration system. In addition, it advised the Ministry of Defence on Skynet V, a PFI project involving the design and implementation phases of a satellite communication system. **Clients:** Bristol & West; CDC Solutions; FirstGroup; Gooch & Housego; New Zealand Milk; TangoZebra; United Biscuits.

Beachcroft Wansbroughs (see firm details p.872) Our researchers were informed that the firm is best known for its niche in IT PFI projects for the health service and other public sector procurement issues. The firm is also active in the private sector, providing advice to over 30 NHS Trusts, the Ministry of Defence and local authorities. Its experience includes licensing, the drafting of maintenance contracts and distribution arrangements. **Clients:** Club Med; Daimler-Benz; Dalgety; Dualit; Farnborough International Air Show; Lucent Technologies; Mercedes Benz; Sotheby's; Trace Computers.

Foot Anstey Sargent (see firm details p.961) The firm undertakes a large amount of work for internet service providers, in particular Eclipse, and has witnessed a growth in domain name disputes. Highlight of the year was winning the tender for the Planning Inspectorate to put the whole planning appeal process online. The firm has also been instructed by a company which provides online dating services to arrange its web audit work, and acted for a major regional newspaper concerning its web design contracts. **Clients:** ISPs; Eclipse; Planning Inspectorate.

Laytons (see firm details p.1031) Handling software contracts, licensing and technology transfer work, the firm recently advised Essilor, the world's largest manufacturer of optical lenses and spectacles, on a domain name dispute involving one of its branded products. The group also advised on various software contracts and dealt with a number of copyright infringement cases for the Zuken Group, an international Bristol-based software company. It is currently advising Intelligent Networking Technology on its joint ventures in the US and Australia. **Clients:** Business Link West; Essilor UK; INTY; Mayrise; Somerfield Stores; Zuken Group.

WALES

INFORMATION TECHNOLOGY • Wales	Ptnrs	Assts
1 **Edwards Geldard** Cardiff	1	3
2 **Eversheds** Cardiff	1	1
Morgan Cole Cardiff	2	3

LEADING INDIVIDUALS
1 **DELEMORE Ceri** Edwards Geldard

This book is the product of 6,552 1/2 hour interviews. See p.7 for BMRB audit.
Within each band, firms are listed alphabetically. *See individuals' profiles p.445*

Edwards Geldard (see firm details p.948) Dominates the Welsh market with its respected client base and a team of "*talented lawyers.*" Niche areas of expertise include IT-related facilities management contracts and public procurement issues. **Ceri Delemore** (see p.503) remains "*possibly the best*" IT practitioner in the region, according to our interviewees. **Clients:** British Chamber of Commerce; Citibank NA; Hyder Services; Life Fitness (UK); Pendragon; S4C; Total Engine Support; The Welsh Academy.

Eversheds (see firm details p.952) Operates with a mixed IP/IT practice. On the non-contentious side, the firm has strengths in outsourcing, system acquisition and advising start-ups, while on the contentious side it is active in disputes relating to specification compliance. The group recently acted for Halifax in its major system acquisition to support a new product. It also acted for Oddbins on the development of a website for online trading, and advised Cotec Computing Services on a high value supply dispute. **Clients:** Anacomp; DVLA; The Mortgage Code Compliance Board.

Morgan Cole (see firm details p.1074) Advises on copyright and database issues including ownership, exploitation and enforcement in the IT field and is best known for its relationships in with Welsh associations. The firm recently advised the Wales Tourist Board in relation to Project Icecube, a destination management system designed to promote tourism services to an international market where internet interface is of prime importance. **Clients:** BP Amoco; Wales Tourist Board.

MIDLANDS & EAST ANGLIA

INFORMATION TECHNOLOGY • Midlands & East Anglia	Ptnrs	Assts
1 **Eversheds** Birmingham, Nottingham	4	14
Wragge & Co Birmingham	13	35
2 **Hewitson Becke + Shaw** Cambridge, Northampton	4	4
Pinsent Curtis Biddle Birmingham	2	9

LEADING INDIVIDUALS	
1 **JONES Bill** Wragge & Co	**YATES John** V-Lex Ltd
2 **ARNOLD Michael** Eversheds	
3 **SASSE Sarah** Wragge & Co	

This book is the product of 6,552 1/2 hour interviews. See p.7 for BMRB audit.
Within each band, firms are listed alphabetically. *See individuals' profiles p.445*

Eversheds (see firm details p.952) Leading the field with its closest rival Wragge & Co, peers acknowledge that the firm has continued to "*strengthen over the past year.*" The group has a track record among software houses and outsourcing providers in matters of data protection, supply agreements and dispute resolution. National IT head **Michael Arnold** (see p.445) is an "*authority on IT outsourcing.*" The team acted for The Phoenix Consortium on the IT arrangements arising out of its purchase of MG Rover. The firm also represented BYG Systems in negotiations for a project to develop, supply and maintain e-commerce kiosks for BP service stations. Instructed by Computerland in the successful settlement of a major IT outsourcing contractual dispute. **Clients:** Computerland; Driving Standards Agency; DuPont; Hays; IBM; Misys; National Computer Centre.

Wragge & Co (see firm details p.1189) Has a stronghold over the financial services, telecoms, utilities and travel sectors, with experience in large outsourcing projects, domain name disputes, corporate finance and data protection. Its "*sheer weight of numbers*" and "*enviable client base*" ensures it top quality work in the field. Head of department **Bill Jones** is rated as "*an esteemed figure*" in the region and **Sarah Sasse** elicited market support. This year the firm completed the British Airways Software Development and IT Outsourcing project, which has a contract value of €600 million over ten years. It also acted for WH Smith on the outsourcing of the IT operations of its retail HQ and all of its high street stores across the UK, in a five year contract with an estimated value of £50 million. Instructed by Global Switch on an international joint venture with Chelsfield and TrizecHahn to create Global Switch SARL. **Clients:** AT&T; British Telecom; COLT; Driving Standards Agency; Interoute; NFU Mutual; Powergen; Recognition Systems; Vodafone.

Hewitson Becke + Shaw (see firm details p.994) Bolstered by the high level of activity in the Cambridge market, this respected team received warm commendations from our interviewees, particularly for its work in the convergence arena. The team acts for both suppliers and purchasers, dealing with licensing, distribution, development, and other procurement issues, and has advised a number of ASPs and ISPs during the year. It advised on a £2.25 million contract for the design and build of a website on behalf of an international client. It has also acted in the sale of a smartcard business, and in the £20 million sale of an IT company. **Clients:** Microsoft Research; Novell.

Pinsent Curtis Biddle (see firm details p.1098) Demonstrating a particular speciality in data protection work, the firm is also strong in PFI/public sector work. Some practitioners perceive the firm to have *"suffered a little"* with Charles Park's move to the London office, although this is counterbalanced by comment that the firm "*still has a genuine focus*" in the field. Significant instructions from the past year include acting for the NHS Executive on the National Payroll and HR Project, advising Luton and Dunstable Hospital NHS Trust on its electronic patient records procurement, and advising Worcester County Council on its financial system. **Clients:** Cendant; ITNET; Lanner Group; Misys; National Exhibition Centre; Premier Brands; Smith & Nephew; TRW.

Other Notable Practitioners **John Yates** (see p.452) of **V-Lex** is thought to have *"consolidated his position as one of the best IT lawyers around"* since joining the newly formed boutique. Peers commend his *"super attitude"* and technical ability as well as his *"masterly handling of clients."*

THE NORTH

INFORMATION TECHNOLOGY • The North	Ptnrs	Assts
1 **Masons** Leeds, Manchester	3	6
2 **Addleshaw Booth & Co** Leeds, Manchester	11	15
Eversheds Leeds	4	10
3 **Halliwell Landau** Manchester	3	7
Pinsent Curtis Biddle Leeds	7	14
4 **Hammond Suddards Edge** Leeds, Manchester	6	4
Irwin Mitchell Leeds	1	3

LEADING INDIVIDUALS	
1 **GASKILL Shelagh** Masons	
2 **PARRY Rex** Eversheds	**PEETERS Michael** Pinsent Curtis Biddle
3 **MOAKES Jonathan** Halliwell Landau	**SAMPSON Ian** Addleshaw Booth & Co
4 **DAVIS Dai** Nabarro Nathanson	**JAY Rosemary** Masons
UP AND COMING	
BOARDMAN Richard Halliwell Landau	
HARVEY Margaret Addleshaw Booth & Co	

This book is the product of 6,552 1/2 hour interviews. See p.7 for BMRB audit.
Within each band, firms are listed alphabetically. *See individuals' profiles p.445*

Masons (see firm details p.1056) Continues to be the "*practice of choice*" for IT in the North. Both the Leeds and Manchester offices have had hallmark years for large outsourcing deals and IT PFI projects, in addition to acknowledged strengths in data protection. Leeds head of department **Shelagh Gaskill** (see p.447) remains "*in a league of her own*" in the eyes of our interviewees. One practitioner claimed that "*in data protection she's the best of the best.*" Recent recruit **Rosemary Jay** (see p.x448) has a background with the Data Protection Commissioner that many clients find attractive; she "*wrote the best textbook on data protection around and puts her expertise into practice.*" Zoe Ollerenshaw has recently left the firm. Major matters from the past year include acting on the £2.5 billion outsourcing of Rolls-Royce to EDS, and drafting corporate and home shopping web site agreements for Express Dairies. The team also advised the Co-operative Bank on various internet banking initiatives. **Clients:** BAE Systems; Bradford & Bingley Building Society; Clariant UK; K2 Direct Mail; Metropolitan Police Authority; Nikoworld UK.

Addleshaw Booth & Co (see firm details p.853) The firm's Leeds and Manchester offices act for a broad range of clients in the field, including software houses, internet service providers and users who range from well-known corporates and financial institutions to public bodies and educational establishments. Interviewees applaud **Ian Sampson** (see p.450) as "*simply superb for IT contracts work,*" while **Margaret Harvey** (see p.448), recently arrived from Shaw Pittman, is said to be particularly adept at "*business process outsourcing*." Highlights from the past year include advising British American Tobacco on its global telecommunications services procurement contract, and acting for AstraZeneca on the implementation of its IT outsourcing to IBM. The firm also advised Minacs Worldwide in connection with customer relationship management services and call centre services to be provided to General Motors. **Clients:** Airtours; Alphameric Retail; British American Tobacco; First Software UK; Going Places; Iceland Foods; 3i; Romerys (Travel); Sabre Group.

Eversheds (see firm details p.952) Areas in which the Leeds office excels include supply arrangements, IT litigation and outsourcing. Department head **Rex Parry** (see p.449) is praised for his work which crosses into e-commerce. The firm recently acted for ITN in its negotiations with French supplier Dalet for the supply of a radio news production system, using its digital radio channels. It also advised Spectrasite UK on its outsourcing of helpdesk operations to EDS in addition to advising a mobile phone retailer in its dispute with a contractor supplying fixed line and internet services. **Clients:** The National Computing Centre; Parker Hannifin Corporation; Pindar; TeleCity; Welcom Software.

Halliwell Landau (see firm details p.982) Experienced in high value system procurement, supply disputes, software infringement issues and domain name disputes. The "*down to earth*" **Jonathan Moakes** (see p.507) is particularly experienced in high value systems procurement, while **Richard Boardman** (see p.501) drew market approval with one practitioner commenting that "*he's one of the most switched-on IT lawyers around – the stuff he knows and the things he's able to do are quite amazing*." Highlights from the past year include creating a suite of commercial and licensing documents for Knowledge Management Software and handling a multi-million pound software procurement for Edison Mission Energy. The firm negotiated a software licence agreement with a major mobile telephone supplier relating to WAP technology. **Clients:** Dedicated Microcomputers Group; Edison Mission Energy; Knowledge Management Software; Knowledge Support Systems Group; Time Group; Voxsurf International.

Pinsent Curtis Biddle (see firm details p.1098) Demonstrating a track record in large scale ICT contracting and outsourcing, the firm has handled systems procurement and managed services under PFI, as well as data protection advice. **Michael Peeters** (see p.450) is said to be "*highly intelligent and active in the outsourcing field*." Highlights from the past year include advising Accenture on the development of a new technology venture, and advising Morgan Stanley on a multi-million pound global framework for IT outsourcing. In addition, the team drafted international contracts for the Vocalis Group, a speech recognition technology company. **Clients:** Accenture; Department of Health; Logica; Prelude Technology; Sema Group; Square Sum; Vocalis; Weir Group.

Hammond Suddards Edge (see firm details p.984) Respected by its peers for its recent high profile work, this firm joins our listings this year. Significant matters include advising Halifax Estate Agencies, Connells and Royal & SunAlliance in relation to the online estate agency joint venture Rightmove.co.uk. The firm also acted for JSB Software Technologies (now Surfcontrol) on the $100 million acquisition of Cyber Patrol, and advised TelMe.com on various licensing deals, including Telewest and Freecom.net. **Clients:** 3i; Automotive Products; Berisford; Bradford & Bingley; Crown Cork & Seal; De Puy International; Egg; Findel; Halifax; Mita; Studentwheels.com; Yates Group.

Irwin Mitchell (see firm details p.1009) Active in both contentious and non-contentious work, the firm has secured its place in high-value transactions for a number of leading software houses, quoted companies and institutional clients. Recent work includes advising the retail chain Bewise on software implementation projects, and acting for Eiger Systems on the contractual arrangements for the licensing of an innovative financial software product. The firm also advised the multi-media division of Leeds Innovations on a number of bespoke contractual arrangements. **Clients:** Bewise; Chess Logistics; Eiger Systems; Leeds Innovations.

Other Notable Practitioners Dai Davis (see p.446) of Nabarro Nathanson heads the firm's Sheffield IT practice. He specialises in non-contentious IT projects and is thought to enjoy a following among suppliers.

SCOTLAND

INFORMATION TECHNOLOGY • Scotland	Ptnrs	Assts
1 **Maclay Murray & Spens** Edinburgh, Glasgow	6	14
2 **McGrigor Donald** Edinburgh, Glasgow	2	10
Shepherd & Wedderburn WS Edinburgh	4	17
3 **Dundas & Wilson CS** Edinburgh	3	20
4 **MacRoberts** Glasgow	2	4
Masons Edinburgh	2	7

LEADING INDIVIDUALS	
1 **FLINT David** MacRoberts	**MACPHERSON Shonaig** McGrigor Donald
NICOLSON Fiona Maclay Murray & Spens	
2 **CAMERON Gillian** Maclay Murray & Spens	
3 **BOAG-THOMSON Joanna** Shepherd & Wedderburn WS	
MCROBB Liz Shepherd & Wedderburn WS	
ORR Alistair Maclay Murray & Spens	**SALMON John** Masons
SAUNDERS James Shepherd & Wedderburn WS	

This book is the product of 6,552 1/2 hour interviews. See p.7 for BMRB audit.
Within each band, firms are listed alphabetically. *See individuals' profiles p.445*

Maclay Murray & Spens (see firm details p.1047) A "*superb IT practice*," which is admired by peers for its relationships with "*brand name software houses*." Experienced in procurement, data and domain protection and secure extranets. **Fiona Nicolson** (see p.508) is "*without a doubt a pioneer in the Scottish IT market*," while **Gillian Cameron** (see p.446) is thought to offer "*pragmatic and commercial advice*." "*Bright*" **Alistair Orr** (see p.449) is rated for his work in IT/IP cross-over work. The firm has been advising on numerous cyber squatting cases. It has also acted for TSN Sport.com, thought to be Scotland's largest dot.com start-up, in its £10 million first round investment from Warburg Pincus to create a sports portal site. In addition, it has been advising BAE on its collaboration with the Swedish airline SAS, regarding the sharing of technology and data. Also instructed by a Californian software company on the incorporation of a European subsidiary based in Scotland. **Clients:** Boehringer Ingelheim GmbH; Core Technologies; Iwerks Entertainment; SmithKlineBeecham; Spalding Sports Worldwide; Speechworks.

McGrigor Donald (see firm details p.1062) Acting for both providers and procurers, the firm has a niche in innovative PFI/PPP projects and web internet contacts. Over the past year it has advised on public sector outsourcing projects, as well as assisting old and new economy clients on website development. Building on a "*solid technology background in both IT and IP*," much of this profile is due to the talents of **Shonaig Macpherson** (see p.448). An innovator, she is credited alongside Fiona Nicholson with spotting the potential in the market. The group advised Mitel Telecom in the Glasgow Council's Secondary Schools PPP (where the ICT contract value was £54 million) and in relation to the provision of ICT services to Glasgow Council's Primary Schools covering 203 schools. The firm also advised Intelligent Finance on its systems contracts in the creation of a start-up internet bank for Halifax, and advised Caminus in its transactions with

PowerGen, London Electricity and Yorkshire Electricity. **Clients:** Caminus; Intelligent Finance; Mitel Telecommunications; Scottish Tourist Board.

Shepherd & Wedderburn WS (see firm details p.1126) Expert in high value outsourcing transactions coupled with a strong technology company client base providing spin-off IT work. UK practice head **Liz McRobb** (see p.449)is recommended for her work in outsourcing and infrastructure, while newly arrived **Joanna Boag-Thomson** (see p.445) now heads the Glasgow office's technology and intellectual property group and is said to bring "*an impressive track record from her time at MacRoberts.*" **James Saunders** (see p.451) is rated by peers for IT/IP issues connected with fundraisings. The firm has been acting for the City of Edinburgh Council in relation to its information and communication technologies project, and for Thus in the outsourcing of its IT Helpdesk function. Advised Scottish Power on the creation of the Calanais joint venture with SAIC as an outsourcing vehicle for the Scottish Power ISD division, which involved negotiating contracts with an estimated value of £400 million. **Clients:** Capital Copiers; Colt Telecommunications; Dow Carter; Flexcon; Infinite Data Storage; Magnum Power; NMT Group; Scottish & Newcastle; Signum Industries.

Dundas & Wilson CS (see firm details p.947) Seen on complex, high value outsourcings and other transactions encompassing software licensing and development, and procurement matters. Lorne Byatt's move in-house is thought to have taken the firm's "*true specialist,*" though peers commend the firm's deep well of clients. The highlight of the year was advising Bank of Scotland in a $1 billion strategic partnership with IBM, with the latter managing the provision of IT operational services. The firm also advised Glasgow City Council on the negotiation and drafting of a £36 million contract for the supply of IT equipment and services to 29 secondary schools. In addition it assisted CC Technology in its provision of software development, licensing and maintenance services. **Clients:** CC Technology; Digital Animations Group; DigMedia; First Banking Systems; Origo Services.

MacRoberts (see firm details p.1048) With a track record in multi-media work, internet-related law and international regulation, the firm has also acted on a number of licensing deals, medical device exploitation, ISP agreements and international trade agreements. The recent loss of Joanna Boag-Thompson and two assistants to Shepherd & Wedderburn is perceived to be "*a blow for the firm, hitting at its depth.*" **David Flint** (see p.447) is considered "*a clever chap who handles a lot of IT,*" although much of his time is devoted to corporate and insolvency matters. Peers credit him with "*holding the team together.*" Recent work includes acting for Giltech on the international licensing of medical products, advising the University of Strathclyde on various technology spinouts, and advising Calligrafix and Scottish Borders Internet on various internet projects. **Clients:** British Energy; Calligrafix; Dunedin International; Giltech; Initiative Software; J&J Denholm; Scottish Internet Exchange; Scottish Council for Education.

Masons (see firm details p.1056) Our research indicates that the firm has seen an increase in outsourcing, PFI work and disputes. Its client roster leans towards the supplier/developer side and peers credit the firm with "*breaking into data protection in particular.*" Practice head **John Salmon** (see p.450) is thought to have a following among a number of leading suppliers. The group advised software developer KAL in its first round of funding and assisted in the ongoing global licensing of its ATM development product, Kalignite. It has also been advising Realise, a UK e-commerce solutions provider, in development agreements with major financial organisations and a number of dot.coms. Instructed by Black Information Design, one of the UK's top ten independent e-services providers, in relation to various e-commerce development agreements. **Clients:** Black Information Design; ICL; KAL; Miller Group; Newell & Budge; Realise; Red Lemon; Spektra Group; Winning Moves.

LEADERS IN INFORMATION TECHNOLOGY

ARCHER, Quentin
Lovells, London (020) 7296 2000

ARNOLD, Michael R
Eversheds, Birmingham (0121) 232 1141
michaelarnold@eversheds.com
Specialisation: System development, outsourcing, e-commerce. Head of *Eversheds* IT group.
Prof. Memberships: Society for Computers and Law.
Career: MA (Cantab). Qualified with *Eversheds* 1984. Partner 1990.
Personal: Cricket.

BAILES, Tony
Nabarro Nathanson, Reading (0118) 925 4602
a.bailes@nabarro.com
Specialisation: Partner and head of technology, media and telecommunications group. Sole area of practice is in IT and e-commerce disputes of all types, acting for a wide range of major US and European owned multinational computer and communication companies, including Sun Microsystems and Siemens. Jointly led the team acting for the major complainant in the landmark Digital case before the EC Commission. Acted with a fast growing specialist team in relation to over 30 substantial high-value disputes arising from systems integration and software development contracts, outsourcing contracts and PFI based projects.
Personal: Born 15.05.51. Married with four children. Lives in Oxford.

BARRETT, David
Simmons & Simmons, London (020) 7628 2020
david.barrett@simmons-simmons.com
Specialisation: Partner and head of information technology practice. Responsible for practice in information technology, communications, computer technology transfer, information systems and business systems outsourcing, IT & telecommunications procurement and supply, multimedia and international projects.

BICKERSTAFF, Roger
Bird & Bird, London (020) 7415 6000
Specialisation: Principle area of practice is information technology. He is Co-Head of the Information Technology group. His particular work focus is large-scale IT-infrastructure projects, including outsourcing, partnering and PFI projects and e-commerce infrastructure development. Other specialities include IT contract management and IT dispute resolution, protection of rights, e-commerce, the impact of EC legislation and impact of new technology. Also advises on all aspects of EC/GATT procurement law. Clients include many government departments and major private sector IT purchasers.
Prof. Memberships: Society for Computers and Law.
Career: Qualified in 1990. At *Linklaters & Paines* 1990-92. Joined *Bird & Bird* in 1992 and became a Partner in 1995.
Personal: Born 1961. Attended King's College, Cambridge 1980-84. Lives in London.

BOAG-THOMSON, Joanna
Shepherd & Wedderburn WS, Glasgow
(0141) 566 8570
joanna.bt@shepwedd.co.uk
Specialisation: Accredited by Law Society of Scotland as a specialist in intellectual property law. Principal areas of practice is e-commerce and IP/IT, with a focus on B2B e-commerce. Was part of Scottish Enterprise's E-commerce Strategy Committee for Scotland.
Prof. Memberships: Law Society of Scotland; Licensing Executives Society; TIPLO; Society for Computers and Law.
Career: Trained *Wright Johnston & Mackenzie*, Glasgow and Edinburgh 1988-90. Assistant *Wright Johnston & Mackenzie Callander* 1990-91. Assistant *Bird Semple Fyfe Ireland* 1991-93. Assistant, associate then partner *MacRoberts* 1993-2000. Partner in IP and technology at *Shepherd & Wedderburn* 2000 to date.
Publications: Numerous magazine and newspaper articles. Co-edited Greens 'Scottish E-commerce Handbook'.
Personal: Educated Craighome School, Glasgow, then LLB and Dip LP at Edinburgh University. Interests – theatre, travel, reading and writing.

BOARDMAN, Richard
Halliwell Landau, Manchester (0161) 831 2905 / 0467 790 981
rboardman@halliwells.co.uk
See under Intellectual Property, p.501

BREWARD, Alastair
Taylor Joynson Garrett, London (020) 7300 7000

BURNETT, Rachel
Salans Hertzfeld & Heilbronn HRK, London (020) 7509 6000
rburnett@salans.com
Specialisation: Partner specialising in information technology. Practice covers contract negotiation, drafting and related commercial advice for the full range of IT and e-commerce industry transactions. Acts for major vendors, system integrators, software publishers, data licensors, service providers, resellers, major corporate and financial services sectors. Co-author of 'Drafting and Negotiating Computer Contracts' (Butterworths, 1994), author of 'Outsourcing IT – The Legal Aspects' (Gower, 1998). Editor of the IT Law Guides Series for the Institute of Chartered Accountants. Writes and lectures widely on IT-related matters.
Prof. Memberships: Institute for Information Systems Management Chairman; Worshipful Company of Information Technologists (Court Livery Member); British Computer Society (Vice-President, Management); Society for Computers & Law; Law Society.
Career: Qualified 1980. Former IT professional.
Personal: Exeter University (BA Soc. Studies, Hons). Associate, Institute of Linguists (French). Chair, Association of Women Solicitors, 1990-91.

CAMERON, Gillian
Maclay Murray & Spens, Glasgow (0141) 248 5011
gjc@maclaymurrayspens.co.uk
Specialisation: Partner in IP & Technology Department. Specialises in IP generally and non-contentious IT/ internet work in particular for a wide range of clients, including advising Scotland's largest dotcom startup and various ISPs. Accredited as an IP specialist by the Law Society of Scotland and an honorary lecturer at Strathclyde University's Hunter Centre for Entrepreneurship.
Prof. Memberships: Member of Licensing Executives Society.
Career: LLB (Hons) Edinburgh University (1987); Dip LP (1988); Joined *Maclay Murray & Spens* in 1996; previously Head of Technology Law Unit at *Bird Semple*.

CARBONI, Anna
Linklaters, London (020) 7456 5810
anna.carboni@linklaters.com
See under Intellectual Property, p.502

CAROLINA, Robert
Tarlo Lyons, London (020) 7405 2000
robert.carolina@tarlolyons.com
Specialisation: Focuses entirely upon commercial transactions and projects involving telecommunications and information technology. Represents users, purchasers, developers and vendors of related products and services, and advises on electronic commerce transactions and projects. Related areas of expertise include technology outsourcing and facilities management arrangements, technology and telecommunications system and services procurement and technology distribution and licensing. Senior visiting fellow with the Information Security Group at Royal Holloway (University of London).
Prof. Memberships: American Bar Association; Illinois State Bar Association; Law Society; Society for Computers and Law; Computer Law Association; The Internet Society.
Career: University of Dayton (BA, 1988); Georgetown University Law Center (JD, 1991); London School of Economics (LLM International Business Law, 1993). Qualified in 1991. Gained experience as an in-house lawyer with an Internet software developer in the US and four years additional experience working in the technology and communications law practice at *Clifford Chance*. Joined *Tarlo Lyons* in 1998.
Publications: Published articles include The European Database Directive: An Introduction for Practitioners, 'The Journal of Proprietary Rights vol 8 no 9 (September 1996); The Internet & Financial Services, 'Tolley's Compliance Monitor' vol 8 no 10 (March 1996, co-author); Commercial Transactions on the Global Information Infrastructure: A European Perspective, 14 'John Marshall Journal of Computer and Information Law 269 (Winter 1996, co-author); Legal Aspects of Software Protection Devices 11 'Computer Law and Security Report 188 (July/August 1995); Multimedia Defamation 12 'International Media Law' (March 1994), co-author.
Personal: Born 1964, Ohio, USA. Married. Resides in central London. Leisure interests include music and cinema.

CHISSICK, Michael
Field Fisher Waterhouse, London (020) 7861 4000
mpc@ffwlaw.com
Specialisation: Head of IT and e-commerce law group which comprises a team of seven partners and 18 specialist lawyers. Main areas of practice include outsourcing projects, data protection, digital mixed media, electronic commerce and m-commerce contracts, linking agreements, software contracts and internet law. In the past year has advised on several major outsourcing projects, including advising Lewisham Council on a major outsourcing of all its IT and communication infrastructures and Thomas Cook on its e-commerce projects.
Prof. Memberships: Law Society; Solicitors European Group; FAST Legal Advisory Group; Computer Law Association.
Career: 1st Class Degree in Law (LLB); Law Society Finals 1st Class; Masters Degree in IT and Telecommunications.
Publications: Author of 'Internet Law' published in October 1997 by FT Publications and co-author of 'Electronic Commerce Law and Practice' published in 1999 and 2000 by Sweet & Maxwell.

DAVIES, Clive
D J Freeman, London (020) 7583 4567
cld@djfreeman.co.uk
Specialisation: Partner media and communications department. All aspects of information technology and communications law particularly PFI, major procurement contracts, outsourcing and software development. Internet and e-commerce work includes website development, content and linking agreements and contracts with ISP's. Regularly advises on related competition and European issues. Acts for a variety of computer, telecommunications and media clients including Bull Information Systems Limited, Consignia, Pilat Media, the British Phonographic Industry (BPI) and Energis.
Prof. Memberships: Member of CBI Intellectual Property Working Group.
Career: Qualified 1977. Joined *D J Freeman* 1990. Partner 1991.
Publications: Author of publications on the internet, 'E-mail and the Law', and 'E-commerce Start Ups' and a chapter of copyright and the internet in a Unicom Electronic Commerce Report. On editorial team of 'Tolleys Communications Law'.
Personal: Born 30.9.52. Educated Royal Grammar School Worcester and Manchester University (LLB Hons). Leisure activities include family, skiing, sailing and tennis.

DAVIS, Dai
Nabarro Nathanson, Sheffield (0114) 279 4000
d.davis@nabarro.com
Specialisation: Consultant. Main areas of practice are computer, internet and technology law. Advises on sale of computer systems, licensing of computer systems, intellectual property, joint ventures, development agreements and facility management agreements. Expert in internet and e-commerce legal issues. Clients range from start-up dot.coms to large plcs. Also advises on the safety of technological products and on compliance with technology related European Union legislation such as Electromagnetic Compatibility Directive. Contributor to and consultant editor to Croner's Electronic Commerce and to Croner's Industrial Equipment Safety. Speaker at many national and international conferences; co-opted legal expert to BSI committee DS/1/1 and convenor of IEC Committee TC56 Legal Working Group.
Prof. Memberships: Solicitor; Member of Institution of Electrical Engineers; Chartered Engineer; Member of Royal Academy for the Arts, Manufacture and Commerce; Honorary Scientific Member of International Association of Cybernetics; Honorary Member of Centre for International Legal Studies; Member of Licensing Executives Society.
Career: Joined *Eversheds Hepworth & Chadwick* in 1987; became a partner in 1992; head of *Eversheds* national IT law practice 1995-98.
Personal: Born 2nd March 1958. Took a Physics MA at Keble College, Oxford 1976-79; then MSc Computing Science at Newcastle University 1981-83. Leisure interests include tennis, reading and cooking. Lives in Boston Spa.

DELEMORE, Ceri
Edwards Geldard, Cardiff (029) 2023 8239
ceri.delemore@geldards.co.uk
See under Intellectual Property, p.503

DINSDALE, Danelle
DLA, London (08700) 111 111

ELLACOTT, Sara
Nabarro Nathanson, Reading (0118) 925 4616
s.ellacott@nabarro.com
Specialisation: Internet related and e-commerce issues, with particular expertise in e-mail issues, cybersquatting, domain names and Meta-tags; largescale IT disputes, mainly acting for large IT suppliers; advising internet start ups on aspects of setting up and running their businesses.
Prof. Memberships: TIPLO. Thames Valley Commercial Lawyers Association.
Career: *Turner Kenneth Brown*, trainee solicitor (March 1989 – 1991); solicitor (March 1991 – May 1995). *Nabarro Nathanson*, solicitor (May 1995 – May 1998); partner (May1998).
Publications: 'Email scanning may breach privacy' – Computing (May 2000). 'IT companies need to pre-

pare for new email privacy rights' – Corporate Briefing (April 2000). 'Private Lives – privacy, human rights and e-mail' – IT Consultant (March 2000). 'Use of emails within the working environment' (Charity Finance Yearbook 2000). 'Domain names explained' – The Business Magazine (October 1999). 'The Year 2000: issues of conformity, discovery and legal privilege' – IT, Communications and Law (February 1999) Commercial Litigation (January 1999).
Personal: Lincoln College Oxford – BA Hons in Jurisprudence. Post Graduate Diploma in UK and European Copyright and Related Rights – Kings College London. Married, one child.

FLINT, David
MacRoberts, Glasgow (0141) 332 9988
df@macroberts.co.uk
Specialisation: Partner in IP and technology law group. Corporate and commercial matters including commercial contracts, patents, trade marks, copyright and other intellectual property licensing, computer and technology contracts, agency and distribution agreements, restrictive practices and competition law in terms of both EU and UK law. Author of 'Liquidation in Scotland'; EU Competition Law section of 'Stair Memorial Encyclopaedia of the Laws of Scotland'; executive editor 'Greens Scottish E-commerce Handbook'. Extensive lecturing experience on a variety of legal and IT subjects.
Prof. Memberships: Licensing Executives Society; Insolvency Practitioners Association; Association of Business Recovery Professionals; Institute of Credit Management; The Computer Law Association Inc; Union Internationale des Avocats; UK Association for European Law; American Bar Association (associate); member of Joint Working Party of Scottish, English and Northern Irish Law Societies and Bars on Competition Law (since 1981); member of CBI Competition Panel; member of Law Society of Scotland Intellectual Property Law and International Relations Committees; licensed insolvency practitioner.
Career: Qualified in 1979. Assistant in *MacRoberts* company and commercial department 1979-84 and partner from May 1984. Admitted Notary Public 1980. Chairman of Scottish Lawyers European Group 1985-95.
Personal: Educated at the High School of Glasgow 1964-73, the University of Glasgow (LLB 1976 and LLM 1982), and the Europa Institut, Universiteit van Amsterdam (Diploma in European Integration 1978). Director of Giltech Ltd, The Shareholding & Investment Trust Ltd, Renfrewshire Chamber of Commerce and Advoc Ltd.

GARDNER, Nick
Herbert Smith, London (020) 7374 8000
Specialisation: Partner in intellectual property and information technology department. Deals with intellectual property and technology, specialising in matters involving technical issues in the computing and electronics field. Contentious and non-contentious work. Admitted as a Solicitor Advocate with rights of audience in all civil proceedings. Appointed expert for internet domain name determinations by the World Intellectual Property Organisation.
Career: A number of years experience in the electronic and computing industries before becoming a solicitor. Qualified in 1988 and became a partner at *Herbert Smith* in 1994. Handled the first Internet domain name case in front of the English courts, acting for Harrods. Acted for Amstrad in its record breaking £50 million plus judgment against Seagate Technology. Acting for National Air Traffic Services in relation to a £50 million plus claim brought by EDS. Also deals with data protection matter and has advised a number of utilities in relation to Data Protection Tribunal Proceedings. Handles a wide range of internet and e-commerce work as well as traditional hardware and software contracts.
Personal: Educated at the University of Nottingham.

GARDNER, Paul
Osborne Clarke, London (020) 7809 1000

GASKILL, Shelagh
Masons, Leeds (0113) 233 8905
shelagh.gaskill@masons.com
Specialisation: Partner and Head of Data Protection Group. Industrial and commercial IT outsourcing deals, information law, data protection law, database design, international data flows, electronic and new media and major infrastructure projects.
Prof. Memberships: Associate Member of BCS.
Career: Lecturer – Faculty of Law, University of Leeds 1979-84. Qualified 1986. At *Dibb Lupton Broomhead* 1984-94 (Partner from 1993). Joined *Masons* as a Partner in 1994.
Personal: Interests: opera and bridge.

GOODGER, Ben
Willoughby & Partners, Oxford (01865) 791 990
ben@iprights.com
Specialisation: Partner in intellectual property department. Advises on all aspects of the commercial exploitation and management of IP. Specialist areas: Internet, e-commerce and IT law; technology transfer, patenting and biotechnology; trade marks and brand management; IP audits and strategy consulting. Also handles other general IP and commercial law, including advertising and trading standards.
Prof. Memberships: Past President of Licensing Executives Society; Secretary: Society for Computers & Law (Thames Valley Group); IPI; INTA, on Editorial Boards for 'Global eCommerce' and 'Euro Watch' journals.
Career: Exhibition to Keble College, Oxford; *Frere Cholmeley* 1986-90; *Denton Hall* 1990-93; *Dallas Brett* 1993-97. *Willoughby & Partners* 1997 to date.
Personal: Married with three children; plays the bassoon; architecture; drama; drawing.

GORNALL-KING, William
Boyes Turner, Reading (0118) 959 7711
wgornall-king@boyesturner.com
Specialisation: Partner and head of technology and commerce group. Main areas of practice are technology and computer law including intellectual property. Advises on e-commerce, internet, multimedia and software development, integration, distribution and outsourcing contracts. Clients include major multinationals in software, data and storage products including Information Resources Inc (CPG data); the Met Office (weather data) and CommVault Inc (data storage and warehousing) as well as peripherals suppliers (Kyocera-Mita, Tally) and ISPs & ASPs. Advises clients on e-commerce strategies and data protection issues.
Prof. Memberships: Law Society, Society for Computers and Law, British Computer Society, ISPA, TVCLA, SEG and Data Protection Forum.
Career: *Clarks* 1980-88 (partner from 1985). Joined *Boyes Turner* as partner 1988.
Publications: Contributes articles of topical interest in technology field for 'Business Magazine' and other publications.
Personal: Brighton College (1971-76); LLB (Hons) University of Exeter (1979). Married with two children. Vice President Redingensians RFC, coaches mini-rugby; cycling; opera and military history. Vice Chairman Reading Area Committee Thames Valley Chamber of Commerce.

GRAHAM, Rory
Osborne Clarke, London (020) 7809 1000

GRIFFITHS, David
Clifford Chance, London (020) 7600 1000
david.griffiths@cliffordchance.com
Specialisation: Partner specialising in computer and IT, and telecommunications.
Career: Cambridge (MA Law). Articled *Clifford Turner/Clifford Chance*; qualified 1983; partner *Clifford Chance* since 1990.

HAMBLIN, Julian
Bond Pearce, Southampton (023) 8082 8888
jhamblin@bondpearce.com
Specialisation: Partner and Head of the Information Technology and Intellectual Property Group. Specialises in information technology, intellectual property, internet and data protection issues acting for major retailers, government bodies, universities, and software companies. Focus is on development and licensing of computer software, outsourcing, online services and e-commerce.
Prof. Memberships: The Intellectual Property Lawyer's Organisation and the Society for Computers and Law.
Career: Qualified 1987 following articles with *Pickering Kenyon.* Joined *Boodle Hatfield* 1987 and *Bond Pearce* in 1995 following the firm's acquisition of *Boodle Hatfield's* Southampton office.

HARRINGTON, Alison
Garretts, Reading (0118) 949 0000
alison.harrington@glegal.com
See under E-commerce, p.295

HART, Michael
Baker & McKenzie, London (020) 7919 1000
michael.hart@bakernet.com
Specialisation: Principal area of practice is contentious and non-contentious IP and IT Law. Work includes copyright, trade marks and passing off, patents and trade secrets, computer copyright disputes, broadcasting and media law. Also deals with government regulations and trade libel. Has represented various trade bodies in lobbying activities relating to UK and EU legislative proposals, including the copyright in the Information Society Directive. Has acted in numerous IP court actions representing companies such as Fila, McLaren, Seiko, Versace, Apple Computer and Sony.
Prof. Memberships: Anti-counterfeiting Group, AIPPI, Intellectual Property Lawyers Association
Career: Qualified in 1983. With *Linklaters & Paines* 1983-87. Joined *Baker & McKenzie* in 1987 and became a partner in 1990.
Personal: Born 12 August 1959. Educated at City of London School 1970-77 and Exeter College, Oxford 1977-80. Leisure activities include theatre, cinema, horse racing and tennis. Lives in London.

HARVEY, Margaret
Addleshaw Booth & Co, Manchester
(0161) 934 6348
mzh@addleshawbooth.co.uk
Specialisation: Technology law including major IT supply and implementation projects and e-commerce related advice. Particular speciality in outsourcing both technology related and business process outsourcing.
Prof. Memberships: Computer Law Group; Society for Computers and Law; Computer Law Association.
Career: Qualified with *Boodle Hatfield* in 1987, legal counsel IBM 1988-93, head of legal for Price Waterhouse Management Consultants 1993 to 1998; partner *Shaw Pittman* 1998 to 2000; partner *Addleshaw Booth & Co* 2000-.
Publications: Various articles on technology and outsourcing related issues. Contributing author 'IBC Distance Learning Course on IT and Telecommunications'; regular speaker on IT and outsourcing Sheffield University LLB 1984.
Personal: Walking, sailing, husband Jack Rockett.

HIGHAM, Nicholas
Denton Wilde Sapte, London (020) 7242 1212
nach@dentonwildesapte.com
See under Telecommunications, p.813

HOLT, Jeremy
Clark Holt, Swindon (01793) 617 444
Specialisation: Partner specialising in computer law. Advises on all aspects of non-contentious work including internet related contracts, software rights, system purchase agreements and maintenance contracts.
Prof. Memberships: Society for Computers and Law, British Computer Society.
Career: Qualified in 1980, co-founded *Clark Holt* Commercial Solicitors in 1995.
Personal: Born 1956. Leisure interests include military history, five-a-side football and reading computer magazines.

JACOBS, Laurence
Allen & Overy, London (020) 7330 3000
laurence.jacobs @allenovery.com
Specialisation: Partner in the Communications, Media and Technology Group specialising in information technology, e-commerce and related intellectual property matters. He advises on system development and integration projects, outsourcing, public procurement, electronic commerce and technology joint ventures.
Prof. Memberships: He was a member of the Computer & Law Society working party on law reform for electronic commerce reporting to the DTJ and is Chairman of the International Communications Round Table Working Party on copyright and new media.
Career: Qualified *Clifford Chance* 1990. Partner *Allen & Overy* 1997.
Personal: Born 1960. Educated Queens College and Kings College, Cambridge University.

JAY, Rosemary
Masons, Manchester (0161) 234 8234
rosemary.jay@masons.com
Specialisation: Personal information law, confidentiality, privacy, freedom of information, human rights, international privacy, and data protection. Legal expert to a European Commission funded Study on the role of standards in achieving privacy protection. Advice on the data protection aspects of Hello Limited v Northern Shell, Michael Douglas and Catherine Zeta-Jones.
Prof. Memberships: Member of the Society for Computers and Law.
Career: Stockport Metropolitan Borough Council 1979-84. Qualified 1981. Principal solicitor at Vale Royal District Council 1984-87. Head of Legal, Office of the Data Protection Register (now Information Commissioner) 1987-99. Joined *Masons* in Novem ber 1999.
Publications: Co-author of Data Protection Law & Practice, general editor of the Encyclopedia of Data Protection and regular columnist for 'Society of Computers and Law' magazine.
Personal: Interests: Gardening and theatre.

JONES, Bill
Wragge & Co, Birmingham (0870) 903 1000

KECK, Colleen
Allen & Overy, London (020) 7330 3000
colleen.keck@allenovery.com
Specialisation: Colleen is a corporate partner who has practised law in both the UK and USA as in-house and external counsel. She has extensive experience in negotiating and drafting all types of agreements used in and by the bioscience, information technology, media and communications industries including emerging bioinformaties field. She acts for both customers and suppliers, with particular expertise in on-line services and products (including e/m-commerce), joint ventures, collaborations, outsourcing and systems integration projects.
Prof. Memberships: International Trade Mark Association, Canadian Bar Association, Alberta Law Society, Licensing Executives Society, Associate Member of the Pharmaceuticals Trade Mark Group.
Career: Barrister and solicitor, Home Oil Company Ltd (1983-88); associate *Allen & Overy* (1988-92), partner (since 1992).
Personal: Born 1958. Educated University of Saskatchewan (LLB 1982, BA 1985); University of London (LLM 1987). Admitted as solicitor/called to Bar Alberta Canada, England & Wales 1988.

KEMP, Richard
Kemp Little LLP, London (020) 7710 1610
richardk@comlegal.com
See under E-commerce, p.296

LISTER, Richard
Freshfields Bruckhaus Deringer, London
(020) 7936 4000
richard.lister@freshfields.com
Specialisation: IT/Telecoms transactional work (procurement, outsourcing, joint ventures) for customers and suppliers. Advises on e-commerce projects and on-line services generally (contract, intellectual property, data protection, security.)
Prof. Memberships: Law Society. American Bar Association. Society for Computers and Law.
Career: Joined *Berwin Leighton* 1989 and became a partner in 1997. Partner at *Freshfields* 1999.
Personal: Born 1966. Educated Manchester Grammar School and University College, Cardiff. Married with two children.

LUBBOCK, Mark
Ashurst Morris Crisp, London (020) 7638 1111
mark.lubbock@ashursts.com
Specialisation: IT/E-commerce/IP.
Prof. Memberships: Law Society; Society for Computers & Law; Associate Member of Trade Mark Agents; and Computer Law Group
Career: Articles *McKenna & Co (1982-84), McKenna & Co* (1984-88); and *Ashurst Morris Crisp* (1988-date).
Publications: Intellectual Property Section of Sweet and Maxwell's 'Practical Commercial Precedents'; Intellectual Property Section of Sweet and Maxwell's 'Practical Commercial Checklists'; 'E-Commerce – Doing Business Electronically, A Practical Guide'. Published by The Stationery Office, 2000.
Personal: Education: Cranleigh and Peterhouse, Cambridge. Interests: Rugby, cricket, tennis, modern art and lately, babies.

MACPHERSON, Shonaig
McGrigor Donald, Edinburgh (0131) 777 7000
Specialisation: Handles all aspects of intellectual property and information technology work. Advises on protection strategies, funding for technology projects, licensing, research contracts, litigation and dispute resolution, expertise on software licensing, systems developments and procurement, outsourcing and facilities management contracts. Speaker at Glasgow IT summits in 1993 and 1994, and at the International Science Festival in Edinburgh in 1992, 1993 and 1994, Chicago 1996.
Prof. Memberships: Law Society (England & Wales), Law Society (Scotland), Licensing Executives Society, Royal Society, Scottish Biomedical Association, Scottish Biomedical Research Trust. Visiting Professor at Heriot-Watt University, Society for Computers and the Law.
Career: Qualified in 1984 in England & Wales with *Norton Rose*. Assistant Company Secretary (Legal) Storehouse plc, then Legal Director of Harrods 1987-89. Partner at *Calow Easton* in London 1989-91. Qualified in Scotland 1991. Joined *McGrigor Donald* in 1991 and became a partner in 1992.
Personal: Born 29th September 1958. Director of Edinburgh Chamber of Commerce and Enterprise. Recreations include theatre, opera and reading. Lives in Edinburgh.

MARTINDALE, Avril
Freshfields Bruckhaus Deringer, London
(020) 7936 4000
avril.martindale@freshfields.com
See under Intellectual Property, p.507

MAUGHAN, Alistair
Shaw Pittman, London (020) 7847 9562
alistair.maughan@shawpittman.com
Specialisation: Partner in Global Technology Group. Acts for major technology users and vendors, government departments, banks and manufacturing entities. Focus on complex and strategic technology projects, particularly outsourcing and e-commerce. Involved in major IT PFI projects (BA – POCL, Inland Revenue – NIRS2, Home Office – Police mobile radio replacement project), DSS – ACCORD. Specialises in IT, e-commerce and technology acquisition supply contracts. Work is mainly non-contentious and divided equally between major government contracts and contracts for private sector clients. Author of several articles on computer law. Lectures on outsourcing, e-commerce and acquiring

computer systems. Contributing author to Sweet and Maxwell's 'Outsourcing Practice Manual'.
Prof. Memberships: Law Society, New York State Bar, NY State Bar Association, Society for Computers and Law, Computer Law Association.
Career: Qualified in 1987. With *Boodle Hatfield* 1985-89, then *Crowell & Moring* in Washington D.C, 1989-92. Qualified in New York in 1990. At *Theodore Goddard* 1992-93, before joining *Dibb Lupton Broomhead* in 1993. Became a partner in 1994. Joined *Shaw Pittman* in 1998.

MCCALLOUGH, Rob
Masons, London (020) 7490 6236
rob.mccallough@masons.com
Specialisation: Partner and Head of Information & Technology Group. Has international experience in handling large commercial and technology-related disputes involving arbitration, litigation and Alternative Dispute Resolution relating to hardware and software procurement, project management, product liability, licensing, outsourcing and PFI contracts. He specialises in legal risk management and dispute resolution for the computer, telecommunications and other technology-related industries. He also lectures widely upon commercial and legal issues relevant to the IT industries.
Prof. Memberships: Hong Kong Law Society; English Law Society; the N.C.C.; European workshop for resolution of telecommunications disputes and the Worshipful Company of Information Technologists.
Career: Qualified in 1975. At *Hill & Perks*, Norwich 1975-78. Member of Attorney General's Chambers in Hong Kong 1978-83. Joined *Masons* (Hong Kong) in 1983. Became a Partner in 1984.

MCROBB, Liz
Shepherd & Wedderburn WS, Glasgow
(0141) 566 9900
liz.mcrobb@shepwedd.co.uk
Specialisation: Head of the firm's technology and intellectual property group which combines specialists in IT and intellectual property for young technology companies and major IT projects. Experienced in advising on all aspects of intellectual property protection and exploitation. Particular interest over recent years in advising public and private sector clients in procurement of IT, outsourcing arrangements, software development and support including recent engagement on major MoD project and leadership of Scottish Electricity Settlements organisation's contractual arrangements to procure systems required for the deregulated electricity market. Also acted recently for Scottish Power UK plc in its £48m outsourcing and joint venture relative to its IS Division and acted for City of Edinburgh Council in its IT PPP outsourcing of the entire IT division which completed earlier this year.
Prof. Memberships: Law Society of Scotland.
Career: Joined *Shepherd & Wedderburn WS* in 1993 and became a partner in 1996. Qualified in English Law 1995.

MILLARD, Christopher
Clifford Chance, London (020) 7600 1000
christopher.millard@cliffordchance.com
See under E-commerce, p.296

MOAKES, Jonathan
Halliwell Landau, Manchester (0161) 835 3003
See under Intellectual Property, p.507

MONAGHAN, Iain
Masons, London (020) 7490 6239
iain.monaghan@masons.com
Specialisation: Partner Information & Technology Group. Iain has advised on some of the UK's largest and most innovative ICT and business process outsourcing transactions. Has led teams handling PFI-funded ICT and business process procurement and the first private sector property outsourcing. In e-commerce, deals with procurement of services for prospective businesses and advises clients, particularly in the financial sector, upon the customer/commercial interface. Led a team advising on the establishment of the first off-shore internet bank in Europe and is involved in various projects relating to the development of e-banking and e-procurement.
Prof. Memberships: Law Society.
Career: MA (Cantab).

MORGAN, Glyn
Taylor Joynson Garrett, London (020) 7300 7000

NICHOLSON, Kim
Olswang, London (020) 7208 8731
kan@olswang.com
Specialisation: Partner and head of IT and telecommunications unit. Practice covers on the corporate side: corporate finance, venture capital, syndicated equity funding, mergers and acquisitions, IPOs, takeovers, all within the online, communications and technology industries; on the commercial side: contracts for exploitation of products, licensing, content deals, distribution exploitation and carriage deals in or related to the online and communications industry for clients ranging from multinational plcs through to internet start-ups, for example Thus plc, NetStore plc, Sportal International Limited, Freeserve plc, Raw Communications Hons Limited, UUNet Technologies Inc and Motorola Inc.
Career: Qualified 1985. Joined *Olswang* as a partner in 1993.
Personal: Born 30 November 1960. Educated at Birmingham University and College of Law, London. Interests include opera, music, hill walking, art and antiques.

NICOLSON, Fiona
Maclay Murray & Spens, Glasgow
(0141) 248 5011
fmmn@maclaymurrayspens.co.uk
See under Intellectual Property, p.508

O'LEARY, Marcus
The Law Offices of Marcus J. O'Leary, Bracknell
(01344) 303044
Specialisation: IT: Main area of practice is IT, including the drafting and negotiation of computer and software distribution, development, tpm, outsourcing, evaluation, VAR and licensing arrangements. All areas covered especially internet and e-commerce issues, (including cybersquatting), multimedia, disaster recovery, database, software piracy, data protection, matters and disputes generally. IP: Other principal area of practice is intellectual property where experience encompasses copyright and designs generally, patents, biotechnology, trade marks, branding, passing off, confidential information, trade libel, music, media and entertainment (particularly the new methods of music delivery), franchising and character merchandising, as well as intellectual property health checks and IP litigation. Advertising and Sales Promotion: Healthy advertising and marketing practice involving copy advice on marketing/advertising and promotional campaigns on TV, in print, on the Internet and in direct marketing – including multimedia material. Dealing with agency/client relationships including drafting suitable contracts. Acts for some of the world's leading international technology companies.
Prof. Memberships: Law Society, Society for Computers and the Law, British Japanese Law Association and member of the legal advisory group to FAST.
Career: Over 20 years experience in the IT industry. Previously an accountant, then qualified as a barrister, later requalifying as a solicitor, Manager of Legal Affairs at Hewlett Packard and was negotiating IT contracts for them as long ago as 1978. In-house as an Intellectual Property Lawyer for the United Biscuits Group in the mid 1980s, moving to *Pitmans* in 1989 and forming their IP/IT department. With two others founded the Reading office of *Garrett & Co* in 1994 and set up *Garrett's* IP/IT function including a worldwide network of IP/IT lawyers. Launched *The Law Offices of Marcus J O'Leary* in 1995, which has gone from strength to strength since that date.
Personal: Born 31st October 1952. Educated at London University and the Inns of Court School of Law. Enjoys sailing, writing, and scrambling in the mountains. Lives in Eversley, Hampshire.

ORR, Alistair C
Maclay Murray & Spens, Edinburgh
(0131) 226 5196
aco@maclaymurrayspens.co.uk
Specialisation: Partner in IP and technology department based in Edinburgh office. Specialises in non-contentious IP and IT issues. Recent experience includes advising Scottish Enterprise on its flagship Project Alba and advising the Information System Division of Scottish Power. Has negotiated a number of significant outsourcing transactions including acting for the purchasers of the Pringle knitwear business from Dawson, and in particular on the trademark aspects of this acquisition; advising Scottish Widows on a variety of IP/IT and outsourcing transactions; adviser in Scotland to Nominet, the UK domain name authority, on a variety of internet related issues. Other clients include 3i, BAe, Claims Direct, Enron, Hibernian FC, John Menzies, the Royal Bank of Scotland and a variety of growing high-tech and dotcom business.
Prof. Memberships: Honorary Secretary of The Internet Society of Scotland; member of Licensing Executives Society; member of IMAS (Interactive Media Alliance Scotland).
Career: Trained *Dundas & Wilson CS*; qualified October 1992; assistant solicitor *Dundas & Wilson* 1992-94; assistant solicitor 1994-96; associate 1996-98; partner since 1998 *Maclay Murray & Spens.*
Personal: Born 1964. Educated at University of Glasgow, Balliol College Oxford (LLB, Dip LP, MLitt). Enjoys rugby, swimming, reading. Resides Edinburgh.

PARRY, Rex
Eversheds, Leeds (0113) 200 4230
rexparry@eversheds.com
Specialisation: All aspects of IT and digital media work except litigation, with particular emphasis on outsourcing, e-commerce, the Internet and related agreements.
Prof. Memberships: Society for Computers and Law and Computer Law Association.

Career: Qualified in 1989; *Frere Cholmeley* from 1987 to 1992. Joined *Eversheds* in 1992, becoming a partner in 1996.
Personal: Born 1965. Fanatical trout fisherman. Interests also include walking and wine.

PEARSON, Hilary
Bird & Bird, London (020) 7415 6000
Specialisation: Partner in Intellectual Property Department. Main areas of practice are intellectual property and computer law. Barrister in patent chambers then worked in Silicon Valley 1980-83, becoming involved in the start of the personal computer industry. Since then has represented a wide range of hardware, software, semiconductor manufacturing equipment and component suppliers. Work includes IT-related patent litigation and computer contract litigation and non-contentious issues.
Prof. Memberships: American Bar Association, Computer Law Association, Licensing Executives Society, American IP Law Association.
Career: Qualified 1976. New Court, Temple 1977-80; *Rosenblum, Parrish & Bacigalupi,* San Francisco 1980-83; *Arnold White & Durkee,* Houston 1983-90. *Simmons & Simmons,* London 1990-95. Joined *Bird & Bird* in 1995. Member of the Californian Bar 1981 and Texas Bar 1985; US Patent Attorney.
Publications: Author of 'Computer Contracts' (1983) and 'Commercial Exploitation of Intellectual Property' (1990). Contributor to 'Internet Law and Regulation' (1996, 1997).
Personal: Born 1943. Holds BA/MA (Oxon) Hons Physics 1965-69, and LLB (London) 1975.

PEETERS, Michael
Pinsent Curtis Biddle, Leeds (0113) 244 5000
michael.peeters@pinsents.com
Specialisation: Head of Commerce, Trade, Technology and Media Group in Leeds. Principal area of practice is information technology law including major IT procurement and outsourcing contracts, data protection, telecommunications, electronic trading, software licensing and distribution, and dispute resolution. Other main area of work is intellectual property law, particularly international software copyright. Frequently addresses seminars and conferences. Registered Trade Mark Agent.
Career: *Clifford Chance* 1986 until 1992, then became Head of IT Unit at *Simpson Curtis* in Leeds.

PRINSLEY, Mark
Rowe & Maw, London (020) 7782 8900
mprinsley@roweandmaw.com
Specialisation: Head of IT Group, specialising in major IT projects. Works particularly on outsourcing transactions. Advises on all aspects of corporate transactions and covers work for e-commerce and internet businesses, in particular, internet infrastructure businesses such as as vignette and a variety of 'incubating' new media businesses.
Career: Articled *McKenna & Co* 1979-81; assistant solicitor 1981; assistant solicitor *Rowe & Mawe* 1984-98; partner 1987 to date.
Personal: Born 1956. Educated Brasenose College, Oxford (1978 Law).

REES, Chris
Herbert Smith, London (020) 7374 8000
christopher.rees@herbertsmith.com
Specialisation: All aspects of IT law including system acquisition, outsourcings, IP licensing and protection, M&A of IT centred business, corporate venturing, dispute resolution (acted for Bull against Kwik-Fit and Graham Technology).
Prof. Memberships: National Computing Centre (Chairman of Legal Affairs Committee); International Bar Association (Chairman of Computers and Database Committee); Law Society.
Career: Qualified *Freshfields* 1979; Data General, European Counsel 1985-90; *Bird & Bird,* 1990-2000 (Founding partner IT group, managing partner 1993-96); *Herbert Smith* 2001 – head of IT group.
Publications: 'Database Law' (Jordans) 1998.
Personal: Christ's College Cambridge.

RENDELL, Simon
Osborne Clarke OWA, London (020) 7809 1000

ROBERTSON, Ranald
Robertson & Co, Technology Law Practice, London (020) 7731 4626
Specialisation: Focus of practice is IT law, with over 20 years' experience in this field within the computer industry and private practice. Advises an international client base of users and vendors. Work includes major IT procurement projects (outsourcing, software development, systems integration), distribution agreements, software licensing, e-commerce/internet issues, international data protection and hi-tech start ups. Author of 'Legal Protection of Computer Software' and Computer Contracts section of Butterworths 'Forms and Precedents'. Co-author of 'European Computer Law' and Sweet & Maxwell 'Outsourcing Practice Manual'. Editorial Panel of 'IT Law Today'.
Prof. Memberships: British Computer Society. Computer Law Association, Worshipful Company of Information Technologists, London Computer Law Group, Founder Chairman of 13 country pan-European IT Law Group/Europe network of which *Roberston & Co* is UK member.
Career: Legal Services Manager with CAP/SEMA (1980-87); Partner and head of IT groups at *Stephenson Harwood, Field Fisher Waterhouse* and *Taylor Johnson Garrett* (1987-97). Set up *Robertson & Co* in September 1997 to provide clients with senior expertise and experience on computing, software and Internet matters at an affordable and reasonable cost. Qualified 1980.
Personal: Born 1948. Graduated Auckland University, New Zealand 1972. Married with 2 children.

ROWE, Heather
Lovells, London (020) 7296 2000
heather.rowe@lovells.com
Specialisation: Non-contentious information technology, telecommunications and multimedia work, including matters relating to electronic commerce, electronic banking, electronic data interchange and agreements and regulation of the IBA; Chairman UK editorial board 'Droit de l'Informatique et des Telecoms'; consultant editor, 'IT Law Today' and 'Computer Law and Security Report'; correspondent 'Computer and Telecommunications Law Review'; editorial panel 'World Telecoms Report', and 'World Internet Law Report', 'Communications Law' and 'Banking Technology'; editorial Board Butterworths Journal of International Banking and Financial Law.
Prof. Memberships: Co-Chairman of Committee R (technology and e-commerce), IBA; Chairman ICC International Working Party on Data Protection and Privacy; Chairman ICC UK Computing, Telecommunications and Information Policies Commission; member International Telecommunication Users Group and Telecommunications Users Association.
Career: Articled *Wilde Sapte,* London: Qualified 1981 with *Wilde Sapte*; Assistant Solicitor, *S J Berwin & Co*: Assistant Solicitor, *Lovells*; Partner 1988.

SALMON, John
Masons, Glasgow (0141) 248 4858
john.salmon@masons.com
Specialisation: Partner and Head of IT in Scotland specialising in providing non-contentious IT and e-commerce advice to new economy and traditional businesses throughout the UK and Europe. Particular experience in dealing with e-commerce and new media suppliers and developers including several computer games companies. John was a founding partners of *Masons'* new media and e-commerce service OUT-LAW.COM.
Prof. Memberships: Law Society of Scotland, Scotland IS and Society for Computers and Law.
Career: Attended Edinburgh University 1987-91 LLB Hons and Strathclyde University 1991-92 DipLP. Formerly IT programmer/consultant. *Bird Semple* 1995-99. Joined *Masons* as Partner in 1999, establishing the firm's Information and Technology Practice in Scotland.
Personal: Born 1969. Resides Glasgow. Leisure interests include hockey and running.

SAMPSON, Ian
Addleshaw Booth & Co, Leeds
ics@addleshaw-booth.co.uk
Specialisation: Head of firm's technology unit within the technology, media and intellectual property department. Advises on all non-contentious aspects of information technology contracts, including outsourcing, e-commerce and systems procurement.
Prof. Memberships: LES, IBA, Society for Computers and Law.
Career: Qualified in 1987. Joined the firm in 1988, partner in 1992.
Personal: Educated at University of Kent. Enjoys competitive distance running.

SANDISON, Hamish
Bird & Bird, London (020) 7415 6000
Specialisation: Partner in Company Department and Co-Chair of Information Technology Group. Main area of practice is IT law. Acts for both public bodies and private sector companies on IT procurement, including major IT PFI projects. Heads team representing CCTA (the Government's Central Computer and Telecommunications Agency). Member of DSS and BBC legal advisers panels. Intellectual property, e-commerce and multimedia work is also covered, especially advising on copyright law. Clients include Motion Picture Export Association of America and numerous scientific and technical publishers. Co-author of 'Computer Software Protection Law', 1989. Contributing Editor 'International Copyright and Neighbouring Rights', 1990. Lectures frequently in both UK and US. Often interviewed on TV and Radio.
Prof. Memberships: Council of Intellectual Property Institute, FAST Legal Advisory Group, Intellectual Property Committee of the British Computer Society.
Career: Admitted to Washington DC Bar 1980. Qualified in UK 1989. Joined *Bird & Bird* 1992 as a Partner.
Personal: Born 1952. Attended University College School, London 1960-70, Jesus College, Cambridge

1971-74, then University of California, Berkeley 1974-75. Lives in Usk, Monmouthshire.

SASSE, Sarah
Wragge & Co, Birmingham (0870) 903 1000

SAUNDERS, James
Shepherd & Wedderburn WS, Edinburgh (0131) 473 5288
james.saunders@shepwedd.co.uk
Specialisation: Partner in corporate department. Main areas of practice are energy law and IP (including computer law). Advises on electricity agreements and on IP agreements including licensing and turnkey.
Career: Qualified in 1984. Trainee with *McClure Naismith*, Glasgow 1983-85. Worked for ICI plc 1986-87 and *Freshfields* 1987-93. Joined *Shepherd & Wedderburn WS* in 1993.

SINGLETON, Susan
Singletons, London (020) 8866 1934
susan@singlelaw.com
Specialisation: Principal of firm since 1994. Main areas of practice are commercial law, competition law and IT/IP law. Handles compliance, competition law, litigation and complaints, and EU law generally. Advises on internet law, copyright, trade marks and patents, ownership of rights, licences, EU IT/IP directives, general commercial law, agency (particularly Commercial Agents (Council Directive) Regulations), distribution and contract law.
Prof. Memberships: Competition Law Association, Licensing Executives Society, Law Society, Society of Computers and Law and Computer Law Association.
Publications: Author of 20 books including 'Business, Internet and the Law' (Tolley 2nd ed 2001), Gower, 'E-Commerce – A Practical Guide to the Law' (2001), 'Commercial Agency' (Butterworths 1998), 'Blackstone's Guide to the Competition Act 1998', 'Jordan's Data Protection' (1998). Editor of 'Comparative Law of Monopolies' looseleaf and journals 'IT' and 'Telecoms Law Today'. Writes and speaks widely on legal issues.
Personal: Born 14 December 1961. Attended Westfield School, Newcastle upon Tyne 1972-79, then Manchester University 1979-82 and Chester Law College 1982-3. Married with five children. Lives on Pinner Hill.

SMALL, Harry
Baker & McKenzie, London (020) 7919 1000
harry.small@bakernet.com
Specialisation: Partner specialising in Information Technology Law including both contentious (IT and telecoms disputes and software protection) and non-contentious (outsourcing, facilities management and multi-jurisdictional software licensing). Other main area of work is IP law, covering enforcement of IP rights, copyright and designs law and multimedia contracts. Acted in many significant computer systems and high technology disputes including, amongst others, Exel v Dun & Bradstreet Software and Vodafone v Orange. Regularly addresses conferences and is lecturer on designs for Bristol University Intellectual Property Diploma course.
Prof. Memberships: Society for Computers and Law (Chairman); Member of Editorial Board of 'IT Law Today'; Expert to the EC Economic and Social Committee on EC IT Harmonisation Measures.
Career: Qualified England and Wales 1981; Qualified Hong Kong 1987; *Baker & McKenzie* Hong Kong 1986; *Baker & McKenzie* London 1987; Partner 1990 – present.
Publications: Contributor to Sweet & Maxwell IT Encyclopaedia' and Sweet & Maxwell 'Outsourcing Practice Manual'. Author of numerous articles on IP and IT law for various legal periodicals.
Personal: St Alban's Boys Grammar School 1968-75; Oriel College, Oxford (1978 BA; 1981 MA) Born 1957; Resides London.

SMITH, Graham
Bird & Bird, London (020) 7415 6000
Specialisation: Computer project disputes, commercial litigation in computer and telecommunications industries. Evidence, document imaging and computer records. Internet law including domain name disputes, website advice, internet/e-mail use policies and regulatory issues. Intellectual property disputes. Gave evidence to the House of Lords Science and Technology Select Committee on Digital Images as Evidence. Advised Guernsey on its electronic transaction legislation.
Prof. Memberships: American Intellectual Property Law Association; Council Member, Society for Computers and Law; Computer Law Association; eCentreUK Legal Advisory Group; Fellow of the Society for Advanced Legal Studies.
Career: Qualified 1978. Joined *Bird & Bird* 1983. Partner 1985.
Publications: Contributes a section on Non-Contractual Liability to the loose-leaf 'Encyclopedia of Information Technology Law' (Sweet & Maxwell). Editor and a co-author of the book 'Internet Law and Regulation' (Sweet & Maxwell, 2nd edition December 1997). Speaks and writes regularly in the UK and abroad mainly on IT and internet legal issues.
Personal: Born 1953. Educated Bristol University (LLB, 1975). Lives London.

SWYCHER, Nigel
Slaughter and May, London (020) 7600 1200
nigel.swycher@slaughterandmay.com
Specialisation: Intellectual property and information technology law; including the IP and IT aspects of acquisitions, disposals, flotations and privatisations; involved in technology, licensing and transfer, franchising and sponsorship and IT procurement and development. Co-head of the firm's technology, media and telecoms group.
Prof. Memberships: ITMA.
Career: Admitted 1987 with*Slaughter and May*. Partner 1994.
Personal: Born 6 June 1962. Educated at Denstone College, Staffordshire and Durham University. Magician.

TIGHE, David
Manches, Oxford (01865) 722106
Specialisation: Main area of practice is IT, dealing with all types of commercial IT agreements and with corporate finance work in the IT sector. Commercial work includes software licensing, distribution and marketing agreements, software development contracts, facilities management outsourcing and computer bureau agreements, system supply agreements, and internet and e-commerce issues. Corporate finance work ranges from start-ups and venture capital deals to acquisitions/disposals and flotations. Also writes articles on IT issues.
Prof. Memberships: Society for Computers and Law.
Career: Attended Marist College, Hull and Trinity College, Cambridge. Qualified as a solicitor in 1982. At *Boodle Hatfield* from 1980-85. Head of legal services at Logica plc from 1986-88. *Manches* since 1989. Partner since 1990.

TURNER, Mark
Herbert Smith, London (020) 7466 3602
mark.turner@herbertsmith.com
Specialisation: Partner specialising in transactional and advisory work in IT and e-business. Regularly advises major corporations, government agencies and leading edge technology companies. Most of his work has a strong international element. At the forefront of developments in e-business, advising on on-line exchanges, regulation of business on-line, contracts and payment on the internet. Work includes acting for BSkyB on new technologies; Freeserve on a range of internet issues; Credit Suisse First Boston, Goldman Sachs, Bear Stearns and Schroders on IT and e-commerce issues arising from IPOs, listings and other transactions by their clients.
Prof. Memberships: International Chamber of Commerce; International Bar Association; Society for Computers and Law; Computer Law Association; City of London Law Society.
Career: Qualified in 1983. *Macfarlanes* 1981-85. Denton Hall 1985-95 (Partner 1988). *Garretts* 1995-97. *Herbert Smith* 1998.
Personal: Born 1956. Educated Latymer Upper School and University College, Oxford (Exhibitioner).

WARD, Conor
Lovells, London (020) 7296 2000
conor.ward@lovells.com
Specialisation: Partner in the firm's computer, communications and media unit. Work includes advising on the contentious and non-contentious aspects of systems acquisition and development; facilities management and outsourcing (including telecommunications services); electronic commerce, electronic data interchange encryption technologies, anti-piracy and computer crime. Practises exclusively in the information technology field, often where the technological issues are most complex. Recent work includes advising in relation to the setting up of public key infrastructures in the UK and abroad and a strategic alliance between Nokia and Cable & Wireless relating to WAP technology.
Prof. Memberships: The British Computer Society Legal Affairs Committee, The Computer Law Association, member of editorial board of the Computer and Telecommunications Law Review published by Sweet and Maxwell. Appointed a Director of the Federation Against Software Theft (FAST) and Chairman of the legal advisory group of FAST.
Career: 1980-84 The Queen's University, Belfast (Law LL.B (Hons)); 1984-88 IBM United Kingdom Laboratories Limited – development programmer; 1987 called to the Bar of England & Wales; 1988-90 *Heald Nickinson* – assistant; 1990 to date *Lovells*, assistant solicitor; partner 1998.

WEBSTER, Michael
Nicholson Graham & Jones, London (020) 7360 8101
michael.webster@ngj.co.uk
Specialisation: Computer & telecoms, software & service supply contracts, ranging from software development & distribution contracts, VAR & franchising, turnkey supply and systems integration agreements, Internet, EDI, ASP, e-commerce and web site issues,

multi-media rights, joint ventures, technology transfer, outsourcing & long term supply of services agreements.
Prof. Memberships: Society for Computers & the Law, British Computer Society, Computer Law Group, Software Business Network, Worshipful Company of Information Technologists.
Career: Articled *Herbert Smith*, qualified in 1967, partner *Rowe & Maw* 1973. Long term involvement with specialisations has led to many invitations to speak and write articles on a number of topics such as outsourcing, joint ventures and liability arising from IT systems contracts.
Personal: Born 1942. Educated at Berkhamsted School and Bristol University (LLB Hons). Interests include tennis, golf, long distance walking and tree felling. Member of The Honourable Artillery Company.

WESTMACOTT, Philip
Bristows, London (020) 7400 8000
philip.westmacott@bristows.com
Specialisation: Partner in intellectual property department. He is one of over 70 lawyers handling intellectual property matters in the firm together with 20 other intellectual property partners: Ian Judge, David Brown, John Allcock, Edward Nodder, Sally Field, Paul Walsh, Kevin Appleton, Alan Johnson, Pat Treacy, Tim Powell, Dr Penny Gilbert, Matthew Warren, David Wilkinson, Simon Ayrton, Christine Hore, Laura Anderson, Dr Justin Watts, Andrew Lykiardopoulos, Ralph Cox and Alastair McCulloch. The full range of intellectual property work, contentious and non-contentious, with an emphasis on disputes involving, and advice to, the IT and computer industries. Has given evidence as an expert on UK IP law in US proceedings. Cases include, for the plaintiff, Philips v VDC, IBM v Phoenix, Monsanto v Maxwell M Hart and Monsanto v Stauffer and, for the defendant, Smith Myers Communications Ltd v Motorola, Iomega v Nomai, and Intel v VIA Technologies. Lecturer and marker on the Bristol University Diploma in Intellectual Property Law and Practice.
Prof. Memberships: Law Society, Associate of Chartered Institute of Patent Agents, London Computer Law Group, AIPPI, Society for Computers and Law.
Career: Undergraduate trainee at Tube Investments Ltd 1971-74. Joined *Bristows* on qualification in 1978 and became a partner in 1985.
Personal: Born 15 April 1954. Educated at Cambridge University 1972-75 (Engineering and Law). Enjoys sailing, walking, skiing and cycling. Lives in London and Yorkshire.

WILDISH, Nigel
Field Fisher Waterhouse, London (020) 7861 4000
ndw@ffwlaw.com
Specialisation: IT Law: acting for suppliers and customers in relation to a wide range of IT contracts, including systems and software development and procurement, networking, marketing and distribution agreements, outsourcing contracts and service level agreements. Electronic Publishing, Electronic Commerce and Internet Law: drafting and negotiating all kinds of e-commerce contracts including web development and exploitation agreement, and linking affinity agreements; advising on all legal aspects of the Internet, including contracts over the Internet, cross-jurisdictional liability and name/brand protection. Mergers and Acquisitions in IT, Telecoms and E-commerce: due diligence, joint ventures, acquisitions and sales.
Prof. Memberships: IBA (Technology and Intellectual Property Committees)National Computing Centre (Member, Law Group) Computer Law Association. Information and Communications Industries Association.
Career: Clare College, Cambridge.Partner: Turner Kenneth Brown (1974-95); Nabarro Nathanson (1995-97); Osborne Clarke (1997-99). *Field Fisher Waterhouse* (1999-date).
Personal: Married with 2 teenage children. Active in squash, golf, cricket. Active member of Church of England. Member: MCC.

WORTHY, John
Denton Wilde Sapte, London (020) 7242 1212
jnw@dentonwildesapte.com
Specialisation: Partner in Technology, Media and Telecoms group. Electronic banking, electronic commerce, internet, IT system integration, software development, facilities management, encryption, export control; data transfer, data protection, multimedia; telecoms transactions and privatisations, joint ventures, regulatory issues, network services, satellite transponder leases, satellite construction and launch, satellite financing. Major clients include: S.W.I.F.T., Credit Suisse First Boston, Bank of Scotland and group companies, Springboard Internet Services, Daiwa Institute of Research Europe, Advanced Radio Telecom, Europay International.
Prof. Memberships: Law Society. Telecommunications Managers Association. Editorial Board, Computer Law and Security Report.
Career: *McKenna & Co* 1983-92; *Allen & Overy* 1992-96; *Denton Wilde Sapte*, partner, 1996. In-house counsel at British Aerospace (1992) and News Digital Systems (1994).

YATES, John
V-Lex Ltd., Worksop (01909) 544 000
Specialisation: Chief Executive Officer. Main area of practice is computer law, including computer contracts and disputes. Author of numerous articles on all aspects of computer law. Regular speaker on outsourcing and computer disputes.
Prof. Memberships: Vice Chairman of Society of Computers and Law.
Career: Qualified in 1984. IBM In-house lawyer 1984-87. Partner at *Theodore Goddard* in computer group, 1987-93. Joined *Oxley & Coward* as a partner in 1993. Co-founder of *V-Lex Limited* in June 2000.
Personal: Born 8 May 1959. Attended Leeds University (LLB) and Oxford University (BCL). Leisure interests include mountaineering and rock climbing. Lives near Sheffield.

INSOLVENCY / CORPORATE RECOVERY

London: 453; South: 457; Thames Valley; 457; Sth West: 458; Wales: 459; Midlands: 459; E. Anglia: 460; Nth West: 461; Yorks; 462; Nth East: 463; Scotland: 464; N. Ireland: 465; *Profiles*: 465

RESEARCH APPROVED BY BMRB: *For this edition,* Chambers' *researchers conducted 6,552 interviews – 4,419 with law firms, 554 with barristers and 1,579 with clients.*

The validity of the research was scrutinised by BMRB International, who audited both the methodology and the results at our offices in July 2001. They interviewed Chambers' *researchers and cross-checked sample interviews. Details of the audit appear on page 7.*

LONDON

INSOLVENCY/CORPORATE RECOVERY • London		Ptnrs	Assts
1	Allen & Overy	5	20
2	Clifford Chance	5	12
	Denton Wilde Sapte	12	19
3	CMS Cameron McKenna	11	15
	Freshfields Bruckhaus Deringer	4	12
	Linklaters	8	14
	Lovells	11	25
4	Cadwalader, Wickersham & Taft	2	8
	Lawrence Graham	10	12
	Norton Rose	9	10
	Simmons & Simmons	3	4
	Stephenson Harwood	6	12
5	Hammond Suddards Edge	4	5
	Herbert Smith	12	10
	Isadore Goldman	n/a	n/a
	Nabarro Nathanson	1	4
	Slaughter and May	7	6
	Travers Smith Braithwaite	4	7
6	Ashurst Morris Crisp	n/a	n/a
	Berwin Leighton Paisner	6	7
	DJ Freeman	7	9
	Eversheds	1	2
	Nicholson Graham & Jones	3	12
	Osborne Clarke	na	n/a
	Richards Butler	3	4
	Sprecher Grier Halberstam	n/a	n/a
	Taylor Joynson Garrett	8	7

This book is the product of 6,552 1/2 hour interviews. See p.7 for BMRB audit.
Within each band, firms are listed alphabetically.

Allen & Overy (see firm details p.856) "*Clearly maintains its number one status.*" Having reached these heights with some "*fancy footwork*" during the last recession, the firm now acts for "*a marvellous clientele*" that includes not only all the major accountancy firms, but also the leading clearing, international, merchant and investment banks. The Business Reconstruction group advises on the largest cross-border restructurings, rescues and insolvencies across the world. Perceived to have a "*highly international focus,*" London remains the driving force on highlight deals such the largest corporate turnaround in Slovakia. Also advised the steering committee of creditors on the US$1.3 billion restructuring of Thai Telephone & Telecommunications, one of the most complex of the Thai restructurings since the financial crisis of mid 1997. On the domestic front, the group has been engaged in matters relating to sectoral shake-outs or mismanagement. Standing astride the domestic market it advised on the largest domestic insolvency of the past year; the receivership of the Independent Energy Group. Competitors acknowledge that both **Gordon Stewart** (see p.477) ("*elder statesman, first rate*") and **Nicholas Segal** (see p.476) ("*effective, a power broker*") are the driving force behind this balanced and deeply talented team. They are "*the names everyone knows*" in the industry and are quite simply "*both superb operators who sit at the top of their profession.*" Any queries in the market concerning the depth of high profile players underneath Segal and Stewart have been answered by recent hire and new partner **Ian Field** (see p.469). "*A real young heavyweight,*" it is anticipated that he will "*undoubtedly prosper under Segal and Stewart,*" adding leverage to the firm. Further highlights for the team include the successful design and completion of the debt restructuring and acquisition of VSZ. **Clients:** Big five accountants; leading clearing banks; international investment banks.

Clifford Chance (see firm details p.919) Multi-jurisdictional work lies at the heart of this practice, involved in high profile restructuring assignments for banking groups and a substantial level of telecom sector insolvencies. Acted for iaxis NV, the parent company of iaxis Ltd, and its largest creditor, which went into administration and was subsequently sold to Dynergy. "*Well placed to prevail in a downturn,*" the firm recently obtained the heavyweight talents of **Nick Frome** (see p.469) from Lovells. Having "*bolstered the practice*" with his "*eminent status,*" he is set to drive hard at the market alongside respected practice head, **Mark Hyde** (see p.472). Talented and innovative, **Adrian Cohen** (see p.468) secured market approval with his work on complex cases, while **David Steinberg** (see p.477) remains the firm's "*big name for insurance insolvency,*" a field in which the "*smart and personable*" **Philip Hertz** (see p.471) is expected to "*seal a good future.*" In the past year, the firm acted for the provisional liquidators and scheme administrators of Chester Street Insurance Holdings (PwC), in the highest profile insurance liquidation of the year. Continues to maintain its relationship with EBRD on a number of assignments, including the sale of First Commercial Bank of Latvia to Nord LB. **Clients:** KPMG; PricewaterhouseCoopers; Ernst & Young; Chase Manhattan; Citigroup; Barclays; NatWest; HSBC; Fuji Bank; Bank of America; Nomura International.

Denton Wilde Sapte (see firm details p.939) Fielding a stellar line-up that "*has made an extraordinary push in the area,*" research has indicated that this "*excellent team*" remains rated a fraction below Allen & Overy. Peers agreed that "*the Transtec and Versailles jobs alone can justify them reaching close to the top.*" The Reconstruction and Insolvency Group continues to undertake the entire range of insolvency work from personal bankruptcy to large workouts and restructurings, with its strongly "*bank-oriented*" practice. Highlights from the past year include acting for Arthur Andersen following its appointment as the administrative receiver of all 30 UK companies within the TransTec Group, which involved major litigation with Ford Motor Company Chair of the CBI's Insolvency panel. The "*first rate*" **Mark Andrews** heads the practice, and **Michael Steiner** is a "*magisterial figure,*" endorsed for his Official Receiver work and adjudged "*technically spot-on.*" "*Pleasant and constructive,*" **Mark Gill** is thought to capture "*many votes from the banking community*" while established figure **Nigel**

LEADING INDIVIDUALS	
1 **ANDREWS Mark** Denton Wilde Sapte	**FROME Nicholas** Clifford Chance
HYDE Mark Clifford Chance	**SEGAL Nicholas** Allen & Overy
STEWART Gordon Allen & Overy	**WHITE John** CMS Cameron McKenna
2 **ANDERSON Hamish** Norton Rose	**BUGG Anthony** Linklaters
ELLIOTT Robert Linklaters	**FOSTER Stephen** CMS Cameron McKenna
GALE Stephen Herbert Smith	**SHANDRO Sandy** Freshfields Bruckhaus
STEINER Michael Denton Wilde Sapte	**VERRILL John** Lawrence Graham
3 **BARNETT Nigel** Denton Wilde Sapte	**FLETCHER Ian** Stephenson Harwood
GILL Mark Denton Wilde Sapte	**GRIERSON Christopher** Lovells
HOUGHTON John Simmons & Simmons	**ROOME James** Bingham Dana LLP
SCHAFFER Danny Isadore Goldman	**SCOPES Richard** Denton Wilde Sapte
4 **BERRY Christopher** Edwin Coe	**BETHELL-JONES Richard** Denton Wilde Sapte
COHEN Adrian Clifford Chance	**GAINES Keith** Lovells
GORDON-SAKER Paul Stephenson Harwood	**GREGORY Deborah** Lovells
GRIER Ian Sprecher Grier Halberstam	**HAMILTON Dan** CMS Cameron McKenna
HIGHAM John Stephenson Harwood	
MALLON Christopher Freshfields Bruckhaus	**MANNING Peter** Simmons & Simmons
MORRIS Howard Denton Wilde Sapte	**OUGHTON Paul** Nicholson Graham & Jones
PIKE Nicholas Lawrence Graham	**POPE Timothy** Hammond Suddards Edge
PRIOR Michael Nabarro Nathanson	**RAJANI Shashi** Nicholson Graham & Jones
RUSHWORTH Jonathan Slaughter and May	**WALSH Jeremy** Travers Smith Braithwaite
WOOLF Geoffrey SJ Berwin	
5 **BAINES Richard** Osborne Clarke	**BORDELL Keith** Berwin Leighton Paisner
MCCARTHY Michael Richards Butler	
UP AND COMING	
CROUCHER Yvette Cadwalader, Wickersham & Taft	
FIELD Ian Allen & Overy	**GODFREY Patricia** Nabarro Nathanson
LOWE Rita CMS Cameron McKenna	**WITHYMAN Tom** Lawrence Graham

LEADING INDIVIDUALS: INSURANCE INSOLVENCY	
1 **FIDLER Peter** Stephenson Harwood	**MONTGOMERY Nigel** DLA
WILKINSON Andrew Cadwalader, Wickersham & Taft	
2 **SPENCER Robin** Lovells	**STEINBERG David** Clifford Chance
YORKE Jonathan Richards Butler	
3 **FRENCH Matthew** Lovells	**TYRELL Vivien** DJ Freeman
UP AND COMING	
HERTZ Philip Clifford Chance	

See individuals' profiles p.465

Barnett always "*gets results.*" Completing the round up of the firm's key players are the "*extremely capable*" **Richard Scopes**, who is "*a seasoned campaigner in both banking and insolvency,*" **Richard Bethell-Jones**, who has secured "*good connections with banks,*" and **Howard Morris**, considered heavily "*focused on reconstruction and turnaround work.*" The firm's relationship with PricewaterhouseCoopers has resulted in winning quality instructions. It advised PwC as the administrative receiver of the Versailles Group and acted on the collapse and subsequent liquidation of Boxman, a substantial pan-European CD e-tailer, which constituted the largest e-tailing collapse after Boo.com. **Clients:** Big five accountancy firms; NatWest, HSBC and Royal Bank of Scotland.

CMS Cameron McKenna (see firm details p.922) Considered "*one of the old hands*" in the industry, the firm acts on substantial multi-bank restructurings both on behalf of lenders and borrowers, with much work originating from the telecoms and internet sectors. The firm acted for the Royal Bank of Scotland and Deloitte & Touche, receivers of the Alpha Telecom Group of companies. It is judged to operate with "*a truly broadly based team with talented lawyers and much better contacts on the banking side than many.*" Senior figure **John White** (see p.478) is applauded as "*an old warhorse,*" whose depth of experience affords him such a high profile, while the "*skilled*" **Stephen Foster** (see p.469) is a "*class act who does deals sensibly.*" **Dan Hamilton** (see p.471) is endorsed as "*good at getting things done*" while **Rita Lowe** (see p.473) is increasing her profile in the non-contentious sphere; "*always positive – not a shrinking violet at all.*" Building on its Eastern European strengths, the firm has been acting for the Russian Rossiyskiy Kredit Bank in establishing the first amicable settlement using laws introduced in 1999, which was subsequently given effect in the USA by an order of the Federal Bankruptcy Court. In addition, the firm advised the joint liquidators of Tamaris on a successful voluntary arrangement leading to the company's return to solvency and allowing it to keep its listing on the LSE. **Clients:** Lloyds TSB, big five accountancy firms; Grant Thornton.

Freshfields Bruckhaus Deringer (see firm details p.965) Has "*come on leaps and bounds*" establishing *a "strong restructuring practice,"* bolstered by its efficiency and "*a mass of complex cross-border work*" for international debtors. The Restructuring and Insolvency Group acts for IPs, creditors, debtors and regulators on corporate restructurings and formal insolvency procedures, with acclaimed strength in the financial sector. The market favours **Sandy Shandro** (see p.476) as "*an excellent operator,*" dominant in the international sphere. **Chris Mallon** (see p.473) has done much to secure his reputation with his advice to KPMG, the provisional liquidators of boo.com, which was the first high profile dot.com failure. Involved in the liquidation of the Eurobank Corporation in the Channel Islands, the group also advised ICO Global Communications across a number of jurisdictions on one of the largest insolvencies worldwide. The latter was one of the first arrangements to use provisional liquidation successfully in combination with Chapter 11 as a workout tool. **Clients:** Lloyds TSB; ICO; Goldman Sachs; Deloitte & Touche; Government of Brunei; ABN AMRO.

Linklaters (see firm details p.1042) Enjoys a high profile in the "*largest restructuring and turnaround work,*" typically with a cross-border element. Head of the firm's Restructuring and Insolvency Group, **Robert Elliott** (see p.469) is appreciated as *an "impressive operator"* who has "*definitely secured his place in the premier league.*" **Anthony Bugg** (see p.467) is best known for his contentious work where his style is adjudged "*aggressive but effective.*" Richard Wright has taken a consultancy role at the firm. The group advised VSZ, the Slovak steel conglomerate, on its corporate and financial restructuring and the disposal of its steel production business, in one of the highest profile cross border deals in 2000. Also conducted the US$4.5 billion restructuring of Guangdong Enterprises Group, and acted for Innogy Holdings in its acquisition from the administrative receivers of Independent Energy. **Clients:** NatWest; HSBC; Barclays; Chase Manhattan; Grant Thornton; PricewaterhouseCoopers; KPMG.

Lovells (see firm details p.1044) Suffered a setback with the "*unexpected defection*" of Nick Frome to Clifford Chance. While the market perceives the group shaken by events, it remains bullish over its future prospects; "*at the heart, they've still got good people and they're out there winning good work.*" In addition to its acclaimed rescue and restructuring advice, the firm commands strength in insurance insolvency. Best known for its continued work acting for BCCI on its worldwide liquidation. The firm advised the Hong Kong Official Receiver and RSM Nelson Wheeler Corporate Advisory Services in their capacity as provisional liquidators of Akai Holdings and Kong Wah Holdings. Over the year, it has been occupied with issues surrounding the fall-out in the TMT sector. **Christopher Grierson** (see p.571) is valued *as "a super litigator and problem solver."* He has just completed the massive Bank of England litigation. **Keith Gaines** (see p.570) is another heavily endorsed for his contentious insolvency work, while **Deborah Gregory** (see p.470) "*has always been someone you can rely on.*" Both **Robin Spencer** (see p.477) and **Matthew French** (see p.469) elicited heavy endorsement for their activities in insurance insolvency. A major highlight for the group includes acting for the Ford Motor Group in the TransTec receivership. Its cross border work continues with instructions from HLB Kidsons as liquidators of Caribbean International Insurance, pursuing asset recoveries in the UK, USA and elsewhere. **Clients:** Big five accountancy firms; Barclays.

Cadwalader, Wickersham & Taft (see firm details p.906) Largely driven by its strong connections with US and European investment banks and hedge funds, much of the caseload involves the workouts of high yield bonds and secondary bank debt in distressed companies. The firm has "*successfully targeted*" its offering and is in "*best position*" to assist bond holders on the US high yield elements. The efforts of **Andrew Wilkinson** (see p.478) ("*one of the pukka names in insurance insolvency*") and his "*impressive*" senior assistant **Yvette Croucher** (see p.468) are applauded, the latter widely perceived to have "*done a good job on Ionica.*" Acted for the bondholders and joint administrators of Ionica, a provider of wireless telecommunications services, obtaining the sanction of the High Court in a scheme of arrangement, which contained cutting-edge features concerning the restructuring high yield debt. The firm has successfully renegotiated the terms and pricing of a tender invitation to rehabilitate the liquidity of Eurotunnel's £9.6 billion junior debt, where it represented a group of over fifteen key junior debt holders based in London and the US. **Clients:** Bondholders; hedge funds; banks; accountants; IPs.

Lawrence Graham (see firm details p.1030) "*A well respected team*" that owes much of its success to the profile of "*fantastic operator*" **John Verrill** (see p.478), with one practitioner commenting *that "if I had a conflict, I'd trust John.*" Handling a broad range of insolvency matters, often in the mid-market, the firm is perceived to have strength in the oil and gas sector. Experienced and well established **Nick Pike** (see p.475) offers a "*considered approach,*" while **Tom Withyman** (see p.479) *has "fine people skills*" and "*really knows his stuff.*" Significant matters include the administration of London Trust Bank, a bank with strong Syrian connections, and the administration of the multi-jurisdictional construction company, Christiani & Nielsen. **Clients:** Pannell Kerr Forster; Ernst & Young; RBS.

Norton Rose (see firm details p.1082) The Corporate Rescue and Insolvency team is still principally concerned with restructurings for both banks and corporates, supported by a strong finance practice and international offices. Scoring well in cross-border insolvency, the motor, telecoms and aviation sectors have engaged much of the group's attention. "*Extremely able*" **Hamish Anderson** (see p.466) enjoys an "*enviable banking clientele*" and is active in receiverships and liquidations. "*He's young, well respected and has the potential to take the practice places.*" Noteworthy cases include the provision of insolvency and restructuring advice to BMW in its sale of Rover, and advising Daewoo Motor Company on the appointment of the provisional liquidators to Daewoo Worthing Technical Centre. The latter being the first time that an English court has appointed a provisional liquidator to assist in the restructuring of a foreign-owned company. Also acted for the provisional liquidators of Kroll Buchler Phillips arising out of the collapse of litigation brought by Optimum Solutions against the electricity industry. **Clients:** Big five accountancy firms; BDO Stoy Hayward; Moore Stephens Booth White; HSBC; RBS; Bank of Scotland; Exim Bank of Japan; FSA; DTI.

Simmons & Simmons (see firm details p.1132) The corporate recovery practice targets complex one-off transactions, the most high profile of which has been the Millennium Dome rescue. "*Big gun*" **John Houghton** (see p.472) elicited praise for his "*highly innovative work*" on this matter. The firm's broad coverage includes strength in nursing homes, telecoms and sports-related insolvencies. **Peter Manning** (see p.473) received due recognition for his "*expertise in rescue and reconstruction issues.*" The firm continues to advise the New Millennium Experience Company on its exit into a solvent liquidation, including the sale to Legacy, and acted for Global TeleSystems in restructuring its business and dealing with bondholders (to the value of US$500 million) of its subsidiary, Espirit Telecommunications. Further cross border work includes advising a creditor on the recovery of its claim against both Iaxis (in administration) and its Dutch parent, Iaxis N.V. **Clients:** Deloitte & Touche; KPMG; RSM Robson Rhodes; Singer & Friedlander.

Stephenson Harwood (see firm details p.1141) Thought to have succeeded in its goal of setting insolvency "*as one of its core areas,*" with the market commending a "*heavyweight team*" bolstered by good banking relationships (particularly with HSBC) and top flight dispute capabilities. "*Highly intelligent*" **Ian Fletcher** (see p.469) is respected for his banking led practice and **Paul Gordon-Saker** (see p.470) uses his "*wealth of experience*" in his role as "*a first class litigator.*" **John Higham QC** (see p.471) has enhanced the firm's advocacy pool, while **Peter Fidler** (see p.469) remains the key player for insurance insolvency. Instructed by HSBC and a syndicate of banks on the £30 million restructuring of luggage manufacturer Carlton International, the firm also successfully defended RBS against a claim for £15 million brought by PwC as the receivers of Wallace International. Also acted for BakerTilly in the voluntary liquidation of ISPG, a holding company with assets to the value of £500 million. **Clients:** StanChart; Nordes Bank; HSBC; Deloitte & Touche; PricewaterhouseCoopers; Grant Thornton; Baker Tilly; Smith & Williamson; IPs; regulators.

Hammond Suddards Edge (see firm details p.984) A national force, the merger with Edge Ellison has built on a "*long established reputation*" in the industry and created a "*force more dynamic than the constituent parts.*" The Business Finance & Recovery Unit offers business regeneration, risk assessment, and insolvency advice. **Tim Pope** (see p.475) specialises in non-contentious receiverships and administration work. Highlights include acting for Kroll Buchler Phillips and PWC as joint liquidators of Leyland Dar in litigation involving a £50 million surplus arising from the receivership. Here a landmark decision was obtained concerning the priority of liquidators' expenses payable from floating charge assets. The firm also acted for the liquidators (KPMG and Smith & Williamson) on Sturmey Archer, one of the largest liquidations of the year, as well as advising the Football League on the administration of Crystal Palace FC. **Clients:** KPMG; Deloitte & Touche; Ernst & Young; Grant Thornton; Barclays; Lloyds TSB; BDO Stoy Hayward; Levy Gee; GE Capital Commercial Finance.

Herbert Smith (see firm details p.993) Thought to cultivate international restructurings and reorganisations, the firm wins high profile assignments with the support of its top-notch litigation and corporate practices. Active in the area of investment trusts and insurance insolvency. Practice head **Stephen Gale** (see p.470) is widely perceived to be "*clearly an excellent lawyer with all the glory and recognition from his presidency of R3.*" Highlights for the firm include acting for the Policyholders Protection Board in connection with a number of insurance companies in financial difficulties. The group also acted for Nomura on its bid to acquire the Millennium Dome, and was instructed by Marconi on the recovery of equipment supplied to Powernet Telecom (in administration). **Clients:** PPB; Eurotunnel; Westpac; big five accountancy firms.

Isadore Goldman The source of the firm's market plaudits is in "*primarily personal bankruptcy,*" where it is nationally regarded as a force to be reckoned with. Adjudged "*a specialist,*" **Danny Schaffer** (see p.476) "*towers over the firm,*" also receiving praise for his directors' disqualification work. His relationship with NatWest is envied; he is "*very much the NatWest man for sorting out problems.*" **Clients:** NatWest; KPMG.

Nabarro Nathanson (see firm details p.1078) Less visible in the market place, the firm's corporate recovery and insolvency group has nonetheless been active in turnaround and restructuring, formal insolvency work and issues affecting the IT and dot.com sector. "*Pre-eminent*" **Michael Prior** (see p.475) acts as a consultant with the firm, as head of department **Patricia Godfrey** (see p.470) is growing her profile in the field. The firm recently acted for a listed plc in a tax driven reorganisation which included a complex solvent liquidation, and advised a rapidly expanding telecom/internet facilities provider in its group restructuring. Further highlights include acting for the purchasers of boo.com in liquidation and activities for the receivers of a commercial kitchen manufacturer. **Clients:** HSBC; Barclays; Bank of Scotland; GE Capital; PricewaterhouseCoopers; Ernst & Young; Begbies Traynor.

Slaughter and May (see firm details p.1135) "*Fleet of foot in both debt and equity, with a grounding in corporate and banking,*" the insolvency offering here is thought by financial institutions to be "*potentially more useful in a recession than those who claim specialist expertise.*" In keeping with the firm's generalist approach, it draws upon talented lawyers firm-wide which may explain its lower profile in the market. Key to much of the group's success is the well respected **Jonathan Rushworth** (see p.476), seen to hold a presence on the biggest, most complex restructurings. The work remains impressive. Significant matters include advising a major creditor in the administration of Iaxis, and its central role in the aftermath of the Barings collapse, acting for Ernst & Young as liquidators of various Barings companies. Recently completed the largest Eastern European cross-border refinancing, that of Slovnaft, a major Slovakian listed oil refining and food distribution company. **Clients:** Major accountants; IPs; banks; corporate clients.

Travers Smith Braithwaite (see firm details p.1160) Stephen Pearson's departure to join RBS has ended a finely tuned double act, which the market believes "*will certainly affect the firm.*" On the non-contentious side, **Jeremy Walsh** (see p.478) has kept the operation "*running smoothly.*" The firm's highlight transactions include advising Barclays Bank over the toy retailer Beatties of London, including its CVA and an equity fundraising exercise by parent company, Era Group. Also acted for the Bank of Scotland and PKF in the receivership of XS Leisure. **Clients:** GEI International; Channel Holding; Deloitte & Touche; PricewaterhouseCoopers.

Ashurst Morris Crisp (see firm details p.866) A busy year in high value reconstruction and formal insolvency work. The practice has expanded into Continental Europe through its Paris and Frankfurt offices, the latter from where Nick Angel now practices. Angel's move has left the firm bereft of a heavy hitter, although quality work shores up its profile. Its recent headline deal involved acting for the receivers of Finelist Group on the largest formal insolvency in the UK this year, where the total value owed to the banking syndicate exceeded £300 million. Furthermore the firm's corporate and litigation prowess is felt to bring in quality instructions to Ben Tidswell's team. On the contentious front, the firm is acting for the liquidators of Barings Futures (Singapore) in their claim for US$2 billion from the company's former auditors, currently the highest value insolvency litigation. It also advised the Virgin Entertainment Group in a complex reconstruction, including debt and equity reorganisation, and substantial disposals (over £200 million). **Clients:** Arthur Andersen Singapore; Ernst & Young; Kroll Buchler Phillips; Levy Gee.

Berwin Leighton Paisner (see firm details p.878) Heavily focused on turnaround work, with at least half of its work concerning distressed companies and their investors with the balance comprising IPs and banks. Head of Business Regeneration, **Keith Bordell** (see p.467) is the standout practitioner here. The group advised on the reconstructions of Eagle Trust, the LEP Group and Dan Air. Also acted for Brown & Jackson (parent company to Poundstretcher retail chain) through its various refinancings, and received instructions from the British Shoe Corporation, part of the Sears Retail Group, which disposed of its retail businesses (including Dolcis, Cable & Co & Shoe Express and Shoe City) through a competitive auction process. **Clients:** BDO Stoy Hayward; Begbies Traynor; Buchler Phillips; Grant Thornton; Royal Bank of Scotland.

DJ Freeman (see firm details p.943) A powerhouse in insurance insolvency offering strong solutions to technically complex issues. Head of the insurance insolvency practice, **Vivien Tyrell** (see p.477) remains endorsed by the market. Recently the group has been dealing with three schemes of arrangement, involving Ramus Insurance (the international solvent scheme), and a section 304 enforcement in the United States. In addition, the practice has been conducting in a five month trial against the directors of Continental Assurance for wrongful trading and misfeasance. **Clients:** Major accountancy firms; Bermuda Fire and Marine.

Eversheds (see firm details p.952) Has undertaken a large amount of advisory work for existing clients over the last year, yet the profile of Brenda Harris' team lies with its regional coverage and in restructuring work. The group advised HSBC Bank in the administration of Crystal Palace Football Club and continues to be instructed by the lead bank on the workout of a major manufacturing company. **Clients:** KPMG; Grant Thornton; Levy Gee.

Nicholson Graham & Jones (see firm details p.1081) Engaged in the mid-market, the team is endorsed for its strength in group restructurings, informal rescues, and section 110 schemes. A player in the financial services sector, it is also handling an increasing number of directors' disqualifications. Established figure **Shashi Rajani** (see p.475) is *a "real academic and technical insolvency man,"* while **Paul Oughton** (see p.474) maintains his profile for contentious matters and secures relationships with a number of the firm's banking clients. **Clients:** KPMG; BDO Stoy Hayward; Baker Tilly; Lloyds TSB; Barclays.

Osborne Clarke (see firm details p.1086) The firm's strength in the TMT sector has led to an influx of work for technology-related companies, particularly venture capitalists, acting on turnaround. A strong synergy between the firm's banking and insolvency groups has seen an increasing level of instructions from clients such as Brown, Shipley & Co, RBS/Natwest and Barclays. **Richard Baines** is endorsed as a "*sound and reliable practitioner.*" The firm advised Close Brothers in its management of equity funds in Gibbs-Palmer, a major garden centre supplier now in administrative receivership. **Clients:** NatWest; ABN AMRO; IPs.

Richards Butler (see firm details p.1107) Commended for its insurance insolvency team, its general insolvency capability has been boosted by the arrival of **Michael McCarthy** (see p.473) from DLA, who "*brings added expertise*" with a track record in work for the receivers and particularly DTI petitions. **Jonathan Yorke** (see p.479) is an acclaimed "*expert on schemes of arrangement.*" The firm continues to advise PwC as provisional liquidators of the North Atlantic and Black Sea and Baltic Insurance companies, and is acting for the Japanese liquidator of Cresvale International, on matters arising from US$2.7 billion bond issues by Princeton Group entities. In addition, the firm is involved in the administrative receivership of Wessex Dairies. **Clients:** PricewaterhouseCoopers; Deloitte & Touche; Royal Bank of Scotland.

Sprecher Grier Halberstam The market acclaims this "*genuine specialist insolvency firm*" that is only limited by its size. Thought to be mostly acting for debtors and borrowers, it also handles a broad range of both corporate and personal insolvency matters. **Ian Grier** (see p.471) is a licensed IP and remains the firm's best known name in the field. **Clients:** Big five accountancy firms; IPs; clearing banks; corporates.

Taylor Joynson Garrett (see firm details p.1150) The Reconstruction and Insolvency department, under the guidance of Michael Frawley, has a number of niche strengths, including property based enforcement, trouble shooting for financial institutions, debt restructuring, and directors' disqualification proceedings. The firm's highlight of the year was acting for the receivers of the Britannic Group, the largest timber group in the UK, which involved the receivership of ten companies. Also instructed by Singer and Freidlander in the administration of Crystal Palace FC, and restructured and recovered a substantial loan made by Lucent to a dot.com company operating in the UK and Europe. **Clients:** KPMG; PricewaterhouseCoopers; Smith & Williamson.

Other Notable Practitioners **Nigel Montgomery** of **DLA** remains "*top drawer*" for insurance insolvency work, while **Christopher Berry** of **Edwin Coe** is rated for his personal insolvency expertise, particularly directors' disqualifications. **James Roome** (see p.476) of **Bingham Dana LLP** is expert on restructuring and recovery work for bondholders and banks. Long established **Geoffrey Woolf** (see p.479) of **SJ Berwin** benefits from a "*broad based, generalist approach*" to insolvency.

THE SOUTH

INSOLVENCY/CORPORATE RECOVERY • The South		Ptnrs	Assts
1	**asb law** Crawley	2	4
	Blake Lapthorn Fareham	2	3
	Sherwin Oliver Solicitors Portsmouth	5	4
2	**Lester Aldridge** Bournemouth	3	4
3	**Bond Pearce** Southampton	3	4
	Paris Smith & Randall Southampton	2	3
4	**Cripps Harries Hall** Tunbridge Wells	1	2
	Paul Davidson Taylor Horsham	2	4

LEADING INDIVIDUALS		
1	**DOBSON Julian** Julian Dobson Solicitors	**KEITLEY Nicholas** Blake Lapthorn
	NIEKIRK Malcolm Lester Aldridge	
2	**BROCKMAN Christopher** Sherwin Oliver	**OLIVER David** Sherwin Oliver
	TAYLOR Andrew asb law	
3	**LE BAS Malcolm** Paris Smith & Randall	
4	**BARKER Matthew** Lester Aldridge	**COOK Nigel** Paul Davidson Taylor
	CRAIG Nigel Sherwin Oliver	**JEFFRIES Graham** Bond Pearce
	MUNRO Rick Lamport Bassitt	

This book is the product of 6,552 1/2-hour interviews. See p.7 for BMRB audit.
Within each band, firms are listed alphabetically. *See individuals' profiles p.465*

asb law (see firm details p.865) A successful merger has resulted in a full corporate and personal insolvency caseload with strengths in DTI matters and voluntary arrangements. **Andrew Taylor** (see p.477) is praised for his skill in directors' disqualification work. Recent highlights for the practice include acting for a major creditor in the Daewoo international receivership and advising independent financial advisers on corporate restructuring in the light of pension mis-selling claims. Conducted a challenge to the validity of a conditional fee arrangement in which the High Court has served proceedings on both the Bar Council and the Law Society as interested parties. **Clients:** Major regional IPs.

Blake Lapthorn (see firm details p.886) Skilled in business rescue the firm is "*held in the highest respect amongst the local IPs,*" although the recent loss of Matthew Barker to Lester Aldridge is a setback. In non-contentious insolvency, **Nicholas Keitley** is judged to be "*highly competent and diligent at what he does.*" The group advised the directors of Darlows, a large chain of estate agents, on its restructuring plans, and drafted a voluntary arrangement proposal for the directors of Hedstrom (UK), a manufacturer and distributor of garden toys. **Clients:** BKL Weeks Green; Ernst & Young; Fanshawe Loft; Grant Thornton; PricewaterhouseCoopers.

Sherwin Oliver Solicitors (see firm details p.1128) A mix of contentious and non-contentious work includes turnaround, asset sales and administrative receiverships. On the contentious side, the firm has seen growth in directors' disqualification defence work and construction insolvency matters. Its respected players are **Christopher Brockman** (see p.467), a "*technically skilled litigator,*" and "*department sage*" **David Oliver** (see p.474) – "so *well-established that everyone knows him.*" **Nigel Craig** (see p.468) has a healthy profile for his work in the region. **Clients:** IPs; accountants; corporates.

Lester Aldridge (see firm details p.1038) "*One to watch in the region,*" it has opened an office in Southampton, which houses the non-contentious arm of its corporate recovery team, while the litigators have remained in Bournemouth. Increasing its presence in turnaround work, particularly in the healthcare sector for major private hospitals. The "*hard-working*" **Malcolm Niekirk** (see p.474) is based in Southampton; "*a sound, sensible chap, he deserves every success.*" The recent arrival of licensed IP **Matthew Barker** (see p.466) from Blake Lapthorn is widely seen as a "*boost*" for the practice, with his non-contentious insolvency experience. **Clients:** Major accountants and IPs.

Bond Pearce (see firm details p.888) Known for its bank-led receivership work, the firm undertakes pre-appointment advice and is active in the motor trade and agricultural sectors. **Graham Jeffries** (see p.119) is valued by clients and peers alike as a safe pair of hands, benefiting from his banking expertise. The firm has undertaken receiverships for Lloyds TSB, and acted on an administrative receivership in the retail telecoms sector for KPMG. Also advised liquidators of the Hayward Group, and undertook restructuring and recovery work for State Securities. **Clients:** IPs, accountants and corporates.

Paris Smith & Randall (see firm details p.1089) Typical work includes sales of businesses and assets on behalf of licensed IPs, as well as a successful track record in insolvency litigation, which has included the discharge of a bankruptcy order in a complex cross-border case. A force in the local market due to the presence of "*senior practitioner*" **Malcolm Le Bas** (see p.473). Recent matters include giving corporate recovery advice to two major institutions in Southampton. **Clients:** KPMG; Radfords; Roger Evans.

Cripps Harries Hall (see firm details p.927) The departure of Julian Dobson is felt to have had "*an enormous impact*" on the practice, as it has yet to find an equivalent force at partner level. The firm continues to undertake a mix of corporate and personal insolvency, mainly for IPs. The department led by Ed Bible has worked on large matters over the past year, including the receivership of a motor dealership. **Clients:** Major accountants and IPs.

Paul Davidson Taylor Endorsed as a "*reasonable presence in its locality*" with "*good connections in the factoring industry.*" **Nigel Cook** "*knows his way around*" particularly in the non-contentious sphere. **Clients:** IPs; major accountants.

Other Notable Practitioners **Rick Munro** (see p.474) of **Lamport Bassitt** is "*well regarded by the local IPs, largely on the contentious side.*" **Julian Dobson** (see p.468) of **Julian Dobson Solicitors** is anticipated to "*make an impact*" with his new Brighton-based firm.

THAMES VALLEY

Boyes Turner (see firm details p.891) Encompassing both personal and corporate insolvency, with a balance between contentious and non-contentious work, it "*belongs at the top of the tree, due to the quality of its work.*" **Chris Branson** (see p.467) draws upon his long-standing expertise, and he is supported by the respected **Phil Smith** (see p.476). Highlights include acting for the receivers of Debug Holdings, a hi-tech business, successfully selling its assets to repay the secured lender in full and provide a surplus for unsecured creditors. In the contentious sphere it acted in a successful appeal, Mulkerrins v PricewaterhouseCoopers, where the Court of Appeal struck out the bankrupt's claim issue proceedings relating to property. **Clients:** Main accountancy firms.

Morgan Cole (see firm details p.1074) The firm is perceived to have expertise in corporate insolvency. The "*extremely able*" **Bruce Potter** is thought to have long since proved the "*substantive quality of his advice.*" **Clients:** Big five accountancy firms and major IPs.

Pitmans (see firm details p.1099) Enjoying "*a rising profile*" and has "*good contact with banks and factoring entities*" in the area. Newly ranked IP **Suzanne Brooker** (see p.467) has impressed the market with her ability

INSOLVENCY/CORPORATE RECOVERY • Thames Valley	Ptnrs	Assts
1 **Boyes Turner** Reading	4	5
2 **Morgan Cole** Reading	4	5
Pitmans Reading	3	4
3 **Clarks** Reading	n/a	n/a
Darbys Oxford	2	1

LEADING INDIVIDUALS	
1 **BRANSON Christopher** Boyes Turner	
2 **ARCHER David** Pitmans	**SMITH Phillip** Boyes Turner
3 **BROOKER Suzanne** Pitmans	**POTTER Bruce** Morgan Cole
TAYLOR Elizabeth Darbys	

This book is the product of 6,552 1/2-hour interviews. See p.7 for BMRB audit.

Within each band, firms are listed alphabetically. *See individuals' profiles p.465*

and one practitioner opined, *"I'd like to see her doing more,"* while **David Archer** (see p.466) continues to be well received. Over the last year, the firm has acted on a number of receiverships, administrations and partnership insolvencies, and has also successfully defended several directors' disqualification proceedings. **Clients:** Main IPs.

Clarks (see firm details p.916) The market believes that the team is *"practical, commercial and knowledgeable of the subject."* The team led by David Clark is also *"perfectly pleasant to deal with."* **Clients:** IPs and accountants.

Darbys (see firm details p.931) The practice's workload is slanted to personal insolvency, such as voluntary arrangements and liquidations. It is generally perceived to handle work for *"all the IPs in Oxfordshire and Berkshire,"* while **Elizabeth Taylor** remains the firm's best known practitioner. **Clients:** Main accountants and IPs.

SOUTH WEST

INSOLVENCY/CORPORATE RECOVERY • South West	Ptnrs	Assts
1 **Osborne Clarke** Bristol	5	17
2 **Bond Pearce** Bristol, Plymouth	3	13
Foot Anstey Sargent Plymouth	2	2
3 **Laytons** Bristol	2	3
4 **Burges Salmon** Bristol	6	10
CMS Cameron McKenna Bristol	2	5
TLT Solicitors Bristol	4	10
5 **Beachcroft Wansbroughs** Bristol	2	2
Clarke Willmott & Clarke Taunton	3	2
Meade-King Bristol	1	2

LEADING INDIVIDUALS	
1 **LAWSON Stephen** Foot Anstey Sargent	**TETTMAR Victor** Bond Pearce
2 **BON Gordon** Bevan Ashford	**BOOBIER Nigel** Osborne Clarke
COOK Patrick Osborne Clarke	**STOBART Guy** Burges Salmon
3 **ALLINSON Stephen** Clarke Willmott & Clarke	**ASKEW Martin** Clarke Willmott & Clarke
HARRIS Anthony Laytons	**HARRIS Clare** Meade-King
MAY Philip TLT Solicitors	**WILTSHIRE Peter** CMS Cameron McKenna
4 **AGAR Nick** CMS Cameron McKenna	**SMITH Gillian** Foot Anstey Sargent

This book is the product of 6,552 1/2-hour interviews. See p.7 for BMRB audit.

Within each band, firms are listed alphabetically. *See individuals' profiles p.465*

Osborne Clarke (see firm details p.1086) Over the past year this firm has seen a steady increase in its IT insolvency caseload, in addition to liquidations and personal insolvency work for IPs. Competitors were united in their praise for *"its depth of resources"* while its DTI work also won plaudits. **Patrick Cook** is the firm's *"long-standing name for insolvency,"* while **Nigel Boobier** has developed his presence with *"client wins and quality of work."* Enjoying strong relationships with major accountancy firms, the group has recently been acting for PricewaterhouseCoopers in the administrative receivership of Patchington Farms and advised Ernst & Young in the receivership of Mallby Ltd. **Clients:** Baker Tilly; Deloitte & Touche; Ernst & Young; KPMG; Smith & Williamson.

Bond Pearce (see firm details p.888) Typical work handled by this practice includes pre-appointment advice to finance houses as well as receiverships and sales. It has been acting in a series of trading relationships for banks (including a high profile hotel in the North), preserving hundreds of jobs following disposals. *"One of the old favourites"* in the field, **Victor Tettmar** (see p.477) is head of the Banking & Business Support department. Highlights include advisory and restructuring work in manufacturing, financial services, motor and construction. In addition, the practice has handled substantial litigation involving IPs and foreign banks in the technology and agri-business sector. **Clients:** BNP Paribas; KPMG; Lloyds TSB Bank.

Foot Anstey Sargent (see firm details p.961) Dominating the Exeter market with niche strengths in advice to the claimant in disqualification cases, and LPA receiverships, both personal and corporate. Competitors are of the view that it is *"a small team with high skill levels." "Elder statesman"* **Stephen Lawson** (see p.473) enjoys *a "huge reputation"* while **Gillian Smith** (see p.476) also received a substantial share of market recognition. Lawson was recently instructed to act as an expert in a major Scottish case, Frost v Unity Bank, which involved complex issues concerning the enforceability of an IVA in Scotland and other cross-border issues. Smith has been involved in the disqualification case concerning Walker Wingsail Systems. **Clients:** National and local IPs.

Laytons (see firm details p.1031) Much of the firm's work has centred on liquidations, voluntary arrangements and turnarounds across the transport, motor industry, IT, engineering and construction sectors. The *"experienced team"* includes **Anthony Harris** (see p.471) (managing partner of the Bristol office), who focuses on non-contentious issues. The firm recently acted for the trustee in the rescue of Overndale School and advised Newport Technology Group in its reconstruction and voluntary liquidation involving £8 million in assets. **Clients:** Main IPs; banks; corporates.

Burges Salmon (see firm details p.902) The majority of the practice involves instructions from financial institutions, while it also advises creditors and directors of troubled companies. Managing partner **Guy Stobart** (see p.477) remains key to much of the firm's profile, particularly in agricultural receiverships. The firm has been acting on behalf of IPs, clearing banks, building societies and other UK financial institutions on the full range of rescue and insolvency matters. **Clients:** Major accountants; Lloyds TSB; UCB Group.

CMS Cameron McKenna (see firm details p.922) Active for both banks and IPs, the firm is thought to be buoyed by its good relationship with Lloyds. The talented team includes **Nick Agar** (see p.465), who handles primarily contentious work for banks and is visible *"doing a huge amount of work for Lloyds,"* and **Peter Wiltshire** (see p.478), skilled on the non-contentious side. The firm recently acted for Lloyds in the Shanning International liquidation matter, which is now going before the House of Lords. **Clients:** Local IPs; Lloyds TSB.

TLT Solicitors (see firm details p.1157) Handles a volume of insolvency matters primarily for IPs and Official Receivers in the region, including administrative receiverships, LPA receiverships, and voluntary arrangements. **Philip May** (see p.473) is appreciated for his technical knowledge and is best known for his bank-led recoveries work. The firm acted for Ernst & Young as receivers of Boing Ltd and also holds a national contract for The Insolvency Service (the Official Receiver offices). **Clients:** Accountants; national clearing banks; IPs.

Beachcroft Wansbroughs (see firm details p.872) Notable recent successes involved off-shore trusts. In addition, the team led by Giles Hindle has acted on behalf of both the DTI and directors in disqualifications proceedings. Judged to be a favourite of IPs in the region, the firm is seen to be winning "*an ever increasing amount of work.*" **Clients:** IPs; accountants.

Clarke Willmott & Clarke (see firm details p.915) Noted as acting both for and against IPs, it is primarily a contentious practice, which has seen several sales of insolvent companies and voluntary arrangements. **Martin Askew** (see p.466) has recently arrived from Beachcroft Wansbroughs and acts primarily for IPs, with particular expertise in investigating the causes of insolvency and pursuing recoveries, while **Stephen Allinson** (see p.465) is acknowledged as a "*sensible and practical*" operator. The firm acted for Deloitte & Touche as liquidators unscrambling a series of undervalue transactions and breaches of fiduciary duty by the directors of a failed company. Also acted on behalf of the Eagle Star Insurance company commercial loans department on matters concerning a professional loan book of approximately 100 cases and enforcing recoveries. **Clients:** IPs, banks, companies.

Meade-King Over the past year, the practice has seen an increasing amount of directors' disqualification defence work, as well as property-related insolvency matters. A balance exists between corporate and personal matters, mainly acting for IPs. **Clare Harris** (see p.471) receives market recognition, particularly for her personal insolvency work. **Clients:** IPs.

Other Notable Practitioners **Gordon Bon** (see p.466) of **Bevan Ashford** is endorsed for his strength in litigation and personal insolvency.

WALES

	INSOLVENCY/CORPORATE RECOVERY • Wales	Ptnrs	Assts
1	**Eversheds** Cardiff	1	2
2	**Edwards Geldard** Cardiff	2	6
	Hugh James Ford Simey Cardiff	3	3
	Morgan Cole Cardiff	4	5
3	**Hunt & Morgan** Cardiff	n/a	n/a

	LEADING INDIVIDUALS	
1	**VAUGHAN Philip** Eversheds	
2	**THOMAS Catrin** Hugh James Ford Simey	
3	**HUNT Matthew** Hunt & Morgan	**REES Bleddyn** Morgan Cole
4	**BARANSKI Karl** Edwards Geldard	**PAY Alex** Morgan Cole
	WILKINS John Dolmans	

This book is the product of 6,552 1/2-hour interviews. See p.7 for BMRB audit.
Within each band, firms are listed alphabetically. *See individuals' profiles p.465*
n/a Figures unavailable at time of going to press.

Eversheds (see firm details p.952) Continues to handle a steady stream of higher-end corporate insolvency matters for a large number of banks and accountancy firms in the region. Competitors acknowledge that the firm "*gets the lion's share of the big-ticket work*" and remains "*legitimately number one*" for corporate insolvency work. Head of the Insolvency unit, **Philip Vaughan** (see p.478) is judged to be "*without peer*" winning "*substantial instructions through the firm's banking clients.*" Highlights of the year include acting for KPMG in the HMG Group motor dealer receivership, one of the largest of the last twelve months. **Clients:** Major accountants; IPs, clearing banks; finance houses; surveyors.

Edwards Geldard (see firm details p.948) Engaged in a mix of corporate and personal insolvency cases on both the contentious and non-contentious side. It has witnessed a recent upsurge in bankruptcy claims, although the bulk of the practice is still corporate work, with **Karl Baranski** developing his profile. Instructed predominantly by IPs, the firm has undertaken a large amount of LPA receivership work for Bass Brewers over the last year. In addition, it recently acted for Bridgend County Borough Council against the administrator of Cosslett Contractors. **Clients:** Big five accountancy firms; IPs; accountants.

Hugh James Ford Simey (see firm details p.1004) Best known for its contentious prowess, the firm continues to shore up the non-contentious side, and displays strengths in compulsory liquidations and bankruptcy. **Catrin Thomas** (see p.477) is applauded as being "*highly active and adept*" in the field of personal insolvency. Significant matters include acting for Grant Thornton in a successful preference claim and also in the liquidation of Eynons' (Pontardawe) Ltd, a long-standing South Wales bakery. It continues to act for PricewaterhouseCoopers in the ongoing administration of Sunrise Homes. **Clients:** BN Jackson Norton; Grant Thornton; PriceWaterhouse Coopers; Solomon Hare.

Morgan Cole (see firm details p.1074) Retains its market approval, although head of the company-commercial department **Bleddyn Rees** is thought to have been less visible in insolvency work in recent times. Perhaps as a consequence of this, **Alex Pay** (see p.475) is said to be "*growing in profile,*" building on his background in banking litigation. **Clients:** Big five accountancy firms; IPs.

Hunt & Morgan Thought to have "*positioned itself well as a niche insolvency firm*" it is highly visible acting for liquidators and trustees in bankruptcy on mid-tier cases. "*Reasonable and skilled,*" **Matthew Hunt** is the standout practitioner here.

Other Notable Practitioners **John Wilkins** of **Dolmans** continues to handle predominantly bankruptcy and liquidation work, with an equal split between contentious and non-contentious matters.

MIDLANDS

Eversheds (see firm details p.952) Winning the "*bulk of the bank work in the region,*" this office has carved a name for its activities in the automotive industry, timeshare property insolvencies and restructurings. The practice also regularly deals with multi-site receiverships and the transfer of appointments. National Head **Jeff Drew** (see p.468) attracted widespread praise, with competitors agreeing that "*the market leader still has to be Drew,*" especially considering his "*historical connection to NatWest.*" Much of the firm's work is said to be won "*due to his name and personal reputation.*" **Louise Pheasant** (see p.475) remains appreciated as "*worthy competition.*" Highlights for the team include acting for KPMG in the administration of Century International, advising Ernst & Young in the receivership of NS Eurowire and acting for Deloitte & Touche in the liquidation of White Mountain Goods. The firm also obtained a pooling order from the High Court in respect of the assets of three companies. **Clients:** Deloitte & Touche; Grant Thornton; KPMG; PricewaterhouseCoopers; Royal Bank of Scotland.

Martineau Johnson (see firm details p.1055) Largely lender-driven, in the past year it has been active on turnarounds and reconstructions. With a

INSOLVENCY/CORPORATE RECOVERY • Midlands	Ptnrs	Assts
1 **Eversheds** Birmingham	3	8
2 **Martineau Johnson** Birmingham	6	10
3 **Wragge & Co** Birmingham	3	18
4 **Gateley Wareing** Birmingham	2	6
Irwin Mitchell Birmingham	1	3
5 **Hammond Suddards Edge** Birmingham	4	2
6 **Actons** Nottingham	2	4
Pinsent Curtis Biddle Birmingham	1	2
Shoosmiths Northampton	n/a	n/a

LEADING INDIVIDUALS	
★ **DREW Jeff** Eversheds	
1 **BAKER Ian** Martineau Johnson	**MCGEEVER Brendan** Gateley Wareing
PALLETT Julian Wragge & Co	**PHEASANT Louise** Eversheds
2 **COOKE David** Pinsent Curtis Biddle	**READETT Helen** Martineau Johnson

This book is the product of 6,552 1/2-hour interviews. See p.7 for BMRB audit.
Within each band, firms are listed alphabetically. *See individuals' profiles p.465*

strong banking expertise, **Ian Baker** (see p.116) remains "*well respected*," while **Helen Readett** (see p.475) ("*she knows her stuff*") is "*strong in property insolvency.*" The firm was recently instructed by a lender on the restructuring of an exposure of £40 million involving five different lenders and a large trading group. Also advised Grant Thornton on a trading receivership involving ten companies. **Clients:** Arthur Andersen; BDO Stoy Hayward; HLB Kidsons; KPMG; Lloyds TSB.

Wragge & Co (see firm details p.1189) The firm continues to run a mixed banking and insolvency team, which undertakes insolvency rescue and restructuring matters. The prosecution of directors' disqualification cases for the DTI is felt to dominate the workload. The "*highly capable*" **Julian Pallett** heads the Debt Finance team and enjoys "*many contacts at the banks.*" The group advised KPMG on the administrative receivership of John Tams Group and acted for Ernst & Young on the receivership of National Homecare. Handled the resultant complications following Derby Cycle Corporation's sale of certain assets to a company that subsequently went into liquidation. **Clients:** Arthur Andersen; Ernst & Young; KPMG; Moore Stephens Booth White; PricewaterhouseCoopers.

Gateley Wareing (see firm details p.969) The firm is perceived to have "*a good following and a good flow of work*" in the field. Its talented lawyers include **Brendan McGeever**, who is "*easy to deal with*" and thought to attract a volume of work from IPs. **Clients:** Deloitte & Touche; Grant Thornton; AIB; Clydesdale Bank.

Irwin Mitchell (see firm details p.1009) One of the few specialist units in the West Midlands where the practitioners deal exclusively with insolvency work. While the majority of its clients are accountants and IPs, the department also has close links with Lloyds TSB, Allied Irish Bank and the Inland Revenue Special Compliance Office. Lawyers also act for high profile directors, and have seen a growth in administration orders. Steven George leads the well-regarded team. The firm acted for Poppleton & Appleby in the successful administration of a major component manufacturing company in Coventry. In one of the largest litigation cases, the firm advised KPMG in its pursuit of directors in a multi-million pound liquidation. Concluded the receivership of a group of companies in the seed and foodstuff market (£15 million turnover) on behalf of Lloyds Bank and Arthur Andersen. **Clients:** KPMG; Poppleston & Appleby; PricewaterhouseCoopers.

Hammond Suddards Edge (see firm details p.984) Now headed by Chris Harlow, the firm continues to achieve a substantial number of instructions in the growing asset finance and invoice discounters sectors. The recent loss of John Sullivan and Duncan Haymes' return to Manchester have dimmed the visibility of the practice. Highlights include acting for Deloitte & Touche in the administration of HKB Steels and for Smith & Williamson in the liquidation of Sturmey Archer. The firm has also been providing ongoing advice to Royal Bank of Scotland on turnaround issues and corporate support. **Clients:** IPs; accountants.

Actons This "*long-established*" Nottingham practice remains "*top notch in its patch.*" The group, headed by Richard Lehman, continues to act for banks, local accountants and other solicitors in the field. **Clients:** IPs and major accountants.

Pinsent Curtis Biddle (see firm details p.1098) The firm continues to work for a number of banks, IPs, corporates and insurance companies. The "*switched-on*" **David Cooke** (see p.117) is "*intellectual and multi-skilled*," although the team in general is felt to lack the depth required to challenge the leading firms. Recently appointed as the independent trustee to the Finelist plc pension schemes and has also been acting for a New York listed insurance company on the restructuring of its UK operations, which will involve the voluntary liquidation of its UK subsidiaries. **Clients:** Main accountants and clearing banks.

Shoosmiths (see firm details p.1129) The Northampton based group, led by Dominic Hopkins, remains respected in the field, handling both corporate and personal insolvency work with "*an experienced and polished approach.*" **Clients:** IPs and major accountants.

EAST ANGLIA

INSOLVENCY/CORPORATE RECOVERY • East Anglia	Ptnrs	Assts
1 **Eversheds** Cambridge, Ipswich, Norwich	2	6
Mills & Reeve Cambridge, Norwich	2	6
2 **Prettys** Ipswich	3	2
Taylor Vinters Cambridge	2	3
3 **Nicholsons** Lowestoft	1	1

LEADING INDIVIDUALS	
1 **MCGURK Anthony** Eversheds	**SHORT John** Taylor Vinters
WAINE Ian Prettys	**WHEATLEY Jamie** Mills & Reeve
2 **NICHOLSON Mark** Nicholsons	
3 **FALKUS Bryony** Mills & Reeve	

This book is the product of 6,552 1/2-hour interviews. See p.7 for BMRB audit.
Within each band, firms are listed alphabetically. *See individuals' profiles p.465*

Eversheds (see firm details p.952) All three offices in the region advise on corporate insolvency matters, winning plaudits for their "*pre-eminence with a big sweep*" of work. Best known for receiverships rather than contentious work. The "*sensible*" **Anthony McGurk** (see p.474) ("*technically a good operator*") is based in Cambridge. In matters of administrative receivership, the firm has acted for KPMG over the Gibbs Palmer Group of companies, advised BDO Stoy Hayward on Hedley House Hotel, and acted for PricewaterhouseCoopers with regards to Eaton International. **Clients:** Grant Thornton; Lovewell Blake.

Mills & Reeve (see firm details p.1069) The insolvency team at this firm has seen an increasing level of formal insolvency appointments over the past twelve months. Has an emphasis on CVAs for biotechnology and new technology companies, turnaround work and LPA receivership work. The "*super*" **Jamie Wheatley** (see p.478) is credited with propelling the contentious side into the limelight. **Bryony Falkus** (see p.245) has a greater corporate element to her practice but remains respected for her insolvency expertise. **Clients:** Banks, accountants and IPs.

Prettys (see firm details p.1100) Operating from the corporate department, the firm remains the "*premier insolvency practice in Ipswich,*" historically linked with Grant Thornton in the region. **Ian Waine** (see p.478) wins the approval of market with his "*approachable, knowledgeable manner.*" The firm has handled a number of receiverships and provided defences to directors' disqualification proceedings, in addition to the administration of a high profile local company. **Clients:** Local accountants.

Taylor Vinters (see firm details p.1150) Close relationships exist between the practice and the corporate recovery specialists in a number of major accountancy firms, including Ernst & Young and Grant Thornton. **John Short** (see p.256) "*has a good following,*" and is seen as key to the firm's success. It has recently been advising Lloyds TSB on issues arising from turnarounds and individual voluntary arrangements. The firm also acts for office-holders and creditors during disputes, and has acted for liquidators in wrongful trading and misfeasance claims against directors. **Clients:** Ernst & Young; Grant Thornton; Lloyds TSB.

Nicholsons The bulk of this practice's workload comprises contentious insolvency, primarily for IPs, and bankruptcy work involving setting aside preferences. In addition, the firm undertakes company liquidations and administration orders. Perceived to have a "*good relationship with local IPs*" and judged to remain a localised operation. **Mark Nicholson** (see p.474) is "*a perfectly capable operator and pleasant to work with.*" **Clients:** BDO Stoy Hayward; Lovell Blake.

NORTH WEST

INSOLVENCY/CORPORATE RECOVERY • North West	Ptnrs	Assts
1 **Addleshaw Booth & Co** Manchester	8	7
2 **Hammond Suddards Edge** Manchester	3	7
3 **Chaffe Street** Manchester	3	3
Davies Wallis Foyster Liverpool	3	6
DLA Liverpool	n/a	n/a
Halliwell Landau Manchester	4	6
4 **Eversheds** Manchester	1	5
5 **Cuff Roberts** Liverpool	2	2
Mace & Jones Manchester	2	3

LEADING INDIVIDUALS	
★ **BROOKS Egan** Addleshaw Booth & Co	
1 **SPENCER Shân** Chaffe Street	
2 **BURROWS Julia** Addleshaw Booth	**HAYMES Duncan** Hammond Suddards Edge
JOYCE John Addleshaw Booth & Co	
3 **BUCHANAN Andrew** Halliwell Landau	**COATES Philip** DLA
GOODMAN Nick NJ Goodman & Co	**GREGORY Andrew** Davies Wallis Foyster
WALLER Simon Eversheds	
4 **JUMP Graeme** Mace & Jones	**PRESTON Dermot** Hammond Suddards Edge
SOMEKH Peter Chaffe Street	**TWEMLOW Tony** Cuff Roberts
UP AND COMING	
ALDERTON John Hammond Suddards Edge	**BARNES Ged** Addleshaw Booth & Co
GRAY David Eversheds	**KELLY Susan** Hammond Suddards Edge

This book is the product of 6,552 1/2-hour interviews. See p.7 for BMRB audit.
Within each band, firms are listed alphabetically. *See individuals' profiles p.465*

Addleshaw Booth & Co (see firm details p.853) "*Sustained last year's growth – a force to be reckoned with*" enjoying a mix of advisory, litigation and turnaround work. Competitors acknowledge that the firm has "*always had a strong presence in Manchester*" with the "*substantial, robust team*" thought to "*dominate the market through its NatWest Bank work.*" Competitors endorsed **Egan Brooks** (see p.467) as "*obviously number one – he's on a different plane to the rest of us.*" Securing the long-standing NatWest ties, "*academically and experience-wise he's streets ahead of the rest of the pack.*" **Julia Burrows** (see p.467) is said to be "*one of Egan's main partners*" and "*long-established, she typifies the Addleshaw's quality.*" **John Joyce** (see p.472) is "*commercial – he pulls in some good work*" while **Ged Barnes** (see p.466) is commended as "*trustworthy, a sound practitioner.*" Notable instructions include advising Arthur Andersen in the administration of Powernet Telecom, the high profile dot.com failure, with the sale of the internet service provider Totalserve. Also advised the agricultural receivers SHM Smith Hodgkinson in National Westminster Bank v Jones, concerning transaction at undervalue. The firm advised Grant Thornton as the receivers of Manchester's noted 'Reform' restaurant in connection with the going concern sale. **Clients:** Main UK clearing banks; factoring companies; leading accountants and IPs.

Hammond Suddards Edge (see firm details p.984) "*Plays off its client base very well – it's really out there getting work and I'm impressed with its attitude.*" The firm has recently recruited senior figures. **John Alderton** (see p.465) (formerly of DLA) is seen to be "*a welcome arrival*" and has "*close connections with the insolvency lawyers' association,*" while **Susan Kelly** (see p.473), a recent recruit from Linklaters, is anticipated to "*do good things.*" **Dermot Preston** (see p.475) is "*one of the senior lawyers who gives the practice its standing.*" Recently returned from the Birmingham office, **Duncan Haymes** (see p.471) is thought to "*rise above the mob – he's been around, knows everybody and has the skill to match his marketing abilities.*" Busy in recoveries and restructuring, the firm has a strong following of IPs and clearing banks. The group acted for GMAC in the administration of Cramlington Textiles, realising nearly £6 million, and advised PwC in the liquidation of Fearnley Construction Group. The firm also acted for KPMG in the administration of DCE, a national utilities contractor with a £50 million turnover and with over 1,200 employees. **Clients:** Royal Bank of Scotland; Lloyds TSB; Co-op Bank; KPMG; Begbies Traynor.

Chaffe Street (see firm details p.911) Market consensus believes that the firm "*punches above its weight and successfully sells itself*" to industry figures, and that it is still yet to realise its "*bags of potential.*" Engaged in a broad range of insolvency and recovery work for the main banks and major accountancy firms. **Shân Spencer** (see p.477) has "*a good name for general all-round expertise.*" Her activity in the local R3 committee ensures that she is a "*serious player with a reputation that precedes her.*" **Peter Somekh** (see p.477) is also rated for his non-contentious work. The firm has been acting for Royal Bank of Scotland in the receivership of E Simpson and was involved in the receiverships of Ravenhead Glass, TBS Cygma and Scanchem UK. **Clients:** Clearing banks; big five accountancy firms; IPs.

Davies Wallis Foyster (see firm details p.935) A force in the Liverpool market "*attracting quality work.*" Niche strengths include acting for breweries in receivership work and utilising the firm's experience in food technology and production. **Andrew Gregory** (see p.470) is "*well-known and liked around town,*" although his new role as managing partner has imposed other demands on his time. The firm acted in the receiverships of Runcorn-based Vantrunk and Grandreams, a national wholesaler of children's books. Also acted for the liquidator in a claim for misfeasance and wrongful trading, against directors of a company in the aviation industry. **Clients:** Bank of Scotland; Deloitte & Touche; Grant Thornton; Huntingdon Moore; Kroll Buchler Phillips; Lloyds TSB.

DLA **Philip Coates** is the top name of a team that advises a range of major clearers, big five accountancy firms, IPs and corporates on insolvency matters.

Halliwell Landau (see firm details p.982) Busy in the automotive and technology industries. A "*traditionally strong practice*" has "*good reciprocal relationships with the banks.*" **Andrew Buchanan** (see p.467) has "*come to the fore*" building on his banking experience, and is appreciated for "*getting his hands well and truly dirty.*" Significant matters include acting for KTH in the acquisition of the automotive division of Transtec and advising Arthur Andersen in the sale of the Cooperheat Group of Companies (in receivership). Also acted for Kroll Buchler Phillips in the liquidation of Switch TV. **Clients:** Main clearing banks; big five accountancy firms; IPs.

Eversheds (see firm details p.952) Fielding experience in new economy failures, accident management companies, the healthcare sector and the motor industry. "*Steadily growing its insolvency practice on the foundations of a huge client base.*" Although not securing the highest profile, **Simon Waller** (see p.478) is "*definitely a player – he's done a lot of good work.*" Bolstered by "*a good name from his days on secondment at RBS,*" **David Gray** (see p.470) is increasingly seen "*working on larger assignments,*" the most recent example being advice to PwC as the administrators of breathe dotcom, the fourth biggest internet service provider in the UK. Another highlight for the team was acting for BDO Stoy Hayward in implementing a corporate voluntary arrangement in the UK, for Kim Von Herzog Properties, a Jersey registered company. **Clients:** Bank of Scotland; HSBC; all major accountants.

Cuff Roberts The market applauds this Liverpool firm for securing a strong connection to AIB in Manchester. **Tony Twemlow** (see p.617) is the "*mainstay*" of the practice whose work includes a mixture of both corporate and personal insolvency matters. Significant matters from the past year include the liquidation of the Merseyside Innovation Centre for Parkin S Booth and the administrative receiverships of a restaurant and an internet company. **Clients:** AIB Bank; Nationwide; KPMG; Grant Thornton; Pricewaterhouse Coopers.

Mace & Jones (see firm details p.1046) Noted for its strength in agricultural receiverships, employment and disqualification proceedings, the firm is endorsed by competitors as "*becoming more and more active.*" "*Technically skilled,*" **Graeme Jump** (see p.472) is viewed as a "*worthy competitor*" in spite of his commitments as managing partner of the firm. **Clients:** Huntington Moore; Pannell Kerr Forster; Parkin S Booth; PricewaterhouseCoopers; RSM Robson Rhodes.

Other Notable Practitioners **Nick Goodman** (see p.470) of **NJ Goodman & Co** is seen to be "*highly active on the liquidation and bankruptcy side,*" advising IPs.

YORKSHIRE

INSOLVENCY/CORPORATE RECOVERY • Yorkshire	Ptnrs	Assts
1 **DLA** Leeds, Sheffield	n/a	n/a
2 **Walker Morris** Leeds	6	15
3 **Addleshaw Booth & Co** Leeds	8	7
Hammond Suddards Edge Leeds	5	15
Pinsent Curtis Biddle Leeds	3	7
4 **Eversheds** Leeds	1	4
5 **Brooke North** Leeds	5	5
6 **Carrick Read Insolvency** Leeds	3	5
Keeble Hawson Sheffield	4	3
Lupton Fawcett Leeds	2	2

LEADING INDIVIDUALS	
1 **CORR Patrick** Pinsent Curtis Biddle	**CRANSTON Peter** DLA
2 **BALLMANN William** Addleshaw Booth	**FRITH Stuart** Brooke North
MUDD Philip Walker Morris	
3 **BROWN Robert** Keeble Hawson	**HINCHLIFFE David** Walker Morris
JACKSON Mark DLA	**JEFFRIES Jonathan** Pinsent Curtis Biddle
4 **BRIGGS Graham** Addleshaw Booth	**FRIEZE Steven** Brooke North
LAYCOCK Andrew Carrick Read	**MARSHALL Richard** Lupton Fawcett
OBANK Richard DLA	**RIDLER Graham** Eversheds
UP AND COMING	
FERGUSSON Richard Keeble Hawson	

This book is the product of 6,552 1/2-hour interviews. See p.7 for BMRB audit.

Within each band, firms are listed alphabetically. *See individuals' profiles p.465*

DLA The Business Support and Restructuring Group services both companies and individuals in asset disposals, property sales, investigation work, litigation and recovery. It acts for major banks and other lenders. National insolvency head **Peter Cranston** is the leading figure here. **Richard Obank** and **Mark Jackson** also receive their share of market commendation.

Walker Morris (see firm details p.1171) Runs the gamut of insolvency work from complex corporate insolvencies to administrations, liquidations and voluntary arrangements. Head of department **Philip Mudd** (see p.474) draws from a healthy background in banking to offer "*true quality*" as a non-contentious lawyer operating on behalf of banks. His status as managing partner leads him to be seen less at the coalface. Respected litigator **David Hinchliffe** (see p.472) is "*always around and about*" and active on procedural issues. The firm advised Arthur Andersen on the administration of Uno and World of Leather, the listed national furniture retailers, in one of the most publicised corporate collapses of the year. Also acted for Caterpillar (UK) in the purchase of two major suppliers from administrative receivers and received instruction from Deloitte & Touche on the receivership of Greatminster Group, the insurance broker and financial intermediary. **Clients:** Lloyds TSB; RBS; Barclays; the big five accountancy firms.

Addleshaw Booth & Co (see firm details p.853) "*Traditionally strong with a fine set of clients,*" it is preferred advisor to Yorkshire Bank as well as the sole Northern panel firm for 3i plc and one of three panel firms for HSBC. The "*eminently experienced*" **William Ballmann** (see p.466) is viewed as the firm's "*big hitter*" for insolvency work, while **Graham Briggs** (see p.467) commands market commendation as an "*excellent technical operator*" who "*always gets the job done.*" In addition to its formal insolvency work, the firm is developing expertise in turnaround for both clearing banks and equity investors. The firm acted for Lloyds TSB in the administrative receiverships of William Denby & Sons, a long-established textile business, and United Kitchens, a retailer operating from 110 nationwide outlets. **Clients:** 3i Group; HSBC; RBS; Lloyds TSB; leading accountants and IPs.

Hammond Suddards Edge (see firm details p.984) The Business Finance and Recovery Group represents local IPs and bankers as well as asset-based lenders, and with a strong corporate base has been increasingly active in sales and turnaround work. "*Hammonds being Hammonds will always get decent work,*" and this view is not altered by the retirement of leading light Paul Rhodes. Under the guidance of Jeremy Bennett the firm's recent highlights include representing the Luxembourg liquidators of BCCI in a claim against a foreign government and advising on the insolvency aspects of a Cayman Islands application. Also advised on the receiverships of T&D Industries, Demaglass, and the Leyland Daf liquidation application. **Clients:** Arthur Andersen; Bank of America; Eurosales Finance; GMAC; Kroll Buchler Phillips; PricewaterhouseCoopers.

Pinsent Curtis Biddle (see firm details p.1098) Expert in high value complex restructuring and recoveries, retaining close connections with clearing banks, particularly HSBC. Witnessed an increase in debtor-led work with clients across the telecoms, energy, retail and insurance sectors. The firm has scored well in targeting the "*the entrepreneurial side*" of the market with a respected corporate department affording "*a steady supply*" of insolvency work. Much of the firm's profile lies with practice head **Patrick Corr** (see p.468), who "*has the blarney*" and is "*highly regarded in R3 circles.*" Established figure **Jonathan Jeffries** (see p.472) is appreciated by peers and clients for his "*honest judgement – you can take him at his word.*" The group was instructed in the administration of Iaxis by a large US listed telecoms company, which was owed in excess of US$40 million. Also acted for the LPA receiver of Demaglass and advised a private debenture holder in relation to the receivership of Saturn Gas. **Clients:** Banks; accountants.

Eversheds (see firm details p.952) The insolvency department has moved from its litigation base to sit within the banking unit of the corporate department. Bank-led recoveries and restructuring are key parts of the workload alongside its strengths in IP led workouts and administrations. "*Practical*" **Graham Ridler** (see p.475) has developed his personal profile, and is said to be successfully driving the firm forward. Instructions of note include acting for PricewaterhouseCoopers in the restructuring and work-out of a multi-million turnover group of companies, and advising KPMG Corporate Recovery in the restructuring that included the sale of a US subsidiary. Also advised Arthur Andersen in the administration of Thomas Weatherald Ltd. **Clients:** Arthur Andersen; KPMG Corporate Recovery; PricewaterhouseCoopers; RBS/Natwest.

Brooke North Expert in contentious insolvency matters, the firm is endorsed for its non-bank and individual insolvency work. Practice head, "*hard-hitting*" **Stuart Frith** is a specialist litigator, both in personal and corporate matters, and is set to be the next national president of the R3 Association. He is supported by **Steven Frieze**, acclaimed as "*at the forefront*" of the industry. The practice has acted in two major insolvency-related cases in the past twelve months: for the Bank of Ireland in the Hollicourt Contracts case (now the leading case on s.127 of the Insolvency Act), and for the trustee in Dennison v Krasner, as a result of which Parliament brought forward the Welfare and Pensions Reform Act. **Clients:** Accountants; banks; corporates.

Carrick Read Insolvency (see firm details p.909) Competitors view this practice as a "*sound if small outfit*" heavily experienced in debtor-led work. **Andrew Laycock** is a "*fearless litigator*" willing to take up challenges to the big IP and industry leaders. Highlight matters include the administration of Cantride, a drill-bit business, and the bankruptcy of Reg Brierley, the chairman of Sheffield United.**Clients:** Accountants/IPs; banks; corporates.

Keeble Hawson "*Tenacious*" practice head **Robert Brown** (see p.467) is endorsed for his work in liquidations and is thought to have a fine hold on the mid-market for voluntary arrangements and administrations. **Richard Fergusson** (see p.469) handles a "*strong mix*" of contentious and non-contentious work, and is judged by peers to be "*a worthy competitor.*" The firm has recently been acting in two administrative receiverships for RBS. **Clients:** Accountants/IPs; banks; corporates.

Lupton Fawcett The firm's insolvency department remains strong in the area of small to medium-sized administrative receiverships and company voluntary arrangements. It is said to be a "*good competitor on the non-bank side,*" with managing partner **Richard Marshall** well respected for his "*real focus.*" **Clients:** Accountants / IPs.

NORTH EAST

INSOLVENCY/CORPORATE RECOVERY • North East	Ptnrs	Assts
1 **Dickinson Dees** Newcastle upon Tyne	4	10
2 **Eversheds** Newcastle upon Tyne	2	4
3 **Hay & Kilner** Newcastle upon Tyne	2	2
Watson Burton Newcastle upon Tyne	3	4
4 **Robert Muckle** Newcastle upon Tyne	1	4
Ward Hadaway Newcastle upon Tyne	3	1

LEADING INDIVIDUALS	
1 **ANDERSON John** Eversheds	**SANDERSON Gordon** Dickinson Dees
2 **BLAIR Jonathan** Dickinson Dees	**PENNIE John** Dickinson Dees
3 **GILL Julian** Watson Burton	**HARROLD Neil** Hay & Kilner
TIPLADY Gillian Watson Burton	
4 **DUTTON Paul** Eversheds	**JAMES Jim** Ward Hadaway
UP AND COMING	
MCNICOL Stephen Robert Muckle	

This book is the product of 6,552 1/2-hour interviews. See p.7 for BMRB audit.
Within each band, firms are listed alphabetically. *See individuals' profiles p.465*

Dickinson Dees (see firm details p.941) Far ahead of the other firms due to the size of its team and the volume of its work. Adjudged "*a well-balanced practice,*" rated for its bank work, directors' disqualification and to a lesser extent administrations. **John Pennie** (see p.475) hits the target in "*anything that's complicated,*" while **Gordon Sanderson** (see p.476) enjoys an enviable relationship with the banks. **Jonathan Blair** (see p.466) undertakes a volume of directors' disqualification work. The firm recently acted for KPMG in successfully settling a claim brought against a District Council in its capacity as a shadow director of a failed company. Also instructed by Jennings Johnson in a large company reconstruction under section 110 of the Insolvency Act and advised Grant Thornton on the administration of Bonds Foundry. **Clients:** Deloitte & Touche; Ernst & Young; Grant Thornton; KPMG; PricewaterhouseCoopers.

Eversheds (see firm details p.952) Increasingly involved in corporate turnaround, the robust practice enjoys a "*clearly defined presence*" supported across the region by offices in Leeds and Manchester. Well respected, **John Anderson** (see p.466) is viewed as an "*exceptionally knowledgeable insolvency lawyer*" albeit sometimes "*a bit academic in his approach.*" **Paul Dutton** (see p.468) is a "*fine competitor*" thought to have given ballast to this office. Recent highlights for the firm include acting for KPMG in the restructuring of Arc Trust (a National Lottery funded arts centre) and in the LPA receivership of Trotters Arms. **Clients:** KPMG Corporate Recovery; NatWest; PricewaterhouseCoopers.

Hay & Kilner "*Technically sound*" **Neil Harrold** (see p.471) is perceived to be the force that "*pulls in the work,*" and is valued for his "*pragmatic and steady approach.*" Niche strengths of this firm include personal insolvency, investigation of suspected wrongdoing by directors and advocacy. The firm has been acting for the joint liquidators of Hails Construction in proceedings against its former directors for misfeasance and preference. This two-year investigation culminated in a settlement of the claim for a six-figure amount. Another notable matter included a complex bankruptcy where concealed assets were traced to the Isle of Man, and legal proceedings resulted in their recovery. **Clients:** IPs; major accountants.

Watson Burton Heavily focused on turnarounds and administrations in the last year, the firm has witnessed growth in liquidation and bankruptcy work for second tier local firms. The market consensus is that **Julian Gill**'s recent arrival from Robert Muckle will "*strengthen its practice.*" **Gillian Tiplady** is endorsed for her litigation skills. She is one of a limited number of lawyers in the area who are licensed IPs. **Clients:** Main accountants.

Robert Muckle The firm continues to advise on insolvency matters of both a corporate and personal insolvency nature. Felt to have suffered with the loss of partners to Eversheds and Watson Burton, the practice is judged to be "*refocusing and rebuilding*" with the successful recruitment of **Steve**

McNicol (see p.120) from Lovells to head up the practice. The firm is now advising Grant Thornton in the receivership of Onyx Internet. **Clients:** Big five accountancy firms; The Co-operative Bank; Lloyds TSB.

Ward Hadaway (see firm details p.1173) Its remit has extended to receivership work, winning appointments from the clearing banks. The firm has also continued to build up its creditor-led base, leading to instructions from IPs nationwide. The quality of the work is endorsed as "*always legally and technically correct, that's why they are a favourite of the local IPs.*" **Jim James** (see p.472) is considered the "*number one operator*" at the firm. Over the past twelve months the group has been undertaking work for the Federation Brewery and has been appointed to advise on the bank receivership of J&K Meats. **Clients:** Major accountancy firms.

SCOTLAND

INSOLVENCY/CORPORATE RECOVERY • Scotland	Ptnrs	Assts
1 **Dundas & Wilson CS** Edinburgh, Glasgow	4	10
2 **Burness** Edinburgh, Glasgow	4	5
Shepherd & Wedderburn WS Edinburgh	5	7
3 **DLA** Glasgow	n/a	n/a
Iain Smith & Company Aberdeen	3	2
MacRoberts Glasgow	1	3
4 **Biggart Baillie** Glasgow	n/a	n/a
Maclay Murray & Spens Glasgow	3	3
McGrigor Donald Glasgow	1	6
5 **Boyds** Edinburgh	n/a	n/a
Paull & Williamsons Aberdeen	n/a	n/a
Steedman Ramage Edinburgh	4	2

LEADING INDIVIDUALS	
1 **BRADY Yvonne** Dundas & Wilson CS	**CUTHBERTSON Ian** Dundas & Wilson CS
ROXBURGH Roy Iain Smith & Company	
2 **HOLLERIN Gordon** DLA	**SLEIGH Andrew** Burness
3 **FLINT David** MacRoberts	**HALLY Paul** Shepherd & Wedderburn WS
LANG Russell Boyds	**MACFARLANE John** McGrigor Donald
SHAW Murray Biggart Baillie	
4 **GIBSON David** Dundas & Wilson CS	**HENRY Graeme** Dundas & Wilson CS
HUGHES Michael Maclay Murray & Spens	**MCNIVEN Alan** Paull & Williamsons
MERSON James Stronachs	
UP AND COMING	
CARTY Gillian Shepherd & Wedderburn WS	**GRANT Rachel** Steedman Ramage
JONES Calum Boyds	

This book is the product of 6,552 1/2-hour interviews. See p.7 for BMRB audit.
Within each band, firms are listed alphabetically. *See individuals' profiles p.465*

Dundas & Wilson CS (see firm details p.947) "*Head and shoulders above everyone else*" fielding a "*large and fully dedicated team*" with "*strong links with the recovery units of the major banks.*" Head of the firm's Corporate Recovery Group **Ian Cuthbertson** is credited with shoring up those strong relationships. Praised for a "*superb client-facing role*" he is "*the main man for insolvency*" in the region. **Yvonne Brady** is "*at the top of her game*" both in her "*excellent knowledge of the subject and the ability to get things done.*" Newly ranked **Graham Henry** is valued as "*sound on the pre-insolvency reconstruction side*" while **David Gibson** is rated for his technical skills. Highlights of the past year include advising the Bank of Scotland on the restructuring of Semple Cochrane, acting for Kroll Buchler Phillips and Clydesdale Bank on the receivership of North Anderson Cars Group, and advising KPMG and the Bank of Scotland on the receivership of Image Precision International. **Clients:** Arthur Andersen; Deloitte & Touche; KPMG; Kroll Buchler Phillips; National Australia Bank.

Burness (see firm details p.903) The firm remains focused on corporate insolvency work, and respected for its relationship with PricewaterhouseCoopers. **Andrew Sleigh** (see p.476), viewed as the "*driving force,*" builds on his corporate background to provide a commercial, client focused offering. The firm acted for the Scottish Football Association in the rescue of the National Football Stadium and for the joint receivers of Gordon & Innes, a potato growing company in North East Scotland. **Clients:** Main accountants; financials.

Shepherd & Wedderburn WS (see firm details p.1126) The firm handles all the VAT enforcement work for Customs & Excise in Scotland as well as half the directors' disqualification work for the DTI. The "*esteemed*" **Paul Hally** (see p.471) is still seen "*around and about*" in the field, although his managing partner status has reduced his profile, while new partner **Gillian Carty** (see p.467) is rated for her "*intellectual expertise.*" Highlights for the group include advising Deloitte & Touche, the joint receivers of Gray Dunn & Co, in issues surrounding the lease of the company's Scottish premises. It also advised KPMG, as liquidator of the internet company Lastorders.com, on the disposal of the company and related intellectual property issues. Work for Deloitte & Touche involved actions to recover debts from European customers in the receivership of Donside Game & Meat Company. **Clients:** Customs & Excise; HSBC; DTI; RBS; Bank of Scotland.

DLA Best known for its contentious work, the firm advises a variety of IPs, accountants and corporates. **Gordon Hollerin** is the leading name here.

Iain Smith & Company Felt to "*dominate the Aberdeen market,*" **Roy Roxburgh** is commended for taking "*a specialist line in formal insolvency work.*" Recent highlights include acting for the receiver of Bain 2000 Ltd, a meat processing company, and successfully representing the trustee in bankruptcy in the Burnett's Trustee v Grainger case concerning property, which is the subject of sale before the appointment of the trustee. **Clients:** IPs; accountants; corporates.

MacRoberts (see firm details p.1048) The firm undertakes a variety of work including receiverships, liquidations, intensive care and workouts. A "*prominent player*" said to enjoy a steady flow of work. **David Flint** (see p.447) is rated as "*a first class insolvency lawyer*" bolstered by his experience in the IT and technology markets. **Clients:** Grant Thornton; Deloitte & Touche.

Biggart Baillie (see firm details p.882) Over the past twelve months, the firm has been instructed to defend a number of disqualification actions and has acted for directors in breach of warranty claims brought as a consequence of insolvency. **Murray Shaw** (see p.581) "*gives sound sensible advice*" combining insolvency with his expertise in general commercial litigation work. He is currently advising the directors in two large insolvencies matters. **Clients:** IPs; accountants; corporates.

Maclay Murray & Spens (see firm details p.1047) Maintained a good flow of work acting for receivers in relation to the sale of businesses, advising companies and directors on restructuring and undertaking litigation. Practice head **Michael Hughes** (see p.472) is rated for his corporate insolvency expertise, bringing to the table a "*measured and thorough approach.*" The firm continues to act for the receivers of APC in a complex case involving allegations of managerial impropriety and construction litigation. In addition, the firm has acted in the receiverships of Westerwood Hotels and Arbride. **Clients:** IPs; accountants; corporates.

McGrigor Donald (see firm details p.1062) Draws upon specialists in other units such as property, intellectual property and corporate tax. Active in pre-insolvency work, the firm has a noted strength in corporate restructuring. At the helm is the *"experienced"* **John Macfarlane** (see p.473) who enjoys a strong following of IPs, particularly in English/Scottish cross border aspects. The firm acted for the joint receivers of AM Russell (agricultural machinery) and is advising PwC in the ongoing liquidation of Monktonhall Colliery. **Clients:** Banks; accountants.

Boyds (see firm details p.890) *"Making strong efforts to secure its position in the insolvency market."* **Callum Jones** (see p.472) is a litigator who specialises in insolvency, and is *"steadily making a mark for himself"* successfully *"building up a practice from scratch."* **Russell Lang** has recently arrived from Morison Bishop. As *"a respected name in the industry"* he is anticipated to win a volume of formal insolvency instructions for the firm. **Clients:** Banks; accountants.

Paull & Williamsons (see firm details p.1091) A presence in the Aberdeen market, the firm undertakes insolvency work with a focus on the corporate and restructuring side while enjoying *"strong local banking connections."* **Alan McNiven** (see p.474) is a *"senior corporate partner"* who displays expertise across a range of insolvency issues. **Clients:** IPs; accountants; corporates.

Steedman Ramage (see firm details p.1139) Acts for IPs, banks, government agencies and both corporates and private clients. Competitors acknowledge that the firm has been *"setting out its stall on the insolvency front."* A *"well known name across Scotland,"* **Rachel Grant** (see p.470) is credited with *"increasing the size of the practice significantly."* The firm acted for Ritzons in resisting the liquidation of Brian McGregor & Sons, and is now responsible for half the directors' disqualification work in Scotland, having been awarded the work by the Department of Trade and Industry Insolvency Service. **Clients:** IPs; accountants; corporates.

Other Notable Practitioners **James Merson** (see p.474) of **Stronachs** is perceived to have a strong following among the local IPs.

NORTHERN IRELAND

INSOLVENCY/CORPORATE RECOVERY • Northern Ireland	Ptnrs	Assts
1 **Napier & Sons** Belfast	3	1
2 **John McKee & Son** Belfast	n/a	n/a
3 **Elliott Duffy Garrett** Belfast	n/a	n/a
McManus & Kearney Belfast	1	1

LEADING INDIVIDUALS
1 **GORDON John Gerard** Napier & Sons
2 **ROSS Alexander** John McKee & Son
3 **KEARNEY Mary Frances** McManus & Kearney
WILSON Michael Elliott Duffy Garrett

This book is the product of 6,552 1/2-hour interviews. See p.7 for BMRB audit.
Within each band, firms are listed alphabetically. *See individuals' profiles p.465*

Napier & Sons The pre-eminent insolvency practice in Northern Ireland. Its main thrust remains voluntary arrangement work, both for the corporate and individual. Closely associated with PwC, instructed as its main adviser in the region. Licensed IP **John Gordon** is considered the *"first port of call for high value referrals"* by fellow solicitors. The practice has continued to act for Global Marine of Texas in its difficulties with Harland & Wolff. Gordon is now handling the first dot.com insolvency in the region, namely Lution Limited, which went into company voluntary arrangement in December 2000. **Clients:** IPs; accountants and corporates.

John McKee & Son (see firm details p.1014) Felt to score well in the mid market, acting for a range of banks and major receivers. **Lex Ross** (see p.476) continues to specialise in receivership work, which he undertakes alongside banking and general corporate work. **Clients:** IPs; accountants and corporates.

Elliott Duffy Garrett (see firm details p.949) **Michael Wilson** (see p.478) once again elicited commendation from the market, with the bulk of his work undertaken for IPs. The practice is also endorsed for its service banks in receivership work. **Clients:** IPs; accountants and corporates.

McManus & Kearney The firm handles approximately 70% personal insolvency work, mainly in voluntary arrangements and trusteeships, with the balance being corporate insolvency. It acts for a number of finance companies, which provide it with spin-off insolvency work, but its main source of work remains referrals from solicitors and accountants. **Mary Kearney** is well respected and is said to be active on behalf of hire purchase companies. **Clients:** IPs; accountants and corporates.

LEADERS IN INSOLVENCY/CORPORATE RECOVERY

AGAR, Nick
CMS Cameron McKenna, Bristol (0117) 9300 200
nsda@cmck.com
Specialisation: Advises banks and insolvency practitioners on all aspects of corporate and personal insolvency and on debt recovery.

ALDERTON, John Charles
Hammond Suddards Edge, Manchester
(0161) 830 5179
john.alderton@hammondse.com
Specialisation: Partner, business finance and recovery. Specialises in contentious and non-contentious insolvency (with particular emphasis on property insolvency), lender security reviews and enhancement and general work-out, reconstruction and business support. Recent work includes administrations of Cramlington Textiles Limited (£7 million realisations), Dewsbury Civil Engineering Limited (a £50 million turnover national utilities contractor) and East Lanes Paper Mill Company Limited (a £35 million turnover paper manufacturer). Also security reviews and enhancement for a major clearing bank of a major oil engineering group and of a large supplier to the film industry.
Prof. Memberships: Society of Practitioners of Insolvency.
Career: Trained *Dibb Lupton Broomhead*; qualified 1989; partner, *Dibb Lupton Broomhead* 1994; partner, *Hammond Suddards Edge* 1999.
Personal: Married with two children. Keen skiier and golfer.

ALLINSON LIP, Stephen
Clarke Willmott & Clarke, Taunton
(01823) 445207
sallinson@cw-c.co.uk
Specialisation: One of a select number of lawyers in the UK who is also a Licenced Insolvency Practitioner and also an IPA Registered Property Receiver. Head of the insolvency and business recovery departments and a member of the firm's management board. Experienced in all aspects of insolvency law (corporate and personal). Acting for major banks and accountants (national firms and niche practices). Also undertakes general insolvency advocacy (for creditors and debtors, with particular experience in defendant director disqualification work). Over the last 12 months has developed the department in two particular areas: insolvency rescue actions and conditional fee litigation for insolvency practitioners. Balance of other professional work is commercial banking litigation and professional negligence in banking and insolvency fields. Recommended defendant solicitor by the Institute of Chartered Accountants in England and Wales in respect of

accountants facing professional disciplinary proceedings. Has extensive lecturing experience with Hawkesmere Lowe & Gordon Seminars, BLS and others.
Prof. Memberships: Law Society; Fellow of the Association of Business Recovery Professionals (South West Branch Committee Member); The Institute of Credit Management (South West Branch Committee Member); The Insolvency Lawyers Association; Chairman of the ACCA Admissions and Licensing Committee.
Career: Trained with *Clarke Willmott & Clarke* in September 1982; admitted in October 1984. Became a partner in January 1989.
Publications: Author of 'Debt Recovery' (3rd edition published May 2001); Legal Update contributor on a bi-monthly basis to 'Credit Today' and contributor of numerous articles to insolvency and debt recovery journals.
Personal: Sport (Director of Yeovil Town Football Club); church activities and youth work; charity and school work; amateur dramatics.

ANDERSON, Hamish
Norton Rose, London (020) 7238 6000
andersonh@nortonrose.com
Specialisation: Partner in the insolvency group. His work covers all aspects of insolvency under the Insolvency Act 1986 and cross-border insolvency. Recent assignments include acting for the provisional liquidators and Daewoo Motor Company Ltd. Assignments frequently involve knowledge of insolvency law in other jurisdictions. Recent examples include: US, France, Germany, Greece, Russia, Indonesia, Singapore Korea and Thailand. Has acted as an expert witness on English insolvency law in US chap II proceedings.
Prof. Memberships: Past president Insolvency Lawyers' Association. Council member, R3. Editor of R3 journal 'Recovery'. Member, Law Society and City of London Law Society Insolvency sub-committees. Publications officer, committee J (creditors' rights) International Bar Association. Member, editorial board 'Insolvency Law & Practice'.
Career: Admitted 1973. Licensed insolvency practitioner since 1987. Partner, *Bond Pearce* 1977-96. Partner, *Norton Rose* since 1996. Author of several insolvency textbooks and numerous articles.

ANDERSON, John
Eversheds, Newcastle upon Tyne (0191) 261 1661
johnanderson@eversheds.com
Specialisation: All aspects of insolvency, corporate and personal, acting for secured and unsecured creditors, office holders and debtors; banking; asset tracing and recovery. Particular interests include landlord and tenant, pensions in bankruptcy and directors disqualification. Ensuring the conversion of the technicalities into results.
Prof. Memberships: The Law Society. Incorporated Law Society of Newcastle upon Tyne.
Career: Education: Royal Grammar School, Newcastle upon Tyne 1976-83. Newcastle University 1983-86. Articles: *Wilkinson Maughan* 1987-89. Partner: 1997 (when *Wilkinson Maughan* joined *Eversheds*).
Personal: Interests include cricket, ancient history and legal history.

ANDREWS, Mark
Denton Wilde Sapte, London (020) 7242 1212

ARCHER, David
Pitmans, Reading (0118) 958 0224
darcher@pitmans.com
Specialisation: All aspects of commercial and personal insolvency including insolvency litigation and insolvency/pensions issues. Acts as an independent trustee to corporate pension schemes of insolvent companies.
Prof. Memberships: Insolvency Lawyers Association; Member of INSOL Europe; Associate Member of R3; Law Society.
Personal: Christianity, skiing and sailing.

ASKEW, Martin
Clarke Willmott & Clarke, Bristol (0117) 971 6600
maskew@cw-c.co.uk
Specialisation: Partner specialising in insolvency and corporate recovery. Martin has dealt with all aspects of bankruptcy and insolvent liquidations and also has considerable experience in dealing with voluntary arrangements, insolvent partnerships, administrations and administrative receiverships. This includes advice on related issues such as retention of title, sales of businesses as going concerns, the disposal of property and construction loss and expense claims.
Career: University of Sheffield. Admitted as solicitor, *Dibb Lupton Broomhead*, Leeds – 1992. Articled *Nabarro Nathanson*, London. Joined *Wansbroughs Willey Hargrave*, Bristol (now *Beachcroft Wansboroughs*) 1996-2001; joined *Clarke Willmott & Clarke* as partner 2001.
Personal: Interests include rugby, squash and family.

BAINES, R.E.
Osborne Clarke, London (020) 7809 1000

BAKER, Ian
Martineau Johnson, Birmingham (0121) 678 1575
ian.baker@martjohn.com
See under Banking, p.116

BALLMANN, William
Addleshaw Booth & Co, Leeds (0113) 209 2036
wb@addleshaw-booth.co.uk
Specialisation: Partner in the Finance Group. Specialises in corporate reconstruction and turnaround work as well as contentious and non-contentious corporate and personal insolvency and related banking issues. German national with extensive contacts in Europe, a substantial proportion of the work is international. Licensed Insolvency Practitioner. Author of articles and legal updates on corporate recovery issues.
Prof. Memberships: Law Society, ABRP (Fellow), ILA (Council Member), AEPPC.
Career: Qualified in 1983. Joined the firm as Partner in 1992.
Personal: Educated at the University of Leeds (LLB 1978). Leisure interests include golf, skiing and scuba diving.

BARANSKI, Karl
Edwards Geldard, Cardiff (029) 2023 8239
karl.baranski@geldards.co.uk

BARKER, Matthew
Lester Aldridge, Bournemouth 023 8082 0407
matthew.barker@lester-aldridge.co.uk
Specialisation: Work includes all aspects of insolvency, business rescue and turnaround relating to companies and individuals. Acts for insolvency practitioners and directors and creditors of companies in financial difficulties. Also acts for invoice discounters and other financiers. Advises on corporate reorganisations and solvent liquidations.
Prof. Memberships: Law Society; Association of Business Recovery Professionals.
Career: Qualified in 1995 following articles with *Blake Lapthorn*. Solicitor in the Insolvency and Business Rescue Group at *Blake Lapthorn* until December 2000. Licensed insolvency practitioner in 2000. Joined Lester Aldridge in January 2001 as an associate in the corporate recovery team.
Personal: Born 1969. Married. Recreations include hockey, tennis, film, music and walking.

BARNES, Ged
Addleshaw Booth & Co, Manchester
(0161) 934 6656
gaba@addleshaw-booth.co.uk
Specialisation: All aspects of corporate recovery and insolvency work, including turnaround and reconstruction, and associated banking and security arrangements.
Career: Articled *Slater Heelis*. Joined *Addleshaw Booth & Co* as an assistant solicitor in 1998. Senior solicitor from 2000.
Personal: Born 1971. Educated at Maricourt High School and Manchester University (1993 LLB Hons). LPC at Chester Law School (1994 Distinction). Resides Greenfield, Saddleworth. Leisure interests include golf, football (Everton FC) and socialising.

BARNETT, Nigel
Denton Wilde Sapte, London (020) 7242 1212

BERRY, Christopher
Edwin Coe, London (020) 7691 4000

BETHELL-JONES, Richard
Denton Wilde Sapte, London (020) 7242 1212

BLAIR, Jonathan
Dickinson Dees, Newcastle upon Tyne
(0191) 279 9219
law@dickinson-dees.com
Specialisation: Partner, insolvency group, head of directors disqualification team. Work includes corporate recoveries, administrations and receiverships as well as individual insolvency work. Jonathan heads up the seven man strong directors disqualification team working for the insolvency service across the North of England. The team was successful in tendering for the expanded North East region in autumn 2000.
Prof. Memberships: Law Society; Committee Member of SPI (North East Region)
Career: LLB; training with *Wragge & Co* 1987-89; 1989 to date *Dickinson Dees*. Partner at *Dickinson Dees* 1997.
Personal: Married, two children; keen mountaineer and rock climber.

BON, Gordon
Bevan Ashford, Bristol (0117) 923 0111
g.bon@bevanashford.co.uk
Specialisation: Partner and head of Bristol insolvency department, specialising in insolvency (contentious and non-contentious). Acting for major, medium-sized and small accountancy firms with insolvency practitioners as well as for British and foreign banks and other commercial clients. Cases include refinancing and restructuring businesses in financial crisis.
Career: Torquay Boys' Grammar School; Queen Mary College, London. Called to the Bar 1983, quali-

fied as a solicitor 1986. Joint insolvency exam 1995. Partner at *Laytons* since 1994. Joined *Bevan Ashford* as partner 2001.
Personal: Born 1959. Lives in Bristol.

BOOBIER, Nigel
Osborne Clarke, Bristol (0117) 917 3000

BORDELL, Keith
Berwin Leighton Paisner, London (020) 7760 1000
keith.bordell@berwinleightonpaisner.com
Specialisation: Partner, head of business reconstruction and insolvency group. Advises on all aspects of business rescues and reconstructions, workout and insolvency law. Clients include distressed companies, company doctors, accountants and insolvency practitioners, investors, lenders and other creditors.
Prof. Memberships: Law Society; R3; Insolvency Lawyers' Association; AEPPC/ EIPA.
Career: Trained at *Cameron Markby.* Qualified 1988. *Watson, Farley & Williams* 1989-95, *Allen & Overy* 1995-98. Partner *Berwin Leighton* 1998.
Personal: Born 1963. Educated at Chigwell School and the London School of Economics. Married with two sons.

BRADY, Yvonne T
Dundas & Wilson CS, Glasgow (0141) 222 2200

BRANSON, Christopher
Boyes Turner, Reading (0118) 959 7711
cbranson@boyesturner.com
Specialisation: Partner in insolvency. Principal area of practice is corporate and individual insolvency. Acts for receivers, liquidators and administrators in corporate insolvency situations and for trustees in bankruptcy as well as nominees and supervisors in CVAs and IVAs. Acts for office-holders in areas of fraud and asset tracing, often abroad. Advises banks and financial institutions on security and lending issues. Clients include all the major accountancy firms, plus many smaller regional firms. Has lectured at IBC Conferences, R3 conferences as well as giving internal lectures and talks to accountancy firms. Charge-out rate of £180 per hour.
Prof. Memberships: Law Society; IPA; fellow R3; Insolvency Lawyers Association; member Insolvency Courts Users committee.
Career: Qualified in 1981. Partner at *Boyes Turner* from 1988. Insolvency practitioner 1989.

BRIGGS, Graham
Addleshaw Booth & Co, Leeds (0113) 209 2000
Specialisation: Insolvency, turnaround and banking law. Grahams broad based skills as an advisor to banks and insolvency practitioners were further enhanced by a one year secondment to a major UK bank as lead advisor to a commercial debt management project. Highlights of last year include advising the receivers of Grampian Care Limited, Scotland's largest nursing home operator.
Prof. Memberships: Leeds Law Society. Insolvency Lawyers Association. Association of Business Recovery Professionals.
Career: Joined *Addleshaw Booth & Co* upon qualifying as a solicitor in 1984. Developed his expertise from a background in bank litigation and bank advisory work.
Personal: Married with 3 children, lives in Menston near Ilkley. He is the holder of a Motor Sports Association competition license and competes in the Thoroughbred Sportscar Championship in a race prepared MGB.

BROCKMAN, Christopher
Sherwin Oliver Solicitors, Portsmouth
(023) 9283 2200
christopher.brockman@sherwinoliver.com
Specialisation: Deals with all aspects of individual and corporate insolvency, from administration to voluntary arrangements, particularly on the contentious side. Acts for many of the leading and smaller insolvency practitioners on the South Coast and regularly appears in court on their behalf. Also prosecutes for the DTI and acts for directors facing disqualification proceedings. Regularly gives talks at professional seminars. Has a particular interest in the effect of the incorporation of the European Convention on Human Rights into UK law on insolvency proceedings. Lectures on all aspects of insolvency law.
Prof. Memberships: Law Society, R3, LawNet Insolvency Unit, Insolvency Lawyers Association.
Career: Called to Bar 1985, transferred to solicitors 1988, joining *Sherwin Oliver Solicitors* in 1992 from a leading London firm.
Personal: Born 1962, lives in Broughton, Hampshire. Sailing.

BROOKER, Suzanne
Pitmans, Reading (0118) 958 0224
sbrooker@pitmans.com
Specialisation: Licensed Insolvency Practitioner dealing with all areas of formal rescue and insolvency for individuals, partnerships and companies.
Prof. Memberships: Member of Association of Business Recovery Professionals (ABRP); committee member for Southern Region for ABRP; member of Insolvency Practitioners Association.
Career: Joined *Pitmans* in 1992. Qualified Licensed Insolvency Practitioner 2000.
Personal: Married. Nine 'O' Levels, three A Levels, LLB (Hons) 2:1. Interests include reading, horse riding, swimming.

BROOKS, Egan
Addleshaw Booth & Co, Manchester
(0161) 934 6000
Specialisation: Head of corporate recovery practice.
Prof. Memberships: The Law Society (Chairman, Insovency Law sub-committee 1999-). Licenced Insolvency Practitioner, Society of Practitioners of Insolvency and Notary Public.
Career: Qualified 1966. *Slater Heelis* 1964-98. Partner 1969. Joined firm 1998 as Partner.
Personal: Educated at Manchester Grammar School and Manchester University (LLB Hons). Lives in Hale. Leisure interests include motoring, architecture and walking.

BROWN, Robert
Keeble Hawson, Leeds (0113) 244 3121
robertbrown@keeblehawson.co.uk
Specialisation: Robert is a partner and head of department at *Keeble Hawson.* He deals with all aspects of insolvency, Directors' Disqualification proceedings, commercial litigation and recovery both personal and corporate. Robert has particular expertise in dealing with contentious claims arising out of insolvency situations both for the insolvency practioners and the respondents.
Prof. Memberships: The Law Society; SPI; ILA; IPA; Licensed Insolvency Practitioner; member of Association of Business Recovery Professions; member of Insolvency Practitioners Association. Member of Leeds Law Society Civil Litigation committee.

Career: Articled *RC Moorhouse & Co.* Qualified 1979, partner 1981.
Personal: Born Harrogate 1955. Resides Wetherby. Educated Leeds University (LLB). A retired goal keeper now concentrating on mountain biking and tennis.

BUCHANAN, Andrew
Halliwell Landau, Manchester (0161) 835 3003
Specialisation: Head of insolvency and corporate recovery. Specialises in corporate and personal insolvency and Turnaround Administrative Receivership of Cooperheat (UK) Limited and Cooperheat International Limited on behalf of Arthur Andersen. Administrative Receivership of Manchester Abattoir on behalf of Pannel Kerr Foster.
Prof. Memberships: Law Society.
Career: Partner with *Haliwell Landau* since joining in March 1999.
Publications: Accountancy books, including 'Corporate Recovery Health Check'.
Personal: Stockport Grammar School, Sheffield University, Trent Polytechnic. Golf, cricket, rugby, walking. Father, retired medical practitioner.

BUGG, Anthony
Linklaters, London (020) 7456 4470
tony.bugg@linklaters.com
Specialisation: Experienced in all aspects of insolvency related work, advising banks and financial institutions, insolvency practitioners and corporate clients in relation to recovery, reconstruction or distressed debt problems. Has acted on a wide range of administrations, receiverships, liquidations and insolvent partnerships. Most recent assignments include advising the bank group of Dialog Corporation plc, the administrator of Ionica plc, the administrative receivers of THI plc, the liquidators of Toshoku Finance UK plc, a bondholder group in relation to Xerox Limited and RBS in relation to Finelist plc.
Prof. Memberships: SPI (Member of PR Committee), Law Society, AEPPC, IPA, IBA, Council Member, Insolvency Lawyers Association immediate past President.
Career: Qualified 1981. Partner *William Prior & Co* 1982. Partner *Dibb Lupton Broomhead* 1990. Joined *Linklaters* 1998; became partner 1998. Licensed Insolvency Practitioner since 1987.

BURROWS, Julia
Addleshaw Booth & Co, Manchester
(0161) 934 6346
jkb@addleshaw-booth.co.uk
Specialisation: Partner Corporate Recovery Department. Specialising in insolvency banking and corporate recoveries.
Prof. Memberships: Law Society; Insolvency Lawyers Association; Society of Practitioners of Insolvency. Association of Business Recovery Professionals.
Career: Educated at Leicester University (1977 LLB Hons). Articled with *Addleshaw Booth & Co.* Qualfied 1980. Made Partner in 1992. Licenced Insolvencey Practitioner.
Personal: Leisure interests include theatre, skiing and walking. Resides Bolton.

CARTY, Gillian
Shepherd & Wedderburn WS, Edinburgh
(0131) 473 5138
Specialisation: Corporate recovery/insolvency (all aspects) and directors disqualification (for DTI).
Prof. Memberships: Licensed Insolvency Practitioner (through Law Society of Scotland).

Career: Qualified 1995. Assumed as partner in May 2001.

COATES, Philip
DLA, Manchester (08700) 111111

COHEN, Adrian Leon
Clifford Chance, London (020) 7600 1000
adrian.cohen@cliffordchance.com
Specialisation: Finance practice partner specialising in all aspects of domestic and international non-contentious insolvency and corporate reconstruction, including negotiation of standstill, inter-creditor and security documentation, advising on counter-party risk, security enforcement, asset realisation, directors' duties and officeholders' duties.
Career: London School of Economics; Queen Mary and Westfield College, London (LLB (Hons) 1985, LLM 1987). Called to the Bar 1988; Barrister at law 1988-90; joined *Clifford Chance* corporate practice 1990; the firm's insolvency group 1991 to date.
Personal: Married with three children, one dog and two cats.

COOK, Nigel
Paul Davidson Taylor, Horsham 0140 383 1213
ncook@pdt.co.uk
Specialisation: Corporate insolvency, particularly administrative and LPA receiverships. Within past year has acted for insolvency practitioners in respect of insolvencies in the manufacturing and retail sectors. Also specialises in advice to directors of companies in financial difficulties or who face disqualification proceeds.
Prof. Memberships: Associate member of the Insolvency Lawyers association.
Career: Assistant Solicitor: commercial department *Clifford – Turner* (1976-81). Head of legal department First National Commercial Bank (1982-89); Partner: *Paul Davidson Taylor* (1995-).
Personal: B.A (Oxon) Jurisprudence. Keen golfer and cricketer. Trustee of penal affairs charity, The Inside Out trust.

COOK, Patrick D.
Osborne Clarke, Bristol (0117) 917 3000

COOKE, David J
Pinsent Curtis Biddle, Birmingham
(0121) 200 1050
david.j.cooke@pinsents.com
See under Banking, p.117

CORR, Patrick
Pinsent Curtis Biddle, Leeds (0113) 244 5000
patrick.corr@pinsents.com
Specialisation: Head of corporate recovery, Leeds. Advises insolvency practitioners and turnaround specialists on all aspects of corporate recovery and turnarounds. Also advises banks and other financial institutions on security issues. Recently acted for a Fortune 500 US corporate in relation to the administration of a UK telecommunications company with a European network (sums at risk were in excess of $40 million) and advised DFEE in relation to the transfer of the Training Enterprise Councils to the Learning Skills Council and other successor bodies. Has presented seminars to accountants and banks on corporate recovery, turnaround and banking issues and regularly presents seminars on behalf of the Association of Business Recovery Professionals most recently at their annual conference in Italy.
Prof. Memberships: Young Solicitors Group; the Insolvency Lawyers Association; subscriber to R3; committee member of the Class of 2000.
Career: LLB (Hons), Leeds Metropolitan University. Joined *Pinsent Curtis Biddle* in 1988. Qualified in 1990. Partner 1996.

CRAIG, Nigel
Sherwin Oliver Solicitors, Portsmouth
(023) 9283 2200
nigel.craig@sherwinoliver.com
Specialisation: Partner in corporate/commercial and corporate rescue department. Principal area of practice is corporate restructuring, mergers, acquisitions and disposals, with and without insolvency related issues. Approximately half of the department's cases are insolvency-related and involve acting for the Insolvency Practitioner on a restructuring/hive down prior to sale, and subsequently on the sale, or acting for the clients acquiring from receivers, administrators or liquidators. Has dealt with numerous re-structurings for groups of various values, the acquisition and disposal of insurance companies and insurance brokerages and the acquisition, disposal and re-structuring of major cross-channel ferry companies and shipping companies. Also handles management buy-outs and provides management and general corporate advice. Has advised on the setting up of nationwide franchise operations and re-structuring of a franchise group.
Prof. Memberships: Law Society, Insolvency Lawyers' Association (Associate Member), LawNet Insolvency Unit.
Career: Qualified 1981. Shortly afterwards set up with David Oliver as *Oliver & Co.*The firm merged with *Sherwins* to produce *Sherwin Oliver* in May 1989.
Publications: Author of a number of articles published in legal journals and newspapers. Lectures regularly and has been interviewed and spoken on radio on legal topics. Charge out rate for normal work is in the region of £165 per hour plus VAT.
Personal: Born 16th December 1956. Educated at Southern Grammar School, Portsmouth 1968-75, Kingston-upon-Thames Polytechnic 1975-78 and Guildford Law College 1978-79. Leisure pursuits include sailing (racing two-man catamarans), and motor biking (including track days). Lives in Emsworth, Hampshire.

CRANSTON, Peter
DLA, Leeds (08700) 111111

CROUCHER, Yvette
Cadwalader, Wickersham & Taft, London
(020) 7456 8514
yvette.croucher@cwt-uk.com
Specialisation: A senior associate in the London financial restructuring practice. She has comprehensive experience of complex corporate insolvencies and restructuring. She also advises on insurance company run-offs, restructurings and investigations. She has advised companies, banks, bondholders and creditors generally and also directors and office holders on their respective duties and liabilities. She is also a licensed insolvency practitioner. Recent work includes advising the joint administrators of Ionica plc and advising bondholder committees on major corporate restructurings.
Prof. Memberships: R3 Association of Business Recovery Professionals; Womens Group.
Career: Graduated in 1990 from Exeter University. Trained and qualified at *Simmons & Simmons*. Spent six months on secondment to the Royal Bank of Scotland, Specialised Lending Services in 1997. Joined *Cadwalader* in February 1998 after a four month sabbatical in Africa.
Personal: Married with one daughter.

CUTHBERTSON, Ian
Dundas & Wilson CS, Glasgow (0141) 222 2200

DOBSON, Julian
Julian Dobson Solicitors, Brighton (01273) 693567
jcd@juliandobson.com
Specialisation: Solicitor and licensed insolvency practitioner by examination, specialising exclusively in insolvency law; full range of insolvency work carried out for insolvency practitioners and other clients including administrations, bankruptcies, CVAs, IVAs, liquidations, PVAs and receiverships. Regularly instructed by Top Five accountancy firms.
Prof. Memberships: Insolvency Lawyers Association. R3. Insolvency Practitioners Association. Law Society.
Career: Articled *Hawley & Rodgers*; qualified 1986; assistant solicitor *Bunkers & Co* 1986-91; partner *Bunkers* 1991; passed JIEB examination to become Insolvency Practitioner 1993.
Personal: Born 1959; resides Lewes. Swimming, golf.

DREW, Jeff
Eversheds, Birmingham (0121) 232 1000
jeffdrew@eversheds.com
Specialisation: Partner in insolvency and banking group. Chairman of *Eversheds* corporate recovery and insolvency group. Advises insolvency practitioners and banks in connection with all aspects of corporate recovery and insolvency law and banks in connection with the taking and realising of charges. Speaks widely at conferences and seminars.
Prof. Memberships: Association of Business Recovery Professionals.
Career: Qualified in 1980. Worked at *Wragge & Co* 1978-82, then *Edge & Ellison* 1982-92 (from 1984 as a partner). Joined *Eversheds* as a partner in 1992.
Personal: Born 12th October 1954. Attended Solihull School and St Edmund Hall, Oxford 1974-77. Leisure interests include tennis, squash and badminton. Lives in Birmingham.

DUTTON, Paul
Eversheds, Newcastle upon Tyne (0191) 2611661
paulnsdutton@eversheds.com
Specialisation: Partner and head of corporate recovery and insolvency. Clients include all the big five accountancy firms, as well as regional specialist insolvency practitoners such as Tait Walker, Tenon Jennings Johnson, JB Taylor & CO and BKR Haines Watts. The firm also acts for HSBC Bank, National Westminster Bank, Royal Bank of Scotland, Bank of Scotland, Lloyds TSB and Co-op Bank. Advises insolvency practitioners, banks and other secured lenders and businesses on all aspects of corporate recovery and insolvency regimes. Particular specialism in non contentious business recovery bank work, including administrative receiverships and administrations, work outs, turn around and intensive care work, security reviews and advice on corporate restructures and bank refinancing. Involved in most high profile recoveries in the North East during and since the recession including Stanley Miller plc, Slaley Hall and Swan Hunter. The most notable case dealt with is the landmark decision on fixed and floating charges in

New Bullas Trading Company limited and he can also claim the dubious accolade of renaming the case following the sale of the company's name by the receiver.
Prof. Memberships: Law Society, R3 Committee Tyne and Wear Region, Insolvency Lawyers' Association.
Career: Date of birth: 06/08/65, Northumbria University LLB (Hons), Chester Law School. Joined *Robert Muckle Solicitors* 1989, qualified 1991, partner 1993, head of insolvency and banking since 1994. Joined *Eversheds* (Newcastle) in January 2001 as head of corporate recovery and insolvency.
Personal: Cricket Northumberland CCC, golf and football.

ELLIOTT, Robert
Linklaters, London (020) 7456 4478
robert.elliott@linklaters.com
Specialisation: Recent significant transactions include the £1.5billion acquisition financing of Southern Electric/Southern Water, GUS/Argos $1.6 billion takeover financing and the British Land Universal £300 million mortgage bond issue.
Career: Partner in the banking department of *Linklaters* since 1990. Co-head, corporate recovery and Insolvency *Linklaters & Alliance.* Leeds Grammar School; London University. Qualified in 1976. *Wilde Sapte* 1976-90. Joined *Linklaters* 1990 to date as a partner. Partner in the banking department of *Linklaters* since 1990. Co-head corporate recovery and insolvency *Linklaters & Alliance.*

FALKUS, Bryony
Mills & Reeve, Norwich (01603) 693225
bryony.falkus@mills-reeve.com
See under Corporate Finance, p.245

FERGUSSON, Richard
Keeble Hawson, Leeds (0113) 244 3121
richardfergusson@keeblehawson.co.uk
Specialisation: Licensed insolvency practitioner dealing with all forms of corporate and personal insolvency and recovery on behalf of practitioners, banks and building societies and debtors. Deals with a full range of contentious and non-contentious insolvencies from bankruptcy to trading receiverships and administrations. Also has experience of court appointed, agricultural and LPA receiverships as well as director disqualification proceedings.
Prof. Memberships: Law Society and ABRP.
Career: Trained at *Dibb Lupton Broomhead* 1989 to 1991; joined *Booth & Co* (now *Addleshaw Booth & Co)* September 1992; partner *Keeble Hawson* June 2000.
Personal: Educated at Batley Grammar School and Leeds University. Interests include hill walking, reading, travelling, food and wine.

FIDLER, Peter
Stephenson Harwood, London (020) 7809 2003
peter.fidler@shlegal.com
Specialisation: Partner, litigation department (recovery and insolvency group). Peter has specialised in banking since 1967 and in insolvency for some 25 years. In the last eight years has specialised in schemes of arrangement for insolvent insurance companies. Has been involved in recovery of assets from abroad using compulsory interrogation techniques in the UK and abroad.
Prof. Memberships: City of London Law Society Insolvency Law Sub-Committee.
Publications: Main Editor, Sheldon & Fidler's Practice and Law of Banking, 11th Edition, 1982. Lectures regularly at conferences on a variety of banking and insolvency topics.
Personal: Interests include music, theatre, the arts and sports. Languages: speaks French. Resides London.

FIELD, Ian T
Allen & Overy, London (020) 7330 3000
ian.field@allenovery.com
Specialisation: Business restructuring and insolvency; banking and finance.
Career: Partner in the banking department dealing with all types of restructuring and corporate insolvency work, acting for banks and other financial institutions, insolvency practitioners and corporations.
Personal: Exeter College, Oxford – Jurisprudence.

FLETCHER, Ian
Stephenson Harwood, London (020) 7809 2025
ian.fletcher@shlegal.com
Specialisation: Partner, Banking Group. Specialist in corporate recovery and restructuring work and also in aquisition finance (MBO's MBI's) against a general corporate and financial background with a significant international element. An authorised insolvency practitioner and former member of the Government Party which considered insolvency regulation in the UK.
Prof. Memberships: Council of the Association of Business Recovery Professionals (R3); Council Insolvency Lawyers' Association.
Publications: WS Joint author 'The Law Practice of Corporate Administrations' 1994, 1st edition, 2nd edition (2001). Joint Editor 'Cross Border Insolvencies' incorporating contributions from 35 jurisdictions published by Oceana Publications Inc 1999.
Personal: Educated Glasgow University (LLB). Qualified Scotland 1971, England 1978.

FLINT, David
MacRoberts, Glasgow (0141) 332 9988
df@macroberts.co.uk
See under Information Technology, p.447

FOSTER, Stephen
CMS Cameron McKenna, London
(020) 7367 3000
stephen.foster@cmck.com
Specialisation: Partner in banking and insolvency department. Principal areas of practice are banking, reconstruction and insolvency. Work includes advising banks and corporates on domestic and international banking questions and pre-insolvency issues, including options to maximise recovery and advising insolvency practitioners in receiverships, administrations and liquidations. Other main areas of practice are European and cross-border reconstructions, UK and US distressed debt issues and advising on documentation and insolvency issues. Has lectured to the Institute of Bankers, R3 and for various commercial lecture providers on banking and insolvency topics and written various articles.
Prof. Memberships: Member of Law Society; Insolvency Lawyers Association; AEPPC; R3; IBA Committee J.
Career: Qualified in 1989. Became a partner at *Cameron Markby Hewitt* (now *CMS Cameron McKenna*) in 1991.
Personal: Born 4 January 1958. Educated at Pembroke College, Cambridge. Interests include walking, music and film. Lives in London.

FRENCH, Matthew
Lovells, London (020) 7296 2000
matthew.french@lovells.com
Specialisation: Business restructuring and insolvency. Particular expertise in (re)insurance run-off and insolvency. Broad experience of default and credit risk management in financings and commercial contracts. Recent assignments include a multi-bank workout of a major UK manufacturing business, the preparation of schemes of arrangement for Equitable Life and provision of pan-European advice on telecoms collapses.
Prof. Memberships: The Association of Business Recovery Professionals. The International Association of Insurance Receivers. The Association of Run-off Companies. The Insolvency Lawyers Association.
Career: Churchhill College, Cambridge University 1984-87 MA (Law). Qualified as a barrister 1988 (Lincoln's Inn and 3/4 South Square, Chambers of Michael Crystal QC). *Wilde Sapte* 1989-99 (partner 1997); *Lovells* 1999-date (partner 2001).
Publications: Contributing editor to Butterworth Tolley's 'Insolvency' loose-leaf. A regular conference speaker. Features published in several journals.
Personal: Married with two children, resides London. Interests include oriental philosophy and contemporary arts. Born 1966.

FRIEZE, Steven A
Brooke North, Leeds (0113) 283 2100

FRITH, Stuart J
Brooke North, Leeds (0113) 283 2100

FROME, Nicholas P
Clifford Chance, London (020) 7600 1000
nicholas.frome@cliffordchance.com
Specialisation: Business restructuring and insolvency. Adviser to bank creditors in relation to the numerous UK and cross-border restructurings including Heron and Wickes; English Law adviser to the US bondholders in relation to Tiphook (CTRL) restructuring; adviser to the bank creditors in relation to aspects of the Queens Moat restructuring; adviser to ING in relation to the acquisition of Barings Bank from administrators and subsequent settlement negotiations with subordinated noteholders; adviser to co-ordinating banks and steering committees in relation to numerous confidential restructurings of international groups including a number of technology companies. Recently advised the receivers of the Hollas Group plc and Yorkshire Foods plc; advising Nortel in relation to Ionica plc and Ford in relation to TransTec plc; adviser to the administrators of Japan Leasing and AY Bank and to bank creditors in relation to restructurings linked to the Russian debt crisis and the Ashanti restructuring; also advised the UK lease and bank creditors in relation to the successful restructuring of the Hong Kong based QPL Group.
Prof. Memberships: Member of the Association of Business Recovery Professionals; INSOL; Insolvency Lawyers' Association; Insolvency Practitioners Association.
Career: Marlborough College and University College London. Formerly with *Lovells* (1975-2001)
Personal: Interests include fly-fishing, golf, cricket, military history and music. Married with three children.

GAINES, Keith
Lovells, London (020) 7296 2000
keith.gaines@lovells.com
See under Litigation, p.570

GALE, Stephen
Herbert Smith, London (020) 7374 8000
stephen.gale@herbertsmith.com
Specialisation: Partner and head of corporate recovery at *Herbert Smith.* Principal area of practice is corporate rescue and company reorganisation. Has wide experience of acting for banks and other financial institutions in work-outs and reorganisations. Also has considerable insolvency related experience, particularly in corporate insolvencies. Lectures widely on insolvency-related issues.
Prof. Memberships: Law Society, Institute of Credit Management, SPI, IPA, AEPPC, President of R3, the Association of Business Recovery Professionals.
Career: Qualified in 1982. Associate with *Simpson Curtis* 1984, then partner with *Masons & Marriott* in Hong Kong, 1985. Joined *Hammond Suddards* in 1987 as a partner. Partner *Herbert Smith* January 1998.
Personal: Born 15th October 1957. Attended Blackpool Grammar School and Sixth Form College, then Sheffield University. Leisure pursuits include fell walking, windsurfing, horseriding, skiing and classical music. Married with three children.

GIBSON, David
Dundas & Wilson CS, Glasgow (0141) 222 2200

GILL, Julian
Watson Burton, Newcastle upon Tyne (0191) 244 4444

GILL, Mark
Denton Wilde Sapte, London (020) 7242 1212

GODFREY, Patricia
Nabarro Nathanson, London (020) 7524 6000
Specialisation: Head of insolvency and corporate recovery group; handles all aspects of insolvency, rescue, turnaround and reorganisation.
Publications: Associate editor: Tolley's 'Insolvency Law & Practice'. Regular contributor: Legal Network TV. Joint author: Tolley's 'Company Secretarial Manual' – Insolvency Section. Regular conference speaker R3 and INSOL Europe. Member of both R3's London region and education courses and conferences committees. Member of NARA (association of non-administrative receivers) professional puposes committee. Head of firm's German group and joint author 'Englische Gesekshaften in der Insolvenz', a guide to UK insolvency proceedings written in collaboration with German Chamber of Commerce, director and trustee, German British Forum.

GOODMAN, Nick
NJ Goodman & Co, Altrincham (0161) 928 0990
nick@njgoodman.co.uk
Specialisation: Specialist with wide experience acting for officeholders in all types of insolvency cases, both personal and corporate. Expertise acquired as a partner within the banking and insolvency groups of two Top 20 law firms. Undertakes director defence work including disqualification proceedings.
Prof. Memberships: ABRP; Law Society; member of the North West Regional Committee of SPI (1994-96).
Career: Qualified 1982; *N J Goodman & Co* (2000); *Addleshaw Booth & Co* (1995-00); *Dibb Lupton Broomhead* (1989-95); Hong Kong (1982-88).
Personal: Attended Southampton University. Leisure pursuits include golf and family. Lives in Cheshire.

GORDON, John Gerard
Napier & Sons, Belfast (028) 9024 4602

GORDON-SAKER, Paul
Stephenson Harwood, London (020) 7809 2367
paul.gordon-saker@shlegal.com
Specialisation: Partner, litigation department. Head of recovery and insolvency group. Paul has specialised in insolvency work for the last 30 years and has substantial experience in all types of insolvency procedures operating in the UK together with more general experience of procedures in the United States, Europe and Hong Kong. He has special expertise in cross border insolvency disputes and is heavily involved in reconstruction and workouts for banking clients. He acts for all the major accountancy practices, banks and building societies. He is involved with many reported decisions of the High Court, Court of Appeal and House of Lords and has a prestigious reputation throughout the insolvency world. He is a frequent lecturer on insolvency topics at various conferences.

GRANT, Rachel
Steedman Ramage, Edinburgh (0131) 260 6641
rachel.grant@steedmanramage.co.uk
Specialisation: Partner and head of corporate recovery and insolvency unit with *Steedman Ramage.* Accredited by the Law Society of Scotland as a specialist in insolvency law. Advises on all aspects of corporate and personal insolvency including receivership, liquidation, administration, CVAs, sequestration and trust deeds. Acts for DTI insolvency service disqualification unit taking disqualification action against directors. Also acts for The Office of the Accountant in Bankruptcy, insolvency practitioners and banks. Advises commercial clients on recovery, reconstruction and insolvency related matters. Has lectured for Institute of Chartered Accountants, Law Society of Scotland, The Association of Business Recovery Professionals (R3), and various other business and commercial organisations on insolvency related matters and directors disqualification.
Prof. Memberships: Law Society of Scotland; Law Society Insolvency Solicitors Committee; Association of Business Recovery Professionals (R3).
Career: 1984-86 trained *DR Calder & Williams,* Dundee; 1986-88 assistant *Alex Morison & Co,* Edinburgh; 1988-99 assistant and thereafter associate *Shepherd & Wedderburn;* head of *Shepherd & Wedderburn* corporate recovery and insolvency unit; joined *Steedman Ramage* 1999 as partner and head of corporate recovery and insolvency unit.
Publications: Various articles and legal updates on insolvency related matters and directors disqualification for professional and commercial journals.
Personal: Education: University of Edinburgh 1981, LLB (Hons); Dundee University, 1983, Dip LP.

GRAY, David
Eversheds, Manchester (0161) 831 8000
dlgray@eversheds.com
Specialisation: Senior solicitor in the corporate recovery and insolvency department. Acts for all main accountancy practices and most banks. Acted for Administrators of breathe.com Limited; acted for a major creditor of Iaxis Limited; acted for listed plc on restructuring and other business.
Prof. Memberships: R3 Licensed Insolvency Practitioner 1999.
Career: Articled *Slater Heelis;* qualified 1995; *Addleshaw Booth & Co* 1995-98; *Chaffe Street* 1998-99; *Eversheds* since 1999.
Personal: Shefield University (LLB Hons); Law Society finals (First Class Honours). Interests include squash, golf and walking. Lives in Buxton.

GREGORY, Andrew
Davies Wallis Foyster, Manchester (0161) 228 3702
ahg@dwf-law.com
Specialisation: Insolvency; banking; corporate recovery; developed the practice and procedure on the transfer of Insolvency Practitioners' appointments, removal from office and change of firms.
Prof. Memberships: Law Society; Association of Business Recovery Professionals.
Career: Partner *Davies Wallis Foyster* 1992 (head of insolvency and banking).
Publications: Editorial board 'The Insolvency Lawyer' (Sweet & Maxwell).
Personal: Paramount Secondary School; St Helens College of Technology; Liverpool John Moores University; walking; reading; theatre; resides Macclesfield.

GREGORY, Deborah
Lovells, London (020) 7296 2000
deborah.gregory@lovells.com
Specialisation: Partner in *Lovells'* business restructuring and insolvency group. A licensed insolvency practitioner who has specialised in restructuring and insolvency work since 1984. Deals with all aspects of corporate insolvency including voluntary arrangements, schemes of arrangements, administrations, receiverships, liquidations and all forms of corporate restructurings. Led the legal team on the administration of the British & Commonwealth Group and acted for ING on the Barings acquisition, Proton on the acquisition of Lotus, the receivers of Yorkshire Food Group plc and its 27 subsidiaries, a consortium of 28 leasing financiers and two banks who had a multi-million dollar exposure to Newport Wafer-Fab Limited, a major western bank on the restructuring of an exposure arising from repo agreements with a group trading in Russia and a multi-million pound restructuring of a debt arising from equity options, a restructuring and receivership of two groups of nursing homes and a major telecoms carrier on the restructuring of two multi-million pound debts owed to it.
Prof. Memberships: Fellow of and Council Member of the Association of Business Recovery Professionals ('R3'), Chairman of the Constitution Committee of R3, Member of INSOL Europe, INSOL, International Association of Insurance Receivers, International Women's Insolvency & Restructuring Confederation (IWIRC), British Insurance Law Association, the Law Society Insolvency Sub-Committee and a member of the Insolvency Court Users' Committee.
Career: Articled *Lovell White & King* 1982-84; qualified 1984; assistant solicitor 1984-89; non-contentious business restructuring and insolvency department since 1983; partner *Lovell White Durrant* 1989-99; consultant 2000; partner 2001.
Personal: Educated at Nuneaton High School for Girls; King Edward VI Sixth Form College; Manchester University (1980 LLB Hons); Guildford College of Law (Law Society Part II).

GRIER, Ian Stephen
Sprecher Grier Halberstam, London
(020) 7544 5555
iang@sprgr.co.uk
Specialisation: Head of litigation and insolvency department. Deals with all aspects of corporate and individual insolvency, principally working for administrative receivers, liquidators and trustees in bankruptcy as well as for banks and creditors. Substantial involvement in rescue schemes for limited companies, partnerships and individuals by way of corporate and individual voluntary arrangements. Also has considerable experience in relation to court appointed receiverships and LPA receiverships. Other main area of practice is corporate litigation including contractual disputes, construction work, intellectual property, banking litigation and debt recovery. Important cases have included Re Brightlife Limited (leading case on fixed and floating charges); Re Cranley Mansions Limited (leading case in relation to individual voluntary arrangement); Scottish Enterprise v Bank of East Asia Limited. Clients include merchant banks, a substantial number of firms of insolvency practitioners and major firms of accountants, international employment agencies and many companies in the IT and technology sectors. Lectures widely to the Association of Business Recovery Professionals (R3), firms of chartered accountants and other professional bodies in relation to the law and practice of insolvency.
Prof. Memberships: Law Society; fellow of the Association of Business Recovery Professionals.
Career: Qualified in 1972. Joined with David Sprecher to form *Sprecher Grier* in 1984.
Publications: Co-author of three published works on corporate and individual insolvency and of numerous articles.
Personal: Born 23 February 1945. Educated at London University (LLB 1967, LLM 1968). Former local councillor. Leisure interests include theatre, playing poker and bridge. Lives in London.

GRIERSON, Christopher
Lovells, London (020) 7296 2000
christopher.grierson@lovells.com
See under Litigation, p.571

HALLY, Paul
Shepherd & Wedderburn WS, Edinburgh
(0131) 473 5183
paul.hally@shepwedd.co.uk
Specialisation: Chief executive and partner in corporate department. Main area of practice is corporate finance.
Prof. Memberships: Law Society of Scotland, Society of Writers to the Signet, Institute of Directors.
Career: Trained *Fyfe Ireland* (1982-84); assistant *Shepherd & Wedderburn* (1984-87), partner (1987-). Lecturer to Joint Insolvency Training Courses (1990-). Member of Law society of Scotland Insolvency Committee (1998-). Qualified Insolvency Practitioner.
Personal: Born 23rd June 1959. Holds an LLB (Hons) Dip LP Edinburgh (1977-84).

HAMILTON, Dan
CMS Cameron McKenna, London
(020) 7367 3000
djh@cmck.com
Specialisation: Partner in banking group. Principal area of practice is insolvency and reconstruction. Has wide experience of insolvency and rescue work including receiverships, administrations, liquidations, corporate and individual voluntary arrangements and schemes of arrangements. Also has wide experience of advising directors of troubled companies, banks and creditor groups on restructuring and rescues. The firm acts for the leading firms of accountants and insolvency practitioners and has numerous banks among its clients. During Summer 1998 he was a member of the team establishing the firm's corporate rescue and recovery practice in Hong Kong and South East Asia. Recently completed the first successful restructuring of a major Russian bank using new Russian corporate rescue laws. Currently advising Scotia Holdings and its administrators on a rescue plan. Regular lecturer to clients and occasional conference speaker.
Prof. Memberships: Associate of Business Recovery Professionals; Insolvency Lawyers Association.
Career: Qualified in 1988. Joined *Cameron Markby* in 1986 and became a partner at *Cameron Markby Hewitt (now CMS Cameron McKenna)* in 1994.
Personal: Educated at Reigate Grammar School 1973-80 and Worcester College, Oxford 1981-84.

HARRIS, Anthony
Laytons, Bristol (0117) 930 9500
Specialisation: Bristol managing partner and part of the Company, Commercial and Insolvency department. Specialises in all aspects of insolvency law and is a licensed insolvency practitioner. Practice also covers company and commercial work including mergers and acquisitions, corporate finance and banking.
Prof. Memberships: Association of Business Recovery Professionals; Insolvency Lawyers Association.
Career: Qualified 1971. Partner at *Laytons* 1977. Editor of 'Laytons Insolvency'.
Personal: Educated at Kings School, Rochester and St. Johns College, Cambridge 1962-66. Born 14th May 1946. Lives near Bath.

HARRIS, Clare
Meade-King, Bristol (0117) 926 4121
ch@meadeking.co.uk
Specialisation: All aspects of personal and corporate insolvency. Predominantly contentious. Acts for a broad range of medium-sized and smaller insolvency practitioners.
Prof. Memberships: Law Society, MABRP, ILA, Licensed Insolvency Practitioner.
Career: LL.B London University. Qualified at *Meade-King* 1989. Insolvency practitioner since 1992. Partner from 1994.
Personal: Born 1962. Married with young and energetic family. Lives in Bristol.

HARROLD, Neil
Hay & Kilner, Newcastle upon Tyne
(0191) 232 8345
neil.harrold@hay-kilner.co.uk
Specialisation: Partner and head of Insolvency Unit. Corporate and personal insolvency, directors' disqualification, asset tracing and recovery. Cases include Official Receiver v Cooper (1997), Kings v Cleghorn (1998) and Ord v Upton (1999).
Prof. Memberships: Member of the Law Society, Insolvency Lawyers' Association and Association of Business Recovery Professionals. Qualified as Licensed Insolvency Practitioner in 1997.
Career: Admitted as barrister and solicitor in Western Australia in 1987. Admitted as a solicitor in England in 1991. Joined *Hay & Kilner* in 1993, becoming a partner in 1997.
Personal: Born 1964. Educated at Guildford Grammar School, Western Australia (1977-81) and University of Western Australia (1982-86). Married with two children. Interests include family, travel and cycling.

HAYMES, Duncan
Hammond Suddards Edge, Manchester
(0161) 830 5000
duncan.haymes@hammondse.com
Specialisation: Partner in business finance and recovery unit. Banking, corporate turnaround and insolvency. Has addressed conferences and seminars.
Prof. Memberships: Law Society; Association of Business Recovery Professionals; Insolvency Lawyers Association.
Career: Joined *JW Hollows & Co* in 1975, moving to *Pilkington Brothers* in 1980. From 1983-90, was at *William Prior & Co* and from 1990-92, was at *Addleshaw Sons & Latham.* Joined *Hammond Suddards* as a partner in 1992.
Personal: Born in 1953. Lives in Manchester.

HENRY, Graeme W
Dundas & Wilson CS, Edinburgh (0131) 228 8000

HERTZ, Philip
Clifford Chance, London (020) 7600 1000
philip.hertz@cliffordchance.com
Specialisation: Senior associate in insolvency group specialising in insurance reconstruction and insolvency, general restructuring, insurance banking and general insolvency including advising on derivature-related products, securitisations and structured financings.
Prof. Memberships: International Association of Insurance Receivers. Association of Run-Off Companies, FSA Sub-Committe member. R3 and ILA.
Career: *Clifford Chance* (1991-97). *Cadwalader, Wickershaw & Taft* (1997-99) and *Clifford Chance* (1999 to date).
Publications: Co-author of chapter entitled 'Insurance Insolvency' in Tolley's 'Insolvency Law' (July 1999) as well as numerous insurance insolvency and insolvency-related articles in 'Insurance Day' and Mealey's 'Insurance Insolvency Report'.
Personal: City of London School, University College, London, Downing College, Cambridge. Interested in all types of sport, wine tasting and relaxing with family and friends. Married with four children.

HIGHAM QC, John
Stephenson Harwood, London (020) 7809 2347
john.higham@shlegal.com
Specialisation: Commercial litigator – particularly experienced in the fields of corporate insolvency, company law, banking, financial services, insurance and professional negligence.
Career: Partner *Stephenson Harwood* 2000. Called to the Bar in 1976. From 1978 to 1999 he was a practising barrister and a member of a leading insolvency set of chambers. He was appointed a QC in 1992. In 1999 he requalified as a solicitor advocate. He is also a Recorder on the Midlands and Oxford Circuit.
Publications: 'The Law and Practice of Corporate Administrations' (Joint Editor/Published 1994).
MA, LL.M Churchill College, Cambridge (1971-5).

HINCHLIFFE, David
Walker Morris, Leeds (0113) 283 2500
Specialisation: Advises insolvency practitioners on all aspects of insolvency with particular emphasis upon company and individual rescue, often through voluntary arrangements and administrations. Also specialises in liquidations and bankruptcies. Significant instructions have included acting for the liquidators of Medchoice Holidays, Sir James Hill and Dunn & Co. Speaker at Regional SPI Conference.
Prof. Memberships: Society of Practitioners of Insolvency, Insolvency Lawyers Association.
Career: Qualified 1989. Became a partner at *Walker Morris* immediately upon joining the firm from *Eversheds* in 1996.
Personal: Born 1965. Played rugby for Otley RUFC. Leisure pursuits include supporting Bradford Bulls, food (preferably lots), generally being noisy and heavy rock music.

HOLLERIN, Gordon Craig
DLA, Glasgow (08700) 111111

HOUGHTON, John
Simmons & Simmons, London 020 7628 2020
john.houghton@simmons-simmons.com
Specialisation: Head of corporate recovery. Rescues and turnarounds: The Dome; Bookers plc's standstill; Heron. Work-outs: The Brent Walker Group plc. Receiverships: Estate agency chain; hotels group; multinational polyester manufacturer; de Savary receiverships; Colorvision plc. Administrations and CVAs: NRC Refrigeration; Richmond Rugby Club; Oxford United FC's CVA; Portsmouth FC on its administration application; Team Lotus; Travers Morgan (construction and surveying consultancy).
Prof. Memberships: R3, Insolvency Lawyers' Association, European Insolvency Practitioners Association and City of London Law Society Insolvency Committee.
Career: LLB, LLM. Partner 1994.

HUGHES, Michael
Maclay Murray & Spens, Glasgow 0141 248 5011
mjh@maclaymurrayspens.co.uk
Specialisation: Partner in IP and technology department based in Glasgow. Principal areas of practice are advising technology companies on fundraising, mergers and acquisitions, corporate joint ventures, venture capital investments, MBOs and MBIs. Recent deals: the start-up of Award plc (contact lens manufacturers) and also the sale of that company to Bausch and Lomb Inc; the start-up and funding of LastOrders.com, the demerger and £4 million equity funding of Actis Technology Limited, advising Mazars Neville Russell on their contract to outsource private tax and executry work for Bank of Scotland, and the acquisition of Trainer Limited and other outdoor advertisers on behalf of Scottish Radio Holdings plc. He has also advised The Sportsmasters Network, Scotland's largest internet start-up to date, on the corporate aspects of their £10m equity investment from US investor Warburg Pincus.
Career: Trained at *Allan McDougall and Co*; qualified 1988; University of Glasgow (LL.B, Dip LP); assistant *McGrigor Donald* 1989-92; assistant/associate/partner *Dundas and Wilson* 1992-97; partner *Maclay Murray and Spens* 1997.
Personal: Born 1964. Running, walking, tennis, golf.

HUNT, Matthew
Hunt & Morgan, Cardiff (029) 20341234

HYDE, Mark
Clifford Chance, London (020) 7600 1000
mark.hyde@cliffordchance.com
Specialisation: Partner and head of the insolvency group specialising in both contentious and non-contentious insolvency work and restructuring work often with a cross-border element.
Prof. Memberships: Member of the Association of Business Recovery Professionals; Council member and past president of The Insolvency Lawyers Association.
Career: Bootham School, York; Birmingham University (LLB Hons1980). Articled *Philip Conway Thomas*; joined *Clifford Turner* on qualification in 1984; made partner *Clifford Chance* 1993; licensed insolvency practitioner; admitted to practise in Hong Kong and Brunei.
Personal: Born 1958; resides London; married with three children.

JACKSON, Mark
DLA, Leeds (08700) 111111

JAMES, Jim
Ward Hadaway, Newcastle upon Tyne (0191) 204 4000
Specialisation: (i) Extensive experience in advising lenders, companies, directors, individuals and creditors on the options available when a business is in crisis or has failed. Has advised banks, insolvency practitioners, directors and creditors on issues as diverse as receiverships of quoted companies, voluntary arrangements for "ex" multi-millionaires and negotiations with banks when businesses are in financial difficulty. Has also been involved in major litigation involving complex construction frauds. (ii) Experience in dealing with Directors' Disqualification and attending creditors' meetings on behalf of creditors. (iii) Is also the partner responsible for the management of the firm's debt collection unit.
Prof. Memberships: Member of Law Society, associate member of R3.
Career: University of Bristol BSc in Politics. Qualified 1990. Employed at *Walker Morris* 1988-98. Joined *Ward Hadaway* 1998 as a partner.

JEFFRIES, Graham
Bond Pearce, Southampton (023) 8033 2001
gjeffries@bondpearce.com
See under Banking, p.119

JEFFRIES, Jonathan
Pinsent Curtis Biddle, Leeds (0113) 244 5000
jonathan.jeffries@pinsents.com
Specialisation: Partner, licensed insolvency practitioner, heavily involved with financial institutions. Advises insolvency practitioners on all aspects of insolvency, and banks and other financial institutions on re-financing and security. Acted for the directors of DC Cook Group plc; the administrators of United Kitchens plc; receivers of O'Hare Limited and the administrator of Evans Group Limited. Also successfully managed turnaround for a number of major corporates. Advises a number of banks on financial recovery strategies. Presents workshops to banks and accountants on corporate recovery, debt recovery and banking law.
Prof. Memberships: Fellow of the Association of Business Recovery Professionals – R3; Fellow of the Insolvency Practitioners Association; Member of the Education Courses and Conference Committee of R3.
Career: Qualified 1983. *Pinsent Curtis Biddle* 1981 to date.

JONES, Calum
Boyds, Glasgow (0141) 221 8251
cjones@boydslaw.com
Specialisation: Head of the corporate and insolvency department and areas of work cover insolvency (both contentious and non-contentious), corporate and complex commercial litigation. Acting for the liquidator of the largest dotcom failure in Scotland so far: Boondoggle.com; liquidators of another dotcom company, Begin Limited; receivers of Robert Jenkins (Shoe Retailers) Limited; former receiver of Glen Scotia Whisky Distillery Co. Limited (Bryan Jackson); firm of Pannell Kerr Forster in defending an action for negligence being pursued by the liquidator. Value:> £2.5m; accountant in bankruptcy in connection with two landmark cases involving the rights of trustees and of the beneficiaries of deceased debtors; the rights of trustees and of secured creditors. Also acted in the Receivership of Gray Dunn & Co Ltd; for the receivers of the Promat Group in Dundee. Consulted by the Receivers of Landmark. Calum Jones was also recently asked to assist the Scottish Law Commission in its comments on the forthcoming Law Commission report on Electronic Commerce. The Law Commission was particularly concerned to ensure that the position of factors who are increasingly dealing with their clients electronically, was not ignored.
Prof. Memberships: Accredited by Law Society of Scotland as a specialist in insolvency law. Membership of Insolvency Lawyers Association. Subscriber member of Association of Business Recovery Professionals (R3). Committee member of Scottish Committee of R3. Secretary of Glasgow Insolvency Forum. Convener of Law Society of Scotland Insolvency Conference
Career: Trained, *Kidstons & Co*; Qualified, 1989; partner in present firm, 1999. 1987-89, trainee solicitor, *Kidstons & Co*; 1989-90, assistant solicitor, *Kidstons & Co* (litigation); 1990-91, associate, *Kidstons & Co* (insolvency); 1991-99, partner, *Kidstons & Co* (head of corporate law and insolvency); 1999-date, partner, *Boyds* (head of corporate and insolvency)
Personal: Main leisure activities: reading, walking, gardening and golf.

JOYCE, John
Addleshaw Booth & Co, Manchester (0161) 934 6180
joj@addleshaw-booth.co.uk
Specialisation: Partner specialising in corporate insolvency work, dealing with all non-contentious and contentious aspects as well as corporate reconstructions and turnaround.
Career: Qualified 1988. Joined firm as Partner in 1998.
Personal: Educated at De La Salle College Salford and Manchester University (1985 LLB Hons). Law Society Finals (1986 Second Class Hons). Resides Chorley.

JUMP, Graeme
Mace & Jones, Manchester (0161) 236 2244
Specialisation: Senior partner. Head of insolvency and recovery department. Licensed insolvency practitioner (1989). Insolvency assessor to the Law Society's post-qualification Case Work Committee (1992). President of the Insolvency Lawyers Association (1997-98). Fellow of the Association of Business Recovery Professional. Member of the Insolvency Practitioners Association. Member of the American Bankruptcy Institute. Member of AEPPC.
Prof. Memberships: Member of the Association of

Partnership Practitioners; president, Manchester Law Society, 1991-92; honorary treasurer, Manchester Law Society 1995-98; founder member and honorary secretary of the Northern Arbitration Association (1990); Associate of the Chartered Institute of Arbitrators (1997). Member of the Chartered Institute of Arbitrators (1999).
Career: Admitted 1969. Joined *Mace & Jones* in 1971. Partner, 1973. Senior partner 1997.

KEARNEY, Mary Frances
McManus & Kearney, Belfast (028) 9024 3658

KEITLEY, Nicholas
Blake Lapthorn, Southampton (023) 8063 1823

KELLY, Susan
Hammond Suddards Edge, Manchester
(0161) 830 5006
susan.kelly@hammondse.com
Specialisation: Partner, business finance and recovery. Specialises in insolvency and reconstruction/rescue work. Acts for major firms of accountants, top tier banks and asset based lenders. Has in depth experience of all forms of insolvency from a variety of angles and advises clients on their options as creditors, debtors and office holders in any given situation. Most recent instructions include, acting for the administrators of Dewsbury Civil Engineering Company Limited, acting for the trustee in bankruptcy of a number of Lloyd's names and carrying out substantial investigations into bankrupts' estates including dealing with trust breaking and fraud issues and emergency applications for repatriation of assets. Also acted for Cadburys Schweppes plc re claim in guarantor's voluntary arrangement – reported Court of Appeal cases re Somji and acted for the administrators of Rostel Limited and Primedeck Limited.
Prof. Memberships: R3; Insolvency Lawyers Association; Law Society.
Career: Qualified in 1988 and joined *Dibb Lupton Broomhead*; partner at *DLB* in 1995; *Linklaters & Alliance* 1997-2000; partner *Hammond Suddards Edge* 2000-present.
Personal: Married with two children; resides South Manchester; enjoys walking, cycling and rowing; blue belt in Woo Shu Kwan

LANG, Russell
Boyds, Glasgow (0141) 221 8251

LAWSON, Stephen
Foot Anstey Sargent, Exeter (01392) 411221
stephen.lawson@foot-ansteys.co.uk
Specialisation: Consultant in insolvency department. Handles all areas of corporate and personal insolvency, including LPA receiverships. Also handles bank litigation and professional negligence, including acting as expert witness in these fields. Author of 'Individual Voluntary Arrangements' and 'LPA Receivers'. Has extensive lecturing experience for *Jordans*, R3 and others.
Prof. Memberships: Law Society, IPA, SPI, Institute of Credit Management.
Career: Qualified in 1969. Former president and secretary of Devon and Exeter Law Society. Deputy High Court Bankruptcy Registrar.
Personal: Born 27 August 1945. Attended Queens College Taunton 1956-64.

LAYCOCK, Andrew
Carrick Read Insolvency, Leeds (0113) 246 7123

LE BAS, Malcolm
Paris Smith & Randall, Southampton
(023) 8048 2482
Specialisation: Senior partner in commercial department. Principal area of practice since 1972 has been insolvency and sales and purchases of businesses, including MBOs. Has an extensive practice acting for both vendors and purchasers. Clients include national firms of insolvency practitioners, the insolvency service and a significant number of local companies. Acts for Southampton Football Club, Portsmouth Football Club and Hampshire County Cricket Club. Increasingly involved in sports law.
Prof. Memberships: Law Society. Insolvency Lawyers Association.
Career: Qualified in 1964. Became a partner at *Paris Smith & Randall* in 1969. Managing partner 1993-98. Senior partner from 1998.
Personal: Born 28th October 1941. Educated at Worksop College 1955-59. Honorary solicitor to Hampshire County Cricket Club; director, Mayflower Theatre Trust; chairman Newscom plc Pension Fund; chairman Alldays Pension Fund. past-president Trojans Sports Club; trustee of Wessex Cancer Trust. Interests include cricket, rugby union, cinema, theatre and jazz. Lives in Southampton.

LOWE, Rita
CMS Cameron McKenna, London
(020) 7367 2798
nal@cmck.com
Specialisation: Member of the banking department of CMS Cameron McKenna, specialising in insolvency and corporate reconstruction.
Prof. Memberships: Association member of R3 (Association of Business Recovery Professionals); member of Education, Courses & Conferences committee of R3; member of Insol Europe.
Career: Queens University Belfast (LLB); University of London (LLM). Called to the Inn of Court of Northern Ireland and converted to solicitor in 1993.
Publications: Associate editor of 'Insolvency Law & Practice'. Contributor to other publications.
Personal: Married with four children.

MACFARLANE, John
McGrigor Donald, Edinburgh (0131) 777 7000
Specialisation: Partner in banking unit. Principal area of practice is corporate insolvency. Also handles corporate banking. Recently acted in the ongoing liquidation of Monktonhall Colliery for PriceWaterhouseCoopers, and acted for the nominees and supervisors in relation to the CVA and restructuring of AGM Leisurewear Limited. Other cases include acting for the receivers of AM Russell Limited and Heat & Control Limited. Major clients include KPMG, Ernst & Young, PriceWaterhouseCoopers, Grant Thorton and Bank of Scotland. Contributor to legal journals on insolvency and related topics (eg 'Impecunias'). Formerly tutor in Diploma of Legal Practice, Strathclyde and Edinburgh Universities. Speaker at various conferences eg 'Insolvency and the Construction Industry'.
Prof. Memberships: Law Society of Scotland; Joint Insolvency Specialists Group.
Career: Qualified 1971. Partner at *Bird Semple*, Fyfe Ireland 1976-90. Joint Convenor, Joint Insolvency Specialists Group (Law Society of Scotland/Institute of C.A. Scotland) 1995-98.
Personal: Born 18th September 1949. Educated at Glasgow University 1967-71 (LL.B Hons). Interests include horse riding and point to point (not riding). Lives in East Lothian.

MALLON, Christopher
Freshfields Bruckhaus Deringer, London
(020) 7936 4000
christopher.mallon@freshfields.com
Specialisation: Manager in restructuring and insolvency group. All areas of Insolvency law and asset tracing. Particular expertise in cross-border insolvency and complex bank fraud.
Prof. Memberships: Insolvency Lawyers Association, City of London Solicitors Company.
Career: Qualified in Australia in 1982. Practised at *Jackson McDonald*, Perth, 1982-85, *Allen & Overy* 1985-86. Joined *Lovell White & King* 1987. Admitted in England 1987. Joined *Biddle* as a partner in July 1995.
Personal: Born 6th May 1956. Attended Aquinas College, Perth, Western Australia and the University of Western Australia. Lives in Stockwell.

MANNING, Peter
Simmons & Simmons, London 020 7628 2020
peter.manning@simmons-simmons.com
Specialisation: Partner, corporate recovery. Corporate insolvency, reconstructions, banking and security reviews. Regular lecturer on banking and insolvency issues.
Prof. Memberships: Law Society, Association of Business Recovery Professionals, Insolvency Lawyers Association.
Career: Qualified 1986. Partner *Alsop Wilkinson* 1990 to 1999.
Personal: Born 1959. Attended Hertford College, Oxford 1978-82.

MARSHALL, Richard
Lupton Fawcett, Leeds (0113) 280 2000

MAY, Philip
TLT Solicitors, Bristol (0117) 917 7912
pmay@tltsolicitors.com
Specialisation: Acts for official receivers and insolvency practitioners nationally. Also acts in relation to corporate restructuring and recovery. For biographical details see Litigation (Commercial) section.

MCCARTHY, Michael
Richards Butler, London (020) 7772 5738
mpm@richardsbutler.com
Specialisation: Specialises in both contentious and non-contentious insolvency matters, dealing with administrations, administrative receiverships, liquidations and in particular provisional liquidations on behalf of the official receiver. Acts for major clearing banks as well as insolvency practitioners from the major accountancy firms. Acted for RBS and administrative receivers of Wessex Dairies Limited; administrators of Northern Ireland Jean Co Limited; and provisional liquidator of CW Cheney & Son Limited.
Prof. Memberships: Insolvency Lawyers Association.
Career: Qualified 1989; asociated partner, *Dibb Lupton Broomhead* – 1991; partner, *Hill Taylor Dickinson* – 1993; partner, *Richards Butler* 1999.
Personal: Finchley Catholic High School; Southampton University LLB (Hons) 2:1; Law Society Finals (Hons). Interests: films, gardening. Married with two children. Lives in Kent.

MCGEEVER, Brendan
Gateley Wareing, Birmingham (0121) 234 0000

MCGURK, Anthony
Eversheds, Cambridge (01223) 224 204
anthonymcgurk@eversheds.com
Specialisation: Handles all aspects of corporate insolvency and reconstruction work, including acting for insolvency practitioners in connection with administrative receiverships, LPA receiverships, administrations, IVAs and liquidations. In addition, specialises in company/corporate work, including mergers and acquisitions and fundraising, in particular with regard to start up and early stage companies.
Prof. Memberships: Eastern Region Committee member of ABRR; Institute of Directors.
Career: Qualified in September 1989. Became a partner at *Eversheds* in May 1995 and relocated to the Cambridge office in December 1998.
Personal: Educated at Downside School, Nr. Bath, Graduated in Law from Hull University. Obtained First Class Honours in Law Society finals.

MCNICOL, Stephen
Robert Muckle, Newcastle upon Tyne
(0191) 244 2904
SMcNicol@robertmuckle.co.uk
See under Banking, p.120

MCNIVEN, Alan
Paull & Williamsons, Aberdeen (01224) 621621
armcniven@paull-williamsons.co.uk
Specialisation: Partner in corporate department, specialising in company acquisitions/disposals/investment; reconstructions; general corporate and insolvency law. Licensed insolvency practitioner and accredited by Law Society as insolvency specialist.
Prof. Memberships: Law Society of Scotland; Society of Advocates in Aberdeen; Joint Insolvency Specialists Group.
Career: Apprentice *AC Bennett & Son*, Edinburgh 1972-74; joined *Paull & Williamsons* 1974 (partner since 1980).
Personal: Educated Alloa Academy (1962-68); Edinburgh University (1968-72). Married with three children. Leisure interests: golf, football, skiing.

MERSON, James
Stronachs, Aberdeen (01224) 845845
james.merson@stronachs.co.uk
Specialisation: Partner in commercial litigation department. Specialist area of practice is insolvency. Licensed insolvency practitioner and certified by Law Society of Scotland as a specialist in insolvency law. Also handles civil litigation, spanning all types of commercial disputes and litigation and employment tribunals.
Prof. Memberships: Law Society of Scotland. Aberdeen Bar Association.
Career: Qualified in 1974. Joined *Stronachs* in 1974, becoming a partner in 1978.
Personal: Born 24th April 1951. Attended Aberdeen University 1969-72. Leisure interests include travel and golf. Lives in Aberdeen.

MONTGOMERY, Nigel
DLA, London (08700) 111 111

MORRIS, Howard
Denton Wilde Sapte, London (020) 7242 1212

MUDD, Philip
Walker Morris, Leeds (0113) 283 2500
Specialisation: Head of banking and insolvency department. Deals with insolvency and banking issues for lenders, insolvency practitioners and corporate clients with an emphasis on debt restructuring and corporate rescue in addition to mainstream insolvency, lending and realisation work. Acted for lender in reconstruction of UK Land plc. Recent work includes administration of US and UK listed company EuroTelecom Corporation Limited, the receiverships of listed companies On Demand Information plc, Peterhead Group plc, Total Office Group. Acted for the purchaser on rescue of Hull City AFC. Speaker at local and regional R3 conferences.
Prof. Memberships: Fellow of Association of Business Recovery Professionals; member, Insolvency Lawyers Association; Licensed Insolvency Practitioner.
Personal: Born 19 January 1959. Attended Bristol University 1977-80. Leisure interests include music, skiing and sailing. Lives in Huddersfield.

MUNRO, Rick
Lamport Bassitt, Southampton (023) 8083 7777
rick.munro@lamportbassitt.co.uk
Specialisation: Rick Munro covers all aspects of corporate and personal insolvency, particularly in liquidations and bankruptcies; fraud/asset tracing work; acting primarily for insolvency practitioners. Recent work includes acting for liquidators in preference and wrongful trading claims against former directors, acting for receivers of property company in enforcement of their equitable charge over shares, acting for trustees in bankruptcy in realising assets such as the matrimonial home and personal pension policies.
Prof. Memberships: Hampshire Incorporated Law Society; Association of Business Recovery Professionals.
Career: Qualified in 1992 following articles with *Lovells*; assistant solicitor with *Lovells*, London (1992 to 1994) and in Hong Kong (1994 to 1997); joined *Lamport Bassitt* in January 1998. Partner in January 2000.
Publications: Contributor to Tolley's 'Insolvency Law and Practice'.
Personal: Born 1967. Birmingham University (LLB Hons) 1985-88. Married with two children. Interests include cricket, golf, diving.

NICHOLSON, Mark
Nicholsons, Lowestoft (01502) 532300
Specialisation: Bankruptcy and personal insolvency and liquidations. Acts for insolvency practitioners.
Career: Qualified May 1977. Licensed insolvency practitioner.
Personal: Born 14.6.52.

NIEKIRK, Malcolm
Lester Aldridge, Bournemouth (01202) 786161
malcolm.niekirk@lester-aldridge.co.uk
Specialisation: Head of the corporate recovery and insolvency team. Licensed insolvency practitioner. Deals almost exclusively with non-contentious corporate insolvency, including turnaround work and restructuring as well as the full range of formal insolvency procedures. Usually advises banks and other financial institutions, insolvency practitioners and sometimes businesses buying assets from receivers and companies in financial difficulties. He has received public attention for his work with insolvent football clubs. Occasional conference speaker. Supports plain English drafting. One of his documents was commended in the 1999 Clarity awards.
Career: Articled *Moore & Blatch*, Southampton; qualified 1987. Joined *Lester Aldridge* 1990. Partner 1994. Insolvency practitioners licence 1998.
Personal: Born 1963. Educated Royal Grammar School, High Wycombe; Southampton University (1984 LLB Hons). Lives in Lyndhurst.

OBANK, Richard
DLA, Leeds (08700) 111111

OLIVER, David
Sherwin Oliver Solicitors, Portsmouth
(023) 9283 2200
david.oliver@sherwinoliver.com
Specialisation: Senior partner in insolvency and litigation department. Practice covers all areas of corporate and individual insolvency, acting for all of the major insolvency practitioners in the Southern region and some outside. Acts for various firms of chartered surveyors in relation to LPA receiverships. Also handles general civil litigation and major fraud prosecutions. Work includes construction arbitration contract disputes, involving claims in excess of £5 million each (obtained an Administration Order in relation to a Lloyds managing agent company with claims against it of approximately £90 million) and major fraudulent trading cases, representing a company with a deficiency in excess of £12 million. Has lectured for Portsmouth University, LawNet, Chambers of Commerce, 3Rs and others.
Prof. Memberships: Law Society, Insolvency Lawyers Association, AEPPC, Chartered Institute of Arbitrators, R3.
Career: Senior litigation partner at *Sherwin Oliver* since 1985. Fellow of Chartered Institute of Arbitrators since 1993. Appointed Deputy District Judge in June 1993. Past Chairman Lawnet Insolvency Unit.
Publications: Written articles on insolvency; radio and TV appearances.
Personal: Born 13th March 1944. Leisure interests include golf, tennis, walking, swimming, films and theatre. Trustee of three national charities. Lives in Portsmouth.

OUGHTON, Paul
Nicholson Graham & Jones, London
020 7648 9000
paul.oughton@ngj.co.uk
Specialisation: Corporate turnaround and recovery work. Traditional insolvency/corporate recovery/corporate rescue areas such as liquidations, receiverships, administrations, corporate voluntary arrangements, bankruptcies, individual voluntary arrangements, structured moratoriums and schemes of arrangement. He has specialist knowledge in media-related work particularly in film/television post-production and the music business. Paul is active in corporate litigation/project finance and development/corporate breakdown and re-financing and corporate work-outs.
Prof. Memberships: R3, ILA, AEPPC, IBA and Law Society.
Career: Partner in the Corporate Rescue and Insolvency Group since July 1997. Joined from *Hill Taylor Dickinson.* Previously practised through to partnership at *William Prior & Co* and *Dibb Lupton Broomhead.*

PALLETT, Julian
Wragge & Co, Birmingham (0870) 903 1000

PAY, Alex
Morgan Cole, Cardiff (02920) 385494
alex.pay@morgan.cole.com
Specialisation: Insolvency, reconstruction and recovery, finance litigation.
Prof. Memberships: Law Society; Association of Business Recovery Professional; associate of Chartered Institute of Bankers.
Career: Trained and qualified with *Allen & Overy.* Joined *Morgan Cole,* partner 1990.
Personal: BA, LLM, BSc in Financial Services. Interests: most sports, cinema, literature. Married with two children.

PENNIE, John
Dickinson Dees, Newcastle upon Tyne
(0191) 279 9255
law@dickinson-dees.com
Specialisation: A specialist in both personal and corporate insolvency, leading a team of nine lawyers. JIEB Moderator in personal insolvency. Member of the Law Society Insolvency Authorisation Casework Committee. Licensed insolvency practitioner.
Prof. Memberships: Law Society, Fellow of the Association of Business Recovery Professionals.
Career: MA (Cantab). Partner with *Dickinson Dees* since 1985.

PHEASANT, Louise
Eversheds, Birmingham 0121 232 1154
louisepheasant@eversheds.com
Specialisation: Banking, corporate recovery and insolvency. Acts for lenders and insolvency practitioners on all aspects of insolvency law, reconstructions, security and asset realisations.
Prof. Memberships: R3, Association of Business Recovery Professionals.
Career: Birmingham University (1st Class Hons). Midland Bank plc 1979-83; *BBC* 1983-84; *Eversheds* 1988. Became partner in 1997.
Personal: Cinema, contemporary art, West Bromwich Albion.

PIKE, Nicholas
Lawrence Graham, London (020) 7759 6721
nick.pike@lawgram.com
Specialisation: Partner in corporate recovery department. Specialist in all aspects of insolvency, recoveries and reconstruction. Instructions over the last year include the receivership of Ledwood Construction Limited, together with a large number of liquidations, administrations and bankruptcies.
Prof. Memberships: Law Society. Insolvency Practitioners' Association. Institute of Credit Management. American Bankruptcy Institute, Insolvency Lawyers' Association.
Career: 1987, qualified as a solicitor (*Alsop Williamson,* later *DLA).* 1992, partner. 1996, partner and head of insolvency, London (*DLA).* 1999, partner, banking and corporate recovery group, *Lawrence Graham.*
Publications: Numerous insolvency articles; Editorial Board Member of Finance and Credit Law.
Personal: Educated Bristol University (LLB).

POPE, Timothy
Hammond Suddards Edge, London
(020) 7655 1000
tim.pope@hammondse.com
Specialisation: Specialising in all types of insolvency both non-contentious and contentious. Particular specialism is non-contentious receivership and administration work. Also experienced in advising banks and other financial institutions on restructuring and workouts and debt equity swaps. Highlights of the Past Year: acting for the joint liquidators of Leyland Daf Limited, Messrs Kroll Buchler Phillips and PricewaterhouseCoopers, in respect of litigation involving a £50 million surplus arising from the receivership in relation to an action bought by the Dutch bondholders of Leyland Daf limited; acting for Levy Gee as receivers of the China Jazz Restaurant Group in London; acting for the administrators of Excel Estates Ltd in relation to substantial asset and property sales relating to the Excel Group, a major motor components group in the Midlands. Recent reported cases include Leyland Daf Limited.
Prof. Memberships: Licensed Insolvency Practitioner (licence held since 1990); fellow of Association of Business Recovery Professionals (R3); member of the AEPPC and Committee J of the International Bar Association (Insolvency and Creditors Rights).
Career: Qualified 1982. 1985, joined what is now *Dibb Lupton Alsop* in the Leeds office, partner 1988. 1990, partner in London office of *Dibb Lupton Alsop.* October 1996, joined *Hammond Suddards* London office.
Personal: BA Hons Law. Leisure interests include ballet, opera, theatre, horse racing, travelling. Single, resides in London.

POTTER, Bruce
Morgan Cole, Reading (0118) 955 3000

PRESTON, Dermot
Hammond Suddards Edge, Manchester
(0161) 830 5146
dermot.preston@hammondse.com
Specialisation: Partner, business finance and recovery. Specialises in all aspects of non-contentious insolvency with a particular emphasis on administration and administrative receiverships, advising secured lenders in relation to enhancing security, turnaround and workout situations. Administration and sale of Cox Long Group – a £40m turnover timber group; administration and restructuring of the Hallis Hudson Group – a £42m turnover textiles and soft furnishings group.
Career: 1986-89, *Slater Heelis;* 1989-91, *Pannone & Partners;* 1991-2000 DLA; *Hammond Suddards Edge,* Sept 2000-present.
Personal: Married with three children. Resides Didsbury, Manchester. Burnley Football Club; Lancashire County Cricket Club.

PRIOR, Michael
Nabarro Nathanson, London (020) 7524 6205
m.prior@nabarro.com
Specialisation: Insolvency, corporate recovery, national/international. Cases include: Maxwell Personal Bankruptcy, Epic Group, Dallhold (Alan Bond), Olympia & York. 1996/97: Facia Group, YC Group, Administration & CVA Millwall Football Club. Lister Group of Textile Companies (1998). Purchasers of boo.com (2000) Compagnie Européene de Réassurance (2001).
Prof. Memberships: COMMJ; IBA; INSOL; Council ABRP (R3); SPI; IPA; ILA various technical committees (ILA, SPI, CBI). Chairman International Commission. ABRP (R3).
Career: Epsom College, England; Sorbonne University, France.
Personal: Heli-skiing, cricket, opera, Peninsular War History. Large growing family.

RAJANI, Shashi
Nicholson Graham & Jones, London
020 7648 9000
shashi.rajani@ngj.co.uk
Specialisation: All aspects of corporate rescue and insolvency matters, acting for accountants and banking and corporate clients. Also advises banking and individual clients on personal insolvency matters. Particularly skilled in director disqualification cases and international aspects of turnarounds and insolvencies. Acts as consultant to the other departments and groups of the firm on insolvency matters. Licensed Insolvency Practitioner since 1986.
Prof. Memberships: The Law Society, including Chief Insolvency Assessor; The City of London Solicitor's Company; The City of London Law Society and its Insolvency Law Sub-Committee; Association of Business Recovers Professionals (R3) and its Membership Committee; INSOL International; INSOL Europe; Appeal Committee of ACCA.
Career: Partner and head of corporate rescue and insolvency group from 1994 to date. In practice as an advocate in Dar es Salaam, Tanzania and Tabora (1956-64). Appointed in 1964 to the Tanzanian Civil Service as Assistant Administrator General. Promoted to Senior Assistant Administrator General in 1967. Coopers & Lybrand London as manager in insolvency department (1970-77). *Linklaters & Paines,* senior assistant solicitor (1977-88). *Cameron Markby Hewitt,* partner (1989-93); *Nicholson Graham & Jones,* partner since 1994.
Publications: Author of Tolley's 'Corporate Insolvency Law Handbook' (1990); Tolley's 'Corporate Insolvency' (1995); chapters in Tolley's 'Company Law on Insolvency'; chapter in 'Theory & Practice' (Sweet & Maxwell, 1993) on 'Equitable Assistance in the Search for Security' in insolvency law; and Tolley's 'Insolvency Fees and Costs' (1995-2000). Chief editor of Tolley's 'Insolvency Law & Practice' and joint consulting editor of Tolley's 'Insolvency Law' (1996). Writes for a number of international journals.

READETT, Helen
Martineau Johnson, Birmingham (0121) 678 1576
helen.readett@martjohn.com
Specialisation: Advises insolvency practitioners on all types of insolvency work and banks and lending institutions on putting security in place and maximising realisations.
Prof. Memberships: Licensed insolvency practitioner and member R3. Law Society member.
Career: Qualified 1982. *Edge Ellison* partner until 1998. Now with *Martineau Johnson.*
Personal: Married with young son.

REES, Bleddyn
Morgan Cole, Cardiff (029) 2038 5385

RIDLER, Graham
Eversheds, Leeds (0113) 243 0391
ridlerg@eversheds.com
Specialisation: Partner and head of insolvency for Leeds. Advises insolvency practitioners on both contentious and non-contentious insolvency work. Advises banks on security and intensive care issues. Particular specialism in receivership, administration and corporate restructuring work. Recent receiverships include Galaxy Air Cargo Limited (PwC/BOS), Appleby Group (RCM Robson Rhodes/Nat West), UVG (Wales) Limited, (Arthur Andersen/RBS), Porcelain Techniques Limited (RSM Robson Rhodes/HSBC), Shop and Stone Investments Limited

(KPMG/HSBC). Recent administrations include Discovery Stores Group, Art Glass Limited.
Prof. Memberships: Law Society, SPI.
Career: Leicester University LLB (Hons), qualified 1987 – joined *Pinsent Curtis*, made partner 1993, joined *Eversheds* as partner in 1996.
Personal: Resides Leeds, leisure interests include golf, shooting and weight training.

ROOME, James
Bingham Dana LLP, London (020) 7375 9787
jroome@bingham.com
Specialisation: Partner in financial restructuring group. Corporate law, including insolvency and reconstructions. Specialist experience in corporate insolvency, including work-outs and reconstructions. Particular experience in multinational insolvencies. He is a licensed insolvency practitioner and has spoken at conferences on topics ranging from professional liability to financial institution insolvency.
Prof. Memberships: R3; Law Society; City of London Law Society; Insolvency Lawyers Association; European Insolvency Practitioners Association.
Personal: Born 7 October 1958.

ROSS, Alexander
John McKee & Son, Belfast (028) 9023 2303
Specialisation: Advises banks and financial institutions on lending and security matters and has particular expertise in acting for funders in private finance initiative work. Also advises insolvency practitioners, particularly administrative receivers, on all legal matters arising from corporate recovery and insolvency including sales of businesses and assets and claims by creditors.
Prof. Memberships: Law Society of Northern Ireland.
Career: Qualified 1967; Partner in *John McKee & Son* from 1972.
Personal: Born 23 December 1942. Educated at Strathallan School, Perthshire and Queens University, Belfast.

ROXBURGH, Roy
Iain Smith & Company, Aberdeen
(01224) 645 454

RUSHWORTH, Jonathan
Slaughter and May, London (020) 7600 1200
jonathan.rushworth@slaughterandmay.com
Specialisation: Partner with a wide-ranging company, corporate finance and capital markets practice both domestic and international, acting in particular for listed and other companies, for partnerships and also for corporate trustees in capital markets issues. He has a particular interest and specialisation in corporate recovery and insolvency work, advising companies and their directors, banks and other creditors and also insolvency practitioners on refinancing and insolvency issues. His practice involves domestic, overseas and cross-border insolvency matters. He has been involved in many of the recent large insolvencies, in particular acting for the administrators of the Barings Group. He has lectured extensively on the subjects of corporate recovery and insolvency, written numerous papers on the subject and has written a book on receivership.
Prof. Memberships: Creditors' Rights Committee of the International Bar Association and the Law Society's Standing Committee on Company Law.

SANDERSON, R Gordon
Dickinson Dees, Newcastle upon Tyne
(0191) 279 9348
law@dickinson-dees.com
Specialisation: Practice covers advising banks and other lending institutions on all aspects of personal and corporate recovery, term loan and other security documentation, enforceability of directors guarantees and other third party security and general banking issues.
Career: Qualified 1985. After qualification spent three years at *Robert Muckle*, Newcastle before moving to *Dickinson Dees* in January 1990. Became partner in 1993 and head of firm's banking unit in 1995. Former lecturer in Banking Law at the University of Northumbria.

SCHAFFER, Danny
Isadore Goldman, London (020) 7242 3000
Specialisation: Partner. Specialises in all aspects of insolvency including related litigation and bank recovery. Licensed insolvency practitioner.
Prof. Memberships: Insolvency Practitioners Association; R3; Insolvency Lawyers Association.
Career: Qualified in 1975. Partner at *Isadore Goldman* since 1978. Appointed Deputy Registrar in Bankruptcy at High Court in February 1992.
Personal: Born 2 September 1950. University of Birmingham 1969-71. Spare time activities include being a football referee. Lives in London.

SCOPES, Richard H
Denton Wilde Sapte, London (020) 7242 1212

SEGAL, Nicholas A
Allen & Overy, London (020) 7330 3000
segaln@allenovery.com
Specialisation: Restructurings; corporate insolvency and litigation. International restructurings including the attempt to rescue and restructure BCCI; the worldwide restructuring of the Heron Group; and restructuring of the Queens Moat House Group, a major Danish multinational corporate, Thai Telecom and Uneximbank of Russia. Recent insolvency assignments include advising the receivers of Leyland Daf Finance and the provisional liquidators of the IWG Group.
Prof. Memberships: Fellow of the Society for Advanced Legal Studies; Fellow of the Association of Business Recovery Professionals; Board of International Insolvency Institute. Visiting lecturer in University of London.
Career: Quartered *Cameron Markby* (1982), Partner (1985); Partner *Allen & Overy* (1989). Editorial board of 'Insolvency Intelligence' and various other journals. Editor of insolvency chapters in 'Gore-Brown on Companies'; and contributor to 'Current Developments in International and Comparative Corporate Insolvency Law' (ed Ziegel, 1994); 'Insolvency of Banks: Management of Risks' (ed Oditah, 1996) 'Restitution and Banking Law' (ed Rose, 1998), Lightman & Moss 'Law of Receivers and Administrators of Companies' (2000).
Personal: St Peter's College, Oxford (1979 MA First Class). Married with one son.

SHANDRO, Sandy
Freshfields Bruckhaus Deringer, London
(020) 7936 4000
sandy.shandro@freshfields.com
Specialisation: Partner in Restructuring and Insolvency Group Advises on all aspects of insolvency from risk-avoidance to restructuring. Also advises officeholders in formal insolvency proceedings. Much cross-border experience. Fluent French. Frequent speaker and author. Member of editorial board of Receivers, Administrators & Liquidators Quarterly.
Prof. Memberships: Vice Chairman, City of London Law Society Insolvency Sub-Committee, Insolvency Lawyer's Association, AEPPC, INSOL, Canadian Bar Association.
Career: Qualified in 1978 (British Columbia) and 1992 (England & Wales). Solicitor Advocate. CEDR Accredited Mediator.
Personal: Born 1951. Educated in Canada (BA, Alberta, 1972; MA McGill, 1974) and at Oxford University (BA 1976, BCL 1978). Past President, Canada-UK Chamber of Commerce. Lives in London.

SHAW, Murray
Biggart Baillie, Glasgow (0141) 228 8000
mshaw@biggartbaillie.co.uk
See under Litigation, p.581

SHORT, John
Taylor Vinters, Cambridge (01223) 423444
See under Corporate Finance, p.256

SLEIGH, Andrew
Burness, Glasgow (0141) 248 4933
afs@burness.co.uk
Specialisation: Andrew acts for many insolvency practitioners and financial institutions in all aspects of company rescue, insolvency related legal issues and procedures. He recently acted for PricewaterhouseCoopers in large agricultural insolvencies – Simmers Group and Gordon & Innes Limited and for major Scottish banks in confidential rescue arrangements. Andrew also acted for SFA in rescue of Hampden Stadium, Glasgow.

SMITH, Gillian
Foot Anstey Sargent, Exeter (01392) 411221
gillian.smith@foot-ansteys.co.uk
Specialisation: Handles all aspects of personal and corporate insolvency, contentious and non-contentious, particularly personal contentious work. Acts for major national insolvency practitioners and for the Insolvency Service in conducting directors' disqualification proceedings under the CDDA 1986. Interested in agricultural insolvency. Law Society CPD course assessor.
Prof. Memberships: Law Society.
Career: BA Birmingham University. Qualified in 1981. LLM at University College London, before moving to Devon in 1982. Partner with *Foot Anstey Sargent* since 1989. Licensed insolvency practitioner since 1990.
Personal: Leisure interests include riding, sailing and skiing.

SMITH, Phillip
Boyes Turner, Reading (0118) 959 7711
psmith@boyesturner.com
Specialisation: All aspects of insolvency work, corporate and personal. Particular experience in dealing with administrations, administrative receiverships and large-scale bankruptcies involving cross-border investigations and asset tracing.
Prof. Memberships: Association of Business Recovery Professionals; Insolvency Lawyers Association; Law Society.
Career: With *Boyes Turner* since articles: qualified

1994, associate 1998, partner April 2000.
Personal: Born 1970. Leisure interests: golf, football and the guitar.

SOMEKH, Peter
Chaffe Street, Manchester (0161) 236 5800
pas@chaffestreet.co.uk
Specialisation: Covers all aspects of non-contentious insolvency and reconstructions. Acts for all major accountancy firms and financial institutions. Recent cases include acting for the administrative receivers of UBH International Limited, administrators of The Phone People plc and the administrative receivers of the Overlander Group of Companies.
Career: Trained and qualified at *Addleshaw Booth & Co* 1990-99. Partner *Chaffe Street* from 1999.
Personal: Attended William Hulme's Grammar School, Manchester. Studied economics and economic history, Liverpool University. Interests include cricket, classic cars, cinema and travel.

SPENCER, Robin
Lovells, London (020) 7296 2000
robin.spencer@lovells.com
Specialisation: Insolvency and business restructuring group specialising in general insolvency, insurance, company reconstruction, insurance-related insolvency matters and troubled financial services companies, as well as other more general types of insolvency and restructuring. Major assignments include Mentor Insurance Limited; Drexel Burnham Lambert Group; British & Commonwealth Merchant Bank plc; OIC Run-Off (formerly The Orion Insurance Company plc); The London and Overseas Insurance Company Ltd; Sovereign Marine & General Insurance Company Limited; New Cap Reinsurance Corporation (Bermuda) Limited and New Cap Re (Australia); Equitable Life Assurance Society; TransTec; Japan Leasing.
Prof. Memberships: Member of International Association of Insurance Receivers, Association of Business Recovery Professionals.
Career: Qualified as Barrister 1981; solicitors' office HM Customs & Excise 1983-86; joined *Lovells* 1987 (including two year secondment to *Appleby, Spurling & Kempe*, attorneys, Bermuda); requalified as solicitor 1991; partner 1994.
Personal: Born 1958. Educated at Birkenhead School (1969-76); Pembroke College, Cambridge (1980 BA Hons (Cantab)); 1984 MA (Cantab)). Resides Chesham, Buckinghamshire.

SPENCER, Shân
Chaffe Street, Manchester 0161 236 5800
sms@chaffestreet.co.uk
Specialisation: Corporate recovery and insolvency dealing with administration, receiverships, liquidations and CVAs. Wide experience of acting for banks and other financial institutions in work out and recovery situations. Recent cases include The Ravenhead Company Limited, The Phone People plc, Azmara plc, Catering Design Services Limited and E Simpson Limited. Licensed Insolvency Practitioner, addresses R3 conferences.
Prof. Memberships: R3 (Chairman, North West Region); Insolvency Practitioners Association, Insolvency Lawyers Association, AEPPC, IBA, Law Society.

STEINBERG, David
Clifford Chance, London (020) 7600 1000
david.steinberg@cliffordchance.com
Specialisation: Insolvency group partner specialising in insurance reconstruction and insolvency, general restructuring and general insolvency.
Prof. Memberships: CBI Insolvency sub-panel.
Career: King Edward VI Grammar School, Southampton; St John's College, Cambridge. Articled *Clifford Chance*; qualified 1988; partner 1994.
Publications: Co-author of chapter on 'Insurance Insolvency' and 'Schemes of Arrangement' in Tolley's looseleaf 'Insolvency'.
Personal: Born 1960; resides Surrey.

STEINER, Michael
Denton Wilde Sapte, London (020) 7242 1212

STEWART, Gordon
Allen & Overy, London (020) 7330 2701
gordon.stewart@allenovery.com
Specialisation: Partner specialising in business restructuring and insolvency, domestic and global: turnarounds, workouts and formal insolvencies geographically spread – from transatlantic through continental Europe to Asia and in industries such as energy, retail, manufacturing, insurance and property. Past highlights include the Maxwell private side administrations and representing the insolvency profession in connection with the Paramount case in the House of Lords. Recent assignments include the restructuring of privatised Slovak steel producer VSŽ (acting for the bank creditors), and also advising foreign governments on insolvency law reform.
Prof. Memberships: Society of Practitioners of Insolvency (past President); Chairman of Law Society's insolvency law sub-committee.
Career: Articled and Associate, *Cameron Markby* (1978-88); Partner *Allen & Overy* (1989).
Publications: Author of 'Administrative Receivers and Administrators', contributed to 'Leasing Law in the European Union' and column in 'Recovery'.
Personal: Oxford University (MA 1977).

STOBART, Guy
Burges Salmon, Bristol (0117) 939 2241
guy.stobart@burges-salmon.com
Specialisation: Corporate rescue and recovery and general insolvency. Major clients include Lloyds TSB, Bank of Scotland and Standard Chartered Bank. His finance work also covers a diverse spectrum of banking transactions and general banking law.
Prof. Memberships: Law Society, member of the Association of Business Recovery Professionals and the Insolvency Lawyers Association and a licensed insolvency practitioner.
Career: Trained and worked at *Slaughter and May* for five years before joining *Burges Salmon* in 1983, becoming a partner in 1986. He was managing partner from 1995-99.

TAYLOR, Andrew
asb law, Brighton 01273 828000
andy.taylor@asb-law.com
Specialisation: Heads seven strong group of insolvency lawyers at asb law. Deals with all aspects of contentious and non-contentious, personal and corporate insolvency work. Involved in many reported cases including Bradley-Hole and Euro Express. The group's work includes conducting directors' disqualification proceedings on behalf of the DTI. Frequent lecturer and contributor to Tolley's Insolvency service.
Prof. Memberships: Law Society, ILA, MABRP.
Career: Qualified in 1983. Joined *Burstows* in 1989 as a partner to create the insolvency group. Joined *Argier Stoneham Burstows* upon merger in 1999. Licensed insolvency practitioner since 1987.
Personal: Born 1958; married with young children. Educated at Nottingham University 1977-80 (LLB). Known locally for his interests in trombone playing and brass bands.

TAYLOR, Elizabeth
Darbys, Oxford (01865) 811700

TETTMAR, Victor
Bond Pearce, Bristol (0117) 929 9197
vtettmar@bondpearce.com
Specialisation: Partner and head of the Banking and Insolvency Group. Licensed insolvency practitioner and Registered Property Receiver specialising in all aspects of insolvency, bank recovery and rescue. Particular expertise in corporate insolvency, security issues, restructuring and the agribusiness sector.
Prof. Memberships: Full member of the Association of Business Recovery Professionals (R3) and Chairman of South West and South Wales region; council member of the Insolvency Lawyers Association and member of the Non Administrative Receivers Association.
Career: Manchester University. Remained with *Bond Pearce* on qualifying in 1985, becoming partner 1991.
Publications: Editor of 'Jordans Agricultural Lending: Security and Enforcement' published 1999. Co-author of Distribution chapter in 'Tolley's Insolvency Law'.

THOMAS, Catrin
Hugh James Ford Simey, Cardiff (029) 2022 4871
catrin.thomas@hjfs.co.uk
Specialisation: Partner and head of insolvency and debt recovery unit. Handles all aspects of personal, partnership and corporate insolvency. Acts on behalf of a variety of clients including insolvency practitioners, banks and other financial institutions, directors, shareholders and many professional individuals (mainly architects and accountants). Deals with contentious and non-contentious insolvency work and also commercial litigation including banking litigation and litigation between directors and shareholders.
Prof. Memberships: Law Society, Insolvency Lawyers' Association.
Career: Qualified in 1983. Became a partner at *Hugh James* in 1986.
Personal: Born 26th September 1956. Educated at the University of Wales, Aberystwyth 1975-78 (LL.B) and Emmanuel College, Cambridge 1980-81 (LL.M). Leisure interests include reading, music, theatre, travel and watching rugby and cricket. Lives in Cardiff.

TIPLADY, Gillian
Watson Burton, Newcastle upon Tyne (0191) 244 4444

TWEMLOW, Tony
Cuff Roberts, Liverpool (0151) 237 7777
tony.twemlow@cuffroberts.co.uk
See under Partnership, p.617

TYRELL, Vivien
D J Freeman, London (020) 7583 4055
vivientyrell@djfreeman.com
Specialisation: Partner in the insurance department. Authorised insolvency practitioner. Acting for officeholders and advising in relation to all aspects of insolvency. The largest proportion of her work is insurance insolvency involving drafting international

schemes of arrangement. She has unwound joint venture agreements and vehicles, pursued actions for the repatriation of assets using injunctions and office-holders' interrogation procedures both here and abroad. Wrongful trading, directors' misfeasance and other directors' liability issues. Advice in relation to exit routes to creditors and shareholders whose interests are in insurance companies in run-off.
Prof. Memberships: International Association of Insurance Receivers, INSOL Europe, INSOL, ILA and ABRP.
Career: Qualified 1980. Joined *D J Freeman* 1981 (partner from 1985).
Personal: Educated at South Shields Grammar School for Girls and Somerville College, Oxford (BA Hons Jurisprudence). Interests include opera, skiing, sailing, hot air ballooning.

VAUGHAN, Philip
Eversheds, Cardiff (029) 2047 1147
Specialisation: Practice covers a wide-range of non-contentious banking and finance work and includes transactional work (including acquisition finance), regulatory advice and drafting of standard documentation for banks, building societies, centralised mortgage lenders and finance companies. Has a particular expertise in consumer credit work. Also involved in a wide range of non-contentious insolvency work acting for receivers, administrators and liquidators and advising lenders on enforcement of security and restructuring/refinancings.
Career: Qualified 1984. Formerly with *Clifford Chance* and National Westminster Bank Legal Department. Joined current firm in 1987 and became partner in 1988.
Personal: Born 14th December 1958. Educated at Haverfordwest Grammar School, St. Edmund Hall, Oxford (M.A.) and Emmanuel College, Cambridge (LL.M).

VERRILL, John
Lawrence Graham, London (020) 7379 0000
john.verrill@lawgram.com
Specialisation: Significant area of practice is insolvency. Joint head of corporate recovery team. Acted in the company voluntary arrangement of London Securities plc and gave advice to boards of British and Commonwealth and Polly Peck after administration orders made. Recent work includes restitution and wrongful trading actions arising out of ultra vires local authority contracts and insolvent construction company Christiani Nielson Ltd. Has also been involved in elements of Thailand's restructuring and the 'Bangkok Principles'. Also has significant area of practice in oil and gas law. Work covers all aspects of upstream asset management.
Prof. Memberships: Insolvency Practitioners Association; fellow and council member, Association of Business Recovery Professionals or R3; Insolvency Lawyers Association (council member); UK Energy Lawyers Group, International Bar Association Section on Energy and Resources Law.
Career: Qualified in 1981. Licensed insolvency practitioner 1990. Joined *Lawrence Graham* in 1983, becoming a partner in 1986.
Publications: Author of Butterworths 'Insolvency Meetings manual'. Frequent speaker and writer on insolvency topics.
Personal: Born 25 March 1954. Attended University College School Hampstead, then University College, London (LLB Hons). Leisure interests include shooting, rowing and gardening. Lives in South Oxfordshire.

WAINE, Ian
Prettys, Ipswich (01473) 232 121
iwaine@prettys.co.uk
Specialisation: Acts for insolvency practitioners, banks, corporate and unincorporated clients on corporate reconstructions and rescues, administrations, receiverships, liquidations, bankruptcies and voluntary arrangements.

WALLER, Simon
Eversheds, Manchester (0161) 831 8000
simonwaller@eversheds.com
Specialisation: Partner; head of corporate recovery and insolvency, Leeds and Manchester. Specialises in insolvency and corporate reconstruction. Acts for all of the main accountancy practices and for a number of banks and secondary lenders; previously acted (whilst at Wilde Sapte) for the receivers of Leyland Daf Limited and the administrators of Paramount Airways Limited amongst others. Currently advising a number of clearing banks on their exposure to the accident management industry and the administrators of Breathe.com Limited, the fourth largest ISP in the UK acting for a major creditor on the collapse of Iaxis Limited and advising listed plcs on restructuring.
Prof. Memberships: SPI.
Career: Articled *Booth & Co*; qualified 1989; *Wilde Sapte* to 1996; partner *Halliwell Landau* 1996-98; partner *Eversheds* 1998; sits on editorial board of 'Receivers, Administrators and Liquidators Quarterly'.
Personal: St Cuthbert's School; Durham University (BA Hons Law). Interests include sport, cinema and reading. Resides Didsbury, has one daughter.

WALSH, Jeremy
Travers Smith Braithwaite, London
(020) 7295 3500
Jeremy.Walsh@TraversSmith.com
Specialisation: Partner specialising in corporate rescue, reconstruction and insolvency, acting for banks, companies, insolvency practitioners, creditors and investors. Has wide experience including rescues, reconstructions, administrations, receiverships, liquidations, voluntary arrangements and schemes of arrangement. Licensed insolvency practitioner since 1994.
Prof. Memberships: Law Society; Association of Business Recovery Professionals; Insolvency Lawyers Association; INSOL Europe; International Bar Association.
Career: Qualified in 1985. Partner in *Travers Smith Braithwaite* since 1994.
Personal: Born 4 November 1960. University of Manchester. Interests include family, films, theatre, swimming and music.

WHEATLEY, Jamie
Mills & Reeve, Cambridge (01223) 222206
jamie.wheatley@mills-reeve.com
Specialisation: Practices in commercial and insolvency litigation.

WHITE, John
CMS Cameron McKenna, London
(020) 7367 3000
jjw@cmck.com
Specialisation: Partner and head of banking and insolvency group. Insolvency work includes multi-bank support operations, administrations and administrative receiverships. Banking work includes clearing bank lending, property and project finance, trade finance and syndicated facilities. Acted for the administrators of Polly Peck, the examiner of the Maxwell Communication Corporation and the administrators of Air Europe. Addresses around 20 conferences per year.
Prof. Memberships: Law Society; Chartered Institute of Bankers; Society of Practitioners in Insolvency; Insolvency Lawyers Association; International Bar Association; City of London Solicitors Company; Association Europeene des Practiciens des Procedures Collectives; International Insolvency Institute.
Career: Qualified in 1963. Having joined *Cameron Markby Hewitt* in 1957, became a partner in 1964. Fellow of the Chartered Institute of Bankers.
Personal: Born 6 July 1938. Leisure interests include hockey, cricket and port. Lives in London. Clubs: Athenaeum and West Herts.

WILKINS, John
Dolmans, Cardiff (029) 2034 5531

WILKINSON, Andrew
Cadwalader, Wickersham & Taft, London
(020) 7456 8540
andrew.wilkinson@cwt-uk.com
Specialisation: Partner in the London financial restructuring practice; managing partner of the London office and a member of the firm's management committee. Andrew has wide experience in both insurance restructuring and general restructuring and insolvency. He has pioneered the use of schemes of arrangement for the work out of troubled insurance companies and is currently acting for investment banks, related hedge funds and insolvency practitioners on general restructuring and insolvency matters. He is a licensed insolvency practitioner. He also writes and lectures extensively on all aspects of restructuring and insolvency.
Prof. Memberships: CLLS insolvency law sub-committee.
Career: Graduate of Jesus College, Oxford. Joined *Cadwalader* in 1998 from a major City firm.

WILSON, Michael
Elliott Duffy Garrett, Belfast (028) 9024 5034
michael.wilson@edgsolicitors.co.uk
Specialisation: Product liability. Insolvency and business turnaround.
Prof. Memberships: Law Society of N Ireland. Fellow, Association of Business Recovery Professionals.

WILTSHIRE, Peter
CMS Cameron McKenna, Bristol (0117) 934 9300
prw@cmck.com
Specialisation: All aspects of insolvency related work advising banks and other financial institutions, insolvency practitioners and property recovery specialists. Includes rescue and work-outs, concentrating on non-contentious insolvency.
Prof. Memberships: Subscriber, member of and regular provider of seminars for R3; NARA council member; Insolvency Lawyers Association.
Career: Articled *Cameron Markby/Cameron Markby Hewitt* 1988-90. Qualified *Cameron Markby Hewitt*, London, 1990. Bristol *Cameron Markby Hewitt* 1991 (now *CMS Cameron McKenna*). Partner 1999.
Personal: Church. Armchair sports critic. Singing. Married, five children.

WITHYMAN, Tom
Lawrence Graham, London (020) 7379 0000
tom.withyman@lawgram.com
Specialisation: Partner handling all aspects of corporate insolvency and reconstructions with particular specialisation in administrations. Recent work includes acting for the administrators of London Trust Bank plc and of Pex plc, the receivers of Luton Town Football Club and the liquidators of ASRS Establishment Ltd. Frequently lectures and writes on insolvency topics.
Prof. Memberships: Law Society, Insolvency Practitioners Association, Association of Business Recovery Professionals, Insolvency Lawyers' Association.
Career: *Lawrence Graham* 1990-95; Senior Crown Counsel, Turks and Caicos Islands 1995-97; *Lawrence Graham* 1997-date (partner 2000); licensed insolvency practitioner 1999.
Personal: Born 1966. Educated at Spalding GS and Emmanuel College, Cambridge. Interests: hiking, golf and most sports. Married with two children.

WOOLF, Geoffrey
SJ Berwin, London (020) 7809 2012
Specialisation: Partner in Banking Department (Insolvency & Asset Recovery Group). Principal area of practice is corporate insolvency and reconstruction. Also handles banking and financial services work and debt restructuring. Advises a clearing bank on its standard forms and procedures. Has acted as an expert witness in a number of cases. Regularly speaks at conferences and publishes articles.
Career: Qualified in 1970 after articles at *Stephenson Harwood.* Former Head of the Property Department and former Finance Partner.
Personal: Born 1946. Educated at Harrow County Grammar School and King's College, London (LL.B 1967).

YORKE, Jonathan
Richards Butler, London (020) 7247 6555
Specialisation: Specialises in all aspects of corporate insolvency in particular receiverships, administrations, liquidations and voluntary arrangements. He has been involved in a number of larger insolvencies over the last decade with considerable involvement in cross border cases. In recent years he has specialised in the insolvency of insurance companies acting for PricewaterhouseCoopers in the North Atlantic and Black Sea and Baltic provisional liquidations.
Prof. Memberships: Society of Practitioners of Insolvency, Law Society European Insolvency Practitioners Association, Insolvency Lawyers Association.
Career: University of Essex LLB (Hons). Qualified as a solicitor 1986; licensed insolvency practitioner 1990; partner at *Richards Butler* 1992.
Personal: Cycling, skiing, sailing, paragliding and trying to get fit. Married with two children.

INSURANCE

OVERVIEW: Insurance in London is divided into the areas of general claims, reinsurance and non-contentious work. Insurance Insolvency remains in the Insolvency section. In the main reinsurance work is done in London. Our interviewees indicated a trend towards advisory work rather than actually going to court with an increase in ADR and mediation. Our lists include both those firms handling a large caseload and those securing instructions in complex, one-off cases.

RESEARCH APPROVED BY BMRB: *For this edition,* Chambers' *researchers conducted 6,552 interviews – 4,419 with law firms, 554 with barristers and 1,579 with clients.*

The validity of the research was scrutinised by BMRB International, who audited both the methodology and the results at our offices in July 2001. They interviewed Chambers' *researchers and cross-checked sample interviews. Details of the audit appear on page 7.*

TOP IN-HOUSE LAWYERS

Bob BRITTON, Solicitor, Hiscox *Syndicate 33*

Peter MAYNARD, Group Legal Services *Director, Prudential plc*

Jane OWEN, Senior Lawyer, *Aon UK Holdings Limited*

Humphrey TOMLINSON, Legal Director, *Royal & Sun Alliance Insurance*

Vyvienne WADE, Group Legal Director *Jardine Lloyd Thompson*

Rhic WEBB, Head of Legal Brockbank

"Immensely cool headed," **Bob Britton** is recognised as a long-standing figure. The *"formidable"* **Jane Owen** remains widely respected. **Vyvienne Wade** is described as *"phenomenally able,"* while **Rhic Webb** at Brockbank continues to pick up accolades. On the life insurance side, **Peter Maynard** *"is one of the most high profile in-house lawyers around."* Another widely recognised figure, **Humphrey Tomlinson** has *"a lot of experience on the non-contentious side"* and is supported by *"a good team."*

In-House lawyers profiles: p.1193

LONDON

GENERAL CLAIMS

Barlow Lyde & Gilbert (see firm details p.870) Specialist insurance firm that stays ahead of the competition by a whisker. Most practitioners see it as *"the number one force,"* although the challenge is a strong one. The size of its team is advantageous and our interviewees considered it to consist of *"good effective lawyers right down to the junior fee-earners."* It has an impressive involvement in all areas of insurance including aviation, marine, personal injury and professional negligence. The range of disputes, subrogation matters and global insurance programmes fall into the areas of special risk such as film/media, credit insurance and contingency. The firm was recently involved in a successful arbitration in Australia, regarding the collapse of a Californian mine. *"Senior figure"* **Tim Hardy** (see p.488) and **Michael Mendelowitz** (see p.489) both received warm commendations during our research. **Clients:** Ace Global Markets; Chubb; Hiscox Group.

Clyde & Co (see firm details p.921) Best known for its *"big shipping presence"* and with a noted expertise in marine and energy insurance, its offering is not confined to these areas. Its team is perceived to be *"an extremely good, impressive bunch"* with a track record in aviation, healthcare and professional negligence. The group acts for insurers across Europe and globally, with its London clients comprising most of the larger Lloyd's Syndicates and companies. Highlight of the year was its high profile case representing the London market insurers of a US defence contractor building nuclear submarines, who presented claims exceeding US$100 million concerning four related workmen's compensation policies. *"Excellent, level headed"* **Michael Payton** (see p.489) and his colleagues **Peter Farthing** (see p.488) (*"top-tier"*) and **Roderick Smith** (see p.490) are all regarded as leading individuals at this firm. **Clients:** Ace; Hiscox; Equitas.

CMS Cameron McKenna (see firm details p.922) A top-flight practice enjoying a good reputation among peers who commend its *"substantial insurance and litigation arm."* Clients rate the high quality service; it is *"highly commercial, incredibly practical and a cost effective unit to instruct."* **Mark Elborne** (see p.487) is *"a rainmaker, suave and charming"* with a *"client friendly approach."* Judged by her peers as *"excellent,"* **Belinda Schofield** (see p.490) is a respected practitioner in the field. The group has expertise in construction insurance, and work includes drafting and due

	INSURANCE: GENERAL CLAIMS • London	Ptnrs	Assts
1	Barlow Lyde & Gilbert	53	109
2	Clyde & Co	42*	20*
	CMS Cameron McKenna	15*	44*
	Ince & Co	25*	24*
3	Kennedys	42	75
	Reynolds Porter Chamberlain	29*	80*
4	Clifford Chance	9*	9*
	DJ Freeman	12*	16*
	Davies Arnold Cooper	36	35
	Freshfields Bruckhaus Deringer	12*	20*
	Herbert Smith	6	20
	Holman Fenwick & Willan	9*	10*
5	Beachcroft Wansbroughs	20	95
	Berrymans Lace Mawer	3	5
	Elborne Mitchell	16*	27*
	Hextall Erskine	15	32
	Hill Taylor Dickinson	5	3
	Lovells	20	50
	Rowe & Maw	11	20
	Vizards, Staples & Bannisters	21	30

	LEADING INDIVIDUALS	
1	**BAKES Martin** Herbert Smith	**ELBORNE Mark** CMS Cameron McKenna
	GREENLEY Simon Reynolds Porter	**PAYTON Michael** Clyde & Co
	SCHOFIELD Belinda CMS Cameron McKenna	
2	**FARTHING Peter** Clyde & Co	**HARDY Tim** Barlow Lyde & Gilbert
	HIGGINS David Herbert Smith	**SMITH Rod** Clyde & Co
3	**KENDALL David** DJ Freeman	**LEONARD Paul** Freshfields Bruckhaus
	MENDELOWITZ Michael Barlow Lyde	**PARKER Raj** Freshfields Bruckhaus
	PERRY William Charles Russell	

This book is the product of 6,552 1/2-hour interviews. See p.7 for BMRB audit.
Within each band, firms are listed alphabetically. *See individuals' profiles p.487*
* *Indicates total team size including General Claims and Reinsurance.*

diligence services concerning the newer classes of cover. Instructions stemming from the recent spate of film finance litigation have increased this year. Acted in HIH Casualty & General Insurance v Chase Manhattan & Others, a pivotal dispute concerning the Phoenix film facility. **Clients:** Insurers.

Ince & Co (see firm details p.1008) Perceived to be an "*excellent firm, no doubt*" holding its own as a "*key competitor*" for trade and shipping. Fielding a "*strong department with a depth of partners and assistants.*" Marine insurance is a key area producing the recent highlight case of 'Vergina', a major casualty off West Africa raising issues of unseaworthiness and proof of loss by peril. Also involved in the Elton John case. The firm has been instructed by banks, commodity traders and oil companies to advise on insurance covers for various nations including Iran and Egypt. **Clients:** Ace; Brockbank Syndicate Management; Newmarket Underwriting.

Kennedys (see firm details p.1018) "*Well connected*" firm that competitors acknowledge is "*having a good run at the moment.*" Areas of expertise include property related disputes, CAR and EAR. It has a notable personal injury practice and handles product liability and travel insurance claims. It has a national impact, receiving endorsement from insurers and fellow solicitors for its capacity to handle a huge volume of work. Recent instructions include dealing with problems arising from an oil platform in the Mexican Gulf, hurricane losses in the Caribbean, and power stations in the Middle East. Securing a place on the reduced AXA panel is a bonus for the firm. **Clients:** AXA; Insurance companies; Lloyd's syndicates.

Reynolds Porter Chamberlain (see firm details p.1106) "*Always there*" in the market, some interviewees indicated that the team has been making a real drive at the sector. Although still felt to have a greater profile for its outstanding professional negligence work, the team is respected for its quality output. It handles claims for several insurers; DP Mann has recently outsourced its employers liability and public liability claims function to this team. It has also created a loss adjusting division. The group has seen an increase in international instructions, particularly relating to South American financial claims. With a following among barristers and competing solicitors, **Simon Greenley** (see p.488) is a "*sound practitioner.*" **Clients:** AIG; Equitas; Hiscox.

Clifford Chance (see firm details p.919) This global insurance practice is a favourite among accountancy firms, and is respected by peers for its skills in insolvency insurance. Our interviewees acknowledge that it "*has a great focus on the complex cases involving multi-million claims.*" The group defended Deloitte & Touche in the litigation arising from the collapse of Barings. **Clients:** Sun Life of Canada; Deloitte & Touche; AON.

DJ Freeman (see firm details p.943) "*Up and coming*" firm seen to be "*a quality offering and so specialist.*" Among the team, "*leading light*" **David Kendall** (see p.489) stands out. Alongside its coverage work, the firm has been involved in film finance litigation acting for AXA. Instructed by Shell in an energy insurance claim relating to defective oil pipelines. **Clients:** AXA; Independent; St Paul.

Davies Arnold Cooper (see firm details p.934) This traditional leading light of the insurance field is thought by peers to have struggled of late with the loss of key personnel. Its foundations in this field are such however, that many believe it can "*ride the storm.*" It continues to be heavily involved in energy, D&O and marine insurance. The group acted for a ferry company in relation to short sea freight claims, and represented an insurer in the investigation of a possible fraudulent claim in excess of £1 million, which related to water damage to trading premises. **Clients:** Insurers.

Freshfields Bruckhaus Deringer (see firm details p.965) Complex, one-off matters are the main feature of this practice, buoyed by "*an enviable big-ticket client list.*" Perceived by clients to field "*talented insurance people,*" including **Paul Leonard** (see p.575), who has been described by one barrister as "*streets ahead of most people,*" and **Raj Parker** (see p.578), "*clever and laid back, a man for the future.*" The firm acted for the Royal Bank of Canada in Commercial Court proceedings arising out of insurance policies written in the mid-1990s. Instructed by English Welsh and Scottish Railways on insurance claims concerning losses arising out of the rail network restrictions imposed by Railtrack. **Clients:** Royal Bank of Canada; English Welsh and Scottish Railways.

Herbert Smith (see firm details p.993) Peers acknowledge that the firm "*does high profile litigation exceptionally well.*" Instructed by Royal & Sun Alliance in its exposure to film finance problems, the firm has also been active in the Selby rail crash and the collapse of the Maxwell companies. Continues to advise Mabey & Johnson on coverage issues flowing from the design of bridges. "*Impressive*" **Martin Bakes** (see p.487) and respected **David Higgins** (see p.488) are its high profile team members. **Clients:** Willis; Royal & Sun Alliance; CGNU.

Holman Fenwick & Willan (see firm details p.999) Predominantly known as a shipping firm with expertise in marine insurance. Described as "*a small team but involved in a lot of matters,*" it continues to secure its following among major insurers. Work tends to be multi-party insurance disputes, often with a multi-jurisdiction element, involving issues of policy coverage and contract interpretation. **Clients:** Insurers.

Beachcroft Wansbroughs (see firm details p.872) "*Extremely effective.*" The London operation handles insurance matters arising from its strengths in professional negligence, EL and PL, fraud, property based PL and educational liability. Trevor Chamberlain and Paul Murray are key members of the team. The firm recently advised on the matter of Callery v Gray, concerning insurance premium recoveries for 'after the event expenses' on legal insurance. **Clients:** Zurich; Royal & Sun Alliance; Ecclesiastical.

Berrymans Lace Mawer (see firm details p.877) In spite of the departure of some personnel, the firm remains an active member of the field. A national insurance firm that handles volume claims, including some generated by its strong personal injury practice, it has a presence on high value recoveries. Recently involved in a case concerning the liability of contractors for a fire, and successfully sued an electricity company for causing a fire at a farm. **Clients:** Independent Insurance Company; Norwich Union; Royal & Sun Alliance.

Elborne Mitchell (see firm details p.949) "*Limited only by size,*" our interviewees commended the quality found among this "*fine bunch of lawyers.*" Recently recruited a new partner, Bill Jarvis. The firm is about to embark on claims relating to asbestos charges for its principal client AIG. Acted for Kuwait Airways with regard to loss of aircraft in the Gulf War. Its workload also includes instructions from brokers Arthur J Gallagher and IRB of Brazil. **Clients:** Kuwait Airways; AIG.

Hextall Erskine Deemed a "*good employers liability firm*" that also handles public and product liability and professional negligence. The sport, leisure and travel unit has been involved in a footballer's insurance matter and has handled FA contingency liability since 1996. Involved in various sport and motor related injury cases. Nigel Bundy is senior partner in this largely insurance based firm that has recently opened an office in Birmingham. It has also been doing a lot of advisory work of late, particularly in the advent of the corporate killing policy. **Clients:** Liberty International; AIG; Farraday.

Hill Taylor Dickinson (see firm details p.997) It was widely felt that the marine and energy insurance work of this firm should be recognised in our lists. Tim Taylor heads "*the strongest marine insurance department there is*" and, with his "*sensible assistants,*" "*handles high quality work extremely well.*" The group acted for the successful party in the Starsea Case, taken to the House of Lords, and was involved in the litigation for the 'Vergina' case (a ship that went down off the coast of Africa). Involved in MII insurance, and in the P-36 platform loss in Brazil, worth £500 million. **Clients:** Insurers.

Lovells (see firm details p.1044) The two principal markets for its insurance practice are its corporate client base and insurers, both of which are largely outside the UK. John Trotter is part of the team, which focuses on high-end matters. Recent cases have included litigation concerning a multi-million dollar life policy protecting a deceased music artist. It also pursued a business interruption claim for a railway operator following the Hatfield rail crash. **Clients:** Non-UK Insurers.

Rowe & Maw (see firm details p.1113) A relatively small insurance department that barristers perceive to have "*an increasing profile.*" It acts for several Lloyd's syndicates and a range of the well-known insurance companies. Sean Connolly heads the team that has expertise in professional negligence and product liability. The firm recently handled a case involving smoke and water damage caused to stock by a fire at a major London fashion retailer, and property damage caused by an explosion at a bottling plant in Ireland. **Clients:** DJ Marshall; Chartwell; ME Brockbank.

Vizards, Staples & Bannisters There is a construction expertise to this practice, and a recent high profile case in Bovis & Eagle Star v Commercial Union. Covers the range of insurance related issues with the exception of personal injury. The firm earned commendations from clients and solicitors as "*pretty active and doing rather well,*" particularly for its EL and PL work. Involved in a recovery action following a fire at a company's headquarters in Rochdale, the firm has also been winning a number of instructions deriving from combustible sandwich panels in the construction field. Richard Houseago is an active member of the team. **Clients:** Insurers; QBE.

Other Notable Practitioners **William Perry** (see p.490) of **Charles Russell** is a respected insurance practitioner. Clients like the fact the he is "*reliable*" and "*responds quickly.*"

REINSURANCE

INSURANCE: REINSURANCE • London	Ptnrs	Assts
1 Barlow Lyde & Gilbert	13	24
Clyde & Co	42*	20*
Ince & Co	25*	24*
2 Clifford Chance	9*	9*
CMS Cameron McKenna	15*	44*
Holman Fenwick & Willan	9*	10*
Lovells	6	12
3 DJ Freeman	12*	16*
Freshfields Bruckhaus Deringer	12*	20*
Herbert Smith	6	20
4 Charles Russell	3	4
Elborne Mitchell	16*	27*
Lawrence Graham	7	5
5 Berwin Leighton Paisner	3	3
Norton Rose	8	23
Reynolds Porter Chamberlain	29*	80*
Richards Butler	9	10

LEADING INDIVIDUALS	
1 **CROLY Colin** Barlow Lyde & Gilbert	**DUFF John** Holman Fenwick & Willan
ROGAN Peter Ince & Co	
2 **BROOK Nigel** Clyde & Co	**KENDALL David** DJ Freeman
LEWIS Stephen Clifford Chance	**McKENNA Ian** Holman Fenwick & Willan
O'NEILL Terry Clifford Chance	
3 **BANDURKA Andrew** Holman Fenwick	**BRADLEY Nicholas** Lawrence Graham
DOBIAS Michael Davies Arnold Cooper	**ELBORNE Mark** CMS Cameron McKenna
HEPWORTH Allan Ince & Co	**MACKIE Francis** Norton Rose
MUNDAY Nicholas Clifford Chance	**PAYTON Michael** Clyde & Co
SCHWARTZ Peter Baker & McKenzie	

This book is the product of 6,552 1/2-hour interviews. See p.7 for BMRB audit.
Within each band, firms are listed alphabetically. *See individuals' profiles p.487*
* *Indicates total team size including General Claims and Reinsurance.*

Barlow Lyde & Gilbert (see firm details p.870) Although our interviewees agree that the firm "*is a leading light, at the forefront of the market,*" there was also a significant body of comment to suggest that it is no longer solely pre-eminent. In dispute resolution work, it continues to play an important role in the long running Unicover pool dispute, and recently handled a multi-million dollar reinsurance claim for new clients involving a Latin American energy and pollution cover arising from clean up costs of a major oil spill. **Colin Croly** (see p.487) elicited numerous commendations from leading players in the market. Further highlights include acting for Swiss Re Life & Health advising on the number of accidents or events in the reinsurance of EL insurance claims. **Clients:** Swiss Re; SVB Syndicates; AXA Global Risks.

Clyde & Co (see firm details p.921) Move into the top band after a weight of recommendations. The firm has a forceful presence in reinsurance with a particular bent towards marine matters. Interviewees described it as "*a major force, with some exceptionally talented practitioners,*" among whom **Nigel Brook** (see p.487) is "*extremely impressive.*" The group acted for Sphere Drake in the workers' compensation reinsurance affair, and for various companies and syndicates against defaulting re-insurers in the Australian market. Senior figure **Michael Payton** (see p.489) remains a respected practitioner at the firm. **Clients:** Ace; Hiscox; Kiln.

Ince & Co (see firm details p.1008) "*Top-flight,*" claim the competitors of this marine based firm. Superstar **Peter Rogan** (see p.490) is doing less day-to-day work as a senior partner but remains well regarded amongst peers, seen to be "*fun to deal with*" and "*the strategic force*" behind the group. The firm acts for Crown Life in relation to arbitrations arising out of the PA Spiral matter, and acted for Brockbank in winning the multi-million pound Risk Capital Re arbitration. **Allan Hepworth** (see p.488) provides valued support and peers anticipate that he will increase his presence in the market place. **Clients:** Ace; Brockbank; Crown Life.

Clifford Chance (see firm details p.919) Maintains a strong reputation in this area with its involvement in several of the major recent reinsurance cases over the past year. By way of example, the firm acted for Manulife in the PA Spiral, and advised J&H Aneco in a House of Lords Appeal. An international presence attractive to many clients, the firm also fields a number of esteemed lawyers. **Terry O'Neill** (see p.489) acted for Sunlife in the Unicover affair and has been described as "*a market leader in reinsurance.*" "*Sound operator*" **Stephen Lewis** (see p.489) is skilled in policy drafting, while the respected **Nicholas Munday** (see p.489)is praised for his focus on political risk and regulatory issues. **Clients:** Sun Life of Canada; Manulife Financial; AON.

CMS Cameron McKenna (see firm details p.922) Peers and clients commend the "*longstanding reputation*" that this firm enjoys for reinsurance work. It is instructed by insurers in the USA, Australia and the Far and Middle East. The group has been involved in many of the major cases of recent years, including acting for GE in disputes arising from credit contingency reinsurance. Advised international insurers on accident and health spiral issues, as well as issues derived from the US Unicover Pool problems. The firm acted on behalf of Equitas in a test case concerning the invasion of Kuwait and the seizure of Kuwait City Airport. "*Experienced*" **Mark Elborne** (see p.487) is a leading partner in the group. **Clients:** Domestic and international insurers.

Holman Fenwick & Willan (see firm details p.999) "*Major firm in this area*" that has been a regular presence on significant pieces of work. Its current portfolio of cases includes film financing, LMX, personal accident and substantial international property disputes. "*Senior and experienced*" **John Duff** (see p.487)strengthens the firm's reputation and is considered to have "*an excellent practice.*" Barristers praised **Ian McKenna** (see p.489) as "*exceptionally impressive*" and **Andrew Bandurka** (see p.487) is respected as a solid practitioner. **Clients:** Domestic and International insurers.

Lovells (see firm details p.1044) "*Tends to come in on the big cases*" according to our interviewees, who also commented favourably on the quality of its offering. The group acted for OIC Run Off in a case relating to whether an agreement reached in 1975 was legally binding. Involved in an arbitration for Sovereign Marine & General Insurance against its insurers, and in a transaction for the sale of Community Re and the take back of pooled reinsurance liabilities to secure an exit for participants. **Clients:** OIC Run-Off; Pearl Assurance; Sovereign Marine & General Insurance.

DJ Freeman (see firm details p.943) "*Outstanding*" **David Kendall** (see p.489) is a key asset, with one barrister describing him as "*one of the best litigation solicitors I've ever worked with; diligent, efficient and extremely well-organised.*" The group was instructed by AXA in the recent film finance disputes, and was successful in the preliminary issues hearing in HIH v New Hampshire and Others. **Clients:** AXA.

Freshfields Bruckhaus Deringer (see firm details p.965) Specialising in big ticket complex cases, interviewees perceived that the firm "is geared up for the big stuff." The firm acted in the Jaffray litigation concerning allegations that it withheld information regarding asbestos related liabilities in the 1980s. Also acted for a number of Life Insurance Companies in their participation in the London Accident Reinsurance Group II underwriting pool. Seen by some as "*the people for the future*" this team includes Paul Leonard. **Clients:** Lloyds; Aon.

Herbert Smith (see firm details p.993) Handles complex cases with reinsurance managed from its respected insurance department. Interviewees acknowledged the firm to be "*particularly strong on complex and detailed, high value work.*" Highlight instructions include advising Willis in a reinsurance dispute between La Reunion Arienne and ACE arising from the Air France Concorde crash, and acting for the Provisional Liquidator of Ocean Marine, a P&I club, which collapsed in March 1999. **Clients:** Willis; Jardine Lloyd Thompson; Provisional Liquidators of Ocean Marine.

Charles Russell (see firm details p.912) "*Involved in the game and good at what they do.*" Stephen Carter heads the department which represented Nationwide Mutual Insurance Company in its international dispute concerning its participation in the M E Rutty Pool. It acted for Sphere Drake and other companies and syndicates in US $40 million-worth of claims arising from a series of reinsurance treaty agreements. **Clients:** Nationwide Mutual; Sphere Drake; Aon.

Elborne Mitchell (see firm details p.949) Tim Brentnall is an active member of the team that advised Transamerica in various disputes connected with the PA LMX Spiral, and has acted for GE Frankona RE, QBE and Munich Re. **Clients:** QBR; Munich Re.

Lawrence Graham (see firm details p.1030) Interviewees described this relatively young reinsurance team as "*capable and impressive*" during research. The team includes the highly recommended **Nicholas Bradley** (see p.487) who is currently acting for Phoenix Home Life Insurance in relation to the PA/LMX disputes. In the main, the group acts for international companies; one such example is its involvement in a dispute on behalf of the Israeli liquidator of an Israeli company against Cigna. **Clients:** Phoenix Home Life Mutual Insurance; IntAP; Gerling Konzern Globale.

Berwin Leighton Paisner (see firm details p.878) A lower profile this year; Jonathan Sacher heads the department which has recently been involved in instructions arising from the reinsurance of Kuwait Airways' losses as a result of the invasion by Iraq in 1990. The firm has also been instructed on a major programme of reinsurance recoveries, involving around 50 reinsurers owing money to a London based reinsurance company. **Clients:** Aon; Brockbank; Equitas.

Norton Rose (see firm details p.1082) Felt to be doing a notable amount of reinsurance work, this firm's reinsurance department is headed by "*outstanding*" **Francis Mackie** (see p.489). The group has a high profile with its work for Lloyd's Syndicates and a number of insurance companies. Recent work includes acting in the Paris Commercial Court for AXA Re and AXA Re (UK) against the UK provisional liquidators of Black Sea and Baltic (UK). **Clients:** AIG; HSBC Insurance Brokers; Equitas.

Reynolds Porter Chamberlain (see firm details p.1106) Aiming to make a mark in reinsurance, peers agree the firm has a presence in the market. The group has secured instructions from Lloyd's and international markets. It acted in the PA LMX spiral. D&O work is an area of specialism, particularly with the recruitment of Ed Smerden from DAC. **Clients:** Chubb; AXA; WURT.

Richards Butler (see firm details p.1107) Peers acknowledge that this firm fields lawyers who "*know what they're talking about*". The group acted on behalf of Signal in a substantial claim on excess loss policies against a German underwriter, and represented Stirling Cooke Brown in the Sphere Drake v Stirling Cooke Brown case. Mark Connoley is head of department. **Clients:** PWC; Willis Faber; American Re.

Other Notable Practitioners **Michael Dobias** (see p.487) of Davies Arnold Cooper continues to draw commendation from both barristers and solicitors. **Peter Schwartz** (see p.490) of Baker & McKenzie received warm endorsement and is felt to be "*well-known and highly experienced*" with a personal reputation which exceeds that of the firm.

NON-CONTENTIOUS

Herbert Smith (see firm details p.993) Securing a following among some of the largest insurers, this firm was endorsed by our interviewees as "*the main player*" in the non-contentious market. Major transactions typical of this group include acting for AXA in connection with the restructuring of the £1.7 billion Inherited Estate of AXA Equity and Law, and advising on the acquisitions of UAG and Scottish Life for Royal London. "*Straight-talking*" **Marian Pell** (see p.490)is rated for her expertise in this area. Peers also endorsed **Geoffrey Maddock** (see p.489), who acted for FPLO on its proposed demutualisation and stock market listing. **Clients:** AXA; Friends Provident; Winterthur.

Lovells (see firm details p.1044) The non-contentious offering at this firm is felt to be "*highly focused.*" Combining an outstanding track record and depth of experience with fine corporate skills, the firm has been busy with transactions in the life assurance industry. Advised Equitable Life on its proposed demutualisation and the subsequent sale of its operating assets and sales force to Halifax Group. "*First rate*" **John Young** (see p.490) heads the team and is perceived to be a "*leading light*" in this field. **Clients:** The Equitable Life Assurance Society.

Clifford Chance (see firm details p.919) A busy year for this "*focused*" practice that is challenging the leading firms hard. **Katherine Coates** (see p.487) was a principal lawyer on the CGU and Norwich Union merger, and the firm has been retained as lawyers in the merged company. **Hilary Evenett** (see p.487)was involved in the establishment of a new managing agency and syndicate at Lloyd's. She is currently advising the company on the establishment of an internet portal, an example of the firm's cross-over expertise in both insurance and e-commerce. **Clients:** CGNU.

Freshfields Bruckhaus Deringer (see firm details p.965) Largely involved in the corporate sphere, where the firm's forte is endorsed by all. The group

INSURANCE: NON-CONTENTIOUS • London		Ptnrs	Assts
1	Herbert Smith	13	22
	Lovells	5	14
2	Clifford Chance	14	40
	Freshfields Bruckhaus Deringer	11	19
3	Linklaters	5	10
	Slaughter and May	9	30
4	Norton Rose	3	7
5	Ashurst Morris Crisp	11	9
	Barlow Lyde & Gilbert	9	20
	Clyde & Co	11	15
	Eversheds	5	4
6	DJ Freeman	4	6
	Lawrence Graham	2	4

LEADING INDIVIDUALS		
1	**COATES Katherine** Clifford Chance	**YOUNG John** Lovells
2	**BATESON James** Norton Rose	**EVENETT Hilary** Clifford Chance
	HILL Jeremy Ashurst Morris Crisp	**HOLDERNESS Andrew** Clyde & Co
	JAMES Glen Slaughter and May	**MADDOCK Geoffrey** Herbert Smith
	MIDDLEDITCH Matthew Linklaters	**PELL Marian** Herbert Smith
	RONALDSON Cheryl Norton Rose	**SOUTHEY Verner** Barlow Lyde & Gilbert

This book is the product of 6,552 1/2-hour interviews. See p.7 for BMRB audit.
Within each band, firms are listed alphabetically. *See individuals' profiles p.487*

acted for Prudential on its international offering of ordinary shares and ADRS, and advised Zurich Financial Services on the unification of its dual headed structure. Philip Richards has moved to the Milan office and Ian Poynton takes over his role as leader of the team. **Clients:** Prudential; Zurich Financial Services; Eureko BV.

Linklaters (see firm details p.1042) A "*good firm*" featuring in "*mega-deals*" on the corporate side. The "*excellent*" **Matthew Middleditch** (see p.517) is a well known member of the team that has been involved in a number of major cases including the Halifax acquisition of equitable life, and is acting for Merill Lynch as sponsors to Friends Provident. The group has also acted in the sale of Winchester's international insurance services worth £400 billion and advised the independent directors of Sunlife and Provincial Holdings last year. **Clients:** Willis; Halifax.

Slaughter and May (see firm details p.1135) This corporate giant is felt to attract choice deals through its M&A expertise rather than a dedicated focus on the insurance market. The group acted for Abbey National in the acquisition, by sponsored demutualisation, of Scottish Provident Institution. "*Excellent chap*" **Glen James** (see p.488) is a partner in this team that was also involved in the CGU-Norwich Union merger. **Clients:** Norwich Union; Abbey National.

Norton Rose (see firm details p.1082) Peers acknowledge that the firm has "*developed an effective practice.*" Recent highlight cases include advising AXA on the £2.37 billion recommended cash offer for the outstanding minority interest in Sun Life Provincial Holdings, and advising QBE Insurance Group in the £375 million offer to acquire Limit. Personable **James Bateson** (see p.487) and **Cheryl Ronaldson** (see p.490) form "*a good team*" and are respected for their work in this area. **Clients:** AXA; CGNU; QBE Insurance Group.

Ashurst Morris Crisp (see firm details p.866) A respected corporate practice, which has secured some first rate insurance instructions. **Jeremy Hill** (see p.488) is on a team that has recently acted for the Royal & Sun Alliance Group on the creation of its UseColor.com internet portal, and advised Skandia on the sale of The National Insurance and Guarantee Corporation to Churchill. **Clients:** Benfield Grieg Group; Royal & Sun Alliance; Skandia.

Barlow Lyde & Gilbert (see firm details p.870) **Verner Southey** (see p.490) brings his wealth of experience to this team which offers a respected degree of specialism to corporate clients. Advisory work forms a significant part of its work and it has recently advised Hiscox Group, Ace Capital Ltd and Munich Re Group. Highlights of the past year include acting for the majority participants in the Lloyd's life insurance market on the sale of Lutine Assurance Services to the St Paul Group. The firm acted on two corporate acquisitions for the Munich Re Group in the UK. **Clients:** Hiscox; ACE Global Markets; Munich Re Underwriting.

Clyde & Co (see firm details p.921) Interviewees judged the firm to be "*more technical and niche focused*" than some in our non-contentious table. Its client roster includes insurers and reinsurers across Europe and Lloyd's brokers, undertaking portfolio transfer projects and MBOs. The firm acted on the restructuring of Winterthur's UK Life Division, and advised a leading broker in the establishment of its ART division. **Andrew Holderness** is the standout practitioner at this firm. **Clients:** Credit Suisse; Atrium Underwriting; Winterthur Life UK.

Eversheds (see firm details p.952) Traditionally linked to the Lloyd's market and felt by peers to demonstrate the requisite technical expertise, the firm has a comparatively low profile in the market. Acted on acquisitions and disposals for Cox Insurance Holdings, including the disposal of its marine assets to Munich Re and Euclidian. The firm also acted for Advent Capital (Holdings) on its acquisition of Kingsmead Underwriting Agency at Lloyd's. **Clients:** Liberty Mutual Insurance Group; Legal & General; Advent Capital (Holdings).

DJ Freeman (see firm details p.943) Technical policy drafting including ART has been the busiest area for this firm, which completed over 12 major transactions this year including acting for UK P&I Club on a ten year balance sheet protection with Swiss Re worth £400 million. Also involved in an entertainment industry securitisation credit wrap. **Clients:** UK P&I Club; Royal & Sun Alliance; Hampden Agencies.

Lawrence Graham (see firm details p.1030) Concentrating on the regulatory rather than M&A side of non-contentious insurance, the firm is thought to be raising its profile in this area. Recent work includes advising HSBC Insurance Brokers on warranty and indemnity insurance in connection with mergers and acquisitions. It has a product development practice that advises on new insurance products. **Clients:** Legal & General Group; HSBC Insurance Brokers; QBE International Group.

THE REGIONS – INSURANCE

Beachcroft Wansbroughs (see firm details p.872) Spread nationally, this firm retains its outstanding reputation and impressive clients, acting for most of the leading insurance companies in the UK. Extending from its stronghold in the North, the areas of litigation encompassed include catastrophic loss, environmental disaster, class action product liability claims, personal injury, property and construction related loss. Entering into a national partnership with Cornhill was a significant move over the last year, it now acts as its primary law firm. **Clients:** Cornhill; Zurich; CGNU.

Berrymans Lace Mawer (see firm details p.877) Our interviewees commended the firm's offices in Manchester and Liverpool as "*excellent centres of practice,*" which are also supported by a Southampton team. The firm covers the range of non-personal injury related insurance work. Typical work involves policy interpretation, fire and flood property damage, engineering claims and recoveries for insurance companies. Instructed on a £2

INSURANCE • The Regions		Ptnrs	Assts
1	**Beachcroft Wansbroughs** Birmingham, Bristol, Leeds, Manchester	43	30
	Berrymans Lace Mawer Birmingham, Liverpool, Southampton	n/a	n/a
2	**Keoghs** Bolton	21	49
	Weightmans Liverpool	25	33
3	**Bond Pearce** Bristol, Exeter, Plymouth	12	23
	Browne Jacobson Nottingham	11	31
	Wragge & Co Birmingham	12	12
4	**Cartwrights Insurance Partners** Bristol	4	13
	Crutes Newcastle upon Tyne	n/a	n/a
	Hill Dickinson Liverpool	32	28
	Jacksons Gateshead	7	11
	James Chapman & Co Manchester	24	23
5	**CMS Cameron McKenna** Bristol	2	7
	Davies Arnold Cooper Manchester	5	9
	Davies Wallis Foyster Liverpool, Manchester	14	17
	Eversheds Cardiff, Ipswich, Newcastle upon Tyne	3	6
	Halliwell Landau Manchester, Sheffield	5	29
	Merricks Chelmsford, Ipswich	10	10
	Mills & Reeve Cambridge, Norwich	n/a	n/a
	Ricksons Preston	9	18

This book is the product of 6,552 1/2-hour interviews. See p.7 for BMRB audit.
Within each band, firms are listed alphabetically.

million fire claim relating to a damaged building in the North West, the firm also handled a similar claim concerning a factory in the Midlands. John Henthorne is one of the partners specialising in insurance. **Clients:** AXA; Ecclesiastical; Abbey National; Halifax.

Keoghs (see firm details p.1020) Mainly handles bulk personal injury work arising from factory and road accidents, public liability claims and product liability. Perceived to "*have skill in attracting and keeping new work*" and described by one solicitor as "*the best non-Manchester firm around.*" Areas of specialism include fraud, disease, product and employers liability, policy interpretation and construction. It has secured a place on the slimmed-down AXA panel. David Tyson is head of department. **Clients:** UK Insurers; loss adjusters; insurance brokers; claims handling agencies.

Weightmans (see firm details p.1176) "*Traditionally strong in the north,*" the firm acts for several of the major insurance companies and covers the full range of insurance work including EL and PL, industrial disease, motor and public sector claims. Tony Pritchard has recently been dealing with stress claims and the North West Water VWF case. Other significant claims handled by the firm have been repetitive strain injury and asbestos claims related. Acts for MIB. AXA Corporate Solutions; NHSLA. **Clients:** Zurich; MMI; MIB.

Bond Pearce (see firm details p.888) According to our interviewees, the firm "*continues to do a lot in the market, has a good reputation and is well respected.*" Professional negligence forms a substantial part of its insurance practice but it also has expertise in defendant personal injury and liability work. Although strongest in the South West, also has an office in Leeds, which was opened on the back of an increased insurance workload. Erik Salomonsen heads the department. **Clients:** Zurich; Royal & Sun Alliance.

Browne Jacobson (see firm details p.898) "*Intellectually strong*" Midlands based firm, involved in defendant personal injury, road traffic accident, employer's liability, public liability industrial disease and deafness cases. Nick Parsons heads the department, which has recently been drafting policy wordings for insurers and has expertise in handling child abuse claims and 'failure to educate' claims. Currently handling over 100 claims with 14 education authorities including those relating to failure to diagnose dyslexia. **Clients:** Hiscox; Municipal Mutual; St Paul International.

Wragge & Co (see firm details p.1189) "*Excellent*" Midlands based firm with a national presence, and that has invested in new and emerging markets. Described as "*a strong practice, universally praised,*" it is known for its size and international claims work. It acted for the London office of a US D&O Insurer in defending a claim brought against the directors of a public listed company. Currently acting for the company that arranged the design, manufacture and distribution of a computer football game in an IP claim. In non-contentious insurance it has acted for insurers in joint ventures with financial intermediaries. Former claims manager of a Lloyd's syndicate, Eddie Breen is a partner here. **Clients:** Assicurazioni Genreali SpA; Hibernian; Royal & Sun Alliance.

Cartwrights Insurance Partners This newly formed firm consists of the former Cartwrights insurance practice, including all the partners, created during the merger of their firm with Bond Pearce. As previously the group intends to play to its key strengths in the personal injury and professional negligence sphere. Over the past year the group has handled brain and spinal injury cases in excess of £1 million and employers liability cases. Deborah Bradley is a partner in the team. **Clients:** Insurers.

Crutes (see firm details p.928) "*Able and professional*" claimant firm generally regarded by its peers as leading the field in the North East. It handles volume defendant personal injury work and has units dedicated to catastrophic personal injury, special claims including stress and bullying, and child abuse claims. The group has a significant practice dealing with public authority claims. **Clients:** Public authorities.

Hill Dickinson (see firm details p.996) Notable presence in the North West with an enviable client roster which includes leading UK insurers. Divides its lawyers into sector specific groups covering policy fraud & transport, public sector services, specialist disease EL, professional negligence and liability services. Christine Atkinson is a partner at the firm. **Clients:** ACE; Churchill; Goldsbury International.

Jacksons (see firm details p.1010) The insurance world is said to "*think well of*" this North East based firm that has "*solid foundations.*" Work mainly consists of ELPL, RTA and property damage related insurance. It has safeguarded its place on the diminishing insurance panels including AXA as well as securing appointments to some of the newly created entities. Richard Clarke is head of insurance litigation and his team has recently been involved in a number of upper limb disorder cases arising from the clothing manufacturing industry. **Clients:** AXA; Insurers.

James Chapman & Co (see firm details p.1011) Insurance is the core area of this firm that is supported by a strong reputation in professional negligence. It handles bulk defence personal injury work, and has a dedicated catastrophic injury team. Kevin Finnegan is a specialist in this area and the firm has been appointed to a panel of only three, to deal with severe cases. The firm also has teams devoted to stress and disease cases, and handles public and employers liability claims. **Clients:** Zurich; AXA; St Paul.

CMS Cameron McKenna (see firm details p.922) Covers most areas of insurance excluding personal injury and has particular expertise in professional negligence and financial institutions claims. The group handles Directors and Officers, warranty and indemnity, and material damage claims. It has witnessed a growth in fraud related claims arising from financial institutions over the past year, and has acted for US bond holders in claims concerning their bonds. Simon Hegarty and Jeremy Barnes are the partners involved in this area. **Clients:** Markel; Chubb; AIG; DJ Marshall.

Davies Arnold Cooper (see firm details p.934) As in London, the general consensus from our interviewees concerning this firm seems to be "*a sound team, that has gone through a rough patch.*" Nevertheless, clients spoken to during research were satisfied with the level of service and indeed the firm retains its good client base. Stephen Gorman is a key member of this team, which has recently acted for an insurer in relation to the recovery of £2 million against a workman who cut into a live gas pipe leading to a catastrophic fire. Also acted in a case relating to flood claims. **Clients:** Insurers.

Davies Wallis Foyster (see firm details p.935) "*Successful firm that has grown a lot*" according to our interviewees. It has been retained on both Royal & Sun Alliance panels, and acted for insurers in the case of Seddon v Teakin, one of the three test cases before the Court of Appeal in the Helphire litigation. **Clients:** Admiral; AXA; Royal & Sun Alliance.

Eversheds (see firm details p.952) "*You've got to hand it to them*" claims one competitor, the firm has combined a commercial insurance presence with a high volume general liability practice. It also has expertise in insidious disease litigation and technical claims. Instructed by Norwich Union in COPD claims against contractors by British Coal, and successfully concluded a matter on behalf of a leading British energy supplier regarding a £3.5 million catastrophic loss claim arising out of an explosion. Recently formed a professional indemnity group in the North East acting for AON, QBE and Royal & Sun Alliance. **Clients:** AON; QBE; Royal & Sun Alliance.

Halliwell Landau (see firm details p.982) Particularly expert in industrial disease, the firm also has units devoted to employers and public liability, transport and, in Sheffield, public authority litigation. Suzanne Liversidge specialises in the latter. The firm acted in the Piper Alpha disaster and has secured its place on a number of panels. **Clients:** AIG; Crowe; Norwich Union.

Merricks (see firm details p.1065) "*A solid pair of hands,*" this firm handles insurance work out of its commercial litigation and personal injury departments. Typical work includes property insurance, advice on policy liability and subrogated claims following fires and floods. It is endorsed by peers for its strength in building subsidence claims, and handles marine and transit insurance as well as professional negligence. Covers the range of EL, PL personal injury related work and was recently involved in a subsidence case, Byers v Department of the Environment. **Clients:** AXA; Cunningham Lindsey.

Mills & Reeve (see firm details p.1069) The firm has a great presence in the East Anglian market due in part to its size. Although best known for its professional negligence practice, the insurance department has attracted a good following among UK insurers. Mark Hazelwood is a partner in the team. **Clients:** Insurers

Ricksons The firm fields a unit for high volume litigation work, as well as handling more complex disease and liability cases. It acted for Iron Trades in recovery cases involving CAPE, and is currently advising on a vendor improvement programme for Norwich Union. It has recently implemented a new IT system called e-Case and e-Tran, which offers transparency to clients and the ability to deliver instructions electronically. Anthony Hughes is managing partner, involved in insurance. **Clients:** Iron Trades; Garwin; Miller Pycraft; Zurich.

REINSURANCE

INSURANCE: REINSURANCE • The Regions	Ptnrs	Assts
1 **Humphreys & Co** Bristol	2	1

This book is the product of 6,552 1/2-hour interviews. See p.7 for BMRB audit.
Within each band, firms are listed alphabetically.

Humphreys & Co (see firm details p.1005) Peter Montgomery is a partner in this niche reinsurance firm, which our interviewees believe is uniquely placed outside of the London stronghold. It acts for international insurance companies, and is currently advising a German company on the collapse of a reinsurance pool in France with thirteen global pool members. Also involved in an arbitration in Tunisia for an English Insurance company. **Clients:** International Reinsurance clients.

SCOTLAND

INSURANCE • Scotland	Ptnrs	Assts
1 **Simpson & Marwick WS** Edinburgh	12	32
2 **Biggart Baillie** Glasgow	5	8
Brechin Tindal Oatts Glasgow	4	9
Dundas & Wilson CS Edinburgh	5	n/a
HBM Sayers Glasgow	n/a	n/a

This book is the product of 6,552 1/2-hour interviews. See p.7 for BMRB audit.
Within each band, firms are listed alphabetically.

Simpson & Marwick WS (see firm details p.1133) "*At the top, the best niche insurance firm in Scotland.*" Paul Wade is a partner in this insurance team that has recently been involved in the Piper-Alpha litigation and the Dunblane inquiry. Acted for Transco in relation to an explosion and in an e-coli inquiry in Lanarkshire. **Clients:** Transco.

Biggart Baillie (see firm details p.882) The firm handles non-contentious as well as contentious insurance matters, and has won a tender process to act for Scottish Amicable in its acquisition of the businesses of M&G Life and M&G Pensions. Alison Grant is heavily involved in professional negligence matters. The client roster includes major insurance companies, and the team advises on employers' and public liability claims. **Clients:** Iron Trades; Zurich Municipal; Scottish Amicable.

Brechin Tindal Oatts (see firm details p.893) A medium sized practice, recommended by our interviewees. Typical work includes motor, employers and public liability claims. The firm is also involved in stress related claims, fatal accident inquiries and road traffic prosecutions. Derek Allan is a member of the team. **Clients:** Insurers.

Dundas & Wilson CS (see firm details p.947) Fields teams dedicated to non-contentious as well as contentious insurance work. Colin Mcleod is the Insurance Litigation Industry group leader and has particular expertise in professional negligence and policy wording disputes. The non-contentious team acts for a number of financial service entities, and insurance companies such as Standard Life and Scottish Widows. It recently handled the Scottish aspects of the acquisition of Scottish Provident by Abbey National, and advised the Royal Bank of Scotland group in its bancassurance joint venture with CGNU valued at £1.2 billion. **Clients:** Royal Scottish Assurance; Norwich Union; Scottish Widows.

HBM Sayers Respected by peers, the firm is thought to offer a first rate litigation service and has secured a good following among leading UK insurance companies. The "*dedicated*" team has been involved in the E-coli inquiry and is on the new AXA panel. **Clients:** AXA.

LEADERS IN INSURANCE

BAKES, Martin
Herbert Smith, London (020) 7374 8000
martin.bakes@herbertsmith.com
Specialisation: Partner in litigation department (insurance section). Has expertise in a wide range of insurance work, including policy disputes between insureds and insurers, subrogated actions against all types of professionals, local authorities, banks and many others, acting for major UK brokers and their errors and omissions insurers.
Career: Qualified in 1980. Became a partner at *Herbert Smith* in 1987.
Personal: Educated at Downing College, Cambridge.

BANDURKA, Andrew
Holman Fenwick & Willan, London
(020) 7488 2300
andrew.bandurka@hfw.co.uk
Specialisation: Partner in insurance/reinsurance department. Well known for his work on marine and PA Spirals. Principal area of practice is large insurance claims and reinsurance related. Work covers large insurance claims and reinsurance and professional negligence (insurance/reinsurance brokers and managing agents). Author of numerous articles in 'Lloyd's List', 'Mealey's' and other publications. Regular speaker at seminars world wide on arbitration and reinsurance. Sits as an arbitrator.
Prof. Memberships: British Insurance Law Association.
Career: Degrees in Mathematics and Statistics. Masters degree in Operational Research. Called to the Bar in 1985. Qualified as a solicitor in 1989. Became a Partner at *Holman Fenwick & Willan* in 1993.
Personal: Born 31st December 1956. Married with three children.

BATESON, James
Norton Rose, London (020) 7283 6000
batesonjgd@nortonrose.com
Specialisation: Advises on the establishment, regulation, sale and purchase of insurance companies and related business in the UK and Europe and in relation to Lloyd's matters. A member of the Insurance Law sub-committee, City of London Solicitors Company. Part of the team which advised AXA on its takeover of Guardian Royal Exchange plc for £3.4 billion. Led the team advising the Law Society in relation to the new Professional Indemnity Scheme.
Prof. Memberships: Law Society; City of London Solicitors Company.
Career: Aldenham School; Southampton University (LLB). Articled *Norton Rose*. Qualified 1986; partner since 1995.
Personal: Born 1961. Resides Harpenden.

BRADLEY, Nicholas
Lawrence Graham, London (020) 7379 0000
nick.bradley@lawgram.com
Specialisation: Insurance and reinsurance. Head of reinsurance group at *Lawrence Graham*.
Prof. Memberships: C.I.I., Law Society.
Career: Admitted 1986. Partner, *Davies Arnold Cooper* 1992-96. *Lawrence Graham* 1996 to date. CEDR accredited mediator.
Personal: Education: Bradford GS, Nottingham University (BA, Hons in Law), Guildford College of Law. Hobbies include sailing.

BROOK, Nigel
Clyde & Co, London (020) 7623 1244
Nigel.Brook@clyde.co.uk
Specialisation: Partner, head of reinsurance. Handles international reinsurance disputes, mainly for London market. On the direct side, his main specialisations are credit insurance, brokers' professional indemnity, and regulatory. Drafts and advises on wordings.
Career: Qualified 1981, partner 1985.
Publications: Author of various articles and many of Clydes' 'Reinsurance Updates'.

COATES, Katherine
Clifford Chance, London (020) 7600 1000
katherine.coates@cliffordchance.com
Specialisation: Partner in corporate finance group specialising in non-contentious insurance matters including UK and European regulation, start-ups, mergers and acquisitions, demutualisations, ART capital raising, distribution arrangements, product development, Lloyd's, investment funds including in particular private equity funds and other financial services matters.
Career: King Edward VI High School for Girls, Edgbaston, Birmingham; Somerville College, Oxford (MA Jurisprudence); Law Society Finals. Articled *Coward Chance/ Clifford Chance*; qualified 1983; partner *Clifford Chance* since 1990.
Personal: Born 1959. Resides Godalming, two children.

CROLY, Colin
Barlow Lyde & Gilbert, London (020) 7247 2277
ccroly@blg.co.uk
Specialisation: Partner and Head of Reinsurance and International Risks. Advises on all areas of reinsurance and international risks, including contract wording and dispute resolution. Joint Editor 'Reinsurance Practice and the Law', published by Informer. Speaks regularly on a number of aspects relating to reinsurance/insurance at various conferences, including such matters as drafting and construction of reinsurance contracts and coverage issues in respect of asbestos, environmental and tobacco issues.
Prof. Memberships: Secretary General of AIDA (Association Internationale de Droits des Assurances), and Chairman of the AIDA Reinsurance Working Party. Chairman, Reinsurance Section, Federation of Insurance and Corporate Counsel (FICC), Government Appointed member Insurance Brokers Registration Counsel (IBRC) 1997-98.
Career: Qualified in 1971 in the Republic of South Africa. Practising attorney in Transvaal 1974-75. Qualified in England and Wales 1980. Joined *Barlow Lyde & Gilbert* 1976, Partner 1980.
Personal: Born 9th October 1949. Read economics and law at Cape Town University, followed by a Masters Degree in International Law at London University. Recreations include gardening, reading, theatre, gym. Lives in Central London.

DOBIAS, Michael
Davies Arnold Cooper, London (020) 7936 2222
mdobias@dac.co.uk
Specialisation: Partner and head of reinsurance and professional indemnity group. Main area of practice is insurance, particularly professional indemnity, financial institutions and directors and officers; also reinsurance matters, both domestic and international, covering arbitration and litigation. Includes facultative and treaty contracts. Represents insurers, reinsurers and brokers. Author of 'The Trials of Treaty Disputes' jointly with David McIntosh and 'The Scales of Justice: the Need for a Defence Bar Representation Body'. Lectured extensively at conferences and seminars on insurance and reinsurance issues.
Prof. Memberships: Law Society, International Association of Defence Counsel, London Solicitors Litigation Association.
Career: Joined *Davies Arnold Cooper* in 1973. Qualified in 1975. Partner 1980. Head of Reinsurance Interest Group.
Personal: Born 28th September 1950. Attended Birmingham University 1969-72. Leisure pursuits include sport, cinema and wine tasting. Lives in Chigwell, Essex.

DUFF, John
Holman Fenwick & Willan, London
(020) 7488 2300
john.duff@hfw.co.uk
Specialisation: Partner in Insurance/Reinsurance Department. Main area of practice is non-marine and marine reinsurance. Author of various articles and a frequent speaker worldwide.
Career: Qualified in 1982. Joined *Holman Fenwick & Willan* in 1983, becoming a Partner in 1987.

ELBORNE, Mark
CMS Cameron McKenna, London
(020) 7367 3057
me@cmck.com
Specialisation: Principal areas of practice involve acting in claims and disputes for insurers and reinsurers of banks and financial institutions, directors and officers, accountants, financial advisers and stockbrokers, Lloyd's agents and Lloyd's brokers; advising insurers and reinsurers on policy wordings and construction in insurance and reinsurance contracts; acting in major reinsurance arbitration and litigation disputes and advising reinsurers generally with clients in the London market, Europe, Middle and Far East, USA and Bermuda. Lectured in Bermuda at International Reinsurance Congress and in Hong Kong and London at various conferences on financial institutions insurance, Directors' and Officers' liability cover and on reinsurance.
Prof. Memberships: Law Society, Chartered Institute of Insurers, Society of Insurance Receivers.
Career: Qualified 1983 while at *Cameron Markby Hewitt* and became a Partner in 1988.
Personal: Born 22nd January 1958. School Trustee. Leisure pursuits include golf, swimming, tennis, shooting and opera. Lives near Uppingham, Rutland. Married with five children.
See under Professional Negligence, p.695.

EVENETT, Hilary
Clifford Chance, London (020) 7600 1000
hilary.evenett@cliffordchance.com
Specialisation: Partner specialising in non-contentious insurance matters, including UK and European regulation, new authorisations, mergers and acquisitions, portfolio transfers, demutualisations, Lloyd's corporate capital transactions, and other financial service matters.
Prof. Memberships: Life Assurance Legal Society.

Career: King Edward VI High School for Girls, Birmingham; Merton College, Oxford (MA Jurisprudence). Called to Bar 1986; requalified as solicitor with *Clifford Chance* 1990; made partner *Clifford Chance* 1997.

FARTHING, Peter

Clyde & Co, London (020) 7623 1244
Peter.Farthing@clyde.co.uk

Specialisation: Partner in insurance and reinsurance department. Has covered almost every aspect of insurance and reinsurance: marine – hull, cargo, war and liability, contract frustration; non-marine – property, jewellers' block, fine art, goods in transit, kidnap and ransom, E&O, D&O, pollution, personal accident, personal stop loss, employers' liability, product liability, performance guarantee, contractors' all risks; reinsurance – excess of loss, quota share, run-off covers, LMX, pools, commutations; brokers' liabilities; issues involving Lloyd's Names, Managing and Members' Agents; recent cases include 'Napier v Kershaw' (1993) (subrogation) and Commercial Union v NRG Victory (1998) ('follow the fortunes'). Member of Council of Law Society (non-constituency, insurance matters); worked on implementation of open market for solicitors' professional indemnity insurance.

Career: *Clyde & Co* 1973 to date. Became a partner in 1977.

GREENLEY, Simon

Reynolds Porter Chamberlain, London
(020) 7242 2877
skg@rpc.co.uk

Specialisation: Partner in insurance, reinsurance and professional indemnity department. Main area of practice is reinsurance and coverage litigation and arbitration, first party property and professional liability litigation. Work includes litigation for London market underwriters, including banks and other financial institutions, directors and officers, bankers' bond, financial services industry, insurance brokers, accountants, engineers and surveyors. Acts in a wide range of non-marine insurance and reinsurance disputes for Lloyd's syndicates and company underwriters, including commercial property risks, liability and contingency. Special studies of financial institutions and 1st party property risks; also e-commerce risks. Handles international insurance and reinsurance and liability litigation (US, South America, European).

Prof. Memberships: Law Society. British Insurance Law Association.

Career: Qualified in 1980. Became a partner in 1983.

Personal: Born 29 January 1957. Leisure interests include golf, tennis, rackets, squash, 20th century art, antique furniture. Hurlingham Club and Walton Heath Golf Club. Married with two children and lives in London.

HARDY, Tim

Barlow Lyde & Gilbert, London (020) 7247 2277
thardy@blg.co.uk

Specialisation: For 20 years has advised and represented participants in the insurance and reinsurance markets in London and around the world upon policy coverage issues and resolution of disputes in multi-national litigation, arbitration or other forms of dispute resolution in most leading jurisdictions. Extensive experience of London Market pooling and underwriting agency problems and coverage issues associated with North American and other long-tail liabilities, insolvencies and commutations. Additional wide experience of insurance cases with an international element in respect of liability/ property programmes, bond and credit and political risk insurance, contingency/cancellation coverage and overseas binders and other schemes. Presently serving on London Market committees advising upon policy drafting in wake of leading insurance and reinsurance cases and in anticipation of new risk transfer problems. In 1998 became CEDR accredited mediator.

Prof. Memberships: Past Chairman of the British Insurance Law Association; Chartered Insurance Institute; British Exporters Association.

Career: *Barlow Lyde & Gilbert* since qualification in 1982, partner since 1987.

Publications: In addition to conference presentations and published articles, contributing author of 'Reinsurance Practice and the Law' (LLP 1993, looseleaf).

Personal: Educated at RGS High Wycombe and Balliol College, Oxford graduating in Jurisprudence. Lives in London.

HEPWORTH, Allan

Ince & Co, London (020) 7623 2011
allan.hepworth@ince.co.uk

Specialisation: Specialises in marine, non-marine and aviation reinsurance litigation. In recent years his practice has had particular emphasis on London market reinsurance problems arising out of the marine, aviation and personal accident LMX spirals. He has also handled major reinsurance disputes such as the 'Pan Atlantic v. Pine Top' litigation and the dispute arising out of the death of Robert Maxwell. His practice also extends to dealing with numerous direct insurance problems involving in recent years major disputes arising out of loss of hire open covers, cargo insurances and political risk contracts.

Career: Educated at Rugby School and obtained a Law with French degree from Birmingham University. He joined *Ince & Co* as an articled clerk in 1986, qualified in 1988 and became a partner in 1995. In the early 1990s, spent 15 months on secondment to the Legal Department of the reinsurance division of a major US insurance and reinsurance company.

HIGGINS, David

Herbert Smith, London (020) 7374 8000

Specialisation: Partner and head of insurance litigation section. Specialises in insurance and reinsurance law. Many of his cases have an international element requiring advice on jurisdiction and choice of law.

Prof. Memberships: Recorder of the Crown Court. He is a solicitor advocate with higher court rights in all courts in all proceedings both civil and criminal, Chairman of the Insurance Law Sub-Committee of the City of London Law Society and member of the Committee of the City of London Law Society.

Career: Qualified in 1970 and joined *Herbert Smith* in 1971. Became a partner of the firm in 1977.

Personal: Educated at St. Peter's School, York and Newcastle University.

HILL, Jeremy

Ashurst Morris Crisp, London (020) 7859 1748
jeremy.hill@ashursts.com

Specialisation: Partner in company/commercial department. Head of insurance. Lloyd's of London and London Market: handles all non-contentious matters, particularly policy wordings; acquisition, disposal, flotation of agencies, brokers and insurance and reinsurance companies; regulatory issues; captive insurance vehicles; insurance reconstructions and insolvencies; and creation and registration of Lloyd's Corporate Members. Has advised on numerous capacity offers in the Lloyd's market (both for cash and securities) as well as conversion schemes. Acted for Iron Trades on the disposal of Iron Trades Insurance Company to QBE; acted for CBS on the largest conversion scheme at Lloyd's, CBS 2000; acted for the St Paul Companies on the sale of Minet to Aon and for Goshawk Insurance Holdings plc on its takeover of Matheson Lloyds Investment Trust plc; acted for Ockham Holdings plc on its takeover of New London Capital plc; acted for Benfield Greig Group plc on its merger with E W Blanch, and for the IVA and LPC in the creation of the 'Ins-sure' joint venture. Author of 'Willis Guide to Directors' and Officers' Liability', and of articles in publications on Lloyd's and the London Insurance market.

Prof. Memberships: Chartered Insurance Institute, Law Society.

Career: Qualified in 1984. Joined *Ashurst Morris Crisp* in 1982, spending a year seconded to Lloyd's of London in 1985, and becoming a partner in 1992.

HOLDERNESS, Andrew

Clyde & Co, Guildford (01483) 555555
Andrew.Holderness@clyde.co.uk

Specialisation: Principal area of practice is corporate finance covering flotations, mergers, acquisitions and disposals (both public and private), MBOs/MBIs, joint ventures, private equity transactions and general corporate advice for the Lloyd's and the companies market. Also specialises in the introduction and structuring of corporate capital to Lloyd's, formation of new Lloyd's Managing Agents and Syndicates. Acted in 1999 for Wren plc on the £250 million merger with BRIT Insurance Holdings plc; Fairfax Financial Holdings on the US$600 million takeover of TGI Holdings, Inc; management of Euclidian plc on the £30 million MBO; Chartwell Re, Swiss Re and Thomas Miller on the new US$50 million joint venture marine hull syndicate; Wren plc on the £130 million group reorganisation; management of Ensign on the £145 million syndicate MBO and Cathedral Capital plc on the Offer for Subscription raising £15 million.

Prof. Memberships: Law Society, Chamber of Commerce.

Career: Articled at *Titmuss Sainer Dechert* 1985-87, became a partner in 1992, joined *Clyde & Co* as a partner in 1997.

Personal: Born 15 February 1962. Educated Marlborough College 1975-80, Exeter University 1981-84. Leisure pursuits include golf and skiing.

JAMES, Glen

Slaughter and May, London (020) 7600 1200
glen.james@slaughterandmay.com

Specialisation: Practice covers all work in the fields of company and corporate finance, including mergers and acquisitions, issues and flotations and corporate restructurings, with a specific interest in non-contentious insurance and reinsurance work.

Prof. Memberships: The Law Society; Securities Institute.

Career: Qualified 1976. Articled at *Slaughter and May* 1974-76. Assistant solicitor 1976-83. Partner since 1983.

Personal: Born 22 August 1952. Educated at King's College School, Wimbledon and New College, Oxford.

KENDALL, David
D J Freeman, London (020) 7583 4055
drk@djfreeman.co.uk
Specialisation: Partner and head of insurance department. Main area of practice is insurance and reinsurance. Acts for major UK and overseas insurers and reinsurers, for scheme administrators and for Lloyd's brokers in litigation and arbitration. Has particular experience of advising on pool and syndicate group reinsurance programmes and on insurance coverage. Advises on regulatory, structural and management issues affecting Lloyd's, particularly in relation to run-off and corporate capital. Lloyd's panel arbitrator. Cases have included 'PCW Syndicates v PCW Reinsurers' (reinsurance), 'Suncorp v Milano' (pools/reinsurance), 'DR Insurance v Central National' (jurisdiction), 'Munich Re v Weavers' (reinsurance), 'Milano v Walbrook' (reinsurance), 'Bermuda Fire & Marine v BF&M' (insurance insolvency) and 'HIH v New Hampshire' (reinsurance). Regularly contributes articles to ReActions, Lloyd's List and other insurance publications. Speaks regularly at conferences and *D J Freeman* seminars.
Prof. Memberships: Law Society, Federation of Insurance and Corporate Counsel, BILA, ARIAS, LMAA, British-German Jurists and SEG.
Career: Qualified in 1981. Worked at *Hedleys* 1979-87, from 1985 as a partner. Joined *D J Freeman* in 1988 as a partner, becoming Head of Department in 1993.
Personal: Born 17th September 1955. Holds an LLB (Hons) 1976, and MA (Business Law) 1982.

LEONARD, Paul
Freshfields Bruckhaus Deringer, London
(020) 7936 4000
paul.leonard@freshfields.com
See under Litigation, p.575

LEWIS, Stephen
Clifford Chance, London (020) 7600 1000
stephen.lewis@cliffordchance.com
Specialisation: Partner specialising in insurance and reinsurance, ADR, arbitration, litigation and advisory work, including reinsurance treaty and policy drafting and review.
Prof. Memberships: Insurance Law Sub-Committee of the Law Society.
Career: St Catherine's College, Oxford (1st class Hons Philosophy, Politics and Economics 1970); University of London (LLB 1980). Qualified 1974; partner *Clifford Chance* 1985; worked with the Law Commission, a branch of the British Government concerned with law reform 1975-80 concentrating particularly on reform of insurance and reinsurance law and the law concerning liability for defective products; written numerous articles and lectured on insurance and reinsurance law and on the London insurance market generally.

MACKIE, Francis
Norton Rose, London (020) 7283 6000
mackiefo@nortonrose.com
Specialisation: Partner practising in the international commercial insurance and reinsurance market, with clients being from the London market (Lloyd's and company market) and the international insurance market. The practice involves both contentious matters and policy advisory work. Current high profile cases include Marc Rich Oil/Sugar claims (in arbitration), the London market film financing insurance/reinsurance disputes, the travel insurance litigation. The practice currently has an emphasis on political risk/CF advise and disputes and also energy related risks.
Career: Admitted 1976. After qualification practised for two years in Newcastle and then moved to London, becoming a partner at *Clyde & Co* in 1984. In November 1993 he moved over to *Norton Rose* to become a partner in the insurance group.

MADDOCK, Geoffrey
Herbert Smith, London (020) 7374 8000
geoffrey.maddock@herbertsmith.com
Specialisation: Partner in the insurance section of the company department. In addition to general company law and corporate finance experience, has expertise in corporate insurance and reinsurance work involving mutual and proprietary life and general insurance companies, including mergers and acquisitions, joint ventures, demutualisation and restructuring of insurance businesses.
Career: Qualified in 1990 and became a partner in 1997.
Personal: Educated at Gonville & Caius College, Cambridge.

McKENNA, Ian
Holman Fenwick & Willan, London
(020) 7488 2300
ian.mckenna@hfw.co.uk
Specialisation: Partner specialising in all aspects of insurance and reinsurance dispute resolution on behalf of cedants, reinsurers and brokers in both the London and overseas insurance and reinsurance markets. Also specialises in brokers' E & O disputes, and disputes arising from the operation of underwriting agencies/reinsurance pools. Has a wide experience of conducting litigation and arbitration both in London and in various overseas jurisdictions.
Prof. Memberships: British Insurance Law Association; The Law Society.
Career: Belfast Royal Academy; University of Birmingham; University of Limoges (France); Munich Re (London) 1985 to 1987; trained and qualified *Holman Fenwick & Willan*; *Barlow Lyde & Gilbert* (1992 to 1994); rejoined *Holman Fenwick & Willan* in 1994. Became partner in 1997.
Personal: Born 1962. Married with two children, resides in Hertfordshire. Interests include reading and watching sport, particularly rugby.

MENDELOWITZ, Michael
Barlow Lyde & Gilbert, London (020) 7247 2277
Specialisation: Partner in reinsurance division. All aspects of insurance and reinsurance, with emphasis on complex reinsurance claims, environmental and other long-tail problems, insurance insolvency and disputes concerning interpretation of contracts.
Prof. Memberships: Association Internationale de Droit des Assurances (Assistant Secretary-General), British Insurance Law Association, UK Environmental Law Association, Law Society and Chartered Insurance Institute.
Career: Practised as a barrister in South Africa before joining *Barlow Lyde & Gilbert* in 1987. Re-qualified as a solicitor in 1989 and became a partner in 1990. Frequent speaker at conferences in UK and overseas on topics ranging from arbitration and alternative dispute resolution in reinsurance to liability for pollution and toxic torts. Numerous articles published in legal and market journals. Co-author and co-ordinating editor of 'Reinsurance Practice and the Law' (Lloyd's of London Press, 1993).
Personal: Born 1952. Educated at University of the Witwatersrand (B.A., LL.B.) and Oxford University (B.C.L.) as a Rhodes Scholar. Lives in North London. Interests include family, music and skiing holidays.

MIDDLEDITCH, Matthew
Linklaters, London (020) 7456 3144
matthew.middleditch@linklaters.com
See under Investment Funds, p.517

MUNDAY, Nicholas
Clifford Chance, London (020) 7600 1000
nicholas.munday@cliffordchance.com
Specialisation: Partner specialising in insurance and reinsurance. Practice focuses on re-insurance, project finance insurance and political risk and Lloyd's matters including Lloyd's regulatory issues.
Career: Forest School, Snaresbrook; BA Law London – South Bank. Qualified 1985; articled *Barlow Lyde & Gilbert*; joined *Clifford Chance* 1990; made partner 1995.
Personal: Horse riding, tennis, motor racing, golf. Born 1959; married two children.

O'NEILL, Terry
Clifford Chance, London (020) 7600 1000
terry.oneill@cliffordchance.com
Specialisation: Partner specialising in contentious and non-contentious insurance, reinsurance, Lloyd's and professional indemnity.
Career: Ratcliffe College, Leicester; University College, London (LLB 1965, PhD 1973). Barrister Lincoln's Inn 1973; joined *Clifford Turner* 1977; qualified 1978; partner *Clifford Chance* since 1980; solicitor advocate (Civil) 1994; co-author (with Jan Woloniecki) 'The Law of Reinsurance', (Sweet & Maxwell 1998).
Personal: Born 1944; resides London.

PARKER, Raj
Freshfields Bruckhaus Deringer, London
(020) 7936 4000
raj.parker@freshfields.com
See under Litigation, p.578

PAYTON, Michael
Clyde & Co, London (020) 7623 1244
Michael.Payton@clyde.co.uk
Specialisation: Partner in insurance and reinsurance department. Adviser to insurers worldwide on most of the major international insurance problems of recent years, notably (and in no particular order) 'Piper Alpha'; the invasion of Kuwait; collapse of US Savings & Loans Banks; breast implants; US environmental and pollution claims; break up of the former Yugoslavia; Scandinavian credit reinsurance; loss of Sleipner GBS; the kidnap of' 'Shergar', the ships 'Braer', 'Estonia', and 'Sea Empress'; Chernobyl related contamination of food crops; and the Lloyd's litigation including reconstruction and renewal, in particular the reinsurance aspects; implications of the break up of the former USSR for the oil and gas industries from an insurance perspective. US and Canadian extended warranty insurance problems; Hatfield rail crash; loss of Rig P.36.
Prof. Memberships: Chairman, Solicitors' Indemnity Mutual Insurance Association. Chairman, British Maritime Law Association. 1995-96 Member of the working party of the President of the Law Society on professional indemnity insurance. 1997 Chairman – Energy Employers Mutual Insurance Association.

PELL, Marian
Herbert Smith, London (020) 7374 8000
marian.pell@herbertsmith.com
Specialisation: Partner and head of insurance section of corporate division. Specialises in corporate insurance and reinsurance transactions and financing involving mutual and proprietary life and general insurance companies, including mergers and acquisitions, demutualisation and the restructuring of insurance businesses.
Career: Qualified in 1976 and became a partner at *Herbert Smith* in 1984.
Personal: Educated at Southampton University.

PERRY, William
Charles Russell, London (020) 7203 5288
billp@cr-law.co.uk
Specialisation: Practice involves both contentious and non-contentious work in national and international insurance and reinsurance; in particular direct property insurance coverage disputes (especially high risk property and fine art); property reinsurance (facultative and treaty); alternative risk transfer programmes. Recent reported cases include the Callaghan litigation, Aetna Re v Central Re, etc. Also competition and trust litigation work. Lectures and writes internationally.
Prof. Memberships: Chartered Institute of Arbitrators; International Association of Defense Counsel; British Insurance Law Association; Institute of Management; International Bar Association; City of London Solicitors Company; Law Society.
Career: *Norton Rose* 1974-85 (qualified with Honours 1977); *Pickering Kenyon* 1985-95 (senior partner 1990-95); *Charles Russell* 1995-date.
Personal: Educated University College, Oxford. Fellow, Royal Society for Arts. Married to Jane; children: Alexandra, Caroline and Michael.

ROGAN, Peter
Ince & Co, London (020) 7623 2011
peter.rogan@ince.co.uk
Specialisation: Became senior partner of the firm in May 2000. Specialises in advising in the insurance and reinsurance fields and is Chairman of the *Ince & Co* Insurance Business Group. Reinsurance practice is litigation oriented and diverse, acting for clients both in London and abroad on high profile non-marine, aviation and marine reinsurance disputes, including such high profile matters as the PA LMX Spiral & Unicover. Past cases included setting a number of important precedents in areas of legal difficulty, such as Pine Top on non-disclosure, and PCW on moral hazard. In direct insurance work, his practice is almost as broad, encompassing a variety of classes, most significantly professional indemnity insurance matters for brokers, accountants and banks and others in a range of high value cases arising from major market losses and disputes since the late 1980s.
Prof. Memberships: Aside from the IBA, he is a Committee member of ARIAS (UK).
Career: Educated at Stellenbosch University and Kings College, London, he spent two years at London brokers *Willis Faber* before joining *Ince & Co* in 1977, becoming a partner in 1982.
Personal: Born 1950, resides London, leisure interests include family, theatre, tennis, golf and skiing.

RONALDSON, Cheryl
Norton Rose, London (020) 7444 3323
ronaldsonca@nortonrose.com
Specialisation: Partner in the corporate insurance group at *Norton Rose.* Has a strong reputation for corporate and regulatory insurance, particularly within the Lloyd's market. Experience covers a broad range of private and public company transactions for insurance companies in all sectors of the insurance industry, Lloyds' managing agencies, brokers and corporate members. Also has expertise in advising participants in the market on a wide variety of insurance regulatory matters – both life and non-life, and on alternative risk products and structures.
Prof. Memberships: The Law Society.
Career: Partner *Norton Rose* Jan 1999. Solicitor *Clifford Chance* 1994-98. Solicitor *Barlow Lyde & Gilbert* 1990-94. Trainee *Barlow Lyde & Gilbert* 1988-90. King's College London – LLB (Hons). Leicester High School for Girls.

SCHOFIELD, Belinda
CMS Cameron McKenna, London (020) 7367 3000
Specialisation: Principal areas of practice are handling professional indemnity claims against accountants, actuaries, financial institutions, insurance brokers and directors' and officers' liability. Acting for insurers and insureds. Growing and significant area of practice is in the field of regulation and risk management acting for professionals and insurers in risk control and avoidance projects, due diligence exercises and advising on the impact of regulatory controls, including representing individuals in regulatory proceedings and monitoring such proceedings for insurers. Work also includes general insurance and reinsurance advice and drafting and construction of policy wordings. Experienced in handling large commercial disputes. Speaks at numerous market seminars.

SCHWARTZ, Peter
Baker & McKenzie, London (020) 7919 1000
peter.schwartz@bakernet.com
Specialisation: Peter is Chair of the European insurance group. He deals with all aspects of liability insurance and non-marine reinsurance, including commercial and financial risks; commercial agreements; discontinued operations; cross-border reinsurance issues; professional liabilities; agency-intermediary relationships; new solutions; dispute resolution.
Prof. Memberships: International Bar Association; British Insurance Law Association; ARIAS; Chartered Insurance Institute.
Career: Trained *Alexander Howden Group Ltd*; qualified 1978; partner *Wilde Sapte* 1991-96; partner *Sonnenschein, Nath & Rosenthal* 1996-99; partner *Baker & McKenzie* 1999 to date.
Publications: Peter contributes articles regularly to professional trade press and is a regular speaker at conferences and seminars both in the UK and worldwide.
Personal: Peter was born in 1953 and resides in Chalfont St Giles. He enjoys all sports, particularly tennis, athletics and football, music, ballet (watching!) and travel. Education: Wembley County Grammar/Alperton High; Leeds University (LLB Hons); College of Law, London.

SMITH, Rod
Clyde & Co, London (020) 7623 1244
Rod.Smith@clyde.co.uk
Specialisation: Partner in insurance & reinsurance department. Acts for London market and overseas insurers in a wide range of insurance and reinsurance disputes, frequently of an international nature. Work areas include marine and non-marine insurance including cargo, goods in transit, jeweller's block, Fine Art, contingency, business interruption, credit, political and financial risks, and personal accident including Key Man insurance. Handles all aspects of reinsurance disputes including excess of loss, quota share, run-off reinsurance and commutations, and has extensive involvement in the drafting and review of insurance and reinsurance wordings including new product development. Experienced in ADR, particularly mediation.
Career: Qualified as an attorney in South Africa 1976. Joined *Clyde & Co.* 1977. Qualified in England and Wales 1980. Partner *Clyde & Co.* 1982.

SOUTHEY, Verner
Barlow Lyde & Gilbert, London (020) 7247 2277
vsouthney@blg.co.uk
Specialisation: Consultant with *Barlow Lyde & Gilbert.* Corporate insurance work in all its aspects for public and private corporations and partnerships engaged in insurance activities at Lloyd's and in the London, European and international insurance markets.
Career: Formerly practised as attorney in Rhodesia (now Zimbabwe). Practised in the City and admitted as a solicitor in England in 1977 and joined *Clyde & Co.* as head of corporate in 1986. From September 1996 until March 1999 acted as consultant to *Clyde & Co* and to entities in the insurance industry. Joined *Barlow Lyde & Gilbert* as consultant in 1999.
Personal: Born 1st October 1942. Educated Grahamstown and University of Cape Town, South Africa. Lives in London and the Dordogne and devotes leisure to wife, wine, sport, music and international commuting.

YOUNG, John
Lovells, London (020) 7296 2000
john.young@lovells.com
Specialisation: Advises on the formation, regulation, sale and purchase of insurance companies and businesses in the UK and internationally. Co-ordinates the activities of *Lovells* lawyers who advise the insurance industry on non-contentious matters. Has acted on numerous transactions within the industry, including several recent life assurance demutualisations. Author of various articles on insurance; author of the insurance chapter in the CCH Common Market Reporter (1996). Regularly speaks on topics relating to the regulation of insurance and mergers and acquisitions in the industry.
Prof. Memberships: Law Society. Member ICC Committee on Insurance. Immediate past President of the Society of Scottish Lawyers in London.
Career: Articled *Lovells* 1979-81; qualified 1981; partner 1987.

INTELLECTUAL PROPERTY

London: 491; The South: 495; Thames Valley: 495; South West: 496; Wales: 496; Midlands: 497; East Anglia: 498; North West: 498; North East: 499; Scotland: 500; *Profiles*: 500

OVERVIEW: By a narrow margin, general market opinion considered that the split of our IP tables into patent and general specialists was still justified. It has become apparent however, that such a distinction is becoming ever more blurred at a number of law firms. This year, although Bristows and Bird & Bird maintain their top status, the gap appears to be narrowing. Our researchers found that Linklaters, Simmons & Simmons and Taylor Joynson Garrett received almost as many plaudits from leading market figures. Indeed, the latter firm has now forced itself into the top band for non-patent IP advice.

RESEARCH APPROVED BY BMRB: *For this edition,* Chambers' *researchers conducted 6,552 interviews – 4,419 with law firms, 554 with barristers and 1,579 with clients.*

The validity of the research was scrutinised by BMRB International, who audited both the methodology and the results at our offices in July 2001. They interviewed Chambers' *researchers and cross-checked sample interviews. Details of the audit appear on page 7.*

TOP IN-HOUSE LAWYERS

Bob BOAD, Assistant Head of *Group Trade Marks, BP*

Alan COX, Head of Trade Marks, *Glaxo SmithKline Beecham*

Sheila HENDERSON, Trade Marks Director at *Reckitt & Benckiser plc*

Richard HEATH, Head of Department, *Corporate Trademarks, Unilever*

Frederick MOSTERT, Intellectual Property Counsel, *Richemont International*

David ROBERTS, Director and Senior Vice President, Corporate Intellectual Property, *Glaxo SmithKline Beecham*

Evie KYRIAKIDES, Market Property Manager, *Mars*

"Thorough, demanding and focussed," **Bob Boad** maintains a *"laid back"* approach. **Alan Cox** has remained steadfast at Glaxo SmithKline Beecham, valued for his *"enormous experience and expertise."* **Sheila Henderson** is endorsed for her *"long experience of the consumer products industries."* **Richard Heath** continues to *"handle his global responsibilities efficiently and effectively." "Certainly one of a kind,"* **Frederick Mostert** is indispensable while **David Roberts** *"holds a key position,"* recommended for his long experience. **Evie Kyriakides** joins the list *"clearly destined to be a leader."*

In-House lawyers profiles: p 1193

LONDON

INTELLECTUAL PROPERTY: PATENT • London	Ptnrs	Assts
1 Bird & Bird	9	5
Bristows	18	23
2 Linklaters	9	33
Simmons & Simmons	6	16
Taylor Joynson Garrett	7	10
3 Herbert Smith	6	25
Lovells	3	10
Wragge & Co incorporating Needham & Grant	8	29
4 Baker & McKenzie	4	14
Clifford Chance	5	17
Eversheds	6	10
5 Allen & Overy	3	12
Roiter Zucker	3	1
6 Stringer Saul	4	4

This book is the product of 6,552 1/2-hour interviews. See p.7 for BMRB audit.
Within each band, firms are listed alphabetically.

Bird & Bird (see firm details p.884) "*Rightly placed at number one,*" this "*powerhouse*" firm's policy of expansion is clearly judged by clients and peers to be succeeding. A "*strong team,*" comprising both patent and trademark specialists, it is especially respected for its pharmaceuticals and biotechnology expertise, and wins particular plaudits for its capacity on the contentious side. The "*practical*" **Trevor Cook** (see p.503) "*knows the law inside out,*" while the "*outstanding*" **Morag Macdonald** (see p.506) was recommended to researchers as a "*formidably clever practitioner.*" Peers still rate **David Harriss** (see p.504) as a "*great name in the business,*" while **Miles Gaythwaite**'s (see p.504) work on the Napro-BMS appeal earned sustained market commendation. The firm acted on two of last year's most notable patent cases, representing Oxford Gene Technology on a patent infringement case brought against Affymetrix, and advising Pfizer on its revocation action concerning the Viagra field of use patent. **Clients:** Pfizer; Nestlé; One2One; Oxford Gene Technology.

Bristows (see firm details p.895) One of the "*great names in the sector,*" the firm is considered by some clients to be "*the firm of choice for patent litigation,*" as well as "*just about number one for trademarks.*" Advising on financing and licensing agreements, regulatory issues, IP strategy and patent litigation, the firm has "*been so good for so long.*" "*User friendly*" **Sally Field** (see p.503) is said to "*know her way around the toughest litigation cases*" and the "*dependable*" **Ian Judge** (see p.506) is a "*first-class lawyer of the old school.*" The "*technically first-class*" **Paul Walsh** (see p.510) is a trademarks expert who is also "*commercial and easy to deal with.*" Clients regularly praise **David Brown** (see p.501) for his contentious expertise, while **Edward Nodder** (see p.508) is a "*solid player, who knows his stuff.*" The firm successfully represented Novartis in a case relating to its immuno-suppressant drug, Certican, and acted for Affymetrix on its victory in the Court of Appeal in a case against Oxford Gene Technology relating to the transferability of a patent licence. **Clients:** Affymetrix; Chiron; GlaxoSmithKline; Monsanto; BP Amoco; British Airways; IBM; ICI; Ericsson; Marconi; Novartis; VIA Technologies.

Linklaters (see firm details p.1042) This firm's "*long-term commitment to IP*" has borne fruit, and resulted in a practice which is noted for its "*tremendous strength in depth.*" Recognised for expertise in patent and trademark litigation, the firm has acknowledged cross-border capability, bolstered by high-profile teams across Europe and South-East Asia. Technology transfer and brand management also constitute an important element of the workload. The "*confident*" **Jeremy Brown** (see p.501) is widely regarded as "*excellent*" and represented American Home Products on its high profile patent infringement action against Novartis. The "*painstaking and intellectual*" **Robin Whaite** (see p.511) advised Hewlett-Packard on

INTELLECTUAL PROPERTY: GENERAL • London	Ptnrs	Assts
1 Bird & Bird	9	5
Bristows	18	23
Taylor Joynson Garrett	7	10
2 Linklaters	9	33
Simmons & Simmons	6	16
3 Baker & McKenzie	4	14
Clifford Chance	5	17
Eversheds	6	10
Herbert Smith	6	25
Lovells	3	10
Wragge & Co	8	29
4 Allen & Overy	3	12
Denton Wilde Sapte	5	8
Olswang	2	4
Slaughter and May	3	16
Willoughby & Partners	9	16
5 Arnander Irvine & Zietman	7	7
Ashurst Morris Crisp	3	25
Field Fisher Waterhouse	6	n/a
Freshfields Bruckhaus Deringer	3	29
Gouldens	2	5
Roiter Zucker	3	1
Rowe & Maw	6	16
6 Briffa	1	2
CMS Cameron McKenna	4	18
Dechert	4	12
H2O (Henry Hepworth Organisation)	2	7
Hammond Suddards Edge	4	11
Norton Rose	4	17
SJ Berwin	3	5

This book is the product of 6,552 1/2-hour interviews. See p.7 for BMRB audit.
Within each band, firms are listed alphabetically.

co-ordinating multi-jurisdictional litigation against ink-jet cartridge suppliers that were believed to infringe some of its patents. **Robert Swift** (see p.510) is a "*sound choice*" and acted on one of the most discussed trademark disputes of the year, representing Davidoff against parallel imports of 'Cool Water' aftershave from Singapore, a case that reached the European Courts of Justice. "*Impressive*" **Ian Karet** (see p.506) and the "*steady*" **Nigel Jones** (see p.505) have both attracted sustained market recommendation, while newly ranked trademark expert **Anna Carboni** (see p.502) attracted rave reviews from clients. She represented Riker Laboratories on an invalidity application against a trademark registration of Glaxo Group. **Clients:** Gucci; Hermès; Johnson & Johnson; Lloyds TSB; Microsoft; Novo Nordisk.

Simmons & Simmons (see firm details p.1132) Competitors, who commend the firm as "*consistently doughty opponents,*" acknowledge its distinguished track record in this practice area. The team is a constant feature on multi-jurisdictional litigation, both in patent cases and more general IP issues. "*Sane, sensible and commercial,*" **Rowan Freeland** (see p.504) is considered to be "*delightful to work with or against,*" and led the defence of Hyundai Electronics in a major piece of patent litigation against Rambus. "*Methodical and knowledgeable,*" **Kevin Mooney** (see p.508) "*has been around.*" He advised on Bristol-Myers Squibb's appeal on the patent covering the second medical use of the cancer drug Taxol. Fellow practitioners rate **Gerry Kamstra** (see p.506)as a "*singularly impressive*" man, while **Helen Newman** (see p.508) is noted for her "*practical*" nature. The firm advised Humbrol in relation to its high profile dispute and settlement with Damien Hirst over the artist's sculpture 'Hymn,' which was copied from Humbrol's educational 'Anatomy Set' toy. **Clients:** 3M; Bacardi-Martini; GlaxoSmithKline; Humbrol; Hyundai Electronics; Procter & Gamble; Leisure Link Group; Time Warner Entertainment; Provensis; NXT plc; XO Communications.

Taylor Joynson Garrett (see firm details p.1150) "*Talented people who have great know-how,*" the team is "*seen all the time*" by its principal rivals. Noted for pharmaceutical and biotechnology patent litigation, the firm also advises on the range of general work, including internet litigation, advertising, design cases and trade mark registry oppositions. **Mark Hodgson** (see p.505)is "*focused and really knows his law,*" and led the firm's advice to Eli Lilly on multiple cases against Novo Nordisk concerning both insulin technology and devices for administration of insulin. **Gary Moss** (see p.508)is a "*forceful litigator,*" who advised Kirin-Amgen and OrthoBiotech against Hoechst Marion Rousel and others on actions related to genetic engineering, most notably the infringement of Kirin-Amgen's patent covering the DNA sequence for erythropoietin. The "*assured*" **Richard Price** (see p.509) and **James Marshall** (see p.507) are others to attract substantial market support. The firm acted for Eli Lilly and ICOS Corp on their successful application in the UK Patents Court to revoke the Pfizer-owned patent that monopolised the use of pharmaceutical compounds including Viagra. Elsewhere, the team represented TNT, the courier company, in a dispute with Turner Network TV relating to the 'TNT' trademark. **Clients:** Eli Lilly; Kirin-Amgen; Johnson Wax; Oxford Natural Products; Pharmax Ltd; Fujitsu; Telsonic; Generics Group.

Herbert Smith (see firm details p.993) Active on a range of IP matters, the firm handles patent, trademark and copyright cases, both on the non-contentious and contentious sides. The "*accomplished*" **Bill Moodie** (see p.508) is rated as a "*good computer contracts litigator,*" and acts for new government outfit DERA, advising on all brand and technology issues inherent in potential privatisations. **Mark Shillito** (see p.509) gives ongoing parallel import advice to Colgate-Palmolive, while **Andrew Rich** (see p.509) advised on The Roche Diagnostics Products v Kirin-Amgen patent case, notable as the biggest patent case of recent times. **Clients:** AstraZeneca; BAA; Vodafone; Time Warner; Trinity Mirror; DERA; Colgate-Palmolive.

Lovells (see firm details p.1044) Long recognised for its strength in patents, the firm continues to advise on a high level of contentious and non-contentious IP work, notably matters arising from the merger and de-merger of Granada Group. Recent overseas mergers give the firm a highly regarded pan-European patent practice. "*Effective patent litigator*" **Robert Anderson** (see p.500) advised DSM NV on the defence of a patent revocation action brought by Danish company Novo Nordisk, in relation to a patent for DSM concerning the cloning and expression of microbial phytase. The "*consistently successful*" **Nick Macfarlane** (see p.507) acted for Merck against Monsanto, one of the biggest biotech patent trials to date, and successfully defended them on a claim involving alleged misuse of confidential information in the formulation and manufacture of insecticides. **Clients:** Reuters; Exxon-Mobil; Nortel; Merck; Napp Pharmaceuticals.

Wragge & Co incorporating Needham & Grant (see firm details p.1189) "*You see the name, you see the cases,*" say rivals of this recently constituted team. Considered to be a "*good fit*" by peers, the firm's all-round IP strength is felt to have grown over the past 12 months. Handling a range of patent disputes in the biotechnology and electronics industries, the team also advises on anti-counterfeiting and brand enforcement cases. Some clients rate the "*affable*" **Gregor Grant** as "*London's top patent lawyer,*" while **Adam Cooke** and **David Gibbins** garner plaudits for their "*proven track record.*" The firm advised on Asahi v Macopharma, a patent dispute concerning blood transfusion bags and equipment, and acted on Millipore v Amersham, another patent case, which concerned chromatography columns. **Clients:** British Telecom; Cadbury Schweppes; Dyson Appliances; PowerGen; British Airways; Carlton Communications.

LEADING INDIVIDUALS	
1 **COOK Trevor** Bird & Bird	**FIELD Sally** Bristows
GRANT Gregor Wragge & Co	**HODGSON Mark** Taylor Joynson Garrett
MACDONALD Morag Bird & Bird	**MOONEY Kevin** Simmons & Simmons
WILLOUGHBY Tony Willoughby & Partners	
2 **BROWN Jeremy** Linklaters	**DAVIES Isabel** Eversheds
FREELAND Rowan Simmons & Simmons	**JUDGE Ian** Bristows
MACFARLANE Nicholas Lovells	**WALSH Paul** Bristows
3 **ANDERSON Robert** Lovells	**COHEN Laurence** McDermott, Will & Emery
HARRISS David Bird & Bird	**MARSLAND Vanessa** Clifford Chance
MOSS Gary Taylor Joynson Garrett	**NEWMAN Helen** Simmons & Simmons
NODDER Edward Bristows	**PERKINS David** Clifford Chance
STARR Ian Ashurst Morris Crisp	
4 **BROWN David** Bristows	**INGLIS Andrew** Olswang
JONES Nigel Linklaters	**JONES Stephen** Baker & McKenzie
KARET Ian Linklaters	**LLEWELYN David** White & Case
MACDONALD-BROWN Charters Gouldens	**MARTINDALE Avril** Freshfields Bruckhaus
MOODIE Bill Herbert Smith	**PRICE Richard** Taylor Joynson Garrett
SMITH Catriona Allen & Overy	**SWIFT Robert** Linklaters
SWYCHER Nigel Slaughter and May	**WHAITE Robin** Linklaters
5 **COOKE Adam** Wragge & Co	**GAYTHWAITE Miles** Bird & Bird
HARRIS Paul Eversheds	**HART Michael** Baker & McKenzie
HENRY Michael Buchanan Ingersoll	**IRVINE James** Arnander Irvine & Zietman
KAMSTRA Gerry Simmons & Simmons	**TAYLOR Peter** Clifford Chance
THORNE Clive Denton Wilde Sapte	
6 **BARRY Robert** Allen & Overy	**BRIFFA Margaret** Briffa
CARBONI Anna Linklaters	**CHALKLEY Simon** Gouldens
DANILUNAS Marija Hammond Suddards	**GARE Stephen** Rowe & Maw
GIBBINS David Wragge & Co	**MARSHALL James** Taylor Joynson Garrett
RAWLINSON Paul Baker & McKenzie	**RICH Andrew** Herbert Smith
SHILLITO Mark Herbert Smith	**TURNER Catrin** H2O (Henry Hepworth)
WOOD Ian Rowe & Maw	
UP AND COMING	
MIDDLEMISS Susie Slaughter and May	

See individuals' profiles p.500

Baker & McKenzie (see firm details p.868) Well-known for its non-contentious capacity, the IP group is highly respected for its patent, trademark and copyright work. The team profits from the firm's powerful IT practice, while a global network of offices gives it a strong position in multi-jurisdictional cases. "*Top quality*" partner **Stephen Jones** (see p.505) and the trademarks team co-ordinate searches and applications for Apple Computers throughout the EU. **Paul Rawlinson** (see p.509) is respected as a leading brand protection lawyer and acted for Sherman Cooper on the acquisition of an IP licence for the worldwide rights to the 'Acupuncture' footwear brand. **Michael Hart** (see p.504) represented the Committee of Vice-Chancellors of the Universities of the UK on its reference to the Copyright Licensing Agency. **Clients:** Sony; Calvin Klein; Levi Strauss; Yahoo!; Tommy Hilfiger; L'Oréal.

Clifford Chance (see firm details p.919) "*Strong at partner level,*" the team is still led by **David Perkins** (see p.509), a "*class act, who knows how to build a practice.*" Patent disputes, trademark cases and the IP elements of big-ticket M&A are core elements of the group's workload. The team also includes "*helpful and client-friendly*" **Vanessa Marsland** (see p.507) and the respected **Peter Taylor** (see p.510). The firm advised Ajinomoto on a substantial patent portfolio relating to artificial sweeteners, and subsequently analysed multi-jurisdictional infringement litigation options. It also acted on the acquisition of the Revlon professional business, a complex transaction involving splitting rights and taking security in various jurisdictions. **Clients:** American Home Products; Aventis; Exxon Mobil; Gap; Lego; Mars; Starbucks; GlaxoSmithKline.

Eversheds (see firm details p.952) "*Active*" practice with a wide-ranging caseload, encompassing contentious and non-contentious patent, trademark and design work. "*Tough operator*" **Isabel Davies** (see p.503) has "*done a wonderful job in cementing the practice,*" and receives stout support from the "*underrated, effective*" **Paul Harris.** (see p.504) The firm successfully represented Boston Scientific in the Court of Appeal, resisting J&J's appeal against the finding of invalidity on two patents. Trademark work has included advising on Unilever v General Housewares over the latter's use in the UK of the mark 'OXO' on its kitchen equipment. **Clients:** Asda; Guinness; Sara Lee; Unilever; Wagamama; Black & Decker.

Allen & Overy (see firm details p.856) "*They've had a great year!*" Often seen on contentious cases, the team handles patent and trademark litigation, brand name protection and transactional and financing work. "*Competent and steady*" **Catriona Smith** (see p.509) and **Robert Barry** (see p.501) are the department's best-known players. The firm acted for William Hill in litigation brought against it by the BHB relating to database rights for horse-racing cards. This was the first UK database rights case under the Database Rights Directive. The team also advised American Home Products on the transfer of a number of intellectual property licences. **Clients:** American Home Products; Bass; BT; Carlton International.

Roiter Zucker (see firm details p.x1110) "*Capable*" niche firm, headed by Anna McKay, which continues to act for pharmaceutical companies on a broad range of IP matters. The team maintains a reputation for "*rarely, if ever, losing a significant patent case.*" It acted for the defendants in the Glaxo v Dowelhurst case at the ECJ, an important case of trademark infringement, raising questions about the relationship between national IP rights and the principle of free movement of goods. It also advised the BAEPD and Dowelhurst in connection with their application for judicial review of certain, allegedly anti-competitive, provisions of the PPRS – a case significant because of its impact on the pricing of pharmaceuticals. **Clients:** IVAX Corp; Bioglan; BAEPD; Dowelhurst; Medihealth.

Stringer Saul (see firm details p.1147) Focusing on pharmaceutical and biotech work, this niche practice, featuring Gary Howes, has its reputation principally in patent cases. It has acted in a series of vaccine patent cases, and co-ordinated cross-border litigation for Medeva. It has also advised Antisoma and SR Pharma on patent licensing. **Clients:** Celtech Group; British Biotech; Antisoma.

Denton Wilde Sapte (see firm details p.939) "*Steady firm,*" which continues to deal with a wide range of contentious and non-contentious work, and focuses on IP advice relating to banking, IT and e-commerce transactions for an "*impressive client roster*" of blue-chips. The "*perfectionist*" **Clive Thorne** (see p.510) handled trademark protection matters for Equitable Life, and is respected for his "*longevity*" in this area. The team managed design right and brand management for Sony Pictures, advised EasyGroup on trademark and domain name protection, and acted for Creightons on TM litigation against John Frieda. **Clients:** Easygroup; Marks & Spencer; Sony; Mattel.

Olswang (see firm details p.1084) Gaining in profile this year, the firm scored a major success with its advice to Dyson Appliances during a high profile patent infringement action against Hoover. "*Dyson was a great result,*" acknowledge competitors, who attribute credit for the group's progress to the "*top-flight*" **Andrew Inglis** (see p.505). Advised Genetix Group on its acquisition of Genpak and the Genetix share placement which included the detailed review of many sets of patents. Advised UK Medical Ventures in relation to the establishment of two start-up biotech companies that included complex patent licensing agreements. **Clients:** Dyson Appliances; Genetix Group; Johnson Matthey; Channel Four.

Slaughter and May (see firm details p.1135) "*Great for non-contentious work*," the firm continues to advise its peerless plc client base on a variety of patent infringement and validity claims. The "*resourceful*" **Nigel Swycher** (see p.510) "*fights the good fight*" and "*does a super job for his clients*." He advised Unilever on the IP aspects of the £100 million disposal of its European bakery supplies business. Having advised on a number of passing off/trademark infringement proceedings concerning use of the REED name on the internet, Chris Hickson retired this year. However, the firm boasts the services of rising name **Susie Middlemiss**, seen by many as "*a potential star*." **Clients:** Stena Lines; Emap; Richemont; Unilever.

Willoughby & Partners (see firm details p.1183) Occupying an "*important position*" in the market, this "*outstanding*" trademark firm continues to appear on high profile litigation work, such as the GlaxoSmithKline parallel import litigation against Dowelhurst. The firm is still felt to lean heavily on the individual talents of "*lateral thinker*" **Tony Willoughby** (see p.511), "*a lawyer with common sense*," who "*has made a lifetime's work of trademarks*." It acted for Asprey & Garrard against William Asprey on a passing off and TM infringement action, and undertakes non-contentious work for publishing, IT and software companies. **Clients:** Ford Motor Company; Cadbury Schweppes; GlaxoSmithKline; Cartier; The Scotch Whisky Assocation; PA Consulting.

Arnander Irvine & Zietman (see firm details p.862) Now renamed following last year's departures, the firm continues to offer an across the board IP service, ranging from commercial work through to patent litigation and advisory work. Said to be "*rebuilding the practice gamely*," the "*focused*" **James Irvine** specialises in big case litigation, and advised Hoover on its appeal against the Dyson patent infringement judgment. **Clients:** DaimlerChrysler; Hoover.

Ashurst Morris Crisp (see firm details p.866) Experiencing substantial growth in e-commerce related work, and active on both contentious and non-contentious work, the firm's "*no frills*" style wins substantial market approval. **Ian Starr** (see p.510)is universally accounted a "*wonderful TM litigator*" by peers, and has acted for Johnson & Johnson on a number of TM disputes. However, the reputation of the department is still felt to rest largely on his shoulders. The firm acted for AltaVista on its £214 million High Court action, and on the non-contentious side, advised on the disposals of Smith & Nephew's personal hygiene division to Beiersdorf. **Clients:** Johnson & Johnson; Motorola; Bell Atlantic; Smith & Nephew.

Field Fisher Waterhouse (see firm details p.957) Known for ability as trademark prosecutors, and managing a portfolio of 13,000 live marks, the team, which includes Mark Abel and John Olsen, acted for Ordnance Survey in High Court proceedings against the Automobile Association concerning infringement of crown copyright – one of the largest copyright disputes in UK history. Other work includes advising antiquesportfolio.com in a copyright infringement claim against Rodney Fitch, and the securing and maintenance of Dell Computers' UK trademark registrations. **Clients:** Laura Ashley; Logica.

Freshfields Bruckhaus Deringer (see firm details p.965) The firm is seen to be "*making an effort*" in this area, and, according to a number of competitors, "*it's beginning to pay off*." Litigation, both patent and trademark, and non-contentious work all form part of a varied caseload. The "*driven*" **Avril Martindale** (see p.507) is considered "*adept*" and "*easy to deal with*." The firm advised LVMH on the De Beers international branding joint venture for the use of the De Beers brand worldwide. It also advised Ford on its acquisition of Land Rover from BMW – a particularly complex deal, due to the trademark law implications of the separation of ownership of 'Rover' and 'Land Rover.' **Clients:** AstraZeneca; Bass; Deutsche Bank; Hewlett-Packard; Microsoft.

Gouldens (see firm details p.976) A 'one stop shop' for trademark filing and management practice advice, this "*good young team*" has also advised on a number of significant contentious cases, and rises in the tables this year. The "*dynamic*" **Charters Macdonald-Brown** (see p.507) knows how to "*put clients at ease*," and newly ranked **Simon Chalkley** (see p.502) is respected by peers as a name to watch on the non-contentious side. The firm advised Boehringer Ingelheim on a case which related to the rights of parallel importers to overlabel or repackage pharmaceutical products, and acted for Acupuncture in four cases relating to infringement of design right and registered design. **Clients:** Bhs; Imperial Tobacco; Schering; Ted Baker; Eidos; Hanson; GlaxoSmithKline; Rank Hovis McDougall.

Rowe & Maw (see firm details p.1113) "*Sound team*," with a well-known trademarks niche, both in contentious and transactional work. **Ian Wood** (see p.511) is a "*tremendously experienced litigator*," while **Stephen Gare** (see p.504) is also commended by peers as a "*safe pair of hands*." The firm acted for BP Amoco in an action against Kelly Fuels over infringement of two of BP's 'green' trademark registrations, covering the livery of BP service stations. Other work has included a patent litigation matter for the UK's fastest growing character merchandising company, Worlds Apart, in relation to tents and other collapsible structures. **Clients:** BP Amoco; Cable & Wireless; Danone; Lear Corporation M&G; Morgan Stanley; McCann Erickson Advertising; NBC/CNBC.

Briffa (see firm details p.894) Based at the Business Design Centre, this "*unique*" niche firm is said to have "*its own style*," and appears on a number of high profile cases. The "*talented*" **Margaret Briffa** is an "*independent thinker*" who does "*some interesting work*." The team commenced High Court and trademark proceedings on behalf of White Stuff, objecting to the Milk Marketing Board's television and poster advertising campaigns, which involved the use of the words 'white stuff.' It also acted for Prism Leisure against Electronic Arts in respect of the trademark 'Football Manager'. **Clients:** Visa international; St. Luke's; White Stuff; Agent Provocateur.

CMS Cameron McKenna (see firm details p.922) Although the firm is by no means the first name on the lips of interviewees in this sector, its outstanding pharmaceutical and biotechnology clientele ensures that the group remains active. Transactional and contentious work remain the focuses for Stephen Whybrow and his team. The firm advised on medical device patent litigation in the Patents Court, as part of a multi-jurisdictional action. It also acted for six leading film companies on a major video counterfeiting action – the largest counterfeiting seizure in the UK. Other work includes acting for a Japanese pharmaceutical company on a significant arbitration with a leading worldwide pharmaceutical company. **Clients:** Asahi Medical; Consignia; Camelot Group; Motion Picture Association.

Dechert (see firm details p.938) "*Competent*" group, whose trademarks practice is considered to be "*holding up well*," and represents the firm's principal strength in the sector. Led by Duncan Black, the team is best known for its international work relating to the trademark 'Diana, Princess of Wales.' The firm recently advised on a significant international financial services re-branding. **Clients:** Thomas Cook; Asprey & Garrard; Vauxhall/General Motors.

H20 (Henry Hepworth Organisation) (see firm details p.981) Maintaining its reputation for acting on behalf of heavyweight retailers, the firm has an especially solid name for its trademark and copyright practice. The "*sensible*" **Catrin Turner** (see p.510) is "*an increasingly prominent trademark litigator*." The firm represented Tesco on its high-profile litigation concerning the Levi international exhaustion campaign – an important case for its issues of sourcing branded goods outside Europe. **Clients:** Tesco; Tottenham Hotspur; Workthing.com; Sportal.com.

Hammond Suddards Edge (see firm details p.984) Busy on a wide range of contentious and non-contentious work, the team advises on trademarks, patents, and parallel importation. The "*tenacious*" **Marija Danilunas** (see p.503) wins praise for her "*technical ability*," and makes her debut in the tables. The team acted for Harrods on worldwide domain name litigation and advised Kodak on parallel imports, passing off and copyright infringements. It also acted for Alpha Fry on patent infringements and distribution/agency agreements, and advises financing clients such as Illinois Tool Works on corporate support work. **Clients:** British Aluminium; Aventis; Kodak; Zeneca Group.

Norton Rose (see firm details p.1082) Although seen comparatively infrequently, the firm's excellent client base keeps it "*there or thereabouts*" in a variety of IP work. Richard Barratt leads the team. The firm acted for BMW on the restructuring and disposal of the Rover Group and Land Rover – a complex deal, splitting the IP rights relating to the names Rover, Land Rover and MG. The team also acted on the first flotation of an easyGroup company, the airline EasyJet, which involved a wide-ranging reformation of the group's brands and the hiving off of trademarks. **Clients:** Arthur Andersen; Del Monte; Cathay Pacific; Burberry.

SJ Berwin (see firm details p.879) Said by peers to be "*doing more these days*," the team, under the aegis of Ray Black, has an established reputation for trademarks and copyright work. The firm acted for the World Wrestling Foundation, which was sued by the World Wide Fund for Nature for breach of contract and trademark infringement arising from a co-existence agreement dating from the 1990s. Other work includes advising leading estate agent Countywide in an action against Homemovers, a residential property internet portal, over database rights, copyright and trademark rights. **Clients:** J Sainsbury; Marks & Spencer; Sony; UEFA; Baileys.

Other Notable Practitioners At White & Case, "*IP heavyweight*" **David Llewelyn** (see p.506) is continuing his quest to build a team to match his own personal reputation. **McDermott, Will & Emery**'s top litigator **Laurence Cohen** (see p.503) is ruefully rated by some peers, who admit: "*You know you're going to get a good fight with Larry!*" **Buchanan Ingersoll** is now home to the experienced **Michael Henry**, a "*distinguished copyright lawyer*" who brings "*years of experience with him*" from H20.

THE SOUTH

INTELLECTUAL PROPERTY • The South	Ptnrs	Assts
1 **Lochners Technology Solicitors** Godalming	3	2
2 **DMH** Brighton	4	2
3 **Lester Aldridge** Bournemouth	1	1

LEADING INDIVIDUALS
1 **LOCHNER Ludi** Lochners Technology Solicitors
2 **ASPINALL Tim** DMH

This book is the product of 6,552 1/2-hour interviews. See p.7 for BMRB audit.
Within each band, firms are listed alphabetically. *See individuals' profiles p.500*

Lochners Technology Solicitors (see firm details p.1043) Renowned for its patent work, this Godalming-based firm specialises exclusively in IP, IT and EU law, and is recognised to be "*fabulous at what it does.*" **Ludi Lochner** is "*a familiar name in the market*" and is regularly mentioned as "*a sound practitioner.*" The firm acted for Remington on its Europe-wide challenge to a patent infringement action brought by Phillips. **Clients:** Remington; Harley Davidson; Nova; AxyGen Scientific.

DMH (see firm details p.944) Still the local firm of choice for contentious IP work, it advises a broad range of clients, drawn mainly from the pharmaceutical, software and engineering sectors. **Tim Aspinall** (see p.564) is said to be a "*serious commercial lawyer.*" The contentious team acted for a multi-national supplier of simulation systems in a copyright/confidentiality claim against a former employee. Non-contentious work includes a multi-jurisdictional investigation into the ownership of rights of a software package for a substantial engineering group. **Clients:** Multi-national pharmaceutical companies; cosmetics companies; writers and artists; software producers and designers.

Lester Aldridge (see firm details p.1038) With a general bias toward IT work, the team operates within a combined technology and IP unit. Boosted by the launch of an in-house UK and community TM registration filing practice, the practice now has the appearance of a one-stop shop. The team has advised on the acquisition of trademark brands for Bournemouth-based Ceuta Healthcare, and Acted for HALMA in acquiring a patent portfolio. On the contentious side, the firm acted for RK Marine in a dispute over registered designs. **Clients:** Ceuta Healthcare; Cobham; Fortis; ITW.

THAMES VALLEY

INTELLECTUAL PROPERTY • Thames Valley	Ptnrs	Assts
1 **The Law Offices of Marcus J O'Leary** Bracknell	2	5
Willoughby & Partners Oxford	3	5
2 **Garretts** Reading	2	4
Nabarro Nathanson Reading	2	6
3 **Manches** Oxford	3	4
Osborne Clarke Reading	2	3

LEADING INDIVIDUALS
1 **BOOY Anna** Willoughby & Partners
2 **HARRINGTON Alison** Garretts
NORTCLIFF Celia The Law Offices of Marcus J O'Leary

This book is the product of 6,552 1/2-hour interviews. See p.7 for BMRB audit.
Within each band, firms are listed alphabetically. *See individuals' profiles p.500*

The Law Offices of Marcus J O'Leary (see firm details p.1030) Bracknell-based firm with "*a fine IP niche*" and a reputation for quality. The firm advises an impressive technology client roster that includes four of the largest software companies in the world. It covers a broad range of IP matters, ranging from copyright and design to patents, biotechnology and passing off. Both peers and clients strongly endorse **Celia Nortcliff** (see p.508). **Clients:** Leading IT companies.

Willoughby & Partners (see firm details p.1183) Still "*a strong commercial practice,*" the Oxford arm of this respected IP boutique concentrates on non-contentious work for a clientele drawn mainly from retail, media and biosciences. The respected **Anna Booy** (see p.501) is "*seen on the lecture circuit*" and gains praise for her "*wide-ranging experience.*" The firm advised Polish Telecom on a major 'business to business' e-commerce deal, acted on the Kingfisher/Woolworths de-merger, and represented entertainment distributors on the installation of CD-burning kiosks in retail outlets. Other work includes advising ex-Buck's Fizz band members in relation to use of the band name. **Clients:** Kingfisher Group; Star Technology Group; Celador; Sega Europe.

Garretts (see firm details p.968) Considered by some clients to be "*better than everyone else in Reading,*" this "*more than competent*" team has niche strengths in technology transfer, licensing and exploitation in the pharmaceuticals and life sciences industries, as well as copyright, design right and trademarks. **Alison Harrington** (see p.295) is a "*decent, hard-working lawyer.*" The firm has advised Scherer on a number of important pan-European and worldwide technology transfer agreements. **Clients:** R P Scherer; Eurobotanicals; Cardionetics.

Nabarro Nathanson (see firm details p.1078) Focused on soft IP work, developed in conjunction with the firm's well known IT and e-commerce practice, the team advises on a range of copyright, patent and licensing issues. Headed by Sara Ellacott, the group has acted for Siemens Medical Services on its claim for copyright infringement against Med Imaging for the unauthorised use and access of Siemens' proprietary service software. The team also advised Sondex on patent and know-how licensing issues and draft general IP agreements for companies including HI-Q Systems, Software Translation Products and Ninth Floor. **Clients:** Direct Wines; Guide Dogs for the Blind; Sun Microsystems.

Manches (see firm details p.1051) Oxford-based practice, covering a broad range of IP work, with niches in biosciences, IT and publishing. The firm has been active on technology transfers for research councils and universities and advised Oxford Gene Technology on a multi-million pound settlement of disputes with Affymetrix, which involved a number of patent-related agreements. **Clients:** Oxford Gene Technology; National Trust (Enterprises); Reed Elsevier; Deutsche Bank.

Osborne Clarke (see firm details p.1086) "*Consolidating its position in the region,*" the firm acts for a wide range of clients in industries including motor and pharmaceuticals. The team, led by Russell Bowyer, advised Profiad on its clinical research trials business, handles the UK brand management, protection and domain name issues for Porsche, and advised NOxMaster on patent licensing to Perkins. **Clients:** BMW GB; Harley Davidson; Panasonic Broadcast; Pharma Ventures.

SOUTH WEST

INTELLECTUAL PROPERTY • South West	Ptnrs	Assts
1 **Osborne Clarke** Bristol	1	3
2 **Bevan Ashford** Bristol	3	5
3 **Beachcroft Wansbroughs** Bristol	3	3
Burges Salmon Bristol	n/a	n/a
Humphreys & Co Bristol	n/a	n/a
4 **Laytons** Bristol	n/a	n/a

LEADING INDIVIDUALS	
1 **BRAITHWAITE Andrew** Osborne Clarke	**HUMPHREYS Robert** Humphreys & Co
JONES Gareth Bevan Ashford	
2 **BROWN Richard** Laytons	**WOOD Alan** Beachcroft Wansbroughs

This book is the product of 6,552 1/2-hour interviews. See p.7 for BMRB audit.
Within each band, firms are listed alphabetically. *See individuals' profiles p.500*

Osborne Clarke (see firm details p.1086) "*The best in the region,*" the firm is considered to possess "*more really commercial lawyers*" than its nearest rivals. Particularly expert on cases that straddle the IP/IT nexus, the team is led by the "*entrepreneurial*" **Andrew Braithwaite**, said by clients to have "*an excellent bedside manner.*" The firm represents Allied Domecq on various brand and trademark issues, and continues to work on the branding and merchandising for the 2001 Ryder Cup. It also advised the University of Bristol on patented licensing for various technology projects, and acted for Nutricia on IP licensing agreements. **Clients:** Morgan Motor Co; Lloyds TSB; University of Bristol.

Bevan Ashford (see firm details p.880) An "*energetic firm,*" seen to be "*growing into IP advice,*" which advises on a range of matters across a number of industries. **Gareth Jones** (see p.505) is respected for "*pushing the firm forward.*" The firm acted on the franchising of a telecommunications service to an Israeli organisation. **Clients:** Orange PCS; Allied Domecq; Biotrace International; World TV.

Beachcroft Wansbroughs (see firm details p.872) Another firm with a strong reputation for IP-related work in the IT sphere, it covers the spectrum of advice for a strong pharmaceutical and healthcare clientele. **Alan Wood** (see p.511) is seen as "*a safe pair of hands.*" **Clients:** Healthcare clients; public sector institutions.

Burges Salmon (see firm details p.902) Still strongest on the non-contentious side of IP, the firm continues to impress peers: "*considering the fact that they're not specialists, they pull in some superb work.*" The group has advised United Biscuits on hi-tech research and development, as well as its patent arrangements. **Clients:** Bristol & West; United Biscuits; New Zealand Milk (UK).

Humphreys & Co (see firm details p.1005) Expanding niche firm, which is highly rated for its advice on trademarks, patents, design and copyright. The caseload includes registration, maintenance, licensing and litigation on IP-related work. The "*assertive*" **Robert Humphreys** (see p.505) is a "*dyed-in-the-wool specialist,*" who is praised for "*broadening the firm's repertoire.*" **Clients:** Food and drinks manufacturers; financial services clients.

Laytons (see firm details p.1031) Respected around the region, the team, headed by **Richard Brown** (see p.502), acted for a major supermarket chain on IP aspects of the outsourcing of its facilities management services. Other work has included advising on the use of Nationwide's trademarks in relation to the marketing of football related products and on its sponsorship of the Football League. **Clients:** Somerfield Stores; Zuken Group; Nationwide Building Society.

WALES

INTELLECTUAL PROPERTY • Wales	Ptnrs	Assts
1 **Edwards Geldard** Cardiff	1	3
2 **Eversheds** Cardiff	n/a	n/a
Morgan Cole Cardiff	1	1

LEADING INDIVIDUALS	
1 **DELEMORE Ceri** Edwards Geldard	**McNABB Heather** Eversheds
2 **LINDSEY Michael** Morgan Cole	

This book is the product of 6,552 1/2-hour interviews. See p.7 for BMRB audit.
Within each band, firms are listed alphabetically. *See individuals' profiles p.500*

Edwards Geldard (see firm details p.948) Still acclaimed for its client base and variety of work, the firm is considered to have the leading IP team in Wales. The team has increasingly advised on infringement actions, and recently acted on a major patent litigation. **Ceri Delemore** (see p.503) is the firm's outstanding practitioner. **Clients:** Chubb; S4C; Citibank NA; British Chamber of Commerce.

Eversheds (see firm details p.952) Handling both contentious and non-contentious matters, the team, led by **Heather McNabb** (see p.507), provides IP support on corporate transactions and has dealt with a number of domain name disputes. The firm advised the Solectron Corporation on the IP aspects of a multi-million pound, multi-jurisdictional corporate deal. **Clients:** UWIC; National Assembly for Wales; Alliance Pharmaceuticals; Ice Hockey Super League.

Morgan Cole (see firm details p.1074) The respected **Michael Lindsey** has a largely contentious practice, while his assistant, a lawyer with a degree in molecular immunology, handles non-contentious matters. The firm advised a mobile telephony client on a High Court trademark and passing off case, and is involved in ongoing trademark litigation for a client in Munich and Leipzig. **Clients:** Rockwool; Gyrus; PHS, Addis; University of Wales College of Medicine; Target Group.

MIDLANDS

INTELLECTUAL PROPERTY • Midlands	Ptnrs	Assts
1 **Wragge & Co incorporating Needham & Grant** Birmingham	5	26
2 **Martineau Johnson** Birmingham	3	3
3 **Pinsent Curtis Biddle** Birmingham	2	8
4 **Browne Jacobson** Nottingham	3	5
Eversheds Birmingham, Nottingham	2	7
Shoosmiths Northampton	2	2
5 **Freethcartwright** Nottingham	1	1
Hammond Suddards Edge Birmingham	1	3

LEADING INDIVIDUALS	
1 **BARKER William** Martineau Johnson	**BARRON David** Wragge & Co
HARRIS Gordon Wragge & Co	
2 **ELLIS Peter** Browne Jacobson	**LUCKMAN Michael** Wragge & Co
WYN DAVIES Cerys Pinsent Curtis Biddle	
3 **ASSIM Gary** Shoosmiths	**DRISCOLL Helen** Martineau Johnson
HEAD-RAPSON Niall Martineau Johnson	

This book is the product of 6,552 1/2-hour interviews. See p.7 for BMRB audit.
Within each band, firms are listed alphabetically. *See individuals' profiles p.500*

Wragge & Co incororating Needham & Grant (see firm details p.1189) The addition of respected former Hammonds Suddards Edge partner **Michael Luckman** to the team has been heralded as another sign of the firm's "*enormous growth.*" Already a "*huge IP force*" with "*mighty litigation capacity,*" the team's acquisition of Luckman's predominantly non-contentious and franchising skills is felt to provide "*an even better balance.*" **David Barron** continues to gather heavy endorsement for his "*absolutely top quality*" contentious work, while counterfeiting expert **Gordon Harris** is commended for his "*vision and control.*" The firm continues to be busy with local engineering and manufacturing work, while increasing its presence in the electronics and telecommunication sectors. It acted for British Airways on a patent dispute relating to first class seats, which was settled by mediation in Singapore, and represented a subsidiary of the BI group in a patent dispute over gas meter technology. **Clients:** British Airways; BI Group; AstraZeneca; British Telecom; Dyson Appliances; Carlton Communications.

Martineau Johnson (see firm details p.1055) Unanimously considered to be "*a firm on the up,*" its acquisition of the esteemed duo of **Helen Driscoll** (see p.503) from Freethcartwright and **Niall Head-Rapson** (see p.504) from the Nottingham office of Eversheds is considered to have broadened its appeal. They join the firm's leading light, the "*knowledgeable and self-effacing*" **William Barker** (see p.501), who commands widespread respect from clients and competitors for his skills as a litigator. The firm has extended its caseload into the biotech sphere, and also represented Magnet on the successful defence of a claim concerning design right infringement. Other work includes advising Booker Cash & Carry on a High Court case involving claims by Mars UK concerning the packaging of own brand chocolate bars. **Clients:** Glynwed International; McKechnie; Manganese Bronze Holdings.

Pinsent Curtis Biddle (see firm details p.1098) A "*huge department*" is clearly rated among the most competitive in the region, although commentators do not believe that its depth of quality is quite the equal of the leading duo. Contentious expert **Cerys Wyn Davies** (see p.511) wins the praise of clients for "*fighting her corner.*" The firm offers a comprehensive filing service, advising, *inter alia*, leisure equipment producers and electronics companies. The firm advised a TI Group subsidiary on the defence of a patent infringement action relating to industrial conveyors. It also acted for 3i-backed Indigo Photonics on the IP aspects of its acquisition of Oxford Fiber Optic Tools, and represented Delphi Automotive Systems on IP issues relating to the acquisition of a braking systems business. **Clients:** TI Group; GKN; Brintons Carpets; Select; MG Rover Group.

Browne Jacobson (see firm details p.898) A frequent recipient of referrals, the firm's profile is in the ascendant, and not merely in the East Midlands. Competitors single out the team's strength in contentious cases, but the firm also appears on a number of high-level transactional matters. "*Trustworthy and reliable*" **Peter Ellis** (see p.503) is accorded much of the credit for the team's progress. The firm advised Charnos on its exploitation of patent rights relating to the Bioform bra. **Clients:** NHS Trusts; Huthwaite Research Group, Charnos.

Eversheds (see firm details p.952) The Birmingham and Nottingham branches of the national firm work in tandem to offer a complete regional service. Philip Atkinson, noted for his expertise in brand strategy, heads the team. Said to have a "*steady workload*" in Birmingham, the firm advises on trademarks, patents and domain dispute cases. The Nottingham office has suffered the loss of leading practitioner Niall Head-Rapson to Martineau Johnson. The firm acted for a large clothing retailer on a contentious trademark infringement action, and advised Diageo on the sale of the Guinness Book of Records. **Clients:** Bass; Bell Fruit Ltd; Novara; Giftware Association; Renault.

Shoosmiths (see firm details p.1129) "*Punchy and well-balanced team,*" which is headed by the respected **Gary Assim** (see p.500), an expert on grey goods cases. The firm represented TK Maxx in the Amsterdam Court of Appeal on a trademark infringement dispute with Polo Ralph Lauren. It also acted for the Waters Corporation in patent revocation proceedings against Agilent Technologies and advised Direct Mail Production Services in an action against Equifax for copyright infringement and breach of confidentiality. **Clients:** TKMaxx; Games Workshop; Dr Martens; Volkswagen Group UK; Conran Design Group; The Open University.

Freethcartwright (see firm details p.964) Despite the departure of litigator Helen Driscoll to Martineau Johnson, market opinion still speaks of a "*solid IP practice.*" The team, headed by Andrew Margiotta-Mills, has a TM filing practice and offers registered design work for a range of international clients. The firm advises Experian on all its IP work, including trademark and patent-related advice, and was instructed by Helly Hansen on its international branding strategy. **Clients:** Paul Smith; Helly Hansen; Plasplugs.

Hammond Suddards Edge (see firm details p.984) The loss of non-contentious heavyweight Michael Luckman to Wragges has clearly been a setback for the firm, although it has acquired the services of hard-IP specialist Jonathan Moore. The focus of the caseload is now on digital communication patents and the IP side of telecoms, media and technology work, and the firm is also active on brand and trademark work for retailers and food manufacturers. The firm recently advised a technology company on an international patent litigation. **Clients:** Apollo Leisure; Quadrant Healthcare; SurfControl; Compass Group.

EAST ANGLIA

	INTELLECTUAL PROPERTY • East Anglia	Ptnrs	Assts
1	**Mills & Reeve** Cambridge, Norwich	6	6
2	**Eversheds** Cambridge, Ipswich, Norwich	n/a	n/a
3	**Hewitson Becke + Shaw** Cambridge	2	7
4	**Greenwoods** Peterborough	1	2
	Taylor Vinters Cambridge	n/a	2

	LEADING INDIVIDUALS	
1	**FARRANT Patrick** Eversheds	**POORE Alasdair** Mills & Reeve
2	**NAPPER Isabel** Mills & Reeve	

This book is the product of 6,552 1/2-hour interviews. See p.7 for BMRB audit.

Within each band, firms are listed alphabetically. *See individuals' profiles p.500*

Mills & Reeve (see firm details p.1069) *"A cut above the rest,"* the firm has been busy representing a leading London-based technology company on its IP licensing and software agreements. The respected **Isabel Napper** (see p.508) leads a team involved in negotiating a £40 million research and development collaboration for a high profile electronics company. Her colleague, the *"cerebral"* **Alasdair Poore** (see p.509), was involved in the IP aspects of a recent £17m AIM listing. **Clients:** Zeus Technology; Cadcentre Group; Xaar; Vocalis.

Eversheds (see firm details p.952) *"Making a push in this area,"* the firm has attracted substantial market approval from clients this year. Covering patent, trademark and copyright work, often on the contentious side, the team has an enviable biotechnology client base. **Patrick Farrant** (see p.503) *"clearly knows what he's doing,"* and heads the team. The firm advised CeNeS Pharmaceuticals on a wide range of regulatory matters, including the sale of AutoPatch equipment to Glaxo Wellcome. **Clients:** Du Pont; Morley Research; Cyan Technology; Plant Bioscience; Catalyst Biomedica.

Hewitson Becke + Shaw (see firm details p.994) The firm's profile in this area is considered to have declined since the departure of leading partners Ian Craig and Niel Ackermann to the London office of US firm Dorsey & Whitney. Now headed by Bill Thatcher, whose forte is in hard IP and IT, the team is busy with technology patents, R&D agreements and licensing. It advised a drug discovery company on licensing arrangements with a Japanese partner, and acted for a biotech company on its joint venture with an Australian company. **Clients:** DaimlerChrysler; Microsoft Research; Millennium Pharmaceuticals.

Greenwoods (see firm details p.978) Philip Sloan leads a team that advises on the spectrum of IP matters, ranging from patent litigation to trademark and copyright cases. Hi-tech companies remain a core element of the firm's clientele.**Clients:** Hi-tech companies; biotech companies; publishing companies.

Taylor Vinters (see firm details p.1150) Featuring qualified barrister David Rainford, the team advises a number of local hi-tech businesses and large international technology consultancies on work ranging from commercial contracts to licensing and agency and distribution agreements. Predominantly a non-contentious firm, it is nevertheless seen acting on the occasional patent case. **Clients:** University of Cambridge; One Ltd.

NORTH WEST

	INTELLECTUAL PROPERTY • North West	Ptnrs	Assts
1	**Addleshaw Booth & Co** Manchester	4	20
	Halliwell Landau Manchester	3	6
2	**Hill Dickinson** Stockport	n/a	n/a
3	**DLA** Liverpool, Manchester	n/a	n/a
	Eversheds Manchester	3	15
	Hammond Suddards Edge Manchester	1	3
	Philip Conn & Co Manchester	1	2
4	**Kuit Steinart Levy** Manchester	3	2
	Lawson Coppock & Hart Manchester	n/a	n/a
	Taylors Blackburn	2	3

	LEADING INDIVIDUALS	
1	**BOARDMAN Richard** Halliwell Landau	**MOAKES Jonathan** Halliwell Landau
	WOODS Philip Hill Dickinson	
2	**BENTHAM Paul** Addleshaw Booth & Co	**JONES Patricia** Hammond Suddards Edge
	OSBORN Terry Philip Conn & Co	**STOKER Robert** Addleshaw Booth & Co

This book is the product of 6,552 1/2-hour interviews. See p.7 for BMRB audit.

Within each band, firms are listed alphabetically. *See individuals' profiles p.500*

Addleshaw Booth & Co (see firm details p.853) The firm's Manchester office has *"the blue-chip clients, the history and the name,"* according to peers, and remains one of the clear market leaders in the region. Renowned for its contentious expertise, the firm also draws on a top-quality corporate department to advise on the IP aspects of a range of high-end transactions. **Robert Stoker** (see p.510) and **Paul Bentham** (see p.501) draw praise from interviewees as *"quality practitioners."* The firm represented Standard Court over allegations by Prefel that use of the name '*Prada Society Café*' infringed Prefel's registered trademark PRADA. Other work includes advising Stockton-on-Tees Borough Council on complex copyright and confidentiality issues involved in the Wellington Square regeneration project. **Clients:** Baxenden Chemicals; Royal Doulton; Birthdays; Packard Bioscience.

Halliwell Landau (see firm details p.982) *"Strong at the top,"* the firm is said to have *"real focus and bags of experience."* Especially well regarded for non-contentious advice, the team includes the *"solutions-oriented"* **Richard Boardman** (see p.501) and the *"knowledgeable"* **Jonathan Moakes** (see p.507). The firm acted for ASICS on a cross-border licensing dispute that involved regional restriction and parallel import issues, and represented Umbro on its sponsorship of Chelsea Football Club. **Clients:** Trinity Pharmaceuticals; Osmetech; Tepnel Life Sciences.

Hill Dickinson (see firm details p.996) **Philip Woods** (see p.511)remains the key figure at a practice that is said to *"excel"* on the contentious aspects of patent and trademark cases. The *"well-schooled"* team advises an enormous range of leading British companies. **Clients:** Medical, pharmaceutical, mobile phone and clothing manufacturers.

DLA Under the guidance of Graham Orchison, the firm continues to act on a range of IP work.

Eversheds (see firm details p.952) Working in close co-operation with the Leeds office, the firm is best known for its work in protecting IP on the internet. Other matters include extensive trademarks advice. The firm acted for textile company COTS on its brand disposals, notably the disposal of the Van Heusen brand. Instructed by Peter Black Healthcare, the firm has also advised on substantial brand-related work and product licences for pharmaceutical products. **Clients:** Peter Black Healthcare; AEA Technology; Manchester Innovation; Kuwait Petroleum; Next.

Hammond Suddards Edge (see firm details p.984) Still active in both contentious and non-contentious brand and patent work, this national firm's Manchester office is considered by peers to have *"a sound IP practice."* The respected **Patricia Jones** (see p.505)concentrates on hard IP. The team acted for a large quarrying company on a patent infringement dispute over the rights to a stone-cleaning machine, and advised British Aluminium on its worldwide IP portfolio. **Clients:** GenCor; Kickers International; Associated Octel; Boots; Bradford & Bingley.

Philip Conn & Co (see firm details p.1096) Twenty years of experience is considered to makes this firm a "*solid IP contender.*" The "*excellent*" **Terry Osborn** makes his debut in this year's tables. Acting for several companies on the acquisition and disposal of intellectual property, the department gives extensive advice on the protection of new concepts and designs and related IT issues. Although predominantly known for non-contentious work, the firm has been prominent in advising on the Designer's Guild v Russell Williams case at the House of Lords. Clients range from engineering to textiles and computers.

Kuit Steinart Levy (see firm details p.1025) Headed by Colin Hoffman, the firm handles most aspects of IP, including, on the non-contentious side, advising sports personalities on their merchandising agreements. A notable upturn in the firm's contentious work is best exemplified by a successful action to enforce the change of name of a Manchester restaurant that had used the brand name of an international designer clothing range without consent. The firm also advised SSL International on a number of brand acquisitions, including the 'Hibi' range of products. **Clients:** SSL International; Wisdom Toothbrushes; sports personalities.

Lawson Coppock & Hart Handling most areas of IP, notably trademark infringement and licensing, this small team maintains a discreet, but respected, regional profile. **Clients:** Include textile companies and mail order companies.

Taylors Known for its long-standing connections with the textile industry, this ten-year old firm is headed by Tony Catterall, and represented the Designer's Guild on a successful House of Lords appeal against Russell Williams Textiles, a case about design protection in the home furnishings industry. **Clients:** The Tensar Group; Graham & Brown; Beckers; Designer's Guild; Ultraframe.

NORTH EAST

	INTELLECTUAL PROPERTY • North East	Ptnrs	Assts
1	**Addleshaw Booth & Co** Leeds	4	20
2	**DLA** Leeds, Sheffield	n/a	n/a
	Pinsent Curtis Biddle Leeds	2	15
3	**Eversheds** Leeds	3	15
	Hammond Suddards Edge Leeds	2	9
	Walker Morris Leeds	2	4
4	**Irwin Mitchell** Leeds	2	4
	Lupton Fawcett Leeds	1	4
5	**Dickinson Dees** Newcastle upon Tyne	2	4

	LEADING INDIVIDUALS	
1	**KEMPNER Richard** Addleshaw Booth & Co	
2	**CHANDLER Stephen** Pinsent Curtis Biddle	**LOVE James** Irwin Mitchell
	TULLEY Christopher DLA	
3	**CANTRILL Patrick** Walker Morris	**CLAY Andrew** Hammond Suddards Edge
	JACKSON Stuart Addleshaw Booth & Co	**SYKES John** Lupton Fawcett

This book is the product of 6,552 1/2-hour interviews. See p.7 for BMRB audit.

Within each band, firms are listed alphabetically. *See individuals' profiles p.500*

Addleshaw Booth & Co (see firm details p.853) Peers admire the firm's Leeds office for its "*strength in depth and versatility,*" and acknowledge it to be "*the region's outstanding practice.*" The "*technically skilled*" **Richard Kempner** (see p.506) is also rated for his "*commercial sense*" and is said to be "*in a league of his own.*" **Stuart Jackson** (see p.505) is also respected as a "*key member of the team.*" The firm acted for the Consortium of Italian Lambrusco Wine Growers in passing off proceedings against Halewood International's 'Lambrini'. It also advised Uponor against Glynwed in patent revocation proceedings, and Granada Media in the choice of a new TV/Internet site health channel. Known for its "*fabulous client base,*" the firm has been involved in several domain name disputes for leading corporate entities. **Clients:** Airtours; Asda; Argos; Bisto; Ferrari; Halifax Building Society.

DLA Although the firm has disposed of its patent filing practice, the firm still has a reputation for general IP work. **Christopher Tulley** is the leading name here.

Pinsent Curtis Biddle (see firm details p.1098) Exclusive advisors on IP to two Government Departments, this "*focused IP team*" continues to expand, and is acknowledged to be "*mopping up a lot of the local business.*" **Stephen Chandler** (see p.502) is "*quite an operator,*" has "*wonderful commercial flair*" and heads a team that includes three registered trademark attorneys. The firm acted for PACE technology on patent litigation relating to digital television, and acted on an appeal against a claim for unregistered design right infringement and breach of copyright, relating to beer bottle design. **Clients:** Covance; PACE; Smith & Nephew; Genzyme.

Eversheds (see firm details p.952) The team has a strong niche in internet-related matters, specifically domain names, advising in relation to new and existing names, infringement and disputes. Transactional work springs from the firm's "*fantastic client base*" that includes a host of sports clients. The firm undertakes contractual, sponsorship and licensing agreements for media clients, and was recently instructed by the Vice-President of the Royal National Rose Society to defend the use of 13 domain names in UDRP proceedings brought by the Diana, Princess of Wales Memorial Fund. **Clients:** Skipton Building Society; Vice President of the Royal National Rose Society.

Hammond Suddards Edge (see firm details p.984) The firm continues to have a strong reputation for its contentious work, notably in the field of patent litigation. Top litigator **Andrew Clay** (see p.502) "*doesn't miss a trick,*" and recently acted on a patent title dispute, representing Automotive Products, a motor-car component manufacturer based in Leamington. **Clients:** Yorkshire Electricity; Halifax; Associated Octel; Depuy International.

Walker Morris (see firm details p.1171) This "*sound firm*" boast a trademarks unit that still files the greatest number of trademarks of any law firm outside London. Rivals respect leading light **Patrick Cantrill** (see p.502) as an "*original thinker.*" The firm has acted on numerous trademark infringements and passing off cases, including the successful defence of Selfridges against a South African retailer. **Clients:** Red Hat; Static; BT Cellnet; Symphony Group.

Irwin Mitchell (see firm details p.1009) "*Focusing well,*" the firm has recently acted on a number of high profile contentious cases. The "*technically proficient*" and "*hugely underrated*" **James Love** (see p.506) moves up in the tables, and represented the world's largest manufacturer of skate blades on a domain name dispute. The team advised Gripple in obtaining an injunction in a Californian wine industry dispute involving patent and trademark infringement. **Clients:** HD Sports; Gripple; Royal Armouries; Sheffield Wednesday FC.

Lupton Fawcett Continuing to service a number of medium-sized businesses in the pharmaceutical, manufacturing and computer sectors, the team is headed by the "*pioneering*" **John Sykes** (see p.510), regarded as "*an IP doyen of the North.*" The team advised Federal Mogul on the disposal of a portfolio of around 50 patents. **Clients:** Tyco Industries; Early Learning Centre; PWS Distribution.

Dickinson Dees (see firm details p.941) Continuing to grow in the sector, the firm is the only Newcastle-based practice with a serious IP reputation. Mark Pearce and the team acted on the IP audit of a soft drinks manufacturer and the related aspects of its sale to Britvic. The firm also acted on the settlement of patent and confidential information litigation that included a clinical waste disposal business and connected licensing agreements. **Clients:** Orchid Drinks; Eurocare Environmental Services; Formica.

SCOTLAND

INTELLECTUAL PROPERTY • Scotland	Ptnrs	Assts
1 **Maclay Murray & Spens** Glasgow	4	16
McGrigor Donald Edinburgh	3	10
2 **MacRoberts** Glasgow	1	6
3 **Dundas & Wilson CS** Glasgow	3	n/a
Shepherd & Wedderburn WS Edinburgh, Glasgow	4	3
4 **Burness** Edinburgh, Glasgow	3	3

LEADING INDIVIDUALS
1 **MACPHERSON Shonaig** McGrigor Donald
NICOLSON Fiona Maclay Murray & Spens
2 **FLINT David** MacRoberts
3 **GRASSIE Gill** Maclay Murray & Spens
McLEAN James Burness
SAUNDERS James Shepherd & Wedderburn WS

This book is the product of 6,552 1/2-hour interviews. See p.7 for BMRB audit.
Within each band, firms are listed alphabetically. *See individuals' profiles p.500*

Maclay Murray & Spens (see firm details p.1047) "*Immensely able firm,*" active in both contentious and non-contentious IP, which is revered for its "*academic and thorough excellence.*" **Fiona Nicolson** (see p.508)provides the "*substance behind the publicity*" and is especially applauded for her licensing work. **Gill Grassie** (see p.504) also maintains her share of market support. The firm continues to advise animal healthcare business Vericore on key commercial contracts, including product licensing, manufacturing, supply and distribution. It acted for a UK company in the establishment of a biotechnology spin-off from a Greek Institute and all accompanying IP matters, and advised BAE on the drafting of its collaboration with the Swedish airline SAS regarding the sharing of technology and data. **Clients:** Scottish Widows; Davidoff; Kodak; GlaxoSmithKline.

McGrigor Donald (see firm details p.1062) A part of the firm's technology group, the IP practice is rated by competitors and clients as "*strong all-round.*" Head of technology **Shonaig Macpherson** (see p.507) is "*a technical whiz*" and is consistently prominent on "*high quality, interesting work.*" The firm offers core expertise in internet software and biosciences, and acted for Scotland's leading technology investor 3i and Elixent in acquisition of rights to intellectual property from Hewlett-Packard, the company's first ever UK spin-out. **Clients:** Scottish Biomedical; Viragen (Scotland); 3i; Ardana Biosciences.

MacRoberts (see firm details p.1048) Offering "*sound IP advice*" with a strong IT flavour, the team's caseload is weighted towards the non-contentious side. This includes copyright, trademarks and patents work. Head of the team **David Flint** (see p.447) is respected for his "*knowledge and all-round ability.*" The firm advised a sports company in relation to general IP matters, and has handled trademarks for motor sales and software companies. **Clients:** Dundee and Strathclyde Universities; Scottish Council for Educational Technology; biotechnology companies.

Dundas & Wilson CS (see firm details p.947) Rated for its strong niche in university spin-off work, the firm recently suffered the departure of leading name Lorne Byatt to an in-house position at Voxar. Now headed by Laurence Ward, the team has a strong life sciences clientele, and advised Intense Photonics on the IP aspects of its establishment and funding. **Clients:** University of Glasgow; Geron Bio-Med; Buck Chemicals (UK); Intense Photonics; Ardana Bioscience.

Shepherd & Wedderburn WS (see firm details p.1126) Seen to be "*steadily building up its numbers,*" the firm has acknowledged expertise in the pharmaceuticals sector. **James Saunders** (see p.509) is characterised as "*a nice guy with a commercial mind.*" The firm completed a review of the IP portfolio of Strakan Group, a pharmaceutical company specialising in skin and bone disease therapies. This involved the review of documentation covering a number of jurisdictions. **Clients:** Flexcon; Scottish & Newcastle; The Royal College of Surgeons.

Burness (see firm details p.903) Perceived by the market as a "*steady*" firm, particularly in the non-contentious field, it is headed by **James McLean** (see p.507). He is rated as an "*outstanding academic lawyer,*" and clients appreciate his "*amazing longevity in the business.*" The firm acted on the sale of Spider Software Systems to Artesyn Technologies – a transaction requiring extensive due diligence, and valued at more than £44 million. **Clients:** Diagnostic Instruments; Harris Tweed Authority; Scottish Football Association; Standard Life.

LEADERS IN INTELLECTUAL PROPERTY

ANDERSON, Robert
Lovells, London (020) 7296 2000
robert.anderson@lovells.com
Specialisation: Intellectual property and technology. Patent litigation – he has particular experience of cases with a chemical, pharmaceutical and biotechnological content. Designs, copyright, trade secrets and trade marks. R&D agreements and acquisitions and joint ventures involving technology based businesses. Also other matters involving computers, pharmaceuticals, biotechnology or otherwise having a high technology content. Lectures on patent litigation for the Bristol University IP Diploma.
Prof. Memberships: AIPPI; Associate Member Chartered Institute of Patent Agents; Solicitors European Group; City of London Law Society Intellectual Property sub-committee; IPLA.
Career: BSc Edinburgh (Natural Sciences), 1968. Articled *Bristows Cooke and Carpmael*, admitted 1972; joined *Lovells* 1974; partner 1978; IP practice area leader.

ASPINALL, Tim
DMH, Brighton (01273) 744319
tim.aspinall@dmh.co.uk
See under Litigation, p.564

ASSIM, Gary
Shoosmiths, Northampton (01908) 488 411
gary.assim@shoosmiths.co.uk
Specialisation: Partner specialising in intellectual property, practice covers trade mark and copyright infringement with particular expertise in parallel importing and anti-counterfeiting; acted on the case of Mackie Designs Inc v Behringer and Others 1999 RPC 717 their leading case on copyright/design rights in electronic circuit boards and S.51 CDPA 1988; acts for retailers and brand owners alike in a variety of business sectors including fashion, automotive and technology.
Prof. Memberships: Institute of Directors; International Trade Mark Association; British Association for Sport and Law; Director and Board Member of Milton Keynes Chamber of Commerce; Board Member of Milton Keynes Economic Partnership.
Career: Trained *Travers Smith Braithwaite*; qualified 1990; joined *Shoosmiths* 1997; partner *Shoosmiths* 1998
Publications: Joint author of 'Enforcement of US judgements in England: an Update, International Commercial Litigation (1996)'; Letters Rogatory: an English Legal Perspective, New York Law Journal

(1996); joint author of four articles on 'Copyright Made Simple' in 'The Bookseller' (1997); one of the first lawyers to be quoted in the press (The Times, Drapers Record) on the ECJ Opinion in Silhouette v Hartlauer regarding parallel importing and rights of trade mark owners (1998).
Personal: Durham University (1987 BA Hons Law); Chester College of Law 1988; Born 1961; resides Bedfordshire; married with two children; leisure interests include rugby, cricket and walking own dogs.

BARKER, William
Martineau Johnson, Birmingham (0121) 678 1632
william.barker@martjohn.com
Specialisation: Senior partner, head of intellectual property department. Areas of practice include contentious and non-contentious intellectual property and computer law. Experienced in anti-counterfeiting and has particular experience of trademarks, copyright and patents. Has written various articles on the protection and enforcement of intellectual property rights and has addressed seminars in Birmingham, Singapore, Sydney, Seattle, Munich and Cincinatti. Experienced in the application and execution of Anton Piller Orders and is on the Birmingham Law Society list of supervising solicitors.
Prof. Memberships: Anti-counterfeiting Group; Licensing Executives Society; TIPLO (the Intellectual Property Lawyers Organisation).
Career: Articled: *Laces & Co*, Liverpool. Qualified 1986; assistant solicitor, *Pinsent & Co* 1986-90; associate, 1990-91; partner, *Martineau Johnson* 1992.
Personal: Born 4 January 1962. Educated at Merchant Taylors School, Crosby, Liverpool. BSc in Law and Mathematics. Leisure interests include tennis, member Edgbaston Priory LTC and golf. Member Moor Hall Golf Club.

BARRON, David
Wragge & Co, Birmingham (0870) 903 1000

BARRY, Robert
Allen & Overy, London (020) 7330 3874
robert.barry@allenovery.com
Specialisation: Considerable experience of the full range of intellectual property litigation with a particular emphasis on patents and trade marks. Acted in many major patent disputes in both High Court and Patents County Court, as well as oppositions in the European Patent Office, covering a number of different technologies and industry sectors including pharmaceutical, electronic, chemical and bioscience industries.
Prof. Memberships: Royal Pharmaceutical Society of Great Britain; International Bar Association; Associate member of the Chartered Institute of Patent Agents; The International Association for the Protection of Industrial Property; INTA; American Intellectual Property Association; AIPLA.
Career: Associate *Bird & Bird* (1985), partner (1991); partner *Eversheds* (1997), head of intellectual property litigation North; partner *Allen & Overy* (2000).
Personal: Kings College Chelsea (B Pharmacy). City University (Dip Law). Called to the Bar 1983. Resides London. Leisure interests include running, sailing, golf and football; season ticket holder at Middlesborough Football Club.

BENTHAM, Paul
Addleshaw Booth & Co, Manchester
(0161) 934 6337
pjbe@addleshaw-booth.co.uk
Specialisation: Partner in Intellectual Property Department, Commercial Group specialising in Intellectual property and technology including patents, trade marks, passing off, copyright and designs, trade secrets and confidential information and related areas of competition law. Particular expertise in information technology contracts including e-commerce, the acquisition of computer systems, the licensing of computer software and databases, and outsourcing agreements. Also has considerable experience in technology licensing and advising on intellectual property matters in respect of corporate acquisitions and joint ventures.
Prof. Memberships: Licensing Executives Society, Solicitors European Group and The Society for Computers and Law.
Career: Qualified in 1989 and became a partner in 1995.
Personal: Educated at the University of Leicester (1984-87), (LL.B Hons, Law with French) Universite de Strasbourg (Diplome d'Etudes juridiques francaises). Leisure interests include foreign travel and supporting Manchester United.

BOARDMAN, Richard
Halliwell Landau, Manchester (0161) 831 2905 / (0467) 790 981
rboardman@halliwells.co.uk
Specialisation: Partner in the intellectual property and information technology department. Has extensive experience of managing large scale, often international, commercial and dispute related IP & IT projects and related anti-trust work. Helps clients to design and implement risk managed solutions to commercial issues or opportunities where IP & IT issues are significant. Projects have included multi-jurisdictional brand litigation (with strategy facilitation and the construction of commercial risk models), commercial patent based technology exploitation within the Indian sub-continent, risk managed software delivery into a life-critical environment and global music collecting society comparative benchmarking to balance revenue maximisation with exploitation control. Increasingly works with clients operating within the internet and e-commerce environments.
Prof. Memberships: The Chartered Institute of Patents Agents (Associate), The Society for Computers and the Law, The Licensing Executives Society, The British Interactive Multimedia Association, The Law Society and The International Association of Entertainment Lawyers.
Career: Qualified in 1989. Employed as trainee solicitor, assistant and associate at *Simpson Curtis* 1987-1994. Joined *Garrett & Co* in 1994. Appointed partner in 1995. *Halliwell Landau* 1998 as partner.

BOOY, Anna
Willoughby & Partners, Oxford (01865) 791 990
anna@iprights.com
Specialisation: Consultant in intellectual property department. All transactional intellectual property work especially in the industry areas of computer software, the internet, multimedia, publishing, music and entertainment, the fine arts, advertising and brand management. She is a founding member of the Working Group on Copyright for Museums and Galleries and is the only privately practising lawyer in the Copyright User Group advising HMSO on the liberalisation of Crown Copyright.
Prof. Memberships: SCL, IPI, SEG.
Career: Qualified both UK and Australia.
Personal: Born 19 June 1962. Educated at the University of Queensland (BA, LLB Hons) and University College, London. (LLM in Intellectual Property).

BRAITHWAITE, Andrew
Osborne Clarke, Bristol (0117) 917 3000

BRIFFA, Margaret
Briffa, London (020) 7288 6003

BROWN, David
Bristows, London (020) 7400 8000
david.brown@bristows.com
Specialisation: Partner in intellectual property department. Practice covers the full range of intellectual property and includes disputes in relation to patents, copyright, design rights, trade secrets and antitrust issues. Co-ordinates multi-forum disputes. Acts for international companies in the manufacturing, pharmaceutical, electronic and engineering industries. Had conduct of major cases such as Pilkington v. PPG and Glaxo v. Generics. Recent cases include Electrolux v. Dyson, Texas Instruments v. Hyundai, and Novartis v. AHP.
Prof. Memberships: Member Royal Corps of Naval Constructors 1960-1966.
Career: Joined *Bristows* 1966. Qualified as Solicitor in 1973; Partner from 1974; Member of Editorial Board of Patent World.
Personal: Born 8 May 1942. Educated at Royal High School Edinburgh, Royal Naval Engineering College Plymouth and Royal Naval College Greenwich (Honours Degree in Naval Architecture). Interests include the Turf.

BROWN, Jeremy
Linklaters, London (020) 7456 5748
jeremy.brown@linklaters.com
Specialisation: Specialist in intellectual property and technology related matters. Degrees in chemical engineering and law. Long experience in commercial and litigious matters involving intellectual property rights and technology related issues. Particular knowledge of, and experience with, issues affecting the healthcare, chemical, computer and luxury goods industries. Main areas of practice include patent, copyright, trademarks and trade secrets litigation; licensing of intellectual property rights and technology transfer generally including EC and UK anti-trust and competition law considerations; pharmaceutical law; computer law. Typical matters include litigating patents, trade marks, copyrights and other intellectual property rights and disputes concerning technology agreements in English courts and co-ordinating parallel multijurisdictional litigation; advising on technology licensing, research and development, marketing and distribution arrangements (including compliance with EC competition law rules); and responsibility for intellectual property, technology and regulatory issues in corporate reorganisations and transactions.
Prof. Memberships: Licensing Executives Society (LES); President of LES International 1995/96 and Member of Executive Committee 1995-97. Member of Council 1988-89 and past President of LES Britain and Ireland 1991-92. Member of Council of AIPPI United Kingdom 1989 to date; UK delegate to Tokyo 1992, Montreal 1995, Rio 1998, Congresses and Copenhagen 1994, Vienna (1997) and Sorrento (2000) Exco meetings. Chartered Institute of Patent Agents (Associate Member), South African Institute

of Intellectual Property (Fellow), American Bar Association, American Intellectual Property Law Association.
Career: 1975 University of South Africa – Bachelor of Law (B.Juris); 1970 University of Natal, South Africa – MSc in Chemical Engineering. Head of intellectual property and technology department, *Linklaters* and Co-Head of intellectual property practice group, *Linklaters & Alliance.* Partner, *Linklaters* 1982 to date. Assistant solicitor, *Linklaters* 1978-82. Spoor & Fisher, Patent Attorneys, South Africa 1971-78.

BROWN, Richard

Laytons, Bristol (0117) 930 9500
richard.brown@laytons.com
Specialisation: Partner in Company and Commercial Department. Work includes mergers and acquisitions, corporate finance (including banking and venture capital), pensions, employment, employee incentive schemes, commercial contracts, agency and distribution, and export law. Also handles intellectual property work, including computers, patents, trade marks, design rights copyright, confidential information and licensing of intellectual property rights, covering both contentious and non-contentious work.
Prof. Memberships: Consular agent for France; Representative of Law Society's European Group for the South West of England.
Career: Qualified in 1976. Worked at *Norton Rose* 1974-79, BAT Industries 1979-84 and joined *Laytons* in 1984, becoming a partner in 1986.
Publications: Author of several articles in local business magazines.

CANTRILL, Patrick

Walker Morris, Leeds (0113) 283 2500
Specialisation: Practice covers the full range of contentious and non-contentious intellectual property and information technology work including advice on the securitisation and the management of IP and e-commerce issues. Case load relates to a broad client base. Has acted in a number of High Court patent and other infringement disputes as well as on high profile IT procurement and technology licensing deals. Has lectured extensively in the UK and abroad on IT, e-commerce and IP issues.
Prof. Memberships: Chairman of the Parallel Imports Committee of International Trademark Association.
Career: Qualified 1984. Also admitted in Hong Kong in 1986. Joined *Walker Morris* as a partner and head of the intellectual property group in 1992.

CARBONI, Anna

Linklaters, London (020) 7456 5810
anna.carboni@linklaters.com
Specialisation: Specialist in contentious and non-contentious intellectual property and information technology work with particular expertise in trade marks, passing off and anti-counterfeiting litigation and breach of confidence matters. Contentious intellectual property work includes co-ordinating major anti-counterfeiting programmes (Microsoft, Gucci); obtaining Anton Piller and Mareva injunctions and enforcement of these through contempt proceedings; representing brand owners in preventing parallel imports of their products; conducting litigation involving computer misuse, data protection and breach of confidence allegations (Virgin v British Airways); appearing as advocate in Trade Mark Registry proceedings and interlocutory hearings in the High Court. Also includes trade mark portfolio management and brands: advising on (re)branding exercises including searches on worldwide availability and registrability of trade marks, and associated copyright issues (British Airways); auditing and maintaining trade mark portfolios (Forte, Centrica); general filing and prosecution work (3M, Forte, Gucci). Also includes commercial IP/IT work: outsourcing agreements (British Airways – ground fleet services, engineering IT; joint ventures (SB/Gist brocades); privatisations (BR/OPRAF).
Prof. Memberships: Member and active participant in the International Trade Marks Association, Anti-Counterfeiting Committee Member, Computer Law Group, Anti-Counterfeiting Group, AIPPI and Ligue Internationale du Droit de la Concurrence (Committee Member of the Bristish Group), Associate Member of the Chartered Institute of Patent Agents, English Board Member of the Editorial Board of European Trade Mark Reports (ETMR). Advocacy: qualified to appear in all civil proceedings in the English courts.
Career: 1984-86 College of Law, Lancaster Gate, Common Professional Examination and Law Society Finals; 1981-84, Girton College, Cambridge, Natural Sciences BA (converted to MA, Cantab.). 1996 to date partner *Linklaters;* 1995 head/co-head of the trade mark and design filing and prosecution practice, *Linklaters;* 1989 secondment to Italian intellectual property firm, *Jacobacci & Perani*; 1988-96 assistant solicitor, *Linklaters;* 1986-88 articled clerk, *Linklaters.*

CHALKLEY, Simon

Gouldens, London (020) 7583 7777
src@gouldens.com
Specialisation: Principally in non-contentious intellectual property advising on the protection, maintenance and commercial exploitation of IP rights. Clients cover a wide spectrum of businesses including brand, technology and e-commerce companies. Substantial experience of drafting and negotiating a broad range of IP and IT contracts including licensing, R&D and rights acquisition agreements.
Prof. Memberships: Licensing Executives Society; Intellectual Property Lawyers's Association; AIPPI; ITMA.
Career: Trained with *Gouldens*, qualified in 1991 and appointed partner in 1998.

CHANDLER, Stephen

Pinsent Curtis Biddle, Leeds (0113) 244 5000
stephen.chandler@pinsents.com
Specialisation: Group head of commerce, trade, technology and media. Intellectual property, including protection, exploitation and enforcement of patents, trade marks, copyrights, design rights and trade secrets, as well as consultancy in the management of IP. Acted in Thomson Multi-media v Pace Microtechnology (digital TV patent infringement); 3M v NAMSA (patent infringement); PLM v Redfearn; for Smith & Nephew plc in healthcare patent matters; for Sema Schlumberger; worked for the NHS in developing a framework for the management of its intellectual property; a number of NHS Hospital Trusts.
Career: Qualified in 1980. Partner in 1985.
Personal: Born 1955. Educated St John's College, Cambridge 1974-77.

CLAY, Andrew J

Hammond Suddards Edge, Leeds (0113) 284 7000
andrew.clay@hammondse.com
Specialisation: Partner specialising in intellectual property litigation and the commercial exploitation of intellectual property. Particular specialisation in heavyweight patent, copyright and breach of confidence litigation. Cases include Re GEC's Patent (patent infringement, breach of confidency, copyright and design right infringement); Single Buoy Engineering Inc v Brown Borthers Limited & Another (patent infringement); R vMaff (ex p ISK Biosciences) – (a case on data protection in relation to pesticide regulatory data); Tensar Inc v Netlon Limited (a major intellectual property infringement); Gadget Shop plc v The Bug.Com Limited (copyright infringement); Ian McGuire and Fleet (Line Markers) Limited v Supaturf (patent infringement); SGB Sevices plc v Birchwood Products Limited (design right infringement); Parsons v Parsons (passing-off and copyright infringement); LUK Leamington Limited v Whitnash plc and Automotive Products (USA) Inc (patent entitlement action); Fromm Family Foods Inc v Window International (passing-off and copyright infringement); Halifax plc v Sutcliffe (trade mark infringement and passing-off in relation to domain names); efax.com v Mark Oglesby (trade mark infringement and passing-off in relation to a domain name); Dennis Degler v M & J Polymers Limited (breach of confidence); Pharmacia & Upjohn AB v Bision Pharmaceuticals Limited (rectification of the Trade Marks Register); Mul-T-Lock Limited v Mul-T-Lock (UK) limited and Wishside (DFL) Limited (patent infringement); Sunderland Football Club v Sutcliffe (trade mark infringement and passing-off relating to a domain name); Statestrong Limited v Sainsbury plc (trade mark infringement and passing-off); Meltog limited v Prodec Precision Manufacturing Co Limited (trade mark infringement relating to a domain name); The English Pewter Company v Fine Art Pewter Design Limited (design right and copyright infringement); Tenneco Packaging (Caerphilly) and Tenneco Packaging Limited v Linpac Plastics Limited (copyright infringement and design right infringement); Caldwell Investments plc and Mothercare (UK Limited (patent infringement); HH Calmon & Co Limited v Kalpac UK Limited (breach of confidency and copyright infringement).
Prof. Memberships: Chartered Institute of Patent Agents, Institute of Trade mark Agents, Solicitors' European Group, Licensing Executive Society, Society for Computers and Law, member of anti-counterfeiting group.
Career: Harrogate Grammar School; St Andrew's University (1st Class Honours BSc degree); Law School in Leeds; Bristol University (Diploma in Intellectual Property); Certificates in EU Competition Law, Open University (Certificate in Analogue and Digital Electronics). *Herbert Smith* 1989-1992. 1992-date *Hammond Suddards.* Partner 1997.
Publications: Patent – Amendments to Particulars of Objections – see V Scott – Paine Orders EIPR 1997, 19 (2), 90-93; Threatening Third Parties – How Far Can You Go?, 'The CIPA Journal' April/May 2001.
Personal: Resides in Harrogate. Hobbies include cinema, theatre, cycling and reading.

COHEN, Larry
McDermott, Will & Emery, London (020) 7577 6909
lcohen@europe.mwe.com
Specialisation: Partner – Intellectual Property Unit. Contentious and non-contentious intellectual property matters including patents, trademarks, copyright, design right and trade secrets. Also deals with regulatory law, particularly in the area of agrochemicals and medicines and genetically modified organisms. Acted in Chiron v. Murex (client), Harrods Limited (client) v. Harrods (Buenos Aires) Limited, GEC v. FKI (client), Coin Controls (client) v. Suzo and Philips Electronics v. Ingman (client); R v DETR ex p Watson (Adventa Seeds intervening-client).
Prof. Memberships: CIPA, ITMA, INTA, IBA, Law Society.
Career: Qualified 1976. Assistant Solicitor with *Bristows Cooke & Carpmael* from 1976, and became a Partner in 1981. Joined *Hammond Suddards* in 1992. Joined *McDermott, Will & Emery* in 2000 and is currently Head of Contentious Intellectual Property.
Publications: Author of 'World Litigation Law and Practice: Unit B1 England and Wales' (1986) and CIPA/ ITMA Trademarks Handbook section on Civil Litigation (1992). Contributor of numerous articles to a variety of specialist publications on intellectual property topics and regular conference speaker.
Personal: Born 12th September 1951. Attended Emmanuel College, Cambridge 1970-73. Leisure pursuits include tennis, cycling and skiing. Lives in Radlett, Hertfordshire.

COOK, Trevor
Bird & Bird, London (020) 7415 6000
Specialisation: Partner in intellectual property department. Main areas of practice are litigation, transactional and advisory work in relation to patents, copyright, other intellectual property rights and associated regulatory law issues, particularly in the information technology and pharmaceutical/biosciences sectors.
Prof. Memberships: Treasurer of the International Association for the Protection of Industrial Property (AIPPI) (UK Group), member of Licensing Executives Society, associate member of Chartered Institute of Patent Agents, Secretary of British Copyright Council Working Group on Copyright & Technology.
Career: Qualified in 1977. Joined *Bird & Bird* in 1974, became a partner in 1981.
Publications: Contributor to 'Information Technology and the Law', 'CIPA Guide to Patents Act' and 'European Patents Handbook', 'Database Law'; co-author of 'Pharmaceuticals Biotechnology and the Law' and 'Practical Intellectual Property Precedents'; author of 'The Protection of Regulatory Data'.
Personal: Born 1951. Attended Southampton University (BSc Chemistry, 1973).

COOKE, Adam
Wragge & Co, London (020) 7242 5866

DANILUNAS, Marija
Hammond Suddards Edge, London (020) 7655 1000
marija.danilunas@hammondse.com
Specialisation: Partner and national head of intellectual property. Specialises in developing IP strategies for multinational corporations using litigation and other commercial tools to enforce patents and trademarks and other IP rights. Marija has considerable hands on experience of foreign IP litigation and performs and active supervisory role resulting in beneficial costs savings to clients. Experience in IP/competition law issues for pharmaceuticals and medical related companies, as well as general industry.
Prof. Memberships: INTA; CIPA; TIPLO; PTIC; ECTA; BELLA; Law Society of UK and Wales; Law Society of Upper Canada; Wadham College Law Society secretary/treasurer.
Career: Dually qualified UK solicitor 1989; Canadian barrister (10 years); part-time deputy judge Ontario; IP unit of *Bird & Bird* 1986-94; *Hammond Suddards Edge*, August 1994; partner *Hammond Suddards Edge*, November 1995.
Personal: Resides in London. Enjoys sailing.

DAVIES, Isabel
Eversheds, London (020) 7919 4555
daviesi@eversheds.com
Specialisation: Partner and head of intellectual property at *Eversheds* London. Head of *Eversheds* national intellectual property group. Work includes patents, trademarks, copyright, designs, competition and EC law. Cases have included Jif, Boston Scientific v Palmaz 1998, Prince Internet Litigation 1998, Tommy Hilfiger v Tesco 1998 and Elvis TM appeal (CA) 1999, Denny v Instance (CA 2001), Unilever v American Housewares Inc (Oxo) and Teleworks Ltd v Telework Group plc 2001.
Prof. Memberships: ITMA, CIPA, INTA, ACG. Member of Intellectual Property Sub-committee of the Law Society.
Career: Qualified in 1976. Partner at *Wragge & Co*, 1979-85. Joined *Woodham Smith* (*Taylor Joynson Garratt*) as partner in 1986, then *Jaques & Lewis* (now *Eversheds*) in 1994.
Publications: Editor of Sweet and Maxwell's 'European Trade Mark Litigation Handbook'. Co-editor of *Eversheds* 'IPEye'. Legal Editor of 'Journal of Brand Management', Editorial Board of Trademark World and Country Correspondent for EIPR. Has spoken widely at conferences on IP issues, often taking the Chair.
Personal: Born 30th May 1952. Attended St Albans Girls' Grammar School, Leicester University and Guildford College of Law. Leisure interests include travel, theatre, squash, skiing, food and wine. Lives in Chelsea.

DELEMORE, Ceri
Edwards Geldard, Cardiff (029) 2023 8239
ceri.delemore@geldards.co.uk
Specialisation: Partner, head of intellectual property/information technology. All aspects of intellectual property and information technology law including transactional work, research and collaboration agreements, licensing, assignments, trade mark applications, IT procurement, FM and outsourcing contracts, bespoke software developments and IP and IT related litigation. Also handles media work.
Prof. Memberships: The Intellectual Property Lawyers Organisation. The Law Society's Solicitors' European Group. Society for Computers & The Law.
Career: Articled *Slaughter and May*, qualified 1986; *Slaughter and May* 1984-88; joined *Edwards Geldard* 1988: partner 1991.
Publications: Author of 'Copyright Explained' published by RIBA.
Personal: BA (Hons) English and French Law Class 1, University of Kent at Canterbury; Diplome de droit francais de l'université de Paris-Sud.

DRISCOLL, Helen
Martineau Johnson, Birmingham (0121) 678 1635
helen.driscoll@martjohn.com
Specialisation: Intellectual property specialist, principally dealing with contentious work. Particular expertise: trademark and passing off actions, design right and copyright actions, injunctions and contempt.
Prof. Memberships: AIPPI. Law Society's European Group.
Career: Articled *Eversheds*, qualified 1993, associate 1996, *Freeth Cartwright, Hunt Dickins* 1997; partner 1998. Education: University College, Cardiff; Leicester University.
Personal: Interests include choral singing, fast cars and languages.

ELLIS, Peter
Browne Jacobson, Nottingham (0115) 976 6000
pellis@brownej.co.uk
Specialisation: Practises in all aspects of Intellectual Property litigation and dispute resolution including patents, copyright and design rights (registered and unregistered), confidential information, passing off trade secrets; acting for computer software and hardware companies, telecommunications, engineering and clothing companies. In 1998 involved in the trademark for major fashion house, assisting/representation with clients in US patent litigation.
Prof. Memberships: TIPLO, LES, AIPPI.
Career: Qualified 1976. At *Wells & Hind* 1976-1980. *Browne Jacobson* 1981 to present (Partner from 1984).
Personal: Born 3.6.52. Interests include family, golf, cricket and sports generally. Lives in Nottingham.

FARRANT, Patrick
Eversheds, Cambridge (01223) 355 933
patrickfarrant@eversheds.com
Specialisation: A commercial lawyer specialising in the exploitation of intellectual property, in particular biotechnology related, and the interaction between IP and competition law. Head of national biosciences group.
Prof. Memberships: Solicitors European Group, AIPPI, AIJA, Licensing Executive Society, BIA.
Career: Trained with *Frere Cholmeley*; qualified in 1989; joined *Eversheds* in 1990; partner in 1995.
Personal: Three children; Swiss and British national; fluent French speaker.

FIELD, Sally
Bristows, London (020) 7400 8000
sally.field@bristows.com
Specialisation: Partner in intellectual property department. Intellectual property litigation. Work covers advising on full range of intellectual property including patents, trade marks, copyright, designs and confidential information. Cases include Allen & Hanbury's (Glaxo) v. Generics, IBM v. Phoenix and Kimberly-Clark v. Procter & Gamble.
Prof. Memberships: Law Society, Associate Member Chartered Institute of Patent Agents, Associate Member Institute of Trade Mark Agents.
Career: Articled with *Clifford Turner* 1979-81, then moved to *Bristows* in 1983. Became a Partner in 1987.
Publications: Writes articles for specialist periodicals. Regular speaker at intellectual property conferences and seminars.
Personal: Born 16th May 1957. Attended Durham University 1975-78. Leisure pursuits include golf, tennis and skiing. Lives in London.

FLINT, David
MacRoberts, Glasgow (0141) 332 9988
df@macroberts.co.uk
See under Information Technology, p.447

FREELAND, Rowan
Simmons & Simmons, London 020 7628 2020
rowan.freeland@simmons-simmons.com
Specialisation: Intellectual property litigation particularly patents and designs. Major cases include Rambus v Hyundai Electronics, Texas Instruments v Hyundai Electronics, Allied Colloids v American Cynamid, General Instrument v Intel, Southco v Dzus and Hallen v Brabantia. Also IT law. Commissioning editor, then editorial board member, 'Patent World'.
Prof. Memberships: AIPPI, AIPLA, TIPLO.
Career: Born 1956. Education Wellington, St Catherines College Oxford (BA 1978). Joined *Simmons & Simmons* 1980, qualified 1982, partner 1988.
Personal: Married with three daughters. Interests: Reading, gardening, opera.

GARE, Stephen
Rowe & Maw, London (020) 7782 8814
sgare@roweandmaw.co.uk
Specialisation: Handles all aspects of intellectual property and IT. He has been involved in numerous corporate and commercial transactions as well as having conducted major litigation in 25 years practising in this area. Experience includes acting in many media matters, particularly music-related matters for EMI, including its relationship with the The Beatles and other major record groups, publishing for Hodder Headline plc and advertising; heading up the team which represented Automated Wagering International Inc, the US company selected by The People's Lottery to provide the gaming system for the UK National Lottery; patent litigation covering a wide range of inventions ranging from PAL colour television systems to children's pop-up play tents; trade mark and passing off litigation, ranging from character merchandising to luxury goods; advising RTL Television on its agreement for broadcasting Formula One motor racing in Germany.
Prof. Memberships: Member of the City of London Solicitors' Company Intellectual Property Sub-Committee, the INTA ADR Committee, AIPPI and the Institute of Patentees and Inventors. He is also an Associate of the Chartered Institute of Patent Agents.
Career: Articled to *Rowe & Maw* 1974. Qualified *Rowe & Maw* 1976. Partner 1981. Founded and is Head of *Rowe & Maw's* IP/IT Group.

GAYTHWAITE, Miles
Bird & Bird, London (020) 7415 6000
Specialisation: Consultant to intellectual property group. Principal area of practice is patents, patent and know-how licensing, trade marks and copyright. Also pharmaceuticals and software. Important cases handled include L.B. Plastics v Swish; Holtite v Jost; Unilever v Gillette; Societe Francaise Hoechst v Allied Colloids Ltd; Kakkar v Ferring; BICC plc v Burndy Corporation; Amersham v Corning; Hässle v SmithKline Beecham, Cynamid and Knoll; Connaught Laboratories v SmithKline Beecham and Napro Biotherapeutics v Bristol Myers Squibb.
Prof. Memberships: Chartered Institute of Patent Agents, Licensing Executives Society, APRAM. Member of Chartered Institute of Arbitrators.
Career: Qualified as Chartered Patent Agent in 1972. Joined *Bird & Bird* in 1974. Partner 1978.
Personal: Born 1943. Educated at Glasgow University 1960-64 (BSc, Chemistry) and Cambridge University 1964-67 (PhD, Organic Chemistry). Lives in London and south-west France.

GIBBINS, David
Wragge & Co, London (020) 7242 5866

GRANT, Gregor
Wragge & Co, London (020) 7242 5866

GRASSIE, Gill
Maclay Murray & Spens, Edinburgh (0131) 226 5196
gg@maclaymurrayspens.co.uk
Specialisation: Contentious IP and technology litigation partner specialising in trademarks, internet and domain name disputes, patents, copyright and confidential information/trade secret disputes. Recent cases included House of Lords copyright appeal case – Redrow Homes v Bett; parallel imports trade marks case Davidoff/Joop v M&S Toiletries; first Scottish domain name case for Scottish Widows; multi-jurisdictional patent/trade secret case. Clients include Microsoft, Glaxo Smith Klein, ICI, BMW, Kymata Ltd, Iwerks, WL Gore & Associates.
Prof. Memberships: Law Society IP committee member; Law Society specialist accreditation in IP law; associate member of CIPA; member of TIPLO and INTA.
Career: Edinburgh University (LLB Hons 1984). Writer to the Signet. Worked for *Bristows* IP litigation department, London (1991-92) and *Drostes*, Munich (1992-93).
Publications: Scottish correspondent for CIPA guide. Member of editorial committee for Sweet & Maxwell 'European Trade Mark Reports' and 'European Copyright and Design Reports'; author of Scottish chapters of Sweet & Maxwell 'European Trade Mark Litigation Handbook' and of Monitor Press 'IT 2000 Handbook'.
Personal: Born 1963. Interests: running; skiing; scuba diving; travelling.

HARRINGTON, Alison
Garretts, Reading (0118) 949 0000
alison.harrington@glegal.com
See under E-commerce, p.295

HARRIS, Gordon
Wragge & Co, Birmingham (0870) 903 1000

HARRIS, Paul
Eversheds, London (020) 7919 4500
harrisp@eversheds.com
Specialisation: Partner *Eversheds* London Intellectual Property Group. Patents, trademarks, copyright, designs. Notable cases include Coloplast (1993); Wagamama v City Centre Restaurants (1995); Electrolux v Black & Decker (1996). Author of various IP articles; regular lecturer including Bristol University: IP Diploma course.
Prof. Memberships: ITMA; CIPA; INTA (Chair of the European Legislation Analysis Sub-committee); AIPPI; UNION; Royal Society of Chemistry; Chariman of the Whittington Committee of the City of London Law Society.
Career: Qualified in 1987. *Bristows Cooke & Carpmael*; *McKenna & Co* (1988-92); *Taylor Joynson Garrett* (1992-94); Eversheds formerly *Jaques & Lewis* (1994-), became Partner in 1995.
Personal: Born 17th May 1961; Keele University; Leisure interests include fitness; running; theatre; Italian wine. Lives in Westminster.

HARRISS, David
Bird & Bird, London (020) 7415 6000
Specialisation: Partner in the intellectual property department. Main area of practice is intellectual property litigation. Includes UK and international patent infringement litigation, trademark infringement, passing off, copyright infringement, design infringement and breach of confidence. Acted in Akzo/Du Pont, PLG/Ardon, BP/Hoechst Celanese, BP/Union Carbide and Exxon/Lubrizol.
Prof. Memberships: Chairman of Law Society IP Working Party; Chartered Institute of Patent Agents (Fellow).
Career: Qualified as Patent Agent 1969. Worked for *AA Thornton & Co* 1965-70, then *Langner Parry* from 1970-73 (Chartered Patent Agents). Joined *Bird & Bird* in 1973. Qualified as a solicitor 1977. Partner 1977. Senior partner 1993.
Publications: Member of Editorial Board of 'Patent World'; co-editor of 'International Intellectual Property Litigation'.
Personal: Born 1943. Educated Christ's College, Cambridge. Lives in Chobham, Surrey.

HART, Michael
Baker & McKenzie, London (020) 7919 1000
michael.hart@bakernet.com
Specialisation: Principal area of practice is contentious and non-contentious IP and IT Law. Work includes copyright, trade marks and passing off, patents and trade secrets, computer copyright disputes, broadcasting and media law. Also deals with government regulations and trade libel. Has represented various trade bodies in lobbying activities relating to UK and EU legislative proposals, including the copyright in the Information Society Directive. Has acted in numerous IP court actions representing companies such as Fila, McLaren, Seiko, Versace, Apple Computer and Sony.
Prof. Memberships: Anti-counterfeiting Group, AIPPI, Intellectual Property Lawyers Association.
Career: Qualified in 1983. With *Linklaters & Paines* 1983-87. Joined *Baker & McKenzie* in 1987 and became a partner in 1990.
Personal: Born 12th August 1959. Educated at City of London School 1970-77 and Exeter College, Oxford 1977-80. Leisure activities include theatre, cinema, horse racing and tennis. Lives in London.

HEAD-RAPSON, Niall
Martineau Johnson, Birmingham (0121) 678 1636
niall.head.rapson@martjohn.com
Specialisation: Partner, intellectual property. First patent case outside London, Elvis case at first instance.
Prof. Memberships: AIPPI, INTA, LES, AURIL.
Career: CPE/LSF Nottingham Law School; Kings College, London – Biotechnology BSc (Hons) 2:1; Diploma in intellectual property – Queen Mary's College, London; Articled and qualified *Gouldens. Freshfields; McKennas, Eversheds.*

HENRY, Michael
Buchanan Ingersoll, London (020) 7920 3700

HODGSON, Mark
Taylor Joynson Garrett, London (020) 7300 7000
mhodgson@tjg.co.uk
Specialisation: Partner in intellectual property department. Head of pharmaceutical and medical group. Specialises in patent litigation in the UK courts and in the European Patent Office. Also handles pharmaceutical, medical device and biotechnology matters, including regulatory issues, product liability, advertising, parallel importation and clinical trial contracts. Acted in respect of Smith Kline and French Laboratories Ltd (Cimetidine) Patents, Bonzel v Intervention, R v Licensing Authority ex p Smith Kline and French Laboratories Ltd Merck/SB v Primecrown, Smithkline Beecham v Norton/LEK, Eli Lilly & Co v Novo Nordisk, Biogen v Medeva and, most recently, on behalf of Lill Icos in their successful action to revoke Pfizer's UK patent for the use of sildenafil (Viagra) to treat impotence. Has written articles for legal and pharmaceutical journals and lectures extensively on matters such as EC medical device regulations, parallel importation and harmonisation of European patent litigation.
Prof. Memberships: Member Law Society; AIPPI; IBA; member of City of London Solicitors' Company (IP sub-committee) and secretary of Intellectual Property Lawyers Association.
Career: Qualified in 1983 whilst at *Woodham Smith* 1981-85. Joined *Simmons & Simmons* in 1985 where he became a partner in 1989. Joined *Taylor Joynson Garrett* in 1998.
Personal: Educated at Barnard Castle School 1969-77 and at Emmanuel College Cambridge 1977-80. Chester Law School 1981. Leisure interests include Newcastle United FC and chauffeuring his children to parties. Lives near Gamlingay, Cambs.

HUMPHREYS, Robert
Humphreys & Co, Bristol (0117) 929 2662
Specialisation: Senior partner in commercial department. Intellectual property, commercial and reinsurance.
Prof. Memberships: Law Society.
Career: Qualified 1981. With *Simmons & Simmons* 1979-85. Partner *Cartwrights* 1985-86. Co-founded *Humphreys & Co* 1986.
Personal: Born 1953. Educated Dr Morgan's School, Bridgwater and New College, Oxford. Leisure interests include cricket. Lives near Bristol.

INGLIS, Andrew
Olswang, London (020) 7208 8975
api@olswang.com
Specialisation: Partner specialising in intellectual property, particularly patents and trade marks. He also deals with copyright issues for media clients of the firms. Andrew heads *Olswang*'s intellectual property group which comprises over 20 lawyers. The practice spans substantial patent and trade mark practices (including patent and trade mark filing practices), as well as meeting the needs of the more traditional clients of the firm in the areas of media, IT and e-commerce. A substantial portion of Andrew's trade mark practice concerns online issues. He splits his time between litigation and deals with branding strategies, advertising and promotion. He acted for Dyson in their recent patent win against Hoover. Other important reported cases he has handled include British Coal Corporation v Glaverbel SA, R Bance & R Bance & Co Ltd's Licence of Right (copyright) Application, Mecklermedia v DC Congress, and Anheuser-Busch Ince v Budejovicky Budvar Navdoni Podnik (the most recent county appeal Budweiser trade mark decision).
Career: Originally qualified in Australia in 1981 where he practised before moving to England. After qualifying in England in 1990 he was a partner at *Nabarro Nathanson* from 1991-97, and has been a partner at *Olswang* since 1997. Active in contributing articles to publications such as the 'European Intellectual Property Review' and public speaking on intellectual property issues at various Hawksmere and IBC seminars.

IRVINE, James
Arnander Irvine & Zietman (Formerly Llewelyn Zietman), London (020) 7842 5400

JACKSON, Stuart
Addleshaw Booth & Co, Leeds (0113) 209 2391
sja@addleshaw-booth.co.uk
Specialisation: Both litigation and licensing in all areas of intellectual property, with a concentration on patents and other areas involving high technical or scientific content. As a Chartered Chemist who has worked as a scientist in the healthcare industry for many years, he specialises particularly in matters involving chemical and pharmaceutical patents. Recent matters include patent infringement and revocation actions: Upnor v Glenwed, concerning polythylene pipes, DSM v Trouw UK, concerning phytase produced by genetically modified microorganisms, and Nutrinova (Hoechst) v Scanchem, concerning alleged infringement of process patent by importing from China acesulphame-K synthetic sweetener. Acted for Sir Roger Penrose in copyright action against Kimberly Clark regarding use of embossing pattern on toilet paper. Also acted for Clayton Plant Protection as intervener in judicial review by Monsanto against decision by MAFF to approve generic glyphosate agricultural herbicide, including taking reference to ECJ, which found in Clayton's favour regarding interpretation of European Directive on pesticides.
Prof. Memberships: Law Society, Royal Society of Chemistry (C Chem, MRSC).
Career: Flavour chemist with *Brewing Research Foundation* (1975-1977). Project Manager in R & D for *Johnson & Johnson Patient Care Limited* (1997-1999). Joined *Addleshaw Booth & Co* in 1994 and qualified as a solicitor in 1996.
Publications: Named inventor on a number of patents. Has published many papers and articles on intellectual property topics, wound healing and chemistry of beer. The author of the chapter 'Parallel Imports into and within the European Union' in 'Intellectual Property in the Global Market Place' (1999).
Personal: BSc Hons (First Class) in chemistry, Imperial College (1969-72); MSc, Oxford University (1972-75). Leisure interests include cycling (racing and touring), running, fell-walking.

JONES, Gareth
Bevan Ashford, Bristol (0117) 975 1687
g.jones@bevanashford.co.uk
Specialisation: Technology transfer agreements, all aspects of IT procurement in public and private sectors including framework agreements, software licencing agreements, Private Finance Initiative funded transactions, and advice on national guidance issued by public sector bodies.
Prof. Memberships: Licensing Executives Society; Society for Computers and Law; The Intellectual Property Organisation.
Career: University College Wales, Aberystwyth – LLB (Hons). Qualified 1980. 1985-91, partner *Eversheds* Cardiff (formerly *Phillips & Buck*). 1991-date, partner – *Bevan Ashford.*
Personal: Golf, rugby, skiing.

JONES, Nigel
Linklaters, London (020) 7456 5804
nigel.jones@linklaters.com
Specialisation: Specialist in intellectual property and technology related matters, particularly in the pharmaceuticals field. Main areas of practice include IP aspects of corporate transactions and IPOS; drafting and negotiating technology agreements; IP litigation, including patent litigation (particularly in the biotech and general healthcare fields), breach of confidence actions and trade mark and copyright disputes.
Prof. Memberships: Fellow of the Chartered Institute of Arbitrators. Past member of Council of Licensing Executives Society, Britain and Ireland, and Past Chairman of its EC/Laws Committee. Past Chair, European Committee of LES International. Associate member of the Chartered Institute of Patent Agents. Foreign Affiliate Member of American Intellectual Property Law Association. Member of Association Française des Praticiens du Droit des Marques et des Modèles.
Career: Chairman of Linklaters' healthcare group. 1995 to date: Partner, *Linklaters*, intellectual property and technology departments; 1998-1995: Assistant solicitor, *Linklaters*; 1986-1988: Trainee solicitor, *Linklaters*. Oxford University, BA Hons (1st class) in Biochemistry.

JONES, Patricia
Hammond Suddards Edge, Manchester (0161) 830 5000
patricia.jones@hammondse.com
Specialisation: Contentious and non-contentious intellectual property, including patents, trade marks, passing off, copyright, designs and confidential information. Particular expertise in patent litigation and biotechnology.
Prof. Memberships: Licensing Executives Society.
Career: Qualified 1995. *Eversheds* (1993-96), *Wacks Caller* (1996-2000), joined *Hammond Suddards Edge* January 2000.
Personal: Strathclyde University – Applied Physics BSc (Hons) (1st class). Manchester University PhD – Structure of Proteins Using X-Rays. Interests include watching rugby union.

JONES, Stephen
Baker & McKenzie, London (020) 7919 1000
stephen.jones@bakernet.com
Specialisation: Partner specialising in intellectual property, in particular patents, trade marks and designs; involved in both contentious and non-contentious areas of practice with an emphasis on litigation and dispute resolution; qualified patent agent and registered trade mark agent as well as solicitor. Partner in charge of the London office Trade Marks Unit and member of the Pharmaceuticals/Healthcare and E-commerce practice groups.
Prof. Memberships: Chartered Institute of Patent Agents (fellow); Institute of Professional Representatives before the European Patent Office (EPI); Institute of Trade Mark Agents (ITMA); European

Communities Trademark Association (ECTA); Licensing Executives Society (LES); AIPPI (UK); International Trademark Association (INTA); Pharmaceutical Trade Marks Group; Competition Law Association; Royal Society of Chemistry (associate); Law Society.
Career: Began career at *Frank B Dehn & Co* 1978-1983; qualified 1981 as patent agent; IP department *Linklaters & Paines* 1983-1985, head of trade marks unit 1987-1993; patent department ICI Pharmaceuticals 1985-1987; partner, head of intellectual property *Boodle Hatfield* 1993-1995; *Allen & Overy* 1995-99; partner *Baker & McKenzie* 1999.
Publications: Editor CIPA Guide to Patents Acts.
Personal: Imperial College, London (1977 BSc Chemistry); University of London (external) (1990 LLB). Born 22 January 1956; married with three children.

JUDGE, Ian
Bristows, London (020) 7400 8000
ian.judge@bristows.com
Specialisation: Partner in intellectual property department. Ian is one of over 70 lawyers handling intellectual property matters in the firm together with 20 other intellectual property partners; David Brown, John Allcock, Philip Westmacott, Edward Nodder, Sally Field, Paul Walsh, Kevin Appleton, Alan Johnson, Pat Treacy, Tim Powell, Dr Penny Gilbert, Matthew Warren, David Wilkinson, Simon Ayrton, Christine Hore, Laura Anderson, Justin Watts, Andrew Lykiardopoulos, Ralph Cox and Alastair McCulloch. Work covers litigation and licensing of the full range of intellectual property, including patents, trade marks, copyright, designs and confidential information. Has had conduct of major patent cases such as Bristol-Myers ats Beecham and Du Pont v. Akzo (both H.L.), Monsento v Stauffer, Chiron v Organon Teknika and Chiron v Evans Medical. Speaker at seminars on specialist intellectual property topics.
Prof. Memberships: Law Society, Chartered Institute of Patent Agents (Associate Member), Chairman – Intellectual Property Lawyers Association, AIPPI, AIPLA.
Career: Joined *Bristows* 1964, qualified as a solicitor in 1967, became a partner in 1969. Head of intellectual property department 1992 to date.
Personal: Born 4th December 1941. Attended Cambridge University (BA Natural Sciences and Law 1963, MA 1967).

KAMSTRA, Gerry
Simmons & Simmons, London 020 7628 2020
gerry.kamstra@simmons-simmons.com
Specialisation: Partner in intellectual property department. Principal area of practice is intellectual property law, including financings, commercial transactions and litigation within the pharmaceutical and biotechnology industries. Clients include AstraZeneca, 3M, Bayer, Bristol-Myers Squibb, Guidant Corporation, Alizyme plc and Inhale Therapeutic Systems. Has written numerous articles and lectures widely.
Prof. Memberships: Member Intellectual Property Advisory Committee of BioIndustry Association and Associate Member of Chartered Institute of Patent Agents.
Career: Qualified in 1986. Joined *Simmons & Simmons* 1986 where he became a partner in 1992.
Personal: Born 13th May 1954. Educated at Hymers College, Hull, Keble College, Oxford (Psychology & Physiology), Leicester University (Ph.D in Neuroendocrinology) and Trent Polytechnic.

KARET, Ian
Linklaters, London (020) 7456 5800
ian.karet@linklaters.com
Specialisation: Specialist in IP and technology related matters, particularly in patents. Main areas of practice include IP aspects of major acquisitions and disposals, corporate fund raising and licensing (including drafting and reviewing patent, know-how, trade mark and software licences, both from the commercial and EC anti-trust viewpoints); drafting and negotiating IP licences, manufacturing agreements and distribution agreements and general advisory work. IP litigation, including patent litigation (biotech, pharmaceutical and chemicals), trade mark and copyright disputes and software exploitation.
Prof. Memberships: Deputy Reporter General of AIPPI. Fellow of the Chartered Institute of Arbitrators. Member of the Royal Society of Chemistry. Associate Member of the Chartered Institute of Patent Agents.
Career: 1997 to date: Partner, intellectual property and technology department, *Linklaters*; 1990-1997: Assistant solicitor, *Linklaters*; 1987-1989 Articled clerk, *Linklaters.* Oxford University, MA (Chemistry). Leo Baeck College, MA (Jewish Studies).

KEMPNER, Richard
Addleshaw Booth & Co, Leeds (0113) 209 2000
rak@addleshaw-booth.co.uk
Specialisation: Partner and joint head of intellectual property. Handles both disputes and transactions involving patents, copyright, trademarks, designs and confidential information. Voted the UK's Top Trade Marks Rising Star for 2000 by the 'Insider Guide to Brands and Trade Marks' and as being "very knowledgeable" and "bright, friendly and proactive". Clients include Asda, Airtours and Ferrari. Recent High Court reported cases include Stoddards v Ryalux (copyright), United Biscuits v Asda (TMs) and Nutrinova v Sanchez and in the ECJ R v Maff ex p Monsanto. Speaks and writes extensively on protection, licensing and enforcement.
Prof. Memberships: LES, INTA, CIPA, IPLA, ITMA.
Career: Joined the firm in 1990. Partner 1992.

LINDSEY, Michael
Morgan Cole, Cardiff (029) 2038 5385

LLEWELYN, David
White & Case, London (020) 7600 7300
Dllewelyn@whitecase.com
Specialisation: Partner in *White & Case's* London office specialising in intellectual property law. Main area of practice is intellectual property. Deals with all aspects, both contentious and non-contentious. Also covers information technology, e-commerce and pharmaceutical law. Has been involved in a number of major IP related transactions and cases, many cross-border. Clients come principally from the cosmetics, food and drink, pharmaceuticals and retail sectors. Also computer companies (especially software) and multimedia. Senior Visiting Fellow in Intellectual Property, Centre for Commercial Law Studies, Queen Mary College, London.
Prof. Memberships: Law Society, Pharmaceutical Trade Marks Group, International Trade Mark Association.
Career: Research Fellow at Max Planck Institute for Patent, Copyright and Competition Law, Munich 1980-81. Qualified in 1985. With *Linklaters & Paines* 1982-87, then Partner at *McKenna & Co* 1987-94. Founded *Llewelyn Zietman* in July 1994. Joined *White & Case's* London office in September 1999.
Publications: Joint author of leading textbook Kerly's 'Law of Trade Marks and Trade Names' (13th ed, 2001). Author of numerous articles published in legal journals. Has also delivered many conference papers in the UK and abroad.
Personal: Born 15th July 1956. Educated at Wallingford Grammar School 1967-74, Southampton University 1974-77 (LL.B) and Worcester College, Oxford 1978-79 (BCL, 1st Class Hons). German speaker. Lives in London SW7.

LOCHNER, Ludi
Lochners Technology Solicitors, Godalming (01483) 414588

LOVE, James
Irwin Mitchell, Leeds (0113) 234 3333
lovej@irwinmitchell.co.uk
Specialisation: Intellectual property. Extensive experience in relation to patent, trade marks, copyright, designs confidentiality, counterfeiting and search and seize orders. Work in the last twelve months includes: handling an oil industry patent dispute which was one of only half a dozen cases since 1977 to reach the House of Lords in connection with the Patents Act 1977; handling defence of dispute featured on national television concerning the extent of Dyno-Rods alleged monopoly in Day-Glo painted vans; major international litigation in US and throughout Europe.
Prof. Memberships: Chartered Institute of Patent Agents. Institute of Trade Mark Agents.
Career: 1989-94: *Bristows*, London. 1994-96: *Eversheds*, Leeds. 1996 to date *Irwin Mtchell*, Leeds (partner from 1997). Named as one of Yorkshire's top three lawyers under 40 in 1999 and as one of the region's leading young professionals. The only young lawyer to win two awards in the inaugural Yorkshire Lawyer Awards 2000, and cited as one of the leading young lawyers outside London in Legal Business.
Publications: Articles in a wide variety of general and specialist press.
Personal: 1984-87: Queens College, Cambridge (Sciences). 1987-1989: The College of Law, Chancery Lane. 1992-1993: Diploma in Intellectual Property, Bristol University.

LUCKMAN, Michael
Wragge & Co, Birmingham (0870) 903 1000

MACDONALD, Morag
Bird & Bird, London (020) 7415 6000
Specialisation: Partner in the intellectual property department. Work includes litigation, transactional and advisory work in relation to all intellectual property rights. In particular, handles pharamaceutical, biotechnology, electronics and software patents and trademarks. Acted in Mentor/Hollister, Compaq/Dell, Richardson Vicks/Reckitt & Colman, Chocosuisse/Cadbury, Unilever/Johnson Wax, Research Corporations SPC, Swiss Miss, Baxter/Pharmacia Upjohn and Genetics Institute, Cartonneries de Thulin/White Knight, Stolt Comex Seaway/Coflexip, Novo Nordick/DSM.
Prof. Memberships: CIPA, ITMA, INTA, ECTA, British Computer Society.

Career: Called to the Bar in 1984. Qualified as a solicitor in 1988, having joined *Bird & Bird* in 1985. Partner 1989.
Publications: Contributor on IP issues to 'Internet Law and Regulation' (Sweet & Maxwell, 2nd edition, December 1997), UK section of 'The New Role of Intellectual Property in Commercial Transactions' (Wiley 1994) and the Legal Aspects chapter of 'Essential IT' (Gee Publishing 1996). Co-author of 'Designs & Copyright Protection of Products: World Law & Practice' (Sweet & Maxwell).
Personal: MA in Mathematics, Physics and Law from Cambridge.

MACDONALD-BROWN, Charters
Gouldens, London (020) 7583 7777
cmb@gouldens.com
Specialisation: Advised in numerous patent, trade mark, copyright design and other IP cases. In the last year, acted for two major pharmaceutical companies in a High Court trademarks/parallel imports case, which is on reference to the ECJ at present (GlaxoSmithKline and Boëhringer v Dowelhurst); acted for the successful claimant in an important design right case (Fulton v Grant Barnett) and had two patent trials in the last year. One at least will be reported on a costs issue. All cases cited are reported.
Prof. Memberships: Law Society, IBA, CIPA, ITMA, IPLA, TIPLO, AIPPI, ABA, AIPLA, INTA, ECTA, Pharmaceutical Trade Mark Group and LES.
Career: Trained with *Gouldens*, partner 1977, founder of IP group and its head. Executive Council of AIPPI (UK) and INTA Committee member. Honorary Advisor to the Legal and Parliamentary Committee of the Royal Society of Chemistry. Lectures on IP Diploma Course at Bristol University.
Publications: Numerous papers and articles for INTA, CIPA, PTMG, EIPR, Bristol University and others.

MACFARLANE, Nicholas
Lovells, London (020) 7296 2000
nicholas.macfarlane@lovells.com
Specialisation: Patents; trade marks; passing-off; copyright; misuse of confidential information; trade libel and other allied areas of competition law; largely involved in litigation. Involved in many leading intellectual property cases concerning inter alia; patentability of software; the movement of patented pharmaceuticals within the EU; extent of relief in Anton Piller Orders; comparative advertising and counterfeiting.
Prof. Memberships: Founder Member of and former Secretary of Intellectual Property Lawyers Association; Council Member British Group of AIPPI; associate member Chartered Institute of Patent Agents and Institute of Trade Mark Agents.
Career: Lancaster University 1974 BA (Hons). Articled *Richards Butler*, qualified 1977. *Faithfull Owen & Fraser* partner 1980. 1985 amalgamated with *Durrant Piesse*, now *Lovells*.

MACPHERSON, Shonaig
McGrigor Donald, Edinburgh (0131) 777 7000
Specialisation: Handles all aspects of intellectual property and information technology work. Advises on protection strategies, funding for technology projects, licensing, research contracts, litigation and dispute resolution with particular expertise in biosciences. Speaker at Glasgow IT summits in 1993 and 1994, and at the International Science Festival in Edinburgh in 1992, 1993 and 1994, Chicago 1996.
Prof. Memberships: Law Society (England & Wales), Law Society (Scotland), Licensing Executives Society, Royal Society, Scottish Biomedical Association, Scottish Biomedical Research Trust. Visiting Professor at Heriot-Watt University, Society for Computers and the Law.
Career: Qualified in 1984 in England & Wales with *Norton Rose*. Assistant Company Secretary (Legal) Storehouse plc, then Legal Director of Harrods 1987-89. Partner at *Calow Easton* in London 1989-91. Qualified in Scotland 1991. Joined *McGrigor Donald* in 1991 and became a partner in 1992.
Personal: Born 29th September 1958. Director of Edinburgh Chamber of Commerce and Enterprise. Recreations include theatre, opera and reading. Lives in Edinburgh.

MARSHALL, James
Taylor Joynson Garrett, London (020) 7300 7000
jmarshall@tjg.co.uk
Specialisation: All areas of intellectual property, both contentious and non-contentious. In particular, patent, trademark, copyright and breach of confidence litigation; licences and other agreements concerning exploitation of intellectual property including in competition law context.
Prof. Memberships: Solicitors Association of Higher Courts Advocates; Associate of Chartered Institute of Patent Agents; AIPPI; IP Advisory Committee of BioIndustry Association.
Career: BSc (Mathematics and Physics), University of Bristol. Called to the Bar in 1986 with pupillage in Chambers of (then) Stephen Gratwick QC. 1987 joined *Lovell White Durrant*, subsequently requalifying as a solicitor. 1995 obtained solicitor advocate (Higher Courts Civil) qualification. 1997 joined partnership of *Taylor Joynson Garrett*.

MARSLAND, Vanessa
Clifford Chance, London (020) 7600 1000
vanessa.marsland@cliffordchance.com
Specialisation: Partner specialising in intellectual property including copyright, patents, trademarks, and designs.
Career: St Leonard's, Mayfield; King's College Cambridge. Admitted 1981; intellectual property partner in *Clifford Chance* since 1987; a former director of the Computer Law Association Inc. and of the Federation Against Software Theft (FAST) the UK's software anti-piracy body; specialist editor of 'Copinger & Skone James on Copyright' (14th Edition).
Personal: Born 1957; resides London.

MARTINDALE, Avril
Freshfields Bruckhaus Deringer, London (020) 7936 4000
avril.martindale@freshfields.com
Specialisation: Partner specialising in intellectual property. Main area of practice covers non-contentious intellectual property and information technology. Deals with commercial, advisory and transactional aspects of intellectual property and information technology.
Prof. Memberships: Law Society of England & Wales, Law Society of Scotland, Licensing Executives Society, Competition Law Society, INTA.
Career: Qualified in Scotland in 1985. With Scottish firm *Dickson Minto WS* 1985-88, then *McKenna & Co.* 1988-92. Qualified in England & Wales in 1992. Joined *Bristows Cooke & Carpmael* and became a partner in 1993. Joined *Freshfields* August 1997.
Personal: Born 1961. Educated at Glasgow University.

McLEAN, James
Burness, Edinburgh (0131) 473 6118
jmcl@burness.co.uk
Specialisation: Graduated in English and Scots Law at Cambridge and Edinburgh Universities. Convenor of the Law Society of Scotland's Intellectual Property Committee. Practice covers assignation disposal and licensing of intellectual property including property and insolvency aspects.

McNABB, Heather
Eversheds, Cardiff (029) 2047 1147
heathermcnabb@eversheds.com
Specialisation: Partner and head of intellectual property and information technology unit. Specialises in all aspects of intellectual property and IT work. Practice covers the full range of contentious and non-contentious IP. Advises on the protection, maintenance and exploitation of intellectual property rights. Particular interest in technology-based businesses and the internet. Extensive experience of exploiting and protecting IP and drafting and negotiating all types of IT contracts, including agreements for licensing and maintenance, turnkey, facilities management, and outsourcing arrangements, (including PFI work). Also particular interest in e-commerce dealing with clients on the supplier and customer side.
Prof. Memberships: Member of the Licensing Executives Society; member of the Society for Computers and Law; Member of the Intellectual Property Lawyers Association and the New Media Development Group.
Career: University of Wales, Cardiff (LLB Hons. 1986). Qualified in 1989. Joined *Eversheds* in 1994, becoming a partner in 1995.
Personal: Married and resides in South Wales.

MIDDLEMISS, Susie
Slaughter and May, London (020) 7600 1200
susie.middlemiss@slaughterandmay.com
Specialisation: Intellectual property partner, dealing with contentious and non-contentious matters, including patent and trade mark issues.
Career: Qualified New South Wales 1986, England and Wales 1991; *Slaughter and May* 1995; partner 2000.
Personal: BSc; LLB (University of Sydney).

MOAKES, Jonathan
Halliwell Landau, Manchester (0161) 835 3003
Specialisation: Partner and head of intellectual property department. Work includes patents, copyright, designs, trade secrets, technology transfer and exploitation agreements, trade marks and disputes. Particular experience in acting for high tech businesses – member of the firm's high tech/biotech unit. Other area of practice is computer law, including software licensing, supply contracts and disputes. Author of 'International Information Technology Law – England and Wales' and the 'Encyclopaedia of Information Technology Law – Export Licensing Control'. Has addressed numerous conferences on intellectual property and computer law issues.
Prof. Memberships: Committee Member of North West Branch of the Licensing Executives Society, Society for Computers and Law, Solicitors European Group.
Career: Qualified 1984. Worked at *Baker & McKenzie* 1982-88, then *Halliwell Landau*, becoming a partner in 1989.
Personal: Born 1960. Attended Queens' College,

Cambridge 1978-81. Leisure interests include sailing, skiing, fell walking, tennis and playing the violin. Lives in Wilmslow.

MOODIE, Bill
Herbert Smith, London 020 7374 8000
bill.moodie@herbertsmith.com
Specialisation: Head of the intellectual property and technology department. Specialises in intellectual property law, particularly patents, copyright and trade marks involving the electronics, communications and the IT and digital media industries. Extensive litigation experience but also substantial non-contentious practice. Clients include Quantel, Cable & Wireless, Guinness, Formula One, BSkyB, Bridgestone/Firestone, PriceWaterhouseCoopers, Warner, Vodafone, Bourns, WH Smith, BAT and Qinetiq.
Career: South African patent agent and attorney – 1975; solicitor in England and Wales – 1979; partner at *Herbert Smith* – 1984; head of IP Group – 1996.
Personal: Education – University of Cape Town (B.Sc Elec. Eng.) First Class Honours – 1969; University of South Africa (LL.B) – 1975.

MOONEY, Kevin
Simmons & Simmons, London 020 7628 2020
kevin.mooney@simmons-simmons.com
Specialisation: Senior partner in intellectual property department. Principal area of practice is patent litigation. Clients include GlaxoSmithKline, Eli Lilly, Bristol Myers Squibb, Pharmacia & Upjohn, 3M, Union Carbide, Procter & Gamble, Gallaher and Norsk Hydro. Member of Nuffield Bioethics Council Working Party on Human Tissue (April 1995). Experienced speaker at conferences.
Prof. Memberships: ABA, AIPLA, AIPPI, City of London Solicitors Company (Member of Intellectual Property Sub-Committee).
Career: Qualified in 1971. Partner at *Simmons & Simmons* since 1973.
Personal: Born 14th November 1945. Educated at Bristol University (LLB 1968). Leisure activities include gardening and supporting QPR. Lives in Ealing, West London.

MOSS, Gary
Taylor Joynson Garrett, London (020) 7300 7000
gmoss@tjg.co.uk
Specialisation: Member of *Taylor Joynson Garrett's* intellectual property department. Practice covers all areas of intellectual property, but with particular emphasis on patents, biotechnology, information technology and technology transfers. Also handles both contentious and non-contentious matters within the field of information technology including licence disputes, fitness for purpose disputes and copying/plagiarism disputes. Examples of important cases handled are Pall Corporation v Commercial Hydraulics, SKM v Wagner Spraytech, Single Buoy Moorings v Brown Brothers and Vickers plc, Brugger v Medic-Aid Limited, Amgen v Roche Diagnostics & Genetics Institute (major litigation relating to biotechnology patents) Amgen v Aventis (ditto) and Taylor v Ishida Co Limited. Clients include Amgen Inc, Visa, Pall Corporation, Haberman Associates, Avery Denison, Geron Corporation Biocompatibles plc, Generics Group AG and SkyPharma plc. Member of the editorial boards of 'The Biotechnology Law Report' and the 'Journal of Brand Management'. Has spoken at seminars on life sciences and information technology, both protection and issues arising on acquisitions of technology based companies.
Prof. Memberships: Law Society (member of Intellectual Property sub-committee).
Career: Qualified in 1977. With *Clifford Turner* 1977-79, then *Woodham Smith* 1979-90 (partner from 1981). Joined *Taylor Joynson Garrett* as a partner in 1990.
Personal: Born 7 April 1953. Educated at the University of Leicester 1971-74 (1st Class Hons) and the College of Law (1st Class Hons). Recreations include theatre, opera and golf. Lives in London.

NAPPER, Isabel
Mills & Reeve, Cambridge (01223) 222379
isabel.napper@mills-reeve.com
Specialisation: Strong City background dealing in all aspects of intellectual property law. Her move to Cambridge, where she has acquired a substantial reputation, enables her to use that experience to the advantage of clients. Enjoys handling a wide variety of IP issues relating to patents, designs, trademarks and confidential information, including advising companies of all sizes on how to deal with their intellectual property in order to protect and exploit it efficiently. Frequently lectures and gives seminars to clients and professional bodies. Extensive practical experience of litigation and licensing. Has a particular interest in technology transfer and biotechnology.
Prof. Memberships: Chartered Institute of Patent Agents, Society for the Application of Research, Licensing Executives' Society.
Career: MA (London). Qualified 1984. Specialist IP lawyer with *Lovell White Durrant.* 1991 IP partner *Hopkins & Wood.* 1994 to 1998, IP team at *Taylor Vinters.* 1998 partner in IP team *Mills & Reeve.*
Personal: Born 1958. Keen on good food, wine and enjoying life.

NEWMAN, Helen
Simmons & Simmons, London 020 7628 2020
helen.newman@simmons-simmons.com
Specialisation: Partner and managing partner of the firm's intellectual property group. Principle area of practice is advising on the acquisition, disposal, restructuring and exploitation of intellectual property rights portfolios (including merchandising deals). Involved in trademark filing and prosecution for clients for an extensive range of global brand owners. Conducts enforcement litigation for merchandising campaigns handles other intellectual property litigation in the United Kingdom and co-ordinates corresponding overseas litigation.
Prof. Memberships: International Trademark Association, Institute of Trademark Agents, MARQUES, Anti-Counterfeiting Group, European Communities Trade Mark Association.
Career: Articled with *Simmons & Simmons.* Qualified 1980 and became a partner in 1985.

NICOLSON, Fiona
Maclay Murray & Spens, Glasgow
(0141) 248 5011
fmmn@maclaymurrayspens.co.uk
Specialisation: Partner and head of IP and technology department. Specialises in intellectual property and information technology work for clients both national and international, including start-ups, listed companies, venture capitalists and educational institutions.
Prof. Memberships: Immediate past president – Licensing Executives Society, 'Britain and Ireland' council member. Chairman of the Law Society of Scotland panel for accreditation of intellectual property.
Career: Joined *Maclay Murray & Spens* in 1993. Previously partner and head of IP at *Bird Semple, Fyfe Ireland.*
Personal: Glasgow University MA (1974) LLB (1983). Born 1954.

NODDER, Edward
Bristows, London (020) 7400 8000
edward.nodder@bristows.com
Specialisation: Partner in intellectual property department. Advises on the full range of contentious and non-contentious intellectual property, including patents, trade marks, copyright, designs and confidential information, computers and IT, pharmaceuticals and biotechnology. This includes advice on European competition and harmonisation laws as they impact on intellectual property, including the European Patent Office and the Community Trade Mark Office. Amongst numerous reported cases, acted for the plaintiff in 3M v. Rennicks (patent infringement and licensing), Gillette v. Edenwest (trademark infringement and passing off), 3M v Plastus (cross border injuction) and 3M v NCI (stay pending EPO opposition) and for the defendant in Kastner v Rizla (patent claim contruction). Has been involved in opposition proceedings at European Patent Office for 3M, British Gas and other clients. Currently responsible for Patents Court, High Court and Appeal Court patent and brands litigation on behalf of 3M, Novartis, Sara Lee (Douwe Egberts), Ciba Vision and closely involved with Novartis v AHP in House of Lords.
Prof. Memberships: Law Society, Associate Member of Chartered Institute of Patent Agents, AIPPI.
Career: Joined *Bristows* in 1978. Became a Partner in 1986.
Publications: Author of articles for specialist periodicals such as 'Patent World' and 'Managing Intellectual Property'. Regular speaker at intellectual property conferences and seminars.
Personal: Born 29th June 1956. Educated at Cambridge University 1974-77 (MA in Natural Sciences and Law). Enjoys opera, chamber music, tennis, gardening and the Languedoc.

NORTCLIFF, Celia
The Law Offices of Marcus J. O'Leary, Bracknell (01344) 303044
Specialisation: Full range of intellectual property and information technology work with emphasis on computer industry; advice includes software licensing and distribution; hardware sales and distribution; competition; advertising and marketing; facility management; e-commerce; CCTA contracts; public procurement; disaster recovery; acts for a number of world renowned companies.
Prof. Memberships: Law Society
Career: Qualified 1971. Ten years in City finally as partner at *Rowe & Maw*; 1982 onwards in Reading becoming partner and head of intellectual property at *Brain & Brain* in 1991; joined *The Law Offices of Marcus J O'Leary* as a partner in 1996.
Personal: Educated Lowestoft Grammar School then Manchester University. Leisure interests – plays flute and piano; enjoys travel and reading.

OSBORN, Terry
Philip Conn & Co, Manchester (0161) 833 9494

PERKINS, David
Clifford Chance, London (020) 7600 1000
david.perkins@cliffordchance.com
Specialisation: Partner and head of intellectual property department specialising in patents, trademarks, designs and pharmaceuticals.
Prof. Memberships: The Law Society; City of London Solicitors Company; The Intellectual Property Lawyers Association (IPLA); International Bar Association; Chartered Institute of Patent Agents (Associate Member); Institute of Trade Mark Agents (Associate Member); European Communities Trade Mark Practitioners' Association; Union of European Practitioners in Industrial Property (Council Member of the British Group); AIPPA (Associate Internationale pour la Protection de la Propriete Industrielle); International Trade Mark Association (Foreign Member); American Bar Association (Foreign Member); American Intellectual Property Law Association (Foreign Member); International Sub-Committee Chair of Anti-trust Law Committee and Co-Chair of International Developments Sub-Committee of the ADR Committee; Common Law Institute of Intellectual Property (Council Member); World Intellectual Property Organisation; listed as WIPO Mediator/Arbitrator; The Intellectual Property Lawyers Organisation (TIPLO),Council Member.
Career: Newcastle Preparatory School; Uppingham School; Newcastle University. Partner *Clifford Chance* 1975.
Publications: Speaks extensively and is widely published.
Personal: Born 1943; three sons, one daughter; resides London. Interests include golf and tennis.

POORE, Alasdair
Mills & Reeve, Cambridge (01223) 222248
alasdair.poore@mills-reeve.com
Specialisation: Wide range of intellectual property work including commercial (licensing and other agreements, computer contracts, competition law and mergers and acquisitions) and litigation and dispute resolution. Experience and particular interest in high-tech areas including electronics, computers and software, and also chemicals and biotechnology. Recent work has included a substantial patent action involving electronic copy protection technology, strategic advice on listing of new engine technology company, licensing negotiations on world beating refining process, licensing and advice on a significant web browsing technology, negotiation of Pathfinder PFI project in the IT sector.
Prof. Memberships: Chartered Patent agent, Registered Trade Mark agent, former council member of CIPA and chairman General Laws' committee, Patent Litigators' Association, Licensing Executives' Society, INTA.
Career: MA (Cantab) Law and Natural Sciences; Shell International Petroleum Co; *Lovell White Durrant*; *Clyde & Co*; *Mills & Reeve*, partner 1996.
Personal: Squash, real tennis, mountaineering, music.

PRICE, Richard
Taylor Joynson Garrett, London (020) 7300 7000
rprice@tjg.co.uk
Specialisation: Intellectual property partner, specialising in patents, trade marks, copyright, confidential information, trade libel litigation, IP intensive acquisitions, disposals and licensing. Important cases include successful defence of SC Johnson and Son, Inc. (2000) in patent infringement proceedings brought by Sara Lee (appeal in October 2001); in 1998-2000 acting successfully (first instance and House of Lords) for Healing Herbs Ltd in revocation action against BACH trade mark registrations for flower remedies (leading case on generic marks); acting successfully for Hoechst Celanese Corporation in patent infringement proceedings against BP Chemicals, first instance and appeal; proceeding to first account of profits in a patent case for 100 years, successful settlement shortly before Judgment (1998); in 1997, successful for Canon in last civil appeal from Hong Kong to the Privy Council (patent and copyright issues); in 1991 successful appeal to House of Lords concerning Asahi Chemical's Patent Application (genetic engineering – priority of competing patent claims and the need for enabling disclosure); in 1988 acted for Reckitt and Colman winning the leading case on trade dress/passing off (JIF Lemon, House of Lords).
Prof. Memberships: Chairman, 1994-97 The Intellectual Property Lawyer's Association (formerly Patent Solicitors Association), City of London Solicitors' Company, Law Society's Intellectual Property Working Party, Solicitors European Group, AIPPI (UK). Lecturer Bristol University post-graduate IP Diploma.
Career: Qualified in 1970. With *Joynson-Hicks and Co* 1968-75 (partner 1973-75), then partner at *Courts and Co* 1975-77 and at *Woodham Smith* 1977-90. Joined *Taylor Joynson Garrett* as a partner in 1990.
Personal: Born 7th January 1946. Educated at Kingston Grammar School 1957-64 and Bristol University (LLB) 1964-67. Leisure interests include natural history, tennis and sailing. Trustee, British Ornithologist's Union. Lives in West Berkshire. Married with three sons.

RAWLINSON, Paul
Baker & McKenzie, London (020) 7919 1000
paul.rawlinson@bakernet.com
Specialisation: 'Soft' intellectual property litigation including trade marks, copyright, unfair competition. Particular emphasis on 'brand' industries where anti-counterfeiting/infringement work is undertaken for clients such as inter alia, Calvin Klein, Polo/Ralph Lauren, Tommy Hilfiger, L'Oreal, Lancome and Stussy.
Prof. Memberships: Steering Committee of the Anti-Counterfeiting Group; International Anti-Counterfeiting Coalition; French Chamber of Commerce.
Career: Trainee with *Baker & McKenzie*; qualified 1988; partner 1995; also admitted Hong Kong; lecturer for ITMA.
Publications: Written articles for 'European Intellectual Property Review'; contributor to 'Encyclopedia of Information Technology Law' (Sweet & Maxwell); editor Baker & McKenzie's 'Guide to Intellectual Property Laws in Central & Eastern Europe'; co-editor of 'Guide to Famous Marks'; editor 'Trade Marks in Europe' and 'Global Brand Protection'.
Personal: Education: St Peter's Grammar School; University of Kent (1983 BA Law); University of Paris XI (1984 Licence en Driot). Born 1962; resides in London. Married to Alison, with one son, Maximilian James. Interests include being a dad as well as soccer (a life-long, so far, Manchester City fan), golf, country living and fine wine.

RICH, Andrew
Herbert Smith, London (020) 7374 8000
andrew.rich@herbertsmith.com
Specialisation: All areas of intellectual property law, contentious and non-contentious. Has been involved in a number of the leading cases in this area including the Roche-Amgen patent litigation (recombinant erythropoietin), the SKB v Connaught appeal, the Sandvik v Iscar and Sandvik v Emporia patent actions, an action for Roche concerning the PCR patents, actions brought by the owners of the UK Quiksilver trade marks to prevent parallel imports, the patent action between Carter-Wallace and Unilever relating to pregnancy test kits, a contested application by BASF for a supplementary protection certificate and a number of oppositions in the European Patent Office.
Prof. Memberships: Member of the Intellectual Property Advisory Committee of the UK BioIndustry Association. Member of Council of the AIPPI UK Group, member of IPLA and associate member of CIPA and ITMA.
Career: Degree in Biology from Liverpool University (First Class Honours) – 1984. Articled at *Lovell White Durrant* – 1987-89. Joined *Hammond Suddards* in Yorkshire in 1992. Joined *Herbert Smith* in 1994. Partner 1996.

SAUNDERS, James
Shepherd & Wedderburn WS, Edinburgh
(0131) 473 5288
james.saunders@shepwedd.co.uk
Specialisation: Partner in corporate department. Main areas of practice are energy law and I.P. (including computer law). Advises on electricity agreements and on I.P. agreements including licensing and turnkey.
Career: Qualified in 1984. Trainee with *McClure Naismith*, Glasgow 1983-85. Worked for ICI plc 1986-87 and *Freshfields* 1987-93. Joined *Shepherd & Wedderburn WS* in 1993.

SHILLITO, Mark
Herbert Smith, London (020) 7374 8000
mark.shillito@herbertsmith.com
Specialisation: All aspects of intellectual property work, contentious and non-contentious; extensive trial experience; has acted in a number of the leading cases in the fields of patents (Chiron v Organon Teknika; Strix v Otter; Fort Dodge v Akzo); trade marks (Vodafone v Orange); plant variety rights (Germinal v Fell & Rowsell); copyright and media (BSkyB v. PRS; Newspaper Licensing Agency Ltd v Marks & Spencer plc); and breach of confidence (Berkeley Administration v McClelland). Specific expertise in law relating to genetically modified organisms.
Prof. Memberships: AIPPI; AIPLA; CIPA; ITMA; INTA; IPLA; TIPLO.
Career: Articled at *Herbert Smith*; qualified 1989; partner 1996. University College London (LLB Hons). Queen Mary & Westfield College, London (Dip.IP).

SMITH, Catriona
Allen & Overy, London (020) 7330 3774
catriona.smith@allenovery.com
Specialisation: Specialises in intellectual property and information technology disputes from patents and domain names. Has wide experience of pharmaceutical and healthcare disputes, protecting

well-known trademarks and acting in international patent litigation.
Prof. Memberships: Secretary to the British Group of the Union of European Practitioners in Industrial Property; Council Member Intellectual Property Lawyers Association; IP sub-committee of the City of London Law society, INTA, AIPPI.
Career: Assistant *Clifford Chance* (1982 -89); Assistant *Allen & Overy* (1989 -1992), Partner 1992.
Personal: MA University of St Andrew's (1977).

STARR, Ian
Ashurst Morris Crisp, London (020) 7638 1111
ian.starr@ashursts.com
Specialisation: Partner in intellectual property and information technology group. Principal area of practice is litigation and arbitration in relation to disputes relating to intellectual property rights and technology. Particular interest in cross-border disputes on patents and trademarks and disputes relating to the interaction between competition law and the enforcement of IP rights.
Career: Qualified in 1979. *Clifford Chance* 1980-83 (partner 1984). *Ashurst Morris Crisp* 1993-date (head of IP group).
Personal: Family and golf.

STOKER, Robert
Addleshaw Booth & Co, Manchester
(0161) 934 6327
rrs@addleshaw-booth.co.uk
Specialisation: Partner in technology, media and intellectual property department. Work includes the acquisition, exploitation and enforcement of patents, trade marks, copyright and designs, confidential information and related areas of competition law. Head of sport, media and entertainment unit advising on broadcasting, publishing, film and music related matters together with sponsorship and image rights agreements. Also advises on information technology matters. Appointed to advise the Organising Committee of the 2002 Commonwealth Games and the Rugby Football League where he is a member of the Consultative Committee. Led *Addleshaw Booth's* team advising Rugby League World Cup 2000 Limited. Has spoken on various intellectual property/ information technology and sport related topics in the UK and USA and broadcasts on television and radio on sports issues.
Prof. Memberships: Licensing Executives Society, INTA, LIDC, Solicitors European Group, Law Society, British Association for Sport and Law, Member of the Board of Governors of Sports Aid North West.
Career: Qualified in 1981. Joined firm in 1989; partner since 1991.
Personal: Educated at St Catharine's College, Cambridge 1972-75 and 1976-77. Leisure interests include angling, music, journalism, photography and Sunderland A.F.C.

SWIFT, Robert
Linklaters, London (020) 7456 5806
robert.swift@linklaters.com
Specialisation: Specialist with over 30 years' experience in the intellectual property field. Typical matters include: resolving disputes about trade marks, copyright, designs and unfair trading through negotiations and litigation where necessary, interim injunctions and damages assessments against 'pirates' and 'counterfeiters'; protection of computer software; drafting and negotiating licence agreements of various IP rights; EC and UK competition law issues arising out of complex licensing structures; IP aspects of major corporate deals.
Prof. Memberships: Member, Law Society Commercial and Consumer Law Committee and IP Sub-Committee. Deputy chairman, Solicitors' Wine Society Committee.
Career: Partner, intellectual property and information technology department. 1980-1995: Head of intellectual property department; 1976 to date: Partner, *Linklaters*; 1975: Six month secondment to *White & Case* New York; 1971-1975: Assistant solicitor, *Linklaters*; 1967-1971: Solicitor, patent and trade mark dept., EMI Limited; 1967: Qualified as solicitor. College of Law; London University; John Marshall High School, Los Angeles.

SWYCHER, Nigel
Slaughter and May, London (020) 7600 1200
nigel.swycher@slaughterandmay.com
Specialisation: Intellectual property and information technology law; including the IP and IT aspects of acquisitions, disposals, flotations and privatisations; involved in technology, licensing and transfer, franchising and sponsorship and IT procurement and development. Co-head of the firm's technology, media and telecoms group.
Prof. Memberships: ITMA.
Career: Admitted 1987 with*Slaughter and May*. Partner 1994.
Personal: Born 6 June 1962. Educated at Denstone College, Staffordshire and Durham University. Magician.

SYKES, John
Lupton Fawcett, Leeds (0113) 280 2000
john.sykes@lupfaw.co.uk
Specialisation: Has substantial experience in handling all aspects of intellectual property work since 1982 when he began specialising in this field. His knowledge and experience is based on both national and international work in this field, whether as part of a dispute or as part of a commercial deal, and covers patents, trade marks, copyright including media and entertainment industry work, confidential information and all types of design rights. John Sykes has particular expertise and interest in patents and trademarks, and intellectual property rights relating to the information technology industry.
Prof. Memberships: Associate Member of the Chartered Institute of Patent Agents; Member of the Licensing Executives Society.
Career: 1982-86, trainee and qualified solicitor with *Philip Conn & Co*, Manchester, a niche intellectual property practice. 1986-89, solicitor with *Dibb Lupton Broomhead*, specialising in intellectual property law, Leeds. 1989-92, partner with *Dibb Lupton Broomhead*, Leeds. 1992-date, partner *Lupton Fawcett*, Leeds.
Personal: Born 8 May 1957. Particular interests include sailing and golf when family and work allow.

TAYLOR, Peter D
Clifford Chance, London (020) 7600 1000
peter.taylor2@cliffordchance.com
Specialisation: Partner dealing with intellectual property, patents, trade mark, copyright, registered design and design right law, contentious and non-contentious, related aspects of competition law, passing off, trade libel and misuse of confidential information.
Prof. Memberships: ECTA; INTA; AIPPI
Career: LLB Hons Law, Birmingham. Articled *Needham & Grant*; qualified 1984; made partner at *Clifford Chance* 1990.
Personal: Born 1959; resides London.

THORNE, Clive
Denton Wilde Sapte, London (020) 7320 6953
cdt@dentonwildesapte.com
Specialisation: Partner in intellectual property group. Specialises in contentious intellectual property work, including copyright law, patents, trade marks, passing off, marketing law, computer law and trade secrets. Also commercial litigation, arbitration and employment law. Leading cases have included Alan Clark v Associated Newspapers; Halifax BS v Urquhart DyRes; Interlego AG v Tyco Industries; Sony Corporation v Saray Electronics; Robin Ray v Classic FM; Dormeuil v Nicolian; Dormeuil v Ferlaglow; Karoon v Bank of Tokyo.
Prof. Memberships: A founding member of The Intellectual Property Lawyers Organisation. Fellow of the Chartered Institute of Arbitrators. Member of Patent Solicitors Association; International Trade Mark Association; Institute of Trade Mark Agents (associate member); Anti-counterfeiting Group; Computer Law Group; Chartered Institute of Patent Agents (associate member); panel of arbitrators WIPO and Patents County Court.
Career: Qualified in 1977. Articled *Clifford Turner*. Admitted in Hong Kong in 1984 and Victoria, Australia in 1985. Joined *Denton Wilde Sapte* as a partner in 1987.
Publications: Co-author of 'Intellectual Property – the New Law,' joint author of 'Sony Guide to Home Taping' and 'Users Guide to Copyright.'

TULLEY, Christopher
DLA, Leeds (08700) 111111

TURNER, Catrin
H2O (Henry Hepworth Organisation), London
(020) 7539 7210
catrin.turner@h2o-law.com
Specialisation: Intellectual property, information technology, privacy and data protection. IP aspects and launch of Learndirect and Arena contribution to go Racing consortium. Adviser to Tesco on IP matters including European case against Levi. Management of reputation risk arising from e-commerce and insurance of those risks.
Prof. Memberships: INTA, ITMA (Associate), Pharmaceutical Trade Marks Group. Fellow of the Royal Society of Arts, Sciences and Maunufacturing.
Career: Qualified 1989 with niche IP/IT firm. *Davies Arnold Cooper* 1991-1999. *H2O* since 1999.
Personal: Interests: Africa, carpentry.

WALSH, Paul
Bristows, London (020) 7400 8000
paul.walsh@bristows.com
Specialisation: Partner in intellectual property department. Practice spans both contentious and non-contentious intellectual property matters including computer contracts and related disputes. Legal adviser to the British Brands Group, an alliance of leading manufacturers in the FMCG industry concerned with lookalike products. Also interested in emergency interlocutory applications, search and seizure and asset freezing orders, and has been appointed by the High Court to supervise in the conduct of such orders. Cases include Pilkington v PPG (confidential information arbitration), PPG v Pilkington (anti-trust arbitration), Assidoman Multipack

v Mead Corporation and Altertext Inc. v Advanced Data Communications Ltd.
Prof. Memberships: Licensing Executives Society, Associate Member of the Institute of Trade Mark Agents, European Community Trade Mark Association, Law Society.
Career: Qualified and joined *Bristows* in 1983. Became a partner in 1988.
Publications: Lecturer on technology transfer litigation, trade mark law, biotechnology law and Anton Piller Orders. Author of various articles for 'Trade Mark World' and 'Corporate Briefing'.
Personal: Born 21st December 1956. Educated at Salvatorian College 1968-75 and Oxford University 1976-79. Leisure interests include tennis, squash, literature and wine. Lives in London.

WHAITE, Robin

Linklaters, London (020) 7456 5828
robin.whaite@linklaters.com
Specialisation: Considerable experience in commercial and litigious matters involving IP rights and technology. Particular knowledge of issues in the healthcare and computer industries. Main areas of practice include patent, copyright, trade marks and trade secrets litigation; technology joint ventures and IP aspects of corporate finance and restructurings; technology transfer generally, including European anti-trust and competition law considerations; pharmaceutical law, including regulatory affairs.
Prof. Memberships: Committee member of the IP Lawyers Association. Represents the British Chamber of Commerce on the UK Government's Standing Advisory Committee on IP. Editorial board of 'Managing Intellectual Property'. Chairs annual conference on international patent litigation.
Career: 1989 to date: Partner, intellectual property department, *Linklaters*; 1986-1989: Assistant solicitor, *Linklaters*; 1978-1986: Articled clerk/assistant solicitor, *Herbert Smith & Co.* 1977-1980: Cambridge University, BA, MA; 1978: Law Society Final Exams.

WILLOUGHBY, Tony

Willoughby & Partners, London (020) 7345 8888
tony@iprights.com
Specialisation: Senior partner. All areas of intellectual property, but particularly litigation relating to trademarks, passing off, copyright, designs and confidential information.
Prof. Memberships: ITMA, INTA, LSLA, TIPLO, SALS, Law Society.
Career: 1970 *The Distillers Co. Ltd.* 1973 *Herbert Smith.* 1994 *Willoughby & Partners.*
Publications: Various papers relating to subjects such as parallel imports; search orders; freezing orders; domain names.
Personal: Born 29 September 1944. Educated at Westminster School. Interests include music, sport and wine. Member of the Governing Body of Westminster School (1990-2000).

WOOD, Alan

Beachcroft Wansbroughs, Bristol (0117) 918 2000
awood@bwlaw.co.uk
Specialisation: Partner in projects department. Main areas of practice are computer and IT, competition and public procurement, and intellectual property. Acts for both public bodies and private sector companies. IT projects range from complex, high-value IT system procurements, with advice on tendering procedures, review and incorporation of technical specifications, contract drafting and award and ongoing contract support, to advice on standard supply, licence and maintenance terms. Also includes advice on public procurement rules, the Private Finance Initiative, out-sourcing and facilities management. Intellectual property advice includes both contentious and non-contentious aspects of IP protection, licensing agreements both national and international, technology led joint ventures and technology transfer generally.
Career: Qualified at *Linklaters & Paines* in 1975. With *Linklaters & Paines* 1975-1987. *Osborne Clarke* 1987-1997. Joined *Wansbroughs Willey Hargrave* May 1997. Partner in *Beachcroft Wansbroughs 1999*.

WOOD, Ian

Rowe & Maw, London (020) 7248 4282
Specialisation: Partner intellectual property department. All aspects of intellectual property law, including patents, trade marks and copyright and allied rights, although primarily involved in the area of dispute resolution. Acts for a broad range of clients from large multinational corporations to smaller more locally based businesses, covering a broad spectrum of industries and services extending from those involved in newly emergent technologies to those in more established areas of business. Responsible for the conduct of several notable actions in the High Court, including the following leading reported patent infringement actions: Molnlycke v Procter & Gamble; Nidek v VISX; Unilever v Akzo and Chefaro; Honeywell v ACL. Other leading cases include Burton v Burton Snowboards and BP Amoco v Kelly. Also advising the European Commission in connection with WTO disputes regarding international obligations on patents. Author of several articles and regularly invited to speak at conferences and seminars (including those attended by fellow professionals).
Prof. Memberships: CIPA; ITMA; INTA; AIPPI; IPLA.
Personal: Born 1950. Attended Durham University (BSc Physics and MSc Nuclear Physics). Qualified as a solicitor in 1977.

WOODS, Philip

Hill Dickinson, Stockport (0161) 429 6767
Specialisation: Partner in technology and intellectual property group of *Hill Dickinson* specialising in all aspects of intellectual property and computer law, both contentious and non-contentious.
Prof. Memberships: Chartered Institute of Patent Agents (associate); Institute of Trade Mark Agents (associate); UNION; FICPI; AIPPI; Society for Computers and Law; committee member of LES (North West Group); TIPLO (founder member).
Career: Qualified 1974. Admitted Hong Kong 1975. *Deacons* (Hong Kong) 1975-81. Partner, *Wilkinson & Grist* (Hong Kong) 1981-89. Partner, *Eversheds Alexander Tatham* (head of IP department) 1989-94. Chairman of *Eversheds* National IP Group until 1994. Partner, *Philip Woods & Co* 1994-97. Presently partner *Hill Dickinson.*
Personal: Leisure pursuits include classic cars, wines, walking, reading and gardening. Lives in Prestbury, Cheshire. Born 23 December 1950.

WYN DAVIES, Cerys

Pinsent Curtis Biddle, Birmingham
(0121) 200 1050
cerys.wyn-davies@pinsents.com
Specialisation: Technology partner. Advises on intellectual property, information technology and e-commerce/e-business and data protection issues, emphasis on non-contentious matters including technology and biotechnology licensing; multimedia licensing; research and development and collaboration agreements; confidentiality arrangements; trademarks advice and licensing and IP/IT due diligence and audits.
Prof. Memberships: Licensing Executives Society. TIPLO. FAST. Intellectual Property Lawyers Association. ICC.
Career: Qualified 1985. *Coward Chance* 1983-87 and *Clifford Chance* 1987-95. Joined *Pinsent Curtis Biddle* in 1995 as partner.
Personal: Born 1961. Graduated from Exeter University 1982 (LLB) 1st Class and Sweet and Maxwell prize winner. Diploma in Intellectual Property Law, University of London 1991 – Distinction in all four heads. Interests include theatre, walking and skiing.

INVESTMENT FUNDS

OVERVIEW: With asset management a burgeoning industry in the UK, many law firms are seizing the opportunity to expand their practices. Against the background of an ageing population, government initiatives are channelling funds into the private sector, a scenario replicated in Europe. Further afield, US clients are acquiring families of funds for the Euromarket. Hedge funds remain an important diet for specialist practices, while property funds are experiencing dynamic growth across Europe, with corporate manufacturers acquiring real estate portfolios. With private equity fund raising reaching remarkable proportions, linked activities such as structured investment products and high yield split capital funds are *"being churned out at a fairly heavy rate."*In Scotland, track record and geographical proximity ensure that long established relationships between the key investment houses and the Edinburgh firms remain hard to corrupt. However with an increasingly proactive approach by fund managers and brokers, the market has witnessed some surprising couplings. One such example was Friends Ivory & Sime's choice of Norton Rose for a major reconstruction matter over traditional advisors, Shepherd & Wedderburn.

RESEARCH APPROVED BY BMRB: *For this edition,* Chambers' *researchers conducted 6,552 interviews – 4,419 with law firms, 554 with barristers and 1,579 with clients.*

The validity of the research was scrutinised by BMRB International, who audited both the methodology and the results at our offices in July 2001. They interviewed Chambers' *researchers and cross-checked sample interviews. Details of the audit appear on page 7.*

TOP IN-HOUSE LAWYERS

Pamela EDWARDS, Executive Director of Legal Services Europe, *Fidelity Investments International*

Kenneth GREIG, Head of Legal Services, *AXA Investment Managers Ltd*

Lucy LYNCH, Head of Law & Compliance for Europe, *Morgan Stanley Dean Witter Investment Management Ltd*

Alexander MARSHALL, Executive Director & Senior Counsel, *Goldman Sachs Asset Management International*

Simon MARTIN, Legal Manager, *Gartmore Investment Management plc*

Jonathan THOMAS, Executive Director & Counsel, *Goldman Sachs Asset Management International*

Jane THORNTON, Head of Legal, *Gartmore Investment Management plc*

Josephine TUBBS, Head of Legal & Secretariat, *Framlington Group Ltd*

Pamela Edwards has a global brief at Fidelity and is considered *"one of the cleverest in-house lawyers in the industry."* **Kenneth Greig** is highly rated as an *"outstanding ambassador"* and an *"excellent lawyer with a great breadth of knowledge."* Praised for being *"strong in financial services generally,"* **Lucy Lynch** brings her enthusiasm to the deal table. **Alex Marshall** continues to attract wide-ranging recommendations. Noted for his *"confidence in standing his ground,"* is **Simon Martin**. A pleasure to work with, **Jane Thornton** is regarded by some as *"one of the best in-house lawyers around."* **Jonathan Thomas** is endorsed as *"well-versed in his field,"* while **Josephine Tubbs** although relatively new to the market, continues to be well regarded.

In-House lawyers profiles: p 1193

LONDON

Clifford Chance (see firm details p.919) Still a *"top firm with the resources to deliver,"* it has been appointed global counsel on several major projects, including advising JP Morgan Chase on the annual collections of legal opinions in 44 jurisdictions, and building a related bespoke internet service. Regulatory *"guru"* **Tim Herrington** (see p.517) and investment trusts expert, the *"efficient"* **Andrew Hougie** (see p.517), jointly advised on the proposed reconstruction of Biotechnology Investments Ltd into 3i Bioscience Investment Trust plc with a £281 million market capitalisation on the London Stock Exchange. **James Barlow** advised Chase on the Man-Glenwood Nexus Guaranteed hedge fund and advised Chase on the outsourcing to it of Schroders Investment Management (totalling US$255 billion assets), the largest outsourcing deal outside the US. A further highlight was advising the DTI on the establishment of the UK High Technology Fund, a £150 million fund of funds, investing in technology private equity funds, involving a £20 million government investment. **Clients:** Aberdeen Asset Managers; ED&F Management Investment Products; Gartmore; Industri Kapital; JP Morgan Chase Fleming; Duke Street Capital; Merrill Lynch; Morgan Stanley.

Linklaters (see firm details p.1042) Organised within its Investment Management Group, this practice has *"strength and quality,"* and builds on *"long-established connections."* Senior corporate finance partner, the *"top-ranking, versatile"* **Matthew Middleditch** (see p.517) is endorsed by peers for his specialist advice, such as the innovative Chase Fleming Rollover Scheme made to ASDA loan holders. Led by its core client base of investment funds and asset managers, the group's profile in hedge funds and offshore work has increased considerably. Key players in this area are Group Head *"Mr Offshore Funds"* **Tim Shipton** (see p.518) (*"jovial and pleasant"*), and *"father of investment funds"* **Paul Harris** (see p.517), who is praised by peers for his ability to *"explain esoteric matters in practical terms to which clients can relate."* Shipton acted on the establishment of Pradera European Retail Fund, raising €300 million on its third closing, while Harris advised the Board of International Biotechnology Trust on proposals for appointing new trust managers. Newly recommended **Jonathan Perkins** (see p.518)advised on the establishment of the AXA Private Equity Fund II. **Clients:** Alliance Capital Management LP; AXA; BC Partners; JP Morgan Fleming; Morely Asset Management; Pincus; Investec Asset Management; Janus Capital Corp; ING Barings.

Herbert Smith (see firm details p.993) *"Serious"* practice, best known for investment trusts expertise, covering fund reorganisations and reconstructions and split capital investment funds. Peers commend it as a *"good team of fantastically capable lawyers – commercial, helpful people."* Advising on the complex reorganisations of Pantheon International Participations and Henderson High Income Trust, the *"excellent"* **Nigel Farr** (see p517)*"understands and drafts new concepts quickly."* With a *"good reputa-*

INVESTMENT FUNDS • London	Ptnrs	Assts
1 Clifford Chance	10	48
Linklaters	12	35
2 Herbert Smith	5	8
Norton Rose	5	15
3 Eversheds	5	7
4 Ashurst Morris Crisp	5	7
Dechert	2	16
Macfarlanes	5	5
Simmons & Simmons	5	13
SJ Berwin	11	15
Slaughter and May	n/a	n/a
5 Field Fisher Waterhouse	3	4
Freshfields Bruckhaus Deringer	2	9
Lovells	n/a	n/a
Stephenson Harwood	3	8
Travers Smith Braithwaite	4	5
6 Allen & Overy	n/a	n/a
Lawrence Graham	3	3
Rowe & Maw	2	2
Speechly Bircham	2	2

LEADING INDIVIDUALS	
1 **FARR Nigel** Herbert Smith	**HERRINGTON Tim** Clifford Chance
MIDDLEDITCH Matthew Linklaters	**SHIPTON Tim** Linklaters
2 **CORNICK Timothy** Macfarlanes	**CRIPPS James** Slaughter and May
HARRIS Paul Linklaters	**MARSDEN Tim** Norton Rose
SLATER Richard Simmons & Simmons	**THOMPSON Pamela** Eversheds
3 **ASTLEFORD Peter** Dechert	**BLAKE Jonathan** SJ Berwin
BROUGH Gordon City Law Partnership	**CULLEN Iain** Simmons & Simmons
STONES Richard Lovells	**SUTCH Andrew** Stephenson Harwood
4 **BAILLIE Kirstene** Field Fisher Waterhouse	**BARLOW James** Clifford Chance
CLARKE Dominic Herbert Smith	**COX Simon** Norton Rose
HOUGIE Andrew Clifford Chance	**IVE David** Rowe & Maw
McWHIRTER Anthony Freshfields Bruckhaus	**PERKINS Jonathan** Linklaters
WALSOM Roger Ashurst Morris Crisp	**WATTERSON Mark** Freshfields Bruckhaus
5 **MITCHELL Andrew** Norton Rose	**ROBINSON Stephen** Macfarlanes
SAUNDERS William Stephenson Harwood	**SHAW Michael** Herbert Smith
UP AND COMING	
MARTIN Stuart Dechert	**THOMPSON Blair** SJ Berwin

This book is the product of 6,552 1/2-hour interviews. See p.7 for BMRB audit.

Within each band, firms are listed alphabetically. *See individuals' profiles p.514*

tion" on the regulatory side, **Dominic Clarke** (see p.516) advised Royal & Sun Alliance on its conversion of unit trusts into OEICs. "*A pleasure to deal with,*" **Michael Shaw** (see p.518) advised Gartmore British Income & Growth Trust on shares placings and related matters. **Clients:** Henderson Global Investors; Merrill Lynch; Gartmore; Dresdner RCM Global Investors; Royal London; BFS Broker Financial Services Investment.

Norton Rose (see firm details p.1082) "*Going from strength to strength and doing exceptionally well,*" this broadly based funds practice has a good reputation in investment trusts and offshore work. Widely admired for its gain in market share, the "*effective*" team has been active on behalf of new entrants such as Collins Stewart, while consolidating established relationships with brokers such as Warburgs. Head of the umbrella Financial Institutions group with expertise in emerging markets, **Tim Marsden** (see p.517) "*delivers a good service*". He advised on the reconstruction of Jupiter International Green Investment Trust and the launch of its successor trust. Also recommended are "*bright*" **Simon Cox** (see p.516) and "*capable*" **Andrew Mitchell** (see p.517), who advised on Merrill Lynch New Energy Technology's successful £200 million launch. **Clients:** Britannic Asset Management; Jupiter Asset Management; Friends Ivory & Sime; Henderson Investors.

Eversheds (see firm details p.952) A "*vast*" practice with a strong reputation in domestic retail unit trusts and OEICs, representing over 20% of the total market in this area. The retail focus carries through to offshore work, with advice to Henderson Global Investors on the conversion and restructuring of 33 unit trusts into OEICs (value £2.3 billion) a key matter, led by head of department **Pamela Thompson** (see p.518). Richard Millar is now a consultant with the firm; he remains an integral part of the group servicing an active client base. A further highlight for the group was acting on the £100 million flotation of Net Investor. **Clients:** CoFunds; AMP; Norwich Union; Henderson Global Investors; UBS Asset Management; Fidelity.

Ashurst Morris Crisp (see firm details p.866) "*Private equity is what they're about,*" although the reputation of the practice also rests on its corporate investment trusts work, where it is perceived to have "*tied up*" key clients including INVESCO and Carlyle. The practice also has expertise in regulatory and offshore work. Heading the group is the "*clever*" **Roger Walsom** (see p.518), who advised Merrill Lynch on its tender offer for 50% share of capital of International Biotechnology Trust, and on the flotation of Aberdeen Growth. Other highlights include acting for GT Japan Investment Trust on the tender offer by Cazenove for 45% of its share capital. **Clients:** JZ Equity Partners; Legal & General; Medical Research; Carlyle; Catalyst; West Private Equity; Cazenove & Co.

Dechert (see firm details p.938) An "*impressive*" practice, whose solid reputation in hedge funds and offshore work generates significant leverage. The practice's transatlantic link is seen as a key advantage both in terms of work referral and cross-border UK/US advisory capability. "*Energetic*" **Peter Astleford** advised on the launch of hedge funds for Gartmore (Alphagen Hokuto Fund) and American Express (Advisory European Equity Fund), as well as the investment trust launch on the London Stock Exchange of the Lindsell Train Investment Trust, sponsored by Cazenove. He is ably assisted by the "*capable, rising*" **Stuart Martin** (see p.517), who makes his debut in this year's rankings. The group also advised on the launch of two UCITS funds for Thames River and the unitisation of the Scudder Latin America Growth Fund. **Clients:** Deutsche Asset Management; Gartmore Investment Management; Zurich Scudder Investments; American Express Asset Management; T Rowe Price; Malta Financial Services Centre.

Macfarlanes (see firm details p.1046) A small team, whose individuals are described as "*extremely pleasant to deal with,*" and which is highly rated in unit trusts, OEICs and private equity funds related work. On the retail side, **Tim Cornick** (see p.516) is recognised for his expertise in regulated funds and collective investment schemes, while **Stephen Robinson** (see p.518) is increasingly seen on private equity related matters. Cornick advised Fidelity Investments on its launch of 'Funds Network' and online supermarket, and acted for Legal & General on a distribution deal with the Alliance & Leicester. The firm also advised Legal & General Ventures on a new annual English limited partnership for pan-European investment, that raised over £135 million. **Clients:** HSBC Private Equity; Legal & General Ventures; Deutsche Asset; Fidelity; Lazard; Legal & General.

Simmons & Simmons (see firm details p.1132) The firm is considered to have "*a good name*" in hedge funds, with this area comprising around half of the practice's client base. Also known for his financial services expertise, the "*excellent*" **Richard Slater** (see p.402) advised on the reconstruction and liquidation of Hill Samuel Emerging Smaller Companies Investment Trust. He also advised Barclays Bank on its strategic alliance with Legal & General in relation to the promotion of L&G's funds and other investment products. Doing "*a fantastic job*" on the hedge funds side, **Iain Cullen** (see p.516)advised on the launch of European equities hedge funds for Merrill Lynch Investment Management. **Clients:** Barclays Funds; INVESCO; Perpetual; Scudder Threadneedle; Henderson Investors; Merrill Lynch.

SJ Berwin (see firm details p.879) The practice's colossal reputation in funds formation tends to eclipse its activity in related areas. Its players have a "*strong*" reputation in acting for domestic private equity funds and VCTs, employing a "*practical and helpful*" approach. Head of the private equity team, **Jonathan Blake** (see p.676) is a leader in the sector, while senior assistant **Blair Thompson** (see p.518) is described by peers as "*pleasant to deal with.*" They jointly advised on the establishment of the Second European Private Equity Fund for Bridgepoint Capital and the Electra European Fund LP for Electra Partners Europe. Other highlights include advice to the Schroder Ventures European Fund II (€3.5 billion). **Clients:** Quilter & Co; Electra Active Management; Beeson Gregory Investment Management SICAV; Ephesus Capital Fund; Bridgepoint Capital Partners; Schroder Ventures.

Slaughter and May (see firm details p.1135) A low profile practice, despite being "*highly active in the market*" on behalf of its "*good range*" of mainly asset management clients. Peers endorse its involvement in "*clever schemes*" such as the issue of 'Conversion Rights' by Genesis Emerging Markets Fund and the Saudi Arabian Investment Fund restructuring, both matters handled by key partner **James Cripps.** (see p.516) The group also advised on European depository receipts issue by Schroder Ventures International Investment Trust and the launch of 3i European Technology Trust. **Clients:** 3i; Abbey National; ING Barings and BAM; Flemings; Fleming Family & Partners; Schroder & Co; Sierra Trading.

Field Fisher Waterhouse (see firm details p.957) Well-versed on the retail side of investment funds, this small team is built around **Kirstene Baillie** (see p.516) who peers believe "*knows her stuff.*" Innovative products are a key area of practice focus, with recent notable work including the mutation of Virgin Direct personal pension scheme into a stakeholder pension scheme. The group also advised SG Asset Management on the establishment of new unit trusts. **Clients:** Chase Fleming; LeggMason Investors; SG Asset Management; Virgin Direct.

Freshfields Bruckhaus Deringer (see firm details p.965) Previously based in the tax department, the investment funds group is now aligned with the financial services group. Offshore work with a strong tax element still counts for approximately 70% of the practice, while limited partnership and property funds are other areas of specialist expertise. Best known among a team of "*good people,*" steeped in tax expertise, are **Anthony McWhirter** (see p.517) and "*high quality*" **Mark Watterson** (see p.518). McWhirter was the leading figure in the structuring of The Blackmoor Limited Partnership as a vehicle for the acquisition of the Oldham Estate (for £500 million), while Watterson led the team advising The Blackstone Group on the establishment of Blackstone Real Estate Partners. **Clients:** Apollo Real Estate Investment Funds; Blackstone Group; Deutsche Bank; Goldman Sachs/Whitehall Funds; JER Partners; Orion Capital Management; State Street Global Advisors.

Lovells (see firm details p.1044) A "*steady*" integrated practice with a growing presence in retail oriented work, unit trusts and property funds. Also well known in the financial services and corporate arena, head of group **Richard Stones** (see p.518) is also highly respected in this area. He advised Lloyd TSB on the launch of Create. The team also advised on the launches of the 'iShares' exchange-traded fund for Barclays Global Investors and Britannic Money. **Clients:** Global Asset Management; Merrill Lynch; Prudential/ M&G; Henderson Investors; CCF Charterhouse; Doughty Hanson; Barclays Global Investors; BAA.

Stephenson Harwood (see firm details p.1141) A "*decent,*" broadly-based investment funds practice, with around 40% of its client base comprising Channel Islands' London-listed funds, and property funds an area of increasing focus. Headed by "*commercial, intelligent and pleasant*" **Andrew Sutch**, the "*active*" team includes **William Saunders** (see p.518), who is recommended for his corporate investment trust work. Several placings and listings of new shares count among recent highlights; the Exeter Enhanced Income Fund (£25.9 million), Framlington Health & Income Fund (£120 million) and the US Growth & Income Fund (£100 million), the latter two listed on the London and Channel Islands Stock Exchanges. **Clients:** Hoare Govette; Collins Stewart; Exeter Asset Management; HSBC Investment Funds (UK); Framlington; Gartmore.

Travers Smith Braithwaite (see firm details p.1160) Often seen acting for private equity investors, the Investment Funds group draws specialist expertise from the financial services, tax and corporate departments. Acting for a range of investment trusts and VCTs, the group, led by Alistair Douglas, advises on fund formation, investment activities and listing. It recently acted for Apax, 3i and Advent on the disposal of their investment in TDL Infomedia for £485 million. **Clients:** F&C Ventures; Geocapital Partners; Mercury Private Equity; ECI Ventures; Lothbury Property Trust; Gartmore Investment Management; Fleming Technology Investment Trust; Shires Investment Trust.

Allen & Overy (see firm details p.856) Against the background of the firm's strong banking client base, the investment structures group is more often seen acting for blue-chip investors, with an increasing amount of work for VC investors. Richard Slynn and the team have been bolstered by the strengthening of resources in the real estate group and additional resources in Germany and New York offices. Key deals include advising on the launch of Merrill Lynch Japan Enhanced Performance plc and advising Bear Stearns on the setting up of Lynx New Media Ventures fund. **Clients:** Bank of Scotland; Bear Stearns Asset Management; CSFB; Deutsche Bank; Merrill Lynch International; Schroder Exempt Property Unit Trust.

Lawrence Graham (see firm details p.1030) Active in the market, and "*picking up nice investment trust work*" according to rivals, the Collective Investments department focuses on closed-ended private equity and VC fund work, representing clients such as Brewin Dolphin. Specialising in investment trust reconstructions and reorganisations, Charles Wilkinson and the group represent an increasing number of foreign investment funds. Highlights include advising St David's Investment Trust in its merger with Prolific Income and advising Media and Income Trust in the reorganisation and restructuring of the its share capital. **Clients:** Gartmore Investment Management; Old Mutual Securities; Premier Asset Management; Media and Income Trust; St David's Investment Trust; Yeoman Investment Trust.

Rowe & Maw (see firm details p.1113) A focused practice, providing expertise in tax, trust and stamp duty aspects of investment funds, the latter being a major issue for fund reorganisations. Key client M&G continues to provide the firm with its principal profile, including advice on the reorganisation of M&G Charifund and Charibond. "*Fearfully clever*" **David Ive** (see p.517)is acknowledged as a tax and stamp duty specialist. **Clients:** M&G Charifund; M&G Charibond.

Speechly Bircham (see firm details p.1136) Its profile lies in retail unit trusts and OEICs, although the practice also covers investment trusts, limited partnerships and offshore funds. With tax comprising an important core element of the work, the group advised on the creation of an umbrella Jersey-based collective investment scheme for Merrill Lynch Investment Managers. The group, which includes Mervyn Couve, acted as principal advisors to Scottish Life on its demutualisation, and advised on the regulatory aspects of A&P's acquisition of NPI. **Clients:** The Scottish Life Assurance Company; Lombard Odier Unit Trust Manager; Ecclesiastical Insurance Group; Bank of New York Trust and Depositary Company; The Royal Bank of Scotland; Tilney Collective Management.

Other Notable Practitioners **Gordon Brough** (see p.516) of **The City Law Partnership** is described by specialists as "*big city firm quality,*" and is said to have an "*idiosyncratic, engaging*" style. He is famed for his "*cosy*" links with his most active client, Aberdeen Asset Managers, as well as links to Friends Ivory & Sime and Collins Stewart. He advised on the $150 million acquisition of Murray Johnson (£4 billion funds under management) and the acquisition of the investment management business of Life Assurance Holding Company.

THE REGIONS

INVESTMENT FUNDS • The Regions	Ptnrs	Assts
1 **Burges Salmon** Bristol	1	2

LEADING INDIVIDUALS
1 **GODFREY Christopher** Burges Salmon

This book is the product of 6,552 1/2-hour interviews. See p.7 for BMRB audit.
Within each band, firms are listed alphabetically. *See individuals' profiles p.514*

Burges Salmon (see firm details p.902) "*The only regional firm with a real reputation*" flourishes as a result of its client list and the presence of the esteemed **Christopher Godfrey**. The group is considered to be a "*useful*" representative for managers located outside London, and handles the lion's share of this region's work. The team advised on a £31 million share placing and fund-raising, sponsored by Collins Stewart for investment trust AMIC, and acted on the launches of Exeter Smaller Companies Income Fund and Exeter Financials Fund. Also involved in a scheme of amalgamation for Premier Portfolio Managers and for Exeter Management. **Clients:** Asset Management Investment Company (AMIC); Premier Portfolio Managers; Exeter Investment Group; Hargreaves Lansdown; St. James's Place Capital; Sarasin Investment Management.

SCOTLAND

INVESTMENT FUNDS • Scotland	Ptnrs	Assts
1 **Dickson Minto WS** Edinburgh	4	5
Dundas & Wilson CS Edinburgh	2	8
2 **Tods Murray WS** Edinburgh	3	2
3 **Maclay Murray & Spens** Glasgow	n/a	n/a
McGrigor Donald Glasgow	2	4
4 **Shepherd & Wedderburn WS** Edinburgh	3	6

LEADING INDIVIDUALS	
1 **ATHANAS Chris** Tods Murray	**MACKAY Philip** Dundas & Wilson CS
2 **DORAN Frank** McGrigor Donald	**MINTO Bruce** Dickson Minto WS
3 **DUNSIRE David** Tods Murray	**POLSON Michael** Dundas & Wilson CS
THURSTON SMITH Martin Tods Murray	**TODD Andrew** Dickson Minto WS

This book is the product of 6,552 1/2-hour interviews. See p.7 for BMRB audit.
Within each band, firms are listed alphabetically. *See individuals' profiles p.514*

Dickson Minto WS (see firm details p.942) "*Strong*" in investment trusts, the "*active*" team is commended for having "*built a fantastic practice.*" Supported by a "*terrific private equity practice,*" it is heavily occupied with VC funds and Scottish limited partnerships. **Andrew Todd** advised on the listing of Standard Life European PE Trust, a £16 million private equity fund of funds trust and the first to be launched by that trust. "*Impressive*" **Bruce Minto** (see p.517) advised on the listing of split capital trust Edinburgh Leveraged Income Trust. Other highlights include advising on the Geared Opportunities Income Trust, a new split capital trust managed by Friends Ivory & Sime. **Clients:** Aberforth Partners; Artemis; Edinburgh Fund Managers; JO Hambro Capital Management.

Dundas & Wilson CS (see firm details p.947) A "*balanced*" practice with "*all round strength*" in a full service range of investment funds work. The client roster includes a broad spectrum of financial services groups, insurance companies, banks, building societies and fund management companies. "*Diligent, down to earth*" **Philip Mackay** is valued for his technical skills while "*thorough and effective*" **Michael Polson** "*gets the job done.*" Notable work includes the launches of Britannic Global Income Trust and of SVM OFEX Fund, while the team is currently handling one of the largest single unit trust conversion projects in the UK. **Clients:** Franklin Templeton; Scottish Widows Investment Partnership; Martin Currie Investment Management; Abbey National; CGNU; Baillie Gifford.

Tods Murray WS (see firm details p.1157) The team has maintained its reputation as the "*pre-eminent group*" in unit trusts and OEICs. "*Leading light*" **Chris Athanas** (see p.516) is "*tenacious and thorough,*" and advised Scottish Equitable Fund Management and SEAM Investment Company ICVC on the rationalisation of its retail open-ended funds range. "*Experienced and technically strong*" **David Dunsire** (see p.516) and "*intelligent*" **Martin Thurston Smith** (see p.632) jointly advised Chase Manhattan and State Side Trustees. The firm also acted for Edinburgh Unit Trust Managers and Edinburgh Investment Company ICVC in the rationalisation of sub-funds within its umbrella OEIC and acted on AEGON's integration project of Guardian Royal Exchange authorised unit trusts into AEGON Investment Company ICVC (aggregate value £1 billion). **Clients:** Edinburgh Fund Managers; AEGON; First Colonial (formerly Stewart Ivory & Co); Clydesdale Bank.

Maclay Murray & Spens (see firm details p.1047) Operating from within the corporate finance department, Michael Livingston and the team are appreciated by competitors as a "*small boutique investment trusts*" outfit. Activity with funds clients gives the firm a respectable profile in the market, and the team was recently involved in the Scottish Widows demutualisation. **Clients:** Glasgow Fund Managers; Edinburgh Investment Trust; Brewin Dolphin.

McGrigor Donald (see firm details p.1062) A broad-based practice, acting for a range of fund managers, banks and insurers. However, the team's key client, Murray Johnson, has had its open-ended portfolio taken over by Aberdeen Asset Managers. Described as "*easy to deal with,*" **Frank Doran** (see p.401) remains highly rated, and acted for the investment trusts of Murray TMT and Murray Emerging Growth & Income Trust. **Clients:** Aberdeen Murray Johnson; Clydesdale Bank; Gartmore; DirectLine.

Shepherd & Wedderburn WS (see firm details p.1126) Handled as part of the firm's financial services department, the investment trusts practice enjoys "*traditionally strong clients.*" Perceived to be "*trying to rebuild*" its profile since the departure of its key partner, the foundation to be able to "*bounce back*" remains solid. The team (which is led by Malcom Gillies) advised Ivory & Sime ISIS Trust on its reorganisation, involving an open offer to raise up to £75 million. **Clients:** Friends Ivory & Sime; Edinburgh Fund Managers; Baillie Gifford & Co.

LEADERS IN INVESTMENT FUNDS

ASTLEFORD, Peter
Dechert, London (020) 7583 5353

ATHANAS, Chris
Tods Murray WS, Edinburgh (0131) 226 4771
chris.athanas@todsmurray.com
Specialisation: Specialises in corporate financial services and investment funds; all aspects of collective investment schemes including open-ended investment companies (OIECs), unit trusts, investment trust companies, investment products (including PEPs and ISAs), related regulatory and compliance law.
Prof. Memberships: Law Society of Scotland; Society of Writers to the Signet; Notary Public.
Career: Qualified 1966 *Paull & Williamsons*; *Dundas & Wilson* 1968, corporate department partner 1969-96 and member of strategy board 1991-95; partner *Tods Murray* since 1996.
Personal: Born 1941. Attended Fettes College, Edinburgh; Aberdeen University (1962 MA) 1964 (LLB); WS Leisure: the arts, collecting, walking, golf, angling; Blairgowrie golf club; Luffness new golf club; the Royal Burgess Golfing Society.

BAILLIE, Kirstene
Field Fisher Waterhouse, London (020) 7861 4000
kmb@ffwlaw.com
Specialisation: Financial services – Head of Investment Funds and Products Group. Advises fund managers, insurance companies, and banks on a wide range of retail and institutional investment funds, insurance and pension products – and related financial services regulatory issues.
Prof. Memberships: City of London Solicitors Company; Association of Pension Lawyers; Life Assurance Legal Society.
Career: Qualified *Bischoff & Co* 1987; partner *Frere Cholmeley Bischoff* 1995-1998; partner *Field Fisher Waterhouse* 1998 to present.
Publications: Article in 'FT Unit Trust and Oeic Yearbook 2001' on Financial Services and Markets Act and its impact on collective investment schemes; Article in FT Unit Trust and Oeic Yearbook 2002 on 'Prospects for UK Investment Funds in 2002; Financial services chapter of 'E-Commerce: Law and Practice' written by fellow partner Michael Chissick and published by Sweet and Maxwell (currently in its second edition).

BARLOW, James
Clifford Chance, London (020) 7600 1000

BLAKE, Jonathan
SJ Berwin, London (020) 7533 2222
jonathan.blake@sjberwin.com
See under Private Equity, p.676

BROUGH, Gordon
The City Law Partnership, London
(020) 7253 5505
gordon@citylaw.com
Specialisation: Corporate with emphasis on fund management and fund transactions including flotations, acquisitions and mergers. Specialist interest in partnership law.
Prof. Memberships: Association of Partnership Practitioners.
Career: Founded *Brough Skerrett* in 1994. Formerly a partner with *Bird Semple Fyfe Ireland WS* and prior to that, *Thorntons WS.*
Publications: 'Private Limited Companies: Formation and Management'. 'The Law of Partnership in Scotland'.
Personal: An enthusiastic socialiser and writer (resting). Married with two children.

CLARKE, Dominic
Herbert Smith, London (020) 7374 8000
dominic.clarke@herbertsmith.com
Specialisation: Partner in corporate division. Specialises in investment funds within the UK and overseas and in the regulation of the financial services and insurance industries. His work in connection with investment funds includes the formation and restructuring of unit trusts, open-ended investment companies, investment trusts, limited partnerships, common investment funds for charities, off-shore funds and other investment vehicles. His regulatory practice covers the application of regulations governing the financial services and insurance industries.
Career: Qualified in 1975. Became a partner at *Herbert Smith* in 1987.
Personal: Educated at Leeds University.

CORNICK, Timothy
Macfarlanes, London (020) 7849 2510
tim.cornick@macfarlanes.com
Specialisation: Partner in corporate department. Practice covers financial services, regulatory and securities work. Main area of practice is investment management and collective investment schemes. Substantial involvement in matters on behalf of investment managers, custodians and trustees. Particular experience of unit trusts and open ended investment companies onshore and offshore. Speaker at conferences and seminars for IBC, Cadogan and Oracle.
Prof. Memberships: Law Society.
Career: Qualified in 1982, having joined *Kenneth Brown Baker Baker* in 1980. Became a partner of *Turner Kenneth Brown* in 1988. Joined *Macfarlanes* as a partner in 1995.
Publications: Contributor to Butterworths Financial Services Law and Practice and Encyclopaedia of Forms and Precedents. Lead editor, Sweet & Maxwell's 'Collective Investment Schemes Law and Practice'. Author of articles in International Business Lawyer, Journal of International Banking and Financial Law and Compliance Monitor. Consultant Editor of 'International Guide to Marketing Investment Funds'.
Personal: Born 1st November 1957. Attended Weymouth Grammar School 1969-76, then Worcester College, Oxford 1976-79 and College of Law Guildford 1979-80. Society of Dorset Men; Primary Club, MCC. Leisure interests include opera, golf, cricket, wine, jogging, reading history. Lives in Kent.

COX, Simon F.T.
Norton Rose, London (020) 7283 6000
Specialisation: Partner in corporate finance department. Has a wide-ranging securities and corporate practice with an emphasis on collective investment and international and domestic corporate finance. Contributor to 'A Practitioner's Guide to the Stock Exchange Yellow Book' and author of various articles. Has spoken at a number of UK and overseas conferences on funds, stock exchange and Financial Services Act issues and on investment in the former Soviet Union.
Prof. Memberships: Securities Institute, IBA, Law Society, City of London Solicitors Company.
Career: Qualified in 1980, having joined *Norton Rose* in 1978. Became a partner in 1988.
Personal: Born 17th January 1956. Attended Eton College 1967-73 and Trinity College, Oxford 1974-77. Trustee of two Charitable Trusts. Lives in London.

CRIPPS, James
Slaughter and May, London (020) 7600 1200
james.cripps@slaughterandmay.com
Specialisation: Partner in commercial department. General and international corporate and corporate finance practice with emphasis on listed and unlisted collective investment schemes (including private equity and emerging markets) and advice (including regulatory advice) to providers of financial services and financial products. Co-ordinator of Asset Management Practice.
Prof. Memberships: Juvenile Diabetes Research Foundation (director); The Law Society; Securities Institute; Worshipful Company of Fullers (Court Member) and the City of London Solicitors' Company.
Career: Joined *Slaughter and May* 1978; qualified 1980; partner 1989.
Personal: Born 15 March 1956. Educated Eton and St. Catharine's College, Cambridge. Married, three sons, two daughters. Lives in London and Buckinghamshire. Leisure interests include farming, forestry, opera and golf.

CULLEN, Iain
Simmons & Simmons, London (020) 7628 2020
iain.cullen@simmons-simmons.com
Specialisation: Partner in financial markets department. Handles all types of work relating to commodities, futures and options, unit trusts, offshore funds and investment management. Author of numerous articles in the professional press. Regular speaker at conferences and seminars.
Prof. Memberships: Law Society, International Bar Association, American Bar Association, Alternative Investment Management Association, Board of Editors of Futures and Derivatives Law Report, Advisory Board of World Securities Law Report.
Career: Qualified in 1980, having joined *Simmons & Simmons* in 1977. Became a Partner in 1986.
Personal: Born 13th May 1953. Took a BA in Law in 1975. Lives in London.

DORAN, Frank
McGrigor Donald, Glasgow (0141) 248 6677
See under Financial Services, p.401

DUNSIRE, David
Tods Murray WS, Edinburgh (0131) 226 4771
david.dunsire@todsmurray.com
Specialisation: Partner in corporate department. Specialises in financial services particularly unit trusts, acting principally for trustee. Also handles corporate finance and general corporate work, with an emphasis on acquisitions and disposals, MBOs and start-ups.
Prof. Memberships: Law Society of Scotland.
Career: Qualified 1982, having joined *Tods Murray WS* in 1980. Partner *Tods Murray WS* 1986. Departmental managing partner 1998.
Personal: Born 1958. Attended Buckhaven High School, Fife 1970-76, then Edinburgh University 1976-80 (LLB). Leisure: family, gardening and music.

FARR, Nigel
Herbert Smith, London (020) 7374 8000
nigel.farr@herbertsmith.com
Specialisation: Main areas of practice are transactional and advisory work in the investment funds sector, general corporate finance and M&A. Particular expertise in relation to investment trusts but with increasing involvement with UK and offshore limited partnerships and offshore funds generally. Has extensive experience of acting for funds, fund management groups and financial advisers, with particular emphasis on the structuring, launch, take-over and merger, reorganisation and reconstruction of funds. Also advises on acquisitions and disposals in the financial services sector.
Career: Joined *Herbert Smith* in 1985; partner in 1994.
Personal: Educated at Wimbledon College and Gonville & Caius College, Cambridge. Interests include food and wine, sport, cinema and travel.

GODFREY, Christopher
Burges Salmon, Bristol (0117) 939 2000

HARRIS, Paul
Linklaters, London (020) 7456 3104
paul.harris@linklaters.com
Specialisation: Specialises in investment funds matters. Has over 25 years experience in structuring, creating and organising funds for investment in property of all types (securities, derivatives, financial instruments, real estate, etc) onshore and offshore, domestic and international, public and private, retail and institutional.
Career: Head of investment funds group. Partner, *Linklaters* 1976 to date; 1969-1976: Assistant solicitor, *Linklaters.* University of Birmingham, LLB (First Class Hons), LLM.

HERRINGTON, Tim
Clifford Chance, London (020) 7600 1000
tim.herrington@cliffordchance.com
Specialisation: Partner specialising in financial services including mutual funds, asset management and investment trust work, securities and derivatives trading and regulatory issues, insurance, mergers and acquisitions, Stock Exchange and other corporate work for the financial services industry. Head of the firm's Global Asset Management Group.
Prof. Memberships: Member Law Society's Company Law Committee (past chairman); Vice Chairman, Investment Funds Committee; International Bar Association.
Career: Queen Mary's Grammar School, Basingstoke; Bristol University (LLB). Articled *Clifford Chance*; qualified 1978; partner *Clifford Chance* since 1985.
Personal: Cricket, travel, walking, gardening and wine. Born 1954; resides London and the Isle of Wight.

HOUGIE, Andrew
Clifford Chance, London (020) 7600 1000
andrew.hougie@cliffordchance.com
Specialisation: Partner specialising in investment companies, closed end funds and other collective investment funds as well as transactional and advisory work in the funds, financial institutions and asset management sectors generally and general corporate finance. He has extensive experience of acting in relation to the design, launch, take-over and merger, reorganisation and reconstruction of funds. Recent work included the reconstruction of Biotechnology Investment Limited and the establishment of its successor, 3i Bioscience Investment Trust plc.
Career: Articled *Slaughter and May* 1984, qualified 1986. Joined *Clifford Chance* 1996, partner 1999.
Personal: Stockport Grammar School; Gonville & Caius College, Cambridge. Married. Interests include cycling, walking and bridge.

IVE, David
Rowe & Maw, London (020) 7248 4282
Specialisation: Partner in corporate taxation department. Experienced in all aspects of taxation, especially in relation to financial services, collective investment schemes, unit trusts, offshore funds, life assurance taxation and also taxation matters relating to trusts generally, and tax litigation. Author of articles in various tax journals, including 'British Tax Review' and 'Tax Journal'. Lecturer on tax topics, especially collective investment schemes and unit trusts. Former member of the Taxation Committee of the Associators of Unit Trusts and Investment Funds. Member Law Society Revenue Law Stamp Duty Committee.
Prof. Memberships: Law Society.
Career: Qualified in 1972. Worked with *Allen & Overy* 1976-84. Spent six months at the Tax Bar (1984-85), then joined *Rowe & Maw* in June 1985. Became a partner in 1986.
Personal: Born 2nd January 1950. Attended Highgate School 1963-68, then Birmingham University 1968-71. Chairman of the Association of Liberal Democrat Lawyers. Joint author of a number of Liberal Democrat publications on constitutional reform. Parliamentary candidate for 1979, 1983 and 1987 General Elections. Leisure pursuits include opera and swimming. Lives in London.

MACKAY, Philip
Dundas & Wilson CS, Edinburgh (0131) 228 8000

MARSDEN, Tim
Norton Rose, London (020) 7283 6000
Specialisation: Partner in Corporate Finance Department. Corporate finance with particular emphasis on financial services operations and collective investment schemes, both on-shore and off-shore. Advises on acquisitions and disposals in the financial services sector and advises both public and private sector entities on financial services regulation generally. Commonly advises on corporate and collective investment transactions involving emerging markets. Lectures on financial services, investment trusts and unit trusts.
Career: Qualified 1984; Barrister 1984-85. Joined *Norton Rose* 1986. Partner in 1993.
Personal: Born 9th September 1961. Honorary solicitor to DEBRA. Leisure interests include sport and social activities.

MARTIN, Stuart
Dechert, London (020) 7775 7542
advice@dechertEU.com
Specialisation: Partner, financial services group London. Specialises in advising on the establishment and structuring of asset management and financial service businesses, financial products and related corporate finance work, retail and institutional funds established in the UK and abroad including emerging fund markets, hedge funds, multi-manger funds, property funds and venture capital funds. Also advising on fund mergers and re-organisation involving UCITS and non-UCTIS funds and UK investment trusts.
Prof. Memberships: Member of the International Bar Association.
Career: Qualified 1985. Specialised in corporate finance, investment fund and financial services work with leading City of London law firm between 1987 and 1993, later becoming head of Legal at a major asset management group. Stuart joined the financial services group of *Titmuss Sainer Dechert* (now the merged firm of *Dechert*) as a partner in 1997.
Personal: Born 1960. Graduate of Manchester University.

McWHIRTER, Anthony
Freshfields Bruckhaus Deringer, London (020) 7936 4000
anthony.mcwhirter@freshfields.com
Specialisation: Partner in tax department. Main practice area is investment funds. Advises on all aspects of the structuring, operation and winding up of investment funds and other collective investment arrangements including tax planning and regulation. Author of various articles; has spoken widely at conferences.
Prof. Memberships: Law Society of City of London, AUTIF.
Career: Qualified in 1979, having joined *Freshfields* in 1977. Became a Partner in 1985.
Personal: Born 1954. Attended Downing College, Cambridge.

MIDDLEDITCH, Matthew
Linklaters, London (020) 7456 3144
matthew.middleditch@linklaters.com
Specialisation: Corporate department. Specialises in UK corporate finance and company law. Main areas of practice include advising companies and merchant banks on: mergers and acquisitions, including public takeovers and private acquisitions of shares and businesses; flotations; secondary issues, including acting on rights issues, vendor placings and open offers; reorganisations; joint ventures and general corporate work.
Career: 1990 to date: Partner, *Linklaters*; 1988-1990; Assistant solicitor, *Linklaters*; 1986-1988: Assistant solicitor, *Mills & Reeve*, Norwich; 1982-1986: Assistant solicitor, *Linklaters*; 1980-1982: Articled clerk, *Linklaters.* 1979-1980: College of Law, Law Society Final Examinations; 1976-1979: Trinity College, Cambridge, MA Law.

MINTO, Bruce
Dickson Minto WS, Edinburgh (0131) 225 4455
bruce.minto@dmws.com
Specialisation: Work includes Stock Exchange listings, Yellow Book work generally, mergers and acquisitions and institutional finance.
Prof. Memberships: Law Society of Scotland.
Career: Qualified in 1981. Formed *Dickson Minto WS* in 1985.
Personal: Born 30 October 1957. Attended Edinburgh University 1975-79. Leisure interests include golf, shooting and music.

MITCHELL, Andrew
Norton Rose, London (020) 7444 3502
mitchellas@nortonrose.com
Specialisation: Partner in the corporate finance department where he specialises in investment fund and financial services related work. He has acted for UK and overseas financial services and fund management groups, dealing with merger and acquisition transactions and all aspects of the launch, operation and restructuring of UK domestic and overseas

investment funds. His clients include asset management houses, investment banks and property development companies.
Career: Joined *Norton Rose* 1988; qualified 1990; partner 1997.
Personal: Born 1964. University of York.

PERKINS, Jonathan
Linklaters, London (020) 7456 3049
jonathan.perkins@linklaters.com
Specialisation: Corporate department. Principal areas of practice are all aspects of investment fund work for managers, promoters and investors, including the structuring, establishment and reorganisation of different forms of collective investment vehicles (open and closed companies, unit trusts and limited partnerships), in both domestic and offshore domiciles and for institutional and retail investors. Also advises on general corporate law matters.
Career: 1999: Partner, *Linklaters*; 1992-1999: Solicitor, *Linklaters*; 1990-1992: Trainee solicitor, *Linklaters*.

POLSON, Michael
Dundas & Wilson CS, Edinburgh (0131) 228 8000

ROBINSON, Stephen
Macfarlanes, London (020) 7831 9222
stephen.robinson@macfarlanes.comm
Specialisation: Partner in investment funds and financial services group. Specialises in all types of investment funds, including both onshore and offshore vehicles, unit trusts, open ended investment companies, private equity and property funds.
Prof. Memberships: Law Society, member of Regulatory Committee of the British Venture Capital Association.
Career: Qualified in 1992 in Scotland. Joined *Macfarlanes* in 1995 and became a partner in 2001.
Publications: Co-Editor FT Law & Tax's 'Collective Investment Schemes: Law & Practice.'
Personal: Born 1968. Educated at Hutchenson's Grammar School and Glasgow University (LLB Hons). Interests include sport (football and swimming) and music.

SAUNDERS, William
Stephenson Harwood, London (020) 7809 2138
william.saunders@shlegal.com
Specialisation: Partner in corporate department: funds and financial services group. Particular areas of expertise: the structuring and restructuring of investment trusts and off-shore funds; a thorough knowledge of the regulatory regime governing financial services. Transactions: a number of flotations; takeovers and reorganisations; mainstream corporate activities including mergers and acquisitions, international joint ventures and schemes of arrangement. Recent highlights: the PAM takeover of CNC; the Collins Stewart group management hive out; the launch of the BC Asset Management and BFS Investments property funds.
Career: Qualified September 1994. Became a partner in November 1999.
Personal: Educated at the University of Kent and the University of Grenoble (English and French Law 2:1 and first in French Law). Captain Old Citizens Cricket Club.

SHAW, Michael
Herbert Smith, London (020) 7466 2201
Michael.shaw@herbertsmith.com
Specialisation: Corporate law including corporate finance, M&A and investment funds. Recent transactions include: Friends Provident on its demutualisation and flotation; the DTI on the conversion of the Post Office into Consignia, a public limited company; New Star Asset Management on its establishment and acquisition of Castle Market Holdings and takeover of Jermyn Investment Properties.
Career: *Clifford Chance* 1988 to 1992. *Herbert Smith* from 1992. Become a Partner 1997. Secretary to the panel on Takeovers and Mergers 1996 –1998.
Personal: St John's College, Cambridge.

SHIPTON, Tim
Linklaters, London (020) 7456 3100
tim.shipton@linklaters.com
Specialisation: Corporate department. Specialist in offshore fund work advising domestic and foreign clients on the corporate, regulatory and tax aspects of structuring, creating, organising and marketing funds for investment in property of all types (securities, derivatives, financial instruments, debt, real estate, onshore and offshore, domestic and international, public and private, retail and institutional). Has been involved in international capital market issues of debt and equity securities joint ventures and project financing work.
Career: Head of investment management group. 1988 to date: Partner, *Linklaters*, corporate department; 1980-1988: Assistant solicitor, *Linklaters* London and New York. 1979: Trinity Hall, Cambridge, MA Law; 1977: Trinity Hall, Cambridge, BA Law. Hitchin Grammar School.

SLATER, Richard
Simmons & Simmons, London 020 7628 2020
richard.slater@simmons-simmons.com
See under Financial Services, p.402

STONES, Richard
Lovells, London (020) 7296 2000
richard.stones@lovells.com
Specialisation: Advises financial services businesses, mostly on regulatory matters, the establishment and marketing of unit trusts and other investment funds and other legal issues affecting the industry. Has a general corporate and commercial training, and deals with corporate transactions involving businesses in his sector. Also advises a number of major pension funds on investment management issues. Has contributed to the CCH 'Financial Services Reporter' and Securities Transactions in Europe. He regularly speaks at seminars on regulatory and investment fund topics.
Prof. Memberships: He is a member of the Securities Institute, and of the City of London Law Society Regulatory Working Party.
Career: Joined *Lovells* 1977; qualified 1980; Partner 1987.

SUTCH, Andrew
Stephenson Harwood, London (020) 7329 4422

THOMPSON, Blair
SJ Berwin, London (020) 7533 2776
blair.thompson@sjberwin.com
Specialisation: Member of *SJ Berwin's* corporate finance group specialising in structuring, establishment and operation of private equity and investment funds and advising on venture and development capital investments.
Prof. Memberships: Law Society of England and Wales; New Zealand Law Society.
Career: Qualified in New Zealand in 1995; *Buddle Findlay* 1995-1997; *SJ Berwin* 1997 – present.
Personal: Educated at University of Canterbury (LLB (Hon) B.Comm).

THOMPSON, Pamela
Eversheds, London (020) 7919 4500
thompspm@eversheds.com
Specialisation: Partner and head of financial services group. Main areas of practice are collective investment schemes, pooled investments and financial services regulatory work. Handles onshore and offshore funds and products including authorised and unauthorised unit trusts, open ended investment companies and limited partnerships both retail and institutional. Advises on the structuring of such products. Also handles insurance company products – life and pensions pooled funds. Also handles general financial services work, including regulatory advice, taxation and promotion of financial products.
Prof. Memberships: Association of Women Solicitors.
Career: Qualified in 1982, having joined *Bischoff & Co* in 1980. Became a partner in 1986.
Personal: Born in 1956. Attended St Hilda's College, Oxford 1975-78.

THURSTON SMITH, Martin
Tods Murray WS, Edinburgh (0131) 226 4771
martin.thurston.smith@todsmurray.com
See under Pensions, p.632

TODD, Andrew
Dickson Minto WS, Edinburgh (0131) 225 4455

WALSOM, Roger
Ashurst Morris Crisp, London (020) 7859 1780
roger.watson@ashursts.com
Specialisation: A partner in the company department involved in a wide range of corporate work including corporate finance and investment funds. Advises on all aspects of investment fund work, including in particular investment trusts and venture capital funds, and has been involved in the launch and restructuring of numerous investment vehicles. Also has substantial experience of a wide range of other corporate transactions, particularly in relation to the raising of capital, mergers and acquisitions and capital restructuring.
Prof. Memberships: Law Society.
Career: Qualified in 1980. Joined *Ashursts* in 1983. Became a partner in 1988.

WATTERSON, Mark
Freshfields Bruckhaus Deringer, London (020) 7936 4000
mark.watterson@freshfields.com
Specialisation: Specialises in transactional and advisory work in the investment funds sector, including the structuring, marketing and taxation of investment funds, including property funds and joint ventures, and structuring fund-based financial products and tax-driven financing transactions.
Prof. Memberships: Law Society, City of London Solicitors Company.
Career: Attended Wymondham College 1974-81, Churchill College, Cambridge 1982-85. Joined *Freshfields* 1986, qualified 1988 and became a partner 1997.
Personal: Born 1963. Leisure interests include golf and motor racing (Le Mans 24 hours).

LICENSING

OVERVIEW: Licensing lawyers hope that the proposed reform of laws relating to the sale of alcohol, and to public entertainment regulations, will eventually come to fruition. In December the Deregulation (Sunday Dancing) Order 2000 created a sizeable body of work. Consolidation in the field overshadows expansion, as public houses apply for increased and varied licences in an effort to extend hours of trading. For the meantime, the licensing of internet based companies remains an area under intense discussion.

RESEARCH APPROVED BY BMRB: *For this edition,* Chambers' *researchers conducted 6,552 interviews – 4,419 with law firms, 554 with barristers and 1,579 with clients.*

The validity of the research was scrutinised by BMRB International, who audited both the methodology and the results at our offices in July 2001. They interviewed Chambers' *researchers and cross-checked sample interviews. Details of the audit appear on page 7.*

LONDON

LICENSING • London	Ptnrs	Assts
1 Berwin Leighton Paisner	2	2
Field Fisher Waterhouse	1	1
Jeffrey Green Russell	2	n/a
Joelson Wilson & Co	2	1
Kingsford Stacey Blackwell	2	2
Richards Butler	1	3
2 Davenport Lyons	1	2
Pullig & Co	1	n/a
3 Pinsent Curtis Biddle	5	4

LEADING INDIVIDUALS	
1 **BAYLIS Craig** Berwin Leighton Paisner	**CLIFTON David** Joelson Wilson & Co
DAVIES Suzanne Joelson Wilson & Co	**EDNEY Robert** Kingsford Stacey Blackwell
GLAZEBROOK Peter Field Fisher Waterhouse	
HALLIWELL Tilly Jeffrey Green Russell	**SOUTHORN Elizabeth** Richards Butler
2 **HARRIS Julian** Pinsent Curtis Biddle	**HEPHER Christopher** Pullig & Co
SKEENS Julian Jeffrey Green Russell	

This book is the product of 6,552 1/2-hour interviews. See p.7 for BMRB audit.
Within each band, firms are listed alphabetically. *See individuals' profiles p.526*

Berwin Leighton Paisner (see firm details p.878) "*The risen star*" **Craig Baylis** (see p.526) has "*an ability to deal with a whole range of people,*" and remains key to the success of the practice. Though the success of the merger is too recent to judge, the licensing group is expected to take on many of the spin-off planning and property clients from Berwin Leighton. It has seen a growth in demand for public entertainment licences, and has been active in Westminster on behalf of Chorion. Obtaining licenses for internet gaming is an area of growing importance for the firm. **Clients:** Chorion; Parisa Group; Whitbread; JD Wetherspoon.

Field Fisher Waterhouse (see firm details p.957) "*Stalwart of the licensing practice,*" **Peter Glazebrook** (see p.528) ("*as he gets older he gains even more gravitas*") remains "*absolutely the best in London.*" Acting for public houses, hotels, clubs, wine bars, restaurants and off-licences throughout England and Wales, the firm is predominantly involved in liquor licensing. It also advises on ancillary matters such as planning law, food safety, and health and safety compliance issues. The firm has witnessed an increase in established premises applying for public entertainment licences for special opening hours. It is retained by Westminster City Council to act in its increasingly stringent licensing arrangements. **Clients:** Burberry; First Quench Retailing; Jamies Wine Bars; Selfridges Retail; Unwins.

Jeffrey Green Russell (see firm details p.1012) Though the two partners at this firm work with entirely separate client bases, each attracts positive press. "*Eclectic,*" the "*Queen of Covent Garden*" **Tilly Halliwell** (see p.528) and "*major force*" **Julian Skeens** (see p.531) maintain their hold over the impressive clients in this arena. Halliwell has been active in late licence cases, particularly contentious work in Westminster. The firm recently won a licence for the Soho House at appeal level, and also secured a major new site for Glendola Leisure at the Trocadero Centre. **Clients:** Glendola Leisure; City bars and restaurants; fish!

Joelson Wilson & Co (see firm details p.1013) Acting for gaming, liquor and entertainment licence clients in equal measure, the firm maintains its impressive reputation as a national player. "*On the ball*" **David Clifton** (see p.527) is "*quiet and cerebral*" and "*the past master at careful preparation.*" With the "*highly impressive*" **Suzanne Davies** (see p.527), he has recently secured Hard Rock Café as a major client. The firm has had success in an appeal at the Crown Court, which raised the issue of the admissibility of video evidence. **Clients:** Hard Rock Café; Grosvenor Casinos; Rank Group; Regent Inns.

Kingsford Stacey Blackwell (see firm details p.1022) Described as "*straightforward with no airs and graces,*" **Robert Edney** (see p.528) "*is able to explain things clearly to magistrates.*" The firm is a "*traditional player*" in this market and has seen an increase in public entertainment work, with the trend towards consolidation reaching its major leisure clients. It advised Fullers on its recent hotel acquisitions. **Clients:** First Quench; Oddbins; Punch; Fullers; Pitcher and Piano.

Richards Butler (see firm details p.1107) "*An excellent, no-nonsense advocate,*" **Elizabeth Southorn** (see p.531) continues to cover the range of licensing issues including liquor, betting and gaming. This year the firm completed the licensing of the Great Eastern Hotel for Sir Terence Conran, and advised on the first Conran restaurant outside London. It also re-licensed the entire estate for Mezzanine Group following the acquisition of Deal's and Smollensky's. **Clients:** Conran Restaurants; Mezzanine Group; Thistle Hotels, Centros Miller.

Davenport Lyons (see firm details p.931) Viewed by peers as "*major players,*" the team boasts a wide range of clients, primarily within the media, entertainment and leisure industries. High profile David Lavender is now a consultant with the firm. Under the guidance of Philip Conway, the firm carries out all the public entertainment work for Scottish & Newcastle and represented Oliver Peyton in a successful application for a new licence at 'The Admiralty,' Somerset House. **Clients:** Atlantic Bar and Grill; Granada; Sodexho; Est Est Est; Planet Hollywood.

Pullig & Co The "*thorough*" **Christopher Hepher** has been joined by Graeme Harris (as consultant) from the recently defunct London firm, Loxleys. The firm works strictly within the fields of liquor and entertainment licensing, with clients ranging from small independent off-licences to the largest licensed premises. With more transfers being granted administratively in the market, the firm has been able to concentrate resources on larger applications. It has an on-going stream of work for four major exhibition centres in London, servicing them in unusual, flexible requirements. **Clients:** Off-licences; exhibition centres; nightclubs.

Pinsent Curtis Biddle (see firm details p.x1098) Renowned for being "*excellent on gaming,*" **Julian Harris** (see p.528) extends his practice to cover casinos, lottery and internet gaming. He also devotes a significant amount of time to liquor licensing, and recently acted for an internet-based liquor company. The firm has advised overseas bookmakers wishing to set up on the Isle of Man. It also acts as advisor to the British Casino Association, and recently persuaded it to approve the licensing of automated roulette machines. **Clients:** Breweries; bookmakers; casinos..

THE SOUTH

LICENSING • The South	Ptnrs	Assts
1 **Blake Lapthorn** Portsmouth	3	4
Fynn & Partners Bournemouth	3	2
2 **asb law** Maidstone	5	1
Trethowans Southampton	2	n/a
3 **DMH** Brighton	2	1
Lester Aldridge Bournemouth	1	1
4 **Girlings** Herne Bay	2	n/a
Lamport Bassitt Southampton	2	1

LEADING INDIVIDUALS	
1 **FYNN Lionel** Fynn & Partners	**MESSENT Michael** Trethowans
PALMER Julia Fynn & Partners	
2 **CRIER Phil** Blake Lapthorn	
3 **HARTWELL Roger** DMH	

This book is the product of 6,552 1/2-hour interviews. See p.7 for BMRB audit.
Within each band, firms are listed alphabetically. *See individuals' profiles p.526*

Blake Lapthorn (see firm details p.886) Joining the team as head of department, "*exceptionally thorough*" **Phil Crier**, is expected to "*bring a high degree of professionalism*" to the offering. The respected team specialises in liquor work, and has seen a marked increase in applications for special hours certificates, and off-licences for convenience stores. This year, it successfully renewed liquor licences for 300 premises. **Clients:** Bass; Whitbread; Lidl; Waitrose; Alldays Stores; Balfour.

Fynn & Partners (see firm details p.967) "*Excellent*" **Lionel Fynn** (see p.528) and the "*confident, measured*" **Julia Palmer** (see p.530) sustain their reputation, forming an "*incredibly well prepared*" team. The firm continues to be active on late night operations for a major client. It covers the range of licensing requirements, undertaking liquor, entertainment and betting work. The group increasingly caters for those clients wishing to apply for the maximum number and range of feasible licenses. **Clients:** SFI; Bowlplex; Hall & Woodhouse.

asb law (see firm details p.865) Headed by Stephen Thomas, this "*substantial department*" acts for public houses, nightclubs and restaurants in liquor and public entertainment licence applications. The firm is increasingly busy acting for various small chains and individual licensees. It recently acted on behalf of a pizza chain wishing to deliver alcohol to the home. **Clients:** Famous Moes; Historic Houses; Whitbread.

Trethowans (see firm details p.1161) Betting forms the majority of this firm's work, and **Michael Messent** (see p.530) maintains his reputation as a "*smooth*" lawyer with "*sound judgement.*" The firm is retained by Ladbrokes in England and Wales, advising it on compliance issues and internet development, and also handling its track licensing. This year, the group acted on behalf of Tower Casino Group, both in objections and new applications. **Clients:** Ladbrokes; Tower Casino Group; Pizza Hut.

DMH (see firm details p.944) The "*friendly, easy-going, patient*" **Roger Hartwell** (see p.528) and his team undertake all aspects of licensing work. A dip in sports ground licensing work, has been compensated for by an increased workload for café-bars. The firm handled a successful appeal to allow stand-up drinking in this type of establishment. **Clients:** Jim Thompsons; Tin Drum; hotel chains; restaurants; café-bars.

Lester Aldridge (see firm details p.1038) Specialising in liquor and public entertainment licences, the firm has built up a niche in working for nightclubs in the region. In line with changes in the legislation, Colin Patrick and the team have been heavily engaged in applying for Sunday dancing licences. The firm also acts for receivers and liquidators on all licensing aspects, and conducts betting and casino licence applications and objections. **Clients:** Bournemouth Hotels and Restaurants Association; night clubs; bars.

Girlings The firm has been acting for Shepherd Neame in its wave of applications for new public houses on estates and business parks. A major part of the work of Francis Elton and the team involves advising private members clubs on licensing issues. The firm acts as an agent for nightclubs nationwide. **Clients:** Shepherd Neame; University of Canterbury, Kent County Cricket Club.

Lamport Bassitt (see firm details p.1026) The "*relaxed and confident*" team led by Adrian Lightfoot is finding that public entertainment licensing is on the increase. The firm undertakes a significant amount of agency work for the leading firms around the country. **Clients:** De Vere Hotels; University of Southampton; Meridian Taverns.

THAMES VALLEY

Morgan Cole (see firm details p.1074) Respected **Paddy Roche** heads the licensing department at this "*stand-out firm*" which primarily deals with liquor licensing issues and, to a lesser extent, public entertainment. The firm is part of the Bass Take Home initiative. Most significantly this year, the firm acted in the R v Inner London Crown Court Ex Parte Provis, challenging the right of the police to make representations about applications (due to the lack of prior notice), which it won in the divisional court. **Clients:** Granada; Young's Brewery; Blanc Restaurants; Punch Taverns.

Field Seymour Parkes (see firm details p.957) This Reading outfit has suffered a double blow in the form of Philip Day's move to Fynn & Partners and Larrisa Lowe's departure to Linells. The firm continues to act in liquor, entertainment, betting and gaming issues. It has been appointed by Swindon Town FC for the licensing of the terraces, and also advised an internet café.

Allan Janes **David Hay** leads the team at this warmly recommended firm that acts for companies within the leisure industry, including pubs with entertainment, and independent bookmakers. The firm has seen an increase in applications for variations on entertainment licences. **Clients:** independent licensees; hotels; public houses.

Blandy & Blandy (see firm details p.886) Head of the liquor-licensing unit, **Sue Dowling** (see p.527), is retained by Wembley National Stadium and continues to act for The Oval. Debenhams is a major client for this firm, which also acts for the rapidly expanding Purple Turtle Partnership.

LICENSING • Thames Valley		Ptnrs	Assts
1	**Morgan Cole** Oxford	1	2
2	**Allan Janes** High Wycombe	1	n/a
	Blandy & Blandy Reading	2	1
	Field Seymour Parkes Reading	n/a	2
	McLellans Hertford	2	2
	Turbervilles with Nelson Cuff Uxbridge	1	1

LEADING INDIVIDUALS		
1	**HAY David** Allan Janes	**ROCHE Paddy** Morgan Cole
2	**LOWE Larissa** Linnells	**SMITH David** Turbervilles with Nelson Cuff
UP AND COMING		
	DOWLING Susan Blandy & Blandy	

This book is the product of 6,552 1/2-hour interviews. See p.7 for BMRB audit.
Within each band, firms are listed alphabetically. *See individuals' profiles p.526*

Recently, the firm has been instructed in relation to Twickenham Rugby Stadium's liquor licensing requirements. **Clients:** Sports grounds; public houses; large retail chains.

McLellans (see firm details p.1064) "*Absolutely top-notch,*" this "*thorough*" team, headed up by Clare Eames, "*exudes confidence*" in its work for nightclubs, hotels, restaurants and independent operators. Recently appointed as solicitors for BDL hotels, the firm continues to handle Wetherspoon's licensing nationwide, and the regional licensing for McMullen & Sons. It is also on the panel for Fleurets, the estate agents to the licensed trade. **Clients:** JD Wetherspoon; McMullen & Sons; Queen Mary and Westfield College.

Turbervilles with Nelson Cuff (see firm details p.1163) Maintaining the firm's "*strong reputation,*" **David Smith** (see p.531) acts for a broad spread of clients, including newly formed pub company, 10 Joy plc. The firm is also heavily involved in new licence applications for Holmes Place Group on a national basis. It secured Virgin Active (in the south) as a new client this year, and continues to act for the Sheraton at Heathrow and the Radisson Group. **Clients:** Holmes Place Group; Budgens Stores; World Duty Free; Diageo Group.

Other Notable Practitioners The "*approachable*" **Larissa Lowe** (see p.529) received warm endorsement from her peers; we await the impact of her recent move from Field Seymour Parkes to **Linnells.**

SOUTH WEST

LICENSING • South West		Ptnrs	Assts
1	**Bond Pearce** Bristol	3	1
2	**Osborne Clarke** Bristol	1	1
3	**Clarke Willmott & Clarke** Taunton	1	2
	Crosse & Crosse Exeter	1	1
	Foot Anstey Sargent Plymouth	1	2
	Gregg Galbraith Quinn Bristol	1	1
4	**Bevan Ashford** Bristol	2	3
	Stephens & Scown Exeter	2	1
	Stones Exeter	1	1
5	**Rickerby Watterson** Cheltenham	2	1

LEADING INDIVIDUALS		
★	**PHILLIPS Jeremy** Osborne Clarke	
1	**DAVIES Tim** Bond Pearce	**PARROTT Michael** Bond Pearce
2	**EARDLEY Kathryn** Bond Pearce	
3	**CROSS James** Crosse & Crosse	**GREGG Andrew** Gregg Galbraith Quinn
	HAYDEN Tim Clarke Willmott & Clarke	**PHIPPS Matthew** Osborne Clarke

This book is the product of 6,552 1/2-hour interviews. See p.7 for BMRB audit.
Within each band, firms are listed alphabetically. *See individuals' profiles p.526*

Bond Pearce (see firm details p.888) Cartwrights is nationally recognised as a leading firm, and the merger with Bond Pearce looks set to bring mutual benefits. "*Exceptionally good*" **Tim Davies** (see p.527) heads the team, and his colleagues, "*flamboyant advocate*" **Michael Parrott** (see p.530) and "*wonderful*" **Kathryn Eardley** (see p.528), continue to attract positive attention. The firm handles a significant amount of work in London, and here it secured the first casino special hours licence. It also continues to undertake work obtaining liquor licences for petrol stations. **Clients:** British Retail Consortium; Greene King; Tesco Stores; Ladbrokes Casinos.

Osborne Clarke (see firm details p.1086) The universally acclaimed **Jeremy Phillips** ("*technically good, tactically thoughtful, with superb academic knowledge*") has moved here from the now defunct Eversheds office in Bristol. Expected to retain his clients, he continues to act as advisor to the Brewers and Licensed Retail Association, particularly in relation to the eagerly anticipated government reforms. He is retained by the Arts Council of England as advisor regarding the proposed reform to public entertainment law. He has been joined recently by "*excellent*" **Matthew Phipps** of Eversheds, Cardiff. **Clients:** Scottish & Newcastle; The Belfry; Capital and Regional; Gastronomie und Tanz.

Clarke Willmott & Clarke (see firm details p.915) The "*assured and confident*" **Tim Hayden** (see p.528) at this "*well respected*" firm specialises in regulatory work and practises as a solicitor advocate. The firm undertakes licensing for retailers, nightclubs, public houses and hotels. It acted in the licensing of the new multi-million pound Bristol & West building in Bristol, and for the Tacchi-Morris Arts Centre in Taunton. **Clients:** CWS; Eurest Sutcliffe; Matthew Clark; InnSpired Pubs.

Crosse & Crosse Endorsed for his skills in court, **James Cross** is renowned for having "*a good range of clients.*" The firm sees entertainment licensing and planning law as closely intertwined, and has also acted for companies wishing to set up off-licences on petrol forecourts. It also licensed the Bishopstock Music Festival, and continues to act for nightclubs across the South West. **Clients:** Convenience stores; nightclubs; festivals.

Foot Anstey Sargent (see firm details p.961) An extremely experienced team under the guidance of Tony Daniel continues to act for public houses, off-licences, clubs, restaurants, hotels and leisure facilities in all aspects of liquor licensing. Viewing sporting venues as a niche market, the firm has witnessed a huge increase in licence applications. It also undertakes betting, gaming, public entertainment and lottery work, and handles agency work for major national firms. **Clients:** Public houses; clubs; restaurants; hotels; leisure facilities.

Gregg Galbraith Quinn **Andrew Gregg** (see p.528) is respected as "*incredibly hard working;*" he "*researches extremely carefully and has a great presence in court.*" The firm acts mainly for clubs, public houses, and catering establishments, and has enjoyed a growth in the whole leisure industry. It also handles a significant amount of agency work for national firms. **Clients:** Nightclubs; public houses; catering establishments.

Bevan Ashford (see firm details p.880) The firm's licensing team, headed up by David Wood, deals with the range of licensing issues. Recently acted for Invicta Leisure in obtaining new licences and arranging transfers, final grants and children's certificates. The group also secured the licensing for Cardiff based brewers SA Brain, and has been advising on the sale of liquor over the internet. **Clients:** SA Brain Brewers; Allied Domecq Retailing; Bath Licensing Committee.

Stephens & Scown *"An extremely thorough and experienced team,"* Martin Clayden and the group specialise in obtaining new licences and securing alterations to existing licences for its strong leisure industry clients. Winning instructions from holiday parks, hotels, breweries and off-licences, the firm also undertakes a small amount of betting and gaming work. **Clients:** St. Austell Brewery; Bourne Leisure; Primex UK.

Stones (see firm details p.1146) Paul Keeling leads a practice that primarily works in the liquor licensing arena, and caters for the range of businesses. The firm arranges new club registrations, applications for both on and off licences and occasional licences. Also active in special orders of exemption, protection orders and transfers. **Clients:** Private landlords; clubs; holiday chalets; campsites.

Rickerby Watterson (see firm details p.1108) Public entertainment and festivals licensing make up a substantial proportion of this firm's workload. Derek Jones and his team also secure racecourse betting licences. Recent highlights include obtaining the licence for the Greenbelt festival on Cheltenham racecourse, and a new licence for the Christian festival, Encounter, held in Montpelier Gardens. **Clients:** Whitbread; Greenbelt; Encounter.

WALES

LICENSING • Wales		Ptnrs	Assts
1	**Morgan Cole** Cardiff	1	4
2	**Cartwrights Adams & Black** Cardiff	1	n/a

LEADING INDIVIDUALS		
1	**FREEMAN Bill** Freemans Solicitors	**RAWLE Claire** Morgan Cole
2	**CHILDS Christopher** Cartwrights Adams & Black	
	MORSE John John Morse Solicitors	

This book is the product of 6,552 1/2-hour interviews. See p.7 for BMRB audit.
Within each band, firms are listed alphabetically. *See individuals' profiles p.526*

Morgan Cole (see firm details p.1074) *"Approachable"* **Claire Rawle** has *"lots of experience and conducts fine presentations to the court."* Undertaking an increasing amount of work obtaining petrol forecourt licences for Spar, the firm has also recently secured a national contract with Bass Take Home. It also acts for a major proportion of local independent operators, including public houses, hotels and off-licences. **Clients:** Spar; Bass Take Home; Punch.

Cartwrights Adams & Black Respected **Christopher Childs** *"knows the system"* and leads the licensing department at this firm. Undertaking the range of licensing and public entertainment work, the firm appears throughout Wales. The team acts for a major brewer and a national hotel chain. **Clients:** breweries, hotel chains.

Other Notable Practitioners The *"extremely thorough"* **Bill Freeman** continues to act as sole practitioner in Cardiff and maintains his excellent reputation. **John Morse**, with a practice that covers both liquor and betting work, dominates his local market: *"bluntly put, he is Swansea licensing."*

MIDLANDS

LICENSING • Midlands		Ptnrs	Assts
1	**Poppleston Allen** Nottingham	3	4
2	**Anthony Collins Solicitors** Birmingham	1	2
	Hammond Suddards Edge Birmingham	2	3
3	**Kenneth Curtis & Co** Birmingham	1	n/a
4	**Berryman Shacklock** Nottingham	1	n/a
	Challinors Lyon Clark West Bromwich	2	1
	Freethcartwright Nottingham	2	1
	Young & Pearce Nottingham	4	1
5	**Eversheds** Birmingham	1	1
	Lanyon Bowdler Shrewsbury	2	n/a
	Nelsons Nottingham	1	1

LEADING INDIVIDUALS		
1	**ALLEN Jeremy** Poppleston Allen	
	COLLINS Anthony Anthony Collins Solicitors	
	CURTIS Anthony Kenneth Curtis & Co	**POPPLESTON Susanna** Poppleston Allen
	POTTS Andrew Hammond Suddards Edge	
2	**PEARCE John** Young & Pearce	**SHAW Deborah** Anthony Collins Solicitors
3	**HUGHES Kirsty** Hammond Suddards	**LEE Trevor** Challinors Lyon Clark
	LUCAS David Nelsons	**RADCLIFFE Malcolm** Freethcartwright
	WILSON Robin Berryman Shacklock	**YOUNG David** Eversheds
4	**SHARKEY Lisa** Poppleston Allen	

This book is the product of 6,552 1/2-hour interviews. See p.7 for BMRB audit.
Within each band, firms are listed alphabetically. *See individuals' profiles p.526*

Poppleston Allen Nationally regarded as *"top of the tree,"* this highly focused firm retains its reputation as the *"obvious choice"* for licensing work. *"Knowledgeable, credible, confident"* **Jeremy Allen** displays *"exceptional experience,"* while with **Susanna Poppleston** and the *"excellent"* **Lisa Sharkey** forms an *"effective team."* The firm also deals with related issues, such as planning and regulatory matters. A substantial level of work this year has come from the de-regulation of Sunday dancing, and the firm has also seen a growth in late-night work. **Clients:** Luminar Leisure; Scottish and Newcastle; Chorion; Pizza Express.

Anthony Collins Solicitors (see firm details p.860) A *"buoyant"* firm, headed by the *"organised and helpful"* **Anthony Collins** (see p.527), continues its liquor licensing work and is expanding the betting and gaming aspects of the practice. **Deborah Shaw** (see p.531) maintains her profile as *"a professional who knows the business."* The firm is retained by Brindley Place and Mail Box for advice on licensing matters. Recently, the firm applied for 14 licences on behalf of National Amusements nationwide. **Clients:** Birmingham Mail Box; Brindley Place; City Centre Restaurants; National Amusements.

Hammond Suddards Edge (see firm details p.984) Though the team has undergone personnel changes recently, it maintains its reputation nationally as experts in this field. *"Key player"* **Andrew Potts** (see p.531) has been joined by the highly rated **Kirsty Hughes** (see p.529) of Poppleston Allen. Recent highlights include obtaining 17 new special hours certificates in one day. It also acts for sports clubs, and recently re-licensed Aston Villa FC and Warwickshire County Cricket Ground. **Clients:** Scottish and Newcastle Breweries; Punch Retail; Granada Compass; Apollo Leisure Group.

Kenneth Curtis & Co *"A good following of supermarkets and off-licences"* remain loyal to this firm, which acts for small businesses in and around Birmingham. Rated for his responsiveness, *"strong advocate"* **Tony Curtis** heads a well regarded team that is felt to be one of the strongest local players. **Clients:** Supermarkets; off-licences.

Berryman Shacklock (see firm details p.877) Regarded by some as having "*elevated the firm,*" **Robin Wilson** brings expertise in liquor and entertainment licensing. This year the firm has seen an influx of work due to the Sunday dancing de-regulations, and a stream of licensees wishing to vary their licences. **Clients:** Wolverhampton & Dudley Breweries; Nottinghamshire County Cricket Club; Nottingham Police.

Challinors Lyon Clark The "*able, measured and thorough*" **Trevor Lee** handles work in Birmingham and throughout the Black Country courts. Benefiting from the buoyancy of the city generally, the firm is receiving an increase in applications from hoteliers in and around Birmingham. **Clients:** Hoteliers; night clubs; sports clubs; registered clubs; public houses; supermarkets; off-licences.

Freethcartwright (see firm details p.964) **Malcolm Radcliffe**'s work for his major client, Aldi, keeps him away from the public eye, but he remains well respected in the market place. The firm has developed a strong niche in new supermarket applications. Though the majority of the work is liquor licensing based, the team also wins instructions in connection with obtaining public entertainment licences for festivals. Recently the firm acted for Leicestershire Police in two major club revocations. **Clients:** Aldi; Leicestershire Police.

Young & Pearce With a "*knock-about style,*" **John Pearce** and his team focus on betting and gaming and have developed a niche in casino and bingo work. The firm has seen a growth in individual entrepreneurs setting up café-bars, taking up the surplus from breweries. This year it guided Nottingham City Council through an application for nine bar outlets at the Nottingham Ice Arena. **Clients:** Casinos; café-bars; off-licences; public houses.

Eversheds (see firm details p.952) In this national firm, the licensing practice operates out of the Environment and Regulatory team. **David Young** (see p.687) retains his enviable client base and impressive reputation. The firm finds that large-scale developers are becoming an increasingly important asset in its client base, and it continues its work for Bass and Eldridge Pope. This year has been distinguished by the firm's late licence work in Cheltenham. **Clients:** Bass; Eldridge Pope; Town & Country Inns.

Lanyon Bowdler Adrian Roberts now heads up the licensing department at the firm, which primarily handles off-licence work, and also acts for independent traders and local developers. **Clients:** Off-licences, independent traders.

Nelsons (see firm details p.1080) "*Reliable*" **David Lucas** (see p.530) is known for "*getting on well with the licensing committee.*" The firm has a strong client base in Nottingham, and is increasingly winning liquor and gaming instructions in Leicestershire, Derby and Grantham. Highlights of the year include obtaining a late licence for the opening of a flagship store for Blue. The firm also re-licensed the whole of Notts County Cricket Club at Trent Bridge. **Clients:** La Tasca; Fat Cat Cafes; Notts County Cricket Club.

EAST ANGLIA

LICENSING • East Anglia	Ptnrs	Assts
1 **Howes Percival** Norwich	1	2
2 **Belmores** Norwich	1	1
Eversheds Cambridge, Ipswich, Norwich	1	2
3 **Kenneth Bush** King's Lynn	1	1
Mills & Reeve Norwich	1	1
Steele & Co Norwich	3	3

LEADING INDIVIDUALS	
1 **KEFFORD Alan** Howes Percival	**PARTRIDGE Malcolm** Eversheds
2 **NICHOLLS Simon** Belmores	

This book is the product of 6,552 1/2-hour interviews. See p.7 for BMRB audit.

Within each band, firms are listed alphabetically. *See individuals' profiles p.526*

Howes Percival (see firm details p.1003) "*Deserves its top reputation;*" the firm is undeniably bolstered by the presence of "*big noise*" **Alan Kefford** (see p.529). A recent client win is a builder of bowling alleys, while it continues to acts for the 21 franchisees of Budgens Local. The group has handled applications opposed by the police for public entertainment licences on Sunday evenings. Prominent in the licensing world, it runs the National Licensee Certificate course and acts as an examiner for the British Institute of Innkeepers. **Clients:** Scottish & Newcastle; Mounts Bay Pub Company; Mystic Knight Pub Company.

Belmores "*Effective*" **Simon Nicholls** runs the well respected licensing department garnering himself plaudits from his peers. Securing pub licences is a niche area for the firm. **Clients:** Hotels; pubs.

Eversheds (see firm details p.952) "*Major players,*" this firm boasts the skills of the "*extremely effective*" **Malcolm Partridge** (see p.530). Handling liquor and public entertainment licences, First Quench is a major client for the firm. Recent highlights include the opposed transfer of a public house, in which two of the three participants voiced opposition. The group also handles a significant level of agency work for other firms nationwide. **Clients:** First Quench; UEA Students.

Kenneth Bush Nigel Dodds is in charge of the department at this well respected firm. Acting for hotels and off-licences, it also undertakes gaming work. It acts for major national leisure companies, and it is in this sector that the firm is expected to expand. **Clients:** Major national leisure companies; hotels; off licences.

Mills & Reeve (see firm details p.1069) "*High profile players,*" Harriet Wells leads the firm in a whole range of licensing applications. The firm achieved four new licences in the very week that the Sunday de-regulation laws came into force. This year it has obtained the licences for a large national bookstore, and it also acts for the National Trust in the transfers of licences, and in securing new off-licences for shops. One notable element of the firm's offering is matters handled for holiday parks on the coast, completing their transfer and alteration licensing work. **Clients:** Norwich City FC; National Trust; University of East Anglia.

Steele & Co (see firm details p.1140) Philip Hyde and his team approach licensing from the public law field, and are presently organising the department into contentious and non-contentious teams. Its major work comes from institutional clients, and the firm is retained by the Mayor of London and the Greater London Authority, which it advises on the licensing of the Royal parks and Trafalgar Square. **Clients:** Institutional clients.

NORTH WEST

LICENSING • North West	Ptnrs	Assts
1 **Cobbetts** Manchester	2	4
2 **Weightmans** Liverpool	2	5
3 **Addleshaw Booth & Co** Manchester	1	2
Elliotts Manchester	1	1
4 **A Halsall & Co** Birkenhead	1	3
Pannone & Partners Manchester	2	n/a
5 **Davies Wallis Foyster** Liverpool	2	6
Halliwell Landau Manchester	2	2

LEADING INDIVIDUALS	
1 **HOLLAND Barry** Elliotts	**LAWSON Hamish** Cobbetts
LYONS Anthony Addleshaw Booth & Co	
2 **JONES Simon** Cobbetts	**OWEN Mark** Weightmans
3 **DICKINSON Nick** Pannone & Partners	**HORNE Anthony** Weightmans
JOHNSON Christopher A Halsall & Co	

This book is the product of 6,552 1/2-hour interviews. See p.7 for BMRB audit.
Within each band, firms are listed alphabetically. *See individuals' profiles p.526*

Cobbetts (see firm details p.923) "*Long recognised as a leader in the field,*" **Hamish Lawson** (see p.529) and the "*tremendous*" **Simon Jones** (see p.529) run a "*cracking practice.*" Universally acclaimed as the best in the region, the firm undertakes liquor and public entertainment licensing, and regulatory work for breweries, pub companies and property developers. The firm has secured a multiple licence application on Salford Quays for Orbit Development. It has also acted for The Lowry in its opening and ancillary applications including a general order of exemption. **Clients:** Whitbread; De Vere Group; Yates Bros.

Weightmans (see firm details p.1176) "*First class*" firm, commanding immense respect from its peer group, which is noted for its efficient, direct approach. "*Your man for the detail,*" **Mark Owen** (see p.530) heads up the team, which includes the respected **Anthony Horne** (see p.529). Growth areas for this expanding team include betting applications with its work for Dones Bookmakers. It acted for The Chase (Hestview Authority) in the high profile case which went to the divisional court. It also obtained an exemption order allowing Liverpool FC to sell alcohol at half time, and resisted attempts by the police to close the nightclub, Cream. **Clients:** The Chase; Punch Retail; Liverpool FC; Cream.

Addleshaw Booth & Co (see firm details p.853) "*Excellent operator, analytical, practical*" **Anthony Lyons** (see p.530) leads an "*imposing team*" which "*inspires confidence.*" It advises on liquor and public entertainment licences for a range of clients. A highlight of the year was representing Bakersfield Entertainment on an appeal in Prestonfield Crown Court, obtaining a new licence despite police opposition. It also obtained a new licence without restrictions for a client in Newcastle-upon-Tyne. **Clients:** AMEC Developments; Sainsburys; Inventive Leisure.

Elliotts (see firm details p.950) "*As either friend or foe, they're impressive.*" The "*larger than life*" **Barry Holland** (see p.529) received warm endorsements from his peers. Perceived to be extremely active, the firm has recently secured the licensing work for the MBI of Mustard Entertainment (from the Brannigans chain), and also secured the national work for the new Woolworth's concept stores. Has also acted for several supermarkets in avoiding convictions. **Clients:** Pelican Group; Brannigans; Safeway Stores; Vernons Pools.

A Halsall & Co "*Thorough*" **Christopher Johnson** (see p.529) is the lead player at this locally prominent firm. Acting for nightclubs, petrol stations, and large national co-operatives, he undertakes all aspects of liquor and entertainment licensing, and has witnessed growth in instructions from nightclubs. **Clients:** Nightclubs; petrol stations; large national co-operatives.

Pannone & Partners (see firm details p.1088) Well regarded by peers and clients, **Nicholas Dickinson** (see p.527) has a particular interest in advocacy. The firm has been developing the licensing practice, pushing it onto the national stage. Its work obtaining petrol forecourt licences has been substantial this year, including securing the first of these in Birmingham. **Clients:** Texaco; Jennings Brothers; Fox Group.

Davies Wallis Foyster (see firm details p.935) Undertaking purely licensing and regulatory work, Carl Bruder continues to act on behalf of off-licences, nightclubs, and casinos. Acting exclusively for TM Retail, its work for rapidly expanding client T&J Morris also constitutes a substantial volume. The firm is prominent acting on licensing issues in Scotland. **Clients:** Daniel Thwaites; Safeway Stores; T&J Morris; TM Retail.

Halliwell Landau (see firm details p.982) Adjudged a "*well prepared, friendly team*" servicing a fine client base. Head of department Chris Eddlestone and the firm enjoy a presence in many sectors of the leisure industry, and recently secured Hand Picked Hotels and Sir Rocco Forte's new group RF as new clients. The RF group's new five star hotel, 'The Lowry,' has created a mass of work for the firm. Recently arranged special hours certificates in Blackpool and Bolton despite a level of historical opposition. **Clients:** International Sports Management; Entrepreneurial Leisure; Bass; Clarinbridge Group.

YORKSHIRE

LICENSING • Yorkshire	Ptnrs	Assts
1 **Gosschalks** Hull	2	1
John Gaunt & Partners Sheffield	5	3
2 **DLA** Sheffield	n/a	n/a
Lupton Fawcett Leeds	1	1

LEADING INDIVIDUALS	
1 **GAUNT John** John Gaunt & Partners	**JOHNSON Clare** Gosschalks
WOODS Andrew Gosschalks	
2 **COWELL Martin** DLA	**WHUR Paddy** Addleshaw Booth & Co

This book is the product of 6,552 1/2-hour interviews. See p.7 for BMRB audit.
Within each band, firms are listed alphabetically. *See individuals' profiles p.526*

Gosschalks Though "*filling the Les Green shoes is not easy,*" **Clare Johnson** ("*shrewd – a good performer and hard worker*") and "*excellent*" **Andy Woods** are "*making a good fist of it.*" The firm maintains its position as among the best in the area, continuing to undertake work in liquor, betting and gaming and public entertainment licensing. Finding that its clients are choosing to maximise current licensed properties rather than apply for new licences, the team has been engaged in the revocation of certain licences. A highlight of the year was obtaining the licences for Crystal Palace, in the face of over 100 resident objectors. **Clients:** William Hill; Yates Wine Lodges; Punch Taverns; First Leisure; Esporta.

John Gaunt & Partners (see firm details p.1014) Much of the focus of the firm lies in licensing, principally handling liquor and public entertainment work, and supplementing this with betting and gaming as these arise. The practice is widely acknowledged to be successful, and **John Gaunt** (see p.528) is recognised as "*knowledgeable and busy.*" The caseload takes it all over the country and this year the firm has lodged over 5000 applications.

DLA **Martin Cowell** retains his profile in the local market. The firm acts across the range of licensing including liquor, public entertainment and in cinemas. **Clients:** Breweries; cinemas; nightclubs.

Lupton Fawcett In the last year, John Norris' team has seen a boom in garage forecourt off-licence applications. Working mainly for the convenience store operators, the firm obtained the first of these licences in Manchester. It also acts for clubs and public houses, and undertakes some agency work. **Clients:** Spar franchisees; Londis; public houses; clubs.

Other Notable Practitioners **Paddy Whur** of **Addleshaw Booth & Co** in Leeds has recently made a break-through, winning all of Ladbrokes' betting work for the North of England. Though described by some as "*still on a learning curve,*" he is "*pro-active advisor.*"

NORTH EAST

LICENSING • North East	Ptnrs	Assts
1 **McKenzie Bell** Sunderland	2	n/a
2 **Dickinson Dees** Newcastle upon Tyne	1	2
Mincoffs Newcastle upon Tyne	2	2
3 **Freemans** Newcastle upon Tyne	n/a	n/a

LEADING INDIVIDUALS	
1 **TEMPERLEY William** McKenzie Bell	
2 **SCIENCE Austen** Mincoffs	
3 **ARNOT Richard** Dickinson Dees	**FREEMAN Keith** Freemans
4 **ROBINSON Sarah** Mincoffs	

This book is the product of 6,552 1/2-hour interviews. See p.7 for BMRB audit.
Within each band, firms are listed alphabetically. *See individuals' profiles p.526*

McKenzie Bell (see firm details p.1063) The firm continues to be regarded as "*in a league ahead of everyone else,*" while **William Temperley** (see p.531) attracts accolades as an "*academic thinker,*" whose "*vast knowledge*" and "*particular style is pleasing and helpful to the court.*" Due to the fragmentation of the breweries, the firm is doing more public entertainment work than previously, acting for individuals, nightclubs and city centre entertainment complexes. It also handles betting office work and acts for a premier league football club in its liquor licensing issues. **Clients:** Major breweries; Northumbria Police; nightclubs; sports clubs.

Dickinson Dees (see firm details p.941) "*Enthusiastic advocate,*" **Richard Arnot** (see p.526) works primarily in liquor licensing for breweries, national hotel chains and the police force. Involved in the development of the politically charged 'pink triangle' of Newcastle, the firm has undertaken a substantial amount of work for Trafalgar Leisure. The department has its focus clearly on developing a nationwide presence. **Clients:** Scottish & Newcastle; Northumbria Police; Thistle Hotels, Trafalgar Leisure.

Mincoffs (see firm details p.1070) "*Great deal maker*" **Austen Science** (see p.531) and up and coming **Sarah Robinson** (see p.531) ("*a regular in the courts*") continue to attract positive press as a formidable team. The market perceives that Robinson is coming to the fore in this well respected team. Amusement arcade operators and smaller leisure companies still feature as a major part of the business. It secured the first night club licence in Sunderland, and has been active in obtaining late night licences for premises throughout the North East. **Clients:** RAL Ltd; Absolute Leisure; Ultimate Leisure; Wessex Taverns.

Freemans The well-known team at this firm undertakes licensing work throughout the North of England. Applauded as "*busy, user-friendly, good with clients,*" **Keith Freeman** is particularly endorsed for doing "*a huge amount of work for Bass – a vast area of work so he is highly experienced.*" **Clients:** Breweries.

SCOTLAND

LICENSING • Scotland	Ptnrs	Assts
1 **Brunton Miller** Glasgow	3	1
R&JM Hill Brown & Co Glasgow	2	n/a
2 **Dundas & Wilson CS** Edinburgh	2	3
3 **Harper Macleod** Glasgow	2	1
McGrigor Donald Glasgow	n/a	6
4 **Blackadders** Dundee	2	n/a
Hasties Edinburgh	1	1
Johnston & Herron Lochgelly	1	n/a
Lindsays WS Edinburgh	1	2

LEADING INDIVIDUALS	
1 **BATTERS John** John Batters & Co	**CUMMINS Jack** R&JM Hill Brown & Co
DALGLEISH Douglas Brunton Miller	**LAWSON Peter** R&JM Hill Brown & Co
LOUDON John Dundas & Wilson CS	
2 **JOHNSTON Tom** Johnston & Herron	**MACIVER Archibald** Brunton Miller
3 **FERRIE Audrey** McGrigor Donald	
4 **MORTON Robin** Brunton Miller	
UP AND COMING	
BRYNES Joanna Harper Macleod	

This book is the product of 6,552 1/2-hour interviews. See p.7 for BMRB audit.
Within each band, firms are listed alphabetically. *See individuals' profiles p.526*

Brunton Miller (see firm details p.899) The "*expertise*" of **Douglas Dalgleish** (see p.527) continues to add weight to this "*pugnacious team*" comprising **Archibald Maciver** (see p.530) and **Robin Morton** (see p.530) who continue to impress their peers. Undertaking the whole range of work from liquor to entertainment, betting and civic government matters, the firm's client base has expanded in the past year. Currently involved in an appeal by Safeway against Glasgow Licensing Board for a refused off sales licence in conjunction with BP. Also acted on behalf of Hamid in Hamid v City of Glasgow Licensing Board, the alleged underage sale that took place when the licence holder was not present. **Clients:** Bass; SFI Group; JD Wetherspoon; Safeway; Debenhams; Whitbread; De Vere Hotels.

R&JM Hill Brown & Co (see firm details p.995) "*Walking encyclopaedia*" and "*wonderful raconteur*" **Jack Cummins** (see p.527) and the "*faultless*" **Peter Lawson** (see p.529) create a "*great combination.*" Moving away from the fluctuating public house trade, the firm is concentrating on nightclubs, in particular Carnegies and Luminar. The group recently acted for Luminar in its acquisition of twelve premises from Scottish & Newcastle. Also has a considerable off-sales workload for Tesco and Somerfield. **Clients:** Carnegies; Luminar; First Leisure; Scottish & Newcastle; Punch.

Dundas & Wilson CS (see firm details p.947) Leading light, **John Loudon** sustains his reputation as one who "*knows how best to present a case.*" The firm has yet to extend its relatively localised reputation. Involved in the liquor, entertainment, and betting arenas, it has also acted for an internet-based liquor company. Draws on the support of a dedicated Hospitality and Leisure team. **Clients:** Edinburgh Festival Inns; Scottish Rugby Unions; Odeon Cinemas; Alldays; Stanley Casinos.

Harper Macleod (see firm details p.987) "*Pleasant and more than capable,*" **Joanna Brynes** (see p.526) is the standout associate here. The firm continues to represent 1700 members of the Scottish Licensed Trade Association (SLTA), ranging from large brewers to individual practitioners. It secured the second internet liquor licence in Glasgow for globalwhiskey.com, and licensed the first sushi conveyor belt restaurant in Scotland. Recently appointed to act for Eadie Cairns in connection with the management of all its licensed premises. **Clients:** William Hill Organisation; Eadie Cairns; SLTA.

McGrigor Donald (see firm details p.1062) "*A certain presence,*" with strengths in betting and gaming, **Audrey Ferrie** (see p.528) "*knows her stuff.*" The firm continues to act for Yates Group and recently advised in relation to the first HaHa Bar and Canteen in Scotland. It also represented the Dublin based Bewley's Hotel in its Glasgow opening and has been instructed by SFI Group as it expands into Scotland. **Clients:** Glasgow Royal Concert Hall; SFI Group; Ladbrokes; Sean Graham Bookmakers.

Blackadders (see firm details p.885) "*A big name in his local area, he certainly merits his reputation,*" Ken Glass acts for hotels and public houses in all liquor and public entertainment issues. Of significance this year, the firm successfully appealed on behalf of a sports facility for a national company. The team is increasingly drawing a profile as agents of choice for the major Edinburgh and Glasgow firms. **Clients:** Hotels; public houses.

Hasties This "*localised*" firm acts primarily for smaller companies, including single outlet operators that have gradually developed into chains. Combining the licensing practice with the firm's property offering, Alistair MacDonald and the team act for nightclubs and off-licences. **Clients:** Public houses; hotels; nightclubs; off-licences.

Johnston & Herron Prominent and warmly endorsed, the firm is reputed to "*have the local market well stitched up.*" Lead player, **Tom Johnston** (see p.529) is described as a "*first rate advocate, definitely a player to be reckoned with.*" **Clients:** Private clients.

Lindsays WS (see firm details p.1041) Nora Kellock heads the department that is perceived by the market to be "*content to appear in the Edinburgh sphere.*" The firm primarily handles liquor licensing, but also betting and gaming. Specialising in the temporary licensing of large outdoor events, Murrayfield stadium is one of its major clients. Also acts for Howies restaurants in its liquor licensing as the company expands to Aberdeen and Dundee. **Clients:** Victoria Wines; Granada Group; BHS in Scotland; Sodexho; Bell Haven.

Other Notable Practitioners **John Batters** sole practice in Glasgow generates consistently good reports from his peer group. Known to be a "*true specialist,*" he is "*well prepared and pragmatic.*" Clients include high profile corporates.

NORTHERN IRELAND

LICENSING • Northern Ireland	Ptnrs	Assts
1 E&L Kennedy Belfast	n/a	n/a
Shean Dickson Merrick Belfast	2	1
2 O'Reilly Stewart Belfast	*	*

This book is the product of 6,552 1/2-hour interviews. See p.7 for BMRB audit.

Within each band, firms are listed alphabetically. *See individuals' profiles p.526*

E&L Kennedy The "*experienced, unflappable*" Roisin McGrath undertakes the licensing work at this firm, which acts for pubs and clubs in Northern Ireland. **Clients:** Public houses; nightclubs.

Shean Dickson Merrick (see firm details p.1124) The respected team are felt to adopt a "*detailed, realistic and pragmatic*" approach. Maura Mackay has been heavily involved in the Millennium Project and Belfast Quay in the past year, where the team secured four licences on one site. It also represents the Northern Ireland Federation of Registered Clubs, and 25 of its members. Also on the books is Croft Inns, the retail arm of Guinness, which recently acquired five new public houses in Belfast. **Clients:** Sheridan Group; Hard Rock Café; Northern Ireland Federation of Registered Clubs.

O'Reilly Stewart (see firm details p.1085) (1 ptnr, 1 asst part-time) "*An experienced*" team including Guy O'Reilly continues to act for hotels, public houses, landlords, off-licences, restaurateurs and bookmakers in their liquor and betting and gaming requirements. Acting from the commercial property department, the firm has recently secured a licence for 'The Ramada Hotel', to be run by Andras House Ltd. **Clients:** Hastings Group; Queens University; Andras House.

LEADERS IN LICENSING

ALLEN, Jeremy
Poppleston Allen, Nottingham (0115) 953 8500

ARNOT, Richard
Dickinson Dees, Newcastle upon Tyne (0191) 279 9000
richard.arnot@dickinson-dees.com
Specialisation: Specialises in liquor licensing law and has presided over a rapidly expanding licensing practice which is well on its way to becoming a national presence.
Prof. Memberships: British Institute of InnKeepers. Association of Licensing Practitioners.
Career: Articled at *Mincoffs* and qualified in1992. Spent a number of years specialising in criminal advocacy before being recruited by the Chief Constable of Northumbria Police to represent the force in licensing matters. In 1998 he was asked to join *Dickinson Dees* to establish and develop a licensing department.
Personal: Enjoys most sports and was a keen but untalented boxer.

BATTERS, John A.
John Batters & Co, Glasgow (0141) 427 6884

BAYLIS, Craig
Berwin Leighton Paisner, London (020) 7760 1000
craig.baylis@berwinleightonpaisner.com
Specialisation: Partner in regulatory department and head of the business regulation unit. Main area of practice is licensing and leisure. Handles all aspects for the leisure, retailing and brewing industries including advocacy at all levels throughout the UK. Other area of expertise is business protection and environmental law. Advises and represents on all regulatory matters, health and safety, food safety, trading standards and environmental health. Author of 'Food Safety: Law and Practice' and 'Environmental Regulation- Its Impact on Foreign Investment'.
Prof. Memberships: Food Law Group.
Career: Qualified 1981. Solicitor for the Metropolitan Police 1981-84; Partner at *Field Fisher Waterhouse* 1984-92. Joined *Paisner & Co* (now *Berwin Leighton Paisner*) in 1992 and became a Partner in 1993.
Personal: Born 9th February 1957. Attended Exeter University 1975-78. Lives in London.

BRYNES, Joanna
Harper Macleod, Glasgow (0141) 221 8888
joanna.brynes@harpermacleod.co.uk
Specialisation: Licensing and leisure. Represents The Scottish Licensed Trade Association, OKO Restaurants in the first sushi conveyor belt restaurant in Scotland, Cairngorm Chairlift Company in the highest restaurant in Scotland, Lidl, and RW Cairns Ltd.
Prof. Memberships: Law Society of Scotland.
Career: Qualified 1996; trained at *Harper Macleod*; associate August 2000.

Personal: Educated at Balfron High School, Stirlingshire; University of Glasgow 1991-96; lives in Glasgow; enjoys visiting some of the licensed premises she represents; cinema and reading.

CHILDS, Christopher
Cartwrights Adams & Black, Cardiff
(029) 2046 5959

CLIFTON, David
Joelson Wilson & Co, London (020) 7580 5721
drgc@joelson-wilson.co.uk
Specialisation: Partner in charge of licensing/leisure department. Liquor, betting, gaming and late-night entertainment licensing and lotteries. Acts for a range of leading public companies, appearing as advocate in magistrates courts and crown courts and before local authorities throughout England and Wales. Advises two of the leading trade organisations in the leisure field which has resulted in involvement in the drafting of national licensing legislation and membership of working parties on licensing law reform. "Legal Expert" for 'The Publican' Newspaper and featured on Sky Television's 'Inn Business' programme. Clients include leaders in the casino, bingo, betting, internet gaming, pub, hotel, resturant and nightclub fields.
Prof. Memberships: Law Society. International Association of Gaming Attorneys, Association of Licensed Multiple Retailers.
Career: Attended Wellingborough School (1963-74) and University of Reading (1974-78). Articled at *Joelson Wilson & Co* in 1979; appointed partner in 1983, head of litigation department 1988 and head of licensing/leisure department in 1993.
Publications: Contributing editor, Smith & Monkcom, 'Law of Betting Gaming & Lotteries' (2nd edition) and 'Halsbury's Laws of England: Betting, Gaming and Lotteries'. Regularly speaks at seminars and conferences.
Personal: Born 14th March 1955. Lives in West Sussex. Leisure interests include family, theatre and cricket.

COLLINS, Anthony
Anthony Collins Solicitors, Birmingham
(0121) 200 3242
Specialisation: Heads up the licensing and leisure law department of the firm. Specialises in licensing applications of all types, particularly for national brewers and entrepreneurs. The majority of the applications are concentrated within the West Midlands conurbation but clients are also advised throughout England and Wales. The firm also arranges secured lending for breweries.
Prof. Memberships: Co. Chairman Association of Licensing Practitioners 2000. Vice President Birmingham Law Society.
Career: Articled *Wragge & Co* and qualified 1970, joined *Tilley Carson & Finlay* in Toronto 1970 and admitted as a Barrister and Solicitor to the Law Society of Upper Canada 1972. Founded *Anthony Collins Solicitors* in 1973.
Personal: Married. Three children. Bradfield College. Family history and fly fishing.

COWELL, Martin
DLA, Sheffield (08700) 111111

CRIER, Phil
Blake Lapthorn, Portsmouth (023) 9222 1122

CROSS, James.G.
Crosse & Crosse, Exeter (01392) 258451

CUMMINS, Jack
R. & J. M. Hill Brown & Co, Glasgow
(0141) 332 3265/333 0636
Specialisation: Partner in licensing department. Handles licensing, gaming, leisure and retail matters, representing a wide range of restaurant, retail and entertainment interests in the licensed trade. Author of 'Licensing Law in Scotland' (Butterworths, 2nd edition, 2001); contributor to 'Scots Law Times', 'Journal of the Law Society of Scotland' and 'Scottish Licensed Trade News'; reporter for 'Scottish Civil Law Reports' and Editor of 'Scottish Licensing Law and Practice'. Contributed chapter on Scottish Licensing Law to 'Licensing Law Guide' (Butterworths, 1998). Accredited as a specialist in liquor licensing law by The Law Society of Scotland. Keynote speaker or Chairman, National Conferences for Licensing Boards 1994-99. Contributor to various radio and television programmes. Law Society of Scotland 'Update' speaker. Convenor of Certificate in Liquor Licensing Course, Central Law Training; Convenor and keynote speaker Annual Licensing Conference, Central Law Training 1996-2001. Keynote speaker 'ACPOS' Conference, York, November 1998. Member of Licensing Law Committee of the Law Society of Scotland.
Prof. Memberships: Law Society of Scotland.
Career: Joined *R & JM Hill & Brown & Co.* in 1976. Qualified in 1978 and became a partner in 1980.
Personal: Born in 1952. Educated at the University of Glasgow (M.A., 1974, LL.B. 1976) and University of Montpellier (1972-73). Leisure pursuits include motoring. Lives in Glasgow.

CURTIS, Anthony G.
Kenneth Curtis & Co, Birmingham
(0121) 356 1161

DALGLEISH, Douglas S.
Brunton Miller, Glasgow (0141) 337 1199
douglasdalgleish@bruntonmiller.com
Specialisation: Senior partner. Has been involved in licensing work for over thirty years. Widely experienced, acting for several major breweries and supermarket chains. Also handles general commercial work. Regular contributor to various licensed trade publications. Has addressed numerous conferences and seminar groups. Scottish Legal Adviser to B.E.D.A. and to Scottish Golf Union.
Prof. Memberships: Law Society of Scotland.
Career: Qualified in 1956. Became senior partner of *Brunton Miller* in 1974. Member of Law Society Working Party on licensing law.
Personal: Born 26 December 1927. Attended Glasgow University 1949-55. Chairman of Dumbarton FC; Past President of Scottish Golf Union; Chairman of Caledonian Golf Travel Limited. Leisure interests include golf and football. Lives in Helensburgh.

DAVIES, Suzanne
Joelson Wilson & Co, London (020) 7580 5721
scd@joelson-wilson.co.uk
Specialisation: Partner in licensing/leisure department. Liquor, betting, gaming and late night entertainment licensing, together with associated compliance and regulatory matters, including health and safety, food safety, trading standards and criminal prosecutions. Appears as advocate in courts throughout England and Wales. Acts for, amongst others, Regent Inns plc, IG Index plc, Grosvenor Casinos Limited, Association of Licensed Multiple Retailers and Hard Rock Cafe. One of the firm's legal experts who writes for 'The Publican'.
Prof. Memberships: Hotel Property Network, International Association of Gaming Attorneys.
Career: Manchester University, American Studies BA (Hons) 1982-86, Pennsylvania State University, USA 1986-87, College of Law, Chester – CPE and LSF 1987-89.
Personal: Interests include theatre, cinema and travelling.

DAVIES, Tim
Bond Pearce, Bristol (0117) 929 9197
tdavies@bondpearce.com
Specialisation: Partner and Head of Liquor Licensing and Gaming at *Bond Pearce* (formerly *Cartwrights*). 18 years continuous specialisation in liquor, gaming and entertainment licensing. Advises on strategy and specific issues and appears as advocate nationally. Examples of clients include Hilton Hotels, Ladbroke (Gala) Casinos and Tesco Stores. Co-ordination with commercial partners on licensed property acquisitions and disposals. Consultant to British Retail Consortium.
Prof. Memberships: A National Licensee's Certificate holder (assisted with writing the syllabus)
Career: Qualified 1978 with *Cartwrights*, becoming partner in 1984. Joined *Bond Pearce* in 2001 on merger.

DICKINSON, Nick
Pannone & Partners, Manchester (0161) 909 4503
nick.dickinson@pannone.co.uk
Specialisation: Represents major clients throughout the United Kingdom, one of very few English solicitors regularly appearing before Licensing Boards in Scotland. Special interest in petrol station forecourt licensing. Has lectured extensively on licensing related matters. Has written staff training manuals and written and produced training videos for clients.
Prof. Memberships: Law Society and Association of Licensing Practitioners.
Career: Qualified in 1975. Partner since joining *Pannone & Partners* in 2000, previously head of licensing at *Davis Wallis Foyster.*
Personal: Born 3rd June 1943. Educated at Uppingham School 1956-61. Leisure interests include shooting and sailing.

DOWLING, Susan
Blandy & Blandy, Reading (0118) 951 6829
Sue_dowling@blandy.co.uk
Specialisation: Partner in charge of licensing and gaming department. The department has considerable experience in sports related liquor licensing, often dealing with licensing issues for football and cricket grounds. Has continued to act for Wembley National Stadium Ltd over the last year. Also acts for Wembley Plc/ Wembley (London) Ltd on licensing matters relating to Wembley Exhibition Halls, Arena and Conference Centre.The department has recently been instructed by The Rugby Football Union and Twickenham Experience Ltd to advise on licensing matters relating to Twickenham Rugby Stadium. Continues to act for Debenhams Plc and this year, has made numerous new licence applications for its stores.
Prof. Memberships: The Law Society. Thames Valley Commercial Lawyers Association.
Career: Articled at *Blandy & Blandy.* Associate (1991), partner 1992 to date.
Personal: LLB (Hons) Business Law (Coventry), College of Law (Guildford). Leisure interests include

family, travel, dance, renovation of antique furniture.

EARDLEY, Kathryn
Bond Pearce, Bristol (0117) 929 9197
keardley@bondpearce.com
Specialisation: Partner in the Liquor Licensing and Gaming team at *Bond Pearce* (formerly *Cartwrights*). Specialises in the administration of licensed estates particularly for national retailers and breweries. Has recently been involved in the firm's development of pioneering licensing case management and database systems, the objective being to automate licensing processes, whilst providing clients with enhanced information on their licensed properties.
Career: Qualified in 1978 following articles with *George Brown & Co.* Moved to *Blatch & Co*, then spent six years with Hampshire Magistrates' Court Committee. Joined *Cartwrights* in 1988 becoming Partner in 1990. Joined *Bond Pearce* in 2001 on merger.

EDNEY, Robert
Kingsford Stacey Blackwell, London
(020) 7447 1200
Specialisation: Partner in Licensing Department. Acts for major brewery clients and others in the leisure industry at all levels in relation to liquor and entertainment licensing and related work.
Career: Qualified in 1970, having joined *Kingsford Stacey* in 1968. Became a Partner in 1972.
Personal: Born 8th September 1946. Educated at Cambridge University (MA 1968). Chairman of local tennis club. Enjoys tennis, food and wine. Lives in Aston, near Stevenage with his wife and family.

FERRIE, Audrey
McGrigor Donald, Glasgow (0141) 248 6677
Specialisation: Liquor, betting, gaming and civic government licensing throughout Scotland, acting for clients in the hotel, restaurant, pub, casino and bookmaking sectors. A regular speaker at industry conferences throughout the UK.
Prof. Memberships: Accredited as a specialist in liquor licensing by Law Society of Scotland.
Career: Educated Notre Dame High School, Glasgow and Glasgow University, trained with well-known criminal litigation firm in Glasgow (*Hughes Dowdall & Co*) then to *Moncrieff Warren Paterson* who merged with *McGrigor Donald.*
Personal: Married to a Glasgow lawyer, two children. Leisure interests include travel and attempting to keep fit – when time permits.

FREEMAN, Bill
Freemans Solicitors, Lower Chepstow
(01291) 623 225

FREEMAN, Keith Michael
Freemans, Newcastle upon Tyne (0191) 222 1030

FYNN, Lionel
Fynn & Partners, Bournemouth (01202) 551991
Specialisation: Partner and head of environmental, licensing and planning department. Regular advocate in a wide range of planning, environmental and licensing matters. Has personally conducted numerous cases involving liquor licensing, betting and gaming and noise related proceedings at Magistrates Court and Crown Court level, as well as many Town Planning Inquiries. Recently involved in substantial objections to the village green and waste disposal proposals. Specialises in High Court Challenges/Judicial Review.
Prof. Memberships: Member of BISL, Associate Member of The Institute of Acoustics.
Career: Lectures at national seminars on licensing and planning matters. Produced "cassette law" audio series with Oyez IBC and Law Society. Has produced two licensing videos and a third on children's certificates to wide acclaim. Currently involved in the production of a town planning video on urban design.

GAUNT, John R.T.
John Gaunt & Partners, Sheffield (0114) 266 8664
Specialisation: Main area of practice is licensing and leisure with over 20 years experience in this field. Has developed a wide client base including many plcs and operates nationally. Exclusively retained by many clients. Has handled a number of high profile licence applications (including the licensing of multi-faceted leisure centres) attracting significant media attention and coverage, particularly in recent years.
Career: Qualified in 1976. Became a partner in *Wake Smith* in 1977 and latterly a member of the firm's Management Committee. Co founded *John Gaunt & Partners* in 1995, a specialist commercial litigation and property practice particularly for the liquor and leisure industries. The practice now handles in excess of 5,000 licence applications per annum and has over nineteen people dedicated to the field of licensing.

GLAZEBROOK, Peter
Field Fisher Waterhouse, London (020) 7861 4000
Specialisation: Partner and head of the Licensing Department. Primary area of practice is liquor and entertainment licensing law. Work includes applications to the licensing justices for liquor licences for public houses, hotels, clubs, wine bars and off-licences including supermarkets and applications to local authorities for public entertainment licences for nightclubs and bars and conducting appeals through to the Crown Courts where appropriate. Legislations relating to environmental issues in respect of licensed premises.
Career: Qualified in 1970. Joined *Field Fisher Waterhouse* in 1974 and became a partner in 1977.

GREGG, Andrew
Gregg Galbraith Quinn, Bristol (0117) 925 8123
Specialisation: All aspects of law concerning food, licensing, employment and health and safety. Acts for wide variety of food and drink manufacturers, processors and retailers. See R v Gateway Foodmarkets Ltd C.A. TLR 2.1.97. Notary Public
Prof. Memberships: Secretary Food Law Group, Past President Bristol Law Society, Council Member Notaries Society.
Career: The Dragon School Oxford, The Kings School Canterbury. Solicitor D.o.A. 1970, Notary Public D.o.A. 1984. For 20 years partner with a leading Bristol firm before setting up own niche practice in 1992.
Personal: Born 12.9.43. Interests include rugby, sailing, motor racing and restoration of vintage cars. Owns and campaigns a 1933 Lagonda. Chairman of Young Bristol.

HALLIWELL, Tilly
Jeffrey Green Russell, London (020) 7339 7000
Specialisation: Liquor and entertainment licensing. Work includes liquor and public entertainment licensing for bars, restaurants, clubs etc. Clients include Glendola Leisure (Rainforest Cafe, CC Club). Hard Rock Cafe, Gioma (Gaucho Grill, Calzone), Shepherd's Bush Empire/Brixton Academy, Soho House, Elbow Room, City Bars & Restaurants plc (The 10 Room, 10 Tokyo Joe's) and Bally more Leisure (Shoeless Joe's Chain).
Prof. Memberships: Law Society.
Career: LLB (Hons), Manchester. Qualified in 1970. Joined Jeffery Green Russell as Company/Commercial/Licensing Partner in 1994.
Personal: LLB (Hons) Manchester.

HARRIS, Julian
Pinsent Curtis Biddle, London (020) 7667 0110
julian.harris@pinsents.com
Specialisation: Partner in Litigation Department, specialising in gambling and licensing law with particular emphasis on internet gambling, advising internet businesses and obtaining the necessary regulatory permits. The firm has advised sports betting operators moving their internet operations offshore, the Fantasy League and several gambling and other sporting web sites. The firm acts for several major casino, leisure and food/catering groups, and recently obtained an internet liquor licence for CERT Group Plc. Spent six years with the solicitors for the Gaming Board. In the past year has represented the British Casino Association. In addition, the firm represents two major casino operators in the UK, with casinos both in London and in other major cities. The firm also advises overseas operators interested in establishing a UK presence. Well known regular contributor to gambling and particularly internet related seminars and international conferences.
Prof. Memberships: International Association of Gaming Attorneys, International Internet Gaming Association, European Forum for the Study of Gambling and the Food Law Group.
Career: Qualified 1980; partner *Nicholson Graham Jones* 1986-88 and *Shoosmiths* 1988-93 where he was Head of Litigation. Joined *Biddle* 1993 where he is head of the Gaming & Leisure Group.
Personal: Born 15 May 1955. Magdalene College, Cambridge.

HARTWELL, Roger
DMH, Worthing (01903) 235 026
Specialisation: Licensing and associated property work. Undertakes own advocacy including appeals.
Career: Qualified 1966. Prosecuting solicitor, Brighton Borough Council 1966-69. Joined *Donne Mileham & Haddock* (now *DMH*) in 1970 and became a partner in 1973. Managing Partner 1994-97.
Personal: Born 1943. Education: Magdalen College School Brackley and Bristol University 1960-63. Interests: endurance sports, astronomy, theatre and gardening. Lives in Worthing.

HAY, David Leslie
Allan Janes, High Wycombe (01494) 521301

HAYDEN, Tim
Clarke Willmott & Clarke, Taunton
(01823) 442 266
thayden@cw-c.co.uk
Specialisation: Partner with an extensive licensing practice covering licensing of major retailers, substantial on-licensed premises and night clubs, as well as vehicle licensing disputes and fraud.
Prof. Memberships: UKELA.
Career: Qualified in 1981. Joined *Clarke Willmott & Clarke* in 1979, becoming a partner in 1985. Qualified as a Higher Courts Advocate in 1995.
Personal: Born 10th December 1956. Attended Bristol Grammar School 1968-74, University College

Cardiff 1974-78 and College of Law Guildford 1978-79. Leisure interests include golf and cricket.

HEPHER, Christopher
Pullig & Co, London (020) 7353 0505

HOLLAND, Barry
Elliotts, Manchester (0161) 834 9933
Specialisation: Notary Public 1980. Head of Licensing and Food Safety Department. Acts for major off licence chains in England and Wales and for a national bookmaker and a pools company. Also handles entertainment and liquor licensing for major brewing clients and night club operators. Other areas of practice are food safety and health and safety at work acting on a nationwide basis for national supermarket chains. Chairman of the Food Law Group. Cases have included a leading authority in the field of petrol stations, convenience stores and the preparation of rules for an 'on line' National Lottery game. Has lectured for the Law Society and given both in-house and client seminars on liquor, betting, licensing, food safety and health & safety.

HORNE, Anthony
Weightmans, Manchester (0161) 833 2601
anthony.horne@weightmans.com
Specialisation: Sole area of practice is licensing and leisure. Work includes liquor, gaming and public entertainment. Acted in the first new casino licence to be granted in Manchester for more than 30 years. Major clients include Gatecrasher, Rank Leisure Division Ltd, Menzies Hotels plc, Grosvenor Casinos Ltd, UMIST and Manchester University.
Prof. Memberships: Law Society. Fellow to the Society of Entertainment Licensing Practitioners. Manchester Doorsafe committee.
Career: MA (Cantab) 1983. Admitted 1985. Progressed to *Weightmans* as a licensing partner March 1999.

HUGHES, Kirsty
Hammond Suddards Edge, Birmingham
(0121) 222 3605
kirsty.huges@hammondse.com
Specialisation: Key member of a specialist team operating exclusively on behalf of the Licensed Trade. Acts on a day to day basis for a wide range of operators from listed companies to individual entrepreneurs, advising and making applications on behalf of theatres, cinemas, concert halls, entertainment venues, breweries, stores, hoteliers, sports facilities, pub and club owners, off-licences, post offices and newsagents. She has considerable experience in acting on behalf of receivers of licensed premises.
Prof. Memberships: Law Society.
Career: Joined *Hammond Suddards Edge* in April 2001 having worked for *Poppleston Allen* for three years and *Eversheds* Birmingham for six years. Educated at Manchester University (law degree) and Chester College of Law.
Personal: Holidays spent exploring and trekking. Leisure time devoted to outdoor pursuits, food and sport. Lives in Solihull.

JOHNSON, Christopher R.
A. Halsall & Co, Birkenhead (0151) 647 6323
Specialisation: Head of licensing department. All aspects of liquor licensing including off licence work. Acting for National Companies England and Wales.
Career: Qualified 1971. Partner 1973.

JOHNSON, M. Clare
Gosschalks, Hull (01482) 324 252

JOHNSTON, Tom
Johnston & Herron, Lochgelly (01592) 780421
tgj@johnston-herron.co.uk
Specialisation: Partner specialising in Liquor Licensing. Main area of practice is liquor licensing. Accredited Liquor Licensing Specialist. Advises on and attends at Licensing Boards. Deals with purchase, sale and finance of licensed properties. Author of 'How Not to Lose Your Licence', published in April 1994. Has lectured extensively to solicitors and to licensees. Regular contributor to Scottish Licensing Law and Practice.
Prof. Memberships: Law Society of Scotland (Member of Specialist Accreditation Committee on Liquor Licensing).
Career: Apprentice and assistant at *Allan McDougall & Co.* 1976-79. Qualified in 1978. Partner *Johnston & Herron* in 1979. Past Dean of Dunfermline District Society of Solicitors. Member of Law Society Council 1989-92.
Personal: Born 10th July 1954. Educated at Edinburgh University 1972-76. Leisure interests include reading, cooking and wine. Lives in Edinburgh.

JONES, Simon
Cobbetts, Manchester (0161) 833 3333
simon.jones@cobbetts.co.uk
Specialisation: Partner in commercial property department. Specialises in licensing and leisure work including all aspects of liquor licensing, public entertainment and Gaming Act matters, representing a wide range of brewing, restaurant and retail interests in the licensed trade. Also provides assistance and representation in related prosecutions – food safety, consumer protection, trading standards, environmental protection, weights and measures and health and safety legislation. Has extensive experience in appearing before courts and committees throughout England and Wales and in negotiating with enforcing authorities.
Prof. Memberships: Law Society, Manchester Law Society, Food Law Group.
Career: Articled with *Leak Almond & Parkinson* which subsequently became *Cobbett Leak Almond* and qualified in 1978. Became a partner in 1982.
Personal: Born 28th March 1953. Educated at Birkenhead School 1965-71 and Oxford University 1972-75.

KEFFORD, Alan
Howes Percival, Norwich (01603) 762103
Specialisation: Managing partner for East Anglian office and head of firm's liquor and leisure division. Main area of practice covers all aspects of liquor and entertainment licensing. Also includes gaming matters. Alan is a staunch believer in the principle of providing a one-stop service to the leisure sector. He has made applications throughout East Anglia and the South East on a regular basis. He acts for two major breweries on licensing matters in East Anglia and counts amongst his clients a number of major hotels in Norfolk. Instrumental in *Howes Percival* being licensed by the Awarding Body of the British Institute of Innkeeping to run courses and examinations for the National Licensee Certificate in four centres: Lowestoft, Great Yarmouth, Thetford and Ipswich. Alan is a director of Anglian Archives plc and his family have close links with the hotel industry. He has spoken at various seminars for representatives of the leisure industry.
Personal: Born 1 May 1944. Attended University College, London 1963-66. Leisure pursuits include walking, cricket and golf. Lives in Norwich.

LAWSON, Hamish K
Cobbetts, Manchester (0161) 833 3333
hamish.lawson@cobbetts.co.uk
Specialisation: Partner in commercial property department. Main area of practice is licensing. Acts for most of the breweries and major licensed retail operators represented in the north west, especially with regard to new site applications. Also handles food law, acting for two major national food manufacturers. Acted in Drury & Samuel Smith Old Brewery (Tadcaster) v Scunthorpe Licensing Justices on surrender of licences. Firm advises North West Brewers and Licensed Retailers Association. Has addressed numerous conferences and seminars including 'The 24 Hour City' in Manchester in 1993.
Prof. Memberships: Law Society of England and Wales, Manchester Law Society.
Career: Qualified in 1978. Joined *Cobbett Leak Almond* in 1976, becoming a partner in 1981.
Personal: Born 23 June 1951. Attended Oxford University 1969-72. Leisure interests include theatre (acting and directing) and sport. Lives in Bramhall, Cheshire.

LAWSON, Peter J.
R. & J. M. Hill Brown & Co, Glasgow
(0141) 332 3265/333 0636
plawson@hillbrown.co.uk
Specialisation: Partner in licensing department. Principal area of practice is licensing. Deals with new licence applications, provides an advice service to multiple operators and individuals, court representation (including trading standards, consumer protection, etc.) and renewal/review service for existing clients. Also handles commercial and conveyancing, in particular with regard to licensed premises, providing a full commercial service and advice. Clients include national brewers, supermarket chains and national entertainment companies. Has written various articles for trade magazines and lectured on Glasgow University Licensing Course. Co-presenter of licensing seminars throughout Scotland.
Prof. Memberships: Law Society of Scotland.
Career: Qualified in 1981. Partner at *McSherry Halliday, Irvine* 1984-90. Joined *Hill Brown* as a partner in 1990.
Personal: Born 25 March 1958. Educated at Glasgow University. Holds various directorships. Chairman of Tron Theatre, Glasgow. Leisure interests include theatre. Lives in Glasgow.

LEE, Trevor A.
Challinors Lyon Clark, Edgbaston
(0121) 455 6333

LOUDON, John A
Dundas & Wilson CS, Edinburgh (0131) 228 8000

LOWE, Larissa
Linnells, Oxford (01865) 248607
larissa.lowe@linnells.co.uk
Specialisation: Liquor, betting (including new outlets), gaming, public, and late night entertainment licensing. Handled licensing for large fleet of taxis, including prosecutions for any breaches. Advised large retail organisation on ongoing compliance

issues. Also handled prosecutions for DTI and RSPCA.
Career: Qualified 2000 *Field Seymour Parkes*, Reading.
Personal: Born 1963; Educated University of Utrecht 1983-9; Kingston University 1995-96; Guildford College of Law 1996-97. Previously professional athlete. Currently ranked top five world pole vaulter and previously competed internationally in rowing and triathlon.

LUCAS, David
Nelsons, Nottingham (0115) 958 6262
Specialisation: Works exclusively in the areas of liquor and entertainment, licensing and gaming. Head of department that represents a wide spectrum of clients from plcs to individual operators and two police authorities advising on a diverse range of applications around the country.
Prof. Memberships: Association of Licensing Practitioners, Association of Entertainment Licensing Practitioners.
Career: Articled at Nottingham City Council joining private practice in 1981. Moved from mixed civil practice to concentrate solely on licensing in 1996.
Publications: Contributor to LNTV video on licensing law, provides material and training to clients and organisations involved in licensing work.
Personal: Vice President of Nottingham Rugby Football Club, Member of Nottinghamshire County Cricket Club.

LYONS, Anthony
Addleshaw Booth & Co, Manchester (0161) 934 6000
axl@addleshaw-booth.co.uk
Specialisation: Partner and head of licensing and gaming department. Specialist licensing solicitor handling all aspects of liquor, gaming and entertainment licensing law including a large volume of agency work. Particular strengths in public house, nightclub, theatre, off licence and restaurant work. Council member of the British Institute of Innkeeping and solicitor to the Federation of Licensed Victuallers Associations. His firm is accredited by the British Institute of Innkeeping as a training and examination centre for licensees seeking either their National Licensee's Certificate or the Entertainment Licensee's National Certificate. Client base includes City Centre Restaurants plc, Granada plc, Punch, Scottish & Newcastle, Ladbrokes, Inventive Leisure plc, Noble House Leisure Limited, Stringfellows, Hale Leisure Limited and many other household names.
Career: Former partner of *Lyons Wilson.* October 1993 formed specialist licensing practice *Copeland Lyons.* February 2000 joined *Addleshaw Booth & Co.*
Personal: Resides Manchester. Leisure interests include cycling, snow skiing, fell walking and classic cars.

MACIVER, Archibald D.
Brunton Miller, Glasgow (0141) 337 1199
archiemaciver@bruntonmiller.com
Specialisation: Partner. Main area of practice is licensing. Extensive experience in all aspects of liquor licensing work. Also involved heavily in licensing under Civic Government (Scotland) Act such as public entertainment licences, street traders and late hours catering licences. Regular columnist in various trade papers. Has addressed many seminar groups on licensing matters.
Prof. Memberships: Law Society of Scotland, Scottish Law Agents Society, Glasgow Bar Association.
Career: Qualified in 1982. Worked at *Levy & McRae* 1981-88, from 1984 as a partner. Joined *Brunton Miller* in 1988 as a partner. Accredited by the Law Society of Scotland as a Specialist in Liquor Licensing Law in 1993.
Personal: Born 13 December 1959. Attended Hutchesons' Grammar School 1972-77 and University of Strathclyde 1977-81. Leisure interests include sport (especially football), cinema and reading. Lives in Glasgow.

MESSENT, Michael
Trethowans, Southampton (023) 8032 1000
michael.messent@trethowans.com
Specialisation: Head of licensing department with extensive experience as advisor and advocate in betting, gaming and liquor licensing law. Retained by Ladbrokes, Tower Casinos, Pizza Hut and other leisure companies. Regularly instructed as Ladbrokes advocate in contested betting licensing cases.
Career: Qualified 1971. Joined *Woodford & Ackroyd* 1973. Partner since 1976.
Personal: Educated CS Wimbledon and Southampton University. Interests include golf, walking, travel, food and drink.

MORSE, John
John Morse Solicitors, Swansea (01792) 648 111

MORTON, Robin J.M.
Brunton Miller, Glasgow (0141) 337 1199
robinmorton@bruntonmiller.com
Specialisation: Mobile telephone no: (07970) 272953. Consultant in licensing department. Handles liquor licensing, leisure and entertainment law. Acts for major organisations as well as individuals in obtaining and operating liquor licences, appearing at many boards throughout Scotland. Also acts for banks, purchasers and sellers in the property and commercial aspects relating to licensed premises. Has been involved in a number of reported cases, including one which resulted in a change of law (Mount Charlotte Investments v City of Glasgow District Licensing Board). Accredited by the Law Society of Scotland as a specialist in liquor licensing. Regular contributor to 'Scottish Licensed Trade News' Legal Clinic. Frequently lectures on liquor licensing law and is on the panel of lecturers for the First Annual Advanced Licensing Seminar.
Prof. Memberships: Law Society of Scotland.
Career: Qualified in 1975. With *Brunton Miller* 1975-78. Assistant Director of Legal Aid for the Hong Kong Government 1978-81. Partner with *Brunton Miller* 1981-88. Joined *McClure Naismith Anderson & Gardiner* as a partner in 1988, established *Robin Morton Solicitors* in 1995. Consultant with *Brunton Miller* 1996-date.
Personal: Born 1 October 1951. Educated at Glasgow Academy 1961-69, then Glasgow University 1969-72. Leisure pursuits include music and football. Lives in Glasgow.

NICHOLLS, Simon J.
Belmores, Norwich (01603) 617947

OWEN, Mark
Weightmans, Liverpool (0151) 227 2601
mark.owen@weightmans.com
Specialisation: Head of the firm's licensing department – handles all areas of liquor licensing as well as public entertainment and betting and gaming. Represents most of the major breweries and major licensed retail operators – particular expertise in new site applications. Acts exclusively for the sixth largest bookmaker in the country. Regularly appears before committees across the country. Acted for the successful party in the landmark Hestview decision. Clients include First Quench, Done Bookmakers, University of Liverpool, Liverpool Football Club and Cream.
Prof. Memberships: Law Society. Founder member of the Association of Licensing Practitioners.
Career: Qualified 1987 – partner 1992.

PALMER, Julia
Fynn & Partners, Bournemouth (01202) 551991
Specialisation: Partner and head of licensing department. Specialising in advocacy for all aspects of liquor and public entertainment licensing, betting and gaming licensing, and local authority matters affecting the leisure industry. Also advises on allied matters, including: food law, health and safety, noise and environmental legislation. Julia is highly experienced in new site licensing, with a good record of obtaining "superpub" licences on previously unlicensed sites. Enjoys a national reputation and appears regularly before Courts and Committees throughout England and Wales. Her clients include: major Leisure plcs, Breweries, entire Managed Estates, Stadia operators and Vineyards.
Career: A former legal adviser to the Licensing Justices, Julia qualified in 1980.

PARROTT, Michael
Bond Pearce, Bristol (0117) 929 9197
mparrott@bondpearce.com
Specialisation: Formerly with *Cartwrights,* Michael is a partner specialising in all aspects of licensing law including liquor, gaming, entertainment and cinema licences on behalf of major plcs. Practice has involved applications for judicial review of interpretation and implementation of licensing justices' policy. Has carried out due diligence excercises in relation to the acquisition and disposal of licensed premises and estates. Also acts for national food retailers on food law matters.
Career: Articled in Magistrates Court Service, qualified 1979 and joined *Cartwrights* in 1985, becoming Partner in 1987. Joined *Bond Pearce* in 2001 on merger.

PARTRIDGE, Malcolm
Eversheds, Norwich (01603) 272 660
malcolmpartridge@eversheds.com
Specialisation: Specialisations include all aspects of liquor and entertainment licensing for both independent operators and national concerns.
Prof. Memberships: Norfolk and Norwich Law Society (Former President), Employment Lawyers Association.
Career: Qualified 1970. Partner in Norwich since 1976. Considerable advocacy experience. Specialist in licensing law for twenty years.
Personal: Born 16th January 1945. University of Sheffield 1964-67.

PEARCE, John
Young & Pearce, Nottingham (0115) 959 8888

PHILLIPS, Jeremy
Osborne Clarke, Bristol (0117) 917 3000

PHIPPS, Matthew
Osborne Clarke, Bristol (0117) 917 3000

POPPLESTON, Susanna
Poppleston Allen, Nottingham (0115) 953 8500

POTTS, Andrew
Hammond Suddards Edge, Birmingham (0121) 222 3206
andrew.potts@hammondse.com
Specialisation: Advises on liquor, gaming and betting licenses, with 27 years' experience in the field. Acts for a number of public company clients as well as numerous private companies and individuals. His experience includes licensing airports, football clubs, public houses, night clubs, off-licences, pop concerts, betting offices and gaming applications.
Prof. Memberships: Law Society, Birmingham Law Society.
Career: Qualified in 1971. Joined *Hammond Suddards Edge* (formerly *Edge Ellison*) in 1970, becoming a partner in 1976. Part time Industrial Tribunal Chairman from 1983-95.
Personal: Born 7th September 1944. Attended Aldenham School 1958-63 and Bristol University 1963-66. Leisure interests include tennis, hockey and cricket. Lives in Leamington Spa.

RADCLIFFE, Malcolm
Freethcartwright, Leicester (0116) 201 4000
malcolm.radcliffe@freethcartwright.co.uk
Specialisation: Partner in licensing and commercial department. Principal area of practice is licensing. Also handles commercial conveyancing. Major clients include Aldi Stores and Leicestershire police. Individual charge-out rate is normally £166 per hour.
Prof. Memberships: Law Society, Solicitors Benevolent Association.
Career: Qualified in 1972. With *Ironsides* from qualification and became a partner in 1974. Partner in *Freeth Cartwright Hunt Dickins* 1998.
Personal: Born 22 November 1948. Educated at Oakham School 1959-66. Parish Councillor and Chairman of local primary school governors.

RAWLE, Claire
Morgan Cole, Cardiff (029) 2038 5385

ROBINSON, Sarah
Mincoffs, Newcastle upon Tyne (0191) 281 6151
Specialisation: Licensing, covering liquor, entertainments, gaming, amusements and planning.
Career: Qualified in1994 and became Partner in 2000. Extensive previous experience in civil litigation.
Personal: Born 12th September 1969. Interests in sport, leisure and maintaining personal awareness of developments in the leisure trade.

ROCHE, Paddy
Morgan Cole, Oxford (01865) 262 600

SCIENCE, Austen
Mincoffs, Newcastle upon Tyne (0191) 281 6151
Specialisation: Leisure Department Head. Main area of practice is licensing, covering liquor, gaming, amusements, and planning. Acted in numerous leading cases including R v Herrod, ex parte Leeds City District Council; R v Newcastle Gaming Licensing Committee, ex parte Whiteheart Enterprises Ltd and R v Burt & Adams. Major clients included Rank, Mecca, Scottish & Newcastle, Century Inns and Pubmaster. Editor of sections on Clubs in Halsbury's Laws of England and in Encyclopaedia of Forms and Precedents.
Prof. Memberships: Law Society Planning Panel, National Vice President of the British Amusement Caterers Trade Association.
Career: Qualified in 1961.
Personal: Born 11th August 1938.

SHARKEY, Lisa
Poppleston Allen, Nottingham (0115) 953 8500

SHAW, Deborah
Anthony Collins Solicitors, Birmingham (0121) 200 3242
Specialisation: Deborah Shaw is a partner in the firm's licensing and leisure department specialising in licensing applications of all types, particularly for national breweries and entrepreneurs. Applications are made throughout England and Wales but with a special concentration in the West Midlands. Deborah has wide experience of handling betting and gaming licensing. The firm's licensing expertise incorporates a licensing property department with a substantial secured lending emphasis.
Career: Qualified in 1984. Deborah has 15 years experience with two leading licensing practices.
Personal: Educated at Birmingham University; interests include mountaineering, fell walking, films and theatre, reading, travel when time and family permit.

SKEENS, Julian
Jeffrey Green Russell, London (020) 7339 7018
jms@jgrlaw.co.uk
Specialisation: Partner in charge of licensing and gaming law department. Specialist in liquor licensing, betting, gaming, public entertainment and lotteries. Undertakes cases throughout the UK including Scotland and Northern Ireland. Described as being at the cutting edge of licensing; known for his creative approach. Represented the industry in the leading case of Shipley. Cases successfully handled include the UK's first multi-activity centre, the UK's first 24-hour public entertainment licence and the UK's largest licensed premises.
Prof. Memberships: Law Society, Business in Sport and Leisure (Director), Society for the Study of Gambling, International Association of Gaming Attorneys, European Society for the Study of Gambling, Society of Entertainment and Licensing Practitioners, Society for Advanced Legal Studies. Sits on the National Licensing Forum.
Career: Qualified 1980. Joined *Jeffrey Green Russell* in 1987 as a partner to establish the now thriving licensing and gaming department.
Personal: Born 26th December 1951. LLB (Hons) (1974).

SMITH, David
Turbervilles with Nelson Cuff, Uxbridge (01895) 201700
david.smith@turbervilles.co.uk
Specialisation: Head of licensing dept., joint head litigation dept. Specialises in all aspects of licensing. Clients include major retailers & wholesalers, health clubs, hotel groups and airport retailers. Defends in criminal proceedings, prosecutes for RSPCA. Advises the Association of Licenced Free Traders.
Prof. Memberships: Law Society, Association of Licensing Practitioners.
Career: Qualified in Magistrates Courts Service. Admitted 1981, Private Practice from 1984, Partner at *Turbervilles* from 1986.
Publications: Columnist in Licensing for London Restaurant News.
Personal: Born 1st Feb. 1953. Married with 2 children. Lives in Ickenham. Leisure – football, music, fine wines.

SOUTHORN, Elizabeth
Richards Butler, London (020) 7247 6555
es@richardsbutler.com
Specialisation: Partner, head of licensing unit specialising in the licensing of liquor, betting, gaming, internet gambling, late night entertainment and large new multi-leisure sites; acts for major players in the leisure industry including the Rank Organisation, the Royal Opera House, The BBC; Thistle Hotels, Mezzanine group plc, national bookmakers Coral, Sir Terence Conran, Park Piaza Europe and many of the most active development companies such as Marylebone, Warwick, Balfour and Centras Miller.
Prof. Memberships: Business in Sport and Leisure; Association of London Brewery Solicitors; the Law Society.
Career: Articled *Oswald Hickson Collier & Co.*; qualified in 1974; *Clyde & Co* 1980-82; *Crossman Block & Keith* 1982-88; partner and head of licensing at *Penningtons (London)* 1988-93. Joined *Richards Butler* in 1993. Currently partner and head of licensing unit.
Personal: St Anne's College, Oxford 1968-71; (MA Jurisprudence) 1975. Leisure interests include family, sailing, opera and reading.

TEMPERLEY, William
McKenzie Bell, Sunderland (0191) 567 4857
mckbell@dial.pipex.com
Specialisation: Partner in licensing and leisure department. Principal area of work covers liquor and public entertainment licensing including sports grounds, betting and theatre licences and all types of applications and offences under the Licensing Act 1964. Handles applications to Justices and local authorities and Appeals to Crown Court throughout five North Eastern counties. Handles objections and applications for late licences, revocations and opposed renewals on behalf of police and licensees.
Prof. Memberships: Association of Licensing Practitioners. Fellow of the Society of Entertainment Licensing Practitioners.
Career: Articled with *McKenzie Bell* and became a partner in 1966.
Personal: Born 1940. Attended Bristol University 1958-61. Leisure pursuits include theatres and railways. Lives in Sunderland.

WHUR, Paddy
Addleshaw Booth & Co, Leeds (0113) 209 2000

WILSON, Robin K
Berryman Shacklock, Nottingham (0115) 945 3700

WOODS, Andrew
Gosschalks, Hull (01482) 324 252

YOUNG, David A
Eversheds, Birmingham (0121) 232 1000
davidyoung@eversheds.com
See under Product Liability, p.687

LITIGATION

General Commercial: 532; Banking & Finance: 551; Civil Fraud: 553; Pensions: 556; Property: 557; *Profiles*: 564

RESEARCH APPROVED BY BMRB: *For this edition,* Chambers' *researchers conducted 6,552 interviews – 4,419 with law firms, 554 with barristers and 1,579 with clients.*

The validity of the research was scrutinised by BMRB International, who audited both the methodology and the results at our offices in July 2001. They interviewed Chambers' *researchers and cross-checked sample interviews. Details of the audit appear on page 7.*

Litigation General Commercial

London: 532; South: 538; Thames Valley: 539; South West: 540; Wales: 541; Midlands: 542; E. Anglia: 543; North West: 544; Yorkshire: 546; North East: 547; Scotland: 548; N. Ireland: 550

OVERVIEW: It is evident from our research that no two firms define or structure their commercial litigation departments in the same way. In this edition of *Chambers* we have included not only those recognised generalists, but also featured specialists in the field of banking and finance, civil fraud, pensions and property litigation. Our General Commercial Litigation tables continue to concentrate on those individuals and teams who have chosen not to specialise to any significant degree and who have been awarded with spontaneous commendation of barristers, clients and their peers.

LONDON

40+ LITIGATORS

LITIGATION: GENERAL COMMERCIAL (40+ LITIGATORS) • London	Ptnrs	Assts
1 Herbert Smith	28	100
2 Clifford Chance	*	*
Freshfields Bruckhaus Deringer	27	105
Lovells	*	*
3 Allen & Overy	17	60
Linklaters	17	60
4 Ashurst Morris Crisp	14	46
Norton Rose	27	93
Slaughter and May	8	32
5 Simmons & Simmons	14	41
6 Barlow Lyde & Gilbert	*	*
CMS Cameron McKenna	*	*
Denton Wilde Sapte	*	*
Richards Butler	22	23

This book is the product of 6,552 1/2 hour interviews. See p.7 for BMRB audit.
Within each band, firms are listed alphabetically.
**See editorial entries for explanation of team sizes.*

Herbert Smith (see firm details p.993) The predominant market view is that this firm remains "*the premier league litigation practice,*" both in terms of "*quality and the enormous depth of resources at its fingertips.*" Operating under the "*best known brand name by far*" in the field. Although clients remain aware of the firm's long-held reputation as "*aggressive, red-meat litigators,*" many saw a slight softening of the ways, where its lawyers demonstrated "*the utmost practicality and commerciality.*" One competitor, typical of many interviewed, agreed: "*litigation is a business where experience counts for a lot and these partners have an awful lot of it.*" Among a depth of talented senior figures, **David Gold** (see p.570) remains "*a first class litigator – he's someone people go to if they're really in trouble.*" Peers acknowledged he is "*undoubtedly top of the tree – a hugely impressive lawyer and one of the toughest blokes around.*" "*Superb*" practice head **Harry Anderson** (see p.564) is "*really pushing the firm forward.*" Considered by peers to be "*distinguished,*" **Ted Greeno** (see p.571) is rated for his expertise in the energy field and led the team which successfully resolved the BSkyB litigation. **Charles Plant** (see p.579) has an "*excellent strategic sense*" and **Campbell McLachlan** (see p.576) is said to be "*focused*" and "*attentive to his clients' needs.*" **Christa Band**'s (see p.565) "*star just keeps rising*" and the "*straight-shooting*" **Paula Hodges** (see p.573) is someone with whom "*you always know where you stand.*" David Natali is now a consultant at the firm. The firm recently completed the last of the BSkyB litigation arising out of the 1990 merger between British Satellite Broadcasting (BSB) and Sky Television, where of the £290 million originally claimed, BSkyB has paid out just £10.7 million. It also represented Coopers & Lybrand Singapore in connection with the litigation brought by the auditors of the Barings Group following its collapse, with claims worth in excess of £1 billion. In addition, the firm advised Arthur Andersen on claims made against it in connection with the collapse of the Bond Group in Australia with debts of around A$3 billion. **Clients:** Arthur Andersen; Automobile Association; BSkyB; Fyffes Group; Messer UK; Rio Tinto; Standard Life.

Clifford Chance (see firm details p.919) (47 ptrs and 173 assts available as required) In terms of mainstream general commercial litigation, this firm is widely seen to have "*had an awesome year,*" lauded for its involvement in a number of "*high quality, high profile* cases" which run the gamut of practice areas. The depth of the firm's expertise across a wide range of sectors continues to attract clients with a structure that encourages an element of specialism. "*Smooth as silk*" **Jeremy Sandelson** (see p.580) attracted endorsement from clients ("*he inspires the utmost confidence*") and from rivals: "*always constructive, an analytical thinker.*" "*Charming but hard-hitting*" **Simon Davis** has impressed many with his successful litigation work for Philip Morris in its High Court claim against Rothmans, alleging entitlement to terminate a Marlboro licence for the UK as a result of the BAT merger with Rothmans. Practice head **John Potts** is seen to have "*taken the practice to another level*" under his stewardship. David Mayhew has recently taken up a post at the FSA. The firm represented Severn Trent in its successful High Court action against WPD, Welsh Water and United Utilities

LEADING INDIVIDUALS

★	**GOLD David** Herbert Smith	**STYLE Christopher** Linklaters
1	**ANDERSON Harry** Herbert Smith	**DAVIES Valerie** Norton Rose
	GREENO Ted Herbert Smith	**MACKIE David** Allen & Overy
	McLACHLAN Campbell Herbert Smith	**PARKER Raj** Freshfields Bruckhaus
	SANDELSON Jeremy Clifford Chance	**SPARROW Edward** Ashurst Morris Crisp
	TURNBULL John Linklaters	
2	**FAGAN Neil** Lovells	**FORDHAM John** Stephenson Harwood
	GOLDSPINK Robert Morgan, Lewis & Bockius	
	HOUSE Tim Allen & Overy	**LEONARD Paul** Freshfields Bruckhaus
	PEARSON Nick Baker & McKenzie	**PLANT Charles** Herbert Smith
	TAYLOR Tim SJ Berwin	
3	**BOWDEN Paul** Freshfields Bruckhaus	**CANNON Lista** Richards Butler
	GOOD Diana Linklaters	**KELLY Jonathan** Simmons & Simmons
	MICKLETHWAITE Neil DLA	**NICHOLSON Brinsley** Linklaters
	REYNOLDS John McDermott, Will & Emery	
	SLEIGH Russell Lovells	**TROTTER John** Lovells
	YORK Stephen Vinson & Elkins LLP	
4	**ARCHER Nick** Slaughter and May	**GRIERSON Christopher** Lovells
	HENDERSON Guy Allen & Overy	**HUMPHRIES Mark** Linklaters
	KING Ronnie Ashurst Morris Crisp	**MAGNIN John** Nicholson Graham & Jones
	SHERRINGTON Patrick Lovells	**SKREIN Michael** Richards Butler
	WATSON Peter Allen & Overy	
5	**BACON Gavin** Simmons & Simmons	**COLE Margaret** White & Case
	DAVIS Simon Clifford Chance	**DE WALDEN Ludovic** Lane & Partners
	ELDER Hugh Gordon Dadds	**FRASER David** Baker & McKenzie
	HEARN Andrew Dechert	**HUNTLEY Graham** Lovells
	LOMAS Paul Freshfields Bruckhaus	**POLLACK Craig** SJ Berwin
	RANDS Harvey Memery Crystal	**TOUT Liz** Denton Wilde Sapte
6	**BAND Christa** Herbert Smith	**FINKLER Deborah** Slaughter and May
	GILL Judith Allen & Overy	**GRANDISON Richard** Slaughter and May
	GRAY Nick Slaughter and May	**POTTS John** Clifford Chance
	SLOWE Richard SJ Berwin	**WOOD Jonathan** Clyde & Co
UP AND COMING		
	FRIEDMAN Paul Baker & McKenzie	**HODGES Paula** Herbert Smith

See Individuals' Profiles p.564

alleging breach of the EU public procurement rules, and is acting for Deloitte & Touche (Singapore) in the Barings litigation. **Clients:** Jupiter; HSBC; Philip Morris; Severn Trent.

Freshfields Bruckhaus Deringer (see firm details p.965) "*Clearly a top quality practice*" and "*an efficient, seriously slick machine*" which handles those "*high-profile, high-value cases that require big teams.*" Rivals commend the firm's breadth of practice and the intelligent approach proffered by its litigators. Clients endorse **Raj Parker** (see p.578) as a "*highly incisive operator*" who "*prioritises well.*" **Paul Leonard** (see p.575) remains a "*formidable presence*" in the market. **Paul Bowden** (see p.566) and **Paul Lomas** (see p.575) also received their share of market commendation. The team successfully defended The Society of Lloyd's in the Jaffrey litigation against wide-ranging allegations that Lloyd's fraudulently withheld information from its Names concerning the true extent of the asbestos-related liabilities, which hit in the 1980's. A further key matter involved acting for Marks and Spencer in breach of contract and estoppel proceedings brought by Baird Textile Holdings, a former clothing supplier, in relation to the former's termination of their 30 year trading relationship. Advised the National Lottery Commission on the procedure to be followed by it to ensure that the selection for the next National Lottery operator was fair as a matter of public law. **Clients:** Abbey National; Bank of England; British American Offshore; Deutsche Bank; Equitas; ICI; Lehman Brothers; Lloyd's; London Regional Transport; Sotheby's.

Lovells (47 ptrs and 160 assts available as required) (see firm details p.1044) "*Tactically superb, these lawyers will always be sensible, will fight hard when they have to and negotiate when they need to – they're a bit more-grown up than many other firms,*" so says one competitor. Clients point to the firm's "*efficient approach,*" and many interviewees commented on the firm's long-running BCCI litigation. **Neil Fagan** (see p.569) has "*an enormous reservoir of legal knowledge.*" Some claim that **John Trotter** (see p.697) is "*deceptively understated*" and "*effective particularly in the professional negligence sphere.*" "*Remarkably energetic*" head of department **Russell Sleigh** (see p.581) "*gets on well with clients,*" while **Christopher Grierson** (see p.571) is described as being "*a smooth operator*" who has secured "*some of the highest profile, quality work,*" notably the Bank of England litigation. Competitors view **Graham Huntley** (see p.573) as "*always a handful – he's such a good lawyer,*" while **Patrick Sherrington** (see p.581) once again proved he has a following. Recent key matters include acting for Imperial Tobacco, Gallaher, British American Tobacco and Rothmans in challenging the EU Directive banning tobacco advertising and sponsorship. The team also acted for BAA and World Duty Free Europe in a claim against Eurotunnel for rescission of a 15 year agreement to operate Eurotunnel's retail sites in England and France. The firm has been instructed to act for the liquidators of BCCI in proceedings before the English High Court under section 213 of the Insolvency Act, seeking a contribution from Bank of America to the deficit of BCCI on the basis that Bank of America was a party to the fraudulent business within BCCI. **Clients:** ALSTOM; BAA; Liquidators of BCCI; EBRD; Nortel Networks Group.

Allen & Overy (see firm details p.856) "*Instructed on a vast array of matters – they have really been forging ahead in the past twelve months,*" both competitors and clients commend the "*tremendous thought processes*" of these lawyers. The most senior figures include **Guy Henderson** (see p.572), considered "*thorough and hands-on.*" **Tim House** (see p.573) is said to be "*first rate*" and "*a really bright chap.*" **David Mackie QC** (see p.575) "*rightfully resides in the top echelon of the market*" as he demonstrates "*outstanding tactical ability.*" **Judith Gill** (see p.87) is said to be "*dedicated*" and "*straight down the line – you know exactly where you stand with her,*" while **Peter Watson** (see p.584) once again received market commendation for his breadth of experience. The firm acted for Anaconda Nickel and Glencore International AG in an insurance claim against a consortium of insurers following the late completion of the world's largest nickel and cobalt mining and processing plant, where the parties received A$113 million under a settlement. In addition, the firm has been acting for First Rand Bank of South Africa in proceedings brought by AIG International (South Africa) in a dispute relating to a joint venture to engage in the gold derivatives business in South Africa. A further matter involved instructions from Marlborough Fine Art Liechenstein in defending claims made against it by the estate of Francis Bacon for undue influence exercised over a period of several decades. **Clients:** Barclays; BNP Paribas; Cable & Wireless; UBS.

Linklaters (see firm details p.1042) A thriving M&A market has generated a large amount of litigation work for this firm in the past year. The general market consensus is summed up by one practitioner's comment that "*it's an outstanding practice with highly talented people doing exceptionally good work.*" Practice head **Christopher Style** (see p.582) is a "*real straight-shooter – he calls it the way he sees it,*" while **John Turnbull** (see p.583) is a "*true generalist.*" Peers describe **Brinsley Nicholson** (see p.577) as "*a class act, one of the elder statesman*" in the field. Thought by some to be a "*famous name for the weighty cases,*" **Diana Good** (see p.570) has a reputation for being "*hard but fair,*" while the "*exemplary*" **Mark Humphries** (see p.573) also garners market support. The team acted on behalf of International Power in litigation concerning the arrangements made by National Power and National Grid for dealing with surpluses in the Electricity Supply Pension Scheme. It also acted in the House of Lords hearing of the high profile judicial review claim made by London Transport against the London Borough of Hillingdon. Instructed by London Metal Exchange in its successful defence of judicial review proceedings commenced against it by Albatros Warehousing BV following earlier disciplinary proceedings.

Clients: Abbey Life; BBL; International Power; London Metal Exchange; Transco.

Ashurst Morris Crisp (see firm details p.866) Our researchers were told that this is a "*major contentious firm*" with "*quality at the top and some pretty bloody good assistants.*" The firm is encountered on a wide range of matters. "*Streetwise and affable*" practice head **Ed Sparrow** (see p.582) is rated for his breadth of knowledge. "*Nothing gets past*" **Ronnie King** (see p.575), who remains best known for his litigious work in the oil and gas field. Key matters for the team include acting for Barings Singapore in its claim to recover losses from its auditors, Coopers & Lybrand (Singapore) and Deloitte & Touche (Singapore). The firm has also been defending Imperial Tobacco in smoking-related claims covering three European jurisdictions, and acted for TV Danmark in the judicial review of the ITC's decision in relation to the broadcast of a World Cup Qualifying match. **Clients:** Amvescap; Benfield Greig; BNP Paribas; Morgan Grenfell Private Equity; N M Rothschild.

Norton Rose (see firm details p.1082) Many interviewees believed that this team is "*up with the Magic Circle firms in terms of quality, producing hard fought litigation,*" while barristers agreed that its instructions are thorough, fair and "*right on the ball.*" **Val Davies** (see p.568) is said to be "*quite aggressive but pretty effective,*" best known for her work in the Maxwell Pensions Fund matter against Coopers & Lybrand, which resulted in the largest ever settlement against a UK firm of auditors. Key matters for the firm include acting for a representative policyholder against The Equitable Life Assurance Society in an action concerning its practice of declaring lower levels of final bonus to GAR policyholders, which affected 100,000 policyholders and the industry at large. The firm also acted successfully for Banque Paribas in a $20 million letter of dispute, and is currently acting for the trustee and protector companies of a substantial Bermuda-based trust in the Thyssen litigation. **Clients:** BNP Paribas; Credit Agricole Indosuez; Société Générale; Thybo Trustees.

Slaughter and May (see firm details p.1135) Built on the foundations of "*a raft of huge corporate clients,*" the firm's policy of "*non-specialisation means they don't target litigation,*" according to the perception of many rival litigators. There was, however, considerable market support for the quality, commerciality and depth of experience across this well-resourced team that consistently secures the most high profile transactions. **Nick Archer** (see p.564) is "*known as a personality*" in addition to being a "*top quality litigator.*" **Deborah Finkler** (see p.569) has been described as being "*pretty special*" with "*the judgment and the guts to go with her instinct.*" **Nick Gray** (see p.571) and the "*extremely professional*" practice head **Richard Grandison** (see p.571) also received warm recommendations during our research. Many admired the team's involvement in high profile cases, such as acting for the liquidators of Barings in their £1 billion claim for negligence against Coopers & Lybrand's London and Singapore offices and Deloitte & Touche Singapore. In addition, the firm has been acting for Unilever on its ground-breaking claim against Mercury Asset Management arising out of the latter's alleged mismanagement of Unilever's pension fund. The team also acting for Marsh & McLennan Companies in its appeal to the High Court from a decision of the Pensions Ombudsman, which raised important questions concerning the equalisation of Guaranteed Minimum Pension. **Clients:** Liquidators of Barings, Marsh & McLennan Companies; RAC; Unilever.

Simmons & Simmons (see firm details p.1132) Considered a team of "*tough operators*" which has "*had a pretty good year,*" particularly applauded for its finance and telecoms matters. **Jonathan Kelly** (see p.574) specialises in large domestic and international litigation arising out of banking, corporate and financial services disputes. **Gavin Bacon**'s (see p.564) practice includes regulatory and defamation cases as well a range of investigation work. The highlight of the past year was continued instruction from Merrill Lynch Investment Managers on its defence in the landmark litigation brought by Unilever's pension fund. The team also successfully defended Donohue and others against an action brought by the US Armco Group, relating to issues arising out of a management buyout. It brought judicial review proceedings on behalf of One2One against the Secretary of State for Trade and Industry, alleging unlawful conduct in allowing Vodafone and Orange to delay in making payment of their 3G mobile licences. **Clients:** Gallaher; Independent Television Commission; Merrill Lynch; Railtrack.

Barlow Lyde & Gilbert (see firm details p.870) (Able to draw from 53 ptrs and 109 assts) General market consensus agrees that this "*pretty sensible outfit*" fields "*competent litigators.*" Peers felt that "*attitude-wise, they've really taken to the new rules and won't be obtuse, properly explaining the client's position.*" Although its niche strengths remain insurance, professional negligence and to a lesser extent construction disputes, the firm is nonetheless active in mainstream commercial disputes. The team acted for PricewaterhouseCoopers in the claim brought by Elton John. The firm was also successful at first instance in the Metro Trading International case, where it is representing the principal defendant against a $400 million claim. It has recently been retained by National Express Group for all its UK litigation, which has already led to two substantial instructions, one dispute relating to bus business and the other dispute relating to rail matters. **Clients:** Dixons; Gulf International Bank; National Express Group; PricewaterhouseCoopers.

CMS Cameron McKenna (see firm details p.922) (Able to draw from 36 ptrs and 105 assts) Competitors are of the view that this firm "*acts for a number of impressive clients,*" forming a regular feature in major pieces of litigation. Many believe its main strengths to be construction and product liability, while the team, although in itself a sensible and reasoned offering, has failed to produce a standout practitioner. The firm acted for DSND Subsea in the £20 million TCC litigation against DGS Offshore Technology AS and another party. It is currently representing Media Most, one of the biggest media outlets in Russia, in a dispute with the Russian government concerning $260 million worth of shares. In addition, the team has been instructed by First Union National Bank in an international shipping fraud matter to the value of £300 million. **Clients:** DSND Subsea; First Union National Bank; The Post Office.

Denton Wilde Sapte (see firm details p.939) (Able to draw from 33 ptrs and 52 assts) The marriage of Wilde Sapte's litigation capability in the specialist areas of banking, insurance and insolvency and Denton Hall's litigation expertise in sectors such as energy, infrastructure and technology has proved to be a happy one. The result is a "*fairly generalist practice that can turn its hand to any dispute.*" Joint head of department **Liz Tout** has "*a realistic attitude*" to litigation and "*doesn't take bad points.*" The firm acted for Credit Lyonnais in a US$200 million dispute between Glencore International and Metro Trading International. It also acted for Wembley National Stadium in its claim for rectification against Wembley (London) arising out of the acquisition of the stadium in 1999. In addition, the firm continues to act for the Equitable Life Assurance Society in its landmark application in the House of Lords relating to guaranteed annuity rates. **Clients:** Credit Lyonnais; Equitable Life Assurance Society; Wembley National Stadium.

Richards Butler (see firm details p.1107) Its strengths lie in investment banking litigation, professional negligence and technology disputes. Competitors view it as "*high quality across the board,*" employing *a "sensible commercial approach,"* while barristers comment that its lawyers are "*always well prepared.*" **Lista Cannon** (see p.566) is visible on "*high profile matters for demanding clients, and she keeps them happy.*" **Michael Skrein** (see p.581) has a practice wider than his media related cases. Key matters for the firm include obtaining a successful ruling from the World Intellectual Property Organisation (WIPO) after filing ICANN complaints at on behalf of Direct Line, NatWest, Dixons and Freeserve, where a cybersquatter had registered these domain names. The team also acted for Express Newspapers where the Court of Appeal made a landmark decision in protecting the privilege of the journalist to protect his source. Also acted for a French company in relation to a prime bank investment fraud. **Clients:** Bar Mutual Indemnity Fund; BBC; Direct Line; Eurocontrol; Express Newspapers; Fiat Auto (UK); Galileo International; Hoverspeed; Lloyds TSB; MTV; The Rank Group; SmithKline Beecham; Trilium Property Service.

FEWER THAN 40 LITIGATORS

LITIGATION: GENERAL COMMERCIAL (FEWER THAN 40 LITIGATORS) • London	Ptnrs	Assts
1 Baker & McKenzie	9	24
SJ Berwin	11	20
Stephenson Harwood	n/a	n/a
2 Clyde & Co	n/a	n/a
Gouldens	6	11
3 DJ Freeman	11	13
Dechert	10	14
Eversheds	n/a	n/a
Nabarro Nathanson	4	14
Nicholson Graham & Jones	10	15
4 Berwin Leighton Paisner	n/a	n/a
Lawrence Graham	n/a	n/a
Macfarlanes	6	17
Reynolds Porter Chamberlain	6	12
Rowe & Maw	n/a	n/a
Taylor Joynson Garrett	17	22
Travers Smith Braithwaite	5	9
5 Hammond Suddards Edge	7	14
Mishcon de Reya	11	12
Theodore Goddard	5	12
6 Charles Russell	12	11
Ince & Co	n/a	n/a
Lane & Partners	3	4
Lewis Silkin	6	9
Masons	n/a	n/a
Memery Crystal	2	4
Pinsent Curtis Biddle	4	3
Reed Smith Warner Cranston	5	6
White & Case	3	8

This book is the product of 6,552 1/2 hour interviews. See p.7 for BMRB audit.
Within each band, firms are listed alphabetically.

Baker & McKenzie (see firm details p.868) Clients and competitors view this firm as "*good at managing the co-ordination of international work and cross-border issues.*" Head of department **Nick Pearson** (see p.578) is seen to be a "*serious individual*" endorsed for his work on the Grupo Torras litigation. **David Fraser** (see p.569) is a "*highly considered individual*" who is "*good at devising a strategy.*" Many commented on his input advising Camelot in its highly publicised proceedings against the National Lottery. He was also instructed by Ken Livingstone in his dispute with the government over PPP plans for London Underground. **Paul Friedman** (see p.569) is described as "*a tough operator*" who "*thinks outside of the box*" and, according to one client, can be "*the lone voice of reason, with his clear advice.*" In disputes arising from the sale of Geest's banana business to Fyffes, the team advised Geest on its defence of a £30 million claim by Fyffes for breach of warranty, and also acted in a £14 million claim brought by Geest against Fyffes for fraudulent misrepresentation. It continues to act for Grupo Torras in its ongoing litigation, in which over US$140 million was recovered from the Bahamas in 2001. **Clients:** Bank Leumi; Camelot; Cooper Industries; Emerson Electric; Federal Express; Grupo Torras; National Bus; Pacific Century Cyberworks; Saudi British Bank; Sony; Transport for London.

SJ Berwin (see firm details p.879) With a "*particular forte in multi-jurisdictional litigation,* the firm is judged to be "*going from strength to strength in the international scene.*" **Tim Taylor** (see p.582) is seen to be "*knowledgeable*" and "*a good manager of client relationships as well as cases.*" He is considered key to much of the firm's success. **Craig Pollack** (see p.579) is described by a leading silk as being "*always on the ball and well-prepared,*" while one client, typical of many, said he had "*a brilliant brain.*" The "*thorough and impressive*" **Richard Slowe** (see p.581) is a solicitor-advocate. Recent key matters for the team include acting for five separate companies in a claim by Tamarind International and others, for compensation/indemnity against subsidiaries of Eastern Electricity (aggregate sum in excess of £100 million). The team defended Viktor Kozeny against a $200 million claim brought by AIG and others, relating to the voucher privatisation scheme in Azerbaijan. Instructed by Morgan Stanley Dean Witter in litigation arising from Visa's alleged anti-competitive exclusion of MSDW from its network in Europe. **Clients:** ANZ Investment Bank; Atlantic Estates; The British Land Company; Carlton Television; Drake Insurance; Fyffes; Hilton Group; Leeds Sporting; Marks & Spencer; Pandora Films; Société Générale; WPP Group.

Stephenson Harwood (see firm details p.1141) "*Quite a litigation force,*" The firm has seen an increase in 'risk advisory' work in the last year, particularly with its roster of financial sector and professional services clients. Practice head **John Fordham** (see p.569) is described by our interviewees as "*a pretty outstanding litigator, and personable with it.*" Key highlights for the team include representing Swiss trading company Noga in the Abacha case, concerning a several hundred million-dollar action against Mohammed Abacha, the son of the late Nigerian dictator. Other matters include acting for the Bank of America on a major international fraud case and advising in the ABN AMRO whistleblowing case. **Clients:** Christie's; Noga; HSBC; Royal Bank of Scotland.

Clyde & Co (see firm details p.921) Much of this firm's contentious work is generated by the shipping, trading, insurance and finance sectors, although it does undertake a significant amount outside of this domain. The bar is of the opinion that it "*always provides well handled instructions.*" Head of department **Jonathan Wood** (see p.585) enters the rankings this year after warm endorsement, and is thought to generate much of his work from the firm's insurance clients. The team has been acting in the Piper Alpha litigation, which arose out of the North Sea disaster, and has also been instructed by the UK government in relation to the BSE Inquiry. It continues its involvement in the high profile Metro Litigation, acting for an international trading company in an attempt to recover $30 million relating to the construction of a refinery in the UAE. **Clients:** CGU; Euler Trade Indemnity; Export Credits Guarantee Department; NCM Credit Insurance.

Gouldens (see firm details p.976) "*Still churning out some impressive work,*" the firm has been active across the board, with many of its disputes international in nature. The team acted for Glaxo Wellcome and Boehringer Ingelheim against Dowelhurst and others (parallel importers in the pharmaceutical sector), and advised SEA Assets in a successful claim against PT Garuda Indonesia, where the court held that the CPR had changed the service regime for foreign companies trading in the UK. Another key highlight saw the team advising Standard Bank in the first case before the English courts under Article 13 of the Brussels Convention on jurisdiction, as to what constitutes specific invitation or advertising for the purposes of obtaining investment business in the EU. **Clients:** Arlington; Ashtenne; Bhs; Cargill; Delancey; Hanson; Miller; Marks & Spencer; Mothercare; Pillar; Tomkins; TT Group.

DJ Freeman (see firm details p.943) Competitors view the firm as being "*good and efficient,*" with clients of the opinion that "*they give accurate and fast advice.*" Its principal target market lies with the major corporates and financial houses. Over the past year the firm has been instructed on a number of matters by Invensys, including acting against three French banks in a multi-million pound action arising out of 1980's lendings. It has also been acting for Mohammed Al Fayed in a further round in the judicial review of the decision not to grant him a British passport, and for Shell in a number of up and downstream litigation matters. **Clients:** Invensys; Mohammed Al Fayed; Shell.

Dechert (see firm details p.938) Clients described these lawyers as "*thorough – they respond quickly, make themselves available and are particularly keen to talk through issues,*" indeed peers commend the firm's commerciality. **Andrew Hearn** (see p.572) has an extensive client base, which includes major retailing chains, travel companies, publishing, and those operating in the food and drink sectors. The team represented the family and associates of the late General Sani Abacha of Nigeria in their worldwide disputes with the Federal Government of Nigeria and the Swiss corporation, Noga. Instructed by a Liechtenstein corporation in a dispute concerning ultimate beneficial entitlements in its parent, which involved proceedings in England, France and Liechtenstein. A further matter involved successfully enforcing a substantial New York judgment against the Government of Peru. **Clients:** Banner Homes; Dixons; Etam; Fiske; Irish Life; J Rothschild Assurance; London Underground; Oasis Group; Saga Group; Telegraph Newspapers; William Hill.

Eversheds (see firm details p.952) Continues to handle a wide range of disputes, with recognised strength in international matters and those arising from the media, insurance and financial services sectors. In the past year the firm has been project managing the defence of the two Libyans accused of sabotaging the Pan-Am jet which crashed in Lockerbie. It also acted for Sir Elton John and his companies in his negligence action against PricewaterhouseCoopers. The firm also successfully acted for Max Kingsley, the former managing director of London Clubs, in his eight year fight to prove that the Gaming Board had failed to grant him a fair hearing after revoking his gaming licence in 1994. **Clients:** BAE Systems; Heath Lambert; Jarvis; KPMG.

Nabarro Nathanson (see firm details p.1078) The firm has had a number of high profile actions in the past year. It acted on the successful assertion of state immunity in the context of a defamation claim in the House of Lords, on behalf of a US Department of Defence employee. It is continuing to advise the US Securities and Exchange Commission in a variety of matters, including freezing injunctions and asset tracing issues. **Clients:** Granada Group; IMG; Securities Exchange Commission; US Department of Justice.

Nicholson Graham & Jones (see firm details p.1081) Clients are attracted by this firm's "*long track record,*" with one commenting that it has "*constantly delivered.*" Its niche strengths include travel, sport, insolvency, banking and financial services, which provide its mainstream litigation work. **John Magnin** (see p.575) has a style described by clients as "*diplomatic,*" with agreement that he "*takes good care of all the points.*" The team acted for Bass Brewers and Britvic Soft Drinks as claimants in the lead action brought by the UK soft drinks industry against Terra Nitrogen and Messer. The firm also defended Union Cal, derivatives and futures brokers, in an action brought by ten overseas claimants concerning currency trading transactions. In addition, the firm acted for Road Tech on its claim against Mandata in relation to meta-tags. **Clients:** Coral Racing; Dynamotive Technologies; PGA European Tour; Merchant Retail Group; Ryder Cup; Thomson Tour Operators; Windsor Life.

Berwin Leighton Paisner (see firm details p.878) While it is still early days since the merger, the general market perception is that the union will be "*beneficial*" in terms of "*resources and complementary practice strengths.*" One client, typical of many, commented on the firm's "*sound commercial advice*" and actions that "*align themselves to our requirements.*" Key matters include successfully representing TV Loonland AG and its French subsidiary in a substantial sales agency dispute, and acting on a large commission dispute for Sumitomo Real Estate Sales (New York) concerning a deal involving the £100 million acquisition of the holding company of Ashdown House. The firm also continues to act for Nottingham Forest in its high profile petition brought by minority shareholders under section 459 of the Companies Act. **Clients:** Active Imaging; Brunswick Public Relations; Computer Futures; Foreign & Colonial Ventures; Goodman & Carr; National Westminster Bank; Nottingham Forest; Oasis Stores; Tesco.

Lawrence Graham (see firm details p.1030) Often seen acting in the financial services and advertising sectors, with a strong base of institutional clients. The team acted in a multi-million pound fraud arising out of oil transactions in Cuba, where it obtained worldwide mareva's to freeze and recover the proceeds of the fraud. A further matter involved acting for the management and investors in an action for the rectification of sale documentation, and in respect of breaches of warranty. **Clients:** 3i; De La Rue; Scottish & Newcastle; University Superannuation Scheme.

Macfarlanes (see firm details p.1046) Seen to have "*a pretty wide-ranging litigation department*" with strengths in employment and property issues. The firm acted for the trustees of the Airways pension scheme and the New Airways pension scheme in the highly publicised proposed merger of the two, which together are worth £10 billion. It has also been advising American International Group and Omega Advisors in fraud proceedings against Viktor Kozeny and others, arising out of investment in the privatisations in Azerbaijan. In addition, it was instructed by Eastgate in relation to warranty claims of over £30 million arising out of its acquisition of Hambro Legal Protection in 1998. **Clients:** A&G Imports; Associated British Ports; BET; Carlton; Gleeds; Intercapital Brokers; JD Wetherspoon; Kingfisher; R&B Falcon Corporation; Reebok International; Saatchi & Saatchi; Virgin Atlantic Airways.

Reynolds Porter Chamberlain (see firm details p.1106) Best known for its work involving insurance and professional negligence claims, the firm is also engaged in a variety of pure commercial disputes. Key matters from the past year include defending AstraZeneca in connection with a claim for personal injury arising out of a clinical trial. The team also defended Swedish paper giant SCA in a product liability claim concerning disposable nappies, and defended North Surrey Water in a £7 million dispute with Thames Water over a bulk water agreement. **Clients:** Associated Newspapers; AstraZeneca; Christies; Dalkia; Mag Instrument; Vivendi; Volvo Penta UK.

Rowe & Maw (see firm details p.1113) Peers commended this firm for its involvement in matters of considerable size, complexity and commercial sensitivity. It is increasingly finding itself involved in multi-jurisdictional matters, often in the fields of IT, product failures, property damage or environmental incidents. Highlights include acting for United Pan-Europe Communications in a $2 billion action against Deutsche Bank, and for Bank of America in a multi-billion dollar action brought by the liquidators of BCCI. The team also acted for Europe's largest software houses in connection with a massive and politically sensitive dispute concerning procurement of IT services by public bodies. **Clients:** Argos; AXA Insurance; Bank of America; Chartwell Underwriting; Deloitte & Touche; EMI; ICI; Lear Corporation; Monsanto; NBC; Smith & Williamson; Unilever.

Taylor Joynson Garrett (see firm details p.1150) Peers perceive the firm's litigation practice to be "*reasonably broad*" with expertise in technology and fraud disputes. The team represented SmithKline Beecham in a potentially groundbreaking judicial review against the Advertising Standards Authority in respect of advertisements for Ribena ToothKind. The firm also acted on various claims for GE Capital Commercial Finance arising out of the receivership of a textile company. In addition, it has been representing the Marchioness Contact Group in the Marchioness/Bowbelle Formal investigation. **Clients:** GE Capital Commercial Finance; Johnson Matthey; The Marchioness Contact Group; Meridiana SpA; The National Farmers' Union; Stoddards International; Toyota (GB); Toyota Financial Services (UK); David Yallop.

Travers Smith Braithwaite (see firm details p.1160) With particular strength in financial disputes, especially those with a banking element, the firm's litigation practice also has considerable expertise in commercial fraud, property disputes and a growing number of IT/IP matters. In a recent highlight, the team represented one of the 'big five' accountancy firms in a substantial multi-million pound litigation brought by a household name in the financial markets, involving the issue of causation and contributory negligence. It continues to represent BAII SA, a subsidiary of one of the largest French banks, in multi-million dollar proceedings in England against the liquidators of BCCI, and also acts for the Mirror Group Pension Scheme in the continuing multi-party, global asset recovery exercise that has constituted the Maxwell litigation. **Clients:** BAII SA; Lloyds Disciplinary Committee; MGN Pension Trustees.

Hammond Suddards Edge (see firm details p.984) "*Much more of a player these days*" according to our interviewees, the London office acts for some major corporate, sporting and media clients in the UK. It acted for a major electricity generator in a £100 million claim against one of its suppliers, and advised a computer service company in connection with a substantial claim against ICL for breach of contract. Another highlight was its advice to a UK business services company in relation to a substantial fraud perpetrated by former employees, which necessitated obtaining and executing a search and seizure order. **Clients:** Amateur Boxing Association; Banking Ombudsman; British Energy; Conoco; English Partnerships; Football League; Hazlewood Foods; London Underground; One2One; Viatel; WPP.

Mishcon de Reya (see firm details p.1071) Undertaking litigation across a range of issues, from new technology to trusts, this firm is perceived by barristers to have "*done an awful lot,*" producing "*a consistently high quality of instructions.*" Known for its fraud and media-related disputes. Significant matters from the past year include advising the liquidator of FX Music in a claim against Barclays Bank, in respect of misapplied funds. The firm also acted for Pharmexo Anstalt in a claim against Glaxomed, a subsidiary of Glaxo Wellcome, concerning a dispute over the operation of an agency agreement for the supply of pharmaceuticals to Libya. In addition, the firm acted in the case of Elegant Hotels v Horney and W.I. Builders, which involved a £30 million breach of warranty claim arising from the sale of a hotel chain owned by a listed company. **Clients:** Auto Credit Trust; Diana, Princess of Wales Memorial Fund; The Arab Republic of Egypt; Locum Group; VCI.

Theodore Goddard (see firm details p.1152) Perceived by competitors to be "*into the media stuff and good at it,*" its litigation work also includes disputes relating to fraud, product liability, contracts, banking, insolvency, defamation and IP. The team acted for Commerzbank AG in a successful action brought against subsidiaries of a public company for recovery of sums underpaid on a credit facility and swaps agreement. The firm also acted for Ryanair in its successful defence of BA's claim for trademark infringement and malicious falsehood. Instructed by Union Transport Worldwide, a NASDAQ-listed freight forwarding company, in proceedings brought by an Italian company concerning the purchase of the latter's subsidiary. **Clients:** ABC International Bank; Banco del Gottardo; Credit Agricole; Delta; Designers Guild; Ericsson; France Telecom; Givenchy SA; GlaxoSmithKline; Investcorp International; National Geographic Society; News Group Newspapers; Oracle; Sony Music International; The Times; Walt Disney.

Charles Russell (see firm details p.912) Particular specialities for this firm include telecommunications, shareholders disputes and music business disputes. Over the past year, it has been successful in defending Cable & Wireless against injunction proceedings brought by Excell, and in representing an individual sued for £7.5 million for alleged insider share dealing. The team also acted for session musicians and the Commissioner for the Rights of Trade Union Members against a judicial review application brought by the Musicians Union. **Clients:** Cable & Wireless; Fine Foods International; ntl.

Ince & Co (see firm details p.1008) Peers regard this firm as being "*good opposition on the general side,*" well known for its insurance and shipping dispute work. In the past year it has advised Banque Paribas and AVAB, a Romanian government entity, on the $100 million recovery of shipping assets around the world. It has also advised Occidental, the operator of the platform in the Piper Alpha loss ($1.5 billion). The team is currently representing Korean clients in relation to a US$2 billion dispute involving allegations of unfair state subsidies. **Clients:** AVAB; Banque Paribas; Chevron; Global Marine; Hitachi; Hyundai; McDermott; Occidental.

Lane & Partners (see firm details p.1027) "*Personality-driven,*" much of the firm's profile in litigation lies with "*good operator*" **Ludovic de Walden** (see p.568). Operating across the board, de Walden also has niche expertise in art world litigation, while the firm undertakes a large amount of commercial disputes encompassing IP, banking and construction and aviation. **Clients:** Corporates and corporate subsidiaries; private individuals.

Lewis Silkin (see firm details p.1040) The firm's strengths in the litigation arena lie with shareholders rights, partnerships, utilities, injunctive and equitable remedies. The team advised EFG Private Group in connection with a claim for the recovery of US$26 million lost from the assets of two companies. Instructed by members of a Kenyan family in a highly complex dispute regarding the distribution of approximately US$15 million following the liquidation of BCCI. The firm also advised Terra Nova Insurance Company, QBE International and GRU as to whether indemnity should be given to an insured, Drake & Skull Engineering, in respect of claims notified (potentially worth in excess of £3 million), on the grounds of non-disclosure and/or misrepresentation. **Clients:** Alex Lawrie Factors; Bass Group; City of Glasgow Council; EFG Private Bank Group; Harrods; Hermes Group; House of Fraser; Integrated Dental Holdings; London Electricity; Telegraph Group.

Masons (see firm details p.1056) "*Traditionally the top for construction litigation*" and "*pretty bloody good at IT disputes,*" our interviewees commended the firm's efforts to broaden its litigation practices. Highlights for the practice include representing TXU Europe Group (formerly Eastern Electricity), in multi-party proceedings involving claims by commercial agents for compensation in excess of £130 million. The firm also acted for the claimant in the case of Inntrepreneur v East Crown where the court ruled that an entire agreement clause in a contract precluded the existence of a collateral contract. Also advised United Assurance Group (now part of Royal London) in relation to a substantial High Court IT claim against Unisys. **Clients:** ABB; Bovis; Carillion/TBV; Dial House Ventures; Electricity Direct (UK); Government of Pakistan; HBG Group; ICL; Mowlem; P&O; Ringway Group; Unistar International; Virgin Energy.

Memery Crystal (see firm details p.1064) Interviewees describe it as "*a firm that gets results in spite of its size.*" Typically winning instructions in insurance, regulatory, company and shareholders disputes, IT/IP and media litigation. A large amount of its commercial disputes work comes from existing clients of the firm, particularly underwriters and traders. Many know **Harvey Rands** (see p.579) for his fraud expertise although, as head of litigation, his remit is much broader. **Clients:** Lloyd's Underwriters; Morant; Seymour Pearce & Ellis; Wembley Corporation.

Pinsent Curtis Biddle (see firm details p.1098) The recent merger is said to have "*strengthened its litigation capabilities,*" and despite its small size, this team has secured a number of high profile matters. It acted for the Bar Council in Hall v Simons, a leading House of Lords decision removing an advocate's immunity from suit. A further key matter involved acting for the successful appellant in the Court of Appeal in Dubai Aluminium v Salaam, a case which concerned the liability of partners for acts undertaken by their partners. It also continues to act in recovering assets for the independent trustees of a number of the Maxwell pension schemes. **Clients:** H M Salaam (Dubai Aluminium case); Independent Trustees of Maxwell Private Side Pension Schemes; Trustor AB.

Reed Smith Warner Cranston The merger of Warner Cranston with the US firm Reed Smith has given the firm a substantially increased client base. The firm is said to "*fight hard*" and is "*straightforward to deal with.*" It undertakes a variety of matters from section 151 share assistance claims through to fraud and agency recoveries. The team recently represented Brierley Investments in relation to fiduciary claims against one of the company's directors in London. It has also continued to act for the Government of Dubai in relation to the fall-out from the Dubai Aluminium Company litigation. **Clients:** Brierley Investments; The Government of Dubai; Petrotrade.

White & Case (see firm details p.1178) Market comment agrees that this is "*one of the US firms that is here to stay and is taking a lot of the litigation talent.*" One solicitor went so far as to claim that "*they're people I'd be starting to worry about if I was a Magic Circle firm.*" In the London office, the litigation team includes litigators qualified in both the UK and the US, and advises on corporate and contract disputes, banking and financial matters, professional negligence, insurance, insolvency and construction. **Margaret Cole** (see p.567) received warm endorsement in the course of our research. **Clients:** Leading international corporates and financial institutions.

Other Notable Practitioners **Hugh Elder** (see p.569) of **Gordon Dadds** "*can hold his own against the big boys,*" while **Neil Micklethwaite** of **DLA** remains respected by his peers. **Robert Goldspink** of **Morgan, Lewis & Bockius** is considered "*more impressive than a lot of other people around town.*" **John Reynolds** (see p.579) of **McDermott, Will & Emery** is "*thorough and proficient.*" Formerly of Hammond Suddards Edge, **Stephen York** (see p.585) of **Vinson & Elkins** is said to be "*a quality act*" who has a "*great name and experience*" in the field of alternative dispute resolution.

THE SOUTH

LITIGATION: GENERAL COMMERCIAL • The South	
1	**Blake Lapthorn** Fareham
2	**Bond Pearce** Southampton
	Cripps Harries Hall Tunbridge Wells
	DMH Brighton
	Thomas Eggar Church Adams Chichester
3	**asb law** Crawley
	Brachers Maidstone
	Clyde & Co Guildford
	Stevens & Bolton Guildford
	Thomson Snell & Passmore Tunbridge Wells
4	**Barlows** Surrey
	Lester Aldridge Bournemouth
	Paris Smith & Randall Southampton

LEADING INDIVIDUALS		
1	**ASPINALL Tim** DMH	**HIGHAM David** Blake Lapthorn

This book is the product of 6,552 1/2 hour interviews. See p.7 for BMRB audit.
Within each band, firms are listed alphabetically. *See individuals' profiles p.564*

Blake Lapthorn (see firm details p.886) Retaining its premier reputation, both clients and peers applaud this firm of "*robust litigators*" that have a recognised "*expertise in insurance*" and "*unsurpassable technical knowledge.*" Rivals concede that the firm "*attracts big clients*" with its multi-disciplinary approach, advising on a wide range of work including regulatory issues. **David Higham** garners plaudits for his "*impressive professionalism*" that "*inspires confidence.*" The group acts for the General Optic Council on all its litigation. Recent highlights include instructions on a major construction dispute for a local authority, that included proceedings in the ICC and covered multi-jurisdictional issues. **Clients:** Kerry Group; GOC; Queensborough Holdings; Alcatel.

Bond Pearce (see firm details p.888) The firm offers "*high quality*" dispute resolution for medium to large sized companies, displaying key strengths in retail, financial services and EU issues. The Southampton team, led by Tony Askham, has acted for the Professional Contractors Group in a judicial review of IR35 legislation. The group also acted for 24 ice cream wholesalers in proceedings under the Commercial Agents Regulations against Birds Eye Walls. Its recent property dispute successes include a case involving a B&Q warehouse at Bidston Moss, Wallasey. **Clients:** Volkswagen Group UK; Peugeot Wholesale; The National Trust; St. Merwyn Meat.

Cripps Harries Hall (see firm details p.927) The firm is admired for its "*commercial edge,*" although peers stress that the loss of SIF work is "*a potential problem*" in terms of volume. The group includes Peter Ashford, a specialist who handles large and complex disputes, including a number of multi-million pound claims. Increasingly the firm is engaged in cases involving internal disputes affecting professional practices and private companies. It continues its high profile work in disputes arising from the construction, insurance and financial services industries. Acted for a leading business in relation to a multi-million pound claim against another company for licence fees on geographical data. **Clients:** Hidden Hearing International; HM Customs & Excise; Swiss Life.

DMH (see firm details p.944) The Brighton office of DMH offers capabilities in major commercial litigation, commercial fraud and defamation. Litigation specialist **Tim Aspinall** (see p.564) is rated as "*innovative*" by his clients while peers agree he shows "*entrepreneurial flair*" but is "*not a point-scorer.*" The group represented a leading hi-tech company against a major financial institution in a claim worth in excess of £1 million arising out of a PFI transaction. Also instructed by a multi-media company in a dispute involving the development of computer games, and advised a company operating in the financial sector in a complex, high value claim concerning the establishment of offshore trusts. **Clients:** Local authorities; accountancy firms; pharmaceutical manufacturers; software houses; multi-media companies.

Thomas Eggar Church Adams (see firm details p.1153) With four offices in the regions, this practice is seen to have grown thanks to "*a merger that works*" and is consistently proffering a "*traditionally high quality standard of work.*" Tom McKeown heads the national commercial litigation team, whose strengths include professional negligence, international fraud and insolvency matters, and shareholder and partnership disputes. The group defended an international business on a multi-jurisdictional freezing of assets order. It also advised on a House of Lords case concerning a dispute over the winding up of a partnership. **Clients:** MJ Gleeson & Co; Nationwide Building Society; Railtrack; Levy Gee.

asb law (see firm details p.865) Peers view this as an "*interesting practice*"; a tripartite merger that has worked well. Its key strength in the Crawley office lies with its expertise in shareholder and company disputes. Andrew Pawlik leads the team which is subdivided into specialist groups; technology/e-commerce, travel and aviation, and environmental litigation. The firm represented Thornton Springer Accountants in connection with a substantial insurance dispute with wide-ranging repercussions. Advised substantial Brazilian clients in international litigation concerning commercial agents regulations, and represented two defendants in a commercial fraud action that resulted in worldwide freezing and search and seizure orders. **Clients:** Unijet; Air Miles; First Choice; Hanson Aggregates.

Brachers (see firm details p.893) The Maidstone head office of this firm is headed up by John Sheath who also runs the clinical negligence practice. Traditionally associated with its agricultural prowess, acting for landed estates, the firm actually undertakes litigation in a range of commercial areas, including debt recovery and insolvency. Also has a focus on the hi-tech sector. The group has been involved in a piece of competition litigation that has been referred to the ECJ. **Clients:** NHS Trusts; health authorities; Eurotunnel; Travis Perkins.

Clyde & Co (see firm details p.921) The Guildford office of the firm offers a breadth of experience in commercial litigation, winning instructions that are the envy of many competitors. Headed by Jonathan Wood, the practice advises clients on all matters from insolvency to environmental claims. The group has recently been involved in several major product liability claims for household names, involving product recall and the ensuing litigation. **Clients:** Glencore; Tate & Lyle; East Point Holdings.

Stevens & Bolton (see firm details p.1143) "*A strong firm*" commended for its commerciality and prowess in the contentious field. Headed by Richard King, much of this department's litigation load comes from construction and engineering disputes. It has a developing niche in adjudication claims made by contractors and sub-contractors. Recently instructed by a joint venture company, formed by IAF Group and Bouygues UK, on its successful claim in the Technology and Construction Court against Portsmouth City Council concerning the abortive Portsmouth Millennium Tower project. The group was also instructed by a leading pharmaceutical manufacturer in a multi-million pound claim of fraud, which involved freezing orders. **Clients:** Hays; Gerling Namur Insurances of Credit; IAF Group; Unilever-Bestfoods; WS Atkins.

Thomson Snell & Passmore (see firm details p.1155) Peers agree that this "*skilled*" group of lawyers is always "*pleasant to deal with.*" Peter Radula-Scott leads the department which is experienced in heavyweight commercial litigation. The team acted on a worldwide freezing order for a client, and brought a successful action against a Greek company. It also defeated an action brought by a major brewing industry company on an alleged breach of patents. **Clients:** Royal Institution of Chartered Surveyors; C&H Fabrics; State Bank of India; Waterers Landscape.

Barlows This Guilford based firm is considered a "*small but high quality*" offering by our interviewees. The commercial litigation practice includes Hamish Cameron Blackie, and services clients that range from public authorities to leading retailers. It has a recognised capability in advising on insolvency and trading agreement disputes, while an admirable proportion of its workload comes in the form of injunctive activity and cross-border instructions. **Clients:** Retailers; public authorities.

Lester Aldridge (see firm details p.1038) Although rivals concede "*managing a commercial practice in Bournemouth is no mean feat,*" the quality of this firm's output and its cohesive team continue to attract plaudits. The team, which fields partner Michael Giddins, offers a complete service with ongoing updates on legal developments, in-house training and risk management advice. The group has been engaged in multi-jurisdictional disputes in the EU and US, specifically working on a cross-jurisdictional distributorship dispute. **Clients:** AFC Bournemouth; Atomic Energy Authority; The Cobham Group; P&O; Severn Trent.

Paris Smith & Randall (see firm details p.1089) Endorsed for its "*admirable client roster*" which includes a broad swathe of regional plcs. Led by Clive Thomson, the team's strengths lie in insolvency disputes and those requiring complex technical knowledge. The group acted on behalf of a local plc in an issue relating to licence agreements for the occupation of land by other parties for leisure purposes. **Clients:** Private and public companies; legal expense insurers; insolvency practitioners.

THAMES VALLEY

LITIGATION: GENERAL COMMERCIAL • Thames Valley	
1	**Clarks** Reading
	Morgan Cole Oxford, Reading
2	**Boyes Turner** Reading
	Nabarro Nathanson Reading
	Shoosmiths Reading
3	**Garretts** Reading

LEADING INDIVIDUALS		
1	**CLARK Tim** Garretts	**ROBINSON Michael** Boyes Turner
	ROWE Claire Shoosmiths	

This book is the product of 6,552 1/2 hour interviews. See p.7 for BMRB audit.

Within each band, firms are listed alphabetically. *See individuals' profiles p.564*

Clarks (see firm details p.916) Declared by competitors to be "*probably the most established firm in the area*" with a portfolio of substantial clients, despite witnessing recent movements at partner level. Thought to have "*found its niche in the market,*" working for Global Crossing as well as other IT and telecoms clients. The last year has seen a rise in conflict and trade secrets litigation, especially in injunctive work. Instructions from a strong following of transport and logistics companies continue to bolster this team's standing in the market place. Antony Morris' department continues to represent BMW GB on all its litigation. **Clients:** Aerotek Europe; Blue Circle Industries; BMW GB; Bunzl; Global Crossing; RMC; Transport Development; University of Reading; Thames Water.

Morgan Cole (see firm details p.1074) Enjoys a strong grounding in high volume insurance "*specialising in finance and factoring.*" Work this year has included a customs and excise fraud investigation. Althought this office has seen some personnel movements, peers acknowledge that it can provide a greater range of specialist expertise than many in the Thames Valley. One recent example lies in its advice on a multi-million pound warranty claim against a construction business. **Clients:** Alex Laurie Factors; Barclays Mercantile; BP; Haymills plc; Miela; Oxford Brookes University; Thames Valley Police; Unipart.

Boyes Turner (see firm details p.891) Researchers were told by its competitors that the firm remains one that can handle the larger, more complex deals. These have included search and seizure orders against the former employees of a company attempting to solicit clients, and a judicial review for a UK trade association. The firm has been successful in an action against a major software supplier, and against a large, high street retailer. **Michael Robinson** (see p.580) received warm recommendations from our interviewees. The department maintains something of a specialism in directors disqualification proceedings. **Clients:** Barratts North London; Baumatic Ltd; Grenco UK; IG Index; Kelly Services; South Bucks District Council.

Nabarro Nathanson (see firm details p.1078) Peter Sheppard's "*competent*" team has seen strong growth across the board, particularly in insolvency, corporate and shareholder matters. With a presence independent of its London office, the team continues to act on trade finance disputes for, inter alia, Brown, Shipley & Co and the Bank of Ireland. Acting for a variety of institutional corporate landlord and tenant clients, the firm also has a foothold in the technology sector, with regular successes for Siemens on contractual issues. **Clients:** Bank of Ireland; Brown, Shipley & Co; SAS Institute; Siemens; Singer & Friedlander; Sun Microsystems; Thorn UK (Box Clever).

Shoosmiths (see firm details p.1129) Like its rivals in the Thames Valley, this team has seen a growth in IT and telecoms litigation. Department head **Claire Rowe**'s (see p.580) "*pragmatic*" style has led to heavy endorsement from the market. The firm benefits from work channelled through its sizeable debt recovery practice and wins a substantial level of instructions from its insolvency and insurance practice by way of "*successful relations, at an effective price.*" **Clients:** ACE Insurance; Coca-Cola; Hogg Robinson.

Garretts (see firm details p.968) The "*excellent service*" afforded by this team is often for clients outside the region, proffered via the Andersen Legal network, which goes some way to explaining its lack of profile among competitors locally. The office does not generally undertake annuity work, focusing primarily on one-off disputes, with a heavy following in the IT and professional negligence sectors. "*Competent and commercial*" **Tim Clark** (see p.567) enters the table this year due to his "*exceptional commitment*" and "*wholeheartedly 100%*" approach. The firm has been involved in a utilities litigation concerning electricity usage and generation, and received a major instruction from Thames Water. **Clients:** Aquazur; Bosch; Gallay Conteneurs et Systemes; Hallmark Cards; The Leasing Group (Lattice Group); SC Johnson Wax; Thames Water Utilities; Timberland; Wordsworth Holdings.

SOUTH WEST

LITIGATION: GENERAL COMMERCIAL • South West ○	
1	**Burges Salmon** Bristol
	Osborne Clarke Bristol
2	**Beachcroft Wansbroughs** Bristol
	Bevan Ashford Bristol
	Bond Pearce Bristol, Exeter, Plymouth
	TLT Solicitors Bristol
	Veale Wasbrough Bristol
3	**Clarke Willmott & Clarke** Bristol
	Foot Anstey Sargent Exeter, Plymouth
	Laytons Bristol

LEADING INDIVIDUALS		
1	**HAGGETT Paul** Burges Salmon	**MAY Philip** TLT Solicitors
	MORRIS Peter Burges Salmon	**PIZZEY Simon** Veale Wasbrough
	PUDDICOMBE Nigel Veale Wasbrough	
2	**CLOUGH Peter** Osborne Clarke	**METCALFE Stephen** Beachcroft Wansbroughs
	OWENS David Bevan Ashford	
3	**ROBINSON Clare** Osborne Clarke	**WILLIAMS Peter** Burges Salmon

This book is the product of 6,552 1/2 hour interviews. See p.7 for BMRB audit.

Within each band, firms are listed alphabetically. *See individuals' profiles p.564*

Burges Salmon (see firm details p.902) Envied by peers for its "*sheer volume of work*" the firm is considered "*the major commercial force in Bristol.*" It handles all manner of commercial disputes including banking, contractual, technical and engineering issues. Judged to put in a "*first rate performance,*" **Paul Haggett** (see p.571) works alongside **Peter Morris** (see p.577), a recent recruit from Eversheds, and the "*experienced*" **Peter Williams** (see p.76). The group has recently been engaged in fraud matters, the resolution of regulatory difficulties and contractual agreement disputes for both national and international clients. Its reach extends to the motor, shipbuilding, aviation and rail industries, as well as disputes over equipment produced in the manufacturing sector. **Clients:** FirstGroup; St Paul International Insurance; Nationwide Building Society.

Osborne Clarke (see firm details p.1086) Interviewees both inside and outside of this region commended the "*high quality service*" and "*volume of work*" produced by the firm to our researchers. Included in a "*credible team*" is "*dedicated and tenacious litigator*" **Clare Robinson** and "*sensible*" **Peter Clough**. Heavily endorsed for its specialist knowledge of IP and IT, financial institutions and construction matters. Cross-border work is on the increase, as exemplified by the team's advice to a Greek Cypriot interest in a dispute concerning exports from Cyprus. The group also advised GE Capital Equipment Finance on a substantial equipment leasing dispute with WPP Group, and acted for Nutricia Holdings on a breach of warranty dispute with Scotia Holdings. **Clients:** Abbey National; Netscape Communications; Prudential Assurance Company; European Telecom; Sun Life.

Beachcroft Wansbroughs (see firm details p.872) Rated for its strengths in professional indemnity, and its knowledge of the insurance market, the group has expanded beyond this core to act on a broad range of substantial commercial disputes. This office fields a "*well prepared team.*" Considered to be a "*confident litigator,*" **Stephen Metcalfe** (see p.576) has advised on a wide range of disputes including multi-million pound claims, winning respect from his peers for his "*self-assured manner.*" **Clients:** Equifax plc.

Bevan Ashford (see firm details p.880) Applauded for its NHS work, both the Exeter and Bristol teams have garnered respect for their output of commercial litigation. The department includes "*safe pair of hands*" **David Owens** (see p.578) whose own practice encompasses a specialism in healthcare. The firm is acting in proceedings initiated by Dubal, the Dubai Government-owned aluminium company, in a dispute involving $23 million. In the financial services sector the firm acted for a major financial planning company in a substantial claim for damage to its business, attributable to the illegal procurement and use of confidential information by another publicly listed IFA. It also advised the London office of a multinational accountancy practice on a claim involving a former corporate client in the IT sector. **Clients:** HSBC; BS Group; Allied Domecq; Biotrace International.

Bond Pearce (see firm details p.888) Fielding lawyers from the Bristol office and a highly integrated unit across the Exeter and Plymouth branches, this firm is winning plaudits for its coverage and expertise in insolvency and banking matters. Also bolstered by a dedicated property litigation group and niche strengths in freehold restrictive covenants. Head of commercial litigation Tony Askham presides over a practice that handles business lease renewals, residential possession actions and adverse possession claims. The group acted for B&Q against Liverpool & Lancashire Properties in a successful prosecution denying the landlord the ability to reduce the area available for exercise of a tenant's right of way. **Clients:** West Country Housing Association; B&Q; Safeway; Comet; The National Trust.

TLT Solicitors (see firm details p.1157) With a team of four heavyweight litigators, including the "*sensible operator*" **Philip May** (see p.576), this firm has seen a significant increase in its cross-border work. The team has specialist sector expertise in insolvency, partnerships and construction, often involving multi-party actions. The group advised Avon Rubber on an international contractual dispute. Through its membership of the European Law Firm network, the firm has gained new clients including a leading European producer of combustion systems and a leading European electronics business. **Clients:** Aardman Animations; Avon Rubber; Brooks Service Group; Proton cars.

Veale Wasbrough (see firm details p.1167) Interviewees acknowledged that this firm has "*strengthened its position*" and secured itself a "*hard-nosed reputation in litigation.*" The "*determined*" **Simon Pizzey** (see p.579) and "*solutions-oriented*" **Nigel Puddicombe** (see p.579) are two of this team's "*experienced lawyers.*" The group undertakes contract-based litigation and partnership work. It acted for a UK subsidiary of a German engineering company in its defence of a substantial claim by a customer, and acted for a household name retailer in a number of contractual disputes with its product suppliers and in its trading standards matters generally. **Clients:** British Aerospace; Bristol & West; SWEB; London Electricity; Great Mills; Bar Mutual; Hemmings Waste Management.

Clarke Willmott & Clarke (see firm details p.915) Head of department Chris Taylor and the team display experience in domestic and international arbitration, and advise on property, construction and a range of general commercial work. One recent highlight saw the firm acting on an international arbitration in defence of an action for breach of contract under US rules (based in London with hearings in the US.) It also defended an engineering company in High Court claims in excess of £1 million, and advised trout farming clients claiming substantial damages arising from oil pollution following an accident in which a fire engine crashed into lakes. **Clients:** Gloucester County Council; Hygrade Foods; University of Bristol.

Foot Anstey Sargent (see firm details p.961) The Exeter and Plymouth branches of this firm are deemed "*a steady force*" by competitors. With expertise in banking and insolvency, the commercial litigation department also has experience in mediations. The team includes Angus McNicol and has acted in a family construction dispute, which resulted in a multi-million pound settlement for its client. The group also acted on a breach of agency contract dispute that resulted in settled mediation (for a small percentage of the original claim), and advised on a partnership dispute involving two brothers and a substantial property portfolio. **Clients:** Northcliffe Group; Mountfield Westwood; Anderton and Rowland.

Laytons (see firm details p.1031) Headed by partner Bill Brydon, this firm is commended by peers for its skill in handling construction and insolvency disputes. The group acted on a claim for breach of confidence and copyright infringement against a University and the DETR, concerned with a vehicle speed-limiting device operated by a GPS system. In addition it has recently been involved in a fraud and deceit claim arising out of investment in an internet café business operating throughout UK. **Clients:** Securicor Information Systems; Zuken UK; Milburns Restaurants; Hamptons.

WALES

LITIGATION: GENERAL COMMERCIAL • Wales	
1	**Edwards Geldard** Cardiff
	Eversheds Cardiff
	Hugh James Ford Simey Cardiff
	Morgan Cole Cardiff, Swansea
2	**Palser Grossman** Cardiff Bay

LEADING INDIVIDUALS		
1	**HOPKINS Paul** Edwards Geldard	**JEFFERIES Michael** Hugh James Ford Simey
	JONES Peter Eversheds	
2	**JONES Michael** Hugh James Ford Simey	**NOTT Christopher** Palser Grossman
	RHYS-JONES Mark Eversheds	**WILLIAMS Gareth** Hugh James Ford Simey
	WILSON Allan Morgan Cole	

This book is the product of 6,552 1/2 hour interviews. See p.7 for BMRB audit.
Within each band, firms are listed alphabetically. *See individuals' profiles p.564*

Edwards Geldard (see firm details p.948) Buoyed by an admired client base and involvement in complex, high profile disputes, this firm remains a force in the Welsh market and beyond. A significant proportion of its client base is situated in other commercial centres around the country. Headed by the respected **Paul Hopkins** (see p.573), the team represented the Welsh Development Agency and three individual defendants in complex litigation initiated by Landare Investments. It also acted for the Wales Art Council and its chief executive in successfully defending at trial, defamation proceedings brought by the Director of Cardiff-based Chapter Arts Centre. **Clients:** Williams plc; Citigroup; Welsh Development Agency; Admiral Insurance Services.

Eversheds (see firm details p.952) Considered "*major players in Cardiff,*" peers rate the team's ability to "*pull in lots of national work.*" Working as part of the dispute resolution and litigation department, this office undoubtedly benefits from the presence of "*sensible*" **Peter Jones** (see p.574) and **Mark Rhys-Jones** (see p.579), "*a guy you can do business with.*" The group's expertise stretches from professional negligence to public sector dispute resolution, as shown by its ongoing involvement in the Bloody Sunday and Shipman inquiries. In the general commercial field it advised Tarmac and Betws Anthracite in pursuing an action through the courts relating to an illegal coal subsidy. **Clients:** Barclays; Lloyds TSB; Cardiff County Council; Royal & SunAlliance; Oddbins; Bovis Homes.

Hugh James Ford Simey (see firm details p.1004) Acknowledged by peers to profit from the interplay between its insurance and commercial litigation units. "*Leading light*" **Michael Jefferies** (see p.574) works alongside the respected players **Michael Jones** (see p.574) and **Gareth Williams** (see p.651). The team represented the WRU in a claim brought against it by the Australian Rugby Union for a substantial compensation alleged to be due following the well publicised transfer from Australia to Wales of Jason Jones-Hughes. The group is also acting in a major dispute involving a private company and the National Assembly over a claim for the repayment of £2 million. **Clients:** Welsh Rugby Union; Millennium Stadium; Hyder plc; S4C; Crawfords.

Morgan Cole (see firm details p.1074) Respected "*highly commercial team*" continues to offer advice on all manner of disputes, with particular expertise in agriculture, banking, and defamation. Headed up by the "*analytical*" **Allan Wilson** (see p.584) ("*a robust performer*") the team has been busy co-ordinating efforts to deal with potential claims arising from the recent foot and mouth epidemic. The group acted on a multi-million pound action for a public company suing the vendor of a group of companies. **Clients:** National Farmers' Union.

Palser Grossman Peers agree this Cardiff Bay based firm is "*developing a healthy commercial litigation department.*" Headed by the "*talented*" **Christopher Nott** the team specialises in property litigation, and is occupied with corporate shareholder and commercial contract disputes including a recent litigation over unlawful disposal of shares in a public company. The team acted for the owners of Wembley Stadium over non-payment for the use of the property. It continues to run a range of actions against the Welsh Rugby Union. **Clients:** The American Furniture Group; TRW Inc; Brunswick Construction; International Greetings; Cardiff Athletic Club.

MIDLANDS

LITIGATION: GENERAL COMMERCIAL • Midlands
1 Pinsent Curtis Biddle Birmingham
Wragge & Co Birmingham
2 Eversheds Birmingham, Nottingham
3 Browne Jacobson Nottingham
DLA Birmingham
Hammond Suddards Edge Birmingham
Martineau Johnson Birmingham
4 Freethcartwright Nottingham
Gateley Wareing Birmingham
Lee Crowder Birmingham
5 Bell Lax Litigation Birmingham
Shakespeares Birmingham
Shoosmiths Northampton
6 Kent Jones and Done Stoke-on-Trent
Moran & Co Tamworth
The Wilkes Partnership Birmingham

LEADING INDIVIDUALS	
1 HOWARD Paul Wragge & Co	
2 GARVIE Carl Pinsent Curtis Biddle	MANNING COX Andrew Wragge & Co
ROSE Digby Hammond Suddards Edge	
3 SINGLETON Bernard Lee Crowder	SPOONER Andrew Martineau Johnson
WILLETTS Jayne Hammond Suddards Edge	
4 BERWICK Guy Freethcartwright	DAVIES Peter Gateley Wareing
LAX Peter Bell Lax Litigation	MUMFORD Nicola Wragge & Co
UP AND COMING	
BYRNE Justin Eversheds	JAMDAR Smita Martineau Johnson

This book is the product of 6,552 1/2 hour interviews. See p.7 for BMRB audit.
Within each band, firms are listed alphabetically. *See individuals' profiles p.564*

Pinsent Curtis Biddle (see firm details p.1098) The practice was a resounding hit with our interviewees due to its "*size, weight of clients and economic muscle.*" The team includes **Carl Garvie** (see p.570) who is deemed "*astute*" and "*an excellent litigator*" by peers and clients alike. Known for its "*high quality work,*" the team has been involved in significant disputes in the power and water industries. Recently acted in two cases in the House of Lords – one of which was against the Secretary of State for Trade and Industry and the Secretary of State for Health. The group was also instructed by an international engineering company in defence of a multi-million pound claim for breach of a joint venture involving complex issues of project finance and overseas jurisdictions. **Clients:** Alstom UK; Axa Sun Life; Rolls-Royce; Saint-Gobain.

Wragge & Co (see firm details p.1189) At the forefront of the market due to its "*size and client base.*" Our researchers were informed that the "*impressive group of knowledgeable lawyers*" has a number of standout practitioners. "*Professional*" **Andrew Manning Cox** has 20 years experience of commercial litigation while Head of Dispute Resolution **Paul Howard** is "*always stiff opposition*" according to his peers. **Nicola Mumford** gains respect for her pragmatic approach. The team is defending a £100 million claim alleging breaches of warranty following the takeover of a leading company. It also acted for a claimant company against one of its former directors alleging breach of duty, resulting in a multi-million pound claim, and received instructions from an internet company in connection with a substantial warranty claim relating to the acquisition. **Clients:** Bank of Scotland; BI Group; Cadbury Schweppes; Hilton Group; Rover Group.

Eversheds (see firm details p.952) Competitors of this "*impressive team*" find them "*tough opposition,*" respecting the consistently "*good quality service.*" The commercial litigation unit includes the warmly endorsed **Justin Byrne** (see p.566). The team has substantially expanded its level of instructions from the education, transport and IT sectors. In the past year it attracted commercial dispute instructions from over 30 UK listed or major international corporates. The firm acted in a multi-million pound completion account dispute for a major automotive manufacturer, and was involved in resolving disputes with rail operators and passenger transport executives. **Clients:** Simons Group; Priory Hospitals; Boots; West Bromwich Building Society.

Browne Jacobson (see firm details p.898) "*The dominant firm of Nottingham*" according to competitors. This "*decent bunch*" is "*skilled at what it does,*" and is headed by partner Peter Ellis. Active promoters of alternative dispute resolution, the firm has a broad client base that spans many sectors including a specialism in professional negligence. The firm has recently advised several leading food manufacturers in disputes. **Clients:** Parceline; Express Dairies; Siemens Communication.

DLA The Birmingham branch of this national firm has a commercial litigation practice with a client base containing retailers and consumer goods manufacturers.

Hammond Suddards Edge (see firm details p.984) In consolidating its team the firm has attracted endorsement from rivals as being "*on the rise.*" It has developed expertise in a number of areas including computer contracts, engineering disputes and shareholders claims. The "*experienced*" **Digby Rose** (see p.580) represented Dunkin' Donuts in significant litigation which involved actions in both Birmingham and the US. Also respected for her practice is the "*impressive litigator*" **Jayne Willetts** (see p.584). The team successfully defended Barpro Group on a £2 million claim, and is acting for the purchasers in two multi-million pound disputes relating to the acquisition of computer systems. **Clients:** Scottish & Newcastle; T&S Stores; Galliford Try; Allied Domecq; Calor Gas.

Martineau Johnson (see firm details p.1055) Respected by competitors as a "*solid and reasonable firm,*" it has acted for corporate and individual clients in major commercial claims over defective machinery, corporate fraud and regulatory matters. Head of department **Andrew Spooner** (see p.574) has handled some major pieces of litigation and arbitrations, while **Smita Jamdar** (see p.574) is developing her profile. Areas of expertise include servicing clients in the education sector, and the firm is witnessing a growth in the level of complex claims from public bodies. The group acted for a public authority in a multi-party action concerning its defence of a claim in excess of £15 million, and acted for the claimant in a major arbitration for a multi-national group of companies – a nuclear industry claim in excess of £3 million. **Clients:** Alstom UK; multi-national corps; local authorities; banks.

Freethcartwright (see firm details p.964) An "*excellent offering*" deemed to be challenging Browne Jacobson in the Nottingham market. The "*problem-solver*" **Guy Berwick** (see p.565) is commended for his "*conciliatory approach*" and peers say he is "*a modern commercial litigator.*" The firm has an expertise that spans many industries, in particular print and textiles. It acted for British Gas Services and Helly Hansen on a substantial breach of contract claim and advised on contractual disputes for HMV Media Group. Instructed by a major plc to investigate a claim under the protection from harassment legislation. **Clients:** HMV Media Group; British Gas Services; Helly Hansen; Paul Smith; Center Parcs.

Gateley Wareing (see firm details p.969) Adjudged an "*assertive*" firm, it is rated as "*sound and reliable*" by competitors. **Peter Davies** ("*straightforward operator*") garners plaudits from our interviewees. Clients are drawn, in the main, from the manufacturing and accountancy sectors. The group has been involved in cross-border litigation, including the representation of manufacturers whose IP rights were being infringed by manufacturers in Hong Kong. Successfully represented an internet company in a software dispute. **Clients:** Commercial clients.

Lee Crowder (see firm details p.1035) Expanding its profile outside of the West Midlands, this "*straightforward*" practice now boasts a growing number of national clients to add to its "*historically strong client base.*" **Bernard Singleton** (see p.581) is esteemed for his "*down to earth approach.*" The group acted for a large private company in a warranty claim valued in excess of £5 million. It also works closely with the firm's e-business unit, with a recent success in advising a national provider of on-line legal services in a case relating to the use of 'meta-tags' by a rival web site. **Clients:** Euromoney Publications; William H. Mercer; Wesleyan Financial Services.

Bell Lax Litigation A "*small but deadly*" offering that engenders respect from practitioners across the region. The "*pro-active*" **Peter Lax** (see p.575) leads the team, rated as a "*good technician – one for the more complex matters.*" The group represents a broad range of clients, on a national basis, including private and public businesses, as well as individuals. **Clients:** Owner-managed businesses.

Shakespeares (see firm details p.1122) A "*well-organised outfit,*" seen by the market to have "*really got its act together.*" The team is led by Mark Beesley who specialises in trust disputes, injunctions and restricted covenance. Its niche strengths are banking litigation, restraint of trade and handling major product liability cases on both national and international bases. The firm also undertakes mediations. It has acted on domestic and international factoring recovery cases, including actions on behalf of suppliers in several European countries. **Clients:** University of Central England; HSBC Invoice Finance; Cradley Print; Braythorns.

Shoosmiths (see firm details p.1129) A "*respected*" offering from the Northampton office, said to provide commercial litigation services of a "*high standard.*" The team, including intellectual property specialist John Hill, has recently acted in matters as diverse as credit card fraud, shareholders' actions and accountancy negligence cases. Acted in a multi-million pound claim involving recovery of a 200 motorcar fleet. **Clients:** Barclays; NatWest; DaimlerChrysler Financial Services; Kier International.

Kent Jones and Done (see firm details p.1020) With a traditional core specialism in pure commercial disputes, this "*highly visible*" firm's dispute resolution department is headed by property litigation specialist Graham Neyt. The group acted for Britannia Building Society in the reported cybersquatting case in which the society was granted summary judgment. It has also been involved in several major cases concerning coal-mining subsidence, of which the firm has a long-standing experience. **Clients:** JCB Group.

Moran & Co This Tamworth based firm is seen as "*doing fine*" in the highly competitive field of commercial litigation. Led by Patrick Moran, the team offers a depth of knowledge and experience in banking, financial litigation and professional negligence. It acted on a complex commercial banking action for a sum in excess of £3 million. **Clients:** Financial institutions.

The Wilkes Partnership (see firm details p.1181) Continues to elicit commendation from its competitors in the region. Headed up by Peter Ewin, the firm advises a number of diverse clients on a broad range of commercial litigation matters, including complex recovery issues. **Clients:** ATS Midlands; Avis Rent A Car; EMI Records; Bank of Ireland.

EAST ANGLIA

LITIGATION: GENERAL COMMERCIAL • East Anglia	
1	**Eversheds** Cambridge, Ipswich, Norwich
	Mills & Reeve Cambridge, Norwich
2	**Hewitson Becke + Shaw** Cambridge
	Taylor Vinters Cambridge
3	**Birketts** Ipswich
	Greenwoods Peterborough
	Prettys Ipswich

LEADING INDIVIDUALS		
1	**CALLAGHAN Edward** Mills & Reeve	**ROESSLER Max** Eversheds
2	**BLAKE Peter** Prettys	**HIGGS Rachel** Mills & Reeve
	MATTHEWS Paul Eversheds	**PERROTT Edward** Taylor Vinters

This book is the product of 6,552 1/2 hour interviews. See p.7 for BMRB audit.
Within each band, firms are listed alphabetically. *See individuals' profiles p.564*

Eversheds (see firm details p.952) "*Obviously a strong offering,*" securing its top-flight reputation once more. Combines a broad range of work with local specialities, such as instructions from Aventis and other biotechnology companies in Cambridge. Most definitely out of the shadow of the London office, the firm is applauded as offering "*quality, client focused advice.*" Standout deal of the year for the team was its protection of Firebond's reputation through the liquidation of Drake Insurance. **Max Roessler** (see p.580), "*an extremely good all-rounder,*" is endorsed by his competitors and clients alike. "*Personable*" **Paul Matthews** (see p.576) is "*articulate and prepared to seek mediated solutions.*" He defended a £9 million warranty claim following a sale of business. **Clients:** AEW-THURNE; Argentaria; Aventis Crop Science; Bloody Sunday enquiry; Broadland District Council; Comtec Cable Accessories; Elan Pharma; Firebond; Frans Maas; IFR; Norfolk Health Authority; Robert Rice (v Great Yarmouth Borough Council); Textron; TXU Europe; Unwin Seeds.

Mills & Reeve (see firm details p.1069) "*A major force,*" the firm's strong presence in the region "*by virtue of its size and reputation*" has it pushing hard for outright leadership. Its peers concede, "*you have to be on your guard*" when opposing this team. It has had growth in work for online and software companies as well as biotech firms. "*Practical and experienced*" **Edward Callaghan** (see p.566) is joined in our tables by **Rachel Higgs** (see p.572), as interviewees commend her "*quality advice*" and "*switched on approach.*" The year has also seen the firm acting for a defence contractor in arbitration in a substantial claim against a US manufacturer for breach of performance warranty. **Clients:** MSI-Defence Systems; SCA Recycling; Targetfollow Estates; Virgin Wines Online; Wiremold.

Hewitson Becke + Shaw (see firm details p.994) The firm has enjoyed an increase in work of a more international flavour and is commended for its involvement in mediations under CEDR-accredited Phillip Saffron. Examples of this work include a series of product defect claims. The firm represented a plc in the IT sector and advised a US telecoms corporation on a variety of disputes. It has also broadened its focus to include risk management advice, including advice to a national logistics plc on its successful withdrawal from a joint venture. **Clients:** Plcs; airline industries; commodities suppliers; agrochemical manufacturers.

Taylor Vinters (see firm details p.1150) "*A force locally,*" the impact of this firm is discerned further afield. It is presently working on a proposed order against a large pharmaceutical company, and on the litigation concerning the flotation of Portuguese football club Benfica. Standout partner **Edward Perrott** (see p.579) has "*a deservedly good reputation*" in the field. The firm has maintained its following in engineering and telecoms work, acting for The Technology Partnership in a claim relating to mobile satellite links over Africa and Asia. **Clients:** Bidwells Property; Eastern Counties Leather;

Nowell Stebbing; Phillips Electronics UK; Redland Aggregates; University of Cambridge.

Birketts A quiet year although the firm continues to bring in work from Ipswich and further afield. Managing Partner Bob Wright's department has filed claims against a number of high street banks for overcharging trust management fees, on behalf of beneficiaries. The firm also advised a pension fund against a major insurance company fund manager. **Clients:** Regional clients.

Greenwoods (see firm details p.978) James Maxey's team is known to field "*extremely professional and knowledgeable lawyers*" with a strong following in the food industries and related sectors, including transport and storage. In the last year, the team has seen an increase in instructions concerning data disputes and e-litigation while professional negligence cases also provide a steady stream of work. **Clients:** Emap; KMPG; Railtrack; Thomas Cook.

Prettys (see firm details p.1100) The "*methodical and reliable*" **Peter Blake** (see p.566) heads the litigation team in what has been a notable year for pensions litigation and international work. Has also acted for a worldwide exporter in a distribution dispute. Unlike the competition in Ipswich, this firm has seen a growth in insolvency-related work and instructions from commercial agents. **Clients:** Pension funds; plant hire companies; shipping companies.

NORTH WEST

LITIGATION: GENERAL COMMERCIAL • North West	
1	**DLA** Liverpool, Manchester
	Eversheds Manchester
2	**Addleshaw Booth & Co** Manchester
	Cobbetts Manchester
	Hammond Suddards Edge Manchester
3	**Halliwell Landau** Manchester
4	**Berg & Co** Manchester
	Brabners Liverpool, Preston
	Davies Wallis Foyster Liverpool, Manchester
	Hill Dickinson Liverpool
5	**Kershaw Abbott** Manchester
	Pannone & Partners Manchester
	Wacks Caller Manchester
6	**Chaffe Street** Manchester
	Cuff Roberts Liverpool
	Mace & Jones Liverpool, Manchester
	Rowe Cohen Manchester

LEADING INDIVIDUALS		
1	**CLAVELL-BATE Michael** Eversheds	**HARRIS Andrew** DLA
	MATTISON Mark Eversheds	**ROPER Robert** Cobbetts
	SORRELL Christopher Wacks Caller	
2	**GATENBY John** Addleshaw Booth & Co	**GOLD Antony** Eversheds
	GOSLING John Addleshaw Booth & Co	**THOMAS Paul** Halliwell Landau
	WINTERBURN Anthony DLA	
3	**AMSDEN Mark** Addleshaw Booth & Co	**GRAY David** DLA
	KERSHAW Anne Kershaw Abbott	**KHAN Charles** Berg & Co
4	**BLAKEMORE Craig** Mace & Jones	**HAYES Philippa** Hammond Suddards Edge
	MANLEY Mark Brabners	**RAWLINSON David** Cuff Roberts
	SMALL Graham Rowe Cohen	**WHITTELL Mark** Cobbetts

This book is the product of 6,552 1/2 hour interviews. See p.7 for BMRB audit.

Within each band, firms are listed alphabetically. *See individuals' profiles p.564*

DLA Active across the UK and Europe in big-ticket commercial disputes, **Andrew Harris** continues to elicit heavy praise from our interviewees and is ably supported by **Anthony Winterburn** and **David Gray**.

Eversheds (see firm details p.952) Commentators continue to remark on the more emollient attitude now taken by a firm once noted for its unyielding approach. IP, IT, construction, insurance, defamation, property, education and banking are all specialisms which fall under the umbrella of this thriving practice, which has "*grown markedly from an excellent base.*" Increasingly the emphasis is on the resolution of commercial disputes whether by ADR, risk management techniques or early case assessment. All qualified members of the team handle disputes worth in excess of £1 million, many of which have an international element to them. Fielding a team of true stars, **Michael Clavell-Bate** (see p.567) is a "*bigger picture litigator of undoubted integrity.*" **Mark Mattison**'s (see p.576) practice is centred around construction disputes where he displays his "*tenacity, intelligence and brilliant technical acumen*" while "*statesman-like*" **Antony Gold** (see p.570) focuses on contentious IP and e-commerce related work. Together they form a "*formidable whole*" engaged on complex litigation such as a £10 million professional negligence claim by a car rental company against a firm of solicitors. Participation is also ongoing in an alleged breach of contract claim worth more than £20 million, which is producing a multiplicity of proceedings.

Addleshaw Booth & Co (see firm details p.853) The bedrock of this practice is its "*superb corporate and commercial client base,*" while a healthy proportion of its activities lies in IT litigation. The quality of the offering is in no doubt, as competitors commend "*an effective, pragmatic team.*" This includes the "*dynamic*" **John Gosling** (see p.571), an expert in professional negligence and insurance related dispute resolution. Reflecting the firm's distinct sympathy towards mediation, **John Gatenby** (see p.80), "*a member of the old guard with an academic bent,*" displays excellence in this and the related dispute resolution field. He is complemented by the energetic **Mark Amsden** (see p.564), "*a good people person, gifted on the IT side,*" who is felt to have "*done something for morale*" since his arrival. The team acted in Winpar Holdings v Joseph Holt, a case of widespread importance for UK listed companies with overseas shareholders. **Clients:** Airtours; Littlewoods; United Utilities.

Cobbetts (see firm details p.923) Smaller than its heavyweight rivals, this Manchester based practice earned fulsome praise for being "*professional, sensible and straight in its dealings.*" Some clients are plcs, but the majority of work is for owner-managed businesses with a discernible bias toward financial services concerns and breweries. Head of department **Mark Whittell** (see p.584) is "*impressive and dependable*" and "*like the firm as a whole, conducts himself with dignity.*" His colleague **Robert Roper** (see p.580) is essentially an IP practitioner who involves himself in broad litigation. A "*quality opponent,*" he is hailed for his "*pragmatism and no-nonsense approach.*" Partner driven, the practice embraces insolvency, contract disputes, banking, defendant insurance, professional negligence, director disqualification and co-operative litigation. **Clients:** UNCL; Lookers; Weir Group; Cheshire Building Society; North British Housing Association.

Hammond Suddards Edge (see firm details p.984) A microcosm of the wider national practice, the Manchester office "*is a small but effective presence with access to meaty clients and jobs.*" Its core lies in mainstream dispute resolution, where reputation for conciliation has been cemented by its increased involvement in ADR. Other signal interests include property litigation, defamation, media, sports, health and environmental work. The departure of the respected Ian Meredith to the London office is seen as only a minor inconvenience due to the continued presence *of "a professional bunch of lawyers you can respect.*" These include **Philippa Hayes** (see p.571), *"a tough cookie and excellent supervisor"* who specialises in defamation and the resolution of commercial disputes. In the past year the team has appeared in High Court proceedings on a complaint to the Banking Ombudsman regarding defamation and breach of contract. **Clients:** BASF; ICI; Ultraframe; Optical Express.

Halliwell Landau (see firm details p.982) The firm remains *"a respected and skilful opponent"* in the eyes of our interviewees. Priding itself on its aggressive approach and commercial awareness, rivals remarked *"you know you're in for a good fight when you see the name."* The client base is split evenly between owner-managed businesses and institutions. Within this broad church property litigation, professional negligence and brewery associated litigation are particular specialities. The enterprise is run by **Paul Thomas** (see p.583) *"a practitioner of long standing and eminence"* who operates with managerial responsibilities. His advisory capability has been seen in such matters as Amec Developments v Jurys Hotel Management UK, a case involving the construction of a 265 bedroom hotel in breach of a restrictive covenant. **Clients:** AEGON Insurance; Kwik-Fit GB; Reebok; Pilkington; Royal Bank of Scotland.

Berg & Co (see firm details p.876) A compact unit, which continues to garner plaudits from its competitors. Catering for the needs of smaller enterprises it handles commercial contractual disputes, insolvency and professional negligence. Its strong showing in our tables is a reflection of the esteem in which **Charles Khan** (see p.574) is held by his peers. His *"intensity and serious quality reap dividends"* and, as one rival commented, *"it is surprising that one of his talents has not been snapped up by the bigger firms."* **Clients:** Textile manufacturers and IT/computer companies.

Brabners (see firm details p.892) This practice's capacity has been enhanced immeasurably by the absorption of the entire commercial litigation department of highly rated Berrymans Lace Mawer. *"A quality old-fashioned firm"* it has a renowned defamation practice with further capabilities in employment, property, professional negligence, IP and debt recovery. **Mark Manley**, known principally for defamation, also doubles up as a *"commercial and approachable"* general litigator. The team has been involved in two complex breach of warranty claims, each worth over £10 million, and a successful defamation action against a national tabloid. **Clients:** Business and Community Services; Stoves; Riverside Housing Association.

Davies Wallis Foyster (see firm details p.935) *"A capable operator that more than punches its weight."* Bolstered successfully by an aggressive recruitment policy, the firm is judged by rivals to have a bright future conducting matters in its stonghold areas of corporate litigation, risk assessment, intellectual property, partnership disputes and regulatory issues. In common with many other practices, the team is presenting a more conciliatory aspect, making an effort to explore non-contentious options within the dispute resolution exercise. **Clients:** Allied Domecq; Anglo International Group; Lloyds TSB; Tulip International (UK).

Hill Dickinson (see firm details p.996) The overwhelming market perception of this firm is of it as *"a highly successful defendant insurance practice."* This view, however, has to be tempered somewhat by its evident involvement in other litigation sectors such as construction, insolvency, banking and finance, professional indemnity and shareholder disputes. Recent highlights include acting on behalf of a lottery millionaire in resisting a claim by his ex-girlfriend for a share of the winnings. Also appeared for a major bank in a breach of confidentiality action against an investment advisor. **Clients:** Insurance companies; manufacturing companies.

Kershaw Abbott (see firm details p.1021) A niche practice *"limited somewhat in size but not in quality."* The practice comprises, inter alia, insurance, construction and professional indemnity work. It is its partnership dispute work which catches the eye, an area in which **Anne Kershaw** (see p.574) excels. Hers is the overwhelming contribution to the reputation of the firm. She is seen as *"an excellent and fearsome litigator"* with *"a tremendous work rate and a reluctance to ever let go."* Admirers of her *"gun-slinging style"* include a number of nationally known plcs. **Clients:** Railtrack; Cruden Construction.

Pannone & Partners (see firm details p.1088) Lacking the heavyweight corporate clients of some of its rivals, this virtually freestanding department relies on the sheer quality of its service to attract business. Much of that takes the form of litigation on behalf of small to medium sized businesses in areas such as PI, insolvency, banking, commercial property and commercial contracts. *"Broad ranging and claimant orientated"* the emphasis is on litigation avoidance through a department sub-divided into specialist teams. Acted in a multi-million pound claim for Royal Bank of Scotland, and in a complex commercial property dispute seeking to recover a fraudulently obtained high value nursing homes empire. **Clients:** Granada Group; Monarch Airlines; Volvo Truck & Bus Company; Manchester Airport.

Wacks Caller (see firm details p.1170) Multi-jurisdictional disputes, professional negligence, defamation and shareholder disputes are all to the fore in this *"increasingly vital department."* Researchers were told that it has *"really come on in the past year,"* much of the impetus being provided by market favourite **Kit Sorrell** (see p.582). *"Results driven and with a number of tricks up his sleeve"* he is *"a hard-nosed fighter who commands a loyal client following."* He has been seen in B&Q v Liverpool and Lancashire Properties, a leading case on landlord and tenants' rights over service areas, and is due to represent the former management of singer Russell Watson in an upcoming claim. **Clients:** Scottish & Newcastle; Cream; Liverpool and Lancashire Properties.

Chaffe Street (see firm details p.911) Regarded as an excellent corporate finance firm the litigation department handles spin-off work from that field. Not surprisingly the focus is predominantly on banking and insolvency matters with further specialisms in IP and contractual disputes. The departure to Hammond Suddards Edge of its main litigation partner is felt to be a blow, but commentators remain sanguine following the lateral hire of a former member of Davies Wallis Foyster. The team appeared in an intellectual property dispute worth in excess of £1 million, and acted in a complex dispute involving an engineering contract. **Clients:** Locker Group; Reticel.

Cuff Roberts *"A tightly knit operation"* commended for its insolvency and debt recovery arms. A broad expertise encompasses employment, property litigation, professional negligence and partnership disputes. **David Rawlinson** (see p.579) is rated for his *"stickability and astute handling of the bigger case."* **Clients:** The Littlewoods Organisation; Littlewoods Pools; Johnson Cleaners.

Mace & Jones (see firm details p.1046) *"A dedicated team"* which tackles medium-sized matters while having the capacity to run the weightier case. IP and property litigation are the mainstay of this practice, but the work extends into IT, professional negligence and shareholder disputes. Co-ordinating affairs is **Craig Blakemore** (see p.566) praised for his *"unhistrionic manner"* and *"ability to tame the more liverish animals in the jungle."* **Clients:** Grant Thornton; Peel Holdings; Co-operative Group (CWS); big five accountancy firms.

Rowe Cohen A PI firm that has successfully expanded into commercial litigation, this is a *"nifty little practice which more than holds its own."* Tending to deal with the entrepreneurial owner managed businesses it is consistently gaining experience in cases with an international flavour in places as diverse as Vietnam, Dubai and North America. Team leader **Graham Small** (see p.581) *"gets his cases through his name and due to his sound commercial grasp."* Recent significant litigation includes acting for David McLean, MP of Penrith, in obtaining an apology from a newspaper, which then appeared on all of their billboards. Also acted for a client on a substantial contractual claim brought against a Taiwanese company in relation to Taiwanese law. **Clients:** Huntley International; Medical Innovations; Freeborders Inc.

YORKSHIRE

LITIGATION: GENERAL COMMERCIAL • Yorkshire
1 **Addleshaw Booth & Co** Leeds
DLA Leeds, Sheffield
Eversheds Leeds
Hammond Suddards Edge Leeds
Walker Morris Leeds
2 **Irwin Mitchell** Sheffield
Pinsent Curtis Biddle Leeds
3 **Lupton Fawcett** Leeds
Rollits Hull
4 **Andrew M Jackson & Co** Hull
Gordons Cranswick Solicitors Bradford, Leeds
Keeble Hawson Leeds
5 **Brooke North** Leeds
Ford & Warren Leeds
Gosschalks Hull
Read Hind Stewart Leeds

LEADING INDIVIDUALS	
1 **HEAPS John** Eversheds	**KAMSTRA Simon** Addleshaw Booth & Co
SINCLAIR Jonathan Eversheds	
2 **CROSSLEY Peter** Hammond Suddards	**GILBERT Ralph** Rollits
KISSACK Nigel Pinsent Curtis Biddle	**STONE Paul** DLA
3 **CHAPMAN Stuart** Pinsent Curtis Biddle	**CHERRY Peter** Addleshaw Booth & Co
CROSSE Damian DLA	**DAVIES Gwendoline** Walker Morris
4 **EVANS Hugh** DLA	**ROTHWELL Charles** Keeble Hawson
SMITH Hugh Andrew M Jackson & Co	
UP AND COMING	
GARRETT Susan Addleshaw Booth & Co	

This book is the product of 6,552 1/2 hour interviews. See p.7 for BMRB audit.
Within each band, firms are listed alphabetically. *See individuals' profiles p.564*

Addleshaw Booth & Co (see firm details p.853) The firm's perennially healthy client base has been further bolstered by the acquisition of household name clients, all with their attendant needs in the commercial litigation field. Its litigation capability stretches across the full range of sectors embracing pockets of specialism in spheres such as mining, railways, pharmaceutical and defamation. Lead individual **Simon Kamstra** (see p.574) is "*something of a polymath*" handling shareholder and contract disputes, professional negligence and property litigation. Praised for his analysis of cases, peers are in awe of this "*general in the field that plots the downfall of his opponents with military precision.*" "*Awesome litigator*" **Peter Cherry** (see p.567) spearheads the burgeoning defamation arm, advising top clients in disputes over television coverage. Increasingly seen on complex matters in London, he retains a foothold in the North. Highlights of a busy year include a £4 million warranty claim on behalf of a company against a plc vendor and action for an employer in connection with the termination of a multi-million pound agreement undertaken. **Susan Garrett** (see p.570) is also developing a name in this field. **Clients:** Halifax; Airtours; Kelda Group; Asda Group; Kingfisher.

DLA Blessed with a strong client base, this team has displayed its skills in corporate litigation encompassing cross-border disputes. The respected team includes **Paul Stone, Hugh Evans** and **Damian Crosse.**

Eversheds (see firm details p.952) "*A historically strong and vital*" department which is sub-divided into specialist teams for construction, environment, insurance and property litigation. The numbers and quality of personnel have allowed it to fashion key strengths in competition, IT, telecoms, auditors' negligence claims and product liability. Head of department **Jonathan Sinclair** (see p.581) "*stands out as first rate*" according to both clients and competitors. He is particularly adept at competition work and acted for Asda in a House of Lords case concerning claims by the Italian Parma Ham trade association alleging that EU law precluded the supermarket chain from slicing and packaging Parma Ham in the UK. **John Heaps** (see p.572) is the national head and consequently divides his time across the country. "*Technically excellent and an organisational whizz,*" he co-ordinated an action for Terra Nitrogen in defending five separate claims worth in excess of £50 million which arose from a major product recall of carbonated drinks. Much of the team's workload now has an international feel, as typified by its advice on claims worth $160 million arising from the construction of a plant in the Far East. **Clients:** Kuwait Petroleum Corp; English Welsh & Scottish Railways; Next.

Hammond Suddards Edge (see firm details p.984) "*Cropping up time and time again on the fatter cases*" this team is judged by rivals to have "*a well defined sense of purpose and the talent to see it through.*" Its spheres of activity include property, environmental, fraud, professional negligence, competition, defamation, contract and shareholder disputes. Adapting to changing times, it puts a sharp accent on mediation and in-house advocacy having appointed a barrister of 20 years' standing to lead a specialist unit. In charge overall is **Peter Crossley** (see p.568), expert in contractual warranty claims and shareholder disputes. "*Addicted to the cut and thrust of litigation,*" barristers feel he "*imperiously sweeps aside the dead wood of any case.*" A string of high value recent cases includes acting for a major plc in a £2 million dispute arising out of the administration of the company's pension scheme, and representing a company in both England and the USA which had been the victim of a financial services fraud. **Clients:** Austin Reed; Bradford & Bingley; Harrods; National Grid Company.

Walker Morris (see firm details p.1171) "*A definite force*" in this area, "*aggressive in its marketing but with the results to back it up.*" Lateral hires at partner level from Eversheds and Irwin Mitchell have boosted both the client base and scope of the practice. Effective in insolvency and property litigation, the team can also turn its hands to other disciplines including media and construction matters. **Gwendoline Davies** (see p.568) is at the helm and has established a name in class actions. Recently involved in a substantial environmental class action with 180 plus claimants, she has also enjoyed Court of Appeal success this year acting for Selby District Council in a long-running dispute with Samuel Smith Old Brewery over the redevelopment of Tadcaster town centre. A clutch of favourable comments has led to this firm entering the upper echelon of our table this year. **Clients:** BUPA; Express Dairies; Northern Foods Group; Selfridges; Waste Recycling Group.

Irwin Mitchell (see firm details p.1009) Operating at the bulk end of the market this is a practice that "*can give the opposition real headaches.*" Business and partnership disputes constitute the bread and butter with medium-sized plcs catered for. Well able to handle all facets of this area, the team has a specialism in the field of commercial agents' regulations disputes both in the UK and Europe. The loss of two partners to Walker Morris and Hammond Suddards Edge has however, caused a certain disquiet in the market. This remains a buoyant operation, further fuelled by the outsourcing of legal work from in-house legal departments at a number of substantial commercial organisations such as Esso. **Clients:** BOC; Esso; AXA Sun Life Services; William Cook; Alfred McAlpine.

Pinsent Curtis Biddle (see firm details p.1098) Not on the same scale as its Birmingham counterpart, this practice is nonetheless "*noteworthy for the weight and quality of its work.*" With an international element and an emphasis on early resolution, it is "*a redoubtable force*" according to our interviewees. The retail sector, IT disputes, trading and regulatory law, product liability, and competition raids are all facets of its experience. An innovative spirit is exemplified in the establishment of the first in-house forensic accounting team in this area. National Head of Litigation, **Nigel Kissack** (see p.566), "*radiates sense and dependability*" on the occasions when he handles cases. More hands-on is **Stuart Chapman** (see p.566) whose general practice is prosecuted in a "*thoughtful and considered*" manner. The team has been involved in a $7.7 million product liability claim mediated in the USA, and has appeared in nine multi-million pound IT disputes in the past year. **Clients:** Argos; Tesco; Jarvis Porter Group; Pace Micro Technology; Groupe Schneider.

Lupton Fawcett Considered to lack the corporate client base to challenge the leaders, this practice "*more than holds its own in its own realm.*" More involved in the high net worth private client sphere, it presents an efficient and economical alternative to the region's businessmen. Affording expertise in engineering disputes, IP, banking, property, debt recovery and professional negligence it can also boast an extensive contentious insurance practice. **Clients:** T & N Federal-Mogul; high street banks and building societies; engineering and manufacturing companies.

Rollits (see firm details p.1110) "*A respected firm with a good client core,*" it is regarded by competitors as "*having the pick of the quality work in Hull.*" Its interests extend to contract and property disputes, professional indemnity, IP and landlord and tenant matters. Targeting companies of significant size, it is enjoying growth in the construction sector benefiting from a more cost-effective approach than is offered by its rivals in Leeds and London. **Ralph Gilbert** (see p.570) has appeared for a major motor dealership in a £6 million claim against it, alleging a conspiracy to destroy the business of an independent parts supplier. The team also acted on behalf of two shareholders and former directors of a football league club in a dispute with other shareholders over control. **Clients:** Anglia Oils; Humbrol; Kingston Communications (Hull); Wabco Automotive (UK).

Andrew M Jackson & Co (see firm details p.860) Shepherding a client base of medium-sized businesses and wealthy individuals the practice "*has a generous portion of the Hull pie.*" Devoted to "*quality over quantity*" the team takes on cases in the areas of commercial property, partnership, professional negligence, insolvency, and litigious construction. Historically connected to the transport industry, it has been engaged on an idiosyncratic case, dating back to 1819, which concerns the disputed purchase of property by Humber pilots. Team leader **Hugh Smith** (see p.581), "*proactive and sound of judgment,*" has also overseen an international dispute relating to the supply of equipment to Africa worth in the region of £1 million. **Clients:** Associated British Ports; MFI Properties; Northern Food Trustees; Central Land Developments.

Gordons Cranswick Solicitors Differing in caseload from the headline firms in the field, this "*fine dependable firm*" attracts bulk commercial litigation. Local textile, retail and technology companies and owner-managed businesses form the lion's share of the practice alongside a number of finance companies, for which advice on asset finance litigation is provided. The jewel in the crown, however, remains its coveted client William Morrisons, the regional supermarket giant. **Clients:** William Morrisons; Peter Blacks; textile companies; finance companies.

Keeble Hawson Mainly based in Leeds, with additional capacity in Sheffield, the practice services the whole of Yorkshire and North Nottinghamshire. Its clients are mainly owner-managed businesses, many being referred from its corporate department. Acting for both claimants and defendants, construction and IP are its core areas, although a recent lateral hire from Hammond Suddards Edge has seen it make strides in the pharmaceutical field. Led by **Charles Rothwell** (see p.580), a lawyer both "*insightful and analytical,*" the team is perceived by competitors to be expanding both in terms of workload and personnel. **Clients:** Several regional based companies in the building, demolition and retail industries.

Brooke North A catholic approach results in involvement in areas as diverse as contractual disputes, construction, property, IP, fraud and partnership disputes. The team lost one partner this year but is still seen as "*an economic alternative to Leeds' bigger players.*" Possessing an "*aggressive style,*" it is led by Lynne Stockdale and has participated in a number of recently reported cases including Bank of Ireland v Holicourt Contracts and Khalatshi v Walker Morris. **Clients:** Evans of Leeds; Linpac Containers; Bank of Ireland; Illingworth Morris; Aram Resources.

Ford & Warren (see firm details p.961) A niche practice heavily allied to the transport and brewing industries, which "*displays commercial acumen and is effective in the difficult case.*" Considered "*a value for money alternative,*" by barristers, it is heavily involved in insurance with coverage in professional negligence, insolvency, construction and contractual disputes. The group has handled 600 claims against the French government following strikes by lorry drivers in that country. It also excels in tenancy disputes in the pub trade and handles all of UPS' debt recovery in the UK. **Clients:** Bass; Punch; UPS; transport companies.

Gosschalks Adopting a "*commercial and pragmatic approach*" this medium sized practice services the needs of its existing commercial clients both as defendant and claimant. Lacking a standout figure, peers acknowledge it can call upon "*uniformly competent practitioners*" in areas such as property, insurance, IP, and contractual disputes. Recent highlights include two major unfair prejudice actions, a lucrative patent action, and a £5 million warranty claim surrounding the sale of a motor company. **Clients:** Wellington Pub Co; William Hill; Thompson Plastics (Hull); nationally known clients in the leisure and licensing trade.

NORTH EAST

LITIGATION: GENERAL COMMERCIAL • North East	
1	**Dickinson Dees** Newcastle upon Tyne
	Ward Hadaway Newcastle upon Tyne
2	**Eversheds** Newcastle upon Tyne
3	**Watson Burton** Newcastle upon Tyne
4	**Hay & Kilner** Newcastle upon Tyne
5	**Robert Muckle** Newcastle upon Tyne

LEADING INDIVIDUALS		
1	**ELLIOTT Robert** Ward Hadaway	
2	**COLLINSON Ian** Ward Hadaway	**HARVEY Guy** Dickinson Dees
	SOLOMAN Martin Hay & Kilner	

This book is the product of 6,552 1/2 hour interviews. See p.7 for BMRB audit.

Within each band, firms are listed alphabetically. *See individuals' profiles p.564*

Dickinson Dees (see firm details p.941) Possessing reach both locally and nationally, the firm "*has clout and a corporate client base to die for.*" With a stress on early resolution, its key areas are fraud, transport and inquiries, shareholders' disputes, commercial agents' regulations cases and professional negligence. The firm's progressive spirit has been illustrated by the establishment of a sister office in the Tees valley and the recruitment to the practice of a former director of forensic services for Deloitte & Touche. The leading personality is **Guy Harvey** (see p.571), "*a definite name to conjure with,*" who successfully led his team on the Ladbroke Grove Inquiry. He has further been involved in a multi-million pound contract claim for a major US corporate, and handled complex trust litigation and tracing claims. **Clients:** Northern Electric; Northumbrian Water; Arriva; GoAhead.

Ward Hadaway (see firm details p.1173) With construction, banking, employment and insolvency work handled by other specialist units within the firm, this is a commercial litigation department in the purest sense.

Its niche strengths are professional negligence and IP with the presence of two "*formidable litigators*" ensuring its top-flight status. **Robert Elliott** (see p.569) is a "*polished and energetic litigator,*" an ex-London practitioner who "*dominates the North Eastern scene.*" Researchers were told that **Ian Collinson** (see p.567) has "*drive and determination*" and "*his results speak for themselves.*" He led a team defending Allerdale Borough Council on a wrongful trading action with sums claimed in excess of £10 million. The firm also acted for Pride Valley Foods on a £15 million professional negligence claim. **Clients:** Safeway Stores; Pride Valley Foods; City Electrical Factors; Allerdale Borough Council; Able UK.

Eversheds (see firm details p.952) "*A front line practice staffed by talented and industrious litigators of a high calibre;*" a claim from one barrister echoed by other interviewees. Its clients are predominantly large plcs harvested both locally and nationally, and serviced by a department with the critical mass to take on the largest cases. Offering the range of commercial litigation, it impresses in competition, commercial insurance, product liability, defamation, and health and environmental law, and has had a key role in the Bloody Sunday Inquiry. Perceived to be going through a period of reorganisation after the closure of its Middlesbrough office, the practice remains highly visible and in the last year has conducted two multi-million pound European competition cases relating to abuses in the coal mining industry. Also advised in respect of a freezing order arising from a high value banking fraud. **Clients:** Rolls-Royce; Northumbria Water; Invensys.

Watson Burton This department, "*deserving of its place in the sun,*" is split into a commercial litigation unit and a construction and engineering/insurance unit. The latter attracts the majority of the laurels, but its general litigation capabilities are manifest. Choosing to specialise more than many of its rivals, it is particularly strong in sale of goods and shareholder disputes while increasingly carving out a name for regulatory work. The arrival of a respected litigator from competitors Robert Muckle is expected to provide ballast, especially on the insolvency side. Notable recent cases include successfully defending a number of claims against Associated Co-operative Creameries, and a contractual claim against Scandinavian Tourist Boards. **Clients:** Co-operative Wholesale Society; Premier Direct Group; Scandinavian Tourist Board; Ultimate Leisure; Metnor Group.

Hay & Kilner Not on the same playing field as the bigger operators, this practice is "*an attractive option for the smaller concerns.*" Catering for SMEs, insurers and professional partnerships, activity is generally confined to the lower value cases. Shareholder disputes, breach of warranty claims, commercial frauds, judicial review and patent disputes form the workload, each approached from a mediation friendly stance. Expert in railway issues, the firm has acted for Railtrack in a number of heavyweight contentious commercial matters including a claim against a quarry company for carrying out work on its property adjacent to a railway line. **Martin Soloman** (see p.582) continues to elicit warm commendations from the market. **Clients:** Railtrack; Noble Organisation; Avon Rubber Company; Northeast Press; insurers.

Robert Muckle Interesting times here with the loss of leading practitioners to rival firms. While a need to re-establish its litigation capacity is evident, the market accepts that this is still "a *reliable, practised outfit.*" It handles commercial contract disputes, insolvency, shareholder disputes and IP for a client base comprising mainly manufacturing companies and owner-managed businesses. Traditionally aggressive in approach, there is universal sentiment among our interviewees that it has "*mellowed of late*" due to the inclusion of a qualified mediator. **Clients:** Sunderland FC; QSP.

SCOTLAND

Brodies WS (see firm details p.x896) "*A traditional practice*" handling contractual disputes, insolvency, IP and partnerships. It is home to **David Williamson** (see p.584) who, as our researchers were informed, is "*by anybody's reckoning the best in the field.*" Wearing a number of hats he has a broad practice and is "*both academically and tactically gifted*" with a capacity for "*driving through the opposition.*" Studded with esteemed practitioners, many of them solicitor advocates, the team can call upon the "*clear-headed*" **William Holligan** (see p.59) who is highly visible on the JR front. **Joyce Cullen** (see p.330) meanwhile lends expertise on property related matters conducting herself in a "*no-nonsense, prompt style.*" In the past year the firm has appeared in large-scale partnership and contractual disputes and a number of commercial/negligence claims. **Clients:** Major corporates.

Dundas & Wilson CS (see firm details p.947) Benefiting from a tie-in with Arthur Andersen the practice concentrates largely on its core clients in banking and finance. It has a "*sound grasp of many areas*" being split into five specialised teams: commercial, construction, insurance, property and employment. IP and IT cases also abound with the firm having established an e-commerce group. Noted for his banking and insurance work, **Colin MacLeod** is "*switched on*" and, like the rest of the team, can take advantage of an enviable client base featuring many of the corporate big hitters in the country. Highlights include advising Scottish Media Group on an £11 million scheme of arrangement and share capital reduction. Also advised a large international client upon the Scottish aspects of a multi-million trade secrets litigation in the USA.

Maclay Murray & Spens (see firm details p.1047) "*Good performers and competent in most areas,*" according to peers, this practice is felt to be generally underrated by the market. It contains four solicitor advocates and offers particular expertise in media, IP, IT and fraud. Receiving referrals from a host of English solicitors, it provides a one-stop UK cross-border service, which allows it to secure simultaneous UK-wide injunctions for its corporate clients. Its two offices are seen as highly complementary and include **Alayne Swanson** (see p.582) "*a fighter with a broad practice.*" **Ewan Easton** (see p.568) is particularly commended for supplying pre-litigation and negotiation skills. The team represented BBC Scotland in seeking rights to televise the Lockerbie trial, and has been involved in a multi-million dollar international fraud investigation conducted in four European countries. On the IP front it participated in the Davidoff/Joop litigation, a significant case for brand owners in the sphere of parallel imports. **Clients:** Highland Distillers; Lloyds TSB; Lithgows; Microsoft; GlaxoSmithKline.

McGrigor Donald (see firm details p.1062) This practice, one of the two largest in Scotland, handles the full array of commercial litigation matters. It is in IP, property litigation, and contract disputes that it presents "*more than a match to anyone.*" Its broad client base stretches from owner-managed businesses to blue-chip companies. A higher profile resulting from involvement in the Lockerbie trial and continued growth have resulted in a heavy recruitment drive. "*The tough, seasoned team*" includes **Craig Connal**, a planning expert who is "*a sensible guy applying the law in a practical way.*" Last year the department advised William Grant & Sons in a passing off action and provided regulatory advice to BP in relation to Health & Safety issues at its petrochemical complex in Grangemouth. **Clients:** BP Amoco; Imperial Tobacco; Forth Ports; The Post Office.

Shepherd & Wedderburn WS (see firm details p.1126) "*A genuinely healthy practice consolidating year on year*" so say our interviewees. Offering a spread of skills, it outstrips its competitors in the areas of aviation and clinical negligence. Out of the game for a while, managing partner **Hugh Donald** (see p.568) has returned to mainstream practice and is revered as "*a senior, sensible and honest practitioner.*" His colleague **Ian MacLeod** (see p.575), "*a first class litigator who never delays,*" proves particularly adept in the realm of public sector litigation. He led the team in an action on behalf of Scottish Power concerning interim interdict proceedings in relation to

LITIGATION: GENERAL COMMERCIAL • Scotland	
1	**Brodies WS** Edinburgh
	Dundas & Wilson CS Edinburgh, Glasgow
	Maclay Murray & Spens Edinburgh, Glasgow
	McGrigor Donald Edinburgh, Glasgow
2	**Shepherd & Wedderburn WS** Edinburgh
3	**Anderson Strathern WS** Edinburgh
	Burness Edinburgh
	Simpson & Marwick WS Edinburgh
4	**Henderson Boyd Jackson WS** Edinburgh
	MacRoberts Edinburgh, Glasgow
	Morison Bishop Glasgow
	Morton Fraser, Solicitors Edinburgh
5	**Anderson Fyfe** Glasgow
	Balfour & Manson Edinburgh
	Biggart Baillie Edinburgh, Glasgow
	Levy & McRae Glasgow

LEADING INDIVIDUALS		
★	**WILLIAMSON David** Brodies WS	
1	**ANDERSON Peter** Simpson & Marwick WS	**CONNAL Craig** McGrigor Donald
	MACLEOD Colin Dundas & Wilson CS	**MACLEOD Ian** Shepherd & Wedderburn WS
2	**HOLLIGAN William** Brodies WS	**SWANSON Alayne** Maclay Murray & Spens
	TYLER Alfred Balfour & Manson	
3	**CULLEN Joyce** Brodies WS	**DONALD Hugh** Shepherd & Wedderburn WS
	EASTON Ewan Maclay Murray & Spens	**HAYWOOD Brent** Burness
	SHAW Murray Biggart Baillie	**STEWART David** Morton Fraser, Solicitors
	WATSON Peter Levy & McRae	

This book is the product of 6,552 1/2 hour interviews. See p.7 for BMRB audit.
Within each band, firms are listed alphabetically. *See individuals' profiles p.564*

the terms of UK procurement regulations. Also acted in King v Bristow Helicopters, a case of international significance which turned on the correct interpretation of the Warsaw Convention. **Clients:** Scottish Power; Scottish Provident Institution; Shell UK; Orange; Miller Group.

Anderson Strathern WS (see firm details p.859) A cross-departmental team, strong in insolvency and viewed by rivals as enjoying *"a steady flow of work from the banks."* Its secure foothold in banking and financial services work has been confirmed by its appointment as one of two providers to Bank of Scotland Business Banking. Regularly seen in both Sheriff Courts and the Court of Session Commercial Court it also handles IP, insurance and construction litigation. A recent highlight was Labinski v BP Oil Development, a £40 million case arising from the exercise of a servitude right on the part of oil companies preventing land development. **Clients:** Clydesdale Bank; Coal Authority; Zurich Commercial; National Trust for Scotland; Scottish Rugby Union.

Burness (see firm details p.903) Drawing on sound connections in Edinburgh commercial circles, this long-standing practice has enjoyed *"consistent growth over the years."* It is broken down into five main units: corporate and commercial, technology, employment, media and entertainment, and product liability. Promoting an ethos of early resolution, it caters for a client base incorporating a number of institutional clients, in addition to the usual corporate favourites. **Brent Haywood** (see p.572), head of the commercial technology section, typifies the firm's approach in being *"young, energetic and forward-thinking."* Significant deals over the last year have included acting on a trademark infringement in relation to Microsoft Software, and instructions from the Scottish Football Association concerning judicial review proceedings. **Clients:** BBC; Dell Computers; Highland Spring; Scottish FA; manufacturing and pharmaceutical companies.

Simpson & Marwick WS (see firm details p.1133) Possessing possibly the biggest defendant practice in the country, this specialist litigation firm is heavily insurance based. Up to 80% of the caseload involves defendant reparation in this field, the residue being taken up by professional negligence, healthcare and routine contractual disputes. **Peter Anderson** impresses on many fronts with peers conceding *"he has fingers in so many pies, it's unbelievable."* His practice is *"prosecuted with startling vigour."* Appeared in Gunn v Newman, a case questioning the potential unfairness to defendants of jury awards. The team also acts for Transco protecting its interests following the Larkhall explosion. **Clients:** Insurers; engineering companies.

Henderson Boyd Jackson WS Established three years ago, this department has *"come up from nowhere."* Initially weighted towards insolvency, it is now more diffuse, combining building arbitration, IP and a presence in general contractual disputes. Commentators applauded the efforts of the team whose recent highlight involved appeal proceedings on a major patent action brought in the Court of Session. **Clients:** KPMG; HLB Kidsons; Ernst & Young.

MacRoberts (see firm details p.1048) Market leaders in construction work, this firm *"makes limited but telling sorties"* into alternative areas according to our interviewees. These include property, health and safety, insolvency, environmental, and professional negligence matters, all handled by a team of *"undoubted ability."* Judicial review is an area of growth both in the review of public body decisions and those of private tribunals. The group acted for Royal Bank of Scotland in a VAT appeal relating to the retrospective capping by Parliament of rights to reclaim VAT paid in error. **Clients:** British Energy; Royal Bank of Scotland; Ford; LAW Mining; Railtrack; Texaco.

Morison Bishop (see firm details p.1075) Undoubtedly large, although peers believe it has yet to punch its weight. Our interviewees agree that the firm produces lawyers who are *"strong and reliable, fusing legal ability with good sense."* Markedly vital on the insurance defender reparation side, it further undertakes banking, insolvency and professional indemnity. Alive to current trends, it is also active in IP/e-commerce disputes, including some cyber-squatter cases. **Clients:** Beazer Homes; computing manufacturers.

Morton Fraser, Solicitors (see firm details p.1076) A traditional Edinburgh firm able to call upon an extensive client base of blue chip companies. Property litigation dominates but construction, IP and judicial review all feature heavily. A sizeable team is well placed to cover the full sweep of litigation as peers commend its *"proficient service"* with individual specialisms in asset finance and employment. Acting in general commercial disputes **David Stewart** is *"never less than thorough."* **Clients:** Halifax; UKAEE, International Oil Pollution Compensation Fund.

Anderson Fyfe (see firm details p.858) A smaller firm undertaking *"volume work to a high standard."* Although lower in profile than some of its competitors, the feeling amongst our interviewees is that the firm is *"a tremendously effective outfit."* Incorporating a specialist insolvency unit it is active across the whole litigation spectrum.

Balfour & Manson (see firm details p.869) Although best known as a private client firm, commercial litigation is handled *"to a high standard."* Obtaining a considerable amount of out of town referrals, it deals with IP, professional negligence and defamation work within a general commercial framework. **Fred Tyler** (see p.650) is busy with building disputes and breach of contract cases and is applauded by his peers as *"one of the best organised lawyers in the business."* The firm acted in Margaret Brown v PF Dunfermline, one of the first cases taken to the Judicial committee of the Privy Council from Scotland under the terms of the European Convention on Human Rights. **Clients:** Law Society of Scotland; UKCC; Royal & SunAlliance.

Biggart Baillie (see firm details p.882) Respected by a wide range of its rivals, this firm is felt to offer *"a decent commercial litigation service."* General litigation is handled with a bias towards insolvency and contract disputes. In the last year it has defended a £9 million breach of contract suit, and represented numerous defenders in breach of warranty claims. "*Intellectual*" **Murray Shaw** (see p.581) is respected for his work in construction and planning law. **Clients:** Scottish Power; Cable & Wireless; Thus.

Levy & McRae (see firm details p.1039) "*Combatants with a close knit group of talented operators.*" Key practitioner **Peter Watson** (see p.288) is a "*tough fighter*" who has been involved in Piper Alpha and Lockerbie, and enjoys international contacts. His practice encompasses media/defamation, IP, software licensing and contractual disputes. Recently the team has seen a boom in aviation work being involved in the Glasgow air crash and the F15 disaster in the Highlands. **Clients:** Scottish Media Group; Scottish Daily Record; Strathclyde Police Federation.

NORTHERN IRELAND

LITIGATION: GENERAL COMMERCIAL • Northern Ireland	
1	**Carson McDowell** Belfast
	Elliott Duffy Garrett Belfast
	L'Estrange & Brett Belfast
2	**C&H Jefferson** Belfast
	Cleaver Fulton Rankin Belfast
	McKinty & Wright Belfast
	Mills Selig Belfast
3	**Johns Elliot** Belfast
	Johnsons Belfast
	Tughan & Co Belfast

LEADING INDIVIDUALS		
1	**BECKETT Sam** L'Estrange & Brett	**HAM Brian** Mills Selig
	LYNCH Michael Elliott Duffy Garrett	**O'DRISCOLL Pat** Cleaver Fulton Rankin
	SPRING Paul Mills Selig	**TURTLE Brian** Carson McDowell
	WILSON Michael Elliott Duffy Garrett	
2	**CRAWFORD Sandra** McKinty & Wright	**FOX Brendan** Cleaver Fulton Rankin

This book is the product of 6,552 1/2 hour interviews. See p.7 for BMRB audit.

Within each band, firms are listed alphabetically. *See individuals' profiles p.564*

Carson McDowell (see firm details p.909) "*As old as Methuselah*" and consistently in the top rank. The benefit of a fat portfolio of blue-chip clients affords it high visibility in the commercial courts. **Brian Turtle** (see p.583) brings "*gravitas and incomparable flair*" to a general practice with an accent on IP and copyright. **Clients:** Blue-chip corporates.

Elliott Duffy Garrett (see firm details p.949) Involved in major disputes with a body of respected practitioners including **Michael Lynch** ("*a good practical lawyer*") and **Michael Wilson** (see p.585) both of whom have the luxury of a good corporate client base. Advice is offered in insolvency, construction, planning, judicial review, defamation and professional indemnity.

L'Estrange & Brett (see firm details p.1038) Well able to negotiate the most complex of cases, this practice is at its best in construction, IP, professional negligence and employment matters. Peers judge **Sam Beckett** (see p.565) as "*well experienced and deadly in the endgame.*" The group acted for BP in a trademarks dispute concerning the particular shade of green used in petrol stations, and for Gilbert Ash in a major construction dispute. **Clients:** Gilbert Ash NI; Morrison Developments.

C&H Jefferson (see firm details p.1012) A major defence litigator with a voluminous practice. Its main line of approach lies in construction law, and it further represents insurance groups. Also covers professional indemnity, judicial review, and commercial agents disputes.

Cleaver Fulton Rankin (see firm details p.918) Observers commented on the intensity brought to bear on this practice's opponents. Taking centre stage are **Pat O'Driscoll** (see p.578) and **Brendan Fox** (see p.202) who juggle a number of disciplines. These include IP, financial services, construction, defamation and employment.

McKinty & Wright (see firm details p.1063) Building on its reputation in property work, this practice has successfully moved into wider litigation. It now attracts large-scale professional indemnity and insurance cases while having a pronounced speciality in medical defence work. **Sandra Crawford** (see p.568) is considered a prime mover by the market, and leads a team also proficient in IT, product liability and defamation.

Mills Selig (see firm details p.1070) A "*well-connected commercial firm,*" with a preponderance of medium-sized business clients. **Brian Ham** (see p.571), "*senior and thoroughly grounded,*" works alongside **Paul Spring** (see p.582) who is known for his work for newspapers on the defamation front. **Clients:** News Group Newspapers; CGU; Northern Bank.

Johns Elliot (see firm details p.1014) A truly eclectic practice active in both the public and private sectors with a client base that include such concerns as the NI Housing Executive. An interest in urban regeneration is illustrated by its involvement in an action for Dunloe Ewart, a major property company, in mounting a challenge to the government over its decision to grant preferred developer status to a Dutch company. The group is also involved in defamation work for newspapers and radio stations, and in professional negligence with the firm assisting on all matters for the Veterinary Defence Society. **Clients:** Belfast International Airport.

Johnsons (see firm details p.1015) Insurance defendant and defamation matters dominate the landscape here. Its insurance clients are of the highest calibre with the firm being appointed to both the AXA and Norwich Union panels of solicitors. As regards defamation, the practice continues to be "*first port of call*" for many such as Liam Neeson who was advised on the libellous implications of reports of his alleged marital difficulties. Other areas tackled include PI and breach of copyright.

Tughan & Co (see firm details p.1163) Insurance defence actions form the foundations of the practice. A healthy commercial department generates spin-off litigation work in the form of contractual disputes, negligence actions and product liability claims. Recent cases have included a major planning action for Tesco and a number of judicial reviews. It is hoped that the recent formalising of a link with a well-known Dublin firm will stimulate yet more growth.

Litigation Banking & Finance

OVERVIEW: For the first year we include a separate banking and finance litigation table. Our intention has been to limit it to complex, high level investment banking work, so the list is an exclusive one. What it demonstrates most clearly is that, as one lawyer agreed "*the people strong in banking litigation are the people with strong relationships to the banks.*" Hence Allen & Overy and Clifford Chance fight it out at the top while Herbert Smith makes a more modest entry. Regulatory expertise is increasingly important in financial litigation. Some of the names in the table approach banking litigation from this angle and it is probably best read in conjunction with our civil fraud and regulatory table. Others will be familiar from general commercial litigation, but the market judges that, while they have the breadth of a commercial litigator, their finance expertise must not be overlooked.

LONDON

LITIGATION: BANKING & FINANCE • London		Ptnrs	Assts
1	Allen & Overy	11	26
	Clifford Chance	12	30
2	Freshfields Bruckhaus Deringer	10	20
3	Linklaters	12	30
	Lovells	11	32
4	Herbert Smith	12	12
	Norton Rose	8	26
	Slaughter and May	*	*
5	Richards Butler	7	11
	Simmons & Simmons	5	14
	Stephenson Harwood	n/a	n/a
6	Ashurst Morris Crisp	4	*
	CMS Cameron McKenna	7	12
	Denton Wilde Sapte	5	9

LEADING INDIVIDUALS		
1	**ARCHER Nick** Slaughter and May	**GRIERSON Christopher** Lovells
	HOUSE Tim Allen & Overy	**STYLE Christopher** Linklaters
	TAYLOR Ian Freshfields Bruckhaus Deringer	
2	**BAGGALLAY Roger** Clifford Chance	**BAND Christa** Herbert Smith
	FAGAN Neil Lovells	**KELLY Jonathan** Simmons & Simmons
	WATSON Peter Allen & Overy	
3	**BAGGE James** Norton Rose	**CAVE Tim** Freshfields Bruckhaus Deringer
	DAVIES Valerie Norton Rose	**FINKLER Deborah** Slaughter and May
	FORDHAM John Stephenson Harwood	**GILL Mark** Denton Wilde Sapte
	GODDARD John Freshfields Bruckhaus Deringer	
	GOOD Diana Linklaters	**GWYNNE Richard** Stephenson Harwood
	WARNE David Richards Butler	
UP AND COMING		
	HART Andrew Freshfields Bruckhaus Deringer	
	O'CONOR John Allen & Overy	

This book is the product of 6,552 1/2-hour interviews. See p.7 for BMRB audit.
Within each band, firms are listed alphabetically. *See individuals' profiles p.564*
**See editorial entries for explanation of team sizes.*

Allen & Overy (see firm details p.856) "*Hot stuff in banking litigation*" with a large, high profile team rated as leaders on the capital markets/derivatives side. "*Good people with a great strength and breadth of practice*" and a "*business like approach*" include **Tim House** (see p.573) whose "*naturally good judgement and tactical sense*" were widely praised by clients and competitors. Head of department **Peter Watson** (see p.584), "*a fair opponent and always pragmatic*" also stands out, while "*excellent*" **John O'Conor**'s (see p.578) "*expertise on derivatives and specific banking products*" sees him emerging this year. The department also receives support from colleagues in fraud and asset tracing and on the regulatory side as these areas become increasingly important in pieces of banking litigation. The firm represented eleven banks in proceedings over the alleged Solo Industries fraud, a multi-jurisdictional case valued at $300 million. Also acted for NatWest in litigation against Rabobank in relation to an insolvent food group. **Clients:** CSFB; UBS; Nomura; Barclays; Chase Manhattan.

Clifford Chance (see firm details p.919) "*It has a strong non-contentious banking practice and, in virtue of that, has one of the strongest banking litigation practices.*" Competitors respect this team as "*good blue chip commercial litigators*" who "*stick out as the real cream.*" It is the team, though, rather than the individuals, which is the focus of attention. With the exception of **Roger Baggallay** (see p.565), considered "*a good name on sovereign debt,*" the partners maintained a relatively low profile in the market. The group – which is an integrated part of the commercial litigation team – is adjudged by some commentators to have the greatest share of the market in this sector. Consolidating its position on a number of panels, the time and effort invested on the regulatory side are paying off, and its global network leaves it well placed as the banking industry reorganises on global lines. The firm is representing Crédit Lyonnais Rouse in proceedings arising from the Sumitomo copper incident. It also acted for a Deutsche Bank subsidiary in its defence against Media Most, to the claim that it had breached contractual obligations by working with Gazprom on a deal which would have resulted in Media Most losing control of TV Channel NTV. **Clients:** ABN AMRO Hoare Govett; Bank of New York; Citigroup; Deutsche Bank; HSBC; JP Morgan Chase; Lehman Brothers; Merrill Lynch; Morgan Stanley; UBS.

Freshfields Bruckhaus Deringer (see firm details p.965) "*Freshfields through and through: utterly dependable and bright*" the banking litigation team garners considerable market approval. "*Impressive operator*" **Ian Taylor** (see p.582) "*has a good reputation, especially amongst American merchant banks*" while barristers confirm that **Tim Cave** (see p.566) has "*good litigation sense and understands the needs of clients.*" Though not thought to be a banking specialist, as "*one of the bank of England boys*" **John Goddard** (see p.570) has a solid profile in this field, while "*aggressive younger partner*" **Andrew Hart** (see p.571) is carving out a reputation. Not considered to have quite the banking client base of the two leaders, the firm is felt by peers and clients to have a "*broader litigation focus*" overall. Supported by a robust regulatory offering, the team represents an enviable list of investment banks on a range of trading disputes, regulatory investigations and other contentious situations. Its continuing involvement in the BCCI proceedings for the Bank of England probably constitutes the year's highest profile work. The firm also represented Deutsche Bank against the claim brought by UPC that it had misused confidential information to secure an advantage in bidding for German cable TV company TeleColumbus. **Clients:** Abbey

National; Bank of England; Deutsche Bank; FSA; Lehman Brothers; Morgan Stanley; Nomura; RBS; CIBC; Crédit Lyonnais; Chase Manhattan; CSFB; Dresdner Kleinwort Benson; UBS Warburg Dillon Reed.

Linklaters (see firm details p.1042) As its transactional banking department goes from strength to strength, banking litigation appears somewhat lower in profile although peers continue to acknowledge a quality output bolstered by robust investment banking relationships. "*Thorough, experienced and shrewd*" **Christopher Style** (see p.582) is "*aggressive, good on the law and leaves no stone unturned,*" while "*highly rated and visible*" **Diana Good** (see p.570) also elicited commendation. A broad client base sees the firm acting for major investment banks on issues arising out of securities sales, rights issues, civil or criminal fraud, derivatives and regulatory matters. A commercial banking arm handles transactional matters including problems surrounding trade finance, letters of credit and loan defaults. As illustration of its global competence, the team assisted on a prospectus liability action in the Danish courts. Also obtained freezing orders in six countries and initiated litigation in England, Switzerland and Cairo following the discovery of fraud by an ex-employee of a major investment bank. **Clients:** Citigroup; CSFB; JP Morgan Chase; Merrill Lynch; Morgan Stanley.

Lovells (see firm details p.1044) "*Heavily involved in BCCI,*" competitors consider that while it "*has a good litigation practice across the board, insolvency related work is where it'll really pick up.*" Hardly surprising that its highest profile financial litigator, "*effective, experienced, high profile guy*" **Christopher Grierson** (see p.571) is closely associated with major insolvency cases. "*Canny operator*" **Neil Fagan** (see p.569), "*an old hand who does a lot of work for Barclays,*" also received considerable market support, though clients stressed "*they're all pretty good there.*" The firm appears in a variety of cases involving issues such as fraud claims, sovereign debt restructuring, derivative related matters and other trading disputes, increasingly of a cross border nature. Its high profile cases include BCCI, where it represents the liquidators, and Barings, where it is acting for ING. Also assisted the EBRD and OPIC in attempting to enforce agreements taken as security from a Romanian borrower under French law but with an English jurisdiction clause. **Clients:** EBRD; OPIC; BCCI (In Liquidation); ING; Barclays; Standard Chartered Bank; Commerzbank; Lloyds TSB; Central Banks of two African countries.

Herbert Smith (see firm details p.993) "*Traditionally known as the number one litigation firm,*" the firm does not have the same profile in pure banking litigation as some of its competitors. Questions were raised about whether the firm's "*hyper-aggressive*" style suited the sector, although commentators recognised that it "*must pick up a lot of bank v bank work.*" The outfit's best known banking litigator is **Christa Band** (see p.565), who competitors praise as pleasant, expert and "*every bit as effective as you'd expect from Herbert Smith.*" The firm represented JP Morgan on an action arising from the settlement of two Russian rouble transactions, and has been advising UBS on multi-jurisdictional proceedings relating to a bank reference. **Clients:** Dresdner Kleinwort Wasserstein; UBS; JP Morgan; ING; Saudi American Bank; Coopers & Lybrand (Singapore).

Norton Rose (see firm details p.1082) An established team with "*significant banking litigation work,*" it is part of a broad based litigation department with expertise in related areas such as fraud, insolvency and asset finance litigation, clients appreciate. "*Highly experienced*" group head **Val Davies** (see p.568) "*always gets good write-ups.*" She is supported on the regulatory side by "*sensible and highly rated*" fraud expert, **James Bagge** (see p.565). Increasingly active in trade finance litigation, the firm represents a strong selection of, frequently foreign, investment banking clients in a variety of work. Represented Banque du Caire in three actions relating to a multi-million dollar letter of credit fraud and the State Bank of Saurashtra in matters arising from allegedly forged letters of indemnity. **Clients:** Société Générale; Komercni Banka; RBS; BHF Bank; Capital Bank; Banque du Caire; SBS; Banque Paribas; HSBC; Crédit Agricole Indosuez.

Slaughter and May (see firm details p.1135) (8 Ptnrs & 15 assts part-time)As with so many areas, the firm is not considered by peers to specialise but "*through the quality of the practice it generates a lot of work.*" Most notable is its representation of the liquidators of Barings in their £1 billion claim for negligence relating to the group's collapse. "*A leader in this field,*" **Nick Archer** (see p.564) is considered by clients "*a civilised opponent: approachable, pleasant, entertaining and fair,*" while on the regulatory side of banking litigation "*technically good*" **Deborah Finkler** (see p.569) was endorsed by clients for having "*judgement and the nerve to follow it.*" Skilled in letter of credit and option contracts, the team acts on a mass of international work for its superb investment bank client base. Represented the Abbey National on a large investor compensation litigation in Jersey following the failure of an offshore investment scheme. **Clients:** Abbey National; Deutsche; Central Bank of Yemen; Liquidators of Barings.

Richards Butler (see firm details p.1107) A growing group with a profile in banking and regulatory litigation, researchers were impressed that a high proportion of the group's work is multi-jurisdictional. Count its international offices, especially in the US, its depth of experience on large, complex litigations and the degree of partner involvement, and the firm is well placed to pick up high-value investment bank work. Typically high profile work includes representing an LME Metal Broker in proceedings resulting from Sumitomo's loss of $3 billion during the 1996 copper markets crisis. "*Lugubrious character*" **David Warne** (see p.584) is "*terribly good fun and charming.*" He represented a number of Brazilian investors against an English investment bank and its Brazilian affiliate in a $30 million claim concerning alleged fraud in the purchase of step down coupon eurobonds. **Clients:** Bank of Scotland; Lloyds TSB; Morgan Stanley Dean Witter; National Bank of Kuwait; Société Générale.

Simmons & Simmons (see firm details p.1132) "*They work well in teams and the quality of the lawyers is high,*" while according to one rival, "*I'd always take them seriously.*" A client-driven reorganisation has created the new financial markets department, and the team represents investment banks and other financial institutions on complex, high value litigation. Also experienced in contentious regulatory matters and risk management. Currently busy advising Merrill Lynch Investment Managers on its defence against Unilever's pension fund. "*Smart operator*" **Jonathan Kelly** (see p.574) wins praise from clients for his "*knowledge, experience and understanding of the products and markets as well as the law.*" **Clients:** CSFB; Deutsche Bank; Merrill Lynch; Prudential Bache; Refco Overseas; UBS Warburg; Aon.

Stephenson Harwood (see firm details p.1141) "*It has a tradition of acting for the banks,*" and is thought by some to be "*making a strong showing at the moment.*" Head of litigation **John Fordham** (see p.569) is "*pragmatic and fair*" while "*shrewd tactician*" **Richard Gwynne** (see p.571) was also typically recommended by clients as "*relaxed, high class and absolutely outstanding.*" Representing a high proportion of the London offices of foreign banks, it also works for leading retail and investment banks. The firm was instructed by KBC Bank in a $500,000 letter of credit dispute with Corus Trading, and assisted Dresdner Bank in attempts to enforce judgments against bank accounts held outside the UK. **Clients:** RBS; HSBC; Standard Bank; Den norske Bank; Arab International Bank; KBC Bank; Dresdner Bank.

Ashurst Morris Crisp (see firm details p.866) (Team includes up to 46 assts as required) Although possessing a low profile this year, clients claim that the team, under Edward Sparrow, "*provides technically excellent, prudent advice.*" Strengthened by the appointment of several new partners with a financial litigation focus, it has been seeing increasing levels of international work. With a strong following of merchant banks, the firm is particularly well represented among private equity houses. Engaged in issues such as derivatives, swaps and documentation disputes along with transactional conflicts and problems surrounding IPOs. Represented the former partners of Phillips & Drew against UBS in their attempt to recover assets misappropriated by another former partner. **Clients:** BNP Paribas; Morgan Grenfell Private Equity; Close Brothers; Deutsche Bank; Indosuez International Finance; ING Barings; NM Rothschild; WestLB.

CMS Cameron McKenna (see firm details p.922) "*The traditional lawyers for Lloyds,*" the banking litigation team, led by Duncan Aldred, has kept a low profile but the market sees them picking up complex work on the back of retail banking strength. The firm has a strong profile in insolvency, while typical retail based work, some of it done from the strong Bristol office, includes large constructive trust disputes and fraud proceedings. It acted for DEG on complex investment bank litigation involving a number of hearings in London and Zambia. **Clients:** Lloyds TSB; RBS; DEG; National Australia Group; Crédit Lyonnais.

Denton Wilde Sapte (see firm details p.939) "*A good litigation practice, and obviously a good banking practice as well with the Wilde Sapte expertise,*" leading competitors agree that "*you cannot ignore it.*" The market sees the team more regularly in retail banking and insolvency related work than on high-end investment bank litigation. While mortgage related work occupies the Milton Keynes office, London handles a wide variety of cases including major product and bond disputes. It represented Crédit Lyonnais in a $200 million dispute between Glencore International and Metro Trading International. **Mark Gill** is carving out a strong reputation in this sector. **Clients:** Bank of Scotland; Citibank; RBS/NatWest.

Litigation: Civil Fraud

LONDON

Allen & Overy (see firm details p.856) **Civil Fraud:** Unique among City firms in having a designated trust, asset tracing and fraud group as distinct from its regulatory counterpart. Endorsed by clients as "*excellent technically and offering a bespoke service,*" it handles high value cases, predominantly acting on the claimant side. Cases often have an off-shore or multi-jurisdictional flavour and work is also undertaken on behalf of the Official Solicitor, Public Trustee and DTI. Team leader **Robert Hunter** (see p.573) is the "*current doyen*" of this type of work, "*a cracking lawyer who makes it look easy,*" according to his peers. **Reg/Inv:** Handles a diffuse portfolio of regulatory work, advising on investigatory and disciplinary proceedings. The group enjoys a strong following among banks and financial institutions under investigation by the SFA, and also provides assistance to the regulatory bodies themselves. Currently acting on one of the biggest investigations to be instigated by the SFO, **Sidney Myers** (see p.577) marshals the team and is "*calmness personified, adept at getting to the bottom of things quickly.*"

Clifford Chance (see firm details p.919) **Civil Fraud:** Acts for victims of fraud bringing civil proceedings, often on a multi-jurisdictional footing. The majority of clients are banks and governments seeking to recover loss. Long established **George Staple QC** gained invaluable experience working for the SFO in the 1990s and forms a "*redoubtable team*" with the "*wonderfully organised*" **Jeremy Sandelson** (see p.580) and "*up and at 'em litigator*" **John Potts**. Recently acted for a Japanese client, tracing assets to the value of £5 million in the USA and Switzerland. **Reg/Inv:** Acts in the main for regulators and official bodies in relation to their disciplinary procedures. Also to be seen defending members of its extensive corporate client base who have fallen foul of the authorities. Of late the group has become more involved in the regulatory side of insurance.

Herbert Smith (see firm details p.993) **Civil Fraud:** "*Experts on asset tracing who operate at the highest level,*" as judged by many of our interviewees. Its international network and depth of resources allows this department to excel whether it is representing claimant, defendant or interested third party. Typical of its activities has been its recent advice to investors in the collapsed BVI incorporated hedge fund in respect of a variety of cross-border claims. David Natali has now retired as a partner but brings his vast experience to bear as a consultant. **Reg/Inv:** A robust practice principally acting for financial services companies in front of the regulator. Wide-ranging in its scope, most of the major regulators have been dealt with including the FSA, SFO, DTI and Inland Revenue. Peers consider **Christa Band** (see p.565) "*a fine practitioner, fully conversant with regulatory work.*" In the last year, the group has advised the Financial Times on the provision of its services over the internet and advised Bradford & Bingley on its demutualisation.

Linklaters (see firm details p.1042) **Civil Fraud:** Largely seen acting in major fraud investigations on behalf of corporates belonging to its highly prized client base. Visible both domestically and internationally, clients feel its resources allow it to "*handle multi-jurisdictional frauds effortlessly.*" "*Fraud supremo*" **Alan Walls** (see p.583) has been praised for his efforts in the Hubco matter, addressing the question of whether allegations of corruption could be settled by international arbitration. The group also acted for Corporate Services Group in relation to its investigation by the SFO. **Reg/Inv:** The department advises on disciplinary procedure and the risk of criminal liability. It has recently been closely involved in an independent investigation by the Paymaster General into Custom & Excise's handling of excise diversion fraud.

Lovells (see firm details p.1044) **Civil Fraud:** Expansion of the firm's international practice, particularly in Germany, Asia and the USA, has resulted in increased multi-jurisdictional activity. Asset tracing remains at the core of operations evidenced by heavyweight cases in the Court of Appeal and House of Lords. These include the long-running BCCI affair, "*a terrific case from which the department has crafted an enviable reputation,*" and the high profile Sultan of Brunei matter where it appeared for HRH Prince Jefri. Peers claim that group head **Keith Gaines** (see p.570) "*cuts through the voluminous paper work like a knife through butter.*" **Reg/Inv:** Assists in internal investigations into company mismanagement and employee fraud. The group is also active in official investigations and disciplinary proceedings under the Companies Act, Banking Act and Financial Services & Markets Act.

Norton Rose (see firm details p.1082) **Civil Fraud:** "*Resource intensive with a host of able practitioners*" this firm is lauded by rivals for its litigation in the bigger frauds. These include advising Czech concern Komercni Banka on matters arising out of a $250 million letter of credit fraud and successfully defending a claim in the Banco Santander case. Work is further generated through a renowned Middle Eastern practice, which has led to the

LITIGATION: CIVIL FRAUD • London
1 Allen & Overy
Clifford Chance
Herbert Smith
Linklaters
Lovells
Norton Rose
2 Ashurst Morris Crisp
Baker & McKenzie
Freshfields Bruckhaus Deringer
Slaughter and May
Stephenson Harwood
3 CMS Cameron McKenna
Denton Wilde Sapte
Mishcon de Reya
Richards Butler
Simmons & Simmons
SJ Berwin
Theodore Goddard
4 Dechert
Kingsley Napley
Macfarlanes
Peters & Peters
5 DLA
Eversheds

LEADING INDIVIDUALS	
1 **BAGGE James** Norton Rose	**HUNTER Robert** Allen & Overy
STAPLE George Clifford Chance	
2 **FORDHAM John** Stephenson Harwood	**GAINES Keith** Lovells
GERRARD Neil DLA	**MYERS Sidney** Allen & Overy
POLLARD Stephen Kingsley Napley	**WALLS Alan** Linklaters
WOODCOCK Tony Stephenson Harwood	
3 **BAND Christa** Herbert Smith	**BARRETT Elizabeth** Slaughter and May
BYRNE David Dechert	**FINKLER Deborah** Slaughter and May
KELLY Jonathan Simmons & Simmons	**OLIVER Keith** Peters & Peters
POTTS John Clifford Chance	**RAPHAEL Monty** Peters & Peters
SANDELSON Jeremy Clifford Chance	**TAYLOR Ian** Freshfields Bruckhaus
WALKER Deirdre Norton Rose	

This book is the product of 6,552 1/2-hour interviews. See p.7 for BMRB audit.

Within each band, firms are listed alphabetically. *See individuals' profiles p.564*

team advising Banque du Caire, a prominent Egyptian bank, on a multi-million dollar letter of credit fraud. **Reg/Inv:** Interviewees applaud **James Bagge** (see p.565) as "*an absolute leader in his field*" and he is felt to dominate the firm's activities in this area. An indication of his prowess lies in his engagement to advise on the review of the FSA's supervision of Equitable Life. His colleague **Deirdre Walker** (see p.583) also received warm market commendation as a "*formidable litigator.*"

Ashurst Morris Crisp (see firm details p.866) **Civil Fraud:** "*A major player in business related frauds*" principally assisting claimants through domestic and international asset tracing. Key cases for the team include acting for the partners of Phillips & Drew in pursuing claims against UBS, and advising Sumitomo in an action against Crédit Lyonnais Rouse arising from unauthorised trading on the London Metal Exchange. The team continues to represent the liquidators of Baring (Futures) Singapore in litigation against the company's auditors. **Reg/Inv:** Low-key in this area, the market feels that the firm nonetheless provides an assured service. The group has acted in a number of FSA regulatory investigations and is currently advising in the continuing DTI inquiry into Mirror Group Newspapers.

Baker & McKenzie (see firm details p.868) **Civil Fraud:** New to the tables after praise from our interviewees for its "*cutting edge*" activities in asset tracing, worldwide interim relief and the penetration of offshore trusts. Grupo Torras, the case on which it cut its teeth, rumbles on keeping the team busy in several jurisdictions and allowing it to fully exploit its global network of offices. The group has also been seen acting for Sony United Kingdom on a large multi-jurisdictional procurement fraud. **Reg/Inv:** Smaller in scale than the civil fraud side, this aspect of the operation generally involves servicing those corporate clients and their individual senior employees who find themselves in trouble with the regulator.

Freshfields Bruckhaus Deringer (see firm details p.965) **Civil Fraud:** Heavily involved in complex, high value international cases for banking, financial services and insurance clients, the group also conducts work for liquidators and administrators. The practice stands on strong ground this year as a result of acting in big ticket cases. Appeared for State of Brunei in one of the biggest claims ever brought in civil proceedings and for Lloyd's of London in the Jefri litigation. Currently engaged in acting for the estate of Francis Bacon in a claim against his former agent. Litigation partner **Ian Taylor** (see p.582) is the stand-out practitioner here, praised for his experience and work on behalf of banks. **Reg/Inv:** Acts in the main for financial institutions on disciplinary and regulatory matters at home and abroad. In the past year alone the team has advised on SFA, London Stock Exchange, IMRO, DTI and London Metal Exchange inquiries.

Slaughter and May (see firm details p.1135) **Civil Fraud:** While our interviewees did not readily associate this type of work with this corporate giant, it carries out corporate fraud work and international asset tracing on behalf of its illustrious clients. Highlights include acting for the liquidators of Barings and advising Deutsche Bank in respect of criminal proceedings following the Peter Young affair. **Reg/Inv:** Displaying "*a measured approach much appreciated by the regulators*" it is in this area that the department truly shines. Strong in financial regulatory litigation, it acts in investigation and disciplinary proceedings brought by the FSA and others. Currently acting for a range of global investment banks under investigation, and on the outstanding DTI enquiry into Queen's Moat Hotels. Industry specialists find team leader **Deborah Finkler** (see p.569) "*both purposeful and highly active.*" **Elizabeth Barrett** (see p.565) was also highly recommended to our researchers.

Stephenson Harwood (see firm details p.1141) **Civil Fraud:** Visible in the more substantial international matters and unusual in having a distinct specialism in marine fraud. Acted for Bank of America on a US$13 million fraud and in the Banco Santander affair. The group also advised a variety of banks in relation to the collapse of Dubai based Solo Industries, as a result of alleged fraudulent trading. At the hub of operations is the well-regarded **John Fordham** (see p.569). **Reg/Inv:** The department appears both for and in front of regulatory and other professional bodies. The group is noted for its work advising various financial institutions in relation to SFO and Inland Revenue inquiries. **Tony Woodcock** (see p.585) is "*a regulatory aficionado constantly on the go.*"

CMS Cameron McKenna (see firm details p.922) **Civil Fraud:** Confined for the most part to the recovery of substantial sums through litigation, the team also undertakes defence work. Activity is focused heavily in the financial services arena acting for banks, insurers and investment companies. Clients appreciate its "*cost effective, efficient service.*" The team has recently acted for a major US bank in the Simetal case, and defended one of the companies that managed the assets of the Cheney Pension Scheme. **Reg/Inv:** Concentrates more on compliance issues rather than pure fraud, being concerned with disciplinary matters in the event of rule breaches. Has spent a good proportion of time advising financial institution clients on the implications of the new regulatory regime born of the Financial Services & Markets Act 2000.

Denton Wilde Sapte (see firm details p.939) **Civil Fraud:** "*Often on the end of good cases,*" according to peers, the practice centres primarily around banking fraud, debt recovery and insurance related matters. Neil Griffiths leads the team, which is expert on asset confiscation and caters for a significant client base, including the State Bank of Australia. **Reg/Inv:** The group handles matters on behalf of the FSA relating to asset freezing and regulatory injunctions.

Mishcon de Reya (see firm details p.1071) **Civil Fraud:** Acts for the victims of fraud and advises on all aspects of recovery and prevention. The group has been retained by Microsoft to advise on its European anti-counterfeiting strategy and made substantial recoveries for W&G Foyle booksellers following a procurement fraud. The team was particularly praised by barristers for "*its expeditious enforcement techniques*" and consequently rises in our rankings this year. **Reg/Inv:** Well-versed in the investigations of suspected frauds and adept at liaising with authorities regarding prosecution and regulatory matters. The department has established a forum of more than 20 City financial institutions committed to researching the legal and commercial measures available to combat fraud.

Richards Butler (see firm details p.1107) **Civil Fraud:** Endorsed by its rivals as "*a healthy practice,*" much of the work is allied to the firm's involvement in financial services litigation. The group has acted for a number of Brazilian investors in claims against an English bank, and advised a consortium of well-known high street companies in an action to recover substantial funds misappropriated by its finance director. **Reg/Inv:** Regulatory and investigatory work is the strong suit of the department. The emphasis lies on fraud prevention, financial services regulation and investigatory asset tracing. The firm has recently taken on a specialist money laundering practitioner in response to marked growth in this area.

Simmons & Simmons (see firm details p.1132) **Civil Fraud:** Acts as both claimant and defendant in loss recovery from within the commercial litigtion department. Clients include governments, multi-national concerns and financial institutions. **Reg/Inv:** Perceived by the market to be strong in this area, the firm is effective on regulatory and financial services matters. The vast proportion of the work centres on regulatory enforcement and disciplinary matters and is undertaken from within a dedicated finance litigation group under the stewardship of **Jonathan Kelly** (see p.574). Amongst the feathers in its cap this year has been its involvement in advising Refco on LIFFE's largest investigation to date.

SJ Berwin (see firm details p.879) **Civil Fraud:** Taking a cross-departmental approach, the firm acts for claimants and defendants in major multi-jurisdictional cases. Asset tracing is to the fore and the team, under the guidance of Tim Taylor, has recently acted for a major telecoms company in one such exercise. It appeared in the Pirate of Prague affair and specialises in obtaining Mareva orders. **Reg/Inv:** Generally the firm appears on behalf of clients under investigation by IMRO and the FSA, and those experiencing difficulties in applications for registration.

Theodore Goddard (see firm details p.1152) **Civil Fraud:** Generally attending to the needs of companies that are the victims of fraud, the firm also acts for governments, banks and individuals. The co-ordination of multi-jurisdictional asset tracing proceedings is the team's forte. **Reg/Inv:** Undertakes complex investigatory work often in a number of jurisdictions simultaneously.

Dechert (see firm details p.938) **Civil Fraud:** Pursuing judgments on behalf of claimants, the firm is also recognised by our interviewees for its defence of plcs and individuals against large scale prosecutions. The group represented the Abacha family in both civil and criminal proceedings, and continues to advise its numerous financial services clients. It has in **David Byrne** (see p.409) "*a protean lawyer, equally at ease with both criminal and civil matters.*" **Reg/Inv:** Active in 19 regulatory investigations in the past year involving, inter alia, the DTI, FSA, and IMRO. The team further advises on money laundering, compliance obligations and director disqualification. A commitment to this area is evidenced by the recent recruitment of a former FSA enforcement lawyer.

Kingsley Napley (see firm details p.1022) **Civil Fraud:** Complementing the firm's more esteemed criminal litigation department, the group handles all aspects of civil fraud, including defence work, asset tracing and recovery on behalf of the victims of fraud. Interviewees consider **Stephen Pollard** (see p.411) "*a smart and sharp individual*" who is noted for his "*dogged defence of the individual.*" Recent highlights include acting for the administrator of a trust alleged to have misappropriated several million pounds. **Reg/Inv:** The team handles Inland Revenue, Customs & Excise and DTI investigations, regulatory enquiries and directors disqualification proceedings.

Macfarlanes (see firm details p.1046) **Civil Fraud:** A number of leading rivals expressed their willingness to refer conflicted work to this team. Working under the umbrella of the commercial litigation department, cases are undertaken for individuals and companies in both defendant and claimant capacities. A recent highlight was acting for claimant American International Group/Omega in fraud proceedings arising out of investment in privatisations in Azerbaijan.

Peters & Peters (see firm details p.1095) **Civil Fraud:** Famed for its defendant work, researchers were told that the firm is "*increasingly displaying a feel in the civil field.*" **Keith Oliver** (see p.411), celebrated for his work on the criminal side, "*does a great job for his clients displaying tenacity and aggression.*" Peers continue to regard **Monty Raphael** (see p.412) as the "*distinguished figurehead*" of the team, and he continues to attract quality clients.

DLA **Civil Fraud:** Respected **Neil Gerrard** heads the team, which undertakes asset tracing. **Reg/Inv:** A broad caseload sees the firm both acting for defendants and advising regulatory bodies.

Eversheds (see firm details p.952) **Civil Fraud:** A nationwide network of offices provides the firm with a certain presence in this field in the eyes of our interviewees. Usually seen acting for the individual or corporate client, it recently featured in the high profile Abache case. **Reg/Inv:** The firm represents those of its corporate clients under investigation by the DTI and other regulatory bodies.

Litigation Pensions

OVERVIEW: Another busy year in the pensions litigation sector, with high profile, long-term cases such as British Airways and National Bus continuing. The National Grid case has now finally been settled by the House of Lords judgment. The Woolf reforms, aimed at making dispute resolution quicker and simpler, have had an impact, with many firms increasingly involved in mediation.

LONDON

LITIGATION: PENSIONS • London	Ptnrs	Assts
1 Eversheds	2	n/a
Lovells	n/a	n/a
2 CMS Cameron McKenna	3	8
Linklaters	3	12
Nabarro Nathanson	4	7
Pinsent Curtis Biddle	4	4
Rowe & Maw	2	2
Sacker & Partners	2	2

LEADING INDIVIDUALS	
1 DIMSDALE GILL Angela Lovells	
ORTON Giles Eversheds	
2 ATKINSON Mark CMS Cameron McKenna	BLYTH Mark Linklaters
CARRUTHERS Andrew Rowe & Maw	COOMBS Monica Sacker & Partners
MONTY Craig Lovells	
3 WARNE Jonathan Nabarro Nathanson	
UP AND COMING	
NURSE-MARSH Isabel Pinsent Curtis Biddle	

This book is the product of 6,552 1/2-hour interviews. See p.7 for BMRB audit.

Within each band, firms are listed alphabetically. *See individuals' profiles p.564*

Eversheds (see firm details p.952) Changes for this firm, as **Giles Orton** (see p.578) (*"a big presence in litigation"*) relocates his practice from Derby to London as part of the firm's national integration strategy. Chairman of the APL Litigation Committee, he is widely respected throughout the industry, having been involved in high profile cases including the Maxwell litigation. Clients appreciate that he is *"willing to listen"* and gives *"a frank appraisal of chances and opportunities."* The group acted for the National Grid on its successful appeal to the House of Lords regarding the use of pension fund surplus. It also advised electricity companies participating in the Electricity Supply Pension Scheme in House of Lords hearings. These concerned part-timer backdated access to pension schemes. **Clients:** National Grid Company.

Lovells (see firm details p.1044) A respected practice that has been involved in many of the major cases – Courage, British Coal, Maxwell – since its inception in the mid-eighties. The group comprises commercial litigators (who also draw on the professional negligence practice) dealing with claims against professionals arising from pensions cases. Clients include insurers, trustees, members and employers, predominantly on large blue-chip schemes. **Angela Dimsdale Gill** (see p.568) (*"thorough – ferocious but great"*) and **Craig Monty** (see p.577), considered by peers *"a decent chap to deal with,"* are key players in the team. The firm acted in the Barclays Bank successful appeal against a decision by the Pensions Ombudsman, and advised members of the National Power Group electricity supply pension scheme in the challenge to the National Power and National Grid use of surplus to satisfy redundancy liabilities. **Clients:** Barclays Bank; trustees of the BT Pension Scheme.

CMS Cameron McKenna (see firm details p.922) Well-known for its Ombudsman work, the pensions department handles contentious work, with a *"young, dynamic"* team also including a specialist Pensions Ombudsman Unit. **Mark Atkinson** is singled out by rivals for praise as *"an efficient and instinctive litigator."* The firm acted for scheme members in a High Court rectification application concerning the provisions of the NPI pension scheme. It also carried out a successful appeal in the High Court over a Pensions Ombudsman ruling against a former trustee of an under-funded pension scheme. **Clients:** Hogg Robinson Trustees.

Linklaters (see firm details p.1042) Enjoying an *"enviably strong client base"* this young team continues to *"drive hard."* Recently made partner, the *"excellent and energetic"* **Mark Blyth** (see p.566) is judged by market sources to be *"knowledgeable and impressive."* The firm acts for employers, trustees, scheme advisers and pension professionals, insurance/life companies and representative members. It advised International Power on arrangements with the National Grid for dealing with surpluses in the Electricity Supply pension scheme. Other work includes advising PwC, the liquidators of the Ferguson Group, in defending proceedings brought by trustees of two Ferguson group schemes. **Clients:** International Power; British Airways; PwC.

Nabarro Nathanson (see firm details p.1078) A team with *"a serious track record"* and *"huge experience"* has recently suffered departures. However, **Jonathan Warne** (*"a good chap"*) remains to emphasise the firm's standing in the market. The group acted for one of the Airways Pension Scheme representative beneficiaries, including both APS pensioners and deferred pensioners, in the proposed BA scheme merger proceedings. It also advised beneficiaries in the National Bus distribution proceedings. **Clients:** National Bus Representative Beneficiaries; British Airways Pension Scheme Representative Beneficiaries.

Pinsent Curtis Biddle (see firm details p.1098) Considered by peers a *"strong firm,"* the market foresees a strengthening to Biddle's litigation practice in the aftermath of its merger with Pinsent Curtis. Involved in a number of significant cases including National Power and Lansing Linde, the firm's clients include trustees, insurers, representative beneficiaries, members, employees and pensions advisors. The group acted for trustees in National Power v Feldon in the House of Lords, and for trustees in Lansing Linde v Alber & Others in the Court of Appeal. It continues to defend trustees in various Pensions Ombudsman complaints. Head of Pensions Litigation, **Isabel Nurse-Marsh** (see p.577) received warm market endorsement. **Clients:** Trustees of National Power Group; Trustees of Lansing Linde Pensions Scheme.

Rowe & Maw (see firm details p.1113) A *"pedigree"* litigation team, acting mainly for the pension department's clients, but also undertaking standalone work. **Andrew Carruthers** (see p.566) remains widely endorsed by clients and rivals. The firm was involved in Merchant Navy Ratings Pension Fund's application for Court approval of proposals designed to rectify substantial MFR deficit in the scheme. It also appeared on an appeal against the decision of the Pensions Ombudsman in Williamson and the Marsh & McLennan Companies, regarding GMP equalisation. **Clients:**

Marsh Mercer Pension Scheme Trustees; Merchant Navy Ratings Pension Fund Trustees Ltd.

Sacker & Partners (see firm details p.1117) Still seen by the market as "*relatively new to litigation,*" the practice has yet to match the firm's reputation for 'pure' pensions work. The firm provides specialist pensions advice, ranging from advising trustees and employers in internal dispute resolution procedures, to bringing and defending complaints to the Pension Ombudsman. Department Head **Monica Coombs** (see p.567) is "*a litigator by instinct*" with "*substantial pensions knowledge*" who is seen to be "*pushing the firm's profile in this area.*" The firm continues to advise Legal & General following its successful appeal against the Pension Ombudsman's jurisdiction to investigate contracts, and acts for independent trustees in asset recovery and professional negligence claims. **Clients:** Chamber of Shipping.

Litigation Property

London: 557; The South & Thames Valley: 560; South West: 560; Wales: 561; Midlands: 561; East Anglia: 562; North West: 562; North East: 563; Scotland: 563

OVERVIEW: While Nabarros maintains its number one spot, many practitioners predict that the newly merged Berwin Leighton Paisner will mount a serious challenge to its dominant position. In the past year, property litigation has not been immune from the downturn in the volume of civil litigation. Nevertheless, true specialists, particularly those with an established reputation, remain busy.

LONDON

Nabarro Nathanson (see firm details p.1078) Described by specialists as a "*first-class practice*" with an "*excellent client base*" perceived to be the leader in this field although the gap is closing ("*it lacks the pre-eminence it once had.*") A "*real force*" and "*extremely busy,*" particularly in rent reviews, dilapidation claims, alienation and redevelopment work. The large team has recently witnessed changes in personnel, but continues to be led by "*rock solid*" **Iain Travers** (see p.583) who has "*a huge amount of experience and common sense.*" He acted for City of London Real Property Company (part of Land Securities) in a case against CGU to obtain rectification of rent review provisions in a lease. **Jennifer Rickard** (see p.580) "*combines a quick mind with an engaging personality*" while peers agree she "*fights her corner but is sensible.*" She is acting for Land Securities in a major redevelopment in Central London involving the demolition and redevelopment of three multi-storey buildings. **Clients:** Allied Dunbar; BL Universal; Capital & Counties; GE Capital; Granada Group; Land Securities.

Berwin Leighton Paisner (see firm details p.878) The market agrees that the firm "*will have an excellent practice with the merger,*" some believing it will "*lead the field*" in the future. Paisner brings expertise in the leisure industry to a firm that already handles a broad sweep of work on behalf of its institutional property clients. **Roger Cohen** (see p.567) ran and organised Berwin Leighton's team and he is described by competitors as "*aggressive, up-front, client focused and effective.*" Admired for his ability to "*mobilise the troops,*" he led the team handling the Hannibal House lease renewal. Equally "*determined to make the merger work*" is Paisner's **David Cox** (see p.568). He is a "*well-liked, good operator*" who acted on a contract dispute for the purchase of land that forms part of a major development in Suffolk. New partner **Ros Morshead** (see p.577) ("*reliable, quick to respond*") was consistently recommended; she led the team acting for Liverpool City Council in proceedings against Walton Group. **Clients:** BAA; Capital and Regional; Lex Service; PACE; Prudential Property Investment Management; Tesco.

Herbert Smith (see firm details p.993) A "*well-ordered and disciplined*" firm which "*trains its litigators extremely well.*" The practice handles management work for institutional funds and large property clients in addition to the usual landlord/tenant type work and large one-off cases. Attracting a raft of client commendations "*tough cookie*" **Lucy Hutchinson** (see p.574) is "*a jolly good opponent – one of the best academic lawyers around*" who, on behalf of Standard Life, successfully defended a claim from Egan Lawson for introduction fees in the Court of Appeal. "*Impressive*" **Martin Thomas** (see p.583) is active on many of the firm's major pieces of work, including the defence of a trespass claim on a landfill site on behalf of Severn Trent Water, and representing Guinness in a dispute over the value of development land at Paddington Basin. **Clients:** ABF; BSkyB; Hermes; London Buildings; Severn Trent Water; Standard Life.

Linklaters (see firm details p.1042) "*Tough and together,*" the team "*serves its client base extremely well.*" The focus of the practice tends to be on rent review and redevelopment work as well as the larger one-off cases. A growing team is "*unquestionably well led*" by the "*high-profile and truly amazing*" **Katie Bradford** (see p.566) who clients believe works "*furiously hard*" and peers agree is "*an opponent to be reckoned with.*" The firm acted for Scottish Widows for its review at 60 London Wall and is retained by Lloyds Bank for its 400 rent reviews nationwide. Work on the redevelopment side included advising Ropemaker Properties on the successful clearing of a 50-tenant site for a major redevelopment in Knightsbridge. **Clients:** Canary Wharf Group; Lloyds Bank; MEPC; Ropemaker Properties; Scottish Widows.

Lovells (see firm details p.1044) "*Aiming big,*" rivals acknowledge the group has a "*wonderful institutional property client base*" and "*markets itself well.*" Developing the mediation side, the team has leaned away from court work towards pre-action work, and has seen an increase in development work and rent reviews. "*Brilliant with no weaknesses*" **Nicholas Cheffings** (see p.567) is "*simply a star*" and he recently advised a hotel operator on the rent review of its London headquarters office accommodation. "*Technical*" **Anne Waltham** (see p.584) ("*extremely sensible, tough when she needs to be*") led the settlement negotiations in the dispute between BAA and Eurotunnel concerning the trading performance of the retail units at the Eurostar rail terminal in Ashford. **Clients:** Prudential; Barclays; Forte; SIF.

Ashurst Morris Crisp (see firm details p.866) A "*growing*" practice with a "*good client base,*" it handles a wide range of commercial property litigation work and is witnessing an upturn in development related work, specialist advisory matters and restricted covenant claims. Led by "*committed and conscientious*" **Michael Madden** (see p.575) who is applauded by peers as "*a damn good pro who fights his cases hard.*" He acted for Kvaerner Construction in successfully resolving proceedings brought by SAVE Britain Heritage in relation to the redevelopment of Baltic Exchange for Swiss Re. **Clients:** BT; British Gas; IBM; Reuters; Thames Water; United News & Media.

LITIGATION: PROPERTY • London	Ptnrs	Assts
1 Nabarro Nathanson	2	13
2 Berwin Leighton Paisner	2	15
Herbert Smith	2	6
Linklaters	2	10
Lovells	2	7
3 Ashurst Morris Crisp	1	8
Clifford Chance	1	4
DJ Freeman	1	3
Denton Wilde Sapte	2	7
Lawrence Graham	2	5
4 CMS Cameron McKenna	2	6
Dechert	2	6
Masons	3	9
SJ Berwin	1	1
5 Boodle Hatfield	1	3
Macfarlanes	2	5
Olswang	1	3
Rowe & Maw	2	7
Simmons & Simmons	1	4
Speechly Bircham	2	3
6 Beachcroft Wansbroughs	2	6
Dewar Hogan	2	3
Radcliffes	1	1

LEADING INDIVIDUALS	
★ **BRADFORD Katie** Linklaters	**CHEFFINGS Nicholas** Lovells
1 **FRANCIS Penelope** Lawrence Graham	**HUTCHINSON Lucy** Herbert Smith
KING Vivien D J Freeman	**MADDEN Michael** Ashurst Morris Crisp
RICKARD Jennifer Nabarro Nathanson	
2 **COHEN Roger** Berwin Leighton Paisner	**PEET Carole** Denton Wilde Sapte
PICKSTON John Clifford Chance	**TRAVERS Iain** Nabarro Nathanson
WALTHAM Anne Lovells	
3 **BRIERLEY Ian** DLA	**COX David** Berwin Leighton Paisner
CROSS Siobhan Masons	**FREYNE Michele** Rowe & Maw
HEWSON Carol Simmons & Simmons	**HIGHMORE Robert** Charles Russell
MOLYNEUX Anne Masons	**WALKER Andrew** CMS Cameron McKenna
WEBBER Lesley Beachcroft Wansbroughs	
4 **CONWAY Keith** Dechert	**FOX-EDWARDS Jane** Lawrence Graham
HINDLE Andrew Boodle Hatfield	**HOGAN Ronald** Dewar Hogan
HUNTER Jason Russell-Cooke	**MASTERS David** Dawson & Co
METLISS Michael SJ Berwin	**THOMAS Martin** Herbert Smith
TUGWELL Andrew Osborne Clarke	
UP AND COMING	
MORSHEAD Ros Berwin Leighton Paisner	

This book is the product of 6,552 1/2-hour interviews. See p.7 for BMRB audit.
Within each band, firms are listed alphabetically. *See individuals' profiles p.564*

Clifford Chance (see firm details p.919) A small group focusing on complex high-value work, advising on the structuring of deals, supported by its strong corporate client portfolio. The firm has been hit by the departure of Ian Brierly to DLA, while the highly regarded Wendy Miller now acts as a consultant. The unit continues to be led by the "*wonderful*" **John Pickston** (see p.579), felt by clients to be "*a delight to deal with*." He acted on behalf of the Burford Group in High Court proceedings against Forte Hotels for damages in excess of £6 million. Highlight of the past year was the representation of Paul Reichman, Canary Wharf Ltd in its case against WPP Group and Ogilvy & Mather in a claim arising out of abortive negotiations for a lease. **Clients:** Burford Group; CGNU; Great Eastern Hotels; HSBC; Storehouse Properties; Woolworths.

DJ Freeman (see firm details p.943) "*Going places*" and building up the necessary strength in depth, it specialises in landlord and tenant issues, such as contested renewals, site clearances, dilapidation claims and, in particular, service charge disputes. Advised on a dispute over responsibility for the continual repair and maintenance of the sewage and drainage systems below a high profile London estate. Researchers were impressed by the market feedback on "*acquired taste*" **Vivien King** (see p.575), "*a legend that doesn't stand still*" and "*an excellent ambassador for the firm*." **Clients:** AXA; Benchmaker; Boxclever; Karen Millen; The Post Office.

Denton Wilde Sapte (see firm details p.939) A "*strong and effective*" practice with a steady supply of portfolio management work and some high profile pieces of litigation, which continues to be based in both London and Milton Keynes. Led by the "*excellent*" **Carole Peet** who advised Sainsburys on the contested rent review of it store at Purley Way, the firm also acted for Wembley National Stadium Ltd in respect of its claim for rectification against Wembley (London) Ltd arising out of the acquisition of Wembley Stadium in 1999. **Clients:** Barclays Bank; English Partnerships; J Sainsbury Group of Companies; Whitbread Group of Companies; The Crown Estate.

Lawrence Graham (see firm details p.1030) "*No airs or graces*" to be found in this "*small but highly effective*" property litigation team. It advised on a number of substantial retail redevelopment schemes, including Crystal Peaks Shopping Centre in Sheffield, Covent Garden for Derwent Valley Holdings and a redevelopment on Oxford Street. "*Tireless worker*" **Penny Francis** (see p.569) heads the firm's property department. Typically described as "*charming, extremely sensible and an excellent litigator,*" she always "*offers a polished service*." Active in rent review work, she acted as the legal assessor on a number of reviews including Marleybone County Court, a major Debenhams store and a tenant in the first round of reviews at Canary Wharf. "*Sensible*" **Jane Fox-Edwards** (see p.569) continues to elicit recommendation. **Clients:** Cellnet; Chartwell Land; Gap; Land Securities; Legal & General Assurance Society; Property Trust.

CMS Cameron McKenna (see firm details p.922) "*Solid and dependable,*" the firm handles all landlord/tenant and property disputes and is active in opposed lease renewals (for development) under the 1954 Act, agents commission disputes, rights to light claims, actions under development agreements and LVT applications. The "*experienced*" **Andrew Walker** (see p.583) "*runs a tight ship*" according to peers and successfully defended (v Pexton and Another) an appeal against the operation of The Wellcome Trust's estate management scheme covering a large part of South Kensington. **Clients:** Alba Life; Heron Land Developments; J Sainsbury; The Crown Estate Commissioners; The Wellcome Trust.

Dechert (see firm details p.938) A "*safe pair of hands*" which is "*seeking to make a greater name*" in property litigation according to sources interviewed by our researchers. The team acts for both landlord and tenant clients on all property litigation matters, including transactional and major rent review work. "*Livewire*" **Keith Conway** (see p.567) is a "*tough litigator*" who represented Banner Homes in Banner Homes v Luff and successfully established the validity of a gentleman's agreement. The firm has also handled rent review work for British Land at Broadgate and Canary Wharf and is acting for Secretary of State v P&O in defending an £18 million dilapidation claim. **Clients:** Banner Homes; British Land; Dixons; Frogmore; PACE.

Masons (see firm details p.1056) A "*good team*" which "*works well away from the spotlight*" in both pure litigation and advisory work. Continues to advise a central London Estate on a range of matters including air space development, dilapidation claims, lease renewals and rent reviews. Inntrepreneur remains the department's major client. The team is led in tandem by **Siobhan Cross** (see p.568) ("*handles complex cases extremely well*") and the highly regarded **Anne Molyneux** (see p.577), who acted in Inntrepreneur v East Crown Ltd. **Clients:** Berkeley Group; Bovis Homes; Burger King; Inntrepreneur Pub Company; Nomura International; Wates Group.

SJ Berwin (see firm details p.879) "*Small team with good clients*" which is viewed as a "*continual threat*" by competitors. Commercially oriented practice acting mainly on behalf of landlords on site clearances, rent reviews, rights to light and redevelopment related work. **Michael Metliss** (see p.576) is "*remarkably popular*" among major clients. He successfully settled a claim brought on behalf of Plaza Estates in the Lands Tribunal to discharge a restrictive covenant. The firm also acted for Newhaven Port & Properties in litigation against the shipping company, James Fisher & Sons. **Clients:** AXA Sun Life; British Land; Marks & Spencer; NHS Executive; Plaza Estates; Sainsbury's.

Boodle Hatfield (see firm details p.889) The firm has a strong market reputation for its residential property litigation practice, acting mainly on behalf of landlord clients ("*small practice with some large clients who they keep extremely happy*") and is witnessing a general increase in the volume of litigation and a flurry of business renewal applications. The "*incredibly able*" **Andrew Hindle** (see p.573) is the department's best known personality. He represented Eaton Square Properties in the reported case Eaton Square Properties Ltd v Ogilvie. **Clients:** Grosvenor; The Bedford Estates; St Giles Hotel.

Macfarlanes (see firm details p.1046) Recommended by interviewees for "*taking a mature approach*" and "*keeping you on your toes,*" Willie Manners' team is also known for its "*timely advice.*" It handles a variety of cases in both commercial and residential disputes, including contested rent reviews, development agreements, dilapidation claims, renewals and removal of squatters. The department advised Comet on a number of contentious matters and represented Abbey Life in a case against various tenants in a site clearance. On the residential side, it acted for the Trustees of a settlement whose sole asset is a warehouse site leased to the Government. **Clients:** Abbey Life; Comet; Industrial Property Fund; Scottish Life; Skanska.

Olswang (see firm details p.1084) "*Impressive – going places,*" the firm boasts a growing property litigation team. It has moved away from its traditional retail client base with the emphasis now on the commercial side. Marcus Barclay heads the team that handles a string of dilapidation claims. The firm acted for Stirling Homes in successfully defending a claim for adverse possession and advised The Carphone Warehouse on a range of issues relating to user clauses and licence to assign. **Clients:** Capital & Regional Properties; Green Property; Helical Bar; Minerva; The Carphone Warehouse.

Rowe & Maw (see firm details p.1113) Active in all areas of property litigation with an emphasis on leasehold work. It acts for both landlords and tenants in the commercial arena and has developed a specialism in injunctions. Although the team is less high profile in the market, clients consider the "*aggressive*" **Michele Freyne** (see p.569) to be "*a real force.*" She successfully represented a subsidiary of Unilever in a substantial compensation case in the Lands Tribunal concerning the blight caused by the Channel Tunnel Rail Link. **Clients:** HMV; Oliver Ashworth; Pearl Assurance; Unilever.

Simmons & Simmons (see firm details p.1132) Heavily involved in work on the commercial side, principally acting on behalf of landlords. Lease renewals and redevelopment issues are prevalent and insolvency related work is beginning to grow. **Carol Hewson** (see p.572) "*doesn't mess around,*" she continues to act for Wereldhave Property in relation to a claim against Mount Cook Land. The team also acted for Eagle Star in relation to the redevelopment of Metropolis House, London. **Clients:** Eagle Star; New Millennium Experience; Wereldhave Property.

Speechly Bircham (see firm details p.1136) Competitors feel that the firm has a "*worthy*" property litigation department and clients agree that it carries out "*good work at a good price.*" Graham Ling heads a team that handles a wide range of matters including dilapidation claims, rent arrears and site clearances on behalf of its largely commercial landlord client base. The firm acted on behalf of P&O Property Holdings in a dilapidation claim of approximately £18 million against a government department. **Clients:** Cable & Wireless; Crown Estate Commissioners; Howard de Walden Estates; Lincoln Assurance; P&P Group; Scottish Life Assurance Company.

Beachcroft Wansbroughs (see firm details p.872) "*A growing practice,*" which is "*bringing on quality assistants*" and winning "*some very good work.*" It has a strong reputation for rent reviews, dilapidation claims, service charge disputes and development issues such as site clearances. The department is led by the "*formidable*" **Lesley Webber** (see p.584) who clients agree "*knows her subject well*" and "*shoots from the hip.*" She represented a consortium of commercial tenants in the case of Fluor Daniels and Others v Shortlands Investments, over service charges in office leases. **Clients:** Universities; Hospitals; GE Capital; Office Angels; Waste Management.

Dewar Hogan (see firm details p.940) "*Efficient and proactive*" niche firm that specialises in property litigation and handles a wide range of commercial and residential matters. Its impressive client roster consists of property companies, public authorities, banks, private investors and individuals. **Ronald Hogan** (see p.573) and the team acted for an occupier of commercial premises in the City over a right of light dispute with a developer of a major project. Also challenged a closing order made to residential premises on the grounds of incompatibility with the Human Rights Act 1998. **Clients:** Deutsche Asset Management, English Partnerships, Tesco Stores; Vodafone.

Radcliffes (see firm details p.1103) An "*old-fashioned*" firm which has "*successfully established a presence for itself*" with "*sound all-round knowledge.*" The market waits to see the effect of leading light Rob Highmore's move to Charles Russell. The group handles a blend of both residential and commercial landlord and tenant work, in addition to dealing with boundary disputes, rights of way disputes, rights to light and property related professional negligence. The team acted for the Crown Estate in a successful mediation and defended a land owning body over a claim for an injunction seeking to restrain access to valuable development land. **Clients:** Church of England Pensions Board; Colonial; Imperial Service Endowment; Terrace Hill Group; The Brewers Company; The Portman Estate.

Other Notable Practitioners DLA recently acquired **Ian Brierley** from Clifford Chance. "*Exceptional*" **Rob Highmore** (see p.572) has moved from Radcliffes to **Charles Russell**, "*sound, not aggressive and effective – actively thinks about clients.*") **Russell-Cooke**'s **Jason Hunter** (see p.573) was highly recommended to *Chambers*' researchers, as was **David Masters** (see p.576) of **Dawson & Co.** Former surveyor **Andrew Tugwell** ("*sensible*") is included as "*a name to watch at Osborne Clarke.*"

THE SOUTH & THAMES VALLEY

LITIGATION: PROPERTY • The South	Ptnrs	Assts
1 **DMH** Brighton	2	2
Thomson Snell & Passmore Tonbridge	1	2
2 **Brachers** Maidstone	3	6
Cripps Harries Hall Tunbridge Wells	1	2
3 **asb law** Crawley	2	3
Coffin Mew & Clover Portsmouth	1	3

LEADING INDIVIDUALS	
1 **ALLEN Martin** DMH	**WAKEFORD Carol** Cripps Harries Hall

This book is the product of 6,552 1/2-hour interviews. See p.7 for BMRB audit.
Within each band, firms are listed alphabetically. *See individuals' profiles p.564*

DMH (see firm details p.944) "*A big presence – active in the market place,*" was one typical comment received. In addition to repossessions, rent arrears, injunctions, dilapidation cases and general property disputes, the firm also handles local government work and portfolio management. It offered policy advice to Wandsworth Borough Council regarding homelessness cases under the Housing Act 1996. "*Experienced*" and "*well known*" **Martin Allen** (see p.564) was recommended to our researchers. **Clients:** Croydon Council; Wandsworth Council; TM Retail Group.

Thomson Snell & Passmore (see firm details p.1155) A "*good quality, substantial*" firm, "*highly visible*" in handling all forms of property litigation, including title disputes, leases enfranchisement and landlord/tenant work. The team is led by commercial litigator Peter Radula-Scott. **Clients:** Antler Homes; Headley Bros; State Bank of India; Trilogy Entertainments.

Brachers (see firm details p.893) John Sheath's team gains property litigation work from a solid commercial property department and from its place on the NFU panel. Flooding related work and environmental litigation is on the increase. The highlight of the year was representing Eurotunnel against BAA. **Clients:** Eurotunnel; NFU.

Cripps Harries Hall (see firm details p.927) The firm has "*a good name*" and is perceived by most interviewees to be "*doing well*" in property litigation. Its expertise covers all contentious property disputes including lease renewals, rent reviews, break clauses and service charges. It has worked on portfolio estate management for a number of government departments and pension funds and acted for the Channel Tunnel Rail Link developer on planning related enforcement litigation in the High Court. High profile **Carol Wakeford** (see p.583) is described by clients as "*extraordinarily capable.*" **Clients:** Brighton & Hove Council; Ralph Kent; Union Railways (South); Youngs Brewery.

asb law (see firm details p.865) The firm has raised its property litigation profile and is now considered a "*major competitor*" in the market. It handles a mixture of commercial and residential matters for a predominantly landlord client base. Rex Cowell's team has dealt with large dilapidation claims, forfeiture, enfranchisement and a disputed adverse possession case. **Clients:** Marley Properties; Marley Pension Fund; private property investment companies.

Coffin Mew & Clover The firm is perceived to be active on the residential side, with an impressive roster of housing association clients. Team leader Robert Wassall has vast experience in working with RSLs. The team worked on a possession proceeding against a shared ownership lessee. **Clients:** Estate agents; a healthcare trust; Portsmouth HA; Eastleigh HA.

SOUTH WEST

LITIGATION: PROPERTY • South West	Ptnrs	Assts
1 **Burges Salmon** Bristol	9	18
2 **Masons** Bristol	1	6
Osborne Clarke Bristol	2	6
3 **Beachcroft Wansbroughs** Bristol	1	4
Veale Wasbrough Bristol	1	3
4 **Bevan Ashford** Bristol	1	2
Bond Pearce Bristol, Exeter, Plymouth	1	6
5 **Lyons Davidson** Bristol	1	2
TLT Solicitors Bristol	1	3

LEADING INDIVIDUALS	
1 **BRIGGS Leona** Osborne Clarke	
2 **BASTOW Martin** Lyons Davidson	**BEDFORD Richard** Burges Salmon
HAM Neil Burges Salmon	**MARTIN Bonnie** Masons
ORME James Osborne Clarke	**PUDDICOMBE Nigel** Veale Wasbrough
UP AND COMING	
BARLEY Mark Bond Pearce	**ROGERS Jane** Osborne Clarke
SEAGER Nicola Masons	

This book is the product of 6,552 1/2-hour interviews. See p.7 for BMRB audit.
Within each band, firms are listed alphabetically. *See individuals' profiles p.564*

Burges Salmon (see firm details p.902) "*Market leader*" with a particularly strong reputation for its agricultural based litigation, which "*casts a long shadow*" over the practice. It is also active in a variety of commercial property disputes including landlord and tenant issues. Recent highlights include involvement in National Westminster Bank v Jones (High Court) and Swift v Dairywise Farms (High Court). "*Aggressive*" **Neil Ham** (see p.571) has a "*good commercial head*" and **Richard Bedford** (see p.565) is considered to be a "*good litigator*" for agricultural banking and insolvency related matters. **Clients:** Anchor; FirstGroup; J Rothschild Assurance; Orange.

Masons (see firm details p.1056) "*One of the strongest and largest property litigation teams*" acknowledge its peers in the region, considered to benefit from a strong London office. Acts mainly on commercial landlord and tenant disputes, specialising in rent reviews, dilapidation claims and industrial estate management, while development related work is increasing. "*Go-getter*" **Bonnie Martin** (see p.576) has a "*good grasp of the technicalities*" and **Nicola Seager** (see p.581) is a "*driving force.*" The team negotiated terms for vacant possession and compensation claims arising from a compulsory purchase order enabling the development of 36 shops in Folkestone. **Clients:** Bath & North East Somerset Council; PRICOA Property Investment Management; Wereldhave Property Corp.

Osborne Clarke (see firm details p.1086) A "*strong practice*" and a force in the field, the team handles a wide range of property litigation for its broad commercial client base, principally drawn from the retail and development sectors. "*Dynamic*" **Leona Briggs** is described by clients as "*sensible, practical and commercial*" and **James Orme** continues to be highly recommended. "*Competent*" **Jane Rogers** is considered to be "*a safe pair of hands.*" **Clients:** Abbey National; Bovis Homes; Imperial Investments; Somerfield Stores.

Beachcroft Wansbroughs (see firm details p.872) An impressive weight of recommendation for a team which is "*gaining strength*" and has some "*good young litigators coming through.*" The firm's Bristol office has a number of retailers among its portfolio management clients, and while landlord/tenant work remains the bread and butter of its workload, development work is increasing. The team, led by Philip Hands, acted in

Edwards and Trollope (trustees of Swansea Yacht and Sub-Aqua Club) v City and County of Swansea, in a complex lease rectification case. **Clients:** Bristol & West; Clarks; Hill House Hammond; Johnsons.

Veale Wasbrough (see firm details p.1167) "*Looking to strengthen,*" according to competitors, and well on the road to achieving this goal. The firm has a strong property practice with excellent clients, and the arrival of **Nigel Puddicombe** (see p.579) from Cartwrights is welcomed as a shrewd hire: "*one of the top property litigators in the country.*" The group handles a range of property litigation matters from contested lease renewals and dilapidation claims to possession actions and injunctions. Recent work includes three substantial judicial reviews for Bristol Harbourside, Gloucester Docks Planning Appeal and the Bath Spa project. **Clients:** Esso; PACE; Somerfield Stores; University of Bristol.

Bevan Ashford (see firm details p.880) A "*knowledgeable*" team with "*strength in depth*" so say its rivals. Lease renewals and injunctions are now more commonplace while the majority of work continues to be drawn from the public sector. Kane Kirkbride's team recently advised the secretary of State for Health on property issues including the defence of a dilapidation claim for office premises in Winchester and the defence of a claim for adverse possession of land included in a property auction. **Clients:** Allied Domecq; Capitec; Lidl; Linden Homes.

Bond Pearce (see firm details p.888) A "*strong litigation team*" is heavily involved in property work, along the lines of lease renewals, rent arrears, rent reviews, dilapidation claims and rights of way disputes. The "*eminently capable*" **Mark Barley** (see p.565) "*stands up for his clients,*" and his team advised on B&Q v Liverpool and Lancashire Properties in a successful prosecution of action denying the landlord the ability to reduce area available for tenant's right of way. Its presence in Bristol has been boosted by a recent merger with Cartwrights. **Clients:** B&Q; Crown Estates; Safeway; The National Trust.

Lyons Davidson (see firm details p.1045) The team acts for a range of landlords, tenants, lenders, borrowers and corporate clients as well as individuals in general residential and commercial property litigation. **Marin Bastow** (see p.565) was consistently recommended to researchers as a "*pragmatic*" and "*sensible*" practitioner. **Clients:** AXA Sun Life Services; Lloyds TSB.

TLT Solicitors (see firm details p.1157) The team, led by Julia Lucas, receives instructions from developer and landlord clients and an increasing flow from the retail sector. Pub owner Punch is a major source of work for the department and, in addition to litigation and estate management issues, it acts in relation to its extensive lease renewal programme. **Clients:** Brandon Hire; First Choice Holidays; Hanson; Lloyds TSB.

WALES

LITIGATION: PROPERTY • Wales	Ptnrs	Assts
1 **Hugh James Ford Simey** Cardiff	1	2
2 **Edwards Geldard** Cardiff	1	2
Morgan Cole Cardiff, Swansea	n/a	3

LEADING INDIVIDUALS	
1 **JONES Siân** Morgan Cole	**MORGAN Neil** Hugh James Ford Simey
UP AND COMING	
MEGGITT Edward Edwards Geldard	

This book is the product of 6,552 1/2-hour interviews. See p.7 for BMRB audit.
Within each band, firms are listed alphabetically. *See individuals' profiles p.564*

Hugh James Ford Simey (see firm details p.1004) A "*busy practice,*" with a strong reputation for residential and housing association work, which clients believe "*actively searches for solutions.*" Handles a range of landlord/tenant disputes for its clients. **Neil Morgan** (see p.577) is a "*good all round, common-sense litigator*" who acted for a major Housing Association in the resolution of compensation claims by over 100 private home owners following a large estate regeneration scheme. **Clients:** Companies House; housing associations; insurance companies.

Edwards Geldard (see firm details p.948) The market feels that the firm has an "*improving*" property litigation department alongside specialist and "*good opponent*" **Ed Meggitt** (see p.576). It is actively involved in conveyancing problems and dilapidation claims, as well as seeing an increase in 1954 Act applications on behalf of clients such as Powergen and Stationery Box. **Clients:** Hyder; Park Properties; Powergen; Stationery Box.

Morgan Cole (see firm details p.1074) The property litigation team draws from the firm's "*excellent property client base*" in handling both commercial and residential matters, including dilapidation claims, rent arrears, lease renewals and disrepair claims. **Siân Jones** (see p.574) is highly recommended. **Clients:** Financial institutions; major plcs; housing associations.

MIDLANDS

LITIGATION: PROPERTY • Midlands	Ptnrs	Assts
1 **Wragge & Co** Birmingham	2	8
2 **Eversheds** Nottingham, Birmingham, Derby	1	7
Hammond Suddards Edge Birmingham	1	4
3 **Browne Jacobson** Nottingham	1	1
Martineau Johnson Birmingham	1	2
Pinsent Curtis Biddle Birmingham	1	2
4 **Anthony Collins Solicitors** Birmingham	2	6

LEADING INDIVIDUALS	
1 **LLOYD HOLT Suzanne** Wragge & Co	
2 **KENT Paul** Pinsent Curtis Biddle	**O'BRIEN Gary** Eversheds
SCOTT Gordon Hammond Suddards Edge	

This book is the product of 6,552 1/2-hour interviews. See p.7 for BMRB audit.
Within each band, firms are listed alphabetically. *See individuals' profiles p.564*

Wragge & Co (see firm details p.1189) Nothing but praise from clients and competitors alike for this "*super practice*" which is "*big, strong and easy to work with.*" Instructed by an "*impressive client list,*" alongside general landlord/tenant issues, the department's workload includes judicial reviews, rights of way, freehold disputes, covenants against the sale of alcohol and site clearances on behalf of developer clients. "*Experienced*" **Suzanne Lloyd Holt** is an "*extremely skilful and adept practitioner*" who "*leads a good team.*" The firm advised a large residential developer on ransom, trespass and public and private nuisance claims involving three landowners to enable a 120 hectare development. **Clients:** British Waterways Board; Calthorpe Estates; Castlemore Securities; HSBC.

Eversheds (see firm details p.952) **Gary O'Brien** (see p.578) "*runs a tight ship,*" with "*super clients*" which is particularly active in freehold property work and gaining more work from landlord clients. On behalf of Birmingham Alliance, the team successfully completed the closure of the Old Bull Ring Indoor Market and the opening of the New Bull Ring Indoor Market involving the service of hundreds of break notices and one injunction application. **Clients:** Birmingham Alliance; Bournville Village Trust; Newey & Eyre.

Hammond Suddards Edge (see firm details p.984) A unit with "*some exceptional clients and big work,*" it operates a "*good efficient service*" on an increasing range of matters, including eviction work, trespassers on commercial land, title disputes and town and village greens. It won a successful slander of title trial for house builder client Galliers Homes. "*Experienced*" **Gordon Scott** (see p.580) "*knows how property works*" according to clients. **Clients:** Calthorpe Estates; Leicester City Football Club; Millenium Point; The Royal Bank of Scotland.

Browne Jacobson (see firm details p.898) A dedicated property litigation team described by the market as "*sound and aggressive when needs be.*" David Potts' team is active almost exclusively in the sphere of real property litigation for commercial clients, particularly retailers, in all landlord and tenant matters. **Clients:** Landlords; manufacturing companies; property developers; retailers.

Martineau Johnson (see firm details p.1055) A "*perfectly steady*" group that "*handles cases well.*" Active in rent recovery, lease renewals, rent reviews, adverse possession, dilapidation claims and eviction of squatters. Martin Edwards' team advised a public authority in its defence of a multi-party trespass action claim. **Clients:** Private clients; landed estates; companies and property developers.

Pinsent Curtis Biddle (see firm details p.1098) A small but busy team handling rent reviews, lease renewals, dilapidation claims and government work. **Paul Kent** (see p.574) is a "*sensible and practical litigator*" who clients feel takes a "*commercial and pragmatic view.*" He recovered £1 million for the Inland Revenue in a professional negligence claim. **Clients:** Birmingham City Council; English Partnerships; Inland Revenue; Lex Service Group.

Anthony Collins Solicitors (see firm details p.860) A strong reputation for its housing association work. Andrew Lancaster heads a team that handles an increasing number of cases on the landlord side, including general eviction work, dilapidation claims and lease renewals. **Clients:** Housing associations.

EAST ANGLIA

LITIGATION: PROPERTY • East Anglia	Ptnrs	Assts
1 **Eversheds** Ipswich, Norwich	n/a	3
Hewitson Becke + Shaw Cambridge	1	2
Mills & Reeve Norwich	1	3

LEADING INDIVIDUALS
1 **FALKNER James** Mills & Reeve
SCANNELL John Eversheds

This book is the product of 6,552 1/2-hour interviews. See p.7 for BMRB audit.
Within each band, firms are listed alphabetically. *See individuals' profiles p.564*

Eversheds (see firm details p.952) The team's work is mainly commercial landlord and tenant (service charges, rent reviews, lease renewals, dilapidation claims, forfeitures, highway disputes) and has the advantage of being able to tap into national resources when required. It represented Ipswich Borough Council v Moore in the Court of Appeal. **John Scannell** (see p.580) continues to win market approval. **Clients:** Crawford & Co; GAP; TXU Europe Group; Rentokil.

Hewitson Becke + Shaw (see firm details p.994) The group acts in commercial property disputes involving service charges, dilapidation claims, professional negligence and in claims for possession by proceedings or by peaceable re-entry. It has a large agricultural base and is active in disputes involving contentious probate and farming partnerships. The team is led by Janet Rees (Cambridge) and Clare Bangor-Jones (Northampton). **Clients:** Cambridge University Colleges; Cambridge University Estate Management Service; property developers; national charitable organisations; private clients.

Mills & Reeve (see firm details p.1069) The property litigation department, which includes the highly regarded **James Falkner** (see p.569), handles disputes for its institutional and higher education client base. Recent work includes the clearance of a major Cambridge development site of business/residential occupiers and High Court action for a landlord on the construction of a rent review clause in an industrial lease (Bellow Properties v Trinity College). **Clients:** Cambridge colleges; Nokia UK Group; Wherry Limited Partnership.

NORTH WEST

LITIGATION: PROPERTY • North West	Ptnrs	Assts
1 **Cobbetts** Manchester	2	3
DLA Liverpool, Manchester	n/a	n/a
2 **Addleshaw Booth & Co** Manchester	1	1
Eversheds Manchester	1	5
Hammond Suddards Edge Manchester	1	4
Pannone & Partners Manchester	3	3

LEADING INDIVIDUALS	
1 **JENNINGS Steven** DLA	
2 **HOATH Helen** Gorna & Co	**O'FARRELL Vincent** Pannone & Partners
RANSON Lee Eversheds	**STONE Peter** Cobbetts
WALKER Alan Cobbetts	

This book is the product of 6,552 1/2-hour interviews. See p.7 for BMRB audit.
Within each band, firms are listed alphabetically. *See individuals' profiles p.564*

Cobbetts (see firm details p.923) A "*specialist*" team with particular strength in brewery and forfeiture work. Department head **Peter Stone** (see p.582) continues to be highly regarded in this field, while **Alan Walker** (see p.583) "*gets to the nitty-gritty quickly.*" The team recently represented the British Rail Property Board, pleading fraud against a purchaser at auction who refused to complete because of 'squatters.' **Clients:** British Rail Property Board; Littlewoods Property; Whitbread Property.

DLA Acting on a wide range of regional property litigation work, the team's leading name is **Steven Jennings.**

Addleshaw Booth & Co (see firm details p.853) The firm continues to be a force in the region according to our research with expertise in mortgage-related property litigation due to its long-standing relationships in the banking and building society sectors. Charles Jagger now heads up the firm's Manchester office, out of which the team acted for Gibson Investments on a dilapidation claim against Chesterton. **Clients:** Comet; Green Property Management; Halifax; Standard Life Investments.

Eversheds (see firm details p.952) The Manchester office of the firm's trans-Pennine team handles all property related disputes and is increasingly involved on the development side. The group advised Wain Homes in judicial review proceedings on the decision to dedicate a portion of land as highway and on issues arising from its sale at a profit. "*Sensible*" **Lee Ranson** (see p.579) is considered to be a "*worthy opponent.*" **Clients:** Barclays Bank; Hammerson; Stanley Leisure.

Hammond Suddards Edge (see firm details p.984) A "*strong firm,*" in which Jan Levinson heads up a team that handles estate management, dilapidation claims, judicial reviews and other disputes on behalf of landlord and development clients. Acted for Aventis CropScience UK in the defence of an environmental pollution claim by a neighbouring landowner and is continuing to advise James Hall (Spar) on matters including rent reviews, contested lease renewals and a combined landlord's disrepair claim. **Clients:** BASF; James Hall (Spar); Luxfer Group; TIP/TLS.

Pannone & Partners (see firm details p.1088) An "*active*" property litigation team involved in a wide variety of disputes, including several land tribunal cases arising out of the Manchester Metrolink project. "*Vicious but sensible*" **Vincent O'Farrell** (see p.578) is reckoned by clients to be "*extremely good for all types of litigation.*" The team acted on a complex dispute seeking to recover a defrauded multi-million pound nursing homes empire. **Clients:** GMPTE; Granada Group; Manchester Airport; Texaco.

Other Notable Practitioners Gorna & Co's **Helen Hoath** (see p.573) is an established figure in the region, described to our researchers as a "*decent operator*" who "*brings some sense to a dispute.*"

NORTH EAST

LITIGATION: PROPERTY • North East	Ptnrs	Assts
1 Addleshaw Booth & Co Leeds	1	2
Pinsent Curtis Biddle Leeds	2	2
2 Dickinson Dees Newcastle upon Tyne	1	3
DLA Leeds, Sheffield	*	*
Eversheds Leeds	0	4
Hammond Suddards Edge Leeds	1	4
Nabarro Nathanson Sheffield	2	6
Walker Morris Leeds	1	4

LEADING INDIVIDUALS	
1 HERBERT Alan Pinsent Curtis Biddle	O'LOUGHLIN Philip Addleshaw Booth & Co
2 BECK Andrew Walker Morris	BELCHER Penny Hammond Suddards Edge
UP AND COMING	
OLDFIELD Alison Eversheds	

This book is the product of 6,552 1/2-hour interviews. See p.7 for BMRB audit.

Within each band, firms are listed alphabetically. *See individuals' profiles p.564*

Addleshaw Booth & Co (see firm details p.853) The "*strongest practice in the region,*" rated by the market for its "*high quality work and clients.*" It handles property management, rent reviews, lease renewals and dilapidation claims for its landlord and tenant clients. Recent highlights include representing Principal Hotels in a case against Bass Pensions. The "*excellent*" **Philip O'Loughlin** (see p.578) is considered to be a "*leading light.*" **Clients:** Comet; Green Property Management; Halifax; Standard Life Investments.

Pinsent Curtis Biddle (see firm details p.1098) A "*strong practice*" with an "*impressive client base,*" active in landlord/client disputes and restrictive covenants. **Alan Herbert** (see p.572) is "*a respected name.*" The firm advised a consortium of seven blue chip tenants in respect of a £3.8 million service charge dispute based on the cladding to a major office block in Leeds. **Clients:** Costcutter Supermarkets; Haemonetics (UK); Hogg Robinson; Weatherall Green & Smith.

Dickinson Dees (see firm details p.941) "*The clear leaders in Newcastle,*" led by Jen Smurthwaite, the team undertakes the full range of property litigation issues. Increases in dilapidation claims and restrictive covenants are witnessed and the firm recently advised Enron on warranties relating to the sale of a business and acted on the removal of squatters from commercial premises in Oxford Street, London. **Clients:** Cheviot Investment; Morrison Residential Investments; Richmondshire District Council; Reg Vardy.

DLA The property litigation team in the region is led by John Kittle and is a focal point for local referrals.

Eversheds (see firm details p.952) Operating an "*efficient service for all property litigation work,*" it is felt by peers to possess a "*good client list*" but "*lacks a natural leader.*" It represented The Sock Company in a solicitor negligence claim involving complex issues of expert valuation. The team's most notable practitioner is the "*thorough and determined*" **Alison Oldfield** (see p.578). **Clients:** ASDA; Barclays Bank; Hammerson; Stanley Leisure.

Hammond Suddards Edge (see firm details p.984) A growing team with "*a good name and good clients,*" active in the utilities sector and handling an increasing number of dilapidation claims. The firm acted for William Morrison Supermarkets in successful High Court appeal proceedings brought against the Secretary of State for the Environment, Transport and the Regions. Assistant Director for Advocacy, **Penny Belcher** (see p.565) (ex Irwin Mitchell) is an "*impressive*" lawyer and has lent the firm credibility and weight. **Clients:** Austin Reed; Boots Properties; Bradford & Bingley; Yorkshire Electricity.

Nabarro Nathanson (see firm details p.1078) A "*sharp and experienced*" practice that wins the approval of clients for adopting a "*realistic, no-nonsense approach*" to property litigation matters. Particularly involved in portfolio work and rent reviews, Jane Turley's team continues to act for Capital Shopping Centres in all management work relating to the MetroCentre, Gateshead. **Clients:** Capital Shopping Centres; MAFF; Railtrack; The Coal Authority.

Walker Morris (see firm details p.1171) A "*good solid team*" considered by peers "*strong in Leeds.*" It handles a range of commercial property disputes, forfeiture cases and service charge disputes (including one valued at £3 million in connection with a property in the city) for a mix of landlord and tenant clients. **Andrew Beck** (see p.565) is viewed by competitors as "*a no-nonsense negotiator to be reckoned with.*" **Clients:** Halifax; Arcadia Group; Tops Estates.

SCOTLAND

Dundas & Wilson CS (see firm details p.947) "*The obvious choice in Scotland,*" the firm has a "*strong, active*" dedicated unit. It deals with rent reviews, planning appeals, proprietorial and leasehold interests and is increasing its presence in the leisure and hospitality sector, handling night club, hotel, restaurant and cinema development. "*Lacking a senior figure,*" the most visible member of the team is "*very able*" associate **Sheila Webster. Clients:** Alldays; Scottish Widows; Standard Life.

Maclay Murray & Spens (see firm details p.1047) A "*strong, easy to deal with*" team which handles all matters from rent arrears through to major disputes and cases. The majority of work is commercial, on behalf of landlord clients particularly in the retail area. The key personality here is "*impressive*" **Ewan Easton** (see p.568), a highly respected litigator, with a "*sharp mind.*" **Clients:** Sears, Stannifer; Hazelmere Estates.

McGrigor Donald (see firm details p.1062) The firm has "*always been highly regarded for property litigation work*" and is recommended to our researchers for its "*able people who meet expectations.*" Craig Connal's team acted for Southgate Developments (a division of BT) in a successful application to the Lands Tribunal to remove burdens on a development site. **Clients:** Banks and building societies; property developers and managers.

Brodies WS (see firm details p.896) A "*strong litigation practice,*" developing a degree of specialism in property litigation. William Holligan's team is active in landlord and tenant matters, both contentious and non-contentious, with a strong reputation for its work in the retail sector. Much of

LITIGATION: PROPERTY • Scotland	Ptnrs	Assts
1 Dundas & Wilson CS Edinburgh	1	4
Maclay Murray & Spens Glasgow	1	4
2 McGrigor Donald Glasgow	2	4
3 Brodies WS Edinburgh	n/a	n/a
Burness Edinburgh	3	4
Semple Fraser WS Glasgow	4	3
Shepherd & Wedderburn WS Edinburgh	2	2
Steedman Ramage Edinburgh	2	2

LEADING INDIVIDUALS
1 EASTON Ewan Maclay Murray & Spens
2 CUMMING Kenny Steedman Ramage
UP AND COMING
WEBSTER Sheila Dundas & Wilson CS

This book is the product of 6,552 1/2-hour interviews. See p.7 for BMRB audit.

Within each band, firms are listed alphabetically. *See individuals' profiles p.564*

the work is gained from the firm's commercial property department. **Clients:** Developers and retailers.

Burness (see firm details p.903) A "*good firm with some very able people,*" with wide experience in disputed rent reviews, dilapidation claims and servitude rights of access. Philip Rodney heads the firm's Dispute Resolution department. **Clients:** British Land Universal; Highland Spring; Newcastle Building Society; Zurich GSG.

Semple Fraser WS (see firm details p.1121) Alison Gow's team works closely with the firm's "*strong*" commercial property department undertaking a wide range of issues. It advised Friends of the Earth, WWF and RSPB on a decision by Lafarge Redland to appeal refusal of planning permission for Harris Superquarry. Also acted for Scotia Pharmaceuticals in arbitration relating to cladding on an Isle of Lewis factory. **Clients:** Clydeport Operations; Lidl Stores GmbH; Scudder Threadneedle Property Fund Managers; Tesco Stores.

Shepherd & Wedderburn WS (see firm details p.1126) A "*good*" litigation team commended by peers as "*recognising the need for specialism,*" it acts principally for landlords in property disputes. David Anderson's unit represented William Alexander in its case against The Royal Hotel. **Clients:** Developers; housing associations; landlords.

Steedman Ramage (see firm details p.1139) A "*fabulous property practice*" with "*good retail tenant clients*" and a good breadth and depth of experience according to interviewees. The team acted for Sears against Coal Pension Properties over an unreasonable withholding of consent to assignation of lease. **Kenny Cumming** (see p.568) is "*one of the biggest names in Scottish property litigation.*" **Clients:** Helical Retail; Mint UK; Next; Sears Group Properties.

LEADERS IN LITIGATION

ALLEN, Martin
DMH, Brighton (01273) 744324
martin.allen@dmh.co.uk
Specialisation: Partner with wide experience of all contentious property related matters, professional negligence, title and covenant cases, arbitrations (rent review, options etc.), construction and insolvency, with particular expertise in commercial leases. Acts for a range of investors, developers, businesses with multiple property holdings as well as public authorities, charities and institutions; has handled numerous cases relating to commercial leases, (eg. privity, rent reviews, user and keep-open covenants and repairs).
Career: Qualified 1972. Partner *Donne Mileham & Haddock* (now *DMH*) 1976. Head of litigation group, 1982-94; head of commercial property 1996-00.
Personal: Interests include sailing, jazz, naval history and sport.

AMSDEN, Mark
Addleshaw Booth & Co, Manchester
(0161) 934 6195
mra@addleshaw-booth.co.uk
Specialisation: I.T. Litigation, Commercial Disputes. Engineering, e-commerce. 1) Won a 3 week, £2 million computer supply trial to do with computer software in the travel industry. 2) Lead Partner in a tens of million pound breach of contract software supply case (on going). 3) Various internet related disputes. 4) Planned a £50 million product liability recall. 5) Extensive experience of warranty and company acquisition related disputes.
Career: Solicitor and Barrister Victoria Australia – admitted 1987, Solicitor admitted England 1992. *Slater Heelis* 1990-98, partner 1996. *Addleshaw Booth & Co* 1998-date. Partner 1998.
Personal: Educated Melbourne Grammar, Monash University, Melbourne. Married 1 son. Cricket, rugby, travel.

ANDERSON, Harry
Herbert Smith, London (020) 7374 8000
Specialisation: Head of litigation and arbitration division since 1998. Also heads one of the firm's general commercial litigation groups with substantial experience in litigation arising out of corporate transactions, such as claims for misrepresentation and breach of warranty, as well as professional negligence cases.
Career: Joined *Herbert Smith* as an articled clerk in 1968. Qualified 1970. Partner since 1976. Started *Herbert Smith's* Hong Kong office in 1982; returned to London 1987.
Personal: Educated at Jesus College, Cambridge.

ANDERSON, Peter
Simpson & Marwick WS, Edinburgh
(0131) 557 1545

ARCHER, Nick
Slaughter and May, London (020) 7710 4073
nick.archer@slaughterandmay.com
Specialisation: Principal area of practice is commercial litigation and arbitration. Handles a wide variety of domestic and international disputes in the commercial context. Has particular experience in banking disputes.
Prof. Memberships: The Law Society; International Bar Association; Indian Council of Arbitration.
Career: Qualified in 1981 with *Slaughter and May* and became a partner in 1988.
Personal: Born 15 May 1956. Attended Oakham School and Durham University. Lives in London.

ASPINALL, Tim
DMH, Brighton (01273) 744319
tim.aspinall@dmh.co.uk
Specialisation: Managing partner and head of litigation. Practice focuses on commercial litigation including intellectual property and computer-related litigation. He has particular experience in the high technology sector, but deals with the full range of commercial disputes on behalf of national and international clients. Skilled at managing complex and difficult cases to a successful conclusion and has been involved in numerous major disputes of this kind over the years. Regularly speaks at conferences and lectures to other lawyers throughout the country on litigation topics including the strategy and tactics of winning cases. Matters in recent years include acting for the successful defendant in the reported case of Hughes Rediffusion v Link Miles (a multi-million pound patent High Court infringement action); acting in an ICC arbitration for a company against a bank in a multi-million pound claim involving a PFI contract.
Prof. Memberships: Society for Computers and Law; branch committee member Institute of Directors.
Career: York University 1975-78 BA (Hons); qualified in 1982 and joined *Donne Mileham & Haddock* (now *DMH*) 1983, partner in 1987; appointed information technology partner 1989; appointed head of litigation in 1994; appointed managing partner 1997.
Publications: Contributor to the new 'Civil Litigation Handbook', published by the Law Society.
Personal: Born1956. Interests are golf, cricket, gardening.

ATKINSON, Mark
CMS Cameron McKenna, London
(020) 7367 3000

BACON, Gavin
Simmons & Simmons, London (020) 7628 2020
gavin.bacon@simmons-simmons.com
Specialisation: Commercial litigation and dispute resolution; regulatory issues. Acted for the majority shareholders of BCCI, Novartis and Railtrack amongst others.

Prof. Memberships: Law Society of England and Wales; IBA; ABA.
Career: Qualified in1982; partner 1988. Worked in the following *Simmons & Simmons* local offices: Adu Dhabi (1993-5); Hong Kong (1995-7); Shanghai (1997-9). Relocated to *Simmons & Simmons'* London office in April 1999.
Personal: Bristol University. Married with two children.

BAGGALLAY, Roger
Clifford Chance, London (020) 7600 1000
roger.baggallay@cliffordchance.com
Specialisation: Partner in financial and corporate litigation group. Main area of practice, usually on behalf of financial institutions, is commercial litigation, particularly general banking, trade finance, asset management, securities, futures and derivatives disputes, regulatory investigations and frauds; and also aircraft finance and leasing disputes. Reported cases include Wahda Bank v Arab Bank and Kleinwort Benson v Sandwell, South Tyneside, Birmingham, Glasgow and Lincoln.
Prof. Memberships: Law Society; Solicitors' European Group.
Career: Born 1954. Attended Marlborough College (1967-71), then Oxford University (New College) for Law degree (1975). Articled with *Clifford Chance* (1976). Head of litigation in Hong Kong (1982-85), partner (1987). Consultant Editor of Butterworths International Litigation Handbook and for the England and Wales chapter of 'Aircraft Liens and Detention Rights'; and Country Correspondent (News) of the Journal of International Banking Law. Regular conference and seminar speaker.

BAGGE, James
Norton Rose, London (020) 7283 6000
baggeajs@nortonrose.com
Specialisation: Partner in commercial litigation department. Practice focuses on fraud and the regulation of investment and banking business, in particular advising on all forms of investigations, statutory or private, and associated legal proceedings involving the SFO, DTI, SRO and Revenue authorities. Advised the Board of Banking Supervision on the Barings inquiry. Has acted for LIFFE in relation to market investigations and enforcement actions. Conducted the Banking Act inquiry into Hambros involvement with the aborted bid for the Co-operative Wholesale Society. Is representing the trustees of the Thyssen Bornemisza Trust in action commenced by Baron Thyssen in Bermuda. Acts for three global investment banks in relation to ongoing regulatory investigations. Is currently assisting with the enquiry with the FSA's supervision of the Equitable Life.
Prof. Memberships: International Bar Association.
Career: Qualified 1979. Spent eight years at the Criminal Bar and two years on secondment to the Serious Fraud Office. Joined *Norton Rose* in 1990 and became a partner in 1993.

BAND, Christa
Herbert Smith, London (020) 7374 8000
Specialisation: Partner in litigation and arbitration division. Specialises in banking and financial services work. Also has wide experience of general commercial litigation including professional negligence work and work with an international element.
Career: Educated at Tiffin Girls' School; Trinity Hall, Cambridge (BA 1985, MA 1988); Inns of Court Law School (Bar Finals 1986); St. Edmund Hall, Oxford (BCL 1987). Qualified 1993; barrister, London, 1987-90; worked with major solicitors' firm, Sydney, Australia, 1990-92; solicitor advocate, all Courts (1994). Partner *Herbert Smith* since 1996.

BARLEY, Mark
Bond Pearce, Plymouth (01752) 266 633
mbarley@bondpearce.com
Specialisation: Associate specialising in business and residential tenancy disputes, lease renewals, dilapidations, restrictive covenants, adverse possession and property-related professional negligence claims.
Prof. Memberships: Member of the Property Litigation Association, the Forum of Insurance Lawyers and a committee member of the Plymouth Law Society.
Career: Oxford University Exhibitioner (French and Latin) 1982-85; Guildford Law College (CPE and LSF 1985-87). Qualified 1989 with Bond Pearce, appointed Associate 1999.

BARRETT, Elizabeth
Slaughter and May, London (020) 7600 1200
elizabeth.barrett@slaughterandmay.com
Specialisation: Partner in litigation department. Principal area of practice is commercial litigation including civil and commercial fraud and corporate crime, and extensive experience of a broad range of statutory, regulatory and disciplinary investigations and enquiries.
Prof. Memberships: The Law Society.
Career: Qualified 1981. Partner *Peter Carter-Ruck and Partners* 1982-86. Joined *Slaughter and May* 1986; partner 1989.
Personal: Born 23 November 1956. Attended University College, London (LLB Hons 1978).

BASTOW, Martin
Lyons Davidson, Bristol (0117) 904 5898
mbastow@lyonsdavidson.co.uk
Specialisation: Partner and Head of Property Litigation Group. Experienced in all aspects of property litigation with particular emphasis on landlord and tenant disputes and complex security enforcement. Work includes dilapidations, forfeiture, 1954 Act renewals, arbitration, possession proceedings, property-related prosecutions and acting for LPA receivers.
Prof. Memberships: Associate of the Chartered Institute of Arbitrators; PACT panel member; member of Property Litigation Association, Bristol Housing Lawyers Group and LSC Funding Review Committee.
Career: Joined *Lyons Davidson* on qualification in 1988. Partner since 1994.

BECK, Andrew
Walker Morris, Leeds (0113) 283 2500
Specialisation: Partner and head of property litigation group. Specialist areas include some charge disputes, lease renewals, removing squatters and landlord and tenant disputes. Andrew has been involved in a number of reported cases including Postel Properties Limited v Boots the Chemist Limited involving a substantial service charge dispute in respect of a shopping centre.
Prof. Memberships: Andrew is a CEDR accredited mediator and a member of the Association of Northern Mediators, Member of the Property Litigation Association.
Career: Qualified in 1988, joined *Walker Morris* 1989.
Personal: Born 1958, resides Leeds, hobbies include family and sport.

BECKETT, Sam
L'Estrange & Brett, Belfast (028) 9023 0426
sam.beckett@lestrangeandbrett.com
Specialisation: Partner. Main area of work: civil litigation, including construction, planning law and professional negligence.
Prof. Memberships: Law Society of Northern Ireland. Member Contentious Business committee, Chancery Division Liaison committee; Commercial Division Liasion committee; Society of Construction Law.
Career: Qualified 1980. Partner in *L'Estrange & Brett* since 1986.
Personal: Born 1957. Education: Queen's University, Belfast (LLB).

BEDFORD, Richard
Burges Salmon, Bristol (0117) 902 2749
richard.bedford@burges-salmon.com
Specialisation: As a specialist property litigator, he deals with professional indemnity claims, agricultural insolvency related matters and real property disputes. Particular specialism is banking disputes relating to agriculture. He has lectured on numerous subjects including agricultural law, secured lending and specialist areas of landlord and tenant law.
Prof. Memberships: Law Society.
Career: Joined *Burges Salmon* in 1983 as a trainee and became a partner in 1992. Joint author of RICS publication, 'Farm Receiverships'.

BELCHER, Penny
Hammond Suddards Edge, Leeds (0113) 284 7000
penny.belcher@hammondse.com
Specialisation: All areas of commercial and property litigation, arbitration, mediation and Tribunal work. Freezing injunctions, search and seizure orders, commercial fraud and landlord and tenant disputes, compensation claims, planning, judicial review.
Prof. Memberships: Attorney State Bar of California. Property Litigation Association.
Career: Barrister 1980. Practised as barrister specialising in property litigation until 1987. Admitted Attorney State Bar of California 1988. Qualified as solicitor 1993. Joined *Eversheds* 1993. Partner 1997. Joined *Hammond Suddards Edge* 2000.
Personal: Educated St Hugh's College, Oxford: BA and MA Jurisprudence. Interests include music and theatre, walking, sailing and squash.

BERWICK, Guy
Freethcartwright, Nottingham (0115) 936 9369
Specialisation: Solving problems, especially complex disputes, at the right time, in the right way, ensuring the most realistic result at the right price. Wide experience of all commercial disputes especially construction, engineering and arbitration. Considerable experience of injunctive work, often acts as supervising solicitor in Search and Seizure orders.
Prof. Memberships: Fellow of the Chartered Institute of Arbitrators.
Career: 1979, LLB Nottingham University. 1994, FCIArb. 1996, LLM Advanced Litigation (with Distinction), Nottingham Law School. External examiner Nottingham Law School 2001. Qualified 1982. Joined present firm 1983. Partner, construction group.

Personal: Interests include football and Blackburn Rovers. Married to Kathy, two daughters, Katrina and Stephanie.

BLAKE, Peter

Prettys, Ipswich (01473) 232121
plb@prettys.co.uk
Specialisation: Handles a range of commercial litigation including construction and engineering, sale of goods, warranty claims, carriage of goods by road and freight forwarding. Clients include insurance, construction, engineering, road haulier and freight forwarding companies.
Prof. Memberships: Law Society.
Career: Qualified in 1987. Partner in *Prettys* commercial litigation department since 1991.
Personal: Born 1963. Educated at King Edward VI School, Norwich 1973-81, Exeter University 1981-84 and Guildford College of Law. Past Chairman of Ipswich and East Suffolk Hockey Club.

BLAKEMORE, Craig

Mace & Jones, Liverpool (0151) 236 8989
craig.blakemore@maceandjones.co.uk
Specialisation: Commercial contract disputes, professional negligence actions (particularly solicitors), insolvency, computer/IT law and intellectual property.
Prof. Memberships: Society for Computers and Law. Association of Business Recovery Professionals.
Career: Articled *Mace & Jones* -80/1982. Solicitor *Mace & Jones* – 1982/1986. Partner *Mace & Jones* -86 onwards. Head of litigation for the firm.
Personal: Interests include rugby, squash, motorcycling.

BLYTH, Mark

Linklaters, London (020) 7456 4246
mark.blyth@linklaters.com
Specialisation: Full-time specialist in all types of pensions litigation, including surplus disputes, trustee applications to court for directions, breach of trust, Pensions Ombudsman complaints, professional negligence of actuaries/professional advisers, administrators and regulatory issues with Opra. High profile cases this year include acting for National Power (Court of Appeal) over arrangements made for dealing with surpluses in the Electricity Supply Pension Scheme (now appealed to the House of Lords).
Prof. Memberships: Association of Pensions Lawyers. Advisory Panel member – The Occupational Pensions Defence Union Limited. Association of Contentious Trust & Probate Specialists.
Career: Articled to *Allen & Overy* 1988-90. Associate partner, head of pensions litigation group 1990 to date.

BOWDEN, Paul

Freshfields Bruckhaus Deringer, London (020) 7936 4000
paul.bowden@freshfields.com
Specialisation: Partner in Litigation Department. Multi-party litigation and judicial review cases in the environmental and product fields.
Prof. Memberships: Membership: Joint Bar/ Law Society Working Party on Civil Justice (1992-93); Lord Woolf's advisory committee on multi-party actions (1995-96); International Nuclear Lawyers Association; Chairman of Nottingham Law School.
Career: Qualified with *Freshfields* in 1981. Partner in 1987, qualified in Hong Kong, 1986.
Personal: Born 1955. Educated: Bristol University 1973-78.

BRADFORD, Katie

Linklaters, London (020) 7456 4234
katie.bradford@linklaters.com
Specialisation: Specialises in all aspects of property litigation and arbitration including landlord and tenant, solicitors'/surveyors' negligence, insolvency related disputes. Leader in rent review arbitration. Has taken over 60 actions to trial and 12 to CA. Recent cases include Prudential v Waterloo (CA 1999) and CLE v Kato Kagaku (1999). Named as 'Expert's Expert' in property litigation by competitors. Blundell Lecturer on rent review (1998).
Prof. Memberships: Women in Property Litigation; Women in Property; Registered mediator (CEDR accreditation); Fellow of Chartered Institute of Arbitrators.; PACT arbitrator; Member of ARBRIX and MEDRIX; Fellow of Royal Society for Art; and aspirant member of MCC.
Career: Articled *Osmond Gaunt & Rose* (Finchley), *Lovell White Durrant*, commercial litigation, *Linklaters* since 1992. Former Chairman of Property Litigation Association. Partner and Head of Property Litigation Unit.

BRIERLEY, Ian P

DLA, London (08700) 111 111

BRIGGS, Leona

Osborne Clarke, Bristol (0117) 917 3000

BYRNE, David

Dechert, London (020) 7775 7415
david.byrne@dechertEU.com
See under Fraud, p.409

BYRNE, Justin

Eversheds, Birmingham (0121) 232 1000
justinbyrne@eversheds.com
Specialisation: Complex multi-party and international litigation. Commercial litigation, with particular emphasis on IT. Professional negligence, shareholder disputes and defamation, often as part of a wider dispute. Reported cases include Investors Compensation Scheme Limited v West Bromwich Building Society (HL), West Bromwich Building Society v Mander Hadley (C/A) and Hertford Foods Limited v Lidl UK Gmbh (C/A). Also has mediation experience, including successful Court of Appeal mediation.
Career: Articled at *Farrer & Co*, 1990-92. Joined *Eversheds* in 1995 from *Harbottle Lewis.*
Personal: Born in 1966. Attended Shrewsbury School and Bristol University.

CALLAGHAN, Edward

Mills & Reeve, Cambridge (01223) 222 242
ed.callaghan@mills-reeve.com
Specialisation: Main areas of practice include building and engineering litigation, arbitration and adjudication. Also covered is professional indemnity work relating to architects, surveyors, engineers and solicitors. Has addressed seminars to audiences in the construction industry.
Prof. Memberships: Law Society, Legal panel. Technology & Construction Solicitors' Association.
Career: Qualified with *Mills & Reeve* in 1974. Became Partner in Commercial Litigation Department in 1979.
Personal: Born 25th February 1950 in Middlesex. Attended Franciscan College, Buckingham 1961-68, then Exeter University 1968-71. Leisure pursuits include squash, reading and viticulture. Lives Norfolk Broads.

CANNON, Lista

Richards Butler, London (020) 7772 5702
lmc@richardsbutler.com
Specialisation: As a lawyer qualified in New York and England & Wales, her practice covers the full range of commercial litigation work with particular emphasis on transnational (cross-border) commercial disputes and litigation, sovereign immunity issues, risk assessment and dispute resoluton and government advisory work. She has a strong banking, finance and regulatory practice. Her work includes ICC arbitration and energy related contract disputes.
Prof. Memberships: In September 1998 she was seconded for six months to the Financial Services Authority as a Senior Legal Advisor and Acting Head of Enforcement. Law Society, admitted to New York State Bar in 1976, Federal Bar Council, ICC UK Environmental Committee.
Career: Litigation lawyer at *Sullivan & Cromwell,* New York, 1975-80. Established commercial litigation department, (*Boodle Hatfield*), London 1980-92; Member of the Partnership Board of *Richards Butler* since May 1998.
Personal: Educated at New York University 1969; University of London LLB (hons) 1971. Trustee British American Educational Foundation since 1980, member of India House, New York and Reform Club.

CARRUTHERS, Andrew

Rowe & Maw, London (020) 7782 8809
acarruthers@roweandmaw.com
Specialisation: Pensions litigation and domestic and international arbitration and mediation.
Prof. Memberships: Law Society; Association of Pensions Lawyers; CEDR; LCIA; Chartered Institute of Arbitrators; Secretary of Pensions Litigation Committee of the Association of Pensions Lawyers.
Career: Solicitor *Lovell White & King* 1975-77; solicitor *Bond Pearce* 1977-80; solicitor *Linklaters & Paines* 1980-83; solicitor *Rowe & Maw* 1983-present; partner 1985; head of litigation and dispute resolution department 1995.
Publications: 'Pensions Litigation' – Tolley's; 'Pensions Law' (2000).
Personal: Educated at Harrow County Boy's School; Pembroke College, Oxford (1972 Jurisprudence; 1975 MA). Enjoys music, travel, family, history and gardening.

CAVE, Tim

Freshfields Bruckhaus Deringer, London (020) 7936 4000
timothy.cave@freshfields.com
Specialisation: Partner in the dispute resolution department dealing with commercial litigation and specialising in banking and property litigation.
Career: Articled *Freshfields.* Qualified 1986. Partner 1994.
Personal: Born 1960. Educated at Bristol University.

CHAPMAN, Stuart

Pinsent Curtis Biddle, Leeds (0113) 244 5000
stuart.chapman@pinsents.com
Specialisation: Partner and head of litigation, Leeds. Independently acknowleged expert in resolution of both commercial and IT disputes.
Prof. Memberships: Chairman, Society for Computers & Law (Northern Group)

Career: *Linklaters* (1989-94). *Eversheds*, Leeds (1994-98). *Pinsent Curtis Biddle*, Leeds (1998-Date).
Personal: Born 1965 and educated in Grimsby. Leisure interests include family, football, sailing, cricket, most other sports.

CHEFFINGS, Nicholas
Lovells, London (020) 7296 2000
nicholas.cheffings@lovells.com
Specialisation: Partner and head of group of 14. PACT arbitrator ADR-Net (1991) and CEDR (2000) accredited mediator and has sat as a mediator and mentor on a number of occasions; also a fellow of the Chartered Institute of Arbitrators (1993) and sits as a legal assessor to surveyor arbitrators and experts. Specialises in all aspects of contentious property work from advisory to House of Lords, such as landlord and tenant (including major rent reviews), planning/judicial review, rights of light, lands tribunal work, professional negligence, agency and vendor/purchaser and joint venture disputes; acted on several reported cases.
Prof. Memberships: Law Society; ARBRIX; Land Institute; Chartered Institute of Arbitrators; Property Litigation Association.
Career: Qualified 1983; partner *Nabarro Nathanson* 1990; partners *Lovells* 1999.
Publications: General editor of 'Commercial Property Disputes: Law and Practice' (1999); author of numerous articles and regular speaker at conferences; Blundell Memorial lecturer.
Personal: Born 1960. Educated at Caistor Grammar School; University of Leicester (LLB 2(1) Hons). Interests include holidays, dining, theatre etc, watching virtually any sport and occasionally complete inactivity. Resides Chelsfield.

CHERRY, Peter
Addleshaw Booth & Co, Leeds (0113) 209 2000
pjc@addleshaw-booth.co.uk
Specialisation: Partner in Litigation and Dispute Resolution Group, dealing with delivery of dispute resolution services to clients, including disputes arising on the sale and purchase of businesses, financial services litigation, product liability related cases, arbitrations, fraud and judicial review.
Prof. Memberships: Qualified 1978, Partner at the firm 1983.
Career: BA Durham 1975.
Personal: Leisure interests include prehistory, wine and numismatics.

CLARK, Tim
Garretts, Reading (0118) 949 0000
Specialisation: Complex commercial litigation, arbitration and dispute resolution. Recent cases include information technology disputes, minority shareholders actions, finance and leasing, professional negligence and energy sector disputes. Recently acted for Thames Water Utilities Ltd in complex litigation concerning the sale and supply of renewable energy. Clients include multinational corporations, major listed plcs and technology companies based in the Thames Valley.
Prof. Memberships: Thames Valley Commercial Lawyers Association.
Career: *Eversheds* London (formerly *Jacques & Lewin*) 1985-96; *Garretts* to date.
Personal: Leisure interests include family, golf, all sports. Married with two children.

CLAVELL-BATE, Michael
Eversheds, Manchester (0161) 831 8000
michaelclavellbate@eversheds.com
Specialisation: Head of the commercial litigation team in Manchester. All areas of management of commercial disputes including mainstream commercial litigation and ADR. Also specialises in all areas of defamation. Received national press coverage following the Football Association's withdrawal of its charges against Brian Clough. Also hit the headlines last year acting for Ros Marks, former nanny to Cherie and Tony Blair. Recently contributed to a chapter on 'Defamation on the Internet' for a legal text published April 2000. Reported cases include Secretary of State v Secure & Provide plc. Current major cases include two very high profile defamation cases, a multiparty product liability case (approx. £50m) and a professional negligence case with a damages claim in excess of £20m.
Prof. Memberships: Chairman of the Civil Litigation Committee of the Manchester Law Society. Council member of the Manchester Law Society. Currently Vice President of Manchester Law Society and President commencing 2001.
Career: Qualified with *Eversheds* in 1990 and became a partner in 1997.
Personal: Born 25 March 1966. Attended Newcastle University and Chester College of Law. Resides in Trawden, North East Lancashire. Leisure interests include all sport.

CLOUGH, Peter
Osborne Clarke, Bristol (0117) 917 3000

COHEN, Roger
Berwin Leighton Paisner, London (020) 7760 1000
roger.cohen@berwinleighton.com
Specialisation: Litigation and dispute resolution partner. Main area of practice is real estate disputes including landlord and tenant, planning-related litigation, environmental claims, rating, ADR and professional indemnity. A mediator. Other areas are general commercial litigation and arbitration. Acted for Tesco in high profile rent review dispute with British Land concerning the valuation of a store in Maidstone. Represents Prudential, Legal & General, Central Government, UBS and other funds and quoted companies.
Prof. Memberships: CEDR registered mediator; Fellow Chartered Institute of Arbitrators; Administrative Law Bar Association; City of London Solicitors' Company; Law Society; Law Reform sub-committee; Property Litigation Association; associate fellow, Society of Advanced Legal Studies; panel member, Dispute Mediation Ltd; mediation panel of Chartered Institute of Arbitrators.
Career: Articled with *Donnelly & Elliott* in Gosport, then joined *Matthew Arnold & Baldwin* in Watford. Joined *Berwin Leighton* in 1984 and became a partner in 1989. Head of real estate disputes group and co-chair of *Berwin Leighton Paisner* Israel desk.

COLE, Margaret R.
White & Case, London (020) 7397 3609
mrcole@whitecase.com
Specialisation: One of the country's leading advisors in commercial litigation.
Prof. Memberships: Law Society of England & Wales, registered CEDR mediator.
Career: Joined *White & Case*, London as partner, 1995.
Personal: MA Cambridge University 1982. Interests include opera and competitive horse riding.

COLLINSON, Ian
Ward Hadaway, Newcastle upon Tyne
(0191) 204 4000
Specialisation: Head of commercial litigation with particular expertise in professional negligence, insurance and defamation.
Career: Birkenhead School and Kings College, London. Qualified in 1982. Articled and subsequently partner with *Dawson & Co*, London. Head of litigation 1989. Moved to Newcastle and *Ward Hadaway* 1991. Partner 1992. Head of litigation 1993.
Personal: Golf, sailing and fishing.

CONNAL, Craig
McGrigor Donald, Glasgow (0141) 248 6677
See under Planning, p.663

CONWAY, Keith
Dechert, London (020) 7583 5353
keith.conway@dechertEU.com
Specialisation: Partner, specialising in property litigation and commercial litigation. Keith deals with all property and landlord and tenant matters. In recent years, Keith has had extensive experience of dealing with major rent review arbitrations. He has built up, and encourages the use of self-help remedies. He also deals with corporate, joint venture and partnership disputes, and commercial, banking and insolvency litigation and arbitration. Keith is featured in the Legal Business Legal Experts list of highly recommended lawyers. Some of Keith's significant cases include Argyll Stores -v- CIS (House of Lords) – Keep Open, Banner Homes Group Plc -v- Luff Developments Ltd – Joint Venture Dispute (Court of Appeal), Belvedere Court -v- Frogmore Estates Plc and Harley House (Marylebone) Ltd -v- Michaels – both Court of Appeal 1987 Act, London & Leeds -v- Paribas (Court of Appeal) – Rent Review. Currently dealing with; BHP Petroleum v Chesterfield Properties – original Landlord release of personal/developers covenants under the 1995 Act and liability for defects and the Broadgate Rent Reviews.
Prof. Memberships: Property Litigation Association, Member of Chartered Institute of Arbitrators, Member of Joint Working Party – Limitation of Actions.
Career: Qualified 1984. Partner in 1990.
Publications: Contributor to the 'Landlord & Tenant Factbook' published by Franey & Co in 1992, Joint Editor of 'Property Law Journal', regularly writes on property and commercial law and litigation practice. Spoken at numerous conferences.

COOMBS, Monica
Sacker & Partners, London (020) 7329 6699
monica.coombs@sacker-partners.co.uk
Specialisation: Specialising in pensions litigation and mediation particularly professional negligence, trust law and asset tracing and recovery.
Prof. Memberships: Association of Pension Lawyers. Association of Pensions Lawyers Pensions Litigation Committee. Law Society.
Career: Admitted in Western Australia 1990. Qualified in England 1996. Partner at *Sacker & Partners* since 1999.
Personal: Educated at the University of Western Australia. Leisure activities include travel, diving and walking.

COX, David
Berwin Leighton Paisner, London (020) 7427 1328
david.cox@berwinleightonpaisner.com
Specialisation: Specialises in a whole range of property-related disputes, including rent collection and service charge disputes, forfeitures, rent reviews, lease renewals, dilapidations claims, title and right to light disputes and professional negligence claims. Clients include institutional investors, retail groups, developers and owner-occupiers. Has led seminars on a variety of property topics (most recently on expert witnesses and property and human rights) and has had articles published recently in 'Estates Gazette' and 'Property Law Journal'.
Prof. Memberships: Law Society, Property Litigation Association.
Career: Qualified 1979. Partner *Lovells* 1985-97. Partner *Berwin Leighton Paisner* 1998.

CRAWFORD, Sandra
McKinty & Wright, Belfast (028) 9024 6751
post@mckinty-wright.co.uk
Specialisation: Practises in all types of commercial litigation including professional negligence, claims arising out of the carriage of goods and marine matters. Also extensive employment law practice, both advisory and litigation, acting for employers.
Prof. Memberships: Law Society of Northern Ireland, Northern Ireland Employment Lawyers Group.
Career: Graduated Queen's University of Belfast in Law (LLB) 1985. Qualified 1987. Partner in *McKinty & Wright* since 1995.
Personal: Born 1962. Married, one child.

CROSS, Siobhan
Masons, London (020) 7490 6277
siobhan.cross@masons.com
Specialisation: Partner in property litigation group. Practice covers all areas of property litigation and dispute resolution including landlord and tenant matters such as rent reviews, dilapidations, possession proceedings, and lease renewals and other property related disputes including disputes over development of land, relevant professional negligence claims and rights of way, light and air. Experienced in alternative methods of dispute resolution including mediation, arbitration and expert determination.
Prof. Memberships: Property Litigation Association.
Career: Qualified in 1987. Joined *Masons* in 1988 and became a partner in 1993.
Personal: Born 21 July 1962 and lives in North London.

CROSSE, Damian
DLA, Leeds (08700) 111111

CROSSLEY, Peter
Hammond Suddards Edge, Leeds (0113) 284 7106
peter.crossley@hammondse.com
Specialisation: National head of commercial dispute resolution unit. Specialises in litigation for corporate clients, primarily heavy/light engineering. Particular experience in large scale contractual warranty claims, shareholders disputes and fraud related work and the international sales of goods. Presently dealing with a high profile DTI investigation into a listed company and a £5 million international arbitration case.
Prof. Memberships: Law Society, Leeds Law Society.
Career: Kearsney College, South Africa, University of Natal, South Africa (BCom, LL.B), St Johns College, Cambridge (MA). Qualified attorney in South Africa (1984); articled *Richards Butler*, assistant solicitor *Richards Butler* (1989-92); assistant solicitor *Hammond Suddards* (1992-95); partner 1995; national head of commercial dispute resolution 1999..
Personal: Resides in Ilkley. Leisure interests include cricket, running, theatre, church and family.

CULLEN, Joyce
Brodies WS, Edinburgh (0131) 228 3777
joyce.cullen@brodies.co.uk
See under Employment, p.330

CUMMING, Kenny
Steedman Ramage, Edinburgh (0131) 260 6600
kenny.cumming@steedmanramage.co.uk
Specialisation: General commercial litigation, dispute resolution and advisory work – in particular, property, planning, rent review and environmental litigation.
Career: Qualified 1981. At *Dundas & Wilson CS* 1979-94 (partner from 1986). Joined *Steedman Ramage WS* as a partner in 1994.
Personal: Born 8 November 1957.

DAVIES, Gwendoline
Walker Morris, Leeds (0113) 283 2500
gxd@walkermorris.co.uk
Specialisation: Partner and head of commercial dispute resolution group engaged in a wide range of High Court and commercial dispute resolution for corporate clients and for various institutional clients. Emphasis on banking; insolvency; contractual disputes; breach of warranty claims; defective products; member of firm's lender services group; involved in four Court of Appeal issues last year including: successfully acted in a leading case on agency defending a bank's right to charged assets (Triffit Nurseries v Salads Etcetera Ltd) and acted on a landmark case involving relief from forfeiture of finance leases (On Demand Information plc, On Demand Information International plc v Michael Gerson Finance plc, Michael Gerson Investments Ltd).
Prof. Memberships: Society of Practitioners of Insolvency (subscriber status); Law Society; Leeds Law Society; CEDR accredited mediator.
Career: Whitland Grammar School; Leicester University (LLB); College of Law, Chester. Articled *Herbert Smith* 1996-98; qualified 1998 with *Herbert Smith* until December 1992, *Mallesons Stephen Jacques* (Australia – six months); joined *Walker Morris* in 1992 and partner May 1994.
Personal: Born 1964; resides Luddendenfoot. Leisure interests include reading, walking, sport, travel and family.

DAVIES, Peter
Gateley Wareing, Birmingham (0121) 234 0000

DAVIES, Valerie E.M.
Norton Rose, London (020) 7444 2673
daviesvem@nortonrose.com
Specialisation: Partner in commercial litigation department. Handles a wide variety of domestic and international disputes of a commercial nature with particular emphasis on banking, corporate and financial litigation, insolvency and commercial fraud. Experienced in tracing and recovering assets. Heads *Norton Rose's* insolvency litigation team and has extensive experience of cross border international insolvency. A CEDR accredited mediator and mediates actions being appealed from a first instance decision to the Court of Appeal. Also handles some high profile defamation cases.
Prof. Memberships: Law Society; City of London Solicitors Company; International Bar Association.
Career: Qualified as a solicitor in 1979 and became a partner in *Norton Rose* in 1986. Was appointed as an Assistant Recorder in 1997 and a Recorder in 2000.

DAVIS, Simon
Clifford Chance, London (020) 7600 1000

DE WALDEN, Ludovic
Lane & Partners, London (020) 7242 2626
dewaldenl@lane.co.uk
Specialisation: Complex multinational litigation and arbitration, art law problems.
Prof. Memberships: Chartered Institute of Arbitrators; IBA; Institute of Art and Law.
Career: Litigation partner since 1985.
Personal: Interests: The arts, opera, theatre, skiing, shooting, golf, reading. Married with three children. Lives Chelsea and Oxfordshire.

DIMSDALE GILL, Angela
Lovells, London (020) 7296 2000
amdg@lovells.com
Specialisation: Commercial chancery, pension fund disputes, professional negligence and fraud. Significant cases include Re Courage, National Power plc v Feldon, British Coal Corporation v British Coal Superannuation Scheme Trustees Ltd and the largest fraud claim arising out of collapse of BCCI. Extensive experience of high value pension and trust disputes and professional negligence work. Advises OPRA and Solicitors Indemnity Fund.
Prof. Memberships: City of London Law Society Litigation Sub-Committee, Association of Pension Lawyers and Pension Litigation committee of that association, Pensions Litigation Court Users' Committee, City of London Law Society Pro Bono Sub-Committee (Chair), Trustee Solicitor's Pro Bono Group.
Career: Qualified 1982, partner *Lovells* 1988.

DONALD, Hugh
Shepherd & Wedderburn WS, Edinburgh (0131) 473 5159
hugh.donald@shepwedd.co.uk
Specialisation: Partner. Specialist in clinical negligence, representing doctors and dentists in civil claims, inquiries and disciplinary proceedings. Also aviation representing airline and helicopter operators in both civil claims and accident inquiries. On the panel appointed to handle claims under Law society of Scotland Charter Policy.
Career: Qualified in 1975, having joined *Shepherd & Wedderburn WS* in 1973. Became a partner in 1977. Administrative head of litigation department 1990-94. Appointed managing partner in April 1994, and chief executive from April 1995 – April 1999.
Personal: Born 5th November 1951. Educated at Edinburgh University. Family Mediator. Chairman, Family Mediation Scotland. Leisure interests include gardening, walking and church. Lives in Edinburgh. Awarded OBE for services to family mediation in Scotland.

EASTON, Ewan
Maclay Murray & Spens, Edinburgh (0131) 226 5196
ere@maclaymurrayspens.co.uk
Specialisation: Partner in Commercial Litigation and Advocacy. Specialises in property litigation, planning issues and employment law. Initiated the series

of 'stay open' clause litigations in Scotland which have resulted in orders requiring banks, a supermarket and numerous other traders to keep trading operations alive. Has acted for Haslemere in shopping centre repossession, and for WISCO in environmental judicial review against the Scottish Executive. Instrumental in the first business petition to the new Scottish Parliament suggesting new Scottish legislation on landlord and tenant Law.
Career: University of Glasgow (LLB 1980). Member of the Arbitration committee of the Law Society of Scotland. Worked for *Herbert Smith*, London (1984-85).
Personal: Born 1958.

ELDER, Hugh
Gordon Dadds, London (020) 7493 6151
hughelder@gordondadds.com
Specialisation: General commercial litigation.
Prof. Memberships: President London Solicitors Litigation Association 1998-00 (honorary treasurer 1996-98). Society for Computers and Law; Law Society.
Career: Qualified 1973. Articled clerk and assistant solicitor *Radcliffes & Co* 1971-76; assistant solicitor *Cameron Kemm Nordon* 1976-79; assistant solicitor *Gordon Dadds* 1980, partner and head of litigation 1981.
Personal: Education: Sherborne School and Edinburgh University (LLB 1970). Leisure interests: family, (married, two daughters), golf, music, arts. Resides London and Dorset.

ELLIOTT, Robert
Ward Hadaway, Newcastle upon Tyne (0191) 204 4319
bob.elliott@wardhadaway.com
Specialisation: Partner dealing with wide range of commercial litigation, primarily heavy/light engineering, IT/hi tech, and other manufacturing businesses. Particular interest in intellectual property, IT sector disputes, company/business sales disputes, faulty machinery/manufacturing processes, EU/international, defamation. CEDR accredited mediator.
Career: Attended RGS Newcastle, then Manchester University. Qualified 1983. Practised in London 1981-93; *Herbert Smith, Clifford Chance, Richards Butler* (partner). Returned to Newcastle 1994 joining *Ward Hadaway* as partner in 1996.
Personal: Lives in Wall (nr Hexham); married, two daughters; interests: hill walking, gardening and cooking.

EVANS, Hugh
DLA, Leeds (08700) 111111

FAGAN, Neil
Lovells, London (020) 7296 2000
neil.fagan@lovells.com
Specialisation: Senior partner of 'city litigation group' specialising in financial, corporate finance and commercial litigation, regulatory issues and commercial dispute resolution. He also heads the firm's public policy practice.
Prof. Memberships: Member of the City of London Solicitors' Company and former Chairman, Employment Law Sub-Committee City of London Solicitors' Company; member International Bar Association Commercial Litigation and Labour Law Committee.
Career: Articled *Lovells*; qualified 1971; partner 1975.

FALKNER, James
Mills & Reeve, Norwich (01603) 693230
james.falkner@mills-reeve.com
Specialisation: Agricultural, commercial and residential property and landlord and tenant disputes.
Prof. Memberships: Law Society; Property Litigation Association; Agricultural Law Association.
Career: Joined *Mills & Reeve*, 1980. Partner 1988.

FINKLER, Deborah
Slaughter and May, London (020) 7600 1200
deborah.finkler@slaughterandmay.com
Specialisation: Broad range of commercial litigation including advising Unilever Superannuation Fund in its negligence claim against Mercury Asset Management, as well as a wide range of financial regulatory matters for a number of global financial institutions.
Career: Partner 1991.

FORDHAM, John
Stephenson Harwood, London (020) 7809 2300
john.fordham@shlegal.com
Specialisation: Partner, head of litigation department. Extensive dispute resolution experience; High Court; international arbitrations; international investigations and asset-tracing; multijurisdictional disputes; commercial, banking, insolvency and fraud litigation; regulatory enquiries; alternative dispute resolution (advocate and mediator). Led team representing liquidators of the Maxwell pension trustee company – approximately £400 million recovered for pensioners. Lectures on banking and fraud matters.
Prof. Memberships: CEDR – Accredited Mediator.
Career: Qualified October 1974. Joined *Stephenson Harwood* in 1972 as a trainee and became partner in 1979. Became head of litigation in 1995.
Personal: Born 1948. Educated at Dulwich College; Gonville & Caius College, Cambridge, MA. Married with two children. Interests include theatre, cinema, art, tennis and cricket. Foreign languages French. Resides Cheam, Surrey.

FOX, Brendan
Cleaver Fulton Rankin, Belfast (028) 9027 1325
b.fox@cfrlaw.co.uk
See under Construction, p.202

FOX-EDWARDS, Jane
Lawrence Graham, London (020) 7759 6527
jane.fox-edwards@lawgram.com
Specialisation: Practice covers all areas of property litigation including shopping centre and portfolio management issues, dilapidations, rent reviews. Also deals with insolvency related property issues, residential property problems and restrictive covenant issues. Gives regular seminars and contributes to the 'Estates Gazette' and other property journals.
Prof. Memberships: Property Litigation Association.
Career: Qualified in 1988. Joined *Lawrence Graham* 1989 from *Boodle Hatfield* and became a partner in 1996. Now head of property litigation.

FRANCIS, Penelope
Lawrence Graham, London (020) 7379 0000
penny.francis@lawgram.com
Specialisation: From 1 May 1998, head of property department. Partner in property litigation team. Main area of practice is property litigation, covering rent reviews, insolvency, shopping centre and portfolio management, lease renewals and dilapidations. Lectures for RICS, ARBRIX, Henry Stewart, AdIdem, TBR and other conferences. Qualified as a PACT arbitrator and on the Law Society's panel of arbitrators.
Prof. Memberships: Law Society; Women in Property; Property Litigation Law Reform Group; RICS Dispute Resolution Panel; Centrepoint Board member.
Career: Qualified in 1984. Worked at *Beachcroft Stanleys* 1982-88. Joined *Lawrence Graham* in 1989, becoming a partner in 1991.
Personal: Born 9 November 1959. Attended University of Bristol 1978-81, then College of Law 1981-82. Leisure interests include ballet, eating and travel. Lives in London.

FRASER, David
Baker & McKenzie, London (020) 7919 1000
david.fraser@bakernet.com
Specialisation: Business disputes with experience in the areas of insurance and reinsurance, trade finance, sovereign immunity, professional liability, carriage by sea, telecommunications, corporate joint ventures, minority shareholders right and contentious insolvency. Has acted as counsel in and managed several major commercial arbitrations in England and elsewhere and has brought a number of cases to trial in the Commercial Court and the Court of Appeal in London. Has recently represented the owners of the Kazakhstan metals industry in complex arbitration proceedings against former joint venture partners. Led the team acting for Geest in the banana wars with Fyffes. Acts for a number of professional consultancy firms including Tillinghast and LEK. Acts in contentious issues for Camelot. Adviser on crisis management and senior management responsibilities. Member of City Disputes Panel Users Committee and LCIA.
Prof. Memberships: The Law Society and New York Bar.
Career: Qualified in 1973. Joined *Baker & McKenzie* in 1975, becoming a partner in 1982.
Publications: 'Arbitration of International Commercial Disputes Under English Law'– The American Review of International Arbitration 1997/vol.8. no.1.
Personal: Education: University of Birmingham. Lives in London. Born 1948.

FREYNE, Michele
Rowe & Maw, London (020) 7248 4282
Specialisation: Main area of practice is property litigation. Started first specialist team in 1980 which has grown into team which she heads of six including two partners. Also specialises in matrimonial law (about 15% of total workload).
Prof. Memberships: Property Litigation Association, Solicitors Family Law Association.
Career: Qualified in 1978. Joined *Rowe & Maw* in 1979, became partner in 1984. Group managing partner, commercial litigation 1993-94.

FRIEDMAN, Paul
Baker & McKenzie, London (020) 7919 1000
paul.friedman@bakernet.com
Specialisation: Litigation; arbitration and dispute resolution. Paul specialises in complex international commercial and financial dispute resolution. He has been involved for a number of years in acting for clients in the Formula One motor racing industry. Paul also acts for high profile companies in the media and digital media industry. He is a specialist in commercial fraud and trust disputes and was a key member of the Grupo Torras litigation team which

involved him working not only in London but also in Jersey, the Bahamas, the Cayman Islands, Spain and Switzerland. This litigation resulted in a number of important reported decisions. Other reported decisions include British Aerospace Plc v Dee Howard and Aleria SpA. Paul also acts for major financial institutions often in relation to disputes outside the United Kingdom.
Prof. Memberships: Association of Contentious Trust and Probate Specialists; British Israel Law Association Executive Committee; Confederation of British Industry Judicial Issues Group; ICC Fraud Advisory Panel E-Commerce Committee; Law Society of England & Wales.
Career: Paul graduated in law from the London School of Economics. He qualified in 1991 and spent one year with *Baker & McKenzie*, Sydney (1995) where amongst other things he assisted the Australian Law Reform Commission with a comparative study of European jurisdiction and choice of law rules. Paul became a partner at *Baker & McKenzie*, London in 1999.
Publications: Paul regularly contributes to external publications such as 'The Banker' (Let the Buyer Beware, May 2001 edition) 'Global Counsel' (European Jurisdiction in an E-Commerce World, March 2001 edition) and the 'British Bankers Association Newsletter' (Suspicion of Money Laundering and Human Rights, March 2001 edition). Paul also gives presentations to clients and at conferences in London and internationally in his specialist areas. These have included recent presentations for Euromoney, IBC and The Securities Institute as well as *Baker & McKenzie* client training conferences in London and elsewhere.
Personal: Paul was born in South Africa and moved to London in 1980. He is married and still resides in London.

GAINES, Keith
Lovells, London (020) 7296 2000
keith.gaines@lovells.com
Specialisation: Principal areas of work: contentious insolvency, commercial fraud, asset tracing. Wide experience with emphasis on cross border situations encompassing many jurisdictions from USA through Caribbean to Europe and Far East. Advised on several key legal developments in last 15 years; acted on several high profile cases, including liquidation of BCCI. Advises UK accountants, overseas lawyers, UK and overseas financial institutions. Experienced in dealings with Serious Fraud Office and other regulatory bodies. Worked for the administrators of British and Commonwealth, ING in the Barings collapse, the receivers of Rosehaugh, and for the court-appointed receivers.
Prof. Memberships: The Law Society, International Bar Association, Society of Practitioners of Insolvency, AEPPC. Committee O. Author of several articles and talks on insolvency.
Career: Qualified 1981; seconded to New York 1984-86; partner 1986, London; admitted Hong Kong solicitor 1986.

GARRETT, Susan
Addleshaw Booth & Co, Leeds (0113) 209 2000
Specialisation: Commercial litigation, human rights and professional negligence with particular expertise in tax, insurance and construction disputes.
Personal: Interests include skiing.

GARVIE, Carl
Pinsent Curtis Biddle, Birmingham
(0121) 200 1050
carl.garvie@pinsents.com
Specialisation: Partner specialises in corporate and commercial litigation including warranty claims, shareholder disputes, fiduciary duty claims and commercial contractual disputes. Considerable experience in injunctive relief applications, including acting as the court-appointed supervisor of search orders.
Prof. Memberships: Law Society.
Career: MA Trinity Hall, Cambridge. Articled at *Pinsent & Co* (now *Pinsent Curtis Biddle*). Qualified in 1986. Partner in 1991.
Personal: Soccer, music, gymnasium.

GATENBY, John
Addleshaw Booth & Co, Manchester
(0161) 934 6548
jkg@addleshaw-booth.co.uk
See under Alternative Dispute Resolution, p.80

GERRARD, Neil
DLA, London (08700) 111 111

GILBERT, Ralph
Rollits, Hull (01482) 323 239
ralph.gilbert@rollits.com
Specialisation: Full range of commercial disputes including contentious insolvency and commercial property work.
Career: Qualified at *Rollit Farrell & Bladon* (1990), Partner (1999).
Personal: Educated at University of Hull (1987). Married with 3 children. Interests include church and charity work.

GILL, Judith A E
Allen & Overy, London (020) 7330 3779
judith.gill@allenovery.com
See under Arbitration (International), p.87

GILL, Mark
Denton Wilde Sapte, London (020) 7242 1212

GODDARD, John
Freshfields Bruckhaus Deringer, London
(020) 7936 4000
john.goddard@freshfields.com
Specialisation: Partner in dispute resolution department, specialising in banking litigation (principally for the Bank of England) and commercial litigation, usually involving company law and shareholder disputes.
Career: Qualified 1980.
Personal: Born 1955. Educated at Magdalene College, Cambridge.

GOLD, Antony
Eversheds, Manchester (0161) 831 8000
antonygold@eversheds.com
Specialisation: Head of intellectual property team, *Eversheds* Leeds/Manchester and head of commercial department at *Eversheds* Manchester. Former Chairman of *Eversheds* national litigation group. Main current area of practice is intellectual property, particularly internet-related, as well as passing off, trade mark, patent and copyright litigation. Other previous experience includes acting in Brady v Brady (House of Lords, 1988), Barlow Clowes, BCCI, Lancashire and Yorkshire Assurance Society. Most recent reported case is Arrow Nominees v GR+MM Blackledge Plc (Court of Appeal July 2000). Has extensive media experience.
Prof. Memberships: Law Society. International Bar Association, International Arbitration Club, London Court of International Arbitration. Member INTA Special Committee on the Internet.
Career: Qualified in 1983, joined *Eversheds Alexander Tatham* in 1984 and became a partner in 1988. Chairman of *Eversheds'* National Litigation Group 1993-98.
Personal: Born 26th August 1958. Attended Birkenhead School 1969-76, then Manchester University 1976-79 and Chester College of Law 1979-80. Leisure interests include climbing and mountaineering. Lives in Adlington, Cheshire. Married, three children.

GOLD, David
Herbert Smith, London (020) 7374 8000
Specialisation: Partner in Litigation and Arbitration Division. Main area of practice is general commercial litigation, often with an international connection. Also handles company/partnership disputes, local authority law, computer law and injunctions. Led the legal team responsible for pursuing the former owner of Rumasa SA, a large private company expropriated in Spain in 1983, involving litigation in England, Jersey, Switzerland, Holland and the United States. Led the teams dealing with the Hammersmith loan swaps dispute and Le Gavroche health prosecution. Represented Tottenham Hotspur plc, Alan Sugar and others against Terry Venables and led the team representing Amstrad in its successful litigation against US disk drive manufacturer, Seagate. He represented a major Israeli company in its successful claim against insurers arising out of the expropriation of a timber concession in Liberia. He also represented one of the Defendants in the Atlantic Computer/B&C litigation which settled at the beginning of 1999 after a successful mediation. He represented Abbey National Treasury Services in litigation arising out of the Barings collapse. He led the team representing John Reid Enterprises in its claim against Michael Flatley which was settled during the trial. He conducted an independent enquiry for Britannia Building Society in relation to their mortgage to Peter Mandelson. He represented one of the defendants in major proceedings brought in Bermuda following the collapse of Bermuda Fire & Marine Insurance Company Limited.
Prof. Memberships: Law Society.
Career: Qualified in 1975. Joined *Herbert Smith* in 1973, becoming a Partner in 1983.
Personal: Born 1st March 1951. Attended LSE 1969-72. Leisure interests include theatre, bridge and family. Lives in Thorpe Bay, Essex and in Hampstead.

GOLDSPINK, Robert
Morgan, Lewis & Bockius, London
(020) 7710 5500

GOOD, Diana
Linklaters, London (020) 7456 4328
diana.good@linklaters.com
Specialisation: Litigation department. Part-time judicial appointment as Recorder. CEDR accredited mediator. Specialises in commercial litigation, and has extensive experience of advising clients, settling and fighting a wide range of commercial disputes involving banking and insurance, and financial services work. Also specialises in EC law disputes including competition law (both EU and UK); and tax litigation.

Career: 1988 to date: Partner, *Linklaters* London; 1989-92 Partner, *Linklaters* Brussels; 1982-88: Assistant solicitor, *Linklaters.* 1981: Aix-en-Provence International Law DESU; 1978: Oxford University BA Jurisprudence.

GOSLING, John
Addleshaw Booth & Co, Manchester (0161) 934 6000 jag@addleshaw-booth.co.uk
Specialisation: Head of Litigation and Dispute Resolution Group. Heavyweight corporate and commercial disputes. Also professional negligence work, particularly financial services industry claims, valuers, surveyors and barristers, predominantly on behalf of insurers.
Prof. Memberships: Law Society, Manchester Law Society.
Career: Qualified in 1984; partner since 1990. Appointed Head of Group in May 1998.
Personal: Educated at Durham University 1978-81. Leisure pursuits include sport and family.

GRANDISON, Richard
Slaughter and May, London (020) 7600 1200 richard.grandison@slaughterandmay.com
Specialisation: Head of commercial litigation and arbitration department. Extensive experience in commercial litigation, arbitration and commercial judicial review for a wide range of corporate clients in commercial disputes in England and overseas.
Prof. Memberships: The Law Society and City of London Solicitors' Society.
Career: Qualified in 1978 with *Slaughter and May.* Partner since 1987. Educated at Fettes College, Edinburgh and Pembroke College, Cambridge.

GRAY, David
DLA, Manchester (08700) 111111

GRAY, Nick
Slaughter and May, London (020) 7600 1200 nick.gray@slaughterandmay.com
Specialisation: Partner specialising in a wide range of commercial disputes in the English Courts, in arbitration proceedings in England and abroad and in judicial review proceedings. Regularly involved in overseeing litigation and co-ordinating local advice in other jurisdictions.
Career: Qualified 1988. Joined *Slaughter and May* in 1988. Partner since 1996.
Personal: Born 1964; resides London. Educated at Daniel Stewert's and Melville College, Edinburgh and at Sidney Sussex College, Cambridge. Leisure interests include music, sport, theatre and Italy.

GREENO, Ted
Herbert Smith, London (020) 7374 8000
Specialisation: Partner in litigation and arbitration division. Wide range of experience in both litigation and arbitration work spanning a number of commercial, industrial and professional sectors including the oil and gas industry, engineering and construction, media, product liability and accountancy.
Career: Qualified 1983. Partner at *Herbert Smith* since 1989.
Personal: Educated at King's College, London.

GRIERSON, Christopher
Lovells, London (020) 7296 2000 christopher.grierson@lovells.com
Specialisation: International and domestic litigation with particular emphasis on insolvency, fraud and asset recovery matters, and insurance and reinsurance. Has acted in a number of prominent cases, including Laker Airways, Mentor Insurance, BCCI, Barings and EMLICO. Has acted for Prince Jefri of Brunei in the KPMG "Chinese Walls" litigation and in defence of the proceedings brought by the Government of Brunei. Is now also acting for the liquidators of BCCI in their claim against the Bank of England. Licensed insolvency practitioner.
Prof. Memberships: International Bar Association, American Bar Association, American Bankruptcy Institute, European Association of Insolvency Practitioners, London Solicitors Litigation Association, The Law Society (England), City of London Solicitors' Company.
Career: 1976-80 Assistant Solicitor in *Durrant Piesse*; 1980 Partner *Lovells*; 1991-94 partner in New York office and 1992-94 managing partner of that office.

GWYNNE, Richard
Stephenson Harwood, London (020) 7809 2321 richard.gwynne@shlegal.com
Specialisation: Partner, litigation department. Wide experience of all types of commercial litigation, international arbitration and ADR. Specialises in particular in banking litigation and jurisdiction issues. Major cases include: multi-party litigation against investment banks and professional advisers arising out of the acquisition of a substantial computer leasing company involving claims of over £500m; successfully defending a shareholders dispute in connection with a satellite broadcasting company; several reported cases involving letters of credit and performance guarantees.
Career: Qualified 1979. Became a partner in November 1986.
Publications: Author of the chapter on enforcement of foreign judgments in England and Wales in 'International Execution against Judgment Debtors'. (Oceana 1999).
Personal: Educated at Trinity College, Cambridge.

HAGGETT, Paul
Burges Salmon, Bristol (0117) 939 2262 paul.haggett@burges-salmon.com
Specialisation: Head of litigation department. Responsibility for firm's contentious banking and insolvency litigation practice. Lead partner of Nationwide Managed Litigation project and team leader for *Burges Salmon's* involvement in Paragon Managed Litigation Project.
Career: Trained at *Freshfields.* Qualified in 1985. Manager (*Freshfields* litigation department) 1985-89. Assistant/associate *Burges Salmon* – 1989-92. Partner *Burges Salmon* – 1992-date. Head of commercial litigation unit – 1997 to 2000. Head of litigation department 2000-date.
Personal: Born 1960, resides Bristol. Interests – golf, vegetable gardening, reading, family.

HAM, Brian E.
Mills Selig, Belfast (028) 9024 3878 brian.ham@nilaw.com
Specialisation: Property based litigation. Acts for a number of major local property developers. Other major area of practice is commercial property work (primarily site aquisition and development) and construction law.
Prof. Memberships: Law Society of Northern Ireland, The Environmental & Planning Law Association for Northern Ireland.
Career: Qualified 1969. Joined *Mills Selig* 1971. Became partner 1984. Senior partner in 2000.
Personal: Sailing, gardening and architecture.

HAM, Neil
Burges Salmon, Bristol (0117) 902 2747 neil.ham@burges-salmon.com
Specialisation: Commercial property disputes including rent and service charge disputes; contested rent reviews and arbitrations; disrepair claims; contested lease renewals; professional negligence claims; risk assessment for major landowners and developers; non-litigious dispute resolution.
Prof. Memberships: Law Society and Property Litigation Association.
Career: Qualified in 1987 and continued with *Simmons & Simmons*, joined *Burges Salmon* in 1991 and became a partner in 1996.

HARRIS, Andrew
DLA, Manchester (08700) 111111

HART, Andrew
Freshfields Bruckhaus Deringer, London (020) 7936 4000 andrew.hart@freshfields.com
Specialisation: Partner specialising in banking, professional negligence and fraud related litigation and regulatory matters. Particular experience in multi-jurisdictional disputes.
Career: Articled *Freshfields.* Qualified 1988.
Personal: Born 1962. Educated at Keble College, Oxford.

HARVEY, Guy
Dickinson Dees, Newcastle upon Tyne 0191 279 9237 law@dickinson-dees.com
Specialisation: Head of commercial disputes group. Practice covers a full range of litigation problems including fraud, disaster recovery and disputes management. Recent matters include Ladbroke Grove Rail Inquiry, successfully representing Northern Racing Ltd (A11ER(0)42(2000), TLR16/2/2000:8/2/2001, BLD 2212003109) in the Companies Court and Court of Appeal, handling other inquiries, including SFO.
Prof. Memberships: Member of ILA, trained mediator.
Career: Qualified 1976; *Simpson Curtis* (now *Pinsent Curtis Biddle*) 1974-7; partner 1978-96; *Dickinson Dees* partner 1997-.
Personal: Born 1951, educated at Stowe School and Trinity College, Cambridge. Interests include the arts, shooting, France. Married with two children. Lives near Darlington.

HAYES, Philippa
Hammond Suddards Edge, Manchester (0161) 830 5264 philippa.hayes@hammondse.com
Specialisation: Partner, commercial dispute resolution unit. Specialises in the resolution of commercial disputes, including contractual disputes, IT claims, shareholder disputes, partnership disputes, warranty claims, international disputes and cross-border litigation, civil fraud, injuctive relief, defamation, breach of confidence and banking litigation. Acted for Esther Rantzen in her claim for defamation against Mirror Group Newspapers – jury trial in 1991 and in the Court of Appeal in 1993. Acted for Lancaster City Council in its claim against Noel Edmonds' company, Unique Group, arising out of the failed 'World of

Crinkley Bottom' in Morecambe, leading to a reported case on strike out. Recently acted for a major bank in successfully defending a claim for defamation and breach of contract which also involved a complaint to the Banking Ombudsman. Other active clients include Luxfer Group, Air 2000, SGL Carbon and TIP Europe.
Prof. Memberships: CEDR Accredited Mediator; Manchester Law Society council member; Law Society.
Career: Articled *Herbert Smith*, qualified 1987; assistant solicitor, *Herbert Smith* to 1993; associate, *Addleshaw Sons & Latham*, 1993-96; partner *Addleshaw Booth & Co* 1996-98; partner *Hammond Suddards Edge* 1998.
Personal: Educated at Nottingham and Cambridge Universities. Lives in Bowdon, Cheshire. Leisure interests include sport, fitness, theatre and cinema.

HAYWOOD, Brent
Burness, Edinburgh (0131) 473 6135
bwh@burness.co.uk
Specialisation: Brent is a partner in the dispute resolution department, handling general commercial litigation and specialising in contractual disputes, insolvency, e-commerce, intellectual property and media law. Particular experience in cross border disputes and interim protective measures.
Career: Qualified in New Zealand (1989), England and Wales (1993), Scotland (1993). Joined *Burness* in 1994; Became partner in 1999.
Personal: Born 1965. Attended Otago University, New Zealand, and Glasgow University. Interests include long distance running and cycling, family and supporting local church.

HEAPS, John
Eversheds, Leeds (0113) 243 0391
johnheaps@eversheds.com
Specialisation: Partner. National head of litigation and dispute management. Main area of practice is the management and negotiation of business disputes. Particular expertise in the fields of cross border disputes, information technology, business risks and product liability.
Prof. Memberships: Senior Vice-Chairman to Committee 12 (Civil Litigation SLP) International Bar Association. Fellow of The Chartered Institute of Arbitrators.
Career: Qualified 1978 *Hepworth & Chadwick*, Leeds. *Freshfields* 1978-84. Joined *Eversheds*, Leeds 1984, partner 1985.
Personal: Born 8th July 1953. Ratcliffe College then Liverpool University 1972-75. Lives near Harrogate, North Yorkshire.

HEARN, Andrew
Dechert, London (020) 7583 5353
andrew.hearn@dechertEU.com
Specialisation: Litigation partner, Andrew specialises in the resolution of commercial disputes and also in the areas of intellectual property and libel (in which areas his broad client base is well represented in the publishing and retail sectors). His work is both national and international in nature and extends to international arbitrations and mediations. Examples of its range in the past year have been a substantial commercial court trial and its connected litigation in several other jurisdictions involving claims of over $1 billion by the state of Nigeria; working with the New York office on the successful enforcement proceedings to recover a multi-million dollar judgment from the State of Peru; acting for members of the British Retail Consortium in their pioneering and successful test case which has now established the registrability of retail service marks in the UK; acting in High Court proceedings, an ICC Arbitration and related foreign proceedings all concerning the entitlement of various parties to the assets of a substantial Liechtenstein entity; successfully invoking the new summary disposal provisions of the Defamation Act 1996 on behalf of a publisher client faced with a claim by a bankrupt claimant; acting on various warranty and post completion disputes and achieving their resolution on good terms, in one case after a two day mediation.
Prof. Memberships: Fellow of the Chartered Institute of Arbitrators; CEDR Accredited Mediator and on W.I.P.O. List of Mediators; former member of the City of London Law Society's Litigation Sub-Committee.
Career: Andrew graduated in law in 1979 from St John's College, Oxford. He was articled to Titmuss Sainer & Webb (now Dechert), qualified in 1982 and became a partner in 1986.
Personal: Born 1957. Married with three sons. Skiing, tennis, the arts, member of Old Gowers Club and Campden Hill Tennis Club.

HENDERSON, Guy
Allen & Overy, London (020) 7330 3000
guy.henderson@allenovery.com
Specialisation: General commercial litigation. He is a CEDR accredited mediator.
Prof. Memberships: Member of the Law Society of Hong Kong; Associate of the Chartered Institute of Arbitrators. Member of the Compliance Committee of the Law Society of Hong Kong 1995-97: Member of the Securities and Futures Appeals Panel of Hong Kong 1994-97; Member of the Editorial Board of Longman's Legal Practice Manuals in Hong Kong 1995-97; Appointed a lay member of the Insider Dealing tribunal of Hong Kong, 1995.
Career: Qualified in 1982, partner *Allen & Overy* 1990. Head of Litigation and Dispute Resolution, *Allen & Overy*, Hong Kong 1993-97. Head of Corporate and Commercial Litigation Group, *Allen & Overy*, London since 1998.
Personal: Born 1958. Educated at Cambridge University (MA).

HERBERT, Alan
Pinsent Curtis Biddle, Leeds (0113) 244 5000
alan.herbert@pinsents.com
Specialisation: All aspects of property dispute resolution and litigation including landlord and tenant, development disputes, dilapidations, portfolio management, rent reviews, rating, possession, vendor/purchaser disputes, enforcement and protection of security, enforcement of restrictive covenants. Arbitration, litigation, mediation and lands tribunal work.
Prof. Memberships: Property Litigation Association.
Career: Articled with *Ashurst Morris Crisp*. Qualified 1989. Joined *Pinsent Curtis Biddle* 1993. Partner and Head of Property Litigation team 1996.
Personal: Walking, fly fishing.

HEWSON, Carol
Simmons & Simmons, London (020) 7628 2020
carol.hewson@simmons-simmons.com
Specialisation: Partner in litigation department. Main area of practice is commercial litigation, with particular experience in all aspects of commercial property and landlord and tenant litigation. Has extensive experience in rent review disputes, including arbitration, service charge disputes, forfeiture claims and litigation under the Landlord and Tenant Act 1954. Experienced in all aspects of property insolvency. Addressed seminars for Central Law Training on commercial property and also for Euroforum on commercial lease insolvency.
Prof. Memberships: Law Society; City of London Solicitors Company; member of Property Litigation Association; member of Women in Property Litigation.
Career: Kings College, London 1974-77; qualified in April 1980; partner in 1986.
Personal: Deputy chairman of Broomleigh Housing Association and chairman of its Audit Committee.

HIGGS, Rachel
Mills & Reeve, Norwich 01603 693 233
rachel.higgs@mills-reeve.com
Specialisation: Commercial litigator, specialising in contract disputes, warranty claims, boardroom disputes, professional negligence and infringements of intellectual property rights. Particular expertise in disputes relating to restrictive covenants and confidential information. Experienced mediator and exponent of alternative dispute resolution. Willing to take cases on a conditional fee basis.
Prof. Memberships: ADR Group (Eastern Region); Mediators in East Anglia; Norwich Businesswomen's Network.
Career: LLB Nottingham University; qualified 1984; partner 1990; LLM in Advanced Litigation, Nottingham Law School 1997; head of commercial dispute resolution team, Norwich.
Personal: Born 1960; resides Norwich. Leisure interests include family, cooking, reading, theatre and film.

HIGHAM, David
Blake Lapthorn, Fareham
(01489) 579 990

HIGHMORE, Robert
Charles Russell, London (020) 7203 5000
roberth@cr-law.co.uk
Specialisation: Litigation partner and head of property litigation and dispute resolution team. Principal area of practice covers full range of property and landlord and tenant litigation and dispute resolution including commercial and residential property and professional negligence actions. Acts for both landlords and tenants including major institutions, pension funds, banks and life assurance companies.
Prof. Memberships: Chairman 1998-99 and founder committee member of Property Litigation Association; active member of British Property Federation; Law Society; City of Westminster Law Society.
Career: Qualified 1982, at *Radcliffes & Co* since 1980. Became a partner in 1987. Partner *Charles Russell* 2001.
Personal: Born 9th February 1957. Educated at Cambridge and County High School (1968-71), Beverley Grammar School, East Yorkshire (1971-75), Trinity Hall, Cambridge (1976-79). Leisure pursuits include squash and Ceroc. Lives in Bromley, Kent.

HINDLE, Andrew
Boodle Hatfield, London (020) 7318 8131
ahindle@boodlehatfield.com
Specialisation: Main areas of practice include property and commercial litigation for both domestic and foreign clients, covering issues relating to business tenancies; residential tendencies, including the Rent Acts and the Housing Act; rent and debt recovery; breaches of covenant; forfeiture and possession; corporate, contractual and employment disputes. In addition, a broad range of general litigation, including insolvency matters and construction disputes, and significant experience in acting for clients in the agrochemical industry.
Prof. Memberships: Lord Chancellor's department: civil procedures for Housing and Land Actions Working Group; editorial board, 'Landlord and Tenant Review' (Sweet & Maxwell); Property Litigation Association.
Career: Qualified 1979. Appointed an associate of *Boodle Hatfield* in 1996.
Publications: Articles in 'New Law Journal', 'Estates Gazette' and 'Landlord and Tenant Review'.
Personal: Born 11 July 1955. Educated at Marlborough and Trinity College, Oxford. Lives in London. Married with two children. Leisure interests include travel, food and wine, theatre and music.

HOATH, Helen
Gorna & Co, Manchester 0161 832 3651
hmh@gorna.co.uk
Specialisation: Property litigation; break clauses; dilapidations; rent reviews; contested business tenancy renewals; specific performance; restrictive covenants; easement disputes; 'rights to light' Allied London Industrial Properties Ltd v Castleguard Properties Inc 1997 EGCS 18; Jolley v Carmel Limited 2000 2EGLR 153; 2000 3 EGLR 68.
Prof. Memberships: Law Society; Association Women Solicitors; Property Litigation Association; Women in Property; MCIA.
Career: Easingwold School; Worcester College Oxford; Articled *Kramer & Co.* London; *McKenna & Co.*

HODGES, Paula
Herbert Smith, London (020) 7374 8000
paula.hodges@herbertsmith.com
Specialisation: Experience in a wide range of commercial litigation and international arbitration with particular expertise in energy, IT and telecommunications disputes. Leading cases include acting for Amoco, British Gas, Amerada Hess, Agip, Fina and Phillips Petroleum in the renowned dispute with Enron regarding the CATS gas pipeline in the Central North Sea (including a successful appeal to the House of Lords) (1995-01); acting for Amerada Hess in an energy dispute with the Bluewater Group (including success before the Court of Appeal); acting for IBM in a highly publicised dispute regarding the provision of an Automatic Fingerprint Recognition System to a consortium of UK police forces (1995-98); acting for MMK UK Limited in a multi-million pound dispute with BT regarding network services provided for the purpose of an on-line lottery system (1999-00).
Prof. Memberships: Member of the United Kingdom Energy Lawyers Group; member of Institute of Petroleum.
Career: Qualified 1989; partner 1996.
Publications: Contributor to PLC 'Legal Risk Management Manual' (2000).
Personal: Read law at Cambridge University. Undertakes legal pro bono work in the UK and overseas.

HOGAN, Ronald
Dewar Hogan, London (020) 7822 7400
ronhogan@dewarhogan.co.uk
Specialisation: All types of contentious property matters and related litigation in connection with commercial and residential property. Instructed in relation to property management disputes (including dilapidations, arrears, forfeiture, and rent reviews); professional negligence cases involving solicitors and valuers; enforcement of securities and other insolvency related work; leasehold enfranchisement and estate management schemes. Instructed in a number of reported cases, author of articles in the property press and speaker at conferences on property issues. Chairman of the Property Litigation Association 1995-96.
Career: Formed the niche property litigation practice of *Dewar Hogan* in 1991. Formerly at *Nabarro Nathanson.*

HOLLIGAN, William
Brodies WS, Edinburgh (0131) 228 3777
william.holligan@brodies.co.uk
See under Administrative & Public Law, p.59

HOPKINS, Paul
Edwards Geldard, Cardiff (029) 2023 8239
paul.hopkins@geldards.co.uk
Specialisation: Head of commercial dispute resolution at *Edwards Geldard* and also the firm's international services partner. He specialises in large scale High Court commercial litigation and commercial dispute resolution including negotiation, arbitration and ADR.
Prof. Memberships: Member of the Law Society; associate member of the American Bar Association; member of the International Bar Association; officer and council member of the Cardiff and District Law Society, responsible for training; coopted to the Council for the Confederation of South Wales Law Societies. Also sits on the Chancery Court Users Committee for the Wales and Chester circuit. Committee member of the South Wales Exporters Association; secretary of Wales Commercial Law Association.
Career: Educated at University College, Oxford. Trained at *Slaughter & May.* Joined *Edwards Geldard* in 1988 from *Slaughter & May's* litigation department. Made a partner in 1992.
Personal: Interests include: history, rugby and music.

HOUSE, Tim
Allen & Overy, London (020) 7330 3000
tim.house@allenovery.com
Specialisation: Tim House has been a partner since 1992 and is Head of the Banking and Finance Litigation Group in London. He specialises in commercial dispute resolution and has wide experience of acting for financial institutions and quoted companies in complex litigation and regulatory disputes. He currently acts for leading US/European banks and other financial institutions in all areas of contentious business, risk management and reputational risk including regulatory. He also has particular experience in derivatives disputes. Admitted as a solicitor in England (1986) and in Hong Kong (1988). Assitant solicitor, *Allen & Overy*, London (1985-92). Partner since 1992.

HOWARD, Paul
Wragge & Co, Birmingham
(0870) 903 1000

HUMPHRIES, Mark
Linklaters, London (020) 7456 4250
mark.humphries@linklaters.com
Specialisation: Main area of practice is commercial litigation. Is an experienced solicitor-advocate and practises in the High Court and many other courts and tribunals. Has experience of handling a wide range of commercial disputes but with an emphasis on industrial and insurance cases.
Prof. Memberships: 1999-00: The Law Society Higher Rights Task Force; 1999: Life Fellow of the Royal Society for the Encouragement of Arts, Manufactures and Commerce (FRSA); 1997-00: The Law Society Insurance Law Committee; 1997: The Law Society Training Committee, Advocacy Training Sub-Committee; 1996-97: The Law Society Civil Litigation Committee. Multi-track Working Group; 1995-96: Woolf Inquiry: Commercial Court Working Group; 1994: Solicitor's Association of Higher Court Advocates (Vice Chairman, 1997-99; Chairman, 1999-00).
Career: Head of structured finance group: 1993 to date. Partner, *Linklaters*; 1994 to date: Solicitor-advocate (Higher Courts, Civil); 1986-93: Assistant solicitor, *Linklaters*; 1988: Secondment to *Morgan, Lewis & Bockius*, Washington DC; 1984-86: Articled clerk, *Winters*, Huntingdon. 1987: MA Cantab; 1983: BA (Hons) Cantab; 1983-84: The College of Law, Guildford; 1980-83: St Catharine's College, Cambridge; 1973-80: King Edward's School, Bath.

HUNTER, Jason
Russell-Cooke, London (020) 7405 6566
hunterj@russell-cooke.co.uk
Specialisation: All aspects of both commercial and residential property disputes.
Prof. Memberships: Property Litigation Association and its Law Reform committee. Mediator (ADR Net).
Career: Qualified at Russell-Cooke in 1992. Partner in 1997.

HUNTER, Robert
Allen & Overy, London (020) 7330 3000
robert.hunter@allenovery.com
Specialisation: Robert Hunter, widely known as one of the leading fraud specialists in the country, became a partner in 1991 and is head of the Trust, Asset Tracing and Fraud Group. He has extensive experience in trust litigation, asset tracing and civil fraud cases ranging from claims involving bribery and secret commissions to commodities fraud and advance fee frauds. He has acted in proceedings in all major offshore centres. He is Secretary of the Association of Contentious Trust and Probate Specialists and writes and lectures internationally on fraud and trust litigation. He is a CEDR accredited mediator.
Career: Admitted as a solicitor 1984; assistant solicitor, *Allen & Overy* 1984-90; partner since 1991.

HUNTLEY, Graham
Lovells, London (020) 7296 2000
graham.huntley@lovells.com
Specialisation: Main areas of practice include corporate and finance litigation, M & A disputes, contentious regulatory and financial services matters, regulatory and corporate investigations and professional negligence. Manager of *Lovells'* City and corporate litigation group.

Prof. Memberships: Assistant Secretary of London Solicitors Litigation Association. Director of RCJ Advice Bureau.
Career: Solicitor since 1986.
Personal: Durham University (BA Hons).

HUTCHINSON, Lucy
Herbert Smith, London (020) 7374 8000
Specialisation: Head of property litigation: partner in litigation and arbitration division. Deals with specialised property litigation involving major property and landlord and tenant disputes relating to commercial, retail, industrial and residential property. Does rent review work, including acting as legal assessor to Arbitrators. Acts for a number of institutional investors including Hermes and Standard Life. Also does regulatory work and general commercial litigation.
Career: Qualified in 1982. Became a partner at *Herbert Smith* in 1989.
Personal: Educated at Southampton University.

JAMDAR, Smita
Martineau Johnson, Birmingham (0121) 678 1332
smita.jamdar@martjohn.com
Specialisation: Commercial and statutory disputes for corporate and institutional clients including High Court, arbitration, judicial review and regulatory disputes. Particular interests include breach of warranty/misrepresentation claims and educational litigation.
Prof. Memberships: Law Society Birmingham, Law Society.
Career: Qualified 1996. Associate 1999.
Publications: Author of articles for Court Brief and Education Brief. Addressed seminars on ADR, the Civil Procedure Rules and Health & Safety.
Personal: Born 1970. Educated at Bolton School Girls' Division and Trinity College, Oxford. Interests include Liverpool FC, the cinema and modern literature.

JEFFERIES, Michael
Hugh James Ford Simey, Cardiff (029) 2022 4871
michael.jefferies@hjfs.co.uk
Specialisation: Partner in construction and civil engineering department. Has specialised in construction law for over 20 years, engaged in major litigation and arbitration for all sectors of the industry, as well as advising on non-contentious matters. Particular emphasis on professional indemnity matters, acting on behalf of a variety of professionals including architects, engineers, surveyors and their insurers (including contractor's design liability insurers). Important cases handled include Mid Glamorgan C.C. v Devonald Williams; H.H.C v W.H.T.S.O and Mid Glamorgan C.C. v Land Authority for Wales. Member of Salford University Working Party on Intelligent Authoring of Building Contracts. Lead partner for the Welsh Rugby Union redevelopment of the National Stadium.
Prof. Memberships: Institute of Arbitrators.
Career: Joined *Hugh James* in 1970. Qualified and became a partner in 1972.
Personal: Born 21st November 1947. Educated at University College, London. Lives in Cardiff.

JENNINGS, Steven
DLA, Manchester (08700) 111111

JONES, Michael
Hugh James Ford Simey, Cardiff (029) 2022 4871
Specialisation: Partner in commercial litigation department. Handles a wide variety of commercial litigation work including intellectual property. Acts for numerous clients including advertising agencies, building companies and manufacturers. Also handles construction arbitration and litigation matters acting for housing associations and architects amongst others. Cases handled include R v South Glamorgan County Council ex parte Evans concerning parents' choice in education. High Court Advocate. Lecturer on civil advocacy courses at Cardiff Law Society.
Prof. Memberships: Chartered Institute of Arbitrators, past President of Cardiff Law Society, Law Society Welsh Spokesman for over 30 years.
Career: Joined *Hugh James* in 1963. Qualified in 1966 and become a partner the same year. Senior partner in 1970.
Personal: Born 14 January 1943. Educated at Neath Boys' Grammar School 1953-60 and Jesus College, Oxford 1960-63. School Governor. Past chairman and current secretary of Parents for Welsh Education. Leisure pursuits include gardening and music. Lives in Peterston-S-Ely, Cardiff.

JONES, Peter Watkin
Eversheds, Cardiff (029) 2047 1147
peterjones@eversheds.com
Specialisation: Commercial litigation, particularly construction and engineering and property related litigation. Has considerable experience in major construction disputes and professional negligence in relation to earthworks design and claims for loss and expense. Also advises on matters of defamation. Is joint lead partner for the provision of legal services to the National Assembly for Wales. Peter is the national head of the Inquiries and Investigations Unit which is now in its third year of working for Lord Saville's Bloody Sunday Inquiry. The Unit also commenced work this year in acting for the Inquiry into the deaths and issues raised by the activities of Harold Shipman. Has practised as a mediator and is an accredited mediator with CEDR and the ADR Group.
Prof. Memberships: Fellow Chartered Institute of Arbitrators; member of the Law Society.
Career: Articled with *Phillips & Buck*, now *Eversheds*. Partner 1986.
Personal: Educated University of Wales; University of Aix-en-Provence; has a university doctorate in Comparative Law. Fluent French and Welsh speaker. Is a semi-professional musician.

JONES, Siân
Morgan Cole, Cardiff (029) 2038 5510
sian.jones@morgan-cole.com
Specialisation: Contentious property specialising in landlord and tenant law, agricultural tenancy disputes and land compensation claims.
Prof. Memberships: Property Litigation Association.
Career: Joined *Morgan Cole (Bruce)* in 1989 as an articled clerk. Qualified in 1991 and has worked as a property litigation solicitor.

KAMSTRA, Simon
Addleshaw Booth & Co, Leeds (0113) 209 2000
spk@addleshaw-booth.co.uk
Specialisation: Partner in Commercial Litigation. Specialising in company and shareholder disputes; sports law; mergers and acquisition related claims; trusts and trustee law; misfeasance and directors duties issues; professional negligence.
Prof. Memberships: IBA. Leeds Law Society.
Career: Educated at University of Manchester (LLB). Partner 1996.
Personal: Interests include music, cricket and photography.

KELLY, Jonathan
Simmons & Simmons, London (020) 7628 2020
jonathan.kelly@simmons-simmons.com
Specialisation: Partner in financial markets department and head of the finance litigation group. Main areas of practice are banking and financial services litigation, specialising in asset management, securities, commodities and derivatives disputes, and regulatory issues arising in these areas. Experienced in corporate disputes and large scale commercial fraud actions. Clients include UK, US and European commercial and investment banks, investment institutions, brokers and commodity houses.
Prof. Memberships: Law Society, Society of English and American Lawyers.
Career: Qualified in 1989 after articled at *Simmons & Simmons*. Became a partner in 1995.
Personal: Born 11th August 1964. Educated at Stonyhurst College 1972-82, Balliol College, Oxford 1983-86.

KENT, Paul
Pinsent Curtis Biddle, Birmingham (0121) 200 1050
paul.kent@pinsents.com
Specialisation: Partner in property litigation. All aspects of property dispute resolution including the tactical value of disputes in corporate transactions in development work and site acquisition. Rent review, Lands tribunal work, dilapidations claims, rates disputes and all contentious landlord and tenant matters. Reported cases: Banks v Kokkinos
Prof. Memberships: Property Litigation Association.
Career: 15 years in wholesale food distribution prior to qualification as solicitor. Several years of commercial litigation and for seven years specialising in property litigation. Joined *Pinsent Curtis Biddle* 1993. Partner 1998.
Personal: Sailing, large-scale landscape gardening, English furniture and ceramics.

KERSHAW, Anne
Kershaw Abbott, Manchester (0161) 839 0998
mail@kershaw-abbott.co.uk
Specialisation: Practises in the field of commercial dispute resolution with particular emphasis on professional partnership disputes, professional liability and commercial and construction disputes.
Prof. Memberships: Member of Association of Partnership Practitioners; Secretary Manchester Professional Forum; Past President Manchester Law Society; Member of Society of Construction Lawyers; CEDR; Accredited Mediator.
Career: Admitted 1975. Practised in North West all working life. Co-founder of *Kershaw Abbott* as niche practice in 1991. Appointed Tax Commissioner in 1995.
Personal: Lives in Ribble Valley with judicial husband and son. Music lover and devoted gardener.

KHAN, Charles
Berg & Co, Manchester (0161) 833 9211
charlesk@berg.co.uk
Specialisation: Charles Khan is a partner in the commercial litigation department. He specialises in

commercial litigation, including contract disputes (special expertise in disputes in the textile and clothing sector), concerning quality, title, non-payment; professional negligence; landlord and tenant; advising office holders, companies and individuals on insolvency related matters.
Prof. Memberships: Law Society; Manchester Law Society.
Career: Qualified in 1980. Joined *Berg & Co* in 1982 and became partner in 1984. Appointed Deputy District Judge in the Northern Circuit in 1994.
Personal: Born 21 June 1956. Educated Stand Grammar School and Hull University. Enjoys cycling, football, cricket, cinema. Lives in Prestwich, Greater Manchester.

KING, Ronnie
Ashurst Morris Crisp, London (020) 7638 1111
ronnie.king@ashursts.com
Specialisation: Commercial litigation and arbitration, both domestic and international with particular experience in oil and gas, power, engineering and projects. Also acts on general contract claims including warranty claims and disputed completion accounts.
Career: Articled *Ashurst Morris Crisp* 1984-86. Assistant solicitor 1986-94. Partner 1994.
Personal: Educated at the Belfast Royal Academy and St Catharine's College, Cambridge (Simmons scholar); MA, LLM.

KING, Vivien
D J Freeman, London (020) 7583 4055
vmk@djfreeman.co.uk
Specialisation: Caseload includes all aspects of contentious property matters including real property, mortgage and leasehold concerns. Venues for dispute include the courts, arbitration and mediation. Particular legal interests include trespass, dilapidations and rent reviews. PACT arbitrator and member of Arbrix. Fellow, Institute of Continuing Professional Development.
Prof. Memberships: Lectures extensively. Member, Property Litigation Association and its Law Reform Committee. Member of organising committee for RICS Oxford Study Weekend and RICS working parties for both dilapidation and disability discrimination.
Career: BA in Law. Qualified solicitor 1987. Partner at *Turner Kenneth & Brown* 1989 – 1993; partner *Bower Cotton & Bower* 1993-94; partner at *SJ Berwin & Co* 1995-99; joined partnership *D J Freeman* 1999.
Publications: Frequent contributor to the property press. Contributed to publications 'Commercial Property Dispute', 'Nuisances' and 'Freemans's Guide to the Property Industry'.
Personal: Old houses, antique glass, cooking and wine. Born 1950. Lives London and South of France.

KISSACK, Nigel
Pinsent Curtis Biddle, Leeds (0113) 244 5000
nigel.kissack@pinsents.com
Specialisation: National head of litigation and managing partner in Leeds. Commercial litigation: recent cases include product liability – acted as co-counsel for European defendant in claim in US Courts for $7 million; defamation – settled claimants case in mediation for £60K + costs; contract – acted for exclusive supplier for national retailer whose contract was terminated without notice. Settled for £4 million + costs.
Career: Partner *Alsop Wilkinson* 1980-96. Partner *Dibb Lupton Alsop* 1996-97. National head of litigation *Pinsent Curtis Biddle* 1997-date.
Personal: King William's College, Isle of Man. Sheffield University LLB (Hons). Married with two children. Reading, travel, arts and motorcycling.

LAX, Peter
Bell Lax Litigation, Birmingham (0121) 355 0011
PeterLax@commercialdispute.com
Specialisation: Partner in specialist commercial and insurance litigation firm. Main areas of practice are commercial litigation and defamation. Handles construction and engineering litigation, professional negligence and employment matters. Pioneer of no-win no-fee agreements for commercial litigation and professional negligence claims. Reported cases include the North West Holdings (advertising public interest petitions) and Fishel and University of Nottingham (employee's entitlement to undertake paid outside work). Has addresses Society of Practitioners in insolvency, Midlands Association of Insolvency Lawyers, Midlands Guild of Newspaper Editors.
Career: Qualified in 1982. Worked with *Duggan Lea & Co* 1980-85, then *Pinsent & Co* 1985-93, from 1988 as a partner. Joint founder with Heather Bell of specialist litigation practice *Bell Lax Litigation.*
Personal: Born 27 March 1958. Attended Barnard Castle School 1969-75, then Durham University 1976-79. Leisure interests include drinking real ale (occasionally) and sipping wine (repeatedly!). Lives in Lichfield.

LEONARD, Paul
Freshfields Bruckhaus Deringer, London (020) 7936 4000
paul.leonard@freshfields.com
Specialisation: Partner in litigation department. Main areas of practice are international litigation, arbitration and mediation. Cases include Ocean Island case (Tito v Waddell), Westinghouse Uranium Contract litigation and the Alexander Howden insurance fraud cases. Acting in numerous ICC arbitrations. Also involved in insurance insolvency litigation, acting in the KWELM and Electric Mutual (EMLICO) cases. A CEDR accredited mediator.
Prof. Memberships: Law Society.
Career: Articled at *Freshfields.* Qualified in 1966. Partner in 1972. Head of litigation department 1988-91.
Personal: Born 14th January 1942. Educated at Finchley Grammar School and Sheffield University (LL.B.). Leisure interests include cricket, contemporary art and an old Aston Martin.

LLOYD HOLT, Suzanne
Wragge & Co, Birmingham (0870) 903 1000

LOMAS, Paul
Freshfields Bruckhaus Deringer, London (020) 7936 4000
paul.lomas@freshfields.com
Specialisation: Particular interests: EC and anti-trust; ECHR; financial services and banking; regulatory or economics dominated cases; art law; crises.
Prof. Memberships: Law Society, Solicitors' European Group, INSEAD Alumni Association.
Career: Sciences and Law, Emmanuel College, Cambridge; *Freshfields* Litigation Department; MBA INSEAD; *Freshfields* Brussels office in 1989; partner 1990; Litigation Department, London from 1993.
Personal: Interests: anything that you can do on a mountain, on a beach or in France, music, food and wine, family (one wife and two daughters); not necessarily mutually exclusive or in that order.

LYNCH, Michael
Elliott Duffy Garrett, Belfast (028) 9024 5034

MACKIE Q C, David L
Allen & Overy, London (020) 7330 3770
david.mackie@allenovery.com
Specialisation: Head of Litigation. Litigation and arbitration.
Prof. Memberships: Law Society. Fellow Chartered Institute of Arbitrators, CEDR Accredited Mediator.
Career: Qualified *Allen & Overy* in (1971), Partner, (1975), Head of Litigation (1988). Recorder of Crown Court 1988. Deputy High Court Judge 1998. Higher Court Advocate (all courts). Queen's Counsel 1998.
Personal: Born 1946. St Edmund Hall, Oxford 1964-7.

MACLEOD, Colin
Dundas & Wilson CS, Edinburgh (0131) 228 8000

MACLEOD, Ian
Shepherd & Wedderburn WS, Edinburgh (0131) 473 5245
ian.macleod@shepwedd.co.uk
Specialisation: Partner in litigation department. Main areas of practice are general commercial litigation and employment law. Accredited as Employment Law Specialist by Law Society of Scotland. Solicitor in Scotland to Department for Education and Employment. Also solicitor in Scotland to HM Customs & Excise and to Health and Safety Executive. Member of Court of Session Rules Council.
Prof. Memberships: Law Society of Scotland, WS Society, Scottish Law Agents Society, Edinburgh Bar Association.
Career: Qualified in 1960. Joined *Shepherd & Wedderburn WS* in 1957, becoming a partner in 1964.
Personal: Born 19th April 1937. Attended Aberdeen and Edinburgh Universities 1954-59 (MA, LLB). Governor of Rannoch School; Lt. Cdr. RNR (Rtd.)

MADDEN, Michael
Ashurst Morris Crisp, London (020) 7859 1539
michael.madden@ashursts.com
Specialisation: Partner in charge of the property litigation group at *Ashurst Morris Crisp.* He specialises in development agreement disputes, property financing actions, landlord and tenant disputes and other general property disputes. Acts for both landlords and tenants in contested rent review arbitrations and expert determinations. Also advises on both liquor and gaming licensing matters.
Prof. Memberships: Accredited mediator with CEDR. FCIArb. Chairman of Property Litigation Group Law Reform Committee.
Career: Qualified as a solicitor in 1987. Joined *Ashursts* in 1993. Partner in litigation since 1995.
Publications: Contributor to 'Commercial Property Disputes: All England Legal Opinion'.

MAGNIN, John
Nicholson Graham & Jones, London (020) 7360 8168
john.magnin@ngj.co.uk
Specialisation: Involved in all aspects of commercial litigation, UK and international, including shareholder disputes; contractual, warranty and agency claims; fraud; defamation; confidential information; boardroom disputes and departures;

restrictive covenants; proceedings under the Companies, Insolvency, Financial Services and Company Directors Disqualification Acts; financial services, regulatory and disciplinary proceedings. Recent work includes metals and currency trading litigation; limited partnership disputes; substantial warranty claims; and acting for financial services, media and sports companies and organisations.
Career: Joined *Nicholson Graham & Jones* in 1985, qualified in 1987, became partner in 1992. Head of Litigation 2001.
Personal: Attended UCL 1981-4. Interests include family, golf, cricket, football, running and trumpet.

MANLEY, Mark
Brabners, Liverpool (0151) 600 3000

MANNING COX, Andrew
Wragge & Co, Birmingham (0870) 903 1000

MARTIN, Bonnie
Masons, Bristol (0117) 924 5678
bonnie.martin@masons.com
Specialisation: Specialises in property litigation. Acts for a number of companies relating to a range of property disputes arising from their retail and leisure outlets. Advises on numerous landlord and tenant problems arising out of all aspects of commercial leases including dilapidations, forfeiture and the Landlord & Tenant Act 1954. Acts for a number of landlords of industrial estates advising on all aspects of management. Has acted for parties to a number of significant Lands tribunal appeals, a high profile arbitration concerning the financial effects of boundary changes and arbitrations relating to land values. Has a particular interest in rent review and arbitration law as it relates to property. Is an appointed arbitrator under the Professional Arbitration on Court Terms (PACT) scheme, a member of ARBRIX and an appointed member of the RICS Presidents Initiative relating to the training of independent experts.
Prof. Memberships: ARBRIX; BURA; UKELA (UK Environmental Law Association); BPAA (Bristol Property Agents Association); BPF; British Council of Offices; TCPA; Law Society; in the process of setting up the Bristol Branch of Property Litigation Association.
Career: Admitted 1985 – partner *Masons* London before moving to set up property litigation department in Bristol in 1990.
Personal: Lives in Somerset with partner and two small boys.

MASTERS, David
Dawson & Co, London (020) 7421 4800
d.masters@dawson-and-co.co.uk
Specialisation: All aspects of property litigation including landlord and tenant advice, commercial property disputes, enforcement of restrictive covenants, rent reviews, forfeiture claims, dilapidations and disrepairs claims, applications under the Landlord and Tenant Act 1954, the Housing Act 1988 and Leasehold Reform Housing and Urban Development Act 1993. Acts for large and small property companies, housing associations, landed estates and private individuals.
Prof. Memberships: Property Litigation Association, The Institute of Continuing Professional Development; Law Society.
Career: Qualified 1981. *Speechly Bircham* 1988 to 1998 (partner from 1990) *Dawson & Co* since 1999(partner).
Personal: Born 7 November 1956. Educated at Felsted School and Reading University. Married. Interests include skiing, tennis, RHS member. Lives in Coggeshall, Essex.

MATTHEWS, Paul
Eversheds, Norwich (01473) 284428
paulmatthews@eversheds.com
Specialisation: Partner in commercial litigation department. Principal area of practice is contract-based litigation and dispute management including sale of goods and services in various commercial and industrial sectors (chemicals, manufacturing, agriculture and motor retail). Also handles insolvency matters. Acts for insolvency practitioners in pursuing and defending a wide variety of claims arising during mainly corporate insolvencies. Has been involved in a wide variety of high value corporate disputes, including shareholders disputes and warranty claims. Insolvency work has included ROT cases, challenging IVA's, director disqualification, wrongful trading and preferences. Has handled disputes in Italy, France, Belgium, the Netherlands and Scandinavian countries and has dealt with numerous disputes involving issues of European law. Experienced in various forms of alternative dispute resolution.
Career: Qualified in 1982. Became a partner at *Eversheds Daynes Hill & Perks* in 1985. Has obtained CEDR Mediator accreditation.
Personal: Born 25th September 1953. Educated at Culford School 1966-71, Hatfield Polytechnic 1971-75 (BA Hons in Business Studies) and the College of Law. Leisure activities include golf, shooting, jazz saxophone, wine and food. Lives in Weybread Suffolk.

MATTISON, Mark
Eversheds, Manchester (0161) 831 8000
markmattison@eversheds.com
Specialisation: Partner in commercial litigation department. Main area of practice is construction and engineering litigation.
Prof. Memberships: Law Society. Past President of Manchester Law Society. Member, Chartered Institute of Arbitrators, Vice Chairman of North West Branch, Member Society of Construction Law. CEDR Accredited Mediator.
Career: Articled at *Alexander Tatham* (now *Eversheds*) 1972-74 and became a partner in 1978.
Personal: Born 26/4/1951. Attended Liverpool College and studied Law in Liverpool. Leisure pursuits include cycling, swimming and overseas travel. Lives in Hale, Cheshire.

MAY, Philip
TLT Solicitors, Bristol (0117) 917 7912
pmay@tltsolicitors.com
Specialisation: Principal area of practice is business breakdown and insolvency. Extensive experience of general commercial disputes, including search and seize orders, freezing orders, cross border litigation, arbitration and mediation. Charge-out rate is £180 per hour. See also Insolvency/Corporate Recovery and Partnership.
Prof. Memberships: Law Society; Bristol Law Society; Insolvency lawyers Association; Association of Business Recovery Professionals; Chartered Institute of Arbitrators; Bristol Chancery Court Users committee.
Career: Educated Southend-on-Sea, Essex and Lincoln College, Oxford. Articled *Osborne Clark*, Bristol 1982-84. Assistant solicitor to partner *Osborne Clarke*, Bristol 1984-95. Joined *Trumps* as partner 1995. *Trumps* merged with Bristol law firm *Lawrence Tucketts* to become *TLT Solicitors* on 1 May 2000.
Personal: Born 16 March 1959. Married with two children. Lives near Bristol. Leisure pursuits include golf, snooker and skiing.

McLACHLAN, Campbell
Herbert Smith, London (020) 7374 8000
Specialisation: Partner in litigation and arbitration department. Specialises in international commercial litigation and arbitration including public and private international law, investment disputes, multi-national fraud and cross-border banking. He is Vice-Chairman of the IBA Committee on International Litigation, and Joint Secretary of the British Branch of the ILA. His book, 'Transnational Tort Litigation', is published by OUP.
Career: Qualified New Zealand 1984 and England and Wales 1991. Partner at *Herbert Smith* since 1992.
Personal: Educated at Victoria University of Wellington, New Zealand, the University of London and Hague Academy of International Law (Diploma cum laude).

MEGGITT, Edward
Edwards Geldard, Cardiff (029) 2023 8239
ed.meggitt@geldards.co.uk
Specialisation: All aspects of property dispute resolution and litigation. This includes advising on numerous landlord and tenant issues arising from commercial leases such as forfeiture; break notices; distraint; breaches of covenant (particularly dilapidation); security of tenure and advice and Court proceeding relating to the Landlord and Tenant Act 1954. Other areas include conveyancing problems such as misrepresentation; specific performance; professional negligence and rectification. Also, involved in issues arising from developments including nuisance/negligence; easement disputes and trespass/adverse possession claims.
Prof. Memberships: Law Society; Property Litigation Association; Member of Regional Committee of the Property Litigation Association (South West and Wales).
Career: Articled *Edwards Geldard* and qualified in 1993.
Personal: Interests include cricket (captain Cardiff Cricket Club 1999 & 2000); golf (Llanishen Golf Club); rugby and travel. Educated at St Illtyd's College, Cardiff and the University of the West of England. Married to Karen with a young daughter, Ella.

METCALFE, Stephen
Beachcroft Wansbroughs, Bristol (0117) 918 2000
smetcalfe@bwlaw.co.uk
Specialisation: Commercial litigation, particularly involving IT and financial institutions.
Prof. Memberships: Law Society.
Career: *Durrant Piesse* 1981-85. *Beachcroft Wansbroughs* 1985-date. Partner 1988.
Personal: BA (Hons) New College, Oxford. Married with four children. Interests: Music, theatre, literature, walking.

METLISS, Michael
SJ Berwin, London (020) 7533 2222
michael.metliss@sjberwin.com
Specialisation: Michael regularly advises property companies, institutional owners and retailers on a wide range of property issues; from redevelopment to rent review, from disclaimer to distraint, from rights

of way to dilapidations, from professional negligence to nuisance, from service charges to forfeiture, from tenant insolvency to trespass and from rectification to misrepresentation. He has written articles for the Property Press, has lectured to the Property Managers' Association, at the Royal Institute of Chartered Surveyors, for IBC UK Conferences and extensively at SJ Berwin's inhouse property seminars. He also acts as an advocate in mediation.
Prof. Memberships: Professional memberships: Property Litigation Association
Career: Articled *Bartletts De Reya*, qualified 1984. Partner *SJ Berwin* 1991.
Publications: Articles in Estate Gazette, Property Week: has lectured to IBC UK Conferences, Property Managers Association, RICS.
Personal: Football, Golf, Music, Middle East, Film.

MICKLETHWAITE, Neil
DLA, London (08700) 111111

MOLYNEUX, Anne
Masons, London (020) 7490 4000
anne.molyneux@masons.com
Specialisation: Partner and head of property litigation group. Handles all areas of High Court litigation. Cases have included Passmore v Morland (House of Lords interpretation of EC Treaty). Courage v Crehan (reference to Luxembourg – right to damages/illegality), Langton v Inntrepreneur (House of Lords – set-off), Little v Courage (covering status of option). Has addressed conferences on the licensed trade, dilapidations, insolvency, litigation and rent review.
Prof. Memberships: Law Society.
Career: Qualified in 1983. Associate at *Lawrence Messer & Co*, before joining *Masons* in 1987. Became a partner in 1989. Appointed Recorder in 2000.
Personal: Born 12 January 1959. Member of Ealing and Fulham Book Club. Lives in Ealing. Has two children.

MONTY, Craig
Lovells, London (020) 7296 2000
craig.monty@lovells.com
Specialisation: Partner in the commercial litigation sector with particular emphasis on professional indemnity work, trust and pensions disputes (important cases include: British Coal Corporation v British Coal Staff Superannuation Scheme Trustees Limited (1995) 1 All ER 912; National Power plc v Hugh Feldon & Others (1999:CA)) and product liability work.
Prof. Memberships: Member London Solicitors Litigation Association; associate member of Association of Pension Lawyers.
Career: Articled *Lovells*; qualified 1988; partner 1998.
Personal: Education: Our Lady and St. Bede's Roman Catholic Comprehensive School, St. Mary's Sixth Form College, University of Newcastle upon Tyne (LLB 1st Class Hons); College of Law, Chester (Law Society Finals).Personal: Born 1964; resides Harpenden.Leisure: All sports, particularly football (Middlesbrough FC) and horse racing.

MORGAN, Neil Christopher
Hugh James Ford Simey, Cardiff (029) 2022 4871
neil.morgan@hjfs.co.uk
Specialisation: Partner. Head of the firm's property litigation department. Extensive experience in all aspects of property litigation including landlord and tenant. Experience both in commercial and residential fields. Clients include government agencies, insurance companies, surveyors, property developers, property management companies, housing associations, letting agents, commercial landlords and tenants and residential landlords, residents' associations. Cases include: Acted on behalf of Companies House in defending a one million pounds dilapidations claim; successful defence of a claim in excess of half a million pounds against a housing association as a result of a disputed boundary; multiparty action seeking judicial review of a decision of a local authority in relation to holiday homes; successfully represented several housing associations in contested possession actions.
Prof. Memberships: Member of the Property Litigation Association.
Career: Graduate of Aberystwyth University and Chester College of Law. Qualified in 1991. Joined the firm in 1991. Partner in 1994. Welsh speaker.

MORRIS, Peter
Burges Salmon, Bristol (0117) 902 7721
peter.morris@burges-salmon.com
Specialisation: Peter Morris is a partner in *Burges Salmon's* Commercial Litigation department. The types of work he undertakes include commercial contract disputes; property disputes; professional negligence for claimants, especially against solicitors and surveyors; risk management and dispute avoidance. Clients include Bristol and West, Co-op group and Rhodia/Aversis.
Prof. Memberships: Law Society, Property Litigation Association.
Career: Trained with *Kenwright & Cox* (Chancery Lane, London) and qualified in 1982. Became a Partner at *Kenwrights & Cox* (Chancery Lane, London) in 1985: Partner at *Holt Phillips* (Bristol) in 1986; Partner at *Eversheds* (Bristol) in 1994 and a Partner at *Burges Salmon* (Bristol) in 2001.
Personal: Peter likes hill walking, fine food, wine and beer.

MORSHEAD, Ros
Berwin Leighton Paisner, London (020) 7760 1000
ros.morsheadberwinleightonpaisner.com
Specialisation: Partner in litigation and dispute resolution. Main area of practice is property litigation including landlord and tenant, planning-related litigation, disputes as to all aspects of real property and professional negligence. Represents retailers, institutions, developers and local government.
Prof. Memberships: The Law Society; Property Litigation Association; member of the Education and Training Sub-committee.
Career: Articled with *Clifford Chance*, September 1990-September 1992. Joined *Berwin Leighton* in 1997 and became partner *Berwin Leighton Paisner* in 2001.
Publications: Regular contributor of articles to property press and presenter at conferences and client seminars.
Personal: Lives in North London. Interests include cinema, theatre, music and socialising.

MUMFORD, Nicola
Wragge & Co, Birmingham
(0870) 903 1000

MYERS, Sidney A
Allen & Overy, London (020) 7330 3000
sidney.myers@allenovery.com
Specialisation: Has been a partner in the litigation department since 1991 and is Head of the Regulatory Investigations Group. He advises clients, principally in the banking and financial services sectors, on all types of regulatory, tax, DTI and on occasion, criminal investigations. He also acts for both firms and individuals in defending disciplinary proceedings brought by all of the major City regulators. In addition, he has extensive experience of litigating and negotiating a broad range of commercial disputes, including judicial review proceeding involving decisions of financial regulatory bodies and the UK tax authorities. Sidney is also qualified as a solicitor in Hong Kong and is a CEDR accredited mediator. Admitted as a solicitor in England (1984) and Hong Kong (1995). Assistant solicitor, *Allen & Overy* 1984-90; partner, *Allen & Overy*, London since 1991; partner, *Allen & Overy* Hong Kong (1994-96). CEDR accredited mediator.

NICHOLSON, Brinsley
Linklaters, London (020) 7456 4364
brinsley.nicholson@linklaters.com
Specialisation: Practised in proceedings before the High Court of Justice and the Commercial Court; experienced in obtaining urgent injunctions (particularly to freeze assets), dealing with jurisdictional issues, questions of conflict of laws and handling substantial disputes. Also experience of arbitration, insolvency, financial services, investigations, banking and white collar crime.
Career: 1992-99: Head of litigation department, *Linklaters*; 1986-89: Partner, *Linklaters* Hong Kong; 1977 to date: Partner, *Linklaters*; 1972-77; Solicitor, *Linklaters*; 1965-71: Articled clerk, *Peacock & Goddard*. Educated at Winchester College.

NOTT, Christopher
Palser Grossman, Cardiff Bay
(029) 2045 2770

NURSE-MARSH, Isabel
Pinsent Curtis Biddle, London (020) 7606 9301
isabel.nurse-marsh@pinsents.com
Specialisation: Head of pensions litigation group and full-time specialist in pensions litigation. Experience includes winding up disputes, claims over surplus, breach of trust, asset tracing and rectification actions, construction of scheme documentation issues, applications to the High Court and Pensions Ombudsman claims. Particular interest in professional negligence claims – bringing and defending claims against pensions professionals. Registered mediator and active promoter of use of mediation in pension disputes. High profile cases this year include acting for the National Power trustees in the House of Lords surplus case and in BESTrustees plc v Ian Stuart and others.
Prof. Memberships: Association of Pension Lawyers; member of Association of Pension Lawyers' Pension Litigation Sub-Committee; member of Centre for Effective Dispute Resolution's Faculty: Member of Association of Contentious Trust and Probate Specialists.
Career: 1989-92 *Slaughter & May*; 1992-01 *Biddle*; 2001 *Pinsent Curtis Biddle*.
Publications: Writes and lectures frequently on pensions litigation and mediation.
Personal: Lincoln College, Oxford. Dual nationality – English and French. Lives in Oxfordshire.

O'BRIEN, Gary
Eversheds, Birmingham (0121) 232 1000
Specialisation: Head of property litigation team in Birmingham and National Chairman of property litigation product group in *Eversheds* which handles all types of landlord and tenant disputes. Gary has particular specialisation in freehold property developments involving difficult restrictive covenants or major boundary and easement disputes as well as enforcement of sale and purchase contracts and clearance of sites for redevelopment schemes.
Career: Qualified in 1985. Joined *Simpson Curtis* in 1987. Partner at *Simpson Curtis* 1990 and at *Eversheds* from 1996.
Personal: Born 1959. Attended KEGS Aston and St. John's College, Oxford. Interests include opera and Aston Villa Football Club.

O'CONOR, John
Allen & Overy, London (020) 7330 3000
john.o'conor@allenovery.com
Specialisation: John O'Conor is a partner in the litigation department and a member of the Banking and Finance Litigation Group based in London. After working initially in the firm's banking department, he moved to litigation where he has advised on a variety of banking and financial disputes and financial regulatory proceedings, as well as advising banks generally on litigation risk issues. In particular, he has acted in many reported cases in London dealing with derivatives markets which have, on a number of occasions, involved jurisdictional disputes with important anti-suit and inconvenient forum contests. In addition, he has substantial experience of arbitration proceedings held both in London and overseas in the financial, insurance and other sectors before the ICC, LCIA and other arbitral bodies in Sweden, Japan, Switzerland and the United States. He has considerable knowledge of banking and international capital markets and specialist knowledge of derivatives and other financial instruments.
Career: Qualified in 1990; assistant solicitor *Allen & Overy* 1990-97; Partner since 1997.

O'DRISCOLL, Pat
Cleaver Fulton Rankin, Belfast (028) 9027 1311
p.o'driscoll@cfrlaw.co.uk
Specialisation: Commercial litigation, serious fraud, multi-document litigation, intellectual property, product liability, judicial review and admiralty.
Prof. Memberships: The Law Society of Northern Ireland.
Career: Educated at Glenstall Abbey School, Republic of Ireland and Queen's University of Belfast (BSc Econ). Qualified 1972. Became a partner in *Cleaver Fulton & Rankin* 1975.

O'FARRELL, Vincent
Pannone & Partners, Manchester (0161) 909 3000
vincent.o'farrell@pannone.co.uk
Specialisation: Partner and Head of Department in Commercial Litigation. He specialises in land disputes, contentious probate and trust issues, civil fraud, judicial review, defamation, contract and pre-emptive remedies. He is also a notary public.
Prof. Memberships: Member of ACTAPS (Association of Contentious Trust and Probate Specialists).
Career: Vincent was admitted in 1971, when he joined *Howards*, a predecessor to *Pannone & Partners*.
Personal: Leisure interests include theatre, sport and music. Lives in Bury.

OLDFIELD, Alison
Eversheds, Leeds (0113) 243 0391
Specialisation: Specialises in all areas of property litigation, acting for institutional landlords and retail tenants on property disputes arising from their leasehold interests as well as advising developers on land assembly issues. Particular niche areas include applications to the Lands Tribunal and Judicial review proceedings. Clients include Asda, Hammerson UK Properties plc and Next plc.
Prof. Memberships: Property Litigation Association (Past Chairman Northern Regional Group); Women in Property.
Career: Articled with *Macfarlanes*; joined *Eversheds*, London on qualification in 1994; transferred to *Eversheds*, Leeds February 1995.
Personal: Educated Harrogate Grammar School; Durham University.

OLIVER, Keith
Peters & Peters, London (020) 7629 7991
See under Fraud, p.411

O'LOUGHLIN, Philip
Addleshaw Booth & Co, Leeds (0113) 209 2000
pho@addleshaw-booth.co.uk
Specialisation: Head of Property Litigation Department, Commercial Property Group. Practice covers all landlord and tenant and property litigation, in particular rent reviews, dilapidations, property related professional negligence. Work also includes Landlord and Tenant 1954 applications, forfeiture, tenant default.
Career: Qualified 1986; joined the firm 1991, becoming a Partner in May 1995.
Personal: Attended Cambridge University 1979-82. Leisure interests include fellwalking, landscape photography, archaeology.

ORME, James
Osborne Clarke, Bristol
(0117) 917 3000

ORTON, Giles
Eversheds, London (020) 7919 4739
gilesorton@eversheds.com
Specialisation: Head of pensions. Main area of practice is pensions litigation, conducting disputes over pension schemes, particularly regarding surplus and winding up. Leading cases include Falconer v Aslef and NUR, Imperial Tobacco, Mirror Group, Lloyd's Bank Pension Scheme. Author of numerous articles on pensions law and Pensions Ombudsman procedure.
Prof. Memberships: Member of Main Committee of Association of Pension Lawyers. Chairman of Pensions Litigation Committee of Association of Pension Lawyers.
Career: Qualified in 1983. Joined *Eversheds* 1987, associate 1988, partner 1989. Head of litigation, East Midlands 1994-01.
Personal: Born 18 August 1959. Attended King Edward VII School, Sheffield 1970-77; The Queen's College, Oxford (Hastings Exhibition) 1977-80 and Chester College of Law 1980-81. Derby City Councillor 1988-92.

OWENS, David
Bevan Ashford, Bristol (0117) 975 1688
d.owens@bevanashford.co.uk
Specialisation: Partner in public sector commercial. After 12 years experience working in the commercial litigation department of *Bevan Ashford*, his focus on public law issues, particularly judicial review, has increased to the extent that he is now working with the public sector commercial team in the health and social care department. His work has involved commercial litigation on a wide range of topics both for NHS and private sector clients, together with a significant degree of advice on more general matters on the law and practice of the NHS and other public sector bodies. Currently main practice areas are judicial review within the NHS and associated advice on public law issues.
Prof. Memberships: Bristol Law Society, Society of Computers and Law.
Career: Joined *Bevan Ashford* in 1982. Qualified 1984. Partner 1990.
Personal: Born 23 July 1958.

PARKER, Raj
Freshfields Bruckhaus Deringer, London
(020) 7936 4000
raj.parker@freshfields.com
Specialisation: Partner in litigation department, Solicitor Advocate. Main area of practice is insurance and reinsurance work. Regular speaker at insurance industry seminars. Substantial general commercial dispute resolution practice. Also deals with sports law, acting for the Football Association in advisory and contentious work.
Prof. Memberships: Law Society; Society of Solicitor Advocates. Nominated Court of Arbitration for Sport ('CAS') Arbitrator. Member of British Insurance Law Association, British Association for Sport and the Law. CEDR accredited mediator.
Career: Joined *Freshfields* in 1986 and became a partner in 1993.
Personal: Born 1960. Educated at Christ's College 1972-79 and Southampton University 1979-82. Recreations include sport, music, theatre and ornithology. Lives in London.

PEARSON, Nick
Baker & McKenzie, London (020) 7919 1000
nick.pearson@bakernet.com
Specialisation: Head of commercial dispute resolution group with emphasis on multi-jurisdictional disputes; commercial fraud and insolvency; head of business recovery practice group and licensed insolvency practitioner; managing the multi-jurisdictional Kuwait Investment Office driven Grupo Torras litigation in London, Jersey, the Bahamas, Switzerland and elsewhere ($800 million international fraud), 1993 and continuing.
Prof. Memberships: Society of Practitioners of Insolvency; Insolvency Lawyers Association; Insol Europe.
Career: Qualified 1976; *Herbert Smith* 1974-79; *Baker & McKenzie* Hong Kong 1979-88; partner 1982; partner *Baker & McKenzie* London 1988-present.
Publications: 'International Tracing of Assets' – Sweet & Maxwell
Personal: Education: King Edward School, Birmingham; Lincoln College, Oxford (1970 BA Jurisprudence). Born 1951; resides London; married with two children.

PEET, Carole
Denton Wilde Sapte, London (020) 7242 1212

PERROTT, Edward
Taylor Vinters, Cambridge (01223) 423444
efvp@taylorvinters.com
Specialisation: Partner and head of commercial litigation. Specialising in leading edge technology, precision engineering and high quality manufacturing clients. Litigation covering infringement of intellectual property rights, contractual disputes and professional negligence.
Prof. Memberships: Law Society.
Career: Jesus College, Cambridge 1965-68. Retail business owner in Beirut 1968-73. Trained and practised in London with *Crossman Block and Keith* 1974-80. Joined *Taylor Vinters* in 1981. Registered mediator.
Personal: Interests include skiing, sailing and cricket.

PICKSTON, John
Clifford Chance, London (020) 7600 1000
john.pickston@cliffordchance.com
Specialisation: Partner. All types of litigation and advice relating to property matters including development issues, rent review, insolvency, environmental, professional negligence and landlord and tenant.
Career: Qualified 1986; partner 1996.

PIZZEY, Simon
Veale Wasbrough, Bristol (0117) 925 2020
spizzey@vwl.co.uk
Specialisation: Managing partner. Commercial litigation in the fields of banking, commercial fraud, business breakdown (corporate and partnership) and professional negligence. Clients include building societies, banks, local authorities, central government agencies, professional partnerships and corporates.
Prof. Memberships: Bristol Law Society panel of supervising solicitors for the enforcement of search and seize orders.
Career: Qualified 1982. Joined *Veale Wasbrough* in 1987. Partner in 1989. Head of *Veale Wasbrough*'s litigation department. Managing partner since 1998.
Personal: Born 1957. Birmingham University.

PLANT, Charles
Herbert Smith, London (020) 7374 8000
Specialisation: Principal area of practice is commercial litigation with particular reference to media, oil and gas and construction industries. Also provides expert advice on international arbitration law.
Prof. Memberships: Law Society, International Bar Association (Secretary of the International Litigation Committee).
Career: Qualified in 1969 while at *Herbert Smith.* Became a partner in 1976. Head of litigation department 1988-95. Member of Lord Chancellor's Advisory Committee on Legal Education and Conduct (1994 – 1999). Member Legal Services Consultative Panel (appointed December 1999.) Governor of College of Law. CEDR Addredited mediator.
Publications: Editor: Blackstone's 'Civil Practice 2001'; 'Civil Procedural Rules' (Blackstone 2000).
Personal: Born 1944. Attended Cambridge University 1963-66. Lives in Tunbridge Wells.

POLLACK, Craig
SJ Berwin, London (020) 7533 2222
craig.pollack@sjberwin.com
Specialisation: Complex commercial litigation often with multi-jurisdictional aspects; cross-border fraud and asset trading and shareholder disputes. Also acts as a mediation advocate. Clients include major public companies, banks and venture capital houses as well as governments.
Prof. Memberships: Law Society. Israel Bar Association.
Career: Joined *SJ Berwin* in 1991. Partner commercial litigation 1997.
Personal: BA (Cape Town); LLB (Jerusalem); LLM (London). Qualified as an advocate in Israel 1989.

POLLARD, Stephen
Kingsley Napley, London (020) 7814 1200
spollard@kingsleynapley.co.uk
See under Fraud, p.411

POTTS, John
Clifford Chance, London (020) 7600 1000

PUDDICOMBE, Nigel
Veale Wasbrough, Bristol (0117) 925 2020
npuddicombe@vwl.co.uk
Specialisation: All aspects of property litigation principally acting for lenders and landlords. Clients include breweries and pub companies, life companies, distribution companies, property companies, and local authorities. Also handles contractual, negligence and passing off disputes.
Prof. Memberships: President, Bristol Law Society 2000. Chairman, Bristol Law Society. Civil Courts committee 1993-98.
Career: Qualified 1979. Partner with *Cartwrights* from 1987. Joined *Veale Wasbrough* as partner 2001.
Personal: Born 1954. Kings College Taunton and Southampton University.

RANDS, Harvey
Memery Crystal, London (020) 7242 5905
dhrands@memerycrystal.com
Specialisation: Head of litigation; leads groups specialising in commercial, commodities, insurance and shipping litigation; company and regulatory enquires and white-collar crime; intellectual property; directors' and officers' liability.
Prof. Memberships: Chartered Institute of Arbitrators
Career: Articled *Charles Mazillius & Co*; qualified 1976; solicitor *Rubinstein Callingham* 1977; solicitor *Stilgoes* 1977; partner *Stilgoes* 1978; partner *Memery Crystal* since 1980.
Personal: Pilgrim School, Bedford; The City University (1972 BSc Philosophy and Physics); College of Law (1976 solicitors finals). Born 1951; resides in London. Leisure interests include family and country pursuits.

RANSON, Lee
Eversheds, Manchester (0161) 831 8000
leeranson@eversheds.com
Specialisation: Property litigation – acting for commercial and institutional landlord clients in Retail, Local Authority and Banking sectors. Specific niche areas include resolution of property disputes in the education and leisure industries. Has a particular interest in property related professional indemnity claims.
Prof. Memberships: Law Society. CEDR qualified mediator. Member of Property Litigation Association.
Career: Qualified 1990. *Jaques & Lewis* (merged *Eversheds* 1994). Transfered to *Eversheds* Manchester, Jan 1997. Partner May 1999.
Personal: Born 16.12.64. Educated Wilmslow Grammer School & Hull University. Married, two children. Interests include golf, football, cricket. Lives in Bramhall.

RAPHAEL, Monty
Peters & Peters, London (020) 7629 7991
See under Fraud, p.412

RAWLINSON, David
Cuff Roberts, Liverpool (0151) 237 7777
david.rawlinson@cuffroberts.co.uk
Specialisation: Commercial contract, construction (and litigation, related professional negligence), arbitration, alternative dispute resolution and defamation.
Prof. Memberships: Law Society; Liverpool Law Society; member of Chartered Institute of Arbitors; member of Society of Construction Law; member of Northern Arbitration Association Council; member of Council of Society for Computers & Law; chairman SCL Liverpool Group.
Career: Qualified 1976. Assistant solicitor, then partner (1978) Banks Kendal Taylor & Gorst, merged with Cuff Roberts 1987. Chairman of firm's Executive Board 1999 to date. Past member of Young Solicitors' Group National committee. Past Chairman YSG Liverpool Group.
Personal: Nottingham University (1970-73). Married, two children. Lives West Kirby, Wirral. Golf, cycling, walking, local and family history. Supporter Tranmere Rovers FC.

REYNOLDS, John
McDermott, Will & Emery, London
(020) 7577 6994
jreynolds@europe.mwe.com
Specialisation: International commercial litigation and arbitration.
Prof. Memberships: Law Society. International Bar Association.
Career: 1985-87: *Lickfolds Wiley & Powles*, London (Articles); 1987-99: *Herbert Smith*, London (New York 1989-90; Partner 1994); 1999 to date: *McDermott, Will & Emery*, London (Partner)
Personal: Born 1963. Educated at Clifton College, Reading University and UCL. Married with two children. Lives in Islington. Leisure: rugby, Formula One motor racing, cooking, music (loud/quiet/dance). Member of the Groucho Club.

RHYS-JONES, Mark
Eversheds, Cardiff (029) 2047 1147
markrhysjones@eversheds.com
Specialisation: Partner in the dispute resolution and commercial litigation department at *Eversheds* Cardiff office. Specialises in conducting litigation in all areas of IT, intellectual property, product liability and general contractual disputes of a substantial value; accredited mediator with the Centre for Dispute Resolution (CEDR) and the ADR Group; Chair of the *Eversheds* Technology Litigation Group.
Prof. Memberships: Wales Commercial Law Association; Society for Computers and Law; British Computer Society; Advisory Board of Centre for Professional Legal Studies, Cardiff Law School.
Career: Educated at Merton College, Oxford (1987 BA Hons Jurisprudence). Articled with *Eversheds*; qualified 1990; became a partner in 1995.
Personal: Born 1966 and resides in Cardiff. Leisure pursuits include aerobics, skiing and badminton.

RICKARD, Jennifer
Nabarro Nathanson, London (020) 7524 6000
j.rickard@nabarro.com
Specialisation: Partner property litigation department. All aspects of property litigation. Acted in 'Mannai Investment Company Ltd v. Eagle Star Assurance Ltd', 'Lewisham Investment Partnership v. Morgan', 'Straudley Investment v. Mount Eden Land', 'Grundy v. Summit Group Holdings' and 'Pontsarn v. Kansallis Osake Panke'. Speaker at Blundell Memorial Lectures, Henry Stewart conferences, RICS, ISVA, IBC conferences, Euroforum, and Contract Property Training, Central Law Training. Speaker on Owlion cassettes on Dilapidations 1996, Lease Renewals 1998, Rent Reviews 1998 and Property law updates 1997-00.
Career: Qualified 1983. Partner 1989.
Publications: Joint author of 'The Rooftop Rents' report on mobile phone base stations, which won the UK Design and Marketing award 2000 in the research category.

ROBINSON, Clare
Osborne Clarke, Bristol (0117) 917 3000

ROBINSON, Michael
Boyes Turner, Reading (0118) 959 7711
mrobinson@boyesturner.com
Specialisation: Partner in dispute resolution group, specialising in commercial litigation. Particular expertise in professional negligence claims for claimants (recovered £2,000,000 in claim against firm of solicitors last year) and intellectual property disputes (defended and settled two claims issued against clients by one of world's largest software suppliers last year, one of them involving freezing and search and seizure orders).
Prof. Memberships: Property Litigation Association; Environmental Law Foundation; Institute of Credit Management; OSS Negligence Referral panel.
Career: With *Boyes Turner* since 1978. Qualified 1980; partner 1985.
Publications: Stowe School, Magdalene College Cambridge. Married with three children. Interests include golf, carp angling, gardening and Reading FC.

ROESSLER, Max
Eversheds, Norwich (01603) 272727
maxroessler@eversheds.com
Specialisation: Professional Negligence, Product Liability.
Prof. Memberships: Law Society.
Career: Admitted 1981. Partner 1986.

ROGERS, Jane
Osborne Clarke, Bristol (0117) 917 3000

ROPER, Robert
Cobbetts, Manchester (0161) 833 5214
robert.roper@cobbetts.co.uk
Specialisation: Principal area of practice is intellectual property. Work includes litigation on all types of trademark, passing off, copyright and design right matters as well as mechanical and electrical patent proceedings. Also handles commercial litigation and dispute resolutions including large commercial contract disputes with overseas elements and/or competition law issues. Has considerable experience in injunction work including Anton Piller Orders both in intellectual property matters and commercial litigation. Important cases handled include McMillan Graham & Others v R R UK Ltd (contempt of court for breach of interlocutory undertakings in passing off/copyright case); DTI v D C Wilson and others (acted for the major intermediaries sued by the DTI in the Barlow Clowes collapse); Watson & Watson v Duton Forshaw and Others (commercial court London – restrictive trade practice and conspiracy to injure by unlawful means); MIG v CSM (2001, commercial court London – commercial agent regulations).
Prof. Memberships: Law Society, Manchester Law Society, Licensing Executive Society.
Career: Qualified in 1979 while at *Cobbett Leak Almond.* Became a partner in 1983.
Personal: Born 11 August 1953. Educated at Altrincham Grammar School 1964-71 and the University of Wales Institute of Science and Technology 1973-76 (LLB Hons). Married with two children. Narrowboating, golf, training.

ROSE, Digby H
Hammond Suddards Edge, Birmingham (0121) 222 3000
digby.rose@hammondse.com
Specialisation: Commercial dispute resolution and litigation. Has wide experience covering contractual disputes, computer claims and contentious intellectual property work. Other areas of interest include defamation and professional negligence. Also advises on partnership issues. Cases include substantial disputes concerning computer systems, industrial machinery, engineering plant and media contracts as well as patent and design right infringement and claims resulting from the acquisition and sale of businesses. Regular contributor to 'Current Law Week', providing the focus articles on civil litigation.
Prof. Memberships: Law Society, Birmingham Law Society.
Career: Qualified in 1975. Worked in London for four years before joining *Edge Ellison* in 1979. Became head of commercial litigation in Birmingham in 1990.
Personal: Born 16 September 1950. MA Gonville & Caius College, Cambridge. Honorary secretary of Birmingham Botanical Gardens. Leisure interests include music. Lives in Birmingham.

ROTHWELL, Charles
Keeble Hawson, Leeds (0113) 244 3121
charlesrothwell@keeblehawson.co.uk
Specialisation: Partner specialising in commercial litigation matters, particularly of a heavyweight nature. Main areas of practice are building and engineering disputes, partnership disputes and professional negligence. The practice covers commercial disputes, construction and property litigation, and expertise in mediation and arbitration.
Career: Articled at, and assistant with *Biddle and Co.* Qualified in 1993. Assistant at *Dibb Lupton Broomhead* 1995 to 1997. Partner at *Keeble Hawson* 1998.
Personal: Born 1968. Resides at Holmfirth. Educated at Queen Elizabeth Grammar School, Wakefield and the University of Liverpool. Interests; horse riding, gardening and walking.

ROWE, Claire
Shoosmiths, Reading (0118) 965 8959
claire.rowe@shoosmiths.co.uk
Specialisation: Head of dispute resolution unit. Insurance lawyer advising major insurers, loss adjusters, loss assessors and self-insured companies. Experience in prosecuting and defending claims for business interruption and consequential loss. Also handles a range of commercial litigation relating to general commercial contract disputes, IT contracts, various internet related disputes, product liability cases and warranty and company acquisition related disputes. Recently has advised on dispute resolution tactics and risk management procedures to a number of companies in the technology, medial and telecommunications sector, including the tactics to be adopted to achieve the successful resolution of a £5 million claim against a software developer in relation to the development of an interactive web site.
Prof. Memberships: Member of the Law Society
Career: Joined *Shoosmiths* in 1984 as a trainee. Qualified in 1986. Associate in 1987. Salaried Partner in 1990 and Equity Partner in 1999.

SANDELSON, Jeremy
Clifford Chance, London (020) 7600 1000
jeremy.sandelson@cliffordchance.com
Specialisation: Specialising in commercial litigation, including securities disputes, mergers and acquisitions litigation and regulatory investigations including DTI and FSA work. Experienced in international trust disputes. Regular speaker at seminars. Recently involved in the Thyssen litigation in Bermuda.
Career: Charterhouse School; Cambridge University (scol). Qualified 1981; partner *Clifford Chance* 1988; Secretary Takeovers and Mergers Panel 1990-92.
Personal: Born 1957.

SCANNELL, John
Eversheds, Norwich (01603) 272727
johnscannell@eversheds.com
Specialisation: Landlord and tenant – commercial and residential. Other property litigation – squatters, adverse possession, title disputes.
Career: University of East Anglia B.Sc. Articles *Daynes Hill and Perks* 1987-89. Non-contentious commercial property/company commercial 1989-92. Civil litigation (now exclusively property litigation) 1992 to date.
Personal: Interests include classical music, jazz guitar, keeping fit, food and wine.

SCOTT, Gordon
Hammond Suddards Edge, Birmingham (0121) 222 3269
gordon.scott@hammondse.com
Specialisation: National head of property litigation and partner in the property litigation unit. Work covers the complete spectrum of property-related disputes and includes landlord and tenant, title disputes, easements and covenants, specific performance, judicial review, professional negligence claims and everything in between. Particular interest in dilapidations claims. Acts for companies across the property sector, including institutional landlords, major retailers, Housing Associations and development groups.
Prof. Memberships: Member Property Litigation Association. Milk Marque Arbitration Panel.
Career: Joined *Edge Ellison* as a partner in 1990 from another local firm, having moved to Birmingham in the early 1980s from *MacFarlanes* and earlier, *DJ Freeman & Co.*
Personal: Born 1951. Educated at Whitgift School and Exeter College, Oxford. External interests include rugby, cricket and walking. Lives in Edgbaston.

SEAGER, Nicola
Masons, Bristol 0117 970 5206
nicola.seager@masons.com
Specialisation: Partner in the property litigation group. Acts for pension funds, property developers, property managers and construction companies, a leading supplier of gas and electricity services, retailers and a distribution and haulage company on all aspects of commercial landlord and tenant and general property disputes. Particular specialisms include contested lease renewal proceedings under the Landlord and Tenant Act 1954, (especially for property developers) dilapidation and service charge disputes; portfolio management; disputes arising on land development including rights of light and party walls; advising landlords and insolvency practitioners on their rights and remedies on tenant insolvency; possession proceedings; promoting and contesting compulsory purchase orders and compensation claims arising on compulsory acquisition.
Prof. Memberships: Property Litigation Association (current Chair of the South West and South Wales group).
Career: Qualified 1991. Joined *Masons* in 1996 and became partner in 2001.
Personal: Lives in Somerset.

SHAW, Murray
Biggart Baillie, Glasgow (0141) 228 8000
mshaw@biggartbaillie.co.uk
Specialisation: Head of Litigation Department. Partner in the litigation department specialising in construction law (contentious and non-contentious) and planning law. Law Society accredited in both areas as well as Licensed Insolvency Practitioner. Work includes commercial litigation including contract disputes, building contract diputes and arbitration, and planning (with particular reference to the energy industry).
Prof. Memberships: International Bar Association; Law Society of Scotland.
Career: Qualified 1982. Assistant solicitor, *Biggart, Baillie & Gifford* 1982-85 and 1986-87 Assistant *Speechly Bircham*, London, 1985-86. Partner, *Biggart, Baillie & Gifford* since 1987.
Publications: Author of chapter on liquidation in 'Scottish Insolvency Casebook', and has written several articles on insolvency for the IBA Journal. Speaker on courses on insolvency and building contracts.
Personal: Educated at Dundee University (LL.B Hons 1980). Leisure pursuits include golf, reading and rugby. Born 25th September 1957. Lives in Glasgow.

SHERRINGTON, Patrick
Lovells, London (020) 7296 2000
patrick.sherrington@lovells.com
Specialisation: Commercial Litigation. Extensive experience of international commercial litigation, arbitration and ADR, especially in the fields of banking and finance, energy, product liability and professional negligence. Leads the firm's ADR practice and regularly sits as a mediator. Author of: 'Civil Litigation' published in Hong Kong by Longmans, 2nd edition 1996; writes and regularly speaks on his specialist areas of practice.
Prof. Memberships: Admitted in the UK, Hong Kong and Australia (NSW). Law Society of England & Wales, Solicitors' European Group, City of London Solicitors' Company, Fellow of the Chartered Institute of Arbitrators, Law Society of Hong Kong, Inter-Pacific Bar Association, LawAsia, International Bar Association.
Career: Articled *Lovells* 1978-80; resident in New York 1982-84; Partner 1985; resident in Hong Kong 1987-96; CEDR accredited mediator; Higher Courts (Civil proceedings) qualification; Law Society of Hong Kong Council Member 1990-96; Vice President 1993-96; Council Member Inter-Pacific Bar Association 1990-96; Governor Advocacy Institute of Hong Kong 1994-96.

SINCLAIR, Jonathan
Eversheds, Leeds (0113) 243 0391
jonathansinclair@eversheds.co.uk
Specialisation: Head of litigation and dispute management department for Leeds and Manchester and of the core commercial dispute management group in those offices. Specialises in the management and resolution of major business disputes for corporate clients. He has extensive experience in a range of substantial corporate and commercial disputes including warranty claims, auditors' negligence claims, product liability and IT disputes. Jonathan has developed a particular expertise in contentious competition work including OFT and EU Commission Dawn Raids. He acted for Asda on its challenges to resale price maintenance on OTC pharmaceuticals and on the widely publicised Parma Ham case in the House of Lords (December 2000).
Prof. Memberships: Law Society.
Career: Qualified in 1987. *Clifford Chance*, London 1985-89. Joined *Eversheds*, Leeds 1989. Partner 1992.
Personal: Born 1961. Oxford University (1st) 1979-82. Lives in Ilkley. Leisure: mainly keeping up with son and two daughters at football, tennis etc.

SINGLETON, Bernard
Lee Crowder, Birmingham (0121) 236 4477
Specialisation: Civil litigation.
Career: Partner 1976.
Personal: Tennis.

SKREIN, Michael
Richards Butler, London (020) 772 5720
spms@richardsbutler.com
Specialisation: A partner specialising in: Administrative law (notably in the aviation field) and competition law, insurance, intellectual property and media. Key successes in the last 12 months include the successful defence of Express Newspapers against Sir Elton John who sought an order to reveal a source; obtaining a mandatory injunction for Irish national broadcaster RTÉ from an English Court that tapes of an Australian TV series be delivered for transmission in Ireland; and the wresting of domain names from infringers (eg brands having their names sullied by the addition of 'sucks.com' to the end of their name) in landmark WIPO arbitration. Michael's team's media work won the prestigious 'The Lawyer's 2001 Litigation Team of the Year' Award. On the aviation side, his work has included acting for airlines and aircraft brokers, including successful Commercial Court and international litigation. He has long acted for EUROCONTROL, the European Organisation for the Safety of Air Navigation.
Prof. Memberships: Fellow of the Society for Advanced Legal Studies; Law Society; The City of London Solicitors' Company; Copinger Society, the Baltic Exchange.
Career: Articled *Richards, Butler & Co* 1971; qualified 1973; partner since 1976; head of litigation department 1990 to 1996; lectured on advertising law, copyright infringement, intellectual property and defamation implications of the Internet, libel and trade marks; chair of the Protecting the Media series of conferences, the market leader.
Personal: Born 1947. Educated at Oxford University (MA, Modern History) and the University of Southern California (AM *magna cum laude* International Relations). Honor Society of *Phi Kappa Phi*.

SLEIGH, Russell
Lovells, London (020) 7296 2000
russell.sleigh@lovells.com
Specialisation: Managing partner, litigation and dispute resolution practice. Experienced in wide range of international commercial litigation, in particular corporate, banking and regulatory disputes and multi-jurisdictional fraud issues. Acted on numerous official investigations on behalf of the authorities and of other parties involved. Also experienced in media law issues.
Career: Qualified 1973. Partner 1980. New York office 1977-80. Paris office 1990-93.

SLOWE, Richard
SJ Berwin, London (020) 7533 2345
richard.slowe@sjberwin.com
Specialisation: Partner in litigation department. Main area of practice is advocacy in commercial litigation. Has fifteen years commercial and common law experience at the Bar as Head of Chambers at 4 Kings Bench Walk, Temple. Also handled Lloyd's litigation: solicitor advocate to the Writs Response Group and others. Acted for the working miners throughout the 1984 strike. Successfully defended Michael Fagin after he had visited the Queen's bedroom.
Prof. Memberships: Secretary of West London Law Society 1972-75. Vice Chairman of Solicitors Association of Higher Court Advocates 1995-97.
Career: Qualified in 1970. Joined *SJ Berwin & Co.* in 1990 as a partner.
Personal: Leisure interests include tennis, cricket, skiing and family. Lives in London.

SMALL, Graham
Rowe Cohen, Manchester 0161 830 4600
Specialisation: Commercial litigation and dispute resolution. Head of Department acting mainly for SMEs/OMBs and high net worth entrepreneurs, covering the full spectrum of commercial disputes. Increasing international dimension to trade disputes and within last 12 months, has handled/advised on issues arising in North America, South Africa, Far East (Hong Kong, Taiwan, Vietnam), Middle East (Dubai, Yemen) and pan-European.
Prof. Memberships: Law Society; British Association for Sport and Law.

SMITH, Hugh
Andrew M. Jackson & Co, Hull (01482) 325242
Specialisation: Substantial area of practice involves retail law covering Trading Standards, Health and Safety, Consumer Protection and Consumer Safety. Particular expertise in the vitamin and fish industry. Commercial Litigation work includes contractual disputes both international and domestic, company and partnership disputes, commercial property disputes, professional negligence, defamation and passing off. Represents finance houses in respect of consumer complaints/recoveries.
Prof. Memberships: Member of the Law Society and the Food Law Group. Also an ADR mediator.

Career: Admitted 1983. Joined present firm in 1989, becoming a partner in 1991 in charge of the commercial litigation division.
Personal: Born 16.01.59. Attended Nottingham University (LLB Hons).

SOLOMAN, Martin
Hay & Kilner, Newcastle upon Tyne
(0191) 232 8345
lawyers@hay-kilner.co.uk
Specialisation: Full range of commercial disputes including contracts, shareholder disputes, professional negligence, partnership disputes, construction, mediation, breach of warranty claims arising out of purchase/sales of businesses, defamation, copyright and trademark litigation, litigation relating to development of land.
Prof. Memberships: Law Society, Chairman of a Health Authority Disciplinary Committee.
Career: Educated at University of Kent 1971 – 1974. Joined *Hay & Kilner* in 1984 becomming a partner that year.
Personal: Born 1953. Lives in Newcastle upon Tyne; leisure pursuits include family, skiing, music and cycling.

SORRELL, Christopher
Wacks Caller, Manchester (0161) 957 8888
Ksorrell@wackscaller.com
Specialisation: Partner and head of the commercial litigation team. Specialises in high value commercial litigation, professional negligence, property litigation and shareholder disputes.
Prof. Memberships: Manchester Law Society, Liverpool Law Society.
Career: BSC (Econ) London, MA (Sheffield). Assistant solicitor, *Bremner Sons & Corlett*, Liverpool 1979-82. Assistant solicitor, *Bermans*, Liverpool 1982-83. Partner and head of the commercial litigation department, *Davies Wallis Foyster*, Liverpool, 1983-00. Since 2000 with *Wacks Caller.*
Personal: Educated at Liverpool Collegiate; North Staffs Polytechnic 1969-72; Sheffield University 1973-74; Liverpool Polytechnic 1974-75. Born 25 October 1949. Lives in Caldy.

SPARROW, Edward
Ashurst Morris Crisp, London (020) 7859 1573
edward.sparrow@ashursts.com
Specialisation: General commercial litigation and dispute resolution (corporate acquisition and disposal and financial disputes; City regulation; mergers and acquisitions; Stock Exchange transactions and management and trading of securities/other financial instruments); professional negligence, insolvency and insurance; corporate fraud claims.
Prof. Memberships: Law Society.
Career: Ampleforth College; Lincoln College, Oxford. Articled *Ashurst Morris Crisp*; qualified 1977; partner 1981; head of litigation department 1993.
Personal: Born 1953; resides London.

SPOONER, Andrew
Martineau Johnson, Birmingham (0121) 200 3300
andrew.spooner@martjohn.com
Specialisation: Partner and head of litigation department. Main area of practice is commercial litigation including major claims for breach of contract and tort. In particular, handles claims arising from product liability and defective goods and machinery. Has acted in a variety of large claims involving landfill sites and the engineering industry, including robots, cranes, mining equipment, furnaces, diesel trains, power stations, industrial conveyors, plastic extrusions, boilers, radiators computers and hi tech devices. Addressed seminars on Trading Conditions, the Woolf Reforms and resolving disputes by mediation.
Prof. Memberships: Chartered Institute of Arbitrators, Centre for Dispute Resolution, Association of Midlands Mediators.
Career: Qualified in 1978. Head of litigation in 1989. Fellow of the Chartered Institute of Arbitrators. Accredited Mediator (CEDR). Solicitor member of the Solicitors Disciplinary tribunal.
Personal: Holds an LLB. Leisure interests include golf, cricket, walking the dogs and the Arts.

SPRING, Paul
Mills Selig, Belfast (028) 9024 3878
paul.spring@nilaw.com
Specialisation: Head of litigation department. Main area of practice is libel. Represents several national newspapers, broadcasting organisations and book and magazine publishers. Extensive experience of libel litigation for both defendants and plaintiffs. Areas of practice include breach of confidence, contempt of Court, press complaints, copyright and pre-publication work. Other major areas of practice are commercial litigation, product liability litigation (clients include British American Tobacco) and IP.
Prof. Memberships: Law Society of Northern Ireland.
Career: Qualified 1983. Litigation partner since 1988.
Personal: Educated Belfast Royal Academy and London School of Economics (graduating in Law in 1981). Leisure interests include cycling, architecture, the countryside and two young children! Lives near Belfast.

STAPLE, George
Clifford Chance, London (020) 7600 1000

STEWART, David L.
Morton Fraser, Solicitors, Edinburgh
(0131) 247 1000

STONE, Paul
DLA, Leeds (08700) 111111

STONE, Peter
Cobbetts, Manchester (0161) 833 5246
peter.stone@cobbetts.co.uk
Specialisation: Over 20 years experience in litigation for national and regional blue chip clients. Particular expertise in commercial property litigation (forfeiture, dilapidations, covenants, contested lease renewals, brewery/licensed retailer work) and in defamation (plaintiff and defendant) for individual and media clients.
Prof. Memberships: Law Society. Notaries Society.
Career: Articled at *Cobbetts*, 1974. Qualified 1976, partner 1979.
Personal: Born 1951. Educated at Rossall School and Liverpool University (LLB Hons 1st class). Leisure interests include fell walking, climbing and mountain biking.

STYLE, Christopher
Linklaters, London (020) 7456 4286
christopher.style@linklaters.com
Specialisation: Specialises in commercial litigation. Has practised in proceedings before the High Court of Justice and Commercial Court. Has conducted numerous arbitrations, both ad hoc and institutional (ICC, LMAA, LCIA etc). Also advised on questions of public international law before international tribunals. Extensive experience of all forms of urgent injunctive relief and a specialist in jurisdictional issues and questions of conflict of laws.
Prof. Memberships: Member of London Solicitors Litigation Association, International Bar Association and the City of London Solicitors' Company. Fellow of Chartered Institute of Arbitrators, Solicitor Advocate (Higher Courts Civil), accredited Mediator.
Career: Partner and head of litigation and arbitration. 1985 to date: Partner, *Linklaters*; 1979-85: Assistant solicitor, *Linklaters* London; 1983: Six months with the litigation department of *Sullivan & Cromwell* New York; 1977-79: Articled clerk, *Linklaters.* 1978: MA Law; 1976-77: City of London Polytechnic, Law Society Part II; 1973-76: Trinity Hall, Cambridge, BA Law (Cantab).

SWANSON, Alayne
Maclay Murray & Spens, Glasgow
(0141) 248 5011
aes@maclaymurrayspens.co.uk
Specialisation: Head of commercial litigation and advocacy; solicitor advocate with 17 years of experience as a commercial litigator; specialist areas include contractual disputes, arbitration, media law, debt collection and insolvency. Major cases include three major Court of Session commercial cases concerning contracts for supply of goods/services; two commercial agency cases; resisting minority shareholder's petition; challenging retention of title clause for receivers and major contractual dispute for Cable & Wireless. Appears regularly in Sheriff Court and Court of Session.
Career: Attended University of Edinburgh (LLB Hons, Dip LP). Articled at *Shepherd & Wedderburn* 1982-84; assistant solicitor Glasgow 1984-85; foreign associate at *Hughes Hubbard & Reed*, New York 1986-87; assistant solicitor *Bird Semple Fyfe* Ireland 1987-90; partner 1990-93; partner *Dundas & Wilson* 1994-97; solicitor advocate 1996.
Personal: Born 1959. Resides Glasgow. Leisure interests include music, playing cello and piano, walking.

TAYLOR, Ian
Freshfields Bruckhaus Deringer, London
(020) 7936 4000
ian.taylor@freshfields.com
Specialisation: Partner in Litigation Department. Main area of practice is commercial litigation, particularly in relation to banking and financial services, fraud and asset recovery. Also represents financial institutions in regulatory, DTI and SFO inquiries.
Prof. Memberships: Law Society; Member of Commercial Court Committee.
Career: Qualified in 1976, having joined *Freshfields* in 1974. Became a Partner in 1982.
Personal: Born 1951. Attended Gonville & Caius College, Cambridge 1969-73. Lives in London.

TAYLOR, Tim
SJ Berwin, London (020) 7533 2222
tim.taylor@sjberwin.com
Specialisation: Complex commercial litigation with an emphasis on cross-border disputes. Co-author of Sweet and Maxwell's European Litigation Handbook. Major cases in the last 12 months include acting in Federal Republic of Nigeria v General Abacha (deceased), Brunei Investment v Agency Prince Jefri Bolkiah, Bergen Industries v Dalmore Products.

Prof. Memberships: International Bar Association; American Bar Association.
Career: MA Oxon.

THOMAS, Martin
Herbert Smith, London (020) 7466 2034
Specialisation: All forms of litigation, arbitration and mediation relating to commercial property including contractual disputes, negligence actions, possession claims, landlord and tenant, rent reviews, dilapidations, nuisance and rights of light claims together with development related work and property related insolvency/corporate recovery matters.
Prof. Memberships: Property Litigation Association.
Career: Joined *Herbert Smith* 1987, qualified 1989, partner 1997.
Publications: Contributes to Estates Gazette and Property Law Journal. Also speaks at public lectures and seminars on property litigation topics.
Personal: Educated at Portsmouth Grammar School and Worcester College Oxford.

THOMAS, Paul
Halliwell Landau, Manchester (0161) 835 3003
pathomas@halliwells.co.uk
Specialisation: Paul Thomas is the Managing Partner of *Halliwell Landau.* He specialises in all types of commercial litigation, professional negligence, interim remedies and freezing orders, landlord and tenant, and other property-related disputes.
Prof. Memberships: Law Society of England and Wales.
Career: Qualified 1979, partner at *Halliwell Landau* since 1981.
Personal: Born 1954; squash, rugby, French language and culture.

TOUT, Liz
Denton Wilde Sapte, London (020) 7242 1212

TRAVERS, Iain
Nabarro Nathanson, London (020) 7524 6283
i.travers@nabarro.com
Specialisation: Head of Property Litigation. Property litigation and arbitration generally.
Prof. Memberships: Chairman of Property Litigation Association. Member of London Court of International Arbitration. Member of ARBRIX. Trained mediator. Appointed by President of Law Society and RICS as Arbitrator on property disputes.
Career: Qualified 1977. Partner 1980. Fellow of Chartered Institute of Arbitrators.
Publications: Joint author of 'Distress for Rent' (Jordons).

TROTTER, John
Lovells, London (020) 7296 2000
john.trotter@lovells.com
See under Professional Negligence, p.697

TUGWELL, Andrew
Osborne Clarke, London (020) 7809 1000

TURNBULL, John
Linklaters, London (020) 7456 4310
john.turnbull@linklaters.com
Specialisation: Specialising in corporate finance litigation, all contentious aspects of mergers and acquisitions work and professional negligence.
Career: 1989 to date: Partner, *Linklaters,* litigation department; 1988-89: Assistant solicitor, *Linklaters* London; 1985-87: Assistant Solicitor: Linklaters Hong Kong; 1983-85: Assistant solicitor, *Linklaters* London; 1980-82: Articled clerk, *Philip Ross & Co.* 1979: Leicester University, LLB.

TURTLE, Brian
Carson McDowell, Belfast (028) 9024 4951
Specialisation: Commercial litigation (30 years of practice in all major areas) to include contractual and tortious disputes. Intellectual property. Professional negligence. Employment law/industrial relations to include unfair dismissal, race, religious and sex discrimination claims.
Prof. Memberships: Law Society of Northern Ireland.
Career: 1968: LLB – QUB; joined *Carson & McDowell* 1968. Admitted as solicitor 1971. Partner in *Carson & McDowell.*

TYLER, Alfred
Balfour & Manson, Edinburgh (0131) 200 1210
fred.tyler@balfour-manson.co.uk
See under Personal Injury, p.650

WAKEFORD, Carol
Cripps Harries Hall, Tunbridge Wells (01892) 506116
caw@crippslaw.com
Specialisation: Commercial property and property related insolvency. Experienced in dealing with all forms of commercial property disputes including landlord and tenant opposed lease renewals; tenant default; rent reviews; dilapidations; unreasonable withholding of consent to assignment; sub-letting; change of use; specific performance; vendor and purchaser disputes; compulsory acquisition and compensation claims; government property work; specialist knowledge of judicial review and other planning litigation. Reported cases: Bass Holdings v Morton Music; Midland Bank v Chart Enterprises; Lloyds Bank SF Nominees v Hassan; Ballard (Kent) v Oliver Ashworth (Holdings).
Prof. Memberships: Women in Property; Property Litigation Association; SPI Womens Group.
Career: Articled with *Nabarro Nathanson* 1983-85; assistant solicitor with *Nabarro Nathanson* 1985-90; became a partner in the property litigation department of that firm 1990. Joined *Cripps Harries Hall* as a partner in 1996.
Personal: Born 1955, resides East Sussex; married to chartered surveyor, two children. Educated Bexhill County Grammar School, University College London (LLB). Speaks fluent French. Enjoys horseriding, sailing, reading, entertaining and France.

WALKER, Alan
Cobbetts, Manchester (0161) 833 7413
alan.walker@cobbetts.co.uk
Specialisation: All aspects of property litigation work, with particular emphasis on landlord and tenant matters, including dilapidations, rent reviews, opposed renewal proceedings, breaches of covenant and associated aspects of property management work.
Prof. Memberships: Law Society. Property Litigation Society.
Career: Magdalene College, Cambridge (M.A., LLM). Articled 1989-91. Admitted 1991; partner 2000.
Personal: Leisure interests include swimming, walking and theatre.

WALKER, Andrew
CMS Cameron McKenna, London
(020) 7367 2710
alw@cmck.com
Specialisation: Partner and head of Property Litigation and Dispute Resolution group. Main area of practice covers all types of property disputes including landlord and tenant (breaches of covenants, rent reviews, statutory renewals of commercial leases, breaches of statutory obligations, insolvency and applications to the Leasehold Valuation tribunal for Estate Management Schemes); claims arising out of contracts for the sale and purchase of land/buildings; breach of statutory obligations; disputes on boundaries, trespass, rights of way, professional negligence by surveyors or solicitors in relation to property matters.
Prof. Memberships: Law Society, Property Litigation Association, The City of London Property Association.
Career: Qualified 1986 and became a partner and head of Property Litigation group in 1993.
Personal: Born 8 December 1959. Leisure pursuits include horse-riding, gardening, cars and family life. Lives in London and Ross-on-Wye.

WALKER, Deirdre
Norton Rose, London (020) 7444 2633
walkerdm@nortonrose.com
Specialisation: Partner in commercial litigation department and head of corporate and banking litigation. Specialising in fraud related litigation. Deirdre has extensive experience of urgent applications for freezing injunctions and ancillary relief and in the recovery of assets. Previous instructions include advising and reporting to the Bank of England following a failed bid for the CWS; advising (and continuing to do so) in connection with the Wickes fraud; advising the Pell Frischman Group in connection with its dispute with Trevor Osborne regarding the diversion of assets from a joint venture; advising beneficiaries in connection with a dispute involving the tracing and recovery of assets wrongfully disposed of in an effort to avoid tax liabilities in various jurisdictions, obtaining Mareva relief in this jurisdiction, the British Virgin Islands and Jersey and eventually recovering in excess of £120m misappropriated assets; advising a plc in respect of its recovery of confidential information unlawfully disseminated through third parties by a previous director of the company and obtaining an injunction to prevent further disclosure; more recently advising Towry Law plc in connection with its warranty claims against Hogg Robinson plc arising out of the disposal of Advizors Limited and the subsequent 'hole' discovered in connection with the pensions misselling provision; advising in connection with the enforceability of a call option and obtaining a freezing order in respect of the relevant shares and advising a Cypriot company in relation to its contractual claim for payment of the fee for services rendered and obtaining a world-wide freezing order in order to protect the client's position pending the outcome of the litigation.
Career: Deirdre was callled to the Bar in 1985. She joined *Norton Rose* in 1989 and became a partner in 1997.

WALLS, Alan
Linklaters, London (020) 7456 4258
alan.walls@linklaters.com
Specialisation: Specialises in contentious commercial practice, principally fraud investigation and asset

recovery, insolvency and banking, encompassing regulatory investigations and other types of commercial dispute.
Career: 1987 to date: Partner, *Linklaters*; 1981-87: Assistant solicitor, *Linklaters*; 1979-81: Articled clerk, *Linklaters*. 1978: Trinity Hall, Cambridge University, Law MA (Cantab).

WALTHAM, Anne
Lovells, London (020) 7296 2000
anne.waltham@lovells.com
Specialisation: A partner in the property litigation group. Specialises in property litigation, dealing with a wide variety of landlord and tenant and real property disputes, including advising the firm's property department on potentially litigious matters. Particular expertise in rent review disputes acting for leading institutional landlords. Familiar with running substantial landlord and tenant cases and has also dealt with a number of property related professional negligence cases and arbitrations. Contributes to a number of publications including the Estates Gazette, Property Week, Property Law Journal and Commercial Lawyer. Regularly presents seminars on aspects of property litigation, to clients and externally, most recently on expert witnesses post Woolf and rent review update.
Prof. Memberships: Law Society; Property Litigation Association.
Career: Qualified in 1982 and joined *Lovells* in 1989; Partner 1998.

WARNE, David
Richards Butler, London (020) 7247 6555
dgw@richardsbutler.com
Specialisation: Commercial litigation. Partner specialising in the banking, insolvency and regulatory fields, nationally and internationally; specialises particularly in cases involving international conflict of law issues, has acted successfully for Barclays Bank in connection with US and UK jurisdictional issues arising in the MCC Administration; has also acted for creditors and bond holders in the Brent Walker reconstruction, for creditors in the Heron reconstruction and has had substantial involvement with the regulatory issues arising out of the collapse of Barings and the losses suffered by Morgan Grenfell by reason of the Peter Young affair; has successfully represented the Personal Investment Authority in connection with judicial review of decisions relating to certain high-profile compensation of investor issues; on the international front, has recently been involved in a very substantial trust dispute in the courts of the Bahamas and Australia, a jurisdiction dispute involving the US and UK courts in respect of the affairs of a US company in chapter 11, and a case for Lloyd's Bank involving evidence of Turkish banking law which raises significant issues for clearing banks in relation to the collection of foreign cheques and the application of Section 4 of the Cheques Act 1957 (see 'The Times' 8th February 1999); has recently succeeded in the Court of Appeal and successfully resisted a petition for leave to appeal to the House of Lords in relation to a trust dispute (Walker v Stokes) concerning French and Hong Kong companies and property in France; is currently acting in relation to a challenge to the English courts jurisdiction under the Brussels Convention raising issues as to domicile: a substantial misselling case involving long dated step-down bonds sold to Brazilian investors; a Prime Bank Instrument fraud claim involving England and continental jurisdictions; a claim for the return of substantial funds wrongly paid to a French Bank under a Letter of Credit and a substantial foreign exchange trading dispute, with a Swiss Bank.
Prof. Memberships: The Law Society.
Career: Qualified 1972; joined *Richards Butler* 1972.
Publications: Joint editor 'Banking Litigation' (Sweet & Maxwell).
Personal: Born 1947. Leisure: walking, wine, cricket, food and literature.

WARNE, Jonathan
Nabarro Nathanson, London (020) 7524 6000

WATSON, Peter
Levy & McRae, Glasgow (0141) 307 2311
peterwatson@lemac.co.uk
See under Defamation, p.288

WATSON, Peter M
Allen & Overy, London (020) 7330 3000
peter.watson@allenovery.com
Specialisation: Deals with the full range of contentious commercial work in particular aviation, freezing orders, conflict of laws, professional negligence, banking, finance and commercial fraud, judicial review and trade promotion issues.
Prof. Memberships: Member of the Civil Procedure Rules Committee (1996-00); CEDR Board Member.
Career: Assistant solicitor *Allen & Overy* 1981-86, seconded to *Allen & Overy* Dubai office 1984-86; partner *Allen & Overy* 1987.
Personal: BA Oxford University 1978. Born 1956.

WEBBER, Lesley
Beachcroft Wansbroughs, London (020) 7242 1011
lwebber@bwlaw.co.uk
Specialisation: Partner, head of property litigation and planning department. Principal area of practice is property litigation including rent reviews, lease renewals, dilapidations and service charge disputes, possession and forfeiture, rating and professional negligence actions. Also acts as arbitrator and as legal assessor to arbitrators. Other main area of work is town and country planning covering planning applications, agreements and appeals, local planning advice and representation, compulsory purchase orders and environmental assessments. Acted in PHIT v Holding & Management, Zubaida v Hargreaves, Sterling Estates v Pickard, Morgan Sindall v Sawston Farms, Fluor Daniels v Shortlands Investments and in the original arbitration of National Westminster Bank v Arthur Young. Member of Law Society/RICS Working Party on Landlord and Tenant Act 1954 and co-draftsman of PACT scheme for lease renewals. Member of Property Advisory group to the Department of the Environment, Transport and the Regions.
Prof. Memberships: Fellow of the Chartered Institute of Arbitrators, honorary member of ARBRIX, Blundell Memorial Lecturer 1999.
Career: Qualified 1980 while with *Freshfields*. Joined *Masons* in 1984 and became a partner in 1985. Partner London office of *Dibb Lupton Broomhead* from 1993. Joined *Beachcroft Stanleys* in 1997.
Personal: Born 10 April 1956. Attended Birmingham University 1974-77. Winner of SLSS Prize for Planning Law.

WEBSTER, Sheila
Dundas & Wilson CS, Edinburgh (0131) 228 8000

WHITTELL, Mark
Cobbetts, Manchester (0161) 833 5252
mark.whittell@cobbetts.co.uk
Specialisation: Commercial litigation including banking professional negligence, franchise disputes, insolvency.
Prof. Memberships: CEDR, accredited mediator.
Career: Articled 1980-82. Assistant solicitor, *Glass Bagshawe Miller*, 1982-84; assistant solicitor, *GW Towells*, 1984-86; *Cobbetts* 1986-present – made partner, 1989.
Personal: 44 years old. Three children. Educated Marple Hall Grammar School and Sheffield University. Lacrosse player at international and veteran international level. Enthusiastic sportsman. Interested in wine, travel.

WILLETTS, Jayne
Hammond Suddards Edge, Birmingham (0121) 222 3000
jayne.willetts@hammondse.com
Specialisation: Partner. Specialises in professional negligence and pensions litigation. Qualified as first woman High Court solicitor advocate 1994.
Prof. Memberships: First female chairman Law Society National Young Solicitors' Group 1990-91; first woman president of Birmingham Law Society 2000-01; member Court Users Committees for both Mercantile Court and the chancery division in Birmingham.
Career: Qualified in 1982. Joined *Edge Ellison* 1988 – partner from 1991.
Personal: Born 1958. Educated at Stourbridge High School for Girls and University College London. Leisure interests include equestrian sports.

WILLIAMS, Gareth
Hugh James Ford Simey, Cardiff (029) 2022 4871
gareth.williams@hjfs.co.uk
See under Personal Injury, p.651

WILLIAMS, Peter Rhys
Burges Salmon, Bristol (0117) 939 2000
peter.williams@burges-salmon.com
See under Agriculture, p.76

WILLIAMSON, David
Brodies WS, Edinburgh (0131) 228 3777
david.williamson@brodies.co.uk
Specialisation: Solicitor advocate handling general commercial litigation and specialising in intellectual property, employment law, partnership disputes and professional negligence. Experienced speaker at conferences and seminars. Lectured for over 5 years at University of Edinburgh in civil procedure.
Career: Qualified in 1971. With *Simpson & Marwick* 1969-75, latterly as partner. Joined *Brodies* as a partner in 1976. Part-time Employment tribunals chairman and part-time sheriff. Criminal Injuries Compensation Panel member.
Personal: Born in 1949. Educated at Royal High School, Edinburgh and University of Edinburgh. Leisure interests include cricket and hill walking. Lives in Edinburgh.

WILSON, Allan
Morgan Cole, Cardiff (029) 2038 5385
allan.wilson@morgan-cole.com
Specialisation: Handles a wide variety of commercial litigation work, including substantial, high profile matters. Has acted for a range of institutional and corporate clients concerning competition, profession-

al indemnity and construction claims, as well as buy-out/acquisition disputes. Work also covers defamation and transportation related claims. Advised rugby clubs on disputes with governing bodies and International Rugby Board on regulatory and competition, matters including dealing with the competition directorate in Brussels. Also dealt with engineering claims resulting from Severn Bridge gantry collapse. Has conducted many mediations and has sat as a mediator.
Prof. Memberships: Law Society, Association of European Lawyers, TECSA, mediator ADR Net Ltd.
Career: Hutton Grammar School, Preston 1968-75; University of Surrey, BSc Linguistics (German) 1975-79; College of law, Guildford 1979-80; *Slaughter and May* 1980-85; *Morgan Cole* 1985 to date, partner from 1986. Currently divisional director for litigation.
Personal: Golf, running and indoor rowing. Married, two sons. Lives near Raglan, Monmouthshire.

WILSON, Michael
Elliott Duffy Garrett, Belfast (028) 9024 5034
michael.wilson@edgsolicitors.co.uk
See under Insolvency/Corporate Recovery, p.585

WINTERBURN, Anthony
DLA, Manchester (08700) 111111

WOOD, Jonathan
Clyde & Co, London (020) 7623 1244
Jonathan.Wood@clyde.co.uk
Specialisation: Co-ordinating partner of commercial litigation department. Main area of practice is insurance and banking work, within the commercial litigation department. Involves advising on export credit guarantee insurance, financial institution insurance, fraud, reinsurance and insolvency matters. International trade work also covered, including conflict of laws, trading contracts, trading disputes and political risk insurance. Frequent speaker on insurance and reinsurance, insolvency, fraud and export credit and political risk insurance.
Prof. Memberships: Law Society, IBA, Vice Chairman of Committees on International Trade, Member of Insurance, Insolvency and International Litigation Committees, Member of London Court of International Arbitration, ABA and DRI.
Career: Qualified 1977. Joined *Clyde & Co* 1984. Partner in 1987. Legal Advisor to Export Credits Guarantee Department, Cardiff 1987.
Personal: Born 11th June 1953. Attended Stockport Grammar, Sheffield University 1971-74. Leisure pursuits include tennis, skiing and scuba diving. Lives in Farnham.

WOODCOCK, Tony
Stephenson Harwood, London (020) 7809 2349
tony.woodcock@shlegal.com
Specialisation: Partner – litigation department; Head of investigation and regulation group. Main area of practice is financial services and professional regulation; fraud; insider dealing; directors liability; white collar crime including health and safely and environmental regulation. Also deals with financial and professional investigations, conducting investigations for regulatory bodies in financial services, accounting and insolvency and advising institutions on money laundering avoidance procedures.
Career: Office of the DPP 1979-85 and the Office of Treasury Solicitor 1985-87. *Slaughter and May* 1987-90. *Stephenson Harwood* 1990; partner, 1994. Solicitor-Advocate (All Courts) 1996.
Publications: Co-author of 'Serious Fraud: Investigation and Trial' (Butterworths). Contributor 'Butterworth's Encyclopaedia of Financial Services Law'.
Personal: LLB (Hons), LLM; Joseph Hume Law Scholar (UCL); Montague Prizeman & Harmsworth Scholar (Middle Temple); Languages: French. Resides London.

YORK, Stephen
Vinson & Elkins LLP, London (020) 7618 6033
syork@velaw.com
Specialisation: Commercial litigation, ADR and international arbitration (both as counsel and as neutral), principally in the projects energy and IT/telecoms sectors. Particularly experienced in work involving complicated technology where there has been a project or risk management failure.
Prof. Memberships: Fellow Chartered Institute of Arbitrators; LCIA; Law Societies of England & Wales and Hong Kong. Board Member CEDR.
Career: St Catharine's College, Cambridge (1979, BA, MA). Admitted solicitor England & Wales 1982; Hong Kong 1984.
Publications: 'Practical ADR' (Sweet & Maxwell); 'A Guide to the Law of Electronic Commerce' (Butterworths).
Personal: Married with four children. A resident of Cambridge.

LOCAL GOVERNMENT

London: 586; South West: 588; Wales: 588; Midlands: 589; East Anglia: 590; The North: 590; Scotland: 591; *Profiles*: 592

RESEARCH APPROVED BY BMRB: *For this edition,* Chambers' *researchers conducted 6,552 interviews – 4,419 with law firms, 554 with barristers and 1,579 with clients.*

The validity of the research was scrutinised by BMRB International, who audited both the methodology and the results at our offices in July 2001. They interviewed Chambers' *researchers and cross-checked sample interviews. Details of the audit appear on page 7.*

LONDON

LOCAL GOVERNMENT • London	Ptnrs	Assts
1 Nabarro Nathanson	9	16
2 Rowe & Maw	2	9
Sharpe Pritchard	n/a	n/a
3 Ashurst Morris Crisp	1	3
Lawrence Graham	1	6
Léonie Cowen & Associates	1	2
Trowers & Hamlins	6	8
4 Berwin Leighton Paisner	2	*
Denton Wilde Sapte	1	*
5 Clifford Chance	*	*
Herbert Smith	*	*
6 DJ Freeman	1	*
Dechert	1	2
Jenkins & Hand	2	n/a
Winckworth Sherwood	*	*

LEADING INDIVIDUALS	
1 **CHILD Tony** Rowe & Maw	**COWEN Léonie** Léonie Cowen & Associates
FORGE Anna Rowe & Maw	**ILEY Malcolm** Nabarro Nathanson
RANDALL Simon Lawrence Graham	
2 **AMBROSE Ray** Nabarro Nathanson	**CURNOW Tony** Ashurst Morris Crisp
GRIFFITHS Trevor Sharpe Pritchard	
3 **DOOLITTLE Ian** Trowers & Hamlins	**HAND Catherine** Jenkins & Hand
4 **RANDALL Helen** Nabarro Nathanson	**SERRELLI Roseanne** Sharpe Pritchard
UP AND COMING	
SHARLAND John Sharpe Pritchard	

This book is the product of 6,552 1/2 hour interviews. See p.7 for BMRB audit.
Within each band, firms are listed alphabetically. *See individuals' profiles p.592*
* *See editorial entries for explanations of team sizes.*

Nabarro Nathanson (see firm details p.1078) "*You can't keep them down.*" Unequivocally the London firm that drew most comment in our research, endorsed "*for the size and competence of its team.*" Anchored in its Public Sector Group, the team acts for private clients as well as a vast array of public sector bodies. Clients applaud lawyers who "*are quite prepared to meet challenging deadlines – we needed a big gun and we got one who works with us rather than for us.*" The impact of PPPs on local government has been reflected by an increase in outsourcing and regeneration work. **Malcolm Iley** was instructed to advise the London Borough of Southwark on the 10-year regeneration of the Elephant & Castle. Iley has "*a real knowledge of local authorities*" and "*gives confidence to clients by being calm and collected.*" He is well supported by **Ray Ambrose**. The firm has also witnessed a growth in e-government and governance issues, being one of the two firms this year to be appointed to advise the National Audit Office. With her work on projects such as Bournemouth Borough Council's first Pathfinder PFI project for a library/ICT network, the "*in demand*" **Helen Randall** (see p.593) enters the tables this year. Clients describe her as "*approachable, she's a specialist.*" It has been aided, like many leading firms in this area, by a reorganisation of the department along lines more familiar to the local government client. **Clients:** Birmingham CC; Bournemouth BC; Brent LBC; Denby; DETR; Islington LBC; Plymouth City Council; Southwark LBC.

Rowe & Maw (see firm details p.1113) "*Huge in the district audit field,*" as NHS and local government external auditors, the firm also enjoys an impressive relationship with the big five accountants, the Audit Commission and private bodies involved in local government matters. "*Probably the foremost local authority lawyer*" is a typical endorsement for department head **Tony Child** (see p.58), "*you'd be hard pressed to find someone with a more encyclopaedic knowledge of case law.*" Clients feel "*kept in the picture, particularly regarding arbitration issues.*" **Anna Forge** (see p.592) has made her mark with "*good judgement,*" technical knowledge and an "*accessible approach.*" The group has been engaged in PFI projects for schools and care centres, and runs training for over 50 local authorities on health and social care and the law. It has also been heavily involved in education, presiding over the first ever successful challenge to a pupil's expulsion from a private school. The group has acted for Transport for London on corporate governance arrangements. **Clients:** Transport for London; local authorities.

Sharpe Pritchard (see firm details p.1123) The firm maintains its high status as the London litigation agents for local authorities. Indeed, it would be difficult to find a local authority that has not dealt with the firm. Clients certainly approve of the quality of its work, "*we keep on being enormously impressed.*" Although the group encompasses other aspects of local government expertise, litigation remains its greatest strength. A complementary growth in non-contentious procurement work ensures that the firm remains "*friendly and low key – they listen to their clients and don't make grand statements.*" Most notable in the team is **Trevor Griffiths** (see p.592) ("*no one beats him for litigation*"), with both the thorough **Roseanne Serrelli** (see p.593) and client friendly **John Sharland** (see p.593) developing the practice. The group has acted for the City of Westminster on an IT system PPP, and on the refurbishment of the Barbican Centre. **Clients:** Cambridgeshire CC; Corporation of London; Hammersmith & Fulham LBC; City of Westminster; Waltham Forest Housing Action Trust.

Ashurst Morris Crisp (see firm details p.866) Best known for its planning expertise, a greater willingness among authorities to look at the commercial aspects of local government has resulted in considerable growth in the firm's town centre regeneration projects. One typical example is advice on the construction of a large, new container port on the former Shell Refinery site for Thurrock Council. The firm has also assisted Ealing LBC on a major section 106 planning negotiation. Our interviewees commended a "*professional, down to earth*" team who "*don't sit on the fence.*" The firm's work on the Channel Tunnel Rail Link Scheme has seen them act for Union Railways Property on a regular basis. The "*pleasant and business-like*" **Tony Curnow** (see p.663) leads a team that has acted on all aspects of the extension and redevelopment of Broadmead Shoppping Centre for Bristol CC as well as for Hackney LBC's 700,000 square foot Hearn Street development. **Clients:** Bath and NE Somerset CC; Brent LBC; Bristol CC;

DLR Limited; Ealing LBC; Hackney LBC; Thurrock; Union Railways Property.

Lawrence Graham (see firm details p.1030) Our research indicates that this is an "*active group, particularly expert on leisure trusts.*" The team maintains a market-leading position on sport, heritage and leisure externalisations for local authorities. Work has included the transfer of two leisure centres in Thurrock to a newly created Charitable Trust, and involvement in a mixed residential/commercial/leisure development in Medway. Peers believe that **Simon Randall** (see p.593) is "*enormously good at dealing with council members*" and "*knows exactly how to perform in a committee environment.*" The firm is also involved in two-fifths of the completed stock transfers in the country, most notably acting on Coventry's £200 million LSVT, one of the biggest to date. **Clients:** Chiltern DC; Coventry CC; Denbighshire CC; Medway Council; Pendle BC; Thurrock Council.

Léonie Cowen & Associates (see firm details p.1037) Its size is thought not to threaten its chief rivals, yet it challenges with its utmost quality and an approach that is "*flexible and knowledgeable, particularly in PFI-type schemes.*" Its clients do not believe size is an issue; "*they can cope with large scale work admirably.*" The "*particularly accessible*" **Léonie Cowen** (see p.592) has an enviable reputation with many leading solicitors claiming she is "*great to work with, I'd recommend her as my first choice.*" The firm's organic growth has kept pace with an increased volume of leisure projects and some sizeable educational projects. It acted in the externalisations of leisure centres at Ellesmere Port, in Dover and Newham creating new, not-for-profit organisations. Also advised WS Atkins on the transfer of Southwark's education services. Its lawyers have impressed clients as "*knowledgeable about the sector and focused on what's important commercially.*" **Clients:** Barking & Dagenham; Dover DC; Dudley MBC; Ellesmere Port; Enfield LBC; Newham LBC; Southwark CC; Tower Hamlets; WS Atkins.

Trowers & Hamlins (see firm details p.1162) "*Obviously a skilled and dedicated team,*" the firm is preceded by its considerable reputation as a social housing specialist. The past year has seen the firm transfer £706 million of housing to the private sector, most notably Coventry City Council. Our researchers were impressed that many of the more junior members of the local government team garnered plaudits. Department head **Ian Doolittle** (see p.592) stands out with his "*national reputation*" for housing association finance and transfers. Clients appreciate a team that is "*clued up and aware of what we can and can't do.*" The firm is also commended for its early risk assessment reports. Its extensive regeneration work for Brent LBC and externalisations for both the leisure and education sectors are typical of the breadth of this offering. **Clients:** Coventry CC; Hackney LBC; Hounslow LBC; Merton LBC; North Wiltshire DC; Sunderland CC.

Berwin Leighton Paisner (see firm details p.878) (2 partners full-time, 3 partners and 12 associates part-time.) Retains its dominance in the planning and property fields, but our interviewees felt that the firm lacks the depth of *'pure local government'* work as undertaken by its rivals. With an outstanding property department headed by Phillip Bretherton, the firm has continued to expand its involvement in the outsourcing of business processes, such as IT projects. The firm has been active in a large number of retail and leisure redevelopments, including Belfast City Centre and Paradise Street in Liverpool. **Clients:** City of Westminster; Department of Social Development in Northern Ireland; Liverpool City Council; London Borough of Enfield; Maidstone Borough Council; Northampton Borough Council; Solihull MBC.

Denton Wilde Sapte (see firm details p.939) (1 partner full-time, 3 partners and 14 associates part-time.) With a firm grounding in the planning and public sector department, the team has seen growth in both PFI and regeneration work. Some commented that its status is reliant on planning strengths, but clients are "*impressed,*" considering them "*excellent and competitive on pricing.*" Recent highlights for Sandra Banks' team include advising on a £54 million infrastructure development for Reigate and Banstead Borough Council, and the London Development Agency's regeneration of the Royal Dock's Area, including the Docklands Light Railway extension to City Airport. The group has also been active on behalf of English Partnerships. Encompassing both private sector and public sector work, it acted for Equion on its procurement facilities for the Metropolitan Police in the South East. **Clients:** Barking LBC; Birmingham City Council; English Partnerships; Essex CC; Herefordshire DC; London Development Agency; Manchester City Council; Portsmouth City Council; Reigate & Banstead BC; South Oxhey Regeneration Scheme; Tower Hamlets LBC.

Clifford Chance (see firm details p.919) (7 partners and 22 assistants part-time.) Best known for its high-end planning expertise, the firm has nonetheless been involved in a number of redevelopment projects, for West Dorset District Council and for Historic Royal Palaces in relation to the Tower Environs scheme for the Tower of London. Brian Hall's team is recognised for its skill in financing issues and training. The group advises public and private bodies and a number of banks on lending to local authorities, and acts for lenders on housing association transfers. Its "*wealth of background experience*" and "*speedy, pleasant manner*" was commented on time and again in our interviews with clients. **Clients:** Corporation of London; East Hertfordshire DC; Hastings BC; Hounslow LBC; Manchester CC; MEPC; Spelthorne BC; West Dorset DC.

Herbert Smith (see firm details p.993) (9 partners and 10 assistants part-time.) Using a high profile in public and administration law as a springboard into the local government field, the firm remains, in the words of one competitor, "*mind-blowingly strong.*" Combining the talents of its litigation and planning departments, the cross-departmental team is skilled in related areas such as construction, rather than setting its stall as a 'pure' operator. It has also seen an expansion of its PPP-related real estate work, with the bias on the private sector. It acted on the redevelopment of Fulham Pools opposite the London Borough of Hammersmith & Fulham, and in the regeneration of the Shoreditch area for Hackney LBC. Most recently it landed instructions in the 'Swindon Front Garden' commercial and leisure development, encompassing 700 acres, 4,000 houses and several schools. **Clients:** Dorset CC; Hackney LBC; Holmes Place; Kensington & Chelsea LBC; Oxfordshire CC.

DJ Freeman (see firm details p.943) (1 full-time partner supported part-time by 2 partners and 3 associates.) Traditionally best known as a property firm, it has recently weighted its local government work away from housing, targeting securitisations and limited partnerships in the private sector. Recent work has included a large number of redevelopments, acting for Camden LBC on a proposed residential and leisure complex at Swiss Cottage, and advising BG plc on the redevelopment of a former gas works site in Hove. Ted Totman has also led work on the agreement and lease of a proposed major phased redevelopment of the town centre at Walton-on-Thames for Elmbridge BC. **Clients:** Camden LBC; Carrick DC; Chichester CC; Commission for New Towns; Elmbridge BC; Enfield LBC; Epsom & Ewell BC; Fareham BC; Hertmere DC; Truro.

Dechert (see firm details p.938) Has continued to refocus its public sector work, turning to larger scale, property development schemes. Notable successes can be seen in a variety of large office developments within London, including a mixed use leisure development in Ilford and the redevelopment of the listed Novella House. Also advised on aspects of the Crown Estate's commercial development of Regents Street properties. Michael Hallowell and the public sector team have utilised their "*good expertise in planning and infrastructure*" on Hemel Hempstead's town centre extension, and advised on the disposal of surplus school land for development in West Sussex. **Clients:** Corporation of London; Crown Estate; Dacorum BC; PACE; Redbridge LBC; Swansea CC; West Sussex CC.

Jenkins & Hand (see firm details p.1013) Though a smaller, "*bright, able and experienced*" firm, it continues to secure big-ticket work that is the envy of larger departments. While noted as having expertise in social housing, it is one of the firms acting for the preferred bidder for the Elephant & Castle's prestigious, long-term regeneration scheme. The well-respected **Catherine Hand** (see p.592) continues to advise the District Audit service and is also an expert legal advisor on Lambeth's Housing Investment Commission. The firm also advised Torbay on its recent housing stock transfer. **Clients:** District Audit Service; Southwark CC; Torbay Council.

Winckworth Sherwood (see firm details p.1185) (All fee-earners working part-time.) Despite a perception from some quarters that the firm is biased towards planning, new requirements for 'best value' have seen a significant increase in not-for-profit outsourcing and procurement work. Andrew Murray's group has been active in infrastructure work, acting on several light rail schemes, including Nottingham Express Transit, the Leeds Supertram and the DLR. It has also worked for the Chester Guided Busway and on the major works at Yorkshire Marina in Bridlington Harbour. In addition the firm handled a regeneration project for Hammersmith & Fulham and the outsourcing of Lewisham's housing management function. **Clients:** Chester Guided Busway; Corporation of London; East Riding BC (Yorkshire Marina); East Sussex CC; Hammersmith Regeneration Project; Hertfordshire CC; Lewisham LBC; Merseyside CC; Metropolitan Police Authority; Mid Glamorgan CC; Oxfordshire CC.

SOUTH WEST

LOCAL GOVERNMENT • South West	Ptnrs	Assts
1 **Bevan Ashford** Bristol, Exeter, Plymouth	4	4
2 **Bond Pearce** Bristol, Exeter	1	*

This book is the product of 6,552 1/2 hour interviews. See p.7 for BMRB audit.
Within each band, firms are listed alphabetically.
* *See editorial entries for explanations of team sizes.*

Bevan Ashford (see firm details p.880) The incorporation of 'best value' into local authority arrangements has complemented the firm's expertise in health and social care. It has secured a high proportion of advisory work, aiding the South West of England Regional Development Agency on a variety of property and planning matters, including the Temple Quay development in Bristol. Local authorities describe them as "*client-focused and keen to work in a manner which suited us.*" John Bosworth and a team of specialists drawn from a variety of departments advised South Somerset Council in its plans to serve discontinuance notices regarding the planning uses of a town centre. **Clients:** Bristol CC; Chichester DC; Gloucestershire CC; Hackney LBC; Havering LBC; Maidstone BC; South Somerset CC; SW England RDA.

Bond Pearce (see firm details p.888) (full time partner and 2 part time assistants) Judged by peers to be "*expanding well and widening its client base.*" The firm has seen an increase to its client base both among local government bodies and commercial entities. The firm is particularly endorsed for its work in the property and planning sphere. Emrys Parry has acted for a number of local authorities on compulsory purchase and highway matters, such as the Reading Oracle shopping centre development. The team has recently been augmented by a new recruit from local government. **Clients:** Caradon DC; Dorset CC; Penwith DC; Plymouth City Council; Reading BC; South Oxfordshire DC.

WALES

LOCAL GOVERNMENT • Wales	Ptnrs	Assts
1 **Eversheds** Cardiff	2	2
2 **Edwards Geldard** Cardiff	n/a	n/a
3 **Morgan Cole** Cardiff, Swansea	*	*

LEADING INDIVIDUALS
1 **EVANS Eric** Eversheds
2 **COLE Alun** Morgan Cole
WILLIAMS Huw Edwards Geldard

This book is the product of 6,552 1/2 hour interviews. See p.7 for BMRB audit.
Within each band, firms are listed alphabetically. *See individuals' profiles p.592*
* *See editorial entries for explanations of team sizes.*

Eversheds (see firm details p.952) Embraced by the market for its "*local strengths and technical expertise,*" partly the product of the firm's overall "*massive local government profile.*" Welsh devolution has led to an increase in constitutional and vires work regarding the establishment of companies by local authorities. For unit head **Eric Evans** (see p.592), PFI and related schemes have provided a staple diet, representing Wiltshire CC on three hospital schemes and two school PFIs. The third major string to its bow is acting on regeneration and redevelopment, including advice to the Vale of Glamorgan Council concerning the Barry Waterfront project, and the completion of Neath Port Talbot County Borough Council's £30 million waste-to-energy scheme. **Clients:** Blaenau Gwent CC; Bridgend CC; Caerphilly; Neath Port Talbot CBC; West Sussex CC; Wiltshire CC.

Edwards Geldard (see firm details p.948) Notable chiefly for property-related work on CPO, planning matters and highways, as shown by its long term work for Wrexham on a new four-phase access road to the Wrexham Industrial Estate. Its "*fine*" local government focus is located within **Huw Williams**' (see p.60) public sector department. The group has been involved in the purchase and planning of town centre developments, such as 'Fountain's Walk' at Pontypridd for Rhondda Cynon Taf County Borough and at Pontypool for Torfaen County Borough. The firm rounds this off with a variety of regeneration schemes for the Welsh Development Agency in Carmarthenshire. Clients have been "*impressed with the standard of preparation*" from the firm. **Clients:** Cardiff CC; Torfaen CB; Welsh Development Agency; Wrexham BC.

Morgan Cole (see firm details p.1074) (Up to 8 partners and 32 assistants available as required.) Recent reorganisation at the firm has seen an increased focus from both Welsh offices towards specifically commercial matters, although the market has yet to perceive the full effects of this move. "*Clients have a lot of confidence in*" **Alun Cole** according to his peers. The firm continues to work on Cardiff CC's 'Sports Village' development, and has been active in a variety of PFI schemes and land disposals. Enjoys a profile as the retained firm of the Welsh Development Agency on the Pembray project, constructing a knowledge-based visitors' centre. **Clients:** Cardiff CC; Welsh Development Agency; local authorities.

MIDLANDS

LOCAL GOVERNMENT • Midlands	Ptnrs	Assts
1 **Wragge & Co** Birmingham	3	10
2 **Pinsent Curtis Biddle** Birmingham	4	3
3 **DLA** Birmingham	n/a	n/a
Eversheds Birmingham, Nottingham	3	8
4 **Anthony Collins Solicitors** Birmingham	2	5
Mills & Reeve Birmingham	6	2

LEADING INDIVIDUALS
1 **KEITH-LUCAS Peter** Wragge & Co
MATTHEW Stephen Eversheds
2 **COOK Mark** Anthony Collins Solicitors
KNOX Martin Anthony Collins Solicitors
3 **STEPHENS Hugo** Pinsent Curtis Biddle

This book is the product of 6,552 1/2 hour interviews. See p.7 for BMRB audit.

Within each band, firms are listed alphabetically. *See individuals' profiles p.592*

Wragge & Co (see firm details p.1189) "*Superb.*" Based in the public sector department, the firm draws on the corporate team, bringing in specialists as and when. Clients state they have "*good confidence*" in this "*reliable*" firm. The range of work has continued to expand and competitors in London view them as "*a definite threat.*" Planning and property developments, especially for town centres, are something of a mainstay. Clients agree: "*for commercial development issues they're pretty sharp and were most competitive on their tender.*" The group has acted on the new Oxford United football ground, encompassing planning powers and restrictive covenants. Acting for both public and private bodies, the firm has developed a speciality in externalisations, overseeing the care homes transfer from Buckinghamshire CC to Heritage Care, while also acting for BUPA. "*Focused*" **Peter Keith-Lucas** "*is a market leader with his own inimitable style.*" He heads the unit and is perceived by peers to have cornered the market in advising on the constitutions of local authorities across England. This includes a recent standards committee enquiry for Congleton BC in an investigation into allegations of misconduct by the leader of the council over local development proposals. **Clients:** Buckinghamshire CC; Congleton BC; Telford & Wrekin Council; Torfaen CC.

Pinsent Curtis Biddle (see firm details p.1098) With PFIs a strong area for the firm, the last year has seen an upsurge in housing and related projects for local authorities. Peers say the firm is "*much more noticeable.*" Variety is the key, acting for Islington LBC on the outsourcing of their management team, for Walsall MBC on an education externalisation and for both on their street lighting projects. Competitors claim "*it has taken steps forward with cohesive support for local government work.*" Combining development and public law skills, the team has represented several councils on town centre developments, including Solihull, Bromsgrove and Aylesbury. "*The level of technical expertise is outstanding.*" Since his arrival from Irwin Mitchell, **Hugo Stephens** (see p.784) ("*a big personality*") has clearly made an impact, said to "*cover all the ground for LSVT nationally,*" including the £420 million, 36,500-unit stock transfer for Sunderland CC, one of the largest such transfers to date. Guidance and advisory work also feature prominently, aiding 4Ps and DETR, inter alia, on social housing and a range of issues. Rounding off this package is an increasing level of instructions from private sector clients for PFI/PPP schemes, such as Nationwide BC, Jarvis and Onyx. **Clients:** 4Ps; Islington LBC; Newham LBC; Sunderland Council; Walsall MBC.

DLA A respected firm that has a profile in the high end of the market, acting on PFI projects, including transportation and infrastructure matters for local authorities and private bodies.

Eversheds (see firm details p.952) With internal reorganisations complete, the "*constructive*" **Stephen Matthew** (see p.712) is now head of the firm's national Projects Group, and it is in this field that the Nottingham office excels. Clients believe "*his leadership has instilled the highest qualities*" in the team. He has overseen the fire service and schools PFIs for Cornwall CC, as well as entering the vehicles procurement programme for Nottinghamshire Police. The headline deal for the year has been representing Nottingham City Council on the £180 million Express Transit Project, the first light rail system to be procured under PFI. Commended by clients as "*absolutely excellent, a prompt service from self-starters who know how to solve problems.*" The team has also been involved in the major externalisation of Lincolnshire's central IT services, and the PFI for the long-term maintenance of Camden LBC's social housing. **Clients:** Cornwall CC; Dorset Police Authority; Hinckley & Bosworth BC; Lincolnshire CC; Newcastle-Under-Lyme Council; Nottinghamshire Police Authority; Somerset CC; Stoke-on-Trent City Council.

Anthony Collins Solicitors (see firm details p.860) Our researchers were told that the firm fields "*good players in the market,*" with their undoubted strength in social housing and regeneration schemes. Working for almost a third of all authorities involved in New Deals for Communities, the team is said to have "*a joined up way of working, with lawyers and quantity surveyors plus community developers on tap.*" Clients pay glowing tribute to partners **Mark Cook** (see p.592) ("*extremely approachable*") and **Martin Knox** (see p.782) ("*clearly a national leader*"). Interviewees believe its success lies in its tailored approach for a variety of clients, whether the large PFI for building new housing for the Stonebridge Housing Action Trust or the smaller urban regeneration scheme for Bassetlaw DC. The group also advised Bretland DC on its e-commerce strategy. **Clients:** Bath and NE Somerset CC; Brent LBC; Bristol City Council; Colchester; DLR Limited; Ealing LBC; Hackney LBC; Havering LBC; Hounslow LBC; Stoke City Council; Thurrock; Union Railways Property.

Mills & Reeve (see firm details p.1069) Many interviewees felt that the full impact of the recent relocation of the majority of the local government team to the Birmingham office (from Norwich) has yet to be felt. Clients value that "*they understand the local authority environment and relate well to us – the quality of work is high.*" A highlight of recent work was the partnership forged with Leicester CC on employment and litigation matters. Nicholas Hancox's "*knowledgeable*" unit also won the contract for the East of England Development Agency and the £60 million Norwich Millennium Library. **Clients:** LB Barking & Dagenham; Bedfordshire; Cambridgeshire; East Hertfordshire DC; Leicester CC; Newham LBC; Norfolk.

EAST ANGLIA

LOCAL GOVERNMENT • East Anglia	Ptnrs	Assts
1 **Steele & Co** Norwich	2	3

This book is the product of 6,552 1/2 hour interviews. See p.7 for BMRB audit.
Within each band, firms are listed alphabetically.

Steele & Co (see firm details p.1140) Based in its public law department, Richard Hewitt's team has emerged in this year's research as the dominant force in East Anglia, due in part to Mills & Reeve's new weighting towards the Midlands but also as direct result of being "*responsive, practical and down to earth.*" It now acts for 11 authorities on a long term basis, including Westminster City Council's civil, property, litigation and debt recovery services. Clients praise "*a tailored service.*" The firm also won the tender for the procurement advice to Merton LBC, and is further involved in providing regulation advice for the East of England Development Agency. **Clients:** Boston DC; Broadland DC; Bromley LBC; Chelmsford BC; Croydon LBC; East of England Development Agency; Merton LBC; Westminster CC.

THE NORTH

LOCAL GOVERNMENT • The North	Ptnrs	Assts
1 **Eversheds** Leeds	4	13
2 **Pinsent Curtis Biddle** Leeds	6	7
3 **Walker Morris** Leeds	1	8
4 **Masons** Leeds	4	9
Pannone & Partners Manchester	3	2

LEADING INDIVIDUALS
1 **CIRELL Stephen** Eversheds
2 **DOBSON Nicholas** Pinsent Curtis Biddle
KILDUFF David Walker Morris

This book is the product of 6,552 1/2 hour interviews. See p.7 for BMRB audit.
Within each band, firms are listed alphabetically. *See individuals' profiles p.592*

Eversheds (see firm details p.952) "*The Rolls Royce of local government work.*" It remains a nationally dominant force. The work is centred on the Leeds office and "*leading light*" **Stephen Cirell** (see p.58). Clients speak of an "*extremely good range of lawyers at their disposal*" who "*supported us with a thorough knowledge of PFI and related legislation.*" Cirell stands out on the national stage, "*he has a big impact on everything,*" while competitors agree "*if I were a local authority in a difficult situation, I would want him on it.*" He is supported by John Bennett, now in a consultancy position. Commanding a constant stream of instructions, a particular success has been PFI-related strategic partnerships and outsourcings, such as for Bedfordshire CC. The firm has advised Havering LBC on its new constitution and Brent LBC on the 'best value' review of its legal services. It is involved in giving advice and assistance to local authorities with LEAs that are subject to sanction action by the government. **Clients:** Bedfordshire CC; Blackburn CC; Brent LBC; Haringey LBC; Havering LBC; Lincolnshire CC; Liverpool CC; Middlesbrough CC.

Pinsent Curtis Biddle (see firm details p.1098) Another strong showing from the "*highly regarded*" **Nicholas Dobson** (see p.592) and his team, who have "*delighted*" clients with their "*quick grasp of the public sector environment.*" Dobson is said to have an "*understanding of the political as well as practical frameworks.*" The team has utilised strategic collaborations and partnerships under 'best value' such as arrangements with Dudley MBC and Bolton MBC. As sole external legal representatives to DfEE, the firm advised on the outsourcing of the local authority LEA management at the London Boroughs of Southwark, Haringey and Waltham Forest. It also handled an integrated PFI/'best value' project on a range of community services for the building of a community facility for Stoke-on-Trent Council and a wide variety of other authorities. **Clients:** Birmingham; Bolton MBC; Bradford MBC; Cheshire Police Authority; Colchester; Dudley MBC; Lancashire County Council; Layton; Leeds City Council; PWC; Stoke on Trent Council; City of Sunderland; Walsall MBC; Waltham Forest LB; York.

Walker Morris (see firm details p.1171) Considered by some observers to be "*sending out a message that they are serious about local government work.*" The firm has been supporting several external auditors on governance and procedures. It has also been involved in advice on the effects and implementation of new human rights legislation. On the commercial side, it represented Liverpool's city-wide regeneration scheme, as well as advising on the pathfinder deal for Leeds CC's education outsourcing. Department head **David Kilduff** (see p.593) "*knows and understands public law*" and is particularly reputed for his projects work. The group combined 'best value' partnership, procurement strategy and PFI/PPP for Sheffield City Council in a 30-year, £1 billion long-term waste management contract. **Clients:** Bradford CC; DETR; Kunick plc; Leeds City Council; Liverpool City Council; MoD; Sheffield City Council.

Masons (see firm details p.1056) Clients proclaim that they "*have been more than happy with the service*" provided by construction partner Mark Richard's team. It has been successful applying construction and its other core strengths such as outsourcing and utilities work to local government clients. The firm has continued to work on major disputes for Leeds CC over the South Leeds stadium, and advises on its pedestrianisation scheme as well as providing general data protection advice. The firm has set up a partnership with North Yorkshire CC legal services and provides legal and other advice for regional small education action zones. **Clients:** Leeds CC; North Yorkshire; other local authorities; public sector PFI projects.

Pannone & Partners (see firm details p.1088) Steven Grant and his team have seen significant instructions this year in major projects and transport work. Most notable of these has been its advice to the Greater Manchester Passenger Transport Authority on the Phase 3 Metrolink project, concerning the granting of concessions, and on the right to operate the city's tram system. The group has also represented Manchester Airport on the major acquisition of the airports division from the National Express Group for £241 million. Also entered into a partnering agreement deal with Tameside MBC. **Clients:** Benefits Agency; Greater Manchester Passenger Transport Authority; Highways Agency; Manchester Airport; North West Regional Assembly; Oldham MBC; Rochdale MBC; Tameside MBC.

SCOTLAND

LOCAL GOVERNMENT • Scotland	Ptnrs	Assts
1 **Dundas & Wilson CS** Edinburgh	n/a	n/a
Shepherd & Wedderburn WS Edinburgh	5	7
2 **McGrigor Donald** Glasgow	*	*
3 **Brodies WS** Edinburgh	3	2
Burness Edinburgh	2	4
Simpson & Marwick WS Edinburgh	2	3
Tods Murray WS Edinburgh	n/a	n/a

LEADING INDIVIDUALS
1 **MACLEOD Ian** Shepherd & Wedderburn WS
SHAW Kate Simpson & Marwick WS

This book is the product of 6,552 1/2 hour interviews. See p.7 for BMRB audit.
Within each band, firms are listed alphabetically. *See individuals' profiles p.592*
* *See editorial entries for explanations of team sizes.*

Dundas & Wilson CS (see firm details p.947) "*Obviously extremely strong in PFI,*" according to our interviewees, which has led to some "*excellent contacts.*" The firm channels local authority work from Michael McAuley's newly restructured government services group, seen as "*a good competent crowd.*" Added to its relationship with Arthur Andersen, the firm has a strong base to challenge for local government work. Highlight of the year was advising the City of Edinburgh and Glasgow City Council on their PPP schools projects. It has also continued its exclusive partnering arrangements with Stirling Council on its Forthside Development, as well as its Balfron High School Project. **Clients:** City of Edinburgh Council; Glasgow City Council; Stirling Council.

Shepherd & Wedderburn WS (see firm details p.1126) A substantial, dedicated local authority team, it is viewed as "*long established and particularly strong.*" Active in the contracting out of local authority functions to companies controlled by them, and any subsequent vires issues. Examples include advising Edinburgh Leisure on the outsourcing of its services and North Ayrshire Leisure Limited on a transfer of its sport and leisure facilities. "*Pushing hard, competing for project work and certainly a force to be reckoned with,*" noted one competitor. **Ian MacLeod** (see p.575) is "*more experienced than most*" and "*comfortable with a range of issues.*" The firm has been pushing its planning experience West, with schools and roads projects for North Ayrshire, as well as a similar project for new client Midlothian Council. Notably the firm represented Aberdeenshire Council in a judicial review under police pensions regulations, while Waterfront Edinburgh instructed it on a major redevelopment of the Edinburgh waterfront. **Clients:** Aberdeenshire Council; Angus Council; Audit Scotland; City of Edinburgh Council; Commissioner for Local Administration; East Dunbartonshire Council; East Renfrewshire Council; Falkirk Council; Fife Council; Highland Council; Midlothian Council; North Ayrshire Council; North Lanarkshire Council; West Lothian Council.

McGrigor Donald (see firm details p.1062) (All staff part-time.) A particular focus on legislative work and statutory interpretation for both private sector clients and local authorities is in evidence. This included setting up a bidding consortium across Scotland for trunk road contracts and ongoing housing work for Aberdeenshire. In what has been a busy year, Alan Boyd's public sector group has worked on the City of Edinburgh's transport PFI scheme procurement, and acted on both Argyll & Bute's and Dumfries & Galloway's waste management PFIs. It also advised the Highland Council on its framework for local economic development using joint venture participation. The firm's "*strong local authority connections*" encourage some to see them as the "*first port of call for Edinburgh*" work, as well as further afield. **Clients:** Aberdeenshire; Argyll & Bute; Dumfries & Galloway; City of Edinburgh; Highland Council; Moray Council; North Lanarkshire; Orkney Islands Council.

Brodies WS (see firm details p.896) Noted particularly for its litigation prowess, the firm has witnessed growth across the board with particular strength in PFIs. It handled the externalisation of Inverclyde County Council's facilities and employment services. William Holligan's public affairs group has acted in several judicial review cases on Scottish Parliament and human rights issues following devolution drawing on cross-departmental support. It has also been involved in a number of employment tribunal hearings on behalf of local authorities, the Scottish Legal Aid Board and the Scottish Prison Service. **Clients:** Inverclyde County Council; numerous local public bodies such as local authorities and government bodies.

Burness (see firm details p.903) The local government team, operating out of the corporate department under Alan Soppitt, continues to strengthen its reputation as a public sector specialist with the resources to tackle large urban regeneration and partnership projects. The group is acting for the City of Edinburgh in the Waterfront Edinburgh joint venture, and is advising over 15 local development agencies in the formulation of legal frameworks. Instructed by Edinburgh City Council on the South East Wedge Project, the largest single property development and regeneration in the UK, creating four new communities. Further instructed by East Lothian Council on the transfer of its entire stock of secondary schools to the private sector, and acted for a number of NHS Trusts on the development or disposal of land sites. **Clients:** Area Tourist Boards, Scotland; Capital City Partnership; East Lothian Land; Edinburgh City Council (South East Wedge Project); Fife Council; Glasgow Alliance; Inverclyde Regeneration; North Ayrshire Council; Waterfront Edinburgh.

Simpson & Marwick WS (see firm details p.1133) Respected for its litigation practice, the firm remains a strong defender of local authorities, most often indirectly through their insurers. This has included a large number of employer representations in cases relating to stress in the workplace. Clients praise the firm "*for its depth of knowledge and client care,*" as well as its "*ability to respond to impossible deadlines.*" **Kate Shaw** received heavy endorsement for her "*great deal of experience*" and "*personable*" approach. "*She exemplifies the quality of service to be expected from Simpson & Marwick.*" **Clients:** Fife Council; North Lanarkshire; Renfrewshire; Strathclyde Police; West Lothian; West of Scotland Water.

Tods Murray WS (see firm details p.1157) A constant flow of work continues to shore up this firm's involvement in the sector. Advising on a number of local government PFI projects in both Scotland and England, Ian McPake's public sector-based group has advised long-standing client Angus Council on judicial reviews. These have related to the Secretary of State for Trade and Industry's exclusion of Arbroath from Assisted Area Status and the Scottish Environmental Protection Agency on conveyancing and planning matters. **Clients:** Angus Council; Dundee City Council; Scottish Environmental Protection Agency; Tay Bridge Joint Board.

LEADERS IN LOCAL GOVERNMENT

AMBROSE, Ray
Nabarro Nathanson, London (020) 7524 6000

CHILD, Tony
Rowe & Maw, London (020) 7782 8686
tchild@roweandmaw.com
See under Administrative & Public Law, p.58

CIRELL, Stephen
Eversheds, Leeds (0113) 243 0391
stephencirell@eversheds.com
See under Administrative & Public Law, p.58

COLE, Alun
Morgan Cole, Cardiff (029) 2038 5385

COOK, Mark
Anthony Collins Solicitors, Birmingham (0121) 200 3242
Specialisation: Public sector commercial lawyer, with particular experience of 'public/private partnerships' in the local government, NHS and education sectors. Advising principally upon service delivery, strategic procurements, facilities management and the Private Finance Initiative, with considerable involvement in EC public procurement, UK competitive tendering legislation and vires issues, along with Best Value.
Prof. Memberships: Law Society.
Career: Joined *Anthony Collins* in 1997 as an associate. Prior to that worked with *Pinsent Curtis* where he was extensively involved in local government work. Has been principally responsible for exploring a legal framework for the 'Public Sector plc' initiative, and contributed to the book of that title.
Personal: Leisure interests – World music, real ale, football and walking. Married with two children.

COWEN, Léonie
Léonie Cowen & Associates, London (020) 7604 5870
leonie.cowen@lcowen.co.uk
Specialisation: Local Authority professional work and consultancy, especially public private partnerships, companies, joint ventures, PFI, project finance, Best Value and quality, high level sensitive investigations and inquiries, social services, education, employment and public procurement. Has advised over 100 local authorities. Recent projects include advising WS Atkins in the externalisation of Southwark's education services, acting for Southwark in the transfer of their residential homes to Anchor Trust, advising Barking & Dagenham on a homes re-provisioning programme and developing standard form social services procurement contracts, Mile End Park (an acclaimed multi-million pound Millenium project), transfers of leisure services for Dover, Ellesmere Port, Hounslow (a first for libraries) and others, a PPP for a new theatre in North Wales and externalising Enfield's theatre, acting for school governors in PFI projects, advising on museums in Basingstoke, Grimsby and elsewhere, community-led social and economic regeneration companies. Regular speaker at conferences and seminars.
Prof. Memberships: Law Society, Association of District Solicitors, Charity Law Association, Education Law Association.
Career: 15 years in local government, latterly as Chief Solicitor to Barnet and Director of Law & Administration/Deputy Chief Executive at Camden. Founded her own practice in 1989.
Personal: Born 1950. Leisure interests include music and her family.

CURNOW, Tony
Ashurst Morris Crisp, London (020) 7638 1111
See under Planning, p.663

DOBSON, Nicholas
Pinsent Curtis Biddle, Leeds (0113) 244 5000
nicholas.dobson@pinsents.com
Specialisation: National head of Local Government Law and partner. Advises on local authority, constitutional and administrative law, Best Value, TUPE and local government modernisation generally. Advises local authorities and others (public and private) and the Improvement and Development Agency for Local Government and the Employers' Organisation for Local Government.
Prof. Memberships: Association of Council Secretaries and Solicitors.
Career: Qualified in 1984 (also qualified in teaching and social work). Has worked as a lawyer with six local authorities. In 1999 left Doncaster MBC (Chief Solicitor). 1999 *Pinsent Curtis*, Partner.
Publications: Writes and lectures extensively on local government law (eg Journal of Local Government Law and Local Government Chronicle). Books: Best Value: Law and Management (Jordan Publishing Limited June 2000); TUPE, Contracting-Out and Best Value (Sweet and Maxwell, December 1998). Conferences: 1999 – Law Society in Paris, Association of Council Secretaries and Solicitors (London), 2000. Law Society Local Government Group Weekend School 2000-01. Contributes to Legal Network Television training videos.

DOOLITTLE, Ian
Trowers & Hamlins, London (020) 7423 8000
idoolittle@trowers.com
Specialisation: All aspects of public sector law, especially property and housing law (including housing stock transfers and arms length housing organisations). Specialises in public/private sector partnerships, especially in the context of urban regeneration. Also specialist in environmental law.

EVANS, Eric
Eversheds, Cardiff (029) 2047 1147
Specialisation: Partner in commercial property department and head of both the planning and PFI units. Specialises in all aspects of property law including complex planning obligations, major town centre regeneration/shopping schemes, site assembly, agreements for the construction of major highways associated with developments, public/private sector joint ventures, planning gain, valuations, urban development/regeneration grants and land reclamation. 30 years public sector experience, dealing with all areas of local government. Extensive experience of PFI and led one of the first PFI/PPP deals in Wales, at University Hospital of Wales NHS Trust. Has since advised on numerous deals including Newport Southern Distributor Road, Chepstow Community Hospital, Wiltshire's grouped schools scheme and 'Waste to Energy' scheme at Neath.
Prof. Memberships: Member of Law Society's Planning Panel.
Career: Qualified in 1980. Town Clerk, Borough of Blaenau Gwent (1981-89). Deputy Chief Executive and Legal Adviser, Land Authority for Wales (1989-92). Partner *Eversheds* 1992.
Personal: Director of Silent Valley Waste Services. Lives in Abertillery.

FORGE, Anna
Rowe & Maw, London (020) 7248 4282
Specialisation: Partner in the firm's Public Law Group; concentrates on work for local authorities; provides advice on statutory powers and administrative law requirements, local authority finance and interest in companies, compulsory purchase and land disposal, EC and domestic grants, housing matters, local government reorganisation disputes, public procurement, pensions issues relating to local government, statutory transfer schemes and the public and finance law implications of a variety of commercial contracts involving public bodies including PFI contracts, ' partnership' arrangements, best value contracts; redevelopment and regeneration schemes.
Prof. Memberships: Administrative Bar Association
Career: Qualified 1982. LB Southwark; 1979-89; *Berwin Leighton* 1989-99, partner 1996; partner *Rowe & Maw* 1999.
Personal: Born 1951. Leisure interests include ballet, theatre, travel, reading. Two children. Lives in Hove.

GRIFFITHS, Trevor
Sharpe Pritchard, London (020) 7405 4600
Specialisation: Partner specialising in judicial review, statutory and planning appeals, including appellate courts. In addition deals with assessment of costs and environmental and planning injunction work.
Career: Joined *Sharpe Pritchard* in 1982, qualified in 1984 and became a partner in 1987.
Personal: Born 6th December 1957. Educated at Bishop Wordsworth School 1969-76 and U.W.I.S.T 1976-79. Recreations include golf and cricket. Lives in London.

HAND, Catherine
Jenkins & Hand, London (020) 7222 5002
jenkins.hand@dial.pipex.com
Specialisation: Partner in housing and local government department. Set up *Jenkins & Hand* in 1996 with Keith Jenkins as a firm specialising in work for the public and not-for-profit sector. Local government work includes advice on local authority powers and district audit issues, numerous housing stock transfers both large scale and estate based, major urban regeneration schemes, procurement issues, tenant management coops and local authority sponsored companies. Also has extensive experience on all aspects of housing association work. Lectures regularly on housing stock transfers and on housing association law.
Career: Qualified 1978. Lecturer in Law at Queen Mary College, London 1978-79 and 1980-84. Lecturer in Law University of Kent 1979-80. In government legal service, Lord Chancellors Department 1984-89. Joined *Winckworth & Pemberton* in 1989, partner 1990. Left to set up new firm 1996.
Personal: Born September 1954. Educated Southampton University 1972-75 (LLB 1st Class Hons). Board member of Rosebery Housing Association.

ILEY, Malcolm
Nabarro Nathanson, London (020) 7524 6000

KEITH-LUCAS, Peter
Wragge & Co, Birmingham (0870) 903 1000

KILDUFF, David
Walker Morris, Leeds (0113) 283 2500
Specialisation: All aspects of public administrative law including powers, joint ventures, audit law, procurement and commercial contracts under best value and PPP. Leads an innovative Human Rights Advisory Service for public bodies and advises the Institute of Waste Management on best value. Substantial major projects experience across the public sector in local government, education, Government Department and health in aspects including integrated wastes management, accommodation services and vehicles.
Prof. Memberships: Law Society: Former member of the specialist Law Society Planning Panel.
Career: Training: Calderdale MBC; Qualified in 1982. Appointments include Assistant Chief Solicitor Stockton on Tees, Deputy Secretary Ashford Borough Council then Borough Secretary and Solicitor 1988-95. Former secretary and honorary legal adviser to the Kent Association of District Councils. Joined *Walker Morris* as Head of Public Sector & PFI in May 1999 from *Eversheds.*
Personal: Born 26 July 1958. Attended the University of Kent. Married with three children. Lives in Shipley.

KNOX, Martin
Anthony Collins Solicitors, Birmingham (0121) 200 3242
See under Social Housing, p.782

MACLEOD, Ian
Shepherd & Wedderburn WS, Edinburgh (0131) 473 5245
ian.macleod@shepwedd.co.uk
See under Litigation, p.575

MATTHEW, Stephen
Eversheds, Nottingham (0115) 950 7000
See under Projects/PFI, p.712

RANDALL, Helen
Nabarro Nathanson, London (020) 7524 6665
h.randall@nabarro.com
Specialisation: Main practice area is public private partnerships including PFI and local government outsourcings acting for both public and private sector clients. Experience in closing PFI pathfinders and firsts and has led teams of innovative best value partnerships in education, libraries, waste, ICT and housing, as well as regeneration and planning. Particular experience in European public procurement especially use of the negotiated procedure. Clients have included London Boroughs, government department, unitary, county and district councils and private sector service providers and funders.
Career: Qualified in 1991. Began career at a City firm, transferred to local government and joined *Nabarro Nathanson* in 1996 and was admitted as a partner in 2001.
Publications: Only lawyer member of Sir Ian Byatt's Procurement Review Taskforce; co-author of Butterworth's 'Guide to the Local Government Act 1999'; contributor to IPPR's 'Report on Public Private Partnerships'; Sweet and Maxwell's 'Outsourcing Practice Manual'; the 'New Local Government Network's' reports – 'Achieving Best Value' and 'Strategic Partnerships'. Helen writes a column on procurement for 'Municipal Journal' and is a regular speaker at national conferences.
Personal: 14 May 1962. Non-executive director of New Local Government Network.

RANDALL, Simon
Lawrence Graham, London (020) 7759 6538
simon.randall@lawgram.com
Specialisation: Principal area of practice is public sector work advising local authorities on externalisation, charitable trusts, urban regeneration and public procurement, PFI, housing and competitive tendering. Involved in large scale voluntary transfers of housing stock to housing associations and local housing companies. Author of many articles and pamphlets on local government and social issues ranging from the private rented sector, large scale voluntary sector of housing stock, local authority companies, community care and housing finance. Organises many seminars on health service, housing and local government related matters.
Prof. Memberships: Law Society.
Career: Articled with *Lawrence Graham* and became a Partner in 1970. Member, London Borough of Bromley 1968-94. Chairman London Borough of Bromley Housing Committee 1971-76 and Leader of the Council 1976-81. Member Greater London Council 1981-86. Chairman, London Boroughs Association Housing and Social Services Committee 1978-94. Non-executive Director Bethlem Royal and Maudsley Special Health Authority 1971-94.
Personal: Born 1944. Attended Westminster School. Appointed CBE in June 1991 for housing work in London. Chairman Kelsey Housing Association Ltd and member of Management Committee of Bromleigh Housing Association Ltd. Member National Housing Federation Council and director H.O.M.E.S. Limited.

SERRELLI, Roseanne
Sharpe Pritchard, London (020) 7405 4600
rserrelli@sharpepritchard.co.uk
Specialisation: All areas of public sector contracting but especially public/private partnerships and PFI. Particular specialities – waste management, social services PFI, leisure provision, information technology procurement, schools PFI and housing regeneration.
Prof. Memberships: Law Society.
Career: Articles *Sharpe Pritchard* 1992-94. Partner *Sharpe Pritchard* 1997.
Publications: Lectures: PFI standardisation documents, waste management, IT contracts and case law.
Personal: Ursuline School; New Hall, Cambridge.

SHARLAND, John
Sharpe Pritchard, London (020) 7405 4600
jsharland@sharpepritchard.co.uk
Specialisation: Partner specialising in local government law including advice on local authority powers, local government finance, public sector contracting, housing regeneration, town and country planning.
Prof. Memberships: Law Society.
Publications: TUPE and the 'Acquired Rights Directive' (co-editor) 1996. 'A Practical Approach to Local Government Law', Blackstones 1997. Articles in various publications. Lectures and presentations to seminars and conferences.
Personal: Educated Dulwich College, LSE, City of London Polytechnic. Leisure interests include history of art and architecture, swimming, walking and theatre.

SHAW, Kate
Simpson & Marwick WS, Edinburgh (0131) 557 1545

STEPHENS, Hugo
Pinsent Curtis Biddle, Birmingham (0121) 212 1828
hugo.stephens@pinsents.com
See under Social Housing, p.784

WILLIAMS, Huw
Edwards Geldard, Cardiff (029) 2023 8239
huw.williams@geldards.co.uk
See under Administrative & Public Law: General, p.60

MEDIA & ENTERTAINMENT

London: 594; The South: 601; Wales: 601; Midlands: 601; The North: 601; Scotland: 602; *Profiles*: 602

OVERVIEW: Another busy year in the media world. In music, the recent spate of management disputes included the Charlotte Church litigation, notable because the defendant was a minor. Theatrewise, the move away from the blockbuster musical continues, with the exception of the subsidised/commercial partnership production of Trevor Nunn's My Fair Lady, and the rise of the 'pop star' musicals, as exemplified by the success of Mamma Mia. The sale and leaseback work in the film world is keeping many lawyers busy, and international co-production fuelled by tax incentives schemes continues its growth. In publishing, the boundaries between screen and page are increasingly eroded.

RESEARCH APPROVED BY BMRB: *For this edition,* Chambers' *researchers conducted 6,552 interviews – 4,419 with law firms, 554 with barristers and 1,579 with clients.*

The validity of the research was scrutinised by BMRB International, who audited both the methodology and the results at our offices in July 2001. They interviewed Chambers' *researchers and cross-checked sample interviews. Details of the audit appear on page 7.*

TOP IN-HOUSE LAWYERS

Television

Martin BAKER, Controller of Legal and Business Affairs, *Carlton*

Deanna BATES, Head of Legal, *BskyB plc*

Colin CAMPBELL, Director of Legal and Business Affairs, *Channel 5*

Antonia DOWNEY, Head of Legal, *The Jim Henson Company*

Svenja GEISSMAR, Vice-President of Business Affairs, *MTV*

Simon JOHNSON, Head of Legal, *ITV*

Sarah TINGAY, Director of Legal and Business Affairs, *Pearson TV*

Catherine WILLIAMS, Senior Business Affairs Executive, *Channel 4*

"There is nothing **Martin Baker** *has not got the ability to do"*, high praise indeed for *"a highly experienced and respected figure"*. Possibly *"the most experienced and well known"* in-house lawyer in television with *"enormous experience of all aspects of the pay television business,"* **Deanna Bates** continues to feature strongly. **Colin Cambell** is *"a master with a wealth of experience."* **Antonia Downey** is commended as *"commercially driven and knowledgeable"*; **Svenja Geissmar** continues to impress. **Simon Johnson** is heavily endorsed while **Sarah Tingay** is rated for her depth of experience. **Catherine Williams** has established herself as *"a bit of an institution."*

Film

Sara CURRAN, Head of Legal and Business Affairs, *Working Title*

Cameron McCRACKEN, Head of Corporate and Business Affairs, *Pathé Distribution*

Angela MORRISON, Chief Operating Officer, *Working Title*

Andrew HILDEBRAND, Director of Business Affairs, *Filmfour*

James SHIRRAS, Financial Director, *Film Finances*

Mark PYBUS, Head of Business Affairs, *Company Television*

Sheeraz SHAH, Vice-President of Legal and Business Affairs, *Working Title*

Both **Sara Curran** and **Angela Morrison** received strong endorsement with **Sheeraz Shah** joining them in recognition of his *"incredible thoroughness and politeness." "Exceptionally good and enormously energetic"* **Cameron McCracken** has his *"own unique style – he somehow manages to make it fun."* **Andrew Hildebrand** continues to command respect while the market appreciates the efficiency of **James Shirras**. *"Outstandingly good and fair,"* **Mark Pybus** successfully combines business and legal skills.

In-House lawyers profiles: p 1193

LONDON

FILM FINANCE / FILM & TV PRODUCTION / BROADCASTING

Richards Butler (see firm details p.1107) "*Rightly at the top of the field,*" and "*traditionally a force*" with the BBC at its core, the team acts for blue chip financiers, broadcasters, and studios. The "*archetypal banking lawyer*" **Richard Philipps** (see p.606) is commended for his "*analytical precision,*" he acted for the lenders to the British film 'Enigma' and the producer of the £15 million feature 'Killing Me Softly.' The "*solutions oriented*" **Michael Maxtone-Smith** (see p.603) used his "*sound judgment*" for the lenders to HBO's forthcoming $120 million mini-series 'Band of Brothers.' **Barry Smith** (see p.607) may appear "*laid back,*" but in advising many major film and TV production companies "*he knows exactly what he's doing.*" **Stephen Edwards** (see p.603) assisted the BBC and other UK broadcasters in their negotiations with the bodies representing television directors, and is trusted for "*knowing TV agreements inside out.*" **Clients:** NatWest; DG Bank; Société Générale; BBC; HSBC; FACT; Carnival Films; MTV.

SJ Berwin (see firm details p.879) A major force in sale and leaseback, the group continues to inspire the confidence of leading financial institutions. A busy team, judged to be "*strong on finance and production,*" it acted for the funders of Sky Pictures on four features last year and represented Intermedia on the production and financing of the Michael Apted film 'Enigma.' Despite the loss of Jacqueline Hurt to Olswang, the roster of leading lights remains impressive. The "*inspired*" **Tim Johnson** (see p.604) and "*lawyer's lawyer*" **Nigel Palmer** (see p.605) acted on the production and financing of the critically acclaimed 'Me Without You.' **Peter McInerney** (see p.605) is "*well known*" in the field, representing Jim Henson Productions in relation to the production of 'The Hoobs' TV series. **Clients:** Columbia Pictures; Société Générale; Gullarme Enter; Banque Internationale a Luxembourg; United Artists Films.

Olswang (see firm details p.1084) Renowned for its strength in broadcasting, a niche that puts it "*firmly at number one.*" **Mark Devereux** (see p.603) is the "*all round best media lawyer in London,*" and wins praise for his "*quality papering of deals.*" **Lisbeth Savill** (see p.606) "*knows what she's doing*" and **Charles Moore** (see p.605) is "*respected.*" The team acted for Fox Searchlight in the production of 'Quills' and advised Miramax Film Corp on all European aspects of the Martin Scorsese film 'Gangs of New York.' The arrival of "*pragmatic*" **Jacqueline Hurt** (see p.604) from SJ Berwin strengthens an already "*established media practice.*" The broadcast team is commended for its "*strong breadth of practice.*" **David Zeffman** (see p.607) is "*a high profile player,*" while **Selina Potter** (see p.606) is "*focused.*" The group acted on the incorporation and setting up of So television – including a deal with Channel 4 for the next three series of 'So Graham Norton.' **Clients:** Granada; Channel 4; Sky Productions.

MEDIA & ENTERTAINMENT: FILM FINANCE • London	Ptnrs	Assts
1 Richards Butler	4	6
SJ Berwin	3	9
2 Olswang	5	4
3 Davenport Lyons	4	6
Denton Wilde Sapte	8	10
The Simkins Partnership	3	2

MEDIA & ENTERTAINMENT: FILM & TV PRODUCTION • London	Ptnrs	Assts
1 Olswang	5	4
2 Harbottle & Lewis	2	4
Lee & Thompson	3	2
3 Davenport Lyons	4	6
SJ Berwin	2	4
The Simkins Partnership	3	3
Theodore Goddard	4	8
4 Harrison Curtis	1	n/a
Richards Butler	5	4
Schilling & Lom and Partners	1	n/a
5 Denton Wilde Sapte	8	11

MEDIA & ENTERTAINMENT: BROADCASTING • London	Ptnrs	Assts
1 Denton Wilde Sapte	8	11
Olswang	4	12
2 Ashurst Morris Crisp	2	11
Clifford Chance	2	4
3 Goodman Derrick	4	3
Richards Butler	5	5
Wiggin & Co	2	2
4 Field Fisher Waterhouse	2	4
5 DJ Freeman	4	4
Davenport Lyons	4	6
Harbottle & Lewis	4	2
SJ Berwin	2	4
The Simkins Partnership	3	2
6 Allen & Overy	6	10
Herbert Smith	n/a	n/a
Lovells	n/a	n/a
Travers Smith Braithwaite	7	10

This book is the product of 6,552 1/2 hour interviews. See p.7 for BMRB audit.
Within each band, firms are listed alphabetically.

Davenport Lyons (see firm details p.931) Involved in the structuring of more than 25 films for a leading financier. "*The grand old man*" **Leon Morgan** (see p.605) acted on all aspects of the Ska Film 'Snatch.' The "*experienced*" **Richard Moxon** (see p.605) advised a Close Brothers sponsored production company on a number of transactions including 'Kiss Kiss Bang Bang.' The team "*gets the job done*" and is admired for "*responding quickly.*" **Clients:** Barclays Bank; Royal Bank of Scotland; Close Brothers.

Denton Wilde Sapte (see firm details p.939) The successful merger has attracted new bank and financier clients, and the firm's "*size and history*" continues to garner "*number one for broadcasting*" plaudits. The past year has found the team involved in over 18 film financing transactions, including single project loans and revolving credit facilities, with an aggregate value of over $180 million. **Michael Ridley** (see p.606) is an "*exceptional TV lawyer*" and the "*technical*" **Ken Dearsley** (see p.603) is seen as "*intellectually astute.*" They are joined in our rankings by the "*bright*" **Chris Hanson** (see p.604) who is "*strong on finance.*" **Clients:** Viacom; Paramount Pictures; Sony Pictures Entertainment; Warner Bros; Universal Studios; Coutts & Co; Cofiloisirs; Natwest Bank.

The Simkins Partnership (see firm details p.1131) A highly focused media firm, with across the board strengths. Rated for its film finance capability, the firm is seen to be "*doing a lot of work*" and to have a heavy presence in the production market. Busy on sale and leaseback transactions, it acted for provider Ingenious Media on over 20 transactions. Advised and assisted on the production contracts for the forthcoming Warner Bros film 'Harry Potter.' **Antony Gostyn** ("*a first class lawyer*") and the well regarded if "*exacting*" **Nigel Bennett** remain key players. **Clients:** Ingenious Media; The Film Consortium; Channel Four Television; Really Useful Films.

Harbottle & Lewis (see firm details p.985) Commended for its "*strength in production*" and envied for a "*great client list.*" The "*charming*" **Robert Storer** (see p.602), "*hardworking*" **Abigail Payne** (see p.606) and "*experienced*" **Medwyn Jones** (see p.604) are a team respected as a "*sage bunch.*" Advised Merchant Ivory on the production aspects of its latest feature 'The Golden Bowl' and advised the founders of Talkback Productions on its sale to Pearson TV. The group also advised World Productions on production and sale and leaseback agreements for the BBC2 series 'Attachments.' **Clients:** Merchant Ivory Productions; Chrysalis Visual Entertainment; Ginger Media Group.

Lee & Thompson Envied for its fantastic roster of "*interesting clients*" and a focus on the production side, the firm also scores well in financing. The "*high profile and specialist*" **Jeremy Gawade** worked on the forthcoming Film Four feature 'Crush' – a Pipe Dream Pictures production directed by John McKay. The group also advised Sacha Baron Cohen, the creator of Ali G, on his film deal with Working Title. "*Dynamic*" **Reno Antoniades** is a "*responsive practitioner*" and has worked on Revolution Film's 'Twenty Four Hour Party People,' starring Steve Coogan. **Clients:** Pipe Dream Pictures; Revolution Films; Ali G; Red Production Co.

Theodore Goddard (see firm details p.1152) Respected for its "*impressive client roster*" and "*city approach,*" the firm acted for Universal Studios on the production of 'Hannibal.' The "*dynamic*" **Jonathan Berger** (see p.603) has a "*strong practice*" and is key to the firm's success. The team has advised major independent producers, such as Renaissance Films on 'Morality Play' and DNA Films on 'The Parole Officer.' **Clients:** Buena Vista International; DNA Films; NatWest Bank; Tiger Aspect Productions.

Harrison Curtis (see firm details p.988) "*A young firm with big clients,*" despite its size. It advised Chris Auty, the producer of the forthcoming 'Dust,' and Kinowelt in connection with the forthcoming feature 'Rain.' Continues to act for the Zone Vision group of channels in the launch of various satellite TV channels across Europe, and also advised Blakeway Productions on all production aspects of the ITV series 'Royal Portraits.' The "*calm*" **Tim Curtis** wins plaudits for being "*responsive and easy to work with.*" **Clients:** Film Four; Kinowelt; Zone Vision Enterprises; Diplomat Films.

Schilling & Lom and Partners (see firm details p.1119) Busy on sale and leaseback transactions for producers, this firm is "*on the scene,*" if not having the highest of profiles. It has been actively involved in the acquisition of rights for internet broadcasters and is widely rated as enjoying a talent driven practice. **Nicholas Lom** (see p.604) is respected for his "*wide experience.*" **Clients:** Castle Communications; Renegade Films; Criminal Productions.

Ashurst Morris Crisp (see firm details p.866) "*A consistent force for years,*" widely rated for its international practice, the team is felt to play on its "*corporate and regulatory strengths.*" Highly respected **Tony Ghee** (see p.603) is

FILM FINANCE/FILM & TV PRODUCTION LEADING INDIVIDUALS	
1 **DEVEREUX Mark** Olswang	**PALMER Nigel** SJ Berwin
PHILIPPS Richard Richards Butler	
2 **ANTONIADES Reno** Lee & Thompson	**BERGER Jonathan** Theodore Goddard
JOHNSON Timothy SJ Berwin	**MORGAN Leon** Davenport Lyons
SAVILL Lisbeth Olswang	**STORER Robert** Harbottle & Lewis
3 **DEARSLEY Ken** Denton Wilde Sapte	**GOSTYN Antony** The Simkins Partnership
MAXTONE-SMITH Michael Richards Butler	
MOORE Charles Olswang	**SMITH Barry** Richards Butler
4 **BENNETT Nigel** The Simkins Partnership	**GAWADE Jeremy** Lee & Thompson
HENRY Michael Buchanan Ingersoll	**HURT Jackie** Olswang
JONES Medwyn Harbottle & Lewis	**LOM Nicholas** Schilling & Lom and Partners
MOXON Richard Davenport Lyons	
5 **CURTIS Tim** Harrison Curtis	**McINERNEY Peter** SJ Berwin
PAYNE Abigail Harbottle & Lewis	
UP AND COMING	
HANSON Christopher Denton Wilde Sapte	
ONES TO WATCH	
BLAIR Jonathan Theodore Goddard	**TATTON-BROWN Sam** Davenport Lyons

BROADCASTING LEADING INDIVIDUALS	
1 **GHEE Tony** Ashurst Morris Crisp	**JAMES Sean** Wiggin & Co
RIDLEY Michael Denton Wilde Sapte	**ZEFFMAN David** Olswang
2 **BALLARD Tony** Field Fisher Waterhouse	**EDWARDS Stephen** Richards Butler
SANDELSON Daniel Clifford Chance	
3 **SWAFFER Patrick** Goodman Derrick	
4 **LEIFER Tony** DJ Freeman	
UP AND COMING	
POTTER Selina Olswang	

See individuals' profiles p.602

"*experienced and sensible.*" The group advised the sponsoring banks on all English law aspects of the IPO of International Media AG, and acted for United Broadcasting and Entertainment on its proposed acquisition of Zenith Media. **Clients:** SBS; UPC Media; National Geographic; Kirch Media.

Clifford Chance (see firm details p.919) Renowned for its strength in "*corporate broadcasting,*" the firm's client base and regulatory expertise mark it out as a leader. The "*well known*" **Daniel Sandelson** (see p.606) is seen as "*the name in corporate.*" The group advised Can West on its multi-million pound joint venture with Granada over broadcasting in Ireland and advised Carlton on structuring and tax in the disposal of Technicolor – the world's largest duplicator of film. **Clients:** ONDigital; Channel 5; Hearst; Can West; Video Networks.

Goodman Derrick (see firm details p.974) This long established practice continues to advise a number of terrestrial broadcast clients. Engaged in a range of ongoing work for ITV Network Centre including regulatory, legislative and policy issues. The esteemed **Patrick Swaffer** (see p.607) "*deserves a long time service award*" and continues to "*do a good job for his clients.*" He led the team representing the ITV companies who challenged the controversial ITC ruling on broadcast times for news. **Clients:** Granada; BBFC; GMTV; ITV2; Channel 5.

Wiggin & Co (see firm details p.1180) Respected for its "*good UK focused practice.*" The "*excellent*" **Sean James** (see p.604) is commended as "*solid, steady, knowledgeable.*" The firm has advised TRG and The Super 12 on the sale of horse racing rights for the next ten years. The firm has continued its successful, long-standing Flextech workload post the merger with Telewest, acting for the merged entity in its acquisition of Pay Per View rights for Football premier league, a three year deal. **Clients:** Telewest; UKTV; Discovery; Fox Kids.

Field Fisher Waterhouse (see firm details p.957) Broad based, "*doing a bit of everything,*" the firm is respected for its "*good individuals*" and "*broadcast capability.*" It acted for the BBC on its acquisition rights and assets in extending its community website and advised the 26 public service broadcasters that make up the Eurosport Consortium. "*Veteran*" **Anthony Bal-**

High Profile Media Cases

Parties	Lawyers	Significance
Time Warner; AOL	• Time Warner – Cravath Swaine & Moore (US); Herbert Smith (UK) • AOL – Simpson Thacher & Bartlett; Wilmer Cutler & Pickering	One of the largest mergers in history valued at $147 billion. The first of various mergers combining new technology and old economy companies.
Hello! v OK!; Michael Douglas and Catherine Zeta Jones	• Hello! – Charles Russell • OK! Michael Douglas and Catherine Zeta Jones – Theodore Goddard	One of the first cases to utilise the new UK human rights law as regards privacy. An injunction was brought against Hello! Magazine for publishing unauthorised photographs of the wedding of Michael Douglas and Catherine Zeta Jones; later overturned by the Court of Appeal.
Northern & Shell; United News & Media (now United Business Media)	• Northern & Shell – Linklaters & Alliance • United News & Media – Ashurst Morris Crisp	£125 million sale of Express Newspapers, comprising the Daily Express; Sunday Express and the Daily Star.
Jonathan Shalit v Charlotte Church	• Jonathan Shalit – Russells • Charlotte Church – Davies Arnold Cooper	Dispute over management contract. Significant case to go to court concerning a child's contract.
Pearson; Bertelsmann; Groupe Bruxelles Lambert	• Pearson – Freshfields Bruckhaus Deringer • Slaughter and May – Bertelsmann; Groupe Bruxelles Lambert	Merger valued at £12 billion, creating the largest European broadcasting company.
ITN v Living Marxism (now LM)	• ITN – Pinsent Curtis Biddle • LM – Christian Fisher	ITN accuses Living Marxism of libel, after allegation that its journalists falsified images from Bosnian concentration camps. The first attack on a news organisation to go to trial. Considerable damages were awarded due to the severity of accusing a news organisation of deceiving the public.
Elton John v PwC	• Elton John – Eversheds • PwC – Barlow Lyde & Gilbert	Elton John accuses PwC of negligence regarding his accounts.
Racecourse Association; Go Racing Consortium	• RCA – Denton Wilde Sapte • Arena Leisure – Freshfields • Channel 4 – Olswang • BSkyB – Inhouse	£387 million media rights deal for all but 10 courses of the Racecourse Association. UK broadcasting rights remain intact, with greater facility for interactive betting services.

lard (see p.602) is commended for his telecoms expertise and *"sensible, learned"* approach. **Clients:** Eurosport Consortium; Quadriga; Time Warner.

DJ Freeman (see firm details p.943) A highly commercial outfit with a long-standing presence in the market due to its Channel Four relationship, the firm advised on the setting up of 4 Ventures – the commercial arm of Channel Four. Advised Channel Five on the sale and leaseback transactions in connection with the television series 'Headless' and the television film 'Hotel'. **Tony Liefer** (see p.604) *"has a good reputation"* and worked on the production, finance and distribution agreement work of the forthcoming Working Title film 'Long Time Dead.' **Clients:** Working Title; Carlton; Universal; Aardman Animation; Channel 4; Channel 5.

Allen & Overy (see firm details p.856) Major broadcasting clients are calling upon the firm's corporate and regulatory expertise. The group acted for British Movietonews in its dispute with ITN, relating to TVAM film archive materials, and acted for The Film Council in connection with a wide range of issues concerning its operations as a public body. The team led by John Wooton acts as corporate legal advisor to the giant created by the merger between United News & Media and Carlton Communications (United Business Media). **Clients:** Cable & Wireless; The Radio Authority; The News Corporation.

Herbert Smith (see firm details p.993) Known for its *"strength in competition and regulatory work,"* although this is in no way the limit of this practice guided by Stephen Wilkinson. The high profile client in this area continues to be BSkyB. The group advised on its acquisition of the majority share holding in Open, the TV shopping and interactive services company. *"Specialists"* in broadcasting, their cross border reach includes advice to Time Warner on the European aspects of its US$350 billion merger with AOL. **Clients:** CNN; Time Warner; Capital Radio.

Lovells (see firm details p.1044) Corporate clients are the bedrock of the broadcasting work undertaken by the firm, with an expansive media team led by Lindy Golding covering the board. The group advised Granada Group on its merger/demerger with Compass group and the formation of Granada, a major independent media group, noted by peers as being a *"great deal to bag."* **Clients:** Granada/LWT; Trinity Mirror; Telewest.

Travers Smith Braithwaite (see firm details p.1160) Enjoying a *"significant client in ntl,"* for whom it does *"a good job,"* the team which includes Margaret Moore is an active force in cable TV and pay per view. The firm advised ntl on its joint venture with ITN to create The News Channel and its work with Universal Studios to create The Studio Channel. It also acted on the acquisition of an interest in the Hessen cable franchises owned by Deutsche Telekom (value €1.2 billion.) **Clients:** Channel 5; ntl; Premium TV.

Other Notable Practitioners *"Crusading workaholic"* **Michael Henry**'s move from H2O to Buchanan Ingersoll is being eagerly monitored by the market.

MUSIC

Russells (see firm details p.1117) Yet again reigning supreme, *"number one for their strength in depth,"* Russells has an unparalleled non-contentious team and a strong litigation capability. *"Commercial animal"* **Tony Russell** has a *"wonderful appetite for work"* and services a *"serious client base."* He represented George Michael on a new publishing deal with Warner Chappell. The *"pre-eminent"* **Brian Howard** represented Jonathan Shalit in the most talked about case of the year – the management dispute against Charlotte Church (who at 15 was a minor), which was resolved after the first day of the trial. **Chris Organ** is *"a solution finder,"* drafting and negotiating deals for both talent and corporate clients. **Steven Tregear** acted for All Saints in connection with their management dispute with Mark Benson, and **Mark Sinnott** represented the Popstars label. **Clients:** Major and independent labels; major artists.

Clintons (see firm details p.920) Representing record and publishing companies, this *"corporate led"* practice is *"rightly thought of as one of the best."* *"Top drawer lawyer"* **Andrew Sharland** is seen as *"effective;"* he represented Jazz Summers – the former manager of Richard Ashcroft – in last year's contentious management dispute. **David Landsman** heads the firm's commercial team, negotiating contracts and arranging deals for dance labels, artists and publishing companies. **Clients:** Record labels; publishing companies; major artists.

Lee & Thompson An *"active music practice,"* peopled by *"a formidable team."* The firm's strength lies in *"handling independent labels and artists,"* while management disputes are the mainstay of the firm's litigation work. Starting the year with four major music related High Court trials, the group also acted for Andrew Morton and handled the injunction proceedings brought by Victoria and David Beckham against their former bodyguard. The *"calm"* **Robert Lee** uses his *"sound judgement"* in re-negotiating artists' recording and publishing agreements. **Robert Horsfall** is rated and **Andrew Thompson** displays his *"tenacious and industrious style"* in representing major artists on publishing deals. **Gordon Williams** garners respect as a *"hardworking litigator,"* **Mike Brookes** is rated for his work representing the claimant in the Spice Girls v Aprilia, and the up and coming **Sofia Robb** is involved in litigation with a growing specialism in artwork/video disputes.

TOP IN-HOUSE LAWYERS

Music

Alistair GEORGE, Head of Legal Affairs UK, *Sony*

Paul JONES, Legal and Business Affairs Director, *Polydor*

James RADICE, Director of Business Affairs, *EMI*

Claire SUGRUE, *Universal/Island Records*

John WATSON, Commercial and Business Director, *Warner Music*

Alistair George is a *"good, tactical lawyer"* judged to be *"the best all-rounder."* With a *"good technical law background,"* **Paul Jones** elicits warm approval, as does **James Radice** who is *"sound, human and personable but no soft touch."* Claire Sugrue is thought to be "the hardest working woman in music" while the *"bright, commercial, common sense approach"* of **John Watson** is appreciated.

Music Publishing

Jane DYBALL, Director of Legal and Business Affairs, *Warner Chappell*

Grenville EVANS, Director of Commercial Affairs, *BMG*

Sarah LEVIN, Head of Legal and Business Affairs, *Universal Music Publishing*

Chris MILESON, Director of Legal and Business Affairs, *EMI Publishing*

Rakesh SANGHVI, General Manger, *Sony Publishing*

"Thorough and commercial," **Jane Dyball** is viewed as a *"safe pair of hands"* with the ability to *"be a terrier when she needs to be."* **Sarah Levin** is an *"absolute pleasure to do deals with"* while **Grenville Evans** is *"excellent; personable and laid back."* *"Bright"* and highly skilled **Chris Mileson** is a valued player and *"bright new kid on the block,"* **Rakesh Sanghvi** *"made huge strides."*

In-House lawyers profiles: p.1193

MEDIA & ENTERTAINMENT: MUSIC • London	Ptnrs	Assts
1 Russells	11	4
2 Clintons	11	11
Lee & Thompson	5	4
3 Sheridans	5	4
4 Bray & Krais	2	2
Mishcon de Reya	7	17
Statham Gill Davies	12	n/a
The Simkins Partnership	5	7
Theodore Goddard	3	7
5 Davenport Lyons	5	4
Denton Wilde Sapte	5	6
Eversheds	3	5
Hamlins	3	5
Harbottle & Lewis	4	7
Harrison Curtis	2	n/a
Searles	2	2
Spraggon Stennett Brabyn	3	2

LEADING INDIVIDUALS	
1 **GRAFTON GREEN Paddy** Theodore Goddard	
HOWARD Brian Russells	**RUSSELL Tony** Russells
SHARLAND Andrew Clintons	**TURTON Julian** The Simkins Partnership
2 **BRAY Richard** Bray & Krais	**GLICK David** Mishcon de Reya
HARMAN James Theodore Goddard	**JONES Howard** Sheridans
LEE Robert Lee & Thompson	**THOMPSON Andrew** Lee & Thompson
3 **ALLAN Robert** Denton Wilde Sapte	**EATON Michael** Mishcon de Reya
FREE Dominic The Simkins Partnership	**GILL Kaz** Statham Gill Davies
GILMORE Laurence Hamlins	**HORSFALL Robert** Lee & Thompson
LANDSMAN David Clintons	**ORGAN Chris** Russells
TREGEAR Steven Russells	
4 **ABRAMSON Lawrence** Harbottle & Lewis	
BROOKES Mike Lee & Thompson	**KRAIS Mark** Bray & Krais
RENNEY Paul Theodore Goddard	**SEARLE Helen** Searles
SINNOTT Mark Russells	**STATHAM John** Statham Gill Davies
WARE James Davenport Lyons	**WILLIAMS Gordon** Lee & Thompson
UP AND COMING	
ROBB Sophia Lee & Thompson	

This book is the product of 6,552 1/2 hour interviews. See p.7 for BMRB audit.
Within each band, firms are listed alphabetically. *See individuals' profiles p.602*

Sheridans (see firm details p.1127) "*Capable and growing*" firm with a "*top bracket*" reputation in the talent driven market. The "*first class*" **Howard Jones** is "*fair and trustworthy*" and acts for a variety of senior record company executives. **Clients:** Artists; industry executives; smaller record companies.

Bray & Krais Known as an artist-focused practice, this firm is shifting towards industry with the representation of record company executives. Involved in the establishment of several joint venture record labels between major record companies and independent labels. Ongoing work on recording agreements for artists and publishing agreements for writers. "*Calm under pressure,*" **Richard Bray** "*impresses with his drafting*" and recently handled the website/internet agreement for a major artist. **Mark Krais** is seen as "*approachable*" and is known for his "*excellent brain* ." He was involved in the Rolling Stones European tour, drafting contracts for the group and their various companies. **Clients:** Sony/ATV Music Publishing (UK); Universal Music Publishing; Blur; Ronan Keating; Artful Dodger; Van Morrison; Westlife.

Mishcon de Reya (see firm details p.1071) "*An interesting merger*" judged by the market as "*potentially great, although the jury is still out.*" The Eatons team has benefited from Mishcon's litigation prowess and corporate finance capability. "*Highly regarded*" **David Glick** (see p.603) works with younger artists including newcomer Craig David, and also representing Pete Tong in the distribution of his worldwide brand Essential Collection. "*Powerhouse*" **Michael Eaton** (see p.603) re-negotiated the long-term recording and publishing contracts for Enya, whilst the firm secured the release of Bush from the LA based Trauma records and concluded a deal with Atlantic Records. **Clients:** Fatboy Slim; Craig David; Bush; Eric Clapton; Bee Gees; Enya; Gabrielle.

Statham Gill Davies (see firm details p.1139) An "*artist-led practice*" that is "*building towards the corporates.*" This year's higher position for the firm is due to its "*strength in commercial work*" and "*reputation for getting things done.*" Enjoying a "*good roster of artists*" bolstered by the growth of corporates. Both **Kaz Gill** ("*strong at deal making*") and **John Statham** retain their reputation as innovative players in the market. **Clients:** Major brands, independent labels.

The Simkins Partnership (see firm details p.1131) Delivering a "*high quality of service,*" the firm continues to be dominated by "*rainmaker and technician*" **Julian Turton**, "*a good operator with over twenty years' experience.*" He represented the vendors of Modern Music GmbH (one of Germany's largest rock labels) in its multi million pound cross border sale. On behalf of Candy Rock Recording, the firm successfully resisted a Court of Appeal case brought by PPL arising from a copyright tribunal decision concerning a standard music industry agreement. **Dominic Free** is credited with "*stabilising their litigation practice.*" **Clients:** Sony Europe; EMI International: Island; BMG (UK); Geri Halliwell; Leftfield.

Theodore Goddard (see firm details p.1152) "*The Bentleys of the profession,*" the firm has been busy advising Universal Music in connection with the establishment of its online music portal Voxstar and its interests in GetMusic.com. "*Genius*" **James Harman** advised Sade on WIPO litigation to recover her domain name from cybersquatters, and on the re-negotiation of her recording contract with Epic Records. **Paddy Grafton Green** (see p.603) remains a popular figure rated for his strength on tax and is considered a lawyer of "*wonderful work habits.*" **Paul Renney** (see p.606) "*knows what he's doing and is still young enough to enjoy it.*" **Clients:** Sony Music; Universal Music International; many major artists.

Davenport Lyons (see firm details p.931) A strong component of the practice is US music, advising on production deals, signings and publishing deals. The firm acts for a variety of music clients, representing established mainstream acts and leading hip hop and reggae artists such as Beenie Man and U God. **James Ware** (see p.607) is rated for his "*sound, knowledgeable approach*" and is said to "*know music publishing inside out.*" **Clients:** Michael Nyman; VP Records; Mediaeval Baebes.

Denton Wilde Sapte (see firm details p.939) "*Charming and confident*" **Robert Allan** (see p.602) led the team in its highlight of the year advising EMI on contractual due diligence towards Time Warner, performing a key supporting role in its submissions to the European Commission on the impact of the proposed joint venture on the European music publishing market. Felt to be corporate focused, the group advised on all matters relating to the production and recording of the Bacharach & David concert at the Royal Albert Hall. **Clients:** Boxman.com; K-Tel Entertainment UK; Warner/Chappell Music.

Eversheds (see firm details p.952) Admired for its understated quality, "*Eversheds are the Lexus of the profession, you get a good safe ride.*" Representing some serious heavyweights in the music industry (consultant Frank Presland is Elton John's manager), Patrick Isherwood's group advised on all legal aspects of Party In The Park 2001, including all the artists' contracts, overseas TV deals, production, sponsorship and merchandising agreements. **Clients:** AEI Music; Apple Corps; Elton John.

Hamlins (see firm details p.983) Busy with mainstay client PPL, the group has advised on its dispute with 500 local authorities that refused to pay royalties for music broadcast in sports centres. **Laurence Gilmour** (see p.603) is an *"intelligent litigator, one of the best,"* although the firm is in danger of being *"a one man firm."* The firm is also involved in the complex management dispute of a major recording artist. **Clients:** Sony; BMG International; BPI.

Harbottle & Lewis (see firm details p.985) Acting for Robbie Williams, the firm successfully fought off an attempt by Ludlow Music to restrain distribution of his multi-platinum selling album over litigation concerning lyrics. It also advised Mushroom Records in the litigation brought by MCA, and Radioactive over rights to the recent album by top band, Garbage. The loss of Andy Stinson has affected the reputation of the firm but the *"excellent"* **Lawrence Abramson** (see p.602) *"makes his presence felt."* **Clients:** 19 Management; Robbie Williams; K-Tel.

Harrison Curtis (see firm details p.988) *"An effective young firm,"* admired for its *"good ratio of hits to misses,"* it acted for a major record label in negotiations of joint venture and label arrangements with independent labels. Lawrence Harrison and his team advised a major UK band's record company on all aspects of their album (live and studio) and all video and touring arrangements. **Clients:** Courtyard Music; Universal Island Records; Siouxsie & The Banshees/The Creatures.

Searles (see firm details p.1120) The *"personable"* **Helen Searle** (see p.606) is seen as *"an effective operator,"* with a focus on artists on the independent side of the industry. **Clients:** Jamiroquai; Moby; Sonique.

Spraggon Stennett Brabyn An artist-led practice, strong on artist relations and peopled by *"charming individuals."* Peers agree that Sarah Spraggon's team has *"great young clients"* and continues to impress with its *"commercial deals in dance and pop music."* **Clients:** Recording artists; songwriters.

THEATRE

Band	MEDIA & ENTERTAINMENT: THEATRE • London	Ptnrs	Assts
1	Clintons	2	2
	Tarlo Lyons	2	1
2	Campbell Hooper	2	1
	The Simkins Partnership	2	1
3	Harrison Curtis	2	n/a
4	Bates, Wells & Braithwaite	3	3
	Harbottle & Lewis	3	3
	Theodore Goddard	3	6

Band	LEADING INDIVIDUALS	
1	**COHEN John** Clintons	**ROSE Michael** Tarlo Lyons
	SHAW Barry Barry Shaw	
2	**EGAN Sean** Bates, Wells & Braithwaite	**FRANKS David** The Simkins Partnership
	HARRISON Lawrence Harrison Curtis	**WILLS David** Campbell Hooper
3	**JENNINGS Carolyn** Campbell Hooper	**MEADON Simon** Tarlo Lyons

This book is the product of 6,552 1/2 hour interviews. See p.7 for BMRB audit.
Within each band, firms are listed alphabetically. *See individuals' profiles p.602*

Clintons (see firm details p.920) *The "top drawer"* **John Cohen** is a *"tour de force,"* advising a range of *"huge talent clients"* including producers, writers and impresarios. Heavily involved in musical theatre, advised on all aspects of Andrew Lloyd Webber's 'Beautiful Game' and arranged the New York production of 'Aida' for Tim Rice. **Clients:** Don Black; PW Productions; Morgan St; David Babani.

Tarlo Lyons (see firm details p.1149) Busy advising on six of the biggest theatre productions this year including 'My Fair Lady' at the National Theatre. The *"elder statesman"* **Michael Rose** (see p.606) acted for several Mackintosh productions both domestically and abroad and made submissions, on behalf of a group of agents, to a government consultation on new law affecting theatrical agents. The *"talented"* **Simon Meadon** (see p.605) advised on 'The Car Man' at the Old Vic and 'The Witches of Eastwick.' **Clients:** Sir Cameron Mackintosh; AMP; SFX Back Row; Donmar Warehouse; ENB.

Campbell Hooper (see firm details p.907) Always *"helpful,"* the firm has been busy advising on productions including 'Medea,' 'Napoleon,' 'Cats,' 'Starlight Express' and 'Oklahoma!' The *"first class"* **Carolyn Jennings** (see p.604) works alongside the *"professional and knowledgeable"* **David Wills.** (see p.607) They act for many high profile artists and advised Trevor Nunn in relation to his directing of 'My Fair Lady' at the National Theatre. **Clients:** Trevor Nunn; Duncan Weldon; Theatre of Comedy; Peter O' Toole; Chichester Festival Theatre.

The Simkins Partnership (see firm details p.1131) *"Known for theatre work,"* the firm has been active with the production of 'The Beautiful Game' and two productions currently in development for its principal theatre client The Really Useful Group. The *"pre-eminent"* **David Franks** *"knows his business"* and has advised various individual clients involved with current West End productions including 'Mamma Mia,' 'Art,' and 'The King and I.' **Clients:** Really Useful Group; The National Theatre; Brian Brolly; Fat Bloke Productions.

Harrison Curtis (see firm details p.988) The warmly recommended, *"theatre focused"* **Laurence Harrison** is acting for the producers of 'Fame', in both its West End run and national tour. The small partnership is also acting for the producers on the transfer and presentation of the Abbey Theatre Production of 'Dolly West's Kitchen' at the Old Vic and advised Background Production and Guy Chapan on the production of 'Another Country' at the Arts Theatre. **Clients:** Lively Arts Production Management; Drill Hall Theatre; Producers of 'Dolly West's Kitchen'.

Bates, Wells & Braithwaite (see firm details p.871) *"Sound"* firm heavily involved with the Royal Shakespeare Company's international co-production of 'The Secret Garden' and filming of 'Macbeth' for Channel Four. The group is dominated by the presence of *"capable"* **Sean Egan**, a *"leading theatre practitioner"* who acted for the producers on the West End production of 'A Midsummer Nights Dream.' The group also advised Adventures in Motion Pictures on 'Car Man' and 'Swan Lake.' **Clients:** E.N.O; RSC; West Yorkshire Playhouse; Adventures in Motion Pictures.

Harbottle & Lewis (see firm details p.985) *"A great name"* in theatre building on its traditional client base. The group led by Colin Howes advised on the redevelopment of the Hampstead theatre – London's first new producing theatre since 1976 – part-funded by a Lottery grant of £9.85 million. An *"all round entertainment practice,"* it advised the Really Useful Group on financing for the London production of 'The Beautiful Game' by Andrew Lloyd Webber and Ben Elton. **Clients:** Cirque du Soleil; Really Useful Group; D'Oyly Carte Opera Productions; Tiger Aspect Productions.

Theodore Goddard (see firm details p.1152) *"Enormously expanded team"* which includes Paul Renney, and has acted for The Ambassador Theatre Group on its £18 million acquisition of seven West End theatres and its joint ventures with Natural Nylon Entertainment and Carlton Television.

Represented the producers of 'Saturday Night Fever' both domestically and abroad. **Clients:** Ambassador Theatre Group; Robert Stigwood Organisation; Capitol Events GmbH.

Other Notable Practitioners The "*grand old man of theatre*" **Barry Shaw** (see p.607) is "*still a serious player*," having had "*more theatre experience than anyone in London*."

PUBLISHING

MEDIA & ENTERTAINMENT: PUBLISHING • London		Ptnrs	Assts
1	Denton Wilde Sapte	4	6
2	Taylor Joynson Garrett	6	5
3	Finers Stephens Innocent	2	3
	H2O (Henry Hepworth Organisation)	2	n/a
	Harbottle & Lewis	6	7
	Lovells	4	9
	The Simkins Partnership	5	2

LEADING INDIVIDUALS		
1	**WILLIAMS Alan** Denton Wilde Sapte	
2	**MITCHELL Paul** Taylor Joynson Garrett	
3	**KAYE Laurence** Garretts	**NYMAN Bernard** BM Nyman & Co
	SOLOMON Nicola Finers Stephens Innocent	

This book is the product of 6,552 1/2 hour interviews. See p.7 for BMRB audit.

Within each band, firms are listed alphabetically. *See individuals' profiles p.602*

TOP IN-HOUSE LAWYERS

Publishing

Andrew CROMPTON, Legal and Business Development Director, *Macmillan*

Roger FIELD, Legal Director, *Random House*

Adrian LAING, Director of Legal Affairs/Company Secretary, *HarperCollins*

Vicky LOCKIE, Director of Legal Services, International Division, *Pearson Education*

Jo MARKS, Head of Legal, *Oxford University Press*

Helena PEACOCK, Head of Legal, *Penguin*

Andrew Crompton is noted for his *"roll your sleeves up and get the work done attitude."* Though not everyone's cup of tea, **Andrew Laing** *"runs a tight ship"* and is indisputably a key player. **Helena Peacock** is valued as a *"sensible and practical"* lawyer. **Vicky Lockie** is the general counsel for the largest education publishing company in the UK. **Jo Marks** at OUP is considered *"bright and practical – pleasant to deal with."*

In-House lawyers profiles: p 1193

Denton Wilde Sapte (see firm details p.939) Widely regarded as "*deserving first place*" for its "*industry knowledge*." The group acted for a leading publishing house in defending a copyright infringement and passing off action brought by the estate of James Joyce over a newly edited 'Ulysses.' It was also involved in a copyright tribunal reference by the UK Committee of Vice-Chancellors and Principals of the Universities, regarding the licensing of copyright materials in universities. The "*sage*" **Alan Williams** (see p.607) is considered a "*leader in the field*." **Clients:** Macmillan; Simon & Schuster UK; John Wiley.

Taylor Joynson Garrett (see firm details p.1150) Known for its strong client roster, this "*serious practice*" represents many publishers in their corporate and commercial publishing matters. The group advised DACS in relation to its proposed intervention in the Copyright Tribunal reference made by The Committee of Vice Chancellors and principals of the Universities of the United Kingdom. The "*rated*" **Paul Mitchell** (see p.605) is considered a "*stand out individual*." **Clients:** Dick Francis; Harper Collins; Roald Dahl Literary Estate; DACS; Macmillan.

Finers Stephens Innocent (see firm details p.958) Considered by some clients to be "*the first port of call*" in publishing. The group advises rights holders and a number of leading agents. Acted for Anthea Turner in the negotiations surrounding the publishing of her autobiography and Barbara Windsor in the dispute with her ghostwriter. The "*technician*" **Nicola Soloman** (see p.607) is seen as "*pragmatic*" and redrafted agreements with various contributors to the New York Times. **Clients:** British Association of Picture Libraries and Agencies; International Herald Tribune; New York Times.

H2O (Henry Hepworth Organisation) (see firm details p.981) Successfully defended Punch and its Editor against contempt proceedings brought in relation to MI5. The group led by Catrin Turner act for several major league publishers. **Clients:** Granta; Hodder Staughton; Harper Collins; IPC Media.

Harbottle & Lewis (see firm details p.985) Seen as "*established in publishing*," the firm acted for Chrysalis Books on various acquisitions, including Quadrillion Publishing and Element books. Advised the late George Carman QC on dealing with contracts for his planned autobiography and negotiating the serialisation of extracts in The Times. **Clients:** Peoplenews.com; Chrysalis Books; George Carman/Harper Collins; Helen Fielding.

Lovells (see firm details p.1044) A "*fantastic team*" advised on the reorganisation of the Guardian Media Group and Hurst Publishing, producers of Autotrader magazines, and acted on the joint venture GCSE revision site 'learn.co.uk.' Seen as "*doing more litigation work*," the firm advised the magazine publisher of titles such as 'Bella,' 'TV Quick' and 'Take A Break' on its dispute with WH Smith Trading. **Clients:** Guardian Media Group; Trinity Mirror; H Bauer Publishing; Reuters.

The Simkins Partnership (see firm details p.1131) "*Good all rounders*," Julian Turton's team advised on the sale of Cover To Cover Cassettes (the UK's largest library of unabridged spoken word recordings) to BBC Worldwide. Known for its niche as an "*e-publishing firm*," it also acts for a large number of photographic libraries, specialist contract publishers, literary agents and authors. **Clients:** Corbis; Sebastian Faulks; Jeremy Paxman; Gillon Aitken Associates.

Other Notable Practitioners **Laurence Kaye** (see p.295) at Garretts retains admiration for his e-publishing work. The "*sui generis practitioner*" **Bernard Nyman** (see p.605) garners respect for his representation of individuals on copyright infringement cases.

THE SOUTH

MEDIA & ENTERTAINMENT • The South	Ptnrs	Assts
1 Manches Oxford	4	5
Wiggin & Co Cheltenham	2	2

This book is the product of 6,552 1/2 hour interviews. See p.7 for BMRB audit.
Within each band, firms are listed alphabetically.

Manches (see firm details p.1051) Coleen Blackburn heads a team that acts for intermediaries and distinct divisions of the Oxford Psychologists Press. Involved in ongoing work for 'The Lord of The Rings' trilogy currently in production by New Line Cinema. The group is advising Tolkein's estate in a protective capacity in relation to all merchandising and commercial agreements. **Clients:** SWETS; Elsevier Science.

Wiggin & Co (see firm details p.1180) Seen as "*TV oriented*," this firm continues to be ranked in our London table and several partners work from both offices. Key areas of the practice are new media, publishing and high profile television work. Acts for a wide range of media clients. **Clients:** TAC (association for independent producers in Wales); Jean Doumanian Productions (Woody Allen films); Scottish Committee for Gaelic Broadcasting.

WALES

MEDIA & ENTERTAINMENT • Wales	Ptnrs	Assts
1 Morgan Cole Cardiff, Swansea	2	1

LEADING INDIVIDUALS
1 LEWIS Emyr Morgan Cole

This book is the product of 6,552 1/2 hour interviews. See p.7 for BMRB audit.
Within each band, firms are listed alphabetically. *See individuals' profiles p.602*

Morgan Cole (see firm details p.1074) Advised on the part lottery-funded 'Beautiful Mistake,' a musical documentary directed by Mark Evans featuring the performances of John Cale and Catatonia, amongst others, and negotiated copyright clearance, financing and production agreements for Boda. Highly focused, **Emyr Lewis** is key to the firm's success. He advised Agenda TV on its joint ventures with directorial talent and its online video streaming and e-learning ventures. **Clients:** Cartoon Cymru; Boda; Agenda TV.

MIDLANDS

MEDIA & ENTERTAINMENT • Midlands	Ptnrs	Assts
1 Hammond Suddards Edge Birmingham	1	n/a
Kent Jones and Done Stoke-on-Trent	2	1

LEADING INDIVIDUALS
1 ANDERSON Frances Lee Crowder

This book is the product of 6,552 1/2 hour interviews. See p.7 for BMRB audit.
Within each band, firms are listed alphabetically. *See individuals' profiles p.602*

Hammond Suddards Edge (see firm details p.984) A successful team which includes David Hull, it advised Apollo Leisure on outsourcing management agreements to operate the Sunderland Empire Theatre and the Leas Cliff Hall. Also advised on the UK tour of the musical 'Miss Saigon', commencing in November 2001, and represented SFX on the disposal of its entire UK ticketing operations to Ticketmaster. **Clients:** Wrightway Marketing; Apollo Leisure Group; SFX Entertainment; Raw Media.

Kent Jones and Done (see firm details p.1020) The firm assisted a world class celebrity with a representation agreement and advised Ravi Shankar on a book publishing agreement. Advised on publishing arrangements surrounding a well known music biography and acted in two disputes regarding other music biography publications. The group headed by Michael Servian continues to advise on profit participation for a number of clients, including in relation to Sir David Lean's Oscar-winning films. **Clients:** David Lean Film Trust; Estate of Patrick Hamilton; Faraway Productions AG.

Other Notable Practitioners **Frances Anderson** (see p.602) of Lee Crowder is rated for her heavy involvement in film and TV.

THE NORTH

MEDIA & ENTERTAINMENT • The North	Ptnrs	Assts
1 McCormicks Leeds	4	5
2 Eversheds Leeds, Manchester	1	2
Lea & Company Stockport	1	n/a
3 Ramsbottom & Co Blackburn	1	n/a

LEADING INDIVIDUALS
1 LEA Stephen Lea & Company
McCORMICK Peter McCormicks

This book is the product of 6,552 1/2 hour interviews. See p.7 for BMRB audit.
Within each band, firms are listed alphabetically. *See individuals' profiles p.602*

McCormicks (see firm details p.1060) The respected and high profile **Peter McCormick** (see p.604) continues to advise on a number of radio franchise bids and proposed mergers and acquisitions. A strong sports broadcasting theme runs through the firm which advised the FAPL on problems encountered with the overseas broadcasting contract with Canal+. Also advised Leeds United Football Club on the club's website rights and its proposed television channel, a joint venture with BSkyB. **Clients:** BBC Radio Leeds; Yorkshire Television; The Music Factory Entertainment Group.

Eversheds (see firm details p.952) This respected firm acts for a wide range of media clients. Led by Joanna Berry, who has considerable television in-house experience, the team has been involved in drawing up contracts between programmes service providers and major digital radio multiplexes. **Clients:** Granada TV; Russell Watson; Channel 5.

Lea & Company This Stockport-based firm acts for artists/songwriters and record/production companies. **Stephen Lea** gains respect from his competitors and clients alike.

Ramsbottom & Co Famed for its circus work, the practice acts for almost all of the major UK touring acts and the two leading booking agents. This Blackburn-based company has a niche in representing touring ice shows, particularly in the Middle East and far East. Its reputation for circus work has brought it a substantial client base among fairground equipment operators. The team, lead by Malcolm Clay, works on contracts, animal welfare legislation as regards performing animals, and outdoor entertainment licensing.

SCOTLAND

MEDIA & ENTERTAINMENT • Scotland	Ptnrs	Assts
1 **Dundas & Wilson CS** Edinburgh	5	4
Tods Murray WS Edinburgh	4	4
2 **Levy & McRae** Glasgow	4	2
McGrigor Donald Glasgow	n/a	n/a
3 **Anderson Strathern WS** Edinburgh	5	3
Bannatyne, Kirkwood, France & Co Glasgow	5	4
Wright, Johnston & Mackenzie Glasgow	2	2

LEADING INDIVIDUALS	
1 **FINDLAY Richard** Tods Murray WS	
2 **SIBBALD Graham** Dundas & Wilson CS	**WATSON Peter** Levy & McRae

This book is the product of 6,552 1/2 hour interviews. See p.7 for BMRB audit.
Within each band, firms are listed alphabetically. *See individuals' profiles p.602*

Dundas & Wilson CS (see firm details p.947) Perceived to have a dominance provided by size, the firm enjoys an "*enviable client list*" which covers commercial work for the Scottish Media Group. Packed with "*good individuals*" including "*mainstream corporate*" figure **Graham Sibald.** Advised Scottish Radio Holdings on launch and roll-out of local digital multiplex services and advised on provision of content to other multiplex providers. The group advised DigMedia Limited on its e-commerce partnership with the association of Independent Music/Musicindie – the largest UK e-commerce venture of it's kind. **Clients:** DigMedia; The Scotsman Publications; SMG; Digital Animations.

Tods Murray WS (see firm details p.1157) A "*leader in the field,*" **Richard Findlay** (see p.603) is heavily involved in production finance agreements. The group negotiated location deals for feature and TV productions including Ridley Scott's 'Gladiator' and the 'Monarch of the Glen' series for the BBC. Acted for the producer in the second series of the ten part drama series for Channel 4's Tinsel Town, and for the TV animation company Skryptonite on fifteen animated series/co-productions. **Clients:** Scottish Screen; Federation of Scottish Theatres; Wark Clements & Company.

Levy & McRae (see firm details p.1039) Known for its "*contentious work,*" heavily involved in newspaper and TV defamation work. **Peter Watson** (see p.288) is seen as "*tough and uncompromising*" and enjoys a "*great client list.*" **Clients:** Scottish Television; Channel Four; Reuters: Granada; GMTV.

McGrigor Donald (see firm details p.1062) With a key strength in non-broadcast media, this firm attract non-broadcast clients because of their "*size and strength.*"

Anderson Strathern WS (see firm details p.859) A firm with a wide ranging media practice, it advised on the start-up of a web based broadcasting site. The team has negotiated license agreements with Phonographic Performance for instore broadcasting. **Clients:** Red Facilities; fabchannel.com; Scottish Publishers Association; Edinburgh College of Art.

Bannatyne, Kirkwood, France & Co (see firm details p.869) Headed by Martin Smith, the team has been instructed by an agent to act for 'Harry Potter' interdict. The firm represented broadcast and print media in HMA v Danskin, successfully challenging a section 4 order prohibiting reporting of the case by arguing the press rights to freedom of expression in terms of Human Rights legislation. **Clients:** Business am; The Independent; The Oban Times Group.

Wright, Johnston & Mackenzie Busy with corporate work for the creative industries, the group, headed by Yvonne Dunn, has also worked with Glasgow Film Finance to generate a tax efficient sheltering facility. **Clients:** Antonine Short Film Factory; Sigma Films; Big Fish Casting Agency.

LEADERS IN MEDIA & ENTERTAINMENT

ABRAMSON, Lawrence
Harbottle & Lewis, London (020) 7667 5000
lawrence.abramson@harbottle.com
Specialisation: Specialist litigator in all areas of the entertainment and media industries, including music, television, film, computer games, publishing and sport.
Prof. Memberships: International Association of Entertainment Lawyers.
Career: Trained at *Sheridans.* Solicitor with *Denton Hall* 1988-97. Joined *Harbottle & Lewis* in 1996.
Personal: Educated at the British School of The Netherlands, University of Manchester, Chester College of Law (LLB 2:1). Married with two children. Interests include sport, music, theatre, travel and entertaining.

ALLAN, Robert
Denton Wilde Sapte, London (020) 7320 6516
rwa@dentonhall.com
Specialisation: Partner in technology, media and telecoms group and head of the music group. Works with music industry clients on music publishing; recording contracts; 'due diligence' reviews of music companies and their assets; music business mergers and acquisitions; video licensing; negotiations with rights bodies and other contractual matters. Advises users of music, for example, TV programme makers and broadcasters, film production companies and advertisers regarding clearances. Also works on the 'talent' side of the music business, advising on contractual and other issues. Has been published widely in leading professional journals and the trade press. Has lectured at MIDEM and New Music Seminar in New York and to the Beverly Hills Bar Association.
Career: Qualified in 1967. Partner with *Roney & Co* 1970-73. Partner with *Simons Muirhead & Allan* 1973-86. Joined *Denton Hall* as a partner in 1986.

ANDERSON, Frances
Lee Crowder, Birmingham (0121) 236 4477
frances.anderson@leecrowder.co.uk
Specialisation: Non-contentious work in music, television, film, the arts, new technology and computer law.
Prof. Memberships: Law Society; Women in Film and Television; PACT; Society for Computers & Law.
Career: Qualified in 1989 at *Wragge & Co*; set up own practice in 1995 and joined *Lee Crowder* in 2000.
Personal: Former chairman and currently a director of Birmingham International Film & Television Festival. Company Secretary and a director of the Grand Theatre, Wolverhampton. Company Secretary and a director of the Media Development Agency for the West Midlands.

ANTONIADES, Reno
Lee & Thompson, London (020) 7935 4665

BALLARD, Tony
Field Fisher Waterhouse, London (020) 7861 4000
jab@ffwlaw.com
Specialisation: Main area of practice is communications with a recent focus on network platforms at the leading edge of recent developments in this field, advising both established operators and new entrants on the new technologies. Acting for television network and service providers in both public and private sectors, including established broadcasters and new entrants. Also acting for telecoms companies entering the content market. Specialisms extend to all forms, so broadcasting as well as major feature film production and distribution, competition, copyright and administrative law. Arbitrator on International Arbitration panel of American Film Marketing Association and trained mediator for alternative dispute resolution. Frequent speaker at conferences.
Prof. Memberships: International Bar Association, Communication Lawyers Association, Royal Television Society, Copinger Society and chairman of UK branch of European Centre for Space Law.
Career: Qualified in 1974, having joined *Allison & Humphreys* in 1971. Became a partner in 1975. Merged with *Field Fisher Waterhouse* in 1998.
Personal: Born 21st August 1945. MA (Cantab) 1964-68. Fellow of Royal Anthropological Institute. Leisure interests include astrophysics, sailing and painting. Lives in London and Suffolk. Athenaeum.

BENNETT, Nigel
The Simkins Partnership, London (020) 7907 3000

BERGER, Jonathan
Theodore Goddard, London (020) 76068855
jonathanberger@theodoregoddard.co.uk
Specialisation: Main area of practice covers legal and business affairs advice on the production, finance and distribution of feature films and television programming. Acts for leading independent producers and distributors. Regular speaker on the film and television industry.
Prof. Memberships: British Academy of Film & Television Arts; Producers Association for Cinema & Television.
Career: Qualified in 1986 with *Bartletts de Reya* and became a partner in *Mishcon de Reya* in 1990 and joined *Theodore Goddard* as a partner in the Media & Entertainment Group in 1995.
Personal: Born 1962. Educated Charterhouse and the University of Kent at Canterbury. Leisure interests include supporting Chelsea FC, cooking and golf.

BLAIR, Jonathan
Theodore Goddard, London (020) 7606 8855

BRAY, Richard
Bray & Krais, London (020) 7493 8840

BROOKES, Mike
Lee & Thompson, London (020) 7935 4665

COHEN, John
Clintons, London (020) 7379 6080

CURTIS, Tim
Harrison Curtis, London (020) 7611 1720

DEARSLEY, Ken
Denton Wilde Sapte, London (020) 7320 6547
krd@dentonwildesapte.com
Specialisation: Partner in technology, media and telecoms group. Specialises in all aspects of film financing with special expertise and reputation in UK sale/leaseback transactions, tax based financing arrangements and working with the major studios, other leading US and European film companies, banks and other lending institutions. Wide experience in film and television production and distribution, video distribution, 'due diligence' reviews in the media industry and copyright matters generally. Has lectured on a wide number of industry subjects in London, America, India and Far East.
Prof. Memberships: International Bar Association.
Career: Has been with *Denton Wilde Sapte* since articles. Qualified in 1974. Became a partner in 1979.

DEVEREUX, Mark
Olswang, London (020) 7208 8888
mjd@olswang.com
Specialisation: Senior partner. Main area of practice is film and television finance, production and distribution. Responsible for all areas of work covered by entertainment, media and communications. Regular contributor to media trade press.
Prof. Memberships: Law Society, State Bar of California.
Career: Qualified in 1981, joining *Simon Olswang & Co* in the same year and becoming a partner in 1982.
Personal: Born 2 August 1956. Attended Lycée Français de Londres 1961-74, then University College London 1975-78. Leisure interests include tennis, skiing, diving and photography. Lives in London.

EATON, Michael
Mishcon de Reya, London (020) 7440 7000
Specialisation: All areas of media and entertainment law, including merchandising, touring, television, film and sport, as well as expertise in corporate law.
Career: Qualified in 1967 and became a corporate partner in the city firm, *Stephenson Harwood.* Joined Dick James Music in 1977 as Head of Business Affairs to gain further industry experience and was responsible for all business and contractual dealings with a vast roster of clients. Returned to private practice with the formation of *Eaton & Burley* in 1980. In 1990 founded *Eatons* together with Jeremy Wakefield and David Glick. The firm merged with *Mishcon de Reya* in 2000.

EDWARDS, Stephen
Richards Butler, London (020) 7247 6555
Specialisation: Broadcasting law including ITC licence applications; satellite and cable transmission and programme contracts; production financing, distribution and co-production agreements and European regulation. Other copyright and media/entertainment work including sports agreements; copyright collecting society transactions; print and multimedia publishing agreements; talent contracts; website agreements; copyright tribunal hearings and music industry agreements. Chairs Hawksmere Conference on Rights Clearances for Television Programmes. Regular speaker at media industry conferences.
Career: Qualified in 1976. Joined the BBC in 1978, and was head of copyright 1981-90. Joined *Richards Butler* as a partner in 1990.
Personal: Attended University of the Witwatersrand, Johannesburg 1968-70 and Trinity Hall, Cambridge 1971-73. Leisure pursuits include sailing, cricket and music.

EGAN, Sean
Bates, Wells & Braithwaite, London (020) 7551 7777

FINDLAY, Richard
Tods Murray WS, Edinburgh (0131) 226 4771
richard.findlay@todsmurray.com
Specialisation: Entertainment and media law partner. Practices exclusively in entertainment and media law acting for a wide range of clients throughout the film, television and music industry sectors and also for companies in the fields of theatre, festival and event management and the arts generally.
Prof. Memberships: International Association of Entertainment Lawyers.
Career: Partner *Ranken & Reid* (1979-90); Partner *Tods Murray* (1990).

FRANKS, David
The Simkins Partnership, London (020) 7907 3000

FREE, Dominic
The Simkins Partnership, London (020) 7907 3000

GAWADE, Jeremy
Lee & Thompson, London (020) 7935 4665

GHEE, Tony
Ashurst Morris Crisp, London (020) 7638 1111
tony.ghee@ashursts.com
Specialisation: Media and entertainment and telecommunications. Regulatory, corporate and commercial advice for cable and telecommunications operators, terrestrial and satellite broadcasters and film and television production companies. Particular expertise: all aspects of satellite and broadcasting law including digital media. Speaks regularly on the convergence of broadcasting, telecoms and information technology industries and broadcasting regulation.
Prof. Memberships: IBA, ICC and BSAC.
Career: Worked: *Blake Dawson Waldron* and TEN television network in Australia. *Denton Wilde Sapte* and partner at *Ashursts* in UK.
Personal: Married.

GILL, Kaz
Statham Gill Davies, London (020) 7487 5565

GILMORE, Laurence
Hamlins, London (020) 7355 6000
lgilmore@hamlins.co.uk
Specialisation: A Managing Partner and head of the entertainment and intellectual property department. Specialises in all aspects of related litigation including copyright, trademark, contract disputes, monopolies and mergers and EC competition law. Practice also covers defamation and passing off actions. Acts for prominent organisations, corporations and individuals from the world of entertainment.
Prof. Memberships: International Association of Entertainment Lawyers.
Career: Articled at *Davenport Lyons* 1984-86. Assistant solicitor *Taylor Joynson Garrett* 1986-87. Partner, *Hamlins* (previously known as *Hamlin Slowe*) since 1988.
Personal: Educated at Preston Manor Grammar School and Trinity Hall, Cambridge. Writes occasional newspaper articles. Leisure pursuits include theatre, music and sport. Born 17 April 1959. Lives in London.

GLICK, David
Mishcon de Reya, London (020) 7440 7000
Specialisation: All areas of entertainment and media law with particular emphasis on music, television, film and sport. Music client base ranges from new and emerging artists/bands to 'superstar artists'. Corporate clients include major record and publishing companies as well as a number of independent record labels and publishing companies in relation to their various spheres of activities. A specialist in co-ordinating substantial joint venture and other 'label' structures, he bridges the gap between the media business and the City.
Career: Qualified in 1989 and co-founded *Eatons* in 1990. Eatons merged with *Mishcon de Reya* in 2000.

GOSTYN, Antony
The Simkins Partnership, London (020) 7907 3000

GRAFTON GREEN, Paddy
Theodore Goddard, London (020) 7606 8855
paddygraftongreen@theodoregoddard.co.uk
Specialisation: Work includes advice on (i) copyright issues in relation to recordings, musical compositions and theatrical productions and (ii) production, distribution, management concert appearance, sponsorship and merchandising agreements. Advice on taxation both within the UK and overseas of income derived by businesses and artists. Cases have included acting as Chairman of BPI Tribunal into chart hyping, and for BMG in the MMC Enquiry into Recorded Music, for PolyGram and Universal Music in relation to a variety of corporate and commercial transactions including PolyGram Filmed Entertainment's acquisition of ITC in 1995 and sale in 1999 and PolyGram's acquisition (1991) and disposal (1999) of its interest in The Really Useful Group, in the sale in 1999 of London Records to the Warner Group, for major companies and artists in structuring international transactions including con-

cert tours (Tina Turner, Michael Jackson, Janet Jackson, Lionel Richie and The Rolling Stones), for David Bowie in relation to the "Bowie Bonds" and Iron Maiden in relation to the securitisation of income. Lecturer and seminar chairman for IBC Legal Studies and others.
Prof. Memberships: Law Society.
Publications: Occasional articles in legal journals.
Personal: Born 30th March 1943. Attended Ampleforth College 1957-62; holds an MA (Oxon), 1963-65. Leisure interests include music and cricket. Lives in London.

HANSON, Christopher
Denton Wilde Sapte, London (020) 7320 6576
czh@dentonwildesapte.com
Specialisation: Specialist in all areas of media financing, film and television production and distribution, copyright and sports sponsorship. Work undertaken includes 'off-balance sheet' finance, single project loans, revolving credit facilities, equity investment, sale and leaseback and other tax based financing, structuring international co-productions and the commissioning, production, licensing, sponsorship, merchandising and exploitation of film and television product. Clients include leading US and European banks in this sector, US 'Hollywood' studios, independent producers, distributors and broadcasters.
Career: Qualified 1992. Partner *Denton Wilde Sapte* 1999.

HARMAN, James
Theodore Goddard, London (020) 7606 8855

HARRISON, Lawrence
Harrison Curtis, London (020) 7611 1720

HENRY, Michael
Buchanan Ingersoll, London (020) 7920 3700

HORSFALL, Robert
Lee & Thompson, London (020) 7935 4665

HOWARD, Brian
Russells, London (020) 7439 8692

HURT, Jackie
Olswang, London (020) 7208 8888
jmh@olswang.com
Specialisation: Partner in the media and communications group, advising on all aspects of media and communications law specialising in the financing, production and distribution of films and television programmes. Has particular experience and expertise in the financing of independent feature films and, in that connection, the structuring of a combination of any one or more of government subsidies, co-productions grants, distribution, pre-sales and bank financing. Also advises producers and acquirers of films on tax driven sale and leaseback transactions.
Prof. Memberships: Law Society, Women in Film & Television.
Career: Trained at *SJ Berwin & Co* qualified 1991, partner at *SJ Berwin & Co* 1998. Joined *Olswang* as a partner in 2000.

JAMES, Sean
Wiggin & Co, London (020) 7290 2424
sean.james@wiggin.co.uk
Specialisation: Partner specialising in cable, satellite, analogue and digital terrestrial, on-line, internet and other television operations and programming including sports media rights, regulatory compliance, programming acquisitions, licences, co-productions and commissions, telecommunications and satellite agreements including uplink, transponder capacity, encryption and compression, facilities agreements, conditional access and subscriber management contracts and licence agreements, cable affiliation agreements and direct-to-home distribution agreements.
Prof. Memberships: Royal Television Society.
Career: Articled *Wiggin & Co*; qualified 1990; 18 months secondment to United Artists 1991-92; Assistant solicitor with *Wiggin & Co* until May 1996; partner 1996.
Personal: Born 1965. Interests include squash, cars, windsurfing and rowing.

JENNINGS, Carolyn
Campbell Hooper, London (020) 7222 9070
CarolynJennings@campbellhooper.com
Specialisation: Head of the media group specialist in intellectual property rights and contract law with a detailed knowledge of the theatre, film, music, television and merchandising industries. Her practice covers all fields of the entertainment and media business representing independent television companies, film producers, film financiers, theatre producers and music companies.
Career: Admitted as a solicitor in 1982 having trained at *Campbell Hooper*.

JOHNSON, Timothy
SJ Berwin, London (020) 7533 2202
tim.johnson@sjberwin.com
Specialisation: Film production, financing and distribution, satellite communications, digital media, broadcasting and communications. Structuring film projects for financing purposes including co-productions and use of local incentives.
Career: MA, Sidney Sussex College, Cambridge. *Denton Hall* 1987-1993, *Yusef & Leader* 1993-1994, *SJ Berwin & Co* 1994-date. Partner 1995.
Personal: Married. Interests include rugby, travel, food, history and the West Country.

JONES, Howard
Sheridans, London (020) 7404 0444

JONES, Medwyn
Harbottle & Lewis, London (020) 7667 5000
medwyn.jones@harbottle.com
Specialisation: Partner and Head of the Broadcasting Group. Main area of practice is film and television production, financing, and distribution and broadcasting. Work includes television and film commissioning, licensing and financing agreements, programme content, sponsorship, broadcasting legislation, carriage and transmission agreements and joint ventures.
Prof. Memberships: Law Society, Royal Television Society, BAFTA.
Career: Qualified in 1980. Worked at *Theodore Goddard* 1978-81, then *Walker Martineau* 1981-92 (from 1983 as a partner). Joined *Cameron Markby Hewitt* as a partner in 1992 and *Harbottle & Lewis* as a partner in 1994. Regular lecturer at conferences and seminars.
Personal: Born 1955. Attended Scorton Grammar School, Chester Grammar School, Sheffield University and College of Law. Leisure interests include skiing, regular exercise and good wine. Lives in Richmond.

KAYE, Laurence
Garretts, London (020) 7304 8255
laurence.kaye@glegal.com
See under E-commerce, p.295

KRAIS, Mark
Bray & Krais, London (020) 7493 8840

LANDSMAN, David
Clintons, London (020) 7379 6080

LEA, Stephen
Lea & Company, Stockport (0161) 480 6691

LEE, Robert
Lee & Thompson, London (020) 7935 4665

LEIFER, Tony
D J Freeman, London (020) 7583 4055
nal@djfreeman.co.uk
Specialisation: Head of media and communications department; both corporate and commercial work for media and hi-tech clients including major start-ups, venture capital, flotations, corporate acquisitions, disposals, joint ventures, programme financing and distribution agreements and e-commerce, internet start-ups and internet and film related broadcasting ventures.
Prof. Memberships: Law Society.
Career: Qualified in 1972, having joined *DJ Freeman* in 1970. Became a partner in 1975.
Personal: Born 17 September 1945. LLB (London) 1968 and LLM (University of California) 1969. Enjoys tennis and cooking. Lives in London.

LEWIS, Emyr
Morgan Cole, Swansea (01792) 634634

LOM, Nicholas
Schilling & Lom and Partners, London (020) 7453 2600
nicholas.lom@schillinglom.co.uk
Specialisation: Senior partner and head of entertainment and commercial department. Main areas of practice – non-contentious internet, film, television, video, music, publishing, multimedia and copyright matters.
Career: Prior to entering the law, worked as a script editor at the BBC and in independent production. Qualified in 1982. Articled at *Wright Webb Syrett* before forming *Schilling & Lom* in 1984.
Personal: Born 29 April 1949. Attended Westminster School and Pembroke College, Cambridge (MA Cantab). Member of the Groucho Club. Leisure interests include his children, chess, book collecting.

MAXTONE-SMITH, Michael
Richards Butler, London (020) 7247 6555
Specialisation: Advises banks, financiers, distributors and sales agents in connection with all aspects of financing film and television both in Europe and the USA including the granting of security over intellectual property rights. Clients include Cobalt Media Group LLC, DG Bank, Deutsche Genossenschaftsgank AG, Royal Bank of Scotland and Societe Generalé.
Career: Articles at *McKenna & Co* (1986-88); assistant at *Richards Butler* (1988-98); partner at *Richards Butler* (1998-).
Personal: Educated at Nottingham High School and St Catharine's College Cambridge. Married with two sons. Leisure interests: playing the piano, cricket and literature.

McCORMICK OBE, Peter
McCormicks, Leeds (0113) 246 0622
p.mccormick@mccormicks-solicitors.com
Specialisation: Substantial area of practice is media and entertainment (allied to extensive portfolio of sports law) with considerable experience in both contentious and non-contentious aspects. Advises a

number of sporting bodies, clubs and individuals on contractual matters as well as media and entertainment law issues. Clients include The FA Premier League, Leeds United FC, a number of sporting personalities such as Leslie Ash, Lee Chapman, Billy Pearce, Freddie Trueman, Richard Whiteley and a number of television presenters, actors, actresses and journalists. Advises on all aspects of broadcasting legislation. Has advised on three radio franchise bids. Deals with a number of defamation actions and advice on behalf of leading public figures, including politicians and personalities. Handles complaints on broadcasting and press issues. Lectures on media and entertainment. Advises a number of clients in the music industry including performers and managers. Considerable experience of broadcast sponsorship and similar issues. Negotiates contracts for personal benefits, corporate sponsorship and ancillary matters. Has 20 years experience of tax investigation and enquiry work, both Revenue and VAT and serious fraud cases. Resident legal expert on Radio Leeds, Yorkshire Television and the Yorkshire Post.
Publications: Author of 'Sport, Business and the Law' published by Jordans.
Personal: Chairman of the Yorkshire Young Achiever Awards. Member of the Advisory Board, Sports Law Centre, Anglia University; vice-president of The Outward Bound Trust; solicitor to The Duke of Edinburgh's Award; member of the Legal Working Party of the FA Premier League; patron, Harrogate Junior Chamber of Commerce; trustee, Friends of War Memorials.

McINERNEY, Peter
SJ Berwin, London (020) 7533 2521
peter.mcinerney@sjberwin.com
Specialisation: Partner in the Media, Communications and Sports Groups. Specialist in entertainment and sport industries including television and film production, distribution and finance, merchandising, sponsorship, advertising and publishing.
Career: Royal National Theatre (1981-1983). Thames Television (1983-1989). *S J Berwin & Co* (1989 to date)

MEADON, Simon
Tarlo Lyons, London (020) 7405 2000
simon.meadon@tarlolyons.com
Specialisation: Having practised as an entertainment lawyer for over 10 years both in private practice and in industry, he then worked as a theatre producer with Bill Kenwright Ltd for five years presenting over 50 theatrical productions in the West End of London and on Broadway. Principal area of practice is theatre and related work particularly for the Donmar Warehouse, Adventures In Motion Pictures, SX Backrow Ltd and Cameron Mackintosh Limited. He also acts for theatrical agents and personal management companies. In addition, his long experience of film production and financing enables him to advise on these and related matters.
Prof. Memberships: Law Society.
Career: Qualified in 1983.
Personal: Born 25 August 1958, in Staffordshire, England. Educated at North Staffordshire Polytechnic where he graduated in 1979 with a BA (Hons) in Law. Leisure pursuits include theatre, film, tennis and bridge.

MITCHELL, Paul
Taylor Joynson Garrett, London (020) 7300 7000
pmitchell@tjg.co.uk
Specialisation: Partner in intellectual property department. Principal area of practice is entertainment and media law including copyright and related work in various areas of the entertainment and media industry including music, books, films, television and multimedia. Other main area involve company law aspects of the acquisition and disposal of companies and joint ventures in the entertainment and media industry. Contributes articles to various professional publications and is co-author of Joynson-Hicks on UK Copyright Law. Addresses various conferences on topics related to entertainment and media law.
Prof. Memberships: Law Society.
Career: Qualified in 1976 while with *Joynson-Hicks* and became a partner in 1978.
Personal: Born 2 November 1951. Attended Canford School 1965-69, then Bristol University 1970-73. Roald Dahl Foundation (Advisory Board member). Leisure pursuits include family life, sailing and walking. Lives in London.

MOORE, Charles
Olswang, London (020) 7208 8699
chm@olswang.com
Specialisation: Partner in media and communications group. Specialist in the development, production, financing, distribution and acquisition of feature films and television programmes. Work includes helping clients structure the financing of productions, including co-production deals, subsidies and UK sale and leaseback deals. Clients include independent producers and major financiers and distributors and, in particular, US studios given unique US experience (see below). Runs the Film Business School in Spain and contributes to the National Film and Television School Finance Module for its Producers Course. Only European member of the Advisory committee for the annual UCLA Business Affairs Symposium for the motion picture industry.
Prof. Memberships: Law Degree from University of Manchester 1984. Qualified as an English solicitor in 1988. Qualified as California lawyer in 1991.
Career: Joined *Olswang* from qualification in 1988. Rejoined *Olswang* in 1998 after four years in Los Angeles working as attorney in motion picture group at Paramount Pictures Corporation (1994-95) and as vice-president, legal affairs at Twentieth Century Fox Film Corporation (1995-97).

MORGAN, Leon
Davenport Lyons, London (020) 7468 2600
lmorgan@davenportlyons.com
Specialisation: A specialist in the production, financing and distribution of films, television and other audio visual material and IP rights generally. Advises funds specialising in film and television sale and leaseback transactions and other similar financing or investment schemes. Major clients include Barclays Bank plc, The Royal Bank of Scotland, Equity Bank, Bank Leumi, Ed Victor Limited, The Mersey Television Company and many individuals including Phil Redmond, Matthew Vaughn, Guy Ritchie, Douglas Adams, Richard Harris and Sylvie Guillem. Is regularly quoted in industry periodicals.
Prof. Memberships: Law Society
Career: Qualified and joined *Davenport Lyons* in 1964. Became a partner in 1969.
Personal: Born 3 July 1939. Educated at Westcliff High School, 1951-1958. Leisure interests include film, books, art, theatre, music and opera. Lives in London

MOXON, Richard
Davenport Lyons, London (020) 7468 2600
rmoxon@davenportlyons.com
Specialisation: Main area of practice is film and television production and finance including animation and children's programming together with involvement in merchandising and character licensing. Has also been particularly active in the area of tax-based financings, film library acquisitions and so-called 'sale and leaseback' transactions.
Prof. Memberships: PACT Council, BAFTA and a co-opted member of the British Screen Advisory Board.
Career: Imperial Tobacco legal department, 1975-1977; *Denton Hall & Burgin* 1977-1984 (partner 1982); Lorimar Productions 1984-1986 (head of legal and business affairs, partner); *Marriott Harrison* 1986-January 1999. (partner)
Personal: University of Birmingham LLB (Hons) 1969-1972. Interests include singing, cinema, golf. Lives Sunbury-on-Thames.

NYMAN, Bernard
B. M. Nyman & Co, London (020) 8365 3060
bernie.nyman@iname.com
Specialisation: Principal area of practice is non-contentious work in publishing (books, magazines, journals, etc), dealing with contracts for all aspects of publishing including electronic publishing, acting for publishers, authors, literary agents, printers, distributors and learned societies. Libel reading (ie pre-publication advice) and dealing with libel complaints post-publication. General intellectual property work including advice on copyright, trade marks and passing off, and agreements in the entertainment industry generally.
Prof. Memberships: Law Society, European Communities Trade Mark Association, The Media Society, TIPLO. Trustee of The Enid Blyton Trust for Children (appointed 2000).
Career: Qualified in 1979. Partner at *Rubinstein Callingham* from 1983. Partner at *Manches & Co* 1994-98. Proprietor *BM Nyman & Co* 1999.
Publications: Author of the copyright section of 'The Encyclopaedia of Forms & Precedents' (5th edn re-issue, 1999, Vol 21(2)), precedents for Adams: 'Character Merchandising' (2nd edn, 1996, Butterworths). Regular contributor to 'Entertainment Law Review'. Specialist contributor to the 14th edn of 'Copinger & Skone James on Copyright' (Sweet & Maxwell, 1999).
Personal: Born 1954. Educated at Royal Liberty School 1965-72 and Sheffield University 1972-75 (BA in Law). Leisure interests include jazz, film and cricket. Lives in North London.

ORGAN, Chris
Russells, London (020) 7439 8692

PALMER, Nigel
SJ Berwin, London (020) 7533 2265
nigel.palmer@sjberwin.com
Specialisation: Head of media and communications group. Main area of practice is media and entertainment work, including film financing, tax shelter financing, merchandising, film and television production, publishing and video distribution. Involved in financing of many notable feature films, and tax based film financing. Lawyer to 'Thomas the Tank Engine' company from back bedroom to public company. Author of Longman's 'Practical Commercial Precedents on Merchandising'. Member of editorial board of 'Yearbook of Copyright and Media Law'.

Prof. Memberships: International Bar Association, Copinger Society, Fellow of Royal Society of Arts.
Career: Joined *Denton Hall & Burgin* in 1976, qualifying in 1979. Partner *Denton Hall Burgin & Warrens* 1983-88. Left to join *SJ Berwin & Co* as a partner in 1988.
Personal: Born 12 May 1950. Attended St Edward's School, Oxford 1963-67, then Christ Church, Oxford 1968-71. Leisure pursuits include swimming, reading and music. Lives in Greenwich.

PAYNE, Abigail
Harbottle & Lewis, London (020) 7667 5000
abigail.payne@harbottle.com
Specialisation: Main areas of practice are film and television production, financing, distribution and copyright issues. Particular expertise in structuring international co-productions to obtain subsidies and tax incentives. Clients include major US production companies and sales agents, leading UK producers, sale and leaseback partnerships, insurance underwriters and talent agencies.
Career: Qualified in 1995, worked at *Theodore Goddard* 1993-95, then BBC (Independent Drama) 1995-97. Joined *Harbottle & Lewis* in 1997. Became senior associate in 2000.
Personal: Born 1968. Attended Lockleaze School 1981- 86, then Bath University. Leisure interests include tennis, skiing, gym and cinema.

PHILIPPS, Richard
Richards Butler, London (020) 7247 6555
rpsp@richardsbutler.com
Specialisation: Partner in media group. Specialises almost exclusively in film finance work, acting for leading banks and other financial institutions active in the market, distribution companies and major overseas organisations. He also acts for producers.
Prof. Memberships: BAFTA.
Career: Qualified 1978. Partner at *Richards Butler* since 1985.
Personal: Born 1952. Educated at Queen's College, Cambridge.

POTTER, Selina
Olswang, London (020) 7208 8734
skp@olswang.com
Specialisation: Broadcasting and publishing industries. Advises on all commercial aspects of broadcasting, including channel launches, licensing sports, movies and other content, distribution deals and ad sales agreements. Particular expertise in technical aspects of broadcasting, such as satellite and uplink contracts, conditional access, electronic programme guide and interactive television deals. Advises on all commercial elements of book and magazine publishing.
Career: Qualified in 1989 with *Frere Cholmeley*; joined *Olswang* in 1994; became a partner 1995.
Personal: Educated, New College, Oxford.

RENNEY, Paul
Theodore Goddard, London (020) 7606 8855
paulrenney@theodoregoddard.co.uk
Specialisation: Head of e-commerce group, overseeing the different legal aspects of internet and other digital businesses, especially distribution of music online; co-ordination of Data Protection advice throughout the firm and advice on non-contentious intellectual property and commercial matters, as well as corporate media acquisitions, disposals and joint venture; advises on theatre rights, acquisitions and production arrangements, especially musicals, general sponsorship and sales promotions, book and magazine publishing and commercial and IPR arrangements for the horseracing industry.

RIDLEY, Michael
Denton Wilde Sapte, London (020) 7320 6526
mfr@dentonwildesapte.com
Specialisation: Partner in technology, media and telecoms group. Practice encompasses all aspects of television industry, especially the establishment and carriage of new television channels, and also includes commissioning, distribution, co-production agreements for films and television, sponsorship agreements, broadcasting regulation, copyright law. Frequently lectures on broadcasting, television production and copyright.
Prof. Memberships: Law Society, Copinger Society, Royal Television Society.
Career: Qualified in 1980. Rights manager, National Theatre 1980-81. Senior solicitor, London Weekend Television 1981-89. Joined *Denton Hall* in 1989 and became a partner in 1990.
Personal: Chairman of St Paul's Arts Trust and on board of Pop Up Theatre Company.

ROBB, Sophia
Lee & Thompson, London (020) 7935 4665

ROSE, Michael
Tarlo Lyons, London (020) 7405 2000
michael.rose@tarlolyons.com
Specialisation: Partner in entertainment and media department. Principal area of practice is theatre and related work, largely involving stage musicals. Also handles copyright disputes, piracy claims and defamation, as well as most other aspects of entertainment law, with background experience in general company and commercial work. Administration trustee of a large theatre-related charity. Major involvement in contract work (including much international licensing) in respect of over 80 first class stage productions, including such well-known musicals as 'Cats', 'The Phantom of The Opera', 'Les Miserables', 'Miss Saigon', 'Five Guys Named Moe', 'Carousel', 'Follies', 'Moby Dick!', 'Oliver', 'Martin of Guerre', 'Tap Dogs', 'Dance of the Vampires', 'Swan Lake', 'Oklahoma' (1998), 'Cinderella', 'Slava's Snow Show', 'Ugly Rumours', 'Fosse' and 'Havana Night'. Experience also in high profile copyright and employment disputes, as well as some film and TV work. Solicitor to Sir Cameron Mackintosh and his group of companies since 1977. Writes a monthly column in 'The Stage' newspaper on entertainment law; contributes to various other publications including 'Musical Stages' and 'Entertainment Law Review'. He has also written a section on Theatre, Opera and Ballet for the 1999 edition of 'Copinger & Skone James on Copyright'. Seminar speaker on various theatre-related topics.
Prof. Memberships: Law Society, International Association of Entertainment Lawyers, Charity Law Association and is a fellow of the Society of Advanced Legal Studies.
Career: Qualified in 1958. Partner in *Randall Rose* from 1960 until merger with *Tarlo Lyons* in 1986.
Personal: Born 27 August 1934. Educated at Rugby School 1948-52 and University College, London 1952-55. Chairman of Allied Cavendish Properties Ltd (30 shareholders) since 1985. Trustee/director of the Mackintosh Foundation since 1988 and the Theatre Investment Fund Ltd since 1997. Chairman of Encore Tickets Ltd, 2001. Leisure pursuits include golf, theatre, reading and walking. Lives in London.

RUSSELL, Tony
Russells, London (020) 7439 8692

SANDELSON, Daniel
Clifford Chance, London (020) 7600 1000
daniel.sandelson@cliffordchance.com
Specialisation: Partner in communications, media and technology group specialising in corporate and commercial law relating to the media industries; acts for media distribution networks and financial institutions particularly in the broadcasting field, advises on television and film production and distribution, broadcast start-ups particularly in on-demand, pay and terrestrial television, broadcasting regulation, pan-European copyright as it relates to the media industries and media asset acquisitions and disposals including film library and content acquisitions and disposals.
Career: St Catherine's, Oxford University (BA Philosophy, Politics & Economics). Articled *Allen & Overy*; qualified 1988; partner *Clifford Chance* 1996; author of 'UK and EC Broadcasting Law' section in Butterworths 'Competition Law Handbook'; contribution editor to Longmans 'Law and Practice of Multimedia' Handbook; contributor to many trade journals including 'Broadcast' and 'Intermedia'.
Personal: Born 1961; married with two children; resides London.

SAVILL, Lisbeth
Olswang, London (020) 7208 8888
ljs@olswang.com
Specialisation: Partner and Head of Media and Communications Group. Specialist in the production, financing, distribution and acquisition of feature films and television programmes. Work includes structuring finance therefor, including loans, subsidies, and tax-based leasing deals. Clients include independent producers, television broadcasters, major US studios and film financiers (including banks). Runs the Film Business School in Spain and contributes to the National Film and Television School Finance Module for its Producers Course.
Prof. Memberships: Women in Film and Television.
Career: Obtained Arts/Law degree from University of New South Wales in 1980; began her career as a litigation solicitor in Sydney in 1981; followed by international finance work for a major city firm in New York and London 1985-89; and became a partner at *Olswang* in 1991.

SEARLE, Helen
Searles, London (020) 7371 0555
helen@searles-solicitors.co.uk
Specialisation: Intellectual property. The firm represents a large number of successful international artists, as well as independent publishers, record companies and distributors. The firm is particularly strong in e-commerce activities.
Career: Became a partner at the now defunct *Siefert Sedley Williams* in her mid-twenties. Joint founding partner of *Searles Solicitors*, a niche practice. Helen has been actively engaged in private practice for the past fourteen years.
Publications: Regularly lectures to both industry and university audiences on the field of agreements relating to the entertainment industry and contributes articles to the music, legal and academic press.

SHARLAND, Andrew
Clintons, London (020) 7379 6080

SHAW, Barry
Barry Shaw, London (020) 8297 8899
barhanelth@compuserve.com
Specialisation: Drafting of documents in connection with theatrical presentations not only in and for the United Kingdom but also overseas. Invariably, but not always, acts for the Producer. Normally involved in the negotiation and preparation of all material documents for clients. Thereafter acts on the further licensing of rights in the ventures. Recent projects have included dealing with the arrangements for 'La Cava'; 'Thunderbirds'; 'The Caretaker'; 'Noises Off'; the production documents for 'Mamma Mia'; the proposed 'Chitty Chitty Bang Bang'. Additionally specialises in music copyright matters, publishing and defamation.
Prof. Memberships: Has been associated with a number of subsidised theatres; has sat on numerous boards and is a director and secretary of Greenwich Theatre and Almeida Productions Limited. Is also actively involved with Blackheath FC (Rugby Union) where he is the Honorary Secretary.
Career: Articled to Oscar Beuselinck and followed him when he rejoined *Wright & Webb* in 1963. Stayed in *Wright & Webb* (which in due course merged with *Syrett & Sons*) until *Wright Webb Syrett* decided to join another firm in 1995 at which point he set up practice on his own.

SIBBALD, Graham I
Dundas & Wilson CS, Glasgow (0141) 222 2200

SINNOTT, Mark
Russells, London (020) 7439 8692

SMITH, Barry
Richards Butler, London (020) 7247 6555
Specialisation: Partner advising on all aspects of copyright law, film and television finance distribution and production, particular expertise in all aspects of sale and leaseback transactions including representing lenders to lessor partnerships. Advises on the Internet, multimedia and other forms of publishing, and on music agreements, also advises clients on character merchandising and licensing, trade marks, passing off and other forms of protection.
Career: Qualified 1974; partner *Richards Butler* 1980.

SOLOMON, Nicola
Finers Stephens Innocent, London
(020) 7344 7652
nsolomon@fsilaw.co.uk
Specialisation: Nicola Solomon is head of publishing and intellectual property at *Finers Stephens Innocent*. She has considerable expertise in all areas of law relating to publishing and book selling. She and her team are unique in that as well as advising a broad range of publishers, both British and international, they also provide specialist advice to rights holders such as authors, illustrators, journalists, photographers and their representatives including agents, literary estates and professional organisations. Nicola advises on both contentious and non-contentious issues, including drafting and negotiating contracts, advice on copyright, moral rights, contractual disputes, passing off and trademark infringement, brand management, defamation and literary estates. She is particularly interested in the ramifications of digitalisation and the electronic delivery of content and she has spent much of this year advising clients on these issues. Clients include the Wall Street Journal, The Society of Authors, The Association of Illustrators and The British Association of Picture Libraries and Agencies, as well as many individual publishers, creators and agents.
Career: Nicola qualified in 1984 and has been a partner since 1988. She also sits as a Deputy District Judge.
Publications: Writes extensively in this area, including a regular column in 'Author' magazine.

STATHAM, John
Statham Gill Davies, London (020) 7487 5565

STORER, Robert
Harbottle & Lewis, London (020) 7667 5000
robert.storer@harbottle.com
Specialisation: Partner and Head of the Film & TV Production Group. Main areas of practice are film and television production and finance and copyright issues. Has over 25 years' experience representing leading producers, including Merchant Ivory Productions, Fragile Films and Kismet Films, as well as financiers, completion guarantors and film financiers. Involved in the production and financing of numerous films and television series and programmes, including most recently Mr Bean, Spice World – The Movie, Ideal Husband, Honest, Golden Bowl, Lucky Break and The Importance of Being Earnest. Addressed a number of conferences on media issues.
Prof. Memberships: Law Society, International Bar Association, Director of Association of Independent Producers (early 1980s), Director of Film Finances Ltd (1983-88).
Career: Joined *Harbottle & Lewis* in 1969, qualifying in 1971. Became partner in 1974, and senior partner in 1999.
Personal: Born 1947. Attended Buxton College 1960-65, then London School of Economics 1965-68. Leisure pursuits include family, golf, tennis and cinema. Lives in Barnes, London.

SWAFFER, Patrick
Goodman Derrick, London (020) 7404 0606
Specialisation: Partner in media department. Main areas of practice are broadcasting and publishing. Includes pre and post-publication advice on defamation, contempt, confidence and copyright, rights exploitation, contractual issues and regulatory advice for the broadcasting industry.
Career: Joined *Goodman Derrick* in 1974. Qualified 1976. Became partner in 1979 in media department.
Personal: Born 12 February 1951. Lives in London.

TATTON-BROWN, Sam
Davenport Lyons, London (020) 7468 2600

THOMPSON, Andrew J.
Lee & Thompson, London (020) 7935 4665

TREGEAR, Steven
Russells, London (020) 7439 8692

TURTON, Julian
The Simkins Partnership, London (020) 7907 3000

WARE, James
Davenport Lyons, London (020) 7468 2600
jware@davenportlyons.com
Specialisation: Copyright and copyright tribunal and has an extensive knowledge of transactional broadcast clearing practice, music industry, broadcasting, entertainment, merchandising, rights administration, theatre, computer media. Clients include substantial independent music publishers and specialist entertainment businesses on the one hand and well-known composers and artists on the other.
Prof. Memberships: International Association of Entertainment Lawyers, International Managers Federation. Deputy chairman of the Guildford School of Acting.
Career: St Johns College, Oxford. Virgin Group, director; CBS Songs, European regional vice-president; *Davenport Lyons*, partner since 1986.
Personal: Music, theatre and hill walking. Members: Athenaeum, MCC.

WATSON, Peter
Levy & McRae, Glasgow (0141) 307 2311
peterwatson@lemac.co.uk
See under Defamation, p.288

WILLIAMS, Alan
Denton Wilde Sapte, London (020) 7320 6249
apw@dentonwildesapte.com
Specialisation: Head of digital media practice. Work includes digital media and e-commerce, electronic publishing, copyright, libel, commercial contract, traditional publishing and theatre. Lectures for Hawksmere, PIRA and others.
Career: Qualified in 1969, having joined *Denton Hall & Burgin* in 1967. Became a partner in 1972.
Publications: Co-author with Michael Flint and Clive Thorne of 'Intellectual Property: the New Law'; contributes to 'Publishing Agreements' edited by Charles Clark and 'International Media Liability' published by John Wiley. Author with Duncan Calow of 'Digital Media: Contracts, Rights and Licensing' (2nd edn 1998 Sweet & Maxwell). Edited Halsbury's Laws of England section on 'Press, Printing and Publishing'.

WILLIAMS, Gordon
Lee & Thompson, London (020) 7935 4665

WILLS, David
Campbell Hooper, London (020) 7654 5141
DavidWills@campbellhooper.com
Specialisation: Consultant in media group. Extensive experience of the law and practice of the theatre. Advises producers, financiers and creative personnel in the West End, on Broadway, off Broadway and all other territories where live theatre is performed. Regularly negotiates production rights, finance agreements, co-production ventures, theatre licences and agreements for the services of creative contributors to theatrical productions. Handles media litigation. Represents writers and performers on stage and screen.
Career: Qualified 1967. Partner at *Campbell Hooper* 1970.
Personal: Lives in London and Wiltshire.

ZEFFMAN, David
Olswang, London (020) 7208 8888
dcz@olswang.com
Specialisation: Partner media and communications group. Principal area of practice involves commercial and corporate aspects of television, sport, music and e-commerce businesses.
Prof. Memberships: IBA, IAEL.
Career: Qualified 1983 while with *Frere Cholmeley* and became a partner in 1989. Appointed head of company and commercial department, *Frere Cholmeley Bischoff* in 1993. Joined *Simon Olswang & Co* as partner in 1994.
Personal: Born 28th February 1958. Attended Haberdashers' Aske's School 1969-76, then Brasenose College, Oxford 1977-80. Lives in London.

PARLIAMENTARY & PUBLIC AFFAIRS

London – Parliamentary Agency 608; London – Public Affairs: 609; *Profiles*: 609

OVERVIEW: The dramatic reduction in the number of private bills presented to Parliament has led to the domination of Transport and Works Act and Harbour Orders for Parliamentary Agents. For the lobbyists, increased attention to the European decision-makers has proven vital in their efforts to protect the interests of their clients.

RESEARCH APPROVED BY BMRB: *For this edition,* Chambers' *researchers conducted 6,552 interviews – 4,419 with law firms, 554 with barristers and 1,579 with clients.*

The validity of the research was scrutinised by BMRB International, who audited both the methodology and the results at our offices in July 2001. They interviewed Chambers' *researchers and cross-checked sample interviews. Details of the audit appear on page 7.*

LONDON

PARLIAMENTARY AGENCY

PARLIAMENTARY AGENCY • London	Ptnrs	Assts
1 Bircham Dyson Bell	6	5
Rees & Freres	3	6
Winckworth Sherwood	4	1
2 Sharpe Pritchard	2	2

LEADING INDIVIDUALS	
1 **DURKIN Joseph** Rees & Freres	**GORLOV Alison** Winckworth Sherwood
THOMPSON Paul Bircham Dyson Bell	
2 **IRVING Paul** Winckworth Sherwood	**McCULLOCH Ian** Bircham Dyson Bell
3 **LEWIS Alastair** Sharpe Pritchard	**OWEN Robert** Bircham Dyson Bell
PETO Monica Rees & Freres	
4 **BROWN Nicholas** Bircham Dyson Bell	

This book is the product of 6,552 1/2-hour interviews. See p.7 for BMRB audit.
Within each band, firms are listed alphabetically. *See individuals' profiles p.609*

Bircham Dyson Bell (see firm details p.883) "*Par excellence*" in this field, due in part to the fact that four members of the team are Roll A parliamentary agents, and also to its unparalleled experience with a complementary public affairs practice. Providing "*excellent scale and depth*" not only in promoting and opposing local and private legislation but also in more general planning, environmental and public law advice. The core of the firm's work derives from the highest profile Transport and Works Act Orders, including the recent promotion of a TWA Order to authorise the £115 million extension of the Docklands Light Railway to London City Airport. The team enjoys expertise in local passenger transport executives, where **Paul Thompson** (see p.610) ("*a man on a mission*") has "*an excellent understanding of the nature of passenger transport executives.*" He is joined by the "*leader*" **Ian McCulloch** (see p.610) and "*rising star*" **Robert Owen** (see p.610). **Nicholas Brown** (see p.609) has been less visible this year due to his managerial role, but is still perceived to be an "*experienced player.*" Significant work is also undertaken within the areas of bank mergers, light rail projects and harbours and ports regulation and development work. **Clients:** Greater Manchester Passenger Transport Executive; English Welsh and Scottish Railway; Edinburgh City Council.

Rees & Freres (see firm details p.1105) Although reputed to be "*weakened by the retirement of Peter Lane,*" it has replenished an "*excellent*" team, which comprises three Roll A parliamentary agents. The "*most experienced player*" in the field, "*with the most distinguished reputation,*" **Joseph Durkin** is supported by the "*exceptionally bright*" **Monica Peto** who has cultivated a prominent presence. The group acted for Railtrack in the Thameslink 2000 and West Coast Mainline Enquiries. The bulk of the workload continues to be advice on Transport and Works Act Orders to corporations and local authorities. Support is provided by property lawyers giving advice to clients who may be affected by TWA orders. It also specialises in harbour and port orders and private bills, undertaking the successful bill to turn Greenham Common into a peaceful tract of land. **Clients:** Railtrack; British Rail; Felixstowe Dock and Railway Co.

Winckworth Sherwood (see firm details p.1185) "*The most active*" of the parliamentary agents according to one interviewee. A "*dynamic, experienced team*" is headed by the "*powerful, clear-thinking*" **Alison Gorlov** (see p.609). Her "*enormous experience*" is bolstered by the support of "*bright, able*" **Paul Irving** (see p.610). The group is acting on a variety of TWA Orders, including the opposition to two Harbour Orders and one TWA Order concerning the regeneration scheme for the Bridlington Bay Marina in Yorkshire. Also assisting in the funding of a light rail transit system in Bristol. The firm is one of only two panel members of the Scottish Parliament's Non-Executive bills unit, performing a drafting service for Committee Bills and Members' Bills.

Sharpe Pritchard (see firm details p.1123) Although perceived to be less active this year, it nevertheless possesses an "*unparalleled parliamentary monitoring research service and a more practical approach than other agents.*" "*Confident and capable*" **Alastair Lewis** (see p.610) is developing into "*a worthy successor to Michael Pritchard.*" Involved in large private bills, such as the promotion of the merger between Barclays and The Woolwich. Particular expertise in planning advice for local authorities, who believe that the team "*really understand the public sector.*" A certain amount of TWA and harbour orders are undertaken, acting for harbour and transport authorities promoting and opposing primary and secondary legislation. **Clients:** English Heritage; London Borough of Lambeth.

LONDON

PUBLIC AFFAIRS

PARLIAMENTARY: PUBLIC AFFAIRS • London	Ptnrs	Assts
1 Bircham Dyson Bell	*	*
Clifford Chance	1	1
DLA	n/a	n/a
Lovells	*	*
SJ Berwin	n/a	n/a

LEADING INDIVIDUALS
1 BRACKEN Jonathan Bircham Dyson Bell CLEMENT-JONES Tim DLA
THOMAS Richard Clifford Chance
2 HOLMES Simon SJ Berwin

This book is the product of 6,552 1/2-hour interviews. See p.7 for BMRB audit.

Within each band, firms are listed alphabetically. *See individuals' profiles p.609*

**See editorial entries for explanation of team sizes.*

Bircham Dyson Bell (see firm details p.883) (6 Ptnrs, 5 Assts part-time) A "*politically astute*" team able to draw upon its knowledge of the political scene from expertise in parliamentary agency. The "*supreme drafter,*" **Jonathan Bracken** (see p.609) has heightened the firm's reputation for drafting public legislation and advising on parliamentary and legislative procedure within the telecommunications, utility, environment and transport sectors. Significant inroads have been achieved on the Utilities Bill, advising the Electricity Association and British Telecom on their desired amendments. Similar work is now undertaken in relation to the Scottish Parliament and the National Assembly for Wales. An extensive client base includes government agencies and non-departmental public bodies, charities and pressure groups. Lobbying advice was recently given to the RSPCA on the fox-hunting bill. **Clients:** Merseyside Passenger Transport Executive; Cable & Wireless; Hampshire County Council.

Clifford Chance (see firm details p.919) The team to aim at according to one of their peers, chiefly due to the extensive experience of **Richard Thomas** (see p.610), who boasts 18 years in UK public service as a legal and policy adviser, campaigner and regulator. Clients are drawn, not simply to the fact that he has "*the broadest portfolio in public affairs work*" but because he "*achieves success against great odds.*" The group provides strategic advice on government policy and legislation, helping clients anticipate and understand issues arising from Whitehall, Westminster and Brussels. A recent success has been the campaign for IMS Health, culminating in the withdrawal of a government clause in the Health and Social Care Bill which allowed the government access to anonymous patient data. An important recent innovation has been the introduction of a 'Public Policy Online Service' detailing relevant legislative proposals for its clients. **Clients:** DETR; Goldman Sachs; Whitehall & Industry Group.

DLA **Tim Clement-Jones** is a leading name in London, and leads a team which has acted with increasing frequency for major e-commerce clients.

Lovells (4 Ptnrs, 1 Asst part-time) (see firm details p.1044) A "*high profile, impressive*" outfit, suffering, however, the loss of Gordon Innes. Head of department Neil Fagan has maintained an impressive client base, with particular growth in the areas of pharmaceuticals, biochemicals, human genome and e-commerce. The group has displayed expertise in helping clients overcome uncertainty regarding the effect of UK and EU laws on data protection and e-commerce. **Clients:** Media; tobacco companies; telecom companies.

SJ Berwin (see firm details p.879) Perceived to possess a large share of "*big ticket*" work, proving to be adept in deploying Human Rights issues within the protection of clients' public policy interests. The team, acting as the advisors to the Conservative Party, persuaded the policy-makers that certain areas of the Financial Services and Markets Bill were not compliant with Article 6 of the European Convention of Human Rights. Currently engaged in lobbying for ENIC against UEFA's ban on multiple football club ownership, which included lobbying the European Parliament and European Commission. A new office opened in Munich in Autumn 2000 and is strategically placed to aid European lobbying efforts. "*Energetic competitor*" **Simon Holmes** (see p.609) has been largely responsible for honing an enviable client base, including high-profile members of the music, media, sport and pharmaceuticals industries. **Clients:** Coca-Cola Enterprises; Procter & Gamble; Warner Brothers.

LEADERS IN PARLIAMENTARY & PUBLIC AFFAIRS

BRACKEN, Jonathan
Bircham Dyson Bell, London (020) 7222 8044
jonathanbracken@bdb-law.co.uk
Specialisation: Principal areas of practice are public affairs, lobbying, legislative drafting, parliamentary procedure, research and advice on public policy issues. During the past year he has worked on the Health Bill, Utilities Bill, Postal Services Bill and Hunting Bill and on the Health Insurance (Amendment) Bill before the Oireachtas (Irish Parliament).
Prof. Memberships: Law Society; Society for Advanced Legal Studies (Associate Fellow); Institute of Public Relations (Government Affairs Group); Administrative Law Bar Association.
Career: Partner *Bircham Dyson Bell* (then *Bircham & Co*) 2000; Scholar in Residence, US Law Library of Congress.

BROWN, Nicholas
Bircham Dyson Bell, London (020) 7222 8044
nicholasbrown@bdb-law.co.uk
Specialisation: Specialises in infrastructure legislation. Adviser to charities and trustees. Is presently engaged in promoting various Harbour Orders and advising on the West Coast Main Line project.
Career: Articled *Bircham Dyson Bell* (then *Bircham & Co*) 1979. Qualified as a Solicitor in 1983. Partner and Roll A Agent 1985. Chairman of Executive Committee 1997-to present.
Personal: Attended Westminster School and Jesus College, Oxford. Plays cricket and golf and is a qualified soccer referee. Two children.

CLEMENT-JONES, Tim
DLA, London (08700) 111 111

DURKIN, Joseph
Rees & Freres, London (020) 7222 5381

GORLOV, Alison
Winckworth Sherwood, London (020) 7222 0441
amhgorlov@winckworths.co.uk
Specialisation: Senior parliamentary partner and parliamentary agent. Specialist in legislation and legislative drafting, parliamentary and legislative procedures, administrative and public law, transport and other infrastructure (railways, harbours, tramways, utilities), public sector bodies, commercial undertakings. Long experience of acting for central and local government, major transport undertakers, port authorities, utility undertakers, banks, building societies, charities and educational bodies.
Prof. Memberships: Law Society. Society of Parliamentary Agents (past president).
Career: Joined *Sherwood & Co.* in 1971. Qualified as a solicitor in 1975, became a partner and Roll A Agent in 1978.

HOLMES, Simon
SJ Berwin, London (020) 7533 2222
simon.holmes@sjberwin.com
Specialisation: European, competition and trade law. Major cases include some of the largest anti-dumping, competition and single market law cases involving lobbying in Brussels, London and other member state capitals.
Prof. Memberships: Recent Chairman, Solicitors' European Group.
Career: 1st Class Honours, Law and Economics from Cambridge. Grande Distinction, Licence Speciale en

Droit Européen, Brussels University.
Personal: Married, 2 daughters. Walking, cycling, tennis, film.

IRVING, Paul
Winckworth Sherwood, London (020) 7593 5000
pirving@winckworths.co.uk
Specialisation: Partner in Parliamentary department. Specialises in drafting, promoting and opposing legislation in Parliament and delegated legislation (including Orders under the Transport and Works Act and the Harbours Act) and in advising on railways, harbours and other infrastructure projects.
Prof. Memberships: Society of Parliamentary Agents (Secretary). Law Society.
Career: Called to the Bar 1986. Requalified as solicitor 1991. Partner at *Sherwood & Co* since 1992.
Personal: Educated at Trinity College, Oxford (MA and D.Phil). Born 7th November 1956.

LEWIS, Alastair
Sharpe Pritchard, London (020) 7405 4600
alewis@sharpepritchard.co.uk
Specialisation: Promotion of and opposition to private and hybrid bills, transport and works orders and harbour revision orders. Work on government bills includes drafting amendments for clients and monitoring progress through parliament. Promoted bill regulating secondhand dealers to Royal Assent in 2001 and is currently promoting a bank reorganisation bill. Acts for a large number of local authorities, statutory bodies, national authorities and companies.
Prof. Memberships: Society of Parliamentary Agents.
Career: LL.B Trent Polytechnic, College of Law.
Personal: Football, walking, cycling.

McCULLOCH, Ian
Bircham Dyson Bell, London (020) 7222 8044
ianmcculloch@bdb-law.co.uk
Specialisation: Parliamentary strategy and procedure, tactics and lobbying. Promoting and opposing primary and subordinate legislation for statutory companies, local authorities, trade associations, transport undertakers, banks, property companies, harbours, charities and sporting and amenity bodies.
Prof. Memberships: Society of Parliamentary Agents (Hon Sec 1989-95; President 1995-98). City of Westminster Law Society (President 1994-95). Law Society. Statute Law Society.
Career: Admitted as a Solicitor 1976. Partner since 1977. Enrolled as a Roll A Parliamentary Agent 1979. Senior Parliamentary Partner since 1992. Senior Partner (1997-).
Personal: Born 13th May 1950. Educated Edinburgh Academy and University of Dundee (LLB Hons. jurisprudence and philosophy).

OWEN, Robert
Bircham Dyson Bell, London (020) 7222 8044
robertowen@bdb-law.co.uk
Specialisation: Main areas of practice continue to be parliamentary and public affairs, town and country planning, transport and environmental law. Over the past year highlights have been: promoting for Docklands Light Railway Limited an order under the Transport and Works Act (TWA) to authorise an extension of the DLR to Silvertown and London City Airport; being appointed by Merseyside Passenger transport Executive and Nottinghamshire County and Nottingham City Councils to promote TWA Orders for, respectively, a MerseyTram System and extension to the Nottingham Express Transit System; acting for objectors in relation to various other orders proposed to be made under the TWA for transport infrastructure; continuing to act for EWS and other landowners affected by the proposed Channel Tunnel Rail Link; advising in relation to various other light rail schemes and railway re-openings; advising the Environment Agency Wales in relation to various matters including a review of its role as Conservancy Authority for the River Dee; advising various ports, harbours and conservancies on local legislation and the Government's new ports policy.
Prof. Memberships: Law Society; United Kingdom Environmental Law Association; Society of Parliamentary Agents.
Career: University of London: 1983-86; College of Law: 1986-87; Qualified as a solicitor: 1989; Partner with *Bircham Dyson Bell* since 1991.
Personal: Married with three children.

PETO, Monica
Rees & Freres, London (020) 7222 5381

THOMAS, Richard
Clifford Chance, London (020) 7600 1000
richard.thomas@cliffordchance.com
Specialisation: Director of Public Policy at *Clifford Chance* since 1992. For the previous 18 years he held various legal, policy and regulatory posts in the public sector including 6 years as Director of Consumer Affairs at the Office of Fair Trading. Helps *Clifford Chance* and its clients to deal with business developments inside Whitehall, Westminster and Brussels. Has in-depth knowledge on governmental structures, procedures and culture and extensive experience of getting legislation onto the statute book and amending Bills. Also has a wide-ranging network of personal contacts – within the civil service, parliament, the media, trade associations, interest groups and the voluntary sector. Writes and speaks extensively on legal and related matters and is regularly used by the media for comment on constitutional, legislative and other pubic sector developments. Member of various governmental and self-regulatory committees and schemes.
Prof. Memberships: Law Society; Royal Society of Arts.
Career: *Freshfields* (1971-74); CAB Legal Service (1974-79); National Consumer Council (1979-86); Office of Fair Trading (1986-92); *Clifford Chance* (1992 – present).

THOMPSON, Paul
Bircham Dyson Bell, London (020) 7222 8044
paulthompson@bdb-law.co.uk
Specialisation: Advice on parliamentary and legislative procedures and tactics, legislative drafting, lobbying and public affairs and the promotion of and opposition to local legislation. Has acted for a wide range of public and private sector bodies including national, local, port and transport authorities, banks and other financial institutions, major plcs, utilities, trade and amenity associations and religious and other charitable bodies. Currently, particularly involved in advising various interests on, and assisting them in relation to, new government legislation and devolved matters, whilst also heavily engaged in the promotion of light rail schemes by Transport and Works Order and port-related work.
Prof. Memberships: Law Society, Society of Parliamentary Agents.
Career: Called to the Bar 1977. Partner in *Dyson Bell & Co* 1982. Partner and Solicitor at *Bircham & Co and Dyson Bell Martin* since 1990.
Personal: Born 26th March 1954.

PARTNERSHIP

OVERVIEW: Firms have observed an increasingly fluid and ever more contentious market with a continued growth in merger activity, restrictive covenant inquiries and garden leave issues. An important development in the legislation has been the incorporation of Limited Liability Partnerships (LLPs), allowing the flexibility of the traditional internal partnership structure, with the added benefit of being able to trade with limited liability. Although generating interest, the early response is hesitant due to the requirement to provide financial information including the filing of annual accounts.

RESEARCH APPROVED BY BMRB: *For this edition,* Chambers' *researchers conducted 6,552 interviews – 4,419 with law firms, 554 with barristers and 1,579 with clients.*

The validity of the research was scrutinised by BMRB International, who audited both the methodology and the results at our offices in July 2001. They interviewed Chambers' *researchers and cross-checked sample interviews. Details of the audit appear on page 7.*

LONDON

PARTNERSHIP • London	Ptnrs	Assts
1 Allen & Overy	4	n/a
Fox Williams	3	n/a
Rowe & Maw	2	n/a
2 Herbert Smith	3	4
Kingsley Napley	4	n/a
3 Bristows	1	n/a
Field Fisher Waterhouse	3	n/a
Finers Stephens Innocent	2	n/a
Reynolds Porter Chamberlain	3	n/a
5 Wright Son & Pepper	1	2

LEADING INDIVIDUALS

1 **FOX Ronnie** Fox Williams — **LINSELL Richard** Rowe & Maw
TURNOR Richard Allen & Overy

2 **SACKER Tony** Kingsley Napley — **WILLIAMS Christine** Fox Williams

3 **GOLD David** Herbert Smith — **MAYER Stephen** Reynolds Porter Chamberlain
SIMMONS Michael Finers Stephens Innocent

4 **LACE John** Bristows — **McARTHUR Colin** Field Fisher Waterhouse
WRIGHT Nicholas Wright Son & Pepper

UP AND COMING

MURRAY Clare Fox Williams

This book is the product of 6,552 1/2-hour interviews. See p.7 for BMRB audit.

Within each band, firms are listed alphabetically. *See individuals' profiles p.615*

PARTNERSHIP: LARGE INTERNATIONAL MERGERS • London	Ptnrs	Assts
1 Allen & Overy	n/a	n/a
Herbert Smith	3	4
Linklaters	4	n/a
Slaughter and May	1	1

LEADING INDIVIDUALS

1 **TRIGGS Jeff** Slaughter and May

2 **GODDEN Richard** Linklaters

UP AND COMING

COHEN Raymond Linklaters

This book is the product of 6,552 1/2-hour interviews. See p.7 for BMRB audit.

Within each band, firms are listed alphabetically. *See individuals' profiles p.615*

Allen & Overy (see firm details p.856) Judged a *"worthy competitor"* by peers **Richard Turnor** (see p.617) owns the most *"serious brain"* in the field of partnership law. He advises professional and non-professional partnerships in all areas ranging from the formation of internal constitutional documents to international mergers. He is currently converting two professional firms into LLPs. The team advised Bear Stearns on the establishment of a new media venture capital fund with Virgin, and advised Schroder Exempt Unit Trust on its investment in West India Quay Limited Partnership. **Clients:** Accountants; law firms; international investment banks.

Fox Williams (see firm details p.963) *"Great ambassador"* **Ronnie Fox** (see p.615) maintains his standing as head of an efficient and admirable team including the well respected **Christine Williams** (see p.617) and the up and coming **Clare Murray** (see p.616). The team acts for individuals and firms in contentious and non-contentious work including mergers, restructuring, restrictive covenants and exits, and in the drafting of initial partnership agreements. It has an active involvement in law firms new to London, particularly US firms. **Clients:** Solicitors; accountants.

Rowe & Maw (see firm details p.1113) *"Probably the guru on partnership law,"* according to clients **Richard Linsell** (see p.616) is the standout partner, acting for an increasing number of law firms. He advises on departures, mergers, splits and stockbroking partnerships, and continues to act for Ernst & Young in its conversion to LLP status. Linsell has also been involved in the selling of a high-profile partnership. **Clients:** Solicitors; accountants; commercial organisations.

Herbert Smith (see firm details p.993) Litigator **David Gold** (see p.615) heads a *"broad practice"* which has had a particularly busy year acting in disputes and advising individuals being poached by other companies. Heavily involved in the majority of high-profile partnership disputes, the firm acted for PricewaterhouseCoopers in a review of global governance arrangements, including a reorganisation of PwC International. **Clients:** Accountants; law firms (including US firms); legal networks.

Kingsley Napley (see firm details p.1022) *"Good at the human side,"* **Tony Sacker** (see p.616) is endorsed by competitors and clients, and uses a broad team of partners in his effort to remain almost exclusively non-contentious. Appointed official solicitor for the Law Commission on the major reform in partnership law, the firm retains its high profile. It has overseen numerous partnership exits, and has drafted the partnership agreement for a major media firm. The team has a niche in regulatory work involving disciplinary tribunals. **Clients:** Solicitors; accountants.

Bristows (see firm details p.895)*"Experienced old hand"* **John Lace** (see p.615) has access to tax and property advice from two fellow partners at this firm. Fielding mainly non-contentious work, acting more for individuals than companies, his work involves drafting partnership agreements for mergers, de-mergers, retirements and dissolutions. The team also offers advice on using limited partnerships as a medium for tax transparent forms of commercial collaboration. **Clients:** Solicitors; accountants; surveyors; veterinary surgeons; architects.

Field Fisher Waterhouse (see firm details p.957) Primarily acting for professional partnerships, the team advises on the whole range of partnership matters, drawing on its tax specialists and the commercial litigation department as appropriate. **Colin McArthur** (see p.616) is endorsed by competitors for his skill in *"getting out of partnerships gently."* The firm also has a niche in collective investment schemes in old style partnerships. It has seen a growth in restrictive covenant and garden leave issues. **Clients:** Accountants; solicitors; architects; quantity surveyors; professional individuals.

Finers Stephens Innocent (see firm details p.958) The *"client oriented"* and *"amusing"* **Michael Simmons** continues to impress his peers. He is equally at home in contentious and non-contentious work, advising and acting for partners wishing to leave and for those wishing to expel a partner. Also active in drafting deeds and advising on limited liability partnerships. **Clients:** Accountants; solicitors; actuaries; architects.

Reynolds Porter Chamberlain (see firm details p.1106) Acting equally for individuals or firms, *"sensible, calm and competent"* **Stephen Mayer** (see p.616) maintains a profile in the field. He successfully assisted a partner in resisting attempts by his fellow partners to remove him. He also frequently advises on restrictive covenants, disputes, and settlements for out-going partners. **Clients:** Solicitors; accountants; estate agents; surveyors; farming and veterinary partnerships.

Wright Son & Pepper (see firm details p.1190) Highly regarded **Nicholas Wright** (see p.617) also draws upon the skills of two partners who deal with the litigious and negligent aspects of partnership law. Whilst the firm maintains its focus on regulatory work, it has a noted increase in issues surrounding the formation of multi-disciplinary firms of solicitors and accountants. **Clients:** Solicitors; accountants; surveyors.

Linklaters (see firm details p.1042) Retaining its team focus, although the *"first rate"* **Richard Godden** (see p.246) continues to be seen as the major player in international mergers. He draws on lengthy experience in the structure of international organisations, where his expertise lies in the global co-ordination of deals for the big five firms of accountants. He acted for Ernst & Young in the disposal of its management consultancy business to Cap Gemini. **Raymond Cohen** (see p.615) is also defining himself as one to watch. **Clients:** Major accountancy firms.

Slaughter and May (see firm details p.1135) Though the firm possesses a reputation for a *"ruthless focus on their M&A base,"* **Jeff Triggs** (see p.617) has been described as a *"leading light"* within the field of international mergers. He has advised Bacon & Woodrow in the transfer of its insurance business to Deloitte & Touche and in the proposed merger of the remainder of the firm with Hewitts in the US. **Clients:** Accountants; actuaries; large professional and commercial partnerships.

THE SOUTH & THAMES VALLEY

PARTNERSHIP • The South & Thames Valley	Ptnrs	Assts
1 **Lester Aldridge** Bournemouth	3	3
Linnells Oxford	2	n/a
2 **Mundays** Esher	1	n/a
Rawlison Butler Crawley	3	2

LEADING INDIVIDUALS
1 **CORKE Andrew** Lester Aldridge
2 **MISCAMPBELL Andrew** Linnells

This book is the product of 6,552 1/2-hour interviews. See p.7 for BMRB audit.
Within each band, firms are listed alphabetically. *See individuals' profiles p.615*

Lester Aldridge (see firm details p.1038) The team, including the respected **Andrew Corke** (see p.615) focuses on general and private medical practitioner partnerships, but also advises and draws up deeds for other professional partnerships. It is also active in retirements, admissions, and disputes issues. **Clients:** Medical practitioners; accountants; solicitors; vets.

Linnells (see firm details p.1043) According to our research the emphasis of this practice is solicitor partnerships, but it also acts for numerous medical partnerships. The *"objective"* **Andrew Miscampbell** (see p.616) heads the non-contentious side of the practice, often dealing with mergers, property complications, and tax issues. **Clients:** Solicitors; medical partnerships.

Mundays (see firm details p.1077) Exploiting his commercial background, David Irving leads a team that focuses on professional partnerships, and has noted a massive growth of interest in LLPs. The team also acts for medical partnerships. **Clients:** Professional partnerships.

Rawlison Butler (see firm details p.1104) Clive Lee heads a bolstered team that advises professional partnerships. The firm receives a regular flow of instructions regarding partnership disputes, and there is a particular interest in the extent to which partners claiming indemnity are liable. **Clients:** Medical partnerships; accountants; surveyors; solicitors.

SOUTH WEST

PARTNERSHIP • South West	Ptnrs	Assts
1 **Burges Salmon** Bristol	3	n/a
TLT Solicitors Bristol	2	n/a
Veale Wasbrough Bristol	2	5
2 **Bond Pearce** Bristol	1	n/a
Osborne Clarke Bristol	3	3

LEADING INDIVIDUALS	
1 **BELLEW Derek** Veale Wasbrough	**LLEWELYN EVANS Adrian** Burges Salmon
MAY Philip TLT Solicitors	
2 **MARSH David** Burges Salmon	**MOULE Jos** Osborne Clarke OWA
STARKS Brian Bond Pearce	
3 **MOSS Nicholas** TLT Solicitors	

This book is the product of 6,552 1/2-hour interviews. See p.7 for BMRB audit.
Within each band, firms are listed alphabetically. *See individuals' profiles p.615*

Burges Salmon (see firm details p.902) *"Senior statesman"* **Adrian Llewelyn Evans** (see p.616) is *"committed to mediation"* and is seen as active in contentious matters by his peers. He works in a team of three partnership lawyers, including the warmly recommended **David Marsh** (see p.616). Agriculture is a strong focus for the firm, and it has also recently overseen a merger of surveyors' firms and the collapsing of a training subsidiary into a partnership. **Clients:** Farming partnerships; solicitors; accountants; surveyors; consulting engineers.

TLT Solicitors (see firm details p.1157) *"Superb allies"* **Philip May** (see p.616) (contentious) and **Nick Moss** (see p.616) (non-contentious) act as a two-pronged fork in their approach to professional partnership inquiries. Medical practices and solicitors' firms constitute the majority of their clients. They draft agreements, advise on taxation and structural issues and deal with exits and dissolutions. **Clients:** Doctors; solicitors; accountants; dentists; vets; surveyors; architects.

Veale Wasbrough (see firm details p.1167) Although much of the partnership work seen by this firm comes from the medical sector, it also deals with an increasing number of solicitor firms' dissolutions. The highly respected **Derek Bellew** (see p.240) and his team also advise vets and pharmacies on the ever more popular move to conglomerate business arrangements. **Clients:** Medical partnerships; solicitors; accountants; veterinarians; pharmacists.

Bond Pearce (see firm details p.888) The "*fantastically methodical*" and almost exclusively contentious lawyer **Brian Starks** (see p.617) stands out of the team of four at this firm, which is known for its ability to settle disputes without involving High Court proceedings. It also formulates partnership agreements, and advises on partners joining and exiting. **Clients:** Professional; business; family; farming partnerships.

Osborne Clarke (see firm details p.1086) **Jos Moule**'s team is endorsed by competitors for its work across the full range of partnership work. It has advised accountants with regard to potential re-structuring as a limited liability partnership, and regularly advises commercial clients as to whether commercial joint ventures can be construed as partnerships. **Clients:** Accountants; solicitors; actuaries; commercial partnerships.

MIDLANDS

PARTNERSHIP • Midlands		Ptnrs	Assts
1	**Pinsent Curtis Biddle** Birmingham	2	2
2	**Freethcartwright** Nottingham	2	7
	Hammond Suddards Edge Birmingham	1	1

LEADING INDIVIDUALS	
1	**COOKE David** Pinsent Curtis Biddle

This book is the product of 6,552 1/2-hour interviews. See p.7 for BMRB audit.
Within each band, firms are listed alphabetically. *See individuals' profiles p.615*

Pinsent Curtis Biddle (see firm details p.1098) **David Cooke** (see p.615) continues to be highly regarded in this field. As a non-contentious lawyer, he acts for firms rather than individuals in mergers, acquisitions and disposals. The team also advises on the drafting of deeds. **Clients:** Solicitors; surveyors; actuaries.

Freethcartwright (see firm details p.964) Paul Thorogood leads a recently bolstered team that advises professionals on mainly non-contentious matters such as formations and mergers and in the more contentious field of dissolution. The seven strong 'Risk Management' team is considered by clients and rivals a skilled force in the market. **Clients:** Accountants; doctors; solicitors.

Hammond Suddards Edge (see firm details p.984) Active in both the contentious (Digby Rose) and non-contentious (Baljit Chohan) arena, the team recently received its first LLP instruction. It has given advice regarding restrictive covenants and has had a significant growth in lawyer breakaway groups and in new business ventures. **Clients:** Lawyers; accountants; surveyors.

THE NORTH

PARTNERSHIP • The North		Ptnrs	Assts
1	**Cuff Roberts** Liverpool	2	n/a
2	**Kershaw Abbott** Manchester	2	n/a
	Mace & Jones Manchester	1	1
3	**Cobbetts** Manchester	2	1

LEADING INDIVIDUALS		
1	**KERSHAW Anne** Kershaw Abbott	**TWEMLOW Tony** Cuff Roberts
2	**JUMP Graeme** Mace & Jones	

This book is the product of 6,552 1/2-hour interviews. See p.7 for BMRB audit.
Within each band, firms are listed alphabetically. *See individuals' profiles p.615*

Cuff Roberts Widely recognised by clients and peers as the leading player in the North, "*your man for the intricacies*" **Tony Twemlow** (see p.617) advises professional partnerships on their formation and dissolution, admission and retirement matters. He is equally involved in contentious matters and recently acted for a firm of accountants in the acrimonious expulsion of a partner. **Clients:** Surveyors; accountants; solicitors; doctors.

Kershaw Abbott (see firm details p.1021) **Anne Kershaw**'s (see p.615) "*direct style*" earns her great reverence amongst her peers. Mainly dealing with contentious work such as expulsions and exits, she has also successfully mediated for a large firm of solicitors. The team is moving towards the area of medical partnership practice and its corresponding property complications. **Clients:** Solicitors; accountants; doctors.

Mace & Jones (see firm details p.1046) **Graeme Jump**'s (see p.472) insolvency and litigation background coupled with his position as senior partner creates a sound basis for both contentious and non-contentious work. His specialist area is medical partnerships and the related property issues. The firm also acts for accountants and solicitors. **Clients:** GPs; dentists; solicitors; accountants.

Cobbetts (see firm details p.923) Regarded by the market as having a niche focus that includes medical partnerships, the firm mainly acts on non-contentious matters. The team (which includes Nicholas Fielden) recently completed a de-merger and re-drafted the partnership deeds for a local accountancy firm. **Clients:** Medical partnerships; accountants; solicitors.

SCOTLAND

PARTNERSHIP • Scotland		Ptnrs	Assts
1	**Dundas & Wilson CS** Edinburgh, Glasgow	1	1
	Maclay Murray & Spens Glasgow	2	n/a
	McGrigor Donald Edinburgh, Glasgow	2	n/a
2	**Burness** Edinburgh	1	2
3	**Bell & Scott WS** Edinburgh	1	1
	Fyfe Ireland WS Edinburgh	n/a	n/a
	Robson McLean WS Edinburgh	2	n/a

This book is the product of 6,552 1/2-hour interviews. See p.7 for BMRB audit.
Within each band, firms are listed alphabetically. *See individuals' profiles p.615*

Dundas & Wilson CS (see firm details p.947) Drawing upon the expertise of tax advisors at Anderson Legal, Christian Hook and his team advise mainly commercial clients in the structuring of corporate partnerships. The firm is also increasingly active in the area of limited partnerships in the property sector. **Clients:** Commercial partnerships; professional partnerships.

Maclay Murray & Spens (see firm details p.1047) The firm deals with contentious and non-contentious work for professionals. **Ian Stubbs** (see p.847) is well regarded by clients for his technical skills; his expertise lies in the formation of partnerships and in the confirmation of deeds for existing firms. The firm also advises those wishing to expel or headhunt partners. **Clients:** Doctors; surveyors; lawyers.

LEADING INDIVIDUALS
1 **STUBBS Ian** Maclay Murray & Spens

See individuals' profiles p.615

McGrigor Donald (see firm details p.1062) "*An extremely knowledgeable team*" led by Ian Gordon, which is seen to be active in the use of partnerships and limited partnerships as a vehicle for special finance or venture capital projects. The team also advises on partnership exit arrangements, and has recently dealt with the acquisition of a law firm partnership. **Clients:** Chartered surveyors; law firms; smaller accountancy firms.

Burness (see firm details p.903) The team led by Alan Soppitt has "*definitely been around the tracks.*" It displays expertise both in potentially contentious partnership disputes and in the non-contentious sphere of Scottish limited partnerships in relation to private equity. **Clients:** Limited and professional partnerships.

Bell & Scott WS (see firm details p.875) Led by Bruce Anderson, the firm offers mainly non-contentious advice on drafting but due to an increasing trend towards internal restructuring it also advises a wide range of professional partnerships on disputes. **Clients:** Accountants; solicitors; doctors; architects.

Fyfe Ireland WS (see firm details p.967) Operating from the corporate department of this medium sized commercial practice, Andrew Cubie's team continues to act for medical, farming and leisure industry partnerships, including joint-venture partnerships. **Clients:** Doctors; hoteliers; farmers.

Robson McLean WS (see firm details p.1109) Although the firm lacks a specialist department, Walter Thompson and his team advises small owner-managed businesses on the reconstitution of partnership liabilities following the addition or loss of a partner. It views medical partnerships as a niche focus. **Clients:** Hoteliers; publicans; small traders; retailers.

NORTHERN IRELAND

PARTNERSHIP • Northern Ireland	Ptnrs	Assts
1 **L'Estrange & Brett** Belfast	3	2
2 **Elliott Duffy Garrett** Belfast	1	n/a

LEADING INDIVIDUALS
1 **IRVINE John** L'Estrange & Brett

This book is the product of 6,552 1/2-hour interviews. See p.7 for BMRB audit.
Within each band, firms are listed alphabetically. *See individuals' profiles p.615*

L'Estrange & Brett (see firm details p.1038) Rated as "*absolutely first class*" by our interviewees **John Irvine** (see p.249) draws upon a large team to deal with particular partnership issues. The firm recently acted for a local estate agency in its merger with DTZ. **Clients:** Accountants; estate agents.

Elliott Duffy Garrett (see firm details p.949) Primarily dealing with contentious disputes, Michael Lynch and his team draw on expertise in litigation. The firm acts mainly for smaller professional partnerships. **Clients:** Accountants; solicitors.

MEDICAL PARTNERSHIPS - NATIONAL

PARTNERSHIP: MEDICAL • National	Ptnrs	Assts
1 **Hempsons**	2	1
2 **BrookStreet Des Roches** Witney	1	2
Payne Marsh Stillwell Southampton	1	1
Veale Wasbrough Bristol	2	5
3 **Bates, Wells & Braithwaite** Sudbury	1	n/a
Clarkson Wright & Jakes Orpington		
Mace & Jones Liverpool	1	1
TLT Solicitors Bristol	2	n/a

LEADING INDIVIDUALS	
1 **ABBESS Lynne** Hempsons	**GREGAN Paddy** BrookStreet Des Roches
2 **BELLEW Derek** Veale Wasbrough	**JUMP Graeme** Mace & Jones
STILLWELL Kevin Payne Marsh Stillwell	

This book is the product of 6,552 1/2-hour interviews. See p.7 for BMRB audit.
Within each band, firms are listed alphabetically. *See individuals' profiles p.615*

Hempsons (see firm details p.990) Maintaining a clear lead over her competitors, the "*practical, knowledgeable*" **Lynne Abbess** (see p.615) remains queen of medical partnerships. Capitalising on continual changes in the medical world, she finds her property background and in-depth understanding of NHS regulations crucial to her success. She continues to advise the GPC of the BMA, and has recently completed an advice paper for GPs. **Clients:** Doctors; solicitors; accountants; architects.

BrookStreet Des Roches (see firm details p.897) The firm continues to be dominated by **Paddy Gregan** (see p.615) whose "*name is cast in stone*" in the field of medical partnerships. Mainly non-contentious, dealing with mergers and exits, he is known as a "*decent chap to have on the other side.*" A considerable amount of his time is also spent acting for other commercial and professional partnerships. **Clients:** GPs; lawyers; farmers; chartered surveyors.

Payne Marsh Stillwell **Kevin Stillwell** (see p.617) continues to head the firm's medical partnership practice. A highly recommended non-contentious lawyer with a background in property, his focus is on the resolution of difficulties, rather than litigation. **Clients:** GPs.

Veale Wasbrough (see firm details p.1167) See the South West editorial.

Bates, Wells & Braithwaite (see firm details p.871) Following the departure of Jacqueline Cooper, David John Morley has taken over the medical department of the firm. Primarily dealing in non-contentious work, the team also acts for medical partnership cases which involve property issues. **Clients:** GPs.

Clarkson Wright & Jakes (see firm details p.917)The firm draws upon the interlocking skills of a team of four, headed by Michael North. Primarily working on formations and expulsions, it has property expertise for those complications peculiar to medical partnerships. Recently, the firm has dealt with the formations of partnerships and with the expulsion of partners. **Clients:** GPs; professional partnerships.

Mace & Jones (see firm details p.1046) See the the The North editorial.

TLT Solicitors (see firm details p.1157) See the South West editorial.

LEADERS IN PARTNERSHIP

ABBESS, Lynne
Hempsons, London (020) 7839 0278
lma@hempsons.co.uk
Specialisation: Partner and head of the professional services department. Principal area of practice is partnership law, encompassing advice on partnership formation, disputes, termination and associated property matters (in particular NHS GP's cost rent schemes and other surgery developments). Acts for doctors, dentists, solicitors, accountants and other professional partnerships. Advises the BMA/GPC on policy issues relating to partnerships and surgery developments affecting all NHS GPs in England and Wales. Author of chapters on partnership in 'The Law and General Practice' and 'When Partners Fall Out' and numerous articles in a variety of professional publications. Co-author of 'Primary Healthcare Premises: An Expert Guide'. Frequent lecturer on partnership issues. Legal correspondent for Medeconomics and regular contributor to the journal 'GP'.
Prof. Memberships: Law Society. Founder member and committee member of Association of Partnership Practitioners.
Career: Qualified 1982 with *Hempsons*. Partner since 1985.

BELLEW, Derek
Veale Wasbrough, Bristol (0117) 925 2020
dbellew@vwl.co.uk
See under Corporate Finance, p.240

COHEN, Raymond
Linklaters, London (020) 7456 3556
raymond.cohen@linklaters.com
Specialisation: Specialist in UK corporate finance and company law with wide ranging international experience, having spent nearly 10 years in Hong Kong. Main areas of practice include public and private mergers and acquisitions, issues, joint ventures and general corporate advise. Member of Linklaters & Alliance Asian Business Group with particular focus on Hong Kong, China and Taiwan. Transactions of significance where substantial involvement can be disclosed have included private mergers and acquisitions and joint ventures, including Coopers & Lybrand merger with Price Waterhouse in the UK and establishment of PriceWaterhouseCooper's worldwide network of locally merged firms and partnership restructuring arrangements, Jardine Motors Group joint venture with Ford Great Britain, to establish the Polar Motor Group, Independent News & Media acquisition of the Belfast Telegraph, Edison Mission Energy acquisition of Fidler's Ferry and Ferrybridge power stations from PowerGen and SEP auction sale of power purchase contracts; public mergers and acquisitions, including Bell Cablemedia bid for Videotron, Cable & Wireless Communications merger with Bell Cablemedia and Nynex Cablecoms, Kwik Save Group merger with Somerfield, Jardine Motors Group bid for Appleyard Group, Polar Motor Group bid for Dagenham Motors and advising on the establishment for Bermuda Takeover Codes for the Jardine Group; flotations and listings, including Cable & Wireless Communications, Coca Cola Beverages, Worldsec, Lomond Underwriting, Jardine Matheson, Jardine Strategic Holdings, Hongkong Land Holdings, Mandarin Oriental and Dairy Farm; reorganisations including restructuring Coca Cola Amatil's Central and Eastern European businesses in the demerger of Coca Cola Beverages and restructuring Entergy Corporation's UK group holding London Electricity as part of its debt restructuring involving the issue of QUIPs.
Career: 1982 Brasenose College, Oxford University, BA Jurisprudence, Manchester Grammar School. 1996 partner *Linklaters* London; 1992-96 partner corporate/corporate finance department *Linklaters* Hong Kong; 1987-92 assistant solicitor corporate/corporate finance department *Linklaters* Hong Kong; 1985-87 assistant solicitor corporate department *Linklaters* London; 1983-85 articled clerk *Linklaters* London.

COOKE, David C
Pinsent Curtis Biddle, Birmingham
(0121) 200 1050
david.c.cooke@pinsents.com
Specialisation: Partner in corporate department. Partnership work including drafting and advising on partnership deeds, partner disputes and retirements, mergers, acquisitions and disposals of professional partnership practices. Clients include a major national firm of chartered accountants, a major national firm of property advisors, accountants, solicitors, actuaries and architects.
Career: Manchester University. Qualified 1961. Partner at *Pinsent Curtis Biddle* (then *Pinsent & Co)* since 1969 and senior partner 1987-94.

CORKE, Andrew
Lester Aldridge, Bournemouth (01202) 786132
andrew.corke@lester-aldridge.co.uk
Specialisation: Commercial litigator specialising in partnership (particularly professional partnership) disputes. Particular specialisation in medical partnership litigation and in the statutory and financial implications of dissolution in GP practices.
Career: Articled *Thomas Eggar Church Adams* (London). Qualified 1980. Solicitor and partner *Coffin Mew & Co* (Southampton) 1980-87. Partner *Lester Aldridge* 1988.

FOX, Ronnie
Fox Williams, London (020) 7614 2501
rdfox@foxwilliams.com
Specialisation: Main areas of practice are employment law and partnership law. Specialises in advising partnerships and partners in professional firms. Regularly deals with partnership disputes involving the departure of partners. Founder and first Chairman of the multi-disciplinary Association of Partnership Practitioners. Chairman of *Fox Williams'* Partnership Law Group. Past Master of the City of London Solicitors' Company. Past Chairman of the Practice Management Sub-Committee of the IBA. Past Member of the Law Society Law Management Section Advisory Group. Frequently broadcasts and is the author of numerous articles in the professional and national press on employment, partnership and management topics.
Prof. Memberships: IBA, Law Society, City of London Law Society, Employment Lawyers' Association, Association of Partnership Practitioners.
Career: Qualified 1972. Senior Partner at *Fox Williams.*

GODDEN, Richard
Linklaters, London (020) 7456 3610
richard.godden@linklaters.com
See under Corporate Finance, p.246

GOLD, David
Herbert Smith, London (020) 7374 8000
See under Litigation, p.570

GREGAN, Paddy
BrookStreet Des Roches, Witney (01993) 771 616
paddy@bsdr.com
Specialisation: All aspects of business law including company acquisitions and disposals, corporate finance, partnership and joint ventures and company restructuring. Also advises on insolvency law. Particularly regarded for his work on behalf of professional partnerships and individual partners. Acts for a wide range of corporate clients, institutions and professionals.
Prof. Memberships: Law Society, Thames Valley Commercial Lawyers Association, Association of Partnership Practitioners, Employment Lawyers Association.
Career: Qualified in 1987. With *Linnells* from 1988 to 1997, as a partner from 1990. Joined *BrookStreet Des Roches* in 1997 as a partner.
Personal: Born 23.6.61. Educated at West Park Grammar School, St. Helens. Leisure interests include all kinds of sport, mountains and spending time with family.

IRVINE, John
L'Estrange & Brett, Belfast (028) 9023 0426
john.irvine@lestrangeandbrett.com
See under Corporate Finance, p.249

JUMP, Graeme
Mace & Jones, Manchester (0161) 236 2244
See under Insolvency/Corporate Recovery, p.472

KERSHAW, Anne
Kershaw Abbott, Manchester (0161) 839 0998
mail@kershaw-abbott.co.uk
Specialisation: Practises in the field of commercial dispute resolution with particular emphasis on professional partnership disputes, professional liability and commercial and construction disputes.
Prof. Memberships: Member of Association of Partnership Practitioners; Secretary Manchester Professional Forum; Past President Manchester Law Society; Member of Society of Construction Lawyers; CEDR; Accredited Mediator.
Career: Admitted 1975. Practised in North West all working life. Co-founder of *Kershaw Abbott* as niche practice in 1991. Appointed Tax Commissioner in 1995.
Personal: Lives in Ribble Valley with judicial husband and son. Music lover and devoted gardener.

LACE, John
Bristows, London (020) 7400 8000
john.lace@bristows.com
Specialisation: Partner in Company Department. Main areas of practice are company, corporate finance, partnership and charity law. Extensive experience in mergers, acquisitions, corporate reorganisations and joint ventures, acting particularly for UK and US corporations. Has advised in relation to many partnership agreements, mergers, demergers and disputes, particularly in the accountancy and legal professions. Advises several professional institutions and other learned societies on their corporate and regulatory affairs.
Prof. Memberships: Law Society, Association of Partnership Practitioners, Charity Law Association.

Career: Qualified in 1973 after articles at *Meade-King & Co*, Bristol. Joined *Bristows* in 1974 and became a Partner in 1978.
Personal: Born 11th September 1947. Educated at Malvern College 1961-66. Enjoys sailing, gardening, photography and cricket. Member of MCC. Lives in London.

LINSELL, Richard
Rowe & Maw, London (020) 7782 8806
rlinsell@roweandmaw.co.uk
Specialisation: Partnership and commercial law. Acts for leading partnerships in all areas of professional practice. Work undertaken ranges from mergers, demergers and strategic alliances, through partnership defections and a wide range of partnerships disputes, to partner assessment and remuneration schemes and regulatory and disciplinary issues. Richard gave evidence to the House of Commons Trade and Industry Select Committee on the subject of LLPs and remains closely involved with the movement, including lecturing and writing on these and other professional topics. Also regularly advising on the adoption of improved partnership agreements with particular emphasis on partner retention, profit sharing and succession issues. He is also a CEDR Accredited Mediator.
Prof. Memberships: IBA, APP
Career: Jesus College, Cambridge 1966-69; Articled *Rowe & Maw*; Partner 1976.

LLEWELYN EVANS, Adrian
Burges Salmon, Bristol (0117) 939 2272
adrian.llewelyn-evans@burges-salmon.com
Specialisation: Broadly-based heavyweight litigation and arbitration with a bias towards technical subject matter, often with an international element. Recent work includes substantial product liability cases for insurers; corporate finance claims; professional indemnity claims; engineering equipment failure in the defence, marine and aircraft industries; partnership disputes of all description; a flourishing practice as a mediator.
Prof. Memberships: Registered mediator CEDR and ADR Group; FCI Arb; Law Society; Bristol Mercantile Court Users Committee; Official Referee Solicitors' Association.
Career: Trained at *Linklaters*, qualifying in 1979 and joining *Burges Salmon* in 1982, becoming a partner in 1984.
Personal: University College of Durham 1973-76. Leisure interests include gardening, walking, fishing and music.

MARSH, David
Burges Salmon, Bristol (0117) 939 2288
david.marsh@burges-salmon.com
Specialisation: Main areas of practice are company/commercial and corporate finance work, and partnerships. Director of Lumination plc.
Prof. Memberships: Law Society.
Career: Joined *Burges Salmon* in 1971, became a partner in 1972, managing partner in 1990 and senior partner from 1995-2001.
Personal: University College, Oxford 1962-65. Leisure interests include skiing, music and golf.

MAY, Philip
TLT Solicitors, Bristol (0117) 917 7912
pmay@tltsolicitors.com
Specialisation: Deals with contentious issues for partnerships. Has acted personally as Court-Appointed receiver. Has also acted as an expert in relation to professional partnership issues. Specialises in shareholder and boardroom disputes and professional partnership breakdowns. For biographical details see Litigation (Commercial) section.

MAYER, Stephen
Reynolds Porter Chamberlain, London
(020) 7242 2877
sdm@rpc.co.uk
Specialisation: Head of commercial litigation. A substantial and increasing area of his practice consists of advice on partnership disputes and their resolution, including advising on restrictive covenants in partnership agreements. Clients include professional and commercial partnerships. He also acts in employment disputes.
Prof. Memberships: Law Society; International Bar Association; Media Society; Association of Partnership Practitioners.
Career: Educated at St Paul's School and Oriel College, Oxford. Qualified in 1974. Partner of *Reynolds Porter Chamberlain* since 1977.
Personal: Married with three children. Leisure interests include erratic golf and slightly less erratic tennis.

McARTHUR, Colin
Field Fisher Waterhouse, London (020) 7861 4000
Specialisation: Partner in company and commercial department. Handles all aspects of corporate and partnership law, including establishment, mergers and acquisitions, sales, retirements, dissolutions and joint ventures. Also deals with commercial contracts.
Prof. Memberships: Law Society, IBA, Institute of Directors.
Career: Qualified in 1969, having joined *Waterhouse & Co* (now *Field Fisher Waterhouse*) in 1967. Became a partner in 1974.
Publications: Co-author of 'A Director's Guide – Duties, Liabilities and Company Law' (1990), and contributor to 'A Directors Guide to Accounting and Auditing' (1991).
Personal: Born 5 November 1944. Educated at Fettes College 1958-63 and Cambridge University 1963-66. Leisure interests include golf and aphorisms. Lives in London.

MISCAMPBELL, Andrew
Linnells, Oxford (01865) 254207
afm@linnells.co.uk
Specialisation: Partnership, especially professional practices including medical practices. Commercial Property. Mediation.
Prof. Memberships: Law Society. Association of Partnership Practitioners.
Career: Qualified 1985; *Anstey Sargent and Probert* 1988-94 (Partner 1990-94); *Linnells* 1995 to date (Partner). Trained Mediator 1993.
Personal: Born 18 June 1959. Educated at St Edwards, Oxford and Nottingham University. Interests: cricket, golf, hockey. Active church member.

MOSS, Nicholas
TLT Solicitors, Bristol (0117) 917 7777
Specialisation: Involved in all areas of corporate and commercial law but main area of practice is partnership and quasi-partnership law. Has wide experience providing strategic and business advice to a large number of professional partnerships, including doctors, dentists, vets, solicitors, accountants, surveyors and architects.
Prof. Memberships: Association of Partnership Practitioners.
Career: Qualified 1982; joined *Trumps* (now merged with *Lawrence Tucketts* to form *TLT*) 1985; partner since 1988.
Personal: Born 1955, lives in Bristol. Recreations include motorbike, trekking and golf.

MOULE, Jos
Osborne Clarke, Bristol (0117) 917 3000

MURRAY, Clare
Fox Williams, London (020) 7614 2554
cmmurray@foxwilliams.com
Specialisation: Employment and partnership law. Clare has a particular interest in international employment law, contracts and disputes. Over the last year she has advised a large number of US and UK law firms on partnership arrangements in the UK, particularly team moves and partner retirement.
Prof. Memberships: Management Committee of the Employment Lawyers Association, International Committee of the Employment Lawyers Association, Labour and Employment Law Section of the American Bar Association, founder and member of Management Committee of the Association of Partnership Practitioners. Member of the Genetic Testing and Employment Sub-Committee of The Recruitment Society.
Career: Articles at *Jacques & Lewis* (subsequently *Eversheds*), qualified 1993, joined *Fox Williams* 1996, appointed partner at *Fox Williams* May 1999.
Publications: Editor of *Fox Williams*' weekly online employment law information service, www.hrlaw.co.uk. Editor of monthly International Employment column in 'Personnel Today'. Provides regular comments on a number of employment and partnership law issues in Legal and National newspapers and television.
Personal: Member of the panel of the Peter Wolff Theatre Trust, a charitable trust set up to promote new British playwrights; regular theatre goer; running and playing tennis.

SACKER, Tony
Kingsley Napley, London (020) 7814 1200
tsacker@kingsleynapley.co.uk
Specialisation: Head of partnership unit. Main area of practice is partnership law. Over 20 years experience advising and negotiating in this area. Also deals with charities.
Prof. Memberships: Association of Partnership Practitioners, City of London Law Society, Westminster Law Society, Association of Charity Lawyers.
Career: Qualified in 1963. Partner from 1967 at *Egerton Sandler*, which merged with *Kingsley Napley* 1989. Partner at *Kingsley Napley* since 1989. President Westminster Law Society 1987-88. Chairman City of London Law Society 1998 -2001. Committee Member Association of Partnership Practitioners 1997 to date. Official Solicitor Consultant to the Law Commission.
Publications: Author, 'Practical Partnership Agreements' (Jordans).
Personal: Born 2nd March 1940. Educated at Owens School to 1958. Recreations include doing communal work and improving computer skills. Lives in London.

SIMMONS, Michael
Finers Stephens Innocent, London
(020) 7323 4000

STARKS, Brian
Bond Pearce, Plymouth (01752) 266633
bstarks@bondpearce.com
Specialisation: Partner in the Commercial Litigation Group. Specialises in partnership litigation and in particular professional partnerships eg solicitors, accountants, doctors, surveyors and valuers, and family farming partnerships.
Prof. Memberships: Member of the Association of Partnership Practitioners.
Career: Qualified 1972 with *Bond Pearce*, becoming partner in 1977.

STILLWELL, Kevin
Payne Marsh Stillwell, Southampton
(023) 8022 3957
kevinstillwell@pms.solicitors.co.uk
Specialisation: Advising GPs (practices and individuals) constitutes the vast majority of his work: partnership formations and restructuring -admissions and retirements- surgery relocation, leasing and building schemes, interpartner disputes. His approach is practical, drawing on extensive experience of general medical practice.
Prof. Memberships: Law Society; Hampshire Law Society; Association of Partnership Practitioners.
Career: LLB Southampton, London articles, qualified 1979, two years with *Ashford Sparkes* in Exeter then relocated to Hampshire in 1981.
Personal: Born 1954. Married with young family. Carriage driving is his main hobby.

STUBBS, Ian
Maclay Murray & Spens, Glasgow
(0141) 248 5011
ims@maclaymurrayspens.co.uk
See under Trusts & Personal Tax, p.847

TRIGGS, Jeff
Slaughter and May, London (020) 7600 1200
jeff.triggs@slaughterandmay.com
Specialisation: General corporate/commercial practice. Recent matters include the merger of Price Waterhouse and Coopers & Lybrand, the takeover of the Savoy Group by Blackstone, the renegotiation of the contracts for the automation of post office counters among ICL, the DSS and Consignia plc, the joint venture between Consignia plc, TNT Post Group NV and Singapore Post Pte Limited relating to international cross-border mail business and the demerger of Bacon & Woodrow, the merger of part of its business with Deloitte & Touche and the proposed merger of the remainder of its business with Hewitts.
Prof. Memberships: The Law Society.
Career: Gorleston Grammar School; University College, London (LLB, Hons).
Personal: Leisure interests include playing trombone in a jazz band, sport and keeping fit.

TURNOR, Richard
Allen & Overy, London (020) 7330 3905
richard.turner@allenovery.com
Specialisation: Partner who advises professional partners and partnerships, joint venture partnerships, banks and others who deal with partnerships.
Prof. Memberships: Association of Partnership Practitioners (Chairman), Chairs APP Working Party on limited liability partnerships.
Career: Articled *Allen & Overy*, qualified 1980, partner 1985.
Personal: Oxford University 1977. Born 1956.

TWEMLOW, Tony
Cuff Roberts, Liverpool (0151) 237 7777
tony.twemlow@cuffroberts.co.uk
Specialisation: Insolvency, partnership, charities and anything with a 'chancery' ring to it.
Prof. Memberships: Insolvency Lawyers' Association.
Career: MA (Cantab). Qualified 1968. Assistant and then partner (1971) in *Cuff Roberts*. Chairman of the Young Solicitors Group of the Law Society (1978). President, Liverpool Law Society (1995). Managing partner, *Cuff Roberts* 1988-94.
Personal: Music, tennis. Married with three children. Lives in Hoylake, Wirral.

WILLIAMS, Christine
Fox Williams, London (020) 7628 2000
Specialisation: Within the context of her corporate work, has extensive experience in the area of professional partnerships. Work has included drafting partnership deeds, restructuring partnerships, negotiating mergers of firms, advising on and implementing the incorporation of partnerships. Has also undertaken much work in the area of partnership disputes, including negotiating the departure of partners. Member of the working party of the Association of Partnership Practitioners which made representations to the Government on the proposed legislation for limited liability partnerships. Has written and spoken extensively on partnership law.
Prof. Memberships: Law Society, City of London Law Society, International Bar Association, Association of Partnership Practitioners.
Career: Qualified in 1977. Partner at *Oppenheimers* 1981-88. Formed and joined *Fox Williams* as a partner in 1989.
Personal: Born 15th February 1953. Educated at St Anne's College, Oxford 1971-74. Leisure interests include theatre and cinema. Lives in Buckinghamshire.

WRIGHT, Nicholas
Wright Son & Pepper, London (020) 7242 5473
Specialisation: Head of Partnership and Professional Department. Main area of practice is partnership law. Advises on partnership creation, disputes and dissolutions, including interventions and practice management of other firms. Member of the Solicitors Assistance Scheme and solicitor member of Defendants' Friends (ICA). Has considerable commercial experience and acts for both UK and overseas corporations.
Prof. Memberships: Law Society. Holborn Law Society, Association of Partnership Practitioners.
Career: Qualified in 1970, having joined *Wright Son & Pepper* in 1960. Became a Partner in 1979.
Personal: Born 2nd February 1943. Educated at Charterhouse 1956-60.

PENSIONS

OVERVIEW: A busy year in the pensions market, with clients' needs driven by new legislation. Product work, including developing the stakeholder pension plans, has been an active area for the legal services market. Mergers, winding ups and restructuring have won heavy attention, with the investment aspect of pensions becoming a priority.

RESEARCH APPROVED BY BMRB: *For this edition,* Chambers' *researchers conducted 6,552 interviews – 4,419 with law firms, 554 with barristers and 1,579 with clients.*

The validity of the research was scrutinised by BMRB International, who audited both the methodology and the results at our offices in July 2001. They interviewed Chambers' *researchers and cross-checked sample interviews. Details of the audit appear on page 7.*

TOP IN-HOUSE LAWYERS

Mark McKEOWN, Litigation Counsel UK & Europe, *William Mercer*

Val VARDY, Principal, *Towers Perrin*

Mark McKeown continues to attract praise. **Val Vardy** is well renowned as an established figure in the market; she is *"knowledgeable and extremely good"*.

In-House lawyers profiles: p 1193

LONDON

PENSIONS • London	Ptnrs	Assts
1 Freshfields Bruckhaus Deringer	3	18
Linklaters	4	23
Rowe & Maw	8	9
Sacker & Partners	20	15
2 Allen & Overy	3	16
Clifford Chance	3	11
Lovells	5	11
Slaughter and May	2	14
3 Baker & McKenzie	2	10
CMS Cameron McKenna	4	13
Nabarro Nathanson	4	13
Travers Smith Braithwaite	3	6
4 Eversheds	4	5
Hammond Suddards Edge	6	11
Herbert Smith	3	7
Pinsent Curtis Biddle	7	7
5 Macfarlanes	3	3
Simmons & Simmons	3	4

This book is the product of 6,552 1/2-hour interviews. See p.7 for BMRB audit.
Within each band, firms are listed alphabetically.

Freshfields Bruckhaus Deringer (see firm details p.965) *"A strong unit in a great firm."* Heavily influenced by the firm's outstanding transactional presence, the team operates as part of the integrated Employment, Pensions and Benefits team, with cross-border expertise and an impressive international focus. Pensions Head **Ken Dierden** (see p.626) is adjudged by clients *"sensible and helpful, consistently level headed,"* while *"exceptional and personable"* **David Pollard** (see p.629) garnered market plaudits for his *"phenomenal knowledge, presented well"* and for combining *"strong academic interest with hands on experience." "Incredibly hard working"* **Daniel Schaffer** (see p.630) is *"punchy and knows his stuff,"* although some find his style *"aggressive."* Clients commend the team for *"working relentlessly"* on their behalf. Advised CAA Pension Scheme trustees on its industry-wide conversion as a result of a PPP proposal for air traffic control. This included liaising with the Government on legislation under the Transport Act 2000. Also acted for Bass on the pensions aspect of its disposal of its brewing arm to Interbrew. **Clients:** AMP UK; Bass; ICI.

Linklaters (see firm details p.1042) *"Exceptionally good group – leading players in terms of documentation."* The team acts for major corporates and trustees of large schemes. **Ruth Goldman** (see p.627) *"has done a fantastic job of gelling a robust team,"* which offers a *"good level of personal service"* and is perceived to be *"going from strength to strength."* Such success has led clients to comment that *"the whole team is strong but for partner attention you're aware you're in a queue." "A lawyer's lawyer"* **Tim Cox** (see p.625) is *"pragmatic and practical,"* while **Claire Petheram** (see p.629) ranks alongside top-flight practitioners. The group advises on the implications of corporate deals on global schemes for clients such as Hewlett-Packard and BP Amoco. Assisted in the implementation of the pension aspects of AstraZeneca's flexible benefits programme and advised on the merger of Post Office Pension Scheme and Post Office Staff Superannuation Scheme. **Clients:** AstraZeneca; British Telecom; Lloyds TSB; The Rank Group; Tesco; Diageo.

Rowe & Maw (see firm details p.1113) *"A strong stand-alone practice"* where *"each client really matters."* Respected for its long established client base, comprising mainly employers and trustees of substantial occupational pension schemes. Despite other commitments *"excellent"* senior partner **Stuart James** (see p.628) remains highly respected by peers. **Andrew White** (see p.632) is an *"all-rounder,"* who *"gets things done quickly,"* while **Anna Rogers** (see p.630) grasps the issues with ease. Overall the team is widely endorsed for its *"proactive approach, relaxed manner and understanding of the practicalities."* Acts for a high proportion of FTSE 100 and FTSE 250 clients. The group handled the pensions aspects surrounding the disposal of Technicolor for Carlton Communications and separated the Storehouse pension scheme into BhS and Mothercare products during the demerger. **Clients:** Abbey National; BG Group; British American Tobacco; London Regional Transport; Nestlé.

Sacker & Partners (see firm details p.1117) *"Stand out specialists"* who continue to be recognised for scheme advice work and as a safe option for referrals. Respected for a client base that includes 21 of the FTSE 100. Acclaimed by industry sources as *"superb"* although some feel the group overall is *"a victim of its own success"* as its junior assistants have yet to reach the high standards that the market has come to expect from the firm. Ex Chairman of the APL **Mark Greenlees** (see p.627) is *"fantastic, clients love him."* **Ian Pittaway** (see p.629) is *"always good to deal with"* and *"doesn't get bogged down with details"* while the talents of **Jonathan Seres** (see p.631) continue to attract market praise. Other members of the team singled out were *"absolutely first class"* **Peter Docking** (see p.626), **Sarah Tier**

("*extremely good,*") **Chris Close** (see p.625) and **Peter Lester** (see p.628). Restructuring instructions taken recently include advising the Third National Swedish Pension Fund with regards to its investment providers. The group also advised Legal & General in the production of new standard terms of business for bulk buyouts by its trustees. Involved in some of the first stakeholder pension schemes to be registered and Revenue approved (includes Abbey National and Legal and General). **Clients:** Jarvis Hotels; Citibank NA; AXA Sun Life; Nationwide Building Society; Yorkshire Bank.

Allen & Overy (see firm details p.856) Widely perceived as "*heavily transactional,*" the practice enjoys an envied client base although is felt to lack the depth of team in comparison to our leaders. Key to the firm's profile remains **Derek Sloan** (see p.631). "*Excellent; incredibly clever and user-friendly*" rivals perceive that "*clients adore him.*" The group advised Mobil on the pensions aspects of its European downstream joint venture with BP, and acted on proposals for the merger of the Mobil Pension and Dependents' Benefits Plan. It also advised Caterpillar on the merger of nine of its UK staff pension schemes into a single plan. **Clients:** Mobil; Caterpillar; Rexam Pension Plan.

Clifford Chance (see firm details p.919) A "*good client base*" is the backbone of this practice, which works closely with the employment and litigation groups. Acts for FTSE 100 companies across a range of sectors, the majority being financial institutions, investment banks and private equity providers while supported by its network offices on cross border arrangements. **Helen Cox** (see p625) and **Nick Sherwin** (see p.631) form a "*good team*" according to rivals but remain "*low profile.*" On the transactional front, the group advised Schroder Ventures on the pensions aspect of its acquisition of Homebase and represented Kvaerner on the sale of its construction business to Skanska. **Clients:** British Energy; Jaguar Cars; Safeway; Unipart.

Lovells (see firm details p.1044) "*A fundamentally sound practice*" with a client base dominated by blue-chip companies but also including smaller clients. President of the Society of Pension Consultants **Jane Samsworth** (see p.630) is "*a joy to work with, pleasant and constructive*" while **John Pearson** (see p.629) is seen by competitors as a "*quality practitioner but low profile.*" "*Dynamic*" **Steve Ito** is "*focused and thorough*" while **Russell Strachan** (see p.631) rounds out this impressive line-up. Acted on pensions aspects of the Exxon/Mobil worldwide merger, and advised Granada on its merger with Compass, the flotation of the Granada Media Division and the acquisition of United Business Media's television arm. **Clients:** BAA; Land Rover Group; Pension Provision Group; Army Benevolent Fund.

Slaughter and May (see firm details p.1135) "*Heads down transactional people,*" the practice handles both corporate and stand-alone work for a client base that reflects the firm's blue chip corporate clientele. **Philip Bennett** (see p.625) is considered by clients a "*great M&A man – technically brilliant,*" while **Howard Jacobs** (see p.628) ("*well respected for being pragmatic*") matches his pensions work with a strong profile in employment matters. Setting "*impressive*" standards the firm "*does a Rolls Royce job on everything.*" Has been engaged in the pensions-related aspects of firms' corporate transactions, most notably the sale of Schroder's investment banking business and the disposal by Tomkins of RHM. **Clients:** Unilever; Blue Circle; Vauxhall Motors.

Baker & McKenzie (see firm details p.868) The firm's major strength remains its international presence, which allows it to draw on overseas expertise for multi-national organisations. An increasing portion of the work comes from stand-alone pensions clients. Chairman of the Association of Pension Lawyers, "*absolute star*" **Robert West** (see p.632) commands an impressive market reputation as "*approachable and pragmatic*" – "*a good communicator capable of expressing complex legal points in simple language.*" The group advised the trustees of National Provident Institution on the merger of its UK pension plan with the AMP scheme and advised the trustees on the implications of the Hanson Quarry Products Pension Scheme merger with the Hanson Industrials Pension Scheme.

LEADING INDIVIDUALS

1	**ARTHUR Hugh** Macfarlanes	**BENNETT Philip** Slaughter and May
	COX Tim Linklaters	**DIERDEN Kenneth** Freshfields Bruckhaus
	GOLDMAN Ruth Linklaters	**GREENLEES Mark** Sacker & Partners
	JAMES Stuart Rowe & Maw	**PITTAWAY Ian** Sacker & Partners
	POLLARD David Freshfields Bruckhaus	**ROGERS Anna** Rowe & Maw
	SLOAN Derek Allen & Overy	**STANNARD Paul** Travers Smith Braithwaite
	WEST Robert Baker & McKenzie	**WHITE Andrew** Rowe & Maw
2	**BENNEY Belinda** Field Fisher	**COX Helen** Clifford Chance
	ELLISON Robin Eversheds	**FENTON Jonathan** DLA
	FORD Peter Norton Rose	**GAULT Ian** Herbert Smith
	ITO Stephen Lovells	**LEWIS Roger** Eversheds
	MARSHALL Jane Hammond Suddards	**MOORE Nigel** CMS Cameron McKenna
	MULLEN Chris Pinsent Curtis Biddle	**QUARRELL John** Nabarro Nathanson
	SAMSWORTH Jane Lovells	**SCHAFFER Daniel** Freshfields Bruckhaus
	SERES Jonathan Sacker & Partners	**SHERWIN Nick** Clifford Chance
	SMITH Stephanie Travers Smith	**TIER Sarah** Sacker & Partners
3	**DOCKING Peter** Sacker & Partners	**PETHERAM Claire** Linklaters
	STRACHAN Russell Lovells	
4	**ANDREWS Sue** Pinsent Curtis Biddle	**ATKINSON Mark** CMS Cameron McKenna
	BERKELEY Christopher Pinsent Curtis Biddle	**CLOSE Chris** Sacker & Partners
	COWLEY Michael Stephenson Harwood	**GRANT Mark** CMS Cameron McKenna
	JACOBS Howard Slaughter and May	**KOWALIK Mark** CMS Cameron McKenna
	LESTER Peter Sacker & Partners	**MEEKS Alastair** Pinsent Curtis Biddle
	MURRAY John Nabarro Nathanson	**PEARSON John** Lovells
	POWELL Andrew Hammond Suddards	**SAUNDERS Carolyn** Taylor Joynson Garrett
	WYMAN Michael Simmons & Simmons	
UP AND COMING		
	BROWNING Lesley Norton Rose	**DERBYSHIRE Wyn** SJ Berwin
	GREENSTREET Ian Hammond Suddards Edge	

See individuals' profiles p.624

Clients: Avis UK Pension Plan; Co-operative Insurance Society Scheme; Merchant Navy Officers' Pension Plan.

CMS Cameron McKenna (see firm details p.922) Adjudged "*a good year;*" the practice handles a range of work including corporate support and enjoys a strong profile in Pensions Ombudsman work. Head of department **Nigel Moore** (see p.629) "*runs a good department*" with a "*fighting team*" that is praised by clients and rivals as "*dynamic, youthful and enthusiastic.*" "*Impressive*" **Mark Grant** (see p.627) displays a "*firm grasp of complicated issues*" while **Mark Kowalik** (see p.628) offers "*snappy advice,*" although some consider him a "*maverick.*" **Mark Atkinson** has a strong profile in litigation work. The group acted for Hogg Robinson Trustees in an action brought before the High Court and advised over 20 sets of trustees in the merging of FirstGroup bus companies' pensions. Retained by the Occupational Pensions Regulatory Authority (OPRA) to give specialist training to their staff. **Clients:** British Land; Motorola; Baker Hughes; First Group Trustees; Independent Insurance.

Nabarro Nathanson (see firm details p.1078) Its revival set back by the loss of Lesley Browning and Peter Ford to Norton Rose, the firm nevertheless is perceived as a vital component of the market. **John Quarrell** (see p.630) divides industry opinion, yet this "*idiosyncratic pioneer of pension law*" is "*not to be underestimated.*" **John Murray** (see p.629) is widely endorsed for the quality of his advice. Servicing a range of clients including trustees, fund managers, insurance companies and company pension schemes, the firm also has a strong reputation in litigation. Acted for the trustees of the AMP UK Staff Pension Scheme in its merger with schemes from Henderson Administration, NPI and London Life. Also advised Unisys in its joint venture with Barclays and Lloyds TSB. **Clients:** Exel; IBM; Littlewoods; AMP UK Staff Pension Scheme trustees.

Travers Smith Braithwaite (see firm details p.1160) A "*class outfit*" which targets the upper end of the insurance market. **Paul Stannard** (see p.631) is recommended by peers as an "*exceptionally able, first rate practitioner*" and "*decent man*" with "*effortless technical command.*" **Stephanie Smith** (see p.631) is admired by clients for her "*tremendous help*" and "*fantastic advice.*" The group acted for Guardian Royal Exchange trustees in the merger with AXA Schemes and continues to advise the merged scheme. **Clients:** Associated British Foods; AXA; Trinity Mirror; NTL.

Eversheds (see firm details p.952) A strong national presence with its UK network offers genuine depth of resources. Interviewees perceived that litigation star Giles Orton's move to London indicates a national integration strategy that places this office at the forefront. **Robin Ellison** (see p.626) is admired as *pleasant and knowledgeable;*" he remains a major figurehead for the operation. **Roger Lewis** (see p.628) is an "*authoritative source of advice.*" Acts for trustee bodies, industry wide schemes and a large group of plc clients. The group advised the Department of the Environment, Transport and the Regions on pensions issues in connection with the Transport Act 2000. **Clients:** National Grid Company.

Hammond Suddards Edge (see firm details p.984) "*A strengthening team*" and certainly one to watch as it develops its London presence. National practice Head, the "*forceful and pragmatic*" **Jane Marshall** (see p.628) is seen by the market as an "*indomitable character.*" **Andrew Powell** (see p.630) has won plaudits for his "*rambunctious*" no-nonsense approach, while new addition to the team **Ian Greenstreet** (see p.627) (from Simmons & Simmons) is viewed as a "*name to watch.*" Merging pension schemes for West-Deutsche Landesbank was a highlight for the year. The group also acted for Sea Containers on Railways Pension Scheme and represented the trustees on the merger of the three main Wessex Water pension schemes. **Clients:** ICI; Allied Dunbar Assurance; Texaco; Northern Electric.

Herbert Smith (see firm details p.993) Although admired and respected for its quality advice for both its corporate driven and stand-alone clients, the team is felt by market sources to employ an approach too "*low key*" to take on the leading firms. "*A tremendous chap,*" **Ian Gault** (see p.627) is "*good at explaining things and client friendly.*" Legal advisors to the Institute of Actuaries. Instructions include reorganisations and wind ups disputes over application of surpluses and advising on public/private sector issues. The group was involved in the pensions aspects of the proposed privatisation of DERA. **Clients:** WS Atkins; Securicor; De La Rue; Iceland; Otis.

Pinsent Curtis Biddle (see firm details p.1098) Too early to tell with regards to the merger, many feel that Pinsent Curtis brings an "*unknown quantity*" to Biddle's existing reputation. Advises a respectable range of international and UK businesses, with increasing instructions from US firms. A recent highlight was involvement in drafting pension sharing on divorce notes for a cartel of major insurers. Head of Pensions **Chris Mullen** (see p.629) has "*taken on Hugh Arthur's role,*" ably supported by **Alastair Meeks** (see p.629) ("*academic*") and the "*super*" **Christopher Berkeley** (see p.625). The team of "*keen, dynamic individuals*" is boosted by the addition of "*powerhouse*" **Sue Andrews** (see p.624) from Eversheds. **Clients:** Friends Provident; Babcock International Group; Jardine Lloyd Thompson.

Macfarlanes (see firm details p.1046) The combination of *a "good corporate practice*" and the presence of "*leading light*" **Hugh Arthur** (see p.624) sees the firm enter the tables this year. Operating as part of the closely integrated Employment, Pensions and Benefits Group, the practice handles a balance of trustee and corporate work. Arthur "*combines decent pragmatism with fine pensions knowledge.*" Continuing to work for trustees of British Airways pension schemes, the team also undertook pensions work for new client Arthur Andersen. **Clients:** Arthur Andersen; British Airways; Patheon; Saatchi & Saatchi.

Simmons & Simmons (see firm details p.1132) "*Fine lawyers but less of a presence*" despite its stellar employment practice, the firm drew less distinctive comment. Head of Department **Michael Wyman** (see p.632) "*knows exactly what he's talking about*" while some commented on the lack of depth beneath him. Acted on the establishment of Interbrew and Bass Brewers pension schemes, the group also advised the trustees of the Next Group Pension Plan on the introduction of a defined contribution section and on the overhaul of their investment arrangements. **Clients:** SmithKline Beecham; Bass Brewers; William Hill; Xerox; Next; Zurich Financial Services.

Other Notable Practitioners "*Watch this space*" at **Norton Rose** with the arrival of **Peter Ford** (see p.626) ("*first class*") and **Lesley Browning** (see p.625) *("sharp mind, good all round solicitor")* from Nabarro Nathanson. **Wyn Derbyshire** (see p.626) at **SJ Berwin** is "*building up a profile.*" The unconventional **Belinda Benney** (see p.625) of **Field Fisher Waterhouse** is endorsed as "*sparky*" and "*she knows her stuff.*" **Jonathan Fenton** at **DLA** is still widely thought of as "*an able practitioner.*" **Carolyn Saunders** of **Taylor Joynson Garrett** continues to raise the profile of the firm and, respected for both pure pensions and litigation work, she wins plaudits from the market for her work on the National Bus case. **Michael Cowley** of **Stephenson Harwood** has a profile greater than that of the firm.

THE SOUTH & SOUTH WEST

PENSIONS • The South & South West	Ptnrs	Assts
1 **Burges Salmon** Bristol	1	6
Osborne Clarke Bristol	3	6
2 **Blake Lapthorn** Fareham, Portsmouth	1	1

LEADING INDIVIDUALS
1 **ILLSTON Tim** Burges Salmon
2 **WOMERSLEY Mark** Osborne Clarke
UP AND COMING
RICCIO Maria Blake Lapthorn

This book is the product of 6,552 1/2-hour interviews. See p.7 for BMRB audit.
Within each band, firms are listed alphabetically. *See individuals' profiles p.624*

Burges Salmon (see firm details p.902) Respected practice, acting mainly for trustees of pension schemes in the financial services, manufacturing and academic sectors. Team leader and "*effective operator*" **Tim Illston** (see p.628) is considered by competitors to be "*a good commercial lawyer*" with a noted tax expertise. Appointed legal advisors to the trustees of the University of Oxford staff pension scheme, the firm also advised trustees of Firstgroup on scheme mergers and a common investment fund. **Clients:** Triumph International; Kenwood Appliances; Axminster Carpets; University of Oxford.

Osborne Clarke (see firm details p.1086) A "*good pensions practice*" with "*an excellent corporate client base.*" Corporate support is mixed with its respected stand-alone advice for a client roster, which includes major plcs across industry and the financial services sector. Head of Pensions and Employee Benefits Unit **Mark Womersley** continues to command respect in the market. The firm negotiated investment management agreements with a contract value of £2.2 billion for the Imperial Tobacco Pension Fund and advised on pension aspects of multiple disposals by Western Power Distribution. **Clients:** Abbey National; Danish Bacon Company; Imperial Tobacco Pension Fund; Kier Group Pension Scheme.

Blake Lapthorn (see firm details p.886) Small team making an impression on the market. As well as offering pensions advice, the team has a litigator specialising in related professional negligence. While providing transactional support, it also has experience of Ombudsman and High Court pensions work. Advised trustees on an MFR under-funding affecting their scheme and drafted a consolidated trust deed for two benefit schemes. Head of Pensions **Maria Riccio** is "*top drawer.*" **Clients:** Chelton; Abbey Life.

THAMES VALLEY

PENSIONS • Thames Valley	Ptnrs	Assts
1 **Clarks** Reading	1	1
2 **Pitmans** Reading	n/a	n/a

LEADING INDIVIDUALS
1 **CLARK David** Clarks
2 **ARCHER David** Pitmans

This book is the product of 6,552 1/2-hour interviews. See p.7 for BMRB audit.

Within each band, firms are listed alphabetically. *See individuals' profiles p.624*

Clarks (see firm details p.916) Known as having a niche in independent trustee work, the firm mostly advises on small to medium sized schemes based in the locality. The practice also receives instructions from employers and insolvency practitioners, as well as providing M&A support and documentation. **David Clark** remains key to the strength of the firm. **Clients:** Scientific Investment Pension Plan; BRG Pension Plan.

Pitmans (see firm details p.1099) This small Pensions department has an emphasis on advising insolvency practitioners and independent trustees, as well as taking up the pensions aspects of corporate acquisitions. Head of Department **David Archer** is praised by peers as "*pleasant to deal with.*" The group acted as statutory independent trustee to the Ferguson Group Pension Schemes. **Clients:** Elf Atochem; Instron Pension Scheme.

WALES

PENSIONS • Wales	Ptnrs	Assts
1 **Eversheds** Cardiff	1	1

LEADING INDIVIDUALS
1 **DAVIES Ian** Eversheds

This book is the product of 6,552 1/2-hour interviews. See p.7 for BMRB audit.

Within each band, firms are listed alphabetically. *See individuals' profiles p.624*

Eversheds (see firm details p.952) Niche strengths in multi-scheme mergers and small self-administered schemes, the offering of this team is only tempered by its small size. Headed by "*extremely busy and able*" **Ian Davies** (see p.626), the practice has national support. Clients praise the "*speedy response*" and are impressed that Davies "*seems to have all the answers at his fingertips.*" The firm advised on the merger of Cardiff International Airport and Belfast International Airport pension schemes, and provided general advice to the National Assembly for Wales. **Clients:** Walkers Snack Foods; National Museum of Wales; Heinz; National Assembly for Wales.

MIDLANDS

PENSIONS • Midlands	Ptnrs	Assts
1 **Wragge & Co** Birmingham	5	12
2 **Hammond Suddards Edge** Birmingham	4	6
Pinsent Curtis Biddle Birmingham	4	3
3 **Eversheds** Birmingham	2	5
4 **Martineau Johnson** Birmingham	1	3

LEADING INDIVIDUALS	
1 **COCKERILL Vivien** Wragge & Co	**FORREST Ian** Hammond Suddards Edge
RYLAND Glyn Wragge & Co	
2 **DAVIS Richard** Browne Jacobson	**HINGLEY Gerald** Wragge & Co
RAMSHAW Simon Pinsent Curtis Biddle	**SHELLEY Daniel** Pinsent Curtis Biddle
3 **BLACK Richard** Wragge & Co	**EVERSON Ingrid** Eversheds
FALLON Liz Eversheds	**GRAVILL Robert** Hammond Suddards Edge
LAIGHT Simon Martineau Johnson	**MILES Helen** DLA
MILTON Kevin Wragge & Co	

This book is the product of 6,552 1/2-hour interviews. See p.7 for BMRB audit.

Within each band, firms are listed alphabetically. *See individuals' profiles p.624*

Wragge & Co (see firm details p.1189) "*Impressive team*" with a determined group of high quality, technically skilled lawyers. Active nationally for employers and trustees in a "*strong client list*" which includes FTSE plcs and private companies. Has a dedicated pensions litigation team responsible for disputes in the High Court and Pensions Ombudsman claims. Although less in the public eye, **Gerald Hingley** is praised by the market as "*excellent; quiet and understated,*" an "*old fashioned lawyer with a smart head on his shoulders.*" The "*personable*" **Glyn Ryland** has a "*high profile in the Birmingham market*" while **Richard Black** "*gets the job done*" and is "*supremely well liked in and outside practice.*" **Vivien Cockerill** remains heavily endorsed as "*one of best people outside London.*" Previously at Garretts, highly personable **Kevin Milton** is "*technically good.*" Advised on the establishment of a stakeholder pension for a financial institution. The group also worked on a merger scheme for the Albright & Wilson Pension Fund trustees and was instructed by the trustees on the merger of the Travis Perkins pension schemes. **Clients:** Gallup Organisation; Police Mutual Assurance Society; Britannic; EMAP; GKN Westland.

Hammond Suddards Edge (see firm details p.984) A "*tremendous team*" re-establishing its prominence after the merger although it remains in the shade of a growing London presence. A year of change, with the departure of Richard Davis to Browne Jacobson ("*will prove to be a loss for them*") and the return of partner **Robert Gravill** (see p.627) ("*always rated*") from London. A high proportion of the practice's work is advisory work, with a considerable number of winding-ups being handled over the year. Acts principally for blue-chip entities including insurance companies, plcs and trustees of major pension schemes. "*Straight-talking*" **Ian Forrest** (see p.626) is considered by rivals an "*excellent pensions lawyer*" and "*great with clients.*" The firm advised trustees to Allied Dunbar pension schemes on the merger with the Zurich Assurance scheme, and also acted on issues arising post-wind up of the Football League Pension and Life Assurance Scheme. Represented trustees of the Misys pension arrangements in a consolidation exercise. **Clients:** Land Rover; GKN; Allied Dunbar; Football League Pension and Life Assurance Scheme.

Pinsent Curtis Biddle (see firm details p.1098) "*Jury's still out on the merger.*" Given the traditional strength of Biddle's pension practice, most sources feel the merger will bolster this team. New regional Head of department, **Simon Ramshaw** (see p.630) is the former head of pensions at Edge Ellison. Adjudged by peers "*a good business man and marketer*" who will gel the team and succeed in driving its growth. "*First class, established*" **Daniel Shelley** (see p.631) is "*highly constructive,*" while the market awaits the impact of his pairing with Ramshaw. The firm carried out a substantial scheme merger for a public company client resulting in a combined fund of £1,700 million. Also restructured a major pension scheme with funds in excess of £120 million, and has been appointed as Independent Trustee to three pension schemes following a major administrative receivership. **Clients:** TI Group; GKN; Cadbury Schweppes.

Eversheds (see firm details p.952) Giles Orton's move to London means that the Derby branch no longer handles pensions litigation. The Birmingham team is seen by the market as "*strong,*" but still requiring the support of this national firm. Particular expertise in small self-administered schemes and a successful independent trustee company has secured the firm its profile. In a recent highlight, the firm advised on pensions aspects of the acquisition of MG Rover. **Liz Fallon** (see p.626) is "*technically very good*" but "*low profile*" while **Ingrid Everson** (see p.626) enters the tables in recognition of her developing stature. **Clients:** Alexander Forbes Trustee Service; Alliance & Leicester; Birmingham International Airport.

Martineau Johnson (see firm details p.1055) "*Good people, building a team.*" **Simon Laight** (see p.628) is endorsed by clients as "*highly knowledgeable,*" and has done much to boost the profile of the practice. Offers a range of pensions-related advice to trustees, employers and other professionals, and is increasingly concentrating on product development. Established the Total Pension Plan (executive pension provision) for Pointon York and assisted in the set up of Britannic Assurance's Stakeholder Pension product. **Clients:** Pointon York; University of Birmingham Pension and Assurance Scheme; University of Coventry; IM Group.

Other Notable Practitioners Richard Davis of **Browne Jacobson** remains "*a recognised force*" in this area.

EAST ANGLIA

PENSIONS • East Anglia	Ptnrs	Assts
1 **Eversheds** Norwich	1	n/a

LEADING INDIVIDUALS
1 **SCOTT Harry** Mills & Reeve

This book is the product of 6,552 1/2-hour interviews. See p.7 for BMRB audit.
Within each band, firms are listed alphabetically. *See individuals' profiles p.624*

Eversheds (see firm details p.952) The group is a recognised force locally as a component of a strong national network, although it has no profile outside the region. Ben Goodfellow has three fee-earners in the department handling non-contentious work, mainly for large privately owned companies in the area. The team negotiated for the scheme externalisation of Norwich County Council works department and the admission of the service provider to the Local Government Scheme. **Clients:** Norwich County Council; Pordage Pension Scheme; Fitzmaurice Holdings.

Other Notable Practitioners **Harry Scott** (see p.631)of **Mills & Reeve** continues to elicit market recommendation.

NORTH WEST

PENSIONS • North West	Ptnrs	Assts
1 **Addleshaw Booth & Co** Manchester	1	3
DLA Liverpool, Manchester	n/a	n/a
2 **Eversheds** Manchester	1	5
Hammond Suddards Edge Manchester	1	4
3 **Masons** Manchester	1	5

LEADING INDIVIDUALS	
1 **WRIGHT David** DLA	
2 **ASHLEY TAYLOR Andrew** Hammond Suddards	**GRAHAM Ronald** Eversheds
GRIFFITHS David Addleshaw Booth & Co	**KENNEDY Patrick** Masons
3 **HARRIS Jeremy** DLA	
SCHOLEFIELD Stephen Addleshaw Booth & Co	
UP AND COMING	
SOUTHERN Steve Hammond Suddards Edge	

This book is the product of 6,552 1/2-hour interviews. See p.7 for BMRB audit.
Within each band, firms are listed alphabetically. *See individuals' profiles p.624*

Addleshaw Booth & Co (see firm details p.853) "*An excellent firm*" which continues its steady dominance of the region. "*Leading light*" **David Griffiths** (see p.627) is "*intense; with sound focus on transactions*" while **Stephen Scholefield** (see p.631) "*has his finger on the pulse*" and clients appreciated that he is "*very quick with advice.*" The group advised trustees on refunds of surplus and on applications for modification orders, and acted for beneficiaries in several contested court proceedings related to the use of scheme surpluses. **Clients:** Cussons (International); Kelloggs; Trinity Mirror; Ciba Speciality Chemicals.

DLA The Liverpool branch is the stronger of the firm's regional offices, with Manchester offering more corporate support. **David Wright** is a leading figure in the North West.

Eversheds (see firm details p.952) A nationally integrated practice, the group is establishing its presence with a team of quality lawyers. Handles scheme merger work for medium to large corporates and is experienced in multi-scheme mergers. Advised Akzo Nobel Trustees on revised structure documentation for their entire UK pensions scheme. **Ronald Graham** is seen by rivals as "*the most personable practitioner you could hope to meet*" and leads "*a strengthening team*" across the Manchester and Leeds offices. Jacqui Timmins is now predominantly based in Leeds. **Clients:** Akzo Nobel Trustees; DuPont.

Hammond Suddards Edge (see firm details p.984) "*Benefiting from having national support,*" the firm offers a complete service with clients including both trustees and employers. "*Gentlemanly*" **Andrew Ashley Taylor** (see p.625) is praised by clients as a "*thorough pensions lawyer.*" He forms a good team with the contrasting style of tough fighter and "*exciting prospect*" **Steve Southern** (see p.631). The team dealt with pensions issues arising from the merger of FKI with Bridon, and advised Kodak on the UK pension aspects of its acquisition of Bell & Howell Company's imaging business. Further transactional advice includes instructions from CWS on the pension aspects of its acquisition of eleven stores from Somerfield. **Clients:** Associated Octel Corporation; FKI; BASF; Motorola; Umbro International.

Masons (see firm details p.1056) "*Professional*" stable team attaining its profile mainly due to the efforts of the popular Head of department **Patrick Kennedy** (see p.628), endorsed by the market as "*a good team leader, committed and enthusiastic.*" Acting for a range of corporates, undertaking trustees work, general advisory and corporate support. Instructions on the data protection aspects of the pensions market are increasing and the firm carried out an audit for an established client. The firm has advised on related aspects of PPP finance projects work for the Metropolitan Police Service and the Ministry of Defence. **Clients:** Lathams Financial Management; London Scottish Bank.

NORTH EAST

PENSIONS • North East	Ptnrs	Assts
1 Addleshaw Booth & Co Leeds	2	7
Hammond Suddards Edge Leeds	2	4
2 DLA Leeds, Sheffield	n/a	n/a
Eversheds Leeds	1	4
3 Dickinson Dees Newcastle upon Tyne	3	2
Wrigleys Leeds	1	4
4 Nabarro Nathanson Sheffield	2	3
Pinsent Curtis Biddle Leeds	1	2
Walker Morris Leeds	1	2

LEADING INDIVIDUALS	
1 AINSCOE Raymond Wrigleys	
2 JENKINS Martin Dickinson Dees	McKENNA Catherine Hammond Suddards
RAWNSLEY Rachel Addleshaw Booth & Co	
3 HOLMES Leigh Wrigleys	MASSARANO SALT Vikki DLA
PAYNE Kate DLA	TURNBULL Andrew Walker Morris
4 ALLISON Margaret Nabarro Nathanson	ARCHER Richard Wrigleys
KNIGHT Timothy Wrigleys	RIDLER Mark Hammond Suddards Edge
THOMAS-GREEN Susan Pinsent Curtis Biddle	
TIMMINS Jacqueline Eversheds	
UP AND COMING	
SAEEDI Terry Hammond Suddards Edge	

This book is the product of 6,552 1/2-hour interviews. See p.7 for BMRB audit.

Within each band, firms are listed alphabetically. *See individuals' profiles p.624*

Addleshaw Booth & Co (see firm details p.853) Top flight firm offering "*a first class service.*" It has broadened its traditional client base of banks and financial institutions with the addition of manufacturing clients, carrying out both 'pure' pensions work and corporate support with niche strength in independent trustee work. **Rachel Rawnsley** (see p.630) is valued by clients as "*clever and able,*" while the highly respected Neville Peel has taken a consultancy role with the firm. Instructed by trustees over an application to OPRA by the employer for a modification order amending the scheme. The group also advised an employer on a large MFR dispute with trustees and acted for Law Debenture in a High Court challenge to the Ombudsman's ruling. **Clients:** Asda; Bradford and Bingley; Skipton Building Society; Logica.

Hammond Suddards Edge (see firm details p.984) "*Good pensions practice*" with "*super clients.*" Acts mainly for corporate clients in utilities, chemical and civil engineering sectors. **Catherine McKenna** (see p.629) "*is good to deal with*" while the "*knowledgeable*" **Mark Ridler** (see p.630) moves up the tables this year on the back of warm market recommendations. **Terry Saeedi** (see p.630) rounds out an impressive offering. Handled Kelda Group's exit from a centralised privatised pension scheme and advised trustees of the Northern Electric Group on the National Power and National Grid litigation and its outsourcing of pension arrangements. **Clients:** Kelda Group; VAW; Kalon Pension Scheme; Carpets International.

DLA **Vikki Massarano Salt** is the leaading figure at a team that maintains a high profile in the region.

Eversheds (see firm details p.952) The departure of Raymond Ainscoe and Leigh Holmes to Wrigleys has "*diminished the team's pre-eminence.*" As part of the firm's integration strategy work is shared between the Leeds and Manchester offices, but this office has yet to match the depth of the latter. **Jacqui Timmins** (see p.632), relocating from Manchester, is "*pleasant to do business with*" and judged by industry sources to be a welcome step on the road to recovery. Highlight of the year was the advice (with the Manchester office) to the Akzo Nobel Trustees on revised structure documentation for their entire UK pensions scheme. **Clients:** Chapelthorpe; Akzo Nobel Trustees.

Dickinson Dees (see firm details p.941) "*Dominant in Newcastle,*" the firm acts primarily for clients in the region and is successfully targeting a broader base. Clients range from national plcs to limited companies and trustees, with scheme mergers and construction a growth area. Panel advisors to OPRA, the firm also undertakes pension litigation. **Martin Jenkins** (see p.628) has a strong regional profile, rated by clients as a "*good practical lawyer – he's going places,*" with most agreeing that he is the architect of the group's success. The firm acted for the trustees of two schemes in Caterpillar Scheme merger. **Clients:** Northern Electric; Northern Rock; Railway Pensions Management; Railways Pension Trustee Company.

Wrigleys (see firm details p.1191) "*More weight than most in the market,*" bolstered by the recruitment of talented lawyers from Eversheds. Both **Tim Knight** and **Richard Archer** are well respected in the market, if in lower profile as they operate mixed practices. Predominantly acting for and as trustees of pension schemes and in conflict situations. Clearly pre-eminent in the market place, **Raymond Ainscoe** is "*one of the best pension lawyers.*" **Leigh Holmes** "*will push things*" and the market awaits the success of the duo's impact. **Clients:** Pension scheme trustees; charities; private clients.

Nabarro Nathanson (see firm details p.1078) "*Unrealised potential*" is thought to lie within a team that is still regarded as a satellite to the London practice. Clients vouch that **Margaret Allison** (see p.624) "*understands our business.*" Works predominantly for trustees and sponsoring companies of occupational pension schemes where the caseload includes documentation, Revenue issues, litigation, and corporate support. Assisted Taylor Nelson Sofres in the pensions aspects of its various corporate acquisitions and advised Sheffield City Council on the pensions issues surrounding a PFI project to provide accommodation for six schools in Sheffield. **Clients:** Deloitte & Touche; East Riding of Yorkshire Council; Trustees of the Cotswold 1999 Pension Scheme.

Pinsent Curtis Biddle (see firm details p.1098) A low-key participant in the market, enjoying an established client base. Felt to be less proactive on the flag-waving front, **Susan Thomas-Green** (see p.631) is praised by rivals as "*a lawyer of high calibre.*" Clients include large non-quoted and FTSE 250 plcs companies and the practice has a niche in winding up work. Acted for the trustees of Ferguson International in the winding up of its two large insolvent schemes and appointed as statutory trustee for Cintel International Pension Scheme. **Clients:** Koppers UK; Thistle; Ferguson International.

Walker Morris (see firm details p.1171) A relatively small team, yet to break into the top end of the market but respected by interviewees for its quality and efficiency. Advises trustees on winding up pension schemes, as well as acting for plcs in merger and general advisory issues. "*Experienced and able*" **Andrew Turnbull** (see p.632) offers "*practical advice.*" The firm acted as a trustee in a windup involving a pension scheme worth £25 million. Active in commercial transactions, it advised the sellers in a £70 million share sale transaction. **Clients:** Grattan; Killgerm; Bradford & Northern Housing Association; Kelda Group.

SCOTLAND

PENSIONS • Scotland	Ptnrs	Assts
1 **Shepherd & Wedderburn WS** Edinburgh	2	4
2 **Morison Bishop** Glasgow	3	2
3 **Burness** Glasgow	1	2
Maclay Murray & Spens Glasgow	2	1
McGrigor Donald Glasgow	1	3

LEADING INDIVIDUALS	
1 **FLEMING Andrew** Burness	**GORDON Ian** McGrigor Donald
HOLEHOUSE Andrew Shepherd & Wedderburn WS	
TALMAN Iain Morison Bishop	
2 **KNOX Louisa** Shepherd & Wedderburn WS	**TROTTER Peter** MacRoberts
3 **CROMBIE June** Morison Bishop	
THURSTON SMITH Martin Tods Murray WS	
UP AND COMING	
HILL Alistair Dundas & Wilson CS	

This book is the product of 6,552 1/2-hour interviews. See p.7 for BMRB audit.
Within each band, firms are listed alphabetically. *See individuals' profiles p.624*

Shepherd & Wedderburn WS (see firm details p.1126) "*Stable, strong team.*" Acts for large institutions and public companies, with niche strengths in the electricity industries. Provides advice on winding up, reorganisation and documentation. Instructed in the winding up of the Scottish Transport Group pension schemes, the group has also established new final salary and money purchase schemes for the Scottish Power group of companies. "*Experienced and on the ball,*" **Andrew Holehouse** (see p.627) brings a "*sensible approach*" to proceedings, while **Louisa Knox** (see p.628) is valued by clients as a "*highly commercial operator.*" **Clients:** Scottish Power; Scottish Transport Group; Scottish Life Pension Scheme; Church of Scotland Pension Scheme; Scottish Amicable.

Morison Bishop (see firm details p.1075) Acclaimed for its trustee work, it lacks a comparable base in the corporate sphere. Acts predominantly for trustees on company schemes with a smaller base of employer clients, and has a growing independent trusteeship practice. Clients include insurance companies, trade organisations and intermediaries such as accountants and actuaries. Peers vouch that **Iain Talman** (see p.631) is "*the most experienced pensions lawyer in Scotland;*" both he and "*personable*" **June Crombie** (see p.626) "*have earned their stripes.*" **Clients:** Rosyth Pension Scheme; Law Society of Pension Schemes.

Burness (see firm details p.903) Anticipated to make a greater impact thanks to the return of "*experienced and able*" **Andrew Fleming**, fresh from his stint as Head of Richards Butler's pensions team, a move that rivals acknowledge "*can only be good news for Burness.*" Furthermore at assistant level, a long-term secondment from William M Mercer has joined the team. The firm advised an LSE-listed group on its move from final salary pension provision to money purchase provision, and acted for a large financial services group on trusteeship issues in a large scheme for unassociated employers. **Clients:** Standard Life; Riley Dunn & Wilson; Clyde Marine; Lees of Scotland.

Maclay Murray & Spens (see firm details p.1047) Arising from the upheaval of key departures, the team has expanded, addressing any questions concerning depth of resources. Boosted by having a London office, the firm has nonetheless concentrated its energies into this group. Acts mostly for plc company schemes and general advice to insurance companies, the team has witnessed growth in issues surrounding scheme mergers and surpluses. Maureen Burnside, better known for her employment work, heads the Employment, Pensions and Benefits department. The firm acted for the trustees of the Bank of Scotland Staff Pension Scheme on its merger with the Capital Bank and Bank of Wales schemes. **Clients:** Coats Viyella; Menzies Pension Fund; Seagram Distillers; Compaq; Scottish Homes.

McGrigor Donald (see firm details p.1062) Continuing to act for larger established companies, as well as assisting smaller entrepreneurial entities, the last year has seen an emphasis on transactions, including mergers, winding ups and the consolidation of schemes. Pragmatic, hardworking **Ian Gordon** (see p.627) owns a "*substantial knowledge*" of pensions law, although his time is drawn upon for tax and share scheme advice. The firm completed the amalgamation of Alba Life pension schemes with Britannic Assurance and presided over merger of schemes operated by Forth Ports. **Clients:** Alba Life; Forth Ports.

Other Notable Practitioners **Peter Trotter** (see p.632) at **MacRoberts** received heavy endorsement from the market, particularly in his independent trustee work. **Martin Thurston Smith** (see p.632) of **Tods Murray WS** has a profile greater than that of the firm's pensions team. **Alistair Hill** of **Dundas & Wilson** is developing a reputation for himself.

LEADERS IN PENSIONS

AINSCOE, Raymond
Wrigleys, Leeds (0113) 244 6100

ALLISON, Margaret
Nabarro Nathanson, Sheffield (0114) 279 4004
m.allison@nabarro.com
Specialisation: Work covers almost every aspect of pension law, including advising trustees and companies on the re-organisation of schemes and the up-dating of scheme documentation. In the last year, has advised increasingly on the pension aspects of local government PFI projects of disposals by several plcs. Enjoys speaking engagements and trustee training.
Prof. Memberships: Full APL member.
Career: Qualified 1987. Specialised in pensions since 1988. Joined *Nabarro Nathanson* 1994 to establish their Sheffield pension team.
Personal: Born 1962. Has lived and worked in Sheffield since 1985. Interests include horses and cats.

ANDREWS, Sue
Pinsent Curtis Biddle, London (020) 7606 9301
susan.andrews@pinsents.com
Specialisation: Partner in Pensions Group of *Pinsent Curtis Biddle*. Advises on all areas of pensions law including trustees' duties and liabilities, winding up, investment management and custody, mergers and acquisitions and stakeholder.
Prof. Memberships: Member and secretary of the Association of Pensions Lawyers; Fellow of the Pensions Management Institute and director of the governing council.
Career: Qualified as barrister in 1984. Requalified as solicitor in 1991. Worked in-house 1986-1989, entering private practice in 1989. Joined *Pinsent Curtis Biddle* in February 2001.
Personal: Born 1st July 1961 and holds an LLB from Thames Valley University. Leisure interests include squash and golf. Lives in Hertford with her daughter.

ARCHER, David
Pitmans, Reading (0118) 958 0224
darcher@pitmans.com
Specialisation: All aspects of commercial and personal insolvency including insolvency litigation and insolvency/pensions issues. Acts as an independent trustee to corporate pension schemes of insolvent companies.
Prof. Memberships: Insolvency Lawyers Association; Member of INSOL Europe; Associate Member of R3; Law Society.
Personal: Christianity, skiing and sailing.

ARCHER, Richard
Wrigleys, Leeds (0113) 244 6100

ARTHUR, Hugh
Macfarlanes, London (020) 7831 9222
Specialisation: Partner in pensions group. Advises on all areas of pensions law, including advice to employers, trustees, actuaries and other pensions pro-

fessionals. Work includes scheme mergers, corporate and business transfers, MFR problems, disputes, and the drafting of complex documentation. Has lectured extensively on pensions topics at all levels. Author of 'Pensions and Trusteeship' (Sweet & Maxwell, 1998), a leading textbook on pensions law in the light of the Pensions Act 1995, and of numerous articles in specialist pensions publications.
Prof. Memberships: Association of Pension Lawyers.
Career: Qualified in 1980. Worked at *Lovell White & King* 1978-84. *Biddle* 1984-1998, *Macfarlanes* 1999-.
Personal: Born 6th November 1955. Attended Cardinal Vaughan Memorial School, London 1967-74, then Magdalene College, Cambridge (Open Scholarship in Classics) 1974-77 (MA Law).

ASHLEY TAYLOR, Andrew M
Hammond Suddards Edge, Manchester (0161) 830 5000
andrew.ashleytaylor@hammondse.com
Specialisation: The law and practice relating to occupational pension schemes and other forms of retirement provision in the UK. Covers a wide variety of pension disciplines for employers, employees and trustees including corporate transactional work, project and merger advice, documentation and pension dispute resolution. Speaks regularly at seminars and writes articles. Qualified mediator for Alternative Dispute Resolution procedures.
Prof. Memberships: Association of Pension Lawyers, Associate of the Pensions Management Institute, Member of the North West Group of the NAPF.
Career: Qualified November 1984 and became an Associate of the Pensions Management Institute in 1990. Worked in industry to 1988 then went into private practice and joined *Baker & Mckenzie* London to specialise in pensions law.
Personal: Golf, travel, cycling, music and theatre.

ATKINSON, Mark
CMS Cameron McKenna, London (020) 7367 3000

BENNETT, Philip
Slaughter and May, London (020) 7600 1200
philip.bennett@slaughterandmay.com
Specialisation: Partner in pensions/employment department. Main area of practice is pensions work. Author of 'Pension Fund Surpluses' (Longman, 2nd ed 1994).
Prof. Memberships: Association of Pensions Lawyers, Past Chairman Legislative & Parliamentary Sub-Committee of the Association of Pensions Lawyers, Former Member, Main Committee of the Association of Pensions Lawyers.
Career: Qualified 1979. Partner 1986 with *Slaughter and May* in London.
Personal: Born 2 March 1954.

BENNEY, Belinda
Field Fisher Waterhouse, London (020) 7861 4190
bxb@ffwlaw.com
Specialisation: Partner in Pensions Department. Full-time pensions specialist since 1986 when switched from private client work. Since then has covered full range of pensions work: documentation and rule drafting, sex discrimination, mergers & acquisitions, privatisations, severance terms, application of surplus, trustee duties and liabilities, asset protection, and all aspects of pension investment. Frequent speaker at pensions seminars and trustee training courses. Author of 'A Guide to the Pensions Act 1995' (Butterworths), and the pensions chapter in the 'Administration of Estates' practitioners' manual published by Tolley's. Appointed by the Board of the Occupational Pensions Regulatory Authority (OPRA) in April 2000.
Prof. Memberships: National Association of Pension Funds, Association of Pension Lawyers, Law Society, Institute of Chartered Accountants Pensions Sub-Committee.
Career: Qualified in 1981. Joined *Field Fisher Waterhouse* in 1996 as head of the pensions practice.
Personal: Holds an LL.B from the University of Bristol.

BERKELEY, Christopher
Pinsent Curtis Biddle, London (020) 7667 0147
christopher.berkeley@pinsents.com
Specialisation: Partner in pensions group. Acted in 2001 for the trustees of the Innogy Group of the ESPS in the National Grid/International Power allocation of surplus case that was decided in the House of Lords. He acted for the trustees of the Lansing Linde Pension Schemes in rule construction/scheme rectification proceedings that was appealed to the Court of Appeal. He has recently been appointed as legal adviser to the trustees of a number of pension schemes in the engineering sector.
Prof. Memberships: APL, Member of APL Investment Sub-Committee, Member of the Committee of the City & Eastern Group of the National Association of Pension Funds; Co-opted member of the NAPF Investment Committee 2000-01; City of London Solicitors Company. Has spoken at both NAPF and APL conferences.
Career: Educated at Sherborne School (1967-71) and Brasenose College, Oxford (1972-76) where he gained a Second Class Honours degree in Classics; MA (1980); articled at *Lemon & Co*, Swindon (1977 to 1979); qualified as a solicitor with *Lemon & Co* in May 1980; commercial property solicitor with *Wansbroughs* in Bristol (1981-85); Assistant Parliamentary Counsel (1985-90); assistant solicitor in the Pensions and Employment department of *Lovell White Durrant* (1990 to 1996); Partner in the Pensions Group of *Biddle* (now *Pinsent Curtis Biddle*) (1996-present).
Personal: Married with three children; armchair cricket and rugby union enthusiast. Membership of MCC and London Wasps RFC.

BLACK, Richard
Wragge & Co, Birmingham (0870) 903 1000

BROWNING, Lesley
Norton Rose, London (020) 7444 2448
browningla@nortonrose.com
Specialisation: Experience of all types of pensions related work including general advisory work for employees and trustees, corporate transactions (including PFI), pension scheme mergers, winding-up of pension schemes and investment and custodian agreements. Also has extensive pensions litigation experience, having been involved in the British Airways, National Bus and Hillsdown Holdings cases as well as numerous complaints to the Pensions Ombudsman.
Prof. Memberships: Association of Pension Lawyers (and currently serving on the Education and Seminars sub-committee), NAPF City and Eastern Group, IPEBLA.
Career: Joined *Norton Rose* in June 2001 having previously been a partner at *Nabarro Nathanson* where she also trained. Studied at Keble College, Oxford and the College of Law and qualified in 1991.
Publications: Contributor to Butterworths 'Pensions Law Handbook' and 'Whitehouse on Revenue'.
Personal: Married. Enjoys reading, cinema, theatre and eating out.

CLARK, David
Clarks, Reading (0118) 958 5321

CLOSE, Chris
Sacker & Partners, London (020) 7329 6699
chris.close@sacker-partners.co.uk
Specialisation: Partner in specialist law firm. All aspects of law relating to pension schemes. Represented the employer in South West trains case. Acted on a number of high profile scheme mergers and demergers. Experienced in transactions including TUPE. Lectures at conferences, seminars and workshops.
Prof. Memberships: Association of Pension Lawyers.
Career: Qualified in April 1987; became a partner at *Sackers* in June 1987.
Personal: Born 14th December 1954, University of York 1973-76. London University (external) 1981-85. Interests: family, cricket, Charlton Athletic, real ale, walking and backgammon. Lives in Sevenoaks.

COCKERILL, Vivien
Wragge & Co, Birmingham (0870) 903 1000

COWLEY, Michael
Stephenson Harwood, London (020) 7329 4422

COX, Helen
Clifford Chance, London (020) 7600 1000
helen.cox@cliffordchance.com
Specialisation: Partner and head of the pensions group specialising in all aspects of pensions law and practice including pension scheme documentation, the establishment, merger and winding-up of pension schemes, the pensions aspects of corporate mergers and acquisitions, sales, flotations and privatisations and international pension arrangements.
Prof. Memberships: Law Society; Liveryman of the City of London Solicitors' Company; Association of Pension Lawyers (APL); International Pension and Employee Benefits Lawyers Association (IPEBLA); former member of the Main Committee of APL; former member of the Legislative and Parliamentary Sub-Committee of APL; former chairman of the International Sub-Committee of APL; former UK representative on the Steering Committee of IPEBLA; former chairman and secretary of the National Association of Pension Funds City and Eastern Group.
Career: Barry County Grammar School for Girls; University College, London (LLB 1st Class Hons 1974). Articled *Coward Chance*; qualified 1977; made partner *Clifford Chance* 1989.
Personal: Travel, cinema, theatre, art and reading. Born 1953; resides London.

COX, Tim
Linklaters, London (020) 7456 3692
tim.cox@linklaters.com
Specialisation: Specialist advice on all aspects of pensions law including the establishment and winding up of schemes; advice on employment and regulatory issues; advice on the application of tax and social security legislation affecting different kinds of pension arrangements; advice on the pension aspects

of corporate takeover and merger work.
Prof. Memberships: Association of Pension Lawyers: member since 1987; member of Legislative & Parliamentary Sub-Committee since 1989; Member of Main committee 1991-96.
Career: Articled at *Linklaters* 1985, assistant solicitor 1987-96, partner 1996. Partner, employment and employee benefits department. Educated at Sir John Deane's Grammar School, BA (Law) (Downing College, Cambridge), BCL (Magdalen College, Oxford).

CROMBIE, June
Morison Bishop, Glasgow (0141) 248 4672
june.crombie@morisonbishop.co.uk
Specialisation: Accredited by the Law Society of Scotland as a specialist in Pension Law. Pensions law and practice, including independent trusteeships through directorship of Mitre Pensions Ltd which is involved in a considerable number of schemes including 6,000 member, Rosyth Royal Dockyard Pension Scheme.
Prof. Memberships: Law Society of Scotland, Association of Pension Lawyers. Secretary of the Scottish Group and full member of the Association of Pension Lawyers. Local member of the Scottish Group of the Pensions Management Institute.
Career: Qualified 1987, partner 1991, partner in pensions unit of corporate division.

DAVIES, Ian
Eversheds, Cardiff (029) 2047 1147
iandavies@eversheds.com
Specialisation: Partner in the pensions unit within the employment and pensions department. Handles all aspects of establishing and running pension schemes; documentation; scheme mergers; winding-up; ownership of surpluses; advice to trustees, acting as independent trustee; and pensions aspects of M&A. Has particular experience of handling multi-scheme mergers and providing SSAS documentation and advice to pensioneer trustees. Also handles taxation work, including share option schemes, ESOPs, business and capital taxation. Has published several articles on pensions and tax issues.
Prof. Memberships: APL.
Career: Qualified in 1984. Joined *Phillips & Buck* (now *Eversheds*) in 1982, becoming a partner in 1988.

DAVIS, Richard GL
Browne Jacobson, Nottingham (0115) 976 6000

DERBYSHIRE, Wyn
SJ Berwin, London (020) 7533 2222
wyn.derbyshire@sjberwin.com
Specialisation: Specialises in all aspects of pensions law, particularly in relation to scheme documentation, advice to trustees and commercial transactions.
Prof. Memberships: APL, IPEBLA, NAPF.
Career: BSc (Hons) Leeds University; PhD Cambridge University. Trained *Clifford Chance*, qualified 1991. Partner and head of the pensions group *SJ Berwin* 1998.
Personal: Born 1962. Married, one daughter. Interests include history, sailing, scuba diving.

DIERDEN, Kenneth
Freshfields Bruckhaus Deringer, London (020) 7936 4000
ken.dierden@freshfields.com
Specialisation: Partner in employment, pensions and benefits department. Work covers all aspects of the establishment and operation of pension schemes (both private and public sector). Experienced in pensions litigation and has wide involvement of the pensions aspects of privatisations. Acts for employers and trustees.
Prof. Memberships: Former Chairman of the Association of Pension Lawyers (APL). Associate of the Institute of Taxation.
Career: Qualified in 1977. Lecturer at College of Law 1977/80. Joined *Freshfields* 1980. Partner 1987.
Personal: Born 1952.

DOCKING, Peter
Sacker & Partners, London (020) 7329 6699
peter.docking@sacker-partners.co.uk
Specialisation: Partner in specialist pensions law firm. Principal area of practice is pensions law. Covers all aspects including litigation, sales and purchases, trust law issues and life office matters. Frequent lecturer and contributor to pensions and academic journals. Former Chairman of APL's Education Committee. Current member of the APL's International Committee. Steering group member of IPEBLA (International Pension and Employee Benefit Lawyers Association).
Prof. Memberships: Association of Pension Lawyers, Law Society.
Career: Qualified in 1987. Partner at *Nicholson Graham & Jones* 1991 to 1996. Joined *Sacker & Partners* as a partner in 1996.
Personal: Born 1st June 1961. Educated at Sutton Manor High School for Boys and the University of Exeter. Leisure activities include mountaineering, climbing, walking, skiing and travel.

ELLISON, Robin
Eversheds, London (020) 7919 4500
robinellison@eversheds.com
Specialisation: National head of pensions. Acted in the Maxwell pensions case. Author of 'Pensions Law and Practice'. Editor of 'Pensions Benefit Law Reports'. Has also published 'Pensions and Divorce', 'The Pension Trustee Handbook' and 'Pensions: Europe and Equality'. Regular broadcaster including frequent contributions to BBC Radio 4's 'Moneybox'.
Prof. Memberships: NAPF, Association of Pensions Lawyers, Law Society.
Career: Fellow of Wolfson College, Cambridge 1975-80. Founded *Ellison Westhorp* in 1980, carrying out exclusively pensions work. Managing Director of Finance for Housing Ltd 1982-87 and Director of Baltic plc 1985-87. Chairman, Pendragon.

EVERSON, Ingrid
Eversheds, Birmingham (0121) 232 1493
ingrideverson@eversheds.com
Specialisation: Partner specialising in all aspects of pensions work, advising companies and trustees and including support in various corporate, commercial, employment and property. Through *Eversheds* Pension Trustees Limited responsible for several trusteeships.
Prof. Memberships: Association of Pensions Lawyers, Midlands Life & Pensions Society and student member of the Pensions Management Institute.
Career: Articled at *Wragge & Co*, qualified 1982. Joined *Eversheds* in 1992 and became a partner in 2001.
Personal: Educated at Bristol University. Sits as part-time Support Child Support Appeal Tribunal chairman. Hobbies – attempting to learn golf and attempting to keep fit.

FALLON, Liz
Eversheds, Birmingham (0121) 232 1000
Specialisation: Partner. Handles all aspects of pensions law including transactional work, scheme reorganisation, advice to insolvency practitioners, establishment of schemes and scheme documentation. Is also a director of *Eversheds* Pension Trustees Limited, which has a substantial portfolio of trusteeships. Has spoken at the Institute of Actuaries Annual Conference and for the Pensions Management and is a regular lecturer for a number of professional training organisations including Industrial Relations Services. Also regularly involved in Trustee training courses.
Prof. Memberships: Law Society, Association of Pension Lawyers, National Association of Pension Funds.
Career: Qualified 1983. Joined *Eversheds* 1981. Became a partner 1997. Heads up pensions team in Birmingham.
Personal: Born 17.2.1959. Attended University of Kent, BA Law and German. Interests include keeping up with two young sons, skiing and horse riding.

FENTON, Jonathan
DLA, London (08700) 111 111

FLEMING, Andrew
Burness, Edinburgh (0131) 473 6000

FORD, Peter
Norton Rose, London (020) 7444 2711
fordp@nortonrose.com
Specialisation: Partner with experience in all aspects of pensions including corporate transactions, scheme mergers and reorganisations, scheme winding-up, investment and custody and pensions litigation.
Prof. Memberships: Currently a member of the Main Committee of the Association of Pensions Lawyers (APL), a position to which he was re-elected for a second term in 1999 by other pension lawyers. He previously chaired the APL Education Sub-Committee and is a member of the JWG Actuarial Committee. Also a member of a number of pensions organisations including the National Association of Pensions Funds and the IEBA.
Career: Qualified April 1988. Partner *Nabarro Nathanson* in 1993. Partner *Norton Rose* 2001.
Personal: Born 8th December 1962. Attended John Fisher School, Purley 1974-81 and the University of Hull 1981-84.

FORREST, Ian
Hammond Suddards Edge, Birmingham (0121) 222 3000
ian.forrest@hammondse.com
Specialisation: Head of the pensions department in the Birmingham office. Practice includes the full range of pensions law work including transactional support, documentation, scheme mergers, trusteeship and 'special projects'. Clients include several public companies, a national sports association, charities and insurance companies. Currently treasurer of the Association of Pension Lawyers.
Prof. Memberships: APL, PMI, IPEBLA.
Career: Qualified with *Edge Ellison* in 1989. Made associate in 1994 and partner in 1995.
Personal: Born 2 April 1951. Educated at Loughborough University (1968-71). Law degree gained through part time study.

GAULT, Ian
Herbert Smith, London (020) 7374 8000
ian.gault@herbertsmith.com
Specialisation: Senior pensions partner. Has extensive experience of advising on all aspects of pensions law and practice. Currently on the legislative and parliamentary sub-committee of the Association of Pensions Lawyers, the executive committee of the Pensions Research Accountant's Group and the Council of the Society of Pensions Consultants.
Prof. Memberships: Association of Pensions Lawyers.
Career: Qualified in 1977. Partner at *Herbert Smith* since 1988.
Personal: Educated at Clare College, Cambridge.

GOLDMAN, Ruth
Linklaters, London (020) 7456 3686
ruth.goldman@linklaters.com
Specialisation: Employment and employee benefits group. Specialises in pensions law and employee benefits. Considerable experience in all main areas of pension law practice including trust law aspects, documentation, mergers and acquisitions, flotations, privatisations, international benefits and industry-wide schemes, as well as international pensions.
Prof. Memberships: Chair of International Committee of Association of Pension Lawyers 1993-1999. Chair of *Linklaters & Alliance* European Pensions Group. Elected member of NAPF Council.
Career: 1992 to date: Partner, *Linklaters*; 1985-1992: Assistant solicitor, *Linklaters*; 1983-1985: Articled clerk, *Linklaters*. 1981-1983: College of Law, Chancery Lane; 1981: Warwick University, MA Industrial Relations; 1980: Lady Margaret Hall, MA Politics, Philosophy and Economics.

GORDON, Ian
McGrigor Donald, Glasgow (0141) 567 9269
iangordon@mcgrigors.com
Specialisation: Principal area of practice is employee benefits, pension schemes, share incentive schemes, option schemes, and employee share ownership arrangements for listed, AIM and Ofex companies. Also advises employees and trustees on pensions law. Work includes establishment of and ongoing advice in relation to approved and unapproved pension arrangements. Frequent lecturer on pensions and taxation issues. Has given TV and radio interviews on pension issues.
Prof. Memberships: Association of Pension Lawyers.
Career: Joined *McGrigor Donald* as a trainee in 1979. Qualified in July 1979. One year secondment to *Thomson McLintock CA* in 1983. Became a Partner at *McGrigor Donald* in the same year.
Personal: Educated at Edinburgh University 1975-79. Born 15th August 1957. Lives in Glasgow.

GRAHAM, Ronald
Eversheds, Manchester (0161) 831 8000

GRANT, Mark
CMS Cameron McKenna, London
(020) 7367 2325
msg@cmck.com
Specialisation: Partner in pensions group advising employers and trustees on all aspects of pensions law, including creation of stakeholder schemes. Established firm's Pensions Ombudsman Unit which defends complaints made against employers, trustees and advisers. Acted for trustee of Coloroll schemes in landmark European Court of Justice case on sex equality issues.
Prof. Memberships: APL, IPEBLA (membership secretary and steering committee member 1997-2001).
Career: Trained *McKenna & Co*, qualified in 1992; secondment to pensions practice of New York firm *Winthrop, Stimson, Putnam & Roberts*, 1995; Law Society working committee on Pensions Bill, 1995; partner *CMS Cameron McKenna* 1999.
Publications: Co-editor 'International Pension Lawyer' 1995-97; assistant editor 'Occupational Pensions Law Reports' 1997-; author of 'The Pensions Ombudsman; Powers, Procedures and Decisions' (Sweet & Maxwell) 1998; numerous articles for trade journals and papers for conferences.
Personal: Hertford College, Oxford 1986-89. Married with two children. Interests: football and cycling.

GRAVILL, Robert
Hammond Suddards Edge, Birmingham
(0121) 222 3000
robert.gravill@hammondse.com
Specialisation: Pensions. Robert Gravill, based in Birmingham, is a partner in the pensions department. Managing Director of Edge Ellison Trustees Ltd. Robert is responsible for many of the firm's larger clients and heads up the documentation and trusteeship work in the department. He numbers amongst his clients several insurance companies and acts as the trustee of many schemes. Robert is a regular speaker on pensions matters and the author of a number of articles. He is involved with the APL, IPEBLA, TACT and NAPF.
Career: Educated Southampton University (LL.B) and College of Law, Guildford.
Personal: Married, lives in Nuneaton and cites his hobbies as walking, skiing and travel.

GREENLEES, Mark
Sacker & Partners, London (020) 7329 6699
mark.greenlees@sacker-partners.co.uk
Specialisation: Partner in specialist pensions law firm. All aspects of law relating to occupational pension schemes. Represented the male beneficiaries in the 'Coloroll' reference to the European Court. Acted for vendor in what was then the second largest MBO in UK business history. Regular contributor to pensions periodicals; regular speaker at major conferences and seminars. Immediate past Chairman of the Association of Pension Lawyers.
Prof. Memberships: Association of Pension Lawyers.
Career: Qualified in 1979. Joined *Sacker & Partners* in 1977, becoming a partner in 1982. Former chairman of APL. Member of the Main Committee of APL 1991-1996. Chairman of Legislative and Parliamentary Committee of APL 1992-1994. Chairman of Legislation Committee of SPC 1991-1992. Member of SPC Council.
Personal: Born 18th April 1954. Attended Berkhamsted 1964-71 and Oxford University 1972-76. Leisure interests include family, old cars and Watford FC. Lives near Berkhamsted.

GREENSTREET, Ian Alexander
Hammond Suddards Edge, London
(020) 7655 1000
ian.greenstreet@hammondse.com
Specialisation: Partner in the London office of the pensions unit advising employers and trustees on all aspects of pension law including general advisory work, scheme mergers and wind ups, documentation work, ombudsman disputes and commercial transactions. Also does product work for providers eg SIPPS and stakeholder schemes. Is a regular speaker on a number of pension related topics.
Prof. Memberships: Association of Pension Lawyers.
Career: Joined *Hammond Suddards Edge* as a partner in October 2000. Before then he worked at *Simmons & Simmons* for ten years specialising exclusively in pensions law.
Publications: Author of 'Stakeholder Pensions – A Special Report' published by Sweet & Maxwell 2001. Past contributor to Sweet & Maxwell's 'Law of Pension Schemes' and 'Pensions the New Regime: A guide to the Pensions Act 1995 and its regulations'. He is also a contributor of articles to many professional journals on topical pension issues.
Personal: Has a psychology degree from Bristol and later re-qualified as a solicitor. Married with two daughters.

GRIFFITHS, David
Addleshaw Booth & Co, Manchester
(0161) 934 6000
Specialisation: Partner in pensions department, commercial group. Pensions law, covering advice to individuals, employers and/or trustees in relation to the maintenance and conduct of occupational pension schemes, scheme mergers and reconstructions, contentious pensions issues and the pensions aspects of mergers and acquisitions. Provides full legal document service.
Prof. Memberships: Association of Pension Lawyers. Currently serving on their Legislative and Parliamentary Sub-Committee.
Career: Qualified as a solicitor in 1990 with the firm. Associate 1993. Partner 1996.
Personal: Educated at the University of Edinburgh, (MA English Language and Literature). Interests include music, literature, hill-walking and badminton. Lives in Bolton.

HARRIS, Jeremy
DLA, Manchester (08700) 111111

HILL, Alistair
Dundas & Wilson CS, Edinburgh
(0131) 228 8000

HINGLEY, Gerald
Wragge & Co, Birmingham (0870) 903 1000

HOLEHOUSE, Andrew
Shepherd & Wedderburn WS, Edinburgh
(0131) 228 9900
andrew.holehouse@shepwedd.co.uk
Specialisation: Partner and head of pensions group. Deals with all legal aspects of pensions law, including establishment, winding up and ongoing advice for major occupational pension schemes, advice to life offices, pensions aspects of company sales, acquisitions, mergers and flotations, pensions litigation and EC aspects. Also handles employee share schemes. Has written journal articles and regularly speaks at seminars on pensions law.
Prof. Memberships: Committee member and immediate past Chairman Scottish Group Association of Pensions Lawyers, Law Society Pensions Law Accreditation Panel, Law Society Working Party on Pensions Law.
Career: Qualified in England & Wales 1981. With

Rooks Rider, London 1981-87 (partner from 1984). Joined *Shepherd & Wedderburn* in 1988. Qualified in Scotland 1989. Became an associate at *Shepherd & Wedderburn* in 1990 and a partner in 1992.
Personal: Born 8th December 1955. Leisure activities include malt whisky, fine wines, opera, classical music, rugby. Lives in Edinburgh.

HOLMES, Leigh
Wrigleys, Leeds (0113) 244 6100

ILLSTON, Tim
Burges Salmon, Bristol (0117) 939 2284
tim.illston@burges-salmon.com
Specialisation: Head of pensions unit. Has expertise in independent trusteeships, trust law, unapproved retirement benefits schemes, public sector schemes, pension fund trustee training, investment management agreements and establishment, merger and winding-up of pension schemes. Drafts insurance company and pension scheme documentation.
Prof. Memberships: Law Society, Association of Pension Lawyers, NAPF, Society of Pension Consultants, PMI and IPEBLA.
Career: Moved from *Freshfields* to *Burges Salmon* in 1988, becoming a partner in 1990.
Personal: University of Manchester 1977-80. Leisure interests include hockey, guitar and cycling.

ITO, Stephen
Lovells, London (020) 7296 2000

JACOBS, Howard
Slaughter and May, London (020) 7600 1200
howard.jacobs@slaughterandmay.com
Specialisation: Pension scheme restructurings, general pension advice.
Prof. Memberships: City of London Solicitors' Company Employment Law Sub-committee.
Career: *Slaughter and May* since 1975.
Personal: Winchester College. Pembroke College, Cambridge. Married, three children. Interests: family and gardening.

JAMES, Stuart
Rowe & Maw, London (020) 7782 8613
sjames@roweandmaw.com
Specialisation: Senior partner pensions department. Pensions law and related trust, tax and commercial law matters. Other main area of work is unit trusts and retail financial services. Member of the Pension Law Review Committee 1992-93.
Prof. Memberships: Law Society, Association of Pensions Lawyers (Past Chairman), Reliance Insurance Group (Chairman), M&G Securities Limited, Fellow, Pensions Management Institute.
Career: Articled with *Rowe & Maw*. Qualified in 1967, then joined *Warren Murton & Co.* 1967-77. Returned to *Rowe & Maw* as a partner in 1977. Senior partner 1996.
Personal: Born 3rd March 1944. Attended Reed's School 1958-62. Lives in Surrey. Enjoys skiing, flying, diving and reading.

JENKINS, Martin
Dickinson Dees, Newcastle upon Tyne
(0191) 279 9528
martin.jenkins@dickinson-dees.com
Specialisation: Pensions law in all its aspects.
Prof. Memberships: Association of Pensions Lawyers; Secretary National Association Pension Funds (Northern Counties Group).
Career: Joined *Dickinson Dees* from *Eversheds* in 1992. Now leads a team of ten pension specialists.
Personal: Cycling and socialising (sometimes simultaneously!).

KENNEDY, Patrick
Masons, Manchester (0161) 234 8234
patrick.kennedy@masons.com
Specialisation: Patrick Kennedy is a partner in *Masons* National Pensions Group, the only national pensions group based in the North West. Patrick is accustomed to giving legal advice on all aspects of pensions and is a Director of *Masons* Trustees Limit ed, the market leader separate independent trustee company in the North West. He is a full member of the Association of Pension Lawyers and has spoken on a wide variety of pensions legal topics including pensions and insolvency, Data Protection and the pensions aspects of corporate transactions.
Career: Graduated in Law from London University in 1988. Qualified as a Solicitor in 1990. Joined *Masons* in 1999.

KNIGHT, Timothy
Wrigleys, Leeds (0113) 244 6100

KNOX, Louisa
Shepherd & Wedderburn WS, Edinburgh
(0131) 228 9900
louisa.knox@shepwedd.co.uk
Specialisation: Partner in pensions group 1998. Deals with all aspects of pensions law, writes journal articles and regularly speaks at seminars.
Prof. Memberships: Committee Member of the Association of Pension Lawyers (Scottish Group), Member of the Association of Pension Lawyers.
Career: Glasgow University (LLB Hons); Qualified 1993; specialised in pensions law since then.
Personal: Hill walking; mountain biking; swimming; socialising – food and drink.

KOWALIK, Mark
CMS Cameron McKenna, London (020) 7367 3000
mak@cmck.com
Specialisation: Specialises in all aspects of law relating to occupational pension schemes, including trust law, documentation, mergers and acquisitions, privatisations, Ombudsman complaints and scheme wind ups. Handles day to day work for several major pension funds.
Prof. Memberships: Association of Pension Lawyers (Treasurer of APL 1996 to 2000, member of Education & Seminars Committee since 1993).
Career: Qualified in 1988. Whole career has been at *McKenna & Co* and then *CMS Cameron McKenna*.
Personal: Born 17 September 1962. Educated at King Henry VIII School, Coventry (1973 to 1981) and St John's College, Oxford (1982 to 1985). Interests include fine art, international athletics and football (Member of Coventry City London Supporters Club).

LAIGHT, Simon
Martineau Johnson, Birmingham (0121) 678 1334
simon.laight@martjohn.com
Specialisation: Handles all aspects of law relating to pension schemes. Acts mainly for trustees of large occupational schemes and employers. Specialises in development work for pension product providers and insurance companies. Experienced in public sector pension issues, in particular pension aspects of PFIs/PPPs.
Prof. Memberships: APL, NAPF (Midlands Region), President of Midlands Life & Pensions Society.
Career: Worked exclusively in pensions since qualifying in 1992 at *Ellison Westhorp*. Norwich Union 1994. Associate at *Martineau Johnson* in 1998 and partner in 2000.
Personal: Educated at London University (BA). Interests include family, cycling and attempts at DIY.

LESTER, Peter
Sacker & Partners, London (020) 7329 6699
peter.lester@sacker-partners.co.uk
Specialisation: Partner in pensions only law firm. Deals with all areas of pensions law with specialist expertise in relation to FURBS and multinational pension provision. Major clients include BBC and the pension funds of leading companies. Contributor to pensions periodicals and speaker at major conferences and seminars.
Prof. Memberships: Association of Pension Lawyers. For many years a co-opted member of the Parliamentary Committee of the National Association of Pension Funds.
Career: Qualified in 1968. Partner at *Walker Martineau* 1970-83. Joined *Sacker & Partners* as a Partner in 1983.
Personal: Born in 1944. Educated at Christ's Hospital 1954-62 and Birmingham University 1962-65 (LL.B). Leisure activities include golf, music, theatre and walking. Lives in Hove.

LEWIS, Roger
Eversheds, London (020) 7919 4815
lewisr@eversheds.com
Specialisation: Head of London pensions group. Advises employers and trustees in relation to all aspects of corporate pension arrangements.
Prof. Memberships: Law Society, APL, NAPF.
Career: Qualified 1978. Employed IBM 1966-68, GEC 1968-72 and Commission of the European Communities 1973-75. Joined *Lewis, Lewis & Co.* (now *Eversheds*) in 1976, becoming a partner in 1979.
Personal: Born 14th April 1945. Attended UCS 1958-63, then Balliol College, Oxford 1963-66 (BA [Hons], MA [Oxon] Physics). Governor of Hebrew University of Jerusalem, trustee of Sobell Foundation. Married with two children. Leisure interests include golf, tennis and theatre.

MARSHALL, Jane
Hammond Suddards Edge, London
(020) 7655 1000
jane.marshall@hammondse.com
Specialisation: Partner and head of pensions unit. Handles all areas of pension law, with particular emphasis on complex advice work and special projects, including scheme mergers, conflicts, privatisation, outsourcing and similar issues affecting the public sector, and pension surpluses. Handled pensions aspects of water privatisation and acted for the trustees in one of the first large surplus refund cases (£50 million). Contributor to professional journals, including 'Pensions Age', 'Professional Pensions' and 'Occupational Pensions Quarterly'. Lectures at conferences and seminars, and is a speaker on radio and TV. Editor and co-author of 'Pensions: The New Law' (Jordans 1995) and 'Pension Disputes: Prevention and Resolution' (Jordans 1998).
Prof. Memberships: Law Society, Association of Pension Lawyers and International Pensions and Employee Benefit Lawyers Association. Member of

the Regulatory Sub-Committee of National Association of Pension Funds. OPAS adviser.
Career: Qualified in 1978. Worked abroad after qualifying. Joined *Lovell White & King* in 1980 to specialise in pensions. Founder partner with pensions specialists *Ellison Westhorp* and became partner with *Hammond Suddards* following its merger with *Ellison Westhorp* in 1994, becoming head of the firm's pension practice.
Personal: Born 17th December 1953. Attended March High School for Girls to 1972, then Dundee University 1972-76 (First Class Honours). Leisure interests include gardening, antiques and local history. Mother of four. Lives in Little Bromley, near Colchester.

MASSARANO SALT, Vikki
DLA, Leeds (08700) 111111

McKENNA, Catherine M P
Hammond Suddards Edge, Leeds (0113) 284 7000
catherine.mckenna@hammondse.com
Specialisation: Partner in pensions department. All work relating to occupational pension schemes. General advice work, including documentation, sales and acquisitions, mergers, insolvency advice, FURBS and trusteeship. Regular speaker at seminars and co-author of 'Pensions – The New Law' (Jordans).
Prof. Memberships: Association of Pension Lawyers, National Association of Pension Funds, Associate of the Pensions Management Institute, Society of Pension Consultants.
Career: Educated at Nottingham University (LLB Hons) and Chester Law School (2nd class honours). Qualified 1989. Joined *Alsop Wilkinson* in Manchester and moved to *Hammond Suddards*, Leeds in January 1994. Committee member NE NAPF and Chairman NE PMI.
Personal: Born 1964. Interests include socialising, food, wine, watching sport. Lives in Ilkley.

MEEKS, Alastair
Pinsent Curtis Biddle, London (020) 7606 9301
alastair.meeks@pinsents.com
Specialisation: Advising trustees and employers on all aspects of the law relating to occupational pension schemes. Clients include Charter plc and ITN.
Prof. Memberships: APL, Associate of the Pensions Management Institute.
Career: Joined *Biddle* on qualification 1992. Became a partner in 1997.
Publications: Assistant Editor of the 'Occupational Pensions Law Reports', Legal Contributor to 'Occupational Pensions' magazine.
Personal: Born 16 November 1967. BA (Hons) Law Durham 1985-88. Lives in London.

MILES, Helen
DLA, Birmingham (08700) 111111

MILTON, Kevin
Wragge & Co, Birmingham (0870) 903 1000

MOORE, Nigel
CMS Cameron McKenna, London
(020) 7367 3000
Specialisation: Partner and Head of Pensions Team. Main area of practice is pensions. Work includes advising on administration of pension schemes; drafting trust deeds and rules; advising on pension aspects of mergers and acquisitions; advising on mergers of schemes; handling litigation in employment tribunals, High Court and European Court of Justice. Advises on investigations by the Pensions Ombudsman. Organises and speaks on trustee training courses. Also handles employment law. Acted in Coloroll's application to the European Court. Speaking experience includes NAPF training courses, APL annual conferences and commercial conferences.
Prof. Memberships: Law Society, City of London Solicitors Company, Association of Pension Lawyers (Chairman of International Committee). OPAS adviser. Member of Training Standing Group of NAPF.
Career: Qualified 1986. Articled at *Radcliffes & Co* 1984-86. Joined *McKenna & Co* (now *CMS Cameron McKenna*) in 1986. Partner 1994.
Personal: Born 13th June 1962. Attended St Albans School 1973-80, Warwick University 1980-83, College of Law Chancery Lane 1983-84 and City of London Polytechnic (MA in Business Law) 1984-86. Leisure interests include golf and football. Lives in Welwyn Garden City.

MULLEN, Chris
Pinsent Curtis Biddle, London (020) 7606 9301
chris.mullen@pinsents.com
Specialisation: Partner in and head of *Pinsent Curtis Biddle* 's 20-lawyer strong Pensions Group. Advises companies and scheme trustees on all aspects of pensions law, relating principally to occupational pension schemes. Heavily involved in complex mergers and pension scheme reorganisations; negotiations concerning benefit improvements allied to surplus refunds; advising trustees and employers on member disputes and Ombudsman complaints; documentation advice, drafting and large-value transaction advice. Specialist knowlege of data protection issues for pension schemes. Clients include Heinz, Lloyd's, Costain Group plc, Vivendi Group, Air France and the NSPCC as well as other UK and US Law firms seeking specialist pensions support.
Prof. Memberships: APL, Member of APL Education Committee, City of London Solicitors Company. Editor of 'Pension Lawyer' magazine. Conference Speaker for IBC, NAPF, APL.
Career: Qualified in 1986 after articles at *Biddle* . Became a partner in 1990. Head of pensions group since 1998. Non-executive member of *Pinsent Curtis Biddle* board.
Personal: Born 11th September 1960. Educated at Jesus College, Cambridge 1979-82 (MA in Law). Married, with three children, a beagle and a swimming pool.

MURRAY, John
Nabarro Nathanson, London (020) 7524 6000
Specialisation: Advises employers, trustees and others on all aspects of pensions law; specialises in scheme re-organisation and documentation for approved and unapproved schemes; experienced in pensions litigation and pensions ombudsman enquiries.
Prof. Memberships: Law Society, APL, IPEBLA, former member Association of Pensioneer Trustees Committee 1991-97.
Career: Leeds University (1976 LL.B). Qualified and joined *Nabarro Nathanson* 1979. Partner 1986.
Personal: Born 1953. Resides London.

PAYNE, Kate
DLA, Sheffield (08700) 111111

PEARSON, John
Lovells, London (020) 7296 2000
john.pearson@lovells.com
Specialisation: Partner in pensions and employment group. Advises employers, trustees and others on all aspects of pensions law and documentation relating to occupational and personal pension schemes and pension products; reorganisations; offshore schemes; pensions aspects of company sales, purchases and insolvencies; and pensions litigation. Acted for Mirror Group Newspapers post-Maxwell in sorting out its pensions problems. Has given many pensions related talks, including one in French.
Prof. Memberships: Law Society, City of London Solicitors Company, Association of Pension Lawyers, International Pension and Employee Benefit Lawyers Association.
Career: Qualified in 1971. Joined *Lovells* and became a partner in 1986.
Personal: Attended King's College, London (LLB 1968).

PETHERAM, Claire
Linklaters, London (020) 7456 3676
claire.petheram@linklaters.com
Specialisation: Employment and employee benefits group. Specialises in all aspects of pension law including pension scheme mergers, pension aspects of commercial transactions, trust law queries relating to pension schemes, investment management issues and plain English documentation.
Career: 1997 to date: Partner, *Linklaters*, employment and employee benefits; 1989-1997: Assistant solicitor, *Linklaters*; 1987-1989: Trainee solicitor, *Nabarro Nathanson*. College of Law, Lancaster Gate; University of Leeds, LLB (Hons).

PITTAWAY, Ian
Sacker & Partners, London (020) 7615 9506
ian.pittaway@sacker-partners.co.uk
Specialisation: Partner in specialist pensions law firm. Covers all aspects of pension law including acting as trustee, arbitrator and expert witness. Author of numerous articles and lectures. Former Chairman and Secretary of APL.
Prof. Memberships: Law Society, Association of Pension Lawyers, Justice.
Personal: Born 28th July 1956. Attended the University of Hull 1974-77. Leisure interests include gardening, wine and reading.

POLLARD, David
Freshfields Bruckhaus Deringer, London London
(020) 7832 7060
david.pollard@freshfields.com
Specialisation: Partner in Employment, Pensions and Benefits Department, and group of over 30 lawyers covering the whole range of pensions, employment and benefits work. Acted for trustees in Drexel pension case. Author of book 'Corporate Insolvency: Employment and Pension Rights' and contributor of chapters to Tolley's 'Employment Law' and Tolley's 'Insolvency Law'. Co-Editor 'Trust Law International' magazine. Editor of 'Guide to the Pensions Act 1995' book. Editorial Board, Occupational Pensions Law Reports. Main Committee of the APL. Awarded APL 'Wallace Prize' in 1998.

POWELL, Andrew M
Hammond Suddards Edge, London
(020) 7655 1000
andrew.powell@hammondse.com
Specialisation: Partner in pensions unit. Handles all aspects of pensions work, including inter alia documentation, deal based work, financial products, mergers and other complex advice work. Contributor to Trust Law International, Accountancy Age, Acquisitions Monthly and others. Co-author of 'Managing a Company Pension Scheme'. Contributor to 'Pensions: The New Law' (Jordans 1995). Editor 'Pension Law Reports' (IDS). Specialist editor for pensions to the Journal for Alternative Dispute Resolution.
Prof. Memberships: Law Society, Institute of Directors, the Society for Advanced Legal Studies.
Career: Qualified in 1980. Articled *Granville West Chivers & Morgan.* Then in-house lawyer covering pensions work for DHSS; adviser to OPB, NHS superannuation fund; responsible for pensions work at *Denton Hall Burgin & Warrens* before becoming a partner at *Ellison Westhorp* in 1990. Joined *Hammond Suddards* in 1994. Former main committee member of Association of Pension Lawyers; member of APL investment sub-committee, IPEBLA and Director of Trustee Corporation Limited.
Personal: Born 26th January 1955. Attended King Henry VIII Grammar School to 1975. Graduated from the University of Wales in 1978; then attended Lancaster Gate College of Law. Lives in Harrow-on-the-Hill.

QUARRELL, John
Nabarro Nathanson, London (020) 7524 6000
Specialisation: Partner and head of pensions department. Work covers all aspects relating to occupational and personal pension schemes, including investment legalities, overseas provision, equality issues, litigation matters and dispute resolution. Acts for and advises most leading firms of accountants, many pension providers and a number of firms of pensions consultants and actuaries. Has acted in a large number of leading cases. Author of numerous articles and papers. Lectures at home and abroad. Advises Russian government.

RAMSHAW, Simon
Pinsent Curtis Biddle, Birmingham
(0121) 200 1050
simon.ramshaw@pinsents.com
Specialisation: Partner and Regional Head of Pensions Group. Main area of practice is pensions, covering documentation, transactional work, scheme mergers, reconstructions and wind-ups, insolvency advice and independent trusteeship. Has handled several major scheme mergers and acted as independent trustee to schemes run by a part of a nationalised industry, a national clothing company, two quoted public companies and a professional practice which is a world leader in its field. Author of various articles for publications issued by pension consultancies, and of a variety of easy-to-read Technical Guides issued by the firm. Regular lecturer for Professional Associations and pension consultancies. Organiser of and speaker at various trustee training courses.
Prof. Memberships: NAPF, APL, IPEBLA, Law Society.
Career: Qualified 1981, working at *Robert Muckle* from 1979 to 1983. Then joined *Edge Ellison*, becoming a Partner in 1986. Joined *Pinsent Curtis Biddle* in 2000.
Personal: Born 28th January 1958. Attended Newcastle upon Tyne University, 1975-78.

RAWNSLEY, Rachel
Addleshaw Booth & Co, Leeds (0113) 209 2000
Specialisation: Partner in pensions department, commercial group. Advises corporate clients and trustees on all aspects of ongoing pension schemes, setting up new schemes, winding up and merging established schemes. Advises insolvency practitioners, including on independent statutory trusteeships.
Prof. Memberships: Association of Pensions Lawyers, National Association of Pension Funds.
Career: Joined the firm in January 1993. Partner in 1997.
Publications: Co-author of the pensions chapter of 'The Business Client Handbook' (Sweet & Maxwell). Editor of 'An Introduction to Pensions Law' written and published by the University of Northumbria.
Personal: Educated at Cambridge University 1983-86 (MA in Law). Lives in Ilkley.

RICCIO, Maria
Blake Lapthorn, Fareham (01489) 579 990

RIDLER, Mark
Hammond Suddards Edge, Leeds (0113) 284 7000
mark.ridler@hammondse.com
Specialisation: Pensions law. Experience includes scheme documentation, trustee and employer advisory work, scheme mergers and legal due diligence and drafting and negotiating documentation for company and business sales and purchases.
Prof. Memberships: Association of Pensions Lawyers.
Career: Qualified with *Bevan Ashford* in 1986. Moved to *Kershaw Tudor*, Sheffield in 1988 and became a partner in 1991. Became a partner in *Irwin Mitchell* in 1994 upon the merger with *Kershaw Tudor*. Joined *Hammond Suddards* in September 1999. Regular speaker at seminars.
Personal: Married with two children. Interests include radio controlled aircraft and jazz.

ROGERS, Anna
Rowe & Maw, London (020) 7248 4282
arogers@roweandmawe.co.uk
Specialisation: Partner in pensions department. Specialises in pensions work including scheme mergers and demergers and all aspects of advisory and documentation work for trustees and employers in defined benefit, defined contribution, hybrid and umbrella occupational pension schemes of all sizes.
Prof. Memberships: Association of Pension Lawyers, Fellow and Council Member of Pensions Management Institute.
Career: Articled at *Nabarro Nathanson.* Qualified in 1985. Became a partner at *Rowe & Maw* in 1989.
Personal: Born 15th May 1961. Educated at Sheffield High School for Girls 1972-79 and Keble College, Oxford 1979-82 (MA Jurisprudence). Lives in London. Enjoys reading, cinema, music and travel.

RYLAND, Glyn
Wragge & Co, Birmingham (0870) 903 1000

SAEEDI, Terry
Hammond Suddards Edge, Leeds (0113) 284 7000
terry.saeedi@hammondse.com
Specialisation: All aspects of pensions law and practice including general advisory work, scheme establishment and re-organisations, insolvency advice, transaction support, documentation. Director of *Hammond Suddards* Pension Trust Ltd (independent trustee company). Regular speaker at seminars and co-author of *Naborro Nathanson's* 'A Guide to UK Pensions Law'.
Prof. Memberships: Association of Pension Lawyers, Pensions Management Institute, Society of Pension Consultants (Yorkshire Group Committee Member), Society of Computers and Law.
Career: Analyst/Programmer with Sheffield Local Education Authority 1988 to 1990. Trainee and assistant solicitor with *Dibb Lupton Broomhead* 1990-1995. *Nabarro Nathanson* 1995-1997. Joined *Hammond Suddards* in September 1997. Partner on 1 May 2000.
Personal: BA (Hons) Law, Msc Software Engineering. Qualified 1992.

SAMSWORTH, Jane
Lovells, London (020) 7296 2000
jane.samsworth@lovells.com
Specialisation: Partner advising on all aspects of pension law and documentation, including establishment, management and termination of occupational pension schemes, (both approved and unapproved and personal pensions); reorganisation and scheme mergers; pension aspects of company sales and acquisitions; pension litigation; pensions in insolvency; advising clients in their relations with the regulatory authorities including the preparation of submissions to the Pensions Ombudsman. Co-author of 'Guide to the Pensions Act 1995'; regular contributor to seminars and conferences on pension issues.
Prof. Memberships: Fellow Pensions Management Institute; Member of Investment Sub-Committee of Association of Pension Lawyers, immediate past Honorary Secretary and former member of its main committee and its Legal and Parliamentary and Education and Training Sub-Committees; Member of the Council of OPAS Ltd; Council Member and President SPC; Law Society; City of London Solicitors; Director *Lovells* Pension Trustees Ltd.
Career: Qualified 1978. 1978-83 Greater London Council. 1983-87 British Telecommunications plc; 1987 joined *Lovells*; partner 1991.

SAUNDERS, Carolyn
Taylor Joynson Garrett, London (020) 7300 7000

SCHAFFER, Daniel
Freshfields Bruckhaus Deringer, London
(020) 7936 4000
daniel.schaffer@freshfields.com
Specialisation: Partner in employment, pensions and benefits group. Pensions. Advises on all aspects of pensions.
Prof. Memberships: Association of Pension Lawyers (Member of International Committee). Sir John Vinelott Trust Law Committee. Sat on Financial Law Panel working party on 'commercial dealings with trustees'. Regular speaker.
Career: Joined *Freshfields* in 1988. Part-time tutor in trusts at LSE (1987-88), Merton College, Oxford (1987-90) and Balliol College, Oxford (1988-92).
Personal: Born 1963. Educated at Haberdashers' Aske's School, Elstree 1971-82, Bristol University 1983-86 (LLB, Simmons Scholar) and Merton College, Oxford 1986-87.(BCL 1st Class). Leisure pursuits include travelling in France. Fluent in French; working knowledge of Spanish.

SCHOLEFIELD, Stephen
Addleshaw Booth & Co, Manchester
(0161) 934 6436
scs@addleshaw-booth.co.uk
Specialisation: Advises on all aspects of pensions law, including the pensions aspects of corporate disposals and acquisitions, pension scheme mergers, trustee issues, contentious matters and documentation.
Prof. Memberships: Association of Pension Lawyers.
Career: Qualified as a solicitor in 1996 and joined the firm in 1997.
Personal: Educated at Cambridge University. Interests include eating, sleeping and drinking.

SCOTT, Harry
Mills & Reeve, Norwich (01603) 693 249
harry.scott@mills-reeve.com
Specialisation: Pensions i.e. law and practice relating to occupational pension schemes including documentation, advice, Pensions Ombudsman Cases and acting as a pension scheme trustee through *Mills & Reeve*'s corporate trustee, Francis House Trustees Limited. Full member of the Association of Pension Lawyers.

SERES, Jonathan
Sacker & Partners, London (020) 7329 6699
jonathan.seres@sacker-partners.co.uk
Specialisation: Senior Partner of specialist pensions law firm. Experienced in all aspects of pension schemes, covering establishment, alteration, merger, booklets, related employment law, Financial Services and Markets Act work, common investment funds and investment management and custody agreements. Advises employers, trustees, trade unions and charities. Acted in application to the ECJ in the Coloroll matter (*Sacker & Partners* were acting for the four classes of male beneficiaries). Acted for GEC Plan in 1999 on £2.5bn separation of MES. Author of 'Pensions: A Practical Guide' (4th edition 1997, FT Law & Tax, 450 pages). Appeared as pensions tax expert on Channel 4's City Programme. Now leads the firm of 36 specialist pensions lawyers.
Prof. Memberships: Association of Pension Lawyers, National Association of Pension Funds, Society of Pension Consultants, Law Society.
Personal: Born 13th June 1945. Oxford University PPE (Hons) 1966. Leisure interests include sailing, history and charities. Lives in London.

SHELLEY, Daniel
Pinsent Curtis Biddle, Birmingham
(0121) 200 1050
daniel.shelley@pinsents.com
Specialisation: All aspects of pension law.
Prof. Memberships: Association of Pension Lawyers.
Career: Articles – *Slaughter and May*; *Pinsent Curtis Biddle* – partner 1995.
Personal: Born 1958.

SHERWIN, Nick
Clifford Chance, London (020) 7600 1000
nick.sherwin@cliffordchance.com
Specialisation: Partner specialising in pensions, also widely experienced in taxation matters, particularly employee share schemes and other benefits.
Career: Manchester Grammar School; St John's College, Cambridge (MA Hons 1982); University of Pennsylvania (LLM 1983); ATII, Gilbert Burr Medal Winner. Articled *Clifford-Turner*; assistant solicitor *Clifford-Turner/Clifford Chance* 1986-1993; made partner *Clifford Chance* 1993; Chairman Investment Sub-Committee of Association of Pension Lawyers; former committee member of Association of Pension Lawyers; former chairman Legislative & Parliamentary Sub-Committee of Association of Pension Lawyers; former NAPF Case Law Standing Group member. Member Pensions Research Accountants Group, Associate Member SIPP Provider Group.
Personal: Born 1961; resides London; married with two daughters.

SLOAN, Derek S
Allen & Overy, London (020) 7330 3000
derek.sloan@allenovery.com
Specialisation: Partner and head of employment, pensions and incentives department. Practice covers all areas of pensions work including establishing, reorganising, merging and terminating schemes, conversion of schemes from defined benefit to defined contribution, investment management and custody arrangements, the pensions implications of business sales, reorganisations and insolvencies, funding issues and equal treatment. Regular speaker at conferences.
Prof. Memberships: Law Society, Association of Pension Lawyers, Chairman of APL Legislative and Parliamentary sub-committee, Pensions Research Accountants Group.
Career: Qualified 1973, having joined *Allen & Overy* in 1971. Became a partner in 1977.
Personal: Attended Oxford University 1967-70 (BA Jurisprudence). Born 1948.

SMITH, Stephanie
Travers Smith Braithwaite, London
(020) 7295 3000
Stephanie.Smith@TraversSmith.com
Specialisation: Partner in pensions department. Handles all aspects of pensions law. Regular public speaker.
Prof. Memberships: Association of Pensions Lawyers.
Career: Qualified in 1986. Joined *Travers Smith Braithwaite* in 1993, becoming a partner in 1994.
Personal: Born 22 March 1962. Holds an LLB from Queen Mary College, London (1983). Lives in London.

SOUTHERN, Steve
Hammond Suddards Edge, Manchester
(0161) 830 5172
steve.southern@hammondse.com
Specialisation: The law and practice relating to occupational pension schemes and other forms of retirement pensions in the UK. Includes advice to employers and trustees, transactional work, mergers, trusteeship, documentation.
Prof. Memberships: Association of Pension Lawyers and Associate of the Pensions Management Institute.
Career: Qualified in September 1996 and became an Associate of Pensions Management Institute in 1998.
Personal: Football, music.

STANNARD, Paul
Travers Smith Braithwaite, London
(020) 7295 3000
Paul.Stannard@TraversSmith.com
Specialisation: Partner in pensions department. All aspects of pensions law.
Prof. Memberships: Fellow of the Pensions Management Institute.
Career: Qualified 1982. Joined *Travers Smith Braithwaite* as a partner in 1989.
Personal: Born 1957.

STRACHAN, Russell
Lovells, London (020) 7296 2000
russell.strachan@lovells.com
Specialisation: Pension law in all its applications, particularly: negotiating scheme reorganisations and mergers, benefit design, sales and acquisitions, conflicts of interest and trustee problems, winding-up, equal pay and contentious issues, investment and regulatory matters, scheme documentation and member communications. Clients include multi-national and UK employers, trustees, insurance companies, investment companies and professional advisers.
Prof. Memberships: Law Society, Association of Pension Lawyers, National Association of Pension Funds; Pension Research Accountants Group.
Career: Articled *Lovells* qualified 1970; partner 1975.

TALMAN, Iain
Morison Bishop, Glasgow (0141) 248 4672
iain.talman@morisonbishop.co.uk
Specialisation: Partner in corporate division (head of pensions unit). Accredited by The Law Society of Scotland as a specialist in pensions law. All aspects of pensions law and practice including pensioneer trusteeships, independent trusteeships through directorship of Mitre Pensions Ltd which acts in relation to a number of schemes including the 6,000 member Rosyth Royal Dockyard Pension Scheme. Acted in Mirror Group Pensions and Lilley Group, Clydesdale Group and Capital Foods independent trusteeships cases. Legal adviser to The Law Society of Scottish Staff Pension Scheme. Author and speaker.
Prof. Memberships: Law Society of Scotland, Association of Pension Lawyers, Association of Pensioneer Trustees, Local Member of the Scottish Group of the Pensions Management Institute, Actuarial Society of Glasgow (Life and Pensions Group). Pensioneer Trustee on the OPRA Panel. Scottish Legal panel member for Occupational Pensions Defence Union.
Career: Qualified in 1976. Partner in 1978. Past chairman, Scottish Group of Association of Pension Lawyers, PMI Working Group on Pensions and Divorce; convener of Law Society Pensions Accreditation panel; convener of Law Society Working Party on Pensions.
Personal: Born 18 July 1952. Leisure interests include movies, people, travel and ardent liquors.

THOMAS-GREEN, Susan
Pinsent Curtis Biddle, Leeds (0113) 244 5000
susan.thomas-green@pinsents.com
Specialisation: Partner in Pensions Group and head of Leeds team. Acts for trustees and employers in relation to scheme mergers (£150 million fund last year). Director of Pinsents Trustees Ltd – recent trustee appointments include Hydra Tools International, Hadleigh, Universal Bulk Handling, Cintel International; Public Sector Pension Arrangements, Pensions Disputes.
Prof. Memberships: Association of Pensions Lawyers, Pensions Management Institute, Society of Pensions Consultants.
Career: Partner *Pinsent Curtis Biddle* and Leeds head of Pensions 1994 to date: *Dundas & Wilson* 1991-94 (established Pensions Unit), *Freshfields* 1987-91. *Nicholson Graham & Jones* 1985-86.
Personal: University of Leicester. Golf, astronomy, swimming and good holidays. Married.

THURSTON SMITH, Martin
Tods Murray WS, Edinburgh (0131) 226 4771
martin.thurston.smith@todsmurray.com
Specialisation: Partner in Corporate Department. Specialises in collective investment schemes and financial services. Also handles pension schemes, corporate and commercial work including other commercial applications of trusts.
Prof. Memberships: Law Society of Scotland; Association of Pension Lawyers.
Career: Joined *Tods Murray* 1974. Qualified 1977. Partner 1978.
Personal: Born 1951. Attended The Edinburgh Academy 1957-69 and Christ's College Cambridge 1970-1974. Leisure: family, hillwalking, wine, classical music and jazz. Fluent in German and French.

TIER, Sarah
Sacker & Partners, London (020) 7329 6699

TIMMINS, Jacqueline
Eversheds, Leeds (0113) 743 0399
jacquelinetimmins@eversheds.com
Specialisation: Partner in employment department. Pensions law including scheme mergers, amalgamations, establishment of schemes, documentation, trusteeship matters, sales and acquisitions and dispute resolution. Presented at APL and external seminars.
Prof. Memberships: Full member APL, secretary to North West APL, secretary and committee member of Manchester NAPF Group and a member of SPC.
Career: Qualified in 1991. Joined *Eversheds* in 1995.
Personal: Born 1965. Married, two sons. Leisure interests include wine (vineyard partner 'La Chevalerie' in the Loire Valley), hill walking and windsurfing.

TROTTER, Peter
MacRoberts, Glasgow (0141) 332 9988
peter.trotter@macroberts.co.uk
Specialisation: Partner and head of pensions and employee benefits group. Pensions law (including professional independent trusteeship) and Employee Share and Management Incentive Schemes.
Prof. Memberships: Associate of Pensions Management Institute (NAPF Prize and Scottish Group Prize 1993); member of Society of Share Scheme Practitioners and Association of Pension Lawyers; PMI Scottish Group Committee member; OPAS adviser.
Career: LLB (Birm); LLB (Edin); Dip LP (Strath); APMI; partner, pensions and employee benefits group, *MacRoberts* 1998.
Publications: Various newspaper and magazine articles.

TURNBULL, Andrew
Walker Morris, Leeds (0113) 283 2500
Specialisation: Practice covers the full range of pension work and includes creation and administration of schemes, scheme mergers, transactions and wind ups whether acting as an individual independent trustee or through Walker Morris Trustees Limited.
Prof. Memberships: North Eastern Group of the Association of Pension Lawyers.
Career: Qualified 1983. Joined *Walker Morris* after qualification becoming a partner in 1985.
Personal: Born 19th April 1957. Educated at Shrewsbury and Birmingham University. Interests include golf, tennis and keep fit.

WEST, Robert
Baker & McKenzie, London (020) 7919 1000
robert.west@bakernet.com
Specialisation: Partner in pensions department. Principal area of practice involves advising on all legal aspects of pensions including trust aspects, litigation, surpluses, sales and purchases, drafting and advice to independent trustees. Other area of work is employee benefits and share schemes. Acted in AMP litigation South West Trains v Wightman, National Bus, The Times Pension Fund litigation, the Drexel Pension Scheme litigation and in the sex discrimination case in the European Court, Neath v Hugh Steeper. Contributor on pensions to Butterworths' Legal Service and author of articles for Pensions World and Pensions Management. Addressed many conferences in UK, USA and Canada.
Prof. Memberships: Law Society, Chairman of Association of Pension Lawyers, former Secretary of International Employee Benefits Association, Member of the Legal Advice Committee of the Occupational Pensions Advisory Service.
Career: Qualified in 1978. Joined *Baker & McKenzie* in 1982 and became a partner in 1985.
Personal: Born 1st January 1952. Attended Maidenhead Grammar School 1963-71 and Clare College, Cambridge 1971-74. Leisure pursuits include sport and archaeology. Lives in Wargrave, Berks.

WHITE, Andrew
Rowe & Maw, London (020) 7782 8632
awhite@roweandmaw.co.uk
Specialisation: Partner in pensions department. All aspects of law relating to company and personal pension schemes. Also handles life insurance, advising insurance companies on life policies and other products. Author of 'Pensions Issues in Mergers and Acquisitions' (FT Law and Tax, 2nd edition 1996); writes a regular monthly article in 'PLC Magazine'. Frequent speaker at conferences.
Prof. Memberships: Law Society, formerly a member of the Main Committee of the Association of Pension Lawyers. Former Chairman of Association's Legal and Parliamentary sub-committee. Current Chairman of Association's Divorce sub-committee.
Career: Qualified 1974. Joined *Rowe & Maw* 1977, becoming a partner in 1979.
Personal: Born 1st January 1950. Attended Manchester Grammar School 1961-68, then University College, Oxford, 1968-72. Leisure pursuits include reading. Lives in London.

WOMERSLEY, Mark
Osborne Clarke, Bristol (0117) 917 3000

WRIGHT, David
DLA, Liverpool (08700) 111111

WYMAN, Michael
Simmons & Simmons, London (020) 7628 2020
michael.wyman@simmons-simmons.com
Specialisation: Partner in pensions group, which covers the whole range of pension work.
Prof. Memberships: Member of European Subcommittee, Society of Pension Consultants. Previously a member of the Legislative Sub-Committee of the Association of Pension Lawyers.
Career: *Slaughter & May*, 1976-1985. With *Simmons & Simmons* since 1985.
Publications: Contributor to 'The Acquisition of Private Companies and Business Assets' 1989, 1992 and 1997; 'Pensions: The New Regime', 1998; Sweet & Maxwell's 'The Law of Pension Schemes', 1998-, and Joint Ventures and Shareholders' Agreements', 2000.

PERSONAL INJURY

RESEARCH APPROVED BY BMRB: *For this edition,* Chambers' *researchers conducted 6,552 interviews – 4,419 with law firms, 554 with barristers and 1,579 with clients.*

The validity of the research was scrutinised by BMRB International, who audited both the methodology and the results at our offices in July 2001. They interviewed Chambers' *researchers and cross-checked sample interviews. Details of the audit appear on page 7.*

LONDON

MAINLY CLAIMANT

PERSONAL INJURY: MAINLY CLAIMANT • London	Ptnrs	Assts
1 Leigh, Day & Co	3	10
Russell Jones & Walker	9	11
Thompsons	4	18
2 Evill and Coleman	4	4
Irwin Mitchell	3	4
Pattinson & Brewer	5	14
3 Anthony Gold	3	4
Field Fisher Waterhouse	3	5
Hodge Jones & Allen	8	6
Rowley Ashworth	5	11
Stewarts	5	7
4 Bolt Burdon	4	6
Levenes	5	20
OH Parsons & Partners	n/a	n/a

LEADING INDIVIDUALS	
1 **DAY Martyn** Leigh, Day & Co	**ETTINGER Colin** Irwin Mitchell
LEE Terry Evill and Coleman	**MCCARTHY Frances** Pattinson & Brewer
WALKER Ian Russell Jones & Walker	
2 **ALLEN Patrick** Hodge Jones & Allen	**CAHILL John** Stewarts
KITSON Paul Russell Jones & Walker	**LAWTON Anthony** Thompsons
MARSHALL David Anthony Gold	**MEERAN Richard** Leigh, Day & Co
NELSON-JONES Rodney Field Fisher Waterhouse	
PARKER Alison Bolt Burdon	

This book is the product of 6,552 1/2-hour interviews. See p.7 for BMRB audit.
Within each band, firms are listed alphabetically. *See individuals' profiles p.644*

Leigh, Day & Co (see firm details p.1036) An "*imaginative and brave*" practice, specialising in complex liability and causation claims, with a partial focus on foreign jurisdiction work. The esteemed **Richard Meeran** (see p.648) continues his involvement in the Cape asbestos case on behalf of South African miners, as well as a mercury poisoning case against Thor Chemicals, also based in South Africa. "*Great campaigner*" **Martyn Day** is also involved in a number of overseas asbestos cases, and is seen by many as a "*one-off*" and "*one of the greats.*" **Clients:** South African miners.

Russell Jones & Walker (see firm details p.1116) Despite a continued increase in private client instruction, trade unions still account for 90% of a practice that has "*enormous strength in depth.*" The firm has a specialised employers' liability unit, and while RTA is the biggest area, RSI, stress and asbestos cases also feature heavily. **Ian Walker** (see p.651) ("*insurers are afraid of him*") is VP of the Bodily Injury Claims Management Association and is senior fellow of the College of Personal Injury Law. **Paul Kitson** (see p.647) was also singled out to our researchers as "*a quality member of the team.*" The team has appeared on numerous criminal compensation appeals over the past year. **Clients:** Police Federation; Iron and Steel Trades Confederation; IPMS; PCS; Royal College of Nursing; TSSA; USDAW.

Thompsons Although the firm has suffered a number of recent departures, it remains the largest of all trade union law firms, and researchers were left in no doubt that this is still "*undeniably a force to be reckoned with.*" **Anthony Lawton** has moved from the firm's Birmingham office to London, and maintains his reputation as a leading player in the field. The team led the campaign to secure compensation for asbestos victims in the aftermath of the collapse of Iron Trades Holdings, and has also advised on the reform of the Criminal Injuries Compensation Authority scheme. The firm won £3.2 million in Wales for Unison members last year and £900,000 for NUJ members in the last 21 months. **Clients:** Unison; AEEU; GMB; PCS; Bectu; Aslef.

Evill and Coleman (see firm details p.952) The team maintains an emphasis on tackling high value claims cases, notably in matters concerning employer's liability. Asbestosis and other chest diseases are areas of niche expertise, as are sporting cases. The firm receives referrals from a wide range of sources, including doctors and other solicitors, and has recovered around £10 million this year. The "*fantastic*" **Terry Lee** (see p.168) has "*a deservedly good reputation*" among his peers. **Clients:** Private clients.

Irwin Mitchell (see firm details p.1009) A firm which does the range of PI work from routine fast track to catastrophic and is consequently seen to "*bridge the gap*" between the niche and union firms. The firm specialises in spinal and head injuries, as well as occupational diseases, 25% of which are union referrals. The firm is part of a new British mesothelioma interest group and also offers financial/employment advice to brain injured clients. **Colin Ettinger** (see p.646) was decribed to our researchers as a "*class act.*" **Clients:** MSF; UNIFY; Royal College of Nursing; BMA.

Pattinson & Brewer (see firm details p.1091) A solid practice with a strong employment department, which provides a comprehensive service to its almost exclusively union clientele. Headed by the "*seasoned*" **Frances McCarthy** (see p.648) (President of APIL), the firm has a growing occupational diseases department. McCarthy has been involved in the Woolf Working Party and has just updated the protocol in the area of occupational disease. Aside from union referrals, the practice also instructs clients from Accident Line. **Clients:** TGWU; RMT; GMB; PCS; UNIFY; CWU.

Anthony Gold (see firm details p.861) The team undertakes a wide range of personal injury claims on behalf of claimants, including brain and spinal injuries, stress at work cases and actions against the police. With no trade union or legal expense insurer clients, the team acts largely for individuals referred by specialist agencies, including Headway, RoadPeace and the London Cycling Campaign. **David Marshall** (see p.648) "*has a fantastic brain*" and "*knows all there is to know about costs.*" **Clients:** Private clients.

Field Fisher Waterhouse (see firm details p.957) One of the leading asbestos disease claims practices in the country, it also covers a variety of transport cases, and is involved in a number of train disaster steering committees. The "*extremely thorough*" **Rodney Nelson-Jones** (see p.648) is a recognised authority on asbestos-related chest diseases. **Clients:** Individuals and institutions.

Hodge Jones & Allen (see firm details p.998) Historically a legal aid practice, the team is now said to be *"doing a fine job on conditional fees."* Having undergone a programme of steady expansion, the practice handles fast-track cases as well as a number of high profile multi-track claims. The firm has a devoted multi-party unit that has recently been involved in Gulf War syndrome and sheep dip claims. Vice President of APIL, **Patrick Allen** (see p.644) continues to command great respect in the market. **Clients:** Private clients.

Rowley Ashworth Predominantly performing trade union-referred PI work, this is a practice with an established stable of headline clients. The past year has seen work on a substantial number of WRULD and asbestosis cases. Although not possessing the high profile of some of its competitors, the firm is reckoned to score more than its share of successes. This year, the team won a notable victory in the House of Lords, recovering £935,000 in a PI case involving a minor. **Clients:** GMB; TGWU; USDAW.

Stewarts (see firm details p.1144) A specialist PI practice headed by the widely admired **John Cahill,** (see p.645) who is chairman of the London branch of Headway, and specialises in head and spinal injuries. Other areas of expertise include abuse litigation, particularly for people with learning difficulties. An increasing caseload of multiparty actions has included the Trilucent breast implant litigation and the representation of the English victims of a coach crash in Nevada. **Clients:** Private clients.

Bolt Burdon Commended to our researchers as a *"good value"* outfit, this Islington-based practice acts exclusively for accident victims, with a particular focus on toxic industrial disease cases, fatal accidents and head injuries. The firm also works on some injuries abroad, and has become a popular destination for referrals. Clients regard **Alison Parker** as an *"insightful, helpful and sympathetic"* practitioner. **Clients:** Private clients.

Levenes (see firm details p.1039) Large team, noted for its high volume of cases, which is said by peers to be *"excellent at what they do."* Working for legal expense insurers and private clients, the firm specialises in RTA and accidents at work, as well as a select number of catastrophic claims. **Clients:** Direct Line; DAS legal expense insurers.

OH Parsons & Partners (see firm details p.1090) *"Traditional"* trade union firm, and one of the oldest of its type in the country. 70% of the team's workload involves straightforward accident claims, with the balance being taken up with disease work, such as VWF, emphysema and mesothelioma cases. Frequently acting for workers in the shipbuilding industry, the firm also has niche expertise in airport-related work. **Clients:** TGWU; UCAT; ISTC; GMB; UNISON.

MAINLY DEFENDANT

	PERSONAL INJURY: MAINLY DEFENDANT • London	Ptnrs	Assts
1	Barlow Lyde & Gilbert	4	26
	Beachcroft Wansbroughs	13	40
	Berrymans Lace Mawer	12	35
2	Kennedys	14	53
	Vizards, Staples & Bannisters	13	31
3	Badhams	n/a	n/a
	Davies Arnold Cooper	3	7
	Hextall Erskine	7	13
	Watmores	8	1

	LEADING INDIVIDUALS
1	**DICKINSON Graham** Barlow Lyde & Gilbert
2	**CHERRY Anthony** Beachcroft Wansbroughs
	RENOUF Terence Berrymans Lace Mawer
	STAPLES Martin Vizards, Staples & Bannisters
3	**IRVINE Mariel** Kennedys
	SLESS Tania Beachcroft Wansbroughs

This book is the product of 6,552 1/2-hour interviews. See p.7 for BMRB audit.
Within each band, firms are listed alphabetically. *See individuals' profiles p.644*

Barlow Lyde & Gilbert (see firm details p.870) An expanding team, commended for its *"progressive approach"* to litigation, although sometimes described to our researchers by claimants as *"peacefully hostile."* A substantial insurance client base remains the bedrock of the firm's caseload. The *"outstanding"* **Graham Dickinson** (see p.646) continues to advise the Secretary of State for Health in respect of the Bristol Royal Infirmary paediatric cardiac surgery litigation. He also has a particular specialisation in the rehabilitation of victims of catastrophic injuries. **Clients:** AXA Insurance; Generali; Zurich Municipal; CGNU; Royal & Sun Alliance; Direct Line.

Beachcroft Wansbroughs (see firm details p.872) Working for a large number of composites, the majority of the PI department's workload is generated from the firm's insurance practice. Our interviewees had *"the highest respect"* for the *"first-class"* **Anthony Cherry** (see p.645), while **Tania Sless** (see p.650) was praised for her *"pragmatic approach."* The firm has advised on issues arising from the storage of waste at a quarry. **Clients:** Independent; RSA; Norwich Union; Alliance Cornhill International.

Berrymans Lace Mawer (see firm details p.877) An *"impressive and fair"* insurance practice that has particular niche strengths in industrial disease, motor, abuse and major trauma injury claims. The firm is on the panel for several leading insurers, including Norwich Union, Royal & SunAlliance and Independent. *"Multi-talented"* **Terry Renouf** (see p.649) is both a *"highly competent defence lawyer and extremely innovative on IT strategies."* He was instrumental in the development of Xclaim, the firm's case management system, which gives clients the facility to check the status of individual claims at any time. **Clients:** AXA Insurance; Chubb Security; Guardian; Norwich Union.

Kennedys (see firm details p.1018) An *"effective outfit"* which handles industrial disease and high value catastrophic motor claims and EL/PL. As well as handling this work for insurers, the team takes instructions from leading players in the railway industry. The firm has an acclaimed separate liability unit, and has retained all its panel positions. Newly ranked **Mariel Irvine** is said to be *"diplomatic, efficient and sensitive to clients' needs."* **Clients:** Insurers; Connex South Central; Railtrack; Virgin Trains.

Vizards, Staples & Bannisters Described to our researchers as the archetypal *"tough guy"* defendant firm, it concentrates on complex issues but also has a fast-track unit that accounts for about 20% of the caseload. Ex-president of FOIL **Martin Staples** (see p.650) heads the team and is respected as *"a man of huge experience."* The group successfully defended Grampian Holdings (insured by Royal & SunAlliance) on the organophosphate sheep dip claims, and has dealt with a number of tourist claims for Airtours. **Clients:** Royal & SunAlliance; Norwich Union; Airtours.

Badhams A *"sensible"* firm of insurance specialists, with an approach that is considered by its peers to be *"suited to the Woolf reforms."* Following a sustained campaign of lateral hires, the team's profile has been considerably raised this year. The group has been involved in a number of successful actions at the Court of Appeal. **Clients:** AXA; Norwich Union; Royal & SunAlliance.

Davies Arnold Cooper (see firm details p.934) Despite some continuing market opinion that it has been *"diminished by departures,"* the team is thought by most to have *"successfully rebuilt and re-established itself."* The firm has niche ability in product liability claims, acting on behalf of a number of large retailers, as well as handling travel and tourism-related claims, aviation personal injury and construction accidents. **Clients:** Independent; Zurich Commercial; Royal & SunAlliance; Tryg-Baltica; Zenith; Rover Group.

Hextall Erskine Said to be "*continuing along steadily,*" the firm is praised by clients for dealing with cases "*quickly and with intelligence.*" Particularly occupied with sports and respiratory claims, emphasis of the firm's caseload is now on multi-track cases. **Clients:** AIG; Ace Europe; CNA; Chaucer Group; Generali; Crawfords; Iron Trades.

Watmores Specialising in insurance-related litigation, the firm remains respected by both peers and clients and is known for its strong local authority client base. **Clients:** Local authorities.

THE SOUTH

MAINLY CLAIMANT

PERSONAL INJURY: MAINLY CLAIMANT • The South		Ptnrs	Assts
1	**Lamport Bassitt** Southampton	1	10
	Shoosmiths Basingstoke	n/a	n/a
2	**Amery-Parkes** Basingstoke	4	6
	George Ide, Phillips Chichester	2	3
	Thomson Snell & Passmore Tunbridge Wells	4	7
3	**Blake Lapthorn** Portsmouth	3	9
	Moore & Blatch Southampton	2	11
	Pattinson & Brewer Chatham	3	3
	Warner Goodman & Streat Fareham	5	8

This book is the product of 6,552 1/2-hour interviews. See p.7 for BMRB audit.
Within each band, firms are listed alphabetically.

Lamport Bassitt (see firm details p.1026) Respected mixed practice, which is split between defendant and claimant work, and has its greatest reputation as an "*excellent major union claimant firm.*" The team has acted extensively for the TGWU on industrial accidents and disease. **Clients:** TGWU.

Shoosmiths (see firm details p.1129) "*Top for sheer volume,*" this "*machine-like*" team remains a major force both in the south and nationally. Dealing principally with fast-track claims for legal expense insurers and motoring organisations, the firm is increasingly developing its 'after the event' PI work. **Clients:** AA; Direct Line Group; Churchill.

Other Notable Firms Although not possessing the prolific caseload of its Basingstoke neighbour Shoosmiths, **Amery-Parkes** is considered to be an "*effective competitor*" in the same market. Researchers again had their attention drawn to **George Ide, Philips** as "*a sound Sussex-based claimant firm,*" dealing with both high volume legal expense insurance claims and high value brain injury claims. According to peers, **Thomson Snell & Passmore**'s claimant department "*really knows what it's talking about.*" The firm achieved a notable success on a walking wounded brain injury case. The "*proactive*" **Blake Lapthorn** strikes a balance between RTA litigation on behalf of legal expense insurers and expertise in more complex work. The team also has a niche in criminal injury compensation awards and claims against LEAs and schools for bullying and harassment. **Moore & Blatch** has a strong RTA presence in Southampton, and is a member of Headway, MASS and APIL. **Pattinson & Brewer**'s Chatham office specialises in trade union-based PI litigation, with a particular reputation for complex cases. The team has a growing private clientele and strong disease department, particularly for asbestosis. **Warner Goodman & Streat** is seen to be moving away from union work towards RTA claims, most notably for Claims Direct.

MAINLY DEFENDANT

PERSONAL INJURY: MAINLY DEFENDANT • The South		Ptnrs	Assts
1	**Beachcroft Wansbroughs** Winchester	n/a	n/a
	Berrymans Lace Mawer Southampton	5	6
	Bond Pearce Southampton	1	6
	Ensor Byfield Southampton	n/a	n/a
2	**AE Wyeth & Co** Dartford	13	14
	Davies Lavery Maidstone	3	18
	Keoghs Southampton	n/a	n/a
	Palser Grossman Southampton	n/a	n/a

LEADING INDIVIDUALS		
1	**BRUFFELL Martin** Berrymans Lace Mawer	**EVANS Rod** Ensor Byfield
	RIGG Bettina Bond Pearce	

This book is the product of 6,552 1/2-hour interviews. See p.7 for BMRB audit.
Within each band, firms are listed alphabetically. *See individuals' profiles p.644*

Beachcroft Wansbroughs (see firm details p.872) Although now seen almost as much doing clinical negligence work, the firm is still considered to have a "*sensible and effective*" insurance-based personal injury practice. The firm has acted on a variety of cases, including mesothelimia, stress-related illness, asthma and asbestosis. **Clients:** Leading insurance companies.

Berrymans Lace Mawer (see firm details p.877) National firm with a strong insurance liability practice in the south, which focuses on motor, local authority, industrial disease and construction cases. Respected former City practitioner **Martin Bruffell** (see p.644) is involved in Work it Out – a joint venture mediation unit with claimant firms. **Clients:** AXA Insurance; Church & General; Independent Insurance; Norwich Union; Royal & Sun Alliance.

Bond Pearce (see firm details p.888) A leading player in the south, the team advises on a broad range of defendant insurance work, most of which is PI-related. Clients cover the range of insurance companies, Lloyd's syndicates and self-insureds, particularly in the retail sector. The firm also has an established name for asbestosis, RSI and stress. **Bettina Rigg** (see p.649) continues to be rated as a "*key*" individual in the region. **Clients:** Royal & SunAlliance; Group Ama; Hiscox Insurance; NFU Mutual; The Post Office.

Ensor Byfield (see firm details p.950) An exclusively insurer PI practice, which focuses on EL/PL and RTA. The team retains its position with a number of key insurers, including AXA and Iron Trades. The firm's employers' liability practice has a particular focus on asbestosis and industrial deafness. **Rod Evans** received strong market recommendation as a "*trustworthy and sharp-witted individual.*" **Clients:** AXA Corporate Solutions; AXA Insurance; Zurich International; Iron Trades; Fortis Insurance.

Other Notable Firms **AE Wyeth & Co** has supplemented its bread and butter lifting injuries practice with recent involvement in two major head and spinal injury cases for local authorities through Zurich Municipal. "*Reliable*" Maidstone firm **Davies Lavery** acts for small and mid-size insurers, and has a specialist RTA department, while **Keoghs**' Southampton office has an insurance-based practice which is beginning to gain market attention. Wales-based firm **Palser Grossman** also has a Southampton office, which is recognised as "*a quality operation, still establishing itself in the region.*" The team acts exclusively on defendant PI claims for insurers.

THAMES VALLEY

MAINLY CLAIMANT

PERSONAL INJURY: MAINLY CLAIMANT • Thames Valley	Ptnrs	Assts
1 **Osborne Morris & Morgan** Leighton Buzzard	3	2
2 **Boyes Turner** Reading	2	2
Fennemores Milton Keynes	4	5
Harris & Cartwright Slough	3	9
3 **Henmans** Oxford	3	10

LEADING INDIVIDUALS
1 **OSBORNE Thomas** Osborne Morris & Morgan
2 **DESMOND Adrian** Boyes Turner

This book is the product of 6,552 1/2-hour interviews. See p.7 for BMRB audit.
Within each band, firms are listed alphabetically. *See individuals' profiles p.644*

Osborne Morris & Morgan A specialist brain and spinal injuries practice with a national reputation. **Tom Osborne** is an authority in this area of the law, and is admired for his "*bold, but sympathetic*" approach. **Clients:** Private clients.

Other Notable Firms Renamed Reading firm **Boyes Turner** continues to focus on complex cases referred by Headway, CICA and non-specialist firms. Peers "*have a lot of time*" for a department that recovered around £5 million in 2000. Described by one client as "*the best that I have ever instructed,*" **Adrian Desmond** (see p.165) earned strong market commendation this year. **Fennemores** has a focus on RTA for legal expense insurers such as Frizzell Financial Services and Liverpool Victoria Friendly Society. The firm also acts in employer, occupier and public liability cases. In Slough, **Harris & Cartwright** has a growing reputation for its work on catastrophic injuries. Acting exclusively for individuals, the firm scored a major success through its involvement in a tetraplegic case which, with a settlement of £9.3 million, was the highest award ever made in the UK for such a matter. Although better known for defence work, **Henmans** has experience of acting for severely injured claimants, in particular those suffering from cerebral palsy.

MAINLY DEFENDANT

PERSONAL INJURY: MAINLY DEFENDANT • Thames Valley	Ptnrs	Assts
1 **Morgan Cole** Reading	8	30
2 **Henmans** Oxford	3	10

LEADING INDIVIDUALS
1 **TENQUIST Iain** Morgan Cole

This book is the product of 6,552 1/2-hour interviews. See p.7 for BMRB audit.
Within each band, firms are listed alphabetically. *See individuals' profiles p.644*

Morgan Cole (see firm details p.1074) The Reading office comprises two PI teams: one for motor, one for EL/PL. Both teams have a marked preponderance of fast-track cases on their books, and the firm continues to be "*the first local name you think of for defendant work,*" according to rivals. The group has seen a substantial increase in industrial disease work, and has maintained its position on all panels. Managing partner **Iain Tenquist** (see p.650) is said to "*run an efficient department.*" **Clients:** Norwich Union; AXA; Alliance Cornhill; Churchill.

Henmans (see firm details p.991) Acting principally on medium and big-ticket cases, the firm's expertise lies in employers' liability and it focuses on RSI, deafness and fatal accidents. The team continues to represent a number of leading insurers, as well as receiving a greater volume of instruction from loss adjusters. **Clients:** Major insurers.

SOUTH WEST

MAINLY CLAIMANT

PERSONAL INJURY: MAINLY CLAIMANT • South West	Ptnrs	Assts
1 **Bond Pearce** Plymouth, Bristol	3	19
Lyons Davidson Bristol	n/a	n/a
Russell Jones & Walker Bristol	2	4
Veale Wasbrough Bristol	3	9
2 **Rowley Ashworth** Exeter	n/a	n/a
Thompsons Bristol	2	6
Wolferstans Plymouth	6	8
3 **David Gist Solicitors** Bristol	n/a	n/a
4 **Bobbetts Mackan** Bristol	2	1

LEADING INDIVIDUALS	
1 **HERBERT Andrew** Thompsons	**ROBERTS Gavin** Thompsons
ROWE Bernard Lyons Davidson	**SOLLY Gillian** Russell Jones & Walker
WEBSTER John Veale Wasbrough	

This book is the product of 6,552 1/2-hour interviews. See p.7 for BMRB audit.
Within each band, firms are listed alphabetically. *See individuals' profiles p.644*

Bond Pearce (see firm details p.888) "*One of the local leaders*" is particularly noted for its strong Plymouth office, with its smaller Bristol team consequently being somewhat overshadowed. The group advises a range of private clients, including trade unions, fleet management and credit hire companies. Niche strengths include occupational disease work, serious injury cases, privately instructed RTA and EL/PL. **Clients:** TGWU; USDAW.

Lyons Davidson (see firm details p.1045) "*A very sound legal expense insurers practice*" which focuses on volume RTA work. **Bernie Rowe** (see p.649) is renowned as a "*mover and shaker*" in the market. The firm has niche expertise in road traffic accident claims, and employs specialist Accident Investigators. Other work covered includes catastrophic injury cases. **Clients:** Royal & SunAlliance; Direct Line; DAS Legal Expenses Insurance.

Russell Jones & Walker (see firm details p.1116) National players, whose Bristol office continues to specialise in injuries suffered by trade union members, and has seen a significant increase in its private client work over the past year. Headed by the popular **Gillian Solly** (see p.650), the department has particular expertise in CICA cases, where fee earners conduct their own advocacy before the board. Niche strengths include chemical poisoning, EL/PL, asbestos, stress, RSI, multi-tort and foreign jurisdiction claims. **Clients:** Police Federation; IPMS; PCS; MSF; TSSA; RCN.

Veale Wasbrough (see firm details p.1167) The firm continues to be involved in multi-party cases, including the Ladbroke Grove train crash, the South African coach crash, the Avonmouth explosion and numerous multi-claimant cases involving asbestos related conditions, industrial deafness and VWF. The firm has recovered over £6.5 million of damages on behalf of its clients. **John Webster** (see p.651) remains highly regarded by his peers. **Clients:** TGWU; CCSL.

Other Notable Firms **Rowley Ashworth** and **Thompsons** both have "*decent*" offices in the South West to serve their union clients, though neither enjoys a profile as high as their London and Northern based colleagues. **Andrew Herbert** and the "*conscientious*" **Gavin Roberts** at **Thompsons** are well-regarded figures. **Wolferstans** has a strong claimant practice in Plymouth, and **David Gist** Solicitors in Bristol has advised on maximum severity claims, and recently achieved a £632,000 settlement for an amputee victim of a severe RTA. **Bobbetts Mackan** has a rapidly expanding practice, doing a range of PI work from RTA through to public liability.

MAINLY DEFENDANT

PERSONAL INJURY: MAINLY DEFENDANT • South West		Ptnrs	Assts
1	**Beachcroft Wansbroughs** Bristol	4	18
2	**Bond Pearce** Bristol, Plymouth	4	2
	Cartwrights Insurance Partners Bristol	4	5
3	**Bevan Ashford** Bristol	1	7
	Hugh James Ford Simey Exeter	3	–
	Palser Grossman Bristol	n/a	n/a
	Veitch Penny Exeter	6	5

LEADING INDIVIDUALS	
1	**BEALE Robert** Beachcroft Wansbroughs
2	**BRADLEY Deborah** Cartwrights Insurance Partners
	DERBYSHIRE Paul Hugh James Ford Simey

This book is the product of 6,552 1/2-hour interviews. See p.7 for BMRB audit.
Within each band, firms are listed alphabetically. *See individuals' profiles p.644*

Beachcroft Wansbroughs (see firm details p.872) "*Top of the tree locally,*" the firm boasts separate multi-track and fast track teams. **Bob Beale** (see p.644) is a leading name for disease work, and his team also deals with back and leg injuries, as well as fraudulent PI claims. The fast-track team, which acts as an increasingly separate unit, deals mostly in RTA and EL.

Other Notable Firms **Cartwrights Insurance Partners** has a broad-based practice, working for insurers, self-insureds and loss adjusters. It has a national reputation in occupational disease work, particularly VWF, and asbestosis. **Deborah Bradley** is said to be an "*outstanding*" litigator. Although more acclaimed for clinical negligence expertise, **Bevan Ashford** has been involved in a wide range of stress claims, including bullying and harassment. **Bond Pearce**'s Plymouth office has attracted widespread recommendations from London firms, and successfully defended a test case on occupational stress for an NHS Trust. **Hugh James Ford Simey**, with offices in Exeter and Bristol, works on heavy personal injury cases for insurers. **Paul Derbyshire** (see p.646), in the Exeter office, was singled out to researchers for his extensive local insurance practice. "*Aggressive*" **Palser Grossman** is expanding rapidly in the region, and "*seems to have a knack of retaining clients,*" while **Veitch Penny** has been commended for its "*sensible*" work on behalf of the RAC, NHSLA and local authorities.

WALES

MAINLY CLAIMANT

PERSONAL INJURY: MAINLY CLAIMANT • Wales		Ptnrs	Assts
1	**Hugh James Ford Simey** Merthyr Tydfil	9	21
2	**Leo Abse & Cohen** Cardiff	6	35
	Thompsons Cardiff	3	11
3	**Loosemores** Cardiff	5	6
	Smith Llewelyn Partnership Swansea	2	3

LEADING INDIVIDUALS		
1	**HARDING Andrew** Hugh James Ford Simey	**HARVEY Mark** Hugh James Ford Simey
	HOPKINS Ian Leo Abse & Cohen	**WILLIAMS Robin** Leo Abse & Cohen

This book is the product of 6,552 1/2-hour interviews. See p.7 for BMRB audit.
Within each band, firms are listed alphabetically. *See individuals' profiles p.644*

Hugh James Ford Simey (see firm details p.1004) High value claims specialists, who are still gaining exposure from their work on the British Coal Respiratory claims where ultimate compensation payments are expected to reach £2-4 billion. The firm has also recently been appointed as the Royal College of Nursing's agent solicitors. Although much of the claimant work is concentrated in the firm's Merthyr Tydfil office, **Andrew Harding** (see p.646) in Cardiff has been favourably mentioned to our researchers for his expertise in head injury cases. The firm also recently gained the services of **Mark Harvey** (see p.647) from the Smith Llewelyn Partnership. Secretary of APIL, he is praised for his "*realistic approach*" to cases. **Clients:** NACODS; Royal College of Nursing.

Leo Abse & Cohen (see firm details p.1037) "*Organised*" and respected union firm with a long-established track record in Wales. Peers paid tribute to the quality of the team's individuals, with **Ian Hopkins** (see p.647) and **Robin Williams** (see p.651) both said to "*know what they're doing.*" **Clients:** Trade unions.

Thompsons Nationally renowned union-focused firm, whose Cardiff office retains its reputation as an "*aggressive unit.*" However, the retirement of Roger Bent has been regarded locally as a setback to the team's profile. **Clients:** Trade unions.

Loosemores A high volume personal injury practice, respected for its "*professionalism,*" it is primarily known for acting on behalf of legal expense insurers and motor organisations. Specialisms include head and spinal injuries. This year, the firm has handled cases for damages in excess of £1 million. **Clients:** Insurers.

Smith Llewelyn Partnership (see firm details p.1136) Known for its expertise in pharmaceuticals and clinical negligence, the firm also has a thriving conditional fee PI practice. However, the departure of the esteemed Mark Harvey to Hugh James Ford Simey has been widely regarded as a temporary setback to the practice. **Clients:** Private clients.

MAINLY DEFENDANT

Hugh James Ford Simey (see firm details p.1004) The defendant practice is based in Cardiff and is known for its "*sensible*" approach, which is "*realistic*" and characterised by "*not taking silly points*". **Gareth Williams** (see p.651) has specialist expertise in health and safety and environmental matters, as well as maximum severity injury cases. Work on several paraplegia and tetraplegia claims has included a case valued at £2m for a hotelier in respect of an accident in Greece. **Clients:** Norwich Union; AIG; Zurich Municipal.

PERSONAL INJURY: MAINLY DEFENDANT • Wales	Ptnrs	Assts
1 **Hugh James Ford Simey** Cardiff	n/a	n/a
Morgan Cole Cardiff	4	15
Palser Grossman Cardiff Bay	n/a	n/a
2 **Dolmans** Cardiff	6	13

LEADING INDIVIDUALS
1 **CRADICK Simon** Morgan Cole
WILLIAMS Gareth Hugh James Ford Simey
2 **PRICE Hugh** Morgan Cole

This book is the product of 6,552 1/2-hour interviews. See p.7 for BMRB audit.
Within each band, firms are listed alphabetically. *See individuals' profiles p.644*

Morgan Cole (see firm details p.1074) A "*premier league*" firm, working for insurers and self-insureds. Among a strong team, department head **Simon Cradick** (see p.645) and **Hugh Price** (see p.645) attract consistent market recommendation. The firm is currently advising insurers on a pair of fatal accident cases. **Clients:** Insurers.

Palser Grossman A large insurance-focused practice, which has grown rapidly in the past two years and remains highly rated for its litigation prowess. **Clients:** Major insurance companies.

Dolmans (see firm details p.944) Continues to hold down its share of market support for its work on behalf of local authorities.

MIDLANDS

MAINLY CLAIMANT

PERSONAL INJURY: MAINLY CLAIMANT • Midlands	Ptnrs	Assts
1 **Irwin Mitchell** Birmingham	3	16
Rowley Ashworth Birmingham	n/a	n/a
Russell Jones & Walker Birmingham	4	18
Thompsons Birmingham	n/a	n/a
2 **Barratt Goff & Tomlinson** Nottingham	4	1
Freethcartwright Nottingham	3	4
Nelsons Nottingham	6	8

LEADING INDIVIDUALS	
1 **HENDERSON Stuart** Irwin Mitchell	
2 **GOODMAN Sarah** Thompsons	**PRAIN David** Rowley Ashworth
ZINDANI Jeffry Russell Jones & Walker	

This book is the product of 6,552 1/2-hour interviews. See p.7 for BMRB audit.
Within each band, firms are listed alphabetically. *See individuals' profiles p.644*

Irwin Mitchell (see firm details p.1009) A firm with a reputation for both high volume and high value work. The firm specialises in high value spinal cord and brain injury cases, as well as complex liability cases. A large claimant LEI department is also based in Birmingham with the combined strengths of two departments giving strong expertise in RTA work at all levels. **Stuart Henderson** (see p.647) "*stands out a mile,*" and has particular expertise in brain and spinal cord injury, fatal accident claims and medical negligence. **Clients:** RCN; BMA; MSF; legal expense insurers.

Rowley Ashworth Union firm, which is respected by peers for its coverage of a broad range of PI work. Among "*a spread of high quality fee-earners,*" the respected **David Prain** earns the warmest recommendation. **Clients:** Trade unions.

Russell Jones & Walker (see firm details p.1116) "*Upwardly mobile*" in the region, the firm is reputed to contain some "*capable operators.*" Now boasting a fast-track RTA department, the team has worked on several high profile cases, including acting for a police officer who suffered PTSD at the scene of a Harrier jump jet crash, obtaining £250,000. **Jeffry Zindani** (see p.651) was mentioned to our researchers as a "*reliable man.*" **Clients:** Trade unions.

Thompsons In spite of the departure of Tony Lawton to the firm's London office, the firm's Birmingham team retains an enviable name for big-ticket cases on behalf of its varied union client base. **Sarah Goodman** remains a "*well-known name on the circuit.*" **Clients:** Trades unions.

Other Notable Firms Three Nottingham firms round out *Chambers'* lists in this area. Although **Freethcartwright** has its highest reputation for clinical negligence, competitors acknowledge the firm's PI capacity, notably on industrial disease matters. **Barrett Goff & Tomlinson** retains its profile as a respected boutique, specialising in high value work, while **Nelsons** continues to be recognised for legal expense insurers' cases.

MAINLY DEFENDANT

PERSONAL INJURY: MAINLY DEFENDANT • Midlands	Ptnrs	Assts
1 **Beachcroft Wansbroughs** Birmingham	3	7
Browne Jacobson Nottingham	7	8
2 **Buller Jeffries** Birmingham	7	5
3 **Everatt & Company** Evesham	4	2
Weightmans Birmingham	7	8
4 **Chapman Everatt** Wolverhampton	3	n/a
Keoghs Coventry	n/a	n/a

This book is the product of 6,552 1/2-hour interviews. See p.7 for BMRB audit.
Within each band, firms are listed alphabetically.

Beachcroft Wansbroughs (see firm details p.872) Commended for a "*professional, reliable, consistent approach,*" the firm's strength in depth is often cited by rivals as a factor in its continued eminence in the region. **Andrew Roach** (see p.649) is "*one of the main guys you would go to in Birmingham.*" The firm remains on most of the major insurance panels, and has advised on a variety of high profile paraplegic, tetraplegic and severe brain damage cases. **Clients:** Leading insurance companies.

Browne Jacobson (see firm details p.898) A "*strong team, which knows the law*" and "*works in everyone's best interest.*" The firm acts on a full range of defendant PI cases, including fast track and high profile multi-party actions. Niche strengths include EL/PL claims for local authorities, defence of stress, deafness and VWF claims, child abuse and failure to educate claims. **Clients:** Gallagher Bassett International; Municipal Mutual; St Paul International.

Other Notable Firms **Buller Jeffries** has remained on the AIG and Prudential panels, and is respected for the range of its caseload. This includes EL/PL, motor cases and child abuse matters. **Derek Adamson** (see p.644) is said to be "*technically streets ahead of most of his competitors,*" while **Geoffrey Lewis** (see p.647) was also recommended. **Everatt & Company**'s rep-

LEADING INDIVIDUALS	
1 ADAMSON Derek Buller Jeffries	
2 ARKELL Catherine Everatt & Company	CHAPMAN Richard Chapman Everatt
DACE Nigel Weightmans	LEWIS Geoffrey Buller Jeffries
PERRY Timothy Weightmans	ROACH Andrew Beachcroft Wansbroughs

See individuals' profiles p.644

utation as "*a niche firm with vast experience*" is boosted by the presence of the respected **Catherine Arkell** (see p.644). An "*aggressive*" team at **Weightmans** owes much of its name to the personal reputations of "*super-competent*" **Nigel Dace** (see p.645) and **Timothy Perry** (see p.648). **Chapman Everatt** is a "*small, but sound*" firm, where **Richard Chapman** (see p.645) has established an enviable name, while **Keoghs**' office in Coventry is newly ranked for its PI work on behalf of insurers.

EAST ANGLIA

MAINLY CLAIMANT

PERSONAL INJURY: MAINLY CLAIMANT • East Anglia	Ptnrs	Assts
1 Cunningham John Thetford	5	12
2 Morgan Jones & Pett Great Yarmouth	3	1
Taylor Vinters Cambridge	3	7
3 Edwards Duthie Ilford	2	6
Leathes Prior Norwich	2	1

LEADING INDIVIDUALS	
1 JOHN Simon Cunningham John	JONES David Morgan Jones & Pett

This book is the product of 6,552 1/2-hour interviews. See p.7 for BMRB audit.
Within each band, firms are listed alphabetically. *See individuals' profiles p.644*

Cunningham John (see firm details p.930) A firm with a "*national reputation,*" which extends from the south coast to Tyneside. The Thetford office specialises in multi-track tetraplegia, head and spinal injury claims while the Bury St Edmunds practice deals exclusively in fast-track RTA and industrial injuries. The firm continues to act on a number of US holiday claims as co-attorney, and in total has recovered in excess of £15 million in damages this year. Leading practitioner **Simon John** (see p.167) is treasurer of UKABIF (United Kingdom Acquired Brain Injury Forum). **Clients:** Private clients.

Other Notable Firms At Yarmouth-based **Morgan Jones & Pett**, the "*plain speaking*" **David Jones** heads a team specialising in offshore litigation and sports injuries. "*Good old-fashioned firm*" **Taylor Vinters** continues to be rated for catastrophic claims cases, while in Ilford, newly merged firm **Edwards Duthie** is rated by peers as "*a firm that will always do a sound job for you.*" **Leathes Prior**'s PI practice embraces both fast track and multi-track cases. The firm has acted on a number of head injury claims, recovering in excess of £1 million.

MAINLY DEFENDANT

PERSONAL INJURY: MAINLY DEFENDANT • East Anglia	Ptnrs	Assts
1 Eversheds Ipswich	2	5
Mills & Reeve Norwich	2	2
2 Edwards Duthie Ilford	2	4
Greenwoods Peterborough	2	n/a
Kennedys Brentwood	4	1
Merricks Ipswich	n/a	n/a
Prettys Ipswich	n/a	n/a

LEADING INDIVIDUALS	
1 CROOK Christopher Edwards Duthie	PADFIELD Brendan Eversheds

This book is the product of 6,552 1/2-hour interviews. See p.7 for BMRB audit.
Within each band, firms are listed alphabetically. *See individuals' profiles p.644*

Eversheds (see firm details p.952) The firm's Ipswich office is universally accounted to be "*good at what it does.*" Expertise in stress claims, sexual abuse cases and high profile multi-party matters is deployed on behalf of a range of local authorities and insurers. Newly ranked **Brendan Padfield** (see p.648) is a well-known name in the area. The firm has advised Transco on a series of multi-party explosion claims. **Clients:** Zurich Municipal; Transco; Provident Insurance.

Mills & Reeve (see firm details p.1069) Despite losing the NHSLA contract, this is still regarded as a "*top local firm.*" The team has acted on a number of high value multiple injury, head injury and spinal injury claims for various insurers. **Clients:** Composite insurers; underwriters; Lloyd's syndicates; loss adjusters.

Other Notable Firms Defendant PI work is thought by local experts to be a strengthening area of **Edwards Duthie's** versatile practice. Insurance companies rate **Chris Crook** as "*one of the best lawyers in the region.*" **Greenwoods** has been "*seen more and more in this field,*" while **Merricks** has a sound reputation for acting on fatal accidents and multi-party claims. **Prettys** is also considered to be "*operating well*" in the region, while **Kennedys**' Brentwood office has gained a strong name for work on behalf of insurers.

NORTH WEST

MAINLY CLAIMANT

Pannone & Partners (see firm details p.1088) This "*top-class*" team is said to be "*bursting with quality,*" and remains the clear leader in the region. The firm concentrates its efforts on high value claims, although it does process some bulk work from LEI referrals. Department head **Carol Jackson** (see p.647) specialises in head injuries, was involved in the raising of funds for Headway House, and is said to "*know her onions.*" "*Utterly professional*" **Cathy Leech** (see p.647) was praised for her "*awareness of the wider issues,*" while **Pauline Chandler** (see p.645) has an outstanding name for disease cases, and this year achieved a precedent-setting Court of Appeal victory against Shell tankers. **Clients:** Mondial; RAC; Eastgate.

John Pickering & Partners The firm's "*awesome*" reputation for industrial disease, notably mesothelioma and asbestosis, persists. **John Pickering** is acknowledged by peers to be a "*committed, thorough and tenacious*" lawyer. **Clients:** Private clients.

Leigh, Day & Co (see firm details p.1036) "*Great team with a bulldog style,*" which has featured on aviation claims, both civilian and military, and car-

PERSONAL INJURY: MAINLY CLAIMANT • North West		Ptnrs	Assts
1	**Pannone & Partners** Manchester	5	18
2	**John Pickering & Partners** Oldham	n/a	n/a
	Leigh, Day & Co Manchester	3	4
	Russell Jones & Walker Manchester	3	12
	Thompsons Liverpool	4	3
3	**Donns Solicitors** Manchester	n/a	n/a
	Whittles Manchester	n/a	n/a
4	**Hugh Potter & Company** Manchester	3	3
	Linder Myers Manchester	5	7

LEADING INDIVIDUALS		
1	**JACKSON Carol** Pannone & Partners	**LEECH Catherine** Pannone & Partners
	PATTERSON Frank Leigh, Day & Co	**PICKERING John** John Pickering & Partners
2	**CHANDLER Pauline** Pannone & Partners	**CONNOR Michael** Russell Jones & Walker
	MANSFIELD Collin Whittles	**MCCOOL Geraldine** Leigh, Day & Co
	POTTER Hugh Hugh Potter & Company	

This book is the product of 6,552 1/2-hour interviews. See p.7 for BMRB audit.
Within each band, firms are listed alphabetically. *See individuals' profiles p.644*

bon monoxide poisoning cases. The firm is also on the Headway panel and has expertise in head and spinal injuries. "*Fearsome litigator*" **Frank Patterson** (see p.648) and **Geraldine McCool** (see p.648), renowned for her "*passion for her work,*" both receive consistent market plaudits. **Clients:** Private clients.

Russell Jones & Walker (see firm details p.1116) The firm's Manchester office is said to have "*an entrepreneurial streak which serves it well.*" Specialists in brain and spinal injuries and fatal accidents, the firm serves an overwhelmingly trade union clientele, and recently recovered damages of £4.8 million for an RTA head injury case. The "*thorough*" **Michael Connor** (see p.645) is renowned for his "*impeccable judgement.*" **Clients:** Police Federation; Royal College of Nursing; PFA.

Thompsons Still doing substantial union work, this team of "*excellent litigators*" retains a respected position in the local pecking order. Disease work remains an area of conspicuous achievement. **Clients:** Trade unions.

Other Notable Firms "*On their way up,*" **Donns Solicitors** has earned a particular reputation for MoD cases. **Whittles**' work on disease cases continues to earn market approval, with **Collin Mansfield** attracting warm recommendation from competitors. Vastly experienced **Hugh Potter** heads an eponymous firm with a sound PI reputation, while **Linder Myers** "*does some weighty cases*" and has "*some acute people in charge.*"

MAINLY DEFENDANT

PERSONAL INJURY: MAINLY DEFENDANT • North West		Ptnrs	Assts
1	**James Chapman & Co** Manchester	13	16
	Keoghs Bolton	18	56
	Weightmans Liverpool, Manchester	27	32
2	**Beachcroft Wansbroughs** Manchester	n/a	n/a
	Berrymans Lace Mawer Liverpool, Manchester	26	70
	Halliwell Landau Manchester	6	35
	Hill Dickinson Liverpool, Manchester	32	16

LEADING INDIVIDUALS		
1	**BROOKS Roger** Keoghs	**FINNIGAN Kevin** James Chapman & Co

This book is the product of 6,552 1/2-hour interviews. See p.7 for BMRB audit.
Within each band, firms are listed alphabetically. *See individuals' profiles p.644*

James Chapman & Co (see firm details p.1011) A "*tough but sensible*" defendant firm, specialising in high value work for insurers. Said to have a "*progressive approach,*" the team is considered to owe much to **Kevin Finnigan** (see p.646), who has "*a positive attitude, and is always willing to listen to good ideas.*" The firm advises on a broad range of PI cases, with stress, asbestos claims and catastrophic injury featuring prominently in the caseload. A highlight case was the successful defence of a £200,000 RSI claim for Zurich Municipal. **Clients:** AXA; NFU/Avon; Zurich Commercial; Zurich Municipal.

Keoghs (see firm details p.1020) In spite of the retirement of Barry Tazik-er, the firm commands the respect of peers for its straightforward approach. "*They don't take silly points and deal with all the issues.*" Working for more than twenty insurers, the team has a growing reputation for disease, employer's liability, product liability and fraudulent claims. **Roger Brooks**' (see p.644) increased profile as "*a sensible, proactive opponent*" sees him ranked for the first time this year. **Clients:** Group Ama; Budget; First Group.

Weightmans (see firm details p.1176) Respected national firm, which has retained its position on most panels and is commended for its "*go-ahead, dynamic*" attitude. The team is renowned for its work on behalf of insurance companies. **Clients:** Insurance companies.

Other Notable Firms Although **Beachcroft Wansbroughs**' Manchester office does not quite have the profile of many of the firm's other teams, it is still felt to produce "*good, solid*" work for insurers. Similar comments have been applied to **Berrymans Lace Mawer**'s regional group, which handles fatal accident claims, stress cases, RSI, VWF and asthma cases. **Halliwell Landau** has an excellent reputation for disease work, and focuses on insurance litigation for corporate clients. **Hill Dickinson**'s "*combative*" team has also maintained its name for disease work.

YORKSHIRE

PERSONAL INJURY: MAINLY CLAIMANT • Yorkshire		Ptnrs	Assts
1	**Irwin Mitchell** Leeds, Sheffield	13	20
2	**Morrish & Co** Leeds	n/a	n/a
	Pattinson & Brewer York	3	4
	Rowley Ashworth Leeds	n/a	n/a
	Russell Jones & Walker Leeds, Sheffield	4	6
3	**Hamers** Hull	1	10

This book is the product of 6,552 1/2-hour interviews. See p.7 for BMRB audit.
Within each band, firms are listed alphabetically. *See individuals' profiles p.644*

MAINLY CLAIMANT

Irwin Mitchell (see firm details p.1009) "*Excellent*" both for routine and complex cases, the firm maintains its position as the premier outfit in Yorkshire. **John Pickering** (see p.648) and **Andrew Tucker** (see p.650) are both known as "*tough negotiators.*" The team acted on behalf of 110,000 miners and 120,000 former miners in a VWF and respiratory disease case against British Coal. The case has given rise to settlements of around £250 million. **Clients:** Private clients.

Morrish & Co Favoured union firm, with an increasingly active profile and a niche in claimant PI work. The caseload covers the spectrum of disease,

LEADING INDIVIDUALS	
1 **PICKERING John** Irwin Mitchell	**TUCKER Andrew** Irwin Mitchell
2 **ALLEN Simon** Russell Jones & Walker	**CARSON Peter** Rowley Ashworth

See individuals' profiles p.644

stress and accident cases. **Clients:** TGWU.

Pattinson & Brewer (see firm details p.1091) Trade union practice, best known for undertaking EL and RTA claims. A recent highlight saw the firm win £440,000 for a railway worker who contracted mesothelioma. **Clients:** GMB; UNIFY; RMT.

Rowley Ashworth The Leeds arm of this nationally prominent union firm is rated for its "*proactive style.*" **Peter Carson** is acclaimed for his "*incredibly deep knowledge of the law.*" **Clients:** Trade unions.

Russell Jones & Walker (see firm details p.1116) Much of the Leeds office's reputation is based on its work for the Police Federation, although it is more widely recognised as "*a good all-round union firm.*" **Simon Allen** (see p.644) has a "*growing influence*" in the market. The firm represented an injured Yorkshire steel worker who received a pay-out of £90,000. **Clients:** ISTC; USDAW; Police Federation.

Other Notable Firms Hull firm **Hamers** is well known locally for its expertise in RTA and employer's liability cases.

PERSONAL INJURY: MAINLY DEFENDANT • Yorkshire	Ptnrs	Assts
1 **Beachcroft Wansbroughs** Leeds	5	13
2 **DLA** Bradford, Leeds, Sheffield	n/a	n/a
3 **Irwin Mitchell** Sheffield	n/a	n/a
Nabarro Nathanson Sheffield	2	16
4 **Keeble Hawson** Leeds, Sheffield	3	4
Praxis Partners Leeds	4	28

LEADING INDIVIDUALS	
1 **ANSON Peter** DLA	**HOTCHIN Samuel** Beachcroft Wansbroughs

This book is the product of 6,552 1/2-hour interviews. See p.7 for BMRB audit.
Within each band, firms are listed alphabetically. *See individuals' profiles p.644*

MAINLY DEFENDANT

Beachcroft Wansbroughs (see firm details p.872) "*Still pre-eminent in the region,*" the Leeds office boasts a team of "*strong fee-earners.*" The team advises on the full range of PI work from small to medium-sized cases including asbestosis, dermatitis and stress. **Samuel Hotchin** (see p.647) has a name as a "*decent, sensible lawyer.*" **Clients:** AXA; Royal & SunAlliance.

Other Notable Firms DLA fields a "*respectable, professional*" insurance practice, headed by "*wily old bird*" **Peter Anson**. Although **Irwin Mitchell**'s defendant team has moved from Sheffield to Leeds, the firm is still thought to "*get through a fair volume of work.*" **Nabarro Nathanson**'s "*improving*" defendant practice has created a favourable impression during its work for British Coal on disease and VWF cases. **Keeble Hawson** has an "*underrated*" PI team, while the former Hammond Suddards Edge team at **Praxis Partners** retains its share of market support.

NORTH EAST

MAINLY CLAIMANT

PERSONAL INJURY: MAINLY CLAIMANT • North East	Ptnrs	Assts
1 **Thompsons** Newcastle upon Tyne	8	4
2 **Browell Smith & Co** Newcastle upon Tyne	n/a	n/a
Marrons Newcastle upon Tyne	n/a	n/a
3 **Hay & Kilner** Newcastle upon Tyne	8	3
Russell Jones & Walker Newcastle upon Tyne	1	2
4 **Beecham Peacock** Newcastle upon Tyne	n/a	n/a

LEADING INDIVIDUALS	
1 **ALLAN David** Marrons	**BRADSHAW David** Hay & Kilner
BROWELL Philip Browell Smith & Co	**PORTEUS Stephen** Marrons

This book is the product of 6,552 1/2-hour interviews. See p.7 for BMRB audit.
Within each band, firms are listed alphabetically. *See individuals' profiles p.644*

Thompsons "*Top dogs*" in the region in spite of the retirement of Roger Maddocks, the firm has particular expertise in representing unions on industrial diseases cases such as VWF, bronchitis and mining cases. The office has a specialist asbestosis department, and produces "*quality as well as volume.*" **Clients:** Durham NUM; Durham Mechanics Association.

Browell Smith & Co (see firm details p.897) Union firm which is said by competitors to be "*gradually increasingly in influence.*" The firm has done 25,000 emphysema cases to date and is acting on an increasing number of asbestos and bladder cancer matters. **Philip Browell** is "*heavily involved in the region.*" **Clients:** GMB; NUM; TGWU.

Marrons (see firm details p.1054) "*Smaller but sensible firm,*" whose attitude is described as "*Woolfian before Woolf.*" **David Allan** and **Stephen Porteus** are the key names here. **Clients:** Private clients.

Other Notable Firms The respected **David Bradshaw** (see p.644) of **Hay & Kilner** deals with multi-party referrals from Accident Line, Recover and Greystoke. The firm also receives referrals from Headway and the Spinal Injuries Association. **Russell Jones & Walker**'s new office in Newcastle has gained market plaudits for its union work, while **Beecham Peacock**'s union practice also enjoys regional respect.

PERSONAL INJURY: MAINLY DEFENDANT • North East	Ptnrs	Assts
1 **Eversheds** Newcastle upon Tyne	5	17
Hay & Kilner Newcastle upon Tyne	4	2
Sinton & Co Newcastle upon Tyne	6	2
2 **Crutes** Newcastle upon Tyne	9	9
Jacksons Stockton on Tees	7	11

This book is the product of 6,552 1/2-hour interviews. See p.7 for BMRB audit.
Within each band, firms are listed alphabetically.

MAINLY DEFENDANT

Eversheds (see firm details p.952) The Newcastle office of this national player has expanded markedly, and has a high-profile clientele of self-insureds. Newly rated **Toby Scott** (see p.650) specialises in RTA multi-party defendant cases. **Clients:** Iron Trades; Norwich Union.

Hay & Kilner The firm's excellent reputation in this area was underlined by its retention on the panels of Royal & SunAlliance and Allianz Cornhill. **Peter Pescod** (see p.648) is a recognised expert in accident-related claims,

LEADING INDIVIDUALS	
1 **DIAS James** Sinton & Co	**PESCOD Peter** Hay & Kilner
2 **CLARKE Richard** Jacksons	**DREWE David** Crutes
SCOTT Toby Eversheds	**WILLIAMS Alun** Hay & Kilner

See individuals' profiles p.644

and receives "*valuable support*" from **Alun Williams** (see p.651). Other areas of the firm's caseload include public liability, stress, disease and asbestos work. **Clients:** Royal & SunAlliance; Allianz Cornhill; Group Ama.

Sinton & Co (see firm details p.1134) Acting for an array of insurance clients, the firm has a fine reputation for EL/PL, industrial disease and cases of maximum severity. **Jim Dias** (see p.646) is a "*good name to conjure with.*" **Clients:** AXA; Provident; Norwich Union; Tokio Marine.

Other Notable Firms Led by **David Drewe** (see p.646), **Crutes** operates a high turnover defendant practice, with the bulk of it on behalf of local authorities and insurers. RTA and EL/PL constitute most of **Jacksons**' workload, where **Richard Clarke** has a long-standing name.

SCOTLAND

MAINLY PURSUER

PERSONAL INJURY: MAINLY PURSUER • Scotland	Ptnrs	Assts
1 **Thompsons** Edinburgh, Glasgow	8	12
2 **Anderson Strathern WS** Edinburgh	8	10
Balfour & Manson Edinburgh	8	10
Burnside Kemp Fraser Aberdeen	3	3
Lawford Kidd Edinburgh	2	5
3 **Digby Brown** Glasgow	11	11
4 **Drummond Miller WS** Edinburgh	6	8
Levy & McRae Glasgow	3	8

LEADING INDIVIDUALS	
1 **KEMP Sandy** Burnside Kemp Fraser	**SHORT David** Lawford Kidd
SMITH Sid Thompsons	**TYLER Alfred** Balfour & Manson
2 **CARR Robert** Anderson Strathern WS	**FIFE Robert** Anderson Strathern WS
GARRETT Graeme Digby Brown	**LUMSDEN Lawrence** Thompsons
MAGUIRE Frank Thompsons	

This book is the product of 6,552 1/2-hour interviews. See p.7 for BMRB audit.
Within each band, firms are listed alphabetically. *See individuals' profiles p.644*

Thompsons Still doing "*as much union work as all the other firms put together,*" and "*clearly number one in Scotland,*" the group divides its time between union work for GPMU, GMB and Unison, and private claims from former workers. **Frank Maguire** ("*well-organised and aggressive*") specialises in asbestos-related lung disease from the Glasgow office, while "*key figures*" **Laurence Lumsden** and **Sid Smith** work from Edinburgh on bronchitis and emphysema cases. **Clients:** GPMU; GMB; Unison.

Anderson Strathern WS (see firm details p.859) Said to be "*chasing the leaders strongly,*" this is a strong pursuer practice which is best known for its work on behalf of the Royal College of Nursing. **Robert Carr** (see p.645) and **Robert Fife** (see p.646) both have sound reputations as "*straightforward people to deal with.*" The former acted on one of the year's most high-profile fatal accident enquiries, following the death of a 10 year old boy during dental treatment. This included a GMC prosecution against the anaesthetist. **Clients:** Royal College of Nursing.

Balfour & Manson (see firm details p.869) A "*top firm*" which combines high-profile cases with some volume work (RTA, slippers and trippers etc), as well as some union cases gained through agency referrals. "*Top-class*" **Fred Tyler** (see p.650) is a recognised head and spinal injuries specialist, and was recently involved in the high profile stress case Cross v Highlands & Islands Enterprise. **Clients:** Private clients; EIS.

Burnside Kemp Fraser (see firm details p.904) "*A tight group,*" based in Aberdeen, whose location partly dictates its expertise in oil industry-related work, including fatal offshore accidents and negotiation of damages. The firm also does some defendant work for offshore marine vessels. The respected **Sandy Kemp** (see p.335) has an excellent reputation as a litigator, and is currently involved in a number of helicopter cases in the House of Lords. **Clients:** Tidewater More North Sea; Gulf Offshore North Sea; Swire Pacific Offshore.

Lawford Kidd (see firm details p.1029) A small but "*high quality*" firm, which deals with a variety of union work, and has a particular niche in industrial disease cases. **David Short** (see p.650) is said to "*work hard for his clients,*" and has developed a particular niche in aviation claims relating to accidents and employment. The firm is also on the panel for RSA. **Clients:** Unison; BALPA.

Digby Brown (see firm details p.942) Specialists in pursuer litigation, the firm has strong links to The Spinal Injuries Association and The Head Injuries Trust for Scotland. The firm also advises a number of union clients. Regarded by peers as "*the maverick we all respect,*" **Graeme Garrett** (see p.646) is a well known local rainmaker. **Clients:** Claims Direct; Keystone; Greystoke; GBMU.

Other Notable Firms **Drummond Miller WS** features a diverse personal injury caseload, featuring union work for the RMT, EMA and PCS, as well as such high profile cases as the Nazareth House child abuse affair. Glasgow firm **Levy & McRae** has appeared on a number of matters that have been in the public eye. The firm advised the Lockerbie Air Disaster Group and co-ordinated all claims for the families, and represented the parents affected by the Dunblane tragedy.

MAINLY DEFENDER

Simpson & Marwick WS (see firm details p.1133) "*The most successful defender litigation firm in Scotland*" is renowned for its "*consistent spread of quality and experience.*" Acting for a number of leading insurance companies, the team has substantial experience of the full range of defender personal injury, including stress, EL/PL and lung disease cases. The respected **Gordon Keyden** is road traffic adviser to the MIB in Scotland, while **Peter Anderson** is still considered by peers to be "*the driving force behind the team.*" Newly rated **Michael Wood** is said by clients to be "*one of our favourites.*" The firm successfully defended Cross v Highlands & Islands Enterprise, a high profile stress case. **Clients:** Norwich Union; Zurich Commercial; Motor Insurers Bureau.

HBM Sayers Specialists in industrial disease, vibration white finger and RTA, the firm advises an impressive array of insurer clients. The "*shrewd*" **George Moore** is renowned for his abilities as a solicitor advocate. **Clients:** RSA; Norwich Union; AXA.

PERSONAL INJURY: MAINLY DEFENDER • Scotland	Ptnrs	Assts
1 **Simpson & Marwick WS** Edinburgh	12	30
2 **HBM Sayers** Glasgow	8	8
3 **Anderson Strathern WS** Edinburgh	4	10
Biggart Baillie Glasgow	5	7
4 **Anderson Partnership** Glasgow	5	6
Brechin Tindal Oatts Glasgow	3	6
Dundas & Wilson CS Edinburgh	1	11
Morison Bishop Glasgow	n/a	n/a
Paull & Williamsons Aberdeen	2	5

LEADING INDIVIDUALS	
1 **ANDERSON Peter** Simpson & Marwick	**KEYDEN Gordon** Simpson & Marwick
MOORE George HBM Sayers	
2 **CARR Robert** Anderson Strathern WS	**ROXBURGH James** Biggart Baillie
WOOD Michael Simpson & Marwick	

This book is the product of 6,552 1/2-hour interviews. See p.7 for BMRB audit.
Within each band, firms are listed alphabetically. *See individuals' profiles p.644*

Anderson Strathern WS (see firm details p.859) Although slightly better known for its pursuer practice, the firm "*can don an insurer's hat when it needs to,*" according to competitors. The "*versatile*" **Robert Carr** (see p.645) is also respected for his defender practice. **Clients:** Garwins Liability Adjusters; Crowe Insurance Group; Co-operative Insurance.

Biggart Baillie (see firm details p.882) Maintaining its leading reputation for expertise in industrial disease, the firm has also included substantial motor accident cases among its workload. Veteran **James Roxburgh** (see p.649) is "*as busy as ever,*" and is widely regarded as an "*indefatigable crusader.*" The firm successfully defended British Shipbuilders from an alleged asbestos claim by a former shipyard worker. **Clients:** Iron Trades; Norwich Union; Zurich Municipal; Scottish Power UK.

Other Notable Firms Three firms are ranked in this area of practice for the first time. **Anderson Partnership** and **Morison Bishop** were both said to be "*doing more and more defender work,*" while **Brechin Tindal Oatts** is also known for its work on behalf of a variety of major insurance companies. **Dundas & Wilson**'s "*juggernaut of a department*" continues to appear regularly on catastrophic injury cases. In Aberdeen, **Paull & Williamsons** continues to mine its niche seam of oil industry related accident and injury cases.

NORTHERN IRELAND

PERSONAL INJURY: MAINLY CLAIMANT • Northern Ireland	Ptnrs	Assts
1 **Agnew, Andress, Higgins** Belfast	4	2
Eamonn McEvoy & Co Lurgan	n/a	n/a
Edwards & Co Belfast	2	4
Francis Hanna & Co Belfast	n/a	n/a
2 **Diamond Heron** Belfast	1	3

LEADING INDIVIDUALS	
1 **AGNEW Seamus** Agnew, Andress, Higgins	**ANDRESS Stephen** Agnew, Andress, Higgins
MCEVOY Eamonn Eamonn McEvoy & Co	
2 **DIAMOND Maurice** Diamond Heron	

This book is the product of 6,552 1/2-hour interviews. See p.7 for BMRB audit.
Within each band, firms are listed alphabetically. *See individuals' profiles p.644*

MAINLY CLAIMANT

Seamus Agnew and **Stephen Andress** continue to be the stand-out names at **Agnew, Andress & Higgins**, regarded by some in the market as "*first among equals*" for claimant personal injury in the province. **Eamonn McEvoy**'s personal reputation enables his eponymous firm to maintain its standing among the local elite, while both **Edwards & Co** and **Francis Hanna & Co** retain their share of market support. A strong union client base sees **Diamond Heron** feature regularly on high profile PI cases. **Maurice Diamond** is still considered to be "*their shining light*" in this area.

PERSONAL INJURY: MAINLY DEFENDANT • Northern Ireland	Ptnrs	Assts
1 **C&H Jefferson** Belfast	8	15
McKinty & Wright Belfast	n/a	n/a
2 **Harrison, Leitch & Logan** Belfast	2	3
Johnsons Belfast	n/a	n/a
O'Reilly Stewart Belfast	n/a	n/a
Tughan & Co Belfast	n/a	n/a

LEADING INDIVIDUALS	
1 **BOWDEN Ronnie** Harrison, Leitch & Logan	**CROSS John** McKinty & Wright
GIBSON Michael Tughan & Co	**JEFFERSON Ian** C&H Jefferson
TAYLOR Derek C&H Jefferson	**TWEED Paul** Johnsons

This book is the product of 6,552 1/2-hour interviews. See p.7 for BMRB audit.
Within each band, firms are listed alphabetically. *See individuals' profiles p.644*

MAINLY DEFENDANT

Belfast's finest exponents in this area remain **C&H Jefferson** and **McKinty & Wright**, both of whom have an imposing insurer-based clientele. At the former firm, **Ian Jefferson** (see p.647) and **Derek Taylor** (see p.650) are commended for their "*realistic approach,*" while **John Cross** (see p.645) of McKinty & Wright gains plaudits as a "*safe pair of hands.*" Among other firms to gain recommendation, **Harrison, Leitch & Logan** is felt to "*owe much*" to the "*irrepressible*" **Ronnie Bowden** (see p.644), while, at **Tughan & Co**, **Michael Gibson** (see p.646) remains widely recognised as the outstanding practitioner. Although **O'Reilly Stewart**'s market profile is not as high as in previous years, the firm is still recommended by a number of regional commentators as "*a decent operation.*" Said to be "*coming up fast,*" **Johnsons** has a noted insurance practice. Leading player **Paul Tweed** (see p.288) is reckoned to "*pull in a lot of work.*"

LEADERS IN PERSONAL INJURY

ADAMSON, Derek
Buller Jeffries, Birmingham (0121) 200 0437
derek.adamson@bullerjeffries.co.uk
Specialisation: Personal injury claims particularly fatal accidents, catastrophic injuries, industrial disease and medical negligence. High profile cases have included motorway disasters, asbestos litigation and products claims. Other principal areas include professional indemnity, fires, construction claims, policy interpretation and defending civil claims against the police.
Prof. Memberships: Law Society; Birmingham Law Society; FOIL.
Career: Articles *Buller Jeffries* 1979-1981. Partner 1985. Deputy District Judge 1993-1997.
Personal: Born 1956. Birmingham University 1975-78. Leisure Interests: mainly sport, manager of youth soccer team.

AGNEW, Seamus
Agnew, Andress, Higgins, Belfast (028) 90320035

ALLAN, David
Marrons, Newcastle upon Tyne (0191) 281 1304

ALLEN, Patrick
Hodge Jones & Allen, London (020) 7284 6634
pallen@hodge-jones-allen.co.uk
Specialisation: Principal area of practice – clinical negligence, personal injury and miscarriage of justice claims. Member of Steering Committee of Plaintiff lawyers in the Kings Cross Fire and Marchioness litigation and represented many survivors and bereaved in each case. Managed the MMR litigation 1998-99 and the Sheep Dip litigation 1998-2000. Since April 1998 coordinating and managing the Gulf War and Kerrin Point group claims. Lecturer on legal aid, personal injury practice and costs.
Prof. Memberships: Law Society; executive committee of APIL since 1992; vice-president April 2000; Law Society Personal Injury panel; AVMA Referral panel; Society of Labour Lawyers; Legal Services Commission Funding Review Committee chairman.
Career: Articled *Offenbach & Co* 1974-76. Qualified 1977 and simultaneously set up *Hodge Jones & Allen* with Henry Hodge. Senior partner of *Hodge Jones & Allen* and head of personal injury team.
Personal: Born 27 May 1950. St Catherine's College, Oxford 1969-72. Married to GP, two daughters. Lives Camden Town, London. Interests – windsurfing, sailing, hillwalking, opera, theatre.

ALLEN, Simon
Russell Jones & Walker, Sheffield (0114) 276 6868
s.j.allen@rjw.co.uk
Specialisation: Claimant personal injury. Involved specifically in industrial accidents, RSI cases, Asbestos cases, multi-handed fume and VWF cases and post traumatic stress cases. Ran the Hillsborough Police PTSD Litigation which was successful before the Court of Appeal in October 1996 and set new law in the House of Lords in 1998. Has been involved in two of the top six RSI settlements ever, winning over £0.5 million in damages in the year 2000.
Prof. Memberships: APIL. American Trial Lawyers Association. Member of Personal Injury Panel. Appointed Assessor for Personal Injury Panel in 2000. Member of Law Society Committee which produced the Pre-Action Protocol and is preparing the Disease protocol for the Lord Chancellors' Dept. Local contact point for Headway. Society of Labour Lawyers. Regular lecturer.
Career: Articled *Favell & Smith*, Sheffield. Qualified 1985. *Brian Thompson & Partners*, Sheffield 1985-89 (Partner 1987). *Russell Jones & Walker* 1989 to date (partner 1990). Local managing partner: Leeds 1996-97. Local managing partner: Sheffield (which he opened in 1997). Heads RSI, PTSD, VWF and Asbestos Units within the firm. Set up the firm's National Occupational Disease Group, which is the first of its kind in the UK, to research and develop knowledge of such illnesses.
Publications: Sol. Journal 1993, 1994, 1997, and 2000; New Law Journal 1997 and 2000; PMILL 1996, 1997, 1998 and 1999; APIL Magazine 1995, 1996, 1997, 1998 and 1999; Legal Times 1996. Regular lecturer on PI and in particular on PTSD, RSI, stress, employers liability, Asbestos and procedure. 'PI Update' provider: Law Society Gazette 1996 to date with four published articles in 2001. Published Sweet & Maxwell paper on PTSD.
Personal: Family, photography. Trades Union Movement, Manchester United supporter.

ANDERSON, Peter
Simpson & Marwick WS, Edinburgh
(0131) 557 1545

ANDRESS, Stephen
Agnew, Andress, Higgins, Belfast (028) 90320035

ANSON, Peter
DLA, Sheffield (08700) 111111

ARKELL, Catherine
Everatt & Company, Evesham (01386) 769161
arkell@everatt.co.uk
Specialisation: Senior Partner. Acts for defendant insurers in a variety of personal injury claims. Work includes serious accident claims involving paraplegia, head injury, etc, and many disease cases including large volume deafness, asbestos-related, RSI, and hand/arm vibration claims. Has also dealt with large (over £1 million) fire-related claims for insurers. Defending HSE prosecutions is a particular interest.
Prof. Memberships: Law Society.
Career: Qualified in 1979. Became a partner in *Everatt & Co* in 1980.
Personal: Born 1954. Educated at Westwood's Grammar School and Bristol University 1973-76.

BEALE, Robert
Beachcroft Wansbroughs, Bristol (0117) 918 2000
rbeale@bwlaw.co.uk
Specialisation: Partner. He has handled property, fraud and fire damage claims, advising on policy wording and coverage disputes on such claims. Now handles public and employer's liability and motor claims, particularly in back injury and malingering cases and industrious diseases as well as product liability cases.
Prof. Memberships: Member of FOIL.
Career: Articled *Robins Hay*; qualified 1971; assistant solicitor *Burges Salmon* 1971. *Wansbroughs Willey Hargrave*, 1974.

BOWDEN, Ronnie
Harrison, Leitch & Logan, Belfast (028) 9032 3843
Ronnie.Bowden@harrisonll.com
Specialisation: Senior Partner Road Traffic, Employers Liability. Matters handled recently have included: serious injury (brain damage and quadriplegia); industrial disease claims; repetitive strain injury; stress in the workplace.
Prof. Memberships: Law Society of Northern Ireland.
Career: Educated at Methodist College, Belfast and Queen's University, Belfast.
Personal: Married: two adult children. Weekend golfer. Soccer fan.

BRADLEY, Deborah
Cartwrights Insurance Partners, Bristol

BRADSHAW, David
Hay & Kilner, Newcastle upon Tyne
(0191) 232 8435
david.bradshaw@hay-kilner.co.uk
Specialisation: Head of claimant personal injury and clinical negligence. Acts in cases of maximum severity (both brain and spinal injury). Member of Spinal Injury Association and Headway Specialist panels. AVMA referral panel member. Involved in a number of multi party actions. Member of the Law Society Multi Party Action Panel. A lead solicitor in connection with the Benzodiazepine litigation. Co-ordinated a substantial number of cases for industrial deafness at Scottish & Newcastle Breweries (highest damages awards at the time). Co-ordinated a number of claims involving carcinogen BiSCME.
Prof. Memberships: Law Society Personal Injury Specialist Panel and medical negligence specialist panel assessor. Member of ATLA. Member of the International Practice Section. APIL, AVMA and Environmental Law Foundation member.
Personal: Born 7.12.51. Lives Tyne Valley, Northumberland. Interests include opera, squash, tennis, reading.

BROOKS, Roger
Keoghs, Bolton (01204) 677240
rbrooks@keoghs.co.uk
Specialisation: Acts for insurers defending personal injury claims arising from ELIPL and road traffic accident liability. His particular speciality is high value claims arising from serious head and spinal injuries.
Prof. Memberships: Law Society. FOIL.
Career: Partner. Articled 1980-82 at *Berrymans*, London. Qualified 1982. Joined *Keoghs* 1983.
Personal: Born in 1958. Educated at The King's School, Ely. LLB Hons at University in Southampton. Resides Bolton. Married with three children. Enjoys tennis, walking, skiing.

BROWELL, Philip
Browell Smith & Co, Newcastle upon Tyne
(0191) 221 1611

BRUFFELL, Martin
Berrymans Lace Mawer, Southampton
(023) 8023 6464
martin.bruffell@blm-law.com
Specialisation: Senior partner, Southampton office and joint national head of the insurance liability group including one of the largest personal injury divisions in the country. Handles personal injury claims with specialisation in occupational disease and employers' liability.
Prof. Memberships: Former President of FOIL (Forum of Insurance Lawyers), previously Editorial Board member of JPIL (Journal of Personal Injury

Litigation). A CEDR accredited mediator.
Career: Joined *Berrymans* in 1979, qualified in 1981, associate in 1982, partner in 1984. Involved in working parties for the Law Society and the Lord Chancellor's Department, government departments (DETR, DSS) and insurance bodies (ABI). Work covered the Ogden tables, Woolf, damages, conditional fee arrangements, the tracing of EL insurers and rehabilitation.
Publications: Contributed to 'Binghams and Berrymans Motor Cases', articles for 'The Lawyer', 'Post Magazine', 'Law Society Gazette' and the publications of ILEX and the Association of District Judges. Radio appearances on BBC Radio 4 and 5 Live as a commentator on litigation issues.
Personal: Born 1955, educated at RGS High Wycombe and Leeds University.

CAHILL, John
Stewarts, London (020) 7242 6462
jcahill@stewarts-solicitors.co.uk
Specialisation: Managing partner and head of personal injury and clinical negligence group. Specialises in foreign personal injury claims and ADR.
Prof. Memberships: Centre for Dispute Resolution; Law Society; Association of Personal Injury Lawyers; Richard Grand Society.
Career: Articled *Kingsford Stacey*. Qualified 1985; partner 1990; CEDR accredited mediator; member of Personal Injury panel; founder of The Richard Grand Society; trustee of Headway, the Brain Injuries Association; chairman Headway, London.
Publications: Spinal Injuries Case Studies; personal injury chapter in the 'Penguin Guide to the Law 2001'.
Personal: Born 1960. Educated at Oratory School and Bristol Polytechnic (1981 LLB Hons). Resides London. Married with two daughters. Enjoys fine wines, golf, swimming, and time off in France.

CARR, Robert
Anderson Strathern WS, Edinburgh
(0131) 220 2345
robert.carr@andersonstrathern.co.uk
Specialisation: Partner in litigation department. Accredited by the Law Society of Scotland as a medical negligence specialist and admitted as a solicitor/advocate with extended rights of audience in the highest Scottish civil courts. Almost 20 years of practice in civil litigation covering all areas of court and tribunal work. One of a team involved in advising insurers, particularly in personal injuries and related actions, and in advising the Royal College of Nursing as their appointed Scottish agents. The RCN instructions cover the full spectrum of criminal and civil court work and employment law matters, including frequent advice on medical negligence issues and regular appearance at fatal accident enquiries. Also speaks and lectures to insurers, nurses and doctors on many aspects of civil law and court procedure and practice. Head of the firm's Parliamentary Unit; assisted the RCN in its evidence before the Scottish Parliament on the Adults with an Incapacity Bill. Represented the Denholm family at the much publicised recent fatal accident enquiry in relation to the death of Darren Denholm who died whilst undergoing dental surgery under general anaesthetic; the case resulted in a finding that dental surgery under general anaesthetic should no longer be conducted outside a hospital setting. *Anderson Strathern* also dealt with the case of Richard Adamson, one of the first medical negligence actions in Scotland to proceed before a jury for almost 50 years, which resulted in an award for pain and suffering of £100,000 for a young man whose only testicle was negligently removed by doctors at a hospital in West Lothian. Has also been pioneering in Scotland damages for children who have suffered disability as a consequence of their mothers undergoing anticonvulsant therapy whilst pregnant.

CARSON, Peter
Rowley Ashworth, Leeds (0113) 244 2018

CHANDLER, Pauline
Pannone & Partners, Manchester (0161) 909 3000
pauline.chandler@pannone.co.uk
Specialisation: Plaintiff personal injury work comprising industrial accidents and disease including asbestos claims Owen v IMI (bystander asbestos case); Jeromson v Shell Tankers in the Court of Appeal (asbestos mesolthelioma in marine engineers); asthma (including a series of groundbreaking AGM asthma cases settled in 2001); lead welders bronchitis (Knox and Others v Cammel Lairds); lung disease; deafness; vibration; repetitive strain; passive smoking cases; solvent damage (Jenkins v MOD, brain damage from trike); professional negligence; fatal disease and accident cases (William v Great Ormond Street Hospital).
Prof. Memberships: Law Society Personal Injury Panel Assessor.
Career: Degree at Manchester University. Admitted 1974. Specialised in personal injury and disease work for 25 years at *Thomsons*. Joined *Pannone & Partners* as a partner in 1999.

CHAPMAN, Richard
Chapman Everatt, Wolverhampton
(01902) 717 700
rdc@chapmaneveratt.co.uk
Specialisation: Partner specialising in defendant personal injury. Specialises in defendant personal injury. The whole firm acts exclusively for insurers and has no private clients. Has appeared on radio and television.
Prof. Memberships: Law Society, Birmingham Law Society, Birmingham Medico Legal Society.
Career: Qualified in 1970. Founding partner of *Chapman Everatt* in May 1992. Birmingham Law Society Council member 1979-2000 and President for 1996/97.
Personal: Born 7 October 1945. Educated at Birchfield School 1952-59, then Denstone College 1959-64. Governor of Birchfield School. Leisure interests include all sports, particularly golf and cricket, as well as theatre and cinema. Lives near Wolverhampton.

CHERRY, Anthony
Beachcroft Wansbroughs, London (020) 7894 6022
acherry@bwlaw.co.uk
Specialisation: Partner specialising in liability insurance claims and related risk management issues, handling cases of long-term exposure to chemical, physical and biological agents in the workplace, through products and in the environment. Has a special interest in the chemical industry. Lectures regularly on related topics and is on the editorial board of JPIL.
Prof. Memberships: President of the Forum of Insurance Lawyers from 1995 to 1997. He is a member of the Law Society Civil Litigation committee and was a member of the Vice Chancellor's working party on Practice Direction.
Career: Admitted May 1979, articles at *Bates & Partners*, Medico Legal section at ICI Legal Department from 1980 to 1983 (developing an expertise in long-term exposure to chemical and physical agents in the work place through products and the environment), *Stanley Simpson North* (then *Beachcroft Stanleys*) from 1983 to date, a partner since 1985.

CLARKE, Richard
Jacksons, Stockton on Tees (01642) 643643

CONNOR, Michael
Russell Jones & Walker, Manchester
(0161) 934 4897
m.j.connor@rjw.co.uk
Specialisation: Claimant personal injury principally on behalf of Trade Unions and Staff Organisations.
Prof. Memberships: APIL, PI Panel, Manchester Law Society (MLS) Council member since 1996, MLS Chair of Public Relations Committee and MLS Parliamentary Liaison Officer.
Career: Articled at *Whittles*, Manchester and Leeds 1989-91. *Thompsons*, Liverpool 1991-93, *Thompsons*, Stoke-on-Trent 1993-96, appointed partner 1995, *Thompsons* Manchester 1996-99, *Russell Jones and Walker* Dec 1999-date, appointed partner Jan 2001.
Publications: Regular contributor to Trade Union and Staff Organisation Journals.
Personal: Married with two boys aged eight and six. Spare time spent entertaining children and supporting Blackburn Rovers FC.

CRADICK, Simon
Morgan Cole, Cardiff (029) 2038 5385
simon.cradick@morgan-cole.com
Specialisation: Partner in general insurance division. Main area of practice is insurance litigation, covering all areas of personal injury work including maximum severity claims, industrial disease, 'RSI', employers' and public liability claims also professional indemnity. Contributes to a regular bulletin on legal update for all insurance clients. Prepared and lectured on all aspects of personal injury litigation.
Prof. Memberships: FOIL. Secretary of the Welsh Personal Injury Lawyers Association.
Career: Qualified in 1984, joined *Morgan Cole* in 1985 and become a partner in 1988.
Personal: Interests include skiing and travel.

CROOK, Christopher
Edwards Duthie, Ilford (020) 8514 9000

CROSS, John
McKinty & Wright, Belfast (028) 9024 6751
post@mckinty-wright.co.uk
Specialisation: Defending claims for motor insurers and defending medical negligence suits.
Prof. Memberships: Law Society of Northern Ireland and member of Contentious Business Committee of the Society.
Career: Qualified 1970. Partner in *McKinty & Wright* since 1975. Graduate of Trinity College Dublin (BA, LLB).
Personal: Married with four children. Leisure interests include computers and travel.

DACE, Nigel
Weightmans, Birmingham (0121) 233 2601
nigel.dace@weightmans.com
Specialisation: Partner specialising in personal injury work including motor, employers liability, public liability and professional and clinical negligence claims. Acts for insurance companies and

Lloyd's syndicates, at both High Court and County Court level. Very considerable experience of cases involving paraplegic and tetraplegic damage, brain damage and cerebral palsy. Has lectured on behalf of Birmingham Law Society and Worcester Law Society on 'The Practice and Procedure in Personal Injury Claims'.
Prof. Memberships: Birmingham Medico-Legal Society.
Career: Qualified 1973. Trained in London. Partner with *George Green & Co* 1982-96. Partner with *Weightmans* since May 1996.
Personal: Educated at Shrewsbury School 1963-67 and Liverpool University 1967-70. Leisure pursuits include playing golf and tennis, watching most sports, particularly football, and also theatre. Born 6th September 1949. Lives in Hagley, Worcestershire.

DAY, Martyn
Leigh, Day & Co, London (020) 7650 1200

DERBYSHIRE, Paul
Hugh James Ford Simey, Exeter (01392) 274 126
pad@fordsimey.co.uk
Specialisation: Partner in insurance division; lead partner at the Exeter office specialising in all aspects of defendant personal injury work. This year has been spent handling catastrophic injury claims and settlement of an amputee claim at one million pounds. Acted for one of the successful defendants in Rastin v British Steel (1994). Promotes use of I.T. in dealing with court applications.
Prof. Memberships: Law Society. Past Chairman of Devon & Exeter Law Society Litigation Committee.
Career: Qualified in 1973. Partner in *Ford Simey Daw Roberts* (now *Hugh James Ford Simey*) since 1979. Deputy District Judge 1986 to date. Recorder 1999.
Personal: Born 13 March 1949. Educated at St Brendans College, Bristol and Exeter University (1967-70). Trustee of Exeter Rugby Club and loves rugby, trout fishing and Dartmoor walking.

DESMOND, Adrian
Boyes Turner, Reading (0118) 952 7219
adesmond@boyesturnerlegal.co.uk
See under Clinical Negligence, p.165

DIAMOND, W. Maurice
Diamond Heron, Belfast (028) 90243726

DIAS, James
Sinton & Co, Newcastle upon Tyne (0191) 212 7800
j.dias@sinton.co.uk
Specialisation: Partner in personal injury department. Sole area of practice is personal injury and medical negligence. The personal injury is mainly on behalf of defendant insurers and the medical negligence on behalf of claimants.
Prof. Memberships: Law Society.
Career: Qualified in 1972 after articles with *John H Sinton & Co.* Became a partner in 1974.
Personal: Born 1948. Educated at Austin Friars School, Carlisle and Leeds University. Deputy District Judge. Deputy district chairman Appeals Service. Past president North of England Medico-Legal Society. Leisure interests where family commitments permit include sport and reading. Lives in Newcastle-upon-Tyne.

DICKINSON, Graham
Barlow Lyde & Gilbert, London (020) 7247 2277
gdickinson@blg.co.uk
Specialisation: All aspects of insurance liability work but primarily employers liability, industrial disease, motor and public liability claims. Extensive experience in major injury and loss claims and defence of group action.
Prof. Memberships: Member of the Chartered Insurance Institute.
Career: Qualified 1978. Partner *Robin Thompson & Partners* 1980. Founding partner *Dickinson Simpson* (Birmingham) 1983. Senior partner *Rowley Dickinson* (Birmingham) 1989. Appointed head of general insurance division, *Barlow Lyde & Gilbert* 1994.

DREWE, David
Crutes, Newcastle upon Tyne (0191) 212 5600
Specialisation: Partner in litigation department. Main area of practice is personal injury, acting largely on behalf of insurers, and professional negligence, acting exclusively for defendants including solicitors, surveyors, brokers and accountants. Making growing use of mediation in both personal injury and professional indemnity matters.
Prof. Memberships: FOIL, Law Society, Deputy Vice President Newcastle Upon Tyne Law Society.
Career: Joined *Crutes* on qualifying in 1981. Became a partner in 1986.
Personal: Born 15th July 1957. Educated at Merchant Taylor's School, Crosby 1968-75, and Newcastle University 1975-78. Leisure interests include walking, theatre, cinema and reading. Lives in Newcastle upon Tyne.

ETTINGER, Colin
Irwin Mitchell, London (020) 7404 3600
Specialisation: Partner specialising in personal injury and trade union law; conducts catastrophic injury cases of a high value and has particular specialities in workplace accident cases and occupational health matters.
Prof. Memberships: Executive council member Association of Personal Injury Lawyers; convenor Health & Safety Group of the Society of Labour Lawyers; patron for the charity Roadpeace; member of the OSS Professional Negligence Panel. Consultant Editor of J.P.I.L.
Career: Articled *Robin Thompson & Partners*; qualified 1978; partner 1980-95; partner *Irwin Mitchell* 1995. Fellow of College of Personal Injury Law.
Personal: Born 1952, London. Interests: current affairs, circuit training, football, cinema, jazz.

EVANS, Rod
Ensor Byfield, Southampton (023) 8048 3200

FIFE, Robert
Anderson Strathern WS, Edinburgh (0131) 220 2345
robert.fife@andersonstrathern.co.uk
Specialisation: All areas of personal injury litigation (pensions and defamation) acting on behalf of trade union clients and insurers. Particular interest in Health Service Law. Regularly lectures to insurers and nursing profession. Also handles general commercial litigation including defamation, professional negligence and advising local authorities.
Career: Qualified 1978. Partner in Litigation Department 1982. Solicitor Advocate 1995. Part-time Chairman of Appeals Committee of the Institute of Chartered Accountants of Scotland. Part-time Sheriff 2000.
Personal: Born 2nd Sept 1955. School Governor. Lives in Edinburgh.

FINNIGAN, Kevin
James Chapman & Co, Manchester (0161) 828 8000
kevin.finnigan@james-chapman.co.uk
Specialisation: Head of personal injury department. He has extensive experience in dealing with severe brain and spine injury claims involving maximum awards. He has pioneered successfully the development of a consensual approach with claimants' solicitors resulting in early economic settlement of the largest personal injury claims. He is a frequent speaker at conferences and seminars on the topic of handling catastrophic personal injury claims. He has worked in true partnership with insurers by assisting them to develop a pro-active approach.
Prof. Memberships: Manchester Law Society and FOIL.
Career: Educated at St Bedes College, Hull University LLB (Hons) – 1975. Articled at *James Chapman & Co.* Admitted 1978.
Personal: Born 18.12.53. Married with three children. Enjoys hill walking particularly in Ireland, reading and consuming Guinness.

GARRETT, Graeme
Digby Brown, Glasgow (0131) 225 8505
ggarrett@digbybrown.co.uk
Specialisation: Personal injury. Acted for several clients in Piper Alpha disaster. Member of Scottish Myodil Steering committee.
Prof. Memberships: Member of APIL since 1991; council member Law Society of Scotland 1992-95; convenor Law Society of Scotland Personal Injury panel 1996-2000; member Ogden Tables Working Party.
Career: Qualified as solicitor 1977. *Allan McDougall & Co*, Edinburgh 1979-91, partner; *Thompsons*, Edinburgh 1991-97, partner; *Digby Brown*, Edinburgh 1997-present, partner, managing partner since 2000.
Personal: Educated Royal High School, Edinburgh and Edinburgh University. Married with two daughters. Interests include rugby, malt whiskies and dogs.

GIBSON MBE, Michael
Tughan & Co, Belfast (028) 9055 3300
michael.gibson@tughan.co.uk
Specialisation: Partner and head of litigation department. Main areas of practice are personal injury, pharmaceutical and asbestos related litigations.

GOODMAN, Sarah
Thompsons, Birmingham (0121) 621 200

HARDING, Andrew
Hugh James Ford Simey, Cardiff (029) 2022 4871
andrew.harding@hjfs.co.uk
Specialisation: Partner and head of the claimant personal injury litigation group in the firm's head office. Specialises in catastrophic injury claims with particular interest and speciality in claims involving head injury. Established the firm's head injury unit in 1998. Also undertakes clinical negligence work and solicitors' negligence claims.
Prof. Memberships: Member of the Law Society's Personal Injury Panel and the Association of Personal Injury Lawyers. Trustee and chairman of Headway Cardiff and Childrens' Brain Injury Trust (CBIT) Cymru. Recorder sitting on Wales and Chester circuit.
Career: Born 10.06.61. Graduate of University Col-

lege Cardiff. Joined the firm in 1982 and qualified in 1984. Partner since 1986.

HARVEY, Mark
Hugh James Ford Simey, Cardiff (029) 2022 4871
mark.harvey@hjfs.co.uk
Specialisation: Personal injury, clinical negligence, product liability; representing victims of transport accidents including P&O Lifeboat; Maidenhead Rail Fire; co-ordinating the Gerona Air crash litigation and member of the steering committees of Southall and Ladbroke Grove rail crashes. Also household product failures including sanitary and cosmetic items.
Prof. Memberships: Secretary of APIL; PEOPIL; ATLA; Swansea Law Society PRO; National Back Pain Association and British Association of Sports and the Law; Editorial Board Wales Law Today; Headway; Holiday Travelwatch.
Career: 1987 Legal Executive, *Owen White*; qualified 1990 *Lawford & Co*; partner *Smith Llewelyn Partnership* 1995 – May 2001; partner, *Hugh James Ford Simey.*
Personal: Born September 1962; Wine Bluffer; Footballer; Golfer and Skier; resides Vale of Glamorgan.

HENDERSON, Stuart
Irwin Mitchell, Birmingham (0121) 212 1828
Specialisation: Partner in personal injury department. Particular emphasis on catastrophic spinal cord and brain injury, fatal accident claims, clinical negligence and travel litigation. Heads firm's plaintiff personal injury department in Birmingham. Acted in a number cases involving some of the highest award of damages in personal injury in the UK including the Leung case, (a record £3.4 million in 1994) and the Luhar case (a record £5.1 million in 2000). Acting in numerous major group actions for illness suffered by holiday makers against tour operators. Has extensive media experience and lectures in-house and externally.
Prof. Memberships: APIL, Law Society.
Career: Qualified in 1992. Joined *Robin Thompson & Partners* in 1979, becoming a partner in 1992. Partner at *Irwin Mitchell* from January 1995.
Personal: Born 20th February 1958. Attended UCE Birmingham.

HERBERT, Andrew
Thompsons, Bristol (0117) 304 2400

HOPKINS, Ian
Leo Abse & Cohen, Cardiff (02920) 383 252
ianhopkins@leoabse.co.uk
Specialisation: Partner in litigation department. Personal injury litigation specialist. Member of Law Society PI panel and scheme contact for Law Society's Accident Line. Handles large personal injury claims for both plaintiffs and defendants including a substantial case load of industrial disease claims (particularly occupational asthma and asbestosis). Clients include Trade Unions, insurance companies and the general public. Supervisor in Legal Aid Board Franchised Legal Aid department. Member of Steering committee for Severn Tunnel train crash.
Prof. Memberships: Law Society, APIL, Personal Injury panel.
Career: Qualified in 1987. Became a partner at *Leo Abse & Cohen* in 1990.
Personal: Born 20 August 1961. Educated at Aberdare Grammar School and Kingston University 1979-82. Masters in Business Administration, University of Glamorgan. Lives in Aberdare.

HOTCHIN, Samuel
Beachcroft Wansbroughs, Leeds (0113) 251 4700
shotchin@bwlaw.co.uk
Specialisation: Consultant in general insurance department. Insurance litigator. Specialises in personal injury, product liability and insurance law, including fraudulent claims, policy interpretation and liability.
Career: Qualified and joined *Wansbroughs Willey Hargrave* in 1979. Became a partner in 1982. Consultant in *Beachcroft Wansbroughs* in 1999.

IRVINE, Mariel
Kennedys, London (020) 7638 3688

JACKSON, Carol
Pannone & Partners, Manchester (0161) 909 3000
carol.jackson@pannone.co.uk
Specialisation: Serious injuries, head, spine and fatal accidents. Settlements: Maidenhead train crash; tetraplegic claim £2.75m; complex liability Clegg v Sunset Holidays diving into swimming pool in Spain; CICA 'baby shaking' case £365k; £2m for serious head injuries sustained by 40 year old when ladder fell off passing van; action against driver and MENCAP for RTA young woman with pre-existing learning difficulties when she strayed out of MENCAP college onto dual carriageway £1.15m; employees liability including acute and serious head injuries £620k; serious head injury cases pending for Hong Kong national. Recently successful in jurisdiction argument for fatally catastrophic accident in Lanzarote second jurisdiction in England. Most recent settlement paraplegic and head injury £3.45m.
Prof. Memberships: Law Society Personal Injury Panel, APIL, Fellow of CPIL, Headway, SIA and Richard Grand Society.
Career: Admitted as a solicitor in 1981, became partner with *Pannone & Partners* in 1994. Head of personal injury department.

JEFFERSON, Ian
C & H Jefferson, Belfast (028) 9032 9545
ianjefferson@chjefferson.co.uk
Specialisation: Senior partner specialising in personal injury work, primarily but not exclusively for defendants. Clients include major insurance companies and Lloyds syndicates. Considerable experience of cases involving catastrophic injuries including brain damage, spinal injuries and fatal accidents.
Prof. Memberships: Council of the Law Society of Northern Ireland; area representative of FOIL; Headway; Spinal Injuries Association; NI Medico-Legal Society; PEOPIL.
Career: Qualified Northern Ireland 1971. England 1990.
Personal: Fishing, sailing, hockey and theatre.

JOHN, Simon
Cunningham John, Thetford (01842) 752401
See under Clinical Negligence, p.167

JONES, David
Morgan Jones & Pett, Great Yarmouth (01493) 334700

KEMP, Sandy
Burnside Kemp Fraser, Aberdeen (01224) 327500
See under Employment, p.335

KEYDEN, Gordon
Simpson & Marwick WS, Edinburgh (0131) 557 1545

KITSON, Paul
Russell Jones & Walker, London (020) 7837 2808
Specialisation: Plaintiff personal injury specialist. Has successfully pursued numerous claims for injuries on the sports field for footballers and rugby players. Has lectured at many conferences on sports injury claims, road traffic accident litigation.
Prof. Memberships: Past committee member of British Association of Sport & the Law; Member of the Association of Personal Injury Lawyers; coordinator of Greater London Regional Group of APIL; Member of Law Society Personal Injury panel.
Career: Partner with *Russell Jones & Walker* since 1992.

LAWTON, Anthony
Thompsons, London (020) 7290 0000

LEE, Terry
Evill and Coleman, London (020) 8789 9221
Terry.Lee@evillandcoleman.co.uk
See under Clinical Negligence, p.168

LEECH, Catherine
Pannone & Partners, Manchester (0161) 909 3000
catherine.leech@pannone.co.uk
Specialisation: All types of personal injury work especially catastrophic injury claims (particularly spinal), aviation law and disaster litigation, product liability litigation and multi-party actions.
Prof. Memberships: Personal Injury Panel since 1995; APIL Co-ordinator Product Liability and Consumer Affairs SIG; Spinal Injury Association Panel; Association of Trial Lawyers of America. Fellow of the College of Personal Injury Law.
Career: Attended University of Wales, Cardiff and College of Law, Chester. Trained at *Ryland Martineau* then *Pannone and Partners.* Admitted September 1987. Became partner with firm May 1991. Lectures in PI law for Law Society/AWS Returners course and other continuing education suppliers.
Personal: Married with three children. Enjoys running, rowing and spending time with family. Member of SIA Ball committee.

LEWIS, Geoffrey
Buller Jeffries, Birmingham (0121) 200 0419
geoff.lewis@bullerjeffries.co.uk
Specialisation: Extensive insurance related practice with some claimant work as well. Catastrophic injury cases, Fatal Accidents Act, employers' liability and property claims. Local authority work and Motor Insurers' Bureau specialist. Policy problems and interpretation. Enjoys unusual or novel accident claims involving points of law.
Prof. Memberships: Law Society; Birmingham Law Society; FOIL.
Career: Articled to Roger Coates at *Buller Jeffries* 1971. Qualified 1973 and partner 1979.
Personal: Born 1949. Graduated 1970 external London University LLB, 2:1 (Hons). Leisure interests include running (London Marathon 1996 and 2001), ballroom dancing, music and DIY.

LUMSDEN, Lawrence
Thompsons, Edinburgh (0131) 225 4297

MAGUIRE, Frank
Thompsons, Glasgow (0141) 221 8840

MANSFIELD, Collin
Whittles, Manchester (0161) 228 2061

LEADERS IN PERSONAL INJURY

MARSHALL, David
Anthony Gold, London (020) 7940 4000
Specialisation: Principal area of practice – personal injury and medical negligence work. Member of the Law Society's Personal Injury and Medical Negligence panels. Acted in APIL campaigns on Legal Aid, Lord Woolf's Report and on the development of Conditional Fees.
Prof. Memberships: Law Society, APIL (executive committee member since 1996 and treasurer since 1998).
Career: Joined *Anthony Gold, Lerman & Muirhead* as a trainee solicitor in 1985, qualifying in 1987 and becoming a partner in 1989. Managing partner 1997.
Personal: Born 5 June 1962. Education – Queen's College, Oxford, 1980-1983. Lives in Herne Hill, South London. Honorary Treasurer, Blackfriars Advice Centre. Leisure interests include foreign travel, history and contemporary fiction.

MCCARTHY, Frances
Pattinson & Brewer, London (020) 7400 5100
Specialisation: Partner in Personal Injury Department. Main area of practice is workplace accident and occupational disease claims. Also handles medical negligence and other areas of personal injury. Has handled successful appeals to the European Court of Justice on the question of equal treatment in matters of Social Security. Regular lecturer for Legal Action Group and other bodies.
Prof. Memberships: Law Society, Association of Personal Injury Lawyers, Association of Trial Lawyers of America, Environmental Law Foundation.
Career: Qualified in 1981. Joined *Pattinson & Brewer* in 1979, becoming a Partner in 1985. President of APIL, Secretary of the International Practice Section of ATLA, founder member of ELF. Editorial Board of Journal for Personal Injury Law.
Publications: Co-author of 'Know How for Personal Injury Lawyers'.

MCCOOL, Geraldine
Leigh, Day & Co, Manchester (0161) 832 7722
gmccool@leighday.co.uk
Specialisation: Main area of practice is aviation for plaintiffs, product liability and MOD claims. Cases have included Lockerbie, British Midland at Kegworth, Piper Alpha and Chinook Mull of Kintyre crash 1994.
Prof. Memberships: APIL, ATLA, past chairman of Young Solicitors Group. Member of Law Society's Personal Injury panel. On panel of mediators in Personal Injury for Court of Appeal cases. Council member Manchester Law Society.
Publications: Co-Author of Longmans 'Know How PI', 'Multi Party Actions' by LAG and 'Civil Litigation Handbook' published by the Law Society.
Personal: Born 20 April 1961.

MCEVOY, Eamonn E.
Eamonn McEvoy & Co, Lurgan (028) 3832 7734

MEERAN, Richard
Leigh, Day & Co, London (020) 7650 1200
Specialisation: Practice covers environmental, product liability and personal injury claims including actions for damage caused by chemicals, noise, lead paint and asbestos; property devaluation arising from contaminated land, overseas claimants against UK companies (several reported cases), many of these actions being multiparty in nature. Numerous publications in scientific and legal journals and newspapers.
Prof. Memberships: APIL; London Legal Aid Area committee chair. Solicitors' Human Rights Group. International Law Association.
Career: Admitted April 1988. Partner at *Leigh Day* since 1991.
Publications: 'Contributing editor Journal of Personal Injury Law'.
Personal: Born 23 June 1961. BSc (London University 1983), LLM Advanced Litigation (Nottingham Law School) 1996.

MOORE, George K.
HBM Sayers, Glasgow (0141) 353 2121

NELSON-JONES, Rodney
Field Fisher Waterhouse, London (020) 7861 4022
rnj@ffwlaw.com
Specialisation: Partner in charge of personal injury litigation department. Personal injury work includes asbestosis, aviation and road accidents. Also handles medical negligence work. Cases have included the M1 Air Crash (Steering Committee Member), Bryce v Swan Hunter Group (Asbestosis), and Pendergast v Sam & Dee (medical negligence).
Prof. Memberships: Law Society.
Career: Qualified in 1975. Worked at *Prothero & Prothero* 1973-77 and *L Bingham & Co* 1977-83. Joined *Field Fisher Waterhouse* in 1983.
Publications: Co-author of 'Product Liability – The New Law Under the Consumer Protection Act 1987' (2nd edn 1988), 'Medical Negligence Case Law' (2nd edn 1995) 'Personal Injury Limitation Law' (1994), 'Computing Personal Injury Damages' (3rd edn 2000), 'Multipliers' (1998) and 'Butterworths Personal Injury Damages Statistics' (4th edn 2001). Contributor to 'Structured Settlements – A Practical Guide', 'Butterworths Personal Injury Litigation Service' and 'The Medical Accidents Handbook'.
Personal: Born on 11 February 1947. Educated at Repton School and Hertford College, Oxford (MA Oxon). Lives in London.

OSBORNE, Thomas R.
Osborne Morris & Morgan, Leighton Buzzard (01525) 378177

PADFIELD, Brendan
Eversheds, Ipswich (01473) 284428
brendanpadfield@eversheds.com
Specialisation: Head of defendant personal injury for *Eversheds* nationally and head of insurance/claims for the East of England. Works on behalf of insurance companies, large self-insureds and P & I clubs, dealing with road traffic employers and public liability claims. Also works for the health service.
Prof. Memberships: Law Society, Norfolk and Norwich Medico Legal Society, Suffolk Medico Legal Society, Association of Serious Injury Solicitors.
Career: Qualified 1984; became a partner in 1990.
Personal: Born October 1959. Attended University College Durham. Lives in Suffolk. Interests include regional history, wine and cooking.

PARKER, Alison
Bolt Burdon, London (020) 7288 4700

PATTERSON, Frank
Leigh, Day & Co, Manchester (0161) 832 7722
Specialisation: Maximum severity cases, including spinal cord injury and acquired brain injury litigation, acting exclusively on behalf of claimants. He is a member of the Spinal Injuries Association Specialist panel and the Headway Specialist panel. He also deals with complex and high value industrial accident and industrial disease litigation on behalf of Trade Union clients. He has experience of coordinating large multi-party PI actions, including international industrial disease litigation. He has experience of dealing with the television, radio and newspaper media in respect of high profile litigation. A regular lecturer on specialist legal topics to the legal profession.
Prof. Memberships: Member of the Law Society's Personal Injury Specialist panel.
Career: Qualified in 1986, having served articles with *Pannone & Partners*. Became a partner in 1990, and head of personal injury litigation in 1993. Partner at *Leigh Day & Co* from December 1995.
Publications: Co-author 'PI Know How' – published by Longmans. Co-author 'Personal Injury Precedents & Pleadings' – published by Sweet & Maxwell, former General Editor 'Personal Injury Precedents & Pleadings.'
Personal: Born 6 December 1959, graduated from University of Manchester.

PERRY, Timothy
Weightmans, Birmingham (0121) 233 2601
tim.perry@weightmans.com
Specialisation: Mainly defendant insurance and associated personal injury work. Predominantly deals with employers' liability and public liability claims, to include catastrophic injuries and asbestosis, deafness and other industrial diseases.
Prof. Memberships: Law Society and Birmingham Law Society.
Career: Educated at Abraham Darby Comprehensive in Telford and then Hull University. After qualifying in 1974, was assistant solicitor at *Browne Jacobson*. Joined *William Hatton* in 1979. Became a partner in 1981.
Personal: Married and lives in Birmingham. Interests include motor sport and football.

PESCOD, Peter
Hay & Kilner, Newcastle upon Tyne
(0191) 232 8345
lawyers@hay-kilner.co.uk
Specialisation: Partner in Litigation Department. Main area of practice is personal injury, acting primarily for major insurers in all types of accident/disease claims. Handles professional negligence work relating to surveyors, accountants, insurance brokers and architects. Has lectured on medical negligence and special damages and expert evidence.
Prof. Memberships: Law Society, Personal Injury Panel, FOIL (Forum of Insurance Lawyers), FHS Appeals Authority, Deputy District Judge. ADR Mediator.
Career: Joined *Hay & Kilner* in 1973. Qualified in 1975 and became a Partner in 1976.
Personal: Born 29th June 1951. Educated at Queen Elizabeth Grammar, Darlington 1962-69 and Newcastle University 1969-72.

PICKERING, John
Irwin Mitchell, Sheffield (0114) 276 7777
pickeringj@irwinmitchell.co.uk
Specialisation: Partner and head of personal injury department; specialist interest in medical negligence, catastrophic injury cases and cases with an international content. Important cases include Hepworth v Kerr (medical negligence case in which a patient suffered paralysis after a routine middle ear operation); Bird v Hussain (a record award for chronic pain suffered as a result of a road traffic accident); Thomas v Charles (head injury sustained abroad, damages

£750,000, then a record award for the Canary Islands); Ward v Newalls Insulations and Cape Contractors (the then highest damages award in this country of £750,000 for an asbestos disease case); Hodgson & Others v Imperial Tobacco Ltd and Gallagher & Hergall Ltd (acting on behalf of smoking related lung cancer victims against the major UK tobacco manufacturers, case included a Court of Appeal decision on conditional fee agreements); Van Oudenhoven v Griffin Inns Ltd (£950,000 damages for head injury as a result of pub blackboard accident); dealt with the two cerebral palsy cases involved in the Heil v Ranking landmark judgment in the Court of Appeal, namely Warren (£3.1 million damages) and Annabel. Subsequent seperate Court of Appeal hearing on Warren dealt with the question of multiplier; other actions include acting in test cases for industrial deafness and Vibration White Finger, the latter leading to *Irwin Mitchell's* involvement in the VWF Solicitors Steering group and the subsequent £500 million settlement scheme with British Coal. Currently involved in the Hatfield and Selby train crash cases.
Prof. Memberships: Claimant Solicitors Representative on the Clinical Disputes Forum. Member of and Assessor for the Law Society's Personal Injury Panel. Member of The Law Society's Medical Negligence Panel and the AVMA Medical Negligence Panel. Former Executive Committee Member and a Secretary of APIL. Member of The Board of Governors of The Association of Trial Lawyers of America (ATLA) . Past co-chair of International Practice Section and Member of the Board of the Birth Trauma Litigation Group, England and Wales Representative of the Pan European Organisation of Personal Injury Lawyers (PEOPIL).
Career: Articled *Irwin Mitchell*; qualified 1979; partner 1980; National Head of Personal Injury Department of *Irwin Mitchell* and member of the Management Board.
Publications: Co-author of the Clinical Negligence Pre-Litigation Protocol. Regularly lectures in in the UK and abroad on the subjects of Medical Negligence amd Personal Injury. Co-author of Jordan's Civil Court Service and contributor to Clinical Negligence in General Practice.
Personal: Born 1955, resides Sheffield. Married with two children. Interests include theatre, squash, golf and motor racing.

PICKERING, John
John Pickering & Partners, Oldham
(0161) 834 1251

PORTEUS, Stephen
Marrons, Newcastle upon Tyne (0191) 281 1304

POTTER, Hugh
Hugh Potter & Company, Serious Injury Solicitors, Manchester (0161) 237 5888
hughpotter.com
Specialisation: Mainly brain and spinal cord injury including medical negligence and professional negligence cases. Has growing caseload of English plaintiffs injured abroad. The firm has franchises for personal injury, clinical negligence and welfare benefits.
Prof. Memberships: Fellow of the College of Personal Injury Law, Member of the Law Society Personal Injury and Medical Negligence Panels, Member of AVMA Panel, Richard Grand Society and 10 year membership of APIL.
Career: Qualified in 1988, became a partner in *Pannone Napier* and *Pannone & Partners* in 1990 and joined *Perkins & Company* as a partner in 1994. Formed *Hugh Potter & Company Serious Injury Solicitors* on 1st May 1998.
Personal: Born 8 June 1962. Fund raiser for Headway and Spinal Injuries Association.

PRAIN, David
Rowley Ashworth, Wolverhampton
(01902) 771551

PRICE, Hugh
Morgan Cole, Cardiff (029) 2038 5385
hugh.price@morgan-cole.com
Specialisation: Partner, insurance division. Main areas of practice are personal injury and professional negligence for insurance clients. Has handled many maximum severity claims including quadraplegia and serious head injury cases. Professional negligence work for solicitors, brokers, engineers, surveyors and accountants. Frequent lecturer on Woolf changes (CPR); also lectured on adequacy of professional indemnity cover to RICS. Member of SIF Protocol drafting working party and CGU reserving guidelines drafting team.
Prof. Memberships: Deputy District Judge 1988-1997. President of Cardiff Law Society 1998/9; member of Law Society Personal Injury panel and FOIL. Trained ADR mediator.
Career: Articled at *Hardwickes* (now *Morgan Cole*) and qualified in 1975; partner in 1978.

RENOUF, Terence
Berrymans Lace Mawer, London (020) 7638 2811
terry.renouf@blm-law.com
Specialisation: Personal injury acting for defendants in all aspects of liability insurance relating to insurers. Particular specialisation in disease related litigation.
Prof. Memberships: Liveryman of City of London Solicitors' Company.
Career: Admitted 1987, joined *Berrymans Lace Mawer* 1987, associate 1989, partner 1991. Member of Pre-Action Protocol Working Group assisting Lord Woolf on both interim and final 'Access to Justice' reports. Member of Law Society pre-action Protocols Working Group and Drafting Group of both Injury and Occupational Diseases Protocols.
Personal: Born 1960. Educated at Hautlieu School, Jersey, Durham University, Manchester Polytechnic.

RIGG, Bettina
Bond Pearce, Southampton (023) 8063 2211
brigg@bondpearce.com
Specialisation: Partner and Head of Insurance Group in Southampton. Specialises in personal injury and medical negligence claims for insurers and self insureds. Work includes a wide range of motor, employers' liability and public liability claims as well as all aspects of Health and Safety. Appears regularly as advocate in the Civil Courts and the Coroners Court.
Prof. Memberships: Member of the British Insurance Law Association, the Forum of Insurance Lawyers, the Chartered Insurance Institute and the Council of The Insurance Institute in Southampton.
Career: Qualified in 1982. Joined *Bond Pearce* in 1980, becoming Partner in 1989.

ROACH, Andrew
Beachcroft Wansbroughs, Birmingham
(0121) 698 5200
ARoach@bwlaw.co.uk
Specialisation: Partner handling all types of personal injury work including serious motor cases and public and employers' liability claims. Specialises in particular in gradual and modern diseases and sports law. Ran the successful defence of the co-defendant in the groundbreaking case of Smoulden v Whitworth & Nolan, the first case where liability attached to a referee for his handling of a rugby game. Also acts on large loss claims, especially arson and product liability (recently acted for Laboratoires Garnier), and advises on policy disputes of all types. Has spoken at AIRMIC and numerous other conferences on trends in industrial diseases and sports law.
Prof. Memberships: BILA, FOIL.
Career: Qualified 1980; solicitor *Lawrence Graham* 1980-82. Solicitor *Herbert Smith* 1982-86. *Wansbroughs Willey Hargrave* (now *Beachcroft Wansbroughs*) 1986.

ROBERTS, Gavin
Thompsons, Bristol (0117) 304 2400

ROWE, Bernard
Lyons Davidson, Bristol (0117) 904 5701
browe@lyonsdavidson.co.uk
Specialisation: Partner and Head of Personal Injury and Insurance. Principal area of practice is personal injury litigation arising from road traffic accidents. Heads a department of 180 personnel, handling personal injury and road traffic litigation for plaintiffs and defendants. Has been involved in numerous substantial personal injury cases, including structured settlements. Experienced lecturer at legal conferences and seminars. Organised 3-day international Conferences on Whiplash Injuries (1997 and 2000), Psychological Injuries (1998) and Fibromyalgia 2000 Conference. Served on Working Party to establish the Disability Assessment Unit and now Treasurer of BICMA (Bodily Injury Claims Management Association).
Prof. Memberships: Treasurer of Motor Accident Solicitors Society (Chairman 1992-94), Member Judicial Advisory Committee to European Whiplash Association. Treasurer of BICMA.
Career: Qualified in 1976. Partner at *Ivesons* in Hull from 1977. Joined *Lyons Davidson* in 1986 and became a Partner in 1987. Managing Partner 1992-94.
Personal: Born 21st December 1951. Educated at Watford Grammar School 1963-70 and Hull University 1970-73 (BA, Politics and Law). Leisure pursuits: fly fishing. Lives in Bristol.

ROXBURGH, James
Biggart Baillie, Glasgow (0141) 228 8000
jroxburgh@biggartbaillie.co.uk
Specialisation: Leading defence practitioner in industrial (particularly lung) disease cases. Scottish Regional Chairman of Forum of Insurance Lawyers and member of Panel of Solicitors advising Law Society's PI Insurers.
Career: Glasgow University BL 1963; partner *Biggart Baillie* 1968; senior partner, *Biggart Baillie* 1990-2000. Acted for claimants in a number of accidents involving oil industry in North Sea.
Personal: Married with two daughters, one son. Leisure interest include skiing, golf, tennis and bridge.

SCOTT, Toby
Eversheds, Newcastle upon Tyne (0191) 261 1661
tobyscott@eversheds.com
Specialisation: Defendant personal injury. Particularly interest and major area of practise is in insidious disease and technical claims. Much of the year has been devoted to advising on insidious disease exposure and other long term liabilities.
Prof. Memberships: Board Director of Northern Dispute Resolutions.
Career: Trained *Cohen Jackson/Ingledoms.* Qualified 1986. Assistant and subsequently partner in *Linley & Moher*, the niche insurance pratcice until merger with *Eversheds* in 2000.
Publications: Contributor to Insurance Day.
Personal: Born 1962. Resides Newcastle upon Tyne. Leisure interests include sailing, travel, wine.

SHORT, David
Lawford Kidd, Edinburgh (0131) 225 5214
law@lawfordkidd.co.uk
Specialisation: Exclusively acts for victims. Extensive practice acting on behalf of Trade Unions including AEEU, UNISON, BALPA and FirstAssist for ULR claims. Main area of practice, work related accidents and disease cases. Particular specialisation in aviation related accidents mainly representing pilots. Past steering committee member of Piper Alpa and Brent Spar disasters.
Prof. Memberships: Law Society of Scotland, Society of Writers to Her Majesty's Signet. Executive Councillor – APIL. ATLA member.
Career: Dundee and Strathclyde Universities, trained at *Lawford & Co,* London for period in 1980s. Qualified 1984.
Personal: Married – one son.

SLESS, Tania
Beachcroft Wansbroughs, London
(020) 7242 1011
tsless@bwlaw.co.uk
Specialisation: Partner in insurance litigation department specialising in employers', public, product liability claims and also serious motor injury claims. Particular expertise in work-related upper limb disorders, and stress claims. Clients include major retailers and motor manufacturers. Retains an interest in Irish claims, and has written and broadcast on comparative levels of compensation between this jurisdiction and Ireland.
Prof. Memberships: Member of Employers' Liability and Disease special interest group of FOIL; committee member of LSLA.
Career: Articled *Miley & Miley*, Dublin. Qualified 1985 in Ireland, 1991 in England and Wales. *Miley & Miley* 1985-88; *Prudential Assurance Company Limited* 1988-90; *Davies Arnold Cooper* 1990-99 (partner 1993); *Beachcroft Wansbroughs* 1999-date.
Personal: Born 1961. Trinity College, Dublin 1978-82. Married with two sons. Resides Highgate. Interests – reading, cinema, theatre, art.

SMITH, Sid
Thompsons, Edinburgh (0131) 225 4297

SOLLY, Gillian
Russell Jones & Walker, Bristol (0117) 927 3098
g.c.solly@rjw.co.uk
Specialisation: Clinical negligence mainly, although some serious personal injury including Heil v Rankin Court of Appeal (the general damages case). Has specialised in clinical negligence and personal injury work for claimants since 1983. The clinical negligence caseload is varied and substantial, during the last year including a £1.7 million CP settlement and several awards over £100,000. Managing partner at Bristol office since 1994.
Prof. Memberships: Founder member of APIL and first treasurer. Member Bristol Law Society, Bristol Medico-Legal Society APIL.
Personal: Educated at Beverley High School for Girls followed by Warwick University for law degree. Qualified April 1981. Joined current firm in 1983. Married with two children.

STAPLES, Martin
Vizards, Staples & Bannisters, London
(020) 7400 9999
mrs@vsb.co.uk
Specialisation: Introduced insurance litigation to *Vizards* in 1974 and became senior partner in its bicentenary year, 1997; spearheaded the development of all aspects of non marine insurance litigation with the firm, culminating in the merger with *Bannisters* to create the presently named firm. Today his concentration is upon policy construction and the resolution of major liability disputes. Also has wide experience of medical negligence claims, having run for seven years the original Thalidomide litigation and acted in Shewan v Westminster Hospitals. Also dealt with the first industrial deafness case Berry v Stone Manganese and other evolving disease claims involving asbestos, mica dust, talcosis, hardwood dust, rubber compounds and presently the test cases involving organophosphates – the Farmers' 'Sheep Dip' claims. Has also dealt with claims in respect of major disasters, employers liability, professional indemnity and coverage. Directly responsible for liability claims with BAA nationwide and acts for Royal & Sunalliance, Iron Trades, Prudential QBE etc.
Prof. Memberships: Immediate past president Forum of Insurance Lawyers (FOIL); associate member Fire Loss Association; founder member Bodily Injuries Claims Manager Association (BICMA).
Career: Articled *Wilkinson Kimbers & Staddon* 1962. Joined *Geoffrey Coombs & Co* Partner 1971 then amalgamation with *Vizards* as partner 1974. Spearheaded insurance litigation in firm. Senior partner *Vizards* 1997.
Personal: Born 1944. Educated Hounslow College. Interests: travel, sport. Reside London and Upper Dicker.

TAYLOR, Derek T
C & H Jefferson, Belfast (028) 9032 9545
Specialisation: Main area of practice is all aspects of industrial chest disease acting for defendants including all asbestos-related conditions and occupational asthma. Has some 15 years experience acting for major insurers who have carried EL and PL risks in industry. Other area of expertise is medical negligence. Has some 13 years experience acting for Health Boards in Northern Ireland in all kinds of medical negligence claims. Has acted for the defence in a number of successfully defended and high-profile obstetric cases.
Prof. Memberships: Law Society of NI, NI Medico-Legal Society.
Career: Qualified in 1975. Assistant Solicitor with *Harrison Leitch & Logan* 1975-1977. *L'Estrange & Brett* 1977-1978. Partner with *C&H Jefferson* 1979 to date.
Personal: Born 17th April 1949. Educated Bangor Grammar School, Co. Down and then Queen's University of Belfast 1968-1972. Leisure interests include hill walking and golf. Member of National Trust.

TENQUIST, Iain
Morgan Cole, Reading (0118) 955 3046
iain.tenquist@morgan.cole.com
Specialisation: Catastrophic injuries, in particular brain injuries. Public liability claims: led the litigation arising from the 60 vehicle pile-up on the M4 in March 1991 involving 10 fatalities; regular contributor of articles to journals; experienced speaker; divisional director.
Prof. Memberships: Law Society, Forum of Insurance Lawyers.
Career: 1969-76 Magdalen College School, Oxford. 1977-80 King's College, London (LLB). 1980-81 College of Law, Guilford. 1982-85 *Humfrys & Symonds*, Hereford (qualified 1994). 1985 to date *Morgan Cole.*

TUCKER, Andrew
Irwin Mitchell, Sheffield (0114) 276 7777
Specialisation: Litigation in respect of products giving rise to injury, particularly pharmaceutical products, medical devices, experience of multi-party litigation both product related and arising from transport disasters and occupational disease. Acted for Plaintiffs in many high profile cases including: Opren, Dalkon Shield, Benzodiazepines, Manchester Aircrash, "Herald of Free Enterprise", Kegworth Aircrash, "Marchioness"/"Bowbelle" collision, North Cornwall Water Pollution, Armley Asbestos, Human Growth Hormone/Creutzfeldt-Jacob Disease, tobacco, silicone implants, Mineworkers V.W.F. and Mineworkers Respiratory Disease.
Prof. Memberships: Law Society, Association of Personal Injury Lawyers, South Yorkshire Medico Legal Society, American Trial Lawyers Association, Australian Plaintiff Lawyers Association.
Career: Articled *Wallace Mitchell*, Nottingham. Qualified 1985. Partner, *Irwin Mitchell*, 1988.
Personal: Born October 1960, University of Liverpool, LL.B. Lives North Derbyshire.

TWEED, Paul
Johnsons, Belfast (02890) 240183
pt@johnsonslaw.co.uk
See under Defamation, p.288

TYLER, Alfred
Balfour & Manson, Edinburgh (0131) 200 1210
fred.tyler@balfour-manson.co.uk
Specialisation: Partner in litigation department. Main area of practice is personal injury (with special interest in head and spinal injuries) and medical negligence (with a special interest in birth cases). Also handles general commercial (including defamation and professional negligence) and aviation matters. Has been involved in major multi-party actions including the 1986 and Mull of Kintyre Chinook disasters, the Piper Alpha disaster, the Lockerbie disaster and the Brent Spar and Cormorant Alpha helicopter crashes, and the Scottish Myodil claims. Represented the pursuer in the House of Lords cases of Herd v Clyde Helicopters; the House of Lords appeal of McFarlane v Tayside Health Board, the failed sterilisation case, which is now the subject of to the European Couts of Human Rights; the current case of King v Bristow Helicopters.
Prof. Memberships: SSC; NP; Association of Personal Injury Lawyers (Scottish coordinator); Spinal

Injuries Association; Headway; Scottish Head Injury Forum (advisor to Management committee).
Career: Qualified in 1975, having joined *Balfour & Manson* in 1973. Became a partner in 1978.
Personal: Born 27 January 1951. Educated at Daniel Stewart's College, Edinburgh 1956-69 and Edinburgh University 1969-73. Enjoys golf. Lives in Edinburgh.

WALKER, Ian
Russell Jones & Walker, London (020) 7837 2808
Specialisation: Chairman and joint senior partner of personal injury department. Has specialised in plaintiff personal injury since 1975. Acted in the then largest CICB award in 1988. Also the then largest ever court fatal award (£920,000) in 1991. Lead solicitor in the Kings Cross fire cases. Regular lecturer for IBC, Jordans, Euroforum, Hawksmere and others. Immediate past president of Association of Personal Injury Lawyers. Former co-chair, International Section of Association of Trial Lawyers of America. 1993-95, co-ordinator for Information Technology Group APIL. Member of Board of Governors, Association of Trial Lawyers of America. Member of ABI and IUA Rehabilitation working parties. Senior Fellow, College of Personal Injury Law. Member of Executive Board, College of Personal Injury Law. Member of Editorial Board, Journal of Personal Injury Litigation. CEDR – accredited mediator. Vice-president, Bodily Injury Claims Management Association.
Prof. Memberships: Association of Personal Injury Lawyers (hon life member); Association of Trial Lawyers of America; Law Society; Holborn Law Society; Medico-Legal Society; Association of Plaintiff Lawyers of Australia; Society for Computers and the Law; London Solicitors Litigation Association; South African Association of Personal Injury Lawyers.
Career: Qualified in 1974. Joined *Russell Jones & Walker* in 1968, becoming a partner in 1977.
Publications: Co-author of 'Tribunal Practice and procedure 1985', 'Know-How for Personal Injury Lawyers 1993 and 1997', and editor in chief of the 'Journal of Personal Injury Litigation 1994/5'.
Personal: Born 15 April 1950. Attended Whitgift School 1961-68. Governor of an independent school. Leisure interests include music, golf, gardening, cooking and walking. Lives in Caterham, Surrey.

WEBSTER, John
Veale Wasbrough, Bristol (0117) 925 2020
jwebster@vwl.co.uk
Specialisation: Personal Injury acting for claimants in accident and disease cases. Special interest in head and spinal injury cases and fatal accident cases. Many asbestos injury and post traumatic stress disorder cases. Much experience of employers' liability, road accidents (including multi-party cases, Paddington rail crash, South African bus crash, M4 Hungerford multi vehicle and Avonmouth explosion) and product liability. Some interest in sports and holiday injury cases.
Prof. Memberships: Fellow of the College of Personal Injury Law; chairman of the Civil Courts committee, Bristol; Member of Bristol Law Society Council; Association of Personal Injury Lawyers; Bristol Medico Legal Society; panel member of Law Society Personal Injury panel; Spinal Injuries Association; Headway; MIND; Roadpeace.
Career: Qualified 1985. Joined *Veale Wasbrough* 1988. Partner in 1994 and head of the firm's personal injury team since 1996.
Personal: Born 1961. Manchester University.

WILLIAMS, Alun C.
Hay & Kilner, Newcastle upon Tyne (0191) 232 8345
lawyers@hay-kilner.co.uk
Specialisation: Partner in Litigation Department. Has specialised in personal injury work for defendants and claimants since 1979. Also handles health and safety and road traffic work. Has a particular interest in stress related and industrial disease claims.
Prof. Memberships: Personal Injury Panel, FOIL.
Career: Qualified in 1979. Joined *Hay & Kilner* in 1977, becoming a Partner in 1982.
Personal: Born 7th August 1955. Attended Newcastle University 1973-76. Leisure interests include military history, football, reading and music. Lives in Newcastle-upon-Tyne.

WILLIAMS, Gareth
Hugh James Ford Simey, Cardiff (029) 2022 4871
gareth.williams@hjfs.co.uk
Specialisation: Partner and head of commercial litigation division. Personal injury litigation for insurers. Has acted for insurers for more than 20 years and undertaken the usual range of personal injury work. Has a particular interest in health and safety matters. Also deals with commercial litigation, acting for a number of local companies and partnerships by whom he is regularly instructed to deal with contractual and other disputes. Advises major sports governing body on litigation and constitutional issues.
Prof. Memberships: Law Society; F.O.I.L.
Career: Joined *Hugh James* in 1975 and qualified in 1976. Became a partner in 1978. First solicitor in Wales to be appointed a Licensed Insolvency Practitioner. Deputy District Judge from 1991 to date.
Personal: Born 5th September 1951. Educated at Glan Clwyd High School 1962-69 and University College of Wales, Aberystwyth 1969-72 (Morgan Owen Law Prizeman). Leisure pursuits include sport, reading and music. Lives in Cowbridge.

WILLIAMS, Robin
Leo Abse & Cohen, Cardiff (02920) 383252
robinw@leoabse.co.uk
Specialisation: Head of trade union services department. Principal area of practice covers personal injury claims, employment and Trade Union law. Advises BFAWU, GMB,TGWU, UNIFI and USDAW business and private clients. Acts in industrial disease cases including asbestosis, deafness, asthma, RSI and dermatitis. Also handles fatal accident claims, employment injunctions and has extensive experience of all complaints to the Employment tribunal including mass dismissal claims, sex discrimination cases, transfer regulations disputes. Has acted in general chancery and commercial cases, particularly contested probate actions, winding up petitions and bankruptcy. Lectures on personal injury, employment and trade union law.
Prof. Memberships: Law Society; Personal Injury panel; APIL (regional coordinator of the South Wales and West Regional group); fellow of College of Personal Injury Lawyers.
Career: Qualified in 1980 while with *Leo Abse & Cohen* and became a partner in 1985.
Personal: Born 15 October 1955. Attended Glanafan Comprehensive School 1966-74 and London School of Economics 1974-77. Leisure pursuits include sport (rugby, soccer and badminton), theatre, art, cinema, modern music and reading. Lives in Cardiff.

WOOD, Michael
Simpson & Marwick WS, Edinburgh (0131) 557 1545

ZINDANI, Jeffry
Russell Jones & Walker, Birmingham (0121) 643 6800
Specialisation: Main area of practice is personal injury acting for a number of Trades Union clients. Acted in the largest noise induced deafness claim for a Police Firearms Officer. Acted in a number of lifting cases, and in particular in the reported case of Colclough v Staffordshire County Council 1993.
Prof. Memberships: Member of the Personal Injury panel, Law Society; Member of the Birmingham Medico-Legal Society; APIL.
Career: Qualified in 1989; April 1989 joined *Russell Jones & Walker* in Birmingham, became a partner in July 1994, local managing partner in 1998.
Publications: Author of book entitled 'Manual Handling Law and Litigation' (CLT Professional Publishing) and several articles.
Personal: Born on the 4 July 1963. Attended Moseley Comprehensive School and UCE LLB (Hons); University of Keele, MA (Industrial Relations).

PLANNING

OVERVIEW: The government's drive to reduce the time spent on enquiries and so shorten planning procedures seems to be working. Enquiry work is, on the whole, declining in favour of complex negotiation. Planners are increasingly focusing on the core areas of negotiation, strategy and CPO. A handful of the lawyers in this section are skilled advocates, and for them enquiry work remains a staple, while there is a marked increase in clients going to smaller niche firms for specific planning instruction.

RESEARCH APPROVED BY BMRB: *For this edition,* Chambers' *researchers conducted 6,552 interviews – 4,419 with law firms, 554 with barristers and 1,579 with clients.*

The validity of the research was scrutinised by BMRB International, who audited both the methodology and the results at our offices in July 2001. They interviewed Chambers' *researchers and cross-checked sample interviews. Details of the audit appear on page 7.*

LONDON

PLANNING • London	Ptnrs	Assts
1 Berwin Leighton Paisner	6	12
2 CMS Cameron McKenna	2	7
Denton Wilde Sapte	3	15
Nabarro Nathanson	4	7
3 Herbert Smith	2	12
Linklaters	4	13
SJ Berwin	2	2
4 Ashurst Morris Crisp	1	5
Clifford Chance	1	6
Lovells	1	4
Norton Rose	1	8
Osborne Clarke	2	n/a
5 Gouldens	2	1
Slaughter and May	1	1
Stephenson Harwood	1	3
Theodore Goddard	3	2
6 Dechert	n/a	4
DJ Freeman	n/a	1
Fladgate Fielder	1	1
Freshfields Bruckhaus Deringer	2	8
Lawrence Graham	3	2
Macfarlanes	1	2
Olswang	1	1
Simmons & Simmons	1	2
Travers Smith Braithwaite	1	2

This book is the product of 6,552 1/2-hour interviews. See p.7 for BMRB audit.
Within each band, firms are listed alphabetically.

Berwin Leighton Paisner (see firm details p.878) "*Undoubtedly in pole position,*" according to a substantial majority of interviewees, fears that this "*first-class outfit*" may be "*overstretched*" by its prodigious workload have been allayed by the elevation of two new partners this year. Although for some, "*size isn't everything,*" the scale and depth of the practice are legendary, and the team is known for its technical expertise and solid back-up. Riding on a strong property client base, the firm's enormous workload for Tesco remains the jewel in an impressive portfolio. A glittering list of clients is studded with plcs engaged in property development, industry and transport. The "*imaginative*" **Tim Hellier** (see p.666) is still "*active and impressive,*" while the "*technically brilliant*" and "*innovative*" **Timothy Pugh** (see p.668) "*keeps a cool head*" and was particularly recommended to researchers for his skill in difficult negotiations. Practice head **Ian Trehearne** (see p.670) is "*a bright cookie,*" with a reputation among his peers as a "*keen strategist.*" "*Co-operative and trustworthy,*" **Tim Smith** (see p.669) also retains his share of market support. The firm represented Blue Circle in a recent public inquiry, and securing planning permission and confirmed compulsory purchase orders for the Ferensway re-development of Hull city centre. **Clients:** Argent Group; BG; Berkeley Homes; Blue Circle Industries; Peel Holdings; Tesco Stores; The British Land Company; Home Office; Railtrack; PACE; Prudential; Southern Water.

CMS Cameron McKenna (see firm details p.922) Although the bulk of the group's profile has been bound up with the T5 project, its work on infrastructure projects and increasing focus on PFI should not be overlooked. The practice is said to be "*maturing nicely,*" with competitors acknowledging that the team "*really know what they are doing.*" Headed by "*planning magician*" **Tony Kitson** (see p.667), the team also includes the respected **Chris Williams**. In addition to T5 work, the firm advised The Wellcome Trust on its new headquarters building, and acted for Hutchison Ports on the development of Thamesport. **Clients:** AA; Berkeley Group; Centros Miller; Pricoa; J Sainsbury; Taylor Woodrow; Biffa Waste Services; Westminster City Council; Wellcome Trust.

Denton Wilde Sapte (see firm details p.939) Wide-ranging planning, with an emphasis on public sector work and a particularly strong reputation for performing its own advocacy. Researchers were impressed by the weight of commendation for the team, which is said to boast some "*impressively intelligent people.*" The team continues to work closely with public bodies such as the GLA, as well as lobbying and planning groups, such as London Tomorrow. Interpretation and advice in matters arising from the Human Rights Act is a niche strength. The team is led by **Stephen Ashworth** (see p.662), whose "*calm and assured*" style is commended by clients – they often refer to him as "*a class act.*" The "*unorthodox*" **Sandra Banks** applies her no-nonsense style to public sector work, while interviewees also continue to endorse **Margaret Casely-Hayford** (see p.662). Notable work over the last year includes acting for Thornfield Properties in securing consent for a transport, retail and leisure scheme in Redditch. The firm also acted for the London Borough of Tower Hamlets on the regeneration of central Stepney, including CPO and enquiry work. **Clients:** Sainsburys; Virgin; Marks & Spencer; Chelsea Village; English Partnerships; Carter Commercial; City Centre Restaurants; Department of the Environment, Transport and the Regions.

Nabarro Nathanson (see firm details p.1078) The firm complements its unsurpassed property litigation and local government practices with an "*able but discreet*" planning outfit. The recent acquisition of the "*clever and energetic*" **Martin Evans** (see p.664) from Ashurst Morris Crisp is a real coup, thought by peers to improve the team's capability to attract major planning instructions. The team is headed by "*the king-pin of compulsory purchase,*" **David Hawkins**. Among a respected team, **Gary Graves** (see

LEADING INDIVIDUALS		
★	**GREENWOOD Brian** Norton Rose	**THOMAS Patricia** SJ Berwin
1	**ASHWORTH Stephen** Denton Wilde Sapte	**CUNLIFFE Michael** Forsters
	GALLIMORE Michael Lovells	**HALL Brian** Clifford Chance
	HELLIER Tim Berwin Leighton Paisner	**JACKSON Ray** Linklaters
	KITSON Tony CMS Cameron McKenna	**MAX Richard** Olswang
	PUGH Tim Berwin Leighton Paisner	**TREHEARNE Ian** Berwin Leighton Paisner
2	**CASELY-HAYFORD Margaret** Denton Wilde Sapte	
	COOPER David Gouldens	**CURNOW Tony** Ashurst Morris Crisp
	DYER Carl Osborne Clarke	**EVANS Martin** Nabarro Nathanson
	GRAVES Gary Nabarro Nathanson	**HILLEBRON Richard** Slaughter and May
	HUGHES Norna Nabarro Nathanson	**QUAYLE Sophie** Herbert Smith
	RICKETTS Simon SJ Berwin	**ROBINSON Patrick** Herbert Smith
3	**BANKS Sandra** Denton Wilde Sapte	**EVANS Douglas** Theodore Goddard
	HAWKINS David Nabarro Nathanson	**JEEPS Barry** Stephenson Harwood
4	**BLANEY Trevor** Lawrence Graham	**FONGENIE Wesley** Osborne Clarke
	FRASER Moira Fladgate Fielder	**LEA Alison** Travers Smith Braithwaite
	QUALTROUGH John Simmons & Simmons	**REDMAN Michael** Clifford Chance
	TRUE Justin Dechert	**TURNER Angela** Gouldens
	WATCHMAN Paul Freshfields Bruckhaus	**WATKINS David** Linklaters
	WELLS Martin Stephenson Harwood	**WILLIAMS Christopher** Cameron McKenna
UP AND COMING		
	HOWARD Karen Ashurst Morris Crisp	**SMITH Tim** Berwin Leighton Paisner

See individuals' profiles p.662

p.665) and **Norna Hughes** (see p.666), who has a "*good grasp of detail and strategy,*" feature prominently. Especially commended for retail projects, the firm secured the quashing of the Secretary of State's blocking of the Brent Cross Shopping Centre development, and advised the Bristol Alliance on the expansion and rebuilding of Bristol's Broadmead shopping district. The firm assisted Sellar Properties and the Civil Service Sports Council in gaining planning permission for new sporting facilities in Portsmouth. **Clients:** Body Shop International; Capital One; Chase Bank; Civil Service Sports Council; Bristol Alliance; London Electricity; Costco Wholesale UK; English Partnerships; Hanover Property Unit Trust; Land Securities.

Herbert Smith (see firm details p.993) Combining 'pure' planning with more transactional property capability, the firm tends to advise on individual big-ticket projects. Minerals work remains a speciality, while an exceptionally strong development client base is also acknowledged by competitors. The practice is headed by the "*ebullient*" **Sophie Quayle** (see p.668), popular with clients and peers for her "*engaging manner.*" She is said to be "*definite*" in her advice, "*honest and straightforward.*" **Patrick Robinson**'s (see p.669) "*intellectual rigour*" is praised by clients, who value his "*spot-on strategic instincts.*" Highlight instructions of the last year include the Lots Road power station in Chelsea, development proposals for Selfridges and some large developments for British Land. **Clients:** Allied London; Schroder Property Investment Management; British Land; CABE; Hutchison Whampoa; Ove Arup; Selfridges; British Museum; Harrods.

Linklaters (see firm details p.1042) Our interviewees were unanimous in their acknowledgment of this firm's "*excellent year.*" Its "*strong*" planning practice feeds off a "*magnificent*" property base, and has won a number of high profile instructions. Clients value the "*extreme caution and thoroughness*" with which the team anticipates obstacles. The practice is headed by "*hardy perennial*" **Ray Jackson** (see p.666), described by clients as "*a wit and a workaholic*" who delivers "*fantastic service.*" He is supported by the "*sensible*" **David Watkins** (see p.670), commended for his "*top quality advice.*" The group advised Heron Corporation on all aspects of its proposed 222 metre tower at Bishopsgate, and assisted the BBC on various redevelopments. Instructed by the SRA in connection with TWA orders for Thameslink infrastructure projects, the firm also acted for Fulham Stadium in ongoing matters relating to the new riverside stadium development, including matters against the Secretary of State in the High Court. **Clients:** Heron Corporation; BBC; Lend Lease Europe; Swiss Re; Strategic Rail Authority; Fulham Stadium; Crown Estate; Development Securities; Goldman Sachs; BT; Railtrack.

SJ Berwin (see firm details p.879) Still presided over by the "*mighty presence*" of the "*awesomely experienced*" **Patricia Thomas**, the team is felt to depend heavily for its profile on her wide-ranging practice, where airports and regulatory work particularly stand out. She is supported by the "*clever*" **Simon Ricketts** (see p.669), whose "*meticulous*" work includes significant levels of advocacy. Recent highlights include advising the Walton Group on a major retail and leisure development, and acting for Sheffield City Airport on the objection to change of use of Finningley Airport. The firm also advised London City Airport in connection with the DLR extension under a TWA Order. **Clients:** Walton Group; London City Airport; Sheffield City Airport; Belfast International Airport; British Land; Marks & Spencer; Southern Water.

Ashurst Morris Crisp (see firm details p.866) The loss of key partner Michael Cunliffe to Forsters and the departure of Martin Evans to Nabarro Nathanson is widely considered to have weakened the firm's profile. However, a number of interviewees anticipate that "*veteran local authority soldier*" **Tony Curnow** (see p.663) will successfully build a fresh and cohesive team. His colleague **Karen Howard** (see p.666) is still regarded by clients as a lawyer of great promise. The firm has acted on the Colchester Garrison redevelopment for Sir Robert McAlpine, and advised Chelsfield on the redevelopment of the Paddington Basin and on the development of the Stratford Rail lands in East London. For the Royal Bank of Canada it advised on plans for a major regeneration project in Yorkshire and for Kvaerner it fended off challenges to plans for the Baltic Exchange. **Clients:** Sir Robert McAlpine; Chelsfield; Royal Bank of Canada; BAE Systems; Berkeley Strategic Land; Friends Provident Life Office.

Clifford Chance (see firm details p.919) Specialising in judicial review and CPO, the planning department gains stand-alone recognition from clients, in addition to benefitting from the presence of the firm's highly respected property practice. Leading figure **Brian Hall** (see p.666) is well served by an experienced team, which includes the "*focused and detailed*" **Michael Redman** (see p.668). Peers regard the two together as "*a great combination*" with particular strength in environmental matters. A profitable year has seen a notable increase in work arising from conflicts between telecoms clients and the government over the issue of mobile communications masts. Busy on behalf of a wide range of clients, including big retail and development names, the firm acted for Safeway Stores on a CPO related matter involving human rights issues, and advised the Burford Group on the long-running Avonmouth matter near Bristol. **Clients:** Burford Group; Canary Wharf Group; Chartwell Land; Coca-Cola Great Britain; Grantchester Group; HJ Heinz; John Laing Developments; Land Lease Europe; Safeway Stores; Railtrack.

Lovells (see firm details p.1044) The "*superb and likeable*" **Michael Gallimore** (see p.665) has combined fee-earning and managerial duties well, with peers reporting that he is "*as active as ever.*" A major boost to the practice is its commission to handle the King's Cross Development work for Argent St. George. Appearing on a number of impressive matters, the firm acted for Cory Environmental on a major appeal relating to its landfill operations and advised Prudential on the proposed redevelopment of the Arndale Centre, Manchester. For Ballymore Properties, the firm acted on proposed redevelopment projects near Canary Wharf and at Arrowhead Quay. It continues to advise Fairview New Homes on its residential development programme. **Clients:** Argent St. George; Ballymore Properties; Prudential; Fairview New Homes; Leading Rule; Church Commissioners; Ikea; Aberdeen Property Investors; Artesian; Greycoat; John Lewis; Waitrose.

Norton Rose (see firm details p.1082) This sizeable and "*tidy practice*" continues its "*sound*" planning work for a range of clients, especially in offices and housing developments, business parks, public inquiries and ports. The "*smooth and plausible*" **Brian Greenwood** (see p.665) remains the guiding star here. "*A tall poppy,*" he was repeatedly commended to researchers, especially for his advocacy. Highlight work for the team includes ongoing negotiations and applications for Castle Cement in connection with projects around the country. The firm acted for English Heritage on the Stonehenge project, and assisted Renewable Energy Systems on enquiries into the building of wind farms. **Clients:** Spitalfield Development Group; Esso; Renewable Energy Systems; Arlington Securities; British Aerospace; Hanover International; Helical Bar; Peabody Trust; Portfolio Holdings.

Osborne Clarke (see firm details p.1086) The merger of planning specialists McGuinness Finch with Osborne Clarke has grafted corporate muscle onto a team which was already a planning force in the retail industry. Clients appreciate the fact that the firm's lawyers are "*competitively priced*" and that work receives attention at partner level. Lead partner is the "*energetic and intelligent*" **Carl Dyer**, who is assisted by the "*sensible*" **Wesley Fongenie**. Key work has included securing planning permission for a factory outlet centre for Norcross, and advising a consortium of landowners on the proposed Cedar Park Business Park. For Immogy the firm assisted with a riverside residential proposal in central London. **Clients:** Asda Stores; Tesco Stores; Budgens Stores; Carter Commercial Developments; Peel Developments UK; Invensys; La Farge Redland Aggregates; Persimmon Homes.

Gouldens (see firm details p.976) Unusually for planning firms in London, the team concentrates on contentious matters. Star partner **David Cooper** (see p.663) was praised to researchers as "*an extraordinary lawyer, dedicated to his clients.*" A widely respected advocate, he has conducted more public enquiries than any other practising planning lawyer. The team also includes the respected **Angela Turner** (see p.670), whose expertise lies principally in environmental matters. The firm advised Arsenal FC on a large redevelopment on three sites, acted for Arlington Securities on a section 106 for Hatfield Aerodrome, and represented Pillar Property on the regeneration of Cricklewood. **Clients:** Pillar Property; Arlington Securities; Arsenal Football Club; Nomura International; Hawksmoor Estates; Bristol Airport; Benchmark Group; Burford Holdings; Waitrose.

Slaughter and May (see firm details p.1135) Pooling talents from across the firm's property and litigation departments, the practice's core work consists of planning applications and negotiation for an envied roster of existing clients. **Richard Hillebron** (see p.666), a senior assistant in the litigation department, is the outstanding practitioner here. He elicited approval for his "*excellent*" work, highlighted by advising Derwent Valley on a redevelopment in Soho. The firm also acted for a well-known investment house on a large development in Docklands as part of the Millennium Quarter Masterplan. **Clients:** Major corporates and financial institutions.

Stephenson Harwood (see firm details p.1141) The star here is the "*mighty impressive*" **Barry Jeeps** (see p.667) whose peers describe him as "*clued up*" and "*honest.*" His colleague **Martin Wells** (see p.670) receives respect for his methodical attention to detail. The firm's niche expertise in regional planning guidance is reflected in its continued work for heavyweight client Peel Holdings on a range of matters including the Trafford Centre, Giant's Field and the Manchester Ship Canal. It has also made a good name for itself in Human Rights Act and TWA matters. The firm continues to act for KPMG on its objections to Thameslink 2000 at Blackfriars, and for Canterbury College on the relocation of its main campus. Large-scale enquiry work and litigation are other core elements of the caseload. **Clients:** Peel Holdings; KPMG; St Martins; Canterbury College; National Mutual and Sun Alliance; Bass Hotels; Royal Albert Hall; University of Greenwich; Wimpey Homes.

Theodore Goddard (see firm details p.1152) The "*unmistakeable*" **Douglas Evans** (see p.664) is key to much of the firm's success in this field. Peers commend him, believing he has "*pretty much cornered the market*" in waste management. The firm's talents in this area are evident in its involvement in EfW projects across the UK, and a client base that includes Minosus and Thames Water Utilities. In a major coup, it has also been appointed to the legal panel of Vivendi. **Clients:** Taywood Homes; Vivendi; Minosus; Surrey Waste Management; Laing Homes; Berkely Group; Bryant Homes; Mobil North sea; Thames Water Utilities.

Dechert (see firm details p.938) Although low profile, this "*quietly efficient, responsive and proactive*" team wins plaudits from its clients. The team is headed by "*reliable and competent*" **Justin True** and advises on a range of complex one-off projects. Key work over the past year includes acting for the estate of M Kingsley on a variety of planning issues, including litigation. The team also advised The Crown Estate on the refurbishment of a listed building in London, assisted Helical Retail on a number of redevelopments in county town centres across the West Country, and acted for PACE on a compulsory purchase compensation claim. **Clients:** The Abbeyfield (Loughborough) Society; The Crown Estate; Dixons; Freeport Leisure; Hampton Trust; Helical Retail; PACE; Shire Properties.

DJ Freeman (see firm details p.943) With the departure of Richard Max to Olswang, the firm is felt to have lost "*the significant player*" in the planning department. However, the firm is still felt to have a sound track record in brownfield regeneration advice.

Fladgate Fielder (see firm details p.960) "*Robust*" **Moira Fraser** (see p.665) now heads the firm's planning team. Her specialities include retail developments, highways, and inquiry work. Highlight work for this team includes advising Amylum UK on strategic issues arising from the government's regeneration strategy for the Greenwich peninsula. The group also acted for Sun Microsystems on infrastructure agreements for its UK HQ and assisted Lower Mill Estate on a section 106 agreement for Redrow Homes (South East). **Clients:** Amylum UK; Sun Microsystems; Lower Mill Estate; Redrow Homes (South East); Capital & Regional Properties; Regal Hotel Group; Terrace Hill Group.

Freshfields Bruckhaus Deringer (see firm details p.965) Better known for environment work, the firm's core specialities in strategy, telecoms, power and PFI give its planning practice a strong government policy flavour. Known for undertaking "*unusual, complex*" instructions, the team is headed by the respected **Paul Watchman** (see p.376). Major instructions include advising on PFI for the MOD and other government agencies, and assisting Conoco on the development of a large CHP plant. The group advised Honda on doubling the size of a manufacturing plant and associated rail link. **Clients:** Conoco; Powergen; Scottish Power; Mercury One2One; Hutchison 3G; Honda; MoD; HSBC; Lafarge Redland; Trillium.

Lawrence Graham (see firm details p.1030) The "*aggressive*" and "*assiduous*" **Trevor Blaney** is an experienced advocate respected by his peers, and heads a team that is often seen on enquiry work and CPO. Notable activity over the year includes acting for London & Regional in the High Court on matters pertaining to the proposed redevelopment of Crystal Palace. The firm also advised Wembley on the planning and listed building consent applications for the redevelopment of the Wembley Stadium complex. For St James Homes, the team acted on the defence to a High Court challenge to a residential scheme near Holland Park. **Clients:** Southgate Developments; BT Property; London & Regional; Cellnet; Crest Strategic Projects; East Sussex CC; Forest Healthcare Trust; St George North London.

Macfarlanes (see firm details p.1046) This mixed practice provides support to the property department as well as undertaking substantial standalone planning work. In a busy year, much of the firm's time has been given to pre-enquiry negotiations for clients attempting to reach agreements with local authorities. The team advised Scottish Life on the redevelopment of the Royal Baths at Harrogate and negotiated for Fred Olsen SA on the redevelopment of its London office. Other work includes acting for Conrad Phoenix Properties on a £40 million retail park in Watford, including advice on highway agreements. **Clients:** Scottish Life; Fred Olsen; Conrad Phoenix Property; London Bridge Holdings; Crest Homes; AXA Real Estate; Comet; Ian Schrager Hotels; P&O.

Olswang (see firm details p.1084) "*Real livewire*" **Richard Max**'s (see p.668) arrival at the firm is judged by competitors and clients to be a coup for the firm, a timely response to the departure of Richard Searle to private practice. "*Aggressive*" and "*energetic,*" Max is a skilled solicitor advocate. Much of the workload at the firm comprises support to an active property group, but there is stand-alone work on behalf of developers, occupiers and private clients. Recent undertakings include advising Minerva on a major development in London and listed building issues. The team also handled public authority work on the CPO aspects of the Channel Tunnel Rail Link. **Clients:** Capital & Regional Properties; Charterhouse Shopping Centre Fund; Delancey Estates; Helical Bar; Minerva; Stralo; Phillips & Drew Property Partnerships; Somerfield; NHS; Shell.

Simmons & Simmons (see firm details p.1132) The team's caseload covers both contentious and non-contentious work, for which it still retains the respect of competitors. Leading light **John Qualtrough** (see p.668) is highly rated by his peers: "*he knows exactly what he is doing,*" especially in the negotiation and drafting of agreements. The group advised the American School in Switzerland on the development of its existing school on greenbelt land in Surrey and assisted Rapid Transit International on mediation to settle judicial review proceedings brought by the client against Northampton Borough Council and English Partnerships. **Clients:** RTI; Tasis.

Travers Smith Braithwaite (see firm details p.1160) The staple diet here is mixed-use leisure and retail developments, and the firm has won some significant town centre redevelopment work in the last year. The "*good and thorough*" **Alison Lea** (see p.667) continues to fly the flag for the firm, and is a particularly experienced enquiry advocate. Highlights this year have been the town centre redevelopments of Solihull and Norwich for Lend Lease Europe, and central Belfast for Multi Development Corporation. The group also acted in litigation for Lafarge Redland Aggregates. **Clients:** Garbe Group; Clearwater Estates and Properties; Greenwich Reach 2000; Multi Development Corporation; Lafarge Redland Aggregates; Lend Lease Europe.

Other Notable Practitioners Drafted in from **Ashurst Morris Crisp** to provide **Forsters**' property practice with a planning capacity, **Michael Cunliffe** (see p.663) has provided an "*immeasurable boost*" to a firm not normally known for such expertise. All eyes are now on what sort of a team he can build. His clients include McDonald's Restaurants, Lattice Property Holdings, Harvington Properties, Schlumberger and Warner Village Cinemas.

THE SOUTH

PLANNING • The South	Ptnrs	Assts
1 **Bond Pearce** Southampton	1	2
2 **Brachers** Maidstone	2	1
DMH Brighton	1	1
3 **Fynn & Partners** Bournemouth	1	1
4 **Lester Aldridge** Southampton	2	1

LEADING INDIVIDUALS	
1 **ABRAHAM Henry** Brachers	**TRINICK Marcus** Bond Pearce
2 **ALLEN Tony** DMH	**HIGNETT Andrew** Lester Aldridge

This book is the product of 6,552 1/2-hour interviews. See p.7 for BMRB audit.
Within each band, firms are listed alphabetically. *See individuals' profiles p.662*

Bond Pearce (see firm details p.888) The firm's reputation for "*great strength and quality people*" was bolstered last year with the arrival of John Houghton as consultant. Peers consider that the recent transfer of "*excellent*" **Marcus Trinick** (see p.670) from the firm's Plymouth office has further enhanced its national reputation for wind power. The firm continues to act for Associated British Ports in connection with the 250-hectare Dibden Terminal, one of the largest infrastructure projects in Europe. It receives instructions in on-shore and offshore renewable energy developments throughout Britain, many of which involve environmental impact statements and concern European Sites of Nature Conservation importance. The firm also acts as advisors to The University of Southampton on development projects, and undertakes retail, industrial, housing and agricultural work across the Southern region. **Clients:** Associated British Ports; Scottish Power; Enron Corporation.

Brachers (see firm details p.893) Interviewees endorsed the "*intellectually strong,*" and "*reliable and assured*" **Henry Abraham** and his team. The group regularly works with the property and corporate departments, and has acted for institutional clients, building developers and objectors on several controversial cases. The team achieved compensation and costs for an objector to a compulsory purchase order, and also acted for an institutional client, obtaining residential development on a greenfield site. **Clients:** Developers; manufacturers; estates owners; farmers.

DMH (see firm details p.944) Researchers discovered a "*major department,*" attracting interesting work and fielding a team of town planners working alongside planning lawyers. Recently, the respected **Tony Allen** (see p.662) has been involved in a £45 million development for Brighton, including shops, hotels, and housing. The firm also acted for Brighton & Hove Albion FC in its complex relocation to a greenfield site, involving ancillary developments and transport links. **Clients:** Millgroup; Brighton & Hove Albion; house builders; leisure developments; waste companies.

Fynn & Partners (see firm details p.967) The firm is another to include a large contingent of town planners, working alongside Lionel Fynn on appeals, planning consents and enforcement cases. Specialists in one-day inquiries, the group also acted on a large enforcement case on a £1 million site, and successfully objected on behalf of local residents in the vicinity of a minerals and waste landfill site. **Clients:** Bowlplex; Woodhouse Inns.

Lester Aldridge (see firm details p.1038) The development of the planning unit has prompted the team's move to a new Southampton office. **Andrew Hignett**'s (see p.666) team inspires "*absolute confidence*" among peers for its work advising on planning applications, appeal inquiries, and compulsory purchase orders. The group acted for a national utility in relation to the use of its compulsory purchase powers in developing a six-mile pipeline in Lancashire. It also advised on a detailed application for a high profile factory outlet scheme and waterfront development, involving a contested highway order and negotiating a section 106 agreement. **Clients:** Goulden Properties; Ibstock; Poole Pottery; Portland Port.

THAMES VALLEY

PLANNING • Thames Valley	Ptnrs	Assts
1 **Clarks** Reading	3	1
Jameson & Hill Hertford	1	n/a
Pitmans Reading	2	1

LEADING INDIVIDUALS	
1 **DIMMICK Simon** Clarks	**JAMESON Robert** Jameson & Hill
VALENTINE Richard Pitmans	
UP AND COMING	
DRUKARZ Daniel Pitmans	

This book is the product of 6,552 1/2-hour interviews. See p.7 for BMRB audit.
Within each band, firms are listed alphabetically. *See individuals' profiles p.662*

Clarks (see firm details p.916) The respected **Simon Dimmick** (see p.663), known primarily for his work on behalf of the University of Reading, heads a team that is widely endorsed by clients and peers. The firm acted in a high profile, successful telecommunications appeal in Leicestershire, and negotiated planning permission for several hundred homes on behalf of the University of Reading. NHS work is a feature of the practice, and the firm has advised on a substantial extension to the John Radcliffe hospital in Oxford. **Clients:** University of Reading; Blue Circle Industries; NHS Trusts.

Jameson & Hill General appeal work for local authorities takes up the majority of this respected firm's time. **Robert Jameson** (see p.667)'s "*clear and understandable*" approach earns him respect from a loyal client base that also includes major retailers and house builders. The firm has recently dealt with several call-in enquiries, acting both for developers and objectors. **Clients:** Local authorities, Somerfield Stores; Persimmon Homes.

Pitmans (see firm details p.1099) **Richard Valentine** (see p.670), recommended by clients for "*finding the right solutions,*" has recently been joined by rising name **Daniel Drukarz** (see p.663) from Fladgate Fielder in London. Acting for large institutional and developer clients, the firm also continues to undertake strategic work for major housing clients relating to new housing settlements. It is involved in urban re-generation projects, including the mixed-use live and work scheme in Hackney. **Clients:** Wimpey; Brookmill Estates; Cala Homes; McAlpine.

SOUTH WEST

PLANNING • South West	Ptnrs	Assts
1 **Clarke Willmott & Clarke** Bristol, Taunton	4	3
2 **Bevan Ashford** Bristol, Exeter	2	3
Burges Salmon Bristol	1	4
3 **Davies and Partners** Gloucester	1	2
Osborne Clarke Bristol	1	3
Stephens & Scown Exeter	5	n/a
TLT Solicitors Bristol	1	1

LEADING INDIVIDUALS	
1 **ENGERT Nick** Clarke Willmott & Clarke	
PASTERFIELD Stephen Clarke Willmott & Clarke	
ROBINSON Patrick Burges Salmon	
2 **BAKER Neil** Clarke Willmott & Clarke	**BOSWORTH John** Bevan Ashford
EVANS Katherine TLT Solicitors	**GIBBS Kevin** Osborne Clarke
HOLMES Sarah Bond Pearce	**WOOD David** Bevan Ashford

This book is the product of 6,552 1/2-hour interviews. See p.7 for BMRB audit.
Within each band, firms are listed alphabetically. *See individuals' profiles p.662*

Clarke Willmott & Clarke (see firm details p.915) Winning instructions from volume house builders, the firm is also moving into complex brownfield site work, advising on environmental complications. Researchers encountered no serious opposition to the firm's continuing presence at the top of the rankings. **Nick Engert** (see p.664)'s weighty reputation among his peers as a serious advocate and a "*major competitor*" is complemented by **Stephen Pasterfield**'s (see p.668) standing as a "*gentlemanly and smooth technician.*" Newly made-up partner **Neil Baker** (see p.369) is also admired for his advocacy skills, although his practice contains a substantial environment element. The group advised Matthew Clark plc in connection with the recycling of a factory and brownfield site as part of a comprehensive development scheme. Increasingly active for local authorities, the firm has been instructed by Torridge District Council for all advocacy work and was recently appointed to the panel for the South West Regional Development Agency. **Clients:** Matthew Clark; Scott UK; Rok Property Solutions.

Bevan Ashford (see firm details p.880) Particularly endorsed by peers for its NHS trust work, redeveloping redundant sites, the firm acts for a wide client base including public sector authorities, developers and housing associations. Planning agreements and highway stopping up orders are developing areas of the caseload. **David Wood** (see p.416) and **John Bosworth** (see p.662) retain high standing among their peers. For Birmingham University Hospital, the team negotiated planning permission and section 106 agreements for a major new hospital, which involved public transport and highway measures. The firm also acted for a consortium of retailers, chambers of commerce and pressure groups to oppose the retail development of the Morlands Factory Site in Glastonbury. **Clients:** Department of Health; Crest Nicholson Residential (South West); Lidl UK; Birmingham University Hospital NHS Trust.

Burges Salmon (see firm details p.902) Each fee-earner in **Patrick Robinson** (see p.669)'s "*well managed team*" hails from a local government background. Though peers "*don't see them so often at public enquiries,*" the firm is rated consistently highly for its niche strengths in telecoms and quarry work. The group recently won the advisory work for FPL/186k on its development of a new national telecoms network for the UK, provides UK Nirex with strategic planning advice on nuclear waste disposal, and advised COLAS on its application for a major landfill and review of mineral permission. **Clients:** UK Nirex; FPL/186k; COLAS; Orange.

Davies and Partners (see firm details p.933) A heavy residential developer bias defines this firm's approach to planning. Michael Morgan has taken over from Rina Bird. High Court challenges in the past year have included responding to a councillors' application to quash a land transfer, and also one provoked by the Land Compensation Act. The team has been particularly active in matters arising from village green applications. **Clients:** Crest; Persimmon Homes; Tayward Homes.

Osborne Clarke (see firm details p.1086) Researchers frequently encountered the suggestion that the firm's merger with London planning operation McGuinness Finch "*should rejuvenate*" its planning team nationally. **Kevin Gibbs** and his team handle all the planning and environmental work for Bristol International Airport, and acted for Countryside Strategic Projects, advising on a local planning objection for a housing site in Taunton. Waste and energy work is closely tied to the environmental department, and a major new client for the firm is London waste management company, Cory Environmental. **Clients:** Barratt Homes; Countryside Strategic Projects; KPMG; Wilson Bowden Developments.

Stephens & Scown Described as "*traditional*" in its style, Ian Lamond's team maintains its focus on minerals and waste disposals, and sustains its close relationship with English China Clay and Aggregate Industries. It continues to act on an enquiry relating to a huge factory outlet scheme at Roche, Cornwall. The firm is also acting for Aggregate Industries in the complex minerals case at Black Hill Quarry. **Clients:** English China Clays; Aggregate Industries; South Crofty; Viridor Waste Management.

TLT Solicitors (see firm details p.1157) "*Forthright*" **Katherine Evans** (see p.664), "*knows her stuff*" although it was suggested to researchers that her profile overshadows that of the the group. The firm primarily deals with housing planning, but is seeing an increase in minerals work. It has prepared section 106 agreements for Hanson Aggregates and Edward Ware New Homes, and completed a minerals local planning enquiry for Wiltshire County Council and the Berkshire Joint Strategic Planning Unit. The team was instructed by Beaufort on two city centre redevelopment mixed scheme sites, which involved infrastructure and contamination issues. **Clients:** Beaufort; Chase Homes; Edward Ware New Homes; Hanson; Wiltshire County Council.

Other Notable Practitioners Although major player Marcus Trinick has relocated to the firm's Southampton branch, **Sarah Holmes** of Bond Pearce continues to impress commentators with her technical ability.

WALES

	PLANNING • Wales	Ptnrs	Assts
1	**Edwards Geldard** Cardiff	1	2
	Eversheds Cardiff	2	2
	Morgan Cole Cardiff	1	2

	LEADING INDIVIDUALS	
1	**BOSWALL Julian** Morgan Cole	**EVANS Eric** Eversheds
	MANSON Stephen Eversheds	**WILLIAMS Huw** Edwards Geldard

This book is the product of 6,552 1/2-hour interviews. See p.7 for BMRB audit.
Within each band, firms are listed alphabetically. *See individuals' profiles p.662*

Edwards Geldard (see firm details p.948) According to clients, respected **Huw Williams** (see p.60) offers a "*superb service,*" and leads a team that takes on substantial work for private clients, notably on enforcement cases concerning alleged breaches of planning regulations. The group advised the acquirer on a complex former metals site purchase in Derbyshire, and drafted planning title reports. It also undertook the planning aspects of the Wales Millennium Centre Project. **Clients:** Cardiff Bay Development Corporation; Welsh Development Agency; Silverlink Trains.

Eversheds (see firm details p.952) Though **Eric Evans** (see p.664) has been indisposed for much of the past year, "*efficient*" **Stephen Manson** (see p.667) has maintained the excellent profile of this firm. With minerals permissions and land assembly/compulsory purchase as niche strengths, the firm provides ongoing advice to Hanson Aggregates South Wales, and undertakes substantial National Assembly land compensation claim work. It has been involved in numerous town and village green enquiries and has represented Business Wales on the Land Use Planning Forum. **Clients:** Hanson Aggregates South Wales; Welsh Development Agency; National Assembly for Wales.

Morgan Cole (see firm details p.1074) "*Sensible, approachable*" **Julian Boswall** (see p.370)has lifted the firm's profile over the past year, leading a team that has advised on complex section 106 agreements and related planning matters on PFI for a new hospital. Expert on highways and CPO work, the group also acted for Gwent Police Authority, preparing the planning aspects of PFI for a major new police station near Caerphilly. **Clients:** Welsh Development Agency; Impregilo/Macob Consortium; Gwent Police Authority.

MIDLANDS

	PLANNING • Midlands	Ptnrs	Assts
1	**Marrons** Leicester	7	7
2	**Eversheds** Birmingham	1	4
	Pinsent Curtis Biddle Birmingham	2	1
	Wragge & Co Birmingham	3	3
3	**Hewitson Becke + Shaw** Northampton	1	2
	Shoosmiths Northampton	2	5
4	**Browne Jacobson** Nottingham	3	6
	Hammond Suddards Edge Birmingham	1	2
5	**Kent Jones and Done** Stoke-on-Trent	3	2
	Knight & Sons Newcastle-under-Lyme	1	1

	LEADING INDIVIDUALS	
1	**BULL Rod** Eversheds	**MARRON Peter** Marrons
2	**DAMMS Martin** Pinsent Curtis Biddle	**EDMOND John** Marrons
	GILBEY Iain Shoosmiths	**HEMMING Dan** Wragge & Co
	TAYLOR Peter Hewitson Becke + Shaw	**THOMSON Morag** Marrons
	WHITE Martin Pinsent Curtis Biddle	
3	**SMITH Brian** Browne Jacobson	

This book is the product of 6,552 1/2-hour interviews. See p.7 for BMRB audit.
Within each band, firms are listed alphabetically. *See individuals' profiles p.662*

Marrons (see firm details p.1054) Researchers were left in no doubt that this "*bright, sharp, commercial,*" team still boasts the leading planning team in the region. Leading figure **Peter Marron** (see p.667) remains an "*obvious choice*" for clients, while rising star **Morag Thompson** (see p.669) elicited scores of positive comments from her peers. Her work on the Alconbury case is considered to have placed her firmly on the map. "*Always excellent*" **John Edmond** (see p.664) completes an imposing team. The team takes on vast quantities of local authority instructions, particularly enforcement work, and an increasing load from the education sector. Acting for household name house-builders and land developers, the team also advises on judicial reviews and section 207 challenges. It was involved in the ground breaking Alconbury case which led to the landmark decision by the High Court that there is an incompatibility between Human Rights legislation and planning legislation. **Clients:** Local authorities; major housebuilders; land promoters; education authorities.

Eversheds (see firm details p.952) Acknowledged by competitors for its quality, the team is overseen by senior practitioner and "*consistent performer*" **Rod Bull** (see p.662). His team serves as the centre of the national network, with a substantial house-builder practice and additional niche minerals and waste experience. Drawing on a strong existing national property client base, the firm successfully negotiated final section 106 and 278 agreements on behalf of Bryant Northern, thereby securing outline planning permission for the Newcastle Great Park Scheme. It continues to act for Birmingham MailBox, on Europe's largest mixed-use development. **Clients:** Bass; Bryant Group; EMDA; Ford Europe.

Pinsent Curtis Biddle (see firm details p.1098) Boasting niche strengths in planning gain, compulsory purchase and regeneration, environmental assessment and judicial review proceedings, the team is a familiar sight, whether acting in the public or private sectors. Peers perceive that this work has earned "*clear and assured*" **Martin Damms** (see p.663) and "*concise*" **Martin White** (see p.671) a loyal and satisfied band of clients. The firm's recent appointment as national advisor to English Partnerships is a coup for a group that also advised on the redevelopment of a 550-acre brownfield site either side of the motorway at Warrington. It also acted on a major call-in enquiry relating to a proposed retail development in Manchester that involved a wide range of issues and the application of new enquiry rules. Other work includes litigation concerning the East Midlands Airport runway extension. **Clients:** East Midlands Airport; Corus; Alstom.

Wragge & Co (see firm details p.1189) "*The heavy hitting property practice*" at this firm is acknowledged by rivals to bring in substantial ancillary work for the planning team, where the respected **Dan Hemming** leads his team through complex and successful work, acting primarily for developers. Most significantly last year, the firm acted on the relocation of Marconi Communications' UK headquarters to Ansty, involving one million square feet of high technology floor space. The group also acted for Cambridge City Council in the redevelopment of the city centre, and represented Castlemore Securities on major retail schemes in Hampshire and Beckton. **Clients:** British Energy; Miller Homes; Prologis Developments.

Hewitson Becke + Shaw (see firm details p.994) "*A major player in the local market,*" **Peter Taylor** (see p.669) heads the firm's Northampton office, which continues to work closely with the Cambridge branch. Acting for landowners, developers and local authorities, he continues to conduct a high level of advocacy at appeals, and had recent success in developing the Turnstone Estates, a case which went to the Court of Appeal. The group also acted for Bedfordia Estates in a recommendation for the allocation for 400 dwellings in Bedford. **Clients:** Bellway Homes; Berkeley Homes; Peterborough City Council.

Shoosmiths (see firm details p.1129) Known by clients for his "*well-schooled advice,*" **Iain Gilbey**'s (see p.665) reputation continues to develop in the region. Working from the commercial property department, the team has expanded, and represents local authorities, house builders, retailers, developers and privatised utilities. Acting as key advisors to Nottingham City Council, the firm has been involved in the £400 million Broadmarsh development. It also acted for Blue Circle Industries on a major storage redistribution centre. **Clients:** Westfield; Blue Circle Industries; St. James Homes.

Browne Jacobson (see firm details p.898) Although not as active on behalf of developers, the firm is highly respected regionally for its enquiry work on behalf of local authorities. Nature conservation and housing are other core elements of the caseload. **Brian Smith** (see p.669) is a prominent local name, and has appeared on wind farm public enquiries for the Countryside Council for Wales. The firm has completed four two-week call-in inquiries for the CCW in the past 12 months, and also handles instructions from English Nature. On the developer side, the group succeeded in a major judicial review challenge by Aldergate Properties against Bassetlaw District Council. **Clients:** Aldergate Properties; The Countryside Council for Wales, Alliance and Leicester.

Hammond Suddards Edge (see firm details p.984) David Goodman's team is respected by interviewees as a "*decent practice.*" Power generation and electricity, including wind farms, and compulsory purchase work, figure strongly at the practice. The firm acts for major regional development agencies, and advised Leicester City FC on a planning application for a new 30,000-seat stadium development on a former power station site. The team also achieved permission for a £2 million sq ft regional distribution centre, involving a call-in application, and major section 106 negotiations. **Clients:** Walsall Borough Council; Persimmon Homes; Derbyshire County Council.

Kent Jones and Done (see firm details p.1020) Grant Anderson's team spends the majority of its time on 'pure' planning matters for developers and landowners. It has particular expertise advising on mineral and waste planning. The team recently obtained a grant for a lawful development certificate for waste recycling following a six-day public inquiry, and advised on securing planning permission for 130 dwellings in Widnes. Other work includes obtaining planning permission for a new country house for an estate landowner in Staffordshire and Derbyshire. **Clients:** Laporte; JE Greenall; JCB Group.

Knight & Sons (see firm details p.1025) Richard Lashmore and the team have expertise in detailed minerals development, while highways issues are an area of increasing expertise. The firm recently advised on planning permission in respect of a mixed-use site comprising supermarket, residential and leisure developments. It also negotiated a section 106 agreement for the development of a new hotel and conference centre at a national leisure park. **Clients:** Hanson Brick; Hanson Waste Management; Morrison Developments.

EAST ANGLIA

PLANNING • East Anglia	Ptnrs	Assts
1 **Mills & Reeve** Cambridge	2	3
2 **Hewitson Becke + Shaw** Cambridge	1	2
Taylor Vinters Cambridge	4	3

LEADING INDIVIDUALS	
1 **BRADY Peter** Hewitson Becke + Shaw	**BROCK David** Mills & Reeve
2 **FIRTH Beverley** Mills & Reeve	**KRATZ Philip** Taylor Vinters

This book is the product of 6,552 1/2-hour interviews. See p.7 for BMRB audit.

Within each band, firms are listed alphabetically. *See individuals' profiles p.662*

Mills & Reeve (see firm details p.1069) All planning lawyers at this firm are also environmental lawyers, and the team enjoys a particularly high local reputation for minerals and waste planning advice. Working closely with the property and development team, the firm acts for landowners, developers, planning authorities and objectors. Higher education and developer matters are other areas of growth. "*First class*" **Beverley Firth** (see p.665) and eminent former City practitioner **David Brock** (see p.662) continue to receive extensive endorsement from peers and clients. The firm has been prominent on urban renaissance work, while in waste management planning, it acted for Hanson Waste Management on a new facility outside Maidstone. **Clients:** Hanson; Tarmac; Redland.

Hewitson Becke + Shaw (see firm details p.994) Sharing clients and work with the Northampton office, the department is built around **Peter Brady** (see p.662), regarded by peers as a "*major competitor.*" The group represents national institutions, commercial developers, industrial operators and academic institutions, and advised a consortium of 14 Devon landowners and funders on a new town development, including 5,000 houses, shops and a leisure area. The firm also represented Shanks Waste Services on a waste landfill site at Bletchley, which included a bypass. **Clients:** Barratt Homes; Cambridge University; Medical Research Council; Norfolk Homes.

Taylor Vinters (see firm details p.1150) Thought by interviewees to "*do well in and around Cambridge,*" the firm's planning and development team remains headed by the "*pleasant*" **Philip Kratz** (see p.667). The team advised Countryside Properties on proposals for large-scale residential developments in Cambridge city centre, and acted for Kajima (Europe) on a major office development. **Clients:** Countryside Properties; Kajima (Europe); educational establishments.

NORTH WEST

PLANNING • North West	Ptnrs	Assts
1 Halliwell Landau Manchester	1	2
2 Addleshaw Booth & Co Manchester	2	2
Eversheds Manchester	2	4
3 DLA Manchester	n/a	n/a
Wake Dyne Lawton Chester	1	1

LEADING INDIVIDUALS	
1 LANCASTER Roger Halliwell Landau	WINTER Paul Eversheds
2 KENWORTHY Michael Addleshaw Booth & Co	
3 MORITZ John Wake Dyne Lawton	PIATT Andrew DLA
4 HOLMES John Halliwell Landau	
UP AND COMING	
RICHARDSON Simon Davies Wallis Foyster	

This book is the product of 6,552 1/2-hour interviews. See p.7 for BMRB audit.
Within each band, firms are listed alphabetically. *See individuals' profiles p.662*

Halliwell Landau (see firm details p.982) Peers are unanimous in acclaiming **Roger Lancaster** (see p.667) for his "*brilliant*" advocacy, commenting that his unrivalled track record is responsible for much of the firm's profile in this area. Newly ranked **John Holmes** (see p.666) has also carved out a reputation which is strongly endorsed by clients. The firm achieved a significant ruling in the Goldfinch (Projects) conversion of a former poultry packing station into a residential development of detached dwellings. Another highlight was a successful appeal against the refusal of Bolton MBC to grant outline planning permission for residential development at Crown Lane, Horwich. This decision led to new guidelines on residential land. **Clients:** Goldfinch (Projects); Malbern Construction; Fairclough Homes; Allen Homes.

Addleshaw Booth & Co (see firm details p.853) Working closely in tandem with the Leeds office, this team historically has had a manufacturing client base, but is picking up a noticeable increase in instructions from the retail sector, property development and the waste industry. **Michael Kenworthy** (see p.667), who elicits warm commendation from contemporaries, recently had success in a judicial review action, which was followed by the reopening of Planning Appeal inquiry for Trafford Park Estates. The group has also obtained injunctions on planning enforcement matters for Macclesfield Borough Council, and represented STMC in a series of appeals relating to building control matters. **Clients:** Arrowcroft North West; Stena Line Ports; Green Property Developments.

Eversheds (see firm details p.952) Dividing his time between Leeds and Manchester, **Paul Winter** gains strong endorsement from clients, who appreciate his "*thoroughness and the time he gives to single projects - he gets into things in a big way.*" Appearing in contentious and non-contentious planning work including judicial reviews, he is also undertaking substantial amounts of CPO, retail residential and waste work. The group advised English Partnerships and the North West Development Agency on strategy for dealing with the landmark Rochdale case. It is also involved in numerous village green schemes, and acted for Manchester City Council in the redevelopment of Piccadilly Gardens. **Clients:** English Partnerships; Manchester City Council; Walmart/Asda.

DLA Planning is conducted from under the Real Estate Group umbrella, and is led by **Andrew Piatt**. The group advises local authorities and applicants on matters relating to commercial and town centre developments, minerals, transport and CPOs.

Wake Dyne Lawton (see firm details p.1170) The firm has a niche market in minerals and environment, in addition to quarry work and waste in quarries. "*Certainly one of the names in planning,*" according to his peers, **John Moritz** (see p.668) acted on a contentious call-in enquiry on behalf of a residential group, concerning buying fuels in an extension to a cement works. The group also appears on behalf of housing developers and in enforcement matters pertaining to the farming industry. **Clients:** Developers; residential groups.

Other Notable Practitioners Simon **Richardson** (see p.668) at Davies Wallis Foyster acts for house-builders, industrial developers and retailers. A solicitor-advocate with a town planning background, he also undertakes expert witness work.

YORKSHIRE

PLANNING • Yorkshire	Ptnrs	Assts
1 Wilbraham & Co Leeds	4	2
2 Eversheds Leeds	2	4
Walker Morris Leeds	4	2
3 Addleshaw Booth & Co Leeds	2	3
Hammond Suddards Edge Leeds	1	3
4 Nabarro Nathanson Sheffield	2	4

LEADING INDIVIDUALS	
★ WILBRAHAM Peter Wilbraham & Co	
1 WILLIAMSON Andrew Walker Morris	
2 WADE-SMITH Richard Wilbraham & Co	
3 BERESFORD Amanda Addleshaw Booth & Co	
GOODMAN David Hammond Suddards Edge	
UP AND COMING	
BUTTERFIELD Kate Wilbraham & Co	GRIFFITHS Marian Eversheds
WALTON David Wilbraham & Co	

This book is the product of 6,552 1/2-hour interviews. See p.7 for BMRB audit.
Within each band, firms are listed alphabetically. *See individuals' profiles p.662*

Wilbraham & Co (see firm details p.1181) Specialist firm which has "*built up the profile of planning in Yorkshire,*" and is recognised nationally to be a leader, regularly competing with London firms. Competitors and clients alike applaud **Peter Wilbraham** as a "*powerful force*" who "*entirely merits his reputation.*" His "*unrivalled*" position in the market is backed up by **Richard Wade-Smith** (see p.670), who is said to have "*created a substantial practice.*" **Kate Butterfield** (see p.662) and **David Walton** (see p.670) are also successfully developing their individual profiles. Highlights this year have included the development of surplus residential and employment land for Severn Trent Property. The group also acted for the joint venture Thorpe Park (Leeds) in the development of a 109-hectare development in the Leeds Green Belt, which incorporates 1.8 million square feet of office space and the largest new park for Leeds this century. **Clients:** Severn Trent Property; Thorpe Park (Leeds); Redhouse Projects (Teesland).

Eversheds (see firm details p.952) Although the office is nominally headed by Paul Winter, he is better known for his practice in Manchester. **Marian Griffiths** (see p.666) receives substantial endorsement for her environmentally-oriented practice. The team advised the Waste Recycling Group on proposed new landfill sites in the Midlands and Yorkshire and an energy from waste plant in Hull. It also advised Asda Walmart on a complex call-in enquiry into a proposed new store in Bishop Auckland. **Clients:** AMEC; Waste Recycling Group; Walmart/Asda.

Walker Morris (see firm details p.1171) Peers are aware that this firm is "*putting the resources in place,*" and while it is still considered a "*quiet but successful unit,*" it does boast the services of the high profile, "*excellent advocate*" **Andrew Williamson** (see p.671). The majority of the firm's workload contains some element of advocacy, and it acts for house builders, regional developers, mineral groups and local government. Acting for Strata Gas, it lodged a contentious proposal for onshore gas exploration, and is involved in landfill work for WRG at a large mixed-use site in Chesterfield. **Clients:** Caterpillar; WRG Group; Thornfield/Asda.

Addleshaw Booth & Co (see firm details p.853) Steven Turnbull's move to Lawrence Graham in London is considered locally to have been a substantial blow to the firm's planning practice in Leeds. Much responsibility now rests on the shoulders of the respected **Amanda Beresford** (see p.662). The firm remains known for its excellent property department, and is still a common sight on major development work. It acted for Berkeley Clarence Dock on the redevelopment of Clarence Dock, Leeds, for mixed use purposes. **Clients:** Berkeley Clarence Dock; Bowdon Charitable Trust; Halifax.

Hammond Suddards Edge (see firm details p.984) Though he has been indisposed for some of the past year, the "*dominant figure*" of **David Goodman** (see p.665) is seen by peers to have been "*back in gear more recently.*" The team is active in the fields of utilities, compulsory purchase orders and judicial review work, advising clients from both the public and private sectors. Its particular focus is power generation and electricity distribution, advising on way leave matters and wind farm projects in England and Wales. The group has also advised on a number of CPOs for English Partnerships, SEEDA, and National Grid. Recent highlights include advising TXU on the proposed CHP plant at Heathrow Terminal 5. Retail is also an important area for the team; it gave advice to Wm. Morrison Supermarkets in a successful High Court challenge in the North East of England. **Clients:** The National Grid Company; BAE Systems; Powergen Renewables; Wm. Morrison Supermarkets.

Nabarro Nathanson (see firm details p.1078) The strengths of this firm lie historically in the fields of waste, minerals and reclamation, acting principally for large engineering developers. Group head Mike Renger recently advised Celtic Energy on compulsory purchase procedures involving common land, and was involved in a four-week public inquiry regarding the East Merthyr Reclamation Scheme. The group has also been heavily involved in the redevelopment of Altrincham Town Centre, advising on road closure procedure and planning agreements, including contamination issues. **Clients:** Coal Authority; Trafford Borough Council; Chatham Maritime.

NORTH EAST

PLANNING • North East	Ptnrs	Assts
1 **Dickinson Dees** Newcastle upon Tyne	2	2
2 **Ward Hadaway** Newcastle upon Tyne	2	1

LEADING INDIVIDUALS	
1 **FINCH Paul** Dickinson Dees	**TAYLOR Paul** Dickinson Dees

This book is the product of 6,552 1/2-hour interviews. See p.7 for BMRB audit.
Within each band, firms are listed alphabetically. *See individuals' profiles p.662*

Dickinson Dees (see firm details p.941) "*Obvious choice,*" in the North East according to our interviewees, this firm has a "*significant presence in planning.*" Clients consider **Paul Taylor** (see p.669) to be "*sound, not flashy - he gets the job done.*" Together with the "*thorough and practical*" **Paul Finch** (see p.665), he is the leading figure at a department that incorporates lawyers and town planners. The firm has undertaken a high level of advocacy in the past year, and is also increasing its non-contentious planning work. Recent highlights include preparation and submission of several planning application and environment statements relating to minerals and waste disposal schemes. The firm negotiated a planning agreement for a complete sector of a new town in Northumberland, and prepared and managed a major planning application for a Discovery Centre in Cumbria. **Clients:** National Grid; Miller Homes; North Eastern Co-op.

Ward Hadaway (see firm details p.1173) Neil Robson's team is best known for residential and commercial development and conservation work. The firm is also developing its public sector work for local authorities, and won an appeal to allow sporting facilities for a school in a conservation area. Other work includes advising on the opposition to the demolition of a World Heritage Site in Durham, and handling a planning enquiry for Cameron's Breweries in connection with a public house extension on a site in Yorkshire. **Clients:** English Heritage; Cameron's Breweries; Barratt Homes; Persimmon Homes.

SCOTLAND

Brodies WS (see firm details p.896) **Neil Collar** (see p.663)'s superb reputation is thought by peers to be driving this practice forward. Known to be "*articulate, academic and extremely knowledgeable,*" his "*great client base*" lends the firm an excellent profile. Major client Wimpey Homes was advised on an objection to the Rural West Edinburgh Local Plan, as well as the human rights issues arising from the inquiry. The team also appeared on behalf of the Grampian Housebuilders Association at the Consolidated Aberdeenshire Local Plan inquiry. The firm recently obtained a Certificate of Appropriate Alternative Development for GKN from the Scottish Ministers for a non-food retail development in Rutherglen. **Clients:** Wimpey Homes; Corus Group; GKN.

Dundas & Wilson CS (see firm details p.947) Our researchers were told that the firm remains at the head of the field, buoyed by the presence of highly respected head of department, **Ann Faulds**. "*Accurate, competent and always producing interesting work,*" her "*planning knowledge is considerable,*" and she remains first choice of a number of clients for "*large complex matters.*" Appointed as sole Scottish representative on the RTPI on Human Rights, Faulds also appeared as advocate on behalf of Scottish Enterprise Edinburgh and the Lothians in the Biotechnology inquiry. She has a "*capable lieutenant*" in **Frances McChlery**. The department incorporates environment, transport and planning, with niche strengths in retail enquiry work, and infrastructure approvals for both public and private clients. Last year, it handled the East Kilbride Retail Inquiry, appearing for Land Securities Properties. In addition, it is acting for the developer in the high profile Castle Tioram case. **Clients:** Carter Commercial Developments; Stirling Council; Land Securities Properties.

Archibald Campbell & Harley WS (see firm details p.861) Our interviewees claimed that "*the reputation of the firm is built around* **David Cockburn**" (see p.663). Known to be a "*low-key, long term player,*" his "*strong reputation*" is a major attraction to clients. Scottish Natural Heritage is said to provide the team with a "*huge chunk of work,*" and the group advised that client on a month-long planning inquiry concerning Bogside, Irvine. On the developer side, the firm has represented Miller Homes and Hanson Waste Management in the consideration of the Rural West Edinburgh Local Plan. **Clients:** Scottish Natural Heritage; Hanson Waste Management; The Miller Group.

PLANNING • Scotland	Ptnrs	Assts
1 **Brodies WS** Edinburgh	1	1
Dundas & Wilson CS Edinburgh	1	3
2 **Archibald Campbell & Harley WS** Edinburgh	3	n/a
McGrigor Donald Glasgow	3	3
Paull & Williamsons Aberdeen	2	n/a
Shepherd & Wedderburn WS Edinburgh	2	2
3 **Burness** Edinburgh	3	1
Maclay Murray & Spens Glasgow	3	2
Semple Fraser Glasgow	4	2
4 **Ledingham Chalmers** Aberdeen	3	2
MacRoberts Glasgow	1	n/a

LEADING INDIVIDUALS	
1 **COLLAR Neil** Brodies WS	**FAULDS Ann** Dundas & Wilson CS
2 **COCKBURN David** Archibald Campbell & Harley WS	
CONNAL Craig McGrigor Donald	
INNES Colin Shepherd & Wedderburn WS	
SALES Martin Burness	**SMITH Bruce** Paull & Williamsons
3 **GILLES June** Semple Fraser	**GRANT James** MacRoberts
McCHLERY Frances Dundas & Wilson CS	
UP AND COMING	
HARRIS Jacqueline McGrigor Donald	

This book is the product of 6,552 1/2-hour interviews. See p.7 for BMRB audit.

Within each band, firms are listed alphabetically. *See individuals' profiles p.662*

McGrigor Donald (see firm details p.1062) This "*heavyweight commercial practice*" is well respected, and is felt to owe much to leading contentious lawyer **Craig Connal** (see p.663). Qualified to handle supreme court advocacy, he has an excellent reputation for his enquiry experience. **Jacqueline Harris** (see p.666) also maintains her share of market support. Town planning, commercial and property litigation, and public policy are key areas of strength for the firm, while waterfront development, retail work and human rights have also generated substantial work in the past year. The group has advised on regeneration projects in both Clydeside and Leith, and acted on a human rights-related enquiry for North Lanarkshire Council. **Clients:** North Lanarkshire Council; Glasgow Harbour; major property developers.

Paull & Williamsons (see firm details p.1091) Proclaimed "*the number one firm in Aberdeen*" by our interviewees, its impact is also felt in the Central Belt. Nationally recognised, the department is headed by the "*excellent advocate*" **Bruce Smith** (see p.669). Acting mainly for residential developers, the firm has arranged consents for negotiating planning agreements, and advised Alfred Stewart Properties on retail development for the Dunfermline local plan. The team also advised on the Midlothian local plan for Betts and a consortium led by CALA Management. **Clients:** Stuart Milne Group; Betts; Wilcon Allan.

Shepherd & Wedderburn WS (see firm details p.1126) The "*all-embracing service*" at this firm earns **Colin Innes** (see p.666) the rare plaudit of being "*well worth whatever fee he asks.*" Known for showing a "*reasonable approach and a focus on getting the deal done,*" he "*certainly knows his way around the system.*" A balanced portfolio of clients includes housing developers, telecoms and the public sector, with the firm involved in all stages of the process, from the outset of major projects to appearing at judicial challenges. Acting for Pillar Properties, the firm secured permission for the development of a gap site left untended for 20 years in the East of Edinburgh. The team was also involved in the Waterfront Edinburgh development of the Granton area of the city. **Clients:** Pillar Properties, Teeside, Waterfront Edinburgh.

Burness (see firm details p.903) Known to be "*quite prominent in minerals,*" **Martin Sales**' (see p.669) team focuses on development in environmentally sensitive areas. With an increasing concentration on urban regeneration, the firm undertakes all cases that involve brownfield sites, listed buildings and issues of architectural merit. The high profile, long-running, Harris superquarry case still keeps the firm occupied; it represented Lafarge Aggregates on its successful judicial review against the Scottish Executive. The team also acted Wimpey Homes Holdings, wining an interdict injunction and appeal for a housing site. This case is now going to the House of Lords. **Clients:** Lafarge Aggregates; Lothian University Hospitals; Wimpey Home Holdings.

Maclay Murray & Spens (see firm details p.1047) Chris Smylie heads this respected department, which is rated by peers for its substantial client base. The firm's new stand-alone Planning and Environmental department is attracting work from both public and private sectors, in particular volume housebuilders. The group advised Wilson Bowden on the 'new-town' developments at Ravenscraig, and also undertook a successful judicial review and court of session for Robert Wiseman Dairies. Other work includes advising Union Square Developments in relation to a retail and leisure redevelopment at Aberdeen Station, including the negotiation of a complex Section 75 Agreement. **Clients:** Wilson Bowden; Barratt Construction; Robert Wiseman.

Semple Fraser (see firm details p.1121) Developing well, the market perceives that its reputation has much to do with the presence of **June Gilles** (see p.665). Her "*thoroughly researched work*" allows her to "*get the job done rather than fight over technicalities.*" The firm continues to advise Tesco Stores in its expansion throughout Scotland, including representation at PLIs. The group also appeared on behalf of Bass developments and successfully challenged the decision by Glasgow Council to promote a compulsory purchase order and to convey property in central Glasgow to a competing developer. **Clients:** Tesco Stores; Barratt Developments; The British Land Corporation.

Ledingham Chalmers (see firm details p.1034) "*Quite properly one of the players,*" the firm is particularly endorsed for its prominence in the Aberdeen market. John Curran and his team act for a number of builder and developer clients, and recently won instructions from new client, The University of Aberdeen. The firm acted for Morrison Development Partnerships on a mixed hotel, leisure and retail development in Aberdeen and represented Aggregate Industries at the Rural West Edinburgh Local Plan Inquiry. **Clients:** Cala; Morrisons; Scottish Capital Group, University of Aberdeen.

MacRoberts (see firm details p.1048) Though perhaps better known for property work rather than contentious planning issues, **Jamie Grant** (see p.371) also draws upon the skills of a ten year qualified town planner. With mining and energy work as an industrial focus for the firm, it recently secured work for new client, Ambient Hydro on a hydro scheme at Loch Lomond. The firm specialises in advice on controversial open cast applications, and acted for the PFI consortium, led by Amey developments in the disposal of 15 former schools sites. **Clients:** Ambient Hydro; TXU Power Europe; Railtrack.

LEADERS IN PLANNING

ABRAHAM, Henry
Brachers, Maidstone (01622) 690691

ALLEN, Tony
DMH, Brighton (01273) 744451
Specialisation: Partner who specialises in town planning, environmental law, waste management and contaminated land; acted in: housing, leisure and retail developments; health authority and university cases, in cases regarding waste deposit licensing, waste transfer stations, planning and licensing, statutory nuisance prosecutions, a waste power plant and mineral extraction.
Prof. Memberships: European Environmental Law Sub-Committee Law Society; International Bar Association; UK Environmental Law Association; Planning & Environmental Law Committee Law Society.
Career: Qualified 1971; partner 1976; with *Donne Mileham & Haddock* (now *DMH*) throughout – latterly specialising in town planning and environmental. Heads a multi-disciplinary planning group of lawyers and chartered town planners.
Publications: Various articles on planning, listed buildings and environmental subjects. A practical guide to the law on contaminated land and its implications for property transactions (Part IIA Environmental Protection Act 1990).

ASHWORTH, Stephen
Denton Wilde Sapte, London (020) 7242 1212
Specialisation: Partner, Planning and Public Law Group. Experience in planning law, including major development inquiries; judicial review; highway law; compulsory purchase orders; Private Finance Initiative Public Private Partnerships projects; waste proposals. Advises on developing policy issues on retailing; planning benefits; private funding of infrastructure through the planning system; and town centre management.
Prof. Memberships: Urban Land Institute. Council member of City Property Association.
Career: Articled *Denton Hall* 1986; qualified 1988; partner 1995; secondment to Sainsbury plc 1992-94; Harkness Fellowship at Lincoln Institute of Land Policy, Cambridge Massachussetts 1995-96 (researching American approaches to regeneration, provision of infrastructure and public participation in the planning process); Member Department of Transport, Private Sector Panel on Developer Contributions and Highways Agreement; Member DETR, Expert Review Group on Town Improvement Zones.
Personal: Born 1963; leisure activities include cycling, 19th century British history, dry-stone walling, cookery.

BAKER, Neil
Clarke Willmott & Clarke, Bristol (0117) 941 6658
nbaker@cw-c.co.uk
See under Environment, p.369

BANKS, Sandra
Denton Wilde Sapte, London (020) 7242 1212

BERESFORD, Amanda
Addleshaw Booth & Co, Leeds (0113) 209 2325
aqb@addleshaw-booth.co.uk
Specialisation: All planning work including retail, leisure, industrial, residential and advocacy at Public Inquiries. Comprehensive environmental advice including pollution control, energy, waste, transport, contaminated land and due diligence. Clients advised include major development and manufacturing companies, utilities, banks and local authorities. Particular expertise in environmental and planning issues in urban regeneration projects. Recognised authoress and speaker at conferences.
Prof. Memberships: Qualified planner. Member U.K.E.L.A.
Career: Qualified in 1985, joined *Addleshaw Booth & Co* in 1997.

BLANEY, Trevor
Lawrence Graham, London (020) 7379 0000

BOSWALL, Julian
Morgan Cole, Cardiff (029) 2038 5385
julian.boswall@morgan-cole.com
See under Environment, p.370

BOSWORTH, John
Bevan Ashford, Bristol (0117) 975 1731
j.bosworth@bevanashford.co.uk
Specialisation: Planning, urban regeneration and local government law. Special expertise in judicial review, compulsory purchase, and regional government. Projects have included regional shopping centres, Canary Wharf, a new village in South Hampshire, renewable energy schemes, town centre regeneration schemes, Temple Quay, Bristol and many PFI hospitals and the redevelopment of major brownfield sites. Advisor to south west branch of Housebuilders Federation.
Prof. Memberships: Legal Associate of RTPI. Member of Law Society's Planning Panel.
Career: Qualified 1988. Articled Portsmouth City Council. Joined *Bevan Ashford* 1995, after six years working for *Ashurst Morris Crisp.*

BRADY, Peter
Hewitson Becke + Shaw, Cambridge (01223) 461155
peterbrady@hewitsons.com
Specialisation: Planning, environment and waste disposal.
Prof. Memberships: Law Society's specialist planning panel.
Career: Leicester University 1973-6 LL.B (Hons). 1977-79: Cheshire County Council. 1979-81: Hertfordshire County Council. 1981-84: Northumberland County Council. 1984-88: *Jameson & Hill*, Hertford. 1988-90: *Berwin Leighton*. 1990: *Hewitson Becke + Shaw*.
Personal: Golf.

BROCK, David
Mills & Reeve, Cambridge (01223) 222 438
david.brock@mills-reeve.com
Specialisation: Has a wide ranging planning, environmental and minerals law practice. His planning work includes new settlements, urban regeneration, minerals and waste planning and PFI projects. He also advises on all aspects of environmental law.
Career: Qualified in 1980. Partner at *Herbert Smith* 1989-2000, *Mills & Reeve* 2000 to date.
Personal: Born in 1954. Educated at Dame Allan's Boys School, Newcastle, Marylebone Grammar School and University College, London (LLB). Practising Christian. Enjoys opera, skiing, modern art and architecture. Lives near Saffron Walden.

BULL, Rod
Eversheds, Birmingham (0121) 232 1000
Specialisation: Head of national *Eversheds* Planning Group. Planning and compulsory purchase/environmental. Experienced advocate. Considerable experience of advising developers on large mixed-use schemes (especially residential). Also specialist in minerals/waste law.
Prof. Memberships: Law Society's Planning Panel, Legal Associate RTPI, UK Environmental Law Association, Associate of Institute of Quarrying.
Career: Educated Rugby, Hull University. Partner of *Eversheds* leading Planning and Environmental Team.
Personal: Married, resides Twycross (Atherstone, Warwick). Interests: walking, computers and reading.

BUTTERFIELD, Kate
Wilbraham & Co, Leeds (0113) 243 2200
kate.butterfield@wilbraham.co.uk
Specialisation: Extensive experience of planning law; recent cases range from advising on planning and environmental matters for motor racing circuits, dealing with compulsory purchase orders, complex planning and highways matters for major commercial developments, advising on strategic infrastructure projects and negotiating planning permission for a 30 storey building in Leeds.
Career: Articled *Hammond Suddards*; qualified 1992; *Hammond Suddards* London & Leeds 1992-95; *Pinsent Curtis*; *Wilbraham & Co* 1995.
Personal: Born 1967. Horse riding, tennis and squash.

CASELY-HAYFORD, Margaret
Denton Wilde Sapte, London (020) 7242 1212
Specialisation: Partner and non-practising barrister, planning and public law group. Practice covers the full range of major project property planning and PFI advice (such as housing, multi-purpose stadium and concert venue developments, police station developments, shopping centres, superstores, hospital development and contaminated land redevelopment proposals, as well as major energy installations). Negotiates planning consents and related agreements, carries out planning audits for funders and developers and co-ordinates and advises on compulsory purchase and land assembly matters and public inquiries covering all regulatory matters related to site development, as well as High Court appeals and judicial review proceedings.
Prof. Memberships: Bar (England and Wales), Grays Inn, UKELA, Association of Women Barristers, firm's representative on Business in Sport and Leisure, Leisure Property Forum.
Career: Called to the Bar by Gray's Inn 1984. Pupilage 4-5 Gray's Inn Square 1985-1987. In house counsel ADC. Joined *Denton Hall* in 1987, partner 1998.
Publications: Author of 'Practical Planning: Permission and the Application' published by FT Law and Tax, December 1995.
Personal: Educated at Streatham Hill High (Girl's Public Day School Trust) and Somerville College, Oxford.

COCKBURN, David
Archibald Campbell & Harley WS, Edinburgh (0131) 220 3000 DWC@achws.co.uk
Specialisation: Handles a full range of commercial property matters, including purchases, development, sales, leasing (for both landlords and tenants), funding and security work. Also advises on planning matters. Accredited planning law specialist. Contributes book reviews and articles to Law Journal of Law Society of Scotland and Scottish Planning and Environmental Law. Regularly contributes by way of lectures to Law Society Update, various professional seminar providers and Edinburgh University.
Prof. Memberships: Society of Writers to HM Signet. Member of Law Society panel awarding accreditation.
Career: Qualified in 1966. Worked with Glasgow Corporation 1966-67 then *Breeze Paterson & Chapman* 1967-70. Joined *Archibald Campbell & Harley WS* in 1970, becoming a partner in 1971.
Personal: Born 4th February 1943. Attended Edinburgh University 1961-1964. Leisure pursuits include sport and reading.

COLLAR, Neil
Brodies WS, Edinburgh (0131) 228 3777 neil.collar@brodies.co.uk
Specialisation: Partner and Head of Planning Law Department, Legal Associate of the Royal Town Planning Institute, LLM for research into use of planning issues 1990. Handles town and country planning matters – planning applications, appeals and inquiries (including inquiry advocacy), court actions, planning issues in relation to land acquisition and disposal, Local Authority compulsory purchase, roads etc. Wide experience of private and public sector clients. Author of 'Planning', published by W.Green & Son and Sweet & Maxwell (Concise Scots Law Series) co-author of 'Pollution Control in Scotland' published by T&T Clark and a number of articles in journals. Member of Editorial Board of Scottish Planning and Environmental Law. Senior tutor for planning law at University of Edinburgh and speaker on aspects of planning law at several conferences.
Prof. Memberships: Law Society of Scotland, Legal Associate of the RTPI, United Kingdom Environmental Law Association.
Career: Qualified in 1992, having joined *Brodies WS* in 1990.
Personal: Born 31st March 1967. Educated at the University of Glasgow 1984-88 and 1989-90 (LLB and Diploma) and Liverpool University 1988-89 (LLM). Enjoys playing the saxophone, lacrosse, hockey and touch rugby. Lives in Edinburgh.

CONNAL, Craig
McGrigor Donald, Glasgow (0141) 248 6677
Specialisation: Partner in commercial litigation unit. Solicitor Advocate. Many years experience of advising on and appearing at Tribunals, Courts and Inquiries in contentious and high profile matters. Recent cases have ranged from successfully acting for the respondent before the Inner House of the Court of Session in the landmark case of East Dunbartonshire Council v McTaggart & Mickel, to appearing successfully for FIFA in claims arising from the abortive Estonia v Scotland football match.
Prof. Memberships: Law Society of Scotland, SSC (Solicitor in the Supreme Courts), Council member, Royal Faculty of Procurators in Glasgow 1995-98.
Career: Joined *McGrigor Donald* in 1977 on qualification, becoming a partner in 1980.
Publications: A regular lecturer and author of many articles, from the general press to, for example, Estates Gazette and JPEL. Contributor, Stair Memorial Encyclopaedia of Scots Law.
Personal: Born 7th July 1954. Educated at Glasgow University (LLB, 1st Class Honours 1975). Rugby referee.

COOPER, David
Gouldens, London (020) 7583 7777
Specialisation: Senior partner in Planning Department. Specialises in Local Government work. Has conducted approximately 900 Planning Inquiries on behalf of clients who include ADT; Alton Towers; ARC Properties; Arlington Securities; Arsenal Football Club; Bristol Airport; British Car Auctions; British Aerospace; Citibank; Flairline Properties; Galliard Homes; GRE Properties; Group Lotus; Hanson Properties Limited; Heron; P&O Developments; Pillar Properties; Port Ramsgate; Sally UK; Sir Emmanuel Kay CBE; Sir Robert McAlpine; Southampton Football Group; Tarmac Properties and Virgin, the majority as Advocate. Has also acted on behalf of groups concerned with the conservation of important buildings in London and the Provinces including SAVE Britain's Heritage, the Covent Garden Resident's Association, the Georgian Society and the Victorian Society. He now also has a major practice specialising in Regulatory, White Collar Crime and Fraud.
Prof. Memberships: Law Society Planning Panel, Legal Associate of the Royal Town Planning Institute.
Career: Qualified in May 1967. Gained experience in the planning field with George Wimpey Limited before joining *Gouldens* as a Partner in 1973.
Personal: Born 8th June 1942. Took an LLB (Hons) in 1960. Lives in London SW1.

CUNLIFFE, Michael
Forsters, London (020) 7863 8477 mdcunliffe@forsters.co.uk
Specialisation: Planning law acting for both developers and local authorities.
Prof. Memberships: Legal Associate of the Royal Town Planning Institute, Member of the Law Society's Planning Panel and Member of the City of London Law Society's Planning and Environmental Law Sub-Committee. Associate Fellow of the Society for Advanced Legal Studies and a Member of the Society's Planning and Environmental Law Reform Working Group.
Career: Qualified 1974. Joined *Ashurst Morris Crisp* 1983. Partner *Ashurst Morris Crisp*, 1987-2001. Partner *Forsters*, 2001.

CURNOW, Tony
Ashurst Morris Crisp, London (020) 7638 1111
Specialisation: Partner and head of planning and public sector group. Advises local authorities and the private sector on planning, regeneration and public infrastructure projects. Major schemes include Channel Tunnel Rail Link, Docklands Highways, Chalkhill Estate for London Borough of Brent, Parkway/M602 in Trafford Park, Hackney Estates Regeneration Strategy, Surrey Heath Borough Council's town centre redevelopment at Camberley, Project Vauxhall in the London Borough of Lambeth, the redevelopment of the Guinness Brewery at Park Royal, the Southgate Shopping Centre in Bath and the extension of Broadmead for Bristol City Council.
Prof. Memberships: Law Society Planning Panel and Legal Associate RTPI.
Career: Qualified 1979. 11 years in local government. Joined *Ashurst Morris Crisp* 1988, Partner in 1996.

DAMMS, Martin
Pinsent Curtis Biddle, Birmingham (0121) 200 1050 martin.damms@pinsents.com
Specialisation: Planning and Environmental Law. Increasingly involved in urban regeneration schemes requiring compulsory purchase proceedings and highways stopping up and diversion orders. Covers full range of contentious and non contentious matters including advising and representing public bodies. Planning applications, appeals, development plan representations, judicial review, negotiating/drafting planning agreements, enforcement action, housing, commercial, retail, leisure and minerals development, highways issues, compulsory purchase proceedings, contaminated land issues and waste regulation, hazardous substances consents. Advocate.
Prof. Memberships: Law Society. Birmingham Law Society. Member of the Law Society's Planning Panel. Legal Associate R.T.P.I. Member of the Midlands Environmental Business club.
Career: Qualified 1976. In Local Government to 1989. Joined *Edge Ellison* in 1989. Partner from 1993. *Pinsent Curtis* 2000 to date.
Personal: Born 17th November 1952. Educated at Mexborough Grammar School and University of Birmingham.

DIMMICK, Simon
Clarks, Reading (0118) 958 5321
Specialisation: Town and Country Planning, highways law, environmental work relating to property development. Advice on local authority matters generally. Advocacy. Acts for land owners, developers and local authorities.
Career: Qualified in 1977. 1983-1988 Assistant County Solicitor, Berkshire County Council. Joined *Clarks* in 1988, becoming a Partner in 1989.
Personal: Born 19 January 1952. Educated Kings School, Worcester, and University College, London – LLB 1974. Leisure time interests include family and Church work.

DRUKARZ, Daniel
Pitmans, Reading (0118) 958 0227 ddrukarz@pitmans.com
Specialisation: Planning department partner specialising in all aspects of planning law and practice, including judicial review and major inquiry work. Wide experience in office and business park schemes, urban regeneration initiatives and other large scale retail, residential and mixed use developments, often involving 'tall' buildings. Many projects endorsed by the GLA and CABE. Expertise in negotiating and drafting planning and infrastructure agreements. Acts for a variety of multinationals (including advice on EC wide environmental strategy), investment and development companies and amenity groups.
Prof. Memberships: Law Society; Member Institute of Petroleum.
Career: Articles *Titmuss Sainer & Webb*, qualified 1989, assistant solicitor with *Nabarro Nathanson* and *S J Berwin* before joining *Fladgate Fielder* in 1994 to set up Planning Unit. Partner since 1997. Joined *Pitmans* as partner in December 2000.
Personal: Born 1960. Married with two children.

Interests include family, Himalayan, African and South American trekking and five-a-side. Lives in London.

DYER, Carl
Osborne Clarke, London (020) 7809 1000

EDMOND, John
Marrons, Leicester (0116) 289 2200
johnedmond@marrons.net
Specialisation: Partner in planning, development and public law department. Has 15 years experience of specialist contentious town planning and associated work, including judicial review and High Court challenges to planning decisions under the 1990 Act, public law matters and compulsory purchase. Has acted in a wide range of cases including new village schemes, major urban regeneration schemes, contaminated land proposals, landfill proposals, motorway service areas, retail and leisure applications, applications involving Conservation Areas, Listed Buildings and Registered Parks; and in negotiating Section 106 agreements and related agreements relating to major infrastructure proposals. Major clients include Persimmon Homes, Barratt Homes, David Wilson Homes, Allison Homes, Hallam Land Managements, Forte UK Ltd, Jelson Homes, Stapleford Park plc, Safeways, Wilson Bowden Properties, CWS. Conducted Local Plan Inquiries on behalf of Local Planning Authorities including Daventry District Council, South Derbyshire District Council and North West Leicestershire District Council.
Prof. Memberships: Law Society, Legal Associate of the Royal Town Planning Institute, Member of the Law Society's Planning Panel.
Career: Qualified in 1983, joined *Marron Dodds* in 1987 becoming a partner in 1988. Prior to joining *Marron Dodds* specialised in Magistrates Court/Crown Court prosecution and defence work. Educated at Hull Grammar School.
Personal: Born 8th February 1959. Attended Wolverhampton University (BA (Hons) Law 1980). Leisure interests include golf (member of Luffenham Health Golf Club), personal fitness and the arts. Lives on the Leicestershire/ Rutland border. Married with four children.

ENGERT, Nick
Clarke Willmott & Clarke, Taunton
(01823) 442 266
nengert@cw-c.co.uk
Specialisation: Chairman and partner heading planning and environmental department now comprising five partners, a consultant on local government matters, a planning barrister, two associates and an assistant. Main areas of practice are town and country planning, compulsory purchase and compensation and land development. Recent appearances as an advocate include a called in application for a major food store development in South Bristol, local plan inquiries for national housebuilders in Bedfordshire, Cheshire, Dorset and Wiltshire, successful section 78 appeals in Devon, Gloucestershire and Somerset. A principal adviser to local authorities and other landowners in respect of several substantial development schemes involving such issues as contaminated land, environmental assessment, flood prevention, listed buildings and conservation areas, renewable energy, retail and traffic impact, design and layout and overall sustainability. Currently advising landowners and local authorities on use of compulsory purchase powers and disputed compensation claims. Is on the Urban Advisory Board for the Regional Development Agency. Regular lecturer on planning related matters to regional branches of the Royal Town Planning Institute and RICS. Recognised nationally as one of the highest rated planning solicitor advocates (as chosen by leading solicitors and planners – Planning Magazine 1999, 2000 and 2001).
Prof. Memberships: Member of the Law Society and UKELA.
Career: Qualified in 1973. Joined *Clarke Willmott & Clarke* in 1975, becoming a partner in 1979.
Personal: Born 28th September 1948. Attended Oundle School and Southampton University. A Governor of the West of England School for Children with little or no sight and an official steward for British Eventing. Leisure interests include riding, shooting, tennis, golf, choral singing and wine tasting.

EVANS, Douglas
Theodore Goddard, London (020) 7880 5789
douglasevans@theodoregoddard.co.uk
Specialisation: Management of multi-disciplinary and inter-firm teams to sucessfully obtain planning and regulatory consents for some of the UK's most contentious development proposals. Advocacy, strategic advice and negotiation of planning permissions and agreements for all forms of development. Advice on environmental assessment and contaminated land is an important part of the practice. Major clients include multi-national waste companies, utility, mining, power generation, commercial and residential developers. Current cases include acting for Onyx Environmental Group, successfully obtaining three EfW planning permissions in Hampshire; acting for SITA on the 25 year Surrey Waste Contract and promoting two EfW incinerators; EPR/Cory, promoting a major EfW plant at Belvedere; acting for Minosus in promoting the UK's first underground special waste facility within a rock salt mine; Bryant Homes, Persimmon Homes, Fairview, Bellway, Countryside Homes and other national house builders – securing major allocations and planning permissions, by negotiation and on appeal, for developments ranging from 50-5,000 dwellings. Additionally, Douglas is acting on various cases including major landfill extensions and the presenting of objections to Emerging RPG, Structure and Local Plans, including appearing at Inquries, to secure development allocations. Thames Water Utilities in the Terminal 5 Inquiry; promoting a 10,000 house development at Stevenage for Persimmon Homes; promoting three major 'waste to energy' incinerators for Hampshire Waste; obtaining planning permission to double the size of the UK's only potashmine for Cleveland Potash; securing planning permission for 1000 dwellings at Banbury for Bryant Homes; advising SITA on the 25 year Surrey Waste Contract and promoting two waste to energy incinerators; promoting three further waste to energy incinerators at various locations; advising on a major landfill site extension; presenting objections to numerous Local Plan Inquiries to secure allocations for retail and housing development.
Prof. Memberships: Member of the Law Society Specialist Planning Panel, Legal Associate of the Royal Town Planning Institute, Member of the City of London Law Society Planning and Environment Law Sub-Committee, Member of the Environmental Services Association, Affiliate Member of the Institute of Wastes Management, Member Editorial Board Institute of Wastes Management Scientific and Technical Review, Member UKELA, Member Renewable Power Association.
Personal: Leisure interests include sailing, shooting and music.

EVANS, Eric
Eversheds, Cardiff (029) 2047 1147
Specialisation: Partner in commercial property department and head of both the planning and PFI units. Specialises in all aspects of property law including complex planning obligations, major town centre regeneration/shopping schemes, site assembly, agreements for the construction of major highways associated with developments, public/private sector joint ventures, planning gain, valuations, urban development/regeneration grants and land reclamation. 30 years public sector experience, dealing with all areas of local government. Extensive experience of PFI and led one of the first PFI/PPP deals in Wales, at University Hospital of Wales NHS Trust. Has since advised on numerous deals including Newport Southern Distributor Road, Chepstow Community Hospital, Wiltshire's grouped schools scheme and 'Waste to Energy' scheme at Neath.
Prof. Memberships: Member of Law Society's Planning Panel.
Career: Qualified in 1980. Town Clerk, Borough of Blaenau Gwent (1981-89). Deputy Chief Executive and Legal Adviser, Land Authority for Wales (1989-92). Partner *Eversheds* 1992.
Personal: Director of Silent Valley Waste Services. Lives in Abertillery.

EVANS, Katherine
TLT Solicitors, Bristol (0117) 917 7777
kevans@TLTsolicitors.com
Specialisation: Specialises in all aspects of development including planning, highways, compulsory purchase/compensation, land acquisition. Also environmental law particularly contaminated land and environmental liability in corporate transactions. Experienced in High Court challenges and judicial reviews. Acts for developers, financial institutions, minerals and waste operators, local authorities, private landowners and individuals.
Prof. Memberships: Law Society, Royal Town Planning Institute.
Career: Qualified planner 1987, solicitor 1997. 1986-96 employed by national housebuilders to acquire and project manage major development sites. *Lawrence Tucketts* (now *TLT Solicitors*, the merged firm of *Trumps* and *Lawrence Tucketts*) since 1998.
Personal: Born 1962. Lives in Bristol. Interests include family and travel.

EVANS, Martin
Nabarro Nathanson, London (020) 7524 6000
Specialisation: Partner in the planning group. Town and country planning and related issues. Particular experience in providing strategic advice on major retail and leisure schemes (both in and out of town) and public inquiries acting both for developer and local authority clients. Major clients include Reuters, Friends Provident, Hammerson, St George and Slough Estates. Also involved in negotiating complex planning and infrastructure agreements on behalf of developers and local authorities.
Prof. Memberships: Law Society, Journal of Leisure Property Forum (Editorial Board).
Career: Qualified 1989.

FAULDS, Ann
Dundas & Wilson CS, Edinburgh (0131) 228 8000

FINCH, Paul
Dickinson Dees, Newcastle upon Tyne (0191) 279 9000
Specialisation: Planning, compulsory purchase and compensation. Involved in major housing projects in the North East, Hampshire and Dorset, major urban regeneration schemes in London and the North East and in various PFI schemes. Highlights of last year include negotiation of bus depot relocation agreement and compensation package. Developer at Purbock local plan inquiry, representation of a number of clients in CPO inquiries, advice on comments issues in rail re-franchise proposals. Negotiation of planning agreements re major development in Basingstoke, successful advocacy in a number of public inquiries.
Prof. Memberships: Law Society. Newcastle Law Society. Member of Law Society Planning & Environmental Committee.
Career: 1979-1982 *Runnymede* BC, 1982-1986 *North Tyneside* MBC, 1986-1990 *Clifford Chance*, 1990-date *Dickinson Dees.*
Publications: Notes to 'Leasehold Reform Housing and Urban Development Act 1993 (Current Law)'. Various articles in property and planning law journals, 'Rights of Way Law Review.'
Personal: Educated Omskirk Grammar School and University of Newcastle Upon Tyne. Married, no children. Outside interests hockey, squash, hill-walking, travel.

FIRTH, Beverley
Mills & Reeve, Cambridge (01223) 222 235
beverley.firth@mills-reeve.com
Specialisation: Partner in the Property Services Department, specialising in all aspects of planning law. Work includes advice on aspects of land development, negotiations with local authorities including planning agreements. Also includes advocacy in planning appeals and in local plan inquiries. Contentious work includes judicial review. Particular environmental expertise in land contamination and waste disposal including clinical waste. Also experienced in health and safety. Recent projects include local airfields, new settlement and University campus.

FONGENIE, Wesley
Osborne Clarke, London (020) 7809 1000

FRASER, Moira A.
Fladgate Fielder, London (020) 7323 4747
mfraser@fladgate.com
Specialisation: Partner. Many years specialist experience in planning, CPO and compensation, highway and other infrastructure issues. Emphasis on inquiry work and appeals. Expertise in negotiating and drafting planning and infrastructure agreements. Advises on development plan policies. Acts for public authorities, private sector and amenity groups. Special expertise in large retail and listed buildings.
Prof. Memberships: The Law Society; Fellow of the Royal Society of Arts; Town and Country Planning Association.
Career: MA (Hons) Cantab. Articled 1977-79 *Norton Rose*, qualified 1979. *D J Freeman* 1988-99, *McGuinness Finch* 1999-2001. *Fladgate Fielder* 2001- .
Personal: Born 1955. Leisure pursuits include golf, art appreciation and family.

GALLIMORE, Michael
Lovells, London (020) 7296 2253
michael.gallimore@lovells.com
Specialisation: Partner in commercial property department and head of planning group. Principal area of practice is property development with particular expertise in the planning and environmental aspects of major development and infrastructure projects. Wide experience in office and business park developments, retail schemes, new housing settlements, leisure projects and waste management schemes. Also experienced in development site acquisitions. Expertise includes negotiations and appeals for planning and associated consents and drafting and negotiation of s.106 agreements and related development/infrastructure agreements. Has acted on numerous judicial review applications and High Court challenges. Experience also on various PFI projects. Acts as an advocate at planning and local plan inquiries.
Prof. Memberships: Law Society Specialist Planning Panel, Law Society Planning and Environmental Law Committee, City of London Law Society Planning and Environmental Law Sub-Committee.
Career: Qualified 1983, Partner 1988.

GIBBS, Kevin
Osborne Clarke, Bristol (0117) 917 3000

GILBEY, Iain
Shoosmiths, Northampton (01604) 543 000
iain.gilbey@shoosmiths.co.uk
Specialisation: Partner and head of planning group. Town and country planning and environmental law. All aspects of property development. Specialises in providing strategic advice on residential, retail and other large scale commercial developments. Experienced in conducting major public inquiries and associated High Court litigation. Acts for privatised utilities, major national housebuilders, landowners, retailers and occupiers.
Prof. Memberships: Law Society and UKELA.
Career: Educated at Royal Grammar School, High Wycombe. Southampton University (LLB). College of Law, Guildford. Trained at *Berwin Leighton.* Qualified 1994. *Ashurst Morris Crisp* 1997-2000. Joined *Shoosmiths* January 2000. Partner May 2000.

GILLES, June
Semple Fraser, Glasgow (0141) 221 3771
june.gilles@semplefraser.co.uk
Specialisation: Commercial property specialising in town and country planning. June has extensive experience of providing legal advice and support in planning inquiries and legal challenges, enforcement and negotiation of planning agreements in the retail, leisure, industrial, minerals and renewable energy sectors. She works with a number of significant clients including Tesco Stores in their Scottish expansion and on windfarm projects for Powergen Renewables.
Career: Trained *Maclay Murray & Spens*; qualified 1983. Spent six years working in property and planning with Motherwell District Council and then Dunbarton District Council. Returned to private practice with *Bird Semple Fyfe Ireland.* Joined *Semple Fraser WS* 1997.
Personal: Born 1960. Educated at Hutchesons' Grammar School and Glasgow. Interests include cinema, music, theatre, photography, reading and skiing.

GOODMAN, David
Hammond Suddards Edge, Leeds (0113) 284 7000
david.goodman@hammondse.com
Specialisation: Partner and head of planning department. Main area of practice is town and country planning handling all aspects of planning issues relating to development, including retailing, residential, office, power generation, mineral extraction, waste disposal and leisure uses. Undertakes advocacy at public inquiries. Also deals with environmental law including environmental assessment and environmentally sensitive developments. Has handled a proposal for an overhead transmission line through Cleveland and North Yorkshire, various power generation projects including windfarms, promotion of clinical waste incinerator proposals, and a football stadium in the North East. Author of articles on planning law. Lectures regularly to RTPI and other professional bodies.
Prof. Memberships: Law Society, British Wind Energy Association.
Career: Qualified in 1980. Articled at Surrey County Council 1978-80, then assistant solicitor at Oldham Metropolitan BC 1980-84. Senior solicitor at Newcastle upon Tyne City Council 1984-88. Joined *Hammond Suddards* in 1988 and became a partner in 1991.
Personal: Born 15th October 1955. Educated at the Royal Grammar School, Newcastle upon Tyne 1967-74 and Sheffield University 1974-77. Recreations include sport, gardening and theatre.

GRANT, James
MacRoberts, Glasgow (0141) 332 9988
jamie.grant@macroberts.co.uk
See under Environment, p.371

GRAVES, Gary
Nabarro Nathanson, London (020) 7524 6000
g.graves@nabarro.com
Specialisation: Partner specialising in all aspects of planning law and practice, including major inquiry work and judicial review.
Prof. Memberships: Member Law Society Planning Panel (1995) and City of London Law Society Planning and Environmental Law Sub-Committee. Legal Associate of RTPI.
Career: Articled *Russells*; qualified 1983. *Herbert Oppenheimer* (1983-1988); *Lovell White Durrant* (1988-1991). Partner *Nabarro Nathanson* (1991 to date).
Personal: Born 1958. Married with one child, resides London.

GREENWOOD, Brian
Norton Rose, London (020) 7283 6000
greenwoodbj@nortonrose.com
Specialisation: Areas of expertise include planning applications, environmental assessment, negotiation of planning and infrastructure agreements and hearings and appeals. Appears as advocate at appeals. Recent instructions encompass industrial processes (Castle Cement), power stations, residential and commercial development, listed buildings (English Heritage) and motorway service areas (Esso).
Prof. Memberships: Chairman, Law Society's Planning and Environmental Law Committee, former Chairman City of London Law Society Planning and Environment Committee; UKELA; Law Society's Specialist Planning Panel.
Publications: Author of 'Butterworths Planning Law Service', co-author of 'Environmental Regulation

and Economic Growth', editor of 'Planning Law Handbook' and 'Butterworths Planning Law Guidance'.

GRIFFITHS, Marian
Eversheds, Leeds (0113) 243 0391
mariangriffiths@eversheds.com
Specialisation: Town and country planning, compulsory purchase. Main areas of practice are retail, minerals and waste disposal and housing, town centre regeneration.
Prof. Memberships: Law Society's Planning Panel. Legal Associate Royal Town Planning Institute.
Career: Law degree from Leeds and qualified as a solicitor in 1981. Articled in local government and worked in the public sector until 1991. Joined *Eversheds* in 1996.
Personal: Born Chester, educated in Wolverhampton. Married with twin daughters aged 10. Lives in Leeds.

HALL, Brian
Clifford Chance, London (020) 7600 1000
brian.hall@cliffordchance.com
Specialisation: Partner and head of firm's planning unit specialising in environment, public law and town planning.
Prof. Memberships: Member of UKELA and Law Society's Planning Panel.
Career: Rutherford Grammar School; King's College, London (LLB, DMA, FCIS). Articled North Tyneside MBC; qualified 1980; partner *Clifford Chance* since 1988.
Personal: Born 1950; resides London.

HARRIS, Jacqueline
McGrigor Donald, Glasgow (0141) 248 6677
www.mcgrigors.com
Specialisation: Partner in Commercial Litigation Unit. Developed expertise in planning through dealing with litigation involving technical and scientific evidence and with plannning applications, appeals, public inquiries and judicial review. Has considerable experience of dealing with technical and scientific issues arising in planning (and litigation) matters. Planning practice now includes advising on all aspects of planning, particularly in relation to major development and infrastructure projects, retail and mineral planning. Conducts advocacy at public inquiries. Planning clients include: The Post Office; Lattice Property Holdings Ltd, Forth Ports plc, I & H Brown Ltd, Glasgow Harbour Ltd. Other key areas of practice are commercial litigation and product liability.
Career: Qualified 1990; Partner *McGrigor Donald* 1999.

HAWKINS, David
Nabarro Nathanson, London (020) 7524 6000

HELLIER, Tim
Berwin Leighton Paisner, London (020) 7760 1000
tim.hellier@berwinleightonpaisner.com
Specialisation: Wide experience in retail, housing, leisure, office developments and major urban regeneration schemes, compulsory purchase, contaminated land, risk management and infrastructure schemes and urban regeneration schemes. Acted for AMEC Developments in securing planning permission for the first freight terminal associated with the Channel Tunnel in the Green Belt. Acted for BAA-McArthur/Glen (UK) Limited, the factory outlet operator in securing planning approvals for over 1.5 million square feet of retail floorspace. Currently acting on major urban regeneration schemes in Bracknell, Hull, Chester and Liverpool, Belfast Guildford. Other major clients: Tesco, Legal and General, London and Amsterdam, Liverpool Council Belfast Regeneration Office and Warner Village.
Prof. Memberships: Law Society, Associate Fellow of the Society of Advanced Legal Studies, UKELA.
Career: Strode College, Egham. Sheffield University LLB (Hons). Law Society Finals, City of London Polytechnic. Qualified 1986; partner *Berwin Leighton* (now *Berwin Leighton Paisner*) 1997.
Personal: Married with two children. Interests include rugby, running and general fitness, music, his children.

HEMMING, Dan
Wragge & Co, Birmingham (0870) 903 1000

HIGNETT, Andrew
Lester Aldridge, Southampton (023) 8082 0419
andrew.hignett@lester-aldridge.co.uk
Specialisation: Retail and residential developments, development of contaminated land, planning appeals and local plan representations, including advocacy at public inquiries. He acts for port authorities and has therefore considerable experience in port and marina developments.
Career: Qualified 1978. With local authorities until 1988, culminating as a Chief Officer in the South West. A planning specialist in private sector since then. Has advised both local authorities and developers in relation to town centre developments including capital spending restrictions. Compulsory purchase work, including compensation, is a major part of his practice, advising both the public sector and national utilities in relation to the promotion of their compulsory purchase powers, together with businesses/individuals affected by CPO's. Andrew Hignett has also lectured extensively to solicitors and other professionals on planning law issues.

HILLEBRON, Richard
Slaughter and May, London (020) 7600 1200
richard.hillebron@slaughterandmay.com
Specialisation: Specialises in all aspects of town and country planning from submission of an application through to decision and appeal, including compulsory purchase, negotiating highways and other agreements with local authorities and certificates of lawful use or development.
Prof. Memberships: Legal Associate of The Royal Town Planning Institute; Member of The Law Society's Planning Panel and Member City of London Law Society Planning and Environmental Law Sub-Committee.
Career: Qualified 1980.

HOLMES, John
Halliwell Landau, Manchester (0161) 831 2998
jholmes@halliwells.co.uk
Specialisation: Specialises in both environmental and planning matters. Acts for a wide range of corporate clients in the UK. Has also contributed to a number of legal journals and is an examiner for the Institute of Fisheries Management.
Prof. Memberships: Law Society.
Career: Qualified in 1999. Senior Legal Advisor to the Environment Agency in its North West Regional Office. Joined *Halliwell Landau* in 1999.
Personal: Born in 1959. BA (Hons) (Government and Politics) 1988. LLB (London) (Hons) 1993. Recreations include football, cricket, hockey and horse riding.

HOLMES, Sarah
Bond Pearce, Plymouth (01752) 266633
sholmes@bondpearce.com
See under Environment, p.372

HOWARD, Karen
Ashurst Morris Crisp, London (020) 7638 1111
Specialisation: Advises on Town Planning and related matters, including urban regeneration, compulsory purchase and highway orders, appeals and public inquiries, High Court challenges, and planning and infrastructure agreements. Wide experience in retail, leisure and housing matters and major mixed use development schemes. Acted for English Partnerships in securing permission for the Millennium Dome and the regeneration of the Greenwich Peninsula. Main adviser to Tesco Stores Limited since 1988. Other major clients have included Amec Developments Limited, Lloyds Bank, BG plc, St James Homes, Hemmingway and DLR.
Prof. Memberships: Fellow of Institute of Legal Executives; Student member of Law Society.
Career: Local Government 1984-1986. Joined *Denton Hall* 1986. Moved to *Berwin Leighton* 1988; became senior manager; left March 2000. Now Legal Manager at *Ashurst Morris Crisp*.
Personal: Born 1964; one child. Interests include motorcycling, personal fitness, socialising and family. Lives in Broomfield, Essex.

HUGHES, Norna
Nabarro Nathanson, London (020) 7524 6000
n.hughes@nabarro.com
Specialisation: Heads planning department. Handles all aspects of planning related work, particularly contentious planning and Judicial Review.
Career: Qualified in 1989. Joined *Nabarro Nathanson* in 1987, becoming a partner in 1989. Previously a Barrister specialising in planning, having been called to the Bar in 1983.
Personal: Leisure interests include family, friends, socialising and tennis. Lives in London.

INNES, Colin
Shepherd & Wedderburn WS, Edinburgh (0131) 228 9900
colin.innes@shepwedd.co.uk
Specialisation: Partner in litigation department. Head of the planning and environmental group specialising exclusively in planning and environmental issues. Has substantial experience of advising on planning or related issues to clients both in the private and public sectors, including on the contentious side representation at public local inquiries, planning appeals and judicial review of planning decisions in the Court of Session. In relation to non-contentious work has extensive experience in providing advice on all types of planning projects and PFI schemes.
Prof. Memberships: Law Society (England and Wales), Law Society (Scotland) and UKELA, WS Society. Legal associate, Royal Town Planning Institute.
Career: LL.B (Hons) University of Aberdeen. LL.M (Environmental Law) University of Aberdeen.

JACKSON, Ray
Linklaters, London (020) 7456 4884
ray.jackson@linklaters.com
Specialisation: Planning and environmental unit in the property department. Specialises in all aspects of environmental law including town planning, public health, control of pollution, compulsory purchase and highways. Typical matters have included a wide

selection of corporate, privatisation and major property transactions where planning, regulatory and environmental issues have been pertinent. Has had extensive involvement in major public local inquiries for motorways, large redevelopment schemes and compulsory purchase orders. Detailed knowledge of the Compensation Code in respect of claims in the Lands Tribunal and as Parliamentary Agent; considerable experience of Private and Hybrid Bill procedures.
Prof. Memberships: Member of the Planning & Environment Committee of the British Property Federation. Member of the London Office Review Panel of the London Planning Advisory Committee (LPAC). Founding Member of the City of London Law Society Planning and Environmental Law Subcommittee.
Career: Joined *Linklaters* in 1985, made partner in 1988.

JAMESON, Robert
Jameson & Hill, Hertford (01992) 554881
Specialisation: Main area of practice is town and country planning, handling all aspects of planning issues, including retailing, residential, office, mineral extraction, waste disposal, and leisure uses; acting both for private clients and local authorities. Considerable local plan experience. Regular advocate at inquiries into local plans. Planning and enforcement appeals. In addition, has extensive experience in negotiating complex planning agreements.
Career: Qualified in 1971. Started legal career in local government. Was principal assistant county secretary at Hertfordshire County Council before co-founding *Jameson & Hill* in 1982. Over 20 years of planning experience.

JEEPS, Barry
Stephenson Harwood, London (020) 7809 2513
barry.jeeps@shlegal.com
Specialisation: Partner, Head of Town and Country Planning Group. Extensive experience in all aspects of town and country planning, compulsory purchase and Transport and Works Act applications with particular emphasis on large-scale public inquiries and litigation. Planning advice in relation to London Bridge City (one of the largest urban regeneration projects in the country) and the Trafford Centre, Manchester (a major shopping centre) planning permission for which was defended successfully in the House of Lords.
Career: Joined *Stephenson Harwood* in 1980 and qualified in 1982. Partner and Head of Town and Country Planning Group in 1989.
Personal: Born 1958. Educated at St Catherine's College, Oxford.

KENWORTHY, Michael
Addleshaw Booth & Co, Manchester
(0161) 934 6000
mbk@addleshaw-booth.co.uk
Specialisation: Partner in commercial property group and head of planning law. Specialises in planning, environmental, highways and compulsory purchase matters. Acts for local authorities, utility companies, waste operators, developers and NHS trusts. Advises international companies on environmental due-diligence in land and corporate acquisitions.
Prof. Memberships: Member of the Law Society and UKELA.
Career: University of Keele 1974-1978. Qualified in 1981. Joined the firm in 1986. Partner in 1990.

KITSON, Tony
CMS Cameron McKenna, London
(020) 7367 3556
abk@cmck.com
Specialisation: Partner in Planning Group. Advises on the planning aspects of all sizes and types of property development. Has handled numerous appeals involving retail, office, industrial and residential developments, and appears as an advocate at public local inquiries. Experienced in negotiating and drafting Section 106 Agreements and other development agreements. Advises on all aspects of local authority law and administration, and PFI schemes. Advises on compulsory purchase and compensation, and Transport and Works Act schemes, the clean-up of contaminated industrial sites and disposal for redevelopment. Speaker at seminars on planning and environmental law, local government law. Contributor to Solicitors Journal, Law Society's Gazette, Journal of Planning and Environmental Law and *CMS Cameron McKenna* publications on planning, highways, compulsory purchase and public sector law and finance.
Prof. Memberships: Law Society, Law Society's Panel of Planning Solicitors. City of London Law Society.
Career: Qualified in 1975. Local authority solicitor before joining *McKenna & Co* in 1988; became a Partner in 1990.
Personal: Born 14th February 1952. Lives in London.

KRATZ, Philip
Taylor Vinters, Cambridge (01223) 423444
prk@taylorvinters.com
Specialisation: All aspects of town and country planning and environmental law. Experienced advocate. Work includes agreements, applications, appeals (including local inquiries), local plan and structure plan representations. Recent experience has included acting in connection with large scale residential proposals in Cambridge and the surrounding area and commercial proposals throughout the country.
Prof. Memberships: Law Society; member of the Law Society's Specialist Planning Panel; Legal Associate member of the Royal Town Planning Institute.
Career: Qualified in 1982. District Solicitor and head of Legal Services with East Cambridgeshire District Council from 1983-1992; Assistant Chief Executive until joining *Taylor Vinters* in May 1995. Head of planning development and construction team.
Personal: Leisure interests include cricket, Jaguar cars and military engineering.

LANCASTER, Roger
Halliwell Landau, Manchester (0161) 835 3003
rlancaster@halliwells.co.uk
Specialisation: Partner and Head of Planning and Environmental Law Department. Specialises in town and country planning, environmental law and compulsory purchase matters and local government issues and general advocacy at inquiries. Has substantial house building retail and developer clients and also acts for public sector authorities.
Prof. Memberships: Law Society.
Career: Qualified in 1975. Solicitor with Humberside County Council and Birmingham City Council. Joined *Halliwell Landau* as a Partner in 1982. Senior Partner 1995-2000.
Personal: Born in 1951. Educated at Biddulph Grammar School and Leicester University (LLB 1971). Recreations include cricket, squash and gardening.

LEA, Alison
Travers Smith Braithwaite, London
(020) 7295 3000
Alison.Lea@TraversSmith.com
Specialisation: Partner and head of planning and environment group. Specialises in all aspects of planning and environmental law including highway matters and compulsory purchase. Has recently acted on a number of successful judicial review applications and High Court challenges for Lafarge Redland Aggregates and Clearwater Estates. Particular experience in negotiating consents for large retail, leisure and residential mixed use schemes including the drafting and negotiation of planning and infrastructure agreements.
Prof. Memberships: City of London Law Society Planning and Environment Law Sub-Committee. Legal associate of Royal Town Planning Institute.
Career: Trained *Norton Rose*; qualified 1989. *Norton Rose* 1987-97. *Travers Smith Braithwaite* 1997 to date; made partner in 1998.
Publications: Author of monthly Planning Focus in 'Property Law Journal', member of contributory board of 'Property Law Journal'. Articles in 'Journal of Planning and Environmental Law', 'Environmental Law Monthly' and 'Environmental Law Review'.
Personal: Educated at Rainford High School and Girton College, Cambridge. Interests include horse riding and playing classical piano and flute.

MANSON, Stephen
Eversheds, Cardiff (029) 2047 1147
stephenmanson@eversheds.com
Specialisation: Partner specialising in town and country planning, Private Finance Initiative/Public Private Partnership work together with general public sector work. Former member of Government's Private Finance Panel Executive. Advises a number of local minerals developers on such matters as the current minerals review procedures. Currently advising United News and Media on planning appeal for alternative use of studio site in Cardiff. Acts for both public and private sectors on PFI schemes in a variety of areas such as education (advised Wiltshire County Council on its three schools deal – £30m), health (advised health trust on local hospital scheme in Cardiff – £15m) and transport (advising Newport County Borough Council on its Southern Distributor Road – £40m).
Career: Bristol University (LLB Hons). Bristol Polytechnic (LSF First Class Hons).
Personal: Recreations include windsurfing and badminton.

MARRON, Peter
Marrons, Leicester (0116) 289 2200
petermarron@marrons.net
Specialisation: Senior partner in planning, development and public law department. Has twenty-five years' experience of contentious town planning, together with associated work advising the development industry. Also handles public law matters, compulsory purchase and judicial review. Has acted in cases ranging from new village schemes, landfill proposals and many other applications of strategic importance. Has given talks over the years to a number of bodies. Major clients include national

house-builders, major land promoters, commercial developers and local authorities.
Prof. Memberships: Law Society, Chartered Institute of Arbitrators.
Career: Qualified in 1970. Founded *Marron Dodds* as a senior partner in 1978. DOT/ RYA Ocean Yacht Master with commercial endorsement. ACIArb 1990. Fellow of the Royal Society of Arts 1995. Legal Associate of the Royal Town Planning Institute. Member of International Bar Assocation. Member of Law Society's Planning Panel. Fellow of the Institute of Advanced Legal Studies.
Personal: Born 3rd June 1944. Attended Liverpool University (LLB Hons 1966). Leisure interests include the arts and off-shore sailing. Lives in Uppingham, Rutland.

MAX, Richard
Olswang, London (020) 7208 8616
rdm@olswang.com
Specialisation: Partner in property department. Head of planning. Deals with all areas of planning law and practice as well as compulsory purchase and highways matters. Noted solicitor-advocate at planning enquiries. Represents both private and public sectors including developers, retailers, housebuilders and local authoritites.
Prof. Memberships: Law Society's Planning Panel; Chairman of the City of London Law Society Planning and Environmental Law Sub-Committee; Legal Associate and Council Member of the Royal Town Planning Institute.
Career: Qualified in 1988. Assistant solicitor at *Macfarlanes* 1988-93. Planning solicitor, Oxford City Council 1993. At *Radcliffes & Co* 1993-95. Joined *D J Freeman* in April 1995 – made partner in May 1997 and head of planning in 1999. *Olswang* – partner and head of planning 2001.
Personal: Born 1 September 1963. Educated at St Paul's School 1976-82, Oxford Polytechnic 1982-85 and The College of Law, Chester 1985-86. Interests include exhibiting and driving a convertible VW Beetle as well as skiing and cycling. Lives in London.

McCHLERY, Frances
Dundas & Wilson CS, Glasgow (0141) 222 2200

MORITZ, John
Wake Dyne Lawton, Chester (01829) 773100
jmm@wdl.co.uk
Specialisation: Initially in local government. Has advised on a number of major development projects in the North West and nationally involving urban regeneration and contaminated land. Advises housebuilders, commercial developers waste management companies and local authorities on planning and infrastructure law, compulsory purchase and environment law.
Prof. Memberships: Member of the Law Society's Planning Panel and a Member of the United Kingdom Environmental Law Association.
Career: Qualified in 1973. Partner at *Lambert Storey* in 1990. Joined *Masons* in 1990 as a partner.
Personal: Born in Manchester 20th September 1948. LLB Manchester University. Leisure interests include travel, theatre and viewing and appreciating art and architecture.

PASTERFIELD, Stephen
Clarke Willmott & Clarke, Bristol (0117) 941 6600
spasterfield@cw-c.co.uk
Specialisation: Partner in the planning and environmental department. Specialises in planning, handling all issues relating to development including mineral extraction, waste disposal, urban regeneration, retailing, office and residential uses; also compensation and environmental law including waste management licensing, contaminated land, nuisance and water pollution. Acts for Government Departments, Developers, Financial Institutions, Minerals and Waste Operators and Local Authorities as well as private individuals. Recent appearances as advocate at appeals have been for a pension fund in Wales and a principal party at the Severnside Inquiry into old permissions for a huge area of industrial land. Is currently advising national companies on legal issues of transportation/compulsory purchase, electro magnetic fields and brownfield regeneration. Stephen has also been selected as joint advocate for a West Country planning authority at its Local Plan Inquiry. Continues to act on a wide range of planning and compulsory purchase issues. Very experienced advocate and lecturer on techniques at inquiries. Author of numerous articles.
Prof. Memberships: Member of Law Society's specialist Planning Panel and Legal Associate of the Royal Town Planning Institute.
Career: Qualified in 1974. Principal solicitor, *Solihull MBC* 1976-79. Deputy City Solicitor, Winchester 1979-1988. Partner at *Lawrence Tucketts* from 1994 to 1999. Joined *Clarke Willmott & Clarke* as partner (1999 to date).
Personal: Born 30th April 1949. Educated Birkenhead School 1960-67. Leisure pursuits include sport of all kinds, especially golf, fishing and horse racing.

PIATT, Andrew
DLA, Manchester (08700) 111111

PUGH, Tim
Berwin Leighton Paisner, London (020) 7760 1000
timothy.pugh@berwinleightonpaisner.com
Specialisation: Partner; Co-Head Planning and Environment Department. Planning and Environmental Law. Particular areas of planning-related expertise: rail and infrastructure projects, urban regeneration, retail, industrial, warehousing, waste disposal, land reclamation and housing projects; compulsory purchase; highway orders; planning and infrastructure agreements; Transport and Works Act Orders. Particular areas of environment-related expertise: contaminated land; waste disposal; environmental impact statements; water law; environmental terms and conditions of contract.
Prof. Memberships: City of London Solicitors Company, IBA, Society for Advanced Legal Studies (SAALS). Member: Planning and Environment Committee of the British Property Federation; Planning and Environment Law Sub-Committee of the City of London Law Society; IBA's Committee on International Environmental Law; and SAALS Planning and Environmental Law Reform Group.
Career: Qualified 1984. Articled at *Donne Mileham & Haddock* 1982-84. Joined *Berwin Leighton* (now *Berwin Leighton Paisner*) 1984; Partner 1990.
Personal: Born 1959. Education Duffryn High School, Newport, Gwent; University College, London; and College of Law, Lancaster Gate. Leisure skiing, cycling and lying under old cars. Resides in Hove.

QUALTROUGH, John
Simmons & Simmons, London (020) 7628 2020
Specialisation: Partner in Property Department. Advises on all areas of planning law and practice including appeals; objections and representations to local plans; and the drafting and negotiation of planning, highway and other infrastructure agreements; highways; compulsory purchase; and compensation issues. In addition he deals with commercial property matters where planning is a significant element, including option agreements, conditional contracts and sales coupled with overage/clawback provisions.
Prof. Memberships: Law Society; City of London Law Society (Committee member of Planning and Environmental Law Sub-Committee).
Career: Qualified 1978. Partner at *Simmons & Simmons* since 1988.
Personal: Born 30th April 1953. Holds a BA (1974).

QUAYLE, Sophie
Herbert Smith, London (020) 7374 8000
sophie.quayle@herbertsmith.com
Specialisation: Partner and Head of Planning department. Wide ranging experience of all matters relating to planning applications, associated documentation and environmental statements; inquiries (appeals of call-ins); section 106 agreements highways agreements and conditions and general strategic planning/property issues; and advising on judicial review and statutory appeals.
Prof. Memberships: City of London Law Society, Planning and Environmental sub-committee.
Career: *Herbert Smith* (1989 to date). Qualified 1991. Partner 1998.
Personal: Born 1964; St. Anthony's Leweston, Dorset; Southampton University. Sporty – especially sailing, diving and skiing; travel.

REDMAN, Michael
Clifford Chance, London (020) 7600 1000
michael.redman@cliffordchance.com
Specialisation: Solicitor advocate (qualified in criminal and civil jurisdiction). Senior member of the planning group of the commercial property practice advising developers on all aspects of planning and development. He is on the DETR Compulsory purchase policy review working group. Appeared in the courts in judicial review proceedings. Negotiating and drafting planning and other statutory agreements. Has advised on the planning aspects of the Canary Wharf development. Has advised power companies in respect of major gas power generating stations. Writes regularly on planning issues and is a contributor to the Journal of Planning Law.
Prof. Memberships: Member of the Law Society's Planning Panel.
Career: Barrister (1975); solicitor (1986).
Personal: Rugby referee.

RICHARDSON, Simon
Davies Wallis Foyster, Manchester (0161) 228 3702
sfr@dwf-law.com
Specialisation: Planning consultancy, applications and appeals and legal development services.
Prof. Memberships: Law Society; Royal Town Planning Institute.
Career: Christchurch Borough Council; Thamesdown Borough Council; *Berwin Leighton*; *Chapman Warren*; *Cobbetts*; *Davies Wallis Foyster* 1997.
Personal: Baines Grammar School; The Queen's

College, Oxford. Landscape photography, food and cookery.

RICKETTS, Simon
SJ Berwin, London (020) 7533 2768
simon.ricketts@sjberwin.com
Specialisation: Planning and local government law, advising institutions and developers on major retail/ business / residential / leisure schemes, including negotiating related agreements, coordinating appeals and legal challenges. Extensive experience in compulsory purchase and related procedures.
Prof. Memberships: Member of Law Society, Member of British Council for Offices Planning Legislation Committee, Member of PLC Property Editorial Board.
Career: Called to the Bar 1985. Member of planning group at *Lovell White Durrant* (now *Lovells*) 1988 before moving to *SJ Berwin* in 1997. Partner 1999. Requalified as a solicitor 1991.

ROBINSON, Patrick
Burges Salmon, Bristol (0117) 902 2740
patrick.robinson@burges-salmon.com
Specialisation: All planning issues including negotiation of planning and other infrastructure agreements and appearing as an advocate at Planning Inquiries. Current projects include acting for motorway service area provider at tri-partite call-in inquiry; advising on nuclear waste disposal.
Prof. Memberships: Legal Associate of the Royal Town Planning Institute and a member of the Law Society specialist Planning Panel.
Career: Before joining *Burges Salmon* in 1990, he worked as a planning solicitor with Southampton City Council. Became a partner and head of planning unit in 1995.
Personal: University of Leicester 1982-85. Enjoys his motorbike and yachting.

ROBINSON, Patrick
Herbert Smith, London (020) 7374 8000
patrick.robinson@herbertsmith.com
Specialisation: Commercial property development and planning work including negotiated planning consents, Inquiries (Appeals and Call-Ins), judicial review, compulsory purchase, and general strategic property and planning advice.
Prof. Memberships: Law Society's Specialist Planning Panel.
Career: Articled at *Herbert Smith* (1978-80). Partner 1986. Joint Editor of Blundell & Dobry's Planning, Applications, Appeals and Proceedings (5th Ed) 1996.
Personal: Born April 1956. Educated at University of Nottingham (LLB 1977). Leisure pursuits include jazz, the Cévennes and family. Lives in London.

SALES, Martin
Burness, Edinburgh (0131) 473 6130
mas@burness.co.uk
Specialisation: As one of Scotland's first Accredited Specialists in Planning Law, Martin Sales is well placed to advise on all aspects of Town & Country Planning specialising in developments involving contentious applications for major projects in environmentally sensitive areas, including brownfield and greenfield sites. Martin has extensive experience of minerals developments in areas of high conservation value, environmental assessment as an integral part of planning applications, the legal aspects of the remediation and disposal of contaminated land, landfill sites and the negotiating of planning and related agreements, management plans and restoration schemes.

SMITH, Brian
Browne Jacobson, Nottingham (0115) 976 6000
bsmith@brownej.co.uk
Specialisation: Managing Partner. Main area of practice is planning and development acting for developers, local planning authorities and national conservation bodies. Has over 20 years post-qualification experience in this field, in local government, commerce and private practice. Handles environmental work, dealing principally with land contamination and environmental liability in corporate acquisitions and disposals, funding transactions and insolvencies. Also deals with local government law, compulsory purchase and rating.
Prof. Memberships: Member of Law Society Planning Panel, Legal Associate of Royal Town Planning Institute, Law Society Advisory Group on Conservation, Heritage and Rural Issues, Fellow of the Land Institute.

SMITH, Bruce
Paull & Williamsons, Aberdeen (01224) 621621
gbsmith@paull-williamsons.co.uk
Specialisation: Partner in Planning and Environmental Law Department. Main area of practice is planning. Advises on planning applications, appeals, enforcement notice appeals, local and structure plans and the conduct of public inquiries. Also handles environmental law. Advises on waste disposal licences, river purification issues and other issues arising out of the Environmental Protection Act. Has acted in many of the major planning inquiries in Scotland over the last decade. Lecturer in planning law at Aberdeen University.
Prof. Memberships: Law Society of Scotland, Society of Advocates in Aberdeen. Law Society accredited specialist in Planning Law.
Career: Qualified in 1967. Joined *Paull & Williamsons* in 1970, becoming a Partner in 1973.
Personal: Born 15th June 1947. Attended Aberdeen University 1964-67 (LLB). Chairman of Abernethy Trust which runs four residential outdoor pursuit centres in Scotland. Leisure interests include golf, skiing and sailing. Lives in Aberdeen.

SMITH, Tim
Berwin Leighton Paisner, London (020) 7760 1000
timothy.smith@berwinleightonpaisner.com
Specialisation: Partner handling all aspects of Planning and Environmental work including inquires and court work, strategic advice infrastructure agreements, compulsory purchase and highways. Acted for Chatsfield in relation to White City, and in relation to West Quay, Southampton. Other major clients include Tesco, British Land and Ministry of Defence.
Prof. Memberships: Member of Planning Inspectorate's advisory "user group" panel.
Career: Educated at Thomas Bedock Upper School Northampton, and Nottingham University. Articled and qualified with *Hewitson Becke & Shaw*. Joined *Berwin Leighton* 1996.
Publications: Planning chapter of 'Commercial Transaction Checklists', and environmental chapter of 'CBI European Business Handbook 1999' (with Andrew Waite).
Personal: Leisure intrests include rugby (lifelong supporter of Northampton RFC) and fell walking.

TAYLOR, Paul AT
Dickinson Dees, Newcastle upon Tyne
(0191) 279 9534
paul.taylor@dickinson-dees.com
Specialisation: Partner in Planning Department. Handles all aspects of planning including the preparation of applications, the conduct of appeals (including advocacy at local inquiries), enforcement procedures and development plan work. Also deals with compulsory purchase orders and land compensation. Experience includes advocacy at many local inquiries, particularly involving housing development and mineral extraction.
Prof. Memberships: Law Society, Law Society Planning Panel. Legal Associate RTPI.
Career: Qualified 1971. Assistant solicitor at Nottinghamshire County Council 1971-74; Senior Assistant Solicitor for Leicestershire County Council 1974-77. Worked for Hoveringham Group Ltd 1977-82 before joining *Eversheds* in Newcastle in 1982. Became a Partner in 1983. Joined *Dickinson Dees* 1994.
Personal: Born 19th August 1947. Holds an LLB, 1968. Leisure interests include gardening. Lives in North Shields.

TAYLOR, Peter
Hewitson Becke + Shaw, Northampton
(01604) 233 233
petertaylor@hewitsons.com
Specialisation: All planning work including advocacy at planning appeals and local plan inquiries; Section 106 Agreements; judicial reviews; enforcements and general planning law. Acts for companies, private individuals and local authorities.
Prof. Memberships: The Law Society; Legal Associate R.T.P.I; Member of The Law Society's Specialist Planning Panel.
Career: Qualified in 1985; *Shacklocks Solicitors* Mansfield 1985-1986; *Hewitson Becke + Shaw* Solicitors Northampton 1986 to date (Partner since 1989).
Personal: Born 2nd October 1960; Educated at Brunts Grammar School, Mansfield; Birmingham University and Chester Law College. Interests include: athletics and marathon running.

THOMAS, Patricia
SJ Berwin, London (020) 7533 2222

THOMSON, Morag
Marrons, Leicester (0116) 289 2200
moragthomson@marrons.net
Specialisation: Partner in planning, development and public law department. Has extensive experience of specialist contentious town planning and associated work, including Judicial Review and High Court Challenges to planning decisions under the 1990 Act, public law matters and compulsory purchase. Previously worked in local government for eight years. Currently advises many national and local house builders, property developers and local authorities concerning a wide range of developments. Acknowledged planning advocate. Continues to advise local authorities in relation to local plans, planning appeals, enforcement matters and other planning related issues. Regularly involved in the formation of infrastructure and planning agreements in relation to large-scale developments. Currently acting for Alconbury Developments Ltd in relation to their proposals for 7 million sq ft of rail-served warehousing at Alconbury Airport and in relation to the leading human rights case, known as 'the Alconbury Cases,'

the subject of a recent landmark judgment by the House of Lords.
Prof. Memberships: The Law Society, Legal Associate of the Royal Town Planning Institute and Member of the Law Society's Planning Panel.
Career: Educated at Banbury School, Nottingham University and Guildford College of Law. Qualified in 1982, following articles with New Forest District Council. 1982-1988 Planning Solicitor with Charnwood Borough Council. 1988 moved into private practice.
Personal: Lives in Mountsorrel, Leicestershire with her husband. Leisure interests include violin playing, the arts generally, golf and football.

TREHEARNE, Ian
Berwin Leighton Paisner, London (020) 7760 1000
ian.trehearne@berwinleightonpaisner.com
Specialisation: Planner and Barrister. Joint Head of Planning and Environment Department. Principal area of work is planning law covering advice and advocacy on development, including major retail and office schemes, transport related development, airports, media and entertainment, factory outlet centres, housing, hotels, utility and waste disposal developments and local plan inquiries. Specialist active on conservation, historic building and design issues. Also environment law advising on contamination liability and threats and European Community matters. Advised on Ludgate development, Regents Place, Euston Centre and tower and other major office sites in London, Ebbsfleet Station and 8.5m sq. ft. development surrounding it, five-star hotel in Bloomsbury, 1.6m sq. ft. shopping in Croydon, the Channel Tunnel Rail Link and environmental cases such as Dartford including Thames Gateway and Medway Cement Works and Welbeck, as well as Finningley and Manston Airports, station related development for Railtrack. PFI issues: redevelopment of DSS estate in Newcastle and Sunderland; rationalisation and rebuilding of University College Hospital, United Medical and Dental Schools and King's College, London. Numerous conferences and seminars. Lectured at City University 1982-84.
Prof. Memberships: Royal Town Planning Institute.
Career: London Borough of Newham, 1972-4, then joined the London Borough of Islington 1974-76. City of Westminster 1977-9. Joined the London Borough of Camden in 1979 and moved to *Berwin Leighton* in 1985. Admitted to Partnership in 1988. Called to the Bar 1980.
Personal: Born 17th May 1950. Attended Durham University 1968-71. Leisure pursuits include sailing, building, books and music. Lives in London.

TRINICK, Marcus
Bond Pearce, Southampton (023) 8063 2211
mtrinick@bondpearce.com
Specialisation: Partner and Head of the Specialist Planning and Environmental Group. Twenty years experience of project development (often in large teams) in all parts of the UK. Advocate at over 300 public inquiries. Especial experience in energy generation, port development, retail work, nature conservation law, EU environmental law and Environmental Impact Assessment (EIA), as well as commercial, retail and housing development.
Prof. Memberships: Secretary of British Wind Energy Association and member of European, Republic of Ireland and US Wind Energy Associations. Legal Associate member of the RTPI and member of UK Environmental Law Association.
Career: Qualified in 1983, joined *Bond Pearce* in 1990, becoming partner in 1991.

TRUE, Justin
Dechert, London (020) 7583 5353

TURNER, Angela
Gouldens, London (020) 7842 6145
at@gouldens.com
Specialisation: Wide range of planning, environmental and local government law including appeals, inquiries, judicial review and agreements. During 12 years in local government (Royal Borough of Kensington & Chelsea), has great experience of planning law from the local government perspective and particularly in relation to listed building and conservation area law and enforcement related matters. During 16 years in private practice has an equivalent depth of experience of advising developers and others on planning strategies relevant to their proposals. Has acted as Advocate at Public Inquiries and other tribunals.
Prof. Memberships: Law Society Planning Panel; Legal Associate of the Royal Town Planning Institute; City of London Law Society's Planning & Environmental Law Sub-Committee; UKELA Town Planning.
Career: Qualified in 1973. Principal Solicitor, Royal Borough of Kensington & Chelsea. Partner at *Gouldens* from 1985.
Publications: Co-author of 'Badlands, Essential Environmental Law for Property Professionals'.
Personal: Sheffield University (LLB). Many interests.

VALENTINE, Richard
Pitmans, Reading (0118) 958 0224
rvalentine@pitmans.com
Specialisation: The co-ordination and implementation of strategies and tactics employed in relation to major planning proposals, particularly in connection with inquiries and judicial reviews. In the last five years, he has increasingly specialised in the judicial review process as a means of challenging planning decision and in the statutory appeal procedures. Notable involvements have involved Copas v Royal Borough of Windsor & Maidenhead; Jones v The Secretary of State for Wales; Somerfield Stores Limited v Hambleton District Council; Baber v SoSETR; McLean Homes Limited v SoSETR and Chelmsford Borough Council; Rockhold v SoSETR; Somerfield Stores Limited v Flintshire County Council.
Prof. Memberships: Law Society.
Career: Partner *Stephenson Harwood* 1973-77. Partner *Pitmans* 1977-.
Personal: Travel, fishing and shooting, classic cars and any lawful intellectual challenge.

WADE-SMITH, Richard
Wilbraham & Co, Leeds (0113) 243 2200
Specialisation: Partner with wide experience in planning work but with special knowledge on environmental assessment for infrastructure and energy projects. Practice covers industrial, retail and leisure development; renewable energy development; on shore gas exploitation; electricity transmission; and water and sewage treatment. Recent projects include major employment schemes in the West Midlands, surface mining in the North East, a mix of renewable energy schemes throughout the UK; and substantial wind energy projects.
Prof. Memberships: Member of the Law Society's Specialist Planning Panel, loyal associate of Royal Town Planning Instutite, consultant editor to the Environmental Law Reports, and lectures regularly on environmental and planning law issues.

WALTON, David
Wilbraham & Co, Leeds (0113) 243 2200
david.walton@wilbraham.co.uk
Specialisation: Partner with wide breadth of practice including housing, retail, leisure and employment applications. Retains strong local government practice including compulsory purchase, Transport and Works Act and other public utility projects.
Prof. Memberships: Legal Associate of the Royal Town Planning Institute.
Career: Qualified 1982; Hereford Council (articled clerk); Oxfordshire Council (assistant solicitor environment); Shrewsbury Council (principal solicitor planning); Leeds City Council (assistant chief legal officer); *Wilbraham & Co* (partner).
Publications: 'Development Plans: Law and Practice', Sweet & Maxwell (1998). Lectured on the post-graduate diploma for planning & environmental law at Leeds Metropolitan University. Diploma in Local Government Law and Practice.
Personal: Born 1958.

WATCHMAN, Paul
Freshfields Bruckhaus Deringer, London
(020) 7936 4000
paul.watchman@freshfields.com
See under Environment, p.376

WATKINS, David
Linklaters, London (020) 7456 4852
david.watkins@linklaters.com
Specialisation: Environmental law specialist. Experienced in all aspects of town planning and development activity, including obtaining all requisite planning and other consents, compulsory purchase orders, road closure orders, planning, highways and drainage agreements. Environmental law expertise includes advising on the contaminated land regime, the development of brownfield sites and the environmental implications of corporate disposals.
Career: 1997 to date: Partner, *Linklaters*, planning and environment unit; 1987-1997: Assistant solicitor, *Linklaters*; 1985-1987: Assistant solicitor *Shepherd & Wedderburn WS*; 1983-1985: Trainee solicitor, *Shepherd & Wedderburn WS*. 1978-1983: Edinburgh University, LLB (Hons).

WELLS, Martin
Stephenson Harwood, London (020) 7809 2529
martin.wells@shlegal.com
Specialisation: Senior associate – planning group. Advises on planning and related matters. Recent cases have included advising on major developments for the University of Greenwich, Accor Group, Chiltern, Den norske Bank, Royal Albert Hall, Canterbury College, South East Essex College, London Development Agency, London Transport Property and KPMG. Regular speaker at internal training seminars.
Prof. Memberships: Legal Associate, RTPI; Law Society's Planning Panel; City of London Law Society's Planning and Environmental Law Sub-Committee.
Career: Legal posts in local government 1965-86; Borough Secretary Runnymede BC 1986-87; assistant, *Denton Hall Burgin & Warrens* 1987-88. Joined

Stephenson Harwood in 1988 and became senior associate in 1989.
Publications: Contributions to 'Property Week', 'Planning', 'Planning in London'.

WHITE, Martin
Pinsent Curtis Biddle, Birmingham
(0121) 200 1050
martin.white@pinsents.com
Specialisation: Handles planning and related areas, including highways and environmental issues, with emphasis on town centre regeneration, planning appeal work, development plans, compulsory purchase, issues of planning gain, Section 106 agreements, rail related scheme and waste matters. Has acted in appeals relating to major inward investment, airports and business parks, for local Planning Authorities and private sector clients. Also handles local government and public law generally. Author of articles, speaker at conferences and seminars on planning gain and general planning issues.
Prof. Memberships: Law Society (Member of Planning Panel), Legal Associate of Royal Town Planning Institute.
Career: Qualified in 1979. Articled at Solihull Council 1977-79. Joined *Pinsent & Co* in 1981. Partner in 1987.
Personal: Born 1953. Attended Cambridge University 1972-76; Newcastle Polytechnic 1976-77. Interests include drama and music.

WILBRAHAM, Peter
Wilbraham & Co, Leeds (0113) 243 2200

WILLIAMS, Christopher
CMS Cameron McKenna, London
(020) 7367 3000

WILLIAMS, Huw
Edwards Geldard, Cardiff (029) 2023 8239
huw.williams@geldards.co.uk
See under Administrative & Public Law, p.60

WILLIAMSON, Andrew
Walker Morris, Leeds (0113) 283 2500
ajw@walkermorris.co.uk
Specialisation: Partner in Planning and Environment Department. Handles all aspects of planning law with an emphasis on advocacy at s.78 appeals, Local Planning Inquiries, compulsory purchase order and enforcement. Also handles Lands Tribunal and CPA Licensing and Environmental Protection Act authorisation appeals.
Prof. Memberships: Corporate Member of Royal Town Planning Institute, Law Society Planning Panel.
Career: Articled at *Race & Newton* in Burnley 1981-83, then joined *Walker Morris* in 1984 and became a Partner in 1985.
Personal: Born 16th February 1957. Lives in Leeds.

WINTER, Paul
Eversheds, Manchester (0161) 831 8000

WOOD, David
Bevan Ashford, Bristol (0117) 975 1635
d.wood@bevanashford.co.uk
See under Health & Safety, p.416

PRIVATE EQUITY

OVERVIEW: The growth of private equity in many companies is benefiting from the current dip in the IPO market and cautious bank lending, while PE houses are now flushed with funds. The last five years have seen an increasing number of US and UK-based sponsors entering the Europe market. Average key deal values have increased from £200 – 300 million to £1 – 2 billion. Not surprisingly the legal market is polarising in favour of firms who can handle cross border pan-European transactions with credible resources in areas such as capital markets, high yield and securitisation. Firms handling large, one-off transactions often off the back of their strong corporate finance practices such as Allen & Overy and Freshfields Bruckhaus Deringer are distinct from 'panel firms' with strong traditional funds practices such as Macfarlanes and SJ Berwin. Against the background of a London-centric market, most private equity work undertaken in the regions tends to gravitate around the North, with the notable exception of Osborne Clarke's well regarded offices in the Thames Valley and South West regions. Deals are mostly domestic in nature, ranging between £50 – 100 million.

RESEARCH APPROVED BY BMRB: *For this edition,* Chambers' *researchers conducted 6,552 interviews – 4,419 with law firms, 554 with barristers and 1,579 with clients.*

The validity of the research was scrutinised by BMRB International, who audited both the methodology and the results at our offices in July 2001. They interviewed Chambers' *researchers and cross-checked sample interviews. Details of the audit appear on page 7.*

LONDON

PRIVATE EQUITY: BUYOUTS & INVESTMENT • London	Ptnrs	Assts
1 Ashurst Morris Crisp	12	n/a
Clifford Chance	9	30
2 Allen & Overy	7	15
Dickson Minto WS	n/a	n/a
3 Lovells	3	12
Macfarlanes	7	12
4 SJ Berwin	9	36
Travers Smith Braithwaite	7	15
5 CMS Cameron McKenna	7	18
Freshfields Bruckhaus Deringer	9	30
6 DLA	n/a	n/a
Nabarro Nathanson	5	20
Olswang	7	12

LEADING INDIVIDUALS	
1 **BAIRD James** Clifford Chance	**DICKSON Alastair** Dickson Minto WS
GEFFEN Charles Ashurst Morris Crisp	**LAYTON Matthew** Clifford Chance
2 **COMPAGNONI Marco** Lovells	**HALE Chris** Travers Smith Braithwaite
HANTON Bruce Ashurst Morris Crisp	**MARTIN Charles** Macfarlanes
PAUL Alan Allen & Overy	
3 **BARTER Charles** Travers Smith Braithwaite	**BEDDOW Simon** Ashurst Morris Crisp
DAVIS Steven SJ Berwin	**GREEN Geoffrey** Ashurst Morris Crisp
MURRAY-JONES Allan Skadden, Arps	**SHEACH Andrew** CMS Cameron
TUFFNELL Kevin Macfarlanes	**WHITE Graham** SJ Berwin
4 **BOWN Christopher** Freshfields Bruckhaus	**CARPANINI Fabrizio** Olswang
HOWARD Susan Allen & Overy	**MEEK Charles** Macfarlanes
SINGH Daljit Jones, Day, Reavis & Pogue	**WAYTE Peter** DLA
UP AND COMING	
BAIRD Derek Dickson Minto WS	**MACKIE Chris** Olswang
ONES TO WATCH	
HAMPTON Alison Lovells	**McNAIR Martin** Dickson Minto WS

This book is the product of 6,552 1/2-hour interviews. See p.7 for BMRB audit.
Within each band, firms are listed alphabetically. *See individuals' profiles p.676*

BUYOUTS & INVESTMENT

Ashurst Morris Crisp (see firm details p.866) "*Clearly a winner*" – an "*up and down private equity practice.*" Competitors have noted its increasing international presence, "*building a strong practice in Paris and beefing up Frankfurt*" while remaining "*attractive*" to US clients. Clients speak well of **Charlie Geffen**'s (see p.677) "*ability to deliver, he knows his stuff inside out.*" He is credited with developing the practice under tutelage of senior partner **Geoffrey Green** (see p.678) who still "*keeps a hand in deals.*" Geffen advised on the £230 million Gilde Investments acquisition of Armstrong Installation Products and the £200 million Berkshire Partners acquisition of Avery Berkel while Green acted on the £11 billion De Beers deal. Seen in action on the Yell £2.1 billion transaction, clients testify to **Bruce Hanton**'s (see p.678) "*unflustered, calm, extremely helpful*" approach on transactions. "*Good allrounder*" **Simon Beddow** (see p.676) advised on the £750 million Baxi Heating for Electra Candover deal. **Clients:** ABN AMRO Private Equity; Advent International; Candover; Chase Capital Partners; Cinven.

Clifford Chance (see firm details p.919) An "*extremely strong, cohesive team*" which continues to scoop accolades, having "*had a good year*" in the wake of high deal activity involving several of key clients. Clients value that it "*covers all areas on a Europe-wide basis with high quality specialists*" and partners who "*know what it's all about.*" Endorsed by market sources for his "*rounded skill base*" **Matthew Layton** (see p.678) has been leading teams on several LBOs for Schroder Ventures including Homebase (£1 billion) and VEBA Electronics (US$2.3 billion.) **James Baird** "*does a good job*" and is recommended to those who require a "*more aggressive touch.*" He advised on major deals for CVC Capital Partners, including the US$400 million acquisition of an Invensys business and the US$300 million cross border LBO of a Revlon business. **Clients:** Candover Partners; CVC Partners; Duke Street Capital; PPM Ventures; Royal Bank Private Equity; Schroder Venture Advisors.

Allen & Overy (see firm details p.856) Although still eclipsed by the strength of the firm's debt practice, the private equity team is widely considered "*more visible than before.*" Well-versed in "*larger, more significant transactions,*" it advised on six of the top European private equity deals last year. "*Hugely experienced*" **Alan Paul** (see p.254) advised on the largest of these, Leconport Estates' £3.5 billion takeover of MEPC. Also rated in the corporate finance arena, he "*holds the equity practice together*" with his ability to see the bigger picture. He also advised Deutsche Bank Capital Partners on its multi-jurisdictional £670 million joint purchase (with Pierre & Vacances) of CenterParcs, Scottish & Newcastle's holiday division. **Susan Howard** (see p.678) acted on the £550 million agreed public to private bid by Nikko Principal Investments for Powell Duffryn and Morgan Grenfell Private Equity's CHF1.6 billion acquisition of the performance polymer business from Ciba Speciality Chemicals. **Clients:** Charterhouse Development Capital; Deutsche Bank Capital Partners; Morgan Grenfell Private Equity; Nikko Principal Investments; West LB; West Private Equity.

Dickson Minto WS (see firm details p.942) "*A specialist firm which picks up cracking work for its size.*" Predominantly focused on transactions with a 70% pure private equity bias, peers describe the team as "*tight, aggressive and well driven*" enjoying "*fiercely loyal clients.*" Counter-comment revolves around its lack of a pan-European presence. A "*brilliant business-doer with an exceptional nose for commercial points,*" **Alastair Dickson** (see p.677) is "*remarkably creative and imaginative.*" He advised on the acquisition of General Healthcare Group for £1.4 billion public to private. **Derek Baird** also continues to be seen in action. **Clients:** BC Partners; Charterhouse; Mercury European Acquisitions Capital; Apax; Close Brothers.

Lovells (see firm details p.1044) "*Well-versed in private equity deals*" although seen as "*a bit thin on the ground*" in London following partner redistribution among the firm's European network of offices. The impact of Allan Murray-Jones' departure to Skadden Arps remains to be seen. Focusing on European mergers, "*terrific*" **Marco Compagnoni** (see p.677) has had a lower profile this year. He acted on the TI Automotive Systems in its demerger from Smiths Group for £940 million. **Clients:** 3i; Mercury Equity; PPMV; CSFB Private Equity; Advent; Allianz Capital.

Macfarlanes (see firm details p.1046) "*Awfully good – they've always had a strong team.*" Clients and competitors agree that the firm has partners with longstanding expertise. Focused on mid-market domestic deals, its recent triumph in gaining Alchemy as a key client adds further kudos to a client roster that includes Kleinwort Benson and 3i, the London law firm on the latter's panel. "*Experienced dealer*" **Charles Martin** (see p.678) acted for Alchemy on the £160 million public to private MBO of Anglian and for Candover on the proposed sale of RIM. "*Sensible and upfront*" **Kevin Tuffnell** (see p.679) acted for the management in the acquisition of MEPC by GE Capital and Hermes, and advised the management of Security Printing and Systems in a £70 million secondary buyout funded by APAX. "*Highly competent*" **Charles Meek** (see p.678) has been acting for the 3i Group and its managed funds on a number of matters including the £200 million secondary buyout of Target Express Holdings Limited and the £110 million purchase of Go from British Airways. **Clients:** 3i; Alchemy; Royal Bank Private Equity; Advent; L&G Ventures; Botts & Company; Kleinwort Benson Development Capital.

SJ Berwin (see firm details p.879) "*Leading fundraising practice by a league,*" the "*excellent operator,*" **Graham White** (see p.679) "*has added strength to the team.*" He led the team advising on the £122 million MBO and subsequent flotation of Collins Stewart, and on Linden's £78 million public to private. Clients seek out the services of "*easy going and extremely able*" **Steven Davis** (see p.677) who advised Pierre & Vacances on the £670 million acquisition of CenterParcs from Scottish & Newcastle and represented Cinven and Vector Industries on the acquisition of Wolseley businesses for £136 million. **Clients:** Apax Partners; JP Morgan Partners; Graphite Capital (formerly Foreign & Colonial Ventures); Lake Capital; Mercury Private Equity; UBS Capital.

Travers Smith Braithwaite (see firm details p.1160) "*A good little private equity practice*" often seen acting for management teams and endorsed by the market for its track record in public to private work. Clients' praise for the "*amazing matrix of well rounded teams they can put on to deals*" is due in large part to "*universally liked*" **Chris Hale** (see p.678) who has "*done a cracking job beefing up the practice.*" He acted for the bidder and management on the £375 million public to private of Fairview Holdings, 3i's largest to date. **Charles Barter** (see p.676) has "*been around the block many times*" bringing that experience to play in advice to Bridgepoint Capital on the £156 million secondary buyout of Golden Wonder. **Clients:** Apax Capital Partners & Co Ventures; ECI Ventures; GMT Communications Partners; Phoenix Private Equity; ABN AMRO; Graphite Capital.

CMS Cameron McKenna (see firm details p.922) This "*straightforward, commercial*" team has "*clearly made progress.*" Although valued in the mid market transactions, the practice boasts a broader deal range value than some of its competitors. "*Brilliant document man*" **Andrew Sheach** (see p.678) is "*loved by clients,*" he acted on the Bridgepoint sale of Riva Clubs (£90 million) and advised on the ABN Amro £20.5 million MBO of Quantum Publishing. **Clients:** Elderstreet Capital Partners; Dresdner Kleinwort Benson Private Equity; Legal & General Ventures; Lloyds TSB Development Capital; Bridgepoint Capital; ABN AMRO Development Capital.

Freshfields Bruckhaus Deringer (see firm details p.965) "*Making big advances*" but currently perceived to lack depth. Competitors opine that the firm has "*so much fire power that can get the expertise they need, but they're not quite there yet.*" With significant international presence, its profile in cross border work has been particularly strong in the US and Germany, supported by the merger with leading private equity firm Bruckhaus. "*Thoughtful*" **Christopher Bown** (see p.677) acted for Lehman Brothers on the recommended £950 million take private (for cash) of the Burford Group. **Clients:** Ineos Capital; Nomura Principal Finance; Cinven; Goldman Sachs; Warburg Pincus; Industri Kapital.

DLA The practice is perceived to be reliant on key individual **Peter Wayte**, and performs substantial buyout work.

Nabarro Nathanson (see firm details p.1078) The firm is widely seen by peers as being "*active in the VC market place*" with a "*newly increasing client list*" which including the high profile NewMedia SPARK. Rhidian Jones leads a team whose recent highlights include acting for the management on the £67 million buyout of Pinewood Studios and on the Pubmistress MBO of Pubmaster Group. **Clients:** Alchemy; Benchmark Capital; Crescendo Ventures; ETF Group; HSBC Ventures; NewMedia SPARK.

Olswang (see firm details p.1084) "*Strong at the lower end of the market.*" The coupling of ex-Berwin Leighton players with the firm's existing VC practice is injecting an institutional flavour to its private equity capabilities. Having ridden the dot.com wave, this experience has resulted in it acting for Gresham Trust in the £12 million investment in Community Careline. Comprising an "*effective double act,*" **Fabrizio Carpanini** (see p.677) "*gets deals done*" and **Chris Mackie** (see p.678) is noted by the market for his "*precise*" approach. Carpanini advised on the £15 million MBO of C-side, while Mackie advised Friends Ivory & Sime on the £18 million MBI of Channel Television. **Clients:** Graphite Capital; Friends Ivory & Sime Private Equity; Gresham Trust; Lloyds TSB Development Capital; Sovereign Capital; bainlab.

Other Notable Practitioners Known to industry sources for his strong relationship with Doughty Hanson while at Lovells, "*the best operator in the team*" **Allan Murray-Jones** (see p.678) has joined **Skadden, Arps, Slate, Meagher & Flom.** Despite his "*immense energy*" **Daljit Singh** (see p.679) of **Jones, Day, Reavis & Pogue** has had a low profile. Still "*well regarded,*" his clients include Carlyle Group and BancBoston.

DEBT

PRIVATE EQUITY: DEBT • London	Ptnrs	Assts
1 Allen & Overy	16	35
Clifford Chance	10	45
2 Ashurst Morris Crisp	3	13
3 Lovells	3	15
Norton Rose	5	17
4 Denton Wilde Sapte	4	13
Dickson Minto WS	n/a	n/a
5 Shearman & Sterling	4	18

LEADING INDIVIDUALS	
1 GILLESPIE Stephen Allen & Overy	JOHNSON James Clifford Chance
STEWART Mark Clifford Chance	VICKERS Mark Ashurst Morris Crisp
2 BARRON Michael Dickson Minto WS	COTTIS Matthew Lovells
GORRIE Euan Allen & Overy	WARD Anthony Shearman & Sterling
3 CAMPBELL Mark Clifford Chance	KEAL Anthony Allen & Overy
MORLEY David Allen & Overy	POLGLASE Timothy Norton Rose
SWEETING Malcolm Clifford Chance	
4 BAMBER Andrew Norton Rose	INGLIS Alan Clifford Chance
WARD Nigel Ashurst Morris Crisp	
UP AND COMING	
EVANS Jacqueline Allen & Overy	FREEMAN Adam Lovells

This book is the product of 6,552 1/2-hour interviews. See p.7 for BMRB audit.
Within each band, firms are listed alphabetically. *See individuals' profiles p.676*

Allen & Overy (see firm details p.856) "*A terrific debt practice – banks look on them as the safe place to go – they do an excellent and thorough job.*" Clients rate its ability to "*cover all related areas with high quality specialists on a Europe-wide basis.*" "*Technical but robust*" in his approach, **Stephen Gillespie** (see p.677) acted for Barclays Capital in its £680 million senior and mezzanine financing for the acquisition of the Rank Holidays division by a consortium comprising Bourne Leisure Group, Candover and Legal & General, in the largest European leisure sector deal last year. "*User-friendly*" **Euan Gorrie** (see p.677) acted for JP Morgan in the £1 billion debt facilities for Doughty Hanson's acquisition of RHM from Tomkins. Although his "*abrasive*" style is "*not everyone's cup of tea,*" **Tony Keal** is commended as "*the real technician*" who "*lives his work and fights hard for his clients.*" He acted for UniCredito Italiano as the arranger of the €800 million facilities for the acquisition of Italtel from Telecom Italia, by a group of investors including Clayton Dubilier & Rice. Covering the work as part of his mixed practice, **David Morley** (see p.119) is "*extremely well-liked,*" while **Jacqueline Evans** (see p.677) "*knows the business.*" Morley acted for CIBC and Merrill Lynch as arrangers of £885 million senior debt and £75 million mezzanine debt to finance the acquisition by Nomura of the Meridien Hotels chain from Compass. **Clients:** Barclays Capital; Goldman Sachs; Merrill Lynch; Lehman Brothers; WestLB; Morgan Grenfell Private Equity; CIBC World Markets; Salomon Schroder Smith; Barney/Citigroup.

Clifford Chance (see firm details p.919) "*Rounded*" team with "*tremendous depth and a pleasure to work with,*" the pan-European practice has advised on 16 of the 30 largest European buyouts. The Rogers & Wells capability enhances expertise in high yield securities issues and the US funded elements of European transactions. "*Tremendous client winner with his big personality*" **James Johnson** (see p.119) is highly praised by banks for his market awareness. He acted for the banks on the LBOs of Ciba Speciality Chemicals (€979 million), Baxi/ Newman (€770 million) and the speciality divisions of Lafarge (€1 billion.) Seen often acting for the borrower, "*pragmatic*" **Mark Stewart** (see p.679) has dealt on the corporate side of key LBOs including Homebase, Holiday Divisions of Rank (£1.1 billion) and BBA Frictions ($585 million.) Other key members who act within a broader spectrum include "*great lawyer and client man*" **Mark Campbell** (see p.116) who acted for Barclays Capital in the buyouts of Adams Childrenswear (£117 million) and Fluor Chemicals (£350 million) and the re-leveraging of Kappa Packaging (€1.75 billion.) "*First class operator*" **Malcolm Sweeting** is prominent in the market with his Goldman Sachs relationship, advising it on the €3 billion buyout of Messer Griesheim, and the acquisition of Competel (€400 million.) **Alan Inglis** (see p.119) acted for the banks on the buyout of Nordrhein-Westfalen cable and telephony business of Deutsche Telecom (€3 billion.) Although less visible on the transactional front, the team undoubtedly benefits from the gravitas of senior partner Stuart Popham. **Clients:** Citigroup; JP Morgan Chase; CSFB; Barclays Capital; Goldman Sachs.

Ashurst Morris Crisp (see firm details p.866) "*A balanced practice doing well*" despite changes within its core group. Bolstered by the addition of a respected capital markets team from Weil Gotshal, increasing its high yield debt capability. The integrated pan-European leverage finance practice provides vital support. Justin Spendlove's role as managing partner has largely reduced his fee-earning time, while **Mark Vickers** (see p.123) continues his "*fantastic job*" in successfully "*boosting the debt practice.*" "*First rate technically,*" he acted for the Royal Bank of Scotland on the £360 million debt financing for the Cannons Group public to private and on the De Beers public to private ($16 billion.) Head of the MBO debt finance practice **Nigel Ward** (see p.679) is praised by peers as "*a good bloke who doesn't waste time.*" He acted for SEB on the €1.1 billion debt financing on the Alfa Laval multi-jurisdiction buyout and advised Merrill Lynch on the £300 million debt financing of the Odeon Cinemas buyout. **Clients:** Merrill Lynch; Bank of Scotland; Royal Bank of Scotland; Lehman Brothers; Dresdner Kleinwort Wasserstein; BNP Paribas; ING Barings.

Lovells (see firm details p.1044) A "*good team – coming out of the forest,*" although the market continues to mourn the loss of John Penson believing that the team is "*not quite the strength it was.*" Endorsed for his "*all round skills,*" **Matthew Cottis** (see p.117) acted for Dresdner Kleinwort Wasserstein on the £111 million buyout of Alliance Medical by Bridgepoint Capital. He also acted alongside "*able*" **Adam Freeman** (see p.677) for CIBC World Markets on the £110 million buyout of the Tom Cobleigh pub chain by Electra Partners. **Clients:** Bank of Scotland; Barclays; CIBC; CSFB; Dresdner Kleinwort Wasserstein; Deutsche Bank.

Norton Rose (see firm details p.1082) A "*good quality practice*" seen by the market as having "*made good strides.*" Its high yield capability will be fortified by the return to practice of former Jones Day US partner Tom Speechly. **Timothy Polglase** (see p.121) ("*forceful but good to deal with*") advised Deutsche Bank in the £550 million senior secured debt to fund the public to private buyout by Prestige Acquisitions of Powell Duffryn. He is also leading the team advising Fuji Bank on the SEK5,590 million debt financing for the leisure appliances business of Electrolux. "*Leading light in banking*" **Andrew Bamber's** (see p.676) profile has increased. A "*reasonable negotiator,*" he advised on the financing of the recommended offer by General London Constructors for of Fairview Holdings (£307 million.) **Clients:** JP Morgan Chase; Deutsche Bank; The Royal Bank of Scotland; Intermediate Capital Group; HSBC; Mezzanine Management.

Denton Wilde Sapte (see firm details p.939) Its key strength in acquisition finance is reflected in its lender dominated client base. Traditionally the designated lawyers for NatWest, the group led by Sarah Coucher has tracked its merger and closed 33 acquisition financings for Royal Bank of Scotland Group. Other highlights include acting for Abbey National in its acquisition of Oldham Estates from MEPC (public to private) arranging £460 million syndicated loan facilities and Baxi Partnership's acquisition of the Blue Circle heating division (£590 million cross border syndicated loan facilities.) **Clients:** Royal Bank of Scotland Leveraged Finance; Société Générale; The Governor and Company of the Bank of Scotland; Lloyds TSB; GE Corporation.

Dickson Minto WS (see firm details p.942) "*Pleasant to deal with and extremely experienced,*" considered by some sources "*the firm of choice*" to have on the other side. Believed to focus primarily on PE sponsors and borrowers rather than banks. Although better known in the domestic context, its track record in multinational buyouts includes the Cinven/Investcorp deal. "*Superlative banking lawyer*" **Michael Barron** (see p.676) is "*commercial and extremely able.*"

Shearman & Sterling (see firm details p.1125) Newly ranked this year, a "*good team*" gaining stature on high profile deals such as financing the acquisition of Yell by Hicks Muse and Apax. Market perception is that the group benefits from the firm's links with US banks and its acknowledged high yield capability. **Anthony Ward** (see p.679)commands "*the highest respect*" from his peers; "*absolutely excellent at technical level*" he "*has a complete grasp of all aspects of a deal.*" He recently acted for Merrill Lynch on the debt financing in DB Capital Partners' acquisition of CenterParcs. Also advised Investcorp in the acquisition of the German public company, Gerresheimer Glas. **Clients:** Morgan Stanley; Merrill Lynch; Deutsche Bank; UBS Warburg; Goldman Sachs; Bear Stearns; CVC; Investcorp.

FUND FORMATION

PRIVATE EQUITY: FUND FORMATION • London	Ptnrs	Assts
1 SJ Berwin	8	14
2 Clifford Chance	3	25
3 Macfarlanes	5	5
4 Ashurst Morris Crisp	4	8

LEADING INDIVIDUALS	
1 BLAKE Jonathan SJ Berwin	
2 BARKER Bridget Macfarlanes	
3 GLOVER Jason Clifford Chance	GOLD Josyane SJ Berwin
MIFSUD Mark SJ Berwin	SHELDON Jeremy Ashurst Morris Crisp

This book is the product of 6,552 1/2-hour interviews. See p.7 for BMRB audit.

Within each band, firms are listed alphabetically. *See individuals' profiles p.676*

SJ Berwin (see firm details p.879) "*Leaders in the field,*" it "*wins by a league*" in terms of volume and experience which dates back to the inception of the industry's growth in the early 1980s. The London team is part of one of the largest dedicated teams in Europe, with extended capability residing in the firm's Munich and Paris offices. Providing a comprehensive full service, it handles the spectrum of work from fund formation for UK and international private equity fund managers to investment and exit transactions. Clients value its "*partner-driven*" approach and "*detailed expertise*" on matters. "*Undoubted*" leader in funds, **Jonathan Blake** (see p.676) mainly advises on the corporate side of funds work. **Josyane Gold** (see p.677) specialises in advising PE fund managers establishing UK and European investment funds and executive incentive arrangements and led on the Advent Private Equity Fund III (£300 million.) Leader on the Benchmark Capital European Fund ($750 million,) **Mark Mifsud** (see p.678) advises PE managers in the structuring of investment funds, incentive schemes and related vehicles. Further highlights for the team include the Apax Europe V fund (€ 4.4 billon.) **Clients:** Amadeus; Apax; B&S Electra; Bridgepoint Capital Partners; Schroder Ventures; UBS; DLJ Phoenix Private Equity.

Clifford Chance (see firm details p.919) "*A strong practice,*" its experience in the field originates from the first ever MBO fund handled for Charterhouse Development Capital in the 1980s. A tight focus on large, complex institutional projects is borne out by a client base of top tier private equity funds and blue chip UK and European fund investors. Last year, it established over 50% of European private equity funds supported by local resource throughout its European offices and specialists in the US. Clients appreciate "*high levels of dedicated resource and hand-holding.*" Co-head of practice **Jason Glover** (see p.677) provides valuable industry insight from his former in-house posts. Highlights for the group include advising Industri Kapital 2000 on the establishment of a PE fund structured as a series of English limited partnerships raising € 2.1 billion and advising the DTI on the establishment of the UK High Technology Fund (a £150 million fund of funds.) Also advised on the establishment of UBS Warburg Co-Investment Plan – 2001 Vintage, a co-investment scheme for senior executives. **Clients:** Bank of America; Candover; EQT; HSBC Private Equity; Industri Kapital; UBS Capital; UBS Warburg; UK Government.

Macfarlanes (see firm details p.1046) Historically associated with fund work for Morgan Grenfell, the team operates from within the investment funds and financial services department, covering the formation and structuring of funds for institutional and retail markets, evaluating critical tax issues. Head of department, "*bright*" **Bridget Barker** (see p.676) represented Morgan Grenfell Private Equity on its pan European new fund which raised € 1.5 billion, and also advised in connection with new funds for ECI Ventures, Close Brothers Private Equity and Parallel Ventures. The group acted for Scottish Equity Partners in the raising of its first PE fund of £80 million. **Clients:** HSBC Private Equity; Morgan Grenfell Private Equity; L&G Ventures; Alchemy.

Ashurst Morris Crisp (see firm details p.866) "*Pretty new to the game*" by comparison with its peers, the group is acknowledged for its presence in the market and links to Cinven. Recognised by peers as a player on the transactional side, key partner **Jeremy Sheldon** (see p.679) advised on the formation of the third Cinven Fund, the £200 million Reuters Greenhouse Fund and the Bracken Investments Guernsey Fund, constituted as a Guernsey limited partnership. The team acted on the €47.5 million launch of Digit Networks European Digital Infrastructure Fund I constituted as Jersey limited partnerships. **Clients:** Cinven; West Private Equity; ICG; Coller Capital; Reuters; Carlyle; Gartmore.

THE REGIONS

Addleshaw Booth & Co (see firm details p.853) Our researchers discovered that a "*commitment to quality*" makes it a top choice for big players in the regions such as 3i and a popular choice for referrals. Operating as the ABC Private Equity group, a network of "*strong*" partners covers the three offices, operating from within the corporate finance department. Highlights handled by the Manchester office include advising 3i on the £300 million public to private of Peter Black Holdings and advising Barclays Private Equity on the £120 million MBO of the CRP Group. **Clients:** HSBC; Barclays Private Equity; 3i Group; Apax Partners; Bridgepoint Capital; Aberdeen Murray Johnstone; Gresham Trust.

Dickson Minto WS (see firm details p.942) "*Private equity boys par excellence.*" Woven together with the firm's estimable investment funds work, this "*terrific*" PE practice has a high profile in London for its VC and limited partnerships work. The firm advised the first new Scottish VC to be established in recent years, Penta Capital Partners, on its formation, IMRO approval and the Penta Fund 1 LP which raised £115 million. Other highlights include advising Close Brothers on the Close Growth Fund LP that raised €84 million. **Clients:** Royal Bank Private Equity; Aberdeen Asset Management; Penta Capital Partners; Close Brothers; Artemis; Standard Life Private Equity.

PRIVATE EQUITY • The Regions	Ptnrs	Assts
1 **Addleshaw Booth & Co** Leeds, Manchester	13	29
Dickson Minto WS Edinburgh	n/a	n/a
DLA Manchester	n/a	n/a
Hammond Suddards Edge Leeds	8	28
Osborne Clarke Bristol	8	21
Wragge & Co Birmingham	4	13

This book is the product of 6,552 1/2-hour interviews. See p.7 for BMRB audit.
Within each band, firms are listed alphabetically.

DLA Its regional coverage is an attractive feature to private equity houses such as Barclays Venture. According to peers, it remains an obvious choice in conflict situations.

Hammond Suddards Edge (see firm details p.984) London remains the perceived focus of the firm's private equity practice although its reputation is primarily as a regional force. The "*strong*" provincial teams are engaged in deals such as advising Royal Bank Development Capital on the £20 million MBI of Dale Joinery. Recent highlights include advising Abbey National Private Equity on the £1.3 billion acquisitions of a Whitbread pub chain and the £2.2 billion investment in Meridian Hotels with Nomura. **Clients:** Barclays Private Equity; Apax Capital Partners; Granville Baird; Internet Capital Group Europe; Royal Bank Development Capital.

Osborne Clarke (see firm details p.1086) According to peers there are "*some excellent people here.*" The firm's "*heavy leaning*" towards technology, media and telecoms gives it "*good visibility*" in London. The three offices handle work throughout the Thames Valley and South West. Acting regularly for management on VC backed transactions, advantaged by a flow of deals from well-known private equity houses including NatWest, Bridgepoint, Lloyds TSB and 3i Group. Key matters for 3i include the £287 million public to private of Fairview Holdings and the further funding by the consortium of Mediasurface (£21.5 million raised.) The firm also advised Close Brothers Private Equity on the £120 million funding for the creation of United Transport International. **Clients:** 3i Group; Lloyds TSB Development Capital; NatWest Development Capital; Bridgepoint Capital; Quester; Barclays Ventures; Barcalys Private Equity.

Wragge & Co (see firm details p.1189) Clearly the "*top corporate finance practice in the Midlands*" according to interviewees although its work has a distinctly national coverage. Operating from within corporate, the team typically works for VCs, management teams and investee companies. Recent highlights include acting for the purchaser of the £101 million IBO of Vickers Turbine Components from Rolls Royce and acting for management on the £1.4 billion IBO of Rank Hovis MacDougall from Tompkins. **Clients:** Friends Ivory & Sime; Apax Partners; Barclays Private Equity; Lloyds TSB Development Capital; Rank Hovis MacDougall; Aberdeen Murray Johnstone.

LEADERS IN PRIVATE EQUITY

BAIRD, Derek
Dickson Minto WS, London (020) 7628 4455

BAIRD, James
Clifford Chance, London (020) 7600 1000

BAMBER, Andrew
Norton Rose, London (020) 7444 3480
bamberawj@nortonrose.com
Specialisation: Andrew Bamber has been a partner at *Norton Rose* since 1991 specialising in structured finance and corporate transactions, in both cases typically in the context of corporate acquisitions. His practice covers acting for corporates, banks and other finance providers and financial advisers. Investment grade-type acquisition financings: acting for the corporate including the Texas Utilities £3.6bn bid for The Energy Group, the Ciba £1.3bn bid for Allied Colloids, the Mannesmann £22bn bid for Orange, the AXA £3.4bn bid for Guardian Royal Exchange, the TXU Europe £3.045bn bid for Hydroelectria Cantabrica, the Trinity £1.05bn merger with Mirror Group, and the Airline Group's £1.4bn acquisition from HM Government of National Air Traffic Services; acting for the banks including the Chase and Deutsche Bank financing for the US$2bn bid by Cemex for Southdown, JP Morgan on certain other bid financings, Deutsche Bank in respect of a series of acquisition financings for Enterprise Inns; and HSBC on Taylor Woodrow's £525 million bid for Bryant Group. Private equity sponsored acquisition financings include over 30 MBO/MBI transactions acting for RBS, ICG, Fortis Bank, Bank of Scotland, HSBC and Chase Capital Partners. Noteable recent deals in this sector include private MBOs/MBIs of Flagship Foods £172.6 million; Mill House Inns £97.5m; Allflex US$156 million and public-to-privates of Concentric £122 million; Ward Homes £54.5m and Fairview Homes £287 million. Also acted for Deutsche Bank as financial adviser on the take private of Powell Duffryn plc £507 million. Other structured deals include acting for TXU Europe on a series of confidential transactions including its acquisition of Norweb Energi and for Kelda on the proposed mutualisation of its regulated water business. Other recent work includes the sale and restructuring of interests in Spitalfields and advising easyRentacar on its fleet financing and other fund raisings. He also acted for Fuji Bank on the US$2.5bn facility for British Airways and for the banks on numerous other aircraft financings for BA and DHL.

BARKER, Bridget
Macfarlanes, London (020) 7831 9222
bcb@macfarlanes.com
Specialisation: Partner in company, commercial and banking department. Specialises in investment funds and financial services, acting for a number of on-shore and off-shore investment funds, covering a range of investment areas. Also experienced in corporate finance work, acting for a number of listed companies. Recent matters include advising on pan European venture capital funds for HSBC Private Equity and Legal & General Venture. Author of articles on investment funds, financial services and money laundering.
Prof. Memberships: Law Society, International Bar Association. Vice Chairman of IBA Committee on Specialised Investment Funds. Association of Women Solicitors.
Career: Qualified with *Macfarlanes* in 1983. Became a partner in 1988.

BARRON, Michael
Dickson Minto WS, London (020) 7628 4455
michael.barron@dmws.com
Specialisation: Private equity transactions, especially structured debt finance and other credit facilities. Acts for major financial institutions and banks active in the private equity and development capital market.
Career: Qualified as a solicitor in Scotland 1977 and in England 1986. Educated University of Edinburgh. Solicitor with 3i plc 1984 to 1987 then with *Dickson Minto WS*, as a partner since 1989.

BARTER, Charles
Travers Smith Braithwaite, London
(020) 7295 3000
Charles.Barter@TraversSmith.com
Specialisation: Partner in corporate finance department. Corporate finance, in particular private equity, buyouts, buyins, disposals and reconstructions.
Prof. Memberships: Law Society, City of London Solicitors Company.
Career: Articled Clerk 1985; partner 1995.
Personal: Motorcycling, gardening, natural history, Church.

BEDDOW, Simon
Ashurst Morris Crisp, London (020) 7638 1111
simon.beddow@ashursts.com
Specialisation: UK and cross-border Corporate and Corporate Finance and venture capital.
Prof. Memberships: City of London Solicitors' Company.
Career: 1987-89 *Pinsent & Co* (Birmingham) (Articled Clerk), 1989-96 *Travers Smith Braithwaite* (Assistant), 1996 – *Ashurst Morris Crisp* (Partner since 1998).
Personal: Married with two daughters and one son.

BLAKE, Jonathan
SJ Berwin, London (020) 7533 2222
jonathan.blake@sjberwin.com
Specialisation: Head of the corporate finance department and the private equity group advising generally on mergers and management buy-outs, venture and development capital investments and related taxation issues. He has a particular specialisation in advising private equity and venture capital fund managers in many countries in Europe and else-

where on the structure of venture capital funds, management companies and carried interest incentive arrangements. Clients for whom he has established funds or carried interest incentive arrangements include ABN Amro, Apax, Bridgepoint Capital, Phoenix Equity Partners, Dresdner Kleinwort Capital, Electra Partners, Mercury Asset Management, PRICOA, Schroder Ventures and UBS Capital.
Prof. Memberships: Associate of the Chartered Institute of Taxation (ATII); British Venture Capital Association; International Bar Association; Chairman – Tax and Legal Committee of the European Venture Capital Association.
Personal: Educated at Haberdashers' Aske's School, Elstree and Queens' College, Cambridge (MA LL.M). Qualified 1979. Born 7th July 1954.

BOWN, Christopher
Freshfields Bruckhaus Deringer, London (020) 7936 4000
christpoher.bown@freshfields.com
Specialisation: Partner in corporate department specialising in private equity and cross-border M&A transactions. Recent transactions include major multi-jurisdictional private equity purchase of chemical business, and other major acquisitions.
Prof. Memberships: Law Society.
Career: Qualified 1981, partner *Baker & McKenzie* 1987-98; partner *Freshfields* since 1998.
Personal: Born 1956, educated Queens' College, Cambridge.

CAMPBELL, Mark
Clifford Chance, London (020) 7600 1000
mark.campbell@cliffordchance.com
See under Banking, p.116

CARPANINI, Fabrizio
Olswang, London (020) 7208 8888
fcp@olswang.com
Specialisation: Specialising in private equity/venture capital transactions, acting for institutions and management teams on buy-outs, buy-ins, institutional buy-outs and development capital deals. Institutional clients include Graphite Capital, Gresham Trust, Lloyds TSB Development Capital and Sovereign Capital Ltd.
Prof. Memberships: British Venture Capital Association. British Italian Law Association. Law Society.
Career: Joined Olswang as a partner in the corporate group in February 2000, having previously been a partner at Berwin Leighton.
Publications: A regular speaker at conferences on private equity and management buyouts.
Personal: Belmont Abbey School, Hereford & Bristol Poly. Leisure: Family, skiing, cycling and golf.

COMPAGNONI, Marco
Lovells, London (020) 7296 2000
marco.compagnoni@lovells.com
Specialisation: Specialises in a range of mergers and acquisitions work and corporate law. A particular specialisation is private equity transactions (MBOs and MBIs) acting primarily for institutional investors. Equity institutions for whom he has acted regularly include HgCapital, Doughty Hanson and Advent International. He also has extensive experience of joint ventures, purchase and sales of companies and businesses (both domestic and cross border). Significant recent transactions include acting for ING in its purchase of Barings, advising Doughty Hanson on its purchases of the BTR Aerospace Business and the demerger of Ti Automotive from Smiths Group.
Prof. Memberships: Member of the British Venture Capital Association, the British Italian Law Association and the City of London Solicitors Company.
Career: Articled at *Lovells*; qualified in 1987 and became a partner in 1993.

COTTIS, Matthew
Lovells, London (020) 7296 2000
matthew.cottis@lovells.com
See under Banking, p.117

DAVIS, Steven
SJ Berwin, London (020) 7533 2660
steven.davis@sjberwin.com
Specialisation: A diversified corporate practice covering mergers and acquisitions (private and public), leveraged buy-outs, venture and development capital investments, flotations, corporate finance and corporate reconstructions, albeit with a particular focus on private equity transactions acting primarily for financial institutions. Equity institutions for whom he acts regularly include Apax Partners and UBS Capital. Significant recent transactions include the public to private of The Limelight Group, advising the management of ERM on their management buyout and Pierre et Vacances on the acquisition of Center Parcs European business.
Prof. Memberships: Member of the New York Bar.
Career: Qualified in 1987 with *SJ Berwin*. Seconded to *Debevoise & Plimpton*, New York office 1992-93 and became a partner in 1994.
Personal: Born 1965. Educated Clifton College, Bristol and Manchester University. Married with one child. Leisure pursuits include golf, squash and cooking. Lives in London.

DICKSON, Alastair
Dickson Minto WS, London (020) 7628 4455
alastair.dickson@dmws.com
Specialisation: Mergers and acquisitions; leveraged buy-outs; acting for major financial institutions and banks. Deals in the last 12 months include acquisition of General Healthcare (£1.3 billion).
Prof. Memberships: Member of Law Society of Scotland; Writer to Her Majesty's Signet.
Career: Educated Edinburgh University 1971. *Dundas & Wilson* 1971-73. *Maclay Murray & Spens* 1973-76. *Dundas & Wilson* 1976-85 (partner from 1978). Founding partner of *Dickson Minto WS* 1985.
Personal: Golf, squash, hill walking.

EVANS, Jacqueline
Allen & Overy, London (020) 7330 3000

FREEMAN, Adam
Lovells, London (020) 7296 2000
adam.freeman@lovells.com
Specialisation: Cross-border and domestic leveraged buy-outs, buy-ins, take privates and other types of acquisition finance and general syndicated loans.
Career: Articled *Lovells*, qualified 1996.
Personal: Married (Louisa) with a daughter (Lily). Interests include rugby, cricket and golf. Education: Birmingham University and Chester College of Law.

GEFFEN, Charles
Ashurst Morris Crisp, London (020) 7638 1111
charlie.geffen@ashursts.com
Specialisation: General corporate and corporate finance.
Career: Head of Private Equity.
Personal: Married, four children.

GILLESPIE, Stephen
Allen & Overy, London (020) 7330 3000
stephen.gillespie@allenovery.com
Specialisation: Steven Gillespie is a partner in the banking department, specialising in leveraged finance, telecoms/telemedia finance and project finance. Recent transactions include Cinven's purchase of Photo Service and Photo Station from GrandVision (for the arrangers); Drax I and II (for the arrangers and the senior lenders), the Rank Holidays/Bourne Leisure LBO (for Barclays Capital), the Wind Telecomunicazioni SpA 2G and 3G financings (for the arrangers and underwriters), the €10 billion 'jumbo' financing for ENEL SpA (for the arrangers) and the €100 million debut financing for Virgin Mobile (for the arrangers/underwriters), the Moyle Interconnector project financing (for RBS/Natwest) and various PFI financings for Edison Capital.
Prof. Memberships: Law Society. City of London Solicitors Company.
Career: Articled *Stephenson Harwood* 1985-87, Solicitor *Freshfields* 1987-91, Solicitor *Allen & Overy* 1991-95, partner 1995.
Personal: Born 1962. Educated at Foyle and Londonderry College and Trinity College, Oxford (MA (Hons) Jurisprudence 1984). Interests include family, reading, outdoor pursuits and music. Lives in St. Albans.

GLOVER, Jason
Clifford Chance, London (020) 7600 1000
Jason.Glover@cliffordchance.com
Specialisation: Specialises in private equity matters including funds establishment, management buy-ins and buy-outs and venture capital.
Career: Operations Director Hambro European Ventures (now Duke Street Capital) 1996-97; Operations Director Asian Infrastructure Fund 1997-98; Partner at *Clifford Chance* since 1998; Articled at *Clifford Chance*; Qualified 1991.

GOLD, Josyane
SJ Berwin, London (020) 7533 2314
josyane.gold@sjberwin.com
Specialisation: Partner in the private equity group. She specialises in advising private equity and venture capital fund managers on the establishment of investment funds in the UK and many other countries across Europe. She also advises on the creation of investment management companies and carried interest and other incentive arrangements. She has extensive experience in private equity financing and other corporate finance and commercial work.
Prof. Memberships: Member of the EVCA Tax & Legal Committee.
Career: *Bartletts de Reya* 1979-87, qualified 1981, partner 1983; joined *SJ Berwin* as partner in 1988.
Personal: Born 1956; resides London. Educated at Bristol (LLB). Speaks French.

GORRIE, Euan
Allen & Overy, London (020) 7330 3000
euan.gorrie@allenovery.com
Specialisation: He specialises in acting for banks, mezzanine lenders or borrowers in connection with acquisition finance, public bids and other leveraged or structured finance transactions, restructurings, syndicated loans and lending to investment funds. Recent transactions include advising the arranging banks on the RHM acquisition, the acquisition of Pubmaster, the acquisition of a portfolio of pubs from Bass plc and the refinancing of Impress.

Career: Glenalmond; New College Oxford; Articled *Allen & Overy*, Partner 1996.
Personal: Married; two children.

GREEN, Geoffrey
Ashurst Morris Crisp, London (020) 7638 1111
geoffrey.green@ashursts.com
Specialisation: Senior Partner. Principal area of work is mergers and acquisitions, including cross-border mergers and acquisitions and corporate finance generally, including new issues. Other main area of work is buy-outs acting primarily for equity institutions.
Prof. Memberships: Law Society.
Career: Qualified in 1975 while with *Ashurst Morris Crisp* and became a partner in 1979.
Personal: Forest School; St. Catharine's College, Cambridge. Leisure pursuits include tennis, golf and riding. Lives in London.

HALE, Chris
Travers Smith Braithwaite, London
(020) 7295 3000
Chris.Hale@TraversSmith.com
Specialisation: Main area of practice: head of *Travers Smith* private equity group. Advises leading buy-out houses in the UK. Also advises on new issues and a number of listed companies, financial advisers and larger private companies on equity raising and mergers and acquisitions. Known particularly for working on more complex, larger buyouts and cross-border transactions.
Prof. Memberships: Hon. Treasurer and Executive Committee member of Society of Advanced Legal Studies.
Career: Qualified as a solicitor in 1981 with *Kingsley Napley*, joined *Travers Smith Braithwaite* in 1983 and became partner in 1987.
Personal: Educated at King's College School, Wimbledon, Emmanuel College, Cambridge (MA) and Wolfson College, Cambridge (LLM). Leisure interests include football, reading, gardening, walking and legal history.

HAMPTON, Alison
Lovells, London (020) 7296 2000

HANTON, Bruce
Ashurst Morris Crisp, London (020) 7638 1111
bruce.hanton@ashursts.com
Specialisation: Principal area of work is corporate finance particularly private equity transactions. Recent transactions include the acquisition of the Foseco and Releasants businesses of Burmah Castrol (Cinven), the IPO of Carphone Warehouse Group plc, the acquisition of the retail business of Allied Domecq plc by Punch Taverns Limited (Texas Pacific Group and Colong Capital) and the acquisition of William Hill (Cinven and CVC).
Prof. Memberships: Law Society.
Career: Qualified in 1988 with *Ashurst Morris Crisp*. Became Partner in 1996.
Personal: Born 7 February 1962. Educated Alleyn's School and Bristol University (LL.B and LL.M). Married with five children.

HOWARD, Susan
Allen & Overy, London (020) 7330 3000
susan.howard@allenovery.com
Specialisation: Experience of all aspects of corporate finance work specialising in larger management buy-outs/ins, private equity work of all sizes (from smaller venture capital investments to large cross-border deals for financial purchasers) and mergers and acquisitions. Her recent experience includes advising Principal Hotels on its sale, and Bass plc on its sale of 988 pubs, in both instances, to Nomura International plc's Principal Finance Group (PFG).
Prof. Memberships: The Law Society.
Career: Articled with *Allen & Overy* (1985-87), qualified (1987), partner (1994).
Personal: Born 1962. Attended Pates Grammar School (1973-78), Cheltenham Grammar School (1978-80) and Exeter College, Oxford (1981-84) (BA Hons). Lives in London.

INGLIS, Alan
Clifford Chance, London (020) 7600 1000
alan.inglis@cliffordchance.com
See under Banking, p.119

JOHNSON, James
Clifford Chance, London (020) 7600 1000
james.johnson@cliffordchance.com
See under Banking, p.119

KEAL, Anthony C.
Allen & Overy, London (020) 7330 3000

LAYTON, Matthew
Clifford Chance, London (020) 7600 1000
matthew.layton@cliffordchance.com
Specialisation: Particular emphasis on domestic and international management, leveraged buy-outs and venture capital transactions as well as general corporate and corporate finance work.
Career: LL.B (Hons) Leeds 1982. Qualified 1986; partner 1991.

MACKIE, Chris
Olswang, London (020) 7208 8888
cam@olswang.com
Specialisation: Private equity and venture capital advising institutions as well as general corporate work.
Prof. Memberships: Law Society.
Career: 1987-94 *Turner Kenneth Brown.*
1994-00 *Berwin Leighton*, partner 1996.
Feburary 2000 joined *Olswang* as a partner.
Personal: Married with 3 children. Lives in London.

MARTIN, Charles
Macfarlanes, London (020) 7831 9222
cdzm@macfarlanes.com
Specialisation: MBOs/Venture capital. M&A (especially cross-border), private equity and Corporate finance/securities.
Career: Bristol University 1982. Qualified 1985. Partner 1990. Worked in the US 1988-89.
Personal: Married with three children. Lives in London.

McNAIR, Martin
Dickson Minto WS, London (020) 7628 4455

MEEK, Charles
Macfarlanes, London (020) 7831 9222
chm@macfarlanes.com
Specialisation: Private equity. UK and cross-border M & A, private equity and corporate finance.
Career: London University 1982. Qualified at *Macfarlanes* 1986. Partner 1992.
Personal: Married with three children. Lives in London.

MIFSUD, Mark
SJ Berwin, London (020) 7533 2222
mark.mifsud@sjberwin.com
Specialisation: Partner in the private equity team of the corporate finance department. Advises private equity managers in relation to the structuring and establishment of private equity investment funds, incentive schemes, carried interest arrangements and co-investment plans. Has extensive experience in a wide range of jurisdictions. Also advises on related matters and general corporate finance. Clients for whom he has established funds, carried interest arrangements or advised on other related matters include Aberdeen Murray Johnstone Private Equity, ABN Amro, Accel Partners, Benchmark Capital, Dresdner Kleinwort Capital, Electra Partners Europe Limited, Lloyds TSB Development Capital, nCoTec, Palamon Capital Partners, PRICOA Capital Group Limited and TLcom Capital Partners.
Prof. Memberships: International Bar Association; Holborn Law Society (Committee Member); Law Society.
Career: Qualified 1993; partner *SJ Berwin* 1999.
Personal: Born 1968. Educated at Magdalen College School and St Catherine's College, Oxford. Speaks Maltese and Italian.

MORLEY, David H.
Allen & Overy, London (020) 7330 2551
david.morley@allenovery.com
See under Banking, p.119

MURRAY-JONES, Allan
Skadden, Arps, Slate, Meagher & Flom LLP, London (020) 7519 7000
amurrayj@skadden.com
Specialisation: Partner specialising in M&A, particularly private equity. Experience includes cross border M&A, all aspects of English law corporate finance and private equity fund raising.
Prof. Memberships: The Law Society.
Career: Qualified in Australia in 1976 and in England in 1981. Became a partner at *Durrant Piesse* in 1986, and joined *Skadden Arps* as a partner in 2001.
Personal: Educated at All Saints' College, Bathurst, and the Australian National University.

PAUL, Alan D.
Allen & Overy, London (020) 7330 3000
alan.paul@allenovery.com
See under Corporate Finance, p.254

POLGLASE, Timothy
Norton Rose, London (020) 7283 6000
polglaset@nortonrose.com
See under Banking, p.121

SHEACH, Andrew
CMS Cameron McKenna, London
(020) 7367 2969
ajs@cmck.com
Specialisation: Specialises in all types of private equity transactions (management buyout/buyin, public to privates (PTPs) and development capital and exit work), mergers and acquisitions and Yellow and Blue Book work. In the last year he has acted on a number of management buyouts/buyins for both equity investors and management teams and also for Luminar plc on its recent acquisition of Northern Leisure plc.
Career: BA (Law) Pembroke College, Cambridge 1981-84; Joined *Cameron Markby* 1985; Partner 1993.

SHELDON, Jeremy
Ashurst Morris Crisp, London (020) 7638 1111
jeremy.n.sheldon@ashursts.com
Specialisation: Partner in company department. Principal area of practice is U.K. and international buyouts acting primarily for equity providers, including Cinven Limited, Candover Investments plc and BZW Private Equity Limited. Other areas of practice include establishing and marketing quoted and unquoted investment funds, mergers and acquisitions, flotations and other Stock Exchange transactions.
Prof. Memberships: Vice-president of the mergers and acquisitions commission of the Union Internationale des Avocats.
Career: Qualified in 1980. Became a partner in 1987.
Personal: Born in 1952.

SINGH, Daljit
Jones, Day, Reavis & Pogue, London
(020) 7236 3939
dsingh@jonesday.com
Specialisation: Fax: (020) 7236 1113. All aspects of corporate finance including Blue & Yellow Book, M&A (UK and cross border); private equity, principal finance transactions (whether for the equity house, management or other funders) and securities work.
Prof. Memberships: Law Society, IOD.
Career: London University, Law College (Chancery Lane), *Baker McKenzie, Alsop Wilkinson, Hammond Suddards, Jones Day, Reavis & Pogue.*
Personal: Football (especially Chelsea Football Club), entertaining, music, business, and the family (married, two girls and one boy).

STEWART, Mark
Clifford Chance, London (020) 7600 1000
mark.stewart@cliffordchance.com
Specialisation: Partner dealing with general corporate banking with an emphasis on acquisition financings.
Career: University College School, London; Bristol University. Articled *Richards Butler*; qualified 1983; trainee and assistant solicitor 1983-86; *Clifford Chance* 1986-90; partner since 1990.
Personal: Born 1958; resides London.

SWEETING, Malcolm
Clifford Chance, London (020) 7600 1000
malcolm.sweeting@cliffordchance.com
Specialisation: Partner in finance practice.

TUFFNELL, Kevin
Macfarlanes, London (020) 7831 9222
kevin.tuffnell@macfarlanes.com
Specialisation: Partner in Corporate Commercial & Banking Department. Venture capital, corporate finance, mergers and acquisitions and flotations. Many substantial buy outs and financial purchases, including acting for management in relation to the financial purchases of IPC Magazines and William Hill, and for Royal Bank Private Equity on the bid for Britax International plc.
Career: Qualified in 1984 while with *Macfarlanes.* Became a Partner in 1989.

VICKERS, Mark
Ashurst Morris Crisp, London (020) 7638 1111
mark.vickers@ashursts.com
See under Banking, p.123

WARD, Anthony
Shearman & Sterling, London (020) 7655 5000
award@shearman.com
Specialisation: Partner specialising in acquisition finance. Advises a variety of leading financial institutions and equity sponsors. Recent transactions include advising Investcorp in connection with the debt financing of the acquisition of Gerresheimer Glas AG. Advising Merrill Lynch in connection with debt financing of the acquisition of Center Parcs. Advising Morgan Stanley in connection with the debt financing of the acquisition of McKechnie Plc.
Career: Qualified in1988. Partner *Ashurst Morris Crisp* in 1996. Partner *Shearman & Sterling* in 1998.
Personal: Education: School of Slavonic and East European Studies, London University, BA in Russian language and literature.

WARD, Nigel
Ashurst Morris Crisp, London (020) 7859 1236
nigel.ward@ashursts.com
Specialisation: International and structured finance with particular emphasis on acquisition and bid finance and debt restructurings. Advises primarily leading US and European investment banks and venture capital houses. Recent transactions include the financing of the Alfa Laval buy-out and the Finelist and Dunlop Slazenger debt restructurings.
Prof. Memberships: Member of Banking Law subcommittee of the City of London Law Society.
Career: Educated St Catherine's College, Oxford. Qualified in 1985. Partner in 1992.
Publications: Author of 'How stands the high yield investor in the European LBO market?'
Personal: Born 1961. Married with three children. Plays golf and tennis.

WAYTE, Peter
DLA, London (08700) 111111

WHITE, Graham
SJ Berwin, London (020) 7533 2240
graham.white @sjberwin.com
Specialisation: Partner in the corporate department specialising in private equity transactions.
Prof. Memberships: Law Society of Scotland.
Career: 1984-86 *Iain Smith & Co* Aberdeen; 1987 *Simmons & Simmons*; 1988-98 *Dickson Minto WS*; 1999 *SJ Berwin.*

PRODUCT LIABILITY

OVERVIEW: The increase in cases brought under the Consumer Protection Act (1987) seems set to continue, despite lingering worries over funding. Diminished legal aid and conditional fee arrangements have not stifled claims with EU legislation and greater consumer awareness fuelling the market. Justice Burton's landmark ruling (March 2001) on Hepatitis C has provided much needed case law on the Consumer Protection Act and spurred on the claimant firms in their search for potential group actions. That said, manufacturers are increasingly aware of the threat from product liability exposures. More initiatives at EU level are placing strict conditions upon manufacturers concerning regulatory and preventative measures. Although it is still making headlines with cases in other countries, the tobacco litigation has been superseded in the UK by big pharmaceutical cases such MMR and the contraceptive pill litigation. Food safety cases such as BSE and CJD typify a new product sector that has emerged over the last few years.

RESEARCH APPROVED BY BMRB: *For this edition,* Chambers' *researchers conducted 6,552 interviews – 4,419 with law firms, 554 with barristers and 1,579 with clients.*

The validity of the research was scrutinised by BMRB International, who audited both the methodology and the results at our offices in July 2001. They interviewed Chambers' *researchers and cross-checked sample interviews. Details of the audit appear on page 7..*

LONDON

MAINLY DEFENDANT

PRODUCT LIABILITY: MAINLY DEFENDANT • London		Ptnrs	Assts
1	CMS Cameron McKenna	7	10
2	Davies Arnold Cooper	4	13
3	Lovells	8	25
4	Ashurst Morris Crisp	3	12
	Kennedys	5	8
5	Beachcroft Wansbroughs	9	20
	Freshfields Bruckhaus Deringer	3	7
	Simmons & Simmons	4	4
	Theodore Goddard	2	4
6	Clifford Chance	3	5
	Herbert Smith	n/a	n/a

LEADING INDIVIDUALS		
1	**DODDS-SMITH Ian** CMS Cameron McKenna	
	HODGES Christopher CMS Cameron McKenna	
2	**KELLEHER John** Theodore Goddard	**MELTZER John** Lovells
	PEARL Simon Davies Arnold Cooper	**WARE Anne** Davies Arnold Cooper
3	**BOWDEN Paul** Freshfields Bruckhaus	**ELVY Mark** Ashurst Morris Crisp
	McDOUGALL Arundel Ashurst Morris Crisp	
	SAYERS Shane Kennedys	**SHERRINGTON Patrick** Lovells
	TYLER Mark CMS Cameron McKenna	

This book is the product of 6,552 1/2 hour interviews. See p.7 for BMRB audit.
Within each band, firms are listed alphabetically. *See individuals' profiles p.684*

CMS Cameron McKenna (see firm details p.922) Once again, this firm of fine "*all-rounders*" retains its position as clear leader in the field. A strong dedicated team, wide manufacturing client base and "*impressive*" technical skills keep it firmly at the cutting edge. Particularly recommended for its pharmaceutical, advisory and regulatory work, the team has been involved in high profile multi-party proceedings such as oral contraceptives, MMR and breast implant claims. "*Elder statesman and legend*" **Ian Dodds-Smith** (see p.684) remains heavily endorsed by clients and colleagues, although it is **Christopher Hodges** (see p.685) ("*a master of the area*") who is increasingly attracting much of the limelight. He is thought by clients to enjoy "*unsurpassed knowledge,*" particularly in relation to European regulatory issues. "*Understated*" **Mark Tyler** (see p.416) is praised as "*an extraordinarily able solicitor.*" **Clients:** Dow Corning; Schering; John Wyeth; Aventis Pasteur MSD.

Davies Arnold Cooper (see firm details p.934) Recommended to researchers as "*a cohesive team,*" widely known for its strength in litigation. Its "*large and steady supply*" of instructions is won mainly from insurers and the firm remains firmly at the forefront of the high profile, multi-party pharmaceutical cases. In a recent highlight, the firm acted for the National Blood Authority in the groundbreaking Hepatitis C litigation. "*Heavyweight*" **Simon Pearl** (see p.686) commands respect from lawyers and clients alike, although his aggressive style is not everybody's cup of tea. "*Tactical*" **Anne Ware** (see p.687) is applauded for her thorough, determined, "*client-conscious*" approach. With "*good support*" and a "*personable approach*" the firm provides "*excellent value for money.*" **Clients:** NHSLA; GlaxoSmithKline; Roche Products.

Lovells (see firm details p.1044) An "*impressive*" team with a broad sweep of experience in the major product categories, the firm has set out its stall as "*a strong force*" in this area. Acclaimed for its litigation prowess, the group has recently been involved in major international tobacco and pharmaceutical cases, including a challenge to the EU directive banning tobacco advertising, and the high profile MMR litigation. Tracking the increased regulation from Europe, the firm has been busy advising across industry sectors such as telecommunications, electronic goods, transport and food manufacturers. "*Amiable*" **John Meltzer** (see p.686) is clearly a leading light, and has attracted substantial endorsement from both lawyers and clients for his work in the tobacco and vaccine litigation. **Patrick Sherrington** (see p.581) enters the tables following heavy endorsement. **Clients:** European tobacco companies; train manufacturers.

Ashurst Morris Crisp (see firm details p.866) Has addressed questions raised by the market concerning its heavy tobacco related caseload by successfully developing expertise in emerging areas. Recent highlights still cover that niche, as the firm has been involved in a high-profile challenge to the EU directive banning tobacco advertising and sponsorship. Other instructions include health & safety issues, product recalls, regulatory and pharmaceutical work. Peers agree that popular **Mark Elvy** (see p.684) "*runs a tight ship,*" while **Arundel McDougall** (see p.685) ("*first class,*") a recent addition to the team from Rowe & Maw, has a reputation for pharmaceuticals that precedes him. **Clients:** Manufacturers of tobacco and pharmaceuticals.

Kennedys (see firm details p.1018) "*Outstandingly good, although relatively small,*" the firm has built on its strengths in the insurance market to produce a dynamic, highly visible product liability offering. It acts for pharmaceuticals and medical product manufacturers. Experienced in risk management and product recall, clients instruct the firm for its "*specialist knowledge*" in the area and commend the team for its "*go-ahead*" proactive attitude. Best known for pharmaceuticals issues and risk management, **Shane Sayers** is described as "*larger than life*" and "*an efficient operator.*" **Clients:** Johnson & Johnson; Novartis; Medeva; motor vehicle manufacturers.

Beachcroft Wansbroughs (see firm details p.872) Acting for both insurers and the insured, the group, under the guidance of Anthony Cherry, has taken the lead in paint and contraceptive cases. Its work on the high profile oral contraceptive litigation has won it praise from clients as an "*impressive, highly organised*" outfit. **Clients:** Major insurers; chemicals manufacturers; pharmaceuticals.

Freshfields Bruckhaus Deringer (see firm details p.965) A newcomer to the rankings following numerous recommendations by competitors and clients, the firm began its tobacco work four years ago, and has since built up its strength. The Bruckhaus merger has given it an established product liability capability overseas. The work is mostly contentious, although the team also advises mobile phone manufacturers and has experience in pan-European product recalls and regulatory work. Frequently described by clients as "*first rate,*" **Paul Bowden** (see p.566) is a star environmental practitioner known for his European tobacco work. **Clients:** JT International; arms manufacturers; multi-national domestic appliances manufacturers.

Simmons & Simmons (see firm details p.1132) A "*significant operation,*" if quieter in the wake of the tobacco furore. A "*really rather good*" team, headed by Miles Alexander, has received instructions in other areas such as telecoms and pharmaceuticals (where the work is more advisory) and is expanding into chemicals and electronics. The tobacco defence cases continue across Europe, and the firm is noted by clients for its expertise in co-ordinating cross-border preparation for anticipated litigation in the telecommunications sector. Also witnessed an increased amount of risk assessment and pre-litigation risk management. **Clients:** Tobacco manufacturers; petrochemicals manufacturers; telecommunications sector.

Theodore Goddard (see firm details p.1152) A quieter year than last, with the MMR and Myodil matters largely over. The team continues to advise pharmaceuticals, MDU members and toy manufacturers. "*Outstanding*" **John Kelleher** sets the measured style for his department, which "*approaches litigation in a moderate way.*" Endorsed by clients for his "*useful mixture of determination and subtlety*" he is said to possess "*terrific judgment.*" **Clients:** Glaxo Wellcome, MDU.

Clifford Chance (see firm details p.919) Peers believe that its generalist corporate approach combined with an internationally weighted client base and substantial proportion of advisory work has afforded this practice a low profile in the market. Nevertheless, the firm boasts an impressive client list and has considerable expertise, most notably in the pharmaceutical and transport sectors. Recent highlights include defending against asbestos-related claims, advising an international pharmaceutical company on its pan-European compliance programme, and advice on clinical trials. Andrew Edgar leads the group. **Clients:** Pharmaceuticals; car manufacturers; mobile phone manufacturers.

Herbert Smith (see firm details p.993) A first rate litigation team, led by David Higgins has handled an extensive amount of work, much of it overseas. Rivals are impressed by highlights, which include the renowned benzene contamination case, and it continues to act on issues relating to telecommunications, asbestos and latex allergies. **Clients:** Major insurers; major corporate organisations.

MAINLY CLAIMANT

PRODUCT LIABILITY: MAINLY CLAIMANT • London	Ptnrs	Assts
1 Leigh, Day & Co	3	6
2 Alexander Harris	1	1

LEADING INDIVIDUALS
1 **DAY Martyn** Leigh, Day & Co
2 **MEERAN Richard** Leigh, Day & Co
3 **BARR Richard** Alexander Harris

This book is the product of 6,552 1/2 hour interviews. See p.7 for BMRB audit.
Within each band, firms are listed alphabetically. *See individuals' profiles p.684*

Leigh, Day & Co (see firm details p.1036) An "*aggressive and professional*" firm which continues to draw strong reactions from the market. Many applaud "*cause-driven*" **Martyn Day**'s "*proactive approach*" in "*breaking new ground,*" although some opine that he is a "*classic showman,*" skilled in "*stirring up publicity for his client.*" The group also fields **Richard Meeran** (see p.648), judged by clients to be "*extremely experienced and an innovator in the area.*" The firm has had a busy year with work continuing on the contraceptive pill litigation, hip replacement claims, breast implant claims and substantial asbestos cases in South Africa.

Alexander Harris (see firm details p.854) "*Serious players,*" the firm is endorsed by colleagues for its breadth of experience. Head of department, **Richard Barr** (see p.684) received commendation from peers for his multi-party action work, especially MMR, where he was "*extremely good at the science and managing the team.*"

THE REGIONS

Irwin Mitchell (see firm details p.1009) Heralded by rivals as a "*switched on firm*" with an impressive depth of experience, the team has had heavy involvement in major multi-party claims such as tobacco, CJD and vCJD, benzodiazepines, breast implants, FACs and asbestos. **David Body**'s (see p.164) recent activities have revolved around work for the families of vCJD victims, to which he "*devoted his heart and soul.*" His exertions bore fruit earlier this year when an interim payout was awarded following the results of the BSE Inquiry Report. "*Extremely intellectual*" **Andrew Tucker** (see p.687) "*plays his cards close to his chest*" while "*forceful*" **John Pickering** (see p.686) is admired by clients as "*a shrewd operator.*"

Freethcartwright (see firm details p.964) "*Upbeat and robust*" **Paul Balen** (see p.164) heads up a "*well-organised*" team, which has been involved in many of the leading multi-party cases. Best known among his competitors for his work on the Trilucent breast implants (which included negotiating a compensation package). Peers applaud the firm for its "*ground-breaking work in pharmaceuticals and healthcare,*" as it is heavily involved in the MMR claims and is co-ordinating the 3M Capital Hip. The firm has also represented claimants in the Hepatitis C litigation.

Alexander Harris (see firm details p.854) Judged by peers to have had a quieter year, this Altrincham based team specialises in pharmaceuticals and medical devices. **David Harris** (see p.685) is endorsed by peers who typi-

PRODUCT LIABILITY • The Regions	Ptnrs	Assts
1 **Irwin Mitchell** Sheffield	5	6
2 **Freethcartwright** Nottingham	1	1
3 **Alexander Harris** Altrincham	1	1
Blackett Hart & Pratt Newcastle upon Tyne	3	n/a
Leigh, Day & Co Manchester	1	n/a

LEADING INDIVIDUALS	
1 **BALEN Paul** Freethcartwright	
2 **BODY David** Irwin Mitchell	**TUCKER Andrew** Irwin Mitchell
3 **HARRIS David** Alexander Harris	**MALLEN Anthony** Blackett Hart & Pratt
McCOOL Geraldine Leigh, Day & Co	**PICKERING John** Irwin Mitchell

This book is the product of 6,552 1/2 hour interviews. See p.7 for BMRB audit.
Within each band, firms are listed alphabetically. *See individuals' profiles p.684*

cally refer to his work on MMR, LSD, Trilucent breast implants and the anti-smoking drug Zyban.

Blackett Hart & Pratt A new addition following its success in the Hepatitis C litigation earlier this year. **Tony Mallen** heads up the team that achieved an *"excellent victory"* which has been hailed by competitors as a landmark for consumer rights.

Leigh, Day & Co (see firm details p.1036) A focused practice specialising in military and commercial aviation product liability. On the military side *"veteran"* **Geraldine McCool** (see p.648) has recently undertaken work in relation to a hawk plane's ejection canopy and faulty Lynx helicopter rotor heads. On the commercial side, McCool and the team have been involved in deep vein thrombosis cases.

SCOTLAND

PRODUCT LIABILITY • Scotland	Ptnrs	Assts
1 **Burness** Edinburgh	2	2
McGrigor Donald Glasgow	2	3
Simpson & Marwick WS Edinburgh	4	6

LEADING INDIVIDUALS
1 **MURRAY Marsali** Burness

This book is the product of 6,552 1/2 hour interviews. See p.7 for BMRB audit.
Within each band, firms are listed alphabetically. *See individuals' profiles p.684*

Burness (see firm details p.903) Continues to build on its *"broad experience,"* most notably on the litigation side where the group is praised by clients for its *"rational"* approach. Peers concur, *"they fight hard but remain open-minded."* *"Reasonable and thorough,"* **Marsali Murray** remains at the helm recognised as a leading light for this type of work in Scotland. **Clients:** Pharmaceuticals; agrichemicals and consumer products manufacturers.

McGrigor Donald (see firm details p.1062) Firmly established and renowned for its work defending tobacco manufacturers, the firm applies its experience across a range of other industries, from petrochemicals to pharmaceuticals. The team, headed by Jacqueline Harris places particular emphasis on the importance of effective risk-management. **Clients:** Tobacco manufacturers.

Simpson & Marwick WS (see firm details p.1133) Comprising *"superb litigators,"* the group led by Peter Anderson is thought by peers to possess a considerable experience in work relating to the motor vehicles and pharmaceuticals industry. **Clients:** Pharmaceuticals manufacturers; motor vehicle manufacturers.

NORTHERN IRELAND

PRODUCT LIABILITY • Northern Ireland	Ptnrs	Assts
1 **Elliott Duffy Garrett** Belfast	2	2
McKinty & Wright Belfast	3	2
Mills Selig Belfast	1	1
O'Reilly Stewart Belfast	1	4

LEADING INDIVIDUALS	
1 **WILSON Michael** Elliott Duffy Garrett	
2 **SPRING Paul** Mills Selig	**STEWART Brian** O'Reilly Stewart

This book is the product of 6,552 1/2 hour interviews. See p.7 for BMRB audit.
Within each band, firms are listed alphabetically. *See individuals' profiles p.684*

Elliott Duffy Garrett (see firm details p.949) Warmly commended for his *"knowledge and capability,"* market opinion once again confirms *"top quality"* **Michael Wilson** (see p.478) as leading individual in the field. **Clients:** Tobacco manufacturers; pharmaceuticals.

McKinty & Wright (see firm details p.1063) Supported by a backbone of insurance clients, the firm continues to build on its profile in a wide range of cases. The group recently defended GlaxoSmithKline in relation to claims made against the drug Myodil, and advised a toy manufacturer on issues surrounding an allegedly defective doll. Paul McDonald heads the team. **Clients:** GlaxoSmithKline; insurers; car manufacturers and supermarkets.

Mills Selig (see firm details p.1070) Acts for both defendants and claimants. With the tobacco litigation an ever-present feature of the firm's workload, the team led by the *"respected"* **Paul Spring** (see p.582) has recently undertaken work for electronic goods and motor vehicle manufacturers. **Clients:** Tobacco companies; electronic goods manufacturers; motor vehicle producers.

O'Reilly Stewart (see firm details p.1085) Known for its work in the benzodiazepine cases during which the *"self-assured"* **Brian Stewart** (see p.687) won praise from fellow solicitors as *"a leading light."* The team over the past year has been involved in defending a pharmaceuticals manufacturer concerning tobacco patches, and a case involving a portion control module that allegedly left a cinema flooded with cola. Its involvement in tobacco litigation is ongoing. **Clients:** Pharmaceuticals; insurers.

FOOD LAW

LONDON

FOOD • London	Ptnrs	Assts
1 Berwin Leighton Paisner	2	2
2 Bird & Bird	2	2
Covington & Burling	2	5
Simmons & Simmons	2	6
Taylor Joynson Garrett	1	n/a
3 Barlow Lyde & Gilbert	1	3
Pinsent Curtis Biddle	1	1

LEADING INDIVIDUALS	
1 **BAYLIS Craig** Berwin Leighton Paisner	**ROSS Hilary** Berwin Leighton Paisner
2 **CODY Nick** Taylor Joynson	**GILBERTSON Kathryn** Berwin Leighton Paisner

This book is the product of 6,552 1/2 hour interviews. See p.7 for BMRB audit.

Within each band, firms are listed alphabetically. *See individuals' profiles p.684*

Berwin Leighton Paisner (see firm details p.878) Fielding stalwart lawyers and a breadth of practice, being one of the few to possess a dedicated team, the firm finds itself once again cream of the crop. The international dimension of its work has continued to expand with "*astute*" **Hilary Ross** (see p.686) advising US and Canadian companies on launching their products in the UK and Europe. Her strong scientific background is felt to be advantageous, and she is proclaimed by peers as a "*leading expert*" on GM foods. **Craig Baylis** (see p.684) has carved out a name for food-safety related matters and is perceived as "*academic and user-friendly – good if it's an issue that needs fighting.*" **Kathryn Gilbertson** (see p.685) is endorsed for her activities defending against the enforcement agencies. **Clients:** Hogshead; Travel Inn; Farm Foods.

Bird & Bird (see firm details p.884) Distinguished by its IP perspective, the "*knowledgeable*" team is recommended by clients in particular for trademark and labeling advice, as well as for regulatory matters. Jane Mutimear heads the team. Recent work has involved advising on the emerging area of neutraceuticals and on GM foods. **Clients:** Nestlé.

Covington & Burling (see firm details p.926) Despite its smaller size, the team is reputed by clients to be "*at the cutting edge of food and health claims.*" It continues to advise McNeil Consumer Nutritionals on its product Benecol (recently concerning advertising proceedings,) and also on new products that are being introduced to the UK and European markets. Further highlights include advisory and regulatory work in relation to additive issues and novel foods. **Clients:** McNeil Consumer Nutritionals.

Simmons & Simmons (see firm details p.1132) Under the guidance of Miles Alexander, the team has cemented its position as a "*solid practice with a wide client base.*" It has recently shifted the emphasis away from contentious labelling work, concentrating more on the advisory and regulatory aspects. The caseload contains a strong international element, notably for US clients in cases relating to novel and GM foods.

Taylor Joynson Garrett (see firm details p.1150) A "*sensible*" team with a strong profile in this area, headed up by the respected **Nick Cody**. Recommended to researchers for defence work in relation to food safety prosecutions, as well as for its IP and advertising work. Over the last year, the firm has made a successful application for permission to conduct a judicial review of an ASA adjudication that advertising claims made for a children's fruit drink were misleading.

Barlow Lyde & Gilbert (see firm details p.870) Undertakes defence work in disputes between manufacturers and their suppliers, the firm also concentrates its "*conciliatory efforts*" on disputes between food manufacturers, retailers or restaurants and the enforcement agencies. The team, which includes Gary Freer, has recently been involved in a major civil dispute between a manufacturer and a supplier with regard to a product recall. **Clients:** Cadburys; manufacturers; restaurant chains.

Pinsent Curtis Biddle (see firm details p.1098) Most often seen stepping in to defend manufacturers and retailers against the enforcement agencies. Well-versed in the spectrum of food related issues, particularly food safety and labeling, Andrew Stacey's team boasts an emergency incident management scheme, and offers risk management advice. Over the last year work has included advising a manufacturer in a claim against a packaging company, for loss of profit due to faulty packaging. It continues its advice to key client Tesco. **Clients:** Tesco; Glanbia Group

THE REGIONS

FOOD • The Regions	Ptnrs	Assts
1 **DLA** Birmingham	2	1
Elliotts Manchester	1	1
Eversheds Birmingham, Norwich	2	1
Gregg Galbraith Quinn Bristol	1	3
Shoosmiths Northampton	3	2
2 **Andrew M Jackson & Co** Hull	3	1
Margetts & Ritchie Birmingham	1	2
3 **Bevan Ashford** Bristol	1	1
Bond Pearce Bristol	1	1
Hammond Suddards Edge Birmingham	n/a	2

This book is the product of 6,552 1/2 hour interviews. See p.7 for BMRB audit.

Within each band, firms are listed alphabetically.

DLA **Steven Edmonds** is the major name at a department that handles all areas of consumer law, including food law, health & safety, product safety, consumer credit and trading standards.

Elliotts (see firm details p.950) "*Technically able*" **Barry Holland** (see p.529), whose enthusiasm and proactive approach continue to win him considerable praise among clients, sits at the helm of the licensing and food safety practice. The team is recommended for its activities defending food retailers. Endorsed for its specialist knowledge in applications for off-licences in petrol station and convenience stores. **Clients:** Pelican Group; supermarket chains.

Eversheds (see firm details p.952) "*Worthy of note due to the breadth of its practice*" is the typical opinion of its peers. The team has had a busy year, involved in the reformulating and relabelling of US products to be launched in the UK and Europe, and in the registration of organic food under the European approval certification system. Norwich-based **Owen Warnock** (see p.343) is a "*prominent*" and respected figure, while "*hard-working*" **David Young** (see p.687) heads up the health & safety team in Birmingham. The latter has recently run successful due diligence defences under the Food Safety Act. The group has considerable experience in food law prosecutions and inquiries. **Clients:** Dairy Crest; MuscleTech.

Gregg Galbraith Quinn "*Magisterial*" **Andrew Gregg** (see p.528) is warmly praised by solicitors and barristers for his expertise in licensing and food-safety issues. Clients are impressed by his "*hands-on*" and "*relaxed*" approach, while peers respect his knowledge of the field. The team has been concentrating on the food labelling arena in the light of new EC directives

LEADING INDIVIDUALS	
1 HOLLAND Barry Elliotts	
2 EDMONDS Steven DLA	GREGG Andrew Gregg Galbraith Quinn
REID Ron Shoosmiths	WARNOCK Owen Eversheds
YOUNG David Eversheds	
3 HETHERINGTON David Margetts & Ritchie	SMITH Hugh Andrew M. Jackson & Co

See individuals' profiles p.684

and FSA guidelines. **Clients:** Restaurants.

Shoosmiths (see firm details p.1129) Reputed to be "*pretty well involved at the hard edge*" and in possession of an envied list of clients, the team specialises in training food companies in issues such as consumer care, due diligence and crisis management. Also has expertise in labelling and in litigation. Leading the team, "*first rate*" **Ron Reid** (see p.686) is said to employ "*tremendous experience and depth of knowledge.*" **Clients:** British Sugar; Just Juice.

Andrew M Jackson & Co (see firm details p.860) Specialists in the fish industry, the team acts for vitamin and international pelagic companies. **Hugh Smith** (see p.687) has secured a reputation in this niche area. On the regulatory side recent work has involved acting for companies in relation to disputed health claims. **Clients:** Vitamin companies; pharmaceuticals.

Margetts & Ritchie **David Hetherington** (see p.685) and the team have advised food retailers in relation to product recalls prompted by the FSA, and acted on issues arising from misleading labeling and contaminated food. Other defence work has included various meat content cases and allegations regarding the importation of contaminated nuts. The group has followed the market trend in witnessing more civil litigation. The firm was appointed as food law consultant to the NFMFT in May 2001. **Clients:** Supermarkets; retailers.

Bevan Ashford (see firm details p.880) Unassuming yet still a force, the team's strength lies in its food labelling advice and food safety regulatory work. **Clients:** Allied Domecq; Meridian Leisure

Bond Pearce (see firm details p.888) The bulk of the work continues to consist principally of issues relating to food safety and hygiene. The firm, led by Michael Parrott defends in cases of prosecutions by environmental health officers, and advises on regulatory matters. **Clients:** Restaurants; supermarkets.

Hammond Suddards Edge (see firm details p.984) Recommended in particular for its regulatory strength, Françoise Snape's team maintains its reputation in the field. **Clients:** Hazelwoods.

LEADERS IN PRODUCT LIABILITY

BALEN, Paul
Freethcartwright, Nottingham (0115) 936 9369
paul.balen@freethcartwright.co.uk
See under Clinical Negligence, p.164

BARR, Richard
Alexander Harris, London (020) 7430 5555
Specialisation: Main areas of practice – personal injury and product liability. Cases: Opren, currently co-ordinating generic MMR vaccine cases at *Alexander Harris.* Co-author of the Penguin Guide to the Law. Writes regular light-hearted column for the Solicitors Journal. Regular live slot as 'Legal Eagle' on BBC Radio Norfolk. Lectures on personal injury, pharmaceutical product and multi party actions to legal and medical audiences. An expert regularly called upon to contribute to news and current affairs programmes, who is frequently quoted in the press.
Prof. Memberships: Panel solicitor for AVMA, Law Society National Personal Injury Panel, Society of Authors.
Career: July 1999 joined *Alexander Harris* – Partner. April 1998 – July 1999 *Hodge Jones & Allen* – Partner. 1974 – April 1998 *Dawbarns.* Qualified 1971.

BAYLIS, Craig
Berwin Leighton Paisner, London (020) 7760 1000
craig.baylis@berwinleightonpaisner.com
Specialisation: Partner in regulatory department and head of the business regulation unit. Main area of practice is licensing and leisure. Handles all aspects for the leisure, retailing and brewing industries including advocacy at all levels throughout the UK. Other area of expertise is business protection and environmental law. Advises and represents on all regulatory matters, health and safety, food safety, trading standards and environmental health. Author of 'Food Safety: Law and Practice' and 'Environmental Regulation- Its Impact on Foreign Investment'.
Prof. Memberships: Food Law Group.
Career: Qualified 1981. Solicitor for the Metropolitan Police 1981-84; Partner at *Field Fisher Waterhouse* 1984-92. Joined *Paisner & Co* (now *Berwin Leighton Paisner*) in 1992 and became a Partner in 1993.
Personal: Born 9th February 1957. Attended Exeter University 1975-78. Lives in London.

BODY, David
Irwin Mitchell, Sheffield (0114) 276 7777
Bodyd@irwinmitchel.co.uk
See under Clinical Negligence, p.164

BOWDEN, Paul
Freshfields Bruckhaus Deringer, London (020) 7936 4000
paul.bowden@freshfields.com
See under Litigation, p.566

CODY, Nick
Taylor Joynson Garrett, London (020) 7300 7000

DAY, Martyn
Leigh, Day & Co, London (020) 7650 1200

DODDS-SMITH, Ian
CMS Cameron McKenna, London (020) 7367 2509
ids@cmck.com
Specialisation: Partner and Head of Healthcare Group. Main area of practice is healthcare relating to pharmaceuticals and products in the medical, cosmetics and food sectors. Specialist in both licensing and related regulatory affairs, pricing and including reimbursant issues. Has dealt with many judicial reviews in the regulation and NHS sector (some with references to the E.C.J.). Practice includes product liability and personal injury litigation. Has handled very many multi-claimant product liability cases, often with international elements and has coordinated cases in Europe as a whole. Major cases include those relating to hormone pregnancy tests, oral contraceptives, blood products, benzodiazepines, IUCDs, breast implants, baby drinks, pesticides, heart valves and vaccines.
Prof. Memberships: Include the American Bar Association, Federation of Insurance & Corporate Counsel, Fellow of the Royal Society of Medicine.
Career: Joined the firm in 1974 and qualified in 1976. Became a Partner in 1984. Member of various working parties on research and medical law issues for Royal College of Physicians, Medical Research Council and Royal College of Pathologists. Temporary Adviser (1987) to W.H.O. on law relating to clinical trials. Previously member of Clinical Sciences Ethics Committee of the University of London and University College Hospital.
Publications: Author of 'Product Liability for Medical Products' in 'Medical Negligence' (Butterworths) and 'Legal Liabilities in Clinical Trials' in 'Early Phase Human Drug Evaluation' (CRC). Author of various other book chapters and articles on regulatory and liability issues. Frequent lecturer in the UK and abroad. Consultant Editor to the 'Personal and Medical Injuries Law Letter' and the 'Regulatory Affairs Journal'.
Personal: Born 31st July 1951. Educated at Solihull School and Downing College, Cambridge 1969-72.

EDMONDS, Steven
DLA, Birmingham (08700) 111111

ELVY, Mark
Ashurst Morris Crisp, London (020) 7859 1567
mark.elvy@ashursts.com
Specialisation: Main areas of practice are product liability and risk management in the health, safety and environmental fields. Particular expertise in the defense of multi-party product related claims and the defense of multi-jurisdictional claims with a focus on Europe. Advised on a number of product recalls and acted in defense of proceedings brought under the General Product Safety Regulations 1994. Also advised on several investigations carried out by City regulators including DTI, IMRO, SIB, SFA and The Stock Exchange.
Prof. Memberships: Law Society; International Association of Defense Council; Defense Research

Institute; International Bar Association.
Career: Admitted as a solicitor of the Supreme Court of New South Wales in 1984. Admitted as a solicitor in England in 1991. Joined *Ashurst Morris Crisp* in 1987; partner 1994.
Publications: Contributing author to publication on Group Actions in England and Wales published by Oxford University press in March 2001. Co-author of chapter in the Risk Management Guide: 2001 published by the London Stock Exchange.
Personal: Born 20 April 1961; attended University of New South Wales (B Comm 1982, LLB 1984). Married with two children, Resides London.

GILBERTSON, Kathryn
Berwin Leighton Paisner, London (020) 7760 1000
kathryn.gilbertson@berwinleightonpaisner.com
Specialisation: Senior solicitor in the regulatory department. Kathryn has extensive experience advising on food safety, hygiene and labelling matters. She also advises clients on trading law, health and safety and consumer issues. Her proactive and commercial approach enables clients to achieve compliance with novel remedies thus minimising the impact of the regulations on their business. She has particular expertise in advising directors on their personal and corporate liabilities. A specialist in the formulation of policies and strategies for crisis management, HACCP, product recall and incident investigation. Frequently writes for Caterer and Hotelkeeper. Lectures extensively on food and safety matters. Recently spoke to the CIEH London Food Study Group on the impact of the Human Rights Act on food law enforcement.
Prof. Memberships: Food Law Group, European Food Law Association, Society of Food Hygiene Technology, Young Fraud Lawyers Association, Road Risk Forum.
Career: Admitted in 1994. Dual qualified as both an environmental health officer and solicitor having 16 years experience in food and safety law.
Personal: Born 14 July 1962. Married with a son. BSc (Hons) Environmental Health, Diploma Health and Safety, Mediator.

GREGG, Andrew
Gregg Galbraith Quinn, Bristol (0117) 925 8123
See under Licensing, p.528

HARRIS, David
Alexander Harris, Altrincham (0161) 925 5555
Specialisation: Joint Senior Partner and Partner in charge of the Pharmaceutical Product and Disaster Litigation Department. All areas of pharmaceutical product litigation, concentrating on multi party action litigation. Lead Solicitor in Myodil litigation and member of Steering Committees in Opren, Human Insulin, and Hillsborough Disaster. Lead Solicitor in Listeriosis claims against the Government and instructed by families of victims of BSE / CJD. Lead Solicitor in the investigation of Septrin claims and in the action for underdosing of Radiotherapy at the North Staffordshire District Hospital. Considerable experience in litigation in the USA, including Shiley Heart Valves, Telectronic Pacemakers and Breast Implant claims. Contributes regularly to television news and current affairs programmes and is an expert frequently consulted by radio reporters and producers, and has been extensively quoted in the Press. Lectures on pharmaceutical product and multi party actions to legal and medical audiences. Investigating claims for 'Persona' multi party action. Responsible for all generic work in LSD multi party action. One of two firms nominated by Legal Aid Board to carry out preliminary investigations into ECT treatment. Lead solicitor investigating claims of overtreatment by Manchester orthodontist, Melvyn Meggitt.
Prof. Memberships: Law Society, APIL, ATLA.
Career: Qualified in 1979 and then became co-founder of *Alexander Harris* in May 1989. First practice in this country specialising exclusively in clinical negligence and pharmaceutical product liability. The practice has now added a specialist personal injury department. Deputy District Judge on the Northern Circuit since 1988. Assessor to Law Society Personal Injury Panel. CEDR Accredited mediator.
Personal: Born 23rd May 1949. Attended Hull University (LL.B 1972).

HETHERINGTON, David
Margetts & Ritchie, Birmingham (0121) 214 5001
david.hetherington@margetts-ritchie.com
Specialisation: Defends businesses and directors prosecuted by local authorities and government departments under regulatory law relating to food safety, trading standards, environmental health, consumer protection, product safety and health & safety. Recovers defence costs. Businesses represented include: poultry, meat, scotch eggs, ice cream, yoghurt and pizza producers; bakery, breweries and vineyard; fish processors, importers and shellfish distributors; nut importers and wholesalers; organic food importers and wholesalers; tinned and general food importers; restaurants, cafés, butchers, baker, grocers and delicatessen; food and non-food supermarkets; electrical distributors and retailers; doors and fire doors manufacturers; glass producer and installer; national / international furnishing retailers; toys importer and retail chain; holiday camp operator; kitchens / conservatory producers and installers; golf professional; university. Recent cases include: The Pesticides Safety Directorate was successfully required to amend 'naming and shaming' report; Food Standards Agency poultry product recall; saucepan flaking metal in contact with food, charges dismissed with costs; unsafe festive lights, charges dismissed with costs; unsafe glass table, charges dismissed with costs; unsafe fire door, charges withdrawn; weights & measures, charges dismissed with costs; café hygiene, charges withdrawn; misleading seafood labelling, charges withdrawn; food past use-by-dates, charges withdrawn; misleading telephone prices, charges withdrawn; under-age sale, charges withdrawn; false descriptions charges, car and electrical servicing; health & safety, food distribution premises; misleading prices charges, £90,000 defence costs recovered.
Prof. Memberships: Law Society. Food Law Group.
Career: With *Margetts & Ritchie,* articles (1975-77), assistant solicitor (1978-84), and partner (1984-01). Instructed as a Prosecution Solicitor agent: West Midlands Trading Standards, Environmental and Fire Service Departments (1981-86), West Midlands Probation Service (1986-91), Crown Prosecution Service (1987-91), Birmingham Trading Standards (1988-89) and M.A.F.F. (1990). Instructed as a Defence Solicitor: general criminal law offences (1978-99), Duty Solicitor (1979-96), West Midlands Fire Service drivers (1981-87), Trading Standards, Environmental Health, M.A.F.F. & Wine Standards cases (1987-2001). Food Law Consultant to The National Federation of Meat and Food Traders (2001).
Personal: English Ski Council Club Instructor.

HODGES, Christopher
CMS Cameron McKenna, London
(020) 7367 3000
Specialisation: Main areas of practice are product liability, product regulatory and safety law and product recall across a wide range of sectors, including medical devices, pharmaceuticals, automotives and electronics. Author 'Multi-Party Actions'. Editor of 'Product Liability: European Laws and Practice', and 'Product Safety', Chapters in 'Product Liability: Law and Insurance', 'The Textbook of Pharmaceutical Medicine' and various other books. Author of 1995 European Commission Study on the Product Liability Directive. Honorary Research Associate, New College, Oxford.
Prof. Memberships: Law Society, CBI Consumer Affairs Committee and Working Parties on Product Liability and General Product Safety, ABHI Council and Legal Committee, International Association of Defense Counsel, Vice-Chair of International Bar Association Committee on Product Liability and Consumer Affairs.
Career: Worked at *Slaughter and May* and *Clifford Chance* before becoming Partner at *McKenna & Co* in 1990.
Personal: Born 19th March 1954. Educated at King Edward's School, Birmingham. Academical Clerk at New College, Oxford. Founder member and Trustee of 'The Sixteen'.

HOLLAND, Barry
Elliotts, Manchester (0161) 834 9933
See under Licensing, p.529

KELLEHER, John
Theodore Goddard, London (020) 7606 8855

MALLEN, Anthony
Blackett Hart & Pratt, Newcastle upon Tyne
(0191) 221 0898

McCOOL, Geraldine
Leigh, Day & Co, Manchester (0161) 832 7722
gmccool@leighday.co.uk
See under Personal Injury, p.648

McDOUGALL, Arundel
Ashurst Morris Crisp, London (020) 7638 1111
Specialisation: Arundel McDougall is a partner in the Product Liability Group at *Ashursts.* His practice focuses on consumer safety, product stewardship and regulatory issues affecting the healthcare, chemical and agrochemical industries. He frequently advises on the product liability aspects of commercial transactions and on the prospects for judicial review of regulatory decisions. He has experience representing claimants or defendants in most forms of dispute resolution. Recently led the defence team for Hoechst Marion Roussel in the Norplant Multi-party litigation which collapsed shortly before trial, and was involved in the defence of the organophosphate (sheep dip) multi-party action on behalf of a major agrochemical producer.
Prof. Memberships: City of London Law Society, International Association of Defence Counsel; Defence Research Institute.
Career: Qualified in November 1978. Became a partner in 1986 at *Rowe & Maw* and joined *Ashursts* as a partner in 2000.
Publications: Monograph; Pharmaceutical Subsidisation and the National Institute of Clinical Excellence, (October 2000); contributed chapter on

Norplant litigation to 'Multi-party Actions' by Christopher Hodges (Oxford University Press 2001). **Personal:** MA (Hons) Christ Church Oxford, 1972. Married with two children, lives in London. Interests: Rugby, rowing, running, music and field sports.

MEERAN, Richard
Leigh, Day & Co, London (020) 7650 1200
See under Personal Injury, p.648

MELTZER, John
Lovells, London (020) 7296 2000
john.meltzer@lovells.com
Specialisation: Main areas of practice are product liability litigation and product safety regulation. Particular experience in defending multi-party claims. Currently representing pharmaceutical companies in the MMR vaccine group action. Also has experience defending cross-border product liability claims. Has assisted UK companies in the co-ordination of the defence of claims in jurisdictions outside the UK including the US, Canada and Australia. As well as defending claims, advises on non-contentious issues such as product safety, risk management, labelling, product recalls, crisis management and media handling. This work is often for clients who have to deal with high profile 'public health' issues, such as EMF (mobile phones), dioxin contamination, ETS ('passive smoking') and BSE. Has also acted in several judicial reviews of the actions of governmental authorities at national and EU levels. Acted for the principal UK tobacco companies in the judicial review proceedings that resulted in the annulment of the EU Directive banning tobacco advertising and sponsorship. Partner in the firm's product liability group whose clients include manufacturers and retailers of motor vehicles (and components), aircraft engines, tobacco, pharmaceutical products, electronic goods, food, guns, toys and beverages.
Prof. Memberships: London Litigation Solicitors Association; International Association of Defense Counsel.
Career: Qualified New South Wales, Australia 1982. Qualified England & Wales 1991. Solicitor at *Freehill Hollongdale & Page* 1984-86. Joined *Lovells* in 1987 and became a partner in 1997.

MURRAY, Marsali
Burness, Edinburgh (0131) 473 6000

PEARL, Simon
Davies Arnold Cooper, London (020) 7936 2222
spearl@dac.co.uk
Specialisation: Partner in Product Liability and Group Action Unit. Main areas of practice are product liability and negligence. Defends pharmaceutical companies and other manufacturers and their insurers. Also handles pharmaceutical regulatory work. Co-ordinating solicitor for the NHS in HIV Haemophilia litigation and Hepatitis C litigation. Defended in the whooping cough vaccine test case, Loveday v. Renton. Represents GSK in the MMR vaccine litigation. Author of a chapter relating to Product Liability Insurance in Lloyd's of London's 'Product Liability and Insurance' publication, edited by Mark Mildred and 'European Product Liability' published by Monitor Press. Writes and speaks widely at conferences.
Prof. Memberships: Law Society. Law Society's Working Party on Group Actions, Medico-legal Society.
Career: Qualified in 1977. Joined *Davies Arnold Cooper* in 1975, becoming a Partner in 1980.
Personal: Born 30th April 1953. Attended Horace Mann School, New York and Birmingham University (LLB (Hons) 1974). Leisure interests include road running, theatre, music and family. Lives in Harpenden, Herts.

PICKERING, John
Irwin Mitchell, Sheffield (0114) 276 7777
pickeringj@irwinmitchell.co.uk
Specialisation: Partner and head of personal injury department; specialist interest in medical negligence, catastrophic injury cases and cases with an international content. Important cases include Hepworth v Kerr (medical negligence case in which a patient suffered paralysis after a routine middle ear operation); Bird v Hussain (a record award for chronic pain suffered as a result of a road traffic accident); Thomas v Charles (head injury sustained abroad, damages £750,000, then a record award for the Canary Islands); Ward v Newalls Insulations and Cape Contractors (the then highest damages award in this country of £750,000 for an asbestos disease case); Hodgson & Others v Imperial Tobacco Ltd and Gallagher & Hergall Ltd (acting on behalf of smoking related lung cancer victims against the major UK tobacco manufacturers case included a Court of Appeal decision on conditional fee agreements); Van Oudenhoven v Griffin Inns Ltd (£950,000 damages for head injury as a result of pub blackboard accident); dealt with the two cerebral palsy cases involved in the Heil v Ranking landmark judgment in the Court of Appeal, namely Warren (£3.1 million damages) and Annabel. Subsequent seperate Court of Appeal hearing on Warren dealt with the question of multiplier; other actions include acting in test cases for industrial deafness and Vibration White Finger, the latter leading to Irwin Mitchell's involvement in the VWF Solicitors Steering group and the subsequent £500 million settlement scheme with British Coal. Currently involved in the Hatfield and Selby train crash cases.
Prof. Memberships: Claimant Solicitors Representative on the Clinical Disputes Forum. Member of and Assessor for the Law Society's Personal Injury Panel. Member of The Law Society's Medical Negligence Panel and the AVMA Medical Negligence Panel. Former Executive Committee Member and a Secretary of APIL. Member of The Board of Governors of The Association of Trial Lawyers of America (ATLA). Past co-chair of International Practice Section and Member of the Board of the Birth Trauma Litigation Group, England and Wales Representative of the Pan European Organisation of Personal Injury Lawyers (PEOPIL).
Career: Articled *Irwin Mitchell*; qualified 1979; partner 1980; National Head of Personal Injury Department of *Irwin Mitchell* and member of the Management Board.
Publications: Co-author of the Clinical Negligence Pre-Litigation Protocol. Regularly lectures in in the UK and abroad on the subjects of Medical Negligence amd Personal Injury. Co-author of 'Jordan's Civil Court Service' and contributor to 'Clinical Negligence in General Practice'.
Personal: Born 1955, resides Sheffield. Married with two children. Interests include theatre, squash, golf and motor racing.

REID, Ron
Shoosmiths, Northampton (01604) 543 000
Specialisation: Main areas of practice are food law, including advice on product liability, trading standards matters and consumer claims. Also advises on health and safety, environmental law and liquor licensing. Under matters of health and safety, Ron has led the launch of *Shoosmiths* Occupational Safety, a department dedicated to offering straight forward advice on all safety matters. Has set up specialist training department to handle the requirements of national and international companies for in-house training and is a regular speaker at conferences and seminars in his areas of specialisation.
Prof. Memberships: Legal advisor to and Honorary Member of Executive Committee of Inter-Company Consumer Affairs Association, a trade association of Consumer Care Managers in the food and drinks manufacturing industry. Member of The Food Law Group. Secretary to both the Food Industry Regional Safety Team and Northamptonshire Occupational Safety & Health Association. Director of the Radon Council.
Career: Qualified in 1983, having previously been a F.I.L.Ex. Joined *Shoosmiths & Harrison* in 1974. Became a partner in 1985.

ROSS, Hilary
Berwin Leighton Paisner, London (020) 7760 1000
hilary.ross@berwinleightonpaisner.com
Specialisation: Partner in Regulatory Department. Advises on EU and UK regulatory compliance issues for foods. Specifically advises US and Canadian manufacturers about how to successfully launch their products in the EU. This includes providing advice on composition, labelling, packaging, claims and advertising. Also advises clients about defending prosecutions for non-compliance issues and represents clients in Court. Has extensive experience in obtaining pre-market approval for novel foods and advises US, Asian and Dutch companies on this matter. Hilary advises many US companies about compliance issues particular to nutraceuticals and food supplements. In the last year has also advised several e-commerce businesses on compliance issues. A specialist in the regulation of GM foods advising manufacturers, retailers and caterers on this topic. Has also been invited to address the Canadian Ministry of Agriculture and the Ontario Ministry of Agriculture on several occasions. Was also asked to address the 8th Asian Congress of Nutrition in Korea on this topic. Regularly participates in the PAGB's one day training course on food supplements.
Prof. Memberships: Food Law Group, European Food Law Association. Food & Drink Federation, President of the London Young Solicitors Group 1996-97.
Career: Qualified in Scotland in 1993; Obtained English Practicing Certificate in April 1994; Solicitor in pharmaceutical department of *McKenna & Co* 1993-95; Associate in Litigation Department of International law firm *Sonnenschein* 1995-98; Joined *Paisner & Co* in 1998. Partner, *Berwin Leighton Paisner* 2001.
Publications: Has recently authored a report for Monitor Law Press called 'Novel Foods: A guide to the Law & Technology of GMOs in Europe'.
Personal: Born 25 April 1969; Graduated from Glasgow University 1991 with an Upper Second Class Honours Degree in Medical Law and Ethics. Lives in London and enjoys dining out, socialising

with friends, hunting for antiques and going to the cinema.

SAYERS, Shane
Kennedys, London (020) 7638 3688

SHERRINGTON, Patrick
Lovells, London (020) 7296 2000
patrick.sherrington@lovells.com
See under Litigation, p.581

SMITH, Hugh
Andrew M. Jackson & Co, Hull (01482) 325242
Specialisation: Substantial area of practice involves retail law covering Trading Standards, Health and Safety, Consumer Protection and Consumer Safety. Particular expertise in the vitamin and fish industry. Commercial litigation work includes contractual disputes both international and domestic, company and partnership disputes, commercial property disputes, professional negligence, defamation and passing off. Represents finance houses in respect of consumer complaints/recoveries.
Prof. Memberships: Member of the Law Society and the Food Law Group. Also an ADR mediator.
Career: Admitted 1983. Joined present firm in 1989, becoming a partner in 1991 in charge of the commercial litigation division.
Personal: Born 16.10.59. Attended Nottingham University (LLB Hons).

SPRING, Paul
Mills Selig, Belfast (028) 9024 3878
paul.spring@nilaw.com
See under Litigation, p.582

STEWART, Brian J.C.
O'Reilly Stewart, Belfast (028) 9032 1000
oreillystewart@dnet.co.uk
Specialisation: Specialises in product liability defence and insurance defence generally, including pharmaceuticals.
Prof. Memberships: Member of the Council of the Law Society of Northern Ireland. Former Chairman of the Belfast Solicitors' Association. Member of the International Association of Defence Counsel.
Career: Qualified 1978. Admitted to the Republic of Ireland Roll of Solicitors 1991.

TUCKER, Andrew
Irwin Mitchell, Sheffield (0114) 276 7777
Specialisation: Litigation in respect of products giving rise to injury, particularly pharmaceutical products, medical devices, experience of multi-party litigation both product related and arising from transport disasters and occupational disease. Acted for Plaintiffs in many high profile cases including: Opren, Dalkon Shield, Benzodiazepines, Manchester Aircrash, "Herald of Free Enterprise", Kegworth Aircrash, "Marchioness"/Bowbelle" collision, North Cornwall Water Pollution, Armley Asbestos, Human Growth Hormone/Creutzfeldt-Jacob Disease, tobacco, silicone implants, Mineworkers V.W.F. and Mineworkers Respiratory Disease.
Prof. Memberships: Law Society, Association of Personal Injury Lawyers, South Yorkshire Medico Legal Society, American Trial Lawyers Association, Australian Plaintiff Lawyers Association.
Career: Articled *Wallace Mitchell*, Nottingham. Qualified 1985. Partner, *Irwin Mitchell*, 1988.
Personal: Born October 1960, University of Liverpool, LL.B. Lives North Derbyshire.

TYLER, Mark
CMS Cameron McKenna, London 020 7367 3000
mlt@cmck.com
See under Health & Safety, p.416

WARE, Anne
Davies Arnold Cooper, London (020) 7293 4062
aware@dac.co.uk
Specialisation: Specialist in product liability litigation with particular expertise in mass tort claims. Major pharmaceutical related litigation experience includes Pertussis, Opren, Benzodiazepines, Lariam; current caseload includes medical device claims; environmental and multi-jurisdictional litigation. Other areas include medical negligence; complex or unusual medically related and personal injury actions; work related stress, sexual harassment and abuse claims; veterinary, cosmetic and food product related claims.

WARNOCK, Owen
Eversheds, Norwich (01603) 272727
owenwarnock@eversheds.com
See under Employment, p.343

WILSON, Michael
Elliott Duffy Garrett, Belfast (028) 9024 5034
michael.wilson@edgsolicitors.co.uk
See under Insolvency/Corporate Recovery, p.478

YOUNG, David A
Eversheds, Birmingham (0121) 232 1000
davidyoung@eversheds.com
Specialisation: Partner in Litigation Department. Acts principally for retail and leisure clients. Work covers all aspects of food, environment, health and safety, product liability and trading law. Acts for a number of recognised operators.
Prof. Memberships: Law Society, Food Law Group.
Career: Qualified in 1984. Became a Partner at *Eversheds* in 1993.
Personal: Born 11th October 1959. Educated at Solihull School 1971-78, University College, London 1978-81 and The College of Law, Chancery Lane 1981-82. Leisure time devoted to his children and partner, sport and travel. Lives Warwick.

PROFESSIONAL NEGLIGENCE

OVERVIEW: The London professional negligence section is split into legal, financial, insurance and construction although there has been a significant increase in negligence claims arising from areas such as IT consultancy and educational psychology. Mis-selling of pensions also continues to generate work. The run-off of SIF has caused some changes to the London ratings; the most successful are those that have secured appointments on to the insurance panels. This diversification has led to firm's targeting the area. Among those our researchers anticipate for inclusion in forthcoming editions of the guide are Richards Butler, which has done work for Bar Mutual, Eversheds and Hill Dickinson, which has successfully won places on the Zurich and CGNU panels. The range of firms featured in London is wide, encompassing those that specialise in professional negligence with a high volume of claims, and those that undertake a relatively small number of complex, high value matters. In the regions, SIF panel cuts have had a dramatic impact resulting in some of those whose mainstay was this work to drop out of our rankings while others reap the benefits.

RESEARCH APPROVED BY BMRB: *For this edition,* Chambers' *researchers conducted 6,552 interviews – 4,419 with law firms, 554 with barristers and 1,579 with clients.*

The validity of the research was scrutinised by BMRB International, who audited both the methodology and the results at our offices in July 2001. They interviewed Chambers' *researchers and cross-checked sample interviews. Details of the audit appear on page 7.*

LONDON

LEADERS ACROSS THE BOARD

Barlow Lyde & Gilbert (see firm details p.870) Universally respected firm whose quality of work is portrayed by a competitor as "*outstanding, experienced and thoroughly excellent.*" Financial cases are a forte and it is felt it has " *a tight hold on accountants work.*" Covering every area of professional negligence including surveyors and stock-brokers, the firm is also making inroads into the post-SIF solicitors market on panels such as Zurich and Bar Mutual. A number of leading individuals stand out in this "*dominant*" team: **Stuart Hall** (see p.696) is involved in large accountants negligence cases including acting for Coopers & Lybrand in the Bermuda Fire & Marine Litigation. **David Arthur** (see p.694), "*well known for years,*" continues to work for PricewaterhouseCoopers, and has been involved in a number of claims against insurance brokers. "*Top notch*" **Richard Dedman** (see p.695) received an impressive level of endorsement in the course of this year's research, and he heads up the firm's solicitor's liability practice. **Ian Jenkins** (see p.696) is a senior figure at the firm, while interviewees commended **Michael Wilson** (see p.698) for his expertise in the field of financial institutions. Respected **Sarah Clover** (see p.694) was the lead partner in co-ordinating solicitors' responses to claims by Nationwide Building Society. **Clients:** Ernst & Young; PwC.

Reynolds Porter Chamberlain (see firm details p.1106) Received effusive praise from solicitors and barristers during research, including plaudits such as "*the most pragmatic firm in London*" and "*one of those rare firms where all the people there are efficient and terribly personable.*" Seen to enjoy "*all-round strengths,*" including particular expertise in legal negligence, the firm is on several panels including Zurich, Hiscox, Denham Direct and Bar Mutual. The firm was recently involved in large Directors and Officers claims in London, and insurance work for Heath Lambert and Lloyd's insurance brokers. Recently recruited **Stuart White** (see p.697) from Hextall Erskine is thought to have bolstered a robust team of highly regarded lawyers. **Paul Nicholas** (see p.696) is popular among his peers, and judged to employ a "*commercial sense as well as a feel for the way cases will go.*" **Simon Greenley** (see p.488) has expertise in financial professional negligence, competitors acknowledge he is "*a real rainmaker, one of those people that can walk into a room and come away with ten instructions.*" **Barney Micklem** (see p.696) is an "*impressive performer*" with specialism in surveyors and solicitors cases. **Clients:** Zurich; Hiscox; Denham Direct.

FIRMS IN ALPHABETICAL ORDER

Beale and Company (see firm details p.874) On panels for ACE and WREN, this firm has displayed a particular expertise in construction claims, although it has continued to diversify and is handling solicitors' negligence work on CGNU panel as well as matters arising from accountants. Described as "*head and shoulders above everyone else for construction,*" it counts leading individuals **John Ward** (see p.697) and **Antony Smith** (see p.697) amongst its number. Involved in the London Millennium Bridge matter, and a large claim against an engineer regarding a highway in South East Asia. **Clients:** Engineers; insurance panels.

Beachcroft Wansbroughs (see firm details p.872) Particularly rated for its legal negligence work, the London branch of this national firm is felt to field "*a terrific team.*" Involved in a wide variety of professional negligence cases including brokers, valuers, architects, accountants and solicitors, the group has witnessed an increase in education liability cases. On the panel for AIG, it has recently been active for the diminishing SIF panel. **Alison MacLennan** (see p.696) is described by our interviewees as "*one of the best professionals in the business*" and " *pretty unflappable.*" **Clients:** Insurance panels.

Berrymans Lace Mawer (see firm details p.877) The firm remains respected in construction and has also moved up a notch in our financial table after heavy endorsement from our interviewees. The London branch of this national firm is seen to "*communicate well*" while clients value the level of partner contact. Continuing to act for a range of core professions including accountants and surveyors, the firm is now branching out to encompass several other professions such as the police, education and computer consultants. The group was involved in the Heathrow fire debacle, acting for a contractor, and was also instructed on issues arising from a proctor's review at Oxford University concerning an undergraduate who had made race discrimination allegations. Charlotte Capstick is the lead practitioner at the firm in this area. **Clients:** Surveyors; accountants; educational institutions.

Clyde & Co (see firm details p.921) One of the firms in our professional negligence overview that deals with a small number of high quality, complex matters and is frequently seen by our interviewees on brokers cases. It acts for insurers in London and overseas, and regularly advises the E&O insurers of major city law firms. The group also receives instructions from the big five accountants and solicitors and occasionally acts for Bar Mutual. Chris Harris is one of four partners substantially involved in this area. **Clients:** Insurers.

CMS Cameron McKenna (see firm details p.922) Particularly well known for the work it undertakes for insurance brokers, the firm has joined our legal listing as it has taken advantage of the changing insurance market, winning a place on the panels of QBE, Independent and ACE. The group also handles a significant amount of work for accountants, acting for the Institute of Chartered Accountants in England. **Stephen Tester** (see p.697) is widely praised as "*a leading light.*" **Mark Elborne** (see p.695) "*has a huge name in the area,*" and **Belinda Schofield** (see p.697) ("*knows what she's doing*") received a healthy level of commendation during research. **Clients:** Insurance panels; accountancy firms.

Denton Wilde Sapte (see firm details p.939) Developing its profile in this field, one barrister described the firm as "*excellent and trying to do more.*" Its involvement in the current spate of film finance cases has been particularly noted by our interviewees. The firm has expertise in D&O (often with a South American or Spanish angle), insurance brokers, pensions advisers and computer consultants. It recently settled a $30 million claim regarding computer consultants in California. Michelle George is a partner involved in this area. **Clients:** Octavian Syndicate 702; AIG; Ace; Newline; SVB Syndicate 1212.

Fishburn Morgan Cole (see firm details p.959) Construction is an area of particular expertise for this firm, perceived to be "*doing jolly well in it.*" The group covers the range of professions including 'new market' matters such as cases arising from computer consultants. John Cayton has specialism in architects and engineers and the group is respected for its number of high quality, multi-million pound cases. **Clients:** Architects; engineers; surveyors.

Herbert Smith (see firm details p.993) Herbert Smith's involvement in this area is aptly summarised by one interviewee: "*top notch, you pay for their intricate knowledge of the case.*" Professional negligence comprises part of this outstanding litigation practice. Two new professional negligence partners, Paul Lewis and Howard Watson, were made up in spring 2001. Highly rated in insurance, the group is often involved in work for the big five accountancy firms. It is representing Coopers & Lybrand Singapore in connection with the litigation brought against it by the auditors of the Barings group following its collapse. Acting for Amey Rail Ltd and its insurers in relation to the Ladbroke Grove accident. **Clients:** Royal & SunAlliance; Willis Group.

Hextall Erskine Perceived to have suffered from the loss of Stuart White to Reynolds Porter Chamberlain, the group nevertheless remains respected for its niche strengths in construction. The firm received such commendations as "*a smaller outfit, undoubtedly pretty clued up*" which is thought to contain lawyers with "*specialist knowledge.*" David Hadfield is an active member of the team. **Clients:** Engineers; surveyors.

Ince & Co (see firm details p.1008) Has particular strength in legal negligence and was described by one insurance panel as "*a technically skilled firm.*" Perceived by peers to be "*professional and commercial,*" it was involved in the Elton John and PricewaterhouseCoopers case, and continues to advise various insurance companies. It acted for an insurance broker and O&E underwriters in relation to a £6 million broker negligence

PROFESSIONAL NEGLIGENCE: LEGAL • London		Ptnrs	Assts
1	Barlow Lyde & Gilbert	22	47
	Reynolds Porter Chamberlain	27	75
2	Beachcroft Wansbroughs	8	19
	Lovells	20	33
3	Ince & Co	7	15
	Pinsent Curtis Biddle	6	16
4	CMS Cameron McKenna	15	44
	Kennedys	22	21

PROFESSIONAL NEGLIGENCE: FINANCIAL • London		Ptnrs	Assts
1	Barlow Lyde & Gilbert	22	47
2	CMS Cameron McKenna	15	44
	Herbert Smith	23	35
	Reynolds Porter Chamberlain	27	75
3	Berrymans Lace Mawer	4	10
	Lovells	20	33
	Rowe & Maw	18	42
4	Denton Wilde Sapte	4	8

PROFESSIONAL NEGLIGENCE: INSURANCE • London		Ptnrs	Assts
1	Barlow Lyde & Gilbert	22	47
2	Reynolds Porter Chamberlain	27	75
3	CMS Cameron McKenna	15	44
4	Clyde & Co	4	24
	Herbert Smith	23	35
	Rowe & Maw	18	42
5	Squire & Co	8	14
6	Beachcroft Wansbroughs	23	35
	Davies Arnold Cooper	9	35
	Fishburn Morgan Cole	10	18
	Ince & Co	7	15

PROFESSIONAL NEGLIGENCE: CONSTRUCTION • London		Ptnrs	Assts
1	Beale and Company	6	4
	Fishburn Morgan Cole	10	18
	Rowe & Maw	18	42
2	Berrymans Lace Mawer	4	10
	CMS Cameron McKenna	15	44
	Kennedys	22	21
	Reynolds Porter Chamberlain	27	75
3	Davies Arnold Cooper	9	35
4	Barlow Lyde & Gilbert	22	47
	Hextall Erskine	7	4
5	Vizard Oldham	5	4
	Williams Davies Meltzer	n/a	n/a

This book is the product of 6,552 1/2 hour interviews. See p.7 for BMRB audit.
Within each band, firms are listed alphabetically.

LEADING INDIVIDUALS	
1 ARTHUR David Barlow Lyde & Gilbert	HALL Stuart Barlow Lyde & Gilbert
NICHOLAS Paul Reynolds Porter Chamberlain	
TESTER Stephen CMS Cameron McKenna	
2 CONNOLLY Sean Rowe & Maw	DEDMAN Richard Barlow Lyde & Gilbert
ELBORNE Mark CMS Cameron McKenna	
GREENLEY Simon Reynolds Porter Chamberlain	
MICKLEM Barney Reynolds Porter Chamberlain	
TROTTER John Lovells	WARD John Beale and Company
WHITE Stuart Reynolds Porter Chamberlain	
3 BARRETT Geoff Mills & Reeve	CLOVER Sarah Barlow Lyde & Gilbert
JENKINS Ian Barlow Lyde & Gilbert	
MACLENNAN Alison Beachcroft Wansbroughs	
REGAN Michael Rowe & Maw	
SCHOFIELD Belinda CMS Cameron McKenna	
SEYMOUR Michael Lovells	SMITH Antony Beale and Company
THOMAS Nick Kennedys	WILSON Michael Barlow Lyde & Gilbert
WYLDE Peter Irwin Mitchell	

See individuals' profiles p.694

claim. David Rutherford and Andrew Otley are partners specialising in professional negligence. **Clients:** Bar Mutual; St Paul; Heath Lambert Group.

Kennedys (see firm details p.1018) A "*superb, user-friendly*" firm that handles claims for most professions. It has reaped the benefits of SIF's disbandment, launching a new IT based solicitors claims service with Alexander Forbes. **Nick Thomas** (see p.697) is a senior member of the team. Instructed by Professional Indemnity at Lloyds on behalf of the successful defendant in the Curry's Group v Martin case. The firm is also involved in a multi-million pound claim regarding North Sea Pipelines. **Clients:** Insurers; architects.

Lovells (see firm details p.1044) Used by SIF for high quality blue-chip work, this firm is a different animal to many in our listings as it tends to be active in a small number of what have been described as "*high profile one-offs.*" Respected by peers and clients alike, the "*charming*" **John Trotter** (see p.697) is the head of the group and **Michael Seymour** (see p.697) is "*a serious player in this field.*" **Clients:** Solicitors; insurers.

Pinsent Curtis Biddle (see firm details p.1098) The recent merger has combined Pinsent Curtis' Bar Mutual instructions with Biddle's well respected expertise. Competitors view the group as "*strong players,*" recommended for its legal negligence work. The firm was involved in RBS v Etridge and continues to manage class actions on behalf of SIF. Anson Game is head of the department. **Clients:** St Paul; Bar Mutual; Marsh.

Rowe & Maw (see firm details p.1113) A highly visible and respected firm that appears in all of our tables with the exception of legal. Described by one client as "*excellent on cases when investigation into fraud or policy issues is involved.*" The firm acted in United Pan-Europe Communications v Deutsche Bank, and Morris & Others v Bank of America. Among its number **Sean Connolly** (see p.694) has the highest profile, often commended to our researchers as an "*outstanding*" lawyer. **Michael Regan** (see p.207) is also well known as a "*good, sensible*" lawyer. **Clients:** AIG (Europe) UK; Chubb Insurance.

Squire & Co (see firm details p.1137) A small yet renowned firm that is most often seen acting on complex insurance broker cases. Competitors feel that this primarily litigation outfit can be "*quite aggressive,*" but there is no doubt that on its clients' behalf, "*it does a high quality job.*" The firm's respected following of clients encompasses a range of professions, including architects, engineers, surveyors, IFAs and barristers. **Clients:** The Admiral; Bar Mutual.

Vizard Oldham (see firm details p.1169) Respected by our interviewees for its construction-related work and this forms the backbone of its practice, typically acting for engineers, architects and surveyors. It is currently involved in two major claims relating to the design and construction of hotels and is acting for one of the parties in a dispute arising from the design of a tram in Sheffield. At its heart lies a strong core of insurance expertise and it is also involved in claims for brokers and accountants. "*Seen a lot*" by peers, it has recently entered into a claims handling arrangement with HSBC. **Clients:** Insurers in the Lloyds market; HSBC; Major composite insurer.

Williams Davies Meltzer This smaller firm is described to our researchers as "*successful at construction.*" Peter Court and the team are involved in professional negligence work for various professions, including accountants and surveyors.

Other Notable Practitioners At **Mills & Reeve**, **Geoff Barrett** (see p.694) does not have an enormous profile but has a solid reputation and is felt to be "*good.*" **Peter Wylde** (see p.698) of **Irwin Mitchell** continues to be highly commended.

THE SOUTH

PROFESSIONAL NEGLIGENCE • The South	Ptnrs	Assts
1 Blake Lapthorn Fareham	2	2
Cripps Harries Hall Tunbridge Wells	3	5
2 Bond Pearce Southampton	2	3

LEADING INDIVIDUALS
1 BROADIE Charles Cripps Harries Hall
PORTLOCK Richard Blake Lapthorn
TRAYHURN Neil Bond Pearce

This book is the product of 6,552 1/2 hour interviews. See p.7 for BMRB audit.

Within each band, firms are listed alphabetically. *See individuals' profiles p.694*

Blake Lapthorn (see firm details p.886) This firm remains respected despite the loss of SIF work, and was described by one referee as "*a really excellent product.*" It is currently broadening its client base, with independent financial advisors being a growth area, although defending claims against solicitors remains its forte. The firm also receives instructions concerning the accountancy profession and surveyors and has been involved in pensions litigation. **Richard Portlock** is a respected practitioner and has been selected to be on the PASS panel. **Clients:** Valuers; accountants; IFAs.

Cripps Harries Hall (see firm details p.927) In the enviable position of being the only firm in the South East not to have been dropped by SIF, it continues to specialise in solicitors' negligence work. Felt to have "*really emerged*" of late, the group is commended by clients as "*sensible, robust and trustworthy.*" It has experienced an increasing number of commercial cases where insurers have looked beyond their London relationships. The group has managed dispute resolutions, including a number of claims against a major high street lender, and is currently co-ordinating the management of 120 claims brought by another similar company. **Charles Broadie** (see p.694) is recognised as a leading individual in the field. **Clients:** SIF; insurers.

Bond Pearce (see firm details p.888) Coming to prominence in this region, the firm is successfully receiving instructions from new insurers, as well as obtaining work from SIF in run-off. Describe by a barrister as "*focused,*" the firm is also said to have "*a well spread client base.*" **Neil Trayhurn** (see p.697) is respected by his peers. He and the group have particular expertise in defending solicitors and matters involving surveyors and IFAs. **Clients:** SIF; Royal & Sun Alliance; Zurich Professional.

THAMES VALLEY

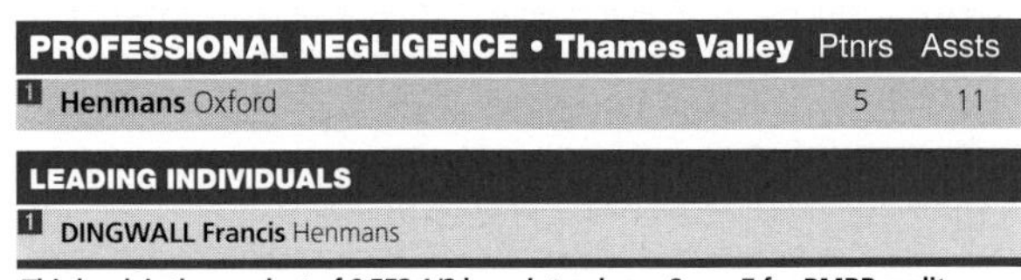

PROFESSIONAL NEGLIGENCE • Thames Valley	Ptnrs	Assts
1 Henmans Oxford	5	11

LEADING INDIVIDUALS
1 DINGWALL Francis Henmans

This book is the product of 6,552 1/2 hour interviews. See p.7 for BMRB audit.

Within each band, firms are listed alphabetically. *See individuals' profiles p.694*

Henmans (see firm details p.991) "*First class,*" this firm attracted the highest praise from barristers, solicitors and clients alike, one of the latter describing it as "*proactive and focused.*" It has a dedicated professional negligence team headed by "*sound operator*" **Francis Dingwall** (see p.695). The firm has successfully made inroads into the new solicitors' insurer market with places on a number of panels constituting the bulk of its instructions. The balance remains with surveyors, civil engineers, architects and insurance brokers. It acted for a number of defendant solicitors against Nationwide Building Society. **Clients:** SIF; St Paul; ACE.

SOUTH WEST

PROFESSIONAL NEGLIGENCE • South West	Ptnrs	Assts
1 Beachcroft Wansbroughs Bristol	5	11
Bond Pearce Bristol, Exeter, Plymouth	5	9
2 CMS Cameron McKenna Bristol	2	7
3 Burges Salmon Bristol	3	6
SJ Cornish Tiverton	n/a	n/a

LEADING INDIVIDUALS	
1 CHALLANDS Richard Bond Pearce	CORNISH Sarah SJ Cornish
HEGARTY Simon CMS Cameron McKenna	SALOMONSEN Erik Bond Pearce
2 PEACOCK Ian Bond Pearce	

This book is the product of 6,552 1/2 hour interviews. See p.7 for BMRB audit.

Within each band, firms are listed alphabetically. *See individuals' profiles p.694*

Beachcroft Wansbroughs (see firm details p.872) The Bristol branch of this national firm is seen to be "*well established*" in the field. It has successfully obtained a position on several new panels and is perceived by our interviewees to field a "*strong team*" covering a "*broad ranging*" set of instructions. Paul Redfern is part of the professional negligence team. **Clients:** Norwich Union panel; Blackmores Brokers.

Bond Pearce (see firm details p.888) Competitors agree that "*you can't knock the quality*" of this offering. **Erik Salomonsen** (see p.696) and **Richard Challands** (see p.694) are respected among their peers while **Ian Peacock** (see p.696) received warm commendations for his expertise in work for IFAs. The firm has won instructions from the new insurance panels and is rated for its work in legal, construction and financial negligence. **Clients:** SIF; Royal & Sun Alliance; Zurich Professional.

CMS Cameron McKenna (see firm details p.922) The firm has recently been specialising in construction and accountancy work and, as a result of the disbanded SIF, has acquired solicitors work to add to claims against professionals such as architects, engineers, academics and auctioneers. The firm has particular expertise in Directors and Officers claims. It successfully defended engineers in a multi-million pound claim brought by a hospital concerning an incinerator project. "*Sensible and able*" **Simon Hegarty** (see p.696) is endorsed by our interviewees. **Clients:** St Paul; RJ Wallace; Markel.

Burges Salmon (see firm details p.902) Particularly praised by the bar as a "*fantastic team, with real strength and depth*" in the light of its work on the Nationwide case. It services a number of corporate and private clients, and has expertise in claimant work alongside its defendant work for Bar Mutual. A recent highlight was the Paragon Finance case, which settled half way through its course. Paul Haggett is part of the team. **Clients:** Bar Mutual; private clients.

SJ Cornish (see firm details p.925) An insurance litigation practice that includes "*feisty*" **Sarah Cornish**, who is thought by peers to "*know her stuff.*" The firm largely acts for construction professionals as well as accountants, brokers and Channel Island advocates. Opened a London office at the start of the year manned by Richard Osborne, with a leaning towards the 'City' type negligence cases. **Clients:** Construction professionals; accountants.

WALES

PROFESSIONAL NEGLIGENCE • Wales	Ptnrs	Assts
1 Morgan Cole Cardiff	3	4

LEADING INDIVIDUALS
1 HUGHES-WILLIAMS Clare Morgan Cole

This book is the product of 6,552 1/2 hour interviews. See p.7 for BMRB audit.

Within each band, firms are listed alphabetically. *See individuals' profiles p.694*

Morgan Cole (see firm details p.1074) This widely respected firm is on many panels and **Clare Hughes-Williams**' "*competent but sensible approach*" has attracted a following among insurers. Our interviewees claimed that these lawyers are "*definitely the people in Wales to turn to,*" and they act for solicitors, barristers, building professionals and accountants. **Clients:** Insurance panels; accountants.

MIDLANDS

Browne Jacobson (see firm details p.898) "*Straightforward, logical and bright*" **Robert Ridgwell** (see p.696) is key to much of this firm's profile. The respected group has recently acted in multi-jurisdictional claims against a high-profile software house, and was involved in policy drafting for the solicitors market. The firm is involved in claims against a range of professions although notable recent cases involved accountants and a hydrology consultant. **Clients:** St Paul; Hiscox; Norwich Union.

Pinsent Curtis Biddle (see firm details p.1098) The firm has recently opened a professional negligence unit in Leeds led by Karen Eckstein, a tax specialist, while the "*excellent*" Birmingham office retains the higher profile. The group acts predominantly for solicitors but is also involved with financial advisors and intermediaries. **Andrew Paton** (see p.82) and **Andrew Long** (see p.696) are a widely praised duo; the former maintains a strong reputation as a mediator, and the latter is described as "*intellectually outstanding.*" **Clients:** SIF; PYV Ltd; New York Life.

Beachcroft Wansbroughs (see firm details p.872) The group acts for major

PROFESSIONAL NEGLIGENCE • Midlands	Ptnrs	Assts
1 **Browne Jacobson** Nottingham	5	9
2 **Pinsent Curtis Biddle** Birmingham	4	16
3 **Beachcroft Wansbroughs** Birmingham	3	6
Wragge & Co Birmingham	6	6

LEADING INDIVIDUALS
1 **LONG Andrew** Pinsent Curtis Biddle
PATON Andrew Pinsent Curtis Biddle
RIDGWELL Robert Browne Jacobson
2 **HICK Mark** Wragge & Co

This book is the product of 6,552 1/2 hour interviews. See p.7 for BMRB audit.

Within each band, firms are listed alphabetically. *See individuals' profiles p.694*

firms of solicitors on a variety of claims and has continued its SIF run-off work. Commentators perceived a stronger presence in Leeds. Philip Steel is an active partner in this "*broad ranging*" team, which has recently been involved in liability cases for accountants, surveyors and architects. **Clients:** SIF; architects; surveyors.

Wragge & Co (see firm details p.1189) Extremely well-regarded by peers, this firm is described as enjoying a "*first class reputation,*" with expertise in financial and construction negligence, as well as employment protection liability and warranty and indemnity claims. It has recently been involved in a £150 million D&O claim and a substantial accountancy claim. The group handles international work, and acts for the insurers of Italian architects and engineers. Respected **Mark Hick** is credited by peers with "*almost single-handedly building up the professional negligence practice.*" **Clients:** ACE Europe; Chubb Insurance; Royal & SunAlliance.

EAST ANGLIA

PROFESSIONAL NEGLIGENCE • East Anglia	Ptnrs	Assts
1 **Mills & Reeve** Cambridge, Norwich	3	10

LEADING INDIVIDUALS
1 **HODGSON Guy** Mills & Reeve

This book is the product of 6,552 1/2 hour interviews. See p.7 for BMRB audit.

Within each band, firms are listed alphabetically. *See individuals' profiles p.694*

Mills & Reeve (see firm details p.1069) Received effusive praise during research, garnering such typical accolades as having "*marvelous strength and depth in its associates.*" Peers agree that this is a "*fantastic firm, always a pleasure to work with.*" The group has expertise in dealing with educational claims and acts for lawyers, accountants, design consultants and brokers. **Guy Hodgson** (see p.696) is an outstanding regional practitioner, thought to be "*impressive on his feet.*" The firm has recently targeted work involving hi-tech professions. **Clients:** Zurich; Hiscox.

NORTH WEST

PROFESSIONAL NEGLIGENCE • North West	Ptnrs	Assts
1 **James Chapman & Co** Manchester	9	8
Weightmans Liverpool	7	12
2 **Hill Dickinson** Liverpool	5	4
3 **Addleshaw Booth & Co** Manchester	5	4
Elliotts Manchester	3	3

LEADING INDIVIDUALS
1 **MAHER Frank** Weightmans
2 **GAUL Patrick** Weightmans
GRANT Mike Addleshaw Booth & Co
TAYLOR Elisabeth James Chapman & Co

This book is the product of 6,552 1/2 hour interviews. See p.7 for BMRB audit.

Within each band, firms are listed alphabetically. *See **Profiles** on p.694*

James Chapman & Co (see firm details p.1011) Respected by peers, it is also praised by clients as "*an excellent firm, with partners well on top of the situation.*" Offering a "*sensible*" approach, it has retained SIF work and secured appointments to new panels such as Zurich and St Paul. The group was recently involved in defending a £1.5 million fire claim against an insurer that was struck out, and acted in the successful defence of a wasted costs order following the collapse of a £1 million malicious prosecution case brought against a police force. Leading light **Elisabeth Taylor** (see p.697) "*justifies her reputation with a consistent display of quality work.*" **Clients:** St Paul; Zurich; Denham.

Weightmans (see firm details p.1176) In the main this firm handles solicitors work, with further instructions in the fields of accountancy, insolvency and IT consultancy. It has obtained a position on a number of panels and remains well liked by peers and clients. "*Superb*" **Frank Maher** (see p.696) generates admiration with one client describing him as "*proactive and creative - he provides the know-how.*" **Patrick Gaul** (see p.695) is also well respected, felt by some to be "*superb*". **Clients:** Bar Mutual; Zurich Professional; St Paul.

Hill Dickinson (see firm details p.996) Taking advantage of the changes created by the demise of SIF, this firm has obtained work from the new panels. Renowned for its expertise in the veterinary and engineering sector, the firm acted in a case in which a vet was held not to be negligent for a decision not to administer prophylactic antibiotics. Further instructions concern construction professionals. Ruth Lawrence is an active member of the team. **Clients:** ACE Europe; St Pauls.

Addleshaw Booth & Co (see firm details p.853) Thought by its peers to have built up a substantial level of work across a range of professions including engineers, brokers, architects and solicitors. Recent cases included acting for engineers in the replacement of a pier and ferry terminal and a large construction claim in Birmingham. **Mike Grant** (see p.695) joined the firm a year ago from Weightmans and is described as an "*experienced and professional practitioner.*" **Clients:** Insurers.

Elliotts (see firm details p.950) John Groome heads the professional negligence department of this "*very good, small niche practice.*" Recently it has seen an increase in mediations and disputes resolved by ADR and an increase in claims by insurance brokers and accountants. Represented the successful defendant in the Court of Appeal in JD Williams & Co v Michael Hyde & Associates, an important case regarding causation in professional liability claims. Also instructed on an Ascension Island pipeline claim and involved in policy advice interpretation for a number of insurers. **Clients:** Accountants; insurance brokers.

YORKSHIRE

PROFESSIONAL NEGLIGENCE • Yorkshire	Ptnrs	Assts
1 **Beachcroft Wansbroughs** Leeds	5	12
2 **Addleshaw Booth & Co** Leeds	7	7
Hammond Suddards Edge Leeds	3	4
Irwin Mitchell Sheffield	3	8

LEADING INDIVIDUALS
1 **COULSON Edward** Hammond Suddards Edge
DAWSON Jane Hammond Suddards Edge
GREENWOOD Duncan Beachcroft Wansbroughs
WILLIS Michael Beachcroft Wansbroughs

This book is the product of 6,552 1/2 hour interviews. See p.7 for BMRB audit.
Within each band, firms are listed alphabetically. *See individuals' profiles p.694*

Beachcroft Wansbroughs (see firm details p.872) "*Reputable and respectable*" the office of this national firm "*stands out*" as handling "*interesting work.*" Recent cases include a £5 million claim against design consultants relating to a failed watertight floor system, and an £800,000 claim against a surveyor in an alleged overvaluation of a golf course. The group counts two leading lights among its number; the esteemed **Duncan Greenwood** (see p.695) and **Mike Willis** (see p.698) who is thought to be a "*bright man who has a nice touch with clients.*" **Clients:** Accountants; electrical engineers; solicitors.

Addleshaw Booth & Co (see firm details p.853) Although felt not to have as high a profile as its sister office in Manchester, the Leeds team is respected for its involvement in claims against solicitors and valuers. The group is headed by John Gosling. **Clients:** Insurers.

Hammond Suddards Edge (see firm details p.984) A "*super firm to work with*" according to clients while competitors admire its "*fine client base.*" The group has secured its share of panel appointments, acting primarily for insurers. It is also involved in claims against architects and consulting engineers. **Jane Dawson** (see p.695) and **Edward Coulson** (see p.695) elicited warm recommendations during our research. **Clients:** Bar Mutual; ACE Global Markets; Independent.

Irwin Mitchell (see firm details p.1009) The firm stands out in the market with its broad based, dedicated claimant professional negligence unit. Its lawyers are typically recognised as experts in their field, handling claims against solicitors and surveyors, and witnessing growth in the number of financial advisor cases as a result of pension mis-selling. The team includes Louise Sykes and Peter Wylde, who divides his time between Sheffield and London. **Clients:** Ring; HSBC Trust Company; Environment Agency.

NORTH EAST

PROFESSIONAL NEGLIGENCE • North East	Ptnrs	Assts
1 **Crutes** Middlesbrough, Newcastle upon Tyne	6	5
2 **Hay & Kilner** Newcastle upon Tyne	8	3

This book is the product of 6,552 1/2 hour interviews. See p.7 for BMRB audit.
Within each band, firms are listed alphabetically.

Crutes (see firm details p.928) Clear leader in the region and seen by many to be "*way ahead*" of the competition with its breadth of coverage. It has been active in matters arising from architects and accountants. Helen Ager is a leading member of the team. Recent work involved acting for a clinic regarding a piercing mishap, and a case that went to the Court of Appeal concerning the importance of terms for borrowers when renewing lending. **Clients:** SIF; St Paul.

Hay & Kilner A respected firm that acts for and against accountants, architects, surveyors and solicitors. Ros Sparrow is a member of the team, whose recent cases include the resolution of a claim brought by a victim of the Piper Alpha disaster against his agents, including quantum specialists and solicitors. Another was a claim against an in-house architectural department for a local authority in relation to the development of an estate of 101 dwellings/sheltered housing units. **Clients:** Architects; accountants; surveyors.

SCOTLAND

PROFESSIONAL NEGLIGENCE • Scotland	Ptnrs	Assts
1 **Simpson & Marwick WS** Edinburgh	3	7
2 **Dundas & Wilson CS** Edinburgh	1	4
3 **Balfour & Manson** Edinburgh	7	1
Morison Bishop Glasgow	2	4
4 **Brechin Tindal Oatts** Glasgow	2	3
Brodies WS Edinburgh	2	3

LEADING INDIVIDUALS	
1 **ANDERSON Peter** Simpson & Marwick WS	**MACLEOD Colin** Dundas & Wilson CS
WELSH John Morison Bishop	
2 **ABERNETHY Pamela** Simpson & Marwick	**ALLAN Derek** Brechin Tindal Oatts
DONALD Hugh Shepherd & Wedderburn	**KENNEDY Spencer** Balfour & Manson
WILLIAMSON David Brodies WS	

This book is the product of 6,552 1/2 hour interviews. See p.7 for BMRB audit.
Within each band, firms are listed alphabetically. *See individuals' profiles p.694*

Simpson & Marwick WS (see firm details p.1133) The leading professional negligence firm in Scotland, it acts for the full range of professionals and is seen to be "*ahead of the game, winning instructions from all over.*" Recent matters include acting on a case of duty of care involving an engineer. Clients number architects, insurance services and IFAs. **Peter Anderson** and **Pamela Abernethy** are described by one client as "*the best of the best in Scotland.*" **Clients:** Engineers; architects; solicitors.

Dundas & Wilson CS (see firm details p.947) A close challenger in the Scottish market, the firm displays expertise in construction and engineering matters, and is on the Association of Consulting Engineers scheme. It also handles cases arising from lawyers and surveyors negligence claims. Typical work involves negotiation and settlement of claims and high value multi-party disputes. **Colin Macleod** is on the Law Society panel in Scotland and is held in high esteem by peers. **Clients:** Composite insurers; London Market Insurers.

Balfour & Manson (see firm details p.869) Acting for both defenders and pursuers, this practice fields the highly rated **Spencer Kennedy** (see p.696). The firm recently successfully completed an insurance broker's claim, resulting in a six figure settlement. **Clients:** Architects; brokers; solicitors.

Morison Bishop (see firm details p.1075) Renowned for its engineers work. The team includes **John Welsh** (see p.209) described by his peers as "*a straightforward, decent player.*" He is on the panel of the Law Society in Scotland and the firm acts for ACE, as well as construction clients, engineers, architects, surveyors and accountants. **Clients:** ACE; accountants.

Brechin Tindal Oatts (see firm details p.893) This firm largely owes its reputation to **Derek Allan** (see p.694) who has secured a place on the Law Society of Scotland panel and is thought to attract a large volume of instructions to the firm. The group handles defender and pursuer work, acting mainly for solicitors, with the balance made up by surveyors and accountants. **Clients:** Solicitors; surveyors; accountants.

Brodies WS (see firm details p.896) Although lower in profile for its professional negligence work, the firm enjoys the presence of "*leading light*" **David Williamson** (see p.584) on its team. Mostly undertakes solicitors work; the firm also acts for surveyors and accountants. **Clients:** Solicitors; surveyors; accountants.

Other Notable Practitioners **Hugh Donald** (see p.695) of **Shepherd & Wedderburn WS** was recommended to *Chambers'* researchers as "*worth a mention.*" He was recently appointed as a panel solicitor.

NORTHERN IRELAND

PROFESSIONAL NEGLIGENCE • Northern Ireland	Ptnrs	Assts
1 Agnew, Andress, Higgins Belfast	2	2
Carson McDowell Belfast	2	2
McKinty & Wright Belfast	2	4

LEADING INDIVIDUALS
1 TURTLE Brian Carson McDowell

This book is the product of 6,552 1/2 hour interviews. See p.7 for BMRB audit.

Within each band, firms are listed alphabetically. *See individuals' profiles p.694*

Agnew, Andress, Higgins A new entrant to the rankings, this firm specialises in solicitors professional negligence matters, often acting for the defendant. Seamus Agnew is on the Northern Ireland Solicitor's panel. **Clients:** Solicitors.

Carson McDowell (see firm details p.909) The firm houses the highly respected **Brian Turtle** (see p.583). A place on the Northern Ireland Solicitors indemnity panel provides the bulk of the instructions for this firm. **Clients:** Solicitors.

McKinty & Wright (see firm details p.1063) On the solicitor's Professional Indemnity Scheme for Northern Ireland. The firm's wide ranging client base includes structural engineers, surveyors, valuers, accountants and brokers. Lester Doake is a partner involved in this area. **Clients:** Solicitors; surveyors; valuers.

LEADERS IN PROFESSIONAL NEGLIGENCE

ABERNETHY, Pamela
Simpson & Marwick WS, Edinburgh (0131) 557 1545

ALLAN, Derek
Brechin Tindal Oatts, Glasgow (0141) 221 8012 dja@bto.co.uk
Specialisation: Principal area of practice is professional negligence, acting on behalf of insurance companies and corporate lenders in professional indemnity claims against solicitors, accountants and surveyors. Mainly defender orientated, but some pursuer/claimant work.
Prof. Memberships: The Law Society of Scotland. The Scottish Law Agents Society.
Career: Joined *Brechin Robb* as apprentice in 1978. Partner since 1984.
Personal: Golf, tennis, walking.

ANDERSON, Peter
Simpson & Marwick WS, Edinburgh (0131) 557 1545

ARTHUR, David
Barlow Lyde & Gilbert, London (020) 7247 2277 darthur@blg.co.uk
Specialisation: Professional negligence disciplinary and regulatory experience involving accountants, insurance brokers, solicitors and financial institutions. Also insurance and reinsurance matters including drafting and construction of policy wordings.
Prof. Memberships: Law Society, International Bar Association, B.I.L.A.
Career: Qualified in 1978. Joined *Barlow Lyde & Gilbert* in 1981. Became a partner in 1984.

BARRETT, Geoff
Mills & Reeve, London (020) 7648 9230 geoff.barrett@mills-reeve.com
Specialisation: Partner in Insurance and Reinsurance Group. Principal areas of practice involve acting in claims and disputes for Insurers and Reinsurers. Has acted in numerous disputes involving professionals such as accountants, financial advisers, insurance brokers, members' agents, surveyors and loss adjusters as well as problems concerning Directors' and Officers' liability cover, both for the Lloyds and company market. Also advises on general insurance and reinsurance matters including drafting and construction of policy wordings and problems arising from the granting of binding authorities.
Prof. Memberships: Law Society.
Career: Read Law at University College London following which he obtained articles with *Hewitt Woollacott & Chown*, as it then was, in 1979. Was admitted as a solicitor in April 1981 and has been a partner since 1986. Joined *Mills & Reeve* as a partner on 1st February 2000.

BROADIE, Charles
Cripps Harries Hall, Tunbridge Wells (01892) 515121
Specialisation: Heads the team that carries out work for the Solicitors Indemnity Fund. Extensive experience in professional indemnity work.
Prof. Memberships: Member of Law Society and local Law Society. Part-time chairman, Pensions Appeal Tribunal.
Career: Education: Bradfield College; Sidney Sussex College, Cambridge University (1966 BA – now MA, 1968 LLB – now LLM); Université de Nancy, France. Articled *Field Roscoe*, London; qualified 1969; *Hedleys*, London 1970-72; secretariat of the European Commission of Human Rights, Strasbourg 1972-74; assistant solicitor *Cripps Harries Hall*, Tunbridge Wells, 1974-76; partner from 1976.
Personal: Reading, foreign languages, walking, local church.

CHALLANDS, Richard
Bond Pearce, Plymouth (01752) 266633 rchallands@bondpearce.com
Specialisation: Partner in the Insurance Group. Specialises in professional indemnity and insurance litigation. Handles work on behalf of accountants, brokers, solicitors, barristers and surveyors. Also deals with policy and coverage disputes and has wide experience of claims involving fraud.
Prof. Memberships: Member of the International Bar Association Insurance Group and the British Insurance Law Association.
Career: Qualified 1975. Joined *Bond Pearce* in 1973, becoming partner 1978.

CLOVER, Sarah
Barlow Lyde & Gilbert, London (020) 7247 2277
Specialisation: Wide experience of dealing with professional liability issues of all kinds, particularly specialising in claims against solicitors. One of the lead partners co-ordinating the professions' response to claims against numerous firms by Nationwide Building Society.
Career: Qualified in 1983, joined *Barlow Lyde & Gilbert* in 1987. Became a partner at *Barlow Lyde & Gilbert* in 1992.
Publications: Has spoken at numerous seminars on professional indemnity and written for a number of publications.
Personal: Educated at University College of London.

CONNOLLY, Sean
Rowe & Maw, London (020) 7327 4144 sconnolly@roweandmaw.com
Specialisation: Specialises in all areas of contentious non marine insurance and reinsurance work including professional indemnity and product liability insurance matters. Has represented a wide range of merchant banks, accountants, insurance brokers,

engineers and surveyors on professional indemnity matters. Has conducted a number of substantial mediations this year. Managing Partner of the firm's insurance and reinsurance group at Lloyd's since 1992. Group managing partner of litigation and dispute resolution department 1999. One of the early proponents of the use of ADR. Participant in market ADR initiative (MAC).
Prof. Memberships: Law Society; International Bar Association; British Insurance Law Association.
Career: University of London 1982 (LL.B). Articled *Rowe & Maw* 1982-84. Assistant solicitor commercial litigation department 1984-86. Solicitor Alexander & Alexander Europe Plc 1986-88. Lloyd's Office *Rowe & Maw* 1989-date.
Personal: Cricket, golf and skiing.

CORNISH, Sarah
SJ Cornish, Tiverton (01884) 243377

COULSON, Edward W H
Hammond Suddards Edge, Leeds (0113) 284 7000
edward.coulson@hammondse.com
Specialisation: Acting for insurers in professional negligence claims against accountants, architects and consulting engineers, licensed conveyancers, insurance brokers and others and insurance related disputes.
Career: Bryanston School 1968-72. St John's College, Cambridge 1973-76.
Personal: Literature, gardening, walking.

DAWSON, Jane S
Hammond Suddards Edge, Leeds (0113) 284 7000
jane.dawson@hammondse.com
Specialisation: Finance/banking litigation with particular emphasis on professional negligence, fraud and asset tracing (including emergency injunctive relief) and receovery actions. Significant experience of managing group actions by mediation; led the team responsible for the settlement of NatWest Home Loans claims against solicitors (team nominated as the Manchester United of Litigation by client for work in this area), the settlement of a large number of Halifax plc claims arising out of shared ownership leases, and most recently the bulk of Halifax plc's current claims against completion solicitors (over 500 claims settled by this process). Acts for a number of leading lending institutions in this work.
Prof. Memberships: The Law Society.
Career: Leicester University LLB (Hons) 2:2. Articled with niche City shipping/insurance firm *Shaw & Croft*. Qualified 1988. Joined *Hammond Suddards* 1989.
Publications: Chairs the *Hammond Suddards Edge* editorial committee for CDR Exchange, the litigation quarterly newsletter. Also contributes articles to CDR Exchange.
Personal: Married to a corporate finance lawyer and has two children. As a result stretched to do anything other than dabble enthusiastically/exhaustedly (and very periodically) in sailing, tennis and hill walking. Cook lots (necessary to live) and reading (anything except legal publications).

DEDMAN, Richard
Barlow Lyde & Gilbert, London (020) 7247 2277
rdedman@blg.co.uk
Specialisation: Professional liability; commercial litigation and arbitration; insurance.
Prof. Memberships: CEDR accredited mediator; Society of Computers & Law; Member of Society of Construction Law.
Career: Trained at *Lovell White & King*; from 1979 at *Barlow Lyde & Gilbert* where formerly joint head of professional liability and commercial litigation department; senior partner May 2001.
Personal: Born 1954; educated at Felsted School and Cambridge University (Clare College – modern languages and law); interests include tennis, golf, football, music and languages.

DINGWALL, Francis
Henmans, Oxford (01865) 722181
francis.dingwall@henamns.co.uk
Specialisation: Partner and head of Henmans Professional Negligence/Commercial Litigation department comprising a team of 16 solicitors. Principally acts on behalf of insurers in professional indemnity claims, on behalf of solicitors, accountants, insurance brokers, surveyors and IT consultants among other purchasers of indemnity insurance products. Also handles broader commercial dispute resolution.
Career: Trained at *Barlow Lyde & Gilbert*. Admitted 1984. Assistant solicitor at *Barlow Lyde & Gilbert* 1984-89. Assistant Parliamentary Counsel 1989-1. Joined *Henmans* 1991.
Personal: Born 1958. Educated at Stonyhurst College and Corpus Christi College, Oxford. Lives in Oxfordshire countryside. Interests include English Language and Literature and coping with young family.

DONALD, Hugh
Shepherd & Wedderburn WS, Edinburgh
(0131) 473 5159
hugh.donald@shepwedd.co.uk
Specialisation: Partner. Specialist in clinical negligence, representing doctors and dentists in civil claims, inquiries and disciplinary proceedings. Also aviation representing airline and helicopter operators in both civil claims and accident inquiries. On the panel appointed to handle claims under Law society of Scotland Charter Policy.
Career: Qualified in 1975, having joined *Shepherd & Wedderburn WS* in 1973. Became a partner in 1977. Administrative head of litigation department 1990-94. Appointed managing partner in April 1994, and chief executive from April 1995 – April 1999.
Personal: Born 5th November 1951. Educated at Edinburgh University. Family Mediator. Chairman, Family Mediation Scotland. Leisure interests include gardening, walking and church. Lives in Edinburgh. Awarded OBE for services to family mediation in Scotland.

ELBORNE, Mark
CMS Cameron McKenna, London
(020) 7367 3057
me@cmck.com
Specialisation: Principal areas of practice involve acting in claims and disputes for insurers and reinsurers of banks and financial institutions, directors and officers, accountants, financial advisers and stockbrokers, Lloyd's agents and Lloyd's brokers; advising insurers and reinsurers on policy wordings and construction in insurance and reinsurance contracts; acting in major reinsurance arbitration and litigation disputes and advising reinsurers generally with clients in the London market, Europe, Middle and Far East, USA and Bermuda. Lectured in Bermuda at International Reinsurance Congress and in Hong Kong and London at various conferences on financial institutions insurance, directors' and officers' liability cover and on reinsurance.
Prof. Memberships: Law Society, Chartered Institute of Insurers, Society of Insurance Receivers.
Career: Qualified 1983 and became a Partner of *CMS Cameron McKenna* in 1988.
Personal: Born 22nd January 1958. School Trustee. Leisure pursuits include golf, swimming, tennis, shooting and opera. Lives near Uppingham, Rutland. Married with five children.

GAUL, Patrick
Weightmans, Liverpool (0151) 227 2601
patrick.gaul@weightmans.com
Specialisation: Professional negligence, solicitors and doctors in particular and industrial disease litigation (bladder cancer). Regularly lectures on variety of topics in civil litigation, especially clinical negligence. Very substantial civil practice. Important cases include Hall v Simons; Whitley v Cook Leathes & Bickerton and others; Roberts v Johnstone; Sa'D v Robinson.
Prof. Memberships: Law Society.
Career: Oxford University BA Jurisprudence.

GRANT, Mike
Addleshaw Booth & Co, Manchester
(0161) 934 6000
Specialisation: Defendant professional indemnity claims, involving all major professions – accountants, solicitors, engineers. Particular experience dealing with large claims made against construction industry professionals – presently dealing with £10M claims defending construction project manager. Many other multi-million pound claims ongoing.
Career: Articled *Percy Hughes & Roberts*; qualified 1988; partner 1990; joined *Weightmans* as partner in January 1996; joined *Addleshaw Booth & Co* as partner in September 2000.
Publications: Contributor to insurance/commercial litigation journals.
Personal: Cardinal Godfrey School, Liverpool; Liverpool University; Chester College of Law. Married, one daughter. Hobbies: tennis, squash.

GREENLEY, Simon
Reynolds Porter Chamberlain, London
(020) 7242 2877
skg@rpc.co.uk
See under Insurance, p.488

GREENWOOD, Duncan
Beachcroft Wansbroughs, Leeds (0113) 251 4700
Specialisation: I have specialised in the PI market for 10 years, particularly in the fields of surveying, engineering, architects, accountants and solicitors negligence. I also advise on policy wording/coverage issues and last year advised a pre-eminent insurer on their claims handling processes on entry into the new solicitors open market. Major cases have included Barclays Bank v Peter Wardle Associates (1997) cited by C.A. in Platform home Loans v Oyston Shipways; Archer v Hickmotts (1998) C.A. NPC 132; Halifax Mortgage Services v Simpson & Others (1998) 64 Con. L.R. 17 and Cottingham v Attey Bower & Jones (1999) 3 W.L.R.873.
Career: Qualified in September 1990 with *Wansbroughs Willey Hargrave*, associate 1994, partner 1997 and joined the partnership of *BW* on merger in May 1999.
Publications: Articles written have appeared in the Estates Gazette, Insurance Post and the Chartered Institute of Insurers Magazine.

HALL, Stuart
Barlow Lyde & Gilbert, London (020) 7247 2277
shall@blg.co.uk
Specialisation: Professional indemnity, especially accountants, directors' and officers' liability and commercial litigation.
Prof. Memberships: English and Hong Kong Law Societies.
Career: Cambridge University; admitted 1975; partner *Dawson & Co* 1976-85; partner *Barlow Lyde & Gilbert* 1985 to date.

HEGARTY, Simon
CMS Cameron McKenna, Bristol (0117) 930 0200
Specialisation: Specialises in insurance litigation (particularly professional indemnity and directors' and officers' liability) and banking litigation.
Career: Trained and qualified with *Cameron Kemm Norden* (1979-81), served with the Royal Navy (1981-86), re-joined *Cameron Markby* (1987) becoming a partner in *Cameron Markby Hewitt* in 1992. Managing Partner of *CMS Cameron McKenna's* Bristol office from 1994.
Personal: Children, amateur dramatics, folk dancing, beer and butterflies are replacing rapidly deteriorating performances on the sports field.

HICK, Mark
Wragge & Co, Birmingham (0870) 903 1000

HODGSON, Guy
Mills & Reeve, Norwich (01603) 693 221
guy.hodgson@mills-reeve.com
Specialisation: Partner and head of insurance Specialises in professional indemnity risks and coverage disputes for insurers, mutual funds and professional firms and D&O. Acts for all professions dealing with claims brought against them and any related insurance issues. Advises on add drafts policy wordings. Joined *Mills & Reeve* in 1984 to develop their professional indemnity practice after gaining a number of years' experience working in the London market. Regular speaker on professional indemnity matters.
Prof. Memberships: British Insurance Law Association. Law Society.

HUGHES-WILLIAMS, Clare
Morgan Cole, Cardiff (029) 2038 5385

JENKINS, Ian
Barlow Lyde & Gilbert, London (020) 7247 2277
ijenkins@blg.co.uk
Specialisation: Insurance, brokers, accountants. Directors' and officers' liability.
Prof. Memberships: International Bar Association.
Career: Partner *Barlow Lyde & Gilbert* 1974. Elected senior partner 1989. Chairman, Kiln Trustees Ltd, CEDR accredited mediator.
Personal: Born 1946. Educated at Denstone College and King's College, London. Leisure interests include family and sailing. Member of Royal Thames Yacht Club. Ocean Cruising Club.

KENNEDY, A J Spencer
Balfour & Manson, Edinburgh (0131) 200 1200
spencer.kennedy@balfour-manson.co.uk
Specialisation: Commercial and professional negligence litigation. Solicitor Advocate enjoying extended rights of audience in Supreme Civil Courts. Panel Solicitor under Law Society of Scotland Master Policy since 1990. Contributor to 'Ensuring Excellence' Risk Management Handbook 1998 and associated seminars.
Prof. Memberships: Law Society of Scotland, SSC Society (Past President), Federation of Insurance Lawyers. Notary Public.
Career: Born 3 May 1945. Educated Royal High School and University of Edinburgh. Partner in *Nightingale & Bell* from 1973 and, after merger, partner in *Balfour & Manson* since 1991.
Personal: Lives in Edinburgh. Enjoys hillwalking and horticulture.

LONG, Andrew
Pinsent Curtis Biddle, Birmingham
(0121) 200 1050
andrew.long@pinsents.com
Specialisation: Partner in Insurance Litigation and Head of Financial Services Litigation. Professional indemnity defendant work, specialising in acting for solicitors and for the financial services industry. Author, speaker and leading expert on pension misselling claims. Acts for mutuals, Lloyd's Underwriters, insurers and the financial services industry. Also sits as a Deputy District Judge.
Career: Qualified in 1980. Joined *Pinsent & Co* in 1986 becoming a Partner in 1989.
Personal: Born 1955. Lives in Worcestershire. Educated at Exeter School and Pembroke College, Oxford. Interests include village sport and bridge.

MACLENNAN, Alison
Beachcroft Wansbroughs, London (020) 7242 1011
amaclennan@bwlaw.co.uk
Specialisation: Partner handling professional negligence advice for solicitors, accountants, architects and surveyors. Also advises on property disputes, policy interpretation and coverage issues in relation to title indemnity policies. Experienced in settlement strategies and mediation. Spent 10 years in industrial personnel management before entering private practice as a solicitor.

MACLEOD, Colin
Dundas & Wilson CS, Edinburgh (0131) 228 8000

MAHER, Frank
Weightmans, Liverpool (0151) 227 2601
Specialisation: Professional Indemnity primarily for solicitors, but also accountants, bankers, engineers, surveyors, valuers. Numerous major fraud investigations, financial services claims, construction litigation and policy wording disputes. Acting for solicitors in 'Alford v West Bromwich Building Society' and others. Home income scheme group action. Advises insurers on professional indemnity policy working and websites.
Prof. Memberships: Law Society – past involvement nationally and locally. Former chairman of National Committee of Young Solicitors Group, member of civil litigation, council membership and professional and public relations committees of the Law Society and general committee of Liverpool Law Society. Joint working partner of the Bar Council and Law Society on the Civil courts – sub-committee chairman.
Career: Liverpool University LLB. Educational Foundation Prize.

MICKLEM, Barney
Reynolds Porter Chamberlain, London
(020) 7242 2877
ctm@rpc.co.uk
Specialisation: Partner in professional indemnity litigation department. Professional indemnity litigation specialist. Work relates principally to solicitors, barristers and surveyors. Has addressed various professional indemnity seminars.
Prof. Memberships: Law Society.
Career: Qualified in 1974. Became a partner in 1977.

NICHOLAS, Paul
Reynolds Porter Chamberlain, London
(020) 7242 2877
Specialisation: Insurance and professional indemnity.
Career: Qualified in 1970, having joined *Reynolds Porter* in 1968. Became a Partner in 1972.
Personal: Born 24th April 1946. Educated at Mill Hill School 1959-63 and Emmanuel College, Cambridge (BA 1967, LLB 1968). Governor of Lockers Park School and Trustee of S.W. Hertfordshire Hospice Charitable Trust.

PATON, Andrew
Pinsent Curtis Biddle, Birmingham
(0121) 200 1050
andrew.paton@pinsents.com
See under Alternative Dispute Resolution, p.82

PEACOCK, Ian
Bond Pearce, Bristol (0117) 929 9197
ipeacock@bondpearce.com
Specialisation: Partner in the Insurance Group and Head of Bond Pearce's professional indemnity practice in the Bristol office. Defends claims on behalf of solicitors, accountants, brokers and financial advisers. Also specialises in the Financial Services sector with particular emphasis on income protection claims.
Career: Qualified in 1984 in London. Joined *Bond Pearce* in 1990, becoming partner 1992.

PORTLOCK, Richard
Blake Lapthorn, Fareham (01489) 579 990

REGAN, Michael
Rowe & Maw, London (020) 7248 4282
See under Construction, p.207

RIDGWELL, Robert
Browne Jacobson, Nottingham (0115) 976 6236
rridgwell@brownej.co.uk
Specialisation: Professional indemnity. Partner advising insurers on policy issues and policy drafting. Risk management and claims avoidance. Advising on commercial claims and professional indemnity litigation, including defending professional indemnity claims against surveyors, solicitors, accountants, intermediaries (financial/insurance/pension consultants). Financial product liability.
Prof. Memberships: Fellow of the Chartered Institute of Arbitrators; founder member of the Institute for Continuing Professional Development.
Career: Qualified 1979; partner *Brown Jacobson* 1980.
Personal: Born 1954; resides Southwell. Education: Lincoln School; Queens College; Cambridge (1976 Law).

SALOMONSEN, Erik
Bond Pearce, Exeter (01392) 211185
esalomonsen@bondpearce.com
Specialisation: Partner and Head of the Insurance Group. Defends claims against a wide range of professionals, including medical professionals. Work also includes employers' and public liability claims including work in the farming industry. Panel solicitor for Composites, Lloyd's underwriters and mutual funds. An accredited mediator.

Prof. Memberships: Member of the International Bar Association. Holder of High Courts Advocacy qualification for all courts.
Career: Qualified in 1975. Joined *Bond Pearce* in 1975, becoming a partner 1979.

SCHOFIELD, Belinda
CMS Cameron McKenna, London
(020) 7367 3000
Specialisation: Principal areas of practice are handling professional indemnity claims against accountants, actuaries, financial institutions, insurance brokers and directors' and officers' liability. Acting for insurers and insureds. Growing and significant area of practice is in the field of regulation and risk management acting for professionals and insurers in risk control and avoidance projects, due diligence exercises and advising on the impact of regulatory controls, including representing individuals in regulatory proceedings and monitoring such proceedings for insurers. Work also includes general insurance and reinsurance advice and drafting and construction of policy wordings. Experienced in handling large commercial disputes. Speaks at numerous market seminars.

SEYMOUR, Michael
Lovells, London (020) 7296 2000
michael.seymour@lovells.com
Specialisation: Main areas of practice: professional negligence, commercial litigation and arbitration often involving an international dimension, particularly in the area of trade and business. Has acted for foreign governments in cases involving state immunity and for banks, insurers and other companies in contract fraud and property related cases.
Prof. Memberships: Law Society, Chartered Institute of Arbitrators, member (President: 1994-96) of London Solicitors Litigation Association, member of the joint working party of the Bar and the Law Society on the Civil Courts.
Career: Articled at *Lovells*; Qualified 1974; Partner 1982.

SMITH, Antony
Beale and Company, London (020) 7240 3474
Specialisation: Partner in professional negligence. Specialises in international and national construction dispute resolution and litigation. Acted in largest ever claim brought in the Technology and Construction Courts. Regularly defends prosecutions under health and safety law. Writes for 'Health and Safety at Work' Journal. Acts on all types of professional negligence claims including accountants, architects, engineers, IFAs and insurance brokers. Member of Law Society panel of solicitors acting on professional negligence actions. Since the end of SIF, acts for the commercial market in defending solicitors.
Prof. Memberships: Institution of Occupational Safety and Health; Centre for Dispute Resolution; Law Society; British Insurance Law Association.
Career: Partner with *Beale and Company* since 1985.
Personal: Liverpool University LLB. (Upper Second Class Hons.). Interests include family, rugby, football and triathlon.

TAYLOR, Elisabeth
James Chapman & Co, Manchester (0161) 828 8000
liz.taylor@james-chapman.co.uk
Specialisation: Defendant professional indemnity work, acting on behalf of insurers and indemnifiers.
Prof. Memberships: The Law Society and The Manchester Law Society.
Career: Educated University of Bristol (LLB). Admitted April 1974. Joined *James Chapman & Co* 1976. Partner 1979. Managing partner 1998. Head of professional indemnity and general insurance department.
Personal: Married, three children. Interests include family, music and theatre.

TESTER, Stephen
CMS Cameron McKenna, London
(020) 7367 2894
skt@cmck.com
Specialisation: Practises in construction and surveyors' PI, Contractors All Risk Insurance, D&O and Transaction Support Insurance. Clients include insurance and reinsurance companies, Lloyds syndicates, insurance brokers and construction companies.
Prof. Memberships: Society of Construction Law.
Career: KCS Wimbledon and St. John's College Cambridge. Qualified 1981. Partner since 1988.
Personal: Interests include family and friends, golf and squash.

THOMAS, Nick
Kennedys, London (020) 7638 3688
Specialisation: Senior Partner. Also Partner in associated Northern Ireland and Hong Kong practices. Principal area of expertise is professional indemnity, particularly in the construction field and CAR/ALOP and property claims, particularly overseas (Middle East and India, Far East and the Americas). Also covers insurance work generally, including disputes as to whether insurers should respond and which insurers should respond. Acted in BBL v. John D. Wood and others, and National Trust v. Hayden Young; Heathrow Express Terminal collapse and Terminal 1 fire. Author of 'Professional Indemnity Claims (An Architect's Guide)', published by Architect's Press in 1981. Regularly addresses conferences and seminars, particularly for insurers.
Prof. Memberships: Member of the Law Society, Fellow of the Chartered Institute of Arbitrators. Also qualified as a solicitor in Hong Kong, Northern Ireland and the Republic of Ireland.
Career: Joined *Kennedys* in 1977 and qualified in 1980. Became a Partner in 1981. Became Senior Partner in 1997.
Personal: Born 16th October 1954. Attended Bristol University 1973-76. School Governor. Leisure pursuits include all sports, travel and the arts. Lives near Berkhamsted, Herts.

TRAYHURN, Neil
Bond Pearce, Southampton (023) 8063 2211
ntrayhurn@bondpearce.com
Specialisation: Partner in the Insurance Group. Specialises in professional indemnity and insurance litigation. Extensive experience of handling claims on behalf of a wide range of professionals including solicitors, surveyors and accountants. Also has experience of construction disputes and policy coverage issues.
Prof. Memberships: Member of the Forum of Insurance Lawyers.
Career: Qualified in 1989 following articles with *Wansbrough Willey Hargreave*. Joined *Bond Pearce* in 1992 becoming partner 1995.

TROTTER, John
Lovells, London (020) 7296 2000
john.trotter@lovells.com
Specialisation: Main area of practice is litigation and other dispute resolution involving insurance and re-insurance, including professional indemnity and product liability. Has been involved in numerous actions and arbitrations in these areas, including the defence of major claims against lawyers. Has written and spoken widely about dispute resolution and issues affecting the insurance industry such as the Civil Procedure Rules and coverage for millennium IT claims.
Prof. Memberships: Vice-chairman of the Insurance Committee of the International Bar Association. Member of the London Solicitors Litigation Association and the City of London Law Society. Member British Insurance Law Association, co-author of 'Liability of Lawyers and indemnity insurance' (Kluwer/IBA).
Career: Qualified in 1977 with *Lovells*; based in New York office 1980-82; partner in 1983. Managing partner, litigation 1994-98.

TURTLE, Brian
Carson McDowell, Belfast (028) 9024 4951
See under Litigation, p.583

WARD, John
Beale and Company, London (020) 7240 3474
Specialisation: Partner in construction department. Has specialised in construction industry law since 1979, on both UK and overseas projects. Work includes advice on contractual structures, contracts, prevention of disputes, resolution of disputes, mediations, adjudications, litigation and arbitration, including ICC arbitrations, and professional indemnity work, especially for engineers and surveyors. A significant proportion of the work relates to projects outside the UK. Also handles health and safety in the construction industry. Work includes advice on duties and obligations under health and safety legislation on systems for compliance (eg CDM regulations) as well as defence of prosecutions brought by the Health and Safety Executive against professionals. Advises insurers and brokers on professional indemnity issues, including policy wordings, and specialist applications of professional indemnity policies. Experienced conference speaker and author of articles on a variety of topics.
Prof. Memberships: Law Society, International Bar Association, International Chamber of Commerce.
Career: Qualified in 1975. Partner with *Beale and Company* since 1977. Now managing partner.
Personal: Born 22nd November 1950. Educated at University College, London 1969-72 (LL.B. Hons). Leisure interests include fly fishing, Formula 1 motor racing and football. Lives in Cobham.

WELSH, John
Morison Bishop, Glasgow (0141) 248 4672
See under Construction, p.209

WHITE, Stuart
Reynolds Porter Chamberlain, London
(020) 7242 2877
sgw@rpc.co.uk
Specialisation: Partner in insurance and reinsurance department. A significant area of practice is professional indemnity, principally construction related, for architects and engineers. Also handles general insurance work, covering insurance disputes,

policy wordings and general liability and property litigation. Extensive experience of mediation. Acted in 'Investors in Industry v South Bedfordshire DC', 'Crown v Mowlem' (re final certificates), 'Citibank v Excess' (re costs liability of insurers), and was also involved in the personal accident claim following the death of Robert Maxwell. Major clients include insurance companies, mutual insurance associations and Lloyd's syndicates. Has given seminars on a range of topics including architects' liability, product liability, liability for pollution, drafting of policy wordings, 'Chapman v Christopher', the impact of the Woolf reforms on insurers, and 'True Professionalism'. Has addressed the Fire Loss Association, the Chartered Institute of Loss Adjusters and the British Insurance Brokers Association. Regularly contributes to various insurance publications. Co-author of the Professional Liability section of LLP publication 'Insurance Disputes'.
Prof. Memberships: Society of Construction Law, British Insurance Law Association, CEDR, Fire Loss Association, Chartered Insurance Institute, FOIL.
Career: Qualified in 1984. Joined *Hextall Erskine* in 1980, becoming a partner in 1987. Partner *Reynold Porter Chamberlain* from 2001.
Personal: Born 1957. Attended The Queen's College Oxford, MA (Hons) 1975-78.

WILLIAMSON, David
Brodies WS, Edinburgh (0131) 228 3777
david.williamson@brodies.co.uk
See under Litigation, p.584

WILLIS, Michael
Beachcroft Wansbroughs, Leeds (0113) 251 4770
mwillis@bwlaw.co.uk
Specialisation: Professional Indemnity: handling claims and insurance issues on behalf of solicitors, surveyors, accountants and financial intermediaries.
Prof. Memberships: Law Society: Leeds Law Society; FOIL.
Career: Articled *Gordon Dudds & Co*, qualified 1985; *Lawrence Messer* 1986; *Wansbroughs Willey Hargrave* 1988; Partner in 1993 *Beachcroft Wansbroughs.*
Publications: Co-author of the Chapter on Solicitors in the LLP Looseleaf: Professional Negligence & Liability (ed. Mark Simpson).
Personal: Redley College; Magdelene College Cambridge. Born 1957; resides North Yorkshire.

WILSON, Michael
Barlow Lyde & Gilbert, London (020) 7247 2277
mgwilson@blg.co.uk
Specialisation: Professional indemnity litigation, in particular, claims against domestic and international banks. Direct involvement in many of the leading cases against merchant banks arising as a result of the takeover activity of the late 80s.
Prof. Memberships: Member of the Law Society; City of London Solicitors Company; Asia Pacific Lawyers Association; International Bar Association; Southwestern Legal Foundation; Inter-Pacific Bar Association; Freeman of the City of London; Fellow of the Royal Society of Art.
Career: Articled with *Slaughter and May*; qualified in 1975; assistant solicitor 1977-79; partner *Berwin Leighton* 1979-99; *Barlow Lyde & Gilbert* 1999 to date.
Personal: Golf, tennis, squash, swimming, travel, reading, music.

WYLDE, Peter
Irwin Mitchell, London (020) 7421 3852
wyldep@irwinmitchell.co.uk
Specialisation: Leads *Irwin Mitchell's* national professional negligence unit which, uniquely, acts primarily for claimants against professionals, particularly solicitors, accountants and financial advisers. Specialises personally in claims arising from commercial transactions, mergers and acquisitions and commercial litigation. A strong proponent of mediation, Peter sits on the Mediation Committee of the Central London County Court and initiated the Wilkinson case which established that legal aid is available for mediation.
Prof. Memberships: ADR Group; Association of Northern Mediators; ADR London Regional Forum; Central London County Court Mediation Committee; London Litigation Solicitors Association; OSS Negligence Panel; ICA Members Advice Panel; Law Society.
Career: Qualified 1983. *Irwin Mitchell* Partner 1985. Educated at Royal Grammar School, Newcastle Upon Tyne and Sheffield University. Head of *Irwin Mitchell* Commercial Dispute Resolution Department. Member *Irwin Mitchell* Management Board 1996-99. Managing Partner, *Irwin Mitchell* London office since 1998. Head of Professional Negligence Unit.
Personal: Leisure: sport, music, cinema/theatre.

PROJECTS / PFI

OVERVIEW: This year, distinct projects and PFI tables have been created for both firms and individuals. While it is recognised that domestic and international PPPs are increasingly difficult to distinguish, it was still felt that the key players in projects and PFI are sufficiently different to warrant separate tables. In particular, American firms are strong on international projects, but take little interest in the domestic PFI market. Abroad, the projects market has started to pick up, especially in the Far East. Magic Circle firms dominate the European mandates for PPP, with many considering that, despite the standardisation of documentation, there is "*still a premium value to using the bigger firms.*" At home, the Treasury forecasts £20 billion worth of PPP projects over the next three years. Complex PPPs such as the London Underground PPP and the National Air Traffic Services PPP have won much comment. Outside transport, firms consider that accommodation projects are likely to remain the mainstay of the PFI market for the foreseeable future. The growth of IT-related projects is also anticipated, while firms are increasingly looking to the expanding market in Ireland.

RESEARCH APPROVED BY BMRB: *For this edition,* Chambers' *researchers conducted 6,552 interviews – 4,419 with law firms, 554 with barristers and 1,579 with clients.*

The validity of the research was scrutinised by BMRB International, who audited both the methodology and the results at our offices in July 2001. They interviewed Chambers' *researchers and cross-checked sample interviews. Details of the audit appear on page 7.*

LONDON

PROJECT FINANCE

PROJECT FINANCE • London	Ptnrs	Assts
1 Allen & Overy	28	65
2 Linklaters	27	n/a
3 Clifford Chance	11	55
Norton Rose	18	49
4 Denton Wilde Sapte	27	32
Freshfields Bruckhaus Deringer	11	32
Milbank, Tweed, Hadley & McCloy	2	11
Shearman & Sterling	4	20
5 Baker & McKenzie	9	31
CMS Cameron McKenna	11	n/a
Slaughter and May	n/a	n/a
White & Case	7	22
6 Ashurst Morris Crisp	n/a	n/a
Herbert Smith	n/a	n/a
Lovells	16*	18*
Masons	5	14
Simmons & Simmons	n/a	n/a

This book is the product of 6,552 1/2-hour interviews. See p.7 for BMRB audit.
Within each band, firms are listed alphabetically.
* *Figures denote combined Projects/PFI team size.*

Allen & Overy (see firm details p.856) "*Dominant*" firm that edges ahead of rivals on account of a top-quality, multi-faceted projects group. Competitors consider it "*the first choice for banks.*" Clients note "*a wealth of experience amongst its senior assistants.*" The firm benefits from having people on the ground internationally, and is increasingly influential in the Middle East. Head of the practice, "*top class*" **Graham Vinter** (see p.715) is a leading light for project owners, sponsors and funders. He acted for the Ministry of Electricity and Water, Yemen in the 400 MW gas-fired Ma'arib IPP project. "*Pre-eminent*" Jonathan Horsfall Turner has now taken a consultancy role with the firm; in the last year he has advised the Greek Government on the privatisation of the municipal water companies in Athens and Thessaloniki. The strong group also includes **Stephen Gillespie** (see p.711) ("*good on big ticket bank deals*") who acted for Deutsche Bank on the financing of the Drax coal-fired station. **Anthony Humphrey**'s (see p.119) caseload has ranged from Croatian waste water and road projects to advising on the continued development of the $2 billion Qatargas LNG Downstream project in Qatar. **Brian Harrison** (see p.712) maintains his reputation for work on behalf of projects companies. Rising names at the firm include "*projects expert*" **Bimal Desai** (see p.710) and **Mark O'Neill**, both of whose emerging markets work has won plaudits from rivals and clients alike. **Clients:** National Grid Company; Japan Bank for International Co-operation; Industrial Bank of Japan.

Linklaters (see firm details p.1042) "*A switched on bunch*" with "*strength in depth.*" Clients praise a "*commercially savvy*" team, which is noted "*for complicated deals requiring international exposure.*" "*Absolutely first-rate assistants*" are a clear asset. Active in all sectors, the firm is most respected for its work in power. Energy specialist **Stuart Salt** (see p.356) acted for the project company on the Sakhalin II Project. A "*plain-speaker,*" he "*has the respect of both sides of the table.*" "*Experienced, precise*" **Alan Black** (see p.709) "*stands out.*" He acted for Sasol on its global joint venture with Chevron. **Clive Ransome** (see p.714) is rated by peers for his work in electricity, oil and gas and transport, often on behalf of the sponsor. **David Weber** (see p.715) advised the sponsor in the Chad-Cameroon Pipeline and Export Terminal Project. The group also advised the project company (a joint venture between Mirant and Reliance Industries) on the Hirma Power Project, and represented the project company and Enron (as sponsor) on the Metgas project in India. **Clients:** ABN AMRO; Amec; Citibank/Schroders Salomon Smith Barney; Deutsche Bank; Mirant; Shell.

Clifford Chance (see firm details p.919) Well established in the market and "*close on the tail of the top tier for international projects work.*" IPP specialist **Peter Blake** (see p.709) heads a group "*packed with quality individuals,*" which has traditionally drawn the bulk of its work from the energy and power sectors. "*Well-respected*" **Tim Soutar** (see p.715) brings a depth of Hong Kong power-related experience to the table and has recently focused on oil and gas, representing the senior debt providers on the Chad-Cameroon Pipeline. **Margaret Gossling** (see p.711) acted on an industrial port project in Egypt, while **Chris Wyman** (see p.716) is recommended for his work in India. New entrant to *Chambers*, **Dan Reynell** (see p.714) is perceived by by the market to have "*done good things in Italy.*" The team advised the sponsors and financial adviser (Citicorp, Sinopec, YPC and BASF) on a $3.4 billion petrochemical complex, represented the IFC on the Meditel financing in Morocco, and assisted on the Blue Stream pipeline between Russia and Turkey. **Clients:** Chase Manhattan; Petrobras.

LEADING INDIVIDUALS	
★ VINTER Graham Allen & Overy	
1 SALT Stuart Linklaters	
2 BARRATT Jeffery Norton Rose	BLACK Alan Linklaters
FLETCHER Phillip Milbank, Tweed	FOX Jason Herbert Smith
GILLESPIE Stephen Allen & Overy	MACRITCHIE Kenneth Shearman & Sterling
3 BLAKE Peter Clifford Chance	BUCKWORTH Nicholas Shearman & Sterling
HARRISON Brian Allen & Overy	HUMPHREY Anthony Allen & Overy
RANSOME Clive Linklaters	ROWEY Kent Freshfields Bruckhaus
4 CRANE David Norton Rose	FINLAY Peter White & Case
GAINES Peter Baker & McKenzie	GOSSLING Margaret Clifford Chance
JOHNSTON Bruce Weil, Gotshal & Manges	McCORMICK Roger Freshfields Bruckhaus
McQUATER Gavin Lovells	PREECE Andrew Herbert Smith
SOUTAR Tim Clifford Chance	WYMAN Chris Clifford Chance
5 BELLHOUSE John White & Case	HALL Peter Norton Rose
PHILLIPS Robert CMS Cameron	REYNELL Daniel Clifford Chance
ROBERTS Martin Slaughter and May	SAUNDERS Christopher Slaughter and May
STOPFORD Philip White & Case	
TEMPLETON-KNIGHT Jane Hunton & Williams	
WEBER David Linklaters	
UP AND COMING	
DESAI Bimal Allen & Overy	O'NEILL Mark Allen & Overy
ONES TO WATCH	
COKER Mark Freshfields Bruckhaus Deringer	

See individuals' profiles p.708

Norton Rose (see firm details p.1082) "*More sponsor-oriented*" according to competitors, with one power company declaring itself "*impressed with its ability to make sure that the project documents and the credit side work well together.*" Bank clients consider that the team is "*in the top drawer for power and oil and gas.*" Michael Taylor's move to Italy strengthens its international presence. An "*amenable, relaxed bunch,*" acknowledged to reach "*high standards,*" includes the "*experienced, diplomatic*" **Jeffery Barratt** (see p.708). Active in the Taweelah A1 independent power and desalination project and the Blue Stream pipeline project, he has also acted for Ashanti Goldfields Company on the development of a number of gold mines in Africa. Renowned for his transport expertise, **David Crane** (see p.710) has advised the arranging groups supporting two preferred bidding consortia in the London Underground PPP. **Peter Hall** (see p.711) acted for the bank group on the financing of a high-speed rail link in the Netherlands. **Clients:** Ashanti Goldfields Company; Bank of America; BNP Paribas; Citibank; Deutsche Bank; Rolls-Royce Power Ventures; Siemens; US Exim.

Denton Wilde Sapte (see firm details p.939) Perceived by competitors to be "*making a push,*" and "*attempting to capitalise on its clout on the banking side.*" Neil Cuthbert heads a team which has been involved in a number of high profile deals in the Middle East, including the privatisation of Oman's water and electricity industries, where it advised the Government of Oman. The group also advised the Icelandic investors on a hydro-electric power plant and aluminium smelter in Iceland, and assisted on the Illijan 1200 MW IPP in the Philippines. **Clients:** Adgas; Bank of China; Chevron; Mobil; Shell; Icelandic Investment Bank; Deutsche Bank; Citibank.

Freshfields Bruckhaus Deringer (see firm details p.965) The group's international spread has led European banks to applaud a proactive reach in the former communist countries of central Europe. Packed with "*core individuals,*" the team includes **Roger McCormick** (see p.713), who is considered by market sources to have "*a long-standing reputation in the field,*" and "*one of the big boys,*" **Kent Rowey** (see p.355). The latter advised US Exim Bank on the financing of the Hamaca heavy oil project in Venezuela's Orinoco Oil Belt. The firm also advised WIND Telecomunicazioni on its bank facility for the development of its fixed-line and GSM networks in Italy. In addition, it is at the forefront of exporting the PFI/PPP concepts to Portugal (the Portuguese toll road programme), Ireland, Italy, Germany and Greece. **Clients:** WIND Telecomunicazioni; Taiwan High Speed Rail Corporation; EIB; Polish Motorways Agency; Hellenic Republic.

Milbank, Tweed, Hadley & McCloy (see firm details p.1068) An "*aggressive*" practice which is "*strong in power*" and perceived by competitors to "*act for institutional investors, thus reflecting its strong bond practice in New York.*" Although its traditional reputation lies as counsel to lenders, it is increasingly involved on the sponsor side, with clients such as Tractebel and TotalFinaElf. Though the practice has suffered a number of defections over the last few years, clients comment on a "*common spirit*" and a "*fair control of partners on the job*" which ensures that "*good standards remain.*" Highly respected by peers and clients alike, **Phillip Fletcher** (see p.711) and his team represented the bridge lenders on the AES Drax £1.2 billion optimisation plan, and TotalFinaElf and Tractebel on the Taweelah A1 power project. The firm has also dominated the financing of power projects in Italy, and is spreading its reach across Turkey and the Middle East. **Clients:** Goldman Sachs; TotalFinaElf; Tractebel.

Shearman & Sterling (see firm details p.1125) "*Has made the biggest impact of the American firms on the London market,*" with successful international integration and a host of talented individuals. "*Core players*" on the global scene well-versed in the oil, gas and communications sectors, the firm offers an envied network of resources. Department head **Kenneth MacRitchie** (see p.712) has a high market profile and is rated for his energy work. He advised Barclays Bank Plc in the £494 million financing for the acquisition of RJB Mining from the Government. "*Excellent*" **Nick Buckworth** (see p.709) is a power specialist who advised the banks on the financing of the Tawleelah A2 power and water generation facility (Abu Dhabi). **Clients:** ABN AMRO; BG plc.

Baker & McKenzie (see firm details p.868) Recommended by international banks as a "*user-friendly team*" which "*understands client needs.*" Although research has indicated a slight lack of visibility, this has been attributed to the decentralising nature of the network. **Peter Gaines** (see p.711) is "*somebody you'd want on your side of the table.*" He acted for Petrobras on the US$3.2 billion Barracuda and Caratinga offshore oil project and advised Dresdner Bank on the restructuring of the DM1.65 billion limited recourse silicon chip wafer manufacturing facility for an affiliate of Advanced Micro Devices Inc. The team also represented Autostrada Wielkopolska SA, the concessionaire for the A2 toll motorway in Poland, and advised the Facility Agent and Lead Arranger on the Oman pipeline. **Clients:** ABN AMRO; British Gas; European Investment Bank; Petrobras; Industrial Bank of Japan; BNP Paribas; Nortel.

CMS Cameron McKenna (see firm details p.922) Considered by banking clients to be forward-driving, with an expansion beyond its traditional public sector work. Rivals commend the firm for "*making UK models work in Portugal.*" **Robert Phillips** (see p.714) specialises in linear transport/communication projects, and acted for the State of the Netherlands in the Dutch HSL infrastructure project. The team also advised the Municipality of Sofia on its water and wastewater system and acted on the Bucharest water project financing. Other work includes advising the Metronet Consortium on the LUL PPP. **Clients:** Schroders, Soloman, Smith, Barney; Dai-Ichi Kangyo Bank; Dresdner Kleinwort Wasserstein; West LB.

Slaughter and May (see firm details p.1135) Recommended by the market for its focus on complex, high value deals, the team's diversity and outstanding client base lead rivals to acknowledge that "*you can't ever ignore them.*" **Martin Roberts** (see p.714) is "*a great energy person*" who acted for the European Investment Bank on the construction, maintenance and operation of the Thessaloniki Metro system in Greece. "*Incredibly professional and focused,*" **Christopher Saunders** (see p.715) advised Chase Manhattan on the Wembley Stadium project and is rated for his oil and gas work. The group also acted for AES on the £1.9 billion refinancing of the Drax coal fired plant, and represented Deutsche Bank on the FirstMark project in Germany. **Clients:** AES; Chase Manhattan; Deutsche Bank; European Investment Bank.

White & Case (see firm details p.1178) The firm is recognised to have "*good people with a strong presence in London.*" Rated by the market for its international PPP work, it is supported by a strong construction department on EPC negotiations. **Peter Finlay** (see p.711) is highly rated for his focus on Turkish power projects, and advised the sponsors on the Iskenderun IPP. With a background in construction, **John Bellhouse** (see p.709) undertakes a mix of UK and international projects, typically acting for developers. "*First-class*" **Philip Stopford** (see p.715)is rated for his transportation and oil and gas work, and acted on the Qatargas LNG project. The team also acted on an ongoing power project in Poland, and the SCECO East power project in Saudi Arabia. **Clients:** International sponsors.

Ashurst Morris Crisp (see firm details p.866) "*Has moved up in the market*" according to banking clients while peers note that "*they're players in the Far East, with interesting IT and telecoms work.*" Overseas work includes advising the Government of Hong Kong SAR on the Cyberport project and involvement in the PPN power project in India. The partners are "*available and of a high quality*" with experience across a range of sectors. In energy the group acted for NRG on its acquisition and non-recourse financing of the Killingholme power station (UK.) **Clients:** Mainly sponsors.

Herbert Smith (see firm details p.993) Recommended by clients as "*practical and accessible,*" with "*a commercial, analytical approach.*" Although the firm continues to be best known for its PFI work, **Jason Fox** (see p.711) has done much to push forward its international profile. "*Head and shoulders above anyone else we've dealt with*" according to clients, he acted for Atlantis in connection with the limited recourse financing of an offshore Tunisian oil field, and advised Chase Manhattan on a number of oil and gas financings. **Andrew Preece** (see p.714) has brought a formidable knowledge of finance and commercial contracts to bear on the Dutch High-Speed Link project, where the group advised the consortium of Bechtel, Amey, Nuon and Dura Vermeer. **Clients:** Chase Manhattan Bank; Eurotunnel; European Investment Bank.

Lovells (see firm details p.1044) Seen on "*big trade financings,*" where banking clients rate its documentation and "*coverage across all sectors.*" **Gavin McQuater** (see p.713) is "*a strong, commercial lawyer.*" He has been involved in a waste to energy project in Singapore, and water-related matters in Europe. The firm is active in airport projects, advising the Leonardo Consortium on the €2 billion financing for Rome Airport and assisting the IVG/PEG consortium on its bid for the Berlin Airport project. Strong too on roads, it represented Bechtel as part of the successful consortium for the Polish A1 Motorway concession. **Clients:** NATS; Sport England; Bechtel; Innisfree; Amey; Barclays Capital; Bank of Scotland.

Masons (see firm details p.1056) Recommended by competitors for its overseas reach, the firm advised the South African government on the Louis Trichardt Prison PPP Project and the Bloemfontein Prison PPP Project. Project companies acknowledge a "*heavily involved*" team. Chris Brown leads a group that advised the Government of Cyprus on the privatisation and infrastructure development of the airports at Larnaka and Pafos. The firm also acted for the sponsor on the development of the special economic zone at Positra, India. At home, the firm won a recent appointment by the European Investment Bank to advise on the financing of one of the London Underground PPP packages. **Clients:** European Investment Bank; Government of Cyprus; Government of South Africa.

Simmons & Simmons (see firm details p.1132) A multi-disciplinary team with a renowned specialisation in the rail sector and a strong presence in China and Southern Europe. Richard Dyton, a partner in the construction group, led a team which advised the Irish Republic's Department of Pub-

Top Ten UK Project Finance Deals (June 2000 to June 2001)

	Project Name	Amount (£million)	Sponsor(s)	Concession Awarder/ Divestor and Legal Advisor	Mandated Arranger / Bookrunner and Leading Legal Advisor	Legal Adviser to Consortium
1	Telecoms Cable & Wireless Communications	9,825.997	NTL Group Ltd	Cable & Wireless **Allen & Overy**	Chase Manhattan Bank, Morgan Stanley Dean Witter; **Clifford Chance, White & Case**	**Travers Smith Braithwaite**
2	Telecoms Hutchison Whampoa 3G Network	3,672.000	Hutchison Whampoa Group, NTT Mobile Communications Network, KPN Mobil Netherlands NV	Ministry of Telecommunications	JP Morgan, HSBC, WestLB, Royal Bank of Scotland, ABN Amro, Citibank, Merrill Lynch; **Allen & Overy** (Steven Kensell)	**Freshfields Bruckhaus Deringer** (Perry Noble)
3	Telecoms TeleWest II Refinancing	2,250.000	Microsoft Corp, Liberty Media	N/a	▲ Syndicated arrangers; **Norton Rose** (Michael Ings)	**Weil Gotshal and Manges** (Bruce Johnston)
4	Water Abacus	1,996.000	Glas Cymru Cyfgedig	Western Power Distribution Ltd, **Allen & Overy**	Royal Bank of Scotland, Salomon Brothers Int; **Clifford Chance**	**Linklaters**
5	Power Drax Power Refinancing	666.483	AES Corp	N/a	Goldman Sachs; **Milbank Tweed Hadley & Mc Cloy** (Phillip Fletcher)	**Davis Polk & Wardwell** (US law) **Slaughter & May** (English law – David Frank)
6	Power Eggborough Power Plant Refinancing	550.000	British Energy	N/a	Barclays Bank; **Allen & Overy** (Tim Arnheim)	**Clifford Chance** (Paul Simpson) **Linklaters** (Jane Woolf)
7	Power Killingholme CCGT Energy Refinancing	507.000	NRG Energy Inc; **Ashurst Morris** Crisp (Michael Johns)	National Power; **Linklaters** (Julia Wolf)	Bank of America; **Shearman & Sterling** (Ken MacRitchie)	**Skadden Arps Slate Meagher & Flom**
8	Telecoms* Eon Communications Cable Network Project	265.637	Madison Dearborn, Incepta, GE Capital Telecom, TDCP	Ministry of Telecommunications	Bank of Scotland, Toronto Dominion Bank; **Norton Rose** (Michael Ings)	**eOn; Taylor Joynson Garrett**
9	Transport Bristol International Airport	260	Macquarie Global Infrastructure Fund, Cintra	Bristol City Council; **Stephenson Harwood**, First Grp; **Burges Salmon**	Abbey National plc; **Freshfields Bruckhaus Deringer** (Perry Noble)	**Shearman & Sterling** (Ken MacRitchie); **Osborne Clarke**
10	Transport East Midlands & Bournemouth Airports	185.77	Manchester Airport; **Pannone & Partners** (Steven Grant)	National Express; **Ashurst Morris Crisp** (Shaun Lascelles)	Royal Bank of Scotland; **Freshfields Bruckhaus Deringer** (Nick Bliss)	**Clifford Chance** (Chris Wyman, financing)

Source: Dealogic Capital Data Project Ware *Source: Law Firms – Chambers & Partners*

* Hybrid arranged under non-recourse basis using an SPV ▲ CIBC World Markets, Bank of New York, Bank of America, Citibank, Deutsche Bank, HypoVereinsbank, WestLB, JP Morgan, Toronto-Dominion Bank, Barclays Bank, Credit Suisse First Boston, Mizuho Financial Group, Royal Bank of Scotland, Fortis Bank

lic Enterprise on the Dublin Rail PPP, and assisted the Province of Noord Brabant on the first PFI road project in the Netherlands. The firm also advised the United Arab Offsets Group on Project Dolphin, and assisted the EIB on its €570 million loan to Wind Telecomunicazioni SpA for the construction of a new fixed and mobile national telecommunications and data network. **Clients:** Abu Dhabi Water & Electricity Authority; Deutsche Telecom; European Investment Bank; Telespazio.

Other Notable Practitioners "*Good on the funding side,*" **Bruce Johnston** (see p.712) of **Weil, Gotshal & Manges** specialises in energy, infrastructure and telecoms projects and advised the EIB on the Athens ring road. **Jane Templeton-Knight** (see p.715) of **Hunton & Williams** is highly experienced in the power and infrastructure sectors and has been active on a number of Brazilian power deals recently. She and fellow partner Mark Frewin form a young, charismatic team who "*close deals in record time,*" according to clients.

LONDON

PFI

Band	PFI • London	Ptnrs	Assts
1	Allen & Overy	28	65
	Clifford Chance	9	40
	Linklaters	27	n/a
2	Freshfields Bruckhaus Deringer	11	32
3	Ashurst Morris Crisp	10	19
	CMS Cameron McKenna	11	n/a
	Denton Wilde Sapte	27	32
	Herbert Smith	30	50
4	Lovells	16*	18*
	Masons	5	14
	Norton Rose	18	49
5	DLA	16	26
	Simmons & Simmons	n/a	n/a
	Slaughter and May	8	n/a
	Theodore Goddard	4	8
6	Berwin Leighton Paisner	6	8
	Bird & Bird	5	6
	Rowe & Maw	6	7
	Trowers & Hamlins	2	n/a

Band	LEADING INDIVIDUALS	
★	**BALDOCK Anne** Allen & Overy	**BLISS Nick** Freshfields Bruckhaus Deringer
	WHITE Bruce Linklaters	
1	**DUFFICY Frank** CMS Cameron	**ELSEY Mark** Ashurst Morris Crisp
	MATHEOU Michael Lovells	**STEADMAN Tim** Clifford Chance
2	**BICKERTON David** Clifford Chance	**GNIADKOWSKI Stan** Denton Wilde Sapte
	IVISON Andrew CMS Cameron	**NOBLE Perry** Freshfields Bruckhaus
	TOTT Nicholas Herbert Smith	
3	**ELLIS Jon** Norton Rose	**FOX Jason** Herbert Smith
	FRANCIS Barry Pinsent Curtis Biddle	**MARLOW Ed** Denton Wilde Sapte
	SEDGLEY David Allen & Overy	
4	**AUSTWICK Malcolm** Beachcroft	**BALLINGALL James** Theodore Goddard
	BECKITT Jonathan CMS Cameron	**BROWN Chris** Masons
	COULTER David Norton Rose	**DARLEY Mark** Lovells
	GATES Ellen Denton Wilde Sapte	**McCANN Martin** Masons
	McCORMACK Carol Berwin Leighton Paisner	
5	**ALLAN Simon** Berwin Leighton Paisner	**GOLDIE Ian** Slaughter and May
	MORRISON Neil Rowe & Maw	**ROLFE Andrew** Clifford Chance
UP AND COMING		
	ARMITAGE Richard Simmons & Simmons	**LEE David** Allen & Overy
	SPACIE Dominic Denton Wilde Sapte	**VERNON Philip** Ashurst Morris Crisp
	WYLES David Herbert Smith	

This book is the product of 6,552 1/2-hour interviews. See p.7 for BMRB audit.
Within each band, firms are listed alphabetically. *See individuals' profiles p.708*
** Figures denote combined Projects/PFI team size.*

Allen & Overy (see firm details p.856) Continues to inspire the confidence of financial institutions, though the balance of the work has tipped slightly in favour of projects companies, sponsors and grantors. Sponsor clients rate the team as "*the best, the most commercially minded,*" and "*full of reasonable and efficient partners.*" "*Top drawer*" **Anne Baldock** (see p.708) acted for MBIA-Ambac International in the Treasury Building PFI project, and advised the arrangers of the Birmingham Northern Relief Road project. **David Sedgley** (see p.715) does a mix of PFI work and North Sea oil and gas financing, and advised NOSWA on the Aberdeen and Moray wastewater projects. Up and coming **David Lee** (see p.712) is "*a sound, pragmatic individual.*" He acted on the Strategic Sea-lift project and the Harnaschpolder waste water treatment project. **Clients:** North of Scotland Water Authority; Premier Prison Services; Edison Capital; West LB; Dresdner Kleinwort Benson; Barclays Bank.

Clifford Chance (see firm details p.919) "*On any bank's shortlist*" and known to "*act for a lot of consortia on bigger deals.*" A pragmatic style wins respect from rivals. "*Clever*" **Tim Steadman** (see p.715) "*knows the market,*" while "*kingpin*" **David Bickerton** (see p.709) "*brings a mix of exuberance and commercial expertise to any transaction.*" Together with **Andrew Rolfe** (see p.714), they advised Modus Services plc on the refurbishment of the MoD's London Headquarters. The firm also represented Greenwich NatWest (arrangers) and MBIA Assurance (guarantors) on the A13 Thames Gateway DBFO, and acted for Greenwich NatWest on a bond financed PPP for a new academy for the Italian tax police in Bari. **Clients:** Abbey National Treasury Services; Amey; Balfour Beatty; Bank of Scotland; Halifax; Lloyds TSB; MBIA; Siemens; Warburg Dillon Read.

Linklaters (see firm details p.1042) "*A high quality PFI team*" according to banks, with "*strength in depth and coverage across all sectors.*" Project companies consider them "*good on complexity.*" "*Always entertaining,*" **Bruce White** (see p.715) is a universally acknowledged star. "*When he's on the case, the job is always done well.*" He acted for the lead arrangers on the Nottingham Express Transit, and for the lead arranger, senior lender and equity shareholder on the Glasgow Schools PFI Project. The firm has also been advising Financial Security Assurance (UK) Limited as monoline insurer and Deutsche Bank as lead manager and underwriter on the GCHQ New Accommodation Project. **Clients:** Bovis Lendlease; Carillion; Group 4; London Electricity; Abbey National; Halifax; HSBC; Royal Bank of Scotland.

Freshfields Bruckhaus Deringer (see firm details p.965) Highly visible on the LUL PPP to which the firm has "*hitched its star*" according to some commentators. Banks rate "*the dogged, confident team,*" while peers and project owners acknowledge a "*professional, high quality service.*" "*Energetic and plain speaking*" **Nick Bliss** (see p.709) advised the National Roads Authority of Ireland on its PPP roads programme, while **Perry Noble** (see p.714) is strong on telecoms and transport PFI. He acted for Abbey National on the Norfolk Police HQ, and for Babcock and Brown on the Derby Courts PFI. The firm has also represented Paradigm Secure Communications in its bid to provide the next generation of secure military satellite communications services to the MoD. **Clients:** Barclays Capital; Innisfree; LUL; The Royal Bank of Scotland; WS Atkins.

Ashurst Morris Crisp (see firm details p.866) Historically a sponsor based practice, some banks are now putting it "*in the top three*" often on their PFI lists. Rivals praise an "*entrepreneurial team which does a thorough job.*" "*Hard-working*" **Mark Elsey** (see p.710) "*really knows what he's doing.*" He acted for the Exchequer Partnership consortium (includes Bovis, Stanhope and Chesterton) on the £150 million GOGGS project. Known recently for his work in transport and accommodation, **Philip Vernon** (see p.715) acted for the Integrated Accommodation Services consortium (includes Carillion, Group 4 and BT) on the £400 million GCHQ New Accommodation project, and advised the funders (includes Deutsche Bank; CIBC and FSA) supporting the Metronet bid for infracos on the London Underground PPP project. The team has successfully exported PPP principles overseas including advising South African National Road Agency on the N4 Platinum toll road. **Clients:** Sir Robert McAlpine Ltd; Carillion; Docklands Light Railway Ltd.

CMS Cameron McKenna (see firm details p.922) Known in the market for its work on behalf of project owners and contractors, the firm also has a strong relationship with Dresdner. The team "*processes a deal very well.*" "*Smooth, commercially driven*" **Frank Dufficy** (see p.710) "*seeks to present arguments in a convincing form,*" and has acted on the Birmingham Schools project. "*Balanced and methodical*" **Andrew Ivison** (see p.712) is recommended by peers for his finance work. He acted for the Metronet Consortium in relation to the LUL PPP. Property expert **Jonathan Beckitt** (see p.709) acted on the North Wiltshire Schools project. The group has also strengthened its IT-related practice, and acted for the Home Office in relation to the IT 2000 project. **Clients:** Dresdner Kleinwort Wasserstein; Barclays Capital; Balfour Beatty Capital Projects; Innisfree Ltd.

Denton Wilde Sapte (see firm details p.939) Considered by banks to present "*a serious challenge to the magic circle,*" the team is "*technically competent, with a high quality of service.*" "*Sensible*" **Stan Gniadkowski** "*clearly knows his stuff.*" A combination projects specialist, he advised Laing Hyder on a number of projects including the Metropolitan Police PFI to provide four new police stations and a firearms training centre. **Ed Marlow**, rated by rivals as "*a good guy who knows his stuff,*" has acted on immigration detention centres and secure training centres for the Home Office. "*Responsive and proactive*" roads expert **Ellen Gates** advised the MoD on Project Aquatrine, and acted for the Highways Agency on the A1 Darrington to Dishforth DBFO road. Recent arrival from Mayer Brown & Platt **Dominic Spacie** has further strengthened the team. **Clients:** MoD; Highways Agency; Newcourt Capital; Laing Hyder; Abbey National.

Herbert Smith (see firm details p.993) "*In it from the start.*" Peers respect the firm for making "*a great contribution towards the correct development of the market.*" Noted for its health expertise, clients consider it "*impressive and able to handle the full complexity.*" "*Pragmatic*" **Nick Tott** (see p.715) has acted for the MoD in its main building project, and for HM Treasury and Partnerships UK in connection with its establishment. "*Hard-working and diligent*" **Jason Fox** (see p.711) possesses "*integrity and a constructive, problem-solving mentality.*" He acted for University College London Hospitals NHS Trust in connection with one of the largest hospital PFI projects. "*Sensible, bright*" **David Wyles** (see p.716) acted for the EIB on the Dudley hospitals PFI. **Clients:** MoD; Partnerships UK; Halifax Bank plc; British Waterways Board; Virgin Trains.

Lovells (see firm details p.1044) "*Heavily involved*" firm which "*wrote the standard documentation for NHS PFI work.*" Rated by clients as "*good on financings*" the group has a strong focus on airports, rail, water, serviced accommodation and defence. "*Diligent*" **Mike Matheou** (see p.712) advised the Board of the Inland Revenue and the Commissioners of Customs and Excise in the STEPS project to transfer their estates to a PFI provider of serviced accommodation. Also assisted the Tube Lines and Surface Lines consortia on bids for the JNP and SSL lines under the London Underground PPPs. **Mark Darley** (see p.710) is considered "*a good lawyer from the banks' perspective.*" He advised a consortium bidding for the Newcastle International Airport PPP. The group also acted for BNP Paribas as senior lender to the project vehicle, Total Schools Solutions Ltd on the Staffordshire 'Two Schools' project. **Clients:** NATS; Sport England; Bechtel; Amey; Barclays Capital; Bank of Scotland.

Masons (see firm details p.1056) Traditionally strong on the sponsor side, the group has made inroads into project financing with "*skilled personnel*" and "*a highly commercial approach.*" Clients applaud "*a multi-faceted team*" that "*knows the Treasury Task Force well.*" **Chris Brown** (see p.709) "*offers a higher standard of public sector work.*" He represented the concessionaire on the Nottingham Express Transit System, and acted for the funder, Bank Gesellschaft Berlin AG on the Humberside Courts development. **Martin McCann**'s (see p.713) "*non-confrontational style works well with both sides of the table.*" He advised BAe systems on the financing of the IT outsourcing requirements to CSC International Systems Management. He also advised the MoD on the multi-jurisdictional procurement of tank training simulators. **Clients:** European Investment Bank; Dexia Public Finance Bank; Bank Gesellschaft Berlin; ING Barings; Royal Bank of Scotland; Innisfree Limited; Carillion.

Norton Rose (see firm details p.1082) Offering "*a comprehensive service,*" the group benefits greatly from an excellent asset finance practice. Transportation PFI projects are a particular area of expertise. Peers agree that **Jon Ellis** (see p.710) "*doesn't suffer fools gladly,*" while clients rate him "*one of the best PFI lawyers in London.*" He advised the Bank of Scotland and Barclays Bank on the financing of an MoD communications project, and advised the preferred bidder on a new main building for the Home Office. "*Conciliatory*" **David Coulter** (see p.710) "*has a broad-based experience*" and "*can see all the facets of a transaction.*" He advised the arranging groups supporting two preferred bidding consortia on the LUL PPP, and has assisted on various projects in the local authority, transport, water and waste sectors. **Clients:** Taylor Woodrow; Royal Bank of Scotland; Paribas; Abbey National; Innisfree; HSBC; Bank of Scotland; Bouygues Construction.

DLA Typically seen acting for government authorities, the team has acted on a range of domestic work, advising the project company on the creation and operation of a new hospital at Farnborough.

Simmons & Simmons (see firm details p.1132) "*Visible,*" multi-faceted practice which "*provides a good, effective service,*" and is well known for its MoD and transport work. The recent lateral hire of an IT expert from Arnold & Porter should help to expand the firm's IT-related projects practice. "*Pragmatic*" **Richard Armitage** (see p.708) "*understands the commercial drivers behind PFI.*" He assisted the MoD on the Future Strategic Tanker Aircraft project. The firm also advised Railtrack on the rescue of the £5.3 billion Channel Tunnel Rail Link, and on the Thameslink 2000 project. In addition, it is assisting the MoD on PPP options for DERA. **Clients:** MoD; Barclays Bank; Carillion and Crown House Engineering; Railtrack; FLAG Atlantic.

Slaughter and May (see firm details p.1135) A significant presence despite a noted pricing pressure in PFI. Competitors agree that the team "*handles major deals sublimely well.*" **Ian Goldie** (see p.711) is a well-respected practitioner with considerable rail expertise. He acted for the LINC Consortium on its bid in connection with the BCV and SSL London Underground infrastructure upgrade PPP project. The firm also acted for the arranging banks on the MoD office redevelopment project, advised Chase Manhattan as lead arranger of the debt financing for the Wembley Stadium project, and assisted the government on the National Air Traffic Services PPP. **Clients:** Chase Manhattan; DETR; Modus; LINC Consortium.

Theodore Goddard (see firm details p.1152) The firm wins the approval of clients for its "*breadth of experience,*" "*wide range of skills*" and "*extensive resources.*" Key lateral hires have further strengthened the department. "*Thorough and good*" **James Ballingall** (see p.708) impresses clients with "*his style of negotiation and the turnaround of contracted documentation.*" The firm has a strong sponsor-based practice, including long-standing relationships with Jarvis and Kier. It advised Bilfinger + Berger on the Wiltshire schools project and assisted the Edmund Nuttall/Halcrow consortium on a flood defences project in the Norfolk Broads. Extending its finance practice, the group acted for Halifax plc as funder, junior debt and equity provider in the pathfinder MoD army foundation college at Harrogate. **Clients:** National Audit Office; Jarvis Projects; Vosper Thornycroft; Halifax plc; Bilfinger + Berger.

Berwin Leighton Paisner (see firm details p.878) Noted in the market as a "*strong healthcare PFI firm*" which is skilled in limited recourse financing techniques. Operates a small team with "*effective, gregarious*" partners. **Carol McCormack** (see p.713) continues to advise the Home Office in relation to its Central London Accomodation Project, while **Simon Allan** (see p.708) acted for the preferred bidder on the Strategic Sealift Project and advised the Government on the sale of the Millennium Dome. The firm has also advised Lex Services on the MoD Whitefleet Project, represented the Trust on the Havering Hospital project, and assisted Southwark Land Regeneration plc on the Elephant and Castle project. **Clients:** Lex Services; Houlder Offshore Engineering; Jarvis; Bouygues/Charterhouse; The Home Office/Partnerships UK; Connex.

Bird & Bird (see firm details p.884) "*Strong on IT, with a clear focus*" the firm continues to dominate this niche strand of the PFI world. Roger Bickerstaff leads a team that has an enviable relationship with central government agencies and plays an active role in policy development. Advised the Employment Service on the £800 million e-commerce scheme rolled out to Job Centres sites in England and Wales and acted for the Prison Service on the renewal of IT infrastructure at 135 prisons and HMPS headquarters. In the international arena the firm advised FCO on the Global Crossing contract to create a global communications network for the embassies and consulates. **Clients:** Foreign & Commenwealth Office; OFSTED; CCTA; HM Prison Service.

Rowe & Maw (see firm details p.1113) "*A competent team*" which is developing its finance capabilities. The firm demonstrates specific expertise in transport, healthcare and education. **Neil Morrison** (see p.713) ("*has the financing expertise you need*") advised Road Management Services (AMEC, Alfred McAlpine, Brown & Root and Dragados) on the A13 Thames Gateway DBFO road. He also assisted the Carillion, Group 4, Société Générale consortium as preferred bidder for the DBFO Contract to provide a new magistrates' court for the City of Manchester. In addition, the firm is advising the Metropolitan Borough of the Wirral on a major bundled schools project comprising nine schools. **Clients:** Alfred McAlpine; AMEC; Brown & Root; Carillion; Department of Trade and Industry; Torbay Borough Council.

Top Ten UK Completed PFI Deals (signed from June 2000 to June 2001)

	Project Name	Amount (£million)	Sponsors	Concession Awarder/ Divestor and Legal Advisor	Mandated Arranger / Bookrunner and Legal Advisor	Legal Adviser to Consortium
1	**Road** Birmingham Northern Relief Road	832.000	Macquarie Infrastructure Projects, Autostrade	DETR **CMS Cameron McKenna**; Robert Phillips, also Trevor Butcher, Nancy Eller	Abbey National, Bank of America, Lloyds TSB Bank, Banca OPI, Prudential Banking, Bank of Scotland, HypoVereinsbank, NIB Capital Bank, NordLB **Allen & Overy**; Anne Baldock	**Ashurst Morris Crisp**; Mark Elsey and John May
2	**Property** MoD Whitehall Building PFI	551.700	Amey Construction, Hyder, Macquarie Infrastructure Projects, Innisfree	Ministry of Defence **Herbert Smith**; Nick Tott	Dresdner Bank, **Slaughter and May**; Steve Edwards, **Allen & Overy**; Anne Baldock	**Clifford Chance**; Andrew Rolfe **Masons**; Cathryn Vickers
3	**School** Glasgow Secondary Schools	373.050	Amey Construction, Miller Construction Mitel (IT suppliers)	Glasgow City Council **Dundas & Wilson**; Michael McAuley	Halifax, **Linklaters**; Bruce White, Benedict James, Richard Ginks	**MacRoberts**; Michael Murphy **Masons**; Cathryn Vickers, advised Amey, **Shepherd & Wedderburn**; advised Miller, **McGrigor Donald** advised Mitel
4	**Property** STEPS (Strategic Transfer of Estate to Private Sector)	294.870	Soros Real Estate Partners, Fortress Investment Corp, Delancey Estates, DTZ Debenham Thorpe	HM Customs and Excise, Inland Revenue, **Lovells**; Mike Matheou (PFI/PPP) and David Lane (property)	Halifax, **Herbert Smith**; Andrew Preece	**Nabarro Nathanson**; Mary Bonar lead, (PFI/PPP) Nigel Heilpern (property), Andrew McLean (finance)
5	**Hospital** University College of London Hospital	280.000	Amec, Balfour Beatty Construction International, Building & Property Group	University College London Hospitals NHS Trust **Herbert Smith**; Jason Fox	Abbey National, **Denton Wilde Sapte**; David Nanson, Joanne Horridge	**Linklaters**; Marshall Levine, Jane Murphy, Cathy Harris
6	**Transport** Nottingham Express Transit Line One System	225.000	Innisfree, CDC Projects, Carillion, Transdev, Adtranz, Nottingham City Transport	Nottingham City Council **Eversheds**; Tim Costello	ABN Amro, Dresdner Kleinwort Wasserstein, Bankgesellschaft Berlin, **Linklaters**; Bruce White, Stuart Rowsen, Anne Vallely	**Masons**; Martin Harman, Chris Brown
7	**Prison** Premier Prison Services Refinancing	198.650	Wackenhut, Serco Group, Kvaerner Construction	Home Office (legal advisers, n/a)	Bank of Scotland, Barclays Bank, Credit Lyonnais, Dai-Ichi Kangyo Bank, WesLB, **Clifford Chance**; Dan Reynell	**Allen & Overy**; Anne Baldock
8	**Social Security Housing** DSS Newcastle Longbenton Estate Refinancing	175.300	Amec, Building & Property Group	N/a	Royal Bank of Scotland **Allen & Overy**	**Berwin Leighton Paisner**; Simon Allan
9	**Hopsital** Dudley Hospital	161.000	Sir Robert McAlpine, Tilbury Douglas, Bank of Scotland	Dudley NHS Trust **Beachcroft Wansboroughs**; Malcolm Austwick	Royal Bank of Canada, European Investment Bank, **Linklaters**; Bruce White	**Ashurst Morris Crisp**; Jan Sanders
10	**Transport** National Traffic Control Centres	160.000	Serco Group, Sir William Halcrow & Partners	Highwyas Agency **Denton Wilde Sapte**; Ian Hodgson, Bonella Ramsey	WestLB, **DLA**; Richard Curl	**Clifford Chance**; Paul Simpson

Source: Dealogic Capital Data.

Trowers & Hamlins (see firm details p.1162) Accommodation specialists who act extensively for the private sector and are rated by clients for "*a pragmatic approach and a first-class level of service.*" Ian Graham heads the firm's cross-departmental PFI group. The team represented the Dexia/Carillion consortium, which is short-listed on four of the eight local authority social housing PFI pathfinder schemes. It also acted for Ryhurst Limited on a Redbridge NHS Trust project, and for North Wiltshire DC on the closing of its office rationalisation project with Jarvis. **Clients:** Ryhurst Limited; Dexia Public Finance Bank; Carillion.

Other Notable Practitioners Despite the firm's loss of its major players to Buchanan Ingersoll, **Malcolm Austwick** (see p.708) of **Beachcroft Wansbroughs** "*has made a reasonable go of things*" and "*retains some good private sector clients.*" The highly respected **Barry Francis** (see p.711) ("*a good operator,*") acted for the NHS Trust on the Walsgrave hospital, mental health and research facilities project. Formerly head of the now disbanded Buchanan Ingersoll PFI unit, at the time of press, he signalled his intention to join the London office of **Pinsent Curtis Biddle**.

THE SOUTH & WALES

PROJECTS/PFI • The South & Wales		Ptnrs	Assts
1	**Bevan Ashford** Bristol	5	8
2	**Burges Salmon** Bristol	3	7
	Eversheds Cardiff	2	2
3	**Morgan Cole** Cardiff	n/a	n/a
4	**Masons** Bristol	2	3

LEADING INDIVIDUALS		
1	**HUGHES Stephen** Bevan Ashford	
2	**EVANS Eric** Eversheds	**WHITFIELD Stuart** Bevan Ashford
3	**FAIRBAIRN Iain** Beachcroft Wansbroughs	**HUTTON David** Bevan Ashford
UP AND COMING		
	MANSON Stephen Eversheds	

This book is the product of 6,552 1/2-hour interviews. See p.7 for BMRB audit.

Within each band, firms are listed alphabetically. *See individuals' profiles p.708*

Bevan Ashford (see firm details p.880)"*Outstanding, professional and cost effective*" according to clients, while rivals acknowledge it "*works well as a team.*" The firm represents a strong roster of NHS Trusts and is increasing its focus on education. It is also starting to build up its financing practice, and is regularly instructed by the Bank of Ireland and the Royal Bank of Scotland. Health expert **Stephen Hughes** (see p.712) "*does an exceptionally good job of pulling in the work.*" Major hospital projects he has acted for are, inter alia, the Bath & West Community NHS Trust, the Cornwall Healthcare NHS Trust and the Essex and Herts Community NHS Trust. "*Technically astute*" **Stuart Whitfield** (see p.716) "*has an excellent knowledge of the MoD sector.*" A regular adviser to AMEC and Bovis Lend Lease, he has been advising AMEC and Vosper Thornycroft on the MoD's Royal School of Military Engineering project. **David Hutton** (see p.712) is endorsed for his work in the education sector. The firm also represented the Isle of Man Government on a £100 million waste to energy plant. **Clients:** Bank of Ireland; Royal Bank of Scotland; Wessex Water; Bovis Lend Lease; Rolls-Royce; AMEC; Vosper Thornycroft; Total Fina Elf.

Burges Salmon (see firm details p.902) The firm is best known for its MoD, transport and rail work. Richard Wynn Jones heads a team, said by clients to "*provide excellent representation,*" that has advised the MoD on Skynet 5. The firm also acted on the Astute PFI for submarine simulator training. Advised the London Fire and Emergency Planning Authority on a major procurement, management and maintenance project, and on a PPP to deliver a new station at Canary Wharf. **Clients:** British Railways Board; London Fire & Emergency Planning Authority; MoD; University of Bristol; West Somerset District Council.

Eversheds (see firm details p.952) "*Admired by public authorities*" and acknowledged by competitors to have "*a stranglehold on education.*" **Eric Evans** (see p.710) is well liked and **Stephen Manson** (see p.712) is recognised as an up and coming force. The firm underlined its education capacity by acting for Wiltshire County Council on the Wiltshire Grouped Schools scheme. It has also acted for an international consortium on the M12 Rijeka-Zagreb motorway and advised Neath County Borough Council on the Neath waste-to-energy PFI. **Clients:** Wiltshire County Council; Neath County Borough Council.

Morgan Cole (see firm details p.1074) Contractors commend a "*thorough, capable and competent*" team buoyed the leadership of Alun Cole. Continues to advise the National Museums and Galleries of Wales in the PPP relocation of the Wales Maritime and Industrial Museum in the Swansea City Waterfront Development. Also advised the South Wales Fire Service on the provision of a new Fire Training Centre (value £11 million). **Clients:** Associated Holdings; Wales Tourist Board; Luton & Dunstable NHS Trust.

Masons (see firm details p.1056) Although the loss of Iain Fairbairn to Beachcroft Wansbroughs is felt by the market to have hit the team hard, high profile work continues to be undertaken, with a keen focus on the accommodation and education sectors. Cathryn Vickers heads a team that advised Amey Business Services Limited on the refurbishment of the MoD main building in Whitehall, and acted on the Glasgow Schools PFI project. The firm has assisted in projects on behalf of consortia led by Ballast, Reliance Custodial Services and Charterhouse. **Clients:** Amey Business Services; Ballast; HBG Construction.

Other Notable Practitioners **Iain Fairbairn** (see p.710) has left Masons and is now focusing on health sector PFI work at **Beachcroft Wansbroughs.**

MIDLANDS & EAST ANGLIA

Eversheds (see firm details p.952) "*Self-starters,*" and "*reassuring to work with*" according to clients. Competitors acknowledge "*an impressive track record in police and fire.*" "*Calm, incisive*" **Stephen Matthew** (see p.713) is now National Head of the Projects Group. He has acted on the Camden Social Housing PFI. The firm maintains its reputation for education projects, and is currently advising Jarvis on the Bridlington Schools PFI. It is also a significant presence on rail matters, representing the Strategic Rail Authority on most of the refranchise negotiations, and assisting Nottingham City Council on the Nottingham Express Transit Project. Large-scale IT outsourcing is an emerging specialisation. **Clients:** Strategic Rail Authority; Ryder; Jarvis; Dorset Police Authority.

Pinsent Curtis Biddle (see firm details p.1098) Bolstered by a group of housing specialists from Irwin Mitchell, peers observe that the team has "*a good PFI track record*" and "*is using it as a platform to enter the housing PFI market.*" Airports expert **Cameron Woodrow** (see p.716) heads the practice. He is assisted by "*commercial*" **Alan Aisbett** (see p.708) who succeeds in "*pulling in the work*" and has been working on the Government's PFI housing standardisation guidance. The firm also acted for Sunderland Housing Group on the 37,000 unit social housing LSVT by Sunderland City Council, advised Walsall MBC on their pathfinder street lighting PFI project, and represented Brighton & East Sussex and Sheffield City Council on their waste management

PROJECTS/PFI • Midlands and East Anglia	Ptnrs	Assts
1 **Eversheds** Nottingham	4	12
Pinsent Curtis Biddle Birmingham	5	7
2 **DLA** Birmingham	n/a	n/a
Mills & Reeve Cambridge	3	6
Wragge & Co Birmingham	3	8

LEADING INDIVIDUALS	
1 **MATTHEW Stephen** Eversheds	**RANDLE Anthony** DLA
2 **KENNY Stephen** Wragge & Co	**PICKUP Raith** Mills & Reeve
WOODROW Cameron Pinsent Curtis Biddle	
3 **AISBETT Alan** Pinsent Curtis Biddle	

This book is the product of 6,552 1/2-hour interviews. See p.7 for BMRB audit.

Within each band, firms are listed alphabetically. *See individuals' profiles p.708*

schemes. **Clients:** Sunderland Housing Group; London Borough of Islington; Natwest.

DLA Tony Randle remains key to the success of the group, claim interviewees. Drawing on support from across the network, the office is recommended for its expertise in the education sector for both public and private clients.

Mills & Reeve (see firm details p.1069) Clients praise "*a commercial and flexible team which offers a first-class service.*" The firm is well known for its public sector health and education work. It completed the Northern Birmingham Mental Health project and is involved in the largest university sector PFI for the University of Hertfordshire. **Raith Pickup** (see p.714) is "*great fun to work with,*" and "*extremely astute and good-humoured.*" **Clients:** NHS Trusts and universities.

Wragge & Co (see firm details p.1189) "*Impressive*" group that acts predominantly for the public sector and project companies, excelling in defence and transport work. The firm advised Adtranz on its involvement in the Nottingham Express Transit and the London Underground PPP. A growing expertise in serviced accommodation projects for local authorities is also recognised by the market. "*Competent, practical*" **Stephen Kenny** is a defence projects specialist who recently completed an 18 month secondment to the Defence Procurement Agency. He assisted Cap Gemini Ernst & Young on the 'DECS' project for the MoD and advised TRW on its £1.7 billion bid for project Bowman. **Clients:** Bedfordshire County Council; Cap Gemini Ernst & Young; Carillion; Adtranz; MoD; Amec; Bullough; Gloucestershire County Council.

THE NORTH

PROJECTS/PFI • The North	Ptnrs	Assts
1 **Addleshaw Booth & Co** Leeds, Manchester	6	6
Pinsent Curtis Biddle Leeds	4	6
2 **Eversheds** Leeds, Manchester	6	21
3 **Dickinson Dees** Newcastle upon Tyne	8	10
DLA Leeds, Manchester	2	6
Nabarro Nathanson Sheffield	3	8
4 **Masons,** Leeds, Manchester	3	2

LEADING INDIVIDUALS	
1 **O'CONNOR Mike** Addleshaw Booth & Co	
2 **CIRELL Stephen** Eversheds	**LOVITT Arthur** Pinsent Curtis Biddle
SUTTIE Frank Addleshaw Booth & Co	
3 **BAKER Huw** Masons	**CLARK Brian** DLA
COCKRAM Richard Addleshaw Booth & Co	**COOKE Ken** Masons
FELLOWS Alison Dickinson Dees	**ROUT Peter** DLA

This book is the product of 6,552 1/2-hour interviews. See p.7 for BMRB audit.

Within each band, firms are listed alphabetically. *See individuals' profiles p.708*

Addleshaw Booth & Co (see firm details p.853) Recognised by the market as "*a major player in Manchester*" and one which "*always offers good strength in depth.*" **Mike O'Connor** (see p.714) is "*good on corporate banking.*" Active in both the public and private sector, he "*sees the equation from both sides.*" He represented Northumbria Health Care NHS Trust on the new DGH at Hexham. Based in Leeds, **Frank Suttie** "*has a hell of a reputation for PFI.*" He advised the MoD on the Landrover PPP. "*Highly competent*" **Richard Cockram** (see p.201)advised the Leeds Community and Mental Health Teaching NHS Trust on the 'Omnibus' accommodation project. **Clients:** Jarvis Projects; University of Sheffield; Energy Services UK; Met Office; Leeds City Council.

Pinsent Curtis Biddle (see firm details p.1098) Has had "*a cracking year,*" say rivals. The team has undertaken "*big deals and proved it can handle a large volume of work.*" It acts for funders (Royal Bank of Scotland, Barclays), consortia (Clugston, Gleesons) and the public sector, and is rated for its expertise in NHS-related PFI work. Recommended by peers for his MoD work, **Arthur Lovitt** (see p.712) represented the Royal Bank of Scotland in the funding of Bradford & Northern's £47 million PFI scheme for Leeds Community Health NHS Trust. The firm has also been representing Nationwide Building Society in connection with its funding of Jarvis's £47 million Kirklees School scheme, and acted for Hull & East Yorkshire NHS Trust on its £30 million maternity scheme. **Clients:** Royal Bank of Scotland; Nationwide Building Society; Barclays; Hull & East Yorkshire Hospitals.

Eversheds (see firm details p.952) The number one in local government "*picks up a huge amount of public sector work.*" Contractors are "*impressed by their representation.*" The partners come from public sector backgrounds and thus know how local authorities tick. **Stephen Cirell** (see p.58) is "*pre-eminent on the local authority side and loved by his clients.*" The group acted for Haringey LBC on a secondary school stock project, and for Kier on an Islington LBC outsourcing. It is representing the Greater Manchester Police on the provision of eighteen new police stations and associated properties. **Clients:** Haringey LBC; Kier; Greater Manchester Police; East Sussex County Council; Liverpool City Council.

Dickinson Dees (see firm details p.941) Expert in NHS PFI work and now strengthening its position in social housing, police and transport sectors. The team is "*breaking out of the NE,*" and is perceived by interviewees to be active in both the public and private sectors. **Alison Fellows** (see p.710) spearheads the group's health expertise. She has been involved in the Newcastle Acute Services Review and the Leeds NHS Trust Rationalisation Strategy. The firm also acted on a £35 million cancer hospital in Belfast, and a schools project for Newcastle City Council. **Clients:** Newcastle Hospitals NHS Trust; HM Prisons; Newcastle City Council.

DLA Specialising in defence and transport the firm also performs public sector outsourcing and procurement. **Brian Clark** is the firm's leading name.

Nabarro Nathanson (see firm details p.1078) "*Constructive, pleasant, and commercial,*" the team is considered by rivals to be a strong public sector force. The projects group is divided up into sector-focused units, with Tim Shaw heading the accommodation unit. The firm acted for Sheffield City Council on the Sheffield Grouped Schools Scheme. It also represented the East Riding of Yorkshire Council on the Humberside Magistrates Courts Scheme, and on the East Riding Grouped Schools Project. In the private sector, the group advised such clients as Bowmer and Kirkland and Shepherd Construction. **Clients:** Sheffield City Council; East Riding of Yorkshire Council; Bolton Metropolitan Borough Council.

Masons (see firm details p.1056) An "*outstanding group.*" The Leeds office has particular experience of the criminal justice sector and education, while Manchester is strong in construction and IT. Leeds based **Ken Cooke** (see p.709) is praised by clients as "*an absolute service provider; nothing's ever too much trouble for him.*" He advised Modern Courts Limited both in the Humberside Magistrates Courts PFI and on courts PFI projects in East Anglia, Bedford and Avon & Somerset. In Manchester, "*PFI master*" **Huw Baker** (see p.708) acted for Carillion Construction on the GCHQ New Accommodation Project. **Clients:** Aqumen Services; John Mowlem & Company; ING Barings; Carillion Construction.

SCOTLAND

PROJECTS/PFI • Scotland		Ptnrs	Assts
1	**Dundas & Wilson CS** Edinburgh, Glasgow	7	26
2	**MacRoberts** Edinburgh, Glasgow	5	16
	McGrigor Donald Edinburgh, Glasgow	7	11
3	**Maclay Murray & Spens** Glasgow	4	n/a
	Masons Glasgow	2	6
	McClure Naismith Edinburgh	6	5
	Shepherd & Wedderburn WS Edinburgh	7	10
4	**Burness** Edinburgh	8	5
	Tods Murray WS Edinburgh	4	5

LEADING INDIVIDUALS		
1	**MURPHY Michael** MacRoberts	
2	**CAMPBELL Alan** Dundas & Wilson CS	**HENDERSON David** MacRoberts
	McAULEY Michael Dundas & Wilson CS	**NASH David** Shepherd & Wedderburn WS
3	**BROWN Steven** McClure Naismith	**GRAHAM Drysdale** McGrigor Donald
	MACAULAY Iain McGrigor Donald	**McEWAN Alastair** Maclay Murray
	READ Anthony Burness	**SIMMONS William** Tods Murray WS

This book is the product of 6,552 1/2-hour interviews. See p.7 for BMRB audit.

Within each band, firms are listed alphabetically. *See individuals' profiles p.708*

Dundas & Wilson CS (see firm details p.947) Recognised to dominate the public sector, where it "*crops up on almost every deal.*" Clients consider it "*an impressive and well-organised firm*" which is "*out on its own for PPPs.*" A notable banking practice lends good support. Niche strengths include the water industry where the firm represents two out of three of the Scottish Water Authorities. **Alan Campbell** "*does a good deal.*" He acted for Lloyds TSB (senior lender) for the St George's Hospital, Tooting. "*Man of the people*" **Michael McAuley** is a "*robust practitioner.*" He acted for Glasgow City Council in the flagship Glasgow batched schools PFI project. The firm also acted for Dexia (senior lender) on the Kirklees Borough Council Waste to Energy Scheme. **Clients:** East of Scotland Water Authority; University of Edinburgh; Bank of Scotland; Barclays Bank; Dexia; Ballast; Newcourt Capital.

MacRoberts (see firm details p.1048) "*A sound projects team*" which "*has reaped the benefits of having the right kind of construction clients when PFI started.*" Pragmatic **Michael Murphy** (see p.713) "*drives the finance through well*" and **David Henderson** (see p.712) remains "*very much on top of deals.*" The team is involved in the Murray Waste Water scheme, Edinburgh schools and Nottingham Police Station projects. Involved in the £50 million Dalmuir Wastewater Project, advising contractors Taylor Woodrow, and acted in the £250 million Glasgow City Schools PFI on behalf of the Miller, Halifax and Amey consortium. **Clients:** Miller Construction; RBS.

McGrigor Donald (see firm details p.1062) Acknowledged by the market to "*have the depth that you need for a major project.*" The "*impressive team*" includes **Drysdale Graham** (see p.711) who advised the NewSchools consortium on the Leyton School project and assisted MBIA Assurance on the Levenmouth water and sewerage project. **Iain Macaulay** (see p.712) wins praise from clients as "*an excellent banking lawyer.*" The Edinburgh office has a private sector bias while public sector work tends to be led out of Glasgow. Following the opening of its Belfast office, the firm is well placed to take advantage of the expanding PFI market in Ireland. It represented the Scottish Tourist Board on an e-commerce project, advised on the Scottish tranche of project Aquatrine and managed the NewSchools consortium and RBS on the Swan Valley Community School's project. The firm is advising the public sector in all three of the Scottish Local Authority Waste Management Projects to be announced to date. **Clients:** MBIA Assurance; The Royal Bank of Scotland; W S Atkins Investments Limited; MoD; The City of Edinburgh Council.

Maclay Murray & Spens (see firm details p.1047) Rated for both sponsor and funder experience. Banks consider that it is "*good at looking at interconnections*" and "*copes with the side issues well.*" Peers agree that the firm has "*a high degree of expertise.*" Strong on water, it is seen to have undertaken a volume of "*difficult health deals.*" "*Cool under pressure*" **Alastair McEwan** (see p.713) has a "*shrewd commercial judgement.*" He advised the preferred bidder on, inter alia, the Aberdeenshire Schools project, the Findlay House project, the Chester-le-Street Community Hospital, and the Copeland Borough Council Accommodation project. **Clients:** North of Scotland Water Authority; Bank of Scotland; Lloyds TSB Bank; Canmore Partnership; Premier Prison Services.

McClure Naismith (see firm details p.1059) "*Well resourced and knowledgeable*" bidder-oriented team that retains the confidence of contractors. Highly rated in health, the team undertakes both private and public sector work. It also acts on law and order, predominantly in the private sector. **Steven Brown** (see p.709) is considered by some sources "*the most knowledgeable person in the PFI market.*" He advised the NHS Trust on the Midlothian Community Hospital, the Secure Care Centre at Stobhill, and the new hospital in Hawick. **Clients:** HBG Construction; Robertson Group; Melville Dundas.

Masons (see firm details p.1056) A relatively young office with a growing reputation. Widely recognised to be "*big on construction,*" clients rate a "*commercial*" team that "*possesses a full understanding of the PFI process.*" Alastair Morrison heads a group that advised Ayr Environmental Services and Caledonian Environmental Services, the preferred suppliers selected to implement two Build-Own-Operate schemes to provide modernised water and sewerage infrastructure. The firm also advised the SPV and the construction JV on a new cancer centre for Belfast City Hospital, and represented Amey Business Services on the Glasgow Schools PFI project. **Clients:** Amec Project Investments; Miller Construction; H&J Martin.

Shepherd & Wedderburn WS (see firm details p.1126) Clients remain "*impressed with the quality*" of this historically public sector firm, which has expanded into the bidders and lenders market. "*Astute and an exceptionally good negotiator,*" **David Nash** (see p.713) is praised by competitors for "*grabbing all the schools projects.*" An engineering and equipment based projects specialist, he acted for the army on a mobile generators project. The firm also acted for Northlink Orkney and Shetland Ferries on the Orkney and Shetland Ferries PFI, and advised Amey-Miller Joint Venture on the Glasgow Schools project. It is acting for East Renfrewshire Council on the Glasgow Southern Orbital/M77 DBFO. **Clients:** Angus Council; MoD; East Renfrewshire Council; Edinburgh City Council; European Investment Bank.

Burness (see firm details p.903) A "*user-friendly*" team with "*a number of good individuals*" and a strong knowledge of the education field. **Anthony**

Read (see p.714) acted for Jarvis on the East Renfrewshire Schools project, and for Barclays on Balfron High School. Bolstered by a recruit from Tods Murray, the group is also well known in the market for its wastewater specialisation, and advised on the financing of the Aberdeen Wastewater project. **Clients:** Ballast; Barclays; BBC; Jarvis; Bank of Scotland; Shanks Group.

Tods Murray WS (see firm details p.1157) Predominantly private sector focused team with noted expertise in hospitals and education where clients commend *"a skilled team across the board."* **William Simmons** (see p.715) *"has a thorough understanding of project agreements."* In 2000, he advised on eleven schools projects, including the Stoke Schools PFI, where he advised the concession company. The firm also acted for the concession company on the Aberdeen Wastewater treatment project, represented the preferred bidder on the Scots law aspects of the Tornado GR4 simulator project, and has been retained by prospective lenders in three schools projects in Scotland. **Clients:** Consort Healthcare; Balfour Beatty Capital Projects; Bank of Scotland; Forestry Commission.

LEADERS IN PROJECTS / PFI

AISBETT, Alan
Pinsent Curtis Biddle, Birmingham (0121) 200 1050
alan.aisbett@pinsents.com
Specialisation: Partner specialising in major projects, PFI and PPP. Acts for both public and private sectors. Major transactions have included £100m concession based financing of London Luton Airport, an £18m schools PFI Project for London Borough of Waltham Forest, a £415m loan facility for Sunderland Housing Group, a £30m schools PFI project for Newham LBC, a £50m housing PFI project for Islington LBC and a £30m outsourcing of Barnsley MBC's leisure facilities. Appointed by DETR/4Ps/TTF to prepare standardisation guidance for local authority housing PFI projects and a contributor to the local authority PFI contract guidance and DFEE schools guidance produced by 4Ps.
Prof. Memberships: Law Society.
Career: LLB University of Hull. LLM University of Exeter. Qualified 1983. South Bucks District Council 1980-82. Waltham Forest LBC 1982-88. *SJ Berwin & Co* 1988-93. *Winckworth & Pemberton* 1993-94. *Prince Evans* 1994-98. *Pinsent Curtis Biddle* to date.
Publications: General editor of 'Local Government Precedents and Procedures', Sweet & Maxwell.
Personal: Married with two children and interests in travel and football.

ALLAN, Simon
Berwin Leighton Paisner, London (020) 7760 1000
simon.allan@berwinleighton.com
Specialisation: Head of finance department and specialist in major developments and infrastructure-related projects. Major projects include the disposal of the Millennium Dome for government, Elephant and Castle project, acting for Lex on the White Fleet transaction, Longbenton PFI project for the project vehicle, Kings College/UMDS PFI project again for the project vehicle, construction of the new Parliamentary building over Westminster tube station and the White City retail development for European Land.
Career: Qualified in 1979, assistant solicitor with *Kenneth Turner Brown* 1979-81 and *Ashurst Morris Crisp* 1981-88. Partner with *Berwin Leighton* since 1988.
Personal: Family of four children. Hobbies include reading, music and wine.

ARMITAGE, Richard
Simmons & Simmons, London (020) 7628 2020
richard.armitage@simmons-simmons.com
Specialisation: Partner specialising in PFI/PPP projects and privatisations. Has particular experience of the defence sector, including the contractorisations of the Royal Dockyards and the Atomic Weapons Establishment, the privatisation of Devonport Royal Dockyard, the DERA PPP and PFI projects, such as the pathfinder Medium Support Helicopter Training Facility Project, and the Future Strategic Tanker Aircraft Project, the largest defence PFI project. He has also advised on projects in the telecommunications and energy sectors and a wide range of commercial transactions such as facilities management and outsourcing contracts.
Career: Articled *Simmons & Simmons*, qualified 1982, partner since 1987
Publications: Author of the defence section of the Butterworth's 'PFI Manual'.

AUSTWICK, Malcolm
Beachcroft Wansbroughs, London (020) 7242 2011
maustwick@bwlaw.co.uk
Specialisation: Projects work for both public and private sector. Concentrates mainly on health sector. Acted for Taylor Woodrow/Innisfree Consortium on the third PFI hospital scheme to achieve financial close with the South Buckinghamshire NHS Trust. Since then has led BW teams on a number of PFI deals including: acting for Dudley Group of Hospital NHS Trust on the largest PFI hospital scheme to date to adapt the standard form contract; acting for the Kier/Tilbury Douglas/Charterhouse Consortium on the largest hopsital PFI scheme in Wales at Neath/Port Talbot. Was also instrumental in bringing Hefeford Hospitals NHS Trust PFI scheme to financial close and a member of the BW team which closed the pathfinder school and office scheme for Pembroke County Council.
Prof. Memberships: Law Society; PPP Forum.
Career: Qualified: 1983, *Beachcroft Ryman Isaacs*. Partner *Beachcroft Stanleys* (now *Beachcroft Wansbroughs*).
Personal: LLB, Exeter University. Reliving childhood dreams on the touchline and other family pursuits. Married with three children.

BAKER, Huw
Masons, Manchester (0161) 234 8357
huw.baker@masons.com
Specialisation: Partner in charge of PFI and major project work in *Masons'* Manchester office. Experienced in all aspects of PFI and major project work including project agreements, finance, building contracts and FM contracts.
Prof. Memberships: Society of Construction Lawyers. Member of TECSA. TECSA accredited adjudicator.
Career: Qualified in 1987. In September 1998 moved from *Addleshaw Booth & Co* where he had been partner in charge of the Manchester construction team to head up PFI and major project work in *Masons'* Manchester office.
Personal: Born 22 September 1962. Graduated from Cambridge University in 1984 with 1st Class Honours in Law. Leisure pursuits include gardening, walking and reading. Lives in Hebden Bridge, West Yorkshire.

BALDOCK, Anne
Allen & Overy, London (020) 7330 2713
anne.baldock@allenovery.com
Specialisation: Head of the PFI/PPP practice and experienced in all aspects of major projects and PFI/PPP in the UK and abroad. She regularly acts for banks, monolines, sponsors and concession-granting authorities. She has advised in all the principal sectors in which PFI/PPP is relevant including rail, roads, Ministry of Defence projects, property and prisons. Anne has been involved (and continues to be involved) in many of the high-profile and prestigious PFI/PPP projects including the Channel Tunnel Rail Link, Docklands Light Railway and the bond financing of the Treasury building ('Goggs').
Career: Articled at *Allen & Overy*; qualified 1984; partner 1990. Secondment with major US bank 1986-88.
Publications: Contributor to several publications on International Banking Law.
Personal: Born 1959. Graduate of LSE.

BALLINGALL, James
Theodore Goddard, London (020) 7606 8855
jamesballingall@theodoregoddard.co.uk
Specialisation: Head of PFI and asset finance teams. Has lead the teams on numerous hospital, schools, further education, colleges, prison, police and railway projects. Has also advised the National Audit Office on their review of nine PFI projects to date. Acts for both banks and consortia. Background in asset finance and banking. Other project finance work includes Euro Tunnel, BSB, Lakeside Thurrock Shopping Centre, and a major cementation project. Specialises in structured finance and lease work, particularly in the transportation field, having set up *Theodore Goddard's* railways group.
Prof. Memberships: Law Society, FRGS.
Career: Born 1958. Educated: Eastbourne College, Cambridge (Emanuel). Qualified 1984.
Personal: Interests include hiking, cycling, squash, piano, writing (wrote 'A Taste of China', published John Murrays 1984), carpentry.

BARRATT, Jeffery
Norton Rose, London (020) 7283 6000
barrattjvc@nortonrose.com
Specialisation: Partner, head of global projects group. All areas of banking, financing and capital markets debt instruments, in particular project related financings. Involved in many complex infrastructure and other project financings in the UK and worldwide, acting for banks, sponsors, project companies, export credit agencies and multilateral

agencies. On the editorial board of Butterworths 'Financial Law and Practice'.
Career: Qualified 1973, joined *Norton Rose* 1976, partner 1979. Established and ran Bahrain office 1979-82. Training partner 1987-91. Headed South East Asian project finance group, based in Hong Kong 1993-95. Chairman Partnership committee 1997 to date.

BECKITT, Jonathan
CMS Cameron McKenna, London
(020) 7367 2113
jonathan.beckitt@cmck.com
Specialisation: Jonathan is a partner in the property group specialising in property and project related transactions. He acts for UK, European and Japanese corporations on such transactions both in the UK and overseas. Jonathan's recent transactions include advising the London Borough of Richmond upon Thames Council on its residential care homes PFI project; Surrey Elderly Services, advising Surrey County Council on the externalisation of sixteen residential care homes for the elderly; North Wiltshire Schools PFI, advising the lenders in relation to this project for the provision of three new schools on a DBFO basis; Hull and East Yorkshire Hospitals PFI, advising the lenders in relation to this project for the provision of a new maternity wing on a DBFO basis; Channel Tunnel Rail Link, leader of the team advising the Department of the Environment, Transport and the Regions.
Career: Admitted 1984. Joined the firm in 1982 and in addition to London, has practised in the Far East and Japan, where he was the resident partner in the firm's Tokyo office from October 1991 to June 1994. Since 1994 he has been a partner in the London office.
Personal: LLB at Bristol (graduated 1981); solicitor of the Supreme Court of England and Wales (1984); licensed foreign lawyer in Japan (1991).

BELLHOUSE, John
White & Case, London (020) 7397 3605
jbellhouse@whitecase.com
Specialisation: Partner specialising in all aspects of major infrastructure projects including project appraisal; project document drafting and negotiation; post contract advice and dispute resolution. In addition to appearing as counsel in arbitrations, he also sits as an arbitrator and on Dispute Review Boards.
Prof. Memberships: Law Society of England & Wales
Career: Partner *McKenna & Co* (London and Hong Kong) 1976-94; partner *White & Case* 1994 to date. Admitted as a solicitor in England and Wales and Hong Kong.
Personal: Born 1946. Resides London.

BICKERTON, David
Clifford Chance, London (020) 7600 1000
david.bickerton@cliffordchance.com
Specialisation: Structured debt capital markets including: project bonds, acquisition finance, warrants and PFI/PPP. Recent transactions include Glas Cymru bond financing of acquisition of Welsh Water, Sutton and East Surrey Water bonds, Nationwide Building Society PIBS receipts, Hexham Hospital PFI/PPP and West Berkshire Hospital PFI/PPP.
Career: *Clifford Chance* 1987 to date. Seconded to Citibank (1992) and Bankers Trust (1993). Partner 1997.
Personal: Education: Downing College, Cambridge – MA. Family Details: three daughters.

BLACK, Alan
Linklaters, London (020) 7456 5948
alan.black@linklaters.com
Specialisation: Main area of practice has been international projects. Extensive experience of acting for governments, sponsors and lenders on major projects for transport, airports and aviation, oil, gas, and derivative products, and projects involving concessions granted by governments to private developers in both civil law and common law countries.
Career: Qualified 1976. Attended Kings College, London. Partner 1983. Head of global projects.

BLAKE, Peter
Clifford Chance, London (020) 7600 1000
peter.blake@cliffordchance.com
Specialisation: Partner specialising in general company and commercial work, energy, oil, gas, natural resources and project finance.
Career: Partner *Clifford Chance* 1983.

BLISS, Nick
Freshfields Bruckhaus Deringer, London
(020) 7936 4000
nicholas.bliss@freshfields.com
Specialisation: Project finance and PFI/PPP. He led the *Freshfields* teams which acted for Road Management Group in the (March 1996) A1(M) and A419/A417 DBFO Road Projects: the first UK monoline insured eurobond infrastructure financing and, subsequently, the M6 DBFO Road monoline insured eurobond infrastructure financing, acting for FSA the monoline insurer. In June 1999 completed the first eurobond financing of a multi-project Programme (Investors Finance). He has been heavily involved in projects in a number of other areas of PFI/PPP (prisons, health and MOD projects).
Prof. Memberships: Law Society.
Career: Barnard Castle School, Corpus Christi College, Cambridge.
Personal: Rowing, cycling, back surgery, childcare and other strenuous pursuits.

BROWN, Chris
Masons, London (020) 7490 4000
chris.brown@masons.com
Specialisation: Head of projects and finance group. Specialises in major infrastructure projects, including advising and negotiating on funding and concession contracts as well as leading the project management of legal input. He also advises on a wide range of domestic and cross-border debt transactions, asset finance, leasing, capital markets and infrastructure finance.
Prof. Memberships: Qualified solicitor in England, Wales and Scotland.
Career: Having qualified in Scotland in 1986 he moved to London. In 1996 he moved to *Masons* as a partner in the projects and finance group. Became head of the group in 1999.
Personal: Born 30 April 1958. Graduated from University of Edinburgh with MA Hons in Economics in 1981 and LLB in 1983. Part time tutor in economics at the Universities of Edinburgh and Cape Town.

BROWN, Steven
McClure Naismith, Edinburgh (0131) 220 1002
sbrown@mcclurenaismith.com
Specialisation: Project finance and PFI. Advises public sector, private sector consortia and banks. Practice covers many PFI sectors and holds overseas appointments on BOO/BOT schemes in power generation, water and sewerage. Represented Grampian Health Board at Stonehaven hospital, Bank of Scotland at Stirling College, the NHS Trust at Hairmyres district general hospital and participated in the consortium advisory team on South Bucks hospital, all amongst the first PFI projects to reach financial closing. Currently advising on a range of projects in health, education, law and order, local authority and transport.
Prof. Memberships: Society of Writers to HM Signet, Law Society of Scotland.
Career: Qualified in 1980. Partner in *McClure Naismith* since 1986, now head of projects group.
Personal: Born 20 November 1956. Educated at Irvine Royal Academy 1969-74, University of Edinburgh 1974-78. Lives near Edinburgh. Leisure pursuits include family, computers, music, golf. Past chairman of a charity for adults with learning difficulties.

BUCKWORTH, Nicholas
Shearman & Sterling, London (020) 7655 5000
nbuckworth@shearman.com
Specialisation: Partner in project finance department. Advising project developers and financial institutions on all aspects of the structuring, negotiation, development and financing of major infrastructure projects particularly in the power and transportation sectors. Nicholas has particular experience of advising developers and lenders in the Middle East and North Africa. He is currently advising the InterGen-Enka consortium on the development and financing of three Build Operate natural gas fired power projects in Turkey, the first to be developed under this regime. He also led the team which advised the lenders on the Taweelah A2 Power Generation and Water Desalination Project, named 'Energy/Project Finance Team of the Year 1999' by Legal Business. He is currently working on projects in Abu Dhabi, Oman, Qatar and elsewhere in the Middle East, as well as in the United Kingdom and mainland Europe.
Career: Qualified in 1986. With *Clifford Chance* 1984-94. Partner *Milbank, Tweed, Hadley & McCloy* 1994-November 1996. Partner, *Shearman & Sterling* November 1996.
Personal: Born 2 February 1961. Educated at Dundee University (LL.B Hons, 1983). Leisure activities include skiing, squash, golf, music and cinema.

CAMPBELL, Alan
Dundas & Wilson CS, Edinburgh (0131) 228 8000

CIRELL, Stephen
Eversheds, Leeds (0113) 243 0391
stephencirell@eversheds.com
See under Administrative & Public Law, p.58

CLARK, Brian
DLA, Leeds (08700) 111111

COCKRAM, Richard
Addleshaw Booth & Co, Leeds (0113) 209 2000
rac@addleshaw-booth.co.uk
See under Construction, p.201

COKER, Mark
Freshfields Bruckhaus Deringer, London
(020) 7936 4000

COOKE, Ken
Masons, Leeds (0113) 233 8905
ken.cooke@masons.com
Specialisation: Specialises in major projects including PFI. Recent work includes projects in the fields of

criminal justice and education. Also specialises in information and technology, including outsourcing projects for financial institutions and advising the Millennium Dome company and DTI on IT procurement.
Prof. Memberships: Law Society.
Career: Fellowship, University of York 1977-87. Qualified 1989 after training at *DLA*. Solicitor, *DLA* to 1994, partner in *Masons* 1998.
Publications: Co-editor of the 'Facilities Management Legal Update', a specialist legal journal for facilities managers.
Personal: MA, DPhil University of York.

COULTER, David
Norton Rose, London (020) 7283 6000
coulterdx@nortonrose.com
Specialisation: PFI, project finance, asset finance, public sector finance and banking – PFI projects in last year have included Oldham Schools; Islington, Newham, Camden and Reading HRA Housing PFI Projects; Eden Project; National Physical Laboratory; London underground sub-surface and JNP Deeplines Projects; National Air Traffic Services; Northlink (Orkney and Shetlands) Ferries Project.
Prof. Memberships: Law Society, Law Society of Scotland, City of London Solicitors Company.
Career: Mainholm Academy, Ayr to 1979; Edinburgh University LLB (1984), DIPLP (1985). Admitted Scotland (1986); Notary Public (Scotland) (1986); admitted England and Wales (1989).
Personal: Sailing, hill walking and travel. Married (Catriona Rose) – one daughter, Fiona, one son, Alasdair.

CRANE, David
Norton Rose, London (020) 7283 6000
Specialisation: Partner in the projects group, specialising in project finance and asset finance. He also handles general commercial work. He has advised on numerous major plant leasing transactions, on sales of leasing companies as well as other company acquisitions and joint ventures. He also has considerable experience of public sector financing, particularly relating to local authorities.
Prof. Memberships: Law Society.
Career: Articled at *Norton Rose*. Qualified 1975. Partner since 1985.

DARLEY, Mark
Lovells, London (020) 7296 2000
mark.darley@lovells.com
Specialisation: Project Finance, focusing primarily on banking and capital markets issues. Extensive experience in all forms of structured and limited recourse financing, securitisation and trade finance as well as projects both in the UK and overseas. Recent transactions include advising on the financing for the Rome airport privatisation, the Berlin airport privatisation, the privatisation of the Greek Tourist Board's portfolio of assets, the Tube Lines Group's successful bid for the JNP network under the London Underground PPP, the financing of three hospital PFI projects and advising in connection with port, airport and railroad developments in the Middle East.
Prof. Memberships: The Law Society.
Career: Bradford Grammar School and Manchester University (1983 LLB Hons). Qualified 1986; partner at *Lovells* 1996.
Personal: Born 1961; resides London. Leisure interests include shooting and fishing.

DESAI, Bimal
Allen & Overy, London (020) 7330 2736
bimal.desai@allenovery.com
Specialisation: Partner in the projects group. Main area of work is major projects in the emerging markets and other forms of structured financings. Currently acting for the project company on Nigeria LNG and the arrangers of the first UK IPP after the introduction of NETA of Vizag IPP Project in India. Has acted for banks, project companies and multilateral institutions, and has considerable experience of Export Credit Agency led financings.
Prof. Memberships: Law Society; City of London Law Society; British India Law Association.
Career: *Macfarlanes* (1989-94); associate, *Allen & Overy* (1995); partner (1998).
Personal: Born 1965. Leisure interests include sailing. Bristol University (LLB, 1984-87); Cambridge University (LLM, 1987-88).

DUFFICY, Frank
CMS Cameron McKenna, London
(020) 7367 2904
fd@cmck.com
Specialisation: Frank Dufficy is a partner in the project finance group, He has extensive experience of advising consortia on all legal aspects of PFI projects, including finance, design, construction, operation and maintenance, within the UK and overseas. In addition he is frequently appointed to manage and lead teams of lawyers highly experienced in the various aspects of PFI work. He has advised on a variety of projects in the defence, health, education, other accommodation and transport sectors in the UK. Frank has also advised on the development, financing, construction and operation of tolled motorways and power projects overseas. He is currently advising project company/sponsors on the Health and Safety Laboratory PFI, the Exeter Courts PFI, Walsgrave and Havering Hospitals PFIs and the A1 Darrington-Dishforth section. He has also advised in respect of infrastructure project financing in other countries, advised the Hungarian Government on the M1/M15; the M5 and M7 roads projects and advised the private sector on the Croatian toll motorway, Ron Brown Highway.
Prof. Memberships: The Law Society, City of London Solicitors Company.
Career: 1981-83; articled clerk – *Linklaters & Paines*. 1983-89; solicitor – *Linklaters & Paines*. 1990 to date; partner, *CMS Cameron McKenna*.
Personal: Education: St Michael's Prep School. St Michael's College. North Carolina State University; BA Political Science. City University; Diploma in Laws. College of Law; Law Society Finals. Leisure Interests: Diving (Olympic Competitor – Munich 1972, British Team 1969-75 inclusive), sailing, skiing, fell walking, shooting, tennis, fishing, golf. Family Details: Married to Alison with three children, Georgia, Jack and Thomas.

ELLIS, Jon
Norton Rose, London (020) 7283 6000
ellisjh@nortonrose.com
Specialisation: Projects work, acting for banks, project companies, export credit agencies and multilateral agencies on various types of projects in the UK and internationally.

ELSEY, Mark
Ashurst Morris Crisp, London (020) 7638 1111
mark.elsey@ashursts.com
Specialisation: Acting for governments, sponsors, contractors and lenders in relation to UK and international infrastructure and energy projects, including PFI/PPP projects. Head of the firm's projects group.

EVANS, Eric
Eversheds, Cardiff (029) 2047 1147
Specialisation: Partner in commercial property department and head of both the planning and PFI units. Specialises in all aspects of property law including complex planning obligations, major town centre regeneration/shopping schemes, site assembly, agreements for the construction of major highways associated with developments, public/private sector joint ventures, planning gain, valuations, urban development/regeneration grants and land reclamation. 30 years public sector experience, dealing with all areas of local government. Extensive experience of PFI and led one of the first PFI/PPP deals in Wales, at University Hospital of Wales NHS Trust. Has since advised on numerous deals including Newport Southern Distributor Road, Chepstow Community Hospital, Wiltshire's grouped schools scheme and 'Waste to Energy' scheme at Neath.
Prof. Memberships: Member of Law Society's Planning Panel.
Career: Qualified in 1980. Town Clerk, Borough of Blaenau Gwent (1981-89). Deputy Chief Executive and Legal Adviser, Land Authority for Wales (1989-92). Partner *Eversheds* 1992.
Personal: Director of Silent Valley Waste Services. Lives in Abertillery.

FAIRBAIRN, Iain
Beachcroft Wansbroughs, Bristol (0117) 918 2000
ifairbairn@bwlaw.co.uk
Specialisation: Head of projects and PFI team in Bristol office. Advising both sides of public private partnerships and including facilities management contracts and procurement and vires issues, covering all fields of PFI but with an emphasis on healthcare schemes.
Prof. Memberships: Law Society.
Career: 1977-82, *Slaughter and May*, assistant solicitor. 1982-96, *Bevan Hancock/Bevan Ashford*. 1996-98, *Bevan Ashford*, head of commercial department. October 1998, *Masons*, partner. January 2001, *Beachcroft Wansbroughs*, January 2001-date, partner.
Personal: Sailing, Skiing, Hill walking.

FELLOWS, Alison
Dickinson Dees, Newcastle upon Tyne
(0191) 279 9289
law@dickinson-dees.com
Specialisation: PFI projects. Lead partner acting for Carlisle Hospital NHS Trust on PFI project for the redevelopment of the Cumberland Infirmary, followed by 6 months secondment to Private Finance Unit of NHS Executive to assist with ongoing projects. Now acting on several further major NHS projects including the Newcastle Hospitals NHS Trust Strategic Review PFI, the Leeds Teaching Hospitals PFI project for St James' Hospital in Leeds, and the new community hospital for Chester le Street.
Career: Cambridge University 1980-83. *Field Fisher Waterhouse* 1985-88. *Dickinson Dees* 1988 to date. Married to Tim Care, also a partner at *Dickinson Dees*, 2 children.

FINLAY, Peter
White & Case, London (020) 7397 3603
pfinlay@whitecase.com
Specialisation: Has a unique range of international project finance and M&A law expertise, focusing particularly on the energy sector.
Prof. Memberships: Law Society of England & Wales, Irish solicitor, New York Bar. French Avocat.
Career: Partner, *White & Case* London. Member of the firm's world-wide management board.

FLETCHER, Phillip
Milbank, Tweed, Hadley & McCloy, London (020) 7448 3000
pfletcher@milbank.com
Specialisation: Partner in project finance group. Specialising in the development and financing of major infrastructure projects, including power plants, pipelines, roads and satellites. Has particular expertise in capital markets and multi-sourced financing. Has represented parties in relation to projects in Europe, the US and Asia, including the Orion and Arianespace satellite financings; Yanpet petrochemicals project, Saudi Arabia; the BGT LNG vessel project, Nigeria; the Birecik and Marmara Ereglisi power projects, Turkey; the Taweelah A1 power project, Abu Dhabi; the Tapada power project, Portugal; the Jawa power project, Indonesia; the Yemen LNG project; the Medway, Shoreham and Drax power projects, UK; the Teverola, Ferrara, Serene, Lomellina and Rosen power project, Italy.
Career: Has been with *Milbank, Tweed* since 1983 and was resident in the firm's Hong Kong office in 1987 and 1988.
Personal: Born 1957. Educated at Georgetown University School of Foreign Service (BS 1979), Fletcher School of Law & Diplomacy (MA, 1983) and the University of California, Berkeley (JD, 1983).

FOX, Jason
Herbert Smith, London (020) 7374 8000
Specialisation: Partner, projects group. Advising the public sector, corporates and banks on all aspects of the structuring, development and financing of projects in a variety of sectors including oil and gas, power, water, property and public infrastructure. Main areas of practice are advising on PFI projects and oil and gas projects. Regular participant in industry conferences on the PFI.
Career: Qualified in 1987 with *Herbert Smith* and became a partner in 1994. Seconded to the Private Finance Panel Executive February to September 1994.
Publications: Author (jointly with Nicholas Tott) of 'The Private Finance Initiative Handbook' (Jordans, December 1998).

FRANCIS, Barry
Buchanan Ingersoll, London (020) 7920 3800
francisb@buchananingersoll.com
Specialisation: Public/private interface transactions including PPP, PFI, major outsourcing projects and other commercial transactions including public sector/private sector joint ventures, facilities management contracts and procurement and administrative law advice. Current projects include major hospital building and services projects (PFI). Managing partner *Buchanan Ingersoll*. Regular speaker at conferences and seminars.
Prof. Memberships: Law Society.
Career: Admitted 1977, at *Beachcroft Hyman Isaacs* (now *Beachcroft Wansbroughs*), associate 1979-80, partner 1980-99, managing partner *Buchanan Ingersoll* 2000.
Publications: Contributor to a range of specialist publications including Butterworth's 'PFI Manual'. A member of the editorial board of 'The PFI Report'.
Personal: Born 14 March 1953. Educated at Enfield Grammar School and University of Bristol. Interests include travel, history and food. Lives in North London.

GAINES, Peter
Baker & McKenzie, London (020) 7919 1000
peter.gaines@bakernet.com
Specialisation: Peter Gaines is a partner and head of the London-based project, acquisition and structured finance group. The London team which Peter leads was named 2000 Legal Team of the Year by Privatisation International. Peter specialises in the representation of lenders and borrowers in all varieties of project and other limited recourse or structured finance transactions. Recent key clients in his areas of specialisation include: Petrobras (in the award-winning Barracuda financing), Telecom Egypt, The Industrial Bank of Japan, Standard Bank, The Sanwa Bank, Dresdner Bank, Union Bank of Switzerland and Barclays Bank.
Prof. Memberships: American Bar Association; International Bar Association.
Career: Qualified 1975; associate *Mayer, Brown & Platt*, Chicago 1975-81; partner *Mayer, Brown & Platt*, Chicago 1981-90; partner *Mayer, Brown & Platt*, London 1990-95; partner *Baker & McKenzie* 1995-present.
Publications: Peter contributes a variety of project finance articles to various publications.
Personal: Education: Peter has a BA from the University of Wisconsin (1972) and a JD from the University of Wisconsin Law School (1975). He was admitted to the Illinois Bar in 1975 and to the New York Bar in 1978. Born 1951 and resides in London.

GATES, Ellen
Denton Wilde Sapte, London (020) 7242 1212

GILLESPIE, Stephen
Allen & Overy, London (020) 7330 3000
stephen.gillespie@allenovery.com
Specialisation: Steven Gillespie is a partner in the banking department, specialising in leveraged finance, telecoms/telemedia finance and project finance. Recent transactions include Cinven's purchase of Photo Service and Photo Station from GrandVision (for the arrangers); Drax I and II (for the arrangers and the senior lenders), the Rank Holidays/Bourne Leisure LBO (for Barclays Capital), the Wind Telecomunicazioni SpA 2G and 3G financings (for the arrangers and underwriters), the €10 billion 'jumbo' financing for ENEL SpA (for the arrangers) and the €100 million debut financing for Virgin Mobile (for the arrangers/underwriters), the Moyle Interconnector project financing (for RBS/Natwest) and various PFI financings for Edison Capital.
Prof. Memberships: Law Society. City of London Solicitors Company.
Career: Articled *Stephenson Harwood* 1985-87, Solicitor *Freshfields* 1987-91, Solicitor *Allen & Overy* 1991-95, Partner 1995.
Personal: Born 1962. Educated at Foyle and Londonderry College and Trinity College, Oxford (MA (Hons) Jurisprudence 1984). Interests include family, reading, outdoor pursuits and music. Lives in St. Albans.

GNIADKOWSKI, Stan
Denton Wilde Sapte, London (020) 7242 1212

GOLDIE, Ian
Slaughter and May, London (020) 7600 1200
ian.goldie@slaughterandmay.com
Specialisation: Energy and natural resources; infrastructure and PFI/PPP projects. Recent projects include: 2000 – London Underground PPP Project, HSL Zuid IP Project (The Netherlands), National Air Traffic Services PPP.
Prof. Memberships: Section on Energy and Natural Resources, International Bar Association; Institute of Petroleum.
Personal: Jesus College, Cambridge; BA, MA.

GOSSLING, Margaret
Clifford Chance, London (020) 7600 1000
margaret.gossling@cliffordchance.com
Specialisation: Partner specialising in international project finance (especially power, oil, gas and natural resources) and general banking and bank mergers (eg the Chase/Chemical merger).
Career: St Anne's College, Oxford (MA Hons) 1980-83. Articled *Coward Chance*; qualified 1986; partner 1993.
Personal: Married with one child; resides London.

GRAHAM, L. Drysdale
McGrigor Donald, Edinburgh (0131) 777 7000
www.mcgrigors.com
Specialisation: Partner in Projects Unit. Specialises in capital projects/PFI work, although has broad experience of corporate finance and general corporate work. Recent projects experience includes advising MBIA on the Levenmouth, the New Schools consortium on the Kent Schools Project, the Tricom consortium on the Defence Korsling Excut Bristol, Bath, Shrivenham and Portsmouth Project and the ikwip consortium on the Royal Berkshire and Bottle Hospital patient management system Project. Currently working on various projects at the preferred bidder stage in the water, schools, accommodation, healthcare and e-commerce sectors.
Prof. Memberships: Law Society of Scotland; Law Society of England and Wales; the Society of Writers to Her Majesty's Signet; Notary Public.
Career: Trained *Biggart Baillie*; qualified Scotland 1982; qualified England and Wales 1990; corporate department *Dundas & Wilson* 1982-84; company department *McGrigor Donald* 1984-87; manager corporate department *Freshfields*, London 1987-91; rejoined *McGrigor Donald*, London office for 18 months; returned to Scotland to become a partner in Edinburgh office 1992.
Personal: Born 1958; resides Edinburgh. Leisure interests include theatre, music, golf, gardening.

HALL, Peter
Norton Rose, London (020) 7283 6000
hallpm@nortonrose.com
Specialisation: A partner in the construction and engineering group with considerable experience of infrastructure projects around the world, including PFI/PPP transactions. Currently acting for both commercial lenders and sponsors on a number of independent power projects and rail projects in the UK and overseas. Contentious work encompasses High Court and international arbitration claims.
Prof. Memberships: Member of the Technology and Construction Court Solicitors Association, an accredited adjudicator and an associate of the Chartered Institute of Arbitrators.

HARRISON, Brian
Allen & Overy, London (020) 7330 2550
brian.harrison@allenovery.com
Specialisation: One of the senior partners in *Allen & Overy's* highly regarded international projects practice. He has a broad client base advising banks, sponsors and multi-laterals on major international telecoms, power and infrastructure projects. His experience includes projects and telecoms fundings based in Europe and Eastern Europe, the Middle East and the United Kingdom. He also has wide international banking and commercial transaction experience including shipping and aircraft financing, acquisition financing, structured financings, property reconstructions and work-outs.
Career: Qualified New Zealand 1976, England 1985; assistant solicitor, *Johnson Stokes & Master*, Hong Kong 1980-83; assistant solicitor *Allen & Overy*, London and Dubai 1983-85; Partner New York and London 1987.
Personal: Born 1953. Auckland University (1975, LLB). Interests include yachting and motorcycling.

HENDERSON, David
MacRoberts, Glasgow (0141) 332 9988
david.henderson@macroberts.co.uk
Specialisation: Partner in construction and projects groups. Main area of practice is construction and engineering law with emphasis on PFI and other infrastructure projects. Currently involved in a variety of PFI projects in the healthcare, railway and waste-water sectors. Led legal team for successful consortium at Highland and Tay sewerage projects and acted for the Trust in the largest healthcare PFI project in Scotland to date.
Career: Qualified in 1979, having joined *MacRoberts* in 1977. Became partner in 1983.
Publications: Co-author of 'MacRoberts on Scottish Building Contracts' and contributor to Butterworths 'PFI Manual'.
Personal: Born 18 July 1955. Educated at Kilmarnock Academy and Edinburgh University.

HUGHES, Stephen
Bevan Ashford, Bristol (0117) 975 1612
s.hughes@bevanashford.co.uk
Specialisation: Head of projects and PFI team. Practice covers private and public sector specialising in healthcare.
Prof. Memberships: Faculty of Building, Society of Construction Law.
Career: *Bevan Ashford* (partner 1993).

HUMPHREY, Tony
Allen & Overy, London (020) 7330 2711
tony.humphrey@allenovery.com
See under Banking, p.119

HUTTON, David
Bevan Ashford, Bristol (0117) 918 8927
d.hutton@bevanashford.co.uk
Specialisation: Partner in PFI and projects team. Practice covers most PFI sectors and private and public sector clients. In the last year, has been involved in schemes in health, defence (closed Defence Animal Centre projects for Project Co), local government (including pathfinder leisure schemes) and specialising in education projects (advising Rhondda Cynon Taff and several bidding consortia on other school projects, closed Newbury College and advising Falmouth College of Arts on a partnership on the Combined Universities in Cornwall project).
Prof. Memberships: Law Society.
Career: *Baker & McKenzie* (1990-95). Qualified 1992. *Linklaters* (1995-97). *Bevan Ashford* (1997 to date). Partner 1999.
Personal: Married with two sons. Leisure includes golf, football and art.

IVISON, Andrew
CMS Cameron McKenna, London
(020) 7367 3410
asi@cmck.com
Specialisation: Project finance and banking partner, advising on major infrastructure, utilities and capital projects in the United Kingdom and overseas. Recent examples of major projects include the NATS Air Traffic Services PPP, the London Underground PPP and the financing of Section 2 of the Channel Tunnel Rail Link.
Career: Partner at *CMS Cameron McKenna* since 1987. Admitted as a solicitor in 1980.

JOHNSTON, Bruce
Weil, Gotshal & Manges, London (020) 7903 1295
bruce.johnston@weil.com
Specialisation: Head of the project finance practice. His project finance experience covers a range of sectors including infrastructure, electricity, oil and gas, telecoms, transportation and waste and water. Recent projects include Athens Ringroad in Greece, Telewest in the UK, Kangal in Turkey, Belchatow II in Poland and VSZ in Slovakia. Frequent speaker at conferences and author of articles.

KENNY, Stephen
Wragge & Co, Birmingham (0870) 903 1000

LEE, David P
Allen & Overy, London (020) 7330 3000
david.lee@allenovery.com
Specialisation: Specialised in public-private partnerships since the PFI started and has acted for banks, project companies and the public sector. In particular acted for banks on Bridgend Prison, the financiers on the Channel Tunnel Rail Link as well as many prison, health and defence projects. International projects include the Istrian Toll Road in Croatia. In 1997, joined Treasury Taskforce HM Treasury and worked on project across all PFI sectors and was the principal author of 'Treasury Taskforce – Standardisation of PFI Contracts'.
Career: Associate *Allen & Overy* (1992-98), Partner (1998). Seconded to the Mitsubishi Bank (1993-94). Member of the original Treasury Taskforce, formed in 1997.
Publications: Principal author of 'Treasury Taskforce – Standardisation of PFI Contracts'.
Personal: Pembroke College, Oxford (1990).

LOVITT, Arthur
Pinsent Curtis Biddle, Leeds (0113) 244 5000
arthur.lovitt@pinsents.com
Specialisation: Partner in property department and major projects team. Involved in significant property developments including a major business park in Rochdale for Wilson Bowden. PFI and Public Sector Partnership work includes: representing, as lead partner, North Durham Acute Hospitals NHS Trust on their PFI scheme; Royal Bank of Scotland plc on £47m major pathfinder community health PFI scheme in Leeds. In 2001 he led the teams advising Royal Bank of Scotland plc on two school schemes at Caerphilly and Fleetwood which closed in April and May respectively. He also led the team advising the MoD on new housing scheme at Wattisham which closed in May.
Prof. Memberships: Round Table (former chairman of Leeds Round Table), Institute of Directors.
Career: Bradford Grammar School and Nottingham University (LLB 2:1). Qualified with *Daynes Hill & Perks* (now *Eversheds*) in Norwich. Three years in commercial property department of *Linklaters & Paines*. Joined *Pinsent Curtis Biddle* in 1990. Partner in 1994.

MACAULAY, Iain
McGrigor Donald, Glasgow (0141) 248 6677
Specialisation: Partner in banking unit. All aspects of debt funding including PFI funding retail finance and consumer credit.
Prof. Memberships: Law Society of Scotland.
Career: Qualified in 1984. Worked in-house with BP Petroleum Development Limited before joining *McGrigor Donald* in 1987. Following a period with *Cameron Markby Hewitt*, returned to *McGrigor Donald* as banking partner in Scotland in 1992.

MACRITCHIE, Kenneth
Shearman & Sterling, London (020) 7448 3000
kmacritchie@shearman.com
Specialisation: Co-head of global project finance group. Advising clients on major infrastructure projects including transport infrastructure, power, telecom, mining and oil and gas. Clients include international banks and project developers.
Prof. Memberships: Law Society, Law Society of Scotland.
Career: Qualified in 1976. Partner, *Clifford Chance* 1991-94. *Milbank, Tweed, Hadley & McCloy* 1994-96. *Shearman & Sterling* partner, since 1996.

MANSON, Stephen
Eversheds, Cardiff (029) 2047 1147
stephenmanson@eversheds.com
Specialisation: Partner specialising in town and country planning, Private Finance Initiative/Public Private Partnership work together with general public sector work. Former member of Government's Private Finance Panel Executive. Advises a number of local minerals developers on such matters as the current minerals review procedures. Currently advising United News and Media on planning appeal for alternative use of studio site in Cardiff. Acts for both public and private sectors on PFI schemes in a variety of areas such as education (advised Wiltshire County Council on its three schools deal – £30m), health (advised health trust on local hospital scheme in Cardiff – £15million) and transport (advising Newport County Borough Council on its Southern Distributor Road – £40million).
Career: Bristol University (LLB Hons). Bristol Polytechnic (LSF First Class Hons).
Personal: Recreations include windsurfing and badminton.

MARLOW, Ed
Denton Wilde Sapte, London (020) 7242 1212

MATHEOU, Michael
Lovells, London (020) 7296 2000
mike.matheou@lovells.com
Specialisation: Working in the firm's Project Finance Unit advising the private sector, financiers and the public sector on PPP/Private Finance Initiative projects (all sectors) and international limited recourse financial projects. Heavily involved in PFI/PPP work across a range of sectors including transport (London Underground PPP/DBFO Roads

and light rail), Healthcare and Government Accommodation (DSS PRIME; STEPS project). Also worked on a range of infrastructure projects internationally including BOT Waste Water Project in Oman, Bauxite mine and harbour development in Guyana and oil refinery and petro-chemicals project in India.
Prof. Memberships: Law Society.
Career: *Lovells*, London and Hong Kong since 1980, Partner 1989. LLB (Hons) Nottingham University.

MATTHEW, Stephen
Eversheds, Nottingham (0115) 950 7000
Specialisation: Joined *Eversheds* in 1995 as partner, having previously worked for fifteen years within local government where he was County Secretary and solicitor of Shropshire County Council. Acts for public sector project sponsors and for bidding contractors, primarily in the field of social infrastructure. Is head of *Eversheds* projects group.
Career: Educated at Farnham Grammar School, University of Sheffield and the College of Law, London. Specialises in local authority and project work and is a member of the Association of Council Secretaries and Solicitors. Began his career with South Yorkshire County Council, moved to Derbyshire County Council and joined Shropshire County Council in 1998.
Personal: Married with three children and lives on the outskirts of Nottingham.

McAULEY, Michael
Dundas & Wilson CS, Glasgow (0141) 222 2200

McCANN, Martin
Masons, London (020) 7490 4000
Specialisation: Martin McCann is a partner in *Masons* projects and finance group. He advises on all manner of domestic/international PFI/project finance/asset finance transactions including Rail: He advised the successful bidder on the first PFI light rail project to close, Nottingham Light Rail. He is currently advising on a number of other rail projects including Manchester Metrolink Phase III and Wales and Borders. Accommodation Projects: He continues to advise leading developers and funders on a wide range of accommodation projects including schools, hospitals and courts. IT Projects: He is currently advising the British Government on one of the first multijurisdictional IT PFI projects. He separately advised Rolls Royce and British Aerospace on the funding of their multi billion pound, multijurisdictional outsourcing/corporate PPP project. Martin previously headed up *Masons* China practice and was recognised as a 'leader in the field' of project finance/restructuring work. He advised governments, developers and banks on all manner of project finance transactions in China, including toll roads, power plants and water projects.
Prof. Memberships: Qualified solicitor in England and Wales. Qualified solicitor in Hong Kong.
Career: Qualified in 1995 and has since been at *Masons*. Head of *Masons* China practice 1996-2001. From 1999-2001 he has been in *Masons'* projects and finance group.
Publications: Advisor to the Chinese government on project finance/asset finance. Legal advisor to British/Dutch/German governments in relation to project finance and investment in China. Currently advising British government on multijurisdictional PPP project.
Personal: Golf.

McCORMACK, Carol
Berwin Leighton Paisner, London (020) 7760 1000
carol.mccormack@berwinleightonpaisner.com
Specialisation: Partner in projects and public sector department. Principal area of work is advising government departments, health bodies, educational establishments, local authorities, private sector consortia and service providers on major commercial transactions such as those undertaken through the Private Finance Initiative, Public Private Partnerships. Has represented HM Treasury and the Home Office on major accommodation PFI projects and represented the Banques Ecovet/Charterhouse consortium on the first NHS PFI to use the standard form contract.
Career: Articled with *Berwin Leighton* 1983-85 and became a partner in 1989.
Personal: Born in Middlesbrough 22 February 1961, attended Selwyn College, Cambridge.

McCORMICK, Roger
Freshfields Bruckhaus Deringer, London
(020) 7936 4000
roger.mccormick@freshfields.com
Specialisation: Project Finance (all sectors, all countries) and other financial/commercial transactions.
Prof. Memberships: International Bar Association.
Career: Partner of *Freshfields* since 1981. Head of Project Finance 1991-97.
Personal: Born 1951, Educated M.G.S. and Oxford.

McEWAN, Alastair
Maclay Murray & Spens, Edinburgh
(0131) 479 2865
ajm@maclaymurrayspens.co.uk
Specialisation: Partner specialising in capital projects and PFI transactions. Completed deals last year included St Georges Hospital PFI project, Dumfries and Galloway Acute Maternity PFI project, Cairngorm Funicular Railway project and Aberdeenshire Schools PFI project. Currently advising in connection with Midlothian Community PFI project, Findley House Care Centre PFI project, Copeland Borough Council PFI project, West Lothian Schools project and Chester-le-street Community Hospital project.
Career: George Watson's College; Edinburgh University (LLB 1979); Scottish School of Business Studies (MBA 1980); Queen's University, Canada (LLM 1982). Articled *Brodies*, 1986-88; assistant solicitor, *Maclay Murray & Spens*, 1988-90, associate 1990-91; partner 1991.
Personal: Born 1958; resides Edinburgh. Enjoys cross country skiing, hill walking.

McQUATER, Gavin
Lovells, London (020) 7296 2000
gavin.mcquater@lovells.com
Specialisation: Project finance. Handles UK (including a number of public/private partnership) projects and international limited recourse transactions, across a range of industries including transport, water and general infrastructure, dealing with sponsors, financial institutions and contracting authorities. Advises on transaction structuring, such as bankable risk allocation and the tender process. Experience of a wide spread of joint ventures, business set ups, corporate reorganisations and M&A transactions. International work includes Europe, Asia and Middle Eastern transactions.
Prof. Memberships: Law Society.
Career: Qualified with *Lovell White & King* in 1979; partner since 1985; 1990-94 in Hong Kong office; now head of firm's project finance unit.

MORRISON, Neil
Rowe & Maw, London (020) 7782 8846
nmorrison@roweandmaw.co.uk
Specialisation: Banking, structured finance and project finance. Advised Road Management Limited on its bid to design, build, finance and operate the A13 Thames Gateway road in East London and has also been advising private sector consortia in PFI projects in the flood defence, urban rapid transit, healthcare and magistrates courts sectors. Advised the Carillion Société Generale Group 4 Consortium on the Manchester Magistrates Courts PFI project, which closed in March 2001. Also involved in heavy rail work (including advising on the Virgin fleet renewals and recently advised Hull Trains on the first open access service in the UK).
Prof. Memberships: Law Society England and Scotland.
Career: Articled *Dundas & Wilson CS*; qualified Scotland 1973; England and Wales 1986; solicitor *Norton Rose* 1973-79; solicitor *Clifford Chance* 1979-82; legal advisor *Britoil plc* 1982-84; legal advisor *Hamilton Bros* 1984-86; partner and head of banking *SJ Berwin & Co* 1987-91; partner and head of banking *McGrigor Donald* 1991-96; group managing partner banking and projects *Rowe & Maw* 1997.
Publications: 'Practical Commercial Precedents' section on credit and finance (FT Law & Tax, Pearson); 'The Private Finance Initiative', a special report (FT Law & Tax, Pearson).
Personal: Born 1946. Leisure interests include hill walking, collecting art, sculpture and music. Lives in Wiltshire.

MURPHY, Michael
MacRoberts, Glasgow (0141) 332 9988
michael.murphy@macroberts.co.uk
Specialisation: Head of *MacRoberts'* projects group, specialising in project finance. Acted for Amey/Halifax/Miller consortium on Glasgow Schools PFI (£400 million). Acting for Amey on Edinburgh Schools PFI (£100 million) and several other schools projects. Acting on numerous health and accommodation projects.
Career: *MacRoberts*. Qualified 1985; assistant solicitor 1986-89; associate 1989-90; partner 1990.
Personal: St Mirin's Academy; Glasgow University 1980, LLB (Hons) 1st Class.

NASH, David
Shepherd & Wedderburn WS, Edinburgh
(0131) 228 9900
david.nash@shepwedd.co.uk
Specialisation: PFI/PPP outsourcing and procurement. Current projects include A92 DBFO, Glasgow Southern Orbital DBFO, Aberdeenshire Schools PFI; Midlothian Schools PFI; MoD Field Electrical Power Supplies; MOD construction vehicles, PFI. Past projects include Aberdenture Schools; Northlink Orkney & Shetland Ferries; Greater Glasgow Sewage Treatment PFI, East Renfrewshire Schools PFI, Scottish Children's Reporters Administration IT PFI, M8 DBFO; M6 DBFO; New Scottish Office; Victoria Quay; Skye Bridge.
Prof. Memberships: Law Society of Scotland.
Career: George Watson University College, Edinburgh. Edinburgh University – Hons MA, LLB (1969-76). Scottish Office Legal Department 1983-98.
Personal: Music, travel, skiing.

NOBLE, Perry
Freshfields Bruckhaus Deringer, London (020) 7936 4000 perry.noble@freshfields.com
Specialisation: Project finance and banking. PFI, transportation and telecommunications projects. Acted for London Underground on Power and Prestige PFI projects. Acts for Abbey National, Babcock & Brown and London Underground on full range of PFI projects. Currently acting for Chase on telecoms financings, Hutchison Whampoa on UMTS financings and First Mark Communications on broadband projects throughout Europe.
Prof. Memberships: Law Society.
Career: Letchworth Grammar School, North East London Polytechnic, Bristol University (LL.M Commercial Law).
Personal: Married, two sons. All sport, particularly cricket. Dog walking and cinema.

O'CONNOR, Mike
Addleshaw Booth & Co, Manchester (0161) 934 6000 mgo@addleshaw-booth.co.uk
Specialisation: Head of PFI/Projects unit. Specialises in PFI, public private partnerships and project finance also in mainstream corporate banking; public/private finance, structured finance; finance transactions involving public bodies of all types. Contributing editor to Butterworths 2 volume 'PFI Handbook'. Contributes to 'CIPFA Handbook on PFI'.
Prof. Memberships: Law Society. British South Africa Lawyers Association. Institute of Fiscal Studies.
Career: Qualified 1989. Partner 1996.
Personal: Leisure interests include horse-racing, electric guitar, travel, piano. Governor of Appleton Thorn County Primary School.

O'NEILL, Mark
Allen & Overy, London (020) 7330 3000

PHILLIPS, Robert
CMS Cameron McKenna, London (020) 7367 2500 rjp@cmck.com
Specialisation: Partner in projects group. Principal area of practice is advising on transactions involving private/public sector participation with particular emphasis on major infrastructure and capital projects. Work covers specialist contract drafting, development with other consultants of a risk profile, and negotiating terms of project documents required for limited recourse financed infrastructure schemes. Major projects include independent power projects (both generation and transmission); road, rail (including high speed rail links), ports and airports transport schemes and information technology. Retained by the World Bank to assist in development courses for the introduction of competition for public/private sector partnerships. Areas of activity include Hong Kong, India, Sub-Saharan Africa, continental Europe and the UK.
Prof. Memberships: Major Projects Association.
Career: Partner at *McKenna & Co* (now *CMS Cameron McKenna)* since 1979, including period as senior resident partner in Hong Kong 1983-88. Admitted as a Solicitor, England and Wales 1971, Hong Kong, 1983 and as a Barrister and Solicitor, State of Victoria, Australia, 1986.
Personal: Born 15th May 1947. Lives in Walton-on-Thames, Surrey.

PICKUP, Raith
Mills & Reeve, Cambridge (01223) 222283 raith.pickup@mills-reeve.com
Specialisation: Leads the PFI team at *Mills & Reeve.* Has considerable experience of advising both the public and private sectors on large projects such as energy plants, power stations, new hospitals and university campuses. Currently leading teams on PFI projects in the health, education, local authority, waste and defence sectors.

PREECE, Andrew
Herbert Smith, London (020) 7374 8000
Specialisation: Partner and head of international projects group. Has considerable experience in major projects work including project finance, lease finance and general commercial work, with particular expertise in oil and gas and infrastructure matters, both domestic (including numerous transactions effected under the Private Finance Initiative) and international, and in complex project, lease and property financings.
Prof. Memberships: Law Society, International Bar Association, Major Projects Association, UK Energy Lawyers Group, Finance & Leasing Association.
Career: Qualified in 1970. Became a partner at *Herbert Smith* in 1977.
Personal: Educated at Selwyn College, Cambridge.

RANDLE, Anthony
DLA, Birmingham (08700) 111111

RANSOME, Clive
Linklaters, London (020) 7456 5904 clive.ransome@linklaters.com
Specialisation: Has worked on a number of major projects, project financings and structured financings in the UK, Europe and Asia. These include the Channel Tunnel (acting for the arranging banks), Northern Ireland's power privatisation (for NIGEN), the Pego power project in Portugal (acting for National Power, EdF and Endesa), the TelecomAsia telecommunications project in Bangkok (acting for KFW and other lenders), power, telecommunications projects and road projects in the PRC, Thailand and Indonesia, Southern's US$2.7 billion acquisition of CEPA (acting for Southern) representing IFC and the offshore banks on the Star refinery project in Thailand, advising Shell Brasil and Petrobras on an LNG import and gas sales joint venture in north-eastern Brazil and advising the project sponsors on the Renor refinery in Brazil.
Career: 1992 to date: Partner in the project and asset finance group, London; 1993-98: Hong Kong based; 1985-92: Assistant solicitor, *Linklaters*; 1985: Admitted as a solicitor. 1982: University College, Cardiff, LLB (Hons); 1978: University of Southampton, BA (Hons).

READ, Anthony
Burness, Edinburgh (0131) 473 6000 ajmr@burness.co.uk
Specialisation: Anthony advises the public sector, bidders and banks on all aspects of the structuring, development and financing of projects. Main area of practice is advising on PFI projects in local authority, education, accommodation and health sectors. Current PFI projects include acting for Fife Council on schools PPP and the service provider on Highland Schools PPP projects. He acted for Strathclyde Police on new training and recruitment centre and Dundee Healthcare Services Ltd on Tayside Primary Care Acute Psychiatric Unit project. Anthony also led Class 98 in the award winning Falkirk Schools project, advised Perth & Kinross Council on office accommodation and car park project and Bank of Scotland on James Watt College, North Ayrshire Campus project. He is a regular speaker at conferences.

REYNELL, Daniel Humphrey
Clifford Chance, London (020) 7600 1000 daniel.reynell@cliffordchance.com
Specialisation: Partner specialising in structured finance, with particular emphasis on project and other limited recourse financings in the energy, telecoms and infrastructure sectors. Recent experience has included transactions in Hungary, Italy, South Africa, Spain and the United Kingdom.
Career: Bradford Grammar School; St John's College, Oxford, BA 1976. Articled at *Coward Chance,* qualified 1977. Partner at *Clifford Chance* since 1987. Secondments to Hong Kong (1986-90) and Tokyo (1990-94)
Personal: Born in 1955; married with two children. Resides in London.

ROBERTS, Martin
Slaughter and May, London (020) 7710 3481 martin.roberts@slaughterandmay.com
Specialisation: Has been involved in more than fifty oil and gas and energy-related projects (acting for purchasers, sellers, sponsors and financiers) since the mid 1970s and more recently power station and other infrastructure projects (including road and rail) in the UK and overseas. Has acted for both sponsors and banks on major PFI projects.
Prof. Memberships: The Law Society; City of London Solicitors' Company; International Bar Association.
Career: *Slaughter and May* 1967, qualified in 1969 and became partner 1975.
Personal: Born 20 March 1944, attended Shrewsbury School and Trinity Hall, Cambridge.

ROLFE, Andrew
Clifford Chance, London (020) 7956 0071 andrew.rolfe@cliffordchance.com
Specialisation: Specialises in major infrastructure project and development work, with particular involvement in PFI/PPP projects. Has led teams acting for sponsors and for financiers on many leading deals in the defence, education, health, local authority and transport sectors.
Career: Qualified in 1982. Partner in *Clifford Chance* since 1988.
Personal: Born 1956. Attended Nottingham University – LLB (Hons) 1977.

ROUT, Peter
DLA, Manchester (08700) 111111

ROWEY, Kent
Freshfields Bruckhaus Deringer, London (020) 7936 4000 kent.rowey@freshfields.com
See under Energy & Natural Resources, p.355

SALT, Stuart
Linklaters, London (020) 7456 5912 stuart.salt@linklaters.com
See under Energy & Natural Resources, p.356

SAUNDERS, Chris
Slaughter and May, London (020) 7600 1200
christopher.saunders@slaughterandmay.com
Specialisation: Joint ventures, project development and financing in wide range of industry sectors.
Career: Qualified with *Slaughter and May* 1979. Partner 1986.

SEDGLEY, David
Allen & Overy, London (020) 7330 2724
david.sedgley@allenovery.com
Specialisation: Project Finance and PFI. Partner with wide experience of projects and structured financing including infrastructure, oil, gas, and power projects. He has particularly extensive experience in PFI transactions in a wide range of sectors.
Career: Articled *Allen & Overy*, qualified 1989, Partner 1995.
Personal: Born 1964.

SIMMONS, William
Tods Murray WS, Edinburgh (0131) 226 4771
william.simmons@todsmurray.com
Specialisation: Work includes infrastructure projects and PFI, corporate finance, mergers and acquisitions, banking and general commercial work including joint ventures.
Prof. Memberships: Law Society of Scotland.
Career: Qualified 1981 *Bishop & Co.* Joined *Dorman Jeffrey & Co* 1983 (partner 1984). Joined *Tods Murray* as a partner in 1986.
Personal: Born 1958. Attended Hutchesons Boys Grammar School 1967-75 and Glasgow University 1975-79 (LLB Hons). Leisure: hill walking and skiing.

SOUTAR, Tim
Clifford Chance, London (020) 7600 1000
tim.soutar@cliffordchance.com
Specialisation: Partner in London office specialising in finance and energy, oil, gas, and natural resource projects. Experience includes power, refinery, petrochemical, pipeline and transport infrastructure projects: Shajiao B and C, Pagbilao and Sual Power Projects – Hopewell Group, Zhuhai Power Project – HSBC, Star Refinery, Thailand – Caltex and PTT, NODCO Expansion – NODCO/QGPC, Luton Airport Expansion – AGI Consortium, Chad – Cameroon Oil Transportation Project – senior lenders.
Prof. Memberships: Power Sector Working Group.
Career: Bradford Grammar School; St Catherine's College, Oxford (BA Jurisprudence 1977); University of East Asia, Macau (Diploma in Chinese Law 1987). Articled *Coward Chance*; qualified 1980, Hong Kong 1983; partner Hong Kong 1988.
Personal: Distance running, golf. Born 1955. Resides Kent.

SPACIE, Dominic
Denton Wilde Sapte, London (020) 7242 1212

STEADMAN, Tim
Clifford Chance, London (020) 7600 1000
tim.steadman@cliffordchance.com
Specialisation: Partner and Head of Construction Group. Member of PFI/PPP Group, specialising in concession and construction aspects of projects arising from the PPP programe in the UK and PFI/PPP schemes elsewhere.
Prof. Memberships: European Construction Institute; IBA committee "T"; CBI Modernising Government Committee; UK PPP Forum; UN/ECE PPP Forum.
Career: Hertford College; Oxford University. Trainee and assistant *Lovell White & King* 1976-82; associate *Baker & McKenzie* 1982-85; partner *Baker & McKenzie* 1985-97; partner *Clifford Chance* since March 1997.
Publications: 'History and Framework of PFI/PPP in the UK', July 2000; 'Public Private Partnerships – A Private Sector Perspective', June 2000; 'Rubbish!' (the future of integrated waste management PPP schemes), Oct 2000; 'BOT/PPP Projects – The Contractor's Perspective', July 2000.
Personal: Born 1955; resides London.

STOPFORD, Philip
White & Case, London (020) 7397 3604
pstopford@whitecase.com
Specialisation: Partner specialising in corporate finance with emphasis on project financings particularly in oil and gas, power and infrastructure. Also handles construction and joint ventures. Head of *White & Case's* Europe, Middle East and Africa Energy, Infrastructure and Project Finance group.
Prof. Memberships: Law Society of England and Wales, American Bar Association, New York State Bar Association.
Career: *White & Case* New York 1980-81; *White & Case* Hong Kong 1981-83; *White & Case* Indonesia 1988-91; *White & Case* Frankfurt 1991-93; *White & Case* London 1993 to present. Admitted as a solicitor in England and Wales; admitted to New York State Bar and to District of Columbia Bar.
Personal: Brunel University (1977 LLB Hons); University of Virginia Law School (LLM 1978).

SUTTIE, Frank
Addleshaw Booth & Co, Leeds (0113) 209 2000

TEMPLETON – KNIGHT, Jane
Hunton & Williams, London (020) 7246 5700
JTempleton-Knight@hunton.com
Specialisation: Partner in project finance group specialising in the development and financing of major power and infrastructure projects often involving export credit agencies and multilaterals. Represented parties in relation to projects in Europe, Middle East, Asia and Africa including Shoreham Power, UK; North Chennai Power, India; Powergen Renewables, UK; Croydon Tramlink; Lisheen Zinc Mine, Ireland; Sea Launch satellite system; New Tagus Bridge, Portugal; Pego and Tapada Power Stations, Portugal; Rosen Power Station, Italy; the Serene group of power stations, Italy; Second Severn Bridge; Newport gold heap leaching project in Uzbekistan; South East London waste-to-energy plant; The Kasese Cobalt Mine, Uganda.
Career: Durham University, BA Honours (upper second), 1985. University of Newcastle -upon-Tyne, Solicitors Final Examination, 1986. *Allen & Overy*, London – qualified 1989. Associate 1989 to December 1995. *Milbank, Tweed, Hadley & McCloy*, London – January 1995 senior associate, elected partner October 1996.

TOTT, Nicholas
Herbert Smith, London (020) 7374 8000
nicholas.tott@herbertsmith.com
Specialisation: Principal areas of work include all forms of financing and banking work with particular emphasis on asset finance, leasing, project financing and PFI/PPP projects. Seconded to the Private Finance Panel Executive for fifteen months with responsibility for PFI Projects in Scotland, Northern Ireland and the Ministry of Defence. Publications include a chapter 'Public Finance in the U.K.' in Leasing Finance (Euromoney 1997, 3rd Edition.) Co-author of 'The PFI Handbook' (Jordans, March 1999).
Prof. Memberships: Law Society; City of London Solicitors' Company.
Career: Qualified Scotland (1985), England and Wales (1991). Partner 1992.
Personal: Born 8th May 1960. Educated at Edinburgh University. Leisure pursuits include golf and skiing.

VERNON, Philip
Ashurst Morris Crisp, London (020) 7859 1705
philip.vernon@ashursts.com
Specialisation: Partner in projects group. Principal areas of practice are infrastructure projects, privatisations and project finance, with particular experience in projects under the UK government's private finance initiative (including light rail, road, prison, hospital and other accommodation projects) and also power and energy projects in the Middle East and Indian sub-continent.
Career: Articled at *Ashurst Morris Crisp*; qualified 1989. Partner at *Ashurst Morris Crisp* since 1998.
Personal: BA (Hons) in Classics, Worcester College, Oxford University 1985: Fulbright Fellowship in US Securities Law 1994.

VINTER, Graham D.
Allen & Overy, London (020) 7330 3000
graham.vinter@allenovery.com
Specialisation: Partner specialising in all aspects of project finance. Involved in numerous projects acting for sponsors and lenders in the oil, gas, mining, electricity, waste, energy and infrastructure sectors worldwide. He has extensive experience of ECA and multilateral financings.
Career: Oxford University (BA 1979). Ludwig-Maximilians University, Munich (1977-78). Born 1956. Articled *Allen & Overy*, qualified 1982, Partner 1988.
Publications: Author of 'Project Finance: A Legal Guide' (2nd. ed., 1998).

WEBER, David
Linklaters, London (020) 7456 5870
david.weber@linklaters.com
Specialisation: Project and project finance department. Specialising in the development and financing of major international projects, including infrastructure, power generation and oil and gas projects, acting for project sponsors, borrowers and lenders.
Career: 1984 to date: Partner, *Linklaters*, projects department; 1981-84: Assistant solicitor, *Linklaters* London; 1980-81: Seconded to *Fulbridge & Jaworski*, Texas; 1978-80: Assistant solicitor, Linklaters, corporate tax; 1976-78: Articled clerk, *Linklaters*. 1979: MA; 1976: College of Law, Lancaster Gate; 1975: BA Law, Clare College, Cambridge. Haberdashers Aske's School, Hertfordshire.

WHITE, Bruce
Linklaters, London (020) 7456 5986
bruce.white@linklaters.com
Specialisation: Specialist in project finance concentrating particularly on its infrastructure projects under the UK government's private finance initiative as well as advising on major international infrastructure projects.
Career: 1995 to date: Partner in the project finance department of *Linklaters*; 1986-95: Assistant solicitor,

Linklaters; 1984-86: Trainee solicitor, *Dorman Jeffrey & Co*, Glasgow. 1981-84: University of Dundee, LLB Law.

WHITFIELD, Stuart
Bevan Ashford, Bristol (0117) 975 1722
s.whitfield@bevanashford.co.uk
Specialisation: Partner in the PFI and projects department. Main area of practice covers project finance and PFI/PPP advisory work. He has advised a wide range of bidding consortia and specialises in projects in the defence sector.
Career: Exeter University. Articled at *Bond Pearce*; qualified 1990; partner at *Veale Wasbrough* 1997. Joined *Bevan Ashford* 1998.
Personal: Lives in Bristol; Leisure interests include family, music and cars.

WOODROW, Cameron
Pinsent Curtis Biddle, Birmingham
(0121) 200 1050
cameron.woodrow@pinsents.com
Specialisation: Major projects; public-private partnerships (including PFI); privatisations; corporate restructuring; joint ventures; acquisitions and disposals; project management. Major transactions have included the pre-franchising reorganisation of the Central Trains Operating Unit of British Rail; the £150 million restructuring and refinancing of Birmingham International Airport; a US$150 million joint venture for LucasVarity; the £100 million concession based financing of London Luton Airport; the acquisition by GEC Alsthom/Tarmac of the Central Infrastructure Maintenance Unit of British Rail. Significant experience in advising both public bodies (including local authorities) and major private sector clients in the transport, automotive and engineering sectors. Expertise in commercial, company, contract and public law.
Prof. Memberships: Law Society.
Career: BA (Jurisprudence), Brasenose College, Oxford. *Freshfields* 1983-93 (qualified 1986). Partner *Pinsent Curtis Biddle* 1993 to date. Birmingham head and national practice coordinator for major projects 1997-2001. Awarded PFI Team of the Year by Legal Business for Birmingham Airport restructuring.
Personal: Common Purpose graduate.

WYLES, David
Herbert Smith, London (020) 7466 2041
david.wyles@herbertsmith.com
Specialisation: PFI and project finance. Has advised sponsors and funders on a wide range of PFI projects including health, education, courts and street lighting. Recent projects include Wirral Schools, Manchester Magistrates Courts and Dudley Hospitals.
Prof. Memberships: City of London Law Society.
Career: Herbert Smith partner 1996.
Publications: Contributor to 'The PFI Handbook' (Jordans March 1999).
Personal: Kings College, London and Sorbonne Panthéon, Paris.

WYMAN, Chris
Clifford Chance, London (020) 7600 1000
chris.wyman@cliffordchance.com
Specialisation: Partner specialising in project acquisition and general finance in the energy, communications and infrastructure sectors.
Career: Epsom College; Cambridge University. Articled *Coward Chance/Clifford Chance*; qualified 1981; partner *Clifford Chance* since 1986.

PROPERTY (COMMERCIAL)

OVERVIEW: The sea change in commercial property continues. The tax-led transactions that followed in the wake of stamp duty rises have now resulted in joint ventures and limited partnerships being the routine rather than the exception. The undervaluation of property companies on the stock market prompted public to private deals. Following PRIME and STEPS, other large scale property users have questioned the value of property ownership and there have been further examples of outsourcing and management through Preps. International, particularly pan-European property investment is becoming a reality, with US funds picking up on the potential.

In this respect, the hotels sector and Eastern Europe are of interest.In this new climate certain firms can be identified as having the critical mass, international capacity and essential associated strengths in tax, finance and corporate matters. Even those without all of these resources and skills find themselves moving away from the traditional approach to property work, although research indicated there was a lesser emphasis on corporatised deals outside London. Urban regeneration has provided a further source of good work for skilled property teams and certain areas, such as the Thames Valley, have also experienced a growth in development work and consequential large scale lettings. Not all property lawyers see this boom continuing and many are keeping a watchful eye for the signs of a slow down.

This year the rankings for London firms have been presented in three tables. Firms with 50 or more property lawyers are grouped together, those with 25-49 appear in a second table and a third covers firms with fewer than 25 property lawyers. The team sizes do not include specialist environmental lawyers, planning lawyers or property litigators. Nor do they include tax or corporate lawyers who are involved with property transactions as a part of their wider practices, and we refer you to those specific sections of our Guide.

TOP IN-HOUSE LAWYERS

Michael ASHLEY-BROWN, Group Legal Counsel, Canary Warf

Mark KINGSTON, European General Counsel, Tishman Speyer

Angeline SWIFT, Legal Manager, BG Property Holdings Ltd

Jayne WALTERS, Commercial Director, Akeler

A *"firm adversary, who manages his team well,"* **Michael Ashley-Brown** remains *"a pleasant man to deal with"* Undoubtedly *"well known,"* commentators are unreserved in vouching for the quality of **Mark Kingston**'s work. **Angeline Smith** at BG Property Holdings is *"no-nonsense and very much in control"* while **Jayne Walters** remains highly regarded.

In-House lawyers profiles: p.1193

'CLIENT ONLY' NATIONAL SURVEY

The table differs from the other tables in this section in two respects. It is derived from a separate survey of commercial property clients across the length and breadth of Britain. It also asked firms to rank firms and individuals on a national basis.
The table below is based on 101 questionnaires and lists the twelve firms with most recommendations in descending order.
(Numbers in brackets denote 2000 positions)

1	**Berwin Leighton Paisner** (5)	6 =	**Linklaters** (3=)
2	**Nabarro Nathanson** (2)	8	**DLA** (11=)
3 =	**Clifford Chance** (3=)	9	**Ashurst Morris Crisp** (8)
3 =	**Lovells** (11=)	10	**CMS Cameron McKenna** (9)
5	**Eversheds** (1)	11=	**Denton Wilde Sapte** (-)
6 =	**Freshfield Bruckhaus Deringer** (11=)	11=	**Herbert Smith** (6)

RESEARCH APPROVED BY BMRB: *For this edition,* Chambers' *researchers conducted 6,552 interviews – 4,419 with law firms, 554 with barristers and 1,579 with clients.*

The validity of the research was scrutinised by BMRB International, who audited both the methodology and the results at our offices in July 2001. They interviewed Chambers' *researchers and cross-checked sample interviews. Details of the audit appear on page 7.*

LONDON

50+ SOLICITORS

Linklaters (see firm details p.1042) *"Outstandingly good at property work"* showing a *"professional approach all the way down the food chain."* The firm wins plaudits from solicitors for its consistently high quality work while clients appreciate its responsiveness and innovative solutions. It pulls apart from many in the pack through its ability to handle the largest and most complex of transactions. It also offers the international capacity required by those clients entering into multi-national real estate deals. Peers commend a truly top-flight team offering *"an extremely good breed"* of property lawyer. Clients typically think of lead name **Martin Elliott** (see p.744) as a *"lateral thinker." "Icon"* **Robert Finch** (see p.744) is an *"effective operator"* capable of leaving the opposition *"dead in the water." "Talented and highly personable with it,"* **Patrick Plant** (see p.751) has a profile in hotel work. **Jeffrey Bailey** (see p.740) has had a big year handling the Cisco Green Park letting in Reading. Head of the group, **Simon Clark** (see p.742) is known for his excellence in tax issues and younger talent **James Knox** (see p.748) has secured his place in our up and coming table through client recommendations of his abilities and pleasant manner. Utilising a large proportion of the team, the firm handled the disposal of MEPC's £1.1 billion

PROPERTY (COMMERCIAL): 50+ SOLICITORS • London	Ptnrs	Assts
1 Linklaters	20	59
2 Clifford Chance	18	82
3 Berwin Leighton Paisner	13	60
Herbert Smith	14	46
Lovells	12	56
4 Freshfields Bruckhaus Deringer	11	43
Nabarro Nathanson	28	75
5 Ashurst Morris Crisp	12	45
CMS Cameron McKenna	12	39
6 Allen & Overy	10	40
Lawrence Graham	23	41

This book is the product of 6,552 1/2-hour interviews. See p.7 for BMRB audit.
Within each band, firms are listed alphabetically.

shopping centre portfolio, by way of joint venture and straightforward sales. In outsourcing, it advised Mapeley on the bid, financing, transfer and management of the Abbey National property portfolio. It demonstrated its European capabilities in the sale of Scottish & Newcastle's Center Parcs business in five countries. **Clients:** Cisco Systems; Lend Lease; Goldman Sachs Whitehall Fund, Lehman Brothers; Development Securities; ABN AMRO.

Clifford Chance (see firm details p.919) Occupying the number two slot alone this year, Clifford Chance is a forceful presence in the world of sophisticated real estate deals. Its giant corporate and finance arms have helped to lift the real estate practice up from the majority of UK-based practices, but the knowledge and skills they offered are now found within the real estate group. Clients value the international nature of the practice. Although assertions that the team is "*institutionalised*" in its approach still exist, our research noted a common assessment that the practice offers "*commercial*" solutions and now operates "*less by the book and more at the cutting edge*" than many other competitors. The "*charming*" **Robert MacGregor** (see p.748) is a "*fine lawyer*" and has a talent for supervising a team on a deal. "*Excellent*" **Iain Morpeth** (see p.750) has achieved high profile, commended especially by institutional and investor clients. All of the recommended lawyers from the team achieve high banding, including the calm and collected **Tony Briam** (see p.741) and "*thinker*" **Jonathan Solomon** (see p.754). Developer clients confirmed their willingness to follow the latter from Norton Rose on his move late last year. Other partners have arrived from CMS Cameron McKenna. The firm continues its work for Canary Wharf with lettings, a development of three new office buildings, and a £1 billion revolving construction loan facility. It advised Tishman Speyer/Travelers Real Estate Venture on the acquisition and financing of Tower Place, with associated lettings. For Railtrack the firm has been involved in the redevelopment of Paddington, Victoria and Bromley South stations. **Clients:** Lend Lease; Spitalfields; Helical Bar; Wates Group; MEPC; Corporation of London.

Berwin Leighton Paisner (see firm details p.878) "*Punctual, prompt, reliable and well organised*," this is a firm that is satisfying longstanding clients. Strong among the institutional investors and in the public and retail sectors (particularly commended for its Tesco relationship). Peers perceive that while the merger with Paisner & Co will not radically change the make up of the property department, the influx of corporate lawyers will enable certain parts of the corporate group to intensify their focus on real estate deals. In addition Paisner has a following among leisure clients. Our researchers were informed that what perhaps sets this group below the two leaders is the lesser degree of international coverage. New head **Philip Bretherton** (see p.741) ("*bloody good*" and an "*incredibly nice guy*") is thought to be an excellent choice, following the departure of David Taylor to Herbert Smith. Most solicitors see this as a fresh start for the group. **Peter Rudolf** (see p.753) has been identified as just about the best lawyer the team can field; "*for him there is no such thing as an unreasonable demand*" and "*his skill is his unflappability.*" The group's younger names received commendation in our research and are not far off the rankings. It is advising the Government in relation to attempts to sell the Millennium Dome. For Southwark Land Regeneration, the firm is assisting in the £1 billion transformation of Elephant and Castle. It acted for key investors (Scottish Widows, the Coal Schemes, the Shell Pension Fund and an overseas investor) who joined BAA in the establishment of the £200 million the BAA Airport Hotels Partnership. **Clients:** Liverpool City Council; CGNU; Compass Group; British Land; Prudential; Legal & General.

Herbert Smith (see firm details p.993) Although operating with a big department for some time now, the Herbert Smith property group is thought to have gained in confidence and is certainly "*beefing up*" its profile. "*Technically extremely good*," it has a reputation for "*dotting all the i's and crossing all the t's*." In line with the Linklaters and Clifford Chance models, it is a direct beneficiary of the firm's corporate credibility. Senior figure **David Taylor** (see p.754) has joined from Berwin Leighton to "*shake a few trees.*" His move has been described as "*interesting*" by clients and "*extraordinary*" by peers, who assume he will ensure the team becomes more entrepreneurial and increasingly "*out there.*" The team includes an admirable number of strong lawyers. **James Barnes** (see p.740) is "*professional and a delight to work with*" and **Christopher Harrison** (see p.746) is deemed by clients to be "*smooth and user friendly.*" **Chris de Pury** (see p.743) is "*a sensible guy and switched on,*" while both **Patrick Robinson** (see p.752) ("*first rate*") and **Chris Tavener** (see p.754) received warm endorsement. **Ian Cox** (see p.743) is ranked as one of this year's new up and coming lawyers. The group advised London & Continental Stations in relation to the regeneration of Stratford City and the Kings Cross site. One of its highest profile acquisitions has been Morgan Stanley's Alban Gate and Heron Quay's joint venture with CIT. Standard Life instructed the team to dispose of the £300 million Cutlers Garden Estate. **Clients:** Hammerson; Halifax; London Stock Exchange; Stanhope; Tishman Speyer; Hermes.

Lovells (see firm details p.1044) A "*non-aggressive*" style from lawyers that "*don't mess around*" and "*take pride in their work.*" The "*stars*" at the top end certainly make competitors realise that "*they are thinking as quickly as the best*." "*Beating a path to new generation work*," **Robert Kidby** (see p.748) is "*keen to make sure the firm second guesses where the market is going.*" Peers typically believe that he has done an excellent job of "*driving the practice*." It is an increasingly internationally focused operation that has the support of an impressive overseas capability. Ex DJ Freeman lawyer **Andrew Sanders** (see p.753) has been a boost for the team and is praised by clients for his commerciality. **Michael Stancombe** (see p.754) also received warm recommendation and "*jolly decent sort*" **Jackie Newstead** (see p.750) enters the up and coming list. The group has received accolades for its work on the Abbey National Columbus £450 million PREPS transaction. In relation to the regeneration of the Kings Cross site, it acted for the Argent St George joint venture purchasing around 55 acres of land. Continuing its leading position in outsourcing, the group is now acting for Shell on proposals to outsource its UK petrol stations. **Clients:** Amey; Lend Lease; Prudential; BAA/Lynton; Waitrose; Post Office.

Freshfields Bruckhaus Deringer (see firm details p.965) "*My Lord they were good!*" one rival told us of the team's performance on a particular transaction. Packed with "*good technical lawyers*" peers acknowledge "*you see their name in a lot of big deals*" of the "*difficult and innovative*" sort. Freshfields' property group has now "*graduated*" and holds a secure position, partly because it is sufficiently resourced in the UK and overseas, and partly because its senior lawyers are "*at least one step ahead of the opposition on a deal*." Our interviewees "*really rate*" **Geoffrey Le Pard** (see p.748); he's "*commercial and gets deals done*," many of those deals being for tenants at Canary Wharf. Head of department **Chris Morris** (see p.750) com-

LEADING INDIVIDUALS: LONDON		
1	**BRETHERTON Philip** Berwin Leighton	**ELLIOTT Martin** Linklaters
	FINCH Robert Linklaters	**KIDBY Robert** Lovells
	LE PARD Geoffrey Freshfields Bruckhaus	**MACGREGOR Robert** Clifford Chance
	MORPETH Iain Clifford Chance	**RYLAND David** SJ Berwin
	TAYLOR David Herbert Smith	
2	**BARNES James** Herbert Smith	**BRIAM Tony** Clifford Chance
	FIELD Christopher Macfarlanes	**HAMILTON Sophie** Forsters
	HARRISON Christopher Herbert Smith	**NISSE Ian** Ashurst Morris Crisp
	PLANT Patrick Linklaters	**RUDOLF Peter** Berwin Leighton Paisner
	SOLOMON Jonathan Clifford Chance	**WHITE Graham** Slaughter and May
	WRIGHT David Nabarro Nathanson	
3	**BAILEY Jeffrey** Linklaters	**BROWN Nicholas** CMS Cameron McKenna
	CLARK Paul DJ Freeman	**CLARK Simon** Linklaters
	DE PURY Chris Herbert Smith	**GNIADKOWSKI Stan** Denton Wilde Sapte
	HOWARD Amanda Nabarro Nathanson	**KUSTOW David** Olswang
	LUST Graham Nabarro Nathanson	**MORRIS Christopher** Freshfields Bruckhaus
	ODY Jonathan Norton Rose	**SAMSON John** Nabarro Nathanson
	SANDERS Andrew Lovells	**STANCOMBE Michael** Lovells
	VIVIAN Jon SJ Berwin	**WATSON Gary** Ashurst Morris Crisp
	WESTHEAD Tim Olswang	
4	**BENZECRY Edward** CMS Cameron McKenna	**BUTLER Alan** Simmons & Simmons
	CLEAL Adam Allen & Overy	**HOLY Julian** Julian Holy
	LAKE Tim Stepien Lake Gilbert & Paling	**OLMER Philip** Olswang
	PATTERSON Anthony Forsters	**PICKUP Bryan** SJ Berwin
	QUICKE Martin Denton Wilde Sapte	**RICE Dermot** Slaughter and May
	ROBINSON Patrick Herbert Smith	**TAVENER Chris** Herbert Smith
	WILLSON Stephen SJ Berwin	
UP AND COMING		
	COX Ian Herbert Smith	**KNOX James** Linklaters
	NEWSTEAD Jackie Lovells	

See individuals' profiles p.739

bines strategic prowess with a pragmatic deal sense. Recent highlights include the instructions from Clifford Chance in connection with its office move to Canary Wharf, acting for Trillium on its bid for STEPS and almost all the subsequent public and private outsourcing bids. It also acted for Granada Compass on the property aspects of its £3.5 billion disposal of the Granada/Forte hotel divisions. **Clients:** London Transport; Scottish Widows; Lehman Brothers; P&O; Bank of England; Kingfisher.

Nabarro Nathanson (see firm details p.1078) A large and "*ever present*" force in property. Its success rests on two strengths: the quality of its leading names and a veritable army of more junior lawyers. For some clients the firm is an "*IBM choice*" for the bulk of its property work. Head of department, **David Wright** (see p.756) falls into the superb category of practitioner, impressing both lawyers and clients. Researchers received outstanding feedback (both in quantity and quality, from clients and other lawyers) for "*top dog*" **Amanda Howard**, who has come to real estate from a corporate background and is admired for her limited partnership experience. **Graham Lust** (see p.748) was described as "*one of the most able lawyers I know.*" **John Samson** is also recommended. The group acted for Australian shopping centre giant Westfield in the joint venture with MEPC to establish a £1 billion portfolio of centres in the UK. It is instructed by preferred STEPS bidder Mapeley, and proving that it has international capability, is instructed by Henderson Global Investors on behalf of Pearl Assurance in connection with a portfolio of shopping centres in eastern and western Europe. **Clients:** Frogmore Investments; Hammerson; Land Securities; Morley Fund Managers; GE Capital Real Estate; Slough Estates.

Ashurst Morris Crisp (see firm details p.866) "*Commitment, thoroughness*" and corporate strength have kept the Ashursts team in a strong position. Partner departures have been a feature of the last year, but in the main these have not made a deep impact. The activity at the top end of the property market is moving towards the type of deal that the team does best – sophisticated finance modules and joint ventures. It has won profile through the massive BT outsourcing project. Heavily responsible for the winning of that work is **Ian Nisse** (see p.750) , whose return to full time practice is welcomed by peers and clients alike. "*Watch this space*" claim competitors as **Gary Watson** (see p.755) ("*a class act*") has moved to the firm from Hammond Suddards Edge, a key win for the group. It acted for the Paddington Basin Development Corporation, its subsidiary, and Chelsfield in connection with pre-lets to Marks & Spencer and Orange. Also advised Canary Wharf on the letting to Clifford Chance. **Clients:** Chelsfield; Grantchester; Tesco; Bristol City Council; Bath & North East Somerset Council; Integrated Accommodation Services (PFI).

CMS Cameron McKenna (see firm details p.922) With serious departures in the last year, including Jon Vivien's move to SJ Berwin, some peers question the firm's direction in this area. Clients continue to report their satisfaction in terms of product; "*excellent on a full range of work, their lawyers are impressive,*" while the group scores well with its "*competitive, cost effective approach.*" The calibre of lawyer found in the property group is first class, and clients gave researchers the impression that no effort is spared on their behalf. "*Excellent*" lawyer **Nick Brown** (see p.741) also manages the group. Clients are "*delighted at the way* **Edward Benzecry** (see p.740) *approaches work*" and competitors also single him out for praise. For Sainsbury's the group conducted two sale and leaseback securitisations of 26 supermarkets, with a combined value of over £550 million. It acted for joint venture company JPPBS Forbury on the development of new offices in the M25 area. The firm also undertook all the work on the Gunwharf development for Berkeley Festival Waterfront Company, including the sale to the Gunwharf Quays LP. **Clients:** John Laing Property; Prudential; Britannic Asset Management; Taylor Woodrow; The Wellcome Trust; Nomura.

Allen & Overy (see firm details p.856) Still heavily involved in property finance and corporate support, the firm is making a concerted effort to build its pure property practice. Seen most often on "*grown up deals*" acting for banks, judged in particular to have "*the German bank market stitched up.*" "*Effective*" **Adam Cleal** (see p.742) is the man responsible for spearheading the drive towards mainstream property clients. The group has been advising WestLB on the £375 million joint venture with British Land to acquire 1 and 10 Fleet Place, 100 New Bridge Street and 33 Cannon Street. Also advised J Henry Schroder on the development of Christchurch Court at Paternoster Square. Granger Trust and Deutsche Bank instructed the firm on the transfer from public to private ownership of the Bradford Property Trust, which included 11500 residential units. **Clients:** Marylebone Warwick Balfour; Saville Gordon Estates; HypoVereinsbank; Habitat; William Pierce; Principle Hotels.

Lawrence Graham (see firm details p.1030) Led by Penny Francis, the team is known to "*give clients a good service.*" One client actually confirmed that they would follow their preferred lawyer "*to the ends of the earth.*" Around a half of the practice is investment work with a good part of the remainder being development projects. The group has been advising London & Regional Properties in connection with the development of a 22 hectare site at Park Royal abutting the A40. Also instructed by that client, the firm is advising on the well-publicised redevelopment of the Crystal Palace site. For Derwent Valley subsidiary, Colebrook Developments, it is working on an office redevelopment in Southampton Row, Covent Garden. **Clients:** AXA Sun Life; Cellnet; J Sainsbury Developments; Universities Superannuation Scheme; Allied Dunbar; Thames Water.

25-49 SOLICITORS

PROPERTY (COMMERCIAL): 25-49 SOLICITORS • London	Ptnrs	Assts
1 SJ Berwin	14	32
2 Dechert	13	24
Denton Wilde Sapte	11	21
3 DJ Freeman	14	16
Macfarlanes	10	27
Norton Rose	9	28
4 Forsters	8	20
Olswang	5	20
Slaughter and May	5	31
5 Field Fisher Waterhouse	15	19
Gouldens	9	16
6 Eversheds	10	24
Richards Butler	12	19
Rowe & Maw	9	16
Simmons & Simmons	11	22

This book is the product of 6,552 1/2-hour interviews. See p.7 for BMRB audit.
Within each band, firms are listed alphabetically.

SJ Berwin (see firm details p.879) A firm that can and does compete happily with firms ranked in the 'larger teams table'. Peers acknowledge that the team knows how to play tough and has lawyers who are "*technically excellent – you expect quality work from them.*" Clients note that the firm is "*particularly good at development and planning*" and is instructed for its "*experience of limited partnerships and collective investments.*" In this latter field, **David Ryland** (see p.753) is described by one client as "*the best legal mind in the country*," while many solicitors proclaim his skill; "*he's in a class of his own.*" **Jon Vivian**'s (see p.754) arrival from CMS Cameron McKenna with a small team is great news for the firm. It is thought that he will add further "*institutional credibility.*" Head of department **Bryan Pickup** (see p.828) is "*experienced and a pleasure to deal with.*" This year, long-standing partner **Stephen Willson** (see p.756) *("spot on, on all the points")* received a number of plaudits from clients and other lawyers; *"you can sit down with him and a blank piece of paper and put something together."* In the last year the group has acted for Peabody Global Real Estate Partners on the purchase of Cutlers Gardens for £300 million, and advised Hilton Group in the sale and leaseback of 11 hotels for £312 million. It was also behind the establishment of the £600 million City of London Unit Trust, acting for Schroders. **Clients:** The British Land Company; AXA Sun Life; Marylebone Warwick Balfour; Sainsbury's; Chelsfield; CB Hillier Parker.

Dechert (see firm details p.938) A long-held reputation in retail property and now displaying a growing interest and capability in property finance. Its clients range across owners and occupiers, in addition to retail developers. It acts as legal adviser to the British Retail Consortium and senior partner Steven Fogel has played a prominent role in legislative changes pertaining to the landlord and tenant relationship. The property team is led by Chris Edwards. On funding work it acted for Nationwide Building Society as senior secured lender, agent and security trustee on the funding for the purchase of Alban Gate from MEPC. It advised Blackfriars Investments on two purchases, one from Slough Estates at £40 million and the other at Orbit House, SE1 for £9.5 million. It has been appointed by Schroders as advisor on its Emerging Retail Fund. **Clients:** BhS; MWB; CGNU; Royal and Sun Alliance; Corporation of London.

Denton Wilde Sapte (see firm details p.939) Clients report on the "*fantastic service*" they receive from this property group with a good number pleased to have followed **Stan Gniadkowski** to the firm last year. His skills in PFI-related and straight property work are valued and other lawyers credit him with much of the team's success. Plaudits are also given to other partners, including newly ranked **Martin Quicke**, who clients say is "*highly efficient and good value for money.*" The group acted on the joint venture between Taylor Woodrow Capital Developments and Hutchison Whampoa Properties on the purchase of Lots Road Power Station. It was instructed by Bishopsbridge (GP) on the purchase of development land at Paddington. For the Crown Estate Commissioners, it purchased Fleet Place House for nearly £60 million. **Clients:** Barclays Bank Group Property Services; The City University; Thornfield Properties and Thornfield Redditch LP; Asticus; Equitable Life; Schroders Exempt Property Unit Trust.

DJ Freeman The loss of five partners from the property division in the last year has brought into question the effectiveness of the firm's sectorised approach. However, its size and long history within the property industry ensure its continued success in attracting high value and complex work. "*It is decent on partnership and structuring*" and its departmental structure ensures that there are corporate, tax and construction lawyers within the group, who are steeped in the property industry. **Paul Clark** (see p.742) is commended by peers for his "*technical and drafting skills*." It advised John Laing on the securitisation of the rental income from the Ashford International Passenger Terminal, raising £70 million through the issue of bonds. It also advised Benchmark JER LP on the acquisition and financing of six properties for £250 million. AXA instructed the team on the £70 million acquisition of retail property from Legal & General. **Clients:** Capital & Regional; Regus; Topland; Land Securities; Wickes; Warner Estate Holdings.

Macfarlanes (see firm details p.1046) A department that takes on a broad range on property matters but secures "*high profile instructions*" and "*consistently gives its clients a good service.*" Peers purport that **Chris Field** (see p.744) "*leaves bite marks on your ankles and gives you a run for your money,*" while clients appreciate his commercial nous and respect his personal touch; "*it's a pleasure to have him on your side.*" At the end of 2000 the group completed the sale of No 1 Poultry for TrizecHahn, having acted on its redevelopment. It was instructed by Allders at Croydon on a redevelopment, sale and leaseback deal raising £50 million, and advised CIT in the purchase, through a limited partnership, of four buildings in East India Dock for £125.5 million. **Clients:** Legal & General; ING Real Estate; AXA Real Estate; Abbey Life; Scottish Life; P&O Developments.

Norton Rose (see firm details p.1082) Waste to energy deals and hotels and leisure have been a feature in the last year as well as sophisticated finance structures. Its activities are balanced between investment, development, finance and projects. **Jonathan Ody** (see p.750) has "*a cracking practice*," clients judge him "*capable, focused and no-nonsense.*" Jonathan Solomon's loss to Clifford Chance has been a blow. The team has been acting for Royal Bank Leasing on the Eden Project, a 'global garden' in Cornwall. It acquired the former Shell Haven refinery in Thurrock for P&O, and advised Legacy on its proposed purchase of the Millennium Dome. **Clients:** CGI; Old Mutual; English Heritage; Standard & Poor's; Workspace Group; DTZ Debenham Tie Leung.

Forsters Widely felt to be "*a firm that has gone out and made a success of itself.*" Even without a large corporate team, this firm is regularly facing London's larger practices on quality deals. Clients told researchers it "*acts quickly and professionally.*" At the helm is "*legendary*" **Sophie Hamilton** (see p.746), she's "*busy, practical and knows what she's doing*." "*Colourful personality*" **Tony Patterson** (see p.751) is "*good value.*" In 2000 the firm sold 16 Grosvenor Place for £8.9 million on behalf of client Benchmark. Several big deals for Clerical Medical Group include a joint venture with Delancey to acquire Rolls House and Arnold House in Fetter Lane, the acquisition of 40 Grosvenor Place for £60 million and the acquisition and forward funding of Phase 2 of the Kensington Village office development at a value of £59.2million. The firm also acted for Redevco on the disposal of properties vacated by C&A. **Clients:** Crown Dilmun; McDonalds' Restaurants; Warner Village; Chester City Council; Shops etc Investments; 552 Kings Road Ltd.

Olswang (see firm details p.1084) An established team that "*gets out and about and makes a lot of noise.*" There is now less of an emphasis on retail clients than in previous years. It benefits from three leading names, who peers believe have "*done an outstanding job and pulled things together and up.*" **David Kustow** (see p.748) is "*commercial, technically good and has been doing it for years.*" Department head **Tim Westhead** (see p.755) is "*effective and pleasant*" and **Philip Olmer** (see p.751) "*knows it's a people business – his clients love him.*" Last year the firm advised Whitehall Green Partnership on its acquisition of P&O's property for more than £400 million, subsequently selling half of the portfolio. Deutsche Property Asset Management also instructed the firm on the sale of a portfolio of bank premises for £20 million. It advised UBS Asset Management on the redevelopment, letting and disposal of '27 West' in Brentford for £33.8 million. **Clients:** Woolworths; Britannia Car Parking; Delancey; Helical Bar; Charterhouse Shopping Centre Fund; Mapeley.

Slaughter and May (see firm details p.1135) Perceived by the market not to target stand-alone work, but performing marvellously on corporate transactional support and serving the property needs of corporate tenants. The group acts for many clients in brewing, leisure and hotels. Head of department **Graham White** (see p.755) is "*out and about and charming,*" while clients endorse **Dermot Rice** (see p.752) as "*bright and slick beyond belief.*" The last year brought two large securitisations for Punch Taverns. Whitbread instructed the firm on the demerger of its pubs and bars division (3000 units), disposing of it to a special purpose vehicle formed by Morgan Grenfell Private Equity. The transaction was all carried out by the use of an interactive web site. It advised Morgan Stanley on the pre-lets of two new buildings in Canary Wharf. **Clients:** Manchester City Council; Guardian; Eldridge Pope; Deutsche Property Asset Management; Pillar Property.

Field Fisher Waterhouse (see firm details p.957) A broad-based and "*sensible*" practice which is strong in industrial property, pipelines and telecoms, and hotels and leisure. It also handles a volume of secured lending and investment. The head of department is Howard Coffell. In the last year the team acted for Whitbread (and latterly for Laurel Pub Company) on the preparation for sale and subsequent securitisation of more than 700 pubs and bars. It acted for the Shell Pension Fund on the acquisition of an SPV owning property in London, and handled the laying of a gas pipeline to a new power station and energy park in the South West of England. **Clients:** BP Amoco; AstraZeneca; ICI; One2One; Accenture; Luminar Leisure.

Gouldens (see firm details p.976) Coming from an interesting foundation in retail, business and industrial parks, the property group has broadened its developer base into the field of investment. Rivals acknowledge its presence on typically large and often complicated deals, an endorsement of the quality of advice. The leading pure property partner is David Roberts. Last year the group acted for long-time client Pillar on its £373.3 million offer for Wates City of London Properties, involving the establishment of a unit trust. It handled the property aspects of the sale by Hanson of its waste management business, and advised Warren & Partners on its first major UK purchase, Garrard House, Gresham Street and then its second, the Goldman Sachs HQ at 120 Fleet Street for £250 million. **Clients:** Delancey Estates; Ashtenne; Arlington Securities; BAE Systems; Burford Holdings; Arsenal Football Club.

Eversheds (see firm details p.952) The group is led in London by Linda Harrison and is divided into four teams – institutional, development, retail and leisure, corporate end users and lenders. It is seeing more PFI and PFI influenced transactions. The group has acted for Lionheart Properties in the £100 million acquisition and development of Lion Plaza in the City of London. Pollen Estate appointed the team to advise in its joint venture with City & West End Properties, concerning the development of four properties in the West End. It is now advising the Electricity Supply Pension Scheme on a projected science research park at Emersons Green, Bristol. **Clients:** BAE Systems; Marconi/Stanhope Pension Trust; Jarvis; Greenwich Group; F&C Properties Investment Management; Scottish Power Pension Scheme.

Richards Butler (see firm details p.1107) The property department, led by Jon Pyke, offers industry sector subgroups in retail, leisure and hotels, investment, finance and development. The firm has witnessed an increase in the amount of international work it handles. It acted for Matra BAe Dynamics on the £80 million development of the Horizon Technology Park in Stevenage. It advised on a series of large transactions for new client, Bavaria Fund, and handled several purchases of property portfolios for Kenmore. **Clients:** Commercial Estates; Naval & Military Club; SLC Langbourn; Microsoft; Skanska Europe; Parkview International London.

Rowe & Maw (see firm details p.1113) Jeremy Clay leads a reinvigorated property group that has laterally hired partners in the last year. In addition to finance, investment and management, development and corporate occupier work, the firm handles a respected volume of corporate support and has bolstered its public sector property work. Its activities in the sale of three of ICI's chemical businesses involved the disposal of over 5000 acres of property. It handled around £400 million of loans for Nationwide, and received instructions from Henderson Global Investors on behalf of Pearl Assurance in the purchase of Kingsmead Business Park, High Wycombe for £46.3 million. **Clients:** Unilever; The Football Association; Charterhouse Shopping Centre Fund II; Ashcroft Estates; HMV Media Group; Morley Fund Management.

Simmons & Simmons (see firm details p.1132) Recommended by clients for its securitisation work, this team is led by "*decent and effective*" **Alan Butler** (see p.742). For Despa he handled the forward funding of the development at Dolcis House Oxford/Bond Streets and, for the same client, the letting of the £100 million 100 Wood Street office premises. Prudential instructed the team to restructure the security for the first mortgage debenture stock of Raglan Estates on that company's acquisition by Pinton Investments. **Clients:** Land Securities; Henderson Investors; Reuters; BP Amoco; Abu Dhabi Investment Authority; Scudder Threadneedle Property Investments.

FEWER THAN 25 SOLICITORS

Boodle Hatfield (see firm details p.889) Respected for the high quality of its work and known to be central property advisor to the Grosvenor Estate. The head of the department is Richard Maughan, and the team works with other lawyers in the Oxford office. The £300 million mixed retail and leisure project at Festival Place, Basingstoke, on which the firm has advised since 1996, has now gone into construction. Treasury Holdings instructed the firm in connection with a £76 million refinancing of a large portfolio, involving senior and junior debt facilities. During 2000 it was appointed by the Grosvenor Estate and Henderson joint venture partnership for the development of the 'Liverpool Paradise Street Development Area'. **Clients:** The Bedford Estates; Margram; Primary Health Care Centres; Highland Developments; Outlet Centres International; overseas banks.

Maxwell Batley (see firm details p.1058) A good name in property and one of the leading smaller teams in London. It is experienced in development finance and investment (both traditional and through joint ventures) and has a strong client base amongst pension funds and institutional investors. In the last year its developer and retail client base has grown. The head of the group is Nigel Wilson. For Consignia Pension Plan it restructured the LP which owns Tower 42 in the City of London and advised Hermes Property Unit Trust in its investment in the partnership. It also advised Ballast Developments on the its purchase of Quays Campus, Salford Quays and BT Pension Scheme in the sale of the Headrow Centre, Leeds. **Clients:** Hermes; National Mutual; Ropemaker Properties; General Electric Pension Trust; Land Securities; British Land.

PROPERTY (COMMERCIAL): FEWER THAN 25 SOLICITORS • London		Ptnrs	Assts
1	Boodle Hatfield	8	9
	Maxwell Batley	8	5
2	Manches	6	8
	Speechly Bircham	6	10
	Travers Smith Braithwaite	7	12
3	Finers Stephens Innocent	5	5
	Julian Holy	5	2
	Mishcon de Reya	8	8
	Nicholson Graham & Jones	9	12
	Stepien Lake Gilbert & Paling	4	4
	Trowers & Hamlins	7	6
4	Coudert Brothers	3	5
	Fladgate Fielder	11	11
	Hamlins	7	4
	Osborne Clarke	8	11
	Park Nelson	6	4

This book is the product of 6,552 1/2-hour interviews. See p.7 for BMRB audit.
Within each band, firms are listed alphabetically.

Manches (see firm details p.1051) Best known for its experience in retail property, but also acting for leading property companies, pension funds and lenders. Louis Manches heads the department. In Leicester, Leeds and Port Solent, it handles developments for Munroe K. The group was instructed by Green Property on the acquisition of a portfolio of properties from P&O, and it acted for Merrill Lynch Asset Management on the sale of Cribbs Causeway. **Clients:** Burford; Quintain; Nationwide; Woolwich; Marylebone Warwick Balfour; WH Smith.

Speechly Bircham (see firm details p.1136) A well regarded, long-established practice, and while commended by many City practices, "*it has not gone City,*" in its approach. Its main activities are for large investors and increasingly developers. Charles Palmer leads the department. It is acquiring office space in the City for Royal Bank of Scotland by way of pre-lets. Scottish Life instructed the team on a joint venture with Arrowcroft to undertake the £50 million redevelopment of the Lower Precinct Shopping Centre, Coventry. It has worked on a mixed use redevelopment in Clerkenwell for Kian Gwan Land. **Clients:** easyEverything; Lincoln Financial Group; Howard de Walden Estates; LB Croydon; P&O Properties; Resolution Property.

Travers Smith Braithwaite (see firm details p.1160) A respected team of "*excellent*" lawyers. Clients commend the partners for their responsive approach and control of a transaction. The head of department is Robert Harman. Last year it completed the Landmark Millennium project in Belfast for the Odyssey Trust Company. For Lothbury Property Trust it acquired the £80 million Clarendon Centre in Oxford through a limited partnership. It currently acts for Guinness in the development of the Western Gateway site at Park Royal. **Clients:** Lend Lease Europe; Clearwater Estates & Properties; LRT; LUL; Redevco; Bourne End.

Finers Stephens Innocent (see firm details p.958) Handling a range of work, including investment, development, finance and leisure and retail, this is a group which works on deals and acts for household name clients that many larger practices would be proud to win. David Battiscombe's group continues with acquisitions, sales and management for several retailers and leisure clients, such as Pizza Hut, Cartier, LA fitness and the Virgin Group. Last year it acted for Marylebone Warwick Balfour on the conversion of a former bank in Pall Mall into a £50 million hotel, and was instructed by Hammerson on the £55 million redevelopment of Crawley Town Centre. **Clients:** Grosvenor Waterside; Office Angels; The Tannen Group; DHL; Radisson Hotels Wordwide; PRICOA.

Julian Holy (see firm details p.???) This niche property firm is known to act for Rotch and is judged to have "*phenomenal contacts*" in the Middle East and Asia. Clients are "*extremely loyal.*" Encountering property lawyers of all types from across the City, in the West End and the provinces, the firm is commended for fielding a team that works hard and knows how to do deals. Both lawyers and clients agree that "*experienced and quick*" **Julian Holy** is an unforgettable presence in the market.

Mishcon de Reya (see firm details p.1071) A "*flourishing property practice*" with lawyers who have proved themselves "*quite a smart bunch.*" A heavy investment and development caseload, with good work in retail and leisure plus finance, is in operation here. The department head is Nick Doffman. Last year the group acted for Frogmore on the sale of land at Paddington Basin for £45.5 million. Other leading property deals included the acquisition of No 1 Poultry for £100 million, and leases for Holmes Place, including one at Shell Mex House. **Clients:** Asda Holdings; Chelsfield; Fairview New Homes; Helical Bar; Heron; Topland.

Nicholson Graham & Jones (see firm details p.1081) Known to handle a lot of lending work, the firm is commended for its high value, traditionally structured transactions. Clients believe that partners show a "*willingness to get things done on time,*" while competitors approve of its supporting lawyers. Richard Smith heads the department. Henderson Investors instructed the team to purchase and subsequently let the £55.5 million premises at 55 Bishopsgate. It acquired Leith House, Gresham Street for Topland at a value of £45 million, and acted for Regalian on the sale of Marble Arch Tower for £69 million. **Clients:** Halifax; HSBC; Heron; Anglo Irish Bank; Allied Dunbar; Ravenbourne Group.

Stepien Lake Gilbert & Paling (see firm details p.1142) The firm was recommended to our researchers as fielding a strong group of high quality partners. The small, niche practice is also thought to attract good assistants. Team head, **Tim Lake** (see p.748) is "*a bright guy*" and well known in the market. Active for overseas investor clients and unquoted property companies. It is seeing an increase in joint venture work on large redevelopment schemes.

Trowers & Hamlins (see firm details p.1162) Under the guidance of Elizabeth Mckibbin, this classic property practice is thought to be "*thorough*" and "*a safe choice,*" but in the eyes of some "*a bit old fashioned.*" The commercial property practice sits side by side with its social housing practice and a good construction team. The firm is steeped in property work for private and public sector clients. It has also been a preferred choice for various UK and US lawyers in corporate support, effectively missing out on the credit for a range of interesting deals. The firm was lead lawyer in the disposal of Guardian Assurance's property portfolio for £700 million. One of its many corporate occupier instructions was from DoubleClick Europe on the acquisition of its new premises in Wigmore Street. **Clients:** Smiths Group; Palmer & Harvey McLane; AXA; Crabtree & Evelyn; NM Rothschild; Bank of Ireland.

Coudert Brothers (see firm details p.925) Kept busy by development, investment and shopping centre work, the services of this small "*highly commercial*" team are of a "*high standard.*" The loss of the previous head of department has had some impact on the client roster but the practice continues to thrive under the lead of Anne O'Neill. **Clients:** Notting Hill Group; Fairview Homes; Capital Shopping Centres; La Salle; Linton.

Fladgate Fielder (see firm details p.960) A team with a one to one partner to assistant ratio and some strong client names. Its work leans towards development with additional focus areas of investment and secured lending. The head of department is Allen Cohen. It advised Capital & Regional Properties on several matters last year, including a joint venture to develop the £100 million Xscape in Milton Keynes, and the £75 million development of Cardiff Bay Sports Village. This is the group behind Nando's Chickenland's continued European expansion, including the acquisition of 30 units in the UK. For Regal Hotel Group it sold ten hotels. **Clients:** Morgan Guaranty Trust Co of New York; Royal Bank of Scotland; Singer & Friedlander Properties; Woolwich BS; AXA Equity & Life; Pillar Property.

Hamlins (see firm details p.983) The firm has a long-standing name in traditional retail, office and industrial property matters. Brian Casey leads the team. **Clients:** NCP; Greycoat.

Osborne Clarke (see firm details p.1086) Earlier in 2001 the firm absorbed the highly rated niche property practice McGuinness Finch. This has added an excellent developer practice to existing investment, finance and corporate occupier work. The firm also has a strong retail client base, and the team is led by Nadine Strahl. For Harwood International, it acted on the letting of Cleveland House, St James Square and acted for Yahoo! on its £2 million pa rental of premises in SW1. It carries out property management work for Eurostar. **Clients:** Chesterton; The Leadenhall Group; Henderson Investors; British Airways Pension Fund; Railtrack; Close Property Investment.

Park Nelson (see firm details p.1089) A very well established retail oriented practice, packed with "*good people,*"and serving some blue chip names. Property is the largest department at the firm, and Eugene O'Keefe's team has an expertise through the range from development to disposal. Many of the partners are also qualified in both the north and south of Ireland. **Clients:** Currys; PC World; Dixons; Asda-Walmart; Sainsbury's Homebase; Allied Carpets.

THE SOUTH

PROPERTY (COMMERCIAL) • The South	Ptnrs	Assts
1 **Blake Lapthorn** Fareham, Portsmouth, Southampton	5	16
2 **Bond Pearce** Southampton	7	11
Paris Smith & Randall Southampton	3	6
Stevens & Bolton Guildford	n/a	n/a
3 **Clyde & Co** Guildford	3	10
Cripps Harries Hall Tunbridge Wells	8	10
Thomson Snell & Passmore Tunbridge Wells	6	2
4 **DMH** Brighton, Crawley	5	12
Laytons Guildford	5	4
Lester Aldridge Bournemouth	8	3
Penningtons Basingstoke, Godalming, Newbury	8	10
Steele Raymond Bournemouth	n/a	n/a
Thomas Eggar Church Adams	n/a	n/a
Chichester, Horsham, Reigate, Worthing	12	12
5 **Brachers** Maidstone	7	2
Coffin Mew & Clover Portsmouth	6	3
GCL Solicitors Guildford	n/a	n/a
Moore & Blatch Southampton	4	5
Rawlison Butler Crawley	3	3
Sherwin Oliver Solicitors Portsmouth	n/a	n/a
Shoosmiths Fareham	1	2

LEADING INDIVIDUALS	
1 **BAILY Tim** Bond Pearce	**BLAKE Carey** Blake Lapthorn
PUGH Nigel Bond Pearce	
2 **BAILEY Michael** asb law	**BENNETT Graham** Shoosmiths
HOWARTH Mark Paris Smith & Randall	**MITCHELL James** Stevens & Bolton
3 **BERRY Paul** Clyde & Co	**BURTON Carl** DMH
GREEN Gilbert Thomson Snell & Passmore	**NEIL Don** Coffin Mew & Clover

This book is the product of 6,552 1/2-hour interviews. See p.7 for BMRB audit.

Within each band, firms are listed alphabetically. *See individuals' profiles p.739*

Blake Lapthorn (see firm details p.886) Overwhelming approval from lawyers and clients for "*the major player*" in the region (with offices in Fareham and Southampton) recognised as having "*grown more than any other regional firm.*" **Carey Blake** is a member of this specialist team that has expertise in retail, leisure and licensed property work, and has been appointed by Whitbread to provide support to the sale of 550 public houses. It also acted on behalf of Haksins Garden Centres in a £7 million acquisition. Clients appreciate the firm's skill in negotiation and its ability to advise on all aspects of commercial property work, "*a large team, it manages to keep on top of new developments.*" **Clients:** Whitbread; Bellway Homes, Fairclough Homes; Premier Marinas.

Bond Pearce (see firm details p.888) Spread across the South and South West and described by rivals as "*supra regional,*" the firm acts for both national and regional clients, and has a strong retail property and development team. The roster of active clients includes investors, PFI funders/developers and educational institutions. "*Courteous, knowledgeable and commercial*" **Tim Baily** (see p.740) is highly regarded by peers, and currently has particular emphasis on marine and port related work. **Nigel Pugh** (see p.751) retains a good reputation and leads the PFI property projects team. Represented Kier Group's project investment arm in its successful bid to build and manage the new Bournemouth Central library and retail complex. **Clients:** Associated British Ports; B&Q; Comet.

Paris Smith & Randall (see firm details p.1089) Recommended to our researchers as a "*skilful, sensible firm*" that has specialist leisure, sports law, retail, and secured lending units. It has also undertaken regeneration projects in the local authority housing sector. Enjoys a variety of leisure clients including football clubs, a retail chain, banks and a number of significant portfolio clients. **Mark Howarth** (see p.746) leads a team that is seen to have "*good assistants at all levels.*" The group acted for Southampton Leisure Holdings on the property aspects of the sale of its existing ground at the Dell and purchase of new stadium site. Also instructed regularly by Rank Group and its subsidiaries. **Clients:** Southampton Leisure Holdings; Alldays Stores; Portsmouth Football Club; Banks of Ireland and Scotland.

Stevens & Bolton (see firm details p.1143) "*Up and coming,*" a growing firm that has trebled in size over the past three years, and is widely regarded by peers as "*a highly commercial, effective operation.*" Instructed by Hammersmith Hospital NHS Trust to negotiate the planning agreement of the new Queen Charlotte's Chelsea Hospital site, the firm subsequently acted on the disposal of the old site to Crest Homes. Clients include NHS trusts, educational institutions and a major pharmaceutical company. Clients commend **James Mitchell** (see p.749) as "*efficient, knowledgeable and flexible – good at looking at the whole picture.*" **Clients:** BOC Group; Hammersmith Hospital NHS Trust; Procter & Gamble.

Clyde & Co (see firm details p.921) Taking the Guildford market by storm, the firm acts in high value deals for major national clients including The Carphone Warehouse and Frogmore Estates. Competitors see the firm acting on "*heavy-hitting corporate work,*" while clients rate the "*well priced and commercially orientated property service.*" The firm retains its "*City*" tag within the local market, undeniably boosted by the London office. Other work includes advising offshore investors, retail property clients and the management of the property portfolio of Unigate Dairies. **Paul Berry**, described by clients as "*commercially minded,*" concentrates on property development and investment, and he is supported by a strong retail practice. **Clients:** The Carphone Warehouse; Frogmore Estates; Kipling UK.

Cripps Harries Hall (see firm details p.927) Public sector, residential and commercial development work are key areas for this "*commercial and effective*" firm. Its relationship with HM Customs and Excise has led to significant, cutting edge work and the firm recently advised on due diligence in the STEPS PFI project (750 properties involved). The group has been appointed by Gravesham Borough Council on a regeneration project in the town centre of Gravesend. Michael Stevens is head of the commercial division and his group concentrates on property portfolio management, advising major landowners and corporate support. **Clients:** HM Customs & Excise; Alan Parker Holdings; Crown Prosecution Service.

Thomson Snell & Passmore (see firm details p.1155) Has a traditional reputation among other lawyers as a highly focused property practice. The firm continues to garner respect from peers and clients with a team that pulls together and "*gets the deal done as smoothly as possible.*" Recent work includes the acquisition of a major industrial complex in Kent, a significant urban development scheme in the South East, and an acquisition of land on behalf of a leading cereal company for a major manufacturing plan. Newly ranked **Gilbert Green** (see p.745) is thought to be "*experienced in commercial property, with a low key approach.*" **Clients:** Colas Ltd; Marley Pension Fund; Mobile Telecom plc.

DMH (see firm details p.944) The inclusion of **Carl Burton** (see p.742) and five other fee earners from Rawlison & Butler has bolstered the commercial property practice, following a major increase to its workload over the past year. The firm has focused its efforts on three 'supergroups' of work: Innovation and Media, Land Development and Dot.org (not-for-profit). Major project work includes advice given to the Brighton Dome refurbishment. Burton specialises in all aspects of property development and is warmly recommended by peers. Strengths are noted in leisure, licensing, and development work for the firm's public sector base. **Clients:** Crest Nichollson Group; Catholic Diocese of Arundel and Brighton; University of Sussex.

Laytons (see firm details p.1031) Recently moved to Guildford after outgrowing previous premises, this "*geared up*" firm specialises in advisory work to the land development and house building sectors. Deemed by clients "*always competent and invariably quick,*" the firm has expertise in brownfield development issues. Ian Cook and the team act on substantial projects including a new settlement in Cambridgeshire and 'Greenwich Getaway,' the development of business, leisure and hotel facilities. **Clients:** Fairclough Homes; Cambourne Development Project; Alfred McAlpine Homes.

Lester Aldridge (see firm details p.1038) Recently opened an office in Southampton to strengthen its commercial property practice, it is looking to broaden the scope of a well-established Bournemouth practice. Bob Robertson and the team continue to serve clients both locally and nationally with expertise in marina and waterside development. Active in the acquisition and disposal of investment properties, the firm is involved in a joint venture providing new airport headquarters for a global plc, and advised Bournemouth AFC on the development of a new stadium. **Clients:** Waste services; investors; leisure groups.

Penningtons (see firm details p.1093) Spread over three offices which operate separately, providing support and additional resources when necessary. The firm undertakes a full range of commercial property work including landlord and tenant, commercial leases for a client roster that comprises national housebuilders, developers and corporate clients. Tom Rossitter and the team (in Newbury) were involved in management issues for New Greenham Business Park, and handled the property financing issues facing Southampton football club. The firm also acts for institutional landlords, commercial lenders and landed estates enjoying strong relationships with US and Australian companies based in London. **Clients:** Audley Developments; Cherwell Land; Sun Life of Canada.

Steele Raymond (see firm details p.1141) Major player in Bournemouth, perceived by peers to have "*come on well,*" with both national and local work. Clients include a major charitable body and a leading maritime company for whom it recently arranged a major site acquisition. Involved in ongoing detailed infrastructure work at a large greenfield site in Hampshire (total value of over £40 million). Bill Oliver and the group have acquired large new clients over past year, and are seen to focus on retail and development. **Clients:** National charity; maritime sector company; national garden centre chain.

Thomas Eggar Church Adams (see firm details p.1153) "*Deal doers, capable of negotiating,*" according to other solicitors. The firm has several offices in the South, winning "*substantial work*" from clients such as Railtrack. Chris Bell is a member of this experienced and "*highly competent*" team. Recent highlights include disposals for a major insurance company to an aggregate value of £16 million. The group also acts for a number of established retailers, highlights of which include advising Gleesons on a joint development with Asda and another party. **Clients:** Railtrack; Halifax; Gleeson Homes; Nationwide Building Society.

Brachers (see firm details p.893) A "*diverse, good quality*" team valued by clients for its "*professional approach.*" Head of department Geoffrey Burr works on development site assembly and acquisitions. The firm has performed a substantial number of disposals for NHS trusts (total value £12 million), and is engaged in sales of factories, warehouses, HQ offices and golf courses. Clients are found all over the UK, in the health sector, manufacturing with a strong roll call of developers. **Clients:** Health sector; manufacturers; developers and development consortia.

Coffin Mew & Clover Largely a residential property firm with a secure standing in the commercial development market. Peers agree that the group is a regular sight in the retail sector. Continues to work on the former Royal Marines Barracks at Deal, Kent, the firm has witnessed an increase in commercial investment acquisitions. Clients include house builders, NHS trusts, commercial investors and land dealers. The standout player here is **Don Neil** (see p.750) who is a dedicated commercial property specialist. **Clients:** Gieves & Hawkes; Bellway Homes.

GCL Solicitors Niche residential practice with a "*high profile*" in house building and winning the approval of clients and lawyers for its quality output. Tony Inkin and the team act for the UK's two leading house builders and a number of other household names in development. **Clients:** Housebuilders.

Moore & Blatch (see firm details p.1072) Well-versed in residential development, this "*respected property practice*" has seen a growth in that sphere. Its expertise lies in land development and related planning matters, and the firm is also engaged in highway agreements, local authority work and waterfront development. Steve Ingram heads up the department that advised a national house builder on the acquisition of a development site for £12 million. **Clients:** Housebuilders; developers; local authorities.

Rawlison Butler (see firm details p.1104) Perceived to have been weakened by the recent break-off of a partner with a small team, although the groundwork for recovery has been well laid. Clients typically speak of it as a "*conscientious team*" well placed to continue the "*strong traditional*" profile. The commercial property team is now headed by Andrew King and Clive Prior, and has recently accomplished acquisitions for a varied roll call of clients including a telecom company, a health club group and developers. One acquisition for Nicholson Estates was in excess of £10 million. **Clients:** Amadeus Services; Dragons Health Clubs; JT Davies & Sons.

Sherwin Oliver Solicitors (see firm details p.1128) Specialist commercial property department felt by rivals to have a "*strong presence in Portsmouth.*" Andrew Peck and the commercial property team recently worked for a multi-national retailer setting up a chain of outlets in London and Bristol, and also advised on a £10 million office development in London. It has a number of franchise-related clients including Domino's Pizza and is engaged in property portfolio work for investors clients. **Clients:** Domino's Pizza; large bank group.

Shoosmiths (see firm details p.1129) **Graham Bennett** (see p.740) is a respected commercial property lawyer, key to much of the office's profile. An inter-office approach supports the broad practice, which has been bolstered by a recruit from Blake Lapthorn. Advised Heinz on the development of a 350,000 sqft national distribution centre, the largest high bay, automated warehouse in Europe. **Clients:** Forelle Estates; H J Heinz Company; Esso; ExxonMobil.

Other Notable Practitioners **Michael Bailey** (see p.740) at **asb law** is endorsed by competitors as an "*intellectually strong*" commercial property lawyer.

THAMES VALLEY

Band	PROPERTY (COMMERCIAL) • Thames Valley	Ptnrs	Assts
1	**Denton Wilde Sapte** Milton Keynes	2	10
	Pitmans Reading	5	16
2	**BrookStreet Des Roches** Witney	6	7
	Morgan Cole Oxford, Reading	5	10
3	**Clarks** Reading	4	6
	Harold Benjamin Littlejohn Harrow	n/a	n/a
	Linnells Oxford	4	3
4	**Iliffes Booth Bennett** Uxbridge	7	9
	Matthew Arnold & Baldwin Watford	4	2
5	**BP Collins** Beaconsfield, Gerrards Cross	6	4
	Boyes Turner Reading	4	3
	Fennemores Milton Keynes	3	4
	~~**Manches** Oxford~~	~~3~~	~~4~~
	Nabarro Nathanson Reading	1	9
	Pictons St Albans	3	1

Band	LEADING INDIVIDUALS	
1	**DAVIES Andrew** Pitmans	
2	**BURGESS James** Pitmans	
3	**BILLINGS Martin** BrookStreet Des Roches	**PAUL Sarah** Harold Benjamin Littlejohn
	SEAWARD Charlie BrookStreet Des Roches	

This book is the product of 6,552 1/2-hour interviews. See p.7 for BMRB audit.

Within each band, firms are listed alphabetically. *See individuals' profiles p.739*

Denton Wilde Sapte (see firm details p.939) Researchers were impressed that the team has added Nokia to an enviable client base that includes the management of property portfolios of Whitbread, KFC and Thornfield Properties. The group continues to advise English Partnerships in relation to major development projects and the disposal of numerous residential and commercial development sites in Milton Keynes. Lawyers typically commented on the "*significant resources*" and "*good quality clients*" belonging to the firm. David Danskin and Chris Denny head the team. **Clients:** English Partnerships; Barclays Bank; Crown Castle

Pitmans (see firm details p.1099) A respected commercial property outfit felt by rivals to "*do contentious property work well,*" securing its "*justifiably strong reputation.*" It has added ballast in the form of new partner David Carr. Clients include commercial developers, investors, banks, and occupiers. Recently involved in the creation of a new campus for a major computer company, the group also acted on the site assembly and development of a £100 million business park. **James Burgess** (see p.741) and the "*efficient*" **Andrew Davies** (see p.743) are acclaimed members of the team. **Clients:** MEPC; Allied Bank of Pakistan; Barratt Homes; Porsche.

BrookStreet Des Roches (see firm details p.897) The arrival of "*client focused*" **Martin Billings** (see p.741) from Morgan Cole has reinforced the practice's reputation as a "*thoroughbred property firm.*" As well as serving its blue chip clients, the emphasis of work is divided between industrial, telecom and energy entities, and landlord work. Instructed by MEPC on its portfolio management work, a highlight of which was the development and letting of its flagship 70,000 sqft office site at Milton Park. The firm now aims to build on its established retail practice, targeting industry. **Charles Seaward** (see p.753) was endorsed by one major client as "*one of our best lawyers, he explains everything in plain English and has a commercial not just legal mind.*" **Clients:** Blockbuster; Co-op; Electronics Boutique; National Grid.

Morgan Cole (see firm details p.1074) Conducts a high quality workload, which encompasses large portfolio landlord and tenant clients. Recent highlights have involved the purchase of a proposed new corporate HQ site worth in excess of £100 million, and a multi-million pound land acquisition for educational development. The Oxford branch, which fields Ruth Morgan, handles a substantial level of telecoms work and is described by a peer as having "*every reason to be optimistic for continued success.*" Its national presence allows the movement of partners between offices when required. The group continues to win exclusive instructions from Hays. **Clients:** Hays; Ernst & Young; MEPC.

Clarks (see firm details p.916) Endorsed by peers for its sizeable amount of work for the NHS. Recent work includes negotiation for a development land option in the West Country, and an acquisition of office space at Green Park in Reading for a US IT company. The group, which includes partner Derek Ching, acted on a major mineral lease for gravel extraction work in Hertfordshire. Has experienced a set back due to the departure of some commercial property lawyers, but remains acknowledged as a key player among its peers. **Clients:** BMW Group; Bunzl Group; CMB.

Harold Benjamin Littlejohn (see firm details p.986) Commercial property is a major area for this firm and the quality of its work is discerned by peers and clients alike. The group is divided into two teams focusing on commercial development and the acquisitions and management of sites. The former handles leases of newly constructed offices, lease renewal work for Ladbrokes and acts for two hi-tech clients in central London. The latter is increasingly instructed in strategic house sales and settlements. **Sarah Paul** (see p.751) is rated as "*efficient*" by her contemporaries and heads the commercial development team. **Clients:** Bellway Homes & Estates.

Linnells (see firm details p.1043) The recruitment of Stanley Beckett from Halliwell Landau has been a significant event for this largely residential firm. He spearheaded the multiple lease acquisitions for Bon Marché and Speedy Hire. The firm has upped its game in the IT stakes by implementing Solcase case management software for its clients. Maintaining its stronghold of an educational clientele, the group recently attracted an Oxford College with £25 million of property holdings as a major client. **Clients:** Berkeley Homes; Coventry Building Society.

Iliffes Booth Bennett (see firm details p.1007) "*Civil and pleasant*" firm according to a solicitor referee. Numbers David Silva among its partners and has recently recruited Ross Humphries. Major areas of work lie in funding and residential development, with recent highlights including acting on behalf of Frontier Estates on the acquisition of Cirrus Place, Crawley. Also assisted on the forward funding for a speculative office development scheme, with an estimated end value of £12 million. Current instructions include a £40 million office park in Milton Keynes and a £20 million office scheme in Birmingham. **Clients:** Lands Improvement; Allied Irish Bank; Dolphin Telecom.

Matthew Arnold & Baldwin (see firm details p.1057) Typically endorsed by peers for its activities on behalf of its major house builder clients. The firm receives continuous instruction from Barclays Bank with regard to sales of repossessed commercial premises. Also involved in sales and leaseback schemes throughout north London and Northern home counties, the department is headed by Richard Hanney. The group is active in receivership sales and recently advised on the sale of a portfolio of 25 investment properties in North West England. **Clients:** Cerplex; Europcar; Watford Football Club.

BP Collins Justin Samuel is a partner in this firm, whose wide-ranging client base includes a FTSE 250 company. The group has been involved in the sale of a large industrial and commercial site in West London with a value of up to £20 million, and continues to handle residential development. **Clients:** Multi-nationals and local companies.

Boyes Turner (see firm details p.891) Work ranges from pure property transactions for developers and investors through to support work for corporate transactions and corporate recovery groups. In what has been a busy year, the firm has received new instructions from the Secretary of State for Health and South Buckinghamshire District Council. Perceived by peers to be *"an efficient and ambitious group looking to expand,"* it recently recruited Simon Doyle, former senior partner of Charlsley Harrison, who has brought along significant new clients. Clients also appreciate its particular experience in landlord and tenant work. **Clients:** Barratt North London; Barclays Bank; South Bucks District Council.

Fennemores Simon Ingram leads this practice for which commercial and residential development and related strategic land acquisitions are major sources of the workload. On-going work includes retail, office, multi-story car park and leisure schemes. **Clients:** Nicholls Brasseries; Pharmacia Ltd; Scania (Great Britain).

Manches (see firm details p.1051) During research, solicitors expressed their appreciation for this commercial property outfit. It has seen significant increase in turnover during the past four years and handles a large amount of development work for local landlord and tenant clients. The firm uses its strong social housing unit to complement commercial property work. Richard Shaw has acted on the redevelopment of a brownfield site for a new HQ building on behalf of a US owned bio-tech company. The firm also acted on the sale of a £4 million residential site by a major regional house builder to a national house builder. **Clients:** Siemens Properties; British Energy; Black & Decker.

Nabarro Nathanson (see firm details p.1078) Recommended as *"an excellent offering"* by a solicitor referee. Andrew Banton has moved to the Reading office from London, and this office continues to assist its City branch on many large-scale transactions. The group acts for local pension fund clients and is involved in funding research for possible solutions to the shortage of office space and employees in Thames Valley caused by the relocation of IT companies. Acted on £20 million acquisition of 28 retail investment properties by the Northern Retail Property Fund (Bank of Scotland). **Clients:** Box Clever/Radio Rentals; Bank of Scotland; GE Capital.

Pictons (see firm details p.1097) Chris Brown leads this team which peers reckon has *"successfully been through a growth period."* The firm regularly handles property transactions and related issues for banks. Favoured with ongoing work for leisure and electronic companies. **Clients:** Citylights Group; SPG; Hemel Hempstead Group of Companies.

SOUTH WEST

PROPERTY (COMMERCIAL) • South West	Ptnrs	Assts
1 **Burges Salmon** Bristol	7	30
Osborne Clarke Bristol	7	18
2 **Beachcroft Wansbroughs** Bristol	n/a	n/a
Bevan Ashford Bristol, Exeter, Plymouth, Taunton	7	10
Bond Pearce Bristol, Exeter, Plymouth	7	17
Michelmores Exeter	5	12
3 **Clarke Willmott & Clarke** Bristol, Taunton	11	11
TLT Solicitors Bristol	6	n/a
Veale Wasbrough Bristol	6	10
4 **Davies and partners** Gloucester	n/a	n/a
Foot Anstey Sargent Plymouth	6	8
Lyons Davidson Bristol	3	3
Rickerby Watterson Cheltenham	8	3
Stephens & Scown Exeter, Liskeard, St Austell, Truro	9	9
5 **Bretherton Price Elgoods** Cheltenham	6	5
Davitt Jones Bould Taunton	3	6
Thring Townsend Swindon	8	9

LEADING INDIVIDUALS	
1 **BOTHAMLEY Michael** Beachcroft Wansbroughs	
DUNN John Burges Salmon	**PRITCHARD Nicholas** TLT Solicitors
2 **GLYNN Andrew** TLT Solicitors	**GUNN David** Bond Pearce
JACOMB Brian Thring Townsend	**LOWLESS Peter** Michelmores
SCOTT Peter Bevan Ashford	**SMITHERS Tim** Veale Wasbrough
3 **BATTERSBY Robin** Burges Salmon	
DAVIES JONES Martin Beachcroft Wansbroughs	
FABIAN Mark Rickerby Watterson	**GIDNEY David** Burges Salmon
McNULTY Stephen Burges Salmon	**SMYTH Robert** Burges Salmon
4 **DUNN Ian** Bond Pearce	**HOGGETT Jonathan** Stephens & Scown
UP AND COMING	
GAIT Charles Osborne Clarke	

This book is the product of 6,552 1/2-hour interviews. See p.7 for BMRB audit.
Within each band, firms are listed alphabetically. *See individuals' profiles p.739*

Burges Salmon (see firm details p.902) Continued growth in the telecoms sector has produced significant work from its client Orange and other telecoms operators. The firm was involved in taking on a 226,000 sqft new HQ for Orange, as well as the development of new call and switching centres. Projects this year include brownfield regeneration, portfolio management, development, investment and rural property and agriculture. Several members of the Burges Salmon team were highly recommended by lawyers and clients during research. **John Dunn** (see p.744) (*"talented and he works hard"*) was warmly endorsed by clients. Several interviewees called for the inclusion of **Stephen McNulty** (see p.749), deeming him to be a *"good commercial lawyer"* as well as *"responsive and proactive."* **David Gidney** (see p.745) is judged to be *"doing well,"* **Robin Battersby** (see p.740) is *"technically skilled"* and **Robert Smyth** *"wins work with his profile for high quality."* **Clients:** Orange; Canadian & Portland Estates; Credit Suisse First Boston.

Osborne Clarke (see firm details p.1086) The firm's impressive client base has grown to include more plcs, institutions, major funders and sizeable corporate occupiers. It boasts an active retail and leisure practice which services over 30 retailers and and e-tailers, and recently added The Perfume Shop to its client roster. Advised Pubmaster Group on portfolio acquisitions including the strategic purchase of GRS Inns, involving a portfolio of 2000 pubs. Described by one solicitor as a *"pull your sleeves up firm,"* the group is judged by clients as *"good value for money."* Among a group that *"knows the business and property market well,"* **Charles Gait** has secured for himself a reputation in the development arena. **Clients:** British Airways Pension Fund; Pubmaster Group; Railtrack.

Beachcroft Wansbroughs (see firm details p.872) Boasts a number of large clients for whom it handles all the property work, including NHS Trusts, local market developers and retailers. The group conducts portfolio management for occupiers in most regions and has recently been appointed by a chain of shopping centres, covering its activities in England and Wales. A significant level of projects and PFI work includes work for a dynamic listed property company that provides residential accommodation to universities and health trusts. Peers deem the group to be *"successful, and delightful to deal with."* **Michael Bothamley** (see p.741) remains extremely well respected, as a *"sensible property lawyer"* who is *"popular with clients."* **Martin Davies Jones** (see p.743) is a senior figure within the team and continues to attract market recommendation. **Clients:** Building societies; national retailers; NHS.

Bevan Ashford (see firm details p.880) Known for its public sector work with clients including NHS trusts and local authorities. The group is active in other areas including the redevelopment of town centres and site acquisitions. Adjudged *"professional"* by peers who also believe it *"a key competitor"* in the marketplace. The firm has recently undertaken a raft of work for the South West Regional Development Agency, including instructions on the 'Eden Project' and the redevelopment of St Austell Town Centre. *"Technically good"* **Peter Scott** (see p.753) remains endorsed by both peers and clients. **Clients:** South West RDA; Devon County Council; Hanson Quarry Products Europe.

Bond Pearce (see firm details p.888) "*A strong practice*" which can be "*fairly aggressive on behalf of its clients,*" it is generally deemed by peers more visible in Plymouth than Bristol. Expert in government department and public sector work, with transport a key area for the firm. It acted on disposals for newly acquired client, Transport for London, and continues to work for Highways Agency. The firm has also been successful in its work for The National Trust and increasingly active for English Heritage across the South of England. Other areas of strength lie with waste and landfill companies and in renewable energy. Clients find "*no short-comings*" among this team of which **David Gunn** (see p.746) is a respected member. **Ian Dunn** (see p.744) is a practitioner thought by rivals to be "*highly visible in the local market.*" **Clients:** Computer Associates; Highways Agency; English Heritage; Transport for London.

Michelmores (see firm details p.1066) A distinguished local firm, which counts **Peter Lowless** as a partner, is seen to have "*expanded a lot*" and was the recipient of praise from peers throughout our research. One solicitor acknowledged he is "*happy to have them on the other side – they know how to do deals.*" Boasts a large public sector practice working for eight government agencies, other clients of the group include educational institutions, developers, local authorities and national house builders. Recent highlights include the acquisition and redevelopment of a redundant office building and the acquisition of a former school. Advised on the development of 20 dwellings and 350 acres of grounds, the firm is also representing a house builder in a joint venture consortium. The firm is instructed on numerous PFI projects nationwide. **Clients:** Regional developers; regional and national house builders; local government and public bodies.

Clarke Willmott & Clarke (see firm details p.915) Largely but not entirely a residential practice, it has recently acted for the MoD on the letting of a distribution warehouse to IKEA. The firm advises BANES on the re-development of hotel, cinema and leisure sites. Activities on an urban re-generation project and advice to a consortium involved in a development scheme outside Bridgewater have kept the team busy this year. Clients appreciate the firm as "*reputable and reliable*" while peers judge it "*technically capable.*" Stephen Rosser heads the PFI and property team primarily advising consortia bidding in the health and safely sector. **Clients:** Beazer Homes; Nationwide Business Finance; University of the West of England.

TLT Solicitors (see firm details p.1157) The in-house legal team from Punch Pub Company has joined this firm, which has seen further success in acquiring Transco as a client. Competitors are witnesses to an increase in activity at this commercial property practice, particularly in secured lending and development matters. The group handled the site assembly and all related issues for Bristol's Harbourside development. A 66 acre waterside location on a brownfield site, it was a mixed development project involving several ownerships and a number of developers. The group has also been involved in the acquisition and disposal of areas near the Millennium Dome, a 12 acre container port at Newport, and the Victoria Deep Water Terminal port facility at Greenwich. Clients appreciate its input on complex property portfolios: "*we don't use them because of their location but because they are efficient and good value for money.*" **Andrew Glynn** (see p.745) and **Nicholas Pritchard** (see p.751) are standout practitioners here, rated by both peers and clients. **Clients:** The Rank Group; Barclays; Sun Life Pensions Management.

Veale Wasbrough (see firm details p.1167) The departure of leading property partner Nigel Somerville is perceived to have been a setback for this firm. It is thought to be fighting back successfully, one solicitor commented "*it has an array of good lawyers, it's definitely a quality commercial property practice.*" **Tim Smithers** (see p.754) maintains his enviable reputation. Activities include advice to local and national property developers including the acquisition of a new site for the National Assembly of Wales and regeneration work at Bristol Harbourside. The firm also worked on the development of old warehouses at Gloucester Docks. Property management and investment for the National Care Services Commission, Defence Estates and PACE has also been high on the work agenda. **Clients:** Local authorities; Defence Estates; Lloyds.

Davies and partners (see firm details p.933) Competitors agree that this firm with particular expertise in house building "*can't be ignored*" because of its "*strong residential development practice.*" The group also handles retail work and investment property management. Julian Born works in the commercial property team. **Clients:** House builders; retailers; investment property companies.

Foot Anstey Sargent (see firm details p.961) The firm is seen by rivals as winning "*significant property work in Exeter.*" Acting for several landowners in both acquisitions and disposals. Typical work for the team includes granting options to a national house builder, the disposal of development land to a national house builder and the acquisition of a school and factory premises. **Clients:** University of Plymouth; Vospers; Wainstones Power.

Lyons Davidson (see firm details p.1045) The firm has targeted the high end of the market. John Hicks acts for one of the largest private healthcare groups in the UK and the team manages portfolios of several nursing homes. It advised on the £7.5 million development of a new education centre for the Charitable Trusts of the United Bristol hospitals. The group is perceived by solicitor referees to be "*a steady and reliable force on deals.*" **Clients:** Highfield Holdings; local authorities and public sector; national retailers.

Rickerby Watterson (see firm details p.1108) Specialists in licensed property work, the firm also has displayed skill in its agriculture and estate work. The firm was recently instructed to purchase the 7.2 acre site of a former school for the development of a new campus for Gloscat. It also acts for one of the largest privately funded nursing homes in the South West. Seen by peers to have "*some talented people*" including **Mark Fabian** (see p.744), who joins the rankings after recommendations from both solicitors and clients. Typical commendations include "*he's quick to grasp the issues.*" **Clients:** Whitbread; Group 4; Lloyds TSB; Gloscat.

Stephens & Scown **Jonathan Hoggett** is the standout practitioner at this team that is thought to have expertise in minerals work and urban regeneration projects in Plymouth and the Thames Valley. The firm is also involved in a trade park project sited in a derelict quarry. Its client base includes landowners and developers involved in housing development projects. **Clients:** House builders; waste disposal companies; mineral extraction companies.

Bretherton Price Elgoods (see firm details p.894) Judged by fellow lawyers to have a "*good strong property department.*" Richard Handley heads the team that has development expertise, as well as strength in property development and landlord and tenant matters.

Davitt Jones Bould (see firm details p.936) A pure property firm set up by a core group of solicitors who used to work for the Government property department. Peter Allinson leads a team that acts for a number of institutions as well as local authorities and banks. Clients feel they provide an "*excellent all-round service.*" Major projects undertaken include Government privatisations and the team has specialist knowledge in areas such as royal parks. The firm is instructed by the Foreign Office on estate matters. **Clients:** MoD; Countryside Agency; Highways Agency.

Thring Townsend (see firm details p.1155) The result of a successful merger between Thrings & Long and Townsends fielding offices in Bath, Swindon and Newbury. Niche areas for the firm include the establishment and running of the property elements of pension schemes, mineral extraction work and the acquisition of sites for telecom companies including Vodafone. Also involved in 'Delta 1200', a large office let in Swindon. Recent instructions include land option work for landowners and developers, landlord and tenant work for licensed premises (pubs, hotels and restaurants), and franchise sites for AUDI and Mercedes. **Brian Jacomb** (see p.747) is well-liked member of the team described as by peers as a "*capable practitioner who brings no airs and graces to the table.*" **Clients:** Vodafone; AUDI; charities.

WALES

PROPERTY (COMMERCIAL) • Wales	Ptnrs	Assts
1 **Eversheds** Cardiff	10	9
2 **Berry Smith** Cardiff	3	2
3 **Edwards Geldard** Cardiff	16	n/a
Morgan Cole Cardiff, Swansea	12	11
Palser Grossman Cardiff Bay, Swansea	4	8
Robertsons Cardiff	n/a	n/a
4 **Hugh James Ford Simey** Cardiff	6	6

LEADING INDIVIDUALS	
1 **BERRY Roger** Berry Smith	**DAVIES Rowland** Edwards Geldard
2 **EVANS Eric** Eversheds	**GATES Kathryn** Edwards Geldard
GEEN Jonathan Palser Grossman	**JAMES Robert** Morgan Cole
JONES Chris Berry Smith	**WILLIAMS Martell** Robertsons
3 **IVIN Alison** Palser Grossman	**JONES Michael** Edwards Geldard
JONES Nefydd Eversheds	**MEREDITH Alan** Eversheds
MORGAN Rosemary Morgan Cole	**ROBERTS David** Hugh James Ford Simey
SELIGMAN David Palser Grossman	**WATKINS David** Eversheds
UP AND COMING	
PRYCE Jonathan Robertsons	

This book is the product of 6,552 1/2-hour interviews. See p.7 for BMRB audit.
Within each band, firms are listed alphabetically. *See individuals' profiles p.739*

Eversheds (see firm details p.952) Remains pre-eminent in Wales due to the quality of its individual lawyers and the scope of its practice. Described by a client as "*excellent, offering a high level of technical expertise, they aim to provide London quality service at provincial rates and achieve this.*" A recent highlight was instruction by Guardian Insurance on the disposal of a major shopping centre in Cardiff, as part of the Guardian Portfolio sale. Other work includes advising Macob Projects on various aspects of a new 200,000 sq ft warehouse for the storage and distribution of L'Oréal products in Europe. The firm has acted for the Welsh Development Agency in several private sector property joint ventures and in a major grant award. Counts a number of high profile lawyers in its group including **Nefydd Jones** (see p.747) and **Eric Evans** (see p.744) , a "*hard working, tough guy.*" **Alan Meredith** (see p.749) remains well respected although lower profile of late and **David Watkins** (see p.755) is developing a name for himself in this area. **Clients:** Investec Bank; National Assembly for Wales; Ministry of Defence.

Berry Smith This "*excellent, niche*" property firm has recently recruited Martin Pursall as a new partner. Clients are "*highly impressed*" with the quality of the group's work. It acted on behalf of Lidl on the acquisition of two regional distribution depots, and advised on a number of site acquisitions for residential development. Has experienced an increase in retail work. **Roger Berry** (see p.741) is seen by other solicitors to be "*go-ahead*" and "*a hard negotiator*" *and* **Chris Jones** (see p.747) is generally felt to be "*popular with clients.*" **Clients:** Gilesports; Driving Standards Agency; British Medical Association.

Edwards Geldard (see firm details p.948) The group handles all the property work for Chevron and remains involved in ongoing urban redevelopment projects. Recently played a role in the acquisition of large parts of the Swansea Docks area, and was involved in the acquisition of land for residential development. This firm boasts a number of well-known personalities amongst its commercial property team. **Rowland Davies** (see p.743) is " *capable and efficient*" and **Kathryn Gates** (see p.745) receives wide praise from clients as "*personable and technically extremely able.*" **Mike Jones** (see p.747) was the subject of spontaneous recommendation during research. **Clients:** Chevron.

Morgan Cole (see firm details p.1074) With offices in Swansea and Cardiff, the team's size is advantageous in the Welsh market. Major projects include a waterside development in Cardiff Bay, and acting for ABP on the sale of its port industrial portfolio. The firm has a strong relationship with BP Oils and acted on the regeneration of the 1,000 acre BP Chemicals works at Baglan Bay. The Welsh Development Agency is a significant client for whom the team handles all property development work. Lawyers rate the "*quality work*" of senior figure **Robert James** (see p.747) while **Rosemary Morgan** (see p.750) is respected for her client-friendly approach. **Clients:** Associated British Ports; Grosvenor Waterside; HSBC Trust Company.

Palser Grossman A small team that includes well-known and respected personalities. **Jonathan Geen** is a new arrival to our rankings after endorsement by peers; "*he's easy to work with and popular with clients.*" **Alison Ivin** is similarly respected by clients and seen to be a "*capable hard worker.*" **David Seligman** is the most experienced member of the team, adjudged "*clever, charming and highly respected by all.*" The group is principally involved in private sector work. Its significant development projects in Wales include the letting and development of Caspian Point in Cardiff, the establishment of a debating chamber for the National Assembly of Wales, and development of the NCM Building in Cardiff Bay.

Robertsons Small, niche property firm that includes "*personable*" **Martell Williams**, who competitors believe has "*good development experience.*" Up and coming **Jonathan Pryce** is said to be "*well liked and technically competent.*" The firm is seen as particularly active in local development work.

Hugh James Ford Simey (see firm details p.1004) A specialist commercial property team whose principal clients are house builders, housing associations and developers. Ongoing work for pension firms and commercial lease work is the order of the day. Most of the group's clients are based in Wales. Major recent deals include the acquisition of two £5 million development sites for Barratt Homes and the disposal of a £5 million site for Glamorgan and Gwent. **David Lloyd Roberts** (see p.752) ("*he knows his stuff*") is the best known of the firm's lawyers. **Clients:** Welsh Water; Barratt Homes; Hafod Housing Association.

MIDLANDS

Eversheds (see firm details p.952) "*An exceptional, thorough, and slick outfit,*" according to competitors, it maintains its position at the top of the pile, and is renowned for its advice on the installation, ownership, operation and maintenance of private infrastructure networks. An "*efficient*" team includes the "*client-friendly*" **Tim Webb** (see p.755), who leads the Birmingham team, and "*driving force*" **Parmjit Singh** (see p.753), who is said by clients to have "*premier league potential.*" Although some regard **Meg Heppel** (see p.746) as "*a demanding task-master,*" she also maintains an "*excellent reputation.*" The firm recently acted for Bourne Leisure on the £700 million purchase of the leisure division of Rank, comprising 77 Holiday Parks and Country House Hotels. The investment team acted on a syndicated £94 million loan facility to fund the purchase of six shopping centres. **Clients:** Bryant Homes; Paramount; Advantage West Midlands; Mailbox.

Wragge & Co (see firm details p.1189) Firms from London and all over the regions regard this as an "*outstanding practice,*" embracing property development, retail and leisure, property management and residential development. The "*formidable*" **Mark Dakeyne** heads a "*keen, proactive team.*" Commended by clients for "*knowing what the end product should be,*" he advised Global Switch on the development and letting of large telecom centres across Europe, and the creation of its joint venture with Chelsfield and

PROPERTY (COMMERCIAL) • Midlands	Ptnrs	Assts
1 **Eversheds** Birmingham, Nottingham	18	80
Wragge & Co Birmingham	19	66
2 **Hammond Suddards Edge** Birmingham	10	20
Pinsent Curtis Biddle Birmingham	11	24
3 **DLA** Birmingham	n/a	n/a
Freethcartwright Leicester, Nottingham	17	11
Lee Crowder Birmingham	5	12
4 **Knight & Sons** Newcastle-under-Lyme	8	22
Martineau Johnson Birmingham	5	12
Shoosmiths Northampton, Nottingham	9	24
5 **Browne Jacobson** Nottingham	9	19
Harvey Ingram Owston Leicester	6	8
Wright Hassall Leamington Spa	4	6
6 **Edwards Geldard** Nottingham	4	6
Higgs & Sons Brierley Hill	4	2

LEADING INDIVIDUALS	
1 **CADDICK Robert** Wragge & Co	**DAKEYNE Mark** Wragge & Co
2 **ASKIN David** Wragge & Co	**BRICE Barry** Pinsent Curtis Biddle
KORDAN Joel Lee Crowder	**WATSON Adrian** DLA
3 **HEPPEL Meg** Eversheds	**O'MEARA Anne** Hammond Suddards Edge
SINGH Parmjit Eversheds	**THORNE Peter** Wragge & Co
WEBB Tim Eversheds	
4 **BURNS John** Wragge & Co	**NEWCOMBE Mark** Hammond Suddards Edge
ROWE Tim Wright Hassall	
UP AND COMING	
YATES Andrew Pinsent Curtis Biddle	

This book is the product of 6,552 1/2-hour interviews. See p.7 for BMRB audit.

Within each band, firms are listed alphabetically. *See individuals' profiles p.739*

TrizecHahn Europe. **Robert Caddick** is admired for his *"hands on approach,"* and acted for Marconi on the development of its new HQ at Ansty, comprising 900,000 square feet of business space. **David Askin** possesses a *"switched on commercial brain,"* while **Peter Thorne** is highly rated by clients for his *"ability to adapt to the ethos of a company." "Diligent"* **John Burns** is said by peers to be *"a good guy to do business with."* The firm has niche strength in setting up and acting for limited partnerships, such as the Clarendon Limited Partnership, which went on to buy the Clarendon Shopping Centre in Oxford. **Clients:** Prologis; Castlemore Securities; MEPC; McDonald's.

Hammond Suddards Edge (see firm details p.984) *"Experts in all fields,"* the firm is a favourite with local clients, who praise a *"broad, well-resourced, cohesive team."* **Anne O'Meara** (see p.751) is recommended for her proficiency on complex deals, while **Mark Newcombe** (see p.750) is said to provide *"up-to-date, innovative advice."* Property finance has been a particularly active part of this year's caseload. The firm gained a place on the panel of Anglo Irish Bank, and advised the Bank of Scotland on the £110 million funding of a development in Solihull. It continues to act as the sole legal advisor to the Millennium Point project in Birmingham, and acted for Prologis on the pre-let of 185,000 sq ft of distribution and warehouse space to Exel Europe. **Clients:** BAA Lynton; Advantage West Midlands; Wolverhampton & Dudley Breweries.

Pinsent Curtis Biddle (see firm details p.1098) *"Deal-oriented without being point-scorers,"* the team is highly regarded by peers and clients alike. The *"knowledgeable and effective"* **Barry Brice** (see p.741) is joined in the rankings by *"impressive performer"* **Andrew Yates** (see p.756), a rising name who recently worked on the largest sale of off-licences in the UK. This involved advice to Whitbread and Punch Retail on the sale of their stake in First Quench Retailing for around £250 million. The team has strengthened its presence in investment work and development projects, as well as advising on joint venture projects in both public and private sectors. The firm acted for Prime (UK) on the establishment of a joint venture with Barclays Infrastructure to carry out primary healthcare developments. The projected development programme involved at least £70 million of development. **Clients:** Lex Service; Morrison Development Partnerships; Lucas Pension Scheme.

DLA Although the firm is not considered to have the evenness of quality of the market leaders, clients still rate it as a sound option. The respected **Adrian Watson** is seen as the department's biggest asset.

Freethcartwright (see firm details p.964) Head of Department George Taylor oversees the firm's impressive retail client list that includes Paul Smith Ltd and Carpet Mill Factory Shops. Following a *"successful"* expansion into Derby, the firm is, according to one client, *"clearly the top firm in the East Midlands."* The team has advised increasingly on urban development, including such schemes as the development of a former industrial site at Grand Union Wharf, Loughborough for 100 homes and 84 student bed spaces. Property finance has also been particularly active this year, and the team has acted on seven transactions in the past year for NatWest, with a total loan value of £16 million. **Clients:** Barratt Homes; Brydon Developments; Multiyork Furniture.

Lee Crowder (see firm details p.1035) The *"excellent"* **Joel Kordan** (see p.748) leads *"a first-class, professional team,"* noted by peers for its burgeoning reputation in development work. Clients love Kordan for his *"sheer responsiveness,"* and the market is unanimous in admiring his enthusiasm: *"He really bangs the drum for the firm."* Although the department has a strong presence in commercial and residential development and general landlord and tenant work, it is best known in the region for housing association charitable property work. The team also has a niche in logistics and telecoms-related work. It advised on the conversion of a lace warehouse and factory into residential development for Morrison Homes. **Clients:** Exel; Morrison Homes; Alfred McAlpine Special Projects; Orange.

Knight & Sons (see firm details p.1025) A comparatively small team, which nevertheless draws high praise from clients, who point to a group with *"the feel, culture and substance of a large practice."* The team comprises *"first rate people who understand law in the real world."* Karl Bamford and his team advised the Trillium Group on its portfolio management, and have niche areas of expertise in mines and minerals, retail acquisition and the licensed trade. **Clients:** Gladman Developments; Punch Taverns; Phones 4U.

Martineau Johnson (see firm details p.1055) Best known for education work, the practice is nevertheless seen by peers to have a *"tidy, commercially-oriented"* property practice. Simon Arrowsmith heads a team with strong investment and management practices, and expertise in the retail and leisure sectors. The firm advised on the completion of a multiple property investment portfolio for West Midlands Metropolitan Authorities Pension Fund. **Clients:** McKechnie; Galliford; CLA Homes (Midlands); IM Properties.

Shoosmiths (see firm details p.1129) *"Excellent technicians,"* whose service has improved over the past year, in the view of its clients. Development has been a particularly active part of this year's caseload. Head of Department John Temple advised Crosby Homes on the acquisition and development of several large city centre schemes in Birmingham, Leeds and Newcastle. **Clients:** Barratt Homes; NatWest; Volkswagen.

Browne Jacobson (see firm details p.898) Researchers had their attention drawn to the firm's *"impressive client base,"* which continues to provide high-quality and varied work for the property team. Secured lending work for several of the country's leading banks, including £15 million worth of deals for Royal Bank of Scotland in the past year, forms the core of this practice. The department, headed by David Hibbert, has also undertaken large retail acquisitions, including the acquisition of eight C&A stores, together with 12 other retail premises for Wilkinson Hardware Stores. **Clients:** Parceline; Wilkinson Hardware Stores.

Harvey Ingram Owston (see firm details p.989) *"The leading firm in Leicester"* is headed by Philip Lane, and is appreciated by clients for *"fostering active partner involvement and appreciating the commercial angles."* Retail remains the mainstay of the firm's property work, with transactions such as the Benson Shoe acquisition of Oliver Timpson Footwear, comprising 300-400 retail outlets nationwide. Substantial urban regeneration work includes the Braunstone Community Association Government Fund Regeneration Project valued at £49.5 million. **Clients:** Persimmon Homes; Everards Brewery; Alliance & Leicester.

Wright Hassall (see firm details p.1190) Retaining a strong reputation for residential development work, the firm is bolstered by the presence of **Tim Rowe** (see p.753), whose *"extensive experience"* in the area and *"refined mind, both commercially and technically,"* earn the appreciation of clients. The practice also specialises in purchase and leaseback of commercial premises, and has acted for British Waterways on various multi-million pound mixed commercial and residential development projects in the South of England. **Clients:** Laing Homes; Britvic Soft Drinks; Lunn Poly.

Edwards Geldard (see firm details p.948) A growing presence in the region, the merger with Eking Manning has greatly strengthened the team, which is headed by David Williams. The firm acted on the acquisition, development and funding of a health and fitness centre. The Derby team specialises in development, while the Nottingham team boasts expertise in retail landlord and tenant work, property finance and secured lending work and is the sole advisor to Powergen in the East Midlands. **Clients:** Miller Homes; Balfour Beatty; Royal Bank of Scotland.

Higgs & Sons (see firm details p.995) A small, *"competent"* team, headed by Ken Cheadle, which has significant expertise in commercial and residential development. Niche areas include agricultural property, landlord and tenant work and the leisure industry. A substantial proportion of work derives from local clients. **Clients:** Regional companies.

EAST ANGLIA

PROPERTY (COMMERCIAL) • East Anglia	Ptnrs	Assts
1 **Eversheds** Cambridge, Ipswich, Norwich	14	30
Hewitson Becke + Shaw Cambridge	9	9
Mills & Reeve Cambridge, Norwich	6	23
2 **Ashton Graham** Bury St Edmunds, Ipswich	8	7
Birketts Ipswich	7	11
Prettys Ipswich	n/a	n/a
Taylor Vinters Cambridge	n/a	n/a
Wollastons Chelmsford	2	4
3 **Ellison & Co** Colchester	5	1
Few & Kester Cambridge	2	2
Greene & Greene Bury St Edmunds	n/a	n/a
Greenwoods Peterborough	n/a	n/a

LEADING INDIVIDUALS	
1 **BRISTOL Jeremy** Birketts	**COWPER Tony** Mills & Reeve
GILLERY Bryan Eversheds	**HAMILTON Keith** Eversheds
MEDVEI Cornelius Eversheds	
2 **GIBBS Robert** Eversheds	**ROBINSON Herbert** Mills & Reeve
3 **BEACH Steven** Taylor Vinters	**BRETT Alan** Hewitson Becke + Shaw
HENSON Michaela Taylor Vinters	**HUTTON Robert** Mills & Reeve
JONES Elizabeth Hewitson Becke + Shaw	

This book is the product of 6,552 1/2-hour interviews. See p.7 for BMRB audit.

Within each band, firms are listed alphabetically. *See individuals' profiles p.739*

Eversheds (see firm details p.952) The national presence of this respected firm is seen to *"give it power"* in this region. The firm fields in each of the three regional centres. Its strengths include property support for major PFI projects and activities for motor trade, nursing homes, house builders, regeneration projects and educational property. The Ipswich office specialises in construction, projects and retail, Norwich focuses on house building and some retail work, while Cambridge, generally felt to be still in its fledgling stages, is currently majoring in development, biotech and IT work. Peers agree that its lawyers *"know what they're about"* and as a unit *"it wins the most work."* Clients typically described the group as *"diligent and conscientious."* Counting a number of leading individuals among its team, **Bryan Gillery** (see p.745) *"knows his stuff"* and is always *"friendly and reasonable."* **Keith Hamilton** (see p.746) is a *"well respected and commercial lawyer"* and *"clever and strategic"* **Cornelius Medvei** (see p.749) is called into play on the more complex matters. **Robert Gibbs** (see p.745) received commendations from solicitors during research. **Clients:** Varrier Jones Trust; GAP; Bernard Matthews; TXU Europe Group.

Hewitson Becke + Shaw (see firm details p.994) Resides at the cutting edge in the fields of construction, planning and development property. The firm is receiving an increasing number of instructions from Cambridge University. Described as a *"good offering"* by solicitor referees, its recent highlights include ongoing work for Cambridge Leisure Complex, pre-let agreements at Capital & Counties Business Park, and major projects for Medical Research Council. **Alan Brett** (see p.741) is viewed by lawyers as *"a practical chap, we like dealing with him"* while **Elizabeth Jones** (see p.747) is respected for her commitment to her clients. **Clients:** University of Cambridge; Millennium Pharmaceuticals; Fairclough Homes.

Mills & Reeve (see firm details p.1069) Dominant in the Cambridge market with expertise in the spheres of higher education, science parks, PFI and development matters. Appointed to the panel of Nationwide Building Society for commercial lending issues. Peers commend the team as *"heavyweight performers, a quality outfit no question."* **Tony Cowper** (see p.742) is *" competent and congenial,"* and **Herbert Robinson** (see p.752) is endorsed as *"quick, efficient and capable."* Clients appreciate **Robert Hutton** (see p.746) who is *"positive, courteous and sensible, you can tell he wants to get the job done."* Recent highlights include the acquisition of local development sites, the drafting of a development agreement and lease to a national leisure chain, and acting for a waste disposal company in various option agreements. **Clients:** University of Cambridge; Health Clients; East of England Development Agency.

Ashton Graham Respected regional firm acting for residential developers and commercial investors. The group, which includes Andrew Roe, recently acted on the reorganisation and sale of an engineering company and in a series of multi-million pound property transactions for foreign-owned developers in the acquisition, development and disposal of major sites in London and the South East. **Clients:** Hotels; GP practices.

Birketts Known among fellow solicitors for its strengths in leisure and licensing industries. The group is involved in the acquisition and disposal of pubs, and in funding matters for banks. The firm has recruited three ex-London lawyers to its commercial property team, including Chris Schwer who rejoins the firm after an absence of fourteen years. **Jeremy Bristol** is felt by peers to fortify the firm's reputation in commercial property, described as an *"experienced practitioner."* **Clients:** Greene King Group.

Prettys (see firm details p.1100) Enjoys a favourable profile among its peers, described by them as *"reputable, competent and reasonable."* David Clark is part of the team that has worked for industrial and commercial developers, offshore companies and lenders. **Clients:** Regional developers; secured lenders.

Taylor Vinters (see firm details p.1150) Remains a respected and well-established firm whose recent work includes investment related matters for

Cambridge University and advice to Resolution plc in the sale of the Martlesham industrial estate to Gordon Saville. **Stephen Beach** (see p.740) is well known in the region and seen to be "*competent and easy to work with.*" "*Rising star*" **Michaela Henson** (see p.746) is judged an asset by solicitor referees who describe her as "*well respected and knowledgeable.*" **Clients:** Granta Park; The Technology Partnership; Biowisdom.

Wollastons (see firm details p.1188) A small but highly regarded firm in this region, characterised as "*decent, energetic and lively* " by a referee. Undertakes a wide range of commercial property work including a significant level of transactions for the motor industry and a number of licensed property matters. The group advised Bulgin on a recent headquarters office move, and regularly advises Global Marine Systems on asset acquisitions. Nicholas Cook is a member of the team. **Clients:** Bulgin; Global Marine Systems; Trace Elliott.

Ellison & Co Commercial property is the major practice area for this small firm whose clients include property investment companies, commercial developers and retail tenants. Peter Powell heads the team.

Few & Kester This "*established*" and "*reputable*" Cambridge firm appears in our listings on the merit of commendations from contemporaries. Charles Webb heads the commercial property department that handles a significant amount of work for Cambridge University colleges. It counts charities, banks and building societies among its clients.

Greene & Greene Makes an appearance in our rankings following recommendations from solicitors during research. Described as "*well established*" and often seen on local deals, the firm also handles a large amount of work outside the local vicinity including activity in London and Cambridge. Niche areas of strength include commercial development in the biotech and IT sectors, leisure, entertainment and transport. Recent highlights include headquarter buildings for major companies. Fraser Paskell is a commercial property partner. **Clients:** Vitech Group; Community Hospitals; Schering Plough; Western Medical.

Greenwoods (see firm details p.978) A "*good commercial firm*" which impressed researchers with its relationships with substantial clients such as Geest and Thomas Cook. Well regarded by fellow solicitors who have worked with them, these lawyers handle leasehold work for EMAP, and receive instructions from the Highways Agency. The latter is a major client for whom they undertake disposal of surplus land and the acquisition of compulsory purchased land. Stephen Illingworth is a partner in the group. **Clients:** EMAP; Highways Agency; Thomas Cook.

NORTH WEST

PROPERTY (COMMERCIAL) • North West	Ptnrs	Assts
1 **Addleshaw Booth & Co** Manchester	9	20
Bullivant Jones Liverpool	8	14
Cobbetts Manchester	22	25
DLA Liverpool, Manchester	n/a	n/a
Eversheds Manchester	6	17
Halliwell Landau Manchester	10	21
2 **Field Cunningham & Co** Manchester	4	3
Hammond Suddards Edge Manchester	4	13
3 **Beachcroft Wansbroughs** Manchester	4	12
Davies Wallis Foyster Liverpool	7	10
Mace & Jones Liverpool, Manchester	4	4
Pannone & Partners Manchester	5	6
4 **Brabners** Liverpool, Preston	8	11
Jones Maidment Wilson Altrincham, Manchester	n/a	n/a
5 **Chaffe Street** Manchester	2	3
Cuff Roberts Liverpool	10	2
Gorna & Co Manchester	4	4
Kuit Steinart Levy Manchester	2	4
Wacks Caller Manchester	3	6
6 **Aaron & Partners** Chester	3	2
Hill Dickinson Chester, Liverpool	n/a	n/a
Walker Smith & Way Chester	2	4
Weightmans Liverpool, Manchester	n/a	n/a

This book is the product of 6,552 1/2-hour interviews. See p.7 for BMRB audit.
Within each band, firms are listed alphabetically. *See individuals' profiles p.739*

Addleshaw Booth & Co (see firm details p.853) Viewed by some clients as the "*regional leaders,*" this large team is felt to provide "*exceptional quality*" in all areas of the property market. Involved in high profile regeneration work, the firm advised on the development of the new 180,000sq ft Asda Walmart near the Commonwealth Games Stadium. Strong across the board, the group has been noted by peers for its advice on portfolio management and local development. "*Stalwart character*" **Diana Craven** (see p.743) is admired as "*an excellent technician.*" The "*knowledgeable and conscientious*" **Peter Kershaw** (see p.748) and **Corin Waller** (see p.755), perceived by other solicitors to be "*commercially switched on,*" also gain strong market endorsement. A recent acquisition from Halliwell Landau, **Paul Conroy** (see p.742) enjoys a reputation among his peers as an "*excellent development lawyer.*" The firm acted for Whitehall Green Partnership on the acquisition of P&O's UK portfolio and subsequent dispersal of substantial parts of it, a deal with an overall value of £450 million. **Clients:** Green Property; AMEC; Birchwood Park Estates; Scudder Threadneedle Property Investments; Railtrack.

Bullivant Jones (see firm details p.901) "*Excellent niche firm,*" with particular expertise in the retail and development sectors, which is regarded by some commentators as "*for quality, the equal of any London-based property practice.*" The team does, however, depend greatly on the presence of "*extraordinarily hard worker*" **Pamela Jones** (see p.747), who is acknowledged to "*know property inside out.*" Her "*firm handle on client relationships*" has assured the firm of a particularly enviable retail clientele, although it also advises on property investment and landlord and tenant matters. The firm acted upon the acquisition, development, letting and sale of the Great Northern Retail Park, Huddersfield. **Clients:** Iceland Foods; MEPC; Development Securities; Kwik Save Stores.

Cobbetts (see firm details p.923) "*Major property player ,*" which is perceived by clients to be "*professional, well-resourced and customer-focused.*" Peers draw the attention of researchers to the firm's "*wonderfully even quality.*" Acting for various development and leisure clients, with a noticeable increase in licensing work, the team features a number of respected individuals. "*Commercial and focused,*" **Stephen Benson** (see p.740) has increased his profile this year, along with **Anthony Fitzmaurice** (see p.744), "*a really sensible lawyer*" who is particularly popular with development clients. Younger partner **Simon Worrall** (see p.756) retains his market reputation for his landlord and tenant work. New to the rankings this year is the "*excellent*" **Stephen White**, who boasts considerable expertise in the retail sector. The firm recently acted on a development agreement for Morrison Developments for six retail units in Swindon, worth around £22 million, and was another to work on the disposal of P&O's vast northern property portfolio. **Clients:** Bellway; Maple Grove Developments; Littlewoods (Construction); Trinity Investments.

DLA Acknowledged by peers for its depth of resources, a "*cohesive team*" is active in development, regeneration, portfolio management and con-

LEADING INDIVIDUALS		
1	BECKETT Roy DLA	GOODMAN Stephen Hammond Suddards Edge
	JONES Pamela Bullivant Jones	
2	ASHWORTH Peter Field Cunningham	MARKS Geoffrey Halliwell Landau
	SORRELL Stephen Eversheds	
3	BENSON Stephen Cobbetts	BUCKLEY Liam Hammond Suddards Edge
	CRAVEN Diana Addleshaw Booth	MOODY John Eversheds
4	EDGE Mike Halliwell Landau	FITZMAURICE Anthony Cobbetts
	LEONARD Tessa Eversheds	PATTISON Mark Beachcroft Wansbroughs
	ROONEY Phillip DLA	STRATTON David Field Cunningham
	WEIGHTMAN Anita DLA	WHITE Stephen Cobbetts
5	BANFI James Jones Maidment Wilson	
	JONES Michael Pannone & Partners	KERSHAW Peter Addleshaw Booth
	WALLIS Guy Davies Wallis Foyster	
UP AND COMING		
	CONROY Paul Addleshaw Booth	JACKSON Karl Mace & Jones
	WALLER Corin Addleshaw Booth	WORRALL Simon Cobbetts

This book is the product of 6,552 1/2-hour interviews. See p.7 for BMRB audit.
Within each band, firms are listed alphabetically. *See individuals' profiles p.739*

struction. **Roy Beckett** has been described as "*a massive presence*" in the market. Head of real estate **Phillip Rooney** and **Anita Weightman** also maintain their share of market opinion.

Eversheds (see firm details p.952) "*A constant presence in the market*" this year, the firm has picked up a number of important new clients, notably the £350 million Littlewoods property portfolio. Residential development, property finance and regeneration advice are central planks of the workload. Opponents concede that "*rainmaker*" **Stephen Sorrell** has "*real presence.*" He heads the property team, and is supported by "*straightforward negotiator*" **John Moody** (see p.749). Clients endorse property development specialist **Tessa Leonard** as a "*capable and diligent performer.*" The firm acted on the £60 million redevelopment of Manchester Airport in conjunction with Railtrack, Manchester City Council and GMPTE, and advised on the redevelopment of Huddersfield Town Centre to provide 275,000 square feet of retail space. **Clients:** Manchester Airport; AMEC; Urban Splash; Royal Bank of Scotland.

Halliwell Landau (see firm details p.982) Although it has suffered the departures of Stephen Goodman to Hammond Suddards Edge and Paul Conroy to Addleshaw Booth, the firm "*has continued to maintain a high standard,*" according to clients. Acclaimed for its development work, the team has acted on various notable retail deals, and has particular expertise in tax syndicated enterprise zone investments. **Geoffrey Marks** (see p.749) has "*been there and done it all,*" and is joined in this year's rankings by **Mike Edge** (see p.744), highly recommended by clients for his commercial outlook. The team advised Middlewood Leisure on a £100 million mixed leisure, retail and office development, including construction of the largest indoor snow slope in Europe. **Clients:** Taylor Woodrow Developments; Tritax Assets; Aldi Stores; Swinton Group.

Field Cunningham & Co (see firm details p.956) A niche firm with, as one peer notes, "*an excellent reputation among house builders.*" This should not obscure, however, "*proficiency and thoroughness*" in the secured lending sector, nor substantial work in the leisure development market. "*Experienced and creative,*" **Peter Ashworth** (see p.739) is described by one client as "*one of the best property lawyers around.*" His colleague **David Stratton** (see p.754) is a development expert who is consistently endorsed by clients. The firm has acted for Barratt Homes on various acquisitions for residential development in the region this year, worth a total of £20 million. **Clients:** Morris Homes; AMEC; Malthouse Developments; Royal Bank of Scotland.

Hammond Suddards Edge (see firm details p.984) Commended by peers for possessing a "*property pedigree away from corporate support,*" the firm has seen a notable upturn in leisure and residential work, especially in city-centre house building. Although still far smaller than its major competitors, the property department created a stir with the hire of **Stephen Goodman** (see p.745) from Halliwell Landau. "*100% a deal-maker,*" he is perceived by some commentators to be "*the best development lawyer around.*" **Liam Buckley** (see p.741) also received a stream of client endorsement for his "*ability to blend commercial and technical expertise.*" The firm acted on the disposal of the £200 million aluminium plate and manufacturing business of Luxfer to Alcoa, and advised on the joint venture of Bryant Homes and Beazer Homes on the North East New Town development, with a value in excess of £1 billion. **Clients:** English Partnerships; British Aerospace; Manchester Airport; Halifax.

Beachcroft Wansbroughs (see firm details p.872) Although its regional profile is not as strong this year, the firm nevertheless retains an enviable client base, and is described by one as "*responsive, improving, and able to find a practical way around complex problems.*" **Mark Pattison** (see p.751) is "*useful to have on one's side, and extremely commercially aware,*" and comes highly recommended by his peers. The firm advised the Secretary of State for Environment on the planned conversion of a former RAF base in Warrington into a new village. It also acted for Realm on the redevelopment of Royal Quays in Doncaster. **Clients:** Balfour Beatty; Defence Estates; Bristol & West; Inland Revenue.

Davies Wallis Foyster (see firm details p.935) "*Expanding and innovative*" practice, seen not only as "*major players in Liverpool,*" but as a regional power. The team, headed by the respected **Guy Wallis** (see p.755), is particularly active on site acquisition and plot sales, urban regeneration, and development funding, with particular expertise in airport work. It advised on the purchase of a 125,000 sq ft building to be converted into a student development worth £20 million for Berkeley College Homes. **Clients:** St Modwen Group; Rothschild's; Manchester Airport; Peel Airports (Liverpool).

Mace & Jones (see firm details p.1046) A firm which has "*established an excellent reputation as a niche player*" amongst peers, with a team which is "*hot, keen and on the ball.*" **Karl Jackson** (see p.747) is considered to stand out as "*an extremely capable technician.*" The firm has seen an increase in out-of-town industrial developments, and is currently working on a partnership between two developers, Pochins and Prologis Development, on the development of their industrial and distribution parks at Middlewich and Crewe. The team also advised on the acquisition and development of RAF Finningley, Doncaster into an international airport for Peel Holdings. **Clients:** Artisan Holdings; The Accident Group; Co-operative Wholesale Society; Cavern City Tours.

Pannone & Partners (see firm details p.1088) "*Professional, experienced and commercially aware,*" the practice is well regarded by clients and solicitors alike. **Mike Jones** (see p.747) is new to the table this year, and was described by a London practitioner as "*particularly practical and efficient on complex and urgent matters.*" Clients include urban developers, members of the petroleum industry, public sector clients and residential developers. The team recently acted on the acquisition of East Midlands Airport for Manchester Airport. **Clients:** Texaco; Urban Splash; Alfred McAlpine; Greater Manchester Passenger Transport Executive.

Brabners (see firm details p.892) The integration of the commercial property team from Berrymans Lace Mawer has greatly strengthened the department, giving it "*an increased presence in the market*" and a new head, Sandy Chapple Gill. Possessing expertise in the leisure and retail sectors, the practice has a strong development bias. It acted on a joint venture between Royal & SunAlliance and Trinity Mirror Properties on a £10 million redevelopment for a new office and exhibition area in Old Hall Street, Liverpool. **Clients:** Royal Bank of Scotland; Project Spark; JD Wetherspoon.

Jones Maidment Wilson incorporating Hatton Scates Horton A relatively small team, considered by peers to be "*proactive and on the ball.*" Leading figure **Jim Banfi** is described as a "*talented communicator.*" Development and regeneration work are primary areas of the firm's caseload. **Clients:** Investment clients.

Chaffe Street (see firm details p.911) Hailed by one peer as "*a firm on the up,*" it has acquired a significant new client in Miller Residential Development Services, which has created work on joint venture residential schemes for city centre living. The team, headed by John Street, provides a full property service, with particular strength in investments and portfolios, development and landlord and tenant work. **Clients:** Boss Group; Bank of Scotland; NM Rothschild & Sons.

Cuff Roberts "*A partner-led practice, without point-scorers*" is considered by peers to have a "*nice steady bunch*" of lawyers. The firm has particular strength in the retail sector. **Clients:** Leading retail and other regional organisations.

Gorna & Co Established firm with "*good people who do the thing properly.*" Recognised experts in development and private investment, the team acts for a number of friendly societies. Headed by Stephen Hindmarsh, it acted on the disposal of a Manchester city centre office investment worth £6 million. **Clients:** National Car Parks; North British Housing; UPS.

Kuit Steinart Levy (see firm details p.1025) Headed by Jonathan Marks, the firm specialises in development, sale and leaseback and portfolio work for large regional investors. Niche expertise exists in the conversion of former textile manufacturing sites into residential premises. Currently advising on a new training ground at Carrington for Manchester City Football Club, the team also advised on the redevelopment of a leisure complex in the region worth £6 million. **Clients:** Manchester City Football Club; Windsmoor Group; Airline Services.

Wacks Caller (see firm details p.1170) Bolstered by the arrival of Elizabeth MacKay from Hill Dickinson, the firm is commended by clients for its "*hands-on personal service and pragmatic legal advice.*" Investment acquisition and funding are important elements of the workload. Recent work includes the development of Blackpool Football Club and the extension of Spinning Gate Shopping Centre in Leigh for the Atmore Group. **Clients:** Modus Properties; Blackpool Football Club; City Living.

Aaron & Partners (see firm details p.853) Best known for private client work, this Chester-based firm does a range of property work, and has a niche in mineral extraction and waste disposal. Other work includes a range of local commercial sales and acquisitions. Headed by Simon Carter, the team advised the Water Hall Group on the acquisition of an area of mineral land in Hertfordshire for sand and gravel extraction. **Clients:** Appchem; Denbighshire County Council; Water Hall Group.

Hill Dickinson (see firm details p.996) A respected team, headed by David Swaffield, which has its primary reputation for advising on commercial redevelopment in the centre of Liverpool for David McLean Developments. Portfolio management, acquisition and disposals for Royal Liver Assurance have also formed a significant element of the department's work. **Clients:** Merchant Navy Pension; Redgrove Fairclough; David McLean Developments.

Walker Smith & Way Headed by Gray Prestt, the department is admired by peers for its "*professionalism,*" with the main bulk of its workload coming from developers, investors and landlords. **Clients:** Developers and investors.

Weightmans (see firm details p.1176) Although the firm is best known for insurance work, its property team also attracts the commendation of peers. Headed by David Morgan, the firm is not only on the property panel of the Post Office, but also responsible for the secured lending portfolio for Carlsberg-Tetley Brewing. The team recently acted for First Quench on the takeover by Nomura of the combined Thresher and Victoria Wine Estates. **Clients:** First Quench Retailing; Oddbins; Maiden Outdoor Advertising.

YORKSHIRE

Addleshaw Booth & Co (see firm details p.853) Still regarded as "*the leading force*" in Yorkshire, the firm's spread of work and nationally admired client base has led clients to view it as "*a cut above their competitors for strength and depth.*" Advising on the full spectrum of work, the team includes a number of the region's leading individual players. "*Sound and sensible*" **John Pike**'s (see p.751) leadership qualities are widely admired by peers. He advised BT on an agreement for the lease of a new office building of around 130,000 sq ft. **Dean Copley** (see p.742) is said to be "*proficient, without being a needless point-scorer,*" while clients view the "*combative*" **Paula Dillon** (see p.743) as "*excellent , keen and proactive.*" **Michael Reevey** (see p.752) is commended as "*a safe pair of hands.*" Particularly active on commercial development, the group acted on the Clarence Dock scheme, comprising a 1 million square foot mixed-use leisure and business site in central Leeds, worth £100 million. **Clients:** Berkeley Group; BT; Standard Life Investments; St James Securities.

Walker Morris (see firm details p.1171) "*Formidable team*", which peers acknowledge for its outstanding client base. This has recently been augmented by instruction from Starbucks to advise on its portfolio management. Particular strength has been noted in development finance, landlord and tenant and retail work. The respected **Richard Innes** (see p.747) is especially commended for his work in the retail sector. The team recently acted on the acquisition of approximately 480 Scottish & Newcastle properties worth £190 million for The Royal Bank of Scotland, and advised Persimmon Homes on a £30 million city centre joint development for Persimmon Homes and Norwich Union. **Clients:** Teeside International Airport; NM Rothschild; Bank of Scotland; Barratt Homes.

DLA Advising on social housing, economic regeneration and education work, the firm also acts for a number of household names on financing and residential development. **Neil McLean** is the team's respected leader. **Clients:** Halifax; MOD.

Eversheds (see firm details p.952) Perceived by peers to possess "*an excellent breadth of experience and a commercial approach to the job,*" the team is considered to owe much to the leadership of head of department **John Foster** (see p.745). Advice on brownfield site development for both public and private sector clients, rail property work and investment are central elements of the workload. The team acted for Lattice Property Holdings on the disposal of the 180,000 square foot Leeds City Office Park to Canada Life. It also advised on a variety of redevelopment and re-lettings at the Brent Cross shopping centre in London. **Clients:** Barnsley Miller Partnership; Royal Bank of Scotland; Asda/Walmart; English Welsh & Scottish Railways; Anglo-American.

Hammond Suddards Edge (see firm details p.984) "*A stronger, more focused team*" this year, "*providing a top-class service.*" This is partly owing to the newly arrived **Nic Crocker** (see p.743) from Eversheds who enjoys a high profile, praised as "*an excellent team leader.*" Advising Allied London Properties this year, on the site assembly and development of the 200,000 sq ft Cumberland House office building in Manchester. Active in public sector regeneration work, often in conjunction with private companies. One such project is the disposal of the Norfolk Park development site, the flagship scheme of Sheffield City Council, which is occurring in phases with private developers. **Clients:** Yorkshire Forward; Bellway Homes; Scottish Power; Wm. Morrison Supermarkets.

Pinsent Curtis Biddle (see firm details p.1098) Some clients rate them as "*one of the best property law firms in the region, tempering commercial advice with good technical knowledge.*" **Nigel McClea** (see p.749) is seen as the team's principal asset, and dispenses advice that is "*succinct and compre-*

PROPERTY (COMMERCIAL) • Yorkshire	Ptnrs	Assts
1 **Addleshaw Booth & Co** Leeds	10	30
2 **Walker Morris** Leeds	11	11
3 **DLA** Leeds, Sheffield	n/a	n/a
Eversheds Leeds	8	23
Hammond Suddards Edge Leeds	7	17
Pinsent Curtis Biddle Leeds	11	22
Read Hind Stewart Leeds	9	4
4 **Andrew M Jackson & Co** Hull	9	8
Gordons Cranswick Solicitors Bradford, Leeds	7	6
Irwin Mitchell Sheffield	5	8
Nabarro Nathanson Sheffield	5	n/a
5 **Denison Till** York	2	3
Gosschalks Hull	9	4
The Frith Partnership Leeds	4	n/a
6 **Keeble Hawson** Sheffield	5	4
Rollits Hull	9	7
Wake Smith Sheffield	1	4

LEADING INDIVIDUALS	
1 **McCLEA Nigel** Pinsent Curtis Biddle	**McLEAN Neil** DLA
2 **FLOUNDERS Andrew** Read Hind Stewart	**INNES Richard** Walker Morris
PIKE John Addleshaw Booth & Co	
3 **AYRE Paul** Gordons Cranswick Solicitors	**COPLEY Dean** Addleshaw Booth & Co
CROCKER Nic Hammond Suddards Edge	**DILLON Paula** Addleshaw Booth & Co
FOSTER John Eversheds	**GRABINER Martin** Nabarro Nathanson
QUINLAN Andrew Pinsent Curtis Biddle	**REEVEY Michael** Addleshaw Booth & Co
STONE David Andrew M Jackson & Co	

This book is the product of 6,552 1/2-hour interviews. See p.7 for BMRB audit.
Within each band, firms are listed alphabetically. *See individuals' profiles p.739*

hensive, with a commercial edge." **Andrew Quinlan** (see p.752), whose client-friendliness has been highly commended, joins him in the leading ranks this year. The team is advising on the long-term development of Curborough New Settlement, a new village outside Lichfield, comprising up to 5000 new homes. It has also secured a place on the English Partnerships Panel, establishing a niche for strategic development advice. **Clients:** Curborough Consortium; Leeds Bradford International Airport; London & Associated Properties; Concert.

Read Hind Stewart (see firm details p.1104) Picking up substantial high-profile work, the team is hailed by commentators for its "*great connections.*" Among a team that "*knows what it's doing,*" **Andrew Flounders** (see p.745) has been commended for his "*technical expertise*" and "*willingness to get the job done.*" Development has been particularly busy this year, and the firm has advised on such schemes as an industrial motorway development at Delta Park in Wakefield, a joint venture between Caddick Developments and Akeler Developments. The firm also advises on inner city leisure schemes and mixed-use industrial, leisure and retail developments. It scored a recent coup through winning the instruction for the Austin Reed property portfolio. **Clients:** Caddick Developments; Helios Properties; Oakgate Group; Broughton Group.

Andrew M Jackson & Co (see firm details p.860) Said by clients to "*know the property business inside out,*" Hull's leading team advises on retail and leisure acquisition, disposal and development. **David Stone** (see p.754) is viewed as a development specialist, and has a "*commercial understanding of the field.*" Work highlights include a development agreement for a 215,000 sq ft retail and leisure development in Scunthorpe Town Centre, comprising 26 retail units and a seven-screen multiplex cinema. **Clients:** MFI Properties; Cannons Health & Fitness; Humberside International Airport; Associated British Ports.

Gordons Cranswick Solicitors A well regarded regional firm with a "*sound*" regional clientele. Researchers were told of a "*commercial, responsive team with good partner involvement.*" A newcomer to the list this year is **Paul Ayre** (see p.739), "*a tremendously able and user-friendly guy*" with a strong niche in retail development. The most significant deal of the year involved acting for the management team on the property aspects of the £300 million public-to private buyout of Peter Black. **Clients:** Wharfdale Finance; William Cook; Replan UK; Bass Brewers; Wm Morrison Supermarkets.

Irwin Mitchell (see firm details p.1009) Kevin Docherty leads a team with particular strength in retail and development, but which also advises on investment sales for pension companies and public sector acquisitions. A high point of last year was acting for Tawnywood on the development and letting of the 140-acre Bermuda Leisure Park and Bermuda Industrial Estate in Nuneaton. The team also advised CVO Fire on the acquisition and development of a flagship store in central London. **Clients:** Peveril Securities; Alfred McAlpine Homes Yorkshire; Sheffield City Council.

Nabarro Nathanson (see firm details p.1078) A "*responsive and commercially aware*" firm with a national presence. The "*pragmatic*" **Martin Grabiner** (see p.745) provides "*first-class client care,*" and heads a team with a niche in waterside developments and leisure regeneration. The firm acted for Capital Shopping Centres on the refinancing of a £770 million metro centre in Gateshead. **Clients:** British Waterways; Jarvis; Coal Authority; Capital Shopping Centres.

Denison Till (see firm details p.939) An "*honourable, traditional firm which gets the job done,*" and has cultivated a niche within the student accommodation sector, working for universities, FE colleges, and housing corporations. Hilary Crook and her team have also advised on substantial development work, and acted for Helmsley Securities on the Merchant Exchange Venture project, involving the acquisition and development of a warehouse into flats and a restaurant/bar. **Clients:** York Diocesan Board of Finance; Unipol Student Homes; Castle Howard.

Gosschalks Best known for licensing work, notably property-related work for breweries, the team, headed by Dick Llewellyn, has advised on numerous portfolio disposals. Among the most notable was the acquisition by the Voyager Pub Group of 1200 properties from Bass. **Clients:** Leisure sector; betting industry; local developers; motor industry.

The Frith Partnership Highly praised by peers for its partner-led ethos, the team is respected by clients for "*the personal quality of their service.*" Barney Frith leads a team with particular strength in retail acquisitions. A highlight of the year was the acquisition for Akeler Developments of the site of a call centre in Merthyr Tydfil pre-letting to One2One.

Keeble Hawson Active in a variety of property projects, the team's workload ranges from lease renewals for Capitec, to the sale of a greenfield site to a major national house-builder. Gareth Owen heads the department, whose specialisms are spread between two offices; the Leeds office specialises in retail and development work, with Sheffield undertaking more general disposals, acquisitions and lease renewals. **Clients:** University of Sheffield; Capitec; Hepworth Properties.

Rollits (see firm details p.1110) "*Well organised and knowledgeable,*" the firm has advised on innovative schemes such as The Deep Millennium Project. Martyn Justice heads the team, whose core areas of practice include commercial development and leasing, city centre retail and residential estate development. **Clients:** Heron Frozen Foods; Persimmon; Peabody Trust.

Wake Smith Clients praise the team for its "*consummate professionalism.*" A highlight of the past year has been advising on the acquisition of a substantial retail unit on The Moor, Sheffield, and subsequent grant of a 125-year lease to J Sainsbury for £4.5 million. The team, headed by Neil Salter, has particular strength in licensed property, industrial property asset management and portfolio management. **Clients:** Retail and other commercial entities.

NORTH EAST

PROPERTY (COMMERCIAL) • North East	Ptnrs	Assts
1 **Dickinson Dees** Newcastle upon Tyne	17	n/a
2 **Eversheds** Newcastle upon Tyne	9	18
3 **Robert Muckle** Newcastle upon Tyne	2	7
Ward Hadaway Newcastle upon Tyne	9	15
4 **Watson Burton** Newcastle upon Tyne	6	4
5 **Jacksons** Stockton on Tees	3	n/a

LEADING INDIVIDUALS	
1 **BRAITHWAITE Neil** Dickinson Dees	
2 **COMBE Jonathan** Robert Muckle	**MORGAN Claire** Eversheds
WARD Ian Dickinson Dees	

This book is the product of 6,552 1/2-hour interviews. See p.7 for BMRB audit.

Within each band, firms are listed alphabetically. *See individuals' profiles p.739*

Dickinson Dees (see firm details p.941) "*Prime movers and shakers in the region,*" the team is said to "*exude confidence and professionalism.*" Clients have even perceived "*still further improvement*" this year. **Neil Braithwaite** (see p.741) is clearly the leading figure in the region; he is perceived to be "*at the top of the tree*" by fellow solicitors, and "*highly intelligent , with an eye for detail*" by clients. **Ian Ward** (see p.755) has a lower profile, although he is still seen to be "*a pragmatic operator*" by his clients. The firm advised on major regeneration work for Gateshead Council, developing the brownfield site of Gateshead Quay into residential, hotel and leisure facilities. Secured lending has also been a noticeable feature of the caseload. **Clients:** Northern Electric; Bellway; GEHE UK; Morrison Group.

Eversheds (see firm details p.952) Retaining its reputation for involvement in cutting-edge property work in the region, the firm has been recently appointed to the panel of English Partnerships and continues to undertake big-ticket work for urban regeneration clients such as One North East. The team is also highly regarded for property finance and portfolio management, with clients describing them as "*first-class, responsive and efficient.*" **Claire Morgan** (see p.749) is "*easy to deal with,*" and is recommended for her work at the head of the urban regeneration team. The firm acted for UK Land Estates on a joint venture with the Duke of Northumberland, developing large industrial estates into high-tech business parks. **Clients:** Newcastle Airport; Bryant Homes; Scottish & Newcastle Pub Enterprises; Barclays Bank.

Robert Muckle Clients praise the firm for its "*timing, delivery and depth of knowledge.*" An acknowledged force in development, the firm has also advised a variety of banks and building societies on investment loan facilities. Development expert **Jonathan Combe** (see p.742) joins the ranks of leading individuals this year, and is respected as a "*pragmatic, experienced and commercial lawyer.*" The firm acted for Easter Developments on the acquisition, development and letting of a new 80,000 sq ft factory at Peaseway, Peterlee. **Clients:** City and Northern Projects; McAleer & Rushe; Miller Homes; Bank of Scotland.

Ward Hadaway (see firm details p.1173) Prominent in the residential development market, the team's strengths also include property investment and commercial development and letting. Richard Freeman-Wallace heads the department. The firm acted on the acquisition and development of 29,000 sq ft of offices at Keel Row House in Newcastle. **Clients:** Persimmon Homes; Trillium; Aldi Stores; Sigma Aerospace.

Watson Burton Headed by Kenneth Millband, this well-established team advises a wide range of clients, including commercial and residential developers, investors and retailers. The group acted on the acquisition and conversion of a late Victorian warehouse, the Turnbull Building, into apartments above Newcastle Quayside. **Clients:** Bellway; Co-operative Wholesale Society; Pillar Property Investment.

Jacksons (see firm details p.1010) Reputed to be "*the best firm in the area,*" and demonstrating considerable skill in portfolio management, the team retains its share of peer support. Headed by Geoff Skeoch, the firm has niche expertise in all areas of freehold and leasehold work. **Clients:** Northern Electric; Tees and Hartlepool Port Authority; Darlington Building Society.

SCOTLAND

Dundas & Wilson CS (see firm details p.947) Again highlighted as one of the top names in Scotland by clients and competition alike, the firm continues to set the benchmark for other firms to match. One competitor admitted: "*They're playing in a different game from the rest of us.*" The largest dedicated property team in Scotland has an enviable roster of heavyweight clients, and handles all aspects of property advice. **Iain Doran**, "*a maverick who knows how to please the clients,*" is one of Scotland's leading names, as is development expert **David Steel**, "*a practical, unassuming, incredibly pleasant person to deal with.*" **Hamish Hodge** remains a firm favourite for his "*tremendous knowledge of all sides of a commercial property transaction.*" New to the ratings this year is **Ian Paterson**, who is commended for "*getting the deal done.*" The firm has acted on national projects such as the £70 million acquisition for PPG Metro of P&O's Scottish property portfolio. It was reappointed as Standard Life's property law firm and is also involved with One2One on a large number of smaller deals concerning sites for third-generation mobile phone masts. **Clients:** Abbey National; CGNU; Land Securities; Lattice; National Car Parks; Odeon; One2One; Premier Properties; Royal & SunAlliance; Transco.

McGrigor Donald (see firm details p.1062) "*It's difficult not to come across them somewhere,*" say peers of a firm that has seen a noticeable increase in property-linked joint ventures. The team, which is respected as "*an invigorating opponent,*" boasts a number of Scotland's top-rated performers. **Tom Anderson** (see p.739) is "*an astute commercial guy*" with "*a great ability to take complicated deals and make them work.*" He led the firm's advice on the redevelopment of Glasgow's Clydeport waterfront area. **David Bankier** (see p.740) is "*vastly experienced,*" while the "*sparky*" **Alison Newton** (see p.750) combines a specialism in retail and leisure with an ongoing management role. **Ewan Alexander**'s (see p.739) "*pragmatic approach*" has earned him a place in this year's rankings. The firm has dealt with many of the out-of-town retail parks currently springing up in Scotland, such as McArthur Glen at Livingstone, and continues to act for the development and letting of call centres, for clients such as Akeler Developments. **Clients:** Akelier; BAA McArthurGlen; Barratt Southampton; Bellhouse Properties; BP Gas and Marketing; BT; Clydeport (Glasgow Harbour); Halladale Group; HF Developments; LNC Properties; Morrison Developments; Morley Fund Management; Resolution Properties; Scottish Mutual Assurance.

Burness (see firm details p.903) The firm is considered by some peers and a number of clients to have closed the gap between itself and the leading duo. "*In a sense they have reinvented themselves, and are coming on strongly.*" A strong, business-minded team strikes "*the right balance between the legal position and the commercial opinion,*" according to clients. Led by **Ian Wattie**, "*a roll your sleeves up, pragmatic lawyer,*" the team's most significant growth has been in the area of property finance and funds. The team also includes **Lionel Most** (see p.750), perceived by peers as "*a good, solid, commercial man to deal with,*" the "*practical, no-nonsense*" **David Reid** (see p.752) and the experienced **Ken Ross**. **Caroline Drummond** (see p.744) "*gets to the commercial points quickly*" and together with **Richard Rennie**

PROPERTY (COMMERCIAL) • Scotland	Ptnrs	Assts
1 **Dundas & Wilson CS** Edinburgh, Glasgow	13	51
McGrigor Donald Edinburgh, Glasgow	13	28
2 **Burness** Edinburgh, Glasgow	11	14
Maclay Murray & Spens Edinburgh, Glasgow	16	45
Semple Fraser Glasgow	6	16
Shepherd & Wedderburn WS Edinburgh, Glasgow	9	30
3 **Brodies WS** Edinburgh	9	11
Fyfe Ireland WS Edinburgh	6	11
Tods Murray WS Edinburgh	10	21
4 **Archibald Campbell & Harley WS** Edinburgh	7	6
MacRoberts Edinburgh, Glasgow	7	15
Paull & Williamsons Aberdeen	8	6
Steedman Ramage Edinburgh	7	12
5 **Biggart Baillie** Glasgow	7	15
Boyds Glasgow	5	5
DLA Edinburgh, Glasgow	7	9
Harper Macleod Glasgow	7	4
Ledingham Chalmers Aberdeen	10	11
Thorntons WS Dundee	4	7
6 **Anderson Strathern WS** Edinburgh	9	12
Davidson Chalmers WS Edinburgh	3	3
Dickson Minto WS Edinburgh	1	5
Henderson Boyd Jackson WS Edinburgh	4	10
Masons Edinburgh	1	4
McClure Naismith Edinburgh, Glasgow	6	13
Miller Samuel & Co Glasgow	4	3
Morison Bishop Edinburgh, Glasgow	6	7
Morton Fraser, Solicitors Edinburgh	6	8

LEADING INDIVIDUALS	
1 **ANDERSON Tom** McGrigor Donald	**DORAN Iain** Dundas & Wilson CS
GARRETT Robin Maclay Murray & Spens	**HANIFORD Paul** Semple Fraser
RYDEN Nick Shepherd & Wedderburn WS	**SMITH David** Shepherd & Wedderburn WS
STEEL David Dundas & Wilson CS	
2 **BANKIER David** McGrigor Donald	**DALGARNO Leslie** Paull & Williamsons
HODGE Hamish Dundas & Wilson CS	**JOHNSON Jennifer** Maclay Murray & Spens
MOST Lionel Burness	**REID David** Burness
REID Sandy Steedman Ramage	**STRACHAN Dale** Brodies WS
WATTIE Ian Burness	
3 **BRYMER Stewart** Thorntons WS	**COCKBURN David** Archibald Campbell & Harley
DEWAR Mark Harper Macleod	**DOBIE James** Shepherd & Wedderburn WS
MACNIVEN Iain Maclay Murray & Spens	**NEWTON Alison** McGrigor Donald
QUIGLEY Ian Maclay Murray & Spens	**ROSCOE James** Fyfe Ireland WS
WALLACE Andrew Archibald Campbell & Harley	
4 **KERR Steven** Fyfe Ireland WS	**KINNIBURGH Linda** Brodies WS
MOFFAT Douglas Tods Murray WS	**PATERSON Ian** Dundas & Wilson CS
ROSS Kenneth Burness	**WILSON Alistair** Fyfe Ireland WS
UP AND COMING	
ALEXANDER Ewan McGrigor Donald	**DRUMMOND Caroline** Burness
ETCHELLS Simon Semple Fraser	**RENNIE Richard** Burness

This book is the product of 6,552 1/2-hour interviews. See p.7 for BMRB audit.

Within each band, firms are listed alphabetically. *See individuals' profiles p.739*

(see p.752), "*one of the stars of the future*," breaks into the rankings for the first time. The firm advised on the disposal of The Royal Infirmary of Edinburgh and related sites for Lothian University Hospital NHS Trust, as well as advising The Royal Bank of Scotland on the acquisition of a portfolio of 450 public houses across the UK. **Clients:** Gordon Ramsay; Grosvenor Development; Ladbrokes; Lothian University NHS Hospital Trust; Royal Bank of Scotland.

Maclay Murray & Spens (see firm details p.1047) The firm is recognised by commentators to have "*upped its game*," through a combination of "*a willingness to be commercial and get on with it*" and its coverage of all areas of property advice. "*Technically excellent and immensely affable,*" **Robin Garrett** (see p.745) heads a team that includes **Jennifer Johnson** (see p.747), who is said to have done "*amazing things*" this year. The "*straightforward*" **Iain Macniven** (see p.749) and the "*readily available*" **Ian Quigley** (see p.752) are prominent on land acquisition and development work. The firm acted for Stannifer's £150 million retail and leisure project in Aberdeen, as well as for the Bank of Scotland on its joint venture with PPG for a mixed portfolio of office and retail properties. It also advised on Prudential's office acquisition at Atlantic Quay for £65 million and the disposal of Hyundai's Dunfermline plant for Scottish Enterprise. **Clients:** Abbey Life; BBC; Bourne End Properties; Caledonian Land Properties; CGNU; Friends Provident; Henderson Property Asset Management; Kilmartin; Prudential; Stannifer.

Semple Fraser (see firm details p.1121) "*A property practice to die for*" maintains its reputation among peers for its specialism this year, notably on the development side. A team of "*extremely able lawyers*" is dominated by "*first class*" **Paul Haniford** (see p.746), "*a fantastic, dogged business-getter,*" who *is noted for his "ability to cut through to the heart of a problem."* Despite the firm's reputation as "*a one-man band*," our researchers found that clients warm to **Simon Etchells** (see p.744) as "*straightforward, personable and impressive.*" The firm acted for Royal & SunAlliance on Phase II of the Eastgate centre development, and advises Tesco on its Scottish purchases and developments. **Clients:** Allied Dunbar; Bass Developments; British Land; Delancey Group; Friends Provident; Halifax; Miller Group; Royal & SunAlliance; SMG; Tesco; Unilodge; Whitbread.

Shepherd & Wedderburn WS (see firm details p.1126) Although not possessing quite the profile of the leading duo, the firm is still acclaimed by clients as a "*pretty impressive outfit*" with "*a good level of commerciality.*" Development and acquisitions and disposals figure prominently in the firm's caseload. **Nick Ryden** (see p.753) has "*a huge reputation*" and "*doesn't suffer fools gladly.*" While some consider him to be excessively aggressive, our research revealed a "*pugnacious man who doesn't get bogged down in the legal issues, and fights the client's corner.*" The "*reasonable and straightforward*" **David Smith** (see p.753) is considered to be an "*admirable foil*" to Ryden. **James Dobie**'s (see p.743) "*pragmatic approach*" also gains accolades from peers and clients. The firm has advised Pillar Property on a variety of major retail and office developments, including Greenside Place, as well as acting on Edinburgh Park and as legal advisor to the Waterfront Edinburgh development. **Clients:** Dunedin Property; Miller Group; Pillar; Scottish Enterprise; Scottish Life; Waterfront Edinburgh.

Brodies WS (see firm details p.896) Comparatively low-profile firm, which is nevertheless viewed by competitors as a "*decent quality operation.*" The team retains a strong client base, notably in retail, and has acted for clients on the acquisition and development of superstores with a value of around £150m. **Dale Strachan** (see p.754) is a "*clever and respected*" lawyer, and receives strong support from **Linda Kinniburgh** (see p.748), commended for her client-friendly style. The firm has advised a number of property investment companies and Far Eastern investors into Scotland. **Clients:** Costcutter Supermarket; easyEverything; The Guinea Group; LVMH; Macdonald Estates; Proibito; Warner Bros Stores; Warner Estate Holdings; Zara.

Fyfe Ireland WS (see firm details p.967) Peers recognise that "*there's an immediate trust which helps get the deal done,*" while clients have drawn researchers' attention to a "*thorough, professional team that gets it just about right.*" The overall impression is of a firm that is "*going places.*" The team has been particularly active on property finance and development work, notably on cross-border transactions for medium-sized property companies. **James Roscoe** (see p.752) "*gets on brilliantly with the business side of any transaction,*" while newly rated **Steven Kerr** (see p.747) is especially noted for his retail work on behalf of the Kingfisher stable of companies. The venerable **Alistair Wilson** (see p.756) retains an "*eminence grise*" status in Scotland. The firm advised Green Property on the joint venture vehicle established for the acquisition and sale of P&O's £70 million Scottish property portfolio. **Clients:** Allied London Properties; B&Q; Deutsche Property Asset Management; Green Property; Matalan; Morrison Homes; Nationwide Building Society; Pizza Hut; Teachers Insurance & Annuity Association; Woolworths.

Tods Murray WS (see firm details p.1157) A stable, "*solid and dependable*" firm, underpinned by a sound client foundation and a recent focus on cross-border work for investors and projects. Particular expertise in property finance includes "*good connections with a number of funders.*" Major deals under respected group head **Douglas Moffat** (see p.749) include the sale of 1 to 3 Atlantic Quay, Glasgow for over £65 million and the acquisition of £14 million-worth of development land and investment properties for Taylor Woodrow. **Clients:** Co-Op Insurance; Dobbies Garden Centre; Hermes; Hill Samuel Property Uni Trust; Nationwide Building Society; Railway Pension Nominees; Scottish Power; Taylor Woodrow.

Archibald Campbell & Harley WS (see firm details p.861) The firm continues to receive a stream of instructions from major retail clients, who praise the property team for "*their focus on keeping us happy.*" **David Cockburn** (see p.742) and **Andrew Wallace** (see p.754) "*concentrate on getting the deal done, not on the gamesmanship.*" The firm has advised clients such as Boots and MFI on UK-wide sale and leaseback deals, as well as major developers and investors such as Northern Rock. **Clients:** Antler Group; Boots; Britannia Building Society; British Gas/Centrica; Direct Line Insurance; MFI; Northern Rock.

MacRoberts (see firm details p.1048) Strong on PFI and PPP work, the firm continues to handle the lion's share of Railtrack's considerable portfolio on both mixed developments and major schemes, such as the joint venture with Stannifer for a retail and leisure development on Aberdeen's Guild Street. Directed in Glasgow by Laurence Fraser and by Allan Mackenzie in Edinburgh, the firm is described by competitors as "*pleasant to deal with.*" The firm acted for Oman Holdings on a joint venture for a substantial Stirling development, advised Amey/Miller Consortium on building and refurbishing 30 secondary schools in Glasgow, and represented Lothian University Hospital NHS Trust on its Managed Equipment Service project. **Clients:** Eurocentral Partnership; Kincaid Companies; Morrison Development; North Glasgow Hospitals NHS Trust; Odeon; Oman Holdings; Railtrack.

Paull & Williamsons (see firm details p.1091) Referred to by some peers as "*the Dundas & Wilson of Aberdeen,*" the firm is recognised to have had a successful year, notably on sales and acquisition work and property rationalisation for oil and gas companies. Praised by clients "*for their expertise and prompt action*" and "*their deal-making capacity,*" the experienced team is led by "*rainmaker*" **Leslie Dalgarno** (see p.743), noted for being "*an astute businessman as well as a good lawyer.*" Work this year has included the development and letting of 100,000 square feet of offices for the European Development Company, as well as office and warehouse accommodation for BAA and the £6 million forward sale of the investment. The team also acted on the disposal of a major leisure development at the Promenade, Aberdeen. **Clients:** BAA; Cromwell Properties; Bett Brothers; Essen Properties; European Development Company; Halliburton Dresser Group.

Steedman Ramage (see firm details p.1139) Despite the firm's moves to broaden the practice into PFI and leisure work, commentators still believe that the firm has "*got some way to go to shake off their 'retailers' friend' image.*" Expertise on investment work has led to advice on acquisitions for Norwich Property Trust as well as Irish investors. Clients recognise that the firm has "*a strong ethos of high standards and quality.*" Under the direction of the "*forceful*" **Sandy Reid** (see p.752), the team has advised Debenhams on its expansion programme across Scotland and the redevelopment and letting of £16.5 million-worth of office space for J Sainsbury in Edinburgh. The firm also acted for Shepherd Developments on the site assembly, development and sale of a new call centre in Glasgow for one of Europe's largest tour operators. **Clients:** Debenhams Retail; EDI Group; Gap; J Sainsbury; Marks & Spencer; Sears Properties (Netherlands); Stannifer Developments; Starbucks.

Biggart Baillie (see firm details p.882) With a wide range of clients, and a workload that includes securitisation, development and retail, Peter Cruickshank and his team continue to attract widespread commendation. The firm remains the leader in railway industry work and has added Highbridge Properties to a portfolio that already includes Tarmac and McCarthy & Stone. Telecoms work is another area of niche expertise, and the firm advised on the property aspects of IBM's £700 million IT outsourcing deal with the Bank of Scotland. The firm also acted as sole legal advisors to Wilcon Homes' 1,200-acre development at Duloch Park. **Clients:** BP Oil UK; David Lloyd Leisure; Habitat UK; IBM United Kingdom; Kleinwort Benson Trustees; Persimmon (City Developments); Royal Bank of Scotland; Scottish Power UK; Wilcon Homes.

Boyds (see firm details p.890) Acknowledged by peers to have "*transformed itself on the commercial side,*" the firm is best known for its developer and investor client base. The team, led by David Boyce, has worked on the acquisition of Prestwick Airport on behalf of an international consortium for £33.4 million, as well as the £2 billion Scottish Property aspects of the Inland Revenue and Customs property portfolio. **Clients:** Belgrave Land; Hagen International; Prestwick Airport; Premier Hotels; Shanks Group; Project STEPS; Safeway.

DLA The team, under Graeme Sunter, provides the full range of commercial property advice to local clients.

Harper Macleod (see firm details p.987) Noted by clients for "*commercialism and speed of response,*" the firm rises in the tables, bolstered by substantial growth in its development clientele. The "*superb*" **Mark Dewar** (see p.743) is the figurehead of the department, and is described as "*hard-working, commercially astute and very personable.*" The team advised on the letting of prominent office premises in the Glasgow Business Park for Arlington Securities. **Clients:** Arlington Securities; Clerical Medical; JJ Gallagher; Luminar; Tulloch; Whitbread; William Hill.

Ledingham Chalmers (see firm details p.1034) "*Through their quality of service, quick response and creative attitude,*" the team, under John Curran's leadership, has scored a number of successes for occupiers, funders and developer clients. The firm advised a consortium of Beazer, Wimpey and Cala on the proposed acquisition of 214 acres of a mixed development site at Bellsdyke Hospital. **Clients:** Aberdeen University; Accenture; Beazer, Cala; Elf Exploration; Morrison Development; Scottish Capital Group.

Thorntons WS The firm has seen a growth in construction-related property work in a practice that continues to be built around the respected **Stewart Brymer**. The firm has undertaken considerable development work for Grantchester Group at The Forge retail park, as well as advising on the refinancing of depot sites for B&Q, and rent review arbitration work for Edge Property Investments. **Clients:** B&Q; Bett Brothers; Big W Letting; Edge Property Investments; Grantchester Group; Imperial Tobacco Pension Trustees.

Anderson Strathern WS (see firm details p.859) A new entry in this year's tables, the firm is an acknowledged player on leasing work for both landlords and tenants. Headed by Alan Menzies, the department has been appointed to the Bank of Scotland's panel in Commercial Heritable Security transactions, and continues to represent the Crown Estate in Scotland. The team has also advised the Coal Authority on its strategic disposals. **Clients:** Allied Irish Bank; BAA; Bank of Scotland; Castle Rock Housing; Clydesdale Bank; Crown Estate; East Lothian Housing Association; Edinburgh College of Art; Halifax; Kwik-Fit; Merlin Entertainments; National Trust for Scotland; National Westminster Bank; Provident Financial Group; Richmond Homes; Royal Bank of Scotland; Scottish Airports.

Davidson Chalmers WS Although the team is comparatively small, clients commend it for its "*prompt response and straightforward and business-like style.*" The firm, headed by Andrew Chalmers, possesses niche expertise in investment sales and purchases and brownfield site redevelopment. Notable work includes the commercial development of 'The Tun' land adjacent to the Scottish Parliament, and the acquisition of the 100-acre Junction 4 M8 Distribution Park. **Clients:** Property companies; developers; banks; house-builders.

Dickson Minto WS (see firm details p.942) "*Thoroughly capable*" department, which continues to function both as a stand-alone operation and as a service arm of the firm's mainstay corporate practice. The team acts for a varied clientele, and is respected by peers as "*full of quality, when we see them.*" **Clients:** Banks; retailers; developers, investment companies.

Henderson Boyd Jackson WS Strong on development, investment and property finance, the team advises both national and overseas banks on funding and refinancing issues. The team acted for British Land on the letting to Debenhams of the anchor store at Scotland's biggest covered retail and leisure development at East Kilbride. Stephen Webster heads a team that also represented ntl on the acquisition of telecommunication sites from Thus. **Clients:** Arrowcroft Group; British Land Company; Dunbar Bank; Futurity; Highfield Group; Jarvis; Martin Currie Investment Management; ntl Group; Reg Vardy; Thomas Pink.

Masons (see firm details p.1056) New to the tables this year, and led by Hugh Bruce-Watt, the department serves both as a property service to the firm's projects and construction clients and as a growing independent property practice with a focus on developments and leasing. The team acted for International Computers on a variety of leasing transactions and the Scottish property aspects of its UK property outsourcing project. It also advised a US investor on the £18 million purchase of a mixed-use property in Edinburgh and on the sale of Shawlands Shopping development in Glasgow. **Clients:** Canonbury Estates; Costco UK; International Computers; Morgan Stanley Dean Witter; Sandown Capital Corporation.

McClure Naismith (see firm details p.1059) Said by peers to be "*quite a PFI/PPP oriented firm,*" this sizeable department is also noted for its expansion and acquisition portfolio work. This year has seen further leisure industry advice for Bass and the Regal Hotel Group. Under Wilson Aitken's leadership, retail work has seen an increase, while the team also advises major national house-builders, including Barratt and Miller. The firm has recently conducted major securitisation work involving nursing homes. **Clients:** Alfred McAlpine; Bass; Brown & Jackson Group; Burford; Care First Group; Coal Pension Properties; Equitable Life Assurance; NHP Properties; Regal Hotel Group.

Miller Samuel & Co (see firm details p.1069) This year has witnessed a growth in retail work on the tenant side and an increase in town centre redevelopment cases. Under the leadership of Douglas Lamb, the team has acted for funds and investors, including advising on the purchase of three office investments for a total of around £25 million. **Clients:** Developers; retailers; investors; banks.

Morison Bishop (see firm details p.1075) Despite the department's size, its profile has been low over the past year. The team continues to act for a number of residential developers and major Scottish institutions. **Clients:** Property developers; commercial lenders; investors; tenants.

Morton Fraser, Solicitors (see firm details p.1075) Viewed by some in the profession as having "*rejuvenated themselves*" in the past year, the firm continues to bring in some major deals off the back of a strong company/commercial base of heavyweight clients. The department is headed by Linda Urquhart and acted on the sale of Scottish & Newcastle's £153 million public house portfolio. The team also advised the Bank of Scotland on the highest office rental in Glasgow and several high street relocations. **Clients:** Accor Group; Bank of Scotland; Clydesdale Bank; Nationwide Building Society; Scottish & Newcastle.

NORTHERN IRELAND

L'Estrange & Brett (see firm details p.1038) With their strength in numbers ("*they're bringing in new people all the time*") and "*a good client base,*" the firm remains the clear leader from our research. Clients describe the firm as "*responsive, thorough, and willing to support us.*" **Alan Hewitt** (see p.746) is said to be "*affable and easy to deal with*" and heads a department that has consolidated its position as the market leader for PFI work, dealing with two educational projects for the Northwin Consortium. **Ian Huddleston** (see p.746) is a rising name who has led the firm's work for the Laganside Corporation and is commended for his "*grasp of commercial considerations.*" The respected **Brian Henderson** (see p.119) is seen as "*practical and easy to get on with.*" The team's construction and development capacity has also grown, and it continues to act for Morrison Homes on its 94-unit scheme at Queen's Square, Belfast. **Clients:** Laganside Corporation; Morrison Homes; Northwin Consortium; Sainsbury's Supermarkets.

Carson McDowell (see firm details p.909) Specialist property firm, which is commended by clients for its "*attention to detail.*" The figurehead remains **Alan Reilly** (see p.752), "*always a leading contender,*" who is seen as "*knowledgeable and thorough, with a strong client base.*" The firm worked on the £70 million Forestside shopping development, the largest in Northern Ireland, as well as the rationalising of Tesco's property portfolio. **Clients:** Arcadia; Argos; Belfast Harbour Commissioner; Electronics Boutique; Forestside; HMV; MFI; Tesco; TK Maxx; Woolworths.

Elliott Duffy Garrett (see firm details p.949) Noted for its expertise in property outsourcing and new development work, the team is headed by **Laurence Mahood** (see p.749), who is described by peers as "*a sharp operator and a good general.*" The firm advised on the redevelopment and pre-letting of C&A stores with RedevCo, and British Land's joint venture with British Land Universal. Other work includes advising on the Northern Irish acquisitions of Homebase for Schroders and on Abbey National's property portfolio for Mapeley. **Clients:** British Land; C&A; Land Securities; Lattice; Mapeley; Schroders.

Tughan & Co (see firm details p.1163) Described as an "*ambitious*" firm with "*a good client roster,*" it is a substantial force in the development sector, acting for a stream of retail clients. Under **Phyllis Agnew**'s (see p.739) "*thorough and meticulous*" leadership, the department "*addresses issues well and is sensible in the manner in which they do it,*" achieving success with both public sector and investment clients. **Clients:** Anglia & General Development; Marks & Spencer; Michael Roden; Northern Ireland Housing Association; Prudential; SV Morrison; Tesco.

Arthur Cox (see firm details p.865) A strong year in property acquisitions has characterised the efforts of a firm that is "*making an effort to expand.*" Described in our research this year as "*a firm to keep an eye on,*" it handled the Northern Irish property work for the sale of the Belfast Telegraph to Independent News and Media. Rowan White's team also advised on the property aspects of the acquisition of a retail chain for Scottish-Midland

PROPERTY (COMMERCIAL) • Northern Ireland	Ptnrs	Assts
1 L'Estrange & Brett Belfast	5	6
2 Carson McDowell Belfast	3	5
Elliott Duffy Garrett Belfast	5	4
Tughan & Co Belfast	4	5
3 Arthur Cox Belfast	1	1
Johns Elliot Belfast	5	2
McKinty & Wright Belfast	2	4
Mills Selig Belfast	4	3
4 C&H Jefferson Belfast	2	3
Cleaver Fulton Rankin Belfast	2	3
Hewitt & Gilpin Belfast	4	3
Johnsons Belfast	1	2

LEADING INDIVIDUALS	
1 AGNEW Phyllis Tughan & Co	MAHOOD Laurence Elliott Duffy Garrett
REILLY Alan Carson McDowell	
2 HEWITT Alan L'Estrange & Brett	
3 FARIS Neil Cleaver Fulton Rankin	FRAZER Ivan McKinty & Wright
HAM Brian Mills Selig	HENDERSON Brian L'Estrange & Brett
LEITCH David Johns Elliot	TINMAN Mark C&H Jefferson
UP AND COMING	
HUDDLESTON Ian L'Estrange & Brett	

This book is the product of 6,552 1/2-hour interviews. See p.7 for BMRB audit.
Within each band, firms are listed alphabetically. *See individuals' profiles p.739*

Co-operative and on the Golden Vale joint venture. **Clients:** Belfast Telegraph; Golden Vale; Musgrave Supervalu.Centra.

Johns Elliot (see firm details p.1014) Continuing to build on its reputation as a developer's firm, this "*fine team*" has acted for MEPC on its Castle Court Shopping Centre development. The "*meticulous*" **David Leitch** is "*a shrewd practitioner who knows what he's doing and gets the job done.*" **Clients:** Belfast International Airport; Dunloe Ewart; Marconi; MEPC; NCP; Northern Bank Pension Trust.

McKinty & Wright (see firm details p.1063) Although best known for its litigation practice, the firm's property department is respected by clients as an "*honest, loyal and dedicated team*." The retail sector is an area of niche expertise. Newly ranked **Ivan Frazer** (see p.745) "*ensures that the job always gets done to deadline.*" The firm represented Phoenix Gas on their extension of gas pipelines across Northern Ireland and Morisson Development on the completion of their Carrickfergus Maritime area. **Clients:** International Computers; Littlewoods; Marks & Spencer; Morrison Development; Next; Phoenix Gas; Stakis Hotels.

Mills Selig (see firm details p.1070) Continues to be seen as an ambitious firm, "*suddenly in real competition for development work.*" Work for national developers is a key part of the caseload. Led by **Brian Ham** (see p.571), the team acted for Allied Dunbar on their £172,000 per annum office relocation and lease, and has advised on £25 million of local transactions for the Herbert Group. **Clients:** Local and national developers; national plcs.

C&H Jefferson (see firm details p.1012) Well known for its work on behalf of retail landlords, the team has broadened into securities advice for Northern Irish banks and PFI work. **Mark Tinman** (see p.754) receives the approval of his peers for "*building the practice into a position of some strength.*" **Clients:** Easons; Electric World; Harland & Wolff; Lidl; Monsoon; New Look; Oasis; Peacocks.

Cleaver Fulton Rankin (see firm details p.918) Clients describe the department as "*totally dedicated,*" and the team continues to act extensively for public authorities and local government clients. **Neil Faris** ("*a very capable fella*") has the highest profile of the team, having acted for the Universities Superannuation Scheme on the sale of Forestside Shopping centre for £70 million. **Clients:** BT Property; Cellnet; Crown Castle Telecommunications; Lisburn Borough Council; The Post Office.

Hewitt & Gilpin A "*solid, dependable*" practice that has focused on acquisition work and a retail client base. Headed by Michael Harrison, the team has acted on the acquisition of a chain of filling stations and on local commercial retail developments. **Clients:** Local commercial entities.

Johnsons (see firm details p.1015) Small but well-respected office under John Marshall, that has a reputation for "*sound*" local retail and development work. **Clients:** Local corporates

LEADERS IN PROPERTY (COMMERCIAL)

AGNEW, Phyllis
Tughan & Co, Belfast (028) 9055 3300
phyllis.agnew@tughan.co.uk
Specialisation: Partner and head of the commercial property department. Main area of practice is commercial property development including property finance, bank and institutional funding, institutional investment, joint venture arrangements and PFI projects.
Prof. Memberships: Law Society of Northern Ireland, IBA and European Lawyers Group.
Career: Qualified 1981. Assistant solicitor at *Tughan & Co* 1981 – 1988. Partner since 1988. Chairman of Special Educational Needs Tribunal.

ALEXANDER, Ewan
McGrigor Donald, Edinburgh (0131) 777 7027
ewan.alexander@mcgrigors.com
Specialisation: Leisure, developments and landlord and tenants. Aspects of Hilton/Royal Banks £312m sale and leaseback and Hilton £230m sale of Casino Division to Gata.
Prof. Memberships: Law Society of Scotland.
Career: Trained McGrigor Donald, Edinburgh and London 1989-1991. Qualified McGrigor Donald, Edinburgh and Glasgow 1991 to date. Assumed January 1999.
Personal: Married with one daughter aged two. Participates in rugby and golf.

ANDERSON, Tom
McGrigor Donald, Glasgow (0141) 248 6677
www.mcgrigors.com
Specialisation: Partner in property unit. Joint ventures, property finance.
Prof. Memberships: Law Society of Scotland.
Career: 1971-75 Edinburgh University (LLB Hons); 1980-89 *Biggart Baillie & Gifford*, partner (Commercial Property/ Corporate); 1989 to date *McGrigor Donald*, partner (Commercial Property).
Personal: Two daughters. Leisure interests include golf, duplicate bridge and skiing.

ASHWORTH, Peter
Field Cunningham & Co, Manchester
(0161) 834 4734
Specialisation: Senior partner. Acts for major developers and housebuilders throughout the North. Responsible for the acquisition of land for approximately 1400 houses annually. Involved with large retail and leisure developments throughout the United Kingdom including superstores, cinemas, bingo clubs and bowling alleys. Deals with numerous joint ventures with other developers and financiers for residential and commercial developments. Handles the funding of major commercial developments. Non-executive director of Barratt Developments plc.
Career: Qualified March 1961. Articled at *Field Cunningham & Co* and became a partner in 1962.
Personal: Born 23 January 1938. Educated at Arnold School Blackpool. Lives in Hale, Cheshire.

ASKIN, David
Wragge & Co, Birmingham (0870) 903 1000

AYRE, Paul
Gordons Cranswick Solicitors, Bradford
01274 202 154
paul.ayre@gordonscranswick.co.uk
Specialisation: Specialist in all types of commercial property work. Clients include retailers, developers, investors and lenders. Has a recognised ability to focus on clients' needs and deliver results accordingly. Recent projects include numerous superstore acquisitions for Wm Morrison Supermarkets plc include the

development of Grays Town Centre; procurement of a contract for the firm to represent Bass Brewers Limited for all lending work throughout England and Wales; acting on the development of the 21 acre Hornbeam Business Park which incorporates 300,000 sq ft of offices, a hotel and a fitness centre. Acquisition of 800,000 sq ft Flush Mills investment complex for Wharfedale Finance.
Career: Qualified in 1989; *Simpson Curtis* until 1993; *Gordons Wright & Wright*, now *Gordons Cranswick* 1993 to present; became partner 1994.
Personal: Born 4th November 1964; married with two children; lives Guiseley. Hobbies include football, skiing, golf, cinema. Newcastle United FC season ticket holder.

BAILEY, Jeffrey
Linklaters, London (020) 7456 4756
jeffrey.bailey@linklaters.com
Specialisation: Real estate department. Joint head of European real estate practice group, *Linklaters & Alliance*. Property law specialist. Significant involvement for overseas clients on inward investment into UK real estate.
Career: Attended Neath Grammar School, attained LLB (Hons) from University of Wales 1971. Qualified in 1974. Partner 1980. Joint head of *Linklaters & Alliance* European property practice.

BAILEY, Michael David
asb law, Croydon
Croydon (020) 8628 2589
Crawley (01293) 603 603
michael.bailey@asb-law.com
Specialisation: Partner in property department. Specialises in commercial property. Work includes handling the development of new sites, construction work, joint ventures, landlord and tenant, sales and purchases of businesses and land transactions for charities. Provides solicitor expert reports on conveyancing practice.
Prof. Memberships: Law Society, Associate of School of Urban and Regional Studies, University of Sussex.
Career: Qualified in 1965. Assistant and partner at *Gates & Co* in Brighton 1966-71. Partner in *Whitley Hughes & Luscombe/Donne Mileham & Haddock*, Crawley and Brighton from 1973-98.
Personal: Educated at Varndean Grammar School; Brighton and College of Law. Positions held include president Sussex Law Society 1995, treasurer/trustee of the Webb Memorial Trust (an educational charity), member of Legal Aid Area committee from 1975, chairman 1990-91. Member Know How Housing team to Eastern Europe. CAB Tutor 1974-84, University of Sussex and Brighton College of Technology part-time lecturer 1967-80.

BAILY, Tim
Bond Pearce, Southampton (023) 8063 2211
tbaily@bondpearce.com
Specialisation: Associate in the Commercial Property Group. Wide experience of all aspects of commercial property work especially development and commercial landlord and tenant. Has been closely involved in a number of the firm's niche areas of work such as wind farms and waste and minerals. Current emphasis is on retail development and port and marine related work.
Career: Qualified 1987, becoming Associate 1997.

BANFI, James P.
Jones Maidment Wilson incorporating Hatton Scates Horton, Manchester (0161) 832 8087

BANKIER, David
McGrigor Donald, Glasgow (0141) 248 6677
davidban@mcgrigors.com
Specialisation: Senior property partner and Chairman of Belfast Office. Main area of practice is property development and investment within tax efficient structures, joint ventures and public/private sector initiatives in commercial property. Acted for BAA-McArthur/Glen in the development of their first designer outlet centre in Scotland and for Resolution Property plc in their first major retail development in Scotland, a 50% interest in the £80m The Forge shopping centre, Glasgow. Advised Downing Corporate Finance as sponsor of major collective investment throughout Scotland, England and Northern Ireland. Advised Akeler Developments, Downing Corporate Finance and Royal Bank on "golden contracts" proior to the expiry of the Renfrewshire Enterprise Zone. Presently advising North Lanarkshire Council on Cumbernauld Town Centre redevelopment, the developer of the Broomielaw, Glasgow's premier office development site, including the funding of a new 100,000 sq. feet headquarters building for Scottish Enterprise, and Akeler Developments on high profile office parts in Glasgow and Livingston.
Career: Qualified in 1972, having joined *McGrigor Donald* in 1970. Became a partner in 1978.
Personal: Born 24th March 1949. Educated at Edinburgh University (LLB 1970). Leisure interests include travel, art history, Scottish contemporary paintings, sailing and skiing. Lives in Glasgow.

BARNES, James
Herbert Smith, London (020) 7374 8000
Specialisation: Partner in the Real Estate Department. He has a broad range of experience in commercial property and property related matters with a particular emphasis on development projects, property joint ventures, property finance and security and, latterly, on schemes promoted under the UK Government's Private Finance Initiative. Projects include Broadgate; Tate Gallery of Modern Art, Bankside; Millbank Tower.
Career: Queen's University, Belfast (LLB); qualified 1980; partner *Herbert Smith* 1989.
Personal: Sport – skiing, sailing, motoring.

BATTERSBY, Robin
Burges Salmon, Bristol (0117) 939 2279
robin.battersby@burges-salmon.com
Specialisation: Commercial property development, acting on development projects for landowners, developers and for consortia of landowners/developers, including the tax aspects of property transactions. Recent projects include acting for consortium of commercial and residential developers in mixed development project in the Midlands, including planning aspects and joint venture documentation.
Prof. Memberships: Law Society.
Career: Joined *Burges Salmon* in 1968 and became a partner in 1972.

BEACH, Steven
Taylor Vinters, Cambridge (01223) 423444
sb@taylorvinters.com
Specialisation: All types of commercial property transactions specialising in institutional investment, development, joint ventures, property insolvency and securities work; dilapidations.
Prof. Memberships: Law Society Member.
Career: Graduated in law at Oxford University and joined *Taylor Vinters* in 1983. Qualified in 1985. Became a partner in 1989 and head of the commercial property department in 1994.
Personal: Enjoys amateur dramatics and sport.

BECKETT, Roy G
DLA, Manchester (08700) 111111

BENNETT, Graham
Shoosmiths, Fareham (01489) 881 010
graham.bennett@shoosmiths.co.uk
Specialisation: Commercial property – all aspects including privatisations (Chatham Docks and Southend Airport), insolvency, funding (1 Cockspur St, Trafalgar Square) and charities (Central Board of Finance of Church of England). Recent transactions include completing finance leasing and property aspects of the Heinz NDC project; advising Aeromatic Fielder on the property and VAT aspects of its acquisition of Galley Systems Limited in Birmingham; acquisition by East Hampshire Housing Association of its new development site in Portsmouth; Simpson Lawrence's disposal of its warehouse at Sopwith Park, Segensworth; acted for Zoffany Hotels in the purchase of the former Post House Hotel, Bournemouth; acted for Esso Petroleum in the disposal of its former depot at Tynemouth.
Prof. Memberships: Law Society; Society of Practitioners of Insolvency; Charity Law Association.
Career: Articled *Ashurst Morris Crisp*, assistant *Clifford-Turner*, Partner *Wilde Sapte*, 1994 Partner *Shoosmiths*.
Publications: Joint author 'Housing Act 1988 – A Practical Guide'.
Personal: Golf, cricket and riding.

BENSON, Stephen
Cobbetts, Manchester (0161) 833 5232
stephen.benson@cobbetts.co.uk
Specialisation: Head of commercial property division. Commercial property in the retail and leisure sector. Acts for household name retailers and licensed premises operators in the pub, restaurant and hotel sector.
Prof. Memberships: Law Society. Associate member of American Bar Association.
Career: Educated at Manchester University and Chester College of Law. Qualified 1980.
Personal: Born 1955. Married with three children. Lives in Knutsford. Leisure interests, exercise, motor cars and vice-chairman of Patrons of Manchester City Art Galleries.

BENZECRY, Edward
CMS Cameron McKenna, London
(020) 7367 2741
evz@cmck.com
Specialisation: Commercial property specialist. Heads the client teams for The Wellcome Trust and Scottish Amicable Investment Fund. Has been involved in many significant deals including several portfolio sales/acquisitions. Currently leading the team on Hutchison 3G's site acquisitions for its third generation network.
Prof. Memberships: Law Society.
Career: Articled with *Hamilin Stowe* 1985-87. Qualified January 1988, joining *Cameron Markby (now CMS Cameron McKenna)* simultaneously. Became a partner in 1994.

Personal: Education: St John's School Leatherhead; Birmingham University; Guildford College of Law. Leisure: golf, tennis, family. Married with two children.

BERRY, Paul
Clyde & Co, Guildford (01483) 555 555

BERRY, Roger John
Berry Smith, Cardiff (029) 2034 5511
Specialisation: Full range of commercial property work including investment and development with particular emphasis on landlord and tenant. Also joint ventures and banking.
Career: Qualified 1978. Articled *Broomheads & Neals* (Sheffield). At *Simpson Curtis* (Leeds) 1978-1981 and *Phillips & Buck* now *Eversheds*, Cardiff 1981-1986. Established *Berry Smith* 1986.
Personal: Born 19 March 1952, Colne, Lancashire. Educated at Sedbergh School and Emmanuel College, Cambridge (MA). Interests: football and cycling.

BILLINGS, Martin J.
BrookStreet Des Roches, Witney (01993) 771616
martin@bsdr.com
Specialisation: Commercial property with wide ranging experience of property financing, development and portfolio management. Recent transactions include pre-let and speculative development projects and strategic acquisitions for MEPC in the UK and forward funding and development projects in the UK and Europe for Tech Data Corporation.
Prof. Memberships: The Law Society.
Career: Qualified 1988. *Cole & Cole/Morgan Cole* 1988–2000. Partner 1994. Joined *BrookStreet Des Roches* in 2000 as a partner.

BLAKE, Carey
Blake Lapthorn, Fareham (01489) 579 990

BOTHAMLEY, Michael
Beachcroft Wansbroughs, Bristol (0117) 918 2000
mbothamley@bwlaw.co.uk
Specialisation: Acts for a range of national and regional developers, retailers and institutions. Has particular expertise in development work where current projects include a number of office, retail and leisure schemes. Also acts for several major residential portfolio investment companies.
Career: Durham University. 1980 joined *Wansbroughs Willey Hargrave*. Partner with *Wansbroughs Willey Hargrave* 1986. 1999, partner in *Beachcroft Wansbroughs*.

BRAITHWAITE, Neil
Dickinson Dees, Newcastle upon Tyne
(0191) 279 9233
law@dickinson-dees.com
Specialisation: Managing partner handles urban regeneration, development agreements and property joint ventures, minerals and waste disposal work, building preservation trusts, historic house rescues. Recent projects include: sale of property portfolio for Northern Electric plc; agreements for development for a series of substantial historic buildings for the Phoenix Trust; sale of waste disposal site portfolio; joint venture for Gateway site adjoining M25; development and part disposal of urban village in East London for Bellway plc.
Career: Trinity College, Cambridge M.A. Law Society Finals. *Joynson Hicks* 1976-78. *Clifford Chance* 1978-80. *Dickinson Dees* 1980 to date. (Partner 1981 onwards – head of property from 1990-98). Managing Partner from 1998.

BRETHERTON, Philip
Berwin Leighton Paisner, London (020) 760 1000
philip.bretherton@berwinleightonpaisner.com
Specialisation: Head of the commercial property department. Specialises in commercial property with particular emphasis on development and tax-led work and, more recently, in projects promoted under the Private Finance Initiative. In the past 18 months, he acted for government offices for London on the contract for the new London Parliament building; for the Ministry of Defence in the disposal of the Duke of York Headquarters; and for the Secretary of State for the Environment, Transport and the regions in the disposal of Bletchley Park to the Bletchley Park Trust. He represented Norwest Holst and MEPC, the promoters of the Bute Avenue scheme in Cardiff and acted for Norwest Holst in relation to the new Dorset Police Headquarters, both schemes being promoted under the PFI.
Prof. Memberships: Member of the Law Society.
Career: Articled *Slaughter and May*; qualified 1974; assistant solicitor 1974-78; assistant solicitor *Simmons & Simmons* 1978-79; property partner *Simmons & Simmons* 1979-94; partner *Berwin Leighton* 1994.
Personal: Born 1950, educated at Oxford University (MA). Leisure interests include opera, collecting 78s, tennis and reading. Lives in Maidenhead.

BRETT, Alan
Hewitson Becke + Shaw, Cambridge
(01223) 461155
alanbrett@hewitsons.com
Specialisation: Managing partner of firm and partner in property department dealing with all aspects of commercial property work, including property funding, development work, joint venture agreements, freehold, leasehold, landlord and tenant matters.
Prof. Memberships: Institute of Directors; Fellow of Centre for Law Firm Management (MBA in legal practice), Nottingham Law School; various management, property and local clubs; Law Society (national and local).
Career: Articled *Evershed & Tompkinson*; qualified 1972; LLM (distinction); Diploma in international law; solicitor *Wild, Hewitson & Shaw* 1973-76, partner 1977-89; partner (following merger) *Hewitson Becke + Shaw* since 1989; membership of various committees with firm including the firm's Heads of Department Committee, Finance Committee, Marketing and Practice Development Committees, Management Committees and Merger Committee; head of commercial property department 1991-94, and managing partner since 1994; supervisor in company law at Cambridge University: 1974-76 Sidney Sussex College, 1975-76 Magdalene College. Lectured in conveyancing law for external London LLB students.
Personal: Resides Cambridge; activities various. Governor of The Perse School for Girls, Cambridge.

BRIAM, Tony
Clifford Chance, London (020) 7600 1000
tony.briam@cliffordchance.com
Specialisation: Partner dealing with all aspects of commercial property work with particular emphasis on advising developers, investors and local authorities in relation to city centre office and retail developments.
Career: Stratton School, Biggleswade; Clare College, Cambridge (MA). Articled *Boodle, Hatfield & Co*; qualified 1974; partner *Clifford Turner/Clifford Chance* since 1981.
Personal: Born 1950.

BRICE, Barry
Pinsent Curtis Biddle, Birmingham
(0121) 200 1050
barry.brice@pinsents.com
Specialisation: Partner specialises in property development and investment. Major projects in last twelve months include: development of site in Kidderminster as a retail park and its sale by way of forward funding; development and letting of business park at Stratford-upon-Avon; town centre retail development scheme at Stoke-on-Trent.
Career: St John's College, Oxford. Qualified in 1975 at *Pinsent Curtis Biddle*. Partner 1980. National head of property 1995.

BRISTOL, Jeremy
Birketts, Ipswich (01473) 232300

BROWN, Nicholas
CMS Cameron McKenna, London
(020) 7367 3000
nick.brown@cmck.com
Specialisation: Partner and manager of property group. Handles property development and investment work for national and international property companies, institutions and retailers. Work includes acquisition and disposal of investment properties, acquisition funding and disposal of office and retail properties and development sites, and leases of all types of commercial property, both completed and in course of construction, and subsequent management of investments. Examples of matters handled are the development of Bristol Harbourside; development of supermarkets; the structuring of joint investments in property; securitisation of property interests; the property aspects of the Channel Tunnel Rail Link.
Prof. Memberships: City of London Law Society, Land Law Committee/Investment Property Forum.
Career: Qualified in 1974. Became a partner of *McKenna & Co* (now *CMS Cameron McKenna*) in 1980 and head of the property group in 1991.
Personal: Born 21 November 1949. Educated at Bristol University 1968-71.

BRYMER, Stewart
Thorntons WS, Dundee (01382) 229111

BUCKLEY, Liam
Hammond Suddards Edge, Manchester
(0161) 830 5000
liam.buckley@hammondse.com
Specialisation: Partner, commercial property. Specialises in commercial property finance and development, property investment and joint ventures. Member of the firm's energy/utilities grouping dealing particularly with power station development.
Career: Articled *Last Suddards*; qualified 1987. Partner *Hammond Suddards* 1994.
Personal: Born 1961. Resides Skipton. Enjoys golf and skiing. Member of Northcliffe Golf Club.

BURGESS, James
Pitmans, Reading (0118) 958 0224
jburgess@pitmans.com
Specialisation: Considerable experience in commercial property matters, including acquisitions, sales, joint venture agreements, funding, investment and developments. He also has significant knowledge pertaining to residential development, land assembly and acquisition.
Prof. Memberships: Law Society.
Career: He qualified in 1982 and joined *Pitmans* in 1989.

Personal: Born 1957. Educated Radley College. Leisure interests include tennis, skiing and fishing.

BURNS, John
Wragge & Co, Birmingham (0870) 903 1000

BURTON, Carl
DMH, Crawley (01293) 605082
carl.burton@dmh.co.uk
Specialisation: Partner who deals with all aspects of residential development work including site acquisitions and disposals, strategic options and collaboration agreements and joint ventures. Acts for household name residential developer clients, local planning authorities, health authorities and major public and private companies. Also deals with planning matters relating primarily, but not exclusively, to residential development sites.
Prof. Memberships: Member of Law Society's Planning panel; legal associate member of Royal Town Planning Institute.
Career: BA (Hons) in Law; diploma in Local Government Law. Qualified 1979; assistant solicitor Horsham District Council (HDC) 1979-81; principal solicitor HDC 1981-83; chief legal officer Dartford Borough Council 1983-85; senior solicitor *Rawlinson & Butler* 1985-86, made partner in 1986; joined *DMH* in July 2000.
Personal: Born 1955. Golf, travel and football.

BUTLER, Alan
Simmons & Simmons, London 020 7628 2020
alan.butler@simmons-simmons.com
Specialisation: Partner 1977. Property department. Broad-based commercial property practice with emphasis on bank and institutional funding, institutional investment and development financing transactions. Acts for banks, institutions and property companies in connection with property transactions. Clients past and present include NatWest Investment Bank, Security Pacific, Chase Manhattan, BNP, Swiss Bank Corporation, Banque Paribas, Mitsubishi Estate Company, DESPA, the Abu Dhabi Investment Authority, Land Securities, MEPC, Railtrack and some of the UK's largest property companies.
Prof. Memberships: Law Society.
Career: Qualified in 1973 while at *Simmons & Simmons* and became a partner in 1977.
Personal: Born 26th April 1947. Attended St. Edmund Hall, Oxford 1966-69. Lives in Oxshott, Surrey.

CADDICK, Robert
Wragge & Co, Birmingham (0870) 903 1000

CLARK, Paul
D J Freeman, London (020) 7583 4055
paulclark@djfreeman.com
Specialisation: Partner, senior property partner commercial property – especially landlord and tenant, shopping centres, development projects, limited partnerships. An advocate of plain English. Author of the leasebook – a new concept in leasing multi-let property. Lectures and writes, principally on landlord and tenant issues.
Prof. Memberships: Law Society; City of London Solicitors Company (chair land law sub-committee); British Council of Shopping Centres; Anglo American Real Property Institute; committee member of Clarity.
Career: Qualified in 1970. *Rubinstein Nash & Co* 1968-72 *Linklaters & Paines* 1972-83. *DJ Freeman* 1984, partner 1985, head of property 1990, senior property partner 2000. UK member of European Board of DePfa-Bank. Commercial property adviser to the Oxford Institute of Legal Practice.
Personal: Born 18 March 1946. Educated at Bemrose Grammar School, Derby 1957-64. Manchester University 1964-67 (LLB Hons). Leisure pursuits include music, reading and the church. Lives in Hitchin.

CLARK, Simon
Linklaters, London (020) 7456 4902
simon.clark@linklaters.com
Specialisation: Specialist in the UK taxation of real estate transactions and investment structuring, advising UK and non-UK institutions, property companies, developers and occupiers. Has long been involved in the UK property markets efforts to create listed tax-transparent real estate vehicles in the UK.
Prof. Memberships: Member of Economic and Legislative Affairs Committee of Association of Foreign Investors in US Real Estate.
Career: Articled at *Linklaters* and qualified in 1981, solicitor in tax department 1981-83, solicitor in commercial property department 1983-88. Made partner in 1988. Head of real estate department since 1999.

CLEAL, Adam
Allen & Overy, London (020) 7330 3000
adamcleal@allenovery.com
Specialisation: Acts for landowners, developers and lenders. Specialises in property acquisitions and disposals, hotels, landlord and tenant transactions, property developments, project financing cross border property transactions, large scale voluntary transfers of housing stock by local authorities to housing associations, property joint ventures, management buy-outs, business acquisitions, the sale and purchase of mortgage portfolios, financing transactions, land law arbitrations and securitisation issues.
Prof. Memberships: The Law Society, City of London Solicitors Company.
Career: LLB Leeds University. Qualified in 1982. Partner *Allen & Overy* since 1991. Head of real estate group since June 2000.
Personal: Cycling, scuba diving, opera, theatre, contemporary art.

COCKBURN, David
Archibald Campbell & Harley WS, Edinburgh (0131) 220 3000
DWC@achws.co.uk
Specialisation: Handles a full range of commercial property matters, including purchases, development, sales, leasing (for both landlords and tenants), funding and security work. Also advises on planning matters. Accredited planning law specialist. Contributes book reviews and articles to Law Journal of Law Society of Scotland and Scottish Planning and Environmental Law. Regularly contributes by way of lectures to Law Society Update, various professional seminar providers and Edinburgh University.
Prof. Memberships: Society of Writers to HM Signet. Member of Law Society panel awarding accreditation.
Career: Qualified in 1966. Worked with Glasgow Corporation 1966-67 then *Breeze Paterson & Chapman* 1967-70. Joined *Archibald Campbell & Harley WS* in 1970, becoming a partner in 1971.
Personal: Born 4th February 1943. Attended Edinburgh University 1961-1964. Leisure pursuits include sport and reading.

COMBE, Jonathan
Robert Muckle, Newcastle upon Tyne (0191) 244 2925
JWCombe@robertmuckle.co.uk
Specialisation: Large scale development projects (both brownfield and greenfield) principally acting on behalf of developers but also commercial lenders and investors. Joint ventures, grant and funding agreements and property investment.
Prof. Memberships: Newcastle upon Tyne Law Society.
Career: Qualified 1989, 1989-1995 *Edge & Ellison.* Joined *Robert Muckle* 1995. Partner and head of property group.
Personal: Educated at The Royal School Armagh, Dundee University, Chester College of Law. Interests include all sports (occasionally pull on rugby boots), three children (so far!) and one wife (again so far!).

CONROY, Paul
Addleshaw Booth & Co, Manchester (0161) 934 6525
pyc@addleshaw-booth.co.uk
Specialisation: All aspects of commercial property with particular emphasis on property development and investment transactions acting for developers and occupiers. Extensive expertise in enterprise zone development projects.
Prof. Memberships: Law Society.
Career: *Field Cunningham & Co* 1992-95; *Hammond Suddards* 1995-96; *Halliwell Landau* 1996-2000 (partner from 1999); *Addleshaw Booth & Co* 2001 to date.
Personal: Married, lives in Altrincham. Educated at St Thomas More RC High School and the University of Manchester. Leisure interests include travel, marathon running and cycling.

COPLEY, Dean
Addleshaw Booth & Co, Leeds (0113) 209 2000
dnc@addleshaw-booth.co.uk
Specialisation: Adviser on all aspects of commercial property development including large office, retail and industrial schemes and urban regeneration projects. Acts for developers, funders and end users. Recent deals include; acting for developer on the major development for retail of a former gas works site in Humberside; acting for developer on 2 Objective One regeneration projects in South Yorkshire; acting for a leading Northern financial institution on the development of its members call centre; acting for an investor in acquiring a major city centre retail investment; acting for a developer in acquiring a portfolio of former utility company properties.
Career: 1986-1988: Articles with *Wright & Wright*, Keighley; 1988-1994: Associate with *Simpson Curtis*, Leeds; 1994-1999: Partner with *Garretts*, Leeds; 1999 to date: Partner with *Addleshaw Booth & Co*, Leeds.
Personal: Plays drums and piano, married with 3 children, interests include snowboarding, photography and wine.

COWPER, Tony
Mills & Reeve, Cambridge (01223) 222231
tony.cowper@mills-reeve.com
Specialisation: Partner with responsibility for commercial property and development and redevelopment issues.
Prof. Memberships: Law Society member, associate member of UKSPA, member of IPF
Career: Director of a former residential property BES company. Acted in setting up one of the Cambridge Colleges. Client partner to some of the largest

property owning educational institutions in the country. Responsible for setting up Cambridge Science Park and all subsequent legal work associated with it. Currently acting in connection with one further Science/Business Park (including site set-up, subsequent lettings and sales), having recently sold another park in its entirety. Recently acted as lead partner on the acquisition of 42 ground lease estates containing some 298 properties. Also acted in connection with what is believed to be the first forward funded PFI job in England.
Personal: Golf.

COX, Ian
Herbert Smith, London (020) 7446 2043
ian.cox@herbertsmith.com
Specialisation: Commercial property development, structured finance, property finance (including insolvency) and all aspects of commercial property investment, in particular limited partnerships. Has acted for the Moorfield Group in connection with investments and disposal upwards of £500m; acted for the London Stock Exchange in connection with their headquarter requirements; acted for Henderson Investors in relation to the funding of retail and leisure developments in Spain; acted for Allied London Properties in connection with the proposed redevelopment of the Brunswick Centre in London; acted for Hammerson UK Properties plc in connection with the proposed redevelopment of Exeter City Centre.
Career: *Herbert Smith* trainee 1987-89; qualified 1989. Partner 1996. Now head of Real Estate Corporate Recovery.
Personal: Educated at St. Brendan's College, Bristol and Exeter Univeristy. Married to Caroline; three children Joe, Matilda and Archie. Leisure interests include sport, now mainly from a spectator's point of view.

CRAVEN, Diana
Addleshaw Booth & Co, Manchester
(0161) 934 6000
dmc@addleshaw-booth.co.uk
Specialisation: Partner in the Commercial Property Group. Wide ranging commercial property interests but specifically including development schemes, land reclamation, property partnerships and joint ventures and funding agreements. Clients include Government agencies, plc developers, banks and companies with substantial property portfolios.
Prof. Memberships: Law Society, Association of Women Solicitors, Network.
Career: Joined firm in 1977 and became a Partner in 1981.
Personal: Interests include professional and managerial level womens groups, gardening and antiques.

CROCKER, Nic
Hammond Suddards Edge, Leeds (0113) 284 7205
nic.crocker@hammondse.com
Specialisation: Partner, property and planning. Specialises in a wide range of commercial property for a variety of property and corporate clients, including shopping centre management, industrial portfolio and waste disposal. Nic is partner in charge of corporate property services. He recently acted for Kelda in the sale of its interests in White Rose Shopping Centre Leeds and two business parks in York and Gateshead for £36.1 million.
Career: Articled *Eversheds* 1984-86; qualified 1986; solicitor, *Eversheds* 1986-91; partner, *Eversheds*, 1991-2000; partner, *Hammond Suddards Edge* 2000-present.
Personal: Born Plymouth. University in Nantes, Hull and Nottingham. Resides Leeds. Married with three children. Plays tennis, golf and hockey. Interests include good food and wine.

DAKEYNE, Mark
Wragge & Co, Birmingham (0870) 903 1000

DALGARNO, Leslie
Paull & Williamsons, Aberdeen (01224) 621621
lsdalgarno@paull-williamsons.co.uk
Specialisation: Head of commercial property department, advising private and public property companies and financial institutions on all aspects of property acquisition, development funding and disposal throughout the whole of Scotland. Acted on all aspects of the acquisition and planning and financial matters in relation to No 1 George Square, Glasgow, a major retail, leisure and lifestyle development in the city centre of Glasgow.
Prof. Memberships: Law Society of Scotland and member of Investment Property Forum.
Career: Graduated from Aberdeen University in 1971, LLB with Distinction. Joined Messrs. *Paull & Williamsons* as trainee in 1971, becoming a partner in the commercial property department in 1977. Head of department since 1986. Notary Public.
Personal: Born 19 March 1950. Educated at Robert Gordon's College and Aberdeen University. Leisure pursuits include golf and football. Lives in Aberdeen.

DAVIES, Andrew
Pitmans, Reading (0118) 958 0224
adavies@pitmans.com
Specialisation: Specialises in all aspects of commercial property, but in particular residential development, site acquisition by conditional contracts options, joint ventures with other residential developers. Clients include a number of publicly quoted residential developers.
Prof. Memberships: Law Society.
Career: Articles *Lovell White Durrant* and joined *Pitmans* in 1995.
Personal: Born in 1962. Educated Birkenhead School and Robinson College, Cambridge. Interests: cricket, rugby and golf. Married with 3 children.

DAVIES, Rowland
Edwards Geldard, Cardiff (029) 2023 8239
rowland.davies@geldards.co.uk
Specialisation: Head of commercial property department at *Edwards Geldard*. Work includes development work, urban regeneration, investment and acquisitions and disposals. Acted for the Cardiff Bay Barrage Scheme and undertook the land assembly and project development for the Millennium Stadium, Cardiff. Is a consultant to Cardiff University Legal Practice Course.
Prof. Memberships: Law Society and Cardiff and District Law Society.
Career: Qualified in 1978. Joined *Edwards Geldard*, becoming a partner 1981.
Personal: Born 27 August 1953. Attended Cardiff High School 1964-71 and Downing College, Cambridge 1972-75. Leisure interests include art, music, literature, cinema, theatre and gardening. Is a founder member of the Academy for Design in Wales and a trustee of Ty Hafen Children's Hospice. Lives in Cardiff.

DAVIES JONES, Martin
Beachcroft Wansbroughs, Bristol (0117) 918 2000
modj@bwlaw.co.uk
Specialisation: Property specialist in property development work.
Career: Assistant solicitor *Herbert Smith* 1966-1968. Partner *Osborne Clarke* 1969-1988. Senior partner *Crawford Owen* 1988-2000. Partner *Beachcroft Wansbroughs* 2000.

DE PURY, Chris
Herbert Smith, London (020) 7466 2095
christopher.de-pury@herbertsmith.com
Specialisation: Varied experience in all principal areas of commercial property law acting for institutions, property companies, developers and occupational tenants. He specialises in large scale infrastructure development projects, joint ventures, and on private finance initiative and corporate outsourcing schemes.
Prof. Memberships: Law Society.
Career: Admitted in 1992. Partnership 1998.
Publications: Author of Property Aspects for Jordans PFI handbook. Written papers and lectured on different aspects of commercial property including joint ventures and corporate outsourcing.
Personal: MA Oxon.

DEWAR, Mark
Harper Macleod, Glasgow (0141) 221 8888
mark.dewar@harpermacleod.co.uk
Specialisation: Commercial leasing, property investment and property development. Acted in purchase, redevelopment and ongoing letting of Princes Square Speciality Shopping Centre, Buchanan Street, Glasgow, development and letting of Stirling Thistle Marches Shopping Centre, Stirling, site acquisition and development of Glasgow Business Park; letting of major office development at 191 West George Street, Glasgow and acquisition and funding of redevelopment for retail purposes of former George Hotel site, Buchanan Street, Glasgow.
Prof. Memberships: Law Society of Scotland accredited Specialist in Commercial Leasing.
Career: Trained at *McGrigor Donald*, Glasgow; Associate *McGrigor Donald* 1989; Partner *Harper Macleod* 1996.
Personal: Born 1959. Educated at Marr College, Troon and University of Glasgow. Married; two children. Interests include golf, football and hillwalking. Lives in Troon.

DILLON, Paula
Addleshaw Booth & Co, Leeds (0113) 209 2000
pmd@addleshaw-booth.co.uk
Specialisation: Specialises in commercial property. Particularly well regarded for development and development finance, acting for developers, lenders, tenants and PFI participants. Recognised as a lawyer who will make deals happen. Skilled negotiator with ability to reconcile potentially conflicting interests.
Prof. Memberships: Law Society
Career: University of Manchester. Qualified 1986. Joined firm as partner in 1999.
Personal: Walking, cycling, skiing.

DOBIE, James
Shepherd & Wedderburn WS, Edinburgh
(0131) 473 5156
james.dobie@shepwedd.co.uk
Specialisation: Property Development and institutional investment with particular emphasis on retail

developments. Acted for Freeport Leisure plc in development of first factory outlet centre in Scotland, and for Pillar Property plc in retail park developments. Acted for New Edinburgh Limited on a number of lettings and onward sales at Edinburgh Park and for the University of Edinburgh in major land sales. Also involved in specialist telecommunication property acquisitions for Orange plc.
Prof. Memberships: Law Society of Scotland. Writer to the Signet.
Career: Educated at Edinburgh University. Joined *Shepherd & Wedderburn WS* 1988 as trainee, became partner in 1995.
Personal: Born 14/08/64. Leisure interests: football, literature, wine and East African culture.

DORAN, Iain
Dundas & Wilson CS, Glasgow (0141) 222 2200

DRUMMOND, Caroline
Burness, Edinburgh (0131) 473 6164
csd@burness.co.uk
Specialisation: Caroline's strength is to see the bigger picture as a result of her expertise in both the fields of property and construction law. Her specialist areas are public sector and development, which frequently overlap. In line with the increasing sophistication of the requirements of property users she has developed experience of complex site assemblies, negotiation of development and funding agreements and all ancilliary documents. Her most recent experience includes advising Lothian University NHS Trust in the sale of Edinburgh Royal Infirmary and advising Grosvenor Developments Limited in the purchase, development, leasing and sale of South Gyle Park, Edinburgh.
Career: Trainee with *W & J Burness* (now *Burness*); qualified 1982; assistant solicitor 1982-87; partner 1987.
Personal: Interests include skiing, climbing, golf, fishing. Member North Berwick Golf Club.

DUNN, Ian
Bond Pearce, Bristol (0117) 929 9197
idunn@bondpearce.com
Specialisation: Formerly with *Cartwrights*, Ian is now a partner in the commercial property group of *Bond Pearce*, handling all aspects of acquisition and disposal of commercial property, particularly block property transactions in the leisure, licensing and transport sector. Specialisation includes conditional acquisition and disposal of development land; estate management work and business lettings; block property auctions; secured lending for institutions, breweries and other commercial lenders.
Career: Qualified in 1981, joined *Cartwrights* in 1988 becoming a partner in 1990. Joined *Bond Pearce* in 2001 on merger.

DUNN, John
Burges Salmon, Bristol (0117) 939 2256
john.dunn@burges-salmon.com
Specialisation: Widely experienced in complex commercial property transactions including portfolio management, development and funding.
Prof. Memberships: Law Society.
Career: Partner with *Cameron Markby* 1987-88. Partner with *Burges Salmon* since 1989.

EDGE, Mike
Halliwell Landau, Manchester (0161) 835 3003
Specialisation: Head of the commercial property department. He advises on all aspects of commercial property, including site assembly and development acquisitions and disposals. He is an expert in environmental law.
Prof. Memberships: United Kingdom Environmental Lawyers' Association.
Career: Qualified 1982; solicitor 1986-89; partner 1989-98 *Slater Heeks*. Made partner at *Halliwell Landau* in 1998.
Personal: Born 1958. Enjoys squash, tennis, skiing, football and theatre.

ELLIOTT, Martin
Linklaters, London (020) 7456 4722
martin.elliott@linklaters.com
Specialisation: Partner and specialist with over 20 years' experience in all aspects of commercial property work with particular emphasis on development, investment and financing work. Transactions involving retail and leisure developments, offices, shops, warehouses and industrial premises, acting for property companies, funds and end-users on sales, purchases, lettings, developments, rent reviews and joint ventures.
Career: 1976 Oxford University BA Law; 1985 to date partner *Linklaters*; 1979-85 assistant solicitor *Linklaters*; 1977-79 articled clerk *Linklaters*.

ETCHELLS, Simon
Semple Fraser, Glasgow (0141) 221 3771
simon.etchells@semplefraser.co.uk
Specialisation: Commercial property partner and finance partner with a special interest in development work and commercial advice to industry. Active in Scotland for *The Miller Group Limited, The Laird Group plc, SMG plc*. Recent projects include acting for the Pacific Quay Developments Ltd Consortium and new Scottish Media Headquarters at Cowcaddens.
Prof. Memberships: The Society of Writers to her Majesty's Signet.
Career: Articled *W & J Burness WS*, qualified 1985; trainee 1985-87; *Bird Semple Fyfe Ireland WS*, 1987-90; *Semple Fraser WS* since 1990, partner since 1992.
Personal: Hermitage Academy; Edinburgh University (1984 LLB Hons; Diploma Legal Practice). Skiing, sailing, books and good wine.

EVANS, Eric
Eversheds, Cardiff (029) 2047 1147
Specialisation: Partner in commercial property department and head of both the planning and PFI units. Specialises in all aspects of property law including complex planning obligations, major town centre regeneration/shopping schemes, site assembly, agreements for the construction of major highways associated with developments, public/private sector joint ventures, planning gain, valuations, urban development/regeneration grants and land reclamation. 30 years public sector experience, dealing with all areas of local government. Extensive experience of PFI and led one of the first PFI/PPP deals in Wales, at University Hospital of Wales NHS Trust. Has since advised on numerous deals including Newport Southern Distributor Road, Chepstow Community Hospital, Wiltshire's grouped schools scheme and 'Waste to Energy' scheme at Neath.
Prof. Memberships: Member of Law Society's Planning Panel.
Career: Qualified in 1980. Town Clerk, Borough of Blaenau Gwent (1981-89). Deputy Chief Executive and Legal Adviser, Land Authority for Wales (1989-92). Partner *Eversheds* 1992.
Personal: Director of Silent Valley Waste Services. Lives in Abertillery.

FABIAN, Mark
Rickerby Watterson, Cheltenham (01242) 246420
mark.fabian@rickerby.co.uk
Specialisation: All aspects of commercial property, with particular emphasis on leasehold office acquisitions and renewals, including property development work. Recent projects include acting on the purchase of a multi-million pound headquarters for UCAS and a freehold site acquisition design and build contract with collateral warranties and an agreement for lease for a new factory and offices for a leading greetings card manufacturer.
Prof. Memberships: Institute of Directors.
Career: 18 years' experience as a commercial property expert. Articled clerk at *Watterson Todman*. Qualified October 1981. Appointed *Rickerby Watterson* managing partner April 1998.
Personal: Law degree from St Edmund Hall, Oxford.

FARIS, Neil
Cleaver Fulton Rankin, Belfast (028) 9024 3141

FIELD, Christopher
Macfarlanes, London (020) 7831 9222
cmf@macfarlanes.com
Specialisation: Specialises in property law with particular emphasis on property development and property financing. Practice includes property investment for domestic and international investors; retail development both in and out of town centres; business park developments; construction projects; development and financing of property in Enterprise Zones; joint ventures. Recent significant work: acting for London Bridge Holdings in the development and letting of Ernst & Young new building at London Bridge, and Dunedin Property in the purchase of a portfolio of shipping centres from Delancey.
Prof. Memberships: City of London Law Society.
Career: Graduated with a law degree from Magdalen College, Oxford in 1974 and joined *Macfarlanes* in 1975. Became a partner in 1981. In 1995 became head of the firm's property department.
Personal: Golf.

FINCH, Robert
Linklaters, London (020) 7456 4722
robert.finch@linklaters.com
Specialisation: Experienced in all aspects of commercial property transactions, including acquisition, development, funding, leasing and disposal of City, Regional and International properties. Also involved in development sector and/or investment property transactions in the USA, Middle East and Europe.
Prof. Memberships: 2000-2001: Master of City of London Solicitors Company; Blundell Memorial Lecturer; 1999-2000: Sheriff of the City of London.
Career: Assistant solicitor *Linklaters* 1969-73. Partner of real estate department 1974 – present.

FITZMAURICE, Anthony
Cobbetts, Manchester (0161) 833 5227
tony.fitzmaurice@cobbetts.co.uk
Specialisation: Specialist in property (commercial, landlord and tenant, development/investment construction (non-contentious).
Career: Articled *Sydney Mitchell & Co* Birmingham; *Bromley Hyde & Robinson*, Ashton-Under-Lyne; qualified 1984.
Personal: Born 1958. Educated at De La Salle Col-

lege; Birmingham University (LLB Hons); Trent Polytechnic. Resides Prestwich. Leisure – children, golf, skiing, tennis.

FLOUNDERS, Andrew
Read Hind Stewart, Leeds (0113) 246 8123
Specialisation: Head of commercial property department. Extensive experience in major out of town industrial retail and leisure schemes including financing and joint venture arrangements. Acts primarily for developers. Emphasis on constructive commercial approach.
Prof. Memberships: Law Society.
Career: Educated – Benton Park Grammar School and Manchester University. Qualified – *Read Hind Stewart* 1983 and partner since 1984.
Personal: Born 1958. Resides Bramhope. Keen sports spectator and plays 5-a-side football. Leisure interests include family, cinema, theatre and Round Table.

FOSTER, John
Eversheds, Leeds (0113) 243 0391
johnfoster@eversheds.com
Specialisation: Head of property development team. Property development of all types to include site assembly, construction, pre-letting, funding and investment sales and participation or profit sharing arrangements. Enterprise Zones work, public and private sector partnerships, grants and PFI.
Prof. Memberships: Law Society.
Career: MA Oxford. Articles with *Macfarlanes.* 1983 joined *Eversheds* becoming a partner in 1985.
Personal: Interests – Munros.

FRAZER, Ivan
McKinty & Wright, Belfast (028) 9024 6751
post@mckinty-wright.co.uk
Specialisation: Commercial property development, acquisitions disposals and lettings on behalf of major retail multiples, joint venture arrangements. Recent work on behalf of developers included a retail park, a sports/leisure centre and a town centre retail, office and other mixed use complex.
Prof. Memberships: Law Society of Northern Ireland, Environmental and Planning Law Association for Northern Ireland.
Career: Graduated Queens University of Belfast in Law (LLB) 1965. Qualified 1968. Partner in *McKinty & Wright* since 1975.

GAIT, Charles
Osborne Clarke, Bristol (0117) 917 3000

GARRETT, Robin
Maclay Murray & Spens, Glasgow (0131) 226 5196
rjg@maclaymurrayspens.co.uk
Specialisation: Head of commercial property department. Main area of practice is development work for developers and occupiers, including site assembly, planning, letting and disposals. Also handles general acquisitions, including freehold purchases and assignations of leases. Has lectured and led groups at various seminars.
Prof. Memberships: Writer to the Signet.
Career: Qualified in 1983. Previously partner with *Steedman Ramage.* Joined *Maclay Murray & Spens* 1997.
Personal: Born 2 April 1959.

GATES, Kathryn
Edwards Geldard, Cardiff (029) 2023 8239
kathryn.gates@geldards.co.uk
Specialisation: Partner in commercial property department. Work includes, broad range of Commercial development and leisure, investment portfolio and residential development land acquisitions on behalf of public and private sectors.
Prof. Memberships: Law Society and Cardiff and District Law Society. Women in Property. Cardiff Business Forum.
Career: Qualified in 1987. Joined *Edwards Geldard* in 1995 and became a partner in 1999.

GEEN, Jonathan
Palser Grossman, Cardiff Bay (029) 2045 2770

GIBBS, Robert
Eversheds, Ipswich (01473) 284428
robertgibbs@eversheds.com
Specialisation: Property development (residential and commercial), investment and portfolio management. Acts for Stock Exchange quoted and non-quoted businesses. Considerable care home sector experience.
Prof. Memberships: Law Society.
Career: Trained in London before moving to East Anglia.
Personal: Upper Second Llb Honours Degree (Leeds). Plays tennis, golf and squash. Married with two children.

GIDNEY, David
Burges Salmon, Bristol (0117) 902 2750
david.gidney@burges-salmon.com
Specialisation: Head of property department unit acting for developers, public sector bodies and landowners. Also specialises in property investment. Recent or current transactions include acting for Orange on new headquarter offices at Paddington Basin; acting for Shearer Property Group and Deutsche Asset Management on retail scheme in Chelmsford; acting for Rugby Estates plc on retail warehouse scheme in Salisbury; acting for Swansea City Council on proposed new national waterfront museum in joint venture with the National Museum and Galleries for Wales.
Prof. Memberships: Member of British Property Federation and Investment Property Forum. On Committee of South West and Wales Chapter of British Council for Offices.
Career: Trained, *Rowe & Maw*; qualified, 1977; made partner at *Burges Salmon,* 1998.
Personal: 1st Class Honours in Literae Humaniores, Oxford. Born 1952. Resides Bristol. Married with four children. Enjoys tennis, theatre.

GILLERY, Bryan
Eversheds, Norwich (01603) 272727
bryangillery@eversheds.com
Specialisation: Residential development acquisitions, volume residential development sales and housing association work.
Prof. Memberships: Law Society, Cambridge Forum for the Construction Industry.
Career: Admitted April 1976. Joined *Eversheds* from local government in 1976. Became a partner in 1979.

GLYNN, Andrew
TLT Solicitors, Bristol (0117) 917 7926
aglynn@tltsolicitors.com
Specialisation: Practising mainly in investment/asset management and secured lending/recoveries. Major transactions of the recent past include disposal of a 600 acre site in Essex for Hanson and acting for Bank and receivers in connection with the sale of a high-profile Televillage development in Wales.
Prof. Memberships: Mining and Minerals Law Group; Non-Administrative Receivers Association.
Career: Qualified with the firm in 1985, then worked in London for more than seven years, principally with City practice *Rowe & Maw.* Returned to the firm in 1992, partner 1994, head of property group 2000.

GNIADKOWSKI, Stan
Denton Wilde Sapte, London (020) 7242 1212

GOODMAN, Stephen
Hammond Suddards Edge, Manchester (0161) 830 5000
stephen.goodman@hammondse.com
Specialisation: Stephen is one of the leading development lawyers in the north west and has and has a comprehensive knowledge of all aspects of development transactions including land assembly, development agreements, funding arrangements, joint ventures and statutory agreements.
Career: Articled *Bennett & Co*; qualified 1985; assistant *Nabarro Nathanson* 1986 – 1989; partner *Gorna & Co*; partner *Halliwell Landau* 1993. Partner *Hammond Suddards Edge* 2001 to present day.
Personal: Born 1961. Resides Cheshire. Keen golfer and Evertonian.

GRABINER, Martin
Nabarro Nathanson, Sheffield (0114) 279 4261
m.grabiner@nabarro.com
Specialisation: All types of commercial property work with emphasis on development and joint venture arrangements involving both the private and public sector. Retail portfolio acquisition and disposal and financing arrangements. Also commercial property and commercial work in relation to infrastructure and transport (in particular waterways and railways).
Prof. Memberships: Director of The Wakefield Metropolitan theatre trust.
Career: 1984-86 First in-house solicitor for the Wickes group of companies, London. 1986-88 partner – *Boodle Hatfield,* London. 1989-98 partner – *Dibb Lupton Broomhead* and *Dibb Lupton Alsop,* Leeds. 1998-date partner *Nabarro Nathanson,* Sheffield.
Personal: Born 1953; Education: St Paul's School, London; Trinity College, Cambridge (MA); resides North Yorkshire. Married to an artist with five children. Leisure: Member of the Leeds Library.

GREEN, Gilbert
Thomson Snell & Passmore, Tunbridge Wells (01892) 701237
fggreen@ts-p.co.uk
Specialisation: The sale and purchase of land for development, particularly negotiation of options, conditional contracts and site assemblies. Works both for leading developers and landowners. Undertakes non-contentious planning work. Major cases in last year include grant of option for major urban green field site to partnership of national developers and acquisition of substantial business site for redevelopment.
Prof. Memberships: Law Society and Agricultural Law Association.
Career: Joined *Thomson Snell & Passmore* as articled

clerk in 1976, qualified 1978 and partner 1980 in commercial property department. Heads development land team and deputy head commercial division.
Personal: Born 30 October 1953. Educated Harrow and Jesus College Cambridge. Married with four children. Interests include field sports, cricket, gardening, cookery and wine. Lives in East Sussex.

GUNN, David
Bond Pearce, Exeter (01392) 211185
dgunn@bondpearce.com
Specialisation: Partner specialising in Commercial Property work dealing with development, investment and funding including joint ventures and major project management. Has a particular interest in waste management, acting for a number of waste disposal companies in connection with site acquisition/disposal and management issues including gas extraction and electricity generation. As a French speaker has worked on property and other commercial transactions involving French companies and organisations.
Prof. Memberships: Member of the Law Society, Association Des Juristes Franco-Britanniques.
Career: Qualified 1982. Joined *Bond Pearce* in 1980, becoming partner in 1987.

HAM, Brian E.
Mills Selig, Belfast (028) 9024 3878
brian.ham@nilaw.com
See under Litigation, p.571

HAMILTON, Keith
Eversheds, Norwich (01603) 272727
keithhamilton@eversheds.com
Specialisation: Landlord and tenant, investment acquisitions and disposals and development work.
Prof. Memberships: Law Society.
Career: Admitted June 1978. Read Jurisprudence at Merton College, Oxford. Spent several years with *Slaughter and May* in London before joining *Eversheds* in 1982. Became a partner in 1985.

HAMILTON, Sophie
Forsters, London (020) 7863 8333
schamilton@forsters.co.uk
Specialisation: Broad-based commercial and institutional property practice including acquisition and funding (clients include Clerical Medical and Goldsmith's Company); acting for occupiers on major relocations; leisure (including Multiplex cinemas for Warner Village); shopping centres (Delancey Estates plc, Shops etc.); private trusts and residential developers.
Career: Educated St Mary's School, Calne; Marlborough College; Clare College, Cambridge. Qualified 1979; partner 1985; head of property department 1991-94 (all at *Frere Cholmeley Bischoff*); founding partner of *Forsters* 1998.
Personal: Married. Lives in London. Enjoys theatre, cinema, reading and cooking.

HANIFORD, Paul
Semple Fraser, Glasgow (0141) 221 3771
paul.haniford@semplefraser.co.uk
Specialisation: Specialist in all aspects of commercial property transactions, including property investment and development, landlord and tenant work and customarily offer advice to a non-Scottish client base.
Prof. Memberships: Society of Writers to HM Signet, Law Society of Scotland. Member: President's committee, Glasgow and Renfrewshire Branch of British Red Cross.
Career: Articled *Fyfe Ireland and Co WS* 1978-1980; legal assistant *Moncrieff Warren Paterson* 1980-81; legal assistant *Bird Semple* 1981-83; partner 1983-90; founding partner *Semple Fraser WS* 1990.
Personal: Born 1955. Educated at Glasgow Academy and Glasgow University (MA-LLB). Interests include skiing, squash, tennis and travel. Lives in Glasgow.

HARRISON, Christopher
Herbert Smith, London (020) 7374 8000
Specialisation: Institutional property investment. The sale of the Ministry of Defence Married Quarters Estate. The redevelopment of the Brent Cross Shopping Centre. The proposed re-development of Kings Cross on behalf of London and Continental Railways. The Ministry of Defence Main Building Redevelopment (PFI). Former member of the Law Society Land Law Committee (led the Law Society's response to the DETR Commercial Lease Best Practice guide).
Career: Harrow School. Articled *Halliley & Morrison.* Joined *Herbert Smith* 1969.
Personal: Cricket, walking (preferably with dog), being with family, Philippa, Oliver and Claudia.

HENDERSON, Brian
L'Estrange & Brett, Belfast (028) 9023 0426
See under Banking, p.119

HENSON, Michaela
Taylor Vinters, Cambridge (01223) 423444
mjh@taylorvinters.com
Specialisation: Commercial acquisitions, sales and lettings. Property development and investments. Corporate support work. Clients include property developers, educational establishments, high-technology businesses and a major airline. Current projects include development of a new Cambridge Technology Park.
Prof. Memberships: Law Society.
Career: Qualified in 1995 with London firm *Baileys Shaw & Gillett.* Joined *Taylor Vinters* in 1997. Specialist diploma in planning and environmental law in 1998. Became a partner in 2001.
Personal: Born 1970. Educated at Hinchingbrooke School, Huntingdon and New Hall College, Cambridge. Interests include sports and horses.

HEPPEL, Meg
Eversheds, Birmingham (0121) 232 1000
megheppel@eversheds.com
Specialisation: Retail investment for clients including Grosvenor Investments and Hammerson and portfolio management for occupiers including Bass, Ryland, Partco Group and Jessops. Lead partner for the Birmingham Alliance's new BullRing and Martineau Galleries Scheme in Birmingham.
Prof. Memberships: Govenor, College of Law.
Career: Joined *Eversheds* in 1979. Partner 1989. Head of property department 1997. Managing Partner Birmingham 2000.

HEWITT, V Alan
L'Estrange & Brett, Belfast (028) 9023 0426
Specialisation: Senior partner and head of commercial property department. Main areas of work: commercial property and trusts.
Prof. Memberships: Law Society of Northern Ireland. (Council Member 1991); chairman, Professional Indemnity Insurance committee 1995-97; chairman, Professional Conduct committee, 1997- 99; chairman, Financial Services committee 1999-2001. Law Reform Advisory committee for Northern Ireland. International Bar Association.
Career: Qualified 1967. Partner in *L'Estrange & Brett* since 1969. Senior partner since 1994.
Personal: Born 1941. Education: Queen's University, Belfast (LLB), University of Michigan (LLM).

HODGE, James (Hamish) S
Dundas & Wilson CS, Edinburgh (0131) 228 8000

HOGGETT, Jonathan
Stephens & Scown, Exeter (01392) 210700

HOLY, Julian
Julian Holy, London (020) 7370 5443

HOWARD, Amanda
Nabarro Nathanson, London (020) 7524 6000

HOWARTH, Mark
Paris Smith & Randall, Southampton (023) 8048 2482
Specialisation: All aspects of commercial property work including portfolio management for large investors; landlord and tenant work; site acquisition and disposal; sales and lease backs; creation and implementation of lease schemes in respect of development sites and subsequent management thereof; Statutory Agreements; development work. Work includes transactions relating to golf course and other leisure related activities. Clients include public authorities, large commercial organisations, friendly societies, retailers, substantial investors (both corporate and private).
Prof. Memberships: Law Society
Career: Joined *Paris Smith & Randall* in 1979, qualifying in 1981. Became a partner in 1985 and has been head of the commercial property department since 1993.
Personal: Attended Southampton University. In his free time enjoys sport, reading and spending time with his family. A governor of Tauntons 6th Form College, Southampton.

HUDDLESTON, Ian
L'Estrange & Brett, Belfast (028) 9023 0426
ian.huddleston@lestrangeandbrett.com
Specialisation: Partner, commercial property department. Practising in all aspects of commercial property but with particular emphasis on property development work and PFI. Retained by a number of major national lenders and the Council of Mortgage Lenders to advise in connection with NI aspects of regularisation and the preparation of standard documentation. Also advises on tax planning and trust issues and acts for a number of charities.
Prof. Memberships: Law Society of Northern Ireland; Society of Trust and Estates Practitioners.
Career: Admitted as a solicitor in Northern Ireland in 1991. Joined *L'Estrange & Brett* in 1991 and became a partner in 1993.
Personal: Born 1965. Educated at Queen's University of Belfast (LLB); University of Bristol (LLM). Former part-time lecturer at Queen's University of Belfast; Course Adviser and Tutor (company law and conveyancing) at the Institute of Professional Legal Studies, Belfast.

HUTTON, Robert
Mills & Reeve, Norwich (01603) 693218
robert.hutton@mills-reeve.com
Specialisation: Commercial property.
Prof. Memberships: Law Society
Career: Articled *Clifford Chance.* Qualified 1977.

Joined *Mills & Reeve* 1981. Partner *Mills & Reeve* 1985.
Personal: Educated St Dunstan's College, London; Magdalen College, Oxford. Married with two children.

INNES, Richard
Walker Morris, Leeds (0113) 283 2500
rhi@walkermorris.co.uk
Specialisation: Retail property with emphasis on acting for anchor tenants and supermarkets.
Career: Qualified 1984. Partner *Walker Morris* since 1987.
Personal: Music and awaiting the day that both children will sleep through the night.

IVIN, Alison
Palser Grossman, Cardiff Bay (029) 2045 2770

JACKSON, Karl
Mace & Jones, Manchester (0161) 236 2244
karl.jackson@maceandjones.co.uk
Specialisation: Broad range of commercial property work with emphasis on commercial property development and in particular urban regeneration projects in Manchester and Liverpool. Established Land Resources Alliance to advise on redevelopment of contaminated land.
Prof. Memberships: Law Society.
Career: Qualified in 1989 with *Vaudrey Osborne & Mellor*. Joined *Mace & Jones* in 1997. Partner since 1998.
Publications: Various published articles, lectured widely.
Personal: Born 1964. Married with one daughter. Lives in Hale, Cheshire. Leisure pursuits: cinema and visual arts, running, sport and theatre. Trustee of Cornerhouse Arts Centre.

JACOMB, Brian
Thring Townsend, Swindon (01793) 412613
bjacomb@thringtownsend.co.uk
Specialisation: Commercial property work including site acquisitions, options and secured lending. Experience in insolvency work.
Prof. Memberships: Solicitors Benevolent Association.
Career: LLB London School of Economics 1970. Law Society finals 1971. Articled at *Coward Chance* and qualified in 1973. Worked in Dubai and the Sharjah offices of *Coward Chance* 1977-82, joining *Townsends* in 1983.
Personal: Honorary Solicitor to St Francis School, Pewsey and chairman of Marlborough Bridge Club.

JAMES, Robert
Morgan Cole, Cardiff (029) 2038 5385
robert.james@morgan-cole.com
Specialisation: Principle area of practice is large scale public and private development work. Advising on joint ventures, disposals for administrative receivers, secured lending, retail and leisure portfiolio work.
Prof. Memberships: One of the first accredited mediators under the Law Society/ RICS PACE scheme for the renewal of business leases. Cardiff Law Society.
Career: Qualified 1978. Joined *Morgan Bruce & Nicholas* becoming partner 1979.
Personal: Born 8 August, 1953. Educated Wrekin College Wellington and Jesus College Oxford. Spare time pursuits include: rugby, cricket and theatre. Morgan Cole liaison partner for the Association of European Lawyers.

JOHNSON, Jennifer
Maclay Murray & Spens, Edinburgh
(0131) 226 5196
jdj@maclaymurrayspens.co.uk
Specialisation: Extensive experience in all aspects of commercial property work. Practice spans a wide range of transactions for occupiers, property companies, developers, institutions and banks including purchase and sale, development, funding and leasing. Has particular experience in cross border property portfolios and the acquisition, letting and sale of shopping centres.
Prof. Memberships: Writer to the Signet and Notary Public.
Career: Edinburgh University. Qualified 1979. Partner in *Maclay Murray & Spens* in 1988.

JONES, Chris
Berry Smith, Cardiff (029) 2034 5511
Specialisation: Full range of commercial property work; investment, commercial and residential development; landlord and tenant and secured lending.
Prof. Memberships: Law Society.
Career: Qualified in 1992. Articled in *Eversheds*, Cardiff. Joined *Berry Smith* in 1994 and became a partner in 1996. Welsh speaker, born 30.12.66. Educated at University College Wales, Aberystwyth and Guildford College of Law.
Personal: Rugby and travel.

JONES, Elizabeth
Hewitson Becke + Shaw, Cambridge
(01223) 461155
elizabethjones@hewitsons.com
Specialisation: Specialises in commercial property law with particular emphasis upon property development including, in particular, pre-let agreements relating to specialised end users. Also specialises in retail property. Recent significant work: acting for Millennium Pharmaceuticals on a major pre-let at Grant Park, Cambridge; acting for i2 Limited at Capital park (the Capital & Countries Business Park); acting for the Medical Research Council on several projects nationwide; also completed the 175th acquisition for the retailer, The Home Entertainment Corporation plc (trading as 'Choices').
Prof. Memberships: Law Society; Cambridge Law Society; Cambridge Business and Professional Club; University Business Club.
Career: After articles with a firm in the City, joined the commercial property department of *Macfarlanes* for a few years; subsequently joined *Hewitson Beck + Shaw* in 1984, becoming a partner in 1988 and is currently Head of Commercial Property in the firm's Cambridge office.
Personal: Leisure interests: reading, travelling.

JONES, Michael
Edwards Geldard, Cardiff (029) 2023 8239
mike.jones@geldards.co.uk
Specialisation: Property development and funding, public/private sector joint ventures and inward investment. Includes £1.8 billion investment by LG at Newport and first Welsh PFI. Currently dealing with Wales Millennium Centre project, the development of Cardiff Gate Business Park and a £24 million spec. funding scheme in Thurrock.
Prof. Memberships: Law Society.
Career: Qualified in 1976 followed by 12 years in local government. Partner at *Edwards Geldard* since 1990.
Personal: Born 1950. Educated Maidenhead Grammar School then Durham University 1969-72. Tennis and music.

JONES, Michael
Pannone & Partners, Manchester (0161) 909 3000
michael.jones@pannone.co.uk
Specialisation: Commercial property, including development, urban regeneration, landlord and tenant. Development agreements relating to refurbishment of Liverpool Collegiate School and its conversion to 90 residential apartments, and the conversion, with grant aid, of Bryant and May former match factory to offices.
Prof. Memberships: Law Society.
Career: Articled to Manchester office of *Eversheds* predecessor *David Blank Alexander* 1968-70. Joined *Pannone & Partners* in 1973 and became partner in 1975. Part-time law lecturer.
Personal: Educated at the Manchester Grammar School and LSE. Married with four children. Leisure interests include golf; Manchester United supporter, Francophile, devotee of Devon.

JONES, Nefydd
Eversheds, Cardiff (029) 2047 1147
nefyddjones@eversheds.com
Specialisation: Deals with all aspects of commercial property investment, development and funding including management and landlord and tenant work. Significant recent experience includes a major office and leisure refurbishment scheme, a retail development involving a joint venture, a shopping centre redevelopment and disposal, a rail-related development transaction and several significant joint ventures involving public bodies.
Prof. Memberships: The Law Society.
Career: Qualified in 1985. *Berwin Leighton* 1988-1995. Partner *Eversheds* 1999.
Personal: Born 1961. Married with two daughters. Reluctant gardener; keen reader; motor racing fan; social golfer.

JONES, Pamela
Bullivant Jones, Liverpool (0151) 227 5671
pj@bullivantjones.co.uk
Specialisation: Senior partner in commercial property department. Deals in all aspects of commercial property especially in development schemes and agreements, retail property for occupiers and as investment and landlord and tenant.
Prof. Memberships: Law Society. Liverpool Law Society.
Career: Qualified in 1977. Joined *Bullivant Jones* in 1973, becoming a partner in 1978 and senior partner in 1994.
Personal: Born 7 January 1951. Attended Holyhead Comprehensive 1962-68. Leisure interests include reading, gardening and walking her dogs. Lives near Tarporley, Cheshire.

KERR, Steven
Fyfe Ireland WS, Edinburgh (0131) 343 2500
skerr@fyfeireland.com
Specialisation: Broad experience of most aspects of commercial property work, particularly in the fields of commercial leasing, site acquisition and development and property related VAT issues. Acted for national retailers (B&Q, Woolworths and Matalan) in letting deals alone exceeding 500,000 square feet in the last year.
Prof. Memberships: Writer to the Signet. Notary Public.

Personal: Born 23 April 1954. Educated Daniel Stewarts College and Edinburgh University. Interests include cricket (playing), golf (striving to beat his son); rugby (spectating) and travel. Married with two active teenagers.

KERSHAW, Peter
Addleshaw Booth & Co, Manchester
(0161) 934 6507
pjk@addleshaw-booth.co.uk
Specialisation: Partner in Commercial Property. Specialising in mainstream commercial property with emphasis on development work.
Prof. Memberships: Law Society.
Career: Qualified 1989. Partner 1996. External Examiner for the Law Society.
Personal: Leisure: Family time and mountain biking.

KIDBY, Robert
Lovells, London (020) 7296 2000
robert.kidby@lovells.com
Specialisation: Property related financing, corporate property outscourcing, PREPs, PFI, secured lending, institutional sales/ purchases/ management, property joint ventures and development projects including shopping centres, offices, airports and hotels. Has lectured extensively on property development and property investment to audiences in England, Europe and Japan.
Prof. Memberships: Policy Committee, British Property Federation, Investment Property Forum, NACORE.
Career: Qualified as a solicitor in 1977 and has specialised in commercial property work ever since. Partner 1985 at *Lovells.* Head of Property since 1995.

KINNIBURGH, Linda
Brodies WS, Edinburgh (0131) 228 3777
linda.kinniburgh@brodies.co.uk
Specialisation: Commercial property department partner. Involved in property investment and banking work, and has particular experience in cross-border corporate finance deals. She also deals with property aspects of insolvency and coal and mineral exploitation law and has recently acted in the large-scale disposals of public sector housing.
Career: Educated at Trinity Academy, Edinburgh and the University of Edinburgh. She qualified as a solicitor in 1982 and has been a partner in *Brodies* since 1985.
Personal: She is married with two young children and spends as much spare time as she has going to the theatre and the opera. She would like to find more time to pursue her interest in micro-liting.

KNOX, James
Linklaters, London (020) 7456 2000
James.Knox@linklaters.com
Specialisation: Experienced in all aspects of commercial property transactions, including sales and purchases of high value investment properties, property development (and funding), property financing, PFI, private real estate partnerships and joint ventures (including joint equity sharing leases, co-ownership trusts and partnership partnership agreements). Transactions of significance where substantial involvement can be disclosed have included; acting for LIFFE on the acquisition and subsequent disposal of part of Spitalfields, E1; acting for Deutsche Bank on the development of its headquarters (300,000 sq ft) in the City of London, including setting up the investment structure through equity sharing leases; acting for DIFA on the purchase and development funding of Thames Court, London, EC4 and subsequent letting to JP Morgan and Rabo Bank; acting for Deutsche Bank, acquiring space at 99 Bishopsgate; acting for Lend Lease on its limited partnership (Retail Partnership) in respect of Bluewater and Touchwood Court, Solihull; acting for the Prudential Global Fund on its disposal of 155 Bishopsgate to British Land; acting for DIFA on the purchase and leaseback to Reader's Digest of 11 Westferry Circus, Canary Wharf; acting for DAKS Simpson on the letting of its former Piccadilly store to Waterstones and the subsequent sale of its interest to Scottish Widows; acting for the CIT Group on the acquisition and financing of Wolsey Place, Woking; acting for the BBC on its real estate outsourcing; acting for Mapeley in respect of its acquisition and financing of the Abbey National property portfolio; acting for Mapeley in respect of its bid for the BT property portfolio.
Career: 1999 to date; Partner, *Linklaters*; 1987-1999: Assistant solicitor, *Linklaters.* Bristol University, LLB (Hons).

KORDAN, Joel
Lee Crowder, Birmingham (0121) 236 4477
joel.kordan@leecrowder.co.uk
Specialisation: All areas of commercial property development including lettings, sales, funding and joint venture agreements, with particular emphasis on large-scale industrial distribution/warehouse/factory schemes. Also, large residential property development practice. Clients include developers, contractors and end users, including many multinational companies.
Career: Articled *Wragge & Co.* Qualified 1990. Joined *Lee Crowder* as a partner in 1997.
Personal: Born 1961, USA. Attended King Edward VI Five Ways Grammar School, Birmingham and LSE (BSc (Econ)).

KUSTOW, David
Olswang, London (020) 7208 8888
dhk@olswang.com
Specialisation: All aspects of commercial property law – investment, development retail centre and funding transactions. Acts for a variety of quoted and unquoted property companies, including large private investment vehicles and property based funds. Also serves the property requirements of various companies in the advertising and media sectors, particularly those involved in film, satellite and cable. Notable transactions recently undertaken include a single investment property disposal for a consideration of £105 million, the property aspects of a re-organisation of assets with values exceeding £200 million, the property aspects of a flotation and the acquisition of a number of investment/ development properties for a single client, over a 12 month period, for an aggregate consideration exceeding £150 million.
Prof. Memberships: A Governor of the British Film Institute and chair of their Property Committee; a member of the International Real Estate Federation (FIABCI).
Career: Admitted 1973; 1970-91 – *Brecher & Co* (partner since 1975); 1991-present – *Olswang* (partner property group).
Personal: Married with two children. Principal leisure interests include reading (particularly modern history), travel, film and food.

LAKE, Tim
Stepien Lake Gilbert & Paling, London
(020) 7655 0000
tim@slgp.co.uk
Specialisation: Partner. Large-scale development work (commercial and residential) including joint venture and consortia arrangements with all attendant property finance issues. Acts for listed and unlisted developers and equity investors.
Career: Qualified December 1980. Set up own practice in 1985 and subsequently merged his practice with *Birkbeck Montagu's.* A founding partner of *Stepien Lake Gilbert & Paling* in 1991.
Personal: Born December 1955. Educated Radley and Exeter University. Interests include shooting, tennis, golf and skiing. Lives in Oxfordshire.

LE PARD, Geoffrey
Freshfields Bruckhaus Deringer, London
020 7936 4000
geoffrey.lepard@freshfields.com
Specialisation: Handles all aspects of commercial property including landlord and tenant, investment, development, planning and finance.
Career: Qualified in 1981. Joined *Freshfields* in 1981, becoming a partner in 1987. Head of property department from 1993 to 2000.
Personal: Born 30th November 1956. Attended Purley Grammar School 1968-70, Brockenhurst Grammar School 1970-75, Bristol University 1975-78 and Guildford College of Law 1978-79. Lives In Dulwich.

LEITCH, David
Johns Elliot, Belfast (028) 9032 6881

LEONARD, Tessa
Eversheds, Manchester (0161) 831 8000

LOWLESS, Peter
Michelmores, Exeter (01392) 436244

LUST, Graham
Nabarro Nathanson, London 020 7524 6200
g.lust@nabarro.com
Specialisation: Property finance specialist. Extensive experience in commercial property investment and development transactions for major property institutions, public property companies and public sector organisations including central government departments. Currently instructed on substantial office developments in Central London. Has developed innovative forms of property financing documentation for inward investors including tax based property financings for multinational clients.
Prof. Memberships: Law Society.
Career: Qualified in New Zealand in 1974, and in England in 1979. Became a commercial property partner in 1980. Member of property finance group.
Personal: Born 1950.

MACGREGOR, Robert
Clifford Chance, London (020) 7600 1000
robert.macgregor@cliffordchance.com
Specialisation: Partner specialising in real estate development, joint ventures, financing and leasing of office.
Prof. Memberships: BCO, Anglo American Real Property Institute.
Career: Berkhamsted School; Nottingham University (Hons). Articled *Titmuss Sainer & Webb*; qualified 1985; partner *Clifford Chance* since 1992.
Personal: Sailing and classic cars. Born 1960; resides London.

MACNIVEN, Iain
Maclay Murray & Spens, Glasgow
(0141) 248 5011
igm@maclaymurrayspens.co.uk
Specialisation: Commercial property partner with extensive experience of all aspects of commercial property work, including investment deals, development work and leasing. Clients include Scottish Amicable Life Assurance Society, ASDA plc and British Waterways Board. Particular areas of interest include joint venture development work, and specialist rent review advice as well as the education sector. Member of the Investment Property Forum and the British Council of Shopping Centres.
Career: Glasgow University (MA 1975, LLB 1977). Been with *Maclay Murray & Spens* throughout his professional career. Past examiner for the Law Society of Scotland.
Personal: Born 1953. Resides Glasgow and West Highlands. Leisure interests include travel, food and drink and crosswords.

MAHOOD, Laurence
Elliott Duffy Garrett, Belfast (028) 9024 5034
laurence.mahood@edgsolicitors.co.uk
Specialisation: Commercial property development, letting and investment, acquisitions and disposals. Current projects include major retail, office and leisure developments and has recently acted in a number of high value investment acquisitions and disposals.
Prof. Memberships: Law Society of N Ireland. Representative on joint Law Society/RICS Forum.
Career: LLB Queen's University, Belfast 1976. Admitted solicitor 1978. Law Society Silver Medal awarded. Partner since 1982.
Personal: Contributing author to Butterworth's 'Property in Europe – Law and Practice'.

MARKS, Geoffrey
Halliwell Landau, Manchester (0161) 835 3003
Specialisation: Deals with full range of property work including development and investment work and all property aspects of property secured lending.
Prof. Memberships: Member of the Royal Chartered Institute of Arbitrators.
Career: Articled *AH Howarth & Co*; qualified 1963; partner *AH Howarth & Co* (now *Howarth Goodman & Co*) 1965-74; partner *Maurice Rubin & Co* 1974-84; partner *Halliwell Landau* 1984.
Personal: Born 1941; resides Prestwich. Educated at Arnold School, Blackpool. Recreations include theatre and opera.

McCLEA, Nigel
Pinsent Curtis Biddle, Leeds 0113 294 5282
nigel.mclea@pinsents.com
Specialisation: National Head of Property. Specialises in large scale commercial property projects, in public and private sectors (with particular focus on leisure, education and health). Major projects: Royal Armouries Museum, Leeds; Relocation of Sunderland Football Club; Redevelopment of Odsal Stadium, Bradford; Disposal of Epsom cluster of redundant hospital sites for Secretary of State; New residential settlement at Lichfield.
Prof. Memberships: Fellow of the Royal Society of Arts, Manufactures and Commerce. Friend of Historic Houses Association.
Career: Qualified 1975. Partner in *Simpson Curtis* (now *Pinsent Curtis Biddle*) 1978.
Personal: Born 1951. Educated at Ashville College, Harrogate and Queen's College, Cambridge.

McLEAN, Neil
DLA, Leeds (08700) 111111

McNULTY, Stephen
Burges Salmon, Bristol (0117) 939 2250
stephen.mcnulty@burges-salmon.com
Specialisation: Commercial property development and social housing. He has a wide experience of commercial property issues arising when working with large corporate clients, especially in the telecommunications and transport sector. He is also head of the highly-regarded social housing unit which advises on all aspects of Registered Social Landlords' legal requirements from regulation and group structures to development management and funding issues. Recent projects include redevelopment of bus depot facilities and major office and data centre acquisitions in Birmingham and Bristol on behalf of a blue chip telecommunications client.
Prof. Memberships: Law Society, British Italian Law Association.
Career: Joined *Burges Salmon* in 1984 becoming a partner in 1988.

MEDVEI, Cornelius
Eversheds, London (0207) 919 4500
corneliusmedvei@eversheds.com
Specialisation: Eversheds head of property practice group. Property finance, property development.
Prof. Memberships: Law Society; British Property Federation; City Property Association.
Career: Admitted 1978; assistant *Markbys/Cameron Markby* (now *Cameron McKenna*); *Mills & Reeve*; partner *Eversheds* 1988 to date.

MEREDITH, Alan
Eversheds, Cardiff (029) 2047 1147
alanmeredith@eversheds.com
Specialisation: Senior partner. Head of commercial property department. Work includes property joint ventures between private and public sector and general commercial conveyancing. Also handles urban regeneration in the public sector, acting for both public and private sector bodies. Has given seminars on contaminated land for the Chartered Surveyors Study Group.
Prof. Memberships: Law Society, Country Landowners Association.
Career: Qualified in 1976. Joined *Phillips & Buck* (now *Eversheds*) as a partner in 1982. Currently head of commercial property department.
Publications: Has co-authored with his environmental partner, Martin Warren, a book entitled 'Contaminated Land – Managing Liabilities'.
Personal: Born 8th January 1952. Attended University of Wales, Aberystwyth. Member of Management Committee of Swansea Cricket and Football Club. Trustee of Dragons Rugby Trust. Leisure interests include golf, rugby and reading. Lives in Cowbridge near Cardiff.

MITCHELL, James
Stevens & Bolton, Guildford (01483) 302264
james.mitchell@stevens-bolton.co.uk
Specialisation: Commercial property; specialises in the development and funding of major property projects on behalf of banks, institutions and developers.
Prof. Memberships: Law Society; Fellow of the Royal Statistical Society and Associate of the Royal College of Science.
Career: Trained *Slaughter and May*, qualified 1980. Assistant solicitor *Slaughter and May* 1980-85. Partner *Barlow Lyde and Gilbert* 1987-95. Joined *Stevens and Bolton* as a partner in 1995.
Personal: Leisure interests include chess, mathematical games and puzzles, satellite and computer technology, football and horse racing. Family; five children aged three months to 15 years.

MOFFAT, Douglas
Tods Murray WS, Glasgow (0141) 275 4771
douglas.moffat@todsmurray.co.uk
Specialisation: Commercial property. Purchase of multi-let George House, Glasgow for Greenwich Group (14.55 million); acting for Baillie Gifford & Co in their taking lease of 105,000 sq ft of offices at Calton Square, Glasgow; acting for Nomura in acquisition of 110 Scottish pubs from Bass; sale of Atlantic Quay, Glasgow (£67.5 million on behalf of Commerz Grunbesitz-Investmentgesellschaft); purchase of Centre Point Retail Park, Aberdeen (£14.6 million on behalf of Railway Pension Nominees).
Prof. Memberships: Law Society, WS Society, British Council of Shopping Centres (Scottish Secretary), British Council of Offices, Investment Property Forum.
Career: Edinburgh University – LLB, apprenticeship and then assistant – *Shepherd & Wedderburn WS* 1968-73, *Tods Murray WS* 1993-date (partner 1974, head of property 1980-98).
Personal: Golf, hill walking, cricket (SCU committee), squash. One daughter and one son.

MOODY, John
Eversheds, Manchester (0161) 831 8000
johnmoody@eversheds.com
Specialisation: Partner in commercial property department. Work covers all aspects of commercial property with a particular emphasis on investment and management work. Involved in several high profile residential and commercial developments and advises several FTSE 100 companies on their strategic property requirements. Contributes articles to professional journals and local press.
Prof. Memberships: Law Society.
Career: Articled 1973-75 at *Ingham Clegg & Crowther* in Preston and became a partner in 1980. Joined *Yates Barnes* in 1989, then moved to *Eversheds Alexander Tatham* in 1990. Became head of commercial property department in 1990 and Managing Partner in 1993. Following the merger of *Eversheds* offices in Leeds and Manchester became Deputy Managing Partner of these offices.
Personal: Born 19th February 1950. Attended Nottingham High School 1961-69, then Jesus College, Cambridge 1969-72. Leisure pursuits include golf (Cambridge Blue 1970-71 and 71-72 and County Golfer), theatre, overseas travel, mowing the lawn and terrorising the cat. Lives in Bowdon, Cheshire.

MORGAN, Claire
Eversheds, Newcastle upon Tyne (0191) 261 1661
Specialisation: Partner in commercial property department. All aspects of urban regeneration and development including site assembly, infrastructure agreements, joint ventures, public/private sector partnerships/PFI, particularly in the health sector, public sector grant funding agreements, portfolio acquisitions and disposals. Recent projects include property joint ventures for a town centre redevelopment scheme and for the development of business parks and acting for the seller in the sale by auction of a

portfolio of nine let industrial estates.
Prof. Memberships: Law Society; Newcastle upon Tyne Law Society.
Career: University of Nottingham; qualified 1975. Partner 1979 onwards.
Personal: Married, three children, lives in Newcastle. Interests include walking, reading, built environment.

MORGAN, Rosemary
Morgan Cole, Swansea (01792) 634634
rosemary.morgan@morgan-cole.com
Specialisation: Public/private sector joint venture property development in the leisure, retail & commercial sectors. Gaming and liquor licensing. Major matters are: The Waterfront Destination, Swansea; two objective 1 priority 6 strategic park developments; re-development of a 400 acre redundant terminal.
Prof. Memberships: The Law Society. Non-executive director of the Swansea NHS Trust; council member of the Council of Wales (Swansea); member of the Court of Governors of the University of Wales (Swansea).
Career: LLB, Birmingham University, Birmingham. Solicitor with *Douglas Jones & Mercer*. Partner with *Morgan Cole.*
Personal: Travelling, wildlife conservation (especially endangered species), and vintage cars.

MORPETH, Iain
Clifford Chance, London (020) 7600 1000
iain.morpeth@cliffordchance.com
Specialisation: Partner specialising in real estate transactions – both domestic and international. Transaction types include real estate funds, joint ventures and private equity; structured finance; project development; single asset and portfolio acquisitions; leasing projects; real estate and FM backed PFI and corporate outsourcing. Clients include investment banks, such as Nomura PFG, Lehman, CSFB, Schroders and Citibank; international investors such as Lend Lease, Witkoff Group, Europa Fund, Curzon Global Partners and Dallah Albaraka Group; and domestic developers and investors such as Thornfield Properties, Minerva, USS and HSBC Pension Trust. Recent transactions include the Shell Mex House transaction for Witkoff Group, Project STEPS for Nomura; the Thornfield/National Car Parks multi site joint venture; the Telecom Italia deal; Minerva's 90 High Holborn development; a variety of investment acquisition, development and joint venture projects.
Prof. Memberships: Law Society; City of London Solicitors Company; Investment Property Forum; British Property Federation.
Career: Partner *Clifford Chance* 1988.
Publications: Contributing author: 'Joint Ventures in Property; Structures and Precedents' published by Sweet and Maxwell; contributor of various articles; regular speaker at real estate conferences.
Personal: Born: December 1953. Educated: Fettes College, Edinburgh; Bristol University, LLB (Hons). Admitted solicitor 1978.

MORRIS, Christopher
Freshfields Bruckhaus Deringer, London (0200 7936 4000
chris.morris@freshfields.com
Specialisation: Commercial property, development, property finance and insolvency law.
Career: Qualified in 1984 and became a partner in 1991. Head of real estate department since May 2000.
Personal: Born 1960. Eastbourne Grammar School 1973-1978. Lincoln College Oxford 1978 to 1981. Lives in Bromley. Interests include family, sport, music and Italy.

MOST, Lionel
Burness, Glasgow (0141) 248 4933
ldm@burness.co.uk
Specialisation: Main area of practice is commercial leasing, and all aspects of property and development work where the main issue is leasing. Law Society of Scotland Accredited Specialist in Commercial Leasing. Occasional Arbiter and Expert Witness in commercial leasing disputes. Part time lecturer in conveyancing for LLB degree and for commercial leasing in LLM in Commercial Law, both at the University of Glasgow. Periodic lecturer for CPD seminars.
Prof. Memberships: Law Society of Scotland (Member of Conveyancing Committee).
Career: Joined *Alexander Stone & Co* in 1977 as apprentice, qualified in 1979, becoming a partner in 1983. Merged with *Burness* and became partner with the firm in 1998.

NEIL, Don
Coffin Mew & Clover, Southampton (023) 8033 4661
cmc@southampton.coffinmew.co.uk
Specialisation: Has headed the firm's commercial property practice in Southampton for many years and has an invaluable knowledge of the local market. Has very wide experience in acting for developers, investors and lessees in all aspects of commercial property work, with a particular expertise in the field of residential development sites.
Prof. Memberships: Member of the Notaries Society.
Career: (LLB) Bristol University, admitted 1966. Joined *Coffin Mew & Clover* in 1971 and became a partner in 1974.
Personal: Married with 3 children. Interests include fishing, skiing and sport.

NEWCOMBE, Mark
Hammond Suddards Edge, Birmingham (0121) 200 2001
mark.newcombe@hammondse.com
Specialisation: Partner in the firm's commercial property department, Mark specialises in the acquisition of all types of greenfield sites, letting of new build offices, retail schemes, warehouses and factories as well as investment sales and forward funding, limited partnerships and effective tax structures for property transactions.
Prof. Memberships: Law Society and British Urban Regeneration Association (BURA). Chairman of the East Midlands Property Forum, co-sponsored by East Midlands Development Agency which is now in its ninth year.
Career: Partner at *Hammond Suddards Edge* since 1989.
Personal: Born 1957, graduate of Manchester University LLB (Hons) and College of Law, Chester. Interests include skiing and motorcycling. Lives in Leicestershire.

NEWSTEAD, Jackie
Lovells, London (020) 7296 2000
jackie.newstead@lovells.com
Specialisation: All aspects of commercial property, particularly development, investment and financing. Last year acted for Prudential on its pre-let of 600,000 sq ft at GreenPark Reading to Cisco Systems (plus options for further 600,000 sq ft). Also acted for Land Securities Trillium on its bid for the London Underground LUPP.
Prof. Memberships: Law Society. British Property Federation. British Council of Shopping Centres.
Career: Trained *Durrant Piesse*; qualified 1986; partner *Lovells* 1997.
Personal: Educated Harrogate Ladies College and St Hugh's College, Oxford. (CBA in jurisprudence 1983); College of Law Lancaster Gate 1984. Leisure interests include opera, archaeology, old buildings, contemporary literature. Married, no children.

NEWTON, Alison
McGrigor Donald, Glasgow (0141) 248 6677
www.mcgrigors.com
Specialisation: Partner, Glasgow office. Recent transactions have included: the development, construction and management contract for a new Glasgow city centre hotel; acquisition work for Tom Cobleigh plc and Yates Brothers plc; the development and lease for a major new call centre at Cardonald for Thomson Holidays; the accquisition strategy, co-ordination and lettings of the £20m redevelopment of St Enoch Centre, Glasgow for Deka; the creation and sale of SPV's for Dawn Developments to provide a new HQfacility for Fullarton Computer Industries in Irvine, and new hotel and student residences at Ballater Street, Glasgow.
Prof. Memberships: Law Society of Scotland. Member of Committee of Scottish Branch of British Council of Shopping Centres and Member The Lighthouse Trust, Glasgow.
Career: 1980-84 Dundee University (LLB, DIP.LP); 1984-86 Trainee, 1986-90 Assistant; 1990-94 Associate; 1994-99 partner; January 1999 to July 2000 Managing Partner, Glasgow office; June 2000 to June 2001 partner in Edinburgh office, charged with development of *McGrigor Donald's* new premises; July 2001 to date partner based in Glasgow office.
Personal: Riding, skiing, cooking and now running.

NISSE, Ian
Ashurst Morris Crisp, London (020) 7638 1111
Specialisation: Commercial property matters with an emphasis on development projects, investment transactions and joint ventures. Clients for whom he is the lead partner include British Telecom, Chelsfield, Church Commissioners for England, Hemingway Pearson and Stanhope.
Career: Became a partner at *Ashursts* in 1987.

ODY, Jonathan
Norton Rose, London (020) 7283 6000
odyjw@nortonrose.com
Specialisation: Partner in the property planning and environmental department. Has extensive experience of property development and investment work and related banking and finance documentation. Also has long involvement with central and local government financing (including PFI and PPP) transactions, tax-based leasing work, and inward investment structures for non-residents.
Prof. Memberships: Anglo American Real Property Institute, British Council for Offices, City of London Law Society, City Architecture Forum.
Career: Articled *Romney Fraser & Ody*, (Malvern, Worcestershire); qualified 1965; assistant solicitor 1964-1967; partner 1967-1968 *Pattinson & Brewer*; assistant solicitor *Freshfields*, 1969-1972; partner.

OLMER, Philip
Olswang, London (020) 7208 8888
pho@olswang.com
Specialisation: Philip is a partner specialising in all areas of office, industrial, retail and leisure property investment and development transactions, including joint ventures and offshore structures for overseas investors; significant transactions have included: acting for a major institutional fund on the joint venture structuring and development of serviced office schemes in London, Middlesex and the West Country; acting for a major housebuilder on the redevelopment of a former utility company headquarters building in North London and a brownfield site in London Docklands as two major residential schemes comprising over 500 units; the acquisition of the former Gucci building in London's Old Bond Street and its redevelopment and letting to DKNY; acting for a major health club operator on the development and pre-leasing of numerous 40,000 sq ft health clubs all over the country; the purchase and leaseback of a new Holiday Inn hotel in the Midlands.
Prof. Memberships: FIABCI, British Israel Chamber of Commerce.
Career: Trained *Campbell Hooper*, qualified 1985; assistant solicitor property, *Forsyte Kerman* 1985-87; assistant solicitor, property department, *Berwin Leighton* 1987-91; equity partner 1991-99; partner *Olswang* 1999.
Personal: Education: Christ's College Grammar School, London; City of London Polytechnic (1982 BA Hons Business Law); College of Law, Guildford (1983 Finals). Born 1960; resides London.

O'MEARA, Anne
Hammond Suddards Edge, Birmingham (0121) 222 3000
anne.o'meara@hammondse.com
Specialisation: Partner in the firm's commercial property department, Anne specialises in property development, property-related regeneration work and in particular acting as a legal project manager for regeneration projects including public/private sector. Over the past five years Anne has acted as a project manager in relation to both the £113 million Millennium Point project in Birmingham and the National Space Science Centre in Leicester. Both of these millennium projects will be opening this year and will reflect a culmination of complex legal agreements and arrangements. Anne acts for Advantage West Midlands, in connection with major regeneration projects, including the regeneration of the former Dunlop area including the Fort Dunlop Building. This year she has acted for Birmingham City Council and Optima Community Association in respect of the regeneration of a large former local authority housing area in central Birmingham.
Prof. Memberships: Birmingham Law Society; Law Society; British Urban Regeneration Association (BURA).
Career: Graduate of Birmingham University LLB (Hons) and College of Law, Chester. Joined *Edge Ellison* in 1978, qualified in 1980 and became a partner in 1984.
Personal: Chairman, CBSO Development Trust and member of the Board of City of Birmingham Symphony Orchestra. Non-executive director, Birmingham Health Authority. A member of Birmingham City Council's 'locate in Birmingham' advisory board.

PATERSON, Ian J C
Dundas & Wilson CS, Edinburgh (0131) 228 8000

PATTERSON, Anthony
Forsters, London (020) 7863 8333
ajpatterson@forsters.co.uk
Specialisation: Broadly-based commercial practice with particular emphasis on investment and development work. Clients include Guardian Properties, Benchmark Group plc, Salmon Harvester Developments, Citygrove Leisure etc.
Prof. Memberships: Investment Property Forum; 100 Property Club; Lansdowne Club, Law Society.
Career: Articled *Frere Cholmeley Bischoff* 1973; qualified 1975; partner 1980; head of property department 1994-98 (all at *Frere Cholmeley Bischoff*); various management committees; founding partner of *Forsters* 1998.
Personal: Divorced with three children. Educated St Joseph's College, Blackpool; University College London. Lives in Shepherds Market.

PATTISON, Mark
Beachcroft Wansbroughs, Manchester (0161) 934 3000
mpattison@bwlaw.co.uk
Specialisation: Property development, strategic and tactical advice, landlord and tenant new letting and management, investment acquisitions and disposals cases. Deals include an agreement for the construction and lease of office buildings for Inland Revenue; the redevelopment, extension and letting of a shopping centre; the development of a new urban village at Warrington.
Career: Articled *Vaudreys*; qualified 1982. Remained at *Vaudreys* until it merged with *Beachcroft Wansbroughs*. Directorships: Disley Properties Limited; Winters Nominees.
Personal: Born 1958, educated at Stockport Grammar School, Manchester University and College of Law Chester. Married with two daughters. Leisure interests include clay pigeon shooting, swimming, running, walking and fishing.

PAUL, Sarah
Harold Benjamin Littlejohn, Harrow (020) 8422 5678
sarah.paul@hben.co.uk
Specialisation: Commercial landlord and tenant property development acting for landlords, developers and tenants; business leases and renewals especially in the office and retail sectors; acquisition, disposal and management of commercial investment property.
Prof. Memberships: Law Society.
Career: Articled *Lovell White & King* (now *Lovells*); partner *Harold Benjamin Littlejohn* since 1992; head of commercial landlord and tenant department.
Personal: Born 1954; North London Collegiate School; St Hilda's College, Oxford; lives in North London.

PICKUP, Bryan
SJ Berwin, London (020) 7533 2468
bryan.pickup@sjberwin.com
See under Travel, p.828

PIKE, John
Addleshaw Booth & Co, Leeds (0113) 209 2000
jdp@@addleshaw-booth.co.uk
Specialisation: Main area of practice is commercial property work, in particular development, banking, investment and private sectors. A particular specialism is land pollution and he frequently advises on land contamination and remediation, waste and lender risk.
Career: Qualified 1972. Partner 1976.
Personal: Jesus College Cambridge (MA: Hons). De Montfort University (MA: Environmental Law). Chairman of Governors Moorlands School, Leeds and Governor of St Peters School, York. Director of Urban Mines Limited and heavily involved in the Brownfields project as a member of the Advisory Group. Interests include sports and family.

PLANT, Patrick
Linklaters, London (020) 7456 4718
patrick.plant@linklaters.com
Specialisation: Partner specialising in commercial property, hotel and leisure. Advises investors, developers, lenders and tenants on all aspects of commercial property in the UK and has particular expertise in joint ventures, management and franchise agreements for hotel and leisure projects.
Career: Educated at St. Joseph's College, Blackpool and Manchester University. Articled *Wilsons*, Salisbury, qualified 1986, with *Linklaters* since qualification (save for 1989-90 when with *Mallesons Stephen Jaques*, Sydney Australia). Partner *Linklaters* since 1994.

PRITCHARD, Nicholas
TLT Solicitors, Bristol (0117) 917 7947
npritchard@tltsolicitors.com
Specialisation: Has specialised in commercial property since 1972. Undertakes a wide range of commercial conveyancing transactions with particular emphasis on leisure and office development both town centre and out of town as well as in town residential developments. Widespread experience of site assembly, acquisition development funding and disposals. Now concentrates on 'problem' properties which are suited to his entrepreneurial approach.
Career: Qualified 1970, moved to Bristol and *Trumps (now TLT Solicitors*, the merged firm of *Trumps* and *Lawrence Tucketts*) in 1972, became partner in 1974.
Personal: Tennis, golf, sailing and generally enjoying life.

PRYCE, Jonathan
Robertsons, Cardiff (029) 20237777

PUGH, Nigel
Bond Pearce, Southampton (023) 8063 2211
npugh@bondpearce.com
Specialisation: Consultant in the Commercial Property Group, dealing with all types of commercial property transactions. Specialises in institutional funding, commercial leases, site acquisition, retail development in town, out of town and edge of town, multiple town centre purchases, construction work, joint ventures, landlord and tenant, statutory agreements, retail parks, student accommodation schemes. Clients include public quoted companies, banks, receivers, a large number of southern based (including London) developers and further education colleges.
Prof. Memberships: Member of the Southampton University Court, Society of Notaries Public, and Solicitors European Group.
Career: Qualified in 1970 and articled in the City. Joined *Hepherd Winstanley & Pugh* in 1973 as a Partner and *Bond Pearce* in 1998 on merger.

QUICKE, Martin
Denton Wilde Sapte, London (020) 7242 1212

QUIGLEY, Ian
Maclay Murray & Spens, Edinburgh (0131) 226 5196 isq@maclaymurrayspens.co.uk
Specialisation: Partner dealing in all aspects of commercial property work, including development and leasing pre-funding, development finance and regeneration projects.
Prof. Memberships: Writer to the Signet and Notary Public.
Career: Glasgow University, LLB (Hons) 1969.
Personal: Born 1946.

QUINLAN, Andrew
Pinsent Curtis Biddle, Leeds (0113) 294 5280 andrew.quinlan@pinsents.com
Specialisation: Property development (options and joint ventures) and property investment.
Prof. Memberships: Investment Property Forum.
Career: *Titmuss Sainer & Webb* 1984-88; *Pinsent Curtis Biddle* 1988 to date.
Personal: Hull University (LLB Hons). Married with two children. Interests include family, wine, food and travel.

REEVEY, Michael
Addleshaw Booth & Co, Leeds (0113) 209 2000 mar@addleshaw-booth.co.uk
Specialisation: Partner in Commercial Property Group. Substantial development projects; the financing of property assets and representing both landlords and tenants of retail property.
Career: Oxford University 1976-1979; joined the firm in 1980; admitted as a solicitor 1982 and made a partner in 1988.

REID, David
Burness, Edinburgh (0131) 473 6000 drr@burness.co.uk
Specialisation: Deals primarily with large commercial and institutional clients, advising on property developments, high street retailing and commercial leases. He is involved very heavily with major joint ventures and pre-funded developments. Also frequently consulted for opinions on property disputes. Major clients include Grosvenor Developments Ltd, Sun Life Assurance Society plc, St Andrews University and Johnson Group Cleaners plc. Spent some time as a conveyancing tutor at Edinburgh University.

REID, Sandy
Steedman Ramage, Edinburgh (0131) 260 6600 alexander.reid@steedmanramage.co.uk
Specialisation: Development, letting, purchase/sale, investment and joint ventures. Experience includes acquisition, development and letting of major shopping centres; mixed use developments both in and out of town; large portfolio transactions. Accredited as a planning specialist by the Law Society of Scotland. Recent transactions include acting for: Marks and Spencer in the £186 million sale of Gyle Shopping Centre, Edinburgh; J Sainsbury Developments in the acquisition, development, letting and sale of a major mixed use development at St Andrew Square, Edinburgh; Helical Retail in acquisition, pre-letting and funding of development of George/Commercial Hotels complex in Glasgow; advising EDI Group on planning for proposed Princes Street Galleries development, Edinburgh.
Prof. Memberships: Law Society of Scotland; Society of Writers to HM Signet; International Bar Association (Scottish Representative committee).
Career: Educated Robert Gordon's College, Aberdeen 1966-1972; Aberdeen University 1972-1975. Joined *Steedman Ramage* 1975, qualified 1977; partner 1980; chairman 1993.
Personal: Born 15 September 1954. Married, two sons. Leisure activities include music and sport.

REILLY, Alan
Carson McDowell, Belfast (028) 9024 4951 alan.reilly@carson-mcdowell.com
Specialisation: Acquisition and disposal of commercial property and all types of interests therein. Development of commercial property. Traditional specialisation in retail property originally for tenants latterly more particularly for landlords including from site acquisition through development to initial letting and ultimately disposal. More recently diversification into commercial property services in higher education, leisure, culture and arts sectors. This year Titanic Quarter Agreement for development of 100 acre waterfront site in central Belfast acting for the Belfast Harbour Commissioners. Acting for the landlord in extension of Abbey Centre Shopping Centre, Newtownabbey. Acting for the landlord in assembling site for extension of Flagship Shopping Centre, Bangor. Acting for Tesco Stores Limited in disposal of off-licence chain of stores.
Career: M.A. (CANTAB). Whole career with *Carson & McDowell* (qualified 1976), partner 1978.
Personal: Married with two daughters.

RENNIE, Richard
Burness, Edinburgh (0131) 473 6168 rvr@burness.co.uk
Specialisation: Richard is experienced in all areas of commercial property, from landlord and tenant, purchases and sales, investment, development, property finance and property tax. He is also qualified under English law and he has used his knowledge of both systems in a number of high profile cross-border transactions. He has a particular interest in the fields of retail and leisure and property tax. However, his wide experience of all areas of commercial property give him the ability to focus in on the key issues on client objectives to optimise value and service to clients.
Career: Studied law at Edinburgh University, graduating in 1991. Gained a diploma in 1992 and qualified at *Burness* (as it is now) in 1994. Became partner in 1999.
Personal: Hobbies are football and golf. Interested in malt whiskey and travel.

RICE, Dermot
Slaughter and May, London (020) 7600 1200 dermot.rice@slaughterandmay.com
Specialisation: Specialises in all types of commercial property work including development, investment, securitisation and structured finance. Recent significant transactions include: acting for Norwich Union Life and Pensions in connection with the first ever UK securitisation of equity release mortgages; various projects for Grosvenor Limited and acting for HRO International in connection with the re-development and letting of 265 Strand.
Career: Articled *Gamlens*; qualified 1984; partner *Slaughter and May* 1991.
Personal: Married, 3 children. Resides: London.

ROBERTS, David
Hugh James Ford Simey, Cardiff (029) 2022 4871 david.roberts@hjfs.co.uk
Specialisation: Partner and head of commercial property department. Work includes site assembly and acquisition, including option work, agreement and grant of lease and forward sale agreements in relation to office, retail and industrial developments. Undertakes large scale land acquisition for large volume house builders, consortia and joint venture agreements. Specialises in Housing Association stock transfers and other social housing initiatives.
Prof. Memberships: Law Society.
Career: Qualified 1974. Joined *Hugh James* in 1972, becoming a partner in 1975. Head of commercial property department.
Personal: Born 1949. Attended Grove Park Grammar School, Wrexham and Selwyn College, Cambridge 1968-72 (MA, LLB). Cambridge Blue at athletics. Member of Bristol Athletics Team 1974-8. Competed at European and Commonwealth Championships. Member of Hawks Club and Achilles Club. Legal advisor and board member of Welsh Sports Hall of Fame. Leisure interests include sport, particularly golf, athletics and rugby. Lives in Cardiff.

ROBINSON, Herbert
Mills & Reeve, Cambridge (01223) 222233 herbert.robinson@mills-reeve.com
Specialisation: Partner specialising in property development advice and transactional work; option agreements; joint venture arrangements; 25 years' experience in the field of commercial property including: major project work for HEIs; setting up Granta Park, Abington, Cambridge; advice to EEDA on major development projects.
Career: Trained *Kenneth Brown Baker Baker*, qualified 1969; assistant solicitor *Taylors*, Newmarket 1970-72; partner 1972-87; partner *Taylor Vintors*, Cambridge 1988-99; chairman 1990-99; partner *Mills & Reeve* since 1999, leading property development team.
Personal: Resides near Newmarket. Sailing, walking, military history.

ROBINSON, Patrick
Herbert Smith, London (020) 7374 8000 patrick.robinson@herbertsmith.com
Specialisation: Commercial property development and planning work including all aspects of planning (see entry under Planning section). Established track record in all aspects of property work, with an emphasis on corporate relocations, site assembly and development cases.
Prof. Memberships: Law Society's Specialist Planning Panel.
Career: Articled at *Herbert Smith* (1978-80). Partner 1986. Joint Editor of Blundell & Dobry's 'Planning, Applications, Appeals and Proceedings' (5th Ed) 1996.
Personal: Born April 1956. Educated at University of Nottingham (LLB 1977). Leisure pursuits include jazz, the Cévennes and family. Lives in London.

ROONEY, Phillip
DLA, Liverpool (08700) 111111

ROSCOE, James
Fyfe Ireland WS, Edinburgh (0131) 343 2500 jroscoe@fyfeireland.com
Specialisation: Qualified in both Scotland and England, with extensive experience of cross-border

transactions. Main specialisms are property investment and property finance. Largely for English-based, American and German investors and lenders including Teachers Insurance, Helaba and Nationwide.
Prof. Memberships: WS, NP, admitted as a solicitor in England and Wales.
Career: Qualified 1988. Partner with *Bird Semple Fyfe Ireland* and thereafter *Fyfe Ireland* since 1992. Head of commercial property department.
Personal: Born 22 December 1960. Educated Dundee High School and Oxford and Edinburgh Universities. Interests include cycling and gardening.

ROSS, Kenneth
Burness, Edinburgh (0131) 473 6000

ROWE, Tim
Wright Hassall, Leamington Spa (01926) 886688
timr@wrighthassall.co.uk
Specialisation: All aspects of commercial property law with a particular emphasis on commercial developments. Acts for a number of household-name clients.
Prof. Memberships: Law Society.
Career: Articled *Boodle Hatfield*; qualified 1987. *Dibb Lupton Broomhead* 1989. Partner *Shoosmiths & Harrison* 1995. Partner *Wright Hassall* 1997.
Personal: Born 1964. Corpus Christi College, Cambridge (1984 BA Hons). Lives North Oxfordshire.

RUDOLF, Peter
Berwin Leighton Paisner, London (020) 7760 1000
peter.rudolf@berwinleightonpaisner.com
Specialisation: Property development, particularly retail and office, and investment. Recent transactions include the acquisition and development of The Mall, Cribbs Causeway (Prudential Assurance); redevelopment, letting and forward sale of 59 Gresham Street, London EC4 (Legal & General); acquisition and development of Serpentine Green regional shopping centre, Peterborough (Tesco); acquisition, development and forward sale of Midsummer Place shopping centre, Milton Keynes (London and Amsterdam Properties); redevelopment of Albert Dock, Liverpool (Arrowcroft); acquisition, development and forward sale of New Bond Street shopping centres, Weymouth (Shearer Property Group); acquisition and development of new London headquarters for OveArup Partnership; conditional acquisition for large mixed-use development at St Stephens, Ferensway, Hull (London and Amsterdam developments).
Prof. Memberships: Law Society.
Career: Bedford School; St Johns, Cambridge – MA 1st Class Honours.
Personal: Participation in sports especially squash and triathalons.

RYDEN, Nick
Shepherd & Wedderburn WS, Edinburgh (0131) 228 9900
nick.ryden@shepwedd.co.uk
Specialisation: All aspects of commercial property and property development.
Prof. Memberships: Member, Governor and former Chairman of Anglo-American Real Property Institute; occasional lecturer Law Society of Scotland post-qualifying legal education, RICS and Heriot-Watt University; member of Investment Property Forum; member of Investment Property Forum Securitisation Working Party; member of BPF Scottish working party.
Career: Articled *Shepherd & Wedderburn WS*; qualified 1976; assistant solicitor 1976-78; partner 1978.
Personal: Born 1953; resides Edinburgh. Leisure interests: Travel, hill walking and photography. Education: Fettes College; Aberdeen University (LLB;WS)

RYLAND, David
SJ Berwin, London (020) 7533 2222
david.ryland@sjberwin.com
Specialisation: Ranked by recent surveys in Euromoney as one of the world's leading real estate lawyers. Has extensive experience of a wide range of property finance mechanisms, including development agreements, joint ventures, forward sale, overage sale, side by side leases, trusts for sale, secured lending and equity kicker agreements. Also widely recognised as a specialist in investment mechanisms including limited partnerships, and unit trusts. Worked on numerous tax-related property transactions including finance and operating leases, enterprise zone schemes, and transactions to securitise cash flow from properties and maximise tax benefits from property related cash flows. Wide experience in development work, including forward fundings and forward purchases. Acted on the establishment of a wide range of property funds including MWB Leisure Funds I, II, and IIB, the Barclays Whitgift Partnership, the Regent Retail Parks Partnership, the Regent Residential Partnership, the Two Rivers Limited Partnership, the Foundation Partnership, the 02 Limited Partnership, the West India Quay Limited Partnership, the retail Park Unit Trust, the Chiswick Park Unit Trust, the Residential Property Unit Trust, the Hercules Unit Trust, the City of London Offices Unit Trust, the West End of London Property Unit Trust, the Strategic Property Partners Fund and the Gresham Property Partners Fund. Acted on numerous syndication of property amongst retail investors and property cashflow securitisations as well as the structuring of funds and asset specific acquisitions in Western and Central Europe.
Career: *Clifford Chance* 1981-88; *SJ Berwin & Co* 1988-date, Dulwich College: 1965-72; Exeter College Oxford University: 1973-77 (double first in Mods and Greats). Frequent lecturer and writer of articles on property investment related matters.
Personal: Married. Interests include sport, music and cinema.

SAMSON, John
Nabarro Nathanson, London (020) 7524 6000

SANDERS, Andrew
Lovells, London (020) 7296 2000
andrew.sanders@lovells.com
Specialisation: Commercial property partner with wide experience of the commercial property market, specialising in all aspects of development investment, joint venture and property finance work.
Prof. Memberships: Law Society.
Career: Articled Welsh Water Authority; qualified 1978; solicitor Islwyn Borough Council, solicitor The Post Office Company; solicitor United Friendly Insurance, partner *DJ Freeman* 1990; joined *Lovells* as a partner 1999.
Personal: Born 1954. Interests include karate, cinema, watching most sport.

SCOTT, Peter
Bevan Ashford, Bristol (0117) 975 1611
p.scott@bevanashford.co.uk
Specialisation: Head of commercial property department. Covers a wide range of property work including commercial development work (particularly in the leisure field), PFI contractual work in the education and health sectors and regeneration schemes.
Prof. Memberships: Law Society.
Career: *Norton Rose* 1969-72; *Boodle Hatfield* 1972-75. Joined *Bevan Ashford* 1975; partner 1977.

SEAWARD, Charlie
BrookStreet Des Roches, Witney (01993) 771616
charlie@bsdr.com
Specialisation: Investment work large scale portfolio management, secured lending, joint ventures, consortium agreements, particular experience in the public energy sector.
Prof. Memberships: The Law Society.
Career: Qualified 1978. Subsequently with *Lovells White and King* (now *Lovells*). Joined *BrookStreet Des Roches* as a partner in 1997.
Personal: City of London Polytechnic.

SELIGMAN, David
Palser Grossman, Cardiff Bay (029) 2045 2770

SINGH, Parmjit
Eversheds, Birmingham (0121) 232 1410
parmjitsingh@eversheds.com
Specialisation: Development: clients include Birmingham Mailbox, RBS Property Development, Severn Trent Property, Stoford Developments and Urban Box. Major projects in the last 12 months include project managing the legals on The Mailbox Scheme (biggest single building mixed use scheme in the UK-1m plus sq ft), in particular deals with The BBC for its Midlands operation in excess of 90,000 sq ft. and Harvey Nichols. Urban regeneration: act for Advantage West Midlands on various strategic schemes including its major inward investment site at Ansty for the development of a new global communications headquarters for GEC Marconi. Investment: clients include The Birmingham Alliance (Hammerson, Henderson and Land Securities) on the redevelopment of the new BullRing, Birmingham.
Prof. Memberships: Investment Property Forum.
Career: Trained *Eversheds*, qualified 1989, partner 1997.
Personal: Born 1965. Warwick University, LLB (Hons). College of Law, Chester. Enjoys watching and playing football. Married, 2 children.

SMITH, David
Shepherd & Wedderburn WS, Edinburgh (0131) 473 5292
david.smith@shepwedd.co.uk
Specialisation: Partner in Commercial Property Department and Chairman of Firm. Main areas of practice are development projects, leases and opinion work. Regular speaker at conferences and seminars.
Prof. Memberships: Law Society of Scotland, Society of Writers to the Signet.
Career: Joined *Shepherd & Wedderburn* in 1969. Partner in 1974.
Personal: Born 17th November 1947. Edinburgh University 1966-69. Leisure pursuits include veterans' hockey, golf, skiing, hill walking, gardening and enjoying good food and wine in good company. Lives in Edinburgh.

SMITHERS, Tim
Veale Wasbrough, Bristol (0117) 925 2020
tsmithers@vwl.co.uk
Specialisation: Partner in property services department. Main areas of practice are development, energy and environmental law with specialisms in wastes management, contaminated land and Pipelines Act work. An editor of Butterworths' 'Property Law Service'. Regular contributor to professional publications and speaker at seminars.
Prof. Memberships: Pipeline Industries Guild, Institute of Wastes Management, Environmental Services Association.
Career: Qualified 1982. Joined *Veale Wasbrough* in 1986, becoming a partner in 1988.
Personal: Born 1958. University of Wales.

SMYTH, Robert
Burges Salmon, Bristol (0117) 939 2000

SOLOMON, Jonathan
Clifford Chance, London (020) 7006 4024
jonathan.solomon@cliffordchance.com
Specialisation: Jonathan is a partner in real estate and specialises in development, funding and investment transactions acting for developer, tenants, investors and lenders. He has extensive experience of Central London office developments and lettings and led the team that won the Legal Business Property Team of the Year Award in 1998 for the proposed 700,000 square foot Liffe development at Spitalfields Market, London EC1. Jonathan also has considerable experience of acting on investment transactions both for overseas and UK clients. Recent examples of work include acting as part of the Nomura legal team on the £1 billion Meridian Hotel group sale and leaseback transaction; acting for Helical Bar plc on major development pre-lettings to law firms, *Slaughter & May* and *Linklaters* at Chiswell Street, London EC1 and continuing to act on the 1 million square foot Spitalfields office development project.
Career: Articled *Norton Rose*; qualified 1986; partner *Norton Rose* 1995; partner *Clifford Chance* 2000.

SORRELL, Stephen
Eversheds, Manchester (0161) 831 8000

STANCOMBE, Michael
Lovells, London (020) 7296 2000
michael.stancombe@lovells.com
Specialisation: Investment, financing and development (acting for both institutions and developers). Investment structures and indirect investment vehicles. Management of major portfolios. Also acts for a major retail group on new developments.
Prof. Memberships: Member of the British Council for Offices, the Investment Property Forum and Urban Land Institute. Fellow of the Society for Advanced Legal Studies. Representative Member of the British Property Federation, City Property Owners Association, Global Real Estate Investors and Westminster Property Owners Association.
Career: Articled at *Durrant Piesse* (now *Lovells*); qualified 1979; Partner 1982.

STEEL, David A
Dundas & Wilson CS, Glasgow (0141) 222 2200

STONE, David J
Andrew M. Jackson & Co, Hull (01482) 325242
Specialisation: Wide range of experience in commercial property development schemes (retail, leisure, and industrial) for developers, funders, owners and tenants. Recent experience includes acquisition, letting and funding of several retail/leisure schemes, joint venture agreements (including joint venture for redevelopment of a regional town centre). Acts for major leisure operator on schemes nationwide.
Prof. Memberships: Law Society.
Career: King Henry VIII School, Coventry and Cambridge University.
Personal: Married, two children. Golf.

STRACHAN, Dale
Brodies WS, Edinburgh (0131) 228 3777
dale.strachan@brodies.co.uk
Specialisation: Commercial property partner dealing with development, investment and property PFI/PPP. Recent/current transactions include acting on behalf of Corus Group (formerly British Steel) in joint venture arrangements for the redevelopment of approx 1100 acres at the former Ravenscraig Steelworks, Motherwell to form Scotland's next 'new town' involving a long term, large scale mixed use scheme of development. Acting on behalf of Trillium/William Pears Consortium in the Scottish aspects of the UK-wide property outsourcing project with British Telecommunications plc.
Prof. Memberships: Society of Writers to Her Majesty's Signet; International Bar Association; Society of Construction Law.
Career: George Heriot's School Edinburgh. University of Aberdeen (1977 LLB). Articled, *Archibald, Campbell & Harley WS* Edinburgh; qualified 1979; assistant Solicitor *Brodies* 1979-83; partner since 1983.
Personal: Fishing, skiing, motorcycling, private flying.

STRATTON, David
Field Cunningham & Co, Manchester (0161) 834 4734
Specialisation: Partner. Undertakes a wide range of commercial conveyancing transactions. Has specialised in major developments of all types, with particular emphasis on retail and office development, both town centre and out of town. Widespread experience of joint venture, institutional funding and secured lending work, as well as acquisition and disposal of major investment portfolios. Increasingly acting for banks in connection with property secured lending, particularly with a development bias.
Prof. Memberships: Law Society.
Career: Articled with Warrington Borough Council. Qualified in 1971. Worked for Christian Salvesen Properties as group legal adviser. Joined *Halliwell Landau* in 1979 and became deputy senior partner. Joined *Field Cunningham & Co* in 1996.
Personal: Born 16 May 1947. Educated at Altrincham Grammar School for Boys and Colwyn Bay Grammar School, then Leeds University 1965-68. Lives in Bowdon, Cheshire.

TAVENER, Chris
Herbert Smith, London (020) 7374 8000
Specialisation: Partner in real estate department. Deals with a full range of commercial real estate work for developer and institutional clients. Particular expertise in landlord and tenant work.
Career: Became a partner of the firm in 1982.
Personal: Born in 1948. Educated at RGS, Guildford and Christ Church, Oxford. Leisure time devoted to golf, skiing, music and family. Lives in Islington and (whenever possible) North Norfolk.

TAYLOR, David
Herbert Smith, London (020) 7374 8000
david.taylor@berwinleighton.com
Specialisation: Head of Property Department. Main areas of practice are commercial property development and investment. Broad commercial practice including acquisition development and joint ventures with specialist involvement for local authority and public sector clients. Recent transactions include significant purchases for the Prudential, Development Projects for AMEC, British Land and Kingspark. In addition, clients include BG Plc, CLS Holdings, Godfrey Bradman and Akeler.
Career: With *Lovell White & King* from 1974 to 1979. Joined *Berwin Leighton* in 1980 and became a Senior Associate in 1987. Became Head of Property Department 1996. Member Contributory Board PLJ. Member of 'PROP's' committee of variety club. Pro Bono Adviser to museum in Docklands.
Personal: Born 5th August 1956. Educated at Shooters Hill Grammar School. Leisure interests include classic cars. Lives in London.

THORNE, Peter
Wragge & Co, Birmingham (0870) 903 1000

TINMAN, Mark
C & H Jefferson, Belfast (02890) 329545
Specialisation: Acquisition development and disposal of commercial property. Acting for a number of retail multiples, developers and banks.
Prof. Memberships: Law Society of Northern Ireland.
Career: Whole career with *C & H Jefferson*. Qualified 1987. Partner since 1993.
Personal: Born 1962. Education: Queens University Belfast (LL.B) 1985. Institute of Professional Legal Studies, Belfast 1986.

VIVIAN, Jon
SJ Berwin, London (020) 7367 2116
jmv@cmck.com
Specialisation: Commercial property. Recent matters include: acting on behalf of Brixton plc on the acquisition of two large estates at Heathrow; acting on behalf of The Crown Estate in connection with regearing of their interest at Millbank Tower; acting on behalf of Gazeley Properties in connection with a development at Marsh Leys, Bedford; acting on behalf of Kumagai Gumi UK Ltd on the disposal of 55 Bishopsgate to Henderson for a consideration of £55m.
Prof. Memberships: City of London Law Society.
Career: *CMS Cameron McKenna* 1989 to August 2001. *SJ Berwin* since August 2001.
Publications: Monthly column in 'Property Week'.
Personal: Rugby School and Cambridge. Sporting.

WALLACE, Andrew
Archibald Campbell & Harley WS, Edinburgh (0131) 220 3000
AW@achws.co.uk
Specialisation: Partner specialising in commercial property, leasing, investment and development acquisition with particular emphasis on investment and industrial property. Known as a hard-nosed deal maker, he excels in concluding deals and identifying where value can be realised. Clients include Ashtenne Holdings plc, Frogmore Developments & Quintiles Transnational Corporation.
Career: Strathclyde University (LLB Hons), qualified in 1985, joined *Archibald Campbell & Harley WS* same year. Appointed partner in 1988. He has been a

regular lecturer to surveyors and the WS Society on leasing and related subjects.

WALLER, Corin
Addleshaw Booth & Co, Manchester (0161) 934 6533
cew@addleshaw-booth.co.uk
Specialisation: Extensive experience acting for investment funds, developers and local authorities on all aspects of commercial property. In particular forward funding arrangements, development and joint venture agreements. Recent transactions include acting for a local authority on its town centre redevelopment project.
Prof. Memberships: Law Society.
Career: Articled *Last Suddards/Hammond Suddards.* Qualified 1988. Joined *Booth & Co* in 1989. Partner at *Addleshaw Booth & Co* since 1996.
Personal: Born 1963. Married with two children. Enjoys skiing (snow and water) and going to the gym.

WALLIS, Guy
Davies Wallis Foyster, Liverpool (0151) 236 6226
gsw@dwf-law.com
Specialisation: Approximately 25 years experience in area of commercial property development with particular emphasis on out-of-town retail, shopping centres and waterfront retail/leisure schemes. Lead solicitor in a £60m town-centre shopping centre in the Midlands. Involved from the outset, and remains involved, with the prestigious Albert Dock scheme in Liverpool – the largest group of Grade I listed buildings in the UK. Involved in the waterfront scheme at Southampton Docks at Ocean Village and acts for the developer of Twelve Quays, Birkenhead, which includes Wallasey Dock and Morpeth Dock. Handled the joint venture arrangements in respect of the London & Amsterdam joint venture with ING Real Estate at Milton Keynes in connection with the CNT Development Agreement. Acted in connection with the project management arrangements between Legal & General and London & Amsterdam Developments Limited in relation to the re-development of the town centre of Bracknell. Dealt with the Development Agreement in respect of the Art Deco former airport terminal building and listed hangars at Liverpool Airport for Neptune Developments Limited, now a Mariott hotel and David Lloyd Leisure Centre respectively. Currently involved in major redevelopment of the Metropolitan Cathedral Precinct, Liverpool.
Prof. Memberships: The Law Society; Liverpool Law Society; Manchester Law Society; Society for Computers and Law.
Career: King William's College, Isle of Man; College of Law; founder partner of *Davies Wallis & Co* in 1977.
Personal: Golf (and not much time for that). Family: Teenage son and nearly teenage daughter. Understanding wife.

WARD, Ian
Dickinson Dees, Newcastle upon Tyne (0191) 279 9244
law@dickinson-dees.com
Specialisation: Urban Regeneration, including public/private sector Joint Ventures, mixed use commercial/residential developments, business parks and town centre developments. Acts for developers, national housebuilders and public authorities such as urban development corporations and local authorities. Also actively engaged in PFI, especially in the NHS. Recent work includes Gateshead Council's Baltic Quays development beside the Millenium Bridge and Arts Centre, advising on Millennium Commission projects and large scale PFI schemes for Leeds Teaching Hospitals and Belfast City Hospitals Regional Cancer Centre for Northern Ireland.
Prof. Memberships: Law Society.
Career: Articled at Eversheds (Newcastle). Qualified 1983, partner 1989-1997. Became a partner at *Dickinson Dees* 1997 – head of property.
Personal: Durham University B.A. Hons Law 1980. Swimming and family holidays.

WATKINS, David
Eversheds, Cardiff (029) 2047 7634
davidwatkins@eversheds.com
Specialisation: All areas of commercial property including acquisitions and disposals, joint ventures, secured lending, landlord and tenant, developments and forward funding arrangements.
Prof. Memberships: Law Society.
Career: *Lovells* 1991-98. Joined *Eversheds* in 1998 and made partner in 2000.
Personal: Educated at Gowerton School, Lancaster University, University of Illinois and Chester College of Law. Interests include rugby, golf and reading.

WATSON, Adrian
DLA, Birmingham (08700) 111111

WATSON, Gary
Ashurst Morris Crisp, London (020) 7638 1111
gary.watson@ashursts.com
Specialisation: All aspects of property law with particular emphasis on institutional investment and funding, property development, leasing and relocation work. Has acted in numerous large relocations including for a number of UK and overseas law firms as well as many tenants at Canary Wharf. Also has particular expertise in advising overseas investors.
Prof. Memberships: Investment Property Forum, Council Member of the International Council of the Urban Land Institute of America, British Property Federation.
Career: Qualified as a solicitor in 1979 and specialised in property law ever since. Assistant solicitor at *Clifford Turner* 1979 to 1982; assistant solicitor *Lovell White Durrant* 1982-1995; partner and head of London office *Hammond Suddards* 1995-2001; partner *Ashurst Morris Crisp* 2001-date.
Personal: Born August 1955. Educated at Oxford University (BA 1976). Leisure pursuits include travel, eating out, cinema and reading.

WATTIE, Ian
Burness, Edinburgh (0131) 473 6000

WEBB, Tim
Eversheds, Birmingham (0121) 232 1354
timwebb@eversheds.com
Specialisation: Development: developers include Chase Midland plc, Folkes Group plc, John Mowlem & Co plc, Lingfield Securities plc, Highbridge Properties plc, Taylor Woodrow and St Modwen Properties plc. Deals include leading on 1,100 acre development of Newcastle Great Park for Bryant/Beazer Homes and Enterprise Zone purchase and forward sales for Highbridge Properties. Major corporates: clients include Headlam Group plc, Hampson Industries plc, Hagemeyer, Carlsberg Tetley, Volvo, Misys Plc, Mentmore Abbey plc. Urban Regeneration: Advantage West Midlands.
Prof. Memberships: Investment Property Forum. Institute of Directors. Director of Birmingham Contemporary Music Group (one of the leading orchestras of its type in the world).
Career: Qualified *Eversheds* Sept 1989. Partner May 1997. Head of property (Birmingham) November 2000.
Personal: Married to Sarah, two children, Lucy and Charles. Jazz, cooking, live music, film and shooting.

WEIGHTMAN, Anita
DLA, Manchester (08700) 111111

WESTHEAD, Tim
Olswang, London (020) 7208 8888
tew@olswang.com
Specialisation: Commercial Property for listed property companies and institutional investors with a specialisation in the acquisition and management of shopping centres. Major transactions include the acquisition of a portfolio of five shopping centres for Capital & Regional plc for £147m, the sale of a portfolio of 44 properties for MEPC for £100m, the acquisition of The Pallasades Shopping Centre, Birmingham and The Ashley Centre, Epsom for £94m and £70m respectively, the acquisition and subsequent development of a series of office sites around the M25 for Green Property plc. Recent highlights include the acquisition of 151 Buckingham Palace Road, London SW1 for £101m on behalf of Delancey Estates plc and the acquisition on behalf of Green Property plc of the P&O property portfolio for £430m.
Career: *Stafford Clarke & Co* – 1980-1985. *Stones Porter* -1985-1996 (Partner 1986). *Olswang* – Partner – 1996 to date – Head of Property 1999 to date.
Personal: Education: Loughborough Grammar, University of Newcastle upon Tyne (LL.B Hons). Leisure Interests: Triathlon, mountain biking, marathon running and watching rugby. Married with three children. Resides – Godalming.

WHITE, Graham
Slaughter and May, London (020) 7600 1200
graham.white@slaughterandmay.com
Specialisation: Experienced in all aspects of commercial property work, including landlord and tenant matters, corporate property outsourcing, structured and tax-based finance, commercial property investment, secured lending and development work. Extensive landlord and tenant practice, frequently acting for tenants. He recently advised Whitbread plc on disposals of its brewing business and its public house estate, a multi-national oil company on a property outsourcing transaction of petrol filling stations and Enron plc on acquiring its UK corporate headquarters space. Regular contributor to Property Week. Member of the committee which has produced the Standard Commercial Property Conditions.
Prof. Memberships: City of London Law Society Land Law Sub-Committee; The Law Society.
Career: Qualified in 1980 after articles at *Slaughter and May.* Became a partner in 1987.
Personal: Born 1955. Educated at Haberdashers' Aske's, Elstree and St. Catherine's College, Oxford.

WHITE, Stephen
Cobbetts, Manchester (0161) 833 3333

WILLIAMS, Martell
Robertsons, Cardiff (029) 20237777

WILLSON, Stephen
SJ Berwin, London (020) 7533 2255
stephen.wilson@sjberwin.com
Specialisation: Head of property division of *SJ Berwin.* Specialist in all aspects of commercial property.
Prof. Memberships: Law Society.
Career: Qualified 1971, articled and subsequently partner at *Burton & Ramsden,* partner *SJ Berwin* 1982.
Personal: Battisborough School Plymouth, Devon College of Law. Married with three children. Interests: squash and tennis.

WILSON, Alistair
Fyfe Ireland WS, Edinburgh (0131) 343 2500
awilson@fyfeireland.com
Specialisation: Senior partner in firm. Acts extensively for investors, retailers, finance providers and developers, with considerable experience of providing strategic commercial advice in substantial property transactions and in negotiating the necessary documentation. Has particular experience of cross-border property transactions involving conflict of laws.
Prof. Memberships: WS, NP.
Career: Qualified 1968. Partner with *Fyfe Ireland WS* since 1971.
Personal: Born 19 July, 1945. Educated Peebles High School and Edinburgh University. Interests include fishing, hill-walking and motorcycling.

WORRALL, Simon
Cobbetts, Manchester (0161) 833 5272
simon.worrall@cobbetts.co.uk
Specialisation: Landlord and tenant, development and investment property, and licensed premises acquisitions.
Prof. Memberships: Law Society
Career: Articled to *Cobbett Leak Almond* 1987. Qualified 1989; partner *Cobbetts* 1999.
Personal: Married with two children. Hulme Grammar School Oldham; Sheffield University (LLB (Hons)); Chester College of Law. Interests include golf, theatre, cinema.

WRIGHT, David
Nabarro Nathanson, London (020) 7524 6000
d.wright@nabarro.com
Specialisation: Head of property dealing exclusively with commercial property with emphasis on development projects and institutional investment; extensive experience of leading teams in acquisition, disposal and leasing of major property portfolios.
Career: Qualified 1971.
Personal: Born 1946. Bishop Vesey's Grammar School, Sutton Coldfield then Bristol University 1965-68. Member of development board of Investment Property Forum. Director of Direct Wines Limited. Leisure: golf, gardening.

YATES, Andrew
Pinsent Curtis Biddle, Birmingham
(0121) 200 1050
andrew.yates@pinsents.com
Specialisation: Property development, joint ventures and leading other major property projects, particularly town centre schemes.
Publications: Joint editor of the chapters of Sweet and Maxwells 'Local Government Precedents and Procedures' dealing with local authority partnership arrangements and joint ventures (D29-D41).
Personal: Interests include martial arts and playing lead guitar in the *Pinsent Curtis Biddle* band.

SHIPPING

OVERVIEW: The wet and dry tables are amalgamated in all regions this year to reflect the continuing drop in the number of casualties at sea. Wet work is increasingly the preserve of a clutch of larger firms equipped with the international resources to respond quickly to disasters. However, there is room in the market for the likes of Waltons & Morse, challengers to Clyde & Co's mantle as chief advisor to the cargo industry, while individual moves such as that of Ben Browne to Shaw & Croft underline the importance of the city's smaller niche firms. Consolidation in the regional P&I club market, acute client pressure to cut fees, and a steady flow of practitioners away from the capital, leaves the regional markets still buoyant.

RESEARCH APPROVED BY BMRB: *For this edition,* Chambers' *researchers conducted 6,552 interviews – 4,419 with law firms, 554 with barristers and 1,579 with clients.*

The validity of the research was scrutinised by BMRB International, who audited both the methodology and the results at our offices in July 2001. They interviewed Chambers' *researchers and cross-checked sample interviews. Details of the audit appear on page 7.*

LONDON

SHIPPING • London		Ptnrs	Assts
1	Holman Fenwick & Willan	36	46
	Ince & Co	60	63
2	Clyde & Co	56	57
3	Hill Taylor Dickinson	15	14
	Richards Butler	19	25
4	Bentleys, Stokes & Lowless	12	8
	Clifford Chance	4	21
	Holmes Hardingham	9	11
	Jackson Parton	10	5
	More Fisher Brown	11	7
	Norton Rose	12	n/a
	Shaw and Croft	9	9
	Sinclair Roche & Temperley	21	39
	Stephenson Harwood	9	21
	Waltons & Morse	5	5
5	Hill Dickinson	4	3
	Lawrence Graham	4	6
	Watson, Farley & Williams	7	18
6	Barlow Lyde & Gilbert	4	5
	Curtis Davis Garrard	6	9
	Fishers	n/a	n/a
	Middleton Potts	8	8
	Thomas Cooper & Stibbard	13	n/a

This book is the product of 6,552 1/2-hour interviews. See p.7 for BMRB audit.
Within each band, firms are listed alphabetically.

Holman Fenwick & Willan (see firm details p.999) Researchers were impressed by continuing market plaudits for an "*extremely sharp and focused shipping firm,*" which "*takes some beating for wet work.*" Deploying "*massive numbers*" to handle the largest casualties, the firm's reputation chiefly rests with an extensive client list of market-leading salvors and shipowners, although an expanding P&I club base has put the dry practice on an almost equal footing. Peers, barristers and clients appreciate the firm's culture, which is said to produce "*easy-going, friendly yet super-confident lawyers.*" Legendary sector doyen and salvage expert Archie Bishop has now left the partnership to take up a client promotional role. However, the team is not short of big hitters. In the dry sphere, litigator **Richard Crump** (see p.766) was described by one prominent client as "*possibly the best shipping lawyer anywhere.*" He's "*incredibly knowledgeable and always in command of the facts.*" New senior partner **Robert Wilson** (see p.773) is "*amazingly diligent and intellectually rigorous. You give him twenty things to do, he does them and stands no nonsense.*" **Hugh Livingstone** (see p.769) has expertise across the range of charterparty and bills of lading disputes. For clients, he "*puts everything in simple terms,*" and "*doesn't take up difficult stances or shout at you down the phone.*" Fellow South African **Marcus Bowman** (see p.765) is another "*tough, effective and hard-nosed litigator.*" The firm acted for the buyers of seven ships previously owned by the collapsed Yugoslavian shipowner Slobodna Plovidba, was involved in the 'Leonidas' High Court case, and was prominent in the final House of Lords judgment in the 'Hill Harmony,' one of the most controversial cases of recent years. On the wet side, the hugely popular **James Gosling** (see p.767) has assumed the mantle of leading lawyer, and is especially noted for his work on behalf of owners in the German market. Clients and barristers routinely sang his praises, describing him as "*both charming and on the ball.*" Highlights from the caseload include the 'Derbyshire' public inquiry, where the firm advised the owners, as well as a series of high-profile total loss cases, including the 'Ievoli Sun,' off the French coast, the 'Treasure,' sunk off South Africa and the 'Egasco Fortune' near Egypt. **Clients:** P&I Clubs; owners; charterers; underwriters; shipyards.

Ince & Co (see firm details p.1008) An immense force in international shipping, the firm is considered by many to be the class of the field. Slick and professional, this is considered to be the "*Kellogg's of the shipping world,*" with tremendous brand power allied to partners of the highest quality. Clients told our researchers that the firm "*can be expensive, but it's worth it because the quality is so high.*" The core strength of the dry team is in the hull underwriting markets ("*Lloyd's and the insurers would always go there*") but the firm also sweeps up the lion's share of wet work: "*There are few large casualties where they don't have a slice of the pie.*" Peers speak of the group's robust approach to disputes. "*You feel a slight shudder before litigation and a few bruises afterwards.*" However, the team's cohesiveness is seen as a major plus. "*When they raise points with you, they consider what they are going to say without shooting from the hip.*" Richard Williams has now retired from partnership to take up a consultancy position, while **Richard Sayer** (see p.771) has returned to fee-earning duties after stepping down as senior partner. He "*led them well for many years, invested wisely and should take credit for having developed a leading international practice.*" Dry lawyer **Paul Herring** (see p.768) received more praise than anyone else this year. His "*case handling skills are superb. You know exactly where you stand. From a client's perspective, he speaks their language, and from a barrister's perspective, he delegates work effectively to counsel.*" Clients also like **Bob Deering** (see p.766), who "*always fits in well with our approach.*" Heading up the wet team, **James Wilson** (see p.773) is a "*superb all-round lawyer,*

LEADING INDIVIDUALS

1	**CRUMP Richard** Holman Fenwick & Willan	**GOSLING James** Holman Fenwick
	HERRING Paul Ince & Co	**SAYER Richard** Ince & Co
	VLASTO Tony Clifford Chance	
2	**BARDOT Andrew** Bentleys, Stokes & Lowless	**DEERING Bob** Ince & Co
	EAST Lindsay Richards Butler	**EVANS John** Hill Taylor Dickinson
	GINSBERG Roy Waltons & Morse	**LAX Michael** Lawrence Graham
	LIVINGSTONE Hugh Holman Fenwick & Willan	**TAYLOR Andrew** Richards Butler
	TAYLOR Tim Hill Taylor Dickinson	**WILSON James** Ince & Co
	WILSON Robert Holman Fenwick & Willan	**WINTER Glenn** Holmes Hardingham
3	**BROWNE Ben** Shaw and Croft	**DE LA RUE Colin** Ince & Co
	DONOGHUE Andrew Middleton Potts	**FISHER Nicholas** Fishers
	JOHNSON Andrew Hill Taylor Dickinson	**PARTON Nicholas** Jackson Parton
	ROOTH Anthony Watson, Farley & Williams	**THORP Clive** Barlow Lyde & Gilbert
4	**ATKINSON Joe** Sinclair Roche & Temperley	**BUSH Philip** Jackson Parton
	CROFT Roger Shaw and Croft	**FLETCHER Simon** Clyde & Co
	GHIRARDANI Paolo Stephenson Harwood	**HARVEY Richard** Richards Butler
	HODGSON Derek Clyde & Co	**LUX Jonathan** Ince & Co
	MOYLAN Adrian More Fisher Brown	**STRONG Malcolm** Ince & Co
	WALLIS Robert Hill Taylor Dickinson	
5	**BOWMAN Marcus** Holman Fenwick & Willan	**BROWN Anthony** AD Brown,
	CURTIS Simon Curtis Davis Garrard	**DUNN Chris** Waltons & Morse
	GRAY Edward More Fisher Brown	**GREENSMITH Nicholas** Clyde & Co
	GRIFFITHS Paul Bentleys, Stokes & Lowless	**HARRIS Graham** Thomas Cooper
	HAWKES Ian More Fisher Brown	**HEBDEN David** Thomas Cooper
	JOHNSTON David Holmes Hardingham	**LEACH Ben** Sinclair Roche
	LOWE Steven Stephenson Harwood	**MOORE Chris** Ince & Co
	MORRISON Mark Clifford Chance	**SCOTT Kenneth** Holmes
	SEWELL Vernon Bentleys, Stokes & Lowless	**SHAW Patrick** Ince & Co
	SLADE Robin Stephenson Harwood	**THOMAS Tony** Clyde & Co
	WILLIAMS Paul Norton Rose	

See individuals' profiles p.765

whom you can always trust. He doesn't take silly points." His team also includes leading oil pollution specialist **Colin de la Rue** (see p.766), and **Patrick Shaw** (see p.771), whose "*preparation is first-class.*" Responsible for a substantial Greek practice, he "*comes up with realistic and commercial proposals, and doesn't just regurgitate the text-books.*" New to the ratings this year, **Chris Moore** (see p.770) is described as "*straight and effective,*" while admiralty manager Chris Beesley was frequently noted for his claims practice. The dry practice is also home to tough litigator **Jonathan Lux** (see p.769) and vastly experienced generalist **Malcolm Strong** (see p.771). Notable cases include advising Harland and Wolff on a dispute arising from delay and costs for the building of two drill ships in Belfast, at a cost of $330 million per vessel. In an unsafe port claim, the firm also represented the owners of the 'Shanghai' tanker, following the grounding of the vessel while carrying a cargo of crude oil. The wet team has advised on matters such as the 'Bunga Teratai Satu,' a container vessel which ran aground off the Great Barrier Reef, and the 'World Discoverer,' a cruise ship abandoned in the Sandfly Passage in the Solomon Islands. **Clients:** Cargo owners; charterers; shipowners; insurers; P&I Clubs.

Clyde & Co (see firm details p.921) The firm's greater concentration on its corporate department has had no discernible effect on its overall shipping profile, where it remains a powerful force. The practice maintains its market-leading position as premier advisor to the cargo industry, but also handles the full range of casualty, salvage, insurance and commodities work. An expanded clientele of overseas shipowners has been a notable feature of the past year. Clients value the range of specialist skills on offer, citing the firm's "*sheer technical expertise.*" Known for a robust approach, the team is "*pretty bullish and terrier-like, but it works.*" The talent at associate level also drew frequent plaudits. "*Even if your partner is away,*" said one cargo client, "*there are any number of other people who can step into their shoes.*" The Guildford office is thought by many to be the equal of London, although the loss of hull and cargo underwriting practitioner Ben Browne, to Shaw and Croft, is seen as something of a blow. However, **Simon Fletcher** (see p.767) was recommended for his wet and energy practice, while newly rated **Nick Greensmith** (see p.767) handled the successful appeal in the 'Sea Empress' litigation. He is seen as a "*quiet man of high calibre.*" Although his negotiating style is not to everyone's taste, **Derek Hodgson** (see p.768) in the London office remains well known for his owners, charterers and hull insurance practice. He acted for slot charterers 'OOCL America' in the biggest ever container loss case. **Tony Thomas** (see p.772) is viewed as "*the archetypal Clyde's cargo man,*" and has strong ties to the Japanese market. The group has been involved in the major High Court 'Metro' litigation, a case concerning loss of oil from storage in Fujairah. The wet team has been busy with a string of notable salvage cases, including the 'Ievoli Sun,' a chemical tanker that sunk off Alderney and the 'Bunga Teratai Satu,' which grounded on the Great Barrier Reef. **Clients:** Les Abeilles International; Tsavliris; Tokio Marine & Fire; MOAC; ACE; AIG; Royal & Sun Alliance; CGNU; AXA; Chubb; Thomas Miller; Charles Taylor; North of England P&I Club; West of England P&I Club; NYK; Pan Ocean; Golden Union; Precious Shipping; D'Amato; Premuda; Glencore; BP; Shell; Société Générale.

Hill Taylor Dickinson (see firm details p.997) Despite some market perception of a reliance on the Lloyd's underwriting and marine insurance markets, the firm has also had exposure to major casualty work and boasts a client list packed with shipowners from Europe and the Middle East. Peers consider the team to be "*a pleasure to deal with,*" while acknowledging that "*they fight hard for their clients.*" Several P&I Clubs and owners were also quick to endorse the firm's credentials, asserting that "*we'd always use it for a big hefty case.*" **John Evans** (see p.766) received substantial recommendation this year. Strong on casualty work, he acts for a clientele of shipowners and P&I insurers, with notable links to the Greek market. **Tim Taylor** (see p.772) runs the ship insurance and re-insurance practice. Described as "*completely unflappable,*" he is a "*fantastic case handler who doesn't merely know the law, but has a great overview.*" Dry litigator **Andrew Johnson** (see p.769), and **Robert Wallis** (see p.772), who has a wet/shipowning practice and acts for Dutch company P&O NedLloyd, were also recommended. The team acted for the owners of the 'Bowbelle' at the public inquiry into the 'Marchioness' riverboat disaster, and was involved in the 'Mighty Servant,' 'Erika,' and 'Castor' casualties. It also acted for Primorsk Shipping in connection with 'Nakhoda' oil spill off Japan, and for hull and liability underwriters Hiscox in connection with the collision between the Mega Yacht 'Auriga,' and the Spanish government ferry 'Millennium.' **Clients:** CGNU; Brockbank; P&O NedLloyd; Primorsk Shipping; Hiscox; P&I Clubs; Stena Line; Associated British Ports; Titan Salvage; Cunard; Festival Cruises; Costa Cruises; MSC; Toisa; Societe Generale Vendor Finance; Fleet Business Credit (UK); Fineline Group; Capital Professions Finance; Tokyo Leasing.

Richards Butler (see firm details p.1107) A substantial force for both wet and dry work, the firm has been involved in a number of the sector's highest-profile cases. The wet practice is smaller than several of its leading competitors, but has acted on a number of major casualties, and also has a track record in container casualties, pollution, and salvage. Respected player **Richard Harvey** (see p.768) led a team which acted for the owners of the cruise liner 'World Discoverer,' which ran aground in the Pacific, and advised on the $60 million Lloyd's Form salvage case, in which the 'Asian Parade' ran aground off the Irish Coast. Senior figurehead **Andrew Taylor** (see p.771) has acted on casualties such as the 'Ievoli Sun,' and on a major pollution case behalf of the owners of the 'Erika'. Taylor also handles dry matters, and has close connections to the Italian market. P&I Club clients rate him as "*fantastic,*" while fellow solicitors admire his commitment: "*He really sticks to his task.*" **Lindsay East** (see p.766) is felt to be the strongest weapon available to the dry practice. Praised by peers, the bar and the clubs, he's "*quick and responsive.*" The team won a successful appeal on behalf of the charterers of the 'Hill Harmony' and also advised the charterers of the 'Treasure,' a sinking off the coast of South Africa involving charter, bill of lading and pollution issues. **Clients:** Steamship Mutual; UK Mutual P&I Club; Louis Dreyfus Group; Elka Shipping; Shinwa KK; Pan Ocean; Standard Steamship Owners P&I Association; Glencore Rotterdam; Wijsmuller Salvage; North of England P&I Club; MSC Mediterranean Shipping; Niarchos; P&O Bulk Carriers; CM Lemos; Far Eastern Shipping Company.

Bentleys, Stokes & Lowless (see firm details p.875) Historical heavyweight which, although it does not have the profile of its salad days, still pulls in "*some bloody good work.*" P&I clubs appreciate the firm's "*competitive fees and high service levels*" for charterparty disputes. The team has strong club connections in Scandinavia, Italy and Greece, notably for hull markets work. Senior partner **Andrew Bardot** (see p.765) balances his managerial responsibilities with extensive fee-earning in the Italian and Greek markets. Hugely popular among fellow lawyers, he has a "*consistently impressive owners and charterparty practice*" and "*a sensible, straightforward approach.*" **Paul Griffiths** (see p.767) also received substantial market endorsement, with clients appreciating his "*pragmatic, problem-solving abilities.*" **Vernon Sewell** (see p.771) has handled a number of complex matters, often for a Scandinavian clientele. Although regarded as an "*awkward opponent,*" peers also confirm that he is "*fun to deal with.*" **Clients:** P&I Clubs; ship owners.

Clifford Chance (see firm details p.919) Such are the resources at its disposal, that the shipping practice has "*the ability to do absolutely everything.*" Although not a feature on bread and butter FD&D claims, the firm's work on high value cases draws universal praise. The group has handled a series of international ship foreclosures, many in the $5 million region, and is said to "*co-ordinate its global approach superbly.*" **Tony Vlasto** (see p.772) remains the litigation department's star attraction. "*Energetic and organised,*" he "*possesses sufficient mastery of any case to understand it quickly and give valuable advice on it.*" His practice includes both dry and wet cases. **Mark Morrison** (see p.770), formerly located in Hong Kong, appears in this year's tables, following some weighty recommendation. A "*hands-on practitioner,*" clients value his "*open and professional*" attitude. The firm advised on a $140 million offshore drilling rig arbitration and has acted on around 50 High Court claims arising from the 'Sea Empress' casualty. **Clients:** ABT International; Brasoil; COSCO; Dubai Shipping Company; Global Crossing; Interorient Navigation; KDD; Norwegian Cruise Line; Oceanco International; Osprey Maritime; Petrobras; Sea-Land Service; Delmas; OceanRig; Phillips Petroleum; Britannia P&I Club; Charterers Club; China P & I; Gard UK; Sociedad Mutua De Seguros; Shell Trading Middle East; Trafigura; Trans Global Projects; Veba Oil Supply & Trading.

Holmes Hardingham (see firm details p.1000) The team continues to register well with the London market. Commentators point to a "*tight, focused, down to earth firm who don't overcharge and do a damn good job.*" The practice is broadly spread, equally adept at both wet and dry work, and has a string of relationships in Northern Europe. Among these, Scandinavian club Skuld is especially notable, while the team also has a sizeable salvage and charterer practice. Dry stalwart **Glenn Winter** (see p.773) received high praise from all quarters. He has "*excellent judgement. His skill is that he knows when to settle and doesn't mislead his clients.*" Clients also speak warmly of "*absolutely superb response times and quality of advice.*" Wet lawyer **Ken Scott** (see p.771) is noted for his impressive Greek clientele, while newly recommended **David Johnston** (see p.769) is regarded as an expert in the yacht and insurance market. The firm has been heavily involved in the complex Metro Oil Trading litigation. In the 'Erika' case, it acted for Total, the charterers of the vessel which sank off the French coast in December 1999, in connection with the resulting claim against the vessel's owners. Other cases include the 'Milasan,' a marine insurance claim, the 'Trade Green,' a cargo insurance matter and a bill of lading case in the Admiralty Court, the 'Chitral.' **Clients:** CGU; Royal & Sun Alliance; BP Amoco; TotalFinaElf; Stolt-Nielsen; Spliethoff; Pacnav (Mexico); Skuld; Howard Smith.

Jackson Parton (see firm details p.1010) A close-knit firm, "*full of great go-ahead guys,*" which appears to some observers to be "*more akin to a bunch of mates than a partnership.*" Although the approach of individual partners varies, with some said to be "*pretty aggressive,*" quality levels here are felt to be consistently high. Our researchers discovered that **Nick Parton** is still regarded as the team's main asset. A popular figure, he "*fights and serves his clients well.*" "*Thorough*" **Philip Bush** is sometimes considered to be "*excessively robust,*" but "*brings in a lot of work.*" Although previously characterised as a dry-oriented firm (as much as 50% of the caseload is devoted to charterparty and demurrage cases for clubs,) the development of the wet practice was highlighted by a recent casualty case on behalf of shipowners Tokio Marine. The practice has also forged close ties to owners, operators and clubs in Greece, Japan and France. **Clients:** P&I Clubs; shipowners; FD&D Clubs; insurers.

More Fisher Brown In spite of the departure of Tony Brown in November 2000 to set up his own practice, the firm has not suffered any noticeable drop in profile. Regarded as one of the best niche practices of its size, it is said to be "*great for maritime cases and arbitrations,*" and to possess a clutch of "*thorough and intelligent litigators who won't take things to court unless they have to.*" Highly recommended this year was **Adrian Moylan** (see p.770), who is well-connected in Scandinavia, the USA and Hong Kong. Market opinion speaks of a "*laid-back, sharp and charming lawyer.*" **Eddie Gray** (see p.767) retains his share of admirers, while **Ian Hawkes** (see p.768) is liked by clients for his "*quick, commercial approach,*" and makes his debut in the tables. Core strength in dry work has seen the team act for a raft of owners, operators and clubs in Norway, Germany and Korea. The practice has also been involved in European Commission dawn raids on carriers investigating alleged breach of competition rules, and a series of disputes involving the incorporation of the Hague rules into charterparties. **Clients:** P&I Clubs; shipowners; charterers; offshore contractors

Norton Rose (see firm details p.1082) Operating almost exclusively on big-ticket litigation and arbitration, the firm is perceived to provide a "*mega-shop service.*" Large plc clients were impressed with the firm's cross-departmental service: "*They really understand our business. It does pay to use a City firm for sheer responsiveness and quality.*" Although the departure of top litigator Chris Hobbs to the firm's Athens office is reckoned to be a setback to the London team, he is thought to leave a "*good young team*" behind him. **Paul Williams** (see p.772) was frequently rated this year. He has expertise in major casualties on behalf of shipowners, P&I Clubs and underwriters, with special attention to the cruise sector. Recently, he acted for owners and their P&I Club following a casualty at Calais involving the Aquitaine. The firm also handled the defence of Sembawang in the Solitaire arbitration, the largest arbitration seen in London. **Clients:** Acomarit; Andika; A. Bilbrough & Co; Enron; ExxonMobil; Festival Cruises; Gard Club; Hyundai Heavy Industries; Louis Cruises Lines; Lukoil; Malta Shipbuilding; Mitsubishi; P&O Princess Cruises; Silversea Cruises; Skuld Copenhagen; Stena; Texaco; TotalFinaElf; UK Club (Thomas Miller); Wallem; Volgo Tanker.

Shaw and Croft (see firm details p.1124) "*One of the cutting-edge firms,*" it has gained particular praise for its wet capacity, notably on salvage and cargo, where it is increasingly seen to be challenging larger firms such as Clyde & Co. The team takes the lion's share of Lloyd's Open Form (LOF) salvage appointments. In June 2000, the firm absorbed Brian Williamson and six members of his team from Williamson and Horrocks, a bolt-on that has elicited warm response from the market. Clients have also praised the group's strength in depth, notably at assistant level. It was something of a coup when the practice hired **Ben Browne**, formerly one of the mainstays at Clyde & Co's Guildford office, in June 2001. He has a track record acting for hull and cargo underwriters. Said to be "*smooth, precise and meticulous,*" he has advised Scopic on salvage law reform. Wet litigator **Roger Croft** (see p.765) received widespread recommendation from peers and barristers, and is described as "*consistently a top choice.*" The firm has an eclectic international clientele, and represents ship and tanker owners, charterers, salvors, insurers and clubs in overseas markets such as Greece, the Middle East and the Baltic. It also continues to represent the owners of the vessel in the long-running 'Marchioness' enquiry. **Clients:** Loucas C Matsas; Tsavliris Salvage; Mediterranean Yachtbrokers Association; Kuwait Oil Tanker Company; Yachting Partners Int; City Cruises; Northern Shipping Co; Curnow Shipping; Bimeh-Iran Insurance; JP Knight Group; Smit-Pentow; Latvian Shipping Co; Smit-Union; UK P&I Club; People's Insurance Co of China.

Sinclair Roche & Temperley (see firm details p.1134) In tandem with its foreign offices in Shanghai and Hong Kong, the firm maintains a high quality name both for dry and wet litigation. A low-key style has not deceived the group's competitors. "*They may not market well, but they crop up repeatedly on sizeable cases,*" said one rival. The key man on the wet side is **Joe Atkinson** ("*a fair and decent opponent*") who has expertise in collisions and container ship matters. The dry practice is personified by **Ben Leach**, who received a number of glowing recommendations from the bar this year. **Clients:** Clubs; shipyards; brokers; owners, charterers and operators from Europe, North America, the Far East and Australia.

Stephenson Harwood (see firm details p.1141) Large, integrated dry and wet litigation practice which, in spite of some recent personnel departures, retains a number of admirers. "*We are coming up against them on big cases a lot more than we used to,*" said one rival solicitor. Dry litigator **Paolo Ghirardani** (see p.767) "*really makes them tick.*" Described as an "*influential and resourceful lawyer,*" "*he reaches the parts that other lawyers don't reach.*" **Steven Lowe** is admired by senior barristers. His practice, which includes banking and re-insurance, has a substantial Greek component. The firm represented Heerema Marine Contractors in connection with the sinking of the 'Mighty Servant 2' and the loss of the deck of the 'North Nemba' platform destined for Angola, which led to a $185 million insurance claim. The group also continues to be involved in the 'Ocean Rig' case, a substantial offshore oil contract dispute where the practice is representing the rig owners in a dispute with Brazilian developer Maritima. Head of the firm's wet practice, **Robin Slade** (see p.771), is a new entrant to our tables on the back of positive client endorsement. The team acted for Cenargo International, in a dispute with a Spanish shipyard, and for Swiss shipowning interests in connection with the total loss of the cruise liner 'Belofin 1' off South Africa. **Clients:** BMM; Cosco; Estonia Ship Management; Lloyd's Claims Office; Solent Towage; UK P&I Club; Warta Insurance; Luktrans Shipping; Iran Shipping Lines; Zanzibar Ports Corporation; Finaval.

Waltons & Morse (see firm details p.1173) "*Strong challengers, who have really come on a lot,*" the firm is now considered to be one of the first ports of call for cargo and salvage work. Home to a number of "*outstanding*" individual partners, the team is also praised by clients for its "*cost-effective service,*" which "*doesn't merely milk a case to run up a fee bill.*" Elder statesman **Roy Ginsberg** is routinely praised by peers and clients for his handling of a "*consistent flow of big cases*" on behalf of cargo interests. **Chris Dunn** is a popular choice with marine cargo insurers and has close ties to the Lloyd's market. "*He deals with the markets on a regular basis, and is always approachable.*" The firm acted for a large Norwegian insurer in tandem with a major oil and gas company in the 'Berge Sisar' House of Lords case, concerning the contamination of a Saudi liquefied propane gas cargo. It also represented cargo interests in a challenge of the right of owners to limit their liability under the 1976 Limitation Convention. **Clients:** Cargo underwriters; hull underwriters; shipowners; foreign insurers.

Hill Dickinson (see firm details p.996) A new entrant to the shipping tables, the small London team works closely with its larger counterparts in the North West, and received extensive stand-alone recommendation this year. Peers and barristers have been quick to praise the "*quality and slickness*" of the unit. Former professional yachtmaster Tony Allen is a key member of a department that is considered to be one of the leading yacht specialists. The team handles yacht insurance litigation and transactions in the superyacht market, such as the negotiation of construction, sale and purchase and financing agreements. **Clients:** Lloyd's underwriters; insurance companies, P&I Clubs; brokers; yacht owners; yacht builders.

Lawrence Graham (see firm details p.1030) Strong ties to Eastern Europe and the former Soviet Union give the practice a distinctive flavour. A partner is based permanently in the Ukraine, and the client roster features a number of owners, charterers and operators from the Black Sea and Baltic region. Individually, however, the efforts of **Michael Lax** (see p.769) continue to overshadow the remainder of the team. Possessing "*a broad range of skills,*" he is commended by P&I Clubs for "*being alive to our needs and not getting bogged down with twenty pages of dense legality.*" Another client appreciated his fighting qualities, and likened him to a pitbull terrier. "*Once he goes in, he keeps going for it.*" The firm advised the Azov Shipping Company on the 'Boris Babochkin' case, which extended the principle of non-arrest of sister ships belonging to ex-Soviet state property funds. On the non-contentious side, the team was involved in obtaining the first bareboat charter registration of Ukrainian vessels on the Maltese Ship Register. **Clients:** West of England P&I Club; Latvian Shipping Company; Steamship Mutual Underwriting Association; CMB Group; MT Maritime; Novorossiysk Shipping Company; Charterers Mutual P&I Club; Meyer Werft; Ocean Rig; Dynegy; Geogas Trading; Tankers International.

Watson, Farley & Williams (see firm details p.1174) Although it is still overshadowed by its ship financing prowess, the firm offers a closely-integrated litigation service, which remains popular with its clients. **Tony Rooth** (see p.770) is regarded by peers as a "*first-class contentious lawyer. He's level-headed, meticulous and technically astute, and tells you the truth, even if it's not what you want to hear.*" The firm acted for seismic support company Inshore Services International, in bringing an action against the National Federation of Fishermen. **Clients:** Commodore Group; Costa Cruise; Dry Tank; Far Eastern Shipping Company; Foresight; P&O NedLloyd; Papachristidis; Pegasus Ocean Services; Pleiades Group; Ravenscroft Ship Management; Renaissance Cruises; Royal Caribbean Cruise; Seatrade Shipping; Stirling; Tankers International; Van Ommeren Shipbroking; Wilh Wilhelmsen Limited; Yangming Marine Transport Corp.

Barlow Lyde & Gilbert (see firm details p.870) The retirement of Ray Mead deprives the firm of its leading shipping lawyer. However, the practice received a boost with the lateral hire of litigator **Clive Thorp** (see p.772) in 2001. He is said to be "*good fun to work with and always comes up with original ideas.*" The practice has expertise in shipping, marine insurance, transport, logistics and international trade. Dry work, notably charterparty disputes, is the practice's forte, with P&I clubs endorsing the quality of the team: "*They take a sensible, commercial view of cases.*" The team has been involved in the big-ticket Glencore v Metro trading litigation, and also acted for Greek oil investors in a dispute with the World Bank and the Albanian Government over oil tank farms and terminal installations. Although the wet practice is comparatively low-profile, it acted for The Swedish Club and Norwegian hull underwriters in respect of the collision between the 'Global Mariner' and the 'Atlantic Crusader' in the Orinoco River. **Clients:** The Swedish Club; Metro Trading; UPS Europe; Smith Bilbrough & Co; Ferguson Shipbuilders; Chaucer Syndicates; Ace Europe; WK Webster & Co; Liberty Syndicate Management; UK P&I Club; London Steamship; Robmarine Shipping Corporation; Skuld; OMMIA; Clipper Group; Maryville Maritime; Sovocomflot; Jardine Lloyd Thompson; Babcock International Group; Zespri International.

Curtis Davis Garrard Based near Heathrow Airport, the firm has augmented its reputation as a leading specialist in shipbuilding, energy and marine/offshore construction. Described as an "*impressive niche firm that occasionally handles big cases,*" it serves a clientele comprising international shipowners, shipyards and offshore contractors. The esteemed **Simon Curtis** (see p.766) is the author of the standard text on shipbuilding contracts. The firm advised Alstom and its subsidiary, Chantiers de l'Atlantique, on a $780 million contract with Carnival Corporation's subsidiary Cunard Line, for the construction of the world's largest cruise vessel, 'Queen Mary II.' It also acted for Nortrans Offshore in connection with the provision of an FPSO for use by Ranger Oil, and represented Brovig Offshore on the acquisition of a tanker for conversion to an FPSO for the ISIS project in Tunisia. **Clients:** Alstom; Louis Dreyfus Armateurs; Kawasaki Heavy Industries; Egon Oldendorff; Ceres Hellenic; Stena Drilling; Empresa Naviera Elcano; Innogy.

Fishers (see firm details p.959) Small, popular firm, which draws favourable comment from across the market. Although not a regular feature on the bigger cases, it is a regular choice for a range of dry shipping matters, frequently advising charterers and cargo interests. Clients consider well-known personality **Nick Fisher** (see p.767) to be *"extremely able and approachable,"* as well as a top-class draftsman, although the question of his lack of comparable support continues to be raised by the market. The practice acted for the charterers of the 'Erika,' for LauritzenCool in relation to the Amer Interpleader case, and for X-Press Container Lines, the charterers of the MV 'Eliza' that was a total loss in the Bay of Bengal in November 1999. It also represents BP Oil International Limited in respect of the fire and total loss of the 'Giovanna' in Beirut in November 1998. **Clients:** Hapag-Lloyd; BP Chemicals Trading; BP Shipping; LauritzenCool; The Miller Insurance Group; Rickmers Linie & Cie KG.

Middleton Potts (see firm details p.1067) *"Low-key"* unit, which is best known for the overlap between its dry shipping team and the firm's top-class commodities practice. *"Extremely clever"* **Andrew Donoghue** (see p.766) is an *"understated performer,"* appreciated by our interviewees for his *"reliable and dependable"* style. The bulk of the team's caseload involves arbitration, including cargo shortage and salvage claims from grain houses, time charter and voyage charter disputes for owners, charterers and P&I Clubs, and claims on behalf of hull & machinery underwriters. The firm also has links with the German and Italian markets, and receives a number of referrals from lawyers there. Highlights from the past year include the 'The Amer Reefer Litigation' in which the practice acted for the owners of eight refrigeration vessels. An unusual case (the 'Kribi,') straddling shipping law and the Human Rights Act, saw the practice act for the owners of a vessel in obtaining an anti-suit injunction preventing cargo interests from proceeding with a claim. **Clients:** Steamship Mutual Club; Alfred C. Toepfer; owners; charterers; hull & machinery underwriters.

Thomas Cooper & Stibbard (see firm details p.1153) Although the firm has enviable international reach, its profile in London is felt to have receded. In part, this has been due to the departure of dry lawyer Douglas Bateson to head up the firm's Greek office. However, the team is still acknowledged by clients to be a sound option for litigation. New arrival **Graham Harris** (see p.767), who joined from Richards Butler in July 2001, received market approval as an *"able lawyer who doesn't posture."* **David Hebden** (see p.768) is the elder statesman of the wet arm of the practice, and is a practitioner with extensive experience of shipping casualties and oil pollution cases. The team represents a clientele of shipowners, shipbuilders and oil companies. **Clients:** Exxon Mobil; P&O; shipbuilders; shipowners.

Other Notable Practitioners More Fisher Brown founding partner **Tony Brown** (see p.765) has now left the firm to set up his own dry shipping litigation, insurance and international trade practice. An *"exceptionally bright man,"* he is expected to compete for *"niche, intellectually intensive work."*

SHIPPING FINANCE

SHIPPING: FINANCE • London	Ptnrs	Assts
1 Norton Rose	9	22
2 Watson, Farley & Williams	16	30
3 Allen & Overy	5	1
Stephenson Harwood	5	12
4 Clifford Chance	4	21
Sinclair Roche & Temperley	8	13
5 Linklaters	*	*

LEADING INDIVIDUALS	
1 **GIBB Jeremy** Norton Rose	**RUSSELL Mark** Stephenson Harwood
SHELTON John Norton Rose	
2 **DUNNE Frank** Watson, Farley & Williams	**HARTLEY Simon** Norton Rose
HODGKINSON George Sinclair Roche	**ROBERTSON Struan** Sinclair Roche
SMITH David Allen & Overy	**WARDER David** Watson, Farley & Williams
WATSON Martin Watson, Farley & Williams	
3 **TURNER Paul** Clifford Chance	

This book is the product of 6,552 1/2-hour interviews. See p.7 for BMRB audit.
Within each band, firms are listed alphabetically. *See individuals' profiles p.765*
**See editorial entries for explanation of team sizes.*

Norton Rose (see firm details p.1082) The ship finance team retains its spot as the clear market front-runner. *"A formidable practice which has made the leading position its own,"* it has a fine client blend of owners and lending banks, and excels in acting on high value structured cross-border transactions. Clients value the range of related departments, such as banking and tax. **Jeremy Gibb** (see p.95) is said to be *"as good as anyone in the market,"* while vastly experienced **John Shelton** (see p.771) also receives universal approval. *"Extremely sharp"* **Simon Hartley** (see p.768) has handled a number of complex securitisation deals, and has now *"really broken through into the top ranks."* Key transactions saw the practice act for Sovereign Finance in respect of the UK lease of a semi-submersible drilling rig for a UK subsidiary of R&B Falcon Corp. The team also acted for the financiers (Bank of Nova Scotia and SEBanken) on a syndicated $328 million and a syndicated DM371 million working capital receivables securitisation to finance the construction of two cruise vessels. **Clients:** Sovereign Finance; Bank of Nova Scotia; Lloyds TSB; ABN AMRO; New Zealand Banking Group; Banca Commerciale Italiana; Bank of Scotland; Crédit Lyonnais; Deutsche Schiffsbank; HSBC; Premuda Group; Shipping Corporation of India; Société Générale.

Watson, Farley & Williams (see firm details p.1174) A changing of the guard at senior level has had little effect on a formidably strong ship finance practice with an extensive client list. Former senior partner Alistair Farley now has a consultancy role, while the experienced **Martin Watson**, although still a highly respected figure in the market, has had a lower profile recently. Considered to have an *"entrepreneurial"* culture, the firm is not reckoned to have the capital markets and corporate finance clout of its chief rival Norton Rose. Instead, it scores highly for its impressive clientele of banks and owners, and its excellent global network. Clients emphasise the group's international credentials: *"We make a lot of use of Piraeus and New York."* A new entrant to our tables, **Frank Dunne** (see p.766) is *"a larger than life figure,"* and acts for a range of UK and international lenders. Former managing partner **David Warder** (see p.772) still *"crops up repeatedly,"* typically advising a range of financial institutions and owners/operators.The firm advised Chase Manhattan on a $376 million financing of the Metrotankers fleet, and represented Fortis Bank on the repackaging of its fleet financing of Royal Olympic Cruises, following the delivery of 'Olympic Voyager,' the fastest cruise ship in the world. Also acted for Carnival on the building contract for the Queen Mary II at Chantiers de L'Atlantique. **Clients:** Carnival; Chase Manhattan; Citibank; Fortis Bank;

Gearbulk Holdings; ICB; Leif Hoegh & Co; Nordstrom & Thulin; Overseas Maritime; Sovcomflot AKB.

Allen & Overy (see firm details p.856) Although the group does not contain specialist ship financing lawyers, such is its quality that the market has no hesitation in rating the firm among the leaders in this discipline. **David Smith** (see p.771), whose practice also spans aviation and rail finance, remains highly recommended by clients. Although the clientele is weighted towards financial institutions, it has recently strengthened its owner/operator portfolio with the addition of Ferretti, the leading Italian yacht manufacturer, and Leif Hoegh & Co, a shipping company listed on the Oslo Stock Exchange. Highlights include advising Celtic Pacific on a complex $140 million UK tax-based operating lease of a luxury cruise liner. The team also advised Chase Manhattan on a $170 million syndicated financing of an LNG carrier under construction for Naviera F Tapias Gas, and for INFI as arranger of the A$23 million acquisition of two passenger ships in the South Pacific. **Clients:** Barclays Mercantile Business Finance; Celtic Pacific; WestLB; Chase Manhattan; Halifax; Société Générale; INFI; Ferretti; Leif Hoegh & Co.

Stephenson Harwood (see firm details p.1141) "*Extremely successful and prolific team*," which is considered to owe much to **Mark Russell** (see p.771), a "*quiet and pragmatic performer*," who holds together a "*tight-knit unit*." A solid clientele of banks and owners were appreciative of the team's "*high legal quality and slick service*." The team represented Fortis Bank on the transfer of the Mees Pierson shipping portfolio, following the merger of Fortis and Mees Pierson. The practice also advised privately owned shipowner Cenargo International on the delivery and financing of two freight/passenger ships each with a value of £44 million. It also acted for the lead arrangers – a syndicate of 19 banks including Bank of America, HSBC and ING Barings – in relation to a $440 million secured multi-currency revolving loan facility to companies in the Stolt Comex Group. **Clients:** ABN AMRO; ANZ Bank; Lloyds TSB; Benor Tankers; PGS Production; Solstad Shipping.

Clifford Chance (see firm details p.919) Ship financing remains an important component of the firm's "*nicely balanced shipping practice*." Taking advantage of a clientele of eminent financial institutions, the firm is a regular player in large structured financings, and has developed expertise in the passenger (cruise) sector, and in offshore oil and gas financings. Although Tom Budgett has departed to an in-house position, **Paul Turner** (see p.772)continues to gain market plaudits. The firm advised Star Cruises on the acquisition of Norwegian Cruise Line, and its subsequent restructuring. **Clients:** Citibank; Commerzbank; Deutsche Verkehrs Bank; Islamic Development Bank; Merrill Lynch International; Nomura; Union Bank of Switzerland; Kvaerner.

Sinclair Roche & Temperley (see firm details p.1134) The transactional finance arm of the practice continues to power on, assisted by respected offices in Singapore and Hong Kong. Home to a mix of old and young lawyers, the blend of experience is widely approved by the market. Department head **George Hodgkinson** (see p.768), well known for his ties to client KfW, is regarded as a cornerstone of the team, while "*thorough and pleasant*" senior partner **Struan Robertson**'s "*ambitious streak has helped develop the practice into a market force*." The practice acted for Merita Bank as agent for a syndicated term loan of FIM900 million and a revolving credit of FIM700 million to Silja Line. It also acted for Kreditanstalt ür Wiederaufbau concerning the delivery to P&O of the newbuilding cruise ship 'Aurora.' **Clients:** Merita Bank; Kreditanstalt ür Wiederaufbau; West L/B.

Linklaters (see firm details p.1042) (All partners and assistants part time) Ron Gibbs, head of the firm's International Asset Finance Group, oversees a team which has a growing reputation for handling large, complex structured ship financings. Clients spoke warmly of the group's cross-departmental abilities. "*The team is well-resourced, well-supported and has the necessary related strengths in finance and tax*." The firm's cross-border prowess was also noted.The team recently represented Pride International in the Amethyst joint venture with Maritima for the financing of two mobile drilling rigs which were let to Petrobras. It also acted for Lloyds TSB Leasing on the UK tax-based financing of three container vessels for the China Ocean Shipping Company, arranged by Allco Finance, and for Prudential Trustees in connection with the leasing of two catamarans to Wightlink. **Clients:** Pride International; Lloyds TSB Leasing; Petrobras; COSCO; Enron.

THE SOUTH & SOUTH WEST

SHIPPING • The South and South West		Ptnrs	Assts
1	**Davies, Johnson & Co** Plymouth	4	2
	Foot Anstey Sargent Exeter, Plymouth	2	4
	Lester Aldridge Southampton	4	2
2	**Bond Pearce** Plymouth, Southampton	6	10
	DMH Brighton	n/a	n/a

LEADING INDIVIDUALS		
1	**HORTON Nicholas** Bond Pearce	**JOHNSON Jonathan** Davies, Johnson
	KELLY Russell Lester Aldridge	
2	**HATTERSLEY Charles** Foot Anstey Sargent	**McFADYEN Laurence** Lester Aldridge
	RUSTEMEYER Alistair DMH	
3	**HADLEY-PIGGIN Jonathan** Lester Aldridge	**HAYES Barry** Hayes

This book is the product of 6,552 1/2-hour interviews. See p.7 for BMRB audit.
Within each band, firms are listed alphabetically. *See individuals' profiles p.765*

Davies, Johnson & Co (see firm details p.934) Partner-heavy niche firm, well known for its non-contentious international dry practice. Featuring a strong P&I Club and FD&D component, the practice has forged strong overseas links with Northern Europe and Greece. Experienced practitioner **Jonny Johnson** (see p.769) remains a popular figure in the region. "*He's always around and gets the work*." The team recently worked closely with Lloyd's Syndicate 623 on the establishment of a new fixed premium P&I and FD&D Club. It also helped with the development of a new scheme of legal defence cover for shippers and traders in the international commodities markets. Although the wet practice does not have as high a profile, the firm acted for the owners of 'John R,' a major casualty on the Norwegian coast. **Clients:** P&I Clubs including Britannia, Steamship Mutual and West of England; owners; commodities traders.

Foot Anstey Sargent (see firm details p.961) The shipping practice is personified by the fierce litigation style of **Charles Hattersley** (see p.768), who is active in a range of marine personal injury and fatal accident claims. Although his uncompromising approach polarises the market, clients love the team's competitive fees and aggressive negotiation tactics. According to the London bar, the tactics usually work. "*He really fights and stops his clients being rolled over*." The Plymouth office, with three ex-mariners, handles the majority of the wet and marine insurance work, while a partner in Exeter handles dry, cargo and freight matters. An increase in non-contentious work has involved handling shipbuilding contracts and ship construction for clients such as DML (a Halliburton subsidiary,) as well as ship finance for Lloyds TSB. Total loss cases have included the 'Baltic Surveyor,' 'Margaretha Maria,' 'Fleur de Lys,' 'Princess Martha' and 'Kym.' **Clients:** Atlantic Marine & Sales Charter; Devonport Management; Everend Insurance Brokers; Riverside Fabrications; Georg Duncker & Co; JW Stevenson & Co; P&I Clubs; owners; AXA; Royal & Sun Alliance; Finnish oil traders.

Lester Aldridge (see firm details p.1038) Newly branded as LA Marine, the team has "*confidently entered the market*" and emerged as a major south coast presence, following a number of lateral hires. P&I Club expert **Russell Kelly** (see p.769) and marine lawyer **Jonathan Hadley-Piggin** (see p.767) joined from Shoosmiths in October 2000, followed in January 2001 by yacht and insurance specialist **Laurence McFadyen** (see p.770) from Holmes Hardingham. All are said to be "*really pulling in the work.*" Active in both the commercial shipping and leisure marine sectors, the team acts for owners, insurers and ship managers. Recent highlights include representing Grant Dalton, skipper of the 108' catamaran 'Club Med' after his prosecution by the Maritime & Coastguard Agency for breaches of the International Regulations for the Prevention of Collisions at Sea. Also represented a company wishing to set up an online auction service for the leisure marine industry, and acted for a large ferry operator in defence of a claim for damage sustained by freight vehicles and their cargo during heavy weather. **Clients:** Amicus Legal; Columbia Ship Management; CNA Maritime; Gard UK P&I Club; Geest Line; Lombard Marine Finance; Maersk-Sealand; Standard P&I Club; St.Margarets Insurances; Sunseeker; UK P&I Club; P&O European Ferries.

Bond Pearce (see firm details p.888) Having recently recruited a shipping specialist in associate Nicky Nelson from Norton Rose in London, the firm has been "*popping up more.*" The addition of marine specialist **Nick Horton** (see p.768) ("*a superb draftsman*") in June 2001 was further evidence of the firm's sustained push into the sector. He brings with him a track record acting for yacht insurers and owners, and shipping vessel casualty cases. Dry shipping (charterparties, bills of lading and cargo,) insurance claims, MCA investigations and ports work form the majority of the caseload. In addition, the practice is expected to benefit from the relocation of the P&O claims office from London to Southampton. The firm advised the MCA on an investigation prompted by Customs and Excise allegations of drug smuggling, after quantities of cocaine were found on a cargo vessel in Falmouth. It also acted on a compensation claim for loss of livelihood from a diver who sustained injuries, and advised yacht brokers Camper & Nicholsons in connection with the sinking of a super yacht. **Clients:** Geest Line; ABP; Maersk; Camper & Nicholsons International; Berkley Handling Group; Brittany Ferries; P&O; UK P&I Club; Gard; Steamship.

DMH (see firm details p.944) Not quite felt to have the profile of rival practices, the firm still maintains a consistent presence, handling dry shipping, including P&I Clubs, yachts and marine insurance. **Alistair Rustemeyer** (see p.771) is recommended as a "*sensible operator*" by clients and fellow lawyers, and is known to act for a number of Greek and overseas clients, as well as leading local yacht companies. **Clients:** Navigators and General; Sunderland Marine.

Other Notable Practitioners Exeter-based sole practitioner **Barry Hayes** continues to offer a "*low-key but effective*" service to a clientele which predominantly consists of P&I Clubs and composite insurers. Small amounts of cargo, salvage and customs & excise round out the workload. His profile was raised recently through acting for Southampton Cargo Handling in a Court of Appeal case against Lotus Cars.

EAST ANGLIA

SHIPPING • East Anglia	Ptnrs	Assts
1 **Dale & Co** Felixstowe	1	2
Eversheds Ipswich	n/a	2
John Weston & Co Felixstowe	1	1
2 **Birketts** Ipswich	2	-
Prettys Ipswich	1	2

LEADING INDIVIDUALS	
1 **DALE Michael** Dale & Co	**KEMP Jonathan** Eversheds
WESTON John John Weston & Co	
2 **DICKIE Paul** Prettys	**WHITE-THOMSON John** Birketts

This book is the product of 6,552 1/2-hour interviews. See p.7 for BMRB audit.
Within each band, firms are listed alphabetically. *See individuals' profiles p.765*

Dale & Co Small niche practice which deals with the full range of shipping work. The "*personable*" **Michael Dale** continues to cement his reputation as one of the region's most prolific dry practitioners. "*He's had a busy year,*" acting for a raft of domestic and international P&I clubs. Clients praised the firm's approach, citing its "*hands-on advice and quick, and often successful settlements.*" In addition to its stock clientele of European and Scandinavian clubs, the practice handles stowaway cases, acts for cross-European ferry operators and has recently pursued a number of large cargo claim actions. Clients: International P&I Clubs; ferry operators; European logistics and distribution companies.

Eversheds (see firm details p.952) A growing shipping force, the firm has been "*increasingly active*" since opening up in Ipswich three years ago. The office, accomplished at handling both dry and wet work, receives support from the national network, most notably the Newcastle office, with which it works closely. Associate **Jonathan Kemp** (see p.769) is a respected figure locally, and is thought to have consolidated his P&I defence and bulk cargo charterparty claims practice. The firm has also recruited a marine claims manager with tanker work expertise from Clyde & Co, thereby reinforcing its wet capability. The team has received a number of marine insurance and superyacht instructions, including one on behalf of an owner, investigating and successfully negotiating a $14 million claim on a vessel's hull and machinery policy following her sinking. **Clients:** London P&I Clubs; Turkish shipowners; container lines.

John Weston & Co Ex-seafarer **John Weston** runs a niche shipping and transport practice that has carved out an impressive reputation, both locally and with overseas clients. Acting for a variety of UK and European P&I clubs, local insurers and cargo recovery agents, his "*lucid style*" is widely admired. The firm has handled a number of high value containerised cargo claims at the port of Felixstowe, and has recent collision and salvage experience. **Clients:** P&I Clubs; insurers; recovery agents; owners.

Birketts Although it has suffered personnel departures in recent years, the firm has bounced back with a new focus, after absorbing a portion of cargo recovery business CRS from the Willis Group. The integration of cargo recovery work for underwriters with a pure shipping practice has prompted one observer to dub the firm "*the Clyde & Co of Ipswich.*" Partner **John White-Thomson** is highly rated for his work on personal injury and cargo defence claims, while consultant John Wynn oversees the relationship with cruise line Fred Olsen. The firm recently handled a large arbitration concerning a supply of sugar, and on the cargo recovery side, is dealing with a series of high value computer parts cases. **Clients:** Port of Ipswich; Port of Felixstowe; Hutchison Whampoa; ABP; Fred Olsen; P&O Ferrymasters.

Prettys (see firm details p.1100) Recently made a partner, former Clifford Chance litigator **Paul Dickie** (see p.766) has developed a reputation as an "*impressive local operator.*" Concentrating on dry shipping (charterparties, bills of lading, sale and purchase) and transport, the practice's non-contentious capacity has been boosted by the addition of a part-time ship finance lawyer from Watson Farley & Williams. Highlights of the past year include advising Norwegian lawyers on the sale of a European ferry line, a High Court litigation on behalf of a leading cross-channel carrier, and acting for a Hong Kong member of a London-based P&I Club in connection with a Norwegian Sale Form dispute. The team also handles a substantial volume of cargo line work for world-wide shipping lines and freight forwarders. **Clients:** Shipping lines; P&I Clubs.

THE NORTH

SHIPPING • The North	Ptnrs	Assts
1 **Andrew M Jackson & Co** Hull	5	3
Eversheds Newcastle upon Tyne	5	7
Mills & Co Newcastle upon Tyne	5	5
Rayfield Mills Newcastle upon Tyne	8	4
2 **Hill Dickinson** Liverpool, Manchester	8	12
3 **DLA** Liverpool, Manchester	n/a	n/a

LEADING INDIVIDUALS	
1 **HILTON Chris** Eversheds	**MILLS Guy** Mills & Co
MILLS Stephen Rayfield Mills	**TAYLOR Silas** Andrew M Jackson & Co
2 **MACKIN Stephen** Eversheds	**WAREING David** Hill Dickinson
3 **HILL Martin** DLA	**JACKSON Peter** Hill Dickinson
MAXWELL John Hill Dickinson	**PENROSE Robert** Andrew M Jackson & Co
RAYFIELD Richard Rayfield Mills	

This book is the product of 6,552 1/2-hour interviews. See p.7 for BMRB audit.

Within each band, firms are listed alphabetically. *See individuals' profiles p.765*

Andrew M Jackson & Co (see firm details p.860) Well known nationally for its wet work, the firm has a track record in total loss and casualty cases, in addition to special expertise in the international fishing vessel industry. It advises Sunderland Marine Mutual, a specialist insurer servicing fishing craft. The dry practice acts for a number of P&I clubs, while the firm also boasts a growing European marine insurance practice. Our researchers were impressed by the volume of client commendation: "*They provide us with exactly what we need and don't take a case too far.*" **Silas Taylor** (see p.772) handles the bulk of the personal injury and casualty investigations, often in respect of fishing boats. An "*astute maritime lawyer, he's a realist but not afraid to knock heads together.*" A litigator with a fearsome reputation, "*as soon as his name is dropped into the hat, people shudder a bit!*" **Rob Penrose** (see p.770) is also a popular client choice, and has a versatile practice spanning fishing vessel transactions, licensing, registering and quota issues. He recently represented Dutch and Belgian vessel owners in criminal prosecutions. The firm acted on the Court of Appeal case concerning the entitlement of jack-up rig workers to claim foreign earnings deductions in respect of their income tax. It was also involved in the first inquiry under Section 61 of the Merchant Shipping Act, where a Master's certificate was suspended pending the inquiry. **Clients:** Sunderland Marine Mutual Insurance Company; P&O North Sea Ferries; Whitaker Group; P&I Clubs; marine insurers; fish producer organisations; Humber area shipping and freight forwarding companies.

Eversheds (see firm details p.952) In tandem with its counterpart in East Anglia, the Newcastle team operates as a national unit, and is regarded as one of the leading teams outside London. Buoyed by the firm's recent expansion into the Netherlands, Singapore and Hong Kong, and aided by a dedicated group of mariners, the firm is felt by competitors to have increased its profile for collision and salvage cases. An impressive dry work caseload has seen the firm acting for a spread of national and overseas P&I clubs, hull underwriters and ship managers, foreign owners and leading lights in the London insurance market. All-rounder **Chris Hilton** (see p.768) is considered as one of the sector's leading lights, and the equal of many lawyers in London. "*Just about faultless,*" he "*brings real strength to a fantastic team.*" His caseload includes wet, dry and marine insurance, and he continues to work with BIMCO on the revision of management contracts and charters. Newly-appointed partner **Steve Mackin** (see p.770), an ex-mariner, is also in great demand. He specialises in tanker disputes and advises clients in Russia, the Baltic States and Cyprus. The firm advised on a $14 million super yacht total loss case and had a high profile involvement in the 'Derbyshire' inquiry. **Clients:** Page & Moy; NEPIA; Graig Shipping; Graig Ship Management; P&I Clubs; ship owners; port authorities; ferry operators.

Mills & Co Through its historical association with British Shipbuilders, the firm has carved out a niche in shipbuilding contracts, ship repair and construction, while consolidating its position as one of the leading regional P&I club players. The wet practice is limited to occasional pieces of salvage work. Although the retirement of paterfamilias Geoff Mills represents a setback to the firm, his son **Guy Mills** (*"sharp and immensely hard-working"*) continues to develop an already impressive reputation among clubs, barristers and competitors. The firm has advised on a number of big-ticket charterparty disputes and ship repair contracts, appeared on the buy-out of a major high speed ferry builder, and acted on a multi-million pound shipping and engineering dispute for a world-wide industrial group. **Clients:** British Shipbuilders; P&I Clubs, including North of England Club; ship repair yards; industrial groups.

Rayfield Mills A prolific regional practice which, through its work on high-profile litigation, has become a fixture on the national stage. Renowned by clients for its "*first class quality levels,*" the team is rated by some as "*at least as good as London, and at far more competitive prices.*" Traditionally strong on the dry side, a steady diet of work for core P&I club clients, the North of England and the UK Club has been bolstered by increased work in ship finance, oil and commodities. A growing shipbuilding practice also complements existing expertise in ship repair. The wet team is small, but handles, inter alia, collisions, salvage, tanker and cargo claims. **Stephen Mills** ("*enthusiastic, works hard and really gets on top of the detail*") generates support from both clients and barristers. Vastly experienced, he has represented Exxon Mobil on a range of ship and trading disputes, the most notable of which is the long-running Metro litigation. Fellow name partner **Richard Rayfield** ("*utterly reliable*") is also widely recommended, predominantly for his expertise in maritime disputes on behalf of clubs and owners. **Clients:** Exxon Mobil; North of England P&I Club; UK P&I Club; ship owners.

Hill Dickinson (see firm details p.996) Seen to offer a comprehensive shipping service, the team has particularly strong dry credentials, although it also receives commendation on the wet side. A diversified client base and a network of offices spanning Liverpool, Manchester and London have helped to keep the firm near the top of most people's lists. The Liverpool office maintains its connections to a shipowning clientele, while Manchester specialises in cargo matters. Liverpool-based managing partner **David Wareing** (see p.772) is acknowledged as a leader in shipping-related personal injury. Heading up the Manchester office, **Peter Jackson** (see p.769) oversees a small team that acts for domestic and international insurers, shipping and transport clients. Clients were also impressed by the litigation skills of **John Maxwell** (see p.770), who has acted on several foreign disputes and casualties, advising both owners and underwriters. He represented UK-based owners in actions involving Greenpeace. **Clients:** Mersey Docks & Harbour; Skuld; Warta; insurers.

DLA The shipping group includes teams of specialists in Liverpool, Manchester and London, who advise on collisions, salvage, marine insurance, charterparty and general carriage of goods disputes. A particular forte is marine insurance. **Martin Hill** is regarded as the key player here.

SCOTLAND

SHIPPING • Scotland	Ptnrs	Assts
1 **Henderson Boyd Jackson WS** Edinburgh	2	2
2 **Mackinnons** Aberdeen	5	3
3 **Maclay Murray & Spens** Glasgow	3	2

LEADING INDIVIDUALS	
1 **LOWE James** Henderson Boyd Jackson WS	
MACLEAN Duncan Henderson Boyd Jackson WS	
MACRAE Keith Mackinnons	
2 **SCOTT Charles** Mackinnons	**VIRGO Bruce** Henderson Boyd Jackson WS

This book is the product of 6,552 1/2-hour interviews. See p.7 for BMRB audit.

Within each band, firms are listed alphabetically. *See individuals' profiles p.765*

Henderson Boyd Jackson WS A ubiquitous presence in Scotland, the practice "*has a hand in almost everything,*" and is at the forefront of a small market where few firms have a shipping specialisation. Clients are attracted to the firm's versatility, and laud a "*broad base of skills that can service most of your shipping needs.*" The firm has a fine Court of Session pedigree and an extensive track record in handling ship litigation. Historically known as a P&I club practice, insurance still forms the bulk of its caseload, although the clientele now includes a broader spread of owners, yards, operators and banks. **Jim Lowe** (see p.769), an ex-mariner, handles casualty, salvage and the majority of the big-ticket wet litigation. A popular and experienced solicitor, he has a "*fantastic grasp of the law, and a real ability to get to the crux of issues.*" **Duncan MacLean** (see p.770) is highly rated as "*an energetic and decent lawyer,*" while associate **Bruce Virgo** (see p.772) is rapidly developing a name of his own. The firm advised on two multi-million pound disputes involving arrest of oil rigs, acted for the survivors of the 'Express Samina' sinking, and represented the fabricators of oil platform topsides which collided with Erskine Bridge. In a case against BP, now at the House of Lords, the practice represented Chevron in a landmark decision regarding harbour damage. **Clients:** Clydeport; Caledonian MacBrayne; Britannia Steam Ship Insurance Association; CGNU; Gard; Skuld; UK P&I Club; Amerada Hess; Clydesdale Bank; Kingsberg Simrad; Northern Marine Management; Tokio Sailing; Shell International Trading & Shipping; MCA P&O Crusies; BP Shipping.

Mackinnons (see firm details p.1047) Aberdeen-based shipping specialists with a substantial offshore wet practice, and a growing niche in harbour law. This builds on acknowledged expertise in the fishing vessel industry where the firm is "*second to none*" in Scotland. A core client base of fishing vessel insurers has seen the practice act on a number of related casualties and personal injury claims. In addition, the unit has picked up a number of instructions from English P&I clubs and marine insurers. Chief casualty litigator **Keith MacRae** (see p.770) has "*superb in-depth knowledge of the industry*" and was recommended for his work on marine insurance, salvage, vessel loss, hulls and personal injury. **Charles Scott** (see p.771) is also a respected senior lawyer with a commercial bent, and has a track record in drafting ship sale and purchase and shipbuilding contracts. He acts for a number of Scottish owners who have built ships in Scandinavia and Southern Europe. The firm advised on the 'Sapphire' total loss case. **Clients:** Sunderland Marine Mutual Insurance; Aberdeen Harbour Authority; Peterhead Bay Authority; Scottish boat owners; P&I Clubs; fishing vessel insurers.

Maclay Murray & Spens (see firm details p.1047) The firm lacks the full-time shipping resources of its leading rivals, but remains a recognised force in ship financing and in the contentious sphere, where the firm's commercial litigators are frequently employed on shipping matters. Bruce Patrick leads a small ship finance practice that acts for the Ship Mortgage Finance Company and Scottish clearing banks in connection with loans and complex leasing transactions. It also acts for owners in the purchase and sale of ships, and on the financing of offshore supply vessels and fishing boats. The litigators have represented oil companies, P&I clubs, cargo interests and marine insurers in a range of disputes. The high value Sullom Voe oil tanker collision damage claim involving BP has now progressed to the House of Lords. Other highlights include acting for Steamship Mutual and the owners of MT Multitank Ascania in a claim involving the grounding of the vessel, and advising Far Eastern cargo interests against the owners of the 'Mandarin Sky' in a multi-million pound dispute over damaged cargo. **Clients:** Ship Mortgage Finance Company; Skuld; West of England P&I Club; Steamship Mutual; North of England P&I Club; Lithgows; J&A Gardner & Co; Clyde Shipping; BP; Schlumberger; NUMAST.

LEADERS IN SHIPPING

ATKINSON, Joe
Sinclair Roche & Temperley, London
(020) 7452 4000

BARDOT, Andrew
Bentleys, Stokes & Lowless, London
(020) 7782 0990
Specialisation: Qualified 1980. Partner 1982. Principal areas of practice: all aspects of dry shipping and insurance related litigation and arbitration and non-contentious matters, including sale and purchase and MOA matters. French speaker.
Prof. Memberships: London Maritime Arbitration Association supporting member. Baltic Exchange member.

BOWMAN, Marcus
Holman Fenwick & Willan, London
(020) 7488 2300
marcus.bowman@hfw.co.uk
Specialisation: Partner in shipping litigation department. Specialising in maritime litigation with emphasis on charterparty, bill of lading and marine insurance disputes; P & I claims handler for seven years.
Career: Oceanus P & I club, 1980-83; Britannia P & I club, 1983-87; articled *Holman Fenwick and Willan*; qualified 1990; partner 1993; solicitor of the Supreme Court of England and Wales. University of Cape Town (BA); University of London (LLM).
Personal: Born 1954. Resides London.

BROWN, Anthony
A.D. Brown, Solicitors, London mob:
(07774) 415 287
adpb@ic24.net
Specialisation: Commercial shipping litigation, in particular dry cases, both P&I and defence, arising under charterparties, bills of lading, MOAs and insurance contracts; sale and purchase transactions; drafting of joint venture, profit/loss sharing, shareholders' and other commercial agreements, mostly in shipping-related matters. Fluent German speaker, hence large client base in Hamburg. Also has a number of further contacts in the Dutch, Croatian, Korean and Taiwanese markets. Frequent speaker on shipping topics both in the UK and overseas.
Prof. Memberships: Law Society, LMAA.
Career: Exeter School and Trinity Hall, Cambridge (graduated 1978). Subsequently with *Richards Butler, Elborne Mitchell* and *More Fisher Brown.* Commenced own practice in November 2000.
Personal: Extensive sailing experience, including a number of professional yacht deliveries in the Biscay and Atlantic areas.

BROWNE, Ben
Shaw and Croft, London (020) 7645 9000

BUSH, Philip
Jackson Parton, London (020) 7702 0085

CROFT, Roger
Shaw and Croft, London (020) 7645 9000
Roger.Croft@shawandcroft.com
Specialisation: Senior partner specialising in admiralty law and insurance law. Principal area of practice

is admiralty and insurance law. Work includes collision, salvage, pollution, environmental damage and total loss. Other main area of practice is fraud and money laundering. Acted in the Goring (House of Lords), the Mare (Court of Appeal) cases and KOTC v Al Bader & Others (House of Lords). Clients include major shipowners, salvors, insurers and P&I clubs.
Prof. Memberships: Law Society; City of London Solicitors Company; London Maritime Arbitrators Association; Royal Institute of Navigation; Average Adjusters Association; Admiralty Solicitors Group; International Bunker Industry Association; Worshipful Company of Shipwrights.
Career: Joined the Royal Navy in 1962. Electronic engineer from 1967. Qualified in 1978. Senior partner at *Shaw and Croft* from 1992.
Personal: Born 19 May 1946. Educated at Wallington County Grammar School and London University. Interests include golf, cricket, music, gardening and reading.

CRUMP, Richard
Holman Fenwick & Willan, London
(020) 7488 2300
richard.crump@hfw.co.uk
Specialisation: Partner in commercial litigation department. Practice encompasses all areas of shipping litigation, including charterparty disputes, cargo claims, ship sale disputes, joint venture and pool agreement disputes, marine insurance claims including total loss and related commercial litigation. Has spoken at seminars in Athens and Bombay. Accredited CEDR Mediator.
Prof. Memberships: Law Society member.
Career: Qualified in 1981 having joined *Holman Fenwick and Willan* in 1979. Became a partner in 1987.
Personal: Born 6 September 1957. Educated at St Paul's School, London 1970-74, Oriel College, Oxford 1975-78 and College of Law, Guildford 1979. Lives in London.

CURTIS, Simon
Curtis Davis Garrard, Heathrow Airport
(020) 8400 2400
simon.curtis@cdg.co.uk
Specialisation: Partner in shipping group. Main area of practice is shipping and offshore (oil and gas) work. Covers range of maritime litigation matters and non-contentious project work principally relating to shipbuilding, conversion and repair. Regular speaker at conferences on maritime law.
Prof. Memberships: London Maritime Arbitrators Association (supporting member). Fellow of the Chartered Institute of Arbitrators.
Publications: Author of 'The Law of Shipbuilding Contracts' (2nd edn), Lloyd's of London Press. Contributor to 'Force Majeure and Frustration of Contracts' (2nd edn), Lloyd's of London Press.
Personal: Born 10 November 1955. Attended Jesus College, Oxford (BA Hons) 1st class (Davies Prize 1977) and Bachelor of Civil Law. Leisure pursuits include scuba diving, skiing and fishing. Lives in Berkshire.

DALE, Michael
Dale & Co, Felixstowe
(07074) 794708/(01394) 284 118

DE LA RUE, Colin
Ince & Co, London (020) 7623 2011
colin.delarue@ince.co.uk
Specialisation: Has acted in most major oil pollution incidents worldwide in the last 15 years. On a day-to-day basis advises shipowners, oil companies, P&I clubs, marine underwriters and others on the ramifications of pollution from ships in various branches of maritime commerce. Has given papers on the subject at seminars and conferences in many countries around the world.
Prof. Memberships: British Maritime Law Association Pollution Sub-Committee; elected titulary member of the Comité Maritime International in 1994.
Career: Bar Finals 1977; admitted as solicitor 1980; partner *Ince & Co* 1986; head of firm's pollution group.
Publications: General Editor of 'Liability for Damage to the Marine Environment' (LLP 1993) and co-author of 'Shipping and the Environment' (LLP, 1998), the main textbook on the subject.
Personal: Born 1953. Education: Elizabeth College, Guernsey and Pembroke College, Cambridge. Married with three children.

DEERING, Bob
Ince & Co, London (020) 7623 2011
bob.deering@ince.co.uk
Specialisation: Joined *Ince & Co* in 1976; partner in 1985. Over the years has become involved in all aspects of the firm's shipping practice and heads its Dry Shipping Group which is regularly adjudged to be No 1 and which comprises some 85 partners and other lawyers. He represents a number of substantial ship owners, charterers and P&I clubs both in their own capacity and on behalf of their shipowner members. He also acts for underwriters in the investigation of hull claims and as a result, has experience of casualties from all sides of the fence.
Prof. Memberships: Law Society.
Career: Pembroke College, Cambridge. Joined *Ince & Co* 1976. Qualified 1978. Partner 1985.
Publications: Bob is a regular on both the UK and the international seminar circuit, speaking on matters as diverse as e-commerce and ship arrest.
Personal: Married, 3 children. Sport – both watching and playing.

DICKIE, Paul
Prettys, Ipswich (01473) 232121
pdickie@prettys.co.uk
Specialisation: Shipping litigation, acting for owners, charterers and their insurers. Also advises in relation to commercial shipping including sale and purchase, shipbuilding and finance.
Prof. Memberships: London Maritime Arbitrators' Association (supporting member).
Career: Qualified in 1988. Worked for *Clifford Chance* 1988-97 in London and Hong Kong. Joined *Prettys* 1997; partner 2000.
Personal: Born 22 April 1964 in Turniff, Aberdeenshire. Robert Gordon's College, Aberdeen 1975-81 and Worcester College, Oxford 1982-85. Leisure interests include most sports, gardening and cooking.

DONOGHUE, Andrew
Middleton Potts, London (020) 7600 2333
Specialisation: Partner in shipping litigation department. Main areas of practice are charterparty, bill of lading and ship sale and purchase disputes together with problems arising under contracts for the international sale of goods. Acts primarily for P&I Clubs, Defence Associations and individual shipowners, charterers and commodity houses.
Prof. Memberships: Supporting member LMAA.
Career: MA Degree in Jurisprudence, Lincoln College, Oxford 1973; articled clerk and assistant solicitor *Richards Butler & Co* 1974-80. With *Middleton Potts* since 1980.
Personal: Born 15 November 1951. Leisure interests: mountaineering, naval and ancient history.

DUNN, Chris
Waltons & Morse, London (020) 7623 4255

DUNNE, Frank
Watson, Farley & Williams, London
(020) 7814 8009
fdunne@wfw.com
Specialisation: Frank is a *Watson, Farley & Williams* partner. Frank's practice involves a broad range of ship finance work for major international shipping finance lenders and commercial shipping transactions for major international shipowners, including joint ventures, charter structures, new building contracts, and ship acquisitions. He has also been closely involved in the development of insurance products for credit enhancement. Having worked in Greece during the 1980s, Frank is well known in Greek shipping and finance circles and continues a close working relationship with the Greek market. He has been involved in a number of high-profile work out and dispute resolution situations.
Career: Articled *Norton Rose*; qualified 1980; established the firm's highly successful office in Piraeus 1984 spending five years there; partner in *Watson, Farley & Williams* since 1984.
Personal: Educated Downing College, Cambridge University (LLM).

EAST, Lindsay
Richards Butler, London (020) 7247 6555
Specialisation: Partner. Former head of shipping and insurance group. Main area of practice is shipping and insurance. Acts for owners and charterers direct or through their insurers (P&I and defence clubs) in all contractual disputes, charterparty, bill of lading, MOA, and building contracts. Particular expertise in drafting and advising on club rules, charterparties and shipbuilding disputes. Also handles general marine and non-marine insurance, acting for cargo insurers, reinsurers and war-risk underwriters. Cases have included 'Antaios', 'Antares', 'Antonis P Lemos', 'Standard Steamship v Gann, Aditya Vaibhav', 'Aegean Maritime v Flender Werft' and 'Sagheera'. Speaker at and chairman of various seminars.
Prof. Memberships: Baltic Exchange.
Career: Qualified in 1973, having joined *Richards Butler* in 1971. Became a partner in 1977.
Personal: Born 24 March 1949. Attended Skinners School to 1966, then Worcester College, Oxford 1967-70 (MA Jurisprudence). Leisure interests include cricket, golf, opera and travel. Lives in Rickmansworth, Herts.

EVANS, John
Hill Taylor Dickinson, London (020) 7283 9033
john.evans@htd-london.com
Specialisation: Shipping and insurance litigation. A partner for 21 years, who has practised shipping and marine insurance litigation/arbitration throughout his career. Wide experience of resolution of charterparty disputes and pursuit of claims arising from

major maritime casualties including actual and constructive total losses of vessels. Group leader of one of the firm's maritime and insurance litigation groups, leading a team of professional staff, including two partners who were formerly Master Mariners. Reported cases of interest handled by the group include Ventouris v Mountain (Italia Express); Choko Star; Royal Volker Stevin v Mountain; ('Dutch Dredgers'); Star Sea; Apostolis; Tjaskemolen and 'Vergina'. He is the partner in London responsible for the firm's Piraeus office.
Prof. Memberships: A supporting Member of LMAA, and inter alia a Member of the British Italian Lawyers' Association, of the BMLA and the IBA. He is a liveryman of the Worshipful Company of Shipwrights.
Career: Llandovery College; University College of Wales, Aberystwyth (1972 LLB).
Personal: Resides Stebbing.

FISHER, Nicholas
Fishers, London (020) 7709 7203
info@fishcity.co.uk
Specialisation: Partner specialising in commercial shipping litigation, insurance and reinsurance litigation. Handles commercial shipping litigation, including significant client base in container, reefer and tanker operations. Also insurance and reinsurance litigation involving brokers' PI claims.
Prof. Memberships: London Maritime Arbitrators Association (Supporting Member), Baltic Exchange, The City of London Solicitors' Company.
Career: Qualified in 1979. Partner at *Richards Butler* 1984-88. Founding partner of *More Fisher Brown* 1988-93. Founded *Fishers* in May 1993.
Personal: Educated at Glyn Grammar School, Epsom, then Clare College, Cambridge (MA).

FLETCHER, Simon
Clyde & Co, Guildford (01483) 555 555
Specialisation: Senior partner in marine casualty department. On the wet side: salvage, collision, transhipment, general average for cargo, ship, salvor and banking clients including cargo, hull, P&I and MII insurance matters – recent cases: Collision between Ever Decent and Norwegian Dream and the sinking of the Mighty Servant 2. On the energy litigation side: acting for insurers, oil companies and contractors, mainly in respect of insurance, construction and operating problems including Piper Alpha and Sleipner A. Seconded to an oil company for 18 months regarding an FPSO construction dispute and now involved in the loss of the P 36.
Prof. Memberships: The Law Society; chairman of the BMLA sub-committee for Offshore Structures.
Career: LLB (Hons) Manchester 1968. Qualified and joined *Clyde & Co* in 1971. Became a partner 1975.

GHIRARDANI, Paolo
Stephenson Harwood, London (020) 7809 2612
paolo.ghirardani@shlegal.com
Specialisation: Partner, Head of Shipping and Insurance Litigation Group. Paolo handles all areas of shipping litigation but has a specialist practice of shipping and insurance fraud – with a particular emphasis on Africa. He regularly represents the interests of leading shipowners, P&I Clubs and underwriters, investigating fraudulent claims. He has gained a reputation as a tough, determined and well respected lawyer with good investigative skills. His most recent and interesting case is the Dubai Valour (Gulf Azov Shipping v Idisi) Lloyd's Rep [2001] 727 which involved the successful recovery of a payment made to release a crew detained in Nigeria for two years.
Career: Qualified 1985. Joined *Stephenson Harwood* in 1989 and became partner in 1992.
Personal: Born 1959. University College Cardiff BA (Hons) Law and Spanish 1978-82. Married. Interests: wine making and photography. Languages: Fluent Spanish, a little French and Italian.

GIBB, Jeremy
Norton Rose, London (020) 7283 6000
gibbsjsp@nortonrose.com
See under Asset Finance & Leasing, p.95

GINSBERG, Roy
Waltons & Morse, London (020) 7623 4255

GOSLING, James
Holman Fenwick & Willan, London (020) 7488 2300
james.gosling@hfw.co.uk
Specialisation: Partner in admiralty department. Principal areas of practice are salvage, collision, total loss, pollution and wreck removal, acting mainly for salvors, shipowners, hull underwriters and P and I Clubs. Also handles marine insurance, general shipping and commercial law MOA disputes, charterparty disputes and cargo claims. Important cases have included Scandanavian Star, Europa collision with Inchon Glory, Happy Fellow collision with Darfur, Estrella Pampeana collision with Sea Parana and Smit Tak B.V. v Selco Salvage. Clients include several leading salvage companies, ship owners, hull underwriters, ship managers, insurance brokers and one southern hemisphere tycoon. Is on the editorial board of the *International Maritime Law*. Has lectured on admiralty law in Mexico and Venezuela in Spanish, and in London and Piraeus.
Prof. Memberships: Member of the Instituto Ibero-Americano De Derecho Maritimo.
Career: Qualified in 1980. Became a partner in 1988.
Personal: Born 28 June 1955. Educated at Ampleforth College, York and at St Catharine's College Cambridge. Leisure interests include rugby, skiing, tennis, sailing, rowing, motor cycling, antiques and crosswords. Speaks French and Spanish. Lives near Saffron Walden.

GRAY, Edward
More Fisher Brown, London (020) 7247 0438
egray@m-f-b.co.uk
Specialisation: Principal area of practice is dispute resolution advice to ship owners and operators, and their insurers. Specialises in contractual and tortious disputes arising in connection with the carriage of goods by sea, and second-hand sale and purchase contracts and newbuilding contracts. Particular experience with tankers, container vessels and offshore vessels/offshore construction projects. Extensively involved in managing and coordinating worldwide multi-jurisdictional disputes. Also advises in contentious and non-contentious matters in the shipping area in connection with EU competition and regulatory matters, sales and acquisitions of businesses, and debt refinancing.
Career: *Richards Butler*, London 1979-83 *Richards Butler*, Hong Kong 1983-91, *More Fisher Brown* since 1992.
Personal: St Edmund Hall, Oxford – BA Jurisprudence, 1st Class Hons.

GREENSMITH, Nicholas
Clyde & Co, Guildford (01483) 555555
nick.greensmith@clyde.co.uk
Specialisation: Partner in marine casualty department. Main areas of practice are collision, salvage, total loss and wreck removal, general average, towage and ship repair disputes. Important cases include M Vatan (salvage); Reijin (capsize/wreck removal); Ya Mawlaya/New World (collision); BOS 400 (towage dispute); Sea Empress (grounding/pollution/criminal prosecution).
Prof. Memberships: The Law Society; City of London Admiralty Solicitors Group; Admiralty Court committee; International Harbour Masters Association.
Career: Qualified in 1980. Became a partner in 1984.
Personal: Born 3 March 1955. Educated at William Hulme's GS Manchester and at St Catharine's College, Cambridge. Married with three children. Interests include rugby, football, skiing, golf and sailing.

GRIFFITHS, Paul
Bentleys, Stokes & Lowless, London (020) 7782 0990
PGriffiths@bentleys.co.uk
Specialisation: The full range of marine, insurance and transport related disputes principally on the "dry" side. Advice given to a broad spectrum of clients in connection with actual or potential problems and their resolution by negotiation, Court process or arbitration.
Career: Qualified 1979. Partner at *Bentleys, Stokes & Lowless* since 1985.
Personal: Married. Two children.

HADLEY-PIGGIN, Jonathan
Lester Aldridge, Southampton (023) 8082 0415
jonathan.hp@lester-aldridge.co.uk
Specialisation: Partner and head of shipping and marine department (LA Marine). Specialises in national and international yachting, acting for owners, insurers and businesses in dispute resolution and drafting agreements such as build, sale and charter parties.
Prof. Memberships: Nautical Institute, British Marine Industries Federation, Professional Yachtsmans Association, Chartered Institute of Transport, LMAA, Royal Southampton Yacht Club.
Career: Deck Officer BP Shipping 1978-83, Royal Navy Officer (Submarines) 1983-91. Qualified 1995. *Stephenson Harwood* 1993-96. *Shoosmiths* 1996-2000, partner in 2000. *Lester Aldridge* partner from 2000.
Personal: Born 1961. Warsash Nautical College, Cardiff University BSc(Hons) Dartmouth Naval College. Married, two children. Interests include walking and shooting.

HARRIS, Graham
Thomas Cooper & Stibbard, London (020) 7481 8851
Specialisation: Wide experience of dispute resolution, commercial negotiation and e-commerce in the shipping and transportation industries including shipbuilding, sale and purchase, charterparties, bills of lading, through transport documentation and insurance.
Career: Qualified October 1981 *Norton Rose* then *Richards Butler*. Partner at *Richards Butler* 1988.
Personal: Born 28th September 1956. Educated at King's School, Canterbury and Oriel College Oxford (MA Jurisprudence, First Class Hons). Lives in London.

HARTLEY, Simon
Norton Rose, London (020) 7283 6000
hartleys@nortonrose.com
Specialisation: Specialising in shipping finance representing shipping companies, banks, export credit agencies and other financial institutions in connection with all types of ship lending and leasing, capital raising, sale and purchase of second-hand ships, ship registration, shipbuilding contracts, bareboat chartering, management agreements and related financial arrangements. The shipping finance group is one of the leading shipping finance practices in London, working closely with other *Norton Rose* lawyers experienced in advising shipping industry clients on competition and regulatory matters, taxation, litigation, insurance, mergers and acquisitions and corporate finance for the shipping industry.
Prof. Memberships: Member of the Law Society and Baltic Exchange.
Career: Trained *Norton Rose*; qualified 1988; partner 1997.
Publications: Has been a regular contributor to the 'Economy Shipping Finance Annual' over the last three years.
Personal: Married with one child. Leisure interests are sport and hill walking.

HARVEY, Richard
Richards Butler, London (020) 7247 6555
rhjph@richardsbutler.com
Specialisation: Heads the firm's casualty response team of mainly legally qualified ex-seafarers, which handles all types of casualty including fires and explosions, groundings, salvage, collisions, wreck removal, reef damage and pollution, and their associated insurance and general average issues. Acts for Clubs, Hull underwriters, shipowners and major salvors. Has handled for owners such cases as the Europa/Inchon Glory, MSC Samia/Carina, Lula 1/Graceous, Polydefkis P/Anna Spiritou collisions and the Sea-Land Mariner fire and explosion. Acted for salvors in the European Gateway and for owners in the salvage of the MSC Rosa M as well as in the Maersk Tokyo, Erika and World Discoverer.
Prof. Memberships: Law Society; British Maritime Law Association; BMLA Arrest Convention sub-committee; City of London Admiralty Solicitors Group.
Career: Served as an officer in the British Merchant Navy before qualifying as a solicitor in 1980. Became a partner in *Richards Butler* in 1983.
Personal: Educated at Christ Church, Oxford (M.A.); Southampton College of Technology. Interests include sailing, gardening, music, photography and engineering.

HATTERSLEY, Charles
Foot Anstey Sargent, Plymouth (01752) 675000
charles.hattersley@foot-ansteys.co.uk
Specialisation: Main area of practice is admiralty law including total losses, collision, salvage marine insurance and pollution together with fatal accidents and personal injury claims arising out of such casualties; ship repair and shipbuilding disputes; non-contentious work relating to ship finance, mortgage, security documentation and shipbuilding contracts; expertise in pilot age and Harbour Authority matters. Recent cases: 'Rema'; 'Fleur De Lys'; 'Margaretha Maria'; 'Baltic Surveyor'; 'Pietertje'.
Prof. Memberships: Nautical Institute; Institute of Directors; CBI; BMIA; BMLA.
Career: 1970-83: Deck officer in submarine service; 1985-89, *Holman Fenwick & Willan*; 1989-91, *Norton Rose*; 1993-2001, *Foot Anstey Sargent*, partner.
Publications: Articles for 'Seaways' (Nautical Institute), 'Lloyd's List', and numerous trade magazines.
Personal: Born 22 March 1949. Attended Marlborough College, 1963-68; Durham University, 1969-71; Law College, 1982-84. Interests include mountaineering, skiing and tennis. Married with three children. Lives in Yelverton, Devon.

HAWKES, Ian
More Fisher Brown, London (020) 7247 0438
ihawkes@m-f-b.co.uk
Specialisation: Principal areas of practice are charterparty, bill of lading and ship sale and purchase disputes. Also regularly involved in disputes arising from contracts for the international sale of goods.
Career: *Baker & McKenzie*, London 1989-93; *More Fisher Brown* since 1994.

HAYES, Barry
Hayes, Exeter (01392) 202 742

HEBDEN, David
Thomas Cooper & Stibbard, London
(020) 7481 8851
david.hebden@tcssol.com
Specialisation: Senior partner. Main area of practice is all aspects of shipping casualties, including collisions, grounding, salvage, total loss, fire, flooding and loss of stability, leading to capsize. Defence of criminal prosecutions in shipping. Casualty and emergency response team management. David is also a management adviser to shipping and marine insurance industries and handles day to day shipping problems including discipline and passenger ship operations.
Prof. Memberships: Law Society; British Maritime Law Association (Salvage & Wreck Removal Committee); Admiralty Solicitors Group; Honourable Company of Master Mariners.
Career: Qualified at *Thomas Cooper & Stibbard* in 1971, became a partner in 1974 and senior partner in 1992.
Personal: Barnard Castle School 1948-52; HMS 'Worcester' 1952-54; School of Navigation, Southampton University 1962-64. ISM Lead Auditor 1997. CEDR Accredited Mediator 2001. Interests: Golf and tennis.

HERRING, Paul
Ince & Co, London (020) 7623 2011
paul.herring@ince.co.uk
Specialisation: Specialises in carriage of goods by sea, charter party, bills of lading, sale and purchase and new building disputes. Regular lecturer on charter party, carriage of goods by sea, sale and purchase issues.
Career: First Class Honours Degree in Law from Leicester University. Articled at *Ince & Co* in 1979 and became a partner in 1987.
Personal: Golf.

HILL, Martin
DLA, Liverpool (08700) 111111

HILTON, Chris
Eversheds, Newcastle upon Tyne (0191) 261 1661
hiltonc@eversheds.com
Specialisation: Head of shipping department. Shipping and maritime law. Has over 25 years experience in London and Newcastle, including 15 years managing a mutual FD & D association. Experienced in all aspects of maritime law ('wet' and 'dry') and is an arbitrator. Also handles insurance policy work. On various drafting committees of BIMCO.
Prof. Memberships: Chartered Institute of Arbitrators (Fellow); member of the BMLA Committee on Carriage of Goods by Sea.
Career: Qualified 1975. Accredited mediator.
Publications: Contributor to 'Practical Guide to Multimodal Transport'.
Personal: Cambridge University 1968-71; Adelaide University in 1972.

HODGKINSON, George
Sinclair Roche & Temperley, London
(020) 7452 4179
george.hodgkinson@srtlaw.com
Specialisation: All aspects of sale and purchase and financing of ships, drillships and FPSOs, both second hand tonnage and newbuildings, for both owners and banks; leasing; advice on foreign flag; and, on the regulatory side, drafting legislation to establish new ship registries. He has developed a strong following in Germany, particularly in connection with the financing of newbuildings constructed at German shipyards.
Prof. Memberships: Non trading member Baltic Exchange
Career: Admitted solicitor 1970 (England and Wales); 1978 (Hong Kong). Articled *Clifford Chance*; solicitor *BT Tanker Company Limited* 1971-3; joined *Sinclair Roche & Temperley* as assistant solicitor 1973; partner at *Sinclair Roche & Temperley* 1975 to date.
Publications: Lloyds Shipping Economist, 'A Unique Field for Financing', 2000; International Cruise and Ferry Review, 'Legal Aspects of Financing Growth', 2000.
Personal: MA Oxon (Jurisprudence) 1966; Liveryman Shipwrights Company.

HODGSON, Derek
Clyde & Co, London (020) 7623 1244
derek.hodgson@clyde.co.uk
Specialisation: Partner in marine department. Shipping/marine/insurance. Experienced in representing shipowners/P&I clubs/hull underwriters, charterers and trading companies in High Court actions and arbitrations. Particular speciality in Thailand, Greece, South America and Africa.

HORTON, Nicholas
Bond Pearce, Plymouth (01752) 266633
nhorton@bondpearce.com
Specialisation: Partner specialising in shipping and marine work. Full legal service to shipping, insurance and marine industries with particular specialism in yachts, both in the UK and internationally; litigation and commercial contract work; marine insurance; sale and purchase; build and refit contracts; international litigation.
Prof. Memberships: Member of the British Marine Industries Federation, Royal Ocean Racing Club, Royal Western Yacht Club.
Career: Qualified 1986. *Ingledew Brown Bennison & Garrett* 1984-88. Partner *Davies Grant & Horton* 1990-97; co-founder of *Grant & Horton, Marine Solicitors*, 1997-2001; partner *Bond Pearce* 2001.

JACKSON, Peter
Hill Dickinson, Manchester (0161) 278 8800
Jacko@HillDicks.com
Specialisation: Main areas of practice are marine, goods in transit and insurance litigation. Work includes cargo claims, for both cargo and liability insurers, particularly international road haulage claims; ship related cargo claims for cargo interests; salvage and monitoring foreign litigation. Also handles marine insurance work, particularly marine insurance policy interpretation for underwriters. Acted in ICI plc v MAT Transport, ITT v Birkart, the Breydon Merchant F & W Freight, the Los Angeles, Microfine v Transferry Shipping and Inco Europe.
Prof. Memberships: Liverpool Underwriters Association, Manchester Marine Insurance Association, London Maritime Arbitrators Association.
Career: Qualified in 1985, having joined *Hill Dickinson Davis Campbell* in 1983. Became a Partner in 1989.
Personal: Born 3rd April 1961. Attended St Edward's College, Liverpool 1972-79, then Exeter College, Oxford 1979-82. Leisure interests include football, season ticket holder at Anfield. Former Chairman of Football Supporters Association. Cricket and squash. Lives in Liverpool.

JOHNSON, Andrew
Hill Taylor Dickinson, London (020) 7283 9033
andrew.johnson@htd-london.com
Specialisation: Partner in Shipping and Maritime Law Department. Main area of practice is shipping litigation, covering charter parties, bills of lading, collision and salvage. Co-author of 'A Guide to the Hamburg Rules'; contributor to 'Marine Claims'.
Prof. Memberships: Law Society.
Career: Qualified in 1984, having joined *Hill Dickinson* in 1980. Became a Partner in 1987.
Personal: Born 5th February 1955. Lives in London.

JOHNSON, Jonathan
Davies, Johnson & Co, Plymouth (01752) 226020
Specialisation: Partner specialising in shipping and maritime law. Shipping and maritime law since 1976, also handles commercial litigation work.
Prof. Memberships: LMAA (Supporting), BMIA.
Career: Qualified in 1976. Worked at *Richards Butler* London and Hong Kong 1976-92, became partner in 1980. Joined *Davies Grant & Horton* in 1992 as partner. Founded *Davies, Johnson & Co* May 1997.
Personal: Born 31 March 1951. Attended Nottingham University, taking LLB in 1972. Lives in Plymouth.

JOHNSTON, David
Holmes Hardingham, London (020) 7283 0222
david.johnston@hhlaw.co.uk
Specialisation: Shipping litigation. All aspects of law pertaining to yachts, including salvage, collision, racing disputes, construction, operation and management, purchase and sale. Particularly marine insurance disputes, policy advice and drafting. Recent cases include 'The Milasan' [2000] 2 LL L Rep 458.
Prof. Memberships: BMIF. Subscriber to YBDSA.
Career: Articled *Paola Wright & Wilkinson*, Durban 1971-2; admitted South Africa 1973. Joined *Ingledew Brown Bennison & Garrett*, London 1974, subsequently admitted in England and appointed partner. Founding partner *Holmes Hardingham* 1989. Managing partner 1989 to date.
Personal: B Com LLB (Natal). Extensive yachting experience under sail and power. Member RYA, CA and local sailing club. Other interests include woodland management and gardening.

KELLY, Russell
Lester Aldridge, Southampton (023) 8082 0416
russell.kelly@lester-aldridge.co.uk
Specialisation: Partner in the shipping and marine department (LA Marine). Specialises in shipping and maritime law; particularly charterparties and contracts for the carriage of goods, defending MCA prosecutions, passenger and crew injury claims, bunker suppliers' claims and claims by repairers and suppliers of goods and services to vessels. Clients include a number of the leading P&I Associations, ferry operators and overseas law firms. Regularly engaged in both Commercial and Admiralty Court litigation and arbitration.
Prof. Memberships: London Maritime Arbitrators Association.
Career: Qualified 1986 with *Thomas Cooper & Stibbard*, London, becoming a partner in 1990. Joined *Bond Pearce* 1997. Joined *Lester Aldridge* in 2000.
Personal: Born 1960. Married with two children. Lives near Winchester.

KEMP, Jonathan
Eversheds, Ipswich (01473) 284428
jonathankemp@eversheds.com
Specialisation: Shipping and maritime law. Handles all types of admiralty claims and commercial shipping dispute resolution. Also deals with port and harbour law, marine insurance and superyacht matters. Acted as arbitrator in two collision claims.
Prof. Memberships: Nautical Institute. Law Society.
Career: Royal Navy (navigating officer) 1976-86. Qualified 1990. Joined *Sinclair Roche & Temperley* in 1988 for articles and practised in Singapore and London. Joined *Eversheds*, Ipswich, 1998.
Personal: Born 1958. Educated at Norwich School and King's College, London. Lives near Felixstowe. Sports: Sailing and skiing.

LAX, Michael
Lawrence Graham, London (020) 7337 7618
mike.lax@lawgram.com
Specialisation: Partner in shipping department. Deals with a range of shipping and maritime law matters. Work includes international trade litigation and arbitration, charterparty disputes, cargo claims, marine insurance disputes, oil pollution claims, ship finance, sale and purchase, and shipbuilding contracts.
Career: Qualified in 1977. BA (Dunelm).
Publications: 'Time limits in arbitration proceeding and representations in Bills of Lading'; 'Legal aspects of oil shortage claims'; 'Liquid cargo disputes'; 'Demurrage for tanker owners/charterers'; 'Keeping your corporate veil in place'; 'Is there a future for mutuality'; 'Laytime definitions' – in particular clauses 6 and 9 of Part 2 of the ASBATANKVOY'; 'Arrest of ships, arrest of bunkers – and how to avoid them'; 'The International Safety Management Code (ISM) the legal implications'; 'Loading and discharging responsibilities, and where the responsibilities lie'.
Personal: Born 22 December 1952. Member of Cannons Sports Club. Lives in Wallington.

LEACH, Ben
Sinclair Roche & Temperley, London
(020) 7452 4000

LIVINGSTONE, Hugh
Holman Fenwick & Willan, London
(020) 7488 2300
hugh.livingstone@hfw.co.uk
Specialisation: Partner in commercial litigation department. Specialising in all types of marine litigation on behalf of shipowners, charterers and insurers (P and I and market), as well as sellers and buyers of ships.
Career: Educated University of Cape Town (BA LLB) and University College London (LLM). Admitted 1976 (South Africa), 1985 (England and Wales) and 1986 (Hong Kong). Partner in *Holman Fenwick & Willan* 1986. Resident partner in Hong Kong office 1986-88 and subsequently at London office.

LOWE, James
Henderson Boyd Jackson WS, Edinburgh
(0131) 226 6881
Specialisation: Principal maritime partner. Handles sale and purchase agreements, ship building and financing, ship registration as well as admiralty work; collisions, salvage, marine pollution, ship building and repair contract disputes.
Prof. Memberships: Law Society of Scotland, Honourable Company of Master Mariners, Writer to the Signet, British Maritime Law Association, Nautical Institute.
Career: Ship's Officer 1966-80. Gained Master Mariners Certificate in 1976. Qualified solicitor 1985; assumed partner 1986.
Publications: Author of Maritime Securities in the 'Stair Memorial Encyclopedia' and various articles for legal, marine and fishing industry press.
Personal: Lives East Lothian. Enjoys sailing.

LOWE, Steven
Stephenson Harwood, London (020) 7329 4422

LUX, Jonathan
Ince & Co, London (020) 7623 2011
jonathan.lux@ince.co.uk
Specialisation: Work includes shipping, international trade and insurance advice and litigation. Has acted in many cases and transactions in these fields. Holds LLB (Hons) (Exhib), 1973, and DES from the University of Aix-Marseilles, 1974.
Prof. Memberships: Law Society, London Maritime Arbitrators Association, Chartered Institute of Arbitrators, CEDR, ADR Net, British Academy of Experts, International Bunker Industry Association, International Bar Association. Freeman of the City of London, liveryman of the Worshipful Company of Solicitors, former chairman of the International Bar Association's Committee on Maritime and Transport Law; Chairman of the Committee 1 (legal systems) of the International Bar Association's Human Rights Institute, fellow of the Chartered Institute of Arbitrators and council member of the International Bunker Industry Association Ltd, member of the Steering Committee of London Shipping Law Centre.
Career: Qualified and joined *Ince & Co.* in 1975. Became a partner in 1983.
Publications: Co- author of 'The Law of Tug, Tow and Pilotage' and 'The Law and Practice of Marine Insurance and Average' and 'Bunkers'. Editor of 'Classification Societies'. Author of various other publications in the fields of maritime law and international trade. Regular speaker at conferences and seminars on shipping, international trade and insurance subjects.
Personal: Leisure interests include opera, theatre,

golf, sailing and single-seater motor racing (holder of a national licence). Participated in the Peking to Paris Car Rally (1997) finishing First in Class and awarded gold medal. Lives in London.

MACKIN, Stephen
Eversheds, Newcastle upon Tyne (0191) 261 1661
stephenmackin@eversheds.com
Specialisation: Charterparty and bill of lading disputes, particularly "oil tanker" related disputes. Oil shortage, cargo contamination, off-hire, unsafe port/berth disputes and market loss claims. Liepaya [1999] 1 Lloyd's Rep. 649.
Prof. Memberships: Member of the Nautical Institute.
Career: Qualified 1994. Previously Navigating Officer – Shell Tankers (UK) Ltd (experience of: VLCCs, product tankers, LNG and OBOs).
Personal: Married with two children. Interests include golf.

MACLEAN, Duncan
Henderson Boyd Jackson WS, Edinburgh (0131) 226 6881
Specialisation: All aspects of contentious shipping and transport work including arrests, cargo claims (sea and land), collisions, marine pollution, personal injury claims in the merchant, offshore and fishing fleets, salvage, ship building and repair disputes, and general commercial disputes. Acts for P&I clubs, insurers, banks, owners, builders and repairers in court and in investigations.
Prof. Memberships: Law Society of Scotland; Writer to the Signet; British Maritime Law Association.
Career: Qualified 1988. Joined *Henderson Boyd Jackson* in 1994. Became partner in 1996.
Publications: Presented papers to marine underwriters, the Nautical Institute and fellow solicitors.
Personal: Married with two daughters. Interests include sports and the outdoors.

MACRAE, Keith G
Mackinnons, Aberdeen (01224) 632464
Specialisation: Partner in maritime and litigation department. Acts for marine insurers, covering hull and machinery and P&I. Has particular experience in fishing vessel insurance and claims. Practice split between hull/admiralty work (collisions, salvage, total loss and casualty investigation) and P&I claims (in particular personal accident/employers liability claims from accidents on oil rigs and ships). Also handles oil pollution cases. Work includes on-site investigation on- and off-shore. Has a substantial case load in the Sheriff Court and Court of Session, acting for Defenders in personal injury claims and for Pursuers in ship repair and ship builders negligence claims and contractual disputes. Gave a paper to Law Society of Scotland's Second Maritime Law Seminar. Presents seminars on Marine Insurance to clients.
Career: Qualified in 1982. Joined *Mackinnons* in 1980, becoming a partner in 1983.
Personal: Born 23rd May 1953. Attended Aberdeen University 1971-76 (MA(Hons)) and 1977-80 (LLB). Honorary Norwegian Consul in Aberdeen; Honorary Danish Vice-Consul in Aberdeen. Leisure interests include football, rock and jazz music and travelling. Lives in Catterline.

MAXWELL, M John
Hill Dickinson, Liverpool (0151) 236 5400
mjm@hilldicks.com
Specialisation: Partner in Marine and Transport department. Specialises in shipping and commercial litigation, in particular on behalf of shipowners, P&I Associations and port authorities. Marine accidents and casualty investigations for UK and foreign clients including collision, salvage, cargo claims, environmental and personal injury investigations. Charterparty and commercial disputes and arbitrations.
Prof. Memberships: London Maritime Arbitrators Association
Career: Qualified 1969. Partner in *Hill Dickinson* since 1976. Notary Public 1977.
Personal: Education: Sedbergh School; Liverpool University.

McFADYEN, Laurence
Lester Aldridge, Southampton (023) 8082 0414
laurence.mcfadyen@lester-aldridge.co.uk
Specialisation: Salvage, collision, charterparty and bill of lading disputes. Involved with 'Sea Empress' acting for Salvors.
Prof. Memberships: Supporting member LMAA.
Career: MN navigating officer 1973-82. Mate on offshore supply and anchor handler on part-time basis between 1982-88. Admitted as solicitor 1991. Two years secondment to SKULD, Oslo. Partner with *Holmes Hardingham* 1996-2000. Joined *Lester Aldridge* 2001.
Personal: Class 2 Certif of Competency. 1st Class Honours Nautical Studies (naval architecture and transport economics). Qualified solicitor.

MILLS, Guy B.
Mills & Co, Newcastle upon Tyne (0191) 233 2222

MILLS, Stephen
Rayfield Mills, Newcastle upon Tyne (0191) 261 2333

MOORE, Chris
Ince & Co, London (020) 7623 2011
chris.moore@ince.co.uk
Specialisation: Partner dealing with shipping casualty work, charter party and cargo defence. Recent cases include 'DB29', 'Agean Sea', 'Western Winner'/'British Trent', 'Ever Decent'/Norwegian Dream, 'Weser Ore'.
Career: Articled *Ince & Co*; qualified 1977; partner 1983; senior resident partner Hong Kong 1987-92; acting president Hong Kong branch Maritime Law Association 1988-92; contributer 'Classification Societies'.
Personal: Education: St Edwards, Christ's College Cambridge (1975 MA), Université d'Aix-Marseille. Leisure: Mountaineering, music and skiing. Personal: Born 1951; resides London, married. Fluent French speaker.

MORRISON, Mark
Clifford Chance, London (020) 7006 4813
mark.morrison@cliffordchance.com
Specialisation: Partner in international maritime and trade group, specialising in disputes (particularly arbitration) in the fields of oil and gas; commodities; and ship/rig construction, repair and conversion contracts.
Prof. Memberships: Fellow of the Chartered Institute of Arbitrators; Baltic Exchange; supporting member of the LMAA; member of the Institute of Petroleum.
Career: LLB 1978; BCL 1980; qualified 1983 (Hong Kong 1995); partner 1993; Hong Kong office 1995-99.
Publications: Numerous articles on shipping, commodity and offshore issues.

MOYLAN, Adrian
More Fisher Brown, London (020) 7247 0438
amoylan@m-f-b.co.uk
Specialisation: Charterparty and bill of lading disputes. Commodity, especially sugar, arbitrations. Marine and non-marine insurance litigation. Reported cases include "Lutetian", "Mexico I" and "Holsten cruiser".
Career: Partner *Richards Butler* 1987; founding partner *More Fisher Brown* 1988-date.
Personal: Cambridge cricket blue 1977, incompetent skiing novice, learning Norwegian.

PARTON, Nicholas
Jackson Parton, London (020) 7702 0085

PENROSE, Robert
Andrew M. Jackson & Co, Hull (01482) 325242
Specialisation: EU fishery law, defence of fishery prosecutions; fishing vessel quota, licence, sale purchase and leasing; international joint ventures and enterprises; commercial ship build, second hand sale and purchase, and finance documentation. Representation in Merchant Shipping Act proceedings. Clients include major UK and European fishing vessel owners, fish producers organisations, P&I clubs, banks and owners in relation to finance. Recent cases include advising on prosecutions in the Southern Oceans; a joint venture in South America; Fishery Protection Vessel contracts in the Indian Ocean; ship build contracts in China.
Prof. Memberships: Law Society.
Career: Nottingham University. Joined *Andrew M. Jackson & Co.* Partner 1985.
Personal: Born 1955, resides near Louth, Lincolnshire. Interests include food, wine and TVR cars.

RAYFIELD, Richard
Rayfield Mills, Newcastle upon Tyne (0191) 261 2333

ROBERTSON, Struan
Sinclair Roche & Temperley, London (020) 7452 4000

ROOTH, Anthony
Watson, Farley & Williams, London (020) 7814 8000
trooth@wfw.com
Specialisation: Partner in International Litigation Group. Shipping litigation including charterparty, bill of lading disputes, cargo claiming, maritime casualties and marine insurance (co-editor Gard P&I Handbook). Acts principally for shipowners, charterers, P&I and defence insurers. Focuses on Scandinavia, Continental Europe and Mediterranean countries, especially Greece & Turkey.
Career: Partner *Clyde & Co* 1979-1998 (opened their Hong Kong office 1981). Partner *Watson, Farley & Williams* 1998.
Personal: BA Queen's College, Cambridge. Interests: horses, tennis, skiing, theatre.

RUSSELL, Mark
Stephenson Harwood, London (020) 7809 2600
mark.russell@shlegal.com
Specialisation: Partner, head of ship finance group. All aspects of non-contentious shipping law, acting for lenders and shipowners. He specialises in project finance and in the energy, oil and gas and natural resources fields. Lectures on syndicated loans, loan transfers, loan participations and work-outs.
Career: Qualified October 1983. *Simmons & Simmons* as assistant solicitor 1983-84. *Sinclair Roche & Temperley* in 1984 and became partner in 1989. Joined *Stephenson Harwood* in 1995 as partner. Head of ship finance group in 1996.
Personal: Born 7 October 1958. Educated at Bradfield College; Bristol University, LLB 2:1 1980. Married with two children. Interests include growing large vegetables. Resides Harpenden.

RUSTEMEYER, Alistair
DMH, Brighton (01273) 744 219
alistair.rustemeyer@dmh.co.uk
Specialisation: Partner specialising in all aspects of shipping and insurance litigation and arbitration including carriage of passengers and goods by sea, sale and purchase and marine insurance work.
Prof. Memberships: LMAA (supporting), BMIF, Law Society.
Career: Dip. Maritime Law; qualified 1994; joined DMH September 1997, appointed partner 2000; accredited CEDR mediator.
Personal: Winton Grammar School; University of Buckingham LLB. Born 1964. Interests: sailing and golf. Married with one daughter.

SAYER, Richard
Ince & Co, London (020) 7623 2011
richard.sayer@ince.co.uk
Specialisation: Partner covering maritime law. Main areas of practice are admiralty (collision, salvage and other casualties), charter party disputes, sale and purchase litigation and maritime fraud. Acted for owners of numerous headline casualties including 'The Braer' following the Shetland disaster in 1993. Also a member of the four-man FERIT (Far East Regional Investigation Team) established by all the major Far East insurance associations to investigate the incidence of maritime fraud in the South China Sea in the 1970s.
Prof. Memberships: Chairman (since 1991) of the City of London Admiralty Solicitors Group (Secretary 1972-91), Chairman of the BMLA Salvage Sub-Committee, member of the Baltic Exchange, supporting member of the Association of Average Adjusters, and of the London Maritime Arbitrators Association, member of the Admiralty Court Committee since 1986, and member of the Lloyd's Form Working Party. Assistant to the Court of the Worshipful Company of Shipwrights. Appointed Examiner in Admiralty by Lord Taylor C.J. 1996.
Career: Qualified in 1966, having joined *Ince & Co.* in 1962. Became a Partner in 1970. Was admitted in Hong Kong in 1979 and spent five months there opening the firm's Hong Kong office. Became Senior Partner in 1995, and stepped down in May 2000 after a 5 year stint.
Personal: Born 7th May 1943. Attended Framlingham College 1956-61. Leisure interests include golf, cricket and jazz. Lives in London.

SCOTT, Charles M
Mackinnons, Aberdeen (01224) 632464
Specialisation: Acts for vessel owners, vessel managers and major harbour authorities. Current specialisation and wide experience in harbour law, negotiating shipbuilding contracts and advising on commercial issues arising from them, purchase and sale of vessels, financing documentation, agreements concerning fishing licences and quota rights, fishing vessel partnership and company structures for fishing enterprises.
Career: Educated at Robert Gordon's College, Aberdeen and University of Aberdeen (LLB with distinction 1973). Qualified in 1975. Joined *Mackinnons* in 1978 and became a partner in 1979. Currently managing partner. Part-time lecturer at University of Aberdeen from 1976 until 1995.
Personal: Born 13th January 1953. Married with daughter and son. Lives in Aberdeen. Leisure interests include hill-walking, golf and music.

SCOTT, Kenneth
Holmes Hardingham, London (020) 7283 0222
Ken.Scott@HHLaw.co.uk
Specialisation: Admiralty law, collision and salvage, marine insurance and total loss. Represents salvors on a national and international level; also acts for owners and P&I clubs in charterparty and bill of lading disputes.
Prof. Memberships: Member of the Baltic Exchange; British Maritime Law Association; and Admiralty Solicitors' Group.
Career: Deck officer on tankers, general cargo and bulk carriers; navigating officer on icebreakers in the Canadian Coastguard. Qualified 1980, partner at *Horrocks & Co* 1981-1990; partner at *Holmes Hardingham* 1990 to date.

SEWELL, Vernon
Bentleys, Stokes & Lowless, London
(020) 7782 0990
law@Bentleys.co.uk
Specialisation: Specialises in all aspects of dry shipping and insurance related litigation and arbitration.
Prof. Memberships: The Law Society, supporting member of London Maritime Arbitrators' Association.
Career: Qualified in 1982. Partner in 1986.
Personal: Born 1956. Married with two children.

SHAW, Patrick
Ince & Co, London (020) 7623 2011
patrick.shaw@ince.co.uk
Specialisation: Has a broad based shipping practice covering both wet (collisions/salvage) and dry (charterparty/sale and purchase/bills of lading). Represents both owners and P&I insurers. Experience of investigating a number of high profile marine casualties.
Career: Joined *Ince & Co* in 1983. 1989-92 in *Ince & Co* Hong Kong and 1992-1997 in *Ince & Co* Singapore. Partner since 1991.

SHELTON, John H.
Norton Rose, London (020) 7283 6000
sheltonjh@nortonrose.com
Specialisation: Shipping finance, acting for owners, lenders, lessors, builders, and others.
Prof. Memberships: The Law Society, The Baltic Exchange.
Career: Articled at *Pinsent & Co*, Birmingham, joined *Norton Rose* on qualifying in 1981. Became partner 1987.
Personal: Married, four children. Principal interests: fatherhood and gardening.

SLADE, Robin
Stephenson Harwood, London (020) 7809 2630
robin.slade@shlegal.com
Specialisation: An admiralty specialist, he heads a specifically dedicated team handling all types of admiralty work and which includes several ex-mariners. He and his group have in-depth experience of handling significant major casualties and is one of the few such groups in the City of London. He has been involved in many well known casualties including major public enquiries such as 'Herald of Free Enterprise', 'Independenta', 'Kowloon Bridge', 'Khark 5', 'Sea Prince', 'Zim Piraeus'/'Leerort' and 'Nakhodka'.
Career: Qualified 1974, first became a partner in 1976 and joined *SH* as a partner in 1995.
Personal: Attended School of Navigation, Warsash. Married. One daughter. Interests include skiing, sailing, collecting pictures, theatre, eating and drinking.

SMITH, David
Allen & Overy, London (020) 7330 2555
david.smith@allenovery.com
Specialisation: Partner specialising in banking and asset finance, particularly in relation to ships representing financiers, owners, operators and in domestic and cross-border structured transactions, both leasing and debt based. Transaction structures have included government-guaranteed debt facilities, tax-based lease structures (including UK tax leases, US Lease-In-Lease-Outs and QTEs), off-balance sheet structures and non taxed – based leases including operating leases both with and without residual value support both singly and in combination (such as UK tax leases with US LILOS). He is also regularly involved in sale and purchase, new building contracts and registration matters relating to ships.
Career: Solicitor *Richards Butler*, 1984, Partner 1989; Partner *Wilde Sapte*, 1991; Partner *Allen & Overy*, 1999.
Personal: Born 1960, married with two children, enjoys family, motor cars, golf, cricket, eating out and theatre. BA Jurisprudence, Brasenose College, Oxford, 1981.

STRONG, Malcolm
Ince & Co, London (020) 7623 2011
malcolm.strong@ince.co.uk
Specialisation: Sale and purchase and finance of ships including related corporate, insurance, charter-party and other aspects. Was partner in the 'Niobe' (House of Lords case on sale of ships in 1995).
Prof. Memberships: Law Society. Supporting member London Maritime Arbitrators' Assocation.
Career: Cambridge University (Sidney Sussex College) MA., LL.M. Partner in *Ince & Co.* since 1970.
Personal: Married with one daughter. Interests: arts, rugby and cricket.

TAYLOR, Andrew
Richards Butler, London (020) 7247 6555
Specialisation: Partner in shipping unit. Specialises in marine casualty response, charter disputes, cargo liabilities, pollution, marine insurance, P&I clubs, club rules and sale and purchase. Speaker at conferences. Co-author of 'Voyage Charters' – Lloyds of London Press.
Career: Qualified in 1980. Partner at *Richards Butler* since 1983.

Personal: Born 1952. Educated at Magdalen College School and Lincoln College, Oxford (MA).

TAYLOR, Silas
Andrew M. Jackson & Co, Hull (01482) 325242
Specialisation: Main area of practice is marine casualty work. Acts on behalf of all main P&I clubs in collisions, salvage and major personal injury cases. Particular expertise in legal matters relating to the fishing industry. Also deals with disputes in respect of towage, pilotage and hull and machinery claims. Acts as a mediator in shipping and other cases. Has spoken on maritime law at conferences arranged by the Nautical Institute.
Career: Qualified and joined *Andrew M Jackson & Co* in 1975. Became partner in 1980.
Publications: Has contributed articles to 'Lloyd's Maritime and Commercial Law Quarterly' and the Nautical Institute's 'Seaways'.
Personal: Born 3 February 1953. Educated at Bedford Modern School 1964-71 and Hull University 1971-74. Leisure pursuits include salmon fishing, football and horticulture.

TAYLOR, Tim
Hill Taylor Dickinson, London (020) 7283 9033
tim.taylor@htd-london.com
Specialisation: Partner in Shipping and Insurance Department. Principal area of practice is insurance and shipping litigation. Cases of interest include the 'Stena Nautica' (1982) 'Piper Alpha' (1989), the 'Bowbelle' (1990) and the 'Wondrous' (1992).
Prof. Memberships: Chairman Marine Insurance Standing Committee, British Maritime Law Association; British Insurance Law Association; Association of Average Adjusters; London Maritime Arbitrators' Association; International Bar Association.
Career: Qualified in 1978 while with *Hill Dickinson & Co.* and became a Partner in 1982. CEDR Accredited Mediator.
Personal: Born 22nd June 1954. Attended Clifton College. Member of the MCC. Leisure pursuits include golf. Lives in Walton-on-the-Hill.

THOMAS, Tony
Clyde & Co, Guildford (01483) 31161
Tony.Thomas@clyde.co.uk
Specialisation: Main area of practice is shipping litigation. Has considerable experience in litigation in the Commercial Court in London, London Arbitration and proceedings overseas. Handles shipping and cargo claims and marine insurance disputes. Works mainly for overseas clients particularly in Japan and the EU, as well as the UN World Food Programme. Has spoken at a number of lectures around the world.
Prof. Memberships: Law Society.
Career: Qualified in 1976, joining *Clyde & Co.* the same year. Partner 1981.
Personal: Born 27 May 1952. Attended Leamington College 1963-70, then Manchester University 1970-73. Leisure interests include sport, art and architecture. Lives in Grayshott, Surrey.

THORP, Clive
Barlow Lyde & Gilbert, London (020) 7247 2277
cthorp@blg.co.uk
Specialisation: Consultant in the shipping department. Main areas of practice are charterparties, commodities, oil, freezing injunctions, search orders, payment of judgment debts, sovereign immunity and demurrage arbitrations. Also handles enforcement of judgments. Acted in 'Sonangol v Lundquist', privilege against self-incrimination; and 'Griparion' on indemnity costs. Lectures on Mareva injunctions, demurrage and shipbroker commissions.
Prof. Memberships: Baltic Exchange; Member of Law Society Committee on Arbitration.
Career: Qualified 1976. Worked at *Holman Fenwick and Willan* 1976-79, joining *Clyde & Co.* in 1979. Became partner in 1982. Joined *Barlow Lyde & Gilbert* as a consultant in 2001.
Personal: Born 28th August 1950. Attended Malvern College 1963-68, Hull University 1969-72 and College of Law. Common Councillor. City of London Committee Member London Court of International Arbitration. Chairman, Association for Research into Stammering in Childhood. Married, two children.

TURNER, Paul Alan
Clifford Chance, London (020) 7600 1000
Specialisation: Main practice covers the negotiation of ship building and conversion contracts, contracts for the sale and purchase of secondhand ships, maritime joint venture agreements, corporate acquisitions and disposals, ship finance and security documents, and other commercial shipping agreements.
Career: Educated at Peterhouse, Cambridge (MA). Joined *Clifford Chance* in 1982. Worked in Hong Kong between 1985 and 1988. Now working in London.
Publications: He is the general editor of 'Ship Sale & Purchase' (published by LLP Limited).

VIRGO, Bruce
Henderson Boyd Jackson WS, Edinburgh (0131) 226 6881
Specialisation: Associate, maritime department. Involved in a range of marine related disputes including: arrests, crew/passenger injury claims (notably asbestos related disease), cargo claims and charter/ownership actions. Also acts in ship sale/purchase transactions, ship registrations, and drafting of trading, contract and charter terms.
Prof. Memberships: Law Societies of Scotland, England & Wales, and Queensland. British Maritime Law Association.
Career: Qualified as solicitor in Australia 1981; England and Wales 1995; Scotland 1999. Accredited as Queensland mediator 1994.
Publications: Author/presenter of various papers for legal, marine/marine insurance groups.
Personal: Married with three young children.

VLASTO, Tony
Clifford Chance, London (020) 7600 1000
tony.vlasto@cliffordchance.com
Specialisation: Partner in international maritime, trade and insurance group. Head of Shipping and Admiralty practice group, specialising in particular in all aspects of casualty work, covering also a wide range of general maritime work including charterparty and bill of lading disputes, marine insurance litigation/arbitration, sale and purchase disputes, offshore oil disputes and mortgage enforcement.
Prof. Memberships: Baltic Exchange; BMLA, City of London Admiralty Solicitors Group; supporting member of the London Maritime Arbitrators Association and the Association of Average Adjusters; Steering Committee member of the London Shipping Law Centre; Liveryman Worshipful Company of Shipwrights.
Career: LLB 1972. Qualified 1975; partner 1981.

WALLIS, Robert
Hill Taylor Dickinson, London (020) 7283 9033
robert.wallis@htd-london.com
Specialisation: Admiralty law, particularly Collision, Salvage, Wreck Removal, Total Loss, Pollution Claims, Limitation of Liability and Marine Insurance Litigation.
Prof. Memberships: Law Society and Solicitors' European Group, British Maritime Law Association, CMI Sub-Committee on LoF 95, International Bar Association, Asia-Pacific Lawyers' Association.
Career: Leicester University LLB 1972, qualified 1975, Partner with Elborne Mitchell 1976-1988, joined *Hill Taylor Dickinson* as Partner 1988. Elected Chairman of Partnership 1999. CEDR accredited mediator.
Personal: Born 1950, married with two children. Interests include golf, tennis and rugby.

WARDER, David
Watson, Farley & Williams, London (020) 7814 8000
dwarder@wfw.com
Specialisation: Managing partner of *Watson, Farley & Williams* and member of the firm's international finance group based in London. Acts for financial institutions engaged in finance for the shipping, container shipping, cruise and offshore industries, specialising in asset-backed finance and structured project-based and securitisation transactions, with particular interest and experience in UK and cross border tax-based leasing. Other clients include shipowners and operators, shipbuilders and offshore contractors, and offshore drilling and production industry participants.
Career: *Norton Rose* 1973-82; joined *Watson, Farley & Williams* 1982.
Personal: King Edward VI School, Southampton; Trinity College, Cambridge.

WAREING, David
Hill Dickinson, Liverpool (0151) 236 5400
Specialisation: Partner. Representing shipowners and their insurers, hull and machinery underwriters and P&I Associations. Particular involvement with crew and stevedore accidents and occupational disease claims. Also acting on behalf of liability underwriters in relation to pleasure craft accidents.
Prof. Memberships: Liverpool Underwriters Association, Manchester Marine Insurance Association.
Career: Qualified 1978 with *Hill Dickinson & Co*. Partner from 1982.

WATSON, Martin
Watson, Farley & Williams, London (020) 7814 8000

WESTON, John
John Weston & Co, Felixstowe (01394) 282527

WHITE-THOMSON, John
Birketts, Ipswich (01473) 232300

WILLIAMS, Paul
Norton Rose, London (020) 7283 6000
williamspl@nortonrose.com
Specialisation: Paul Williams is a partner in the shipping litigation group. Whilst involved in all aspects of shipping disputes, he specialises in major casualties on behalf of shipowners, P&I Clubs and underwriters, as well as personal injuries. Paul has become a particular expert in multi-party disaster litigation and has wide experience in court and arbi-

tration proceedings, both in England and internationally.
Prof. Memberships: Paul is a member of the British Maritime Law Association and the Baltic Exchange. He is also a supporting member of the London Maritime Arbitration Association.
Career: Trained *Norton Rose*, qualified 1982 and made partner 1990.
Personal: Pembroke College, Cambridge (MA).

WILSON, James
Ince & Co, London (020) 7623 2011
james.wilson@ince.co.uk
Specialisation: James initially worked mainly on the charter party and cargo claims side of the firm's business. In later years however, he has concentrated more on the 'wet' side of the practice and has been increasingly involved in marine casualties, including the 'Braer' and 'Sea Empress', where the breadth of his admiralty experience was of great value. His client base is drawn from across the maritime industry and includes owners, clubs and marine underwriters. James now leads the firms admiralty group and is qualified both in England and Hong Kong.
Prof. Memberships: CEDR accredited mediator.
Career: James graduated from Cambridge with an Honours Degree in Law. He joined *Ince* in 1983. He became a partner in 1991.
Publications: Co-author of the admiralty section of 'Halisbury's Laws of England'.

WILSON, Robert
Holman Fenwick & Willan, London
(020) 7488 2300
robert.wilson@hfw.co.uk
Specialisation: Partner in commercial litigation department and senior partner of the firm. Principal area of practice is shipping and commercial law. Work covers commercial legal advice, handling and resolving disputes, negotiations, conducting litigation and arbitration including newbuildings; conversion and repair (ship/offshore); MOA; pools; charters; bills of lading; P and I and defence club work; marine insurance (including total losses); international trade, especially tankers and the oil trade. Also deals with insurance, commercial and banking law where related to shipping and trading interests. House of Lords and Court of Appeal cases include Delfini (title to sue), Kyzikos (laytime), Evpo Agnic (arrest), Arta (shipbrokers negligence), Apj Priti (safe berth) and Padre Island (P&I club/third party claims), Factortame (European law) and Haji-Ioannou v Frangos (European Convention and ship arrests).
Prof. Memberships: Law Society, London Maritime Arbitrators Association (supporting member).
Career: Qualified in 1977, having joined *Holman Fenwick & Willan* in 1975. Became a partner in 1982. Appointed senior partner in November 2000.
Personal: Born 8 February 1952. Educated at Watford Grammar School 1962-69 and Corpus Christi College, Cambridge 1970-74 (MA Maths, History; Law). Interests include family, golf and travel. Lives in Hadley Wood, Herts.

WINTER, Glenn
Holmes Hardingham, London (020) 7283 0222
Glenn.Winter@HHLaw.co.uk
Specialisation: Main areas of specialisation are charterparty disputes and bulk liquid cargo claims. Major cases handled include 'The Mito' (1987), ' The Stena Pacifica' (1990), 'The Holstencruiser' (1992) and 'The Stolt Sydness' (1996), 'The Sun Sapphire' (1999) and 'The Erika' (2000).
Career: Qualified in 1982. Founding partner of *Holmes Hardingham.*
Personal: Attended Keble College, Oxford and the University of Illinois. Born 7th May 1956. Married with two children.

SOCIAL HOUSING

OVERVIEW: The Social Housing sector cuts a swathe across many practice areas including complex mixed funding, PFI, property and development, and litigation issues. Panel cuts and the increasingly sophisticated tender process used by Housing Associations have affected firms in the sector with some opting to provide full service. Smaller firms with a specialist niche continue to hold their own. Rent harmonisation, right to buy issues and the increasing prospects of litigation have contributed to an active market.

RESEARCH APPROVED BY BMRB: *For this edition,* Chambers' *researchers conducted 6,552 interviews – 4,419 with law firms, 554 with barristers and 1,579 with clients.*

The validity of the research was scrutinised by BMRB International, who audited both the methodology and the results at our offices in July 2001. They interviewed Chambers' *researchers and cross-checked sample interviews. Details of the audit appear on page 7.*

LONDON

SOCIAL HOUSING • London	Ptnrs	Assts
1 Trowers & Hamlins	14	28
2 Devonshires	14	23
3 Jenkins & Hand	2	n/a
Lewis Silkin	4	5
Prince Evans	3	19
Winckworth Sherwood	4	16
4 Lawrence Graham	4	12
5 Maclay Murray & Spens	1	4
Sharratts	3	n/a
6 Coudert Brothers	3	4
Dawson & Co	2	2
Evans Butler Wade	n/a	n/a
GL Hockfield & Co	1	2
Hodge Jones & Allen	1	1

LEADING INDIVIDUALS	
1 ADLINGTON Jonathan Trowers & Hamlins	BASTOW Gillian Lewis Silkin
GRAHAM Ian Trowers & Hamlins	HAND Catherine Jenkins & Hand
JENKINS Keith Jenkins & Hand	MURRAY Andrew Winckworth Sherwood
ROBERT Louis Prince Evans	
2 DOOLITTLE Ian Trowers & Hamlins	HALL Gareth Devonshires
MORLEY Trevor Prince Evans	RANDALL Simon Lawrence Graham
3 EVANS Chris Evans Butler Wade	FITTON Roger Winckworth Sherwood
HART Rosemary Trowers & Hamlins	HAWKINS James Trowers & Hamlins
HUDSON Allan Devonshires	JENNINGS Robert Prince Evans
SMITH Chris Maclay Murray & Spens	

This book is the product of 6,552 1/2-hour interviews. See p.7 for BMRB audit.
Within each band, firms are listed alphabetically. *See individuals' profiles p.780*

Trowers & Hamlins (see firm details p.1162) Considered by peers and clients alike to be "*head and shoulders*" above the market, with quality work securing the "*biggest and the best*" client base. Clients praise "*an excellent, efficient and responsive*" unit which undertakes complex stock transfers, large scale regeneration projects and PFI. "*Great professional*" **Jonathan Adlington** (see p.780) "*brings his sense of humour to the table.*" Rated for his work in structuring, stock transfer and management issues, "*fantastic*" **Ian Graham** (see p.781) is "*co-operative,*" with clients agreeing that he is "*undoubtedly expert in the field.*" **Ian Doolittle** (see p.781) is a specialist in LSVT and public/private partnerships, while **Rosemary Hart** (see p.781) adopts *a "consistently positive approach*" to development and acquisition matters. **James Hawkins** (see p.781) also elicited commendation for his housing stock transfer expertise. On the lender side, the "*respected and bright*" **Sarah Hayes** (see p.782) and **Adrian Carter** (see p.780), who "*makes deals happen,*" also command a high level of market support. The firm advised Network HA on the transfer of Brent Council's sheltered stock (including redevelopment and partnership contracts), and acted for RSLs on constitutional reorganisations including Drum and Downland Housing Groups. Lender expertise includes bond issues, group borrowings and monoline insured deals. The team advised Dexia Group on over 90 separate loans (including security structures) to housing associations with an aggregate value of £750 million, and acted for New Charter Housing Group on a £213 million loan facility. **Clients:** Metropolitan Housing Trust; Network HA; Sanctuary HA; Horizon Housing Group; Dexia Public Finance; Abbey National Treasury Services; Lloyds TSB.

Devonshires (see firm details p.940) A dedicated practice, heavily endorsed by interviewees for its governance and development advice, while consolidating a profile in the funder market. **Gareth Hall** (see p.781) is best known for his work in corporate and constitutional matters, and **Allan Hudson** (see p.782) is highly rated for his expertise in property issues. The group advised on merger issues for Places for People, Bristol Churches and Edinvar. PFI also plays a major role in the firm's portfolio. On the lender front **Andrew Cowan** (see p.780) "*doesn't miss a point.*" Not averse to playing the "*tough guy,*" clients feel he is "*clearly enthusiastic in every instruction.*" The group has advised on bond issues for HSL, Haven and RSL Finance, acted for Circle Thirty Three in a £65 million acquisition facility and was involved in the £90 million refinancing of Evesham & Pershore HA's loan book. **Clients:** Circle Thirty Three; London & Quadrant; Places for People.

Jenkins & Hand (see firm details p.1013) Clearly defined by the market as "*the specialists*" to turn to for an opinion, the firm comprises a "*heavy-hitting duo*" who command "*the highest level of expertise.*" "*Talented*" **Catherine Hand** (see p.592) acted for Richmond Housing Partnership on the transfer of 7500 properties from the London Borough of Richmond. "*Leading light*" **Keith Jenkins** (see p.782) advised Chichester District Community Housing on its acquisition of 5000 properties from Chichester Council and acted on the first tenanted stock transfer in Wales. **Clients:** Southern Housing Group; William Sutton; Richmond Housing Partnership.

Lewis Silkin (see firm details p.1040) Acting for over 65 RSLs and other voluntary organisations, the group advises on a range of housing matters including constitutional issues, employment, financing and anti-social behaviour disputes. "*First-class*" **Gillian Bastow** (see p.780) is "*quietly efficient*" according to interviewees and advised the United Women's Homes Association on its structure and inter-group agreements with Circle 33. The group also acted for the London Borough of Newham on the formation of Passmore Urban Renewal Ltd. **Clients:** Broomleigh HA; Anchor Housing Trust; Family Housing Association; South London Family HA.

Prince Evans (see firm details p.1101) Winning "*decent work*" with a dedicated, broad-based practice, the firm is led by "*Dominant force*" **Louis Robert**, rated for his "*vast technical ability.*" Clients *appreciate his "instant advice – he's highly knowledgeable, sensible and friendly.*" **Trevor Morley** (see p.783) is an expert in housing finance issues, including complex group borrowing arrangements, while **Robert Jennings** leads one of the largest landlord and tenant litigation groups in the country. **Clients:** Notting Hill Housing Group; London & Quadrant.

Winckworth Sherwood (see firm details p.1185) A committed force in the social housing market, the team provides a "*first rate service*" to over 100 HA clients. Head of department **Andrew Murray** (see p.783) is "*friendly and approachable*" and focused on the finance side, while **Roger Fitton** (see p.781) is recommended by the market for his work in urban regeneration projects and advice on constitutional issues. **Clients:** Southern Housing Group; Paddington Churches HA; Thames Valley HA; Anchor Trust; Hanover HA.

Lawrence Graham (see firm details p.1030) Rated for its "*specialist advice*" in the LSTV arena, the firm regularly advises RSLs on regeneration and development projects. Key to the firm's prominence in the market are the warmly recommended **Simon Randall** (see p.783), who "*gives consistently good advice,*" and the finance-focused **Nick Turner** (see p.784). The firm advised West Wiltshire Housing Society on the transfer of the Council's remaining stock, involving a £100 million refinancing package and conversion to a limited company. **Clients:** Flagship Housing Group; Peabody Trust; Longhurst Group Ltd.

Maclay Murray & Spens (see firm details p.1047) "*A sound commercial practice,*" witnessing growth in employment, site acquisition work and association mergers. "*Sound and reliable*" **Chris Smith** (see p.784) is active in regeneration projects and constitutional issues, including a 250 property project on the south coast. **Clients:** Beacon HA; Guinness Trust; Oxford Citizens HA.

Sharratts Led by Richard Locke, the firm is rated by industry specialists for its "*efficiency and cost-effective approach*" to development and management issues. The group is active in volume property transfers, restructuring and advice to tenants.

Coudert Brothers (see firm details p.925) Focused on the complex development side of the HA market, the firm often advises private developers and investors. Anne O'Neill and the group are active on PFI bids, restructuring and funding, and advised on a development in Kensington. **Clients:** Notting Hill HA; Soho HA; Hastoe HA.

Dawson & Co (see firm details p.936) Bill Smith heads an experienced and established, if small team. The firm advised on a £50 million property mortgage, and was involved in a major urban regeneration project involving property acquisition and facilities provision. **Clients:** Family HA; Landmark HA; Octavia Hill Housing Trust.

Evans Butler Wade "*Respected*" **Chris Evans** leads an experienced group that is active for over 60 HA clients on regeneration and development issues. The team is also involved in acquisitions, financing, constitutional and employment issues. **Clients:** Housing Associations.

GL Hockfield & Co (see firm details p.998) A "*commercial team*" led by James Garvey, it has a strong focus on its RSL client base. Increasing its development and management work, the firm also has a respected contentious capacity. **Clients:** Paddington Churches HA; Southern HA; St Marylebone HA.

Hodge Jones & Allen (see firm details p.998) "*Cost-effective and responsive,*" according to its clients. Charles Piggott and the group give advice on corporate, property and employment issues, with a strong roster of RSL clients. The team acted for an RSL on the injection of housing corporation funding to refurbish a hostel in East London. **Clients:** Novas Ouvertures Group.

ADVISING LENDERS – NATIONWIDE

SOCIAL HOUSING: ADVISING LENDERS • Nationwide	Ptnrs	Assts
1 **Clifford Chance** London	7	25
2 **Addleshaw Booth & Co** Leeds	3	10
3 **Allen & Overy** London	3	n/a
Denton Wilde Sapte London	3	10
Trowers & Hamlins London	4	4
4 **Devonshires** London	2	8

LEADING INDIVIDUALS	
1 **PANTELIA Despina** Clifford Chance	**PAPWORTH Richard** Addleshaw Booth
2 **CARTER Adrian** Towers & Hamlins	**COWAN Andrew** Devonshires
HAYES Sarah Towers & Hamlins	**ROBERTS Ian** Denton Wilde Sapte
TURNER Nicholas Lawrence Graham	

This book is the product of 6,552 1/2-hour interviews. See p.7 for BMRB audit.
Within each band, firms are listed alphabetically. *See individuals' profiles p.780*

Clifford Chance (see firm details p.919) Buoyed by "*a strong brand name*" and an abundance *of "talented practitioners,*" research has indicated that the team leads this field, with clients agreeing that "*safety in numbers counts.*" **Despina Pantelia** (see p.783) is "*simply great,*" rated by peers and clients for her commerciality and her "*fine strategic mind.*" The group maintains its role as advisor to the funders of the Government's transfer programme, and has been active in product development ,involving pooled lending mechanisms. **Clients:** Halifax; Abbey National Treasury Services; Nationwide Building Society.

Addleshaw Booth & Co (see firm details p.853) "*Pushing hard*" at Clifford Chance, this "*first-rate*" team is recommended by rivals for its command of "*the most complex, high value*" syndicated facilities. Clients are loud in their praise for this "*extremely experienced, dependable*" team. "*Commercially astute*" and "*utterly focused,*" **Richard Papworth** (see p.783) is a leading figure in the funder market, and is felt to "*know how to pull together a deal.*" He led the team that advised Nationwide Building Society and RBS Housing Finance on the syndicated £240 million loan facility to the Whitefriars Housing Group for the funding of its LSVT of 20125 properties from Coventry City Council. **Clients:** Bradford & Bingley; Natiowide Building Society; Barclays Bank; Yorkshire Bank.

Allen & Overy (see firm details p.856) Although perceived by the market to lack the focus of the market leaders, the practice is at the cutting edge of bond issues and complex structured financing arrangements, drawing on partners across the banking, corporate and property departments. A team led by banking partner Andrew Joyce acted for the Royal Bank of Canada, ABN AMRO and Nationwide on a £415 million LSVT financing for the Sunderland Housing Group in its acquisition of 36,000 housing properties from Sunderland City Council. **Clients:** Abbey National; Halifax; Nationwide; NatWest Bank.

Denton Wilde Sapte (see firm details p.939) "*A focused, dedicated team,*" led by **Ian Roberts** (see p.783), has acted on complex structuring of bank debt and mixed funding, and is noted for its strong relationship with RBS. The team acted for RBS, Britannia and the Prudential on the funding of Swan Housing Association's development and long-terms needs. Also acted for Nationwide, RBS, Halifax and Abbey National on the funding of an LSVT from Blackburn and Darwen Borough Council to Twin Valley Homes. **Clients:** RBS; Nationwide Building Society.

Trowers & Hamlins (see firm details p.1162) See under previous section.

Devonshires (see firm details p.940) See under previous section.

THE SOUTH

SOCIAL HOUSING • The South	Ptnrs	Assts
1 **Coffin Mew & Clover** Portsmouth	3	8
2 **Cripps Harries Hall** Tunbridge Wells	3	3
Marsons Solicitors Bromley	1	3
Penningtons Newbury	3	3
3 **DMH** Brighton	2	2

LEADING INDIVIDUALS
1 **BENNETT Jennifer** Coffin Mew & Clover

This book is the product of 6,552 1/2-hour interviews. See p.7 for BMRB audit.
Within each band, firms are listed alphabetically. *See individuals' profiles p.780*

Coffin Mew & Clover "*Pre-eminent across all areas*," peers agree that the firm "*leads the field*" in the region. Heavily involved in litigation and funding, the firm acts for over 55 HAs. **Jennifer Bennett** (see p.780) dominates the local market and has a national reputation for her work in general housing management. The team represented a bank on a £20 million facility for an RSL, and advised on a new residential and multi-cultural resource centre. **Clients:** Town & Country Housing Group; Parchment Housing Group.

Cripps Harries Hall (see firm details p.927) "*A fine set of lawyers*," benefiting from a steady flow of litigation work, including possession actions against tenants. Mike Vos leads a team that has experience in finance and stock transfer work matters. **Clients:** High Weald HA

Marsons Solicitors Gerald O'Toole leads a team with a focus on tenancy management, including nuisance, succession rights and leasehold work, as well as service charge disputes. **Clients:** Hyde Housing Association; Broomleigh HA; Amicus Group.

Penningtons (see firm details p.1093) A well regarded player, which also draws on resources from both the Newbury and Basingstoke offices. Litigator Jonathan Rouse and the residential property team act for HA clients in development and management issues, right to buy and possessions work. **Clients:** Oakfern HA; Sovereign HA.

DMH (see firm details p.944) Endorsed by the market for its "*varied workload*," the firm scores well in litigation, structuring site acquisitions for HAs. Adopting a multi-disciplinary approach, property litigator Martin Allen also draws upon strong commercial, employment and residential property practices. **Clients:** Brighton Housing Trust; Guiness Trust; Sanctuary HA.

THAMES VALLEY

SOCIAL HOUSING • Thames Valley	Ptnrs	Assts
1 **Owen White** Slough	4	4
2 **Manches** Oxford	1	4
3 **Sherrards** St Albans	2	n/a

This book is the product of 6,552 1/2-hour interviews. See p.7 for BMRB audit.
Within each band, firms are listed alphabetically.

Owen White A dedicated and "*highly commercial team*" is rated by peers to be "*clearly the local leaders*." Led by Philip Lawrence, the group is active in stock transfers, right to buy, and housing management, including nuisance possession work. Other work includes regeneration and development cases, and contentious matters. **Clients:** Paradigm Housing Group; Windsor & District HA; Maidenhead & District HA; Northern Counties; Ealing Family HA.

Manches (see firm details p.1051) With a "*national profile*" for HA work, and bolstered by a fine PFI focus, the group, led by Paul Butterworth, has seen a growth in its mainstream development work. Active in constitutional and regulatory matters involving tenancy and shared ownership matters, the team advised Jephson HA on two development sites in Bristol. It also advised Anchor on a major transfer from Redbridge Council of Docklands redevelopment land. **Clients:** Swan HA; Anchor Trust; Christian Action HA; Jephson HA.

Sherrards (see firm details p.1128) "*A fine and talented team*" seen by competitors as acting for over 30 HAs and local authorities. Almost exclusively a landlord practice, it is led by litigator Simon Braun, and the group is recommended for its strengths in anti-social tenant litigation. **Clients:** Aldwyck HA; East Hertfordshire DC; Granta HA.

SOUTH WEST

SOCIAL HOUSING • South West	Ptnrs	Assts
1 **Towers & Hamlins** Exeter	2	2
2 **Bevan Ashford** Bristol	8	14
Burges Salmon Bristol	4	5
3 **Stones** Exeter	1	1

LEADING INDIVIDUALS	
1 **KEULS Peter** Trowers & Hamlins	**McNULTY Stephen** Burges Salmon
2 **ACTON Joseph** Trowers & Hamlins	**DYER Nick** Stones
3 **MORTIMER Ken** Bevan Ashford	

This book is the product of 6,552 1/2-hour interviews. See p.7 for BMRB audit.
Within each band, firms are listed alphabetically. *See individuals' profiles p.780*

Trowers & Hamlins (see firm details p.1162) Leading the pack, and matching expertise on the ground with an envied brand name, the firm includes "*senior figure*" **Peter Keuls** (see p.782) and **Joseph Acton** (see p.780), who clients believe brings a "*thorough knowledge of the law to the table*." The firm advised Restormel Housing Trust on the LSVT of 3577 properties (transfer price £25 million) and acted for North Devon Homes Ltd on the LSVT of 3382 properties (£45.5 million), both completed in the same month. **Clients:** Over 30 RSLs; Restormel Housing Trust; North Devon Homes; Devon & Cornwall HA.

Bevan Ashford (see firm details p.880) Focusing heavily on litigation, property transactions and developing niche strength in environmental issues, the firm dominates the public sector. Clients praise "*an approachable team, happy to take up the fight*", while **Ken Mortimer** (see p.783) "*is constantly working hard.*" The firm assisted Knightstone HA on the Foyer project, providing accommodation and training for young people, and advised on the redevelopment of tower blocks in Cheltenham (for the Gloucester & Bromfield Group). **Clients:** Knightstone HA; Places for People.

Burges Salmon (see firm details p.902) "*A classy practice*," active in development regulation, which draws on the skills of the firm's experienced commercial property team. Head of the Social Housing Unit **Stephen McNulty** (see p.783) utilises expertise from across the property, finance and employment teams to service a well regarded client base. The group has been engaged in development site acquisitions along the M40 corridor, Hampshire, Somerset and Berkshire, and in contentious matters, won a Court of Appeal case, Jephson HA v Moisejevs. **Clients:** Hyde HA; Guiness Trust; Oakfern HA.

Stones (see firm details p.1146) Enjoying a "*fine client list*," this small operation is spearheaded by the esteemed **Nick Dyer** (see p.781). Although rivals perceived it to be "*making a push in the sector*," the firm is not yet perceived to have the resources to match the market leaders. Active in site acquisition and development matters, the team acted for Western Challenge HA on the acquisition of 38 residential care homes, valued at £12 million, from a Health Authority. **Clients:** Western Challenge HA; South Hams Housing.

WALES

	SOCIAL HOUSING • Wales	Ptnrs	Assts
1	**Eversheds** Cardiff	2	5
	Hugh James Ford Simey Cardiff	3	3
2	**Edwards Geldard** Cardiff	3	3
	Morgan Cole Cardiff	2	n/a

This book is the product of 6,552 1/2-hour interviews. See p.7 for BMRB audit.
Within each band, firms are listed alphabetically.

Eversheds (see firm details p.952) Operating a national practice from its base in Cardiff, the team offers expertise in financing and residential development. National head, Anne Hayward leads a team which was appointed to the five-member panel of Places for People. The group also advised Principality Building Society on a £20 million loan facility to Pembroke HA, and acted for Torfaen Council on its regeneration project in Pontypool. **Clients:** Barclays Bank; Principality Building Society; Torfaen Council; Bourneville Village Trust.

Hugh James Ford Simey (see firm details p.1004) "*Traditionally a leader in this field*," David Roberts and his "*approachable*" team are active in redevelopment, home ownership initiatives and constitutional issues. It advised on a site disposal for Glamorgan & Gwent HA and has acted for housing associations on their charitable activities. **Clients:** Hafod HA; Charter HA; Glamorgan & Gwent HA.

Edwards Geldard (see firm details p.948) Work for its mainstay client United Welsh HA continues to keep the firm's profile high. Michael Jones leads a group that undertakes funding, development and restructuring cases, and advises on anti-social behaviour and landlord and tenant issues. **Clients:** United Welsh HA; Wales & West HA; Taff HA.

Morgan Cole (see firm details p.1074) Involved in urban and rural regeneration and financing, the team, headed by Philip Stewart, is said to have "*an appreciation of the issues at stake*." Typical examples of the group's larger projects include a £20 million long-term financing facility. **Clients:** HAs; social landlords.

MIDLANDS

	SOCIAL HOUSING • Midlands	Ptnrs	Assts
1	**Anthony Collins Solicitors** Birmingham	4	8
2	**Browne Jacobson** Nottingham	2	3
	Lee Crowder Birmingham	3	7
3	**Freethcartwright** Nottingham	2	3
	Needham & James Stratford-upon-Avon	3	5
	Pinsent Curtis Biddle Birmingham	3	5
	Wright Hassall Leamington Spa	3	3
4	**Harvey Ingram Owston** Leicester	3	1

	LEADING INDIVIDUALS	
1	**KNOX Martin** Anthony Collins Solicitors	**STEPHENS Hugo** Pinsent Curtis Biddle
2	**BALLARD Andy** Lee Crowder	**HEATH Philip** Wright Hassall
3	**DUDLEY Andrew** Needham & James	**HUDDLESTON David** Browne Jacobson
	MATTHEWS Carol Wright Hassall	

This book is the product of 6,552 1/2-hour interviews. See p.7 for BMRB audit.
Within each band, firms are listed alphabetically. *See individuals' profiles p.780*

Anthony Collins Solicitors (see firm details p.860) "*The specialists in regeneration*" are "*rightly at the head of the pack*" as claimed by rivals, with a strengthened team this year. **Martin Knox** (see p.782) is "*more knowledgeable than most*," particularly on governance issues. The group acted for Castle Vale Housing Action Trust on anti-social behaviour litigation, and implemented the New Deal for Communities Initiative on a national basis. It continues to advise RSLs on stock transfer and structural matters. **Clients:** Optima Community Association; Castle Vale Housing Action Trust.

Browne Jacobson (see firm details p.898) The firm is especially noted for its focus on funding, shared ownership and right to buy issues. Highly rated for his financing work, **David Huddleston** (see p.782) advises RSLs on their funding, and acted on a regeneration project in Berinsfield, Oxfordshire. The firm is also experienced in anti-social behaviour issues and tenancy disputes. **Clients:** Metropolitan Housing Trust; East Midlands HA; SOHA Housing.

Lee Crowder (see firm details p.1035) Acting for over 50 HAs and local authorities, the firm has long experience of constitutional and funding issues. **Andy Ballard** (see p.780) is viewed as a high profile litigator, skilled in housing management. The team has undertaken housing management on behalf of Prime Focus, and advised Midland Area HA on disrepair claims. Anti-social behaviour cases and human resources concerns are other integral features of the workload. **Clients:** Prime Focus Housing Group; Midland Area Housing Association; West Mercia Housing Group.

Freethcartwright (see firm details p.964) Retaining its profile as a leading player in the market, the firm's particular strength lies in financing. Led by Gary Reynolds, the team advised Nottingham Community HA on the acquisition of stock from Amber Valley District Council, and has been active in regeneration, partnership, self build projects, stock refurbishment, stock transfers from local authorities, landlord and tenant disputes and employment issues. **Clients:** Nottingham Community HA; Derwent HA; The Salvation Army.

Needham & James "*Moving up in the world*," the firm is commended by interviewees for its high-profile relationships with local authorities, and its enviable client roster of HAs. **Andrew Dudley** "*rolls up his sleeves*" and is the leading figure at a team which acted for Staffordshire Moorland District Council on the transfer of 3000 units, and advised Calderdale MBC on the transfer of 13000 properties to Pennine Housing 2000. The group is particularly involved in development and right to buy issues. **Clients:** South Warwickshire HA; Orbit HA; Focus HA.

Pinsent Curtis Biddle (see firm details p.1098) A new entrant to *Chambers'* tables, the firm is considered to owe much to **Hugo Stephens** (see p.784), formerly of Irwin Mitchell, who has developed a "*successful and highly committed*" team. An expert in LSVTs, Stephens is judged to have widened the firm's profile from PFI. The group advised Sunderland Housing Group on its 37,000 unit LSVT from Sunderland CC and advised Pennine Housing 2000 and Moorlands Housing on its LSVTs. **Clients:**

Sunderland Housing Group; Moorlands Housing; Pennine Housing 2000; Islington LBC.

Wright Hassall (see firm details p.1190) An experienced and expanding team, recently bolstered by the "*weighty addition*" of **Philip Heath** (see p.782) from Lawrence Graham, who is noted for his track record with local authorities. Head of department, the "*approachable*" **Carol Matthews** (see p.782), continues to attract substantial market endorsement. The group has strengths in constitutional, shared ownership and right to buy issues, and advised on the LSVTs of Saxon Weald Homes, East Northamptonshire Council, and West Oxfordshire DC. **Clients:** Orbit Housing; Housing 21; Focus Housing; Moat Housing Society; Rural Housing Trust.

Harvey Ingram Owston (see firm details p.989) Retaining a strong grip on the development market, the firm has an extensive Housing Association client base. Henry Doyle and his team have acted on development issues for de Montfort HA and Foundation Housing. **Clients:** Leicester HA; Riverside HA; Wolds HA.

NORTH WEST

SOCIAL HOUSING • North West		Ptnrs	Assts
1	**Cobbetts** Manchester	5	5
	Trowers & Hamlins Manchester	4	2
2	**Brabners** Liverpool	3	10
	Howarth Goodman Manchester	3	3
3	**Eversheds** Manchester	1	2
4	**Croftons** Manchester	3	3
	Gorna & Co Manchester	1	1
5	**A Halsall & Co** Birkenhead	1	2
	Bremner Sons & Corlett Liverpool	1	n/a

LEADING INDIVIDUALS		
1	**GASKELL Mike** Cobbetts	
2	**HOLDEN Lawrence** Brabners	**TURNER Graham** Trowers & Hamlins
3	**BODE Adrian** Trowers & Hamlins	**RHATIGAN Michael** Eversheds

This book is the product of 6,552 1/2-hour interviews. See p.7 for BMRB audit.
Within each band, firms are listed alphabetically. *See individuals' profiles p.780*

Cobbetts (see firm details p.923) "*Outstanding, and getting better,*" so say its rivals, the firm's expanded team is rated as among the national leaders in this market. "*Approachable and skilled*" **Mike Gaskell** (see p.781) has a profile for stock transfer and constitutional issues. The team has an extensive HA client base and advised on the Blackburn with Darwen/Twin Valley Homes LSVT and on the acquisition of YWCA Hostels for Selhal Community Housing. **Clients:** Places for People Group; Progress Housing Group; Twin Valley Homes.

Trowers & Hamlins (see firm details p.1162) "*Market leaders*" in part due to the strength of the network, this is also recognised as a "*strong, knowledgeable stand-alone team,*" although it is more often recommended for big-ticket work rather than everyday matters. "*Experienced*" **Graham Turner** (see p.784) "*doesn't flap*" and brings a calming influence to any negotiations. **Adrian Bode** (see p.780) has expertise in management and development issues. The team acted for West Kent Housing Associations on a £115 million refinancing facility with Halifax, and advised Manchester Methodist HA and Collingwood HA on overspill estate transfers. **Clients:** Equity Housing Group; Bromford Housing Group; Irwell Housing Trust; Willow Park Housing Trust; Waterloo HA.

Brabners (see firm details p.892) Operating a large regeneration team from both Liverpool and Preston, the team also profits from the firm's commerical property presence. Although lower in profile this year, **Lawrence Holden** (see p.147) continues to "*adopt a solid commercial approach*" in his mixed HA and charities practice. The group has acted on inner-city flat developments and large scale student accommodation projects across Manchester, Birmingham and Liverpool. **Clients:** City Living Syndicate; Riverside Housing Association; Liverpool Housing Trust.

Howarth Goodman The team has a "*traditional breadth of practice*" and, according to rivals, "*appears to be successfully holding its own,*" despite the recent loss of a place on an HA panel. Best known for its work in large scale developments and funding, the firm retains a respected client base.

Eversheds (see firm details p.952) "*Travelling up the learning curve,*" the firm has scored a coup in securing a place on the Places for People (North British HA) panel. Peers agree that **Michael Rhatigan** (see p.783) is "*one of the big names,*" and is warmly recommended for his landlord and tenant practice. The team is felt to focus on the higher end of the market, including site acquisitions and developments. **Clients:** Places for People; RSLs.

Croftons Lower profile, recommended for its work in the volume end of the market. Said to be "*commercial in outlook,*" the firm remains focused on the financing angle. **Clients:** Housing Associations.

Gorna & Co With a strong focus on refinancing, right to buy, and part ownership sales, Stephen Hindmarsh heads a respected team, which is supported by a strong property practice. **Clients:** North British HA.

A Halsall & Co Small team, featuring John Barnes, which has a long-standing national client base of HAs, for which the firm appears on constitutional matters. The firm recently advised on the conversion of a non-charitable organisation to charitable status. **Clients:** Harewood Housing Society.

Bremner Sons & Corlett "*Long-established*" team, which retains a strong profile in the local market, largely through its activities for key client Royal Liver. **Clients:** Royal Liver Assurance; regional RSLs.

NORTH EAST

Dickinson Dees (see firm details p.941) "*Utterly dominant*" in the region, claims one competitor, the firm operates a "*thriving social housing practice.*" The firm regularly advises on management and development for HA and local authorities, and has expertise in complex restructuring and funding arrangements. Head of the Social Housing Group **Mitch Brown** (see p.780) is "*clearly a leading light,*" and focuses on development funding and governance issues. The firm advised on a PFI accommodation scheme with Selby District Council and acted on a PPP transaction for Durham County Council and Gateshead MBC. It also remains on the slimmed down Places for People Group (North British HA) panel. **Clients:** 30 HAs.

Eversheds (see firm details p.952) Adrian Stanley and the team are seen to be matching the drive of the Manchester office "*to become one of the regional leaders,*" securing significant clients in the North East. The team advised Three Rivers HA on its development programme involving the acquisition of ten sites. **Clients:** Three Rivers HA; The Home Group; Enterprise 5.

Rollits (see firm details p.1110) A sound player with a substantial share of the local market, the firm also undertakes work on a national scale. Clive Gardener and the group advised the Joseph Rowntree Foundation in developing a continuing care community at Hartrigg Oaks. The team also con-

SOCIAL HOUSING • North East	Ptnrs	Assts
1 **Dickinson Dees** Newcastle upon Tyne	4	10
2 **Eversheds** Newcastle upon Tyne	1	3
Rollits Hull	4	2
Walker Charlesworth & Foster Leeds	2	3
3 **Gordons Cranswick Solicitors** Bradford	3	2
Savage Crangle Skipton	2	1

LEADING INDIVIDUALS	
1 **BROWN Mitch** Dickinson Dees	
2 **BIRTWISTLE Colin** Walker Charlesworth & Foster	**HURST Andrew** Savage Crangle

This book is the product of 6,552 1/2-hour interviews. See p.7 for BMRB audit.
Within each band, firms are listed alphabetically. *See individuals' profiles p.780*

tinues to be involved in grant funded projects and development work, including PFI. **Clients:** Joseph Rowntree Housing Trust.

Walker Charlesworth & Foster (see firm details p.1170) Operating from a strong base in Leeds, the firm's outstanding player is **Colin Birtwistle** (see p.780), said to be "*always helpful – he knows his way around the law.*" Active in shared ownership sales and large scale funding issues, the firm recently advised on a £20 million mortgage arrangement for an HA, as well as regeneration and development matters. **Clients:** Yorkshire Community Housing; Leeds Federated Housing; Unity Housing.

Gordons Cranswick Solicitors "*A niche practice doing good work,*" it is especially well regarded in the development and financing sphere. Commercial property partner Deborah Powell can also draw upon a strong litigation team to undertakes nuisance and behavioural matters. **Clients:** Anchor Trust; Jephson HA.

Savage Crangle (see firm details p.1119) "*Solid players in the market,*" the firm continues to prosper under the guidance of the "*committed*" **Andrew Hurst**. The caseload includes development, restructuring matters and funding arrangments for HAs. **Clients:** Accord.

SCOTLAND

SOCIAL HOUSING • Scotland	Ptnrs	Assts
1 **Harper Macleod** Glasgow	6	5
TC Young & Son Glasgow	6	3
2 **Brechin Tindal Oatts** Glasgow	4	10
Ledingham Chalmers Aberdeen, Edinburgh	3	1
3 **Henderson Boyd Jackson WS** Edinburgh	3	7
4 **Burness** Edinburgh	2	2
Dundas & Wilson CS Edinburgh	3	7
Golds Glasgow	2	3
5 **Baird & Company** Kirkcaldy	3	1
Macleod & MacCallum Inverness	1	1

LEADING INDIVIDUALS	
1 **FREEDMAN Len** Harper Macleod	
2 **COWAN Andrew** TC Young & Son	**DEWAR Kate** Henderson Boyd Jackson WS
EWING Mark TC Young & Son	**HOGG Derek** Ledingham Chalmers
MACGREGOR Stephen TC Young & Son	**ROBERTSON Andrew** TC Young & Son
3 **PIA Paul** Burness	
THOMPSON Alison TC Young & Son	

This book is the product of 6,552 1/2-hour interviews. See p.7 for BMRB audit.
Within each band, firms are listed alphabetically. *See individuals' profiles p.780*

Harper Macleod (see firm details p.987) Acclaimed by peers for its "*unrivalled spread of clients,*" the firm remains ahead of the social housing pack in Scotland. One of the keys to the firm's success, **Len Freedman** is described *as "a force of nature,"* and is particularly visible on major stock transfer issues. The group acted for Nationwide Building Society on the £20 million acquisition of housing stock at Cumbernauld, Glasgow, and has noted expertise in debt finance, local authority transfers and employment issues. It acted for Bellsmyre HA on the amendment to its LSVT Agreement with Scottish Homes, and has been appointed by Dumfries and Galloway Council to act on a proposed stock transfer to a New Housing Partnership. **Clients:** Aberdeen City Council; Ayrshire North Community Housing Association; Abbey National.

TC Young & Son (see firm details p.1191) At the time of going to press great changes are afoot at this firm, which is setting out its stall as a leader in the market. The firm has scored a coup in the recruitment of **Stephen MacGregor** (see p.782) from Brechin Tindall Oatts adding a much needed focus on "*the higher value end of market.*" Furthermore, it has won the talents of a team from Shepherd & Wedderburn that includes the "*dependable*" **Alison Thompson.** A "*dignified figure*" **Andrew Robertson** (see p.784), retains his role as "*guru*" to a practice filled with "*specialists.*" **Mark Ewing** (see p.781) is noted for his work on the corporate structuring of housing associations and **Andrew Cowan** (see p.781) has a noted expertise in the private housing management and HA tenancy issues. Heavily committed to the area, the firm is applauded for "*devoting a large proportion of its resources*" to the field. **Clients:** Sanctuary; Places for People; Horizon; Home in Scotland.

Brechin Tindal Oatts (see firm details p.893) Although the loss of Stephen MacGregor to T.C.Young is considered to be a blow, this "*capable and solid*" firm continues to be rated as a "*talented group.*" Karen Brodie acts with a team that undertakes stock transfers and funding and tenants' choice transfers. The group acted for Cumbernauld Housing Partnership in the transfer of 2000 units and advised Thistle Housing Association in the transfer of 1000 units in Toryglen. **Clients:** HAs; 57 RSLs.

Ledingham Chalmers (see firm details p.1034) Rated for its "*commercial, pragmatic approach,*" the group has been bolstered by the "*highly significant arrival*" of **Derek Hogg** (see p.782), from Skene Edwards. Peers agree that he has the "*clout*" to promote the practice. The team advised Scottish Borders Housing Association on its acquisition of 7000 homes from Scottish Borders Council. Active in council stock transfer and development partnerships, the team has also been involved in the West Lothian Housing project and the Cumbernauld housing partnership. **Clients:** Bridgewater Housing Association; West Lothian Housing Partnership.

Henderson Boyd Jackson WS A highly commercial operation, which includes **Kate Dewar** (see p.781), a high-profile lawyer, known by peers for her "*involvement in the big transactions.*" The team advised Homes for Life Housing Partnership in the acquisition of sites, contractual arrangements for special needs projects and the development of a mortgage rescue scheme. It also acted for Paragon HA on its award of Approved Landlord Status and acted on the acquisition of over 90 tenants' choice transfer properties in Falkirk, Denny and Stirling. **Clients:** Weslo Housing Management; Paragon Housing Association; City of Edinburgh Council.

Burness (see firm details p.903) "*Always a presence,*" the team has a focus on the high value end of the market. **Paul Pia** (see p.783) is active in constitutional group structures and joint ventures in the public, private and voluntary sectors. The firm continues a long-standing relationship with the Scottish Federation of Housing Associations and prepared the merger agreement for Scottish Borders Council to form Scottish Borders HA. **Clients:** Scottish Homes; SFHA; Link Housing Association.

Dundas & Wilson CS (see firm details p.947) "*A first rate banking presence*" with an envied client base, the team, led by Chris Dun, acts almost exclusively for funders. It advised Abbey National Treasury Services both on a club loan financing to ten of the principal Scottish HAs and on a £11.8 million facility financing for an LSVT to East Ayrshire Housing Partnership. **Clients:** Abbey National Treasury Services; Lloyds TSB Scotland; Halifax.

Golds A lender driven practice, led by Craig Marshall, with involvement in a high volume of fundings. Considered by peers to be a "*focused operation,*" it is especially noted for its cutting-edge work in information technology solutions. **Clients:** Bank of Scotland; Britannia.

Baird & Company Always "*reasonable and user-friendly,*" Charles Milne leads a group experienced in LSVT, development and funding work for both HAs and lenders. **Clients:** RSLs.

Macleod & MacCallum Thought to be driven by the local market, the team generally acts on development issues and stock transfers for Highlands associations.

LEADERS IN SOCIAL HOUSING

ACTON, Joseph
Trowers & Hamlins, Exeter (01392) 217466
jacton@trowers.com
Specialisation: Advises upon all areas of Housing Association law and practice including acquisition and development, building contracts, partnering and construction issues, PFI matters, homelessness initiatives, funding and major consortium agreements and joint ventures. Speaks regularly at client seminars on matters of current interest.
Prof. Memberships: Member of the Law Society.
Career: Torquay Grammar School (1977-84); Magdalen College Oxford (1984-87); *Trowers & Hamlins* (1989-date). Partner from 1995.

ADLINGTON, Jonathan
Trowers & Hamlins, London (020) 7423 8000
jadlington@trowers.com
Specialisation: Senior partner. Head of property department. Vast experience of housing law and the Housing Association movement having built a specialist practice over more than 25 years. Deals with all aspects of commercial and residential property, from purchases, sales and mortgages to development agreements, structures and funding. Instrumental in the development of private finance for social housing. Acts for Housing Associations, Local Authorities and lenders. Regular speaker at housing events and for funding bodies.

BALLARD, Andy
Lee Crowder, Birmingham (0121) 236 4477
Specialisation: Heads the housing group at *Lee Crowder* which is one of the largest within the region advising in excess of 50 Registered Social Landlords. Lectures and trains nationally and locally on a full range of housing management and human resource issues.
Prof. Memberships: Law Society.
Career: Qualified in 1981 before joining the Birmingham practice of *Rigbeys* in 1983. Became a partner in *Rigbeys* in 1985 which in due course merged with *Irwin Mitchell in 1996.* Became a partner in *Lee Crowder* when transferring his team in 1999.

BASTOW, Gillian
Lewis Silkin, London (020) 7074 8029
gillian.bastow@lewissilkin.com
Specialisation: Partner and head of social housing group. All aspects of housing association activity including land acquisition and development, regeneration schemes, partnerships involving RSLs, local authorities/health authorities, private and public finance, care in the community schemes, landlord and tenant issues, constitutional/corporate matters and specialist work with housing co-operatives.
Prof. Memberships: Law Society, NHF Lawyers Sub-Group, Housing Association Committee Member.
Career: Qualified 1981 with *Lewis Silkin.* Partner 1984.
Personal: Born October 1953. Attended Somerville College Oxford (MA) and Leicester University (LLM). Lives in London.

BENNETT, Jennifer
Coffin Mew & Clover, Fareham (01329) 825617
socialhousing@fareham.coffinmew.co.uk
Specialisation: Partner. Head of social housing department. Over 20 years experience in housing law, with particular interest in new housing initiatives and low cost home ownership schemes, but with a very broad expertise in this sector. Heads one of the largest teams of dedicated housing professionals outside London who provide comprehensive services to local and regional RSLs as well as funders.
Prof. Memberships: Member of Chartered Institute of Housing.
Personal: Born 1955. Educated University College, London. Admitted 1979. Non-executive Director of Portsmouth Hospitals NHS Trust.

BIRTWISTLE, Colin
Walker Charlesworth & Foster, Leeds
(0113) 297 2913
colinbirtwistle@walkercharlesworth.co.uk
Specialisation: Housing Association Law and Practice particularly in the field of constitutional matters for Housing Associations e.g. dealing with several rule changes and mergers. Also heavily involved from 1989 with Leeds Partnership Homes which dealt with the transfer of £33m of City Council land largely for Housing Association development but also for outright sale. Now involved with the Single Regeneration Budget Agreement for Leeds and related sales. Also involved with Health Service Reprovision Agreements for two charities.
Prof. Memberships: The Law Society, and Solicitor Benevolent Fund Member.
Personal: Family: married with three children aged 22, 20 and 16. Outside interests – sport, fell walking and charity work.

BODE, Adrian
Trowers & Hamlins, Manchester (0161) 211 0000
abode@trowers.com
Specialisation: A partner since 1983 and has acquired wide ranging experience. Particular specialisations are large-scale acquisitions and disposals, joint venture work and private finance.
Career: University of Nottingham. Qualified 1978. *Trowers & Hamlins* (1978 to date). Partner 1983.

BROWN, Mitch
Dickinson Dees, Newcastle upon Tyne
(0191) 279 9291
law@dickinson-dees.com
Specialisation: Partner in the commercial property department and head of the public sector development group. Handles all aspects of RSL work in the fields of development, governance and finance. Has in the past year dealt with social housing lending facilities on behalf of RSLs and lenders, social housing PFI and PPP transactions, and the establishment of RSL Group structures.
Prof. Memberships: Law Society.
Career: Born 1962. Educated Royal Grammar School, Newcastle upon Tyne. University of Newcastle upon Tyne 1984 (LLB). Qualified 1987, became a partner in 1995.
Personal: Leisure interests include sport, music, art and reading. Married with three daughters.

CARTER, Adrian
Trowers & Hamlins, London (020) 7423 8000
acarter@trowers.com
Specialisation: Partner, Housing Finance Group. Specialist in housing finance, acting for borrowers and lenders. Experience includes innovative work on group borrowing arrangements, hedging arrangements, stock and bond issues, as well as bilateral and syndicated lending and borrowing. Regular speaker.
Career: University of Exeter. *Trowers & Hamlins* 1987-date. Qualified 1989, partner 1994.
Personal: Married, four children.

COWAN, Andrew
Devonshires, London (020) 7628 7576
andrew.cowan@devonshires.co.uk
Specialisation: Partner and head of finance. The RSL finance unit has negotiated over £2 billion of housing association funding and group structures since 1988 from the capital markets, banks, building societies and new initiatives; Andrew acts for ten banks, building societies and over 165 RSL based all

over England and Wales and a group association borrowing vehicle. Andrew and his team act for over 50 RSLs on their group structures, including in relation to mergers and private company acquisitions, PFI, and new initiatives. In the last year he has advised on three new pathfinder regeneration projects. Lectures widely on finance, group structures and RSL corporate strategies.
Career: Articled *Hobson Audley*; qualified 1989; *Trowers & Hamlins* 1990-1991; *Devonshires* 1991; partner 1993; regular speaker; credit committee member of an international charity.
Personal: Educated University of East Anglia. Born 1964: resides London. Leisure: backpacking, football, swimming, Latin America.

COWAN, Andrew
TC Young & Son, Glasgow (0141) 221 5562
asc@tc-young.co.uk
Specialisation: Housing association tenancies and housing management issues. Representation in all areas of litigation and employment related disputes. He has an extensive knowledge of the regulatory regime for secured and assured tenancies and regularly contributes to training conferences and seminars. Has a developing caseload dealing with construction related disputes. Currently extensively involved in a number of transfer of engagements between housing associations. Housing management expertise complements fellow *TC Young* partners' corporate funding, stock transfer and special projects specialisations.
Prof. Memberships: Law Society of Scotland and Chartered Institute of Arbitrators.
Career: Dundee University, LLB 1984; *TC Young & Son* trainee 1985-87; *McArthur Stanton* partner 1986-95; *TC Young & Son* partner 1995.

DEWAR, Kate
Henderson Boyd Jackson WS, Edinburgh (0131) 226 6881
Specialisation: Worked extensively on a variety of innovative transactions promoting community ownership and regeneration for and involving housing associations, housing management companies, local housing companies and local authorities considering stock transfer. Involved in all aspects of large-scale voluntary transfers, in the legal formation of housing associations, housing companies and housing partnerships and following on from acting as one of the lead solicitors in one of the first New Housing Partnership deals in Scotland a few years ago. Has since acted in numerous similar deals since.
Prof. Memberships: Law Society of Scotland. Writer to the Signet. Notary Public.
Career: Qualified 1982; partner specialising in housing and public sector work.
Personal: Edinburgh University graduate; lives Edinburgh; interests include swimming and travelling.

DOOLITTLE, Ian
Trowers & Hamlins, London (020) 7423 8000
idoolittle@trowers.com
Specialisation: Team leader on many housing stock transfers, first LSVT and more recently urban estate-based transfers. Now a specialist adviser on complex metropolitan transfers. At the forefront of establishing arms length housing organisations. Is an authority on public/private sector partnerships. Also specialist in environmental law.

DUDLEY, Andrew P
Needham & James, Stratford-upon-Avon (01789) 414 444

DYER, Nick
Stones, Exeter (01392) 666819
nickdyer@stones-solicitors.co.uk
Specialisation: Specialised in social housing work for nearly 20 years. Experience of site acquisition and development funding, management and transfer agreements with health trusts and local authorities, shared ownership and LSE schemes, and a wide variety of other issues involving registered social landlords.
Career: Law graduate (Trinity Hall, Cambridge). Formerly partner (latterly managing partner) in *Cann & Hallett* and now partner in *Stones* in charge of social housing work.

EVANS, Chris
Evans Butler Wade, London (020) 8858 8926

EWING, Mark
TC Young & Son, Glasgow (0141) 221 5562
mee@tc-young.co.uk
Specialisation: Represents a large number of social housing providers with extensive experience in all aspects of stock transfers from local authorities, Scottish Homes, NHS and the Ministry of Defence. Has acted in numerous transfers of engagements between housing associations. Regularly provides advice on corporate structures and governance issues and has developed group structures for Scottish and UK organisations. Also experienced in preparing multi-agency and private sector development agreements. Currently instructed in relation to a number of New Housing Partnership stock transfers from local authorities throughout Scotland. Corporate and special projects expertise complements fellow *TC Young* partners' funding, stock transfer and housing management specialisations.
Prof. Memberships: Law Society of Scotland.
Career: Qualified in 1983; *TC Young & Son* partner (1987). Co-ordinating housing association work.

FITTON, Roger
Winckworth Sherwood, London (020) 7593 5000
drfitton@winckworths.co.uk
Specialisation: Housing law with emphasis on public and private schemes, brownfield urban regeneration projects, externalisations in social services, staff, student and NHS projects and a wide range of charitable and constitutional work.
Prof. Memberships: Law Society.
Career: Oulder Hill Community School, Rochdale 1974-1979; Exeter College, Oxford, Law 1980-1983; Trained, *Boodle Hatfield* 1984-1986; Assistant Solicitor, *Denton Hall* 1986-1989; Assistant, then partner, *Winckworth Sherwood* 1989-2001.

FREEDMAN, Len
Harper Macleod, Glasgow (0141) 221 8888

GASKELL, Mike
Cobbetts, Manchester (0161) 833 7499
michael.gaskell@cobbetts.co.uk
Specialisation: Advising registered social landlords and local authorities on housing related matters; group structures and constitutional issues; joint ventures; tenant involvement; stock transfer; acquisition and development; landlord and tenant. Currently advising on a number of group structures, stock transfers and tenant involvement initiatives.
Prof. Memberships: Law Society.
Career: LLB Liverpool. Advising housing associations for 18 years.
Personal: Married with three children. Trustee of school charity and voluntary board member of Manchester Care and Repair.

GRAHAM, Ian
Trowers & Hamlins, London (020) 7423 8000
igraham@trowers.com
Specialisation: Partner, housing. Work for associations includes advising on PFI and PPP projects; group structures; governance and vires issues; joint ventures and partnership projects in health, care and urban regeneration. A prolific author and public speaker.

HALL, Gareth
Devonshires, London (020) 7628 7576
gareth.hall@devonshires.co.uk
Specialisation: A broad finance and company/commercial practice, advising housing associations and general corporate clients. Advice includes banking and capital market finance (recently completed a PFI financing acting for lead bank); corporate/constitutional including housing group structures (just completed structure for a leading UK association); mergers, acquisitions and joint ventures; information technology. He has negotiated over 40 IT supply and support contracts over 2 years, ranging from standard packages to bespoke projects.
Career: Trainee at *Lovell White & King* 1982-1984; assistant (corporate) solicitor, *Simmons & Simmons* 1984-1994; joined *Devonshires* 1994, partner since 1995.
Personal: Born 1959. Educated Manchester Grammar School and Merton College, Oxford. Lives in Beckenham. Leisure interests include playing and listening to music of all eras, cycling and the National Trust.

HAND, Catherine
Jenkins & Hand, London (020) 7222 5002
jenkins.hand@dial.pipex.com
See under Local Government, p.592

HART, Rosemary
Trowers & Hamlins, London (020) 7423 8000
rhart@trowers.com
Specialisation: Partner, Housing. Works primarily for housing associations, voluntary and public sector bodies. Experience includes: property acquisition and development including projects in the Private Finance Initiative relating to staff and student accommodation, nursing and care homes, joint ventures and security work; nomination agreements, leases, tenancies, constitutional advice, care in the community and management schemes. Regular author and speaker.

HAWKINS, James
Trowers & Hamlins, London (020) 7423 8000
jhawkins@trowers.com
Specialisation: Partner public sector department. Specialist in public/private sector partnerships. Is an authority on housing stock transfers and, in particular, urban transfers, local housing companies and regeneration schemes. Also specialises in group structure and residential care home transfers.
Career: University of Birmingham; Qualified 1989. *Trowers & Hamlins* 1991 to date. Partner 1996.

HAYES, Sarah
Trowers & Hamlins, London (020) 7423 8000
shayes@trowers.com
Specialisation: Partner, head of Housing Finance/Corporate Finance. General expertise in property finance, secured and unsecured. Particular specialism in housing finance, acting for borrowers and lenders. Experience covers hedging arrangements; bond issues (domestic and Eurobond, rated and insured, own name and group issues); syndicated lending; bonds and securities; group structures and borrowing arrangements; and charitable issues. Experienced speaker at housing, charitable and funding events.

HEATH, Philip
Wright Hassall, Leamington Spa (01926) 886688
philiph@wrighthassall.co.uk
Specialisation: Large scale voluntary transfer of housing stock. He has worked on some 26 completed projects, the most recent being the transfer by West Oxfordshire DC to West Oxfordshire Housing. He has also recently completed the transfer by Horsham DC to Saxon Weald Homes Ltd where he acted for the Company and the Mendip District Council's transfer to Mendip Housing Ltd. He is currently working on Glasgow's proposed transfer of its housing stock.
Prof. Memberships: Law Society.
Career: Called to the Bar by Grays Inn 1988. Assistant then senior assistant solicitor (Barrister) with Oxfordshire County Council. Deputy District Secretary and then head of legal services for South Northamptonshire council. Joined *Lawrence Graham* in 1994 as a senior assistant in the local and public authority unit. Admitted as solicitor January 2000. Joined *Wright Hassall* as a partner in October 2000.
Personal: LLB (Hons) UWE 1978; MA De Montfort 1994 (Environmental Law). Leisure interests include walking, choral music and literature.

HOGG, Derek
Ledingham Chalmers, Aberdeen (0131) 200 1071
derek.hogg@ledinghamchalmers.com
Specialisation: All aspects of social housing work, specialising in stock transfers, corporate structures, funding and advisory work. Heads the firm's social housing team, responsible for all contractual and financial aspects of transactions. Acted for Fife Special Housing Association in largest Scottish LSVT to date. Major clients include Bridgewater, Cunninghame, Fife Special and Scottish Borders HAs. Currently acting for Glasgow City Council in the UK's biggest stock transfer proposal.
Prof. Memberships: Committee member of Kirk Care and Old Town Housing Associations.
Career: Trained with local authority. Joined *Skene Edwards* in 1988 and became partner in 1994. Joined *Ledingham Chalmers* as partner in 2000.

HOLDEN, Lawrence
Brabners, Liverpool (0151) 600 3000
lawrence.holden@brabners.com
See under Charities, p.147

HUDDLESTON, David
Browne Jacobson, Nottingham (0115) 976 6000
dhuddleston@brownej.co.uk
Specialisation: Partner in property department. Advising both local and national Housing Associations on acquisitions of sites for residential developments including a consortium of a number of Associations. Advising Housing Associations on private financing and security agreements. Continues to receive instructions in connection with large value security work for Housing Associations and from banks lending to the sector. Clients include Metropolitan Housing Trust Limited, East Midlands Housing Association Limited, Leicester Housing Association Limited, South Oxfordshire Housing Association Limited. With the recent opening of the Birmingham office instructions are being received from Associations in the West Midlands and the firm now acts for 25 Associations. Other work includes advising on acquisition of development sites for residential, office and industrial developments. Advising on development agreements associated with acquisition of sites and subsequent sales and leases. Acting for developers on the development of sites including financing and subsequent sales by either grant of leases (including industrial, retail and offices) or to investors of whole developments.

HUDSON, Allan
Devonshires, London (020) 7628 7576
Specialisation: Senior Partner and head of property department. Principal area is complex consortium developments of sites, PFI type projects and provision of private finance. Also patient hotels. Practice also covers commercial property work, including acquisition, disposal and management of investment property. Has done pioneering work on patient hotels in Glasgow, Liverpool and Nottingham.
Career: Qualified in 1978. At *Penningtons* 1978-81, *Nabarro Nathanson* 1981-82 and *Knapp Fishers* 1982-84. Joined *Devonshires* in 1984 and became a partner in 1985.
Personal: Born 7th July 1954. Educated at Poole Grammar School and Durham University (BA 1st Class Hons). Leisure interests include theatre, cinema and gardening. Lives in Godalming, Surrey.

HURST, Andrew LT
Savage Crangle, Skipton (01756) 794611

JENKINS, Keith
Jenkins & Hand, London (020) 7222 5002
jenkins.hand@dial.pipex.com
Specialisation: Closely involved with the housing association movement for over 20 years; specialises in housing, co-ops and local authorities. Has made a significant contribution to the growth and development of social housing. Is regarded as one of the most imaginative achievers in this sector.
Career: Qualified in 1974. Joined *Winckworth & Pemberton* in 1972, becoming a partner in 1977. Set up *Jenkins & Hand* 1996.
Personal: Born 10 May 1949. Read law at Lincoln College, Oxford. Leisure interests include reading and rock music. Lives in London. Board member Poplar HARCH and BCHT.

JENNINGS, Robert
Prince Evans, London (020) 8567 3477

KEULS, Peter
Trowers & Hamlins, Exeter (01392) 217466
pkeuls@trowers.com
Specialisation: Housing associations, local housing companies, group structures, large-scale voluntary transfers of housing stock: East Dorset; West Dorset; Penwith; North Dorset; Basingstoke and Deane; Kennet; Kerrier; West Somerset; West Devon; South Hams; Bath and North East Somerset; Restormel; North Devon; Weymouth; Portland and Torbay and Mendip. PFI and PPP projects with educational bodies and local authorities.
Career: Worth School, Sussex; College of Law, Guildford. Qualified 1977. *Trowers & Hamlins* (1972-date), partner 1982.

KNOX, Martin
Anthony Collins Solicitors, Birmingham (0121) 200 3242
Specialisation: Provides specialist legal services on housing and local government law to a significant number of Local Authorites and Registered Social Landlords and numerous community associations, charities and businesses. Pioneered significant iniatives for community regeneration and increased investment in the provision and management of social housing. Particular experience of major urban regeneration and transfer work including SRB, particularly local housing companies and recently NDCs.
Career: Qualified 1980. Worked as legal adviser to Sheffield and Birmingham City Councils' Housing Committees. Since joining *Anthony Collins Solicitors* in 1989, has been closely involved in creating innovative solutions to housing and regeneration in urban local authorities. Has developed the community association model in a number of locations throughout the country both for provision of new stock and improvement of existing council housing.

MACGREGOR, Stephen
TC Young & Son, Glasgow (0141) 221 5562
sxm@tc-young.co.uk
Specialisation: Has acted on behalf of housing associations and housing co-operatives throughout his career and specialises in large-scale voluntary transfers and funding. Extensive experience in funding issues, and has had regular instruction by Scottish clearing banks and other UK and European lenders. Advises on constitutional and corporate structures. He was appointed by Scottish Homes to head a statutory inquiry into the affairs of Bridgeton and Dalmarnock Housing Association in 1999. Has advised 47 RSLs and acted for syndicate of borrowers in the Abbey National Club deal. Corporate, funding and stock transfer expertise complements *TC Young's* recognised special projects and housing management skills.
Prof. Memberships: Law Society of Scotland.
Career: Qualified in 1993. Partner *BTO* 1986-2001. Consultant *TC Young & Son* 2001.

MATTHEWS, Carol
Wright Hassall, Leamington Spa (01926) 886 688
carolm@wrighthassall.co.uk
Specialisation: Solicitor in constitutional issues and structures for registered social landlords and housing groups. Solicitor in LSVTs in acting for both housing associations and councils and with property work. Advises on purchase of development sites and housing management issues. Gives seminars and lectures on all aspects of housing law.
Prof. Memberships: Law Society.
Career: Qualified in 1980. With *Winckworth & Pemberton* in Westminster before joining *Wright Hassall* in June 1995. Head of the housing and local government department.
Personal: Warwick University, History 2:1 BA Hons. Married with two daughters. Lives in Stratford-upon-Avon. Leisure interests include literature and theatre.

McNULTY, Stephen
Burges Salmon, Bristol (0117) 939 2250
stephen.mcnulty@burges-salmon.com
Specialisation: Commercial property development and social housing. He has a wide experience of commercial property issues arising when working with large corporate clients, especially in the telecommunications and transport sector. He is also head of the highly-regarded social housing unit which advises on all aspects of Registered Social Landlords' legal requirements from regulation and group structures to development management and funding issues. Recent projects include redevelopment of bus depot facilities and major office and data centre acquisitions in Birmingham and Bristol on behalf of a blue chip telecommunications client.
Prof. Memberships: Law Society, British Italian Law Association.
Career: Joined *Burges Salmon* in 1984, becoming a partner in 1988.

MORLEY, Trevor
Prince Evans, London (020) 8567 3477
Specialisation: Managing partner and head of housing finance and low cost home ownership departments; considerable experience in advising both lenders and borrowers of housing and public sector finance; acting on behalf of numerous borrowers in a range of transactions from bilateral and syndicated loans to group borrowing arrangements and capital market issues; expertise in advising on all aspects of banking law; including treasury management and related issues; head of largest low cost home ownership unit in the UK responsible for land acquisition and low cost home ownership development schemes including mixed use/tenure regeneration projects primarily on behalf of registered social landlords; acts for the majority of London based low cost home ownership registered social landlord providers; recent projects include: conduct of the sale of shared ownership portfolios; acting for the consortium of developer and housing association in the Trowbridge Regeneration project in the London Borough of Hackney.
Career: Articled Cambridgeshire; qualified 1979; partner *Prince Evans* 1982.
Personal: Born 1953. Resides Cobham, Surrey.

MORTIMER, Ken
Bevan Ashford, Bristol (0117) 975 1638
k.mortimer@bevanashford.co.uk
Specialisation: Partner specialising in commercial property with particular emphasis on public sector clients including RSLs; development acquisition and disposals; planning and statutory agreements; nomination agreements; management agreements and other agreements with local and similar authorities.
Career: Qualified with *Bevan Hancock & Co* in 1975 and returned to *Bevan Ashford* in 1984 having worked in the mean time with *Laurence & Co*. Partner at *Bevan Ashford* 2001.
Personal: Married with three children and formerly in the Territorial Army for 28 years; hobby – canal narrow boating.

MURRAY, Andrew
Winckworth Sherwood, London (020) 7593 5000
ajmurray@winckworths.co.uk
Specialisation: Partner in housing and local government. Main area of practice is public sector and housing law, with particular expertise in finance and projects. Addresses various seminars organised by professional bodies and clients.
Prof. Memberships: Law Society.
Career: Qualified in 1987. Joined *Winckworth Sherwood* in 1988, becoming a Partner in 1989.
Personal: Attended Manchester University 1978-81 (English Language and Literature). Lives in Richmond, Surrey.

PANTELIA, Despina
Clifford Chance, London (020) 7600 1000
despina.pantelia@cliffordchance.com
Specialisation: Public sector finance and general bank lending.
Career: Admitted 1987; *Clifford Chance* 1987-95; *Allen & Overy* 1996-97; *Clifford Chance* 1997 – head of housing finance. Partner since 2000.

PAPWORTH, Richard
Addleshaw Booth & Co, Leeds (0113) 209 2310
rnp@addleshaw-booth.co.uk
Specialisation: Leads the firm's banking unit. Specialist in banking, acquisition finance, property finance, social housing finance, project finance, education sector finance, building society treasury work, capital markets and derivatives. Particular responsibility for the firm's social housing finance practice. Worked extensively for funders on LSVT financings and refinancings and mainstream RSL funding. Acted for the funders on the majority of LSVTs in the 2000/2001 programme (13 of the last 21 to complete to end March 2001) including the £240m funding for the Coventary LSVT arranged by Nationwide and RBS. Has led social housing finance transactions aggregating in excess of £7 billion. Acted for Bradley & Bingley on the only Scottish LSVT to date (Berwickshire). Heavily involved in the Pathfinder Local Authority Housing PFI projects.
Prof. Memberships: Law Society, Leeds Law Society.
Career: Qualified 1989 with *Travers Smith Braithwaite*. Joined the firm 1991. Appointed partner 1995.
Personal: Educated at Christ Church, Oxford. Interests include golf, cricket and football. Lives in Knaresborough. Married with two sons.

PIA, Paul
Burness, Edinburgh (0131) 473 6106
pdp@burness.co.uk
Specialisation: A corporate lawyer specialising in corporate governance issues, business and company formations and reorganisations and corporate contracts across the private, public and not-for-profit sectors. He also sets up joint venture and partnering arrangements between different bodies and companies across the sectors. He has extensive knowledge of social housing issues and of the regulatory regimes which impinge upon the activities of housing associations; Scottish homes registration; charity law and the requirements of the Registrar of Friendly Societies. Also provides legal advice to funders of social housing projects and prepares security documentation. Lead legal advisor to the Scottish Federation of Housing Associations; the Institute of Housing in Scotland and a large number of housing associations.
Publications: Co-author of 'Care, Diligence and Skill', a handbook for directors of not-for-profit companies.

RANDALL, Simon
Lawrence Graham, London (020) 7759 6538
simon.randall@lawgram.com
Specialisation: Principal area of practice is public sector work advising local authorities on externalisation, charitable trusts, urban regeneration and public procurement, PFI, housing and competitive tendering. Involved in large-scale voluntary transfers of housing stock to housing associations and local housing companies. Author of many articles and pamphlets on local government and social issues ranging from the private rented sector, large scale voluntary sector of housing stock, local authority companies, community care and housing finance. Organises many seminars on health service, housing and local government related matters.
Prof. Memberships: Appointed CBE in June 1991 for housing work in London. Chairman, Kelsey Housing Association Ltd and member of Management committee of Broomleigh Housing Association Ltd. Member National Housing Federation council and director HOMES Limited. Member, London Borough of Bromley 1968-94. Member, Greater London Council 1981-86. Chairman, London Boroughs Association Housing and Social Services commiettee 1978-94. Non-executive director, Bethlem Royal and Maudsley Special Health Authority 1971-94.
Career: Articled with *Lawrence Graham* and became a partner in 1970. Head of housing and local government services.
Publications: 'Lock, Stock & Transfer – Making LSVTs Happen'; 'PFI for Housing – Key Legal and Practical Issues'; 'Local Housing Companies'; 'Delivery Vehicles for Best Value within Well-Being Powers: An A-Z Guide'; 'New Arrangements for Local Authority Governance under The Local Government Act 2000'.

RHATIGAN, Michael
Eversheds, Manchester (0161) 831 8000
michaelrhatigan@eversheds.com
Specialisation: Partner in commercial property department. All property aspects for Housing Association law including acquisition development and letting of properties and funding.
Career: Partner *Maurice Rubin Clare* 1979-90; partner *Davies Arnold Cooper* 1990-95; partner *Eversheds* 1995.
Personal: Born 1952. Leisure interests include Bolton Wanderers and opera.

ROBERT, Louis
Prince Evans, London (020) 8567 3477

ROBERTS, Ian
Denton Wilde Sapte, London (020) 7246 7056
imr@dentonwildesapte.com
Specialisation: Ian leads the *Denton Wilde Sapte* social housing finance team with substantial experience acting on a full range of matters in the social housing finance sector (primarily for funders), including LSVTs, group structures, trickle transfers, development, care homes and keyworker facilities. The team is a cross-departmental group of 15 experienced social housing finance and property lawyers, working closely together and supported by leading projects/PFI, construction and environmental specialists. The firm's property department also has expertise in the public sector acting for government departments as well as being on the legal adviser panel for DETR (including advising on the development of PFI/PPP practice), the MoD, the Home Office, certain local authorities and other similar public sector bodies. The firm is on the legal panel for a number of RSLs and has been retained to advise on a wide range of matters including construction dis-

putes, planning issues and tenant consultation. The firm also has significant experience in acting for local authorities in relation to the disposal and development of social housing land and the administration and payment of social housing grants.
Career: Joined *Denton Wilde Sapte* in 1983, becoming a partner in 1990.
Personal: Ian read law at Pembroke College, Cambridge before joining *Denton Wilde Sapte.* He is married with three children. Interests include rugby, motor racing, reading and, more recently, skiing and his Yamaha Fazer.

ROBERTSON, Andrew
TC Young & Son, Glasgow (0141) 221 5562
aor@tcyoung.co.uk
Specialisation: Senior partner. Works for community based charitable and generalist Housing Associations as well as fully mutual and non-fully mutual Co-ops. He acts on behalf of Housing Associations across the whole field of their activity. He was instrumental in the forming of the first Employers' Federation for Housing Association Committees (now EVH) and provided full administrative and advisory support during its early years.
Prof. Memberships: Law Society of Scotland.
Career: LLB Edinburgh 1964. Trainee *Maclay Murray & Spens* 1964-67. Partner, *TC Young & Son* 1968.
Personal: Chairman of the Scottish Housing Associations Charitable Trust from 1992 to date. Trustee of HACT from 1991 to 1997.

SMITH, Chris
Maclay Murray & Spens, London (0171) 606 6130
cps@maclaymurrayspens.co.uk
Specialisation: Partner in social housing department. Principal area of practice covers all aspects of social housing work with particular expertise in employment law, constitutional work, urban regeneration and Care in the Community. Other main area of practice is development work including consortium arrangements. Currently engaged in a major south coast reprovision project involving 250 properties and associated amenities, and the social housing aspects of a new settlement in Cambridge.
Career: Qualified in 1978. Became a partner with *Asshetons* in 1980 and in the merged firm of *Manches & Co*, then joined *Stones Porter* as a partner in 1993, and *Maclays* (associated with *Maclay Murray & Spens*) in 1998.
Personal: Born 22 October 1953. Attended University College, Cardiff 1972-75. Leisure pursuits include golf and squash. Lives in Godalming.

STEPHENS, Hugo
Pinsent Curtis Biddle, Birmingham
(0121) 212 1828
hugo.stephens@pinsents.com
Specialisation: An acknowledged leader in this field with expertise in all forms of corporate, constitutional and finance work for registered social landlords. Has advised on all forms of housing stock transfer including Sunderland Housing Group on the largest transfer to date – 37,000 houses to seven companies; group structures, amalgamations and mergers; PFI/PPP projects, care home transfers and charities; particular expertise in housing finance acting for borrowers and lenders in over £5 million of loans; wrote the National Housing Federation's guide to understanding loan documentation and the loan and security documentation sections for their new revised Private Finance Manual.
Prof. Memberships: Law Society.
Career: Qualified in 1989 with *Trowers & Hamlins*; 1989-94, assistant solicitor *Trowers & Hamlins*; 1994-97, senior assistant solicitor *Prince Evans*; 1997, partner *Irwin Mitchell*; 2001, head of housing at *Pinsent Curtis Biddle.*
Personal: Born 20 March 1956. Member of the Magic Circle.

THOMPSON, Alison
TC Young & Son, Edinburgh (0131) 473 5135
alison.thompson@shepwedd.co.uk
Specialisation: Handles all aspects of social housing law including stock transfers, public/private housing partnerships, commercial contracts, funding, policy, corporate structures, tenancies, tenures, shared ownership developments, site acquisition and development.
Prof. Memberships: Law Society (Scotland), Notary Public.
Career: Qualified 1988; Associate *Shepherd & Wedderburn WS* 1995.

TURNER, Graham
Trowers & Hamlins, Manchester (0161) 211 0000
gturner@trowers.com
Specialisation: Partner, head of Manchester Office. Has specialised in Housing Association law for 25 years, heading a team of six Manchester lawyers (four partners) who provide a comprehensive housing law service on a regional and national basis. Experience ranges from stock transfer major development and partnership projects, urban renewal and regeneration to private finance and group structures. Constitutional vires and PFI issues. All legal issues relating to the housing movement are covered by the Manchester office, including litigation, construction and environmental matters.

TURNER, Nicholas
Lawrence Graham, London (020) 7379 0000
nicholas.turner@lawgram.com
Specialisation: Partner in *Lawrence Graham* 's banking team and specialises in advising housing associations and local housing companies on all aspects of financing. Particular specialisation in the funding aspects of large scale voluntary transfers, syndicated and bilateral lending arrangements, restructuring and refinancing of facilities, capital markets facilities and bond issues, funding issues relating to group structures, security documentation and issues relevant to all of the above. Experience also includes development facilities, derivatives, PFI and ERCF. General experience in most aspects of banking and finance (and in particular property finance) and capital markets.
Career: Prior to joining *Lawrence Graham* spent one year as a money/derivatives broker with EXCO Plc. Qualified at *Lawrence Graham* in 1989 and became a partner in 1997.
Personal: Educated at University of East Anglia, LLB (Hons). Lives in North London. Married with three children.

SPORT

London: 785; South West: 787; wales: 788; Midlands: 788; The North: 788; Scotland: 789; *Profiles*: 789

OVERVIEW: A split within sports law has emerged. In the regions there remain a number of strong sports firms, such as James Chapman & Co and McCormicks, who can handle both the traditional needs of sport and the new concerns that heavy investment brings. In the capital, however, the differences in the varying demands of sports law have been more clearly defined, with the result that the tables for London this year have been split into the new categories of Regulatory and Commercial/Media.

RESEARCH APPROVED BY BMRB: *For this edition,* Chambers' *researchers conducted 6,552 interviews – 4,419 with law firms, 554 with barristers and 1,579 with clients.*

The validity of the research was scrutinised by BMRB International, who audited both the methodology and the results at our offices in July 2001. They interviewed Chambers' *researchers and cross-checked sample interviews. Details of the audit appear on page 7.*

TOP IN-HOUSE LAWYERS

Heather BARTON, Head of Legal and Special Projects, *Scottish Football Association*

Darren BERMAN, Company Solicitor, Football Association

Nic COWARD, Company Secretary, *Football Association*

Andy GRAY, Head of Legal Affairs, *British Swimming Association*

Jonathon HALL, Secretary and Legal Officer, *Rugby Football Union*

Bruce MELLSTROM, Lawyer, *Lawn Tennis Association*

Holly ROPER-KURSTON, Club Solicitor, *MCC*

Sascha WOODWARD-HILL, Lawyer, *Formula One*

"Excellent" **Heather Barton** has established a good reputation at the Scottish Football Association, dealing with constitutional matters. A *"sound commercial lawyer"* **Darren Berman** is highly rated; *"he knows exactly what he is doing."* Considered by some *"the most able of in-house lawyers"* **Nic Coward** is acclaimed as *"excellent at what he does."* The *"extremely efficient"* **Jonathan Hall**, though still a relatively young talent, *"always has plenty of substance to his views."* With his *"wide ranging knowledge of swimming related issues,"* **Andy Gray** continues to pick up accolades. **Bruce Mellstrom** continues to be highly regarded. **Holly Roper-Kurston** is renowned for her *"wide ranging commercial experience."* Rated as an *"expert"* who *"knows the business,"* **Sascha Woodward-Hill** is judged *"a very quick thinker."*

In-House lawyers profiles: p 1193

LONDON

REGULATORY

SPORT: REGULATORY • London	Ptnrs	Assts
1 Denton Wilde Sapte	3	5
Townleys	2	9
2 Farrer & Co	8	5
Max Bitel, Greene	1	2
3 Charles Russell	4	2
Grower Freeman & Goldberg	1	3
4 Mishcon de Reya	3	3
Simmons & Simmons	5	5

LEADING INDIVIDUALS	
1 **BITEL Nicholas** Max Bitel, Greene	**GAY Mark** Denton Wilde Sapte
TOWNLEY Stephen Townleys	
2 **GOLDBERG Mel** Grower Freeman & Goldberg	
VLECK Karena Farrer & Co	
3 **RUSSELL Patrick** Charles Russell	

This book is the product of 6,552 1/2-hour interviews. See p.7 for BMRB audit.

Within each band, firms are listed alphabetically. *See individuals' profiles p.789*

Denton Wilde Sapte (see firm details p.939) One of the major forces for regulatory work, the firm has recently advised on a raft of contentious athletics cases. However, the team also has expertise in the regulatory aspects of a vast range of team sports. **Mark Gay** (see p.790) *"gets through a huge volume of high quality work,"* and has a high profile for acting on drugs-related cases. He advised the IAAF on prosecuting nine athletes before the Sydney Olympics, including Javier Sotomayor, Merlene Ottey and Dieter Baumann. **Clients:** The Premier League; The Racehorse Association; The Motor Sports Association.

Townleys (see firm details p.1159) *"Colossally able,"* the renowned sports boutique maintains its position in the regulatory aspects of sports law, in spite of substantial personnel changes. *"Industry guru"* **Stephen Townley**'s (see p.793) reputation remains unsurpassed. Known for its expertise in rugby union, the firm advised on the structuring of rules and regulations for the proposed Celtic League, and acted for the International Rugby Board on the 'Grannygate' eligibility cases. At the time of going to press, the practice was finalising a merger with national firm Hammond Suddards Edge. **Clients:** Celtic Unions; Six Nations Committee.

Farrer & Co (see firm details p.954) The firm with the strongest reputation for focusing on purely regulatory work, it has a unique clientele, almost exclusively representing governing bodies on constitutional matters. **Karena Vleck** (see p.793) is the team's leading light, and is commended as *"a huge talent"* who has *"moulded her skills to this type of work."* The firm has acted for both the IAAF and UK Athletics in high profile doping cases, and advised the LTA on a new template for a constitution. **Clients:** British Athletic Federation; The Football Association; The Lawn Tennis Association.

Max Bitel, Greene Praised as a *"truly professional outfit,"* the practice has an interesting client mixture of both individuals and establishments. Although a comparatively small operation, its chief player **Nick Bitel** gives it *"real stature."* Possessor of *"one of the best client bases in London,"* he *"really understands the workings of the industry,"* and maintains his position as Chief Executive of The London Marathon. The firm has advised various institutions on contract and commercial issues, and represents individuals from all sports on contracts, doping and IP rights. **Clients:** The London Marathon; Ryder Cup.

Charles Russell (see firm details p.912) **Patrick Russell** (see p.793), *"one of the last of the real gentlemen,"* is largely responsible for the firm's profile in this area. This derives from his work on behalf of the Jockey Club, whose disciplinary and licensing committees he advises on contentious matters involving the regulation of professional jockeys and trainers. **Clients:** The Jockey Club.

Grower Freeman & Goldberg Best known for representing individual sports people, the firm advises on contracts, transfers, management and IP rights for footballers, boxers, tennis players and athletes in many other disciplines. "*Great character*" **Mel Goldberg** (see p.790) remains the team's principal asset and public face. **Clients:** Various sports individuals.

Mishcon de Reya (see firm details p.1071) Led by Tony Morton-Hooper, the team is recognised for its niche in contentious work. Regularly in the headlines as a result of its work on the Diane Modahl saga, the firm also has expertise in advising sports bodies on internal disciplinary enquiries. The team acted for British triathlete Spencer Smith on his successful case before the Court of Arbitration for Sport in New York. **Clients:** Diane Modahl; Arrows Formula One; United Cricket Board of South Africa.

Simmons & Simmons (see firm details p.1132) Including both the MCC and ICC among its clientele, the firm's niche expertise in cricket is unquestioned. Mark Hewland's "*friendly and approachable*" team advises on both regulatory and contentious matters, and was recently involved in the establishment of the ICC's anti-corruption unit. **Clients:** MCC; ICC.

COMMERCIAL / MEDIA

SPORT: COMMERCIAL/MEDIA • London	Ptnrs	Assts
1 Denton Wilde Sapte	5	6
2 Bird & Bird	6	7
Nicholson Graham & Jones	3	4
3 Olswang	6	6
SJ Berwin	7	6
Townleys	2	9
4 Freshfields Bruckhaus Deringer	6	6
Theodore Goddard	1	1
5 Ashurst Morris Crisp	3	3
Clintons	2	2
Collyer-Bristow	2	1
Field Fisher Waterhouse	3	3
Harbottle & Lewis	2	2
Herbert Smith	4	6
Memery Crystal	3	n/a
The Simkins Partnership	2	3

LEADING INDIVIDUALS	
1 BARR-SMITH Adrian Denton Wilde Sapte	
2 PHELOPS Warren Nicholson Graham & Jones	
3 WALKEY Justin Bird & Bird	
4 BELL Alasdair Olswang	COUCHMAN Nicholas Couchman Harrington
HIGTON Jonathan Townleys	McINERNEY Peter SJ Berwin
METLISS Jonathan SJ Berwin	PARKER Raj Freshfields Bruckhaus Deringer
REEVE Felicity Bird & Bird	REID Fraser Theodore Goddard
ZEFFMAN David Olswang	
5 BURDON-COOPER Alan Collyer-Bristow	HORNSBY Stephen The Simkins Partnership
STINSON Philip Clintons	
UP AND COMING	
BROWN Jacqueline Clintons	FITZPATRICK Nick Denton Wilde Sapte

This book is the product of 6,552 1/2-hour interviews. See p.7 for BMRB audit.
Within each band, firms are listed alphabetically. *See individuals' profiles p.789*

Denton Wilde Sapte (see firm details p.939) Acknowledged for its "*utterly professional, hugely commercial*" team, and possessing "*apparently bottomless*" resources, the firm stands supreme in this area of sports law. The "*brilliant and peerless*" **Adrian Barr-Smith** (see p.789), who is praised for "*understanding everything you throw at him,*" leads the group. He receives valuable support from rising star **Nick Fitzpatrick** (see p.790), commended for his "*unstinting enthusiasm.*" The firm represented The Racecourse Association on its innovative sale of media rights, as well as advising on the high-profile broadcast rights for the FA Premiership. **Clients:** The FA Premier League; The Racecourse Association; England and Wales Cricket Board.

Bird & Bird (see firm details p.884) "*Top quality sports department*" with a wide range of expertise, acting for corporate entities, sports rights agencies and high net-worth individuals, and handling commercial work for governing bodies. The team makes good use of the firm's outstanding IP, IT and e-commerce practices. **Justin Walkey** (see p.793) "*has a great name,*" while **Felicity Reeve** (see p.792) also retains her share of market recognition. The team acted for Octagon on its acquisition of Silverstone racetrack and advised the FA on its TV and radio deals and IT rights. **Clients:** The Football Association; Octagon Worldwide; Eurosport.

Nicholson Graham & Jones (see firm details p.1081) A corporate firm with "*a strong understanding of sport*" and an acknowledged name for event packaging, exploitation and acquisition, as well as financing advice. The team is felt to depend heavily on the talents of its "*active, resourceful*" leader **Warren Phelops** (see p.792). It acted for the commercial arm of the ICC in the sale of broadcast and internet rights for the next two World Cups, and advised Lloyds TSB on its renewal of sponsorship for the Six Nations Rugby Championship. **Clients:** ICC Development (International); Lloyds TSB; Sportech.

Olswang (see firm details p.1084) "*Doing more and more sports-related stuff,*" the firm's profile has flourished. "*An invigorating team*" advises a client base that includes a cross-section of broadcasters, rights holders, sponsors and internet companies. The acquisition of "*top class*" competition specialist **Alasdair Bell** (see p.789) from White & Case is considered to have strengthened the team markedly, while broadcasting lawyer **David Zeffman**'s (see p.607) practice has increasingly encompassed the sporting arena. The firm advised Channel Four on its £400 million bid for British horse racing rights, and acted for Granada Media on its acquisition of 5% of the share capital of Arsenal FC. **Clients:** Channel 4; RFU; Granada Media Group.

SJ Berwin (see firm details p.879) Respected sports practice with a client base that includes clubs, broadcasters, rights owners, merchandisers and sports personalities. The team is headed by the "*wonderfully commercial, if a little pushy*" **Jonathan Metliss** (see p.792), and also features the "*industrious*" **Peter McInerney** (see p.791). Highlights of the last year include representing ENIC on its purchase of Sir Alan Sugar's holdings in Tottenham Hotspur FC and advising on contracts for the England and Wales Cricket Board. **Clients:** ENIC; Ondigital; England and Wales Cricket Board.

Townleys (see firm details p.1159) Although still competing hard in this area, the departures of Darren Bailey (to an in-house position) and Nick Couchman (to his own practice) mean that "*for now, the jury must be out*" on the firm's current strength in the commercial sector. The impending merger with Hammond Suddards Edge is expected to provide valuable ballast. The firm does, however, retain its strong client base of rights holders, broadcasters, IT companies and sponsors, as well as the services of the "*astute*" **Jonathan Higton** (see p.791). Highlights of the past year include World Sport Group's acquisition of commercial rights for the next two cricket World Cups, and dealing with the television agreements for the European Rugby Cup. Recently the team dealt with the largest M&A deal in its history, advising World Sport Group on its £66 million merger with Parallel Group. At the time of going to press, the practice was finalising a merger with national firm Hammond Suddards Edge. **Clients:** Six Nations Committee; Carlsberg-Tetley Brewing; Channel 5 Broadcasting.

Freshfields Bruckhaus Deringer (see firm details p.965) Although the firm has experience in regulatory cases, having advised the FA on various disciplinary matters, its presence is far more apparent on transactional issues. "*User friendly*" litigator **Raj Parker** (see p.578) and his team have acted on the flotations of various European football clubs, and advised on a European broadcast dispute for Formula One Administration. **Clients:** FA; FOA.

Theodore Goddard (see firm details p.1152) The recruitment of "*fantastic litigator*" **Fraser Reid** (see p.793) from Russell Jones & Walker is felt to have given the sports team a new impetus. Representing governing bodies, individuals and sports marketing companies, the firm is recognised for its strong commercial focus. Particularly focused on IP-related issues, the team deals with contracts, marketing, and the creation, protection and exploitation of rights. A highlight of the last year was advising on the sale of horse racing rights for the British Horse Racing Board. **Clients:** British Horse Racing Board; World Sports Network; Players Sport Management.

Ashurst Morris Crisp (see firm details p.866) "*Corporate led*" team, which features former Olympic rower Jonny Searle, and retains a reputation as an operation that "*keeps up with developments.*" As well as a strong media company and sponsor clientele, the firm has seen a growth in instructions from football clubs in the past year. The firm has advised football teams, both in Britain and Germany, on stadium development and means of fund raising, and it also represented TV Danmark 1 on its dispute with the ITC, a case that has now gone to the House of Lords. **Clients:** Prima International Television; 365 Corporation; Golf Club Holdings.

Clintons (see firm details p.920) Best known as a media firm, it keeps its place in these rankings through its expertise in sports marketing and sponsorship. "*Knowledgeable*" head of department **Philip Stinson** and litigator **Jacqueline Brown** are both respected by their peers. Acting for sports agencies, professional bodies, clubs and individual players, the firm handles rights and commercial management issues. **Clients:** Sports marketing agencies; high net worth individuals; manufacturers.

Collyer-Bristow (see firm details p.924) Focusing mainly on the sponsorship side of sport, the firm's client base includes governing bodies, rights holders, marketing agencies and sponsors. Department head **Alan Burdon-Cooper** (see p.789) is praised for his expertise in contracts issues. The firm has advised Sports England extensively on National Lottery grants. **Clients:** Sports England; Fast Track Events.

Field Fisher Waterhouse (see firm details p.957) Respected media/new technology-oriented firm, which acts for a client roster that includes sponsors, teams and internet companies, and handles fund-raising, establishing and exploiting brands and sponsorship. The highlights for Patrick Cannon's team in the last year include advising Sporting Edge on a new software application and acting for London Irish Holdings on fund-raising matters. **Clients:** Sports Media Group; Sporting Edge; London Irish Holdings.

Harbottle & Lewis (see firm details p.985) "*Quietly efficient team,*" said to be "*popping up more frequently this year,*" typically on sponsorship, broadcasting and IP work. Led by Bob Mitchell, the team acts for large media companies, sponsors, events, clubs and individuals. The firm advised on the new centralised contracts for the ECB and on the joint venture company Rivals Europe – responsible for building the largest online network of sports team sites in Europe. **Clients:** English Cricket Squad; Ryder Cup; QPR Football & Athletic Club.

Herbert Smith (see firm details p.993) Inevitably strong on the contentious side, Alan Watts and his team advise broadcasters, clubs, pools companies and individuals on a broad range of media and high-tech-related cases. The firm advised Talksport in a dispute with the BBC, and represented Tottenham Hotspur in a recent libel case. **Clients:** BSkyB; Tottenham Hotspur FC; Littlewoods Organisation.

Memery Crystal (see firm details p.1064) Renowned for AIM flotation work and a powerful clientele, the firm, under the guidance of Peter Crystal, also offers advice on merchandising, sponsorship, IT/IP and e-commerce within the sports field. Digital radio is an area of niche expertise. **Clients:** Sponsors.

The Simkins Partnership (see firm details p.1131) **Stephen Hornsby** "*knows his stuff*" on competition-related sports law and leads a team that has a focus on media and entertainment. With expertise in new media and internet law, the firm acts for clients such as SFX and West Ham United on cyber space disputes. The team also advised on the foundation of the European Clubs Association. **Clients:** West Ham United; SFX; Test Match Grounds Consortium.

Other Notable Practitioners Esteemed former Townleys man **Nicholas Couchman** continues to represent broadcasters, rights agencies and individuals at his new firm **Couchman Harrington Associates.**

SOUTH WEST

SPORT • South West	Ptnrs	Assts
1 **Clarke Willmott & Clarke** Bristol	2	1
2 **Osborne Clarke** Bristol	1	2

LEADING INDIVIDUALS
1 **POWELL David** Clarke Willmott & Clarke
2 **BRAITHWAITE Andrew** Osborne Clarke
3 **JEACOCK David** David Jeacock

This book is the product of 6,552 1/2-hour interviews. See p.7 for BMRB audit.

Within each band, firms are listed alphabetically. *See individuals' profiles p.789*

Clarke Willmott & Clarke (see firm details p.915) Although often viewed as a rugby-focused practice, the region's undisputed number one also boasts clients from football, cricket and athletics. **David Powell** (see p.792) leads the team and is said to "*know intuitively what will work.*" The firm successfully defended Pontypool RFC against the WRU on eligibility issues. **Clients:** PRA; Cardiff RFC; Pontypool RFC.

Osborne Clarke (see firm details p.1086) Advising clients from a range of sports, the firm deals with employment, property, contract, litigation, IP and sponsorship issues from across the sector. The respected **Andrew Braithwaite** leads the department. The firm has advised on sponsorship matters for the Professional Golfers Association (PGA). **Clients:** PGA; Gloucestershire County Cricket Club; Bass.

Other Notable Practitioners Swindon-based sole practitioner **David Jeacock** (see p.791) retains his reputation, notably in his niche areas of athletics and disabled sport.

WALES

SPORT • Wales	Ptnrs	Assts
1 Hugh James Ford Simey Cardiff	3	1

This book is the product of 6,552 1/2-hour interviews. See p.7 for BMRB audit.
Within each band, firms are listed alphabetically.

Hugh James Ford Simey (see firm details p.1004) Seen as "*the only firm in Wales*" doing this type of work, the practice is included this year primarily for its work on behalf of the WRU. It handles arrangements for the national team, player contracts, youth development work and IP/copyright issues. Bill Snowdon's team also represents the Cardiff Devils ice hockey team and a number of top athletes. **Clients:** WRU; Cardiff Devils; Millennium Stadium.

MIDLANDS

SPORT • Midlands	Ptnrs	Assts
1 Hammond Suddards Edge Birmingham	2	3

LEADING INDIVIDUALS
1 ALDERSON Richard Hammond Suddards Edge

This book is the product of 6,552 1/2-hour interviews. See p.7 for BMRB audit.
Within each band, firms are listed alphabetically. *See individuals' profiles p.789*

Hammond Suddards Edge (see firm details p.984) Although much of the practice has moved to London, it still retains a presence in the Midlands, and it is here that its reputation remains strongest. Department head **Richard Alderson** (see p.789) is considered to be "*one of the most talented and exceptional sports lawyers anywhere.*" The Football League remains the team's single biggest client, with instructions including the internet, digital broadcasting and stadium contracts. **Clients:** The Football League; Amateur Swimming Association; Aston Villa FC.

THE NORTH

SPORT • The North	Ptnrs	Assts
1 James Chapman & Co Manchester	3	2
McCormicks Leeds	5	1
2 George Davies Manchester	2	2
Walker Morris Leeds	3	3
3 Addleshaw Booth & Co Manchester	4	3
Gorna & Co Manchester	1	2
4 Zermansky & Partners Leeds	2	n/a

LEADING INDIVIDUALS	
★ WATKINS Maurice James Chapman & Co	
1 McCORMICK Peter McCormicks	
2 CAISLEY Christopher Walker Morris	
3 CRAMER Richard McCormicks	MORRISON Michael Gorna & Co
4 HEWISON John George Davies	HOVELL Mark George Davies
SMITH Jason James Chapman & Co	

This book is the product of 6,552 1/2-hour interviews. See p.7 for BMRB audit.
Within each band, firms are listed alphabetically. *See individuals' profiles p.789*

James Chapman & Co (see firm details p.1011) Seen as "*The football firm,*" through its work with FIFA and UEFA, it has now moved in public perception from being regarded as merely the Manchester United firm. The team is still headed by the "*legendary*" **Maurice Watkins** (see p.793), who has been appointed to the UEFA panel of external legal experts, and worked for FIFA/UEFA on the EC challenge to the transfer system. New partner **Jason Smith** (see p.793) is said to be "*coming through nicely.*" The team has expertise in regulatory, commercial and media matters, and advises major clients in rugby, swimming and motor racing. **Clients:** Manchester United; Swansea City; The Amateur Swimming Association.

McCormicks (see firm details p.1060) A wide-ranging sports practice with a huge reputation in the region. "*Fabulous lawyer and great marketer*" **Peter McCormick** (see p.791) "*drives everything forward*" and is a member of the legal working party of the FA Premier League. He receives sound support from the "*sensible, competent*" **Richard Cramer** (see p.790). The team advised on the new broadcasting deal for the FA Premier League, and represented the boxer Richie Woodall in his dispute with Frank Warren. As well as its close links with Leeds United, the firm acts extensively on rugby, cricket and horse racing cases. **Clients:** FA Premier League; Leeds Utd FC; The Rugby Football League.

George Davies (see firm details p.969) Although it has a traditional interest in rugby, the firm is most noted for its work on behalf of the Professional Footballers Association (PFA). The "*sensible*" **Mark Hovell** (see p.791) and **John Hewison**, who "*obviously understands this work,*" both stand out at the practice. The team deals with contracts, transfers and disputes, and is frequently called in to advise clubs that have slipped into insolvency. **Clients:** PFA.

Walker Morris (see firm details p.1171) Renowned for advice on rugby league, the highly respected **Chris Caisley** (see p.790) and his team act for the Bradford Bulls, the Professional Rugby Players Association and the rugby league Super League. The caseload covers disciplinary matters, broadcasting and sponsorship issues. Football, cricket and individual sports also provide substance to an "*impressive clientele.*" **Clients:** Bradford Bulls; Professional Cricket Players Association; Professional Rugby Players Association.

Addleshaw Booth & Co (see firm details p.853) The team has accumulated great kudos through its role as advisor to the 2002 Commonwealth Games in Manchester. The firm has dealt with accommodation, ticketing, internet and broadcasting rights and sponsorship deals. Although this work is perceived to overshadow the rest of the practice, Robert Stoker's team also advises extensively on football and rugby. **Clients:** Manchester 2002 Commonwealth Games; Adidas UK.

Gorna & Co Representing a number of prominent individual sports personalities, the firm advises players and managers on employment, contracts, IP/IT and sponsorship issues. "*Sound practitioner*" **Michael Morrison** (see p.792) leads the team, which is said to offer "*an incredibly good service.*" **Clients:** Sports individuals.

Zermansky & Partners (see firm details p.1192) Richard Lindley and his team continue to be prominent for rugby expertise. The firm acts on a wide range of issues, ranging from player and club disputes to financial problems and matters of competition law. Other work includes disputes involving sponsorship and broadcasting revenue. **Clients:** Rugby League clients.

SCOTLAND

SPORT • Scotland	Ptnrs	Assts
1 **Anderson Strathern WS** Edinburgh	3	2
Harper Macleod Glasgow	3	3
2 **Burness** Glasgow	3	3
Dundas & Wilson CS Edinburgh	3	5
Henderson Boyd Jackson WS Edinburgh	1	2
Morison Bishop Edinburgh	2	2

LEADING INDIVIDUALS	
1 **KERR John** Anderson Strathern WS	
2 **DUFF Alistair** Henderson Boyd Jackson WS	**GROSSET Alan** Morison Bishop
McKENZIE Rod Harper Macleod	**SLEIGH Andrew** Burness
3 **MILLER Stephen** Harper Macleod	

This book is the product of 6,552 1/2-hour interviews. See p.7 for BMRB audit.

Within each band, firms are listed alphabetically. *See individuals' profiles p.789*

Anderson Strathern WS (see firm details p.859) Hailed for its work for the SRU, the practice also handles a wide range of sports work, dealing with straight corporate matters, commercial work, stadium management and so called 'Grannygate' eligibility cases. "*Solid*" **John Kerr** (see p.791) is described as an "*expert on governing bodies.*" The firm has recently been instructed by Sportscotland on the distribution of National Lottery funds, the redevelopment of playing fields and employment work. **Clients:** SRU; Sportscotland.

Harper Macleod (see firm details p.987) "*Busy*" team whose main client is perceived as the SPL, for whom it acts on all legal matters. In the past year, the firm has dealt with constitutional matters in the light of the Human Rights Act, the renewal of sponsorship, disciplinary disputes with players and broadcasting rights, including the arrangement of the first pay per view scheme in Scotland. "*First-rate litigators*" **Rod McKenzie** (see p.791) and **Stephen Miller** (see p.337) are widely commended by peers and clients. The team's client portfolio includes rugby, bowling and hockey bodies, as well as individual clubs and players. **Clients:** Scottish Premier League; Scottish Rugby Union; Glasgow Celtic FC.

Burness (see firm details p.903) "*Hard-nosed*" corporate lawyer **Andrew Sleigh** (see p.257) runs a team whose main client is the Scottish Football Association. Handling the whole gamut of sporting law for the SFA, the firm advises on disciplinary, constitutional and commercial matters. Other leading clients exist in boxing and rugby. The firm also keeps a strong media presence through its advice on behalf of Radio First. **Clients:** SFA; Radio First; Clansman Sporting Club.

Dundas & Wilson CS (see firm details p.947) Although lacking the single eminent practitioner of its major rivals, the firm is acknowledged to have "*serious resources.*" Primarily known for its advice to Rangers, the firm handles issues ranging from player disputes to exploitation of rights. It also advises the SRU on a number of constitutional and commercial cases. **Clients:** Glasgow Rangers FC; SRU.

Henderson Boyd Jackson WS The well-known **Alistair Duff** (see p.790) leads a team with a wide client base. Although primarily known for its representation of individuals, the firm also advises governing bodies, clubs and sponsors. Individual disputes, employment matters, sponsorship deals and television work are core elements of the workload. **Clients:** Hearts FC; British Telecom; sporting personalities.

Morison Bishop (see firm details p.1075) The "*expert*" **Alan Grosset** (see p.790) "*has a great understanding and knowledge*" of the sports arena. Although the firm has a broad range of sporting clients, it is primarily associated with acting for the Lawn Tennis Association on constitutional, contractual and restructuring matters. **Clients:** LTA; Scottish Badminton Union.

LEADERS IN SPORT

ALDERSON, Richard
Hammond Suddards Edge, Birmingham
(0121) 222 3300
richard.alderson@hammondse.com
Specialisation: Partner and head of sports unit. Since 1987, sole area of practice is sport administration and associated commercial activities, advising governing bodies on television, new media and internet rights, sponsorship, discipline and constitutional matters. Also works for industry, covering sport and event sponsorship and broadcast sponsorship. Acts for The Football League and other sports governing bodies.
Prof. Memberships: British Association for Sport and the Law.
Career: Qualified in 1976 with *Edge Ellison*, becoming a partner in 1981.
Personal: Born 17th July 1951. Attended Bristol University 1970-73. Trustee of St Giles' Hospice (Special interest: charity shops). Leisure interests include tennis and Aston Villa. Lives in Birmingham.

BARR-SMITH, Adrian
Denton Wilde Sapte, London (020) 7320 6501
abs@dentonwildesapte.com
Specialisation: Main area of practice is sport, covering broadcasting contracts, licensing and merchandising, event regulation, official supplier contracts and disciplinary matters. Also covers media finance, film and TV production and distribution. Has acted for the FA Premier League, Commonwealth Games Federation, England and Wales Cricket Board and Rugby Football Union. Hon. legal adviser to Sports Aid Foundation. Consulting Editor 'Law and the Business of Sport' (Butterworths, 1997). Specialist Editor 'Copinger and Skone James on Copyright' 14th Edition (Sweet & Maxwell, 1998). Panel Member of the Arbitrators of the American Film Marketing Association.
Prof. Memberships: Design & Artists Copyright Society (Honorary Secretary).
Career: Qualified in 1977. Solicitor at *Rubinstein Callingham* 1977-79. Legal Director of Artlaw Services 1980-81; Joined *Denton Wilde Sapte* in 1982, becoming a partner in 1986.
Personal: Born 1952. Emmanuel College, Cambridge, 1970-73. Governor of Sports Aid Trust. Leisure pursuits include cricket, golf and film. Lives in London.

BELL, Alasdair
Olswang, London (020) 7290 7946
azb@olswang.com
Specialisation: EU and competition. Experienced in all aspects of EU and UK competition law and practised in Brussels for many years. Has been involved in many cases before the European Commission and the European Courts, including cartels, abuse of monopoly power and merger control. Particular experience in the areas of TV broadcasting and professional sport, and has represented the European governing body for football (UEFA) in relation to a wide range of EU legal issues, including player transfers, marketing of television rights, club-ownership rules, advertising and sponsorship, league governance issues and ticketing matters.
Prof. Memberships: Law Society of Scotland.
Career: Previous career: Partner, *White & Case*, London and Brussels.

BITEL, Nicholas
Max Bitel, Greene, London (020) 7354 2767

BRAITHWAITE, Andrew
Osborne Clarke, Bristol (0117) 917 3000

BROWN, Jacqueline
Clintons, London (020) 7379 6080

BURDON-COOPER, Alan
Collyer-Bristow, London (020) 7242 7363
alan.burdon-cooper@collyerbristow.com
Specialisation: Sponsorship in sports, arts and television; licensing and merchandising. Recent work has included advising on a sponsorship of a Formula 1

Championship Event; contracts with Premier League Football Clubs in relation to the running of residential coaching courses; an appointment of a marketing agent for FISU and advice to Sport England on issues relating to lottery funding. Co-author 'Vol 39, Sports and Sponsorship: Encyclopaedia of Forms and Precendents' (Butterworths).
Prof. Memberships: Chairman of the Institute of Sports Sponsorship.
Career: Articled at *Collyer-Bristow*, qualified 1968, partner 1969.
Personal: Born 1942. Educated at Oundle School (1955-61), Emmanuel College, Cambridge (1964 MA LLB). Governor of the Rose Bruford College of Speech and Drama. Liveryman of the Worshipful Company of Dyers. Leisure pursuits include music, sport and gardening. Lives near Hemel Hempstead.

CAISLEY, Christopher
Walker Morris, Leeds (0113) 283 2500
Specialisation: Former Chairman of the firm, the Head of the firm's Commercial Dispute Resolution Department and Sports Division. Main area of practice is sports law. Work includes sports broadcasting rights, contract negotiations and disputes, personality merchandising, licensing agreements, publishing contracts and acting for sports personalities, clubs and associations. Other area of practice is commercial litigation. Cases involve restraint of trade claims and the consequential effects of salary laps in sport; breach of player contract claims in soccer; the prosecution of actions by football league managers against their former clubs subsequent to dismissal; and applications for declaratory relief by Football League players for release from their contracts. Chairman of Bradford Bulls RLFC and of The Rugby Super League and a director of the Rugby Football League, creating regular contact with the media.
Prof. Memberships: The Rugby Football League, The British Association for Sport and the Law.
Career: Qualified in 1978, becoming a Partner in 1979. Also Practice Development Partner.
Personal: Born 2nd June 1951. Attended Grange Boys Grammar School, Bradford. Vice-Consul for the Netherlands Yorkshire and Derbyshire. Leisure interests include running, reading and an interest in most sports. Lives in Lancashire.

COUCHMAN, Nicholas
Couchman Harrington Associates, London (020) 7611 9660

CRAMER, Richard
McCormicks, Leeds (0113) 246 0622
r.cramer@mccormicks-solicitors.com
Specialisation: Partner. Substantial experience in sports law and in particular Rugby League, Rugby Union and Football, dealing with both contentious and non-contentious aspects. Acts for Keighley Cougars RLFC, Wakefield Trinity RLFC, Dewsbury Rams RLFC, Oldham Bears RLFC, Workington Town RLFC, Barrow Braves RLFC, Castleford Tigers RLFC, and a number of top rugby league players and coaches. Represented Ellery Hanley with regard to disciplinary proceedings brought by his club, St Helens, and subsequent wrongful dismissal claim; represented Malcolm Reilley, the former Great Britain Coach, in a claim for compensation following the merger of Huddersfield and Sheffield RLFC; continues to represent the interests of the Australian Rugby League in the UK; represents the Rugby League Players' Association. Successfully conducted the first personal injury claim for a Rugby League Player arising from the field of play and continues to deal with a number of sporting injury cases. Represented the Super-Middleweight World boxing Champion, Richie Woodhall, in his dispute with the promoter Frank Warren which was the first case of its type dealt with by Mediation; represented the Scunthorpe United Director, Des Comerford, in his litigation with the club, again resolved by mediation; represented the Newcastle United 'Save Our Seats' Campaign in proceedings against Newcastle United FC.

DUFF, Alistair
Henderson Boyd Jackson WS, Edinburgh (0131) 346 3617
a.duff@hbj.co.uk
Specialisation: Litigation/Sports Partner. Handles all types of sports work including damages actions between players, team contracts with players, commercial agreements regarding sponsorship/merchandising and other related matters.
Prof. Memberships: Law Society of Scotland, Writer to the Signet, committee member and on the Advisory Board for British Association for Sport and the Law. Scottish Arbiter for 'The Sports Dispute Resolution Panel Ltd'.
Career: Qualified Solicitor since 1982. Joined *Henderson Boyd Jackson* as Litigation Partner in 1992; specialised in sports law since 1994.
Publications: Has published 34 articles for journals on sporting matters and is regularly quoted in the national press.
Personal: Married to a doctor, has 2 young children and lives in Edinburgh. Has completed 13 marathons and has taken part in several climbing trips to the Himalayas.

FITZPATRICK, Nick
Denton Wilde Sapte, London (020) 7242 1212
nef@dentonwildesaspte.com
Specialisation: Partner with substantial media and intellectual property experience, including all aspects of the commercial exploitation of sport (e.g. disposal and acquisition of analogue/digital media rights, brand protection and licensing, agency appointments, event management, sponsorship/official supplier relationships, corporate hospitality, event management etc). Has advised clients including The FA Premier League (FAPL), The England and Wales Cricket Board (ECB), The World Professional Snooker and Billiards Association, The Racecourse Association, ITV, CGU Insurance and Tracy Edwards MBE. Highlights include: the FAPL's sale of international television rights; all licensing, brand protection and commercial arrangements for the Cricket World Cup 1999; ITV's acquisition of F1 television rights; CGU's sponsorship of UK Athletics; Royal & Sun Alliance's sponsorship of Tracy Edwards MBE; ECB's sale of domestic television rights and the sale of media rights by 49 RCA member racecourses.
Prof. Memberships: Law Society.
Career: Educated at Jesus College Oxford (Exhibitioner). Qualified *Denton Wilde Sapte* 1993, 'Assistant Solicitor of the Year' ('Lawyer' awards 1998/9). Partner *Denton Wilde Sapte* 2001.
Publications: Co-author of 'Flint, Fitzpatrick and Thorne – A User's Guide to Copyright' (now in its 5th edition). Numerous articles in trade and legal publications.
Personal: Interest in the arts and music.

GAY, Mark
Denton Wilde Sapte, London (020) 7242 1212
meg@dentonwildesapte.com
Specialisation: Partner in technology, media and telecoms department. Has substantial experience in both the contentious and non-contentious aspects of sports law and advises various sporting bodies on constitutional media rights issues, disciplinary and contractual issues.
Career: Qualified in 1988. Became a partner at *Herbert Smith* in 1995. Joined *Denton Wilde Sapte* 1 January 1999.
Personal: Educated at Lady Margaret Hall, Oxford.

GOLDBERG, Mel
Grower Freeman & Goldberg, London (020) 7723 3040
Specialisation: A partner and head of the sports division at *Grower Freeman & Goldberg* in London. He has represented numerous international football players and clubs, olympic gold medallists and several world champions in boxing, squash, tennis and athletics. He has arranged the transfers of several million pound football players from one club to another. He was the legal advisor of the International Squash Players Association (ISPA) and was Vice-Chairman of the British Olympic Travel Association to the Moscow Olympic Games in 1980. He has written several articles for leading sports magazines both in the USA and the UK, and has appeared on several television programmes both in the UK and in the USA. He recently represented Hans Segers in the successful defence of that footballer in the match fixing trial which was billed as the football trial of the century.
Prof. Memberships: Committee member of the British Association for Sport & Law. Professional member of the Sport Dispute Resolution Panel and an associate mediator of the Sports Dispute Resolution Panel of Mediators.
Career: Founded own firm under the style of *Douglas Goldberg & Co.*
Publications: He is co-author of the book entitled 'The Final Score' published by Robson Books.
Personal: Educated at St. John's College, Cambridge.

GROSSET, Alan
Morison Bishop, Edinburgh (0131) 226 6541
alan.grosset@morisonbishop.co.uk
Specialisation: Sports law. Legal advisor to the Scottish Sports Association and numerous other sports governing bodies, representative bodies, clubs and charities. Has advised on corporate governance and constitutional issues for governing bodies and sports clubs as well as disciplinary procedures, doping control issues and sponsorship agreements. Centrally involved in the campaign for rate relief for amateur sports clubs in Scotland and led the successful valuation appeal Lasswade RFC and Others v Lothian Regional Assessor. Has spoken at several conferences on sports law topics including the 1992 Barcelona Sport and the Law Conference on 'Nations without Countries and Sport'. In 2000-01 has acted for the Lawn Tennis Association in Scotland, and in governing body and other sports club incorporations, and contributed chapter on Drugs and Sport to 'Sport and the Law: A Scots Perspective'. Has also represented Confederation of British Sport at the Brussels

'Corporate Governance and Sport' Conference and the Council of Europe Committee for the Development of Sport in Strasbourg.
Prof. Memberships: Law Society of Scotland (member of E-commerce committee); Society of Writers to her Majesty's Signet; British Association for Sport and the Law. Founder member of the Financial and Legal Advisory panel of the SSC/SSA. Secretary Scottish Society for Computers and Law,
Career: Educated Royal High School and Edinburgh University. Joined *Alex Morison & Co* (now known as *Morison Bishop*) in 1965, qualified 1967, became a partner in 1970.
Personal: Born 18 January 1942. Leisure interests include tennis and golf, past chairman Scottish Sports Association; past president Scottish Lawn Tennis Association; past captain Duddingston Golf Club Limited; currently vice-chairman of the Scottish Sports Council; currently vice-chairman of the Sports Dispute Resolution panel Limited and vice-chairman, Confederation of British Sport.

HEWISON, John
George Davies, Manchester (0161) 236 8992

HIGTON, Jonathan
Townleys, London (020) 7655 1000
Specialisation: Partner. All television and new media sports matters, in particular sports content acquisition, representation and exploitation agreements throughout the world.
Career: Called to the Bar 1984. Joined ITV Sport in 1987 with responsibility for all the ITV Network's sports agreements, including the first exclusive Football League television agreement. Joined *Townleys* 1991. Responsible for all television and related issues both domestically and internationally for sports clients and specialist sports television distributors/agents. Has advised on projects including Rugby World Cup, Davis Cup, Fed Cup, 6 – Nations Rugby, European Rugby Cup, IRB World Sevens Series, Cricket World Cup, other International Cricket and worldwide distribution and other exploitation of both domestic and international football and other domestic and international sports rights, programming and content.
Personal: Born 1958. Attended Wycliffe College, Reading University and the University of Westminster.

HORNSBY, Stephen
The Simkins Partnership, London (020) 7907 3000

HOVELL, Mark
George Davies, Manchester (0161) 234 8810
mail@georgedavies.co.uk
Specialisation: Partner in the commercial department specialising in sports law. Acts for various professional footballers, rugby players, basketball players and other sportspeople on contractual, employment, taxation and insolvency related matters. Advises the Professional Footballers Association and the Basketball Players Association on commercial and trade union related matters. Recently appointed the head of David Seaman's Testimonial Committee and advised the administrators at Chesterfield Football Club.
Prof. Memberships: British Association for Sport and Law. Licensed insolvency practitioner.
Personal: Lives in Manchester.

JEACOCK, David
David Jeacock, Swindon (01793) 854111
jeacock@lineone.net
Specialisation: Sole principal specialising in sports law. Main area of practice is sports law, concentrating on constitutional and drug related issues, but including intellectual property issues arising out of sport. Also handles company and commercial matters. Major clients include sports governing bodies. Currently General Secretary of and Legal Adviser to British Athletics League and Legal Adviser to the Sportshall Athletic Federation. Formerly Secretary to British Athletics Federation Drug Advisory Committee. Vice chairman British Wheelchair Sport Foundation.
Prof. Memberships: Law Society, British Association for Sport & Law.
Personal: Born in 1946. Educated at Exeter College, Oxford 1964-67. Member Swindon Harriers. Lives in Wootton Bassett.

KERR, John
Anderson Strathern WS, Edinburgh
(0131) 220 2345
john.kerr@andersonstrathern.co.uk
Specialisation: Handles general corporate and commercial work, including acquisitions and disposals, corporate finance, banking law, general contract work, agency, distribution and EU law. Specialises in sports law. Acts as lead partner for Scottish Rugby Union and Sportscotland as well as other governing bodies and clubs; involved with constitutional issues, sport sponsorship and product endorsement, discipline and drug related issues as well as the provision of new facilities.
Prof. Memberships: Founder member of Financial and Legal Advisory Panel of Sportscotland; member of British Association of Sport and Law; Professional Member of Sports Dispute Resolution Panel; member of Napier University Sports Law Forum.
Career: LL.B (Hons) Edinburgh 1978; Qualified 1980, partner in *Strathern & Blair* in 1984 and became partner in merged *Anderson Strathern* in 1992.
Personal: Born 1956. Lives in Edinburgh. Enjoys sport at all levels.

McCORMICK OBE, Peter
McCormicks, Leeds (0113) 246 0622
p.mccormick@mccormicks-solicitors.com
Specialisation: Substantial area of practice is Sports Law (allied to portfolio of media and entertainment) with considerable experience in both contentious and non-contentious aspects. Acts for Leeds United Football Club and is Associate Director and Legal Counsel. Dealt with the multi-million pound sale of the Club to Leeds Sporting plc and continues to advise the Club and its associated/subsidiary companies and Leeds Sporting plc. Acts for a number of other sports clubs and bodies and professional sportsmen. Also has expertise in horse-racing, particularly disciplinary hearings and appeals; the only British lawyer to have appeared before the Jockey Club of Germany. Also handles matters relating to Rugby (Union and League), athletics, cricket, boxing, shooting (advises renowned Yorkshire Shoot) and motor racing. Other clients include The F.A. Premier League, The Football Association, Jenny Pitman, Freddie Trueman, Howard Wilkinson, Gordon Strachan, Gary Speed, Harry Kewell, Gary McAllister, David Batty, Castleford RLFC, Wakefield Trinity RLFC, Keighley Cougars RLFC, Otley RUFC and a number of other personalities and the Football Supporters Association. Negotiates contracts for personal benefits, corporate sponsorship and ancillary matters including broadcasting and deals with a substantial workload of intellectual property matters (registration, protection and enforcement). Advised on IP enforcement in Euro '96 tournament for UEFA and World Cup 1998. Deals with litigation cases including defamation and complaints relating to broadcasting and the Press. Acted in the Leeds United/Stuttgart UEFA Disciplinary Hearing in Zurich. Also has twenty years experience of tax investigation and enquiry work, both Revenue and VAT and serious fraud cases. Handles increasing amount of commercial work acting for DFS Furniture Company plc, Iceland Frozen Foods plc, Polypipe plc, The Duke of Edinburgh's Award, Hays plc and others. Columnist with the Yorkshire Post. Writes for a number of publications. Author of 'Sport, Business and the Law', published by Jordans. Lectures widely. Awarded the Higher Courts (Criminal Proceedings) Qualification in 1994. Resident legal expert on Radio Leeds, Yorkshire Television and the Yorkshire Post.
Personal: Vice President of the Outward Bound Trust. Chairman of the Yorkshire Young Achiever Awards. Member of the Advisory Board, Sports Law Centre, Anglia University; Solicitor to The Duke of Edinburgh's Award. Patron, Harrogate Junior Chamber of Commerce; Trustee, Friends of War Memorials.

McINERNEY, Peter
SJ Berwin, London (020) 7533 2521
peter.mcinerney@sjberwin.com
Specialisation: Partner in the Media, Communications and Sports Groups. Specialist in entertainment and sport industries including television and film production, distribution and finance, merchandising, sponsorship, advertising and publishing.
Career: Royal National Theatre (1981-1983). Thames Television (1983-1989). *SJ Berwin & Co* (1989 to date)

McKENZIE, Rod
Harper Macleod, Glasgow (0141) 221 8888
Specialisation: Lead partner in the litigation department specialising in employment and sports law. Involved in the full range of UK and EU employment law work for corporate clients and public and local authorities. Has dealt with many of Scotland's precedent creating cases and is a regular attendee at the Employment Appeal Tribunal. Law Society of Scotland accredited specialist in employment law. Recently listed as one of 'the world's leading employment lawyers'. Regularly lectures and writes on the subject. Also specialises in planning and environmental law, construction law and mining and mineral law. Chairman of Scottish Rugby Union Disciplinary Appeals Committee and International Rugby Football Board Disciplinary Appeals Panel.
Prof. Memberships: Law Society of Scotland; Industrial Law Group.
Career: Qualified 1982. Assistant solicitor, *Harper Macleod* 1982-84. Partner since 1984.
Personal: Educated at High School of Stirling 1970-76, Strathclyde University 1976-79, and Stirling University 1979-80. Leisure pursuits include golf and

gardening. Born 1st July 1958. Lives in Uddingston, Lanarkshire.

METLISS, Jonathan
SJ Berwin, London (020) 7533 2220
jonathan.metliss@sjberwin.com
Specialisation: Is a senior partner in the corporate finance department and a founder member of the firm in 1982. He is actively involved in the property sector representing, inter alia, The British Land Company plc, and acted for them on the acquisition of the Broadgate Estate in the City of London and the Meadowhall Shopping Centre in Sheffield (the UK's largest single site property transaction at £1.17 billion) which won *SJ Berwin* 'The Property Team of the Year' at The Lawyer Awards 2000. He has also established and developed the Sports Business Group (of which he is head) within the firm dealing with all aspects of the business of sport which is now recognised as one of the leading dedicated sports practices in the UK. Has recently been described as one of the top sports lawyers in the country. Has been involved in sports and soccer related businesses for a number of years. Has acted on numerous sports related transactions such as the takeover of the Tottenham Hotspur Football Club in the early 1980s, the acquisition by Pentland Group of the Speedo business and the investment by ENIC plc, of which he was a non-executive director, in Glasgow Rangers Football Club (the single largest investment in a UK football club), the acquisition by ENIC of interests in Vicenza Calcio, AEK Athens, Slavia Prague and FC Basel, the flotation and subsequent fund raisings by Birmingham City Football Club and the flotation of Sports Internet Group. Has been involved in English Premier League clubs such as Arsenal, Chelsea, Derby County, Leeds United, Manchester United and West Ham and for nationwide football league clubs such as Birmingham City, Sheffield United, Swindon Town and Watford. Has advised companies in the sports and leisure area, such as Blacks Leisure, Claremont Garments, ENIC plc and Pentland. Is advising the England and Wales Cricket Board on the issue of central contracts and other related matters. Actively involved in South African sport, in particular the United Cricket Board of South Africa. Is a commercial adviser to the Football Taskforce and a member of the British Association of Sport and Law. His opinion is often sought on sporting issues and is widely quoted in the sports press and regularly speaks at sports related conferences and seminars.
Prof. Memberships: The executive committee of the Weizmann Institute Foundation; joint secretary and member of the executive of the Inter-Parliamentary Council against Anti-Semitism; vice-president of the Commonwealth Jewish Council; member of the board of the British Israel Public Affairs Centre (BIPAC); member Israel-Britain Business Council; member of the Executive of the British-Israel Chamber of Commerce and chairman of the British-Israel Chamber of Commerce Professional Services Committee; member of advisory board of Tel Aviv University Business School; member of the board of governors of Haifa University and chairman of the British Friends of Haifa University; member of UJIA (United Jewish Israel Appeal) Sports Committee, Jewish Care Sports Club, member of the Committee on South African Trade (COSAT) which provides commercial advice to the Department of Trade and Industry on Britain's trade promotion activities in South Africa; member of Government working group on Football Disorder; Law Society; Holborn Law Society; member IoD; Lord's Taverner's; member of Trade Partners UK; Africa and Middle East Advisers; member of the Cricketers Club.
Career: Articled *Nabarro Nathanson*, qualified 1973; assistant solicitor *Nabarro Nathanson* 1973-76; merchant banker, Capel Court Merchant Bank, Sydney 1976-78; assistant solicitor, *Berwin Leighton* 1978-82; senior corporate finance partner and founder member, *SJ Berwin* 1982; director of ENIC plc, Lindow Investment Company Ltd, Pownall Investment Company Limited, Interlaw Limited, The Weizman Institute Foundation, the Southern Africa Business Association, and the Parkes Centre Development Board (University of Southampton).
Publications: Articles for 'Sport Business'; 'Travel Trade Gazette'; 'Commercial Lawyer'; 'Law Society Gazette'.
Personal: Born 1949, resides London and Sussex. Education: Haberdashers' Aske's, Elstree; Southampton University (LLB Hons). Leisure: Squash, cricket, rugby, football, travel, Israel and South Africa; clubs: Arundel CC, Middx CCC, Sussex CCC; RAC; Saracens RFC; Alcester RFC; MCC, Surrey CC, Rugby Club, Cricketers Club; Middlesex County Rugby Football Union, Broadgate Club, Marks Club.

MILLER, Stephen
Harper Macleod, Glasgow (0141) 221 8888
stephen.miller@harpermacleod.co.uk
See under Employment, p.337

MORRISON, Michael
Gorna & Co, Manchester (0161) 832 3651
mjm@gorna.co.uk
Specialisation: Vast experience in a wide range of sport related business, including employment law (contentious and non-contentious); endorsement and sponsorship agreements; exploitation and protection of intellectual property rights, media law including publishing and defamation; administrative law. Involved principally in professional football, acting for clubs, players and agents, dealing with a variety of work including contracts, claims, commercial agreements, arbitrations and disciplinary tribunals. Has for over thirty years acted for the majority of managers of premier league and football league clubs in the negotiation and documentation of contracts and the pursuit and settlement of Unfair and Wrongful Dismissal claims as well as disciplinary proceedings. Other sports include rugby (both codes), swimming, golf and tennis.
Prof. Memberships: Law Society; British Association for Sport and Law; Manchester Law Society; Employment Lawyers Association.
Career: Educated at Cardinal Langley School and St Ambrose College. Joined *Gorna & Co* in July 1967, admitted 1974, partner 1976.
Personal: Married 1971 with two sons. Enthusiastic but incompetent golfer, passionate Manchester United supporter, member of the Variety Club of Great Britain.

PARKER, Raj
Freshfields Bruckhaus Deringer, London
(020) 7936 4000
raj.parker@freshfields.com
See under Litigation, p.578

PHELOPS, Warren
Nicholson Graham & Jones, London
(020) 7360 8129
warren.phelops@ngj.co.uk
Specialisation: Business issues relating to sport: in particular rights ownership and exploitation; corporate structuring and strategy, company, commercial and media (including media, sponsorship, hospitality and merchandising).
Prof. Memberships: Director of Institute of Sports Sponsorship, City of London Solicitors Company, British Association of Sport and the Law.
Career: *Slaughter and May*: trainee solicitor, March 1990-1992; Assistant Solicitor, March 1992-June 1993. *Nicholson, Graham and Jones*: Assistant Solicitor, June 1993 to Jan 1996. Partner and Head of Sports Group, January 1996 to date.
Personal: Fanatical sports player (rugby, football, cricket (for any teams that will have him), squash and tennis) and watcher, especially rugby (Wasps), football (Arsenal) and cricket (Middlesex).

POWELL, David
Clarke Willmott & Clarke, Bristol (0117) 941 6600
dpowell@cw-c.co.uk
Specialisation: Partner. Developed a nationally renowned sports department. Advises footballers, rugby players, athletes, golfers and cricketers as well as acting on behalf of a number of golf clubs. The department lists among its clients the current Bath Rugby squad and Wasps Rugby Squad. Represented the England squad and Anglo-Irish members of the Irish squad in negotiating their World Cup contracts with their respective unions and the British and Irish Lions Squad in their negotiations with British Lions Ltd. The department also acts for the Professional Cricketers Association, the Federation of International Cricketers Associations, the Springbok Supporters Club UK and cricnet.com, givemefootball.com and Destination football. Specialist advice in all relevant fields of law from commercial contracts, employment to litigation and personal injury.
Prof. Memberships: British Association for Sport and Law; Executive Committee of the players' union, the Professional Rugby Players Association (PRA) with Brian Moore, Martin Bayfield and Damien Hopley.
Career: Qualified in 1981, articled at *Herbert Alpass & Co* in Bristol, set up own practice in 1984, took over Bristol offices of *Alsters* in 1989 with two other partners. Joined *Clarke Wilmott & Clarke* in October 1999 as partner.
Personal: Leisure interests include scratch golfer, representing Gloucester since 1978, and rugby – played for Bristol in 1970s. Educated at St. Brendan's College Bristol and University of the West of England.

REEVE, Felicity
Bird & Bird, London (020) 7415 6000
Specialisation: Partner in Sports Group. Advises governing bodies, broadcasters, sports marketing agencies, sponsors and individuals on the creation, acquisition and exploitation of sports related rights. Advises on new digital forms of rights distribution and delivery including the acquisition of content for exploitation via the Internet and via on demand services. Advises on the application of traditional legal principles to the Internet including terms and conditions of sale, on-line gambling and jurisdiction and rights clearance issues. Author of a number of articles

on sports related issues in the national, legal and sports industry press. Clients include The Football Association, FLPTV, Octagon.
Prof. Memberships: Law Society, British Association for Sport and Law.
Career: Qualified 1993. Joined *Bird & Bird* from *Macfarlanes* in 1994. Became a partner in 1998.
Personal: Educated at School of St Helen and St Katherine and Lady Margaret Hall, Oxford.

REID, Fraser
Theodore Goddard, London (020) 7606 8855
fraserreid@theodoregoddard.co.uk
Specialisation: Sports law, entertainment/media law, commercial law, disciplinary proceedings. Specialising from 1997 in sports related work. Provide advice on the protection and exploitation of commercial rights in sport including sponsorship, merchandising and broadcasting rights. Also advises on players' contracts. Niche specialisation in disciplinary issues, particularly doping. Clients include individuals in sports and entertainment fields, sports marketing companies, sports governing bodies and sponsors. Represented the athletes Mark Richardson and Mark Hylton in doping cases before UK Athletics and IAAF in 2000/2001.
Prof. Memberships: Committee member of the British Association for Sport and Law. Member of the Law Society and the International Bar Association – Sports and Gaming Law Group Member. Internationale Association Jenes Advocats ('AIJA'). Sports group member.
Career: Qualified 1992 with *Beale & Co.* Advantage International (1997-98). Joined *Theodore Goddard* as head of sports group in June 2000.
Personal: Football, golf, rugby, squash, diving. Member of Lancashire Cricket Club and Blackburn Rovers supporter.

RUSSELL, Patrick
Charles Russell, London (020) 7203 5018
patrickr@cr-law.co.uk
Specialisation: Partner in Litigation Department. Acts for sporting regulatory authorities and clubs in the regulatory and disciplinary field. Experienced in public law, judicial review restraint of trade and including human rights. Also handles building and construction disputes and is head of *Charles Russell's* Trust and Fidiciary Disputes Group. Acted in judicial review decisions for the Jockey Club (including ex parte HH, Aga Khan), The Law Society and Swindon Town FC.
Prof. Memberships: Law Society, British Association for Sport and Law.
Career: Joined *Charles Russell* in 1976 and qualified in 1979. Became a Partner in 1980. Director of the Solicitors Indemnity Mutual Insurance Association Ltd. Contributing Editor, 'Cordery on Solicitors'.
Personal: Born 11th May 1952. Educated at Ampleforth College 1965-70 and University College, Oxford 1971-74. Recreations include golf, sailing, tennis and motorcycling. Lives near Towcester, Northants.

SLEIGH, Andrew
Burness, Glasgow (0141) 248 4933
afs@burness.co.uk
See under Corporate Finance, p.257, Insolvency/Corporate Recovery, p.476

SMITH, Jason
James Chapman & Co, Manchester
(0161) 828 8000
jason.smith@james-chapman.co.uk
Specialisation: Specialises in the protection and exploitation of rights in the areas of event organisation, sponsorship, licenced merchandise, broadcasting and new media for governing bodies, sports marketing companies, clubs and leading individuals. In particular, advises Manchester United plc on all forms of rights protection and exploitation including through sponsorship, promotions, licencing, the Internet, new media and tours. Recent work includes Manchester United's kit sponsorship and transfer of its merchandising business effective from August 2002 and its co-operative marketing agreement with the New York Yankees; advising the Football Association Premier League in the implications of Arsenal v Reed; and a Formula 1 driver's agreement. Has also advised on contracts relating to the FIFA World Cups 2002 and 2006, FIFA Club World Championship 2000, UEFA's EURO 2000, African Cup of Nations, Chinese Football Association, US Championship Auto Racing Teams, Inc. series, FINA World Swimming Championships 2000 and 2003, and the IAAF World Championships 1999. Also advises the Swimmers Competitors Association, leading footballers, Rugby League players, swimmers and cyclists. Guest Lecturer, MA (Sport and Law), Manchester Metropolitan University. Member of the Editorial Board, 'Sports Law Administration & Practice'.
Prof. Memberships: British Association for Sport and Law. The Law Society.
Career: Qualified *Denton Hall* 1995. Solicitor, *Cobbetts* 1995-1998. Legal Counsel ISL Marketing AG, Switzerland 1998-1999. Senior assistant solicitor, *James Chapman & Co*, 1999-July 2000. Partner August 2000 to date.
Personal: Born 1970. Brasenose College, Oxford 1988-1991 (Blues Soccer Player, Vincent's Club Member). Leisure interests include skiing and golf.

STINSON, Philip
Clintons, London (020) 7379 6080

TOWNLEY, Stephen
Townleys, London (020) 7655 1000
Specialisation: Partner and founder. Main area of practice covers sports rights. Assists and advises on the creation, management and exploitation of media rights, sponsorship rights, television and merchandising. Has been involved in this capacity with various events in the UK and internationally
Prof. Memberships: IBA (former Chairman of Sports Committee), Board Member SLA, ANZSLA, European Sponsorship Consultants Association (Co-founder). Arbitrator – Court of Arbitration for Sport, Switzerland. Fellow of the Chartered Institute of Arbitrators.
Career: Qualified in 1978, having trained in the City of London.
Personal: Born 15th December 1952. Took an LLM in 1975. Leisure interests include tennis and game fishing. Lives in London and Grosmont.

VLECK, Karena
Farrer & Co, London (020) 7242 2022
Specialisation: Partner in the commercial team. Principal area of practice is sports law providing specialist advice for sports governing and representative bodies, individual sports people, sports charities and sponsors. Areas of practice include sponsorship agreements, broadcasting agreements, disciplinary procedures and rules, sports doping cases, formations and advice on constitutions both corporate and unincorporated, merchandising and representation agreements. Other areas of practice are intellectual property generally, charity law and company and commercial law. Appointed Director of UK Athletics 98, the interim governing body for athletics in the UK and appointed a member of the Non-Executive Council of UK Athletics, the new governing body for athletics in the UK. Acted for the British Athletic Federation in relation to Diane Modahl. Acting for UK Athletics in relation to Doug Walker, Linford Christie, Mark Richardson and Paul Edwards. Other clients include Sport England, the British Olympic Association, the Central Council of Physical Recreation, the Football Association, the British Paralympic Association, the British Canoe Union and the All England Netball Association.
Prof. Memberships: Committee member of British Association for Sport and Law.
Career: Qualified in 1992 after articles at *Farrer & Co.* Partner 1998.
Personal: Born 10 March 1967. Educated at Millfield School, Street, Somerset 1983-85 and St John's College, Cambridge 1986-89. Lives in London.

WALKEY, Justin
Bird & Bird, London (020) 7415 6000
Specialisation: Partner in company department and head of sports group. In-depth knowledge covers the media, sports and entertainment industries. Particular expertise includes sports marketing (creation, protection and exploitation of events; sale and purchase of events; constitutional and disciplinary matters; TV, video, film and publishing rights deals; sponsorship; licensing and merchandising) and individual representation (general business management, tax planning, endorsement and appearance contracts). Founder of Sportslink Worldwide. Other area of practice is general corporate and commercial law, both nationally and internationally, primarily in the areas of media and communications to include digital media, telecommunications, broadcasting, advertising, publishing and promotion. Recent high profile work in football for The F.A. in relation to the New National Stadium project and The F.A.'s broadcast arrangements for England internationals and F.A. Cup matches.
Prof. Memberships: Law Society, Licensing Executives Society.
Career: Qualified in 1984. Joined *Bird & Bird* the same year and became a partner in 1987.
Personal: Born 1957. Attended Sherborne School, then the University of Westminster. Lives in London.

WATKINS, Maurice
James Chapman & Co, Manchester
(0161) 828 8000
Specialisation: Partner in commercial department. Sports law specialist. Solicitor for Manchester United Football Club since 1976 and, since flotation, Manchester United plc. Also an adviser to the Football Association Premier League and other Premier and Football League clubs on various matters. Member of the Premier League Legal Working Party. Premier League representative on Association of European Union Premier Professional Football Leagues. Also

solicitor to a number of first-class sportsmen and administrators. Director of Manchester United Football Club PLC and Manchester United PLC. Has handled numerous high-value soccer transfers at home and abroad. Represents clubs and players before UEFA and FA Disciplinary bodies and International and League Compensation Tribunals and negotiates TV, sponsorship, licensing and advertising contracts. Extensive media experience on football related matters. Appointed in August 2000 to the UEFA Panel of External Legal Experts. Chairman of the FIFA/UEFA Task Force Juridical sub-committee dealing with the EC challenge to the transfer system. Local Director for Coutts Bank.
Prof. Memberships: President of the British Association for Sport and the Law.
Career: Qualified in 1966. Solicitor for the Co-operative Insurance Society 1966-68. Joined *James Chapman & Co* as a partner in 1968. Senior partner with effect from May 1999.
Personal: Educated at Manchester Grammar School and University College, London (LLB and LLM). Interests include cricket, soccer and tennis.

ZEFFMAN, David
Olswang, London (020) 7208 8888
dcz@olswang.com
See under Media & Entertainment, p.607

TAX (CORPORATE)

London: 795; South & South West: 799; Midlands & East Anglia: 800; The North: 800; Scotland: 801; *Profiles*: 802

OVERVIEW: Corporate, finance and property transactions are increasingly driven by complex tax structures. Growth areas for instruction can be found in the development of innovative financial products, cross-border structuring, share schemes and contentious matters. Once again our research indicates that the big five accountants lead in the more routine and indirect tax matters, forming direct competition for some regional players.

RESEARCH APPROVED BY BMRB: *For this edition,* Chambers' *researchers conducted 6,552 interviews – 4,419 with law firms, 554 with barristers and 1,579 with clients.*

The validity of the research was scrutinised by BMRB International, who audited both the methodology and the results at our offices in July 2001. They interviewed Chambers' *researchers and cross-checked sample interviews. Details of the audit appear on page 7.*

LONDON

TAX • London		Ptnrs	Assts
1	Freshfields Bruckhaus Deringer	13	27
	Linklaters	13	30
	Slaughter and May	9	20
2	Allen & Overy	7	30
	Clifford Chance	17	36
3	Ashurst Morris Crisp	5	20
	Herbert Smith	4	16
	Norton Rose	6	11
	SJ Berwin	6	10
4	Berwin Leighton Paisner	3	5
	Denton Wilde Sapte	8	10
	Lovells	9	10
	Macfarlanes	3	4
	Nabarro Nathanson	3	5
	Olswang	3	3
	Simmons & Simmons	6	9
	Travers Smith Braithwaite	3	10
5	Clyde & Co	2	1
	CMS Cameron McKenna	4	6
	Field Fisher Waterhouse	3	4
	McDermott, Will & Emery	2	4
6	Hammond Suddards Edge	2	1
	Theodore Goddard	3	7
	Watson, Farley & Williams	6	9

This book is the product of 6,552 1/2-hour interviews. See p.7 for BMRB audit.
Within each band, firms are listed alphabetically.

Freshfields Bruckhaus Deringer (see firm details p.965) A "*first-class*" team, held in the highest regard by peers and clients alike. The practice is known for its "*superb quality,*" excelling at big-ticket M&A and finance-driven transactions, and is a leader in own account work. The group is packed with leading individuals, and is acknowledged to be the leader for cross-border work, aided by a small but respected offering in New York. Head of department, **David Taylor** (see p.808) combines "*talent with a pleasant manner*" in dealing with asset and tax-based financing. **Ben Staveley** (see p.808), who specialises in banking and derivatives, is seen by our interviewees to be going from "*strength to strength.*" **Richard Ballard** (see p.802) is highly respected for his cross-border and structured financial products work, while **Sarah Falk** (see p.804) was recommended to researchers for her "*impressive*" M&A work. In the securitisation sphere, **Sue Porter** (see p.807) ("*excellent reputation*") and **Michael Thompson** (see p.808) are the team's major names. Insurance tax specialist **Stephen Hoyle** (see p.805) is described by clients as a "*constructive lawyer who is always looking for a solution*" and **Timothy Ling** (see p.806), who heads up the firm's corporate finance team, is a "*solid and reliable performer.*" **Murray Clayson** (see p.803) specialises in international tax-based financing and **Colin Hargreaves** (see p.805) received market recommendation for his work in projects financing and complex leasing arrangements. "*Clever*" **Francis Sandison** (see p.808) is heavily endorsed by peers for his expertise in VAT issues, which he combines with mainstream tax work. Significant deals over the past year include advising the Compass Group on its £19 billion merger with Granada Group to form Granada Compass, and advising Bass on the £2.3 billion acquisition of its brewery arm by Interbrew. The group was instructed by Ford on its €3 billion acquisition of Land Rover from BMW, and the team also advised Mannesmann on the £80 billion hostile takeover bid by Vodafone AirTouch. **Clients:** Bass; Royal Bank of Scotland; Compass Group; EMI; Marconi; Ford; Lazards; Pearson; Rank; P&O; Morgan Stanley Dean Witter; Barclays Bank/Barclays Capital; Deutsche Bank; Bank of America; National Australia Bank.

Linklaters (see firm details p.1042) A practice which oozes "*consistency and quality,*" the calibre of its lawyers is felt by clients to be "*unsurpassed.*" An eclectic workload encompasses complex cross-border transactions and financial products advice for the firm's outstanding existing corporate client base and a growing roster of leading financial institutions. Head of department **Guy Brannan** (see p.802) is a "*straightforward thinker,*" whom peers believe provides sensible solutions to the most complex problems. Head of contentious tax is **Nikhil Mehta** (see p.802), who has an "*increasingly excellent reputation for international structuring issues.*" A big plus for the team has been the return of **Yash Rupal** (see p.802) from secondment at Merrill Lynch. He is commended to researchers for his skill in structured finance and derivatives. Corporate restructuring and M&A is the forte of "*switched on*" **Michael Hardwick** (see p.805), while **Tom Scott** (see p.808) is regarded as "*outstanding*" on the M&A side. In VAT matters, **Martin Lynchehan** (see p.806) received commendation from clients for his "*creative thinking*" and his expertise in structured finance. **Simon Clark** (see p.742) is strongly endorsed as a property tax specialist. The group advised Barclays Capital in relation to the first directly issued tax deductible Tier 1 capital for a UK bank, and has received subsequent instructions from leading financiers in relation to further Reserve Capital Instruments. The team also advised on National Power's £8.4 billion demerger of its UK generation and supply business to form Innogy and International Power, and advised BG on its £13 billion restructuring and on the subsequent £15 billion demerger of Lattice. **Clients:** ABN AMRO; AstraZeneca; BAE SYSTEMS; BP Amoco; Dixons; GUS; Innogy Holdings Lend Lease; Rio Tinto; WH Smith; Vodafone Group; Barclays Capital; Merrill Lynch; Morgan Stanley; UBS Warburg.

Slaughter and May (see firm details p.1135) Retaining its reputation as a "*stellar*" team, involved in top level work, it receives a constant flow of

LEADING INDIVIDUALS

★	**EDGE Steve** Slaughter and May	
1	**FRENCH Douglas** Clifford Chance	**MARTIN David** Herbert Smith
	MEARS Patrick Allen & Overy	**NORFOLK Edward** Norton Rose
	NOWLAN Howard Slaughter and May	**STAVELEY Ben** Freshfields Bruckhaus
	TAYLOR David Freshfields Bruckhaus	
2	**AIRS Graham** Slaughter and May	**BALLARD Richard** Freshfields Bruckhaus
	ELMAN Jonathan Clifford Chance	**FALK Sarah** Freshfields Bruckhaus
	LEWIS David Allen & Overy	**RUPAL Yash** Linklaters
	WATSON John Ashurst Morris Crisp	
3	**BALDWIN Mark** Macfarlanes	**BALL Susan** Clyde & Co
	BEARE Tony Slaughter and May	**BRANNAN Guy** Linklaters
	CRAWFORD Susan Ashurst Morris Crisp	**ELLIOTT Peter** Clifford Chance
	FRASER Ross Herbert Smith	**HARDWICK Michael** Linklaters
	JOHNSON Ian Ashurst Morris Crisp	**LING Timothy** Freshfields Bruckhaus
	MEHTA Nikhil Linklaters	**NIAS Peter** McDermott, Will & Emery
	NOBLE Nicholas Field Fisher Waterhouse	**PORTER Sue** Freshfields Bruckhaus
	SANDISON Francis Freshfields Bruckhaus	**THOMPSON Michael** Freshfields Bruckhaus
	TROUP Edward Simmons & Simmons	**WALTON Miles** Allen & Overy
4	**BRAILSFORD Mark** Allen & Overy	**BUTLER Kay** Olswang
	CHALLONER John Norton Rose	**COLEMAN Brenda** Allen & Overy
	DORAN Nigel Macfarlanes	**DOUGLAS Alasdair** Travers Smith
	EHRLICH Michael Clifford Chance	**GETHING Heather** Herbert Smith
	GREENBANK Ashley Macfarlanes	**HARKNESS David** Clifford Chance
	HOYLE Stephen Freshfields Bruckhaus	**KELLY Don** Lovells
	LYNCHEHAN Martin Linklaters	**McGOWAN Michael** Allen & Overy
	OVERS John Berwin Leighton Paisner	**ROSS Howard** Clifford Chance
	SANDERS Tim McDermott, Will & Emery	**SCOTT Tom** Linklaters
	SMITH Isla Norton Rose	**WHITTY Oonagh** Latham & Watkins
	WISTOW Michael Clifford Chance	
5	**BLAKE Jonathan** SJ Berwin	**CLAYSON Murray** Freshfields Bruckhaus
	HARGREAVES Colin Freshfields Bruckhaus	
	HIGGINBOTTOM Louise Norton Rose	
	JACOBS Russell Milbank, Tweed, Hadley & McCloy	
	LUDER Sara Slaughter and May	
	NORWOOD Andrew Weil, Gotshal & Manges	
	PRESTON Christopher Watson, Farley & Williams	
	STRATTON Richard Travers Smith Braithwaite	
UP AND COMING		
	DUGDALE Pat Olswang	**FRIEL Daniel** Lovells

LEADING INDIVIDUALS: VAT

★	**SINFIELD Greg** Lovells	
1	**BALDWIN Mark** Macfarlanes	**CANT Michael** Nabarro Nathanson
	HUMPHREY Ann Sole Practitioner	**ROSE Simon** SJ Berwin
	WARRINER Neil Herbert Smith	**WONG Etienne** Clifford Chance
2	**AVERY JONES John** Speechly Bircham	**CLARK Simon** Linklaters
	CROKER Richard CMS Cameron McKenna	**GARCIA Dario** Ernst & Young
	HALE Paul Simmons & Simmons	**LYNCHEHAN Martin** Linklaters
	MAINPRICE Hugh Hutchinson Mainprice	
	PRESTON Christopher Watson, Farley & Williams	
	SANDISON Francis Freshfields Bruckhaus Deringer	
	STAPLETON Mark Dechert	

See individuals' profiles p.802

instructions from its marvellous corporate client base, as well as being a dominant presence in structured finance, asset finance and new product development. The ever popular **Steve Edge** (see p.804) remains the sector's star practitioner, with clients and competitors applauding his ability to combine "*technical genius with superb client handling skills and the ability to put things into economic context.*" A force in the transactional market, **Howard Nowlan** (see p.807) is "*confident in his abilities and has every right to be.*" Typical of the firm's overall style, his robust and highly pragmatic approach wins him a following among clients "*who just want to know if it will work.*" Researchers received regular recommendation for **Graham Airs** (see p.802), and **Tony Beare** (see p.802) "*is talented and straightforward.*" New to the rankings this year is **Sara Luder** (see p.802) who is developing a reputation among clients as a "*strong young performer who can turn her hand to a number of things.*" Corporate highlights include a number of top-flight M&A transactions of the past year, including matters between Schroders and Citibank, Diageo and Seagram, and the Chase Manhattan link up with Fleming. Major business disposals include BAE Systems/Airbus Consortium, Tomkins/European Foods and Shell International coal disposal. Tax-related financings have involved advising British Airways (Aircraft Financings) and acting for LNC Consortium in the London Underground financing. **Clients:** US based multi-national companies; UK public companies; financiers.

Allen & Overy (see firm details p.856) A practice which has extended its comprehensive banking profile to take high quality instructions involving M&A and own account tax work. Peers have witnessed the firm putting substantial resources and effort into building the practice, and the group's status as "*a class act*" is assured. The team's leading practitioner is **Patrick Mears** (see p.806), who was acclaimed to researchers as an "*outstanding performer*" with "*real breadth of expertise.*" He advised Carphone Warehouse on the tax ramifications of a $277.5 million M&A deal. **Brenda Coleman** (see p.803) is respected for the "*quality and complexity of her work,*" with the past year seeing her advising Robert Fleming on a £4.88 billion bid by Chase Manhattan, and acting for United News & Media on the £1.75 billion merger of the company's TV assets with Granada. **David Lewis** (see p.806) retains high standing for his experience of big-ticket deals. He advised Finmeccanica on the £1.46 billion merger of the company's subsidiary Agusta with Westland. **Miles Walton** (see p.809) is well-known for tax based leasing work and was involved in advising in various Tier 1 capital issues including Northern Rock, Abbey National, Bank of Scotland and Lloyds TSB. **Michael McGowan** (see p.806) is also involved in the finance side and advised SSSB as to both UK and NY law in connection with the £2.256 billion securitisation of part of Abbey National's mortgage portfolio, and Smiths Industries in its £1.77 billion bid for TI Group. **Mark Brailsford** (see p.802) received substantial endorsement from clients for his all-round skills. **Clients:** ABN AMRO; Alliance and Leicester; ANZ; Bank of America; Barclays Mercantile; Cable & Wireless; Commerzbank; Deutsche Asset Management; General Motors; Imperial Chemical Industries; Marconi; Misys; Rexam; Thomson Corporation; Thomson Travel; TI Group; TXU; United News & Media; West LB.

Clifford Chance (see firm details p.919) Among the first ports of call for financial transactions, the team is acknowledged by peers for its range of expertise. The advice proffered by this team is said by clients to be "*sensible and pragmatic.*" **Douglas French** (see p.804) is the best known lawyer in the group and is considered by competitors to be "*a top corporate player and a real problem solver.*" His highlight deals included advising on the tax aspects of Barclays' takeover of Woolwich. **Jonathan Elman** (see p.804) is "*exceptionally clever*" and advised HSBC on a substantial Tier One funding. **Michael Wistow** (see p.809) and **David Harkness** (see p.805) both have a strong reputation for securitisation work. **Howard Ross** (see p.807) continues to receive recommendation, this year representing Woolwich, Halifax, Northern Rock and Alliance & Leicester in a landmark case against the Inland Revenue. **Peter Elliott** (see p.804) advised Chase Manhattan Bank on the tax aspects on its £4.88 billion acquisition of Robert Fleming, and **Michael Ehrlich** (see p.804) also received substantial recommendation for his "*user friendly*" style. On the VAT front, **Etienne Wong** (see p.809) is "*personable, practical and technically astute.*" In the past year he advised Morgan Stanley on the VAT aspects of two property securitisations for J Sainsbury, raising a total of £550 million. **Clients:** ABN AMRO; Arcadia; Canary Wharf; CGNU; Deutsche Bank; EDS; Enron Corporation; HSBC; JP Morgan; Merrill Lynch; National Australia Bank; Nomura Securities; On Digital; Paribas; Phillip Morris; UBS; Woolwich; Zurich Capital Markets.

Ashurst Morris Crisp (see firm details p.866) Smaller than the top players, the team still draws rave reviews from clients, who drew researchers' attention to "*as good a quality tax department as you will ever get.*" Rivals agree that the "*brilliant*" **John Watson** (see p.809) "*is a delight to deal with; the clients love him.*" **Sue Crawford** (see p.803) is felt to bring energy and enthusiasm to her work in corporate restructuring, and **Ian Johnson** (see p.805) is recommended for his innovative approach for clients both in the UK and overseas. Transactional highlights of the past year include acting for AMVESCAP on its £1.16 billion acquisition of Trimark Financial Corporation and advising Carphone Warehouse on its £1.6 billion public offering. Demonstrating its expertise in venture capital transactions, the group advised Carlyle Internet Partners Europe on its internet and information technology businesses fund of €400 million. The team was also instructed by Atlantic Telecom Group on its £323 million high yield bond offering and its acquisition of First Telecom Group for £250 million. **Clients:** ABN AMRO; JP Morgan Capital; Berkeley Homes; Royal & SunAlliance; Deutsche Telekom; Imetal; CapVest; Invesco; National Express; Canary Wharf Group; Finmeccanica; West Private Equity; IBM; Royal Bank of Scotland.

Herbert Smith (see firm details p.993) Judged by rivals to be a "*personable*" team and a major force in the M&A field, the team is also strongly endorsed by clients for its "*quality of advice and fast turnaround times.*" Of particular note is **Heather Gething** (see p.804), described by clients as "*one of the best of her generation,*" and consistently displaying "*excellent analytical skills.*" In the past year, she advised Goldman Sachs and Donaldson Lufkin & Jenrette in the structured financing of the £1.75 billion acquisition of the Drax Power Station by AES Corporation from National Power. **David Martin** (see p.806) continues to have a strong reputation and advised Time Warner in relation to the $20 billion combination of its Warner Music division with the music businesses of EMI Group. **Ross Fraser** (see p.804) advised Royal London Mutual Insurance Society on its £1.5 billion recommended bid through subsidiary RLM Finance to acquire United Assurance Group. Head of department **Neil Warriner** (see p.809) is highly rated for his VAT work. In the past year he has advised BT Pension Scheme on its £1.9 billion acquisition of MEPC jointly with GE Capital, through the vehicle of an unlimited company, Lecanport Estates. **Clients:** Seeboard; BAT; Iceland Group; BG Group International; Merrill Lynch; Morgan Stanley Dean Witter; Goldman Sachs; Citibank; AXA; Winterthur; Hammerson Friends Provident; BT Pension Fund; Donaldson Lufkin & Jenrette; Citibank; HSBC; CSFB; Windsor Life; National Provident; Royal London.

Norton Rose (see firm details p.1082) An "*able, team-oriented*" practice with "*strong technical skills,*" it was particularly commended to researchers for its asset finance-related work. Vastly experienced **Chris Norfolk** (see p.807) retains a high profile among competitors for his "*broad skills and depth of expertise.*" Other members of the department to attract consistent market support were **John Challoner** (see p.803), **Louise Higginbottom** (see p.805) and **Isla Smith** (see p.808). A highlight of the team's year was acting for BMW on the disposal of its Land Rover and Rover businesses to Ford and the Phoenix consortium respectively. Other recent matters include advising DHL on the acquisition of 34 Boeing 757 aircraft, their conversion from passenger to freighter aircraft and their financing by a combination of operating finance and UK tax leases with an umbrella debt facility, arranged by Deutsche Bank. The team also advised Norsk Hydro on the $540 million sale of oil and gas interests to Conoco (UK). **Clients:** Abbey National; AXA; Britannia Airways; Chase Manhattan; Harvey Nichols; HSCS; Northern Foods; P&O; Robert Bosch; Siemens; Stena Line; Taylor Woodrow; TXU.

SJ Berwin (see firm details p.879) A "*strong, commercial*" team on the funds side and a key presence for own account tax work, for clients it remains an "*obvious alternative*" to some of the larger organisations. Head of the Private Equity Group **Jonathan Blake** (see p.676) received recommendation for his corporate and taxation advice relating to MBOs and venture and development capital issues. With a healthy portfolio of clients, particularly in the property field, the firm acted for the British Land Company in relation to its £357 million joint venture with West LB. In the private equity world, it advised the management team of Mercury Private Equity in connection with its buyout from Merrill Lynch Investment Managers, and acted for the management team of F&C Ventures in its buyout from Hypo-und Vereinsbank AG. **Simon Rose** (see p.807) has been involved in a number of high profile VAT litigation matters. **Clients:** Apax Partners & Co Ventures; Atlas Venture; Bridegpoint Capital; The British Land Company; Candover; Chelsfield; Delancey Group; Foreign & Colonial; Hill Samuel; NM Rothschild; Schroder Ventures.

Berwin Leighton Paisner (see firm details p.878) A department of "*depth and quality*" which has strength in property-related and corporate M&A matters. Its team size has increased by a further partner and assistant as a result of the merger with Paisner & Co. Head of department **John Overs** (see p.807) handles both mainstream and VAT tax matters and is respected as a "*competent generalist.*" In the property field, the team acted for the Prudential on the combined corporate and property acquisition of four major City office developments for Wates at a value of £250 million. It acted for Lex Service in the restructuring of the RAC loan notes so as to permit a tax efficient roll over into a unit trust, and advised La Salle Investment, Scottish Widows and Kodak Pension Fund on structuring their investment into the Industrial Development Partnership II for £250 million. **Clients:** Tesco; Lex Service; Prudential Property Investment Managers; Legal and General Assurance Society; CGNU; Amec Developments; Godfrey Bradman; GAP; Monsoon.

Denton Wilde Sapte (see firm details p.939) An "active" mid-tier practice headed by Charlotte Sallabank, which clients value for its "commercial and all-inclusive" approach. It was instructed by Alstom on a pre-emptive financing involving the £200 million purchase of new trains by a syndicate of banks. The firm also advised Landmark Millennium Projects on the lease financing of the National Botantic Garden of Wales, the @ Bristol centre, the Magna Project and the Norfolk and Norwich Millenium Project. Other work includes advising Ingenius Media on film partnerships in repect of sale and leaseback for a number of feature films and TV series. **Clients:** Royal Bank of Scotland; J Sainsbury; McQuarry Bank; Airtours; Lombard Corporate Finance; Barclays Mercantile Business Finance; Rentokil Initial; MBNA; Sony; Toshiba; Enel Power SpA; Liberty Media Corporation; Energis; Allied Leisure; Pearson Television; Equitable Life; OFREG; Incepta; Encyclopaedia Britannica.

Lovells (see firm details p.1044) A tax team which has seen a number of high-profile transactions owing to its strong corporate practice. Fielding a number of high profile individuals, the best known is VAT-dedicated **Greg Sinfield** (see p.808), who is still commended to researchers as "*a star,*" and is described by some competitors as "*the best analyst by a long shot.*" The department also benefits from the "*experience and balance*" of **Don Kelly** (see p.806). **Daniel Friel** is beginning to catch the eye of his competitors and was responsible for structuring and planning the £18 billion merger of Granada and Compass, and the £9 billion IPO of Granada Media. Other highlights for the group included advising Barclays on its £5.5 billion merger with the Woolwich, and assisting OM Gruppen on its £1 billion hostile offer for the London Stock Exchange. **Clients:** Granada Group; Barclays; OM Gruppen; National Air Traffic Control; Equitable Life; South African Breweries; The Sports Council; Doughty Hanson; Abbey National; Merrill Lynch Mercury; Doughty Hanson; Ford Credit; Ranks Hovis McDougall; Dresdner Bank; Chase Manhattan.

Macfarlanes (see firm details p.1046) Led by the "*likeable, energetic and knowledgeable*" **Mark Baldwin** (see p.802), the team focuses on supporting the equity, debt and commercial property deals which the corporate department attracts. Other partners in the group include **Ashley Greenbank** (see p.804), who is respected by the leading lights in the tax world, and advises Carlton Communications and the Virgin Group. **Nigel Doran** (see p.803) also received market recommendation for his advice to high profile buyout teams. Group highlights for the past year include tax planning for the establishment of two limited partnerships involving Morgan Stanley and the CIT Group, and the acquisition by those partnerships of £156.5 million Alban Gate and £125.5 million East India Dock. The group also advised on the £1.2 billion takeover (by scheme of arrangement) of Saatchi & Saatchi by Publicis, and acted for the Virgin Group in establishing a joint venture with Singapore Telecommunications to create a virtual mobile network in South East Asia, with committed funding of about $500 million. Recent matters with a significant VAT element have included the VAT efficient structuring of the Alban Gate Partnership and its acquisition of Alban Gate. **Clients:** Newton; Coults; Lazards; Wellington; Deutsche Asset management; Hawkpoint; Cordian; HSBC; The CIT Group; Abbey Life; Lend Lease; Vivendi; Pernod-Ricard; Carlton Communications; Virgin Group.

Nabarro Nathanson (see firm details p.1078) Best known for its property-related tax advice, but also active in corporate transactions and international tax planning, the team has attracted clients investing in the UK and Europe, such as Benchmark and Keen.com. **Michael Cant** (see p.803) is respected for his property-related direct and indirect tax advice. The group advised Mapeley on a PFI contract, under which it is to provide accommodation to the Inland Revenue and HM Customs & Excise. In the M&A sphere, it has advised on matters for Mayflower Corporation, assisted Deuton SA in its investment in a UK Hotels Group, and advised City Reach International on a corporate structure and a bond issue. The team also acted on behalf of Granada Group in proceedings brought by its insurance subsidiary and rental arm against Customs & Excise. **Clients:** Alphameric; Hammeson; Heron International; Land Securities; Leisure at Work Communications; Optus; Westfield.

Olswang (see firm details p.1084) An "*industrious*" team enjoying a strong reputation for IP/IT related tax advice; it works as an integral part of the firm's corporate and TMT groups. Head of department **Kay Butler** (see p.803) is thought by clients to offer "*a high level of strategic advice.*" She is ably supported by **Pat Dugdale** (see p.804), who received plaudits for her work in high-tech investment funds and corporate structuring. Recent highlights for the group include advising on the reorganisation of Genetix Group with the introduction of three new share plans and its subsequent flotation. It also acted as one of the advisers on the Carphone Warehouse flotation, and acted on the introduction of five new share plans. The firm advised on the tax issues arising from the acquisition by the Whitehall Green Partnership of a £400 million portfolio of properties from P&O Properties. **Clients:** BBC Worldwide; Bank of Boston; The Carphone Warehouse Group; epartners; Genetix Group; Gresham Trust; Macro 4; Motorola; Soros Fund Management; Talk Radio; Thus; Warner Bros/Warner Music

Simmons & Simmons (see firm details p.1132) A "*strong*" broad-based department, with a reputation among competitors for its involvement in complex deals. **Edward Troup** (see p.809) is the Head of Tax Strategy and is described by opponents as "*a bright ideas man,*" while **Paul Hale** (see p.804) received market commendation for his VAT work. Major M&A transactions include advising Interbrew on its £2.3 billion acquisition of the brewing business of Bass, and the £400 million acquisition of Whitbread Beer Company. The team also advised fund managers Perpetual on the £1.05 billion recommended cash and share offer made to it by Schroder Salomon Smith Barney on behalf of AMVESCAP, and advised ED&F Man on the £569 million demerger of its agricultural products business to a management buyout group. **Clients:** BASF; Cadbury Schweppes; Despa; GKN; MCI Worldcom; Railtrack; The British Land Company; Vivendi; BNP Paribas; Citibank; Lehman Brothers; Schroders; Interbrew; Perpetual PLC; ED&F Man Holdings.

Travers Smith Braithwaite (see firm details p.1160) Interviewees agreed that this "*well-respected*" department is gathering pace and strengthening its offering. Clients are impressed with the team's ability to handle "*complex matters without being overly legalistic.*" The return to full-time tax work of **Alasdair Douglas** (see p.804) is seen as a positive coup for the group, while the depth of the team is indicated by **Richard Stratton** (see p.808) who "*impresses at the junior end.*" The group recently advised on the £610 million securitisation of the Trafford Centre in Manchester for Peel Holdings, and advised on the cross-border tax structuring of the £485 million institutional sale of Thomson Directories Infomedia. Engaged in the structuring over 30 private equity deals in the past year, the firm acted on the £370 million public to private of Fairview Holdings, and advised management on the €2.6 billion BIMBO of the Memec electronics division from German conglomerate E.ON. **Clients:** Peel Holdings; Universe Group; Candover Investments.

Clyde & Co (see firm details p.921) A "*niche*" practice headed up by **Susan Ball**, who writes extensively and is said by peers to be "*impressive*" on transactions. Best known for its shipping, insurance and litigation expertise, the tax team continues to win major corporate and private client instructions. Over the past year, the team has provided taxation advice to Microgen on the acquisition of Telesmart Developments, and advised Count Burkitt Company on the merger establishing Burkitt DDB. **Clients:** Insurance companies; Lloyd's vehicles; brokers; reinsurers; credit insurers; Crédit Suisse First Boston; Swiss Re; Pacific Dunlop; Dell; Hewlett-Packard; Microgen.

CMS Cameron McKenna (see firm details p.922) Property-focused and a "*good team to have on your side*" say clients of a team which is acknowledged to "*cut to the chase.*" **Richard Croker** (see p.803) is particularly respected for his VAT advice. The firm advised on the second tranche of an innovative tax restructuring and property securitisation for J Sainsbury, and acted for the National Australia Bank on a £250 million tax based gilt repo transaction. Other work includes advising Enterprise Inns on its purchase of a major portfolio of pubs, while overseas the firm advised the Grohe high yield bond issue of Germany. **Clients:** Black & Decker; BAA; National Australia Bank; Delphi; Taylor Woodrow Property Company; National Grid group; J Sainsbury; Royal Bank of Scotland; Angel Trains Contracts; BsoftB; NSB Retail Services.

Field Fisher Waterhouse (see firm details p.957) Peers attribute the growth of this practice to **Nick Noble's** (see p.807) ability to "*attract good quality work from international institutions.*" Busy in the field of venture capital fundings, asset finance and structured finance, the firm has attracted a following among the leading City financial institutions. Highlights of the past year include advising JP Morgan Chase, Schroder Salomon Smith Barney, Deutsche Bank, Lazard Bank and others on the taxation aspects of financial instruments and financial services. The team also advised on the tax aspects of the merger of Thomas Cook Holidays and British Airways Holidays, which required and received European Commission approval. The team also assisted in the taxation aspects of various property matters, including major developments of hotel, leisure and banking premises. **Clients:** Deutsche Bank; JP Morgan Chase; Lazard Bank; Schroder Salomon Smith Barney; BG; Lattice Group; Macquarie Bank; Smiths Group; Thomas Cook Holdings; Accenture; Delta Property Services; General Medical Council.

McDermott, Will & Emery (see firm details p.1061) A small group with "*high profile individuals*" and one of the few US firms with a "*serious UK tax capability.*" **Peter Nias** (see p.807) is described as "*seriously clever*" and

Tim Sanders (see p.808) "*has the ability and the profile*," in the opinion of clients. The focus of the team is advisory work, almost invariably with an international element. Recent highlights include acting for BAE Systems on the tax structuring of its innovative joint venture with Xchanging, for the outsourcing of its HR function. It also advised the shareholders of the QD Group on the tax aspects of their share disposal to TMP. **Clients:** Amway; Arjo Wiggins Appleton; BAE Systems; Caterpillar; Dun & Bradstreet; Eli Lilly; Morgan Staney; Office Depot; QD Group; Signet Group; Svenska Handelsbanken; Telegraph Group; TXU Corporation; Zeus Technology Group.

Hammond Suddards Edge (see firm details p.984) A small team acting as part of a national whole, headed up by Bernhard Gilbey. The team has a strong property focus, although this does not prevent it from covering a broad range of matters. Corporate transactions with an overseas element are not uncommon in this group. It led iQrom Communications and its UK subsidiaries through a complex group restructuring, leading to a reversal into a company listed on NASDAQ. The group also advised the Goldsmith Foundation for European Affairs on its successful appeal to the VAT Tribunal relating to the overseas supply of services for VAT purposes. **Clients:** Goldsmith Foundation for European Affairs; Hazlewood Foods; Warwick International Group; Wassall; WPP Group; IP Powerhouse Holdings; SurfControl; iQrom Communications.

Theodore Goddard (see firm details p.1152) Headed up by Peter Sayer, this group has seen growth over the past year and is praised for encouraging partners who have "*commercial skills and business understanding.*" The group's highlights include advising Anglogold on its $335 million agreed joint venture investment in Tanzania's Geita goldmine, and advising AHL Services on a pre-sale reorganisation and subsequent $185 million disposal to Securicor. The team advised Halifax as funder, junior debt and equity provider in the PFI pathfinder for the MoD Army Foundation College at Harrogate. Indirect tax work includes advising the waste management division of a French multi-national on a substantial landfill tax dispute with HM Customs & Excise. **Clients:** Universal Pictures; Signet Group; Lehman Brothers; Anglia Railways; Blagden; Ambassador Theatre Group.

Watson, Farley & Williams (see firm details p.1174) Best known for its domestic and cross-border tax leasing work and asset finance, the firm is considered to have weathered the departure of Oonagh Whitty to Latham & Watkins. The versatile **Chris Preston** (see p.807) remains strongly recommended by clients and peers. Highlights of the past year include advising P&O Nedlloyd on tax leases including an off-balance sheet structure for further container vessels. It acted for a Scandanavian container line on a series of UK leases and advised PIL Lines on a series of leases for a fleet of vessels. On the VAT side, the group was instructed by Insmarsat on the VAT and Customs aspects arising from its effective privatisation, and advised on the VAT implications of lending transactions to borrowers in jurisdictions outside the EU. **Clients:** Citibank; Crédit Lyonnais; Daiwa; Insmarsat; Petroleum Geo-Services; Vivendi; Seascope; Dresdner Kleinwort Benson.

Other Notable Practitioners **Andrew Norwood** is a "*securitisation tax specialist*" and part of a growing team at **Weil Gotshal & Manges**. He recently acted for Bear Stearns on the RMAC 2001 NSI Mortgage Securitisation. **Russell Jacobs** (see p.805) of **Milbank Tweed Hadley and McCloy** also maintains high standing among his clients. **Ann Humphrey** (see p.805) is a sole practitioner who advises on VAT matters and is seen by her peers as "*extremely bright and capable.*" **Hugh Mainprice** (see p.806) from **Hutchinson Mainprice** is a specialist in contentious VAT matters who "*likes to take up the battle*" and is described as an "*adventurous thinker.*" Formerly of Watson, Farley & Williams, **Oonagh Whitty** (see p.809) at **Latham & Watkins** is regarded by opponents as "*immense fun to deal with.*" **John Avery Jones** (see p.802) of **Speechly Bircham** is a senior partner who is "*absolutely brilliant*" and **Mark Stapleton** (see p.808) at **Dechert** is thought to be "*strong on the property side.*" Of practitioners at the accountancy firms, **Dario Garcia** at **Ernst & Young** is a "*well-known VAT*" man who is active in contentious matters.

THE SOUTH & SOUTH WEST

TAX • The South & South West	Ptnrs	Assts
1 **Burges Salmon** Bristol	3	3
Osborne Clarke Bristol	4	5
2 **Blake Lapthorn** Fareham	1	1
Wiggin & Co Cheltenham	2	1

LEADING INDIVIDUALS	
1 **BIRD David** TLT Solicitors	**MOSS Philip** Osborne Clarke
MURPHY Niall Blake Lapthorn	**POPPLEWELL Nigel** Burges Salmon

This book is the product of 6,552 1/2-hour interviews. See p.7 for BMRB audit.

Within each band, firms are listed alphabetically. *See individuals' profiles p.802*

Burges Salmon (see firm details p.902) A team which has boosted its numbers in the past year and has seen an increase in investigative and contentious work, as well as continuing to secure envied instructions from its first rate client base. Head of department **Nigel Popplewell** (see p.807)is a "*good negotiator*" and is perceived by peers to have "*a great focus on tax.*" Highlights of the past year include major M&A transactions, Customs & Excise investigations and VAT tribunals. The team was also involved in litigation to reclaim tax and national insurance from former employees and acted on stamp duty, capital allowances and VAT matters arising from an acquisition for Bristol & West. International matters have included instructions from US investment funds concerning UK tax issues, the use of offshore structures for ownership of UK properties, and the implementation of offshore tax planning schemes. **Clients:** First Group; National Mobility; Denmans.

Osborne Clarke (see firm details p.1086) A "*well-respected group*" bolstered in the past year with the recruitment of two new partners and three new assistants. Clients typically consider Head of Department **Philip Moss** to be "*extremely sensible and pragmatic,*" valuing his "*nice, easy manner.*" Highlights of the past year include acting for management in the LBO of Pubmaster Group, and advising a private company in a demerger followed by LBO, obtaining the relevant tax clearances. The group also advised on the float of Stepstone in London and Oslo, and advised Quester VCT on its investments in emerging IT companies. **Clients:** 3i; Airsprung Furniture; Alusuisse Lonza; Bank of Scotland; Bristol Water; British Airways Pension Fund; Invensys; Newcourt Credit; Prism Rail; Quester VCT; Western Power Distribution.

Blake Lapthorn (see firm details p.886) The firm continues to be a force in the market, with its focus on property tax, sales and reorganisations and share schemes. Our researchers were told that **Niall Murphy** is "*sensible and easy to deal with.*" The group advised Wave 105 FM during its sale to Wireless Group and assisted Chelton (Randomes) in its purchase of part of the business of British Aerospace. Instructed by Sotel in the sale of its group of companies, the firm also advised Saunders Jeffries in its sale. **Clients:** Sotel; Alcatel; Murlen; Saunders Jeffries; Fat Face.

Wiggin & Co (see firm details p.1180) The international focus of this "*highly competent*" practice may account for its relatively low profile in the domestic market. The firm is rated by our interviewees for its skills in arranging international tax structures.

Other Notable Practitioners **David Bird** (see p.802)of **TLT Solicitors** is developing his presence in the market, and is praised for being "*personable and having the necessary drive*" to create an effective practice.

MIDLANDS & EAST ANGLIA

TAX • Midlands & East Anglia	Ptnrs	Assts
1 **Pinsent Curtis Biddle** Birmingham	3	3
Wragge & Co Birmingham	2	6
2 **DLA** Birmingham	3	n/a
Eversheds Norwich, Nottingham	3	14
3 **Mills & Reeve** Cambridge	2	2

LEADING INDIVIDUALS	
1 **COLECLOUGH Stephen** PricewaterhouseCoopers	**HYDE Ian** Pinsent Curtis Biddle
LOWE Kevin Wragge & Co	**MORRIS Gregory** DLA
TAILBY Christopher PricewaterhouseCoopers	

This book is the product of 6,552 1/2-hour interviews. See p.7 for BMRB audit.

Within each band, firms are listed alphabetically. *See individuals' profiles p.802*

Pinsent Curtis Biddle (see firm details p.1098) A "*professional and high quality team*" that operates as part of a national practice, and is said by rivals to field a "*good stable of talent.*" Peers believe the "*real name*" here is **Ian Hyde** (see p.805), who leads the Birmingham team and has expertise in property tax. The group recently advised a large worldwide insurance company on the tax driven reconstruction of its UK group. It acted for Whitbread and Punch Retail on the £225 million sale to Nomura of First Quench, which included advising on termination of joint venture arrangements and surrender of tax losses. The team also advised internet testing company GOAL on a £55 million AIM flotation, including pre-float reconstruction. **Clients:**Pemberstone; Murray Johnstone; IMI; Bristol Street Holdings; Onyx Environmental Group; Glanbia; Connex.

Wragge & Co (see firm details p.1189) Proffering "*utter credibility,*" the tax team is seen on some high profile corporate transactions. **Kevin Lowe** is considered by peers to be the "*best in the team,*" and has really helped to "*bolster the firm's tax focus.*" Quality instructions received by the team include advising the management of Rank Hovis McDougall on the share option schemes and personal tax elements of its disposal to Doughty Hanson & Co. The firm advised the institutional investors in the Clarendon limited partnerships and a number of other property investment LPs, and offered advice on the grant of options under the new EMI scheme and the implementation of the new All Employee Share Ownership Plan. **Clients:** 3i; British Airways; Castlemore Securities; HJ Heinz Europe; MEPC; Phoenix Pharmahandel; PowerGen; Preussag; Tilbury Douglas.

DLA A respected practice, which includes **Gregory Morris**, is known for its advice on the tax consequences of take privates and buy-outs. It also advises on share-based incentives and arrangements for dot.com companies.

Eversheds (see firm details p.952) With the loss of Philip Harrison to industry, the practice is thought by some to be operating "*without a full set of armour.*" It does however retain some strong and respected players, including new Head of Department Robert Jones. Tax matters play a large part in all the firm's offices across the region, with niche strength apparent in property and M&A transactions. Highlights include acting for Techtronic (2000) on its purchase of Rover Group from BMW. The firm also advised Harvest Capital in the establishment of the first VCT, and acted for Solectron Corporation in the purchase of a multi-national computer component manufacturing business from Nortel Networks for $900 million. **Clients:**Techtronic (2000); Harvest Capital; Solectron Corporation; Advantage West Midlands; Bryant Group; Jessops International.

Mills & Reeve (see firm details p.1069) Operating out of Cambridge, the firm is naturally blessed with a "*focus on high-tech clients.*" The team is headed up by Ted Powell, and in the past year has provided tax structuring advice for a $100 million venture capital fund to invest in UK and continental European high-tech companies. Other work also includes providing tax structuring advice for a property joint venture, involving the £14 million acquisition of a shopping complex.

Other Notable Practitioners **Stephen Coleclough** at **PricewaterhouseCoopers** has a "*roving brief and wears a number of hats,*" but is particularly rated by peers for his stamp duty work, and is known for his "*bullish*" approach. His colleague **Christopher Tailby** specialises in VAT and has an increasingly global focus.

THE NORTH

TAX • The North	Ptnrs	Assts
1 **Addleshaw Booth & Co** Leeds, Manchester	4	6
Pinsent Curtis Biddle Leeds	3	4
2 **Eversheds** Leeds, Manchester	2	4
Hammond Suddards Edge Leeds, Manchester	3	4
3 **Dickinson Dees** Newcastle upon Tyne	1	3
Walker Morris Leeds	1	3

LEADING INDIVIDUALS	
1 **CHRISTIAN John** Pinsent Curtis Biddle	**JENKINS Edmund** Addleshaw Booth & Co
SIMPSON Mark Hammond Suddards Edge	
2 **CONCANNON Simon** Walker Morris	**GREAVES Judith** Pinsent Curtis Biddle
HENNESSY Tony Dickinson Dees	**JERVIS David** Eversheds
JONES Janet Addleshaw Booth & Co	**TOON John** Addleshaw Booth & Co
TOWNSEND Peter Cobbetts	

This book is the product of 6,552 1/2-hour interviews. See p.7 for BMRB audit.

Within each band, firms are listed alphabetically. *See individuals' profiles p.802*

Addleshaw Booth & Co (see firm details p.853) Top flight, in the eyes of our interviewees, owing to the combination of "*two strong centres in the North*" which boast "*impressive organisation*" and "*technically strong lawyers.*" **Ed Jenkins** (see p.805) is rated as a "*pro-active lawyer who can see past the trees and get straight to the main issues.*" **John Toon** (see p.809) is "*technically able,*" and particularly well-regarded for his property-related tax advice. **Janet Jones** (see p.805) received warm endorsement from her competitors who admire her "*technical and practical skills*" and her "*attention to detail.*" Highlights of the past year include advising Trinity Mirror in relation to its sale of The Belfast Telegraph for over £300 million, and representing the shareholders in the sale of Pennine Retail Systems. **Clients:** Airtours; GEHE Limited; Skillsgroup; Barclays Private Equity; 3i Group; Aberdeen Murray Johnstone.

Pinsent Curtis Biddle (see firm details p.1098) This innovative team provides "*strong and practical*" advice on high level corporate transactions. Researchers were told that **John Christian** (see p.803) is "*commercial, sensible and gets the deal done.*" National head of tax **Judith Greaves** also retains a strong reputation in the local market. The team acted for Hanson on the acquisition of Northern Quarry businesses of Tarmac and advised Whitbread/Punch Retail in the £225 million disposal of FirstQuench to Nomura. International instructions include advising US Industries on the disposal of UK and European interests of Selkirk Europe, which involved multi-jurisdictional structural issues. **Clients:** Hanson; US Industries; BPT; Barclays Private Equity; University of Leeds.

Eversheds (see firm details p.952) A "*sensible and commercial*" team, which is also strong on share schemes. Joint head of department and "*leading light*" **David Jervis** is judged to be a "*sensible operator*" by both peers and clients. He splits his time between corporate tax and share scheme work. The group advised HSBC on the £450 million purchase of Caradon Plumbing Group and acted for Peter Black Holdings on a £300 million take private by the management team, which involved a complex equity structure. Also advised Telecity on a £550 million flotation. **Clients:** HSBC; Peter Black Holdings; Telecity; Holidaybreak; AEA Technology; Chaplethorpe.

Hammond Suddards Edge (see firm details p.984) A "*quality*" team acting as part of a vibrant national practice and providing a corporate support role across the North. National head of tax **Mark Simpson** (see p.808) has a broad tax practice, and competitors acknowledge he is "*experienced, with good leadership skills.*" The firm is also skilled in VAT and property-based issues. Highlights of the past year include advising Bastionen on tax issues relating to its UK property portfolio, and advising Ellis & Everard on the takeover bid by Vopak. Assisting in all areas of corporate finance and tax structuring, the firm advised Allied London Properties in tax issues relating to acquisitions and disposals of properties and joint ventures. **Clients:** Allied London Properties; Darchem; English Partnerships; Findel; FKI; Royal Bank Development Capital.

Dickinson Dees (see firm details p.941) A well-regarded, if smaller, team advises the firm's high quality corporate client base. Clients are attracted by the presence of **Tony Hennessy** (see p.805), nationally regarded as a "*quality lawyer with a good deal of experience.*" Players on the international scene, the group advises on cross-border leasing arrangements from quoted plcs, and advised the Go-Ahead Group on its acquisition of the ground handling business of British Midland Airways. The team also assisted in the tax aspects of the disposal of a private company for £80 million, and is advising on the sale of Orchid Drinks to Britvic. **Clients:** The Go-Ahead Group; ARRIVA; Northern Rock.

Walker Morris (see firm details p.1171) A solid team acting for locally prominent companies and enjoying a boom in stamp duty advice. Head of department **Simon Concannon** (see p.803) is rated by clients for being "*able and commercial.*" The firm advised Bradford Particle Design on a tax incentivised public offer and on a take-over. It assisted Bradford City Football Club on the development of a new stand and continues advising VCTs on tax based investments. Also instructed a large software house on its international structuring and UK investments. **Clients:** Allied Kunick; Cordwell Leisure Developments; Goldsborough Hospitals & Residential Homes; UK Superbowl; United News Shops.

Other Notable Practitioners **Peter Townsend** (see p.809) of **Cobbetts** has some substantial international clients, and is increasingly crossing the paths of leading practitioners. He is known for his academic background and "*technical expertise.*"

SCOTLAND

TAX • Scotland	Ptnrs	Assts
1 **McGrigor Donald** Glasgow	2	2
2 **Maclay Murray & Spens** Glasgow	n/a	3
MacRoberts Glasgow	1	2
3 **Brodies WS** Edinburgh	2	4
Burness Edinburgh	1	1

LEADING INDIVIDUALS	
1 **D'INVERNO Isobel** MacRoberts	**GORDON Ian** McGrigor Donald
JONES Martyn Maclay Murray & Spens	
2 **BARR Alan** Brodies WS	**HOYLE Susan** McGrigor Donald
UP AND COMING	
TOSH Nial Dickson Minto WS	

This book is the product of 6,552 1/2-hour interviews. See p.7 for BMRB audit.

Within each band, firms are listed alphabetically. *See individuals' profiles p.802*

McGrigor Donald (see firm details p.1062) "*Standing alone in the market,*" the team has the benefit of size, talent and high-profile deals including tax-driven financing. Head of department **Ian Gordon** (see p.804) is regarded by his peers as a "*senior player with a great deal of experience, combined with a sensible, commercial attitude.*" **Susan Hoyle** (see p.805), who is based in Glasgow, is a "*competent all-rounder*" and "*brings enthusiasm to the job.*" Highlights of the past year include advising on the tax aspects of the sale of WH Malcolm Group to Grampian Holding and providing finance lease arrangements for the £80 million rejuvenation of the Forth & Clyde Canal (Millennium Link Project). The team provided all the share scheme advice in relation to the sale of Morrison to Anglian Water. **Clients:** Royal Bank of Scotland; Forth Ports; British Waterways; Indigo Vision; Elphinstone Property Group; Channel Health.

Maclay Murray & Spens (see firm details p.1047) A robust team, involved in quality transactional work, it has recently been bolstered by the recruitment of a tax specialist from Deloitte & Touche. Head of the unit is **Martyn Jones** (see p.806). Both competitors and clients find him to be "*likeable and competent, always balanced and constructive in his opinions.*" The firm advised on the £600 million acquisition of Highland Distilleries by 1887 plc, and assisted in Motherwell Bride Holdings' £75 million disposal of its Information Systems Division, funded by 3i. Skilled across the board, the firm advised on the stamp duty aspects of the flotation of Claims Direct, and was involved in the sale of Strategic Software Solutions to US investors. **Clients:** Vericore Holdings; national plcs; private corporates.

MacRoberts (see firm details p.1048) Encompassing a broad swathe of tax matters, including stamp duty planning, corporate support, projects and CGT tax planning for vendor companies, the firm continues to take high ranking in Scotland. Director of Tax **Isobel d'Inverno** (see p.803) is a qualified chartered accountant, and well respected in the market. Recent highlights for the group include advising Johnston Press in various acquisitions, and assisting Horncastle Titles in the acquisition of Newark Trader and Glasgow East News titles. Instructed by Railtrack in the Aberdeen Station redevelopment joint venture with Stannifer, the firm also advised Glenvarigill Company in the acquisition of businesses from the Abercrombie Motor Group. MBOs have also proved to be a significant part of the firm's transactional tax advice. **Clients:** AMEC Group; Bank of Scotland; Campbell Distillers; Ford Motor Company; Keydata UK; Morrison; Omnia Books; Peebles Publishing; 3i Group.

Brodies WS (see firm details p.896) Judged by our interviewees to be a "*sizeable*" team, which includes a mix of lawyers and chartered accountants. Particularly visible on recent corporate and property-based transactions, the group is headed by **Alan Barr** (see p.802), who writes extensively and is "*experienced and active on transactions.*" The firm recently acted as lead advisor on the sale of leading specialist publishing house T & T Clark to Continuum Publishing and advised IFA Portfolio in a joint venture with Bankhall. It was instructed by the shareholders of Martyn Scott in its 90% sale to Witzenmann. **Clients:** Corporates; financials.

Burness (see firm details p.903) The loss of Victoria Nelson to KPMG is a blow, but the firm has employed a chartered accountant in her place. Respected finance man John Rafferty is also part of the team. Instructions include corporate support together with stand-alone tax advisory matters. Significant deals over the past year include advising Big Beat on the tax aspects of the £38 million disposal of Beat 106, and advising Ladbrokes on the tax issues relating to the £5 million acquisition of John Smith & Son. The team also assisted Diagnostic Instruments and its shareholders on its sale. **Clients:** Big Beat Group; Diagnostic Instruments; GE Capital Bank; GE Capital Fleet Services; Ladbrokes; Ritchie & Co; Royal Bank of Scotland.

Other Notable Practitioners Nial Tosh (see p.809) at **Dickson Minto WS** is a "*mature player in the market*" who continues to offer respected support to the firm's wide-ranging corporate activities.

LEADERS IN TAX

AIRS, Graham
Slaughter and May, London (020) 7600 1200
graham.airs@slaughterandmay.com
Specialisation: Principal area of practice is corporate tax. Particular experience of privatisations, securitisations, mergers and acquisitions.
Prof. Memberships: Member of The Law Society's Revenue Law Committee, The Law Society, European American Taxation Institute.
Career: Qualified in 1978 after articles at *Slaughter and May* and stayed at firm until 1980. Partner in *Airs Dickinson* 1980-84. Returned to *Slaughter and May* 1984 and became a partner in 1987.
Publications: Author of chapter on EC Direct Tax Measures in 'Tolley's Tax Planning'.
Personal: Born 8 August 1953. Married Stephanie 1981. Educated Newport (Essex) Grammar, Emmanuel College, Cambridge.

AVERY JONES CBE, John
Speechly Bircham, London (020) 7427 6454
john.averyjones@speechlys.com
Specialisation: Taxation of all kinds.
Prof. Memberships: Member of Treasury appointed Tax Law Rewrite Steering Committee, Law Society (Member and past Chairman of Revenue Law Committee), Chartered Institute of Taxation (Past President), International Fiscal Association, Institute for Fiscal Studies, International Academy of Estate & Trust Law, International Bar Association.
Career: Partner in *Speechly Bircham* since 1970, senior partner since 1985, Deputy Special Commissioner of Income Tax and part-time Chairman of VAT and Duties Tribunals, Consulting Editor of British Tax Review, Member of the Editorial Board of Simon's Taxes, Chairman of the Board of Trustees of the International Bureau of Fiscal Documentation.
Personal: Born 1940, educated at Rugby School and Trinity College, Cambridge.

BALDWIN, Mark
Macfarlanes, London (020) 7831 9222
mark.baldwin@macfarlanes.com
Specialisation: Partner in corporate tax group. Handles a broad spectrum of corporate/business tax work, including private equity and 'public to private' transactions and cross border investment. Has particular expertise in indirect tax (especially VAT), real estate investment development and finance and the structuring of collective investment vehicles (particularly domestic and pan-European private equity and real estate funds) and associated carried interest and co-investment structures.
Prof. Memberships: Member of the Law Society's VAT and Duties Sub-Committee, VAT Practitioners Group, IBA.
Career: Qualified in 1987. Assistant Solicitor at *Freshfields* between 1987 and 1995, when he returned to *Macfarlanes*, becoming a partner in May 1997.
Publications: Regular conference speaker and writer. A contributor to 'De Voil's Indirect Tax Intelligence' and Reporter on UK Taxes for 1999 and 2000 IBA Conferences.
Personal: Born 24 January 1963. German speaker.

BALL, Susan
Clyde & Co, London (020) 7623 1244

BALLARD, Richard
Freshfields Bruckhaus Deringer, London (020) 7936 4000
richard.ballard@freshfields.com
Specialisation: Partner. Specialises in corporate finance (including mergers, demergers, reconstructions and cross border transactions); tax-based and structured financing of all types, including cross border transactions; capital markets work including structured bond issues, hybrid instruments, repackaging and securitisation; derivatives transactions of all types; experience in Inland Revenue enquiries and in Commissioners and court litigation. Contributor to 'Tolley's Tax Planning' and 'Tolley's Company Law' and frequent contributor to tax journals and to various *Freshfields* publications.
Career: Qualified 1978. Became a Partner at *Freshfields* in 1984.
Personal: Born 1953. Attended Queens' College, Cambridge.

BARR, Alan
Brodies WS, Edinburgh (0131) 228 3777
alan.barr@brodies.co.uk
Specialisation: Alan Barr is one of Scotland's leading authorities in the field of tax law. He has carried out substantial research on the subject and his papers and books have been published widely. He is a frequent speaker at professional seminars.
Prof. Memberships: Law Society of Scotland Tax Committee, Convenor of the VAT Sub-Committee.
Career: Admitted as a solicitor in Scotland in 1984, Alan has spent much of his career as a senior lecturer specialising in all areas of taxation, and is currently director of Edinburgh University's Legal Practice Unit (The Diploma Course). Joined *Brodies* as the firm's corporate tax and VAT consultant by agreement with Edinburgh University. He consolidates *Brodies'* position as a leading legal firm in the field of taxation generally, and the aspect of tax on property in particular. When added to the specialist areas of environmental and planning law, Alan's expertise ensures full coverage in all disciplines relevant to property development and acquisition.
Personal: Alan is married and, despite the fact that he lives in Edinburgh, keeps an optimistic eye on the progress of St Mirren Football Club. He enjoys watching rugby and cricket and collecting Marvel Comics.

BEARE, Tony
Slaughter and May, London (020) 7600 1200
tony.beare@slaughterandmay.com
Specialisation: Corporate tax. Main area of practice is corporate tax and, in particular, structured finance, corporate finance and capital markets.
Prof. Memberships: The Law Society.
Career: Qualified 1987. Partner 1994.
Personal: Born 30 November 1959. Educated at Durban High School, Haberdashers' Aske's, Elstree, St. Catharine's College, Cambridge and St. Edmund Hall, Oxford.

BIRD, David
TLT Solicitors, Bristol (0117) 917 7866
dbird@tltsolicitors
Specialisation: Tax and estate planning, specifically inheritance tax and capital gains tax planning for business clients, creating and advising on trusts and trust law, advising on taxation of group companies and VAT and stamp duty issues. Working alongside corporate finance team in drafting and negotiating the tax elements of the sale documentation.
Prof. Memberships: Fellow of the Chartered Insurance Institute; Associate of the Chartered Institute of Taxation.
Career: *Wilsons*, 1992-96; *Osborne Clarke*, 1996-98; *TLT* (formerly *Lawrence Tucketts*), 1998-present.
Personal: Interests include golf, cricket and football (spectator only).

BLAKE, Jonathan
SJ Berwin, London (020) 7533 2222
jonathan.blake@sjberwin.com
See under Private Equity, p.676

BRAILSFORD, Mark R
Allen & Overy, London (020) 7330 3606
mark.brailsford@allenovery.com
Specialisation: He has specialised in corporate tax since qualification and handles the corporate tax aspects of transactions in a wide range of areas. His experience covers in particular the giving of UK tax advice in the fields of domestic and cross-border mergers and acquisitions, domestic and cross-border corporate reorganisations and restructurings, flotations, takeovers, intellectual property, domestic and international banking and capital markets issues.
Prof. Memberships: Member of the European Tax Committee of the International Swaps and Derivatives Association.
Career: Articled *Allen & Overy* (1987), qualified (1989), partner (1996).
Personal: Married with one daughter. Keen tennis and football enthusiast. Member of the AFA Council. Cambridge University (MA 1988).

BRANNAN, Guy
Linklaters, London (020) 7456 5690
guy.brannan@linklaters.com
Specialisation: Specialises in corporate tax matters. Main areas of practice include mergers and acquisi-

tions, reorganisations, reconstructions, cross-border transactions, capital markets and finance transactions, EC tax law and tax litigation.
Prof. Memberships: Member of the permanent Tax Commission on the Union Internationale des Avocats. Member of the American Bar Association (Taxation Section).
Career: Qualified 1981. Partner 1987, resident tax partner New York office 1989-93. Partner and head of tax department since 1998.

BUTLER, Kay
Olswang, London (020) 7208 8888
kbb@olswang.com
Specialisation: Partner, head of tax unit. Spans the spectrum of tax work including corporate tax strategy, international group structuring, joint ventures (particularly in the property and media sectors) both domestic and cross border, limited partnerships, sale and lease backs, film investment, employee incentives and VAT and other tax disputes. She has lobbied the EC Commission, the Inland Revenue and HM Customs and Excise for changes in the law. She was also the only legal representative on the British Screen Advisory Counsel's committee which negotiated the statement of practice concerning the new relief for investment in film with the Inland Revenue.
Prof. Memberships: Law Society; VAT Practitioners Group.
Career: Qualified 1987 at *Oppenheimers*; assistant solicitor *Richards Butler* 1988-90; *SJ Berwin & Co* 1990-95, becoming a partner in 1993. Joined *Olswang* in 1995 as head of tax.
Personal: Interests include perfecting her golf swing and entertaining her young daughter.

CANT, Michael
Nabarro Nathanson, London (020) 7524 6000
m.cant@nabarro.com
Specialisation: Partner in corporate tax department. Specialises in corporate tax, particularly VAT and stamp duties.
Prof. Memberships: Law Society, VAT practitioners group.
Career: Qualified in 1984. Joined *Turner Kenneth Brown* as an assistant in 1988.
Personal: Born 19th September 1958. Attended Leeds Polytechnic 1976-79, then Guildford Law School 1980. Leisure interests include golf. Lives in Haslemere, Surrey.

CHALLONER, John
Norton Rose, London (020) 7444 3389
challonerj@nortonrose.com
Specialisation: Partner in commercial tax department. Principal area of practice is corporate taxation. Extensive experience in relation to the taxation of company acquisitions; property developments; UK corporate restructurings; collective investment schemes; dealing with the complex VAT and other tax issues relating to international ventures.
Prof. Memberships: International Fiscal Association.
Career: Qualified 1977 while with *Nelson & Steele* in Stoke-on-Trent. HM Inspector of Taxes 1979-84. Joined *Norton Rose* in 1984 and became a partner in 1988.
Personal: Born 9 August 1952. Attended Wilmslow School and Exeter University. Lives in Saffron Walden.

CHRISTIAN, John
Pinsent Curtis Biddle, Leeds (0113) 244 5000
john.christian@pinsents.com
Specialisation: Partner and head of corporate tax group. Corporate and property tax, including corporate finance, reconstructions and demergers, asset finance, treasury and financing, property taxation, employee incentives, VAT, collective investment schemes and public bodies.
Prof. Memberships: VAT Practitioners Group. Member of the Corporation Tax Sub-Committee of Law Society Revenue Law Committee. Fellow of the Chartered Institute of Taxation.
Career: Qualified 1985. *Freshfields* 1983-89. Joined *Simpson Curtis* in 1990 (now *Pinsent Curtis Biddle*). Partner in 1991.

CLARK, Simon
Linklaters, London (020) 7456 4902
simon.clark@linklaters.com
See under Property (Commercial), p.742

CLAYSON, Murray
Freshfields Bruckhaus Deringer, London (020) 7936 4000
murray.clayson@freshfields.com
Specialisation: International tax, corporate structuring especially cross-border, financing, banking, securities, capital markets, derivatives, structured finance.
Prof. Memberships: Chartered Institute of Taxation (FTII). Member of International Tax Sub-Committee. International Fiscal Association: Chairman of British Branch.
Career: Sidney Sussex College, Cambridge (MA, LL.M). Partner 1993.

COLECLOUGH, Stephen
PricewaterhouseCoopers, Birmingham (0121) 265 5000

COLEMAN, Brenda
Allen & Overy, London (020) 7330 3625
brenda.coleman@allenovery.com
Specialisation: Partner in the tax department advising on all aspects of corporate tax but has a particular interest in mergers and acquisitions, reorganisations, joint ventures, investment vehicles, tax litigation, financial instruments and tax (and property clawback) advice on privatisations and PFI projects. She is a member of *Allen & Overy's* Tax Investigations Unit and Investment Funds Group.
Career: Qualified *Slaughter and May* (1984); Partner *Herbert Smith* (1991-98); Partner *Allen & Overy* (1998).
Personal: Born 1959. King's College London 1979-81, LL.B Hons, AKC.

CONCANNON, Simon
Walker Morris, Leeds (0113) 283 2500
stc@walkermorris.co.uk
Specialisation: Partner in corporate department, head of tax unit. Principal area of practice is corporate and property tax. Work includes restructuring, leasing, structured bank financing, MBOs, venture capital funding, employee remuneration schemes and VAT planning. Also handles tax disputes including dealing with the Inland Revenue Special Compliance Office and the Special Investigation Section. Major clients include Redcats, Persimmon, Bank of Scotland, Royal Bank of Scotland, Roseby's, Selfridges, Tay Homes, Capital for Companies VCT, Murray Johnstone, Bradford City Football Club, Caterpillar and Debenhams.
Career: Educated at Hertford College, Oxford; qualified in 1990.

CRAWFORD, Susan
Ashurst Morris Crisp, London (020) 7859 1293
susan.crawford@ashursts.com
Specialisation: Partner in tax department. Principal area of practice is corporate tax with particular emphasis on corporate reorganisations, mergers, demergers, and acquisitions including cross-border transactions. Also specialises in property taxation (including tax based structured financing and fund structures, extending to securitisation, leasing and enterprise zones) and oil and gas tax.
Career: Articled *Coward Chance (Clifford Chance)*; qualified 1984. Partner *Ashurst Morris Crisp* since 1994.
Personal: Educated at Wycombe Abbey School; Girton College Cambridge University.

CROKER, Richard
CMS Cameron McKenna, London (020) 7367 2149
radc@cmck.com
Specialisation: All aspects of corporate tax with particular emphasis on VAT and other indirect taxes, tax planning for property transactions, PPP, mergers/acquisitions and joint ventures.
Prof. Memberships: Member of City Chapter of VAT Practitioners Group; member of VAT and Duties Sub-Committee of Law Society's Revenue Law Committee.
Career: Qualified 1989. Partner *CMS Cameron McKenna* 1997.
Personal: Married with three sons. Lives Winchester.

D'INVERNO, Isobel
MacRoberts, Edinburgh (0131) 229 5046
isobel.d'inverno@macroberts.co.uk
Specialisation: Director – corporate tax and head of corporate tax group. Main area of practice is corporate taxation work. Includes corporate acquisitions, disposals, re-organisations, EIS and Reinvestment Relief issues, PFIs, stamp duty planning and VAT on commercial property and corporate transactions. Frequent speaker at seminars on PFI tax, VAT and Stamp Duty and company re-organisations. VAT examiner for Chartered Institute of Taxation.
Prof. Memberships: Institute of Chartered Accountants (England and Wales), Chartered Institute of Taxation, VAT Practitioners Group, member of Tax Law Committee of Law Society of Scotland.
Career: Trained as chartered accountant with *Ernst & Whinney* in London. Practised with *Ernst & Young* as corporate tax specialist. Joined *Brodies WS* as VAT and corporate tax specialist in June 1991. Joined *MacRoberts* in August 1997.
Personal: Educated at St Andrew's University (MA Russian Language and Literature 1979). Gained ACA 1983, then ATII 1984. Non-executive member of the National Board for Nursing, Midwifery and Health Visiting for Scotland.

DORAN, Nigel
Macfarlanes, London (020) 7831 9222
nigel.doran@macfarlanes.com
Specialisation: Partner in corporate tax group. Work includes mergers and acquisitions, joint ventures, MBO's, MBI's, corporate finance, international, employment, investment funds, banking and proper-

ty. Important transactions include the sale of Saatchi & Saatchi and acting for management on the sale of William Hill.
Prof. Memberships: City of London Law Society (Chairman of Revenue Law Subcommittee), Chartered Institute of Taxation, Association of Certified Accountants, Chartered Institute of Bankers, AUTIF Tax Committee.
Career: Qualified in 1984 having joined *Macfarlanes* in 1982. Became a partner in 1988.
Publications: Regular speaker at tax conferences, author of 'Taxation of Corporate Joint Ventures' (Butterworths) and joint author of 'Collective Investment Schemes: the Law and Practice' (FT Law and Tax).
Personal: Born 11th March 1950. Educated at Trinity College, Glenalmond 1963-69 and St. Edmund Hall, Oxford 1969-73. Leisure interests include golf and modern languages. Lives in Twickenham.

DOUGLAS, Alasdair
Travers Smith Braithwaite, London (020) 7295 3000
Alasdair.Douglas@TraversSmith.com
Specialisation: Head of 18-strong corporate tax department. Main areas of work are corporate finance, investment funds and tax investigation work.
Prof. Memberships: Member of the Law Societies of Scotland, England and Wales; Fellow of the Society for Advanced Legal Studies; member of the Executive Board of the Committee for Careers Service of Oxford University; member of the City of London Law Society Revenue Law sub-committee; member of the IBA and American Bar Association.

DUGDALE, Pat
Olswang, London (020) 7208 8888
apd@olswang.com
Specialisation: General, corporate, property and international tax, including tax planning for international groups and corporate reconstructions, acquisitions and disposals. Particular areas of specialist expertise include UK and overseas investment funds, EIS, corporate venturing and private equity transactions and e-commerce. Recent transactions include the establishment of a number of incubator and other new media investment funds.
Prof. Memberships: British German Jurists Association. International Fiscal Association.
Career: Qualified 1985. Corporate and commercial assistant at *Kennedys* 1986-89 and *SJ Berwin* 1989 to 1992; tax assistant at *Norton Rose* 1992-98, tax partner *Olswang* May 1998.
Publications: Editor of Taxation chapter of Sweet & Maxwell's 'Encyclopaedia of International Technology Law'. Articles on international tax and incorporation of partnerships. Regular conference speaker on taxation of e-commerce and general corporate taxation.
Personal: University College Cardiff and Heidelberg University 1978-82. BA Law and German (1st Class Hons). LLM Taxation: Kings College London 1992. Married with two energetic small boys.

EDGE, Steve
Slaughter and May, London (020) 7600 1200
steve.edge@slaughterandmay.com
Specialisation: Partner in corporate tax department. Principal area of practice is corporate taxation with a particular emphasis on corporate finance and structured asset finance. Expertise in investment funds, financial instruments, cross border financial transactions, securitisations and other capital markets work. Advises many UK and non-UK multinationals and banks on a wide range of tax matters. Contributes to a number of publications on corporate tax.
Career: Qualified in 1975 while with *Slaughter and May* and became a partner in 1982.
Personal: Born 29 November 1950. Attended Canon Slade Grammar School, Bolton 1962-69, then Exeter University 1969-72. Lives in London.

EHRLICH, Michael
Clifford Chance, London (020) 7600 1000
michael.ehrlich@cliffordchance.com
Specialisation: Partner specialising in tax on financing transactions and real estate (including VAT).
Career: Bedales School; Southampton University; Warwick University (BSc Mathematics, MSc). Articled *Dawson & Co*; qualified 1977; partner *Clifford Chance* since 1986.

ELLIOTT, Peter
Clifford Chance, London (020) 7600 1000
peter.elliott@cliffordchance.com
Specialisation: Partner and head of international tax. Principal area of practice is corporate and financial taxation including international cross-border structures and transactions.
Career: Partner *Clifford Chance* since 1980.

ELMAN, Jonathan
Clifford Chance, London (020) 7600 1000
jonathan.elman@cliffordchance.com
Specialisation: Partner. Taxation of corporate and financing transactions.
Career: Solicitor 1987; partner 1994.

FALK, Sarah
Freshfields Bruckhaus Deringer, London (020) 7936 4000
sarah.falk@freshfields.com
Specialisation: Partner in tax department. Main area of practice is corporate tax. Work covers corporate tax planning and corporate finance.
Prof. Memberships: Law Society.
Career: Qualified 1986, having joined *Freshfields* in 1984. Became a partner in 1994.
Personal: Born 1962. Attended Sidney Sussex College, Cambridge, 1980-83.

FRASER, Ross
Herbert Smith, London (020) 7374 8000
ross.fraser@herbertsmith.com
Specialisation: Main practice areas include insurance company mergers and acquisitions (recent highlights include acting on the acquisition of United Assurance group by Royal London); and various structured finance transactions. On the non-insurance side, recent transactions include the acquisition by Ireland Group of Booker.
Career: London School of Economics (LLM 1970); qualified 1973; partner *Herbert Smith* 1982.

FRENCH, Douglas
Clifford Chance, London (020) 7600 1000
douglas.french@cliffordchance.com
Specialisation: Partner specialising in tax, particularly tax related to corporate and commercial transactions.
Career: Walbottle High School, Newcastle; Oxford (MA Law) ATII. Articled *Freshfields*; qualified 1981; partner *Clifford Chance* since 1988.
Personal: Born 1956; married, three children.

FRIEL, Daniel
Lovells, London (020) 7296 2000

GARCIA, Dario
Ernst & Young, London (020) 7951 2000

GETHING, Heather
Herbert Smith, London (020) 7466 2346
heather.gething@herbertsmith.com
Specialisation: Heather's tax practice is broadly based. It includes domestic and international tax planning for a variety of multinational companies, structuring and implementing a range of corporate transactions such as public and private mergers and acquisitions, reconstructions and amalgamations, joint ventures, management buyouts and buy ins, and structuring, advising on and implementing financing products and proposals.
Prof. Memberships: Member of the International Bar Association and regular speaker at the Annual Meetings of the Tax Committee of the IBA; Member of the Life Offices Policy and Discussion Group.
Career: Deputy head of corporate tax group. Qualified *Herbert Smith* 1984. Partner 1991.
Publications: Joint author of 'Demutualisation' published by FT Law & Tax, 1997.

GORDON, Ian
McGrigor Donald, Glasgow (0141) 567 9269
iangordon@mcgrigors.com
Specialisation: Principal area of practice is employee benefits, including share incentive schemes, option schemes, and employee share ownership arrangements for listed, AIM and Ofex companies. Also advises on corporate acquisitions, reconstructions and tax driven financing arrangements. Frequent lecturer on taxation issues.
Prof. Memberships: Association of Pension Lawyers.
Career: Joined *McGrigor Donald* as a trainee in 1979. Qualified in July 1979. One year secondment to *Thomson McLintock CA* in 1983. Became a Partner at *McGrigor Donald* in the same year.
Personal: Educated at Edinburgh University 1975-79. Born 15th August 1957. Lives in Glasgow.

GREAVES, Judith
Pinsent Curtis Biddle, Leeds (0113) 244 5000
judith.greaves@pinsents.com
See under Employee Share Schemes, p.309

GREENBANK, Ashley
Macfarlanes, London (020) 7831 9222
ashley.greenbank@macfarlanes.com
Specialisation: Partner in the corporate tax group specialising in UK and cross border tax aspects of corporate finance transactions, mergers and acquisitions and venture capital work.
Prof. Memberships: Law Society (Member of Corporation Tax Sub-Committee of the Revenue Law Committee); BVCA (Tax Committee).
Career: King Edwards School Birmingham, Selwyn College Cambridge MA (1985), Lincoln College Oxford BCL (1989). Qualified 1988. Articles at *Freshfields* (1986-88). Assistant solicitor *Freshfields* tax department (1989-94). Assistant solicitor *Macfarlanes* company commercial and banking department (1994-97). Partner 1997.

HALE, Paul
Simmons & Simmons, London (020) 7628 2020
paul.hale@simmons-simmons.com
Specialisation: Partner in corporate and indirect

taxes group. Main area of practice is corporate tax and value added tax. Work includes mergers and acquisitions, stock exchange listings, project finance, structured finance and property transactions. Also handles taxation of collective investment schemes, including unit trusts, investment trusts and offshore funds.
Prof. Memberships: Law Society, City of London Solicitors' Company (member of Revenue Law Sub-Committee), VAT Practitioners Group, International Bar Association.
Career: Qualified 1985, having joined *Simmons & Simmons* in 1983. Became a partner in 1990.

HARDWICK, Michael
Linklaters, London (020) 7456 5658
michael.hardwick@linklaters.com
Specialisation: Specialises in tax aspects of mergers and acquisitions, takeovers, joint ventures, flotations, privatisations and PFI transactions.
Prof. Memberships: Member, Revenue Law Committee and International Tax Sub-Committee of The Law Society. Chairman, Revenue Law Committee of City of London Law Society.
Career: 1991 to date: Partner, *Linklaters*; 1984-91: Assistant solicitor, *Linklaters*. 1980-81: Gonville & Caius College, Cambridge, LLM (First Class); 1977-80: University College, Oxford. MA (First Class).

HARGREAVES, Colin
Freshfields Bruckhaus Deringer, London (020) 7936 4000
colin.hargreaves@freshfields.com
Specialisation: Corporate tax.
Prof. Memberships: Law Society. City of London Law Society (member, CLLS Revenue Law Sub-Committee).
Career: Uppingham School; Leeds University; qualified 1988; partner *Freshfields* 1996.
Personal: Sailing (member, Burnham Overy Staithe Sailing Club).

HARKNESS, David
Clifford Chance, London (020) 7600 1000
david.harkness@cliffordchance.com
Specialisation: Partner specialising in corporate tax including mergers and acquisitions, corporate restructurings, joint ventures, international tax planning, financing transactions and securitisations.
Career: Colchester Royal Grammar School; Sheffield University (LLB Law 1985). Articled *Clifford Chance*; qualified 1989; partner 1996.
Personal: Interests: family, football, golf, juggling with fire, pig breeding. Born 1963; resides London.

HENNESSY, Tony
Dickinson Dees, Newcastle upon Tyne (0191) 279 9207
law@dickinson-dees.com
Specialisation: A broad range of corporate tax work, including all tax aspects of mergers, acquisitions, corporate reorganisations and flotations together with employee share scheme and remuneration planning work, asset financing and leasing and VAT planning.
Career: Called to the Bar 1979. Practised corporate tax in both a City of London practice and in a major provincial firm before being appointed as head of the corporate tax group at *Dickinson Dees* in 1992.
Personal: Educated St. Mary's College Crosby and University College Oxford (MA). Leisure interests include rugby, hill walking and 18th century music.

HIGGINBOTTOM, Louise
Norton Rose, London (020) 7283 6000
higginbottomal@nortonrose.com
Specialisation: Partner in tax department. Corporate and asset finance.
Prof. Memberships: Law Society, Associate of Institute of Tax, member of Corporation Tax sub-committee of Revenue Law committee of Law Society, IBA, ABA.
Career: Joined *Norton Rose* 1981. Qualified 1983. Partner 1991.
Personal: Born 17 August 1958. Attended Southampton University 1977-80.

HOYLE, Stephen
Freshfields Bruckhaus Deringer, London (020) 7936 4000
stephen.hoyle@freshfields.com
Specialisation: Partner 1988. Tax department. Main area of practice is the taxation of insurance business, financings and general corporate.
Personal: Born 17.9.1955. Attended St Catherine's College Oxford 1973-76, Gonville & Caius College Cambridge, 1976-77, and Northwestern Law School, Chicago, 1977-78.

HOYLE, Susan
McGrigor Donald, Glasgow (0141) 248 6677
susan.hoyle@mcgrigors.com
Specialisation: Partner in corporate unit. Main area of practice is corporate tax, dealing with acquisitions and disposals, group reorganisations and MBO's. Also deals with employee share schemes.
Prof. Memberships: The Chartered Institute of Taxation.
Career: Qualified in October 1986. Worked for *Ernst & Young* and *Coopers & Lybrand*. Joined *McGrigor Donald* in 1995.

HUMPHREY, Ann L
Ann L. Humphrey, London (020) 7378 9370
annlhumphrey@dial.pipex.com
Specialisation: Wide-ranging tax experience during 15 years in the City, with particular emphasis on VAT. Tax litigation experience at all levels, from VAT tribunal or Special Commissioners up to the Court of Appeal. Managing Editor 'EC Tax Journal'.
Prof. Memberships: Member of the Law Society's Revenue Law Committee and its VAT and Duties Sub-Committee; HM Customs VAT Land and Property Liaison Group; VAT Practitioners Group.
Career: Admitted as a solicitor in 1977. MA in Law. Master of Business Administration. Corporate tax partner in City firm until May 1993. Set up her own practice in July 1993 concentrating on VAT and corporate tax. The firm's work is around 40% corporate tax and 60% VAT. In 1997 the firm moved to new custom-built offices at the Tower Bridge.
Personal: French and Japanese speaker. Deputy Social Security Commissioner.

HYDE, Ian
Pinsent Curtis Biddle, Birmingham (0121) 200 1050
ian.hyde@pinsents.com
Specialisation: Partner specialising in corporate and property taxation including tax efficient structures for joint ventures, demergers, reconstructions and property development. Ian also advises on VAT planning, stamp duty, taxation of intellectual property and tax based investment structures.
Prof. Memberships: VAT Practitioners group.
Career: BA Oxford University (1987). *Rowe & Maw* (1988 – 1992). *Pinsent Curtis Biddle* (1992 – date).
Publications: Consulting editor to Butterworth's 'Encyclopaedia of Forms and Precedents on VAT and Stamp Duty'.

JACOBS, Russell
Milbank, Tweed, Hadley & McCloy, London (020) 7448 3009
rljacobs@milbank.com
Specialisation: Has significant expertise in the corporate and financial services sectors, focusing on the development and implementation of new financial cross-border products and the structuring of international consortia and joint ventures in mergers, acquisitions and corporate reconstructions.
Prof. Memberships: The Law Society of England & Wales. President, European – American Tax Institute, London.
Career: Trained *Slaughter & May*; qualified 1985; partner, tax department, *Wilde Sapte* 1992-97, partner, *Cadwalader Wickersham & Taft* 1997-00.
Publications: Written articles for: Butterworths 'Finance Bill Handbook,' 'Tax Journal,' 'Financial Instrument Tax and Accounting Review.'

JENKINS, Edmund
Addleshaw Booth & Co, Manchester (0161) 934 6000
egj@addleshaw-booth.co.uk
Specialisation: Partner in Commercial Tax Department, Commercial Group. Practice covers all areas of business and property tax and includes advising upon the tax aspects of mergers and acquisitions, reorganisations and restructurings, exiting strategies for persons selling their business and MBOs and other venture capital transactions. Acts for a mixture of quoted and private companies, individuals and venture capital houses.
Career: Called to the bar 1985. Re-qualified as a Solicitor 1991. Joined the firm as a Partner in 1996.
Personal: Educated at Princethorpe College and Liverpool University. Interests include playing squash, golf and Italian wines. Married with two daughters and a son. Lives in Hale, Cheshire.

JERVIS, David
Eversheds, Leeds (0113) 243 0391

JOHNSON, Ian
Ashurst Morris Crisp, London (020) 7638 1111
ian.johnson@ashursts.com
Specialisation: Partner in tax department. Involved in advising on the taxation implications of a wide range of corporate transactions advising both overseas and UK clients.
Prof. Memberships: Associate of the Chartered Institute of Taxation.
Career: Graduated in law from Edinburgh University.
Publications: Co-author of Butterworth's 'Taxation of Loan Relationships, Financial Instruments and Foreign Exchange'.

JONES, Janet
Addleshaw Booth & Co, Leeds (0113) 209 2000
Specialisation: Partner with considerable experience in advising on all aspects of taxation for UK corporate and other clients. Experience of advising at a senior level on the taxation aspects of a wide range of corporate finance and employee benefit matters.
Career: Educated at UCW, Aberystwyth and UCL, London. Joined firm in 1998; Partner 1999.

JONES, Martyn
Maclay Murray & Spens, Glasgow (0141) 248 5011
mhj@maclaymurrayspens.co.uk
Specialisation: Partner, head of tax department and formerly senior tax lecturer at Glasgow University. Advises on VAT and property, company taxation, capital allowances, stamp duty and capital gains.
Prof. Memberships: Member of the Tax Law committee of the Law Society of Scotland and its income tax, VAT and stamp duty sub-committees, and CBI Scotland's Economics and Taxation committee.
Career: Glasgow University (LLB 1974).
Personal: Born 1952.

KELLY, Don
Lovells, London (020) 7296 2000
don.kelly@lovells.com
Specialisation: Corporate tax partner specialising in all aspects of business tax including taxation implications of mergers, acquisitions and joint ventures (particularly cross-border), UK equipment leasing and property transactions and North Sea oil tax.
Prof. Memberships: Law Society, City of London Solicitors' Company.
Career: Articled *Lovells*; qualified 1980; partner 1986; specialised in UK corporate tax since qualification.

LEWIS, David E
Allen & Overy, London (020) 7330 3601
david.lewis@allenovery.com
Specialisation: Partner dealing with all aspects of UK international corporate tax work. His experience is primarily in the fields of corporate acquisitions, disposals, mergers, reconstructions and joint ventures and their structuring on a tax efficient basis. He also has wide experience of a range of banking and bond transactions and tax-based structured financing.
Prof. Memberships: Member Law Society Revenue Committee, Chairman of the Stamp Duty Sub-Committee of the Law Society Revenue Law Committee; Member Corporation Tax Sub-Committee of The Law Society Revenue Law Committee.
Career: Articled *Allen & Overy*, qualified 1976, Partner 1982.
Personal: Exeter University 1973. Born 1952.

LING, Timothy
Freshfields Bruckhaus Deringer, London (020) 7936 4000
timothy.ling@freshfields.com
Specialisation: Partner in tax department. All aspects of corporate tax, and particularly UK and cross-border mergers and acquisitions, reconstructions, joint ventures, demergers, private company acquisitions and disposals, new issues.
Prof. Memberships: Law Society and City of London Law Society.
Career: Qualified in 1973. Became partner in *Freshfields* 1977. Head of tax department 1985-91. Member of Law Society Revenue Law Committee 1981-91.
Personal: Born 17th September 1948. Educated The King's School, Canterbury and The Queen's College, Oxford (MA). Leisure interests include sailing and music. Member of Royal Harwich Yacht Club.

LOWE, Kevin
Wragge & Co, Birmingham (0870) 903 1000

LUDER, Sara
Slaughter and May, London (020) 7600 1200
sara.luder@slaughterandmay.com
Specialisation: Sara's practice covers all direct taxes and value added tax, but, in particular, corporation tax. She has extensive experience of corporate transactions including acquisitions, disposals and flotations. She also has considerable experience in leasing and other structured finance transactions. Sara has a particular interest in e-commerce, and is a member of the firm's e-commerce group.
Career: Qualified 1991; joined *Slaughter and May* 1992; partner 1998.

LYNCHEHAN, Martin
Linklaters, London (020) 7456 5716
martin.lynchehan@linklaters.com
Specialisation: Considerable experience of the taxation issues arising in corporate and corporate finance transactions including public and private company disposals and acquisitions and securities offerings as well as extensive experience of structured finance transactions. Proven track record in building successful transactional working relationships with other tax professionals both from in-house tax departments and external accounting firms.
Career: 1998 to date: Partner, *Linklaters*; 1993-98: Assistant solicitor, *Linklaters*; 1998: Trainee solicitor/assistant solicitor, *Richards Butler*. Queen Mary College, London University, LLM (Tax); University of Nottingham BA (Law); St Ignatius, Enfield.

MAINPRICE, Hugh
Hutchinson Mainprice, London (020) 7259 0121
hmainprice@aol.com
Specialisation: Value Added Tax and Insurance Premium Tax. Has appeared in more VAT tribunal cases for appellants than any one else in the UK commencing with the case of Rentokil v C & E Commrs 1973 VATTR 31 heard on the 4 April 1973 and since then has been involved in over 50 cases in the Higher Courts including the House of Lords.
Prof. Memberships: Law Society; Chartered Institute of Taxation; Ordem dos Advogados, Portugal; Royal Geographical Society.
Career: Called to the Bar, Gray's Inn in 1961, became a solicitor in 1978. Employed in the Colonial Legal Service from 1950 to 1964. Joined the Solicitors Office HM Customs & Excise in 1965 and, as a senior legal assistant participated in the drafting of the original VAT legislation. Resigned from the Customs in March 1972 to set up his own legal/consultancy practice on VAT. Was the first person to be awarded a fellowship of the Chartered Institute of Taxation for a thesis on VAT. Author of 'Concise Guide VAT' (1972); 'Mainprice & Willson on VAT' (1973); 'Mainprice on VAT' (Butterworths) (1978); 'Practical VAT Planning' (Tolleys) (1983); 'VAT Disputes' (CCH) (1986). Wrote and edited the original CCH 'British VAT Reporter' (1984). Original editor of the News letters 'VAT Intelligence' (Gee & Co) and 'Practical VAT' (Legal Studies & Services). Author of numerous articles in Accountancy Age, British Tax Review, Taxation and Tax Practitioner. Has made frequent broadcasts on Television and Radio.
Personal: Born 24 April 1928. Educated at Sherborne and London University. Interests include music, photography and travel.

MARTIN, David
Herbert Smith, London (020) 7374 8000
Specialisation: Partner heading the firm's tax department advising on all kinds of business-related tax matters and has played a significant role in many high-profile transactions including company reorganisations, demergers, disposals and acquisitions of companies and businesses; has also been involved in many finance leasing transactions and other financing methods as well as advising on several substantial tax litigation matters.
Career: Qualified 1979; partner *Herbert Smith* 1986.
Personal: Educated at St John's College, Cambridge.

McGOWAN, Michael T
Allen & Overy, London (020) 7330 3620
michael.mcgowan@allenovery.com
Specialisation: Experienced in most areas of UK taxation, particularly structured finance transactions, including securitisations. He advised on the 1996 and 1997 takeover bids for Northern Electricity and Yorkshire Electricity, on the 1997 Canary Wharf securitisation and 1999 flotation, as well as the 1999 securitisation of the Broadgate Estate. More recently he has acted on the securitisation of the Trafford Centre in Manchester, the takeover bid for MEPC plc and the acquisition of TI Group by Smiths Industries plc.
Career: Articled and qualified *Clifford Chance* (1987-90); Assistant solicitor, *Linklaters & Paines* (1990-95) including secondment at *Sullivan & Cromwell* New York (1993); Assistant *Allen & Overy* (1995-97), partner (1997).
Personal: Born 1963. Magdalen College, Oxford (MA BCL). Married with two daughters. Interests: reading, music, being a parent, drinking wine and playing golf.

MEARS, Patrick M.
Allen & Overy, London (020) 7330 3600
patrick.mears@allenovery.com
Specialisation: Managing Partner in the corporate tax department, advises on the corporate tax aspects of transactions in a wide range of areas including UK tax advice in the fields of domestic and cross-border acquisitions, corporate reorganisations, IPO's, transfer pricing and tax investigations, domestic and international banking, asset and tax structured financing, capital markets issues and securities trading and lending.
Prof. Memberships: City of London Law Society's Revenue Law Sub-committee.
Career: Articled *Allen & Overy*, qualified (1982), partner (1988).
Personal: Born 1958. London School of Economics 1979.

MEHTA, Nikhil
Linklaters, London (020) 7456 5686
nikhil.mehta@linklaters.com
Specialisation: Tax department. Specialises in corporate taxation with particular emphasis on international and structured finance, contentious tax, derivatives, mergers and acquisitions, cross-border structures and joint ventures. Head of the India business group.
Career: 1992 to date: Head of the India business group, *Linklaters*; 1989 to date: Partner, *Linklaters*; 1983-89: Legal assistant/assistant solicitor, *Linklaters*; 1981-83: Legal assistant, Inland Revenue Solicitor's Office; 1997-80: Practising as tax advocate, India. Bristol University LLB (Hons).

MORRIS, Gregory
DLA, Birmingham (08700) 111111

MOSS, Philip GS
Osborne Clarke, Bristol (0117) 917 3000

MURPHY, Niall
Blake Lapthorn, Fareham (01489) 579 990

NIAS, Peter
McDermott, Will & Emery, London (020) 7577 6920
pnias@europe.mwe.com
Specialisation: Main areas of practice are corporate, commercial and international taxation. Work includes cross border transactions (in particular, mergers, acquisitions, reorganisations), transfer pricing and thin capitalisation, finance leasing and structured finance transactions.
Prof. Memberships: Law Society. Chairman and Member of Law Society International Tax Sub-committee, and Vice Chairman Chartered Institute of Taxation International Tax Sub-committee, member of ICC UK Tax Committee, International Fiscal Association, International Tax Planning Association, European-American Tax Institute.
Career: Qualified in 1979. Joined *Simmons & Simmons* in 1976, becoming a partner in 1982 and Head of Tax Department in 1992. Joined *McDermott, Will & Emery*, November 1998 as Head of Tax to set up full-service London office.
Publications: Author of the PLC Tax Manual – 'Tax Clearances' chapter; frequent speaker at conferences and seminars and regular contributor of articles on EU and international tax issues.
Personal: Born 24th November 1953. Attended Manchester University 1973-76. LLB. Leisure interests include family and outdoor life, clay and game shooting, music and skiing. Lives in Great Horkesley.

NOBLE, Nicholas
Field Fisher Waterhouse, London (020) 7861 4000
mm@ffwlaw.com
Specialisation: Partner and head of tax department. Practice covers the taxation of UK and international transactions, and in particular companies and company reorganisations, securities and transactions in securities.
Prof. Memberships: ATII.
Career: Qualified in 1979 having joined *Field Fisher Waterhouse* in 1977. Became a partner in 1984.
Publications: Co-author of 'Butterworths Company Reorganisations: Tax and Tax Planning' and 'Butterworths International Taxation of Financial Instruments and Transactions' and joint editor of and contributor to 'Butterworths Tax Planning Service'.
Personal: Born 1 October 1953. Educated at Winchester College and Durham University. Recreations include fencing, walking and reading.

NORFOLK, Edward Christopher Dominic
Norton Rose, London (020) 7283 6000
norfolkecd@nortonrose.com
Specialisation: Partner in commercial tax department. Principal area of work involves advising on tax aspects of mergers and acquisitions, corporate structuring (domestic and international), banking and oil and gas. Author of 'Taxation Treatment of Interest and Loan Relationships' (Butterworths, 3rd edn 1997). Member of editorial committee 'Practical Law for Companies'. Frequent speaker at conferences and seminars.
Prof. Memberships: Law Society (member, Revenue Law committee); Chartered Institute of Taxation (FTII), International Bar Association, International Fiscal Association, American Bar Association (Foreign Lawyers Forum of the Section of Taxation).
Career: Articled at *Longmores* in Hertford, then joined *Gabb & Co* in Abergavenny. Joined *Norton Rose* in 1975 and became a partner in 1979.
Personal: Born 8 August 1948. Attended St John's School, Leatherhead 1962-66, then Southampton University (LLB) 1966-69. Leisure pursuits include skiing and fishing. Lives Somerset and Wimbledon.

NORWOOD, Andrew
Weil, Gotshal & Manges, London (020) 7903 1000

NOWLAN, Howard
Slaughter and May, London (020) 7600 1200
howard.nowlan@slaughterandmay.com
Specialisation: Corporate tax – general, restructurings, demutualisations, transfer pricing.
Personal: MA Oxon.

OVERS, John
Berwin Leighton Paisner, London (020) 7760 1000
john.overs@berwinleightonpaisner.com
Specialisation: Partner in tax department. Principal area of practice covers corporate taxation and VAT.
Prof. Memberships: Law Society.
Career: Qualified in 1978 while at *Berwin Leighton*. Became a partner in 1981.
Personal: Born 15 August 1953. Attended Kilburn Grammar 1964-69, then St Peter's College, Oxford 1972-75. Leisure pursuits include music, photography and tennis. Lives in London.

POPPLEWELL, Nigel
Burges Salmon, Bristol (0117) 902 2782
nigel.popplewell@burges-salmon.com
Specialisation: Head of corporate tax unit, specialising in all aspects of corporate, commercial and property taxation (both direct and indirect), including cross border transactions, restructuring, inward investment, financing arrangements and property investment structure. Considerable experience in representing clients before the general and special commissioners and VAT tribunals. Further extensive experience in advising clients in investigations ranging from small scale enquiries to full-blown SCO investigations and subsequent criminal proceedings.
Prof. Memberships: Fellow, Chartered Institute of Taxation; Law Society.
Career: Natural Sciences degree at Cambridge, then seven years playing professional cricket for Somerset, teaching biology and chemistry during the winters. In 1985 retrained as a lawyer, joined *Clarke Wilmott & Clarke* in 1987, partner 1993; joined *Burges Salmon* in 1999 as a partner.

PORTER, Sue
Freshfields Bruckhaus Deringer, London (020) 7936 4000
sue.porter@freshfields.com
Specialisation: Specialises in corporate taxation and corporate tax planning, particularly in the finance/capital markets area, including structured finance, securitisation, derivatives, banking and bond issues and general corporate tax advice. Acts for banks, building societies, consumer finance, media and corporates. Contributor, Tolley's 'Tax Planning'.
Career: Qualified 1984. Partner 1992 in tax department.

PRESTON, Christopher
Watson, Farley & Williams, London (020) 7814 8000
cpreston@wfw.com
Specialisation: Partner in international tax group. Main area of practice covers leasing and asset finance/structured finance, company taxation and international tax planning. Leasing work typically involves large sophisticated transactions. Also specialises in VAT and customs duties, including both contentious and non-contentious matters and appearing before the VAT tribunal.
Prof. Memberships: Law Society (member of Revenue Law Committee and VAT & Duties Sub-Committee), VAT Practitioners Group (founder member). Fellow of the Institute of Taxation. Lectures extensively on leasing topics.
Career: Admitted 1975. Joined *Watson, Farley & Williams* as a partner in 1982. Chairman 1999-
Personal: Born 9 October 1950.

ROSE, Simon
SJ Berwin, London (020) 7533 2222
simon.rose@sjberwin.com
Specialisation: VAT, indirect and direct taxes in property and commercial transactions, private equity and offshore funds, including venture capital trusts and investment trusts; property joint ventures and fund vehicles; VAT litigation in the UK and the EC.
Prof. Memberships: Law Society, Institute of Indirect Taxation, VAT Practitioners Group, Law Society Revenue Law Committee, Law Society VAT and Duties Sub Committee.
Career: Articled *Lovell White Durrant* 1990-92. Qualified 1992. Joined *SJ Berwin & Co* 1994.
Personal: Born 1968: Exeter University 1986-89 LLB (Law); London University 1996-98 LLM (Taxation).

ROSS, Howard
Clifford Chance, London (020) 7600 1000
howard.ross@cliffordchance.com
Specialisation: Consultant, having retired as a partner in 2000. Specialises in corporate and commercial tax, international corporate tax planning, transfer pricing, oil and gas taxation and tax disputes. Continues to head up both the firm's transfer pricing group and its tax disputes.
Career: LLB (first class) LSE 1966. Qualified 1971; partner 1981.
Personal: Married with three children. Interests include tennis.

RUPAL, Yash
Linklaters, London (020) 7456 5646
yash.rupal@linklaters.com
Specialisation: Tax Department. Specialises in general corporate tax with particular emphasis on structured finance/product development, derivatives and other financial instruments. Currently on long term client secondment with *Merrill Lynch* (investment banking division) working on cross-border mergers and acquisitions and other corporate finance transactions.
Career: 1996 to date: Partner, *Linklaters*; 1988-96: Assistant solicitor, *Linklaters*; 1986-88: Articled clerk, *Linklaters*. 1995: Cambridge, LLM; 1984: East Anglia, LLB.

SANDERS, Tim
McDermott, Will & Emery, London
(020) 7577 3456
TSanders@europe.mwe.com
Specialisation: All corporate and banking related tax matters including cross-border financial structuring.
Prof. Memberships: Law Society; Fellow of the Chartered Institute of Taxation.
Career: Llandovery College (Thomas Phillips Scholar), Thames Valley GS, London University (LLB). Joined *McDermott, Will & Emery*, (MWE) in May 2000, as a Partner in the Corporate Tax Department. Head of the Corporate Tax Department at *Theodore Goddard* prior to joining *MWE*.
Publications: Co-author of Butterworths Tax Indemnities and Warranties. Contributor to Tolleys Company Law.
Personal: Born 1959. Qualified 1984. Married with 2 children. Interests (pre-children) included rowing, golf, cinema, theatre and gardening. Current (post children) interests include televised sport and watching rented videos. Lives in Epsom.

SANDISON, Francis
Freshfields Bruckhaus Deringer, London
(020) 7936 4000
francis.sandison@freshfields.com
Specialisation: Partner. Main area of practice is corporate tax and VAT. Cases have included Collard v Mining and Industrial Holdings (H.L. 1989), R v HM Treasury, ex parte Daily Mail and General Trust (ECJ 1988). Worked on SmithKline Beckman's merger with Beecham, Varity's merger with Lucas, Amoco's merger with BP and Compass's merger with Granada. Co-author of 'Whiteman on Income Tax' (3rd edition, 1988). Member, Tax Law Review Committee.
Prof. Memberships: Law Society (Member, Revenue Law Committee,) City of London Law Society (Distinguished Service Award 1997), Addington Society, VAT Practitioners' Group.
Career: Qualified in 1974. Partner 1980.
Personal: Born 1949. Educated Charterhouse and Magdalen College Oxford.

SCOTT, Tom
Linklaters, London (020) 7456 5692
tom.scott@linklaters.com
Specialisation: Tax department. Specialist in the corporate taxation aspects of domestic and cross-border mergers, acquisitions and capital restructurings with almost 20 years' experience in this area.
Career: 1990 to date: Partner, *Linklaters*; 1983-90: Assistant solicitor, *Linklaters*; 1981-83: Articled clerk, *Linklaters*; 1980: Lecturer in Law, Lincoln College, Oxford. 1979: Magdalen College, Oxford University (MA Law, First Class Honours).

SIMPSON, Mark
Hammond Suddards Edge, Leeds (0113) 243 0391
mark.simpson@hammondse.com
Specialisation: Partner and head of tax unit. Deals with the tax aspects of all types of business transactions, including corporate and asset finance and banking matters, employment tax including employee share schemes and VAT with particular reference to property transactions. Also undertakes tax planning for business proprietors (tax mitigation on investment and disposals including venture capital). Regular contributor at conferences and seminars; author of chapter in 'PLC Tax Manual'.
Prof. Memberships: Law Society, VAT Practitioners Group.
Career: Qualified 1985. With *Freshfields* until joining *Hammond Suddards Edge* in 1991.
Personal: Downing College, Cambridge 1978-82 (MA, LLB). Lives in North Yorkshire.

SINFIELD, Greg
Lovells, London (020) 7296 2000
greg.sinfield@lovells.com
Specialisation: Head of Indirect Tax. VAT and other indirect taxes (customs/excise duty, insurance premium tax, landfill tax, climate change levy) relating to commercial, financial services and property sectors. Investigation and litigation regarding indirect taxes including judicial review, condemnation proceedings and appeals to the VAT and Duties Tribunal and the higher courts and judicial reviews. Represents clients in VAT Tribunals and has appeared in the High Court, Court of Appeal and European Court of Justice as a solicitor advocate. Writes articles on VAT matters and lectures in the UK and Europe on the above.
Prof. Memberships: Law Society, VAT Practitioners' Group.
Career: Called to the Bar 1981. Customs & Excise Solicitor's Office 1983-88. *Durrant Piesse* 1988. Qualified as a Solicitor 1989. Partner *Lovells* 1993. Solicitor advocate 1994.

SMITH, Isla
Norton Rose, London (020) 7283 6000
smithim@nortonrose.com
Specialisation: Partner in taxation department. Principal area of practice is the tax aspect of financing transactions, including leasing and asset finance, banking, structured finance and securitisation, project finance and international corporate tax structuring. Other main areas of practice are tax issues relevant to the insurance sector, corporate restructuring and company acquisitions and disposals. Has dealt with a substantial number of tax based aircraft, ship, rolling-stock and project financings and cross-border asset finance transactions. Clients include banks, bank leasing companies, airlines, shipping companies, rolling stock companies, multinational groups of companies, financial intermediaries and arrangers. Author of chapters in the ICAEW 'Taxation Service' and Longman's 'Practical Tax Planning'. Speaker at a number of conferences.
Prof. Memberships: Law Society, City of London Law Society, Chartered Institute of Taxation, International Fiscal Association, International Bar Association, Finance and Leasing Association.
Career: Admitted as an Attorney of the Supreme Court of S Africa in 1974. Qualified as a solicitor in England and Wales in 1980. Became a partner at *Norton Rose* in 1985.
Personal: Born 17 February 1952. Educated at Westville Girls' High School, Natal, SA 1960-68, the University of Pretoria and the University of Natal, Durban 1969-72. Leisure pursuits include keeping up with two children, aerobics, music, tennis and skiing. Lives in Wimbledon.

STAPLETON, Mark
Dechert, London (020) 7583 5353
advice@dechertEU.com
Specialisation: Partner, tax, advises on UK and international direct and indirect taxation issues, in particular VAT. Specialises in property sector work such as commercial property developments, joint ventures and overseas aspects. Also, taxation of corporate mergers and acquisitions works and onshore and offshore investment funds.
Prof. Memberships: Associate of the institute of Taxation (1989-), National Secretary of the VAT Practitioners Group.
Career: Articles at *Turner Kenneth Brown*. Qualified in 1988. Solicitor at *Turner Kenneth Brown* until 1993. Joined *Titmuss Sainer Webb* (now *Dechert*) 1993. Appointed partner at *Dechert* 1996-date.
Publications: Has written articles for the Tax Journal and has appeared on videos for both Television Education Network and Legal Network Television. Conference speaker for Henry Stewart Conferences and Marcus Evans Conferences.
Personal: Born 1964. Educated at King Edward VI Grammar School, Chelmsford. Graduated from Nottingham University (LLB). Resides in London. Interests include tennis, football, cinema and theatre.

STAVELEY, Ben
Freshfields Bruckhaus Deringer, London
(020) 7936 4000
ben.staveley@freshfields.com
Specialisation: Specialisations include the tax treatment of capital markets, derivatives and securities transactions and the tax position of banks and other financial institutions.
Career: Education – Magdalene College, Cambridge. Became partner 1987.

STRATTON, Richard
Travers Smith Braithwaite, London
(020) 7295 3000
Specialisation: Partner in corporate tax department. Handles corporate tax matters. Specialist in funds and investment structures including onshore and offshore funds, limited partnerships, venture capital trusts, property-based structures and structured finance.
Career: Qualified in 1983. Partner at *Travers Smith Braithwaite* since 1989.
Publications: Recent articles – Venture Capital Trusts chapter in Tolleys 'Tax Plannning'; articles concerning CREST and SDRT in 'PLC' magazine.

TAILBY, Christopher
PricewaterhouseCoopers, Birmingham
(0121) 265 5000

TAYLOR, David
Freshfields Bruckhaus Deringer, London
(020) 7936 4000
david.taylor@freshfields.com
Specialisation: Partner in tax department. Main area of work is corporate tax including banking, asset and structured finance, and some corporate finance.
Prof. Memberships: Law Society, City of London Solicitors' Company.
Career: Qualified in 1984.
Personal: Born 26th July 1959. Attended Cambridge University 1977-80 and 1981-82. Lives in Hampshire.

THOMPSON, Michael
Freshfields Bruckhaus Deringer, London
(020) 7936 4000
michael.thompson@freshfields.com
Specialisation: Partner in tax department. Advises on most UK tax aspects of corporate transactions. Has a particular specialisation in oil and gas taxation and a second specialisation in structuring the financing of all types of receivable through securitisation techniques. Acts for a number of oil and gas companies and banks. Chairs the Law Society's

sub-committee on oil taxation and was the first lawyer representative for professional firms on the Steering Group of the UK Oil Industry Taxation Committee.
Prof. Memberships: Law Society. UK Oil Industry Taxation Committee.
Career: Became a partner at *Freshfields* in 1985.
Personal: Educated at Bradford Grammar School and Trinity College, Cambridge.

TOON, John
Addleshaw Booth & Co, Leeds (0113) 209 2000
jtt@addleshaw-booth.co.uk
Specialisation: To a significant degree, his practice focuses on tax advice for property transactions and capital projects for a mix of retail, developer, institutional and public sector clients. Also heavily involved in the tax aspects of a broad range of corporate and commercial transactions.
Prof. Memberships: Law Society, Chartered Institute of Taxation, VAT Practitioners Group.
Career: Qualified as a solicitor in 1991; Joined firm in January 1995.
Personal: Married with two children. Enjoys golf, theatre and gardening.

TOSH, Nial
Dickson Minto WS, Edinburgh (0131) 225 4455
nial.tosh@dmws.com
Specialisation: Experienced in a wide range of corporate tax matters, with a particular focus on mergers and acquisitions work, MBOs and employee share schemes and benefits.
Prof. Memberships: Law Society of Scotland.
Career: Joined *Dickson Minto WS* in 1994. Based in the Edinburgh and London offices.
Personal: Educated at Edinburgh University.

TOWNSEND, Peter
Cobbetts, Manchester (0161) 833 7493
peter.townsend@cobbetts.co.uk
Specialisation: Corporate tax partner and head of the tax and pensions team. Advises both public and private companies on a broad range of taxation issues including tax planning, employee share incentives, group reorganisations, disputes with taxation authorities and mergers/acquisitions.
Prof. Memberships: Law Society; Manchester Law Society; AITT; TEP; (committee member of the Manchester branch of STEP).
Career: Qualified in 1987. *Gorna & Co* 1987-88; London School of Economics; University of London (LLM Revenue Law 1989); *Slater Heelis* 1990-98 (partner 1996). Joined *Cobbetts* as a partner 1998 on *Slater Heelis* demerger. Formerly a lecturer in revenue law (part-time) at the University of Manchester (1990-94).
Personal: Leisure interests include skiing, football, tennis and walking. Lives in Sale, Cheshire.

TROUP, Edward
Simmons & Simmons, London (020) 7628 2020
edward.troup@simmons-simmons.com
Specialisation: He was head of the corporate tax group at *Simmons & Simmons* until 1995 when he was appointed Special Adviser on tax at the Treasury. He returned to the firm in 1997, since when he has advised on a wide range of corporate and financial transactions, and at the same time has remained active in tax policy, advising and commenting on numerous legislative changes, both in the UK and the EU. Corporate tax, including financing and corporate transactions. Advises on tax policy and strategic tax planning.
Prof. Memberships: Law Society (Chairman, Revenue Law Committee), Chartered Institute of Taxation, Institute for Fiscal Studies, International Fiscal Association, Chairman of British Branch.
Career: MA, MSc (Oxon).
Publications: Numerous articles in Financial Times and various professional journals.
Personal: Cinema, cycling, opera, Anglo-Saxon history, sleep.

WALTON, Miles
Allen & Overy, London (020) 7330 3605
miles.walton@allenovery.com
Specialisation: Partner in Corporate Tax Department. Deals with all aspects of corporate tax but has particular experience of bank taxation and tax-related financing transactions, including domestic and cross-border asset finance, project finance, structured finance, securitisation and capital markets.
Prof. Memberships: Law Society, Institution of Taxation (Associate).
Career: Qualified 1980. Partner *Wilde Sapte* (1994); partner *Allen & Overy* (1997).
Publications: Co-author of 'Taxation and Banking' (Sweet & Maxwell). Has written various articles for legal journals and is a regular speaker at conferences on tax-based asset finance techniques and other tax subjects.
Personal: Born 1955. Brasenose College, Oxford (MA). Leisure interests include saxophone, wine, skiing and clocks.

WARRINER, Neil
Herbert Smith, London (020) 7374 8000
Specialisation: Partner dealing with corporate tax matters generally with particular expertise in indirect taxes (VAT, stamp duty), PFI projects and the tax aspects of transactions in the energy and property industries. Major transactions include the redevelopment of the Bull Ring, Birmingham, the opening of the electricity supply market to greater competition the outsourcing PSI project for the Department of National Savings and the recommended offer by Leconport Estates for MEPC.
Prof. Memberships: The Law Society; The City of London Solicitor's Company; UKOITC.
Career: St Peter's College, Oxford 1981-84; qualified 1987; partner *Herbert Smith* 1994.
Personal: Keen golfer.

WATSON, John
Ashurst Morris Crisp, London (020) 7638 1111
Specialisation: Partner in tax department. Fund work, enterprise zones, private equity, international tax, general corporate tax, tax litigation and property tax. Legal adviser to the EZPUTA. Leads IFMA Steering Committee on UK aspects of PFPVs. Contributor to Tolleys 'Tax Planning' and other textbooks.
Career: Christ's College, Cambridge (1970-73). Exhibition and MA in mathematics. Barrister 1975-78; *Neville Russell* 1978-83. Joined *Ashurst Morris Crisp* in 1983. Partner in 1989.
Personal: Born 23 April 1951.

WHITTY, Oonagh
Latham & Watkins, London (020) 7710 1000
oonagh.whitty@lw.com
Specialisation: Partner, advises clients on tax matters and multi-jurisdictional tax transactions, as well as structured finance, high yield and mergers and acquisitions transactions. Extensive experience in tax-based financing both in financial instruments and asset finance and leasing.
Career: Qualified 1981; Partner *Watson, Farley & Williams* 1987-00. Partner *Latham & Watkins* 2000.
Personal: Born 1954; resides London; attended Imperial College, London University (BSc).

WISTOW, Michael John
Clifford Chance, London (020) 7600 1000
michael.wistow@cliffordchance.com
Specialisation: Tax partner specialising in finance transactions including securitisation, leasing, and tax-based structured and property financings.
Career: Manchester University; Trained *Clifford Chance*; partner 1997.

WONG, Etienne
Clifford Chance, London (020) 7956 0206
etienne.wong@cliffordchance.com
Specialisation: Partner specialising in VAT and other indirect taxes (such as stamp duty and IPT), e-commerce, online services and the Internet, financing transactions (including securitisations) and property transactions.
Prof. Memberships: Institute of Indirect Taxation (associate); VAT Practitioners Group (City Chapter).
Career: Uppingham School; University of Bristol. Trained at *Clifford Chance.*
Personal: Writing, film, computer graphics, music.

TELECOMMUNICATIONS

London: 810; The Regions: 812; *Profiles*: 813

RESEARCH APPROVED BY BMRB: *For this edition,* Chambers' *researchers conducted 6,552 interviews – 4,419 with law firms, 554 with barristers and 1,579 with clients.*

The validity of the research was scrutinised by BMRB International, who audited both the methodology and the results at our offices in July 2001. They interviewed Chambers' *researchers and cross-checked sample interviews. Details of the audit appear on page 7.*

LONDON

Bird & Bird (see firm details p.884) Many interviewees acknowledged that this "*superb all-round practice remains at the top of the market*" with its "*tremendous focus in the sector*" combining strengths in the commercial sector and regulatory work. Some peers typically commented, that "*strategically they've done well – the only question is where do they go next,*" as an indication that the firm has to concentrate on its successes overseas to retain its stellar profile. The Communications Group is engaged in the interconnection of systems, outsourcing of networks, submissions to regulatory authorities including competition law, and often advising on substantial corporate activity. Practice head and managing partner **David Kerr** (see p.813) has an "*unchallengeable*" position in the market, advising on both commercial and regulatory issues, as well as an envied record in international corporate transactions. Highlights for the group include acting for mainstay client BT in the outsourcing to it of Barclay's UK data network, and advising Viatel on the acquisition on the UK business of AT&T. The firm also advised American Express on a global service procurement agreement with Concert Communications. **Clients:** British Telecommunications; Video Networks; Viatel.

Clifford Chance (see firm details p.919) Thought to enjoy "*impressive international coverage,*" having now established specialised teams in its offices across the world. Running the gamut of services from regulatory issues to financing and litigation, it has also been concerned with 3G and other wireless auctions. "*Terrific*" team leader **Liz Hiester** (see p.813) has an approach that is "*to the point,*" and she is respected by peers for her "*premium corporate work.*" "*Technical guru*" **Tim Schwarz** (see p.814) is admired for his emerging markets activities, undertaking telco work in the Caribbean, Africa and the Middle East. **Joachim Fleury** recently arrived from the Amsterdam office, attracting commendation for his cross border M&A expertise. Both competitors and clients agree that he is "*a bright and capable addition to the London office.*" The firm advised Chase Manhattan as advisers to Atlantic Telecom, on its £520 million bid for First Telecom by way of a share offer. Also instructed by Crescent Wireless on complex corporate structuring and financing arrangements to secure funding for a UK 3G licence bid, and advised Deutsche Telekom on its Euro 5.4 billion acquisition of a 51% stake in debis Systemhaus GmbH. **Clients:** Financial institutions; operators; multi-nationals.

Allen & Overy (see firm details p.856) Playing on a global stage among telecommunications and cable operators, equipment and technology suppliers, governments, regulators, broadcasters and investors. It has expertise on corporate, finance, regulatory and competition activities. Researchers were informed that the recruitment of "*knowledgeable*" **Chris Watson** (see p.814) from Simmons and Simmons has balanced the loss of Clare Wright to the Hong Kong office. Practice head **Ian Ferguson** (see p.813) is admired for his finance expertise. Highlight transactions include advising Marconi on the formation of a new joint venture with Railtrack, namely 'EuroMast'. The firm also represented KPN Mobile on the US$5

TOP IN-HOUSE LAWYERS

Robert BRATBY, Head of Telecommunications, *Colt Telecommunications*

Phillip BROMWELL, General Counsel and Secretary, *BT Wireless*

Tim COWEN, Chief Counsel, Competition Law and Public Policy, *Ignite*

Dan FITZ, General Counsel, *Cable & Wireless*

Anne FLETCHER, Group General Counsel, *BT*

Chris SMEDLEY, Legal Director, *Colt Telecommunications*

Stewart WHITE, Group Public Policy Director, *Vodafone Group Services Ltd*

A *"leading light"* in the liberalised telecoms market, **Robert Bratby** continues to be highly regarded. **Phillip Bromwell**, experienced in mobile communications across Europe is *"commercial and has a solid background"*. **Tim Cowen** is considered *"a remarkable competition lawyer"* who has *"done an incredible job,"* while **Dan Fitz**, who has wider responsibilities is highly rated. **Anne Fletcher** has *"formidable organisation skills."* **Chris Smedley** is well renowned as *"an excellent all-round lawyer."* **Stuart White** at Vodafone is recognised as a long-standing figure in the industry; *"knows the business."*

In-House lawyers profiles: p.1193

	TELECOMMUNICATIONS • London	Ptnrs	Assts
1	Bird & Bird	28	60
	Clifford Chance	13	n/a
2	Allen & Overy	8	26
	Linklaters	16	36
	Olswang	10	29
3	Baker & McKenzie	14	30
	Denton Wilde Sapte	13	16
4	Ashurst Morris Crisp	11	21
	Field Fisher Waterhouse	6	12
	Freshfields Bruckhaus Deringer	n/a	n/a
	Simmons & Simmons	11	17
	Taylor Joynson Garrett	15	n/a
5	Charles Russell	7	13
	Norton Rose	11	10
	Osborne Clarke	10	10
	Rowe & Maw	n/a	n/a
	Steptoe & Johnson Rakisons	n/a	n/a

	LEADING INDIVIDUALS	
1	**HIESTER Elizabeth** Clifford Chance	**LONG Colin** Olswang
2	**KERR David** Bird & Bird	**MERCER Edward** Taylor Joynson Garrett
	SCHWARZ Tim Clifford Chance	**STRIVENS Peter** Baker & McKenzie
	WATSON Chris Allen & Overy	**WHEADON Tom** Simmons & Simmons
3	**BALLARD Tony** Field Fisher Waterhouse	**DURIE Robyn** Linklaters
	EDWARDS John Taylor Joynson Garrett	**HIGHAM Nicholas** Denton Wilde Sapte
	LISTON Stephanie McDermott, Will & Emery	**NICHOLSON Kim** Olswang
4	**DICKINSON Peter** Rowe & Maw	**FERGUSON Ian** Allen & Overy
	FLEURY Joachim Clifford Chance	**MONCREIFFE Mark** Charles Russell
	PREISKEL Daniel Steptoe & Johnson Rakisons	**WILLIAMS Rhys** Simmons & Simmons

This book is the product of 6,552 1/2 hour interviews. See p.7 for BMRB audit.

Within each band, firms are listed alphabetically. *See individuals' profiles p.813*

billion sale of 15% of its share capital to NTT DoCoMo, and advised Cable & Wireless on the US$38 billion takeover bid by Pacific Century CyberWorks for Cable & Wireless HKT, Hong Kong's major telecoms operator. **Clients:** Cable & Wireless; Radio Communications Agency; KPN Telecom.

Linklaters (see firm details p.1042) The firm's wider communications-oriented practice has continued to grow over the last year, and undertakes self-standing commercial and regulatory telecoms work, as well as providing support to other departments on related aspects such as project finance and securities matters. The firm's relationship with BT and Vodafone is once more at the heart of its profile in this sector, with peers typically commending its corporate and anti-trust activity. *"A forceful personality,"* **Robyn Durie** (see p.813) is rated for her depth of regulatory knowledge and involvement in the UK 3G auction. The firm is currently advising World Online in the procurement of a proposed £50 million voice-over IP network, and acting for Citylink Telecommunications on a PFI deal enabling it to operate the transmission and radio networks of London Underground, which also involved obtaining the requisite telecoms and radio frequency licences. **Clients:** Vodafone AirTouch; Freeserve; Bell Canada.

Olswang (see firm details p.1084) Rivals acknowledge that "*its star is remarkably ascendant,*" having successfully "*created a differentiated offering*" with a "*genuine telecoms practice grown out of its technology focus.*" The firm operates with a respected client base including major telcos, ISPs, mobile operators, virtual operators, broadband network owners, funders, VC investors and regulatory agencies. Its anti-trust activity has received particular endorsement from our interviewees this year. "*Pre-eminent*" **Colin Long** (see p.813) is an admired regulatory figure and is thought to be key to attracting clients of the calibre of WorldCom. **Kim Nicholson** (see p.814) is thought to be the blueprint for those wishing to succeed in the crossover of a converging technology market. The group advised WorldCom on its UK third generation mobile licence auction bid and acted for US multi-national Enron Broadband on broadband content delivery. Also advised Thus plc on the UK local loop unbundling. **Clients:** Enron Broadband; Genuity; OnCue Telecommunications; Thus; WorldCom.

Baker & McKenzie (see firm details p.868) Has displayed expertise in negotiating the building out of networks throughout Europe. Many of its lawyers are trained in both telecommunications and IT law, keeping it at the cutting-edge of convergence. "*Focused*" practice head **Peter Strivens** (see p.814) is judged a "*real facilitator*" and is involved in significant regulatory litigation, privatisation and re-regulation projects across Eastern Europe. The firm acted for France Telecom on the US$4.3 billion sale of 35% of the Polish national telecoms provider to a consortium of France Telecom and Kulczyk Holding SA, the large privatisation and M&A transaction to date. It provided advice on the build-out of pan-European telecommunications work, including assignments for COLT, Pangea, Tycom Networks and Metromedia Fiber Networks. In addition, the firm acted for Nortel on the proposed outsourcing to it of the voice network of Cable & Wireless and the upgrading of that network to a VOIP network. **Clients:** AOL; COLT; France Telecom; Orange; Pangea; Saudi Telecom Company; Telecom Egypt; Teledesic; Telstra.

Denton Wilde Sapte (see firm details p.939) Particularly active this year in 3G/UTMS network financings, telecom projects and vendor finance. On the regulatory side, the firm has seen growth in the mobile sector, securing 3G mobile work in a number of European countries, and has continued its move into telecoms-related property work. International pursuits have intensified and the firm has now advised on the regulatory regimes of 20 jurisdictions and landed new international cable systems in a dozen countries. Admired by peers for its satellite practice, interviewees comment that "*they tend to be writing laws and outline cases rather than doing big corporate transactions or privatisation work.*" **Nick Higham** (see p.813) dominates the regulatory field. The firm handled the 3G/UTMS financing for Bouygues Telecom (France) and acted for ECI Telecom (Israel) on a number of equipment vendor financings during the past year, including Atlantic Telecom, Globe Telecom and Viatel. It also acted for NatWest in the bridge financing of Patientline Holdings assisting its IPO, and advised the issuer in the Pacific Century US$200 million private bond issue. **Clients:** Crown Castle; Energis; Fibernet; States of Guernsey.

Ashurst Morris Crisp (see firm details p.866) Encompassing M&A, financing, regulatory, competition and commercial law. The firm has expertise in satellite matters, as well as increased involvement in telecoms-related restructurings. Known in the market for its "*broad corporate practice,*" which counts Kingston Communications as a key client. Highlights have included advising Centrica on its £58 million acquisition of One.Tel, the UK's biggest indirect access telecoms company. The firm also advised BT on the corporatisation of the inter-governmental organisation EUTELSAT, and advised Thus plc on its major strategic multi-year alliance with Apple, the US computer maker. **Clients:** Deutsche Telekom; Atlantic Telecom Communications; DirectNet Telecommunications (UK).

Field Fisher Waterhouse (see firm details p.957) Increasingly active in competition, planning and litigation matters arising from the sector. The firm recently won a hotly contested beauty parade to represent the industry in local loop unbundling. Described by clients as a "*high quality, robust if small practice,*" dedicated to the sector and with a niche in property arrangements for a number of operators. Peers endorse its infrastructure activities and agree that its success "*revolves around*" **Tony Ballard** (see p.813), who is "*incredibly academic and skilled in the regulatory sphere.*" On the infrastructure side, the firm recently handled the property aspects of the acquisition by One2One of the Pocket Phone Shop involving more than 160 properties. On the corporate front, the firm continues to advise RSL Communications, a major US long distance operator, on its European acquisition program. It secured instructions from OFTEL under the Telecommunications Act to oblige BT to comply with its licence obligations concerning its calls and access product. **Clients:** COLT; Dexterus; Level 3 Communications; One2One Personal Communications. Orange; 360 Networks.

Freshfields Bruckhaus Deringer (see firm details p.965) In the past year the firm has provided advice on M&A and joint ventures, IPOs and private equity investments, contracts agreements and competition issues. Researchers were informed that the practice is "*corporate-oriented,*" providing "*heavyweight advice to telcos.*" Many practitioners praised the resources provided by its lawyers in Germany. Highlights from the past year include acting for Wind Telecommunicazioni on the Euro 2.4 billion facility for its GSM and fixed line services and the subsequent Euro 3.3 billion facility for its successful UMTS bid, one of the first UMTS project facilities completed and funded in the European market. The firm also acted for Hutchison Whampoa on all aspects of its European 3G strategy and advised the joint global co-ordinators in the IPO of Orange. Also acted for Virgin Mobile on its groundbreaking VNO project financing. **Clients:** Modern Times Group; Telewest Communications; MCI Worldcom.

Simmons & Simmons (see firm details p.1132) Continues to advise clients on regulatory issues in the UK and Europe, providing corporate, banking, litigation and competition support to a growing number of large telecoms operators seeking to raise funds or enter several markets simultaneously. Peers commented that the firm has had success "*striving for more of a European presence.*" "*Largely driving the practice*" is **Tom Wheadon** (see p.814), thought to have an "*excellent understanding of what's going on in the industry.*" The group advised Pacific Century CyberWorks on its £24.3 billion acquisition of Cable &Wireless HKT, the largest ever Asian merger outside Japan and the first leveraged acquisition funding for a quoted Hong Kong company. It also advised on the multi-billion dollar strategic alliance of PCCW with Telstra Corporation, and acted for WorldCom International in its successful application to OFTEL to receive flat rate internet access as an interconnect service from BT. **Rhys Williams** (see p.814) is "*on the ball*" and has "*good attention to detail.*" **Clients:** Excel Communications; First Telecom Group; FirstMark Communications; FLAG Atlantic UK; Global Telesystems Group; IX Europe; Mitsubishi Corporation; Nokia Ventures; One2One Communications; Telewest Communications; Wave European Technologies.

Taylor Joynson Garrett (see firm details p.1150) The firm has expertise in the regulatory, corporate and finance spheres of the industry and advises a range of clients from start-ups to established corporations. It has a particular niche in assisting operators to pilot through the use of new technologies, from IP voice to 40 GHz wireless local loop. Has expanded its telecoms competition and European law practice over the past year. Clients and competitors agree that it fields "*quite a bit of prowess across the board with the combined firepower of Mercer and Edwards.*" **Ted Mercer** is endorsed for his regulatory expertise and his funder client base, while **John Edwards** is seen more on the corporate side, acting for operators and equipment manufacturers. The group acted in the funding of the Isle of Wight Cable and Telephone Company, and advised GN Comtext on the sale of its global non-maritime telex-filing business to Swift Telecommunications. Also retained by a number of the founder shareholders in the sale of Aerial Group to SpectraSite Transco Communications. **Clients:** IDT; Iaxis; Convergence Group.

Charles Russell (see firm details p.912) Described by peers as "*one of the few medium-sized firms to have a keen focus on the communications area,*" much of its profile lies with its work for Cable & Wireless. Active in corporate and commercial transactions including outsourcings, the firm also displays expertise in its knowledge of regulatory issues, dispute resolution and property matters. Practice head **Mark Moncreiffe** (see p.814) is seen to successfully "*cross over between telecoms and media work*" utilising the inherent strengths of the firm and the growing convergence within the industry. Major matters from the past year include representing NTL Mobile in its application for a UMTS licence, and successfully defending Cable & Wireless in an injunction application brought by Excell in Scotland, concerning outsourcing of call centre management. The firm also acted for Scoot.com on its acquisition of Loot. **Clients:** Bulldog Communications; Cable & Wireless; Inquam; MLL Telecom; ntl Group; Scoot.com.

Norton Rose (see firm details p.1082) Acting across the range of telecoms matters with clients in the fixed cable, wireless and broadcasting sector, as well as ISP providers, equipment manufacturers and suppliers. The team has extensive expertise in financing, regulatory and commercial matters including M&A transactions throughout Europe. Both clients and competitors agree that the firm has "*good industry knowledge,*" and is a respected force with its relationship to France Telecom. The group advised the latter on the £25.1 billion acquisition of Orange and also acted for Dataflex Holdings on its LSE flotation and subsequent acquisition of Telephony Experts. In addition, the firm advised on the flotation and subsequent expansion of Redbus Interhouse, which operates neutral internet co-location facilities. **Clients:** Completel; Dataflex Holdings; Ericsson; Flagtelecom; France Telecom; Nortel; Siemens.

Osborne Clarke (see firm details p.1086) While this firm has traditionally represented a number of US telecoms companies in the UK, peers acknowledge that this year its "*profile has gone through the roof.*" In that time the firm has undertaken substantial work for clients such as Viatel, Virgin, Vodafone, Sonera Zed, Station 12 and General Motors. The group acted for Redstone Telecom on all its corporate and commercial matters, including rights issues valued at £125 million and an extensive acquisitions programme (purchase of DIALnet, Isomatrix UK, and Interglobal Telecommunications). Following the rescue from bankruptcy of ICO Global Communications by Telesdic, the firm now advises the newly formed ICO-Telesdic on its corporate and commercial matters, with deal values in the range of US$1 billion. The firm has also been advising on a £3 billion global telecoms outsourcing project on behalf of a service provider. **Clients:** ACC Long Distance UK; Cable & Wireless; General Motors; Nortel; Onstar; World Telecom; Yahoo!

Rowe & Maw (see firm details p.1113) Heavily involved in the construction, rollout and operation of the pan-European dark fibre network, the firm also offers specialist advice in procurement and regulatory work. Competitors regard **Peter Dickinson** (see p.813) as the "*linchpin*" of the practice, particularly for his work leading the £1 billion "Project Apollo" for Cable & Wireless, creating the world's most advanced internet protocol transatlantic cable. The firm was also involved in the Interoute Communications Group's I-21 Network and Telia International Carrier AB's Viking Network, both of which involved the acquisition or sale of indefeasible rights of use, in terrestrial and submarine ducts and dark fibre, alongside the sale and purchase of wavelengths and other managed services. **Clients:** Cable & Wireless Communications; EMI Group; Inmarsat Limited; Metromedia; Reuters Group; Telia AB.

Steptoe & Johnson Rakisons (see firm details p.1142) The firm has a niche in obtaining licences for new operators throughout the world, in addition to obtaining indirect access codes, negotiating interconnection agreements and advising on a range of corporate and commercial issues. It also receives instructions from both service providers and multi-national users in outsourcing issues. Peers commend the firm's capability to field lawyers from different jurisdictions, all based in the London office, and judge it to be "*highly successful in licensing work.*" Head of practice **Danny Preiskel** (see p.814) is recommended for his "*licensing know-how.*"

Other Notable Practitioners **Stephanie Liston** (see p.813) of **McDermott Will & Emery** continues to be rated for her corporate and regulatory advice in the sector, with strength in cross border activities.

THE REGIONS

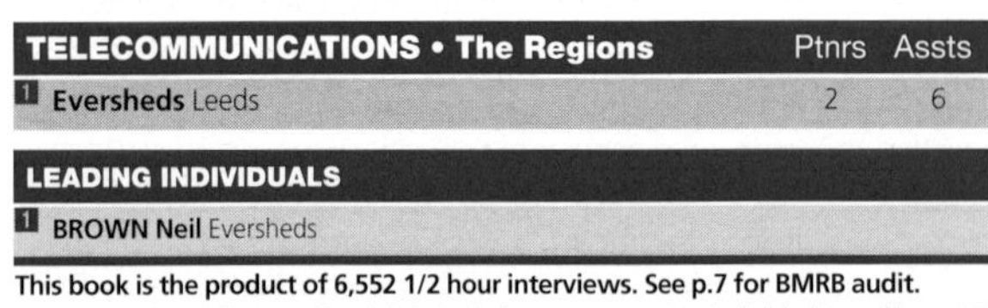

TELECOMMUNICATIONS • The Regions	Ptnrs	Assts
1 **Eversheds** Leeds	2	6

LEADING INDIVIDUALS
1 **BROWN Neil** Eversheds

This book is the product of 6,552 1/2 hour interviews. See p.7 for BMRB audit.

Within each band, firms are listed alphabetically. *See individuals' profiles p.813*

Eversheds (see firm details p.952) "*Still the leading regional practice by a country mile*" and with an increasingly national presence in the sector, the firm's Leeds office boasts a strong corporate, regulatory and infrastructure practice. With an "*ambitious approach to securing decent work,*" **Neil Brown** (see p.813) is respected as the firm's standout practitioner. It acted for the British Waterways Board in the £80 million restructuring of the Fibreway joint venture with Marconi and advised SpectraSite Communications on its £260 million joint venture with BG Transco to develop a mobile communications network infrastructure business. The group also advised satellite services company Inmarsat on a range of commercial and regulatory issues arising from its plans to launch a range of innovative services. **Clients:** British Waterways Board; Inmarsat; Torch Communications; Spectra Site Communications; Via Networks.

LEADERS IN TELECOMMUNICATIONS

BALLARD, Tony
Field Fisher Waterhouse, London (020) 7861 4000
jab@ffwlaw.com
Specialisation: Main area of practice is communications with a recent focus on network platforms at the leading edge of recent developments in this field; including telecommunications, broadcasting and IT; advising both established operators and new entrants on the new technologies. Other areas of practice include television network and service providers in both public and private sectors, including established broadcasters and new entrants in the satellite, cable, multimedia and general major feature film production and distribution, competition, copyright and administrative law. Arbitrator on International Arbitration panel of American Film Marketing Association and trained mediator for alternative dispute resolution. Frequent speaker at conferences.
Prof. Memberships: International Bar Association, Communication Lawyers Association, Royal Television Society and Chairman of UK branch of European Centre for Space Law.
Career: Qualified in 1974, having joined *Allison & Humphreys* in 1971. Became a Partner in 1975. Merged with *Field Fisher Waterhouse* in 1998.
Personal: Born 21st August 1945. MA (Cantab) 1964-68. Fellow of Royal Anthropological Institute. Leisure interests include astrophysics and painting. Lives in London and Suffolk.

BROWN, Neil
Eversheds, Leeds (0113) 243 0391
neilbrown@eversheds.com
Specialisation: Partner. Head of *Eversheds* Telecoms and TMT Groups. Heads team of eight full time specialist telecom lawyers. The team has a leading reputation in regulatory advice, industry specific commercial work, network infrastructure development and increasingly in corporate and international projects. Clients include Kingston Communications, SpectraSite, Project Telecom, Telia, Inmarsat, IMS, Landwell.
Prof. Memberships: International Bar Association (Communications Utilities Committee).
Career: Joined *Breeze & Wyles*, Hertford 1981. Qualified 1983 and left to join *Watson Burton*, Newcastle. Moved to *Eversheds* in 1986. Partner 1988.
Personal: Born 17th January 1957. Attended Richard Hale, Hertford 1969-77, then Warwick University 1977-80. Leisure pursuits include supporting Newcastle United FC; performing magic; the theatre. Speaks Spanish and French. Lives near Ilkley.

DICKINSON, Peter
Rowe & Maw, London (020) 7782 8747
pdickinson@roweandmaw.com
Specialisation: Partner, corporate department. Head of communications group. Main area of practice is corporate and commercial work involving transactions in the telecommunications and related converging industries, including mergers and acquisitions, disposals, joint ventures, network infrastructure projects and outsourcing.
Prof. Memberships: Law Society.
Career: Articled clerk *Clifford Turner* 1986-88; assistant solicitor 1988-93; assistant solicitor *Lovell White Durrant* 1993-94; senior legal adviser Mercury Communications Limited 1994-95; *Rowe & Maw* 1995 to present.
Personal: Born 24th March 1962. Educated at Wells Cathedral School and Southampton University (LLB Hons). Leisure activities include sailing, cycling and skiing. Married to Sarah, they have three children, Ben, Ellen and James. Lives in London.

DURIE, Robyn
Linklaters, London (020) 7456 3256
robyn.durie@linklaters.com
Specialisation: Wide experience in broadcasting, telecommunications, both commercial and regulatory, and intellectual property, e-commerce and information technology work over the past 15 years.
Career: Partner corporate department, information technology, communications group since 1990. Qualified 1977 Australia; 1987 England & Wales.

EDWARDS, John
Taylor Joynson Garrett, London (020) 7300 7000

FERGUSON, Ian
Allen & Overy, London (020) 7330 3038
ian.ferguson@allenovery.com
Specialisation: Partner in the Communications, Media and Technology Group specialising in telecommunications advising internationally on strategic investments, privatisations, mergers and acquisitions, joint ventures, regulation and various types of commercial contracts in the telecommunications sector, equipment and services; he has substantial experience of telecoms privatisations, acting for both governments and investors, having advised on privatisations in Austria, the Czech Republic, Belgium, Bulgaria, South Africa, Turkey, Estonia, Jordan and Pakistan; he has been involved in telecommunications investments and ventures in Europe as well as in Argentina, Brazil, India, Israel, Malaysia and Japan; he has also advised on network infrastructure and services projects.
Prof. Memberships: International Bar Association; ICC Committees on E-Commerce and on Telecommunications & Information Technologies.
Career: Articled *Allen & Overy*, qualified 1985, Partner 1992.
Personal: Educated at Southampton University 1982 (LLB). Born 1959.

FLEURY, Joachim
Clifford Chance, London (020) 7600 1000

HIESTER, Elizabeth
Clifford Chance, London (020) 7600 1000
elizabeth.hiester@cliffordchance.com
Specialisation: Partner in corporate practice area with primary responsibility for telecommunications, computer, IT and media industry practice group, focusing on international and domestic projects, commercial contracts, joint ventures, regulatory advice and antitrust and intellectual property law issues pertinent to those sectors.
Prof. Memberships: Member of Law Society of England and Wales; International Bar Association Communication Sub-Committee; America Bar Association; International Telecommunications Committee; Telecommunications Industry Association; Royal Television Society; INTUG; International Institute of Communications.
Career: Manchester (LLB 1st class Hons 1973); Amsterdam (Diploma in European Integration 1974). Articled *Clifford Chance* 1980-1982; qualified 1982; lecturer in law University of Kent 1974-1980; solicitor *Clifford Chance* 1982-1988; partner since 1988; author of 'Telecommunications' in 'UK and EC Competition Law Encyclopaedia' (Butterworth).
Personal: Music. Born 1952; resides Canterbury.

HIGHAM, Nicholas
Denton Wilde Sapte, London (020) 7242 1212
nach@dentonwildesapte.com
Specialisation: Main areas of practice are telecommunications, internet and digital media. Work includes telecoms regulation (19 countries), privatisations (five countries), market entry and acquisitions, network services and interconnection, internet start-ups, content and netcasting, data protection, systems development and outsourcing. Regular lecturer on telecommunications and internet.

KERR, David
Bird & Bird, London (020) 7415 6000
Specialisation: Joint Head of Communications Group and CEO of firm. Main area of practice is corporate and commercial work involving deals in the telecommunications, e-commerce, media and information technology sectors. Has extensive experience of major transactions in these areas, including acquisitions, joint ventures, project finance, privatisation and outsourcing agreements. Frequent speaker at conferences on the global issues relating to telecommunications, e-commerce and information technology.
Prof. Memberships: IBA, Law Society.
Career: Qualified in 1985. Joined *Bird & Bird* in 1985, becoming a Partner in 1987.
Personal: Born 1960. Attended Jesus College, Cambridge (MA Hons, 1982). Lives in London.

LISTON, Stephanie
McDermott, Will & Emery, London
(020) 7577 6985
sliston@europe.mwe.com
Specialisation: Partner, Corporate Department, leads the firm's European Communications and Technology Practice. Communications work includes advising upon, drafting and negotiating communications related contracts and commercial transactions and providing EC and UK regulatory advice in connection with telecommunications and broadcasting activities. Regular guest speaker.
Career: Qualified in England (1994); District of Columbia (1988) and Texas (1985). Associate with *Fulbright & Jaworski*, in London, Houston, Texas, and Washington, D.C. 1984-89. Senior attorney with MCI 1990-92. *Freshfields'* Company Department 1992-95. *Baker & McKenzie*, London 1995-1999. Joined *McDermott, Will & Emery* in 1999.
Personal: Born 15th March 1958. Attended The Colorado College (BA in History/Political Science 1980), University of San Diego Law School 1980-82 and University of Notre Dame London Law Centre 1982-83 (Juris Doctor 1983). Attended Trinity Hall, Cambridge University (LL.M. in English Law – 1st Class – 1984). Lives in Hampstead.

LONG, Colin
Olswang, London (020) 7208 8888
cdl@olswang.com
Specialisation: Partner and joint head of telecommunications in the UK law firm *Olswang*. Has guided many of the world's leading telecommunication com-

panies over the years in a variety of deals related to fixed, mobile and satellite-based services. Work encompasses regulation and competition law, commercial legal issues, corporate transactions including privatisations, M&A, joint ventures and start-ups, as well as development funding in the communications, IT and general hi-tech sectors. Recent work includes acting for a bidder on the UK third generation mobile auction, advising an industry group of operators on DSL services, acting for a successful bidder in the UK broadband fixed wireless auction, advising on a global satellite-based Internet service and advising various UK public operators on competition-related issues and proceedings before the regulator OFTEL. He is author of the leading text-book 'Global Telecommunications Law and Practice' (pub. Sweet & Maxwell), a guest speaker at numerous conferences and a frequent writer of articles in the telecoms press.
Prof. Memberships: Former chairman of the Communications Law Committee of the International Bar Association and a member of the UK Parliamentary Information Technology Committee.
Career: A graduate of Bristol Unversity, trained and worked at *Clifford Turner* before becoming a partner at *Bird & Bird* and later *Coudert Brothers*, before moving to *Olswang* in 1998.

MERCER, Edward
Taylor Joynson Garrett, London (020) 7300 7000

MONCREIFFE, Mark
Charles Russell, London (020) 7203 5113
markm@cr-law.co.uk
Specialisation: Partner in company/commercial department, Head of media and communications group. Main area of specialisation is the corporate commercial and regulatory aspects of telecommunications, both in the UK and internationally. He heads *Charles Russell's* Telecommunications Unit which promotes industry focused advice to clients in the telecommunications field. He speaks at conferences and contributes specialist articles to journals.
Prof. Memberships: Law Society.
Career: Qualified in 1978. Joined *Charles Russell* in 1984 and became a partner in 1985.
Personal: Born 23rd March 1953. Attended Uppingham School 1966-70, Queens' College, Cambridge, 1971-4, and Université Libre de Bruxelles 1974-75, (licence en droit européen). Leisure interests include varied outdoor sports

NICHOLSON, Kim
Olswang, London (020) 7208 8731
kan@olswang.com
Specialisation: Partner and head of IT and telecommunications unit. Practice covers on the corporate side: corporate finance, venture capital, syndicated equity funding, mergers and acquisitions, IPOs, takeovers, all within the online, communications and technology industries; on the commercial side: contracts for exploitation of products, licensing, content deals, distribution exploitation and carriage deals in or related to the online and communications industry for clients ranging from multinational plcs through to internet start-ups, for example Thus plc, NetStore plc, Sportal International Limited, Freeserve plc, Raw Communications Hons Limited, UUNet Technologies Inc and Motorola Inc.
Career: Qualified 1985. Joined *Olswang* as a partner in 1993.
Personal: Born 30 November 1960. Educated at Birmingham University and College of Law, London. Interests include opera, music, hill walking, art and antiques.

PREISKEL, Daniel
Steptoe & Johnson Rakisons, London (020) 7367 8000
Specialisation: Regulatory and commercial aspects of fixed and wireless international telecommunications, strategic sales, acquisitions and privatisations of operators as well as e-commerce and IT. Particular expertise on European regulatory and commercial developments and strategic knowledge of the telecoms market. Speaks seven languages and has successfully negotiated with regulators, PTTs and alternative operators in numerous juridictions and has achieved regulatory breakthroughs on behalf of various clients. Typical clients range from PTTs, RBOCs and NASDAQ telecoms operators, MVNOs, a leading mobile handset provider, as well as more innovative media companies, operators and ISPs. He led a large international team advising Dynegy on the most significant European telecoms work-out to date when it acquired Iaxis. Previously worked as an investment banker in Morgan Grenfell's telecoms team advising telecoms privatisations, M&A and financing, which has helped in providing the commercially focused legal advice for which he is known.
Prof. Memberships: Federal Communications Bar Association, ECTA British Israel Law Association.
Career: Qualified in 1991 at *SJ Berwin*; joined *Rakisons* (now *Steptoe & Johnson Rakisons*) in February 1996 from Morgan Grenfell with partnership in summer 1997.
Personal: Born 1965. MA Hons in law from Jesus College, Cambridge; passed the Securities and Futures Authority exams in 1994. Interests include languages, travel, opera and football.

SCHWARZ, Tim
Clifford Chance, London (020) 7600 1000
tim.schwarz@cliffordchance.com
Specialisation: Partner focusing on international telecoms, internet posts and IT.
Career: Oxford University (BA Jurisprudence); Oxford University (BCL); Université de Bruxelles (Première et deuxième licences en droit européen); trainee lawyer *Clifford Chance* 1987-89; seconded to OFTEL's Legal Department 1989-90; associate *Clifford Chance* 1989-95; main telecoms lawyer World Bank legal department 1995-97; partner *Clifford Chance* 1997.

STRIVENS, Peter
Baker & McKenzie, London (020) 7919 1000
peter.strivens@bakernet.com
Specialisation: Partner and head of the telecommunications practice group. Work includes advice on licensing and regulatory issues in the UK and other jurisdictions, investments and joint ventures in the telecommunications industry and advising on a wide range of industry issues, including contractual negotiations and disputes. Has extensive experience of cross-border transactions and telecoms privatisations. Gives frequent conference presentations on telecommunications issues and has written the UK and International Chapters of 'Baker & McKenzie – Telecommunications Laws in Europe', Butterworths 1998. Qualified in 1984 with *Baker & McKenzie* and became a partner in 1990.
Career: Educated at St Johns College, Johannesburg, University of Witwatersrand (1971-75) and Balliol College, Oxford (1979-81).
Personal: Born 15 December 1954. Leisure activities include painting, tennis and looking after a growing family. Lives in London.

WATSON, Chris
Allen & Overy, London (020) 7330 3000
chris.watson@allenovery.com
Specialisation: He specialises in telecommunications, particularly competition and EU law issues and questions of regulatory policy. He has advised on projects and issues throughout Europe, in India, the Lebanon and elsewhere in the world. He speaks a number of European languages. He is recognised as a leading individual in the telecommunications law field.
Prof. Memberships: Solicitor, England and Wales. Avocat à la Cour (Member of Paris Bar).
Career: Admitted as a solicitor in 1983; partner *Simmons & Simmons* 1988; admitted as an Avocat à la cour Paris 1993; partner, communications, Media and Technology Group, *Allen & Overy*, 2000.
Publications: He is joint author of 'Telecommunications: the EU Law' and general editor of Sweet and Maxwell's Encyclopedia of European Telecommunications Laws.
Personal: Leisure interests: Chablis growing; fly fishing; bird watching; hockey (Honourable Artillery Company); cricket; music and books. Education: Marlborough College 1970-74, New College Oxford 1976-79; MA (Modern Languages); College of Law, Guildford 1980 (CPE) and 1981 Law Society Finals. Languages: French, German, Italian (all spoken), Spanish, Portuguese, Russian (reading only).

WHEADON, Tom
Simmons & Simmons, London (020) 7825 3603
tom.wheadon@simmons-simmons.com
Specialisation: Specialisation is in the law, regulation and policy of telecommunications.
Prof. Memberships: Law Society and International Bar Association.
Career: Southampton University, Guildford Law School, admitted as a solicitor in England and Wales in 1989. 1987-1989: Trainee solicitor, *Ashurst Morris Crisp.* 1989-1995: Solicitor, *Ashurst Morris Crisp.* 1995-1996: Corporate and regulatory affairs solicitor, Videotron Corporation Ltd. 1996 to date: Partner, communications practice at *Simmons & Simmons.*
Personal: Married to Kate with three sons, Fred, Henry and George.

WILLIAMS, Rhys
Simmons & Simmons, London (020) 7628 2020
rhys.williams@simmons-simmons.com
Specialisation: Main area of practice is in commercial and regulatory aspects of communications law in the UK and internationally, in particular in respect of licensing, interconnection, and submarine cable and pan-European construction/infrastructure issues. Contributor to 'Telecommunications: The EU Law' (Palladian Law Publishing, 1999).
Prof. Memberships: Law Society.
Career: Educated at Emmanuel College, Cambridge; Manchester University and University of North Carolina, Chapel Hill.
Personal: Born 29 October 1965. Married. Interests include mountaineering, playing and listening to blues, American literature; Welsh rugby.

TRANSPORT

RESEARCH APPROVED BY BMRB: *For this edition,* Chambers' *researchers conducted 6,552 interviews – 4,419 with law firms, 554 with barristers and 1,579 with clients.*

The validity of the research was scrutinised by BMRB International, who audited both the methodology and the results at our offices in July 2001. They interviewed Chambers' *researchers and cross-checked sample interviews. Details of the audit appear on page 7.*

OVERVIEW:

Carriage/Commercial: A specialised area of law seeing distinct change, it is increasingly international, with operators growing in size as greater rationalisation takes place. The knock-on effect of the fuel crisis has led many companies to consolidate and become more aware of risk management issues. Cases are now sent to mediation as a matter of course, with both ADR and CMR well established.

Regulatory: A heavily regulated area, which involves over 90% of all domestic freight, the industry is going through a tough period. The 1999 Immigration and Asylum Act ensures that lorry drivers coming into Britain are fined £2,000 for each clandestine immigrant found in their vehicle, unless they follow a strenuous code of practice. A new breed of tough traffic commissioner has now settled into its role, and has overseen an increase in public inquiries. The Vehicle Inspectorate is carrying out more enforcement work and the the influence of the Health and Safety Executive has also increased. The industry is now bracing itself for the impact of the Working Time Regulations on mobile workers.

Rail: The first round of franchises is coming to an end, with negotiations already underway on the next tranche of re-franchising. There is a noted shift in Government requirements; bidders are now required to provide a large capital investment into the infrastructure, alongside well-defined plans leading to service improvements. The market has seen consolidation, as the big players snap up an even greater share.

ROAD: CARRIAGE / COMMERCIAL

ROAD: CARRIAGE/COMMERCIAL • Nationwide	Ptnrs	Assts
1 **Hill Dickinson** London, Manchester	3	1
Holmes Hardingham London	4	5
2 **Waltons & Morse** London	3	4
3 **Clyde & Co** London, Guildford	6	15
Davies Arnold Cooper London	1	1
Davies Lavery London	1	n/a
DLA London, Liverpool, Manchester	6	9
John Weston & Co Felixstowe	2	1
4 **Andrew M Jackson & Co** Hull	1	1
Prettys Ipswich	2	2

LEADING INDIVIDUALS	
1 **HARDINGHAM Adrian** Holmes Hardingham	**KNIGHT Tim** Holmes Hardingham
MARSHALL Julia Hill Dickinson	**MESSENT Andrew** Holmes Hardingham
2 **DUNN Chris** Waltons & Morse	**JACKSON Peter** Hill Dickinson
PYSDEN Kay Davies Lavery	**SILK Ken** Davies Arnold Cooper
3 **HILL Martin** DLA	**HOBBS Jane** Holmes Hardingham
WESTON John John Weston & Co	
4 **ARMSTRONG Stuart** Hill Dickinson	**HENNING Caroline** DLA
MELBOURNE William Clyde & Co	**SHARP Roland** Prettys
THOMAS Tony Clyde & Co	**WARD Dominic** Andrew M Jackson & Co

This book is the product of 6,552 1/2-hour interviews. See p.7 for BMRB audit.
Within each band, firms are listed alphabetically. *See individuals' profiles p.819*

Hill Dickinson (see firm details p.996) Operating from a strong base of three offices, the team includes the *"excellent, feisty and good negotiator"* **Julia Marshall** (see p.821) and the *"good pragmatic realistic and sensible,"* **Peter Jackson.** (see p.821) Peers hold this *"excellent"* firm in high regard, characterising the group as *"easy to deal with – they know their stuff."* Renowned for its international intermodal transit work, the firm also deals with insurance and commercial contracts. The team has recently been bolstered by the addition of **Stuart Armstrong** (see p.819) from Berrymans Lace Mawer.

Holmes Hardingham (see firm details p.1000) *"Packed with good people,"* the firm is *"strong, sensible and good to deal with."* **Andrew Messent** (see p.821) is both *"pragmatic and academic,"* although *"you won't take points from him, there is no posturing."* The *"excellent"* **Adrian Hardingham** (see p.820) is *"a good litigator,"* **Jane Hobbs** (see p.820) is endorsed by peers as a *"thoughtful"* practitioner, while **Tim Knight** (see p.821) also receives strong personal recommendation. Often advising insurers on contentious cases, the group specialises in warehousing, freight forwarding, domestic road haulage work, CMR and insurance cover queries. Highlights included bringing the first judicial review under the Immigration Act 1999.

Waltons & Morse (see firm details p.1173) Bringing a *"highly commercial"* approach to the table, much of the firm's workload involves acting for insurers in multi-modal transport matters. *"Able and popular"* **Chris Dunn** has, market sources indicate, *"a good team behind him."* Specialising in carriage of goods by road, rail and air, the team represents subrogated cargo and hauliers' liability insurers.

Clyde & Co (see firm details p.921) Despite the retirement of David Hall, the firm is still recognised by competitors to have *"a number of good people."* **Tony Thomas** (see p.822) and the group primarily act out of the Guildford office, advising insurers of both carriers and cargo owners. **William Melbourne** (see p.821) continues to be respected by the market. The team has recently been occupied with high value cases with an international slant.

Davies Arnold Cooper (see firm details p.934) Active on intermodal carriage of goods for insurers and cargo interests, recovery agents and freight forwarders, the caseload also includes advice on coverage disputes. The department owes much to *"lone wolf"* **Ken Silk** (see p.822), *"a good man with a fine practice."*

Davies Lavery (see firm details p.935) Based in London, the department deals with multi-modal transport, cargo and carrier claims for both defendant and claimant, as well as clandestine entrants, transit damage to goods and risk policy disputes. The *"sensible, occasionally aggressive"* **Kay Pysden** is the dominant personality here.

DLA **Martin Hill** and **Caroline Henning** maintain a high profile in this area.

John Weston & Co Acting mostly for carrier and cargo insurers, hauliers and freight forwarders, the firm also undertakes debt collection on behalf of the transport industry. Said by the market to be *"gaining ground,"* the team also handles substantial work with an Italian dimension. **John Weston** *"is a good man – you know where you are with him."*

Andrew M Jackson & Co (see firm details p.860) Well-versed in lien disputes and CMR work, the firm acts for domestic and foreign forwarders, trailer operators hauliers and their insurers. *"Likeable"* **Dominic Ward** (see p.822) is the key player in this dedicated practice.

Prettys (see firm details p.1100) Specialising in CMR, domestic haulage disputes and drafting conditions of carriage, the firm also conducts corporate, contentious, lien and logistic work. It has close connections to transport entities both locally and overseas. Clients and rivals recommend **Roland Sharp** (see p.822) as *"sensible and pragmatic,"* while the group is respected for its *"business-like and efficient"* approach.

ROAD: REGULATORY

ROAD: REGULATORY • Nationwide	Ptnrs	Assts
1 Ford & Warren Leeds	3	2
2 Backhouse Jones Clitheroe	3	2
3 Barker Gotelee Ipswich	2	2
Jeffrey Aitken Solicitors Glasgow	1	n/a
Wake Dyne Lawton Chester	2	1
4 Bond Pearce Bristol	1	1
Carless Davies & Co Halesowen	1	n/a
Jeremy Fear & Co Enfield	1	1
Rothera Dowson Nottingham	3	n/a
Wedlake Saint London	3	1
5 Arthur Cox Belfast	1	1
Bannister Preston Sale	1	n/a
Michael S Allen Aberdeen	1	n/a
Over Taylor Biggs Exeter	2	1

LEADING INDIVIDUALS

1
- BACKHOUSE James Backhouse Jones
- KIRKBRIGHT Stephen Ford & Warren
- ROTHERA Ian Rothera Dowson

2
- GOTELEE Michael Barker Gotelee
- HODGSON Gary Ford & Warren
- WHITEFORD Michael Jeffrey Aitken Solicitors

3
- CARLESS Michael Carless Davies & Co
- FEAR Jeremy Jeremy Fear & Co
- HEATON John Bannister Preston
- JONES Geoffrey Bond Pearce
- OVER Christopher Over Taylor Biggs
- PRIOR Barry Wedlake Saint

4
- ALLEN Michael Michael S Allen
- BUTTERFIELD Christopher Herbert Mallam Gowers
- WOOLFALL Andrew Wake Dyne Lawton

5
- HALLSWORTH Chris Foinette Quinn

UP AND COMING
- WYLIE Amanda Arthur Cox

This book is the product of 6,552 1/2-hour interviews. See p.7 for BMRB audit.
Within each band, firms are listed alphabetically. *See individuals' profiles p.819*

Ford & Warren (see firm details p.961) *"The biggest players in the sector."* A full service transport firm engaged in a substantial amount of civil litigation, including CMR, goods in transit claims, haulage contracts and insurance claims. Experienced and encyclopaedic in his HGV knowledge, **Stephen Kirkbright** (see p.821) is seen by some as *"the best in the country,"* while **Gary Hodgson** (see p.820) is appreciated by peers as *"an able and professional transport lawyer."*

Backhouse Jones (see firm details p.867) *"A big practice nation-wide, they know what they are doing." "Top flight among transport lawyers,"* the *"cerebral"* **James Backhouse** (see p.819) *"knows the relevant legislation inside out."* Specialising in transport, the firm is busy with regulatory and compliance issues, defending claims brought against bus companies and handling both passenger and goods vehicles cases. The team is also heavily involved in defence work in the PI field, often for bus companies. Highlights include the Court of Appeal case of Ribble Motor Services v Traffic Commission.

Barker Gotelee *"An excellent road transport firm"* is headed by **Michael Gotelee** (see p.819), *"an absolute gentleman"* who *"inspires loyalty in his clients."* The group's activities include representing defendants in the magistrate's court and operators at public inquiries. It is also involved in auditing operator systems, employment, health and safety issues and clandestine entrant cases.

Jeffrey Aitken Solicitors Dedicated to road transport law, the firm maintains its position as the market leader in Scotland. Defending cases for major haulage companies and dealing with operator licence public inquiries for haulage and freight companies, the *"hot as mustard"* **Michael Whiteford** (see p.822) is judged by his peers as *"absolutely brilliant – he's not scared of a fight and is good at dealing with technically complex points of law."*

Wake Dyne Lawton (see firm details p.1170) An *"experienced"* firm, which is a familiar sight in the road haulage and passenger transport industries. It performs defence work, public inquiries, operator licensing, liens, conditions of carriage and CMR. Clients run from owner drivers through to large international hauliers. The group benefits greatly from the presence of *"extremely able"* **Andrew Woolfall** (see p.822) who, competitors acknowledge, always shows *"good judgement,"* while Jonathan Lawton now acts as a consultant.

Bond Pearce (see firm details p.888) Bolstering its presence in the South West by its merger with Bond Pearce, the former Cartwrights group led by **Geoffrey Jones** (see p.821), acts for transport associations, bus, haulage and distribution companies. The team is considered by the market to be *"close to the top echelons,"* for its work in public inquiries, employment matters and applications for operator licences.

Carless Davies & Co Acting for hauliers in the magistrates courts and on public inquiries, the firm remains *"a major player in the West Midlands." "With years of experience,"* **Michael Carless** is *"one of the sector's leading lawyers."* One haulier admitted *"I never want to be on the other side of a court from him again!"*

Jeremy Fear & Co With hauliers forming 90% of the caseload, the firm is busy with public inquiries, magistrates court work, tribunals and employment matters. Still overwhelmingly known in the market for his work on the London Lorry Ban, *"extremely knowledgeable"* **Jeremy Fear** has a much broader practice. Servicing insurers and hauliers, he is acknowledged as *"an expert on London Borough Transport Scheme matters."*

Rothera Dowson (see firm details p.1113) Engaged in public inquiries, magistrate and Crown Court work, the firm also advises on employment, litigation, operator licensing, terms and conditions and acquisitions/disposals. It has also developed a niche in asylum work, undertaking over 150 cases under the new regulations. Universally respected, **Ian Rothera** (see p.822) operates a *"fine road regulatory practice,"* and is leading the field in *"making a specialism out of asylum."*

Wedlake Saint **Barry Prior** (see p.822) remains at *"the top of the tree for passenger vehicle work."* The firm advises on both passenger and goods vehicles and is often called upon to advise on personal injury issues, including employers liability, commercial matters and the administration of operators' licences.

Arthur Cox (see firm details p.865) Towering over the market in Northern Ireland, the firm benefits from a steady flow of cross-border work from insurers and hauliers. Conducting defence work in PI litigation and RTAs, the firm has an envied roster of clients, including hauliers and warehouse operatives. *"Highly respected"* **Amanda Wylie** (see p.822) leads the team.

Bannister Preston *"Hugely cerebral and highly experienced"* **John Heaton** (see p.820) leads the firm in its high profile Vehicle Inspectorate work. Undertaking prosecution and defence work, the firm also represents the Traffic Commissioners on appeals against their decisions. Heaton has recognised expertise in drivers' hours, tachograph and construction and use regulations.

Michael S Allen Acting on public inquiries and drivers' hours for international and long distance hauliers. One of two specialists in Scotland. Devoted to road haulage work, **Michael Allen** has been heavily involved in the Dutch flagging case and, say clients, *"understands the commercial issues at stake."*

Over Taylor Biggs *"Charm personified,"* **Christopher Over** secures *"substantial cases"* for the firm, according to rivals, including tachograph, PI litigation and operator licences.

Other Notable Practitioners **Chris Hallsworth** (see p.820) of **Foinette Quinn** has a growing reputation for his Vehicles Inspectorate work while **Christopher Butterfield** of **Herbert Mallam Gowers** acts regularly for transport operators.

RAIL

RAIL • Nationwide	Ptnrs	Assts
1 **Freshfields Bruckhaus Deringer** London	16	32
2 **Linklaters** London	n/a	n/a
3 **Clifford Chance** London	11	15
Denton Wilde Sapte London	8	7
Eversheds London, Birmingham, Leeds	3	7
Hollingworth Bissell London	2	n/a
Simmons & Simmons London	n/a	n/a
4 **Burges Salmon** Bristol	n/a	n/a
DLA London	8	16
Field Fisher Waterhouse London	5	5
Herbert Smith London	n/a	n/a
Norton Rose London	4	n/a
Slaughter and May London	n/a	n/a
5 **Ashurst Morris Crisp** London	6	12
Edwards Geldard Derby	2	4
Nabarro Nathanson	9	9
Osborne Clarke Bristol	6	5
Rowe & Maw London	4	4
6 **Allen & Overy** London	9	n/a
Dickinson Dees Newcastle upon Tyne	4	4
Wragge & Co Birmingham	3	7

LEADING INDIVIDUALS	
1 **CHARLTON Bob** Freshfields Bruckhaus Deringer	
ELLARD John Linklaters	
McGEE-OSBORNE Christopher Denton Wilde Sapte	
PHILLIPS Richard Freshfields Bruckhaus	
2 **THOMPSELL Nicholas** Field Fisher Waterhouse	
3 **BONAR Mary** Nabarro Nathanson	**COPPEN Simon** Burges Salmon
GWYNNE Simon Linklaters	**HARRIS Anne** Eversheds
HOLLINGWORTH Sara Hollingworth Bissell	**HORTON Naomi** Rowe & Maw
4 **BEVEN Ray** Ashurst Morris Crisp	**BISSELL Helen** Hollingworth Bissell
LITTLEJOHNS Andrew Freshfields Bruckhaus	**PHILLIPS Simon** Slaughter and May
WHITEHOUSE Michael Wragge & Co	
UP AND COMING	
BUCKLEY William Linklaters	
HANSLIP WARD Matthew Denton Wilde Sapte	

This book is the product of 6,552 1/2-hour interviews. See p.7 for BMRB audit.
Within each band, firms are listed alphabetically. *See individuals' profiles p.819*

Freshfields Bruckhaus Deringer (see firm details p.965) *"A team with outstanding ability"* continues its work with EWS, including advice on the post-Hatfield regulatory upheavals and part acquisition by Canadian Railways. The firm is also heavily involved in the PPP restructuring of London Underground, and has advised Angel trains on rolling stock financings and procurements. *"Impressive"* **Richard Phillips** (see p.821) has *"an excellent rail practice."* Peers agree that *"he is a clever man who did a massive job on the tube."* Highly respected **Andrew Littlejohns** (see p.96) is *"excellent on asset finance,"* while on the procurement side, **Bob Charlton** (see p.94) received heavy client endorsement. **Clients:** EWS; Angel Trains; London Transport.

Linklaters (see firm details p.1042) Clients value the team as one which *"knows the industry inside out."* **Simon Gwynne** is *"incredibly commercial and good to work with,"* and possesses *"a practical and analytical approach,"* while **William Buckley** (see p.819) joins our list in recognition of his corporate work. **John Ellard** (see p.819) remains *"one of the most knowledgeable rail industry players."* Acting primarily as the corporate lawyers for the SRA, the firm is advising on rail replacement franchises, financings and acquisitions of passenger rolling stock, the Thameslink 2000 and West Coast Mainline upgrades. The group also acted for the lead arrangers on the Nottingham Express Transit. **Clients:** SRA; SNCF; NS.

Clifford Chance (see firm details p.919) A quality practice, boasting strong ties to the Department of Transport, Environment and the Regions. Recently advising on the procurement of new rolling stock, a *"highly knowledgeable team,"* featuring Raj Parkash, acts for a substantial client base, including both funders and industry bodies. The team advised Railtrack on its fixed rail infrastructure UK tax-leasing facility, and acted for Dresdner Kleinwort Benson on the pre-emptive build financing of 200 passenger rolling stock vehicles. **Clients:** DTER; Railtrack; Thameslink.

Denton Wilde Sapte (see firm details p.939) *"Well regarded within the industry,"* the team advised ATOC on post Hatfield liabilities, re-franchising and new model agreements for access to stations and track. **Christopher McGee-Osborne** is rated by clients *"among the best rail lawyers in the country,"* while **Matthew Hanslip Ward** (see p.820) joins the up and coming ranks. Dealing with commercial, regulatory and finance work, the firm advised ALSTOM on the financing of trains valued at £200 million. **Clients:** ATOC; Alstom Transport; GB Railways.

Eversheds (see firm details p.952) *"Doing a lot of work for the SRA,"* and consistently endorsed by peers, the *"first-rate"* team is bolstered by the presence of **Anne Harris** (see p.820). Extensively involved in the franchise replacements for the SRA, recent highlights include securing the first two replacement franchises to Preferred Counter Party Status. The firm has also been involved in the Nottingham Express Transit. **Client:** SRA.

Hollingworth Bissell (see firm details p.999) *"Punching far above their weight,"* according to the market both **Sara Hollingworth** (see p.820) and **Helen Bissell** (see p.819) *"know the industry well and are good to deal with."* Undertaking rail passenger partnership work, restructuring and commercial property issues, the firm acts for a number of train operators, freight operating companies and the SRA. Bissell advised on the replacement of the Chiltern Railways Franchise and the current disaggregation of rail franchisers for the SRA. **Clients:** SRA; ATOC; Rail Europe Limited.

Simmons & Simmons (see firm details p.1132) Railtrack remains central to the firm's high marketprofile, and the firm has advised on high value and complex work such as the £5.8 billion project to upgrade and modernise the West Coast Mainline under the guidance of Jerry Walters. The firm has also advised on part of the Rail Regulator's periodic review of Railtrack's access charges and issues. **Clients:** Railtrack; Rapid Transit International; Department of Public Enterprise in Ireland.

Burges Salmon (see firm details p.902) Led by **Simon Coppen** (see p.182), *"a good guy with lots of experience,"* the team *"is highly regarded for its track access work."* It acted on the First Group bids for rail franchises and is also acting for First Great Eastern, First Great Northern and First Great Western on the procurement of new trains. The team acted for all TOCs through ATOC during the Cullen Inquiry and continues to advise on the strategic issues raised by the inquiry. **Clients:** First Group; ATOC.

DLA The team remains respected for its work with light and heavy rail, retaining its high profile client, Connex.

Field Fisher Waterhouse (see firm details p.957) A respected team is personified by **Nicholas Thompsell** (see p.822), considered by rivals as a *"team player and deal-doer"* who always adopts *"a practical approach."* The group acted for Arriva plc and Arriva Northwest on the unbundling of a franchise, and continue to advise SWT on its participation in the South Hampshire Rapid Transit Scheme. **Clients:** Arriva; London Underground; South West Trains.

Herbert Smith (see firm details p.993) Clients praise an *"excellent group of commercial lawyers,"* which operates a broad-based rail practice and has been involved in the franchise replacement rounds, as well as heavy rail projects. The firm advises on M&A, project financing, rolling stock leasing, rail regulation and property development. Although lacking a standout individual, the firm continues to advise on the Channel Tunnel Rail Link for London and Continental Airways, and acted on the disposal of Porterbrook Leasing. **Clients:** Virgin Rail Group; Stagecoach Holdings; South West Trains.

Norton Rose (see firm details p.1082) Led by Gordon Hall, this *"highly regarded"* department acted for Govia on its successful bid for the first round of refranchising for the South Central replacement franchise, and has continued to advise on its £1.5 billion development plans for the network. It also acted for HSBC on its asset financing for the £250 million fixed rail infrastructure UK tax-leasing facility with Railtrack. **Clients:** Porterbrook Leasing Company; HSBC (Rail) UK.

Slaughter and May (see firm details p.1135) **Simon Phillips** (see p.822) is the key player in a team which has been re-appointed to act for the Office of the Rail Regulator. Acknowledged by industry sources to perform *"a lot of interesting work,"* the firm remains a significant player in the market. Acted for Abbey National on the acquisition of Porterbrook Leasing and advised Prism Rail on the offer by National Express Group. **Clients:** ORR; First Group; Central Railway.

Ashurst Morris Crisp (see firm details p.866) The *"excellent, collaborative"* and *"client-friendly"* **Ray Beven** (see p.819) and his team are the main corporate lawyers for the National Express Group and acted on the £166 million takeover of Prism Rail. The group also acted for Docklands Light Railway on the City Airport extension project and is advising on the privatisation of the Tanzanian Railways Corporation. The firm is heavily involved in the current re-franchising and restructuring of the industry. **Clients:** Docklands Light Rail; National Express Group.

Edwards Geldard (see firm details p.948) The team, led by Roman Shurma, has had a busy year acting on the re-franchising rounds, and remains appreciated for its track access specialisation. It continues to advise National Express, and is involved in the Midland Mainline extension. **Clients:** National Express Group; Midland Mainline.

Nabarro Nathanson (see firm details p.1078) The *"indomitable"* **Mary Bonar** (see p.819) is the outstanding personality here. Peers agree that she *"really knows her stuff – she's quite outstanding."* The group acted for Siemens on its design, build and maintenance contract with a ROSCO for new rolling stock. It also advised on the operation and maintenance of a joint venture company in connection with the £200 million Nottingham Light Rail project. **Clients:** National Express Group; The Go-Ahead Group; Siemens.

Osborne Clarke (see firm details p.1086) The team, led by Claire Wagner, is recommended by competitors as *"good, commercial and usually right first time."* It advised c2c Rail on £120 million contracts for the supply, lease and maintenance of new rolling stock, and acted for Prism Rail on operational and regulatory matters connected with the share offer by National Express. **Clients:** Prism Rail; c2c Rail; STVA (UK).

Rowe & Maw (see firm details p.1113) The *"exceptional"* **Naomi Horton** (see p.820) is seen by the market as the key to the group's success, with clients agreeing that she's *"up there with the very best."* Although no longer on the Virgin panel, the firm continues to advise Virgin on the procurement of rolling stock, including the financing of the Cross Country Fleet by Lombard Leasing. Elsewhere, the group advised Hull Trains Company on the conclusion of its open track access arrangements with Railtrack and a number of TOCs on the establishment of internet ticketing facilities on websites. **Clients:** Cross Country; Arriva; West Coast Trains.

Allen & Overy (see firm details p.856) Perceived in industry circles to undertake transportation work on the back of its banking, asset and project finance work, one client noted that *"if one of our firms were conflicted out, we would use Jonathan Bevan's team."* Offering an *"extremely professional"* service, the team advised NM Rothschilds and Railtrack in connection with the review of the track access agreement model clauses and Stagecoach Holdings on a £1 billion rolling stock and service provision order. **Clients:** GB Railways; Angel; Railtrack.

Dickinson Dees (see firm details p.941) Simon Watts and his team are judged by peers to *"do a good job,"* and the firm raised its profile by acting for Govia on its acquisition of the South Central Rail Franchise. The team also advised The Go-Ahead Group on its successful defence of the £326 million takeover bid by C3D. **Clients:** Thameslink; The Go-Ahead Group; Govia.

Wragge & Co (see firm details p.1189) An extensive national practice is led by the *"unfailingly courteous"* **Michael Whitehouse**. The team acted for Bombardier on its three London Underground bids, and concluded the engine supply and maintenance contract for Virgin Cross Country Trains Operation. **Clients:** Bombardier; Cummins Engine; BMW.

LEADERS IN TRANSPORT

ALLEN, Michael
Michael S. Allen, Aberdeen (01224) 480 890

ARMSTRONG, Stuart
Hill Dickinson, London (020) 7695 1016
sarmstrong@hilldicks.com
Specialisation: Main areas of practice are cargo and goods in transit claims (charterparties, bills of lading, CMR and domestic road haulage, Warsaw Convention) and related cargo and G.I.T. liability insurance disputes. Acts for cargo underwriters, recovery agents, hauliers' liability underwriters, freight forwarders and hauliers.
Prof. Memberships: London Maritime Arbitrators' Association (supporting member).
Career: Articled with *Ingledew Brown Bennison & Garrett*, qualified in 1983 and became a partner in 1985. Joined *Hill Dickinson* in February 2001.
Personal: Born 1958. Educated at The King's School, Canterbury 1971-76 and Southampton University 1976-79 (LLB Hons). Leisure interests include golf and chess.

BACKHOUSE, James
Backhouse Jones, Clitheroe (01254) 828300
james@backhouses.co.uk
Specialisation: Commercial transport law including defending prosecutions brought by the Vehicle Inspectorate, Police and Trading Standards, Environment Agency, Health & Safety Executive; Operators and Vocational Licensing including inquiries, environmental, maintenance and financial; employment all issues; health and safety all issues. Recent cases include the successful defence in Nuttall v Wing in the House of Lords dealing with tachograph issues and R v Hennessey (Court of Appeal) an appeal against conviction of causing death by dangerous driving. Successfully dealt with eight cases of causing death by dangerous driving in the past four years, arising out of the passenger and goods transport industry. Has lectured on Article 177 references to the European Courts of Justice and involvement in two such references to the ECJ. Experience in rebated diesel cases, including Vat & Duties Tribunal. Successfully defended alleged illegal transportation of arms to Nigeria prosecution.

BEVEN, Ray
Ashurst Morris Crisp, London (020) 7859 1897
raymond.beven@ashursts.com
Specialisation: Partner in Energy, Transport and Infrastructure Department; Head of Transport Group. Extensively involved in privatisation, concessioning, corporate, commercial, regulatory and infrastructure project matters in transport, particularly in rail. Actively working in the UK passenger rail restructuring and re-franchising process, advising National Express and Govia. Involved in the London Underground PPP and Croydon Tramlink projects, and in corporate finance and M&A matters in transport. Internationally, involved in rail privatisation and rail projects in Africa, Ireland and the Netherlands.
Prof. Memberships: LLB (Hons) and MBA (Adelaide University). Admitted 1984 South Australia; 1999 England & Wales. Institute of Logistics and Transport, Law Society.
Career: Partner *Minter Ellison*, Adelaide 1992-1996. Partner *Kelly & Co*, Adelaide 1996-1998. With *Ashurst Morris Crisp* from 1998 (Partner 2001).
Personal: Born 1963, lives in London.

BISSELL, Helen
Hollingworth Bissell, London (020) 7233 3300
hb@hollingworthbissell.co.uk
Specialisation: Provides wide ranging advice to the railway industry, including on replacement franchise agreements, franchise remapping, track, freight facility and station access, rail infrastructure development agreements, construction and bringing new stations into operational use, station trading and landlord and tenant matters.
Career: Born and educated in Nottingham and Sheffield University. Qualified 1990. From 1992 worked as an in-house lawyer for British Railways Board. Partner in *Hollingworth Bissell* in 1997.
Personal: Lives in London. Interests include food and wine, gardening, reading and the gym.

BONAR, Mary
Nabarro Nathanson, London (020) 7524 6000
m.bonar@nabarro.com
Specialisation: Partner in the projects group and head of rail sector group. Main areas of practice are rail law, project finance and asset finance. Experience commercialisation of rail industry, financing of rail infrastructure (including using Public Private Partnerships) and rolling stock. In domestic market, specialises in track access, regulation and franchising. Clients include public sector, major banks, lessors, ECAs, governments, franchise groups and other corporates. Lectures and writes on rail industry and project finance.
Prof. Memberships: Liveryman, Worshipful Company of Carmen and City of London Solicitors Company; Women Solicitors Association. Member of Chartered Institute of Transport/Institute of Lagisties and Transport.
Career: LLB. London. Admitted in 1971. Partner *Wilde Sapte* banking department 1989 to 1999.

BUCKLEY, William
Linklaters, London (020) 7456 3312
william.buckley@linklaters.com
Specialisation: Transactions of significance where substantial involvement can be disclosed have included advising Republic of Argentina as international counsel on trade sale of state savings and life assurance bank (1993); advising UK government on privatisations of British Rail train operating companies (1994-96); numerous private acquisitions and disposals involving due diligence exercise, data room management, ongoing relationship between vendor and purchaser, drafting negotiation of sale agreements, confidentiality agreements and shareholder agreements.
Career: 1984-88 Magdalen College, Oxford (Classics Mods First, Law Finals First). 1999 Partner *Linklaters.* 1992-99 assistant solicitor, *Linklaters.* 1990-92 trainee solicitor, *Linklaters.*

BUTTERFIELD, Christopher
Herbert Mallam Gowers, Oxford (01865) 244661

CARLESS, Michael
Carless Davies & Co, Halesowen (0121) 550 2181

CHARLTON, Bob
Freshfields Bruckhaus Deringer, London (020) 7936 4000
bob.charlton@freshfields.com
See under Asset Finance & Leasing, p.94

COPPEN, Simon
Burges Salmon, Bristol (0117) 939 2291
simon.coppen@burges-salmon.com
See under Competition/Anti-trust, p.182

DUNN, Chris
Waltons & Morse, London (020) 7623 4255

ELLARD, John
Linklaters, London (020) 7456 3324
john.ellard@linklaters.com
Specialisation: Significant experience in corporate finance, international equity issues and privatisations. Transactions of significance where substantial involvement can be disclosed have included advising the UK government on all three stages of the privatisation of British Telecommunications plc (1982-84, 1991, 1993 (team leader); advising the UK government on the privatisation of the UK passenger rail industry and European Passenger Services 1992-97 (team leader 1996 onwards); advising the UK government on the Thameslink 2000 and West Coast Main Line rail infrastructure projects 1996 to date; advising the global co-ordinators of the Wellcome (1992) and Elf (1994) global share offers, the government of the Netherlands on the privatisation of KPN (1994), the Republic of Italy on the privatisation of Telecom Italia (1997) and the global co-ordinators on the privatisation of Telecom Eireann (1998 to date); advising Coca-Cola beverages on its demerger from Coca-Cola Amatil and listing on the London Stock Exchange, the second largest equity offer of 1998, and on its proposed acquisition by Hellenic Bottling SA; advising the Tube Rail Consortium on its bid for the London Underground public/private partnership and advising a consortium bidding for the Dutch High Speed Link Infrastructure project; advising the Shadow Strategic Rail Authority on the rail franchise renegotiation programme. Also advised on the privatisations of Associated British Ports, BP, British Airways, Jaguar, Wessex Water, the UK Regional Electricity Companies, National Power PLC and PowerGen PLC and Forth Ports.
Career: 1971-74 Trinity Hall Cambridge M.A. Law (First Class Honours). 1989 to date partner *Linklaters* London, corporate department; 1986-89 partner *Linklaters* New York; 1983-86 partner *Linklaters* London tax department; 1977-83 assistant solicitor *Linklaters* tax department; 1975-77 articled clerk *Linklaters.*

FEAR, Jeremy
Jeremy Fear & Co, Enfield (020) 8367 4466

GOTELEE, Michael
Barker Gotelee, Ipswich (01473) 611211
Specialisation: Road haulage and public service vehicle licensing, vehicle operation, prosecutions, disciplinary and environmental public inquiries, accidents, drivers' hours, CMR and employment. The firm covers other commercial aspects for businesses, tax, land, planning, pollution and waste.
Career: Qualified 1963. Since 1966 has acted for a wide range of operators and RHA and FTA members.
Personal: Born 1938. Interests are old vehicles, sailing and walking.

GWYNNE, Simon
Linklaters, London (020) 7456 2000

HALLSWORTH, Chris
Foinette Quinn, Milton Keynes (01908) 366333
Specialisation: Senior partner specialising in road transport law since 1983. Undertakes wide range of work and prosecutes for the Vehicle Inspectorate as well as defending operators and their employees. Specialises in HGV and PCV Law. Undertakes all types of public inquiries before Traffic Commissioners including environmental and disciplinary hearings. Represents clients at Crown Court as a Solicitor-Advocate. Represents FTA and RHA members and has been involved in advising and representing a number of well known UK and European companies. Also specialises in health and safety issues, environmental matters, planning appeals and defending complex criminal prosecutions. Contributes to Road Rescue Recovery Association Magazine and to Commercial Motor Magazine.
Career: Qualified July 1973. Prosecuted for Nottinghamshire and Sussex Police Authorities. Joined *Foinette Quinn* 1982. Solicitor-Advocate (Higher Courts Criminal) 1997. Deputy District Judge (Magistrates Courts).
Personal: Born 5th August 1948. LLB (Hons) London 1966-1969.

HANSLIP WARD, Matthew
Denton Wilde Sapte, London (020) 7242 1212
Specialisation: All aspects of the rail industry, including advising train companies on commercial contracts and regulatory and competition issues. Seconded to a train operator in 1996 to assist the company in preparing for privatisation. More recently, advised Virgin on its CrossCountry project (a network-wide infrastructure upgrade and track access transaction in relation to the introduction of two new fleets of trains), the Association of Train Operating Companies on regulatory enforcement action in the wake of the Hatfield derailment, and a company on its bids for replacement franchises.
Prof. Memberships: The Law Society.
Career: Partner, *Denton Wilde Sapte* 2001.
Publications: 'Legal Lines' columnist for 'Modern Railways 1999-2000'.
Personal: Magdalene College, Cambridge. Interests include history, fine and decorative arts, and motor racing.

HARDINGHAM, Adrian
Holmes Hardingham, London (020) 7283 0222
Adrian.Hardingham@HHLaw.co.uk
Specialisation: Senior partner. Principal areas of practice are transport and shipping law, encompassing international and domestic carriage of goods by road, sea and air. Other main areas of work are marine insurance, particularly cargo risks, and general commercial insurance. Major cases handled include Buchanan v Babco (H.L.) (1978), Silber v Islander Trucking (1985), ITT v Birkart (1988), the 'Rewia' (1991), and Spectra v Hayesoak (1997). Major clients include UK and overseas underwriters, traders, freight forwarders, hauliers and insurance recovery agents. Contributor of various articles on the CMR Convention in Lloyd's Maritime & Commercial Law Quarterly.
Career: Qualified 1978. Founding partner of *Holmes Hardingham*.
Personal: Attended University College, Oxford. Holds private pilot's licence.

HARRIS, Anne
Eversheds, Birmingham (0121) 232 1204
anneharris@eversheds.com
Specialisation: Specialises in commercial law and project work, in particular relating to railways. Having advised on railway facility access agreements, infrastructure developments, rolling stock and regulatory issues. Worked on the privatisation (pre-franchising) of West Coast Trains, and since 1997 for OPRAF/SRA, most recently on franchise replacement.
Prof. Memberships: Law Society; Railway Study Association.
Career: Qualified 1987 with *Eversheds*, partner 1994. Head of *Eversheds* rail group.
Personal: BA English and American Literature. Married (to Simon). Has a keen interest in sport particularly Aston Villa FC. Friend of Barber Institute of Fine Arts.

HEATON, John Graham
Bannister Preston, Sale (0161) 973 2434
info@bannisterpreston.co.uk
Specialisation: Road transport law (prosecuting and defending). Acted for the Crown in Bird v Vehicle Inspectorate, Case C235/94.
Career: 1967-75 William Hulme Grammar School, Manchester; LLB (Hons) Liverpool University 1978; qualified 1981; partner, *Bannister Preston & Ormerod* 1985.
Publications: Articles in legal journals on road transport law.
Personal: Married, two sons. Interests include travel, choral singing, transport generally, family life.

HENNING, Caroline
DLA, Manchester (08700) 111111

HILL, Martin
DLA, Liverpool (08700) 111111

HOBBS, Jane
Holmes Hardingham, London (020) 7283 0222
Jane.Hobbs@HHLaw.co.uk
Specialisation: Transport: Road-carriage/commercial. Main areas of practice are carriage of goods by road and sea and related insurance issues. Handles a wide range of cases involving domestic road haulage and CMR, including freight forwarding and warehousing. Insurance work includes advising on policy disputes and handling subrogated claims on behalf of underwriters. Experienced in pursuing and defending bill of lading and charterparty cargo claims.
Career: Attended Merton College, Oxford 1985 – 1988. Qualified 1991. Joined *Holmes Hardingham* in 1992 and became a partner in 1997. Contributor to 'Multimodal Transport' and 'Insurance Disputes'.

HODGSON, Gary
Ford & Warren, Leeds (0113) 243 6601
clientmail@forwarn.com
Specialisation: Partner in the Commercial Litigation Department. Main area of expertise – goods and passenger transport operations. Extensive experience in all aspects of operators licensing and other regulatory matters, defence expertise before Magistrates Courts and Crown Courts throughout England and Wales on a full range of road traffic matters. Experience in transport related health and safety prosecutions including prosecutions of utmost seriousness. Regular appearance before Coroner's Court following fatal road traffic and transport related accidents. Particular specialisation in Environment Agency prosecutions and environmental problems generally, particularly waste disposal, transportation and storage of hazardous chemicals and environmental problems arising out of the use of the Operating Centres. Wide experience and particular specialisation in prosecutions arising from drivers hours, records offences, construction use offences and particularly prosecutions arising from the lost wheels mystery. Recommended Solicitor for the Road Haulage Association and the Freight Transport Association. Retained solicitor for many national and international transport logistic operators on regulatory transport matters. Heads team providing consultancy services on internal systems for monitoring safety and quality. Advises on and prepares documentation for applications for BS5750 and ISO9002 quality accreditations. Extensive experience in European Transport Law. Leading member of the Ford & Warren team, advising hauliers throughout Europe on "flagging out". Subsequently representing hauliers who are currently being prosecuted for flagging out unlawfully. Regularly lectures to trade associations on transport related matters. Co-author of the 'Commercial Motor Legal Bulletin' and sole author of the 'Truck and Driver Legal Columns'. Regular contributor to the Trade Press generally.
Career: Qualified 1977. Joined *Ford & Warren* in 1978. Became partner in 1985.
Personal: Bachelor of Laws; holder of the Certificate of Professional Competence in Freight and Passenger at national level and in freight at international level.

HOLLINGWORTH, Sara
Hollingworth Bissell, London (020) 7233 3300
Specialisation: Provides a wide range of legal services to the railway industry, dealing with the negotiation and drafting of many types of commercial contracts; advises on foreign railway privatisations; joint ventures, station trading, sales promotion and advertising copy.
Career: Born and educated in Derbyshire and at Durham University. Trained at Cameron Markby and since 1985 has worked in the railway industry, initially as a lawyer with the British Railways Board (Head of Commercial within legal department 1993-96) and latterly as a partner in Hollingworth Bissell.
Personal: Married with two sons and lives in rural Kent. Interests include tennis, cookery, antique furniture and the theatre. Member of the English-Speaking Union.

HORTON, Naomi
Rowe & Maw, London (020) 7782 8871
nhorton@roweandmaw.co.uk
Specialisation: Specialises in infrastructure projects and PFI projects, including heavy and light rail and general rail related commercial advice. Advised Virgin Rail Group on the procurement of new rolling stock for each of the West Coast and Cross Country passenger rail franchises, the largest train procurements in the UK (value in excess of £2bn).
Prof. Memberships: Law Society.
Career: Educated at Sheffield High School, Merton College Oxford and Chester Law School. Articled at *Clifford Chance*, admitted 1992, joined *Rowe & Maw* in 1997 and became a partner in 1998. Now head of Rail Group at *Rowe & Maw* within the banking and projects group. Published (as co-author) a Special Report on the Private Finance Initiative (Pearson Professional) and articles for IFLR and PFI journals.

Personal: Born 1967. Rowed at Women's Henley Regatta and UK National Rowing Championships. Associate of the London College of Music. Enjoys running, rowing, gym training and mountain biking.

JACKSON, Peter

Hill Dickinson, Manchester (0161) 278 8800
Jacko@HillDicks.com

Specialisation: Main areas of practice are marine, goods in transit and insurance litigation. Work includes cargo claims, for both cargo and liability insurers, particularly international road haulage claims; ship related cargo claims for cargo interests; salvage and monitoring foreign litigation. Also handles marine insurance work, particularly marine insurance policy interpretation for underwriters. Acted in ICI plc v MAT Transport, ITT v Birkart, the Breydon Merchant F & W Freight, the Los Angeles, Microfine v Transferry Shipping and Inco Europe.
Prof. Memberships: Liverpool Underwriters Association, Manchester Marine Insurance Association, London Maritime Arbitrators Association.
Career: Qualified in 1985, having joined *Hill Dickinson Davis Campbell* in 1983. Became a partner in 1989.
Personal: Born 3 April 1961. Attended St Edward's College, Liverpool 1972-79, then Exeter College, Oxford 1979-82. Leisure interests include football, season ticket holder at Anfield. Former Chairman of Football Supporters Association. Cricket – member of Lancashire County Cricket Club. Lives in Liverpool.

JONES, Geoffrey

Bond Pearce, Bristol (0117) 929 9197
gjones@bondpearce.com

Specialisation: Formerly with *Cartwrights*, Geoffrey is a partner practising transport law with over 25 years experience in relation to all aspects of bus and lorry licensing and related public inquiries, road use public inquiries and judicial review challenges to local authorities. Also specialises in employment and industrial relations law with experience of all aspects of employment and industrial relations matters in contracts, service agreements and disciplinary procedures; multi-applicant employment tribunals; TUPE; commercial transactions and advice and legal action in relation to industrial action.
Career: Qualified in 1962 following articles with *Granville West Chivers & Dunford.* Joined *Cartwrights* 1964 becoming partner 1966. Joined *Bond Pearce* 2001 on merger.
Publications: Co-author of 'Basic Planning Law and Practice'.

KIRKBRIGHT, Stephen

Ford & Warren, Leeds (0113) 243 6601

Specialisation: Main area of practice is transport. Experienced since 1970 in all aspects of road transport law. Particular specialisation in LGV and PCV, nationally and internationally. Regularly appears before traffic commissioners on Public Inquiries and Transport Tribunals on appeals. Extensive experience in all aspects of criminal defence work. Particular experience in cases of utmost severity including HSE prosecutions, manslaughter and corporate manslaughter. Acted in inquests, criminal proceedings and Public Inquiries following Sowerby Bridge disaster. Acted in Bowles 'A2' manslaughter prosecution and subsequent Public Inquiries. Handled leading cases on 'causing and permitting' (Yorkshire Traction v Vehicle Inspectorate, Kelly v Shulman, Redhead Freight v Shulman) and on using (Travel-gas Midlands Ltd v Reynolds and others). Acted in leading authorities before the Transport Tribunal on finance for HGV and PCV operators (Rosswood, RHA v John Dee Limited and JJ Adam Limited). Acts throughout the UK for PCV operators at Public Enquiries and Transport Tribunal in relation to PSV operator's licenses and registration of local bus services. Acted in leading authorities before the Transport Tribunal on local services and fuel duty rebate (Midland Bluebird, Yorkshire Rider Limited, First Bristol Buses Limited) and for operators in Manchester and Merseyside Public Inquiries. Acts as legal advisor to the Road Haulage Association and recommended solicitor for the Freight Transport Association, the Irish Haulage Association and is recommended solicitor to the FTA, Irish RHA and Transport Logistik Netherlands. Acted in 500 plus claims against the French government following the French lorry drivers strike on behalf of Irish, UK, Dutch and Spanish hauliers. Co-ordinated the RHA 'flagging out scheme' following the 1999 budget to assist hauliers to relocate to other EU member states. Heads a department dealing with civil claims throughout Europe under CMR domestic conditions of carriage and GIT. Principle solicitor of Commercial Motor Legal Bulletin and regular contributor to trade press.
Prof. Memberships: Fellow of the Chartered Institute of Logistics and Transport.
Career: Qualified in 1968. Joined *Ford & Warren* in 1966 becoming a Partner in 1970. Currently Head of Business Law and member of Managing Board of *Ford & Warren.* Born 18 October 1941. Attended Sheffield University 1961-64 and College of Law 1965-66.
Personal: Leisure interests include music (plays guitar and piano) and painting. Lives in Wakefield.

KNIGHT, Tim

Holmes Hardingham, London (020) 7283 0222
Tim.Knight@HHLaw.co.uk

Specialisation: Partner in cargo claims department. Main area of practice is carriage of goods by road, covering national and international carriage by road, warehousekeeping, related insurance matters and terms and conditions of business. Also experienced in carriage by sea work, including bill of lading claims, and carriage by air and rail.
Career: Joined *Ingledew Brown* in 1986, qualifying in 1988. Joined *Holmes Hardingham* in 1989. Became partner in 1993.
Personal: Born 17th March 1964. Attended University of Kent 1983-85. Leisure pursuits include golf and squash. Lives in Hertfordshire.

LITTLEJOHNS, Andrew

Freshfields Bruckhaus Deringer, London (020) 7936 4000
andrew.littlejohns@freshfields.com
See under Asset Finance & Leasing, p.96

MARSHALL, Julia

Hill Dickinson, London (020) 7695 1000

Specialisation: Partner in Marine and Transit Department (London). Advice and litigation in the field of insurance (marine and non-marine) and goods in transit inter-modally. Has a particular interest in the emerging rail freight industry. Drafts and advises underwriters on policy wordings and advises merchants and carriers on conditions of trading. Has been involved in a number of leading decisions relating to CMR, e.g. Cicatiello and others v Anglo European Shipping Services Ltd and others, which successfully argued the first armed hijack defence under CMR Article 17.2. Founder of ELLSA (European Lawyers for Land, Sea and Air), a specialist European group ensuring expedient international assistance in shipping, transit, insurance, company and commercial areas.
Prof. Memberships: LL.B 1974: F.C.I.Arb 1995. Supporting Member of the London Maritime Arbitrators Association. Director of the Rail Freight Group. Freeman of the City of London Solicitors Company.
Career: Admitted 1977 after first training and working in the medical field. Proprietor of own firm 1981. May 1994 merged with and became a partner in the current firm of *Hill Dickinson*.

McGEE-OSBORNE, Christopher

Denton Wilde Sapte, London (020) 7242 1212

MELBOURNE, William

Clyde & Co, Guildford (01483) 555555
William.Melbourne@clyde.co.uk

Specialisation: In addition to road carriage, including GIT and removers block/warehousing related disputes, domestic and international road haulage and heavy haulage; also specialises in marine insurance (including rejection risks) and dry shipping/cargo claims, with particular experience of reefer cargoes (especially bananas and frozen meat), bulk ore, refractories (magnesite) and groundnuts (especially inherent vice-related issues). Also has experience of international sale of goods (especially steel), including ICC Arbitration.
Prof. Memberships: Solicitor (admitted 1985)
Career: BA (Hons) (C.N.A.A.) 1981; LLM (Lond) 1986.

MESSENT, Andrew

Holmes Hardingham, London (020) 7283 0222
Andrew.Messent@HHLaw.co.uk

Specialisation: Partner in cargo claims department. Main area of practice is claims arising from the carriage of goods by sea, road and air, and other related areas, such as warehousing. Also advises on all related insurance issues. Co-author of 'CMR: Contracts for the International Carriage of Goods by Road' (3rd edition 2000). Contributor to 'International Carriage of Goods by Road (CMR)' (1987).
Career: Attended Gonville and Caius College, Cambridge. Qualified 1975, then took up a lecturing post in 1976 until 1985. Returned to marine practice in the City, and moved to *Holmes Hardingham* as one of the founding partners in 1989.

OVER, Christopher

Over Taylor Biggs, Exeter (01392) 823811

PHILLIPS, Richard

Freshfields Bruckhaus Deringer, London (020) 7936 4000
richard.phillips@freshfields.com

Specialisation: Work includes asset and project finance, commercial and corporate law, mergers and acquisitions, joint ventures, disposals and privatisations. Specialist industry focus of railways,wide experience of high profile corporate, project and finance work within this industry.
Prof. Memberships: Law Society, Chartered Institute of Transport, City Solicitors' Company.
Career: Qualified in 1981. (1985 joined Freshfields,

1989 became partner).
Personal: Born 1955, lives in London.

PHILLIPS, Simon
Slaughter and May, London (020) 7600 1200
simon.phillips@slaughterandmay.com
Specialisation: Corporate finance, M&A, general corporate.
Career: Educated Winchester College and Queens' College, Cambridge. Joined *Slaughter and May* 1982. Partner since 1991.

PRIOR, Barry
Wedlake Saint, London (020) 7405 9446
barryp@wsch.co.uk
Specialisation: Partner and head of firm's transport law team of five fee-earners and para-legals. Main area of practice is road transport law for goods and passenger vehicles; work covers operators licensing, defence of prosecutions, personal injury (road traffic and employers' liability), contract drafting, and commercial litigation associated with the industry. Also handles carriage of goods and passengers claims, including CMR/Domestic contracts and local authority tendering bus contracts. Cases have included litigation arising from many major motorway multi-vehicle accidents, public inquiries into operators licenses and major driver's hours/records prosecutions. Contributor to 'Coach and Bus Week'.
Prof. Memberships: Law Society, Chartered Institute of Transport, Institute of Logistics and Transport, Freight Transport Association, Confederation of Passenger Transport, Law Society Personal Injury Panel.
Career: Qualified in 1969. Joined *Wedlake Saint* as a partner in 1985.
Personal: Born 24 October 1943. Attended Lawrence Sheriff School, Rugby, then Sheffield University. Fellow of the Chartered Institute of Transport; and of Institute of Logistics and Transport. Affiliate Member Institute of Road Transport Engineers; sector of the Society of Operations Engineers, Council Member of CPT UK. Lives in Marlow, Bucks.

PYSDEN, Kay
Davies Lavery, London (020) 7780 6868

ROTHERA, Ian
Rothera Dowson, Nottingham (0115) 9100 600
i.rothera@rotheradowson.co.uk
Specialisation: Head of transport department. Since qualifying in 1973, has specialised in all aspects of road transport and traffic law. Acts for national and international HGV and PCV operators and drivers. Defence of prosecutions in Magistrates and Crown Courts throughout the UK, including construction and use offences and drivers' hours and tachograph cases. Defends Immigration Act carriers liability penalties in "stowaway" cases. Handles Operator's Licence applications, disciplinary and environmental public inquiries before the Traffic Commissioners and appeals to the Transport Tribunal. Panel solicitor for the RHA and the FTA. Member of Nottinghamshire Chamber of Commerce Transport Committee. Deputy Coroner for Nottinghamshire.

SHARP, Roland
Prettys, Ipswich (01473) 298234
rsharp@prettys.co.uk
Specialisation: Significant practice in carriage of goods by road – national and CMR. In addition to contentious work, advises on business terms, distribution, warehousing and logistics aspects and related transport matters.
Career: Attended Wellington College and Leeds University. Qualified 1986.

SILK, Ken
Davies Arnold Cooper, London (020) 7936 2222
ksilk@dac.co.uk
Specialisation: Senior Associate, Property, Construction and Insurance.

THOMAS, Tony
Clyde & Co, Guildford (01483) 31161
Tony.Thomas@clyde.co.uk
Specialisation: In addition to road carriage, including GIT and removers block/warehousing related disputes, domestic and international road haulage and heavy haulage, also specialises in marine insurance and dry shipping/cargo claims.
Prof. Memberships: Law Society.
Career: Qualified in 1976, joining *Clyde & Co* the same year. Partner 1981.
Personal: Born 27 May 1952. Attended Leamington College 1963-70, then Manchester University 1970-73. Leisure interests include sport, art and architecture. Lives in Grayshott, Surrey.

THOMPSELL, Nicholas
Field Fisher Waterhouse, London (020) 7861 4000
Specialisation: Corporate/commercial lawyer. Particular interests include transport/travel (especially rail) and privatisation/PFI. Acts for South West Trains in relation to commercial/regulatory aspects of its rail operations. Advised Northern Spirit on rolling stock leasing. Acted for British Railways in relation to numerous disposals. Acted for The Thomas Cook Group Limited in various transactions. Acted for an airline in relation to BA Franchise. Advised London Underground on its police accommodation PPP scheme and has advised on various other PFI schemes. Advised on the privatisation of HMSO and the Paymaster Agency.
Prof. Memberships: Law Society. City of London Law Society, Rail Study Association, Association of Partnership Practitioners.
Career: School: Bablake School, Coventry. University: King's College, London (LLB, AKC). Law School: College of Law, Chester. Articled *Slaughter and May*. Assistant Solicitor *Slaughter and May* 1987 – 92. Assistant Solicitor *Field Fisher Waterhouse* 1992, becoming a partner in 1993.
Personal: Trying to keep up with daughters' interests in music and computers. Trustee London Suzuki Group.

WARD, Dominic
Andrew M. Jackson & Co, Hull (01482) 325242
Specialisation: Partner in 1992. Disputes involving carriage of goods by sea and road including advising transport intermediaries. International trade disputes, other contractual disputes involving marine or transport related matters.
Prof. Memberships: AIJA, SEG.
Career: Qualified 1987.
Personal: Born 30.3.63 in London. Education to age 14 in Germany. Speaks German. Interests include rugby, golf, badminton, cinema, books and travel.

WESTON, John
John Weston & Co, Felixstowe (01394) 282527

WHITEFORD, Michael G.
Jeffrey Aitken Solicitors, Glasgow (0141) 221 5983
m.whiteford@jeffrey-aitken.co.uk
Specialisation: Road transport law. Practice covers representation at operator licence public inquiries before the Traffic Commissioner and appeals to the Transport Tribunal, employment tribunals and defending in prosecutions in the Scottish courts. Acts for many leading haulage and bus operators.
Prof. Memberships: Law Society of Scotland. Panel Solicitor for the Freight Transport Association. The Royal Faculty of Procurators in Glasgow.
Career: Qualified 1971. Joined *Jeffrey Aitken* and has been a partner since 1972.
Personal: Born 15th December 1946. Educated Glasgow University.

WHITEHOUSE, Michael
Wragge & Co, Birmingham (0870) 903 1000

WOOLFALL, Andrew
Wake Dyne Lawton, Chester (01829) 773106
aaw@wdl.co.uk
Specialisation: Road transport law, covering goods and passenger vehicles. Representing clients in Magistrates and Crown Courts as well as at Public Inquiries. Also been involved in cases before High Court and House of Lords. Appears at courts and tribunals throughout England and Wales. Provides consultancy advice to companies on internal systems for compliance with road transport law and operators' licensing requirements. Acted for companies and individuals in relation to drugs/smuggling seizures on the continent.
Prof. Memberships: The Law Society. Member of the Institute of Transport Administrators. Practice membership of HTA and RHA.
Career: Lancaster University. Early career in general practice before moving on to specialise in transport.

WYLIE, Amanda
Arthur Cox – Northern Ireland, Belfast
(02890) 230 007
awylie@arthurcox.ie
Specialisation: Defence personal injury litigation, magistrates court work, Doe and Ruc Prosecutions, construction and use regulations, tachographs, speed limiters, vehicle excise – any transport related matters.
Prof. Memberships: Freight Transport Association Panel Solicitor; Contentious Business Committee Member Law Society; Medico – Legal Society; Treasurer of FOIL Northern Ireland.
Career: Solicitor, FTA Panel Solicitor six years.
Personal: Queens University, Belfast LLB Hons, 1993. Interests – cinema, theatre.

TRAVEL

OVERVIEW: TRAVEL: The enormous growth in travel and leisure has led to increases in almost all types of work in this area. An increasingly aware public has also led to more class actions, disaster cases and corporate manslaughter actions. The established travel firms in this area maintain their top position while firms who specialise in claimant and defence work have prospered.

HOTELS & LEISURE: A specialist area of law which often necessitates cross-departmental support, the sector has been dominated by the fallout of the Compass sale of its £3.5 billion Forte hotel estate. Home to the global hotel chains, with international operators increasingly entering the market, much of the work is now cross-border. The creation of super-group hotel brands has led to greater consolidation. The leisure sector has seen a ready supply of schemes that are now being converted into retail, while the health and fitness industry continues to blossom.

TIMESHARE: Forecast to expand at twice the rate of overall world travel and tourism over the next decade. Since the introduction of the 1997 European Timeshare Regulations, prospective purchasers now have a 14-day cooling off period to cancel any sales agreement. New initiatives such as the introduction of exchange and points systems and the creation of holiday clubs where points act as currency to buy a holiday, are fuelling the market and enticing more firms to the sector.

TOP IN-HOUSE LAWYERS

Richard ASTON, Legal Manager and Company Secretary of Thomson Travel Group Legal, *Thomsons Travel Group Ltd.*

Andrew COOPER, Company Secretary and Head of Legal Services, *Airtours*

Riccardo NARDI, Head of Legal Services, *ABTA*

Anything **Richard Aston** *"has not dealt with is not worth dealing with,"* and he is respected as an *"absolute font of experience."* **Andrew Cooper**, combines *"the solid foundations of common sense"* with a *"grasp on the industry."* **Ricardo Nardi** has *"done a fantastic job,"* providing *"legal direction"* at ABTA through *"his persistence and often courageous use of the law."*

In-House lawyers profiles: p.1193

RESEARCH APPROVED BY BMRB: *For this edition,* Chambers' *researchers conducted 6,552 interviews – 4,419 with law firms, 554 with barristers and 1,579 with clients.*

The validity of the research was scrutinised by BMRB International, who audited both the methodology and the results at our offices in July 2001. They interviewed Chambers' *researchers and cross-checked sample interviews. Details of the audit appear on page 7.*

LONDON

TRAVEL • London	Ptnrs	Assts
1 Field Fisher Waterhouse	2	4
2 Nicholson Graham & Jones	3	4
3 Badhams	2	5
Barlow Lyde & Gilbert	2	4
Norton Rose	*	*
4 Davenport Lyons	1	1
Lane & Partners	1	2
Piper Smith & Basham	3	1
5 Herbert Smith	n/a	n/a
Vizards, Staples & Bannisters	2	3

LEADING INDIVIDUALS	
1 **BARBOR Cynthia** Nicholson Graham	**STEWART Peter** Field Fisher Waterhouse
2 **CHAMBERLAIN Simon** Field Fisher	**FARRELL Patrick** Norton Rose
GIMBLETT Richard Barlow Lyde &	**ROBINSON Tim** Nicholson Graham
3 **GWILLIAM Michael** Vizards, Staples	**MULLIGAN Claire** Badhams
SEARS Trevor Davenport Lyons	**SKUSE Ian** Piper Smith & Basham

This book is the product of 6,552 1/2-hour interviews. See p.7 for BMRB audit.
Within each band, firms are listed alphabetically. *See individuals' profiles p.826*
* *See editorial entries for explanations of team sizes.*

Field Fisher Waterhouse (see firm details p.957) Keeps its top position with the *"excellent, competent and professional team"* who provide *"an all round service,"* handling corporate, regulatory, commercial and contentious matters including class actions. Led by the *"experienced and renowned"* **Peter Stewart** (see p.829), noted for being *"a tough negotiator"* and who interviewees agree is both *"charming and shrewd,"* and *"fights the industry's corner."* **Simon Chamberlain** (see p.827) was also highly rated by colleagues and clients as being *"good on commercial issues."* **Clients:** Thomas Cook Holdings; ITT; AITO.

Nicholson Graham & Jones (see firm details p.1081) *"The best travel solicitor in the country,"* **Cynthia Barbor** (see p.826) heads the team here. Described by clients as *"head and shoulders above the rest"* she is judged by fellow solicitors as *"a terrific lawyer"* who *"takes a reasonable approach."* The Travel and Leisure Law Unit deals with a wide range of consumer, commercial, regulatory and contentious matters including defending class actions for tour operators. The firm acted on the continuation of recovery of passenger service charges from airlines on behalf of ABTA's members. The Unit also acts for hotels, online travel agents, car hire companies and their insurers. **Tim Robinson** (see p.828) is also rated highly by clients and peers. **Clients:** Thomsons; Crystal Holidays; Federation of Tour Operators.

Badhams An *"on the ball team"* evaluated by the market as *"the specialist's specialist,"* the firm has benefited from the wholesale move of Tim Oliver and his team from Berrymans. **Claire Mulligan** (see p.828) is *"bright and ambitious."* The team deals predominantly with defence litigation and has been heavily involved in work for Thomson Holiday and the Thomson Travel Group. Highlights include the Court of Appeal case of Codd v Thomson Holidays which established that foreign standards would apply when abroad. *"The quality of the work is very good,"* and the firm recently established a separate class action department. **Clients:** Thomson Holidays; Thomson Travel Group; First Choice.

Barlow Lyde & Gilbert (see firm details p.870) A regulatory practice also occupied with industry affairs. The "*superb*" **Richard Gimblett** (see p.102) is "*an awesome man*" with "*an excellent legal brain – good on negotiation.*" The team is valued by peers as "*particularly good on airline accidents*" and well-versed in regulatory work for IATA, trust funds and licensing. It continues to act for the CAA and the Air Travel Trust. **Clients:** Federation of Tour Operators (FTO); International Federation of Tour Operators.

Norton Rose (see firm details p.1082) (20 ptnrs & 37 assts available in the Travel Tourism and Leisure Group). **Patrick Farrell** (see p.827) heads up "*a good team on regulatory matters generally.*" Engaged in corporate and competition law, the group advise tour operators and travel groups on contentious matters and dispute resolution. Prominent for its insolvency work within the sector, the firm also scores well with its work for the Thomson Travel Group. **Clients:** Thomson Holidays; TV Travel Shop; easygroup.

Davenport Lyons (see firm details p.931) A "*smooth operator*" valued by clients as "*a pragmatic problem solver,*" **Trevor Sears** (see p.828) "*knows the business inside out.*" As "*the IATA man*" he is UK Counsel to the International Airline Transport Association (IATA) in airline failure and travel agency problems. Highlights for 2000 have included British Airways and Other IATA Airlines v Frequentguide, which raised a number of insolvency issues. **Clients:** IATA.

Lane & Partners (see firm details p.1027) A "*major player on the regulatory front,*" and enjoying an envied insurance client base, the firm deals largely with tour operators and CAA licensing matters. It will be interesting to see how the team develops now that its leading light in this area, Richard Venables, has moved across to consultant status. **Clients:** Trident Aviation; Travel Club of Upminster; tour operators.

Piper Smith & Basham (see firm details p.1098) A regulatory and commercial practice "*well known for this area of work.*" **Ian Skuse** (see p.828) "*knows a lot about the industry*" bringing "*expertise*" to the table. The firm is occupied by all aspects of commercial work for the travel industry, M&A and insolvency work for liquidators. **Clients:** Air France; Omega World Travel; Kuoni.

Herbert Smith (see firm details p.993) Though not a specialist travel practice, it remains roundly endorsed by competitors and clients for its competition and regulatory work within the sector and has a extensive relationship with First Choice Holidays. Acted for First Choice on its alliance with Royal Carribean Cruises involving the creation of a joint venture cruise line. **Clients:** First Choice.

Vizards, Staples & Bannisters Occupied primarily with personal injury litigation on behalf of travel and insurance companies, the firm has been involved in accidents which happen abroad (such as swimming pool incidents) and class actions, appreciated for its approach that can be "*quite hard – but not unfairly so.*" Peers agree that **Michael Gwilliam** (see p.827) is "*a sensible litigator who is tough when he needs to be.*" **Clients:** Airtours.

THE REGIONS

TRAVEL • The Regions	Ptnrs	Assts
1 **Mason Bond** Leeds	4	3
2 **Eversheds** Newcastle upon Tyne	1	2
Irwin Mitchell Birmingham	2	4
Stones Exeter	5	6
3 **Andrea & Co** Guildford	1	4
4 **Clairmonts** Glasgow	2	1
Shakespeares Birmingham	1	3
Tozers Exeter	2	1
5 **asb law** Croydon	2	2

LEADING INDIVIDUALS	
1 **MASON Stephen** Mason Bond	
2 **GARNER Clive** Irwin Mitchell	**HENDERSON Stuart** Irwin Mitchell
PEARS Melanie Eversheds	
3 **ANDREA Costas** Andrea & Co	**COURTENAY-STAMP Bronwen** Stones
INGLEBY Claire Mason Bond	

This book is the product of 6,552 1/2-hour interviews. See p.7 for BMRB audit.
Within each band, firms are listed alphabetically. *See individuals' profiles p.826*

Mason Bond (see firm details p.1055) Respected by City and regional firms alike, the "*excellent team*" which "*still deserve to be Number 1,*" is headed by "*the doyen of travel lawyers,*" **Stephen Mason** (see p.827). With the support of "*very good*" **Claire Ingleby** (see p.827) the firm is consistently quoted within the top 3 firms for travel in the UK. Clients appreciate quality advice that is "*well worth the money.*" Recent highlights on the civil and criminal side respectively, have been Patrick v Cosmosair which established the limits on tour operators for excursions and Hotelplan (Inghams) v Tamesidehotel allocation for MBC on late availability bookings. "*Top rate in all aspects of its criminal and injury related work,*" much of the caseload lies with tour operators with regulatory, litigation, commercial and employment matters as key practice areas. **Clients:** Thomson Holidays; JMC Holidays; Cosmos.

Eversheds (see firm details p.952) Felt by peers to have had a steady year, the firm has been engaged in employment work, business to consumer terms and conditions and work for franchise travel agencies. "*A good person in the industry*" **Melanie Pears** (see p.828) and the team has been involved in the setting up of a new holiday venture and the establishment of a UK trading subsidiary to provide summer camp training holidays. **Clients:** Center Parcs; Eurodisney; Fjordline.

Irwin Mitchell (see firm details p.1009) "*A premier firm in the big league,*" the team "*know what they are talking about.*" With a wealth of experience, its "*notoriously aggressive*" methods do not win friends among fellow solicitors, although peers concede that the firm "*gets good results for their clients.*" "*Dogmatic and vastly experienced,*" **Clive Garner** (see p.827) forms a "*cracking duo*" with **Stuart Henderson**, their "*quality of work should not be underestimated.*" Specialises in claims against tour operators and foreign domiciled defendants, class actions, accident and group action illness claims arising abroad. **Clients:** Eastgate; First Assist; Countrywide/Composite.

Stones (see firm details p.1146) "*A niche firm*" whose "*reputation is well established.*" Initially recommended for its specialisation in skiing accidents, the firm has now seen growth in other accident types, in both contentious and non-contentious matters and insurance disputes. Acting for claimants and defendants the firm is headed by **Bronwen Courtenay-Stamp** ("*respected, knows her stuff*") and rated by clients as "*first class, a good value return.*" **Clients:** Fogg Travel; Europ Assist; T&C Adjusters.

Andrea & Co Specialising in claimant travel work, this niche practice, headed by **Costas Andrea** (see p.826), "*punches far above its weight.*" Dealing almost exclusively with personal injury out of accidents abroad including the collapse of a hotel and test cases on the Package Travel Regulations, the team has recently been joined by an experienced recruit from Prettys. **Clients:** First Assist; numerous individuals and groups.

Clairmonts Dominating Scotland for the top UK tour operators and travel agents. David Kaye and the firm deal with contract and trading standards cases as well as extensive property transactions. **Clients:** Major UK tour operators and agents.

Shakespeares (see firm details p.1122) Led by Mark Beesely and described by clients and rivals as highly experienced, "*the specialists*" in waterways law deal with incorporation and petitioning while the increased litigation area handles disputes over boat building and mooring. 'Continuous cruising' is a growing problem that the firm is also dealing with. **Clients:** Inland Waterways Association and subsidiaries; individuals.

Tozers (see firm details p.1160) Tony Beard and the group act for owners of park homes estates and holiday parks across the range of clients. Although this area has been affected by the foot and mouth crisis, the firm has been inundated with enquiries in its capacity acting for the British Holiday and Home Parks Association. It has recently undertaken a number of high profile buyouts from one of the UK's largest leisure operators. **Clients:** Caravan park owners and developers.

ASB law (see firm details p.865) A new entrant this year, the firm is "*emerging in the market.*" Clients found the team "*good to use.*" Acts on a wide range of work from civil prosecutions against 'air rage' defendants to corporate advice. **Clients:** First Choice; Unijet; Hayes & Jarvis.

HOTELS & LEISURE

Band	TRAVEL: HOTELS & LEISURE • London	Ptnrs	Assts
1	Clifford Chance	6	n/a
	SJ Berwin	3	8
2	Richards Butler	*	*
3	Berwin Leighton Paisner	14	16
	Denton Wilde Sapte	7	8
	Field Fisher Waterhouse	3	11
	Linklaters	2	1
	Lovells	10	n/a
4	Allen & Overy	n/a	n/a
	Douglas Wignall & Co	1	n/a
5	Freshfields Bruckhaus Deringer	3	13
	Garretts	2	3
	Stephenson Harwood	8	8
	Taylor Joynson Garrett	12	9

Band	LEADING INDIVIDUALS	
1	**CARNEGIE Andrew** Clifford Chance	**PICKUP Bryan** SJ Berwin
	RYLAND David SJ Berwin	
2	**PLANT Patrick** Linklaters	
3	**HOUSTON Paul** Field Fisher Waterhouse	**LEVY David** Berwin Leighton Paisner
	LITTLE Andrew Garretts	**NICOLL Richard** Richards Butler
	PHILLIPS Rachel Berwin Leighton Paisner	**QUICKE Martin** Denton Wilde Sapte
	WIGNALL Douglas Douglas Wignall & Co	

This book is the product of 6,552 1/2-hour interviews. See p.7 for BMRB audit.

Within each band, firms are listed alphabetically. *See individuals' profiles p.826*

* *See editorial entries for explanation of team sizes.*

Clifford Chance (see firm details p.919) Providing structuring, tax, financing, leasing, JV and planning advice, the firm is respected as having "*a lot of big leisure clients.*" **Andrew Carnegie** (see p.827) "*well known and respected – absolutely superb*" is the standout player in an efficient, experienced team. Highlights include advising Burford Holdings on a composite restructuring deal with Chorion and representing Nomura on its £350 million acquisition of Principal Hotels. **Clients:** Sol Melia Hotels; Millennium and Copthorne Hotels; Jarvis Hotels.

SJ Berwin (see firm details p.879) "*Sharp and innovative*" **David Ryland** (see p.828) is praised by clients as "*understanding instantly the commercial aspect of a transaction,*"although he remains an acquired taste among peers. Head of Property, **Bryan Pickup** (see p.828) is still a key player in the sector. The "*excellent team*" advises on hotel management contracts, financing and restructuring. It acted on the sale and leaseback of Brannigans to First Leisure and on the acquisition of the Malmaison Group for MWB. **Clients:** Hilton Group; MWB; JLL Hotels.

Richards Butler (see firm details p.1107) (18 ptnrs & 30 assts available from varoius departments as required) "*Well honed and effective,*" the team is "*easy to deal with – on the ball.*" Operating across "*the full width and depth*" of the leisure industry, it undertakes property and management issues. Clients rate **Richard Nicoll** (see p.828) as "*a good pro-active lawyer*" who "*thinks around instructions.*" Highlights include acting on the disposals by the Rank Group of its holiday division (£700 million) and Odeon Cinemas (£280 million.) It has also completed the site acquisition at Battersea Power Station on behalf of Parkview International. **Clients:** The Rank Group; Mecca Bingo; Thistle Hotels.

Berwin Leighton Paisner (see firm details p.878) "*Impressive – it knows the industry,*" the firm acted for Chorion in its roll out of the Tiger Tiger Bar concept and advised Starwood Hotels and Resorts on its European Hotel Franchises. **David Levy** (see p.827) is noted by interviewees as being "*fantastic*" with an "*encyclopaedic knowledge of everything he has ever done*" while **Rachel Phillips** (see p.828) is "*good at looking after clients.*" **Clients:** First Leisure Corporation; Chorion; Starwood Hotels & Resorts Worldwide.

Denton Wilde Sapte (see firm details p.939) "*Taking a real interest in this sector*" recommended for its hotel and stadium work. Clients approve of the "*good team, responsive and quick,*" which draws upon specialist planning expertise and includes "*highly efficient and good value for money,*" **Martin Quicke**. The firm has conducted the second stage of development in the Chelsea Village complex and advised on the re-development of Somerset House. **Clients:** Virgin Active; Chelsea FC; RFU.

Field Fisher Waterhouse (see firm details p.957) Described by peers as a "*top leisure firm*" with a "*dedicated, young and professional team,*" valued by clients as "*excellent and efficient.*" **Paul Houston** (see p.827) "*clearly understands the business very well.*" Highlights include acting as lead property solicitors for Luminar and the firm advises David Lloyd on all aspects of its new health clubs. **Clients:** Marriott Hotels; Travel Inn; David Lloyd Leisure.

Linklaters (see firm details p.1042) Active in the sector advising Scottish and Newcastle on the sale of 13 Center Parc Holiday Villages in five countries and advising Jolly Hotels on the purchase of the Hilton St Ermin's Hotel, St James's for £57 million. Much of the caseload is derived from a first rate property practice engaged in site acquisition, development and letting advice for clients such as Richardson Developments (on Printworks Leisure Scheme, value £110 million.) "*Quite an expert*" **Patrick Plant** (see p.751)is endorsed by peers alongside an experienced team with a serious approach to both contract and corporate work in the sector. **Clients:** S&N; Lehman Brothers; Mandarin Hotels.

Lovells (see firm details p.1044) "*Good to have on a transaction,*" highlights for the firm include advising mainstay client Granada on its contested purchase of Forte and acting for BAA on the creation of a limited partnership fund. Known for its big-ticket corporate expertise, Bob Kidby and the team also acted on the sale of Browns Hotels chain and the Hyde Park and Howard Hotels. **Clients:** Cliveden; Wyndham International; BAA.

Allen & Overy (see firm details p.856) Providing expertise in corporate, banking and property matters, the group which includes Adam Cleal has advised DB Capital Partners on the acquisition of Center Parcs, represented Principal Hotels on the disposal of a portfolio of hotels for £255 million and Bass on the sale of 988 pubs for £625 million. **Clients:** Bass; De Vere Group; Thomson Travel Group.

Douglas Wignall & Co (see firm details p.946) Specialising in management agreements, the "*resourceful*" and "*particularly good*" **Douglas Wignall** has completed contracts for the millennium project for Belfast (the Odyssey Arena Project) as well as agreements for Morrisons' International Development joint venture with Thistle Hotels. **Clients:** Developers; Blakes Hotel.

Freshfields Bruckhaus Deringer (see firm details p.965) "*Absolutely first class*" on the merger and demerger of Granada Compass which included the £1.9 billion sale of Meridien Hotels following its £1.36 billion disposal of the Signature, Posthouse and Heritage hotel chains. Mark Wheelhouse belongs to the group that also acted on the corporate side of the Rank sale of its holiday division and on the Cinven acquisition of Odeon Cinemas. **Clients:** Compass; The Rank Group; Cinven.

Garretts (see firm details p.968) Hotel management, operating and franchise agreements, joint ventures, purchases and disposals form the bulk of the firm's workload. It is also well-versed in outsourcing agreements and general commercial law. The roll-call of clients principally contains owners, developers and investors. The firm acted for MWB on the purchase of the Howard Hotel and on the negotiation of a long-term management agreement with Marriott at Marble Arch. "*The best,*" **Andrew Little** is perceived by clients to be "*as good as it gets on individual hotel matters.*" **Clients:** Petter Olsen AS (Norway); MWB; Capricorn International.

Stephenson Harwood (see firm details p.1141) Active in acquisition, development and financing deals, the firm is associated with its work for the Accor Hotel Group. It acted on the acquisition and financing of eight hotels for Accor, and advised Andrew Weir & Co on the sale of its hotel division. The lead practitioner here is Robert Newman. **Clients:** Accor Group; Andrew Weir Hotels; Bass Hotels & Resorts.

Taylor Joynson Garrett (see firm details p.1150) A specialist knowledge of the leisure industry applies to the firms institutional investment clients. Highlights include completing all property work associated with the £140 million pub rental securitisation for Avebury and the re-organisation and securitisation of the Really Useful Group theatre operating business. **Clients:** Avebury Group; Stoll Moss Theatres; UGC Cinemas Limited.

TIMESHARE

TRAVEL: TIMESHARE • Nationwide	Ptnrs	Assts
1 Tods Murray WS Edinburgh	3	2
2 Baker & McKenzie London	5	6
Stones Exeter	5	6
3 Amhurst Brown Colombotti London	5	3

LEADING INDIVIDUALS
1 ANDERSON David Tods Murray WS
2 BOURNE Tim Stones

This book is the product of 6,552 1/2-hour interviews. See p.7 for BMRB audit.
Within each band, firms are listed alphabetically. *See individuals' profiles p.826*

Tods Murray WS (see firm details p.1157) Headed by the "*godfather*" of timeshare, **David Anderson** (see p.826), the firm acts for and in all areas of the timeshare industry including management agreements, trust deeds and marketing contracts. Increasingly engaged in IP matters, it has been involved in the AIM flotation of Keyworld Investments plc and the introduction of packaging a timeshare product as an investment bond. **Clients:** OTE; RCI; Barrett International Resorts and Keyworld.

Baker & McKenzie (see firm details p.868) The arrival of Mark Henrick and his team from Rowe & Mawe has added substantially to the firm's expertise in this area. Operating from a base of expertise in the regulatory and commercial field, the team acts for timeshare developers, exchange organisations and financiers. **Clients:** RCI, Sunterra Corporation.

Stones (see firm details p.1146) An "*experienced practitioner in the field – well respected*" **Tim Bourne** and his team continue to act for consumers. Concentrating on the supply side of matters, the firm also deals with contentious issues on construction, owners committees and consumer claims. Also dealt with the establishment of a London timeshare scheme and a subsequent European points scheme. It is experienced in corporate, development and trust company work. **Clients:** Owners associations; timeshare developers; timeshare funders.

Amhurst Brown Colombotti (see firm details p.858) Acting for corporate clients only, the "*knowledgeable and intelligent*" Eric Gummers and the group look after the hospitality sector in the UK and Spain. **Clients:** Interval International; Textron Financial; RMi.

LEADERS IN TRAVEL

ANDERSON, David
Tods Murray WS, Edinburgh (0131) 226 4771
david.anderson@todsmurray.com
Specialisation: All aspects of timeshare and leisure related work throughout the UK and Europe; 1975 devised legal structure for first UK timeshare project; advises developers, banks, management companies, trade bodies and other suppliers of services to timeshare industry; legal advisor and secretary to Timeshare Council; author of numerous articles.
Prof. Memberships: Law Society of Scotland.
Career: Qualified *Tods Murray* 1972; partner 1974.
Personal: Born 1948. Attended Perth Academy and Edinburgh University (1970 LLB). Leisure – golf.

ANDREA, Costas
Andrea & Co, Guildford (01483) 889880
ca@andreaco.com
Specialisation: Principal of the firm of *Andrea & Co.* Deals exclusively with travel and tourism law predominantly acting for claimants injured abroad. Currently pursuing personal injury claims in over 50 countries, as well as against UK defendants, primarily tour operators. Acted on higher profile claims such as Estonia ferry disaster and the Ethiopian airline hijacking.
Prof. Memberships: The Law Society Personal Injury Panel; Travel and Tourism Lawyers Association; Pan European Organisation of Personal Injury Lawyers. Founder member of the International Personal Injury Lawyers Association, being a network of personal injury lawyers throughout the world.
Career: Qualified in 1990 and set up the firm of *Andrea & Co* in 1997, which has quadrupled in size in its first four years.
Publications: The author of numerous articles and a consultant to the BBC and 'Holiday Which' magazine.
Personal: Born 28 December 1962. Traveled extensively prior to obtaining an LLB in 1987 before coaching the Guildford College of Law Volleyball Club. Lives in Guildford, Surrey.

BARBOR, Cynthia
Nicholson Graham & Jones, London
(020) 7360 8170
cynthia.barbor@ngj.co.uk
Specialisation: Partner in litigation department and joint head travel and leisure law unit. Main area of practice is travel and leisure law. Has over twenty years experience in acting for major UK and international tour operators, travel agents, ground handlers, insurers, hotels, airlines, car hire companies and trade associations, advising on substantial litigation, commercial agreements and regulatory issues. Also handles general commercial litigation, including insurance and personal injury actions. Writes regularly for 'Travel Trade Gazette' and other travel publications. Speaks frequently on travel law at UK and international conferences.
Prof. Memberships: Fellow of the Institute of Travel and Tourism, Incentive Travel and Meetings Association. Law Society.

BOURNE, Tim
Stones, Exeter (01392) 666 777

CARNEGIE, Andrew
Clifford Chance, London (020) 7600 1000
andrew.carnegie@cliffordchance.com
Specialisation: Partner with real estate background but specialising in property finance and hotel related work, particularly large, complex transactions. Advises hotel owners and financiers on acquisitions, sales, development projects, financings (including securitisations), management contracts and joint venture agreements.
Career: Dollar Academy, Scotland; University of Newcastle-upon-Tyne. Articled *Cartmell Shepherd*, Carlisle; solicitor *Cameron Markby* 1986-88; partner *Clifford Chance* 1996.
Personal: Fishing, shooting, skiing, hill walking. Born 1962.

CHAMBERLAIN, Simon
Field Fisher Waterhouse, London (020) 7861 4000
Specialisation: Partner in the Aviation & Travel Department specialising in commercial, corporate and regulatory work within the aviation and travel industries.
Career: Qualified in 1977. *Richards Butler & Co* 1973-81. British Airways Plc 1981-1990. *Rowe & Maw* 1990-1994. Partner at *Field Fisher Waterhouse* since 1994.
Personal: Educated at Downside School. Born 8th August 1953. Lives in East Sussex.

COURTENAY-STAMP, Bronwen
Stones, Exeter (01392) 666 777

FARRELL, Patrick
Norton Rose, London (020) 7283 6000
farrellpa@nortonrose.com
Specialisation: Advises tour operators, travel agents and airlines on claims handling, contractual disputes of all descriptions, brochure terms and conditions, bonding arrangements and regulatory matters. Also acts for airlines (including start ups) and financiers advising on domestic and European regulatory matters. Acts regularly in aircraft finance litigation.
Prof. Memberships: MRAeS, Chairman of the Royal Aeronautical Society Air Law Group, Chairman of the UK ICC Commission on Air Transport, Member of Institute of Travel and Tourism, IBA, LSLA, CLLS (Chairman of the CLLS Aeronautical Law Sub-Committee).

GARNER, Clive
Irwin Mitchell, Birmingham (0121) 212 1828
GarnerC@IrwinMitchell.co.uk
Specialisation: Partner heading *Irwin Mitchell*'s expanding International Travel Litigation Group. Acts for Claimants in accident and illness claims arising abroad. Successfully acted in many high value head and spinal injury claims and coordinated a large number of multi-party claims against English tour operators arising from illness outbreaks, coach, aviation and maritime accidents. Acted in several reported and precedent setting cases, recovering many millions of pounds in damages for clients injured abroad. Lectured nationally and internationally on personal injury, foreign claims and multi-party issues.
Prof. Memberships: Law Society Personal Injury Panel; Association of Personal Injury Lawyers; American Trial Lawyers Association; Australian Plaintiff Lawyers Association; Pan European Organisation of Personal Injury Lawyers; Travel and Tourism Lawyers Association; Society for Advanced Legal Studies; Vice-Chair of the International Practice Section of the Association of Trial Lawyers of America.
Career: Education: LLB (1988), MA (1989), LLM (1997). Articled *Irwin Mitchell*. Qualified in 1992; Partner 1997.
Publications: Author of several published articles in various journals. Regular commentator on television, radio and in the press on travel and personal injury related issues.
Personal: Born 3 April 1966. Lives in Sheffield.

GIMBLETT, Richard
Barlow Lyde & Gilbert, London (020) 7247 2277
rgimblett@blg.co.uk
See under Aviation, p.102

GWILLIAM, Michael
Vizards, Staples & Bannisters, London (020) 7400 9999
mjg@vsb.co.uk
Specialisation: Heads the Travel and Tourism Unit. Acts on behalf of tour operators and travel agents both directly and on the instruction of their liability insurers. Involved in litigation both in this jurisdiction and overseas in cross-border disputes. Acted on behalf of the Defendants in the recent cases of Brannan v Airtours Holiday Ltd, Hone v Going Places and Gallagher v Airtours Holiday Ltd. Involved in the defence of large multi-party actions brought against tour operators in relation to illness suffered abroad, as well as in relation to major incidents involving fatalities and serious injury.
Career: Articled *Vizards* 1989. Partner 1995. Partner *Vizards Staples and Bannisters* 1999.
Personal: Educated Leeds Grammar School and Exeter University. Interests include skiing, sailing and scuba-diving. Resides London.

HENDERSON, Stuart
Irwin Mitchell, Birmingham (0121) 212 1828
See under Personal Injury, p.647

HOUSTON, Paul
Field Fisher Waterhouse, London (020) 7861 4000
Specialisation: Paul has specialised in hotel and leisure property work since qualification. He has extensive experience of managing the roll-out of branded leisure concepts and franchise operations. In addition, he advises institutional investors in the acquisition, development, disposal and forward funding of properties in the hotel and leisure sector. His clients include Luminar PLC, Marriott, Travel Inn, David Lloyd Leisure and Deutsche Property Asset Management.
Prof. Memberships: Law Society.
Career: Qualified as a solicitor in Scotland in 1989 and in England and Wales in 1991. Paul was articled at *Ross Harper & Murphy* in Glasgow, joined *FFW* in 1989 and became a partner in 1995.
Personal: Born 3 April 1965. Chryston High School; University of Strathclyde. Married, 2 children. Leisure interests include golf, skiing and music.

INGLEBY, Claire
Mason Bond, Leeds (0113) 242 4444
Specialisation: Partner in travel law department. Specialises in drafting and advising on contractual and other documentation of all descriptions for tour operators. Has drafted booking conditions for many major operators and prepares, amongst others, supplier's contracts, agency agreements, promotional agreements and conditions and brochure wording. Presently particularly involved in advising on "unfair terms" in booking conditions. Also advises on regulatory matters. Conducts in-house seminars for tour operators on a number of subjects, including the Disability Discrimination Act. Provides advice on all areas of law affecting tour operators. Firm acts on behalf of more than 100 tour operators of varying sizes. Also represents travel agents, newspapers and a trade association. Author of a number of articles for the 'Travel Law Journal' and one for 'The Legal Executive'. Has lectured for the University of Northumbria and addressed the annual conference of ABTOF in 1994, 1995 and 1996.
Prof. Memberships: Law Society.
Career: Joined *Mason Bond* on qualification in 1990. Became a partner in 1994.
Personal: Born 5th December 1965. Exeter University 1984-87. Leisure activities include hill walking. Lives near Skipton, North Yorkshire.

LEVY, David N
Berwin Leighton Paisner, London (020) 7760 1000
david.levy@berwinleightonpaisner.com
Specialisation: Partner in property department specialising in all types of commercial property work including planning. Acts in particular for the leading companies in the hotel and leisure fields and over 20 years has dealt with the acquisition and disposal of many hundreds of hotels, restaurants and leisure properties of all types. Also has specialist involvement with motorway service areas. Most recent large transaction involvement in disposal of entire hotel portfolio by Compass Group plc for sums in excess of £3 billion.
Prof. Memberships: Law Society. Business In Sport & Leisure. British Israel Law Association.
Career: Educated at Wanstead County High School and Hertford College Oxford. Qualified in 1972. Became a partner at *Paisner & Co* in 1976 (now *Berwin Leighton Paisner*).
Personal: Born 1948. Resides Finchley, London. Married with two children.

LITTLE, Andrew
Garretts, London (020) 7344 0344

MASON, Stephen
Mason Bond, Leeds (0113) 242 4444
Specialisation: Partner in travel law department. Advises tour operators and travel agents. Work includes defending claims brought by consumers, advocacy, dealing with trading standards departments, conducting seminars. Also handles commercial aspects of travel law, including commercial disputes and litigation, copyright, trademarks and passing off. Acted in Bowerman and Wallace v ABTA 1995 CA, Thomson Holidays v Birch 1999 DC and in many first instance travel law cases reported in Current Law. Joint Editor of the 'Travel Law Journal'. Has addressed numerous seminars on travel law topics advertised by the University of Northumbria, held at the Institute of Advanced Legal Studies, London; and also teaches Civil Advocacy. Higher Courts (Civil Pro-

ceedings) Qualification 1994. Used these Rights of Audience to defend a major tour operator successfully against a large claim in the High Court, January 1997 and to appear in the Divisional Court in Dudley v Inspirations East Ltd 1997. Joint Author 'Holiday Law' Sweet & Maxwell (2nd ed) 1998; Member of the Law Society Civil Litigation Committee since 1997.
Prof. Memberships: Law Society, International Federation of Travel and Tourism Advocates.
Career: Qualified 1974. Senior partner since 1986.
Personal: Married, three children. Attended Bradford Grammar School to 1967, and Cambridge University to 1971. Leisure interests include travel, acting and supporting Leeds United FC. Lives in Ilkley, West Yorkshire.

MULLIGAN, Claire
Badhams, London (020) 7242 4154
claire.mulligan@blm-law.com
Specialisation: One of the firm's two partners specialising in travel litigation, as part of the firm's travel litigation unit. Advises tour operators, insurers, travel agents and hotels. Handles a variety of claims including class actions, diving accidents, substantial litigation and resort outbreaks. Recent court successes included the Court of Appeal case of Codd v Thomson Travel which confirmed that local regulations, not British standards, apply to Package Travel Litigation. Usually acts for tour operators or insurers as opposed to individuals. Regularly contributes to insurance press and many recent successes are reported in law reports. Provides in-house seminars to tour operators.
Prof. Memberships: Travel and Tourism Lawyers Association.
Career: Qualified in 1995, made partner in 2000.

NICOLL, Richard
Richards Butler, London (020) 7247 6555
rxn@richardsbutler.com
Specialisation: Has over 25 years experience in all aspects of commercial property investment and development. Acts for a broad range of investors, developers and end users of commercial and residential properties in the UK and internationally. Specialises in high profile and complex development projects (often involving leisure/hotel operator) and on innovative property owning and management structures. Clients included the Rank Group, Parkview (Battersea Power Station), Trillium, Britannia Building Society, Warner holdings, Oasis Villages and British Gas pension fund.
Prof. Memberships: Law Society.
Career: Qualified 1974, joined *Richards Butler* in 1972. Headed property group between 1995-2000. Appointed to the partnership board in 2000.
Personal: Born 1950. Leisure interests include fishing, rugby and sports generally. Member of MCC.

PEARS, Melanie
Eversheds, Newcastle upon Tyne (0191) 2611661
melaniepears@eversheds.com
Specialisation: Partner. Acts as adviser to many household name travel sector clients. Work involves client compliance audits, drafting of terms and conditions, consumer complaint handling, intellectual property disputes and general commercial matters. Has written for the Travel Law Journal and has presented papers at many recent IBA conferences.
Career: Qualified in 1994. Originally trained as a barrister, after which worked in industry for Shell and then in publishing, before joining *Eversheds* 1989.
Personal: Born 10th February 1965.

PHILLIPS, Rachel
Berwin Leighton Paisner, London (020) 7760 1000
rachel.phillips@berwinleightonpaisner.com
Specialisation: All aspects of commercial real estate, especially in the hospitality and leisure sectors. 2000/01 acted on property aspects of the sale by Compass Hotels of its entire hotel portfolio for over £3 billion.
Prof. Memberships: Hotel Property Network (steering committee member since 1997).
Career: Articled in *Paisner & Co*; qualified 1989. Assistant solicitor *Paisner & Co* 1989-96. Assistant solicitor *Wilde Sapte* 1996-99. Partner *Paisner & Co* 1999-2001. Partner *Berwin Leighton Paisner* 2001.
Personal: Born 1964. Educated North London Collegiate School and Cambridge University (Newnham College). Church organist/choirmaster.

PICKUP, Bryan
SJ Berwin, London (020) 7533 2468
bryan.pickup@sjberwin.com
Specialisation: Head of Property Department. Covers a wide variety of property transactions for investors and developers. Also handles the sale, purchase and funding of leisure businesses such as golf clubs, hotels, bingo clubs, cinemas, arenas and sports facilities. Has acted on the funding and acquisition and disposal of leisure parks, the flotation of Holmes Place plc, the acquisition of the nightclubs and bars businesses of First Leisure and a number of restaurant transactions.
Prof. Memberships: Business in Sport & Leisure. British Property Federation.
Career: Qualified in 1981. Joined *SJ Berwin & Co* in 1988 as a Partner.
Personal: Born 15th April 1953. Attended Whitgift School Croydon 1961-69 and Fitzwilliam College, Cambridge 1970-74. Leisure interests include golf and hockey. Lives in Wimbledon.

PLANT, Patrick
Linklaters, London (020) 7456 4718
patrick.plant@linklaters.com
See under Property (Commercial), p.751

QUICKE, Martin
Denton Wilde Sapte, London (020) 7242 1212

ROBINSON, Tim
Nicholson Graham & Jones, London (020) 7360 8162
tim.robinson@ngj.co.uk
Specialisation: Partner in Litigation Department, joint Head Travel and Leisure Law Group. Travel, Tourism and Leisure law. Acts for tour operators, travel agents, hotel groups, insurers, airlines and trade associations. Also handles general commercial litigation, libel and media acting for newspaper and magazine publishers. Writes for Travel Trade Gazette and major travel and tourism publications, the national press, TV and radio. Speaks at travel industry conferences in the UK and worldwide.
Prof. Memberships: Institute of Travel and Tourism, Media Society, Incentive Travel and Meeting Association, Pacific Asia Travel Association (UK chairman and worldwide board director), European Tour Operators Association, International Hotel and Restaurant Association.
Career: Qualified 1977. Joined *Nicholson Graham & Jones* 1979. Partner 1982.
Personal: Born in 1953. Attended St Edmund Hall, Oxford 1971-73. Leisure interests include music, reading, and classic cars.

RYLAND, David
SJ Berwin, London (020) 7533 2222
david.ryland@sjberwin.com
Specialisation: Hotel and leisure sales and purchases, structured finance transactions, management contracts, joint ventures and the establishment of collective investment schemes. Transactions dealt with in the last year relating to the hotel and leisure industry include the negotiation of forward funding agreements relating to substantial leisure parks, the negotiation of new Mal Maison chain of hotels including the negotiation of the joint venture SAS, the sale and leaseback of 11 Hilton Hotels and regulatory agreements relating to a number of new Hilton Hotels, a portfolio of seven hotels for Hilton and the redevelopment of the Great Western Hotel. He has also been involved in the establishment of a wide range of tax efficient collective investment vehicles for property investment for an aggregate value of £2.5 billion.
Career: *Clifford Chance* 1981-88; *SJ Berwin & Co* 1988-date. Dulwich College: 1965-72; Exeter College Oxford University: 1973-77 (double first in Mods and Greats). Frequent lecturer and writer of articles on property investment related matters.
Personal: Married. Interests include sport, music and cinema.

SEARS, Trevor
Davenport Lyons, London (020) 7468 2600
tsears@kingsfords.co.uk
Specialisation: Local counsel to the International Air Transport Association (IATA) and consultant to airlines with particular regard to their relationship with travel agents. Licensed Insolvency Practitioner and speaker at airline and travel seminars, radio and TV.
Prof. Memberships: FABRP
Career: Qualified 1972. Joined *Booth and Blackwell*. Partner 1974. Senior partner 1990.
Publications: Author of chapter 'Travel Insolvency' in Tolley's 'Insolvency Law'.
Personal: Born 1948. Educated at Epsom College. Lives in Surrey. Interests include travel, music, hockey and people.

SKUSE, Ian
Piper Smith & Basham, London (020) 7828 8685
Specialisation: Partner and Head of Travel and Litigation. Acts for large and small travel agents, tour operators, airlines and for business travel agents. Practice covers claims, corporate and commercial work of all kinds including negotiations with Regulators including ABTA, CAA, IATA and Trading Standards Officers. Extensive experience in negotiating commercial agreements concerning all aspects of the travel business, both leisure and business. Excellent track record at managing litigation of all kinds in the Courts and with trade association and Regulators. Expert guidance offered through the regulatory framework of ATOL Licensing, Code of Conduct matters and Airline Regulation. The firm has recently acted in a number of major corporate acquistitions in both the leisure and business sector. A regular columnist for Business Travel World and the Independent

on Sunday and founder member of the consultancy group, Travel Resources.
Prof. Memberships: Institute of Travel and Tourism, CIMTIG.
Career: Qualified in 1980. *Piper Smith & Basham* in 1983 . Partner since 1987.

STEWART, Peter
Field Fisher Waterhouse, London (020) 7861 4000
Specialisation: Partner and Head of Aviation Travel and Tourism Department. Practice covers commercial areas (contentious and non-contentious) concerning the travel industry. Non-contentious work includes contractual arrangements between travel companies and their suppliers, compliance with regulatory requirements, joint ventures and business sales/purchases. Contentious work includes disputes with suppliers, other travel companies and customers. Author of 'A Practical Guide to Package Holiday Law and Contracts' (third edition 1993) and regular articles for ITT journal and other trade papers. Regularly lectures for IBC and ITT at travel industry conferences.
Prof. Memberships: IFTTA, ITT.
Career: Qualified 1982, having joined *Field Fisher Waterhouse* in 1980. Became a Partner in 1985.
Personal: Born 3rd February 1956. Attended Campbell College in Belfast 1969-73, then Pembroke College Cambridge 1974-77. Leisure interests include golf, tennis and music. Lives near Sevenoaks, Kent.

WIGNALL, Douglas
Douglas Wignall & Co, London (020) 7583 1362

TRUSTS & PERSONAL TAX

London: 830; South: 833; Thames Valley: 834; South West: 834; Wales: 836; Midlands: 836; East Anglia: 837; North West: 837; North East: 838; Scotland: 839; N. Ireland: 839; *Profiles*: 740

RESEARCH APPROVED BY BMRB: *For this edition,* Chambers' *researchers conducted 6,552 interviews – 4,419 with law firms, 554 with barristers and 1,579 with clients.*

The validity of the research was scrutinised by BMRB International, who audited both the methodology and the results at our offices in July 2001. They interviewed Chambers' *researchers and cross-checked sample interviews. Details of the audit appear on page 7.*

LONDON

TRUSTS & PERSONAL TAX • London	Ptnrs	Assts
1 Allen & Overy	4	17
Macfarlanes	7	14
Withers	19	18
2 Lawrence Graham	9	13
3 Boodle Hatfield	6	7
Charles Russell	8	6
Currey & Co	7	4
Payne Hicks Beach	8	2
4 Bircham Dyson Bell	8	9
Farrer & Co	12	7
Forsters	5	6
Nicholson Graham & Jones	4	2
Speechly Bircham	7	12
Taylor Joynson Garrett	9	7
5 Baker & McKenzie	4	3
Hunters	7	1
Linklaters	1	5
Radcliffes	7	6
Rooks Rider	7	8
Simmons & Simmons	n/a	n/a
Wedlake Bell	6	5
6 Berwin Leighton Paisner	6	4
Dawson & Co	6	4
Lee & Pembertons	2	1
Maxwell Batley	1	3
May, May & Merrimans	*	*
Trowers & Hamlins	4	2
Witham Weld	2	2

This book is the product of 6,552 1/2 hour interviews. See p.7 for BMRB audit.
Within each band, firms are listed alphabetically.

Allen & Overy (see firm details p.856) "*The only magic circle firm to take this area seriously,*" it is especially known for its strong commercial focus. "*Particularly impressive on the international front,*" the team has an imposing international client base, and was said by one client to be "*an exceptional team, doing cutting edge work.*" **Richard Turnor** (see p.848) handles complex trusts and partnership matters and is praised by fellow lawyers for "*fighting in a balanced way and finding solutions to problems.*" The "*competent and professional*" **Clare Maurice** (see p.845) continues to attract substantial market approval, while **Ceris Gardner** (see p.842)'s star continues in the ascendant. Popular among peers and clients, she is regarded as an "*increasingly impressive practitioner.*" The firm advised on the restructuring of the international holding vehicles of Venezuelan clients in advance of the 31 December 2000 deadline, using English law trusts and Dutch limited partnerships. Trust litigation work includes advising a major trust company on court proceedings relating to sums totalling in excess of £100 million, in respect of which title is subject to dispute.

Macfarlanes (see firm details p.1046) "*Superb across the board,*" the trusts team is regarded as the "*quintessence of quality and expertise.*" A large team advises international entities and a notable stable of entrepreneurial clients on a range of big-ticket work. The "*excellent*" **John Rhodes** (see p.846), an expert on wealth structuring, and "*outstanding technician*" **Michael Hayes** (see p.843) constitute the group's formidable spearhead. Said to ally practical sense with technical expertise, the duo receive high marks for "*explaining difficult concepts without resorting to jargon.*" Rising star **Matthew Pintus** (see p.846) joins the rankings following peer commendation of his predominantly onshore tax and trust practice.The firm's wide-ranging caseload has included the completion of the administration of a multi-billion dollar off-shore estate and advising on an enquiry by the UK Revenue into the affairs of an internationally renowned family and its associated business interests and trusts. Other work includes representing a widow in negotiating a partition of her late husband's £80 million estate, and advising large international financial institutions and wealthy South American families on the use of trusts governed by English law.

Withers (see firm details p.1187) An enormous private client practice with an emphasis on the more traditional landed client has continued to advance in prestige, aided by the acquisition of a number of new lateral hires. Said to have "*a good sense of direction and proportion,*" the department includes a number of recognised experts in the private client field. Foremost among these are **Stephen Cooke** (see p.841), "*a tremendously able, down to earth, pragmatic practitioner with a firm grasp of the issues,*" and the "*level-headed and sensible*" **Tony Thompson** (see p.847). Newly ranked **Murray Hallam** (see p.843) has a reputation for being "*pleasant to deal with*" and is known for his "*sound academic approach*" to trusts matters. **John Riches** (see p.846) has an established name on the banking side, while **Robin Paul** (see p.846) is "*solid and practical.*" Highlights of the past year include acting for the founding shareholders of Carphone Warehouse Group on personal tax issues arising from the IPO of the company, and advising the major shareholders of Chernikeef Networks on tax and trust issues relating to the sale of the company for £200 million. The team also advised offshore trustees and beneficiaries on the release of value from a property company listed on the London Stock Exchange following its takeover. This included applications to court for the variation of trusts and for directions on resolution of contentious issues.

Lawrence Graham (see firm details p.1030) A practice with a large private banking client base and a strong commercial focus, it is commended by clients for its "*dynamism and responsiveness.*" The team's name is still founded on the rock of the personal reputation of the "*first-rate*" **Martyn Gowar** (see p.842), described to *Chambers'* researchers as "*an obvious star.*" He leads a department which recently advised a client on the restructuring of the trust-based ownership of a billion pound art collection, following changes to the underlying beneficiary's tax position. The team was also instructed on the UK's largest ever offer of heritage chattels to the nation in lieu of death duties, and continues to administer the estate of the late Diana, Princess of Wales.

LEADING INDIVIDUALS

1	**AVERY JONES John** Speechly Bircham	**GOWAR Martyn** Lawrence Graham
	HAYES Michael Macfarlanes	**MOYSE Richard** Boodle Hatfield
	RHODES John Macfarlanes	
2	**BRIDGES Mark** Farrer & Co	**BROWN Graham** Payne Hicks Beach
	MELLOR Eliza Nicholson Graham & Jones	
	POWELL Nicholas Currey & Co	**TURNOR Richard** Allen & Overy
3	**BOYD-CARPENTER Henry** Farrer & Co	**COOKE Stephen** Withers
	DOLMAN Robert Wedlake Bell	**GARNHAM Caroline** Simmons & Simmons
	JARMAN Chris Payne Hicks Beach	**MAURICE Clare** Allen & Overy
	REID Nigel Linklaters	**STANFORD-TUCK Michael** Taylor Joynson
	SYED Catriona Charles Russell	**THOMPSON Tony** Withers
	WILLIS David Forsters	
4	**BUZZONI Mark** Taylor Joynson Garrett	**GARDNER Ceris** Allen & Overy
	GOODWIN Peter Bircham Dyson Bell	**HALLAM Murray** Withers
	HOWE Kate Boodle Hatfield	**JACOB Nicholas** Rooks Rider
	JACOBS Michael Nicholson Graham	**KENNEDY John** Hunters
	KIRBY Richard Speechly Bircham	**LONG David** Charles Russell
	MURDIE Alastair Payne Hicks Beach	**PAUL Robin** Withers
	RICHARDSON Joseph Dawson & Co	**RICHES John** Withers
	ROBINSON David Forsters	**STIBBARD Paul** Baker & McKenzie
UP AND COMING		
	PINTUS Matthew Macfarlanes	

See individuals' profiles p.740

Boodle Hatfield (see firm details p.889) A solid track record in landed estates work, combined with an increasing reputation for international advice keep the firm near the top of most people's private client ratings. Senior partner **Richard Moyse** (see p.845) maintains a high profile and receives praise for his "*astute and sensible leadership.*" He acted as an expert witness to one of the parties in a high-profile dispute in Bermuda. **Kate Howe** (see p.843), who specialises in tax planning, also receives market commendation, and is considered to be "*coming along nicely.*" She has advised on the restructuring of complex and high value family trusts, as well as the review and restructure of a number of offshore structures holding UK residential property. The team has provided tax advice to property developers and investors including Grosvenor, advised on a multi-million pound probate, following a sudden death, and represented a Swiss family on a major hotel development.

Charles Russell (see firm details p.912) The injection of the Norton Rose private client team is seen to have brought real strength to the practice, which is considered by peers to be "*motoring ahead.*" Advising both traditional and newer clients, the team was described by one as a "*responsive, thoughtful and thorough group.*" **Catriona Syed** (see p.847), head of the department, has been characterised as "*a genuinely impressive force.*" In the past year, she and her team have advised leading businessmen and their trustees on tax planning prior to the sale of their companies and on tax-efficient single stock diversification planning. The firm also advised on the establishment of a substantial international charitable foundation in Switzerland for a UK client, and acted on the restructuring of offshore trusts for non-UK based clients. **David Long**, who advised on an international trust dispute involving funds in excess of $100 million, remains recommended for his private client work.

Currey & Co Handling all aspects of traditional tax and trusts work, this niche private client firm continues to be rated as "*the country's best kept secret.*" The team is considered to be "*nothing short of brilliant*" in the traditional landed estates arena, where **Nicholas Powell** stands out as a "*precise, straightforward, solution-oriented*" lawyer.

Payne Hicks Beach (see firm details p.1092) The recipient of widespread market praise this year, the private client team rises in the *Chambers* tables, and is renowned for the quality of its individual lawyers. **Graham Brown** (see p.840) runs a diverse practice and wins peer approval as a "*civilised operator with fine technical skills.*" **Chris Jarman** (see p.843) specialises in the taxation of land transactions, property development and charities and is said to be "*precise and scholarly.*" **Alastair Murdie** has a focus on the taxation of agricultural estates, farms and related matters. He is rated for his "*lightness of touch and ability to make matters simple.*" The firm has advised on high profile offshore trust litigation, and acted for wealthy businessmen and the private banking department of a major bank. Heritage property transactions have involved works of art, stately homes and museums.

Bircham Dyson Bell (see firm details p.883) Consolidating its position in the market, the firm earns high marks from clients for its level of partner involvement and "*ability to relate to the businessman.*" **Peter Goodwin** (see p.842) is accorded much of the credit for the group's progress and is described by fellow practitioners as "*intellectually able, honourable and a cracking good practitioner.*" His team advised on a complex tax-saving scheme, involving a trust in which the sole asset was a valuable house, which was settled by mediation. The firm also acted on an international probate and trust dispute involving several English trusts, an estate with assets in five jurisdictions, and litigation in Florida and Switzerland.

Farrer & Co (see firm details p.954) Although retaining a reputation for being "*ultra-conservative,*" the firm is also acknowledged to have few peers for expertise in landed transactions, where it boasts a huge array of clients. The "*technically able*" **Henry Boyd-Carpenter** (see p.840) continues in his high profile role as solicitor to the Queen, while **Mark Bridges** (see p.840) is viewed as an "*industrious and bright performer.*" Recent work has included the creation of tax saving schemes and international structures to hold the wealth of entrepreneurs with assets around the world. The firm has also been active in the development and creation of income and capital tax structuring schemes, and advised the Wernher Foundation during the sale of part of the Wernher Collection. Other work has included the administration of the worldwide estate and intellectual property of the late novelist Patrick O'Brien.

Forsters Perceived to be developing well, the firm's private client capacity includes a respected offshore practice. **David Willis** (see p.848) is well regarded by peers as a "*sensible deal-doer,*" while head of department **David Robinson** (see p.847) is also warmly recommended for his extensive experience. Highlights of the past year include advising the trustees of family settlements on their duties and liabilities following a de-merger of underlying companies. The firm also advised the executors of an estate in respect of claims against the German Government for compensation due to the deceased for expropriation of property during World War II.

Nicholson Graham & Jones (see firm details p.1081) Still felt to be competing successfully with larger rivals, the firm continues to advise a number of leading international families in relation to estate planning. Leading figure **Eliza Mellor** (see p.845) has earned the respect of peers for her "*highly intelligent, forthright and sensible manner.*" Her colleague **Michael Jacobs** (see p.843) is also rated as a "*sound technician.*" The firm advised two concert pianists of worldwide renown on international tax planning issues, as well as several individuals involved in institutional fund management on their personal tax planning.

Speechly Bircham (see firm details p.1136) Offering tax and succession advice at home and boasting a substantial international dimension, the department continues to benefit from the presence of the "*extraordinary*" **John Avery Jones** (see p.840). "*Phenomenally learned and a technical master,*" he continues to be one of the sector's main points of reference. **Richard Kirby** (see p.844) received specific commendation for his work on financial products, and is characterised as an "*intelligent lawyer with commercial acumen.*" The firm advised on the establishment of trusts for an Italian company flotation, incorporating the use of double tax legislation. International trust work also includes co-ordinating investment strategies and hedge funds, and dovetailing UK, French, Canadian and Caribbean tax systems.

Taylor Joynson Garrett (see firm details p.1150) Known for advising wealthy families on special structures both onshore and off, this "*decent*" practice has a substantial reputation and some significant clients. **Michael Stanford-Tuck** (see p.847) is "*a wily operator,*" while **Mark Buzzoni** has an "*efficient manner and pitches his advice ideally.*" The team has advised in relation to the taxation of intellectual property rights held by creators such as new economy entrepreneurs.

Baker & McKenzie (see firm details p.868) Building a strong reputation for advising banks and for its work overseas, the private client team enters the rankings this year. Clients see **Paul Stibbard** (see p.847) as someone who "*has a feel for the needs of the international company.*" The firm has advised international banks and their clients in relation to modifications to offshore structures necessary as a result of the Mexican/Venezuelan anti-avoidance legislation. This has involved restructuring trusts and offshore company structures through the use of UK trusts and dual resident UK and Swiss trusts.

Hunters (see firm details p.1006) A sound general all-round practice which was recently augmented by the addition of another partner and assistant from Alexanders. The firm advises substantial landed estates, together with an increased number of professionals. The popular **John Kennedy** (see p.844) is "*good to deal with on complex matters.*" Recent work includes heritage property matters, probate, wills, works trusts and inheritance tax planning.

Linklaters (see firm details p.1042) A small but well-respected practice is headed by **Nigel Reid** (see p.846), admired by his peers for his "*impressive efforts*" in keeping the department in the public eye. Work over the past year has included acting for a partnership on the purchase of an existing trust business and advising a major banking client in establishing a bare trust which also constituted a separate legal entity for US tax purposes. The firm also represented a body of non-UK trustees on an application to the English Court under the Variation of Trusts Act 1958 to allow the trustees to reimburse the tax liabilities of the settler.

Radcliffes (see firm details p.1103) Considered to be increasing its strength in depth, the team, headed by Clara Trounson, gains high marks from clients who appreciate the group's "*commitment to the task in hand*" and the "*nice balance they strike between a big team and the personal touch.*" The past year's caseload has involved, *inter alia,* advising an entrepreneur on residency issues and mitigation of potential capital gains tax liability in excess of £3 million. The team also advised on the creation of a charitable foundation with assets in excess of £60 million. Overseas, the firm has represented US intermediaries and financial advisers on the mitigation of liability to US and Mexican tax through the establishment of UK and offshore structures.

Rooks Rider (see firm details p.1110) Small, but highly respected, the firm has a sound reputation both for domestic and international tax and trusts work. The "*intellectual*" **Nicholas Jacob** (see p.843) is said to "*know his stuff*" and has built an excellent reputation for his international work. The firm has seen an increase in instructions from the Far East, advising on trust variations and offshore trusts for non-UK domiciled clients. The team also handles high value international probates for overseas clients with interests in the UK.

Simmons & Simmons (see firm details p.1132) A "*small team with a big reputation,*" it acts for a variety of high-powered clients, and is particularly acclaimed for its cutting-edge international work. Head of department **Caroline Garnham** (see p.842) is respected for her "*forthright and straightforward approach.*"

Wedlake Bell (see firm details p.1175) A mixed practice advises a variety of domestic clients, including traditional landed gentry and entrepreneurs, as well as handling offshore matters for overseas individuals. The team is especially known for its expertise in heritage property and works of art. **Robert Dolman** (see p.841) focuses much of his time on advising overseas-domiciled clients, and has an "*effective and undemonstrative*" style. Work over the past year has included creating open-ended investment companies for private individuals, and representing the private offices of wealthy families.

Berwin Leighton Paisner (see firm details p.878) The recently merged firm continues to maintain a respected private client practice, typically dealing with entrepreneurial clients and one-off structuring for international banks and trust companies. Recent work includes advising on the restructuring requirements of a number of trusts, including a trust matter for a client from the Far East with a value in excess of $250 million. The team also acted on the reported case *Re Ratcliffe,* concerning whether non-charitable beneficiaries under a will should receive their bequest subject to inheritance tax.

Dawson & Co (see firm details p.936) The "*technically able, practical and easy-going*" **Joseph Richardson** (see p.846) heads a solid team which undertakes the administration of sizeable and complex estates, many involving an overseas element, as well as advising on heritage, business and agricultural property and on all aspects of taxation. The team's recent caseload has included capital tax planning by way of reinvestment relief and enterprise investment schemes devised to defer or avoid capital gains tax.

Lee & Pembertons (see firm details p.1035) A firm with a hard-working reputation, which continues to serve a loyal clientele on a range of tax issues, including tax planning. Clients include wealthy individuals and overseas trusts.

Maxwell Batley (see firm details p.1058) A small practice headed up by the well-respected Frank O'Shea. Recent matters handled include a large international trust dispute and UK and cross-border probate from all over the world, referred by banks and other asset holders.

May, May & Merrimans (see firm details p.1058) An old style, traditional private client practice with a "*straight as a die*" reputation and an admirable client base, it remains especially noted for its expertise in heritage property matters.

Trowers & Hamlins (see firm details p.1162) Although possessing a comparatively low profile, the department, headed by Michael Williamson, maintains the approval of its peers and clients. Among a varied workload, the team has advised on multi-jurisdictional testamentary and tax planning and multi-jurisdictional probate work, including advice on tax aspects. The team also acts for entrepreneurs and City professionals on wills, trusts and tax planning, and has also advised on offshore structures for investing in property in the Caribbean.

Witham Weld (see firm details p.1187) A "*small but focused practice,*" it is best known for advising on revenue and tax planning, wills and probates for a mixed clientele, among which religious institutions are particularly notable.

THE SOUTH

TRUSTS & PERSONAL TAX • The South	Ptnrs	Assts
1 **Cripps Harries Hall** Tunbridge Wells	8	3
Thomas Eggar Church Adams Chichester	11	3
2 **Adams & Remers** Lewes	3	2
Stevens & Bolton Guildford	3	3
Thomson Snell & Passmore Tunbridge Wells	6	4
White & Bowker Winchester	3	2
3 **Blake Lapthorn** Portsmouth	3	4
Moore & Blatch Lymington	1	2
Mundays Esher	5	2
Paris Smith & Randall Southampton	1	2
Penningtons Godalming	4	4
4 **Brachers** Maidstone	2	1
Charles Russell Guildford	1	4
DMH Brighton	1	1
Lester Aldridge Bournemouth	4	4
5 **Barlows** Surrey	1	1
Buss Murton Tunbridge Wells	2	n/a
George Ide, Phillips Chichester	4	3
Griffith Smith Brighton	2	2
Whitehead Monckton Maidstone	3	2

LEADING INDIVIDUALS	
1 **KING-JONES Amanda** Thomas Eggar Church Adams	
LENEY Simon Cripps Harries Hall	
THORNELY Richard Thomas Eggar Church Adams	
2 **ACOMB Nick** Stevens & Bolton	**GLAZIER Barry** Lester Aldridge
KRAFFT James Thomson Snell & Passmore	**ROGERSON Gary** Cripps Harries Hall
THURSTON Martyn White & Bowker	**WALLEY Ray** Mundays

This book is the product of 6,552 1/2 hour interviews. See p.7 for BMRB audit.

Within each band, firms are listed alphabetically. *See individuals' profiles p.740*

Cripps Harries Hall (see firm details p.927) A practice with a strong reputation, particularly for its tax planning advice and investment work. Head of department **Simon Leney** (see p.844) has a stellar list of clients and is commended for his "*sensible and constructive advice.*" The "*impressive*" **Gary Rogerson** (see p.847) is also highly respected by his peers. The firm has advised a number of wealthy individuals on their personal affairs, specialising in integrated legal, tax and financial advice.

Thomas Eggar Church Adams (see firm details p.1153) Renowned for its investment arm, this "*highly competitive*" practice includes two of the region's outstanding practitioners. **Amanda King-Jones** (see p.844) is particularly noted for her probate work and inheritance tax planning advice, while **Richard Thornely** (see p.848) is involved in estate planning both domestically and offshore, and has a charitable aspect to his practice. The team has been involved in a broad range of Court of Protection work and estate planning, and has been responsible for administrating over 500 trusts. A stand-alone pension trusteeship department has recently been established at the firm.

Adams & Remers Reckoned to be "*developing quietly but effectively,*" the firm continues to act for a high number of landed estates and individuals of high net worth. The past year has seen a noticeable increase in offshore work.

Stevens & Bolton (see firm details p.1143) Now acknowledged by rivals as "*serious competitors,*" the firm's presence on cutting-edge work sees it rise in this year's tables. Head of department **Nick Acomb** (see p.840) also received widespread market endorsement. Significant work over the past year includes advising on the mitigation of capital gains liability to shareholders who sold an IT company for £20 million. The firm also advised on the implementation of tax schemes for UK corporate clients of a leading national firm of accountants, using employee benefit trusts. Elsewhere, the team acted on the reorganisation of an offshore trust structure for an overseas-domiciled individual, who owned UK property worth around £5 million.

Thomson Snell & Passmore (see firm details p.1155) "*High quality*" traditional private client practice, whose head of department, **James Krafft** (see p.844), remains highly rated for his "*steadying experience.*" The firm has advised on several multi-million pound estates and probates and has continued to act for substantial trusts, including an individual trust worth over £75 million. The firm also represented the interests of a number of wealthy individuals.

White & Bowker (see firm details p.1178) The practice's reputation has strengthened considerably over the past year, and it continues to advise a mixture of landed clients and entrepreneurs on high value estates and trusts matters. Held in high regard by his peers, **Martyn Thurston** (see p.848)'s presence is seen as a "*a real plus for the firm,*" and he is respected for his "*ability to get the job done without fuss.*"

Blake Lapthorn (see firm details p.886) The focus of the department is now on its newly consolidated personal tax, trust and probate teams. Work over the past year includes the handling of the purchase and sale of properties in France, along with associated tax and trust work. The department, which includes two French Notaires Stagières, handled over 200 French property matters in 2000.

Moore & Blatch (see firm details p.1072) A multi-disciplinary practice, with a reputation for "*quality and depth,*" which also provides investment services. The practice focuses on complete wealth management, including inheritance planning and the preparation of tax-effective wills for high net worth individuals.

Mundays (see firm details p.1077) Especially noted for its onshore prowess, the firm continues to progress up the rankings. **Ray Walley** (see p.848) makes his debut in the tables, following recommendation from both peers and clients. The team has advised on agricultural and business property relief, retirement relief and the creation of charitable trusts.

Paris Smith & Randall (see firm details p.1089) A "*reliable*" department, praised by its peers for its work on behalf of a mix of both old and new money clients. The team undertakes a range of trust planning and estate work and includes a substantial international aspect in its practice.

Penningtons (see firm details p.1093) Best known for its private client work in the agricultural sector, the team administers around 300 charitable and private trusts and deals with tax compliance work and personal tax planning. Agricultural work has included the restructuring of a number of farming businesses to take advantage of inheritance tax relief. The firm also advised on the acceleration of an inheritance tax exemption through the variation of a will.

Brachers (see firm details p.893) Another firm with a high reputation for agricultural work, where it is reported to be "*superb.*" The practice focuses on advising high net worth individuals, and it recently acted for one of the world's largest law firms on its equity partner benefits package. The team has also dealt with probate in respect of 18 estates, each valued at over a million pounds.

Charles Russell (see firm details p.912) Traditional private client firm, respected locally, which is also felt to benefit from the expertise of its London office. The practice acts for high profile, wealthy individuals, including those in senior positions in business and industry. The team recently advised on a large and complex settled estate in the West Country.

DMH (see firm details p.944) A private client practice with a corporate slant, advising on probate, trusts, wills and estate planning. The team advises high net worth individuals and family companies, with an emphasis on offshore and cross-border taxation.

Lester Aldridge (see firm details p.1038) The only private client firm to have made an impact in Dorset, it still boasts the services of the respected **Barry Glazier** (see p.842). A varied caseload has included preparing and implementing a pre-death tax saving scheme for a terminally ill client and the repatriation of three offshore family trusts under the Variation of Trusts Act. The team has also acted on various matrimonial finance disputes with aggregate assets in dispute of over £50 million, involving overseas and substantial corporate interests.

Other Notable Firms A long-established name in Guildford, **Barlows** has an especially good reputation for onshore work. **George Ide, Phillips** is widely respected for its trusts advice, while **Griffith Smith** and **Whitehead Monckton** are both described as "*professional and straightforward*" practices. **Buss Murton** also continues to maintain its share of market support.

THAMES VALLEY

TRUSTS & PERSONAL TAX • Thames Valley		Ptnrs	Assts
1	**Boodle Hatfield** Oxford	1	3
2	**Blandy & Blandy** Reading	2	3
	Henmans Oxford	3	4
3	**Boyes Turner** Reading	1	2
	Iliffes Booth Bennett Uxbridge	3	2
4	**BP Collins** Gerrards Cross	2	1
	Pictons Hemel Hempstead	2	1
5	**Clarks** Reading	2	1
	Matthew Arnold & Baldwin Watford	1	3
	Stanley Tee Bishop's Stortford	1	2

LEADING INDIVIDUALS	
1	**LAING Sue** Boodle Hatfield
	WILKIN Ashley Boyes Turner

This book is the product of 6,552 1/2 hour interviews. See p.7 for BMRB audit.

Within each band, firms are listed alphabetically. *See individuals' profiles p.740*

Boodle Hatfield (see firm details p.889) Operating in conjunction with a strong London office, the firm is regarded by clients as "*head and shoulders above the rest in the region.*" **Sue Laing** (see p.844) has made a name for herself by acting for a substantial national and international client base, including some of the largest rural and urban landed estates in the UK, wealthy entrepreneurs and financiers, often with a foreign connection. Work over the past year includes advising the Grosvenor trustees on issues arising from the restructuring of the huge privately owned property business.

Blandy & Blandy (see firm details p.886) A long-established firm with a reputation for providing "*sensible and robust*" advice to clients including wealthy individuals and landed gentry. The team advises on a wide range of private client matters, and is headed by Graham Blenwell, who specialises in advising owner-managers of businesses in the IT sector.

Henmans (see firm details p.991) Headed by Zandra Houston, the team specialises in capital tax planning, trusts and larger probate matters. The firm also advises some non-resident clients, and prepares discretionary trusts for individuals in the diplomatic service. Recent work has included advising on the administration of estates for charity clients.

Boyes Turner (see firm details p.891) An "*efficient*" practice, which is perceived to have "*come into the picture*" over the past year. Head of department **Ashley Wilkin** (see p.848) is admired for being "*practical, innovative and sensible.*" Since his arrival from Fladgate Fielder, the team has become more focused on representing the interests of businessmen, and has advised on director and shareholder protection, inheritance tax and capital gains mitigation.

Iliffes Booth Bennett (see firm details p.1007) A practice with a strong local following and a client base including wealthy estates and institutions. The firm is also a panel solicitor for the Alzheimer's Society. Headed by Gillian Outram, the team deals with general estate planning, probate, tax and trust work, including private charitable trusts. It also advises the elderly and disabled on discretionary trusts and enduring powers of attorney.

BP Collins Credited with a "*problem-solving approach,*" the firm represents high net worth individuals, leaders of small to medium businesses and entrepreneurs. David Wilkinson's team's caseload has covered trusts, tax planning and charities matters, advising on capital gains tax relief and family trusts.

Pictons (see firm details p.1097) Perceived to be growing noticeably, the firm has provided tax advice to local businessmen, commercial clients and sporting celebrities. Work over the past year includes green form wills and appointing guardians to those wanting to mitigate inheritance tax liabilities of up to £2 million. Probate work includes interpretation of wills, deeds of variation, creation and running of trusts and Court of Protection applications.

Other Notable Firms **Clarks**' general commercial practice has a respected private client capability, and has advised on the administration of a number of estates over £5 million, as well as inheritance tax planning. At **Matthew Arnold & Baldwin**, a "*commercially focused*" team practises both on and offshore private client work. Led by Iain Donaldson, the group has acted on multi-jurisdictional issues and contentious trust and estate matters. **Stanley Tee & Co** boasts a multi-disciplinary private client group, headed by Richard Tee, which advises on a range of trusts, tax, agricultural and integrated wealth planning.

SOUTH WEST

Burges Salmon (see firm details p.902) A "*real leader in the field,*" the firm's excellent reputation is ascribed to its "*depth of experience and comprehensive level of advice,*" notably in tax matters. **Martin Mitchell** (see p.845) is "*the kind of experienced player to whom you're happy to refer work.*" Head of department, the "*terrific*" **Charles Wyld** (see p.848), advises on tax and estate planning for UK and overseas clients, while **Michael Evans** (see p.841) heads up the international tax and trust unit, and is described as "*a real livewire who gets himself noticed.*" Offshore tax planning over the past year includes restructuring more than 100 trusts for South American clients and restructuring the ownership of a £70 million piece of real estate from a Liechtenstein to a Jersey structure. Substantial tax and estate planning expertise has involved acting for large landed estates, and advising a group of landowners on an innovative use of pool trust arrangements for a land development worth over £100 million.

Osborne Clarke OWA (see firm details p.1086) Commended for its "*uniformity of quality,*" the group is headed by **Sandra Brown**, who is said to be "*tough, efficient and professional.*" The group advises clients including business owners, landowners and lottery winners, with an increasing

TRUSTS & PERSONAL TAX • South West		Ptnrs	Assts
1	**Burges Salmon** Bristol	3	9
	Osborne Clarke OWA Bristol	7	14
	Wiggin & Co Cheltenham	6	2
	Wilsons Salisbury	6	15
2	**Bond Pearce** Plymouth	1	3
	Charles Russell Cheltenham	3	3
	Foot Anstey Sargent Plymouth	3	4
3	**Clarke Willmott & Clarke** Taunton	3	5
	Hooper & Wollen Torquay	3	2
4	**Coodes** St Austell	n/a	n/a
	Meade-King Bristol	3	n/a
	Michelmores Exeter	n/a	n/a
	TLT Solicitors Bristol	n/a	8
	Veale Wasbrough Bristol	2	1
5	**Rickerby Watterson** Cheltenham	2	4
	Stephens & Scown Exeter	3	1
	Stones Exeter	2	3
	Woollcombe Beer Watts Newton Abbot	4	1

LEADING INDIVIDUALS		
1	**BROWN Sandra** Osborne Clarke	**FITZGERALD Peter** Wilsons
	MILLER Adrian Foot Anstey Sargent	**NICHOLSON Jonathan** Bond Pearce
	WOLLEN Nigel Hooper & Wollen	**WYLD Charles** Burges Salmon
2	**ELPHINSTON Alex** Foot Anstey Sargent	**EMMERSON John** Wilsons
	EVANS Michael Burges Salmon	**FULLERLOVE Michael** Wiggin & Co
	MITCHELL Martin Burges Salmon	
3	**NELLIST Peter** Clarke Willmott & Clarke	**VOREMBERG Rhoderick** Wilsons

This book is the product of 6,552 1/2 hour interviews. See p.7 for BMRB audit.
Within each band, firms are listed alphabetically. *See individuals' profiles p.740*

emphasis on managing the affairs and tax planning of entrepreneurs in the TMT sector. The department also acts for private banks and other institutions in the private client field, providing consultancy advice on all aspects of tax planning, trusts and general wealth management.

Wiggin & Co (see firm details p.1180) Continuing its reputation as a "*focused and specialised*" practice, the team's forte is still considered to lie in offshore work. **Michael Fullerlove** (see p.842) is a familiar name in the market and specialises in work with an international aspect. The practice advises wealthy families in the UK and overseas on matters including investments, structuring and tax planning. It has also received fund work instructions from syndicated investment clubs.

Wilsons (see firm details p.1185) Numbering several former City lawyers in its private client group, the firm is renowned for its "*serious and bespoke*" landed estates practice. **Peter Fitzgerald** remains rated as the firm's number one practitioner in this area, while the respected **John Emmerson** continues to advise a strong clientele of wealthy individuals and substantial family trusts. **Roddy Voremberg** also maintains his name for his estate planning practice. The group has advised a number of owners of substantial farms and estates on heritage issues and international tax planning.

Bond Pearce (see firm details p.888) Small private client team, which maintains its level of market support for its tax planning and trusts expertise. Peers hold **Jonathan Nicholson** (see p.846) "*in the highest regard,*" and he is described as "*a real technician.*" The firm acts for a number of overseas-domiciled individuals on trust matters, as well as advising on probate and substantial estates work in the UK.

Charles Russell (see firm details p.912) Seen as "*a fine foil*" for the London team, the Cheltenham office deals with substantial private client matters. These have included advice on around 25 landed estates, and acting on tax structures, VAT and inheritance tax issues.

Foot Anstey Sargent (see firm details p.961) A force in the west of the region, this is considered to be a "*conscientious*" team, dealing with a comprehensive range of private client issues. The "*vastly knowledgeable*" **Adrian Miller** (see p.845) and the "*supremely competent*" **Alex Elphinston** (see p.841) are the outstanding names here. The team deals with a range of trust and estate administration, fund management and tax planning and has long experience in the agricultural sector.

Clarke Willmott & Clarke (see firm details p.915) Felt to be making "*a real impact*" in the region, the firm's asset management team is headed by **Peter Nellist** (see p.845), who is both a qualified lawyer and a financial adviser. The firm has advised on the use of impaired annuities for elderly clients with health problems and acted on an agricultural property relief claim for a bungalow supported by five acres of commercially managed orchard. COT matters have included a case concerning the inheritance income exemption for a gift of £200,000.

Hooper & Wollen (see firm details p.1001) Torquay firm with an increasingly high profile as a "*high quality private client practice.*" **Nigel Wollen** (see p.848) has the respect of his peers for his "*calm and practical advice.*" His team advises on the administration of estates, establishment of trusts and settlements, inheritance tax mitigation and the preparation and administration of Court of Protection receiverships.

Other Notable Firms Perceived to be "*showing up well locally,*" particularly for landed estates work, Cornish firm **Coodes** is felt to have a "*tight grip on the private client market on their own patch.*" Although sometimes overshadowed by its larger Bristol rivals, **Meade-King** is still regarded as a "*thoroughly reliable operation,*" while in Exeter, **Michelmores** is acknowledged as a "*young team of good technical lawyers.*" **TLT Solicitors** has an established niche in estates planning and has acted for a major clearing bank in dealing with the UK estates of foreign domiciled individuals. Headed by Mary McCartney, **Veale Wasbrough's** private client team is most noted for its expertise in inheritance tax and capital gains tax issues. **Rickerby Watterson** enjoys a sound reputation for a range of work carried out for landowners, businessmen, private individuals and private and charitable trusts. This includes advice on wills and the creation of lifetime trusts. **Stephens & Scown's** private client practice is spread over five offices in Devon and Cornwall and is regarded as "*a decent local choice,*" while at Stones, recent work has included preparation of wills and creation of trusts, tax planning for individuals and administration of estates. **Woollcombe Beer Watts**' small team in Newton Abbot maintains a high degree of local client approval.

WALES

TRUSTS & PERSONAL TAX • Wales	Ptnrs	Assts
1 **Edwards Geldard** Cardiff	1	2
2 **Hugh James Ford Simey** Cardiff	1	1
3 **Margraves** Llandrindod Wells	1	3

LEADING INDIVIDUALS	
1 **MARGRAVE-JONES Clive** Margraves	**MORTIMER Fay** Edwards Geldard
WRIGHT Cherry Hugh James Ford Simey	

This book is the product of 6,552 1/2 hour interviews. See p.7 for BMRB audit.
Within each band, firms are listed alphabetically. *See individuals' profiles p.740*

Edwards Geldard (see firm details p.948) An established force in the principality, the private client team is headed by the esteemed **Fay Mortimer** (see p.845). Recent matters handled include probate, estates and tax planning for a mixture of old and new money clients. Trusts and new money work are undertaken in conjunction with the corporate department, and the group's clients include wealthy individuals and entrepreneurs.

Hugh James Ford Simey (see firm details p.1004) Known for its expertise in probate matters and its "*scholarly style*," the team handles complex capital tax planning for commercial clients, as well as advising on the administration of substantial estates. Head of department **Cherry Wright** (see p.848) is considered to possess "*a formidable intellect.*" The firm has advised on systems to cover probate for more than 5000 deceased miners, arising from a recent successful multi-party action.

Margraves Niche private client firm, which is seen to be run "*in the image*" of its leading figure, "*excellent client man*" **Clive Margrave-Jones**. The firm handles several substantial landed estates and advises a number of well-known actors on their affairs. Specialisms include trusts, wills and inheritance tax planning.

MIDLANDS

TRUSTS & PERSONAL TAX • Midlands	Ptnrs	Assts
1 **Martineau Johnson** Birmingham	5	4
2 **Browne Jacobson** Nottingham	2	3
Hewitson Becke + Shaw Northampton	2	8
Lee Crowder Birmingham	2	4
Lodders Stratford-upon-Avon	2	6
Wragge & Co Birmingham	3	5
3 **Higgs & Sons** Brierley Hill	5	2
Pinsent Curtis Biddle Birmingham	2	1
4 **Freethcartwright** Nottingham	1	2
Gateley Wareing Birmingham	1	3
Shakespeares Birmingham	2	2
The Wilkes Partnership Birmingham	n/a	n/a
Willcox Lane Clutterbuck Birmingham	n/a	n/a

LEADING INDIVIDUALS	
1 **CARSLAKE Hugh** Martineau Johnson	**HANSELL Matthew** Martineau Johnson
JENKINS Paul Browne Jacobson	
2 **COLACICCHI Clare** Hewitson Becke + Shaw	**GREEN Martin** Lodders
KERR Drummond Lee Crowder	**LEEK Robert** Higgs & Sons
PALLISTER Stephen Pinsent Curtis Biddle	**THOMPSON Wenna** Browne Jacobson
WOODHEAD Louise Wragge & Co	
UP AND COMING	
FOX Julie Wragge & Co	

This book is the product of 6,552 1/2 hour interviews. See p.7 for BMRB audit.
Within each band, firms are listed alphabetically. *See individuals' profiles p.740*

Martineau Johnson (see firm details p.1055) Still rated as the "*first port of call*" in the region, the firm's resources and "*cutting-edge expertise*" keeps it well clear of its rivals. Particularly highly regarded for its old money practice, the team includes **Hugh Carslake** (see p.841), "*the local doyen,*" who specialises in tax planning, trusts and estate planning, particularly for the owners of landed estates. **Matthew Hansell** (see p.843) who has more of an international aspect to his practice, is new to the rankings this year and is seen as a "*thoroughly safe pair of hands.*"

Browne Jacobson (see firm details p.898) Acting for a number of top accounting practices, the firm receives excellent reviews for its "*sound commercial ethos*" and the quality of its individual lawyers. **Paul Jenkins** (see p.843) continues to have a strong presence in the market and newly ranked **Wenna Thompson** (see p.848) also received market praise as "*a quality operator.*" The team advises wealthy entrepreneurs, landed estate owners, retired people and trustees, and includes practitioners who are on the Camelot Winners Advisory Panel. The past year has seen the practice advise on a contentious trust matter worth over £100 million.

Hewitson Becke + Shaw (see firm details p.994) "*Versatile*" department with a strong investment management flavour. Headed by **Clare Colacicchi** (see p.841), rated by competitors as a "*first-class lawyer and a real fighter,*" the team has advised extensively on the amalgamation and variation of large trusts, together with providing advice on the implications of the Trustee Act 2000. About 20% of the work has an international aspect and features a number of instructions from North American clients with UK interests.

Lee Crowder (see firm details p.1035) Acknowledged by rivals as an "*outward-looking*" firm with sound individual lawyers, it provides personal tax planning for wealthy individuals, notably owner-managers. Head of department **Drummond Kerr** (see p.844) specialises in personal tax planning, and is recommended as a "*solid and trustworthy*" practitioner. The team deals with a wide range of private client matters, from trust administration to tax planning and the provision of financial services.

Lodders A sizeable private client team, perceived to be "*a happy ship,*" earns the approval of clients for its "*focus on quality.*" The "*client-friendly*" **Martin Green** (see p.842), a tax and financial planning lawyer, is described by his competitors as "*well-organised and charming to deal with.*" Clients include landed individuals and figures from the entertainment world, for which the team advise on tax planning and trust administration. The group also performs substantial offshore work for non-domiciled individuals, and has acted on a number of deeds of variation.

Wragge & Co (see firm details p.1189) "*Progressive and competitive*" practice, which attracts a high quality business clientele and is seen to benefit from a strong corporate department. The team's recent growth is widely credited to the efforts of the "*influential*" **Louise Woodhead**. Her younger colleague, **Julie Fox**, is rated as "*a highly promising*" lawyer.Work over the past year includes acting for the executors of several probates with a value in excess of £1 million, some with significant international aspects. The practice is also receiving instructions from foreign lawyers to reseal or reprove foreign grants, where the deceased has assets in the UK.

Higgs & Sons (see firm details p.995) Known for advising an "*old Black Country*" client base,the team continues to be led by the "*affable*" **Bob Leek**

(see p.844), renowned for his "*impeccable technical skills.*" The caseload encompasses probate, tax planning and trusts advice including repatriation, restructuring and setting up of trusts. Significant matters over the past year include an abortive 'flip-flop' CGT scheme for offshore trusts, and the use of loan notes for relief planning and importation of offshore trusts for a client selling an interest in a family company.

Pinsent Curtis Biddle (see firm details p.1098) Focusing strongly on its business client base, the firm is considered to stand out for its tax advice. **Stephen Pallister** (see p.846) joins the rankings this year, and is judged to "*know what he's doing.*" The team acts for technology business entrepreneurs and investors and international entrepreneurs and wealth creators, as well as offshore trust companies, private banks and some old money clients. Work over the past year includes tax planning advice following the de-listing of Dawson Group and related personal tax/trust work.

Other Notable Firms **Freethcartwright** boasts a small generalist practice with a focus on personal injury trusts and a client base which combines old money and new entrepreneurs. The team continues to manage over 200 trusts. In spite of its comparatively diminutive size, the private client team at **Gateley Wareing** continues to be respected for its technical ability. Shakespeares maintains its traditional practice, which is known for its investment management expertise. At **The Wilkes Partnership**, an "*authoritative and serious*" group is said to be "*creeping higher in people's consciousness,*" while **Willcox Lane Clutterbuck** is considered to be "*as good as anyone for probate work.*"

EAST ANGLIA

	TRUSTS & PERSONAL TAX • East Anglia	Ptnrs	Assts
1	**Mills & Reeve** Norwich	6	9
2	**Hewitson Becke + Shaw** Cambridge	2	4
3	**Greene & Greene** Bury St Edmunds	1	1
	Howes Percival Norwich	2	1
	Roythorne & Co Spalding	3	2
	Taylor Vinters Cambridge	4	4
4	**Ashton Graham** Bury St Edmunds	n/a	n/a
	Cozens-Hardy & Jewson Norwich	2	2
	Hood Vores & Allwood Dereham	2	n/a
	Prettys Ipswich	2	2
	Ward Gethin King's Lynn	n/a	n/a
	Willcox & Lewis Norwich	4	2

	LEADING INDIVIDUALS	
1	**BARCLAY Jonathan** Mills & Reeve	**RIPMAN Justin** Mills & Reeve
2	**BRADLEY David** Hewitson Becke + Shaw	**EWART Peter** Hewitson Becke + Shaw
	FOX Jocelyn Taylor Vinters	**HEAL Jeremy** Howes Percival

This book is the product of 6,552 1/2 hour interviews. See p.7 for BMRB audit.

Within each band, firms are listed alphabetically. *See individuals' profiles p.740*

Mills & Reeve (see firm details p.1069) A "*responsible and respectable*" practice which remains the clear market leader in the region, laying claim to the top local individual lawyers and a powerful client base. The "*first class*" **Justin Ripman** (see p.846) provides strategic tax and trusts advice, while **Jonathan Barclay** (see p.840)("*really knows his onions*") handles a number of substantial landed estates. The firm advises landowners, businessmen and other high net worth individuals, and has acted on private tax and trust arrangements offshore for businessmen in relation to the establishment of a substantial investment fund.

Hewitson Becke + Shaw (see firm details p.994) Firmly established as the number two in the region, the private client team is driven by the esteemed duo of **David Bradley** (see p.840) and **Peter Ewart** (see p.842). Acting in conjunction with the Northampton office, the team has advised entrepreneur clients in science-based industries and owners of landed estates, administering more than 300 trusts with a value of over £200 million. The group also includes a substantial international dimension to its caseload.

Greene & Greene Strong department, with a particularly good reputation for agricultural work. Work has included enterprise management incentive schemes, pure tax and trusts, advising the executors of large estates, post-death planning and discretionary trusts.

Howes Percival (see firm details p.1003) A "*small but solid*" team, providing advice on tax planning, investment, trust creation and management, probate and administration of estates. **Jeremy Heal** (see p.73) continues to have a good reputation among his peers. Recent work includes estate planning, especially for farmers where there is potential development of land.

Roythorne & Co Known above all for its superb agriculture practice, the firm has an established clientele in the farming community and among local landed gentry. It advises on a range of private client matters, from estate planning to tax matters.

Taylor Vinters (see firm details p.1150) Among the team's "*knowledgeable*" group of lawyers, head of department **Jocelyn Fox** (see p.842) is considered to stand out. The team advises farmers, company directors and business owner-managers, including an increased number of hi-tech businessmen. Tax planning is an area of particular expertise and the team has been active in creating, structuring and administering private and public trusts. The group recently handled the $210 million donation from the Bill Gates Cambridge Scholars Trust to Cambridge University.

Other Notable Firms **Ashton Graham** is felt to have a "*technically competent*" private client group, while an "*aggressive*" team at **Cozens-Hardy & Jewson** continues to advise local landed interests. In spite of its position in the regional outpost of Dereham, **Hood Vores & Allwood** is considered by larger rivals to run a "*highly respectable landed practice.*" **Prettys** has niche expertise in advising clients with interests in France, while **Ward Gethin** and **Willcox & Lewis** retain sound reputations for their work on behalf of entrepreneurs.

NORTH WEST

Brabners (see firm details p.892) Continuing to expand, after taking on the private client practice of Berrymans Lace Mawer, the team is regarded as an "*obvious place to refer work.*" **Mark Feeny** is considered to be an "*excellent team builder.*" A tax planning expert, he leads a department with a notable old money clientele. The caseload includes advising on the formation and administration of trusts to deal with succession in family companies and an increasing amount of tax planning work for high net worth individuals. The team handles Chancery issues in conjunction with the litigation department. The past year saw the team act for an ex-services client in a successful attempt to gain relief against inheritance tax.

Halliwell Landau (see firm details p.982) Noted for its "*evenness of quality,*" the firm continues to offer "*top-class*"advice on estate planning and trust creation to a client base that includes names such as Barclays Bank Trust Co Ltd and St James's Place Partnership. **Geoffrey Shindler** (see p.847), the team's leading light, is commended as a "*hands on and go-getting lawyer.*"

Addleshaw Booth & Co (see firm details p.853) Said to be "*getting a strong team together,*" this "*aggressive*" team is felt to benefit from the firm's outstanding corporate practice. The firm acts for a range of clients, typically

TRUSTS & PERSONAL TAX • North West		Ptnrs	Assts
1	**Brabners** Liverpool	3	10
	Halliwell Landau Manchester	2	5
2	**Addleshaw Booth & Co** Manchester	2	6
	Birch Cullimore Chester	n/a	n/a
	Cuff Roberts Liverpool	1	1
3	**Cobbetts** Manchester	3	2
	Davies Wallis Foyster Liverpool	1	1
	Pannone & Partners Manchester	3	n/a

LEADING INDIVIDUALS		
1	**SHINDLER Geoffrey** Halliwell Landau	
2	**BISHOP David** David Bishop & Co	**FEENY Mark** Brabners
	MASON Carol Cuff Roberts	**TAYLOR Philip** Bullivant Jones

This book is the product of 6,552 1/2 hour interviews. See p.7 for BMRB audit.

Within each band, firms are listed alphabetically. *See individuals' profiles p.740*

with landed estates or from the business community. It assisted the corporate finance team by undertaking pre-sale tax planning work for a number of business clients advising shareholders in tax planning schemes.

Birch Cullimore Established private client department with "*a wealth of expertise*" in agriculture and landed estates issues. Considered to be "*a team with backbone,*" its caseload also includes substantial probate work.

Cuff Roberts Said to be "*thriving*" under the aegis of the "*industrious*" **Carol Mason** (see p.845), the firm undertakes the full range of private client matters. An enviable regional client base includes a number of wealthy individuals.

Other Notable Firms and Practitioners **Cobbetts** retains a strong private client team and benefits from its top-class family/matrimonial client base. This is also true of **Pannone & Partners**, whose strength in that area is said to be "*colossal.*" **Davies Wallis Foyster** also retains a sound reputation among its peers in Liverpool. **David Bishop** (see p.840) of **David Bishop & Co** is an "*excellent*" practitioner who acts for a mix of old and new money clients and advises on matters with an offshore element. **Philip Taylor** (see p.847) at **Bullivant Jones** retains the respect of his fellow practitioners for his work on wills, trusts and probate.

NORTH EAST

TRUSTS & PERSONAL TAX • North East		Ptnrs	Assts
1	**Dickinson Dees** Newcastle upon Tyne	9	16
	Wrigleys Leeds	6	8
2	**Addleshaw Booth & Co** Leeds	3	11
	Pinsent Curtis Biddle Leeds	1	6
3	**Andrew M Jackson & Co** Hull	1	2
	Brooke North Leeds	1	1
	Grays York	n/a	n/a
	Irwin Mitchell Sheffield	2	2
	Lupton Fawcett Leeds	1	3
	Rollits Hull	6	2
	Ward Hadaway Newcastle upon Tyne	3	3
4	**Gordons Cranswick Solicitors** Bradford, Leeds	2	2
	Walker Morris Leeds	1	2

EADING INDIVIDUALS		
1	**BINKS Nigel** Pinsent Curtis Biddle	**CHADWICK Peter** Wrigleys
	DICKINSON Alexander Dickinson Dees	**WRIGLEY Matthew** Wrigleys
2	**EATON John** Lupton Fawcett	**GIFFORD Adrian** Dickinson Dees
	HOWELL Paul Addleshaw Booth & Co	**LYALL George** Dickinson Dees

This book is the product of 6,552 1/2 hour interviews. See p.7 for BMRB audit.

Within each band, firms are listed alphabetically. *See individuals' profiles p.740*

Dickinson Dees (see firm details p.941) "*Serious competition to us all,*" by virtue of its size and quality of clients, the firm's enormous reputation is founded in its expertise in the agriculture sector. **Alexander Dickinson** (see p.841) and **Adrian Gifford** (see p.842) are both respected as lawyers who are "*fabulous to deal with,*" while **George Lyall** (see p.844) is recommended for his technical expertise. The workload encompasses capital tax planning, trust creation and administration and tax administration, often with an offshore element. Over the past year the team has advised clients who have acquired wealth on flotation, sale or development of their business as well as windfall clients who are the recipients of large damages awards, lottery winnings and life assurance proceeds.

Wrigleys (see firm details p.1191) Considered to have "*cornered the private client market in Leeds,*" the group is felt to attract a high quality of practitioner and is "*going from strength to strength.*" **Matthew Wrigley** ("*I have the highest respect for him*") is renowned for his expertise in heritage property issues, while the "*reliable*" **Peter Chadwick**'s practice has its emphasis on trusts, estate planning and agricultural work. Work over the past year includes inheritance tax planning through the use of gifts or trusts, including offshore structures, wills and the administration of estates and trusts. Clients include landed estates together with clients from industry and commerce.

Addleshaw Booth & Co (see firm details p.853) Said to be showing "*real commitment*" to private client work, the team is said to have a "*lot of muscle.*" **Paul Howell** (see p.843) is the department's outstanding practitioner. The firm has advised on Variation of Trusts Act applications, the migration of offshore settlements to different jurisdictions and tax and succession planning. Scottish Provident, Chase de Vere and Yorkshire Bank are prominent among a high-powered clientele.

Pinsent Curtis Biddle (see firm details p.1098) Small but "*uniformly well-schooled*" team, which continues to be a consistent home for conflict-led referrals. **Nigel Binks**' (see p.840) "*quiet, clever*" leadership has earned him rave reviews from competitors. Acting for entrepreneurs, estate owners, private banks and offshore trust companies, the firm is especially recognised for its trust restructuring expertise. The team has advised on the transfer of trusts to Mauritius and the UK, and the establishment of new UK trusts, worth over £100 million.

Other Notable Firms and Practitioners In Hull, **Andrew M Jackson & Co** enjoys a reputation as a "*small group, punching above its weight.*" **Brooke North** is renowned for its powerful local clientele, while York firm **Grays**, in spite of recent retirements at partner level, is regarded as an "*authority*" on private client work for ecclesiastical and local landed clients. **Irwin Mitchell's** commercial department in Sheffield provides a consistent flow of private client work, while at **Lupton Fawcett, John Eaton**'s (see p.841) financial services expertise in the private client context is widely acknowledged. Back in Hull, **Rollits** is seen as a "*strong competitor,*" advising old money clients and looking after substantial trusts. **Ward Hadaway** focuses on estate planning and asset protection for owner-managed businesses and landowners. **Gordons Cranswick** boasts an on-shore practice, specialising in estate administration and trusts, while **Walker Morris**' potent corporate department generates a substantial private client caseload.

SCOTLAND

TRUSTS & PERSONAL TAX • Scotland	Ptnrs	Assts
1 **Turcan Connell** Edinburgh	7	25
2 **Brodies WS** Edinburgh	2	4
Maclay Murray & Spens Glasgow	3	4
3 **Anderson Strathern WS** Edinburgh	4	3
Balfour & Manson Edinburgh	4	1
MacRoberts Glasgow	2	3
Morton Fraser, Solicitors Edinburgh	4	2
Murray Beith Murray WS Edinburgh	6	5
Tods Murray WS Edinburgh	5	6
4 **Ledingham Chalmers** Aberdeen	3	2
McGrigor Donald Edinburgh	2	5
Pagan Osborne Cupar	6	1
Wright, Johnston & Mackenzie Glasgow	3	3

LEADING INDIVIDUALS	
1 **BIGGAR John** Tods Murray WS	**CONNELL Douglas** Turcan Connell
DALGLEISH Andrew Brodies WS	**MACKINTOSH Simon** Turcan Connell
RAE Scott Morton Fraser, Solicitors	**STUBBS Ian** Maclay Murray & Spens
2 **FULTON Robin** Turcan Connell	**MACROBERT David** MacRoberts
ROSS Hubert Turcan Connell	
UP AND COMING	
HENDERSON Colin Anderson Strathern WS	

This book is the product of 6,552 1/2 hour interviews. See p.7 for BMRB audit.
Within each band, firms are listed alphabetically. *See individuals' profiles p.740*

Turcan Connell (see firm details p.1164) Scotland's leading private client firm continues to pull away from its competitors. The largest team, its clients enthuse about the "*outstanding service*" on offer. **Simon Mackintosh** (see p.844) is said to be a "*competent and professional*" lawyer, while **Douglas Connell** (see p.841) is a "*prominent client-getter.*" **Robin Fulton** (see p.842) and **Hubert Ross** (see p.847) are also said to be "*valuable weapons in the firm's armoury.*" Core expertise in personal tax planning and asset protection is supported by substantial advice on Scottish limited liability partnerships structures used for international tax planning. In heritage property matters, the firm continues to act as advisor to the owners of more than 150 historic houses in Scotland. The team advises a large number of wealthy entrepreneurial clients in Scotland, England and overseas and is heavily involved in structured self-invested personal pension arrangements.

Brodies WS (see firm details p.896) Renowned for its landed estate practice, the private client team is led by **Andrew Dalgleish** (see p.841), who is "*bright, punchy and competent.*" The team advises on heritage property trusts (both onshore and off) and tax planning. Work over the past year includes advising large estate clients on the running of their agricultural or other rural-based businesses. The practice also advises financial institutions and a growing number of independent financial advisors on private client and trust matters.

Maclay Murray & Spens (see firm details p.1047) A "*strong force*" in the west of Scotland, the team is praised for its "*common sense approach,*" as personified by the "*practical*" **Ian Stubbs** (see p.847). Expert in trusts establishment and administration, the group also handles tax planning and probate issues. The firm advises on management of trusts, capital gains tax planning, advising on the structuring of assets in association with partnerships, companies and trusts.

Anderson Strathern WS (see firm details p.859) Traditionally known for its superb landed estate work, the firm has gained an increased reputation for its tax and trusts advice for more entrepreneurial clients. **Colin Henderson** (see p.843) maintains his standing as a lawyer of "*maturing quality.*" The team advises wealthy individuals and families on tax matters including asset protection and capital gains tax. Increasingly advising new money clients in addition to its established clients, the firm currently has investment funds under management and administration in excess of £230 million.

Balfour & Manson (see firm details p.869) Strong on the tax side, the firm is considered to provide "*sound, reasoned*" advice for traditional wealthy clients.

MacRoberts (see firm details p.1048) Headed by the respected **David MacRobert** (see p.845), the team acts for high net worth individuals and works closely with the firm's commercial practice. Covering a broad spread of work, the team has advised on the creation of a number of new trusts for company directors and shareholders as part of tax planning arrangements.

Morton Fraser, Solicitors (see firm details p.1076) A team with "*real aptitude,*" it is led by **Scott Rae**, who is commended for his "*straightforward attitude.*" Primarily known for its advice on trusts creation, the team advises a number of local financial institutions.

Murray Beith Murray WS (see firm details p.1078) Strong on the financial services side of private client work, the firm advises a mixed old and new money clientele. The caseload includes trusts creation and probate advice.

Tods Murray WS (see firm details p.1157) Although active on the spectrum of private client work, the firm is best known for estate management advice for landed clients and entrepreneurs. In spite of his duties as a Member of the Scottish Parliament, **John Biggar** (see p.840) retains his reputation as a practitioner of "*outstanding skill.*"

Other Notable Firms In Aberdeen, **Ledingham Chalmers** retains a "*solid*" reputation. Substantial trusts work for its corporate clientele sees **McGrigor Donald** enter this year's rankings. **Pagan Osborne** has a strong rural practice in Fife, while **Wright, Johnston & Mackenzie** has a "*genuine, discrete private client focus.*"

NORTHERN IRELAND

TRUSTS & PERSONAL TAX • Northern Ireland	Ptnrs	Assts
1 **Cleaver Fulton Rankin** Belfast	3	3
L'Estrange & Brett Belfast	2	1
2 **C&J Black** Belfast	n/a	n/a
Johns Elliot Belfast	n/a	n/a

LEADING INDIVIDUALS	
1 **HEWITT Alan** L'Estrange & Brett	**RANKIN Alastair** Cleaver Fulton Rankin
2 **McCAW Elma** C&J Black	

This book is the product of 6,552 1/2 hour interviews. See p.7 for BMRB audit.
Within each band, firms are listed alphabetically. *See individuals' profiles p.740*

Cleaver Fulton Rankin (see firm details p.918) "*Undoubtedly one of the market leaders,*" the firm continues to benefit from the presence of the "*diligent and knowledgeable*" **Alastair Rankin** (see p.846). Work includes creating lifetime trusts and inheritance tax planning. Clients are typically wealthy or landed individuals, who are advised on preservation trusts and legislative schemes.

L'Estrange & Brett (see firm details p.1038) Long-established private client department, headed by the "*knowledgeable*" **Alan Hewitt** (see p.746), a lawyer of "*utter integrity.*" The firm handles discretionary trusts, and advises on tax planning for established families, company directors and entrepreneurs.

C&J Black Small, all-purpose private client team, led by the "*highly capable*" **Elma McCaw** (see p.845). Probate and trusts advice forms the core of the group's caseload.

Johns Elliot (see firm details p.1014) Respected for its "*enthusiasm*," the group continues to advise on a range of tax and trust matters, as well as standard probate issues.

LEADERS IN TRUSTS & PERSONAL TAX

ACOMB, Nick
Stevens & Bolton, Guildford (01483) 302264
nick.acomb@stevens-bolton.co.uk
Specialisation: Tax and trusts including offshore tax planning, tax planning for foreign domiciles, inheritance tax, capital gains tax, employee benefit trusts and employee share schemes, trust law advice to trustees.
Prof. Memberships: Law Society, Society of Trust and Estate Practitioners (STEP).
Career: Articles *Clifford Turner* 1982-84, solicitor tax department *Clifford Turner (Clifford Chance)* 1984-91, solicitor *Stevens and Bolton* 1991-92, partner *Stevens and Bolton* 1992 to date.
Personal: Education: Bramcote Hills Grammar School (Nottingham); Birmingham University LLB (Hons); Guildford College of Law (2nd class honours). Family: Married with two boys; lives in Guildford.

AVERY JONES CBE, John
Speechly Bircham, London (020) 7427 6454
john.averyjones@speechlys.com
Specialisation: Taxation of all kinds.
Prof. Memberships: Member of Treasury appointed Tax Law Rewrite Steering Committee, Law Society (Member and past Chairman of Revenue Law Committee), Chartered Institute of Taxation (Past President), International Fiscal Association, Institute for Fiscal Studies, International Academy of Estate & Trust Law, International Bar Association.
Career: Partner in *Speechly Bircham* since 1970, senior partner since 1985, Deputy Special Commissioner of Income Tax and part-time Chairman of VAT and Duties Tribunals, Consulting Editor of British Tax Review, Member of the Editorial Board of Simon's Taxes, Chairman of the Board of Trustees of the International Bureau of Fiscal Documentation.
Personal: Born 1940, educated at Rugby School and Trinity College, Cambridge.

BARCLAY, Jonathan
Mills & Reeve, Norwich (01603) 693211
jonathan.barclay@mills-reeve.com
Specialisation: Specialises in tax and estate planning with particular emphasis on trust and tax issues affecting landed estates.
Career: Articled *Whithers*; qualified 1971; partner *Mills & Reeve* 1976; managing partner 1987-90; chairman *Norton Rose* M5 Group 1990-94; senior partner 1995 to date. Other appointments director *Jarrold & Sons Ltd*; East of England Investment Agency Ltd; chairman Norwich Area Development Agency Ltd; Theatre Royal (Norwich) Trust Ltd; Britten Sinfonia.
Personal: Born 1947; resides Norfolk.

BIGGAR, John
Tods Murray WS, Edinburgh (0131) 226 4771
john.biggar@todsmurray.com
Specialisation: Wills; tax and asset protection planning; trusts, formation and administration; probate; personal financial planning.
Prof. Memberships: Society of Trust and Estate Practitioners; Society for Computers and Law; Law Management Section; WS Society.
Career: Articled *Murray Beith & Murray* 1973-75; admitted solicitor 1975; assistant solicitor *Murray Beith & Murray* 1975-77; admitted *WS* 1976; partner *Murray Beith & Murray* 1977-91; partner *Tods Murray* 1991; managing partner 1998-date.
Publications: Co-author 'Drafting Wills in Scotland' (Butterworths 1994); occassional professional magazine contributions.
Personal: Oundle School; University of Edinburgh. Family; golf; music; married; four sons.

BINKS, Nigel
Pinsent Curtis Biddle, Leeds (0113) 244 5000
nigel.binks@pinsents.com
Specialisation: Wide experience of tax and trust work with particular expertise in capital gains tax and inheritance tax planning for entrepreneurs and owner-managed businesses and estate planning, trusts and off-shore structures.
Prof. Memberships: STEP.
Career: Born 1951. Educated at Repton School and Trinity College, Cambridge. Qualified in 1976. Partner in *Simpson Curtis* (now *Pinsent Curtis Biddle*) in 1978. Consultant with *Pinsent Curtis Biddle* from 1995.
Personal: Leisure interests include golf and skiing.

BISHOP, David
David Bishop & Co, Liverpool (01704) 878421
David_Bishop@compuserve.com
Specialisation: Main areas of specialisation are trusts and tax planning for individuals and private companies including offshore arrangements; all aspects of occupational pensions and charities. Notary Public.
Prof. Memberships: Law Society; chairman, Liverpool Branch Society of Trust and Estate Practitioners 1991-99; International Tax Planning Association; Association of Pension Lawyers.
Career: Qualified 1972. Partner *Laces & Co* (now *Berrymans Lace Mawer*) 1974. Head of private client department 1995-00. 2000 principal, *David Bishop & Co.*
Personal: Born 6 April 1947. Educated Sedbergh School 1960-65, Caius College, Cambridge 1966-69. Lives in Formby.

BOYD-CARPENTER, Henry
Farrer & Co, London (020) 7242 2022
hbc@farrer.co.uk
Specialisation: Main areas of practice are general private client work, wills, settlements, probate, settled land, landed estates and charities.
Prof. Memberships: Law Society, Holborn Law Society.
Career: Joined *Farrer & Co* in 1962. Qualified in 1966, became a partner in 1968. Private solicitor to the Queen since 1995. Solicitor to the Duchy of Cornwall 1976-94.
Personal: Born 11 October 1939. Educated at Charterhouse 1953-58 and Balliol College, Oxford 1959-62. School governor and charity trustee. Member of the Board of the British Library since 1999 and chairman of the governing body of Charterhouse. Trustee and council member of many charities: The Merlin Trust, Sutton's Hospital, the Chelsea Physic Garden, the Institute of Cancer Research, among several others. Enjoys reading, music, hill walking and gardening. Lives in Ascot, Berkshire.

BRADLEY, David
Hewitson Becke + Shaw, Cambridge (01223) 461155
davidbradley@hewitsons.com
Specialisation: Probate, trusts, tax, charities.
Prof. Memberships: Law Society; STEP (past chairman Cambridge branch); Charity Law Association.
Career: Articles *Payne Hicks Beach*; admitted 1972; joined *Wild Hewitson & Shaw* now *Hewitson Becke + Shaw* 1975, partner 1977.
Personal: Kings School, Ely; Christ's College Cambridge (language/law). Married with three children. Leisure interests – garden, natural history, France.

BRIDGES, Mark
Farrer & Co, London (020) 7242 2022
mtb@farrer.co.uk
Specialisation: Partner, head of international private client team. Handles tax and trust matters, particularly for non-domiciled and non-resident individuals.
Prof. Memberships: Law Society, Member of STAR Group, Trust Law committee, IBA and ITPA.
Career: Joined *Farrer & Co* in 1978. Qualified in 1980, became a partner in 1985. Solicitor to the Duchy of Lancaster 1998.
Personal: Born 25 July 1954. Educated at Cambridge University 1973-77. Special trustee of Middlesex Hospital and of University College Hospital. Treasurer of Bach Choir 1992-97. Governor of the Purcell School. Treasurer of music in country churches. Council member of Royal School of Church Music 1989-97. Recreations include sailing and music. Lives in London and Suffolk.

BROWN, Graham
Payne Hicks Beach, London (020) 7465 4300
Specialisation: Senior partner, and head of tax and trust department. Areas of practice include legal and fiscal advice to shareholders and boards of family and other private companies; landed estates and heritage property; international trusts, probates and family property; charities and educational institutions; French property and succession. Delivered papers on charities and non-profit organisations, trusts and estates at international conferences in London, Paris, Amsterdam, Munich and Taipei.
Prof. Memberships: Associate of Institute of Taxation in Ireland; sometime member of Law Society's Revenue Law Committee Capital Taxes Sub-Committee and of Law Society's Working Party on the Financial Services Act, Committee of Holborn Law Society; member: International Fiscal Association,

Franco-British Lawyers' Association.
Personal: Born 1944. Educated at Bristol University (LLB, 1966), Catholic University of Louvain (Diploma, 1970), and King's College, London (LLM, 1975). Leisure interests include arts, heritage and music. Fellow of the Royal Society of Arts; Liveryman Clockmakers' Company. Lives in Bath.

BROWN, Sandra
Osborne Clarke, Bristol (0117) 917 3000

BUZZONI, Mark
Taylor Joynson Garrett, London (020) 7300 7000

CARSLAKE, Hugh
Martineau Johnson, Birmingham (0121) 678 1486
hugh.carslake@martjohn.com
Specialisation: Main area of practice covers tax planning, trusts and estate planning and ecclesiastical law. Acts for the owners of landed estates and private individuals in their personal and trustee capacities. Registrar for and legal adviser to the Diocese of Birmingham.
Prof. Memberships: Law Society, STEP. Ecclesiastical Law Association (ELA).
Career: Qualified in 1973, having joined *Martineau Johnson* in 1972. Became a partner in 1974, Notary Public in 1981, head of private client department in 1991 and Diocesan Registrar in 1992.
Personal: Born 15 November 1946. Attended Rugby School, 1960-65, then Trinity College, Dublin, 1966-70. Chairman of the Barber Institute of Fine Arts (University of Birmingham); trustee of the Worcester Cathedral Appeal Trust. Council member of the Notaries Society. Leisure interests include family, music and gardening. Lives in Warwickshire.

CHADWICK, Peter
Wrigleys, Leeds (0113) 244 6100

COLACICCHI, Clare
Hewitson Becke + Shaw, Northampton (01604) 233233
clarecolacicchi@hewitsons.com
Specialisation: Specialises in advice to individuals and trustees on estate planning, in particular as to the use of trusts with a view to alleviating capital taxation and advice to non-UK domiciliaries and non-UK residents.
Prof. Memberships: Deputy Chairman of the Society of Trust and Estate Practitioners and Chairman of its Technical Committee. Member of Charity Law Association.
Career: Qualified 1983. *Macfarlanes* 1981-89. Joined *Hewitson Becke + Shaw* 1989. Became a partner in 1990.
Personal: Born 3 August 1958. Attended Somerville College, Oxford.

CONNELL, Douglas
Turcan Connell, Edinburgh (0131) 228 8111
dac@turcanconnell.com
Specialisation: Joint senior partner. Specialist in trusts, tax planning, asset protection, charities and heritage property; acts as principal adviser to many chairmen and chief executives regarding their personal business and to the trustees of a number of major national charities, as well as private charitable foundations.
Prof. Memberships: President Scottish Young Lawyers Association 1975-76; member of Revenue Committee the Law Society of Scotland 1979-92; chairman Edinburgh Book Festival 1991-95; member Scottish Arts Council and chairman Lottery Committee, Scottish Arts Council 1994-97.
Career: Attended University of Edinburgh (LLB). Articled *Dundas & Wilson CS*; qualified 1976; partner 1979-97.
Personal: Born 1954. Resides Edinburgh. Leisure interests include books, travel and good food.

COOKE, Stephen
Withers, London (020) 7597 6000
Specialisation: Partner in private client department. Main area of practice is tax and asset management planning for the private client, both in the UK and offshore. Speaker at seminars on a wide range of trust, tax and related issues.
Prof. Memberships: City of London Law Society, International Fiscal Association, Society of Trust and Estate Practitioners.
Career: Qualified in 1971, having articled with *Clay Allison & Clark*, Nottinghamshire. Awarded the Law Society SH Clay prize. Joined *Withers* in 1971; partner in 1973.
Publications: Contributor to 'Tax Cases Analysis' and co-author of 'Inheritance Tax on Lifetime Gifts' (1987).
Personal: Born 30th July 1946. Attended Stamford School 1956-64 and Leicester School of Architecture. Chairman of the London Handel Society Ltd. Leisure interests include art, music, cricket, gardening and tennis. Lives in Well, Basingstoke.

DALGLEISH, Andrew
Brodies WS, Edinburgh (0131) 228 3777
andrew.dalgleish@brodies.co.uk
Specialisation: Main areas of practice are capital tax planning, trusts (private client, commercial and public), wills and executries. Co-author Barr Biggar Dalgleish and Stevens, 'Drafting Wills in Scotland'; contributor to Withers, 'International Personal Tax Planning Encyclopaedia'; Norrie & Scobbie, 'Trusts'; and George, 'International Charitable Giving'.
Prof. Memberships: Law Society of Scotland, Society of Trust and Estate Practitioners, Association of Pension Lawyers (associate); fellow of the Society of Advanced Legal Studies.
Career: Qualified 1975. Partner at *Brodies* since 1978.
Personal: Born in 1951, resides in Edinburgh.

DICKINSON, Alexander
Dickinson Dees, Newcastle upon Tyne (0191) 279 9615
law@dickinson-dees.com
Specialisation: Partner in private client department advising wealthy individuals and their families. Particular emphasis on capital taxation, heritage property, maintenance funds, trusts, wills and probates. Acts mainly for individuals with significant property interests (landed estates, commercial and residential portfolios) and entrepreneurs.
Prof. Memberships: Law Society; Society of Trust and Estates Practitioner.
Career: Qualified 1989. Joined *Dickinson Dees* in 1993 and appointed partner in 1997.
Personal: Born 1964 and lives in Northumberland. Keen sportsman and follower of Leeds United. School Governor and Charity Trustee. Travels extensively when time permits.

DOLMAN, Robert
Wedlake Bell, London (020) 7395 3000
Specialisation: Specialises principally in private client tax and trusts both in UK and offshore.
Prof. Memberships: Law Society: STAR group.
Personal: Born 15 October 1945. Educated at Felsted and Oxford University. Chairman of Family Assurance Society. Chairman of the Jesters Club. Lives in West Sussex. Interests are court games and theatre.

EATON, John
Lupton Fawcett, Leeds (0113) 280 2092
john.eaton@lupfaw.co.uk
Specialisation: Financial services partner 32 years specialisation in financial, tax, trust, and investment matters for private clients.
Prof. Memberships: Law Society – Law Society Financial Services Subcommittee; S.B.A.; Institute of Financial Planning; Solicitors for Independent Financial Advice; Association of Solicitor Investment Managers; Securities Institute; Society of Trusts & Estates Practitioners; fellow, Institute of Directors.
Career: Qualified 1965. President Bradford Law Society 1984. Senior partner, *Eaton & Co.*, Bradford until 1988, then Financial Services partner at *Lupton Fawcett*, Leeds. Won 1997 HIFAL Award for Best Financial Services Firm.
Publications: Author, 'Midland Guide to Inheritance and Investment of Inherited Moneys'. Regular contributor to financial, legal, and business journals, broadcaster and speaker at legal and financial seminars.
Personal: Born June 1943. Educated at Charterhouse and Trinity Hall, Cambridge. Cambridge Footlights 1961-64. Keen musician. Trustee of various charities.

ELPHINSTON, Alex
Foot Anstey Sargent, Exeter (01392) 411221
alex.elphinston@foot-ansteys.co.uk
Specialisation: Partner in private client department. Tax planning for individuals through wills and trusts: particular involvement in attorneyship and court of protection work as well as living wills. Also trustee of and advisor to various charities.
Prof. Memberships: Member of the Law Society: secretary of STEP (West of England).
Career: Qualified with *Waterhouse* in London, before moving to Devon, joining *Foot Anstey Sargent* in 1987.
Personal: Born 6 June 1955. Repton School and Durham University. Married with four young children. Interests include theatre, cricket, jazz and jigsaw puzzles. Trustee and governor of local school.

EMMERSON, John
Wilsons, Salisbury (01722) 412412

EVANS, Michael
Burges Salmon, Bristol (0117) 939 2249
michael.evans@burges-salmon.com
Specialisation: Head of international tax and trust unit, focusing on international work for both UK and non-UK based clients. Recent work includes: trust structures for South American clients; reviewing standard trust documentation for a major US bank for use by their customers world-wide; advice to private banks on real estate holding structures; advice to private banks on UK real estate holding structures; tax and estate planning for substantial international families; advice on Double Tax Treaty schemes; analysis of existing and new offshore structures in light of the newly applicable Transfer Pricing legislation; capital gains tax planning for owner managers on company sales, including offshore trust schemes and non-residence.
Prof. Memberships: Law Society, STEP (member of International Committee).

Career: Joined Burges Salmon as a trainee in 1990 and became a partner in tax and trusts in 1999.
Personal: University of Bristol 1986-89. Enjoys golf and cricket.

EWART, Peter
Hewitson Becke + Shaw, Cambridge (01223) 461155
peterewart@hewitsons.com
Prof. Memberships: Society of Trust & Estate Practitioners. Charity Law Association.

FEENY, Mark
Brabners, Liverpool (0151) 600 3000

FITZGERALD, Peter
Wilsons, Salisbury (01722) 412412

FOX, Jocelyn
Taylor Vinters, Cambridge (01223) 423444
jaf@taylorvinters.com
Specialisation: Estate planning and inheritance tax, UK trusts, elderly client services, Court of Protection (head injury patients), wills.
Prof. Memberships: STEP.
Career: Qualified 1985 and joined *Taylor Vinters.* Became partner 1995.
Personal: Cambs High School for Girls, University of Reading (LLB), University of Stirling (M.Phil).

FOX, Julie
Wragge & Co, Birmingham (0870) 903 1000

FULLERLOVE, Michael
Wiggin & Co, Cheltenham (01242) 224114
Specialisation: Private client work for high net worth individuals, both in the UK and elsewhere. A large part of his practice involves international asset and tax structuring on work inbound and outbound to and from the USA.
Prof. Memberships: The Law Society; International Tax Planning Association; STEP.
Career: University of Birmingham – LLB; Magdalen College, Oxford – BCL. Articles and assistant solicitor: *Freshfields*, City of London.
Personal: Born 1948. Gardening, genealogy and alpaca breeding.

FULTON, Robin
Turcan Connell, Edinburgh (0131) 228 8111
rdf@turcanconnell.com
Specialisation: Partner. Specialist areas taxation, trusts and estates, partnerships and charity law.
Prof. Memberships: Qualified Solicitor Scotland 1979. Law Society of Scotland and Society of Writers to HM Signet. STEP.
Career: *Shepherd & Wedderburn;* qualified 1979; assistant solicitor 1979-82, partner 1982-99; partner *Turcan Connell WS* 1999. Senior tutor in wills, trusts and executries, Edinburgh University Diploma in Legal Education.
Publications: Scottish Editor 'Sergeant & Sims on Stamp Duties' and 'Foster's Inheritance Tax';
Personal: Born 1956; resides Edinburgh. Interests include sport generally but particularly squash, tennis, golf and skiing.

GARDNER, Ceris
Allen & Overy, London (020) 7330 3901
ceris.gardner@allenovery.com
Specialisation: She has experience in the whole range of trust issues, advising trustees and beneficiaries on establishing UK and offshore trusts, advising on the powers, duties and liabilities of trustees and the rights of beneficiaries. She has particular expertise in UK direct taxation and the relationship between UK and overseas taxation and the contentious and non-contentious administration of estates.
Prof. Memberships: IBA; Society of Trust and Estate Practitioners; Charity Law Association; European Association for Planned Giving and Immigration Law Practitioners Association.
Career: Assistant Allen & Overy (1988-91), Partner (1991).
Publications: 'Tax Planning the Ingram Way' published in Trusts and Estates Legal Times Supplement. Contributed to 'Disputes Involving Trusts'.
Personal: University of London (BA 1975).

GARNHAM, Caroline
Simmons & Simmons, London (020) 7628 2020
caroline.garnham@simmons-simmons.com
Specialisation: Partner and head of the private capital, family office, and private banking group, providing a dedicated service to the high net worth client and the institutions which advise them. Wide experience of international and domestic tax and estate planning for private clients. Advises wealthy entrepreneurs, family offices and private banks.
Prof. Memberships: Awarded Fellowship of the Chartered Institute of Tax for thesis on tax planning for non-UK domiciliaries investing in commercial property. Member of the Technical Committee and the International Committee of the Society of Trusts and Estate Practitioners ('STEP'). Member of the editorial boards of Butterworths' 'Offshore Cases and Tax Havens' publication and STEP's publication of Wills and Trust Law Reports published by Legalease Limited.
Career: BSc Exeter University. Solicitor, qualified in 1981.
Publications: Regular contributor to national newspapers, in particular the 'Financial Times', on trust and tax matters.

GIFFORD, Adrian
Dickinson Dees, Newcastle upon Tyne (0191) 279 9622
law@dickinson-dees.com
Specialisation: Advises major landowners and businessmen on their personal affairs.
Prof. Memberships: Society of Trusts and Estates Practitioner.
Career: Qualified in 1977. Became partner at *Dickinson Dees* in 1979.
Personal: Born 1946. Educated at Merchant Taylors School and St Andrew's University. Lives in Northumberland.

GLAZIER, Barry
Lester Aldridge, Bournemouth (01202) 786 190
barry.glazier@lester-aldridge.co.uk
Specialisation: Trusts, tax and wills team leader. Corporate and personal tax, particularly for family-owned businesses, as well as landed estates, onshore and offshore trusts, and charities. Managing partner 1994-00.
Prof. Memberships: Articled *Penningtons*, London; qualified 1966; solicitor *Clifford Turner* 1966-71; partner *Lester Aldridge* since 1972; president of Dorset Chamber of Commerce and Industry 1992-93, president Bournemouth and Dorset District Law Society 1991-92; director and company secretary, Dorset Training and Enterprise Council 1989-2001; chairman of Eurolegal 1991-95; chairman of Hurstpierpoint Lawyer's Society.
Personal: Born 1941; resides Wimborne Minster. Educated at Hurstpierpoint College (1950-60); St Peter's College, Oxford (1960-63 BA, 1968 MA Oxon); Notary Public. Recreations include concerts and opera, piano playing, walking, ornithology, gardening.

GOODWIN, Peter
Bircham Dyson Bell, London (020) 7222 8044
petergoodwin@bdb-law.co.uk
Specialisation: Estate planning for UK families and non-UK domiciliaries; advice on UK and non-UK trusts.
Prof. Memberships: Law Society; Westminster Law Society; STAR Group; STEP.
Career: Qualified as solicitor (1968). Partner: *Freshfields* (1974-90). Partner: *Bircham Dyson Bell* (then *Bircham & Co*) (1990 to date).
Personal: Born October 1943. Shrewsbury School (1957-62). Worcester College, Oxford (1962-65). Member of Committee of 1930 Fund for District Nurses.

GOWAR, Martyn
Lawrence Graham, London (020) 7379 0000
martyn.gowar@lawgram.com
Specialisation: Senior partner and partner in tax department. Specialises principally in private client tax, acting for large landed estates, trustees (particularly offshore trusts), and private clients with business interests. Also inter-generational transfers of family businesses and general tax work, income tax, capital gains tax and inheritance tax advice generally, including income tax on structured settlements and tax on insurance policies.
Prof. Memberships: Law Society; Chartered Institute of Taxation (associate 1976, fellow 1981); secretary of International Academy of Estate and Trust Law. Member Addington Society.
Career: Joined *Lawrence Graham* in 1967, qualifying in 1970 and becoming partner in 1973 and senior partner in 1997. Member of numerous revenue law committees including the Tax Committee of the Association of Corporate Trustees (1987-96) and the Capital Taxes Committee of the Chartered Institute of Taxation. Also clerk to the governors of Wellington College and clerk to the trustees of the Hamlyn Trust. A trustee of the Laura Ashley Foundation and the Council of St Paul's Cathedral Choir School. Fellow of the Royal Society of Arts.
Publications: Editor of Butterworths' 'Encyclopaedia of Forms and Precedents' (Vol 30 on partnership) and contributor to Simon's 'Taxes on the tax and trust treatment of demerger shares issues and enhanced scrip dividends'. Has lectured widely over the last 20 years.
Personal: Born 11 July 1946. Educated at King's College School, Wimbledon and Magdalen College, Oxford 1964-67. Lives in Elstead, Surrey and enjoys golf, cricket and gardening.

GREEN, Martin
Lodders, Stratford-upon-Avon (01789) 293259
martin.green@lodders.co.uk
Specialisation: Trusts and tax planning with a special interest in all personal financial planning issues. In addition to the usual tax planning matters, in the last 12 months he has been involved in writing death in service and other pension benefits in trust for clients and also in advising the elderly in connection with funding of care costs.
Prof. Memberships: Law Society Capital Taxes Sub-Committee (former chair of Birmingham Rev-

enue Law Committee Birmingham Law Society); STEP. Associate member Securities Institute.
Career: Articled *Pinsent & Co* (later *Pinsent Curtis*) 1978-80. Partner in Private Client department of *Pinsent & Co* 1984-85. Partner in charge of Private Client department *Lodders* January 1986 to present day.
Publications: In the past contributed to CTT 'News and Reports' and articles in the 'Law Society Gazette'.
Personal: Married with four children. Interested in tennis, table tennis, golf and the countryside. Educated Cheltenham College and Birmingham University.

HALLAM, Murray
Withers, London (020) 7597 6000
murray.hallam@withers.co.uk
Specialisation: Partner in the private client department, specialising in trust and tax planning for the private client, partnership law, heritage property and charity law.
Prof. Memberships: Westminster Law Society, Society of Trusts & Estates Practitioners (STEP), Charity Law Association, The Fletchers Livery Company, The Historic Houses Association, The Hellenic Society.
Career: Articled at *Withers*. Qualified in 1970. Partner in 1977.
Publications: Co-author of 'Practical Trusts Precedents', 'Practical Will Precedents' and 'International Trust Precedents'. Contributor to 'Practical Tax Planning with Precedents'. Lectures on trusts and wills and charity matters.
Personal: Born 1946 and resides in London. Interests include theatre, classical civilisation, chess, cricket and tennis.

HANSELL, Matthew
Martineau Johnson, Birmingham (0121) 678 1504
matthew.hansell@martjohn.com
Specialisation: Private client solicitor specialising in wills, trusts and estate planning for entrepreneurs and high net worth individuals.
Prof. Memberships: Member of the Society of Trust and Estate Practitioners (STEP), the Securities Institute and Capital Taxes sub-committee of the Revenue Law committee of the Law Society.
Career: Partner in *Martineau Johnson* since 1993. Former Chairman of the Birmingham branch of STEP and former secretary of the Revenue Law committee of Birmingham Law Society.
Personal: Married with two children. Interests include badminton and theatre.

HAYES, Michael
Macfarlanes, London (020) 7831 9222
michael.hayes@macfarlanes.com
Specialisation: Specialises in private client tax planning.Work includes tax and estate planning, both national and international, for high net worth individuals, their trusts and closely held companies. Also wills and probate. Other area of practice is charities, including formation of charitable trusts and companies; establishing subsidiary trading vehicles; and negotiations with Charity Commission and Inland Revenue.
Prof. Memberships: Law Society, City of London Law Society, Society of Trusts and Estates Practitioners, Committee Member of the Law Society Wills and Equity Committee, Association of Pension Lawyers, Association of Contentious Trust and Probate Specialists. Member of Camelot Winners Advisory Panel.
Career: Qualified in 1968 while with *Macfarlanes*. Became a partner in 1974. Head of tax and financial planning from 1991-99.
Publications: Contributor to Tolley's 'Administration of Estates' and to Tolley's 'Administration of Trusts'. Has spoken at numerous national and international conferences.

HEAL, Jeremy
Howes Percival, Norwich (01603) 762103
jpwh@howes-percival.co.uk
See under Agriculture, p.73

HENDERSON, Colin
Anderson Strathern WS, Edinburgh
(0131) 220 2345
colin.henderson@andersonstrathern.co.uk
Specialisation: Capital taxes planning for high net worth individuals and trusts, landowners, family businesses, non-domiciliaries.
Prof. Memberships: Society of Trust and Estate Practioners. Chartered Institute of Taxation. Member of Law Society of Scotland Tax Law committee.
Career: Qualified in 1990 after army service; 1990-96 *Coopers & Lybrand* CA; partner *Anderson Strathern WS* 1997.
Publications: Articles on taxation subjects in trade press. Conference speaker.
Personal: Born 1960; resides Edinburgh. Interests: fishing, walking, military history and national heritage.

HEWITT, V Alan
L'Estrange & Brett, Belfast (028) 9023 0426
See under Property (Commercial), p.746

HOWE, Kate
Boodle Hatfield, London (020) 7318 8107
khowe@boodlehatfield.co.uk
Specialisation: Private client taxation, including planning for the landed estate and international tax planning for UK and non-UK residents and domiciliaries; UK and offshore trust advice; heritage property; commercial property taxation, particularly VAT.
Prof. Memberships: STEP (Society of Trust & Estate Practitioners), Westminster Law Society.
Career: Qualified 1982. Trained at *Boodle Hatfield*. Was an assistant from 1982-87, and became a partner in 1987.
Publications: Has lectured widely on tax planning and contributed to 'Legal Network Television'.
Personal: Attended the London School of Economics. Lives in London.

HOWELL, Paul
Addleshaw Booth & Co, Leeds (0113) 209 2000
Specialisation: Head of the firm's private client group. Main areas of expertise are in UK and offshore personal tax planning and trusts, and charities.
Prof. Memberships: Memberships: Society of Estate and Trust Practitioners. Country Land Owners Association. Law Society.
Career: Liverpool University 1974; admitted in 1977; joined the firm in 1990 as a partner.
Personal: Tennis, skiing, sailing, windsurfing and bridge.

JACOB, Nicholas
Rooks Rider, London (020) 7689 7111
njacob@rooksrider.co.uk
Specialisation: Partner specialising in international tax planning structures, offshore and UK trusts, tax and estate planning, and related company and commercial transactions. Specialist advice on trusts relating to divorces. Heavy focus on Hong Kong and Singapore and inward investment into the UK.
Prof. Memberships: International Fiscal Association; Society of Trust and Estate Practitioners (National Council and Development committee)
Career: Articled *Baileys Shaw & Gillett*. Qualified 1982. Assistant solicitor *Rooks Rider* 1987-88, partner *Rooks Rider* 1988. Lectures widely on trusts and tax planning in the UK and abroad.
Personal: Born 1957. Educated Framlingham College Suffolk, Brunel University. Resides London

JACOBS, Michael
Nicholson Graham & Jones, London
(020) 7648 9000
michael.jacobs@ngj.co.uk
Specialisation: Tax; employee share schemes; international tax, trusts, charities and public sector bodies. Author of 'Tax on Take-overs' (7 editions) and 'Rewarding Leadership' (published by CISCO, now Quoted Companies Alliance, February 1998); contributor to 'Tolley's Tax Planning' and 'Tolley's VAT Planning'. Consultant editor of Tolley's 'Trust Law International'.
Prof. Memberships: Trust Law Committee (Founder Member and Secretary, 1994-97, Executive Committee member); Share Scheme Lawyers Group (Founder Member and Vice-Chairman); Executive Committee (member) and Employee Share Schemes Committee (Chairman) Quoted Companies Alliance; STEP; IFA; IFS; Charity Law Association; FRSA; Academician of the Academy of the Learned Societies for the Social Sciences; Fellow of The Society for Advanced Legal Studies.
Career: Articled at *Nicholson Graham & Jones* (1970). Partner 1976. Head of Private Client Department 1981.

JARMAN, Chris
Payne Hicks Beach, London (020) 7465 4300
cjarman@paynehicksbeach.co.uk
Specialisation: Partner in tax, trust and probate department. Deals with a wide range of domestic and international trust, estate and tax planning for both old and new money clients, whether based in the UK or abroad; advice to 'private' and institutional charities; property-related VAT advice for charity, commercial and land-owning clients; commercial property advice to landowners seeking to realise potential development value. Member of Law Society's Revenue Law Committee and Capital Taxes Sub-Committee.
Prof. Memberships: Law Society; Holborn Law Society; STEP; Charity Law Association; Charities Property Association.
Career: Called to the Bar 1976, qualified as solicitor 1980. *Freshfields* 1978-84, *Payne Hicks Beach* 1984 to date. (Partner in 1986).
Personal: Born 1954, educated at Sherborne School and Magdalene College, Cambridge. Leisure interests include singing and music generally, 'social' cricket, golf and cycling.

JENKINS, Paul
Browne Jacobson, Nottingham (0115) 976 6000
pjenkins@brownej.co.uk
Specialisation: Has over 30 years experience in the field of personal tax planning and trusts. Acts for clients of very substantial means, including entrepreneurs and landowners and their respective families. Deals with the creation, settlement, variation and termination of both domestic and offshore trusts. The

aggregate value of trusts with which he is concerned exceeds £1 billion.

KENNEDY, John
Hunters, London (020) 7412 0050
jmsk@hunters-solicitors.co.uk
Specialisation: Private client work including landed estates, national heritage property, inheritance tax planning, trusts and probate.
Prof. Memberships: Law Society, STEP.
Career: Sherborne School. Emmanuel College, Cambridge. Articled at *Hunters*, qualified in 1967, became a partner in 1970 and senior partner 2000.
Personal: Cricket, skiing, gardening.

KERR, Drummond
Lee Crowder, Birmingham (0121) 237 2508
drummond.kerr@leecrowder.co.uk
Specialisation: Drummond Kerr is the head of the private client department at *Lee Crowder* Birmingham, comprising a team of 18 (including support staff) of whom seven lawyers are members of the Society of Trust and Estate Practitioners. It is one of the largest specialist private client teams outside London. Drummond specialises in estate planning and tax planning which will typically involve advising on inheritance tax and capital gains tax planning including structures to minimise tax exposure and maximise use of reliefs and tax shelters. His particular emphasis is on estate planning for owner managers, where the planning will also include advice on corporate wills, cross option agreements and share protection. A feature which distinguishes Drummond (and his department) from many other law firms is his commercial approach to the provision of private client services.
Prof. Memberships: Drummond is a trustee of numerous private and charitable trusts and is a member of the Society of Trust and Estate Practitioners and the Charity Law Association.
Personal: Born November 1960. Married with three children.

KING-JONES, Amanda
Thomas Eggar Church Adams, Chichester (01243) 786 111
amanda.king-jones@teca.co.uk
Specialisation: Partner. Main areas of practice are personal tax and financial planning, administration of estates and trusts and the affairs of the elderly. Instructed as professional witness for probate related matters. Holding appointments as Judicial Trustee and Administrator appointed by the Court.
Prof. Memberships: Law Society, Society of Trust and Estate Practitioners and Solicitors for the Elderly.
Career: Joined *TECA* in 1981. Qualified 1983. Partner 1987.
Publications: Co-author of 'Probate Practice Manual' (Sweet & Maxwell).
Personal: Born 5th February 1959. Educated at Roedean School 1969-77. Exeter University (LLB) 1978-81.

KIRBY, Richard
Speechly Bircham, London (020) 7427 6498
richard.kirby@speechlys.com
Specialisation: Partner 1973. Main area of practice is private client work, handling estate and tax planning for UK and non-UK domiciliaries and trusts. Has written numerous articles for national newspapers and specialist taxation periodicals.
Prof. Memberships: Law Society.
Career: Head Private Client and Charity Team 1980. Solicitor Worshipful Company of Pewterers 1981 (Hon. Freeman 1991, Liveryman 2000).
Personal: Born 18th September 1946. Educated Sevenoaks School 1960-65 and Jesus College, Oxford 1965-68 MA. Member Council Mental After Care Association 1982 (Hon. Treasurer 1987-). Member Carlton Club. Enjoys reading, theatre and cycling. Lives in Dulwich.

KRAFFT, James
Thomson Snell & Passmore, Tunbridge Wells (01892) 510000
jkrafft@ts-p.co.uk
Specialisation: Partner and head of private client department. Main areas of practice are general private client work, personal financial planning, tax planning, wills, settlements, powers of attorney and probate. In addition to numerous executorships and trusteeships, he has been appointed attorney by a substantial number of elderly clients who need help in managing their financial affairs.
Prof. Memberships: Law Society and Society of Trust and Estate Practitioners.
Career: Qualified in 1971, Articled and practised in London before joining *Thomson Snell & Passmore* in 1976.
Personal: Born 1 May 1944. Educated at Downside School and St.Catherine's College, Oxford. Leisure interests include golf, tennis, bridge, reading and psychology. Lives in Langton Green, Kent.

LAING, Sue
Boodle Hatfield, Oxford (01865) 265101
slaing@boodlehatfield.co.uk
Specialisation: Handles UK capital, income and corporation tax planning for landed estates, individuals, trusts, partnerships and private companies; the creation, running and termination of UK and overseas trusts; the interaction of UK and foreign taxes via double tax treaties or UK unilateral relief; the taxation of land transactions within the UK or involving UK entities; UK and overseas taxation of complex trust/corporate structures; long-term planning for individuals, particularly with a foreign element.
Prof. Memberships: STEP (Society of Trust & Estate Practitioners).
Career: Qualified 1978. Trained at *Boodle Hatfield*, became a partner in 1981. Became the first resident partner in the Oxford office in 1994.
Publications: Regular contributor to various articles in tax publications and to 'Legal Network Television'.
Personal: Born 1954. MA (Oxon) 1978. Lives near Oxford.

LEEK, Robert
Higgs & Sons, Brierley Hill (01384) 342100
rel@higgs-and-sons.co.uk
Specialisation: Inheritance tax and estate planning; capital gains tax advice; all aspects of onshore/offshore trust work. Probate and wills.
Prof. Memberships: Law Society; Society of Trust and Estate Practitioners. Member of Birmingham STEP Branch Technical Sub-committee (formerly branch technical officer); former member of Birmingham Law Society Revenue Law Committee.
Career: 1974-76: Lloyds Bank Trust Division; joined *Higgs & Sons* in 1978; qualified 1980 and became a partner in 1987.
Personal: Born 1952. BA (Hons); LLM (Lond). Interests include travel, sport and music. Married with three children. Lives in South Staffordshire.

LENEY, Simon
Cripps Harries Hall, Tunbridge Wells (01892) 506 009
sdl@crippslaw.com
Specialisation: Head of private client department and member of firm's private office group. Handles creation/use of settlements and will trusts; trusteeships and executorships; wills and administration of estates; powers of attorney and attorneyships; inheritance tax and estate planning; charity law; Inheritance (Provision for Family and Dependants) Act claims and other trust or inheritance disputes or claims; appointed to represent large estate in high profile professional trustee and fraud case.
Prof. Memberships: Member of Securities Institute, Director of Solicitors Benevolent Association, member of Society of Trust and Estate Practitioners (STEP), Notary Public.
Career: Articled at *Donne Mileham and Haddock*; qualified1977; salaried partner 1979; equity partner 1982; head of private client department 1989; joined *Cripps Harries Hall* 1994; Educated at Sherborne School, Dorset. Head of private client department 1996 to date.
Personal: Married with two children. Interests include rugby, vintage and classic cars, home and garden.

LONG, David
Charles Russell, London (020) 7203 5000

LYALL, George
Dickinson Dees, Newcastle upon Tyne (0191) 279 9643
law@dickinson-dees.com
Specialisation: Personal tax partner and private/charitable trust specialist. Provides advice on domicile and related issues to UK expatriates in Northern Europe, including appeals of EC rulings and international estate planning.
Career: 1976-82 Edinburgh University – B.Com, LLB and Dip. LP; 1982-85 Scottish Court solicitor and Notary Public; 1985-94 chartered accountant and senior tax manager at *Arthur/Ernst and Young*; March 1994 joined *Dickinson Dees*. Qualifications: English and Scottish Solicitor, CA, NP and TEP.
Personal: Married to Roz with three sons.

MACKINTOSH, Simon
Turcan Connell, Edinburgh (0131) 228 8111
sam@turcanconnell.com
Specialisation: Main areas of practice are tax, trusts and charities. Work includes tax planning, heritage property, often with an international element, charity law and practice, often with an international element; and trust establishment, variation and practice. Lead partner for a number of the firm's major charity clients. Joint head of the firm's charity unit. Convener of the Law Society of Scotland Tax Law Committee and of its panel on Trust Law Accreditation.
Prof. Memberships: Society of Trust and Estate Practitioners, International Academy of Estate and Trust Law.
Career: Partner *Turcan Connell* 1997; partner *W & J Burness WS* 1985-97; non-executive director of Macphie of Glenbervie Ltd and past board member of the Edinburgh International Book Festival. Member of the Scottish Executive Commission on reform of charity law.
Publications: Co-author of 'Revenue Law of Scotland', 1987

MACROBERT, David
MacRoberts, Glasgow (0141) 332 9988
david.macrobert@macroberts.co.uk
Specialisation: Partner and head of private client group. Specialist areas include wills, trusts, inheritance tax, capital gains tax, income tax, executries, power of attorney, charities and investments.
Prof. Memberships: Member Revenue Committee Law Society of Scotland; Capital Taxes Sub-committee of Chartered Accountants of Scotland. Trustee of Scottish Civic Trust.
Career: Glenalmond College; Dundee University (1975 LLB). Trainee *Brechin Robb*; qualified 1977; assistant solicitor *MacRoberts* 1977-801; partner 1980; former senior tutor Glasgow University; former external examiner in finance tax and investment Edinburgh University, Diploma in Legal Practice.
Personal: Born 1953; resides Paisley. Leisure: skiing, sailing, shooting, fishing, gardening. Member: Royal Gourock Yacht Club, Royal Western Yacht Club, Western Club, Western Club, RSAC.

MARGRAVE-JONES, Clive
Margraves, Llandrindod Wells (01597) 825565

MASON, Carol
Cuff Roberts, Liverpool (0151) 237 7777
carol.mason@cuffroberts.co.uk
Specialisation: Trust creation and administration personal tax advice. Administration of high value probate matters and advising individual clients on all matters of personal estate planning. Independent financial advice on portfolio management.
Prof. Memberships: Law Society; Liverpool Law Society; Society of Trust & Estate Practitioners. Lectures widely on estate planning.
Career: Qualified 1984. Assistant solicitor with *Banks Kendall*; merged with *Cuff Roberts* 1987; partner and head of trust and probate department. Member of STEP and ASIM Qualified Person by the Law Society in portfolio management.
Personal: Liverpool University (1977-80). Mother with one son. Lives in South Liverpool. Leisure interests include swimming, tennis, gardening, music and travel.

MAURICE, Clare M
Allen & Overy, London (020) 7330 3904
clare.maurice@allenovery.com
Specialisation: Partner specialising in advising UK and non-UK domiciled individuals and families on how to structure their assets both on shore and internationally. She has special experience advising on the UK taxation of offshore structures and Inland Revenue investigations into such activities. She also acts for grant-making and operational charitable organisations advising on all aspects of their activities.
Career: Articled *Allen & Overy*; qualified 1978, partner 1985, Chairman of the St Bartholomew's and Royal London Charitable Foundation, Director United Response in Business Limited.
Publications: Contributor to the fifth edition 'The Encyclopaedia of Forms and Precedents' vols 42(1) and (2).
Personal: Educated Sherborne School for Girls. Birmingham University (1975 LL.B). Born 1954. Resides London.

McCAW, Elma
C & J Black, Belfast (028) 9032 1441
cjblack@dnet.co.uk
Specialisation: Probate, inheritance tax planning, discretionary trusts, wills, deeds of family arrangement.
Prof. Memberships: Member of the Incorporated Law Society of Northern Ireland, Belfast Solicitors' Association.
Career: LLB (2:1), Queens University, Belfast. Qualified as a solicitor in 1976. Partner in *C & J Black, Solicitors* since 1982.

MELLOR, Eliza
Nicholson Graham & Jones, London
(020) 7648 9000
eliza.mellor@ngj.co.uk
Specialisation: Partner in Private Client Department. Has over 25 years experience advising UK and overseas-based clients on UK and international estate planning and trust matters, including trust litigation and UK domestic tax issues, domicile and residence.
Prof. Memberships: Law Society; International Academy of Estate & Trust Lawyers; Vice President, Europe (London); Technical and International Committees of STEP (1992-00).
Career: Qualified in 1974. Became a Partner of *Nicholson Graham & Jones* in 1985.
Personal: Educated at City of Worcester Grammar School for Girls and Newnham College, Cambridge. Lives in London.

MILLER, Adrian
Foot Anstey Sargent, Exeter (01392) 411221
adrian.miller@foot-ansteys.co.uk
Specialisation: Exeter-based senior partner. Family and financial planning for individuals, families, entrepreneurs, and landed estates; tax, trusts and attorneyship, equity and offshore, advance directives, charities and friendly society work.
Prof. Memberships: Law Society Probate Section Executive committee, vice chairman STEP (West of England).
Career: Joined *Foot Anstey Sargent* in 1974 from *Gregory Rowcliffe & Co.*
Personal: Born 7 November 1947. Radley College and Corpus Christi College, Oxford (Jurisprudence). Chief personal interest is his family and their home and grounds in mid-Devon where he is church warden. His family Scottish estate and French holiday property absorb the rest of his leisure time.

MITCHELL, Martin
Burges Salmon, Bristol (0117) 902 2792
martin.mitchell@burges-salmon.com
Specialisation: Tax and trusts. He advises on all aspects of UK and offshore trusts and probate, and on capital taxation and charity law. Clients are private individuals with commercial, agricultural and non-resident interests.
Prof. Memberships: Law Society, STEP.
Career: Joined *Burges Salmon* from *Macfarlanes* in 1981 and became a partner in 1983.

MORTIMER, Fay
Edwards Geldard, Cardiff (029) 2023 8239
fay.mortimer@geldards.co.uk
Specialisation: Deals with both old and new money clients of substantial means. All areas of estate planning covered including advising entrepreneurs prior to acquisition or start up of businesses and on disposal. Considerable expertise in advising elderly clients. Works closely with clinical negligence team regarding Court of Protection applications and the subsequent investment and management of settlement monies.
Prof. Memberships: Local Branch Secretary of STEP; Law Society Probate Section; The Notaries Society.
Career: Cardiff University (LLB); Articles with large Liverpool firm housing substantial private client department. Associate and subsequently Senior Associate with *Edwards Geldard* since 1988. Notary Public 1995.
Personal: Three young children, juggling home and career a speciality. Leisure interests include tennis, skiing, cooking and theatre.

MOYSE, Richard
Boodle Hatfield, London (020) 7318 8178
rmoyse@boodlehatfield.co.uk
Specialisation: Senior partner of the firm. Has an international practice and reputation, and is one of the UK's leading specialists in tax and financial planning. Advises chiefly on capital taxation; succession; heritage property; trusts and probates, including contentious matters, often with an international focus. Also acts as an expert witness.
Prof. Memberships: Former member of the Revenue Law committee of the Law Society and member of the Capital Taxes sub-committee; president elect of the International Academy of Estate and Trust Law; member of STEP (Society of Trust & Estate Practitioners; founding member of the Solicitor's Tax and Revenue (STAR) group.
Career: Qualified 1970. With *Lawrence Graham* from 1969-73. Joined *Boodle Hatfield* in 1973, became a partner in 1974 and elected senior partner in 1999.
Publications: Tolley's 'Administration of Estates Handbook' publication 1999.
Personal: Born 1943. Educated at Oxford University. Married with four children. Enjoys choral singing, fly fishing, painting, cricket and travel.

MURDIE, Alastair
Payne Hicks Beach, London (020) 7465 4300

NELLIST, Peter
Clarke Willmott & Clarke, Taunton
(01823) 329 842
pnellist@cw-c.co.uk
Specialisation: Trust, probate and inheritance tax planning, general financial advice. The winner of the Money Management's 2000 'Retirement Planner' section and 1999 'Investment Planner' section of its IFA of the Year competition. Runner up 'Investment and Investment Planning' section of Planned Savings 2000 IFA of the Year competition. In January 1999 took and passed the Chartered Insurance Institute's Advanced Financial Planning G60 pension exam. Believed to be the only practising solicitor holding (by virtue of examination passes) all three Law Society financial qualifications – retail branded packaged products, securities and portfolio management and corporate pensions. A member of and lectures for the Society of Financial Advisers.
Prof. Memberships: Society of Trusts and Estates Practitioners (STEP); chairman of the Bristol Law Society Tax Trust and Probate Committee for 2000; clerk to the Somerton Tax Commissioners; chairman of the Association of Solicitor Investment Managers (ASIM).
Career: Articled with *Theodore Goddard*. Qualified in 1973; associate partner from 1977; joined *Clarke Willmott & Clarke* in July 1978; made partner in 1980.
Publications: Has had investment based articles published recently in the Law Society's Gazette, 'Corporate Solutions', Trust and Estates Law Journal ('Investment advice – hidden agendas') and 'Money

Management'.

Personal: Born 1948. Guilford College of Law; Bristol University (LLB). Leisure activities include art and antiques, upholstery, surfing, travel, gardening, hedge laying and chain sawing. Married with two children currently at university.

NICHOLSON, Jonathan

Bond Pearce, Plymouth (01752) 266633
jnicholson@bondpearce.com

Specialisation: Partner and Head of the Private Client Group. Almost forty years experience in wills, trusts and personal tax. Specialist in charity law and solicitor to several major charities.

Prof. Memberships: Member of the Society of Trust and Estate Practitioners (former Chairman of West of England branch) and the Association of Charity Lawyers.

Career: Graduate of Trinity College, Dublin, qualified in 1968 and joined the University of Zambia as lecturer in law, returning to the UK in 1971. Joined *Meade King* in Bristol and was solicitor to the Bristol Municipal Charities. Moved to *Bond Pearce* in 1983, becoming partner 1985.

PALLISTER, Stephen

Pinsent Curtis Biddle, Birmingham
(0121) 200 1050
stephen.pallister@pinsents.com

Specialisation: Partner heading personal tax/trust team in the Birmingham office. Specialises in UK and international tax and estate planning, with a strong focus towards entrepreneurs and business clients. Within this sector he acts in particular for clients in the technology field. Also specialises in advising charitable companies and trusts, and leads the charities group in the firm. Highlights of the year include acting for one of the founders of Carphone Warehouse on the flotation of the company; setting up ownership structures for investors and directors of several technology businesses; acting for the family members and trustees on the £60M de-listing of Dawsongroup plc.

Prof. Memberships: Member, Law Society's Wills and Equity committee; member, Society of Trust and Estate practitioners.

Career: Qualified 1989; *Macfarlanes*, 1987-93; *Osborne Clarke*, 1994-98; *Pinsent Curtis Biddle*, 1998 to date.

Publications: Co-author of 'International Taxation of Low-Tax Transactions'. Contributor to legal journals and other publications.

Personal: Born 1963. Resides Cheltenham; educated Queen Elizabeth Grammar, Penrith, 1976-81; Downing College, Cambridge 1982-86.

PAUL, Robin

Withers, London (020) 7597 6000

Specialisation: Partner in private client department. Main area of practice is probate and succession. Head of probate group, advising executors and beneficiaries on all aspects of probate and post death tax planning, often with an international element. Also deals with trusts, tax and estate planning and heritage property.

Prof. Memberships: STEP, Law Society, Westminster Law Society.

Career: Qualified in 1977, having joined *Withers* in 1975. Became a partner in 1982.

Publications: Co-author of 'The Lawyers Factbook' (Administration of Estates section), 'Practical Will Precedents' and Tolley's 'Administration of Estates' (Chapter on Business and Agricultural Property). Contributor to various legal journals, 'Practical Tax Planning with Precedents' and to the Succession section of 'Practical Commercial Law'. Has lectured at various conferences on wills and succession, with particular emphasis on international aspects.

Personal: Born 19th December 1952. Educated at Malvern College, then Brasenose College, Oxford 1971-74. Lives in London.

PINTUS, Matthew

Macfarlanes, London (020) 7831 9222
mdp@macfarlanes.com

Specialisation: UK inheritance and capital gains tax, and tax and estate planning, both offshore and onshore. Particular expertise in the administration of estates and related tax planning.

Prof. Memberships: STEP, ACTAPs, IBA.

Career: Articled *Russell-Cooke, Potter & Chapman*. Joined *Macfarlanes* 1985, becoming a partner in 1993.

Publications: Co-author of 'Contentious Matters' section of Butterworths Wills, Probate and Administration Service. Author of the insolvent estates section of Butterworths' Encyclopedia of Forms and Precedents.

Personal: Ampleforth College, Warwick University. Interests include opera, sailing and film. Single. Lives in London.

POWELL, Nicholas RD

Currey & Co, London (020) 7802 2700

RAE, Scott A

Morton Fraser, Solicitors, Edinburgh
(0131) 247 1000

RANKIN, Alastair

Cleaver Fulton Rankin, Belfast (028) 9024 3141

Specialisation: Chancery and equity, probate, taxation, trusts and estates and wills.

Prof. Memberships: Member of Council The Law Society of Northern Ireland since 1985: treasurer 1991-95; junior vice-president 1995-96; president 1996-97. senior vice-president 1997-98.

Career: Qualified as solicitor 1977 (Northern Ireland 1977) (Republic of Ireland 1997). Partner 1980. Part-time lecturer on wills, revenue and administration of estates since 1988 at the Institute of Professional Legal Studies, Queens University of Belfast. General Commissioner of Income Tax. Part-time chairman Pensions Appeal Tribunals for Northern Ireland.

Publications: Consultant to 'Succession Law in Northern Ireland' by Sheena Grattan (SLS Publications); Northern Ireland editor, 'Which? Consumer Guides: Wills and Probate'.

Personal: Born 5 September 1951. Educated Trinity College Dublin (BA Dublin University). Member, Society of Trust and Estate Practitioners.

REID, Nigel

Linklaters, London (020) 7456 5702
nigel.reid@linklaters.com

Specialisation: Head of trust department. Specialist in trusts and trust taxation in both commercial and family contexts; commercial and family trusteeships; tax and estate planning for individuals; charities; chancery litigation.

Career: 1994 to date: Head of trust department, *Linklaters*; 1987 to date: Partner, *Linklaters*; 1980-87: Assistant solicitor, *Linklaters*; 1978-80: Articled clerk, *Linklaters*. 1974-77: Christ Church, Oxford; 1963-73: Nottingham High School.

RHODES, John

Macfarlanes, London (020) 7831 9222
john.rhodes@macfarlanes.com

Specialisation: Partner and head of tax and financial planning department. Particular areas of interest include UK inheritance and capital gains tax. Advises on UK and offshore trusts, the law of domicile and international trust and estate planning.

Prof. Memberships: Law Society, Society of Trust and Estate Practitioners.

Career: Qualified in 1970 while with *Macfarlanes*. Became a partner in 1975.

RICHARDSON, Joseph

Dawson & Co, London (020) 7421 4800
J.Richardson@Dawson-and-co.co.uk

Specialisation: Senior partner in private client department. Main area of specialisation is taxation. Covers all areas, particularly capital taxation planning (CGT and IHT) and all aspects of settlements (offshore, variation, etc) and heritage property. Also deals with a range of general private client work for high net worth individuals and families (both old and new money) and some charity work. Acts for a number of major landed estates and offshore clients. Has lectured on IHT and agricultural tenancies, and specialises in all kinds of IHT and CGT planning.

Prof. Memberships: Law Society, Society of Trusts and Estates Practitioners and the Heritage Group.

Career: Qualified in 1974. Partner at *Dawson & Co* since 1976.

Personal: Born 21st October 1949. Educated at St Olave's and St Peter's Schools, York 1959-68, then Durham University 1968-71 (BA in Law). Ex-squash international and former Chairman of Selectors, Squash Racket Association. Leisure interests include reading, walking, cricket, golf and squash. Married with three children and lives near Basingstoke, Hants.

RICHES, John

Withers, London (020) 7597 6000
john.riches@withers.co.uk

Specialisation: Partner in private client department leading commercial group. Main practice areas are estate and capital tax planning for UK and non UK domiciled individuals and advice on concentrated equity holdings in quoted companies. Clients include entrepreneurs, private banks and offshore trustees. Has lectured at major conferences in UK and overseas and contributes to professional journals and professional training videos.

Prof. Memberships: Council Member of STEP serving on the Technical and Education Committees.

Career: Qualified in 1985. Worked with two major regional firms before joining *Simpson Curtis* in 1990. Partner *Simpson Curtis/Pinsent Curtis* 1992-96, partner of *Withers* since May 1996.

Personal: Born 1961. Squash, theatre, walking. Active member of local church.

RIPMAN, Justin

Mills & Reeve, Norwich (01603) 693256
justin.ripman@mills-reeve.com

Specialisation: Partner specialising in tax and estate planning with particular emphasis on trust and tax issues affecting landed estates and offshore trusts.

Prof. Memberships: Member of CLA Tax committee and STEP Technical committee.

Publications: Contributor to Tolley's 'Administration of Trusts'.

ROBINSON, David
Forsters, London (020) 7863 8333
djrrobinson@forsters.co.uk
Specialisation: Partner. Private client specialist, with particular expertise in estate planning, capital taxation and heritage property.
Prof. Memberships: Holborn Law Society; the City of London Law Society; Society of Trust and Estate Practitioners.
Career: Qualified in 1981. With *Glover & Co* 1982-85. Joined *Frere Cholmeley* in 1985 and became a partner in 1989. Founding partner of *Forsters* August 1998.
Personal: Born in 1955. Educated at Westminster School and Pembroke College, Cambridge. Leisure interests include collecting books, music, art and travel.

ROGERSON, Gary
Cripps Harries Hall, Tunbridge Wells
(01892) 506 004
gr@crippslaw.com
Specialisation: Tax planning, trusts and probate; international estate planning, especially involving US citizens; member of the firm's Private Office group.
Prof. Memberships: Society of Trust and Estate Practitioners.
Career: Articled *Cripps Harries Hall*; qualified 1984; partner *Cripps Harries Hall* since 1989.
Personal: Brinkburn Grammar School, Hartlepool; Christ Church, Oxford (BA Jurisprudence). Bridge, sport, gardening. Born 1960; married, three children.

ROSS, Hubert
Turcan Connell, Edinburgh (0131) 228 8111
hjr@turcanconnell.com
Specialisation: Specialises in advising family companies and businesses, entrepreneurs and high net worth individuals on all aspects of personal and corporate taxation. Having worked for seven years as a merchant banker, he brings an understanding of finance as well as taxation to bear. He liaises with firm's Guernsey office when acting for non-residents, non-domiciliaries and offshore groups of companies.
Prof. Memberships: Law Society of Scotland; Society of Writers to HM Signet; Securities Institute; Society of Trust and Estate Practitioners
Career: Partner *Turcan Connell* 1997; partner *W&J Burness WS* 1984; Group Company Secretary, Leopold Joseph (Holdings) plc 1977; Parliamentary Draftsman, Lord Advocates Department 1976.

SHINDLER, Geoffrey
Halliwell Landau, Manchester (0161) 835 3003
Specialisation: Head of trust and estate planning department. Specialises in trusts, personal taxation with specific reference to inheritance tax and capital gains, and wills and probate.
Prof. Memberships: Chairman Society of Trust and Estate Practitioners (STEP) 1994-98, now Vice-President; International Bar Association; American Bar Association Real Property, Probate and Trust Law Section; Institute for Fiscal Studies; Securities Institute; Trust Law Committee; Academician International Academy of Estate and Trust Law; Member Editorial Board Tolley's Trust Law International.
Career: Qualified in 1969. Articled at *March Pearson.* Joined *Halliwell Landau* as a partner in 1986. Honorary Associate of Centre for Law and Business, Manchester University. Director of various local companies.
Publications: Consulting editor of Trusts and Estates Law Journal, Trusts and Estates Tax Journal. Member editorial board Wills and Trusts Law Reports. Regular conference speaker.
Personal: Born 1942. Attended Bury Grammar School and Cambridge University (MA LLM Cantab). Leisure interests include Marylebone Cricket Club, Lancashire CCC, Manchester United FC, Manchester Literary and Philosophical Society and Portico Library; Chairman Development Committee Royal Exchange Theatre, Manchester. Lives in Prestwich, Manchester.

STANFORD-TUCK, Michael
Taylor Joynson Garrett, London (020) 7300 4954
mstanford-tuck@tjg.co.uk
Specialisation: Partner in and head of tax and personal planning department. Principal area of practice is international trust and tax planning, acting for high net worth individuals, mainly those who are non-UK domiciled. Work includes protection of assets, structuring cross-border investments, asset enhancement, diversification and protection. Also deals with domestic private client work, encompassing UK-based estate and tax planning, landed estates, heritage property, contentious and non-contentious probate and chancery litigation. Has administered a major multinational estate, principally in Japan involving detailed assessment of Japanese estate tax and capital gains tax law. Also undertakes trust restructuring for high net worth families relocating to or investing in the UK and has handled high profile contentious and non-contentious chancery proceedings under the Settled Land Act 1925. Experienced lecturer and author of various articles.
Prof. Memberships: Law Society, City of London Solicitors Company, Freeman of the City of London, Society of Trust and Estate Practitioners, Bermuda Society (Committee Member), Star Group.
Career: Qualified in 1972. With *Lovell White & King,* 1972-75. Partner with *Appleby Spurling & Kempe* (Bermuda), 1975-84. Admitted Barrister and Attorney Supreme Court of Bermuda 1978. Joined *Taylor Joynson Garrett* as a partner in 1985.
Personal: Born 3 November 1946. Educated at Radley College 1960-65 and Southampton University 1965-68. Leisure activities include golf, gardening, skiing and country sports. Lives in Newbury, Berks.

STIBBARD, Paul
Baker & McKenzie, London (020) 7919 1000
paul.stibbard@bakernet.com
Specialisation: This includes advising on tax planning strategies for resident, non-resident and non-domiciled individuals, particular specialisation in offshore trust structures and effective tax planning for those coming to and leaving the UK, offshore trust litigation support and inheritance and probate matters involving an overseas aspect. Contributor to various legal journals. Has lectured at various conferences on tax and trust related issues with particular emphasis on international aspects.
Prof. Memberships: Law Society, STEP, ACTAPS, ITPA and member of the British Invisibles International Private Wealth Management Working Group.
Career: Qualified in 1972, partner *Baker & McKenzie* 1991, to date.
Publications: Author of chapter on Offshore Financial Centres in 'Tolley's Tax Havens', author of chapter on Succession Planning in 'Credit Suisse Guide to Managing your Wealth'.
Personal: Education: Marlborough College; Magdalene College, Cambridge; Insead Business School, France MBA (Deans List).

STUBBS, Ian
Maclay Murray & Spens, Glasgow
(0141) 248 5011
ims@maclaymurrayspens.co.uk
Specialisation: Tax and private capital partner specialising in personal tax planning, trusts, partnership law, agricultural property and forestry investment. Also a qualified chartered accountant.
Prof. Memberships: Member of Institute of Chartered Accountants of Scotland. Fellow of the Chartered Institute of Taxation. Sits on the Council of the Law Society of Scotland and a member of the Tax Law Committee. Member of the Society of Trust and Estate Practitioners.
Career: Glasgow University, LLB 1965, CA 1968, FTII 1991.
Publications: 'The Interpretation of Cross Border Taxation Issues in Practice' (1991 Thesis & Chartered Institute of Tax edition).
Personal: Born 1943.

SYED, Catriona
Charles Russell, London (020) 7203 5000
catrions@cr-law.co.uk
Specialisation: International and domestic private client work, including tax and estate planning for UK and non-UK domiciliaries; trusts; charity law and practice; trust aspects of commercial transactions.
Prof. Memberships: STEP Technical Committee member; Charity Law Association; City of London Solicitors Company; Law Society; Fellow of the Society of Advanced Legal Studies.
Career: Practised at the Chancery Bar 1983-86. *Norton Rose* 1986-97. Joined *Charles Russell* (partner 1997).
Personal: Leisure interests include family, opera, fine wine, walking, travel and reading.

TAYLOR, Philip
Bullivant Jones, Liverpool (0151) 227 5671
pgt@bullivantjones.co.uk
Specialisation: Main area of practice in probate, wills and trusts.
Prof. Memberships: Law Society, STEP Membership, Liverpool Law Society.
Career: Qualified in 1973. Joined *Bullivant Jones* in 1986. Partner in 1994.
Personal: Golf, cricket and gardening.

THOMPSON, Tony
Withers, London (020) 7597 6000
Specialisation: Partner in private client department. Main areas of practice are tax planning, asset structuring, trusts and probate. Clients include proprietors of landed estates, proprietors of businesses (particularly in the property industry) and offshore trustees.
Prof. Memberships: Law Society, Society of Trust and Estate Practitioners. Member of Advisory Committee of FTSE International Private Client Indices.
Career: Qualified in 1968. Partner of *Withers* since 1970. Head of Private Client Department 1980-87. Managing Partner 1987-93.
Publications: Editor of Trusts Section of Private Client Business.
Personal: Born 29th May 1943. Educated at Haberdashers Aske's School 1956-60 and Trinity College, Cambridge 1961-65. Chairman of Governors Glenesk

School. President of Horsley & Send Cricket Club. Recreations include golf and amateur dramatics. Lives near Guildford.

THOMPSON, Wenna
Browne Jacobson, Nottingham (0115) 976 6000
Specialisation: Trusts, tax and estate planning, charity law and practice.
Prof. Memberships: Society of trust and estate practitioners.
Career: Articled *Macfarlanes*; qualified 1986; *Macfarlanes* 1984-89; *Browne Jacobson* 1989; partner *Browne Jacobson* 1991.
Personal: Education: MA (Oxon).

THORNELY, Richard
Thomas Eggar Church Adams, Horsham (01403) 214500
richard.thornely@teca.co.uk
Specialisation: Partner and head of private client department. Main areas of practice are personal tax planning, wills, probate and trusts, charities and the affairs of the elderly.
Prof. Memberships: Law Society, S.T.E.P.
Career: Qualified in 1981. After several years at *Slaughter and May*, joined current firm in 1992 and became a partner in 1993.
Personal: Born 20th January 1957. Educated at Rugby School 1969-74 and Trinity Hall, Cambridge 1975-78. Governor of Queen Alexandra Hospital Home, Worthing and honorary solicitor to various charities. Married with three sons. Recreations include mountaineering, skiing and music, particularly playing the piano. Lives near Horsham.

THURSTON, Martyn
White & Bowker, Winchester (01962) 844440
martyn.thurston@wandb.co.uk
Specialisation: Partner and head of tax and trusts. Main areas of practice are tax planning for individuals and trusts, both UK and offshore, wills and succession planning.
Prof. Memberships: STEP, International Tax Planning Association.
Career: Partner *Woodham Smith* 1976-90; partner *Radcliffes* 1990-97; partner *White & Bowker* 1998 to present.
Personal: Born 1946. Interests include climbing and music. Lives in London.

TURNOR, Richard
Allen & Overy, London (020) 7330 3905
richard.turner@allenovery.com
Specialisation: Partner who advises wealthy private individuals, their families and trustees in connection with all aspects of tax and estate planning, especially where there is an international aspect. Also advises private banks and professional trustees about the related services provided by them to private clients and about trust litigation and banks and corporates in connection with any transaction working a trust structure. Also advises museums and other institutions on heritage and cultural property matters.
Prof. Memberships: Member Society of Trust and Estate practitioners; Trustee of International Bar Association Educational Trust; member Law Society Regulatory Review Working Party.
Career: Articled *Allen & Overy*, qualified 1980, Partner 1985.
Personal: Oxford University 1977. Born 1956.

VOREMBERG, Rhoderick
Wilsons, Salisbury (01722) 412412

WALLEY, Ray
Mundays, Esher (01372) 809044
Ray.walley@mundays.co.uk
Specialisation: Partner specialising in tax planning, trusts, will, probate and charity law. Particular interest in work for owners of businesses and corporate shareholders.
Prof. Memberships: Member of Institute of Directors, Chartered Institute of Bankers, chairman of STEP Surrey Branch.
Career: At Lloyds Bank executor and trustee department 1963-72. Qualified in 1976. Became a partner in *Mundays* in 1976. Notary Public.
Personal: Born 29 July 1944. Educated at King Edward VII GS, Sheffield 1956-62, and at Durham University. Leisure interests include computing and walking. Lives in Cobham, Surrey.

WILKIN, Ashley
Boyes Turner, Reading (0118) 959 7711
awilkin@boyesturnerlegal.co.uk
Specialisation: Partner and head of group. Principal area of practice being capital tax planning for individuals and private shareholders through trusts, wills and financial products. Leads a team dedicated to all private client matters such as probate, Public Guardianship Office issues, trusts for the disabled, attorneyships, deeds of variation and living together agreements. Ashley has a reputation for his proactive practical approach to solving client issues and his clients include partners of the major law and accountancy firms. He lectures to finanacial advisers and accountants and has appeared in the College of Law training videos and helps with their editorial.
Prof. Memberships: Law Society Probate section, Society of Trust and Estate practitioners.
Career: Admitted 1975. Partner from 1977 with *Fladgate Fielder*. Joined *Boyes Turner* in 1998 as partner.
Publications: Taxation and daily newspapers.
Personal: Born 1951. Married to Susan. He loves his labradors, theatre and travel. Ex Major in the Territorial Army.

WILLIS, David
Forsters, London (020) 7863 8333
dcwillis@forsters.co.uk
Specialisation: Senior partner of *Forsters*. Trusts (UK and Offshore), estates and personal taxation together with some family law work.
Prof. Memberships: Society of Trusts and Estate Practitioners; Country Landowners Association; Solicitor's Family Law Association.
Career: Oxford University (MA). Qualified initially as a barrister before becoming a solicitor. Partner in *Frere Cholmeley Bischoff* 1978-98. Founding partner of *Forsters* August 1998.

WOLLEN, Nigel
Hooper & Wollen, Torquay (01803) 213251
Specialisation: Partner in probate, tax and trust department. Qualified 1969. Partner 1971. Specialises in wills, trust, probate, personal family and financial planning (including landed estates and non-residents) and charities. Heads a specialist department of five fee earners.
Prof. Memberships: Law Society, STEP.
Career: Qualified in 1969, having joined *Hooper & Wollen* in 1965. Assistant solicitor at *Herbert Smith* 1970-71; partner at *Hooper & Wollen* from 1971.
Personal: Born 16 August 1945. Attended Marlborough College 1959-64. Vice Admiral of Royal Torbay Yacht Club. Leisure interests include sailing and skiing. Lives in Torquay.

WOODHEAD, Louise
Wragge & Co, Birmingham (0870) 903 1000

WRIGHT, Cherry
Hugh James Ford Simey, Cardiff (029) 2022 4871
cherry.wright@hjfs.co.uk
Specialisation: Partner and head of wills, probate and trusts department. Handles all aspects of wills, probate, trusts, tax (especially capital tax) and Court of Protection receiverships, but in particular tax planning trusts for private clients, company directors and shareholders, special needs trusts for accident victims and those with learning difficulties; charitable trusts for both large and fledgling institutions and the constitutional aspects of registered social landlords with charitable rules.
Prof. Memberships: Law Society, STEP.
Career: Qualified in 1969. Became a partner in *Shaen, Roscoe and Bracewell* (London) in 1972. Lecturer UCL 1974-6. Lecturer University of Wales, Cardiff 1976 – 1988. Consultant at *Hugh James* 1980 – 1988. Became partner in *Hugh James* 1988.
Publications: 'Succession – Cases and Materials' (Butterworths 1986); Editor Butterworths 'Wills Probate and Administration Service' (loose-leaf).
Personal: Educated at Wolverhampton Girls High School and then at UCL. Graduated UCL LLB first class honours 1966. Obtained honours in Solicitors Finals. Leisure interests include tennis, opera, fell walking and reading. Lives in Vale of Glamorgan, one child.

WRIGLEY, Matthew
Wrigleys, Leeds (0113) 244 6100

WYLD, Charles
Burges Salmon, Bristol (0117) 902 2773
charles.wyld@burges-salmon.com
Specialisation: Head of tax and trusts department where his practice encompasses tax and estate planning for UK and overseas clients; advising on formation and ongoing legal requirements of charities, whether trusts or companies.
Prof. Memberships: Law Society; Capital Taxes Sub-committee of the Revenue Law Committee of the Law Society; International Tax Planning Association; Charity Law Association; STEP; Institute of Financial Planning.
Career: Trained, qualified and practised at *Frere Cholmeley*, joining *Burges Salmon* in 1986, becoming a partner in 1989. Qualified as financial planner in 1996.
Personal: New College, Oxford (MA) 1975-79.

OFFSHORE: CORPORATE / COMMERCIAL

Guernsey: 849; Isle of Man: 849; Jersey: 850; *Profiles*: 850

OVERVIEW: This year for the first time *Chambers* includes an Offshore section in the UK Guide, covering the full spectrum of commercial law in Guernsey, the Isle of Man and Jersey.

RESEARCH APPROVED BY BMRB: *For this edition,* Chambers' *researchers conducted 6,552 interviews – 4,419 with law firms, 554 with barristers and 1,579 with clients.*

The validity of the research was scrutinised by BMRB International, who audited both the methodology and the results at our offices in July 2001. They interviewed Chambers' *researchers and cross-checked sample interviews. Details of the audit appear on page 7.*

GUERNSEY

OFFSHORE: CORPORATE/COMMERCIAL • Guernsey	Ptnrs	Assts
1 **Carey Langlois** St Peter Port	11	8
Ozannes St Peter Port	10	10
2 **Collas Day** St Peter Port	8	7
3 **Babbe Le Pelley Tostevin** St Peter Port	8	4

LEADING INDIVIDUALS	
1 **CAREY Nigel** Carey Langlois	**HALL Graham** Carey Langlois
HARWOOD Peter Ozannes	**SIMPSON William** Ozannes
2 **HOWITT Simon** Babbe Le Pelley Tostevin	**KIRK Ian** Collas Day
LANGLOIS John Carey Langlois	

This book is the product of 6,552 1/2-hour interviews. See p.7 for BMRB audit.
Within each band, firms are listed alphabetically. *See individuals' profiles p.850*

Carey Langlois One of the "*big two,*" the firm is well known for its investment fund and trusts advice. "*Highly regarded*" **Nigel Carey** and **Graham Hall** are the two leading lawyers on commercial matters, while **John Langlois** is also held in high esteem. The firm acted on the rights issue for the Channel Islands Stock Exchange. **Clients:** Guernsey Stock Exchange; Princess Group; Schroeder Ventures; Alchemy Partners.

Ozannes (see firm details p.1087) "*One of the leading firms on the island,*" competitors informed our researchers. The firm is expanding, and has an established name for buy-outs and securitisation work. **Peter Harwood** has "*wide commercial knowledge,*" while the "*competent and personable*" **William Simpson** also comes highly recommended. Acted on the Aurigny Air Services management buyout, as well as securitisations for BUPA and Citibank. **Clients:** Lloyds TSB; Rothschild.

Collas Day Although felt to lack the punch of the two market leaders, the firm retains a sound reputation for general corporate and financial work, particularly in lending and structured finance. The experienced **Ian Kirk** is "*a significant player in the corporate field.*" The firm acted on the sale of the trust and corporate administration businesses of Ernst & Young to Royal Bank of Canada. **Clients:** Clearing banks and international financial institutions.

Babbe Le Pelley Tostevin A recent merger has formed a large team with "*a decent balance of expertise.*" The firm has increased its workload in banking, trusts and funds, and has its strongest reputation in the insurance industry. **Simon Howitt** has been referred to as "*the main man*" for the firm, which advised on the Columbus sale of assets. **Clients:** HSBC; Credit Suisse Trust; Walbrook Trustees.

ISLE OF MAN

OFFSHORE: CORPORATE/COMMERCIAL • Isle of Man	Ptnrs	Assts
1 **Cains** Douglas	6	14
Dickinson Cruickshank & Co Douglas	11	5
2 **Maitland & Co** Douglas	2	4

LEADING INDIVIDUALS	
1 **CORLETT Andrew** Cains	**DOYLE David** Dickinson Cruickshank
VANDERPLANK Richard Cains	
2 **DOUGHERTY Paul** Dougherty & Associates	
3 **WENTZEL Peter** Maitland & Co	
UP AND COMING	
RIMMER John Dickinson Cruickshank	**SHERLOCK David** Cains

This book is the product of 6,552 1/2-hour interviews. See p.7 for BMRB audit.
Within each band, firms are listed alphabetically. *See individuals' profiles p.850*

Cains (see firm details p.907) "*One can only have glowing comments*" for this large Manx firm, which has a strong bias towards commercial work. E-commerce and mutual fund advice constitute growing elements of the practice. Managing Director **Andrew Corlett** is, competitors commented to our researchers, "*a practical individual, full of common sense,*" whose name extends beyond the island, and **Richard Vanderplank** is "*an excellent corporate lawyer.*" **David Sherlock** is respected for his e-commerce expertise. The firm advised the Isle of Man government on its first foray into the capital bonds market, borrowing £75 million to fund infrastructure projects. **Clients:** Cathay Pacific; Bank of Bermuda; major shipping companies.

Dickinson Cruickshank & Co Clearly one of the two leaders on the island, the firm has seen substantial work in IT transactional and regulatory matters, as well as advising on the potential impact of human rights legislation on the commercial arena. The "*likeable*" **David Doyle** is held in high esteem, while **John Rimmer** has experience in the City. The firm acted for KPMG when its trust and fiduciary services division was acquired by Singer & Friedlander. **Clients:** Financial Institutions; domestic and foreign corporates; private clients.

Maitland & Co Part of a partnership covering several countries, the firm has been operating on the island for ten years. Interviewees endorse its niche in international tax and corporate structuring, typically servicing South African clients. **Peter Wentzel** is the leading name here. The team acted on the establishment of Bidvest which acquired Booker. **Clients:** South African mining and banking groups.

Other Notable Practitioners The "*extremely able*" **Paul Dougherty** heads a niche firm dealing exclusively in corporate, commercial and trusts advice. Clients include Royal Bank of Scotland, Anglo Irish Bank and Royal Scandia Life Assurance.

JERSEY

OFFSHORE: CORPORATE/COMMERCIAL • Jersey	Ptnrs	Assts
1 **Mourant du Feu & Jeune** St Helier	21	36
Ogier & Le Masurier St Helier	7	25
2 **Bedell Cristin** St Helier	12	15
3 **Olsens** St Helier	9	39

LEADING INDIVIDUALS	
1 **BYRNE Chris** Ogier & Le Masurier	**HOWARD Simon** Bedell Cristin
JAMES Ian Mourant du Feu & Jeune	**LOMBARDI Michael** Ogier & Le Masurier
RICHOMME Jacqueline Mourant du Feu & Jeune	
THOMAS Richard Ogier & Le Masurier	
2 **CHAPLIN Clive** Ogier & Le Masurier	**HERBERT Tim** Mourant du Feu & Jeune
KERSHAW Nick Ogier & Le Masurier	
UP AND COMING	
GERWAT Richard Bedell Cristin	**OHLSSON Alex** Olsens

This book is the product of 6,552 1/2-hour interviews. See p.7 for BMRB audit.

Within each band, firms are listed alphabetically. *See individuals' profiles p.850*

Mourant du Feu & Jeune (see firm details p.1076) The oldest firm on the island, it has "*traditionally secured some of the better work*" in international finance and commerce. **Ian James** has for years been "*well regarded as a finance practitioner*" and **Jacqueline Richomme** "*does difficult transactions well.*" **Tim Herbert** is another corporate partner of high standing. The team advised on Arran One Ltd, a $1.6 billion credit card securitisation for the Royal Bank of Scotland. **Clients:** Royal Bank of Scotland International; Deutsche Bank; NTL; Royal Bank of Canada.

Ogier & Le Masurier (see firm details p.1083) Banking, securitisation, structured finance and capital markets are growth areas. **Michael Lombardi** and **Richard Thomas** have a "*high profile and presence,*" while the "*first-class*" **Chris Byrne**, **Clive Chaplin** and **Nick Kershaw** are also recommended to our researchers. The firm advised Bank of America on the disposal of its EMEA private bank business to UBS, and Morgan Stanley on a $1.4 billion acquisition financing to Punch Taverns in connection with the Allied Domecq bid. **Clients:** ANZ; BNP; Flemings; Merrill Lynch.

Bedell Cristin Regarded as "*the third firm in Jersey,*" it offers advice on structured finance, investment funds and trusts. Considered to field a number of "*able partners,*" the team includes **Simon Howard**, who has an excellent name for funds advice, and **Richard Gerwat**, a younger lawyer who our researchers found is "*making his mark in structured finance.*" The team acted on the European Monthly Income Trust, listed in London and on the CISX, which raised gross assets of £195 million and was managed by Aberdeen Asset Managers. **Clients:** Deutsche Bank; Aberdeen Asset Managers.

Olsens A growing firm with a growing reputation, and formerly known as Olsen, Backhurst & Dorey, it re-launched under its new name in April 2000. The firm specialises in sophisticated offshore corporate finance, and in **Alex Ohlsson**, it has a "*go-getting young lawyer*" who is held in high esteem. The team advised Morgan Stanley on the securitisation of Sainsbury's properties for £335 million. **Clients:** Investment banks and large local banks.

LEADERS IN OFFSHORE: CORPORATE/COMMERCIAL

BYRNE, Chris
Ogier & Le Masurier, St Helier (01534) 504 000

CAREY, Nigel
Carey Langlois, St Peter Port (01481) 727 272

CHAPLIN, Clive
Ogier & Le Masurier, St Helier (01534) 504 000

CORLETT, Andrew
Cains, Douglas (01624) 638 300

DOUGHERTY, Paul
Dougherty & Associates, Douglas (01624) 671 155

DOYLE, David
Dickinson Cruickshank & Co, Douglas (01624) 647 647

GERWAT, Richard
Bedell Cristin, St Helier (01534) 814 814

HALL, Graham
Carey Langlois, St Peter Port (01481) 727 272

HARWOOD, Peter
Ozannes, St Peter Port (01481) 723 466

HERBERT, Tim
Mourant du Feu & Jeune, St Helier (01534) 609 000

HOWARD, Simon
Bedell Cristin, St Helier (01534) 814 814

HOWITT, Simon
Babbe Le Pelley Tostevin, St Peter Port (01481) 713 371

JAMES, Ian
Mourant du Feu & Jeune, St Helier (01534) 609 000

KERSHAW, Nick
Ogier & Le Masurier, St Helier (01534) 504 000

KIRK, Ian
Collas Day, St Peter Port (01481) 723 191

LANGLOIS, John
Carey Langlois, St Peter Port (01481) 727 272

LOMBARDI, Michael
Ogier & Le Masurier, St Helier (01534) 504 000

OHLSSON, Alex
Olsens, St Helier (01534) 888 900

RICHOMME, Jacqueline
Mourant du Feu & Jeune, St Helier (01534) 609 000

RIMMER, John
Dickinson Cruickshank & Co, Douglas (01624) 647 647

SHERLOCK, David
Cains, Douglas (01624) 638 300

SIMPSON, William
Ozannes, St Peter Port (01481) 723 466

THOMAS, Richard
Ogier & Le Masurier, St Helier (01534) 504 000

VANDERPLANK, Richard
Cains, Douglas (01624) 638 300

WENTZEL, Peter
Maitland & Co, Douglas (01624) 630 000

SOLICITORS
A-Z OF LAW FIRMS

A & L GOODBODY

Augustine House, Austin Friars, London, EC2N 2HA **Tel:** (020) 7382 0800 **Fax:** (020) 7382 0810 **Email:** info@algoodbody.com **Website:** www.algoodbody.ie • Advises on Irish corporate and commercial law; Irish aspects of major corporate transactions including demutualisations, Irish listings, mergers and acquisitions; inward investment projects; financial services; media and entertainment law.

AARON & PARTNERS

Grosvenor Court, Foregate St, Chester, CH1 1HG **Tel:** (01244) 405555 **Fax:** (01244) 405566 **DX:** 19990 **Email:** enquiries@aaronandpartners.com **Website:** www.aaronandpartners.com **Ptnrs:** 11 **Asst solrs:** 10 **Other fee-earners:** 9 **Contact:** Simon Carter • Commercial law practice covering property, litigation and company commercial. Niche specialisms include: planning; environment; minerals and waste; transport and warehousing; employment; insolvency; construction; agriculture.

AREAS OF PRACTICE

Corporate & Commercial	30%
Commercial Litigation	25%
Property	15%
Minerals & Waste	10%
Planning & Environmental	10%
Transport	5%
Insolvency	3%
Private Client	2%

A

ACTONS

2 King Street, Nottingham, NG1 2AX **Tel:** (0115) 910 0200 **Fax:** (0115) 910 0290 **DX:** 1001 Nottingham 1 **Email:** enquiries@actons.co.uk **Website:** www.actons.co.uk **Ptnrs:** 10 **Asst solrs:** 12 **Other fee-earners:** 12

ADAMS & REMERS

Trinity House, School Hill, Lewes, BN7 2NN **Tel:** (01273) 480616 **Fax:** (01273) 480618 **DX:** 3100 Lewes 1 **Email:** post@adams-remers.co.uk **Website:** adams-remers.co.uk **Ptnrs:** 7 **Asst solrs:** 7 **Other fee-earners:** 18

ADAMS WHYTE

14/16 Frederick Street, Edinburgh, EH2 2HB **Tel:** (0131) 225 8813 **Fax:** (0131) 226 0949 **DX:** ED212 **Email:** hotline@adamswhyte.com **Website:** www.adamswhyte.com **Ptnrs:** 5 **Asst solrs:** 3

ADDLESHAW BOOTH & CO

Sovereign House, P.O. Box 8, Sovereign Street, Leeds, LS1 1HQ
Tel: (0113) 209 2000 **Fax:** (0113) 209 2060 **DX:** 12004 Leeds
Email: info@addleshaw-booth.co.uk **Website:** www.addleshaw-booth.co.uk

25 Cannon Street, London, EC4M 5TB
Tel: (020) 7788 5000 **Fax:** (020) 7788 5060 **DX:** 98948 Cheapside 2
Email: info@addleshaw-booth.co.uk

100 Barbirolli Square, Manchester, M2 3AB
Tel: (0161) 934 6000 **Fax:** (0161) 934 6060 **DX:** 14301 Manchester
Email: info@addleshaw-booth.co.uk

Managing Partner	Mark Jones
Senior Partner	Paul Lee
Number of partners	128
Assistant solicitors	244
Other fee-earners	273

AREAS OF PRACTICE

Commercial Property	24%
Corporate Finance	22%
Commercial Services	19%
Banking & Finance	12%
Litigation & Dispute Resolution	10%
Housing	7%
Private Client	6%

CONTACTS

Banking & Finance	Mark Chidley
Commercial Property	John Pike
Commercial Services	Richard Kempner
Corporate Finance	Sean Lippell
Housing	Anthony Ruane
Litigation & Dispute Resolution	Simon Twigden
Private Client	Paul Howell

THE FIRM: Addleshaw Booth & Co is a leading national law firm with an international capability offering a full range of commercial legal services. A business which works for business, the firm has developed quickly its national markets to provide commercial solutions to a wide range of clients in the corporate, financial, public and private sectors. With offices in Leeds, Manchester and London, the firm combines top level expertise and experience with strength in depth to provide clients with a range of legal services that their businesses need. Clients have a dedicated contact partner who creates a tailor-made team, drawing on the skills of the firm's many nationally recognised specialists. The wide range of clients from the corporate, financial, public and private sectors includes, amongst others, 3i plc, Airtours plc, British Vita, BT plc, Trinity Mirror plc and GEHE (UK) plc, as well as over 135 UK based financial institutions. In the past year Addleshaw Booth & Co has further developed its capabilities and now has 128 partners, a further 244 lawyers and 273 other fee earners firmwide.

PRINCIPAL AREAS OF WORK:

Corporate Finance: Addleshaw Booth & Co's corporate finance practice is one of the most significant in the UK. The practice has a tradition of deal-making, not just providing outstanding technical advice but also in making deals happen through extensive business and professional networks and by strategic input to deals at every stage. The group had its most successful year in 2000, advising on deals with a total value of £6 billion.
Banking: During 2000, the firm's banking and finance practice acted on significant transactions involving total funding/facilities of £8 billion, a 50% increase on the previous year's total funding figure.
Commercial Property: In commercial property, the firm is recognised as one of the leading practices in volume and diversity of market sectors in the UK. It has a national reputation for work in retail and leisure.
Commercial Services: Commercial services' expertise is provided in intellectual property, European and competition law, commercial contracts, employment law, pensions, share schemes and tax issues.

Continued overleaf

Litigation/Dispute Resolution: The firm's litigation and dispute resolution group has widely respected practices in international litigation and arbitration, recognition and enforcement of foreign judgements and regularly provides corporate support advice on international and UK transactions on choice of law, jurisdiction and dispute resolution agreements.
Private Client: The private client practice is regarded as a leading practice across the UK with an increasing number of national appointments and a strong national reputation in family law.
Housing: Addleshaw Booth & Co's housing group incorporates arrears litigation, sales in possession, mortgage shortfall recovery and in 2000 the firm launched 'enact', a fast, efficient and innovative service for clients in the re-mortgage and transactional conveyancing markets.
Other: In addition the firm has a number of cross-disciplinary units, including technology, media and telecommunications, together with pharmaceuticals, sport and entertainment and PFI, which bring together experts in a variety of legal disciplines.

CLIENTELE: The firm's clients include: 3i Group plc; Abbey National plc; Airtours plc; ASDA Group Limited; British Aerospace plc; BT plc; GEHE UK plc; Halifax plc; HSBC Bank plc; J Sainsbury plc; Manchester 2002: Commonwealth Games; Ministry of Defence; Nationwide Building Society; Scapa Group plc; Stadium Group; Trinity Mirror plc; Yorkshire Bank; Yorkshire Electricity Group plc.

RECRUITMENT: In addition, the firm has invested substantially in state-of-the-art hardware, software, training and support across all offices. The firm continues to win significant new appointments through competitive tenders and client recommendations. For further information please visit Addleshaw Booth & Co's website (address given above) or contact Carolyn Roberson, Director of Marketing and Business Development on (0161) 934 6000.

AGNEW, ANDRESS, HIGGINS

92 High Street, Belfast, BT1 2DG **Tel:** (028) 90320035 **Fax:** (028) 90249380 **Ptnrs:** 3 **Asst solrs:** 2 **Other fee-earners:** 1

AITKEN NAIRN WS

7 Abercromby Place, Edinburgh, EH3 6LA
Tel: (0131) 556 6644 **Fax:** (0131) 556 6509 **DX:** 18 Edinburgh
Email: reception@aitkennairn.co.uk **Website:** www.aitkennairn.co.uk

Managing Partner	Kenneth Stanley
Number of partners	5
Assistant solicitors	3
Other fee-earners	3

AREAS OF PRACTICE

Residential Property 30%
Litigation 25%
Private Client 25%
Commercial Property 20%

CONTACTS

Commercial Property ....Kenneth Stanley
Litigation ....Paul Harper
Private Client ....Morag Yellowlees
Residential Property ....Philip Harris

THE FIRM: Aitken Nairn WS is a long established Scottish practice located in Edinburgh's New Town. It has two distinct areas of expertise for both of which it enjoys a strong reputation. Three partners and their staff deal with estate agency, property management, domestic and commercial conveyancing, domestic and commercial leasing, executries, trusts and private client advice. The emphasis is on a quality service at the top end of the market. Two partners and their litigation team handle personal injury, family law, commercial litigation, housing law, bankruptcies, judicial review and Industrial Tribunals. They will resolve disputes at whatever end of the market.

INTERNATIONAL: Languages spoken include Spanish.

ALEXANDER HARRIS

Ashley House, Ashley Road, Altrincham, WA14 2DW
Tel: (0161) 925 5555 **Fax:** (0161) 925 5500 **DX:** 19866 Altrincham 1
Email: info@alexharris.co.uk **Website:** www.alexharris.co.uk

1 Dyers Buildings, London, EC1N 2JT
Tel: (020) 7430 5555 **Fax:** (020) 7430 5500 **DX:** 460 London Chancery Lane
Email: info@alexharris.co.uk

Managing Partner	Ann Alexander
Senior Partner	David Harris
Number of partners	8
Assistant solicitors	14
Other fee-earners	28

AREAS OF PRACTICE

Claimant Clinical Negligence 60%
Pharmaceutical Product Liability/ Medical Devices/Disasters & Multi-Party Actions 20%
Claimant Personal Injury 20%

CONTACTS

Clinical Negligence ....Ann Alexander, ...Lesley Herbertson, Grainne Barton
Personal Injury ....Jenny Kennedy
Pharmaceutical Product Liability & Multi-Party Actions ....David Harris ....Richard Barr

THE FIRM: Specialists in health related litigation work in the UK and abroad, including clinical and dental negligence, personal injury and pharmaceutical product liability. Founded in 1989 by Ann Alexander and David Harris, the firm has offices in London and Altrincham (Cheshire). The firm's lawyers are amongst the leaders in the country in their chosen fields, and boast a US qualified lawyer with close links to other practices in North America. Alexander Harris has the largest number of Law Society Clinical Negligence and AVMA panel members nationwide. The quality of service is confirmed by their being awarded a Legal Service Commission franchise in clinical negligence, personal injury and mental health. Alexander Harris is one of only 18 firms on the Legal Service Commission's multi-party action panel.

PRINCIPAL AREAS OF WORK:
Clinical Negligence: A wide range of clinical negligence cases are dealt with, including matters relating to cerebral palsy, birth injury, anaesthesia, misdiagnosis claims, surgical error, radiation damage, cancer, keyhole surgery and dental work. The team represented the parents of the victims of Lincolnshire nurse, Beverley Allitt

and the families of the victims and alleged victims of Harold Shipman in their successful judicial review of the Secretary of State for Health, Alan Milburn's decision to hold the inquiry into these matters in private. A team of medico-legal assistants supports the department, all of whom are qualified nurses and midwives.

Pharmaceutical Product Liability & Multi-Party Actions: The firm has expertise in all areas of pharmaceutical product litigation. The department is currently co-ordinating and jointly heading all generic Measles, Mumps and Rubella (MMR) vaccine claims, and is responsible for all generic work in the LSD multi-party actions and co-ordinating ECT claims. Work includes investigating over 300 claims of over-treatment by Manchester orthodontist Melvyn Meggitt and representing women who have had their Trilucent breast implants explanted. The firm also investigates claims of adverse effects after taking the anti-smoking drug Zyban, and receiving the meningitis C and DPT vaccine. The treatment of back pain was radically revised after the firm's lawyers pursued a long campaign against Glaxo, manufacturer of Myodil. More than 175 law firms followed the campaign, and as a result £7 million in damages was shared between 400 patients. The firm has considerable experience of litigation in the USA, including Shiley heart valves, Teletronic pacemakers and silicon breast implant claims.

Personal Injury: The firm has specialist lawyers who have considerable expertise in dealing with major cases, in particular brain, spinal and catastrophic injury in the UK and abroad. The firm acts for claimants in all areas of personal injury law – covering injuries on the road, at work, at home, through sporting activities, or as a result of industrial disease. The department also includes a specialist unit handling transatlantic compensation claims.

CLIENTELE: Clients include UK citizens injured during visits to the US and Canada, and claimants against US-based manufacturers. The firm receives an increasing volume of referrals from non-specialist solicitors.

Alexander Harris
solicitors

A

ALEXIOU FISHER PHILIPPS

54 South Molton Street, London, W1K 5SG
Tel: (020) 7409 1222 **Fax:** (020) 7409 7222 **DX:** 44610 Mayfair
Email: mail@afp-law.co.uk **Website:** www.afp-law.co.uk

Number of partners	4
Assistant solicitors	2

THE FIRM: Alexiou Fisher Philipps is a specialist niche matrimonial and family law practice founded by Douglas Alexiou, Jeremy Fisher and Susan Philipps who are all very experienced family lawyers. Douglas Alexiou is the President of the International Academy of Matrimonial Lawyers which boasts an elected fellowship of 300 of the best regarded specialist family lawyers from around the world. Jeremy Fisher is a fellow of the International Academy of Matrimonial Lawyers and lectures widely on the impact of divorce on international financial structures, trusts and business assets. Susan Philipps is an SFLA trained mediator and sits on the education committee of the Solicitors Family Law Association. The firm has a wide ranging client base from the professional to the aristocracy, from entrepreneurs to entertainers, from the media to merchant bankers and their husbands and wives.

ALISTAIR MELDRUM & CO

8-9 Genotin Terrace, Enfield, EN1 2AF
Tel: (020) 8367 0064 **Fax:** (020) 8366 8578 **DX:** 90609 Enfield

Abbey Chambers, 10 Bull Plain, Hertford, SG14 1DT
Tel: (01992) 535866 **Fax:** (01992) 535867 **DX:** 57919 Hertford

Managing Partner	Richard Pugh
Senior Partner	Alistair Meldrum
Number of partners	3
Assistant solicitors	3
Other fee-earners	6

AREAS OF PRACTICE

Crime	85%
Family/Matrimonial	15%

CONTACTS

Criminal	Alistair Meldrum
Family	Mark Bowman

THE FIRM: Founded 10 years ago, Alistair Meldrum & Co has always specialised in criminal defence work and has become one of the foremost criminal firms in North London.

PRINCIPAL AREAS OF WORK: The firm undertakes work in the areas of criminal and family law, including agency and legally aided work.

CLIENTELE: The firm deals with both privately paying and legally aided clients.

ALLAN JANES

21-23 Easton Street, High Wycombe, HP11 1NU **Tel:** (01494) 521301 **Fax:** (01494) 442315 **DX:** 4402 High Wycombe
Email: enquiries@allanjanes.com **Website:** www.allanjanes.com **Ptnrs:** 7 **Asst solrs:** 4 **Other fee-earners:** 4

ALLEN & OVERY

One New Change, London, EC4M 9QQ
Tel: (020) 7330 3000 **Fax:** (020) 7330 9999 **DX:** 73
Email: information@allenovery.com **Website:** www.allenovery.com

Managing Partner	John Rink
Senior Partner	Guy Beringer
UK	
Number of partners	174
Assistant solicitors	634
Other fee earners	262
International	
Number of partners	211
Assistant solicitors	562
Other fee earners	356

THE FIRM: Allen & Overy is a premier international law firm. Founded in 1930, it now has 4,000 staff, including some 350 partners, working in 25 major centres on three continents serving businesses, financial institutions, governments and private individuals where there is a need for decisive legal advice on complex transactions.

PRINCIPAL AREAS OF WORK:

Corporate: The firm's corporate department advises on all aspects of company, corporate finance and commercial law. Lawyers in the department act extensively on public takeovers, international and cross border mergers and acquisitions, Stock Exchange flotations, international equity offerings, private equity, joint ventures and strategic alliances, corporate restructuring, management buyouts and public private partnerships. In addition, the corporate department is actively involved in the work of specialist cross-departmental practice groups including energy, environmental law, insurance, media and communications (including telecommunications, new digital media, broadcasting and satellite), healthcare, financial services and compliance, international projects, construction, mining and metals, European anti-trust, intellectual property and information technology.

Banking: The firm advises financial institutions and borrowers on all types of domestic and international financing transactions including acquisition finance, general bank lending, project finance, property finance, trade finance, restructurings and workouts, all forms of structured finance, asset finance (including aviation and shipping), telecommunications finance and securitisations. The practice acts for over 800 international banks worldwide in deals involving more than 100 jurisdictions.

International Capital Markets: The firm advises in relation to capital markets transactions by issuers from all over the world (including developing countries as well as those with developed economies). These include eurobond issues, euro-equity offerings, equity linked issues, securitisations and derivatives. The firm also has a highly regarded US law practice which now numbers 25 partners and over 120 US qualified lawyers. The practice advises on a wide range of transactions with a significant or dominant US element. For example, Allen & Overy was the first non-US firm to advise the underwriters on a public securitisation deal in the US.

Litigation: The firm's litigation and dispute resolution practice deals with all forms of commercial dispute including administrative and public law, banking and finance, business crime and corporate governance, civil fraud, communications and e-commerce, construction, defamation and media, employment and pensions, energy, environmental law, EU and competition, information technology, insolvency, insurance, intellectual property, investigations, inquiries and crisis management, product liability, professional negligence, projects, property, regulatory proceedings and trust litigation.

Private Client: The firm's large practice provides comprehensive advice to wealthy individuals, entrepreneurs and senior directors, trustees, families, museums, universities and charities worldwide on trusts and estate planning, private capital and personal tax, professional partnerships, immigration, heritage property and private banking.

Project Finance: The firm has one of the leading project finance practices advising all parties in major projects in the UK, Europe (including Western, Central and Eastern Europe), the Middle East, South East Asia and China, and Latin America, acting for sponsors, project companies, lenders and governments.

Property: The firm provides a full commercial property service. Clients include leading national and international investors, landowners, institutions, property companies, developers, contractors, banks and government agencies. The group specialises in multi-property and structured transactions (including public to private deals for UK property companies and beneficial tax structures), as well as advising on building contracts, business rating, commercial leases and underlettings, compulsory purchase, construction law, development agreements, dilapidations, environmental audits, equity sharing leases, housing association law, joint ventures, letting and sale of completed developments, limited recourse funding, pension fund acquisitions, planning procedures and appeals, general property taxation and redevelopments. In conjunction with the firm's insolvency group, it has extensive experience of advising insolvency practitioners.

Taxation: The firm provides a comprehensive corporate tax service including advice on employee benefits and share schemes, and VAT and other indirect taxation.

INTERNATIONAL: The firm has offices in Amsterdam, Antwerp, Bangkok, Beijing, Bratislava, Brussels, Budapest, Dubai, Frankfurt, Hamburg, Hong Kong, Luxembourg, Madrid, Milan, Moscow, New York, Paris, Prague, Rome, Singapore, Tirana, Tokyo, Turin and Warsaw. Languages spoken include Afrikaans, Arabic, Bengali, Bulgarian, Byelorussian, Cantonese, Czech, Danish, Dutch, Finnish, French, German, Greek, Gujarati, Hebrew, Hindi, Hungarian, Italian, Japanese, Korean, Malay, Mandarin, Persian, Polish, Portuguese, Punjabi, Russian, Spanish, Swedish, Tamil and Urdu.

CONTACTS

Acquisition Finance	Tony Keal
Asset Finance	Graham Smith
Banking	David Morley
Bioscience	Robert Barry
Business Reconstruction & Insolvency	Gordon Stewart
Communications/Media/Technology	Ian Ferguson
Construction	John Scriven
Corporate/Commercial	Richard Cranfield
Derivative Products	Jeff Golden
Employment/Pensions & Incentives	Derek Sloan
Energy	Roger Davies
Environmental	Owen Lomas
European Anti-Trust	Mark Friend
Financial Services	Paul Phillips
Housing Association Finance	Richard Cranfield
Insurance	Ian Stanley
Intellectual Property	Colleen Keck
International Capital Markets	Boyan Wells
Litigation	Andrew Clark
MBOs	Alan Paul
Mergers/Acquisitions/Takeovers	Alan Paul
Private Clients	Richard Turnor
Projects & Project Finance	Graham Vinter
Property (Commercial)	Adam Cleal
Property (Finance)	Mark O'Neill
Public Private Partnerships	Anne Baldock
Securitisation	David Krischer
Tax (Corporate)	Patrick Mears
VAT & Indirect Tax	Peter Mendham

ALLEN & OVERY

ALLINGTON HUGHES

10 Grosvenor Rd, Wrexham, LL11 1SD **Tel:** (01978) 291000 **Fax:** (01978) 290493 **DX:** 26651 **Email:** AllingtonW@aol.com **Ptnrs:** 11 **Asst solrs:** 5 **Other fee-earners:** 8

AMBROSE APPELBE

7 New Square, Lincoln's Inn, London, WC2A 3RA
Tel: (020) 7242 7000 **Fax:** (020) 7242 0268 **DX:** LDE 467
Email: mailbox@ambrose.appelbe.co.uk **Website:** www.ambrose.appelbe.co.uk

Managing Partner	Lisa Bolgar Smith
Senior Partner	Lisa Bolgar Smith

AREAS OF PRACTICE

Family	30%
Trusts, Probate, Wills & Charities	30%
Conveyancing	21%
Litigation	19%

CONTACTS

Conveyancing	Felix Appelbe
Family	Lisa Bolgar Smith
Litigation	Duncan Cromarty
Trusts, Probate, Wills & Charities	Felix Appelbe

THE FIRM: Based in Lincoln's Inn, the firm has notable expertise in family law, private client services and charity law. Litigation, property, company and commercial work are also handled, and there is a substantial agency department. Established in 1935 by Ambrose Appelbe, the practice maintains the principles by which he operated: personal attention, excellent service, and simple, innovative solutions to clients' needs. The firm is at the forefront of the legal world. It is a member of the Solicitors Family Law Association and the Relate Quality Partnership. Felix Appelbe is a member of the National Association of Estate Agents. The firm operates as a team, rather than being rigidly compartmentalised.

PRINCIPAL AREAS OF WORK:

Family Law: The department deals with all aspects of marriage and co-habitation breakdown. It enjoys a niche reputation in high finance issues, cases with an international element, property issues and arrangements concerning children. Child abduction is also handled, and advice is given on pre-marriage arrangements.

Litigation: The litigation department handles a range of civil matters and has particular expertise in personal injury, including road traffic, work place and leisure incidents. Professional negligence is a specialism, notably in cases concerning solicitors. Advice is given in partnership disputes, all aspects of employment law, including contracts, termination and tribunal cases, on behalf of both employers and employees, defamation cases are also handled. Alternative dispute resolution is offered wherever appropriate.

Private Client: Extensive private client practice advises on all matters relating to wills and the administration of probates, estates and trusts. Advice is given on tax planning, and on the construction of trusts, in order to achieve significant tax savings. The firm has also helped to achieve excellent investment returns for clients. The practice has acted in the formation of many well-known national charities, and helps them in fundraising and sponsorship.

Conveyancing: All types of residential and commercial conveyancing are dealt with, including landlord and tenant disputes. The firm has a property sales service and Ambrose Appelbe's agency services include actions before the Central London County Court, the High Court and the Privy Council.

CLIENTELE: The large and diverse client base includes individuals and businesses worldwide, as well as charities. Solicitors around the UK, from small provincial firms, to local authorities, instruct the firm in agency matters.

INTERNATIONAL: There is an associate office in Vienna, Alex Frank Rechtsanwaelte KEG.

AMERY-PARKES

Law Courts Chambers, 33 Chancery Lane, London, WC2A 1EN **Tel:** (020) 7404 7100 **Fax:** (020) 7404 6588 **DX:** 162 Lon Chancery Lane WC2 **Email:** lond@ameryparkes.co.uk **Website:** www.ameryparkes.co.uk **Ptnrs:** 23 **Asst solrs:** 16 **Other fee-earners:** 42

AMHURST BROWN COLOMBOTTI

2 Duke Street, St. James's, London, SW1Y 6BJ
Tel: (020) 7930 2366 **Fax:** (020) 7930 2250 **DX:** 412
Email: amlaw@abc-solicitors.com **Website:** www.abc-solicitors.com

Managing Partner	Chris Langford
Senior Partner	Peter Smithson
Number of partners	19
Assistant solicitors	13
Other fee-earners	6

AREAS OF PRACTICE

Commercial Property	30%
Company Commercial	30%
Litigation	30%
Private Clients	10%

CONTACTS

Corporate	Tom Mackay
Employment	Nigel Forsyth
Internet Hi-tech	Tom Mackay
Leisure	Eric Gummers
Litigation & ADR	Steven Morris
Private Client	Peter Smithson
Property	Paul Amandini

THE FIRM: Amhurst Brown Colombotti is a highly progressive international practice. Recognised as one of the leading central London firms for providing high quality commercial services, the firm attributes its success to a dynamic and entrepreneurial approach by its use of multi-talented lawyers combining legal, commercial and language skills.The firm is a well-established international practice respected for its commercial acumen. It has a high quality reputation in its chosen specialisations including property, leisure, employment, international commercial litigation and hi-tech/Internet. The firm has particular expertise in handling cross-border matters spanning Italy, Spain, Poland and Middle East. Amhurst Brown Colombotti provides a committed and reliable service to its clients. It recognises the importance of delivering clients' business objectives by means of practical, creative and cost effective expertise.

PRINCIPAL AREAS OF WORK: Amhurst Brown Colombotti is divided into four core groups: corporate, property, litigation and private client. However the firm also works through other specialist teams which combine lawyers from each of these disciplines. These include employment, leisure and insolvency.

A

ANDERSON BEATON LAMOND

22 St John Street, Perth, PH1 5SP **Tel:** (01738) 639 999 **Fax:** (01738) 630 063 **Ptnrs:** 3 **Asst solrs:** 1

ANDERSON FYFE

90 St. Vincent Street, Glasgow, G2 5UB
Tel: (0141) 248 4381 **Fax:** (0141) 204 1418 **DX:** GW 138
Email: mail@andersonfyfe.co.uk **Website:** www.andersonfyfe.co.uk

Managing Partner	David Chaplin
Number of partners	6
Assistant solicitors	8
Other fee-earners	22

AREAS OF PRACTICE

Property	32%
Litigation & Recovery	29%
Corporate/Business Law/Insolvency	26%
Private Client/Trust/Executry	13%

CONTACTS

Public Sector	Kenneth Meldrum
Private Client Services	Christopher Wilkin
Business Law	David Chaplin
Public Sector	David Chaplin
Commercial Property	Kenneth Meldrum
Residential Property	Lesley Forrest
Litigation	Rhoderick McIlvride
Employment Law	Tom McEntegart

Anderson Fyfe *Solicitors*

THE FIRM: Anderson Fyfe provides services in business, company and employment law, while its private client division provides a comprehensive portfolio of services to individuals. The practice is responsive and flexible to the changing needs of its clients.

PRINCIPAL AREAS OF WORK:
Business Law: The firm's corporate division provides a range of services including company formation, finance, acquisitions and sales. The firm also advises on commercial contracts, intellectual property and trade protection, and has an expanding employment law division.
Private Client: The private practice division looks after individual clients' investments, trusts, tax, wills and executry matters as well as residential conveyancing.
Commercial Property: Services include land acquisition and development, house building developments, leasing, retail leasing, quarrying, security work, planning appeals and Housing Association work.
Litigation: The firm has an extensive commercial and public sector litigation and recoveries department and has been instructed in a number of leading Scottish cases in the Court of Session and House of Lords. The team leader is a solicitor advocate with rights of audience in the Court of Session and the House of Lords.
Public Sector: The firm carries out work for public sector bodies in education, enterprise and housing.

ANDERSON PARTNERSHIP

125 West Regent Street, Glasgow, G2 2SA
Tel: (0141) 248 6688 **Fax:** (0141) 248 9697 **DX:** 512403 Glasgow – Bath St
Email: mailbox@anderson-partnership.co.uk

1 St Colme Street, Edinburgh, EH3 6AA
Tel: (0131) 220 8242 **Fax:** (0131) 220 8342 **DX:** 551112 Edinburgh 7
Email: edinburgh@anderson-partnership.co.uk

Senior Partner	Gilbert Anderson
Number of partners	9
Assistant solicitors	10
Other fee-earners	8

AREAS OF PRACTICE

Insurance/Insurance Litigation & Recoveries	70%
Company/Commercial Property	20%
Private Client	10%

THE FIRM: Established in 1994 under Gilbert Anderson & Partners, the practice has since more than doubled in size. At the end of 1999, the firm opened its Edinburgh office.

PRINCIPAL AREAS OF WORK:

Insurance Law/Insurance Litigation & Claims: Including advice on coverage, conduct of litigation in the Court of Session and in Sheriff Courts throughout Scotland, and representation at fatal accident inquiries. The firm provides advice on all aspects of road traffic claims/public/employers' liability, product liability and undertake all related investigative work for insurers throughout Scotland. The firm has two members of FOIL.

Commercial/Commercial Property & Employment Law: Work includes commercial leasing; security; business acquisition; disposal and start-ups for sole traders, partnerships and companies; contractual advice; employment law; commercial dispute resolution; asset recovery.

Private Client: Including residential conveyancing; tax planning; wills and executries; financial services; matrimonial dispute resolution.

CONTACTS	
Administrative Law	Frank Hughes
Co/Comm Property	David Morris, Alan Paton
Commercial Litigation	Andrew Ireland
Employment Law	James Herd
Ins/Ins Lit & Recoveries	Gilbert Anderson
	John Maillie
	Alan Taylor
Private Client	Morag Gibb

The Anderson Partnership
Solicitors

ANDERSON STRATHERN WS

48 Castle Street, Edinburgh, EH2 3LX
Tel: (0131) 220 2345 **Fax:** (0131) 226 7788 **DX:** 3 Edinburgh
Email: forename.surname@andersonstrathern.co.uk
Website: www.andersonstrathern.co.uk

Managing Partner	Robin Stimpson
Chairman	Alan Menzies
Number of partners	25
Assistant solicitors	43
Other fee-earners	37

THE FIRM: One of Scotland's leading commercial firms with a strong private client practice, Anderson Strathern's genuine full service approach has led to particular success in its principal practice areas of property, private client and corporate services. The firm has also made significant ground in niche practice areas including employment, intellectual property, entertainment and media, banking and services to and for the Scottish Parliament. In the last two years Anderson Strathern has grown considerably to reflect a rapid growth in business, primarily in the commercial sector. Clients include national and international companies, public bodies, banks and property investors, developers and many substantial landowners. Anderson Strathern offers the resources of a large legal practice but features a high level of personal attention combined with genuine specialist advisers. The firm provides expertise in the Scottish aspects of cross-border transactions for England based and international legal firms and as a member of the Association of European Lawyers is strongly placed to provide advice on any European legal issues. The firm continues to introduce bespoke IT systems to improve client service and was the first large Scottish legal firm to be awarded the Investor in People standard.

PRINCIPAL AREAS OF WORK:

Banking: The firm specialises in providing services to banks in property, corporate and litigation work.

Commercial Property: A growing team covers all aspects of commercial property law supported by specialists in landlord and tenant law, planning, construction and environmental law. Two partners are accredited commercial leasing law specialists. One is accredited as a planning law specialist.

Agricultural/Rural Property: This is an award-winning team recognised as a leader in agricultural law and estates work. Two partners are accredited specialists in agricultural law.

Employment: The firm has one of the largest dedicated employment teams in Scotland led by an accredited specialist employment lawyer. All aspects of employment law for both employer and employee are undertaken and in the last 12 months the employment team has acted in a number of landmark employment cases.

Litigation: With particular strengths in areas of liability insurance work and health service law, one partner is accredited as a specialist in medical negligence. Three partners are admitted as solicitor advocates with rights of audience in the highest law courts in Scotland.

Private Client: Recognised as one of the foremost private client practices in Scotland, the firm continues to develop with a particular emphasis on providing investment and tax advice to high net worth individuals.

Parliamentary: A specialist parliamentary team advises on all aspects of work in the Scottish Parliament and Anderson Strathern is the only law firm in Scotland to be appointed to the panel retained for the preparation of legislation on behalf of the Scottish Executive.

CLIENTELE: Clients include The Royal College of Nursing, Napier University, The National Trust for Scotland, the Scottish Rugby Union, The Coal Authority, The Crown Estate, Manor Kingdom, Bank of Scotland, The Royal Bank of Scotland and Scotmid.

CONTACTS	
Agriculture	Alasdair Fox
	James Drysdale
Banking	Ruari MacNeill
Charities	George Russell
Commercial Property	Alan Menzies
	David Hunter
	Andrew Morris
Construction	Michael Essery
	Neil Smith
Corporate	Jonathan MacQueen
Corporate/Sports	John Kerr
Employment	Alun Thomas
Entertainment/Media	Simon Brown
Family Law	Mac Rigg
Intellectual Property/IT	Simon Brown
Litigation	Robert Carr
	Robert Fife
	Ruari MacNeill
	Fiona Stephen
Parliamentary	Morag Ross
Personal Tax	Colin Henderson
Planning	Alastair McKie
Private Client	John Blair
	Colin Henderson
	Lynda Pennell
	Robin Watt
Residential Property	Jean Broadwood
Rural Property	James Drysdale
	Alasdair Fox
	Fiona Gibb
	Robin Stimpson

A

ANDREA & CO

Triatha House, Millbrook, Guildford, GU1 3XJ **Tel:** (01483) 889 880 **Fax:** (01483) 889 881 **DX:** 83156 Guildford 2 **Email:** ca@andreaco.com
Website: www.andreaco.com **Ptnrs:** 1 **Asst solrs:** 2 **Other fee-earners:** 5

ANDREW BRYCE & CO

7 Queen St, Coggeshall, CO6 1UF **Tel:** (01376) 563123 **Fax:** (01376) 563336 **Email:** bryce@ehslaw.co.uk **Ptnrs:** 1

ANDREW KEENAN & CO

Nickleby House, Charles Dickens Terrace, Maple Road, London, SE20 8RE **Tel:** (020) 8659 0332 **Fax:** (020) 8659 3689 **DX:** 34860 Penge
Ptnrs: 1 **Asst solrs:** 1 **Other fee-earners:** 4

ANDREW M. JACKSON & CO

Essex House, Manor Street, Hull, HU1 1XH
Tel: (01482) 325242 **Fax:** (01482) 212974 **DX:** 11920
Email: lawyers@amj.co.uk **Website:** www.amj.co.uk

Managing Partner	John Hammersley
Number of partners	23
Assistant solicitors	31
Other fee-earners	20

AREAS OF PRACTICE

Commercial Property	30%
Corporate	10%
Shipping	20%
Litigation	20%
Private Client	20%

CONTACTS

Commercial Property	Bill Fisher
Company	Martin Whitehead
Family	Andrew J Haines
Litigation	Hugh Smith
Private Client	Kevin Webster
Shipping	Silas Taylor

THE FIRM: The firm's services are founded on committed and well-motivated lawyers delivering top quality advice and value for money.

PRINCIPAL AREAS OF WORK:
Corporate: M&A, corporate finance, partnership, franchise and agency agreements and joint ventures.
Shipping & Fishing: Ship sale, purchase and finance, collision, salvage, charterparty, and Bills of Lading disputes.
Commercial Property: Landlord and tenant, property development and planning.
Private Client: Tax, trusts and tax planning.
Agency Work: Undertaken in all local civil courts.
Legal Aid: Family law and family mediation. Franchise holder.
Litigation: Commercial, property, personal injury and employment.

CLIENTELE: Local and national companies both public and private including MFI, Carpetright, Northern Foods, Express Dairies, Associated British Ports and P&O North Sea Ferries.

ANNE HALL DICK & CO.

157 Kilmarnock Road, Shawlands, Glasgow, G41 3JE **Tel:** (0141) 636 0003 **Fax:** (0141) 636 0303 **DX:** 501146 Shawlands
Email: ahdco@globalnet.uk **Ptnrs:** 2 **Asst solrs:** 2

ANN L. HUMPHREY

The Boathouse Office, 57a Gainsford Street, London, SE1 2NB
Tel: (020) 7378 9370 **Fax:** (020) 7378 9360
Email: annlhumphrey@dial.pipex.com

Senior Partner	Ann L Humphrey

AREAS OF PRACTICE

Corporate Tax & VAT	100%

THE FIRM: The firm provides a tax consultancy service for businesses and other professionals and has extensive experience of all aspects of VAT and business taxation. The firm offers other professionals specialised tax advice designed to help them meet their clients' needs, assistance with in-house training and the preparation of standard form tax documentation and client seminars in the firm's specialisms, as well as help in identifying appropriate tax marketing opportunities. Because the firm concentrates on what it does best, clients pay only for that dedicated expertise.

PRINCIPAL AREAS OF WORK: The firm is dedicated to the provision of high level corporate tax and VAT advice. 60% of its work by fee income is corporate tax related (including stamp duty) and 40% VAT and duties. The firm also from time-to-time provides business advice to other lawyers.

CLIENTELE: Mainly other professionals, both lawyers and accountants, UK and non-UK, and professional bodies.

ANTHONY COLLINS SOLICITORS

St Philip's Gate, 5 Waterloo Street, Birmingham, B2 5PG **Tel:** (0121) 200 3242 **Fax:** (0121) 212 7442
DX: 13055 Birmingham 1 **Email:** acs@acollins-sol.co.uk **Website:** www.anthonycollinssolicitors.com
Ptners: 17 **Asst solrs:** 33 **Consultants:** 2 **Other fee-earners:** 28 **Contact:** Deborah Evans • A proactive niche market practice providing services primarily to the voluntary sector, the business sector, the housing sector, local government and the individual.

AREAS OF PRACTICE

Housing & Local Government	33%
Commercial Property	18%
Business Law/Licensing	16%
Litigation/PI/Medical Negligence	16%
Private Client (Family)	12%
Charities/Church Law	5%

ANTHONY GOLD

New London Bridge House, 25 London Bridge Street, London, SE1 9TW
Tel: (020) 7940 4000 **Fax:** (020) 7378 8025 **DX:** 39915 London Bridge South
Email: mail@anthonygold.co.uk **Website:** www.anthonygold.co.uk

43 Streatham Hill, London, SW2 4TP
Tel: (020) 8678 5500 **Fax:** (020) 8674 8004 **DX:** 58604 Streatham
Email: mail@anthonygold.co.uk

Managing Partner	David Marshall
Number of partners	11
Assistant solicitors	10
Other fee-earners	11

CONTACTS

Admin/Public/Property Litigation	Andrew Brookes
Clinical Negligence	Jon Nicholson
Commercial Property	Howard Lerman
Corporate & Commercial	David Marshall
Family Law/Mediation	Kim Beatson
	Caroline Bowden
Personal Injury	Jon Nicholson
Residential Property	Stephen Whitaker
Trusts & Estates	Mark Politz

THE FIRM: Anthony Gold was founded in 1963. The firm is a progressive and expanding practice with specialist departments who represent both business and individual clients. Based at London Bridge, and also with offices in SW2, the firm excels at meeting the needs of both individual and business clients. The firm's highly regarded litigation practice is largely claimant-focused and aims to work in a way which matches clients' ability to pay its fees. In particular, it has been instrumental in the development of conditional fee agreements. David Marshall is co-author of *Conditional Fees: Law and Practice* (Sweet and Maxwell, 1999).

PRINCIPAL AREAS OF WORK:

Company & Commercial: The acquisition and disposal of companies and unincorporated businesses, all general commercial agreements including joint ventures, agency and distribution and IT and intellectual property matters.
Commercial Dispute Resolution: General commercial contracts of both a national and international content with particular expertise in computer, engineering and construction disputes.
Employment: Advising businesses and individuals on contracts of employment, redundancy, dismissal, European law, HR/employment policies at work and discrimination claims.
Family & Divorce: Financial cases, maintenance and property, children's cases (including abductions), mediation and Inheritance Act cases. Kim Beatson is on the National Committee of the Solitors' Family Law Association. Both Kim Beatson and Partner, Caroline Bowden, are accredited family mediators. The firm has wide experience in international financial matters including high net worth individuals and freezing injunctions in multiple jurisdictions.
Landlord & Tenant/Property: Residential and commercial landlord and tenant claims (for either party), disrepair, dilapidations, possession, forfeiture and lease renewals.
Clinical Negligence: All categories of clinical negligence, with particular expertise in cerebral palsy and other brain injuries, obstetrics and gynaecology, infectious diseases, neurosurgery, orthopaedics, anaesthetics, accident and emergency medicine and general practice. Jon Nicholson and David Marshall are members of the Law Society's Clinical Negligence panel.
Personal Injury: A wide spectrum of personal injury claims for claimants, ranging from catastrophic brain and spinal injuries to road traffic accidents, accidents at work and tripping cases. All personal injury solicitors are members of APIL and those with more than three years post-qualification experience are on the Law Society's Personal Injury panel.
Professional Negligence: Acting for businesses and individuals in claims against solicitors, accountants, surveyors and financial advisors.
Public Law: Judicial reviews of the decisions of local and public authorities in particular the housing, community care and education sectors. Andrew Brookes is Chair of the Housing Law Practitioners' Association.
Property: Acquisitions, development and financial work for retailers, investors, landlords and homebuyers.
Trusts & Estates: Specialising in tax planning, wills and the administration of estates and trusts. Mark Politz is a Chartered Tax Adviser.

ARCHIBALD CAMPBELL & HARLEY WS

37 Queen Street, Edinburgh, EH2 1JX **Tel:** (0131) 220 3000 **Fax:** (0131) 220 2288 **DX:** 181 Edinburgh **Email:** admin@achws.co.uk **Website:** www.achws.co.uk **Ptnrs:** 15 **Asst solrs:** 11 **Other fee-earners:** 16 **Contact:** Andrew Wallace • Known for innovative work in commercial property, corporate, planning, environment, debt recovery/insolvency, litigation and housing. Reputation for quality service, commercial flair and relevant, expert, practical advice.

AREAS OF PRACTICE	
Commercial Property	49%
Private Clients	25%
Litigation	12%
Corporate/Commercial	9%
Planning/Environmental	5%

ARCHON (FORMERLY LANGLEY & CO)

66-67 Cornhill, London, EC3V 3NB
Tel: (020) 7397 9650 **Fax:** (020) 7929 6316 **DX:** 706 London/City
Email: [nameoffeeearner]@archonlaw.co.uk

Number of partners	3
Assistant solicitors	4
Other fee-earners	4

AREAS OF PRACTICE

Employment	90%
General Commercial Advice	10%

THE FIRM: Archon was established in 1993 and specialises exclusively in employment law. Its principals are Jill Andrew, Nick Ralph and Susan Thompson, who between them have over 40 years' experience, and all of whom were previously with major City firms.

PRINCIPAL AREAS OF WORK: The firm deals with all aspects of employment law for corporate clients including contentious and non-contentious matters and also acts for individuals in employment disputes. It aims to provide a highly personalised and responsive service geared to the needs of clients. It is pleased to offer competitive fee quotations and also has a range of fixed price services including the conduct of and representation at Employment Tribunals. Other services which the firm currently provides include bespoke employment law training courses for clients and the legal profession.

ARNANDER IRVINE & ZIETMAN (FORMERLY LLEWELYN ZIETMAN)

Temple Bar House, 23-28 Fleet Street, London, EC4Y 1AA
Tel: (020) 7842 5400 **Fax:** (020) 7842 5444 **DX:** 209 Chancery Lane London WC2
Email: postmaster@aiz-law.com **Website:** www.aiz-law.com

Managing Partner	Ian Macdonald
Senior Partner	Clive Zietman
Number of partners	14
Assistant solicitors	12
Other fee-earners	15

AREAS OF PRACTICE

Commercial Litigation	60%
Intellectual Property	40%

CONTACTS

Banking Litigation	Duncan McNair
	Geoffrey Gauci
Brand Protection	Belinda Isaac
	Andrew Shaw
Commercial & Fraud Litigation	Clive Zietman
	John Bramhall
Commercial Law	Ian Macdonald
E-commerce	Lorna Robertson
	Belinda Isaac
Financial Services Regulation	Clive Zietman
Insolvency Litigation	Charles Pugh
International Commercial Arbitration	Geoffrey Gauci
Patents/Designs & Copyright	James Irvine
	Conrad Arnander
	Gerard Cronin
Trademarks (Registration & Enforcement)	Belinda Isaac
	Andrew Shaw

THE FIRM: Arnander Irvine & Zietman is a young commercial law practice specialising in the resolution of commercial disputes, and in the protection, exploitation and enforcement of intellectual property rights. The specialist services of the commercial litigation department have an emphasis on fraud and financial services, and the intellectual property department is extensively experienced in all aspects of contentious and non-contentious matters. Arnander Irvine & Zietman was founded in 1994 as a specialist niche practice focusing on commercial litigation and intellectual property, and has since greatly expanded its strengths in its chosen areas of expertise. The firm focuses on bringing a pro-active and partner driven approach to the resolution of commercial disputes, and to its intellectual property practice. It seeks to provide services with the highest of standards, but at competitive prices.

PRINCIPAL AREAS OF WORK:

Commercial: Commercial disputes of all kinds are dealt with. Expertise includes banking, including the enforcement of securities, actions based on guarantees and performance bonds, letters of credit and negligence; and a wide range of financial services and insolvency matters. There is significant expertise within the firm in the fields of tracing and the recovery of assets, both within the UK and abroad. In that connection the firm has extensive practical experience in the application of the Brussels and Lugano Conventions and the conduct of multijurisdictional proceedings.

Fraud: The firm advises on all aspects of fraud, including prevention and investigation, as well as assisting in the recovery of monies. It has considerable experience in dealing with Serious Fraud Office, DTI and LIFFE investigations, and the senior partner – who has written extensively about fraud – is an acknowledged expert in the field.

Intellectual Property: Intellectual property expertise includes all aspects of patents, trademarks and service marks, copyright, registered and unregistered design and breach of confidence, together with all types of litigation and intellectual property aspects of corporate transactions.

Patents & Trademarks: Arnander Irvine & Zietman has special expertise in three areas: European patent litigation, including obtaining provisional and protective remedies; chemical, pharmaceutical and software patents; brand protection, from advice on new product development with a view to gaining maximum legal protection; clearance searches in respect of new brand names; registration of trade marks and designs (in the UK and elsewhere) and enforcement of rights.

CLIENTELE: The firm's client base ranges from individuals to major multinationals, with about 75% of the work being of an international nature.

INTERNATIONAL: The firm has French, German and Italian speaking solicitors, and because of the nature of the work carried out, it has a strong international focus, and is conversant with the languages, laws and procedures of a number of foreign jurisdictions.

ARNOLD & PORTER

Tower 42, 25 Old Broad Street, London, EC2N 1HQ
Tel: (020) 7786 6100 **Fax:** (020) 7786 6299
Website: www.arnoldporter.com

Chairman	Michael Sohn
Managing Partner	James Sandman
London Responsible Partner	Fern O'Brian
UK	
Number of partners	8
Assistant solicitors	16
US associates	1
UK total	25
International	
Number of partners	236
Associates	338
Of counsel	19
Special counsel	24
Staff attorneys	35
International total	652

CONTACTS

UK
Anti-trust, Competition & Trade Regulation .... Tim Frazer
Corporate & Securities .... Jeremy Willcocks
Intellectual Property & Technology Litigation .... Ian Kirby
Life Sciences .... Julian Thurston
Litigation .... Fern O'Brian
Product Liability .... Fern O'Brian
Technology .... Sarah Kirk
.... Andrew Hooles
Telecommunications .... Michael Ryan
US
Anti-trust, Competition & Trade Regulation .... Bill Baer
Bankruptcy .... Daniel Lewis
Benefits & Employment Law .... Edward Bintz
Corporate & Securities .... Steven Kaplan
Environmental .... Thomas Milch
Financial Institutions .... Patrick Doyle
Food, Drug & Medical Devices William Vodra
Government Contracts .... Joseph West
Health Care .... Grant Bagley
Intellectual Property & Technology .... David Apatoff
.... Joel Freed
International .... Lawrence Schneider
Legislative/Public Policy .... Jeffrey Smith
Life Sciences .... Richard Johnson
Litigation .... Peter Grossi
Product Liability .... Robert Weiner
Product Finance .... Whitney Debevoise
Real Estate .... George Covucci
Tax .... Richard Hubbard
Telecommunications .... Norman Sinel

THE FIRM: Arnold & Porter was established in Washington, DC in 1946. The firm has a deserved reputation for providing high quality and efficient legal services. Central to the historic practice of the firm has been a focus on the intersection of law, business and public policy and an understanding of the industries in which clients operate. The firm's lawyers have frequently been retained by clients confronted with the most complex legal and business problems, often with a regulatory or governmental component, requiring innovative and practical solutions. Arnold & Porter provides a multidisciplinary approach to client matters and works together across borders to develop international commercial and regulatory strategies for clients operating on a global basis.

London Office: In recent years, the integration of the world economy has accelerated at an unprecedented pace. Governments, companies and the legal profession are all evolving in response to these developments. To support its European clients, and US clients with European interests, the London office was established in 1997. The focus in London is on selected areas in which the firm provides sophisticated representation of the highest calibre. These areas include telecommunications, IP/IT, competition, life sciences, product regulation and liability, corporate, commercial and regulatory counselling.

PRINCIPAL AREAS OF WORK:

Competition: Arnold & Porter's London competition and EU team provides advice to clients undertaking national and international transactions, or who need to resolve competition issues at a European level or at a national level within Europe. The firm represents clients from a broad array of industries before the EC Commission, the Office of Fair Trading and the Competition Commission in relation to a range of competition concerns under EU and United Kingdom laws, including allegations of abuse of dominant position or anti-competitive prices. In addition, the team's lawyers have experience in dealing with major anti-trust inquiries, price fixing issues, distribution and licensing agreements, strategic alliances and joint ventures. Members of the London team undertake and co-ordinate work necessary to obtain competition clearances for mergers, acquisitions and joint ventures from the EC Commission and from national authorities in the EU, Central/Eastern Europe and beyond. The London team specialises in finding solutions to complex competition problems for large and multinational firms. In addition to competition work, the team advises on other aspects of EU law, particularly relating to the free movement of goods within the EU.

Intellectual Property: The intellectual property team in London focuses on contentious and transactional intellectual issues with a special emphasis on hi-tech matters. The firm's intellectual property specialists have comprehensive experience in the acquisition, protection, commercialisation and enforcement of all types of intellectual property rights. The team also has the ability to enforce or defend intellectual property rights, including patents, through litigation or arbitration when that proves necessary. For example, members of the intellectual property litigation team are currently involved in a headline-grabbing microchip patent dispute.

Information Technology: London's information technology practice group understands the complex issues presented by transactions involving technology and provides advice on a wide range of information technology related transactions and regularly restructures, drafts and negotiates outsourcing and distribution of technology products and services. Other work involves issues relating to the protection of data, computer misuse, protection of know-how or confidential information, the transfer of software and rights in software. The London IT practice group also has considerable experience in outsourcing arrangements and in establishing strategic relationships. Group members all have a long track record of advising companies involved in outsourcing transactions, including some of the largest and most complex UK and global outsourcing deals undertaken to date.

Life Sciences: The life sciences group in London is one of a very few groups in the world specialising exclusively in collaborative development and licensing agreements, strategic partnering agreements and other forms of licensing agreement between biotechs and large pharmaceutical companies, whether the biotech is a product company or a platform technology company. The group has unparalleled experience of these sorts of transactions. The London office life science practice is also able to offer an unparalleled service conducting mid-cap mergers and acquisitions for pharmaceutical and biotech companies in the European market either directly, in the UK, or as co-ordinating counsel in the case of other countries in Europe. With its knowledge of the business sector the firm is one of the leading groups in the UK for pharmaceutical and biotech sector transactions, whether commercial or corporate, with the exception of large, set-piece, industry headline, multi-billion dollar mergers and acquisition transactions.

Telecommunications: The telecommunications industry, with its wide array of existing and emerging technologies, poses complex problems and presents challenging opportunities that require effective legal strategies. Arnold & Porter has a broad and innovative practice representing entities grappling with telecommunications issues. Established more than 40 years ago by one of the firm's founding partners, a former chairman of the US Federal Communications Commission (FCC), the firm's practice covers the spectrum of activities that defines the telecommunications industry today, including traditional telephone, data

Continued overleaf

A

and wireless communications; cable, satellite and broadcasting; Internet and advanced technologies. The London practice provides commercial, regulatory, litigation and legislative counsel and strategic advice to corporations, government entities, institutions and individuals before the regulatory agencies, the courts and governments. Governments and international institutions also seek the firm's counsel on the domestic and international implications of existing and emerging technologies and in new regulatory and marketplace structures.

Corporate & Commercial: The team of corporate lawyers in London has extensive experience in advising clients on a broad range of corporate transactions such as domestic and cross-border mergers and acquisitions, joint ventures, flotations/IPOs, secondary issues (such as placings or rights issues), private equity funding and venture capital investments. The corporate group also assists clients in establishing a wide range of commercial relationships, including asset acquisitions, distributorships and other sales relationships. For many relatively routine transactions, the firm strives to maximize value by closing quickly and cost-effectively. It also takes pride in its success in structuring complex and novel transactions. The lawyers in the London office work closely with lawyers in the firm's other offices to achieve client objectives in matters with cross-border implications.

Product Liability/Litigation: Managing some of the largest and most complex product liability matters in the world, Arnold & Porter acts both as national counsel and as trial counsel in many individual cases in the US. For example, the firm serves as the US national co-ordinating counsel and trial counsel for American Home Products in its phen-fen diet drug litigation, which involves a wide range of issues, including compliance with Food and Drug Administration (FDA); new drug and adverse event reporting regulations; the development and evaluation of epidemiological and clinical data; and novel class action issues in both the litigation and settlement contexts. The firm is defending approximately 15,000 cases in 49 US states, as well as the 1,000 federal cases that have been consolidated in Philadelphia. The firm's lawyers have drafted most of the class action briefs and argued those motions. Arnold & Porter is also responsible for working with approximately 500 scientific and regulatory experts who have appeared in one or more of the cases. Most recently, the attorneys were the principal architects of a $4.75 billion settlement that should resolve much of that litigation. Arnold & Porter served as US national defence counsel for a large volunteer blood collector in cases concerning individuals who allegedly contracted the AIDS virus from blood transfusions. The firm obtained numerous rulings granting summary judgment on negligence, strict liability and breach of warranty claims and won favourable verdicts in four cases that have been tried before juries.

Pro Bono Work: Arnold & Porter's distinguished 55 year tradition of pro bono service has established an exceptional reputation in the legal community as a whole. The firm has special ties with many important public interest organisations that provide critical legal services to the disadvantaged. The firm's pro bono work is characterised by diversity – the issues it takes on are as wide-ranging as the interests of its lawyers and staff. The firm has a long-standing tradition of groundbreaking representation in matters involving the arts, civil rights, education, employment discrimination, free speech, international human rights and criminal matters. The firm has grown and changed dramatically since the early pro bono days of its defence of US government employees accused of disloyalty during the McCarthy era. The London office is now following in the tradition of pro bono work.

CLIENTELE: Arnold & Porter's clients range from Fortune 500 corporations to hi-tech start-up companies. With such a broad spectrum of legal specialties and experience, the firm's approach to service is multidimensional.

INTERNATIONAL: With over 650 attorneys firmwide, the firm has a broad international practice, in addition to its Washington DC and London offices, the firm maintains offices in New York, Los Angeles, Century City, Denver and Northern Virginia, and an extensive network of working relationships with law firms throughout the world.

RECRUITMENT: The firm's hiring standards are rigorous. It seeks candidates who have demonstrated academic excellence. Arnold & Porter's growing London office is located in the International Financial Centre in the City of London. The firm strives to foster a collegial and informal atmosphere, which is enhanced by twice weekly informal social gatherings and other events, casual dress, associate mentoring programmes and team based assignment policies. Arnold & Porter encourages attorneys at all levels to be involved in the administration of the office and the development of the firm's transatlantic practice. Associates are expected to work on several matters at once and to assume responsibility quickly. The firm emphasises teamwork and exposure to a number of different partners and clients. It tries to accommodate associates' areas of interests. The firm's commitment to excellence ensures that training is a continuous process with a series of training programmes, seminars and discussion groups and on a day to day basis with partners, who are specialists in their own areas. There is an excellent mentoring programme, which is a continuous form of feedback with partners and associates. Associates receive evaluations on a yearly basis and at that time there is an opportunity to discuss his or her career with the firm's associate evaluation committee. Associates also provide feedback on a periodic basis to the partners with whom they work. Arnold & Porter is committed to equal employment opportunity and to a programme of affirmative action to fulfil that policy. The firm values diversity and affirmatively solicits applications from all qualified applicants, including women, minorities and individuals with disabilities.

ARNOLD THOMSON

205 Watling Street West, Towcester, NN12 6BX **Tel:** (01327) 350266 **Fax:** (01327) 353567 **DX:** 16932 Towcester **Email:** enquiries@arnoldthomson.com **Website:** www.arnoldthomson.com **Contact:** M Thomson • Mike Thomson heads a team including several senior lawyers with extensive experience in areas of work handled across England and Wales. It regularly deals with agricultural tenancy work for other solicitors.

AREAS OF PRACTICE	
Sales, Purchases & Development Work	35%
Trusts/Tax & Probate	25%
Agricultural Tenancies	15%
Civil Litigation	10%
Partnerships	10%
Quotas	5%

ARTHUR COX - NORTHERN IRELAND

Stokes House, 17-25 College Square East, Belfast, BT1 6HD
Tel: (028) 9023 0007 **Fax:** (028) 9026 2650 **DX:** 2012 NR Belfast 2
Email: bt@arthurcox.ie **Website:** www.arthurcox.com

Contact Partner	Angus Creed
Number of partners	6
Assistant solicitors	7
Other fee-earners	5

AREAS OF PRACTICE	
Property	30%
Litigation (inc. Employment)	30%
Banking/Financial Services	20%
Company/Commercial Law	20%

CONTACTS	
Banking/Financial Services	Angus Creed
	Judith Brown
Civil Litigation	Peter Martin
	Angela Maguire
	Amanda Wylie
	Anna Beggan
Commercial Property	Rowan White
	Anne Donnelly
	Patricia Lyons
Company/Commercial	Kerry Canavan
	Peter Stafford
Competition/European	John Meade

THE FIRM: Arthur Cox – Northern Ireland was established in 1996, following the merger of the Belfast office of Arthur Cox, one of the largest practices in the Republic of Ireland, with the long established law firm of Norman Wilson & Co which has particular strengths in the areas of corporate banking, commercial, property and employment law. The firm merged in December 1997 with Martin & Brownlie to give added strength to its employment and litigation departments. The firm is in a unique position to provide a range of cross-border services from its Belfast and Dublin Offices.

PRINCIPAL AREAS OF WORK:
Banking/Financial Services: The firm is established as one of the leading practices in all aspects of banking and secured lending.
Company/Commercial: Includes all types of company/commercial law matters, mergers and acquisitions, joint ventures, agency and distribution agreements with particular emphasis on cross-border transactions.
Competition/European: Competition and EU regulatory advice with particular reference to cross-border transactions.
Commercial Property: Covers a significant range of property and commercial property related transactions including commercial development for private and public companies and financial institutions.
Litigation/Employment: A wide range of litigation services with particular reference to employment and commercial litigation.

INTERNATIONAL: The firm has offices in Dublin, London and New York.

A

ASB LAW

8 Ifield Road, Crawley, RH11 7YY
Tel: (01293) 603603 **Fax:** (01293) 603666 **DX:** 57100 Crawley 1
Email: crawley@asb-law.com **Website:** www.asb-law.com

Chief Executive	Christopher Honeyman Brown
Number of partners	42
Number of fee-earners	140
Total staff	338

AREAS OF PRACTICE	
Commercial Property (inc. Planning)	17%
Commercial Litigation	15%
Corporate & Commercial	14%
Employment	12%
Residential Property	10%
Family	9%
Personal Injury	8%
Insolvency	7%
Wills, Trusts & Probate	7%

CONTACTS	
Aviation	Lee Hills
Commercial Litigation & Debt Recovery	Andrew Pawlik
Commercial Property	Carol Fletcher
Corporate & Commercial	Don Burstow
Employment	Rebecca Thornley-Gibson
Family	Ursula Danagher
Franchising	Don Burstow
General Civil Litigation	Albert Passmore
Insolvency	Andrew Taylor
IP	Karen Lord
IT Contracts	Andrew Clinton
Licensing	Stephen Thomas
Personal Injury	Francis Lacy Scott
Property Litigation	Rex Cowell

THE FIRM: As a result of its unique three-way merger in late 1999, asb *law* has launched itself into the top three firms in the South East. It is now well established as one of the strongest law firms in the region. It has unrivalled service coverage throughout Kent, Surrey and Sussex, providing a range of specialist legal services to businesses, private clients and the public sector.

PRINCIPAL AREAS OF WORK: In the past 12 months, the firm has further strengthened its position through the addition of expertise and the development of new products and services to meet clients' needs.
Travel & Aviation: The team has expanded significantly, and is ideally positioned to provide specialist legal advice to one of the world's most rapidly expanding industries.
Technology, E-Commerce & Computer (TeC): The group was formed last year to meet client demand for support with e-commerce, information technology and intellectual property issues. It already has a substantial client base and has been involved in a range of significant transactions.
Corporate: The 10-lawyer team specialises solely in corporate work and handles a full range of high-value corporate finance, merger and acquisition and company restructuring work. The team has rapidly won a reputation as one of the largest and most experienced corporate groups in the region.
Commercial Contracts: This six-lawyer team regularly deals with high value procurement contracts and has a very strong reputation in the public sector, with work handled ranging from IT contracts to IPR licences and disposals.
Planning & Environmental: The firm's established unit of five lawyers deals with planning, environmental and property litigation issues for a broad range of national clients, local authorities and representative groups.
Employment: The firm has further developed Praesidium, a service which offers employers a 24 hour, 365 days a year telephone helpline providing access to a solicitor specialising in employment law and insurance cover for up to £50,000 of legal fees and awards per claim.

Continued overleaf

The firm's Employee Benefit Scheme (EBS) appeals to companies who prefer to offer a range of benefits to employees as a way of attracting and retaining good staff. Under the scheme, employees receive a free initial consultation and a 10 per cent discount on legal fees.

Commercial Property: This group is one of the strongest teams in the South, with 22 lawyers providing advice on acquisitions, leasing, disposal of commercial property, agricultural interests, hotels and licensed premises, offices and shops.

Insolvency: A licensed insolvency practitioner heads an expanding team of five solicitors acknowledged as the leading insolvency group in the South East.

Commercial Litigation: The firm has considerable expertise in commercial disputes, professional negligence, construction, property and debt collection. A wide range of liquor licensing and gaming matters are also dealt with.

Family: The family group has recruited strongly over the past 12 months, bringing in five highly experienced lawyers with established reputations in their field. The group has continued to target and attract high net worth clients.

Wills, Trusts & Probate: The group has further developed its longstanding relationships with a number of City based law firms. As a result, it now receives a regular stream of London based client referrals which require highly technical but speedy guidance on personal tax and estate planning issues.

Personal Injury & Medical Negligence: The group continues to expand its defendant work for insurance companies and plaintiff medical negligence and personal injury work.

CONTACTS CONTINUED

Residential Property	Robert Moyle
Town & Country Planning	Roger Curtis
Trusts, Personal Tax & Probate	John Catterick

asb *law*

ARGLES STONEHAM BURSTOWS

ASHOK PATEL & CO

1 Crane Court, Fleet Street, London, EC4A 2EG **Tel:** (020) 7797 6300 **Fax:** (020) 7797 6315 **Ptnrs:** 4 **Asst solrs:** 7 **Other fee-earners:** 15

ASHTON GRAHAM

Electric House, Lloyds Avenue, Ipswich, IP1 3HZ **Tel:** (01473) 232425 **Fax:** (01473) 230505 **DX:** 3221 IPSWICH
Email: lawyers@ashtongraham.co.uk **Website:** www.ashtongraham.co.uk **Ptnrs:** 22 **Asst solrs:** 15 **Other fee-earners:** 34

ASHURST MORRIS CRISP

Broadwalk House, 5 Appold St, London, EC2A 2HA
Tel: (020) 7638 1111 **Fax:** (020) 7638 1112 **DX:** 639 London
Email: enquiries@ashursts.com **Website:** www.ashursts.com

THE FIRM: Ashurst Morris Crisp is a major international law firm with offices in Europe, Asia and America. Ashursts provides a high quality integrated legal service across all its offices, focused on all major aspects of business and financial law, with specialist sector knowledge and highly developed transaction management skills, supported by major investment in training and know-how infrastructure.

PRINCIPAL AREAS OF WORK: Ashursts operates in all principal areas of commercial law including:

Company & Commercial: The firm advises clients on cross-border mergers and acquisitions, joint ventures, private equity transactions, corporate finance, EU and competition law, reconstruction and insolvency, IP, IT, insurance and employment.

Banking & Capital Markets: The firm advises lenders, issuers, borrowers and advisers in the fields of corporate debt derivatives, bond issues, acquisitions and project finance, leveraged finance transactions and trade finance.

Commercial/Real Estate: Ashursts works with landlords, developers, tenants and public authorities, offering general property, planning, environmental law and litigation advice.

Commercial Litigation: Advice is given on construction and development issues, international arbitration and dispute resolution, EU and competition law, product liability, insolvency and professional negligence and property litigation.

Tax: The firm handles all aspects of cross-border work including international buy-outs, collective investment schemes, demergers, securitisations and debt trading.

Employment/Employment Benefits & Incentives: Ashursts advises on employment and employee benefits including pensions and employee share schemes.

INTERNATIONAL: The firm has offices in Brussels, Frankfurt, London, Madrid, Milan, Munich, New York, Paris, Singapore and Tokyo. It also has a liaison office in New Delhi. All business and commercial languages are spoken.

RECRUITMENT: The firm recruits both qualified and trainee solicitors to all areas of its practice. Applicants need not only to have achieved high academic standards, but also to possess individuality and commercial awareness that can be applied to issues, ensuring the most appropriate solution for the client. For more information, please visit the firm's website or contact Isabelle Mörling, graduate recruitment manager.

Senior Partner	Geoffrey Green
Managing Partner	Justin Spendlove

CONTACTS

Banking & Capital Markets	Nigel Ward
Buy-Outs/Private Equity	Charles Geffen
Commercial Contracts	Jeremy Hill
Commercial Litigation	Edward Sparrow
Construction & Engineering	Christopher Vigrass
Corporate	David Macfarlane
E-commerce	Mark Lubbock
Employment & Benefits	Caroline Carter
Energy & Natural Resources	Michael Johns
EU/Competition	Julian Ellison
	Nigel Parr
Financial Services	James Perry
Information Technology	Mark Lubbock
Insurance & Reinsurance	Jeremy Hill
Intellectual Property	Ian Starr
International Arbitration & Dispute Resolution	Ronnie King
Investment Banking	Chris Ashworth
Investment Funds	Roger Walsom
Life Sciences	Mark Lubbock
Media & Film	Tony Ghee
Planning	Anthony Curnow
Product Liability	Martin Evans
Projects	Mark Elsey
Property Litigation & Licensing	Michael Madden
Public Sector	Anthony Curnow
Real Estate	Simon Cookson
Reconstruction & Insolvency	Ben Tidswell
Tax	John Watson
Telecommunications	Chris Ashworth
	Tony Ghee
World Trade	Mark Clough QC

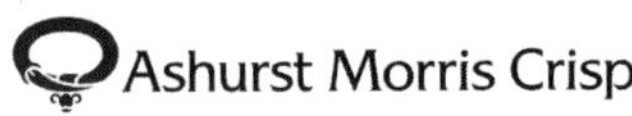

ASKEWS

4-6 West Terrace, Redcar, TS10 3BX **Tel:** (01642) 475252 **Fax:** (01642) 482793 **DX:** 60020 Redcar **Email:** info@askews.com **Website:** www.askews.com **Ptnrs:** 3 **Asst solrs:** 6 **Other fee-earners:** 2

A S LAW

Myrtle Parade, Liverpool, L7 7EL **Tel:** (0151) 707 1212 **Fax:** (0151) 707 2458 **DX:** 28953 Liverpool 2 **Email:** aslaw@dircon.co.uk **Ptnrs:** 3 **Asst solrs:** 3 **Other fee-earners:** 5

BRAY & KRAIS

70-71 New Bond Street, London, W1S 1DE **Tel:** (020) 7493 8840 **Fax:** (020) 7493 8841 **Email:** bbk@bbandk.com **Ptnrs:** 2 **Asst solrs:** 2

BABINGTON & CROASDAILE

9 Limavady Road, Waterside, Londonderry, BT47 1JV **Tel:** (02871) 349531 **Fax:** (02871) 345785 **DX:** 3060 Nr Londonderry 1 **Email:** bab.cro@lineone.net **Ptnrs:** 7 **Asst solrs:** 4 **Other fee-earners:** 3

B

BACKHOUSE JONES

The Printworks, Ribble Valley Enterprise Park, Clitheroe, BB7 9WD **Tel:** (01254) 828300 **Fax:** (01254) 828301 **Email:** enquiries@backhouses.co.uk **Website:** www.backhouses.co.uk **Ptnrs:** 3 **Asst solrs:** 4 **Contact:** James Backhouse • Expertise in law relating to the transport industry, both HGV and coach/passenger travel.

AREAS OF PRACTICE

Road Transport Law (Bus/Coach/Haulage Offences)	50%
Transport Licensing (Driver/Vehicle/Operator)	25%
Personal Injury Litigation	20%
Other	5%

BADHAMS

95 Aldwych, London, WC2B 4JF **Tel:** (020) 7242 4154 **Fax:** (020) 7404 0009 **DX:** 14 Ch.Ln. **Ptnrs:** 17 **Asst solrs:** 16 **Other fee-earners:** 13

BAIRD & COMPANY

2 Park Place, Kirkcaldy, KY1 1XL **Tel:** (01592) 268608 **Fax:** (01592) 203369 **DX:** 9 Kirkcaldy **Ptnrs:** 9 **Asst solrs:** 4 **Other fee-earners:** 4

BAKER BOTTS

45 Ludgate Hill, London, EC4M 7JU
Tel: (020) 7778 1400 **Fax:** (020) 7778 1450
Email: antony.higginson@bakerbotts.com **Website:** www.bakerbotts.com

THE FIRM: Founded in 1840 in Houston, Baker Botts is the legal and business adviser of choice to many of the world's leading companies, with over 600 lawyers in eight US and international offices. Its business is global in scope, influence and perspective, numbering among its partners James A Baker III, the former Secretary of State to President George Bush and adviser to the current President George W.Bush, with leading practices in the energy, high-tech, telecommunications and life-sciences sectors. A significant number of its lawyers have science Ph.Ds. The *Petroleum Economist* ranks Baker Botts among the top three US law firms in the energy sector and amongst the top five worldwide. *IP Worldwide* ranks the firm as one of the top five intellectual property firms.

London Office: The London office was established in 1998 with lawyers having leading reputations in the energy sector including experience in international projects in the oil and gas, power and petrochemicals industries. Currently, its corporate, project and finance practice includes both UK and international transactions in the energy industry, and is at the forefront of advising clients on the impact of and opportunities in new and liberalising markets for gas and power and infrastructure projects in the gas and power sectors. The London office acts for clients in the UK, Europe, the Middle East, Africa, the Russian Federation, CIS, Asia and South America, and works closely with lawyers in other offices including developing key strategic alliances. The London office has a specialist litigation and international arbitration group.

INTERNATIONAL: Baker Botts has other offices in Austin, Baku, Dallas, Houston, London, New York, Riyadh and Washington DC.

Managing Partner (International)	Richard C. Johnson
Managing Partner (London)	Tony Higginson
London	
Number of partners	6
Number of associates	8
Number of other fee-earners	2
International	
Number of partners	239
Number of associates	366
Number of other fee-earners	195

BAKER BOTTS

BAKER & MCKENZIE

100 New Bridge Street, London, EC4V 6JA
Tel: (020) 7919 1000 **Fax:** (020) 7919 1999 **DX:** 233 Chancery Lane, WC2
Email: london.info@bakernet.com **Website:** www.bakernet.com

THE FIRM: Baker & McKenzie, founded in 1949, is one of the world's leading law firms. The firm has grown by anticipating trade and capital flows around the world. Today Baker & McKenzie has 62 offices in 35 jurisdictions. Its strategy is to provide for its clients the best combination of local legal and commercial knowledge and international expertise and resources. Baker & McKenzie aims, above all, to provide commercially orientated advice of the highest quality which adds value to the client's business. The firm looks at the best method of service delivery in each case. It is sensitive to the need to provide not only legal excellence, but also a user friendly service which is efficient, transparent and value for money. To this end the firm implements a variety of client care and quality management programmes. Baker & McKenzie is uniquely placed to blend advice on the law and practice of a number of jurisdictions to help clients achieve their objectives; its lawyers work in national, European and international practice groups in their areas of expertise.
London Office: The London office is an established City firm with a strong domestic and foreign client base. The London office has more than 350 legal professionals, the vast majority of whom are UK qualified, together with resident US admitted banking and securities specialists. Many lawyers have worked in other offices of the firm, enabling them to bring a fresh perspective even to purely domestic assignments. It provides a full range of legal services to corporations, financial institutions, governments and entrepreneurs. The office offers 'hot line' arrangements and secondments of its lawyers to major clients. As an integral part of its service, the firm offers to its clients regular seminars and workshops, newsletters and bulletins on legal developments, magazines and publications. The firm also offers access to its library services and to a number of commercial and legal databases, and rapid internal and external communications through its proprietary Bakernet email network and other networks.

PRINCIPAL AREAS OF WORK: International and domestic banking and finance; derivatives and related markets; financial services; privatisations; domestic and cross-border corporate and commercial transactions; the structuring of multinational groups; domestic and international equity and debt offerings; corporate finance and flotations; venture capital; privately financed projects; international tax; VAT and import/export questions; litigation, arbitration and ADR; civil and commercial fraud; insolvency; European Union and competition law; trade law (WTO); energy; environmental; intellectual property; patents and trademarks; biotechnology; pharmaceuticals and healthcare; information technology; online services and e-commerce, telecommunications, entertainment and media; employment and pension matters; insurance and reinsurance; construction and engineering; commercial property; tax and trust planning; the legal aspects of lobbying.

INTERNATIONAL: The firm has offices in Almaty, Amsterdam, Bahrain, Baku, Bangkok, Barcelona, Beijing, Berlin, Bogota, Brasilia, Brussels, Budapest, Buenos Aires, Cairo, Calgary, Caracas, Chicago, Dallas, Düsseldorf, Frankfurt, Geneva, Guadalajara, Hanoi, Ho Chi Minh City, Hong Kong, Houston, Hsinchu, Juarez, Kyiv, Madrid, Manila, Melbourne, Mexico City, Miami, Milan, Monterrey, Moscow, Munich, New York, Palo Alto, Paris, Prague, Rio de Janeiro, Riyadh, Rome, St Petersburg, San Diego, San Francisco, Sao Paulo, Santiago, Singapore, Stockholm, Sydney, Taipei, Tijuana, Tokyo, Toronto, Valencia, Warsaw, Washington DC, Zurich. The firm conducts business in Afrikaans, Bulgarian, Cantonese, Czech, English, French, German, Greek, Hebrew, Hindi, Hungarian, Italian, Indonesian, Japanese, Kiswahili, Malay, Marathi, Polish, Portuguese, Punjabi, Russian, Spanish and Taiwanese.

RECRUITMENT: For graduate recruitment opportunities, please contact Katie Allen on (020) 7919 1000 or email her at katie.allen@bakernet.com. Alternatively visit the firm's graduate website at www.ukgraduates.bakernet.com.

Managing Partner	Russell Lewin
UK	
No. of partners	67
Assistant solicitors	208
Other fee-earners	82
International	
No. of partners	618
Assistant solicitors	3064
Other fee-earners	1107

AREAS OF PRACTICE

Corporate/Finance/EC/Tax/Commercial	53%
Litigation/Construction	15%
Employment/Pensions/Immigration	16%
Intellectual Property	11%
Commercial Property	5%

CONTACTS

Banking & Finance	Chris Hogan
Capital Markets	Peter Magyar
Civil & Commercial Fraud	Nick Pearson
Commercial	Beatriz Araujo
Commercial Property	Stephen Turner
	Mike Smith
Construction	Jeremy Winter
Derivatives	Chris Hogan
Dispute Resolution	Nick Pearson
	Andrew Keltie
E-commerce	Robbie Downing
Employee Benefits	Michael Ingle
Employment	Christine O'Brien
Energy	Hugh Stewart
Environment	Alison Flood
EU, Competition & Trade	Lynda Martin Alegi
Financial Services	Marwan Al-Turki
Insolvency	Jeremy Goldring
Insurance	Peter Schwartz
Intellectual Property	Michael Hart
	Paul Rawlinson
IT	Michael Hart
	Harry Small
Pensions	Robert West
Pharmaceuticals & Healthcare	Beatriz Araujo
Projects	Mike Webster
Securities	Michael Caro
	Tim Gee
Structured & Project Finance	Peter Gaines
Tax	James maclachlan
Telecommunications	Peter Strivens
VAT, Customs & Excise	Geoffrey Kay
Venture Capital	Charles Whitefoord

BAKER & MCKENZIE

BALFOUR & MANSON

54-66 Frederick Street, Edinburgh, EH2 1LS
Tel: (0131) 200 1200 **Fax:** (0131) 200 1300 **DX:** 4 Edinburgh
Email: enquiry@balfour-manson.co.uk

Chairman	Andrew Gibb
Number of partners	20
Assistant solicitors	18
Other fee-earners	24

AREAS OF PRACTICE

Litigation	50%
Private Client	20%
Property	20%
Commercial/Commercial Property	10%

CONTACTS

Commercial Property	John Hodge
Corporate	Alastair Keatinge
Domestic Property	Anne Pacey
	Kenneth Robertson
Employment	Katherine Taylor
Family	Andrew Gibb
Financial Services & Tax	Murray Burns
Litigation	Spencer Kennedy
	Ian Leach
	Maggie Neilson
	Alfred Tyler
Private Client	Brenda Rennie

THE FIRM: One of the leading Scottish litigation practices, Balfour & Manson also has substantial commercial, private client and property client bases. The practice provides a comprehensive range of legal, financial and general advice, from a wide variety of departments with in-depth expertise, for Scottish, English and foreign clients and solicitors. The principal departments are litigation, commercial/corporate, private client and property.

PRINCIPAL AREAS OF WORK:
Litigation: Headed by Maggie Neilson, the firm has a strong litigation department which handles all aspects of litigation. It has particular expertise in acting in personal injury; professional negligence and contractual claims; multi-party actions; and family law, with considerable experience in international child abduction. Additionally, this department handles commercial work, including insurance; intellectual property disputes; tribunal work; planning and building contracts.
Commercial/Commercial Property: Led by John Hodge, this department handles purchase, lease, sale and security work for clients of all types and sizes and provides corporate services for medium-sized private companies.
Private Client: Headed by Brenda Rennie, the department advises clients from within and without Scotland, providing wills, trusts and executries; tax work; finance and investment advice; and insurance services. This department offers unique support for elderly and infirm clients and their families.
Property: Led by Kenneth Robertson, services include estate agency; mortgage advice; house purchase and sale and repossession work.

INTERNATIONAL: Scottish Member of the PARLEX Group of European Lawyers. The firm handles work in French and German.

B

BAND HATTON

1 Copthall House, Station Square, Coventry, CV1 2FY
Tel: (024) 7663 2121 **Fax:** (024) 7622 9038 **DX:** 11207
Email: law@bandhatton.co.uk **Website:** www.bandhatton.co.uk

Contact Partner	Philip Costigan
Number of partners	6
Assistant solicitors	2
Other fee-earners	7

CONTACTS

Commercial Litigation	Jon Wilby
Commercial Property	Philip Costigan
Other Commercial/Corporate	Haydn Jones
Private Client Litigation	Paul Wright
Private Client Non-contentious	Helen Dodd

THE FIRM: A well-established practice, Band Hatton offers a high quality legal service to both business and private clients, utilising up-to-date working methods, while maintaining traditional values and a commitment to a personal and approachable service. The firm combines a thorough and accurate technical approach with a commitment to providing a very personal service, which offers good value for money. The firm enjoys a strong reputation in the commercial field, in particular for its commercial property work. The litigation practice is expanding rapidly in the areas of commercial, employment and family law. Band Hatton is a member of LawNet, the Federation of Independent Law Firms and LawNet Europe, and has attained accreditation under ISO 9002 as well as holding a CLS Franchise.

BANNATYNE, KIRKWOOD, FRANCE & CO

Exchange House, 16 Royal Exchange Square, Glasgow, G1 3AG **Tel:** (0141) 221 6020 **Fax:** (0141) 221 5120 **Email:** martin@b-k-f.demon.co.uk **Website:** www.bfk.co.uk **Contact:** Martin Smith • Established in 1785, the firm specialises in media law and defamation, representing several national newspaper companies. Other areas of expertise include employment law, reparation and trusts.

BANNERS JONES MIDDLETON

Marsden Chambers, 2 Marsden Street, Saltergate, Chesterfield, S40 1JY **Tel:** (01246) 560560 **Fax:** (01246) 231188 **DX:** 12370 Chesterfield 1 **Email:** info@bjm-soicitors.co.uk **Website:** www.bjm-solicitors.co.uk **Ptnrs:** 14 **Asst solrs:** 4 **Other fee-earners:** 8

BANNISTER PRESTON

30 Washway Road, Sale, M33 7QY **Tel:** (0161) 973 2434 **Fax:** (0161) 962 9562 **DX:** 19269 SALE 1 **Email:** info@bannisterpreston.co.uk **Ptnrs:** 5 **Asst solrs:** 3 **Other fee-earners:** 3

BARBARA CARTER

117 Vicarage Road, King's Heath, Birmingham, B14 7QG **Tel:** (0121) 441 3238 **Fax:** (0121) 441 2191 **Ptnrs:** 1 **Other fee-earners:** 1

BARCAN WOODWARD

King William House, 13 Queen Square, Bristol, BS1 4NT **Tel:** (0117) 925 8080 **Fax:** (0117) 925 8081 **DX:** 7854 (Bristol) **Ptnrs:** 5 **Asst solrs:** 5 **Other fee-earners:** 7

BARKER GOTELEE

41 Barrack Square, Martlesham Heath, Ipswich, IP5 3RF **Tel:** (01473) 611211 **Fax:** (01473) 610560 **DX:** 124722 MARTLESHAM HEATH **Email:** bg@barkergotelee.co.uk **Ptnrs:** 6 **Asst solrs:** 6 **Other fee-earners:** 6

BARLOW LYDE & GILBERT

Beaufort House, 15 St Botolph Street, London, EC3A 7NJ
Tel: (020) 7247 2277 **Fax:** (020) 7643 8500 **DX:** 155 London CDE
Website: www.blg.co.uk

Senior Partner	Richard Dedman
Managing Partner	Kennan Michel
Number of partners	68
Assistant solicitors	144
Other fee-earners	80

CONTACTS

Aviation	Nicholas Hughes
Banking	Graham Wedlake
Commercial Litigation	Richard Dedman
Commercial Property	Malcolm Rogerson
Competition & EU	David Strang
Corporate & Finance	John Longdon
Corporate Insurance	Stephen Browning
Employment	Gary Freer
Environment	Valerie Fogleman
Information Technology/ E-commerce	David Strang
Insolvency	Douglas Howie
Insurance Litigation	John Hanson
Medical Negligence	Kevin Bitmead
Personal Injury	Graham Dickinson
Professional Indemnity	David Arthur
Reinsurance	Colin Croly
Shipping	Nigel Wagland
Travel & Tourism	Richard Gimblett

Barlow Lyde & Gilbert

THE FIRM: Barlow Lyde & Gilbert is a major law firm with the main office located in the City of London. In addition, in the UK, BLG has a strategic presence in Oxford from where it advises clients in the technology sector, and a presence at Lloyd's to serve the insurance market. The firm also has an office in Hong Kong and has recently opened a second overseas office in Shanghai. BLG advises corporate organisations, government bodies, financial and other institutions in all spheres of business activity. The firm is recommended in all of its core areas – in commercial litigation, in insurance and reinsurance where the firm is regarded as pre-eminent, and in corporate and commercial work, especially in relation to e-business issues. The firm's long-term strategy is to build its strength in these chosen areas.

PRINCIPAL AREAS OF WORK:

Litigation: The firm has an outstanding reputation for its expertise in litigation and other forms of dispute resolution – it is the breadth and depth of the practice that distinguishes it from competitors. As well as acting for corporates in relation to a wide range of general commercial disputes, the firm is well known for several sector specialisms. Of particular note are the reinsurance, insurance, professional services and aerospace teams, which are all recognised as market leaders. Also highly regarded are the banking and financial institutions, employment, information technology and shipping teams. The firm's lawyers are geared to obtain the best possible result for the clients – alternative dispute resolution methods are used whenever appropriate and several partners are CEDR accredited mediators.

Corporate: The corporate and finance practice is the fastest expanding area of the firm. The team handles the full range of corporate, finance and commercial work including buy-outs, joint ventures, flotations, reconstructions, corporate finance, corporate capital, banking regulatory investigations, taxation, insolvency, commercial property and EU and competition. The team has a particular focus on technology and e-business matters, containing one of the largest IT practices in the country. In this area BLG acts for a range of clients including banks lending to Internet ventures, consultants advising on e-business strategy and applications, insurers providing Internet based policies and manufacturers supplying essential companies for the transmission of data. BLG's corporate and finance skills combined with the pre-eminence in insurance and reinsurance work uniquely places the firm in a position to undertake corporate and corporate finance transactions for the insurance sector, and to remain at the forefront of alternative risk transfer and innovative bancassurance products.

INTERNATIONAL: The firm also has offices in Hong Kong and Shanghai.

RECRUITMENT: The provision of more than just legal services has always been at the heart of BLG's philosophy and this is demonstrated through the firm's impressive education and training programme. An extensive range of in-house publications and regular seminars on topical areas of aviation, banking, commercial, corporate finance, insurance, reinsurance, professional liability, employment and environmental law are provided for clients. Dedicated training programmes ensure that the firm's solicitors are completely up-to-date with all legal and practice developments and the firm puts great emphasis on effective commercial, as well as technically sound advice. The firm offers 16 training contracts each year. Prospective trainees should contact Caroline Walsh (cwalsh@blg.co.uk) for details of the recruitment programme. Further information on Barlow Lyde & Gilbert is available at the firm's offices or can be viewed on the website.

BARLOWS

55 Quarry Street, Guildford, Surrey, GU1 3UE **Tel:** 01483 562 901 **Fax:** 01483 573 325 **DX:** 2407 **Email:** enquiries@barlows.co.uk **Website:** www.barlows-legal.co.uk **Ptnrs:** 14 **Asst solrs:** 24 **Other fee-earners:** 18

BARNETT SAMPSON

High Holborn House, 52-54 High Holborn, London, WC1V 6RL
Tel: (020) 7831 7181 **Fax:** (020) 7269 5141 **DX:** 254 LDE
Email: lawyers@barnett-sampson.co.uk

Number of partners	4
Assistant solicitors	4
Other fee-earners	2

CONTACTS

Commercial (inc. Company & Litigation) .... Richard Barnett
Family .... Rosemary Carter
.... Ellie Chapman
Property .... Ros Joseph

THE FIRM: Barnett Sampson is a niche firm able to 'punch above its weight'. It consistently works on transactions with leaders in the field. A hands-on approach by all fee-earners ensures a thorough, efficient and professional service to a range of clients.

PRINCIPAL AREAS OF WORK:

Commercial (inc. Company & Litigation): The firm deals with substantial value transactions and claims involving multijurisdictions and financial services.
Family: The firm is experienced in all aspects of family work, including high value ancillary relief, public and private child work, adoption and international. All members of the family department adopt the Solicitors' Family Law Association code and partners are immediate past officers of that association.
Property: All types of commercial and residential property are dealt with, specialising in developments, franchises and shopping centre leases.

B

BARRATT GOFF & TOMLINSON

The Old Dairy, 67a Melton Road, West Bridgford, Nottingham, NG2 5GR **Tel:** (0115) 981 5115 **Fax:** (0115) 981 9409 **DX:** 719903 West Bridgford **Ptnrs:** 5 **Asst solrs:** 2 **Other fee-earners:** 5

BARRIE WARD & JULIAN GRIFFITHS

5 Clarendon Street, Nottingham, NG1 5HS **Tel:** (0115) 941 2622 **Fax:** (0115) 924 0485 **DX:** 711344 NOTTM 16 **Ptnrs:** 3 **Asst solrs:** 1 **Other fee-earners:** 4

BARRY SHAW

13 Blackheath Village, London, SE3 9LA **Tel:** (020) 8297 8899 **Fax:** (020) 8297 2122 **Ptnrs:** 1

BARTRAM & CO

1st Floor, 302 Bath Road, Hounslow, TW4 7DN **Tel:** (020) 8814 1414 **Fax:** (020) 8814 1515 **Email:** info@bartram.uk.com **Ptnrs:** 1 **Other fee-earners:** 3

BATE EDMOND SNAPE

6 The Quadrant, Coventry, CV1 2ED **Tel:** (02476) 220 707 **Fax:** (02476) 256 278 **DX:** 11213 Cov 1 **Email:** bescov1@aol.com **Website:** www.BateEdmondsSnape.co.uk **Ptnrs:** 2 **Asst solrs:** 4 **Other fee-earners:** 13

BATES, WELLS & BRAITHWAITE

Cheapside House, 138 Cheapside, London, EC2V 6BB
Tel: (020) 7551 7777 **Fax:** (020) 7551 7800 **DX:** 42609 CHEAPSIDE 1
Email: mail@bateswells.co.uk **Website:** www.bateswells.co.uk

Number of partners	31
Assistant solicitors	19
Other fee-earners	21

AREAS OF PRACTICE

Charity	25%
Litigation	15%
Property	15%
Company/Commercial	10%
Employment	10%
Immigration	8%
Media	7%
Private Client	5%

CONTACTS

Arts & Media .... Sean Egan
Charity .... Philip Kirkpatrick
.... Stephen Lloyd
.... Fiona Middleton
.... Christine Rigby
.... Rosamund Smith
Commercial Litigation .... Malcolm Robson
Company/Commercial .... Julian Blake
.... Hugh Craig
Employment .... Martin Bunch
.... William Garnett
Immigration .... Emma Cohen
.... Peter Moss
.... Philip Trott

THE FIRM: Bates, Wells & Braithwaite was founded more than 100 years ago and the main office in London was opened in 1970. Originally handling the needs of smaller business clients the firm has developed a strong reputation for administrative law, employment and immigration law as well as a pre-eminence in charity law. The firm is particularly notable for the large proportion of individuals, which actively participate in the sectors on which they advise in both a legal and non-legal capacity. Located in the City, Bates, Wells & Braithwaite is a unique firm combining a strong commercial and charity practice with a general emphasis on public interest work and the arts. The firm is renowned for its expertise in advising charities, businesses and individuals according to their particular needs.

PRINCIPAL AREAS OF WORK:

Charity Law: The charity department has one of the largest charity law practices in the country and acts for many household names and international charities. It has particular expertise in obtaining charitable status for new groups and for initiatives within the charity sector. The firm provides a national advisory service to solicitors on charity matters and has been responsible through the years for many books, articles, and other publications.
Company & Commercial: The company/commercial department undertakes work for a wide range of businesses and has developed considerable expertise. The work undertaken includes company takeovers, joint ventures, management buy-outs, commercial contracts and tax advice.
Litigation: The litigation department handles commercial litigation, mediation, and has a particular expertise in the field of administrative law/judicial review and human rights.

Continued overleaf

Property: The property department handles all types of commercial property work and related financing and development work. There is particular expertise in advising charities.
Immigration: The well-respected immigration department handles all aspects of immigration and nationality law including work permits, citizenship, residency and asylum work and human rights.
Employment: The employment department advises on all aspects of employment law, including restrictive covenants, employee rights, discrimination, service agreements, dismissals and redundancies.
Arts & Media: The recently expanded arts and media department advises on all aspects of the theatre, film and television industries. The department deals with theatrical production in the West End and throughout the UK, feature film production, all types of television production, and internet multimedia issues.
Private Client: The firm now has a thriving private client department, which handles a wide range of tax and trust work.
Family Law: The firm's family law department is now the niche practice Hughes Fowler Carruthers. The two firms retain a close professional relationship.

INTERNATIONAL: Bates, Wells & Braithwaite has significant involvement in international legal developments, being a co-founder of the Parlex Group of European Lawyers (EEIG No. 00001), which consists of a network of firms throughout western Europe.

CONTACTS CONTINUED

Private Client	Con Alexander
	Alice Faure-Walker
Property	Tony Cartmell
	Nick Ivey
Property Litigation	Eve Smith
Public Law	John Trotter

B

BATT BROADBENT

Minster Chambers, 42-44 Castle Street, Salisbury, SP1 3TX **Tel:** (01722) 411 141 **Fax:** (01722) 411 566

BATTENS (WITH POOLE & CO)

Church House, Yeovil, BA20 1HB **Tel:** 01935 423 685 **Fax:** 01935 706 054 **DX:** 100503 **Email:** enquiries@battens.co.uk
Website: www.battens.co.uk **Ptnrs:** 20 **Asst solrs:** 17 **Other fee-earners:** 25

BEACHCROFT WANSBROUGHS

100 Fetter Lane, London, EC4A 1BN
Tel: (020) 7242 1011 **Fax:** (020) 7831 6630 **DX:** 45 London Chancery Lane
Email: rheslett@bwlaw.co.uk **Website:** www.bwlaw.co.uk

30-40 Eastcheap, London, EC3M 1HD
Tel: (020) 7208 6800 **Fax:** (020) 7208 6801 **DX:** 753 London City EC3

10-22 Victoria Street, Bristol, BS99 7UD
Tel: (0117) 918 2000 **Fax:** (0117) 918 2100 **DX:** 7846 Bristol 1

Nine Brindleyplace, Oozells Square, Birmingham, B1 2HE
Tel: (0121) 698 5200 **Fax:** (0121) 698 5290 **DX:** 13057 Birmingham 1

7 Park Square East, Leeds, LS1 2LW
Tel: (0113) 251 4700 **Fax:** (0113) 251 4900 **DX:** 14099 Leeds Park Square

St Ann's House, St Ann Street, Manchester, M2 7LP
Tel: (0161) 934 3000 **Fax:** (0161) 934 3288 **DX:** 14341 Manchester 1

St Swithun's House, 1a St Cross Road, Winchester, SO23 9WP
Tel: (01962) 705500 **Fax:** (01962) 705510 **DX:** 2540 Winchester 1

Senior Partner	The Rt Honourable The Lord Hunt of Wirral MBE
Managing Partner	Robert Heslett
Number of partners	126
Assistant solicitors	271
Other fee-earners	266

AREAS OF PRACTICE

Insurance	50%
Commercial	30%
Health/Public Sector	20%

CONTACTS

Commercial	Simon Hodson
Insurance	Trevor Chamberlain
Corporate Services	Laurence Markham
Employment	Elizabeth Adams
Health/Public Sector	Trevor Blythe
Litigation	Paul Murray
Projects	Malcolm Austwick
Advertising & Marketing	Simon Hodson
Property	John Phelps
Alternative Dispute Resolution	Richard Evans
Charity	Julian Korn
Chemical & Pharmaceutical	Anthony Cherry
Construction	John Vasey
European Community	Julie Nazerali
Education	Julian Gizzi
Fraud	Glenn Miller
Health & Safety	Iain Moore
Housing Association	Jane Staveley
Insolvency	Peter Rees
Information Technology	Alan Wood
Intellectual Property	Jeremy Roper
Personal Injury	Tania Sless
Professional Indemnity	Paul Murray
Product Liability	Chris Wilkes
Public Law	Julian Gizzi
Retail	Laurence Markham
Tax & Trust	Paul Solon

THE FIRM: Beachcroft Wansbroughs provides an integrated and consistent national service capability across its strong regional office network and its major offices in the City of London. With a particular reputation in litigation, Beachcroft Wansbroughs provides a comprehensive legal service to the insurance sector, coupled with in-depth capability for the commercial, financial and public sectors. The firm is one of the top twenty law firms in the UK with over 600 professional staff and 1300 staff in total. It is the largest law firm in the country to obtain the 'Investors in People' award across all of its offices. As you would expect from a firm of such size and standing, the firm takes its commitment to staff very seriously. Beachcroft Wansbroughs' people are its future. By investing in them the firm is investing in the future success of its business and that of its clients. The firm is constantly evaluating and implementing improved mechanisms for excellent service delivery. The latest service to be launched by Beachcroft Wansbroughs is Law Mutual. Law Mutual represents a total re-engineering of case management systems, client assistance, contract management, and client access to data to meet the claims management requirements of the Insurance industry. Feedback from long-standing clients acknowledges that Law Mutual is a unique and innovative service that reflects both the depth of expertise and the approachable nature of the firm.

PRINCIPAL AREAS OF WORK:

LITIGATION SERVICES: The specialist nature of the firm's litigation services is reflected by its ranking in the Higher Courts. In a recent survey by a leading legal journal, Beachcroft Wansbroughs was named as one of

the top five litigation firms in the country, handling the highest number of successful Court of Appeal cases in the last year. The firm's litigation capability reflects its committment to the financial services and insurance industry. Sixty of its 126 partners and over 300 of its lawyers advise the insurance industry on a daily basis, providing tailored solutions to a broad range of issues. Clients include the top ten composite insurers, specialist companies, leading re-insurers, Lloyd's syndicates, professional associations and self-insureds. In the health care and commercial world, the firm's litigators handle a range of medical and clinical negligence, employers' liability and public liability cases and a variety of advisory work on corporate governance, public sector law, patient care issues and the management of ad hoc incidents and crises. The firm has invested heavily in new technology and worked closely with its clients to deliver on-going solutions aimed at improving the results of both its client's business and that of the insured. Law Mutual, a sophisticated claims management service, is the result of constant development of new and innovative legal solutions that challenge the traditional ways of working. The aim is to add value to the firm's client's business through pushing the boundaries of its own.

COMMERCIAL SERVICES: Fifty-nine partners and over 110 lawyers fulfill Beachcroft Wansbroughs' commercial capability in the areas of corporate services, employment, property, projects and public sector work. All areas of commercial work are fully supported by its Brussels based European and Competition unit.

Corporate Services Department: The firm's corporate services department is based in the City of London and provides expansive nationwide coverage to guarantee its clients a seamless service. It advises on a comprehensive set of issues from intellectual property and product liability to insolvency and has a strong capability in M&A, disposals, listings, new issues, capital restructuring and joint ventures for a variety of UK and international clients. This is supplemented by additional specialist expertise in the advertising and media, construction, education, European Union law, information technology, retail, sports and water sectors. The firm works with a diverse range of businesses, providing up-to-the-minute know how on the legal implications of human resource management. It undertakes employment work for both the public and private sectors and acts for health service providers, local authorities, educational establishments and employers' covering the full range of contentious and non-contentious matters, including High Court and tribunal actions and all forms of discrimination and industrial relations matters.

Property Department: With a team of more than 60 property lawyers the property department is one of the largest practices in the country specialising in non-contentious work, complemented by a strong contentious capability. It provides a full range of services in property management, property investment and finance, dispute resolution and property litigation, planning and environment, construction, lease negotiation and total facility management.

Health: The firm acts for over 200 NHS public and private sector bodies involved in the health economy providing a countrywide service. The firm is a member of the National Health Service Litigation Authority's Panel for medical negligence claims work and also provides the full range of associated patient care advisory services. The firm has focused its strategic effort on developing transactional and advisory work so as to meet the commercial and governance needs of its clients in anticipation of the continuing changes in the health market.

Projects: The projects team has a market leading reputation and a track record to match with clients extending across the public and private sectors. Its lawyers are experienced in structuring complex, large-scale, high value transactions, working with clients in construction, IT, facilities management and the provision of major services. In particular, it has played a pivotal role in developing PFI projects in the health sector; the firm's knowledge and expertise in the health industry has been instrumental in its appointment on a significant number of the principal PFI health projects during the last few years.

INTERNATIONAL: Beachcroft Wansbroughs' Brussels office works mainly in English, French and German and has substantial practical experience of advising on the impact of EU law to clients in both the commercial and public sectors. It has extensive experience of advising on EU and national competition rules and seeking clearance of transactional arrangements before the European Commission and national regulatory authorities. The Brussels office has pursued legal proceedings before the European Court of Justice (ECJ) and provides a full EU legal service to clients on areas as diverse as single market rules (including public procurement, intellectual property, free movement and pharmaceuticals), telecommunications, energy and trade.

B

BEALE AND COMPANY

Garrick Hse, 27-32 King St, Covent Garden, London, WC2E 8JD
Tel: (020) 7240 3474 **Fax:** (020) 7240 9111 **DX:** 51632 Covent Garden
Email: reception@beale-law.com **Website:** www.beale-law.com

Managing & Senior Partner	John Ward
Number of partners	10
Assistant solicitors	6
Other fee-earners	9

AREAS OF PRACTICE

Construction	30%
Professional Negligence/Insurance	30%
Company & Commercial/IT	25%
Other Commercial Litigation	10%
Private Client	5%

CONTACTS

Company and Commercial	Michael Archer
Construction	John Ward
Engineers	Rachel Barnes
Insurance	Antony Smith
Litigation	Mark Jones
Private Client	Rachel Barnes
Professional Negligence	Antony Smith

THE FIRM: Beale and Company is a long established firm (founded in 1837) which provides a comprehensive range of services to commercial clients. The main areas of the firm's practice are construction, professional negligence and IT. It has a strong international practice. Beale and Company provides high quality legal advice combined with a practical and commercial approach.

PRINCIPAL AREAS OF WORK:
Professional Negligence: The firm acts for insurers and their insureds in handling professional indemnity claims and advises on risk management and other ways of reducing or preventing claims. It also advises insurers on policy wording, coverage issues and disputes between insurer and insured.
Construction: The firm provides legal advice and, where necessary, representation, in relation to projects in the UK and throughout the world, to employers, contractors and professionals, on all aspects of civil and structural engineering contracts; related insurance and bond provisions and collateral warranties; joint ventures; corporate structures; partnerships; DBFO forms of contract and other forms of contract; disputes and dispute resolution; on and in negotiations, litigation, arbitration and other alternative forms of dispute resolution.
Engineers: This is a special section of the firm's construction practice. The firm is the solicitors for the Association of Consulting Engineers and has acted for more than 30 of the top 50 firms of consulting engineers in the UK. The firm acts for engineers and others prosecuted under Health and Safety legislation.
Litigation: The firm handles a wide range of other commercial litigation, including disputes in the fields of banking, IT, intellectual property, supply of goods and services and employment. It also handles a large amount of international litigation and is a Privy Council agent.
Company & Commercial: The firm advises on all aspects of company commercial transactions, including acquisitions and disposals of businesses; setting up joint ventures; corporate finance arrangements; restructuring of companies and partnerships; establishing commercial contractual relationships such as distribution, agency and licensing networks; intellectual property; directors' duties and liabilities; employment problems and claims; partnership disputes; corporate compliance. There is a strong emphasis on acting for clients in the IT and digital media industries. These range from dot com businesses (the firm having represented some of the first dot com enterprises in selling their businesses and raising finance) to national and multinational companies including a number of technology companies quoted on Nasdaq.
Private Client: The firm advises private clients, domiciled and non-domiciled, on tax planning, formation of trusts, wills and probates.

INTERNATIONAL: The firm is the founder member of a European network of correspondent law firms. The firm also has correspondent law firms in Bombay, Calcutta, Dhaka, Kampala, Karachi, Mombasa, Nairobi and Port Louis.

RECRUITMENT: The firm recruits on average three graduate trainees each year. Currently there are six graduate trainees in the firm.

BEAUMONT AND SON

Lloyds Chambers, 1 Portsoken St, London, E1 8AW **Tel:** (020) 7709 5000 **Fax:** (020) 7481 3353 **DX:** 551 **Ptnrs:** 19 **Asst solrs:** 21 **Other fee-earners:** 12

BECKFORD & CO

35A Prince of Wales Road, Norwich, NR1 1BG **Tel:** (01603) 660 000 **Fax:** (01603) 660 010 **Asst solrs:** 2 **Other fee-earners:** 2

BEDELL CRISTIN

PO Box 75, 26 New Street, St Helier, JE4 8PP **Tel:** (01534) 814814 **Fax:** (01534) 814815 **Email:** enquiries@bedellcristin.com **Website:** www.bedellcristin.com **Ptnrs:** 12 **Asst solrs:** 22 **Other fee-earners:** 47

BEECHAM PEACOCK

7 Collingwood Street, Newcastle upon Tyne, NE1 1JE **Tel:** (0191) 232 3048 **Fax:** (0191) 261 7255 **DX:** 61041 Newcastle upon Tyne **Email:** genenquiry@beechampeacock.co.uk **Website:** www.beechampeacock.co.uk **Ptnrs:** 6 **Asst solrs:** 4 **Other fee-earners:** 7

BELL & BUXTON

Telegraph House, High Street, Sheffield, S1 2GA **Tel:** (0114) 249 5969 **Fax:** (0114) 249 3804 **DX:** 10529 SHEFFIELD **Email:** legals@bellbuxton.co.uk **Website:** www.bellbuxton.co.uk **Ptnrs:** 6 **Asst solrs:** 5 **Other fee-earners:** 5

BELL LAX LITIGATION

New Bank House, 21 Maney Corner, Sutton Coldfield, Birmingham, B72 1QL **Tel:** (0121) 355 0011 **Fax:** (0121) 355 0099 **DX:** 15736 Sutton Coldfield **Email:** mail@litigation.demon.co.uk **Ptnrs:** 3 **Asst solrs:** 4 **Other fee-earners:** 6

BELL & SCOTT WS

16 Hill Street, Edinburgh, EH2 3LD
Tel: (0131) 226 6703 **Fax:** (0131) 226 7602 **DX:** 114 Edinburgh
Email: maildesk@bellscott.co.uk **Website:** www.bellscott.co.uk

Managing Partner	Iain MacDonald
Senior Partner	Simon Guest
Number of partners	8
Assistant solicitors	7
Other fee-earners	10

CONTACTS

Commercial Property & Development .... Paul Jennings
Corporate & Partnership ...... Bruce Anderson
Litigation & Employment .... Colin Heggie
Private Client .... Alan Sharp
Residential Conveyancing .... Susan Calder
Residential Development .... Simon Guest
.... Iain MacDonald

THE FIRM: Bell & Scott WS is a niche firm servicing the Scottish property development sector. The firm delivers practical and innovative legal advice to commercial and residential property developers, complemented by litigation and private client services.

PRINCIPAL AREAS OF WORK:
Commercial Property & Development: The unit provides an integrated property service covering property development and management, sale and acquisition, contentious and non-contentious construction law, leasing, planning and joint ventures.
Residential Development: Over thirty years of expertise has earned the firm a reputation for the provision of high quality legal services to the housebuilding industry.

BELMORES

Goodchild House, 27 Castle Meadow, Norwich, NR1 3DS **Tel:** (01603) 617947 **Fax:** (01603) 630086 **Ptnrs:** 6 **Asst solrs:** 7 **Other fee-earners:** 6

BELTRAMI & CO

93 West Nile Street, Glasgow, G1 2FH **Tel:** (0141) 221 0981 **Fax:** (0141) 332 9892 **DX:** GW8 **Ptnrs:** 2 **Asst solrs:** 3 **Other fee-earners:** 1 **Contact:** Murray Macara • Long-established and prominent criminal defence practice with substantial reputation in many high profile cases, specialising in all aspects of criminal defence work throughout Scotland.

AREAS OF PRACTICE

Criminal Litigation	95%
Other	5%

BENSON MAZURE & CO

22 Bentinck St, London, W1U 2AB **Tel:** (020) 7486 8091 **Fax:** (020) 7935 8825 **DX:** 9007 London West End **Email:** info@bensonmazure.co.uk **Ptnrs:** 2 **Asst solrs:** 1 **Other fee-earners:** 1 **Contact:** Anthony Levy • Commercial and residential conveyancing; landlord and tenant; commercial litigation and company commercial; personal injuries, matrimonial and general litigation; probate and trusts.

AREAS OF PRACTICE

Conveyancing/Landlord & Tenant	50%
Litigation (inc. Commercial)	20%
Company Commercial	17%
Probate & Trusts	13%

BENTLEYS, STOKES & LOWLESS

International House, 1 St. Katharine's Way, London, E1 9YL
Tel: (020) 7782 0990 **Fax:** (020) 7782 0991 **DX:** 1074
Email: law@bentleys.co.uk

Senior Partner	Andrew Bardot
Number of partners	11
Assistant solicitors	7
Other fee-earners	4

AREAS OF PRACTICE

Shipping, Marine & Non-Marine Insurance	100%

CONTACTS

Admiralty .... J Quain
Charterparty/Marine Insurance .... A D Bardot
.... W J Chetwood

THE FIRM: Bentleys, Stokes & Lowless is traditionally associated with the maritime and insurance sectors.

PRINCIPAL AREAS OF WORK:
Admiralty: Specialist advice and representation is offered in relation to: salvage, pollution, total loss, groundings, unsafe port claims, damage claims, collisions and public, official and casualty inquiries and investigations.
Shipping, Insurance & Litigation: The department advises on a wide range of marine and insurance related matters, including charterparty/bill of lading contracts, marine, cargo and aviation insurance, cargo claims, road transport, commodity contracts, commercial contracts, ship sale and purchase, construction, building and general litigation.

INTERNATIONAL: The firm handles work in French, Greek, Italian, Japanese and Spanish.

B

BERG & CO

Scottish Mutual House, 35 Peter Street, Manchester, M2 5BG
Tel: (0161) 833 9211 **Fax:** (0161) 834 5566 **DX:** MDX 14379
Email: help@berg.co.uk **Website:** www.berg.co.uk

Senior Partner	Reuben Berg
Number of partners	9
Assistant solicitors	8
Other fee-earners	7

CONTACTS

Commercial Litigation ..... Sydney Fulda
..... Charles Khan
Commercial Property ..... Jonathan Dover
..... Stephanie Klass
..... Gabriel Rechnitzer
Corporate & Commercial ..... Reuben Berg
..... Stephen Foster
Human Resources ..... Stephanie Klass
..... Alison Loveday
Matrimonial Finance & Professional Negligence ..... Peter Woolf

THE FIRM: Occupying modern offices at the heart of Manchester's commercial district, Berg & Co is a leading Manchester-based law firm, with a reputation for innovative and effective commercial problem-solving. The firm provides decisive, commercial advice to businesses of all sizes.

PRINCIPAL AREAS OF WORK:

Corporate & Commercial: Including choice of business structure, mergers and acquisitions, joint ventures and shareholders' agreements, directors' duties and responsibilities, banking and finance, stock exchange and other regulatory issues, insolvency procedures, commercial contracts, standard terms and conditions, internet law, agency and distribution agreements, intellectual property and information technology, EC law and competition law.
Litigation: Including contractual claims, shareholders' actions, boardroom disputes and corporate fraud, professional negligence, insolvency, intellectual property, emergency applications, debt collection and matrimonial finance.
Commercial Property: Including sales and purchases, leases, development work, multi-let units and secured lending.
Human Resources: Including employment contracts, contested dismissals and severance issues, business transfers, redundancy, discrimination, sickness and maternity, legislative changes and audit of employment practices.

CLIENTELE: Clients include public (including listed) and private companies, education institutions, financial institutions, partnerships, innovative entrepreneurs seeking an innovative and practical approach to legal services.

INTERNATIONAL: The firm has an extensive range of contacts in Europe, the USA and the Far East which enable it to progress its clients' affairs beyond UK boundaries. Languages spoken include French and German.

B

BERMANS

Pioneer Buildings, 65-67 Dale St, Liverpool, L2 2NS **Tel:** (0151) 227 3351 **Fax:** (0151) 236 2107 **DX:** 14116 **Email:** info@bermans.co.uk **Website:** www.bermans.co.uk **Ptnrs:** 10 **Asst solrs:** 7 **Other fee-earners:** 41

BERRY & BERRY

11 Church Road, Tunbridge Wells, TN1 1JA
Tel: (01892) 526344 **Fax:** (01892) 511223 **DX:** 3908 Tunbridge Wells
Email: mail@the-solicitors.co.uk

185 High Street, Tonbridge, TN9 1BX
Tel: (01732) 355911 **Fax:** (01732) 355191 **DX:** 5500 Tonbridge
Email: mail@the-solicitors.co.uk

3 Tonbridge Road, Maidstone, ME16 8RL
Tel: (01622) 690777 **Fax:** (01622) 662555 **DX:** 400307 Maidstone West
Email: mail@the-solicitors.co.uk

Senior Partner	Anthony Herman
Number of partners	7
Assistant solicitors	11
Other fee-earners	10

AREAS OF PRACTICE

Civil Litigation	30%
Matrimonial & Family	20%
Property/Commercial	20%
Criminal Litigation	15%
Probate	15%

CONTACTS

Civil Litigation ..... Ian Tysh
Commercial ..... Anthony Herman
Criminal Litigation ..... Iain Reed
Matrimonial & Family ..... Yashin Masoliver
Probate/Finance ..... Nigel Stratton
Property ..... Zai Koder

THE FIRM: Established over 260 years ago. The Tunbridge Wells and Maidstone offices are very close to the courts.

PRINCIPAL AREAS OF WORK:

Litigation: Employment, personal injury, landlord and tenant, housing, commercial disputes.
Crime: Magistrates and Crown Court Scheme.
Family: Divorce, ancillary relief, public and private, child cases, cohabitee disputes, domestic violence.
Property & Commercial: All types of conveyancing and general commercial work.
Probate: Wills, probate tax, trusts, enduring power of attorney, elderly client care.
Agency Work: Available for Magistrates, County and Crown Courts covering a wide area of the South East.
Legal Aid: Franchised in family, crime and personal injury. Member of Law Net.

INTERNATIONAL: Spanish, French, Arabic, German, Punjabi, Hindi and Welsh spoken.

BERRYMAN SHACKLOCK

Park House, Friar Lane, Nottingham, NG1 6DN
Tel: (0115) 945 3700 **Fax:** (0115) 948 0234 **DX:** 10004 Nottingham 1
Email: legal@berrymanshacklock.co.uk **Website:** www.berrymanshacklock.co.uk

Managing Partner	Andy Matthews
Number of partners	11
Assistant solicitors	18
Other fee-earners	13

AREAS OF PRACTICE

Corporate & Commercial 70%
Private Client 30%

CONTACTS

Corporate/Commercial ....Duncan James
Commercial Litigation ....Richard Brackenbury
Commercial Property ....Ashley Cooper
Insurance Litigation ....Virginia Harvey
Family ....Mike Smith
Licensing ....Robin Wilson
Immigration ....Thalej Vasishta

THE FIRM: An exciting and dynamic firm based in Nottingham, delivering a wide range of specialist legal services for business, the insurance industry and individuals. It takes a no-nonsense approach, maintaining a consistent focus on the client's needs. Berryman Shacklock was created by the merger of two respected Nottinghamshire firms, Berryman & Co and Shacklocks, in December 1999.

PRINCIPAL AREAS OF WORK: Business work includes corporate/commercial; commercial property; IT/e-commerce; employment; intellectual property; dispute resolution (with a niche strength in construction industry); debt recovery; insolvency; licensing. The firm also specialises in insurance litigation. Work done for individuals includes family; wills, trusts and probate; conveyancing; compensation claims; immigration.

BERRYMANS LACE MAWER

Salisbury House, London Wall, London, EC2M 5QN
Tel: (020) 7638 2811 **Fax:** (020) 7920 0361 **DX:** 33861 Finsbury Sq.
Email: info@blm-law.com **Website:** www.blm-law.com

Castle Chambers, 43 Castle Street, Liverpool, L2 9SU
Tel: (0151) 236 2002 **Fax:** (0151) 236 2585 **DX:** 14159 Liverpool 1
Email: info@blm-law.com

King's House, 42 King Street West, Manchester, M3 2NU
Tel: (0161) 236 2002 **Fax:** (0161) 832 7956 **DX:** 14302 Manchester 1
Email: info@blm-law.com

Senior Partner	Paul Taylor
Number of partners	65
Assistant solicitors	129
Other fee-earners	112
Total staff	643

CONTACTS

UK
Birmingham ....Christopher Wiggin
Leeds ....Jonathan Clay
Liverpool ....David Evans
London ....Paul Taylor
Manchester ....Nigel Roden
Southampton ....Martin Bruffell
INTERNATIONAL
Dubai ....Paul Taylor

THE FIRM: Berrymans Lace Mawer is a specialist insurance law firm with the UK's largest personal injury practice. One of the few truly national firms, it has offices is Birmingham, Leeds, Liverpool, London, Southampton and Dubai, each providing a comprehensive legal service to clients. The firm is divided into two groups (insurance liability and specialist insurance); within each are distinct market-specific divisions. BLM has grown significantly in the four years since it merged. Innovative solutions and standardised high levels of service (all offices are ISO 9001 accredited) have resulted in increased numbers of instructions. The firm employs high-calibre lawyers who are experts in their areas of practice. BLM recruits 12 trainees per year across the firm and they benefit from a national training and professional development programme designed to ensure that clients receive the same high standards of service from all offices. The firm has developed a leading edge computerised case management system, XClaim™ that provided clients with online access to check the status of individual claims and generate customised management information reports. XClaim™ sets new standards for computerised case management systems and will set the benchmark for service and efficiency in insurance claims handling.

PRINCIPAL AREAS OF WORK: The firm has a number of units dedicated to specific practice areas with members in each of the offices. These include catastrophe/major trauma; child abuse; clinical negligence, construction; debt collection; disciplinary hearings; education; emergency services; employers' liability; employment; environment; fraud; general insurance; health and safety; holiday and travel; housing; insurance and reinsurance; local authority; marine; motor; occupational disease; personal injury; product liability; professional indemnity; property insurance; public liability; regulatory and compliance issues; retail and leisure; risk management; stress; transportation of people and goods.

CLIENTELE: Berrymans Lace Mawer acts for many large insurance companies, Lloyds syndicates, professional firms, government bodies, utility companies, major policy holders and commercial companies in the UK and overseas. BLM is committed to the provision of an efficient, proactive, cost-effective and pragmatic legal service. It aims to provide that service at levels tailored to clients' specific requirements, in partnership with them, and in a way which delivers a consistent quality of service. BLM's success is reflected by the increasing number of clients who are attracted to the firm.

INTERNATIONAL: The firm has an overseas office in Dubai. In addition, through the BLM Europe EIG, the firm works closely with associate and correspondent firms in 28 other European jurisdictions. It also has an associate firm in Singapore.

BERRY SMITH

Brackla House, Brackla Street, Bridgend, CF31 1BZ **Tel:** (01656) 645525 **Fax:** (01656) 645174 **DX:** 38004 Bridgend
Email: Bridgend@Berrysmith.com **Ptnrs:** 7 **Asst solrs:** 10 **Other fee-earners:** 8

BERWIN LEIGHTON PAISNER

Adelaide House, London Bridge, London, EC4R 9HA
Tel: (020) 7760 1000 **Fax:** (020) 7760 1111 **DX:** 92 London Chancery Lane WC2
Email: firstname.surname@berwinleightonpaisner.com
Website: www.berwinleightonpaisner.com

Bouverie House, 154 Fleet St, London, EC4A 2JD
Tel: (020) 7760 1000 **Fax:** (020) 7760 1111 **DX:** 198
Email: firstname.surname@paisner.com

THE FIRM: The merger of Berwin Leighton and Paisner & Co on May 1 2001 created a major City law firm with substantial corporate and property practices alongside a strong finance capability. Berwin Leighton Paisner has a clear client service focus and a blue chip client base. The firm places a premium on creative and commercial as well as technical advice, and quality, partner-led transactional care. The firm has an entrepreneurial, tenacious and innovative approach. Berwin Leighton Paisner acts for a wide range of UK and international institutions and high growth companies, across a wide range of industry sectors. The firm has offices in the City of London and Brussels and a formal association with Paris firm Uettwiller Grelon Gout Canat and Associés (UGGC). In addition, it has close working relationships with a number of overseas law firms in major centres, particularly in Europe and North America. Berwin Leighton Paisner is committed to service innovation. It operates personalised client extranets, provides a free online legal briefing service via its website and is a joint venture partner with Deloitte & Touche on 'beprofessional', which is a developing business solutions for small and medium-sized enterprises via the web.

PRINCIPAL AREAS OF WORK: The firm's four core practice areas are corporate, real estate, finance and litigation and dispute resolution.
Corporate: A broad range of corporate work is undertaken, including corporate finance, mergers and acquisitions, venture capital, corporate recovery and insolvency and, on the commercial side, asset/consumer finance, retail banking, data protection, franchising and other commercial agreements. All aspects of EU and competition work are also undertaken. The tech media team has expanded considerably and is particularly well known for its work in the IT, publishing, digital media and e-commerce fields. The firm also has a dedicated trademark unit.
Real Estate: The firm's commercial property practice is one of the leading providers of high value services to the property sector. It undertakes work for institutions, investors, developers, retailers, banks, government bodies and major leisure operators. It includes one of the country's leading planning and environment teams and one of the largest combined contentious and non-contentious construction and engineering teams, together with a team of specialist property litigators.
Finance: The finance team advises lenders, issuers and borrowers on all principal financing techniques, specialising in project finance, property finance, banking and capital markets, asset finance and acquisition finance. It is one of the leaders in PFI/PPP work and has been involved in some of the UK's flagship schemes.
Dispute Resolution: The litigation and dispute resolution team deals with a wide range of UK and international commercial disputes by means of negotiation, ADR, arbitration or through the courts. The four core practice areas are complemented by specialist teams in the following disciplines:
Employment: The firm advises employers and employees on both contentious and non-contentious aspects of employment law and on all aspects of occupational pensions schemes.
Insurance & Reinsurance: The insurance and reinsurance team deals with dispute resolution, arbitration, litigation, commercial and corporate insurance and reinsurance matters, acting for insurers, reinsurers, brokers, agents and intermediaries.
Tax and Trusts: The corporate tax group provides a comprehensive advisory service on the UK and international tax aspects of all areas of the firm's practice. The well known trusts and estate planning team advises individuals and trustees on estate and tax planning, trusts and offshore arrangements. They are also recognised for their expertise in contentious probate and charity work.
Regulatory: The high-profile regulatory group, comprising four solicitor advocates, is dedicated to food law, licensing, health and safety and product liability issues.

RECRUITMENT: The firm recruits around thirty trainee solicitors each year. A brochure and application details are available from the firm or via its website.

Senior Partner	Harold Paisner
Managing Partner	Neville Eisenberg
Number of partners	130
Number of fee-earners	430
Total staff	920

AREAS OF PRACTICE

Property	36%
Corporate	35%
Finance	17%
Litigation & Dispute Resolution	12%

CONTACTS

Banking & Capital Markets	Jennifer Mackerras
Charities	Moira Protani
Commercial	Jonathan Kropman
Commercial Property	Philip Bretherton
Construction & Engineering	Terry Fleet
Consumer Finance	Dennis Rosenthal
Corporate Finance	John Bennett
	David Collins
	David Robins
Corporate/International Tax	John Overs
Employment	Rob Eldridge
Environment	Andrew Waite
EU & Competition	Adrian Magnus
	Velia Leone
Insolvency & Regeneration	Keith Bordell
Insurance/Reinsurance	Jonathan Sacher
Licensing/Food Law/Health & Safety	Craig Baylis
Litigation & Dispute Resolution	Michael Goldmeier
	David Parkin
Pensions	Norman Russell
PFI/Projects	Simon Allan
	Jim Buchanan
Planning	Tim Pugh
	Ian Trehearne
Property Finance	Mark Waghorn
Property Litigation	Roger Cohen
Tech Media	Adam Rose
Trade Marks	Debrett Lyons
Trusts & Estate Planning	Wynne Thomas

*berwin leighton paisner

SJ BERWIN

222 Gray's Inn Road, London, WC1X 8XF
Tel: (020) 7533 2222 **Fax:** (020) 7533 2000 **DX:** 255 London Chancery Lane WC2
Email: info@sjberwin.com **Website:** www.sjberwin.com

THE FIRM: Founded in 1982, SJ Berwin's rapid growth and success is best explained by its ability to handle complex corporate and commercial transactions, coupled with a creative approach to clients' problems, a speedy response, and close involvement in their strategic decision making. SJ Berwin acts for clients ranging from major multinational business corporations and financial institutions, to internet entrepreneurs and to high net worth individuals. The firm is especially favoured by entrepreneurial business clients, who find the firm particularly well attuned to their outlook and needs. Increasingly, the firm is focusing on industry sectors including e-commerce, pharmaceuticals and biotechnology, media, communications and information technology, sport and leisure. SJ Berwin was named Law Firm of the Year at The Lawyer Awards 2000.

PRINCIPAL AREAS OF WORK:

Corporate: The firm is well known for its corporate work and offers a full range of corporate finance services, including mergers and acquisitions, capital markets, private equity, management buy-outs, financial services and securities regulation, coupled with an active international banking practice. The firm was named Private Equity Law Firm of the Year by the European Venture Capital Journal in 2001.

Commercial Property: Winner of The Lawyer Awards 2000 Property Team of the Year. All aspects of commercial property work are handled for a wide range of clients, including property companies, developers, institutions, retailers and hoteliers. Specialist groups advise on public and private funding programmes for major infrastructure projects, construction and local government finance issues. A highly regarded planning and environment team is an integral part of this growing and expanded practice. The property finance team is an established market leader in the development of innovative fund structures.

EU & Competition: The firm has a strong European dimension. Its EU, competition and trade law practice is conducted principally through the London, Brussels, Madrid and Munich offices, and advises on domestic and EU mergers and acquisitions, competition, anti-trust and anti-dumping, regulatory work and judicial review proceedings. The firm was named Competition Team of the Year in the annual Legal Business Awards in 2001, following success in 1998.

Litigation: The firm's litigation practice handles a broad range of substantial international and domestic commercial litigation as well as mediation and arbitration which is undertaken by the specialist ADR Services Unit. In addition, the practice includes groups specialising in property litigation, defamation, public law and judicial review, an employment and pensions group and an advocacy group.

Reconstruction & Insolvency: An active insolvency group handles the whole spectrum of insolvency work, from corporate insolvency and bankruptcy to reconstructions.

Intellectual Property: International trademark, copyright and patent litigation, international trademark registration and the identification, exploitation and protection of intellectual property rights are undertaken by a specialist intellectual property group.

Tax: National and international taxation advice, including the structuring of international transactions and property development, is provided by the tax group. Estate planning and asset protection advice is given to private clients in the UK and overseas.

Other Areas: E-commerce work is handled across the firm, with particular strengths in the venture capital, flotations, commercial, financial services, reconstruction and competition practices. Other leading areas of commercial work include film financing and animation production and also communications, as well as commercial contracts, frequently with an international dimension, including franchising, agency distributorship, joint venture and trading agreements, and information technology. The firm also handles pro bono work.

INTERNATIONAL: Internationally, the firm operates through its own network of law firms in Europe and is also the English member of Interlaw.

Brussels: Directly connected and working closely with the EU and Competition Department in London, the office comprises UK qualified solicitors, Spanish *abogados*, French and Belgian *avocats* and trainee solicitors. The office extends a multilingual environment to clients with fluency in several European languages. Key experience and strength lies in matters involving Article 81 (ex Article 85) and Article 82 (ex Article 86) of the EC Treaty and the EC merger control regulation and lobbying contact with various European institutions. Specific areas of practice include biotech regulation, tax law, environment, telecommunications and fishery law.

Madrid: The firm provides corporate legal services with a strong focus on private equity, mergers and acquisitions and tax work. EU and competition law is also practised. Clients include major corporations acquiring top local companies or entering into joint-venture agreements with local partners in the IT business. Specialisation covers advising investment services companies in matters related to setting up local branches, launching venture capital funds and cooperating in pan-European Investment funds.

Frankfurt: In association with SJ Berwin Knopf Tulloch Steininger, the operation in Germany has offices in Frankfurt, Munich and Berlin and consists of the law firm SJ Berwin Knopf Tulloch Steininger, the tax advising firm of Knopf, Tulloch & Partner GmbH and the auditing firm of GKT Industrie- und Handelstreuhand

Continued overleaf

UK	
Number of partners	86
Assistant solicitors	193
Other fee-earners	69
International	
Number of partners	29
Assistant solicitors	54

AREAS OF PRACTICE

Company/Commercial	49%
Commercial Property	19%
Litigation	17%
EU/Competition	9%
Tax	7%

CONTACTS

ADR	David Shapiro
Advocacy	Richard Slowe
Banking	Gillian Smith
Commercial Litigation	Tim Taylor
Company & Commercial	Andrew Shindler
Construction	Ian Insley
Corporate Finance	Jonathan Blake
	Robert Burrow
Defamation	Hilton Mervis
E-commerce	Martin Bowen
	Simon Holmes
Employment	Nicola Kerr
Environment	Mark Brumwell
EU/Competition	Stephen Kon
	Ralph Cohen
Financial Services	Charles Abrams
	Tamasin Little
Hotels	David Ryland
Intellectual Property	Ray Black
	Jeremy Schrire
Investment Funds	Josyane Gold
Leisure	Bryan Pickup
Media & Communications	Nigel Palmer
Parliamentary Lobbying	Simon Holmes
Pensions	Wyn Derbyshire
Pharmaceuticals & Biotechnology	
	Jeremy Schrire
Planning	Patricia Thomas
Projects/PFI	Simon McLeod
Property	Stephen Willson
Property Finance	David Ryland
Property Litigation	Michael Metliss
Reconstruction & Insolvency	Stephen Maffey
Sport	Peter McInerney
	Jonathan Metliss
Tax	Heather Corben
Trademark Litigation	Ray Black

B

AG. They design tax-effective structures to accommodate mergers, acquisitions, sales, corporate divestitures and reorganisations. EU and competition law is also practised. The firm does not merely combine legal and tax expertise, it designs consistent business solutions which take all the relevant financial aspects into account. **Paris:** The office provides corporate legal services with a strong focus on private equity, mergers and acquisitions and tax work.

RECRUITMENT: In order to maintain its commitment to organic growth and development, SJ Berwin will recruit up to 40 ambitious, commercially-minded individuals to begin training in September 2003. All trainees will be required to undertake two corporate seats as part of their training programme. Apply to Charlotte Bishop, Recruitment Manager.

BETESH FOX & CO

17 Ralli Courts, West Riverside, Manchester, M3 5FT
Tel: (0161) 832 6131 **Fax:** (0161) 832 8172 **DX:** 14359 Manchester 1
Email: chambers@beteshfox.co.uk **Website:** www.beteshfox.co.uk

Managing Partner	Martin Coyne
Senior Partner	Stephen Fox
Number of partners	7
Assistant solicitors	16
Other fee-earners	15

AREAS OF PRACTICE

Personal Injury	45%
Commercial Litigation	20%
Company/Commercial & Property	20%
Commercial Crime	15%

B

THE FIRM: Operating nationally and internationally from Manchester city centre, Betesh Fox & Co combines the traditional high standards expected of the legal profession with a progressive outlook.

PRINCIPAL AREAS OF WORK: Personal injury; company/commercial and property; commercial litigation; regulatory offences and commercial fraud; serious crime.

BEVAN ASHFORD

35 Colston Avenue, Bristol, BS1 4TT
Tel: (0117) 923 0111 **Fax:** (0117) 929 1865 **DX:** 7828 Bristol 1
Email: njk@bevanashford.co.uk **Website:** www.bevanashford.co.uk

Alpha Tower, Suffolk Street, Queensway, Birmingham, B1 1TT
Tel: (0121) 634 5000 **Fax:** (0121) 634 5001 **DX:** 715470 Birmingham 41
Email: j.sapeta@bevanashford.co.uk

Curzon House, Southernhay West, Exeter, EX1 1AB
Tel: (01392) 411111 **Fax:** (01392) 250764 **DX:** 8301 Exeter
Email: s.rous@bevan-ashford.com

1 Chancery Lane, London, WC2A 1LF
Tel: (020) 7421 4400 **Fax:** (020) 7421 4422 **DX:** 1058 Chancery Lane
Email: d.widdowson@bevanashford.co.uk

Princess Court, 23 Princess Street, Plymouth, PL1 2EX
Tel: (01752) 256888 **Fax:** (01752) 250508 **DX:** 8273 Plymouth 2
Email: d.beadel@bevan-ashford.com

41 St James Street, Taunton, TR1 1JR
Tel: (01823) 284444 **Fax:** (01823) 270869 **DX:** 32115 Taunton
Email: i.daniells@bevan-ashford.com

Gotham House, Tiverton, EX16 6LT
Tel: (01884) 242111 **Fax:** (01884) 259303 **DX:** 49002 Tiverton
Email: c.palmer@bevan-ashford.com

Chairman of the Board	Nick Jarrett-Kerr
Number of partners	76
Assistant solicitors	145
Number of fee-earners	103
Total staff	629

AREAS OF PRACTICE

Company/Commercial/Projects	28%
Property	24%
Health	21%
Litigation	21%
Private Client	6%

CONTACTS

Birmingham	Jean Sapeta
Bristol	Nick Jarrett-Kerr
Exeter	Simon Rous
London	David Widdowson
Plymouth	David Beadel
Taunton	Ian Daniells
Tiverton	Christopher Palmer

THE FIRM: In the past 12 months, Bevan Ashford has firmly established itself as a truly national commercial law firm following the opening of a substantial Birmingham practice and the tripling in size of its London office. With fee income growing at around 20% per annum and the total number of staff well over 600, the firm offers the breadth and depth of skills, experience and expertise to meet the full range of legal services requirements for its clients in the public and private sector. Bevan Ashford has 76 partners, over 320 lawyers in total and operates out of seven offices in the South West, London and Birmingham. For all clients, the Bevan Ashford approach is to develop pragmatic and realistic solutions to the business and legal issues they face. The firm focuses on the results and realises that the starting point of any successful client relationship is first of all to listen and understand. Bevan Ashford is responsive to each client's own unique needs, unconstrained in its thinking and flexible in the way it delivers its service. It is at the leading edge of IT in developing case management and knowledge management systems for the sole purpose of streamlining its service to be as efficient and cost effective as possible. Above all, Bevan Ashford recognises that the most important prerequisite of a quality service is a team of lawyers and support staff dedicated to service excellence. Many of its lawyers are

INVESTOR IN PEOPLE

dual qualified as barristers, doctors and engineers, whilst others are qualified arbitrators and mediators. The firm hold Investors in People accreditation and is committed to ongoing training and development programmes geared around the continuous improvement of client services.

PRINCIPAL AREAS OF WORK: Bevan Ashford's traditional reputation as a substantial and highly successful healthcare and public sector practice is now balanced by its rapidly growing and nationally recognised private sector teams. Much of the work undertaken is not just national, but international and many of the firm's partners are widely accepted as leaders in their specialist fields. Across all departments, Bevan Ashford continues to attract high profile clients, challenging and ground-breaking work and staff of the highest calibre. With a genuine and demonstrable commitment to exceptional quality and service excellence, clients can be assured of the very best support and advice at all times.

Litigation: The range of litigation and dispute resolution work undertaken by Bevan Ashford – in areas such as employment, insurance, banking, property, construction, IT/IP, professional indemnity and medical – confirms this cross department practice area as one of the largest and most talented teams outside London. The firm acts for clients in Europe, USA and the Middle East, including many of the UK's top companies.

Corporate & Commercial: Bevan Ashford's corporate and commercial department continues to thrive and offers the full range of banking, finance and insolvency services to national and international clients. Other non-contentious 'business services' are provided by experienced and highly regarded teams covering employment, commercial property (including bulk conveyancing), energy, planning and environment, construction and IT/IP.

PFI: The firm's PFI and projects group continues to build a formidable reputation as one of the leading practices in the country. The team has a track record of over 145 projects spanning the health, defence, waste and education sectors and has closed nine schemes in the past year alone. Bevan Ashford is working with Government departments on several Pathfinder schemes and has experience in acting for the public sector, private sector and project funders.

Healthcare: The cross departmental health & social care group operating out of Bristol, Birmingham and London offers a complete range of specialist advisory services, including clinical governance, mental health, child care, registered homes, joint working and partnering. This highly focused grouping is the dominant legal provider to NHS trusts, health authorities, PCGs/PCTs and local authorities in the Midlands and South of England and regularly attracts work in particularly unusual, complex and sensitive matters, often in preference to the client's regular panel firm. Bevan Ashford's dedicated NHS Claims department has been reappointed to the NHS Litigation Authority panel for defendant clinical negligence work for a further three years. With 10 partners divided between Bristol, Birmingham, London and Plymouth, it is the largest team in the country.

INTERNATIONAL: French, German, Italian, Punjabi, Russian, Spanish, Urdu and Welsh are spoken fluently by solicitors within the firm.

B

BEVISS & BECKINGSALE

Law Chambers, Holyrood Street, Chard, TA20 2AJ **Tel:** (01460) 61494 **Fax:** (01460) 63821 **DX:** 43701 Chard **Email:** enquiries@bevissandbeckingsale.co.uk **Website:** www.bevissandbeckingsale.co.uk **Ptnrs:** 7 **Asst solrs:** 5 **Other fee-earners:** 7 **Contact:** Martin Hicks • Substantial agricultural and general practice in South Somerset, West Dorset and East Devon.

BHATT MURPHY

23 Pitfield Street, London, N1 6HB **Tel:** (020) 7253 7744 **Fax:** (020) 7253 7766 **DX:** 36626 Finsbury **Email:** mail@bhattmurphy.demon.co.uk **Ptnrs:** 4 **Asst solrs:** 1 **Other fee-earners:** 2

BIGGART BAILLIE

Dalmore House, 310 St. Vincent Street, Glasgow, G2 5QR
Tel: (0141) 228 8000 **Fax:** (0141) 228 8310 **DX:** GW9
Email: info@biggartbaillie.co.uk **Website:** www.biggartbaillie.co.uk

7 Castle Street, Edinburgh, EH2 3AP
Tel: (0131) 226 5541 **Fax:** (0131) 226 2278 **DX:** ED15
Email: info@biggartbaillie.co.uk

Managing Partner	Campbell Smith
Chairman & Senior Partner	David Ross
Number of partners	25
Assistant solicitors	38
Other fee-earners	26

AREAS OF PRACTICE

Commercial Property	30%
Litigation	30%
Corporate	29%
Private Client	11%

CONTACTS

Banking	Derek Ellery
Charities	Gordon Wyllie
Construction/Planning	Murray Shaw
Corporate Finance	David Allan
Employment	Paul Brown
Aviation, Energy & Utilities/PFI	David Ross
Insurance Litigation	David Stevenson
IT/IP	Colin Miller
Litigation	Murray Shaw
Property/Projects	Peter Cruickshank

BIGGART BAILLIE
SOLICITORS

THE FIRM: One of Scotland's leading commercial law firms with a balance of quality work across the main practice areas of litigation, corporate and property. The firm has strength and depth of expertise in a number of specialist areas and has an excellent reputation amongst the Scottish business community. Biggart Baillie is well placed to provide clients with a wide range of forward-looking expertise delivered by people who understand the business. Training anddevelopment of all of its staff is regarded by the firm as vital to its future and the continuing provision of service which exceeds clients' expectations.

PRINCIPAL AREAS OF WORK: Specialisms are in the areas of corporate finance, banking, PFI, IT/IP, mergers and acquisitions, construction and planning, employment, energy and utilities, property, defender reparation (especially professional negligence and industrial disease cases), ADR and insolvency.

CLIENTELE: The firm acts for major industrial, financial and commercial enterprises across Scotland and with its membership of the Euro-American Lawyers Group it has access to legal representation in many of the world's most important centres of commerce. With offices in both Edinburgh and Glasgow, the firm is able to serve the client base which ranges from small businesses to national and multinational companies including banks and financial institutions, hi-tech companies, insurance companies, utilities, energy companies, retailers and property developers.

B

BILL GOYDER – SOLE PRACTITIONER
42 Lowgreen, Gainford, Darlington, DL2 3DS **Tel:** (01325) 730 234 **Fax:** (01325) 730 234 **Email:** wgoyder@freeserve.co.uk

BINDMAN & PARTNERS

275 Gray's Inn Rd, London, WC1X 8QB
Tel: (020) 7833 4433 **Fax:** (020) 7837 9792 **DX:** 37904 King's Cross
Email: info@bindmans.com **Website:** www.bindmans.com

Senior Partner	Geoffrey Bindman
Number of partners	12
Assistant solicitors	18
Other fee-earners	8

CONTACTS

Prisoners	Tony Murphy
Defamation/Media	Tamsin Allen
Employment/Discrimination	Camilla Palmer
Housing	Barbara Wyatt
Immigration	Alison Stanley
Medical Negligence	Claire Fazan
Civil Litigation	Robin Lewis
Family Law	Felicity Crowther
Children	Katherine Gieve
Criminal Law & Prisoners	Neil O'May
Mental Health	Saimo Chahal
Administrative Law	Stephen Grosz
Personal Injury	Terrence Donovan

THE FIRM: Founded in 1974, Bindman & Partners are specialists in civil liberties and human rights issues and have a commitment to acting for publicly-funded clients. The firm has the resources to handle major litigation of all types, and considerable specific experience and expertise in the following areas.

PRINCIPAL AREAS OF WORK:
Defamation & Media Law: Wide experience in representing individuals, newspapers, TV companies and other media organisations in defamation, copyright, confidentiality and contract claims cases.
Administrative Law: Work includes judicial review, human rights, environmental protection, discrimination and police powers.
Civil Litigation: General litigation including actions against the police.
Employment: In addition to its large employment practice, the firm acts for many employers, notably from the not for profit sector, including colleges and public authorities, voluntary groups, charities and pressure groups, in a wide range of casework. It has particular experience and expertise in discrimination issues.
Crime: Work ranges from major fraud cases and serious crimes to minor offences.
Housing: The firm deals with a wide range of landlord and tenant law, especially for tenants.
Family: An extensive matrimonial and family practice including legally-aided clients.
Children: Work includes wardship, adoption, care proceedings, child abduction, residence and contact disputes.
Medical Negligence & Personal Injury: The firm has an established expertise in medical negligence and other personal injury cases.
Mental Health: This covers advising patients on their rights when detained, on false imprisonment and consent to treatment.
Immigration & Nationality: An established practice in all areas of immigration and nationality law, including business and EU-related applications, personal immigration and asylum.
Prisoners: Acting for prisoners against prison authorities.

BINGHAM DANA LLP
8-10 Mansion House Place, London, EC4N 8LB **Tel:** (020) 7375 9770 **Fax:** (020) 7220 7431 **Ptnrs:** 3 **Asst solrs:** 5

BIRCHALL BLACKBURN

Crystal House, Birley Street, Preston, PR1 2AQ
Tel: (01772) 561663 **Fax:** (01772) 202438 **DX:** 713290
Email: ixjones@birchallblackburn.co.uk

Senior Partner	W. Denison Robbins
Number of partners	9
Assistant solicitors	14
Other fee-earners	30

THE FIRM: Birchall Blackburn has offices in Preston, Manchester and Chorley, allowing clients ready access to a comprehensive range of legal services. Founded in 1950 to provide a full range of legal service for corporate, institutional and private clients, Birchall Blackburn is one of the most progressive firms in the North West with a growing reputation within the commercial field. The firm has specialist departments which include commercial and company law, commercial property, commercial and civil litigation, licensing and the leisure sector, family law, housing, corporate and personal insolvency, immigration, debt recovery and private client work. Close partner contact is central within the service which combines commercial awareness and experience with a pragmatic down to earth approach. Legal Aid work is also undertaken and the firm is a holder of the Legal Aid franchise. The aim is to provide the very highest level of service in a friendly and professional manner to all clients, irrespective of whether they are private paying businesses or individuals in receipt of legal aid. The firm has a particularly strong litigation department.

B

BIRCHAM DYSON BELL

1 Dean Farrar St, Westminster, London, SW1H 0DY
Tel: (020) 7222 8044 **Fax:** (020) 7222 3480 **DX:** 2317 VICTORIA
Email: reception@bdb-law.co.uk **Website:** www.bdb-law.co.uk

Senior Partner	Ian McCulloch
Executive Committee Chairman	Nicholas Brown
Number of partners	35
Assistant solicitors	29
Other fee-earners	48

AREAS OF PRACTICE

Private Client/Charities	34%
Company/Commercial	16%
Litigation	16%
Parliamentary/Public Affairs	16%
Property	16%
Investment Management	2%

CONTACTS

Charities	Simon Weil
Company/Commercial	John Turnbull
Employment	Ian Adamson
Investment Management	Christopher Jones-Warner
Litigation	George Josselyn
Matrimonial	John Darnton
Parliamentary & Public Law	Robert Owen
Private Client	Sarah Stowell
Property	John Stephenson

Bircham Dyson Bell

THE FIRM: In October 2000, Bircham & Co. combined its firm name with the name of its parliamentary and public law department, Dyson Bell Martin, to become Bircham Dyson Bell. The firm's new name and corporate identity reflects the integrated working methods of all its departments. Bircham Dyson Bell continues to provide all of the services for which Bircham & Co. and Dyson Bell Martin were known. To coincide with its change of name, the firm launched a new website (see above). Established for many years in London SW1, Bircham Dyson Bell is highly regarded for its charities and private client work and has a leading parliamentary and public law practice. The firm also has strong company commercial, property, litigation and investment management teams. The firm is continuing to expand and now has 220 staff in total, following the arrival of teams from Radcliffes and Bower Cotton in 2000. The new arrivals have strengthened Bircham Dyson Bell's corporate, private client, litigation and commercial property teams. By attracting partners and senior lawyers from other firms and maintaining a high percentage of internal partner promotions, the firm has grown to be the largest in Westminster. Recent developments have included a significant expansion in the volume of corporate finance work undertaken. In addition, the private client department, one of the largest of any central London firm, is closely linked to a growing investment management division. The firm's work in leasehold reform has grown strongly as has the civil litigation practice. The charities group has expanded to become one of the largest teams in the country since the arrival of several senior practitioners. Because the firm places strong emphasis on maintaining a close working relationship between partners and clients, it is noted for the quality of the service it is able to provide.

PRINCIPAL AREAS OF WORK:

Private Client: Private client services include all aspects of financial planning for the individual including wills, trusts and tax compliance for individuals and trustees. In the area of tax planning, the firm acts increasingly for foreign nationals both within the UK and internationally. The department also includes a substantial probate practice.

Charities: Charity clients range from major national charities to family charitable trusts, the firm advising on all aspects, including formation, administration and promotion. All commercial aspects of charities' activities are covered including acquiring and disposing of businesses and undertakings, fund-raising and commercial participation/commercial arrangements with third parties.

Investment Management: The investment management team offers private clients a comprehensive investment management service. Funds under management are growing steadily and the department is a sponsored member of the CREST settlement system using the firm's nominee company. It aims to provide a seamless service between private client legal services and investment management, managing private client, trust and charity funds on a discretionary and advisory basis. Bircham Dyson Bell is authorised by the Law Society to conduct investment business.

Property: Commercial property expertise covers all the main areas, in particular investment, retail, landlord and tenant, development schemes, project management, funding loan arrangements and site acquisitions and

Continued overleaf

disposals. Property activities for private clients include all aspects of landed estates, both urban and rural, such as estate management, agricultural and other tenancies and town and country planning. The firm also has a leading practice in the leasehold reform field.

Company & Commercial: Services include corporate finance (in particular flotations on the Official List, AIM and OFEX), company acquisitions and disposals, partnerships and joint ventures and all types of commercial agreements. The department undertakes a substantial amount and variety of employment work and also gives advice on intellectual property matters.

Litigation: All aspects of commercial litigation are handled, including building litigation, property disputes and insurance litigation. Matrimonial and family law matters are dealt with and civil litigation services are provided, covering such areas as personal injury and medical negligence.

Parliamentary & Public Law: This department advises on all aspects of the law-making process, whether at a European, national or local level. This includes advice on influencing government policy and resulting legislation, advice on transport infrastructure and other major public works, public enquiries and promoting and opposing private and local legislation.

INTERNATIONAL: As a member of Lexwork International, an association of independent law firms, Bircham Dyson Bell has associated firms in other European cities.

BIRCH CULLIMORE

Friars, White Friars, Chester, CH1 1XS **Tel:** (01244) 321066 **Fax:** (01244) 312582 **DX:** 19985 Chester **Ptnrs:** 8 **Asst solrs:** 2 **Other fee-earners:** 7

BIRD & BIRD

90 Fetter Lane, London, EC4A 1JP
Tel: (020) 7415 6000 **Fax:** (020) 7415 6111 **DX:** 119 London
Email: info@twobirds.com **Website:** www.twobirds.com

Chief Executive	David Kerr
Non-Executive Chairman	Hamish Sandison
Number of partners	72
Assistant solicitors	140
Other fee-earners	76

AREAS OF PRACTICE

Company	56%
Intellectual Property	23%
Litigation	12%
Property	8%
Private Client	1%

CONTACTS

Banking	Trystan Tether
Brands & Trademarks	Morag Macdonald
Communications	David Kerr
Corporate/Commercial	Christopher Barrett
	Justin Walkey
E-Commerce	Graham Defries
Employment	Corinne Aldridge
	Ian Hunter
EU & Competition	Jean-Paul Hordies
	Simon Topping
Intellectual Property	Trevor Cook
	Morag Macdonald
IT	Roger Bickerstaff
	Hamish Sandison
Litigation	Trevor Asserson
	Duncan Quinan
PFI	Roger Bickerstaff
Pharmaceuticals & Biosciences	Trevor Cook
	John Wilkinson
Property	Jonathan Baker
Sport	Felicity Reeve
	Justin Walkey
Tax	Richard Ward

THE FIRM: Working with some of the world's most innovative and technologically advanced companies, Bird & Bird has established a formidable reputation for advice at the cutting edge of law. Yet the firm's approach is strongly commercial too, enabling its clients to capitalise on business opportunities and manage change effectively. Combining entrepreneurial ethos and hi-tech know-how in this way brings the firm's clients significant benefits. Sectoral focus has been pivotal to Bird & Bird's success, borne out by the fact that the firm is amongst the market leaders in the sectors in which it is active. As convergence issues increasingly affect every business, the firm's unrivalled expertise in e-commerce, communications, information technology, intellectual property, sport, media, pharmaceuticals and biosciences gives it a unique perspective. Across each of these sectors, it offers a fully comprehensive service. With offices in London, Brussels, Paris, Hong Kong and Stockholm, Bird & Bird's lawyers are strategically placed to offer local expertise within a global context. That's how they've been successful in realising their clients' business goals, both domestically and internationally.

PRINCIPAL AREAS OF WORK: By providing a full range of legal services within its principal industry sectors, Bird & Bird offers both breadth and depth of expertise, in the following areas:

Banking: Working with leading banks and financial institutions, the firm advises on a full range of banking issues including e-banking, project finance, PFI, secured and syndicated lending, insolvency, corporate reconstruction and banking litigation.

Commercial Litigation: The department offers specialist dispute resolution advice, both in the UK and internationally, focusing, in particular, on the communications, IT and sports sectors.

Commercial Property: Advising telecoms providers, government departments and financial institutions, the firm's expertise ranges from PFI structures and commercial agreements to pan-European regulatory issues.

Communications: The firm advises both telecoms users and suppliers on a variety of domestic and international issues including major infrastructure projects; regulatory issues; joint ventures and strategic alliances; M&A; interconnection agreements, outsourcing arrangements and 3G licences.

Corporate: Offering a comprehensive range of corporate services, including tax, the firm's corporate lawyers undertake a wide variety of transactional work spanning M&A, joint ventures, strategic alliances, investment, equity financing, venture capital and public offerings.

E-commerce: One of Europe's leading practices in e-commerce, expertise spans all the firm's principal departments and encompasses every aspect of e-commerce including: VC and Incubators funds; 'dot-com' start-ups; funding and IPO's; established businesses developing an Internet presence and e-banking.

Employment: Working with companies and individuals, the firm advises on both non-contentious and litigious issues, ranging from employee contracts and termination agreements to changes in employment regulation.

EU: With substantial offices in both Brussels and Paris, the firm has a significant EU and competition capability, concentrating on anti-trust enforcement and legislative developments.

IP: One the largest IP practices in Europe, the firm offers comprehensive expertise across all areas. Lawyers advise on brands and trademark strategy, advertising, media and Internet domain name issues. They have established a strong reputation for conducting successful patent actions as well as providing transactional and litigation advice.

IT: With considerable experience gained in-house within the IT industry and specialist technical backgrounds, the firm's lawyers advise both IT users and suppliers from the public, private and utilities sectors on a variety of major projects.

Media: The firm's expertise spans all areas of media including music, film, TV, publishing and computer games, with a particular focus on negotiating and drafting finance and distribution agreements, publishing deals and issues of digital convergence.

Pharmaceuticals & Biosciences: The firm offers wide-ranging advice on IP, corporate and commercial issues, to diverse UK and multi-national companies within these sectors.

Sport: The firm's sports lawyers have extensive experience of advising governing bodies, rights purchasers, broadcasters, sponsors and leading sportsmen and women.

INTERNATIONAL: The firm has offices in Brussels, Paris, Hong Kong, and Stockholm.

BIRKETT LONG

Essex House, 42 Crouch St, Colchester, CO3 3HH **Tel:** (01206) 217300 **Fax:** (01206) 572393 **DX:** 3603 Colchester **Email:** mail@birkettlong.co.uk **Website:** www.birkettlong.co.uk **Ptnrs:** 16 **Asst solrs:** 9 **Other fee-earners:** 23 **Contact:** Philip George • Birkett Longís team of specialist lawyers offer expertise, professionalism and cost effective solutions to both business and private clients.

AREAS OF PRACTICE

Litigation (inc. Commercial & PI)	30%
Private Client, Family & Financial Services	30%
Property	20%
Company & Employment	20%

B

BIRKETTS

24-26 Museum St, Ipswich, IP1 1HZ **Tel:** (01473) 232300 **Fax:** (01473) 230524 **DX:** 3206 Ipswich **Website:** www.birketts.co.uk **Ptnrs:** 20 **Asst solrs:** 9 **Other fee-earners:** 38

BIRNBERG PEIRCE & PARTNERS

14 Inverness Street, Camden Town, London, NW1 7HJ **Tel:** (020) 7284 4620 **Fax:** (020) 7911 0170 **DX:** 57059 Camden Town **Email:** [name]@birnberg.demon.co.uk **Ptnrs:** 2 **Asst solrs:** 11 **Other fee-earners:** 8

BLACKADDERS

30 & 34 Reform Street, Dundee, DD1 1RJ **Tel:** (01382) 229222 **Fax:** (01382) 342220 **Email:** solicitors@blackadders.co.uk **Website:** www.blackadders.co.uk **Contact:** Johnston Clark • The firm has a large client base of individual and business clients. Particular areas of expertise include corporate finance, employment law and insolvency.

AREAS OF PRACTICE

Private Client	27%
Conveyancing	18%
Commercial/Corporate	14%
Litigation	13%
Financial Services	12%
Branches	9%
Estate Agency	7%

BLACKETT HART & PRATT

11 Market Place, Durham, DH1 3NE **Tel:** 0191 384 0840 **Fax:** 0191 384 1523 **DX:** 60209 DURHAM CITY **Email:** info@b-h-p.com **Website:** www.b-h-p.com **Ptnrs:** 23 **Asst solrs:** 11 **Other fee-earners:** 15

BLACKLOCK THORLEY

89 Constitution Street, Leith, Edinburgh, EH6 7AD **Tel:** (0131) 555 3399 **Fax:** (0131) 555 5535

BLAIR ALLISON & CO

Fountain Court, Steelhouse Lane, Birmingham, B4 6EE **Tel:** (0121) 233 2904 **Fax:** (0121) 236 8913 **DX:** 23534 **Ptnrs:** 3 **Asst solrs:** 2 **Other fee-earners:** 4 **Contact:** Mari Meisel • Concentrates on family law. Nine fee-earners all highly specialist and experienced. Strong in finance, children, care and mediation. High level work, national reputation.

AREAS OF PRACTICE

Family Law (inc. Care & Mediation)	85%
Probate	3%
Conveyancing	9%
Civil Litigation inc. Agency	3%

BLAIR & BRYDEN

27 Union Street, Greenock, PA16 8DD **Tel:** (01475) 888777 **Fax:** (01475) 781836 **DX:** GR2 Greenock-1 **Ptnrs:** 15 **Asst solrs:** 12 **Other fee-earners:** 12

BLAKE DAWSON WALDRON

5th Floor, 66 Gresham Street, London, EC2V 7PL **Tel:** (020) 7600 3030 **Fax:** (020) 7600 3392 **Email:** legal.info@bdw.co.uk **Website:** www.bdw.com.au **Ptnrs:** 2 **Asst solrs:** 1 **Other fee-earners:** 1 **Contact:** Mary Padbury • Australian lawyers. Mergers and acquisitions; Stock Exchange compliance; capital markets; banking and finance; taxation; insolvency; joint ventures; foreign investment; intellectual property; communications; corporate advice; anti-trust; commercial law.

BLAKE LAPTHORN

Holbrook House, 14 Great Queen Street, London, WC2B 5DG
Tel: (020) 7430 1709 **Fax:** (020) 7831 4441 **DX:** 37957 Kingsway
Email: post@blakelapthorn.co.uk

New Court, 1 Barnes Wallis Road, Segensworth, Fareham, PO15 5UA
Tel: (01489) 579990 **Fax:** (01489) 579126 **DX:** 132290 Fareham 5

Harbour Court, Compass Road, North Harbour, Portsmouth, PO6 4ST
Tel: (023) 9222 1122 **Fax:** (023) 9222 1123 **DX:** 124490 Portsmouth 9

Kings Court, 21 Brunswick Place, Southampton, SO15 2AQ
Tel: (023) 8063 1823 **Fax:** (023) 8022 6294 **DX:** 38538 Southampton

Managing Partner	Walter Cha
Senior Partner	David Russell
Number of partners	47
Assistant solicitors	66
Other fee-earners	68

AREAS OF PRACTICE

Property 32%
Commercial 30%
Litigation 30%
Private Client 8%

CONTACTS

Aviation ....Chris McClure
Banking ....Kathryn Shimmin
Charities ....Elizabeth Davis
Clinical Negligence ....Alison McClure
Company/Commercial ....Mark Shepherd
Construction ....Peter Barber
Debt Collection ....Sadak Miah
Education ....Sarah Palmer
Employment ....Max Craft
Environment ....David Rayner
Insolvency & Business Rescue ....Nicholas Keitley
Intellectual Property ....Chris McClure
IT ....Chris McClure
Licensing ....Phil Crier
Litigation ....Stephen Murfitt
Pensions ....Maria Riccio
Personal Injury ....Alison McClure
Planning ....Tim Driver
Private Client ....David Russell
Property (Commercial) ....Carey Blake
Property (Residential) ....Debbie Castle
Regulatory ....Bradley Albuery
Tax ....Niall Murphy

Blake Lapthorn
solicitors

THE FIRM: Established in 1869, and currently with almost 50 partners, 134 solicitors and executives and a total of 410 staff, Blake Lapthorn is one of the largest law firms based in the south of England. With a good proportion of its senior staff having joined the firm from major city law firms, Blake Lapthorn prides itself on being able to offer its clients a level of service comparable to most city-based firms. The firm acts for a wide variety of clients, both commercial and private. The recent growth in its commercial client base has attracted clients nationally and internationally. The firm also acts for many major commercial household names, as well as for a number of local authorities, educational establishments, government agencies and various other public bodies.

PRINCIPAL AREAS OF WORK:
Commercial: The firm has developed a high reputation for its corporate finance work in MBOs, MBIs, acquisitions, disposals and mergers as well as general advice to public and private companies. Within the firm there are specialist lawyers dealing with employment, pensions, intellectual property, IT, insolvency and corporate re-organisations, banking, aviation and tax. In addition, Blake Lapthorn has one of the country's leading licensing practices and a regulatory unit that handles all aspects of regulatory law for commercial clients.
Property: The firm acts for a number of household names in connection with their property portfolios and undertakes a wide variety of property work including major office, retail and leisure developments. The property team is supported by highly expert environmental and planning teams. There is also a large residential conveyancing team servicing private clients, banks and building societies.
Litigation: The firm acts as a resolver of disputes, whether by litigation, arbitration, mediation or negotiation. Specialist areas of expertise include all aspects of construction, engineering and property disputes, general contractual disputes, information technology and computer law, environmental law, foreign export insurance, professional negligence, and professional disciplinary tribunals. The firm also has a recognised specialism in personal injury and medical negligence work and a high-volume debt recovery team.
Private Client: The firm offers its clients the full range of private client advice including inheritance and tax planning, wills and probate, matrimonial and family, including a particular specialism in handling cases involving children. It also has a niche expertise in handling the sale and purchase of properties in France.

INTERNATIONAL: The firm has an associated office in Brussels.

RECRUITMENT: The breadth of the firm's business offers both trainees and qualified lawyers all the challenges and opportunities of a big City firm, yet with all the advantages of a regional firm.

BLANDY & BLANDY

1 Friar St, Reading, RG1 1DA
Tel: (0118) 958 7111 **Fax:** (0118) 958 3032 **DX:** 4008 Reading
Email: law@blandy.co.uk **Website:** www.blandy.co.uk

Senior Partner	Richard Griffiths
Number of partners	14
Assistant solicitors	13
Other fee-earners	9

AREAS OF PRACTICE

Corporate & Commercial 23%
Family 19%
Private Client 19%
Residential Property 16%
Litigation 14%
Commercial Property 9%

THE FIRM: Founded in 1733, Blandy & Blandy is the oldest established legal practice in Reading. Despite its longevity, the firm is modern and progressive in outlook, whilst remaining friendly and approachable. The firm's work is organised into specialist departments providing a full range of legal services to both business and individual clients.

PRINCIPAL AREAS OF WORK:
Commercial: The firm's commercial services are organised under the umbrella of the commercial group. Emphasis is placed on providing a practical and pro-active service and clients can expect a high degree of partner involvement.
Corporate & Commercial: The department deals with a wide range of corporate and other non-contentious commercial work and has particular expertise in the area of mergers and acquisitions and other corporate transactional work, as well as in IT and intellectual property law.

Employment: All aspects of employment law, both contentious and non-contentious, are dealt with. One of the partners sits as a part-time chairman of employment tribunals and the firm is accordingly well placed to advise on industrial disputes and TUPE issues.
Litigation: The firm has built a particularly strong reputation for litigation. Particular specialisms have been developed in relation to insurance litigation and betting, gaming and liquor licensing, and the department is regularly involved in heavy licensing work. A computerised debt collection service is offered and agency work is undertaken.
Commercial Property: All aspects of commercial conveyancing work are handled including landlord and tenant, development and planning.
Private Client: The firm has an enviable reputation for its private client work and its clients range from private individuals and commercial entrepreneurs to large landed estates.
Trusts, Probate & Tax Planning: The department specialises in all aspects of trusts and tax planning work, including the preparation of wills and has a substantial probate practice. The firm has particular expertise in handling the administration of large (including landed) estates.
Conveyancing: The department's workload includes estate development, planning matters, work for housing associations as well as routine residential conveyancing.
Family: The firm has an extensive and highly regarded matrimonial and family law practice. The firm is able to offer the services of trained mediators and has expertise in child-care and child support work. The firm's StepAhead initiative offers a 'one-stop' legal advice, mediation and counselling service.
Civil Litigation: A full range of civil litigation work is dealt with including personal injury claims, probate litigation and bankruptcy. The firm holds a Legal Aid franchise and Legal Aid or conditional fee arrangements are available in appropriate cases.

CONTACTS

Child Care	Brenda Long
Commercial Property	Jane Gunnell
Corporate & Commercial	Philip Tranter
Employment	Richard Griffiths
Family	Andrew Don
Intellectual Property	Philip Tranter
Licensing	Susan Dowling
Litigation	Jacques Smith
Personal Injury	Philip D'Arcy
Pharmaceutical & Healthcare	Kathryn Minter
Private Client	Graham Benwell
Residential Property	Nicholas Blandy

B

BLYTHE LIGGINS

Edmund House, Rugby Road, Leamington Spa, CV32 6EL **Tel:** (01926) 831231 **Fax:** (01926) 831331 **DX:** 11872 Leamington Spa **Email:** blythe-liggins.co.uk **Website:** www.blytheliggins.co.uk **Ptnrs:** 9 **Asst solrs:** 3 **Other fee-earners:** 12

B. M. NYMAN & CO

181 Creighton Avenue, London, N2 9BN **Tel:** (020) 8365 3060 **Fax:** (020) 8883 5151 **Email:** bernie.nyman@iname.com **Ptnrs:** 1

BOBBETTS MACKAN

17 Berkeley Square, Clifton, Bristol, BS8 1HB
Tel: (0117) 929 9001 **Fax:** (0117) 922 5697 **DX:** 37011 Clifton (Bristol)
Email: mail@bobbettsmackan.co.uk

THE FIRM: Committed to providing quality, independent, efficient and cost-effective legal services. Provides a contemporary service based upon an established reputation. Organised in specialist teams, it aims to ensure that the service offered meets the clients' needs, be they 'lay clients' or referral and agency work for the profession. Advocacy services, including higher courts, are available. Member of LawGroup UK, an independent grouping of quality law firms subject to an annual and external quality audit. The firm undertakes franchised and contracted legal aid work.

PRINCIPAL AREAS OF WORK: Civil litigation, including personal injury, employment, medical and professional negligence with expertise in judicial review and public law. Education and social welfare law, family and childcare including divorce, complex financial matters and children. Criminal defence including motoring matters, fraud and courts martial. Real property including conveyancing.
Agency Work: Civil litigation; criminal defence; family and childcare.

Managing Partner	Anthony Miles
Senior Partner	Anthony Miles
Number of partners	5
Assistant solicitors	14
Other fee-earners	18

AREAS OF PRACTICE

Civil Litigation	35%
Matrimonial, Care, Children	20%
Criminal Defence	35%
Non-contentious	10%

CONTACTS

Criminal Defence	Anthony Miles
Employment	Kevin Wood
Family & Childcare	Sally Mitchell
Non-contentious	Tim Platel
Personal Injury	Jo Hillman

BOGUE AND MCNULTY

3 Carlisle Gardens, Belfast, BT14 6AT **Tel:** (028) 9035 1502 **Fax:** (028) 90742185

BOLT BURDON

16 Theberton Street, Islington, London, N1 0QX **Tel:** (020) 7288 4700 **Fax:** (020) 7288 4701 **DX:** 122237 Upper Islington
Email: boltburdon@boltburdon.co.uk **Website:** www.boltburdon.co.uk **Ptnrs:** 6 **Asst solrs:** 20 **Other fee-earners:** 20

BONAR MACKENZIE WS

9 Hill Street, Edinburgh, EH2 3JT
Tel: (0131) 225 8371 **Fax:** (0131) 225 2048/240 0749 **DX:** 7 Edinburgh
Email: law@bonarmac.co.uk **Website:** www.bonarmac.co.uk

Senior Partner	David Flint
Number of partners	9
Assistant solicitors	4
Other fee-earners	8

CONTACTS

Commercial Conveyancing & Business Law ....David Jennings
Debt Recovery & General Litigation ....David Flint
Estate Agency & Residential Conveyancing ....Stephen Murray
Matrimonial & Employment ..Lisa Girdwood
Wills & Trust ....Alistair Bowman

THE FIRM: Bonar Mackenzie has long enjoyed a reputation for providing a very high level of personal attention from partners and associates to their clients. As part of the firm's commitment to enhancing their level of client service, heavy investment is now being undertaken in IT, including the installation of case management and extranet services to provide clients with reports and information when convenient to them. This is seen as part of the added value that the firm strives to provide to all clients. Bonar Mackenzie has for many years been highly regarded for its expertise and efficiency in debt recovery and repossessions, having acted for various banks and building societies. In recent years, the firm has increased its profile in family law. The firm continues to provide a full range of legal services, including residential property, commercial conveyancing and business law, and is committed to client service in all areas. Enquiries from prospective clients are welcomed. The initial meeting is free and an estimate of costs is provided.

B

BOND PEARCE

Bristol Bridge House, Redcliff Street, Bristol, BS1 6BJ
Tel: (0117) 929 9197 **Fax:** (0117) 929 9198 **DX:** 200561 Bristol Temple Meads
Email: info@bondpearce.com **Website:** www.bondpearce.com

Marsh House, 11 Marsh House, Bristol, BS99 7BB
Tel: (0117) 929 9197 **Fax:** (0117) 926 2403 **DX:** 7851 Bristol

Darwin House, Southernhay Gardens, Exeter, EX1 1LA
Tel: (01392) 211185 **Fax:** (01392) 435543 **DX:** 8321 Exeter

1 City Square, Leeds, LS1 2ES
Tel: (0113) 300 2026 **Fax:** (0113) 300 2020

10 Fenchurch Avenue, London, EC3M 5BN
Tel: (020) 7663 5607 **Fax:** (020) 7663 5978

Ballard House, West Hoe Road, Plymouth, PL1 3AE
Tel: (01752) 266633 **Fax:** (01752) 225350 **DX:** 8251 Plymouth

Town Quay House, 7 Town Quay, Southampton, SO14 2PT
Tel: (023) 8063 2211 **Fax:** (023) 8022 2480 **DX:** 2005 Southampton

Senior Partner	Richard Challands
Managing Partner	Simon Richardson
Number of partners	64
Assistant solicitors	137
Other fee-earners	88

AREAS OF PRACTICE

Property 25%
Commercial, Banking & Insolvency 19%
Insurance 18%
Litigation 18%
Personal Injury & Private Client 12%
Employment 8%

CONTACTS

Commercial ....Nick Page
Compulsory Purchase & Local Government ....Emrys Parry
Construction ....Christine Hanley
Corporate Finance ....Simon Hewes
Corporate Recovery & Banking ....Victor Tettmar
Employment ....Nikki Duncan
Food Safety & Consumer Protection ....Michael Parrott
Health & Safety ....Jon Cooper
Insurance & Professional Indemnity ....Erik Salomonsen
IP & IT ....Julian Hamblin
International ....Nick Page
Licencing, Leisure & Gambling ....Tim Davies
Dispute Resolution ....Tony Askham
Mediation & ADR ....Andrew Tobey
Personal Injury ....Mark Thompson
Private Client ....Jonathan Nicholson
Marine & Shipping ....Nicholas Horton
Property, Planning & Environment ....Luke Gabb
Technology & E-commerce ......Nigel Williams
Transport ....Peter Woodhouse

THE FIRM: Bond Pearce's merger in July 2001 with Bristol based Cartwrights consolidated its position as one of the UK's leading law firms and one of the fastest growing. Its sustained growth is based on strong client relationships and a national reputation for excellence. Commercially aware, progressive and innovative, Bond Pearce has the resources to deliver real expertise with people you will want to do business with – plain speaking, direct and open, clear about fees and fast on their feet. Advising commercial and institutional clients throughout the UK, the firm's legal teams work closely with clients to deliver fast and effective business solutions. Recognising that commercial clients need much more than just legal advice, Bond Pearce provides a level of service, commitment and practical understanding one would expect from an in house legal team. The firm's clients include a number of FTSE 100 companies, major UK leisure and brewery companies, supermarket chains, retailers, manufacturers, banks, financiers and insurance companies. Sectors in which the firm is highly regarded include construction, education, energy, finance, insurance, IT and ecommerce, leisure, property, retail, transport, waste and the public sector. The firm's services are provided within the framework of modern office facilities and the latest technology.

PRINCIPAL AREAS OF WORK:

Banking & Corporate Recovery: This team, including two licensed insolvency practitioners, has established a national reputation acting for financial institutions, on M&A work as well as corporate recovery.

Commercial: This work is handled by a specialist team advising on the full spectrum of commercial agreements, often with an international element, which includes advice on intellectual property rights, trade marks, research and development agreements, licensing, joint ventures and competition law. The team advises on all forms of brand protection and identity and IP disputes.

Corporate: The corporate team has built its reputation acting for management teams, lending institutions and investors in MBOs, MBIs, IBIs, acquisitions, disposals and mergers.

Commercial Property: Bond Pearce undertakes a variety of property work, especially retail, commercial and industrial park developments, dealing with a wide range of investment, development, property litigation, project management, construction and H&S issues. A significant profile in the public sector arises from its work for Government departments on regional and national projects, and Bond Pearce's strong planning and environmental unit remains at the forefront of work relating to renewable energy and waste management. The firm is equally well known for its town centre regeneration, compulsory purchase expertise and port development work. Other specialisms include licensed premises and the education and transport sectors.

Dispute Resolution: Bond Pearce is nationally regarded for its work in the fields of professional indemnity, insurance, personal injury, corporate recovery, construction, property, employment, insolvency, transport, intellectual property and e-commerce. The firm also acts for national and local retailers, advising in areas such as customer complaints, consumer credit, security issues, employment matters, food law, licensing, trading standards and Sunday trading. Recent cases include a number of cross border matters and actions in the European Court of Justice. Bond Pearce accepts all types of agency work and is at the forefront of Alternative Dispute Resolution with trained and experienced mediators. A major provider of ADR experience to others, Bond Pearce acts regularly at mediations on behalf of clients.

Employment: With in-house advocacy and mediation experts, this team has a strong national practice and provides a complete service to employers combining legal, human resources and industrial relations skills in a seamless package supplemented by practical training and HR consultancy services.

Leisure & Licensing: A complete nationwide and EU-wide service to clients operating in the food and drink retailing, licensed trade, bingo, casino, cinema and leisure sectors, including many high street names. Further specialisation is also available in food hygiene, packaging and labelling matters.

INTERNATIONAL: Bond Pearce continues to generate an increasing volume of cross-border work through overseas clients and contacts particularly in Europe, the USA, the Far East and Australia. It is a member of international organisations such as Euro Link for Lawyers.

B

BOODLE HATFIELD

61 Brook Street, London, W1K 4BL
Tel: (020) 7629 7411 **Fax:** (020) 7629 2621 **DX:** 53 CHANCERY LANE
Email: law@boodlehatfield.com **Website:** www.boodlehatfield.com

6 Worcester Street, Oxford, OX1 2BX
Tel: (01865) 790744 **Fax:** (01865) 798764 **DX:** 4329 OXFORD 1
Email: law@boodlehatfield.com

Senior Partner	Richard Moyse
Managing Partner	Chris Putt
Number of partners	33
Assistant solicitors	37
Other fee-earners	16

AREAS OF PRACTICE

Property	42%
Corporate & Employment	23%
Tax & Financial Planning	23%
Litigation	12%

CONTACTS

Anglo-German Service	Chris Putt
Banking	Nigel Stone
Charities	Andrew Farley (London)
	Nigel Roots (Oxford)
Commercial	Andrew Drake
Commercial Litigation	Simon Fitzpatrick
Commercial Property	
	Richard Maughan (London)
	Michael Wood (Oxford)
Contentious Trust & Probate	Alison Meek
Corporate & Property Tax	Sara Maccallum
Corporate Finance/M&A	Jonathan Brooks
Employment	Russell Brimelow
Environment	Hugh Devas
Family	Michael Tulloch
	Vivien Gifford (London)
	Barbara Simpson (Oxford)
IT/E-commerce	Andrew Drake
	Jonathan Brooks
Partnership	Andrew Drake
Personal Tax	David Way (London)
	Alan Ciechan (Oxford)
Private Client, Trusts	David Way (London)
	Sue Laing (Oxford)
Private Equity	Chris Putt
	Nigel Stone
Property Litigation	Michael Tulloch
Residential Property	Jane Littlejohn (London)
	Richard Bell (Oxford)
Town & Country Planning	
	Lucy Slater
	Deborah Ceadel (Oxford)

THE FIRM: Boodle Hatfield is a leading central London practice, with a fast-growing second office in Oxford. Known originally for representing wealthy individuals and landed estates, and still outstanding in those fields, it now acts for a wide, international corporate, commercial and private client base. The firm aims to combine technical excellence with genuinely personal service and to provide practical, cost-effective advice. Services are tailored to the needs and methods of each client, who can rely upon the close, continuing involvement of partners with broad experience as well as specialist knowledge. Clients have commended the firm's high standard of advice, efficiency, commitment and ability to 'think outside the box'. The partnership has grown rapidly in recent years as the firm has invested in its core business and developed complementary skills. Several cross-departmental groups have been created. The private capital group, for example, assists high net worth individuals and entrepreneurs to complete their transactions in tax-efficient ways. Other groups specialise in agrochemicals, Anglo-German services, employment law, IT and e-commerce and inward investment.

PRINCIPAL AREAS OF WORK:

Property: The highly-rated property department is involved in major town centre and out-of-town office, retail and leisure developments and in large urban estate transactions with associated landlord and tenant matters, including leasehold reform issues. It acts for developers, owners, occupiers, funders and UK-based and international corporate and private investors. Skills include property finance and secured lending, property taxes, town and country planning, construction and environmental law and, especially in Oxford, agricultural, university and college property. Sector specialisations include golf clubs, petrol filling stations and primary health care centres.

Tax & Financial Planning: The department is a leader in its field, domestically and internationally, and handles tax planning for large complex estates, private companies, high net worth individuals and families, trustees, executors and charities. It advises on inheritance, capital gains and income tax planning, wills and probate, domicile and residence issues, VAT, property and corporate taxes, the establishment of UK and overseas trusts, and on trust and probate disputes.

Corporate: The expanding corporate department acts for entrepreneurs, private and public companies, partnerships and overseas businesses investing in the UK, with many clients in IT-related sectors. It advises on mergers and acquisitions, MBOs and private equity transactions, joint ventures, banking transactions (especially property-related), listings and the issue of securities, and commercial agreements. The employment group has built an excellent reputation and acts both for major multinationals and high profile individuals.

Continued overleaf

Litigation: The department is active in a broad range of commercial disputes and has substantial, well-regarded expertise in property litigation, employment and agrochemicals. Its established and growing matrimonial and family law practice has notable international experience, including child abduction cases.

INTERNATIONAL: Much of the firm's work is international, arising in particular from the USA, Germany, France, the Middle East and the Far East.

RECRUITMENT: The firm has openings for assistant solicitors in each department. Four or five trainees are recruited each year; some spend six months on secondment to ICI. Application forms are available from Christine Jones.

BOODLE
HATFIELD

BOYDS

Thistle House, 146 West Regent Street, Glasgow, G2 2RZ
Tel: (0141) 221 8251 **Fax:** (0141) 226 4799 **DX:** 120 Glasgow
Email: mail@boydslaw.com **Website:** www.boydslaw.com

5 Commercial Street, Edinburgh, EH6 6JA
Tel: (0131) 554 8251 **Fax:** (0131) 555 0570 **DX:** 550864 Leith

Managing Partner	Robert Gall
Senior Partner	David Boyce
Number of partners	13
Assistant solicitors	16
Other fee-earners	5

AREAS OF PRACTICE

Commercial Property	42%
Litigation	22%
Corporate/Commercial	21%
Insolvency	10%
Private Client	5%

CONTACTS

Commercial Property	David Boyce
Corporate	Calum Jones
Insolvency	Calum Jones
IT & IP Law	Emily Wiewiorka
Litigation	Denise Loney
Private Client	Robert Weir

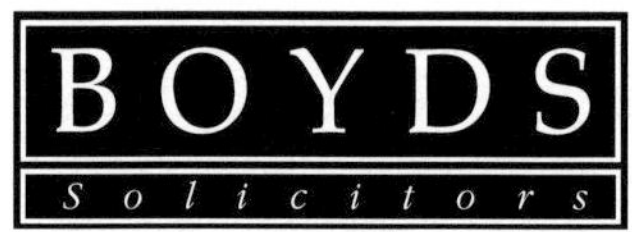

THE FIRM: Boyds is a long established medium-sized law firm with offices in both Glasgow and Edinburgh and is at the centre of the Scottish commercial market. It handles a wide range of UK work, having lawyers qualified in both Scottish and English law. Additionally, as a member of Law Exchange International, Boyds handles international work. The firm prides itself on its approachable, dynamic and progressive attitude to business and was one of the first Scottish legal firms to be accredited with Investors in People. In addition Boyds is the only legal firm authorised by Scotland the Brand, which promotes the highest quality Scottish products and services. Boyds' commitment to training and development ensures the skills of its people are constantly developed to retain the firm's competitive edge. Clients benefit from the highest quality service and the firm's IT system ensures maximum efficiency throughout the business.

PRINCIPAL AREAS OF WORK:
Commercial Property: Work handled includes commercial leases; purchases and sales; development and management work; security work.
Corporate: The firm handles mergers and acquisitions; buy-outs; buy-ins; corporate finance; commercial contracts; insolvency advice; competition law advice; PFI and PPP.
Litigation: Work includes employment; construction disputes; landlord and tenant disputes; repossession work; general contractual disputes; debt recovery; matrimonial; environmental law.
IT Law & IP Law: Work handled includes contractual issues; copyright; design disputes; advice on the Internet; e-commerce.
Private Client: Work includes house purchase and sales, with relevant mortgage and policy advice.

CLIENTELE: Boyds' client base extends from entrepreneurs and those in fast growing sectors through to established medium-sized companies, as well as substantial companies which are household names and plcs. The firm is committed to getting close to their clients, to being in tune with them, and to understanding what is and is not important to them so that it can give them tailored, focused advice.

RECRUITMENT: The practice continues to grow and is still looking to recruit lawyers in all disciplines who are commercially focused.

BOYES TURNER

Abbots House, Abbey Street, Reading, RG1 3BD
Tel: (0118) 959 7711 **Fax:** (0118) 957 3257 **DX:** 54741 Reading 2
Email: mail@boyesturner.com/mail@boyesturnerlegal.co.uk
Website: www.boyesturner.com/www.boyesturnerlegal.co.uk

Senior Partner	Peter Daniel
Chief Executive	Andrew Chalkley
Number of partners	17
Assistant solicitors	17
Other fee-earners	16

AREAS OF PRACTICE

Corporate/Commercial (inc. Corporate Recovery)	25%
Commercial Property & Planning	20%
Dispute Resolution (inc. Employment)	20%
Clinical Negligence/Personal Injury	20%
Private Client	10%
Family	5%

CONTACTS

Banking & Insolvency	Christopher Branson
Clinical Negligence	Susan Brown
	Adrian Desmond
Commercial	William Gornall-King
Corporate	Roy Butler
Debt Recovery	Elaine Price
Dispute Resolution	Gary Parkinson
	Michael Robinson
Employment	Michael Farrier
Family	Anthony Roe
Human Resources	Helen Barnett
Intellectual Property/IT	William Gornall-King
Partnership Secretary	John Brunnen
Personal Injury	Kim Smerdon
Private Client	Ashley Wilkin
Property	Mark Appleton
	Peter Daniel
	Simon Doyle
Town & Country Planning	Anthony Cooley

THE FIRM: Boyes Turner is a leading law firm in the Thames Valley, successfully providing high quality commercial and individual client services. All of its lawyers specialise in their respective areas of law – from partners to legal executives – enabling the firm to offer clients a high degree of expertise and a rare depth of support and experience. The firm has achieved wide respect in commercial property, dispute resolution, employment, intellectual property, corporate recovery and clinical negligence, working in close contact with clients to achieve the right solution for them. In October 2000 the firm changed its name from Boyes Turner & Burrows to Boyes Turner. The change marked the re-branding and re-focusing of the practice and the development of a strategy of expansion and repositioning to ensure the firm is well placed to service the growing and broader needs of the market and its existing client base. In order to meet the firm's actual and planned growth, it has taken new premises in a prestigious Reading town centre location in March 2001.

PRINCIPAL AREAS OF WORK:

Banking & Corporate Recovery: Headed by an LIP, the firm acts for all the major insolvency practices as well as for clearing banks and other financial institutions in both corporate and personal insolvency and securities work.

Corporate: Business formations, acquisitions and disposals, partnerships and joint ventures, inward investment, and corporate restructuring.

Commercial: The firm acts for many substantial businesses including UK subsidiaries of multinationals. Advice includes general business law, commercial and trading agreements, including distribution and licensing, competition law, EU issues and company secretarial work.

Debt Recovery: A fully computerised system providing competitive rates and handling bulk recoveries for trading companies and financial institutions.

Employment: Preparation of employment contracts, advice on disciplinary issues, industrial tribunal representation, restraint of trade, wrongful dismissal, and sex and race discrimination.

Family: Divorce and separation, financial provision, children, emergency procedures, education (members of SFLA).

Intellectual Property: Ownership and exploitation of IPR, licensing, disputes, computer contracts (software and hardware), product liability. Clients include engineering, electronics and computer companies as well as Internet and software houses.

Litigation: Contract disputes, shareholder and partnership disputes, negligence claims, property disputes, mortgage repossessions, landlord and tenant. Agency work undertaken.

Clinical Negligence: A specialist team acts exclusively for the victims of medical accidents (AVMA and Law Society referral solicitors, members of APIL).

Personal Injury: RTAs; work related injuries, CICB/A, Personal Injury Panel; SIA referral panel and Headway, maximum severity claims. (Members of APIL and Accident Line).

Private Client: Wills, trusts, probate, personal tax planning and residential conveyancing.

Property: Sales and leases of commercial property, commercial and residential development projects, commercial lending, landlord and tenant.

Planning: Planning advice for property development projects as well as for appeals and planning enforcement.

CLIENTELE: Its clients in the Thames Valley and, increasingly, in London, range from multinationals to start-ups and growing businesses, many in the hi-tech sector. These include manufacturers and distributors of computers and peripherals, software houses and Internet companies. Among the firm's other clients are white goods manufacturers, engineering companies and service organisations. Private client work continues to form an important part of the practice.

RECRUITMENT: The targeted recruitment of high quality specialist lawyers in the growth areas of the practice. Four new property lawyers have joined the property group, an additional employment lawyer and two additional lawyers for the technology and commerce group further underline the strategy of growth. An additional lawyer has also been added to each of the corporate, corporate recovery and family groups, all these appointments were as a result of increased work within these groups.

B P COLLINS

Collins House, 32-38 Station Rd, Gerrards Cross, SL9 8EL **Tel:** (01753) 889995 **Fax:** (01753) 889851 **DX:** 40256 Gerrards Cross **Email:** enquiries@bpcollins.co.uk **Website:** www.bpcollins.co.uk **Ptnrs:** 16 **Asst solrs:** 14 **Other fee-earners:** 14

BRABNERS

1 Dale St, Liverpool, L2 2ET
Tel: (0151) 600 3000 **Fax:** (0151) 227 3185 **DX:** 14118 Liverpool
Email: tony.harper@brabners.com **Website:** www.brabners.com

7-8 Chapel Street, Preston, PR1 8AN
Tel: (01772) 823921 **Fax:** (01772) 201918 **DX:** 17118 Preston
Email: chris.scott@brabners1.com

Managing Partner	Michael Brabner
Number of partners	28
Assistant solicitors	37
Other fee-earners	37

AREAS OF PRACTICE

Property	29%
Corporate	27%
Dispute Resolution	19%
Private Client	18%
Employment	7%

CONTACTS

Agency	Mark Manley
	Amanda Webster
Banking & Finance	Tony Harper
Charities	Stephen Brodie
Commercial/IP	Terry Montague
Construction	Daniel Brawn
Corporate	Denise Walker
Debt Recovery	Jacqui Lloyd
Defamation	Mark Manley
Dispute Resolution	Mark Manley
	Amanda Webster
Employment	Andrew Cross
Environmental & Planning	Jeff Gillbanks
Housing Associations	Valerie Braide
Insolvency	Denise Walker
IT/New Media	Nicholas White
Matrimonial	Helen Richardson
Private Client & Wealth Protection	Mark Feeny
	George Erdozain
Property	Sandy Chapple Gill
	Ross Shine

THE FIRM: Brabners is a leading corporate and commercial law firm serving the North West. Its business focus is on providing the full range of legal services to the OMB/SME sector; specialised services to the plc and larger corporate; private client services to business owners and other high net worth individuals. The firm's client base includes plcs, public sector bodies, banks and a wide range of commercial, corporate and professional businesses. Brabners has expanded by 50% in the last year enabling it to provide a greater range of services and increased strength in depth. Brabner's objective is to use its experience to provide creative solutions to clients' problems with the emphasis on results, service delivery and value for money.

PRINCIPAL AREAS OF WORK:
Corporate: The firm is highly regarded for its corporate work. Commercial work includes a considerable growth of activity in IP and IT particularly for the computer games software and multi-media markets.
Property: The property team is one of the largest in the North West and has the resources and expertise to handle any type and size of commercial property work. The team is particularly experienced in the retail sector operating nationally for a number of clients. The social housing team enjoys a national reputation and the team is also strong on property development and finance work.
Litigation & Dispute Resolution: The department's work includes contractual disputes; construction litigation; intellectual property actions; landlord and tenant; competition law. The team is nationally recognised for its media and defamation work (Lloyds panel) and for its environmental protestor litigation. The team conducts mediations and is accredited by ADR and CEDR.
Employment: The team is one of the largest specialist departments in the North West and acts primarily for employers on the full spectrum of contentious and non-contentious employment issues.
Private Client/Charities: This team works closely with the firm's OMB/SME clients to provide tax planning, trust administration, matrimonial, probate and conveyancing services to an impressive base of high net worth clients. The firm also has an enviable reputation in the area of charity law.

INTERNATIONAL: Brabners is an active participant in Eurolegal and The Association of European Lawyers providing representation in 83 offices in 35 countries throughout Europe and elsewhere overseas.

RECRUITMENT: Recruiting seven trainee solicitors annually, the firm is committed to a comprehensive personnel development programme for all staff.

BRABY & WALLER (DEBT RECOVERY DIVISION OF IRWIN MITCHELL SOLICITORS)

150 Holborn, London, EC1N 2NS
Tel: (020) 7404 3600 **Fax:** (020) 7404 0208 **DX:** 87 Ch.Ln.
Email: braby&waller@irwinmitchell.co.uk **Website:** www.imonline.co.uk

Managing Partner	Howard Culley
Senior Partner	Michael Napier
Number of partners	5
Assistant solicitors	10
Other fee-earners	11

THE FIRM: Braby & Waller was founded in the 19th century and developed as a City of London commercial practice with particularly close connections to the building materials, manufacturing, finance and supply industries. The firm merged with Irwin Mitchell (see separate entry) in May 1998. The well known Braby & Waller name has been retained for the merged recovery and credit control services.

PRINCIPAL AREAS OF WORK: Debt recovery, nationally and internationally; credit control and insolvency. There is a particular emphasis on trade, commercial and professional debt recovery.
Debt Recovery: Braby & Waller has historically been one of the best known and highly regarded firms in London and the South East for commercial debt recovery and credit control services. The merger with Irwin Mitchell has enhanced the delivery of these services through added resource and the firm's national presence. The senior managers in the debt recovery department have over 150 years combined experience in the field. The services provided include advice and training in pre-legal credit control, trading terms and credit management. The department is fully integrated with Irwin Mitchell's insolvency practice. The firm acts for major national and international manufacturers, suppliers, distributors, communication providers, lenders and professional firms.

BRACHER RAWLINS

180 Fleet Street, London, EC4A 2HG
Tel: (020) 7404 9400 **Fax:** (020) 7404 9401 **DX:** LDE 168
Email: info@bracherrawlins.co.uk **Website:** www.bracherrawlins.co.uk

Senior Partner	Alan Bracher
Number of partners	6
Assistant solicitors	5
Other fee-earners	2

AREAS OF PRACTICE

Corporate/Commercial	40%
Litigation	35%
Property	15%
Employment	10%

CONTACTS

Corporate/Commercial	Alan Bracher
Litigation	Simon Rawlins
Property	John Gaymer
Employment	John Hayes

THE FIRM: Founded in April 1994, Bracher Rawlins is a commercial law practice based in the City. The firm is dedicated to servicing the needs of its clients in the business community.

PRINCIPAL AREAS OF WORK:

Corporate/Commercial: All areas of company and commercial matters are undertaken for both public and private companies and individuals.

Litigation: The firm handles commercial litigation, insolvency and debt collection, professional negligence, medical negligence, auctioneering law and defamation.

Property: Work includes retail, office and industrial property, development, investment/management and residential property.

Employment: The firm deals with all aspects of contentious and non-contentious employment law for both employers and employees.

B

BRACHERS

Somerfield House, 59 London Road, Maidstone, ME16 8JH
Tel: (01622) 690691 **Fax:** (01622) 681430 **DX:** 4806 Maidstone 1
Email: name@brachers.co.uk **Website:** www.brachers.co.uk

Managing Partner	Geoffrey Dearing
Number of partners	21
Assistant solicitors	30
Other fee-earners	44

CONTACTS

Company/Commercial	Stuart Butler-Gallie
Debt Collection & Insolvency	John Craig
Litigation	John Sheath
Private Client	Simon Palmer
Property	Geoffrey Burr
Employment	Alan Hannah

THE FIRM: Brachers is a major regional firm with an established city office at 12 New Fetter Lane, London, EC4.

PRINCIPAL AREAS OF WORK: The firm has a powerful commercial practice, accounting for 85% of its work, accompanied by a private client practice closely focused on high net worth individuals. From its Kent base, the firm is capitalising on its proximity both to Europe and the City of London. Attraction of major European work including commercial contract, ECJ litigation, and pan-European post invoice credit management has led to the recruitment of French qualified legal staff. The London office has developed a large employment practice and also provides the firm's connection to the City in corporate finance and commercial work. The firm has grown strong niche areas of work and also strength in a number of industry sectors. Its prominence in the healthcare sector is reflected in NHS Litigation Panel appointment, one of 14 firms nationally, and its 15 strong client list of NHS Trusts and Authorities. A major team works under contract with legal expenses insurers, and debt recovery and insolvency services are delivered by the largest single office operation in the South East. The well established private client department provides tax planning and trust work for directors and key executives and for the landed sector.

BRECHIN TINDAL OATTS

48 St. Vincent Street, Glasgow, G2 5HS
Tel: (0141) 221 8012 **Fax:** (0141) 221 7803 **DX:** GW96
Email: lawyers@bto.co.uk **Website:** www.bto.co.uk

13 Great Stuart Street, Edinburgh, EH3 7TP
Tel: (0131) 220 2777 **Fax:** (0131) 220 0010 **DX:** ED77
Email: lawyers@bto.co.uk

Managing Partner	William Young
Number of partners	15
Assistant solicitors	23
Other fee-earners	26

CONTACTS

Commercial Property	Alan Borthwick
Corporate	Jeremy Glen
Employment Law Consultancy	Caroline Carr
Insurers' Representation Unit	Louise Hay
Intellectual Property Consultancy	Lisa Forsythe
Litigation	William Speirs
Social Housing Unit	Karen Brodie

BRECHIN TINDAL OATTS

THE FIRM: Brechin Tindal Oatts advises on a range of commercial, corporate and personal matters as well as insurance and commercial litigation. Specialised areas of law are served by niche units, such as the employment law consultancy, intellectual property consultancy, insurers' representation unit and social housing unit, each of which draws on knowledge and experience available in other areas of the firm. Brechin Tindal Oatts consistently aims to provide timely and intuitive advice and to ensure that at all times its solicitors are talking the same language as its clients.

BREMNER SONS & CORLETT
1 Crosshall Street, Liverpool, L1 6DH **Tel:** (0151) 227 1301 **Fax:** (0151) 227 1300 **DX:** 14119 Liverpool 1 **Email:** post@bsclaw.co.uk **Website:** www.bscbw.co.uk **Ptnrs:** 9 **Asst solrs:** 3 **Other fee-earners:** 8

BRENDAN KEARNEY KELLY & CO
4 Clarendon Street, Derry, BT48 7EX **Tel:** (028) 71266935 **Fax:** (028) 7137 1845 **Ptnrs:** 2 **Asst solrs:** 3 **Other fee-earners:** 1

BRETHERTON PRICE ELGOODS

St James's House, St James' Square, Cheltenham, GL50 3PR
Tel: (01242) 224433 **Fax:** (01242) 574285 **DX:** 141660 Cheltenham 11
Email: bpe@bpe.co.uk **Website:** www.bpe.co.uk

Managing Partner	Malcolm Price
Senior Partner	David Oldham
Number of partners	18
Assistant solicitors	10
Other fee-earners	41

AREAS OF PRACTICE

Lender Services 32%
Commercial Property 19%
Corporate Finance 15%
Personal Injury 14%
Commercial Litigation 9%
Residential Sales & Purchases 9%
Employment 2%

CONTACTS

Commercial Litigation ....Philip Radford
Commercial Property ....Richard Handley
Construction ....John Beevor
Corporate/Corporate Finance
..........John Workman
..........Richard Bretherton
Employment ....Matthew Jenkin
Lender Services ....David Oldham
Personal Injury ....Mark Ovington
Residential Sales & Purchases
..........Natalie Claridge

BRETHERTON
PRICE
Total solutions in Law ELGOODS
Solicitors

THE FIRM: Bretherton Price Elgoods was formed in 1989 by the merger of two strong commercial practices. The firm serves a wide range of business, corporate and institutional clients, locally and nationally, through its two divisions, Business Services and Volume Residential Property. Operating from offices in Cheltenham and London, BPE is rapidly growing and commercially driven. Over the past few years, the firm has more than tripled in turnover and staff. The focus for the firm is, simply, to understand each client's business and then to provide a service precisely to the client's specification.

PRINCIPAL AREAS OF WORK:

BUSINESS SERVICES

Corporate: BPE has a strong and proactive corporate department, advising on a wide range of corporate and company/commercial matters, particularly mergers and acquisitions, AIM flotations, venture capital and banking transactions (on behalf of clearing banks and clients). The department also operates in a number of commercial niches including substantial building and civil engineering contracts and IT matters. Within the department, a dedicated employment team deals with both contentious and non-contentious matters, including share option schemes. The team also specialises in planning and implementation of preventative procedures and its lead partner sits as a tribunal chairman in London.

Commercial Property: The large commercial property team acts for a number of public companies including a substantial retail multiple chain. The department has special niche strengths in portfolio management and innovative property investment and development.

Commercial Litigation: This department has a reputation for its 'no nonsense' forensic approach to its business-to-business litigation. The team has particular expertise in complex commercial disputes and intellectual property work. Other specialisms include construction and property litigation and arbitration.

Personal Injury: This department handles defendant work for a number of major insurance companies and a high volume of plaintiff cases for union members and private clients. The department also advises on claimant fraud, policy interpretation and other contractual insurance elements.

RESIDENTIAL PROPERTY DIVISION

Remortgages & Repossession Sales: This team-based division undertakes substantial work for major institutional lenders working to demanding service standards. The division, which represents 42% of total turnover, has dealt with over 30,000 remortgages in the past five years.

Residential Conveyancing: The firm provides a customer focused high volume residential conveyancing service to clients introduced by institutions and substantial estate agency chains.

BRETHERTONS

16 Church St, Rugby, CV21 3PW **Tel:** (01788) 579579 **Fax:** (01788) 570949 **DX:** 11672 Rugby **Email:** clientcare@brethertons.co.uk **Website:** www.brethertons.co.uk **Ptnrs:** 10 **Asst solrs:** 12 **Other fee-earners:** 21

BRIAN KOFFMAN & CO

Queen's Chambers, 5 John Dalton St, Manchester, M2 6ET **Tel:** (0161) 832 3852 **Fax:** (0161) 833 2547 **Ptnrs:** 3 **Asst solrs:** 4 **Other fee-earners:** 9

BRIFFA

Business Design Centre, Upper St, Islington, London, N1 0QH
Tel: (020) 7288 6003 **Fax:** (020) 7288 6004
Email: mail@briffa.com **Website:** www.briffa.com

Number of partners	1
Assistant solicitors	6
Other fee-earners	1

AREAS OF PRACTICE

Intellectual Property & New Media 100%

CONTACTS

Intellectual Property ....Margaret Briffa
..........Ralph Wehrle
..........Teresa Walsh
..........Clare Griffiths
..........Alex Chapman

THE FIRM: Briffa is a leading and award winning intellectual property practice and new media practice. Its strength lies in offering the expertise of a specialist department within a large practice coupled with a personal service. Briffa lawyers are focused on getting results and creative problem solving. The team has experience across all media and is perfectly placed to undertake complex cross-media work. The service is genuinely different and refreshing. Fees are always fixed.

PRINCIPAL AREAS OF WORK: Briffa undertakes a wide range of work within its specialist areas covering both contentious and non-contentious work and business affairs. Briffa competes with the largest city and national firms in its areas of expertise. It has a high level of success.

CLIENTELE: Briffa has a diverse client base which spans most industry sectors. Notably, many clients are recognised innovators within their own industries.

BRISTOWS

3 Lincoln's Inn Fields, London, WC2A 3AA
Tel: (020) 7400 8000 **Fax:** (020) 7400 8050 **DX:** 269 London/Chancery Lane
Email: info@bristows.com **Website:** www.bristows.com

Senior Partner	Ian Judge
Number of partners	28
Assistant solicitors	53
Other fee-earners	30

AREAS OF PRACTICE

- **Intellectual Property** 47%
- **IT** 20%
- **Company/Commercial** 18%
- **Litigation (inc. Employment)** 10%
- **Property (inc. Environmental)** 5%

CONTACTS

- **Charities** ....John Lace
- **Commercial** ....Laura Anderson
- **Partnership** ....John Lace
- **Commercial Litigation** ....Kevin Appleton ....Linda Farrell
- **Commercial Property** ....Michael Rowles ....Alexandra Lethbridge
- **Company** ....Paul Cooke, John Lace
- **Competition & Anti-trust** ....Patricia Treacy
- **Computer Games** ....Paul Cooke
- **Corporate Finance** ..Paul Cooke, Mark Hawes
- **Data Protection** ....Linda Farrell
- **E-business** ..Matthew Warren, David Wilkinson
- **Employment** ....Linda Farrell
- **Environmental** ....Alexandra Lethbridge
- **IP: Biotechnology** ....Tim Powell, Penny Gilbert
- **IP: Pharmaceuticals** ....Edward Nodder ....Simon Ayrton
- **IP: Brands/Trademk** ....Sally Field, Paul Walsh
- **IP: Commercial** ....Matthew Warren ....Laura Anderson
- **IP: General** ....Alan Johnson ....Andrew Lykiardopoulos
- **IP: Patents** ....Ian Judge, David Brown
- **IP: Regulatory** ....Christine Hore, Tim Powell
- **IT** ....Philip Westmacott, Justin Watts
- **Media** ....Paul Walsh, David Wilkinson
- **Tax** ....Miranda Cass

THE FIRM: Bristows is a law firm dedicated to serving businesses with interests in technology or intellectual property, ranging from pharmaceuticals, electronics, IT, and telecommunications to brands, media and e-business. The firm is a market leader in this area and acts for many FTSE 100 and Fortune 500 multinationals. With over 150 years of experience in this field, Bristows has earned an enviable international reputation and has developed one of the largest intellectual property practices in the world; yet remains a friendly niche firm compatible with the needs of new and growing companies. Bristows is a young partnership in a long established firm committed to excellence in its chosen fields. With the continuing recruitment of lawyers and scientists of the highest quality, Bristows aims to stay at the forefront of specialist firms advising businesses with a strong technology or intellectual property base.

PRINCIPAL AREAS OF WORK: The firm has a substantial number of lawyers who first trained as scientists and who are readily able to understand sophisticated technology. This factor sets it apart from its competitors and has generated unparalleled expertise in litigation and corporate and commercial transactions in which intellectual property or an understanding of technology plays a significant part. The firm's litigation expertise also extends to commercial disputes of all kinds, including product liability and employment matters. Bristows is able to field teams of lawyers to handle litigation and transactions demanding multidisciplinary skills, often with an international or cross-border flavour. This is an increasingly important aspect of its business, particularly in the light of European integration and its effect on the development of intellectual property and competition law. Bristows has lawyers who are experienced in corporate and commercial law and in all forms of transaction from take-overs and mergers to joint ventures and technology spin-offs from universities. The firm also has significant complementary practices in real property, tax, competition, charity, employment and environmental law.

RECRUITMENT: Bristows recruits outstanding trainee solicitors each year. The long-term prospects are excellent; many of the firm's present partners trained with the firm. Applicants from all academic disciplines are encouraged to apply and scientific degrees are particularly relevant for certain areas of intellectual property. In-house training is comprehensive and many trainees and associates spend time on secondment at multinational companies including IBM, Gillette and Guinness UDV. Bristows' culture is different to that of many other law firms. Fee-earners are not set targets. This positive approach to work is passed down from the top and ensures that all Bristows' lawyers are committed to achieving excellence in their chosen field.

BROBECK HALE AND DORR

Alder Castle, 10 Noble Street, London, EC2V 7QJ
Tel: (020) 7645 2400 **Fax:** (020) 7645 2424
Email: info@bhd.com **Website:** www.bhd.com

25 Milton Park, Oxford, OX14 4SH
Tel: (01235) 823 000 **Fax:** (01235) 823 030
Email: info@bhd.com

Managing Partner	Thomas W Kellerman
Number of partners	14
Assistant solicitors	41
Other fee-earners	6

CONTACTS

- **Biotechnology** ....Pierre-Andre Dubois
- **Brands & Trade Marks** ....Pierre-Andre Dubois
- **Capital Markets** ....David Ayres
- **Company Commercial** ....David Gent
- **Corporate Finance/Governance** ....Thomas W Kellerman
- **Employment** ....Henry Clinton-Davis
- **Intellectual Property** ....Pierre-Andre Dubois
- **IT/Internet** ....Christopher Grew
- **M&A** ....Richard Eaton
- **Tax** ....Simon Court
- **Venture Capital** ....Thomas W Kellerman

THE FIRM: Brobeck Hale and Dorr is a multinational partnership founded in 1990 by the independent law firms of Brobeck, Phleger & Harrison LLP and Hale and Dorr LLP. BHD is a leading international law firm dedicated to advising clients in the global technology industry. BHD's clients include a wide range of companies in the Internet, information technology, computer software/hardware, biotechnology and life sciences industries, as well as the investment banks, venture capitalists and other financial intermediaries that serve technology companies.

PRINCIPAL AREAS OF WORK: High technology, venture capital, biotechnology, mergers and acquisitions, public offerings, intellectual property, information technology, employment and human resources and tax.

INTERNATIONAL: The firm has a branch office in Munich. Hale and Dorr LLP has offices in Boston, New York, Princeton, Reston, Waltham, Washington DC and Wellesley. Brobeck, Phleger & Harrison LLP has offices in San Francisco, Los Angeles, Palo Alto, San Diego, Irvine, Austin, Dallas, Denver, New York and Washington DC.

Brobeck Hale and Dorr

BRODIES WS

15 Atholl Crescent, Edinburgh, EH3 8HA
Tel: (0131) 228 3777 **Fax:** (0131) 228 3878 **DX:** ED10 Edinburgh
Email: mailbox@brodies.co.uk **Website:** www.brodies.co.uk

Managing Partner	William Drummond
Chairman	Alistair Campbell
Number of partners	32
Assistant solicitors	53
Other fee-earners	30

AREAS OF PRACTICE

Property	45%
Litigation	25%
Corporate	15%
Trust & Tax	15%

CONTACTS

Administrative Law	William Holligan
Banking	Linda Kinniburgh
Competition/Anti-Trust	Rodger Murray
Construction	Moira Clark
Corporate	Alistair Campbell
Corporate Tax	Alan Barr
Devolution	William Holligan
Employment	Susan Craig
Environment	Charles Smith
Family	Karen Bruce Lockhart
Financial Planning	Hew Dalrymple
Franchising	Julian Voge
Intellectual Property	Grant Campbell
Inward Investment	Alistair Campbell
Litigation	William Holligan
Local Authority	Charles Smith
Minerals	Hew Dalrymple
PFI	Charles Smith
Planning	Neil Collar
Property (Agricultural & Estates)	David Houldsworth
Property (Commercial)	Dale Strachan
Property (Residential)	Jim Clark
Property Marketing	Mark Atkinson
Trust & Tax	Andrew Dalgleish
Wills & Executries	Hugh Stevens

SOLICITORS

THE FIRM: Brodies is one of Scotland's leading independent commercial law firms. The firm has developed its commercial practice to include a strong public and private sector client base and continues to advise UK and overseas private individuals on their personal and business affairs. It offers legal advice in its core business areas of corporate and commercial, litigation, property and trust and tax. Brodies adds value through its specialist expertise in employment, public affairs and regulatory matters, planning and environment, banking, IP/IT and pensions. The firm's commercial property team continues to build its credentials in retail, development, investment and banking. PFI/PPP instructions are growing from significant capital projects. The planning and environmental group provides a resource across the firm and works particularly to support property and litigation clients. The corporate team has added two new partners and has significantly expanded its IP/IT practice and advisory work in EC and UK competition law. Significant tender wins in the educational and government sectors have contributed to further success. The firm's employment group has experienced tremendous growth in the last year – it now has eight full time lawyers and has added notable new clients in the financial, recruitment, educational, transport and logistics and public sectors. In commercial litigation the firm continues to earn its place at the top of league tables and the public affairs group has been particularly active in advising on human rights and regulatory issues.

PRINCIPAL AREAS OF WORK:

Corporate: The team gives advice on all areas of corporate and commercial law. The corporate team continues to concentrate on mergers, acquisitions, corporate finance, banking, franchising and corporate tax. In addition it has further developed the range of commercial legal advice supplied to its public and education sector client base, including providing advice on regulatory, competition, pensions and employee benefit issues.

COMMERCIAL PROPERTY

Investment & Finance: Expanded by the addition of a new partner this year, the group provides advice on acquisition, finance, development and disposal of commercial land and buildings for private and institutional investors, which has included acting in some of the largest office investment acquisitions in the strong Edinburgh market.

Development: The property development group acts for commercial property developers active in the commercial, industrial and retail sectors. It also has particular experience in leisure and sporting developments.

Retail: One of the largest retail practices in Scotland, the firm's retail property group has won instructions from a range of new national and international retail clients in the past year. Brodies' property team offers consultancy services to local government and other public authority bodies and advises on agricultural and forestry matters.

OTHER AREAS OF WORK

Corporate Tax & VAT: The group's core work is in support of the transactional activities of the firm's commercial clients by providing dedicated in-house advice on property and corporate deals. In the past year this has included work on the structuring of major property investments and developments.

Commercial & Civil Litigation: The firm has expertise in banking, employment, intellectual property, corporate, insurance, reparation, property including building contracts, professional negligence, partnership, shipping and licensing. It has an excellent reputation in personal injury and family law and provides a substantial debt recovery service. The firm has four solicitor-advocates with extended rights of audience in the Court of Session, House of Lords and the judicial committee of the Privy Council and two Law Society accredited specialists in employment law and a part-time chairman of employment tribunals.

Private Client: Brodies has one of the strongest teams in Scotland on private client, trust, tax and rural business. The firm is well known for its expertise in personal finance planning, inheritance tax advice and trust work, as well as agricultural law, sporting estates and forestry. It also offers a comprehensive residential and rural property service.

BROOKE NORTH

Crown House, Great George Street, Leeds, LS1 3BR **Tel:** (0113) 283 2100 **Fax:** (0113) 283 3999 **DX:** 713100 Leeds, Park Square **Email:** address@brookenorth.co.uk **Website:** www.brookenorth.co.uk **Ptnrs:** 17 **Asst solrs:** 9 **Other fee-earners:** 8

BROOKSTREET DES ROCHES

1 Des Roches Square, Witan Way, Witney, OX8 6BE
Tel: (01993) 771616 **Fax:** (01993) 779030 **DX:** 144160 Witney 2
Email: bsdr@bsdr.com **Website:** www.bsdr.com

Managing & Senior Partner	Nigel Street

AREAS OF PRACTICE	
Commercial Property	45%
Commercial Litigation	25%
Company	25%
Other	5%

THE FIRM: BSDR was established in 1994. It is committed to delivering a responsive high quality and cost effective legal service in a relaxed atmosphere. The firm's primary objective is to provide pragmatic advice and solutions.

PRINCIPAL AREAS OF WORK: BSDR is one of the leading law firms in the South East with particular expertise in commercial property and commercial litigation.
Property: The group handles retail, warehouse, factory and office acquisitions advising on property finance and landlord and tenant matters.
Litigation: The team scored notable success in the Court of Appeal in 1999 for National Grid plc and Nurdin & Peacock plc.
Corporate & Commercial: The team advises on a range of business matters, particularly in the high-tech and bioscience sectors. The technology group is very familiar with the OFEX market.

B

BROWELL SMITH & CO

Pearl Assurance House, 7 New Bridge Street, Newcastle upon Tyne, NE1 8AQ
Tel: (0191) 221 1611 **Fax:** (0191) 241 8200 **DX:** 61084 Newcastle
Email: advice@browells.co.uk **Website:** www.browells.co.uk

Number of partners	4
Assistant solicitors	22
Other fee-earners	52

AREAS OF PRACTICE	
Personal Injury	70%
Private Client	30%

THE FIRM: Browell Smith & Co specialises in personal injury and industrial disease cases on behalf on trade union clients and their members, as well as for the general public. In particular, the firm undertakes work for the National Union of Mineworkers, GMB, Transport & General Workers Union, NUM (COSA) and NACODS. The firm continues to grow and develop in the plaintiff personal injury and industrial disease areas where expertise covers industrial deafness, chronic bronchitis and emphysema, vibration white finger, asbestos related diseases, industrial cancers, work related upper limb disorders and stress cases. Product liability cases are handled and the firm also deals with a variety of employment law cases on behalf of complainants only. At its satellite offices, family law, probate, wills and trusts, domestic conveyancing and crime are undertaken on behalf of private clients of the firm. The practice has also established an immigration and asylum department which continues to expand.

A.D. BROWN, SOLICITORS

One Liverpool Street, London, EC2M 7QD **Tel:** 020 7956 2029 **Fax:** 020 7956 2229 **Email:** adpb@ic24.net

BROWN & WOOD

Princes Court, 7 Princes Street, London, EC2R 8AQ **Tel:** (020) 7778 1800 **Fax:** (020) 7796 1807
DX: 580 LONDON CITY • Brown & Wood merged on 1 May 2001 with Sidley & Austin. The new firm is known as Sidley Austin Brown & Wood; please see the full-page entry under S.

BROWN COOPER

7 Southampton Place, London, WC1A 2DR
Tel: (020) 7404 0422 **Fax:** (020) 7831 9856 **DX:** 35731 Bloomsbury
Email: clientcare@browncooper.com **Website:** www.browncooper.com

Senior Partner	Robin Cooper
Number of partners	5
Assistant solicitors	1
Other fee-earners	3

THE FIRM: Brown Cooper provides a distinctive, high quality but cost-effective service for commercial clients. Matters are invariably handled or supervised by an experienced partner. As well as bringing to bear extensive experience in the fields of corporate commercial, property transactions and litigation, the firm has in depth knowledge of industries including film and television, upstream oil and gas, publishing and printing, fashion, hotel and restaurant, and travel. The impressive litigation team has particular expertise in VAT litigation, insurance, medical negligence, employment, crossborder debt recovery, libel and media litigation as well as domestic and international arbitration.

INTERNATIONAL: Italian, French and German are spoken at the firm.

BROWNE JACOBSON

44 Castle Gate, Nottingham, NG1 7BJ
Tel: (0115) 976 6000 **Fax:** (0115) 947 5246 **DX:** 718130 Nottingham 27
Email: info@brownej.co.uk **Website:** www.brownej.co.uk

Aldwych House, 81 Aldwych, London, WC2B 4HN
Tel: (020) 7404 1546 **Fax:** (020) 7836 3882 **DX:** 142420 Kingsway 3
Email: lon@brownej.co.uk

102 Colmore Row, Birmingham, B3 3AG
Tel: (0121) 237 3900 **Fax:** (0121) 236 1291 **DX:** 13009 Birmingham 1
Email: birmingham@brownej.co.uk

Managing Partner	Brian Smith
Senior Partner	David Hibbert
Head of Commercial Group	Rob Metcalfe
Head of Insurance Group	Nick Parsons
Number of partners	47
Assistant solicitors	82
Other fee-earners	64

AREAS OF PRACTICE

Insurance & Personal Injury Litigation	36%
Corporate/Commercial	35%
Commercial & Other Litigation	14%
Professional Indemnity	9%
Taxation/Trusts	5%
Other	1%

CONTACTS

Banking/Security	Duncan Murray
Biosciences	Sharon Jones
Clinical Negligence	Carol Ayre
Commercial Litigation	Peter Ellis
Commercial Property	David Hibbert
Company/Commercial	Nigel Blackwell
Construction	Nigel Blundell
Corporate Finance	Rob Metcalfe
Debt Recovery	Paul Southby
Employment	Edward Benson
Environmental	Richard Barlow
Freight/Logistics	Caroline Green
Health Law	Gay Wilder
Information Technology/E-commerce	Mark Snelgrove
Intellectual Property	Peter Ellis
	Mark Snelgrove
Pensions	Richard Davis
Personal Injury	Nick Parsons
Planning	Brian Smith
Professional Indemnity	Derek Bambury
Public & Administrative	Richard Barlow
Retail	Maggie O'Mahony
Social Housing	David Huddleston
Sport	David Hibbert
Taxation/Trusts	Maryvonne Hands

THE FIRM: Browne Jacobson is a substantial commercial and institutional law firm, which has a practical approach providing a first class client service. Already acknowledged as a leading regional practice offering a comprehensive range of services, the firm has continued to develop a nationwide reputation for quality and has a growing international presence. It operates from Nottingham, London and Birmingham. International development is driven primarily through London and Paris where the firm has an associated office and through key relationships with selected US law firms.The firm's planned expansion continued through 2000 with a 20.6% rise in income, a total staff increase of 9% and new partners in banking and insolvency, corporate and public authority appointed during the year. Browne Jacobson has experienced and enthusiastic teams which adopt an integrated, problem solving approach for all its clients. This is coupled with a firm-wide philosophy of being dedicated to providing value for money without compromising quality.

PRINCIPAL AREAS OF WORK: Services to clients are focused through the firm's insurance and commercial operating groups.

INSURANCE GROUP: Led by Nick Parsons, the insurance division is divided into four specialist, areas of public authority, professional indemnity, medical negligence and technical insurance. Each has teams of experts with a breadth of knowledge and experience and can provide a full legal service to the insurance industry.

Personal Injury Litigation Group: Acting for major insurers, public and private institutions on a national basis handling personal injury, employers' liability, motor liability, industrial disease, public liability, property claims and product liability. A particular specialism is handling complex multi-party personal injury claims. An increasing area of practice is risk management and post incident investigation services.

Professional Indemnity: The team includes a CEDR accredited mediator and works for the insurers and a broad range of professional clients. The firm also has an established record in risk management, policy drafting and insurance law work.

Public Authority: The public authority group acts for more than 100 Local Authorities and their insurers. It has five senior lawyers with direct experience of working in Local Government. The teams offer environmental, administrative and public law advice.

Medical Negligence: The team includes legal experts with a background in public bodies and medicine including registered medical practitioners. It represents clients throughout the public sector, including health authorities and all types of trusts. The firm is appointed to the National Health Service Litigation Authority Panel.

COMMERCIAL GROUP: Led by Rob Metcalfe, the corporate and commercial teams provide a broad spectrum of expertise including: corporate, commercial, commercial property, commercial litigation and tax.

Corporate: The corporate team acts on flotation and new issues, fund raising, M&A, MBO/MBI/IBO and private equity transactions (in the last 15 months to an aggregate value in excess of £1billion). Sector focus groups (IT & telecoms, retail, freight/logistics, bio-science and sport) provide a tailored service to targeted industry sectors.

Commercial: The commercial team advises on all commercial contracts or arrangements (including joint ventures, agency, distribution, franchising and competition matters) and regulatory matters.

Corporate Tax: The firm is also noted for high level corporate tax and personal financial planning expertise (being concerned with individuals and settlements with an aggregate net worth in excess of £1.5 billion) and expert advice on pensions, employee benefits and general employment.

Commercial Property: Clients include investors, developers, local authorities, housing associations and major retailers. The market facing team advises on all planning and environmental issues, construction law and landlord and tenant matters.

Commercial Litigation: Employment disputes, contentious intellectual property matters, licensing, debt collection and trading standards matters are all within the scope of the commercial litigation team. The firm is a founder member of the Centre for Dispute Resolution and actively seeks alternative solutions to disputes.

BRUNTON MILLER

Herbert House, 22 Herbert Street, Glasgow, G20 6NB **Tel:** (0141) 337 1199 **Fax:** (0141) 337 3300 **DX:** GW21 **Email:** bruntonmil@aol.com **Ptnrs:** 7 **Asst solrs:** 4 **Other fee-earners:** 7 **Contact:** Archie MacIver • The firm is well-known for its licensing expertise and also advises on criminal matters, debt collection, family/matrimonial law, and commercial and domestic conveyancing.

AREAS OF PRACTICE	
Licensing	42%
Conveyancing	24%
Court (Legal Aid & Non-Legal Aid)	20%
Commercial	14%

BRUTTON & CO

West End House, 288 West Street, Fareham, PO16 0AJ **Tel:** (01329) 236171 **Fax:** (01329) 289915 **DX:** 40809 **Email:** mail@brutton.co.uk **Ptnrs:** 5 **Asst solrs:** 3 **Other fee-earners:** 6

BRYAN CAVE

33 Cannon Street, London, EC4M 5TE
Tel: (020) 7246 5800 **Fax:** (020) 7246 5858
Email: chattlee@bryancave.com **Website:** www.bryancave.com

Lead Partner & Resident Manager	Charles Attlee
Number of partners	10
Counsel	3
Associates	11
Other fee-earners	4

THE FIRM: Founded in 1873, Bryan Cave is an international law firm with sixteen offices around the world. A leader in corporate, transaction and litigation representation with a diversified international practice, the firm has over 700 fee earners, ranking it among the 30 largest law firms in the United States and among the 50 largest worldwide. The firm acts for a variety of public and privately-held businesses; financial, institutional and individual clients. Bryan Cave's London office was established in 1982 and was reorganised in 1999 as a multinational partnership of US lawyers and English solicitors. The London office offers clients a distinct service advantage by combining the best practices of UK and US law firms. The office has grown substantially in the last two years and its UK and US qualified lawyers have broad multijurisdictional experience.

PRINCIPAL AREAS OF WORK: The office advises on a wide range of corporate and commercial issues including cross-border transactions, mergers and acquisitions, investment funds, international trade, competition, regulatory work, conventional and Islamic finance, insolvency, intellectual property, telecommunications and technology work. The office has a growing UK commercial litigation capability as well as an international arbitration practice and international trust litigation expertise. In addition, there is a UK/EU employment practice and an international trade regulation and competition practice. The London office has the largest US private client practice outside the US representing US citizens residing in or investing in Europe and Europeans moving to or investing in the US. The practice has a strong US tax focus including advising on ownership structures for closely held businesses and international trust structures, in addition to offering estate planning advice and documentation. The private client practitioners work closely with UK and other advisers to provide integrated US advice to international clients.

CLIENTELE: The firm's clients include major publicly held multinational corporations, major and mid-sized publicly and privately held companies, financial institutions, partnerships, emerging enterprises, charities, private offices and high net worth individuals as well as governmental entities.

INTERNATIONAL: The firm has nine US offices located in New York; Washington, DC; St Louis and Jefferson City, Missouri; two in the Kansas City area; Phoenix, Arizona; Santa Monica and Irvine, California. The firm has seven international offices located in London, Riyadh, Kuwait City, Dubai, Abu Dhabi, Hong Kong and Shanghai. The firm has long standing links with other law firms around the world.

RECRUITMENT: The London office has expanded rapidly and has taken on seven lateral hires over the past twelve months. In particular, the firm has recruited Sarah Linton, Counsel, who heads the UK/EU Employment Practice; Rod Cowper, Partner, who heads the UK Commercial Litigation Practice as well as three associates and two other fee earners. In the lateral hires it has made, the firm has aimed to attract professionals who are well-experienced in their own right, comfortable in combining the best practices of UK and US law firms and who will support the firm's broad corporate/commercial and litigation practices. The London office has put in place a programme for trainee solicitors and recruits two trainees every year. Bryan Cave is keen to encourage lawyers to work in other offices for periods of time. This reflects Bryan Cave's "One Firm" approach and is of great benefit to the firm's culture and cohesion. The London office will be continuing its programme of recruitment throughout 2001/2002.

CONTACTS	
Corporate/Commercial	Charles Attlee
	Anthony Fiducia
International Trade/Competition	Anita Esslinger
Banking & Finance	Walter White
	Richard Stewart
Investment Funds	Charles Attlee
Media & Entertainment	Anthony Fiducia
Islamic Finance	Richard Stewart
Middle East	David Pfeiffer
Employment	Sarah Linton
International Arbitration	Paul Hauser
Commercial Litigation	Rod Cowper
Private Client/Charities	Joe Field
	Richard Cassell
International Tax	Paul Hauser
	Dyke Davies
	Richard Cassell
International Trust Litigation	Joe Field

BRYAN CAVE

BUCHANAN INGERSOLL

Tower 42, International Financial Centre, 25 Old Broad Street, London, EC2N 1HQ
Tel: (020) 7920 3700 **Fax:** (020) 7374 8884 **DX:** 671 London City
Email: info@buchananingersoll.com **Website:** www.buchananingersoll.com

Managing Partner (London)	Barry Francis
UK	
Number of partners	16
Assistant solicitors	10
Other fee-earners	3
International (Worldwide)	
Number of partners	184
Number of associates	193

CONTACTS

Administrative & Competition Law	Diane Wilson
Banking & Finance	David Halliday
	Michael Park
Biotechnology	Ron Schuler
Commercial & Corporate	Peter Brazel
Construction	David Hartley
Corporate Finance	Jonathan Griffiths
Healthcare	Jerry Mansmann
International Arbitrations	Steven Blair
IP & Media	Michael Henry
IT	George Gardiner
Private Equity	Keir Barrie
Projects & PFI/PPP	Barry Francis
Property	Rupert Jones
Tax	Jenny Cottrell

THE FIRM: Buchanan Ingersoll opened in January 2000 with 18 lawyers. Ten further lawyers have since joined reflecting the firm's commitment to grow by recruiting lawyers acknowledged as leaders in their respective fields. It is the London office of Buchanan Ingersoll Professional Corporation, one of the 75 largest law firms in the United States, with more than 400 lawyers in 15 offices across the United States. The firm's international advisory board, consisting of prominent European business leaders, provides strategic counsel and insight for future growth. The firm's lawyers strive to provide prompt high quality commercial and legal advice. Lawyers are committed to understanding and delivering clients' requirements. The firm works with its clients and their other advisers in identifying and developing opportunities, assessing risks, overcoming obstacles and achieving commercially realistic solutions. The office's objectives include developing its projects and healthcare practices and establishing, in London, a substantial biotechnology practice by building on the firm's technology law reputation in the United States. The biotechnology group is advising clients impacted by some of the world's top headline stories – the recall of genetically modified corn products, BSE, human tissue-based implants and issues concerning wireless technology and cancer. The firm's growth in New York advising financial institutions will facilitate a similar growth in London. International tax is a major component of the tax practices in both London and Washington, DC. As well, Buchanan Ingersoll is building Euro-American practices in the construction and insurance/reinsurance industries and in IP and media. Members of the firm have learnt deal making skills in a range of sectors and transactions: corporate finance, public/private partnerships, joint ventures, private placements, share issues, corporate reconstructions, construction, intellectual property, lending, securitisation: the whole range of transaction types in the healthcare, banking, commercial property, technology, security, transport and property development sectors as well as information technology, media and advertising, local government, manufacturing and hotel and leisure sectors.

PRINCIPAL AREAS OF WORK: The London office enjoys a significant transactional practice.

Banking & Finance: Lawyers in the office have advised major British clearing, Northern American and European financial institutions in relation to all aspects of finance and regulatory work including venture capital, project and asset finance (including PPP/PFI), business regeneration, impaired debt trading, trade finance, derivatives, debt capital markets and leasing transactions. In addition to providing the full range of banking advice, finance lawyers have acted for the providers of, and those seeking finance for, businesses at the point of change (development capital, start-up, MBO/MBI and upon exit).

Projects: The initial focus in London was on major projects including public private partnerships. The office's commitment to such projects and, in particular to PFI/PPP, has been enhanced by the additional lawyers who have joined the office over the last year. Highlights include the largest PFI project in Wales (£432 million), the first primary school in Wales procured under PFI, and financing the variation to the £150 million South Tees hospital redevelopment.

Media & IP: Media and intellectual property lawyers are committed to serving clients from the media, entertainment retail and leisure and e-commerce industry sectors. They advise on all aspects of the acquisition, disposal and licensing of intellectual property rights. They are experienced in providing legal advice on brand protection and the co-ordination of the protection of IP assets. The office has expertise in developing anti-counterfeiting programmes.

Technology: The firm's technology lawyers have expertise in global IT procurement and supply arrangements, outsourcing, software and data protection.

Tax: The London office offers a full range of tax, VAT and stamp duty planning services, with a particular expertise in taxation aspects of e-commerce. International tax law is a growth area in the London practice and London liaises on tax efficient cross border structuring with its US colleagues (including the renowned Silverstein and Mullens tax lawyers, a division in the US since early 2000) to provide a comprehensive, one-stop international tax service.

Healthcare: The London office is acting on a range of healthcare transactions: PFI projects in the UK, financing transactions in Ireland and private healthcare provision in the UK and elsewhere in Europe.

INTERNATIONAL: The firm is the London Office of Buchanan Ingersoll Professional Corporation founded in Pittsburgh in 1850. The firm's level of business has quadrupled in the past decade demonstrating dramatic long-term growth. During the past three years the firm has advised in the US on transactions with a value in excess of £95 billion. The new London office is part of the US firm's strategic growth.This has seen the US firm open a new office in New York, focusing on venture capital and technology companies, and expanding its Washington DC office through a merger with Silverstein and Mullens, a major international tax practice known for its editorial role in the Tax Management publication series. In 2001 the firm opened offices in Wilmington and San Diego.

BUCKLE MELLOWS

35/51 Priestgate, Peterborough, PE1 1LB **Tel:** (01733) 568175 **Fax:** (01733) 562064 **DX:** 12312 P'Boro 1 **Email:** bucklemellows.co.uk **Website:** www.bucklemellows.co.uk **Ptnrs:** 16 **Asst solrs:** 6 **Other fee-earners:** 23

BULLER JEFFRIES

36 Bennetts Hill, Birmingham, B2 5SN **Tel:** (0121) 212 2620 **Fax:** (0121) 212 2210 **DX:** 13051 Birmingham 1 **Email:** info@bullerjeffries.co.uk **Website:** www.bullerjeffries.co.uk **Ptnrs:** 8 **Asst solrs:** 6 **Other fee-earners:** 8 **Contact:** Roger Coates • Specialists insurance practice: EL, motor, local authority, products, professional indemnity and construction. Volume personal injury and disease for leading insurers.

AREAS OF PRACTICE	
Civil Litigation	95%
Private Client/Commercial	5%

BULLIVANT JONES

State House, 22 Dale St, Liverpool, L2 4UR
Tel: (0151) 227 5671 **Fax:** (0151) 227 5632 **DX:** 14120 Liverpool
Email: mail@bullivantjones.co.uk

Senior Partner	Pamela Jones
Number of partners	13
Assistant solicitors	18
Other fee-earners	7

AREAS OF PRACTICE	
Commercial Property	70%
Litigation & Employment Law	20%
Company/Commercial	5%
Probate, Trust & Residential Conveyancing	5%

THE FIRM: Bullivant Jones has built on a long-standing reputation for excellence in the commercial property field to expand into other practice areas where the emphasis is still on sound commercial principles. The firm has historically maintained a small but high quality client base in order to ensure that the provision of first rate client services is not compromised. Whilst not jeopardising this policy, in recent years the firm has strategically expanded its range of clients and developed the resources to meet their needs.
The partners aim to be innovative and forward-looking in their approach to transactions and are equipped to advise where appropriate on all the commercial aspects of a client's business. At present the firm has 13 partners and 38 fee earners in all, and is constantly seeking to enhance its level of service. In 1999 Bullivant Jones was among the first practices in the country to be awarded the Law Society's Lexcel badge of quality, and the firm has been an accredited Investor in People since 1996.

PRINCIPAL AREAS OF WORK: The firm concentrates largely on commercial conveyancing. It also has departments in general commercial work, litigation, employment, probate, trusts and residential conveyancing.
Commercial Conveyancing: This department generates the largest portion of work carried out by the firm. Work includes sales, purchases and leases of offices, businesses and shops, and new developments such as out-of-town retail parks as well as high street premises. Clients include developers, retailers and investors.
Litigation: The litigation department deals with a considerable volume of commercial and property-based matters, including building contract disputes. In addition it handles cases concerning food safety, health and safety litigation and liquor licensing.
Employment: The firm's expanded resource in employment law deals with all aspects of both contentious and non-contentious employment law, including redundancy, unfair and wrongful dismissal, discrimination claims, Employment Tribunal and Employment Appeal Tribunal cases, as well as drafting service agreements.
Private Client: The firm has expanded its private client department from a sound base of considerable experience in wills, settlements, probate and trust work, as well as residential conveyancing.
Company Commercial: The department deals with acquisitions and disposals, joint ventures and general commercial transactions.

Bullivant Jones

B

BURGES SALMON

Narrow Quay House, Narrow Quay, Bristol, BS1 4AH
Tel: (0117) 939 2000 **Fax:** (0117) 902 4400 **DX:** 7829 (Bristol)
Email: email@burges-salmon.com **Website:** www.burges-salmon.com

Senior Partner	Richard Wynn-Jones
Managing Partner	Guy Stobart
Number of partners	50
Assistant solicitors	125
Other fee-earners	48

AREAS OF PRACTICE

Corporate	25%
Property	25%
Agriculture	17%
Commercial Litigation	13%
Private Client	12%
Banking & Insolvency	8%

CONTACTS

Agriculture	Roger Hawes
	William Neville
Arbitration	Adrian Llewelyn Evans
Asset Finance	Sandra Forbes
Construction	Marcus Harling
Corporate Banking	Sandra Forbes
Corporate Finance	Christopher Godfrey
Corporate Rescue	Guy Stobart
Corporate Tax	Nigel Popplewell
Dispute Resolution	Adrian Llewelyn Evans
Employment	Christopher Seaton
Environment/Land Use	Ian Salter
EU/Competition	Laura Claydon
Financial Services	Christopher Godfrey
Housing Associations	Stephen McNulty
Insurance	Christopher Jackson
Intellectual Property/IT	Simon Coppen
M&A	Alan Barr
Pensions	Tim Illston
PFI & Partnering	Richard Wynn-Jones
Planning	Patrick Robinson
Private Client	Martin Mitchell
Product Liability	Adrian Llewelyn Evans
Professional Indemnity	Paul Haggett
Property	Robert Smyth
Property Development	David Gidney
Property Finance	Paul Browne
Property Litigation	Neil Ham
Rail	Nicholas Olley
Trade & Industry	Richard Wynn-Jones
Transport & Distribution	Philip Davey
Unit Trusts	Christopher Godfrey
Venture Capital	Richard Spink

THE FIRM: Burges Salmon is one of the UK's leading commercial law firms. Based in Bristol, with a presence in London, the firm provides national and international clients with a full commercial service through four departments: tax and trusts, company commercial, litigation and property. Over recent years Burges Salmon has witnessed an extraordinarily high and sustainable rate of growth reflected by some 75% of the firm's clients being situated outside its South West base. This stems from a client-centric culture, which pervades throughout the firm and is reflected in the acquisition of new clients and in the secure relationships maintained with them.

PRINCIPAL AREAS OF WORK:

Company Commercial: The company commercial ('CoCo') department is the largest in the firm and covers a wide range of disciplines. In effect, the department is made up of five principal groups: corporate finance, finance, EPI (employment, pensions and incentives), corporate tax and commercial. The firm's highly regarded corporate finance unit provides a full service to corporate and business clients, ranging from emerging enterprises to multinational corporations. The core team covers the whole variety of corporate finance work. Burges Salmon's finance group provides a full range of services on all aspects of banking and finance. The EPI unit provides advice to public and private sector clients on all aspects of employment, pensions law and employee benefits. Burges Salmon's team of corporate tax lawyers is recognised as having significant expertise and is able to advise on all aspects of corporate tax law. The commercial unit has an outstanding reputation, advising on general commercial; competition; food law; technology and e-commerce; intellectual property and media; PFI; project finance and transport (including rail issues).

Litigation: Burges Salmon's litigation department is one of the largest regional practices and covers a wide range of work including banking; rail; contracts; defamation and media; financial disputes; insurance; professional negligence; technical and engineering disputes. The litigation department is home to the firm's nationally respected agricultural unit. The unit provides expert legal advice and representation to commercial and private clients with businesses founded in agriculture, land use and the rural economy generally. The firm's property litigation team specialises in commercial property disputes including landlord and tenant issues. The core work in this area is complex commercial disputes and flagship agricultural and commercial property cases.

Property: The firm's property department enjoys a reputation for being a pre-eminent practice offering a first class service throughout the UK. The firm's geographical market for property services is truly national. The department consists of teams that cater for a number of specialist areas including occupiers and portfolio management; brown land regeneration; property investment; rural property and agriculture; town and country planning and compulsory purchase; projects and construction; property development and property finance work.

Tax & Trusts: Burges Salmon's tax and trusts department is one of the largest in the UK and provides a growing national and international client base with a full range of services including tax and estate planning, international tax planning, trusts, trust administration, wills and probate, tax compliance and investigations, property taxation, matrimonial/co-habitation disputes and agriculture as well as specialist units focusing remuneration and charities.

RECRUITMENT: The firm recruits law, non-law and mature graduates and offers both in-house training and residential courses. Vacation experience is also available – apply two years in advance to Lisa Head (lisa.head@burges-salmon.com).

B

BURNESS

50 Lothian Road, Festival Square, Edinburgh, EH3 9WJ
Tel: (0131) 473 6000 **Fax:** (0131) 473 6006 **DX:** ED73 Edinburgh
Website: www.burness.co.uk

242 West George Street, Glasgow, G2 4QY
Tel: (0141) 248 4933 **Fax:** (0141) 204 1601 **DX:** GW154 GLASGOW

Chairman	John Rafferty
Managing Partner	Alan Stewart
Number of partners	33
Assistant solicitors	38
Other fee-earners	19

AREAS OF PRACTICE

Corporate	35%
Commercial Property	33%
Capital Projects	16%
Dispute Resolution	14%
Other	2%

CONTACTS

Corporate	Peter Lawson
	Andrew Sleigh
Commercial Property	Ian Wattie
	David Gibson
Projects	John Miller
Dispute Resolution	Philip Rodney
	Brent Haywood

THE FIRM: Burness is one of Scotland's premier commercial law firms, with a strong UK and overseas client base. The firm is ranked second in the Legal Experts league tables (Scotland), with many of the 33 partners singled out as leaders in their field. A recent survey of Scotland's legal market reports that 80% of Burness clients are very satisfied with the service they receive – some 20% ahead of the nearest competitor surveyed. In the last year the firm successfully recruited five partner level lateral hires including the managing partner, who joined the corporate finance team; a UK pensions law expert, who now heads up the firm's pensions unit; a leading wastewater adviser, as head of projects; a renowned defamation specialist, who leads the firm's media unit. The firm also appointed new directors in finance and IT, portraying commitment to the firm's goal to deliver a consistently first class legal service to commercial clients.

PRINCIPAL AREAS OF WORK: Business is sharply focused on commercial work, and the firm services its clients from four core groups, which are corporate, property, projects and dispute resolution.

Corporate: There are three key features of the firm's corporate service: corporate finance, banking and pensions. In corporate finance, the firm has closed a number of high profile new economy deals, while continuing to manage sizeable and complex old economy deals. The firm covers the full M&A, MBO, JV and flotation spectrum, and regularly manages cross-border transactions. The firm's dedicated banking group continues to receive an impressive range and quality of instruction, from substantial PFI and other capital projects work, to property, mezzanine and acquisition finance. The firm's commitment to expansion in banking and finance, means the group is one of the most highly resourced in Scotland. Its pensions practice is now regarded as being a clear market leader. Specialists in employment, tax, IP/commercial technology and EU/Competition, provide significant back up to the three core areas. The firm also has particular strength in corporate recovery, public/third sector law and inward investment.

Commercial Property: The Burness property team is recognised as having real strength in depth in commercial property, focusing on four core areas, which are development; property finance; investment; retail and leisure. Property lawyers work hand in glove with specialists in construction, planning/environmental law, corporate law and property tax, to deliver a truly integrated service to meet all the property needs of clients. Members of the firm are actively involved in several major developments across Scotland, and the firm is emerging as a leading player in property finance, advising leading UK banks in a number of high profile transactions. On the investment side, the firm has built a strong reputation as a major player in the acquisition of licensed premises portfolios, while in the retail and leisure market, it advises many blue chip household names.

Dispute Resolution: The firm's dispute resolution group adopts a progressive approach. As well as conducting complex high value litigation, it provides clients with conflict avoidance and dispute resolution strategies. It has a vast range of litigation experience, having been involved in substantial high profile litigation during the last year. The group has specialist teams working in product liability, where they have one of the most extensive defender practices in Scotland, media, commercial technology, which brings together a highly skilled team focused on the resolution of disputes involving new technology, and employment, where the focus is largely in the health sector.

Projects: The firm's award winning projects team has an outstanding reputation. Members have been involved in all but one of the Scottish Schools projects to reach financial close. In the last three years they closed 18 projects and are currently working on a wide range of projects including transport, health, education, waste, accommodation, IT and wastewater in Scotland, England, Eire and the Netherlands. The projects group embraces specialist projects and construction teams. Burness is a founder member of the Scottish North American Business Council and the only Scottish member of the State Capital law firm group. Member firms of the State Capital law firm group practise independently and not in a relationship for the joint practice of law.

BURNETT & REID

15 Golden Square, Aberdeen, AB10 1WF **Tel:** (01224) 644333 **Fax:** (01224) 632173 **DX:** AB19 Aberdeen **Email:** mail@burnett-reid.co.uk
Ptnrs: 10 **Asst solrs:** 3 **Other fee-earners:** 9

BURNETTS

6 Victoria Place, Carlisle, CA1 1ES **Tel:** (01228) 552222 **Fax:** (01228) 522399 **DX:** 63005 Carlisle **Email:** info@burnetts.co.uk
Website: www.burnettssolicitors.com **Ptnrs:** 14 **Asst solrs:** 11 **Other fee-earners:** 19

B

BURNSIDE KEMP FRASER

48 Queens Road, Aberdeen, AB15 4YE
Tel: (01224) 327500 **Fax:** (01224) 327501 **DX:** 78 Aberdeen
Email: law@burnside-kemp-fraser.co.uk **Website:** www.burnside-kemp-fraser.co.uk

Managing Partner	Sandy Kemp
Senior Partner	David Burnside

AREAS OF PRACTICE

Employment	40%
Personal Injury	35%
Other	15%
Matrimonial	10%

THE FIRM: The firm specialises in all aspects of civil litigation. It has a particularly strong reputation in employment law in the offshore oil industry, in higher and further education and in the field of personal injury work. The firm has two employment law specialists accredited by the Law Society of Scotland and is alone in the north east of Scotland in having that distinction.

BURROUGHS DAY

14-16 Charlotte St, Bristol, BS1 5PT **Tel:** (0117) 929 0333 **Fax:** (0117) 927 2342 **DX:** 7825 **Email:** burroughs.day@compuserve.com. **Ptnrs:** 14 **Asst solrs:** 13 **Other fee-earners:** 22

B

BURT BRILL & CARDENS

30 Old Steyne, Brighton, BN1 1FL
Tel: (01273) 604123 **Fax:** (01273) 570837 **DX:** 2709 Brighton 1
Email: help@bbc-law.co.uk **Website:** www.bbc-law.co.uk

Senior Partner	J R Summers
Number of partners	5
Assistant solicitors	4
Other fee-earners	8

AREAS OF PRACTICE

Private Client	45%
Litigation	40%
Corporate/Commercial	15%

CONTACTS

Commercial	J R Summers
Litigation	K G Smyth
Private Client	D J Edwards

THE FIRM: Burt Brill & Cardens was established in 1897. Offices in Brighton and Worthing serve both businesses and private clients. Whenever consulted, the firm's policy is to remain independent and objective, and to identify the best results desirable in each case. Members of the firm are approachable, understanding and courteous and provide a service that is both practical and reliable. Clients are regularly kept informed about the progress of their cases and about costs.

PRINCIPAL AREAS OF WORK: Company and commercial law, personal injury, medical negligence, family, employment, commercial disputes, conveyancing, wills, trusts, probate and tax planning.

CLIENTELE: The firm acts for a wide range of clients including the University of Brighton, a plc, businesses, charities, churches, trusts, schools, as well as numerous private clients.

BURTON COPELAND (LONDON)

51 Lincoln's Inn Fields, London, WC2A 3LZ
Tel: (020) 7430 2277 **Fax:** (020) 7430 1101 **DX:** 37981 Kingsway
Email: law@burtoncopeland.co.uk **Website:** www.burtoncopeland.co.uk

Senior Partner	Ian Burton
Number of partners	10
Assistant solicitors	7
Other fee-earners	4

AREAS OF PRACTICE

Commercial/Tax Fraud Investigations/Proceedings/ Prosecutions	60%
Regulatory/Disciplinary Investigations/Proceedings	25%
Serious Crime	15%

CONTACTS

Commercial/Tax Fraud Investigations/Prosecutions/ Regulation	Ian Burton
	Harry Travers
	Jane Glass
General Crime	Mark Haslam

THE FIRM: This specialist practice is widely regarded as one of the most prominent in the areas of commercial fraud, international financial regulation and investigation by the tax authorities, and serious crime. In 1991, Ian Burton, the founding partner of Burton Copeland, established the London office of the firm, which has recently become a separate partnership. The firm is renowned for its dynamic approach to problem-solving and solution implementation in both the national and international contexts, and for its expertise in acting for those who are the subject of, or affected by, investigation and prosecution of commercial fraud, tax fraud and serious crime and regulatory/disciplinary proceedings. Its partners and fee-earners have backgrounds from City law firms, specialised criminal law practices and leading prosecuting authorities, and have been instructed in most of the largest commercial fraud prosecutions in the last 10-15 years. Its clients range from large international corporations to foreign governments, major City law practices and individuals. For many years it has brought its experience to bear in protecting the rights and liberties of its clients in accordance with the European Convention on Human Rights and other international treaties.

PRINCIPAL AREAS OF WORK:

Commercial Fraud: The firm has one of the largest commercial fraud departments in the country, with 10 partners practising in this area and 10 assistants. It is able to offer representation in commercial fraud prosecutions brought throughout the country. Its expertise developed in major prosecutions brought by the SFO and DTI such as Barlow Clowes, Maxwell, BCCI, and various UN sanctions cases, has given it particular speciality in accountancy, banking, and international investment matters. It has substantial experience of large-scale prosecutions resulting from investigations brought by other authorities such as the Inland Revenue, HM Customs & Excise, the MoD and British Transport Police. This expertise and experience is carried over into the related areas of international mutual assistance, confiscation, restraint, money laundering and extradition. The firm's increasingly international practice has resulted in recent instructions on complex matters in numerous jurisdictions, including the United States, Switzerland, Liechtenstein, various members of the European Union, and a variety of Middle Eastern and Far Eastern countries, often working alongside governments and major legal practices in those jurisdictions.

Regulatory & Disciplinary: The firm has substantial experience in advising companies and individuals in respect of investigations and proceedings brought by the FSA, Lloyd's, the SFA, and other bodies responsible for investigation and regulation in national and international financial markets. It also acts for professionals facing disciplinary enquiries/proceedings before tribunals such as the Bar Council, the Law Society, the General Medical Council and Courts Martial. Its work ranges from protecting individuals in an area where procedural safeguards are ill-defined, to conducting internal investigations on behalf of companies concerned with potential regulatory breaches.
Inland Revenue/Customs & Excise Investigations: The practice has particular expertise in relation to Inland Revenue and Customs & Excise investigations and prosecutions, and litigation concerning the tax authorities, an area where the client's best interests often lie in a negotiated settlement. Often working closely with eminent accountancy practices, Burton Copeland specialises in the protection of its clients' interests in the face of the exceptional powers of investigation of the Inland Revenue and Customs & Excise. It has substantial expertise in securing negotiated financial settlements with the tax authorities and/or bringing judicial review proceedings in respect of their actions, particularly in relation to their extensive information gathering powers, and the conduct of raids under powers conferred by warrants obtained under section 20C of the Taxes Management Act 1970 and Schedule 11 of the Value Added Tax Act 1994.
Environmental & Health & Safety Matters: The firm acts for individuals and companies facing prosecutions for breaches of environmental protection, trading standards and health and safety legislation, and/or orders for the compulsory provision of information.
Criminal Law: Burton Copeland has an established reputation as market leader in the largest and most high profile serious criminal cases, and a number of its partners are recognised as leading individuals in this field. It offers specialist advice across the whole spectrum from homicide to road traffic. Where relevant this expertise is again carried over into the related areas of confiscation and restraint proceedings.
Civil Litigation: The firm also acts in a range of civil proceedings ancillary to its core specialisms.

B

BURTON COPELAND (NORTH)

Royal London House, 196 Deansgate, Manchester, M3 3NE
Tel: (0161) 834 7374 **Fax:** (0161) 839 0364 **DX:** 14362 Manchester 1
Email: commfrauddept@burtoncopeland.com **Website:** www.burtoncopeland.com

34 Castle Street, Liverpool, L2 0RN
Tel: (0151) 243 7500 **Fax:** (0151) 243 7501 **DX:** 14117 Liverpool
Email: lpl@burtoncopeland.com

7-9 Bexley Square, Salford, M3 6DB
Tel: (0161) 833 9398 **Fax:** (0161) 833 9975 **DX:** 14362 Manchester 1
Email: salford@burton-copeland.co.uk

Managing Partner	Michael Mackey
Number of partners	17
Assistant solicitors	12
Other fee-earners	30

AREAS OF PRACTICE

General Crime/Road Traffic	55%
Commercial Fraud/Regulation	25%
Customs/VAT & Tax Controversy	20%

CONTACTS

Commercial Fraud/Regulation/ Customs/VAT & Tax Investigation (Manchester & Liverpool)	Lesley Burrows
	Ian Cooper
	Michael Kenyon
General Crime (Manchester)	Michael Mackey
General Crime (Liverpool)	Colin Downie
General Crime (Salford)	Tim Andrew
Regulation/Employee Representation (Manchester)	Louise Straw
Road Traffic (Manchester)	Gwyn Lewis

THE FIRM: Burton Copeland in the North, formerly in partnership and still in association with Burton Copeland (London), is one of the leading firms nationally in the areas of commercial and corporate fraud, investigations and prosecutions by the Customs & Excise and Inland Revenue, regulatory proceedings and serious crime. With offices in Manchester, Salford and now Liverpool, the firm has long been recognised for its established pre-eminence in these areas. The simple strategy of the firm is to concentrate on providing the highest levels of service and expertise in these core disciplines whilst continuing to expand its office network. Clients range from large international corporations to individuals and instructions are received from all areas of the UK and from clients abroad who may have interests to protect within the UK. The firm is committed to the increasing use of information technology, not only in the management of the practice, but also in relation to case work and has developed its own systems to assist in the preparation of financial fraud cases which grow ever more complex.

PRINCIPAL AREAS OF WORK:

Corporate & Commercial Fraud: The firm has one of the largest and longest established commercial fraud departments in the country with four partners practising full-time in this area and seven assistants. The department became a member of the Serious Fraud panel at its inception and all four partners are accredited by the panel as supervisors of the most serious and complex cases. They are able to offer representation in commercial fraud and other similar prosecutions brought throughout the country. The partners are regarded as being amongst the leaders in the field with experience developed in many of the major prosecutions brought by the SFO and other agencies such as Barlow Clowes, Arrows, Butte Mining and Richmond Oil & Gas. The firm is at the forefront of cases involving stock exchange, accountancy, banking and international investment matters. This expertise and experience is carried over into the related areas of confiscation and civil restraint proceedings, money laundering and extradition.
Inland Revenue & Customs & Excise Investigations: The firm is an acknowledged leading practice in this area, where the client's best interests often lie in a negotiated settlement. Burton Copeland specialises in the protection of its clients' interests in the face of the exceptional powers of investigation which the Inland Rev-

Continued overleaf

enue and Customs & Excise possess. Often working with expert accountancy practices it has substantial experience in securing negotiated financial settlements with the tax authorities as an alternative to prosecution. Nevertheless, if a prosecution is commenced the practice is able to bring to bear its long experience of the criminal law process in the defence of its clients interests.

Regulation & Employee Protection: The firm advises and represents both companies and individuals in respect of investigations and proceedings brought by the many other regulatory and investigatory bodies that have proliferated in recent years such as Trading Standards, the HSE and the Environment Agency. Apart from representation its work ranges from advising potential witnesses to conducting internal investigations on behalf of companies concerned with potential regulatory breaches. In addition, instructions are regularly accepted from trade unions, particularly in the public sector, to advise and represent members being investigated in connection with allegations arising from their employment.

General Crime: The practice has an established reputation as a market leader in the North in general criminal law, and offers specialist advice across the whole spectrum from Courts Martial to homicide. It has substantial experience in areas such as serious crime, drug trafficking cases and confiscation proceedings. Earlier this year the firm was appointed to protect the rights of the players during the Rugby League World Cup. A number of the firms' advocates have Higher Court Rights of Audience, which enables the firm to provide a seamless and cost effective service to its clients in appropriate cases. The recent opening of a major new office in Liverpool emphasises the firms' commitment to provide a full service to its clients and further expansion is planned.

Road Traffic: A specialist area in which Burton Copeland has long had a significant reputation. This is maintained by regular instructions on behalf of a wide spectrum of both corporate and private clients and an innovative approach to problems is always sought.

BURY & WALKERS

4 Butts Court, Leeds, LS1 5JS
Tel: (0113) 244 4227 **Fax:** (0113) 246 5965 **DX:** 12048 Leeds 1
Email: leeds@burywalkers.com

Managing Partners	Simon Nuttall
	Michael Burke
Senior Partner	John Clark

AREAS OF PRACTICE

Litigation	40%
Commercial Property	28%
Private Client	20%
Commercial	12%

CONTACTS

Commercial	John Clark
Commercial Property	Michael Burke
Litigation	Simon Nuttall
Private Client	Alan Duffin

THE FIRM: Bury & Walkers was established over 150 years ago. Its property department is well respected and is currently expanding; it was recently involved with the Bolton Arena and the acquisition of a number of substantial retail and warehouse properties. It aims to provide sound practical advice on a cost effective basis.

PRINCIPAL AREAS OF WORK:

Commercial: Company acquisitions; acts on behalf of national franchiser; Shareholder Agreements including television industry and professional practices.

Commercial Property: Acquisitions and sales, development work, funding, construction and planning. National reputation in relation to residential landlord and tenant work.

Litigation: Expanding department with international disputes and property disputes. Personal injury and general litigation in other offices.

Private Client: Provides a full range of services to private individuals.

CLIENTELE: The firm acts on behalf of private individuals through to three Metropolitan Councils and large commercial organisations.

INTERNATIONAL: Members of Euro Link, an organisation of lawyers throughout Europe, USA and Asia.

BUSS MURTON

The Priory, Tunbridge Wells, TN1 1JJ **Tel:** (01892) 510222 **Fax:** (01892) 522500 **DX:** 3913 Tunbridge Wells **Email:** info@bussmurton.co.uk
Ptnrs: 21 **Asst solrs:** 8 **Other fee-earners:** 32

CADWALADER, WICKERSHAM & TAFT

55 Gracechurch Street, London, EC3V 0EE
Tel: 020 7456 8500 **Fax:** 020 7456 8600 **DX:** 98944 Cheapside 2
Email: cwtinfo@cwt.com **Website:** www.cadwalader.com

Managing Partner	Robert Link Jr
UK	
Number of partners	7
Assistant solicitors	25
Other fee-earners	9
International	
Number of partners	85
Assistant solicitors	295
Other fee-earners	86

THE FIRM: Cadwalader Wickersham & Taft is one of the world's leading international law practices, providing financial institutions, Fortune 500 companies and other leading corporations, government entities, charitable and health care organisations, and private clients with innovative solutions to complex legal and business issues. Cadwalader's London office, staffed primarily with solicitors qualified in England and Wales, was established in 1997 to help clients capitalise on European and worldwide markets, as well as to serve those desiring US style services and access to American financial markets.

PRINCIPAL AREAS OF WORK: Fully integrated with Cadwalader's US offices, the London group is renowned for expertise in financial restructuring, capital markets, energy, project finance and privatisation, litigation, real estate and tax matters.

Financial Restructuring: The London office has substantial experience in contentious and non-contentious insolvency and insolvency litigation, with a particular focus on the insurance and reinsurance industry. In addition, the firm's London lawyers advise clients in all aspects of corporate and corporate finance transactions, including mergers and acquisitions and joint ventures. Members also specialise in debt and equity derivatives (including hedging transactions in relation to corporate mergers and acquisitions and ESOPs) and debt and equity offerings in both the private placement and capital markets. Cadwalader lawyers have extensive experience in both domestic and cross-border transactions and are adept at the coordination of foreign legal, regulatory and other professional advice.

Project Finance: In the project finance sector, Cadwalader's London lawyers have experience in a wide variety of disciplines including energy and power, oil and gas, energy trading, rail, privatisation, telecoms and financing. The group has particular expertise in Europe, Africa, the Far East, the Indian sub-continent and the Middle East.

Capital Markets: Cadwalader is a recognised market leader in the area of capital markets transactions, having assisted clients in over $1 trillion in residential mortgage, commercial mortgage and asset backed deals. The firm represents leading financial institutions in the full range of capital markets transactions, including all forms of bond and note issues, swaps, options, leasing deals and tax driven products and other OTC derivatives.

Real Estate: The firm's leading real estate finance practice is complemented by a practice in London which employs the talents of US and UK lawyers to provide the complete spectrum of real estate representations, from financing, acquisitions, sales and exchanges to development, construction, joint ventures, management and leasing.

Litigation: The litigation department handles significant disputes for a broad spectrum of financial institutions, as well as major commercial, industrial and service corporations and high net worth individuals. The firm also advises on both banking and corporate conflicts arising from the transactions carried out by the financial restructuring and capital markets departments.

CONTACTS

UK CONTACTS

Financial Restructuring & Corporate ....Andrew Wilkinson
....Lyndon Norley
Projects ....Paul Biggs
....Vinay Ganga
Capital Markets ....James Croke
Real Estate ....Alan Lawrence
....Richard Streat
Litigation ....Michelle Duncan

INTERNATIONAL CONTACTS

Financial Restructuring ....Mitchell Sonkin
Corporate & Litigation ....Dennis Block
Projects ....Robert Vitale
Capital Markets ....Robert Link Jr
Real Estate ....W. Christopher White

C

CAINS

15-19 Athol St, Douglas, IM1 1LB **Tel:** (01624) 638 300 **Fax:** (01624) 638 333 **Email:** law@cains.co.im **Website:** www.cains.co.im **Ptnrs:** 6 **Asst solrs:** 14 **Other fee-earners:** 7 **Contact:** Andrew Corlett • The firm handles a comprehensive range of cross-border financial, corporate, commercial and property transactions and has considerable expertise in all areas of litigation and dispute resolution.

CAMPBELL HOOPER

35 Old Queen St, London, SW1H 9JD
Tel: (020) 7222 9070 **Fax:** (020) 7222 5591 **DX:** 2364 Victoria
Email: marketing@campbellhooper.com **Website:** www.campbellhooper.com

Managing Partner	Martin Wright
Number of partners	18
Assistant solicitors	14
Other fee-earners	21

AREAS OF PRACTICE

Corporate & Commercial 30%
Property 25%
Construction 20%
Private Client 17%
Employment 8%

CONTACTS

Corporate/Commercial ....Martin Wright
Media ....Carolyn Jennings
Property ....Stephen Siddall
Construction ....Duncan Salmon
Private Client ....Alex Cuppage
Employment ....William Granger

THE FIRM: Campbell Hooper is a medium-sized commercial practice with an established base of commercial and individual clients. The firm is also a member of Proteus, which is an association of independent European law firms. This gives Campbell Hooper the ability to provide a complete service to its clients by being able to provide immediate access to local advice within Europe.

PRINCIPAL AREAS OF WORK:

Corporate/Commercial (inc. Media): Multidisciplinary teams provide cross-border corporate expertise to domestic and overseas business clients in the fields of mergers and acquisitions; joint ventures; management buy-outs; corporate finance and project finance. The department has a consistent deal flow in the £25-100 million range. It has particular expertise in telecommunications, IT contracts, banking, finance, financial services, and business immigration. As part of the corporate/commercial department, the firm's expertise in media has long been recognised in the market. It has extensive experience in film; TV; theatre; broadcasting; recording and music publishing and collecting societies; video; cable and satellite TV; character and other merchandising and publishing; trademarks and intellectual property. Clients include writers, performers, and creative personnel – many of them leaders in their field.

Property: The firm is well respected within the industry for its expertise in residential and commercial work; mixed-use developments; development and funding; urban regeneration projects; retail; town centre redevelopment; international business parks; property investment. The group acts for a wide range of clients including local authorities, charities, developers, retailers, house builders and banks.

Construction: The construction department works closely with the property department and has extensive experience in all types of traditionally structured development projects. It is increasingly developing its profile in specialist areas which include urban regeneration, private finance initiative and public/private partnerships, and design build finance and operate projects.

Continued overleaf

Private Client (inc. Charities, Estate Planning, Conveyancing & Family): The team offers a full range of services for domestic residential conveyancing which covers sales, purchases, leases, tenancies and mortgages. Through the estate planning section, the department advises both domestic and off-shore clients on all aspects of wealth management including the creation and maintenance of both UK and off-shore trusts, multijurisdictional administration and succession issues. The charities group acts for over 30 national charities.
Employment: The firm advises on the drafting of contracts and procedures, day-to-day employee issues, the employment dimension to commercial transactions as well as on all aspects of contentious employment law in tribunals and courts. Clients' businesses include banks, international corporations, charities, trade unions, advertising and recruitment agencies.

CAMPBELL SMITH WS

21 York Place, Edinburgh, EH1 3EN **Tel:** (0131) 556 3737 **Fax:** (0131) 473 7700 **DX:** 51 Edinburgh **Email:** mailbox@camsmith.co.uk **Ptnrs:** 5 **Asst solrs:** 4 **Other fee-earners:** 3

C

CAPSTICKS

77-83 Upper Richmond Road, London, SW15 2TT
Tel: (020) 8780 2211 **Fax:** (020) 8780 1141 **DX:** 59461 Putney
Email: info@capsticks.co.uk **Website:** www.capsticks.com

Senior Partner	Brian Capstick
Number of partners	21
Assistant solicitors	31
Other fee-earners	20

AREAS OF PRACTICE

Clinical Law	54%
Property	15%
Employment	18%
Dispute Resolution	7%
Commercial	6%

CONTACTS

Administrative Law	James Reynolds
Clinical Law	Janice Smith
Commercial	Christopher Brophy
Commercial Litigation & Regulatory	John Witt
Commercial Property	Hilary Blackwell
Employment	Peter Edwards
Private Finance Initiative	Colin Lynch

THE FIRM: CAPSTICKS is one of the leading legal advisers to the National Health Service. It handles litigation, advisory, commercial and property work for over 100 NHS bodies, as well as other health-related public sector and regulatory bodies and voluntary organisations. Founded in the 1970s to act on behalf of the NHS, CAPSTICKS has developed an outstanding level of expertise through a modern infrastructure of research, training and data management. The firm operates modern quality controls and has held the ISO 9001 standard of quality assurance for professional firms since 1994. It was also in the first wave of firms to be awarded the Law Society's quality standard, LEXCEL, in 1998. CAPSTICKS' innovative approach and standards of excellence have helped the firm to attract an exceptionally able team of lawyers. CAPSTICKS' website includes 'NHS Online', an innovative healthcare legal advice area which draws on the firm's 20 years of experience at the forefront of NHS law and provides online answers to questions on issues such as the NHS plan, Primary Care Groups and the Human Rights Act. Supporting all of this work is an expert system which provides on-line access to CAPSTICKS' database of previous advice, articles and precedents derived from more than 25,000 NHS cases. The firm maintains its own information technology company (which also looks after about 30 other legal practices) and has one of the most advanced IT applications in private practice. CAPSTICKS sees its future in further expansion in the health service and the public sector, through development of all its areas of expertise and innovative services.

PRINCIPAL AREAS OF WORK: The firm's work is divided between the clinical law, commercial, disputes resolution, employment and property departments.
Clinical Law: This department deals with a large volume of cases, ranging from small clinical negligence claims to disasters arising from obstetric accidents, which comprise some of the largest PI claims in this country. Part of CAPSTICKS' research has been into how such accidents may be avoided and this work forms a large part of the firm's pro bono programme. This department also deals with issues arising under the Human Rights and Mental Health Acts.
Commercial: This department advises on the contractual aspects of major PFI and other projects. This work is carried out in multidisciplinary teams with members of the property and employment departments. The department has already completed several major PFI schemes including the first specialist mental health facility and the country's first dedicated ambulatory care and diagnostic centre. The commercial department has particular expertise in the procurement of computer and facilitates management services to the NHS, including the European Union Rules.
Dispute Resolution: This department guides clients through some of the most sensitive decisions taken by the NHS, such as decisions to close major hospitals or departments, from which judicial reviews may well follow. The department also has a growing reputation in the field of healthcare regulatory advice. The department's commercial litigators continue to recover substantial sums of money lost through fraud on the NHS.
Employment: This department provides employment law advice and representation to the NHS, which takes account of the ever growing volume of regulations and guidance which applies to Europe's largest employer.
Property: This department carries out major property development work for the NHS, one of the largest land owners in the country, including PFI. Innovative work is also being carried out in conjunction with other departments including development of new state of the primary care facilities and joint ventures between health authorities and local authorities.

CAREY LANGLOIS

7 New Street, St Peter Port, St Peter Port, GU1 4BZ **Tel:** (01481) 727272 **Fax:** (01481) 711052 **Email:** info@careylanglois.com
Website: www.careylanglois.com

CARLESS DAVIES & CO
140 Stourbridge Road, Halesowen, B63 3UL **Tel:** (0121) 550 2181 **Fax:** (0121) 550 9954 **DX:** 14506 Halesowen **Ptnrs:** 2 **Asst solrs:** 1 **Other fee-earners:** 1

CARNSON MORROW GRAHAM
80 Main Street, Bangor, BT20 5AE **Tel:** (028) 9145 7911 **Fax:** (028) 9145 0679 **DX:** 2501 NR BANGOR 1 **Email:** mail@cmgbangorlaw.demon.co.uk **Website:** www.cmgsolicitors.co.uk **Ptnrs:** 6 **Asst solrs:** 4 **Other fee-earners:** 3

CARRICK CARR & WRIGHT

Norwich House, Savile Street, Kingston upon Hull, HU1 3ES
Tel: (01482) 325385/590000 **Fax:** (01482) 327584 **DX:** 11935 Hull
Email: info@carricks.solicitors.co.uk **Website:** www.carricks-solicitors.co.uk

Appleton House, 3a Wednesday Market, Beverley, HU17 0DG
Tel: (01482) 869342 **Fax:** (01482) 867796 **DX:** 28321 Beverley
Email: info@carricks.solicitors.co.uk

Senior Partner	John Wright
Number of partners	5
Assistant solicitors	4
Other fee-earners	16

PRINCIPAL AREAS OF WORK: Best known for its debt recovery, accident claims, commercial litigation and company/commercial work. Also handles commercial property; conveyancing; family and private client matters; medical negligence.

CARRICK READ INSOLVENCY

Trafalgar House, 29 Park Place, Leeds, LS1 2SP
Tel: (0113) 246 7123 **Fax:** (0113) 244 2863 **DX:** 14085 Leeds

Norwich House, Saville Street, Hull, HU1 3ES
Tel: (01482) 211160 **Fax:** (01482) 585798 **DX:** 119935 Hull

Managing Partner	Christopher Garwood
Number of partners	3
Assistant solicitors	7
Other fee-earners	14

AREAS OF PRACTICE	
Insolvency	100%

THE FIRM: Carrick Read Insolvency is the merged insolvency departments of Read Hind Stewart and Garwood Devine forming a specialist insolvency practice operating from offices in Hull and Leeds. The firm is backed by the combined resources of two offices and more than 140 staff. The partners are all licensed insolvency practitioners and the practice acts on behalf of liquidators, receivers, administrators, trustees and those on both sides of the insolvency procedure.

CARSON MCDOWELL

Murray House, Murray Street, Belfast, BT1 6DN
Tel: (028) 9024 4951 **Fax:** (028) 9024 5768 **DX:** 403 NR Belfast
Email: law@carson-mcdowell.com **Website:** www.carson-mcdowell.com

Senior Partner	Brian Turtle
Number of partners	9
Assistant solicitors	13
Other fee-earners	10

AREAS OF PRACTICE	
Company/Commercial	30%
Commercial Property	30%
Civil Litigation	35%
Private Client	5%

CONTACTS	
Civil Litigation	Brian Turtle
Commercial Lit./Arbitration	Peter Davison
Commercial Property	Alan Reilly
Commercial Security	Tom Adair
Company/Commercial	Michael Johnston
Employment	Brian Turtle
PFI	Michael Johnston
Professional Negligence	Kenneth Gouk

THE FIRM: Founded in 1852, Carson McDowell has an outstanding reputation in Northern Ireland and beyond for its experience in all aspects of corporate and commercial practice, PFI, commercial property, corporate finance, employment, commercial contracts, insolvency, civil litigation and arbitration. It has strong relationships with leading firms in London and the regional centres and also in Scotland, often operating as the NI link in projects for inward investment. The firm's experience and reliability are complemented by the latest technology and by its commitment to achieving its clients' business objectives. To this end Carson McDowell has formed a strategic alliance with leading Dublin firm Mason Hayes & Curran under the title 'i-law'. The firms remain independent, but are now able to offer a seamless and comprehensive legal service covering the whole of the island.

PRINCIPAL AREAS OF WORK:
Company & Commercial: The department offers a complete service, covering all areas of practice and involving close co-operation with other professionals. It has established links with a number of firms in the city of London through working alongside them on many transactions and has acted in the privatisation of Northern Ireland public utilities and in PFI projects. The department is also a leading practice in information and communication technology issues.
Commercial Property: The department deals with the purchase, development, management and sale of business property, from the single shop unit to the city centre office building. It provides a complete package, including planning applications, site assembly, project management, developments by way of lease, mortgage and onward investment sale. This year the department acted as lead adviser to the purchaser in the largest ever single property transaction in Northern Ireland. It is equally experienced in residential development.

Continued overleaf

C

Commercial Security & Banking: The firm has an established finance department which has built sound relationships with financial institutions in the province and beyond. It has extensive experience with the various forms of security which are available and will also deal with investigation of property title, land searches and enquiries, companies office file searches, property insurance cover and appropriate legal registrations and statutory notices.

Litigation: An experienced team, not only in the traditional court system but also in equal opportunity, employment and lands tribunal and building arbitrations. The firm also acts in more specialised fields of law such as professional negligence, marine law, defamation, carriage of goods and environment, as well as in areas which are unique to Northern Ireland such as the Criminal Damage Legislation, Fair Employment Law, and the licensing of the sale of intoxicating liquor and bookmakers' premises. In the business field it handles all types of commercial litigation, from simple debt collection (the firm's debt collection system has its own dedicated computer base) through normal contractual claims, intellectual property and employment problems to the major commercial dispute which may involve domestic and European law. In addition, the firm will deal with all aspects of corporate insolvency, both contentious and non-contentious.

CARTER HODGE

18 Hoghton St, Southport, PR9 0PB
Tel: (01704) 531991 **Fax:** (01704) 537475 **DX:** 20102
Email: information@carterhodge.co.uk **Website:** www.carterhodge.co.uk

Managing Partners	Mark Robinson David M Rigby
Number of partners	7
Assistant solicitors	6
Other fee-earners	8

THE FIRM: Carter Hodge is a general practice offering a wide range of services to business and private clients.Tracing its origins from 1889, the firm has a modern and progressive outlook highlighted by its involvement with Legal Aid Franchising, Investors in People and Practice Management Standards.

PRINCIPAL AREAS OF WORK: Litigation (High Court work, commercial litigation, PI and professional negligence); family; company/commercial; property; private client; and employment. The firm has other offices in Ainsdale, Birkdale, and Heswall.

CONTACTS

Clinical Negligence	Rachael Vasmer
Commercial Conveyancing	Guy Wigmore
General Litigation	Mark Robinson
Matrimonial	Philip Porter
Personal Injury	Mark Robinson
Probate & Trust	David Byard
Residential Conveyancing	David Byard

CARTER LEMON CAMERONS

11 Breams Building, London, EC4A 1DW **Tel:** (020) 7405 7554 **Fax:** (020) 7242 3926 **DX:** 25 London/Chancery Lane **Email:** [name]@cartercameros.co.uk **Website:** www.cartercamerons.com **Ptnrs:** 17 **Asst solrs:** 3 **Other fee-earners:** 8

CARTMELL SHEPHERD

Viaduct House, Carlisle, CA3 8EZ **Tel:** (01228) 516666 **Fax:** (01228) 401490 **DX:** 63006 **Email:** post@cartmells.co.uk **Website:** www.cartmells.co.uk **Ptnrs:** 16 **Asst solrs:** 12 **Other fee-earners:** 12

CARTWRIGHT KING

Norwich Union House, South Parade, Old Market Square, Nottingham, NG1 2LJ **Tel:** (0115) 958 7444 **Fax:** (0115) 958 8666 **DX:** 10032 Nottingham **Email:** ck@cartwrightking.co.uk **Website:** www.cartwrightking.co.uk **Ptnrs:** 4 **Asst solrs:** 5 **Other fee-earners:** 7

CARTWRIGHT & LEWIS

100 Hagley Road, Edgbaston, Birmingham, B16 8LT **Tel:** (0121) 246 3000 **Fax:** (0121) 246 3050 **DX:** 707293 Edgbaston **Email:** legal@cartwrightlewis.co.uk **Website:** www.cartwrightlewis.co.uk **Ptnrs:** 9 **Asst solrs:** 12 **Other fee-earners:** 18 **Contact:** Anthony Rich • The firm has one of the largest personal injury departments in the West Midlands. It is known for commercial litigation, commercial property, employment law and comprehensive private client services.

AREAS OF PRACTICE

Personal Injury	32%
Private Client	24%
Property	22%
Commercial Litigation	11%
Company/Commercial	11%

CARTWRIGHTS ADAMS & BLACK

36 West Bute Street, Cardiff, CF10 5UA **Tel:** (029) 2046 5959 **Fax:** (029) 2048 0006 **DX:** 200751 Cardiff Bay **Ptnrs:** 5 **Asst solrs:** 5 **Other fee-earners:** 1

CARTWRIGHTS INSURANCE PARTNERS

2nd Floor, Netherton House, 23-29 Marsh St, Bristol, BS1 4AQ **Email:** info@ci.partners.co.uk **Website:** www.ci.partners.co.uk

CAWDERY KAYE FIREMAN & TAYLOR

25-26 Hampstead High Street, London, NW3 1QA
Tel: (020) 7431 7262 **Fax:** (020) 7431 7261 **DX:** 57567 Hampstead
Email: law@ckft.com

Number of partners	9
Assistant solicitors	5
Other fee-earners	5
Total staff	35

THE FIRM: This highly regarded firm has an established reputation for advising commercial clients and high net worth individuals. Its focus and speciality is consistent with firms of a similar type in the West End and the City, whilst its location in Hampstead ensures a continuing emphasis on cost effectiveness. Founded in 1992 by three of its current partners, Graham Kaye, Daniel Fireman and Simon Taylor, the firm has expanded rapidly and now acts for substantial companies in London, nationally and abroad. It aims to offer clients success with an innovative approach to solving complex legal problems, and has invested heavily to ensure that its information technology is, and remains, at the cutting edge. Cawdery Kaye Fireman & Taylor strives continually to establish and maintain its close relationship with clients. Their needs are understood and their requirements dealt with quickly and effectively.

PRINCIPAL AREAS OF WORK: The firm has particular strengths in commercial litigation, business and company transactions, landlord and tenant, property development and matrimonial work.
Litigation: The litigation department, headed by Simon Taylor, handles commercial, contractual and negligence claims, shareholder disputes, banking litigation, insolvency, debt recovery and high value personal injury work.
Property: The firm has a strong property group whose work includes development (from site acquisition through to individual plot sales), investment, all types of commercial property acquisitions and disposals, and landlord and tenant matters.
Corporate: The corporate department is regularly retained to deal with company purchases and sales, start-ups, partnerships and joint ventures.
Private Client: The firm's traditional private client base has benefited from the recent expansion of the practice and the firm is able to advise on all aspects of wills, trusts, probate and inheritance tax planning.
Family & Matrimonial: With a team of seven lawyers, this department handles all family law issues for high net worth individuals, with many cases involving international elements such as property held offshore or by foreign trusts.Cawdery Kaye Fireman & Taylor provides its clients with the highest quality service. Further expansion in all areas is expected.

RECRUITMENT: Although the firm is committed to organic growth, key appointments have been made from outside, with Pamela Collis joining the firm in 1999 to expand and head its highly regarded matrimonial department.

CCL

196 Old Street, London, EC1V 9FR **Tel:** 020 7253 2277 **Fax:** 020 7253 2288 **Email:** info@cclsolicitors.com **Ptnrs:** 2 **Other fee-earners:** 3

CEDR SOLVE

Princes House, 95 Gresham Street, London, EC2V 7NA **Tel:** (020) 7600 0500 **Fax:** (020) 7600 0501

CHAFFE STREET

Brook House, 77 Fountain Street, Manchester, M2 2EE
Tel: (0161) 236 5800 **Fax:** (0161) 228 6862 **DX:** 14431 Manchester
Email: lawyer@chaffestreet.co.uk

Senior Partner	Robert Street
Number of partners	16
Assistant solicitors	11
Other fee-earners	7

AREAS OF PRACTICE

Company/Commercial/ Corporate Recovery	65%
Commercial Property	25%
Commercial Litigation	10%

THE FIRM: The firm provides a full range of specialist commercial legal services, namely company/commmercial work, commercial property, corporate recovery and commercial orientated litigation.

PRINCIPAL AREAS OF WORK: The services available include flotations, acqusitions and disposals, mergers, management buy-outs, banking law, venture and investment capital, project and asset financing, corporate finance, insolvency, intellectual property, competition law, employment law, pensions, aircraft, commercial property and environmental law.

CHALLINORS LYON CLARK

Guardian House, Cronehills Linkway, West Bromwich, B70 8SW **Tel:** (0121) 553 3211 **Fax:** (0121) 553 2079 **DX:** 713650 West Bromwich 6
Email: jr@challinors.co.uk **Website:** www.challinors.co.uk **Ptnrs:** 28 **Asst solrs:** 18 **Other fee-earners:** 24

CHAMBERS & CO

Jonathan Scott Hall, Thorpe Road, Norwich, NR1 1UH **Tel:** (01603) 616 155 **Fax:** (01603) 616 156 **Ptnrs:** 1 **Asst solrs:** 1 **Other fee-earners:** 1

CHAPMAN EVERATT

5 Shaw Park, Shaw Road, Wolverhampton, WV10 9LE **Tel:** (01902) 717700 **Fax:** (01902) 717447 **DX:** 13025 Birmingham 1
Email: richardchapman@chapmaneveratt.co.uk **Ptnrs:** 4 **Asst solrs:** 1 **Other fee-earners:** 2

CHARLES DODSON – SOLE PRACTITIONER

Lone Barn, Brown Candover, Alresford, SO24 9TW **Tel:** 07802 389 127 **Fax:** 01256 389 575 **Email:** CPDodson@CandoverMediation.com

CHARLES LUCAS & MARSHALL

Radnor House, 28 Bartholomew Street, Newbury, RG14 5EU
Tel: (01635) 521212 **Fax:** (01635) 37784 **DX:** 30802 Newbury
Email: ask@clmsolicitors.co.uk **Website:** www.clmsolicitors.co.uk

Senior Partner	Susan Burnell
Managing Partner	Peter Graham
Finance Partner	Christopher Ball
Head of Practice Development	Hemant Amin
Number of partners	11
Associates	6
Other fee-earners	16

CONTACTS

Agricultural	David Thomas
Charity Law	Michael Overend
Commercial Property	David Thomas
Corporate Services	Stewart McMinn
Litigation	Michael Berrett
Residential Property	Neil Angel
Wills & Estate Planning	Richard Mead

THE FIRM: Charles Lucas & Marshall focuses on giving its clients the very best quality service. The firm places client care at the heart of its business strategy and has acted for businesses of all sizes and advised families over many generations. The firm is now a substantial commercial practice with offices in Newbury, Hungerford, Wantage and Swindon, covering a wide area throughout south east England.

PRINCIPAL AREAS OF WORK:
Corporate Services: Acquisitions disposals and restructuring of companies, intellectual property, employment law, franchising, contract law, joint ventures, management buyouts and buy-ins, partnerships, EU law and IT. The firm also deals with trademarks and patents and has a trademark agent.
Commercial Property: Acquisitions and disposals, development sites, planning and infrastructure agreements, land options, farms, retail and office and business sales and purchases.
Residential Property: Comprehensive service from small flats to country houses and large estates offering speed and efficiency.
Litigation: Specialist areas: medical negligence, personal injury, employment law, family, childcare, property disputes, contentious probate and mediation.
Agricultural: The firm handles sale and purchase of farms, leases, agricultural holdings, partnerships.
Wills & Estate Planning: Wills, administration of estates, setting up of lifetime trusts, management of financial affairs through to inheritance tax planning.
Charity Law: Registration, formation and disputes are covered. The firm is a member of the Charity Lawyers Association.

RECRUITMENT: Applications by letter and CV to Lance Parker.

CHARLES RUSSELL

8-10 New Fetter Lane, London, EC4A 1RS
Tel: (020) 7203 5000 **Fax:** (020) 7203 0200 **DX:** 19 London/Chancery Lane
Email: enquiry@cr-law.co.uk **Website:** www.charlesrussell.co.uk

Buryfields House, Bury Fields, Guildford, GU2 4AZ
Tel: (01483) 252525 **Fax:** (01483) 252550 **DX:** 2436 Guildford 1
Email: guildford@cr-law.co.uk

Killowen House, Bayshill Road, Cheltenham, GL50 3AW
Tel: (01242) 221122 **Fax:** (01242) 584700 **DX:** 7442 Cheltenham 1
Email: enquiry@cr-law.co.uk

Senior Partner	Laurence Watt
Managing Partner	Grant Howell
Number of partners	76
Assistant solicitors	95
Other fee-earners	66

AREAS OF PRACTICE

Private Capital/Family	26%
Media & Communications	20%
Charities	12%
Employment	12%
Commercial Property	10%
Litigation (Commercial)	10%
Other Corporate & Commercial	10%

CONTACTS

Charities	Michael Scott
Commercial Property	David Horner
Computer Law	David Berry
Corporate & Commercial	Simon Gilbert
Employment	David Green
Family	David Davidson
Insurance/Reinsurance	Stephen Carter
Intellectual Property	Robin Bynoe
Litigation	Richard Vallance
Media & Communications	Mark Moncreiffe
Pensions & Employee Benefits	George Duncan
Planning	Geoffrey Jordan
Private Capital	Catriona Syed
Private Property	Ian Cooke
Sport	Patrick Russell
Tax	Tarl Lall

THE FIRM: Charles Russell may have a long standing reputation for family and private client work, but today around 70% of the firm's work is commercial, with major corporate clients in the media, telecoms, IT, employment and voluntary sectors. Unlike many of their competitors in the UK top 50, the firm is not in the business of shedding private clients for more lucrative commercial work. The two kinds of practice are viewed as complementary. Today's wealthy private clients may well be leaders in business, and successful business people have private lives too. Both have extensive involvements overseas, where the firm has long established and important connections. The result is that the firm is growing rapidly on all fronts, driven by a single-minded commitment to being in the top echelon in each of its core areas. It is not just commercial and professional enthusiasm that motivates the firm. It manages to retain many of the more human traits that make it an invigorating and enjoyable place to work. A strong team spirit is proving a potent recipe for success across both the workforce and an unusually broad client base.

PRINCIPAL AREAS OF WORK:
Media & Communications: The media and communications group provides an integrated service to the converging industries which includes telecommunications, information technology, multimedia, film, music, entertainment and sport.

Employment: The employment group is now one of the largest employment teams in the City and provides a comprehensive service.
Charities: A long-established and expanding charity practice comprises a team of specialists who provide a wide range of legal services to the voluntary sector. The annual Charles Russell Charity Conference is becoming 'an institution' in the conference calendar for not-for-profit organisations.
Private Client & Family: One of the UK's leading private client and family practices. The family team deals with all issues relating to marriage, its breakdown, separation and divorce, residence, adoption and child abduction, often involving legal and financial disputes in different jurisdictions. The private capital team advises individuals and institutions, both here and internationally, on tax, trusts, estate restructuring, probate, trust administration, agriculture and property transactions and management.
Corporate/Commercial: Transactions handled include stock market flotations; mergers and acquisitions; venture capital financing; banking; institutional funding arrangements; management buy-outs and buy-ins; business start-ups and corporate rescues; commercial contracts of all kinds; agency and distribution agreements; joint ventures and outsourcing; partnership matters; all aspects of corporate tax.
Dispute Resolution: The dispute resolution team deals with litigation, arbitration and mediation both in the UK and overseas, with a special emphasis on commercial disputes, contentious IP, sports regulation, judicial review, pharmacy law and clinical and professional negligence.
Insurance: The firm's specialist insurance group advises international insurance/reinsurance companies and consultants, Lloyd's syndicates, mutuals, brokers, underwriting agents and run-off managers on both contentious and non-contentious matters.
Commercial Property: The commercial property group advises investors, developers and occupiers. In addition to handling the acquisition/disposal of industrial, commercial and retail property, the team devises and negotiates development and financing transactions. It also handles landlord and tenant agreements, all aspects of management for commercial property and planning matters.

C

CHARSLEY HARRISON

Madeira House, Madeira Walk, Windsor, SL4 1EU
Tel: (01753) 851591 **Fax:** (01753) 832550 **DX:** 3800 Windsor
Email: mail@charsleyharrison.com **Website:** www.charsleyharrison.co.uk

Notaries Public	Phillip Jones (01753) 851591
	Giles Shedden (01753) 496500
	Peter Beech (01753) 517600
Number of partners	5
Assistant solicitors	5
Other fee-earners	6

AREAS OF PRACTICE

Property	40%
Company/Commercial	35%
Litigation/Family Law	20%
Probate/Trust	5%

CONTACTS

Company/Commercial/Property	Phillip Jones
Litigation/Family Law	Kate McCulloch
Probate/Trust	Giles Shedden

THE FIRM: Formed by the merger in 1973 of two long established and well respected Thames Valley practices, Charsley Harrison is a modern, forward-thinking firm geared to meet the needs of both commercial and private clients. The practice has developed rapidly in recent years to represent a wide range of business clients throughout the UK, the EC, the USA and the Pacific Basin and has established links with commercial lawyers in the major cities of the USA, Australia and throughout Europe. Two offices of the practice have recently joined forces in Windsor which will enable a high degree of partner involvement in the day-to-day matters of clients, together with a prompt, efficient and professional service. Other offices are located in Ascot and Slough.

PRINCIPAL AREAS OF WORK:
Company/Commercial: A comprehensive service both domestically and internationally encompassing corporate finance; competition; acquisitions and disposals; mergers; MBOs and joint ventures; distribution and agency agreements; intellectual property rights; taxation; insolvency and employment law matters.
Litigation: All aspects of litigation for both corporate and private clients in the UK and abroad before a wide range of courts and tribunals. Work includes general contractual and commercial disputes; misrepresentation; employment matters; insolvency and banking-related litigation; personal injury; professional negligence and defamation.
Property: Extensive experience of property transactions including purchase; sale; leasing and mortgaging of commercial and retail property; estate development; planning and environmental advice; licensing; site assembly; joint ventures and agricultural property.
Private Client: The firm has a long tradition in providing a friendly and efficient service to individuals in all aspects of their private legal affairs. Work includes wills; tax and estate planning; personal and family finance; investment management; pensions; saving schemes and school fees planning; charity law and Court of Protection work. A full service is also provided in relation to matrimonial and family law including childcare and adoption.

INTERNATIONAL: The firm works with an associate firm in the Netherlands.

CHIOMENTI STUDIO LEGALE

20 Berkeley Square, London, W1J 6HF
Tel: (020) 7569 1500 **Fax:** (020) 7569 1501
Email: london@chiomenti.net

Managing Partner	Giorgio Cappelli
Senior Partner	Luigi Bendi
Number of partners	3
Assistant solicitors	7
Of-counsel	1

AREAS OF PRACTICE

Banking & Finance 40%
Securities & Capital Markets 30%
Taxation 20%
Corporate/M&A 10%

CONTACTS

Banking & Finance .... Luigi Bendi
Corporate/M&A ...... Fillippo Domenico Vassalli
Securities & Capital Markets Giorgio Cappelli
Taxation .... Giulia Battaglia

THE FIRM: Chiomenti Studio Legale continues the practice started by Avv. Pasquale Chiomenti in Rome in the mid 40s. The firm was established in England during 1993, has developed rapidly, particularly during the latter parts of the 90s, and now has a strong presence in the market. It is currently composed of 11 fee-earners.

PRINCIPAL AREAS OF WORK: The firm handles banking and finance; corporate, mergers and acquisitions; anti-trust and EU legislation; taxation; real estate; litigation and arbitration; telecommunications and IT.

CLIENTELE: The firm's clients are predominantly Italian and foreign industrial corporations, banks, insurance companies, financial institutions and corporations. The firm has also acted for the Italian government and local authorities, foreign governments and public entities (including central banks), and international organisations (including the Commission of the European Communities).

INTERNATIONAL: The firm has advised on a substantial number of Italy's major business transactions including IPOs, privatisations, mergers and acquisitions, structured finance and capital markets. The firm is associated with Lex Mundi. Languages spoken are English and Italian.

RECRUITMENT: The firm is always looking for individuals who can make a contribution to its success. Recent growth provides opportunities for qualified solicitors across a range of specialisms. There are also vacancies for trainee solicitors. Candidates must have an Italian J.D. Long term prospects are excellent. Contact S. Djemili for application information.

C

CHIVERS WALSH SMITH & IRVINE & CO

Broadway House, 9 Bank Street, Bradford, BD1 6HN **Tel:** (01274) 740 077 **Fax:** (01274) 740 442 **Email:** solicitors@cwslaw.co.uk **Ptnrs:** 5 **Asst solrs:** 2 **Other fee-earners:** 6

CHRISTIAN FISHER

42 Museum Street, Bloomsbury, London, WC1A 1LY
Tel: (020) 7831 1750 **Fax:** (020) 7831 1726 **DX:** 35737 Bloomsbury
Email: info@christianf.co.uk **Website:** www.christianf.co.uk

Number of partners	5
Assistant solicitors	15
Other fee-earners	5

THE FIRM: Christian Fisher was set up in 1985 and specialises in civil liberties and human rights work. The firm has a long-standing reputation for undertaking high profile test cases in these areas and a commitment to delivering high quality legal aid work. It has franchises in personal injury, crime, housing, employment and immigration, cases against the police, family, mental health, clinical negligence, education, community care and public law.

PRINCIPAL AREAS OF WORK:
Human Rights Cases: The firm expects to bring many test cases under the new Human Rights Act. Past cases have included the lead Court of Appeal case on damages against the police (Hsu). Cases on suing the police for negligence (Osman in the ECHR and Reeves in the House of Lords), racial attacks and murders (Ricky Reel), deaths in custody (Wayne Douglas), many judicial reviews of government and miscarriage of justice cases.
Personal Injury: The firm has a particular profile in the areas of construction, environmental and transport safety and a substantial caseload in these areas. It has acted in the Lockerbie and Marchioness disasters and is the lead firm in the Steering Committees representing the victims of the Paddington and Southall train crashes.
Medical Negligence: Wrongful birth and obstetric cases; accident and emergency cases; GP and hospital negligence; GMC prosecutions.
Crime: Major criminal trials including fraud, political crime and miscarriages of justice.
Family: Childcare and other work.
Mental Health: Tribunal representation.
Employment: Particularly race and sex discrimination and trades union cases.
Housing: For tenants – disrepair and homelessness.
Immigration: A track record in acting for asylum seekers.
Public Law: Inquests and judicial reviews.

THE CITY LAW PARTNERSHIP

99 Charterhouse Street, London, EC1M 6NQ **Tel:** (020) 7253 5505 **Fax:** (020) 7253 5525 **DX:** 53346 CLERKENWELL **Email:** law@citylaw.com **Website:** www.citylaw.com **Ptnrs:** 4 **Asst solrs:** 10 **Other fee-earners:** 2

C & J BLACK

Linenhall House, 13 Linenhall Street, Belfast, BT2 8AA **Tel:** (028) 90550060 **Fax:** (028) 90234125 **DX:** 431 NR Belfast 1 **Ptnrs:** 3 **Asst solrs:** 1

CLAIRMONTS

9 Clairmont Gardens, Glasgow, G3 7LW **Tel:** (0141) 331 4000 **Fax:** (0141) 221 0123 **DX:** 512212 Glasgow **Email:** info@clairmonts.co.uk **Website:** www.clairmonts.co.uk **Ptnrs:** 4 **Asst solrs:** 2

CLARICOAT PHILLIPS

140 Barnsbury Road, London, N1 0ER **Tel:** (020) 7226 7000 **Fax:** (020) 7833 4408 **Email:** Philcoat@aol.com **Ptnrs:** 2

CLARKE WILLMOTT & CLARKE

St James Court, St James Parade, Bristol, BS1 3LH
Tel: (0117) 941 6600 **Fax:** (0117) 941 6622 **DX:** 78247 Bristol 1
Website: www.cw-c.co.uk

Blackbrook Gate, Blackbrook Park Avenue, Taunton, TA1 2PG
Tel: (01823) 442266 **Fax:** (01823) 445800 **DX:** 97175 Taunton Blackbrook

Number of partners	45
Assistant solicitors	56
Directors	4
Other fee-earners	125

AREAS OF PRACTICE

Property & Planning Services	33%
Litigation Services	30%
Private Client Services	19%
Commercial Services	18%

CONTACTS

Agriculture & Estates	Tim Russ
Asset Management	Peter Nellist
Banking & Lender Services	Philip Tebbatt
Clinical Negligence	Andrew Hannam
Commercial Litigation	Chris Taylor
Commercial Property	Roger Seaton
Corporate	Nigel Lindsay
Employment	Kevin Jones
Environmental	Neil Baker
	Tim Hayden
Family	Felicity Shakespear
Financial Services	Robert Morfee
Insolvency & Debt Collection	Stephen Allinson LIP
IT/IP	Richard Harrap
Licensing	Tim Hayden
Mediation/ADR/CEDR	David Sedgwick
Personal Injury	Peter Livingstone
Planning	Nick Engert
Private Client	Stuart Thorne
Probate & Trusts	Peter Nellist
Professional Indemnity	Tim Russ
Sports Law	David Powell
Volume (Residential) Conveyancing	Angela Thompson

THE FIRM: Clarke Willmott & Clarke is one of the leading regional South West firms, with a reputation and client base that extends far outside the region. The firm's reputation has been built not only on the strengths of both its litigation and property teams, but on its complementary skills in commercial services and private client work. Increasingly, clients require skills taken from several discipline areas and this has led to the growing importance of the firm's market sector teams, which include agriculture and food services, lender services, land developers, volume conveyancing for lenders and legal expenses insurers (personal injury). CW&C's client research shows that the firm is consistently regarded for their practical, results-orientated, commercial solutions with an emphasis on cost-effective delivery. In recognition of this, CW&C has been awarded the Law Society's Lexcel accreditation. The firm is equally recognised for its ability to grow and maintain long-term client relationships using multi-disciplinary teams. Technology plays an increasingly vital role in maintaining internal communications, reducing client costs, providing management data and enhancing client relationships.

PRINCIPAL AREAS OF WORK:

Litigation: This remains a key part of the practice and CW&C is particularly regarded for its work in the areas of professional negligence, claimant personal injury, clinical negligence, corporate recovery and insolvency, employment disputes, landlord and tenant, international contract disputes and specialist prosecution services, such as health and safety, environmental pollution offences, food safety and fraud. Through the merger with Alsters, the firm now has a nationally regarded sports law practice, which handles both contentious and non-contentious work in this sector.

Property: The property team continues to develop its three key areas of expertise: land development, planning and environmental and commercial property. It has seen substantial growth in its client base in all three practice areas, particularly in land development and planning and environmental work. The firm is now able to offer land developers a full range of services including strategic land advice, land acquisition and plot sales. CW&C work on behalf of an expanding list of land developers throughout the South and Midlands. The firm's planning and environmental team has unrivalled expertise regionally and is particularly recognised for its advice regarding town and country planning, 'Brown land' issues, Section 106 agreements and public inquiry representation. The environmental team offers a full range of contentious and non-contentious advice, particularly in the areas of contaminated land, minerals and waste disposal. The commercial property team specialises in secured lending, licensed premises, project management of complex sites and commercial developments, including PFI contracts.

Commercial/Corporate: The commercial/corporate teams continue to support these teams by providing transactional advice on take-overs, MBOs, MBIs, joint ventures, share holder agreements, management restructures, acquisitions and sales, intellectual property and competition law.

Private Client: Private client and asset management also play a key role in complementing the two main practice strengths. CW&C is recognised as the South West's leading private client team. Private client services include personal tax planning, asset management, wills, trusts and probate, and family and matrimonial.

RECRUITMENT: Training and personal development continue to be given high prominence and the firm has been awarded the Investor in People accreditation in recognition of this. The firm has a commitment to fast-tracking talented individuals.

CLARKE WILLMOTT & CLARKE SOLICITORS

INVESTOR IN PEOPLE

CLARK HOLT

1 Sanford Street, Swindon, SN1 1HJ **Tel:** (01793) 617444 **Fax:** (01793) 617436 **DX:** 38606 Swindon (2) **Email:** richardc@clarkholt.com **Website:** www.clarkholt.com **Ptnrs:** 5 **Asst solrs:** 2 **Other fee-earners:** 1 **Contact:** Richard Clark • Specialises exclusively in commercial law in the area of corporate, commercial and computer law, and commercial property.

AREAS OF PRACTICE	
Corporate	45%
Commercial Property	35%
Commmercial/Computer	20%

CLARK RICKETTS

Kingsway House, 103 Kingsway, London, WC2B 6QX **Tel:** (020) 7404 1551 **Fax:** (020) 7404 2662 **Email:** aviationlaw@clarkricketts.com **Ptnrs:** 2 **Asst solrs:** 1 **Other fee-earners:** 1

CLARKS

Great Western House, Station Rd, Reading, RG1 1JX
Tel: (0118) 958 5321 **Fax:** (0118) 960 4611 **DX:** 54700 Reading 2
Email: inmail@clarks-solicitors.co.uk **Website:** www.clarks-solicitors.co.uk

Managing Partner	Michael Sippitt
Number of partners	15
Assistant solicitors	26
Other fee-earners	30

CONTACTS	
Advertising	Peter James
Banking & Finance	David Clark
Commercial & European	Peter James
Commercial Dispute Resolution & Litigation	Antony Morris
Commercial Property	Derek Ching
Company & Corporate Finance	Richard Lee
Construction	David Rintoul
Corporate Recovery	David Clark
Debt Recovery	Kirstin Wells
Employment Services	Michael Sippitt
Environment	Derek Ching
Health & Medical Services	Derek Ching
Information Technology	Peter James
Intellectual Property	Peter James
Pensions	David Clark
Planning	Simon Dimmick
Public Sector	Derek Ching
Residential Property	Mary Robertson
Wills, Trusts & Tax Planning	Jo Barton

Clarks
Solicitors

C

THE FIRM: Clarks is a commercial law firm with a proven track record across the UK and overseas. Its clients range from small and medium sized enterprises to multinationals. Clarks is particularly recognised for the number of international and FTSE 250 clients who have chosen to use the firm. Clarks is committed to a strategy based on forging proactive relationships. Clarks' lawyers are supported by the latest technologies and the best of in-house resources. This provides maximum opportunity for efficiency and innovation. The end result is that whatever clients' legal needs, a specialist team at Clarks can be depended upon to work in partnership with the client to meet its objectives. Clarks is determined to stay one step ahead in the evolving market place by listening carefully to its clients and responding quickly to their needs. In over 85 years Clarks has built the practice its clients want. Clarks' lawyers take pride in providing high standards of skill and service. They share a common objective which is to provide clear and constructive commercial advice. The firm enjoys a straightforward business relationship with its clients and offers a variety of approaches to pricing. Clarks creates training programmes geared to individual clients and industry sectors. These are specifically designed to equip managers to identify and avoid potential legal problems. Clarks is part of TAGLaw, an international network of law firms providing clients with professional services in numerous locations around the world. It operates on the principles of transparency of business terms, close client relationships, consistent quality and the provision of timely and cost-effective service.

PRINCIPAL AREAS OF WORK:

Corporate: Clarks has a long established and highly regarded corporate practice. It manages substantial and specialist transactions. It has a growing reputation for its work in finance related fields, particularly consumer finance and advertising and insolvency. This combines with general commercial work to offer a highly resourced general corporate/commercial service.

Commercial Litigation: Clarks remains the principal regional commercial litigation practice offering specialist expertise, including hands-on experience of successful ADR. The construction law services provided include both contentious and non-contentious work.

Commercial Property: A large commercial property team acts for owners, developers, tenants, investors and funders, providing a comprehensive service. A highly skilled planning and development team handles planning applications and appeals. COMBAT (Clarks' Owner Managed Business Advisory Team) is a service provided that combines cross-departmental skills to offer a tailored team to meet the particular needs of owner managed businesses.

Employment: The employment services unit is one of the fastest growing of the firm's practice areas and enjoys an enviable national reputation. It also carries out extensive training and is particularly proactive in developing new employment related services including workshops, in-house seminars and human resources support.

IT & IP: The firm's IT and intellectual property unit handles a varied portfolio of contentious and non-contentious work. Services include copyright, e-commerce, Internet domain name issues, trademark, passing off, patents, licensing and infringement issues, computer system supply and software licence terms and IT outsourcing.

Private Client: The firm has busy private client and residential conveyancing teams, offering private client services to corporate quality standards.

CLIENTELE: Clients include listed companies, public sector bodies and not-for-profit organisations especially health, education and local government. Clarks assigns a partner to each client, providing a consistent personal point of contact. The firm actively encourages the development of relationships with other specialists from different disciplines, providing clients with a known and trusted team of lawyers to help with more complex projects. The firm strongly believes in working in partnership with clients and has developed case plans and client protocols to facilitate this. Case plans provide a client with a project snapshot detailing timings, key events and estimated costs. Client protocols clearly define the basis of an ongoing relationship and the manner in which services are provided. Clarks' lawyers also devise and deliver highly successful client training workshops, enhancing management performance through greater knowledge of the relevant law and procedures.

RECRUITMENT: The firm continues to seek individuals who can contribute to its success. Current growth provides opportunities for qualified solicitors across a range of specialisms.

CLARKSON WRIGHT & JAKES

Valiant House, 12 Knoll Rise, Orpington, BR6 0PG
Tel: (01689) 887887 **Fax:** (01689) 887888 **DX:** 31603 Orpington
Email: cwj@cwj.co.uk **Website:** www.cwj.co.uk

Managing Partner	Claire Singleton
Senior Partner	Leslie Seldon
Number of partners	11
Assistant solicitors	6
Other fee-earners	19

AREAS OF PRACTICE

Private Client	25%
Personal Injury Litigation	20%
Commercial Litigation	15%
Commercial Property	15%
Company/Commercial (including Notarial)	15%
Employment	10%

CONTACTS

Commercial	Michael North
Commercial Litigation	Leslie Seldon
Personal Injury	David Greenhalgh
Private Client	Amanda Custis
	Peter Giblin

THE FIRM: Established in 1875, Clarkson Wright & Jakes is a substantial commercial practice whose aim is to offer a personal service tailored to clients' specific needs. The firm, a member of LawNet, undertakes a wide range of legal work, and offers notarial services and the expertise of units specialising in employment, partnership and doctors' matters. The firm advises French commercial clients and UK clients with interests in France. It has been recognized as an Investor in People and has achieved ISO 9002 accreditation.

PRINCIPAL AREAS OF WORK:

Company & Commercial: Company and business acquisitions and sales; MBOs and MBIs; franchise; agency; distribution and other commercial agreements; conditions of sale; terms of business; partnership especially for doctors; business start-ups.
Employment: Contracts of employment and other employment documentation; claims in the industrial tribunals and civil courts for dismissal, discrimination and breach of contract.
Commercial Property: Acquisition; mortgage and disposal of freehold and leasehold shops; factories and other properties; landlord and tenant matters (including lease renewals and surrenders).
Commercial Litigation: Company; commercial and partnership disputes; construction disputes; arbitration; landlord and tenant matters; defamation; professional negligence; passing off actions and contractual disputes; licensing; debt collection.
Personal Injury Litigation: Motor; employers' and public liability claims; industrial disease and professional indemnity claims; and medical negligence.
Private Client: Residential property; wills and trusts; tax planning; enduring powers of attorney; winding-up of estates and executorships; Court of Protection; and matrimonial.

INTERNATIONAL: Members of the firm also conduct business in French, German and Spanish.

CLAUDE HORNBY & COX

35-36 Great Marlborough Street, London, W1F 7JE
Tel: (020) 7437 8873 **Fax:** (020) 7494 3070 **DX:** 37211 Piccadilly
Email: law@claudehornbycox.fsnet.co.uk

Senior Partner	Richard Hallam
Number of partners	2
Assistant solicitors	6
Other fee-earners	5

CONTACTS

Civil Litigation/Conveyancing	Mohammed Mir
Criminal Litigation/Disciplinary Proceedings	Richard Hallam

THE FIRM: A leading specialist criminal practice for over 70 years, providing all its clients, whether privately paying or legally aided, with high quality but reasonably priced advice and representation on any criminal matter.

PRINCIPAL AREAS OF WORK:

Crime: The firm defends clients in cases ranging from murder, terrorism, firearms and drug-related offences, and corporate fraud on a multi-million pound scale, to driving offences and shoplifting. The fraud work includes acting in major SFO, HM Customs and Excise, and Inland Revenue Investigations. The practice also prosecutes for individuals and corporate clients. The partners regularly represent defendants in Court Martial cases tried in the UK and abroad.
Other Areas: General civil litigation, personal injury, and both commercial and residential conveyancing. The firm provides representation before Professional Disciplinary tribunals.

RECRUITMENT: Two trainee solicitors are recruited each year. Applications to the training partner, Andrew Moxon.

CLAYTONS

PO Box 38, 22 Rothesay Rd, Luton, LU1 1PT **Tel:** (01582) 724501 **Fax:** (01582) 405815 **DX:** 5909 Luton **Email:** mail@claytonssolicitors.co.uk
Ptnrs: 4 **Asst solrs:** 4 **Other fee-earners:** 5

CLEARY, GOTTLIEB, STEEN & HAMILTON

City Place House, 55 Basinghall Street, London, EC2V 5EH
Tel: (020) 7614 2200 **Fax:** (020) 7600 1698
Website: www.cgsh.com

AREAS OF PRACTICE	
Corporate	100%

THE FIRM: A leading US and international law firm with offices in New York, Washington DC, Paris, Brussels, London, Frankfurt, Rome, Tokyo and Hong Kong. The firm is well known for its expertise in finance, mergers and acquisitions, and for its tax, regulatory and litigation practice. The London office advises on all areas of international financial transactions, practising both English and US law.

C

CLEAVER FULTON RANKIN

50 Bedford Street, Belfast, BT2 7FW
Tel: (028) 9024 3141 **Fax:** (028) 9024 9096 **DX:** 421 NR Belfast
Email: info@cfrlaw.co.uk **Website:** www.cfrlawonline.com

Contact Partner	Neil Faris
Number of partners	15
Assistant solicitors	11
Other fee-earners	16

AREAS OF PRACTICE	
Company/Commercial	25%
Litigation	25%
Commercial Property	25%
Private Client	15%
Employment	10%

CONTACTS	
Commercial Property	Kathryn Collie
	James Houston
Company/Commercial	Stephen Cross
	Jennifer Ebbage
Consultancy	Karen Blair
	Neil Faris
Employment	Alyn Hicks
	Rosalie Prytherch
Litigation	William Cross
	Brendan Fox
Private Client	Alastair Rankin
	Joy Scott

THE FIRM: Cleaver Fulton Rankin's aim is world class law in Northern Ireland: in particular to provide clients with a thorough understanding of the legal context of their matters and to offer them sound and practical legal advice and assistance. It specialises in working with lawyers from other jurisdictions.

PRINCIPAL AREAS OF WORK:

Commercial Property: Work includes all aspects of acquisition, development and investment. The practice's property lawyers assist clients in all aspects of business start-ups, development agreements and in lease negotiations, renewal and rent review. The practice also specialises in advisory and litigation services relating to property.

Company Commercial: The firm provides a comprehensive service which includes mergers and acquisitions; management buy-outs; joint ventures; corporate finance; banking; securities; commercial contracts; business start-ups. The company and commercial lawyers aim to provide a speedy and effective service and specialise particularly in working with lawyers from other jurisdictions.

Litigation: The department aims to provide clients and lawyers from other jurisdictions with an experienced and able assistance in litigation matters including the specialist areas of commercial litigation, employment law, defamation, product liability, licensing, intellectual property and construction law.

Private Client: An extensive service to private clients entails giving advice on a variety of legal matters and maintaining close working relationships with other professionals including accountants, stockbrokers and estate agents. Some aspects of matrimonial law and children's law are also covered.

Consultancy: The firm has established a team to service the specialised needs of clients in legal consultancy and legal advisory work in Northern Ireland, including public law and judicial review. Training seminars are organised for clients and their employees on the impact of new legislation.

Employment & Labour: The firm handles all aspects of employment, including tribunals, TUPE and Northern Ireland's special discrimination legislation.

Agency Work: The firm specialises in providing agency services to lawyers in other jurisdictions. Contact the partner or associate in the relevant area.

Pro Bono Work: The firm is a member of the Environmental Law Foundation and the Professional Firms Group of Business in the Community (NI).

IT/Computer Law: The firm has a growing experience in this area and has an IT team dedicated to providing a complete legal service to clients in the IT and technology sector. The IT team has a dedicated website at www.inside-e-law.com.

RECRUITMENT: The firm currently takes four trainee solicitors per year. Applications to commence in September of each year should be made, in writing, early in the year, to Patrick Cross.

CLIFFORD CHANCE

200 Aldersgate Street, London, EC1A 4JJ
Tel: (020) 7600 1000 **Fax:** (020) 7600 5555 **DX:** 606 London
Email: info@cliffordchance.com **Website:** www.cliffordchance.com

Managing Partner	Peter Charlton
Chairman	Keith Clark
Number of partners	234
Assistant solicitors	852
Other fee-earners	256

THE FIRM: Clifford Chance Limited Liability Partnership is the first (and largest) fully integrated global law firm. The firm was created through the January 1 2000 merger of three international firms: New York-based Rogers & Wells, London-based Clifford Chance and Frankfurt-based Punder, Volhard, Weber & Axster. The firm provides seamless global services to the world's leading financial institutions and multinational business, and offers depth and breadth of expertise in Asia, the Americas, Continental Europe and the UK. Unrivalled in its international resources, the firm has 3,504 legal advisers comprising 672 partners and 2,832 other fee earners. The firm's practice is organised around six global practice areas: banking and finance, corporate (including M&A), capital markets, litigation and dispute resolution, real estate, and tax, pensions and employment law.

PRINCIPAL AREAS OF WORK: The firm provides a comprehensive range of legal services in the areas listed above.

Finance: The firm has the world's largest finance practice with over 1000 partners and lawyers located in major financial and commercial centres worldwide. The practice provides advice across the full spectrum of financial products including banking, asset finance, derivative products, project finance, securitisation and structured finance. It is the first firm to bring together lawyers in Europe, the United States and Asia to advise on national and international regulatory issues and the relationship between regulatory systems. The firm acts for all the world's leading investment and commercial banks across many major jurisdictions as well as many corporates. It also advises regulatory authorities, supranational bodies, governments and government agencies.

Corporate: The corporate practice handles some of the world's largest and most complex M&A transactions, combining global transaction capability with a full service of English, US and civil law expertise in the key financial centres across Europe, the Americas and Asia. Apart from mainstream M&A, the firm also encompasses leading specialist practices in private equity; investment banking; funds; financial institutions; insurance; communications, media and technology; energy; commercial contracts; competition and anti-trust. The practice focuses on providing practical, commercial legal advice and its clients include investment banks and financial institutions, multinationals and other public and private corporations, private equity providers and management teams, asset management clients, international partnerships and governments.

Capital Markets: The firm's capital markets practice comprises over 500 partners and lawyers. The practice is founded on a full-service US and UK securities law capability – the law of choice for the majority of international transactions – complemented by local securities law expertise in each of the key financial centres. This combination of local and international perspectives is brought to bear, for example, when helping to apply US disclosure standards to European, Asian and Latin American issuers. The firm acts on the whole range of securities offerings, whether public or private, where the proceeds may be used to finance mergers or acquisitions or for general capital. The firm is well known for its innovative approach to developing solutions and its clients include issuers, guarantors, arrangers, managers, investors, trustees and regulatory bodies such as banks and financial institutions, specialised lenders, corporate originators, security and share trustees, rating agencies, monoline insurers and swap counterparties.

Litigation & Dispute Resolution: The firm has a team of more than 660 litigators internationally – the world's largest and most comprehensive practice of its kind – and has experience in virtually all segments of the business and financial markets across multiple jurisdictions. The lawyers work with clients to resolve disputes efficiently and effectively – whether through arbitration, litigation or other techniques, in a manner that promotes their business objectives. They also work with clients to develop compliance programmes and other techniques to minimise future litigation risks. The firm is currently representing clients in some of the largest and significant actions underway, particularly in the areas of anti-trust and competition law, white collar and regulatory, intellectual property, insurance and banking and securities.

Real Estate: The firm has one of the world's leading international real estate practices which provides comprehensive, domestic and cross-border advice on all transaction types where real estate is the core asset. This ranges from acquisition, development and construction work to joint ventures, tax structuring, debt and equity financing and securitisaions, real estate investment banking, indirect investment, real estate funds, corporate outsourcing and PFI/PPP deals. The practice acts for market leading clients in a broad range of sectors and has a client base which includes developers and investors, landowners, occupiers, lenders, hotwires/leisure operators, investment banks, commercial/mortgage banks, funds and major corporates, for whom they can act in both single and multiple jurisdictions.

Tax: The firm has the largest tax group of any single law firm internationally, providing advice on international and domestic taxation, covering a wide range of financing, investment, corporate and commercial issues, together with advice on tax litigation, disputes and transfer pricing.

INTERNATIONAL: The firm has offices in Europe (Amsterdam, Barcelona, Berlin, Brussels, Budapest, Düsseldorf, Frankfurt, Leipzig, London, Luxembourg, Madrid, Milan, Moscow, Munich, Padua, Paris, Prague, Rome,

Continued overleaf

CONTACTS

Asset Finance .... Geoffrey White
Banking .... Mark Campbell
.... Stuart Popham
Collective Investments .... James Barlow
.... Tim Herrington
.... Stephen Ross
Commercial .... Raj Parkash
Commercial Litigation .... Peter Blake
.... John Potts
Commodities .... Ed Patton
.... Tim Plews
Construction & Engineering .... John Beechey
.... Tim Steadman
Corporate Finance .... David Childs
Corporate Immigration
.... Christopher Paul Goodwill
Derivatives .... Claude Brown
.... Habib Motani
.... Tim Plews
Employee Benefits .... Kevin Thompson
.... Robin Tremaine
Employment .... Chris Osman
Energy & Natural Resources
.... Tony Bankes-Jones
Environment .... Brian Hall
EU & Competition .... Simon Baxter
.... Alex Nourry
Financial Services .... Chris Bates
.... Mark Harding
.... Tim Herrington
Hotels .... Andrew Carnegie
Housing Association Finance
.... Despina Pantelia
.... Robert Smith
Insolvency .... Mark Hyde
.... David Steinberg
Insurance & Reinsurance .... Katherine Coates
Insurance Litigation .... Nicholas Munday
Intellectual Property .... David Perkins
International Capital Markets
.... David Dunnigan
.... Kevin Kelley
.... Robert MacVicar
International Financial Markets .... Tim Plews
Local Government .... Brian Hall
M&A .... David Childs
Marketing & Advertising .... Richard Thomas
MBOs .... James Baird
Media .... Daniel Sandelson
Pensions .... Helen Cox
Pharmaceuticals .... Peter Dieners
Planning .... Brian Hall
Product Liability .... Andrew Edgar
Project Finance .... Peter Blake
Public Policy .... Richard Thomas
Public Sector .... Richard Thomas
Real Estate .... Tony Briam
.... Robert MacGregor
.... Cliff McAuley
Real Estate Finance .... Andrew Carnegie
.... Mark Rees-Jones
Real Estate Litigation .... John Pickston
Retail .... Michael Edwards
Securitisation .... Kevin Ingram
.... Chris Oakley
.... John Woodhall
Shipping .... Mark Morrison
.... Tony Vlasto
Sovereign Debt Rescheduling .... Cliff Godfrey
.... Andrew Yianni
Tax .... Douglas French
Technology .... David Griffiths
.... Christopher Millard

C

Warsaw), North America (New York, Washington DC), South America (São Paulo), Asia (Bangkok, Beijing, Hong Kong, Singapore, Shanghai, Tokyo) and the Middle East (Dubai). Business is conducted in all known business and commercial languages.

RECRUITMENT:

Trainee: The firm is aiming to recruit up to 130 trainee lawyers to join the firm in September 2003/March 2004. It believes that trainees are the future of the firm and therefore provides them with first class training as part of the Clifford Chance Academy. As a client focused organisation it is looking for those with the potential to be a new kind of lawyer – a more rounded business adviser with an understanding of the international business environment and to feel confident operating in different cultures. Applications are welcome from the law or other disciplines. The firm keeps in touch while trainees are studying their CPE/LPC course and pay their fees and maintenance. It wants the LPC to be a stimulating and relevant course, balancing legal and practical training. This is why it has been part of the consortium of city firms who have worked with Nottingham, Oxford and BPP law schools to create a LPC that reflects the needs of the major commercial law firms. When trainees begin their training contract, they are given an introduction to the firm and each practice area runs a focused induction course at the start of each 'seat'. The firm aims to provide the trainee with a mix of experience, both general and specialist, to maximise the chances of the trainee finding a qualification 'home' which fits his or her skills and aptitudes. Those trainees who would like to spend time working overseas can do so in one of our international offices.

Qualified: The firm offers excellent career opportunities for qualified lawyers at all levels. The Clifford Chance Academy provides industry leading training and development programmes and opportunities for all its lawyers. The Academy helps them to develop their legal knowledge and business and personal skills through a variety of formal training programmes, practical experience and structured performance management. To find out more about the opportunities available and to apply on-line go to www.cliffordchance.com/careers.

CONTACTS CONTINUED

Telecommunications	Joachim Fleury
	Elizabeth Hiester
	Tim Schwarz
VAT	Tim Schwarz
	Etienne Wong

C L I F F O R D

C H A N C E

C

CLINTONS

55 Drury Lane, London, WC2B 5RZ
Tel: (020) 7379 6080 **Fax:** (020) 7240 9310 **DX:** 40021 Covent Gdn. 1
Email: info@clintons.co.uk **Website:** www.clintons.co.uk

Senior Partner	John Cohen
Number of partners	17
Assistant solicitors	14
Other fee-earners	12

THE FIRM: Clintons is widely recognised as one of the foremost media and entertainment law firms. The firm also has an extensive general commercial practice and has acknowledged strengths in litigation, family and property.

PRINCIPAL AREAS OF WORK:

Media & Entertainment: The firm acts for a wide range of clients, from high profile individuals to major corporations. Specialist advice is provided in the businesses of music, theatre, television, e-commerce, advertising and marketing, merchandising and sport, film and publishing and generally in the protection and exploitation of intellectual property rights.

Litigation: Clintons is recognised for the strength of its practice in this area and for its ability to deal with heavyweight and high profile litigation. The firm advises on a wide range of contentious work in its core practice areas, as well as in banking, employment and personal injury.

Corporate & Commercial: The firm provides advice in all aspects of the commercial world including new ventures, corporate restructuring, e-ventures, international taxation, employment, liquidation and receivership.

Family: Clintons has a significant and highly regarded practice in family law and divorce, offering advice in all aspects, often for clients in the public eye. The family team is noted for its expertise in the detailed financial arrangements surrounding marriage breakdown and in advising on complex issues concerning children.

Property: Clintons handles all types of property transaction, from commercial developments to residential conveyancing. The firm has special expertise in secured lending and includes banking and other lending institutions as its clients.

Private Client: Clintons advises on all aspects of arrangements for private individuals, including offshore settlements, tax, wills, probate, trusts and matrimonial finance. The work undertaken includes advice relating to the links between the business and personal assets of private individuals. The firm works closely with other professional advisers in the establishment of tax-efficient and practical arrangements for the benefit of its clients.

INTERNATIONAL: Clintons has considerable overseas connections, particularly in the USA, continental Europe, Ireland, Israel, the Channel Islands, Cayman and the Bahamas.

CONTACTS

Advertising & Marketing	Philip Stinson
Corporate/Commercial & Employment	
	John Seigal
E-commerce	James Jones
Family	Maggie Rae
	Tim Bienias
	Elizabeth Vernon
Film & Television	David Landsman
Litigation	David Davis
	Tim Bienias
	Jacqueline Brown
	Andrew Sharland
	Stephen Joelson
Music	David Landsman
	Peter Button
	Andrew Myers
Property	Laurence Middleweek
	Michael Goldman
	David Benain
Publishing	Sally Hamwee
Sport	Philip Stinson
	Jacqueline Brown
Tax, Trusts & Private Client	Sally Hamwee
Theatre	John Cohen
	James Jones

CLYDE & CO

51 Eastcheap, London, EC3M 1JP
Tel: (020) 7623 1244 **Fax:** (020) 7623 5427 **DX:** 1071
Email: joan.radley@clyde.co.uk **Website:** www.clydeco.com

THE FIRM: Clyde & Co is an international commercial law firm with an outstanding reputation in insurance and reinsurance work in both the contentious and corporate fields. The firm is a dominant force in the shipping, transport, trade and energy sectors. There are over 290 lawyers, who are qualified in 17 jurisdictions. Clients are served by offices in Europe (London, Guildford, Cardiff, Paris, St Petersburg and Piraeus), Asia (Hong Kong and Singapore), the Gulf (Dubai) and South America (Caracas). The firm also has an association in Belgrade. Clyde & Co's litigation practice is one of the largest in the United Kingdom.

PRINCIPAL AREAS OF WORK:

Contentious: Advice is given on disputes in a wide range of areas including aviation; general liability; insolvency and recovery; marine and energy; medical negligence; personal injury; political and credit risks; professional indemnity; property and construction.

Non-Contentious: Clyde & Co was one of the first City firms to establish a distinct corporate insurance group. The group specialises in insurance-related corporate transactions and regulatory matters of all kinds including: mergers and acquisitions and alternative risk transfer projects in the life and non-life sectors; the establishment of insurance and reinsurance companies; captives (including Lloyd's captive syndicates) and Lloyd's underwriting vehicles; Lloyd's capacity offers and the provision of all kinds of insurance regulatory advice.

Marine & Transport: Specialists handle all areas of shipping work including disputes arising from salvage and collision; carriage of goods; charterparties; marine insurance policies; general average; pollution; ship repairs. On the non-contentious side, Clyde & Co advises all sectors of the maritime industry on an international basis on all aspects of ship sale and purchase; new building contracts; the management and operation of ships and ship finance transactions. Expertise extends to all litigious aspects of aviation work. Acting for aircraft manufacturers, airlines and lessors on the non-contentious side, the firm has developed a particular specialisation in cross-border financing. The firm is also involved in disputes arising out of the carriage of goods by road and rail.

Commodities & International Trade: Specialist advice is provided to clients through the firm's global network of offices. The full spectrum of commodities is covered including oil, gas, rice, sugar, grain, coffee, oil and fats, coals and metals. Areas of work range from preparing contracts, commodity financing, derivatives and credit enhancement (especially in emerging markets and turbulent jurisdictions) to resolving disputes of every kind, including trade arbitrations before GAFTA, FOSFA, RSA and the London Metal Exchange.

Corporate & Commercial: Clyde & Co's corporate and commercial group handles a wide range of corporate and commercial transactions including flotations; mergers and acquisitions; MBOs; MBIs; joint ventures; inward investment. The corporate and commercial teams also advise on intellectual property rights, e-commerce, data protection issues and on all types of commercial contracts, including distribution and agency arrangements. They act for suppliers and users of IT equipment and services and advise on a broad range of issues relating to the IT and telecommunications industries. Specialists cover the UK and European regulatory and competition implications of corporate transactions, financing arrangements and commercial contracts, including sports law. The banking group advises on a broad range of international and domestic financing arrangements, including asset and project finance. The firm also has an experienced WTO law team.

Commercial Litigation: The breadth of the firm's litigation practice is extensive. It encapsulates many of the work areas identified separately. Litigation and arbitration before courts and tribunals in the UK and worldwide is undertaken through overseas business and correspondent lawyers. Particular areas of expertise also embrace commodity and trade disputes. Resolution of all types of commercial disputes including through mediation is a major strength of the practice.

Energy & Natural Resources: The firm advises on the commercial, regulatory and environmental aspects of petroleum exploration and production worldwide; oil refining; product distribution and transportation and petrochemical investment. Advice is given on power projects throughout the world from large scale combustion plants to combined heat and power plants designed for industrial purposes. The financing aspects of energy projects and regulatory issues affecting the energy sector are also covered. A comprehensive range of legal services is provided for international mining and minerals transactions. This includes advice on acquiring mineral rights, mineral exploration, mine finance, processing, tolling, smelting and distribution. All aspects of trading commodities in the energy and natural resources sectors, and on energy derivatives and the regulatory implications of trading activity are covered. The firm has been involved in advising on the aftermath of major casualties, including Exxon Valdez, Piper Alpha and the Braer. Energy group clients include governments, state oil companies, recognised regulatory bodies, privatised utilities, banks, independent companies, some of the world's largest commodities traders and mining exploration and production companies. A number of the group's lawyers were previously in-house lawyers with energy companies and so have particular insight into the sector's requirements.

Property: The firm represents UK and international developers, contractors, consultants, funders and investors in relation to property transactions. It has been involved in a number of high profile property transactions during the year. Advice is also given on all litigious aspects of the construction industry.

Continued overleaf

Senior Partner	Michael Payton
Number of partners	91
Assistant solicitors	99
Other fee-earners	92

AREAS OF PRACTICE

Insurance/Reinsurance	27%
Banking/Corporate/Commercial & Tax	26%
Marine & Transport	22%
Commercial Litigation	10%
Property	6%
Energy & Natural Resources	5%
Employment	4%

CONTACTS

Alternative Dispute Resolution	Jane Andrewartha
Arbitration	Jonathan Wood
Asset Finance & Leasing	Austen Hall
	Simon Poland
Aviation	Jane Andrewartha
	Colin Franke
Banking	David Page
Commercial Litigation	Stuart Macdonald
	Jonathan Wood
Commodities (Physical)	Paul Turner
Commodities (Transactional/Derivatives)	Clare Hatcher
	Andrew Wells
Construction	John Morris
Corporate & Commercial	Andrew Holderness
	David Page
	David Salt
Corporate Finance	Tim Matthews
	Gary Thorpe
Corporate Insurance - General	James O'Shea
	David Salt
Corporate Insurance - Lloyd's	Andrew Holderness
	Diane Rickard
Corporate Litigation	Conrad Walker
EC, Competition Law & WTO	Stuart Macdonald
	Philippe Ruttley
Employment	Chris Duffy
Energy & Natural Resources - Electricity	Clare Hatcher
Energy & Natural Resources - Mining	Martin Byatt
Energy & Natural Resources: Oil & Gas	Martin Byatt
	Peter Felter
	Andrew Wells
Immigration	Paul Newdick
Insolvency	Mark Fennessy
	Paul Newdick
	Jonathan Wood
Insurance - Marine	Nigel Chapman
	John Dunt
Insurance (Contentious) - Non-Marine/General	Michael Payton
	Rod Smith
Intellectual Property	David Page
	Sally Shorthose
International Trade	David Best
	John Whittaker
IT & Telecommunications	Philip Hooley
	Tim Matthews
Licensing Law	John Mitchell
Life Assurance	James O'Shea
Medical Negligence	John Mitchell
Personal Injury	Angela Horne
Product Liability	Chris Harris
Professional Indemnity	Peter Farthing
	Chris Harris
Property	Paul Berry
	Robert Pilcher
Reinsurance	Nigel Brook
	Paul Bugden
Ship Finance	Simon Poland

C

Employment: The firm's expertise in employment law extends to preparing service and consultancy agreements; terms and conditions of employment; staff handbooks; health and safety policies; equal opportunities policies; restrictive covenants; unfair dismissal disputes; discrimination cases; redundancy programmmes and directors' duties and liabilities. Immigration is another area in which the firm has considerable expertise.

Taxation: Highly-regarded tax specialists advise all practice areas. They deal with all aspects of corporate and personal taxation, including company reorganisations; financings; employee remuneration packages; equity incentive schemes; estate planning and settlements.

INTERNATIONAL: Clyde & Co has overseas offices in Caracas, Dubai, Hong Kong, Paris, Piraeus, Singapore and St Petersburg, as well as an association in Belgrade.

RECRUITMENT: A number of assistant solicitors will be required due to expansion in 2001/2002. All enquiries should be made to Claire Kohler on (020) 7623 1244. For details of our trainee solicitor recruitment programme, call Georgia de Saram on (020) 7648 1580.

CONTACTS CONTINUED

Shipping	Simon Fletcher
	Derek Hodgson
	Brian Nash
	Tony Thomas
Sport	Michael Breen
Tax	Susan Ball
Transport	Michael Parker

CMS CAMERON MCKENNA

Mitre House, 160 Aldersgate Street, London, EC1A 4DD
Tel: (020) 7367 3000 **Fax:** (020) 7367 2000 **DX:** 135316 BARBICAN 2
Email: info@cmck.com **Website:** www.cmck.com

Managing Partner	Dick Tyler
Senior Partner	Bill Shelford
Chief Executive	Robert Derry-Evans
UK	
Number of partners	154
Assistant solicitors	344
Other fee-earners	138
International	
Number of partners	57
Assistant solicitors	158

THE FIRM: CMS Cameron McKenna is an award-winning, full service international commercial law firm advising businesses, financial institutions, governments and public sector bodies. It is a founding member of CMS – the transnational legal services organisation. CMS member firms provide clients with access to integrated pan-European legal and tax services, managed by a single point of contact and with common high calibre service standards. The organisation has 39 offices, currently employs in excess of 1700 lawyers, with a total staff of 3500 in 24 jurisdictions. In Europe, CMS Cameron McKenna is a top ten law firm in its own right, with over 145 partners and more than 800 fee earners. The firm has the resources and experience to advise clients on a wide range of transactions and projects both in the UK and internationally. It has offices and associated offices in various key business centres worldwide including the UK, Central and Eastern Europe, Central, East and South East Asia and North America.

PRINCIPAL AREAS OF WORK: The firm's lawyers have strong specialist expertise in areas such as finance and financial services; corporate; utilities and natural resources; real estate and environment; insurance and reinsurance; cross-border investment; technology, life sciences and intellectual property; infrastructure and projects; human resources and pensions; competition and European law; arbitration and litigation. Its expertise in these areas is reflected in its listing in *Chambers Guide to the Legal Profession 1999-2000*, where it is ranked in 34 areas. The firm is committed to providing the highest quality professional advice and building enduring relationships with its clients. It places great emphasis on the training and development of its partners and staff in both current legal and business issues. The firm's investment in know-how and information systems allows it to share its knowledge and experience throughout the firm, helping to ensure that all its lawyers add value to the services they provide. CMS Cameron McKenna works with its clients to identify their business needs and provide them with comprehensive, cost-effective commercial guidance. The firm offers a clear business lead – not just legal opinion.

INTERNATIONAL: The locations of the firm's offices and associated offices are: Berlin, Brussels, London, Paris, Utrecht, Vienna, Zürich, Aberdeen, Amsterdam, Arnhem, Beijing, Belgrade, Bratislava, Bristol, Bucharest, Budapest, Buenos Aires, Cape Town, Casablanca, Chemnitz, Dresden, Düsseldorf, Frankfurt, Hamburg, Hilversum, Hong Kong, Leipzig, Lyon, Madrid, Moscow, Munich, New York, Prague, Singapore, Stuttgart, Toronto, Warsaw and Washington DC. CMS member firms are CMS Bureau Francis Lefebvre, CMS Cameron McKenna, CMS Derks Star Bustmann Hanotiau, CMS Hasch Sigle Eschenlohr Peltzer Schäfer, and CMS Strommer Reich-Rohrwig Karasek Hainz.

CONTACTS

Aviation	Tim Brymer
Banking	Duncan Aldred
Charities	Andrew Crawford
Construction	John Uwins
Corporate Finance	Sean Watson
Corporate Tax	Mark Nichols
EC Law/Competition/Anti-trust	Richard Taylor
Employment	Simon Jeffreys
Energy	Fiona Woolf
Environment	Paul Sheridan
Financial Services Regulation	Simon Morris
Health & Safety	Mark Tyler
Immigration	Julia Onslow-Cole
Infrastructure Projects/PFI	Robert Phillips
Insolvency	John White
Insurance & Reinsurance	Anthony Hobkinson
IP/Advertising & Mktg	Stephen Whybrow
IT/Telecoms	John Armstrong
Life Sciences	Ian Dodds-Smith
Litigaton/Arbititration & Dispute Management	Tim Hardy
M&A	Richard Price
Media Complaints	Tim Hardy
Pensions	Nigel Moore
Planning	Tony Kitson
Product Liability	Christopher Hodges
Project Finance	Andrew Ivison
Property	Nicholas Brown
Transport	Trevor Butcher
Venture Capital	Andrew Sheach
Water	Richard Temple

COBBETTS

Ship Canal House, King Street, Manchester, M2 4WB
Tel: (0161) 833 3333 **Fax:** (0161) 833 3030 **DX:** 14374 Manchester 1
Email: lawyers@cobbetts.co.uk **Website:** www.cobbetts.co.uk

Managing Partner	Michael Shaw
Senior Partner	Stephen White
Number of partners	50
Assistant solicitors	54
Other fee-earners	33
Total fee-earners	137
Total staff (inc. support)	270

THE FIRM: Cobbetts, with its long history in the city and strong independent stance, continues to impress its clients with the virtues of using a purely 'Manchester' firm. Although Cobbetts has always represented quality of work and high service standards, it has, in recent years, undergone a programme of radical internal changes under the direction of Managing Partner Michael Shaw which are now being reflected in changing external perceptions about the firm. Its overall image continues to be one of quiet conservatism, but this underlying drive for structured progression now places it at the forefront of successful long-term relationship building. For example, the firm's sustained IT investment and ambitious programme of implementation now places it amongst the most technologically sophisticated of any legal firm. It remains committed to further development of intranet and extranet technology and the application of e-commerce in order to better service client needs. Over the past four years the firm has achieved an enviable record of controlled, sustained growth of around 20% pa through good management of the business as a whole and an emphasis on identifying and meeting the needs and expectations of clients, intermediaries and the firm's own personnel. However, unlike many of its competitors, the general ethos of the firm is not geared solely towards financial reward, and strong and continuing emphasis is placed on relationships, quality of environment and job satisfaction for all. This commitment was formally recognised in January 2000 when the firm became the first in the North West to simultaneously receive accreditation in both Investors in People and Lexcel (the Law Society's Quality Award). Cobbetts is a member of the European legal network Eurolegal, has an associated office in Brussels, Renouf & Co, and is a member of the US State Capital Law Firm Group. These affiliations, together with other close relationships around the world, ensure that the firm can meet clients' needs for international legal services and enables it to offer proactive advice to clients in respect of international commerce and trade.

PRINCIPAL AREAS OF WORK: Cobbetts operates through a number of flexible service teams based on work type and managed within two divisions.
Property: The Property Division is the largest under one roof in the North West and incorporates the resources and expertise capable of handling commercial property work of any type and size from greenfield acquisitions through development, letting and general property management. The division has particular expertise in the retail and licensed trade sectors with the licensing and planning team in particular enjoying a national reputation. There is also a flourishing housing association client base.
Corporate: The Corporate Division has the resources and expertise to handle all M&A-related work, corporate finance transactions and banking work. Within this division dedicated teams include lawyers specialising in contentious and non-contentious industrial relations and employment law, IT and computer contracts, agency and distribution agreements and intellectual property work, and an expertise in co-operative law which is unrivalled outside London. The firm's strong OMB client base is supplemented with numerous multinational plcs and public sector organisations. The firm's private client team is the largest within a major Manchester commercial firm and has been supplemented by the recruitment of an independent financial adviser, enabling Cobbetts to offer OMB clients in particular, a true 'one stop shop' for legal and financial advice.

INTERNATIONAL: Languages spoken include French, German, Italian and Spanish.

RECRUITMENT: The firm recruits at least six trainee solicitors every year. Application form can be downloaded from the website and should be sent for the attention of Richard Webb.

AREAS OF PRACTICE

Commercial Property	37%
Company/Commercial	28%
Litigation	27%
Private Client	9%

CONTACTS

Banking	Paul Brown
Commercial Litigation	Mark Whittell
Commercial Property	Stephen Benson
Commercial/IP	Robert Roper
Construction	Peter Taylor
Co-ops & Mutuals	Kevin Jaquiss
	Cliff Mills
Corporate Finance	Robert Turnbull
Debt Recovery	Richard Webb
Defamation	Peter Stone
Education	Kevin Jaquiss
Employment	Judith Watson
Environmental	Simon Jones
Housing Associations	Mike Gaskell
Insolvency	Mark Whittell
IT	Susan Hall
Licensing	Hamish Lawson
Planning	Peter Oldham
Private Client	David Pickering
Sport	Jeremy Orrell

COBLEYS

19-23 Sir Thomas Street, Salford, L1 6BW **Tel:** (0151) 242 9000 **Fax:** (0151) 236 2911

COFFIN MEW & CLOVER

17 Hampshire Terrace, Portsmouth, PO1 2PU **Tel:** (023) 9281 2511 **Fax:** (023) 9229 1847 **DX:** 2207 Portsmouth 1
Email: cmc@portsmouth.coffinmew.co.uk **Website:** www.coffinmew.co.uk **Ptnrs:** 20 **Asst solrs:** 21 **Other fee-earners:** 40

COKER VIS PARTNERSHIP

49 Broad Lane, Tottenham, London, N15 4DJ **Tel:** (020) 8885 1415 **Fax:** (020) 8885 2882 **DX:** 55604 Sth Tottenham
Email: broadlane@cokervis.com **Ptnrs:** 2 **Asst solrs:** 1 **Other fee-earners:** 3

COLE & CO

St Andrew House, 141 West Nile Street, Glasgow, G1 2RN **Tel:** (0141) 353 0007 **Fax:** (0141) 353 1110 **DX:** GW15 Glasgow 1 **Email:** ron@coleandco.co.uk **Ptnrs:** 1 **Associates:** 3 **Contact:** Ron Cole • Commercial property practice established in 1996 by experienced former property partner of a large national firm.

AREAS OF PRACTICE

Commercial Property	98%
Residential Property	2%

COLE & CO

23 Tombland, Norwich, NR3 1RF **Tel:** (01603) 617018 **Fax:** (01603) 630050 **DX:** 5220 Norwich **Ptnrs:** 5

COLE'S

4-5 Rigbys Court, St Giles Street, Norwich, NR2 1NT **Tel:** (01603) 441 111 **Fax:** (01603) 442 222 **DX:** 133140 Norwich 12 **Ptnrs:** 1 **Asst solrs:** 8 **Other fee-earners:** 3

COLIN JONES

17A Thompson Street, Barry, CF63 4JL **Tel:** (01446) 420 043 **Fax:** (01446) 420 045

COLLYER-BRISTOW

4 Bedford Row, London, WC1R 4DF
Tel: (020) 7242 7363 **Fax:** (020) 7405 0555 **DX:** 163 Ch.Ln.
Email: firstname.lastname@collyer-bristow.com **Website:** www.collyer-bristow.com

C

THE FIRM: Collyer-Bristow is an imaginative and innovative firm based in Bedford Row. It was established in 1760 but its environment and approach is progressive and friendly. The firm acts for a wide range of institutional clients; public and private companies; charities; businesses; professional partnerships; and private clients. An association with a group of European practices provides valuable continental links. The bright modernised offices now contain a professionally run art gallery where regular and varied exhibitions are held.

PRINCIPAL AREAS OF WORK:
Company/Commercial: The department's work includes company formations; mergers; acquisitions; sales; buy-outs; reorganisations and all the related range of contractual and commercial advice.
Commercial Property: The work includes freehold and leasehold sales and disposals; residential and office development schemes; major shopping centre developments; agricultural matters; planning and other related work; residential and domestic transactions, including leasehold enfranchisement advice.
Litigation: This strong team has experience in property-related and construction litigation and arbitration; judicial review work; commercial and contractual disputes; professional negligence; defamation; personal injury and in representation before professional tribunals.
Intellectual Property: The firm has an excellent reputation for handling contentious trademark and patent disputes; and in the licensing of rights, publishing, franchising and technology transfer.
Private Client: The firm has maintained and expanded its private client practice, for whom it handles tax planning; trusts; financial and investment advice within the UK and offshore; wills; and the administration of estates and charities.
Family: This is one of the leading matrimonial practices in the country. Its work includes divorce; substantial financial disputes; children cases; cohabitation; international juristiction disputes and forum-shopping, and child abduction. It is one of the appointed firms on the Lord Chancellor's child abduction panel.
Employment: The team handles a wide range of employment and boardroom disputes, industrial tribunal applications, executive service contract advice, and the preparation of employment terms and conditions and advice on business-related immigration.
Sport, Entertainment, Music & Marketing: The firm acts for sponsorship, promotions and merchandising consultancies; advertising and marketing agencies; governing bodies; sponsors; sports photographers and publishers; film and video producers; and distributors. In the music industry, the firm acts for artists, managers, record labels and publishers.
Agency Work: The agency litigation department provides a service for more than 100 firms outside the capital and overseas.

RECRUITMENT: For those candidates who do not believe that biggest necessarily means best, the firm offers a refreshing alternative. CV and references to John Saner.

Senior Partner	Roger Woolfe
Number of partners	24
Assistant solicitors	13
Other fee-earners	25

AREAS OF PRACTICE

Litigation	25%
Matrimonial & Family	20%
Property (Commercial)	20%
Private Client	18%
Commercial	12%
Sport, Entertainment & Marketing	5%

CONTACTS

Area	Contact
Agency	Matthew Marsh
Banking	Stephen Rosen
Commercial Property	Janet Armstrong-Fox
Charity	Daniel Simon
Company/Commercial	John Bailey
Construction	Joanna Kennedy
Defamation	Joanna Kennedy
E-commerce & IT	Paul Sillis
Employment	Keith Corkan
Entertainment/Music	Howard Ricklow
Family	Michael Drake
Immigration	Joe Cohen
Intellectual Property	Joe Cohen
Litigation	Joanna Kennedy
Personal Injury	Joanna Kennedy
Residential Property	Janet Armstrong-Fox
Sport & Sponsorship	Alan Burdon-Cooper
Tax Planning & Trusts	Paul Clark
Wills & Probate	John Saner

CONDIES

2 Tay Street, Perth, PH1 5LJ **Tel:** (01738) 440088 **Fax:** (01738) 441131 **DX:** LP 6 Perth **Email:** enquiry@condies.co.uk **Ptnrs:** 5 **Asst solrs:** 4 **Other fee-earners:** 6

CONINGSBYS

87-89 High Street, Croydon, CR9 1XE **Tel:** (020) 8680 5575 **Fax:** (020) 8681 3941 **DX:** 2611 Croydon 1 **Email:** reception@coningsbys.co.uk **Website:** www.coningsbys.co.uk **Ptnrs:** 3 **Other fee-earners:** 7 **Contact:** Paul Conrathe • A niche practice specialising in human rights, health, education and community care. Its client base is nationwide. Traditional high street work is undertaken.

AREAS OF PRACTICE

Education	34%
Conveyancing	28%
Matrimonial	11%
Human Rights	8%
Personal Injury	5%
Probate	3%

COODES

8 Market Street, St Austell, PL25 4BB **Tel:** (01726) 75021 **Fax:** (01726) 69103 **DX:** 81250 **Email:** coodes@link.org **Ptnrs:** 15 **Asst solrs:** 7 **Other fee-earners:** 19

COOLE & HADDOCK

14 Carfax, Horsham, RH12 1DZ
Tel: (01403) 210200 **Fax:** (01403) 241275 **DX:** 57600 Horsham

5 The Steyne, Worthing, BN11 3DT
Tel: (01903) 213511 **Fax:** (01903) 237053 **DX:** 3717 Worthing

Managing Partner	Paul Burke
Senior Partner	Frank Haddock
Number of partners	10
Assistant solicitors	7
Other fee-earners	5

CONTACTS
Commercial & Civil Litigation/ Employment ....Stephen Loosemore
Company/Commercial/ Commercial Property ....Iain Swalwell
Matrimonial/Childcare ....Penelope Barker
Probate & Trusts ....Jennifer Murphy
Residential Conveyancing ....Paul Burke
....Peter Graves

THE FIRM: Established in Horsham in 1898 and Worthing in 1960, Coole & Haddock built its reputation initially on an extensive private client base mainly in Sussex. This is now complemented by expanding commercial and litigation departments which offer a comprehensive service to businesses over a wider area.

PRINCIPAL AREAS OF WORK: Work handled includes company; commercial/commercial property; town and country planning; commercial and civil litigation/employment/personal injury; property litigation; residential conveyancing; probate and trusts; wills and estate planning; matrimonial/childcare; debt recovery; crime.

C

COPLEYS

Red House, 10 Market Hill, St Ives, PE17 4AW **Tel:** (01480) 464515 **Fax:** (01480) 467171 **DX:** 46402 **Ptnrs:** 5 **Asst solrs:** 4 **Other fee-earners:** 6

CORBETT & CO

Churcham House, 1 Bridgeman Road, Teddington, TW11 9AJ **Tel:** (020) 8943 9885 **Fax:** (020) 8977 3122 **Email:** mail@corbett.co.uk **Website:** www.corbett.co.uk **Ptnrs:** 1 **Asst solrs:** 3 **Other fee-earners:** 1 **Contact:** Edward Corbett • The firm has a growing reputation as a specialist in international and UK construction projects and disputes. Established in 1993, when Edward Corbett left the partnership of Masons, the firm has advised on a wide range of projects in the UK and all over the world. Dispute work includes TCC litigation, ICC arbitration and ADR including adjudication.

AREAS OF PRACTICE
International Construction Projects/ Disputes 60%
UK Construction Projects/Disputes 40%

SJ CORNISH

Twyford House, Kennedy Way, Tiverton, EX16 6RZ
Tel: (01884) 243377 **Fax:** (01884) 243388 **DX:** 49014 Tiverton
Email: solicitors@sjcornish.co.uk **Website:** www.SJCornish.co.uk

Bankside House, 107/112 Leadenhall Street, London, EC3A 4AH
Tel: (020) 7891 2470 **Fax:** (020) 7891 2471 **DX:** 528 London city

Senior Partner	Sarah Cornish
Number of partners	4
Assistant solicitors	2
Other fee-earners	1

AREAS OF PRACTICE
Professional Indemnity 70%
Personal Injury 25%
Commercial Litigation/Debt Collection ..5%

THE FIRM: SJ Cornish is a niche insurance litigation practice dedicated to resolving claims against professionals for insurers. Established in 1991, the firm opened a London office in February 2001 with one resident partner.

PRINCIPAL AREAS OF WORK: Work handled includes defendants' professional indemnity claims (valuers, surveyors, all construction professionals, accountants, insurance brokers, IFAs and solicitors); defendants' personal injury and liability claims ; commercial litigation; debt collection.

COUDERT BROTHERS

60 Cannon Street, London, EC4N 6JP
Tel: (020) 7248 3000 **Fax:** (020) 7248 3001 **DX:** LDE 49
Email: info@london.coudert.com **Website:** www.coudert.com

Managing & Senior Partner	Steven Beharrell
Number of partners	10
Assistant solicitors	16
Other fee-earners	14

AREAS OF PRACTICE
Corporate Finance 30%
Banking/Project/Structured Finance 15%
Litigation/Arbitration 15%
Capital Markets/Funds 10%
Energy/Telecoms/Multimedia 10%
Real Property 10%
Other 10%

THE FIRM: Coudert Brothers in London is a multinational partnership of registered foreign lawyers and solicitors. It is part of a worldwide network of offices established in 32 cities in 19 countries around the world. Coudert Brothers is one global partnership and the London office provides the facilities of a full service London law firm as well as access to the international network of Coudert Brothers. The London office has 10 partners, nine of whom are solicitors and one of whom is a US attorney. The London office specialises in international investment; trade and finance (with particular expertise in corporate finance); mergers and acquisitions; joint ventures; capital markets; banking and project finance; international tax and trust planning;

Continued overleaf

telecommunications and IT law; energy privatisation and infrastructure projects; real estate; arbitration and litigation.

INTERNATIONAL: Coudert Brothers has offices in the major financial centres in Europe, Central Asia, North America and the Asia Pacific region. In Europe, the firm has offices in London, Paris, Brussels, Antwerp, Ghent, Berlin, Frankfurt, Munich, Milan, Moscow, St. Petersburg and Almaty. The North American offices are established in New York, Washington, Los Angeles, San Francisco, San Jose, Palo Alto, Denver and Montreal and the Asia Pacific offices in Bangkok, Beijing, Hong Kong, Jakarta, Singapore, Sydney and Tokyo. Coudert Brothers has associated offices in Budapest, Stockholm, Prague and Mexico City. The firm's Moscow office was the first established by a foreign law firm (1988) and is now one of the largest in Moscow, servicing all the states of the former Soviet Union. Coudert Brothers opened an office in Kazakhstan in 1998.

CONTACTS

Banking/Finance	Alexander Janes
Competition/Telecoms	Alastair Gorrie
Corporate Finance	Steven Beharrell
Energy	Steven Beharrell
Funds	Alasdair Gordon
Litigation/Arbitration	Maria Frangeskides
Project Finance	Peter O'Driscoll
Real Property	Anne O'Neill

COUDERT BROTHERS
INTERNATIONAL LAWYERS

COURTS & CO

15 Wimpole St, London, W1G 9SY
Tel: (020) 7637 1651 **Fax:** (020) 7637 0205 **DX:** 42722 Oxford Circus North
Email: law@courtsandco.com **Website:** www.courtsandco.com

Senior Partner	Bill Holmes
Number of partners	6
Assistant solicitors	4
Other fee-earners	1

AREAS OF PRACTICE

Company, Commercial & Tax	40%
Commercial Litigation	30%
Conveyancing/Trusts, Wills & Probate	30%

CONTACTS

Company/Commercial	Ian Paterson
	Patrick Gilmour
Conveyancing/Probate & Trusts	Bill Holmes
Employment	Frank Ryan
Intellectual Property	Michael Krantz
Litigation	Michael Krantz
	Frank Ryan

THE FIRM: Courts & Co is a niche firm, specialising in company and commercial work. The firm provides an in-depth, personal service to companies and their directors, working closely with their business advisers, particularly their accountants. The firm's policy is to combine the highest level of technical expertise with a close understanding of the client's business and commercial requirements.

PRINCIPAL AREAS OF WORK: A large part of the firm's work consists of advising on the purchase and sale of businesses, corporate mergers and reorganisations, as well as a full range of business and commercial matters, including taxation and intellectual property work. The firm handles commercial conveyancing; heavy commercial litigation (including environmental and town and country planning matters); employment work (both litigious and non-litigious) mainly (but not exclusively) for employers; and estate planning, trusts and probate work.

CLIENTELE: Clients include private and public companies, professional partnerships and individual entrepreneurs in all areas of business; charities and trusts. Much of the firm's work is for overseas clients.

COVINGTON & BURLING

Leconfield House, Curzon Street, London, W1J 5HY
Tel: (020) 7495 5655 **Fax:** (020) 7495 3101
Email: rkingham@cov.com **Website:** www.cov.com

Managing Partner	Kurt A Wimmer
Senior Partner	Charles Lister
Number of partners	8
Assistant solicitors	19
Other fee-earners	9

AREAS OF PRACTICE

Corporate & Commercial	30%
Intellectual Property	30%
Medicines & Consumer Product Regulation	25%
International Taxation	10%
General Litigation & Arbitration	5%

THE FIRM: Covington & Burling was founded in Washington DC in 1919 and now has approximately 440 lawyers in the Washington DC, New York and San Francisco offices, 40 lawyers and solicitors in the London and Brussels offices, and a correspondent office in Paris. The London office was established in 1988 and founded a multinational partnership in 1993. It has 13 UK qualified staff, in addition to US and German lawyers. The office maintains extensive collections of EU and national legal resources and is a focal point for multinational issues for Covington & Burling and clients worldwide. The London office has particular expertise in coordinating, on behalf of multinational clients, legal matters involving a number of jurisdictions and the firm has an informal network of international local counsel contacts in over 40 countries throughout Western and Eastern Europe, Australasia, Africa, the Middle East and the Americas. In particular, the firm has developed an ability to advise clients on policy issues and to lobby policy makers, particularly in connection with the IT and pharmaceutical industries.

PRINCIPAL AREAS OF WORK: Major practice areas in London include intellectual property; communications and technology issues; regulation of food, drugs and other consumer products; corporate and securities law; international taxation; litigation and arbitration; competition and trade. The firm acts as principal legal adviser for a wide range of companies that depend on and provide advanced technology, both in the IT industries and the life sciences industries.

INTERNATIONAL: Work is handled in English, French, German, Italian, Portuguese and Spanish.

COVINGTON & BURLING

COZENS-HARDY & JEWSON

Castle Chambers, Opie St, Norwich, NR1 3DP **Tel:** (01603) 625231 **Fax:** (01603) 627160 **DX:** 5214 **Email:** lawyers@cozens-hardy.com
Website: www.cozens-hardy.com **Ptnrs:** 9 **Asst solrs:** 8 **Other fee-earners:** 12

CRIPPS HARRIES HALL

Seymour House, 11-13 Mount Ephraim Road, Tunbridge Wells, TN1 1EG
Tel: (01892) 515121 **Fax:** (01892) 544878 **DX:** 3954 Tunbridge Wells
Email: reception@crippslaw.com **Website:** www.e-cripps.co.uk

14 Buckingham Street, London, WC2N 6DF
Tel: (020) 7930 0004 **Fax:** (020) 7839 9224
Email: reception.london@crippslaw.com

Managing Partner	Jonathan Denny
Senior Partner	Andrew Fermor
Number of partners	30
Assistant solicitors	40
Other fee-earners	73

AREAS OF PRACTICE

Commercial 30%
Finance & Investment 27%
Dispute Resolution 24%
Private Client 19%

CONTACTS

Alternative Dispute Resolution ....Charles Broadie
Charities ....Peter Scott
Commercial Litigation ....Peter Ashford
Commercial Property ....Michael Stevens
Construction ....Jane Ryland
Corporate Finance (inc. Buyouts) ....Trevor Carney
Debt Recovery ....Russell Simpson
E-commerce ....Lawrence Leporte
Employment ....Roger Byard
Environment ....Jason Towell
Family/Matrimonial ....Michael Rowlands
Information Technology ....Lawrence Leporte
Insolvency & Corporate Recovery ....Ed Bible
Personal Injury (Claimant) ....Myles McIntosh
PFI Projects ....Stephen Williams
Planning ....Jason Towell
Private Client: Financial Services & Investment Business ....David Lough
Professional Negligence ....Gavin Tyler
Property Litigation ....Carol Wakeford
Social Housing ....Michael Vos
Trusts & Personal Tax ....Simon Leney

THE FIRM: Cripps Harries Hall is regarded by many businesses and institutions in the South East as the natural first choice among the region's commercial law firms. A large part of the reason for this success is to be found in the firm's claim to provide 'London style skills at out of London prices'. The high calibre of its legal advisers is evidenced by the high proportion of the commercial partners and solicitors who have either joined from or trained at London firms, including several of the 'top ten' City firms. With headquarters out of London, yet within easy reach of the City, the firm's low overheads are reflected in charges to clients which, typically, are at least one third less than those of comparable London firms. In addition to competitive hourly charging rates, the firm is happy to agree to a wide range of other methods of remuneration if these are preferred by the client. The desire to deliver standards of service associated with the best London firms led Cripps Harries Hall to become the first 'top 100' law firm to achieve accreditation to the Law Society's quality assurance standard for solicitors' firms known as Lexcel. This involves the practice being subjected to rigorous assessments by the British Standards Institution for compliance with the exacting standards set by the Law Society designed to encourage excellence in law firms. Cripps Harries Hall is committed to integrating the provision of legal advice with the effective use of IT; having recently invested over £1 million on a new computer system, benefits for clients include developments such as a secure extranet. In summary, Cripps Harries Hall has grown to become a leading commercial law firm in the South East and believes it is on course to become one of the top regional law firms in the country.

PRINCIPAL AREAS OF WORK: The broad spectrum of commercial and institutional clients is drawn from an increasingly wide area with many new clients being based in London and outside of the South East, including several national clients. All clients have ready access to a very wide range of services. The firm has developed a particularly strong practice in a number of markets, as follows. A significant part of the firm's client base is mid-sized corporates, with the high technology sector well represented. The firm is also respected for its employment and PFI work. Among the firm's institutional property clients are government departments, a top ten City law firm, utility companies, insurance companies, asset management companies, national pension funds, property portfolio companies and housing associations. A particular niche for the firm is property developers and house builders. The specialist team defending solicitors' professional liability claims has been retained by SIF to handle run-off claims, in addition to being instructed by two major insurers new to this market. The firm's dispute resolution practice is broad and includes mediation, arbitration, litigation and risk management.

Private Client: In private client work, the firm has extensive experience and has developed a reputation for managing the affairs of wealthy private clients to rival the top London firms in this field. The firm is believed to have the most comprehensive integrated legal and financial services operation of any solicitors' firm in the country.

INTERNATIONAL: The firm is a member of a network of independent law firms in 18 European countries.

CROFTONS

Television House, Mount Street, Manchester, M2 5FA **Tel:** (0161) 214 6180 **Fax:** (0161) 839 1743 **DX:** 18572 Manchester 7
Email: michael@croftons.demon.co.uk **Website:** www.croftons-solicitors.co.uk **Ptnrs:** 5 **Asst solrs:** 3 **Other fee-earners:** 7

CROMBIE WILKINSON

Clifford House, 19 Clifford Street, York, YO1 9RJ **Tel:** (01904) 624185 **Fax:** (01904) 623078 **DX:** 61501 **Email:** york@crombiewilkinson.co.uk
Website: www.crombiewilkinson.co.uk **Ptnrs:** 8 **Asst solrs:** 8 **Other fee-earners:** 9

CROSSE & CROSSE

14 Southernhay West, Exeter, EX1 1PL **Tel:** (01392) 258451 **Fax:** (01392) 278938 **DX:** 8313 EXETER **Ptnrs:** 10 **Asst solrs:** 8
Other fee-earners: 11

CROWELL & MORING LLP

180 Fleet Street, London, EC4A 2HG
Tel: (020) 7413 0011 **Fax:** (020) 7413 0333 **DX:** 91 London Chancery Lane
Website: www.crowell.com

Managing Partner	Peter Teare
UK	
Number of partners	2
Assistant solicitors	5
Other fee-earners	1
International	
Number of partners	94
Senior counsel	6
Of counsel	33
Associates	95
Other fee-earners	59

CONTACTS

Corporate/Commercial	Peter Teare
Competition	James Ashe-Taylor
Communications/IT	Peter Teare
Privacy	Rachael Ott
Employment	David Keefe
International Trade	Gordon Mackenzie
Legislative	Peter Sellar
Litigation/Arbitration	Pippa Wheeler
Healthcare	Natasha Singarayer

THE FIRM: Crowell & Moring is a leading international law firm with offices in London, Brussels, Washington DC and Irvine CA. It provides a full range of transactional, counselling, regulatory and litigation capabilities, with a particular emphasis within Europe on the technology, new media and communications sectors. The firm makes an effort to learn its clients' business and goals, and understands the importance of providing practical business advice clearly, concisely and quickly. Responsiveness and the accessibility of its lawyers are practice priorities.

PRINCIPAL AREAS OF WORK: Crowell & Moring's offices in London and Brussels operate together as an integrated European practice group, offering advice on corporate and commercial transactions, competition law, communications/IT law, privacy, regulation employment law, international trade law, legislative counselling, health care regulation, litigation and international arbitration. The firm has extensive experience of mergers, acquisitions, and joint ventures – particularly those involving cross-border investments. It regularly assists clients with the establishment of new branches and subsidiaries, particularly for international businesses expanding into new European markets. The firm has expertise in the negotiation and drafting of all forms of corporate and commercial agreements commonly used in modern business. Its transactional capabilities are complemented by one of the leading international anti-trust practices in the world. Crowell & Moring provides competition law advice to some of the very largest international corporations and has obtained successful clearance of the full range of transactions requiring anti-trust approvals both in Brussels and in Washington.

CLIENTELE: Clients range from major multinationals to New Economy start-ups and venture capital funds. Many clients are in the technology, new media and communications sectors. Lawyers combine a range of transactional, regulatory and litigation skills with an in depth understanding of the evolving legal, commercial and policy issues presented by the digital revolution and the convergence of the telecoms, broadcast and information technology industries. Many clients in these sectors are fast moving and innovative businesses with which the firm keeps pace in providing dynamic and creative legal solutions.

CRUTES

7 Osborne Terrace, Newcastle upon Tyne, NE2 1RQ
Tel: (0191) 212 5600 **Fax:** (0191) 212 5601 **DX:** 62553 Jesmond
Email: advice@crutes.co.uk **Website:** www.crutes.co.uk

28 Portland Square, Carlisle, CA1 1PE
Tel: (01228) 525446 **Fax:** (01228) 511517 **DX:** 63000 Carlisle
Email: advice@crutes.co.uk

93 Borough Road, Middlesbrough, TS1 3YS
Tel: (01642) 230103 **Fax:** (01642) 231549 **DX:** 60502 Middlesborough
Email: advice@crutes.co.uk

37-38 West Sunniside, Sunderland, SR1 1BY
Tel: (0191) 568 0710 **Fax:** (0191) 514 5247 **DX:** 60701 Sunderland
Email: advice@crutes.co.uk

Senior Partner	Tim Wallis
Managing Partner	Stephen Crute
Number of partners	20
Assistant solicitors	20
Other fee-earners	20

AREAS OF PRACTICE

Insurance/Personal Injury	59%
Insurance/Professional Indemnity	16%
Commercial	8%
Private Client	8%
Health Related Work	6%
Employment	3%

CONTACTS

ADR/Mediation	Helen Ager
Commercial	Stuart Palmer
Employment	Tim Smith
Health Related Work	Tim Wallis
Insurance/Personal Injury	David Drewe
Insurance/Professional Indemnity	John Parker
Private Client	Stuart Palmer

THE FIRM: Crutes is a forward thinking law firm with four offices based in the north of England – the firm services clients on a national basis. Crutes is renowned for its insurance litigation and, with computer networked offices and case management systems, ensures its clients continuity and accuracy of services. The firm is a leader in alternative dispute resolution and is committed to resolving disputes efficiently and speedily, which gives its clients a more cost-effective service. Paramount to the firm's ethos is the importance of listening to clients. Crutes carries out independent client research as part of its commitment to client satisfaction. The firm not only covers the principal areas listed below but now also has a reputable employment unit which acts for the Treasury solicitors. Crutes has a specialist claims unit, a team of dedicated and experienced solicitors, dealing with the increasing number of stress related and abuse claims. The firm has 20 partners in total, six of whom were appointed within the last year. With all the endorsements one would expect from a professional law firm, including ISO 9001 and Investors in People, Crutes is proud of its 94 year history and excited by challenges, both in the legal and technological sense. The firm is dedicated to providing first class legal services.

PRINCIPAL AREAS OF WORK:

Insurance: Insurance work is a particular strength of Crutes, and the firm acts for a large number of the major insurance companies. The firm has maintained a strong presence on a number of insurance panels following several re-tendering exercises – including Norwich Union and Zurich Municipal. Much of the work is personal injury. The firm has a reputation for providing a complete portfolio, including some of the more specialist work areas eg. physical and sexual abuse claims by children. Its dedicated stress unit now handles a number of stress liability claims.

Public Sector Services: Across all four offices, Crutes acts for virtually all of the local authorities in the North. The firm provides a complete range of services, including employment, commercial, property, health and insurance litigation. As a result of the Human Rights Act, Crutes has been involved with the training and development of public sector clients and the impact of the Act. Crutes also acts for the police and fire brigade in their insurance litigation claims.

Professional Indemnity: Crutes has had a high profile professional indemnity practice for many years, and through its dedicated team not only continues to act for SIF, but also represents other professionals such as accountants and surveyors.

Health: Crutes has acted for the NHS since its inception, and now acts for many of the NHS Trusts in the North, for litigation, employment, property and commercial matters.

Commercial: Crutes now boasts a range of services in this sector, ranging from commercial property and company commercial, to intellectual property, insolvency and debt recovery. The firm has seen a significant increase in the amount of cases it now handles.

Dispute Resolution: Crutes is committed to ADR and has been a pioneer of its development since 1992. All Crutes litigators are trained in ADR and the firm has gained a wealth of experience through its involvement in a substantial number of mediation whether as a party, mediator or trainee mediator.

CUFF ROBERTS

100 Old Hall Street, Liverpool, L3 9TD **Tel:** (0151) 237 7777 **Fax:** (0151) 237 7676 **DX:** 14126 Liverpool 1 **Email:** email@cuffroberts.co.uk **Website:** www.cuffroberts.co.uk

CULBERT AND MARTIN

7 Donegall Square West, Belfast, BT1 6JB **Tel:** (028) 9032 5508 **Fax:** (028) 90438669 **DX:** 498 NR Belfast 1 **Ptnrs:** 2 **Asst solrs:** 2 **Other fee-earners:** 2

CUMBERLAND ELLIS PEIRS INCORPORATING BARTH & PARTNERS

Columbia Hse, 69 Aldwych, London, WC2B 4RW
Tel: (020) 7242 0422 **Fax:** (020) 7831 9081 **DX:** 250 Ch.Ln.
Email: cep@cep-law.co.uk **Website:** www.cep-law.co.uk

Managing Partner	Suzanne Eva
Senior Partner	Lionel Judd
Number of partners	12
Assistant solicitors	7
Other fee-earners	11

CONTACTS

Commercial Property	Rod Forsyth
Company/Commercial	Suzanne Eva
Litigation	Neil Turner
Private Client	Roger Hollinshead
Residential Conveyancing	Robert Maclean

THE FIRM: A merger of two long-established central London practices, the firm has attracted considerable company/commercial and commercial property work and has a substantial litigation department; it also continues to provide the full range of private client services. The firm's philosophy is to combine high quality advice with a positive, personal service, at reasonable cost.

PRINCIPAL AREAS OF WORK:

Company/Commercial: A wide variety of work is handled, including takeovers; buy-outs; flotations; intellectual property; and employment law for businesses of all sizes.

Litigation: The firm is active in High Court and County Court work (both commercial and private), including personal injury, landlord and tenant, and debt recovery. It is particularly strong in employment and family law.

Property: The department acts for institutions and companies in a wide variety of commercial property work. A separate section deals with residential conveyancing.

Private Client: The department handles all aspects of a client's personal affairs, including probate; wills; trusts; tax planning and landed estates. It also has expertise in charity law.

CLIENTELE: The firm acts for public and private companies; institutions; charities (particularly City Livery companies); NGOs; sports associations; and a large number of private individuals.

CUNNINGHAM JOHN

Fairstead House, 7 Bury Road, Thetford, IP24 3PL
Tel: (01842) 752401 **Fax:** (01842) 753555 **DX:** 124810
Email: postmaster@cunningham-john.co.uk **Website:** www.cunningham-john.co.uk

Senior Partner	David Cunningham
Senior Partner	Simon John
Managing Partner	Tom Cook
Number of partners	10
Assistant solicitors	13
Other fee-earners	24

CONTACTS

Commercial/Corporate ....David Cunningham
....Clive Wadham Smith
Company..........................Simon Cunningham
Family...Amita Terry
General Litigation ....Donal Sheahan
Private Client........................Robert Chalmers
....Helen Wingfield
PI/CN...Simon John
...............................Tom Cook, Sandra Patton
.......................Graeme Peart, William Jackson

THE FIRM: Cunningham John's successful growth can be best explained by its extensive expertise and ability to handle high profile personal injury/clinical negligence actions and corporate and commercial transactions.

PRINCIPAL AREAS OF WORK:

Company/Commercial: Clients include leading plc and property companies; one transaction of £500m major waste merger illustrates expertise in complex dealings. Clients nationwide, a London presence and a reputation as problem solvers.

Personal Injury/Clinical Negligence: See 'Leaders in their Field', Simon John.

Other Areas: General and commercial litigation, full private client service, family, child care, residential work and education law.

C

CUNNINGHAMS

Second Floor, Bridge Street Chambers, 72 Bridge Street, Manchester, M3 2RJ
Tel: (0161) 833 1600 **Fax:** (0161) 833 1060

Talbot House, 22 The Crescent, Salford, M50 4PF
Tel: 0161 745 9000 **Fax:** 0161 745 9500

Senior Partner	Martin Cunningham
Number of partners	4
Assistant solicitors	4
Other fee-earners	12

AREAS OF PRACTICE

Crime 100%

CONTACTS

Crime - Legal Aid ....David Caplin
Private Client & Business Crime/Fraud
....Martin Cunningham

THE FIRM: The firm operates from offices in central Manchester and practises exclusively in criminal law. The firm now has a second office on The Crescent in Salford, dedicated to its serious crime, serious fraud and private client departments.

PRINCIPAL AREAS OF WORK: Serious crime, serious fraud and private client are the main areas of work. The practice represents both private and publicly funded clients in all aspects of criminal law, ranging from homicide to road traffic cases. The senior partner heads up the firm's serious fraud department, and specialises in white collar crime, including Customs and Excise cases, Inland Revenue investigations and business fraud. A full criminal defence service is offered to all of the firms clients including a specifically dedicated prison law department for advice and representation to the firms clients held within the prison system. The practice has the privilege of being one of only a handful of firms in Greater Manchester who have been appointed to the Criminal Defence Services Serious Fraud panel. The practice is willing to undertake agency work and to accept instructions from firms who are not themselves on the Serious Fraud panel, and as a result unable to accept instructions for publicly funded serious fraud cases.

INTERNATIONAL: The practice benefits from Punjabi and Urdu speaking lawyers and continues to expand with 8 solicitors now within this 4-partner practice.

CURREY & CO
21 Buckingham Gate, London, SW1E 6LS **Tel:** (020) 7802 2700 **Fax:** (020) 7828 5049 **DX:** 2300 Victoria **Ptnrs:** 8 **Asst solrs:** 3 **Other fee-earners:** 2

CURTIS DAVIS GARRARD
Bedfont Cross, Stanwell Road, Heathrow Airport, Feltham, TW14 8NY **Tel:** (020) 8400 2400 **Fax:** (020) 8400 2420/1 **Email:** cdg@cdg.co.uk **Website:** www.cdg.co.uk **Ptnrs:** 6 **Asst solrs:** 9 **Other fee-earners:** 1

CUTTLE & CO
Bridge Street Chambers, 72 Bridge St, Manchester, M3 2RJ **Tel:** (0161) 835 2050 **Fax:** (0161) 831 7986 **Email:** cuttles_mcr@lineone.net **Ptnrs:** 4 **Asst solrs:** 2 **Other fee-earners:** 14

DALE & CO
10 Victoria Street, Felixstowe, IP11 7ER **Tel:** 07074 794708 / 01394 284 118 **Fax:** 07074 794709 / 01394 276 097 **Email:** law@daleandco.com **Ptnrs:** 1 **Asst solrs:** 1 **Other fee-earners:** 1

DALE LANGLEY & CO
60 Lombard Street, London, EC3V 9EA **Tel:** (020) 7464 8433 **Fax:** (020) 7464 8659 **Email:** dale.lan@btinternet.com **Ptnrs:** 1 **Other fee-earners:** 2

DARBYS

Sun Alliance House, 52 New Inn Hall Street, Oxford, OX1 2QD
Tel: (01865) 811 700 **Fax:** (01865) 811 777 **DX:** 4304 Oxford
Email: info@darbys.co.uk **Website:** www.darbys.co.uk

Senior Partner	Sturge Taylor
Number of partners	18
Assistant solicitors	16
Other fee-earners	16

AREAS OF PRACTICE

Commercial Property & Conveyancing	26%
Matrimonial	15%
Litigation	14%
Criminal & Immigration	12%
Company, Commercial & IP	10%
Clinical Negligence & Personal Injury	10%
Trusts & Probate	10%
Employment	3%

CONTACTS

Company, Commercial & IP ......Nick Hedges
..........Dallia Appleton
Commercial Property & Conveyancing
..........Sturge Taylor, Mark Taylor
..........Mike Simmie, Rupert Curtis
Litigation ....Paul Lowe, Elizabeth Taylor
Criminal & Immigration ....Jim Astle
..........Robin Smith, Jenny Harvey
Matrimonial ....Catherine Eddy
..........Victoria Smith, William Selby-Lowndes
Clinical Negligence & Personal Injury
..........Helen Niebuhr
Trusts & Probate..........Sian Jeffrey
Employment..........David Parry

THE FIRM: This recently merged Oxford practice serves business and private clients in a variety of fields. It is a family firm with a long history and deep rooted ties to Oxfordshire's community and enjoys sharing in the challenges faced by local people and businesses. The 18 partners and specialist client service teams provide a wide range of services to both private and business clients.

PRINCIPAL AREAS OF WORK: The firm operates through three specialist departments: Business Services; Private Client; Crime and Immigration.
Business Services: Teamwork is essential in ensuring business clients' legal needs are met. Four teams operate namely commercial litigation, commercial property, company and commercial, and employment – each providing its own specialist advice. Specialisms include acquisitions; mergers and disposals; corporate finance; business start ups; intellectual property and technology; commercial property; employment; litigation.
Private Client Services: The firm continues to believe that servicing the needs of the private individuals is as important as the business client. Five teams operate namely clinical negligence; family; personal injury; residential conveyancing and probate; tax; wills. All of the teams enjoy excellent reputations with the clinical negligence team having an AVMA panel member; the personal injury team have personal injury panel members; the family team membership of the children panel; family law panel; solicitors family law membership.
Crime & Immigration: Two distinct teams comprise this department. The criminal team is one of the largest in the Thames Valley with its aim to be the largest single provider of criminal services in the area. The team increasingly acts in relation to the defence of commercial and regulatory offences such as fraud, health and safety and Environmental Act prosecutions. The team also has a busy liquor and gaming licence practice. The immigration team enjoys a national reputation and acts for an increasingly large number of employers in obtaining work permits for those wishing to employ foreign nationals.
The firm is also a member of LawNet, the nationwide group of independent law firms who share technical knowledge and resources.

CLIENTELE: Clients include multinational companies, University Colleges, start up companies, partnerships and private individuals. Many partners enjoy an excellent reputation with one qualified insolvency practitioner having a national reputation.

MC DARLINGTON
Diocesan Registry, Church House, 90 Deansgate, Manchester, M3 2QH **Tel:** (0161) 834 7545 **Fax:** (0161) 839 0093

DARLINGTON & PARKINSON
78 Pitshanger Lane, Ealing, London, W5 1QX **Tel:** 0208 998 4343 **Fax:** (020) 8566 8285 **DX:** 5149 EALING **Ptnrs:** 2 **Asst solrs:** 5
Other fee-earners: 3

DAVENPORT LYONS

1 Old Burlington Street, London, W1S 3NL
Tel: (020) 7468 2600 **Fax:** (020) 7437 8216 **DX:** 37233 Piccadilly 1
Email: dl@davenportlyons.com **Website:** www.davenportlyons.com

Number of partners	28
Assistant solicitors	38
Other fee-earners	16

AREAS OF PRACTICE

Company Commercial	25%
Litigation	23%
Entertainment/Media	22%
Commercial Property	20%
Private Client	10%

CONTACTS

Banking & Finance..........Alon Domb
Company/Commercial ....Alon Domb
..........Rebecca Ferguson
..........Michael Hatchwell
Competition ....David Marchese
Copyright & Trademark Litigation
..........David Gore
..........Stuart Lockyear
Corporate Tax..........Leslie Powell
Defamation ....Kevin Bays
..........Philip Conway
..........Robin Shaw
Employment ....Kathryn Pavey

THE FIRM: Davenport Lyons is a long-established firm in the West End of London. The firm is a leading media and entertainment practice and also has an excellent reputation in company and commercial work providing a service normally associated with larger city firms. The firm has wide experience in providing comprehensive legal services to corporate and commercial clients across a broad spectrum of market sectors. Those markets include media in all its forms (film, television, radio, music, theatre, publishing and the newspaper industry); information technology, e-commerce and new media; the retail sector; advertising; the restaurant, hotel, sport, leisure and travel industries; property investment and development. The firm prides itself on an unusual blend of high quality legal expertise and commercial sensitivity to clients' needs. This service is provided with speed and efficiency and at a competitive price. The firm's continuing expansion has broadened its experience and expertise but it still recognises the importance to clients of partner attention. The firm also enjoys close involvement with many US and EU businesses and lawyers and the practice has a significant international dimension. Two of the firm's partners are admitted in New York and California respectively.

PRINCIPAL AREAS OF WORK: The firm provides legal services to a wide range of corporate and individual clients and has expertise in a number of particular specialised fields:
Company & Commercial: Advice on formations, reorganisations, acquisitions, venture capital, business start-ups, joint ventures, competition issues, corporate tax planning, employment matters and banking and finance.

Continued overleaf

The firm is particularly well known for its work for growing companies up to and including stock exchange quotations.

Media: The firm's wide experience in the fields of intellectual property, media, IT, technology, e-commerce, new media and entertainment law is reflected in its client list which includes substantial film and television companies, national newspapers, magazines, book and music publishers, record companies and advertising and media agencies. The firm covers every aspect of the entertainment market and is the principal legal adviser to several banks and other financial institutions lending to the film and television sector.

Music, Entertainment & Theatre: The firm has a strong reputation in the UK and US, and acts for many leading music publishing corporations and individual musicians advising on recording contracts, copyright and the problems of performers and artists. The firm covers every aspect of the entertainment market and advises on the impact of EU legislation.

Property: A strong commercial property department acts for major developers, property investors and lending institutions. It is particularly active in the retail sector in a broad range of substantial property and property related matters. A strong property litigation team supports the department. The firm also provides a first class specialist residential property service.

Liquor Licensing: The firm has developed its liquor and entertainment licensing work for its large numbers of clients in restaurant and nightclub businesses.

Defamation: A leader in this field, the firm's clients include a large number of national newspapers, book and magazine publishers as well as *Private Eye* magazine. The firm represents both plaintiffs and defendants.

Litigation: Commercial litigation is a long-established, substantial and successful element of the practice servicing not only the firm's corporate, property, media and entertainment clients, but also businesses in a wide range of sectors.

Employment: The firm provides specialist and comprehensive advice in all areas of employment law and represents and defends cases in the Employment Tribunal, the County Court and the High Court.

Private Client: This department provides a full service to private clients, both domestic and overseas, including matrimonial matters, advice on tax planning, compliance and appeals trust charities and pensions; wills and administration of estates and Court of Protection practice.

Sport: The firm has a well-established practice advising promoters of sporting events and individual sportsmen in connection with protecting and enhancing their interests.

INTERNATIONAL: Davenport Lyons has wide and long-standing contacts in the international sphere particularly with US and EU businesses and lawyers.

CONTACTS CONTINUED

Entertainment & Liquor Licensing	Philip Conway
	David Lavender
Insolvency	Trevor Sears
Intellectual Property & New Media	Stephen Digby
	David Marchese
International Coordinator	Michael Hatchwell
IT/Technology/E-commerce	Stephen Digby
	Michael Hatchwell
	David Marchese
Litigation (General)	Kevin Bays
	David Gore
	Robin Shaw
Litigation (Property)	Jonathan Aubrey
Media/Film/TV	Laurence Brown
	Melanie Haddad
	Leon Morgan
	Richard Moxon
Music/Entertainment/Theatre	Jay Quatrini
	James Ware
Private Client (Matrimonial)	John Burrell
Private Client (Tax & Trusts)	Judith Spells
	Jeffrey Cohen
Property	Graham Atkins
	John Downing
	Marilyn Elstow
	Richard Kelsey
	Paul McCombie
Publishing	Leon Morgan
	James Ware
Sport	Kevin Bays
Travel	Trevor Sears

DAVID BISHOP & CO

14 Chapel Lane, Formby, Liverpool, L37 4DY **Tel:** 01704 878 421 **Fax:** 01704 878 959 **Email:** David_Bishop@compuserve.com **Ptnrs:** 1

E. DAVID BRAIN & CO

8 Church Street, St Austell, PL25 4AT **Tel:** (01726) 68111 **Fax:** (01726) 61433 **DX:** 81252 St. Austell **Email:** info@david-brain.co.uk **Website:** www.david-brain.co.uk **Ptnrs:** 2 **Asst solrs:** 1 **Other fee-earners:** 6

DAVID CHARNLEY & CO

Phoenix House, 102-106 South Street, Romford, RM1 1RX **Tel:** (01708) 766 155 **Fax:** (01708) 730 743 **DX:** 4614 Romford **Ptnrs:** 1 **Asst solrs:** 14 **Other fee-earners:** 16 **Contact:** Ben Thomas • A large specialist Essex/East London criminal practice. Amongst general work undertaken, fraud and other serious cases are a particular strength. Higher Court advocacy is undertaken.

AREAS OF PRACTICE

Crime	100%

DAVID CORKER SOLICITORS

Natwest Bank Chambers, 218 Strand, London, WC2R 1AT **Tel:** 0207 353 6007 **Fax:** 0207 353 6008 **Email:** dc@davidcorker.co.uk **Website:** www.davidcorker.co.uk **Ptnrs:** 2 **Asst solrs:** 1 **Other fee-earners:** 2

DAVID DU PRÉ & CO

90-92 Parkway, Regents Park, London, NW1 7AN
Tel: (020) 7284 3040 **Fax:** (020) 7485 1145 **DX:** 57070
Email: info@daviddupre.co.uk **Website:** www.daviddupre.co.uk

Senior Partner	David du Pré
Number of partners	1
Assistant solicitors	1

THE FIRM: Established by David du Pré, a former matrimonial barrister, who later qualified as a solicitor in 1980 and held senior positions in leading City family departments before setting up his own specialist matrimonial practice in 1991. He is a member of the Solicitors Family Law Association, the International Society of Family Law, the Family Mediators Association, and the UK College of Family Mediators.

PRINCIPAL AREAS OF WORK: Matrimonial, family and co-habitation law including: separation and parental responsibility agreements; divorce petitions; financial applications, including complex and emergency applications, cases involving substantial assets/income or where there is an international dimension. Although both big and small cases are welcomed, a publicly funded service is not available.

AREAS OF PRACTICE

Family/Matrimonial/Divorce	100%

CONTACTS

Family/Matrimonial/Divorce	David du Pré

DAVID GIST SOLICITORS

21/23 Clare Street, Bristol, BS1 1TZ **Tel:** (0117) 927 9111 **Fax:** (0117) 927 9101 **DX:** 7880 Bristol **Email:** info@davidgist.co.uk **Ptnrs:**4 **Asst solrs:**8 **Associates:**1 **Contact:** Susan Brewster • David Gist Solicitors deals mainly with claimant personal injury claims, predominantly those arising from motor accidents, and also an increasing number of clinical negligence and industrial accident claims.

DAVID GRAY SOLICITORS

Old County Court, 56 Westgate Road, Newcastle upon Tyne, NE1 5XU **Tel:** (0191) 232 9547 **Fax:** (0191) 230 4149 **DX:** 61036 Newcastle upon Tyne **Email:** lawyers@davidgray.co.uk **Website:** davidgray.co.uk **Ptnrs:** 5 **Asst solrs:** 13 **Other fee-earners:** 12

DAVID JEACOCK

16 Church St, Wootton Bassett, Swindon, SN4 7BQ
Tel: (01793) 854 111 **Fax:** (01793) 853 600
Email: jeacock@lineone.net

Principal	David Jeacock
Number of partners	1

AREAS OF PRACTICE

Company/Commercial	50%
Sports Law	30%
Private & General	20%

THE FIRM: After 10 years' personal experience as an in-house lawyer, David Jeacock established the practice in 1984 to provide practical commercial advice to business clients. Because of his involvement and experience in sports administration and doping control, the practice soon provided practical advice in those areas as well and is now well established in this field. Clients include three national governing bodies of sports. This is a small personal practice that clearly enjoys working with all its clients, to solve their problems.

D

DAVID PRICE SOLICITORS & ADVOCATES

5 Great James Street, London, WC1N 3DB **Tel:** (020) 7916 9911 **Fax:** (020) 7916 9910 **Email:** enquiries@lawyers-media.com **Website:** www.lawyers-media.com **Ptnrs:** 1 **Asst solrs:** 1 **Other fee-earners:** 6

DAVIDSON CHALMERS WS

10 Castle Terrace, Edinburgh, EH1 2DP **Tel:** (0131) 228 9191 **Fax:** (0131) 228 9003 **DX:** 408 Edinburgh **Email:** mailbox@dcws.co.uk **Website:** www.dcws.co.uk **Ptnrs:** 5 **Asst solrs:** 10 **Other fee-earners:** 2

DAVIES AND PARTNERS

135 Aztec West, Almondsbury, Bristol, BS32 4AW
Tel: (01454) 619 619 **Fax:** (01454) 619 696 **DX:** 35007 Almondsbury

5 Highlands Court, Cranmore Avenue, Solihull, Birmingham, B90 4LE
Tel: (0121) 711 7107 **Fax:** (0121) 711 4851 **DX:** 715358 Solihull 19

Rowan House, Barnett Way, Barnwood, Gloucester, GL4 3RT
Tel: (01452) 612 345 **Fax:** (01452) 611 922 **DX:** 55253

Senior Partner	D B Davies
Number of partners	18
Assistant solicitors	29
Other fee-earners	24

CONTACTS

Commercial Litigation	Geoffrey Hand
Commercial Property	Peter Mitchell
Company/Commercial	Thomas Brennan
Land Development	Barrie Davies
Personal Injury & Medical Negligence	Evan Lockhart
Private Client	Richard Maisey

THE FIRM: Davies and Partners is forward-thinking and objective in approach. The firm handles a large amount of commercial property, estate conveyancing, company and commercial, commercial litigation, and secured lending work and has also developed a strong personal injury and medical negligence practice.

PRINCIPAL AREAS OF WORK:

Land Development: The firm handles all aspects of development land, from initial site acquisition to individual unit transfers and ancillary documentation, planning applications and appeals, building contracts and freehold and leasehold matters.

Company/Commercial: The firm has extensive experience in the whole range of company and commercial work, including corporate finance; mergers, acquisitions and restructuring; MBOs; publicly-quoted companies; company and partnership formation; joint ventures; shareholders' agreements; banking; financial services and franchising; intellectual property, including international, EU and UK competition implications.

Commercial Property: The firm handles all aspects of commercial property including industrial, office and retail premises for both landlords and tenants and all associated funding, development and property management issues.

Commercial Litigation: Work includes building contracts; judicial review; landlord and tenant; employment; insurance; professional negligence; public liability; economic torts; corporate insolvency; unlawful trading; licensing; debt collection and banking litigation.

Continued overleaf

Personal Injury & Medical Negligence: The firm handles extensively both plaintiff and defendant personal injury work. Medical negligence work is plaintiff-orientated. Two fee earners are members of the Law Society Personal Injury Panel.
Other Areas: All aspects of corporate and personal tax and financial planning, agricultural law (including land acquisition and disposal, agricultural holdings, grazing agreements, share farming agreements, EU implications and business tenancies) and private client work (including residential conveyancing, re-mortgaging, wills, trusts and estate management, and distribution and winding-up of estates).

DAVIES ARNOLD COOPER

6-8 Bouverie Street, London, EC4Y 8DD
Tel: (020) 7936 2222 **Fax:** (020) 7936 2020 **DX:** 172 London Chancery Lane WC2
Email: daclon@dac.co.uk **Website:** www.dac.co.uk

85 Gracechurch Street, London, EC3V 0AA
Tel: (020) 7936 2222 **Fax:** (020) 7410 7998 **DX:** 172 London Chancery Lane WC2
Email: daclon@dac.co.uk

60 Fountain Street, Manchester, M2 2FE
Tel: (0161) 839 8396 **Fax:** (0161) 839 8309 **DX:** 14363 Manchester
Email: dacman@dac.co.uk

Milburn House, Dean Street, Newcastle upon Tyne, NE1 1LE
Tel: (0191) 230 5115 **Fax:** (0191) 230 0296 **DX:** 716751 Newcastle upon Tyne 20
Email: dacnew@dac.co.uk

Senior Partner	David McIntosh
Executive Partner	Daniel Gowan
Operations Partner	David Hertzell
International	
Number of partners	42
Assistant solicitors	82
Other fee-earners	47

CONTACTS

ADR	Michael Dobias
Banking	John Nelmes
Banking Disputes	Allan Reason
Commercial Litigation	Pippa Ellis
	David McIntosh
Commercial Property	Robert Lee
Construction & Engineering	Daniel Gowan
Construction & Property/Insurance	Nick Young
Corporate & Employment	David Smellie
Education	Pradeep Dandiker
Energy	Akbar Ali
E-risk	Richard Highley
Fraud	Nick Young
General Commercial	Robert Lee
Health & Safety	Richard Tovell
Healthcare	Simon Pearl
Insolvency	Bryan Green
Insurance Litigation	Michael Dobias
International Transport/ European Competition	Marjorie Holmes
Marine/Shipping	Marjorie Holmes
Medical Negligence - Defendants	Simon Pearl
Occupational Health	Geoff Meyer
Personal Injury - EL/PL	Allison Dias
Personal Injury - Motor	Alan Jones
Product Liability	Anne Ware
Professional Indemnity/D&O	Kenneth McKenzie
Reinsurance	Michael Dobias
Sports Injuries	John Smith

THE FIRM: At DAC, the focus is on the firm's core strengths. It is a leading practice in dispute resolution (including all forms of litigation, arbitration and alternative dispute resolution), corporate risk and commercial property services. Its commercial and pragmatic approach demonstrates a genuine market commitment to the clients it serves in the industry sectors of insurance, financial services, construction, commercial property, pharmaceutical, healthcare, manufacturing and retailing. The firm has collaborative relationships with its clients and focuses its resources towards developing products and service delivery which add value to their businesses. A passion for its clients' markets has led to the firm championing issues affecting its clients' business. DAC looks towards the issues of the future and has recently been at the forefront of such issues as transnational litigation, rehabilitation, corporate governance/accountability, human rights, e-risks, occupational health and employee issues, reputation management, corporate accountability and health and safety. It has taken a lead in the firm-wide usage of ADR and technological advances such as paperless litigation. The firm remains the number one choice for multi-party actions arising in the UK and internationally relating to product liability or physical disasters and accidents. Examples of high profile litigation include actions arising out of the collapse of the Maxwell empire, Barings, Polly Peck, Banesto, Piper Alpha, haemophilia and the Heathrow Tunnel collapse. In high profile and high value disputes, DAC is the preferred choice. The firm also undertakes high volume work and is seen to be the nation's number one personal injury defence firm. Davies Arnold Cooper was established in 1927. It has offices in London, the London Market, Manchester, Newcastle and Madrid, as well as strong contacts with leading foreign law firms throughout the world.

CLIENTELE: DAC works for major British and international insurance and reinsurance companies, Lloyd's and many quoted and non-quoted property companies. The firm also acts for numerous banks, financial institutions and professional partnerships of all disciplines.

INTERNATIONAL: The firm has an overseas office in Madrid, Spain.

DAVIES, JOHNSON & CO

The Old Harbour Office, Guy's Quay, Sutton Harbour, Plymouth, PL4 0ES **Tel:** (01752) 226 020 **Fax:** (01752) 225 882 **DX:** 8254 Plymouth 2 **Email:** admin@djco.co.uk **Website:** www.djco.co.uk **Ptnrs:** 4 **Asst solrs:** 1 **Other fee-earners:** 2 **Contact:** Jonathan Johnson • A niche practice providing a complete range of services to the commercial shipping industry and the international trading community. An extensive website provides full details.

DAVIES LAVERY

Victoria Court, 17-21 Ashford Road, Maidstone, ME14 5FA
Tel: (01622) 625 625 **Fax:** (01622) 625 600 **DX:** 51971 Maidstone 2
Email: victoria.court@davies-lavery.co.uk **Website:** www.davies-lavery.co.uk

82-86 Fenchurch Street, London, EC3M 4BY
Tel: (020) 7780 6868 **Fax:** (020) 7780 6800 **DX:** 623 London/City EC3
Email: fenchurch.street@davies-lavery.co.uk

King Edward House, 135A New Street, Birmingham, B2 4QQ
Tel: (0121) 689 8900 **Fax:** (0121) 689 8901 **DX:** 13043 Birmingham
Email: new.street@davies-lavery.co.uk

Managing Partners	Kathy Dwyer (Maidstone) Claire McKinney (Birmingham) Philip West (London)
Number of partners	19
Assistant solicitors	42
Other fee-earners	13

AREAS OF PRACTICE

Product Liability & Personal Injury/Insurance	68%
Property Litigation	10%
Commercial Property	7%
Commercial Litigation	5%
Company/Commercial	5%
Transit	5%

THE FIRM: Davies Lavery provides the insurance and commercial sectors with a proactive, professional and expert service at a competitive rate. The firm is forward looking and innovative and its lawyers combine considerable experience and expertise with a progressive approach to work. Davies Lavery was voted Insurance Law Firm of the Year at the Insurance Industry Awards 2000. With over 50 fee-earners, Davies Lavery is able to deal with a wide range of insurance disputes in terms of complexity and quantum. For further information, visit the firm's website.

PRINCIPAL AREAS OF WORK: Specialists in insurance-related work, Davies Lavery is particularly experienced in such areas as: personal injury; policy disputes; property damage; professional negligence; property liability; transit matters; company and commercial law; commercial property.

DAVIES WALLIS FOYSTER

5 Castle Street, Liverpool, L2 4XE
Tel: (0151) 236 6226 **Fax:** (0151) 236 3088 **DX:** 14128 Liverpool
Email: enquiries@dwf-law.com **Website:** www.dwf.law.co.uk

Harvester House, 37 Peter Street, Manchester, M2 5GB
Tel: (0161) 228 3702 **Fax:** (0161) 835 2407 **DX:** 14313 Manchester
Email: enquiries@dwf-law.com

Senior Partner	Jim Davies
Number of partners	51
Assistant solicitors	65
Other fee-earners	62

AREAS OF PRACTICE

Corporate & Commercial	65%
Insurance	35%

CONTACTS

Asset Finance	Tony Bochenski
Banking	Tony Bochenski
Business Agreements	Mark O'Connor
Competition	Laurence Pritchard
Construction	Ross Wellman
Corporate	Mark O'Connor
Debt Recovery	Mary Barlow
Dispute Resolution	Graham Dagnall
Employment	Andrew Leatherland
Health/Safety & Environment	Sarah Fulton
Insolvency	Andrew Gregory
Insurance	Paul Berry
Intellectual Property	Laurence Pritchard
Internet & Technology	Laurence Pritchard
Licensing	Carl Bruder
Music & Media	Francis McEntegart
Pensions	Gerald Power
Planning	Simon Richardson
Property	Guy Wallis
Public Company Work	Mark O'Connor
Training Services	Nigel Wallis
Wealth Protection	Paul Liddle

THE FIRM: Davies Wallis Foyster is one of the leading law firms in the North West, providing a full range of services for corporate and commercial clients and insurance clients. The firm acts for a substantial number of successful and growing businesses in most market sectors and has a proven track record of helping busineses to grow and compete. It has a reputation for the quality, style and energy of its people and its willingness to provide client references. Over the years, the firm has recruited recognised market leaders in all its service areas and has built strong, multi-skilled teams around them. It is, therefore, capable of providing clients with a comprehensive menu of world-class services to help them achieve their business objectives.

PRINCIPAL AREAS OF WORK:

Corporate & Commercial: Services for corporate and commercial clients include asset finance, banking, business agreements, competition, construction, corporate transactions and advice, debt recovery, dispute resolution, employment, health/safety and environment, insolvency, insurance, intellectual property, Internet and technology, licensing, music and media, pensions, planning, property, public company work, training services and wealth protection.

Insurance: Services for insurance clients include accident and injury claims, commercial claims, policy documentation, recovery services and training services.

INTERNATIONAL: DWF is a member of EU-LEX International Practice Group, a well integrated network of international law firms, enabling the firm to coordinate legal work on behalf of clients wherever their business takes them.

RECRUITMENT: DWF is actively recruiting in all its service areas and is looking for lawyers and others who enjoy working as part of a busy team, who respond positively to a challenge and have what it takes to deliver results for clients.

DAVIES WALLIS FOYSTER
SOLICITORS

DAVIS BLANK FURNISS

90 Deansgate, Manchester, M3 2QJ **Tel:** (0161) 832 3304 **Fax:** (0161) 834 3568 **DX:** 14311 Manchester **Email:** dbf-solicitors@tvc.org.uk
Ptnrs: 14 **Asst solrs:** 8 **Other fee-earners:** 9

DAVITT JONES BOULD

15 The Crescent, Taunton, TA1 4EB
Tel: (01823) 279 279 **Fax:** (01823) 279 111 **DX:** 32129 Taunton
Email: general@djblaw.co.uk **Website:** www.djblaw.co.uk

Managing Partner	Madeleine F Davitt
Chief Executive	Peter A Allinson
Number of partners	3
Assistant solicitors	6
Other fee-earners	4

AREAS OF PRACTICE

Commercial Property (inc. Planning, Environmental Law & Litigation)........100%

CONTACTS

Commercial Property........Madeleine F Davitt
Environmental Law..........Tim Sylvester Jones
Public Law........................Tim Sylvester Jones
Landlord & Tenant......................Stuart Bould
Planning & Litigation............Peter A Allinson

DAVITT JONES BOULD

THE FIRM: Davitt Jones Bould was established in 1999 by a team of lawyers that had formerly worked within central government for the Government Property Lawyers. Since establishment the firm has expanded to include experienced commercial property lawyers from both the public and private sectors. The firm offers experience across the full breadth of commercial property transactions including major undertakings such as the property aspects of government privatisations, large scale developments and disposals. The firm's offices are based in Taunton but the firm acts for clients nationwide. Most of the firm's work currently centres on London and the south east of England.

PRINCIPAL AREAS OF WORK:

Commercial Property: All manner of commercial property work is undertaken ranging from small and large scale acquisitions, disposals, lettings and all aspects of property management through to development work and PFI/PPP transactions. In addition to transactional work the firm offers high quality technical legal advice on all matters involving property. Notable projects recently undertaken include the property aspects of the Ministry of Defence's privatisation of DERA and the refurbishment and reletting of high value office buildings in Central London. The firm deals with all associated areas of law relating to commercial property including planning and environmental law. The firm has particular experience in dealing with transactions involving clawback and overage, not only in the drafting and working of such provisions but also in their enforcement.
Property Litigation: The firm has the ability to deal with all aspects of litigation involving commercial property.
Landlord & Tenant: The firm handles all types of landlord and tenant work from the perspective of both landlord and tenant including the grant of and entry into leases, assignments, underlettings, lease renewals and termination of leases. Additionally, the full range of property management work is undertaken including licences for alterations and advice on rent review and other matters. Specialist work is also undertaken such as mobile phone aerial mast leases and wind farms.

CLIENTELE:

Public Sector: The practice has established a reputation and expertise in acting for the public sector. This includes administrative and public law aspects and the political dimensions of such work. Notably the firm is one of the four term commission lawyers for the Ministry of Defence undertaking all property related work on their behalf in London and the South East of England. Other government departments and local authorities are listed amongst the firm's clients. The firm is accustomed to accepting instructions of a most complex and sensitive nature.
Corporate: The firm acts for a range of institutions and corporate clients including manufacturers, banks and small businesses.

DAWSON & CO

2 New Square, Lincoln's Inn, London, WC2A 3RZ
Tel: (020) 7421 4800 **Fax:** (020) 7421 4848 **DX:** 38 LDE
Email: legal@dawson-and-co.co.uk **Website:** www.dawsonslaw.com

Senior Partner	Joseph Richardson
Number of partners	21
Assistant solicitors	13
Other fee-earners	14

AREAS OF PRACTICE

Property..........25%
Family..........18%
Litigation..........18%
Probate/Trusts..........15%
Tax..........15%
Company..........9%

CONTACTS

Corporate & Commercial....Michael Edwards
Family..........Peter Alexander
..........Mary Hakendorf
Litigation..........Joanne Keddie
..........Mathew Rea
Partnership Law..........Stephen Ralph
Private Client..........Joseph Richardson
Property..........Bill Smith

THE FIRM: Situated in Lincoln's Inn, this medium-sized practice offers a wide spectrum of services. In particular it carries out private client work and provides litigation, family, property and corporate, and commercial services for individuals, partnerships, businesses, charities and institutional clients. Over the course of the last five years the firm has expanded dynamically and continues to grow in all departments in order to provide a specialist and full service to meet its clients' needs. The firm combines high professional and personal standards with a commercial approach to its work. Underpinning all its dealings with clients is the fundamental principle of the contact partner. That partner takes a personal responsibility for all the affairs of the clients in his or her care, whichever department is dealing with a particular matter. It is part of the firm's philosophy to understand the nature of a client's business and broader concerns. For members of the firm the aim is to combine quality of work with quality of life. The firm operates a London High Court and County Court agency service, acting mostly for substantial provincial practices.

PRINCIPAL AREAS OF WORK:

Private Client: Services focus on all aspects of tax planning, including international tax, as well as wills, probate, settlements, trust administration and investment management.
Family Law: The firm handles all aspects of family law for high net worth individuals or their spouses including divorce, judicial separation, disputes between cohabitees, financial provision, children and, where appropriate, conciliation.
Litigation: This department offers a proactive and commercial approach to resolving disputes and undertakes work in all courts (including the European Court of Justice) and a number of tribunals as well as engag-

ing in alternative dispute resolution (arbitration and mediation). Particular areas of expertise include commercial contracts, commercial fraud, insolvency and asset tracing, employment law, defamation, contentious probate and trust disputes, contentious and non-contentious partnership law, shareholder and company disputes, property, professional negligence, agricultural disputes and quotas.

Corporate & Commercial: This group deals with all aspects of work, both national and international, from the most complex e-commerce transaction to the most straightforward consultancy agreement. One partner is a licensed insolvency practitioner.

Property: Property services are a notable specialism, including commercial and residential conveyancing, acquisition, management and disposal of investment properties, and landlord and tenant matters. Expertise is also provided in agricultural law, farm quotas, property development, construction contracts, Settled Land Act and trust conveyancing, waste disposal, mineral extraction and housing association law.

CLIENTELE: The practice acts for a broad range of commercial and private clients, for whom it aims to provide comprehensive expertise positively, imaginatively and cost-effectively. Clients include businesses of many types, landed estates, families and individuals, partnerships, charities, housing associations, educational institutions and professionals. Corporate work now has a strong international element. The firm's matrimonial team is known for its work for high profile and wealthy families.

RECRUITMENT: The firm expects to develop through organic growth driven by the very high standard of trainees it recruits and by some lateral hiring.

D

DAWSON CORNWELL

16 Red Lion Square, Holborn, London, WC1R 4QT
Tel: (020) 7242 2556 **Fax:** (020) 7831 0478 **DX:** 35725 Bloomsbury
Email: mail@dawsoncornwell.co.uk **Website:** www.dawsoncornwell.co.uk

Senior Partner	John Cornwell
Number of partners	9
Assistant solicitors	3
Other fee-earners	2

AREAS OF PRACTICE

Family & Matrimonial	73%
Conveyancing	12%
Wills, Trusts & Probate	10%
Litigation & Miscellaneous	4%

CONTACTS

Children's Issues	Anne-Marie Hutchinson
Family Law	Rhiannon Lewis

THE FIRM: Dawson Cornwell is a specialist family law firm. All areas of matrimonial and family law are covered including divorces, separations, pre-marriage agreements, emergency procedures and all issues relating to children. Many cases involve the resolution of complex financial issues. Others involve child abduction and international custody disputes. The firm runs a well-established mediation service. The senior partner founded the Solicitors Family Law Association in 1982 and, in accordance with the principles of the SFLA, the firm aims to resolve family disputes in a constructive and cost effective manner. Other areas of practice include property, probate, tax and family financial planning.

DEAN WILSON LAING

96 Church Street, Brighton, BN1 1UJ
Tel: (01273) 327 241 **Fax:** (01273) 770 913 **DX:** 2706 Brighton
Email: thelawyers@deanwilson.co.uk

Managing Partner	Ian Wilson
Number of partners	8
Assistant solicitors	4
Other fee-earners	7

AREAS OF PRACTICE

Domestic Conveyancing/Probate	21%
General Litigation	15%
Commercial Property	14%
Landlord & Tenant	14%
Employment	12%
Matrimonial	12%
Company Commercial	9%
Planning	3%

CONTACTS

Children	Seema Roberts
Commercial, Commercial Property, Landlord & Tenant (Non-contentious)	David Barling
Domestic Conveyancing/Probate	Georgina James
Employment	Ian Wilson
Family	David Laing
Financial Services	John Atkinson
Landlord & Tenant Litigation	Claire Whiteman
Leasehold Enfranchisement	Jane Pritchard
Licensing	Nicholas Perkins
Planning	David Barling
Sport	David Laing

THE FIRM: The firm offers high quality service to its clients over a comprehensive range of areas. The partners include a Recorder, a former local authority planning committee chairman, a former chairman of industrial tribunals, the holder of a High Courts Advocates Certificate, members of the Personal Injury Panel and the Family Law Panel, an accredited family law mediator and a member of the Society of Trust and Estate Practitioners. The firm also has the benefit of a public funding franchise in family and housing specialities.

PRINCIPAL AREAS OF WORK:

Corporate & Commercial: The firm can advise on all aspects of corporate, commercial and financial matters, including company and partnership formation, restructuring, acquisitions and disposals, and company and partnership disputes. A full range of commercial property work is undertaken including estate development, planning work, commercial leasing and commercial conveyancing.

Landlord & Tenant: The firm specialises in all aspects of landlord and tenant law, both residential and commercial. A substantial amount of litigation for both landlords and tenants is dealt with. The firm are honorary solicitors to the Association of Residential Letting Agents and also to the Southern Private Landlords Association. Leasehold enfranchisement is fully covered.

Employment: The firm is most experienced in all areas of this work, acting for both employers and employees.

Family Law: The family law department covers all aspects of family law, including mediation and has particular experience of substantial settlements.

Personal Injury: The firm has wide experience acting for both claimants and defendants.

Sports Law: The firm has experience acting for a number of this country's international sports persons before their sports disciplinary tribunals and also dealing with complex constitutional issues.

Litigation: A range of civil litigation is undertaken including professional negligence actions, civil engineering and construction disputes, marine disputes, disputes including applications for restraint of trade and non-competition injunctions and debt recovery. Agency work for mortgage lenders and others is also undertaken.

Continued overleaf

Private Client: Private client service includes wills, probate, administration of estates, trusts and tax planning, residential conveyancing and leases, charity law and immigration law.
Licensing: The firm has specialist experience in licensing law relating to pubs, clubs, restaurants and gaming.
Financial Services: The firm is authorised to carry out discrete investment business.

BLACKETT HART & PRATT

Eldon Chambers, 23 The Quayside, Newcastle upon Tyne, NE1 3DE **Tel:** (0191) 221 0898 **Fax:** (0191) 232 0930 **DX:** 61085
Email: advice@deas-mallen.co.uk **Ptnrs:** 23 **Asst solrs:** 11 **Other fee-earners:** 15

DEBEVOISE & PLIMPTON

Tower 42, International Financial Centre, 25 Old Broad Street, London, EC2N 1HQ
Tel: (020) 7786 9000 **Fax:** (020) 7588 4180
Website: www.debevoise.com

Managing Partner	James Kiernan
Number of partners	8
Assistant solicitors	25
Other fee-earners	4
Total lawyers worldwide	479

CONTACTS

M&A .... James Kiernan
.... Andrew Sommer
.... Colin Bogie
Corporate Finance .... Robert Bruce
.... Katherine Ashton
Project Finance .... Craig Bowman
.... Geoffrey Burgess
Dispute Resolution .... Arthur Marriott QC
Tax .... Peter Schuur

THE FIRM: Debevoise & Plimpton is a leading international firm practicing in the areas of corporate law, litigation, tax, real estate and trusts and estates.

PRINCIPAL AREAS OF WORK: The London office, which advises on matters of US and English law, represents US, UK and other clients in connection with mergers, acquisitions and joint ventures; global offerings and other securities transactions; telecommunications, including privatisations; acquisitions, projects and other financings; private investment funds, tax planning; international commercial arbitration and dispute resolution. The office works closely with the firm's head office in New York and branch offices in Paris, Frankfurt, Moscow, Hong Kong and Washington DC.

INTERNATIONAL: Work is handled in French, German, Hungarian, Italian, Potuguese, Russian and Spanish.

DECHERT

2 Serjeants' Inn, London, EC4Y 1LT
Tel: (020) 7583 5353 **Fax:** (020) 7775 7894 **DX:** 30 London
Email: advice@dechertEU.com **Website:** www.dechert.com

Senior Partner	Steven Fogel
Chief Executive	Peter Duffell
UK	
Number of partners	49
Assistant solicitors	90
Other fee-earners	69
International	
Number of partners	168
Assistant solicitors	276
Other fee-earners	155

CONTACTS

Banking/Finance & Securitisation
.... Trevor Beadle
Commercial .... Peter Crockford
Construction .... Charles Brown
Corporate .... David Vogel
Corporate Recovery .... Sally Unwin
Customs & Excise/VAT
.... Malachy Cornwell-Kelly
Employment .... Charles Wynn-Evans
EU & Competition .... Peter Crockford
Financial Services .... Peter Astleford
Insurance/Reinsurance .... Robin Williams
Investigations & Fraud .... David Byrne
IP/Defamation .... Andrew Hearn
IT/E-commerce .... Renzo Marchini
Litigation .... David Byrne
Planning .... Justin True
Property .... Chris Edwards
Property Litigation .... Jeremy Grose
Retail .... Paul Harding
Tax & VAT .... Mark Stapleton
Trade Marks .... Paul Kavanagh

THE FIRM: On 1 July 2000, City of London law firm Titmuss Sainer Dechert merged with US law firm Dechert Price & Rhoads to form an international legal practice called Dechert. The merger followed a successful six-year alliance between the two firms. Dechert has more than 290 lawyers in twelve offices located in the US and Europe serving clients operating in markets around the globe.

PRINCIPAL AREAS OF WORK: The London office of Dechert offers:
Corporate Services: Core services include flotations, capital issues, transborder and domestic mergers, acquisitions and disposals and corporate reorganisations and recoveries. Specialist teams handle banking, securitisation and insolvency work.
Property: A comprehensive range of property services including commercial, industrial and retail development, investment, planning, environment, property litigation and construction. Clients include investment funds, major retailers, property developers, large corporations and public authorities.
Financial Services: Legal, regulatory and tax advice to financial service firms and advice on the legal aspects of operating an investment management business in Europe, North America and other markets around the globe.
Insurance: Serves Lloyd's and non-Lloyd's insurance and reinsurance clients and deals with mergers and acquisitions in the insurance market, insurance litigation and arbitration.
Investigations: The firm handles all civil and criminal aspects of corporate fraud, DTI inquiries, SFO investigations, Inland Revenue and Customs & Excise investigations, disciplinary proceedings, insider dealing, investigations by the SROs, money laundering and compliance.
Litigation: A broad range of national and international commercial disputes in most areas of civil law with particular expertise in anti-trust, take-over, fraud-related cross-border tracing, intellectual property and defamation. The firm also provides ADR services.
Commercial: The firm handles intellectual property, UK and EU competition law, computer law, product liability, overseas joint ventures and general commercial contracts. The trade mark practice offers a unified approach to the selection, requisition, exploitation and enforcement of intellectual property rights. Dechert also has specialist practices in employment, tax and private client, customs and excise and international trade.

CLIENTELE: The firm's clients include substantial UK and international listed and private companies from a wide cross-section of industry and commerce.

RECRUITMENT: In London, the firm recruits up to 15 trainees annually. Contact Lynn Muncey for a trainee solicitor recruitment brochure.

DEIGHTON GUEDALLA

Top Floor, 30-31 Islington Green, London, N1 8DU **Tel:** (020) 7359 5700 **Fax:** (020) 7359 9909 **DX:** 58251 Islington **Ptnrs:** 2 **Asst solrs:** 2 **Other fee-earners:** 3

DENISON TILL

Stamford House, Piccadilly, York, YO1 9PP
Tel: (01904) 611 411 **Fax:** (01904) 646 972 **DX:** 65206 YORK6
Email: mail@denisontill.com **Website:** www.denisontill.com

Goodbard House, Infirmary Street, Leeds, LS1 2JS
Tel: (0113) 246 7161 **Fax:** (0113) 246 7518
Email: mail@denisontill.com

Managing Partner	Christopher Barton
Senior Partner	Anthony Ridge

AREAS OF PRACTICE

Company/Commercial	22%
Dispute Resolution	20%
Commercial Property	20%
Construction	18%
Private Litigation	10%
Tax, Trusts & Wills	6%
Residential Property	4%

CONTACTS

Agriculture & Estates	David Grice
Banking	Andrew Lindsay
Commercial Property	David Grice
Company/Commercial	Anthony Ridge
Construction	Gareth Hevey
Debt Recovery	Jonathan Cripwell
Dispute Resolution	Johanne Spittle
Employment	Brian Harrington
Family	Mark Hepworth
Insolvency	Helen O'Hara
Pensions	Alistair Duncan
Planning	Lionel Lennox
Tax, Trusts & Wills	John Goodrich

THE FIRM: Denison Till is generally recognised as the leading commercial practice in York. Denison Till has expanded through developing various specialisations, including construction law, dispute resolution, personal injury litigation, insolvency, company law, employment, pensions, commercial property, agriculture and ecclesiastical law. The firm has grown strongly over the last few years and has been able to attract experienced high calibre staff from a number of the leading national law firms. Denison Till plans to grow steadily and more expertise in niche areas is being and will be established.

PRINCIPAL AREAS OF WORK: The firm comprises eight principal departments with a strong commercial bias: company/commercial; insolvency; employment and pensions; dispute resolution; construction; commercial property; ecclesiastical; private client.

CLIENTELE: Clients include prominent construction, property and industrial companies many of which are plcs. The firm also acts for public institutions and a wide range of private companies, partnerships and individuals. Denison Till is the largest commercial and private practice in York.

INTERNATIONAL: Denison Till has established overseas contacts and clients and is a member of Lawspan International, an international grouping of commercial lawyers. Partners are proficient in a number of European languages.

DENTON WILDE SAPTE

Five Chancery Lane, Clifford's Inn, London, EC4A 1BU
Tel: (020) 7242 1212 **Fax:** (020) 7404 0087 **DX:** 242
Email: info@dentonwildesapte.com **Website:** www.dentonwildesapte.com

One Fleet Place, London, EC4M 7WS
Tel: (020) 7242 1212 **Fax:** (020) 7246 7777 **DX:** 145 London City EC4

Bankside House, 107-112 Leadenhall Street, London, EC3A 4AA
Tel: (020) 7242 1212 **Fax:** (020) 7246 7722

Regency Court, 206/208 Upper Fifth Street, Milton Keynes, MK9 2HR
Tel: (01908) 690 260 **Fax:** (01908) 668 535 **DX:** 31431

UK Managing Partner	Virginia Glastonbury
UK	
Number of partners	164
Assistant solicitors	289
Other fee-earners	177
International	
Number of partners	38
Assistant solicitors	130
Other fee-earners	77

CONTACTS

Alternative Risk Transfer	George Sandars
Aviation	Hugh O'Donovan
Banking & Finance	Geoffrey Wynne
Charities	Alastair Collett
Construction	Julian Pope
Corporate & Commercial	Philip Goodwin
Employment	Stephanie Dale
Energy & Natural Resources	Michael Doble
Environmental	Jacqui O'Keeffe
EU & Competition	Polly Weitzman
Financial Markets	Robert Finney
Insurance & Reinsurance	Adrian Mecz
Intellectual Property	Clive Thorne
IT & E-commerce	John Worthy
Leasing	Lisa Marks
Litigation	Mark Gill
	Liz Tout
Pensions	Alan Jarvis
PFI	Ed Marlow
Project Finance	Howard Barrie
Property	Stephen Ashworth
Rail	Christopher McGee-Osborne
Reconstruction & Insolvency	Mark Andrews
Sports	Adrian Barr-Smith
Tax	Charlotte Sallabank
Technology, Media & Telecoms	Tony Grant
Trade	John Miles

THE FIRM: Denton Wilde Sapte is a leading international law firm based in the City of London. Formed by the merger of Denton Hall and Wilde Sapte on 1 February 2000, this truly international organisation offers a comprehensive range of the highest quality and affordable commercial legal advice. The combination of Denton Hall and Wilde Sapte has created a premier law firm that is heralded for its innovative and commercial approach. The firm's business is focused on a number of key sectors which ensures that its lawyers provide clients with a real understanding of the market as well as a comprehensive command of the law. Denton Wilde Sapte has 18 offices across Europe, the Middle East and Asia – a network that is further strengthened by Denton International, a group of leading law firms that brings the overall total to 35 offices in 23 jurisdictions around the world.

PRINCIPAL AREAS OF WORK: Denton Wilde Sapte provides a wealth of contentious and non-contentious commercial legal advice. Its extensive knowledge and experience spans many jurisdictions and different business sectors, both public and private.
Banking & Finance: The banking and finance department acts for banks and finance houses on both routine and complex ground-breaking transactions. It covers a wide range of work from corporate lending, project finance, PFI and acquisition finance through to general asset finance (including shipping and aviation), trade finance, structured finance, financial markets and regulation and insolvency and workouts.
Corporate & Commercial: Handling all aspects of corporate finance law, the department acts for many major public listed companies, advising on mergers and acquisitions, joint ventures, IPOs, employment law, regulatory and competition matters, EU law and corporate tax. *Continued overleaf*

Energy & Infrastructure: This leading practice brings together extensive international experience across a wide range of energy industries including oil and gas, electricity, water, mining and minerals and construction.
International Projects: Boasting an extensive international projects practice, the firm works in a wide range of sectors including electricity, oil and gas, water, mining and minerals, telecommunications infrastructure, transportation and environmental issues. The firm acts for banks, sponsors, governments and contractors.
Litigation: The firm deals with all forms of commercial disputes including administrative law, arbitration, aviation law, banking, finance and financial services regulation, fraud, construction disputes, environmental law, business reconstruction, intellectual property, judicial review, mergers and acquisitions, professional negligence, shipping and tax.
Technology, Media & Telecommunications: Denton Wilde Sapte is a leader in media and technology. Its highly experienced department has worked extensively in broadcasting, publishing, IT, film, TV, telecommunications, sport, digital media and music.
Property: The property department advises on all aspects of commercial property and combines development, retail, institutional investment, property finance, planning and public sector.
Other: In addition to these key areas, the firm has built up considerable expertise in a large number of specialist sectors such as insurance, aviation, rail, shipping and retail.

DENTON WILDE SAPTE

INTERNATIONAL: The firm has offices in Abu Dhabi, Almaty, Beijing, Brussels, Cairo, Dubai, Gibraltar, Hong Kong, Istanbul, Moscow, Muscat, Paris, Singapore, Tashkent and Tokyo. The firm also has associated offices in Barcelona, Berlin, Budapest, Chemnitz, Cologne, Copenhagen, Dar es Salaam, Düsseldorf, Frankfurt, Gothenburg, Hamburg, Lusaka, Madrid, Malmö, Potsdam, Stockholm and Vienna.

D

DEVONSHIRES

Salisbury House, London Wall, London, EC2M 5QY
Tel: (020) 7628 7576 **Fax:** (020) 7256 7318 **DX:** 33856 Finsbury Square
Email: info@devonshires.com **Website:** www.devonshires.com

Managing Partner	Julie Bradley
Senior Partner	Allan Hudson
Number of partners	14
Assistant solicitors	26
Other fee-earners	24

AREAS OF PRACTICE

Property	30%
Litigation	25%
Banking & Corporate	20%
PPP/PFI	10%
Construction	5%
Employment	5%
Religious Charities	5%

CONTACTS

Commercial Property	Allan Hudson
Company/Commercial	Gareth Hall
Development	David Brittain
Employment	Amanda Harvey
Finance/Corporate	Andrew Cowan
Housing Management	Nick Billingham
	Jane Mogollon
Litigation/Dispute Resolution	Philip Barden
Low Cost Home Ownership	Jane Nunnerley
PPP/PFI/Projects/Construction	Duncan Brown
	Paul Buckland
Religious Charities	Daniel Clifford
Securitisation/Local Authorities	Julie Bradley

THE FIRM: Devonshires is different. The focus is on clients and providing them with a genuine personal service – working in partnership with them and seeking to build long-term relationships, which benefit both the client and the firm. All fee earners are encouraged to develop clients and share in the development of Devonshires. The firm actively seeks to support staff and to avoid the City treadmill approach – weekend work is not encouraged. A balanced life leads to good advice. This approach has helped the firm grow five fold in the past five years. Devonshires is a City firm with a strong client focus towards business with a public/private dimension and recognised as a leading firm advising on social housing. Devonshires has a broad client base including registered social landlords, charities, companies, governments and individuals engaged in many different types of commercial activities. The firm deals with cases as diverse as securitising loans books to the Bloody Sunday Inquiry. Devonshires' lawyers offer practical and cutting-edge solutions to commercial problems. Staff training and personal development is given high priority to ensure staff retention and continuing strength in depth. Many professionals have joined the firm from larger City practices.

PRINCIPAL AREAS OF WORK: Particular areas of expertise include all aspects of social housing including care, charities, contracts (including IT), commercial, employment, group structures, lending and securitisation; litigation, public-private partnership projects; outsourcing and PFI (especially in education, leisure, housing and municipal services); property acquisition, development and construction; public and administrative law (including EU law, Human Rights Act and judicial review).

RECRUITMENT: Training at Devonshires is a challenge; new recruits will gain hands-on experience in many areas of law and develop the essential skills required to be a successful lawyer. From day one trainees will be valued fee-earners and will be fully integrated into the firm. All partners and fee earners operate an 'open-door' policy enabling trainees to benefit from their knowledge and experience. There will be plenty of opportunity for the new recruit to oversee their own files and develop relationships with clients.

DEWAR HOGAN

15 New Bridge St, London, EC4V 6AU
Tel: (020) 7822 7400 **Fax:** (020) 7822 7401 **DX:** 98939 Cheapside 2
Email: info@dewarhogan.co.uk

Managing & Senior Partner	R Hogan
Number of partners	2
Assistant solicitors	3
Other fee-earners	2

AREAS OF PRACTICE

Property Litigation	100%

CONTACTS

Property Litigation	John Cox
	Ronald Hogan

THE FIRM: Dewar Hogan specialises exclusively in contentious property matters and property litigation in relation to commercial and residential property. The firm's clients include property companies, property funds, retailers, public authorities, banks and private investors. All of its solicitors were formerly with leading London firms.

PRINCIPAL AREAS OF WORK: Contractual disputes, solicitors' negligence and landlord and tenant.

DEWEY BALLANTINE

1 Undershaft, London, EC3A 8LP
Tel: (020) 7456 6000 **Fax:** (020) 7456 6001
Email: fred.gander@deweyballantine.com **Website:** www.deweyballantine.com

Managing Partner	Fred Gander
Senior Partner	Stuart Odell
Number of partners	10
Other fee-earners	33

AREAS OF PRACTICE

M&A	25%
Capital Markets	20%
Project Finance	20%
Energy	15%
Leasing	10%
Tax/Structured Finance	10%

CONTACTS

Capital Markets	Camille Abousleiman
	Louise Bernstein
	Alain Checri
Central & Eastern Europe	Stephen Jones
	James Simpson
Energy	Mark Saunders
	James Simpson
M&A	Douglas Getter
	Stephen Jones
	Mark Saunders
Project Finance	James Simpson
Securitisations	Christopher Caperton
	Alain Checri
Tax, Leasing	Stuart Odell
Tax, Structured Finance	Fred Gander
Technology	Douglas Getter

THE FIRM: Dewey Ballantine LLP is an international law firm with over 500 attorneys located in New York, Washington DC, Los Angeles, Menlo Park, London, Hong Kong, Budapest, Prague and Warsaw. Founded in 1909, Dewey Ballantine's tradition of excellence has made it one of the world's pre-eminent law firms. It provides the highest quality legal representation with the utmost attention to client service. As the businesses of its clients have grown to encompass new types of matters in locations around the globe, so too has its practice. With offices in the key financial centres around the world and a full complement of practice areas, clients regularly turn to Dewey Ballantine for creative solutions to their changing legal needs. Dewey Ballantine, London, has been in existence for 10 years and has provided English as well as US legal advice to its clients since 1996. The firm's strategic focus in London is on financial markets work: mergers and acquisitions, capital markets, project finance, securitisations, structured finance, energy, international tax and cross-border leasing. Its industry focus, where the firm is known and has wide experience, includes energy, infrastructure, technology, telecommunications and transportation.

PRINCIPAL AREAS OF WORK: On mergers and acquisitions work, Dewey Ballantine was ranked number two worldwide in terms of completed deals in 2000 by Thomson Data and Corporate Control Alert (and number one in terms of representation of investment banks). In capital markets the firm is recognised as a leader in debt finance in the emerging markets of central, southern and eastern Europe, the Middle East, North Africa and Latin America. In project finance Dewey Ballantine is active in power, infrastructure, energy and telecommunications projects throughout Europe, the Middle East and North Africa. In particular, it has a prominent position in all areas of projects work in central and eastern Europe, including the former Soviet Union; a profile which is aided by its highly-regarded local offices in Warsaw, Prague and Budapest. The firm's energy practice is led by one of the UK's leading energy lawyers and handles a mix of mergers and acquisitions, corporate and commercial work. The firm has one of the largest US tax practices in London handling cross-border structured finance transactions, leasing and mergers and acuqisitions as well as general corporate advisory work.

CLIENTELE: Dewey Ballantine's client base includes a wide range of global financial institutions and FTSE 100 and Fortune 100 companies. The firm's regular clients include multinational companies, commercial and investment banks, governmental organisations, energy companies, telecommunications service providers and insurance companies.

DIAMOND HERON

Corry House, 7-19 Royal Avenue, Belfast, BT1 1FB **Tel:** (028) 90243726 **Fax:** (028) 90230651 **Ptnrs:** 5 **Asst solrs:** 8 **Other fee-earners:** 2

DICKINSON CRUICKSHANK & CO

33-37 Athol Street, Douglas, IM1 1LB **Tel:** (01624) 647 647 **Fax:** (01624) 620 992 **Email:** advocates@enterprise.net

DICKINSON DEES

St. Ann's Wharf, 112 Quayside, Newcastle upon Tyne, NE99 1SB
Tel: (0191) 279 9000 **Fax:** (0191) 279 9100 **DX:** 61191
Email: law@dickinson-dees.co.uk **Website:** www.dickinson-dees.com

Senior Partner	Graham Wright
Business Development Partner	John Flynn
UK	
Number of partners	57
Assistant solicitors	83
Other fee-earners	84

CONTACTS

Commercial Property	Ian Ward
Company & Commercial	Nigel Bellis
Litigation	Glenn Calvert
Private Client	George Lyall

THE FIRM: Dickinson Dees is the largest firm of solicitors in the North East region, with a total staff of over 470.

PRINCIPAL AREAS OF WORK: The practice offers both commercial and private client services. Specialist services include development and construction; banking and commercial lending; corporate tax; pensions; employee incentives; public procurement; commercial and EU law (based locally and in Brussels); health sector; environmental and planning; local authority and public sector work; employment; information technology; social housing; agriculture. The firm has an office in the Tees Valley and an associated office in Brussels. For further information contact the Business Development Partner or the Senior Partner.

DICKSON MINTO WS

11 Walker Street, Edinburgh, EH3 7NE
Tel: (0131) 225 4455 **Fax:** (0131) 225 2

Royal London House, 22-25 Finsbury Square, London, EC2A 1DX
Tel: (020) 7628 4455 **Fax:** (020) 7628 0027

Managing Partner	Bruce Minto
Senior Partner	Alastair Dickson
Number of partners	15

AREAS OF PRACTICE

Company/Commercial/ Corporate Finance	85%
Banking	15%

CONTACTS

Banking	Michael Barron
Company/Commercial/ Corporate Finance	Alastair Dickson

THE FIRM: Established in 1985, the firm, through its offices in London, Edinburgh and Glasgow, has grown substantially and handles a full range of corporate transactions. The firm deals with transactions of all sizes and complexity for its wide range of clients, including private companies, listed companies and financial institutions. Dickson Minto has advised on some of the largest MBOs and MBIs in Europe, frequently involving numerous other jurisdictions in the USA, South America, Australasia and the Far East. The firm was lead adviser on the largest LBOs in Europe in each of the 1980s and 1990s.

PRINCIPAL AREAS OF WORK: Although best known for its private equity work for financial institutions, the firm has specialist resources in the areas of investment funds, banking, financial services, EU and competition law, pensions law, information technology, intellectual property and taxation which enable it to advise its clients on a full range of corporate transactions. The firm has wide experience in dealing with and coordinating transactions involving other advisers, such as accountants, actuaries and environmental specialists and through its well established contacts with foreign lawyers in international transactions. The firm instructed lawyers in over fifty jurisdictions in the last year on behalf of its clients. Dickson Minto continues to expand and, through its emphasis on the recruitment and intensive training of high-quality staff, it has been able to maintain and continues to provide a flexible service, responsive and dedicated to the needs of all corporate clients, whether large, medium or small, private or public.

D

DIGBY BROWN

The Savoy Tower, 77 Renfrew Street, Glasgow, G2 3BZ
Tel: (0141) 566 9494 **Fax:** (0141) 566 9500 **DX:** GW17
Email: maildesk@digbybrown.co.uk **Website:** www.digbybrown.co.uk

7 Albyn Place, Edinburgh, EH2 4NG
Tel: (0131) 225 8505 **Fax:** (0131) 240 0949 **DX:** ED 182
Email: maildesk@digbybrown.co.uk

Royal Exchange, Panmure Street, Dundee, DD1 1DU
Tel: (01382) 322 197 **Fax:** (01382) 205 915 **DX:** DD 26
Email: maildesk@digbybrown.co.uk

Managing Partner	Graeme Garrett
Number of partners	11
Assistant solicitors	11
Other fee-earners	13

AREAS OF PRACTICE

Pursuer Litigation	90%
Employment	4%
Conveyancing/Executry	6%

THE FIRM: Digby Brown is one of the largest personal injury firms in Scotland with almost 90 years of experience in providing legal services. The firm has a strong geographical presence, with five offices across central Scotland. It specialises in pursurer reparation (approximately 90% of its work), where the firm has built up a reputation as a field leader in claims arising from accidents at work, industrial disease and road traffic accidents. The firm also covers employment law, conveyancing and welfare rights advice. It acts for Trade Union members as well as a large number of private clients on a no win no fee basis. The firm is also heavily committed to use of the latest technology in its everyday business, using permanent data link and digital voice lines between its offices, and constant desktop internet access for each fee-earner. All staff are well versed in the use of such technology to aide the progress of the case work. There are presently 11 partners in the firm, employing two associates, 11 assistant solicitors, four trainee solicitors and eight paralegals. The firm has expanded significantly over the last few years and continues to look towards further development. The firm is aware that the main strength of the firm lies in its personnel, and it remains committed to developing its talents and experience for the benefit of clients. Digby Brown's fee-earners work in litigation teams, representing clients in the Court of Session and the Sheriff Courts throughout the country. The firm has offices in Edinburgh, Glasgow, Dundee and Glenrothes.

DIXON, COLES & GILL

Bank House, Burton Street, Wakefield, WF1 2DA **Tel:** (01924) 373467 **Fax:** (01924) 366234 **DX:** 15030 **Email:** box@dixon-coles-gill.co.uk
Website: www.dixon-coles-gill.co.uk **Ptnrs:** 3 **Asst solrs:** 1 **Other fee-earners:** 2

D J FREEMAN

43 Fetter Lane, London, EC4A 1JU
Tel: (020) 7583 4055 **Fax:** (020) 7353 7377 **DX:** 103 London Chancery Lane WC2
Email: marketing@djfreeman.com **Website:** www.djfreeman.com

Managing Partner & Chief Executive	Jonathan Lewis
Senior Partner	Toby Greenbury
Number of partners	58
Assistant solicitors	56
Other fee-earners	35

AREAS OF PRACTICE

Property Services	42%
Insurance Services	29%
Media & Communications	15%
Commercial Litigation	14%

CONTACTS

Commercial Litigation	Kevin Perry
Construction	David Johnson
Employment	David Von Hagen
Insolvency	Christine Derrett
Insurance Insolvency	Vivien Tyrell
Insurance Litigation	David Kendall
IP & Branding	Alexander Carter-Silk
IT & E-commerce	Clive Davies
Media & Communications (Corporate)	Tony Leifer
Property	Susan Hall
Property Corporate & Joint Ventures	Graham Barber
Property Finance	John Clark
Property Litigation	Vivien King
Public International Law	Timothy Daniel
Public Sector	Edward Totman
Retail Property	Monica Blake
Taxation	Graham Chase

THE FIRM: D J Freeman continues to expand and excel in its four chosen areas of business: commercial litigation, insurance, media and communications and property. In each market sector, multidisciplinary teams of lawyers combine legal services of the highest standard with a commercial approach and deep understanding of their clients' business. This strategy means the lawyers become wholly familiar with the issues, opportunities, competitive advantages and pressures of their clients – a highly effective out-of-house resource for in-house lawyers. The firm is acknowledged as a leader and innovator in its use of technology in all areas of business and has a reputation as a promoter of the use of plain English in legal documents. The firm's regular newsletters are read by thousands of professionals within these industries. They complement the many workshops, seminars and conferences arranged by the firm on a range of topical issues.

PRINCIPAL AREAS OF WORK:

Insurance & Reinsurance: One of the leading insurance practices, this 40-strong team specialises in coverage disputes, reinsurance, commercial, corporate finance, and insolvency. Clients include major insurance companies, Lloyd's syndicates, reinsurers, brokers, underwriting agents, P&I clubs, and finance providers. Insurance litigators handle market and coverage disputes, third party and product liability claims, and shipping contracts. A specialist team handles all aspects of insurance company insolvency. Insurance, corporate finance and commercial lawyers handle flotations, rights issues, the formation and authorisation of insurance and reinsurance companies, mergers and acquisitions, restructurings, and joint ventures including consortium and pool arrangements. D J Freeman is one of the leading firms advising on Lloyd's corporate capital with a particular expertise in insurance derivatives and other innovative risk financing products.
Media & Communications: The rapidly expanding 30-strong media and communications team has clients that include three of the five leading terrestrial television broadcasters, satellite channels, international publishing houses, telecommunications and computer companies, and a growing number of e-commerce and dot.com clients. Media litigators handle high profile libel, copyright and contempt issues as well as contract and other disputes. Corporate and commercial lawyers handle corporate finance transactions, give regulatory advice to broadcasters, deal with programme acquisitions and advise on computer contracts and joint ventures. The department also has a highly regarded specialist IP and branding team.
Property: The 60-strong property services team includes construction law specialists and property litigators who handle landlord and tenant disputes, rent reviews and arbitration. Corporate finance and tax lawyers are involved in some of the largest limited partnerships, joint ventures, corporate acquisitions and restructuring work in the property sector. A specialist property finance team advises banks, lending institutions and borrowers on all types of property finance and finance leasing transactions. Property lawyers deal with leasing, disposals and property development in relation to some of the most important schemes in the UK. Planning lawyers handle town planning appeals and local plan inquiries and frequently undertake advocacy work.
Commercial Litigation: The 30-strong commercial litigation team acts for major corporates in relation to a wide range of disputes. It focuses on the special requirements of in-house lawyers and works to achieve results that put the client first. It handles some of the largest and most complex contractual disputes in the High Court as well as employment, insolvency and regulatory matters, including judicial review. The department's public international law team is regarded as one of the top five in the UK.

DJ WEBB & CO

61 Old Street, London, EC1V 9HW **Tel:** (020) 7253 2400 **Fax:** (020) 7253 2800
Email: djwebb@webbimmigration.com **Website:** www.webbimmigration.com **Contact:** David J Webb • Specialist City practice devoted exclusively to UK immigration and nationality law. The Principal is recognised as a leading practitioner in his field.

AREAS OF PRACTICE

Immigration & Nationality	100%

DLA

3 Noble Street, London, EC2V 7EE **Tel:** (08700) 111 111 **Fax:** (020) 7796 6666 **DX:** 33866 London Finsbury Square
Website: www.dla.com

DMH

100 Queens Road, Brighton, BN1 3YB
Tel: (01273) 329 833 **Fax:** (01273) 747 500 **DX:** 2703 Brighton 1
Email: tim.aspinall@dmh.co.uk **Website:** www.dmh.co.uk

Managing Partner	Tim Aspinall
Chairman	Derek Sparrow
Number of partners	28
Assistant solicitors	29
Other fee-earners	66

CONTACTS

Asset Management .... Rod Gentry
Commercial Litigation .... Tim Aspinall
Commercial Property .... Marion Wilcock
Corporate/Commercial .... Mike Long
E-commerce .... Justin Ellis
Employment .... Rustom Tata
Innovation & Media .... Tim Ashdown
Israeli Desk .... Penina Shepherd
Planning & Environment .... Tony Allen
Private Client .... Richard Pollins
Property Litigation .... Martin Allen

THE FIRM: The acquisition of niche practice Fairbairn Morris gives DMH a London office, a necessary development given the gradual increase in the number of London-based clients in its portfolio. It remains a forward-looking, dynamic firm whose highly specialist groups offer services structured around its clients' markets, primarily in the technology media and telecoms, land development, arts and leisure, retail and public service sectors. Such a structure ensures that clients receive complete and creative solutions to the legal challenges they face. In addition to this commercial practice, conducted out of the Crawley, Brighton and London centres, a wide range of high-quality private client services are offered, both from these centres and the firm's office in Worthing. Company directors are catered for by the firm's private office, which can also offer onshore and offshore tax planning.

PRINCIPAL AREAS OF WORK:

Corporate/Commercial: An experienced team handles a comprehensive range of high value projects on a regular basis including company partnership formations, takeovers, mergers and acquisitions, MBOs, Stock Exchange flotations, franchises, intellectual property work, e-commerce and commercial contracts. The firm acts on behalf of fast growth businesses, high profile national and international clients.

Employment: The firm has extensive experience in acting for employers, employees and TUs on such matters as service contracts, redundancies and unfair dismissal, disciplinary and grievance procedures, discrimination, pensions and incentive schemes.

Litigation: The firm is well known for its litigation expertise and is skilled in handling large and complicated cases. The firm's litigators are particularly experienced in property and construction cases; trademark, domain name and IT disputes; major commercial cases; professional negligence; shipping; foreign litigation matters.

Commercial Property: Leading specialists in commercial conveyancing, planning and property and construction litigations act for land developers and investors, as well as a full range of businesses and institutions. All forms of freehold and leasehold transactions are handled, with particular expertise in site assembly and development, development funding and joint ventures, planning and environmental law, institutional secured funding and property litigation.

Other Areas: The firm provides a wide range of private client services to address personal injury, residential conveyancing, asset management, wills, trust and probate, family matters and on and offshore tax planning.

INTERNATIONAL: Clients with international interests benefit from the firm's membership of Law Europe and its associated offices in the USA. Many find this association particularly useful in the context of the Internet. To assist those with a business interest in Israel, DMH has an Israeli desk.

DOLMANS

17-20 Windsor Place, Cardiff, CF10 3DS
Tel: (029) 2034 5531 **Fax:** (029) 2039 8206 DX: 33005 Cardiff

18A Merthyr Road, Whitchurch, Cardiff, CF4 1DG
Tel: (029) 2069 2979 **Fax:** (029) 2062 4415

Managing Partner	Adrian Oliver
Senior Partner	Jeffrey MacWilkinson
Number of partners	12
Assistant solicitors	20
Other fee-earners	15

CONTACTS

Agency .... John Wilkins
Company & Commercial .... John Wilkins
Employment .... Adrian Oliver
Insolvency .... John Wilkins
Institutional Defendant Litigation .... Jeffrey MacWilkinson
Landlord & Tenant .... Roger Morgan
Licensing .... John Wilkins
Matrimonial .... Randolph Jones
Motor Claims Plaintiff Litigation .... Philip Bradley
Private & Commercial Litigation .... John Wilkins
Private Client & Small Company .... John Wilkins
Property .... Moy Lewis
Wills, Trusts and Probate .... Roger Morgan

THE FIRM: With roots going back over 180 years and a presence in South Wales since 1893, Dolmans is a large Cardiff firm providing commercial legal services to corporate, public sector and individual clients. The partnership was restructured in 1970, with the Cardiff practice retaining and continuing under the name of Dolmans and has, since then, expanded to meet client needs. It considers the supervision of assistant solicitors by the partners to be of primary importance in ensuring a thorough quality service to its clients.

PRINCIPAL AREAS OF WORK:

Litigation: The firm is well known for its experience and expertise in the field of litigation, becoming the dominant firm in the region for insurance and public sector defendant work, with the majority of instructions coming from local authorities and constabularies, either direct or through insurers or others. Its workload covers employers' and public liability, personal injury and landlord and tenant work and includes private sector work. Dolmans is well respected also in the field of plaintiff litigation and a specialist team was established five years ago to deal with motor claims. It is now the leading firm in the region for plaintiff motor claims litigation. Its insurance workload has increasingly become national.

Property, Commercial & Private Client: Dolmans has a strong reputation for property, commercial and private client work. This includes commercial and domestic conveyancing; property development; landlord and tenant and institutional mortgages; business start-ups; company formation; partnership agreements; takeovers; insolvency; finance; employment and contract. It also deals with matrimonial and family law, trusts, wills, probate and taxation.

DONALD RENNIE WS

7 Blinkbonny Cresent, Edinburgh, EH4 3NB **Tel:** (0131) 476 7007 **Fax:** (0131) 476 7008 **DX:** 539943 Edinburgh 19
Email: donald.rennie@cableinet.co.uk **Ptnrs:** 1

DONNELLY & WALL

Callender House, 58/60 Upper Arthur Street, Belfast, BT1 4GP **Tel:** (028) 9023 3157 **Fax:** (028) 9032 9743
Email: mail@donnelly-wall.freeserve.co.uk **Website:** http://go.to/ni-law **Ptnrs:** 4 **Asst solrs:** 3 **Other fee-earners:** 3

DONNS SOLICITORS

PO Box 41, The Observatory, Chapel Walks, Manchester, M60 1DZ **Tel:** (0161) 834 3311 **Fax:** (0161) 834 2317 **DX:** 14312
Email: lawyers@donnlaw.co.uk **Website:** www.donnslaw.co.uk **Ptnrs:** 11 **Asst solrs:** 12 **Other fee-earners:** 237

DORSEY & WHITNEY LLP

21 Wilson Street, London, EC2M 2TD
Tel: (020) 7588 0800 **Fax:** (020) 7588 0555 **DX:** 33890 Finsbury Square
Email: london@dorsleylaw.com

Senior Partner	John Byrne
Number of partners	8
Assistant solicitors	14
Other fee-earners	4

CONTACTS	
Company/Commercial	John Byrne
Private Equity	George Hagerty
	Michael McFall
Capital Markets	Jeffrey Hurlburt
	Peter Kohl
Intellectual Property	Ian Craig
	Niel Ackermann
Commercial Property	Nadeem Khan
Taxation	Elaine Bradley

THE FIRM: Dorsey & Whitney is a full service law firm with over 700 lawyers in 22 offices around the world. The firm has had an office in London since 1986, although up until 1998 it was made up of American lawyers only. It started to offer English legal advice in 1998 when John Byrne and Andrew Rimmington joined from Nabarro Nathanson. They currently employ 26 lawyers in the London office, of whom more than two thirds are English qualified lawyers. In Europe the firm has developed a growing reputation in three specific areas: capital market, private equity and mergers and acquisitions. The firm's origins are in Minneapolis, and the culture of the firm, coming from the mid-west, is more relaxed than that of some other US law firms.

PRINCIPAL AREAS OF WORK:

Company Commercial: The firm's corporate department offers a wide range of services including mergers and acquisitions advice, business reorganisation advice and business start-ups and corporate rescues. Advice is also given on commercial contracts of all kinds, including agency distribution agreements and all aspects of corporate tax.

Private Equity: The firm acts for a significant number of venture capital funds providing venture capital/private equity to UK and European companies. The firm also acts for a large number of companies in their fund raising transactions. The private equity team is made up of US and UK qualified lawyers.

Capital Markets: The firm has an established capital markets practice advising its own clients, and often instructing as US lawyers for other firms where there is an international component to a public offering. The capital market's team has lead transactions in a number of European capital markets and the US.

Intellectual Property: The recent recruitment of a highly respected team of intellectual property lawyers from the Cambridge firm of Hewitson Becke + Shaw has strengthened the firm. The team will continue to act for such companies as DaimlerChrysler and Nike. It advises on a whole range of intellectual property matters from commercial restructuring for the better utilisation of intellectual property assets to major patent and other intellectual property litigation.

Commercial Property: The firm has recently established a commercial property department which now offers a full range of commercial property services to clients of the firm.

Taxation: The firm advises on all aspects of corporate taxation (domestic and international).

CLIENTELE: The firm's clientele range from Fortune 500 companies to start-ups. It acts for a large number of US clients, but, interestingly, approximately 80% of the work undertaken by the firm in London is generated by the team in the London office from clients based in the United Kingdom and in Europe.

INTERNATIONAL: The firm has 22 offices worldwide. Whilst the majority of the offices are in the United States (including New York, Washington, Denver, Seattle and Minneapolis), it has international offices in Brussels, Hong Kong, Tokyo, Shanghai, Toronto and Vancouver. The London office acts for a significant number of European clients and often leads on transactions focused on the continent, and, as a consequence, has assembled a network of European firms with which it has a close association.

RECRUITMENT: Over three years, the London office has grown from four to 26 lawyers. Most recently it has hired Nadeem Khan from Bird & Bird to head a commercial property section; Ian Craig, Niel Ackermann, Rob Downing and Anastasia Fowle to form the nucleus for the new intellectual property department; John Basnage from Freshfields; Rodney Cannon from Linklaters. The firm has been continuously recruiting for the last three years and that exercise is ongoing. There are currently three trainees employed in the London office, and there is the possibility for trainees to undertake part of their training in the Brussels office.

DOUGLAS-JONES MERCER

147 St Helens Rd, Swansea, SA1 4DB **Tel:** (01792) 650 000 **Fax:** (01792) 656 500 **DX:** 656500 **Email:** post@djm.law.co.uk **Contact:** Marshall Phillips • A large provincial practice with specialist departments in conveyancing, probate, family, personal injury, insurance, crime, commercial and employment.

AREAS OF PRACTICE	
Defendant & Claimant PI	21%
Family	20%
Commercial	18%
Crime	16%
Conveyancing & Probate	15%
Civil	10%

DOUGLAS & PARTNERS

116 Grosvenor Road, St. Pauls, Bristol, BS2 8YA **Tel:** (0117) 955 2663 **Fax:** (0117) 954 0527 **Ptnrs:** 4 **Asst solrs:** 5 **Other fee-earners:** 8

DOUGLAS WIGNALL & CO

44 Essex Street, Strand, London, WC2R 3JF
Tel: (020) 7583 1362 **Fax:** (020) 7583 0532 **DX:** 48 London/Chancery Lane
Email: doug@easynet.co.uk

Sole Principal	Douglas Wignall

AREAS OF PRACTICE	
Hotels & Leisure	75%
Commercial & Residential Conveyancing	15%
Other Company/Commercial	10%

CONTACTS	
All Areas of Practice	Douglas Wignall

THE FIRM: Douglas Wignall & Co specialises in hotels and leisure. Its niche is the drafting and negotiation of international management agreements mainly for hotels but also for other buildings such as arenas. Work also includes acquisitions and disposals of hotels, hotel franchise agreements and advising on all aspects of hotel operational matters. The practice also has experience in resort developments including timeshare and lease-back arrangements. The firm has been involved in many major hotel and resort projects in Europe (including the former CIS countries) as well as the UK and has many foreign clients. Douglas Wignall is a member of the International Society of Hospitality Consultants.

DOWNS

156 High Street, Dorking, RH4 1BQ
Tel: (01306) 880 110 **Fax:** (01306) 876 266 **DX:** 57300 Dorking
Email: downs@downslaw.co.uk **Website:** www.downslaw.co.uk

Senior Partner	David Rea
Number of partners	8
Assistant solicitors	10
Other fee-earners	5

AREAS OF PRACTICE	
Commercial Property	20%
Company/Commercial	20%
Trusts/Probate	20%
Litigation	20%
Matrimonial	10%
Conveyancing	10%

CONTACTS	
Commercial Property	Michael Debens
Company Commercial	Christopher Shipley
Conveyancing	Celia Perry
Litigation	Christopher Millar
Matrimonial	Andrew Christmas
Trusts/Probate	Tim Hughes

THE FIRM: Founded in 1835, Downs is a leading regional firm, offering a pro-active and effective approach.

PRINCIPAL AREAS OF WORK:
General Business: Centered around corporate and commercial, commercial property and litigation sections, specialist teams also focus on employment law, IP/IT and planning/local government law. Clients range from multinationals to single entrepreneurs and around 10% of work has an international element. The firm has particular expertise in mergers and acquisitions, corporate finance, industrial/office developments, nursing homes, agricultural property, cross border litigation and arbitrations.
Private Client: Core sections are residential property, trusts, tax planning, wills and probate, matrimonial and personal injury.

INTERNATIONAL: A well-developed network of contacts exists throughout Europe, USA and the Middle East.

DOYLE CLAYTON

69-70 Mark Lane, London, EC3R 7HS **Tel:** (020) 7702 3355 **Fax:** (020) 7702 3322 **Email:** info@doyleclayton.co.uk **Website:** www.doyleclayton.co.uk **Ptnrs:** 3 **Asst solrs:** 2 **Other fee-earners:** 5

DRAYCOTT BROWNE

Peel Court, 45 Hardman Street, Manchester, M3 3PL **Tel:** (0161) 833 1333 **Fax:** (0161) 833 1444

DRUMMOND MILLER WS

32 Moray Place, Edinburgh, EH3 6BZ **Tel:** (0131) 226 5151 **Fax:** (0131) 225 2608 **DX:** 104 Edinburgh **Email:** mail@drumil.demon.co.uk **Website:** www.drummond-miller.co.uk **Contact:** Grant McCulloch • Litigation department handles a large volume of Court of Session actions on behalf of correspondent solicitors. Also a private client department and a large conveyancing department handling commercial and residential work.

AREAS OF PRACTICE	
Residential Conveyancing	24%
Sheriff Court (Civil)	23%
Court of Session (Reparation & Commercial Litigation)	22%
Trust/Executry	12%
Other	19%

DUKES ARNOLD DU FEU

19 / 20 Easton Street, High Wycombe, HP11 1NT **Tel:** (01494) 511900 **Fax:** (01494) 511505

DUNDAS & WILSON CS

Saltire Court, 20 Castle Terrace, Edinburgh, EH1 2EN
Tel: (0131) 228 8000 **Fax:** (0131) 228 8888 **DX:** 553001 Edinburgh-18
Email: dw-enquiries@dundas-wilson.com **Website:** www.dundas-wilson.com

2 Arundel Street, London, WC2R 3DW
Tel: (020) 7240 2401 **Fax:** (020) 7240 2448 **DX:** 137 London Chancery Lane

191 West George Street, Glasgow, G2 2LB
Tel: (0141) 222 2200 **Fax:** (0141) 222 2201 **DX:** 561475 GLASGOW 16

Chairman	Neil Cochran
Managing Partner	Chris Campbell
Number of partners	54
Assistant solicitors	163
Other fee-earners	48

CONTACTS

INDUSTRY CONTACTS
Financial Services .... Michael Stoneham
Technology .... Laurence Ward
Government Services .... Michael McAuley
Real Estate .... Donald Shaw
Energy .... David McGowan
SPECIALIST CONTACTS
Banking .... Stephen Phillips
Corporate .... David Hardie
Employment, Pensions & Incentives .... Eilidh Cameron
Infrastructure .... Alan Campbell
Litigation .... Colin Macleod
Property .... Iain Doran
Technology .... Maureen Coutts

Dundas & Wilson

Andersen Legal

THE FIRM: Dundas & Wilson is a leading corporate and commercial law firm with a spread and depth of specialist skills largely unmatched in Scotland. The firm differentiates itself from its competitors in its industry-focused approach and international reach. Dundas & Wilson is one of the largest commercial law firms in Scotland, with 265 lawyers, including 54 partners. It uses a client-orientated approach to business. The operational structure is industry-focused, using teams of lawyers with different technical skills including banking, corporate, IP and IT, employment, pensions and incentives, property, litigation and infrastructure. Each team works closely together to service the needs of particular industry sectors, with a particular focus in financial services, technology, government services and real estate industries. Last year's Chambers rated the firm top choice in 14 areas including financial services, banking, planning, insolvency, investment funds, local government, property and PFI. Dundas & Wilson is a member firm of Andersen Legal and is associated with Garretts in England. Together with Garretts, it ranks in the UK's top 20 law firms by size and fee income. Andersen Legal is a global legal services network associated with Andersen Worldwide SC. The network operates as integrated practices by sharing knowledge, resources and technology, and offers a broad range of commercial legal services to clients around the world. Through its association with Andersen Worldwide SC, Andersen Legal has unique access to the professional services of Andersen and therefore an unmatched ability to provide integrated legal and business solutions to clients when required. For example, client teams can be tailored to provide all the skills and resources to meet the legal, financial, accounting, tax and consulting requirements of major projects, whilst offering a single point of contact to provide strategic advice and facilitate project management. The Andersen Legal network, including its member law firms as well as several correspondent firms and practices, comprises more than 2,900 lawyers working in 102 offices in 35 countries throughout Europe, Asia Pacific and Latin America.

PRINCIPAL AREAS OF WORK: Dundas & Wilson has an exclusively corporate and commercial practice, providing the legal services listed in the specialist contacts box.

CLIENTELE: Dundas & Wilson services a wide range of blue chip clients, including major corporates, financial institutions and public sector organisations, both at home and abroad.

DUNDONS

261 Lavender Hill, London, SW11 1JD **Tel:** (020) 7228 2277 **Fax:** (020) 7924 2759 **DX:** 58556 **Ptnrs:** 1 **Asst solrs:** 5 **Other fee-earners:** 1

EAMONN MCEVOY & CO

22 Church Place, Lurgan, BT66 6EY **Tel:** (028) 3832 7734 **Fax:** (028) 3832 1760 **DX:** 2104 NR Lurgan **Email:** law@e-mcevoy.co.uk **Ptnrs:** 3 **Asst solrs:** 4

EDMONDS BOWEN

4 Old Park Lane, London, W1K 1QW **Tel:** (020) 7629 8000 **Fax:** (020) 7221 9334 **DX:** 37217 Piccadilly **Email:** (name)@edmondsbowen.co.uk **Ptnrs:** 4 **Asst solrs:** 1 **Other fee-earners:** 5 • Provides client-orientated advice including corporate; employment; property; media/entertainment; sport; litigation and dispute resolution; matrimonial.

AREAS OF PRACTICE

Property/Private Client 35%
Media/Entertainment 25%
Company/Commercial 25%
Litigation/Dispute Resolution 15%

EDWARD FAIL BRADSHAW & WATERSON

402 Commercial Road, Stepney, London, E1 0LG
Tel: (020) 7790 4032 **Fax:** (020) 7790 2739 **DX:** 300701 Tower Hamlets

Managing Partner	John Lafferty
Senior Partner	Edward Preston
Number of partners	5
Assistant solicitors	5
Other fee-earners	7

CONTACTS

Civil Litigation .... John Lafferty
Criminal .... Edward Preston
Family .... Maeve O'Higgins

THE FIRM: One of the oldest established firms in East London, Edward Fail has had a reputation as specialists in criminal law since the 1920s. A merger in 1961 with the general practice of Bradshaw & Waterson (founded in 1887) brought a wide range of legal services to the firm, and the merged practices have over a century of experience of dealing with the family and business problems of the area.

PRINCIPAL AREAS OF WORK: The firm has a particularly strong reputation in the area of criminal law and deals with the whole spectrum of criminal offences, including serious crime, petty crime and white collar fraud. The firm also has thriving departments in family law and litigation.

EDWARDS & CO

28 Hill Street, Belfast, BT1 2LA **Tel:** (028) 90321863 **Fax:** (028) 90332723 **DX:** 410 NR Belfast **Email:** edwards.itm@tibus.com **Ptnrs:** 3

EDWARDS DUTHIE

9-15 York Road, Ilford, IG1 3AD **Tel:** (020) 8514 9000 **Fax:** (020) 8514 9009 **DX:** 200850 Ilford 4 **Email:** eesn@solicitors.uk.com **Website:** www.solicitors.uk.com **Ptnrs:** 15 **Asst solrs:** 47 **Other fee-earners:** 42

EDWARDS GELDARD

Dumfries House, Dumfries Place, Cardiff, CF10 3ZF
Tel: (029) 2023 8239 **Fax:** (029) 2023 7268 **DX:** 33001
Email: info@geldards.co.uk **Website:** www.geldards.com

44 The Ropewalk, Nottingham, NG1 5EL
Tel: (0115) 840 4499 **Fax:** (0115) 840 4500 **DX:** 10010
Email: info@geldards.co.uk

St Michaels Court, St Michaels Lane, Derby, DE1 3HQ
Tel: (01332) 331 631 **Fax:** (01332) 294 295 **DX:** 11509
Email: info@geldards.co.uk

Senior Partner	Roderick Thurman
Number of partners	42
Assistant solicitors	63
Other fee-earners	57

AREAS OF PRACTICE	
Company/Commercial	40%
Property	25%
Litigation	20%
Other	15%

E

THE FIRM: Edwards Geldard is one of the leading regional law firms. The firm's offices are located in Cardiff, Derby and Nottingham. Whilst continuing to expand the traditional areas of work in the company and commercial, commercial property, litigation and private client departments, the firm has acquired particular expertise in a variety of niche areas of legal work. These include mergers and acquisitions, corporate finance and banking, intellectual property, public law, planning and environmental law, energy law, rail and transport law, construction contracts and building arbitration, employment law, insolvency (in the UK and abroad), trusts and tax, secured lending, property litigation and clinical negligence. The firm's growth in recent years has been characterised by an expansion of its work for major Stock Exchange listed clients and for City of London based organisations and by the growing reputation of its work for public sector bodies and utilities. The firm also benefits from a strong core of work from the small to medium size enterprise sector.

PRINCIPAL AREAS OF WORK: The following services are offered from each office (initial enquiries can be directed to the most convenient office): company/corporate; intellectual property; EU law; environmental law; secured lending; construction and engineering; banking and insolvency; tax, trusts and estate administration; commercial contracts/utilities; employment; commercial property; property and development; planning and public law; commercial dispute resolution and clinical negligence; personal injury; private client.

INTERNATIONAL: A variety of languages are spoken by members of the firm. These include French, German, Italian, Polish, Spanish, Ukrainian and Welsh.

EDWIN COE

2 Stone Buildings, Lincoln's Inn, London, WC2A 3TH
Tel: (020) 7691 4000 **Fax:** (020) 7691 4111 **DX:** 191 London Chancery Lane WC2
Email: law@edwincoe.com **Website:** www.edwincoe.com

Senior Partner	John Tomlins
Number of partners	22
Assistant solicitors	11
Other fee-earners	13

AREAS OF PRACTICE	
Litigation	33%
Corporate	31%
Property	17%
Private Client	13%
Insolvency	6%

CONTACTS	
Corporate	Russel Shear
Employment	Rachel Harrap
Insolvency	Christopher Berry
Litigation	David Greene
Private Client	John Shelford
Property	John Tomlins

THE FIRM: The emphasis of this thriving London firm is on providing high quality advice on commercial and business issues to a worldwide client base. The firm is committed to providing a partner led service, which is responsive to clients' needs and achieves their objectives quickly and cost effectively.

PRINCIPAL AREAS OF WORK:

Corporate: The firm's corporate and commercial group acts for clients in all areas of business law and corporate activity including mergers, acquisitions, joint ventures and investments. Commercial work includes intellectual property, IT, sales and marketing activities. The group also has an acknowledged reputation in cross-border and international transactions, public offerings/flotations, banking work and new business start-ups.

Litigation: The litigation group offers a complete dispute resolution service including arbitration and mediation, asset protection and recovery, banking, commercial litigation, factoring, fraud, insurance claims, intellectual property, landlord and tenant protection, professional and disciplinary tribunals and professional negligence claims.

Property: The property group advises investors and developers, insurance companies, banks and retailers and undertakes all aspects of banking security work, property development, landlord and tenant, licensing, mortgages and debentures, planning, investment acquisitions, property portfolios and rent review advice.

Index to leading lawyers: p.1647 • In-House lawyers profiles: p.1193 • www.ChambersandPartners.com

Private Client: The private client group specialises in the commercial development and management of the affairs of individuals and families and the creation and management of domestic and foreign trusts, charities, estate planning and administration, tax planning and wills.
Insolvency & Corporate Recovery: The insolvency department is headed by a licensed practitioner and has strong connections with banks and accountants. It advises on all aspects of corporate reconstruction and recovery, on personal insolvency, company disqualification, professional licensing and disciplinary questions.
Employment: The employment team advises on terms of employment, remuneration, relocation, wrongful dismissal, discrimination and redundancy, including representation at employment tribunals.

CLIENTELE: Edwin Coe ensures that it understands the business of its clients and offers clear, practical advice. Clients include public and private companies, institutions, sovereign states, charities, unincorporated associations and private individuals. The firm receives instructions and referrals from other law firms. The firm has a seminar and briefing programme for clients and contacts, and partners have written standard works on several areas of law including insolvency and the responsibility of directors.

INTERNATIONAL: Work is handled in Cantonese, French, German, Hebrew, Italian, Mandarin, Polish, Romanian, Russian and Spanish.

Edwin Coe

E

ELAINE MAXWELL & CO
26 Sun Street, Lancaster, LA1 1EW **Tel:** (01524) 840810 **Fax:** (01524) 840811 **Email:** elaine.maxwell@virgin.net **Ptnrs:** 1 **Asst solrs:** 1 **Other fee-earners:** 3

ELBORNE MITCHELL

One America Square, Crosswall, London, EC3N 2PR
Tel: (020) 7320 9000 **Fax:** (020) 7320 9111 **DX:** 1063
Email: lawyers@elbornes.com **Website:** www.elbornes.com

THE FIRM: Elborne Mitchell is a specialist insurance and marine/transport law firm, which has a track record in acting in complex and high value cases within its particular areas of specialisation. In recent years the firm has widened its field to include engineering disputes and health and safety issues. The firm has also gained a reputation in the area of regulatory issues and alternative risk transfer. The firm is a forward-looking group of lawyers, ready to give constructive and independent advice to clients worldwide.

PRINCIPAL AREAS OF WORK: Areas of specialism include insurance and reinsurance; marine and transport; commercial litigation; commercial, regulatory and alternative risk transfer .

Managing Partner	Alasdair Gillies
Senior Partner	Tim Brentnall

AREAS OF PRACTICE

Insurance & Reinsurance	60%
Marine/Transport	20%
Commercial/Regulatory/ART	20%

CONTACTS

ART	Andrew Pincott
Commercial	Philip Greig
Insurance	Alan Fisher
Marine/Transport	Peter Tribe
Professional Negligence	Jolyon Patten
Regulatory	Tim Brentnall
Reinsurance	Tim Akeroyd

ANSELM ELDERGILL
Solicitors Chambers, 169 Malden Road, London, NW5 4HT **Tel:** (020) 7284 1006 **Fax:** (020) 7267 5113 **Email:** medicolegal@hotmail.com **Ptnrs:** 1

ELIZABETH CAIRNS
Knowle Hill Farm, Ulcombe, Maidstone, ME17 1ES **Tel:** (01622) 858191 **Fax:** (01622) 858004 **Email:** Elizabeth.Cairns@btinternet.com **Ptnrs:** 1

ELIZABETH RIVERS – SOLE PRACTITIONER
24 Diana Road, London, E17 5LF **Tel:** (020) 8527 8654 **Fax:** (020) 8523 4549 **Email:** mediate@elizabethrivers.co.uk

E & L KENNEDY
72 High Street, Belfast, BT1 2BE **Tel:** (028) 9023 2352 **Fax:** (028) 9023 3118 **Ptnrs:** 3

ELLIOT MATHER
The Courtyard, 49 Low Pavement, Chesterfield, S40 1PB **Tel:** (01246) 231288 **Fax:** (01246) 204081 **DX:** 12362 Chesterfield **Email:** admin@elliotmather.co.uk **Ptnrs:** 13 **Asst solrs:** 6 **Other fee-earners:** 16

ELLIOTT DUFFY GARRETT

Royston House, 34 Upper Queen Street, Belfast, BT1 6FD
Tel: (028) 9024 5034 **Fax:** (028) 9024 1337 **DX:** 400 NR Belfast
Email: edg@edgsolicitors.co.uk **Website:** www.edgsolicitors.co.uk

Managing Partner	Michael P Lynch
Senior Partner	Harry Coll
Number of partners	12
Assistant solicitors	9
Other fee-earners	6

THE FIRM: Established in 1973, Elliott Duffy Garrett is well regarded for its role in serving the business community in Northern Ireland, and for its links with international clients. A wide range of commercial legal services is offered with particular emphasis on company law, commercial property and planning, litigation and insolvency. The firm is a member of IBA, R3, INSOL and Business in the Community (Professional Firms Group).

Continued overleaf

PRINCIPAL AREAS OF WORK:
Company Law: A full service is provided with particular emphasis on corporate finance; mergers and acquisitions; joint ventures; management buy-outs; secured lending and related banking work; inward investment and venture capital services.
Commercial Property & Planning: Work includes commercial property development; letting and investment acquisitions and disposals; planning and environmental law.
Employment Law: Including specialist advice provided in relation to all aspects of employment and anti-discrimination law and practice.
Litigation: Work includes advice and representation covering product liability; construction law; professional negligence; insurance; insolvency and general litigation.

INTERNATIONAL: The firm has a formal association with A & L Goodbody, one of Dublin's principal law firms, through the A & L Goodbody (NI) Association. Members of the firm speak a variety of languages including French, German and Italian.

AREAS OF PRACTICE	
Company/Commercial	25%
Commercial Property	25%
Labour/Employment	20%
Commercial Litigation	20%
Private Client	5%
Insolvency	5%

CONTACTS	
Commercial Property	W Laurence Mahood
Company/Commercial	Michael Wilson
Employment Law	Harry Coll
Insolvency	Michael Wilson
Litigation	Michael P Lynch
Private Client	Barry E Thompson

E

ELLIOTTS

Centurion House, Deansgate, Manchester, M3 3WT
Tel: (0161) 834 9933 **Fax:** (0161) 832 3693 **DX:** 14346
Email: mail@elliott-law.co.uk

Senior Partner	Katharine Mellor
Number of partners	14
Assistant solicitors	16
Other fee-earners	8

THE FIRM: A well-established independent firm, founded in Manchester in 1968, Elliotts offers a comprehensive and commercially-aware service to its client base, both in the UK and internationally.

PRINCIPAL AREAS OF WORK:
Litigation: The firm specialises in contentious work, and has particular experience in insurance law, handling work ranging from professional indemnity, employer and public liability cases to fire and disaster claims and international claims. A wide variety of commercial litigation is undertaken, including construction disputes, product liability, insolvency work, debt recovery, personal injury claims, and consumer problems.
Company/Commercial: A full range of commercial services is available. Work includes corporate finance matters, mergers and acquisitions, franchising, computer law, aviation law, intellectual property work and employment law.
Licensing: The specialist licensing department handles liquor, entertainment and gaming licenses.
Property: Work includes commercial and residential conveyancing and agricultural law. The firm has significant experience in retail property and in the fields of planning and environmental law.
Food Safety: Barry Holland is currently chairman of the Law Society's food law group, in which the firm has a national reputation.

INTERNATIONAL: The firm is a founder member of the Euro-American Lawyers Group, which provides instant access to expert advice throughout Europe and America.

CONTACTS	
Aviation Law	Katharine Mellor
Commercial Litigation	Fiona Miller
Commercial Property	David Walton
Company Commercial	Katharine Mellor
Construction	Michael Woolley
Employment Law	Fiona Miller
Insurance Litigation	John Groome
	Graham Hughes
Intellectual Property	Robert Jones
Licensing	Barry Holland
Motor Litigation	Clare Edwards
Personal Injury	Julian Holt
	Neal Samarji
Private Client	Tim Chapman
Professional Negligence	John Groome

ELLISON & CO

Headgate Court, Head Street, Colchester, CO1 1NP **Tel:** (01206) 764477 **Fax:** (01206) 764455 **DX:** 3601 Colchester
Email: mail@ellison-and-co.com **Ptnrs:** 17 **Asst solrs:** 5 **Other fee-earners:** 22

ELLIS WOOD

Langdales, New Garden House, 78 Hatton Garden, London, EC1N 8LD **Tel:** (020) 7242 1194 **Fax:** (020) 7831 9480 **DX:** 248 Ch.Ln.
Email: enquiries@elliswood.co.uk **Ptnrs:** 3 **Asst solrs:** 2 **Other fee-earners:** 1

ENSOR BYFIELD

Equity Court, 73-75 Millbrook Road East, Southampton, SO15 1RJ
Tel: (023) 8048 3200 **Fax:** (023) 8021 2127 **DX:** 49665 Southampton 2
Email: law@ensorbyfield.com **Website:** www.ensorbyfield.com

63-66 Hatton Garden, London, EC1N 8LE
Tel: (020) 7242 7444 **Fax:** (020) 7242 7445
Email: law@ensorbyfield.com

Senior Partners	Rod Evans
	John Byfield
Number of partners	6
Assistant solicitors	5
Other fee-earners	19

THE FIRM: Ensor Byfield is a regional business-focused law firm based in Southampton and London, committed to supporting local, national and international companies in all aspects of their business activities, from start-up to the realisation of their objectives. A brochure is available on request and more information is available via the firm's website.

PRINCIPAL AREAS OF WORK: The firm falls broadly into three departments: commercial, insurance litigation, and sport.

AREAS OF PRACTICE	
Insurance Litigation	50%
Commercial	32%
Commercial Property	10%
Commercial Litigation	7%
Private Client	1%

Commercial: The department provides a wide range of commercial, contractual and intellectual property advice to both companies and individuals. Particular strengths are in the following sectors: information technology, healthcare, biotechnology and leisure. Within the department there are experts dealing with all aspects of employment law, both contentious and non-contentious, and commercial property. The firm also has a small private client department.
Insurance Litigation: The department is the largest and longest established defendant insurance litigation department in the southern region, and provides advice to insurance companies nationwide.
Sport: The department specialises in motor sport, particularly Formula 1 and football, acting for a number of Football League clubs, and has dealings with golf and rugby.

CONTACTS

Commercial	John Byfield
Commercial Litigation	Michael Wilson
Commercial Property	Tim Southorn
Defendant Insurance Litigation	Rod Evans
Intellectual Property	David Walker
Private Client	Robert O'Connor
Sport	Trevor Watkins

ERIC ROBINSON & CO

359 Bitterne Road, Bitterne, Southampton, SO18 1DN **Tel:** (02380) 425000 **Fax:** (02380) 446594 **DX:** 52750 Bitterne **Ptnrs:** 10 **Asst solrs:** 14 **Other fee-earners:** 20

ERNST & YOUNG

Becket House, 1 Lambeth Palace Road, London, SE1 7EU **Tel:** (020) 7951 2000 **Fax:** (020) 7951 1345

ERSKINE MACASKILL & CO

21 Stafford Street, Edinburgh, EH3 7BJ **Tel:** (0131) 622 6062 **Fax:** (0131) 622 6066 **DX:** 191 Edinburgh **Ptnrs:**2 **Associates:**2 **Asst solrs:**1 **Contact:** Sarah Erskine • Specialist matrimonial and child law practice. Also undertakes conveyancing and criminal defence work.

AREAS OF PRACTICE

Matrimonial/Child Law	53%
Criminal Defence Work	22%
Conveyancing	20%
Other	5%

E

EVANS BUTLER WADE

165 Greenwich High Road, London, SE10 8JA **Tel:** (020) 8858 8926 **Fax:** (020) 8293 4851 **Email:** info@evansbutlerwade.co.uk **Website:** www.evansbutlerwade.co.uk **Ptnrs:** 4 **Asst solrs:** 4 **Other fee-earners:** 2

EVANS DODD

5 Balfour Place, Mount Street, London, W1K 2AU
Tel: (020) 7491 4729 **Fax:** (020) 7499 2297 **DX:** 44644 Mayfair
Email: mail@evansdodd.co.uk

Managing Partner	Geoffrey Dodd
Senior Partner	Geoffrey Dodd
Number of partners	5
Assistant solicitors	2
Other fee-earners	2

THE FIRM: Established in 1975 as a commercial practice with a strong international bias.

PRINCIPAL AREAS OF WORK:
Company & Commercial: All aspects of company and commercial work including public and private corporate law; acquisitions; new issues; joint ventures; banking and finance; aircraft acquisitions; financing and tax planning.
Commercial Property: Commercial property acquisitions, sales, leases and financing. Domestic property work also undertaken.
Litigation: All types of claims, including commercial litigation, contractual disputes, employment and matrimonial matters, debt recovery and professional negligence.

AREAS OF PRACTICE

Company & Commercial	50%
Litigation	25%
Property	15%
Taxation	10%

CONTACTS

Commercial Property	Joseph Hyde
Company & Commercial	Geoffrey Dodd
Litigation	Jeremy Hershkom

EVERATT & COMPANY

104 High Street, Evesham, WR11 4EU
Tel: (01386) 47 191 **Fax:** (01386) 48 515 **DX:** 16167 EVESHAM
Email: post@everatt.co.uk

Senior Partner	Catherine Arkell
Number of partners	5
Assistant solicitors	3
Other fee-earners	8

THE FIRM: Specialists in defendant personal injury litigation since its foundation in 1970, Everatt & Company has earned a reputation within its field that is the envy of many a large legal firm. Its size and independence has played a significant part in this success, ensuring levels of flexibility, internal communication and access to partners that clients rarely see elsewhere. Its central location, too, has been a factor, placing the majority of UK courts within serviceable reach.

PRINCIPAL AREAS OF WORK:
Defendant Personal Injury Litigation: Work includes employers' liability; motor accident claims; industrial deafness; work-related upper limb disorders; asbestos-related claims; other respiratory claims; hand/arm vibration syndrome/VWF; catastrophic injury; work-related stress claims.

CLIENTELE: The firm acts for insurance companies, both large and small, and various liability adjusters.

RECRUITMENT: The firm has recruited individuals and trained them through to qualification. It is strongly committed to internal training.

AREAS OF PRACTICE

Defendant Personal Injury	90%
Other	10%

EVERSHEDS

Senator House, 85 Queen Victoria Street, London, EC4V 4JL
Tel: (020) 7919 4500 **Fax:** (020) 7919 4919 **DX:** 83 Chancery Lane WC2
Website: www.eversheds.com

11 St James Court, Friar Gate, Derby, DE1 1BT
Tel: (01332) 360 992 **Fax:** (01332) 371 469 **DX:** 11535

115 Colmore Row, Birmingham, B3 3AL
Tel: (0121) 232 1000 **Fax:** (0121) 236 1900 **DX:** 13004

Cloth Hall Court, Infirmary Street, Leeds, LS1 2JB
Tel: (0113) 243 0391 **Fax:** (0113) 245 6188 **DX:** 12027 Leeds-27

Daedalus House, Station Road, Cambridge, CB1 2RE
Tel: (01223) 355 933 **Fax:** (01223) 460 266 **DX:** 5807

Fitzalan House, Fitzalan Road, Cardiff, CF24 0EE
Tel: (029) 2047 1147 **Fax:** (029) 20 46 4347 **DX:** 33016

1 Royal Standard Place, Nottingham, NG1 6FZ
Tel: (0115) 950 7000 **Fax:** (0115) 950 7111 **DX:** 10031
Email: nottingham@eversheds.com

Franciscan House, 51 Princes Street, Ipswich, IP1 1UR
Tel: (01473) 284 428 **Fax:** (01473) 233 666 **DX:** 3249

Holland Court, The Close, Norwich, NR1 4DX
Tel: (01603) 272 727 **Fax:** (01603) 610 535 **DX:** 5206

Eversheds House, 70 Great Bridgewater Street, Manchester, M1 5ES
Tel: (0161) 831 8000 **Fax:** (0161) 832 5337 **DX:** 14344

Sun Alliance House, 35 Mosley Street, Newcastle upon Tyne, NE1 1XX
Tel: (0191) 261 1661 **Fax:** (0191) 261 8267 **DX:** 61166

Managing Partner	David Ansbro
Chairman	Keith James
Number of partners	329
Assistant solicitors	791
Other fee-earners	745

AREAS OF PRACTICE

Corporate/Commercial	39%
Litigation/Dispute Management	27%
Property	24%
Employment	10%

E

THE FIRM: A European law firm, Eversheds has over 2000 legal and business advisers based in 17 offices in Europe and three associated offices in Asia. Each office provides a wide range of services to the business and financial community and to the public sector. Its distinctive approach gives clients access to a large team of lawyers who combine local market knowledge with an international perspective. Most commercial law firms offer clients the same core services, and Eversheds is no exception. Its difference, and its competitive advantage, lies in its strength and depth. It has vast resources and an unparalleled breadth of expertise and industry know-how.

PRINCIPAL AREAS OF WORK: Alongside the five core areas of corporate, commercial, litigation and dispute management, commercial property and employment, Eversheds has established a sixth practice group which consolidates volume conveyancing, mortgaging, recoveries and claims management services. Each Eversheds office provides expertise in a range of specialist legal services and market sectors. Specialist services are: business risk services; computer/IT; corporate tax; environment/health and safety; EU/competition; franchising; insolvency; intellectual property; international public law; licensing; PFI; planning; pensions; private capital/tax and venture capital. Market sectors include: banking; bioscience; chemicals; construction; education; energy; engineering; financial services; insurance and reinsurance; e-commerce; technology; media and communications; public sector and retail/leisure.

INTERNATIONAL: The firm has overseas offices in Brussels, Monaco and Paris. Associated offices are located in Amsterdam, Copenhagen and Sofia and three offices in Asia.

EVILL AND COLEMAN

113 Upper Richmond Road, Putney, London, SW15 2TL **Tel:** (020) 8789 9221 **Fax:** (020) 8789 7978 **DX:** 59451 Putney **Email:** enquiries@evillandcoleman.co.uk **Website:** www.evillandcoleman.co.uk **Ptnrs:** 4 **Asst solrs:** 3 **Other fee-earners:** 4 **Contact:** Stewart Graham • Leading reputation in personal injury and clinical negligence claims. Legal Services Commission franchise in personal injury and clinical negligence. Conducted many ground breaking cases in these fields.

FAEGRE BENSON HOBSON AUDLEY

7 Pilgrim Street, London, EC4V 6LB
Tel: (020) 7450 4510 **Fax:** (020) 7450 4544 **DX:** 401 London
Email: lawyers@faegre.com **Website:** www.faegre.com

Joint Managing Partners	Gerald Hobson Gale Mellum

AREAS OF PRACTICE

Corporate Finance/M&A	20%
Company/Commercial/ Financial Services	25%
Employment & Labour Law	10%
Innovation & Technology	10%
Dispute Resolution	20%
Property	15%

THE FIRM: Faegre Benson Hobson Audley is a multinational partnership of English and American lawyers in London, formed between Faegre & Benson LLP and Hobson Audley to provide English business law services to US clients and American business law services to English clients. Faegre & Benson LLP is a firm of more than 375 lawyers with offices in Minneapolis, Minnesota; Denver, Colorado; Des Moines, Iowa; Frankfurt, Germany. Hobson Audley is a firm of more than 35 solicitors in London. In the London office, English business law services are provided in corporate and commercial finance; intellectual property; innovation and technology; employment, dispute solution and real estate matters. American business law advice is provided in London and through the US offices of Faegre & Benson LLP, both on US corporate law and on commercial transactions, including acquisitions; incorporations; joint ventures; distribution agreements; product liability; employment and labour law and immigration.

INTERNATIONAL: The firm handles transactions in French, German, Italian, Portuguese and Spanish.

F

FAIRMAYS

10 Babmaes St, London, SW1Y 6HD
Tel: (020) 7959 0202 **Fax:** (020) 7959 0234 **DX:** 37219 Piccadilly
Email: advice@fairmays.com **Website:** www.fairmays.com

Managing Partner	Alistair Langford
Senior Partner	Anthony Cowen
Number of partners	12
Assistant solicitors	9
Other fee-earners	10

AREAS OF PRACTICE

Company/Commercial	27%
Litigation	27%
Property	27%
Employment	8%
Private Client	7%
Matrimonial	4%

CONTACTS

Company/Commercial	Robert Brooks
Employment	Alistair Langford
IP/IT	Rosanna Cooper
Litigation	Anthony Cowen
Private Client	Andrew Miller
Property	Nicholas Plaut

THE FIRM: Fairmays is a progressive international commercial practice specialising in company/commercial, litigation, property and private client work. The firm has considerable experience of doing business in India and the Middle East, having a branch office in Bahrain. The firm's international clientele includes a significant proportion of high net worth individuals and SMEs. As a consequence, it has developed the skills necessary to meet the demands of that particular market sector and handles a significant amount of new start-up, corporate finance and flotation work coupled with specialist advice in the fields of IP/IT, employment and immigration (both individual and corporate). Its private client department offers a sophisticated tax planning service and works closely with the company/commercial department to provide strategic planning advice to the firm's client both on an individual and on a corporate level. Fairmays has established an infrastructure in its new offices in St James' to augment the service which it provides to its clients both on and off-line, including the availability of video conferencing facilities. Fairmays strives to offer a competitively priced yet high quality personal service to its clients, working in tandem with them to produce innovative solutions to their business problems.

PRINCIPAL AREAS OF WORK:

Company/Commercial: The cornerstone of the practice, adapting to the needs of new media clients. A dedicated IP/IT unit has been formed. Services offered include acquisitions and disposals, flotations, restructuring corporate finance, joint ventures, partnerships, communications law, sports law, taxation, distribution and agency and international and domestic commercial agreements of all kinds.

Litigation: The firm handles all aspects of commercial litigation, insolvency, insurance/fraud, negligence and personal injury, matrimonial, defamation and building disputes.

Property: The full range of commercial property matters, planning and construction law is handled. Particular strengths include secured lending, portfolio, leisure and retail work.

Employment: Both contentious and non-contentious work is handled, mainly on behalf of employers or senior executives. The firm has wide experience of employment disputes, representing clients at the ET, County Court or High Court involving matters such as wrongful dismissal, unfair dismissal and discrimination cases, and other statutory claims.

Private Client: The work of this department includes estate planning and administration, immigration, wills, trusts, probate and personal taxation. A significant amount of offshore work is undertaken.

RECRUITMENT: Two trainees are recruited annually and it is planned that they spend six months in each of the company/commercial, private client, property and litigation departments. The firm looks for an engaging personality with both a creative and sensible approach to work. CVs to Andrew Miller. Further details can be found on the firm's website www.fairmays.com.

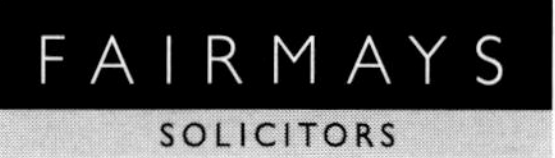

THE FAMILY LAW CONSORTIUM

2 Henrietta Street, London, WC2E 8PS
Tel: (020) 7420 5000 **Fax:** (020) 7420 5005 **DX:** 40012 Covent Garden
Email: flc@tflc.co.uk **Website:** www.tflc.co.uk

Number of partners	6
Assistant solicitors	5
Other fee-earners	3

THE FIRM: The firm has five (=10%) of London's family/matrimonial leaders (*Chambers 1999/2000*) and two of the capital's most respected non-lawyer mediators. As a result the firm has expertise in law, mediation and counselling, which it can offer alone or in combination to provide ground-breaking services for all stages of the relationship, from its formation, through difficulties, to its end and the development of post-separation arrangements. The firm helps clients reach their own agreements or offers effective action through lawyer-led settlements or the courts. Detailed information is available on their website, which was recently voted the best 'Brochure' website in the country. The emergency out of hours contact is James Pirrie, on (01727) 811478.

FARLEYS

F

22-27 Richmond Terrace, Blackburn, BB1 7AQ
Tel: (01254) 606 000 **Fax:** (01254) 583 526 **DX:** 13604 Blackburn 3
Email: info@farleys.com **Website:** www.farleys.com

Senior Partner	Michael Corrigan
Number of partners	10
Assistant solicitors	29
Other fee-earners	35

AREAS OF PRACTICE

Civil Litigation	30%
Criminal	25%
Family	25%
Commercial & Property	15%
Probate/Private Client	5%

CONTACTS

Actions Against the Police	Joanne Kearsley
Company/Commercial	Chris Porter
	Ian Liddle, Debbie King
Crime	Paul Schofield, Andrew Church-Taylor
	Bernard Horne, Kevin Preston
Matrimonial	Kathryn Hughes, Ann Bamford
	Barbara Crook, Anthony Rebello
Mental Health	Joseph Mulderig
Personal Injury/Litigation	Michael Corrigan
	Des Draper, Stephen McNeill
	Kieran O'Connor, Jonathan Bridge
	Beverley Jenkinson, Martin Thomas
Property & Private Client	Peter Leyland
	Philip Taylor

THE FIRM: Established in 1957, Farleys is a broad-based practice encompassing a number of specialised departments in its offices in Blackburn, Accrington and Burnley. The firm has built up a reputation in the North West of England for providing a high level of service both to private clients and to an increasing number of well-known commercial clients. Farleys has Public Funding franchises for family, criminal, actions against the police and mental health.

PRINCIPAL AREAS OF WORK:

Commercial: This successful and growing department covers all aspects of company and commercial work, with a growing expertise in entrepreneurial and manager-owned businesses.

Personal Injury/General Litigation: The firm handles personal injury, both clinical and professional negligence, employment matters and environmental disputes. Members of the Personal Injury panel and the Mental Health Review Tribunal panel.

Family/Matrimonial: The firm has one of the largest family law departments in the North West dealing with all aspects of family law, especially care proceedings and substantial ancillary relief matters.

Criminal: This is one of Lancashire's busiest and most effective criminal practices, dealing with all matters. The department has a special case work unit dealing with serious fraud/crime.

Property: The firm handles all aspects of private client property transactions.

Private Client: An extensive range of services is offered in the area of wills, probate, trustee and executorship.

FARRER & CO

66 Lincoln's Inn Fields, London, WC2A 3LH
Tel: (020) 7242 2022 **Fax:** (020) 7242 9899 **DX:** 32 London Chancery Lane WC2
Email: enquiries@farrer.co.uk **Website:** www.farrer.co.uk

Senior Partner	Henry Boyd-Carpenter
Chief Executive	Andrew Mills-Baker
Number of partners	43
Assistant solicitors	46
Other fee-earners	25

CONTACTS

Agriculture	Simon Pring
Banking & FSA	Jonathan Bayliss
Charities	Judith Hill
	Julian Smith
Commercial Property	Raymond Cooper
Company/Commercial	James Thorne
E-commerce	Peter Wienand
Employment & Pensions	David Smellie
Estates & Private Property	James Furber
Family	Richard Parry
Heritage Property	Judith Hill
	Michael Chantler
Intellectual Property	Peter Wienand
International Private Client	Mark Bridges
Litigation	Adrian Parkhouse
Media	Robert Clinton
Private Client	Richard Powles
	Anthony Edwards

THE FIRM: Farrer & Co is one of the UK's leading law practices. It provides a range of specialist advice to private, institutional and corporate clients. The firm has long been recognised for the quality of its service, both technical and personal. This has been achieved by consistently recruiting team players possessing flair and intellect coupled with a desire to exceed clients' expectations. Their client base is worldwide and clients are frequently leaders in their fields. To meet the increasingly specialised demands of clients, the firm is divided into flexible, client-focused teams. Its breadth of expertise is reflected in the fact that it has an outstanding reputation in fields as diverse as family law, offshore tax planning, employment, heritage work, charity law and defamation.

PRINCIPAL AREAS OF WORK:

Private Client: The firm is recognised as an established leader in the services it provides to its private clients. Core work includes tax planning, heritage property, wills and the administration of estates, probate and trusts. Agricultural estates and private property specialists advise on property matters, while clients also benefit from the firm's strong reputation in management and employment practices. The family team is highly regarded and advises on family disputes arising from marriage breakdown or inheritance claims, family provision and child-related issues.

Institutional: Work for institutions is focused on a highly successful and expanding charities team. In addition to charity law, teams advise these clients on taxation, employment, sponsorship and intellectual property issues. The firm has long had a reputation for advising sports industry clients and for its work for museums, galleries and educational organisations.

Commercial: A full range of work is undertaken for commercial clients, with notable expertise in the media industry. Specialisations include employment and pensions, mergers and acquisitions, intellectual property, corporate tax, e-business, banking and FSA. The commercial property team manages all types of work for clients, while the litigation team has advised on almost every type of business dispute: contract, fraud, insolvency, construction, asset recovery, libel, government inspections and prosecutions.

INTERNATIONAL: The firm handles work in French and German.

RECRUITMENT: Six trainee solicitors are recruited annually; a 2:1 degree is preferred, not necessarily in law. Applications to the Graduate Recruitment Manager.

CONTACTS CONTINUED

Probate & Trust Administration .... Catherine McAleavey
Sport .... Karena Vleck

FENNEMORES

200 Silbury Boulevard, Central Milton Keynes, Milton Keynes, MK9 1LL **Tel:** (01908) 678241 **Fax:** (01908) 665985 **DX:** 84757 Milton Keynes - 3
Email: info@fennemores.co.uk **Website:** www.fennemores.co.uk **Ptnrs:** 13 **Asst solrs:** 8 **Other fee-earners:** 40

F

FENNERS

15 New Bridge Street, London, EC4V 6AU
Tel: (020) 7936 8000 **Fax:** (020) 7936 8100 **DX:** 256 Chancery Lane, London WC2
Email: info@fenners.com **Website:** www.fenners.com

Senior Partner	John Fenner
Managing Partner	Robert Fenner
Number of partners	5
Other fee-earners	12

AREAS OF PRACTICE

Corporate/Commercial 40%
Commercial Property 40%
Banking 20%

CONTACTS

Banking .... David Wisbey
Commercial Property .... John Fenner
.... Caroline Frampton
Corporate/Commercial .... Robert Fenner
Property Development .... Caroline Frampton
.... Jeremy Raj

THE FIRM: Fenners is a City based firm specialising in company/commercial law, corporate finance, commercial property, banking, technology law, planning and residential development, and offers a leading capability in urban regeneration. The firm has a broad client base including public and private companies, financial advisers, banks and other institutions.

PRINCIPAL AREAS OF WORK:

Corporate: Work includes IPOs; rights issues and other secondary issues; venture capital funding; public takeovers; share and asset sales; MBOs; MBIs; public to private transactions; joint venture arrangements; corporate reorganisations; investment funds.

Commercial Property: The firm handles investment acquisitions and disposals; site assembly and development (retail, office and industrial); regional and city centre schemes involving both the public and private sectors; institutional funding and forward sale agreements; commercial lettings for landlords and tenants; building agreements; environmental issues.

Commercial: Work includes joint ventures; intellectual property; the laws relating to the internet and e-commerce; data protection; consumer credit; franchising; employment law; employee share option schemes; competition law.

Banking: The firm undertakes secured and unsecured lending; syndicated lending; mezzanine financing; property financing; securitisations.

Planning: The firm handles redevelopment schemes; urban regeneration schemes; planning agreements for infrastructure work; planning gain and use restrictions; planning appeals and inquiries.

Development: Work includes site assembly and acquisition; management schemes; sales; town planning and related matters.

INTERNATIONAL: The firm maintains associations with law firms throughout Europe and the USA. Languages spoken include French, German, Italian and Portuguese.

Fenners

FENWICK ELLIOTT

353 Strand, London, WC2R 0HS
Tel: (020) 7956 9354 **Fax:** (020) 7956 9355 **DX:** 178 LDE
Email: reception@fenwickelliott.co.uk **Website:** www.fenwickelliott.co.uk

Senior Partner	Robert Fenwick
Number of partners	8
Assistant solicitors	8
Other fee-earners	1

AREAS OF PRACTICE

Contentious Construction (inc. ADR & Arbitration)	60%
Non-contentious Construction	30%
Other Related Work	10%

THE FIRM: Fenwick Elliott is a commercial law firm, which specialises exclusively in building, engineering and energy law. The firm provides a cost effective service, drawing on a wealth of expertise to provide commercially aware and practical advice. The partners of the firm are members of the Technology and Construction Solicitors Association and the Society of Construction Law. Members of the firm are CEDR accredited mediators and are Fellows of the Chartered Institute of Arbitrators. All partners are TeCSA accredited adjudicators and several partners are on other industry panels. The partners speak regularly on construction law matters at conferences and contribute to Television Education Network and LNTV programmes on construction and dispute resolution. A member of the firm is a commissioner of the Foundation for International Arbitration. Another member is Chairman of the Society of Construction Law, Vice-President of the European Society of Construction Law, Senior Warden of the Worshipful Company of Arbitrators and a Fellow of the Chartered Institute of Building. Another member is editor of the *Construction Industry Law Letter*.

F

PRINCIPAL AREAS OF WORK:

Contentious: The firm handles large volumes of litigation, arbitration, adjudication and alternative dispute resolution. Defects claims, loss and expense claims, the securing of prompt payment, design liability, professional negligence and jurisdictional disputes are among the issues frequently dealt with. Particular regard is given to troubleshooting to assist the early resolution of any dispute.
Non-contentious: The firm's burgeoning non-contentious practice includes pre-contract advice on terms and conditions of tender, negotiation and drafting of all types of contracts, from sub-contracts to joint venture agreements, including contracts for the engagement of professionals, bonds and warranties. Planning and environmental law considerations and insurance matters are also dealt with. The practice also has considerable experience of BOT type schemes in the areas of water and power and PFI schemes, in particular in the health and education sectors.

CLIENTELE: The firm acts nationally and internationally for developers, institutional investors, local authorities, utilities, main contractors, specialist subcontractors, architects, engineers, surveyors, PFI consortia and private clients. Further, the firm acts for various foreign government corporations. Most of the firm's clients are well known in the construction industry.

Fenwick Elliott
SOLICITORS

INTERNATIONAL: Work is also handled in French.

FEW & KESTER
Chequers House, 77-81 Newmarket Rd, Cambridge, CB5 8EU **Tel:** (01223) 363111 **Fax:** (01223) 323370 **DX:** 122893 Cambridge 4 **Email:** mail@fewandkester.co.uk **Ptnrs:** 8 **Asst solrs:** 5 **Other fee-earners:** 9

FIELD CUNNINGHAM & CO

St. John's Court, 70 Quay St, Manchester, M3 3EJ
Tel: (0161) 834 4734 **Fax:** (0161) 834 1772 **DX:** 728855 Manchester 4

Senior Partner	Peter Ashworth
Number of partners	3
Assistant solicitors	4
Other fee-earners	9

AREAS OF PRACTICE

Commercial Property	78%
Commercial Litigation	15%
Company Commercial	5%
Private Client	2%

THE FIRM: Established in 1867, Field Cunningham & Co is a successful niche commercial property practice specialising in development work and associated commercial and property litigation. It places much importance on providing a high level of personal service and commitment within a commercial environment.

PRINCIPAL AREAS OF WORK:

Commercial Property: The firm deals with all aspects of commercial property, with particular emphasis on development work in the retail, residential, office, leisure and commercial sectors, development funding, and joint ventures. Activities include work in associated planning, environmental and Lands Tribunal matters. An increasing volume of property secured lending work is being undertaken on behalf of banks. In addition to its commercial development and redevelopment work, the firm acts for national and local house-builders; the volume of new house sales undertaken is approximately one per cent annually of all UK private housing starts.
Commercial Litigation: Especially in property and construction-related and environmental matters. Also intellectual property; employment and general commercial disputes.
Company/Commercial: Private company sales and purchases; joint ventures; MBOs; business start-ups; partnerships; intellectual property and employment.

RECRUITMENT: The firm normally takes one law graduate (2:1 required) annually. Applications by covering letter and CV.

FIELD FISHER WATERHOUSE

35 Vine Street, London, EC3N 2AA
Tel: (020) 7861 4000 **Fax:** (020) 7488 0084 **DX:** 823 London City EC3
Email: info@ffwlaw.com **Website:** www.ffwlaw.com

Managing Partner	Colin McArthur
Senior Partner	John Wilson
Number of partners	71
Assistant solicitors	107
Other fee-earners	70

CONTACTS

Advertising & Marketing	Shelly Nedler
Anglo-French Trade	Marie-Caroline Frochot
Anglo-German/Austrian Trade	Babette Marzheuser-Wood
Aviation	Simon Chamberlain
Banking & Finance	Jon Fife, John Wilson
Capital Markets	Jon Fife, Guy Usher
Charity	Catherine Newcombe
Commercial Property	Howard Coffell, John Pedder
Competition	Charles Whiddington
Construction	Lawrence Bruce, Mark Lowe
Corporate	Tim Davies
Derivatives	Guy Usher, Jon Fife
E-commerce	Michael Chissick
Employee Benefits	Graeme Nuttall
Employment	Margaret Davis
Energy & Pipelines	Howard Coffell
Financial Services Regulation	Christopher Bond
Franchising & Licensing	Mark Abell
Hotels & Leisure	Paul Houston
Immigration	Heather Prescott
Intellectual Property	Mark Abell
International Trade & Projects	John Wilson
Investment Funds & Products	Kirstene Baillie
IT	Michael Chissick
Licensing	Peter Glazebrook
Litigation (Commercial)	Mark Lowe
Litigation (IP/IT)	Nick Rose
Media	Ellen Fleming
Medical Litigation	Paul McNeil
Partnership	Colin McArthur
Patents	Jonathan Radcliffe
Pensions	Belinda Benney
Personal Injury	Rodney Nelson-Jones
PFI/Projects	Nicholas Thompsell, Lawrence Bruce
Planning & Environmental	Richard Webber
Private Client	Penny Wotton
Professional Regulation	Matthew Lohn
Rail	Nicholas Thompsell
Shipbuilding	John Wilson
Sports Business	Patrick Cannon
Tax (Corporate)	Nicholas Noble
Telecommunications	Tony Ballard
Trade Marks	John Olsen
Travel & Tourism	Peter Stewart

THE FIRM: Field Fisher Waterhouse is a City-based firm with a substantial corporate and commercial practice. It has a reputation for providing an excellent all-round service to an impressive list of UK and international clients. The firm is expanding rapidly. In the past year, turnover rose by approximately 20% and total staff by some 15%. Much of this was due to the firm's expanding international practice. Seven new partners were made up in 2001 in the following areas: corporate; Anglo-German trade; trademarks and brand protection; IP/IT litigation; institutional property; employment; personal injury/clinical negligence. In addition, partner Jonathan Radcliffe joined as head of patents, and partner Lawrence Bruce joined to strengthen the firm's projects practice. A distinctive feature of the firm is the number of close and long-standing relationships which it has developed with its clients, achieved by ensuring a high quality service and maintaining a high level of partner involvement in clients' affairs. The firm is well known for its commercial and practical approach, and for its ability to create innovative solutions to legal problems. These qualities are well illustrated by comments from some of its clients: 'Imperial Chemical Industries plc has used FFW for its industrial property work for many years and its performance in handling a large volume of highly complex transactions has been quite outstanding'; 'HM Treasury can add FFW to the short list of 'lawyers with a human touch'. FFW's advice and helmsmanship was always sound and given in a way that continually challenged HM Treasury's views and contributed greatly to its success'.

PRINCIPAL AREAS OF WORK: The firm's core practice areas are brands, technology, media and telecommunications, banking and finance; corporate finance; commercial property. Other areas in which the firm has a leading reputation are: corporate tax; employment; employee share schemes; pensions; investment funds and products; commercial litigation; partnership; personal injury and medical negligence. The firm is also well known for its expertise in a number of industry sectors including: advertising; aviation; communications and media; energy; financial services; franchising; health; hotels and leisure; rail; ship building and ship finance; sport; travel and tourism.

CLIENTELE: The firm has a wide-ranging UK and overseas client base. It includes commercial and industrial companies; banks and other financial institutions; governments; trade associations; regulatory bodies and professional partnerships.

INTERNATIONAL: The firm also acts for a substantial number of overseas clients and has particularly strong connections with China, France, Germany, Italy, Japan, Korea, Scandinavia and the US. The firm works closely with firms in these and other countries and has developed especially close relationships with leading firms in France, Germany, Ireland and Scotland. Partners at the firm include French, German, American and Japanese qualified lawyers. The firm's lawyers speak a wide range of European languages, as well as Japanese, Korean and Mandarin.

RECRUITMENT: Trainees are the firm's future partners. FFW believe in investing considerable time and reources in them so that they qualify as outstanding solicitors. The firm's aim is to take on 100% of its trainees upon qualification. With this in mind, FFW looks to recruit graduates with proven academic ability, excellent personal skills, creativity, determination and ambition. At least 10 trainees are recruited annually. Literature about the firm and its specialist services is available from the marketing department or from the firm's web site. The firm also has several specialist websites at: www.AD-visers.com (advertising and marketing); www.ecomlex.com (European e-commerce lawyers' association); www.ecommerceincubator.net (internet start-ups); www.europeanfranchising.com (franchising); www.e-ploymentlaw.com (employment); www.globalrewardplangroup.com (international network of specialists in employee benefits); www.sponsorshiplaw.com (sponsorship).

FIELD FISHER
WATERHOUSE

FIELDINGS PORTER

Silverwell House, Silverwell Street, Bolton, BL1 1PT **Tel:** (01204) 387742 **Fax:** (01204) 362129 **DX:** 24144 **Email:** info@fpsols.co.uk
Website: fpools.co.uk **Ptnrs:** 11 **Asst solrs:** 11 **Other fee-earners:** 12

FIELD SEYMOUR PARKES

The Old Coroner's Court, 1 London Street, PO Box 174, Reading, RG1 4QW **Tel:** (01189) 516 200 **Fax:** (01189) 502 704 **DX:** 4001 Reading **Email:** enquiry@fsp-law.com **Website:** www.yoursolicitors.com **Ptnrs:** 7 **Asst solrs:** 14 **Other fee-earners:** 18 **Contact:** Christine Bradfield • A general practice handling all areas of company/commercial, litigation, licensing, residential and commercial property, planning, employment, probate, wills and trusts.

AREAS OF PRACTICE	
Civil Litigation	22%
Company/Commercial	21%
Commercial Conveyancing	15%
Domestic Conveyancing	14%
Probate, Wills and Trusts	14%
Matrimonial	5%
Debt Collection	5%

FINERS STEPHENS INNOCENT

179 Great Portland St, London, W1W 5LF
Tel: (020) 7323 4000 **Fax:** (020) 7580 7069 **DX:** 42739 Oxford Circus North
Email: mralli@fsilaw.co.uk **Website:** www.fsilaw.com

Managing Partner	Anthony Barling
Senior Partner	Peter Jay
Number of partners	39
Assistant solicitors	40
Other fee-earners	11

CONTACTS

Commercial	Anthony Barling
Commercial Litigation	Philip Rubens
Construction Law	James Harvey
Corporate	Peter Jay
Corporate Finance	Paul Millett
Defamation	Mark Stephens
Employment	Howard Goulden
Flotations	Ashley Reeback
Hotels	Richard Gerstein
Information Technology	Anthony Barling
Intellectual Property	Chris Parkinson
International	Mark Stephens
Litigation	Richard Gerstein
Matrimonial	David Taylor
Media	Mark Stephens
Medical Negligence	Daniel Marks
Offshore Tax	Michael Lewis
Partnership	Michael Simmons
Personal Injury	Leon Marks
Planning	Nicola Armstrong
Professional Negligence	Richard Gerstein
Property	David Battiscombe
Property Development	Michael Kutner
Property Investment	Melvyn Orton
Property Litigation	John Hewitt
Property Retail	Katherine Miller
Property Trading	Sam Charkham
Publishing	Nicola Solomon
Sports Law	Daniel Marks
Tax	Brian Slater
Trusts & Charities	Robert Craig

Finers Stephens Innocent

THE FIRM: Finers Stephens Innocent is a fast growing mid-sized property, corporate and IP media practice. The firm provides a focused range of services to meet the requirements of its primarily commercial client base. Partner involvement, for which the firm is recognised, ensures that the firm's reputation for understanding the client's business, as well as it understands its own, is maintained. The firm has a finely targeted market-place for each of its departments and ensures that each is fully supported by cross-discipline and industry-led groups. The ability to provide an all-round commercial service ensures that many clients are serviced across departments according to their specific needs. The success of this strategy is evidenced by the number of new services that are now being provided to clients in such areas as intellectual property, construction, tax and employment. The firm has grown by identifying new markets and implementing a strategy to secure a position in these markets. The last two years have seen the firm evolve in line with its strategy of providing commercial clients with the range of expertise and skills they would find in a considerably larger firm but with the client support and speed of response associated with small firms. Teams are put together to support particular clients, or for specific transactions, and come from individual departments or from across the firm. The success of the strategy is seen in the firm's ability to win clients often against much larger firms and to put together teams to enable it to take on substantial corporate and property transactions.

PRINCIPAL AREAS OF WORK: In terms of client services the strategy is to build strongly focused departments which are supported by a range of specialists. The development, construction and retail/leisure teams in commercial property are supported by units specialising in tax, construction, planning, property dispute resolution and finance. Similarly, the corporate and commercial teams are supported by corporate tax, employment and tax planning units.
Media: A particular feature of the last year has been the development of a media department in the firm. Recent recruitment in the area of non-contentious media has strengthened the department, which now covers defamation, IP, IT, film and TV work and financing and various other aspects of media law.
Property: The property department has seen a year of significant transactions for Marylebone Warwick Balfour Group plc, Grosvenor Waterside and the Tannen Group as well as for major retailers.
Corporate & Commercial: Corporate and commercial has seen a year of rapid growth both in terms of the number and the size of transactions. The largest flotation that the firm handled was the AIM listing of Sportingbet(UK).com plc. This was accompanied by a large number of other AIM and OFEX listings. Merger and acquisition deals included the sale of the Whitecross Dental Care Group and New Media Investors as well as the sale of Profile Pursuit Group Limited to London and Edinburgh Publishing plc.
Private Client: The services of the private client department have continued to develop with an emphasis on estate management and offshore tax planning which has grown rapidly.

INTERNATIONAL: In the international arena the firm continues to service the needs of its clients on both sides of the Atlantic via the Network of Leading Law Firms and in Europe through membership of Lawrope an EEIG.

RECRUITMENT: The firm has continued with its policy of using lateral hires to provide or support key strategic areas. The last year has seen the recruitment of Brian Slater who now oversees corporate tax within the firm. The contentious media skills of Mark Stephens have been complemented with the recruitment of Chris Parkinson, who now heads up non-contentious IP and media.

FINN, GLEDHILL

1-4 Harrison Rd, Halifax, HX1 2AG **Tel:** (01422) 330 000 **Fax:** (01422) 342 604 **DX:** 16022 Halifax **Email:** marc.gledhill@finngledhill.co.uk **Website:** www.finngledhill.co.uk **Ptnrs:** 10 **Asst solrs:** 2 **Other fee-earners:** 7 **Contact:** Michael Gledhill • By continually building on the foundations of a successful law practice spanning 200 years, Finn, Gledhill has become one of the most respected law firms in West Yorkshire.

AREAS OF PRACTICE

Commercial	35%
Civil Litigation (Commercial & Other)	18%
Conveyancing	12%
Crime	10%
Divorce & Matrimonial	10%
Probate & Trust	9%

FISHBURN MORGAN COLE

61 St Mary Axe, London, EC3A 8AA **Tel:** (020) 7743 7300 **Fax:** (020) 7743 7301 **DX:** 584 London **Email:** info@fishburn-morgan-cole.co.uk **Ptnrs:** 10 **Asst solrs:** 19 **Other fee-earners:** 12 **Contact:** John Cayton • Fishburn Morgan Cole is the specialist professional indemnity division of Morgan Cole. For further information, please refer to the main entry for Morgan Cole.

FISHER MEREDITH

2 Binfield Road, Stockwell, London, SW4 6TA
Tel: (020) 7622 4468 **Fax:** (020) 7498 0415 **DX:** 37050
Email: mail@fishermeredith.co.uk **Website:** www.fishermeredith.co.uk

Managing Partner	Stephen Hewitt
Senior Partner	Eileen Pembridge
Number of partners	9
Assistant solicitors	24
Other fee-earners	16

AREAS OF PRACTICE

Civil	40%
Crime	32%
Family (inc. Children)	24%
Conveyancing	4%

CONTACTS

Children	Judith Bishton
Community Care/Education	Patricia Wilkins
Conveyancing	Jason Halberstam
Crime	Stephen Hewitt
Employment	David Tyme
Family	Eileen Pembridge
Housing	David Foster
Immigration	Douglas Noble
Mental Health	Rebecca Ellison
Police Actions/Prison Law	David Tyme
Welfare Benefits	Rachel Burley

THE FIRM: Founded by Eileen Meredith Pembridge and another in 1975, Fisher Meredith now consists of nine partners and 76 other staff. The firm remains firmly committed to personal litigation and state funded work. It is departmentalised for increased efficiency and to meet specialisation needs. There are departments specialising in family work of all types including a children's team dealing with children's advocacy and civil domestic violence; all aspects of criminal law; civil actions against the police; prison law; mental health work; conveyancing; community care and education; immigration; welfare benefits; housing law; employment law. The senior partner is the Law Society Council member for London South, and a former Chair of the Law Society's Family Law Committee. The firm has Legal Aid franchises in family, crime, housing, immigration, welfare benefits, mental health, civil actions against the police, employment, community care and education, prison law and public law.

PRINCIPAL AREAS OF WORK:

Crime: A large thriving department well known for expertise in acting for defendants across a range of offences including difficult human rights and civil liberties issues and complex appellate cases. It offers a breadth of expertise including high calibre business crime specialists.
Police & Prison Law: A cutting edge civil liberties service is offered.
Community Care & Education: This department provides a high level specialist service.
Immigration: The firm covers all aspects from asylum to judicial review.
Residential & Commercial Conveyancing: A friendly personalised service from an experienced team.
Mental Health Law: A caring specialist service which includes Court of Protection work.
Housing Law: A specialist service for tenants and residential occupiers.
Welfare Benefits: All aspects of social security law including judicial review.
Employment Law: A specialist service for employers and employees with specialisms in discrimination claims.
Public Law: This department is well known for expertise in house in judicial review.
Agency Work: Fisher Meredith accepts instructions in its areas of expertise.
Charges: For Legal Aid work, the charges are as fixed by the LCD. For private clients, the firm charges between £100 and £180 per hour.

FISHERS

9-13 Fenchurch Buildings, London, EC3M 5HR
Tel: (020) 7709 7203 **Fax:** (020) 7709 7204
Email: info@fishcity.co.uk

Number of partners	3
Assistant solicitors	2

AREAS OF PRACTICE

Commercial Shipping & International Trade Litigation	70%
Professional Indemnity & Insurance Litigation	25%
Drafting Shipping & Insurance Documentation	5%

CONTACTS

General	Nicholas Fisher
	Graeme Lloyd
	Jamie Lyons

THE FIRM: Founded in 1993. Small, independently minded City firm specialising in commercial shipping and international trade litigation, also with significant practice in insurance and re-insurance disputes.

PRINCIPAL AREAS OF WORK:

Shipping: Commercial litigation work, predominantly for shipowners and charterers. Strong following of container and liner operators, tanker and gas carriers and reefer operators. The firm has close links with a number of P&I Clubs and Defence Associations. Experienced also in drafting charterparties and bills of lading.
International Trade: Advises on disputes relating to buying and selling of hard and soft commodities and petroleum products, and on drafting sale contracts.
Insurance & Reinsurance: Litigation, principally on behalf of Lloyd's brokers. Advises on compliance and Lloyd's proceedings.

F

FLADGATE FIELDER

25 North Row, London, W1K 6DJ
Tel: (020) 7323 4747 **Fax:** (020) 7629 4414 **DX:** 9057 West End
Email: fladgate@fladgate.com **Website:** www.fladgate.com

Number of partners	34
Other fee-earners	21
Assistants	30
Total	85

AREAS OF PRACTICE

Corporate/Commercial	38%
Property	37%
Litigation	20%
Tax	5%

CONTACTS

Anglo-American	Nicolas Greenstone
Anglo-French	Nicolas Greenstone
Anglo-Germanic	Andrew Kaufman
Anglo-Israeli	Avram Kelman
Commercial Contracts	Charles Boundy
Corporate	Nicolas Greenstone
Corporate Recovery	Rupert Connell
Employment	Charles Boundy
Immigration	Charles Boundy
Libel	Simon Ekins
Litigation	Paul Leese
Property	Allen Cohen
Tax	Andrew McKenzie
Town Planning	Moira Fraser

THE FIRM: Fladgate Fielder is one of the leading business law practices in the West End of London, providing legal advice of the highest quality for a diverse portfolio of clients. Pivotal to the firm's success are the following factors: namely its standard of excellence in client service, the calibre of its expertise, its innovative and commercial approach to the solution of problems and the combination of efficiency and cost-effectiveness to reach the optimum result.

PRINCIPAL AREAS OF WORK:
Corporate: The firm handles corporate; listings and flotations; AIM, EASDAQ and OFEX quotations; mergers and acquisitions; venture capital; MBOs; UK and cross-border corporate and commercial transactions; employment; immigration; computer and intellectual property law; banking; partnership law; corporate restructuring; insolvency; company secretarial work.
Property: Work includes acquisition and disposal; funding; construction and development; investment; secured lending; landlord and tenant; housing associations; joint ventures; portfolio management; residential estate conveyancing; town and country planning; environmental issues; enterprise zone development.
Litigation: Work includes general commercial litigation; professional negligence; asset recovery; corporate recovery; landlord and tenant; intellectual property; libel; matrimonial; construction disputes; building and product liability; insurance litigation.
Tax: All aspects of taxation are handled including corporate and business taxes as well as off-shore and international aspects; personal tax planning; wills; probate; charities; land estate matters.

CLIENTELE: The firm's client base has a strong commercial focus, comprising leading public and private companies, financial institutions and entrepreneurs in the UK and overseas.

INTERNATIONAL: Fladgate Fielder has an expanding international dimension based on multi-lingual lawyers working in London. The firm has Anglo-American, Germanic, Israeli and French Desks. The firm is able to conduct business in French, German, Hebrew, Italian and Spanish.

F

FLEETWOOD & ROBB
11 Queensgate, Inverness, IV1 1DF **Tel:** (01463) 226 232 **Fax:** (01463) 713 447 **DX:** LP 7 - INI **Ptnrs:** 3

FLETCHERS
111 Carrington Street, Nottingham, NG1 7FE **Tel:** (0115) 959 9550 **Fax:** (0115) 959 9597 **Ptnrs:** 3 **Asst solrs:** 4 **Other fee-earners:** 5

FLYNN & MCGETTRICK
9 Clarence Street, Belfast, BT2 8DX **Tel:** (028) 90244212 **Fax:** (028) 90236490 **Ptnrs:** 3 **Asst solrs:** 3

FOINETTE QUINN
125-131 Queensway, Milton Keynes, MK2 2DH **Tel:** (01908) 366333 **Fax:** (01908)644096 **DX:** 100012 Bletchley **Ptnrs:** 3 **Asst solrs:** 2 **Other fee-earners:** 4

FOLLETT STOCK
Malpas Road, Truro, TR1 1QH **Tel:** (01872) 241700 **Fax:** (01872) 225052 **DX:** 81225 Truro **Email:** martin.follett@follettstock.co.uk **Website:** www.follettstock.co.uk **Ptnrs:** 3 **Asst solrs:** 3 **Other fee-earners:** 2

FOOT ANSTEY SARGENT

21 Derry's Cross, Plymouth, PL1 2SW
Tel: (01752) 675 000 **Fax:** (01752) 671 802 **DX:** 118102 Plymouth 2
Email: info@foot-ansteys.co.uk **Website:** www.foot-ansteys.co.uk

4-6 Barnfield Crescent, Exeter, EX1 1RF
Tel: (01392) 411 221 **Fax:** (01392) 218 554 **DX:** 8308 Exeter

Managing Partner	Jane Lister
Number of partners	33
Assistant solicitors	43
Other fee-earners	30

CONTACTS

Advocacy ....Tony Daniel
Banking ....Robin Brown
Childcare......Margaret Bonner, Vanessa Priddis
Commercial Litigation....Angus McNicol
Commercial Property....Simon Gregory
....Cindy Rai
Company & Commercial......Richard Coombs
....Mark Lewis
E-commerce/IT....Edmund Probert
Employment....Jon Loney
Family Finance....Fiona Meadows
Insolvency....Gillian Smith
Investment Management....John Crowley
Marine....Charles Hattersley
Media....Tony Jaffa
Planning & Land Use....Isabel Diver
....Michael Horwood
Private Client/Tax Planning......Adrian Miller
Property Litigation....John Westwell

Foot Anstey Sargent

THE FIRM: Foot Anstey Sargent is a major regional practice with a growing national and international client base. The firm prides itself on providing a level of service and expertise which can be compared with the best in the country, but from a south west base and at regional rates. The firm is recruiting young and talented lawyers with established track records in many specialist areas of the law in order to provide that high level of service. Investment in the latest technology and office facilities ensures the best possible service to clients.

PRINCIPAL AREAS OF WORK: The firm acts for businesses, individuals and institutions, and provides a comprehensive range of specialist services for clients. Cross-departmental teams can handle large and complex corporate transactions across a broad range of business sectors. The corporate team works closely with the firm's specialists in commercial property, property litigation, planning, employment and commercial litigation. Private clients benefit from expertise in the most complex areas of trust and estate planning, and there is a growing portfolio management team. The firm has clients throughout the UK and is particularly recognised nationally for banking, employment, insolvency, marine and media law.

CLIENTELE: Clients include Northcliffe Newspaper Group, The Wrigley Company Ltd, Exeter Friendly Society Ltd, University of Plymouth, UKRD Group Ltd, South West Highways, Arbuthnot Latham & Co, Bank of Scotland, The Wireless Group plc and local authorities.

F

FORBES

Rutherford House, 4 Wellington Street, (St John's), Blackburn, BB1 8DD **Tel:** 01254 54374 **Fax:** 01254 52347 **DX:** 17952 Blackburn-1
Email: forbes@f-p.co.uk **Website:** www.forbessolicitors.co.uk **Ptnrs:** 24 **Asst solrs:** 46 **Other fee-earners:** 62

FORD & WARREN

Westgate Point, Westgate, Leeds, LS1 2AX
Tel: (0113) 243 6601 **Fax:** (0113) 242 0905 **DX:** 706968 Leeds
Email: clientmail@forwarn.com **Website:** www.forwarn.com

Managing Partner	Keith Hearn
Number of partners	16
Assistant solicitors	44
Other fee-earners	42

THE FIRM: Ford & Warren is a major commercial firm in the North of England. The size and strength of the firm enables expert teams of lawyers to be put together helping clients achieve their business objectives.

PRINCIPAL AREAS OF WORK:

Business: The business law department provides a full range of management advice to employers. The Managing Partner is in this department as head of employment law. The employment team deals with issues right across the board from tribunal claims, fraudulent directors, trade union disputes and injunctions. Corporate law encompasses mergers, acquisitions, MBOs, MBIs and commercial contracts along with intellectual property issues. Gary Gillman, of the Ontario and Quebec Bars and based in Toronto, is the firm's North America Consultant.

Commercial: The commercial law department provides a full range of contentious and non-contentious services, from property litigation, planning and environment through to transport public inquiries. This department handles major commercial litigation in close liaison with the business law department. The head of department has enormous expertise in the transport industry.

Claims: The claims department has strong teams acting for major insurance companies throughout the country. Litigation includes employers liability, road traffic, fire and insurance fraud claims. As well as the defendant claims team, the department has a plaintiff team which has unrivalled expertise in high profile multi-plaintiff claims, including Bradford stadium fire, Zeebrugge ferry sinking and the Hillsborough stadium disaster. The firm's medical negligence team goes from strength to strength.

Private Client: This department caters for all the needs of the private client from matrimonial law to employee relocation. Residential conveyancing is also handled.

FORD & WARREN
Solicitors

FOREMAN LAWS

25 Bancroft, Hitchin, SG5 1JW **Tel:** (01462) 458 711 **Fax:** (01462) 459 242 **DX:** 7102 Hitchin **Email:** lawyers@foremanlaws.co.uk **Contact:** Martin Foreman • Strong commercial, property development and construction base, alongside full range of private client services. Well-developed use of IT.

AREAS OF PRACTICE	
Company	30%
Commercial Property	25%
Civil Litigation	15%
Family	10%
Probate & Trusts	10%
Residential	10%

FORSTERS

67 Grosvenor Street, London, W1K 3JN **Tel:** (020) 7863 8333 **Fax:** (020) 7863 8444 **DX:** 82 988 Mayfair **Email:** mail@forsters.co.uk **Website:** www.forsters.co.uk **Ptnrs:** 21 **Asst solrs:** 32 **Other fee-earners:** 15

F

FOSTER BAXTER COOKSEY

6-10 George Street, Snow Hill, Wolverhampton, WV2 4DN
Tel: (01902) 311 711 **Fax:** (01902) 311 102 **DX:** 702433 Wolverhampton 5
Email: solicitors@fbc-sol.co.uk

Managing Partner	Graham Sower
Senior Partner	David Nixon
Number of partners	14
Assistant solicitors	11
Other fee-earners	27

CONTACTS	
Commercial Property	Simon Bowdler
Corporate Services	James Hayes
Employment	Tracy Worthington
Insolvency	Guy Birkett
Legal Audits	James Hayes
Litigation	Timothy Gray
Private Client	Kim Carr

THE FIRM: Formed by the merger of four well-established Midlands firms, Foster Baxter Cooksey now has over 100 staff and serves a broad spectrum of private and business clients. The firm has particular expertise in corporate work, commercial property, intellectual property, civil litigation, matrimonial and family. It has other offices in Telford and Willenhall.

PRINCIPAL AREAS OF WORK: Work includes commercial, property, corporate finance, building societies, civil litigation, family and trusts.

RECRUITMENT: The firm recruits two trainee solicitors (with at least a 2:1 degree) each year. Applicants should write to James Hayes, Training Partner, with a full CV.

FOSTERS

William House, 19 Bank Plain, Norwich, NR2 4FS
Tel: (01603) 620508 **Fax:** (01603) 624090 **DX:** 5225 Norwich-1
Email: enquiries@fosters-solicitors.co.uk

Managing Partner	Andrew Saul

CONTACTS	
Commercial Litigation	Karim Mohamed
Commercial Property	Anne Kirby
Company Commercial	Alison Bignell
Matrimonial & Family	Iain McClay
Mediation	Catherine Iliff
Mental Health	Bruce Chilton
Personal Injury	Jeremy Ives
Professional Negligence	Karim Mohamed
Residential Property/Probate	Anne Kirby

THE FIRM: Fosters is a high street practice committed to the local community and excellent client care. Established in 1761, it merged with local firm Russell Steward in July 2001 and has won a number of national awards.

PRINCIPAL AREAS OF WORK:

Family Law: Substantial specialist family team with mixed client base.
Mediation: This service is the biggest growth area and has been extended to cover five branch offices.
Commercial: Advice is given on all aspects of company and commercial law.
Professional Negligence: National client base with particular expertise in solicitors' negligence.

RECRUITMENT: Unique, award-winning contracts are offered to trainee solicitors.

Index to leading lawyers: p.1647 • In-House lawyers profiles: p.1193 • www.ChambersandPartners.com

FOX WILLIAMS

City Gate House, 39-45 Finsbury Square, London, EC2A 1UU
Tel: (020) 7628 2000 **Fax:** (020) 7628 2100 **DX:** 33873 Finsbury Sq.
Email: mail@foxwilliams.com **Website:** www.foxwilliams.com

Senior Partner	Ronnie Fox
Number of partners	16
Assistant solicitors	32
Other fee-earners	6

AREAS OF PRACTICE

Employment	37%
Corporate	31%
E-commerce	14%
Litigation	13%
Property	5%

CONTACTS

Commercial Agreements	Stephen Sidkin
Commercial Litigation	Gavin Foggo
Commercial Property	Bryan Emden
Corporate Finance	Paul Osborne
Corporate/Financial Services	Tina Williams
Discrimination & Business Immigration	Jane Mann
E-commerce & Internet Law	Nigel Miller
E-commerce & IT Law	Robin Baron
Employment (Executive Termination & International)	Clare Murray
Employment (UK & Corporate)	Mark Watson
M&A	Mark Tasker
Partnership	Ronnie Fox

THE FIRM: Fox Williams is a City firm handling a wide variety of company and commercial work, with particular skills in corporate and employment law. Fox Williams adopts a particular approach to its work, involving a special effort to understand the business needs of its clients, a close relationship between clients and members of the Fox Williams team and a fast, responsive service. The firm pays meticulous attention to detail and to quality assurance, and strives to create a happy and efficient working environment for members of the firm.

PRINCIPAL AREAS OF WORK: The firm is organised into departments focused on corporate law, e-commerce law, employment, commercial litigation and commercial property. A cross-departmental group advises on partnership law.
Corporate: Corporate work includes international and domestic takeovers and mergers, company acquisitions and disposals, share issues, management buy-ins and buy-outs, private placings, flotations, film financing and venture capital projects. General corporate matters such as business start-ups, restructurings and shareholder agreements are also handled.
E-commerce: Fox Williams has specialist expertise in advising on legal issues arising from online commerce and the use of the Internet. This expertise is based on its considerable experience in advising on distribution and agency agreements, joint ventures, technology licensing and IT agreements, intellectual property and EU and UK competition law.
Employment: The firm is well-known for its employment law expertise which includes service agreements, employee rights and restrictive covenants, share incentive and option schemes, golden handshakes, dismissals and redundancies. Employment litigation is handled by employment lawyers in the employment department.
Litigation: A broad range of substantial UK and international litigation and arbitration is undertaken by the litigation department. It resolves disputes relating to intellectual property, trading, shareholder and joint venture arrangements. The litigation department also presents cases for mediation.
Partnership: Fox Williams has an outstanding reputation for partnership work. Partners at Fox Williams have been closely involved in the new rules which apply to limited liability partnerships. Fox Williams has also advised a number of US law firms on the development of their offices in London.
Property: Commercial property work is concerned with a wide range of matters including land acquisitions and disposals, secured lending, business leases, and landlord and tenant issues.

CLIENTELE: The firm's clients range from multinational corporations and major public companies to family businesses and individual entrepreneurs. They include banks, other financial institutions, regulatory authorities, accountants and other professionals (including overseas lawyers). Firms of solicitors often refer work to Fox Williams when City expertise is required.

FOY & CO

PO Box 111, 63 Hallgate, Doncaster, DN1 3DQ
Tel: (01302) 327 136 **Fax:** (01302) 367 656 **DX:** 12563 Doncaster
Email: info@foyandco.co.uk **Website:** www.foyandco.uk

Drakehouse Crescent, Waterthorpe, Sheffield, S20 7HT
Tel: (0114) 251 1702 **Fax:** (0114) 251 1750 **DX:** 717230 Sheffield 28

Church Steps, All Saints Square, Rotherham, S60 1QD
Tel: (01709) 375 561 **Fax:** (01709) 828 479 **DX:** 12601 Rotherham

102 Bridge Street, Worksop, S80 1HZ
Tel: (01909) 473 560 **Fax:** (01909) 482 760 **DX:** 12207 Worksop

102/112 Burncross Road, Chapeltown, Sheffield, S35 1TG
Tel: (0114) 246 7609 **Fax:** (0114) 240 2625 **DX:** 19836 Chapeltown

Managing Partner	Paul Evans
Senior Partner	Stephen Paramore
Number of partners	8
Assistant solicitors	11
Other fee-earners	19

THE FIRM: Established legal practice offering a wide range of domestic and commercial services including conveyancing, litigation, matrimonial and family, criminal and motoring, wills and probate, and all commercial matters.

FRANCIS HANNA & CO

Central Chambers, 75-77 May Street, Belfast, BT1 3JL **Tel:** (028) 90243901 **Fax:** (028) 90244215 **DX:** 473NR Belfast **Email:** info@fhanna.co.uk **Website:** www.fhanna.co.uk **Ptnrs:** 3 **Asst solrs:** 4 **Other fee-earners:** 6

F

FREEMAN & CO

Rodesia House, 52 Princess Street, Manchester, M1 6JX **Tel:** 0161 236 7007 **Fax:** 0161 236 0440 **Ptnrs:** 1 **Other fee-earners:** 4

FREEMANS SOLICITORS

Stuart House, Lower Chepstow, NP16 5HH **Tel:** (01291) 623 225 **Fax:** (01291) 628 162

FREEMANS

7 St Mary's Place, Newcastle upon Tyne, NE1 7PG **Tel:** (0191) 222 1030 **Fax:** (0191) 222 1819 **DX:** 61100 Newcastle-upon-Tyne
Email: freemans@btinternet.com **Ptnrs:** 3 **Asst solrs:** 2

FREETHCARTWRIGHT

Imperial House, 108-110 New Walk, Leicester, LE1 7EA
Tel: (0116) 201 4000 **Fax:** (0116) 201 4001 **DX:** 715612 Leicester 2
Email: postmaster@freethcartwright.co.uk

Willoughby House, 20 Low Pavement, Nottingham, NG1 7EA
Tel: (0115) 936 9369 **Fax:** (0115) 936 9358 **DX:** 10039 Nottingham
Email: postmaster@freethcartwright.co.uk

Norman House, Friargate, Derby, DE1 1NU
Tel: (01332) 361 000 **Fax:** (01332) 207 177 **DX:** 11502 Derby 1
Email: postmaster@freethcartwright.co.uk

Senior Partner	Ian Payne
Chief Executive	Peter Smith
Chairman	Colin Flanagan
Number of partners	49
Assistant solicitors	55
Other fee-earners	55

AREAS OF PRACTICE

Dispute Resolution	31%
Commercial Property	28%
Private Client	21%
Corporate & Commercial Services	20%

CONTACTS

Admin/Public Law	Richard Beverley
Banking	Paul Thorogood
Charities	Nigel Cullen
Company/Commercial	Paul Thorogood
Competition	Phillip Raven
Construction	Guy Berwick
Corporate Finance	Karl Jansen
Employment	David Potter
Family/Childcare	Beth Henderson
Housing Associations	Gary Reynolds
Immigration	Sue Miles
Insolvency	Graham Greenfield
Internet	Andrew Margotta-Mills
IP	Andrew Margotta-Mills
IT	Andrew Margotta-Mills
Licensing	Malcolm Radcliffe
Litigation (Commercial)	Philippa Dempster
Litigation (Property)	Martin Lee
Pensions	John Heaphy
Personal Injury	Jane Goulding
Planning	Ian Tempest
Private Client	Nigel Cullen
Product Liability	Paul Balen
Professional Negligence	Richard Beverley
Property (Commercial)	George Taylor
Risk Management	Philippa Dempster
Sports	Simon Taylor

THE FIRM: Freethcartwright is a major Midlands practice offering services to both commercial and private clients across the entire legal spectrum. Although based in Nottingham, Derby and Leicester, the firm has a wide range of clients throughout the UK and many of its clients have strong international connections. Freethcartwright has grown rapidly in recent years and now ranks as one of the leading East Midlands' firms offering comprehensive legal services in the public and private sectors. Whilst aiming to provide the very best service possible in all areas, the firm also prides itself on its wish and ability to understand the businesses of its clients and to demonstrate to them that with a properly developed relationship it can significantly add value. It believes that major legal practices should be in 'partnership' with their clients, not merely reacting to clients' specific instructions and dealing with problems after they have arisen. The firm aims to combine first-class legal expertise with a thorough knowledge of our clients' business. Its lawyers are encouraged and trained to be both practical and commercial in their approach to the provision of legal services.

PRINCIPAL AREAS OF WORK:

Commercial: The firm's commercial practice covers a broad spectrum of corporate, commercial and financial work from small day-to-day transactions to significant mergers and acquisitions, some with an international content.

Corporate & Commercial: The corporate and commercial team provides the full range of services specialising in MBOs, MBIs, the re-organisation and financing of businesses, mergers, acquisitions and joint ventures. The firm also has a significant capability in specialist areas including pensions, competition, EU law, corporate tax and sport and entertainment law. It has a specialist intellectual property unit dealing with both contentious and non-contentious work including a comprehensive international trademark registration service and significant work in the telecommunications, Internet and IT sectors.

Commercial Property: With one of the largest commercial property departments in the Midlands, the firm acts for developers of industrial, residential and commercial property; institutional lenders and investors; privatised utilities; housing associations; commercial landlords and tenants. The firm has dedicated units covering planning, environment issues and construction.

Dispute Resolution: The emphasis in dispute resolution is on risk management and risk avoidance. The firm has specialist groups in employment, landlord and tenant, construction litigation, professional negligence and insurance. The firm also undertakes significant insolvency, recovery and litigation work for major banks and accountants. The firm acts for Lloyds underwriters, insurers and indemnity institutions. The firm has particular expertise in medical negligence and product liability under the leadership of Paul Balen who enjoys an established national reputation in the field. The group has significant experience in coordinating high profile group actions, both in the UK and overseas.

Private Client: Emphasising the firm's range of services, the private client units provide expertise in family and childcare matters, housing litigation, immigration, personal injury, residential conveyancing and wills and probate. The firm plans to continue growth through organic development, by pursuing pro-active strategic and marketing policies and by investing in high calibre people, from trainee solicitors to partners.

FRESHFIELDS BRUCKHAUS DERINGER

65 Fleet Street, London, EC4Y 1HS
Tel: (020) 7936 4000 **Fax:** (020) 7832 7001 **DX:** 23
Email: email@freshfields.com **Website:** www.freshfields.com

UK	
Number of partners	161
Number of fee-earners	1093
International	
Number of partners	313
Number of fee-earners	1380
Total staff	4853

CONTACTS

Arbitration	Nigel Rawding
Asset Finance	Tim Lintott
Banking	Edward Evans
Construction & Engineering	Sally Roe
Corporate/M&A	Barry O'Brien
Dispute Resolution	Josanne Rickard
Employment	Peter Jeffcote
Energy	Jonathan Rees
Environment	Paul Bowden
EU/Competition	Deirdre Trapp
Finance	Peter Hall
Financial Services	Guy Morton
Insolvency	Peter Bloxham
Insurance	Ian Poynton
Intellectual Property/IT	Avril Martindale
Investment Funds	Anthony McWhirter
Private Equity	Christopher Bown
Project Finance	Kent Rowey
Real Estate	Claire Morris
Securities	Tom Joyce
	Tim Jones
Structured Finance	Ian Falconer
Tax	Ian Taylor
Telecoms, Media & Technology	Simon Marchant
Telecoms, Media & Technology - Regulatory	Rachel Brandenburger
Associate Recruitment	Judith Hesketh
Graduate Recruitment	Deborah Dalgliesh

FRESHFIELDS BRUCKHAUS DERINGER

THE FIRM: Freshfields Bruckhaus Deringer is a leading international law firm providing a range of business legal services. It specialises in producing innovative, commercial solutions to the most complex issues based on its substantial business experience. The firm provides clients with exceptional advice that makes a real difference to their businesses. This approach demands the highest standards of intellectual rigour and service delivery as it strives to exceed the expectations of clients. The firm has a wealth of experience in its chosen practice areas and also invests in developing the specialist industry knowledge of its people so that they can combine their legal skills with genuine understanding of the markets in which their clients operate. Freshfields Bruckhaus Deringer lawyers think ahead – identifying the challenges of the future, and advising clients on how best to meet them.

PRINCIPAL AREAS OF WORK: The firm is widely recognised as a world leader in a number of fields including arbitration, environment, competition, mergers and acquisitions, pensions, corporate tax, PFI and securitisation. It has thriving practices in the areas of IP/IT and e-commerce related issues. Overall, it specialises in providing a seamless service across practice areas and geographies.

CLIENTELE: Freshfields Bruckhaus Deringer has advised most of the world's largest corporations and all of the leading investment banks. It frequently acts for governments and public bodies.

INTERNATIONAL: Its international approach is founded on leading local capabilities and experience backed up by the knowledge and experience of the wider firm. With over 2,000 lawyers in 19 countries across Europe, Asia and the US the firm has the resources to coordinate and execute even the largest and most complex matters involving numerous jurisdictions. The firm has offices in Amsterdam, Bangkok, Barcelona, Beijing, Berlin, Bratislava, Brussels, Budapest, Cologne, Düsseldorf, Frankfurt, Hamburg, Hanoi, Ho Chi Minh City, Hong Kong, Madrid, Milan, Moscow, Munich, New York, Paris, Prague, Rome, Singapore, Tokyo, Vienna, and Washington. It also has an associated office in Shanghai.

RECRUITMENT: Great emphasis is placed on the training and development of the firm's lawyers to meet the changing needs of its clients. As well as the usual training tools, secondments to client organisations are actively encouraged. The firm has a range of state of the art e-services for clients to keep them up to date with progress on deals and legal developments of interest to them. Lawyers and trainees also have access to bespoke electronic databanks and services, ensuring that the combined sum of the firm's knowledge and experience can be applied to individual matters and the more routine parts of the job can be performed efficiently and cost-effectively.

FRIED, FRANK, HARRIS, SHRIVER & JACOBSON

99 City Road, London, EC1Y 1AX
Tel: (020) 7972 9600 **Fax:** (020) 7972 9602
Email: info@ffhsj.com **Website:** www.ffhsj.com

Managing Partners	Peter v. Z Cobb Michael H Rauch
International	
Number of partners worldwide	132
Number of other lawyers worldwide	368
UK	
Partners	5
Assistant solicitors	13
Other fee-earners	3
Total fee-earners	21
Total staff	38

AREAS OF PRACTICE

Corporate	52%
Litigation	26%
Real Estate	6%
Bankruptcy	5%
Tax	5%
Benefits/Employment	3%
Antitrust	2%
Trust & Estate	1%

THE FIRM: An international law firm with approximately 500 attorneys, Fried Frank has offices in New York, Washington DC, Los Angeles, London and Paris. Firm practice areas include antitrust; bankruptcy; benefits and compensation; corporate, litigation; real estate; securities regulation compliance and enforcement; tax; technology transactions and services; trust and estates. The London office concentrates on corporate matters such as cross-border mergers and acquisitions, including leveraged buyouts, joint ventures and private equity investments; global capital markets transactions; senior and mezzanine leveraged financings; structured finance and securitisations matters.

PRINCIPAL AREAS OF WORK: The London office advises US clients investing or raising capital abroad and non-US clients making acquisitions or investments or raising capital in the US or abroad. The firm's London attorneys represent both underwriters and issuers in global, US and euro securities offerings involving equity and debt. They provide the full slate of acquisition finance legal services to capital providers and borrowers, including sourcing funds in senior, mezzanine and other yield markets. They also represent commercial and investment banks, insurance companies and other participants in complex structured finance securitisations. They provide US securities law advice and advise multinational professional services organisations including the Big Five, on mergers and acquisitions and structural and regulatory issues.

INTERNATIONAL: Fried Frank has an established international practice with a concentration in cross-border mergers, acquisitions and joint ventures; private equity investments; US registered and Rule 144A securities offerings; cross-border non-US debt and equity offerings, including high yield debt; commercial financing

Continued overleaf

F

transactions; structured and securitised financings; establishment of LBO funds; international trade and investment; tax; trust and estate planning. The practice is conducted from the firm's US offices and its offices in London and Paris. Lawyers in its London office practice US, English and international law. Lawyers in the firm's Paris office practice French, US and international law. Recent international representations include Bestfoods Inc. in its merger with Unilever plc; WPP Group plc in its acquisition of Young & Rubicam Inc; Invensys plc in connection with the merger of Siebe plc and BTR plc to form one of the world's largest engineering and industrial controls group; Goldman, Sachs & Co when it acted as financial adviser to, among others, Grupo Financiero Banamex-Accival (Banacci) in its acquisition by Citigroup Inc, PaineWebber Group, Inc in its acquisition by UBS AG, Hong Kong and Shanghai Bank Corporation in its acquisition of Crédit Commercial de France SA. Recent international capital markets representations include the Spanish government in the privatization of Iberia SA; KPNQwest NV in its offering of high yield bonds; Procter & Gamble Company or its underwriters, including Goldman Sachs, Deutsche Bank and JP Morgan, in a series of domestic and international financings, including the largest euro offering by a US company at that time; Grupo Televisa SA and Grupo Televicentro in the largest non-privatization equity offering by a Latin American company.

THE FRITH PARTNERSHIP

53 The Calls, Leeds, LS2 7EY **Tel:** (0113) 242 6633 **Fax:** (0113) 242 6620 **DX:** 22124 Leeds 1 **Email:** robertkelly@thefrithpartnership.co.uk
Ptnrs: 4

F

FRORIEP RENGGLI

1 Knightrider Court, St Paul's, London, EC4V 5JP
Tel: (020) 7236 6000 **Fax:** (020) 7248 0209
Email: london@froriep.ch **Website:** www.froriep.com

Resident Partner	Bruno Boesch
Total number of lawyers	4

THE FIRM: Froriep Renggli provides unique expertise and experience advising and representing UK-based clients in transactions and litigation involving Switzerland or calling on Swiss law. The firm also directs Swiss and other clients into UK.

PRINCIPAL AREAS OF WORK: The firm specialises in corporate, commercial, securities, securities dealers and stock exchange, M&A, private equity, banking (transactions and regulations), litigation (including international judicial assistance), international commercial arbitration, estate planning.

INTERNATIONAL: The firm has no international connections or associations. Languages spoken include English, German, French, Italian and Swedish.

FURLEY PAGE

39 St Margaret's Street, Canterbury, CT1 2TX
Tel: (01227) 763 939 **Fax:** (01227) 762 829 **DX:** 5301 Canterbury
Email: postmaster@furleypage.co.uk **Website:** www.furleypage.co.uk

52-54 High Street, Whitstable, CT5 1BG
Tel: (01227) 274 241 **Fax:** (01227) 275 704 **DX:** 32352 Whitstable
Email: postmaster@furleypage.co.uk

Senior Partner	Peter Hawkes
Number of partners	17
Assistant solicitors	10
Other fee-earners	19

AREAS OF PRACTICE

Litigation	32%
Commercial Services	30%
Trust & Estates	25%
Residential	13%

CONTACTS

Company/Commercial	Christopher Wacher
Employment	Jonathan Gauton
Litigation	Peter Hawkes
Private Client	Harvey Barrett

THE FIRM: Furley Page is one of the largest practices in Kent. Lawyers are organised in specialist groups and offer a level of service that competes both regionally and nationally. The firm has associations with commercial practices in many countries to handle an increasing volume of overseas work.

PRINCIPAL AREAS OF WORK:

Commercial Services: Clients include national and international plcs, insurers and a wide range of private companies. Work includes company commercial, commercial property, intellectual property, competition, planning and environmental. There is a specialist e-business group.
Education & Charities: The firm acts for charities, higher education institutions, colleges and schools.
Agriculture: This is a long-standing and significant area of practice for the firm.
Litigation: Groups specialise in personal injury and clinical negligence, commercial and building, landlord and tenant and matrimonial. Agency work is regularly undertaken.
Employment: A team of lawyers and specialist consultants advises nationally and internationally on employment, human resources, health and safety and commercial immigration.
Debt Recovery: The firm offers a specialist computer-supported service operating debt recovery at fixed rates.
Private Client: Work includes comprehensive tax planning, domestic conveyancing, probate, court of protection and wills.
Financial Services: The firm advises on investment, life assurance, pensions and other financial matters.

FYFE IRELAND WS

99 Charterhouse Street, London, EC1M 6NQ
Tel: (020) 7253 5202 **Fax:** (020) 7253 5525 **DX:** 53346 Clerkenwell

Orchard Brae House, 30 Queensferry Road, Edinburgh, EH4 2HG
Tel: (0131) 343 2500 **Fax:** (0131) 343 3166 **DX:** ED 23
Email: mail@fyfeireland.com

Senior Partner	Alistair Wilson
Number of partners	14
Assistant solicitors	14
Other fee-earners	17

AREAS OF PRACTICE

Commercial Property	39%
Private Client & Lender Services	28%
Corporate	25%
Litigation	8%

CONTACTS

Commercial Property	James Roscoe
Corporate	David Lindgren
Litigation	Andrew Taylor
Private Client & Lender Services	Greig Honeyman

THE FIRM: Based in Edinburgh, Fyfe Ireland is primarily a business-to-business law firm with a particular emphasis on commercial property. The firm has a strong client base across its many practice areas and is very well regarded in the market. Its major strength continues to be the provision of a personal, partner-led service. Fyfe Ireland, with its 14 partners, is often referred to as 'punching above its weight' and is well known in London. Clients include a significant number of substantial foreign and UK organisations, particularly banks, building societies, other financial institutions, educational establishments, retailers and IT companies.

PRINCIPAL AREAS OF WORK: The principal focus of the firm continues to be on commercial law, the main work areas being commercial property, corporate and commercial and lender services.
Commercial Property: The firm's commercial property expertise has been well established for many years and is provided to a significant number of financiers and investors, developers, retailers, and builders in both the private and public sectors. All aspects of work are undertaken but there is particular expertise in cross-border security transactions and an expanding construction practice.
Corporate & Commercial: Following a restructuring of the corporate and commercial departments in the early part of last year, the reputations of the three newly appointed partners have been growing steadily, crowned in the latter part of 2000 by the Quadstone cross-border fundraising in which the team helped the company raise £21m. Practice areas include every aspect of private company work, contracts, joint ventures, intellectual property, banking, corporate finance and public/private partnerships.
Commercial Litigation: The head of the commercial litigation department is accredited by the Law Society of Scotland as a specialist in construction law and is also on the Society's list of adjudicators. There is particular expertise in the areas of construction, commercial property and employment.
Private Client & Lender Services: In the lender services division there is much experience in the provision of advice and services to financial institutions including Halifax plc, Yorkshire Building Society, Barclays Bank plc and West Bromwich Building Society. The firm also retains a high quality private client base with core advice areas being wills, trusts and executries, tax planning and financial services. Owner-managed businesses, professional partnerships, agriculture and estates are also particular areas of expertise. A major practice area also exists in conveyancing on behalf of national housebuilders.

RECRUITMENT: The firm is always keen to consider quality candidates. Any application with an appropriate CV should be sent to Steve Kerr (skerr@fyfeireland.com).

FYNN & PARTNERS

70 Richmond Hill, Bournemouth, BH2 6JA
Tel: (01202) 551991 **Fax:** (01202) 295403 **DX:** 7608 Bournemouth
Email: info@fynnpartners.co.uk **Website:** www.fynnpartners.co.uk

Managing Partner	Alan Arnold
Number of partners	6
Assistant solicitors	5
Other fee-earners	11

THE FIRM: Fynn & Partners' national reputation in environmental, licensing and planning law is enhanced by its in-house planning consultancy and advocate teams and supported by a commercial property department with extensive expertise in leisure/licensed and foreign property matters. All aspects of company and commercial (including e-commerce and immigration), employment and private client law work are undertaken.

GABB & CO

32 Monk St, Abergavenny, NP7 5NW **Tel:** (01873) 852 432 **Fax:** (01873) 857 589 **DX:** 43752 Abergavenny **Email:** abergavenny@gabb.co.uk **Website:** www.gabb.co.uk **Contact:** D.J. Vaughan • A long established and high quality practice best known for company/commercial, employment, residential and commercial conveyancing, wills and tax planning.

AREAS OF PRACTICE

Property & Agriculture	35%
Litigation	30%
Private Client & Tax & Probate	25%
Commercial	10%

GADSBY WICKS

91-99 New London Road, Chelmsford, CM2 OPP
Tel: (01245) 494929 **Fax:** (01245) 495347 **DX:** 89707 Chelmsford 2
Email: mail@gadsbywicks.co.uk

Managing Partner	Gillian Gadsby
Senior Partner	Roger Wicks
Number of partners	2
Assistant solicitors	3
Other fee-earners	2

THE FIRM: Gadsby Wicks was founded in 1993 as a specialist practice dealing with clinical negligence and medical products liability litigation on behalf of claimants. The firm now comprises eight lawyers, an in-house medical adviser and a dedicated team of support staff. The firm holds a clinical negligence Legal Aid franchise,

Continued overleaf

is a member of the Legal Aid Board Multi Action panel and has members of both the Law Society Clinical Negligence and AVMA Referral panels. Gadsby Wicks has been at the leading edge of innovation in finding alternative methods of funding litigation and is able to offer affordable litigation to all clients with viable cases.

PRINCIPAL AREAS OF WORK:
Clinical Negligence: The firm is well known for its clinical negligence work obtaining several million pounds in compensation for its clients every year.
Medical Products Liability: The firm has considerable experience and expertise in litigating successful claims on behalf of clients who have been injured by pharmaceutical or other medical products.

AREAS OF PRACTICE	
Medical Negligence	83%
Medical Products Liability	15%
Personal Injury	2%

CONTACTS	
Clinical Negligence	Gillian Gadsby
Medical Products Liability	Roger Wicks

GALLEN & CO
40 Carlton Place, 142 Queen Street, Glasgow, G5 9TW **Tel:** (0141) 420 1441 **Fax:** (0141) 420 8258 **DX:** GW204 **Ptnrs:** 4 **Asst solrs:** 1 **Other fee-earners:** 1

GAMLINS
31-37 Russell Road, Rhyl, LL18 3DB **Tel:** (01745) 343500 **Fax:** (01745) 343616 **DX:** 17352 RHYL **Email:** Gamlins@gamlins.co.uk **Ptnrs:** 11 **Asst solrs:** 16 **Other fee-earners:** 12

G

GAMON ARDEN & CO
Church House, 1 Hanover Street, Liverpool, L1 3DW **Tel:** (0151) 709 2222 **Fax:** (0151) 709 3095 **Ptnrs:** 2 **Other fee-earners:** 2

GARRETTS

2 Arundel Street, London, WC2R 3GA
Tel: (020) 7344 0344 **Fax:** (020) 7438 2518 **DX:** 127 LDE
Website: www.andersenlegal.com/england

1 Victoria Square, Birmingham, B1 1BD
Tel: (0121) 698 9000 **Fax:** (0121) 698 9050 **DX:** 13017 Birmingham

Betjeman House, 104 Hills Road, Cambridge, CB2 1LH
Tel: (01223) 355 977 **Fax:** (01223) 535 327 **DX:** 88010 Cambridge

Bank House, 9 Charlotte Street, Manchester, M1 4EU
Tel: (0161) 228 0707 **Fax:** (0161) 228 1926 **DX:** 14349 Manchester 1

Abbots House, Abbey Street, Reading, RG1 3BD
Tel: (0118) 949 0000 **Fax:** (0118) 949 0049 **DX:** 54711 Reading 2

Senior Partner	Tony Williams
Number of partners	52
Assistant solicitors	125
Other fee-earners	64

CONTACTS	
Banking	Douglas Colliver
Capital Markets	Gilles Thieffry
Collective Investments	Simon Atiyah
Construction	Siobhan McCloskey-Oudahar
Corporate & Commercial	Andrew Smith
Dispute Resolution	Ashley Booker
E-business & New Media	Laurence Kaye
EC & Competition	Phil McDonnell
Employment	Sean Nesbitt
Environment	Susan Guy
Financial Services	James Greig
Hospitality & Leisure	Andrew Little
Immigration	Sean Nesbitt
Information Technology	Mark Crichard
Intellectual Property	Angus Phang
Mergers & Acquisitions	David Roberts
New Media & IT	Laurence Kaye
Pensions	Duncan Buchanan
PFI	Hamid Yunis
Pharmaceuticals/Biotechnology	Gerry Fitzsimons
Planning	Stephen McNaught
Private Client	Judith Powell
Projects	Hamid Yunis
Real Estate	Keith Barnett
Travel	Andrew Smith

THE FIRM: Andersen Legal member firm Garretts is a leading provider of first rate, business-focused legal services to major corporates, financial institutions, governments and agencies, at home and internationally. It is a client-centred law firm with a reputation for leading the field in innovative approaches to meeting clients' needs. With a comprehensive range of commercial legal services, it can add value to virtually any project or transaction, from the simplest to the most complex, from a single country to multiple jurisdictions. It was the first UK law firm to associate with a premier professional services organisation in order to develop first rate, integrated, high added-value commercial solutions to a wide range of business problems and issues. Eight years on, it continues to lead the field through its continuing relationship with Andersen and its considerable investment in new technology and its applications. A typical example is DealSight, its secure, on-line deal-room. Its lawyers have a totally different approach. By working and training with their colleagues at Andersen, they develop a broad commercial perspective which helps them to have a greater awareness of the business issues specific to the client and the sector, and to help the client find the creative solutions it needs.

PRINCIPAL AREAS OF WORK: Legal services include mergers and acquisitions; banking and financial services; e-business, intellectual property and information technology; competition and trade; litigation and arbitration; real estate and labour law. Garretts specialises in a number of industry sectors including: health-care, pharmaceuticals and biotechnology; hospitality, leisure and travel; technology, media and communications; financial services.

GARSTANGS

115A Chancery Lane, London, WC2A 1PP
Tel: (020) 7242 4324 **Fax:** (020) 7242 4329 **DX:** 496 LDE Chancery Lane
Email: rcornthwaite@garstangs.co.uk **Website:** www.garstangs.co.uk

Number of partners	4
Assistant solicitors	7
Other fee-earners	9

AREAS OF PRACTICE	
Criminal/Civil Litigation	60%
Criminal General	30%
Company/Commercial	10%

THE FIRM: A leading radical specialist practice in the fields of white-collar crime, extradition, restraint proceedings and ancillary civil and public litigation. The firm was established in 1989 and specialises in criminal law. The London office was opened in 1990.

PRINCIPAL AREAS OF WORK:
Criminal Litigation: White-collar crime, including major SFO, HM Customs and Excise and Inland Revenue prosecutions; money laundering, restraint proceedings and asset tracing investigations. The firm also handles general crime from both offices.
Other Areas: The Greater Manchester office is more broadly based with specialist property/commercial acquisitions and family departments.

INTERNATIONAL: The firm handles work in French, German, Greek, Italian and Spanish (Castilian and Catalan).

CONTACTS

Criminal Litigation	Richard Cornthwaite
General Crime (London)	Roger Ingram
General Crime (Bolton)	Michael Garstang
Probate/Private Client	Martin Ryan
Family	Rhona Jackson
Fraud Litigation	Richard Cornthwaite
Conveyancing	Nicholas Horsfall
Company/Commercial	Nicholas Horsfall

GATELEY WAREING

Windsor House, 3 Temple Row, Birmingham, B2 5JR
Tel: (0121) 234 0000 **Fax:** (0121) 234 0001 **DX:** 13033 B'ham 1
Email: gw@gateleywareing.com **Website:** www.gateleywareing.com

Knightsbridge House, Lower Brown Street, Leicester, LE1 5NL
Tel: (0116) 285 9000 **Fax:** (0116) 285 9001 **DX:** 10829 Leicester 1

14 Regent Street, Nottingham, NG1 5BQ
Tel: (0115) 983 8200 **Fax:** (0115) 983 8201 **DX:** 15491 Nottingham 2

Senior Partner	Michael Ward
Number of partners	15
Assistant solicitors	53
Other fee-earners	19

AREAS OF PRACTICE

Corporate Services	35%
Banking & Recoveries	23%
Construction	16%
Commercial Property	12%
Dispute Resolution	7%
Private Client	4%
Others	3%

CONTACTS

Asset Finance	Philip Jones
Banking	Andrew Madden
	Brendan McGeever
Commercial	Andrew Evans
Commercial Property	John Beckett
	Craig Mitchell
Construction	Peter Davies
Corporate Services	Michael Ward
Dispute Resolution	Stephen Goodrham
Employment	Ruth Armstrong
Housing Associations	Neil Handel
Private Client	Jonathan Howard
Recoveries	Brendan McGeever

THE FIRM: With offices in Birmingham, Leicester and Nottingham, Gateley Wareing is the Midlands leading independent firm of solicitors specialising in owner-led businesses. The firm is keen to remain a medium sized practice and offers its extensive client base partner-led commercial advice on the legal issues that face businesses today. With a strong reputation for an innovative and practical approach, the firm has an impressive client list from sole traders, partnerships and family ventures to corporate groups, fully quoted public companies and financial institutions. Although much of the client base is located in the Midlands, increasingly Gateley Wareing is gaining a reputation for working with national and international companies.

PRINCIPAL AREAS OF WORK: Although the company does undertake private client work, its main areas of expertise are in:
Corporate Services: Gateley Wareing has developed a particular reputation for its MBO work, whether acting for management, vendors, equity or senior debt providers.
Banking & Recoveries: This department has an emphasis on realisations for financial institutions of all kinds and a growing asset finance practice.
Commercial Property: This growing department acts for a number of property developers across the UK and has an expertise in housing association law.
Construction: The firm has one of the most highly regarded construction departments in the country.
Dispute Resolution: The firm acts for a wide range of organisations engaged in contentious and non-contentious work.
Employment: The employment department continues to go from strength to strength, providing hands on support for the HR needs of all sizes of businesses in this fast changing area of law.
Commercial: Gateley Wareing provides commercial support to the contractual needs of owner-led businesses, with a particular emphasis on e-commerce and intellectual property.
Private Client: Gateley Wareing is one of the few commercial firms operating in the Midlands to provide advice in relation to capital taxes and estate planning.

GCL SOLICITORS

Connaught House, Alexandra Terrace, Guildford, GU1 3DA **Tel:** (01483) 577091 **Fax:** (01483) 579252 **DX:** 141450 Guildford 12 **Email:** partners@gcl-solicitors.co.uk **Website:** www.gcl-solicitors.co.uk **Ptnrs:** 4 **Other fee-earners:** 7

GEORGE DAVIES

Fountain Court, 68 Fountain Street, Manchester, M2 2FB
Tel: (0161) 236 8992 **Fax:** (0161) 228 0030 **DX:** 14316 Manchester 1
Email: mail@georgedavies.co.uk **Website:** www.georgedavies.co.uk

Managing & Senior Partner	John Hewison
Number of partners	15
Assistant solicitors	25
Other fee-earners	9

CONTACTS

Healthcare	Claire Batchelor
Insolvency	Mark Hovell
Sports	John Hewison

THE FIRM: Historically a general practice, the firm has in recent years developed noted specialisms in healthcare, sports and insolvency law. It acts for NHS trusts and health authorities throughout the region and is on the NHSLA panel. In the field of sports law, it has acted for the Professional Footballers' Association for over 40 years. A qualified insolvency practitioner heads the firm's growing insolvency department. A member of LawNet, it was the first large law firm in Manchester to become an Investor in People, and has gained ISO 9002 reflecting its commitment to quality standards.

GEORGE GREEN

195 High St, Cradley Heath, West Midlands, B64 5HW
Tel: (01384) 410 410 **Fax:** (01384) 634 237 **DX:** 20752 Cradley Heath
Email: gg@georgegreen.co.uk **Website:** www.georgegreen.co.uk

Old Bank Chambers, 1 Summer Hill, Halesowen, West Midlands, B63 3BU
Tel: (01384) 410 410 **Fax:** (0121) 585 5455 **DX:** 14523 Halesowen
Email: gg@georgegreen.co.uk

Senior Partner	Richard Cliff
Number of partners	13
Assistant solicitors	6
Other fee-earners	12

CONTACTS

Company/Commercial ....Richard Cliff
Commercial Litigation ....Neil Cutler
Commercial Property ....Cheryl Leyser
Private Client ....Neill Robb

THE FIRM: Established in 1897 and based in the heart of the Black Country, George Green is acknowledged to provide the business community with a real cost effective alternative to City firms, whilst retaining its commitment to the provision of legal advice to its private clientele. Its strong reputation has attracted work from well beyond its Black Country base.

PRINCIPAL AREAS OF WORK:

Company/Commercial: Work includes start-ups, acquisition and mergers, reconstructions, corporate finance, MBOs, flotations, partnerships, commercial agreements, joint ventures and taxation.
Commercial Litigation: Work includes contract disputes, debt collection, employment, intellectual property, building disputes, landlord and tenant, planning disputes, insolvency, defamation, European law and emergency injunctions and claims litigation. The work involves both High Court and County Court actions, in addition to arbitrations and industrial tribunal hearings.
Property Development/Planning: The department undertakes and advises on acquisitions and disposals of land and buildings, leasing, building and development contracts, taxation, property finance, commercial/residential estate development and planning.
Private Client: Work includes wills, probate, estate planning, trusts, charities, pensions, matrimonial law, residential conveyancing and personal taxation.

GEORGE IDE, PHILLIPS

Lion House, 79 St Pancras, Chichester, PO19 4NL
Tel: (01243) 786668 **Fax:** (01243) 831300 **DX:** 30306 Chichester
Email: maildesk@chi.georgeide.co.uk **Website:** www.georgeide.chi.co.uk

52 North Street, Chichester, PO19 1NQ
Tel: (01243) 786668 **Fax:** (01243) 831000 **DX:** 30306 Chichester
Email: maildesk@chi.georgeide.co.uk

Belmont Lodge, Belmont Street, Bognor Regis, PO21 1LE
Tel: (01243) 829231 **Fax:** (01243) 825553 **DX:** 31204 Bognor Regis
Email: maildesk@bognor.georgeide.co.uk

Senior Partner	Jeffrey Hopkins
Number of partners	11
Assistant solicitors	9
Other fee-earners	16

AREAS OF PRACTICE

Personal Injury/Clinical Negligence 50%
Private Client 30%
Other Litigation 20%

CONTACTS

Clinical Negligence ....Julian Bobak
....Philip Lea
Commercial Property.............Jeffrey Hopkins
Commercial/Company ....Robert Enticott
Crime ....Ian Mellor
Employment........................Dorlee Monschau
Family/Children ....Fraser Poole
Mediation ....Renella Squires
Mental Health................................Ian Oliver
Personal Injury.........................Anthony Goff
Trust & Probate ....Ursula Watt
Civil Actions Against Police ....Ian Oliver

THE FIRM: George Ide, Phillips has become one of the leading firms in this part of the South East. With its niche areas of practice and broader specialities, the firm is well placed to serve both its business and private clientele. Each office has Lexcel accreditation.

PRINCIPAL AREAS OF WORK:

Personal Injury: This department concentrates on claimant work and the firm represents many of the major legal costs insurers. The firm was a founder member of MASS (Motor Accident Solicitors Society). Much of the personal injury work is of a high value and profile. The firm has a specialist head injury department and an association with the charity Headway. Members of the department are on the Law Society's Personal Injury panel and one is a fellow of the College of Personal Injury Lawyers.
Clinical Negligence: One of the team is a member of Scope and specialises in cerebral palsy cases. Law Society and AVMA referral panellists.
Other Litigation: The firm has specialists dealing with landlord and tenant, clinical negligence and other mental health work, crime, building disputes, professional negligence, employment and civil actions against the police.
Commercial Property: The firm has a substantial commercial property department with an established reputation and expertise in the range of commercial property issues and acts for a large national property company.
Business Services: Flexible teams support business clients through advice on commercial activities of all types and related areas of finance and employment.
Family/Children: A strong team with members of SFLA and Law Society Family and Children panels.
Investment: In-house investment advice is available and the firm is authorised to conduct discrete investment business.
Public Funding Franchises: The firm holds current franchises and contracts in housing, clinical negligence, employment, mental health, family and personal injury and civil actions against the police.

GEORGE MATHERS & CO

23 Adelphi, Aberdeen, AB1 2BL **Tel:** (01224) 588599 **Fax:** (01224) 584147 **Ptnrs:** 3 **Asst solrs:** 12 **Other fee-earners:** 2

GEPP & SONS

58 New London Rd, Chelmsford, CM2 0PA **Tel:** (01245) 493939 **Fax:** (01245) 493940 **DX:** 3306 Chelmsford **Email:** mail@gepp.co.uk
Ptnrs: 11 **Asst solrs:** 8 **Other fee-earners:** 16

GHERSON & CO

1 Great Cumberland Place, London, W1H 7AL
Tel: (020) 7724 4488 **Fax:** (020) 7724 4888
Email: gherson@macline.co.uk **Website:** www.gherson.com

Senior Partner	Roger Gherson
Number of partners	1
Assistant solicitors	3
Other fee-earners	3

AREAS OF PRACTICE

UK Immigration/Nationality Law/ EU Freedom of Movement 98%

CONTACTS

Immigration & Nationality ....Roger Gherson

THE FIRM: Established in 1988 and now in its 13th year, Gherson & Co is one of the few specialist practices providing in-depth advice on UK immigration law, British nationality law and European Union freedom of movement of persons. The senior partner is a well-known solicitor with many years' experience in the field of immigration law. The firm is committed to solving the most challenging problems.

PRINCIPAL AREAS OF WORK: The firm has particular expertise in employment and work permits for a wide range of employers, banks, financial institutions, software houses, film production companies, sports clubs and other business related immigration (including executive relocation, and the admission of entrepreneurs, investors, innovators, sole representatives, writers, artists and composers). In addition to a strong corporate caseload, the firm also deals with EU associate nationals; EU related immigration issues; an increasing number of cases under the same sex concession; the acquisition of settlement and citizenship; complex nationality issues; family reunion; students and other temporary categories; appeals to adjudicators and the Immigration Tribunal against the refusal of entry clearance, further leave to remain, threatened deportation, etc; judicial review to the High Court.

CLIENTELE: The firm has a wide corporate and private client base including other firms of solicitors.

INTERNATIONAL: Gherson & Co has extensive links overseas, particularly in China (including Hong Kong), FSU, South Africa and the USA. The firm has an associate office in Hong Kong.

GIBSON, DUNN & CRUTCHER LLP

2-4 Temple Avenue, London, EC4Y 0HB
Tel: (020) 7071 4000 **Fax:** (020) 7071 4244 **DX:** 217 London/Chancery Lane
Email: initialsurname@gibsondunn.com **Website:** www.gibsondunn.com

Managing Partner	Wesley G Howell, Jr
Chair of European Operations	Bernard Grinspan
Number of partners	9
Assistant solicitors	15
Other fee-earners	4

AREAS OF PRACTICE

Corporate 60%
Finance 20%
Real Estate 10%
Taxation 10%

CONTACTS

Corporate ....Paul Harter
....................Judith Shepherd
Finance ....Stephen Ball
Project Finance ....Andrew Thomas
Real Estate ....Alan Samson
Taxation ....Anthony Bonanno
....................Nicholas Aleksander

THE FIRM: Gibson, Dunn & Crutcher is one of the leading law firms in the world, with over 700 lawyers in 11 major cities across the US and in Europe. The firm is known for its commitment to providing the highest quality legal services in a personal, responsive manner and is a recognised leader in representing companies from start-up ventures to multinational corporations in industries ranging from high technology to financial services. The firm's offices are operated on an integrated basis so that clients may draw on the depth, expertise and resources provided by its multi-office structure. This ensures that specialists with expertise in appropriate legal disciplines are used, regardless of location. The London office, founded more than 20 years ago, has expanded significantly in the last 12 months as the result of a strategic decision to bring on board English lawyers to enhance the firm's ability to provide high quality legal services to clients with national and international interests. In London, US and English lawyers work together to meet the complex international needs of the firm's clients.

PRINCIPAL AREAS OF WORK: The firm provides the following services in the UK:
Corporate: Top-level UK and multijurisdictional mergers, acquisitions and joint ventures; international public offerings involving single or multiple listings on European and US stock exchanges; public and private takeovers; international and private equity offerings; corporate restructuring; management buyouts; strategic alliances.
Finance: Advice to investors and borrowers on a wide range of financial transactions including acquisition finance, debt finance, project finance, property finance, public bond offerings and private debt placement in the global markets.
Real Estate: The firm advises on property transactions on behalf of financial institutions, investors, developers, retailers and others including joint ventures, development agreements, site acquisition, planning procedures, building contracts and commercial leases.
Taxation: The firm offers a full range of tax services to corporates, partnerships, financial institutions, foreign entities and others, as well as tax effective structuring on national and international transactions.

INTERNATIONAL: The firm has other offices in Century City, Dallas, Denver, Los Angeles, New York, Orange County, Palo Alto, Paris, San Francisco and Washington DC.

GIBSON, DUNN & CRUTCHER

GILFEDDER & MCINNES

34 Leith Walk, Edinburgh, EH6 5AA **Tel:** (0131) 553 4333 **Fax:** (0131) 555 3712 **Ptnrs:** 7 **Asst solrs:** 5 **Other fee-earners:** 1

GILL AKASTER

25 Lockyer Street, Plymouth, PL1 2QW **Tel:** (01752) 203500 **Fax:** (01752) 203503 **DX:** 8284 Plymouth 2 **Email:** rhm@gillakaster.co.uk **Contact:** Malcolm Pillar • Particular knowledge of commercial and property, employment and members of the Children and Mental Health panel with an SLFA mediator. Also offices at Scott Lodge, Milehouse, Plymouth.

AREAS OF PRACTICE	
Commercial & Property	27%
Residential Property	25%
Matrimonial & Family	20%
Civil Litigation	15%
Probate/Trusts/Tax	13%

GILL & CO

37 Grays Inn Road, London, WC1X 8PP **Tel:** 020 7242 0404 **Fax:** 020 7831 8537 **DX:** 35747 BLOOMSBURY 1 **Email:** gillandco@easynet.co.uk **Ptnrs:** 2 **Asst solrs:** 3 **Other fee-earners:** 2

G

GILLESPIE MACANDREW WS

31 Melville Street, Edinburgh, EH3 7JQ
Tel: (0131) 225 1677 **Fax:** (0131) 225 4519 **DX:** ED 113 Edinburgh-1
Email: mail@gillespiemacandrew.co.uk **Website:** www.gillespiemacandrew.co.uk

Managing Partner	Ian Turnbull
Senior Office Manager	David Macfarlane
Number of partners	9
Assistant solicitors	9
Other fee-earners	18

AREAS OF PRACTICE	
Corporate/Commercial	30%
Private Client Tax & Trust	30%
Property (Commercial & Rural)	20%
Investment Management	20%

CONTACTS	
Agriculture/Estates	Simon Leslie
Charities	Thomas Murray
Commercial Property	Neil Wilson
Corporate/Commercial	Derek McCulloch
Corporate/Small Business	Christopher Smith
Employment	Ian Turnbull
Energy (Electricity)	Derek McCulloch
Executry/Probate	John McArthur
Investment/Fund Management	Charles Fotheringham
Litigation	Ian Turnbull
Residential Property	Michael Grey
Tax & Trust	Simon Leslie

THE FIRM: Gillespie Macandrew, with roots established for more than 300 years, has developed leading specialist disciplines for private and business clients and emphasis on high level partner/associate contact. Gillespie Macandrew's private client department is a leader in offering a fully integrated investment management, tax and financial planning service. The commercial department represents Scottish and European interests of both multinational companies and investors abroad. The firm's activities now also focus on charities, professional partnerships, farmers, and the developing SME business sectors of Scotland.

PRINCIPAL AREAS OF WORK:
Agriculture & Farming: This core specialist practice advises on partnerships, contract farming, crofting, landlord/tenant relations, quotas, mineral rights, fish farming and sporting estates. The firm is provider of NFU Scotland legal Helpline.
Charities: Charities are a specialist focus of management and advice from the combined corporate, tax and investment teams. Clients include leading animal, disability, ex-service, arts and rural/environmental charities.
Corporate Client: Company formation, acquisition and business support services include specific areas in technology, agribusiness, employment, and equity finance. Partners are experienced in providing general counsel to companies and assisting with negotiations. The firm supports Edinburgh Business Development with free consultancy for start-up and developing businesses and also Edinburgh International Trade.
Commercial Property/Lending Finance: The firm is experienced in investment, leasing and development of property including leisure, brownfield, agribusiness, licensed property, construction, and planning and environmental law.
Energy & Electricity: Energy and electricity is an area of specialist expertise and Gillespie Macandrew advises generators, industrial users and hydro/windpower SRO and NFFO projects.
Litigation & Employment Law: Contentious and non-contentious cases are handled with specialist expertise in construction, employment, commercial and rural property, trust and family law disputes. The firm operates a debt recovery service.
Private Client/Tax Trust & Financial Planning: This team of over 20 fee-earners combines tax, trust and financial planning advice with discretionary and advisory fund management and an execution-only dealing service.
Investment: The investment department has six professionals from a wide range of investment disciplines with average experience of over 20 years each; and is an active participant in the Law Society of Scotland, ASIM and SIFA.
Residential Property: The department maintains a full range of estate agency, conveyancing, relocation and letting services.

INTERNATIONAL: The firm is the Scottish member of Lexwork International in Europe and maintains additional USA, Asian and other international contacts for both corporate and private client transactions.

GILLS

Equity Chambers, 5 Hortus Road, Southall, UB2 4AJ **Tel:** (020) 8893 6869 **Fax:** (020) 8893 6396 **DX:** 52256 Southall 2 **Email:** jgill@gills-solicitors.co.uk **Website:** www.gills-solicitors.co.uk **Ptnrs:** 2 **Other fee-earners:** 2 **Contact:** Jaswinder Gill • Specialises in education law.

AREAS OF PRACTICE	
Education	55%
General Civil Litigation	45%

GIRLINGS

Crown Chambers, Broad Street, Margate, CT9 1BN **Tel:** (01843) 220 274 **Fax:** (01843) 297 828 **Email:** Andrewwatson@Girlings.com **Website:** www.girlings.com **Ptnrs:** 26 **Asst solrs:** 3 **Other fee-earners:** 30

GLAISYERS

10 Rowchester Court, Printing House St, Birmingham, B4 6DZ
Tel: (0121) 233 2971 **Fax:** (0121) 236 1534 **DX:** 24933 Birmingham 4
Email: advice@glaisyers.co.uk **Website:** www.glaisyers.co.uk

Managing Partner	John Loveday
Senior Partner	Charles Royle
Number of partners	11
Assistant solicitors	11
Other fee-earners	17

THE FIRM: The firm specialises in services for the individual in the areas of crime, family law, personal injury, civil litigation and private client matters. Members of a variety of Law Society panels including PI, childcare and family law, expert solicitors offer a broad range of services to clients. Also members of the Serious Fraud Panel and accredited by the Legal Services Commission to act in High Cost Criminal Cases. Close to all courts, all types of agency work undertaken.

GLAZER DELMAR

223-229 Rye Lane, Peckham, London, SE15 4TZ **Tel:** (020) 7639 8801 **Fax:** (020) 7358 0581 **DX:** 34258 Peckham **Ptnrs:** 4 **Asst solrs:** 7 **Other fee-earners:** 5

GLENISTERS

Television House, 269 Field End Road, Eastcote, Ruislip, HA4 9LS
Tel: (020) 8868 4343 **Fax:** (020) 8429 3606 **DX:** 35150 Eastcote
Email: sols@glenisters.com **Website:** www.glenisters.com

7 King Street Cloisters, Clifton Walk, King Street, London, W6 0GY
Tel: (020) 8453 7790

Managing Partner	Robert Moseley
Senior Partner	Michael O'Brien
Number of partners	3
Assistant solicitors	4
Other fee-earners	12

AREAS OF PRACTICE

Litigation & Family	30%
Property	30%
Banking & Finance	25%
Private Client	15%

CONTACTS

Banking & Finance	Doreen Jones
Litigation & Family Law	Mark Faith
Private Client	Michael O'Brien
Property	Robert Moseley

THE FIRM: Established in 1906, Glenisters aims to provide innovative solutions to many of the problems which face its commercial, corporate, institutional and individual clients.

PRINCIPAL AREAS OF WORK:

Banking & finance: A dedicated banking and finance unit responds quickly to the needs of the firm's lending clients in the areas of mortgage arrears recovery, repossession sales, shortfall recoveries and professional indemnity recovery.

Corporate Services: Work includes commercial litigation, company and partnership, and advice on all employment matters.

Family Law: Advice on divorce and separations, financial matters and children. The firm also provides a mediation service.

Personal Injury: A committed claimant personal injury unit.

Property: Commercial and residential conveyancing, advice on planning matters and landlord and tenant.

Private Client: Work includes wills and probate, administration of estates, trusts and settlements, tax and financial services.

GLOVERS

115 Park Street, London, W1Y 4DY
Tel: (020) 7629 5121 **Fax:** (020) 7491 0930 **DX:** 44438 Marble Arch
Email: central@glovers.co.uk **Website:** www.glovers.co.uk

Senior Partner	Tony Bourne
Number of partners	8
Assistant solicitors	10
Other fee-earners	5

CONTACTS

Banking	Catherine Cava
Commercial Litigation	Tony Bourne
Commercial Property	John Barber
Company/Commercial	John Barber
Construction	David Miles
Employment	Peter Pitt
Professional Negligence	Edward Vaughan

PRINCIPAL AREAS OF WORK: Glovers is an established firm which specialises in the following principal areas:

Commercial Property: The firm has an acknowledged reputation in commercial property, development and in commercial landlord and tenant matters. Work includes development agreements, acting for major retailers, developers, maufacturers and investors, planning negotiations, selling and leasing of commercial developments, rent reviews and all other aspects of landlord and tenant law.

Company/Commercial: Work includes company formations, purchases and sales, joint ventures, general commercial agreements and the drafting of conditions of sale.

Banking & Finance: The firm acts for a number of UK and overseas banks on a wide variety of banking matters, including secured lending and the restructuring of loans and charges.

Commercial Litigation: The department is proactive in its approach to litigation, but does not ignore the value of forceful and structured negotiations in the litigation process. Work includes landlord and tenant and other property matters, commercial disputes, banking cases, insolvency and white collar fraud. Glovers is one of the four original firms reponsible for implementation of ADR in this country and has its own ADR unit.

Construction: The firm acts for one of the UK's leading construction companies and has wide experience in advising on construction contracts, collateral warranties and complex building disputes.

Continued overleaf

Employment: The firm covers all areas of employment law, both contentious and non-contentious, discrimination, transfer of undertakings and compromise agreements.
Professional Negligence: The firm handles claims involving various kinds of professionals, in particular, accountants, architects, engineers, lawyers, surveyors and valuers.

GOLDKORN MATHIAS

6 Coptic Street, Bloomsbury, London, WC1A 1NW
Tel: (020) 7631 1811 **Fax:** (020) 7631 0431 **DX:** 35705 Bloomsbury
Email: gmlaw@btinternet.com

Managing Partner	Roy Mathias
Number of partners	4
Other fee-earners	4

AREAS OF PRACTICE

Litigation	30%
Criminal Work	30%
Conveyancing	15%
Probate	15%
Commercial	10%

CONTACTS

Litigation	Geoffrey Goldkorn
Commercial	Roy Mathias
Crime	Philip Smith
Probate/Conveyancing	David Barchan

THE FIRM: Established in 1979 and reconstituted in its present form in March 2000. The Bloomsbury office is a niche practice specialising in civil litigation, commercial work and probate. The associated office at Camberwell practising under the name Goldkorns is an exclusively criminal practice.

PRINCIPAL AREAS OF WORK:
Civil Litigation: The partners are very experienced litigators, including a Deputy District Judge and solicitor with rights of audience in the High Court. The firm offers a comprehensive litigation service including in-house advocacy in the County Court, the High Court and the Court of Appeal. The firm has an acknowledged reputation for handling complex legal disputes and for assimilating cases involving large volumes of documents. The firm has particular experience in a variety of commercial disputes, litigious probate, breach of trust, copyright, designright and passing off disputes, professional negligence (lawyers and accountants) and civil actions against the police. Agency work is regularly undertaken.
Crime: The Camberwell office is a well run very substantial criminal practice with a Legal Aid franchise in crime and is one of the firms on the Serious Fraud panel. The workload dealt with each year is very high – in excess of 1,000 individual cases.
Property: Work includes commercial and residential conveyancing; landlord and tenant cases.
Probate: Departmental work involves drafting wills and estate planning as well as winding-up estates.
Commercial: Work includes employment contracts, partnerships, sports agreements.

G

GOLDS

8 Newton Terrace, Glasgow, G3 7PJ **Tel:** (0141) 300 4300 **Fax:** (0141) 300 4350 **DX:** GW40 **Email:** golds@golds.co.uk
Website: www.golds.co.uk **Ptnrs:** 11 **Asst solrs:** 19 **Other fee-earners:** 31

GOODMAN DERRICK

90 Fetter Lane, London, EC4A 1PT
Tel: (020) 7404 0606 **Fax:** (020) 7831 6407 **DX:** 122
Email: law@goodmanderrick.co.uk **Website:** www.goodmanderrick.co.uk

Managing Partner	Patrick Swaffer
Senior Partner	John Roberts
Number of partners	20
Assistant solicitors	9
Other fee-earners	8

AREAS OF PRACTICE

Corporate	31%
Media	24%
Commercial Litigation	18%
Property	15%
Employment	8%
Charities/Private Client	4%

CONTACTS

Charities/Private Client	Diana Rawstron
Commercial Litigation	Annabel Crumley
	Tim Langton
Company Commercial	David Edwards
Construction	Susan White
Corporate	John Roberts
Defamation	Patrick Swaffer
Employment	Noel Deans
Film	Keith Northrop
Insurance	Tim Langton
Media	Paul Herbert
	Patrick Swaffer
Property	Gregor Hamlen
	Michael Collins
Publishing	Nicholas Armstrong
Tax	Ian Montrose

THE FIRM: Goodman Derrick is a medium-sized City practice, founded in 1954 by Lord Goodman. It has a broad commercial practice focusing on commercial and corporate finance, property and litigation work with an excellent reputation for media work in television, publishing and related industries.

PRINCIPAL AREAS OF WORK: The main groups for Goodman Derrick are media, corporate, property, litigation, tax, employment, private client and charities.
Media: This department advises both corporate and individual clients on the whole range of contentious and non-contentious matters in the fields of broadcasting, television, film and publishing, as well as other areas of the media and arts. These include film and television production and financing, cable and satellite, distribution, digital broadcasting, book and magazine publishing, sponsorship and licensing agreements. Notable experience has been developed in defamation and in other clearance advice relating to broadcast material, newspaper and magazine articles and book manuscripts.
Property: Work includes all aspects of commercial property transactions, especially work for retail companies, investors, property development, funding, leases, planning and agricultural holdings. In addition, the firm handles some high-quality residential work.
Commercial Litigation: Work includes a broad range of commercial disputes, property litigation, professional negligence, insolvency, insurance, fraud, intellectual property, property litigation and debt recovery.
Corporate: Work includes mergers and acquisitions, flotations, banking and finance, joint ventures, business start-ups, shareholders' agreements, management buy-outs rights issues, share offers, mergers and reorganisations, commercial agreements, European law, intellectual property and IT law.
Private Clients/Charities: Work includes establishment and drafting, tax and financial planning, wills and estates, probate, and trusts.
Employment: This department offers the whole range of contentious and non-contentious advice and specialist advice to the recruitment industry.

CLIENTELE: Goodman Derrick has an impressive client list acting for many public figures, public and private companies, charities, large retail chains, property companies and developers, television companies, broadcasters and independent producers, publishers and newspapers, and trade associations.

GOODMANDERRICK

RECRUITMENT: Applications by letter and CV to Mr Nicholas Armstrong, Recruitment Partner.

GOODMAN RAY

450 Kingsland Road, Dalston, London, E8 4AE **Tel:** (020) 7254 8855 **Fax:** (020) 7923 4345 **DX:** 46807 Dalston **Email:** mail@goodmanray.com **Ptnrs:** 3 **Asst solrs:** 4 **Other fee-earners:** 2 **Contact:** Peggy Ray • Specialist family law. Strong reputation for child-related work. All partners are members of the Law Society Children Panel. Legal Aid franchise.

AREAS OF PRACTICE	
Family	100%

GORDON & SMYTH

Sovereign Centre, 153 Queen Street, Glasgow, G2 3BP **Tel:** (0141) 275 4875 **Fax:** (0141) 275 4800 **DX:** GW33 **Ptnrs:** 1 **Asst solrs:** 1

G

GORDON DADDS

80 Brook Street, Mayfair, London, W1K 5DD
Tel: (020) 7493 6151 **Fax:** (020) 7491 1065 **DX:** 131 Chancery Lane
Email: info@gordondadds.com **Website:** www.gordondadds.com

Senior Partner	Roger Peters
Managing Partner	David Goff
Number of partners	15
Assistant solicitors	11
Other fee-earners	8

AREAS OF PRACTICE	
Family	45%
Company & Commercial	15%
Litigation	15%
Private Client	15%
Property	10%

CONTACTS	
Company & Commercial	Michael Jepson
Family	Sue Bland
Litigation	Hugh Elder
Private Client	Roger Peters
Property	David Goff

GORDON DADDS
SOLICITORS

THE FIRM: Gordon Dadds provides a broad range of services for private and corporate clients. Founded in 1921, the firm has always been pre-eminent in the field of family and private client work. Merging with the City litigation and commercial firm Camillins in August 2001 has reinforced specialist skills in company and commercial law, property, litigation, media and privatised utilities. The merger has also strengthened contacts with law firms worldwide.

PRINCIPAL AREAS OF WORK:

Company & Commercial: This department handles a range of substantial corporate transactions, including national and international corporate tax planning, company acquisitions and sales in a broad range of business sectors, MBOs and corporate reorganisations. The firm advises on the full range of employment, pensions, intellectual property, environmental and regulatory matters, banking and commercial contracts, and has particular expertise in the utilities sector.

Family Law: Combining determination with sensitivity, the family law team deals with complex financial cases, frequently with international elements, as well as all matters in relation to children, divorce, separation agreements and pre-nuptial contracts. Emergency procedures, injunction proceedings and problems arising from cohabitation are also specialist areas.

Litigation & Dispute Resolution: The litigation department handles a wide range of litigation, including high profile cases, for commercial and private clients. The firm's expertise covers media, employment, breach of contract, commercial fraud, directors' disqualification, copyright and intellectual property, insolvency and asset recovery, defamation, health and safety, IT, inheritance disputes, insolvency, professional negligence, property (including landlord and tenant), road traffic (civil and criminal) and shareholder and partnership disputes. Where appropriate, disputes are resolved by arbitration and ADR techniques. Two members of the firm are accredited mediators.

Private Client & Property: Advice is given in the fields of tax and estate planning and administration, with particular regard to overall personal considerations as well as to strictly legal matters. Assignments include administration of estates and post death tax planning, advice on tax returns, drawing up and executing wills and financial management. The firm has a well established and growing charity law practice.

INTERNATIONAL: Languages spoken include French, Greek and Italian.

RECRUITMENT: The firm recruits two high calibre graduates a year as trainee solicitors. Applications should be received by July, two years before training commences. Please address applications to Miss Sue Bland.

GORDONS CRANSWICK SOLICITORS

14 Piccadilly, Bradford, BD1 3LX **Tel:** (01274) 202202 **Fax:** (01274) 202100 **DX:** 11716 Bradford **Email:** mail@gordonscranswick.co.uk **Website:** www.gordonscranwick.co.uk **Ptnrs:** 31 **Asst solrs:** 18 **Other fee-earners:** 21

GORNA & CO

Virginia House, Cheapside, King St, Manchester, M2 4NB **Tel:** (0161) 832 3651 **Fax:** (0161) 834 8572 **DX:** 14339 **Ptnrs:** 7 **Asst solrs:** 6 **Other fee-earners:** 4

GORVIN SMITH FORT

6-14 Millgate, Stockport, SK1 2NN
Tel: (0161) 930 5151 **Fax:** (0161) 930 5252 **DX:** 719421 Stockport 7
Email: enquiries@gorvin.co.uk **Website:** www.gorvin.co.uk

Managing Partner	Andrew Callaghan
Senior Partner	George Marriott
Number of partners	12
Assistant solicitors	18
Other fee-earners	23

AREAS OF PRACTICE

Company/Commercial	28%
Commercial Property	17%
Commercial Litigation	17%
Residential Conveyancing & Estate Planning	12%
Accident/Personal Injury	12%
Employment	5%
Professional Negligence	5%
Family/Matrimonial	4%

CONTACTS

Accident/Personal Injury	Duncan Manners
Commercial Property	Ian Fletcher
	Lorraine Lockie
	Neil Sutcliffe
Company/Commercial	Tim Dennis
	Paul Lupton
Employment	Nigel Crebin
	Lee Jefcott
Estate Planning	Andrew Cusworth
Family/Matrimonial	Matthew Lord
Litigation	Iain Campbell
	Paul Humphreys
Professional Negligence	George Marriott
Residential Conveyancing	Andrew Callaghan

THE FIRM: Gorvin Smith Fort is one of the largest practices in South Manchester, specialising in corporate and private client work. The firm acts for a wide variety of clients, from large companies to small business, partnerships and individuals. A major investment has been made in technology to maximise communication and efficiency. The firm has a programme of expansion and over the past year has opened dedicated professional negligence and corporate recovery departments. A strong commitment is made to recruiting high-calibre lawyers and other staff, as well as providing appropriate training for those already with the firm. The high level of dedication to staff development was recently recognised by the Investors in People award. The firm runs a popular series of seminars, and is actively involved in community life. Gorvin Smith Fort is willing to act as agent on behalf of other solicitors in litigation and family matters.

PRINCIPAL AREAS OF WORK:
Company & Commercial: The Company and Commercial Department's expertise covers all aspects of business disposals, acquisitions and reconstruction; IT and other intellectual property protection; EU restrictive trade practices and commercial contract, health and safety; agency distribution and franchise agreements; partnerships; pensions, share options and shareholder agreements, and venture capital funding. Commercial and industrial retail property; building construction contracts and site developments; joint venture agreements, finance, funding and security documentation; landlord and tenant issues, including leases, lease renewals, sales or lease backs and options are all dealt with by the firm's specialist Commercial Property Department.
Commercial Litigation: The Commercial Litigation Department deals with contractual and commercial disputes, shareholder disputes and minority shareholder protection; partnership disputes and dissolutions, landlord and tenant and other property disputes; emergency order applications, licensing, unfair competition and intellectual property disputes. Specialist Higher Education and Healthcare units also fall under the remit of the department. The departmental head, Iain Campbell, is an ADR Group accredited mediator.
Employment: The Employment Department undertakes work for employers, covering such areas as drafting contracts of employment, service agreements, business transfers; recruitment and unfair dismissal/wrongful dismissal/discrimination actions; advice on compromise agreements; tribunal and court work. Areas of work undertaken on behalf of employees includes unfair dismissal and wrongful dismissal claims; deduction from wages claims; discrimination claims over race, sexuality, gender, disability or age; executive severance; tribunal representation, and health and safety issues.
Corporate Recovery: Credit control, insolvency and debt collection are dealt with by the recently formed Corporate Recovery Unit.

GOSSCHALKS
Queens Gardens, Hull, HU1 3DZ **Tel:** (01482) 324 252 **Fax:** (01482) 590 290 **DX:** 11902 Hull 1 **Email:** info@gosschalks.co.uk
Website: www.gosschalks.co.uk **Ptnrs:** 26 **Asst solrs:** 20 **Other fee-earners:** 24

GOTELEE & GOLDSMITH
31-41 Elm St, Ipswich, IP1 2AY **Tel:** (01473) 211121 **Fax:** (01473) 230387 **DX:** 3220 Ipswich **Email:** mail@gotelee.co.uk
Website: www.gotelee.co.uk **Ptnrs:** 13 **Asst solrs:** 8 **Other fee-earners:** 14

GOULDENS

10 Old Bailey, London, EC4M 7NG
Tel: (020) 7583 7777 **Fax:** (020) 7583 6777 **DX:** 67 City
Email: info@gouldens.com **Website:** www.gouldens.com

Managing Partners	Charters Macdonald-Brown
	Russell Carmedy
Senior Partner	Patrick Burgess
Number of partners	37
Assistant solicitors	63
Other fee-earners	35

AREAS OF PRACTICE

Company/Commercial (inc. Corporate Tax)	42%
Property (inc. Planning)	25%
Litigation (inc. IP)	20%
Banking/Capital Markets	12%
Personal/International Tax Planning	1%

THE FIRM: Gouldens is the twelfth most profitable firm in the UK, has a policy of paying among the highest salaries of UK firms to its lawyers and, belying its size, is one of the few firms truly to 'punch above its weight'. The firm announced four new partners in 2001, bringing the total number of partners to 37 and the average age to 40. There are 63 assistant solicitors and 135 fee-earners in total. Gouldens is a commercial firm with leading practices and individuals in the traditional cornerstones of corporate, property and litigation as well as specialist teams which utilise the expertise of lawyers from these disciplines. Its dynamic and individual culture encourages innovation and a practical approach which achieves clients' objectives.

PRINCIPAL AREAS OF WORK: Gouldens divides its work into the main practice areas described below. There are also a number of specialist areas staffed by multi-skilled teams such as construction, environment, insurance and reinsurance, communications, media and information technology, intellectual property, employment, employee benefits and pensions, regulatory, fraud and white collar crime.

Company/Commercial: The firm's company and commercial department has a strong reputation in the City and advises, amongst others, major public companies and institutions on all aspects of commercial activity including corporate finance, public company takeovers and flotations, mergers and acquisitions, joint ventures, venture capital, management buy-outs, international agreements and franchise and distribution networks and agreements, as well as providing specialist support in areas such as EU and competition law, intellectual property and pensions and employee benefits.
Corporate Recovery & Insolvency: The corporate recovery and insolvency group undertakes a wide range of assignments for insolvency practitioners, banks and other providers of debt and equity finance. Increasingly, this involves advising the full range of stakeholders in companies operating in dynamic business sectors where timely restructuring advice may avoid the need for formal insolvency procedures.
Banking: The banking department has extensive experience in corporate lending and syndications, structured finance, trade finance, property finance, project finance, securitisation, capital markets and debt restructuring, acting for banks and financial institutions as well as borrowers.
Property & Planning: The firm's property and planning departments advise developers, institutional investors, surveyors, and other professionals on the financing, planning implications, tax structuring, and implementation of major developments.
Litigation, Insurance & Reinsurance: The firm handles a wide variety of domestic and international commercial disputes relating to construction, defamation, employment, financial and corporate matters, insurance and reinsurance and intellectual property and has a strong reputation in the field of patent and trade mark disputes. The insurance and reinsurance practice is broadly based, advising Lloyds and other London market insurers on many classes of risk including professional indemnity and directors' and officers' liability, increasingly with an international bias.

INTERNATIONAL: As well as dealing with high profile EU legal and trade issues, the international practice includes advising major companies and institutions on infrastructure projects, privatisations and joint ventures as well as governments on a number of issues including the development of new banking, securities, and foreign investment-related legislation. Languages spoken include Czech, Dutch, German, Greek, Hebrew, Italian, Polish, Romanian, Russian, Spanish and Welsh.

RECRUITMENT: The firm seeks to recruit (and retain) solicitors and trainees who wish to accept the challenge of responsibility in an atmosphere where not only technical expertise but flair, originality and enthusiasm are highly regarded and rewarded. Its system of training is unique and up to 20 trainees are recruited each year.

CONTACTS	
Banking	Tom Budd
CIS/Central Europe	James Campbell
Commercial Litigation	Charters Macdonald-Brown
Commercial Property	Clare Deanesly
Communications, Media & IT	Simon Chalkley
Company/Commercial	Max Thorneycroft
Construction	Craig Shuttleworth
Corporate Finance	Russell Carmedy
Corporate Recovery & Insolvency	Barry Donnelly
	Adrian Owen
Corporate Tax	Blaise Marin-Curtoud
Defamation	Barton Taylor
Employment	Martin Piers
Environment	Clare Deanesly
EU & International	Charters Macdonald-Brown
Fraud/White Collar Crime	David Cooper
Insurance/Reinsurance	Ian Lupson
Intellectual Property	Charters Macdonald-Brown
	Simon Chalkley
Pensions/Employee Benefits	John Papadakis
Personal/Int'l Tax Planning	Jennet Davies
Regulatory	Barry Donnelly

Gouldens

G

GRAEME CARMICHAEL
9 Paget Road, Ipswich, IP1 3RP **Tel:** (01473) 252159 **Fax:** (01473) 214778 **Ptnrs:** 1

GRAHAME STOWE, BATESON
5-7 Portland St, Leeds, LS1 3DR **Tel:** (0113) 246 8163 **Fax:** (0113) 260 1749 **DX:** 12022 **Email:** janet@grahamestowebateson.freeserve.co.uk
Ptnrs: 10 **Asst solrs:** 10 **Other fee-earners:** 11

GRAHAM EVANS & PARTNERS
Moorgate House, 6 Christina Street, Swansea, SA1 4EP **Tel:** (01792) 655822 **Fax:** (01792) 645387 **DX:** 39573 Swansea **Ptnrs:** 9 **Asst solrs:** 4
Other fee-earners: 10

GRANGE WINTRINGHAM
St. Mary's Chambers, Grimsby, DN31 1LD
Tel: (01472) 253 900 **Fax:** (01472) 359 904 **DX:** 13505 Grimsby-1
Email: juliet.savage@grangewintringham.com

Managing Partner	Juliet Savage
Senior Partners	David Overton
	Stephen Savage
Number of partners	10
Assistant solicitors	4
Other fee-earners	10
Other staff	52

THE FIRM: Established in 1770 the practice has changed radically and is one of the largest corporate and commercial practices in the region.

PRINCIPAL AREAS OF WORK:
Corporate/Commercial: The firm has full corporate capability including e-commerce.
Commercial Property: The firm has considerable expertise in advising national clients on all property and related funding matters. The firm has a particular speciality in the sale securitisation and development of properties within enterprise zones.
Employment: The firm has a specialist employment department advising on all types of employment issues from tribunals to share options.
Agriculture: The agricultural department is based at the Market Rasen office and advises agricultural clients on all matters appertaining to farming both contentious and non-contentious.
Litigation: The firm provides a full range of litigation services.
Private Client: The firm continues to have a strong private client department dealing with residential conveyancing, probate, tax and matrimonial.

Continued overleaf

CLIENTELE: The firm handles work for the full range of clients, from private clients to national clearing banks.

RECRUITMENT: This year Ruth Brewin (previously a partner with Martineau Johnson in Birmingham) has been made an equity partner and Jane Eatock (a partner with Birkett Long of Colchester) has joined the partnership.

GRANVILLE-WEST

23 Commercial Street, Pontypool, Torfaen, NP4 6XT **Tel:** (01495) 751111 **Fax:** (01495) 753858 **DX:** 44250 Pontypool **Email:** pontypool@g-west.co.uk **Website:** www.g-west.co.uk **Ptnrs:** 9 **Asst solrs:** 4 **Other fee-earners:** 7

GRAYS

Duncombe Place, York, YO1 7DY **Tel:** (01904) 634771 **Fax:** (01904) 610711 **DX:** 61505 **Email:** enquiries@grayssolicitors.co.uk **Website:** www.grayssolicitors.co.uk **Ptnrs:** 6 **Asst solrs:** 1 **Other fee-earners:** 4 **Contact:** Helen Mellors • Best known for trusts and taxation, charities (Tony Lawton), agriculture and property work. Also increasing specialism in employment and high value matrimonial financial disputes.

AREAS OF PRACTICE	
Private Client & Charity	52%
Agricultural, Commercial & Residential Property	30%
Litigation	5%
Family	4%
Other	9%

GREEN & CO

Alberton House, St. Mary's Passage, Manchester, M3 2WJ **Tel:** (0161) 834 8980 **Fax:** (0161) 834 8981 **Email:** info@greenandcosolicitors.co.uk **Website:** www.greenandcosolicitors.co.uk **Ptnrs:** 1 **Asst solrs:** 6 **Other fee-earners:** 1

GREENE & GREENE

80 Guildhall Street, Bury St Edmunds, IP33 1QB **Tel:** (01284) 762211 **Fax:** (01284) 705739 **DX:** 57205 **Ptnrs:** 9 **Asst solrs:** 2 **Other fee-earners:** 9

GREENLAND HOUCHEN

38 Prince of Wales Rd, Norwich, NR1 1HZ
Tel: (01603) 660744 **Fax:** (01603) 610700 **DX:** 5217 Norwich
Email: mail@ghlaw.co.uk **Website:** greenland-houchen.co.uk

Senior Partner	Robert Plumbly
Number of partners	10
Assistant solicitors	2
Other fee-earners	6

THE FIRM: A long established general practice which seeks to offer at its three offices a full range of legal services. The partners include in their clientele builders and developers, housing associations, members of the local farming community and other commercial and corporate enterprises, as well as the private client. All aspects of litigation are undertaken with a significant legal aid element.

GREENWOODS

Monkstone House, City Road, Peterborough, PE1 1JE
Tel: (01733) 887700 **Fax:** (01733) 424900 **DX:** 12599 Peterborough 4
Email: showard@greenwoods.co.uk **Website:** www.greenwoods.co.uk

Managing Partner	Shelagh Smith
Senior Partner	David Weekes
Number of partners	16
Assistant solicitors	17
Other fee-earners	22

THE FIRM: Greenwoods is one of the leading commercial law firms in East Anglia and the East Midlands, providing a comprehensive range of legal services to corporate clients, tailored to meet specific clients' needs. The Greenwoods approach is to provide clients with strong, responsive, partner-led teams who take a practical approach, within the legal framework, to enable clients to achieve their objectives. The firm's teams look for innovative solutions and actively seek opportunities to provide an added-value service. Looking to the future, the firm is growing by recognising its strengths and developing them. The firm continues to invest in its employees and in information technology and telecommunications to ensure that it is at the leading edge of service delivery.

PRINCIPAL AREAS OF WORK: The firm's legal services include commercial litigation; commercial property and planning; company and commercial; construction and engineering; employment and employee benefits; EU and competition law; health and safety; information technology; insolvency; intellectual property, including significant work in the bioscience sector; mediation; property litigation and private client advice.

CLIENTELE: Greenwoods' client base includes local, regional, national and international companies and organisations. It services its clients in their operations nationally, throughout Europe and in some cases worldwide.

INTERNATIONAL: The firm has an association with Crivello Carlson Mentkowski Steeves s.c. in Milwaukee.

RECRUITMENT: Greenwoods generally recruits up to four trainees annually. Financial support may be provided in some circumstances. A minimum 2:1 degree is required, not necessarily in law. Apply by handwritten letter (plus typed CV) to Rosemary Gearing.

CONTACTS	
Agriculture	Nick Plumb
Commercial Dispute Resolution	James Maxey
Commercial Property/Planning	Stephen Illingworth
Company/Commercial	Michael Evans
Construction & Engineering	Martin Wood
Employment/Employee Benefits	Robert Dillarstone
Family	Jane Proctor
Property Litigation	Michael Taylor
IT/Telecoms	Nigel Moore
Insolvency	James Maxey
Insurance Litigation	David Weekes
Intellectual Property	Philip Sloan
Probate, Wills & Trusts	Nick Monsell

GREGG GALBRAITH QUINN

6 Queen Square, Bristol, BS1 4JE **Tel:** (0117) 925 8123 **Fax:** (0117) 925 5567 **DX:** 7845 Bristol **Ptnrs:** 3 **Asst solrs:** 5

GREGORY, ROWCLIFFE & MILNERS

1 Bedford Row, London, WC1R 4BZ
Tel: (020) 7242 0631 **Fax:** (020) 7242 6652 **DX:** 95
Email: law@grm.co.uk **Website:** www.grm.co.uk

Number of partners	18
Assistant solicitors	2
Other fee-earners	13

AREAS OF PRACTICE	
Litigation	29%
Property	29%
Company/Commercial	26%
Private Client	16%

CONTACTS	
Anglo German	Lesley Pendlebury Cox
Company/Commercial	Paul Holloway
	Adrian Mezzetti
Employment	Jane Laidler
	Ingrid McKeown
Family/Matrimonial	Fenella Pringle
Litigation	Christopher Harper
	Jack Sadleir
Personal Injury/ Clinical Negligence	Anthony Benbow
Private Client	Michael Parnell-King
Property	William Bennett
	David King
Tax	Michael Parnell-King

THE FIRM: Gregory, Rowcliffe & Milners is a progressive firm with an established reputation in quality private client advice, litigation services, corporate and business law. The firm has its roots going back to 1784. It consists of a well-established private client, company/commercial and litigation practice with strongly developed Anglo-German connections, (with fluent German-speakers at all levels throughout the firm); and long standing links with a number of organisations concerned with Anglo-German trade.

PRINCIPAL AREAS OF WORK:

Company/Commercial: The department has excellent international links with Europe, especially Germany, the USA and the Far East, and represents national and multinational concerns, providing practical legal and taxation solutions to business problems and objectives over a broad spectrum of commerce and industry.
Litigation: The firm provides a full range of litigation services to institutional, business and private clients in respect of administrative law (especially judicial review applications against public bodies); commercial, employment and property disputes; family law, including matrimonial disputes with legal aid where appropriate; personal injury, clinical negligence and claims relating to trusts and wills. The firm is noted for the international (especially German) aspect of its commercial and family litigation. It also has an extensive and well regarded London agency practice.
Employment: A strong employment group specialising on employment contracts, negotiations on termination of senior executives, unfair dismissals and discrimination claims.
Private Client: The firm has expertise in inheritance and tax planning, including the preservation of listed buildings and works of art, the creation of charitable trusts, and the administration of estates, often with an international dimension.
Property: All aspects of commercial, industrial, agricultural, residential and investment conveyancing including estate management, planning and tax planning.

GRIFFITH SMITH

47 Old Steyne, Brighton, BN1 1NW **Tel:** (01273) 324041 **Fax:** (01273) 384000 **DX:** 2701 Brighton-1 **Email:** brighton@griffithsmith.co.uk **Website:** www.griffithsmith.co.uk **Contact:** Nicholas Evans • Company/commercial, civil litigation, and private client with specialist skills including planning and environmental law and charity services.

GRINDEYS

Glebe Court, Stoke-on-Trent, ST4 1ET **Tel:** (01782) 846441 **Fax:** (01782) 416220 **DX:** 21053 Stoke **Email:** grindeys@aol.com **Website:** www.grindeys.co.uk **Contact:** Robert Bailey • Grindeys is a long-established firm. Strengths in company/commercial work, commercial litigation, commercial property and personal injury litigation. ISO 9001 accredited.

AREAS OF PRACTICE	
Corporate Services	40%
Insurance Litigation/PI	35%
Private Client	25%

GROSS & CO.

84 Guildhall Street, Bury St Edmunds, IP33 1PR
Tel: (01284) 763333 **Fax:** (01284) 762207 **DX:** 57203
Email: gdk@gross.co.uk

23 Bentinck Street, London, W1M 6AB
Tel: (020) 7935 5541 **Fax:** (020) 7935 6638
Email: gdk@gross.co.uk

Senior Partner	G D Kirk
Number of partners	4
Assistant solicitors	5
Other fee-earners	4

AREAS OF PRACTICE	
Immigration & Nationality Law	20%
Company/Commercial	15%
Wills & Probate	15%
Civil Litigation	12%
Residential Conveyancing	10%
Matrimonial	10%
Commercial Property & Agriculture	10%
Employment	8%

THE FIRM: Established in West Suffolk for over 150 years, this progressive firm offers a specialist immigration service and has a fast-expanding commercial practice as well as a traditional general practice. The firm has an unusually international clientele, as well as sizeable private companies, small businesses and private clients. It is a member of the NIS Group of Independent Solicitors. The firm has an office in London W1 to service its London and international clients.

Continued overleaf

PRINCIPAL AREAS OF WORK:
Immigration & Nationality: The majority of work handled is in the field of business immigration. Assistance is also given in US and Canadian immigration law, and a consultancy service is offered to other solicitors through the ImmLaw service (brochure available).
Company/Commercial: The firm has expertise in most areas of commercial practice, including commercial property, for a wide range of business clients. It acts for many doctors and dentists.
Litigation: All types of litigation are handled, including commercial, civil, matrimonial and Legal Aid. Agency work is undertaken.
Private Client: Work includes conveyancing and wills/estate planning.

INTERNATIONAL: The firm has overseas associate offices in USA, Canada, South Africa, India, Spain, Russia and Hong Kong. Languages spoken include French, German and Russian.

CONTACTS	
Civil Litigation	S Kerr
Commercial Property & Agriculture	J Cobbold
Company/Commercial	G Kirk
Employment	N Amor
Immigration/Nationality Law	G Kirk
Matrimonial	E Hodder
Residential Conveyancing	A Gordon-Stables
Wills & Probate	A Day

GROWER FREEMAN & GOLDBERG

Suite Two, Fourth Floor, One Great Cumberland Place, London, W1H 8DQ **Tel:** (020) 7723 3040 **Fax:** (020) 7723 9015 **DX:** 44433 Marble Arch
Email: sportslaw@gfg-law.co.uk **Website:** www.gfg-law.co.uk **Ptnrs:** 3 **Asst solrs:** 4 **Other fee-earners:** 2

G

GSC SOLICITORS

31-32 Ely Place, London, EC1N 6TD
Tel: (020) 7822 2222 **Fax:** (020) 7822 2211 **DX:** 462 London/Chancery Lane
Email: info@gsc-solicitors.co.uk **Website:** www.gsc-solicitors.co.uk

Senior Partner	S R Sheikh
Number of partners	5
Other fee-earners	10

THE FIRM: This City firm undertakes a broad range of legal work for business and private clients. It is known for its expertise in media and intellectual property, commercial property, corporate and international work. GSC Solicitors, previously Green David Conway & Co, was founded in 1972 and over the years has established a reputation for excellence in its chosen fields. Clients range from small businesses and family-owned companies to multinational plcs and industry bodies, as well as individuals. Recent developments in the firm include an increase in international work, particularly in Asia, Africa and the Middle East.

CONTACTS	
Commercial Litigation	P J Leathem
Commercial Property	P L Belcher
	H D Posener
Corporate Commercial/IT/ Employment	C J Halperin
	S R Sheikh
Media/Intellectual Property	P J Leathem
Private Client/Tax/Trusts/ International	S R Sheikh

GULBENKIAN HARRIS ANDONIAN

181 Kensington High Street, London, W8 6SH
Tel: (020) 7937 1542 **Fax:** (020) 7938 2059 **DX:** 47204 Kensington
Email: gulbenk@nildram.co.uk

Number of partners	11
Assistant solicitors	5
Other fee-earners	3

THE FIRM: Whilst the firm engages in a wide range of commercial work (including litigation), it is best known for its expertise in immigration and nationality law which is undertaken for both commercial and private clients. The highlight of 1998/9 was a successful House of Lords Appeal in the case of Shah and Islam reported in *The Times* on the 26 March 1999 under the heading Pakistan's Failure to Protect Women.

PRINCIPAL AREAS OF WORK:
Immigration & Nationality Law: Work includes nationality applications, all aspects of UK immigration and advice (business and private), refugee and asylum work and obtaining work permits. The firm has experience in US immigration, Hong Kong, Eastern Europe (including Russia), Middle East, Sri Lanka and South Africa. The firm is a founder member of the European Immigration Lawyers Group of which the senior partner is the President. Two of the partners are part-time Immigration Adjudicators and have been appointed to the Law Society Immigration Law Panel.
Matrimonial & Family Law: Comprehensive services are provided including advice on separation, divorce, wardship, custody, adoption and all related financial, property and taxation matters. The senior partner is one of the founder members of the Solicitors Family Law Association.

CLIENTELE: A largely international client base including multinationals as well as small to medium sized companies and private individuals.

INTERNATIONAL: The firm handles work in Armenian, Arabic, Chinese, Danish, Farsi, French, Spanish and Swedish.

AREAS OF PRACTICE	
Immigration	70%
Matrimonial	20%
General	10%

CONTACTS	
General	Paul Gulbenkian
Immigration	Peter Wyatt
	Bernard Andonian
Matrimonial	Paul Gulbenkian
	Bernard Andonian

GWYNNES

Edgbaston House, Walker Street, Wellington, Telford, Wellington, TF1 1HF **Tel:** (01952) 641651 **Fax:** (01952) 247441 **DX:** 23107
Email: info@gwynnes.com **Website:** www.gwynnes.com **Ptnrs:** 7 **Asst solrs:** 9 **Other fee-earners:** 8

H2O (HENRY HEPWORTH ORGANISATION)

5 John Street, London, WC1N 2HH
Tel: (020) 7539 7200 **Fax:** (020) 7539 7201
Email: h2o@h2o-law.com **Website:** www.h2o-law.com

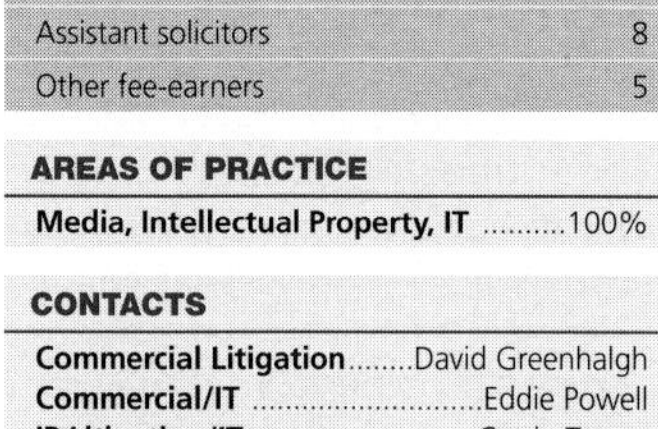

Number of partners	4
Assistant solicitors	8
Other fee-earners	5

AREAS OF PRACTICE

Media, Intellectual Property, IT 100%

CONTACTS

Commercial Litigation........David Greenhalgh
Commercial/IT ....Eddie Powell
IP Litigation/IT............................Catrin Turner
Media/Media Litigation (Defamation) ....Paul Fox
....Jason McCue

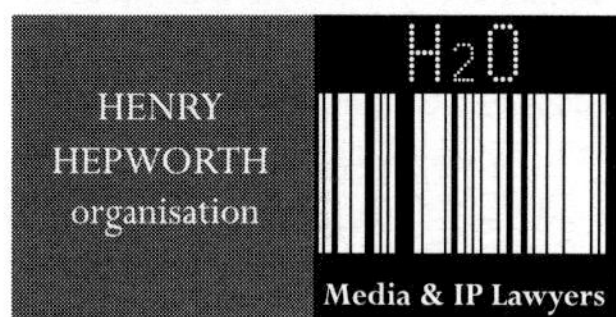

THE FIRM: H2O (Henry Hepworth Organisation), based close to Grays Inn, is a specialist law firm offering a full media, intellectual property and information technology legal service to domestic and international clients. H2O is dedicated to working with the following industry sectors: entertainment; IT/technology; leisure; media; retail. H2O is a single solution for the above industry sectors, dedicated to advise on commercial, transactional and litigation issues. H2O is a friendly firm with a knowledge-led culture whose objectives are to provide a top quality commercial service to its clients from a secure and happy environment. H2O understands its clients' business (and their commercial objectives) and works closely with its clients, in-house lawyers and agents to deliver effective commercial advice. The firm is active in the following fields of activity (recognised by *Chambers Guide to the Legal Profession*): advertising/marketing; broadcasting; defamation; digital media; education, fashion, films, intellectual property; music; publishing; sports; theatre. H2O is a highly organised, successful firm. It has invested heavily in technology and has implemented its radical 'New Ways to Work' programme, including encouraging lawyers to work flexibly from home one day a week. The firm has devised and implemented an active social re-investment policy (which contributes towards projects in the developing world and towards the encouragement of education and the arts).

PRINCIPAL AREAS OF WORK: Entertainment; intellectual property; IT/technology; leisure; media; retail.

CLIENTELE: Clients include: Arena Leisure plc, Carlton UK Television Limited, Tottenham Hotspur plc, Express Newspapers plc, IPC Media Limited, News International plc, NBC News Inc, Time Warner Inc, Tesco Stores Limited, Times Newspapers Limited, Best People Limited, workthing.com, learndirect.

INTERNATIONAL: H2O have established working relationships worldwide with specialist media/intellectual property lawyers. Partners are also qualified in the Republic of Ireland and Hong Kong. The firm has a reputation for multijurisdictional actions and overseeing European actions for clients (including insurance companies). Members of the firm are fluent in French, Spanish, and German.

RECRUITMENT: The firm has an active recruitment and training progamme at all levels. Those interested in joining the H2O team should visit the firm's website.

HAARMANN HEMMELRATH

Tower 42, 25 Old Broad Street, London, EC2N 1HQ
Tel: (020) 7382 4800 **Fax:** (020) 7382 4833
Website: www.hhp.de

Number of partners	9
Assistant solicitors	12
Other fee-earners	2

AREAS OF PRACTICE

M&A 40%
International Tax & Tax Structuring......15%
Company & Corporate Law 10%
Capital Markets, Corporate Finance 10%
Structured Finance 10%
Private Equity 10%
IP & IT 5%

CONTACTS

M&A.............................Claus Köhler, Jay Birch
.....................Philip Newhouse, Ursula Lennerz
Company & Corporate Law ......Claus Köhler
...............................Jay Birch, Philip Newhouse
Capital Markets ....Jay Birch
....David von Saucken
Corporate Finance............................Jay Birch,
Philip Newhouse, Anthony Webb, Ursula Lennerz
Structured Finance.......................Ray Breden
....Philip Newhouse
International Tax & Tax Structuring ....Peter Vaines
..............................Ray Breden, Adrian Murphy
Private Equity ....Philip Newhouse
..................................Nicholas Foss-Pedersen
IP & IT ....Claus Köhler, Chris Hubbard

THE FIRM: Haarmann Hemmelrath, the English arm of Haarmann, Hemmelrath & Partner, opened its London office in spring 2000 in the heart of the City of London. Since then it has grown consistently. The London office comprises English solicitors, registered foreign lawyers and registered European lawyers. A speciality of Haarmann, Hemmelrath & Partner is its multidisciplinary approach, which provides clients with integrated legal and tax advice from a single source on domestic and cross-border issues. Through its close co-operation with all other Haarmann, Hemmelrath & Partner offices, the firm ensures immediate access to the most recent legal and economic developments.

PRINCIPAL AREAS OF WORK: The London office offers services across the spectrum of M&A; IPO; corporate and commercial law; IP; IT; e-commerce; capital markets; corporate finance; tax structuring and international tax advice.

CLIENTELE: The firm's clients include UK and German listed and private companies; leading multinational corporations; high-net-worth individuals and government organisations.

INTERNATIONAL: Founded in 1987, Haarmann, Hemmelrath & Partner has 22 offices in Western, Central and Eastern Europe and Asia including seven offices in Germany's major business centres. An office in Rome will be opened during this year. The firm is a member of various international, professional and other associations and organisations, and regularly takes part in events organised by them. The result is a constant exchange of professional experience with recognised advisers on a worldwide basis. Further, the firm is a member of the RSM international network, an international association of independent firms of auditors with over

Continued overleaf

H

520 offices in more than 70 countries. The languages spoken are German, English, French, Italian, Polish, Czech, Russian, Japanese, Mandarin, Cantonese, and many others according to the location of its offices.

RECRUITMENT: The firm has set up a training contract scheme for trainee solicitors and provides funding for the vocational stage of the training. Candidates with first or upper second class degrees are preferred. Applications should be sent to Sandra Puhr-Westerheide in London.

HACKING ASHTON

Berkeley Court, Borough Road, Newcastle-under-Lyme, ST5 1TT **Tel:** (01782) 715555 **Fax:** (01782) 715566 **DX:** 20954 **Email:** hackingashton@dial.pipex.com **Website:** www.hackingashton.co.uk **Ptnrs:** 7 **Asst solrs:** 5 **Other fee-earners:** 4 **Contact:** R F Ashton • Commercial practice covering a broad spectrum of litigation, property and company commercial work. Specialises in construction and development work, alternative dispute resolution, employment law and agricultural matters. Wide-ranging foreign connections.

AREAS OF PRACTICE	
Commercial Property	35%
Commercial Litigation	30%
Company/Commercial	20%
Private Client	10%
Agricultural	5%

HADENS (FORMERLY HADEN STRETTON SLATER MILLER)

Leicester Buildings, Bridge Street, Walsall, WS1 1EL **Tel:** (0121)-5262626 **Fax:** (01922) 720023 **DX:** 12122 Walsall **Email:** walsall@hadens.co.uk **Website:** www.hadens.co.uk **Ptnrs:** 14 **Asst solrs:** 10 **Other fee-earners:** 23

H

HALLETT & CO

11 Bank St, Ashford, TN23 1DA **Tel:** (01233) 625 711 **Fax:** (01233) 643 841 **DX:** 30202 Ashford **Email:** info@hallettandco.co.uk **Ptnrs:** 8 **Asst solrs:** 2 **Other fee-earners:** 13 **Contact:** C A McDonald • One of the largest firms in Ashford, with renowned expertise in agricultural and employment law, trust and private client with an expanding commercial practice.

AREAS OF PRACTICE	
Property, Commercial Property & Agriculture	40%
Litigation	40%
Probate & Trust	20%

HALL & HAUGHEY

Ground Floor, 63 Carlton Place, Glasgow, G5 9TW **Tel:** (0141) 418 0505 **Fax:** (0141) 429 3131 **DX:** GW 395 **Email:** hh@hallhaughey.fsnet.co.uk **Ptnrs:** 2 **Asst solrs:** 1 **Other fee-earners:** 1

HALLINAN, BLACKBURN, GITTINGS & NOTT

Suite 22, Westminster Palace Gardens, Artillery Row, London, SW1P 1RR **Tel:** (020) 7233 3999 **Fax:** (020) 7233 3888 **Email:** hallinans@btconnect.com **Ptnrs:** 1 **Asst solrs:** 3 **Other fee-earners:** 1 **Contact:** Valerie Walsh • Specialises in crime, extradition, fraud, infanticide and road traffic offences. Legal Aid franchise/private client. Experienced and well respected in the defence of a broad spectrum of clients.

HALLIWELL LANDAU

St. James's Court, Brown St, Manchester, M2 2JF
Tel: (0161) 835 3003 **Fax:** (0161) 835 2994 **DX:** 14317
Email: info@halliwells.com **Website:** www.halliwells.co.uk

Managing Partner	Paul Thomas
Senior Partner	Alec Craig
Number of partners	56
Assistant solicitors	104
Other fee-earners	60

THE FIRM: Halliwell Landau is a leading independent UK law firm. The firm has an impressive client list and provides a comprehensive range of commercial legal advice to support its business activities. The partnership has a reputation for combining experience, commercial awareness and a willingness to consider new approaches and ideas. The firm's philosophy of entrepreneurial awareness with close attention to detail and dedication to high professional standards has become the hallmark of its work.

PRINCIPAL AREAS OF WORK:

Corporate: This is one of the largest departments in the region, advising on mergers, acquisitions, disposals, MBOs/MBIs, banking law and corporate finance.

Commercial Property: The firm is one of the leading commercial property advisers in the North West, advising on a range of commercial property issues including the acquisition and disposal of properties, site assembly and negotiation of leases.

Commercial Litigation: Advice is given on all aspects of commercial litigation including property litigation, banking and recovery work and professional negligence.

Planning & Environmental: The firm is widely acknowledged as one of the most respected planning appeal practices in the country, advising some of the region's top companies and local and national developers.

Construction & Bonds: Halliwell Landau advises on all facets of construction law including bonds and guarantees, which play a crucial role in construction agreements.

Employment: The firm advises clients on both contentious and non-contentious aspects of legislation.

Trusts & Estate Planning: The firm is acknowledged as one of the leaders in the field in the North West, advis-

AREAS OF PRACTICE	
Corporate & Banking	24%
Commercial Litigation	20%
Commercial Property	17%
Insolvency	12%
Insurance Litigation	12%
Intellectual Property	4%
Planning & Environmental Law	4%
Trust & Estate Planning	4%
Employment	3%

CONTACTS	
Commercial Litigation	Ian Austin
Commercial Property	Mike Edge
Corporate	Mark Halliwell
Employment	Stephen Hills
Insolvency	Andrew Buchanan
Insurance Litigation	Christopher Phillips
Intellectual Property	Jonathan Moakes
Planning & Environmental Law	Roger Lancaster
Trusts & Estate Planning	Geoffrey Shindler

ing senior business executives and individuals of high net worth on income and estate planning, the creation of trusts and the administration of investments. It also advises trustees and charities.
Intellectual Property: This department advises on traditional categories of patents, copyright, trademarks and registered designs as well as advice on any form of intangible rights.
Insolvency & Corporate Recovery: This team is principally directed at supporting banks and insolvency practitioners on specialised insolvency matters. It also advises companies and directors on the legal aspects of restructuring, reorganising and refining.
Insurance Litigation: The department advises on general insurance issues, policy disputes and indemnity and warranty issues. All types of defendant personal injury work are handled.

halliwell landau

A. HALSALL & CO

47-48 Hamilton Square, Birkenhead, CH41 5BD **Tel:** (0151) 647 6323 **Fax:** (0151) 647 9818 **DX:** 17853 **Email:** info@halsalls **Ptnrs:** 6 **Asst solrs:** 2 **Other fee-earners:** 2

HAMERS

9-11 Scale Lane, Hull, HU1 1PH **Tel:** (01482) 326666 **Fax:** (01482) 324432 **DX:** 11933 Hull **Email:** info@hamers.com **Website:** www.hamers.com **Ptnrs:** 6 **Asst solrs:** 28 **Other fee-earners:** 18

H

HAMLINS

Roxburghe House, 273-287 Regent St, London, W1B 2AD
Tel: (020) 7355 6000 **Fax:** (020) 7518 9100 **DX:** 53803 Oxford Circus North
Email: admin@hamlins.co.uk **Website:** www.hamlins.co.uk

Managing Partners	Brian Casey
	Laurence Gilmore
	Nigel Mason
Number of partners	17
Assistant solicitors	13
Other fee-earners	21

AREAS OF PRACTICE

Company & Commercial	19%
Property Services	37%
Entertainment/Intellectual Property	18%
Litigation Services	14%
Secured Lending	12%

CONTACTS

Company & Commercial	Gordon Oliver
Litigation (inc. Entertainment, Media & Intellectual Property)	Laurence Gilmore
Property Services	Brian Casey
Secured Lending	Keith Roffey

THE FIRM: This medium sized London practice, formerly known as Hamlin Slowe, is property-orientated with a substantial commercial client base. Founded in 1906, the firm undertakes a wide variety of work, but has particular expertise in commercial property, commercial, secured lending, intellectual property, entertainment and media matters. The firm's clients include several public companies and many large and well-known private companies.

PRINCIPAL AREAS OF WORK:
Property: The department has a long and established reputation in financing, acquisition, letting and disposal of shop, office and industrial property as well as handling development, town and country planning, compulsory purchase and landlord and tenant matters.
Secured Lending: The department acts for lenders in professional negligence, possession, mortgage documentation, arrears, sales, insolvency, consumer credit and unsecured loss recovery matters. The department has developed on-line computer systems for mortgage and arrears recovery.
Litigation: The firm is known for the strength of its litigation department which supports the non-litigious departments, handles heavy commercial litigation, matrimonial and personal injury matters and includes the entertainment, media and intellectual property department which has an outstanding reputation in the entertainment sector, particularly in the areas of copyright infringement. It handles all aspects of entertainment law for clients who include copyright societies, music publishers, record companies, record producers, composers, authors, recording artists, and film and video production companies. The department also advises on matters of defamation, libel, information technology, multi-media, trade marks, passing off and design right.
Company & Commercial: The department deals with mergers, acquisitions, disposals, franchising, employment and partnership matters. The department also advises on share and rights issues, public flotations, corporate reorganisations, liquidations and joint ventures. This department encompasses a division which specialises in advising the leisure industry and has an asset planning division which handles personal taxation, inheritance tax planning, pensions, trusts, wills and probates. Hamlins has a strong client base of both large and small clients. The firm's brochure describing the services that the firm has to offer is available upon request.

HAMLINS

HAMMOND SUDDARDS EDGE

7 Devonshire Square, Cutlers Gardens, London, EC2M 4YH
Tel: (020) 7655 1000 **Fax:** (020) 7655 1001 **DX:** 33885 Finsbury Square
Email: enquiries@hammondsuddardsedge.co.uk
Website: www.hammondsuddardsedge.com

Lloyd's of London, Suite 688 Lloyd's, One Lime Street, London, EC3M 7HA
Tel: (020) 7327 3388 **Fax:** (020) 7621 1217 **DX:** 807 London City EC3

2 Park Lane, Leeds, LS3 1ES
Tel: (0113) 284 7000 **Fax:** (0113) 284 7001 **DX:** 26441 Leeds-1
Email: enquiries@hammondsuddardsedge.com

Trinity Court, 16 John Dalton Street, Manchester, M60 8HS
Tel: (0161) 830 5000 **Fax:** (0161) 830 5001 **DX:** 14347 Manchester-1
Email: enquiries@hammondsuddardsedge.com

Rutland House, 148 Edmund St, Birmingham, B3 2JR
Tel: (0121) 222 3000 **Fax:** (0121) 222 3001 **DX:** 708611 Birmingham-17
Email: enquiries@hammondsuddardsedge.com

Pennine House, 39-45 Well Street, Bradford, BD1 5NU
Tel: (01274) 764 400 **Fax:** (01274) 730 484 **DX:** 11796
Email: enquiries@hammondsuddardsedge.com

Senior Partner	John Heller
Managing Partners	Chris Jones, Gil Hayward
Number of partners	213
Other lawyers	900
Total staff	2000

CONTACTS

Advocacy .... Patrick Walker
Asset Finance .... Angela Davis
Banking .... Patrick Mitchell
Business Finance & Recovery .... Chris Jones
Commercial Dispute Resolution .... Peter Crossley
Computer Law & E-Commerce .... Mike Henley
Construction & Engineering .... David Jones
Corporate Finance .... Nick Allen
Corporate Tax .... Mark Simpson
EC & Competition .... Konstantinos Adamantopoulos
Employment .... Sue Nickson
Environmental .... Paul Bratt
.... Caroline May
HammondsDirect .... Luciano Dammone
Insurance .... Michael Robin
IP .... Marija Danilunas
Licensing .... Stephanie Perraton
.... Andrew Potts
Media & Entertainment .... Hubert Best
.... Robert Wegenek
Pensions .... Jane Marshall
PFI .... Jonathan Hosie
Property & Planning .... Chris Marks
Sports Law .... Richard Alderson

THE FIRM: Hammond Suddards Edge is a leading commercial law firm with a formidable London corporate practice and top-flight status in all the major financial and industrial centres of England: Birmingham, Manchester, Leeds and Bradford. The firm also has offices in Brussels, Paris, Munich and Berlin. The firm has 213 partners, 904 lawyers and a total staff of 2,000, operating as an integrated international practice using the best IT networking systems available to deliver a seamless service to clients, irrespective of location.

PRINCIPAL AREAS OF WORK:

Corporate Finance: The corporate finance unit has an outstanding record in mergers and acquisitions both domestically and overseas. The unit is respected for its considerable expertise and experience in flotations, disposals, reorganisations, joint ventures, MBOs, funding operations and the full range of corporate and commercial services. The majority of the work is for listed companies; indeed, the firm acts for more than 80 UK Stock Market listed companies and 16 US Fortune 500 companies. Other corporate clients include private companies, UK subsidiaries of overseas companies and various financial institutions, including six of the top 10 UK building societies.

Banking: The banking unit undertakes all types of banking work for financial institutions including UK and overseas banks, building societies and borrowers on a broad range of secured and unsecured transactions and restructerings. A dedicated financial law team draws together specialists from disciplines including banking, treasury products, factoring and discounting, asset-based lending, capital markets, compliance, insolvency, composite recovery, banking litigation and bespoke debt recovery systems.

Corporate Tax: The corporate tax unit provides advice on tax planning at all levels, employee share option schemes and offshore tax.

Commercial Dispute Resolution: The commercial dispute resolution unit encompasses all aspects of commercial claims and disputes for the firm's corporate clients. The firm has particular expertise in ADR and arbitration, which was recognised in 2000 when the firm won the CEDR (Centre for Dispute Resolution) award for excellence in ADR for the second time in succession. The unit also handles regulatory work, directors' and officers' liabilities and other aspects of criminal law which present risks for businesses. In addition there is a safety, health and environmental team carrying out all litigious and non-litigious environmental work.

Business Finance & Recovery: The insolvency and corporate recovery unit provides advice to insolvency practitioners and banks on all aspects of their work as receivers, liquidators, trustees, administrators and supervisors. The unit also advises companies and partnerships experiencing serious financial difficulties. Much of the work has an international focus.

Property & Planning: The property unit advises major national developers, institutions and end-users on all aspects of commercial property, particularly major City centre schemes and out of town developments. The planning team continues to go from strength to strength with large scale involvement in major national planning enquiries for UK and international companies and utilities. A dedicated retail team advised a wide range of retailers from high street names to breweries and charities.

Intellectual Property: The intellectual property unit has established itself as a market leader in both litigious and non-litigious IP matters for a broad spectrum of multinationals and UK companies. The unit has specific teams dedicated to telecommunications, media and film, pharmaceuticals, IT and e-commerce. In addition, a dedicated enterprise and technology team has expertise in advertising and brand clearance, character merchandising, computer contracts for hardware and software, domain name recovery, e-commerce, media contracts, rights agreements for sports governing bodies, companies, clubs and sales promotions.

Insurance: The commercial insurance unit, one of the largest based at Lloyd's of London, is recognised for its expertise in professional indemnity for accountants, solicitors, surveyors, architects, engineers, computer consultants and financial institutions. The unit also advises on policy coverage disputes, product liability matters and non-contentious insurance work.
Construction & Engineering: The construction and engineering unit is one of the largest bespoke practices in the UK. The unit acts for employers and contractors both in the UK and overseas on all aspects of contentious and non-contentious construction law from building projects (including operation and facilities management contracts) to civil, process and chemical engineering projects.
Employment: Hammond Suddards Edge has one of the UK's largest employment practices with a large team of dedicated employment lawyers across all locations. Work encompasses all aspects of contentious and non-contentious employment advice.
Pensions: The pensions unit is widely recognised as one of the UK's largest and most experienced pensions advisers. The unit advises employers and trustees on all aspects of pensions arrangements from large occupational schemes to product development work for providers and unapproved top-up schemes.
Lender Services: HammondsDirect is the UK's leading high volume legal support service for lenders and financial institutions. Through sophisticated IT solutions, HammondsDirect offers the ability to handle effectively and efficiently large volumes of litigation cases, conveyancing transactions and mortgage arrears management services.
EU Law: An increasing part of the firm's work is of an international flavour. The Brussels office is now among the largest of those operated by a UK firm in the EU capital and provides specialist expertise in EU, commercial and environmental law. Many of the firm's clients have international interests and/or are making overseas acquisitions, particularly in Europe, the US, Canada and Australia. The firm accepts EU work in Brussels from other solicitors and overseas law firms.

CLIENTELE: With an impressive range of major national and international companies and institutions on its client list, Hammond Suddards Edge advises more than 80 UK Stock Market listed companies, including 18 of the FTSE 100 companies, and 16 US Fortune 500 companies. The firm is recognised and respected for its entrepreneurial and innovative approach and is constantly looking for new ways to enhance client service.

INTERNATIONAL: The firm has offices in Brussels, Paris, Munich and Berlin. Many of the firm's clients have international interests and/or are making overseas acquisitions, particularly in Europe, the US, Canada and Australia. The firm accepts EU work in Brussels from other solicitors and overseas law firms.

RECRUITMENT: Hammond Suddards Edge continues to recruit qualified staff for most areas of the practice across all offices. Enquiries should be addressed to Rebecca Ellis, based in the Manchester office. In addition, some 45 trainees are recruited each year. Applications (in the form of a CV and covering letter) should be sent to Alison Archer at the London office.

HARBOTTLE & LEWIS

Hanover House, 14 Hanover Square, London, W1S 1HP
Tel: (020) 7667 5000 **Fax:** (020) 7667 5100 **DX:** 44617 Mayfair
Email: info@harbottle.com **Website:** www.harbottle.com

Managing Partner	Samantha Phillips
Number of partners	17
Assistant solicitors	51
Other fee-earners	18

CONTACTS

Advertising & Marketing	Gerrard Tyrrell
Aviation	Dermot Scully
Brand Management & Protection; IP Rights	Mark Owen
Broadcasting	Medwyn Jones
Charities	Robert Porter
Company & Commercial	Colin Howes
Corporate Finance	Mark Bertram
Corporate Recovery & Insolvency	Samantha Phillips
E-commerce & New Media	Mark Phillips
Employment	Marian Derham
	Dermot Scully
Film & TV Production	Robert Storer
Immigration	Sue May
Interactive Entertainment	Sebastian Belcher
IT & Technology	Mark Owen
Leisure	Justin Dunlop
Litigation	Gerrard Tyrrell
Music	Ann Harrison
Property Development & Investment	Alan Patten
Publishing	Rachel Atkins
Sponsorship	Bob Mitchell
Sport	Bob Mitchell
Theatre & Performing Arts	Colin Howes

THE FIRM: Harbottle & Lewis provides specialist advice to the media, entertainment and communications industries. It remains unique in having expertise right across these sectors and is consistently recognised as a leading firm by independent sources. Whilst its key practice areas continue to expand, the original values of the firm – to provide efficient legal advice, encourage originality and enjoy what it does – remain constant.

PRINCIPAL AREAS OF WORK: The firm's work encompasses the core areas of media and entertainment, including film, television, broadcasting, sports, publishing, advertising, theatre and the travel and leisure market. The advent of new technologies has inevitably shaped the firm's work and highly successful practices in complementary areas such as e-commerce, new media and interactive entertainment have emerged in recent years. The firm provides a complete range of commercial legal advice to its clients including areas such as corporate, technology, litigation, intellectual property, defamation, property, employment, finance, tax and franchising. The scope of the firm's work is extremely varied and has involved many high profile cases and deals. Recent highlights have included acting for Chris Evans on the £225m sale of Ginger Media Group, advising Chrysalis on their new media investments and negotiating the groundbreaking central contracts for the English Cricket Team. The firm marks itself out with its knowledge and interests in the industries in which it specialises, combined with its legal skills. In undertaking any work the firm aims to understand its clients' business and to add real value. The firm meets clients' expectations of concise, commercial and strategic advice offered proactively but cost-effectively. Harbottle & Lewis's range of cross-departmental groups and other initiatives ensure that lawyers within the firm are constantly exchanging information and ideas in relation to the latest developments in the law and those industries. Good communication is also a key part of how the firm successfully manages client relationships and it aims to achieve this through the innovative use of

Continued overleaf

technology, training, seconded arrangements, seminars, e-newsletters and bulletins. A selection of these and further information about the firm can be found on its website (see above).

CLIENTELE: Clients of the firm range from actors, musicians and other celebrities to plcs, NASDAQ and AIM-quoted companies, emerging growth companies, multinational rights-owners, entrepreneurs and charities.

HARDING EVANS

Queen Chambers, 2 North Street, Newport, NP2 1TE **Tel:** (01633) 244233 **Fax:** (01633) 246453 **DX:** 33202 **Email:** info@hevans.com **Website:** www.hevans.com **Ptnrs:** 8 **Asst solrs:** 13 **Other fee-earners:** 12

HARDWICK STALLARDS

Centurion House, 37 Jewry Street, London, EC3N 2ER
Tel: (020) 7423 1000 **Fax:** (020) 7481 3002 **DX:** 822 London/City
Email: mail@hardwickstallards.com **Website:** www.hardwickstallards.com

Managing Partner	Simon Hardwick
Senior Partner	Keith Robinson
Number of partners	13
Assistant solicitors	8
Other fee-earners	4

CONTACTS

Commercial Property	Michael Pearson
Company & Commercial	Alan Williams
Corporate Finance	Keith Robinson
Employment	Tola Ogundimu
Litigation	Rhodri James
Transportation	Paul Bugden

PRINCIPAL AREAS OF WORK:

Company & Commercial: A broad range of corporate and commercial work, including intellectual property, partnerships, mergers and acquisitions, sales and other disposals, joint ventures, commercial contracts, share option arrangements and general commercial advice.
Corporate Finance: Stock Exchange and regulatory advice, advising on issues, including official list, AIM and OFEX flotations, debt/equity issues, venture capital investment, institutional funding and secured lending, MBOs and MBIs, and corporate reconstructions.
Commercial Property: Commercial development and investment work for private and public companies, overseas investors, financial institutions and individual entrepreneurs, together with all aspects of landlord and tenant work, estate management and work for local authorities.
Litigation: Dealing with most kinds of commercial disputes, particular experience in the areas of landlord and tenant, construction contracts, factoring and banking, together with personal injury work.
Employment: Contentious and non-contentious work.
Transportation: Contentious and non-contentious shipping matters, multi-modal transport, containerisation, and trade finance and insurance.

CLIENTELE: Clientele consists principally of entrepreneur-managed businesses and a number of listed companies. The partner-led approach provides an in-house style of service with an emphasis on business experience.

HAROLD BENJAMIN LITTLEJOHN

Hill House, 67-71 Lowlands Road, Harrow, HA1 3EQ
Tel: (020) 8422 5678 **Fax:** (020) 8864 7530 **DX:** 4243 Harrow
Email: hbl@hben.co.uk **Website:** www.hben.co.uk

Senior Partner	Roger Lane
Number of partners	14
Assistant solicitors	2
Other fee-earners	10

AREAS OF PRACTICE

Commercial Property	40%
Litigation	25%
Corporate	20%
Private Client, Family & Probate	15%

CONTACTS

Commercial Leases	Sarah Paul
Company/Commercial	Roger Duncan
Development	Chris Batty
Family	Keith Flavell
General Litigation	Keith Boddy
Personal Injury	Andrew Tilsiter
Private Client	Jonathan Dorman
Property Litigation	Richard Crowe

THE FIRM: Known as Harold Benjamin & Collins until April 2000, the firm has undergone rapid growth in the past five years, investing in key people and information technology. Widely known for development and commercial conveyancing and property litigation, the firm is ideally located in central Harrow, which is increasingly convenient for a rapidly expanding base of property and other commercial clients, at regional and national levels. The increase in volume and quality of work has seen a series of expansions led by the property department but teams from all departments are fielded for multidisciplinary and high value transactions. The company/commercial and litigation departments continue to expand and attract new clients through recommendation.

PRINCIPAL AREAS OF WORK:

Property: The firm handles development, commercial and residential conveyancing, including the acquisition and legal management of sites for residential and mixed commercial, leisure and residential development; town planning and environmental law; commercial leasehold premises work acting for both landlords and tenants, including the grant and renewal of leases of commercial property and the sale and purchase of tenanted commercial property for investment; retail premises; commercial mortgage work for institutional lenders.
Litigation: Work includes building and property litigation with particular emphasis on the Landlord and Tenant Act 1954; personal injury and clinical negligence; employment law; general litigation; housing association tenant management.
Corporate/Commercial: The firm has a wide range of corporate clients, dealing with a broad spread of work including acquisitions, joint ventures, intellectual property, partnership, general commercial contracts, agency distribution, finance and competition law.

Private Client: The firm provides a full service of family law; wills and probate; residential conveyancing, especially substantial properties.
Family: Recent expansion has led to the strengthening of the family department to include members of the Solicitors Family Law Association, Family Law panel and qualified mediators enabling the firm to offer a broad range of services in family law but particularly in high value ancillary relief work.

CLIENTELE: The firm acts for a wide range of clients on a national basis including plcs, national house builders and private property developers engaged in both residential and commercial property development. The company commercial and litigation departments have national and local clients. The firm acts for a company with an excess of 1,500 retail units spread throughout the country. High value residential transactions are carried out for international clients, and the firm continues to value its associations with private clients, many of whom are local and have been with the firm for many years.

HARPER MACLEOD

The Ca'd'oro, 45 Gordon Street, Glasgow, G1 3PE
Tel: (0141) 221 8888 **Fax:** (0141) 226 4198 **DX:** GW86
Email: maildesk@harpermacleod.co.uk **Website:** www.harpermacleod.co.uk

Managing Partner	Lorne D Crerar
Number of partners	18
Assistant solicitors	15
Other fee-earners	10

CONTACTS

Banking	Lorne D Crerar
Commercial Litigation	Rod McKenzie
Commercial Property	Mark Dewar
Construction	Michael Conroy
Corporate	Donald Munro
Employment	Stephen Miller
Human Rights	Melanie Kerr
Insolvency	James Lloyd
Insurance	Richard Henderson
Intellectual Property & Technology	Tom Thomas
Licensing	Graeme Nisbet
Medical	Claire McManus
Planning & Environmental	Peter Ferguson
Private Client	Gordon Stoddart
Projects	Chris Kerr
Public Sector & Housing	Len Freedman
Recoveries	Dawn McKenzie
Sport	Stephen Miller

HARPERMACLEOD
SOLICITORS

THE FIRM: Harper Macleod, based in Glasgow's city centre, has a reputation for innovation and a progressive approach to law. The firm is well known for providing practical solutions to the demands of the corporate market place. The firm has grown rapidly since its inception. This expansion can be attributed to the dynamism of the firm's partners and Harper Macleod's readiness to challenge conventional approaches to legal problems. The firm has developed particular areas of specialism by establishing teams of solicitors with relevant expertise, known as Practice Groups. This structure encourages the development of flexible and tailored legal services to meet the individual needs of clients. A key feature of Harper Macleod is the long-standing relationships it develops with clients. The firm prides itself on getting to know clients' business in the same way that clients are encouraged to become involved in Harper Macleod. The firm is well resourced to meet the needs of clients with European and international interests. Harper Macleod is the Scottish member firm of ecomlex, an association of leading European e-commerce lawyers, and Commercial Law Affiliates, which provides access to a world-wide network of quality-assured law firms in over 70 jurisdictions.

PRINCIPAL AREAS OF WORK: The work undertaken by the firm is as wide ranging as its clients, from blue-chip UK and multinational companies to entrepreneurs and small business start-ups, and from both private and public sectors. In addition to the five traditional departments of corporate, commercial property, litigation, private client and recoveries, the firm operates 17 multi-disciplinary practice groups covering its main areas of specialism: banking, commercial property, construction, corporate and commercial, employment, human rights, IP&T, insolvency, medical, recoveries, licensing, planning and environmental, private client, projects, public sector and housing, insurance and sports law. The firm is particularly well known and has a leading reputation in social housing, employment, energy and sports law. Harper Macleod's national conferences have a successful track record and the firm is organising the sixth national housing conference and the fourth national employment conference in 2001. In addition, the firm acts for the largest mineral supplier in Scotland together with country's top football league.
E-commerce: One of Harper Macleod's high growth areas is e-commerce. Harper Macleod was the first firm in Scotland to launch a web-based legal package, dotcomstartup. The dotcom team acts for a wide range of online businesses and is ideally placed to provide a comprehensive business solutions package through the dotcom network (www.dotcomstartup.co.uk).
Commercial Property: The firm is active in the commercial property market with a wide range of clients including institutional property owners, developers and retailers. The firm's banking expertise has previously been described as 'one of a few of any substantial size'. Harper Macleod's commercial litigation expertise speaks for itself in the high profile cases in which the firm is instructed.

HARRIS & CARTWRIGHT

Windsor Crown House, 7 Windsor Rd, Slough, SL1 2DX
Tel: (01753) 810710 **Fax:** (01753) 810720 **DX:** 42268 Slough (West)
Email: enquiries@harrcart.co.uk **Website:** www.harrcart.co.uk

Senior Partner	Paul Norris
Number of partners	8
Assistant solicitors	19
Other fee-earners	16

AREAS OF PRACTICE

Company/Commercial	32%
Civil Litigation	29%
Conveyancing	20%
Family	14%
Wills, Probate, Trusts	5%

THE FIRM: Established in 1922, Harris & Cartwright is a progressive and enlightened firm, building on its accumulated knowledge and experience to provide a high quality, responsive and cost-effective service to all its clients. With two offices in Slough (one dedicated to company/commercial work) and others in nearby Langley and Burnham, the firm is one of the largest in the Thames Valley. The firm operates in London out of premises in Lincoln's Inn in partnership with well-respected sole practitioner Lawrence Cartier as Harris & Cartwright Cartier (tel 020 8400 7082), and provides a wide range of corporate and commercial services.

Continued overleaf

PRINCIPAL AREAS OF WORK:

Company & Commercial: A rapidly expanding department, now accounting for approximately one third of total fee income, assists business clients across the full spectrum of problems faced from start-up to flotation and beyond. Services include commercial conveyancing, business sales, takeovers, mergers and acquisitions, partnership formations and agreements, commercial negotiations, company secretarial and administrative matters, commercial litigation, insolvency and receivership, employment, terms and conditions of sale, service contracts and similar agreements. A growing niche market is advising organisations in the international context – British companies trading overseas and foreign companies wishing to operate in the UK.

Personal Injury & Clinical Negligence: All members of the department specialise in the work they undertake and are, variously, members of the Law Society's Personal Injury and Clinical Negligence panels, the AVMA Referral panel, APIL Clinical Negligence Special Interest Group, MASS, PEOPIL, ATLA, the Spinal Injuries Association and Headway. The practice has considerable experience in dealing with catastrophic injury cases, having achieved the highest and second highest awards of damages for personal injury cases in English courts (£9.3m and £5.1m).

Family: All qualified staff are members of the Solicitors Family Law Association and are specialists in this field. They are also, variously, members of the Law Society's Family and Children panels. Matters dealt with include high profile ancillary relief, divorce, children and injunction proceedings.

Financial Services: Headed by an independent financial adviser with 30 years industry experience, the department provides advice on investment, insurance and pensions to both individuals and organisations.

Residential Conveyancing: Operating from offices in Slough, Burnham and Langley, this department offers a full conveyancing service together with advice on development, planning and finance for residential properties.

Probate & Trusts: Working closely with the financial services department, a full range of wills, probate, trusts and estate administration, tax and inheritance tax planning is provided.

INTERNATIONAL: Work is handled in French, German and Punjabi.

CONTACTS

Clinical Negligence	Christopher Gooderidge
Commercial Litigation	Andrew Grant
Commercial Property	Paul Norris
Company/Commercial	Stephen Fuller
	Raj Dhokia
Debt Collection	Andrew Grant
E-commerce	Nick Burrows
Employment	Raj Dhokia
Family	Suzanne Allen
Financial Services	David McIntosh
Intellectual Property	Nick Burrows
Landlord & Tenant	Andrew Grant
Personal Injury	Kent Pattinson
Residential Conveyancing	Richard Palmer
Wills, Probate, Trusts	Ron Kerslake

H

HARRIS & HARRIS

14 Market Place, Wells, BA5 2RE
Tel: (01749) 674747 **Fax:** (01749) 834060 **DX:** 44900 Wells
Email: enquiries@harris-harris.co.uk **Website:** www.harris-harris.co.uk

Senior Partner	Timothy Berry

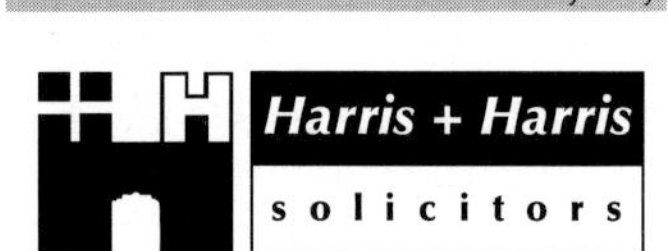

THE FIRM: Established for over 150 years, the firm has a broad client base and prides itself on its commitment to client care. The firm also has an office in Frome and a consultant in France.

PRINCIPAL AREAS OF WORK: Commercial, charity, ecclesiastical, education, employment, family, insolvency, mental health and personal injury law.

HARRISON BUNDEY & CO.

219-223 Chapeltown Road, Leeds, LS7 3DX **Tel:** (0113) 200 7400 **Fax:** (0113) 237 4685 **DX:** 713106 Leeds Park Square **Website:** www.harrisonbundey.co.uk **Ptnrs:** 15 **Asst solrs:** 8 **Other fee-earners:** 9 **Contact:** Jo Trythall • A Legal Aid franchised inner city high street practice specialising in crime, civil liberties, immigration and family, childcare, inquests and personal injury.

HARRISON CURTIS

8 Jockey's Fields, London, WC1R 4BF
Tel: (020) 7611 1720 **Fax:** (020) 7611 1721
Email: mail@harrisoncurtis.co.uk **Website:** www.harrisoncurtis.co.uk

Number of partners	4

CONTACTS

Advertising & Marketing	Vanessa Hall-Smith
Film & Television	Tim Curtis
Immigration	Vanessa Hall-Smith
Music	Nora Mullally
Theatre	Lawrence Harrison

HARRISON CURTIS
Solicitors

THE FIRM: A small niche practice set up in 1998 which is already established as a leading provider of legal services to the media, communication and entertainment industries. The firm's four partners each have recognised expertise within their own practice areas. Emphasis is placed on providing a high quality and accessible service at competitive rates and on effectively meeting client needs and expectations within a friendly working environment.

PRINCIPAL AREAS OF WORK: Areas covered include music, TV and film, theatre, advertising and marketing, e-commerce, sport, immigration.

HARRISON, LEITCH & LOGAN

Victoria House, 54 - 58 Chichester Street, Belfast, BT1 4HN
Tel: (028) 9032 3843 **Fax:** (028) 9033 2644 **DX:** 401 NR Belfast
Email: HarrisonLL@compuserve.com

Senior Partner	Ronnie Bowden

AREAS OF PRACTICE	
Litigation	40%
Company/Commercial/Employment	30%
Property	25%
Private Client/Other	15%

THE FIRM: Harrison Leitch & Logan continues to build upon its expertise in litigation, borne, initially out of a strong insurance base and in the company commercial and property field the firm is involved in many of the most substantial and prestigious transactions in the province. Quality assurance – ISO 9001. First private practice in Belfast to achieve Lexcel (Law Society Standard).

PRINCIPAL AREAS OF WORK:

Litigation: A large emphasis on personal injury, defence litigation, but also represents a broad base of insurers, loss adjusters and travel companies, lending institutions and large UK listed companies.

Property: Acquisition, disposal, development, financing and management of commercial as well as residential property.

Company/Commercial: Company formations, sale and purchase of assets, acquisition of companies, licensing, partnership agreements and shareholder agreements.

Private Client: A large following to whom the firm provides advices on property, wills and probate, trusts and tax planning.

H

HARROWELL SHAFTOE

1 St Saviourgate, York, YO1 2NQ **Tel:** (01904) 620 331 **Fax:** (01904) 655 855 **DX:** 61506 York **Email:** jfy@harrowell-shaftoe.co.uk **Website:** www.harrowells.co.uk **Ptnrs:** 15 **Asst solrs:** 12 **Other fee-earners:** 8 **Contact:** John Yeomans • Large York-based practice with eight specialist departments, offering commercial and private client services. Visit the firm's website for full details.

AREAS OF PRACTICE	
Private Client	50%
Litigation	35%
Company/Commercial	15%

HARTNELL & CO

20 Cathedral Yard, Exeter, EX1 1HB **Tel:** (01392) 421777 **Fax:** (01392) 421237 **DX:** 8388 Exeter **Ptnrs:** 2 **Asst solrs:** 4 **Other fee-earners:** 1

HARTWIG

15 William Mews, London, SW1X 9HF
Tel: (020) 7235 1504 **Fax:** (020) 8681 8183
Email: hartwig@beeb.net

Senior Partner	H.J. Hartwig

THE FIRM: London's largest firm of solicitor-notaries, with English, European and US lawyers; Rechtsanwälte, licensed in Germany since 1978. London-based multinational commercial, industrial, corporate, finance and property practice. The firm handles international litigation and private clients work. A substantial part of the firm's work is at pre-arranged fees on counsel basis for law firms and in-house lawyers.

HARVEY INGRAM OWSTON

20 New Walk, Leicester, LE1 6TX
Tel: (0116) 254 5454 **Fax:** (0116) 255 4559 **DX:** 17014 Leicester 2
Email: hio@hio.co.uk **Website:** www.hio.co.uk

Managing Partner	Chris Finlay
Senior Partner	Stephen Woolfe
Number of partners	23
Assistant solicitors	27
Other fee-earners	44

AREAS OF PRACTICE	
Litigation	33%
Commercial Property	26%
Company/Commercial	18%
Residential Property	15%
Probate & Trusts	8%

THE FIRM: Based in Leicestershire, this prominent practice acts for commercial and other clients not only in the East Midlands but also nationally. The firm makes client service a priority and has been accredited to ISO9001 since 1995. It is dedicated to further improvements to quality of service within a total quality programme.

PRINCIPAL AREAS OF WORK: The firm has five departments: company commercial; commercial property; residential property; litigation; and trusts.

Company/Commercial: For the company commercial department there have been a number of major corporate deals involving comprehensive commercial expertise including bank and development capital financing, MBOs and MBIs, business purchases and sales, commercial contracts, insolvencies, partnerships, pension funds, terms and conditions of trading and competition law. Particularly prominent deals over the last 12 months have included the acquisition of Jones Bootmaker and the Benson Shoe Ltd. take-over of the Oliver Group plc. The emergence of e-commerce and its growing importance to business has led to the expansion of work undertaken in this area, not only on the basis of legal skills, but also in relation to the level of service offered to clients. The firm has advised a number of Internet start-ups on all issues relating to e-commerce as well as updating clients on all forthcoming legislative changes in the electronic world.

Continued overleaf

Commercial Property: This department covers all aspects of commercial property dealings, including freehold and leasehold transactions, site acquisition, landlord and tenant law, rent control, agricultural and environmental law. Retail property is a particular strength and there has been significant growth in the area of planning and development.
Residential Property: Apart from private conveyancing this department specialises in housing association work and repossession sales for major institutions.
Litigation: Expertise includes commercial matters such as intellectual property, insolvency, building disputes, all aspects of employment law, licensing and professional negligence. A range of general litigation is also handled including personal injury and debt collection. The firm's growing family law group also works within the litigation department.
Trusts: Expertise includes estate planning, the drafting of trusts and wills, trust and estate administration as well as charity and Court of Protection work.

CLIENTELE: A prominent provider of legal services to national and regional companies, as well as looking after the needs of smaller businesses. Clients include Alliance & Leicester plc, Everards Brewery, The BSS Group plc, De Montfort Housing Association, Leicester Housing Association, National Car Rentals, Stead & Simpson, Benson Shoe, Golden Wonder, Weetabix, Vision Express (UK) and Samworth Brothers. A network of overseas contacts enables the firm to advise on foreign matters, particularly in Europe and the United States.

HASTIES

51 South Bridge, Edinburgh, EH1 1PP **Tel:** (0131) 556 7951 **Fax:** (0131) 558 1596 **DX:** 16 Edinburgh **Email:** edin.hastie@ukonline.co.uk
Ptnrs: 2 **Asst solrs:** 3 **Other fee-earners:** 4

HATCH BRENNER

4 Theatre Street, Norwich, NR2 1QY **Tel:** (01603) 660811 **Fax:** (01603) 619473 **DX:** 5237 Norwich
Ptnrs: 9 **Asst solrs:** 2 **Other fee-earners:** 10 **Contact:** Richard Cassel • Property, commercial, civil litigation (including employment and personal injury), family and crime. Legal Aid Franchise, Personal Injury and Children Panels.

HAYES

63-64 Magdalen Street, Exeter, EX2 4HN **Tel:** (01392) 202 742 **Fax:** (01392) 202 743 **Ptnrs:** 1 **Other fee-earners:** 1

HAY & KILNER

Merchant House, 30 Cloth Market, Newcastle upon Tyne, NE1 1EE **Tel:** (0191) 232 8345 **Fax:** (0191) 221 0514 **DX:** 61019 Newcastle upon Tyne
Email: Lawyers@hay-kilner.co.uk **Website:** www.hay-kilner.co.uk **Ptnrs:** 22 **Asst solrs:** 11 **Other fee-earners:** 8

HBM SAYERS

13 Bath Street, Glasgow, G2 1HY **Tel:** (0141) 353 2121 **Fax:** (0141) 353 2181 **DX:** 47 Glasgow **Email:** mail@hmbsayers.com **Ptnrs:** 13
Asst solrs: 14 **Other fee-earners:** 7

HEGARTY & CO

48 Broadway, Peterborough, PE1 1YW **Tel:** (01733) 346333 **Fax:** (01733) 562338 **DX:** 16850 Peterborough **Email:** mail@hegarty.co.uk
Website: www.hegarty.co.uk **Ptnrs:** 5 **Asst solrs:** 12 **Other fee-earners:** 24

HEMPSONS

Hempsons House, 40 Villiers Street, London, WC2N 6NJ
Tel: (020) 7839 0278 **Fax:** (020) 7839 8212 **DX:** 138411 Charing Cross 1
Email: london@hempsons.co.uk **Website:** www.hempsons.co.uk

Clarendon House, 9 Victoria Avenue, Harrogate, HG1 1DY
Tel: (01423) 522 331 **Fax:** (01423) 500 733 **DX:** 11965 Harrogate 1
Email: harrogate@hempsons.co.uk

Portland Tower, Portland Street, Manchester, M1 3LF
Tel: (0161) 228 0011 **Fax:** (0161) 236 6734 **DX:** 14482 Manchester 2
Email: manchester@hempsons.co.uk

Managing Partner	Janice Barber
Senior Partner	Bertie Leigh
Number of partners	27
Assistant solicitors	80
Other fee-earners	20

CONTACTS

Charity........Ian Hempseed (London)
Commercial........Ian Hempseed (London)
Commercial Litigation..David Stone (London)
Commercial Property....Graham Lea (London)
........Jane Donnison (Manchester)
........Louise Holroyd (Harrogate)
Defamation........Mark Shaw (London)
Employment........Janice Barber (London)
........Kerry Devlin (Harrogate)
........Sean Reynolds (Manchester)
Healthcare........Bertie Leigh (London)
........Bill Leason (Manchester)
........John Taylor (Harrogate)

THE FIRM: Hempsons is well known for its particular expertise in the field of medical and healthcare law, partnership work and charity law. The firm has long provided a comprehensive range of services to the NHS, the professions and charities.

PRINCIPAL AREAS OF WORK:

Clinical Litigation: The firm has long been renowned for its expertise in this field and handles matters relating to medical and dental negligence (all areas of hospital and general practice). Also covered are class actions;

disciplinary cases for NHS trusts, professional organisations and individual practitioners; codes of professional practice and medical crime. Hempsons is one of the national firms on the NHS Litigation Authority's panel of healthcare solicitors to act in defence of clinical negligence claims, and all three offices are represented.

Healthcare: The firm advises a range of healthcare organisations on all aspects of law and ethics, mental health and community care law, administrative law, NHS regulatory law and the constitution and formation of PCGs and PCTs.

Partnership: Advice is given to doctors and other professionals on the formation of partnerships and partnership agreements; the accession and retirement of partners; the dissolution of partnerships and partnership disputes.

Commercial Litigation/Defamation: The firm advises on all forms of UK commercial disputes, including litigation in respect of employment, insurance, arbitration and ADR work. Defamation work is principally carried out for local authorities.

Commercial Property: The department handles commercial, institutional, professional property, including acquisitions and developments, grant, renewal and termination of leases, rent reviews and the Cost Rent Scheme for general practitioners, including funding proposed surgery developments. Recent deals have included the funding of a large scale indoor real snow ski slope and leisure centre in West Yorkshire with a developed value of between £50 and £60 million; acting for one of the world's largest power suppliers on substantial sub-lettings at its headquarters building in the City of London; the acquisition of a new HQ for a newly established College for the Association of British Dispensing Opticians (ABDO) – The ABDO College of Education and the funding and leasing of London Zoo.

Charity Law: The firm provides a complete service to charities, large and small and currently numbering well in excess of 100. This includes: formation and restructuring of charities; advice to trustees and management on legal duties and powers; updating constitutions; employment issues; dealings with the Charity Commission and the Inland Revenue; financial and commercial activities; trading subsidiaries; fundraising and appeals; disputed legacies. The firm has been active in running seminars on topics of concern to charities and other 'not for profit' organisations.

Commercial Work: The firm specialises in dealing with the commercial and contractual issues of NHS Trusts and Health Authorities, charities and professional clients.

Employment: Hempsons has a lively and proactive team of employment lawyers providing solutions to HR problems in the NHS, for employers and professionals, and those of its charity clients. The firm has particular experience in all types of discrimination work and all the relevant NHS circulars.

CLIENTELE: Clients include health authorities, NHS trusts, healthcare organisations, professional bodies, Royal Colleges, learned societies and individual professionals.

CONTACTS CONTINUED

Medical Crime	Anne Ball (Manchester)
	Jill Crombie (London)
Medical Litigation	Bertie Leigh (London)
	Frances Harrison (Manchester)
	Adrienne D'Arcy (Harrogate)
Partnership	Lynne Abbess (London)

HEMPSONS SOLICITORS

HENDERSON BOYD JACKSON WS

19 Ainslie Place, Edinburgh, EH3 6AU **Tel:** (0131) 226 6881 **Fax:** (0131) 225 1103 **DX:** ED27 EDINBURGH **Email:** hbj@hbj.co.uk
Website: http://www.hbj.co.uk **Ptnrs:** 22 **Asst solrs:** 32 **Other fee-earners:** 48

HENMANS

116 St. Aldates, Oxford, OX1 1HA
Tel: (01865) 722181 **Fax:** (01865) 792376 **DX:** 4311 Oxford 1
Email: welcome@henmans.co.uk **Website:** www.henmans.co.uk

Managing Partner	Sam Eeley
Senior Partner	Anthony Henman
Number of partners	19
Assistant solicitors	30
Other fee-earners	15

AREAS OF PRACTICE

Professional Negligence & Commercial Litigation	29%
Personal Injury	26%
Property	17%
Private Client (inc. Family)/ Charities/Trusts	16%
Corporate/Employment	12%

THE FIRM: Henmans is an established Oxford-based practice with a national reputation, serving both corporate and private clients. Henmans' philosophy is to be extremely client focused to deliver exceptional levels of service. The firm achieves this through an emphasis on teamwork to ensure clients always have access to a specific partner with specialist support, and through an ongoing programme of recruitment and training to guarantee clients optimum advice and guidance. Henmans has invested heavily in IT and has implemented a case management system to enhance services and client care. Henmans' policy of bespoke services and controlled costs ensure that both corporate and private clients benefit from City level litigation standards at competitive regional prices

PRINCIPAL AREAS OF WORK: Henmans has continued to expand and further enhance its presence at national and regional scales.

Professional Negligence: Henmans has greatly expanded its specialist professional indemnity work on behalf of solicitors and other professionals, and has assembled a large team of lawyers (including a higher courts solicitor-advocate) with expertise in professional negligence litigation. Henmans has emerged as one of the top 'post-SIF' firms and is a key player in the new insurance marketplace. The firm also undertakes an increasing volume of insurance and commercial litigation and has the capacity to handle marine insurance disputes.

Personal Injury & Clinical Negligence: The firm has a substantial insurance company client list. Both departments are particularly strong and have a number of AVMA and personal injury panelists.

Employment: Employer and employee work undertaken across the spectrum, with a policy of in-house representation at Employment tribunals. The employer client base includes major national and international companies.

Continued overleaf

Corporate: Henmans offers wide-ranging corporate work for both listed and private companies, including venture capital, sales and acquisitions. The corporate team is experienced in copyright, publishing and computer law, and the firm acts for several leading trade organisations. There is a strong commitment to the enterprise movement and to emergent businesses.
Commercial Property: Specialist commercial property advice focuses on planning and development, option deals, management techniques, sales, purchases, landlord and tenant and employee relocation. Henmans' agricultural and land practice has developed to meet client needs both regionally and nationally. The firm represents a number of substantial estates, Oxford colleges and national charities.
Charities: The firm's reputation for charity law continues to grow with a specialist department concentrating on legacy recovery work, charity start-ups, commercial ventures for charities, property matters and all types of advice to charity trustees.
Private Client: There is a strong private client department providing tax planning for high-net-worth individuals and all types of trust and probate work, including contentious probate actions. Three members of the team belong to the Society of Trust and Estate Practitioners. Matrimonial and family work is undertaken (including a substantial amount of high quality financial work). Residential property work is also offered in the full range of services for private individuals. All the lawyers at Henmans are effective, hard negotiators, respected by competitors for their integrity, expertise and enthusiasm to obtain the best possible results for their clients.

HENRY HYAMS & CO
7 South Parade, Leeds, LS1 5QX **Tel:** (0113) 243 2288 **Fax:** (0113) 242 9714 **DX:** 12028 **Email:** info@henryhyams.com **Ptnrs:** 8 **Asst solrs:** 6 **Other fee-earners:** 19

HENRY MILNER & CO
County House, 14 Hatton Garden, London, EC1N 8AT **Tel:** (020) 7831 9944 **Fax:** (020) 7831 9941 **DX:** 53305 Clerkenwell
Number of partners::1 **Other fee-earners::**1

HEPTONSTALLS

7-15 Gladstone Terrace, Goole, DN14 5AH
Tel: (01405) 765661 **Fax:** (01405) 764201 **DX:** 28831 Goole
Email: legal@heponstalls.co.uk

1 Vicar Lane, Howden, DN14 7BP
Tel: (01430) 430209 **Fax:** (01430) 432101 **DX:** 700844 Howden
Email: legal@heponstalls.co.uk

9-11 Ropergate End, Pontefract, WF8 1JU
Tel: (01977) 602804 **Fax:** (01977) 602805 **DX:** 22255 Pontefract
Email: legal@heponstalls.co.uk

72 Mary Street, Scunthorpe, DN15 6LA
Tel: (01724) 289959 **Fax:** (01724) 289965 **DX:** 14732 Scunthorpe
Email: legal@heponstalls.co.uk

Senior Partner	Roger Beattie
Number of partners	8
Assistant solicitors	10
Other fee-earners	19

AREAS OF PRACTICE	
PI/Clinical Negligence	55%
Property/Common Law/Civil	18%
Matrimonial	10%
Criminal	9%
Trusts, Probate & Tax	8%

CONTACTS	
Agriculture	M G Walker
Clinical Negligence	J Burman
Commercial/Property	R Beattie
Criminal	A S Pinchbeck
Employment	A S Pinchbeck
Personal Injury	J Burman
Tax/Probate & Trust	M G Walker
Welfare & Family	C Luckett

THE FIRM: Heptonstalls, with its four offices in Goole, Pontefract, Scunthorpe and Howden, is a major provider of legal services in Yorkshire and North Lincolnshire. The firm aims to ensure that clients receive an efficient personal and friendly service whatever their legal needs.

PRINCIPAL AREAS OF WORK:
Personal Injury & Clinical Negligence: This department has a leading regional reputation for claimant work arising from medical treatment, road traffic accidents, industrial accidents and disease, defective products and related matters. Special interests include obstetrics and gynaecology, head and spinal injuries, and traumatic brain injury. John Burman is one of two members of the AVMA and Law Society Clinical Negligence panels and three members of the Personal Injury Panel. The department has both clinical negligence and personal injury franchises in Goole, Pontefract and Scunthorpe.
Commercial/Agriculture: Advice on a wide range of business and commercial law including employment and commercial litigation. The firm has extensive experience in advising agricultural businesses on such areas as land law, conservation, agricultural tenancies and other aspects of land management.
Private Client: The firm advises on property, tax and family finance, wills, probate and trusts, landlord and tenant disputes, family and matrimonial law, and welfare benefits.

HERBERT MALLAM GOWERS
126 High St, Oxford, OX1 4DG **Tel:** (01865) 244661 **Fax:** (01865) 721263 **DX:** 4321 Oxford **Ptnrs:** 6 **Asst solrs:** 4 **Other fee-earners:** 2

HERBERT SMITH

Exchange House, Primrose Street, London, EC2A 2HS
Tel: (020) 7374 8000 **Fax:** (020) 7374 0888 **DX:** 28
Email: contact@herbertsmith.com **Website:** www.herbertsmith.co.uk

THE FIRM: Founded in 1882, Herbert Smith is an international law firm with offices throughout Europe and Asia. With 188 partners, 800 other lawyers and a total staff of more than 1,800, it provides clients worldwide with industry-tailored advice. The firm is committed to providing high quality and innovative legal services to major corporations, governments, financial institutions and all types of commercial organisations. Herbert Smith offers an unrivalled balance of corporate, commercial and dispute resolution advice to its clients worldwide. Each of the firm's offices has access to the firm's global expertise, resources and capabilities.

PRINCIPAL AREAS OF WORK:
Corporate & Commercial: Herbert Smith provides a comprehensive range of legal services across all areas of corporate and commercial life. The firm is consistently highly placed in legal league tables and rankings. Frequently, its role puts it at the centre of industries which are reshaping, and the firm is well known for its innovative work in groundbreaking deals and restructurings. The firm has a long-standing reputation for advice on mergers, acquisitions and takeovers and is highly regarded for its expertise in corporate finance. Other areas of corporate expertise include competition law; corporate recovery; employment; European law; insurance; investment funds; media; telecommunications; pensions and share schemes; trusts and charities.
Finance & Banking: Herbert Smith is one of the leading firms in debt finance transactions and finance is central to the firm's practice. Propelled by dramatic growth over the last few years, the firm's debt finance practice continues to advise on international and domestic deals in the bank lending (including acquisition finance and property finance), securitisation and capital markets, asset finance and project finance markets, as well as on corporate recovery matters. The firm's finance lawyers are experienced in operating at the highest level in more than one sector of the debt finance market. The experience of acting for parties on all sides of transactions, together with the range of work carried out by all partners and assistants, gives the firm a broad perspective when approaching transactions, particularly those that are innovative.
Litigation & Arbitration: Herbert Smith enjoys a formidable reputation for its expertise in both domestic and international litigation and arbitration – a pre-eminent position it has held for several decades. The firm has consistently been ranked as the leading UK and Asian firm for commercial litigation. In this area the breadth of the firm's practice distinguishes Herbert Smith from its competitors. Areas of specialism include administrative and public law; banking; civil fraud; construction; defamation; employment; energy; environment; information technology; insurance and reinsurance; intellectual property; public and private international law; professional indemnity; regulatory and compliance cases; sport. Herbert Smith has experience before every type of court and tribunal and conducts arbitrations in all parts of the world. It is the firm's consistent aim to add value to its client's business as a whole, and not to concentrate alone on the narrow issues in dispute. It uses alternative dispute resolution procedures in appropriate cases and several of the partners are accredited mediators.

CLIENTELE: The firm's clients represent many of the world's leading companies including a high proportion of the FTSE 250.

INTERNATIONAL: During the last year Herbert Smith continued the rapid development of its international network of offices. In the last two years the firm has opened offices in Beijing, Moscow, Bangkok and Tokyo, and has recently formed a formal relationship with Gleiss Lutz (a top five German law firm) as well as an association with a leading team of commercial lawyers in Indonesia, Hiswara Bunjamin and Tandjung (HBT). The firm also has a formal alliance with the highly rated Singapore corporate specialist law firm, Arfat & Gunasingham. The firm has offices in Moscow, Beijing, Bangkok and Tokyo that complement its long-established offices in London, Brussels, Paris, Hong Kong and Singapore. All Herbert Smith offices cooperate closely with one another to ensure the client recieves a seamless cross-border service. This is in accordance with the firm's stated objective of meeting the needs of its clients in the major financial and commercial centres of the world together with the continued expansion of operations in Europe and Asia.

Senior Partner	Richard Bond
Worldwide Figures	
Number of partners	188
Assistants solicitors	523
Other fee-earners	277

CONTACTS

Acquisition Finance	Clive Barnard
Administrative & Public Law	Andrew Lidbetter
Arbitration	Julian Lew
Construction & Engineering	Michael Davis
Corporate Recovery	Stephen Gale
Debt Capital Markets	Dina Albagli
Employee Incentives	Colin Chamberlain
Employment	John Farr
Energy, Natural Resources & Utilities	Ted Greeno
	Alan Jowett
Entertainment & Media	Stephen Wilkinson
	Charles Plant
Equity Capital Markets	Caroline Goodall
EU, Competition & Regulation	Jonathan Scott
Finance & Banking	Clive Barnard
Financial Institutions	Marian Pell
Financial Services	Marian Pell
IT & E-commerce	Chris Rees
PFI/PPP/Infrastructure	Andrew Preece
Insurance & Reinsurance Litigation	David Higgins
	David Reston
Intellectual Property	Bill Moodie
International Law	Campbell McLachlan
Investment Funds	Nigel Farr
Leisure & Sport	Alan Watts
	Stephen Wilkinson
Life Sciences	Henry Raine
	Andrew Rich
Litigation	Harry Anderson
M&A	Michael Walter
Pensions	Ian Gault
Planning & Environment	Patrick Robinson
	Sophie Quayle
Private Equity	Tim Steadman
Project Finance	Andrew Preece
Real Estate	Iain Rothnie
Securitisation	Jane Borrows
Tax	David Martin
Telecoms	Tim Bellis
	Philip Carrington
Trusts & Charities	John Wood
WTO/World Trade Law	Craig Pouncey

HERBERT SMITH

H

HEWITSON BECKE + SHAW

Shakespeare House, 42 Newmarket Road, Cambridge, CB5 8EP
Tel: (01223) 461155 **Fax:** (01223) 316511 **DX:** 133155 Cambridge 8
Email: mail@hewitsons.com

7 Spencer Parade, Northampton, NN1 5AB
Tel: (01604) 233233 **Fax:** (01604) 627941 **DX:** 12401 Northampton

53 High Street, Saffron Walden, CB10 1AR
Tel: (01799) 522471 **Fax:** (01799) 524742 **DX:** 200300 Saffron Walden

Managing Partner	Alan Brett
Senior Partner	Ian Barnett
Number of partners	51
Assistant solicitors	40
Other fee-earners	53

AREAS OF PRACTICE

Corporate	33%
Property	30%
Technology	18%
Private	19%

CONTACTS

ADR	Dominic Hopkins
Agriculture	Ian Barnett
Biotechnology	Simon Portman
Commercial Property	Alan Brett
Company/Commercial	John Dix
Construction	Timothy Richards
Debt Services	Clare Bangor-Jones
Employment	Nicholas Sayer
Investment Services	Andrew Lowin
IT & IP	William Thatcher
Litigation	Dominic Hopkins
Pensions	Clare Colacicchi
Planning & Environmental	Peter Brady
Private Client	Peter Ewart
Property Funding	Alan Brett
Residential Property	David Sabberton

THE FIRM: Hewitson Becke + Shaw is one of the UK's leading corporate and commercial firms. It also has a substantial private client practice. With origins in 1865 and established in its current form in 1989, the firm continues to show substantial growth year on year through a policy of high investment in senior personnel and commitment to a dynamic corporate management structure and quality care systems providing flexibility and responsiveness to client needs. HB+S has a total of 110 lawyers, including 51 partners, meeting growing demand for its services regionally, nationally and internationally. The firm has established a leading reputation in many specific areas of law, including company/commercial, intellectual property, information technology, commercial litigation, commercial property, construction, employment, competition law, planning and pensions. Its private client section is one of the largest outside London. HB+S has been closely associated over many years with the development of Cambridge and the 'Silicon Fen' region as a world-leading centre for hi-tech and IT-based business. The firm's legal expertise and professional approach matches that of major City of London firms, but HB+S' strategic locations in East Anglia and the East Midlands add the benefits of cost-effectiveness and extensive local knowledge. The firm provides a valuable international dimension to its client services through LawExchange International, a dynamic and growing network of like-minded firms in Europe, North America and the Pacific Rim, which HB+S co-founded in 1994.

PRINCIPAL AREAS OF WORK:

Commercial Property: The firm handles a large volume of commercial property work, from the construction of major commercial residential developments and science parks to small retail and industrial units. The firm is increasingly used by major concerns abroad, including Hong Kong. Work includes the acquisition, development and letting of all manner of commercial sites. The firm has particular expertise in complex funding mechanisms and joint ventures.

Company/Commercial: Work includes mergers and acquisitions, company structuring and restructuring, venture and development capital investment, management buy-outs/buy-ins, rights issues, Stock Exchange flotations, European Union and International law, merger control, OFT/Commission investigations, joint ventures, pensions, employee share option and incentive schemes, partnerships and insolvency. The firm acts for a significant number of public limited companies as well as owner-managed businesses and is doing an increasing amount of UK-related work from an expanded US client base.

Intellectual Property: The firm advises on all aspects of obtaining, exploiting and enforcing intellectual property rights, with particular expertise in computer hardware and software, biotechnology, pharmaceutical, film, music and book publishing industries.

Information Technology: HB+S acts for users and suppliers including major IT companies, software houses and ISPs. The firm handles licensing, distribution, development, support and other procurement issues, as well as disputes, data protection and e-commerce.

Private Client: Work includes administration of estates, trusts, tax, wills, enduring powers of attorney, pensions, charities, residential property advice, landed estates, court of protection and matrimonial.

Litigation: The services are provided through eight groups each consisting of staff dedicated to one of the following areas of specialisation: banking, intellectual property, personal injury, crime and family. The firm acts nationally for several major clearing banks.

Employment: Work includes injunctions, service contracts, pensions, dismissal, redundancy, compensation for unfair dismissal, profit sharing and share option schemes and general employee benefits. The firm is a member of the Employment Lawyers Association and six members of the firm are individual members of the Association.

Agriculture: Work includes the granting of development options by landowners, joint venture and share farming agreements, farm partnerships, taxation and environmental matters, sales and tenancies and mineral exploitation. The firm has a significant number of landed estates and farming clients.

Bloodstock: The firm advises on all aspects of bloodstock law with particular emphasis on property transactions and general litigation.

Planning & Environmental: Work includes planning appeals and local plan inquiries, advising developers, investors, local authorities, conservation and amenity groups, and individuals. The firm has two members of the Law Society's Specialist Planning Panel.

Residential Property: Work includes sales, purchases and mortgages of freehold/leasehold houses/flats for private clients and institutions as well as builders and developers.

Investment Services: Work includes a comprehensive range of services for individuals, company executives, private trustees, pension fund trustees and charities.
Debt Services: Work includes consultancy, outsourced credit control, pre-legal service and debt recovery.

HEWITT & GILPIN

Thomas House, 14-16 James Street South, Belfast, BT2 7GA **Tel:** (028) 9057 3573 **Fax:** (028) 9057 3574 **DX:** 2000 NR Belfast 2 **Email:** law@hewittandgilpin.co.uk **Website:** www.hewittandgilpin.co.uk **Ptnrs:** 7 **Asst solrs:** 3

HEXTALL ERSKINE

28 Leman Street, London, E1 8ER **Tel:** (020) 7488 1424 **Fax:** (020) 7481 0232 **DX:** 562 CITY **Email:** info@hextalls.com **Website:** www.hextalls.com **Ptnrs:** 18 **Asst solrs:** 15 **Other fee-earners:** 22

HIBBERT DURRAD DAVIES

25 Barker Street, Nantwich, CW5 5EN **Tel:** (01270) 624225 **Fax:** (01270) 628065 **DX:** 22004 Nantwich **Ptnrs:** 10 **Asst solrs:** 11 **Other fee-earners:** 10 **Contact:** Martin Measures • The firm specialises in agriculture; commercial and domestic property; probate and trusts; licencing; litigation.

CONTACTS

Agriculture	David Young
Commercial & Domestic Property	Martin Measures
Licencing	David Sayer
Litigation	Richard Large
Probate & Trusts	Derek Dale

HICKMAN & ROSE

144 Liverpool Road, London, N1 0LA
Tel: (020) 7700 2211 **Fax:** (020) 7609 6044 **DX:** 122234 Upper Islington
Email: mail@hickmanandrose.co.uk

Number of partners	4
Assistant solicitors	25
Other fee-earners	12

THE FIRM: Hickman & Rose is a leading criminal law and human rights firm. It delivers a consistently high quality of work across the full spectrum of criminal justice issues. The firm has an excellent reputation in serious crime and commercial fraud and is renowned for its work on behalf of prisoners.

PRINCIPAL AREAS OF WORK:
Crime: A substantial criminal caseload is run with total commitment to quality and client care. A small group of highly experienced lawyers specialises in larger matters.
Serious Fraud: Serious and international fraud work is backed by the commitment to hold prosecution authorities to the letter and the spirit of the law.
Police Actions: This team has fought and won many cases involving police wrongdoing.
Prisoners Rights: A tough and combative prison rights practice has succeeded on securing improvements in conditions for many prisoners.
Public Law/ECHR: Specialist litigation in the UK and Strasbourg challenging human rights abuses across the criminal justice system.
Mental Health: A growing team works for those detained under the Mental Health Act or affected by community care legislation.
Discrimination: A small team specialises in sex, race and disability discrimination within the criminal justice and mental health systems.

AREAS OF PRACTICE

Crime	50%
Serious Fraud	15%
Police Actions	10%
Prisoners Rights	10%
Discrimination	5%
Mental Health	5%
Public Law	5%

CONTACTS

Crime	Ross Dixon
Discrimination Law	Sarah Ricca
Mental Health	Dawn Lofters
Police Actions	Hope Liebersohn
Prisoners Rights	Liz Sutcliffe
Public Law	Daniel Machover
Serious Fraud	Ben Rose

HIGGS & SONS

Blythe House, 134 High Street, Brierley Hill, DY5 3BG **Tel:** (01384) 342 100 **Fax:** (01384) 342 000 **DX:** 22751 Brierley Hill **Email:** law@higgs-and-sons.co.uk **Ptnrs:** 26 **Asst solrs:** 16 **Other fee-earners:** 11 **Contact:** David Morgan • Established 1875. Legal Aid franchise. ISO 9002. Company/commercial; insolvency; commercial/residential/agricultural property; planning; environment; employment/sex discrimination; personal injury/medical negligence; motor accidents; commercial and consumer litigation; crime.

AREAS OF PRACTICE

Common Law	48%
Domestic Conveyancing	16%
Probate, Wills & Trusts	13%
Company/Commercial	12%
Commercial Conveyancing	11%

R. & J. M. HILL BROWN & CO

3 Newton Place, Glasgow, G3 7PU **Tel:** (0141) 332 3265/333 0636 **Fax:** (0141) 332 2613/332 0414 **DX:** 512207 Glasgow-Sandyford Place **Email:** info@hillbrown.co.uk **Ptnrs:** 6 **Asst solrs:** 1 **Other fee-earners:** 1 **Contact:** Jack Cummins • General practice specialising in licensing work for licensed trade and the entertainment industry.

AREAS OF PRACTICE

Licensing	35%
Domestic/Commercial Conveyancing	25%
Trusts and Securities	21%
General Court	19%

HILL DICKINSON

Pearl Assurance House, 2 Derby Square, Liverpool, L2 9XL
Tel: (0151) 236 5400 **Fax:** (0151) 236 2175 **DX:** 14129 Liverpool 1
Email: law@hilldicks.com **Website:** www.hilldickinson.com

34 Cuppin Street, Chester, CH1 2BN
Tel: (01244) 896 600 **Fax:** (01244) 896 601 **DX:** 19991 Chester

50 Fountain Street, Manchester, M2 2AS
Tel: (0161) 278 8800 **Fax:** (0161) 278 8801 **DX:** 14487 Manchester 2

Sun Court, 66/67 Cornhill, London, EC3V 3NB
Tel: (020) 7695 1000 **Fax:** (020) 7695 1001 **DX:** 98940 Cheapside 2

Managing Partner	David Wareing
Senior Partner	Tony Wilson
Number of partners	79
Assistant solicitors	57
Other fee-earners	85

AREAS OF PRACTICE

Litigation (inc. Insurance/Construction/ Professional Negligence)	40%
Commercial Property/ Planning & Environmental	17%
Shipping	16%
Health/Medical Negligence	14%
Company/Commercial/Pensions/ Tax/Intellectual Property/PFI	13%

CONTACTS

Commercial	David Swaffield
Corporate	Glyn Dale-Jones
Health	Allan Mowat
Insurance	David Scott
	Simon Parrington
Marine & Cargo	John Hulmes
	Julia Marshall
Private Client	Mike Quinn
Property/Construction	David Chinn
	David Swaffield

H

THE FIRM: Founded in 1810, Hill Dickinson is now one of the largest commercial law firms in the North West, providing a portfolio of specialist legal advice to both the domestic and international market. It is fundamental to the Hill Dickinson philosophy to care for clients, whilst delivering a highly professional, cost effective service. ISO 9001 accreditation reflects a demonstrated and on-going commitment to client care. The practice has a strong and marked reputation in the insurance, litigation, company commercial, commercial property, marine and transport domain, and provides specialists to deal with an increasingly wide range of legal requirements. The firm has a total of 400 staff, including more than 70 partners. Operations have been substantially extended over recent years with offices now in Liverpool, Manchester, Chester and the City of London. All offices have full conference facilities, online communication links, an extensive reference library and access to a number of electronic legal data sources. Literature, outlining in detail all aspects of the firm's activities, is available on request and members of the firm are pleased to have a preliminary discussion on any specific requirement.

PRINCIPAL AREAS OF WORK: With a wealth of specialist advisers, the firm undertakes a wide range of legal work in the commercial and private domain and is structured into specialist groups.
Insurance: One of the largest departments of its kind in the country, Hill Dickinson acts for most major insurers and, through them, a large proportion of their corporate and individual policy holders. The department has the capacity and resources to deal with a wide range of litigation issues, including the most complex of 'test' or multi-party actions, and to react quickly to incidents or claims requiring immediate legal assistance.
Health: The firm has one of the UK's largest medico-legal practices, acting on behalf of health authorities, NHS trusts and other health service bodies. The firm is a member of the panel of solicitors maintained by the National Health Service Litigation Authority and was the first in the country licensed to provide health/ medical negligence elements within training contracts.
Property & Construction: The Hill Dickinson property and construction team provides legal advice across the full range of property matters, including construction and engineering projects. It acts for retailers, manufacturers, service providers, developers, investors, contractors and public sector clients. It has experience in retail, office, industrial, leisure and residential projects and provides specialist advice in relation to environmental and planning issues.
Commercial: The commercial group advises on a broad range of matters as diverse as intellectual property, European law, franchising, employment, pensions and PFI. It is one of the leading commercial litigation firms in the North West and where litigation is inevitable the commercial litigation team provides full support.
Corporate: Lawyers in the corporate group provide advice on all aspects of corporate law including company formation, mergers, acquisitions, management buy-outs and buy-ins, venture capital, flotation and insolvency.
Marine & Cargo: Recognised as one of the leading specialist shipping solicitors in the UK, Hill Dickinson has provided advice to both national and international clients since 1810. The department also has well-established experts handling cargo and transit matters, and consequently has the resources to offer a truly comprehensive service.
Private Client: The firm retains a strong private client base, providing specialist advice on, for example, tax and estate planning, wills, trusts, probate and financial planning matters.

HILL TAYLOR DICKINSON

Irongate House, Duke's Place, London, EC3A 7HX
Tel: (020) 7283 9033 **Fax:** (020) 7283 1144 **DX:** 550
Email: enquiry@htd-london.com **Website:** www.htd-law.com

Managing Partner	Rhys Clift
Chairman	Robert Wallis
UK	
Number of partners	22
Assistant solicitors	21
Other fee-earners	9
International	
Number of partners	5
Assistant solicitors	6

AREAS OF PRACTICE

Shipping & Commodities	56%
Insurance	18%
Commercial Transactional	17%
Personal Injury	8%
Others	1%

CONTACTS

Commercial Property	Richard Taylor
Commodities	Jeffrey Isaacs
Company/Commercial	Malcolm Entwistle
Insurance	Tim Taylor
Personal Injury	Maria Pittordis
Shipping	John Evans
	Stephen Cropper
	Robert Wallis
	Andrew Johnson

Hill
Taylor
Dickinson
solicitors

THE FIRM: Hill Taylor Dickinson is a commercial firm servicing the business and financial community in the United Kingdom and internationally. The firm is based in the City of London, and also has offices in Dubai and Greece. The firm has expanded considerably with overseas offices being established and new areas of business being developed. This growth has been achieved by organic growth within the firm complemented by external recruitment (including at partner level). Clients range from major international corporations to owner managed businesses. Critical to the success of the firm's relationship with all of them is close partner involvement and understanding of their operations and markets. Hill Taylor Dickinson is a progressive and dynamic firm seeking to provide an effective personal service to both national and international clients and a commercial approach to legal problems and their resolution.

PRINCIPAL AREAS OF WORK: Hill Taylor Dickinson's practice is entirely commercial.

Company/Commercial & Finance: The firm's transactional work includes company/commercial and financing, including venture capital, leasing and asset finance, ship building and finance, corporate buy-outs and buy-ins, as well as commercial property. Its clients include banks and other financial institutions, both City-based and overseas, insurers, employers' organisations and a wide variety of corporate clients, notably in the leisure, manufacturing and publishing sectors.

Personal Injury, ITF & Employment: This department acts mainly for employers, insurers, owners and P&I clubs in shipping and transport and a wide variety of industries. It deals with mass and individual claims. The department's work includes preventative and practical advice, including the drafting of accident reporting documents and procedures, drafting contractual clauses and employment contracts, safety policies and a whole spectrum of employment and personal injury claims.

Shipping: Hill Taylor Dickinson's expertise in shipping, an area in which it acts for shipowners, P&I clubs, insurers, as well as major oil companies, makes it one of the foremost practices in this field. The shipping department handles the full range of commercial problems arising out of international trade and transport, including major maritime casualties, disaster litigation, pollution claims, charterparty disputes and cargo claims.

Commodities: The firm has also significantly increased its practice in commodities disputes in recent years. Its clientele in this area includes trading houses and a number of trade associations.

Insurance & Reinsurance: This division acts for underwriters, insurance companies, brokers and assureds. London – both Lloyd's and the companies market – is a major source of the division's work, but the firm derives its clients from all over the world. Hill Taylor Dickinson's reputation in marine insurance is well established.

HOBSON AUDLEY

7 Pilgrim Street, London, EC4V 6LB
Tel: (020) 7450 4500 **Fax:** (020) 7450 4545 **DX:** 401 London
Email: lawyers@hobsonaudley.co.uk **Website:** www.hobsonaudley.co.uk

Managing Partner	Gerald Hobson
Number of partners	13
Assistant solicitors	22
Other fee-earners	5

AREAS OF PRACTICE

Corporate Finance/ Company Commercial	31%
Dispute Solution	22%
Innovation & Technology	20%
Property	18%
Employment	9%

CONTACTS

Commercial Property	Malcolm Headley
	Simon Smith
Corporate Finance/ Company Commercial	Max Audley
	Anthony Gordon
	Paul Taylor
Dispute Solution	Gerald Hobson
	Roger Hopkins
Employment	Caroline Whiteley
Innovation & Technology (inc. IP)	Robert Bond
	Edward Hoare
	Claire Poll

THE FIRM: Hobson Audley is a City firm specialising in business law with a broad range of international and UK corporate clients and an emphasis on the technology, media and telecommunications sectors. The firm represents many leading companies in these sectors and also in more traditional areas of business such as energy, manufacturing, banking and finance and property. The firm's comprehensive range of legal skills is coupled with an international perspective and an awareness of business needs.

PRINCIPAL AREAS OF WORK: Hobson Audley combines strength in corporate law, dispute solutions, commercial property with specialist areas such as innovation and technology, multimedia, electronic commerce, and employment.

CLIENTELE: The firm's client base is drawn principally from the UK, Continental Europe and North America. Clients are involved in innovation and technology, e-commerce, publishing, direct selling, healthcare, energy, manufacturing, banking and financial services and property investment and development.

INTERNATIONAL: In 1997 Hobson Audley formed a multinational partnership with Faegre & Benson LLP under the name of Faegre Benson Hobson Audley. Faegre & Benson has offices in Minneapolis, Denver, Des Moines, Frankfurt and Shanghai. Association with Faegre & Benson LLP has enhanced the firm's international contacts with the introduction of a number of substantial US corporations whose UK interests are now represented by Faegre Benson Hobson Audley. Languages spoken include French, German, Italian, Spanish and Portuguese.

G.L. HOCKFIELD & CO

41 Reedworth Street, Kennington Rd, London, SE11 4PQ **Tel:** (020) 7735 0489 **Fax:** (020) 7820 1707 **DX:** 33252 **Email:** mail@hockfield.co.uk **Contact:** James Garvey • Principal areas of work are housing litigation, claimant personal injury and professional negligence work.

AREAS OF PRACTICE	
Housing	48%
Personal Injury	39%
Professional Negligence	7%
Miscellaneous Areas	6%

HODGE JONES & ALLEN

31-39 Camden Road, London, NW1 9LR
Tel: (020) 7482 1974 **Fax:** (020) 7267 3476 **Emergency:** (01459) 111 192
DX: 57050 Camden Town
Email: hja@hodge-jones-allen.co.uk **Website:** www.hodgejonesallen.co.uk

Senior Partner	Patrick Allen
Number of partners	21
Assistant solicitors	32
Other fee-earners	21

AREAS OF PRACTICE	
Personal Injury & Clinical Negligence	36%
Crime	28%
Family	20%
Employment & Discrimination	7%
Housing & Landlord & Tenant Litigation	7%
Property/Corporate	2%

CONTACTS	
Clinical Negligence	Nicola Mooney
Crime	Nigel Richardson
Employment/Discrimination	Ian Pettifer
Family & Children	Lynn Roberts
Housing Litigation	Wendy Backhouse
Mental Health Tribunals	Matthew Evans
Multi-Party (PI/Med Neg/ Product Liability)	Patrick Allen
Personal Injury	Louise Whitfield
Police Claims	Tina Salvidge
Property/Commercial	Elaine Morris
Property/Residential	Paul Browne

THE FIRM: Hodge Jones & Allen was established in 1977 and has expanded rapidly, especially since moving to new premises in September 1997. It has been involved in a number of high profile and leading cases, notably cases involving racial discrimination and personal injury cases arising from the King's Cross fire and the Marchioness disaster. The firm is handling two major group claims including Gulf War Syndrome.

PRINCIPAL AREAS OF WORK:
Criminal: The criminal team deals with the full range of magistrates and crown court work. Specialist fields include fraud, extradition, homicide, drug related offences, youth work and mentally disordered offenders. Solicitors can be contacted outside of office hours on the emergency phone number given above.
Employment: The employment team deals with all types of employment and discrimination claims for employees and employers. All members of the team do their own advocacy. The team also provides non-contentious advice predominantly to voluntary and statutory sector employers. No win no fee contingency arrangements are available.
Family: The family team covers all aspects of family work including property disputes following separation or divorce, conflicts over children, care proceedings and applications for emergency injunctions. Five members of the team are on the child care panel and two on the Lord Chancellor's Department's Child Abduction panel. All solicitors belong to the Solicitor's Family Law Association. Mediation is now offered by accredited family mediators
Housing: The housing team deals with disrepair, homelessness claims including applications for judicial review, possession cases and all aspects of landlord and tenant work, principally on behalf of tenants. The leader of the team was Chair of the Housing Law Practitioner's Group for four years.
Personal Injury: The personal injury team is led by the senior partner. The team acts for claimants, particularly those who have been injured in road accidents, tripping cases, accidents at work or as a result of medical negligence and claims against the police. The team has six solicitors on the Personal Injury panel and two on the clinical negligence panel. The multi-party unit is handling two group actions – Gulf War Illness and Kerrin Point. In each action the firm holds a generic contract with the Legal Services Commission. It also acts for large numbers of children with MMR claims. The police claims unit deals with unlawful arrest, assault, malicious prosecution and false imprisonment. It is handling compensation claims for the Bridgewater Four and other notable miscarriage cases.
Property: This teams handles residential and commercial property work for private individuals, local businesses and charities.
Other: Other significant areas of work include corporate and contractual advice; representation at mental health tribunals; public law; wills and probate.

RECRUITMENT: The firm runs a structured and popular training scheme for trainee solicitors. The annual intake is presently five. Interviews take place in October for training places the following September.

HODKINSONS

42-43 Locks Heath Centre, Locks Heath, SO3 6DX **Tel:** (01489) 885664 **Fax:** (01489) 579149 **DX:** 45251 Park Gate **Ptnrs:** 1 **Asst solrs:** 2 **Other fee-earners:** 4

HOLLINGWORTH BISSELL

10 Storey's Gate, London, SW1P 3AY
Tel: (020) 7233 3300 **Fax:** (020) 7233 3336

AREAS OF PRACTICE

Contracts	75%
Commercial Property	15%
Sales Promotions	10%

THE FIRM: Hollingworth Bissell provides legal services (both general and specialist rail related) to the railway industry.

PRINCIPAL AREAS OF WORK:

Commercial – General: Sales and acquisitions of companies and businesses, joint ventures, shareholders' agreements, reorganisations, procurement contracts, advice on foreign railway privatisations, intellectual property rights, computer contracts, agency contracts, conditions of trading and advice on the legal aspects of advertising, including the running of sales promotions.
Commercial – Rail Specific: Advice on refranchising, licence conditions, station redevelopments. Agreements for access to rail facilities, connection agreements, agreements for railway services, traffic agreements and variations to Franchise Agreements.
Property: Station trading and general commercial property advice.

H

HOLMAN FENWICK & WILLAN

Marlow House, Lloyd's Avenue, London, EC3N 3AL
Tel: (020) 7488 2300 **Fax:** (020) 7481 0316 **DX:** 1069 London City EC3
Email: holmans@hfw.co.uk **Website:** www.holmanfenwick.com

UK	
Number of partners	54
Assistant solicitors	51
Trainee solicitors	15
Other fee-earners	32
International	
Number of partners	27
Assistant solicitors	32
Other fee-earners	9

CONTACTS

Admiralty & Crisis Management	Hugh Brown
	James Gosling
Air, Rail & Road	Marcus Bowman
	Glenn Moore
Commercial Litigation	Peter Bennett
	Guy Hardaker
Corporate & Financial	Nick Hutton
	Jay Tooker
Employment	Andrew Dekany
Energy	Keith Michel
	Roderic O'Sullivan
EU & Competition	Phillip Wareham
Information Technology	Steven Baker
	George Eddings
Insolvency	Noel Campbell
	Steven Paull
Insurance & Reinsurance	Andrew Bandurka
	John Duff
International Trade & Commodities	Patricia Martin
	Christopher Swart
Marine Litigation	Richard Crump
	Hugh Livingstone
Personal Injury	Alan Walls
Private Client	David de Pass
Property	Nick Barr
Ship & Asset Finance	Stephen Drury
	Dan Tindall

HOLMAN FENWICK & WILLAN

THE FIRM: Holman Fenwick & Willan is an international law firm specialising in shipping and transportation, international trade and commodities, insurance and reinsurance, energy, information technology, banking and insolvency. The firm has a reputation worldwide for excellence and innovation and its international litigation, arbitration and dispute resolution practice is one of the largest and most specialist of its kind throughout the world.

PRINCIPAL AREAS OF WORK:

Admiralty & Marine Litigation: Holman Fenwick & Willan is pre-eminent in maritime work. It has one of the world's largest practices with a wealth of experience in the field. It is a recognised leader in dry shipping work including charter parties, bills of lading, other carriage contracts, marine insurance and related disputes. The firm is also renowned as a leader in admiralty and crisis management and operates a 24 hour emergency service geared to providing an immediate response to maritime casualties worldwide. Specialists deal with all forms of contractual disputes, marine insurance claims, collisions, fire and explosions, salvage, towage, wreck removal and recovery, personal injury, damage to oil terminals, rigs and offshore structures, pollution, environmental damage and clean up.
International Trade & Commodities: The department complements the maritime practice. It provides the international trading and financial community with services including advising on sale, purchase and futures contracts, quality claims, damage and shortfall disputes, swaps and barter trade, trade finance, EU law, and transportation agreements.
Energy: Energy is one of the firm's specialist work areas and covers power generation, oil and gas, coal and liquid natural gas.
Insurance & Reinsurance: The firm's practice is recognised internationally as an industry leader. It advises on all aspects of insurance and reinsurance contentious and non-contentious matters including facultative insurance and reinsurance coverage issues and policy interpretation; captive insurance and reinsurance; errors and omissions and professional negligence; property damage, business interruption and liability insurance; insolvency and schemes of arrangement; contract drafting and regulatory issues.
Commercial Litigation, Arbitration & Disputes: The firm has considerable strength in these practice areas, particularly in the areas of financial disputes, technology, coal, oil and gas, environmental claims, professional negligence, sovereign debt and fraud and asset recovery.
Fraud & Asset Recovery: Work focuses on the civil side with an emphasis on asset tracing and recovery in overseas jurisdictions. Other methods of recovery are also pursued using constructive trust, negligence and fraud proceedings.
Insolvency: The full spread of work is undertaken including voluntary arrangements, receiverships, provisional liquidations, liquidations and administrations. Much of the work focuses on international aspects, fraud related insolvency and the insurance industry (including schemes of arrangement).
Company & Finance: The firm advises some of the world's largest ship owners and operators on a wide variety of contractual issues, ranging from shipbuilding, and other offshore and construction contracts, financing documentation, the raising of capital, corporate finance and acquisitions, project and asset finance and joint ventures, as well as advising banks and financial institutions. The department also advises clients on EC and competition law, intellectual property and commercial property matters.

Continued overleaf

Information Technology: IT is a rapidly growing area for the firm and advice is given on every aspect of e-commerce and information technology.
Air, Road & Rail: The firm advises operators, financiers and underwriters on transactions, litigation and regulatory issues.
Trusts, Succession & Taxation: The practice provides private client services.
Employment: The firm handles all aspects of employment law, both contentious and non-contentious.

INTERNATIONAL: Holman Fenwick & Willan's international practice is founded upon its principal offices in London, Paris, Piraeus, Hong Kong, Singapore and Shanghai and over 120 years experience of working with other law firms in jurisdictions throughout the world. The firm also has other offices in Nantes and Rouen.

HOLME ROBERTS & OWEN

Heathcoat House, 20 Savile Row, London, W1X 1AE
Tel: (020) 7494 5600 **Fax:** (020) 7287 9344
Email: thompsp@hro.com **Website:** www.hro.com

Managing Partner	Paul Thompson
Number of partners	6
Assistant solicitors	8
Other fee-earners	2

CONTACTS

Finance .... Martha Collins Rolle
Securities .... Thomas Laursen

H

THE FIRM: Holme Roberts & Owen (HRO) was founded in Denver in 1898 and now has approximately 200 lawyers in Colorado, Utah and London. The firm's London office was established in 1991 to help its clients expand their businesses across Europe. With leading clients in the technology, telecommunications and media sectors, HRO's European practice has expanded rapidly, corresponding to the growth in those fields. The London office also represents clients in the breweries, entertainment/sports, and natural resources industries.

PRINCIPAL AREAS OF WORK: HRO's London practice focuses on corporate finance, public and private securities offerings, complex multi-jurisdictional commercial transactions, market entry strategies, joint ventures and acquisitions as well as general corporate and commercial law matters. In particular, the office has substantial experience representing companies establishing or expanding European operations, assisting them with legal and regulatory requirements of multiple jurisdictions. The firm's experience includes acting in the UK and continental Europe, including Central and Eastern Europe.

INTERNATIONAL: HRO's lawyers are qualified to practice in many jurisdictions including the UK, the US, Germany, and Belgium. In addition to English, the office has lawyers who are fluent in French, German, Spanish, Dutch and Italian.

HOLMES HARDINGHAM

22-23 Great Tower Street, London, EC3R 5HE
Tel: (020) 7283 0222 **Fax:** (020) 7283 0768 **DX:** 636
Email: firstname.surname@HHlaw.co.uk

Managing Partner	David Johnston
Senior Partner	Adrian Hardingham
Number of partners	11
Assistant solicitors	7
Other fee-earners	12

THE FIRM: Holmes Hardingham is a commercial and maritime law firm with an international practice, concentrating on litigation and arbitration related to shipping and transportation.

PRINCIPAL AREAS OF WORK: The firm was founded 12 years ago and has more than doubled in size in that time. Further expansion is expected in response to a growing work-load. All 11 partners and 19 other fee earners handle a variety of shipping and transport related matters including carriage of goods by sea, road and air; commercial and admiralty litigation and arbitration; marine and goods in transit insurance; collision and salvage; commodity sale disputes; ship sale, purchase and finance; oil and gas exploration; yachts and pleasure craft.

HOLMES MACKILLOP

109 Douglas Street, Glasgow, G2 4HB
Tel: (0141) 226 4942 **Fax:** (0141) 204 0136 **DX:** GW50
Email: general@homack.co.uk

Managing Partner	J Stuart McNeill
Contact	William Duffy

AREAS OF PRACTICE

Commercial Property	40%
Private Client	20%
Corporate	20%
Litigation	20%

THE FIRM: The firm was established over 200 years ago and now has a well established commercial and private client base.

PRINCIPAL AREAS OF WORK: The firm has been involved in a number of major corporate transactions and commercial property deals within the last year. These are expanding areas of work together with the firm's specialist strengths in commercial litigation, agricultural law and charity law.

CLIENTELE: The firm has acted in a number of major property developments and investment sales in the last year. It has also represented landlord and tenant in a number of major lettings. Clients include major developers, property companies, house builders and one of Scotland's leading motor retailers. The firm has also represented two of the major UK Banks in substantial security transactions as well as acting for vendors and purchasers in substantial corporate deals and is frequently handling transactions with a value in excess of £10 million.

RECRUITMENT: The firm has expanded its commercial property department within the last year and is anxious to look at further expansion in personnel in this area and also in its corporate department.

H

HOOD VORES & ALLWOOD

The Priory, Church St, Dereham, NR19 1DW **Tel:** (01362) 692424 **Fax:** (01362) 698858 **DX:** 45050 **Ptnrs:** 6 **Asst solrs:** 1 **Other fee-earners:** 7

HOOPER & WOLLEN

Carlton House, 30 The Terrace, Torquay, TQ1 1BS **Tel:** (01803) 213251 **Fax:** (01803) 296871 **DX:** 59204 Torquay (2) **Email:** lawyers@hooperwollen.co.uk **Website:** www.hooperwollen.co.uk **Ptnrs:** 10 **Asst solrs:** 5 **Other fee-earners:** 9 **Contact:** Chris Hart • Specialising in conveyancing, family, child care, litigation, employment, PI, probate, trust, commercial, company, private client. Agency instructions accepted.

HORSEY LIGHTLY

20 West Mills, Newbury, RG14 5HG **Tel:** 01635 580 858 **Fax:** 01635 582 813 **DX:** 30835 Newbury **Email:** info@horseybomer.co.uk **Website:** www.horseybomer.co.uk

HOWARD KENNEDY

19 Cavendish Square, London, W1A 2AW
Tel: (020) 7636 1616 **Fax:** (020) 7499 6871 **DX:** 42748 Oxford Circus North
Email: webmaster@howardkennedy.com **Website:** www.howardkennedy.com

Senior Partner	Trevor Newey
Number of partners	41
Total staff	206
Number of fee-earners	66

AREAS OF PRACTICE

Property	46%
Corporate/Commercial (inc. Media, Entertainment & International)	34%
Litigation	18%
Trust & Estate Planning	2%

CONTACTS

Banking & Property Finance	Nigel Emerson
Construction	James Stewart
Corporate/Commercial	Alan Banes
Employment	Michael Harris
IT & IP	John Fleming
Licensing	Michael Dobrin
Litigation	Craig Emden
Media & Entertainment	Brian Eagles
Project Finance	Philip Leacock
Property	Paul Springall
Taxation	Zafar Rezvi
Trusts & Estate Planning	Roger Seaton

THE FIRM: Howard Kennedy is a leading West End law firm providing a wide range of legal services. Clients range from independent entrepreneurs to listed public companies. Founded in 1936, the practice provides coordinated and comprehensive legal services both in the UK and abroad. The firm's policy is to ensure that legal services are provided with a clear understanding of clients' general and specific commercial aspirations and the special requirements of their particular business. It has developed a range of services appropriate to the needs of business, from finance and set-up stage to maturity, acquisition and disposal. Howard Kennedy is a registered Sponsor on the London Stock Exchange.

PRINCIPAL AREAS OF WORK: The practice is divided into five main departments: corporate and commercial, property, litigation, international and trusts and estate planning, together with a number of specialist groups.
Corporate & Commercial: This department handles a high-quality workload of corporate and corporate finance matters. This includes full Stock Exchange, AIM and OFEX flotations, Venture Capital Trusts, rights issues and unquoted public share offerings, including those under the Enterprise Investment Scheme. In addition, the department acts for providers and recipients of venture capital. It is experienced in takeovers, mergers and acquisitions, both public and private. The department also advises on shareholder disputes and has specialists in pensions, project and commodity finance. Other commercial services include commercial contracts, commercially related immigration with specialist group's dealing in both taxation and employment work.
IT & IP: This group handles a wide range of issues including hi-tech matters.
Media & Entertainment: The group deals with all aspects of entertainment, media and sports law, including film and television finance, production and distribution, music, theatre, publishing, merchandising and sponsorship. Specialist areas include tax, mediation and arbitration.

Continued overleaf

Commercial Property: The development and financing of retail, industrial, office and residential premises is handled, with particular emphasis on the retail and leisure industries together with groups specialising in liquor licensing, betting licensing and property development.
Banking & Property Finance: The group deals with a wide range of banking and finance matters, especially offshore aspects. Clients range from UK clearing banks and building societies to borrowers based in the UK and overseas.
Litigation: The department advises on a wide range of disputes for both commercial and private clients, covering the areas of contract, negligence (including professional negligence), landlord and tenant, property litigation, personal injury, matrimonial, immigration, and debt collecting. There are specialist groups dealing with construction, mediation and ADR.
Trusts & Estate Planning: The department deals with matters ranging from personal taxations, estate planning, wills, trusts, offshore arrangements, probate and related conveyancing. It also advises on the law relating to charities.

INTERNATIONAL: Howard Kennedy has international professional connections worldwide, and is a member of Cercle Juridique European (CJE), Inter Counsel, Transnational Taxation Network, Euro Defi, and Lawyers and Lawyers Associated Worldwide (LAW). All principal European languages are spoken.
International Group: The group deals with overseas clients investing in and conducting business in the UK and internationally. Areas of work covered include cross-border mergers and acquisitions, international project finance, international trade agreements, commodities, European Union law, international property and hotel transactions, international corporate structures, agency and distribution agreements.
International Trade & Project Finance Group: This deals with commodities, derivatives and their regulation, cross-border disputes and international arbitration.

HOWARTH GOODMAN

8 King Street, Manchester, M60 8HG **Tel:** (0161) 832 5068 **Fax:** (0161) 819 7878 **DX:** 14308 Manchester 1 **Email:** sb-@howarthgoodman.com
Website: www.howarthgoodman.com **Ptnrs:** 4 **Asst solrs:** 4 **Other fee-earners:** 10

HOWELLS

427-431 London Road, Sheffield, S2 4HJ
Tel: (0114) 249 6666 **Fax:** (0114) 250 0656 **DX:** 10584

The Avery Buildings, 15-17 Bridge Street, Sheffield, S3 8NL
Tel: (0114) 249 6666 **Fax:** (0114) 249 1455 **DX:** 10584

42 Spital Hill, Sheffield, S4 7LG
Tel: (0114) 249 6666 **Fax:** (0114) 249 6700 **DX:** 10584

Managing Partner	Jonathan Whybrow
Number of partners	12
Assistant solicitors	22
Other fee-earners	36

AREAS OF PRACTICE

Civil & Community	33%
Crime	33%
Family	33%

CONTACTS

Civil & Community	Guy Baddeley
Crime	Danny Simpson
Family	Alyson Siddall

THE FIRM: Established in 1979 to specialise in protecting the rights of individuals, the firm has grown to be one of the country's largest Legal Aid practices with Legal Aid quality franchises in all available areas of work.

PRINCIPAL AREAS OF WORK:
Crime: The criminal department is now one of the largest in the country having four partners and a further 14 fee earners. Work includes all criminal matters with particular expertise in public order offences, serious fraud, juveniles and youth, cases involving mentally disordered defendants and road traffic law. Increasing caseload in civil liberties work including miscarriages of justice, prisoners' rights and judicial reviews.
Family Law: The family department is the largest in Sheffield and one of the largest in the country. The department is divided into two teams covering children and matrimonial law. The children team consists of nine fee-earners (including three partners) of whom five are members of the Law Society's Children's Panel. The team covers all areas of child law, including private and public law children cases, adoption and education advice and representation covering special educational needs, school admissions and exclusions appeals, grant disputes and higher and further education proceedings. Jonathan Whybrow (Head of the Children Team) is a co-author of Emergency Remedies in Family Courts and contributory editor to Children Law and Practice. A former civil servant, he worked on the Children Act 1989 as it was devised and enacted. The matrimonial team consists of ten fee-earners (including two partners) of whom four are members of The Law Society's Family Law Panel. The team deals with all aspects of matrimonial law with particular expertise in domestic violence and financial relief of matrimonial breakdown. The family department also offers a family mediation service and has two qualified mediators.
Civil & Community: The department provides a wide range of legal services for individuals through its litigation and community law teams.
Litigation: Services include accident claims, industrial disease claims, clinical negligence and actions against the police. A strong team consists of three partners supported by a further seven fee-earners. The team has three Law Society personal injury panelists and one clinical negligence panelist.

Community Law: The team provides specialist advice and representation in housing, employment and equal opportunities law, immigration, mental health and welfare benefits. The firm has one of the few specialist housing law teams in South Yorkshire and is a member of the South Yorkshire Housing Practitioners Group and deals with possession proceedings, disrepair, harassment by landlords etc. The employment team specialises in advising employees in the full range of employment problems and are members of The Discrimination Law Association, Equal Opportunities Commission Equality Exchange, Stonewall and Lawyers for Liberty. The immigration team has been the leading firm of immigration lawyers in the region for 20 years and deals with the full range of immigration cases. The team is led by John Donkersley who has over 10 years' immigration law experience and is South Yorkshire's leading immigration lawyer. The mental health team are members of The Law Society Mental Health Review Tribunal Panel and specialise in representing patients before tribunals and provide general mental health law advice and help. An experienced welfare benefits team is able to provide an in-depth service advising clients on all benefits administered by the Government or the Local Authority together with judicial reveiws, advocacy and representation.

HOWES PERCIVAL

Oxford House, Cliftonville, Northampton, NN1 5PN
Tel: (01604) 230400 **Fax:** (01604) 620956 **DX:** 12413 Northampton
Email: law@howes-percival.co.uk **Website:** www.howes-percival.co.uk

Senior Partner	Michael Percival
Number of partners	29
Assistant solicitors	25
Other fee-earners	36

AREAS OF PRACTICE

Company Commercial	30%
Commercial Property	25%
Commercial Litigation	20%
Insolvency	10%
Employment	10%
Private Client	5%

CONTACTS

Company Commercial	Jit Singh
Commercial Litigation	Ashwin Mody
Corporate Fraud	Ashwin Mody
Commercial Property	Roger Burnell
Employment	Chris Maddock
Insolvency	Gerald Couldrake
Private Client	Michael Percival
Licensing	Alan Kefford
Motor Trade	Brandon Ransley

THE FIRM: Howes Percival is a 29 partner commercial law firm with offices in Leicester, Milton Keynes, Northampton and Norwich. It is the firm's aim to be the leading provider of commercial legal services in each of the locations that it has a presence. The vast proportion of new instructions received by Howes Percival are from referrals or recommendations by banks, accountants, financial institutions and existing clients. It is not uncommon for Howes Percival to be instructed by clients who they have previously acted against in corporate or commercial transactions. Specialist seminars and workshops are regularly given for existing and prospective clients. Howes Percival is willing to act as an agent for other solicitors in High Court and County Court cases.

PRINCIPAL AREAS OF WORK:

Company Commercial: Howes Percival provides wide-ranging company and commercial services, with notable experience in corporate finance, acquisitions and disposals, MBOs and MBIs. In addition the firm also has considerable experience in private equity transaction and AIM flotations. A variety of outsourcing agreements are also handled. All aspects of banking law are dealt with and insolvency is a particular specialism.
Commercial Litigation: A variety of commercial litigation services are provided, including specialised work handling directors' disqualifications for the insolvency service of the DTI. A debt recovery service is also provided. The firm has two partners who have been accredited by the Centre for Dispute Resolution as mediators. White collar crime is another area of expertise.
Corporate Fraud: Serious Fraud Office enquiries and HMCE and Inland Revenue defence cases are undertaken by the firm's Leicester office.
Licensing: The firm is recognised as an expert in liquor and entertainment licensing and provides a range of bespoke training courses, including the National Licensee Certificate, to leisure industry clients.
Employment: Employment law matters are undertaken and advice is given on taxation issues. Employee relocation services are also offered.
Private Client: The firm's private client work has seen substantial growth, particularly in trusts, probates and independent financial services.
Commercial Property: Commercial property expertise is strengthened by specialisms in development work and environmental law.
Motor Trade: The firm has commendable experience in the motor trade, acting for several manufacturers and for many dealerships around the country.

CLIENTELE: The top quality work that is carried out by the firm places them in a market whereby they are able to attract instructions from major companies such as DaimlerChrysler (UK) Ltd, easyJet airline co Ltd, Scania (Great Britain) Ltd, Shanks Group plc and Start-Rite Shoes Ltd. City standards of work are provided to clients at prices lower than those of the City. Howes Percival acts for both private and public companies of varying sizes throughout the UK and abroad. It also has informal links with law firms around the world. Clients include major UK financial institutions, manufacturers, retailers, drinks companies, transport companies, businesses in the leisure industry as well as private clients with substantial assets.

RECRUITMENT: Howes Percival aims to develop all four of its offices with a recruitment drive at all levels, in order to further improve its position as a forward-thinking, high quality provider of legal services.

HUGHES FOWLER CARRUTHERS

Academy Court, 94 Chancery Lane, London, WC2A 1DT
Tel: (020) 7421 8383 **Fax:** (020) 7421 8384 **DX:** 251 London/Chancery Lane
Email: mail@hfclaw.com **Website:** www.hfclaw.com

Senior & Managing Partner	Frances Hughes
Number of partners	3
Number of fee-earners	7
Total staff	21

CONTACTS

Matrimonial & Family Law....Frances Hughes
.....Pauline Fowler
.....Alex Carruthers

THE FIRM: This niche family law practice is based in Chancery Lane in Central London and specialises in all aspects of matrimonial and family law. Hughes Fowler Carruthers is a newly established niche practice incorporating the family department from the highly regarded City practice of Bates, Wells & Braithwaite Solicitors. It is to be one of London's leading family law practices. The partners are Frances Hughes, who set up the Bates, Wells & Braithwaite department in 1983, Pauline Fowler and Alex Carruthers, all of whom worked at Bates, Wells & Braithwaite for many years. The firm continues to enjoy a close professional association with this firm which now concentrates on its other core business. All the partners share a considerable breadth of experience which enables them to offer a wide range of skills to suit the individual demands of each client. They are able to provide expertise covering all areas of family law from skilful negotiation to complex litigation. The partners conduct their work with a high degree of professionalism and dedication and provide a high quality sensitive service to all their clients. All members of the firm are members of the Solicitors Family Law Association. The firm is part of an extensive international family law network through memberships of associations such as the International Academy of Matrimonial Lawyers and the International Bar Association. This means Hughes Fowler Carruthers can provide a fully international service through the partners' close connections worldwide.

PRINCIPAL AREAS OF WORK: The firm handles all kinds of family law work but puts a strong emphasis on work with financial complexity and international aspects. Fields of expertise also include defending and attacking trust structures, tracing hidden assets, jurisdictional disputes and pension issues. The firm takes pride in its reputation for creative tailor made settlements as well as its reputation as first class litigators. The partners also have special expertise in complex children and child abduction work. The firm's client base continues to cover a broad spectrum of UK and internationally based men and women including those in the City or in business elsewhere as well as those from the media, the arts and other professionals.

HUGH JAMES FORD SIMEY

Arlbee House, Greyfriars Rd, Cardiff, CF10 3QB
Tel: (029) 2022 4871 **Fax:** (029) 2038 8222 **DX:** 33300 Cardiff
Email: cardiff@hjfs.co.uk **Website:** www.hjfs.co.uk

Managing Partners	Simon Sanger-Anderson Matthew Tossell
Senior Partners	Michael Horwood Russel Jenkins
Number of partners	59
Assistant solicitors	59
Other fee-earners	86

AREAS OF PRACTICE

Claimant Personal Injury	30%
Commercial & Insurance Litigation	25%
Commercial Services	15%
Commercial Property	12%
Private Client	10%
Construction & Professional Indemnity	10%

CONTACTS

Agency .....Alun Jones
Claimant Personal Injury.....Andrew Harding
Commercial & Insurance Litigation
.....Gareth Williams
Commercial Property.....David Roberts
Commercial Services .....Geoffrey Adams
Construction & Professional Indemnity
.....Michael Jefferies
Employment.....Alison Love
Insolvency .....Catrin Thomas
Private Client.....Cherry Wright

THE FIRM: Hugh James Ford Simey is one of the largest regional law firms in the UK. It is a practice which provides a comprehensive range of commercial and private client services through its network of offices across South Wales and the West Country. Hugh James Ford Simey has experienced phenomenal growth and success since it was formed in 1960. It is a dynamic firm, which has an enthusiastic and forward thinking approach to its work and the way in which its services are provided, without sacrificing traditional qualities. Its commitment to embracing new technology is reflected in the recent launch of www.click2law.com, the firm's on-line legal services website which comprises automated document creation, client instruction questionnaires and fixed fee packages for the business community and general public. The firm has a national reputation for its commercial and insurance litigation practice. It also has a strong reputation for its commercial property and insolvency work and has a rapidly growing commercial practice. The firm is proud of its commitment to private client work and the Community Legal Services scheme and continues to be involved in high profile claimant litigation.

PRINCIPAL AREAS OF WORK: The practice is divided into four core areas: commercial litigation, commercial services, commercial property and private client. Specialist teams have been established to serve niche areas of the law. The firm has a multi-disciplinary and holistic approach to the provision of legal services, with these teams comprising not only of solicitors and non-practising barristers, but also individuals with non-legal professional qualifications. The firm's personal injury team, for example, includes a caseworker who is a qualified social worker as well as qualified nursing staff.

Commercial Litigation: The commercial litigation team is recognised as a formidable force in the Wales and West region. The firm's insurance services division has expertise in all areas of insurance work acting for national and international insurers in cases including personal injury, product liability and professional negligence. The firm also has highly regarded construction and professional indemnity departments and specialist units, dealing with property litigation and insolvency. It also provides high quality and wide ranging commercial litigation services to institutional and private clients.

Commercial Services: The commercial services group provides a full range of services to its clients and has an exceptionally wide client base, including quoted companies, sports bodies, housing associations and charitable organisations through to sole traders. The firm has a specialist e-business team which offers advice on e-business start-ups and an e-business support package. The sports law unit provides commercial advice to professional sportspeople and organisations, clubs, promoters and TV production companies in relation to

the major sporting categories. The commercial services group incorporates a specialist employment team, which as well as providing clients with the full range of employment law advice and representation, offers a tailor-made employment services package at a fixed cost together with human resources consultancy services.
Commercial Property: The commercial property group is highly regarded and has achieved national recognition for its work. A full range of services is offered with particular expertise including planning, landlord and tenant, housing association law, acquisitions and disposals, building contracts and commercial and residential development. The firm's secured lending division has experienced a rapid expansion and, due to advances in technology, is able to service its clients' needs on a national basis from one location.
Private Client: The full range of traditional private client services are offered including conveyancing, wills, trusts and probate, family law and crime. The firm has a national reputation for its work in the field of claimant personal injury litigation work, is appointed to the Community Legal Services Multi-Party Actions panel and represented claims in lead cases involving miners respiratory illnesses and vibration white finger. The firm undertakes union work and has a dedicated team dealing with catastrophic injury claims, in particular brain injury. Clinical negligence franchises are held in five of the firm's offices.

INTERNATIONAL: The firm also has informal associations with legal practices in Nantes, Madrid, Dusseldorf, Rome, Milan and Naples. Many partners are Welsh speakers and are delighted to conduct business in that language.

HUGH POTTER & COMPANY, SERIOUS INJURY SOLICITORS

14-32 Hewitt, Manchester, M15 49B **Tel:** (0161) 237 5888 **Fax:** (0161) 237 5999 **Ptnrs:** 2 **Asst solrs:** 3 **Other fee-earners:** 4

HUMPHREYS & CO

14 King St, Bristol, BS1 4EF **Tel:** (0117) 929 2662 **Fax:** (0117) 929 2722 **DX:** 78239
Email: lawyers@humphreys.co.uk **Website:** www.humphreys.co.uk **Ptnrs:** 5 **Asst solrs:** 5
Other fee-earners: 2 **Contact:** R A Humphreys • Principal areas of work are company/commercial, litigation, employment, intellectual property, reinsurance, property, insurance, personal injury, entertainment, professional (including clinical) negligence, competition and insolvency.

HUMPHRIES KIRK

Glebe House, North Street, Wareham, BH20 4AN
Tel: (01929) 552141 **Fax:** (01929) 556701 **DX:** 49700 Wareham
Email: wareham@humphrieskirk.co.uk **Website:** www.humphrieskirk.co.uk

Senior Partner	M J Greenleaves
Number of partners	10
Assistant solicitors	8
Other fee-earners	13

AREAS OF PRACTICE	
Trusts & Probate	30%
Conveyancing	29%
Commercial	19%
Matrimonial	12%
Litigation	7%
Personal Injury	3%

THE FIRM: Humphries Kirk is one of the most innovative firms in the South, which manages to retain a successful balance between catering for substantial commercial clients and its traditional private client base. Humphries Kirk was one of the first firms to qualify for ISO 9001 in this region. Other offices are located at Bournemouth, Dorchester, London (consulting rooms), Poole and Swanage.

PRINCIPAL AREAS OF WORK:
Company/Commercial: Work includes intellectual property (the firm acts for the Design Business Association) and mergers and acquisitions (including international).
Commercial Litigation: All work from industrial tribunal, to High Court, international litigation and arbitrations is undertaken.
Banking & Financial Law: The firm acts for a number of substantial German financial institutions and also for several German savings banks.
Other Areas: Full range of private client services, including an in-house nominee company, trustee company and off-shore client account. The firm has trained mediators, family mediators and arbitrators.

INTERNATIONAL: Humphries Kirk has associated offices in Versailles, France and Cologne, Germany. It maintains a network of relationships with lawyers worldwide. Work is handled in French, German, Italian and Spanish.

HUNT & MORGAN

46-48 Charles Street, Cardiff, CF10 2GE **Tel:** (029) 20341234 **Fax:** (029) 20342350 **DX:** 33031 Cardiff 2

HUNT & COOMBS

35 Thorpe Rd, Peterborough, PE3 6AG **Tel:** (01733) 565312 **Fax:** (01733) 552748 **DX:** 12302 **Email:** reception@hunt-and-coombs.co.uk
Website: www.hunt-and-coombs.co.uk **Ptnrs:** 10 **Asst solrs:** 13 **Other fee-earners:** 14

HUNTERS

9 New Square, Lincoln's Inn, London, WC2A 3QN
Tel: (020) 7412 0050 **Fax:** (020) 7412 0049 **DX:** 61 Chancery Lane.London
Email: mail@hunters-solicitors.co.uk **Website:** www.hunters-solicitors.co.uk

Senior Partner	John Kennedy
Number of partners	14
Assistant solicitors	5
Other fee-earners	12

THE FIRM: Although founded in the early 18th century, the firm is a thriving modern partnership, serving a broadly-based private and institutional clientele.

PRINCIPAL AREAS OF WORK: The firm has a long-established reputation in private client, charity, banking security, and matrimonial work, and an increasing emphasis on commercial property, company/commercial law, employment and litigation.
Private Client: A wide range of work includes trusts, tax planning, tax returns, heritage and agricultural property, wills, probate and conveyancing.
Charities: Work includes acting for major charities; registrations, schemes, trading arrangements, and housing associations.
Banking Security Work: Work includes security work for banks.
Matrimonial: All aspects of work are covered, but particularly cases with a substantial financial element.
Commercial Property: Work includes acquiring and selling property investments, and business tenancies.
Company/Commercial Law & Employment: The firm advises private companies and partnerships on commercial contracts, acquisitions and disposals, employment, contracts and staff handbooks, unfair and wrongful dismissal, redundancy, service occupancies, equal opportunity and race discrimination.
Litigation: Work includes wide range of High Court/County Court work; breach of contract; landlord and tenant disputes, and enforcement of security.

INTERNATIONAL: The firm has a close relationship with firms in Australia.

RECRUITMENT: One trainee solicitor with a good degree is recruited annually. Fortnightly seminars are given. There is a wide spread of work and direct client contact.

HUNTON & WILLIAMS
Fleetway House, 25 Farrington Street, London, EC4A 4AB **Tel:** (020) 7246 5700 **Fax:** (020) 7246 5772 **Email:** ifelmingham@hunton.com
Website: www.hunton.com **Ptnrs:** 6 **Asst solrs:** 4 **Other fee-earners:** 1

HUTCHINSON MAINPRICE

60 Ebury Street, London, SW1W 9QD
Tel: (020) 7259 0121 **Fax:** (020) 7259 0051
Email: reception@hutchinson-mainprice.co.uk **Website:** www.hutchinson-mainprice.co.uk

Number of partners	2
Assistant solicitors	2
Other fee-earners	3

THE FIRM: Hutchinson Mainprice was established on 1 May 1999, when Hugh Mainprice joined Alastair Hutchinson & Co, a leading firm of property law specialists in Belgravia. With the increasing complexity of VAT in relation to property, the new firm will be in a unique position to offer an unrivalled service in the property field. Alastair Hutchinson has had over 20 years experience in property law, while Hugh Mainprice, who assisted in the drafting of the original VAT legislation in 1972, has acted for more clients in the VAT Tribunals, the High Court, the Court of Appeal, the House of Lords, and the European Court of Justice than any other solicitor in the UK. These have included a large number of cases involving property which resulted in a change in the law or Customs' practice.

INTERNATIONAL: The firm has an associated office in Quinta do Lago. Languages spoken include Japanese, French, German, Punjabi, and Swahili.

HUTTONS

16-18 St Andrews Crescent, Cardiff, CF1 3DD
Tel: (029) 2037 8621 **Fax:** (029) 2038 8450 **DX:** 33065 Cardiff
Email: email@huttons-solicitors.co.uk

Senior Partner	Stuart Hutton
Finance Partner	Clare Strowbridge
Number of partners	5
Associates	6
Assistant solicitors	2
Other fee-earners	4

THE FIRM: Huttons is a leading litigation practice in Wales, noted for plaintiff personal injury and medical negligence law, family and childcare law and criminal defence advocacy. The firm was ranked as 'leaders in their field' in clinical negligence (mainly claimant) and crime by *Chambers* (2000-2001). It has been awarded membership of several Law Society Panels, AVMA and Spinal Injuries Association and has been franchised by the Legal Aid Board. The firm is expanding its commercial division.

PRINCIPAL AREAS OF WORK: The firm provides specialist litigation services.
Personal Injury & Medical Negligence: Work ranges from RTA cases (including CFAs) to brain injury in children and multi-party actions.
Litigation: Work done has an emphasis on miscarriages of justice including police actions and judicial review; employment disputes, housing disrepair, landlord and tenant and general contractual disputes.
Family & Child Care: The firm handles divorce, children matters, high value ancillary relief applications and Court of Appeal work.
Criminal Advocacy: High profile murder cases are handled, including the Lynette White murder trial and the Tooze murder and appeal case.
Commercial: Work includes business formation, acquisitions and sales, partnership disputes, property matters, insolvency, employment, probate and wills.

AREAS OF PRACTICE	
Criminal Advocacy	35%
Family/Childcare	20%
PI/Medical Negligence	20%
Litigation	15%
Commercial	10%

CONTACTS	
Litigation	David Evans
Commercial	Clare Strowbridge
Family/Childcare	Christine O'Brien
Criminal Advocacy	Stuart Hutton
PI/Medical Negligence	Tim Musgrave

IAIN SMITH & COMPANY

18-20 Queen's Road, Aberdeen, AB15 4ZT **Tel:** (01224) 645 454 **Fax:** (01224) 646 671 **DX:** AB4 Aberdeen **Email:** info@iainsmith.com **Website:** www.iainsmith.com **Ptnrs:** 5 **Asst solrs:** 9 **Other fee-earners:** 8 **Contact:** Peter A Macari (Managing Partner) • An investor in people. Specialist expertise in corporate, insolvency, employment law, commercial law, commercial litigation and debt recovery.

AREAS OF PRACTICE	
Corporate/Commercial	30%
Litigation/Family Law	25%
Domestic Conveyancing	15%
Commercial Conveyancing	15%
Wills & Executives	10%
Insolvency	5%

I

IAN DOWNING FAMILY LAW PRACTICE

8 The Crescent, Plymouth, PL1 3AB **Tel:** (01752) 226224 **Fax:** (01752) 226213 **Email:** ian.downing@virgin.net **Ptnrs:** 1 **Asst solrs:** 1

ILIFFES BOOTH BENNETT

Lovell House, 271 High Street, Uxbridge, UB8 1LQ
Tel: (01895) 230941 **Fax:** (01895) 811926 **DX:** 45105 Uxbridge
Email: Reception.lh@ibblaw.co.uk **Website:** www.ibblaw.co.uk

Managing Partner	Steven Booth
Number of partners	20
Assistant solicitors	39
Other fee-earners	31

THE FIRM: With offices in Middlesex, Berkshire, Buckinghamshire and Essex, this firm is one of the largest practices in the South East outside central London. Its principal aim is to deliver efficient and effective legal services to an extensive business and private client community. It has particular strengths in commercial property and litigation including employment, private client work, personal injury litigation, family and criminal law.

PRINCIPAL AREAS OF WORK:
Commercial Property: The firm handles all aspects of commercial property work including purchase and sale of retail, office and industrial property, lease negotiations and renewals, portfolio acquisitions and disposals, major construction and development work. Agricultural property is dealt with. Secured lending work for banks and financial institutions is handled.
Company & Commercial: A broad range of corporate work is handled, mainly sales and acquisitions, restructuring and mergers, start-ups, intellectual property, commercial contracts, company formations and franchise and distribution agreements.
Litigation: The firm has an extensive litigation practice acting for both business and private clients. For business clients, the work includes company and partnership disputes, commercial property and construction matters, negligence claims, insolvency, landlord and tenant actions and substantial debt recovery. Private client litigation includes divorce and financial relief and all matters relating to children, personal injury and criminal defence including white collar crime.
Private Client: Work handled includes wills, probate, estate administration, taxation advice and trusts. The firm covers residential conveyancing and gives independent financial advice.
Employment: The firm handles service contracts, unfair and wrongful dismissal, redundancy, discrimination at work, contracts of employment and pensions, compromise agreements.
Charities: All aspects of charities law are covered, including advice on commercial and residential conveyancing, employment and litigation.

CLIENTELE: Business clients range from major public companies to family business and individual entrepreneurs. High net worth private clients form a significant part of the client base.

RECRUITMENT: IBB has a full training programme for all professional and support staff, being fully aware of the need to maintain an appropriately skilled and motivated workforce. Trainee solicitors are offered a structured period of training with extensive professional supervision and maximum client contact. IBB is a member of Lawnet – a federation of independent law firms – and is ISO 9002 accredited. For more details visit the firm's website (see above).

AREAS OF PRACTICE	
Commercial Property	28%
Crime & Fraud	21%
Private Client	19%
Family/Matrimonial	13%
Company/Commercial & Commercial Litigation	12%
Personal Injury	7%

CONTACTS	
Charities	Peter Burnett
Commercial Litigation	Andrew Olins
Commercial Property	Susan Mawson
Company/Commercial	David Jackson
Crime & Fraud	Tan Ikram
Employment	Victoria Harris
Family	Shôn Roberts
Personal Injury Litigation	Anthony Wiseman
Residential Conveyancing	Gillian Outram
Wills, Probate, Tax & Trusts	Gillian Murray

INCE & CO

Knollys House, 11 Byward Street, London, EC3R 5EN
Tel: (020) 7623 2011 **Fax:** (020) 7623 3225 **DX:** 1070 London City EC3
Email: firstname.lastname@ince.co.uk **Website:** www.ince.co.uk

Senior Partner	Peter Rogan
Recruitment Partner	Chris Sprague
UK	
Number of partners	42
Number of assistants	48
Other fee-earners	37
Total	127

CONTACTS

Admiralty	James Wilson
ADR/Mediation	Jonathan Lux
Asset Finance	Tony Suchy
Asset Recovery	Ben Horn
Aviation	Anthony Fitzsimmons
Commercial Insurance	David Coupe
Commercial Litigation	Steven Fox
Construction	Mike Pollen
Corporate	Nick Gould
Dry Shipping	Bob Deering
E-commerce	Nick Gould
EU & Competition	Denys Hickey
Energy	David Steward
Environment & Pollution	Colin de la Rue
Insurance & Reinsurance	Peter Rogan
Insurance Fraud	Alan Weir
International Commercial Arbitration	Chris Jefferis
International Trade & Commodities	Stuart Shepherd
Marine Insurance	Simon Todd
P&I Clubs	Mike Volikas
Personal Injury	Chris Sprague
Political Risk Insurance	Tony George
Professional Indemnity	David Rutherford
Project/Trade Finance	Tony Suchy
Property & Private Client	Albert Levy
Shipbuilding	Mike Pollen
Ship Finance	Malcolm Strong
Sale & Purchase	Paul Herring
Sports & Media	Chris Jefferis
Transport	Louise Krenca
Total Loss Investigation	Paul Arditti
Yachts/Superyachts	Albert Levy

THE FIRM: Founded in 1870, and based in the City of London, the firm has offices in Hong Kong, Singapore, Piraeus and Shanghai, providing legal services to the shipping, insurance and business communities in the Pacific Rim and Mediterranean areas. The Shanghai office, opened in Autumn 2000, is already making a major contribution to maritime and commercial clients in the region. The firm also has an international network of correspondent lawyers in collaboration with whom it can provide legal services at short notice wherever the need arises. The firm prides itself on the quality and dedication of its people and is unusual in that the majority of its partners and assistants are 'home-grown', many having been with the firm throughout their legal careers. The firm is acknowledged for clear legal analysis and tenacious, imaginative dispute resolution, deploying ADR, including mediation, arbitration and litigation. Underpinning this expertise is an understanding of clients' commercial needs. Another feature of the firm's service is continuity. Clients deal with the same partner or team from initial advice to resolution, be it settlement or trial.

PRINCIPAL AREAS OF WORK:

Maritime: Ince & Co handles every aspect of maritime law, including collisions, salvage, charterparty, carriage of goods, marine insurance, ship finance, general average, personal injury, pollution and clean-up, and has been involved in virtually every major maritime casualty from the Torrey Canyon in 1967 to the recent Kristal incident. The firm represents all major P&I Clubs, shipowners, charterers and their underwriters. Ince & Co also operates a 24 hour emergency response service 365 days a year in respect of maritime, aviation and energy related casualties with a dedicated telephone number: (020) 7283 6999.

Insurance/Reinsurance: In its long history Ince & Co has participated in the majority of the leading insurance cases which have contributed to the evolution of insurance law. The firm covers all aspects of insurance and reinsurance, including marine, aviation and non-marine insurance and reinsurance, regulatory and commercial insurance, political risks, personal injury and professional indemnity. The senior partner, considered by many to be the leading insurance practitioner in the London market, heads the insurance practice.

International Trade & Commodities: The firm has been a leader in the development of English law in this area, and is widely experienced in drafting contracts, joint venture, distribution and agency agreements, documentary aspects of trade finance and interpretation of standard contract wordings. The firm advises upon trading of oil and gas, metals and soft commodities and disputes relating thereto as well as political contingency credit and financial risk insurance.

Energy: Energy, both contentious and non-contentious, is an increasingly significant practice area, covering drafting and negotiating contracts, vessels of all kinds, including oil field supply vessels, drilling ships, on and offshore pipelines and installations as well as contractual disputes relating to their use or construction. The firm maintains close links with offshore operators and with shipowners and P&I Clubs, receiving instructions in most major incidents, including such high-profile matters as Piper Alpha, Exxon Valdez and The Braer.

Commercial/Corporate: Ince & Co has a thriving corporate group advising on general corporate and commercial issues ranging from employment to corporate finance through to international joint ventures.

Other: The firm also has significant practices in the areas of property and private client, asset recovery, EU and competition, sports and media, personal injury, and international commercial litigation and arbitration.

RECRUITMENT: Ince & Co recruits in the region of ten trainee solicitors annually. Full details of the firm's training regime and also of current vacancies for all legal staff are posted on the recruitment section of the firm's website.

INTERNATIONAL FAMILY LAW CHAMBERS

218 Strand, London, WC2R 1AP
Tel: (020) 7583 5040 **Fax:** (020) 7583 5151 **DX:** 252 London/Chancery Lane
Email: mail@internationalfamilylaw.com **Website:** www.internationalfamilylaw.com

Head of Chambers	David Truex
Number of principals	4
Other fee-earners	3

AREAS OF PRACTICE

English and international family law (including consultancy and agency) ..100%

CONTACTS

Family Law	David Truex
	Lorna Samuels
	Kirsten Beyer
	Madeleine Dimitroff

THE FIRM: Chambers specialising in international family law with principal members qualified in England and Wales, Australia, Germany and USA. Head of Chambers, David Truex, also qualified as an Australian barrister and solicitor, is an SFLA accredited specialist family lawyer. He is Chairman of the SFLA International Committee and the UK Host Committee for the 2001 World Congress on Family Law and the Rights of Children and Youth. Members of the Chambers have expertise in dealing with multijurisdictional disputes in England and overseas.

PRINCIPAL AREAS OF WORK: Most litigation is conducted in the English courts, generally involving international issues. Particular expertise is claimed in forum disputes, international enforcement, analysis of foreign laws, international treaties and complex financial matters where off-shore assets are in issue. International consultancy and agency work for other lawyers is a substantial part of the practice. Most clients are referred by law societies, embassies and other lawyers.

IRWIN MITCHELL

St. Peter's House, Hartshead, Sheffield, S1 2EL
Tel: (0114) 276 7777 **Fax:** (0114) 275 3306 **DX:** 10513
Email: enquiries@irwinmitchell.co.uk **Website:** www.imonline.co.uk

Managing Partner	Howard Culley
Senior Partner	Michael Napier
Number of partners	77
Assistant solicitors	148
Other fee earners	444

AREAS OF PRACTICE

Insurance Litigation Services	36%
Corporate Services	27%
Plaintiff Personal Injury Litigation	26%
Private Client	11%

CONTACTS

Business Crime	Kevin Robinson
Commercial Litigation	Peter Bellamy
Commercial Property	Kevin Docherty
Company/Commercial	Kevin Cunningham
Competition	Michael Jelly
Corporate Services	Kevin Cunningham
Employment	Simon Coates
Family & Matrimonial	Martin Loxley
Insurance	Joe Simpson
Intellectual Property	James Love
Personal Injury	John Pickering
Police Prosecution	Michael Whitworth
Residential Conveyancing	Steven Martin
Wills & Trusts	Paul Hirst

THE FIRM: Irwin Mitchell is a broad-based national firm operating in four national practice areas: Birmingham, Leeds, London and Sheffield. Now firmly established as one of the top national firms in the UK, Irwin Mitchell offers a distinctive approach to its clients' needs. Whether acting for national or international companies, family businesses or private clients, the firm provides the highest levels of service delivery and customer care. Whatever the area of work, Irwin Mitchell provides clear, direct and positive advice with a firm focus on the needs of the client. The firm has a strong customer service culture and a very high level of client retention. Widely regarded as a law firm with a difference, demand continues to grow for Irwin Mitchell's services. The practice is accredited to ISO 9001 and is authorised by the Law Society to conduct investment business.

PRINCIPAL AREAS OF WORK: The five practice areas provide a complete legal service for clients of the firm.
Corporate Services: The corporate services department comprises four national groups. The commercial and transactions group handles mergers and acquisitions both in the UK and cross-border, buy outs, corporate finance, banking, public sector transactions and commercial contracts. The human resources group covers employment contracts, disputes and pensions and employee benefits. The commercial litigation group represents clients in national and international disputes, mediation and advises on risk management. Its activities include the Braby & Waller debt recovery division; administrative and public law; business crime, professional negligence; insolvency; legal expenses; insurance, commercial and property litigation. The property group handles property acquisition, disposal, leasing, site assembly, development and construction.
Personal Injury: The firm also has an established national reputation for personal injury, clinical negligence and product liability work. It has successfully litigated in a number of multi-party cases as well as achieving substantial awards for individuals. Frequently working at the cutting edge of the law, it has won many significant cases that have often reshaped the law and set new precedents. Recent major victories have included the Armley asbestos claims, the CJD human growth hormone litigation and the Vibration White Finger and Chest Disease cases against British Coal.
Insurance: The firm handles both contentious and non-contentious insurance work in the form of advising on policy conditions and insurance litigation. It acts for insurers in defending claims particularly in the fields of employers liability, product liability and public liability. The firm also operates a large expenses unit which deals with over 60,000 cases per year.
Private Client: The private client practice area covers family, residential property, wills, trusts, probate and includes a Court of Protection unit. It acts for high net worth individuals particularly in ancillary relief disputes and the movements of trusts. Commercial clients provide instructions in the volume areas of will writing and domestic property. In all areas the use of specialist IT has enhanced the firm' s ability to obtain and retain work.
Investment Management: The investment management division provides a full suite of financial and investment management services, which allows the firm to provide a fully holistic approach to its clients. It acts for a wide range of clients including high net worth individuals and personal injury claimants. It creates individually tailored solutions designed to match each client's particular needs, taking into account the degrees of flexibility and risks needed to deliver the results that the clients want.

CLIENTELE: Clients range from the private individual and the family business to public companies and institutions on a national and international scale.

INTERNATIONAL: Irwin Mitchell has well established links with lawyers in the USA and most other foreign jurisdictions. It has particular expertise in transatlantic and Far Eastern work.

ISADORE GOLDMAN

125 High Holborn, London, WC1V 6QF **Tel:** (020) 7242 3000 **Fax:** (020) 7242 9160 **DX:** 124 **Ptnrs:** 10 **Asst solrs:** 3 **Other fee-earners:** 2

ISON HARRISON & CO

Duke House, 54 Wellington Street, Leeds, LS1 2EE
Tel: (0113) 284 5000 **Fax:** (0113) 284 5020 **DX:** 713106 - Leeds Park Square
Website: www.isonharrison.co.uk

Managing Partner	Beverley Coates
Senior Partner	Stephen Harrison

AREAS OF PRACTICE

Personal Injury & Clinical Negligence	40%
Business Clients	20%
Crime	15%
Conveyancing	15%
Family	10%

THE FIRM: Over the last year, Ison Harrison has doubled in size leading to the expansion of existing private client and corporate departments and the launch of a new commercial collections team called 'Equilibrium'. The firm has invested heavily in IT and case management systems. It has IIP accreditation and a LSC franchise and seeks Lexcel accreditation.

Continued overleaf

PRINCIPAL AREAS OF WORK:
Business Client: Specialisation in acquisition, disposals, property, employment, insolvency, partnership and debt recovery.
Private Client: Specialisation in clinical negligence, personal injury, family, crime and immigration. The financial services team enhances the probate, wills, trust and conveyancing departments.

CONTACTS	
Business clients	R J Timperley
Clinical Negligence/PI	Neil Fearn
Family/Immigration	Jo Trythall
Financial Services	Dave Martell
Property	Nigel Cowley

JACKSON & CANTER

32 Princes Road, Liverpool, L8 1TH
Tel: (0151) 282 1732 **Fax:** (0151) 282 1735 **DX:** 14156
Email: mailbox@jacksoncanter.co.uk **Website:** jacksoncanter.co.uk

Senior Partner	Andrew Holroyd

AREAS OF PRACTICE	
Litigation	30%
Crime	18%
Family	15%
Immigration	10%
Welfare	10%

THE FIRM: One of the leading civil rights firms in the North West undertaking a wide range of private client work both privately and publicly funded.

PRINCIPAL AREAS OF WORK: The firm is strong in immigration including business; public law, particularly suing the police and sexual abuse litigation; mental health; children and family work; housing; welfare benefits; crime. The firm also has strong links with the ethnic minority communities on Merseyside and helps and advises new businesses in the community.

J

JACKSON PARTON

18 Mansell Street, London, E1 8AA
Tel: (020) 7702 0085 **Fax:** (020) 7702 0858
Email: mail@jacksonparton.com

Managing & Senior Partner	Graham Jackson
Number of partners	10
Assistant solicitors	6
Other fee-earners	4

AREAS OF PRACTICE	
Commercial Shipping: Owners, Charterers, Cargo Owners & Insurers	70%
Admiralty: Collision and Salvage	30%

CONTACTS	
Admiralty	Brian Roberts
Commercial Shipping	Nicholas Parton
Industrial Diseases & Injury	Brian Roberts

THE FIRM: Jackson Parton is a medium-sized niche City practice specialising in shipping, commodity, insurance and related commercial litigation and arbitration. The firm was founded in 1992 and has flourished ever since.

PRINCIPAL AREAS OF WORK: The firm offers expertise in the full range of P&I and FD&D work, including charter disputes, cargo claims, pollution and general average. Other work includes sale and purchase, shipbuilding, mortgage enforcement disputes, marine insurance matters, commodity disputes, grounding, collision and salvage cases.

INTERNATIONAL: Work is handled in Arabic, Dutch, French, German, Greek, Italian, Japanese, Norwegian, Persian (Farsi) and Spanish.

JACKSONS

Innovation House, Yarm Road, Stockton on Tees, TS18 3TN
Tel: (01642) 643643 **Fax:** (01642) 873737 **DX:** 715796 Stockton
Email: genquiry@jacksons.law.co.uk **Website:** www.jacksons.law.co.uk

Queens House, Wellington Street, Leeds, LS1 2DE
Tel: (0113) 244 1666 **Fax:** (0113) 386 0600 **DX:** 706967 Leeds Park Square

Mayflower House, Fifth Avenue Business Park, Team Valley, Gateshead, NE11 0HF
Tel: (0191) 497 7300 **Fax:** (0191) 497 7301 **DX:** 60407 Whickham

Managing Partner	Richard Clarke
Senior Partner	Kevin Fletcher
Number of partners	16
Assistant solicitors	11
Other fee-earners	28
Total staff	130

AREAS OF PRACTICE	
Insurance Litigation	50%
Company/Commercial & Commercial Property	25%
Commercial Litigation	15%
Employment Law	10%

CONTACTS	
Agricultural	Adrienne Patterson
Commercial Litigation	Nigel Kidwell
Commercial Property	Geoffrey Skeoch
Company/Commercial	Anthony Wentworth
Employment	Kevin Fletcher
Insolvency	Stephen Wiles
Insurance Litigation	Richard Clarke

THE FIRM: Currently celebrating 125 years of service to the business community, Jacksons has a strong reputation as an efficient and progressive firm. The firm's philosophy is based upon a modern approach to business, incorporating the most up to date information technology and a commercial style management structure. Jacksons serves clients nationally in the field of both defendant insurance litigation and employment law and is renowned for providing high quality legal services to commercial clients in the North East. During the past two years the firm has expanded through the opening of a new office in the centre of Leeds and has taken on larger premises in Tyneside.

PRINCIPAL AREAS OF WORK:
Insurance Litigation: With a client list which includes eight out of the UK's top ten insurers, the firm's insurance litigation department offers expertise in disease work for defendants as well as traumatic injury, property damage and road traffic accidents.
Employment: The firm has a national reputation for its experience in employment law and offers specialist representation at employment tribunals throughout the UK, as well as in the Employment Appeal Tribunal.
Company Commercial: The firm covers the full range of services for the business client including sales and acquisitions, corporate finance and commercial contracts.

Commercial Property: The commercial property team deals with all areas of commercial property including freehold, disposals and acquisitions, leasehold matters, development agreements and planning agreements.
Commercial Litigation: The firm offers expertise in contract disputes, debt recovery, insurance recovery and professional negligence. The firm additionally advises on all aspects of criminal and civil liability in connection with environmental issues. Jacksons has been at the forefront of alternative dispute resolution and has pioneered mediation techniques as founder members of ADR Net Limited.
Agriculture: Jacksons was recently appointed by NFU as its panel firm for the North East region, an area extending from the Humber River to the Scottish Border. The agricultural department covers areas of work such as agricultural property, litigation and other rural business matters.
Insolvency: The expanding insolvency department acts for a number of insolvency practitioners, whilst advising companies, partnerships and individuals.

JAMES & CO

99 Manningham Lane, Bradford, BD1 3BN **Tel:** (01274) 729900 **Fax:** (01274) 721100
DX: 712442 Bradford 8 **Email:** jamesco@ukimmigration.co.uk **Website:** www.ukimmigration.co.uk
Ptnrs: 1 **Asst solrs:** 2 **Other fee-earners:** 5 **Contact:** Charles James • Specialist immigration firm. Charles James is on the Law Society Immigration panel for business, general immigration and political asylum.

AREAS OF PRACTICE	
Immigration	95%

JAMES CHAPMAN & CO

76 King Street, Manchester, M2 4NH
Tel: (0161) 828 8000 **Fax:** (0161) 828 8018 **DX:** 14492 Manchester 2
Email: generalenquiries@james-chapman.co.uk

Managing Partner	Elisabeth Taylor
Senior Partner	Maurice Watkins
Number of partners	28
Assistant solicitors	24
Other fee-earners	25

AREAS OF PRACTICE	
Defendant Insurance/Indemnity	80%
Company Work	10%
Plaintiff Personal Injury	5%
Conveyancing Residential/ Commercial & Probate	5%

CONTACTS	
Company/Commercial & Sports Law	Maurice Watkins
Personal Injury	Kevin Finnigan
Professional Indemnity	Elisabeth Taylor
Property/Private Client	Peter Marsden

THE FIRM: James Chapman & Co was established over 100 years ago and from its earliest days concentrated on insurance and indemnity work. It has maintained this specialisation and also handles corporate and commercial work, commercial and residential conveyancing and private client work. The firm also has a recognised specialisation in sports and media law. Clients of the firm include many major insurance companies and substantial corporate entities. The firm is one of the leading practices in the insurance and indemnity field in the North West. With 67 dedicated fee earners, the firm can handle an individual claim or a series of claims, of any size and complexity. James Chapman & Co intends to sustain the high quality provision of insurance and indemnity services that has been its hallmark since the firm was founded, as well as developing its expertise in other areas. In recent years, the practice has expanded steadily and has invested heavily in its office infrastructure and IT systems. It believes it will maintain this growth. The firm's policy is to increase the number of qualified staff, not only to meet the increase in demand for its services, but also to ensure that all clients receive a cost-efficient service.

PRINCIPAL AREAS OF WORK: The firm consists of four departments: personal injury work on behalf of defendants and insurers, insurance and professional indemnity work on behalf of defendants, company/commercial work, including sports law and media and entertainment law, and property and private client work.
Personal Injury: The department has dedicated specialists for cases of catastrophic injury, involving brain and spine injuries. The firm has been appointed as a member of restricted panels to several major insurers to deal with cases of the utmost severity and has a team of lawyers exclusively handling these cases. James Chapman & Co has pioneered a pro-active consensual approach to the settlement of significant personal injury cases and the encouragement of negotiations between solicitors. The firm has handled an increasing number of stress and other occupational disease claims.
Professional Indemnity: The department undertakes a wide range of high quality, complex claims on behalf of solicitors, surveyors, architects, barristers, valuers, insurance brokers, accountants and other professional groups. The firm has wide experience in general litigation and handles a variety of actions in product liability, building and construction risks, policy disputes, subrogation recoveries, motor claims, fire damage and employers' and public liability claims.
Company/Commercial: The department provides services to a variety of clients from listed public companies to smaller owner-run businesses. The services include advice on general company law, including acquisition and sales of companies, commercial contracts, intellectual property law, employment law, commercial litigation and debt recovery, with a growing media and IT practice.
Commercial Property & Private Client: The firm advises commercial property clients on property development, commercial leases, planning applications, estate management, landlord and tenant matters and secured lending. Private clients are advised on all aspects of financial planning, including personal tax advice, inheritance tax and estate planning, probates and trusts including wills, estate administration and preparing and administering settlements, and residential conveyancing.
Sports Law: James Chapman & Co's sports law team is led by partner Maurice Watkins, who is also a director of Manchester United plc and Manchester United Football Club. Maurice Watkins chaired the FIFA/UEFA

Continued overleaf

Task Force Juridical sub-committee coordinating the FIFA/UEFA response to the EC challenge to the world football transfer system. The team's work also includes sponsorship, broadcasting and merchandising. It has also been at the forefront in advising world-leaders in this sector for many years, acting for sporting bodies, event organisers, clubs and managers, as well as for individual sportsmen and women. Highlights during the year include advising the British Olympic swimming team in its dispute with the British Olympic Association and Speedo regarding freedom of choice to wear the revolutionary Speedo Fast Skin swimwear at the 2000 Olympic Games in Sydney; advising Manchester United plc on a cooperative marketing agreement with the New York Yankees; advising Jason Queally and QR 2001 on his attempt at the human powered land speed record. The team also advised Manchester United Football Club on two record-breaking signings, the British record transfer fee for a goalkeeper of £7.8 million for France's World Cup goalkeeper, Fabien Barthez, and the £19 million signing of Dutch striker, Ruud van Nistelrooy.

RECRUITMENT: The firm recruits four trainees a year, as well as additional assistant solicitors.

JAMESON & HILL

72-74 Fore Street, Hertford, SG14 1BY **Tel:** (01992) 554881 **Fax:** (01992) 551885 **DX:** 57908 Hertford **Email:** jail@nildram.co.uk **Ptnrs:** 5 **Asst solrs:** 6 **Other fee-earners:** 6

J

C & H JEFFERSON

Norwich Union House, 7 Fountain Street, Belfast, BT1 5EA
Tel: (028) 9032 9545 **Fax:** (028) 9024 4644 **DX:** 439 NR.Belfast
Email: infor@jefferson.u-net.com **Website:** www.jefferson.u-net.com

Number of partners	8
Assistant solicitors	14
Other fee-earners	4

AREAS OF PRACTICE

Litigation	65%
Commercial	20%
Employment	10%
Private Client	5%

CONTACTS

Commercial	Kenneth Rutherford
Employment	Mark Tinman
Litigation	Gareth Jones
Private Client	David G Lennon
Professional Indemnity	Gareth Jones

THE FIRM: Established in 1898, C & H Jefferson is one of the leading practices in Northern Ireland with an excellent reputation for its comprehensive legal and agency services.

PRINCIPAL AREAS OF WORK:

Litigation: The firm is one of the largest litigation practices in Northern Ireland, specialising in all areas of defence and commercial litigation and has corporate membership of FOIL.

Commercial: The firm has a strong commercial department embracing commercial property transactions; banking and securities, company formations, sales, acquisitions and reconstructions; partnerships; insolvency; debt recovery; agency work for leading firms in Great Britain and elsewhere, maritime law and defamation.

Employment: The firm has a vibrant employment law practice with a dedicated team, acting for employers, with extensive expertise in discrimination law (sex, religion and disability), and advising on contracts of employment.

Private Client: The firm provides a full range of services commensurate with a long-established practice including conveyancing; wills and administration of estates; tax planning and trusts and family law.

INTERNATIONAL: Members of the firm are fluent in French, Italian and Spanish.

JEFFREY AITKEN SOLICITORS

Fortune House, 74 Waterloo Street, Glasgow, G2 7DA **Tel:** (0141) 221 5983 **Fax:** (0141) 225 5750 **Email:** maildesk@jeffrey-aitken.co.uk **Ptnrs:** 4 **Asst solrs:** 1

JEFFREY GREEN RUSSELL

Apollo House, 56 New Bond Street, London, W1S 1RG
Tel: (020) 7339 7000 **Fax:** (020) 7339 7001 **DX:** 44627 Mayfair
Email: jgr@jgrlaw.co.uk **Website:** www.jgrweb.com

Managing Partner	Clive Whitfield-Jones
Senior Partner	Anthony Coles
Number of partners	23
Assistant solicitors	18
Other fee-earners	14

CONTACTS

Company/Commercial	John O'Connell
Insurance Litigation	R Bryan Lincoln
Leisure & Licensing	Julian Skeens
Litigation	Phillip Cohen
Private Client	Phillip Harris
Property	Peter Johnson

THE FIRM: Jeffrey Green Russell is a medium-sized commercial law firm based in Bond Street, London W1. The practice is committed to technology and human resources development, both of which have made a significant contribution to its success. The practice prides itself on being at the cutting edge in the use of technology to achieve its business goals.

PRINCIPAL AREAS OF WORK:

Company/Commercial: A broad spectrum of services focus on commercial and financial activity. Corporate work includes formations, mergers, acquisitions, MBOs, joint ventures, reorganisations and share issues. Other areas of expertise are commercial work (including computer contracts and the Internet), banking and finance, intellectual property and franchising, and corporate taxation.

Litigation: Rapid, positive, effective action is the hallmark of this department in general commercial litigation, insurance disputes including professional negligence and product liability, property litigation, employment matters, debt collection and insolvency, mortgage repossession and commercial fraud including computer and technology-related offences, and personal injury and legal expenses insurance.

Property: The department offers a full range of services including planning, development work, property finance, investment, dealing (including portfolio break-ups and auction work) and landlord and tenant law.
Licensing & Leisure: A strong department caters for the special demands of the leisure industry offering a comprehensive service representing clients in courts throughout the country. The firm deals with bingo, night-clubs and discos, pubs, off-licences, restaurants and catering, hotels, cinemas, amusement arcades and gaming.
Personal Finance: The department provides a specialist service dedicated to the protection and enhancement of clients' personal wealth. The range of services includes wills and probate, estate and financial planning, trusts and settlements, administration of estates and overseas tax arrangements.

CLIENTELE: Clients cover a spectrum of commerce, finance and industry, ranging from small businesses to multinational corporations. Activities include banking, finance, mortgage lenders, the Internet, technology, leisure, restaurants, the licensed trade, brewers, insurance, airlines and property development.

INTERNATIONAL: The firm is a member of ACL International, an association of commercial lawyers world-wide. For further information contact the senior partner.

JENKINS & HAND

Clutha House, 10 Storey's Gate, London, SW1P 3AY **Tel:** (020) 7222 5002 **Fax:** (020) 7222 5004 **DX:** 99924 Victoria **Ptnrs:** 2 **Contact:** Keith Jenkins • Specialising in work for social landlords, local authorities and public sector bodies, including stock transfers, urban regeneration projects, governance of housing associations and local authority powers.

AREAS OF PRACTICE	
Housing Association	70%
Local Authority	30%

JEREMY FEAR & CO

5a St. Onge Parade, Southbury Road, Enfield, EN1 1YU **Tel:** (020) 8367 4466 **Fax:** (020) 8367 3481 **Asst solrs:** 1

JJ RICE

Law Society House, 94 Victoria House, Belfast, **Tel:** (028) 9028 8688 **Fax:** (028) 9028 8588 **Email:** j_rice_llm@compuserve.com

JOELSON WILSON & CO

70 New Cavendish Street, London, W1G 8AT
Tel: (020) 7580 5721 **Fax:** (020) 7580 2251
Email: info@joelson-wilson.co.uk **Website:** www.joelson-wilson.co.uk

Managing Partner	Paul Baglee
Senior Partner	Paul Wilson
Number of partners	7
Assistant solicitors	5
Other fee-earners	4

AREAS OF PRACTICE	
Company/Commercial	34%
Licensing Liquor/Gaming/Betting/ Entertainment	34%
Commercial Litigation & Employment	20%
Property	12%

THE FIRM: Established in 1957, Joelson Wilson & Co provides a personal and individual approach and a highly commercial service to its clients. Traditionally known for its strong company/commercial, commercial litigation and commercial property practice, the firm has an established reputation for its work in the leisure industry in the UK and overseas. Solicitors in its specialised licensing department appear in Licensing Courts throughout the entire country. The firm's employment law unit has a growing reputation. There is a strong international element to the firm's practice. It is the UK member of European Lawyers Network (EEIG) working closely with the other member firms in Amsterdam, Brussels, Frankfurt, Paris and Stockholm and the US associated member firms in Pittsburgh, PA and Sacremento, CA.

JOHN BATTERS & CO

Craigie Hall, 6 Rowan Road, Glasgow, G41 5BS **Tel:** (0141) 427 6884 **Fax:** (0141) 427 7909 **Ptnrs:** 1

JOHN BOYLE AND CO

The Square, 5 West End, Redruth, TR15 2SB **Tel:** (01209) 213507 **Fax:** (01209) 219470 **DX:** 81758 Redruth **Ptnrs:** 3 **Asst solrs:** 3 **Other fee-earners:** 4

JOHN COLLINS & PARTNERS WITH EDWARD HARRIS & SON

Copper Court, Phoenix Way, Enterprise Park, Swansea, SA7 9EH **Tel:** (01792) 773773 **Fax:** (01792) 774775 **DX:** 82804 SWANSEA 2 **Email:** law@johncollins.co.uk **Website:** www.johncollins.co.uk **Ptnrs:** 9 **Asst solrs:** 31 **Other fee-earners:** 5

JOHN FORD MORRISON

Third Floor, Sun Court House, 18-26 Essex Road, London, N1 8LN **Tel:** (020) 8800 6464 **Fax:** (020) 8800 6066 **Email:** admin@johnfordmorisson.co.uk **Ptnrs:** 2 **Asst solrs:** 8 **Other fee-earners:** 6

JOHN GAUNT & PARTNERS

Omega Court, 372 Cemetery Road, Sheffield, S11 8FT **Tel:** (0114) 266 8664 **Fax:** (0114) 266 0101 **DX:** 717212 Sheffield 27 **Email:** post@john-gaunt.co.uk **Website:** www.john-gaunt.co.uk **Ptnrs:** 4 **Asst solrs:** 2 **Other fee-earners:** 3 **Contact:** John R.T. Gaunt • Specialist commercial practice, particularly for the licensed and leisure industries, handling over 5,000 licence applications each year

AREAS OF PRACTICE

Liquor Licensing	80%
Commercial Litigation	10%
Landlord & Tenant (Contentious/ Non-contentious)	10%

JOHN HODGE & CO

27/31 Boulevard, Weston-super-Mare, BS23 1NY **Tel:** (01934) 623511 **Fax:** (01934) 418210 **DX:** 8403 **Ptnrs:** 7 **Asst solrs:** 7 **Other fee-earners:** 11

JOHN KENDALL

The Manor House, St. David's Street, Presteigne, LD8 2BP **Tel:** (01544) 260019 **Fax:** (01544) 260717 **Email:** jkendall@btinternet.com **Ptnrs:** 1

J

JOHN MCKEE & SON

55 Royal Avenue, Belfast, BT1 1FD
Tel: (028) 9023 2303 **Fax:** (028) 9023 0081 **DX:** 470 NR Belfast
Email: info@jmckee.co.uk **Website:** www.jmckee.co.uk

Senior Partner	Lex Ross
Number of partners	5
Assistant solicitors	6
Other fee-earners	2

AREAS OF PRACTICE

Commercial	42%
Litigation	41%
Private client	14%
Other	3%

CONTACTS

Corporate/Commercial	Avril McCammon
	Lex Ross
Litigation	Leonard Edgar
	Melanie Jones
Property	Albert Jordan

THE FIRM: John McKee & Son is a major Belfast law firm, highly regarded for its corporate and litigation expertise. Founded in 1887, the firm is a progressive law firm which continues to enjoy rapid growth. The firm's lawyers have extensive experience in their fields, enabling them to serve the needs of both local and national clients.

PRINCIPAL AREAS OF WORK:

Corporate/Commercial: The firm advises business clients on all aspects of corporate and commercial law. Work includes advice on company acquisitions and disposals, corporate insolvency and personal insolvency acting in the main for insolvency practitioners, and banking and secured lending together with private finance initiative work, acting on behalf of the lending institutions.
Litigation: The firm has an excellent reputation in insurance litigation, commercial and insolvency litigation, employment tribunals and debt recovery.
Property: All aspects of commercial property transactions are undertaken together with building society repossession work.
Other Areas: The firm also provides a full range of private client advice, including wills, tax planning, residential conveyancing and matrimonial matters.

JOHN MORSE SOLICITORS

St Helen's House, 156 St Helen's Road, Swansea, SA1 5DG **Tel:** (01792) 648 111 **Fax:** (01792) 648 028 **Email:** mail@johnmorse.co.uk **Ptnrs:** 1 **Other fee-earners:** 2

JOHN PICKERING & PARTNERS

9 Church Lane, Oldham, OL1 3AN **Tel:** (0161) 834 1251 **Fax:** (0161) 626 1671 **DX:** 23616 **Website:** www.johnpickering.co.uk **Ptnrs:** 6 **Asst solrs:** 6 **Other fee-earners:** 1

JOHNS ELLIOT

40 Linenhall Street, Belfast, BT2 8BA
Tel: (028) 9032 6881 **Fax:** (028) 9024 8236 **DX:** 419 NR Belfast
Email: info@johnselliot.com **Website:** www.johnselliot.com

Managing & Senior Partner	Maurice Butler
Number of partners	8
Assistant solicitors	3
Other fee-earners	9

AREAS OF PRACTICE

Company/Commercial	45%
Litigation and Employment	25%
Probate & Tax	15%
Other	15%

CONTACTS

Company/Commercial	Maurice Butler
Litigation	Ronald Robinson
Private Client	David Leitch

THE FIRM: Johns Elliot is a leading City firm offering a wide range of legal services, with particular emphasis on commercial and corporate matters. The firm was established in 1837. Each client has contact with a single partner who bears responsibility for the conduct of that client's business, although individual aspects will be dealt with by specialist lawyers.

PRINCIPAL AREAS OF WORK:

Company/Commercial Property: Work includes company formations, reconstructions and acquisitions, and all aspects of commercial property, from initial planning applications to satisfying the requirements of the developers' financiers.

Employment: An increasingly problematic area for commercial clients, legal advice is given at an early stage to assess the potential impact of legislation, evolve efficient working practices and ensure good industrial relations are established and maintained.

Litigation: A major part of the firm's practice, this department deals with commercial litigation, building contract arbitrations, medical negligence, personal injury claims and debt collection, and is also involved in defamation actions for newspapers and local broadcasting networks.

THE JOHNSON PARTNERSHIP

Cannon Courtyard, Off Long Row, Nottingham, NG1 6JE **Tel:** (0115) 941 9141 **Fax:** (0115) 947 0178 **DX:** 10082
Email: mail@thejohnsonpartnership.co.uk **Website:** www.thejohnsonpartnership.co.uk **Ptnrs:** 14 **Asst solrs:** 9 **Other fee-earners:** 17

JOHNSONS

Johnson House, 50-56 Wellington Place, Belfast, BT1 6GF
Tel: (028) 9024 0183 **Fax:** (028) 9024 9239 **DX:** 405 NR Belfast 1
Email: pt@johnsonslaw.co.uk

Senior Partners	John Marshall Paul Tweed
Number of partners	6
Assistant solicitors	10
Other fee-earners	1

AREAS OF PRACTICE

Litigation	50%
Defamation/Media & Entertainment Law	25%
Company/Commercial/Employment	20%
Private Client	5%

THE FIRM: Johnsons offers a partner-driven, pragmatic and cost-effective legal service to commercial and private clients.

PRINCIPAL AREAS OF WORK: Johnsons has an extensive defence litigation practice representing many insurance companies. In addition, the firm has developed a recognised expertise in the fields of defamation and media-related law, and corporate law acting for, inter alia, the largest financial institution in Northern Ireland

JOHNSTON & HERRON

George Johnston House, Bank Street, Lochgelly, KY5 9QN **Tel:** (01592) 780421 **Fax:** (01592) 782726 **Email:** mail@johnston-herron.co.uk
Ptnrs: 4 **Asst solrs:** 3 **Other fee-earners:** 2

JOHN WESTON & CO

10 Victoria Street, Felixstowe, IP11 7ER **Tel:** (01394) 282527 **Fax:** (01394) 276097 **DX:** 31467 Felixstowe **Email:** info@johnweston.co.uk
Website: www.johnweston.co.uk **Ptnrs:** 1 **Other fee-earners:** 2

JOHN WINKWORTH-SMITH

Churchdale Farm, Ashford-in-the-Water, Bakewell, DE45 1NX **Tel:** (01629) 640269 **Fax:** (01629) 640608 **Email:** john.winkworth@easynet.co.uk
Ptnrs: 1

JONAS ROY BLOOM

Citadel, 190 Corporation Street, Birmingham, B4 6QD
Tel: (0121) 212 4111 **Fax:** (0121) 212 1770 **DX:** 13013
Email: jonas1@jonasroybloom.co.uk **Website:** www.jonasroybloom.co.uk

Number of partners	6
Assistant solicitors	4
Other fee-earners	14

AREAS OF PRACTICE

Crime	75%
Personal Injury	25%

THE FIRM: The firm specialises in crime, libel, and personal injury law, including medical negligence and civil actions against the police. Its longstanding reputation of dealing with the most serious criminal trials has been extended in recent years into white collar crime and fraud trials, and it is often instructed by professionals. Agency commissions undertaken.

JONATHAN STEPHENS & CO

Ty Cornel, 11 Castle Parade, Usk, NP15 1AA **Tel:** (01291) 673344 **Fax:** (01291) 673575 **DX:** 32552 Usk **Email:** js.agrilaw@oyeznet.co.uk
Ptnrs: 2 **Other fee-earners:** 1

JONES & CASSIDY

220 Ormeau Road, Belfast, BT7 2FY **Tel:** (028) 90642290 **Fax:** (028) 90642297 **Ptnrs:** 2 **Asst solrs:** 1 **Other fee-earners:** 3

JONES, DAY, REAVIS & POGUE

Bucklersbury House, 3 Queen Victoria Street, London, EC4N 8NA
Tel: (020) 7236 3939 **Fax:** (020) 7236 1113 **DX:** 98949 Cheapside 2
Website: www.jonesday.com

Senior Partner	Robert Thomson
Number of partners	8
Assistant solicitors	45
Other fee-earners	12

THE FIRM: Founded in 1893, Jones Day is one of the world's largest law firms, employing more than 1,450 lawyers resident in 26 locations in major centres of business and finance around the globe. Established over 25 years ago, Jones Day London is a multinational partnership, providing UK and US legal advice through UK, US and dually qualified lawyers. The London office provides a full range of business legal services to UK and overseas clients, focusing principally on UK and cross-border M&A; corporate finance transactions; investment funds; private equity; corporate tax planning; banking, tax and tax-based structured finance; litigation/dispute resolution and arbitration; competition/antitrust; commercial property and environmental law; share schemes, employment and pension matters; intellectual property and information technology. The London office is part of Jones Day Europe, which includes approximately 200 lawyers in Brussels, Frankfurt, Geneva, Madrid and Paris. Jones Day Europe functions as an integrated organisation, with a wide range of skills and experience available to meet the needs of its clients.

J

PRINCIPAL AREAS OF WORK:

Corporate, Corporate Finance & Commercial: One of the strengths of the London office is its corporate practice and it is able to offer its clients the full range of high quality legal services required for all corporate transactions. The office has substantial expertise in public and private, domestic and cross-border mergers and acquisitions, reorganisations, auction sales, joint ventures and general commercial transactions. The corporate finance team advises companies, institutions, investment banks and funds on a wide variety of equity and debt issues, capital markets and securities work, funds structuring and financial services law. The private equity team advises a wide range of private equity providers, vendors and management teams. Members of the team have extensive experience in relation to all kinds of private equity transactions such as start-ups, second and subsequent round financings, buy-outs and buy-ins (including 'take private' deals). The team also includes highly regarded acquisition finance, high yield and securitisation specialists and is able to draw upon the advice and experience of the worldwide Jones Day network. The breadth of all this expertise enables the firm to advise both UK and international clients from a broad range of industries and business sectors.

Taxation: The London office tax group, which is the largest tax practice of any non-English firm in London, advises UK, US and other overseas enterprises on the tax aspects of international transactions and investments. It provides both UK and US tax expertise, with particular emphasis on the tax dimensions of cross-border mergers, acquisitions, post-acquisition restructurings, and other internal reorganisations and associated tax planning. The London office is a recognised leader in tax-based structured finance transactions.

Finance: The London office handles a variety of financing and banking transactions, including leveraged acquisition financing, high-yield debt issues and other forms of capital market issues, tax-based structured finance, securitisations, and other secured and unsecured financial transactions.

Litigation & Arbitration: The London office represents clients in English High Court litigation, English and other European arbitration proceedings, and alternative dispute resolutions in a broad range of substantive areas of law. The litigation group also frequently advises on the many complex issues that arise in cross-border litigation and arbitration, including questions of jurisdiction, conflicts of law, pre-trial investigations, disclosure, and enforcement of judgments. Jones Day's London-based lawyers have significant experience in matters that include fraud and white-collar crime, disputes arising out of international trade, commodities, shipping, energy, insurance, employment, product liability, tax, and other general contractual and tortious actions.

Property & Environmental Matters: The London team advises on a full range of real estate transactions for both UK and overseas clients with a particular focus on maximising the value of the corporate real estate asset for clients. The team is also a key part of all corporate transactions providing advice on the liabilities relating to real estate and environmental issues, and in particular the negotiation of environmental indemnities. The environmental team also provides regulatory advice for clients on a wide range of environmental issues.

Employment, Pensions & Share Schemes: The London office has a team of employment and pensions lawyers who advise on transactional and ongoing employee and pensions matters. They play a key role in the mergers and acquisitions practice and advise on all aspects of contentious and non-contentious employment and pensions issues. In addition, they work closely with members of the tax group in advising on and designing employment benefit schemes, such as profit sharing schemes and phantom share plans.

Competition: The firm has a leading reputation in providing innovative competition law advice. As part of the Jones Day European competition team, the London office advises on merger control and the full range of EU and UK competition matters. Members of the team have significant experience in dealing with the European Commission and the UK regulatory authorities.

Intellectual Property & Information Technology: The London office intellectual property/information technology group offers expertise on all aspects of patent, trademark, copyright, domain name and design right issues. The group also advises on software licensing and protection (having a number of leading technology clients for M&A and commercial work) and assists numerous hi-tech and industrial clients on e-commerce/Internet issues. The group is equally experienced in offering sophisticated transactional and litigation support and is fully integrated into the firm's market leading practices in the US and Europe.

INTERNATIONAL: The firm has other offices in Atlanta, Brussels, Chicago, Cleveland, Columbus, Dallas, Frankfurt, Geneva, Hong Kong, Houston, Irvine, Los Angeles, Madrid, New York, Palo Alto, Paris, Pittsburgh, Shanghai, Singapore, Sydney, Taipei, Tokyo, Washington DC, New Delhi (associate office) and Mumbai (associate office). Work is handled in Cantonese, German, French, Italian and Turkish.

JONES MAIDMENT WILSON INCORPORATING HATTON SCATES HORTON

5 Byrom Street, Manchester, M3 4PF **Tel:** (0161) 832 8087 **Fax:** (0161) 835 3123 **DX:** 14372 Manchester 1 **Email:** manager@jmw.co.uk **Website:** www.jmw.co.uk **Ptnrs:** 13 **Asst solrs:** 18 **Other fee-earners:** 4

JONES MYERS GORDON

The Pearl Building, 22 East Parade, Leeds, LS1 5BZ **Tel:** (0113) 246 0055 **Fax:** (0113) 246 7446 **DX:** 14080 Leeds Park Square **Email:** info@jmg.co.uk **Website:** www.jmg.co.uk **Ptnrs:** 4 **Asst solrs:** 2 **Other fee-earners:** 2 **Contact:** John Myers • A specialist family and child care practice.

AREAS OF PRACTICE

Matrimonial/Childcare	95%
Conveyancing	5%

JONES & WARNER

60 Lombard Street, London, EC3V 9EA
Tel: (020) 7464 8454 **Fax:** (020) 7464 8747
Email: jw@jwlaw.co.uk

Number of partners	4
Assistant solicitors	2
Other fee-earners	2

AREAS OF PRACTICE

Employment	100%

CONTACTS

Non-Contentious Aspects/Senior Executives/Employee Benefits/Pensions & Tax ....David Warner
Strategic Issues/Statutory & Regulatory Aspects/Employment Tribunals/Litigation & Arbitration
..........Anne Bevitt
..........Jennie Wade
..........Simeon Spencer

THE FIRM: Jones & Warner, based in the City of London, was established in 1999 as a niche employment law firm. An unusual feature of the firm is that it brings together the complementary skills of solicitors, barristers and human resource professionals to provide a one-stop-solution for employment and labour relations requirements. The firm has four partners, two of whom are dual qualified as barristers and solicitors. One partner holds the qualification of Solicitor Advocate (Higher Courts Civil), giving a right of audience in all civil courts. The firm also retains the services of a senior human resources professional with wide international experience, formerly the Group HR Director of a leading investment bank. The firm's approach is to provide proactive and preventative legal services, to enable its clients to minimise the risk of problems arising and to deal with them from a position of strength. It does not believe that lawyers should simply react after a problem has arisen. Jones & Warner is committed to innovative legal practice and embraces contemporary management ideas, including a strong emphasis on work-life balance.

PRINCIPAL AREAS OF WORK: The firm advises on all aspects of employment law, contentious and non-contentious.

CLIENTELE: The firm works for major employers, national and multinational and for senior executives.

JOY MERRIAM & CO

67 Burdett Road, London, E3 4TN **Tel:** (020) 8980 7171 **Fax:** (020) 8981 7981 **DX:** 55652 Bow **Email:** solicitors@joymerriman.co.uk **Ptnrs:** 3 **Asst solrs:** 2 **Other fee-earners:** 4

J.R. JONES

56A The Mall, Ealing, W5 3TA
Tel: (020) 8566 2595 **Fax:** (020) 8579 4288 **DX:** 5134 Ealing
Email: Solicitors@jrjones.co.uk

Managing Partner	T Raza
Number of partners	3
Assistant solicitors	11
Other fee-earners	7

THE FIRM: Established in 1989 as a sole practice the firm now has three partners and a total staff of 35. The firm has Legal Aid franchises in the areas of personal injury, immigration, family, criminal, employment, housing, welfare and debt. The practice is organised into specialised departments providing a full range of legal services to its clients. The firm has been involved in several high profile cases of recent times. It fought for justice on behalf of the parents of the black teenager Stephen Lawrence, culminating in a public inquiry set up by the Home Secretary under the Chairmanship of Sir William Macpherson. The firm also acted for the family of Dr Joan Francisco. This case made English legal history as the first case of civil murder in which there had been no previous criminal proceedings.

JULIAN DOBSON SOLICITORS

6 Marllborough Place, Brighton, BN1 1UB **Tel:** (01273) 693 567 **Fax:** (01273) 620 742 **Email:** jcd@juliandobson.com

JULIAN HOLY

31 Brechin Place, London, SW7 4QD **Tel:** (020) 7370 5443 **Fax:** (020) 7244 7371 **DX:** 35765 South Ken. **Email:** law@julianholy.co.uk **Ptnrs:** 6 **Asst solrs:** 2 **Other fee-earners:** 3 **Contact:** Simon J Edwards • Specialises in commercial property and litigation, renowned for rapid reaction time. Provides clear incisive advice, high standard of service, personal attention, determined to achieve clients' needs.

AREAS OF PRACTICE

Commercial Property	60%
Commercial Litigation	25%
Company/Commercial	15%

KAYE SCHOLER LLP

10th Floor, 88 Wood Street, London, EC2V 7RS **Tel:** (020) 8528 1006 **Fax:** (020) 8528 1206 **Email:** samiles@kayescholar.com **Website:** www.kayescholer.com **Ptnrs:** 1 **Other fee-earners:** 2

KEEBLE HAWSON

Old Cathedral Vicarage, St. James' Row, Sheffield, S1 1XA **Tel:** (0114) 272 2061 **Fax:** (0114) 270 0813 **Email:** postroom@keeblehawson.co.uk **Website:** www.keeblehawson.co.uk **Ptnrs:** 26 **Asst solrs:** 19 **Other fee-earners:** 33

K

KEMP LITTLE LLP

Saddlers House, Gutter Lane, London, EC2V 6BR **Tel:** (020) 7600 8080 **Fax:** (020) 7600 7878 **Email:** info@comlegal.com **Website:** www.comlegal.com **Ptnrs:** 6 **Asst solrs:** 13 **Other fee-earners:** 1 **Contact:** Richard Kemp • 'A law firm for business and technology' servicing corporate, employment, regulatory and commercial work for computer, e-commerce and communications industry clients.

AREAS OF PRACTICE

Corporate	30%
Commercial	20%
Competition & Regulatory	20%
Intellectual Property	15%
Employment	15%

KENNEDYS

Longbow House, 14-20 Chiswell Street, London, EC1Y 4TW
Tel: (020) 7638 3688 **Fax:** (020) 7638 2212 **DX:** 46628 Barbican
Email: mailbox@kennedys-law.com **Website:** www.kennedys-law.com

50 Mark Lane, London, EC3R 7QT
Tel: (020) 7638 3688 **Fax:** (020) 7702 9757 **DX:** 514 London/City

Ewing House, 130 Kings Road, Brentwood, CM14 4EA
Tel: (01277) 233 636 **Fax:** (01277) 219 175 **DX:** 124462 Brentwood 5

64-66 Upper Church Lane, Belfast, BT1 4QL
Tel: (028) 90 240 067 **Fax:** (028) 90 315 557 **DX:** 490 NR Belfast 1

THE FIRM: Kennedys is one of the leading litigation firms in the UK, known primarily for its insurance-driven commercial practice. The firm is also recognised for its skills in the non-contentious field, particularly in the insurance, financial, construction and transport industries. During 2000 Kennedys expanded considerably. In May 2000 a partner from Gepp & Sons and three members of his liability team joined Kennedys' Brentwood office and in London the firm doubled the size of the Mark Lane office in EC3, the heart of the insurance industry. Following the firms' appointment to the National Health Service Litigation Authority's legal panel, the firm has opened an office in Newmarket. Two new partners and their teams, originally from Mills and Reeve, are now based there. These and other international strategic business developments (the opening of offices in Hong Kong, Auckland and New Delhi) have enabled Kennedys to build on its strengths and increase the firm's profile within the insurance and other market sectors.

PRINCIPAL AREAS OF WORK:

Dispute Resolution: Acting for a wide range of clients both nationally and internationally, Kennedys is one of the leading dispute resolution firms in the country. The practice is structured to allow specialised litigation teams to handle the whole spectrum of insurance work, including professional indemnity, personal injury, reinsurance, product liability, banking and finance, clinical negligence, directors' and officers' liability and employers' and public liability.

Clinical Negligence: Kennedys' healthcare team was established 16 years ago. The firm was recently selected as one of the panel members for the NHS Litigation Authority in both London and East Anglia following a tender process in September 2000.

Personal Injury: Kennedys' liability unit concentrates the firm's diversity of liability experience into one focused group which continues to handle both complex/catastrophic claims and high volume personal injury claims.

Construction Law: The firm's construction team continues to build on its successes in handling both contentious and non-contentious mainstream construction matters as well as dealing with professional indemnity issues for the insurance industry.

Commercial Law: The commercial unit comprising the insolvency, company, commercial property and commercial arbitration teams, provides a wide range of commercial services for several industry sectors.

Senior Partner	Nick Thomas
Chairman	Stephen Cantle
Number of partners	56
Assistant solicitors	68
Other fee-earners	62

AREAS OF PRACTICE

Insurance Litigation	83%
Company/Commercial	6%
Employment	6%
Construction (Non-Contentious)	3%
Commercial Property	2%

CONTACTS

Banking/Finance	John Harvey
Clinical Negligence	Janet Sayers
Commercial Property	Jeremy Palmer
Company/Commercial	James Shaw
Construction (Contentious)	Nick Thomas
	Geoffrey Lord
Construction (Non-Contentious)	James Shaw
Defamation	Philip Hartley
Employment	Marc Meryon
Financial Institutions Private Insurance	Chris Sharrock
Insolvency	Dino Paganuzzi
Insurance	Stephen Cantle
Motor	John Yates
	Richard West
Personal Injury	Timothy Wilson
	Jane Smith
Pharmaceutical/Product Liability	Shane Sayers
Professional Indemnity	Nick Thomas
Railway Litigation	Andrew Gilbert
Reinsurance	Nicholas Williams

Kennedys
Legal advice in black and white

Employment: The expanding employment team's work is a mix of litigation and advisory, transactional matters for the railway, healthcare insurance and financial sectors.
Railway Litigation: Kennedys' large and experienced railway litigation team has specialist knowledge of railway operation, business and personnel. The team advises on employment issues, corporate manslaughter, health and safety and personal injury in particular.
IT/E-commerce: The firm has spent time developing its e-business and technological capabilities. Clients are now able to access details of their cases online via a case management system specifically tailored to their individual requirements.

INTERNATIONAL: Internationally Kennedys continues to expand. In the early part of 2000 Kennedys opened an office in Hong Kong (Skrine Thomas Sharrock). The firm strengthened its Spanish connections with the signing of a partnership agreement with a law firm in Madrid. In November 2000 Kennedys opened an office in Auckland, New Zealand. Kennedys also announced plans in late 2000 to establish an office in New Delhi. This latest international office is now open with legal services provided by a team of locally qualified lawyers and headed by Neeraj Tuli, a former partner of Kennedys, now admitted to the New Delhi Bar.

RECRUITMENT: The firm are always keen to consider applications from commercially driven, enthusiastic and committed lawyers with a strong interest in insurance litigation. Contact the personnel department for details.

KENNETH BUSH

Evershed House, 23/25 King Street, King's Lynn, PE30 1DU **Tel:** (01553) 692737 **Fax:** (01553) 691729 **DX:** 57802 King's Lynn
Email: kenbush@aol.com **Ptnrs:** 15 **Asst solrs:** 3 **Other fee-earners:** 9

KENNETH CURTIS & CO

88 Aldridge Road, Perry Barr, Birmingham, B42 2TP **Tel:** (0121) 356 1161 **Fax:** (0121) 356 2973 **DX:** 21502 **Ptnrs:** 3 **Asst solrs:** 3
Other fee-earners: 1

KENNETH ELLIOTT & ROWE

162-166 South Street, Romford, RM1 1SX
Tel: (01708) 757 575 **Fax:** (01708) 766 674 **DX:** 4602 Romford
Email: law@ker.co.uk **Website:** www.ker.co.uk

24 Buckingham Gate, London, SW1E 6LB
Tel: (020) 7834 6464 **Fax:** (020) 7834 6470 **DX:** 99921 Victoria

Managing Partner	Chris Dixon
Number of partners	12
Assistant solicitors	7
Other fee-earners	13

AREAS OF PRACTICE

Commercial Property	35%
Common Law	30%
Employment	10%
Insolvency	10%
Private Client	10%
Licensing	5%

CONTACTS

Commercial Property	Chris Dixon
Employment	Michael Flynn
Financial Services	David Rogers
Insolvency	Mark Dixon
Licensing	Beverley Hamblin
Matrimonial	Rebecca Gardiner
Personal Injury Litigation	Neville Filar
Private Client	David Farr

THE FIRM: Whilst the firm's foundations were laid in the 1930s, its largely organic growth has taken place over the last 15 years, as the firm has evolved from its high street roots to one with offices in London's West End and Essex, serving an increasingly commercial and cosmopolitan client base with a substantial foreign element. The firm's administrative base remains in Essex, where it is known as a major player in the metropolitan Essex region, acting for local authorities, as well as major manufacturers, shipping companies and many others in addition to a burgeoning personal injury practice.

PRINCIPAL AREAS OF WORK:
Commercial Property: The firm's best known expertise is in the field of commercial property and it has added specialist property litigation to its range of services. Its property team is one of the largest in the region with six partners and five assistants and it continues to top the regional league tables for its work. The breadth of its work is extensive and highly respected, going beyond routine matters and frequently identifying deals for its domestic and international clients. It represents developers, retail chains, local authorities and overseas investment clients on complex property matters.
Insolvency: The firm has its own licensed insolvency practitioner.
Company/Commercial: The firm regularly acts on acquisitions, disposals, MBOs and MBIs of varying descriptions.
Licensing: The firm acts as agents for the legal departments of large brewers and their independent law firms, as well as local licensing committees and businesses.
Personal Injury: The personal injury department comprises two partners and two solicitors plus paralegal support, making it one of the largest plaintiff only departments in the region.
Private Client: The firm represents senior diplomats and forces personnel.

INTERNATIONAL: The firm is a founder member of LAWorld, an international law firm network and has close links with clients and lawyers in China, India and the Far and Middle East.

RECRUITMENT: The firm takes three trainees a year and currently employs seven. It looks for plenty of brains and a sense of humour. Trainees may be sent on overseas work experience with other firms within the LAWorld network.

KENT JONES AND DONE

Churchill House, Regent Road, Stoke-on-Trent, ST1 3RQ **Tel:** (01782) 202 020 **Fax:** (01782) 202 040 **DX:** 20727 Hanley **Email:** mail@kjd.co.uk **Website:** www.kjd.co.uk **Ptnrs:** 15 **Asst solrs:** 10 **Other fee-earners:** 12 **Contact:** Adrian Ross • The dominant corporate practice in the region outside Birmingham, providing a range of specialist and general commercial advice. The firm received Lexcel accreditation during the year.

AREAS OF PRACTICE	
Dispute Resolution	30%
Corporate	29%
Property	22%
Employment	8%
Planning & Environmental	7%
Personal	3%

KEOGHS

2 The Parklands, Bolton, BL6 4SE
Tel: (01204) 677 000 **Fax:** (01204) 677 111 **DX:** 723540 Bolton (Lostock)
Email: info@keoghs.co.uk **Website:** www.keoghs.co.uk

4 Saxon Gate, Back of the Walls, Southampton, SO14 2HA
Tel: (023) 8023 5642 **Fax:** (023) 8023 0765 **DX:** 2014 Southampton 1
Email: info@keoghs.co.uk

1 Eastwood Business Village, Harry Weston Road, Binley, Coventry, CV3 2UB
Tel: (024) 7665 8200 **Fax:** (024) 7665 8262 **DX:** 700127 Coventry 4
Email: info@keoghs.co.uk

K

Chief Executive Officer	Paul Smith
Insurance Managing Partner	David Tyson
Commercial Managing Partner	Alan Robins
Number of partners	23
Assistant solicitors	47
Other fee-earners	107

AREAS OF PRACTICE	
Insurance Litigation	85%
Company/Commercial	15%

CONTACTS	
Commercial Litigation	Jonathan Lowe
Commercial Property	David Johnson
Company/Commercial	Alan Robins
Construction	David Johnson
Employment	Alan Lewis
Fraud	Mark Whalley
Insurance Litigation	David Tyson
Professional Indemnity	Nicola McLoughlin

THE FIRM: Sustained growth over recent years has seen Keoghs develop into one of the country's leading commercial law firms, specialising in insurance litigation and commercial business advice. The practice's success is based upon a combination of its no-nonsense, commercial outlook, the depth and variety of the legal services it provides, the approachability of its staff and, above all, its commitment to both high quality service delivery and competitive charges. Keoghs has full ISO quality accreditation and its clients range from national 'blue chip' organisations to small, growing businesses.

PRINCIPAL AREAS OF WORK:

Defendant Litigation: Keoghs is one of the country's leading advisers to the insurance industry, currently acting for more than thirty insurance organisations including the majority of the UK's top ten composite insurers and many Lloyds syndicates. Working closely with clients to avoid costly, protracted disputes, Keoghs has the capacity and experience to handle not only large volume defendant personal injury litigation including RTA cases but also high-profile, specialist cases including catastrophic injury and disease and deafness. The firm has also developed a wide base of expertise in other insurance related areas ranging from employer's and public liability, product liability and negligence to insurance property work, subsidence claims and good-in-transit cases.

Fraud: Over recent years and to anticipate insurer clients' needs for specialist assistance Keoghs has established specific units to deal with both motor fraud and general fraud. The motor fraud unit now operates in tandem with many insurers' claims departments to identify fraud cases at an early stage and deal with them rapidly and effectively. The results have demonstrated substantial cost savings for clients.

Commercial Litigation: Keoghs commercial litigation team acts for both insurer and commercial business clients dealing with professional negligence claims, building and contractual disputes, injunctions, financial disputes and the recovery of outstanding debts. The team actively employs ADR methods wherever possible, saving clients both time and money.

Company/Commercial: The company and commercial team provides advice to a wide variety of clients from national organisations to privately owned and managed businesses. It offers down-to-earth advisory services including corporate finance, company formation, disposals and acquisitions, contract drafting, buy-outs and shareholders' agreements. In addition it offers a full range of commercial property advice and assistance. The commercial team specialises in providing assistance to small and medium sized business.

Employment: Keoghs employment team has abandoned the traditional methods of dealing with employment related disputes in favour of a new preventative approach. This approach, embodied in the firm's 'PeoplePack' product, not only ensures that employers receive the right advice and take the correct steps before problems arise, but also provides insurance to cover any legal fees that may be incurred where disputes are unavoidable.

Private Client: The firm has a dedicated team dealing with trusts and estate planning and wills and domestic conveyancing for clients who require these specialist services.

KERSHAW ABBOTT

Queen's Chambers, 5 John Dalton Street, Manchester, M2 6FT
Tel: (0161) 839 0998 **Fax:** (0161) 839 1019 **DX:** 14348 Manchester 1
Email: mail@kershaw-abbott.co.uk **Website:** www.kershaw-abbott.co.uk

Contact Partners	Anne Kershaw Christopher Abbott
Number of partners	4
Assistant solicitors	2
Other fee-earners	3

THE FIRM: Based in the centre of the Manchester business community, Kershaw Abbott is a modern and progressive practice serving commercial and insurance clients. Work of quality is handled in an effective and individual manner by partner-led teams, conscious always to provide a cost-effective service.

PRINCIPAL AREAS OF WORK: The firm is best known for its work in the fields of construction, professional partnership disputes, commercial and insurance litigation and employment. Expertise is offered in alternative forms of dispute resolution including mediation, adjudication and arbitration. The firm undertakes agency work in the specialist courts of the North West.

KIDSTONS & CO

K

1 Royal Bank Place, Buchanan Street, Glasgow, G1 3AA
Tel: (0141) 221 6551 **Fax:** (0141) 204 0507
Email: mail@kidstons.co.uk **Website:** www.kidstons.co.uk

3rd Floor, Conference House, The Exchange, 152 Morrison Street, Edinburgh, EH3 8EB
Tel: (0131) 200 6272 **Fax:** (0131) 200 6200

Managing & Senior Partner	Iain Atack
Number of partners	9
Assistant solicitors	2
Other fee-earners	9

AREAS OF PRACTICE

Employment Law	20%
Commercial Property	20%
Business Law/Corporate	18%
Trusts and Probate	18%
Civil Litigation	14%
Residential Property	10%

CONTACTS

Civil Litigation	Iain Atack
Commercial Property	Kenneth Gerber
Corporate/Business Law	Kenneth Gerber
Employment	Iain Atack
Insolvency	Sandy Reid
Residential Property	Alison Atack
Trusts	Douglas McKerrell

THE FIRM: Established in Glasgow over 150 years ago, Kidstons & Co. has grown to provide expertise in employment law, commercial property, civil litigation, trusts, corporate and business law, insolvency law and residential property. The firm has two partners who are accredited by the Law Society of Scotland: Iain Atack, specialist in employment law and Kenneth Gerber, specialist in commercial leasing. The firm has nine partners and two associates with full support from assistant solicitors; the firm has numerous contacts in Hong Kong, the Middle East and the Republic of Ireland. A significant part of the client base is from outwith Scotland.

CLIENTELE: The firm has a varied client base of UK manufacturing and retail plcs, commercial private companies, medical and other partnerships, trusts and family owned property investment and other businesses, many of whom are based in England and Europe. The firm's philosophy is that transactions should be very much partner led with the emphasis on proactive and commercially orientated advice being given so as to enable clients to achieve their goals effectively.

KIERAN & CO
20 The Cross, Worcester, WR1 3PZ **Tel:** (01905) 28635 **Fax:** (01905) 21803 **DX:** 16265 **Ptnrs:** 1

KIMBELLS

352 Silbury Court, Silbury Boulevard, Milton Keynes, MK9 2AF
Tel: (01908) 668 555 **Fax:** (01908) 674 344 **DX:** 31408
Email: recep@kimbells.com **Website:** www.kimbells.com

Senior Partner	Stephen Kimbell
Number of partners	8
Assistant solicitors	11
Other fee-earners	7

AREAS OF PRACTICE

Corporate	30%
Litigation	27%
Commercial Property	22%
Commercial/IT	21%

CONTACTS

Brewing/Services	Peter Holden
Commercial Litigation	Richard Brown
Commercial Property	Timothy Clark
Corporate	Jonathan Hambleton
IT	Robert Cain

THE FIRM: Established in 1986 by former City solicitors, Kimbells aims to offer corporate clients practical, commercial advice. The firm has particularly strong links with the brewing, distribution and hi-tech industries and also with the financial services sector.

PRINCIPAL AREAS OF WORK:
Corporate: The firm has built a reputation for buy-outs and mergers and acquisitions.
Commercial Litigation: Specific experience is offered in property-related matters, insolvency, recovery and EU competition law.
Commercial Property: Expertise covers large commercial developments, acquisitions and disposals and landlord and tenant, with particular experience in the retail sector.
Employment: Advice is offered on a wide range of contentious and non-contentious issues.
Information Technology: All aspects of IT law are covered, including e-commerce, Internet, data protection and competition law.
Services to the Brewing/Licensed Trade Sector: A specialist knowledge of the UK regulatory regime has been developed through working for major national and regional brewers and pub companies.

KINGSFORD STACEY BLACKWELL

14 Old Square, Lincoln's Inn, London, WC2A 3UB
Tel: (020) 7447 1200 **Fax:** (020) 7831 2915 **DX:** 141 Chancery Lane
Email: ksb@kingsfords.co.uk **Website:** www.kingsfords.co.uk

Elan House, 5-11 Fetter Lane, London, EC4A 1QD
Tel: (020) 7822 7500 **Fax:** (020) 7822 7600 **DX:** 117 Chancery Lane

Lincoln House, 34 High Street, Harpenden, AL5 2SX
Tel: (01582) 766 866 **Fax:** (01582) 712 424 **DX:** 80454 Harpenden

Managing Partner	Charles Rankmore
Senior Partner	Jonathan Wood
Number of partners	23
Assistant solicitors	17
Other fee-earners	75

AREAS OF PRACTICE

Litigation & Personal Injury	52%
Property (Residential & Commercial)	21%
Company/Commercial	11%
Private Client	3%
Licensing	3%

CONTACTS

Agency	Minhaj Saiyid
Commercial Litigation	Niki Olympitis
Company/International	Robert Neville
Employment	Jonathan Roper
Family	Andrew Hamilton
Insolvency	Julie Killip
Licensing	Robert Edney
Personal Injury	Simon Pinner
Private Client	Susan Floyd
Property Litigation	David White
Residential Property	Richard Martin

THE FIRM: Kingsford Stacey Blackwell is a progressive, commercial law firm, based in Lincoln's Inn. The firm prides itself on its approachable partner-led range of services. Technical expertise is matched by practical, commercial advice and competitive fees. Clients include local authorities, major breweries and airlines, property developers, large insurers, national retailers, banks, newspapers and publishing houses, building societies and public companies.

PRINCIPAL AREAS OF WORK: Commercial litigation; insolvency; company/commercial; commercial property; licensing; defamation; employment; private client; factoring; landlord and tenant; family; private client; residential property; competition law; personal injury. The firm offers a specialist London Agency Service and is able to provide notarial services. Kingsford Stacey Blackwell has experienced rapid expansion over the last five years, particularly in its personal injury, commercial property, company/commercial, commercial litigation and family law departments.

INTERNATIONAL: The firm is a founder member of Consulegis, a closely coordinated network of over 100 independent English speaking law firms throughout Europe, USA, Latin America and the Far East. Languages spoken by members of the firm include French, German, Greek, Italian, Spanish and Portuguese.

RECRUITMENT: Kingsford Stacey Blackwell is committed to continued expansion in its key departments. Lawyers with expertise and a following in these areas and who are considering a move are invited to contact the firm's practice manager with details. For further information about the firm, visit the website.

KINGSLEY NAPLEY

Knights Quarter, 14 St John's Lane, London, EC1M 4AJ
Tel: (020) 7814 1200 **Fax:** (020) 7490 2288 **DX:** 22 Ch.Ln.
Email: mail@kingsleynapley.co.uk **Website:** www.kingsleynapley.co.uk

Senior/Managing Partner	David Speker
Number of partners	36
Assistant solicitors	33
Other fee-earners	9

AREAS OF PRACTICE

Commercial Property	20%
Criminal Litigation	19%
Litigation	17%
Corporate & Commercial	14%
Family	10%
Business Immigration	10%
Clinical Negligence & Personal Injury	10%

CONTACTS

Clinical Negligence & Personal Injury	Julia Cahill
Commercial Property	Francis Weaver
Construction	Michael Janney
Corporate & Commercial	David Walsh
Criminal Litigation	Christopher Murray
Employment	Richard Fox
Family	Jane Keir
Immigration	Hilary Belchak
Licensing	Michael Caplan
Litigation	Barry Samuels
Partnership	Tony Sacker

THE FIRM: Kingsley Napley is an internationally recognised commercial law firm based in the City of London. The firm has expertise in corporate and commercial work, criminal and commercial litigation, commercial property, employment, immigration, clinical negligence and family law. Kingsley Napley specialises in dealing with matters of particular complexity and difficulty in all branches of the law. The client base is wide and varied, ranging from large public companies to owner-managed businesses and individuals.

PRINCIPAL AREAS OF WORK:

Litigation: Work encompasses commercial and civil litigation and dispute resolution, professional negligence, construction disputes, landlord and tenant, and defamation. There is particular experience in asset tracing investigations.

Employment: The department handles contentious and non-contentious employment law issues for companies and individuals.

Criminal Litigation: Work covers a broad spectrum including corporate and City fraud, SFO, DTI and Inland Revenue investigations, money-laundering, asset tracing enquiries and mutual assistance. The department is internationally recognised for advising on extradition matters and crime. Members of the department appear regularly before various regulatory and professional bodies, both prosecuting and defending. Two of the partners also undertake licensing work.

Family: All aspects of family and matrimonial work are undertaken, including issues concerning childcare, such as child abduction, surrogacy and adoption, through to cohabitation and complex financial matters on divorce.

Corporate & Commercial: Advice on a wide range of business issues including joint ventures, corporate finance, taxation, flotations, rights issues, takeovers, insolvency and liquidation and partnerships.

Property: All aspects of conveyancing of commercial freehold and leasehold property undertaken, together with a small amount of residential property work.

Clinical Negligence & Personal Injury: Expertise in the management of all forms of serious personal injury claims including those arising out of medical negligence in the NHS as well as the private medical sector. It

has particular interest in providing advice and assistance in relation to inquests and to complaints procedures, including General Medical Council. A range of funding options are available.
Immigration: A highly personalised specialist business immigration service is provided to both corporate clients and individuals, advising on all aspects of UK and EU immigration and nationality issues.

INTERNATIONAL: Work is handled in French, German and Spanish.

KIRBYS

32 Victoria Avenue, Harrogate, HG1 5PR **Tel:** (01423) 542 000 **Fax:** (01423) 542 001 **DX:** 11956 HARROGATE 1
Email: mail@kirbyssolicitors.demon.co.uk **Ptnrs:** 5 **Asst solrs:** 6 **Other fee-earners:** 1

KIRK JACKSON

97 Chorley Rd, Swinton, Manchester, M27 2AB **Tel:** (0161) 794 0431 **Fax:** (0161) 794 4957 **DX:** 28201 **Email:** law@kirk-jackson.com **Ptnrs:** 6
Asst solrs: 1 **Other fee-earners:** 2

KIRKLAND & ELLIS

Tower 42, 25 Old Broad Street, London, EC2N 1HQ
Tel: (020) 7816 8700 **Fax:** (020) 7816 8800
Email: william_scarbrough@uk.kirkland.com **Website:** www.kirkland.com

Office Administrator William Scarbrough

CONTACTS

Arbitration	Samuel Haubold
Capital Markets & Securities	Barbara Jones
German Practice	Thomas Verhoeven
Intellectual Property	Jeffrey Mills
Venture Capital	James Learner
	Stuart Mills

THE FIRM: Kirkland & Ellis handles complicated transactional, intellectual property, litigation and counseling matters for major US and international clients. The firm works with a base of long-standing clients engaged in varied industries such as hi-tech, manufacturing, computers , transportation, private equity capital, oil and gas, health care, real estate, chemicals, food products, finance, insurance, advertising and accounting.
London Office: The London office, with over 20 lawyers, focuses on private equity, mergers and acquisitions, capital markets, arbitration and intellectual property matters. It has been serving UK, European and US clients since 1995.

PRINCIPAL AREAS OF WORK: Kirkland is known for its ability to negotiate and close highly sophisticated transactions, representing venture capital investors and public and private companies in mergers and acquisitions, securities, spin-off and split-off, and private equity transactions.
Private Equity: The firm has a premier private equity practice, having represented private investment funds, the private equity groups at several major money centre banks and other participants in this industry for over 25 years. During the last five years, Kirkland's private equity practice has represented more than 50 different clients in hundreds of leveraged acquisitions and other types of transactions and has been principal counsel in over US$50 billion in fund formations.
M&A & Securities: In the mergers and acquisitions and securities area, Kirkland has recently represented clients ranging from some of the world's largest corporations through major banks and investment banks in some of the world's largest and most complex mergers and acquisitions transactions and securities offerings.
Litigation & Arbitration: The firm has earned a reputation for successfully defending companies with business-threatening lawsuits and class actions in diverse legal areas such as commercial, intellectual property, product liability, insurance coverage, environmental, employment, securities law, mass torts, and antitrust issues, handling the trial, appellate, and US Supreme Court phases. This trial-ready reputation has been the impetus for favourable and prompt results for the firm's clients through settlements as well as through the various Alternative Dispute Resolution mechanisms (ADRs) employed whenever practicable and desired by the client.
IP & IT: Kirkland & Ellis advises some of the world's leading technology companies and handles all areas of intellectual property, including biotechnology, semiconductor processing, telecommunications, and Internet and e-commerce technology. Kirkland & Ellis has adopted and adapted to the Internet and e-commerce, and its 130 intellectual property lawyers specialise in the intricacies, implications, legal issues and arguments surrounding today's and tomorrow's communication and emerging technologies.

CLIENTELE: Kirkland & Ellis bases its commitment to client service on developing an intimate knowledge of each client's needs and objectives. The firm seeks long-term, partnering relationships with clients, to the end of providing the best total solution to the client's multi-disciplined and industry specific legal service needs. The firm's goal is to be an instrumental part of each client's success.

INTERNATIONAL: The firm has other offices in Chicago, Los Angeles, New York and Washington DC. It handles work in English, French, German and Spanish.

KIRKLAND & ELLIS
INTERNATIONAL

KLEGAL

1-2 Dorset Rise, London, EC4Y 8AE
Tel: (020) 7694 2500 **Fax:** (020) 7694 2501 **DX:** 38053 BLACKFRIARS
Email: nick.holt@kpmg.co.uk **Website:** www.klegal.com

Managing & Senior Partner	Nick Holt
Number of partners	17
Assistant solicitors	66
Other fee-earners	30

AREAS OF PRACTICE

Corporate	37%
TEC (Technology, E-business & Communications)	13%
Intellectual Property	12%
Real Estate	12%
Employment	10%
Banking & Finance	8%
Tax Litigation	8%

CONTACTS

Banking	Timothy Parsons
Corporate	Colin Fergusson
Commercial	Arun Singh OBE
Competition	Rob Murray
Dispute Resolution	Anthony Maton
E-business & Digital Media	Mark Haftke
Employment (UK)	Stephen Levinson
Employment (International)	Tim Johnson
Financial Regulation	Alastair Holmes
Intellectual Property	James Hodgson
IT & Telecoms	Chris Hoyle
Projects/PPP	Gareth Davies
Real Estate	Philip Burroughs
Tax Litigation	James Bullock

THE FIRM: Since its formation, KLegal has grown from strength to strength, appointing its 100th lawyer in early summer 2001. The firm's objective is to provide expert legal services both on a stand-alone basis and as part of a multidisciplinary offering alongside KPMG (assurance; consulting; corporate finance; forensic accounting; tax and transaction services). Current practice areas, all of which complement the services offered by KPMG, include banking and finance; company and commercial; competition; dispute resolution; e-business and digital media; employment; financial regulation; intellectual property; IT and telecoms; project finance/PPP; real estate; tax litigation. The firm's route to market is focused on six industry facing groups made up of lawyers from each of the firm's practice areas, namely information, communications and entertainment (ICE); financial services (FS); consumer markets (CM); industrial markets (IM); infrastructure and government (I&G) and owner managed businesses (OMB). There are no plans to open regional offices, the initial focus being London and overseas. However, the firm has set up London-based, partner-led teams to act as principal points of contacts for each of the KPMG regional business units.

PRINCIPAL AREAS OF WORK: KLegal provides legal advice and assistance in relation to a wide variety of corporate and commercial transactions (in particular acquisitions and disposals, MBOs and joint ventures), banking and finance related matters (including structured and acquisition finance transactions, treasury products and financial regulation issues), competition law issues; e-business and digital media contracts and content; employment and HR issues; intellectual property matters (both contentious and non-contentious); IT and telecoms work; real estate matters; project finance, including PFI/PPP and tax litigation.

CLIENTELE: Clients include national to multinational corporations, government bodies, banks and financial institutions, Internet start-ups and entrepreneurs. They are introduced to the firm from a variety of sources, including KPMG, KLegal International member firms and external introductions.

INTERNATIONAL: KLegal's presence extends to nearly 50 countries with more than 1,650 lawyers in Europe. There is also a growing presence in South America, Asia, Australia and New Zealand.

RECRUITMENT: The firm is actively seeking exceptional lawyers at all levels from partner to recently qualified. Applications are invited from ambitious and energetic lawyers with good academic backgrounds (min 2:1) and outstanding experience gained in either private practice or industry who are attracted by the prospect of working in a dynamic, cutting-edge, multidisciplinary environment. Please apply to Sarah Bowyer (Human Resources) or Kate Hedstrom (Graduate Recruitment). KLegal has an ambitious education programme designed to develop specialist technical expertise alongside professional skills and business development. The firm has the advantage of access to KPMG's exceptional training resources, ranging from innovative on line learning programmes to residential courses at dedicated locations. Training at all levels aims to integrate lawyers and trainees into the wider context of a multidisciplinary professional services environment. The firm has benefited from a number of significant hires over the last 12 months including former Clifford Chance competition lawyer, Rob Murray; Stephenson Harwood corporate partners, Colin Fergusson and Peter Bradley; former Coudert International managing partner and head of property, Philip Burroughs; former Bond Pearce corporate partner, Moray Macpherson; Slaughter & May litigator, Anthony Maton; former Jones Day Reavis & Pogue employment lawyer Guy Abbiss. Hires from industry include former Head of BT Legal Services, Alan Whitfield; Gilbert McClung from IBM; John Buyers from Cap Gemini, Peter Cashmore from Telecom New Zealand; Stuart Brothers from NPI Limited.

KNIGHTS

Regency House, 25 High Street, Tunbridge Wells, TN1 1UT **Tel:** (01892) 537311 **Fax:** (01892) 526141 **DX:** 3919 Tunbridge Wells
Email: knights@atlas.co.uk **Website:** www.knights-solicitors.co.uk **Ptnrs:** 2 **Asst solrs:** 1 **Other fee-earners:** 4

KNIGHT & SONS

The Brampton, Newcastle-under-Lyme, ST5 0QW
Tel: (01782) 619225 **Fax:** (01782) 717260 **DX:** 711120 Newcastle under Lyme 7
Email: commercial@knightandsons.co.uk

Managing Partner	Robert Hoyle
Senior Partner	Anthony Bell
Number of partners	19
Assistant solicitors	12
Other fee-earners	27

AREAS OF PRACTICE

Commercial Property	40%
Commercial Litigation	22%
Corporate & Commercial	20%
Private Client	18%

CONTACTS

Agriculture	Robert Hoyle
Charities	Charles Jones
Commercial Property	Ian White
Commercial/Competition	Derek Miller
Construction	Richard Lashmore
Corporate Finance	Derek Miller
Employment	Christine Dyson
Licensing	Richard Jones
Litigation (Commercial)	Andrew Davidson
Mines & Minerals	Paul Calladine
Planning & Environment	Andrea Bruce
Taxation	Henry Davenport

THE FIRM: Founded in 1767, Knight & Sons brings a highly specialised, innovative and proactive approach to clients' needs while still retaining traditional values of client care. The firm is primarily a commercial practice but has a very strong client department. The overhaul and restructuring of the management and fee-earning departments continued through the first half of the year 2000 to ensure that clients continue to be provided with the high expertise and service which is the firm's hallmark. The greater autonomy vested in the departments and specialist units has resulted in a more focused approach to fee-earning work, increasing expertise in specialist areas with a consequent increase in profile and new business. The firm now engages the services of two IT consultants and continues to upgrade its information technology commitment to take it well into the twenty-first century. The decision taken by the partners to bring an even more dedicated and purposeful approach to servicing clients' needs, coupled with high staff retention, has resulted in an increase in both quality and quantity of instructions from existing and new partners.

PRINCIPAL AREAS OF WORK:

Agriculture: Knight & Sons is one of the leaders in the field of agricultural work, acting for both private and commercial clients and an increasing number of very substantial landed estates. It is one of the nine firms on the NFU national panel.

Commercial Property: The reputation of the commercial property department continues to grow. In particular the niche areas of mines and minerals, portfolio management, development and local authority work make the firm a dominant force both within the West Midlands and nationally. Planning and environment work, integral to the property market, is provided by a dedicated unit with considerable depth of expertise.

Corporate & Commercial: Work in this area continued to increase during 2000, with a substantial increase in the value of transactional work (including the completion of the firm's first securitisation project for a leading university) and commercial work for a number of clients which are household names.

Litigation: This department has particularly benefited from restructuring, both in the areas of commercial litigation and personal injury. Commercial litigation is attracting more high quality instructions and continues to recruit to service the influx. Similarly, personal injury instructions are being received at an unprecedented rate and the unit is continually having to recruit.

Employment: This unit has flourished from a clear and dedicated approach to focused marketing and is winning many new clients for the firm for both agricultural and wider commercial work.

Tax Trust & Private Client: This department is now ranked as one of the leading teams in the West Midlands with only a few firms in Birmingham and Manchester able to compete with the expertise offered to an ever-increasing client base.

Charities: This unit is also reaping the benefits of focused specialisation and, by working closely with a charities consultant, is rapidly developing a reputation in this field.

KRISTINA HARRISON SOLICITORS

277-279 Chapel Street, Salford, M3 5JQ **Tel:** (0161) 832 7766 **Fax:** (0161) 832 3399 **Ptnrs:** 1 **Asst solrs:** 8 **Other fee-earners:** 15

KUIT STEINART LEVY

3 St. Mary's Parsonage, Manchester, M3 2RD
Tel: (0161) 832 3434 **Fax:** (0161) 832 6650 **DX:** 14325
Email: ksllaw@kuits.com **Website:** www.kuits.com

Executive Partner	Robert Levy
Managing Partner	Jonathan Marks
Number of partners	13
Assistant solicitors	15
Other fee-earners	8

AREAS OF PRACTICE

Corporate	25%
Litigation/Employment	25%
Property	25%
Tax & Trusts	15%
Banking	10%

CONTACTS

Corporate	Robert Levy
Litigation	Jeff Lewis
	Jai Ramsahoye
Employment	Lydia Edgar
Property	Jonathan Marks
Tax & Trusts	Jan Fidler
Banking	Steve Eccleston

THE FIRM: Kuit Steinart Levy is securely established as a leading Manchester practice and continues to grow and develop its range of expertise to meet changing market needs. Its aim is to implement its dynamic growth strategy, while remaining committed to its client-focused approach to law. The firm is forward thinking and dynamic, and all clients receive a service that is professional and comprehensive. Direct access is provided to a partner who takes individual responsibility for work carried out on a client's behalf.

PRINCIPAL AREAS OF WORK:

Corporate/Commercial: The department has a strong corporate and corporate finance skill base, and advises on all aspects of company law and commercial matters, including corporate finance; mergers and acquisitions; management buy-outs and buy-ins; reconstructions; insolvency; agency and distribution. Expertise also extends to terms of trading; commercial contracts; competition law and employment law; intellectual property and brand acquisitions, which is a particular specialism.

Litigation: A variety of litigation services are provided, including all commercial and contract disputes; landlord and tenant work; restraint of trade and competition disputes; professional negligence; personal injury;

Continued overleaf

directors disqualification proceedings; debt collection. In addition the firm has a CEDR-accredited mediator and provides a full dispute resolution service.

Property: The commercial property team advises on a wide range of property matters, including acquisitions and disposals, development and planning, construction contracts, project finance, funding and joint ventures, leases, property investment and environmental law.

Tax & Trusts: The firm specialises in tax and trust matters, including inheritance tax planning; estate planning; mitigation of taxation and Inland Revenue; Customs & Excise enquiries and investigations. All aspects of wills and probate are also handled.

Banking: Kuits' cross departmental banking and secured lending team incorporates expertise in corporate, commercial property and securities law. Areas covered include loan syndication; acquisition banking; facility agreements; capital; mezzanine and asset finance; approval of security including inspection of title to real property.

CLIENTELE: The client base ranges from large public companies through a broad base of small and medium-sized enterprises, to start-ups and vehicles for management buy-outs and buy-ins. The firm also acts for a number of banks and financial institutions and high profile individuals.

RECRUITMENT: Every member of the firm's legal staff has been recruited for their exceptional ability, expertise and knowledge. Several have trained and worked at national and international law firms in the City. The firm has six trainees, and places great emphasis on training and career development. Trainees usually spend six months in each of the firm's main departments, thus gaining a broad experience in the different aspects of legal work. The firm has an internal seminar programme, covering a variety of legal topics and adding to the stimulating working environment.

LAMPORT BASSITT

The Atrium Court, Apex Plaza, Reading, RG1 1AX
Tel: (0118) 925 4242 **Fax:** (0118) 950 5580

46 The Avenue, Southampton, SO17 1AX
Tel: (023) 8083 7777 **Fax:** (023) 8083 7788 **DX:** 38529 Southampton 3
Email: e-mail@lamportbassitt.co.uk

Senior Partner	Adrian Lightfoot
Number of partners	11
Assistant solicitors	20
Other fee-earners	10

AREAS OF PRACTICE	
Litigation	63%
Company/Commercial	24%
Private Client	13%

CONTACTS	
Commercial	Sean Kelly
Litigation	Robert Solomon
Private Client	John Excell

THE FIRM: The firm operates an expanding and predominantly commercial practice, and places particular emphasis on technical ability and specialisation. The firm is a niche practice aiming to provide high quality services within specialist areas. The firm makes full use of modern technology. Most senior fee-earners are highly experienced in their chosen fields. The firm is ISO 9001 registered.

PRINCIPAL AREAS OF WORK:

Commercial: A wide range of corporate, employment, insolvency, planning, property, and liquor, betting and gaming licensing work.

Litigation: The firm is involved in the full range of litigation work including building disputes, commercial contracts, debt collection, employment disputes, intellectual property matters, maritime law, property disputes, professional negligence, and has a large personal injury department. Agency work undertaken.

Private Client: Residential property, personal tax, probate, trusts, wills and matrimonial.

CLIENTELE: Clients include substantial UK and overseas-based listed and private companies from a wide area of industry and commerce, insurance companies, trade unions and trade associations.

RECRUITMENT: A minimum of two trainee solicitors are recruited each year. Enquiries to Mr John Newton, partner.

LANDWELL

St Andrew's House, 20 St Andrew Street, London, EC4A 3TL
Tel: (020) 7212 1616 **Fax:** (020) 7212 1570 **DX:** 218 Chancery Lane, London WC2
Email: firstname.lastname@uk.landwellglobal.com **Website:** www.landwell.co.uk

Senior Partner	Chris Arnheim
Number of partners	16
Assistant solicitors	47
Other fee-earners	12
Total	130

CONTACTS	
Mergers & Acquisitions	Leon Flavell
	Simon Walker
	Shirley Brookes
Corporate Restructuring	Richard Edmundson
	Sarah Holmes

THE FIRM: Landwell is one of the largest global law practices with 2,600 lawyers in over 40 countries. Its links with PricewaterhouseCoopers have enabled it to grow rapidly by attracting high quality lawyers and clients. Clients benefit from Landwell's international network in two ways. Firstly, Landwell has greater local law capability in European, Australian and South American jurisdictions, in particular, than many leading international law practices, enabling it to resource international transactions effectively; and secondly, Landwell is able, together with PricewaterhouseCoopers, to provide solutions to client problems, combining the technical skills of a range of different professionals. Landwell has demonstrated the value of this approach in a number of different practice areas such as mergers and acquisitions, international reorganisations, HR (employment, immigration and pensions), e-business/intellectual property/information technology, financial services and real estate. Landwell lawyers benefit from the high quality assignments for leading global corporates, won through Landwell's international practice groups. These groups share skills across borders, generating opportunities for international secondments. Landwell's lawyers also have access to the world class training programmes and knowledge databases of PricewaterhouseCoopers. Landwell in the UK is based in London, and is focused on building a law practice that will benefit from its international network and its links with PricewaterhouseCoopers. Landwell is confident these benefits will enable it to continue to grow its practice throughout the economic cycle, thereby providing a dynamic and rewarding career platform for its lawyers, and a high quality service for its growing client base.

CONTACTS CONTINUED

E-business/IP/IT .... Latika Sharma
HR (Employment, Immigration, Pensions)
.... Darryl Evans
.... Nick Willis
.... Julia Smye-Rumsby
Financial Services .... Laura Cox
Banking .... Celia Gardiner
Real Estate .... Amanda Benham
Dispute Resolution .... Simon Whitehead

Correspondent law firms of PricewaterhouseCoopers

PRINCIPAL AREAS OF WORK:

Mergers & Acquisitions: Work includes UK and international acquisitions, disposals, joint ventures, IPOs and private equity work.
Corporate Restructuring: Work handled includes financial, commercial and tax-based reorganisations.
E-business/IP/IT: Including protection and exploitation of intellectual property, IT procurement and outsourcing, data protection and e-business.
HR: Areas covered include recruitment, immigration (inbound and outbound) and nationality, HR policies and compliance, occupational, personal and individual pension schemes, discrimination, dismissals and internal reorganisations, transactions and compliance.
Financial Services: Work includes establishment of collective investment schemes, advice on FSA compliance, operational legal advice to financial institutions, broker dealers and financial intermediaries etc.
Banking: Areas covered include advising banks and corporates on lending, treasury products, security, refinancings and insolvency.
Real Estate: Work includes the acquisition and development of commercial property, planning and environmental issues.
Dispute Resolution: Including the resolution of commercial, IP, employment and tax disputes.

INTERNATIONAL: Landwell has 100 offices across Europe, Australia and Asia Pacific, South America and Africa.

LANE & PARTNERS

15 Bloomsbury Square, London, WC1A 2LP
Tel: (020) 7242 2626 **Fax:** (020) 7242 0387 **DX:** 134442 Bloomsbury
Email: info@lane.co.uk **Website:** www.lane.co.uk

Senior Partner	Richard Hardman
Contact Partner	William Morton
Number of partners	11
Assistant solicitors	9
Other fee-earners	5

AREAS OF PRACTICE

Company/Commercial 29%
Litigation 28%
Property (Commercial) 16%
Aviation & Travel 10%
Construction & Arbitration 10%
Intellectual Property & Marketing 7%

CONTACTS

Aviation & Travel .... Richard Venables
.... William Morton
Company & Commercial .... Keith Gallon
.... William Morton
.... Nicholas Sayers
Construction & Arbitration .... Colin Hall
Intellectual Property & Marketing
.... Michael Varvill
Litigation .... Ludovic de Walden
.... Piers Lane
.... Robin Springthorpe
Property .... Richard Hardman
.... Mark Barber

THE FIRM: Lane & Partners concentrates on providing a partner-led service at competitive rates to commercial clients, covering all the main areas of law of relevance to them. It is well known for its work in the areas of international arbitration, construction, aviation and travel law.

PRINCIPAL AREAS OF WORK:

Company & Commercial: The firm advises clients on all aspects of company and commercial law, including mergers and acquisitions, joint ventures, listings, financial services, telecommunications, insolvency and employment and competition law.
Intellectual Property: The firm advises in respect of patent, trade mark and copyright matters, including licensing, franchising, merchandising, all aspects of infringement and on IT and e-commerce issues.
Litigation: The firm is active in all aspects of commercial litigation with particular emphasis on actions in the commercial court.
Arbitration: The firm has an active international arbitration practice, with particular emphasis on major construction disputes.
Commercial Property: The firm is involved on behalf of commercial clients in all aspects of property work including the acquisition of freehold and leasehold properties for occupation, investment or development, the sale and management of properties, planning law and appeals and environmental law.
Construction: The firm advises on all aspects of construction law, including the negotiation and preparation of construction contracts, the interpretation of the standard forms used by the industry and the preparation and handling of claims.
Aviation & Travel: The firm advises UK and foreign airlines and tour operators and travel agents. Advice is also given on aviation insurance and liability cases and on aircraft acquisition and leasing transactions.

CLIENTELE: As well as acting for UK companies, the firm has a considerable number of foreign clients, particularly Swedish, American and Japanese companies. In size, they range from well-known multinationals to small private companies. Their businesses are equally diverse, stretching from international construction and heavy engineering to cosmetics, computers and tour operating.

INTERNATIONAL: The firm has associated offices in Europe, North America, Asia and the Far East. Languages spoken include French and Italian.

RECRUITMENT: One to two trainees are taken on per annum.

LANGLEYS

Queens House, Micklegate, York, YO1 6WG
Tel: (01904) 610 886 **Fax:** (01904) 611 086 **DX:** 720620 York 21
Email: mike.williamson@langleys.co.uk **Website:** www.langleys.co.uk

Newporte House, Doddington Road Business Park, Lincoln, LN6 3JY
Tel: (01522) 888 555 **Fax:** (01522) 888 556 **DX:** 700678 North Hykeham-2
Email: andrew.fearn@langleys.co.uk

34 Silver St, Lincoln, LN2 1ES
Tel: (01522) 531 461 **Fax:** (01522) 510 476 **DX:** 11010 Lincoln
Email: philip.cragg@langleys.co.uk

Managing Partners	Mike Williamson Philip Cragg
Senior Partner	John Morgan
Number of partners	20
Assistant solicitors	17
Other fee-earners	40

AREAS OF PRACTICE

Defendant Insurance Claims	37%
Commercial	21%
Claimant Personal Injury & Medical Negligence	19%
Family/Matrimonial	12%
Residential Conveyancing	6%
Criminal Defence	3%
Wills & Probate	2%

CONTACTS

Defendant Insurance Claims	David Thompson
Commercial	Roger Taylor
Claimant Personal Injury & Medical Negligence	Chris Jones
Family/Matrimonial	Philip Cragg
Residential Conveyancing	Mark Hodges
Criminal Defence	Jerry Bowling
Wills & Probate	Andrew Fearn
Agriculture	Andrew Fearn

THE FIRM: Based in York and Lincoln, Langleys provides a comprehensive range of legal services to businesses, organisations and private clients with a focus on insurance claims work. Established in 1890, the firm has developed a thriving commercial practice whilst retaining and expanding its traditional private client services. The firm was recently accredited with the Investors in People standard, reinforcing its commitment to the continued training and development of both legal and support staff. In recent years, the firm has made a substantial investment into an innovative and progressive IT programme which has already been successful in enhancing efficiency and communications. Ultimately, Langleys is committed to the provision of a quality legal service, and continually strives to exceed clients' expectations.

PRINCIPAL AREAS OF WORK: The firm's activities can be divided into three main areas: insurance claims, commercial and private client work.
Insurance Claims: This is the single largest department at Langleys, offering specialist advice across the whole spectrum of insurance claims for a client base that includes major insurance companies, loss adjusters and local authorities. The insurance claims department has a long-established reputation for its work in this field.
Commercial: This rapidly expanding department offers a comprehensive range of services to businesses including corporate, commercial property, commercial litigation, banking, employment, agriculture and debt recovery services. The team prides itself on its pro-active, cost-effective, commercial advice and its success is reflected in the department's diverse and growing client base.
Private Client: Family law (including divorce/separation, childcare, domestic violence, adoption and mediation), clinical negligence and claimant personal injury, residential conveyancing, civil litigation, wills and probate, employment and crime. The firm has legal aid franchises for the majority of its private client specialisms and notably for clinical negligence work.

RECRUITMENT: Sustained organic growth has resulted in a continuous recruitment policy in all practice specialisms, with a concentration on defendant insurance claims and all aspects of commercial law. CVs from interested solicitors, paralegals and support staff should be sent for the attention of Tracey Connor. In addition, the firm currently takes on two trainee solicitors each year and offers a comprehensive trainee programme.

LANYON BOWDLER
23 Swan Hill, Shrewsbury, SY1 1NN **Tel:** (01952) 291222 **Fax:** (01952) 292585 **DX:** 19721 Shrewsbury **Ptnrs:** 14 **Other fee-earners:** 33

LARBY WILLIAMS
53 Mount Stuart Square, Cardiff, CF10 5LR **Tel:** (029) 20472100 **Fax:** (029) 20472011 **DX:** 200750 Cardiff Bay **Email:** cardiff@larby-williams.co.uk **Ptnrs:** 2 **Asst solrs:** 1 **Other fee-earners:** 3

LARCOMES
168 London Rd, North End, Portsmouth, PO2 9DN **Tel:** (023) 9266 1531 **Fax:** (023) 9266 5701 **DX:** 42401 **Ptnrs:** 4 **Asst solrs:** 9 **Other fee-earners:** 9

LAST CAWTHRA FEATHER
Airedale House, 128 Sunbridge Road, Bradford, BD1 2AT **Tel:** (01274) 848800 **Fax:** (01274) 370552 **DX:** 11723 Bradford 1 **Email:** mail@lcf.co.uk **Website:** www.lcf.co.uk **Ptnrs:** 12 **Asst solrs:** 12 **Other fee-earners:** 15 **Contact:** Simon Stell • An expanding West Yorkshire practice with three offices and a total of 87 staff, undertaking work for businesses and private individuals.

AREAS OF PRACTICE

Property	30%
Litigation (incl. Liquor Licensing)	25%
Company/Commercial	15%
Family	10%
Employment	10%
Wills/Probate/Trusts	10%

LATHAM & WATKINS

99 Bishopsgate, London, EC2M 3XF
Tel: (020) 7710 1000 **Fax:** (020) 7374 4460
Email: webmaster2@lw.com **Website:** www.lw.com

Managing Partner (office)	Joe Blum
Managing Partner (firm)	Robert Dell
Number of partners	18
Assistant solicitors	50
Other fee-earners	7

AREAS OF PRACTICE

Project Finance	30%
Corporate Finance	30%
Company/Commercial	25%
Bank Finance	15%

THE FIRM: Latham & Watkins is a multinational partnership with 11 US and seven international offices. The lawyers in the London office practice English and US law, focusing on capital markets, leveraged finance, mergers and acquisitions and project finance. As client needs dictate, London-based lawyers can also call upon the collective expertise of over 1,200 Latham & Watkins lawyers practising worldwide in disciplines encompassing virtually every aspect of business-related law.
London Office: Latham's London office is well known for its expertise in equity financing, private equity, high yield debt, project finance, acquisition finance and mergers and acquisitions. The office also has specific industry and regional focuses – media and telecoms, venture and technology, an Italian practice, a Scandinavian practice and a Spanish practice.

INTERNATIONAL: The firm also has offices in Los Angeles, New York, Chicago, San Diego, Orange County, New Jersey, Washington DC, San Francisco, Silicon Valley, Boston, New Jersey, Frankfurt, Hamburg, Hong Kong, Moscow, Singapore and Tokyo. The firm handles work in a number of languages including French, German, Italian, Spanish, Japanese and Urdu.

L

LATIMER HINKS

5-8 Priestgate, Darlington, DL1 1NL **Tel:** (01325) 341500 **Fax:** (01325) 381072 **DX:** 69282 Darlington 6 **Email:** lh@latimerhinks.co.uk **Ptnrs:** 8 **Asst solrs:** 7 **Other fee-earners:** 15

LAWFORD KIDD

12 Hill Street, Edinburgh, EH2 3LB **Tel:** (0131) 225 5214 **Fax:** (0131) 226 2069 **DX:** ED 159 EDINBURGH **Email:** law@lawfordkidd.co.uk **Ptnrs:** 3 **Asst solrs:** 4 **Other fee-earners:** 2 **Contact:** David Sandison
• Specialises in personal injury litigation for trade union clients; medical negligence; aviation accidents; Court of Session litigation; relocation conveyancing. Associate office Lawfords, London.

AREAS OF PRACTICE

Personal Injury	60%
Conveyancing/Estate Agency/ General Business	25%
Litigation (General)/Employment	10%
Wills & Executries	5%

LAWFORDS

5 Richbell Place, London, WC1N 3LA
Tel: (020) 7871 8500 **Fax:** (020) 7871 8511 **DX:** 53311 Clerkenwell
Email: enquiries@lawford.co.uk **Website:** www.lawfordslaw.co.uk

Senior Partner	Graham Humby
Managing Partner	Linda Fletcher
Number of partners	18
Assistant solicitors	9
Other fee-earners	17

AREAS OF PRACTICE

Personal Injury	75%
Education/Civil Litigation/ Commercial Property/ Company Commercial	13%
Employment	12%

CONTACTS

Personal Injury	Graham Humby
Employment	Joy Drummond
Education	Clive Robertson
Property	Clive Robertson

LAWFORDS
SOLICITORS

THE FIRM: Established in 1954, Lawfords is a medium-sized practice with offices in London, Manchester and Nottingham and an associated office, Lawford Kidd, in Edinburgh. It is well known for its expertise in claimant PI litigation. The firm offers clients the personal attention of a smaller firm as well as the breadth of legal knowledge offered by a large nationwide practice.

PRINCIPAL AREAS OF WORK:
Personal Injury: The personal injury department receives instructions from a wide range of trade unions and other membership organisations. The firm has particular expertise in representing claimants following accidents at work and has delivered some of the largest UK financial awards and settlements in recent years. The firm employs 31 case-handlers in England and Wales and has an associate office with Lawford Kidd in Scotland to provide national coverage.
Employment: Lawfords has a large and thriving employment department representing both trade union members and private clients. The firm has dealt with some of the leading cases to reach the courts in the last 40 years. The department specialises in all aspects of employment law, including breach of contract, unfair dismissal, redundancy, transfer of undertakings, pensions and discrimination.
Education: The firm acts for a number of institutions in further and higher education, advising and acting in all education related matters such as property acquisition and financing, commercial contracts and company formation, and student and staff issues.
Property: Lawfords acts on behalf of commercial and institutional clients and deals with all aspects of property work. This includes the acquisition and disposal of substantial freehold and leasehold properties for investment, development, occupation or management.

CLIENTELE: Clients include trade unions and employee associations, universities, higher education institutions, legal expenses insurers and membership organisations of private clients.

THE LAW OFFICES OF MARCUS J. O'LEARY

Centennial Court, Easthampstead Road, Bracknell, RG12 1YQ
Tel: (01344) 303044 **Fax:** (01344) 300808
Email: moleary@mjol.co.uk **Website:** www.mjol.co.uk

Number of partners	5
Assistant solicitors	3
Other fee-earners	2

AREAS OF PRACTICE

IT/IP/Internet/Multimedia	75%
Company/Commercial	10%
Litigation	5%
Advertising/Media/Entertainment	5%
Employment	5%

CONTACTS

Advert/Media/Entertainment	
	Marcus O'Leary
	Celia Nortcliff
Company/Commercial	Rupert Wright
Employment	Andrew Fishleigh
IT/IP/Internet/Multimedia	Marcus O'Leary
	Paul Milton
	Celia Nortcliff
Litigation	Andrew Fishleigh

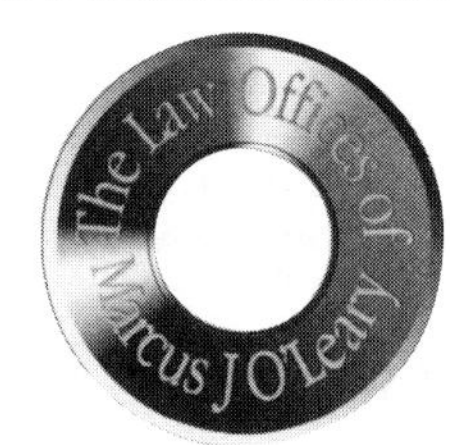

THE FIRM: A well-known and innovative practice specialising in information technology, e-commerce, intellectual property and related commercial matters. Comprising established practitioners in these fields, the practice is modern, progressive and provides an excellent cost effective service to all of its clients.

PRINCIPAL AREAS OF WORK:

Information Technology: Experienced practitioners with in-house experience offer a full range of advice to high technology companies and other companies using high technology products.
Intellectual Property: All copyright, design, patent, biotechnology, trade mark, passing off and confidential information issues handled quickly and efficiently with regard to the client's best interest.
Internet/E-commerce: The firm acts for well-known international companies active in this specialist area. Good quality leading edge advice on all web-related matters is assured.
Music, Media & Entertainment: Advice and contracts for musicians and composers, particularly regarding rights maintenance and digital music delivery.
Advertising: The firm has extensive experience in dealing with advertisements and promotions in different media formats both nationally, internationally and on the Internet.
Competition Law: Advice on UK and EU Competition law is available in relation to all matters dealt with by the firm.
Company/Commercial: The firm provides a full range of legal services including mergers and acquisitions, restructuring, joint ventures and MBOs and MBIs, particularly in connection with high technology companies.
Employment: Advice on all aspects of employment law and human rights issues is available, tempered with down-to-earth practical advice relevant to the situation.
Litigation: Can be undertaken by the firm in connection with any of the matters listed above.

CLIENTELE: Mainly well known international high technology companies.

INTERNATIONAL: Languages spoken include French, German and Spanish.

RECRUITMENT: A small number of very highly qualified and experienced assistant solicitors are needed each year.

LAWRENCE GRAHAM

61 St Mary Axe, London, EC3A 8JN
Tel: (020) 7379 0000 **Fax:** (020) 7480 5156 **DX:** 1072 London City LDE
Email: info@lawgram.com **Website:** www.lawgram.com

190 Strand, London, WC2R 1JN
Tel: (020) 7379 0000 **Fax:** (020) 7379 6854 **DX:** 39 Chancery Lane WC2
Email: info@lawgram.com

Senior Partner	Martyn Gowar
Number of partners	80
Assistant solicitors	92
Other fee-earners	67

AREAS OF PRACTICE

Property	36%
Corporate & Commercial	29%
Litigation	23%
Tax & Financial Management	12%

THE FIRM: Lawrence Graham is a London based firm acting principally for UK and international public and private companies, pension funds, financial institutions, public authorities, shipping companies, small businesses and private individuals. The firm's business is divided into four principal practice areas; company and commercial, commercial property, litigation and tax and financial management. Each of these areas is organised into specialist teams according to clients' requirements or the services being provided. The firm has associations with many law firms throughout the world including North America, Europe, the Middle and Far East. It also has an office in the Ukraine, serving clients since the 1920s primarily, but not exclusively, involved in shipping. The firm works in partnership with clients to achieve their objectives in the most cost effective and practical way. The aim is to add value to client's businesses.

PRINCIPAL AREAS OF WORK:

Company/Commercial: The department advises on a wide range of transactions including public company takeovers, mergers and acquisitions (both domestic and international) bank and other financings, new media/internet and EU/Competition related issues. It is organised into three main focus groups; corporate, finance and commerce/technology, with four other specialist teams supplying advice on employment/employee benefits, insolvency, energy and pensions/insurance. The firm's highly regarded public authority/housing association practice is also located in the company and commercial department.
Commercial Property: The department acts for major institutions, corporate occupiers, pension funds, banks, developers and investors (both plc and private companies), retailers, local authorities and many other public

bodies. The range of work undertaken is comprehensive. It includes acquisitions, disposals and financings, joint ventures, securitisation and telecommunications code powers. Construction, planning and property litigation teams are all located in this department.
Litigation: The department is organised into teams advising on disputes relating to insurance, reinsurance, shipping and more general business disputes including, in particular, those arising out of banking and insolvency, financial services, intellectual property issues and employment rights. A feature of our litigation practice is that much of our work has an international dimension to it. In addition to its extensive High Court practice, the department is actively engaged in arbitrations and other forms of dispute resolution. The tax and financial management department provides various specialist services. They include input as part of larger teams working on corporate and property transactions, fiduciary risk management for both UK and international corporate trustees and a wide range of advice to private individuals. The latter includes tax, trust and estate planning work, much of which has an international element to it. In addition, the firm has an established investment management business for its private clients.

LAWSON COPPOCK & HART

18 Tib Lane, Cross St, Manchester, M2 4JA **Tel:** (0161) 832 5944 **Fax:** (0161) 834 4409 **DX:** 14370 **Email:** info@lawsons-uk.com
Website: www.lawsons-uk.com **Ptnrs:** 8 **Asst solrs:** 1 **Other fee-earners:** 1

L

LAYTONS

Saint Batholomews, Lewins Head, Bristol, BS1 2NH
Tel: (0117) 930 9500 **Fax:** (0117) 929 3369 **DX:** 7895 Bristol-1
Email: bristol@laytons.com **Website:** www.laytons.com

Carmelite, 50 Victoria Embankment, Blackfriars, London, EC4Y 0LS
Tel: (020) 7842 8000 **Fax:** (020) 7842 8080 **DX:** 253 Chancery Lane
Email: london@laytons.com

Tempus Court, Onslow Street, Guildford, GU1 4SS
Tel: (01483) 407 000 **Fax:** (01483) 407 070 **DX:** 2410 Guildford
Email: guildford@laytons.com

22 St John St, Manchester, M3 4EB
Tel: (0161) 834 2100 **Fax:** (0161) 834 6862 **DX:** 14382 Manchester-1
Email: manchester@laytons.com

Chief Executive Partner	Richard Kennett
Number of partners	29
Assistant solicitors	42
Other fee-earners	27

AREAS OF PRACTICE	
Company/Commercial	51%
Commercial Property/ Land Development	19%
General Litigation	12%
Employment	10%
Trusts, Private Client & Private Tax	4%
Building Litigation	2%
Insolvency	2%

THE FIRM: Laytons is a commercial law firm whose primary focus is corporate/commercial and property and land development/construction. The firm's commitment is service to its clients, providing advice which combines technical excellence, practical effectiveness and timely service. Laytons assigns a core legal team to each client who knows its business and can advise directly or by deploying the specialist skills of colleagues. The approach to legal issues is practical, creative and energetic, providing high quality advice founded on a range of complementary specialist skills relevant to the firm's primary fields of focus. The firm is a single national team operating through its four offices, each of which draws on the strengths of the whole with the benefit of excellent IT and communications. Internally, the firm shares and supports, in an environment in which each can learn and contribute; Laytons pools its knowledge to the benefit of all.

PRINCIPAL AREAS OF WORK:

Corporate/Commercial: The firm handles corporate finance (domestic and cross-border mergers, acquisitions and joint ventures, stock exchange work, regulatory compliance, venture capital, management buy-outs, reconstructions, bank lending); commercial (commercial contracts, e-commerce, competition, product safety, international trade); intellectual property and technology (acquisition, protection, licensing and enforcement; internet, advertising law); human resources (employment contracts, share-related and other incentives, pensions, termination of employment, redundancy programmes, TUPE, health & safety); and insolvency and turnaround.
Property, Land Development & Construction Services: The firm offers a range of skills serving these industries and the commercial property interests of clients generally. Laytons is project solicitor for a number of land development consortia (site acquisition, land warehousing, housebuilding, joint ventures, planning advice, hearings and infrastructure agreements). The firm also deals with environmental services (contaminated land projects, environmental claims, waste management, mineral extraction, contracts/tenders for environmental services); construction law (adjudication, arbitration, contract preparation, collateral warranty advice); and land portfolio management. Both fields of focus draw on the skills of each other and also on specialist teams working in both fields: corporate tax (corporation tax, employment taxation, capital taxation, value added tax, property taxation, customs duties); and regulatory compliance (environmental, transport, licensing petroleum and other licensing, property misdescriptions). Strong dispute resolution skills are an integral part of the service provided across the range of the firm's services, with specialist skills in particular fields of work, including UK and international mediation, litigation and arbitration; property disputes; insur-

Continued overleaf

ance and professional negligence; product safety; land and environment; debt recovery; intellectual property; and employment-related issues.

Private Client: This is an essential element of the firm's approach and service to clients. A strong family law team is complemented by a comprehensive and specialist service concentrating on the traditional areas of private client work. The firm provides practical advice focusing on the modern day needs and demands of its client base of high net worth individuals and trustees, covering tax and estate planning for UK resident and non-resident individuals and all aspects of charity law, including tax, fundraising and trading issues.

INTERNATIONAL: International advice is a natural part of the commercial capability and is provided partly from the UK offices and partly through associated overseas law firms.

LCA - LEGALI COMMERCIALISTI ASSOCIATI

16 Old Bailey, London, EC4M 7EG
Tel: (020) 7597 6491 **Fax:** (020) 7329 2521 **DX:** 160
Email: crivellaro@slg.it

London Partner	Roberta Crivellaro
Number of partners	1
Other fee-earners	1

L

THE FIRM: LCA is a full service, multi-disciplinary Italian partnership based in Padua with branches in Milan, Venice, Munich and London. The London branch handles Italian-EU corporate law and international commercial transactions and litigation and assists Italian companies operating abroad and foreign companies with interests in Italy. Sports law, debt recovery, insolvency and property conveyancing are additional specialisations. Correspondents in Eastern Europe. LCA, formed as the result of the merger of Studio Legale Giordano, Studio Legale Camilotti Polettini Rolandi and Studio Commercialisti Bombassei Cerchiai Vidal, is the largest independent practice in the North East of Italy.

LEA & COMPANY

Bank Chambers, Market Place, Stockport, SK1 1UN **Tel:** (0161) 480 6691 **Fax:** (0161) 480 0904 **DX:** 19651 STOCKPORT 1
Email: mail@lealaw.com **Ptnrs:** 2 **Other fee-earners:** 2

LEATHES PRIOR

74 The Close, Norwich, NR1 4DR **Tel:** (01603) 610911 **Fax:** (01603) 610088 **DX:** 5205 Norwich **Email:** info@leathesprior.co.uk
Website: www.leathesprior.co.uk **Ptnrs:** 13 **Asst solrs:** 5 **Other fee-earners:** 15

LEBOEUF, LAMB, GREENE & MACRAE

No 1, Minster Court, Mincing Lane, London, EC3R 7AA
Tel: (020) 7459 5000 **Fax:** (020) 7459 5099 **DX:** 520 London/City
Website: www.llgm.com

Managing Partner	Garry Pegg
Number of partners	12
Assistant solicitors	38
Other fee-earners	10

THE FIRM: LeBoeuf, Lamb, Greene & MacRae is a multinational partnership affiliated with LeBoeuf, Lamb, Greene & MacRae LLP, a United States law firm with over 750 lawyers in 14 US and 9 other international offices. The lawyers in the London office include English solicitors and US lawyers, as well as lawyers from other jurisdictions and represent a cross-section of the firm's clientele in corporate, finance, litigation and regulatory matters. Close co-ordination is maintained between the lawyers in the London office and those in other LeBoeuf offices so that the full resource of the firm may be called upon to assist clients in virtually every aspect of the law.

PRINCIPAL AREAS OF WORK: The London office principally serves clients in the insurance/reinsurance, banking, asset finance, energy, aviation and marine industries. A full range of legal services including civil litigation, US, UK and EU insurance regulations, corporate/commercial, property, energy/utilities/project finance, insolvency, telecommunications, aircraft and ship finance, tax and banking regulation are provided.

Insurance & Reinsurance: US, UK and EU corporate regulation and litigation matters of all types.

Civil/Commercial Litigation: Litigation, arbitration and alternative dispute resolution of all types, including transnational and in particular US/UK disputes.

Energy/Utilities: Electricity, oil and gas transactional and advisory matters; regulatory advice and privatisations.

Project Finance: Major international project work in numerous industry sectors including oil/gas, power and telecommunications.

Corporate/Commercial: Corporate mergers and acquisitions, joint ventures and general corporate finance/commercial advice.

Banking & Finance: All kinds of secured and unsecured lending and lease finance and lititgation with specialist knowledge in the aviation and shipping industries.

Insolvency: All matters involving insolvencies in the US, UK and EU including, in particular, insurance insolvency.

Commercial Property: All aspects of commercial property investment and transactions.

CONTACTS

Asset Finance	Robert Dibble
Aviation	Robert Dibble
	Mitri Najjar
Banking	Robert Dibble
Civil/Commercial Litigation	Nicholas Rochez
	Peter Sharp
Commercial Property	Nick Shepherd
Corporate Finance	Charles Ashton
	Anthony Richmond
Corporate/Commercial	Alan Jones
	Garry Pegg
Energy/Utilities	Alan Jones
	Garry Pegg
I-business & Telecommunications	
	Anthony Richmond
	David Waldron
Insolvency	Peter Sharp
Insurance/Reinsurance	William Marcoux
	Nicholas Rochez
	Peter Sharp
Project/Finance	Garry Pegg
	Anthony Richmond
Shipping & Marine	Robert Dibble
Tax	Andrew Terry

INTERNATIONAL: LeBoeuf, Lamb, Greene & MacRae LLP has offices in the United States in New York, Washington DC, San Francisco, Albany, Boston, Denver, Harrisburg, Hartford, Houston, Jacksonville, Los Angeles, Newark, Pittsburgh, Salt Lake City, and elsewhere in Almaty, Bishkek, Beijing, Brussels, Johannesburg, Moscow, Paris, Riyadh and Tashkent together with working arrangements with local lawyers in numerous other jurisdictions.

LE BRASSEUR J TICKLE

Drury House, 34-43 Russell Street, London, WC2B 5HA
Tel: (020) 7836 0099 **Fax:** (020) 7831 2215 **DX:** 37985 Kingsway
Email: enquiries@lbjt.co.uk

6-7 Park Place, Leeds, LS1 2RU
Tel: (0113) 234 1220 **Fax:** (0113) 234 1573 **DX:** 14086 Leeds Park Square

Windsor House, Windsor Lane, Cardiff, CF10 3DE
Tel: (029) 2034 3035 **Fax:** (029) 2034 3045 **DX:** 33063 Cardiff 1

Senior Partner	Robert Sumerling
Managing Partner	Stephen Janisch (London)
Number of partners	28
Assistant solicitors	30
Other fee-earners	8

AREAS OF PRACTICE

Clinical Negligence	30%
Litigation	15%
Personal Injury	5%
Property	10%
Commercial Law	15%
Employment	20%
Crime	5%

CONTACTS

Clinical Negligence	Stephen Janisch (London)
	Nick Rawson (Leeds)
Commercial Law	Stephen Everett (Leeds)
	Geoff Sparks (London)
Corporate Law	Jonathan North (London)
Employment	Simon Dinnick (London)
	Alex Leslie (London)
	Kate Williams (Leeds)
Environmental	Geoff Sparks (London)
Insurance	Michael Scanlan (London)
Litigation	Simon Dinnick (London)
	Oliver Mayes (London)
Personal Injury	Stephen Janisch (London)
	Kate Williams (Leeds)
PFI	Geoff Sparks (London)
Property	Philip Garland (London)
	Michael Thorniley-Walker (Leeds)

THE FIRM: Le Brasseur J Tickle is a leading health and commercial law firm, with offices in London, Leeds and Cardiff, with a national reputation for its healthcare practice. The firm has continued to grow with the opening of their new Cardiff office and further individual appointments. It has a thriving commercial practice, which complements its pre-eminent medical practice. Le Brasseur J Tickle is dedicated to providing clients with the very highest standards of service. It strives to build strong relationships with its clients through accessibility, responsiveness, and quality of legal service. A clear management structure ensures that clients have direct contact with lawyers acting on their behalf and that clients receive frequent and appropriate feedback on an ongoing basis. The firm prides itself on its efficient and cost effective delivery of legal advice, and places great importance on rigorous and systematic procedures designed specifically to meet each clients requirements. The firm has an established client service programme, which ensures that client's views on service are continually monitored and acted upon.

PRINCIPAL AREAS OF WORK: Le Brasseur J Tickle is a long established forward thinking firm that is constantly striving to expand through good work practice and the development of new work areas. The firm provides a highly proactive and responsive service.

Healthcare law: Le Brasseur J Tickle has a leading reputation for its health law practice. There exists considerable expertise within the firm in both the clinical negligence and personal injury fields and it is one of the few specialist healthcare law practices in the country. It is a market leader in the field of the representation and defence of doctors and dentists and other healthcare professionals. Work in this specialist area continues to expand. As well as the representation of medical defence organisations, health authorities and trusts, the firm also acts for and advises private hospitals, insurance companies, healthcare partnerships and professionals.

Litigation: The firm's experience in litigation and dispute resolution is long established, with many members of the firm having extensive working familiarity with professional negligence (especially medical and dental negligence), commercial disputes and personal injury litigation.

Public Authority Law: In addition the firm has an in depth knowledge of public authority law, including corporate governance, statutory regulation and judicial review. The firm is able to provide practical advice facilitating management decisions and service development in order to avoid conflict and confrontation wherever possible. Lawyers at the firm advise NHS clients on the fiduciary duties of individual directors, Trust Boards on their responsibilities under NHS legislation and individuals about the protection of individual reputation. The provision of fast pro-active advice to Chief Executives and managers is a specialism of the firm and its lead partners.

Employment: The firm has a specialist employment group with extensive experience in advising a client base, which includes public sector, institutional clients, multinational and publicly quoted companies. The employment group gives independent practical advice on a wide range of employment issues, including agreements with senior members of staff, trade unions and employment legislation, as well as advising on such issues as TUPE and redundancy. The representation of healthcare professionals in employment and disciplinary situations is a hallmark of the firm's expertise.

Commercial Law: The firm has a strong and broad company commercial practice, with experience of M&A, joint ventures, partnerships, corporate finance, IT and telecoms law, insurance and commercial litigation as well as experience of company restructuring and bringing companies onto the Alternative Investment Market and full stock exchange quotations. In addition it offers contentious and non-contentious commercial advice including property advice to its clients across the country.

Property: There is a strong commercial property team both in London and Leeds specialising in commercial property development and investment, and landlord and tenant issues. The firm is committed to providing its commercial clients and its well-established private client practice, with top quality advice. The firm continues to advise on all matters relating to wills and probate, and trusts and tax planning.

LEDINGHAM CHALMERS

5 Melville Crescent, Edinburgh, EH3 7JA
Tel: (0131) 200 1000 **Fax:** (0131) 200 1080 **DX:** LP-98 Edinburgh - 2
Email: mail@ledinghamchalmers.com **Website:** www.ledinghamchalmers.com

Johnstone House, 52-54 Rose Street, Aberdeen, AB10 1UD
Tel: (01224) 408408 **Fax:** (01224) 408400 **DX:** LP-39 Aberdeen-1

Kintail House, Beechwood Business Park, Inverness, IV2 3BW
Tel: (01463) 667400 **Fax:** (01463) 713755 **DX:** LP-1 Inverness-2

Senior Partner	David Laing
UK	
Number of partners	29
Assistant solicitors	30
Other fee-earners	23
International	
Assistant solicitors	9

AREAS OF PRACTICE

Company/Commercial/Oil 40%
Commercial Property 23%
Litigation 16%
Residential Property 14%
Private Client 7%

CONTACTS

Agriculture ....Allan Collie (Aberdeen)
Commercial Property John Curran (Aberdeen)
Company/Commercial
...............................Malcolm Laing (Aberdeen)
Construction ....Jennifer Howitt (Aberdeen)
Corporate Finance ....David Laing (Edinburgh)
Employment ....Peter Sharp (Aberdeen)
International ......Gavin Faraquhar (Edinburgh)
Litigation ....Marysia Lewis (Aberdeen)
Oil & Gas............Robert Ruddiman (Aberdeen)
Private Client ....Daniel Stewart (Aberdeen)
Technology ....Roger Connon (Aberdeen)

THE FIRM: Ledingham Chalmers offers 'exportable skills': skills and experience rooted in the rich Scottish legal tradition, developed in an enterprising economy and now offered to an international market. The firm provides a full range of business law services from a unique network of offices in three Scottish locations – Edinburgh, Aberdeen and Inverness – and in three overseas locations – Baku (Azerbaijan), Istanbul (Turkey) and Stanley (Falkland Islands). The firm has developed a reputation for its entrepreneurial, 'can do' approach, giving clients the benefit of its own business experience. The development of an international practice adds an important dimension which is further evidenced by the firm's membership of the Trans European Law Firms Alliance.

PRINCIPAL AREAS OF WORK: The domestic practice in Scotland is structured in divisions – corporate, commercial property, dispute resolution, oil and gas and private client. The firm encourages individual excellence within teams without suffering the extremes of rigid specialisation, with the aim of developing rounded business lawyers who can provide pragmatic solutions. There is also a focus on exportable skills which, while developed at home, can be applied to work overseas in both developed and developing jurisdictions. The firm has developed a particularly strong reputation within the oil and gas and oil services sectors and the land, leisure and construction sectors. Within the Scottish offices, the main services are corporate/commercial; corporate and project finance; commercial property (including planning and environmental); construction; employment; energy law and practice; intellectual property; information technology; insolvency; litigation and dispute resolution; agriculture and estates; private client (which in Scotland includes residential property).

INTERNATIONAL: The overseas offices have a special focus on oil and gas, transportation, infrastructure projects, banking and project finance in their respective regions and are supported by the projects team based in the firm's Edinburgh office. The firm regularly works alongside lawyers in other jurisdictions, sometimes as instructing counsel for UK clients or as part of a larger professional team.

THE BUSINESS OF LAW
LEDINGHAM
CHALMERS
SOLICITORS

LEE BOLTON & LEE

1 The Sanctuary, Westminster, London, SW1P 3JT
Tel: (020) 7222 5381 **Fax:** (020) 7222 7502 **DX:** 2301 Victoria
Email: enquiries@1thesanctuary.com **Website:** www.leeboltonlee.com

Senior Partner	PF Beesley
Number of partners	14
Assistant solicitors	7
Other fee-earners	13

CONTACTS

Charities ....P F Beesley
....A C James
Commercial Property..................G J Fountain
Company/Commercial ....J P Sergeant
Ecclesiastical/Education ....P F Beesley
....N J Richens
Litigation.....................................J P Sergeant
Parliamentary ....J A Durkin
Private Client...........................M J G Fletcher
Public Law ....M A R Peto
Railway Property ....J Taplin
....K E Wallace
....P Robinson

THE FIRM: Established at 1 The Sanctuary in 1855, Lee Bolton & Lee is a well-established Westminster practice, incorporating both commercial, charity, education and private client work. The firm offers extensive experience and advice across a wide spectrum of activities, and is associated with a firm of solicitors and parliamentary agents, Rees and Freres, to provide a specialist service in parliamentary, public and administrative law.

PRINCIPAL AREAS OF WORK:
Private Client: The firm provides expert advice on a full range of private client matters including domestic property, personal taxation and individual financial planning, wills, trusts, probate and the administration of estates. In addition, a separate department handles all aspects of family and matrimonial law.
Ecclesiastical, Education & Charities: As well as general advice on ecclesiastical matters and disciplinary proceedings, the firm advises three diocesan bishops as Registrars. Advice is provided to independent schools on all matters from establishing a new school or hiving-off a school from a larger charity to day-to-day operational and employment issues. In the maintained sector the firm has considerable knowledge of the Education Acts and advises a number of diocese and many individual schools and trustees on education law and the law relating to school sites. The firm's charity practice is linked, but not confined to, its educational and ecclesiastical work and covers all aspects of charity creation, registration and administration including trusts, tax and charitable property.
Corporate Services: Advice is provided for clients ranging from established organisations to emerging businesses and entrepreneurs on every aspect of commercial life including company formations, reconstructions, mergers, MBOs, joint ventures, Stock Exchange work, employment law and pensions, banking and financial services. Funding, planning and development work is handled for banks, institutional clients, investors and developers.
Litigation: A thriving litigation department handles a range of matters including general commercial contracts, employment disputes, professional and medical negligence, property building and landlord and tenant

disputes, defamation, insurance and personal injury claims. The firm has long standing relations with numerous public bodies and has developed a considerable expertise in the area of judicial review proceedings.
Commercial Property: This Department acts for a wide variety of clients from small businesses to major companies, banks, institutional clients, housing associations, investors and developers. All types of commercial property transactions are undertaken including acquisitions and disposals, leasing of commercial property whether acting for Landlord or Tenant, renewal or termination of business lettings, Development Agreements and Joint Venture Agreements. The department draws on expertise elsewhere in the firm; for example where litigation or tax aspects arise. In addition, Rees & Freres have a large commercial property department currently handling work from the major rail transport providers and operators.

LEE CROWDER

39 Newhall Street, Birmingham, B3 3DY
Tel: (0121) 236 4477 **Fax:** (0121) 236 4710 **DX:** 13034
Email: info@leecrowder.co.uk **Website:** www.leecrowder.co.uk

Senior Partner	Stephen Gilmore
Number of partners	22
Assistant solicitors	38
Other fee-earners	25

AREAS OF PRACTICE

Corporate	25%
Property	15%
Commercial Dispute Resolution	15%
Construction & Engineering	15%
Private Client	10%
Housing	10%
Charity Services	5%
Employment	5%

CONTACTS

Corporate	Graham Muth
	Stephen Gilmore
Property	Kevin Nagle
	Joel Kordan
Commercial Dispute Resolution	Richard Whittingham
	Bernard Singleton
Construction & Engineering	Jeffrey Brown
	Stephen Belshaw
Private Client	Drummond Kerr
Housing	Andy Ballard
	Simon Denslow
Charities	Martin Woodward
Employment	Michael Gillespie

THE FIRM: Lee Crowder is a dynamic modern practice based in Birmingham city centre. It has grown dramatically over the last few years, and is one of the oldest firms in the country. It is the firm's intention to continue its growth by recruiting only the highest quality fee-earners at all levels. The firm is committed to providing an excellent client focused, partner led service, and is enhancing its reputation, both regionally and nationally. The firm acts for a broad range of clients throughout the UK and overseas including publicly quoted companies, substantial private companies, banks, charities and other not-for-profit organisations.

PRINCIPAL AREAS OF WORK:
Corporate Services: The department deals with commercial as well as corporate and corporate finance matters. Principal activities involve acquisitions, mergers and disposals, AIM flotations, joint ventures and shareholder agreements, non-contentious insolvency, venture capital and commercial agreements. It is also recognised as a leading firm in e-commerce, media and entertainment on a regional and national basis.
Property Services: The department now has an extremely high profile and acts for commercial and residential property developers, institutions, retailers and landed estates. The firm has a logistics unit, which is recognised as a leader in its field, as well as dealing with acquisitions and disposals, major commercial and residential developments, landlord and tenant matters and joint ventures.
Commercial Dispute Resolution: The department handles a broad range of disputes, specialising in professional negligence claims, particularly in the financial services sector, property litigation and IT disputes.
Private Client: The firm is now a major player in the regional market dealing with all aspects of estate and tax planning and has particular expertise in financial services.
Housing: With over 30 years experience as Housing Corporation panel solicitors, the firm currently acts for over 50 housing associations nationwide and assists several local authorities.
Construction & Engineering: The department deals with the drafting of bespoke contracts and approval of special amendments produced in relation to standard forms. It advises national main contractors, major subcontractors, developers and their insurers.
Employment: The team advises on all aspects of employment problems including contracts, dismissals, discrimination, human rights and all issues arising out of employment legislation at home or in the EU.
Charities: The department acts for over 100 charities across the UK, advising charitable trustees and assisting in dealings with the Charity Commission.

LEE CROWDER
Solicitors

LEE & PEMBERTONS

142 Buckingham Palace Road, London, SW1W 8TR
Tel: (020) 7824 9111 **Fax:** (020) 7824 8804
Email: law@leepem.co.uk **Website:** www.leepem.co.uk

Senior Partner	Julian Whately
Number of partners	9
Assistant solicitors	4
Other fee-earners	8

AREAS OF PRACTICE

Property (Agri, Res & Comm)	35%
Trusts, Probate & Tax Planning	25%
Dispute Resolution	20%
Company/Commercial	10%
Matrimonial & Family	10%

CONTACTS

Property	Julian Whately
Trusts, Probate & Tax Planning	
	Tristram Rae Smith
Dispute Resolution	John Roney
Company/Commercial	Richard Roney
Matrimonial & Family	Jacqueline Fitzgerald

THE FIRM: Established in the late eighteenth century, Lee & Pembertons recently moved to new offices in Victoria. The firm offers a full range of specialist services to private clients, a number of whom are owners of landed estates. The emphasis is on providing a partner led personal service.

PRINCIPAL AREAS OF WORK: Agricultural, charities, commercial, dispute resolution, employment, matrimonial and family, property, wills, trusts, and tax planning.

CLIENTELE: A wide range of private clients, including landowners and entrepreneurs, and their related companies and businesses.

RECRUITMENT: Three new partners have been appointed this year from outside the firm. There are no current vacancies for trainees.

LEES LLOYD WHITLEY

Castle Chambers, 43 Castle Street, Liverpool, L2 9TJ **Tel:** (0151) 227 3541 **Fax:** (0151) 227 2460 **DX:** 14164 Liverpool **Ptnrs:** 11 **Asst solrs:** 8 **Other fee-earners:** 43

LEE & THOMPSON

Greengarden House, 15-22 St. Christopher's Place, London, W1U 1NL **Tel:** (020) 7935 4665 **Fax:** (020) 7563 4949 **Website:** www.leeandthompson.com **Ptnrs:** 9 **Asst solrs:** 5

LEIGH, DAY & CO

Priory House, 25 St. John's Lane, London, EC1M 4LB
Tel: (020) 7650 1200 **Fax:** (020) 7253 4433 **DX:** 53326 Clerkenwell
Email: postbox@leighday.co.uk **Website:** www.leighday.co.uk

International House, 82-86 Deansgate, Manchester, M3 2ER
Tel: (0161) 832 7722 **Fax:** (0161) 839 2329 **DX:** 718178 Manchester 3
Email: postman@leighday.co.uk

Senior Partner	Martyn Day
Number of partners	16
Assistant solicitors	17
Other fee-earners	20

CONTACTS

Accident	Sally Moore (London)
	Geraldine McCool (Manchester)
Administrative Law	Richard Stein
Clinical Negligence	Sarah Leigh (London)
	Frank Patterson (Manchester)
Multi-Party Actions	Martyn Day

THE FIRM: A leading firm specialising in all aspects of complex personal injury work and multi-party actions.

PRINCIPAL AREAS OF WORK:

Multi-party Actions: Specialising in claims as a result of exposure to pollution (radiation, chemicals, pesticides, sewage in the sea) together with industrial disease and nuisance claims. Also acts in multi-party product liability claims.

Clinical Negligence: Concentrates on cases involving serious disabilities or death. Also specialises in medical devices such as artificial heart valves, pacemakers and silicone breast implants.

Accident Litigation: This department deals with a full range of personal injury claims including road traffic accidents, accidents at work and product liability claims. There is a special expertise in actions against the MOD and aviation disasters.

Administrative Law: The department's clients include local authorities and objectors concerning plan making, development control, enforcement and appeals. It undertakes a large number of judicial reviews and utilises human rights legislation.

LEMON & CO

34 Regent Circus, Swindon, SN1 1PY
Tel: (01793) 527141 **Fax:** (01793) 614168 **DX:** 400912 Swindon 6
Email: enquiries@lemon-co.co.uk **Website:** www.lemon-co.co.uk

Chelsea House, 1 Little London Court, Albert Street, Swindon, SN1 3HY
Tel: (01793) 496341 **Fax:** (01793) 511639 **DX:** 400912 Swindon 6
Email: mac@lemonco.star.co.uk

Senior Partner	Richard Fry
Number of partners	7
Assistant solicitors	6
Other fee-earners	8

AREAS OF PRACTICE

Conveyancing	35%
Litigation	30%
Company/Commercial	20%
Trusts & Probate	15%

CONTACTS

Commercial Litigation	Nita King
Commercial Property	Martin Evans
Company/Commercial	Nial Ledingham
Employment	Paul Archer
Family	Stephen Moss
Personal Injury	Timothy Dixon
Private Client	Deirdre Moss
Residential Property	David Halfhead

THE FIRM: Founded in 1914, Lemon & Co is one of the largest and longest established firms in Swindon, providing an extensive range of services for businesses and private clients and is dedicated to client care. It is one of the few Swindon firms specialising in commercial law and has participated in several complex property and corporate transactions in recent years.

PRINCIPAL AREAS OF WORK:

Company/Commercial: Work includes company formations, acquisitions and disposals, MBO/MBI, employment contracts and conditions, shareholders and partnership agreements, jv agreements, intellectual property, franchise, agency and distribution agreements, commercial property and all aspects of landlord and tenant law.

Litigation: All matters are undertaken. Specialists in commercial litigation, employment, personal injury, family, and childcare.

Private Client: Work handled includes estate planning, wills, charity law, management of trusts and settlements, probate work, administration of estates and financial and tax advisory services. The firm's specialist residential conveyancing department is also widely acknowledged for providing a quality service.

LEO ABSE & COHEN

40 Churchill Way, Cardiff, CF10 2SS
Tel: (029) 2038 3252 **Fax:** (029) 2034 5572 **DX:** 33002
Email: law@leoabse.co.uk

Conwy House, Castle Court, Phoenix Way, Enterprise Park, Swansea, SA7 9LA
Tel: 01792 762030 **Fax:** 01792 762031 **DX:** 82803 Swansea 2
Email: law@leoabse.co.uk

Managing Partner	Ian Hopkins
Senior Partner	John Sherratt
Number of partners	11
Assistant solicitors	47
Other fee-earners	21

AREAS OF PRACTICE

Plaintiff Personal Injury	49%
Commercial	23%
Insurance Litigation	18%
Legal Aid	10%

THE FIRM: Leo Abse & Cohen has an outstanding reputation in Litigation with specialist services in personal injury, insurance litigation, medical negligence, commercial and general litigation, employment, family and serious crime. In addition, the firm has a strong property section and deals with an increasing amount of company commercial matters. Leo Abse & Cohen has enjoyed considerable growth in recent years, continuously recruiting high calibre solicitors from all over England and Wales. The firm is the first in Wales to achieve Lexcel status and only the third firm nationally to achieve both Lexcel and ISO9001.

LEONARD GRAY

72-74 Duke St, Chelmsford, CM1 1JY **Tel:** (01245) 504904 **Fax:** (01245) 490728 **DX:** 3309 Chelmsford 1 **Email:** legal@leonardgray.co.uk **Website:** www.leonardgray.co.uk **Ptnrs:** 5 **Asst solrs:** 2 **Other fee-earners:** 9 **Contact:** B Morgan • Committed to providing quality, independent legal services with specialist departments. All aspects of family law with an emphasis on middle and higher income financial cases. Childcare, mediation and adoption.

LÉONIE COWEN & ASSOCIATES

3A Loveridge Mews, London, NW6 2DP
Tel: (020) 7604 5870 **Fax:** (020) 7604 5871
Email: leonie.cowen@lcowen.co.uk **Website:** www.lcowen.co.uk

Principal	Léonie Cowen
Number of partners	1
Other fee-earners	1

AREAS OF PRACTICE

Local Government Law	80%
Charities	10%
Corporate	5%
Commercial Property	5%

CONTACTS

Charities	Léonie Cowen
	Andrew Riddell
Commercial Property	Andrew Riddell
Corporate	Léonie Cowen
	Andrew Riddell
Local Government Law	Léonie Cowen

THE FIRM: Founded in 1989, the firm specialises in local government and administrative law. Léonie Cowen spent 15 years at senior level in local government.

PRINCIPAL AREAS OF WORK:

Powers, Functions & Vires

Public Private Partnerships & Joint Ventures: The firm advises on local authority companies, company structures for service transfers (including sport and leisure, arts, culture and libraries, economic development, social services and housing companies), commercial and not-for-profit projects, and the Part V framework and its impact.

Leisure, Arts, Culture, Libraries & Heritage: Work handled includes reviews, service transfers and contracting.

Economic Development & Regeneration Projects

Local Authority Finance: Including the capital finance regime, project funding, PFI, lottery, audit issues and relationships with external auditors.

Social Services: The firm specialises in community care procurement, transfers of residential homes for older people/adults and securing capital funding for re-provisioning.

Best Value, Quality Systems & Benchmarking

Public Procurement: Advice is given on the public procurement regime, safe procurement processes and drafting contracts.

Employment: Including TUPE, local authority terms and conditions (including sensitive senior level cases), superannuation schemes and pensions.

Investigations & Inquiries

Education: The firm works for LEAs and governors of schools and higher education establishments.

Charities: Particularly the setting-up and management of charities and other non-profit bodies.

Municipal & Cross-Authority Trading

Corporate: The firm handles business transfers, joint ventures, and shareholders agreements.

Commercial Property: Work covered includes acquisition, funding, management and disposal of property for public authorities, housing associations, businesses and investors.

L

LESTER ALDRIDGE

Russell House, Oxford Road, Bournemouth, BH8 8EX
Tel: (01202) 786161 **Fax:** (01202) 786110 **DX:** 7623 Bournemouth 1
Email: info@lester-aldridge.co.uk **Website:** www.lester-aldridge.co.uk

Alleyn House, Carlton Crescent, Southampton, SO15 2EU
Tel: (023) 8082 0400 **Fax:** (023) 8082 0410 **DX:** 96882 Southampton 10

Managing Partner	Roger Woolley
Chairman	Colin Patrick
Number of partners	34
Assistant solicitors	28
Other fee-earners	48

CONTACTS

Asset Finance & Banking	Martin Roderick
Business Property	Bob Robertson
Commercial Litigation	Michael Giddins
Corporate	David Ashplant
Corporate Recovery	Malcolm Niekirk
Employment	Susan Evans
Family Law	Stephen Foster
Health & Community Care	Peter Grose
Health & Safety	Richard Byrne
Intellectual Property	David Ashplant
Investment Services	Steve Dean
LA Fast Track (Debt Services)	Andrew Corke
LA Marine	Jonathan Hadley-Piggin
Personal Injury	Karen Thompson
Planning & Development	Andrew Hignett
Residential Property	Rachel Lapworth
Trusts, Tax & Wills	Barry Glazier

THE FIRM: LA is a dynamic legal business. Based on the south coast, it aims to provide a one stop shop for its entrepreneurial client base and combines high quality commercial legal advice with wealth management. LA has a corporate structure with 16 legal teams reporting to a full time managing partner and lawyers are supported by directors of finance, personnel and marketing. The firm continues to invest heavily in tailored management training. The exciting developments at LA have been much written about in the legal press during the past year, and the firm has lived up to its reputation for ambition, vigour and energy. LA started the year by acquiring a team of marine lawyers from Shoosmiths to form LA Marine – a cornerstone for the firm's new Southampton office. A number of strategic recruitments have seen the firm grow in size by 25% over the past six months. Whilst developing its Southampton office, the firm has also built on its strengths in niche areas such as asset finance. The firm's approach was summed up in a recent client satisfaction survey (undertaken by The Change Partnership) as being "Very customer focused. Nothing is too much trouble, and as soon as we tell them about a problem they jump on it...They will resolve it face to face if necessary; get in their car and go out. They're more like a normal business than a firm of solicitors," or, as another client put it, "They are shockingly normal for solicitors."

RECRUITMENT: LA continues its growth strategy and is actively seeking high calibre lawyers. For more information contact Sarah Jones, head of personnel.

L'ESTRANGE & BRETT

Arnott House, 12-16 Bridge Street, Belfast, BT1 1LS
Tel: (028) 9023 0426 **Fax:** (028) 9024 6396 **DX:** 424 NR Belfast 1
Email: law@lestrangeandbrett.com **Website:** www.lestrangeandbrett.com

Senior Partner	V Alan Hewitt
Number of partners	10
Assistant solicitors	18
Other fee-earners	7

AREAS OF PRACTICE

Corporate & Commercial Law	39%
Commercial Property	38%
Litigation (incl. Employment Law)	18%
Private Client	5%

CONTACTS

Banking & Financial Services/Insolvency	Brian Henderson
Commercial Law	Richard Gray
Commercial Property	V Alan Hewitt
Construction Law	Andrea McIlroy-Rose
Corporate Law	John Irvine
Employment	Adam Brett
Litigation	Sam Beckett
Private Client	Ian Huddleston
Projects & PFI	Richard Gray
Technology	Paul McBride

THE FIRM: L'Estrange & Brett is one of the leading commercial firms in Northern Ireland and one of the oldest practices in Ireland, having been in existence since 1796. Today, it is a modern practice geared to the demands of a fast moving business environment and committed to giving clients the best professional advice and support available in the market. The firm has strong links with many City of London, national and regional firms in Great Britain. It also works on international transactions with firms in many parts of the world. Along with leading Dublin practice McCann FitzGerald, L'Estrange & Brett formed the North South Legal Alliance in 1999. The two firms retain their independence, but work together to provide clients with an integrated service in matters involving elements in both Northern Ireland and the Republic of Ireland.

PRINCIPAL AREAS OF WORK:

Corporate Law: The firm provides fast and effective legal advice across all types of work in the corporate sector, ranging from acquisitions, disposals and mergers to management buy-outs, buy-ins, joint ventures and new inward investment projects.

Commercial Law: The firm advises on diverse areas ranging from sales/distribution and competition law to intellectual property information.

Commercial Property: L'Estrange & Brett has extensive experience across a full range of property related matters with an emphasis on commercial property. The firm's skills cover site acquisition and development, planning, building contracts and arbitration, landlord and tenant, housing developments and environmental law.

Construction Law: The firm's construction unit advises contractors, employers and funders on all types of contentious and non-contentious construction matters.

Litigation: The litigation department is focused on the requirements of commercial clients. Its work covers commercial actions, building contracts, litigation, professional negligence, administrative law and judicial review, as well as personal injury claims.

Banking & Financial Services/Insolvency: The firm's cross-disciplinary unit advises on all aspects of borrowing, lending and corporate finance, including asset and project finance, corporate reconstructions and reorganisations. Its insolvency practice has wide experience of corporate rescue and recovery involving receivership, administration and liquidation.

Projects/PFI: The firm has unrivalled experience of project finance and PFI transactions in Northern Ireland, acting for both public and private sector clients.

Employment: The firm provides a comprehensive service for employers and employees advising on all aspects of litigious and non-litigious employment work.

Private Client: The firm provides legal services to private clients across a wide range of matters, including domestic conveyancing, wills and trusts, probate and tax planning.

Technology: The firm's business technology unit advises a range of clients, from dot.com start-ups to traditional businesses on all technology aspects of their businesses.

LEVENES

Ashley House, 235-239 High Road, Wood Green, London, N22 8HF
Tel: (020) 8881 7777 **Fax:** (020) 8889 6395 **DX:** 135576 Wood Green 4
Email: info@levenes.co.uk **Website:** www.levenes.co.uk

The McLaren Building, 35 Dale End, Birmingham, B4 7LN
Tel: (0121) 212 0000 **Fax:** (0121) 233 1878 **DX:** 23502 Birmingham 3
Email: enquiries@levenes.co.uk

South Gate House, Wood Street, Cardiff, CF10 1EW
Tel: (029) 2039 0777 **Fax:** (029) 2023 0777 **DX:** 122790 CARDIFF 13
Email: contact@levenes.co.uk

Number of partners	12
Assistant solicitors	47
Other fee-earners	48

AREAS OF PRACTICE

Personal Injury	55%
Employment	20%
Crime	10%
Education, Disability & Human Rights	10%
Family & Other Legal Aid	5%

CONTACTS

Crime	David Nicolls
Education/Disability & Human Rights	David Ruebain
Employment	Audrey Onwukwe
Family	Katy Rensten
Personal Injury	David Levene

THE FIRM: Levenes is a socially aware firm providing a national service to both individual and commercial clients. The 250 staff are grouped in specialist teams at five locations across England and Wales (Birmingham, Cardiff and three offices in London). The firm has a particularly strong reputation for personal injury and employment. The innovative work undertaken by the education and disability department is nationally recognised and has an expanding human rights dimension.

PRINCIPAL AREAS OF WORK:
Personal Injury: A leading team of more than 50 lawyers handling all types of personal injury claims including spinal and head injury cases with several recent successful appeal decisions.
Employment: An expert team specialising in employment litigation for both employers and employees with particular expertise in race, sex and disability discrimination.
Education, Disability & Human Rights Law: A specialist department offering a unique service in the areas of special educational needs, school and college matters, care assessments, and disability discrimination. The department is already one of the key advisers on human rights.
Family: All types of family work, including the full range of children's cases, as well as property and financial matters following separation or divorce are handled.
Legal Aid: Work includes family, crime, housing and welfare benefits.

LEVI & CO
33 St. Pauls Street, Leeds, LS1 2JJ **Tel:** (0113) 244 9931 **Fax:** (0113) 244 6789 **DX:** 12033 Leeds **Ptnrs:** 7 **Asst solrs:** 2 **Other fee-earners:** 11

LEVISON MELTZER PIGOTT

9-13 St Andrew Street, London, EC4A 3AE
Tel: (020) 7556 2400 **Fax:** (020) 7556 2401 **DX:** 200 London Chancery Lane
Email: lmp@lmplaw.co.uk

Number of partners	3
Assistant solicitors	2

AREAS OF PRACTICE

Family/Matrimonial/Finance	60%
Children	30%
Cohabitation	10%

THE FIRM: Levison Meltzer Pigott is a specialist divorce and family law firm formed on 1 June 1998. The three partners have, however, worked together for almost 16 years. The firm deals with all areas of divorce and family law, including advising on pensions and the rights of unmarried couples. Jeremy Levison is a founder member of the International Academy of Matrimonial Lawyers and has been vice-president of its European section. His contact with family lawyers worldwide assists in the significant proportion of cases that have an international dimension. Claire Meltzer regularly broadcasts on television and radio, particularly on the subject of pensions and divorce, and has written numerous articles and papers on matters of divorce and family law. Simon Pigott is a member of the International Academy of Matrimonial Lawyers, has lectured for the College of Law, was one of the first family law mediators trained by the Family Mediators Association, was its Chair between 1995 and 1997, and was Vice-Chair of the United Kingdom College of Family Mediators between 1996 and 1998. Each of the partners is an associate of the American Bar Association (Family Section) and all the firm's solicitors are members of the Solicitors Family Law Association.

LEVY & MCRAE

266 St Vincent Street, Glasgow, G2 5RL
Tel: (0141) 307 2311 **Fax:** (0141) 307 6857/8 **DX:** GW149 Glasgow
Email: peterwatson@lemac.co.uk **Website:** www.lemac.co.uk

Senior Partner	Peter Watson
Number of partners	4
Assistant solicitors	6
Other fee-earners	9

THE FIRM: Levy & McRae is one of Scotland's leading law firms. The firm has a particularly strong reputation for litigation, media and personal injury.

PRINCIPAL AREAS OF WORK:
Litigation: All types of litigation work are handled.

Continued overleaf

Media: One of the largest media law practices in the country providing advice to an extensive range of clients in the print and broadcast media.
Personal Injury: Work handled includes claims resulting from car accidents, aircraft and shipping, wrongful death etc.

INTERNATIONAL: Levy & McRae is involved in litigation around the world including in France, Spain, Turkey, Italy and the United States. As part of Legal Netlink, the firm offers worldwide access to local counsel.

LEWIS SILKIN

12 Gough Square, London, EC4A 3DW
Tel: (020) 7074 8000 **Fax:** (020) 7832 1200 **DX:** 182 Chancery Lane
Email: info@lewissilkin.com **Website:** www.lewissilkin.com

Managing Partner	Trevor Watkins
Senior Partner	Roger Alexander
Number of partners	34
Assistant solicitors	40
Other fee-earners	20
Total	94

AREAS OF PRACTICE

Corporate Finance/Commercial	25%
Property/Project Finance/ Construction/Social Housing	25%
Employment	18%
Litigation & Dispute Resolution	16%
Advertising/Media/Defamation/IP/IT	16%

CONTACTS

Advertising & Marketing Services	Roger Alexander
	Brinsley Dresden
Company Commercial	Trevor Watkins
Construction	Peter Morris
Corporate Finance	Clare Grayston
Defamation	Roderick Dadak
Employment	Michael Burd
	James Davies
Intellectual Property	Ian Jeffery
IT	Gillian Cordall
Litigation & Dispute Resolution	Thomas Coates
	Clive Greenwood
Project Finance	Lynne Murray
Property & Planning	Leonard Goodrich
Social Housing	Gillian Bastow

lewissilkin

THE FIRM: Lewis Silkin is a medium-sized commercial law firm which punches well above its weight, competing on equal terms with anyone in its chosen specialist areas. In tone as well as substance, it is distinctive; notably relaxed and unstuffy, it prides itself on friendly and productive working relationships.

PRINCIPAL AREAS OF WORK:
Corporate Services: The firm aims not just to come in at the tail-end of a transaction to document the deal, but to play a far more active role as a business adviser, helping clients to structure deals and conducting complex negotiations on their behalf. An impressive range of work includes flotations, employee benefits, shareholder agreements and regulatory advice, acting on behalf of venture capitalists and sponsors. Commercial work includes project finance, franchising and outsourcing.
Litigation & Dispute Resolution: The firm is known for its success in winning disputes, as a result of a string of high-profile victories. But, more broadly, Lewis Silkin takes the view that problems can be resolved with appropriate dispute resolution techniques. From highly sensitive mediation to High Court litigation, the firm works with clients to achieve their commercial objectives.
Property: A 'seamless' approach enables the firm to take care of all a client's property-related needs, from leases to litigation, finance to planning issues, development to environmental issues.
Marketing Services: From long-established advertising agencies to web marketing start-ups, clients value Lewis Silkin's understanding of the challenges they face, the result of over 30 years spent advising many of the industry's leading names. The firm's track record in this sector is second to none.
Employment: The firm has one of the highest-rated teams in London, a group of outstanding lawyers with a reputation for straightforward practical advice when a sensitive and commercial approach is needed.
Housing & Project Finance: A recognised leader in this field, Lewis Silkin's innovative thinking and long experience have resulted in a strong record of challenging work in the social housing sector, and the financing of grant-aided projects.
Technology & Communications: In a field where moving quickly is not just desirable but essential, the firm helps drive projects forward, ensuring clients avoid the many pitfalls that await the unwary. The firm acts for IT and new media companies and advises on sales and development, procurement and outsourcing, intellectual property and regulatory issues.
Construction: Highly regarded in this area, the firm works as part of the project team from the outset. A comprehensive service, covering everything from new-build property to heavyweight civil engineering.
Defamation: Lewis Silkin offers expert and practical advice to corporations, firms or individuals whose reputation has been put at risk by libel, slander or malicious falsehood.
Sports Law: Drawing upon Lewis Silkin's strength in employment, immigration, intellectual property and corporate finance, the sports law team advises on a wide range of issues, from player contracts to sponsorship, stadium construction to club ownership.

CLIENTELE: The firm's clients range from large corporations and plcs to entrepreneurs, across a very wide range of sectors – from advertising and the Internet to social housing and property, restaurants and retailers to government agencies and utilities.

INTERNATIONAL: Lewis Silkin is the UK representative of the Global Advertising Lawyers' Alliance (GALA), an association of corporate communications lawyers.

LIGHTFOOTS

The Old Red Lion, 1-3 High Street, Thame, OX9 2BX
Tel: (01844) 212305 or 212574/5 **Fax:** (01844) 214984 **DX:** 80550 Thame
Website: www.lightfoots.co.uk

Senior Partner	Martin Hector
Number of partners	5
Assistant solicitors	4
Other fee-earners	12

THE FIRM: This progressive firm, the first nationally to gain and be re-awarded the Investors in People award, provides sound advice on most aspects of English corporate and private client law.

PRINCIPAL AREAS OF WORK:
Commercial: Services include company/commercial, commercial property, employment, tax, property litigation and specialist debt collection, mortgage repossession and asset management, professional negligence and pharmaceutical consulting departments.
Private Client: Work includes wills, probate, trusts, residential conveyancing, other general civil litigation and a specialist family law and mediation department. The firm also has a thriving estate agency and a property letting and management business.

INTERNATIONAL: Members of the firm speak French and Hungarian.

AREAS OF PRACTICE	
Commercial Litigation	28%
Domestic Conveyancing	16%
Trusts & Probate	16%
Commercial	14%
Family	13%
Pharmaceutical	8%
Commercial Conveyancing	3%
Employment	2%

LINDER MYERS

Phoenix House, 45 Cross Street, Manchester, M2 4JF **Tel:** (0161) 832 6972 **Fax:** (0161) 834 0718 **DX:** 14360 **Email:** law@lindermyers.co.uk **Ptnrs:** 13 **Asst solrs:** 21 **Other fee-earners:** 20 **Contact:** Bernard Seymour • Commercial and litigation practice carrying out services of all kinds for business clients. Strong employment department. Also well known for personal injury and clinical negligence ability.

AREAS OF PRACTICE	
Company/Commercial	25%
Personal Injury	25%
General Litigation	15%
Medical Negligence	13%
Matrimonial	12%
Private Client	10%

LINDSAY FORD SOLICITORS

93 Cardiff Road, Caerphilly, CF83 1WS **Tel:** (029) 2088 2441 **Fax:** (029) 2085 1386

L

LINDSAYS WS

11 Atholl Crescent, Edinburgh, EH3 8HE
Tel: (0131) 229 1212 **Fax:** (0131) 229 5611 **DX:** 25 Edinburgh
Email: mail@lindsays.co.uk **Website:** www.lindsays.co.uk

77 Main Street, Davidsons Mains, Edinburgh, EH4 5AD
Tel: (0131) 312 7276 **Fax:** (0131) 312 6029 **DX:** ED 115
Email: cmc@lindseys.co.uk

201-203 Bruntsfield Place, Edinburgh, EH10 4DH
Tel: (0131) 228 6993 **Fax:** (0131) 228 5584 **DX:** 25 Edinburgh
Email: mt@lindsays.co.uk

Barlas & Sharpe WS, 33a Westgate, North Berwick, EH39 4AG
Tel: (01620) 893481 **Fax:** (01620) 894442 **DX:** ED 1245
Email: rfm@lindsays.co.uk

Senior Partner	John Elliot
Number of partners	17
Assistant solicitors	9
Other fee-earners	39

AREAS OF PRACTICE	
Private Client	34%
Commercial	27%
Residential Conveyancing	21%
Litigation	18%

CONTACTS	
Asset Finance	Alasdair Cummings
Banking	Alasdair Cummings
Building Arbitration	Alan MacKay
Charitable Companies	Kathleen Preston
Commercial Contracts	William McIntosh
Commercial Property	David Reith
Corporate	Alasdair Cummings
Crofting/Agriculture	Roy Shearer
Education	Roy Shearer
Employment	Douglas Tullis
Executry & Wills	Callum Kennedy
Intellectual Property	William McIntosh
Investments	Rodger Urquhart
Liquor Licensing	William McIntosh
Litigation	Alistair Mackie
Personal Financial Planning	John Elliot
Residential Property	Robert Arbuthnott
Trusts & Tax Planning	Brian Robertson

THE FIRM: Lindsays provides a partner-led personal service with an emphasis on quality. The firm has a substantial private client base as well as a strong commercial and litigation practice. To complement these legal services, Lindsays has developed a significant presence in the residential property market through its estate agency service. Lindsays was one of the first legal practices in Scotland to recognise the benefit to its clients of adopting written quality procedures, and has gained approval under the quality standard ISO 9001.

PRINCIPAL AREAS OF WORK:
Company/Commercial: All aspects of commercial property work are covered: purchases, sales, leasing and secured lending, asset finance, asset recovery and building contracts, particularly in relation to disputes. Other more specialised areas of expertise are education, intellectual property (especially licensing agreements), road haulage and liquor licensing, including the purchase and sale of licensed premises. The department deals with company formations and secretarial services, take-overs and acquisitions and the formation and management of charitable trusts and companies.
Litigation: A comprehensive debt-recovery service is offered as is advice on employment law, contractual disputes, damages claims, arbitration and matters falling within the jurisdiction of the Scottish land courts. The members of the department are also experienced in dealing with personal litigation and can offer advice in connection with divorce and other family disputes and motoring offences.
Residential Conveyancing: The department assists with all aspects of buying and selling residential property and is authorised to arrange mortgages and insurance.
Private Client: In addition to traditional private client work involving the preparation of wills, acting for and as executors in winding up estates, setting up and administering trusts, this department now offers an in-house Investment Management service which has some £200,000,000 under management. Complementary income tax, tax planning and other independent financial advice is also available.

CLIENTELE: Lindsays has a wide range of clients including plcs, large and small companies, building societies, financial and educational institutions, charities, farmers and a broad spectrum of private individuals.

LINKLATERS

One Silk Street, London, EC2Y 8HQ
Tel: (020) 7456 2000 **Fax:** (020) 7456 2222 **DX:** 10 London City EC3
Website: www.linklaters.com

Senior Partner	Anthony Cann
Managing Partner	Tony Angel
Worldwide figures	
Number of partners	425
Assistant solicitors	1800

CONTACTS

Asset Finance ....Ronald Gibbs
Banking ....John Tucker
Capital Markets ....Michael Canby
Construction & Engineering ..Marshall Levine
Corporate & M&A ....David Cheyne
Corporate Tax ....Guy Brannan
Employment, Pensions & Incentives
............Janet Cooper
............Ruth Goldman
............Raymond Jeffers
Environment (inc. Planning) ......Ray Jackson
EU & Competition ....Bill Allan
Financial Markets ....Paul Nelson
Intellectual Property ....Jeremy Brown
Investment Management ....Tim Shipton
IT & Communications ....Ian Karet
Litigation & Arbitration ......Christopher Style
Projects ....Alan Black
Real Estate ....Simon Clark
Restructuring & Insolvency ......Robert Elliott
Structured Finance ....Julian Davies
Trusts ....Nigel Reid

THE FIRM: Linklaters is one of the leading global law firms, with first-class corporate, finance and specialist teams operating throughout the world. The firm's lawyers work closely with leading corporates, investment banks and other major institutions offering the highest quality advice and innovative use of technology to meet its clients' needs.

PRINCIPAL AREAS OF WORK:
Asset Finance: All principal financing techniques in the global asset finance industry, the financing of specific assets and the acquisition, disposal and financing of asset portfolios.
Banking: Bank lending, telecom acquisition, trade, project and property finance, PFI and tax structured finance.
Capital Markets: International capital markets and securities issues, debt and equity, structured and derivative products, project bonds and securitisations.
Construction & Engineering: Domestic construction and engineering projects, major international projects, PFI/PPP work, construction finance, insolvencies, insurance contracts and claims analysis and negotiation.
Corporate & M&A: Finance and commercial transactions including share offerings, M&A, restructurings and privatisations.
Corporate Tax: Corporate tax advice including large international transactions, litigation and international tax planning.
Employment, Pensions & Incentives: A comprehensive service covering disputes, remuneration, benefits and pensions.
Environment (inc. Planning): Environmental risks and liabilities; prepares, litigates and defends cases on risk assessment and crisis management; regulatory issues; development and planning law, policy and practice.
EU & Competition Law: EU and competition/antitrust issues: merger control, dominance and dealings with national, EU regulatory and WTO authorities.
Financial Markets: Advises investment and commercial banks, securities houses and their affiliates.
Intellectual Property: Exploitation and protection of patents, trade marks and other intellectual property rights.
Investment Management: Structuring and organising offshore open and closed-ended investment companies, unit trusts, UCITS, limited partnerships, fonds communs de placement and other vehicles.
IT & Communications: Commercial and regulatory advice on e-commerce, telecoms and other forms of media.
Litigation & Arbitration: Litigation and arbitration expertise, as well as ADR.
Projects: Power, infrastructure, oil and gas, petrochemical, telecommunications, water and PFI projects.
Real Estate: Investment and funds; retail, leisure and headquarters projects; construction and engineering matters; tax and financing; planning and environmental issues; rent review and real estate-related litigation.
Restructuring & Insolvency: Corporate recovery and workouts, including cross-border restructuring and insolvency.
Structured Finance: Domestic and international expertise in securitisations, project bonds, high-yield debt and structured finance.
Trusts: Trusts and estate planning are handled, both domestic and offshore.

INTERNATIONAL: Work is handled in all commercial languages and local languages of countries in which Linklaters has offices.

RECRUITMENT: In order to maintain Linklaters' premier position the firm actively recruits the highest calibre candidates. Undergraduates interested in making an application can visit the firm's website at www.linklaters.com or contact the firm at graduate.recruitment@linklaters.com.

LINNELLS

Greyfriars Court, Paradise Square, Oxford, OX1 1BB
Tel: (01865) 248607 **Fax:** (01865) 728445 **DX:** 723000 Oxford 5
Email: law@linnells.co.uk **Website:** www.linnells.co.uk

Senior Partner	Jonathan Lloyd-Jones
Number of partners	17
Assistant solicitors	13
Other fee-earners	27

AREAS OF PRACTICE

Residential Property/Development	25%
Commercial Property	16%
Corporate/Commercial	24%
Commercial Dispute Resolution	18%
Private Client	17%

CONTACTS

Asset Finance	Richard Humphreys
Charities	Joss Saunders
Clinical Negligence	Jeremy Irwin-Singer
Commercial Litigation	Jonathan Lloyd-Jones
Commercial Property	John Deech
Construction	Richard Wade
Corporate Finance	Edward Lee
Corporate/Commercial	Edward Lee
Employment	James Whiter
Family	Christine Plews
Intellectual Property	Joss Saunders
Licensing	Carol Oster
Partnerships	Andrew Miscampbell
Publishing	Joss Saunders
Residential Property/Development	Anne Cowell

Linnells
SOLICITORS

THE FIRM: Linnells is one of the South East's leading property and commercial firms. It has a national reputation for its work in the specialist sectors of charities, publishing, construction and asset finance litigation. The firm also has a strong private client practice. A successful refocus for growth in 2000 has brought rapid growth with new personnel at every level contributing to the breadth of services for the corporate client. Linnells has strong associations with the Oxford academic community, and is involved with many of the pioneering university spin-out ventures, assisting young entrepreneurs as well as serving established retail and technology businesses in the area. Intellectual property and IT, two major growth sectors in legal practice, are where the firm's media and technology team is at the forefront of developments with clients involved in e-commerce, mobile telephony, media and data management. More generally, the firm is attracting larger corporations and higher value transactions, many involving cross-border negotiations, as its reputation for high quality, professional, accessible advice becomes more widely recognised.

PRINCIPAL AREAS OF WORK:

Commercial Property: The firm handles a high volume of property transactions ranging from large commercial residential developments to portfolio management for a number of large retail chains. This involves the acquisition, letting and development of major retail sites.

Corporate/Commercial: The quality of Linnells' corporate work has increased steadily with the firm now receiving regular instructions on multi-million pound deals. A new partner appointment has expanded expertise in plc, risk management, competition and EU law. The firm is actively forging links with European and North American firms to assist its larger corporate clients engaged in international commerce.

Commercial Dispute Resolution: The dispute resolution team continues to grow and to attract work from across southern England. In addition to the firm's strengths in claimant professional negligence disputes and (increasingly) IT-related disputes, there are specialist teams for construction, asset and credit finance, and intellectual property. Alternative dispute resolution, in its widest sense, remains core to the ethos of the department.

Private Client: Tailoring services to high net worth individuals enables the firm to provide a high level, competitive service, with work feeding from its corporate practice and vice versa. The firm has specialists in high value ancillary relief, probate, tax and trust planning, as well as personal injury and clinical negligence.

LINSKILLS SOLICITORS

6-8 Castle Street, Liverpool, L2 0NA **Tel:** (0151) 236 2224 **Fax:** (0151) 236 0151 **DX:** 14215 **Ptnrs:** 1 **Asst solrs:** 8 **Other fee-earners:** 20 **Contact:** J S Linskill • Legal Aid franchise in crime, family, welfare, police actions and personal injury. Branch office (welfare advice & civil litigation) 195 Kensington, Liverpool L7 2RF Tel: (0151) 260 1001 Fax: (0151) 261 1936. Legal Aid Franchise in welfare, family and housing.

AREAS OF PRACTICE

Criminal	58%
Road Traffic Accident	17%
Welfare	8%
Conveyancing	7%
Matrimonial	6%
Civil Litigation	4%

LIVINGSTONE BROWNE

84 Carlton Place, Glasgow, G5 9TD **Tel:** (0141) 429 8166 **Fax:** (0141) 420 1337 **DX:** LPI Glasgow - 2 **Email:** ea@livbrown.co.uk **Website:** www.livbrown.co.uk **Ptnrs:** 6 **Asst solrs:** 5 **Other fee-earners:** 2

LOCHNERS TECHNOLOGY SOLICITORS

Craven House, Station Road, Godalming, GU7 1EX **Tel:** (01483) 414588 **Fax:** (01483) 416065 **DX:** 58370 Godalming 2 **Email:** lochners@lochners.co.uk **Website:** www.lochners.co.uk **Ptnrs:** 3 **Asst solrs:** 2 **Other fee-earners:** 1 **Contact:** Ludi Lochner • Specialists in technology-related law and associated areas of the law including patents, trade marks, copyright, design, confidential information and information technology.

AREAS OF PRACTICE

Intellectual Property	75%
Information Technology	25%

LODDERS

7 Warwick Road, Stratford-upon-Avon, CV37 6YL **Tel:** (01789) 293259 **Fax:** (01789) 268093 **Email:** lawyers@lodders.co.uk **Website:** www.lodders.co.uk

LOOSEMORES

Alliance House, 18-19 High St, Cardiff, CF10 1BP **Tel:** (029) 2022 4433 **Fax:** (029) 2080 3100 **DX:** 33008 CARDIFF 1 **Email:** post@loosemores.co.uk **Website:** www.loosemores.co.uk **Ptnrs:** 8 **Asst solrs:** 7 **Other fee-earners:** 14

LORENZO ZURBRUGG

15-17 Jockey's Fields, London, WC1R 4BW
Tel: (020) 7404 5641 **Fax:** (020) 7831 8460 **DX:** 0061 London/Chancery Lane
Email: info@lorenzo-zurbrugg.co.uk **Website:** www.lorenzo-zurbrugg.co.uk

Managing & Senior Partner	Michael Zurbrugg
Number of partners	2
Assistant solicitors	4
Other fee-earners	4

THE FIRM: Lorenzo Zurbrugg specialises in insurance and personal injury litigation, both on behalf of insurers and private clients within the UK and other European countries. The firm also specialises in serious injury work particularly head injury. Clients include a number of Lloyd's syndicates and insurance companies, both UK and foreign, including legal expense insurers.

INTERNATIONAL: Several languages are spoken fluently and the firm has established connections in most European countries with particular emphasis on France, Spain, Portugal, Belgium, Switzerland and Germany. The firm includes a Spanish partner whose main area of work consists of personal injury claims in Spain and giving evidence before English courts in relation to Spanish law. In addition, he deals with general litigation, property transactions, child abduction and custody cases.

L

LOVELLS

65 Holborn Viaduct, London, EC1A 2DY
Tel: (020) 7296 2000 **Fax:** (020) 7296 2001 **DX:** Box 57
Email: information@lovells.com **Website:** www.lovells.com

Managing Partner	Lesley MacDonagh
Senior Partner	Andrew Walker
Number of partners	139
Assistant solicitors	359
Other fee-earners	245

CONTACTS

Advertising/Consumer Law	Andrew Skipper
Arbitration/ADR	Andrew Foyle
	Patrick Sherrington
Asset Finance	Robin Hallam
Banking	Matthew Cottis
	Andrew Gamble
Broadcasting	Michael Golding
	Jennifer McDermott
Business Restructuring	Robin Spencer
Capital Markets	David Hudd
Commodities	David Moss
Computers/IT	Quentin Archer
Construction/Engineering	Phillip Capper
	Nicholas Gould
Corporate Finance/M&A	Hugh Nineham
Defamation	Jennifer McDermott
Employee Benefits	Louise Whitewright
Employment	David Harper
	Andrew Williamson
Energy	David Moss
	Michael Stanger
Environmental	Louise Moore
EU/Competition	Simon Polito
Financial Services	Richard Stones
Fraud/Asset Recovery	Keith Gaines
Insurance/Reinsurance	John Young
	John Powell
Intellectual Property	Robert Anderson
Litigation	Russell Sleigh
Media Law	Jennifer McDermott
Pensions	Jane Samsworth
Planning	Michael Gallimore
Private Equity	Marco Compagnoni
Product Liability	John Meltzer
Professional Indemnity	John Trotter
Project Finance	Gavin McQuater
Property	Robert Kidby
Property Litigation	Nicholas Cheffings
Public Policy	Neil Fagan
Shipping/International Trade	David Moss
Tax	Daniel Friel
Telecommunications	Heather Rowe
VAT	Greg Sinfield

THE FIRM: Lovells is one of the leading international law firms, with more than 1,300 lawyers across 26 offices in 19 countries. Lovells combines the expertise of two leading practices – Lovell White Durrant and Boesebeck Droste. In May 2001 Lovells merged with the highly regarded Dutch firm Ekelmans Den Hollander. Building upon strong and broadly based domestic practices, Lovells provides co-ordinated, multijurisdictional services from their offices around the world.

Lovells places great emphasis on helping clients to achieve their business objectives by providing legal advice that is both imaginative and commercially aware. It is also known for nurturing its working relationships with clients both large and small and consistently achieves very high ratings for client satisfaction in independent research. The size and international strengths of the firm enable it to put together expert teams of lawyers with direct experience of advising on some of the largest and most complex transactions and cases of recent years, both in the UK and elsewhere in the world.Lovells' services are tailored to the needs of individual clients, drawing on the collective knowledge of the firm. Size, experience and international strengths enable the firm to assemble expert teams of lawyers to advise on transactions or issues that concern its clients. Lovells aims to add value at all stages of a project, from its initiation, through its planning to its execution.

Lawyers at Lovells are members of broad practice areas which work together closely. These practice areas operate internationally and are structured to facilitate the sharing of technical know-how and the development of a consistently high standard of legal advice across the firm.

INTERNATIONAL: The practice of each of the firm's international offices reflects the requirements of clients and the nature of local and regional markets. London is the largest office and offers the full range of the firm's specialist services. The firm's German practice mirrors the decentralised structure of Germany in the heart of the 'Euro-zone', with offices in Frankfurt, Dusseldorf, Hamburg, Munich and Berlin from which it provides legal services in all business matters whether domestic or international.

Elsewhere in Continental Europe, the Amsterdam, Brussels, Budapest, Milan, Moscow, Paris, Prague, Rome, Warsaw, Vienna and Zagreb offices offer a combination of local and cross-border legal services covering the areas of banking, corporate finance, private equity, project finance, capital markets, tax, IP, competition and trade regulation, financial services and property. The firm's office in Alicante specialises in trademark matters with the European Trademark Office.

The Asia practice of Lovells is managed from the Hong Kong office and focuses on regional banking, project finance, capital markets, corporate transactions, insolvency, construction, IP, litigation and property.

The North America offices in New York, Chicago and Washington DC concentrate particularly on UK and EU advice on corporate transactions, US securities law advice, insurance and reinsurance litigation, insurance insolvency, consumer financial services including regulatory advice and product liability.

RECRUITMENT: Prospective trainee solicitors should contact Clare Walton for details of the recruitment programme. Further information is available from any Lovells office or via the firm's website. A comprehensive selection of brochures, client notes and newsletters is available from Jan Frangs in the London office.

LOYENS & LOEFF

26 Throgmorton Street, London, EC2N 2AN
Tel: (020) 7826 3070 **Fax:** (020) 7826 3080
Email: marc.klerks@loyensloeff.com **Website:** www.loyensloeff.com

Number of partners	2
Assistant solicitors	8
Other fee-earners	1

LOYENS & LOEFF

THE FIRM: Loyens & Loeff is an independent law firm, which sets new standards in the field of tax and civil law services. The combination of tax, corporate and notarial law as equal components makes Loyens & Loeff unique in comparison to other domestic and international providers of legal services. Loyens & Loeff's multidisciplinary co-operation enables them to offer their specialisations as part of an integrated service. Characteristics of this dynamic firm are creativity and efficient service at the highest professional and legal standards.

PRINCIPAL AREAS OF WORK: The firm advises on capital markets, banking and securities, commercial law and litigation, corporate law, M&A, joint ventures, economic regulatory law, structured finance, project finance, treaty laws, corporate taxation, international, and energy.

INTERNATIONAL: Other offices in Amsterdam, Arnhem, Eindhoven, Rotterdam, The Hague, Brussels (Loyens & Volkmaars), Curaçao, Frankfurt, Geneva, Luxembourg, New York, Paris, Singapore and Tokyo. Languages spoken include English, French, German, Dutch.

LUCAS & WYLLYS

5 South Quay, Great Yarmouth, NR30 2QJ **Tel:** (01493) 855555 **Fax:** (01493) 330055 **DX:** 41100 **Ptnrs:** 7 **Asst solrs:** 2 **Other fee-earners:** 9

LUPTON FAWCETT

Yorkshire Hse, Greek St, Leeds, LS1 5SX **Tel:** (0113) 280 2000 **Fax:** (0113) 245 6782 **DX:** 12035 Leeds **Website:** www.lupton-fawcett.co.uk **Ptnrs:** 23 **Asst solrs:** 32 **Other fee-earners:** 37

LUQMANI THOMPSON

77-79 High Road, Wood Green, London, N22 6BB **Tel:** (020) 8365 7800 **Fax:** (020) 8826 0169 **DX:** 34715 WOOD GREEN 2 **Email:** luqthom@btinternet.com **Website:** www.luqmanithompson.com **Ptnrs:** 2 **Asst solrs:** 2 **Other fee-earners:** 1

LYONS DAVIDSON

Victoria House, 51 Victoria Street, Bristol, BS1 6AD
Tel: (0117) 904 6000 **Fax:** (0117) 904 6006 **DX:** 7834
Email: info@lyonsdavidson.co.uk **Website:** www.lyonsdavidson.co.uk

Senior Partner	Richard Squire
Number of partners	20
Assistant solicitors	42
Other fee-earners	96

THE FIRM: A group of exceptionally bright individuals working together as a team in partnership with their clients. The firm's specialist lawyers provide accurate information, guidance and advice in clear and understandable terms. Twenty eight years of representing clients from individuals to large corporate entities has seen Lyons Davidson develop into one of the largest practices in the region. Whilst growing with, and utilising, the latest technology, the firm prides itself on providing practical advice to clients that answers their needs through a traditional level of personal care and the experience of specialists.

MACDONALDS

1 Claremont Terrace, Glasgow, G3 7UQ **Tel:** (0141) 248 6221 **Fax:** (0141) 333 0318 **DX:** 142 Glasgow **Email:** enquiries@macdonalds-uk.com **Website:** www.macdonalds-uk.com **Ptnrs:** 11 **Asst solrs:** 8 **Other fee-earners:** 5

MACE & JONES

Drury House, 19 Water Street, Liverpool, L2 0RP
Tel: (0151) 236 8989 **Fax:** (0151) 227 5010 **DX:** 14166 Liverpool
Email: law@maceandjones.co.uk **Website:** www.maceandjones.co.ukl

14 Oxford Court, Bishopsgate, Manchester, M2 3WQ
Tel: (0161) 236 2244 **Fax:** (0161) 228 7285 **DX:** 18564 Manchester 7
Email: law@maceandjones.co.uk

30 Sherborne Square, Huyton, L36 9UR
Tel: (0151) 480 7000 **Fax:** (0151) 449 1953 **DX:** 15453 Huyton
Email: law@maceandjones.co.uk

98 King Street, Knutsford, WA16 6EP
Tel: (01565) 634234 **Fax:** (01565) 652711 **DX:** 22959 Knutsford
Email: law@maceandjones.co.uk

Managing Partner	Lawrence Downey
Senior Partner	Graeme Jump
Number of partners	27
Assistant solicitors	42
Other fee-earners	22

AREAS OF PRACTICE

Commercial Litigation/Insolvency 20%
Commercial Property 20%
Company/Commercial 20%
Employment 20%
PI/Private Client/Family 20%

CONTACTS

Commercial Litigation ....Craig Blakemore
Commercial Property ....Tim Williams
Company/Commercial ....Alan Thompson
Employment ....Martin Edwards
Insolvency ....Graeme Jump
Personal Injury ....Stewart McCulloch

M

THE FIRM: A leading regional practice in the North West, Mace & Jones remains a full service firm, while enjoying a national reputation for its commercial expertise, especially in employment, litigation/insolvency, corporate and property, with the firm being voted Property Law Firm of the Year 2000 by *Insider North West* magazine.The firm's clients range from national and multinational companies and public sector bodies to owner-managed businesses and private individuals, reflecting the broad nature of the work undertaken. Sound practical advice is given always on a value-for-money basis. Today, nearly 100 lawyers deliver a service which is founded on an intimate understanding of the needs and objectives of their clients. Low staff turnover leads to a continuity of service which is rarely found in firms of this size. This in turn ensures an understanding of the client, whether in the business or private sector, which enables problems to be anticipated and a pro-active approach adopted.

MACFARLANES

10 Norwich Street, London, EC4A 1BD
Tel: (020) 7831 9222 **Fax:** (020) 7831 9607 **DX:** 138
Email: cpp@macfarlanes.com **Website:** www.macfarlanes.com

Number of partners	56
Assistant solicitors	116
Other fee-earners	61

AREAS OF PRACTICE

Company/Commercial/Banking 55%
Property 20%
Private Client 14%
Litigation 11%

CONTACTS

Advertising & Marketing ....Jeremy Courtenay-Stamp
Banking & Debt Finance ....Julian Howard
Buy-outs/Private Equity ....Charles Meek
Construction ....Tony Blackler
Corporate Tax ....Nigel Doran
Employment ....Tony Thompson
Pensions ....Hugh Arthur
Benefits ....Douglas Shugar
EU/Competition ....Jane Whittaker
Financial Services & Investment Funds ....Bridget Barker
Intellectual Property Jeremy Courtenay-Stamp
Litigation & Dispute Resolution ....Willie Manners
M&A/Corporate ....Robert Sutton
PFI ....John Skelton
Tax & Financial Planning ....John Rhodes

THE FIRM: Macfarlanes is an unconventional City law firm, offering a remarkable concentration of excellence. Its distinctive market position as a leading law firm is built on a reputation for the quality of its client service. Macfarlanes is widely recognised as one of a handful of high quality, unaligned law firms in the UK. The firm's focus on the practice of English law comes together with substantial experience of working on international transactions with equivalent law firms in other jurisdictions.

PRINCIPAL AREAS OF WORK:

Corporate: Macfarlanes is regarded particularly highly for its work in the areas of corporate finance and mergers and acquisitions, including private equity and takeovers. Together this represents over half the firm's work. The firm's related specialist areas such as intellectual property, corporate tax, banking and employee benefits mean that it can provide its broad range of commercial clients with high quality legal services both in relation to corporate transactional work and at the clients' operational level. The firm has a particularly strong reputation for advertising and marketing work as well as investment funds and financial services.

Property: By City standards, Macfarlanes' property practice is substantial in size. The quality of the advice it provides is widely recognised. Property work accounts for over 20% of the firm's business – unusual for a successful City firm. Work for the property sector covers all transactions involving the ownership, development, investment in, and financing of land. Commercial property investment and development transactions are at the core of the firm's property practice.

Litigation & Dispute Resolution: The wide range of business litigation and dispute resolution work includes: leading employment law cases; acting for insured and insurer, especially in advertising and surveying cases; IP cases and disputes over computer hardware and software; financial services regulatory issues and queries; Lloyd's related work; sovereign debt; securities and other banking disputes; judicial review; breach of contract and professional negligence claims; major shipping and construction arbitration and jurisdictional disputes and EU jurisdiction questions.

Private Client: Macfarlanes' pre-eminent private client service commands a leading position. Combined with its strong corporate and property capability, the firm is in a particularly good position to advise the private client entrepreneur. The firm has a longstanding reputation for advising private clients and their family trusts, both domestically and internationally. Tax planning, including the creation and administration of trusts, the preparation of wills and the administration of estates, is central to this work. The international element of its work is of special importance both for UK based families and for overseas taxpayers seeking advice on tax and trust law. The firm is frequently instructed at the request of many of the largest US firms and private banks for this work.

MACKAY SIMON

Mackay Simon have now merged with Maclay Murray & Spens. For further details, see entry for Maclay Murray & Spens.

MACKINNONS

21 Albert Street, Aberdeen, AB25 1XX
Tel: (01224) 632464 **Fax:** (01224) 632184 **DX:** AB 34
Email: admin@mackinnons.com **Website:** www.mackinnons.com

379 North Deeside Road, Cults, Aberdeen, AB15 9SX
Tel: (01244) 868687 **Fax:** (01224) 861012 **DX:** AB34
Email: admin@mackinnons.com

Managing Partner	Charles M Scott
Senior Partner	Denis N Yule
Number of partners	6
Assistant solicitors	4
Other fee-earners	5

CONTACTS

Commercial .... Charles M Scott
.... Graham E Jones
Marine & Litigation .... Denis N Yule
.... Keith G MacRae
.... Bruce Craig
Private Client & Property .. Mrs Patricia J Gray

THE FIRM: Progressive six-partner practice specialising in shipping and commercial law with substantial private client department providing a full range of legal services. The firm is very experienced in all aspects of marine and admiralty law including marine insurance, collisions, salvage, litigation and personal injury as well as acting in the defence of prosecutions under the full range of merchant shipping, pollution and fisheries legislation. The firm acts for numerous P&I clubs and fishing mutuals providing a hands-on service aboard ships, fishing boats and oil rigs. Mackinnons has a substantial marine and commercial practice dealing with purchase, sale, finance and chartering of fishing boats, offshore oil supply and stand-by vessels, and other vessels.

M

MACKINTOSH DUNCAN

103 Borough High Street, London, SE1 1NN **Tel:** (020) 7357 6464 **Fax:** (020) 7357 8448 **DX:** 39921 London Bridge South
Email: admin@mackdunc.co.uk **Ptnrs:** 2 **Asst solrs:** 1

MACLAY MURRAY & SPENS

151 St. Vincent Street, Glasgow, G2 5NJ
Tel: (0141) 248 5011 **Fax:** (0141) 248 5819 **DX:** GW 67
Email: lawyer@maclaymurrayspens.co.uk **Website:** www.maclaymurrayspens.co.uk

3 Glenfinlas Street, Edinburgh, EH3 6AQ
Tel: (0131) 226 5196 **Fax:** (0131) 226 3174 **DX:** ED137

10 Foster Lane, London, EC2V 6HR
Tel: (020) 7606 6130 **Fax:** (020) 7600 0992 **DX:** 42616

Managing Partner	Michael Walker
Senior Partner	Bruce Patrick
Number of partners	57
Assistant solicitors	131
Other fee-earners	50

AREAS OF PRACTICE

Company/Commercial	40%
Commercial Property	28%
Litigation	17%
Private Client	15%

CONTACTS

Banking & Finance .... Susan Kelly
Capital Projects .... Alastair McEwan
Commercial Litigation & Advocacy
.... Alayne Swanson
Construction & Engineering .. Mark Macaulay
Corporate Tax .... Martyn Jones
.... Gwen Souter
Employment .... Malcolm Mackay
European & Competition .... Michael Dean
Financial Markets .... Michael Livingston
IP & Technology .... Fiona Nicolson
Pensions & Employee Benefits
.... Maureen Burnside
Planning & Environmental .... Chris Smylie
Private Equity .... Kenneth Shand
Property .... Robin Garrett
Social Housing .... Chris Smith
Tax & Private Capital .... Andrew Biggart

THE FIRM: Maclay Murray & Spens is a forward looking, practical, commercial legal firm which has a stated objective of providing its clients with the best possible service across the broad range of legal advice provided by the firm. As one of the largest firms to have originally developed from a Scottish base, Maclay Murray & Spens is well placed to offer clients throughout the UK and beyond commercial advice at competitive prices. The firm has a significant English, European and international client base, which can be serviced from any or all of the firm's four offices in Edinburgh, Glasgow, London and Brussels. These are linked by an integrated computer, video-conferencing and telephone network ensuring a fast, efficient service and expert advice are delivered. The London office, which offers a full English law service, provides an ideal platform both for Scottish clients doing business in the City and for London-based clients looking for a premier law firm without City overheads. The development and growth of the Brussels office reflects the firm's commitment to meet client needs.

PRINCIPAL AREAS OF WORK: In the last year the firm's commitment to improving its service has resulted in an internal restructuring to create 11 departments. These are banking and finance, capital projects, commercial litigation and advocacy, construction and engineering, employment, pensions and benefits, European and competition, financial markets, IP and technology, private equity, property (including English property), social housing and tax and private capital. This approach has already paid off in spectacular fashion with the announcement in March of this year that the firm was to merge with specialist employment lawyers Mackay Simon, ensuring that the firm now has one of the best respected employment practices in the marketplace. The firm recognises that many transactions require hand-picked teams made up of lawyers with differing skills from differing departments if the specific needs of the client and the transaction are to be fully met. To this end, the firm ensures that all departments and units are closely linked to give the client the best possible service.

INTERNATIONAL: The firm has an overseas office in Brussels, and handles work in French, German, Italian, and Norwegian.

Continued overleaf

RECRUITMENT: The firm is also committed to recruiting high-quality assistant solicitors in all areas of work and takes on approximately 20 trainees every year. The growth of activity in the firm's London and Brussels offices and the firm's commitment to a policy of regular exchanges of lawyers with firms in other jurisdictions (both in Europe and further afield) ensure that those recruited receive the widest possible training. Maclay Murray & Spens is committed to investing in its people and their development, and continuing to improve its efficiency, quality and service.

MACLEOD & MACCALLUM

P.O. Box No.4, 28 Queensgate, Inverness, IV1 1YN **Tel:** (01463) 239393 **Fax:** (01463) 222879 **DX:** LP 17 Inverness 1
Email: mail@macardmac.co.uk **Website:** www.macardmac.co.uk **Ptnrs:** 10 **Asst solrs:** 4 **Other fee-earners:** 11

MACROBERTS

M

152 Bath Street, Glasgow, G2 4TB
Tel: (0141) 332 9988 **Fax:** (0141) 332 8886 **DX:** GW70
Email: maildesk@macroberts.co.uk **Website:** www.macroberts.co.uk

Excel House, 30 Semple Street, Edinburgh, EH3 8BL
Tel: (0131) 229 5046 **Fax:** (0131) 229 0849 **DX:** ED 207
Email: maildesk@macroberts.co.uk

Managing Partner	John Macmillan
Senior Partner	Raymond Williamson
Number of partners	30
Assistant solicitors	81
Other fee-earners	12

CONTACTS

Banking	Norman Martin
Charities	David MacRobert
Commercial Property	Laurence Fraser
	Allan MacKenzie
Construction	Lindy Patterson
Corporate	Ian Dickson
	Norman Martin
Corporate Tax & VAT	Isobel d'Inverno
Debt Recovery & General Litigation	Craig Turnbull
Employment	John Macmillan
Energy Law	Ian Dickson
Environmental & Planning	Jamie Grant
EU & Competition	David Flint
Intellectual Property/IT	David Flint
Litigation & Arbitration	Richard Barrier
	Lindy Patterson
Pensions & Employee Benefits	Pete Troffer
PFI & Capital Projects	Michael Murphy
	David Henderson
Private Client	David MacRobert

THE FIRM: MacRoberts is a leading commercial law firm offering a comprehensive range of legal services to corporate, commercial, public sector and private clients. Established almost 150 years ago, MacRoberts, through its offices in Edinburgh and Glasgow, provides quality legal services in a prompt, efficient and friendly manner. The firm is committed to delivering the highest standards of professional advice and expertise.

PRINCIPAL AREAS OF WORK:

Corporate: All aspects of corporate and commercial law including incorporations, reorganisations, take-overs and mergers, management buy-outs and joint ventures (UK and international); loan debenture and equity finance, syndications, consumer credit; banking flotations, Stock Exchange requirements, new issues, placings and other issues, employee share schemes and pension schemes; receivership, administration, liquidation and bankruptcy; partnership agreements; EU law; commercial contracts, including agency distribution and finance agreements; entertainment law; privatisations.
Commercial Property: Corporate clients are advised on all aspects of property matters including acquisition, sale and leasing of commercial and industrial property; commercial, industrial and housing development, investment and finance; commercial secured loans; environmental law; agricultural law, including forestry; company relocation schemes; timeshare and leisure developments; planning law; licensing and gaming law.
Construction: Advice in connection with drafting of construction contracts, professional appointments, collateral warranties; and building and engineering disputes and arbitration.
Corporate Tax & VAT: Including tax and VAT aspects of corporate acquisitions, disposals and reorganisations, commercial property transactions and PFI/PPP projects.
Employment: Employment and service contracts, disciplinary and grievance procedures, other procedural rules, employment policies including health & safety, sex and race discrimination, equal pay and trade union disputes are all covered.
Intellectual Property & IT: Work includes franchising, patents and patent licensing, copyright, trademarks and know-how agreements, data protection and computer contracts.
Litigation & Arbitration: The group acts for and advises on all aspects of civil litigation in both Sheriff Courts and the Court of Session; building and engineering disputes and arbitration; insurance and other commercial litigation; rating and valuation; planning; professional negligence; liquidation, administration, receivership and bankruptcy; product liability; debt recovery; reparation claims; intellectual property disputes; licensing.
PFI/PPP & Capital Projects: One of the largest practices in Scotland, clients include NHS Trusts, local authorities, bidding consortia and banks in a wide range of sectors including healthcare, education, roads, waste-water and office accommodation.
Private Client: Specialist advice to individuals, trustees and executors in relation to tax planning and mitigation; preparation of tax returns; investment advice; establishment and administration of trusts; wills; administration of estates; preparation of Powers of Attorney; financial services; acquisition, sale and leasing of estate and domestic property; setting up and administration of curatories.

INTERNATIONAL: Member of ADVOC, an international network of independent lawyers, providing access to legal services throughout Europe and Asia. Languages spoken include Dutch, French, German, Greek, Italian and Norwegian.

MADDEN & FINUCANE

88 Castle Street, Belfast, BT1 1HE **Tel:** (028) 9023 8007 **Fax:** (028) 9043 9276 **DX:** 434 NR Belfast **Email:** Enquiries@Madden-Finucane.com **Website:** www.Madden-Finucane.co **Contact:** Peter Madden • Leading criminal and human rights practice with substantial civil law practice and speciality in judicial review. Main firm involved in the Bloody Sunday enquiry. Branch offices in Downpatrick, Armagh and Derry.

AREAS OF PRACTICE	
Criminal	30%
Civil	30%
General Practice	25%
Administrative Law/Human Rights	15%

MADGE LLOYD & GIBSON

34 Brunswick Road, Gloucester, GL1 1JW **Tel:** (01452) 520 224 **Fax:** (01452) 306 866 **DX:** 7505 GLOUCESTER **Ptnrs:** 3 **Asst solrs:** 2

MAGRATH & CO

52-54 Maddox Street, London, W1S 1PA
Tel: (020) 7495 3003 **Fax:** (020) 7409 1745 **DX:** 9009 West End
Email: magrath@magrath.co.uk **Website:** www.magrath.co.uk

Senior Partner	Chris Magrath
Managing Partners	Rosalind Morris
	David Ashton
Number of partners	8
Assistant solicitors	19
Other fee-earners	10

AREAS OF PRACTICE	
Immigration/Employment	56%
Corporate Fraud/Crime (General)	16%
Civil Litigation	12%
Entertainment	8%
Commercial	4%
Property	4%

CONTACTS	
Civil Litigation	Nick Goldstone
Commercial	David Ashton
Corporate Fraud/Crime (General)	Gary Summers
Employment	Jessica Knight
	Chris Magrath
Entertainment	Alexis Grower
Immigration	Chris Magrath
Property	David Ashton

MAGRATH & CO
SOLICITORS

THE FIRM: Founded in 1990, Magrath & Co has niche expertise in corporate immigration/employment, fraud and entertainment law, as well as providing general commercial and litigation services. The firm's lawyers have extensive experience in their fields, and are dedicated to providing prompt, expert advice which meets and anticipates their clients' requirements.

PRINCIPAL AREAS OF WORK:

Immigration: The firm's dedicated immigration department covers the full range of immigration issues but advises primarily on commercial immigration including global expatriation planning, work permits, applications and appeals. The firm has particular experience in US-UK immigration matters and produces a regular bulletin each quarter to provide legal updates on immigration and employment law.

Employment Law: The firm's employment department deals with all aspects of employment law including contentious employment disputes, mass redundancies, consultation and industrial action, contract drafting and discrimination issues.

Corporate Fraud: The firm is experienced in a wide variety of 'white collar' crime, and can also advise in cases of investigation by agencies such as the Serious Fraud Office, DTI, Inland Revenue and Customs & Excise. Additionally the firm handles a wide range of criminal allegations of a more general nature including confiscation and forfeiture matters.

Civil Litigation: The firm is instructed by a wide range of clients on a variety of commercial and entertainment related issues. Although increasingly geared towards the corporate sector, the firm welcomes private clients on both a fee paying and legally aided basis.

Entertainment Law: Advice on music and literature publishing, recording, production and management agreements; financing, production, distribution and marketing of TV, film, theatre and commercials. Also: merchandising and sponsorship agreements; sports-related advice; and gaming and betting law.

Other Areas: All aspects of company and commercial law and commercial property.

CLIENTELE: The firm acts for a large number of major multinationals, together with other public companies, owner-managed businesses and private individuals throughout Britain, the US and Europe.

INTERNATIONAL: The practice is affiliated to New York-based Gibney Anthony & Flaherty, and to Munich-based David Hole and has links with other legal and professional services firms throughout the rest of the world's major commercial centres. Chris Magrath is also a qualified US Attorney, admitted to the New York State Bar.

MAIDMENTS

St Johns Court, 74 Gartside Street, Manchester, M3 3EL **Tel:** (0161) 834 0008 **Fax:** (0161) 832 4140 **DX:** 14307 Manchester 1 **Email:** law@amaidment.fsnet.co.uk **Website:** www.maidments.com **Ptnrs:** 7 **Asst solrs:** 14 **Other fee-earners:** 38 **Contact:** Allan Maidment • National criminal lawyers specialising in serious crime and commercial fraud. Manchester, Liverpool, Birmingham, London, Leeds, Bolton, Sale.

AREAS OF PRACTICE	
Commercial Fraud	40%
Criminal	30%
Serious Crime	30%

M

MAITLAND & CO

5th Floor, 44-48 Dover Street, London, W1S 4NX
Tel: (020) 7344 7500 **Fax:** (020) 7344 7555
Email: london@maitlandco.com **Website:** www.maitlandco.com

Senior Partner	Eric Pfaff
Number of partners	5
Assistant solicitors	6

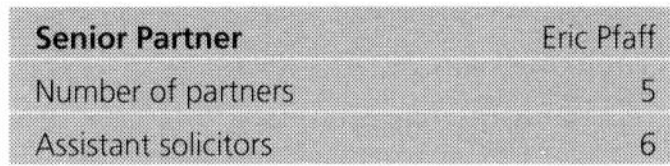

THE FIRM: Maitland & Co is the European presence of Webber Wentzel Bowens, one of Southern Africa's largest law firms.

PRINCIPAL AREAS OF WORK: Maitland & Co's main practice areas are corporate commercial; corporate and personal tax; private client; investment funds; commodities and trade.

INTERNATIONAL: The firm has other offices in Paris, Luxembourg, the Isle of Man, Geneva, Dublin, Johannesburg and Cape Town.

MAITLAND WALKER

22 The Parks, Minehead, TA24 8BT
Tel: (01643) 707777 **Fax:** (01643) 700020 **DX:** 117408 Minehead
Email: office@maitwalk.co.uk

Managing Partner	J H Maitland-Walker
Number of partners	1
Assistant solicitors	1
Other fee-earners	4

AREAS OF PRACTICE	
Competition/IP Law	40%
EC/Trade Law	20%
Commercial Litigation	20%
General Commercial	10%
Private Client	10%

M

THE FIRM: Established in 1996 by Julian Maitland-Walker, the firm has expanded rapidly to become one of the leading niche EU and competition law practices. The firm acts for a wide range of commercial clients. In addition, a consultancy service is offered as a facility to other law firms in both the UK and abroad in specialist EU and competition law matters.

PRINCIPAL AREAS OF WORK:
EU/Trade Law: Including free movement of goods, persons and freedom of establishment, national and international trade, operational logistics, anti-dumping investigations, state aids and public procurement.
Competition/IP Law: Advising EC & UK competition law, representing clients before the EU Commission and the UK Competition Authorities in anti-trust investigations. Advising on all aspects of intellectual property rights, registration, enforcement and licensing.
Commercial Litigation: All aspects of commercial and property litigation, arbitration and employment law.
General Company & Commercial: Advice on incorporations, mergers and acquisitions, joint ventures, commercial agreements and commercial property.
Private Client: Residential property, matrimonial, wills, taxation and probate.
Consultancy Services: The firm offers a unique consultancy service to other law firms both in the UK and abroad providing specialist advice on competition and trade law and other areas of EU law. Julian Maitland Walker is currently a consultant with (inter alia) the following firms: Gouldens (London), Campbell Hooper (London), Brabner Holden Banks Wilson (Liverpool), Veale Wasbrough (Bristol) and Clark Holt (Swindon).

INTERNATIONAL: Work is handled in French, German and Italian.

MALLESONS STEPHEN JAQUES

2nd Floor, Aldermary House, 15 Queen Street, London, EC4N 1TX **Tel:** (020) 7982 0982 **Fax:** (020) 7982 9820 **Email:** lon@msj.com.au **Website:** www.msj.com.au **Ptnrs:** 1 **Asst solrs:** 4 **Contact:** Tim Blue • Mergers and acquisitions, foreign investment in Australia, banking and capital markets, international and domestic securities offerings, telecommunications law, general corporate/commercial, stamp duty and taxation, energy and resources law.

AREAS OF PRACTICE	
Mergers & Acquisitions	30%
Securities Law	30%
Capital Markets	20%
Foreign Investment	10%
General Commercial Work	10%

MANBY & STEWARD

George House, St John's Square, Wolverhampton, WV2 4BZ
Tel: (01902) 578000 **Fax:** (01902) 311886 **DX:** 702431
Website: www.manbys.co.uk

Senior & Managing Partner	Clive Williams
Number of partners	14
Assistant solicitors	13
Other fee-earners	20

CONTACTS	
Agricultural	Steven Corfield
Commercial Litigation	Peter Taylor
Commercial Property	Kevin Styles
Company Commercial	Gavin Southall
Ecclesiastic	John Thorneycroft
Employment	Sue Massey
Planning	Niall Blackie

THE FIRM: Established in Wolverhampton for more than 175 years and with offices in Telford and Bridgnorth, Manby & Steward provides an extensive range of services for the business and private client. The firm has a structure of specialist groups, which are partner led. It has invested extensively in information technology (to ensure it is an efficient and competitive operation) and has achieved IIP and ISO 9002 status. Manby & Steward aims to provide practical, responsive advice in accordance with its clients' requirements.

PRINCIPAL AREAS OF WORK: All aspects of commercial property; company and commercial; commercial litigation; town and country planning; employment; agricultural; private client; family and childcare; residential conveyancing.

INTERNATIONAL: The firm is a founder member of LAWNET and a member of Eurojuris.

MANCHES

Aldwych House, 81 Aldwych, London, WC2B 4RP
Tel: (020) 7404 4433 **Fax:** (020) 7430 1133 **DX:** 76
Email: manches@manches.co.uk **Website:** www.manches.com

3 Worcester Street, Oxford, OX1 2PZ
Tel: (01865) 722106 **Fax:** 01865 201012 **DX:** 4322

Senior Partner	Alasdair Simpson
Chief Executive	Alun Lamerton
Number of partners	47
Assistant solicitors	60
Other fee-earners	26

AREAS OF PRACTICE

Corporate	25%
Commercial Property	20%
Commercial Litigation	16%
Employment	11%
Family Law	10%
Construction	10%
Intellectual Property	8%

CONTACTS

Commercial Property	Louis Manches
Commercial Tax	Stephen Goldstraw
Commercial/IT	Peter Stevens
Construction	Robert Oakes
Corporate	Melvin Pedro
Employment	Alasdair Simpson
Environment/Planning	George Gandy
	Richard Smith
Family Law	Jane Simpson
Insolvency	Vernon Dennis
Insurance	Peter Angel
Intellectual Property	John Rubinstein
Litigation	James Foster
Personal Estate Planning	Alan Poulter
Publishing	John Rubinstein
Social Housing	Paul Butterworth

THE FIRM: Manches continues to provide a broad spectrum of services to its clients. However, the strategy for 2001 and beyond will see greater concentration and focus on its four core commercial sectors of technology, property, construction and retail. This strategy, which largely reflects the existing business mix, is geared to establish it firmly as a market leader in these sectors, whilst retaining that standing in family law. Manches commits itself to innovative problem solving. It offers a level of service and support which reflects the immediacy of its commercial clients' requirements.

PRINCIPAL AREAS OF WORK:
Corporate & Technology: The firm handles mergers and acquisitions, venture capital, corporate reorganisations, AIM flotations, IPOs, joint ventures and partnerships, Enterprise Investment Schemes, Private Finance Initiatives, competition law and franchising.
Property: All aspects of commercial property are handled, including investment and development work for institutions and property companies; retail property; secured lending and joint ventures; social housing.
Construction: A wide range of domestic and international instructions, including contentious and non-contentious work in Europe, the Far East, India and Africa. Work is handled in the areas of litigation; arbitration; adjudication; mediation; PFI and PPP project work; contract drafting and negotiation; advisory work.
Litigation: Commercial dispute resolution with particular expertise in construction, property, banking, insolvency, insurance, product liability, breach of contract and intellectual property.
Intellectual Property: IT; computer law; biotechnology; advertising; sales promotions; marketing and trade description law is handled, including copyrights; film; television and entertainment products and services; multimedia exploitation; passing off; publishing; defamation; UK and EU competition.
Family: Work includes divorce, children, financial provision, separation agreements, adoption, guardianship, affiliation proceedings and jurisdiction crossing.
Employment: The firm deals with executive renumeration and benefits; service agreements; share options and other executive incentive schemes; termination packages; staff manuals; discrimination policies; unfair and wrongful dismissal claims in the Employment Tribunal, County and High Court.
Tax: Areas covered include mergers and acquisitions; joint ventures; flotation planning; profit extraction; leasing; management buy-outs; employee benefits; property tax; VAT planning; stamp duty planning; partnership tax; off-shore trading agreements; insurance and tax; company pension schemes; tax appeals.
Personal Estate Planning: The firm covers estate planning, preparation of wills, establishment of trusts, and the administration of estates and charities.

RECRUITMENT: There are currently 20 trainee solicitors. The firm's Director of Education and Training has responsibility for directing and monitoring each individual's training. Application forms can be obtained by telephoning the recruitment line (020) 7872 8690 or by e-mailing sheona.clark@manches.co.uk.

M AND A SOLICITORS

Kenneth Pollard House, 5-19 Cowbridge Road East, Cardiff, CF11 9AB
Tel: (029) 2066 5793 **Fax:** (029) 2066 5798
Email: enquiries@manda.uk.com **Website:** www.mandasolicitors.co.uk

Managing Partner	Stephen Berry
Senior Partner	Alan Whiteley
Number of partners	4
Assistant solicitors	2
Other fee-earners	1

AREAS OF PRACTICE

Corporate	70%
Commercial	15%
Commercial Property	15%

CONTACTS

Corporate/Commercial	Stephen Berry
Commercial Property	Robert Twigg

THE FIRM: M and A Solicitors is a specialist corporate and commercial practice, established in 1999 to provide a high quality, partner-led service. The emphasis is on understanding a client's business in order to provide practical commercial advice. The firm's association with Gambit Corporate Finance allows it to offer an integrated approach where required, which can add real value to a transaction.

PRINCIPAL AREAS OF WORK: The firm handles all aspects of corporate finance, general commercial work, joint ventures and commercial property, with particular expertise in the IT and technology sectors.

INTERNATIONAL: Welsh is spoken.

MAPLES AND CALDER EUROPE

7 Princes Street, London, EC2R 8AQ
Tel: (020) 7466 1600 **Fax:** (020) 7466 1700
Email: ukinfo@maplesandcalder.com **Website:** www.maplesandcalder.com

Senior Partner	Anthony Travers
Number of partners	1
Associates	9
Other fee-earners	1
Number of partners (other offices)	19
Number of associates (other offices)	42

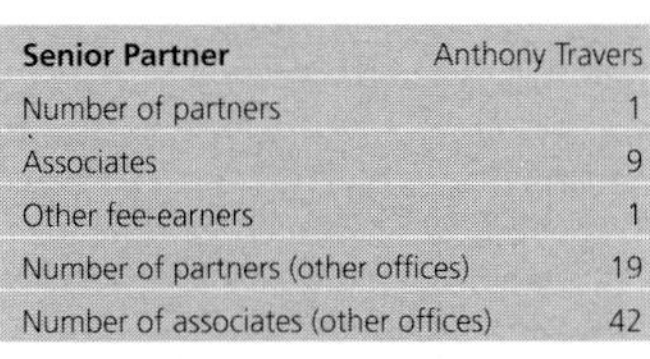

MAPLES and CALDER Europe
Cayman Islands Attorneys-at-Law

THE FIRM: Maples and Calder Europe is a full execution office opened in 1997 as an affiliated office of Maples and Calder, the largest law firm in the Cayman Islands, to provide greater proximity to the firm's client base and enable the firm to provide time zone sensitive advice. Maples and Calder now has over 275 lawyers and staff worldwide. Advice is given to leading international and domestic law firms, major financial institutions and high net worth clients in relation to Cayman Islands law. The firm also offers a highly specialised management service to structured finance transactions through its controlling interest in QSPV Limited and QSPV (Jersey) Limited, licensed trust company administrators of Cayman Islands structured debt special purpose vehicles.

PRINCIPAL AREAS OF WORK: Specialisations include banking, capital markets, structured debt, securitisation, asset financing, captive insurance, international equity offerings and listings, mutual and hedge funds, venture capital, commercial and private trusts and commercial and trust litigation.

INTERNATIONAL: Maples and Calder in the Cayman Islands is based in George Town, Grand Cayman, and Maples and Calder Asia is based in Hong Kong.

M

MAPLES TEESDALE

21 Lincoln's Inn Fields, London, WC2A 3DU
Tel: (020) 7831 6501 **Fax:** (020) 7405 3867 **DX:** 192 London
Email: enq@maplesteesdale.co.uk **Website:** www.maplesteesdale.co.uk

Managing Partner	Andrew Whittaker
Number of partners	10
Assistant solicitors	7
Other fee-earners	10

CONTACTS

Commercial Property ....Mark Bryan
Private Client ....Sally Wilkins

THE FIRM: Maples Teesdale is a long-established firm tracing its roots to 1782 that delivers legal services in its chosen areas of practice in a thoroughly contemporary manner. The firm's core areas of practice are commercial property and construction and private client. It has company/commercial and litigation expertise although this is primarily (but not exclusively) utilised in support of the two main practice areas. The firm does not pretend to or aspire to be a full service practice. Its strategy is to concentrate upon and develop its core areas of expertise within the framework of a small and focused practice in the belief that this offers the optimum working and business environment and constitutes the most effective vehicle for providing a service of the highest quality.

PRINCIPAL AREAS OF WORK:

Commercial Property & Construction: The firm deals with all aspects of commercial property and construction including: property acquisition, occupation and disposal; property construction and development; property investment; property lending; property and portfolio management; all necessary incidental planning and environmental matters. This extends to dedicated litigation and corporate support. Three of the partners are recommended in the *Insiders Guide to Commercial Property* and one partner is an adjudicator approved for the purposes of the Housing Grants, Construction and Regeneration Act 1996.

Private Client: The firm advises on all contentious and non-contentious aspects of family and private business affairs including: the preparation of wills; financial and tax planning; the formation, administration and termination of trusts, both onshore and offshore; the administration of estates; matrimonial matters. The firm also advises on the formation of and advice to charities and provides a full range of residential and agricultural property services.

MARCHANT HARRIES

Bute Chambers, 17-19 Cardiff Street, Aberdare, CF44 7DP **Tel:** (01685) 885 500 **Fax:** (01685) 885 535 **DX:** 53851 Aberdare
Email: [feeearner]@marchantharries.co.uk **Website:** www.marchantharries.co.uk **Ptnrs:** 6 **Asst solrs:** 3 **Other fee-earners:** 5

MARGARET BENNETT

Charlton House, 5A Bloomsbury Square, London, WC1A 2LX
Tel: (020) 7404 6465 **Fax:** (020) 7240 5492 **DX:** 35740 Bloomsbury 1
Email: exclusive@divorce.uk.com

Senior Partner	Margaret H Bennett
Managing Partner	Judith Goodman
Number of partners	3
Assistant solicitors	2
Other fee-earners	2

AREAS OF PRACTICE

Family Law 100%

CONTACTS

Family Law ....Margaret H Bennett

THE FIRM: Established in 1990, as the first law firm practising exclusively in family law (uniquely with in-house divorce counselling, as well), Margaret Bennett Solicitors provides outstanding experience in this specialist field. The principal, Margaret Bennett, is a former chairman of the Family Law committee of the International Bar Association and now chairman of its Hague Child Abduction Task Force; founder member and former vice-president of the International Academy of Matrimonial Lawyers; founder of the Institute of Family Mediation and Arbitration and a Deputy District Judge, Principal Registry of the Family Division, High Court, London. Christopher Creagh Brown has an established reputation in private client and family law including contentious probate and Inheritance Act claims as a partner and consultant at well known London firms including Lawrence Graham and Dawson & Co before joining Margaret Bennett. He is a member of the Association of Contentious Trust and Probate Specialists. Judith Goodman who has an outstanding record in family law was formerly a partner at Goodman Ray having built up the high reputation of that firm since 1985 before joining Margaret Bennett Solicitors. Judith Goodman is a Deputy District Judge of the London County Courts and a trained mediator. The consultant, John D Bieber, is a former partner of Price Bieber and author of *If Divorce is the Only Way*, published by Penguin Books. The consultant counsellor, the Countess of Minto, is former chairman of Marie Curie Cancer Care and Cruse Bereavement Care and a personal coach with Therapist U. In addition to counselling, Caroline Minto also deals with family mediation.

PRINCIPAL AREAS OF WORK:

Family: Practising exclusively in family law, the firm's focus is on helping clients with the emotional burden of marital breakdown creating better awareness of client needs and how their problems may best be resolved. Selective with its clientele, Margaret Bennett Solicitors can devote the time and attention to each matter that it deserves. In complex international cases, the firm's work is facilitated by a close connection with family lawyers and other specialists around the world.

INTERNATIONAL: Languages spoken include French, German and Italian.

MARGETTS & RITCHIE

Coleridge Chambers, 177 Corporation Street, Birmingham, B4 6RL **Tel:** 0121 236 5517 **Fax:** 0121 236 5520 **Email:** dh@margetts-ritchie.com **Website:** www.margetts-ritchie.com **Ptnrs:** 2 **Asst solrs:** 1 **Other fee-earners:** 2

MARGRAVES

Old Court Chambers, Llandrindod Wells, LD1 5EY **Tel:** (01597) 825565 **Fax:** (01597) 825220 **DX:** 200154 Llandrindod **Email:** law@margraves.co.uk **Website:** www.margraves.co.uk **Ptnrs:** 1 **Asst solrs:** 3 **Other fee-earners:** 1

MARK JACKSON-STOPS – SOLE PRACTITIONER

In Place of Strife, 212 Piccadilly, London, W1V 9LD **Tel:** (020) 7917 9449 **Fax:** (020) 7917 9450

MARRIOTT HARRISON

12 Great James Street, London, WC1N 3DR
Tel: (020) 7209 2000 **Fax:** (020) 7209 2001 **DX:** 0001 London Chancery Lane
Email: email@marriottharrison.co.uk **Website:** www.marriottharrison.com

Managing Partner	Tony Morris
Number of partners	10
Assistant solicitors	3
Other fee-earners	5

AREAS OF PRACTICE

Corporate/Corporate Finance 50%
Media/Commercial 35%
Litigation 10%
Property 5%

CONTACTS

Company ....Jon Sweet
Venture Capital ....Duncan Innes
Media/Entertainment ....Tony Morris
IT/Commercial ....Mark Halama
Litigation ....Peter Curnock
Property ....Vivienne Elson

THE FIRM: Originally established in 1985 by a group of media specialists, with its rapidly growing corporate and corporate finance practice, the firm has repositioned itself as a leading corporate/media niche player. Most of the partners have backgrounds with major London firms which they left with a commitment to provide a high quality personalised service to clients. Marriott Harrison's traditional client base of television and film production companies and broadcasters has generated significant corporate finance work which led to the establishment of a dedicated corporate team in the mid-nineties. In addition to servicing the requirements of the media clients, the corporate department now has a significant client-base of its own which includes venture capitalists, VCT's, financial institutions, private equity providers, banks and new technology companies. The media group has broadened the range of its clientele beyond the film and television sectors to include all aspects of new media and e-commerce, information technology, the music industry, entertainment software and computer games, the internet, publishing, the visual and performing arts and other activities in which intellectual property rights play a key role. Regular referral work is received from overseas lawyers, particularly leading firms in USA, Canada, and the EU.

Continued overleaf

MARRIOTT HARRISON
SOLICITORS

PRINCIPAL AREAS OF WORK:
Media: The commercial media team deals with all aspects of the creation and exploitation of content – films, television, music and sound recordings, computer games, software programs and the like. In addition to negotiating contracts and advising on copyright and intellectual property rights and regulatory matters, the team uses its knowledge and experience to advise on the way in which the business of each sector functions. The group has also developed an expertise in advising on large-scale IT procurement contracts in respect of which it is generally retained by a major bank and one of the major record companies. Clients include multinational media corporations, cable channels and operators, television and film production companies, record companies and music publishers, computer games publishers and developers, software developers and IT providers, book and magazine publishers, photographers, website designers, authors, composers and performers, and internet service providers.
Company & Commercial: Company and commercial expertise is provided in such areas as mergers, acquisitions and disposals, management buy-outs and venture capital, restructuring, banking and financial services, share option schemes, OFEX and AIM Listings. Recent projects include advising on the establishment of new funds such as VCT's and extensive work with those involved in the e-commerce and new technology sectors. The group is particularly strong in venture capital and corporate acquisitions both within and without the firm's media industry clients, which it increasingly supports in a broad range of complex commercial transactions, including acquisition and disposal of companies whose assets include extensive portfolios of IP assets, such as sound recordings, software, computer games, films and TV programmes. The department also advises on a wide variety of commercial agreements and arrangements. Major projects undertaken in 2000 included the AIM flotation of Online Travel Corporation plc in which the firm acted for the company, acquisition by Eagle Rock Entertainment plc of production company Cromwell Publishing Limited and various transactions involving Formula One Motor Racing.
Litigation: The litigation group is widely experienced in commercial litigation with particular expertise in media-related cases and general intellectual property matters. Considerable work is undertaken in co-operation with US lawyers in international litigation involving intellectual property rights. There is a substantial proportion of interlocutory work seeking injunctive relief.
Property: The Property Group supports the activities of the Corporate and Media teams, advising on a wide range of freehold and leasehold acquisitions and disposals.

M

MARRONS

1 Meridian South, Meridian Business Park, Leicester, LE3 2WY
Tel: (0116) 289 2200 **Fax:** (0116) 289 3733 **DX:** 710910 Leicester Meridian
Email: enquiries@marrons.net **Website:** www.marrons.net

Number of partners	7
Assistant solicitors	6
Other fee-earners	3

CONTACTS

Company Commercial	Kevin Sumner
Planning	Morag Thomson
Environment	Mike Jones
Property	Nick Robinson
Judicial Review	Simon Stanion

THE FIRM: The practice has an established reputation in the areas of planning, property development, environmental and public law. The RTPI publication *Planning* recently published a league table showing three of the partners as being amongst the highest rated individual planning solicitors as chosen by leading solicitors and planners. Marrons also has a thriving company commercial department based on a small number of high value transactions and also provides commercial litigation support for its commercial clients. The firm is deliberately located on junction 21 of the M1 motorway to allow national accessibility.

CLIENTELE: Marrons acts on behalf of most of the major national house builders, a large number of developers and local authorities.

MARRONS
58 Jesmond Road West, Newcastle upon Tyne, NE2 4PQ **Tel:** (0191) 281 1304 **Fax:** (0191) 212 0080 **DX:** 62555 Jesmond **Ptnrs:** 2 **Asst solrs:** 6 **Other fee-earners:** 3

MARSHALL ROSS & PREVEZER

4 Frederick's Place, London, EC2R 8AB
Tel: (020) 7367 9000 **Fax:** (020) 7367 9001 **DX:** 133107 CHEAPSIDE 2
Email: mail@mrp-law.co.uk

Senior Partner	Mark Prevezer
Managing Partner	Richard Marshall
Number of partners	9
Assistant solicitors	3
Consultants	4
Other fee-earners	8

THE FIRM: Established in the early 1980s, Marshall Ross & Prevezer is a well-regarded City firm, which has attracted a strong property, corporate, commercial and private client base. The firm is best known for commercial property, company/ commercial, commercial litigation (including insolvency and large debt recoveries), computer law, white collar crime, franchise and trade finance. The firm also has strong overseas connections in India, China, Hong Kong, Africa, the United States, as well as most European countries. Acting for a number of household names Marshall Ross & Prevezer has grown on its reputation of being one of the youngest firms in the City, and for being able, as a result of its size, to give a personal and individual service to its clients at partner level.

MARSONS SOLICITORS

Amadeus House, 33-39 Elmfield Road, Bromley, BR1 1LT **Tel:** (020) 8313 1300 **Fax:** (020) 8466 7920 **DX:** 121100 Bromley 9
Email: bromley@marsons.co.uk **Ptnrs:** 5 **Asst solrs:** 11 **Other fee-earners:** 106

MARTINEAU JOHNSON

St. Philips House, St. Philips Place, Birmingham, B3 2PP
Tel: (0121) 200 3300 **Fax:** (0121) 200 3330 **DX:** 721090 Birmingham 50
Email: marketing@martjohn.com **Website:** www.martineau-johnson.co.uk

78 Cannon Street, London, EC4N 6NQ
Tel: (020) 7618 6610 **Fax:** (020) 7618 8130

Managing Partner	David Gwyther
Senior Partner	William Barker
Number of partners	43
Assistant solicitors	63
Other fee-earners	35

CONTACTS	
ADR	Andrew Spooner
Automotive	Geraldine Tickle
Banking & Insolvency	Ian Baker
Charities	Keith Dudley
Commercial	Roger Blears
	Richard Wrigley
Commercial Litigation	Andrew Spooner
Commercial Property	Simon Arrowsmith
Construction	Paul Mountain
Debt Recovery	Andrew Adams
Education	Nicola Hart
Employment	Ian Marshall
Energy/Utilities	Andrew Whitehead
Environmental	Simon Arrowsmith
EU & Competition	Geraldine Tickle
Intellectual Property	William Barker
IT/Computers	Tom McGuire
Licensing	Andrew Spooner
Life Sciences	Niall Head-Rapson
Pensions	Simon Laight
PFI	Andrew Whitehead
Professional Indemnity	David Gwyther
Property Litigation	Martin Edwards
Tax (Corporate)	Yvonne Redfern
Wills, Tax & Trusts	Hugh Carslake

THE FIRM: As a full service commercial law firm, Martineau Johnson's practice dates back to the early 19th century, but is now divided into teams operating in specialist focused areas of law. The firm's approach to business encourages continuity and the development of long-term relationships. This has formed the basis of the firm's expansion into new areas of activity. The firm is large enough to offer the specialist skills that clients demand and small enough to maintain partner contact at every level, whilst looking to introduce the lawyer into the bloodstream of the client's organisation and to become part of the decision-making process at the earliest stage. It has invested substantially in information technology and systems to ensure efficiency and more accessibility. It has recruited carefully to assemble teams which are experts not only in the law, but in the business and activities of the clients they represent. It has responded both to the needs of its clients and anticipated them. It does not pay lip service to the fashionable concept of partnership with clients. The firm's lawyers are business professionals who understand the importance of being part of their clients' team. What all their clients have in common is a need for solutions which address the key issues directly and solve their problems. It delivers! Its service is based on people. They are team players and clients respond to this personal involvement; they know who they are dealing with. It is committed to working long-term with all clients. Whatever the nature of the case, it explores every angle in order to achieve the best possible result for clients. It has combined modern expertise with personal service and maintained the continuing contact for clients with the individual partner. Martineau Johnson addresses legal affairs via the know-how of specialist teams, works on behalf of its clients with passion and prides itself on its practicality and plain speaking. It's the way that Martineau Johnson conducts its business that distinguishes it, a method which has resulted in an impressive portfolio of done deals and a client list which is the envy of many other law firms.

INTERNATIONAL: The firm is a founder member of MultiLaw, an international association of independent law firms, which has more than 55 members worldwide and enables it to deliver legal services internationally.

RECRUITMENT: Committed to the personal supervision and training of trainees, the firm takes on 14 trainees per year. Each trainee has a mentor and benefits from a unique system of seat rotation. There is also a formal structured training programme. The majority of trainees stay with the firm after qualification. Those interested in applying for an open day or training contract should visit the firm's graduate website www.graduates4law.co.uk or email Emily Dean at emily.dean@martjohn.com.

MARTIN-KAYE

Hazledine House, Central Sq., Telford Centre, Telford, TF3 4JL **Tel:** (01952) 291757 **Fax:** (01952) 291759 **DX:** 28073 **Email:** law@martinkaye.co.uk **Website:** www.martinkaye.co.uk **Ptnrs:** 6 **Asst solrs:** 8 **Other fee-earners:** 38 **Contact:** Andrew Green • A progressive practice in the expanding new town of Telford dealing with all aspects of commercial, corporate, intellectual property, employment, litigation and property. Agency work is undertaken.

MARTYN PROWEL SOLICITORS

Hallinans House, 22 Newport Road, Cardiff, CF24 0TD **Tel:** (029) 2047 0909 **Fax:** (029) 2049 8566 **DX:** Cardiff 33037 **Email:** mped@globalnet.co.uk **Contact:** Martyn Prowel • Established in 1996 by three partners of the demerged Hallinans. Remaining at the same location, the new practice undertakes criminal, civil litigation, employment, family and conveyancing work.

AREAS OF PRACTICE	
Crime	30%
Civil Litigation	30%
Conveyancing	15%
Family	15%
Other	10%

MASON BOND

King Charles House, King Charles Croft, Leeds, LS1 6LA **Tel:** (0113) 242 4444 **Fax:** (0113) 246 7542 **DX:** 12064 Leeds 1 **Email:** stephen@masonbond.co.uk **Website:** www.masonbond.co.uk **Ptnrs:** 6 **Asst solrs:** 3 **Other fee-earners:** 5 **Contact:** Stephen Mason • A leading young practice working nationwide in the holiday and travel industries including litigation, commercial and employment, plus family and childcare department.

MASON AND CO

Bridge Street, Bakewell, DE45 1DS **Tel:** (01629) 815 175 **Fax:** (01629) 815 176 **Email:** helen@masonandco.co.uk
Website: www.masonandco.co.uk

MASON & MOORE DUTTON

Kirkton House, 4 Hunter St, Chester, CH1 2AS **Tel:** (01244) 348881 **Fax:** (01244) 351513 **DX:** 22151 **Email:** users@mmd.u-net.com
Website: www.mmd.u-net.com **Ptnrs:** 7 **Asst solrs:** 1

MASONS

30 Aylesbury Street, London, EC1R 0ER
Tel: (020) 7490 4000 **Fax:** (020) 7490 2545 **DX:** 53313 Clerkenwell
Website: www.masons.com

1-4 Portland Square, Bristol, BS2 8RR
Tel: (0117) 924 5678 **Fax:** (0117) 924 6699 **DX:** 78154 BRISTOL

M

9/10 St Andrew Square, Edinburgh, EH2 2AF (Regulated by the Law Society of Scotland)
Tel: (0131) 718 6006 **Fax:** (0131) 718 6100

33 Bothwell Street, Glasgow, G2 6NL (Regulated by the Law Society of Scotland)
Tel: (0141) 248 4858 **Fax:** (0141) 248 6655 **DX:** GW74 Glasgow

Springfield House, 76 Wellington Street, Leeds, LS1 2AY
Tel: (0113) 233 8905 **Fax:** (0113) 245 4285 **DX:** 706955 Leeds Park Square

100 Barbirolli Square, Manchester, M2 3SS
Tel: (0161) 234 8234 **Fax:** (0161) 234 8235 **DX:** 14490 Manchester 2

Worldwide Managing Partner	Anthony Bunch
UK Managing Partner	Peter Wood
International	
Number of partners	91
Assistant solicitors	275
Other fee-earners	67
Total staff	816

CONTACTS

Arbitration ....Mark Roe
Commercial Dispute Resolution ....Raymond Werbicki
Construction & Engineering ......John Bishop
..................Martin Roberts
Corporate & Commercial ....Russell Booker
Data Protection ....Shelagh Gaskill
E-commerce & New Media ....Jon Fell
..................John Salmon
Employment ....Michael Ryley
Energy ....Anthony Bunch
..................Peter Cassidy
Infrastructure ....Martin Harman
..................Ron Nobbs
Insolvency ....Chris Williams
Intellectual Property ....Paul Sanderson
IT ....Rob McCallough
..................Clive Seddon
..................Andrew Smith
Pensions ....Patrick Kennedy
Projects & Finance ....Chris Brown
Property Litigation ....Siobhan Cross
Property/Planning/Environment Guy Jordan

THE FIRM: Masons is one of the most highly regarded specialist law firms in Europe and the Asia Pacific region, aiming to be recognised as pre-eminent advisers to the information and technology, construction and engineering, energy and infrastructure industries as well as a major player in the projects field. Founded in the 1940s, Masons has over 90 partners and 800 staff working in offices located in five different regions in the UK as well as elsewhere in Europe and the Asia Pacific region. The UK practice is operated on a 'one firm' approach. Each office is viewed as equally important, and each offers a national service range based on the same focus areas, a consistent standard of service, the transfer of resources and effective communications. Resources can be provided from any office as necessary and clients have immediate access to the widest possible range of knowledge available within the firm. Clients are attracted to Masons because of the firm's depth of knowledge of their particular industry and continuing commitment to provide the highest quality legal and commercial advice tailored to a client's individual requirements. The firm is proud to have worked on a number of exciting and innovative projects and has been pleased to play its part in some of its clients' greatest achievements. In July 2000, Masons was awarded the Investors in People accreditation, publicly acknowledging it as a firm that recognises the importance of communicating with and training and developing its staff. Out-Law.com, Mason's innovative specialist e-commerce and new media service launched in May 2000, won industry acclaim when it was rated the Best Law Firm Web Site of the Year by the *Insider's Guide* to e-commerce, followed by the Legal IT award in the category Best Use of New Media.

PRINCIPAL AREAS OF WORK: Masons operates in four distinct practice groups serving the needs of clients operating in the information and technology, construction and engineering, and energy and infrastructure industries. These clients also benefit from the industry knowledge of the firm's complementary teams of specialist lawyers who provide a comprehensive service in the areas of project finance, corporate and commercial, commercial property, planning, environment, health and safety, dispute resolution (property and commercial), data protection, employment, pensions, insolvency and taxation.

INTERNATIONAL: International matters are handled by offices in Brussels, Dublin, Hong Kong, Guangzhou (PRC) and Singapore, as well as by the firm's UK based lawyers who work regularly in continental and central Europe, Scandinavia, the Middle East, the Pacific Rim, Africa and the Indian subcontinent.

MASONS

MATTHEW ARNOLD & BALDWIN

21 Station Road, Watford, WD17 1HT
Tel: (01923) 202020 **Fax:** (01923) 215050 **DX:** 4508 Watford
Email: info@mablaw.co.uk **Website:** www.mablaw.co.uk

Senior Partner	Richard Hanney
Number of partners	18
Assistant solicitors	16
Other fee-earners	32

AREAS OF PRACTICE

Company Commercial	25%
Commercial Litigation/Banking/Debt Recovery	18%
Commercial Property & Estate Development	16%
Residential Conveyancing	11%
Tax, Trusts & Probate	9%
Insolvency	8%
Intellectual Property & IT	5%
Family & Childcare	5%
Personal Injury	3%

CONTACTS

Commercial Litigation/Banking & Debt Collection	Steven Mills
Commercial Property	Richard Hanney
Corporate & Commercial	Christopher Green
Employment	Alan Piper
Family	Juliet Wilson
IT	Christopher Green
Insolvency & Corporate Reconstruction	Alistair Bacon
	Adrian Hyde
Intellectual Property	Clare Stothard
Licensing	Alan Piper
Personal Injury	Anna Bailey
Residential Conveyancing & Estate Development	David Marsden
Tax, Trusts & Probate	Iain Donaldson

THE FIRM: Based in Watford since its foundation in 1900, its client base is now national and international. Recognised as the major firm in the region, Matthew Arnold & Baldwin has established a considerable reputation for its commercial services. It also has a strong reputation for its private client work. As a member of both LawNet, the federation of independent UK law firms, and Eurojuris International, the firm has developed strong links throughout Europe and in particular Scandinavia. The commitment to quality and continuous improvement has been recognised by the award of the LawNet Standard, (presently being accredited for ISO 9002). The firm prides itself on forming strong relationships with its clients.

PRINCIPAL AREAS OF WORK:

Commercial: The commercial team is one of the largest in the region. The size and background of the team gives them the strength and depth to handle multiple, complex, commercial transactions. Some of the team have worked 'in house' and are widely respected for their commercial awareness. Specialist units dealing with employment, insolvency, IP, IT, commercial property and company secretarial support them.
Information Technology: Building on its long experience of the computer industry, the IT team has developed a reputation for its support of the e-commerce sector.
Commercial Litigation/Banking/Debt Recovery: The commercial litigation, banking and debt recovery team is particularly well known for its recovery work for Barclays Bank and defence of other financial institutions. This large team has the depth and experience to handle all types of major commercial dispute, especially pre-emptive remedies.
Insolvency & Corporate Recovery: As well as servicing the firm's banking and financial sector clients, the team is well regarded by corporate recovery specialists.
Commercial Property: The commercial property team deals with all aspects of the acquisition, financing and disposal of freehold and leasehold property, from shops to large residential and industrial developments.
Intellectual Property: The intellectual property unit has created an enviable and much reported reputation for its contentious IP work. It advises both listed and small businesses in all areas of IP and IT law. Clients include those in the media, healthcare and e-commerce sectors.
Employment & Employee Benefits: The unit supports the needs of personnel departments, and is noted for its work on restraints, on TUPE and in tribunals. Services for senior executives also feature in its workload, as does the creation of share and other employee benefit plans. The team includes HR professionals and an Employment Tribunal Chairman.
Private Client: A full range of private client services is offered including residential conveyancing, family, personal injury and advice on personal tax, trusts and related financial planning.

MAX BARFORD & CO

16 Mount Pleasant Road, Tunbridge Wells, TN1 1QU **Tel:** (01892) 539379 **Fax:** (01892) 521874 **DX:** 3918 **Email:** alert@mbarford-u-net.com
Ptnrs: 4 **Asst solrs:** 5 **Other fee-earners:** 5

MAX BITEL, GREENE

1 Canonbury Place, London, N1 2NG **Tel:** (020) 7354 2767 **Fax:** (020) 7226 1210 **DX:** 51852 Highbury **Email:** office@MBG.co.uk **Ptnrs:** 4
Asst solrs: 3 **Other fee-earners:** 4

THE MAX GOLD PARTNERSHIP

Suffolk House, 21 Silver Street, Hull, HU1 1JJ **Tel:** (01482) 224900 **Fax:** (01482) 216068 **DX:** 11939 Hull **Email:** law@maxgold.demon.co.uk
Ptnrs: 3 **Asst solrs:** 11 **Other fee-earners:** 12

MAXWELL BATLEY

27 Chancery Lane, London, WC2A 1PA
Tel: (020) 7440 4400 **Fax:** (020) 7440 4444 **DX:** 190 London Chancery Lane WC2
Email: mailroom@maxwellbatley.com **Website:** www:maxwellbatley.com

Senior Partner	Michael Cassidy
Number of partners	17
Assistant solicitors	8
Other fee-earners	10

AREAS OF PRACTICE

Property & Construction	40%
Company/Commercial	20%
Banking	12%
Litigation & Employment	20%
Private Client	8%

CONTACTS

Banking	Fraser McColl
Commercial Property	Nigel Wilson
Company/Commercial	Ian McIntyre
Contruction & Property Development	Raymond Levine
Employment	Philip Wood
Litigation	Philip Knights
Private Client	Frank O'Shea

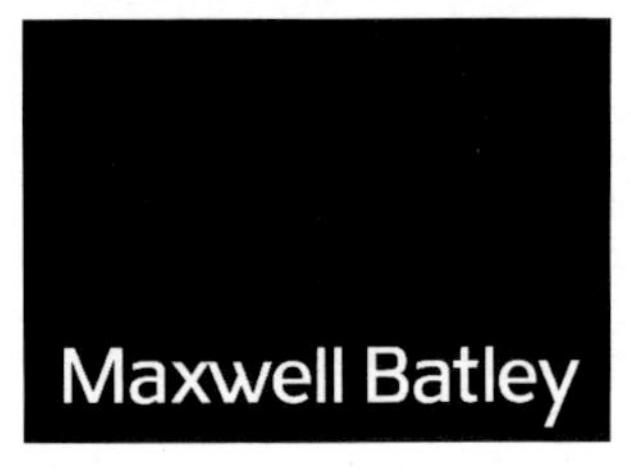

THE FIRM: Maxwell Batley is a multidisciplinary City law firm with highly regarded commercial property expertise and a strong reputation in corporate, banking, litigation and private client work. The firm is known for working in partnership with clients and for providing a partner-led service, using the latest technology. Maxwell Batley takes a business-like approach to the law, by offering practical, innovative advice, good value for money and prompt service.

PRINCIPAL AREAS OF WORK:

Property & Construction: The firm's largest discipline is recognised as a real alternative to the large international firms. Advice is based on the assessment of risk in a competitive and commercial context – not merely legal analysis. The group has substantial experience in acquisitions and sales, property finance and development, joint ventures, landlord and tenant matters and portfolio management. A key expertise is construction work. Clients include leading pension funds, institutional investors, and blue chip property companies, developers and occupiers of all types of property. A wide range of innovative transactions is handled, including development finance transactions and setting up of creative structures to deal with the joint ownership of property. The group advises on the use of various types of corporate and non-corporate vehicles, ensuring that the right balance between risk, control and taxation is achieved in the structure adopted. The group also acts extensively for smaller investors and occupiers.

Banking & Finance: The group works extensively with both UK and international banks and financial institutions, as well as their clients in all types of banking and financial transactions. It provides an expert, cost-effective service, enabling clients to achieve their commercial objectives with their interests being fully protected. Transactions handled include secured and unsecured lending, project finance, structured finance, acquisition finance, portfolio acquisitions and securitisations.

Company & Commercial: The group adopts a practical approach, working closely with its clients to achieve their commercial aims. It advises on mergers and acquisitions, venture capital, loan capital, management buy-outs, PFI, local authority and competitive tendering, distribution and marketing agreements, information technology and insolvency. The corporate finance team advises companies and their financial advisors on flotations, take-overs, placings and rights issues. The group also advises on joint ventures, shareholder agreements and the resolution of corporate disputes.

Litigation & Dispute Resolution: The aim is to prevent contentious situations arising. Where they do arise, expert representation in tribunal or court applications is provided. The group acts for institutional, corporate and private clients and is particularly strong on property-related litigation, including construction disputes. It also handles banking, commercial disputes, insolvency, partnership disputes, professional negligence and general insurance work (including employers and product liability claims).

Employment: The employment group provides comprehensive, pragmatic advice to business and private clients on the whole range of employment related law. It advises on service and consultancy agreements, recruitment and all areas of remuneration, including changes in terms of conditions. The group's expertise extends to intellectual property matters, restrictive covenants, maternity and discrimination issues.

Private Client: The group provides a comprehensive service for private capital and family affairs. It deals with estate planning, trusts, probate and wills, both UK and offshore, and capital tax planning; charities; residential conveyancing for offshore buyers, sellers and lenders as well as UK based.

MAXWELL MACLAURIN

100 West Regent Street, Glasgow, G2 2QB **Tel:** (0141) 332 5666 **Fax:** (0141) 332 6757 **DX:** 95 Glasgow **Email:** mailbox@maxwellmaclaurin.co.uk **Website:** www.maxwellmaclaurin.co.uk **Ptnrs:** 8 **Asst solrs:** 3 **Other fee-earners:** 1

MAY, MAY & MERRIMANS

12 South Square, Gray's Inn, London, WC1R 5HH
Tel: (020) 7405 8932 **Fax:** (020) 7831 0011 **DX:** 225 London
Email: mmm@elawuk.com

Senior Partner	Christopher Walsh
Number of partners	12
Assistant solicitors	4
Other fee-earners	2

AREAS OF PRACTICE

Private Client (Tax, Trust & Probate)	50%
Property (Domestic, Agricultural & Commercial)	30%
Litigation/Matrimonial	15%
Company/Commercial	5%

THE FIRM: Founded in 1786, May, May & Merrimans is best known for its private client work, offering a high-quality personal service to individuals and families, some of whom are the owners of substantial residential and agricultural estates, including heritage property. The firm brings the same quality of service to its corporate clients and undertakes a broad range of company and commercial business.

PRINCIPAL AREAS OF WORK:

Private Client: Specialist advice includes estate planning, will drafting, the creation and variation of all types of settlements including offshore and charitable trusts, and personal and estate taxation. A considerable vol-

ume of probate work is handled, often involving large estates which may include overseas property.
Property: A full range of property work is undertaken, ranging from new town sites to mineral excavations, office and shop leases, agricultural tenancies, estate sales and substantial domestic conveyancing transactions.
Litigation: The litigation element of the practice deals with most types of contentious civil law, including landlord and tenant issues, negligence claims, employment, defamation and general commercial disputes.
Matrimonial: This department handles all aspects of family law, including marriage breakdown and related financial issues, disputes involving children and Inheritance Act claims.
Company & Commercial: The firm can assist in the formation of companies and partnerships, in the sale and acquisition of existing enterprises and in all matters which arise in the course of running a business or private company, including share issues, the drafting of contracts and employment questions.

CONTACTS

Civil Litigation	Sarah Gillette
Company/Commercial	Alexandra Sarkis
Family/Matrimonial	Susan Black
Private Client	Giles Gostwick
Property	Sandy Schofield

MAYER, BROWN & PLATT

Bucklersbury House, 3 Queen Victoria Street, London, EC4N 8EL **Tel:** (020) 7246 6200 **Fax:** (020) 7329 4465 **Email:** rherbert@mayerbrown.com **Website:** www.mayerbrown.com **Resident lawyers:** 32 **Total lawyers:** 1123 **Contact:** Ian R. Coles • Mayer, Brown & Platt has European offices in Cologne, Frankfurt, London and Paris, a representative office in Mexico and 6 offices in the US.

McCLENAHAN CROSSEY & CO

41 New Row, Coleraine, BT52 1AE **Tel:** (028) 7034 3491 **Fax:** (028) 7034 2377 **Email:** info@colerainesolicitors.co.uk **Ptnrs:** 2 **Asst solrs:** 1

McCLOSKEYS

Rochester Building, 28 Adelaide Street, Belfast, BT2 8GD
Tel: (028) 9024 0310 **Fax:** (028) 9024 0312 **DX:** 495 NR Belfast 1
Email: mccloskeys@mccloskeys.co.uk

Senior Partner	Joseph McGuigan
Number of partners	2
Assistant solicitors	2

AREAS OF PRACTICE

Professional Negligence	40%
Other Defence Negligence	40%
General	20%

CONTACTS

Other Defence Litigation	H McGrattan
Professional Negligence	J McGuigan

THE FIRM: McCloskeys is a long-established and predominantly defendants litigation practice. Litigation clients include UK insurers, Lloyds syndicates and government bodies.

PRINCIPAL AREAS OF WORK: The firm is one of Northern Ireland's leading insurance litigation practices. It has expertise in professional negligence, public liability, employers' liability, product liability, road traffic claims, and all other areas of insurance litigation. It has developed a particular expertise in dealing with the defence of fraudulent fire claims.

McCLURE NAISMITH

49 Queen Street, Edinburgh, EH2 3NH
Tel: (0131) 220 1002 **Fax:** (0131) 220 1003 **DX:** 135 Edinburgh
Email: Edinburgh@McClureNaismith.com **Website:** www.mcclurenaismith.com

Pountney Hill House, 6 Laurence Pountney Hill, London, EC4R 0BL
Tel: (020) 7623 9155 **Fax:** (020) 7623 9154 **DX:** 764 CDE London
Email: London@McClureNaismith.com

292 St Vincent Street, Glasgow, G2 5TQ
Tel: (0141) 204 2700 **Fax:** (0141) 248 3998 **DX:** 64 Glasgow
Email: Glasgow@McClureNaismith.com

Senior Partner	Kenneth Chrystie
Number of partners	24
Assistant solicitors	41
Other fee-earners	20

AREAS OF PRACTICE

Litigation	25%
Commercial Property	25%
Corporate/Commercial	25%
Banking/Finance	10%
Private Client	10%
Intellectual Property	5%

CONTACTS

Banking/Asset Finance	John Blackwood
Commercial Property	Wilson Aitken
Consumer Credit/Debt	Frank Johnstone
Corporate/Commercial	Kenneth Chrystie
Employment	Alan Thomson
Intellectual Property	Kenneth Chrystie
Litigation	William Walker
Private Client	Gordon Shearer
Project Finance/PFI	Steven Brown

THE FIRM: McClure Naismith is a commercially focused law firm dedicated to providing the highest quality legal services to its clients in Scotland, England and overseas. Through its membership of the World Law Group the firm enjoys access through similar commercial firms to all major jurisdictions in the Americas, Europe and the Far East. McClure Naismith has continued to develop its range of specialist commercial services and its reputation for a determined approach to achieving results for clients. All of its offices have grown substantially in the last three years and it is one of the few Scottish firms with a London office, providing a full range of English law advice in the fields of corporate, banking, commercial property and commercial litigation.

PRINCIPAL AREAS OF WORK:

Corporate/Commercial: The firm advises on all aspects of corporate and commercial law. It has a particularly strong reputation for handling complex commercial negotiations and commercial contracts. Specialist advice is offered on corporate finance; MBOs and MBIs; mergers, acquisitions and joint ventures; shareholder disputes; agency distribution and licensing contracts; insolvency; competition law; and oil and gas developments. Industrial expertise embraces the mining, transport, pharmaceuticals, distilling and electronic sectors.
Project Finance & PFI: The firm provides project finance advice to companies promoting infrastructure pro-

Continued overleaf

jects principally in the energy and water industries in the UK and overseas, as well as a range of public sector organisations, construction consortia and banks in PFI projects, mainly in the health, water and education sectors.

McCLURE NAISMITH
The Determining Factor
GLASGOW EDINBURGH LONDON

Commercial Property: The firm handles property development work for institutional, corporate and private clients including site acquisition; sale and leasing; secured lending and funding; factory, shop and office developments; private sector rented housing contracts; housing associations; joint venture agreements. The firm advises landlords and tenants on commercial, agricultural and residential leasing and also advises on environmental law.

Litigation: Litigation work of all types is undertaken in all courts, tribunals and inquiries throughout Scotland and in the High Court and county courts in England. The firm is well regarded for its personal injury/reparation practice acting for many leading defence insurers. It also covers property planning and construction litigation, intellectual property disputes and matrimonial and family litigation.

Consumer Credit/Debt Recovery: This department's clients include many of the country's leading finance houses, leasing companies and banks and advises the Consumer Credit Trade Association. The firm is a member of the Finance and Leasing Association. It gives advice on drafting credit documentation and increasingly on data protection issues, as well as providing a volume debt and asset recovery service to a wide range of commercial and financial companies.

Banking & Asset Finance: The firm acts for many UK and overseas banks, including all of the Scottish clearing banks, on secured lending, corporate lending and asset finance as well as in relation to PFI projects. Contentious banking/recovery work is also carried out for leading banks and building societies.

Employment: In this growing area of practice the firm advises principally employers on all aspects of employment law, contentious and non-contentious, including drafting terms and conditions of employment, advice on individual employment rights, claims for unfair and wrongful dismissal and common law claims before employment tribunals and courts throughout the UK.

Intellectual Property: The firm has considerable expertise in negotiating licence agreements for client companies worldwide and for its handling of IP disputes including patent infringement, breach of copyright or trademark and passing off. It has a growing practice in computer contracts and e-commerce.

Private Client: The firm offers advice on estate planning, wills, trusts and executries, insurance, pensions, investments and the purchase sale and leasing of residential property.

M

MCCORMACKS

122 Mile End Road, London, E1 4UN **Tel:** (020) 7790 4339 **Fax:** (020) 7790 5846 **DX:** 300704 Tower Hamlets **Email:** city@mccormacks.co.uk
Website: www.mccormacks.co.uk **Ptnrs:** 4 **Asst solrs:** 15 **Other fee-earners:** 2

McCORMICKS

Britannia Chambers, 4 Oxford Place, Leeds, LS1 3AX
Tel: (0113) 246 0622 **Fax:** (0113) 246 7488 **DX:** 26427 Leeds Park Square
Email: enquiries@mccormicks-solicitors.com

Wharfedale House, 37 East Parade, Harrogate, HG1 5LQ
Tel: (01423) 530630 **Fax:** (01423) 530709 **DX:** 11974 Harrogate 1
Email: d.ezard@mccormicks-solicitors.com

Managing & Senior Partner	Peter McCormick OBE
Number of partners	8
Assistant solicitors	13
Other fee-earners	16

AREAS OF PRACTICE

Company/Commercial & Litigation	75%
Matrimonial, Private Client & Conveyancing	15%
Criminal	10%

CONTACTS

Charity	Peter McCormick O.B.E.
Commercial Litigation	Roger Hutton
	Richard Cramer
Company/Commercial (inc. Property)	Clive Lawrence
	Richard Moran
Debt Collection	Richard Cramer
	Mark Burns
Defamation	Peter McCormick OBE
	Clive Lawrence
Employment	Neil Goodrum, Richard Cramer
European Law	Richard Moran
Family/Matrimonial	Mark Burns
	Geoff Rogers
Insolvency	Richard Cramer
	Roger Hutton
Intellectual Property & IT	Clive Lawrence
	Richard Moran
Media & Entertainment Law	Peter McCormick OBE, Clive Lawrence
Partnership	Peter McCormick OBE

THE FIRM: McCormicks is a high-profile, progressive and highly regarded firm, which has expanded by planned organic growth to attain a reputation for expertise in a number of fields. It has offices in Leeds and Harrogate and associated offices throughout Europe. It offers a comprehensive range of legal services, both to its national and international corporate clients as well as to many notable private clients. It has been described in a survey of the law firms in Yorkshire and Humberside by the *Yorkshire Post* as 'a law firm in the top rank' and by Yorkshire Television as 'one of the region's top law firms'. The firm is admired for its continued ability to operate successfully in the company and commercial field, whilst at the same time maintaining its commitment to the private client. The average age of the partners is 35, and the firm has a reputation for a vibrant and dynamic atmosphere. Currently, company/commercial and litigation account for 75% of the fee income, criminal (serious fraud, tax cases and complex criminal matters) 10% and matrimonial, private client and conveyancing 15%. Partners hold the Higher Courts Qualification, memberships of the Law Society's Personal Injury, Family and Childcare panels and Fellowship of the Chartered Institute of Arbitrators; partners are also trained and experienced in mediation and alternative dispute resolution. The firm is a member of the Law Society's Accident Line scheme. Both the Leeds and Harrogate practices were the first in the region to be awarded Legal Aid franchises and membership of the Law Society's Family Law Scheme. The firm has strengthened its corporate recovery department dealing with all aspects of insolvency work with personnel having worked on the Maxwell and BCCI cases.

PRINCIPAL AREAS OF WORK: Commercial litigation, company and commercial, corporate and white collar crime including VAT and Inland Revenue investigation work and tribunals, debt collection and mortgage repossession, employment, European law, family law, intellectual property, IT, media and entertainment, partnership, property, sports law (one of the premier practices in the country), insolvency, personal injury, general crime (especially road traffic), private client, defamation, charity law. Agency instructions welcomed.

INTERNATIONAL: Associated offices in France, Germany, The Netherlands, Belgium, Eire, Spain, Italy, Portugal and Gibraltar. Fluent French, German, Italian and Spanish spoken.

CONTACTS CONTINUED

Personal Injury	Neil Goodrum
Serious Fraud	Peter McCormick OBE
	Geoff Rogers
Sports Law	Peter McCormick OBE
	Richard Cramer

McCormicks
SOLICITORS

MCCOURTS

53 George IV Bridge, Edinburgh, EH1 1EJ **Tel:** (0131) 225 6555 **Fax:** (0131) 225 5054 **Ptnrs:** 3 **Asst solrs:** 4 **Other fee-earners:** 2

MCDERMOTT, WILL & EMERY

7 Bishopsgate, London, EC2N 3AQ
Tel: (020) 7577 6900 **Fax:** (020) 7577 6950 **DX:** 42619 Cheapside
Website: www.mwe.com/london

Senior Partner	William Charnley
Managing Partner	John Reynolds
UK	
Number of partners	17
Associate lawyers	45
Other fee earners	7
Total	69
International	
Number of partners	498
Associate lawyers and other fee earners	439
Total	937

THE FIRM: McDermott, Will & Emery was founded in 1934 and is now one of the world's largest international law firms, with more than 900 lawyers in 11 offices worldwide, advising major corporate and institutional clients on a variety of legal issues. The international practice is founded on the excellent credentials of the firm's lawyers, as well as its practical and responsive approach. The London office was opened in November 1998 to service clients' international and domestic legal needs. It provides comprehensive legal advice to a broad range of multinational and national corporates (including FTSE 100 institutional, governmental) and private clients across Europe and elsewhere.

PRINCIPAL AREAS OF WORK: The London office provides a comprehensive range of legal services in the following areas:

Banking, Capital Markets, High Yield Debt & Finance: Advice on eurobond issues, MTN and ECP programmes, syndicated and bilateral loans, acquisition and venture capital finance, asset and project finance, structured finance, swaps, high yield debt, derivatives and other treasury products, treasury management and electronic banking, and the regulation of the UK's banking and financial services sectors.

Communications: Advice on communications-related contracts and commercial transactions and the provision of strategic and regulatory advice on telecommunications and broadcasting activities. The firm acts for numerous companies entering the UK, European and international communications markets, including international telecoms operators, Internet providers, equipment suppliers and electricity companies.

Corporate Finance/Merger & Acquisitions/Securities: Advice on a broad range of general corporate issues, including reorganisations, restructurings and joint ventures including corporate finance issues, flotations, debenture issues, bond issues and securitisations. The firm also has extensive experience in the purchase, sale and merger of businesses, public takeovers and private acquisitions and disposals - both domestic and cross border - MBOs and MBIs, LBOs and LBIs. The firm represents issuers of equity and debt securities in the public markets and underwriting syndicates. It also handles public offerings involving industrial revenue bonds and limited partnership interests.

E-Business: The firm has far reaching experience ranging from advising multinationals in both b2b and b2c contexts to ISP and dot.com start-ups, to media companies dealing with convergence. The firm regularly advises on cross-border e-business issues and has drafted and negotiated contracts which establish and regulate the conduct of business via electronic means.

Employment: Advice on wrongful and unfair dismissal, executive severance, confidentiality and restrictive covenants, breaches of fiduciary duty, fraud by employees, sex/race/disability discrimination, Working Time Regulations, union recognition and works councils, industrial disputes, EU employment law, corporate governance, TUPE and the employment aspects of acquisitions.

Information Technology/Intellectual Property: The IT/IP group has particular expertise in IT infrastructure projects across a range of industries, in particular financial services. The group undertakes all aspects of intellectual property work both contentious and non-contentious, and has specific expertise in the pharmaceuticals and biotechnology industries.

Litigation: Broad experience in commercial disputes, both in the UK and internationally and in public international law. The firm litigates in all UK courts and is also involved regularly in international arbitrations. Presently, the firm is advising in disputes concerning international trade, complex contracts, shareholder/boardroom issues, environmental issues, fraud, technology and media.

Pensions: A broad range of issues, including pensions aspects of mergers, acquisitions, disposals, flotations, MBO's and MBI's; litigation and Pensions Ombudsman disputes; investment management and custody agreements; issues affecting internationally mobile employees; plan mergers, reorganisations and terminations;

Continued overleaf

CONTACTS

Banking & International Capital Markets	Graham Rowbotham
Communications/Media & Technology	Stephanie Liston
Corporate/Corporate Finance/Commercial	William Charnley
	Rick Mitchell
	Robert Rakison
E-Business	Rafi Azim-Khan
Employment	Fraser Younson
	David Dalgarno
	Alison Wetherfield
Financial Markets Technology	Phillip Rees
Information Technology	Phillip Rees
Intellectual Property/Biotech & Pharmaceuticals	Larry Cohen
Insolvency	Chris Forrest
Litigation	John Reynolds
Marketing & Advertising	Rafi Azim-Khan
Mergers & Acquisitions	William Charnley
	Robert Rakison
MBOs	William Charnley
Pensions & Employee Benefits	Steven Hull
Projects & Project Finance	Andrew Watson
Securities/US Securities	William Charnley
	Rick Mitchell
Taxation	Peter Nias
	Tim Sanders

McDERMOTT, WILL & EMERY
SOLICITORS AND U.S. ATTORNEYS

design and establishment of new plans; best practice audits; outsourcing from the public sector to the private sector

Taxation: Advice on UK and international tax issues with regard to corporate and commercial business matters, including mergers and acquisitions, spinoffs, flotations, corporate structuring, asset and structured finance, cross border transactions, and transfer pricing.

INTERNATIONAL: The firm has an extensive network of offices in the US. In addition to the practice in the UK, there are also offices in Lithuania and Russia.

McGRATH & CO

4th Floor, King Edward House, 135a New Street, Birmingham, B2 4QJ **Tel:** (0121) 643 4121 **Fax:** (0121) 624 1060 **Ptnrs:** 7 **Asst solrs:** 14 **Other fee-earners:** 57

McGRIGOR DONALD

Pacific House, 70 Wellington Street, Glasgow, G2 6SB
Tel: (0141) 248 6677 **Fax:** (0141) 204 1351 **DX:** GW 135
Email: enquiries@mcgrigors.com **Website:** www.mcgrigors.com

M

Senior Partner	Robert Glennie
UK Managing Partner	Kirk Murdoch
Number of partners	58
Assistant solicitors	125
Other fee-earners	62

AREAS OF PRACTICE

Corporate	29%
Property	26%
Commercial Litigation	16%
Construction	8%
Projects	7%
Employment	5%
Banking	5%
Private Capital	4%

CONTACTS

Banking	Colin McKay
Commercial Litigation	Niall Scott
Competition	Helen Matheson
Construction	Brandon Nolan
Corporate	Colin Gray
Employment	James Young
Financial Services	Frank Doran
Human Rights	Alan Miller
MDTS (Training Services)	Stuart Neilson
Planning & Environment	Steven Scates
Private Capital	Allan Nicolson
Projects	Donna Stevenson
Project Finance	Michael Watson
Commercial Property	Tom Ferrier
Public Law	Alan Boyd
Public Policy	Adam Bruce
Tax & Pensions	Ian Gordon
Technology	Shonaig Macpherson

THE FIRM: McGrigor Donald is a leading business and commercial law practice with offices in Belfast, Brussels, Edinburgh, Glasgow and London. The firm's ability to provide a truly UK-wide service is increasingly attractive to both national and international clients operating throughout Britain – it remains the only UK law firm offering a full range of specialist legal services across all three UK jurisdictions. The firm aims to be a constructive and effective force in achieving the objectives of clients. Its handling of legal work is widely recognised as direct and forthright. With over 220 lawyers across five offices, the firm prides itself on its commitment to providing expert, seamless advice guided by the needs of the client and the individual project. Reflecting the ambitions of its client base, the firm is increasingly transnational with its recent 'best friends' agreement with Philadelphia-based law firm Pepper Hamilton. The firm is exploring strategic alliances with law firms in the USA and Europe to enable it to offer clients extensive cover in European and US jurisdictions. McGrigor Donald's focus on supporting clients drives it to add value in each and every business relationship. The firm aims to add value to deal-making and all of its other corporate legal services by being business advisers – not just transaction driven lawyers.

PRINCIPAL AREAS OF WORK: Working in partnership with each client, experienced teams of accomplished advisers are drawn from across the firm's principal business specialisms.

Corporate/Technology: New issues, public take-overs, M&A, corporate finance, taxation, MBOs and MBIs, acquisition and disposal, interactive media law, IT/IP.

Commercial Property: Investment, development, finance (including secured lending), landlord and tenant, retail, office, industrial and licensing/leisure, portfolio management, joint ventures and tax driven property schemes including enterprise zones, planning and environment.

Projects: In the top ten UK firms advising on PFI/PPP (across all principal sectors, including schools, waste, water and sewage, hospitals, roads, defence, IT). High profile practice extends beyond PPP to energy, power, oil and gas in the UK and beyond.

Banking: Full range of legal services to both lenders and borrowers. Advice extends across all key banking practice areas, including project finance, property finance, retail banking and acquisition finance.

Construction: Advice in drafting construction contracts, claims and dispute resolution, appointment documentation, advocacy and arbitration, procurement and risk allocation.

Litigation: Planning law, intellectual property disputes, professional negligence actions, general contractual litigation, media law, credit management, debt recovery and licensing. The firm also provides a complete in-house advocacy service in relation to arbitrations, tribunals, sheriff courts and the Court of Session and House of Lords.

Employment: Full range of contentious and non-contentious employment law advice including: drafting employment contracts, policies and handbooks, managing terminations of the employment relationships, disciplinary and grievance issues, reorganisations and redundancies, trade union disputes, injunctive and interdict proceedings, employment tribunals, working time regulation, sex, race and disability claims. The team recently launched MDTS, its training and consultancy arm, to complement the wide range of employment services currently offered by the team.

INTERNATIONAL: In 2001, the firm's lawyers were at work for clients in Georgia, Norway, Canada, Zambia, Uganda, Malta, Finland, Ireland and the USA.

RECRUITMENT: McGrigor Donald has built up an enviable internal technical training programme, using both its internal lawyers acting as coaches and reputable external presenters within the legal or business arena. This technical training is complemented by a structured skills training programme that every trainee and lawyer undertakes. The objective of this is to ensure that the firm's lawyers are equipped with commercial awareness and business skills in addition to their excellent technical competence. The firm currently has 46 trainee solicitors.

MCKAY & NORWELL WS

5 & 7 Rutland Square, Edinburgh, EH1 2AS **Tel:** (0131) 229 2212 **Fax:** (0131) 228 4538 **DX:** 138 Edinburgh **Email:** mail@mckaynorwell.co.uk **Website:** www.mckaynorwell.co.uk **Ptnrs:** 8 **Asst solrs:** 11 **Other fee-earners:** 11

MCKENZIE BELL

19 John St, Sunderland, SR1 1JG
Tel: (0191) 567 4857 **Fax:** (0191) 510 9347 **DX:** 60719
Email: mckbell@dial.pipex.com

Managing Partner	Paul Heron
Senior Partner	William Temperley
Number of partners	8
Assistant solicitors	1
Other fee-earners	5

THE FIRM: McKenzie Bell has been established in Sunderland for well over 100 years, providing legal services throughout the North East. Other offices: Washington.

PRINCIPAL AREAS OF WORK:

Company/Commercial: Work undertaken by the department includes commercial leases, partnerships, limited companies, business transfers and contracts.

Property: A full range of residential and commercial property services are offered.

Litigation: Full range of civil and criminal work undertaken. The firm has a legal aid franchise.

Private Client: Advice includes matters relating to family/matrimonial law, childcare, landlord and tenant, employment, wills, trusts and probate.

Licensing: The firm undertakes work regarding all aspects of the application for, or opposition to, liquor, betting and public entertainment licences.

MCKINTY & WRIGHT

5-7 Upper Queen Street, Belfast, BT1 6FS
Tel: (028) 9024 6751 **Fax:** (028) 9023 1432 **DX:** 510 NR Belfast 1
Email: post@mckinty-wright.co.uk **Website:** www.mckinty-wright.co.uk

Senior Partner	John Cross
Number of partners	13
Assistant solicitors	11
Other fee-earners	6

CONTACTS

Commercial Property	Ivan Frazer
Company/Commercial	Eric Boyd
Litigation	Paul Johnston

McKINTY & WRIGHT

THE FIRM: McKinty & Wright is a Belfast-based firm with a client-oriented, commercial and litigation practice. Although the firm offers specialist expertise on matters peculiar to Northern Ireland, it has a wide client base outside the province, including international and multinational companies. It is also pleased to include amongst its clients many leading insurance companies, Lloyds syndicates and insurance intermediaries. McKinty and Wright strives to provide an efficient and cost-effective service to all its clients and to maintain a close working relationship.

PRINCIPAL AREAS OF WORK: McKinty & Wright offers a wide range of services to the commercial and insurance client, from routine advice to insolvency, property, insurance matters and litigation. The firm's litigation department has extensive experience in all aspects of commercial litigation with specialised expertise in personal injury, construction, professional negligence, defamation, insurance and general commercial litigation. The firm also has departments handling employment, licensing, corporate finance, property and general commercial advice.

MCLEAN & STEWART

51/53 High Street, Dunblane, FK15 0EG **Tel:** (01786) 823217 **Fax:** (01786) 822575 **DX:** 631 Dunblane **Ptnrs:** 4 **Asst solrs:** 1

McLELLANS

Old Cross House, Old Cross, Hertford, SG14 1RB
Tel: (01992) 300800 **Fax:** (01992) 300844 **DX:** 57921 Hertford
Email: slocke@mclellans.co.uk **Website:** www.mclellans.co.uk

Senior Partner	Nigel Mahoney
Number of partners	4
Assistant solicitors	4
Other fee-earners	1

AREAS OF PRACTICE

Commercial Property	45%
Licensing	25%
Employment	15%
Property Litigation	10%
Civil Litigation	5%

CONTACTS

Commercial Property	Sylvia Goulding
Employment	Nigel Mahoney
Licensing	Clare Eames
Property Litigation	Martin Miller

THE FIRM: McLellans is a niche commercial practice specialising in commercial property, licensing and employment law and is one of the leading leisure practices in the northern home counties. Four fee earners are experienced advocates (including one former barrister).

PRINCIPAL AREAS OF WORK:

Commercial Property: The firm provides a comprehensive commercial property service, including planning, development work, landlord and tenant, complex property acquisitions, disposals and the specialist aspects of licensed premises.

Licensing: The firm has a dedicated liquor licensing department which handles advocacy from within its own ranks throughout England and Wales.

Employment: The firm advises on all aspects of employment and disciplinary matters and handles advocacy in the Employment Tribunal and Employment Appeal Tribunal, particularly in relation to licensed trade employment matters.

Property Litigation: The firm advises and assists in resolving a variety of commercial and landlord and tenant disputes.

CLIENTELE: Clients include a national pub chain, a regional brewer, a national airline and other leisure, travel, manufacturing and property investment companies.

McMANUS & KEARNEY

Law Society House, 106 Victoria Street, Belfast, BT 1 3JZ **Tel:** (028) 90243658 **Fax:** (028) 90332151 **Email:** law@mcmanus-kearney.co.uk
Ptnrs: 2 **Asst solrs:** 2 **Other fee-earners:** 1

McNEIVE SOLICITORS

26 Cowper Street, London, EC2A 4AP **Tel:** (020) 7253 0535 **Fax:** (020) 7253 0537 **Email:** law@mcneive.com **Website:** www.mcneive.com
Ptnrs: 1 **Asst solrs:** 2 **Other fee-earners:** 2

MEADE-KING

24 Orchard Street, Bristol, BS1 5DF **Tel:** (0117) 926 4121 **Fax:** (0117) 929 7578 **DX:** 7812 **Email:** gen@meadeking.co.uk **Ptnrs:** 10
Asst solrs: 4 **Other fee-earners:** 4

MEMERY CRYSTAL

31 Southampton Row, London, WC1B 5HT
Tel: (020) 7242 5905 **Fax:** (020) 7242 2058 **DX:** 156 Chancery Lane
Email: info@memerycrystal.com **Website:** www.memerycrystal.com

Managing Partner	Jonathan Davies
Senior Partner	Peter Crystal
Number of partners	14
Assistant solicitors	16
Other fee-earners	12

AREAS OF PRACTICE

Corporate Finance & IP/IT	48%
Litigation	21%
Property & Property Litigation	24%
Employment	7%

CONTACTS

Corporate Finance	Lesley Gregory
Employment	Merrill April
Litigation	Harvey Rands
Property & Property Litigation	Douglas Robertson

THE FIRM: The emphasis in this thriving London firm is on commercial business and corporate issues. The firm focuses on providing its clients with practical and commercially viable advice with an entrepreneurial flair and a strong sense of commitment. The partners all have backgrounds in large City practices and have come together with the same belief that only through direct partner involvement can the best possible legal service be given, based on skills and experience built up over many years.

Memery Crystal operates in corporate finance, commercial litigation and property. Within these areas, specialist groups deal with company/commercial matters, intellectual property, digital technology and e-commerce, sports law, tax, insolvency, construction, insurance, corporate crime and regulatory law, employment and property litigation.

Memery Crystal is a progressive and growing firm, able to deal with all the requirements of small to medium sized companies and specialist requirements of larger companies. The firm is committed to establishing long term relationships with its clients, providing a cost effective, personal, partner-led service.

MERCY MESSENGER – SOLE PRACTITIONER

1683B High Street, Knoll, Solihull, B93 0LL **Tel:** (01564) 779 427 **Fax:** (01564) 778 732

MERRICKS

150 Minories, London, EC3N 1LS
Tel: (0870) 241 4848 **Fax:** (0870) 241 4847 **DX:** 522 London/City
Email: london@merricks.co.uk **Website:** www.merricks.co.uk

Lancaster House, 67 Newhall Street, Birmingham, B3 1LX
Tel: (0121) 233 0062 **Fax:** (0121) 233 9880 **DX:** 13145 Birmingham 1
Email: birmingham@merricks.co.uk

207-208 Moulsham Street, Chelmsford, CM2 0LG
Tel: (01245) 491414 **Fax:** (01245) 263829 **DX:** 89702 Chelmsford 2
Email: chelmsford@merricks.co.uk

8 Lion Street, Ipswich, IP1 1DQ
Tel: (01473) 231331 **Fax:** (01473) 230041 **DX:** 3264 Ipswich
Email: ipswich@merricks.co.uk

Senior Partner	Anthony Sheppard
Chief Executive	Michael Lambert
Number of partners	16
Assistant solicitors	17
Other fee-earners	20

AREAS OF PRACTICE

Personal Injury	25%
Insurance Litigation (eg Professional Indemnity, Recoveries, Liability, Fraud)	25%
Construction	20%
Commercial/Property	15%
Employment	9%
Marine & Transit	6%

CONTACTS

Commercial/Property	Mike Alexander
Construction/Engineering	Philip Harris
Employment	Sean Staunton-Dunne
Insurance	Andrew Hunn
Marine & Transit	Mariel Monk
Personal Injury	John Webster

THE FIRM: Merricks is predominantly a commercial practice with particular expertise in construction, insurance and personal injury litigation, servicing clients throughout the country from its London and regional offices. It also handles marine and transit, commercial property, conveyancing and employment work.

PRINCIPAL AREAS OF WORK:
Insurance: Merricks has a long and close relationship with clients in the insurance markets. Work includes a substantial volume of personal injury and industrial disease work, property damage, contractors all risks, fraudulent claims and policy disputes.
Professional Indemnity: The firm acts for leading players including accountants, solicitors and construction related professionals.
Construction/Engineering: An expert team handles the full range of dispute resolution techniques and non-contentious work, contractual claims, payment of certificates, liability disputes, contract drafting and interpretation, duty of care warranties, joint venture agreements and insurance claims.
Personal Injury: The firm acts for claimants and defendants, handling volume instructions and serious injury claims.
Marine & Transit: Areas handled include cargo and charter party disputes, cargo claims and recoveries, marine insurance, collision and salvage, international trade, CMR and domestic road haulage, freight forwarding, warehouse keeping, Road Traffic Act defences and vehicle operators licences.
Commercial Property: Investment property work of all description undertaken including property management, commercial development, commercial conveyancing and landlord and tenant.
Employment: All aspects of employment law in both the contentious and non-contentious fields covered.

MERRIMAN WHITE

3 King's Bench Walk, Inner Temple, London, EC4Y 7DJ
Tel: (020) 7936 2050 **Fax:** (020) 7353 0914 **DX:** 1015 London Chancery Lane
Email: info@merrimanwhite.com **Website:** www.merrimanwhite.com

Merlaw House, 12 The Mount, Guildford, GU2 4HN
Tel: (01483) 574466 **Fax:** (01483) 306184 **DX:** 2457 GUILDFORD
Email: j.wolff@merrimanwhite.co.uk

61 Fleet Street, London, EC4Y 1JU
Tel: (020) 7936 2050 **Fax:** (020) 7583 1783 **DX:** 1015 London Chancery Lane
Email: info@merrimanwhite.com

Managing Partner	Jeremy Wolff
Senior Partner	Raymond Murphy
Number of partners	2
Assistant solicitors	14
Other fee-earners	24

AREAS OF PRACTICE

Litigation	60%
Property	20%
Commercial	10%
Private Client	10%

THE FIRM: A long-established City firm acting on behalf of UK and overseas clients. Merriman White are Privy Council agents.

PRINCIPAL AREAS OF WORK: Merriman White carries out litigation, property and commercial work for business clients of all sizes including major companies in house building, contracting and publishing. It does adjudication and arbitration work in both the construction and commodities fields. It provides a wide spectrum of property, estate, tax and matrimonial services for private clients, as well as specialising in insurance and personal injury work. The firm advises individuals and companies facing criminal investigation and prosecution and has acted for defendants in prosecutions brought by the Inland Revenue, Customs and Excise and by the SFO. The firm also advises individuals and companies facing prosecution for breaches of health and safety and environmental protection legislation.

INTERNATIONAL: The firm benefits from staff who are fluent in a variety of languages including French, Spanish, Italian, German, Yoruba and Farsi.

METCALFE COPEMAN & PETTEFAR

8 York Row, Wisbech, PE13 1EF
Tel: (01945) 464 331 **Fax:** (01945) 476 695 **DX:** 41350 Wisbech
Email: info@mcp-law.co.uk

25 Priestgate, Peterborough, PE1 1JL
Tel: (01733) 349 151 **Fax:** (01733) 312 728 **DX:** 12319 Peterborough
Email: info@mcp-law.co.uk

Cage Lane, Thetford, IP24 2DT
Tel: (01842) 764 141 **Fax:** (01842) 752 818 **DX:** 100902 Thetford
Email: info@mcp-law.co.uk

28-32 King Street, King's Lynn, PE30 1HQ
Tel: (01553) 765 231 **Fax:** (01553) 766 807 **DX:** 57811 King's Lynn
Email: info@mcp-law.co.uk

Senior Partner	Richard Carlson
Number of partners	12
Assistant solicitors	12
Other fee-earners	13

AREAS OF PRACTICE

Residential Property	29%
Commercial/Property/Retail Law	22%
Family	19%
Personal Injury/Litigation	18%
Crime	7%
Probate/Trusts/Tax Planning	5%

CONTACTS

Commercial Property	Jonathan Burton (Peterborough)
Company/Commercial	Tim Stevenson (Thetford)
Crime	Alison Muir (King's Lynn)
Employment	Paul Garner (Wisbech)
Family	Steve Welcomme (Wisbech)
Litigation/ADR	David Rutter (Wisbech)
Personal Injury	David Rutter (Wisbech)
Probate/Trusts	Simon Scott (King's Lynn)
Residential Property	Andrew Davies (Thetford)
Retail	Richard Carlson (Wisbech)

M

THE FIRM: Metcalfe Copeman & Pettefar is a commercial practice with a national reputation, particularly among retail clients. The firm is rated for the quality of its service to commercial clients which is characterised by partner-level attention, accessibility and responsiveness. There is a well established sector team providing specialist services to retailers. The firm is also a high street general practice providing a full range of legal services to private clients including residential conveyancing and other property matters, family law, probate, wills, trusts and tax planning. The personal injury group acts for claimants both from the local area and nationally under the brand name Accident Action.

RECRUITMENT: Applications for training places are welcomed and should be addressed to Alison Muir.

MICHAEL HUTCHINGS

Sandhayes, Corsley, Warminster, BA12 7QQ **Tel:** (07768) 105777 **Fax:** (01373) 832785 **Email:** mbh@dircon.co.uk • Michael Hutchings specialises in EU law and advises on competition cases before the Office of Fair Trading, Competition Commission, European Commission and European Court.

MICHAEL S. ALLEN

Unit 5, Tillydrone Shopping Centre, Hayton Road, Aberdeen, AB24 2UY **Tel:** (01224) 480 890 **Fax:** (01224) 480 980

MICHELMORES

18 Cathedral Yard, Exeter, EX1 1HE
Tel: (01392) 436244 **Fax:** (01392) 215579 **DX:** 8304
Email: enquiries@michelmores.com **Website:** www.michelmores.com

Managing Partner	Andrew Maynard
Senior Partner	Andrew Maynard
Number of partners	20
Assistant solicitors	21
Other fee-earners	27

CONTACTS

ADR	Tim Richards
Charities	Richard Wheeler
Commercial Property	Peter Lowless
Company/Commercial	Malcolm Dickinson
Corporate Finance	Rupert Cattell
Employment	Nick Benson
Family	Simon Thomas
Litigation	Trevor Coleman
Medical Negligence	Lawrence Vick
Private Client	Will Michelmore
Private Equity	Stephen Morse

THE FIRM: Michelmores is a dynamic law practice which takes a practical approach to providing a first class service to a wide range of clients. The firm has an entrepreneurial management team and the last year has seen the firm handle some of the largest and most complex transactions in the south of England and attract London based Internet clients keen to use the firm's expertise and competitive cost base. Michelmores combines state of the art technology with a progressive management style which promotes the highest possible professional standards yet respects the individual. The firm believes in the maxim that a happy firm is a successful firm. Its modern practices, youthful atmosphere and attractive location make it an unrivalled place in which to work which means it attracts top lawyers who want a better career and a better life. Michelmores is a regionally based alternative for national and international commercial clients who are looking for service, intellectual quality and value for money. Many of the firm's partners trained in the City of London and are experienced in acting for large commercial clients which range from multinational and local businesses to institutions, government departments and high net worth entrepreneurs.

MIDDLETON POTTS

3 Cloth Street, Barbican, London, EC1A 7NP
Tel: (020) 7600 2333 **Fax:** (020) 7600 0108 **DX:** 46621
Email: mail@middletonpotts.co.uk

Senior Partner	David Lucas
Number of partners	14
Assistant solicitors	11
Other fee-earners	9

CONTACTS

Commercial Litigation ....Patrick Hann
................Edwin Cheyney
Corporate/Commercial/ Banking/Insurance ....David Godfrey
................David Rabagliati
................Stephen Morrall
................Lindsey Hemingway
Property ....Richard Schmidt
................Howard Lupton
Shipping/Commodities Litigation
................Christopher Potts
................David Lucas
................Andrew Donoghue
................Andrew Ridings
................Faye Doherty

THE FIRM: Middleton Potts was founded in 1976 by six partners, all of whom had previously been with a well-established City practice, and has grown steadily over the past two and a half decades. The firm acts for shipping, commodity, financial, commercial and industrial clients from all over the world. It has four principal areas of work, as described below, and where a matter requires the involvement of lawyers from more than one discipline the client partner will ensure close co-ordination between the disciplines and provide continuity and a regular point of contact between the client and the firm.

PRINCIPAL AREAS OF WORK:

Shipping/Commodities Litigation: The firm's commodities practice has long been one of the most respected in the City, and the department contains several of the best known names in this field. Cases involving all types of commodities are handled, the main clients being international trading houses. The shipping practice also has a long-established and solid reputation. The cases handled are primarily charterparty and bill of lading disputes, though salvage, wreck removal and pollution cases are also undertaken. The main clients are P&I and defence clubs, shipowners, charterers and their insurers, and companies in the off-shore energy field.

Corporate/Commercial/Banking/Insurance: This department has also achieved considerable success, enjoys work of the highest calibre and often acts in transactions where the largest City firms are on the other side. The department handles international and domestic banking and financial matters of all kinds (including ship and project finance transactions); insurance and reinsurance work; the establishment by foreign entities of branches and subsidiaries in the UK; regulatory, compliance and administrative work; the preparation of standard documentation; acquisitions and disposals of shares and assets; corporate reorganisations; joint ventures; ship sales and purchases; international construction contracts and other major industrial, commercial and infrastructure projects (including schemes under the Private Finance Initiative); tax matters; a very broad spectrum of corporate and general commercial matters (including employment law, pensions law, insolvency and intellectual property work).

Commercial Litigation: This expanding group handles commercial disputes of all kinds and conducts both High Court litigation and domestic and international arbitration proceedings. The main areas of work are insurance and reinsurance; construction and technical disputes; banking and financial services litigation; insolvency; commercial fraud; tracing actions and cross-border litigation; and disputes in relation to real property, intellectual property, employment and corporate matters.

Property: The areas handled by this department include the acquisition, funding, development and disposal of freehold and leasehold office and residential premises, industrial sites and other commercial property units and portfolios, planning matters, the general management of property interests, and general commercial transactions related to property.

CLIENTELE: The client base covers a very broad spectrum and includes: commodity trading houses; shipowners and charterers; P&I clubs; oil majors and traders; major international banks, insurance companies and other financial institutions; freight forwarders and transportation companies; airlines; multinational manufacturing and trading corporations; property companies; international construction companies and project joint ventures; foreign state enterprises.

INTERNATIONAL: With a very strong international focus to the practice, Middleton Potts has developed close contacts with clients, lawyers and other professionals from different jurisdictions throughout the world. Many of the firm's lawyers speak at least one, and some speak several, of the following languages: Arabic, Bengali, French, German, Greek, Italian, Malay, Norwegian, Portuguese, Spanish and Turkish.

MILBANK, TWEED, HADLEY & MCCLOY

Dashwood House, 69 Old Broad Street, London, EC2M 1QS
Tel: (020) 7448 3000 **Fax:** (020) 7448 3029
Website: www.milbank.com

Managing Partner	Phillip Fletcher
Worldwide fee-earners	470
Number of UK partners	7
Number of UK associates	35
Total UK staff	60

AREAS OF PRACTICE

M&A, Corporate & Acquisition Finance	40%
Project Finance	35%
Banking & Structured Finance	25%

CONTACTS

Project Finance	John Dewar
Acquisition Finance	Kevin Muzilla
Banking	Patrick Holmes
Capital Markets	Tom Siebens
M&A	Michael Goroff
Securitisations	John Walker
Tax	Russel Jacobs

THE FIRM: The firm has international offices around the world, and clients of its multinational practice in London are offered a range of transactional services under English and New York law. These include banking, capital markets, project finance, securitisation, mergers and acquisitions and acquisition finance. The roots of the practice can be traced back to 1866, with the establishment of the firm that acquired its present name in 1962. It was one of the first US practices to expand internationally and it opened its London office more than 20 years ago.

PRINCIPAL AREAS OF WORK: In the UK, the firm has long been ranked on an equal footing with leading English firms in the area of project finance. More recently, the firm has drawn on its capital markets and mergers and acquisitions expertise to broaden its London practice to achieve prominence in each of these additional areas. The firm's London mergers and acquisitions group focuses on cross-border investments. For example, the group recently represented Goldman Sachs' private equity funds in their acquisition of Messer Griesheim, a German-based industrial gases company, in what is among the largest LBOs ever in Europe. The firm also advised Scottish Power in its acquisition of a US electrical utility in the first such acquisition by a foreign investor. Milbank's London lawyers also have growing reputations in the areas of structured finance, securitisations and acquisition finance. In the field of high yield acquisition finance, the firm acted for the underwriters on the bridge loan and high yield portions of the £1.3 billion leverage buyout of United Biscuits, accredited European Leveraged Loan of the Year for 2000 by International Financing Review. The office also acted on the financing of AES's acquisition of the 4,000 MW Drax power station in the UK partly by means of a £650 million senior and high yield project bond – the first of its kind in Europe; and on the recent Messer Griesheim €550 million high yield bond – the biggest such issue by a European industrial company. The London office has recognised expertise in securitisations involving collateralised loans and other debt portfolios, telecoms vendor financings, aircraft portfolios and natural resources receivables, and regularly acts for the leading underwriters of such issuances. The firm's enlarged corporate finance practice in London now also offers specialist tax advice in cross-border deals, adding significant value to tax-driven structured products as well as mergers and acquisitions transactional work. Milbank's projects practice remains a leader in the field in London, as it has been for nearly a decade. The firm recently advised the sponsors in the US $1.4 billion financing of the Taweelah A1 power and desalination project in Abu Dhabi, which was accorded regional Project Deal of the Year status for 2000 by International Financing Review, as well as parties in a range of other projects from Yemen to the UK.

CLIENTELE: Clients of the London office include major European, US and Japanese financial institutions as well as prominent multinational corporations and international utilities.

INTERNATIONAL: Milbank has other offices in New York, Los Angeles, Washington, Palo Alto, Singapore, Hong Kong and Tokyo.

MILES PRESTON & CO

10 Bolt Court, London, EC4A 3DQ
Tel: (020) 7583 0583 **Fax:** (020) 7583 0128
Email: milespreston@aol.com

Managing Partner	Miles Preston
Senior Partner	Miles Preston
Number of partners	4
Assistant solicitors	2

AREAS OF PRACTICE

Family & Matrimonial	90%
Cohabitation/Paternity Disputes	10%

THE FIRM: Miles Preston & Co is a specialist matrimonial and family law practice formed in May 1994, the three founding partners having previously worked together for over 10 years in a large central London general practice.

PRINCIPAL AREAS OF WORK:

Family: The firm deals with all aspects of matrimonial and family law including divorce and separation, cohabitation and pre-marriage agreements, all issues relating to children and the full range of emergency procedures. Many of the cases involve the resolution of complex financial issues usually concerning substantial assets, some with an international dimension. The practice aims to adopt a firm, effective and fair approach to the conduct of its cases and to offer a high quality and cost efficient service to its clients. All its solicitors are members of the Solicitors' Family Law Association.

CLIENTELE: The firm acts for UK and foreign individuals from a wide variety of backgrounds including business people, professionals and those in the entertainment world and the media.

INTERNATIONAL: The practice has close contacts with a number of other family lawyers worldwide. In addition, two of the partners are members of the International Academy of Matrimonial Lawyers, an association of over 300 prominent international family lawyers practising in various countries around the world.

MILLAR SHEARER & BLACK

40 Molesworth Street, Cookstown, BT80 8PH **Tel:** (028) 8676 2346 **Fax:** (028) 8676 6761 **DX:** 3272 Nr Cookstown **Ptnrs:** 5 **Asst solrs:** 4 **Other fee-earners:** 14

MILLER SAMUEL & CO

RWF House, 5 Renfield Street, Glasgow, G2 5EZ
Tel: (0141) 221 1919 **Fax:** (0141) 221 3796 **DX:** 161 Glasgow
Email: email@milsam.demon.co.uk

Managing Partner	Michael Samuel
Senior Partner	Michael Samuel
Number of partners	14
Assistant solicitors	8
Other fee-earners	12

AREAS OF PRACTICE

Commercial Litigation, Employment & Reparation	50%
Commercial Property & Corporate	40%
Personal (inc. Residential, Conveyancing, Wills, Trusts)	10%

CONTACTS

Commercial Litigation	Robert Kerr
	Laura Doherty
Commercial	Douglas Lamb
	Kelsey Gibson
	John McQuillan
Employment Law	Marie MacDonald
Matrimonial	Robert Kerr
Motor Claims	Diane Cainey
Reparation	Robert Skelly
Residential Conveyancing/ Wills & Trusts	Michael Samuel

THE FIRM: Founded in 1973, Miller Samuel is a well-established city centre firm, which provides a comprehensive legal service to commercial clients, with particular expertise in property development and leasing. The firm has developed a thriving litigation practice which complements the commercial work, including landlord and tenant litigation and employment law. It also handles a substantial amount of debt recovery, personal injury and matrimonial work. Its range of services include all private client fields.

PRINCIPAL AREAS OF WORK:

Commercial: Work handled includes corporate property development; commercial leasing; investment; funding; construction etc, service with specialist rent review arbitration/expert services. Private company work and general commercial contracts also handled.
Litigation: Work includes contract disputes; employment; reparation; debt collection; recovery of possession of heritable property; finance leasing; consumer credit; arbitration; road traffic accident claims; matrimonial.
Private Client: A comprehensive service is provided, offering clients advice on the administration of estates, tax planning, charities and wills. This department also deals with the purchase and sale of residential property.

MILLER SANDS

75-79 Regent St, Cambridge, CB2 1BE **Tel:** (01223) 366741 **Fax:** (01223) 227300 **DX:** 5816 Cambridge **Email:** info@millersands.com **Website:** www.millersands.com **Ptnrs:** 5 **Asst solrs:** 4 **Other fee-earners:** 6

MILLS & CO

Milburn House, Dean Street, Newcastle upon Tyne, NE1 1LE **Tel:** (0191) 233 2222 **Fax:** (0191) 233 2220 **Email:** law@mills-co.com **Website:** www.mills-co.com **Ptnrs:** 4 **Asst solrs:** 5 **Other fee-earners:** 1

MILLS & REEVE

Francis House, 112 Hills Road, Cambridge, CB2 1PH
Tel: (01223) 364422 **Fax:** (01223) 355848 **DX:** 122891 Cambridge 4
Email: duncan.oglivy@mills-reeve.com **Website:** www.mills-reeve.com

Bankside House, 107/112 Leadenhall Street, London, EC3A 4AF
Tel: (020) 7648 9220 **Fax:** (020) 7648 9221 **DX:** 508 London City
Email: duncan.oglivy@mills-reeve.com

Midland House, 132 Hagley Road, Edgbaston, Birmingham, B16 9NN
Tel: (0121) 454 4000 **Fax:** (0121) 456 3631 **DX:** 707290 Edgbaston 3
Email: duncan.oglivy@mills-reeve.com

Francis House, 3-7 Redwell Street, Norwich, NR2 4TJ
Tel: (01603) 660155 **Fax:** (01603) 633027 **DX:** 5210 Norwich
Email: duncan.oglivy@mills-reeve.com

Managing Partner	Duncan Ogilvy
Senior Partner	Jonathan Barclay
Number of partners	57
Assistant solicitors	135
Other fee-earners	91

AREAS OF PRACTICE

Corporate	25%
Property	15%
Private Client	10%
Land & Agriculture	10%
Health	15%
Education	10%
Local Authorities	5%
Insurance	10%

CONTACTS

Corporate	Ted Powell
Education	Glynne Stanfield
Health	Sheila Waddington
Insurance	Guy Hodgson
Land & Agriculture	William Barr
Local Authorities	Nick Hancox
Private Client	Matthew Arrowsmith-Brown
Property	Beverley Firth

THE FIRM: Mills & Reeve is one of the UK's largest regional law firms with 57 partners, 250 lawyers and a total strength of over 500. It operates nationwide from offices in Birmingham, Cambridge, London and Norwich. The firm has a national reputation for the quality of its advice and service, in particular to businesses and entrepreneurs and those who finance them, especially in the hi-tech sector; owners and developers of commercial property; the main carriers of professional indemnity risks; the NHS; higher and further education institutions; and large scale owners and occupiers of agricultural land. For all its clients the firm's aim is to provide creative solutions to their problems, be innovative in developing new products and services to meet their needs and meet consistently the high standards of delivery and quality of service they expect.

PRINCIPAL AREAS OF WORK:

Corporate & Property: The corporate and property teams handle matters as diverse as the businesses they advise. As well as substantial corporate, commercial, property and dispute resolution teams, the firm has spe-

Continued overleaf

M

cialist teams in intellectual property, tax, employment, pensions, insolvency, building and engineering, PFI, planning and environmental matters and licensing. The firm is developing a particular specialism in advising hi-tech and bio-tech businesses with the highest concentration in Europe of such businesses now located in the East of England. The firm is able to provide clients with a complete service including advocacy in-house at all levels of the civil and criminal courts and the use of alternative dispute resolution (ADR).

Healthcare: NHS Trust and health authority work continues to expand over a wide geographical basis throughout the UK. The firm is one of the top three healthcare law practices in the country, acting for over 150 NHS bodies and is currently advising on over 20 PFIs within the healthcare sector.

Education: Significant growth continues to be achieved in work for higher education institutions where the firm has acted for over 60 universities and colleges and is a recognised national leader. A full range of work is undertaken including PFI schemes and tax efficient funding schemes. The firm also has a growing reputation acting for further education institutions.

Local Authorities: Alongside its commitment to healthcare and educational institutions in the public sector, the firm also has a growing practice advising local authorities. In the past year the team advised over 25 local government institutions.

Insurance: The insurance team focuses on the main carriers of professional indemnity risk and the firm's decision in 2000 to open an office in London reflects this commitment. There are now specialist professional indemnity teams in each of the four offices.The team promotes the use of ADR and a number of lawyers have extensive experience in ADR techniques.

Land & Agriculture: The firm enjoys a well-established national reputation in farming and food, expanding its range of advice to clients at all points on the food chain.

Private Client: The firm also has one of the largest landed estate and private client practices outside London advising a wide range of landowners, entrepreneurs and business people on the full range of private client services including personal tax planning both in the UK and offshore.

MILLS SELIG

21 Arthur Street, Belfast, BT1 4GA
Tel: (028) 9024 3878 **Fax:** (028) 9023 1956 **DX:** 459 NR BELFAST
Email: info@nilaw.com **Website:** www.millsselig.com

Managing Partner	Richard Fulton
Senior Partner	Brian Ham
Number of partners	7
Associate partners	1
Assistant solicitors	5
Consultants	2
Other fee-earners	4

THE FIRM: Founded in 1959, Mills Selig has since developed to become a major force both in Northern Ireland and beyond, providing a comprehensive range of services to its predominantly corporate clientele. The firm's traditional strengths are in commercial property and corporate/corporate finance work but it has also developed a strong presence in litigation, particularly defamation, commercial litigation, product liability, intellectual property and employment law. Placing a strong emphasis on high quality service and developing close working relationships with clients, each client has an assigned partner to act as a contact point with overall knowledge of the client's affairs.

PRINCIPAL AREAS OF WORK:

Commercial Property: Acting for developers of retail, industrial, commercial and residential property, institutional lenders and investors and commercial landlords and tenants.

Company & Commercial: Complete range of company and commercial services with particular expertise in merger and acquisition of companies and businesses, joint ventures both locally and internationally, corporate finance, distribution and agency agreements. Specialist knowledge of retail, pharmaceuticals, energy, textiles, food industries, agrichemicals and franchising.

Litigation: Full range of civil litigation and tribunal services, with particular expertise in commercial litigation (including injunction work), defamation, product liability, intellectual property, professional indemnity, employment, construction, criminal damage and property litigation.

Private Client: Residential conveyancing, wills, trusts, estate planning and probate.

AREAS OF PRACTICE

Commercial Property	40%
Company & Commercial	30%
Litigation	25%
Other	5%

CONTACTS

Commercial Litigation	Paul Spring
	Brian Ham
	Adam Curry
Commercial Property	Brian Ham
	Jeremy Mills
	Michael Burns
Company & Commercial	Richard Fulton
	Bill McCann
Corporate Finance	Richard Fulton
Defamation	Paul Spring
Employment	Bill McCann
	Adam Curry
Environment & Planning	Michael Burns
Insolvency	John Kearns
Intellectual Property	Paul Spring
	Adam Curry
Private Client	Jeremy Mills
Product Liability	Paul Spring

MINCOFFS

Kensington House, 4-6 Osborne Road, Newcastle upon Tyne, NE2 2AA **Tel:** (0191) 281 6151 **Fax:** (0191) 281 8069 **DX:** 62550 **Email:** mail@mincoffs.u-net.com **Ptnrs:** 8 **Asst solrs:** 7 **Other fee-earners:** 11 **Contact:** Austen Science • Established over 50 years with strong focus on commercial property and corporate services (highest level of AIM listings in the area) leisure industry, professional negligence and employment.

AREAS OF PRACTICE

Corporate Services & Commercial Property	40%
Civil Litigation	30%
Private Client	20%
Licensing & Planning	10%

MINTER ELLISON

20 Lincoln's Inn Fields, London, WC2A 3ED **Tel:** (020) 7831 7871 **Fax:** (020) 7404 6722
Email: minters.mail@minters.com.au **Website:** www.minters.com.au **Number of partners (London):** 2
Number of partners (worldwide): 200 **Fee earners (London):** 6 **Fee earners (worldwide):** 600
Contact: Michael Whalley • Minter Ellison is a leading Australian law firm with offices and associated firms in most Australian states and in London, New York, Hong Kong, Bangkok, Jakarta and New Zealand.

MinterEllison
ENGLISH & AUSTRALIAN SOLICITORS

MISHCON DE REYA

21 Southampton Row, London, WC1B 5HS
Tel: (020) 7440 7000 **Fax:** (020) 7404 5982 **DX:** 37954 Kingsway
Email: feedback@mishcon.co.uk **Website:** www.mishcon.co.uk

Chairman	John Jackson
Joint Managing Partners	Kevin Gold
	Philip Freedman
Number of partners	36
Assistant solicitors	38
Other fee-earners	22
Trainees	19

AREAS OF PRACTICE

Corporate	33%
Litigation	30%
Property	28%
Family	9%

CONTACTS

Banking & Finance	Richard Tyler
	Eric Bettelheim
Competition Law	Michael Cover
Corporate & Commercial	Larry Nathan
E-Commerce	Grant Gordon
Employment	Rowena Herdman-Smith
	James Libson
Family	Sandra Davis
Film & TV Production	Martin Dacre
	Andrew Millett
Fraud	Gary Miller
	Kasra Nouroozi
Immigration	Philip Bath
	Kamal Rahman
Intellectual Property	Michael Cover
Landlord & Tenant (Residential)	Nick Doffman
Litigation	Tony Morton-Hooper
Media & Communications	Andrew Millett
Media inc. Defamation (Contentious)	Karen Sanig
Music	Martin Dacre
Planning & Environmental	Gordon Campell
Property	Nick Doffman
Retail & Leisure	Nick Doffman
Sport	Tony Morton-Hooper
	Grant Gordon

THE FIRM: Mishcon de Reya is not just any law firm. It is an unconventional commercial law firm, run by lawyers who understand business. Its lawyers have sound commercial knowledge and believe that the partnership with clients extends beyond office walls. Mishcon de Reya is an energetic and innovative practice committed to providing intelligent and creative legal advice. The practice has an open culture and many of its partners are young. The firm is chaired by John Jackson, a senior business figure and chairman of Hilton Group plc.

PRINCIPAL AREAS OF WORK: Organised internally into litigation, corporate and commercial, property and family departments, the firm has also developed specialist groups to meet the demands and opportunities of a constantly evolving commercial world.

Commercial Litigation: The firm's commercial litigation department is internationally respected for its work, which includes defamation, corporate disputes, employment law, fraud and all contentious media. The department also acts for high profile individuals and institutions. Other niche contentious practices include art, design, financial services and sport. Consideration is always given to alternative dispute resolution.

Property: The property department acts for a broad range of clients. Among them are publicly quoted companies, developers, pension funds, banks, house builders as well as private investors and occupiers. It has a growing reputation in the retail and leisure sector and in urban regeneration. Work ranges from major site assemblies, sale and purchase of investment portfolios, joint venture structuring, secured lending, planning and environment, to construction, pre-lets and plot sales.

Corporate & Commercial: The corporate and commercial department has developed a niche in new start-ups and technology, media and communications, including music, television and radio carriage, film and TV production, theatre and computer games. It advises on mergers, acquisitions and disposals, MBOs, flotations, joint ventures and venture capital, as well as providing general commercial advice including contracts, strategic alliances and distribution agreements. Other areas of work include competition and EU law, non-contentious employment and IP advice. The financial services group specialises in US and European regulation of financial institutions with expertise in derivatives, hedge funds, secured lending, cross-border transactions and structured products. The immigration group provides strategic advice from minimising clients' overseas tax liability to helping establish new business in the UK. In 2000, the successful merger with media and entertainment firm Eatons rounded off the firm's technology, media and communications capability.

Family: One of the leading practices in this field, the highly respected family department advises comprehensively on complex money and tax issues emanating from both domestic and international divorce and separation, together with conflicts arising over children that require sensitive and creative solutions. Other key areas of expertise range from advising on co-habitation disputes, pre-nuptial contracts and international child abduction cases. The firm has established a particular expertise in acting for high net worth, high profile individuals, who are under the media spotlight. The partners are trained mediators and use these skills as an enhancement to the practice.

CLIENTELE: Mishcon de Reya provides legal services to a wide range of corporate, entrepreneurial and individual clients and has a continuing commitment to a range of pro bono causes. Further details of the firm's services are available from its main website.

MLM

Waterloo House, Fitzalan Court, Newport Road, Cardiff, CF24 0BA **Tel:** 029 20 462 562 **Fax:** 029 20 491 118 **DX:** 33011 Cardiff
Email: info@mlmsolicitors.com **Website:** www.mlmsolicitors.com **Ptnrs:** 4 **Asst solrs:** 6 **Other fee-earners:** 5

M

M

MONIER-WILLIAMS & BOXALLS

71 Lincoln's Inn Fields, London, WC2A 3JF
Tel: (020) 7405 6195 **Fax:** (020) 7405 1453 **DX:** 37975 Kingsway
Email: mwb@71lif.com

Number of partners	6
Other fee-earners	3

CONTACTS

Charity Law	Michael Dunn
Company/Commercial & Partnership	John Randall
Employment	Peter McRoberts
Litigation	Gerald Neylan
Property	Christopher Hughes
Surrogacy	Gerald Neylan
Wine Trade Matters	David Silks

THE FIRM: Monier-Williams & Boxalls originated in 1790, and has developed a comprehensive range of services for business clients and for private individuals. The firm has been well known since the last century for its expertise in the wine trade and has a unique reputation in related intellectual property law. It has also acquired and developed particular expertise in employment law, professional partnerships, charity and surrogacy law.

CLIENTELE: The firm's clients include major public companies, banks, multiple retailers, insurance companies, educational establishments and well known charities. The approach is one of providing a personal service, with close involvement of partners, both in its specialised areas of work and in its wider general practice.

INTERNATIONAL: Include acting for agencies of the French, Spanish and Mexican governments. Work is handled in French and Spanish.

H. MONTLAKE & CO

197 High Rd, Ilford, IG1 1LX
Tel: (020) 8553 1311 **Fax:** (020) 8553 3066 **DX:** 124842 Ilford 7
Email: mail@montlake.co.uk

Senior Partner	Michael Bonehill
Number of partners	4
Assistant solicitors	1
Consultants	1

CONTACTS

Commercial Property	Michael Bonehill
Company & Commercial	Andrew Montlake
Litigation	Daniel Hockman
Probate & Trusts	Jeremy Davies
Residential Conveyancing	Jacqueline Josephs

THE FIRM: H Montlake & Co has been established since 1953 and has always specialised in carrying out property, company and commercial work and litigation for business clients of all sizes. A wide spectrum of property, tax, estate and matrimonial services is also available to private clients. The practice also has substantial experience in the sporting field where its clients include two football league clubs. Michael Bonehill, the managing partner, also has extensive experience in relation to theatrical work and charitable work and is the chairman of the National Youth Theatre of Great Britain and a Life Governor of the Imperial Cancer Research Fund. The practice has formed and acted for a large number of charities including theatrical, musical and medical charities.

MOORE & BLATCH

11 The Avenue, Southampton, SO17 1XF
Tel: (023) 8071 8000 **Fax:** (023) 8033 2205 **DX:** 38507 Southampton 3
Email: marketing@m-b.co.uk **Website:** www.mooreandblatch.co.uk

London Court, 64 London Road, Southampton, SO15 2EH
Tel: 023 8071 8000 **Fax:** 023 8033 3104 **DX:** 38524 Southampton 3

48 High Street, Lymington, SO41 9ZQ
Tel: (01590) 625 800 **Fax:** (01590) 672 371 **DX:** 34050 Lymington

73 High Street, Milford-on-Sea, Lymington, SO41 0QG
Tel: (01590) 642 172 **Fax:** (01590) 644 905

Managing Partner	Michael Caton
Senior Partner	Robert Miles
Number of partners	15
Assistant solicitors	29
Other fee-earners	61

AREAS OF PRACTICE

Insurance & Personal Injury	35%
Property	28%
Corporate	20%
Private Client	17%

CONTACTS

Commercial Property	Stephen Ingram
Company	Roger Bailey
Commercial	Peter Jeffrey
Insurance	David Thompson
Intellectual Property	Peter Jeffrey
Litigation	Dinshaw Printer
Private Client	Jessica Wiltshire
Town Planning	John Barrington

THE FIRM: Moore & Blatch is one of the major law firms in central southern England, with separate commercial and insurance offices in Southampton and a private client office in Lymington. Moore & Blatch prides itself on producing high-quality work and developing the services it provides to clients. Particular areas of strength are company, personal injury, commercial property, private client and wealth management.

PRINCIPAL AREAS OF WORK:

Corporate & Commercial: This department specialises in corporate transactions, including share and business acquisitions, MBOs and public offers and has been involved in bringing companies to AIM. The firm advises on company law, directors' responsibilities, insolvency, competition and EU law, intellectual property, partnership, employment and commercial matters.

Personal Injury & Insurance: This department handles all aspects of personal injury work, including industrial disease, medical negligence and road traffic injuries for both claimants and defendants. Within the department is a specialist serious injury team dealing with brain damage and other serious injuries. The department also advises insurers on all aspects of insurance law.

Litigation: The department provides a range of litigation services including employment law, health and safety, insolvency work, banking litigation, substantial trade and construction disputes, professional negligence, debt collection, intellectual property and admiralty work.

Property: The department handles the acquisition, disposal and management of commercial property, joint ventures, loan work and social housing schemes. The department also handles volume residential conveyancing schemes, landlord and tenant work, and residential and commercial land development and planning.
Planning & Development: Work includes planning agreements, planning appeals and inquiries and judicial reviews on behalf of national housebuilders, other developers, landowners and local authorities.
Private Client: The department provides a complete wealth administration service for private client families and work includes tax and estate planning, investments, wills, trusts, charitable trusts, probate and retirement finance, family law, general civil litigation and property. The department includes ATII and ACIB qualified specialists and has four members of STEP. The firm is a full member of the Association of Solicitor Investment Managers. In March 2001, the investment management services were hived off and merged with Thesis Asset Management plc through whom investment advice is now provided.
Transport Law: The firm has 25 years experience in acting for the transport industry, dealing with prosecutions, public enquiries, and operator licensing issues. Clients range from owner operator business to plcs.

MOORHEAD JAMES

21 New Fetter Lane, London, EC4A 1AW
Tel: (020) 7831 8888 **Fax:** (020) 7936 3635 **DX:** 288 London/Chancery Lane
Email: mail@moorheadjames.com

Senior Partner	Ben Moorhead
Number of partners	7
Assistant solicitors	2
Other fee-earners	6

CONTACTS

Company/Commercial	David James
	Ben Moorhead
Corporate Finance	David James
	Ben Moorhead
Employment	Christine Bowyer-Jones
	Wayne de Nicolo
	Edward Wheen
Insolvency	Edward Wheen
Litigation	Christine Bowyer-Jones
	Wayne de Nicolo
	Edward Wheen
Matrimonial/Family	Susan Leon
Offshore Tax Planning	R Moorhead
Oil & Gas	Julian Bishop
Property	Julian Bishop
	Susan Leon
Sports & Leisure	Ben Moorhead

THE FIRM: Moorhead James is a commercial practice offering a comprehensive range of services to clients ranging from private individuals to multinational businesses.

PRINCIPAL AREAS OF WORK:

Corporate & Commercial: Work includes formations, flotations, corporate restructuring, franchising and licensing, sports and leisure, banking, corporate finance, education, EU law and aviation.
Property: The department advises on all aspects of commercial and residential conveyancing; environmental law; construction and development; oil and gas; landlord and tenant.
Litigation: This includes High Court and County Court actions, landlord and tenant and other property disputes, employment matters, debt collection, professional negligence and insolvency.
Matrimonial: All aspects of divorce, financial settlements and cohabitation are handled.
Private Client: Work includes tax planning, charities, wills and probate.

INTERNATIONAL: The firm has offices in Frankfurt, Rome, Milan, Paris, Hong Kong, Beijing, Prague and Budapest. Work is handled in Cantonese, French and German.

MORAN & CO
40 Upper Gungate, Tamworth, B79 8AA **Tel:** 01827 546 31 **Fax:** 01827 689 05 **DX:** 12659 Tamworth **Email:** moranlaw.co.uk **Ptnrs:** 3 **Other fee-earners:** 2

MORE & CO
19 Dublin Street, Edinburgh, EH1 3PG **Tel:** (0131) 557 1110 **Fax:** (0131) 557 8882 **Ptnrs:** 3 **Asst solrs:** 15 **Other fee-earners:** 3

MORECROFT URQUHART
8 Dale Street, Liverpool, L2 4TQ **Tel:** (0151) 236 8871 **Fax:** (0151) 236 8109 **DX:** 14142 **Email:** mail@morecroft.co.uk **Website:** www.morecroft.co.uk **Ptnrs:** 11 **Asst solrs:** 6 **Other fee-earners:** 24

MORE FISHER BROWN
1 Norton Folgate, London, E1 6DA **Tel:** (020) 7247 0438 **Fax:** (020) 7247 0649 **Email:** mail@m-f-b.co.uk **Website:** www.m.f.b.co.uk **Ptnrs:** 10 **Asst solrs:** 7 **Other fee-earners:** 1

MORGAN COLE

167 Fleet Street, London, EC4A 2JB
Tel: (020) 7822 8000 **Fax:** (020) 7822 8222 **DX:** 261 London
Email: info@morgan-cole.com **Website:** www.morgan-cole.com

Bradley Court, Park Place, Cardiff, CF10 3DP
Tel: (029) 2038 5385 **Fax:** (029) 2038 5300 **DX:** 33014 Cardiff
Email: info@morgan-cole.com

Buxton Court, 3 West Way, Oxford, OX2 0SZ
Tel: (01865) 262 600 **Fax:** (01865) 721 367 **DX:** 96200 Oxford West
Email: info@morgan-cole.com

Apex Plaza, Forbury Road, Reading, RG1 1AX
Tel: (0118) 955 3000 **Fax:** (0118) 939 3210 **DX:** 117878 Reading Apex Plaza
Email: info@morgan-cole.com

Chairman	John Cole
Chief Executive	David Main
Number of partners	94
Assistant solicitors	155
Other fee-earners	139

AREAS OF PRACTICE

Insurance Litigation	31%
Business Services	26%
Commercial Litigation	21%
Property	17%
Private Client	5%

CONTACTS

Commercial Litigation	Allan Wilson
Commercial Property	Philip Jardine
Company/Commercial	Graeme Guthrie
	Bruce Potter
Construction	Andrew Campbell
Corporate Finance	Duncan Macintosh
Dispute Resolution	Phillip Howell-Richardson
Employment	Anthony Rees
Energy	Paul Dillon
Health	Philip Jardine
Insurance	Iain Tenquist
IT & IP	Alison Sarsfield-Hall
Landlord & Tenant	Jonathan Cantor
Public Law & PFI/Projects	Alun Cole

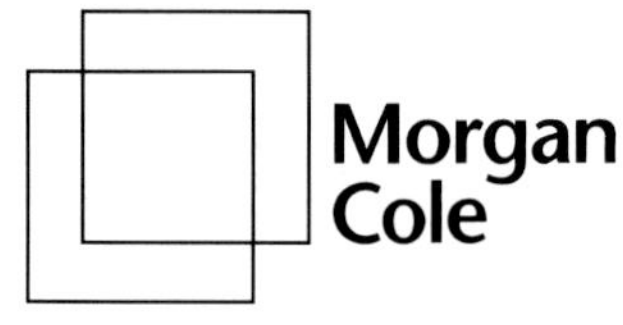

M

THE FIRM: Morgan Cole is a major law firm holding an unrivalled position across the southern half of the UK. With eight offices in London, Thames Valley and South Wales the firm provides a comprehensive service to commercial clients throughout the UK. Morgan Cole is a forward-looking firm committed to providing its clients with legal services to the highest possible standards. The firm enjoys a reputation for being both commercially aware and progressive and for giving strong and practical advice. Its aim is to be one of the UK's leading business law firms providing services to clients in the UK, Europe and beyond. It is committed to investment in clients, staff, IT and training, and to innovation and the continual pursuit of excellence. Partnership is key to the firm's approach and the reason for its commitment to gaining a real understanding of clients' businesses and building relationships. Lawyers work cross-office providing clients with access to greater resources and skills from all offices. A number of industry-focused groups are set up within the firm to ensure that specialised knowledge is always the basis on which advice is given. These groups include agriculture, banking, construction, education, energy, health, housing, IT, leisure, and media.

PRINCIPAL AREAS OF WORK: The firm services a wide range of organisations in a variety of sectors. Main areas of work include ADR; agriculture; banking; charities; commercial litigation; construction; corporate and commercial; debt recovery; EU and competition law; employment; energy; health; insolvency; insurance litigation; intellectual property; information technology; landlord and tenant; leisure and licensing; PFI and projects; professional negligence; property, planning and environmental; public law.
ADR: At the forefront of alternative dispute resolution for many years, the firm has 27 trained mediators who have experience in mediating a wide range of cases.
Insurance: Fishburn Morgan Cole is the firm's specialist insurance division, dealing with professional indemnity litigation, Lloyds and the London market, financial services and reinsurance. It has a strong track record in the defence of claims against professionals such as architects, engineers, surveyors, brokers, accountants and financial advisers. The specialist claims department is staffed by a unique mixture of personnel qualified in law and insurance and currently administers a number of individually designed schemes where a full claims service is provided. Additional services include pre-risk surveys and claims audits.

INTERNATIONAL: Enjoying strong international links, Morgan Cole is a founder member of the Association of European Lawyers and has established connections with law firms in North America and the Far East.

MORGAN JONES & PETT

95 St. Georges Road, Great Yarmouth, NR30 2NR **Tel:** (01493) 334700 **Fax:** (01493) 334710 **DX:** 41102 **Email:** yarmouth@m-j-p.co.uk
Website: www.m-j-p.co.uk **Ptnrs:** 3 **Asst solrs:** 2 **Other fee-earners:** 3

MORGAN, LEWIS & BOCKIUS

2 Gresham Street, London, EC2V 7PE
Tel: (020) 7710 5500 **Fax:** (020) 7710 5600 **DX:** 42603 Cheapside 1
Website: www.morganlewis.com

UK	
Number of partners	7
Assistant solicitors	17
Other fee-earners	4
International	
Number of partners	330
Other fee-earners	1100

AREAS OF PRACTICE

Corporate/Commercial	40%
Litigation	33%
Tax	20%
Pharmacuetical	5%
Other	2%

THE FIRM: Founded in Philadelphia in 1873, Morgan Lewis & Bockius LLP is one of the oldest and largest law firms in the US with over 300 partners and more than 1,100 lawyers. Morgan Lewis ranks among the top ten US law firms in the world. Every area of the firm's practice – from anti-trust to litigation – has a strong international component. Morgan Lewis represents clients in mergers and acquisitions, technology and emerging business all over the world, resolving differing and sometimes conflicting laws in a number of jurisdictions to reproduce the optimum results. Additionally, the firm's lawyers understand the problems and complexities of transnational litigation and can advise on US and EU regulatory matters. Morgan Lewis' clients are diverse and include Fortune 250 companies, leading financial services and investment banking

organisations, as well as pioneers in the e-commerce and Internet sector. All of the firm's clients receive the same high level of care and the firm recognises why they chose Morgan Lewis – because they want a professional firm with experienced, quality people who are as internationally minded as they are.
London Office: The London office of Morgan Lewis, which was founded in 1981, is fully integrated with the firm's other offices and works closely not only with the US offices, but also with the offices located outside the US, in particular Brussels and Frankfurt. In addition, the lawyers in the London office frequently act as liaison with clients who seek to have their legal representation co-ordinated with local counsel in countries where the firm does not have offices. In this regard, the firm has developed a comprehensive network of contacts and leading law firms in such countries.

PRINCIPAL AREAS OF WORK: The firm handles a vast diversity of legal work including: anti-trust, business and commercial litigation, business and finance, corporate transactions, employment, labour and benefits, energy and utilities, intellectual property, investment management, life sciences, personal law, mergers and acquisitions, real estate, securities, tax and technology.

INTERNATIONAL: The firm has other offices in Brussels, Frankfurt, Tokyo, New York, Harrisburg, Los Angeles, Philadelphia, Pittsburgh, Princeton, Miami, Washington, Northern Virginia.

CONTACTS

Corporate/Commercial	Thomas Benz
	Peter Wallace
	Zoë Ashcroft
Litigation	Robert Goldspink
	Neville Byford
Pharmaceutical	Anthony Warnock-Smith
Trust & Tax	Charles Lubar
	Michael Cashman

Morgan Lewis

REGISTERED FOREIGN LAWYERS & SOLICITORS

M

MORISON BISHOP

2 Blythswood Square, Glasgow, G2 4AD
Tel: (0141) 248 4672 **Fax:** (0141) 221 9270 **DX:** GW 11
Email: mail@morisonbishop.co.uk **Website:** www.morisonbishop.co.uk

Erskine House, 68 Queen Street, Edinburgh, EH2 4NN
Tel: (0131) 226 6541 **Fax:** (0131) 226 3156 **DX:** ED 38
Email: mail@morisonbishop.co.uk

51 Frederick Street, Edinburgh, EH2 1LH
Tel: (0131) 226 6000 **Fax:** (0131) 226 2540 **DX:** ED 38
Email: mail@morisonbishop.co.uk

Managing Partner	Ewan Dyce (Edinburgh)
Chairman	John Welsh (Glasgow)
Number of partners	28
Assistant solicitors	30
Other fee-earners	39

THE FIRM: Morison Bishop is a leading commercial law firm focused on delivering high quality professional advice to corporate and commercial clients. Morison Bishop has strengths and abilities in corporate law, commercial property and litigation, with dedicated units for asset recovery, reparation, insolvency, employment and debt recovery. The firm also has an enviable reputation in the fields of pensions, construction and environmental law. Morison Bishop is one of the biggest legal practices in Scotland, with offices located in Glasgow and Edinburgh. The depth of knowledge and breadth of experience within the firm provides Morison Bishop with the ability to assist clients across the full spectrum of legal services. This varies from one-to-one legal advice for a private client, to specialist teams working with a large corporate client.

PRINCIPAL AREAS OF WORK:
Corporate: Specialist areas of work within this division include corporate finance, pensions, constitutional, competition and EU law, intellectual property and IT, general corporate, insolvency, and media and sports law.
Commercial Property: Specialist advice includes: purchase and sale, leasing, property investment, shopping and retail centres, environmental law, licensing and franchising. This division also includes a house builders unit which deals with land acquisition and disposals, leasing and redevelopment.
Litigation: Specialist areas of work within this division include reparation, family law, employment law, debt recovery, alternative dispute resolution, construction, professional negligence, health and safety, and general civil litigation.
Asset Recovery: Specialist services within this division include repossessions, recovery of mortgage arrears; property management, estate agency service and financial advice.
Private Client: Specialist advice includes wills, tax, trusts and executries, financial and investment advice and elderly client service.

MORRISH & CO

Oxford House, Oxford Row, Leeds, LS1 3BE **Tel:** (0113) 245 0733 **Fax:** (0113) 242 5168 **DX:** 12044 **Email:** Morrish.Co@dial.pipex.com
Ptnrs: 8 **Asst solrs:** 3 **Other fee-earners:** 7

MORTON FISHER

Carlton House, Worcester St, Kidderminster, DY10 1BA
Tel: (01562) 820 181 **Fax:** (01562) 820 066 **DX:** 16301/16302
Website: www.mortonfisher.co.uk

Managing Partner	M V Burton
Senior Partner	J S Quinn
Number of partners	17
Assistant solicitors	18
Other fee-earners	21

CONTACTS

Agricultural	J S Quinn
Charity	D C Bishop
Commercial Litigation & Planning	T M L Jones
Debts	N Robertson Smith
Family	G Trenchard
	K Reynolds
Health	J S Quinn
Medical Negligence	C G A Stanley
Personal Injury	N Robertson Smith
	C G A Stanley
	M V Burton

THE FIRM: Morton Fisher has six offices covering a wide geographical area throughout Worcestershire. The firm serves the needs of the local community, specialising in company/commercial work for business, agricultural law, and private client work. The firm handles a substantial amount of litigation, including matrimonial work, commercial litigation, planning, property and estate administration. Members of the firm are on the Law Society's Children panel, the Personal Injury panel and the Family Law panel. It holds the Legal Aid Franchise. Other offices are in Stourport-on-Severn, Bromsgrove, Bewdley, Worcester and Cleobury Mortimer.

PRINCIPAL AREAS OF WORK:

Financial Services: Morton Fisher is one of the first firms to start a financial services department, employing two IFAs and support staff.

Additional Areas: Agricultural, charity, childcare, commercial litigation and planning, debts, health, matrimonial, medical negligence and personal injury.

N

MORTON FRASER, SOLICITORS

30-31 Queen Street, Edinburgh, EH2 1JX **Tel:** (0131) 247 1000 **Fax:** (0131) 247 1007 **DX:** ED119 **Email:** infodesk@morton-fraser.com **Website:** www.morton-fraser.com **Ptnrs:** 20 **Asst solrs:** 31 **Other fee-earners:** 92 **Contact:** Mrs Debbie Entwistle • Commercial firm with a strong private clients practice – specialisms in asset finance, family, employment, e-business and online legal services the firm deals with a growing number of cross border transactions.

AREAS OF PRACTICE

Commercial Property	34%
Litigation	27%
Private Client	14%
Residential Property	13%
Corporate	12%

MOURANT DU FEU & JEUNE

PO Box 87, 22 Grenville Street, St Helier, JE4 8PX
Tel: (01534) 609000 **Fax:** (01534) 609333
Email: enquiry@mourant.com **Website:** www.mourant.com

Mourant du Feu & Jeune, London, 4th Floor, 35 New Bridge Street, Blackfriars, London, EC4V 6BW
Tel: (020) 7332 6161 **Fax:** (020) 7332 6199
Email: jonathan.walker@mourant.com

Managing Partner	Richard Jeune
Senior Partner	Conrad Coutanche
Jersey	
Number of partners	21
Assistant solicitors	7
Other fee-earners	46

CONTACTS

Commercial Litigation	Beverley Lacey
Commercial Property	Liz Breen
Corporate Structures	Nicola Davies
Corporate/Commercial	Tim Herbert
Employee Benefits	James Crill
International Finance	Jacqueline Richomme

Mourant du Feu & Jeune

THE FIRM: A world leader in offshore legal services, Mourant du Feu & Jeune has expanded rapidly through the past five years, in keeping with the increasing growth and strength of the financial sector in Jersey. Established in 1947, the firm now has 21 partners and 26 other lawyers. Mourant du Feu & Jeune prides itself on having some of the finest lawyers in Jersey, many of whom gained experience in major City firms before practising Jersey law. It is a true innovator and has led the way in many aspects of the development of Jersey's world-renowned financial services industry. In 2000 Mourant du Feu & Jeune and Mourant & Co acted for 70% of the FTSE 100 companies and 22% of the top 100 companies in *Business Week Global 1000*. Recognising the importance of its City client base, the firm opened a London branch office in April 2000, the first Channel Islands law firm to do so.

PRINCIPAL AREAS OF WORK:

International Finance: The international finance team advises global financial institutions in the Jersey legal aspects of securitisation, capital markets transactions, structured and corporate finance and banking. These have been areas of particular growth for the firm in recent years and these are fields in which it has established a particularly strong reputation, having advised in many innovative and high profile transactions. In the securitisations category of the *Fitzrovia Funds Encyclopaedia 2000-2001*, Mourant du Feu & Jeune is ranked as top legal adviser, having advised on 71 individual transactions between 1 July 1999 and 30 June 2000. The *Fitzrovia Funds Encyclopaedia 2000-2001* also shows that Mourant du Feu & Jeune continues to hold a dominant position in Jersey's fund industry, ranked once again as outright legal market leaders and listed as legal adviser to 46% of Jersey-domiciled funds.

Commercial: The commercial team specialises in advising businesses on matters of Jersey commercial and corporate law. Its particular areas of expertise include trust and company law, collective investments, regulation of financial services, mergers and acquisitions and employment law.

Commercial Litigation: The four partner, 35-strong litigation department has a pre-eminent reputation for dealing with Jersey-related litigation, alternative dispute resolution and regulatory investigations. The department regularly works in conjunction with City law firms and professional advisers worldwide. Dedicated service groups, focusing primarily on the requirements of financial institutions, cover all aspects of financial services regulation, contentious banking and trust law issues, asset tracing, employment law, insolvency and company law issues/shareholder disputes.

Corporate Structures: The firm's trust and company administration organisation, Mourant & Co, specialises in providing a full range of administration services for onshore and offshore structures for a range of commercial applications. Areas of particular growth in recent years include structures for employee share plans (over $6 billion of assets under administration), capital markets transactions (in excess of $60 billion of assets under administration) and collective investment funds assets (over $6 billion of assets under administration). Structures for international property and ownership have also proved a particular growth area in recent months.

Private Wealth Management: Mourant & Co's highly-regarded private wealth management group is trusted by many high-profile individuals to manage their financial and legal affairs in a discreet, innovative and competent fashion.

MOWAT DEAN & CO WS

45 Queen Charlotte Street, Leith, Edinburgh, EH6 7HD **Tel:** (0131) 555 0616 **Fax:** (0131) 553 1523 **Email:** mailroom@mowatdean.demon.co.uk
Ptnrs: 4 **Asst solrs:** 4 **Other fee-earners:** 3

N

MULLIS & PEAKE

8-10 Eastern Road, Romford, RM1 3PJ **Tel:** (01708) 784000 **Fax:** (01708) 784099 **DX:** 138126 Romford 4 **Email:** office@mplaw.co.uk **Website:** www.mplaw.co.uk **Ptnrs:** 11 **Asst solrs:** 4 **Other fee-earners:** 6 **Contact:** John Poulten • Well known locally for commercial development conveyancing, commercial and probate work. The firm also specialises in both gaming and liquor licensing.

AREAS OF PRACTICE	
Private Client	60%
Commercial	25%
Probate	15%

MUNDAYS

Crown House, Church Road, Claygate, Esher, KT10 0LP
Tel: (01372) 809000 **Fax:** (01372) 463782 **DX:** 36300 Esher
Email: hub@mundays.co.uk **Website:** mundays.co.uk

Hamilton House, 1 Temple Avenue, London, EC4Y 0HA
Tel: (020) 7437 8080 **Fax:** (020) 7437 8180

Oak House, 39-41 The Parade, Claygate, Esher, KT10 0PZ
Tel: (01372) 809000 **Fax:** (01372) 460661 **DX:** 36301 ESHER

Chief Executive	Roger Formby
Senior Partner	Peter Munday
Number of partners	17
Other fee-earners	8
Assistant solicitors	13
Notaries public	3

AREAS OF PRACTICE	
Corporate/Commercial	35%
Commercial Property	24%
Dispute Resolution/Litigation	15%
Family	9%
Private Wealth	9%
Residential Conveyancing	8%

CONTACTS	
Aviation Law	David Irving
Commercial Property	Simon Withers
Corporate Finance	Richard Powell
Dispute Resolution	Fiona McAllister
E-commerce	Valerie Toon
Employment	Sarah Allen
Family	Ian Connell
Franchising	Manzoor Ishani
Mergers & Acquisitions	Peter Munday
Partnership	David Irving
Residential Property	Susan Poulton
Wills, Probate & Tax	Ray Walley

THE FIRM: Mundays is a comprehensive regional practice that is particularly strong in the corporate and commercial fields. Established in 1960, Mundays has a diverse client base that includes major international and national companies as well as small local businesses and individuals.

PRINCIPAL AREAS OF WORK:

Corporate/Commercial: This department is made up of several teams: mergers and acquisitions (takeovers, share and asset sales, MBOs, MBIs, public to private transactions, joint ventures and corporate re-organisations); corporate finance (fundraising including IPOs, rights issues, venture capital funding and private placings); IP (copyright, trademarks, know-how, IT law); franchising (agreements, disputes, international franchising and property transactions); employment (from employers and employee perspectives); commercial (general aspects of commercial law).

Property: The complete range of transactions is handled by this department, including leasehold transactions, sale and purchase of unincorporated businesses, and town and country planning matters.

Dispute Resolution: This department provides advice on disputes concerning commercial matters, franchising, property, employment, IP/IT and software and private client services.

Private Client: This team deals with private wealth, family, conveyancing and dispute resolution.

MURRAY BEITH MURRAY W.S.

39 Castle Street, Edinburgh, EH2 3BH
Tel: (0131) 225 1200 **Fax:** (0131) 225 4412 **DX:** ED40, Edinburgh
Email: mbm@murraybeith.co.uk **Website:** www.murraybeith.co.uk

Managing Partner	John K Scott Moncrieff
Chairman	William Berry
Number of partners	12
Assistant solicitors	15
Other fee-earners	26

AREAS OF PRACTICE

Asset Management	35%
Private Client	34%
Commercial	31%

CONTACTS

Asset Management	W R Gemmell
Commercial Property	F A J More
Corporate	W A Finlayson
Litigation	N J Pollock
Private Client	H P Younger

THE FIRM: This progressive Edinburgh-based practice offers an extensive range of services to private and business clients, with specialities including asset management and tax planning, agricultural law and land purchase, and advising high growth young companies. Established in 1849, Murray Beith Murray actively seeks to combine its traditional strength of a dedicated client service with modern management and innovative use of technology. The firm's services are provided through three separate divisions, namely private client, asset management and commercial.

PRINCIPAL AREAS OF WORK:
Private Client: Murray Beith Murray's core business is private client work and the firm is regarded as one of the leading private client legal firms in Scotland. This division provides a comprehensive range of legal, financial and administrative services, including wills and estate planning, trusts, taxation and executries. In the area of property law it offers a full service on agricultural law and rural property matters alongside a residential estate agency and conveyancing service.
Asset Management: The asset management division offers a full financial planning service including a comprehensive, independent overview of a client's investment and financial needs. Advice is given on a wide range of financial planning issues, including protection of the family, school fees planning, insurance, pensions advice for retirement planning and investment.
Investment: Measured by funds under management, Murray Beith Murray is one of the largest solicitor investment managers in the United Kingdom. It provides a full range of investment management and administration services on both a discretionary and advisory basis.
Commercial: The commercial division offers an extensive range of legal services to assist companies from start-up, through the early years to flotation and beyond. An efficient, competitive and personal service is combined with excellent financial contacts, deal-making skills and information technology systems.
Commercial Property: Services include the acquisition, development and realisation of commercial property of all kinds, together with advice on regulatory planning and environmental issues. These are supported by a litigation service, which includes amongst its specialities work in the areas of professional negligence claims, property and commercial disputes.

MURRAY BEITH MURRAY WS
SOLICITORS AND ASSET MANAGERS

CLIENTELE: Murray Beith Murray's client base includes national and international companies, property investors and developers, financial institutions and private investors and a significant number of land owning interests. The firm's aim is to create, enhance and protect the wealth of its clients.

MYER WOLFF

King William House, Lowgate, Hull, HU1 1YE **Tel:** (01482) 223693 **Fax:** (01482) 225089 **DX:** 11904 **Email:** info@myer-wolff.co.uk **Ptnrs:** 7 **Asst solrs:** 3 **Other fee-earners:** 11 • A long established and regionally known public funding and private client practice specialising in criminal law, child care, matrimonial and mental health tribunal work.

AREAS OF PRACTICE

Crime	47%
Family (inc. Childcare and Mental Health)	21%
Personal Injury/Claims	13%
Matrimonial	10%
Conveyancing/Probate	9%

NABARRO NATHANSON

Lacon House, 84 Theobald's Road, London, WC1X 8RW
Tel: (020) 7524 6000 **Fax:** (020) 7524 6524 **DX:** 77 London/Chancery
Email: info@nabarro.com **Website:** www.nabarro.com

The Anchorage, 34 Bridge Street, Reading, RG1 2LU
Tel: (0118) 950 4700 **Fax:** (0118) 950 5640 **DX:** 4068 Reading
Email: info@nabarro.com

1 South Quay, Victoria Quays, Wharf Street, Sheffield, S2 5SY
Tel: (0114) 279 4000 **Fax:** (0114) 278 6123 **DX:** 712550 Sheffield 20
Email: info@nabarro.com

Senior Partner	Simon Johnston
Managing Partner	Nicole Paradise
Number of partners	110
Assistant solicitors	228
Other fee-earners	149

CONTACTS

Banking	Andrew McLean
Charities	Jonathan Burchfield
Commercial Litigation	David Anderson
Construction	Justin Ede
Corporate/Commercial	Rhidian Jones
	Clive Lightburn
Electricity	Robert Tudway
Employment	Valmai Adams
	Keith Pugh
Environment	Mike Renger
EU/Competition	Cyrus Mehta
Health	David Anderson
Health & Safety	Gareth Watkins
Information Technology	Tony Bailes

THE FIRM: Nabarro Nathanson is one of the country's leading commercial practices, providing the full range of legal services to national and international clients. The firm is a focused commercial practice, with more than 100 partners and some 300 fee-earners. The firm has recently undergone a period of growth that has seen major infrastructure changes, significant increases in fee earning and a new emphasis on client relationships. The firm is recognised as a leading player in many areas of the law including the corporate sector, property, IT, pensions, public sector, planning, property litigation and PFI. More than 25 per cent of the firm's work is with clients based overseas. In 1999 the firm moved its London office to new premises between the City and the West End, where it can optimise investments in IT and other support systems. There is also a new focus on training and development from which all members of Nabarro Nathanson now benefit. The breadth of work undertaken is matched by the quality of service provided – Nabarro Nathanson prides itself in being a highly commercial and forward-thinking practice with friendly, high quality professional staff.

PRINCIPAL AREAS OF WORK: Nabarro Nathanson's strength and diversity is a reflection of its varied, and growing, client base. Clients' needs are addressed through a range of industry sector groupings that run alongside traditional legal departments. These groupings comprise commercial property, energy, computers, communications and electronic publishing, pensions, insurance and financial services, public and private projects, corporate finance and a national centre for law in industry which services the needs of the manufacturing sector.

Corporate: The corporate department covers mergers and acquisitions, flotations, venture capital and management buyouts, EU law, intellectual property, tax, energy and insurance. The firm is also a leader in banking transactions for domestic and international banks and other major financial institutions.

Property: Nabarro Nathanson has long been one of Britain's leading property law firms specialising in development, portfolio management, property finance, large-scale acquisitions and investments and overseas property. Separate departments deal with property litigation, construction law work, and public sector matters (including planning, PFI and CPO).

Other Areas: Other areas where the firm has significant strengths are IT (based in Reading), tax, health and community care, personal injury, charities and pensions. Nabarro Nathanson also has a high reputation for its general litigation and corporate insolvency work.

INTERNATIONAL: Nabarro Nathanson has an office in Brussels. It is also in association with Cabinet Lipworth in Paris and has associated offices in Dubai and Hong Kong.

RECRUITMENT: The firm is always looking for individuals who can make a contribution to its success. Recent growth provides opportunities for qualified solicitors across a range of specialisms. There are also vacancies for trainee solicitors – mostly in London but also in the firm's Reading and Sheffield offices. Candidates must have an upper second degree, although not necessarily in law. Long-term prospects are excellent. Contact Jane Drew for application information.

CONTACTS CONTINUED

Insolvency .... Patricia Godfrey
IP .... Guy Heath
.... Jim Kinnier-Wilson
International Tax .... Huw Witty
Litigation .... Gareth Jones
Litigation/Dispute Resolution .... Peter Sigler
.... Gareth Watkins
.... Peter Sheppard
National Centre for Law in Industry
.... Gareth Watkins
Oil & Gas .... Gareth Jones
Pensions .... John Quarrell
Personal Injury .... Peter Goodwill
PFI .... Malcolm Iley
.... Timothy Shaw
Planning .... David Hawkins
.... Norna Hughes
Property .... David Wright
.... Martin Grabiner
.... Amanda Howard
Property Litigation .... Iain Travers
Public Sector .... Malcolm Iley
Sports .... Michael Hales
Tax .... Huw Witty
Timeshare .... David Anderson
Trusts/Private Client .... Jim Edmondson
Venture Capital .... Rhidian Jones

N

NAPIER & SONS

1/9 Castle Arcade, Belfast, BT1 5DF **Tel:** (028) 90244602 **Fax:** (028) 90330330 **Email:** jgg@napiers.com **Website:** www.napiers.com **Ptnrs:** 4 **Asst solrs:** 6 **Other fee-earners:** 2

NAPTHEN HOUGHTON CRAVEN

7 Winckley Square, Preston, PR1 3JD
Tel: (01772) 883883 **Fax:** (01772) 257805 **DX:** 714572 Preston 14
Email: napthen.houghton.craven@nhc-sol.co.uk

Senior Partner	Peter Hosker
Number of partners	13
Assistant solicitors	7
Other fee-earners	12

THE FIRM: Created on the merger in 1990 of two of Preston's leading firms, Houghton Craven & Dicksons and Napthens. Since the merger, the firm has continued to expand, concentrating on the development of specialist departments. The firm is partner-managed and led, and designed to provide a speedy response for all clients, with particular emphasis on commercial work. Whilst the practice is based in the North West, the firm's clients are spread throughout the country and include offshore companies and trusts. Much of the firm's work is carried out on a national level.

PRINCIPAL AREAS OF WORK:

Commercial: The firm provides a wide range of legal services for commerce, industry, and investor clients. Best known for its commercial property (including planning and compensation) and corporate work, the firm has developed a thriving department specialising in employment law, and also specialises in commercial litigation. The firm has been appointed as sole panel solicitors for the North West region by the National Farmers Union and deals with agricultural legal work of all kinds.

Private Client: Napthen Houghton Craven handles property, probate and trust work, and family matters. A specialist department handles personal injury work with particular emphasis on road traffic accidents.

NAUTADUTILH

Bowman House, 29 Wilson Street, London, EC2M 2SJ
Tel: (020) 7786 9100 **Fax:** (020) 7588 6888
Email: ndlondon@nautadutilh.com **Website:** www.nautadutilh.com

Resident Partner	Gijs Gerretsen
Number of fee-earners	8

• NautaDutilh

THE FIRM: NautaDutilh is one of continental Europe's leading law firms. With more than 400 attorneys, civil law notaries and tax advisers, the firm operates from three main offices in Amsterdam, Brussels and Rotterdam, as well as from offices in London, Madrid, New York and Paris.

PRINCIPAL AREAS OF WORK: The London office specialises in the following types of work: corporate, corporate finance, mergers and acquisitions, banking and structured finance.

CLIENTELE: Clients include financial institutions, corporates and referrals from other firms.

INTERNATIONAL: Despite the increasingly global nature of the firm's practice and intensive ties with many law firms in other jurisdictions, NautaDutilh has clearly and publicly chosen to remain independent.

N

NEEDHAM & JAMES

25 Meer Street, Stratford-upon-Avon, CV37 6QB **Tel:** (01789) 414 444 **Fax:** (01789) 296 608 **DX:** 16202 Stratford upon Avon **Email:** info@neejam.co.uk **Website:** www.needham-james.co.uk **Ptnrs:** 15 **Asst solrs:** 14 **Other fee-earners:** 11

NEIL MYERSON SOLICITORS

The Cottages, Regent Road, Altrincham, WA14 1RX **Tel:** (0161) 941 4000 **Fax:** (0161) 941 4411 **Email:** lawyers@neil-myerson.co.uk **Website:** www.neil-myerson.co.uk **Ptnrs:** 6 **Asst solrs:** 14 **Other fee-earners:** 10 **Contact:** Neil Myerson • Established in 1982, Neil Myerson Solicitors is a company/commercial law firm which also offers specialist expertise in IT, Internet and motor law.

AREAS OF PRACTICE	
Company Commercial	70%
Personal Injury/Housing	20%
Private Client	10%

NELSONS

Pennine House, 8 Stanford Street, Nottingham, NG1 7BQ
Tel: (0115) 958 6262 **Fax:** (0115) 958 4702 **DX:** 179462 Nottingham 35
Email: mailbox@nelsons-solicitors.co.uk **Website:** www.nelsonsonline.com

Managing Partner	Tim Hastings
Senior Partner	Richard Nelson
Number of partners	57
Assistant solicitors	57
Other fee-earners	94

CONTACTS	
Advocacy & Higher Court	Simon Chaplin
Business Defence	Richard Nelson
Corporate	Duncan Taylor
Family	Hilary Freeman
Immigration	David Smith
Licensing	David Lucas
Litigation	Chris Adams
PI	Bruce Williams
Private Client	Richard Grosberg
Property	Noel Tornbohm

THE FIRM: With headquarters in Nottingham and other offices in Derby, Leicester and Grantham, Nelsons is a prominent broad-based practice for commercial, private and Legal Aid clients. Nelsons is one of the few firms in the region to offer strength and depth in all areas. In May 2000 the four-way merger with Leicester based practices Ironsides, Tollers and Greene Deavin created a new practice in Leicester and significantly strengthened the core practice.

PRINCIPAL AREAS OF WORK: The firm has a national reputation in business defence work and has recently been appointed to the Serious Fraud panel. Company and commercial expertise includes corporate finance, venture capital work and all forms of agreements. All aspects of litigation are handled, including cross-border cases. Liquor, gaming and bingo licensing are also dealt with. Construction and employment are both rapidly expanding specialisms. The personal injury department has particular expertise in asbestos-related cases and group actions. The firm has been accepted onto the Multi-party Action panel. Family law, crime, immigration and mental health are also areas of strength. All forms of property work are undertaken, including acting for major property developer clients. The firm has a thriving private client department, which also provides tax advice.

RECRUITMENT: The recruitment of partner Philippa Dawkins in March 2001 has enhanced the corporate services department in Leicester.

NESS GALLAGHER

95 Stewarton Street, Wishew, ML2 8AG **Tel:** (01698) 355 525 **Fax:** (01698) 262012 **DX:** 571075 WISHAW
Email: post@nessgallagher.pretsel.co.uk **Ptnrs:** 4 **Asst solrs:** 8 **Other fee-earners:** 2

NEWSOME VAUGHAN

Greyfriars House, Greyfriars Lane, Coventry, CV1 2GW
Tel: (024) 7633 3433 **Fax:** (024) 7625 6496 **DX:** 18,854 Coventry 2
Email: pauls@n-v.co.uk **Website:** www.n-v.co.uk

Senior Partner	Rupert M B Griffiths
Number of partners	4
Assistant solicitors	12
Other fee-earners	16

AREAS OF PRACTICE

Litigation	55%
Private Clients	25%
Commercial/Business	20%

THE FIRM: Newsome Vaughan is a leading practice in Coventry and Warwickshire, enjoying a strong reputation in personal injury litigation. The firm continues to attract high quality instructions in corporate and commercial property work, and has recently been appointed as solicitor for a large Midlands housing association, as well as for a large American corporation, acting as their UK lawyers and assisting the in-house European Legal Office. The firm has attained the ISO 9001 Quality Standard.

PRINCIPAL AREAS OF WORK: The firm specialises in civil litigation; claimant personal injury litigation; commercial property; company and commercial; employment law; housing association law; private client work; mortgage repossessions; mortgage lending law; professional negligence.

NICHOLAS PRYOR – SOLE PRACTITIONER
19 Sotheby Rd, Highbury, London, N5 2UP **Tel:** (020) 7359 2819 **Fax:** (020) 7359 4984

N

NICHOLSON GRAHAM & JONES

110 Cannon Street, London, EC4N 6AR
Tel: (020) 7648 9000 **Fax:** (020) 7648 9001 **DX:** 58 London Chancery Lane
Email: info@ngj.co.uk **Website:** www.ngj.co.uk

Managing Partner	Michael Johns
Number of partners	52
Assistant solicitors	51
Other fee-earners	24

CONTACTS

Banking	Paul Salsbury
Charities	Carole Cook
Corporate & Commercial	Richard Talbot
Commercial Litigation	John Magnin
Competition	Peter Bond
Construction & Engineering	David Race
Corporate Finance	Richard Herbert
Corporate & Property Tax	Richard Woolich
Election Law	Piers Coleman
Employee Share Schemes	Michael Jacobs
Employment	Jane Liddington
Healthcare & Pharmaceuticals	Owen Waft
Insolvency	Shashi Rajani
	Paul Oughton
Intellectual Property	Peter McBride
New Technologies	Michael Webster
Planning & Environment	Michael Broughton
Private Client & Tax	Eliza Mellor
	Michael Jacobs
Projects/PFI/PPP	Christopher Causer
Property	Richard Smith
Property Finance	Paul Salsbury
Property Litigation	Jane Harte-Lovelace
Public Sector	David Race
Sport & Sponsorship	Warren Phelops
Travel & Leisure	Tim Robinson
	Cynthia Barbor

THE FIRM: The firm aims to deliver a better partnership with, and for, its clients. It does this by creating and developing close, integrated and professional relationships amongst all partners and staff. This helps to deliver to clients consistent, cost-effective and commercial legal advice. It also provides its lawyers with a stimulating and satisfying career, and staff with an enjoyable working environment. Over the past 10 years the firm has doubled in size, enabling it to undertake an increasingly complex workload, extending its specialist capabilities.

PRINCIPAL AREAS OF WORK: The six main departments provide the combination of legal expertise necessary to provide relevant high quality advice to a range of industry and service sectors. Cross-departmental groups bring a commercial understanding of all areas such as sport, travel and leisure, employment and media.
Corporate Commercial: The firm is particularly well known for its corporate work. This includes flotations, mergers and acquisitions, corporate finance, joint venture structures and all UK, EU and international business transactions. It has specialist expertise in banking, insolvency, venture capital, UK and EC competition, corporate tax, property tax, employee share schemes, sport and sponsorship.
Litigation: The firm has extensive experience in commercial dispute resolution, both domestic and internationally, through ADR, arbitration and the courts. It specialises in financial services and banking, insolvency, employment, travel and leisure. The firm also covers a wide range of general commercial, corporate and property litigation.
Property: The firm has one of the leading and most experienced teams in this sector covering property, property investment, finance, planning and environment law. It has provided advice and innovative solutions to some of the largest and most complex property projects of recent times.
Construction & Engineering: This department is one of the largest and strongest in the country, advising on contentious and non-contentious matters. It offers a unique range of services. This covers project and contract work through to litigation, arbitration and alternative dispute resolution, which includes adjudication, mediation and conciliation.
Intellectual Property, Technologies & Sport: This expanding department includes recognised leaders in their field, and acts for some household names. It has a strong commercial understanding of companies and individuals in these areas, combined with wide experience and in-depth legal expertise.
Private Client & Tax: There are few City firms that still have a strong private client department. This firm is one. It advises on all aspects of estate and individual tax planning, frequently with an international element. It specialises in international trust and tax advice, probate and acting for charities.

CLIENTELE: The firm acts for a wide range of clients, ranging from listed companies to individual entrepreneurs; from financial institutions to charities; from public sector bodies to sports and media companies.

INTERNATIONAL: The firm is a founder member of GlobaLex, an international alliance of law firms with offices across the USA, Europe and the Far East, and an office in Brussels.

RECRUITMENT: Always keen to consider applications from qualified lawyers who are confident and commercially driven, the firm also recruits up to ten trainee solicitors each year. For more information contact Gail Harcus or visit the firm's website.

NICHOLSONS

23 Alexandra Rd, Lowestoft, NR32 1PP **Tel:** (01502) 532300 **Fax:** (01502) 568814 **DX:** 41204 **Email:** tbaker@nicholsons-uk.com **Website:** www.nicholsons-uk.com **Ptnrs:** 4 **Asst solrs:** 1 **Other fee-earners:** 5

NICOL, DENVIR & PURNELL

798 Newport Road, Rumney, Cardiff, CF5 8DH **Tel:** (029) 20796311 **Fax:** (029) 20779261 **DX:** 118475 Rumney Cardiff **Ptnrs:** 4 **Asst solrs:** 4 **Other fee-earners:** 2

NIGEL DAVIS – SOLE PRACTITIONER

The Sheepfold, Carr Hall Farm, Turnditch, Belper, DE56 2LW **Tel:** 01335 372889 **Fax:** 01335 372891 **Email:** nigeldavis@talk21.com

NJ GOODMAN & CO

14 Market Street, Altrincham, WA14 1QB **Tel:** (0161) 928 0990 **Fax:** (0161) 941 6254 **Email:** nick@njgoodman.co.uk

NOLAN MACLEOD

39 Donaldson Street, Kirkintilloch, Glasgow, G66 1XE **Tel:** (0141) 777 6366 **Fax:** (0141) 777 8639 **Email:** nolmac@dial.pipex.com

NORTON ROSE

Kempson House, Camomile Street, London, EC3A 7AN
Tel: (020) 7283 6000 **Fax:** (020) 7283 6500 **DX:** 85 London/1064 City
Website: www.nortonrose.com

Managing Partner	Roger Birkby
Senior Partner	David Lewis
UK	
Number of partners	122
Assistant solicitors	330
Other fee-earners	173
International	
Number of partners	65
Assistant solicitors	144
Other fee-earners	21

AREAS OF PRACTICE

Banking & Asset Finance	29%
Litigation	25%
Corporate Finance	24%
Technology	14%
Property, Planning & Environmental	8%

CONTACTS

Aviation	Jeremy Edwards
Banking	Stephen Parish
Capital Markets	Jonathan Walsh
Commercial Litigation & Arbitration	Peter Rees
Construction	Peter Hall
Corporate Finance	Robin Brooks
	Barbara Stephenson
Energy	Michael Taylor
EU & Competition	Martin Coleman
Human Resources	Timothy Russell
Insolvency	Peter Rees
Insurance	Francis Mackie
Intellectual Property	Richard Barratt
Media & Telecommunications	Martin Coleman
Project Finance	Jeffery Barratt
Property Planning & Environmental	Robin Mitchell
Railways	Gordon Hall
Shipping	Jeremy Gibb
Taxation	John Challoner
	Isla Smith

THE FIRM: Norton Rose continues to excel as the finance and business firm uppermost in its chosen markets – corporate finance, asset finance, project finance, acquisition finance, development finance and financial litigation. The firm has offices in Bahrain, Bangkok, Brussels, London, Milan, Moscow, Paris, Singapore and Warsaw, with associated offices in Athens, Jakarta and Prague. Expansion will be continued in 2001 with the merger between Norton Rose and the Cologne office of German firm Gaedertz, to which will be added offices in Frankfurt and Munich. In addition Norton Rose has significant experience in advising clients in Scandinavia, Central, Eastern and Southern Europe and throughout the Middle East, East Asia and Sub-Saharan Africa. Norton Rose provides expert services to a select number of international industry and market sectors. The firm is clearly established as an acknowledged leading professional adviser in banking, insurance, shipping, aviation, railways, construction, energy, media and telecoms. Clients rely upon Norton Rose's in-depth understanding of industry issues, commitment to industrial expansion and ability to develop new techniques to accelerate commercial advantage. For each sector, Norton Rose provides banking and corporate clients with asset finance, equity and structured financial advice, development, acquisition, consolidation and restructuring services, contractual, tax and employee relations advice, regulatory and competition advice, real and intellectual property services, and, where necessary, risk management, arbitration, litigation, workouts and insolvency advice. The firm's specialist teams in corporate finance, capital markets, project finance and commercial litigation build long term relations with clients both internationally and in their various domestic markets.

PRINCIPAL AREAS OF WORK:

Corporate Finance: The firm's corporate finance teams advise on public and private company mergers and acquisitions, privatisations, international joint ventures, inward investments, collective investment media, venture capital and general commercial work.

Capital Markets: The capital markets teams advise banks and other financial institutions on international and domestic equity issues, securities trading, bonds, convertibles, derivatives, swaps, options, and asset, property and development finance securitisations. Norton Rose also offers its clients fully integrated UK/US securities law advice. This adds an important dimension to an already thriving capital markets practice and enables the firm to advise on a full range of US securities matters.

Project Finance: The firm's project finance teams act for banks, contractors, sponsors, ECAs and mezzanine finance interests. They advise on all financial issues, inter-creditor agreements, risk management, receivables and trading issues, securitisation and restructuring, land, environmental, property and construction matters. Projects include energy, oil and gas, water, telecoms, infrastructure and transportation.

Commercial Litigation: The commercial litigation teams undertake a high proportion of multijurisdictional and international disputes. Clients are advised on risk management, arbitration and alternative dispute resolution, litigation, regulatory disputes, work outs and insolvency.

Other Areas: Other specialist teams cover intellectual property; competition and EC law, state aid, public procurement and international trade and utilities regulation; employment law, employee benefits, pension and employment-related immigration matters; international, corporate and commercial taxation; property development, investment and management, planning and the environment. During the past year, Norton Rose has advised on significant matters for, amongst others, Attiki Odos, BMW, BSkyB, ENI SpA, Deutsche Bank, Deutsche Borse, France Telecom, Norsk Hydro, QBE, Redbus Interhouse, Siemens, and Wanadoo S.A.

The firm also acted for BNP Paribas S.A. and Citibank N.A. as lead arrangers on the debt financing of the Taweelah A1 Power Generation and Sea Water Desalination Project in Abu Dhabi. This is the largest power project financing to have reached financial close in the Middle East to date.

CLIENTELE: The firm's clients are international banks, financial institutions and funds, multinational corporate businesses, major public and private companies in the firm's various domestic markets, government departments and agencies, statutory undertakings and sovereign states.

RECRUITMENT: The firm's team structure enables partners and assistants to work closely together on related types of work. This provides a more in-depth and pro-active level of service to clients, improves know-how and quality of training, and gives better support and career development for trainee solicitors and junior assistants. As the firm expands it creates excellent career prospects, including opportunities to work overseas both before and after qualification. Norton Rose recruits 85 trainee solicitors every year. It encourages high quality graduates of any discipline to apply: intellectual ability, personality, determination, and the ability to get on with others are more highly prized than degree subject matter. The firm has always been a pioneer of training and personal development. It has a training programme dedicated specifically to trainee solicitors. Highly competitive salaries are offered, as well as other benefits including sports club, regular social events, and a staff restaurant. Recruitment brochures and application forms are available from Brendan Monaghan, Graduate Recruitment Manager. Norton Rose remains one of the most genuinely pleasant places to work. There is a cohesiveness and camaraderie in the firm that is hard to find elsewhere. This provides real benefits for the firm's clients. The ability to field teams of lawyers who work effectively together and who enjoy the development and achievement of long-term relationships with their clients is clearly welcomed.

OGIER & LE MASURIER

PO Box 404, Whiteley Chambers, Don Street, St Helier, JE4 9WG
Tel: (01534) 504 000 **Fax:** (01534) 735 328
Email: legal@ogier.com **Website:** www.ogier.com

Managing Partner	Sarah Fitz
Chairman	Jonathan White

AREAS OF PRACTICE

Banking	20%
Litigation	20%
Structured Finance	20%
Investment Funds	15%
Trust	15%
Property	10%

CONTACTS

Banking & Finance	Chris Byrne (St Helier)
	Roger Le Tissier (St Peter Port)
Employment Benefits	Clive Chaplin (St Helier)
	Marcus Leese (St Peter Port)
Investment Funds	Nick Kershaw (St Helier)
	Roger Le Tissier (St Peter Port)
Litigation	Matthew Thompson (St Helier)
	Timothy Le Cocq (St Helier)
Securitisation & Capital Markets	
	Michael Lombardi (St Helier)
	Marc Yates (St Helier)
	Roger Le Tissier (St Peter Port)
Trusts	Steve Meiklejohn (St Helier)
	Jonathan White (St Helier)
	Marcus Leese (St Peter Port)

THE FIRM: Ogier & Le Masurier is one of the largest practices in the Channel Islands and is unique in having the first presence in both jurisdictions of Jersey and Guernsey, through associated offices. The firm is able to trace its roots back to 1867 and has grown in parallel with the development of the Channel Islands as an international finance centre. The firm now has more than 50 lawyers and some 210 professional and support staff across both Islands. The firm provides a specialised range of legal services to financial institutions and business clients with banking and finance work, securitisations, investment funds and commercial litigation forming the core of its practice. All the work done by the firm is undertaken by teams of specialists, led by a partner, selected to achieve the commercial objectives of the client. A large proportion of qualified lawyers have worked in major financial centres outside Jersey and bring to the firm the international experience and commercial awareness sought by today's clients. The firm places a great importance on the referral of work to them by professional advisers in other jurisdictions, and seeks to work closely with those advisers not only to meet client requirements but to exceed their expectations.

PRINCIPAL AREAS OF WORK:

Banking & Finance: Ogier & Le Masurier is widely regarded as the premier for banking and international finance work in Jersey. The banking team specialises in advising on all areas of banking, security, banking regulation and on structured finance transactions.

Securitisation: Securitisation of assets is a particular expertise of the firm. With particular expertise in asset-backed securities, CP conduits and structured debt instruments, the firm is able to add value to the structuring process.

Investment Funds: In the field of investment funds, the firm advises on the establishment and structuring of funds, as well as on regulatory and compliance aspects. The firm also advises on listings on the Channel Islands Stock Exchange.

Trusts: The trust and estate planning group has one of the largest teams of lawyers in the Channel Islands exclusively dedicated to advising trust companies, intermediaries and individuals in matters of trust law. The group has particular expertise in the commercial application of trusts in structured financing and the employee benefits sphere.

Litigation: The litigation group is the sole litigation practice in the Island specialising exclusively in commercial litigation. Its areas of expertise include trust disputes, shareholder remedies and asset tracing and freezing orders.

CLIENTELE: Clients for whom the firm acts on a regular basis include Abbey National, ANZ, Bank of America, Bank of Scotland, Barclays Private Bank, BNP, Cazenove, JP Morgan, Chase, Citibank, Deutsche Bank, Dresdner, Hill Samuel, HSBC, ING, Lloyds/TSB, Lazards, Merrill Lynch, Morgan, Guaranty, Schroders, UBS and Zurich Financial Services. The firm's client list also includes many private clients worldwide who use Jersey structures to preserve and manage their wealth as well as trust companies providing trustee services.

OGIER & Le MASURIER

OGLETHORPE STURTON & GILLIBRAND

16 Castle Park, Lancaster, LA1 1YG **Tel:** (01524) 846 846 **Fax:** (01524) 382247 **DX:** 63500 Lancaster **Email:** osg@provider.co.uk **Ptnrs:** 7 **Asst solrs:** 8 **Other fee-earners:** 4 **Contact:** Philip Oglethorpe
• The firm has significant expertise in agricultural, farming and property law; strong private client department; niche company commercial practice (both contentious and non-contentious).

AREAS OF PRACTICE

Agricultural Law	23%
Litigation	22%
Private Client (Wills, Probate)	19%
Property (Commercial & Residential)	14%
Commercial	13%
Family	9%

OLSENS

47 Esplanade, St Helier, St Helier, JE1 0BD **Tel:** (01534) 888 900 **Fax:** (01534) 887 744 **Email:** enquiry@olsenlaw.com

OLSWANG

90 Long Acre, London, WC2E 9TT
Tel: (020) 7208 8888 **Fax:** (020) 7208 8800 **DX:** 37972 London Kingsway
Email: olsmail@olswang.com **Website:** www.olswang.com

Senior Partner	Mark Devereux
Chairman	Simon Olswang
Chief Executive	Jonathan Goldstein
UK	
Number of partners	56
Assistant solicitors	125
Other fee-earners	51
International	
Number of partners	1
Assistant solicitors	3

THE FIRM: Olswang does things differently. Established in 1981, Olswang is a specialist law firm providing a broad range of legal and business advice to clients in the media, communications and technology sectors. The firm's impressive growth record has been fuelled by strong client demand, an insistence on excellence, a deep understanding of its core markets and its application of modern management practices. In January 2001 the firm had a total staff of more than 470.

PRINCIPAL AREAS OF WORK: Olswang offers the full range of services for the areas below. Consult the firm's website for more information.

Advertising: Corporate structure; brand protection; agency services; regulation; employment; sponsorship; taxation and clearance; defamation.

Banking: All aspects of corporate debt financing and insolvency.

Commercial Litigation: Contractual claims for breach of warranty and other breaches of contract; shareholder and boardroom disputes; negligence claims; film and production disputes; claims involving fraud.

Corporate & Commercial: Flotations; private fundraisings; MBOs; MBIs; start-ups; secured lending; acquisitions and disposals; share option schemes.

Defamation: Libel and content related litigation for media defendants; pre-publication/broadcast advice; challenging reporting restrictions by Courts and internet libel and content.

E-commerce: ISP terms and conditions; finance raising; start-ups; www; online trading.

Employment: Employee packages; incentive schemes and disciplinary issues; unfair dismissal; redundancy programmes; discrimination; restrictive covenants; employment disputes; High Court and employment tribunal work; industrial relations; legal and tactical issues relating to team moves.

EU & Competition: Merger control; clearances; commercial agreements; special rules for businesses with market power; handling investigations; dealing with government bodies; protecting/improving clients' competitive position.

Film & TV (Finance/Production): Production finance and services; talent agreements; accessing UK benefits; international co-productions; international sales and distribution; dispute resolution and risk avoidance; corporate finance.

Information Technology: Hardware/software procurement and maintenance; systems integration; outsourcing agreements; development; implementation and maintenance of e-commerce systems and website development.

Intellectual Property: Intellectual protection; acquisition strategy; intellectual property rights; trade secrets; copyright; cross border intellectual protection litigation including multijurisdictional internet/e-commerce patent issues and trademark problems; trademark design and patent filings.

Music: Mergers and acquisitions; competition law; intellectual property; e-commerce; digital distribution; copyright enforcement; anti-piracy; artist disputes.

Private Equity/Venture Capital: MBOs; MBIs; development capital; start ups; corporate reconstructions; debt and mezzanine financing.

Property: Investment with specialisation in shopping centres; development funding; planning; construction; property litigation.

Publishing: Prepublication; negotiating commercial contracts; contractual and intellectual property disputes.

Sport: Broadcasting rights; sports finance; EU and competition law regulation; intellectual property rights; sponsorship; online business; dispute resolution; risk avoidance.

Tax: Acquisitions and disposals; corporate reorganisations; partnerships; joint ventures; structured finance arrangements; property transactions; employee incentives; designing new financial products; VAT.

Telecommunications: Pan-European and global telecom projects investments in network infrastructure; terrestrial (both fixed and mobile) and satellite services; ISPs; mergers and acquisitions; financings; commercial contracts; regulation; competition issues; litigation.

TV/Broadcasting: Technical elements involved in compression, encryption and transmission to the com-

CONTACTS

Advertising	Jonathan Goldstein, Jane Moore
Banking	Graeme Levy, Moni Mannings
Commercial Litigation	Martin Davies, David Stewart
Construction	Richard Wilson
Corporate	Adrian Bott, Stephen Hermer, Moni Mannings, Richard Hildeband, Simon Morgan, Heather Wilby
Defamation	Debbie Ashenhurst, Julia Palca, Geraldine Proudler
E-commerce	Matthew Cowan, John Enser, Kim Nicholson, Victor Timon
Employee Benefits	Nicky Griffin
Employment	Sarah Keeble, Julia Palca, Catherine Taylor
EU & Competition	Howard Cartlidge, Dirk Van Liedekerke
Film & TV Finance	Mark Devereux, Jackie Hurt, Jane Moore, Charles Moore, Lisbeth Savill
Film & TV Production	Mark Devereux, Charles Moore, Lisbeth Savill
Information Technology	Kim Nicholson, Victor Timon
Insolvency	Graeme Levy
Intellectual Property	Andrew Inglis, Paul Stevens, Kim Walker
Music	Martin Davies, John Enser, Stephen Hermer
Planning	Richard Max
Private Equity/Venture Capital	Fabrizio Carpanini, Tina Cowan, Chris Mackie
Property	Martyn Needham, Philip Olmer, Tim Westhead
Property Litigation	Marcus Barclay
Publishing	Selina Potter, Geraldine Proudler, Kim Walker
Sport	Michael Brader
Tax	Kay Butler, Mark Joscelyne
Telecommunications	Colin Long, Kim Nicholson
TV/Broadcasting	Selina Potter, David Zeffman

mercial aspects of producing original programming. Launches and day to day operations of channels in UK, Europe, Middle East, Africa and Asia.

O'MELVENY & MYERS

3 Finsbury Square, London, EC2A 1LA **Tel:** (020) 7256 8451 **Fax:** (020) 7638 8205 **Email:** omminfo@omm.com **Website:** www.omm.com **Ptnrs:** 4 **Asst solrs:** 3 **Other fee-earners:** 1 **Contact:** Adrian Harris • Acquisition and leveraged financing facilities, high yield and other securities transactions, corporate recovery, insolvency and restructuring work, film finance, project finance and trade, property finance, securitisation, mergers and acquisitions, general banking matters.

O'REILLY STEWART

O'Reilly Stewart House, 114-116 Royal Avenue, Belfast, BT1 1DL
Tel: (028) 9032 1000 **Fax:** (028) 9032 3003 **DX:** 3700 NR Belfast
Email: oreillystewart@dnet.co.uk **Website:** www.oreilly-stewart.co.uk

Number of partners	3
Assistant solicitors	12
Other fee-earners	7

AREAS OF PRACTICE	
Litigation	45%
Company/Commercial	20%
Conveyancing	15%
Criminal	5%
Family	5%
Licensing & Gaming	5%
Building Society Work	5%

CONTACTS	
Commercial	Linus Murray
Conveyancing	Janet McMillan
Litigation	Joe Moore

THE FIRM: O'Reilly Stewart can trace its roots back to 1920 and combines a wealth of experience with a steadily increasing number of young highly qualified solicitors familiar with all the latest developments in law, business and technology.

PRINCIPAL AREAS OF WORK:
Litigation: One of the senior partners has practised in the province since 1980 and now deals primarily with defence work. He is a member of the International Association of Defence Counsel and Chairman of the Legal Aid Committee. He leads a team of six solicitors with emphasis on insurance defence work, multijurisdictional class actions, product liability, plaintiff personal injury, medical negligence and a strong emphasis in commercial litigation.
Commercial/Licensing: One of the senior partners has a long established reputation in relation to licensing and commercial property work. He leads a team of five solicitors with emphasis on all aspects of commercial conveyancing and property work including acquisition of freehold and leasehold properties for investment or development, planning law and appeals, multinational property transactions, agency work for English firms, Building Society panel work, mortgage portfolio acquisitions and all aspects of liquor licensing, gaming and entertainment law.
General: Within the firm there are also individual solicitors who practice in employment law, criminal law, domestic conveyancing, matrimonial and probate law.

CLIENTELE: Direct Line Insurance, Hastings Hotels, Bradford & Bingley Building Society, Irish Permanent, Privilege Insurance and Amazon.com.

ORMERODS

Green Dragon House, 64-70 High Street, Croydon, CR0 9XN **Tel:** (020) 8686 5000 **Fax:** (020) 8680 0972 **Email:** enquiries@ormerods.co.uk **Website:** www.ormerods.co.uk

ORRICK, HERRINGTON & SUTCLIFFE

4 Broadgate, London, EC2M 2DA
Tel: (020) 7562 5000 **Fax:** (020) 7628 0078
Website: www.orrick.com

Managing Partners	Jeanne Bartlett Paul Weiffenbach
Chairman USA	Ralph Baxter
Number of partners	6
Assistant solicitors	6
Other fee-earners	5
Total staff (worldwide)	1452

AREAS OF PRACTICE	
Litigation	18%
Corporate & Technology	17%
Structured Finance	12%
Public Finance	10%
Intellectual Property	9%
Global Infrastructure Projects	7%
Employment	7%
Private Finance	7%
Real Estate	6%
Tax	5%
Compensation & Benefits	2%

THE FIRM: Orrick Herrington & Sutcliffe is one of the world's leading finance and technology law firms, headquartered in San Francisco with six further offices across the US, and offices in Tokyo and Singapore. Orrick established a presence in London in 1998. The origins of Orrick, Herrington & Sutcliffe go back to 1863 in California, where it assisted in the formation of some of the state's oldest institutions and industrial corporations, as well as the financing of much of the state's infrastructure. The firm has since expanded successfully to New York and elsewhere in the United States as well as into Asia and Europe, with especially strong growth in recent years. Today it is among the world's top law practices. Orrick, Herrington & Sutcliffe plans to further strengthen and expand its practice in London as well as its other overseas practices in Singapore and Tokyo. In addition, it will expand its corporate practice and its alliance with the Venture Law Group in California's Silicon Valley, and its company and commercial practice across the firm.

PRINCIPAL AREAS OF WORK: The firm's core strategic practices are global energy; communications and infrastructure; structured finance; private equity; mergers and acquisitions; a corporate and technology practice advising both established and emerging companies. The London office has particular expertise in structured finance capital markets transactions, with an emphasis on securitisation of all kinds. Project finance is

Continued overleaf

also a core specialism including privatisations, infrastructure and energy related work and the office is also active in the telecommunications and new media markets. The practice is organised to provide integrated international legal services, applying focused local attention on a full range of commercial issues. This structure, together with an excellent communications network, enables it to deal with client matters originating virtually anywhere in the world. In the United States the firm has earned leading rankings in structured finance, municipal finance, project finance and representation in initial public offerings. In addition many Orrick litigators are recognised as leaders in their areas of expertise. Other strengths include intellectual property, employment law, taxation, real estate, bankruptcy and restructuring, derivatives, market regulation and financial services.

CLIENTELE: US and international clients include major industrial and financial corporations, commercial and investment banks, developers and high technology companies, as well as universities, cities, states and other governmental entities, charities and public service organisations.

INTERNATIONAL: Orrick has offices in New York, Los Angeles, Seattle, Sacramento, San Francisco, Silicon Valley, Washington DC, Singapore, Tokyo.

CONTACTS

Structured Finance ....Paul Weiffenbach
..............Jeanne Bartlett
Global Energy & Communications
..............Martin Stewart-Smith
Infrastructure Projects ....Paul Stock
Mergers & Acquisitions ....Lee Jay
Private Equity ....Lorraine McGowen
Corporate & Technology ....Lee Jay

P

OSBORNE CLARKE

Hillgate House, 26 Old Bailey, London, EC4M 7HW
Tel: (020) 7809 1000 **Fax:** (020) 7809 1005 **DX:** 466 LONDON CHANCERY LANE WC2
Email: info@osborneclarke.com **Website:** www.osborneclarke.com

50 Queen Charlotte Street, Bristol, BS1 4HE
Tel: (0117) 917 3000 **Fax:** (0117) 917 3005 **DX:** 7818 Bristol - 1

Apex Plaza, Forbury Road, Reading, RG1 1AX
Tel: (0118) 925 2000 **Fax:** (0118) 925 2005 **DX:** 117882 - Reading Apex Plaza
Email: info@osborneclarke.com

Managing Partner	Leslie Perrin
Senior Partner	Chris Curling
Number of partners	110
Assistant solicitors	0
Other fee-earners	0
Total staff	0

AREAS OF PRACTICE

Corporate & Commercial	35%
Real Estate & Construction	15%
Employment, Pensions & Incentives	15%
Dispute Resolution	15%
IT	10%
Tax	5%
Banking	5%

THE FIRM: With its strong brand, international reputation and unique geographical reach – Silicon Valley, the M4 corridor and Continental Europe – Osborne Clarke is one of the most dynamic and enterprising law firms in the UK. A dominant commercial force across the south of England, Osborne Clarke's expansion on behalf of its clients has also secured its reputation as an international law firm. In Europe, Osborne Clarke Alliance now fields 550 lawyers in 15 cities, providing a genuinely seamless service in corporate finance, private equity, mergers and acquisitions, tax, employment and other commercial services, largely to the TMT, banking and finance and real estate and construction sectors. In 2001 it radically expanded its German operations in Frankfurt and Cologne, further strengthening its position in international corporate finance and private equity markets. The firm boasts the strongest Anglo-Danish team in the commercial legal services market, operating out of London and Copenhagen. In the UK, Osborne Clarke has a commanding reputation in key corporate and commercial areas. Its corporate team operates across three south of England locations – the City of London, Bristol and the Thames Valley – advising on some of the ground-breaking deals of recent times. It offers extensive services, from funding for growth and restructuring, to mergers, acquisitions and disposals. In 2001, Osborne Clarke merged with McGuinness Finch, a leading niche property practice in London to boost its property practice.

PRINCIPAL AREAS OF WORK: Osborne Clarke has been described as the corporate team of the future. The firm worked on some of the defining deals of 2001, and utilised its technology focus to maximum advantage by combining the skills of its TMT lawyers with its private equity and corporate finance teams – one of the keys to its success. It was one of the leaders in company new issues work, with the corporate team acting on 15 IPOs last year. Osborne Clarke's mergers and acquisitions practice is helping more businesses than ever before to fulfil their acquisition and growth strategies – locally, nationally and internationally. In terms of venture capital, the corporate team acted for over 15 VC houses last year alone, and as one of the leading legal advisers to the private equity market, Osborne Clarke has rapidly expanded its pan-European focus, along with its share of the TMT convergent markets. Despite its success in international and domestic markets, the firm remains true to its two original objectives: looking after its clients and looking after its people.
TMT: Osborne Clarke's TMT team is now one of the largest in Europe. The IT team has doubled in size in the last 12 months, and the firm's established technology client base continues to grow rapidly. It is also acknowledged as having the UK's leading interactive entertainment lawyers, and in October 2000 launched the first online business resource for the sector, gamesbiz.net.
Employment: The employment team also operates across Europe, providing the full suite of human resources advice – from employment to pensions and incentives.
Banking: The firm's banking team advises financial institutions and borrowers on all aspects of banking and financial services, providing a partner-led service based on specialist knowledge of the sector.
Corporate Tax: The corporate tax department provides specialist tax services to both domestic and international clients.

CONTACTS

Advertising & Marketing ....Tim Birt
..............Stephen Groom
Anglo-Danish Matters ....Roy Lambert
..............Per Troen
Anglo-German Matters ....Adrian Taylor
Competition ....Claire Wagner
..............Neil Baylis
Corporate Banking ....Chris Sykes
..............Jeremy Cross
..............Hugh Jones
Corporate Finance ....Andrew Saul
..............Patrick Graves
..............Andrew Gowans
Corporate Tax ....Philip G S Moss
..............Stuart Long
Dispute Resolution ....Clare Robinson
..............Adrian Lifely
Employment ....Julian Hemming
..............Ralph Nathan
..............Danielle Kingdon
Insolvency ....Patrick D Cook
Pensions & Incentives ....Mark Womersley
Private Capital & Personal Trusts ....Sandra Brown
Private Equity ....Kieran O'Connor
..............Alisdair Livingstone
..............Greg Leyshon
..............Simon Beswick
Real Estate & Construction ....Simon Speirs
..............Nadine Strall
TMT ....Simon Rendell
..............Andrew Braithwaite
..............Russell Bowyer

Real Estate & Construction: The firm's commercial property team advises on all of the commercial and legal aspects of UK development and landlord and tenant transactions, including development, investment, acquisition, disposal and management, property litigation and dispute resolution.

INTERNATIONAL: The firm has offices in Barcelona, Brussels, Copenhagen, Helsinki, Madrid, Paris, Rotterdam, St Petersburg, Tallinn.

OSBORNE MORRIS & MORGAN

Danbury House, West Street, Leighton Buzzard, LU7 7DD **Tel:** (01525) 378177 **Fax:** (01525) 851006 **DX:** 90804 Leighton Buzzard **Ptnrs:** 5 **Asst solrs:** 6 **Other fee-earners:** 4

OSWALD GOODIER & CO

10 Chapel St, Preston, PR1 8AY
Tel: (01772) 253841 **Fax:** (01772) 201713 **DX:** 714571 Preston 14
Email: oswgoodier@aol.com

Senior Partner	Mark Belderbos
Number of partners	3
Other fee-earners	1

AREAS OF PRACTICE	
Charity, Trust & Probate	30%
Residential Property & Landlord & Tenant	30%
Commercial Property/Company	18%
Personal Injury & Other Litigation	11%
Matrimonial & Family	7%
Other	4%

THE FIRM: Established in 1897 in central Preston, the firm has a substantial charity, trust, property and private client practice in the North West and further afield. For very many years, Oswald Goodier & Co has represented numerous charities, both religious and secular, involving much work in the fields of trusts, property, educational and ecclesiastical law. Highlights include regular substantial property transactions, and continuous involvement in charity law matters. The firm is highly regarded as experienced in all aspects of private client work, as well as being much involved in civil litigation, licensing, employment and elderly client work.

CLIENTELE: Substantial connections in private client work and several religious, diocesan and secular charities, schools and colleges and long-established trust and estate clients.

OURY CLARK SOLICITORS

5 Arlington Street, London, SW1A 1RA **Tel:** (020) 7629 8844 **Fax:** (020) 7629 8855 **DX:** 140543 Piccadilly 5 **Email:** james.oury@ouryclarksolicitors.com **Website:** www.ouryclark.com **Ptnrs:** 2 **Asst solrs:** 5 **Other fee-earners:** 3 **Contact:** James Oury LLB ACA • Specialists in criminal defence work (particularly white-collar crime, human rights and commercial inward investment) adopting a multidisciplinary legal/accountancy approach.

OVERBURY STEWARD EATON & WOOLSEY

3 Upper King St, Norwich, NR3 1RL **Tel:** (01603) 610481 **Fax:** (01603) 632460 **DX:** 5208 Norwich **Email:** info@overburys.co.uk **Website:** www.overburys.co.uk **Ptnrs:** 14 **Asst solrs:** 4 **Other fee-earners:** 14

OVER TAYLOR BIGGS

1 Oak Tree Place, Manaton Close, Matford Business Park, Exeter, EX2 8WA **Tel:** (01392) 823811 **Fax:** (01392) 823812 **DX:** 300350 Exeter 5 **Email:** law@otb.uk.com **Ptnrs:** 4 **Asst solrs:** 3 **Other fee-earners:** 3

OWEN WHITE

Senate House, 62-70 Bath Road, Slough, SL2 3SR **Tel:** (01753) 876800 **Fax:** (01753) 876876 **DX:** 3409 **Email:** law@owenwhite.com **Website:** www.owenwhite.com **Ptnrs:** 8 **Asst solrs:** 6 **Other fee-earners:** 2

OZANNES

PO Box 186, 1 Le Marchant Street, St Peter Port, GY1 4HP **Tel:** (01481) 723466 **Fax:** (01481) 727935 **Email:** advocates@ozannes.com **Website:** www.ozannes.com • Ozannes is Guernsey's leading law firm, specialising in offshore commercial and corporate work, in particular mutual funds, company and trust law, banking, finance and litigation.

PAGAN OSBORNE

12 St. Catherine Street, Cupar, KY15 4HN **Tel:** (01334) 653777 **Fax:** (01334) 655063 **DX:** 560543 **Email:** enquiries@pagan.co.uk **Website:** www.pagan.co.uk **Ptnrs:** 12 **Asst solrs:** 7 **Other fee-earners:** 13

PALSER GROSSMAN

Discovery House, Scott Harbour, Cardiff Bay, CF10 4HA **Tel:** (029) 2045 2770 **Fax:** (029) 2045 2328 **DX:** 33064 Cardiff 1 **Email:** law@palser-grossman.co.uk **Ptnrs:** 21 **Asst solrs:** 22 **Other fee-earners:** 25

PANEL OF INDEPENDENT MEDIATORS

Panel of Independent Mediators, 47 Campden Hill Square, London, W8 7JR **Tel:** (020) 7221 5893 **Fax:** (020) 7727 6321

PANNONE & PARTNERS

123 Deansgate, Manchester, M3 2BU
Tel: (0161) 909 3000 **Fax:** (0161) 909 4444 **DX:** 14314 Manchester 1
Email: law@pannone.co.uk **Website:** www.pannone.com

Managing Partner	Joy Kingsley
Senior Partner	Rodger Pannone
Number of partners	61
Assistant solicitors	60
Other fee-earners	63

AREAS OF PRACTICE

Personal Injury	26%
Commercial Litigation	19%
Corporate	14%
Commercial Property	12%
Family	8%
Clinical Negligence	8%
Private Client	8%
Employment	5%

CONTACTS

Business Crime	Paul Taylor
Clinical Negligence	John Kitchingman
Commercial Litigation	Vincent O'Farrell
Commercial Property	Andrew Simpkin
Construction	Tom Ellis
Corporate & Commercial	Søren Tattam
Debt Collection	Simon McCrum
Employment	Christine Bradley
Family	Catherine Jones
Financial Services	Tony Ashton
French Property	Lindsay Kinnealy
Insolvency	Paul Johnson
Intellectual Property	John McMuldroch
Licensing	Nick Dickinson
Personal Injury	Carol Jackson
Private Client	Hugh Jones
Public Sector	Steven Grant

THE FIRM: Pannone & Partners is the largest single-site practice in Manchester. It has strengths not shared by firms of a similar size in its ability to service all types of work for both commercial and personal clients, with the firm's strength and size being split evenly between the two. Pannone & Partners was the first law firm to achieve BS5750 accreditation, now ISO 9001, and has held this quality mark for the last 10 years. The firm prides itself on its ability to work in partnership with its clients and to offer practical and cost-effective solutions to meet clients' needs.

PRINCIPAL AREAS OF WORK:

Corporate & Commercial: A comprehensive range of corporate services is available including all aspects of business start-up and formation, banking and finance, commercial contracts, company law and competition law. The department also has a number of specialists offering particular expertise in public sector, intellectual property and advertising and marketing law.

Commercial Property: This department provides a full range of advice on commercial property transactions including purchases, sales, mortgages, planning, development, leases, joint ventures and portfolio management.

Commercial Litigation: This progressive and successful department is acknowledged by its competitors to be tough, knowledgeable and effective. Experienced in litigating in all courts and tribunals, its watchword is commerciality. It also houses the debt collection unit.

Employment: This team handles its own tribunal advocacy and provides quality advice nationally and locally, predominantly for employers, but also for employees, dealing with all aspects of the employment relationship.

Business Crime: An experienced, highly-regarded team advising on white collar, serious and complex criminal/regulatory cases and investigations.

Construction: A dedicated team of construction specialists who carry out work of both a contentious and non-contentious nature.

Insolvency: This team aims to give prompt considered practical advice from which clients, who include banks, receivers, creditors and debtors, can derive financial commercial benefit.

Licensing: This department provides a full range of liquor licensing services with a particular specialism in licensed forecourts. It is the only accredited training provider for the British Innkeepers' Institute National Licensing Course in central Manchester – and offers on-site training and examinations.

Personal Injury: This department is consistently accredited as the strongest personal injury team in the North West, with a demonstrable national and international reputation for the quality of its work, the size of settlements obtained and expertise in handling multi-party and complex claims. The department also handles many hundreds of claims each year arising out of less serious accidents. As with clinical negligence, a significant amount of work is referred from other non-specialist solicitors.

Clinical Negligence: This dedicated team of medical negligence specialists act for clients throughout the country seeking redress for sometimes catastrophic injuries received during medical treatment. Members of this department do not undertake any other form of personal injury work thereby guaranteeing a high degree of specialism.

Family: This is one of the pre-eminent family law departments in the country, handling divorce and all that goes with it. Its specialities include substantial and complex financial cases acting for high net worth individuals and contested adoption.

Private Client: A large department dealing with residential conveyancing, tax planning, wills and estates and Court of Protection work. The staff provide a caring and efficient service when undertaking their clients' most personal transactions.

INTERNATIONAL: The firm is a founder member of the Pannone Law Group, Europe's first integrated international law group taking the form of a European Economic Interest Grouping. Its lawyers recognised the need to offer creative, imaginative and practical advice on a pan-European basis. PLG maintains offices in Andorra, Belgium, Brazil, Canada, France, Germany, Italy, Luxembourg, Netherlands, Portugal, Spain, Sweden, Switzerland and the UK. The firm recognises the importance of communication between different cultures and often transacts business in French, German, Swedish and Danish.

RECRUITMENT: The firm offers eight training contracts each year with a programme of in-house lectures and seminars. The firm encourages trainees to stay on qualification. Application forms are available from Julia Jessop.

PARDOES

6-9 King Square, Bridgwater, TA6 3YB **Tel:** (01278) 457891 **Fax:** (01278) 429249 **DX:** 80602 **Website:** www.pardoes.co.uk **Ptnrs:** 13
Asst solrs: 10 **Other fee-earners:** 17

PARIS SMITH & RANDALL

Number 1 London Road, Southampton, SO15 2AE
Tel: (023) 8048 2482 **Fax:** (023) 8063 1835 **DX:** 38534 Southampton 3
Email: info@parissmith.co.uk **Website:** www.parissmith.co.uk

Number of partners	14
Assistant solicitors	25
Other fee-earners	20

AREAS OF PRACTICE

Company & Commercial	21%
Commercial Property	20%
Family	14%
Tax & Estate Planning	14%
Residential Property	13%
Litigation	13%
Employment	5%

CONTACTS

Child Care	Justin Belcher
Company & Commercial	Andrew Heathcock
Employment	Mary Siddall
Family & Mediation	Neil Davies
Insolvency	Malcolm Le Bas
Litigation	Clive Thomson
Probate/Tax/Trusts	Crispin Jameson
Property (Commercial)	Mark Howarth
Property (Residential)	Peter Gammie

THE FIRM: Paris Smith & Randall is totally dedicated to providing exceptional service to its clients. This means the firm spends the majority of the time listening to its clients. From this it learns each day how to serve them better. The firm's greatest satisfaction is sharing in its client's hopes, aspirations and ambitions.The firm is accredited as an Investor in People and with Lexcel, the Law Society's practice management standard.

PRINCIPAL AREAS OF WORK: As Southampton's premier solicitors and a leading firm in the South, the firm prides itself in serving both commercial clients and private clients. Commercial clients have access to a complete range of services including legal advice on company and commercial, IT, intellectual property, employment and commercial property advice. Private clients can take advantage of a full range of services: family, child protection, personal injury, wills, personal taxation, estate planning, financial and pension advice.

RECRUITMENT: CV's are always welcome from applicants for training contracts, qualified staff and secretarial and administrative staff. These should be sent to the Practice Manager. The firm is committed to providing all its staff with interesting and fulfilling careers, provided they are prepared to become actively involved in learning more about their clients and their businesses and always have a thirst for knowledge and acquiring new skills.

P

PARKER BULLEN

45 Castle Street, Salisbury, SP1 3SS **Tel:** (01722) 412000 **Fax:** (01722) 411822 **DX:** Salisbury 58001 **Email:** law@parkerbullen.com **Website:** www.parkerbullen.co.uk **Ptnrs:** 10 **Asst solrs:** 12 **Other fee-earners:** 7

PARKER & GREGO

18-19 Freeman Street, Birmingham, B5 5H2 **Tel:** (0121) 633 3031 **Fax:** 0121 633 3029 **Ptnrs:** 3 **Asst solrs:** 2 **Other fee-earners:** 5

PARK NELSON

1 Bell Yard, London, WC2A 2JP
Tel: (020) 7539 2000 **Fax:** (020) 7405 4266 **DX:** 186 Chancery Lane WC2
Email: law@parknelson.co.uk **Website:** www.parknelson.co.uk

Managing Partner	Timothy Ford
Senior Partner	Eugene O'Keeffe
Number of partners	19
Assistant solicitors	11
Other fee-earners	7

AREAS OF PRACTICE

Commercial Property	46%
Resolution/Construction/Insurance	31%
Private Client Services	12%
Corporate	11%
Litigation/Dispute	

CONTACTS

Commercial Property	Eugene O'Keefe
Corporate	Tim Ford
Litigation/Construction	John Kings
Private Client Services	Richard Fairbairn

THE FIRM: Park Nelson is one of the oldest firms of solicitors having celebrated its 200th birthday in 1996. It is now continuing its independent development with the most advanced technology pursuing controlled growth through strong management and a determination that services will be partner-led. Clients always have immediate access to partners who supervise the provision of services day to day and control the work of the firm to ensure constant excellence of standards. The four-partner specialist insurance law firm, Rayfields, joined Park Nelson's litigation and dispute resolution department on 25 January 1999.

PRINCIPAL AREAS OF WORK:

Commercial Property: The firm believes that its considerable strengths in commercial property are equal to those of much larger practices. It is particularly well known for its expertise in handling developments, funding agreements and commercial leases in the retail and other fields. Special areas of property expertise include negotiating and advising on retail licensing and franchising agreements, as well as advice on all aspects of town and country planning, compulsory purchase negotiations, and public inquiries and appeals.

Litigation, Dispute Resolution & Insurance: The firm is prominent in construction litigation and dispute resolution, and also in non-contentious construction law as well as contract matters. The litigation department handles specialist professional indemnity work for leading underwriters and professional firms, personal injury and medical negligence cases, landlord and tenant disputes, commercial and contractual matters and employment issues, intellectual property litigation and judicial review proceedings.

Corporate & Business Services: Includes acquisitions and disposals of companies and their businesses, advice on drafting and negotiating commercial agreements, handling joint venture and marketing agreements and preparing financing, banking and loan, funding agreements and insolvency. The firm has specialist and extensive skills in employment law matters, as it does for consumer and consumer credit matters. With its strong international connections, UK and Irish business operations for overseas companies is an important feature and there is a rapidly growing expertise and client base in e-commerce ventures.

Private Client Services: The work of the private client department involves trust management, probate, estate and tax planning, tax returns and the preparation of wills, with particular expertise in French, South African and Italian cases.

Continued overleaf

CLIENTELE: The firm's clients include substantial UK companies, as well as private, professional, institutional and commercial firms in Europe and internationally. A number of French, Belgian and Dutch governmental, cultural and educational institutions in London are also clients. Many of the firm's lawyers are fluent in foreign languages.

INTERNATIONAL: The firm has strong international connections and conducts work throughout the world, in the United States, southern Africa, the Far East and Australia. These connections include eastern Europe, but are particularly strong in the European Union member states and neighbouring territories, especially France and Ireland. Three of the partners are also admitted as solicitors in the Republic of Ireland. The firm has associated offices in Dublin, Paris, Rome and Milan.

PARLBY CALDER

First Floor, 7 Whimple Street, Plymouth, PL1 2DH **Tel:** (01752) 600 833 **Fax:** (01752) 600 933 **Email:** office@parlbycalder.co.uk **Ptnrs:** 2 **Asst solrs:** 1 **Other fee-earners:** 1

P

PARLETT KENT

Signet House, 49-51 Farringdon Rd, London, EC1M 3PP
Tel: (020) 7430 0712 **Fax:** (020) 7430 1796 **DX:** 53308 Clerkenwell
Email: enquiries@parlettkent.co.uk

Portland House, Longbrook Street, Exeter, EX4 6AB
Tel: (01392) 494455 **Fax:** (01392) 491199 **DX:** 134052 - Exeter 15
Email: enquiries@exeter.partlettkent.co.uk

Senior Partner	Caroline Jenkins
Number of partners	7
Assistant solicitors	1
Other fee-earners	5

AREAS OF PRACTICE	
Clinical Negligence	70%
Conveyancing & General Non-Contentious	10%
Personal Injury	10%
Matrimonial	5%
Professional Negligence	5%

CONTACTS	
Clinical Negligence	Caroline Jenkins (London)
	Magi Young (Exeter)
Family	Elizabeth Batten
Personal Injury	Mary Hassell
Private Client	Maggie Leiper

THE FIRM: Established in the 1950s, Parlett Kent is a firm noted in particular for its expertise in a wide range of complex, clinical negligence and personal injury litigation. The firm has in house paramedical support and is committed to applying its expertise to cases of merit regardless of venue or quantum of case. The firm has legal aid franchises for personal injury and clinical negligence litigation and undertakes private work including conditional fee agreement cases. Four partners are members of the Law Society's Medical Negligence panel, the Association of Personal Injury Lawyers and the AVMA referral panel; two members of the firm are members of the Law Society's Personal Injury panel; and two are members of the Association of Trial Lawyers of America. The firm has an office in Exeter where they specialise in clinical negligence and personal injury litigation.

PRINCIPAL AREAS OF WORK:
Clinical Negligence: This department deals with cases of the utmost severity (accidents at birth, brain injuries and spinal injuries) as well as a wide range of both High Court and County Court claims. The firm has particular expertise in cases of obstetric and psychiatric negligence as well as cases arising out of failures to diagnose and treat cancer. It also specialises in claims against the legal profession arising out of mishandling of clinical negligence claims. Members of the practice regularly lecture lawyers, doctors, nurses, health service managers and social workers on medical negligence and risk management.
Personal Injury: This department deals with a full range of personal injury claims, including road traffic accidents and accidents at work, for both claimants and defendants. Two of the partners are members of the Personal Injury panel.
Other Areas: The firm also covers conveyancing, wills, trusts, probate, taxation and family.

INTERNATIONAL: Business is handled in French, Punjabi and Urdu.

RECRUITMENT: At least one trainee solicitor is recruited annually. The firm has an equal opportunities policy and all posts are advertised.

O.H. PARSONS & PARTNERS

Sovereign Hse, 212-224 Shaftesbury Avenue, London, WC2H 8PR **Tel:** (020) 7379 7277 **Fax:** (020) 7240 1577 **Ptnrs:** 6 **Asst solrs:** 4 **Other fee-earners:** 4 **Contact:** Barry Sullivan • Best known for Trade Union work, personal injury litigation and employment law. Founded 1949.

AREAS OF PRACTICE	
Personal Injury	80%
Employment	15%
Crime, Consumer Entertainment Law & Defamation	5%

PATIENCE & BUCHAN

13 Bon Accord Square, Aberdeen, AB11 6DJ **Tel:** (01224) 588333 **Fax:** (01224) 588555 **DX:** AB **Email:** ian@patiencebuchanan.com **Ptnrs:** 2 **Other fee-earners:** 1

PATTINSON & BREWER

30 Great James Street, London, WC1N 3HA
Tel: (020) 7400 5100 **Fax:** (020) 7400 5101 **DX:** 394
Email: enquiries@pattinsonbrewer.co.uk **Website:** www.pattinsonbrewer.co.uk

Managing Partner	John Davies
Number of partners	14
Assistant solicitors	14
Other fee-earners	32

AREAS OF PRACTICE

Personal Injury	59%
Employment/Labour Law	18%
Medical Negligence	10%
General Litigation	6%
Conveyancing/Commercial	5%
Criminal	2%

THE FIRM: The firm of Pattinson & Brewer was founded in about 1892. It has long been a leading trade union practice, having connections going back to the Taff Vale case in 1901 and the formation of the TGWU in 1921. It has a proud commitment to claimant personal injury and disease work, and a well-established reputation in the fields of equal opportunities, and clinical and professional negligence. It has developed a leading profile in the field of employment law and acts frequently for directors and senior executives on their personal employment issues. It has a strong team of general litigators and a very experienced property department. The firm also has offices in Chatham, Bristol, York and Kingsway WC2.

RECRUITMENT: The firm presently recruits one or two trainee solicitors each year, and looks for an interest in claimant-orientated work.

PAUL DAVIDSON TAYLOR

Chancery Court, Queen Street, Horsham, RH13 5AD **Tel:** (01403) 262 333 **Fax:** (01403) 262 444 **DX:** 57617 Horsham **Email:** law@pdt.co.uk
Website: www.pdt.co.uk **Ptnrs:** 10 **Asst solrs:** 5 **Other fee-earners:** 9

P

PAULL & WILLIAMSONS

Investment House, 6 Union Row, Aberdeen, AB10 1DQ
Tel: (01224) 621621 **Fax:** (01224) 640446 **DX:** 35 Aberdeen
Email: info@paull-williamsons.co.uk **Website:** www.paull-williamsons.co.uk

New Investment House, 214 Union Street, Aberdeen, AB10 8QY
Tel: (01224) 621621 **Fax:** (01224) 627437 **DX:** 82 Aberdeen

13 North Bank Street, Edinburgh, EH1 2LP
Tel: (0131) 226 6180 **Fax:** (0131) 226 6797 **DX:** ED 261 Edinburgh

Senior Partner	Bruce Smith
Number of partners	29
Assistant solicitors	34
Other fee-earners	14

CONTACTS

Commercial Property	Leslie Dalgarno
Corporate	Sidney Barrie
Litigation	Sean Saluja
Oil & Gas	Gordon Buchan
Planning & Environment	Bruce Smith
Private Client	George Alpine
	David Geddie

THE FIRM: One of the largest firms in Aberdeen, Paull & Williamsons have enhanced their legal services to meet the increased pace of economic activity in the North East of Scotland in recent years. Moreover, the client benefits from an efficient cross referral system, which provides immediate access to other departments on other areas of the law. The firm also conducts seminars for clients on matters of concern to them, including employment, industrial relations and the effects of new legislation.

PRINCIPAL AREAS OF WORK:

Corporate Services: The firm has an established reputation for serving commercial clients in the North East and has close links with the local financial community. The department handles all types of corporate and commercial transactions including business start-ups, partnerships and incorporations; company administration; takeovers and acquisitions; disposals; management buy-outs; insolvency, receivership, liquidation and administration; commercial contract, licensing and intellectual property; shipping and vessel finance; venture capital financing and investment. The oil and gas unit has acquired a specialist reputation for upstream North Sea work.

Commercial Property Services: The department has recently expanded its operations and now has considerable experience in commercial property developments throughout Scotland. Valuable connections are maintained with other professionals in the commercial property field, such as surveyors, architects and project managers. The firm offers a comprehensive service covering the acquisition and development, leasing and funding of both office and industrial developments. In addition, proven experience has been demonstrated in the fields of retail development, major residential development, licensed premises, agricultural and sporting estates, and woodland and aquacultural development. The planning and environmental unit is active throughout Scotland and is gaining in its profile of resource and expertise.

Private Client Services: The first practice in Aberdeen to open a separate estate agency office, the department now operates from large premises in the heart of the city. The service includes advice on valuation, marketing strategy, mortgages, insurance, contracts of sale and purchase and the handling of enquiries prior to sale. The firm also meets the client's personal financial requirements in the areas of tax planning, succession, trusts, insurance and personal financial management. This expertise extends to cover agricultural partnerships and estate work.

Litigation: The firm has the experience to deal with all areas of contentious work either prior to formal litigation or arbitration or through representation in the courts and tribunals. The department's work ranges from matters which might face the commercial client, including commercial contracts, employment matters,

Continued overleaf

credit control, health and safety at work, and insolvency, to matters of personal concern, such as matrimonial disputes and employment problems. Having developed expertise in the negotiation, pursuit and defence of personal injury claims, the firm has also recently achieved a significant reputation in advising clients and their insurers following major disasters and representing them at subsequent public inquiries.

THE PAUL ROONEY PARTNERSHIP

19-23 Stanley Street, Liverpool, L1 6AA **Tel:** (0151) 227 2851 **Fax:** (0151) 255 0455 **DX:** 14183 **Ptnrs:** 5 **Asst solrs:** 11 **Other fee-earners:** 20 **Contact:** Paul Rooney • Established in 1977. Specialist civil and criminal litigation firm dealing mainly with personal injury claims including factory accidents, industrial diseases, medical and professional negligence, sports injuries and road traffic accidents.

AREAS OF PRACTICE

Road Traffic Accidents/Personal Injury	85%
Crime	10%

PAYNE HICKS BEACH

10 New Square, Lincoln's Inn, London, WC2A 3QG
Tel: (020) 7465 4300 **Fax:** (020) 7465 4400 **DX:** 40 Ch.Ln.
Email: mail@paynehicksbeach.co.uk

Senior Partner	Graham Brown
Managing Partner	Guy Green
Number of partners	22
Assistant solicitors	16
Other fee-earners	19

AREAS OF PRACTICE

Private Client	33%
Commerical Litigation	13%
Commercial Property	12%
Matrimonial & Family Law/Litigation	12%
Residential/Agricultural Property	10%
Tax (Business & Corporate)	10%
Corporate/Commercial	10%

CONTACTS

Commercial Litgation	Richard Butcher
Commercial Property	David FitzGerald
Corporate/Commercial	Guy Green
	Max Hudson
Employment/Sports	Richard Butcher
Family/Matrimonial	Ian Airey
	Fiona Shackleton
	David Leverton
General Conveyancing	Andrew Crawford
	David FitzGerald
Intellectual Property	Richard Butcher
Probate	Alastair Murdie
Tax/Trust	Graham Brown

THE FIRM: A well-known and respected Inns of Court firm, Payne Hicks Beach was established in the early eighteenth century. Although the firm draws strength from its long traditions, the character of the firm is an entirely modern one which has been created by the present partners' own chosen specialisations, several of which have been the object of favourable comment in journals in the last few years.

PRINCIPAL AREAS OF WORK: The firm is organised into five departments.
Tax, Trust & Probate: These are areas of specialisation for which the firm has a reputation as one of the best in London. The range of work undertaken is wider than traditionally associated with private client work, and extends from heritage and agricultural work and property development taxation, to advising entrepreneurs and senior directors, charities, and to off-shore and continental transactions.
Corporate/Commercial: This department deals with the full range of corporate and business law, acting for public and private companies and a range of individual entrepreneurs. The international section deals with many clients and correspondents abroad, and has strong connections both within the European Community and elsewhere, including North America and Japan. Work includes acquisitions and mergers; banking; competition law; employment law; EC law; intellectual property including computers and franchising; management buy-outs; marketing and sale of goods law; new issues and partnership agreements.
Commercial Litigation: The firm has a strong commercial litigation department handling a broad range of work including commercial disputes requiring urgent injunctive relief, arbitration, intellectual property, commercial, landlord and tenant and town and country planning. There is also particular experience in representing clients before regulatory enquiries. Specialised areas of work include advising clients in yacht racing and design and construction, building contract work, partnership disputes and all other aspects of insolvency for both corporate and individual clients.
Family Law: This department is well known for its specialisation in all aspects of family law including divorce and separation, adoption, custody and wardship, and financial claims. Personal injury actions are also handled.
Commercial Property: This section deals with all aspects of property transactions, leases, secured lending, management of investment property, development work including joint ventures and planning agreements.
Residential & Agricultural Conveyancing: This section deals with residential conveyancing, farm and forestry transactions and agricultural property.

INTERNATIONAL: The firm has associates in Paris with a network of other correspondents internationally. Several of the partners conduct legal work in French, German or Danish.

RECRUITMENT: There are usually two or three vacancies for trainee solicitors every year. The minimum educational requirement is a good degree, but emphasis is placed on personality as well as academic achievements. Applications should be made by letter (with CV and references) to the recruitment partner. The firm is also always interested to receive applications from high quality solicitors seeking to move from the City.

PAYNE MARSH STILLWELL

6 Carlton Crescent, Southampton, SO15 2EY **Tel:** (023) 8022 3957 **Fax:** (023) 8022 5261 **DX:** 38514 Southampton 3
Email: enquiries@pms-solicitors.co.uk **Ptnrs:** 6 **Asst solrs:** 1 **Other fee-earners:** 4

PEDEN & REID

22 Callender Street, Belfast, BT1 5BU
Tel: (028) 9032 5617 **Fax:** (028) 9024 7343 **DX:** 389 NR Belfast
Email: peden-reid@dnet.co.uk

Senior Partner	George A Palmer
Number of partners	5
Assistant solicitors	3

CONTACTS

Commercial Property .... Richard Palmer
Company/Employment .... Niall Browne
Family .... Richard Palmer
Litigation .... Nicholas Harvey

THE FIRM: The firm acts in a general advisory capacity for a number of large public and private companies, public sector and statutory bodies, agricultural and marketing organisations, lending institutions, insurers and property developers.

PRINCIPAL AREAS OF WORK:
Company & Commercial Property: Formation and structuring of companies and inter-shareholder arrangements; preparation of vending and purchase agreements; partnerships and joint venture agreements relating to business acquisitions and disposals; capital and other finance sourcing; commercial mortgages and secured lending.
Employment: Advising on drafting of complex service agreements and in disputes arising out of employment contracts including fair employment, discrimination and Industrial Tribunal cases.
Family: Marriage breakdown and divorce. The firm has a large and successful family law practice often involving complex and substantial financial settlements.
Litigation: Wide experience in prosecuting and defending all types of civil actions including personal injuries, professional negligence, employer's and public liability, breach of contract, repossession proceedings, defamation, disputes relating to property rights and product liability including representation of insurers and the interests of other parties.

P

PENNINGTONS

Bucklersbury House, 83 Cannon Street, London, EC4N 8PE
Tel: (020) 7457 3000 **Fax:** (020) 7457 3240 **DX:** 98946 Cheapside 2
Email: info@penningtons.co.uk **Website:** www.penningtons.co.uk

Clifton House, Bunnian Place, Basingstoke, RG21 7QY
Tel: (01256) 406300 **Fax:** (01256) 479425 **DX:** 122362 Basingstoke 8
Email: info@penningtons.co.uk

Phoenix House, 9 London Road, Newbury, RG14 1DH
Tel: (01635) 571000 **Fax:** (01635) 523444 **DX:** 30801 Newbury
Email: info@penningtons.co.uk

Highfield, Brighton Road, Godalming, GU7 1NS
Tel: (01483) 791800 **Fax:** (01483) 424177 **DX:** 58300 Godalming 1
Email: info@penningtons.co.uk

Managing Partner	Lesley Lintott
Number of partners	52
Assistant solicitors	76
Other fee-earners	33

AREAS OF PRACTICE

Property 35%
Litigation (including Shipping) 32%
Corporate 20%
Private Client (including Family) 13%

CONTACTS

ADR .... Henry Brown
.... Sue Dixon
Agricultural .... Michael Fellingham
.... Julian Chadwick
Banking .... Richard Tyson
Clinical Negligence .... David Raine
Commercial Property .... Catriona Smith
.... Anthony Bussy
.... Tom Rossiter
.... Tim Rafter
Construction .... Roger Loveland
.... Sue Dixon
Corporate & Commercial .... Ron Allsopp
.... Charles Brooks
.... Robin Peile
.... David Wilson
Corporate Recovery & Insolvency
.... Noel McMichael
.... Sue Dixon
Employment .... Paul Hadow
.... Mike Cole
.... Simon Fenton
.... Jonathan Rouse
Environmental .... John Mathé
Family .... Jeremy Abraham
Immigration .... Henry Brown
.... Gülay Mehmet
Intellectual Property .... Geoffrey Walkley
Litigation .... Paul Hadow
.... Jonathan Rouse
.... John Sommerville
.... Michael Felce
Personal Injury .... David Raine
Planning .... Roger Bullworthy

THE FIRM: Penningtons is a commercial law firm which provides legal services tailored to individual requirements. Specialist teams address the specific objectives of each client and provide a partner led service with an emphasis on team working. The firm's aims are to match client expectations in the areas of quality, time of delivery and cost of service and to add value. The firm's principal office is in the City of London. There are further UK offices in Basingstoke, Godalming and Newbury and an office in Paris. In addition, Penningtons has close links with law firms in jurisdictions throughout the world. It is therefore able to offer flexibility in the scope of the specialist commercial and private client services it delivers to a wide range of clients with differing requirements.

PRINCIPAL AREAS OF WORK: The main areas of legal services provided are property, litigation (including shipping), corporate and commercial (including intellectual property), and private client (including immigration, family and matrimonial). The firm also has several specialist teams providing focused and co-ordinated services to specific industry sectors, often on a cross departmental basis.
Corporate & Commercial: The department offers a full range of legal skills and experience in corporate finance, management buy-outs and buy-ins, mergers and acquisitions and joint ventures. Multi-disciplinary and cross-border transactions are regularly undertaken. Advice is also given on most aspects of commercial law, including intellectual property (where there is a particular expertise in information technology, especially e-commerce and computer law) publishing, trade marks and technology transfer, distribution, agency and supply, competition law, inward investment and establishment in the UK, banking, pensions and employees' benefits schemes. The department can provide taxation support in relation to all aspects of its corporate and commercial work.
Litigation: The department handles a broad range of national and international work, including banking; construction disputes; employment matters; insolvency work; insurance; partnership disputes; personal injury

Continued overleaf

and clinical negligence claims (for which community legal services quality marks are held in the firm's Godalming and Basingstoke offices); professional indemnity claims; secured lending recoveries; share sale and purchase disputes; trade arbitrations; all aspects of commercial property and landlord and tenant matters. Agency work is also carried out. Members of the department are familiar with ADR techniques in addition to litigation and arbitration. The shipping group provides a worldwide international commercial and corporate shipping and arbitration service from the firm's London and Paris offices. The group has extensive experience of major marine casualties and total losses. The professional regulation group acts for a number of professional bodies, not only investigating and presenting cases for hearing by their disciplinary committees, but also advising on rules, procedures and codes of conduct and conducting appeals and applications for judicial review.

Property: The department has wide experience in dealing with a range of property related transactions including investment sales and purchases, funding agreements, development schemes, landlord and tenant matters, portfolio management, agricultural investments, as well as general commercial property work and high value residential sales and purchases. Specialist town and country planning, environmental and construction law advice is also available.

Private Client: A wide range of services is provided, including, in particular, all aspects of personal tax planning (including offshore), wills, trusts, charities and the administration of estates. All aspects of immigration and nationality law are covered, including investors, work permits, business applications and sole representatives of overseas companies.

Family: The group deals with all areas of family law including property disputes between partners, separation, divorce, the welfare of children, child abduction and adoption. Members of the group are members of the Solicitors Family Law Association and the Family Mediators Association.

INTERNATIONAL: A full international service is provided by Penningtons in association with the member firms of MULTILAW and the European Law Group (ELG). The firm, through its merger with Walker Martineau, is a founder member of MULTILAW, a multinational association of over 50 law firms in more than 40 countries, and is also a founder member of ELG, an association of business law firms in the EU, Norway and Switzerland. It is also a member of the Law Society Solicitors European Group. Penningtons has in-house lawyers qualified in several overseas jurisdictions. Overseas activity includes specialist knowledge of and experience in many different jurisdictions, particularly France, Hong Kong and the Far East, India, Italy, South Africa and the USA. Work is handled in Chinese, French, German, Gujerati, Italian, Spanish and Turkish.

RECRUITMENT: For training placements and recruitment enquiries contact Lesley Lintott at our London office or visit our website. Penningtons is always interested to hear from first class individuals who wish to advance their careers within a progressive and entrepreneurial firm.

CONTACTS CONTINUED

Private Client	Lesley Lintott
	Richard Underwood
	Michael Fellingham
	Julian Chadwick
Professional Negligence	Michael Felce
Professional Regulation	Katrina Wingfield
	Geoffrey Hudson
Relocation/Housing Ass'ns	Andrew Templeman
	Jonathan Rouse
Residential Property	Paul Collard
	Anthony Bussy
	Tim Rafter
	Richard Hornsby
Shipping	Peter Allan
	Greg O'Neill

PETER CARTER-RUCK AND PARTNERS

International Press Centre, 76 Shoe Lane, London, EC4A 3JB
Tel: (020) 7353 5005 **Fax:** (020) 7353 5553 **DX:** 333 Ch.Ln.
Email: lawyers@carter-ruck.com **Website:** www.carter-ruck.com

THE FIRM: Peter Carter Ruck and Partners sees itself as a young and progressive partnership. It is committed to retaining, and indeed expanding upon, its undoubted predominance in the field of defamation, whilst at the same time building upon its name and client base to develop a higher profile and presence on the part of its intellectual property and entertainment media practice. The firm runs a Conditional Fee Agreement ('no win no fee') scheme for actions involving defamation, intellectual property and other media related matters.

PRINCIPAL AREAS OF WORK: The firm handles both contentious and non contentious media work. The media litigation group, offers both pre and post publication advice on libel, slander, contempt, breach of confidence, privacy and advertising law and regulatory and Official Secrets Act issues. The intellectual property and media group advises both in relation to contentious matters, including infringement of copyright, passing off and trade mark disputes, and non contentious matters, including licensing, commercial and Internet content agreements.

CLIENTELE: The firm's clients are drawn equally from the media and from those seeking advice on dealing with the media.

Senior Partner	Andrew Stephenson
Number of partners	8
Assistant solicitors	6
Other fee-earners	4

CONTACTS

Employment	Nigel Tait
Intellectual Property	Guy Martin
Media Litigation	Ruth Collard
	Cameron Doley
	Claire Gill
	Alasdair Pepper
	Andrew Stephenson
	Nigel Tait
	Charlotte Watson

Peter
Carter-Ruck
and Partners

PETER EDWARDS & CO

Ventura, 8 Market Street, Hoylake, CH47 2AE **Tel:** (0151) 632 6699 **Fax:** (0151) 632 0090 **Email:** Peter@imhl.com
Website: www.Peteredwardslaw.com **Ptnrs:** 2 **Asst solrs:** 1 **Other fee-earners:** 5

PETERKINS

100 Union Street, Aberdeen, AB10 1QR
Tel: (01224) 428000 **Fax:** (01224) 626123 **DX:** AB3
Email: maildesk@peterkins.com **Website:** www.peterkins.com

Senior Partner	Philip Anderson
Number of partners	18
Assistant solicitors	8
Other fee-earners	17

CONTACTS

Corporate & Commercial	Neil Hunter
Banking	Brian Aitken
Oil & Gas/Sea Fishing	Duncan MacNiven
IP/IT	Thomas Rennie
Commercial Property	Philip Anderson
Litigation	Colin Forbes
Private Client	Hartley Lumsden

PETERKINS

THE FIRM: Peterkins is a progressive Aberdeen firm with an office in Glasgow. The firm combines traditional skills with new methods and is committed to making full use of technology to provide high quality, cost effective solutions for clients.

PRINCIPAL AREAS OF WORK: Commercial work includes IP/IT, oil and gas, sea fishing industry and commercial property. The banking group carries out high-volume, case-managed security work as well as higher value corporate lending transactions.

INTERNATIONAL: North Sea Group member, with associated offices in Belgium, Denmark, England and Germany. Oil industry clients include companies based in Russia and the firm has Russian speakers.

P

PETER MAUGHAN & CO

15A Walker Terrace, Gateshead, NE8 1EB **Tel:** (0191) 477 9779 **Fax:** (0191) 477 7997 **DX:** 60323 Gateshead **Email:** mailroom@gatlaw.demon.co.uk **Ptnrs:** 2 **Asst solrs:** 1 **Other fee-earners:** 3

PETER RICKSON AND PARTNERS

6 Winckley Square, Preston, PR1 3JJ **Tel:** (01772) 556677 **Fax:** (01772) 562030 **DX:** 714570 Preston 14 **Email:** info@ricksons.co.uk
Number of partners: 21 **Assistant solicitors:** 13 **Consultants:** 2 **Other fee-earners:** 28

PETERS & PETERS

2 Harewood Place, Hanover Square, London, W1S 1BX
Tel: (020) 7629 7991 **Fax:** (020) 7499 6792 **DX:** 44625 Mayfair
Email: law@petersandpeters.co.uk **Website:** www.petersandpeters.co.uk

Managing Partner	Julia Balfour-Lynn

AREAS OF PRACTICE

Financial Regulation/Business Crime	65%
Commercial Litigation	30%
Commercial Conveyancing	5%

CONTACTS

Business Crime	Monty Raphael
	Louise Delahunty
	Keith Oliver
	Jo Rickards
	Peter Binning
	Claire Lipworth
Commercial Conveyancing	Geoffrey Herman
Commercial Litigation	Keith Oliver
	Kathryn Garbett
	Sarah Gabriel
Customs & Excise	Monty Raphael
	Louise Delahunty
	Jo Rickards
	Peter Binning
Financial Regulation	Monty Raphael
	Keith Oliver
	Jo Rickards
	Peter Binning
Tax	Monty Raphael
	Louise Delahunty
	Sarah Gabriel

THE FIRM: This specialist practice is best known as a leading firm in the areas of business crime, financial regulation and commercial litigation involving fraud. The firm has particular experience in dealing with civil and criminal litigation with an international flavour, including extradition and mutual legal assistance matters. In addition, the firm offers high quality services in employment law, anti money laundering and prevention of corruption advice. Peters & Peters concentrates not only on the quality of the service it provides but also on the technical expertise and practical know-how. It aims to be innovative and to provide solutions to problems that cut across traditional boundaries separating the criminal and civil law practitioner. The firm believes it is one of the first practices to develop such a multidisciplinary approach; consequently both partners and assistants at the firm have built up a considerable level of expertise acting for companies, institutions and regulators as well as individual clients. Much of the practice's work is high profile and is frequently international in scope. The firm has built up a close working relationship with law firms overseas. As a result, it regularly receives instructions by way of referral and invitations to speak at international conferences and seminars, as well as invitations to contribute to business and legal journals throughout the world. Members of the firm have served on government committees and advised foreign regulators and international organisations. Members also contribute to law reform and human rights initiatives both here and overseas.

PRINCIPAL AREAS OF WORK: Areas in which the firm's practice has expanded rapidly include commercial litigation and financial regulation, which complement the firm's traditional strengths in tax, customs and commercial fraud.

Commercial Litigation: Peters & Peters' depth of expertise has been put to good use in a number of cases involving substantial litigation both here and overseas, including asset tracing aided by freezing orders and search orders. The firm has acted both for claimants and defendants, as well as performing the supervisory role in search orders. The firm's expertise covers the whole range of contentious work including civil fraud, contractual disputes, employment law and defamation, together with personal and corporate bankruptcy and related insolvency matters. Due to the firm's particular mixture of expertise, it is often asked to deal with civil litigation matters where criminal and/or regulatory proceedings are also contemplated, with all the complications of parallel litigation. Such cases often include the further complexities of private or public international law.

Business Crime: The practice's long-standing experience and pre-eminence in business crime is universally recognised. It has been built up over a huge variety of cases in which it has acted for large organisations in both an investigative and preventative role, as well as for many private clients. Case loads encompass all forms of corporate fraud, cross-border issues including extradition and mutual assistance, as well as forensic tax and revenue work. Expertise includes VAT and customs infractions, insolvency crimes, securities offences and all examples of business delinquency. Money laundering has become of universal concern and the firm is pre-eminent in giving advice, not only to financial firms, but also to the professions.

Continued overleaf

Financial Regulation: The firm has been instructed in most of the high profile cases involving alleged financial mismanagement in the last two decades. As a result, it has built up a group of fee earners with an in-depth knowledge of the domestic and international regulation of the markets. Their work has contributed significantly to legal developments in this area. Cases have regularly involved the DTI, the FSA and other regulators.
General Crime & Regulation: The firm's expertise in criminal matters is frequently called upon in sensitive cases involving serious criminal investigations of many kinds. Other cases involve investigations relating to Health and Safety, Trading Standards and other regulatory bodies.
Other: The firm also provides a service to corporate and private clients in commercial conveyancing and conducts agency work in all its specialist areas.

PETTMAN SMITH

79 Knightsbridge, London, SW1X 7RB
Tel: (020) 7235 1288 **Fax:** (020) 7235 2683 **DX:** 38168 Knightsbridge
Email: ps@pslaw.co.uk

Managing Partner	Ann Glaves-Smith
Senior Partner	Michael Pettman
Number of partners	7
Assistant solicitors	2
Other fee-earners	2

AREAS OF PRACTICE

Litigation	33%
Company & Commercial	33%
Property	33%

CONTACTS

Commercial Litigation	Jonathan Sachs
Commercial Property	Ann Glaves-Smith
	Marie-Gerrard Newton
Company & Commercial	Michael Pettman
Intellectual Property	Peter Jennings

THE FIRM: A modern commercial practice, established in 1982, which has since grown considerably. The firm seeks to provide practical and commercially viable solutions to legal and business problems in a friendly, professional manner. The practice is particularly noted for its work in intellectual property.

PRINCIPAL AREAS OF WORK:
Commercial Litigation: A comprehensive service includes commercial fraud, employment disputes and property and building contract litigation.
Commercial Property: The firm handles development work from acquisition to sale, mortgage and other bank security work.
Intellectual Property: Both contentious and non-contentious work is handled. Actions include copyright and designs, patents, trademarks, passing-off and confidential information. The firm has particular experience in interlocutory proceedings. Non-contentious work includes software licensing and character merchandising.
Company/Commercial: Company acquisitions and mergers, joint ventures and shareholders' agreements. Venture capital funding and technology-related work. Company reorganisations and restructuring. Business acquisitions and disposals. Management buy-outs and investments. Financial services work including disciplinary and regulatory work. Shareholder and partnership disputes. Insolvency advice, personal and corporate. Company formation and administration. Commercial agreements in particular intellectual property licensing agreements. Software licencing and development and hardware contracts. Service and consultancy agreements. Other commercial advice.
Taxation: International tax planning is a particular strength, and immigration and nationality questions are also handled.

CLIENTELE: Clients include major public companies, small businesses and entrepreneurs. There is a substantial client base in America and the Middle East.

PHILIP CONN & CO

Parsonage Court, 1 North Parade, Parsonage Gardens, Manchester, M3 2HN
Tel: (0161) 833 9494 **Fax:** (0161) 834 4540
Email: enquiries@philip-conn.co.uk **Website:** www.philip-conn.co.uk

Managing Partner	Ian Morris
Number of partners	4
Assistant solicitors	3
Other fee-earners	4

AREAS OF PRACTICE

Corporate/Commercial	35%
Intellectual Property (Contentious & Non-Contentious)	35%
Commercial Conveyancing	15%
Commercial Litigation	15%

CONTACTS

Conveyancing	N Greene
Corporate	Terry Osborn
Intellectual Property	Ian Morris
IP Litigation & Employment	A P Gibson

THE FIRM: Philip Conn & Co was founded in 1975 solely as a commercial practice. It has now established a reputation for having one of the strongest intellectual law practices outside of London with an equal emphasis on contentious and non-contentious work. A multidisciplinary approach is taken, and scientists are recruited to meet the needs of intellectual property. Clients range from multinational public companies to medium-sized and owner managed companies. In the last year the volume of corporate work has continued to grow with a variety of multi-million pound transactions for both publicly quoted and private companies taking place. Corporate deals included a sophisticated innovative funding venture for four hi-tech companies. Commercial property continues to expand with transactions exceeding £60 million undertaken in the year.

INTERNATIONAL: The firm has strong links with lawyers, patent attorneys and firms in the EU, USA and Australasia in particular, and extensive experience in the conduct of both litigation and intellectual property licensing overseas.

PICKWORTHS

55 Marlowes, Hemel Hempstead, HP1 1LE **Tel:** (01442) 261731 **Fax:** (01442) 230356 **DX:** 8809 Hemel Hempstead **Email:** hemel@pickworths.co.uk **Website:** www.pickworths.co.uk **Ptnrs:** 5 **Asst solrs:** 8 **Other fee-earners:** 3 **Contact:** Dorothy Pluck • Major Hertfordshire firm with recognised specialists in employment and planning law. Range of services for business and private clients including commercial/civil litigation, insolvency, property.

PICTONS

Keystone, 60 London Rd, St Albans, AL1 1NG
Tel: (01727) 798 000 **Fax:** (01727) 798 002 **DX:** 122730 St. Albans 10
Email: comm@pictons.co.uk **Website:** www.pictons.co.uk

30-32 Bromham Road, Bedford, MK40 2QD
Tel: (01234) 273 273 **Fax:** (01234) 353 110 **DX:** 5614

1 The Waterhouse, Waterhouse Street, Hemel Hempstead, HP1 1ES
Tel: (01442) 242 441 **Fax:** (01442) 248 569 **DX:** 8800

28 Dunstable Road, Luton, LU1 1DY
Tel: (01582) 870 870 **Fax:** (01582) 870 871 **DX:** 144220 Luton 14

Ashton House, 409 Silbury Boulevard, Central Milton Keynes, MK9 2LJ
Tel: (01908) 663 511 **Fax:** (01908) 661 800 **DX:** 31411

13 Town Square, Stevenage, SG1 1BP
Tel: (01438) 342 400 **Fax:** (01438) 359 255 **DX:** 6006

24 The Avenue, Watford, WD1 3NS
Tel: (01923) 237 631 **Fax:** (01923) 226 135 **DX:** 4505

Managing Partner	Gerard Sampson
Number of partners	31
Assistant solicitors	27
Other fee-earners	64

AREAS OF PRACTICE

Commercial	25%
Crime	22%
Litigation/PI	19%
Family	17%
Domestic Conveyancing	16%
Probate, Trusts & Wills	1%

CONTACTS

Civil Litigation/PI/Medical Negligence ....Sue Jarvis (Central Milton Keynes)
Commercial ....Stephen Ryan (St Albans)
Commercial Dispute Resolution ....Sarah Staines (St Albans)
Commercial Property ....Christopher Brown (St Albans)
Corporate ....Roger Talbot (St Albans)
Crime ....David Healey (Luton)
Employment ....David Fagan (St Albans)
Family......Drenne Dunphy (Hemel Hempstead)
Insolvency ....Antony Sampson (St Albans)
Residential Conveyancing ....Christopher Tate (Luton)
Wills, Trusts & Probate ....Elizabeth Harrold (Hemel Hempstead)

THE FIRM: Offering a comprehensive range of legal services to both commercial and private clients, Pictons Solicitors, established in 1967, remains a dominant legal force across Herts, Beds, and Bucks. The firm provides practical solutions, actionable advice and support in a friendly, helpful and accessible environment. Within each department of the firm there are specific areas of specialisation, to provide a significant depth of expertise and client service.

PRINCIPAL AREAS OF WORK:

COMMERCIAL DEPARTMENT

Corporate Finance: The team provides expertise and advice on any corporate transaction, with particular emphasis in the areas of: mergers and acquisitions, buy ins and buy outs, share and asset sales/purchases, and venture capital.

Employment: The team gives advice to the employer or the employee on all aspects of employment law including sex discrimination, race relation and disability discrimination.

Commercial Property: Dealing with everything from major property development on behalf of large plcs to individual business leases. Within this broad portfolio the team also address such associated issues as planning, housing associations, environmental matters, and security work for lending institutions.

Insolvency: The team primarily advises and acts for IPs although some work is carried out for companies and privately owned business.

Dispute Resolution: With two qualified mediators and an arbitrator in their number, the team is well equipped to provide practical solutions to any dispute arising from business transactions including those in the areas of information technology and e-commerce.

Intellectual Property: Handling both contentious and non-contentious matters, with its main body of work stemming from both the music and information technology industry.

OTHER DEPARTMENTS

Crime: One of the leading criminal departments in the area, undertaking a wide spectrum of criminal matters including those which are more serious and complex such as drug offences, rape, murder and white collar fraud. All police stations within the firm's branch network are covered on a 24 hours a day basis throughout the year.

Domestic Conveyancing: The team's increasing focus is on bulk conveyancing and relocation. The team offers a private client service which aims to takes the stress and strain out of completing a conveyance, by providing an efficient IT lead service.

Personal Injury & Clinical Negligence: A substantial area of the firm's practice, for which it has an excellent reputation especially in cases involving head injuries and multi-party actions. The firm was one of the first in the country to gain the Legal Aid Franchise for clinical negligence in all of its branches.

Wills, Trust & Probate: The team offers expert guidance in will drafting, an imaginative approach to tax planning tailored to meet individual needs, and a sympathetic approach to the administration of estates.

Family: Specialisms include divorce, pension, ancillary relief and children law. Pictons' children's law team consists of five children's panel members who deal with a wide spectrum of children's law matters including abuse and abduction.

PINSENT CURTIS BIDDLE

Dashwood House, 69 Old Broad Street, London, EC2M 1NR
Tel: (020) 7418 7000 **Fax:** (020) 7418 7050 **DX:** 119516 Finsbury Square
Email: martin.lane@pinsents.com **Website:** www.pinsents.com

3 Colmore Circus, Birmingham, B4 6BH
Tel: (0121) 200 1050 **Fax:** (0121) 626 1040 **DX:** 703167 Birmingham 12
Email: john.pratt@pinsents.com

1 Park Row, Leeds, LS1 5AB
Tel: (0113) 244 5000 **Fax:** (0113) 244 8000 **DX:** 26440 Leeds 28
Email: nigel.kissack@pinsents.com

1 Gresham St, London, EC2V 7BU
Tel: (020) 7606 9301 **Fax:** (020) 7606 3305 **DX:** 1008 London Chancery Lane
Email: martin.lane@pinsents.com

National Managing Partner	David Ryan
Senior Partner	Julian Tonks
Number of partners	157
Assistant solicitors	257
Other fee-earners	102

P

THE FIRM: Pinsent Curtis Biddle is the result of the merger on 1 February 2001 of Pinsent Curtis, one of the highest quality national UK firms, and Biddle, a highly regarded City player. The merger doubled the strength in London for each firm and increased its capability across a range of disciplines critical to the successful pursuit of the firm's chosen markets strategy. It also brought together two firms known for and strongly committed to client service. The merged firm has a strong blue chip client base, is ranked in the top ten of legal advisers to UK listed plcs, has a reputation for quality work and an extensive list of lawyers independently rated for their specialist expertise. Independent market surveys have, in fact, shown that clients of Pinsent Curtis Biddle are most likely to be satisfied with the service they receive. The firm now has more than 150 partners, a full legal team of over 500 and total UK staff approaching 1000.

PRINCIPAL AREAS OF WORK: The firm is committed strategically to achieving growth in certain chosen areas, aiming to achieve a leading position in those areas in the next three to five years. The areas are: financial institutions; foreign controlled companies; insurance; major projects; pensions; private equity; property; public companies; technology and media. Within the public companies and foreign controlled companies markets the firm is further focusing its business on a sectoral basis, targeting automotive, food, manufacturing and engineering, retail and leisure and transport and distribution. The firm's strategy is driven forward by specialist cross-discipline teams drawn from its core areas of legal expertise in corporate finance, commerce, trade, technology and media, employment, insurance, litigation, pensions, property and tax. In each of these areas the firm has independently named national experts.

INTERNATIONAL: In November 2000, as part of its international growth, the firm entered into a strategic alliance with leading Swedish law firm, Magnusson Wahlin. The two firms have agreed an exclusive referral relationship, crystallising a well-established existing relationship. The firm is further committed to expanding its work in Gemany and with US companies. It has a dedicated German desk, with dual qualified and German national lawyers, and an experienced US team.

PIPER SMITH & BASHAM

31 Warwick Square, London, SW1V 2AF
Tel: (020) 7828 8685 **Fax:** (020) 7630 6976 **DX:** 110 Ch.Ln.
Email: postmaster@pipersmith.co.uk **Website:** www.pipersmith.co.uk

Managing Partner	Mark Spash
Senior Partner	Richard Berns
Number of partners	6
Assistant solicitors	5
Other fee-earners	1

CONTACTS

Commercial & Other Real Property ....Richard Berns
Private Client ....Mark Spash
Tour Operating & Travel ....Ian Skuse
Litigation ....Richard Twyman

THE FIRM: A long established firm based in Westminster since 1875. The firm still retains its Pimlico roots, but has developed into a number of areas of property, commercial, travel and tour operating work, commercial litigation, company commercial, and employment advice and litigation.

PRINCIPAL AREAS OF WORK:
Tour Operating & Travel: The firm acts for many companies in this industry both large and small.
Commercial & Other Real Property: Development and investment property, landlord and tenant, housing association and local authority work together with residential conveyancing.
Other Areas: Private client, corporate, and general litigation, company, immigration and employment.

PITMANS

47 Castle Street, Reading, RG1 7SR
Tel: (0118) 958 0224 **Fax:** (0118) 958 5097 **DX:** 40102 Reading (Castle Street)
Email: cavery@pitmans.com **Website:** www.pitmans.com

Managing Partner	Christopher Avery
Senior Partner	Tony Jones
Number of partners	16
Assistant solicitors	44
Other fee-earners	49

AREAS OF PRACTICE

Property (Commercial)	24%
Company/Commercial	23%
Commercial Litigation	21%
Residential Development	12%
Planning & Environmental	6%
Employment	6%
Intellectual Property	4%
Corporate Recovery	3%
Private Client	1%

CONTACTS

Commercial Property	Christopher Avery
Company Commercial	John Hutchinson
Corporate Recovery	David Archer
Employment	Mark Symons
Environmental	Daniel Drukarz
Intellectual Property	Philip Weaver
Litigation	Sue O'Brien
Planning	Daniel Drukarz
Private Client	Tony Jones

THE FIRM: Pitmans is one of Thames Valley's leading commercial practices, offering a comprehensive legal service to local, national and international businesses. In recent years the partnership has grown and with it, the breadth of skills and specialisations offered. Pitmans' membership of InterAct Europe 1993 EEIG has proved to be invaluable to the success and growth of the practice.

PRINCIPAL AREAS OF WORK:
Company/Commercial: The company/commercial department is one of the largest in the South East, outside London. It handles a wide variety of work including company formations, mergers and acquisitions, management buy-outs, institutional investment agreements, trading agreements, employment issues, share option schemes and financial services. It advises overseas clients on questions of location and handles work overseas for British clients. The department also offers specialist reports tailored to the needs of individual clients on developing European law affecting them, and is able to review legal frameworks in other countries.
Corporate Security & Insolvency: A specialist department is dedicated to corporate security and insolvency work.
Intellectual Property: The intellectual property department has gone from strength to strength and acts for a large number of the international computer and software companies both in the Thames Valley and overseas. The department offers a wide range of services both of a contentious and non-contentious nature in the patent, copyright, trademark, know-how and entertainment sectors.
Commercial Property: A significant percentage of Pitmans' work is in the commercial property sector. The firm is renowned for its work in land acquisitions, joint venture arrangements and particularly for its expertise in planning and public enquiries. The department's clients include some of the largest housebuilders in the country, a number of substantial plcs, and local authorities. It also has a department specialising in the sale of new homes for residential developers.
Environmental Law: The environmental law department integrates well with the existing commercial property, general commercial and planning work. This department offers a wide range of services within this complex area of law with particular emphasis on the new laws developing in the European Union.
Litigation: The litigation department has wide experience in all areas of commercial litigation, especially in the hi-tech, construction and finance industries and in international trade. It regularly works with other departments to provide a team approach for larger litigation matters. A debt collection service is available to clients. Criminal and matrimonial litigation is not undertaken.
Planning: Nearly all the commercial property partners have specialist knowledge of planning law, and a broad range of expertise covers: development strategy, agreements with highway and planning authorities, major planning appeals and judicial reviews of planning decisions.

CLIENTELE: Clients include both public and private companies, banks and local authorities throughout the UK, as well as an increasing number of organisations in Europe.

INTERNATIONAL: Pitmans is a founder member of an EEIG, with associated law firms in Amsterdam, Berlin, Copenhagen, Finland, Hamburg, Leipzig, Lisbon, London, Madrid, Malmo, Moscow, Munich, New York, Oslo and Paris.

POPPLESTON ALLEN

37 Stoney Street, The Lace Market, Nottingham, NG1 1LS **Tel:** (0115) 953 8500 **Fax:** (0115) 953 8501 **DX:** 10100 Nottingham
Email: mail@popall.co.uk **Website:** www.popall.co.uk **Ptnrs:** 3 **Asst solrs:** 4 **Other fee-earners:** 10

PORTER DODSON

Central House, Church Street, Yeovil, BA20 1HH
Tel: (01935) 424581 **Fax:** (01935) 706063 **DX:** 100501 Yeovil
Email: porterdodson@porterdodson.co.uk **Website:** www.porterdodson.co.uk

Managing Partner	David Perratt
Senior Partner	Stephen Priest
Number of partners	24
Assistant solicitors	18
Other fee-earners	42

AREAS OF PRACTICE

Litigation	42%
Commercial	10%
Probate	22%
Conveyancing	26%

THE FIRM: Porter Dodson is a substantial high street practice with specialist departments offering a wide range of specialist advice with the philosophy of total client care. There are six offices across Somerset and Dorset.

PRINCIPAL AREAS OF WORK: The firm's core areas of practice are litigation, probate, tax and trusts, commercial law, and conveyancing.

CLIENTELE: The firm has a substantial commercial and private client base across a broad spectrum, together

Continued overleaf

with insurance companies, county and local authorities and substantial corporations. There is strong representation of the farming and land owning community.

RECRUITMENT: Porter Dodson has a very healthy recruitment policy. It appoints three trainee solicitors each year and is currently recruiting strongly due to continuing expansion and development of services.

CONTACTS

Litigation	Mike Pitt
Conveyancing	Steve Mahoney
Commercial	David Perratt
Probate	Bill Morris

PORTRAIT SOLICITORS IN ASSOCIATION WITH DENTON WILDE SAPTE

1 Chancery Lane, London, WC2A 1LF **Tel:** (020) 7320 3888 **Fax:** (020) 7430 1242 **DX:** 69
Email: dbf@dentonwildesapte.com **Contact:** Judith Portrait or Dominic Flynn • Specialist private client and charity practice.

POTHECARY & BARRATT

Talbot Hse, Talbot Court, Gracechurch St, London, EC3V 0BS **Tel:** (020) 7623 7520 **Fax:** (020) 7623 9815 **DX:** 590 City
Email: advice@pothecary.co.uk **Ptnrs:** 7 **Asst solrs:** 4 **Other fee-earners:** 4

P

POWELL & CO

77 Woolwich New Road, Woolwich, London, SE18 6ED **Tel:** (020) 8854 9131 **Fax:** (020) 8855 4174 **Ptnrs:** 2 **Asst solrs:** 1
Other fee-earners: 5

POWELL SPENCER & PARTNERS

290 Kilburn High Rd, London, NW6 2DD
Tel: (020) 7624 8888 **Fax:** (020) 7328 1221 **DX:** 123862 Kilburn 2
Email: enquiries@psplaw.co.uk

Managing & Senior Partner:	G. Powell
Number of partners	7
Assistant solicitors	16
Other fee-earners	14

AREAS OF PRACTICE

Criminal Defence	60%
Civil Family	18%
Personal Injury	18%
Welfare Benefits	4%

THE FIRM: Powell Spencer & Partners is one of London's foremost legal aid practices, with a strong reputation for its work in the areas of criminal, family, matrimonial, personal injury, clinical negligence, political asylum and human rights litigation. The firm offers a community-based service, has adapted its offices to meet the requirements of clients with disabilities and undertakes home visits.

PRINCIPAL AREAS OF WORK:
Litigation: A specialist range of litigation is undertaken, namely criminal defence, personal injury and medical negligence, child care, family and matrimonial work, and welfare benefits advice.

PRAXIS PARTNERS

2 Park Lane, Leeds, LS3 1ES **Tel:** (0113) 207 6700 **Fax:** (0113) 207 6701 **DX:** 14093 Leeds **Website:** www.praxispartners.co.uk **Ptnrs:** 7
Asst solrs: 22 **Other fee-earners:** 52

PRESTON GOLDBURN

The Old Brewery Yard, High Street, Falmouth, TR11 2BY **Tel:** (01326) 318900 **Fax:** (01326) 311275 **DX:** 81169
Email: mail@prestongoldburn.co.uk **Website:** prestongoldburn.com **Ptnrs:** 3 **Asst solrs:** 2 **Other fee-earners:** 4

PRETTYS

Elm House, 25 Elm Street, Ipswich, IP1 2AD
Tel: (01473) 232121 **Fax:** (01473) 230002 **DX:** 3218
Email: mail@prettys.co.uk **Website:** www.prettys.co.uk

Managing Partner	Jonathan Gorst
Senior Partner	Clive Brynley-Jones
Number of partners	16
Assistant solicitors	20
Other fee-earners	29

CONTACTS

Agriculture	Toby Pound
Clinical Negligence	Stephen Skinner
Commercial Litigation	Peter Blake
Commercial Property	David Clark
Company/Commercial	Ian Waine
Employment	Richard Stace
Insurance	Clive Brynley-Jones
IT/IP	Roland Sharp
Personal Law	Carol Lockett
Shipping	Paul Dickie
Transport	Roland Sharp

THE FIRM: Prettys is one of the largest practices in East Anglia, with an established private client base and a comprehensive commercial law service. The majority of its commercial clients are small to medium sized companies key to the regional economy. The firm's insurance clients are large composite insurers for whom it operates internationally.

PRINCIPAL AREAS OF WORK: Company, commercial property, litigation, alternative dispute resolution, construction, employment, insolvency, credit management, intellectual property, health and safety, estates, financial services, family, French property, personal injury, clinical negligence, transport, shipping, agriculture and insurance.

RECRUITMENT: Four to five high calibre graduates gain training contracts each year. Brochure available.

PRICEWATERHOUSECOOPERS

10-18 Union Street, London, SE1 1SZ **Tel:** (020) 7939 3000 **Fax:** (020) 7804 1200 **Website:** www.pricewaterhousecoopers.co.uk

PRINCE EVANS

77 Uxbridge Rd, Ealing, London, W5 5ST
Tel: (020) 8567 3477 **Fax:** (020) 8840 7757 **DX:** 5100 Ealing
Email: rjennings@prince-evans.co.uk

Managing Partner	Trevor Morley
Senior Partner	Louis Robert
Number of partners	6
Assistant solicitors	24
Other fee-earners	18

AREAS OF PRACTICE

Housing & Public Sector (inc. Banking & Finance)	50%
Litigation	25%
Personal Injury	10%
Private Client (inc. Company/Commercial)	10%
Crime (inc. Childcare)	5%

CONTACTS

Banking & Finance	Trevor Morley
Company/Commercial	Tom Lemon
Crime/Childcare	Philip Eldin–Taylor
Housing & Public Sector	Louis Robert
Litigation	Robert Jennings
Personal Injury	Bryan Neill
Private Client	Tom Lemon

PRINCE

EVANS

THE FIRM: This broad based West London firm has an enviable reputation in housing and public sector work. It has also built strong specialisms in banking/finance, litigation, company/commercial, personal injury and private client work. Prince Evans has one of the largest dedicated housing and public sector departments in the UK, acting for over 100 registered social landlords and numerous local authorities. The firm prides itself on its innovative and energetic approach to work with the highest commitment to client care. The partners hold regular seminars and have forged a significant client base of public/private limited companies together with residential/commercial landlords.

PRINCIPAL AREAS OF WORK:

Housing & Public Sector: This is the largest area of the firm's practice, for which it has developed a reputation for innovation. It involves constitutional development of registered social landlords; land acquisition and development for individuals/consortium registered social landlords; stock transfers of rundown estates using ERCF funding; HAT succession projects; Pathfinder PFI projects with social services/health authorities; reprovision schemes involving PFI; residential care home transfers with VAT and capital finance efficiency; regeneration and on estate planning gain schemes; foyer schemes; mixed tenure, multi-tenure and flexible tenure projects; joint venture company/off-balance sheet transactions using special purpose vehicles. The department is involved in the development of the next generation PFI and quasi-PFI schemes utilising housing revenue account assets and has the largest Low Cost Home Ownership Unit in the UK. Recently the department has been instructed to advise the Housing Corporation and it is at the forefront of high profile estate regeneration involving mixed tenure in the London Borough of Hackney, Trowbridge Estate. It has also acquired Lovell Partnerships Limited as a client.

Banking/Finance: This department continues to be an expanding area of practice. It acts for both lenders and borrowers of housing and public sector finance on a range of transactions from bilateral and syndicated loans to group borrowing arrangements, capital market issues, and large scale security based transactions. Advice is provided on all aspects of banking law, including treasury management.

Litigation: Prince Evans has a strong reputation for conducting all types of commercial disputes before the Courts, arbitration and adjudication. The firm has developed one of the largest dedicated landlord and tenant litigation functions in London providing a variety of housing management advice. It has also received recoginition for its growth in contentious/non-contentious construction work together with employment advice including the transfer of undertakings and matters before the Employment Tribunal. The commercial litigation department has acquired new prestigious pharmaceutical/chemical manufacturing plc clients whilst the property litigation department's profile has continued to rise, having advised on a number of high profile issues. The construction department has increased in size to include new building contractor clients, whilst the employment department has successfully undertaken a large number of sex/race discrimination cases.

Company/Commercial: The firm has considerable expertise in company/commercial transactions including formation, mergers, acquisitions and take-overs together with partnership matters, service/commercial agreements and lettings/disposals both for occupation and investment companies.

Personal Injury & Medical Negligence: The firm handles all aspects of personal injury and medical negligence. Particular specialisms include severe spinal injury (tetraplegic and paraplegic) and head injury claims. The firm has a pioneering reputation in cases involving major catastrophic injury and disability, obtaining UK record damages on several occasions.

Private Client: A wide range of work is also undertaken including tax, trusts and wills/probate. Residential conveyancing has been expanded to three fee-earners.

Crime/Childcare: The department has considerable experience in the conduct of all criminal matters and has a strong reputation in childcare.

PRITCHARD ENGLEFIELD

14 New St, London, EC2M 4HE
Tel: (020) 7972 9720 **Fax:** (020) 7972 9722 **DX:** 88 London
Email: po@pritchardenglefield.eu.com **Website:** www.pritchardenglefield.eu.com

Managing Partner	Stuart McInnes
Senior Partner	Michael Cohn
Number of partners	25
Assistant solicitors	11
Other fee-earners	24

CONTACTS

Banking	Anthony Harris
Clinical Negligence	Brenda Gilligan
Company/Commercial	David Glass
Employment	Belinda Avery
	Howard Hymanson
Family	Marian Joseph
	Frances Sieber
German	John Rhodes
Insolvency	Anthony Harris
Litigation	Michael Cohn
Personal Injury	Ros Ashby
Private Client	David King-Farlow
Property	David Levene

PRITCHARD ENGLEFIELD
SOLICITORS

THE FIRM: Pritchard Englefield, which can trace its origins to 1848, practises primarily in general commercial law.

PRINCIPAL AREAS OF WORK:
Company/Commercial: Mergers and acquisitions, joint ventures, banking and insolvency and corporate restructuring.
Litigation: Cross-border disputes and conflicts of law as well as arbitration, mediation and alternative dispute resolution.
Property: The firm covers all aspects of property investment and development including commercial property and landlord and tenant work, secured lending, property insolvency and property finance.
Employment: The firm has a dedicated and specialist employment team with a broad range of experience in all aspects of employment.
Personal Injury: Representing claimants (modest value claims to claims of maximum severity) and representing defendants referred primarily by European motor insurers. (A.P.I.L. and Accident Line membership).
Clinical Negligence: The firm acts exclusively for claimants, undertaking a varied caseload. The firm is a member of the Law Society's specialist Clinical Negligence Panel, A.P.I.L., Equestrian Lawyers Association and the Medical Equestrian Society.
Private Client: Wills, trusts, the administration of estates, inheritance tax planning, powers of attorney, offshore trusts, pensions and charities.
Family: The firm undertakes work for both married and unmarried clients in relation to finance and children in the UK and internationally. The firm is a member of the SFLA and is accredited by the Law Society.

CLIENTELE: The firm advises both foreign and UK clients including major financial institutions, multinational corporations, public and private companies, government agencies and individual clients.

INTERNATIONAL: The firm is committed to working in and with Europe and is one of the leading law firms in the areas of Anglo-German and Anglo-French trade. Many of the lawyers and support staff are multilingual (French and German) and some fee-earners are dual-qualified.

PRYCE COLLARD CHAMBERLAIN

6 East Saint Helen Street, Abingdon, OX14 5EW **Tel:** (01235) 523411 **Fax:** (01235) 533283 **DX:** 35853 Abingdon **Email:** pryce.ab@virgin.net **Contact:** Stuart Capel • Established 1820s. General practice with particular experience in agriculture, company, property and personal injury work. Also at 1 Church Street, Wantage, Oxon.

AREAS OF PRACTICE

Probate, Wills, Trusts	24%
Agriculture	22%
Personal Injury	14%

PUBLIC INTEREST LAWYERS

Centre Court, 50-54 St Paul's Square, Birmingham, B3 1QS **Tel:** (0121) 702 2110 **Fax:** (0121) 702 2206
Email: phil_shiner@publicinterestlawyers.co.uk

PULLIG & CO

Bridewell House, 9 Bridewell Place, London, EC4V 6AZ **Tel:** (020) 7353 0505 **Fax:** (020) 7936 2548 **DX:** 123 Chancery Lane **Ptnrs:** 4
Asst solrs: 6 **Other fee-earners:** 9

PURCELL PARKER

204-206 Corporation Street, Birmingham, B4 6QB **Tel:** (0121) 236 9781 **Fax:** (0121) 236 8218

RD BLACK & CO.

31 Old Jewry, London, EC2R 8DQ **Tel:** (020) 7600 8282 **Fax:** (020) 7600 8228 • Established in 1996 by Richard Black, formerly of Middleton Potts, this niche practice is renowned for its expertise in handling commodity, shipping and commercial disputes.

AREAS OF PRACTICE

Commodities	40%
Shipping	40%
Commercial Litigation	20%

R

RADCLIFFES

5 Great College Street, Westminster, London, SW1P 3SJ
Tel: (020) 7222 7040 **Fax:** (020) 7222 6208 **DX:** 113 London Chancery Lane WC2
Email: radcliffes@radcliffes.com **Website:** www.radcliffes.com

Chief Executive	Vincent Denham
Senior Partner	Robert Vallings
Number of partners	36
Assistant solicitors	28
Other fee-earners	30

CONTACTS

Charities ....Robert Bieber
....Guy Greenhous
Company/Commercial ....Roland Gillott
Corporate Finance ....Rupert Lescher
Employment ....Mike Thomas
European Law ....Rupert Lescher
Family ....Roger Cobden-Ramsay
Growing Businesses ....Roland Gillott
Health ....Andrew Parsons
Immigration ....Tim Newsome
International – Italy ....Michael Nathanson
International – Other ....Phillip Peacock
International – South Africa ..Tim Newsome
International – USA/Canada ..Paul Clements
IT ....Roland Gillott
Litigation & Dispute Resolution (Commercial) ....Michael Elks
Litigation & Dispute Resolution (Property) ....Robert Highmore
Property Investment & Development
....Charles Farrar
....Michael Higginson
Residential Property ....Karen Mayne
Tax & Private Client ....Clara Trounson

THE FIRM: A distinctive, medium-sized commercial law firm, Radcliffes combines traditional values like integrity and prompt response with a client-focused approach to everything it does. The firm handles commercial matters and private client work with equal skill, empathy and understanding of clients' individual needs.

PRINCIPAL AREAS OF WORK: Cross-departmental teams from across the firm have particular strengths and expertise in the following areas:

Growing Businesses: The firm has an outstanding reputation as a principal adviser to growing businesses, notably hi-tech companies. It provides advice and guidance to businesses not only on legal issues, but also on commercial issues.

Corporate: The firm handles joint ventures, limited partnerships, cooperation agreements for on-going businesses, venture capital, project finance and equity offerings, due diligence reviews, acquisitions and disposals, management buy-outs and buy-ins and listings on AIM and the Stock Exchange.

Business Issues: Areas covered include IP, marketing, distribution and agency agreements, standard terms, outsourcing, competition law in the UK and EU and industry specific legislation.

Employment & Human Resources: The firm advises on all aspects of contentious and non-contentious employment and HR matters including pensions advice.

Technology: Areas covered include e-commerce, internet trading, software and hardware supply and procurement, IP, data protection and licensing.

Dispute Resolution: The firm works in the areas of negotiation; arbitration; mediation and litigation of business disputes in both domestic and overseas markets including those relating to general contract and tort; shareholder and partnership disputes; contractual claims; negligence; the sale of goods and services.

Property Investment & Development: Clients are provided with proactive, commercial advice to aid their business. Acting for property investors, developers and occupiers, including institutions, livery companies and landed estates, the firm's specialist property group handles mainstream property work in addition to advising on property dispute resolution, planning (including consultancy and advocacy) environmental law, property VAT and secured lending.

Private Client: The firm is committed to serving the needs of the private client and advises business owners, senior executives, professionals, individuals, executors and trustees on a wide range of matters. The work covers both UK and international tax considerations and includes tax and estate planning, tax compliance and investigation, uses and variation of trusts, wills, estate and trust administration, receivership, elderly care, family law and residential property.

Charity: Radcliffes is a recognised name in the field of charity law providing services to national and international charities, not for profit organisations, schools and colleges. The firm is ranked in the top 15 of charity legal advisers according to the *Top 3000 Charities Guide to UK Charities 2000* and currently acts for more than 170 charities and not-for-profit organisations, with a particular strength in advising health, mental health and welfare charities.

Health: Radcliffes has been acting for the health sector for over 30 years, providing high quality, commercial advice and assistance to health authorities, NHS Trusts, GPs, Primary Care Groups, insurers, the Royal Colleges, nursing homes and the private sector healthcare providers. The health group has particular expertise in the field of mental health and acts for some of the largest Mental Health NHS trusts. It is frequently called upon to advise on the operation of the Mental Health Act, the impact of government reforms and on all aspects relating to the treatment and detention of the mentally ill and people with learning disabilities.

RECRUITMENT: Four trainees are taken on each year. A recruitment brochure is available on request and application is by CV or employer's application form with covering letter, to the Administration Secretary.

RAEBURN CHRISTIE & CO

16 Albyn Place, Aberdeen, AB9 1PS **Tel:** (01224) 640101 **Fax:** (01224) 638434 **DX:** 2 Aberdeen **Email:** info@raeburns.co.uk
Website: www.raeburns.co.uk **Ptnrs:** 15 **Asst solrs:** 13 **Other fee-earners:** 13

RAMSBOTTOM & CO

25-29 Victoria St, Blackburn, BB1 6DN **Tel:** (01254) 672222 **Fax:** (01254) 681723 **DX:** 15251 Blackburn 2 **Ptnrs:** 5 **Asst solrs:** 7
Other fee-earners: 6

R

RAWLISON BUTLER

Griffin House, 135 High Street, Crawley, RH10 1DQ
Tel: (01293) 527744 **Fax:** (01293) 520202 **DX:** 120750 Crawley 8
Email: info@rawlisonbutler.com **Website:** www.rawlisonbutler.com

15 Carfax, Horsham, RH12 1DY
Tel: (01403) 252492 **Fax:** (01403) 241545 **DX:** 57602 Horsham

Senior Partner	James Chatfield
Number of partners	11
Assistant solicitors	11
Other fee-earners	12

AREAS OF PRACTICE

Commercial Property	30%
Company Commercial	25%
Commercial Litigation	24%
Private Client	21%

CONTACTS

Commercial	Mark O'Shea (Crawley)
Commercial Litigation	Clive Lee (Crawley)
Commercial Property	Clive Prior (Crawley)
Corporate Finance	Tim Sadka (Crawley)
Employment	Louise Dabbs (Crawley)
Insolvency	Stuart Evans (Crawley)
Family	Robert Worthing (Horsham)
Private client	Digby Armstrong (Horsham)

Rawlison Butler

THE FIRM: Rawlison Butler is a dynamic and ambitious law firm delivering imaginative and workable solutions to its commercial clients nationally and internationally, complemented by extensive experience advising on wealth management. Rawlison Butler provides commercial services from its offices in Crawley and private client services from its office in Horsham, West Sussex. Its geographical positioning – close to London Gatwick Airport – enables the firm to provide the highest standards of service to UK and foreign-owned businesses. The diversity of the client base – from owner-managed businesses to listed companies and multinational corporations – ensures a depth of understanding about the issues affecting businesses in a wide range of sectors and regions.

PRINCIPAL AREAS OF WORK: Rawlison Butler is organised on a team basis offering partner-led representation in each area of expertise. Where appropriate, teams work together in order to provide the best and most informed solution for the client whilst maintaining a consistency of service and symmetry of style. High service standards are combined with the latest specialist legal knowledge.
Corporate: The firm specialises in company formation and reorganisation; business acquisitions and disposals; joint ventures; share sales and purchases; acquisition finance; venture capital financing; flotations and fundraising; management buyouts and buyins; partnership and shareholder agreements; exit planning and strategic advice.
Commercial Litigation: The firm handles contractual and trade disputes; product liability; partner or shareholder disputes; IP/IT/E-business disputes; defamation; insolvency and commercial fraud; tax investigations; and regulatory matters.
Property: Work undertaken includes property development agreements; building contracts, appointments and collateral warranties; leases and leasehold management; property investment, joint ventures, acquisition, disposal and management; finance and funding.
Employment: Advice on contracts and employment policies; remuneration packages and stakeholder pensions; related tax matters; parental leave and anti-discrimination policies; internet and communication policies; disciplinary, grievance and termination procedures; and dispute resolution.
Commercial & IT: Work includes outsourcing; supply and purchase contracts; agency and distribution agreements; franchising; terms of business; data protection; due diligence; competition law; confidentiality; technology licensing; domain name registration and disputes; website terms and conditions; facilities management agreements; all aspects of intellectual property law.
Private Client Asset Management: The firm advises on inheritance tax planning; trusts; wills and probates; care for the elderly and enduring power of attorney; independent personal finance advice; residential conveyancing, land sales or purchases, mortgages and security; all aspects of private client litigation.
Family: Rawlison Butler handles divorce; separation and cohabitation disputes; high net worth financial disputes; complex children and residence cases.

RECRUITMENT: Rawlison Butler is keen to recruit driven high calibre qualified lawyers with a proven record of high academic achievement and professional success.

RAYFIELD MILLS

3 Collingwood Street, Newcastle upon Tyne, NE1 1JE **Tel:** (0191) 261 2333 **Fax:** (0191) 261 2444 **Email:** law@rayfield-mills.co.uk
Website: www.rayfield-mills.co.uk **Ptnrs:** 8 **Asst solrs:** 4

READ HIND STEWART

Trafalgar House, 29 Park Place, Leeds, LS1 2SP
Tel: (0113) 246 8123 **Fax:** (0113) 244 2863 **DX:** 14085
Email: rhslaw@rhs-law.co.uk **Website:** www.rhs_law.co.uk

Managing Partner	David Hymas
Number of partners	17
Assistant solicitors	8
Other fee-earners	30

AREAS OF PRACTICE

Commercial Property	35%
Company/Commercial	25%
Commercial Litigation	23%
Employment	9%
Debt Recovery	8%

THE FIRM: Read Hind Stewart was established in 1987, and has now developed into a major practice in the commercial centre of Leeds.

PRINCIPAL AREAS OF WORK: The practice undertakes commercial work and has particularly strong corporate, commercial property, commercial litigation and employment departments. European law is a specialisation, specifically German law related matters.

RECRUITMENT: As a developing practice, Read Hind Stewart is continually looking for outstanding candidates. Please contact the Managing Partner.

REED SMITH WARNER CRANSTON

Pickfords Wharf, Clink St, London, SE1 9DG **Tel:** (020) 7403 2900 **Fax:** (020) 7403 4221 **DX:** 39904 London Bridge South **Email:** firstinitialsurname@reedsmith.co.uk **Website:** www.reedsmith.co.uk **Ptnrs:** 27 **Asst solrs:** 29 **Other fee-earners:** 22

REES & FRERES

1 The Sanctuary, Westminster, London, SW1P 3JT **Tel:** (020) 7222 5381 **Fax:** (020) 7222 4646 **DX:** 2301 Victoria **Email:** enquiries@1thesanctuary.com **Website:** www.reesandfreres.com **Ptnrs:** 12 **Asst solrs:** 12 **Other fee-earners:** 13 **Contact:** Joseph Durkin • Specialists in commercial property, public, parliamentary and local government law, transport infrastructure projects, planning, compulsory acquisition and commercial litigation.

REID MINTY

14 Grosvenor Street, Mayfair, London, W1K 4PS
Tel: (020) 7318 4444 **Fax:** (020) 7318 4445 **DX:** 44615 Mayfair
Email: lawyers@reidminty.co.uk **Website:** www.reidminty.co.uk

Managing Partner	Stephen Moss
Senior Partner	Andrew Reid
Number of partners	12
Assistant solicitors	10
Other fee-earners	56

AREAS OF PRACTICE

Commercial Litigation	50%
Personal Injury	20%
Healthcare	10%
Other	10%

CONTACTS

Banking	Ian Searle
	David Pacey
Commercial Litigation	Stephen Moss
	Simon Goldhill
Commercial Property	Martin Gunson
Corporate/Sports	Jonathan Ebsworth
Costs Consultancy	Andrew Reid
Employment	Nick Neocleous
Health Authority	Ashley Irons
Horseracing	Andrew Reid
Insolvency	Ian Searle
Insurance	Simon Edwards
Personal Injury	Sue Brown

THE FIRM: Reid Minty is renowned for its ability to successfully handle substantial commercial litigation matters. The firm handles City work with a lower cost base and no difference in quality, and is recognised as an expert in this field.

PRINCIPAL AREAS OF WORK: The firm advises on major domestic and international commercial disputes, banking and insolvency matters, and covers the full range of commercial litigation from the House of Lords, and Privy Council, through to the Commercial Court, High Court and County Courts. Recent reported cases include Dubai Aluminium v Salaam, Dardana v Yukos Oil and Ashworth v MGN. The firm advises specialist hospitals on sensitive issues concerning secure unit patients (Ian Brady v Ashworth Hospital, R v Broadmoor SHSA ex p S), on local authority healthcare regulations and on a wide range of specialist employment matters. It also provides supporting commercial and property advice. The firm carries out a number of insurance related services including risk and cost assessment, and volume personal injury work.

CLIENTELE: Prominent clients include domestic and international banks, financial institutions, international insurers, plcs, substantial multinational corporations, health authorities, international transport and container leasing companies, private companies and individuals.

RECRUITMENT: Reid Minty has a comprehensive programme for trainee solicitors, and recruits five to six trainees per year, as well as taking on a number of paralegals.

REYNOLDS DAWSON

34 John Adams Street, Charing Cross, London, WC2N 6HW
Tel: (020) 7839 2373 **Fax:** (020) 7839 2344
24-Hour Emergency Number: (08457) 056767 (code 957)
DX: 40040 Covent Garden 1 **Email:** inquiries@reynoldsdawson.com
Website: www.reynoldsdawson.com

Partner	Colin Reynolds
Salaried Partner	Elizabeth Fox

THE FIRM: Reynolds Dawson was established in 1982 by Colin Reynolds and Stephen Dawson, who is now a District Judge (Crime) and Recorder. Colin Reynolds is a well established and highly respected criminal practitioner and former President of the LCCSA. The practice, which holds a Legal Aid franchise, specialises in crime and is a member of the Serious Fraud Panel. The practice also undertakes extradition work. Reynolds Dawson enjoys a long established private client basis that extends to Personal Injury and Employment Tribunal work. The partners have both been involved in high profile criminal cases as well as participating in the Stephen Lawrence, Marchioness and Laming Inquiries.

REYNOLDS PORTER CHAMBERLAIN

Chichester House, 278-282 High Holborn, London, WC1V 7HA
Tel: (020) 7242 2877 **Fax:** (020) 7242 1431 **DX:** 81 Chancery Lane
Email: rpc@rpc.co.uk **Website:** www.rpc.co.uk

Senior Partner	Alan Toulson
Number of partners	50
Assistant solicitors	83
Other fee-earners	69

AREAS OF PRACTICE

Professional Indemnity	25%
Insurance/Reinsurance	25%
Corporate	10%
Commercial Litigation	10%
Property	10%
Construction	10%
Media & Technology	5%
Private Client/Family	5%

CONTACTS

Commercial Litigation	Stephen Mayer
Commercial Property	Edward Meerloo
	David Haywood
Company/Commercial	Alan Toulson
Construction	Robert Hogarth
Corporate Finance	Jonathan Watmough
Defamation	Liz Hartley
Education	Geraldine Elliott
Employment	Geraldine Elliott
Family	James Stewart
Insolvency	Justin Westhead
Insurance/Reinsurance	Simon Greenley
Intellectual Property	Andrew Hobson
Media & Technology	Tim Anderson
Personal Injury	Duncan Harman-Wilson
Private Client	Colin Russell
Professional Indemnity	Paul Nicholas
Tax & Pensions	Charles Suchett-Kaye

REYNOLDS PORTER CHAMBERLAIN

THE FIRM: Reynolds Porter Chamberlain is a substantial commercial firm and one of the country's leading insurance and litigation practices. The firm also has a strong corporate and commercial practice providing a wide range of legal services to both UK and international businesses, institutions and private individuals. It has well established overseas connections and is a founder member of TerraLex, an international association of law firms across over 100 jurisdictions.

PRINCIPAL AREAS OF WORK:
Insurance/Reinsurance: The department acts for insurance and reinsurance companies and Lloyd's underwriters. It handles general insurance, reinsurance market litigation as well as professional indemnity work, acting for the insurers of accountants, architects, barristers, brokers, engineers, financial advisers, solicitors and other professionals. It also has a substantial practice acting for the insurers of directors and officers, banks and financial institutions. In addition to pure legal services, the firm also offers claims handling and loss adjusting services. Its office in Leadenhall Street provides easy access for the surrounding insurance market.
Corporate: The corporate department acts for publicly quoted companies, multinational corporations, private companies, trade associations and partnerships. Work includes mergers and acquisitions, corporate finance, banking, Yellow Book work, insolvency, franchise and distribution, tax, competition law and financial services regulations.
Media & Technology: The firm's expertise in this area covers publishing, IT and internet law, defamation, media-related litigation and commercial agreements. Media clients include national newspapers, broadcasters and IT companies. This group specialises in both contentious and non-contentious media and IT related work.
Clinical Negligence: This department acts for the NHSLA, NHS Trusts, health authorities and the insurers of private clinics.
Commercial Litigation: The firm handles disputes relating to contracts, product liability, shareholder agreements, agency and franchising, insolvency, personal injury, partnership and property.
Intellectual Property: Patents, trademarks, designs, copyright and licensing are handled for industries ranging from pharmaceutical companies to computing, publishing and entertainment companies.
Employment: The firm deals with contracts, restrictive covenants, misuse of confidential information and trade secrets, employee benefits, pensions and industrial tribunal hearings.
Education: The firm acts for teachers' professional associations, universities, colleges and schools and advises on all aspects of education law including the further and higher education sectors.
Commercial Property: The department acts for publicly quoted property companies and investment funds as well as general trading companies. Areas of work include property investment, site acquisitions, joint ventures, development, town and country planning and landlord and tenant law.
Construction: The firm gives advice on building contracts and related documentation and a substantial amount of arbitration and litigation.
Private Client: The department offers a considerable range of services to private clients, including financial services, personal taxation, wills, trusts and probate.
Family: This department handles all aspects of matrimonial and family law and is especially noted for high value complex divorce work, as well as high profile child abduction work and wardship cases on behalf of local authorities and the Lord Chancellor's department.

CLIENTELE: Clients include multinational corporations, publicly quoted companies, private companies, publishers and broadcasters, new media companies, property developers, professional and trade associations, insurance and reinsurance companies, underwriters, mutuals, private individuals and partnerships.

RECRUITMENT: The firm recruits ten trainee solicitors a year. Bursaries are available. There is also a summer vacation scheme for prospective trainees. Application forms are available from Sally Andrews, Head of Personnel.

RICHARD BUXTON
40 Clarendon Street, Cambridge, CB1 1JX **Tel:** (01223) 328933 **Fax:** (01223) 301308 **Email:** law@richardbuxton.co.uk
Website: www.richardbuxton.co.uk **Ptnrs:** 2 **Asst solrs:** 1

RICHARD MONTEITH
34 Portmore Street, Portadown, BT62 3NG **Tel:** (028) 3833 0780 **Fax:** (028) 3835 0271 **Ptnrs:** 3 **Asst solrs:** 2 **Contact:** Richard Monteith • Specialisation in criminal law in addition to general practice of conveyancing, wills and probate, matrimonial and civil litigation.

RICHARDS BUTLER

Beaufort House, 15 St Botolph Street, London, EC3A 7EE
Tel: (020) 7247 6555 **Fax:** (020) 7247 5091 **DX:** 1066 City/18 London
Email: law@richardsbutler.com **Website:** www.richardsbutler.com

Chairman	Andrew Taylor
Managing Partner	Roger Parker
Worldwide:	
Number of partners	105
Number of fee-earners	417
Total staff	766

THE FIRM: Richards Butler is one of the country's pre-eminent medium to large law firms. Its core strategy is to invest in key practice areas, enabling it to establish renowned capabilities that appeal to significant international concerns. The firm's principal practice areas for this purpose are corporate finance, finance and banking, media/entertainment/leisure, shipping, insurance, commodities, telecommunications, IT and commercial property. Its rated corporate finance team acted for Skanska on the acquisition of Kvaerner interests, and on two bids for the East Coast Mainline and South West Trains rail franchises for GNER Ltd, as well as handling the disposal for the Rank Group of Odeon Cinemas and the Tom Cobleigh chain of public houses. Its specialist finance practice recently acted on what is believed to be the world's largest financial restructuring. The disputes group has continued to represent City financial institutions on investigatory and regulatory work and, in the area of media, has represented the BBC, Express Newspapers and Direct Line in high profile disputes. In shipping, the Admiralty unit acted in practically all the major European casualties, including the 'Erika'. The property group launched an on-line management tool, 'RBAssetsOnLine', which helped the firm win work from Trillium Group, the largest property management company in the UK and Europe, against stiff competition from six competitor law firms. Over two thirds of Richards Butler's work contains an international dimension, a fact reflected in our long-held belief of investing in overseas offices. Its Hong Kong office alone is rightly regarded as the leading British law firm in the region and, with a physical presence in not less than three of the Gulf states, the firm has been providing advice to the Gulf region for a quarter of a century. The European offices continue to expand – with the Paris branch being forced to move to larger premises this year. Richard Butler's aim is to provide the best advice in the areas it specialises in to all clients, irrespective of their size, and to ensure each of them receives the same quality of service and care. The rigorous control of costs is just another pleasant surprise.

PRINCIPAL AREAS OF WORK: Richards Butler advises in all major areas of commercial law, including:
Corporate & Commercial: The firm advises clients on domestic and international mergers and acquisitions; IPOs and stock exchange listings; management buy-outs and buy-ins; corporate and government debt restructuring; joint ventures and inward investment; regulatory environments; project finance including asset financing; venture capital; cross border leasing and PFI; unit trusts; EU and competition law; intellectual property and IT; insurance; media and entertainment law; anti-piracy and copyright protection; pensions; employment and industrial relations; energy.
Dispute Resolution: Advice is given on all matters requiring dispute resolution skills including litigation at all court levels. As one of the largest litigation practices in the UK, the group has expertise in all major litigation areas including financial services/regulatory and banking, all aspects of media and information technology, insurance, employment and general corporate litigation. It also has substantial experience in arbitration and mediation techniques. The firm has acted in many of the major commercial disputes in the City.
Property: The firm advises on all aspects of property, environment and planning law, including investment and financing of land and commercial property; VAT; planning requirements for local authorities; construction and contract negotiations; financing and claim preparation; advice related to licensing of hotels and leisure premises, including liquor licensing, betting, gaming, late-night licensing and multi-leisure site licensing.
Shipping: The group advises on all aspects of shipping, including charterparty disputes; bill of lading claims; ship sale and purchase; drafting of and disputes concerning shipbuilding contracts; marine insurance and reinsurance (such as P&I and defence clubs); salvage; collision and major casualties (the firm has a 24 hour casualty response line); all aspects of ship finance acting both for banks and borrowers; trade and commodities including buying and selling of hard and soft commodities; trade finance.

INTERNATIONAL: The firm has offices in Abu Dhabi, Beijing, Brussels, Hong Kong, Paris, Piraeus, São Paulo and Warsaw, and associated offices in Doha and Muscat.

CONTACTS

Admiralty & Casualty (Wet)	Richard Harvey
ADR	John Hull
Anti-piracy	Mike Northern
Aviation & Aircraft Finance	Adam Morgan
Banking & Financial Services	Gordon Stewart
Commercial	Stephen Sayer
Commercial Disputes	Charles Hewetson
Competition & EU	Katherine Holmes
Corporate Finance	David Boutcher
Defamation	Michael Skrein
E-commerce	Stephen Edwards
Employment	Robin Jeffcott
Energy	Stephen Sayer
Financial Services Regulation & Compliance	Richard Parlour
Insolvency	Jon Yorke
Insurance & Reinsurance	Mark Connoley
Intellectual Property	Graham Simkin
International Arbitration (Commercial)	Roger Parker
International Arbitration (Shipping)	Andrew Hughes
International Banking	Gordon Stewart
International Trade & Commodities	David Pullen
IT & Telecommunications	Graham Simkin
Licensing	Elizabeth Southorn
Litigation	Charles Hewetson
Marine Casualty Response	Richard Harvey
Media & Entertainment	Stephen Edwards
Pensions	Simon Hartley
Planning, Environment & Construction	John Aylwin
Professional Negligence	Roger Parker
Property	Jon Pike
Ship Finance	Adam Morgan
Shipping	Adam Morgan
Tax	Richard Sowler
Unit Trusts & Investment Funds	Simon Hartley

R

RICHARD WHISH – SOLE PRACTITIONER

School of Law, King's College, The Strand, London, WC2R 2LS **Tel:** (020) 7848 2237 **Fax:** (020) 7848 2211 **Email:** richard.whish@kcl.ac.uk

RICKERBY WATTERSON

Ellenborough House, Wellington Street, Cheltenham, GL50 1YD
Tel: (01242) 224422 **Fax:** (01242) 518428 **DX:** 7415 Cheltenham
Email: rw@rickerby.co.uk **Website:** www.rickerby.co.uk

Managing Partner	Mark Fabian
Senior Partner	John Clarke
Number of partners	17
Assistant solicitors	17
Other fee-earners	23

AREAS OF PRACTICE

Property	35%
Private Client/Asset Management	26%
Company Commercial	15%
Commercial Litigation & Insolvency	14%
Employment	5%
Family	5%

CONTACTS

Agriculture	Robin Beckley
Asset Management	Mark Hartley
Commercial Litigation	Tom Esler
Commercial Property	Robin Beckley
Company Commercial	Richard Knight
Education	John Clarke
Employment	Kristine Scott
EU & Competition Law	Anne Compton
Family Law	Carolyn Green
Insolvency & Realisation	Derek Jones
Private Client	Mark Hartley
Residential Property	Henry Marshall

THE FIRM: Rickerby Watterson is a leading Gloucestershire firm with an established commercial law practice and a strong private client base. The firm is innovative, progressive and committed to meeting a wide range of clients' needs. It has a reputation for delivering city expertise and value for money.

PRINCIPAL AREAS OF WORK:

Company Commercial: Work handled includes the sale and purchase of businesses, re-structuring and re-financing, shareholder agreements, raising finance and venture capital. The firm also advises on partnership and joint venture agreements, agency and distribution agreements, UK and EU competition law, e-commerce and intellectual property, and all aspects of employment law, dispute resolution, litigation and insolvency.
Property: The firm advises on acquisitions, funding, development and disposal, environmental and planning work, licensing and landlord and tenant matters. It also has an active residential property team that undertakes bulk re-mortgage, security and banking work.
Private Client: The firm provides specialist advice in areas such as family law, capital tax planning, trusts, investments, mental incapacity and care for the elderly. The firm's asset management team manages funds in excess of £90m on behalf of clients.

CLIENTELE: Clients include plcs and owner-managed companies, local subsidiaries of national and multinational plcs, and leisure and commercial property companies. Many schools and colleges instruct the firm, as do high net worth individuals who are typically business owners, company shareholders, senior business executives, landowners and families with complex estates.

R

RIDLEY & HALL

Permanent House, 1 Dundas Street, Huddersfield, HD1 1LE **Tel:** (01484) 538421 **Fax:** (01484) 533076 **DX:** 710083 Huddersfield 8 **Email:** info@ridleyhall.co.uk **Ptnrs:** 5 **Asst solrs:** 3 **Other fee-earners:** 5 **Contact:** Liz Ryan • Specialists in education, disability and community care. Strong in licensing and issues involving the elderly as well as property, private client, personal injury and matrimonial.

RM BROUDIE & CO

1-3 Sir Thomas St, Liverpool, L1 8BW **Tel:** (0151) 227 1429 **Fax:** (0151) 236 5161 **DX:** 14248 **Ptnrs:** 2 **Asst solrs:** 7 **Other fee-earners:** 10

ROBERTA MCDONALD – SOLE PRACTITIONER

12 Wake Green Road, Moseley, Birmingham, B13 9EZ **Tel:** (0121) 449 6821 **Fax:** (0121) 449 5160

ROBERT LIZAR

159 Princess Road, Moss Side, Manchester, M14 4RE **Tel:** (0161) 226 2319 **Fax:** (0161) 226 7985 **Email:** robertlizar@lizar.fsnet.co.uk **Ptnrs:** 6 **Asst solrs:** 1 **Other fee-earners:** 5

ROBERT MUCKLE

Norham House, 12 New Bridge Street West, Newcastle upon Tyne, NE1 8AS **Tel:** (0191) 232 4402 **Fax:** (0191) 261 6954 **DX:** 61011 **Email:** enquiries@robertmuckle.co.uk **Website:** www.robertmuckle.co.uk **Ptnrs:** 11 **Asst solrs:** 22 **Other fee-earners:** 18

ROBERTSON & CO, TECHNOLOGY LAW PRACTICE

18 Broomhouse Road, London, SW6 3QX **Tel:** (020) 7731 4626 **Fax:** (020) 7731 4598 **Ptnrs:**1 **Email:** drcr@techlaw.co.uk **Contact:** Ranald Robertson • Specialist legal support to users and suppliers on computing, software and Internet issues. Benefits include speedy access to senior IT/computer law experience at a reasonable and affordable cost.

ROBERTSONS

6 Park Place, Cardiff, CF1 3DP **Tel:** (029) 20237777 **Fax:** (029) 2034 0219 **DX:** 33039 Cardiff **Email:** law@robsols.co.uk **Ptnrs:** 9 **Asst solrs:** 2 **Other fee-earners:** 7

ROBSON MCLEAN WS

28 Abercromby Place, Edinburgh, EH3 6QF
Tel: (0131) 556 0556 **Fax:** (0131) 556 9939 **DX:** LP11-Edin 2
Email: info@robson-mclean.co.uk **Website:** www.robson-mclean.co.uk

Senior Partner	William F MacTaggart
Number of partners	12
Assistant solicitors	10
Other fee-earners	10

AREAS OF PRACTICE

Litigation 50%
Commercial/Corporate 25%
Private Client 25%

CONTACTS

Commercial Property ....Nick Atkins
Corporate ....Walter Thomson
Litigation ....Robin Macpherson
Private Client ....Neil Paterson

THE FIRM: This leading Scottish firm, operating from Edinburgh's city centre, continues to see growth in its commercial litigation and commercial/corporate departments. It has a strong client focus offering value-for-money services tailored to individual client needs. The firm is approved to ISO 9001 and is the only Scottish member of LawGroup UK.

PRINCIPAL AREAS OF WORK: Specialisms include commercial litigation, corporate, employment, environmental/planning, IP/technology, personal injury, matrimonial, PFI, commercial property and private client.

CLIENTELE: Major clients include government bodies, local authorities, leading insurers and financial institutions, property companies, charities and special interest groups, trade unions and associations.

ROCHMAN LANDAU

45 Mortimer Street, London, W1N 7TD
Tel: (020) 7544 2424 **Fax:** (020) 7544 2400 **DX:** 42700 Oxford Circus North
Email: mail@rochmanlandau.co.uk

Managing Partner	Teresa Cullen John Rochman
Number of partners	9
Assistant solicitors	3
Other fee-earners	3

CONTACTS

Property ....John Rochman
....Edward Landau
Litigation ....David Liebeck
....Alan Langleben
Employment ....Teresa Cullen
Insolvency ....David Liebeck
Company/Commercial ....John Godby
....John Rochman
Private Client ....Edward Landau
....John Rochman
Licencing ....Patricia Negus-Fancy
Matrimonial ....Teresa Cullen
....Philippa Dolan

THE FIRM: This West End law firm provides a high quality, cost effective legal service to clients, both in the UK and overseas. It combines technical expertise with a commercial approach.

PRINCIPAL AREAS OF WORK: Rochman Landau have considerable expertise in the following areas: business; property; litigation; family matters; wills and probate; trusts – UK and overseas; tax; employment; landlord and tenant, both commercial and residential; licensing; insolvency; immigration. The firm can also offer mediation and ADR services.

CLIENTELE: Clients are both within the UK and overseas, and consist of corporate clients, banks, plcs, mid-sized companies, entrepreneurs and professionals.

INTERNATIONAL: The firm has strong links with the Far East, Australia and America. It also has French speaking fee-earners.

RECRUITMENT: The firm has recently welcomed Alan Langleben (ex Nicholson Graham and Jones) and Stephen Alter (ex Jay Benning and Peltz). The firm takes pride in the fact that a number of its former trainees have remained with the firm, and are represented amongst the partners.

RODGERS & BURTON

15-17 Church Rd, Barnes, London, SW13 9HG
Tel: (020) 8939 6300 **Fax:** (020) 8876 8228 **DX:** 59702 Barnes
Email: info@randb.law.co.uk

Senior Partner	David Moore
Number of partners	5
Other fee-earners	4

AREAS OF PRACTICE

Private & Commercial Conveyancing 52%
Civil Litigation 33%
Matrimonial 10%
Wills & Probate 5%

CONTACTS

Conveyancing/Wills & Probate
....Kathryn Kinnear
Landlord & Tenant ....David Moore
Matrimonial ....Gillian Tyndall
Personal Injury/Employment/
Debt Recovery ....Mark Woloshak

THE FIRM: The firm was founded in 1835, and has had a presence in Barnes since 1952. The firm occupies offices overlooking Barnes Common and incorporated another local firm, Messrs Ashbys, in 1998.

PRINCIPAL AREAS OF WORK: Whilst being a general High Street practice, Rodgers & Burton offers certain specialist advice in servicing landlords and Housing Associations. In particular, the firm offers experience in landlord and tenant litigation, housing association law and finance, disposals and acquisitions of property, lease back financing of acquisitions, shared ownership schemes, construction contracts and disputes.
Other Areas: Rodgers & Burton also have fee earners with experience in employment law, personal injury, debt recovery, contractual disputes, commercial litigation and a busy matrimonial department. Conditional fee arrangements are available if appropriate. The firm will draft wills, where no tax planning or will trust advice is required, for a fixed fee. The firm has obtained a franchise for community legal service specialist help in family. The firm offers an Agency Service in Wandsworth, West London and Brentford County Courts. Rodgers & Burton have a well respected residential conveyancing department and, following the incorporation of Messrs Ashbys, have considerable expertise in commercial conveyancing.

ROEBUCKS

12 Richmond Terrace, Blackburn, BB1 7BG **Tel:** (01254) 274000 **Fax:** (01254) 274002 **DX:** 15254 Blackburn 2 **Ptnrs:** 6 **Asst solrs:** 3
Other fee-earners: 4

ROGER TABAKIN – SOLE PRACTITIONER

61 Onslow Gardens, London, N10 3JY **Tel:** (020) 8374 2562 **Fax:** (020) 8883 8352

ROITER ZUCKER

5-7 Broadhurst Gardens, Swiss Cottage, London, NW6 3RZ
Tel: (020) 7328 9111 **Fax:** (020) 7644 8900 **DX:** 38850 Swiss Cottage
Email: mail@roiterzucker.co.uk **Website:** www.roiterzucker.co.uk

Number of partners	8
Assistant solicitors	8
Other fee-earners	2

AREAS OF PRACTICE

Intellectual Property (including Pharmaceutical)	50%
Private Client	25%
Commercial	13%
Litigation Non IP	12%

CONTACTS

General Contact	Anna McKay

THE FIRM: Roiter Zucker is well known for its intellectual property and competition law work. The firm has an excellent reputation for litigation, having acted in many of the leading IP and competition law cases, including the terfenadine and paclitaxel patent cases, the Glaxo/Dowelhurst case concerning parallel imports and the extent of the free movement of goods, and judicial review cases, most recently for parallel importers in connection with their claim of illegality of the 1999 PPRS governing reimbursement for pharmaceutical products. As well as its high profile litigation, RZ does a full range of non-contentious IP work for clients in various fields: pharmaceutical (from start-up biotech companies to multinational companies), media and an increasing amount of brand work. RZ is small, but highly skilled. It is used to working in the international arena and can draw on expert advice worldwide.

R

ROLLITS

Wilberforce Court, High Street, Hull, HU1 1YJ
Tel: (01482) 323239 **Fax:** (01482) 326239 **DX:** 715756 Hull 15
Email: info@rollits.com **Website:** www.rollits.com

Rowntree Wharf, Navigation Road, York, YO1 9WE
Tel: (01904) 625790 **Fax:** (01904) 625807 **DX:** 61534 York

Managing Partner	Stephen Trynka
Senior Partner	James Brennand
Number of partners	31
Assistant solicitors	17
Other fee-earners	25

AREAS OF PRACTICE

Company & Commercial	34%
Property	24%
Litigation	18%
Private Capital	12%
Planning & Development	7%
Employment	5%

CONTACTS

Commercial	Keith Benton
Commercial Litigation	George Coyle
Company	Richard Field
Employment	Neil Maidment
Environmental	Steve Hawkins
Planning	John Downing
Private Capital	John Lane
Property	Martyn Justice

THE FIRM: One of the principal firms in the Yorkshire region offering a highly regarded comprehensive commercial legal service. Its expertise in corporate and commercial law is unrivalled in East Yorkshire.

PRINCIPAL AREAS OF WORK:
Company: Work includes acquisitions and disposals, flotations, share issues, fund raising, joint ventures, MBOs, finance and credit agreements, corporate recovery, employment law and telecommunications.
Commercial: Including e-commerce, intellectual property, trading agreements, franchising, and competition law.
Commercial & Residential Property: Work includes commercial conveyancing, planning and development, environmental law, landlord and tenant, housing association work and agriculture.
Litigation: Work undertaken includes commercial litigation, intellectual property disputes, building and construction, mediation debt recovery, insurance litigation, professional indemnity, licensing and matrimonial.
Private Capital: Including tax and estate planning, settlements, asset protection, wills, estate administration, education and charity law.

ROOKS RIDER

Challoner House, 19 Clerkenwell Close, London, EC1R 0RR
Tel: (020) 7689 7000 **Fax:** (020) 7689 7001 **DX:** 53324 Clerkenwell
Email: csimm@rooksrider.co.uk **Website:** www.rooksrider.co.uk

Managing Partner	Clare Foinette
Senior Partner	Christopher Cooke
Number of partners	12
Assistant solicitors	22
Other fee-earners	12

AREAS OF PRACTICE

Company/Commercial	40%
Litigation	22%
Private Client	20%
Property	18%

CONTACTS

Banking	Clare Foinette
Commercial Litigation	Paul Whitaker
Company/Commercial	Christopher Cooke
	Keir Gordon
	Nicholas Jacob
	Jeremy Whiteson
Employment	Paul Whitaker

THE FIRM: Established in 1761 (making Rooks Rider one of the oldest law firms in the country) it has a tradition of offering a high quality service to individuals and businesses. Building from this foundation, the partnership is continually expanding the breadth of its expertise to respond to the needs of its clients and the changing business environment. It has a friendly and informal atmosphere and prides itself on finding creative and practical solutions to its clients needs. The firm is committed to the continued development of both the private client and commercial sides of its practice. It achieved Investors in People accreditation in 1999. In addition to offering a comprehensive, high quality service to businesses and individuals Rooks Rider has developed an international reputation for its tax planning skills both in the UK and offshore. It has particular expertise in serving growing businesses (from startup to major listed company). It is a leading firm in the private client field.

PRINCIPAL AREAS OF WORK: The firm has growing practices in a broad spread of commercial and private client areas.

Commercial: Rooks Rider commercial clients range from substantial listed companies to family businesses and in a diverse array of market sectors. The firm offers clients a full service in handling transactions, managing disputes and providing advice on commercial issues. The firm's commercial practice is dovetailed with its international tax practice, and within the commercial practice, solicitors are encouraged to develop a broad legal knowledge. This structure has allowed the firm to provide balanced, practical advice to entrepreneurs and entrepreneurial business in a seamless manner and to create a stimulating working environment. The approach has worked particularly well for inward investment into the UK, business start ups and company sales.

E-Commerce: Existing strengths in advising start ups, intellectual property and corporate sales have been applied to good effect to the growing group of e-commerce clients.

International Tax: The international tax practice has particular strengths in the fields of offshore trusts and international corporate structures for companies and individuals. It is instructed by professional trustees, banks and individuals around the world and partners visit virtually all of the major low tax jurisdictions each year. Team members regularly contribute to conferences and journals in this area and are invited to lecture as far afield as Hong Kong and New Zealand.

Private Client: Its traditional private client base has expanded considerably, advising in relation to landed estates, wills, trusts, probate, and tax planning. This enables the firm to provide an extensive service to wealthy individuals be they UK residents, foreign nationals or expatriates. It works closely with the matrimonial practice which has dedicated specialists dealing with family law issues including complex financial cases.

Property: The property team handles all types of commercial and residential property transactions, and landlord and tenant matters. It has developed a particular expertise on leasehold reform and is a founder member of the Leasehold Advisory Group. It counts developers and investment funds amongst its regular clients and has built a major specialisation in designing tax efficient structures for property purchases in the UK by foreign nationals and residents.

Litigation: Commercial disputes are dealt with by the litigation department which has particular focuses upon, patent litigation, contentious employment matters, family disputes, property litigation and professional negligence.

Other: Cross departmental teams deal with employment, intellectual property, banking and insolvency.

RECRUITMENT: The firm is always seeking to recruit high calibre qualified staff and recruits at least two trainee solicitors each year. All areas of the practice are expanding. Enquiries should be sent to the staff partner.

CONTACTS CONTINUED

Insolvency	Jeremy Whiteson
Intellectual Property	Paul Whitaker
International Tax	Gerald Chappell
	Christopher Cooke
	Nicholas Jacob
	Karen Methold
Matrimonial	Paul Whitaker
Private Client	Nicholas Jenkins
	Charlotte Simm
	Christopher Wright
Property	Clare Foinette
	John Spencer-Silver

ROOKS RIDER SOLICITORS

R

ROSLING KING

2-3 Hind Court, Fleet St, London, EC4A 3DL
Tel: (020) 7353 2353 **Fax:** (020) 7583 2035 **DX:** 154
Email: info@roslingking.co.uk **Website:** www.roslingking.co.uk

Senior Partner	Owen Rafferty
Number of partners	9
Assistant solicitors	28
Other fee-earners	22

AREAS OF PRACTICE

Litigation/Insurance	45%
Property/Construction/Environmental	30%
Company/Commercial/Banking/ Sports/Employment	25%

CONTACTS

Banking/Finance	Owen Rafferty
Company/Commercial	Owen Rafferty
Construction	John Beagley
E-commerce	Ruth Neil
Employment	Helen Thurkettle
Environmental	Paul Lowe
Insurance & Reinsurance	Georgina Squire
Litigation	Georgina Squire
Property	Owen Rafferty
	Malcolm Macfarlane
Sports	John Beagley

THE FIRM: Rosling King is a young, dynamic commercial firm based in the City of London. The firm's main office is on Fleet Street. They also have a London insurance market office in Leadenhall Street, EC1. The firm offers an imaginative and practical approach to working with clients to achieve their objectives. Rosling King values its clients and is constantly looking for ways to improve its relationships with them. With this in mind it has developed a unique client care programme.

PRINCIPAL AREAS OF WORK: This niche firm provides advice in the following areas:

Banking/Finance: Banking advice for both secured and unsecured lending, including loan and other standard form documentation, debt enforcement, insolvency, refinancing, securitisation and risk sharing, structuring of lending and underwriting.

Commercial Property: Including development from conception to completion, funding, landlord and tenant, leasehold enfranchisement, planning, portfolio acquisition and management and property investment and taxation.

Company & Commercial: Including intellectual property, joint ventures, mergers and acquisitions, new business ventures and investments and taxation planning.

Construction: Including all forms of construction documentation for contractors, sub-contractors and professionals, collateral warranties and advice on regulatory matters.

Litigation: All forms of litigation and dispute resolution, including professional indemnity, civil fraud, IT, defamation, sale of goods and general commercial claims as well as disputes in all the firm's listed areas of expertise.

Employment: Including contracts, impact of legislation on the workplace, business restructuring, redundancy and other forms of disputes.

Environment: Including appointment documentation for advisors and contractors, environmental liabilities for business and the impact of EU legislation.

Health & Safety: Including CDM regulations, developments in EU law, risk assessments, HSE matters and all forms of dispute.

Continued overleaf

Insurance & Reinsurance: Including claims handling coverage and market disputes, policy and treaty drafting and interpretation, investigations and commutations of problem portfolios, ART, regulatory work, risk assessment advice and dealing with run-offs, all of which advice is for domestic and international clients.
Sport: Including contractual advice, global representation of overseas interests, branding, IP and sponsorship negotiation, merchandising and promotions.

CLIENTELE: The firm's clientele has developed significantly over the last 10 years. It is an almost exclusively commercial firm and its client base reflects its established areas of expertise. They include a significant number of banks, lenders, building societies, major financial institutions, insurance and reinsurance companies, Lloyd's Syndicates and other insurance professionals, property companies, developers and investors.

INTERNATIONAL: The firm has developed a large international network of associated firms in over 150 cities worldwide to assist its clients' internationally based work requirements. It also offers international surgeries for clients in the UK.

ROSS & CONNEL

10 Viewfield Terrace, Dunfermline, KY12 7JH **Tel:** (01383) 721156 **Fax:** (01383) 721150 **DX:** DF 11 **Ptnrs:** 6 **Asst solrs:** 1 **Other fee-earners:** 1

ROSS & CRAIG

12A Upper Berkeley Street, London, W1H 7PE
Tel: (020) 7262 3077 **Fax:** (020) 7724 6427 **DX:** 44416 Marble Arch
Email: reception@rosscraig.com

Managing Partner	David Leadercramer
Senior Partner	Leonard Ross
Number of partners	9
Assistant solicitors	8
Other fee-earners	5

AREAS OF PRACTICE

Property	50%
Company/Commercial/Media	20%
Litigation	12%
Family	10%
Employment	6%
Private Client	2%

CONTACTS

Company/Commercial/Media	Ian Bloom
Employment	Gill Sage
Environmental	Hugh Barrett
Family/Private Client	Simone Katzenberg
Litigation	David Leadercramer
Property	Stephen Gilbert

THE FIRM: Established in the 1950s with an emphasis on commercial client work, acting for public and private companies, businesses and individual entrepreneurs but with strong teams in respect of private client matters, family, personal injury, trusts, financial planning and bankruptcy.

PRINCIPAL AREAS OF WORK:
Commercial Property: Work includes development projects, acquisitions, portfolio break-ups, structuring joint venture schemes of varying complexity with associated planning and funding requirements conducted through tax efficient procedures. Clients number major developers retailers and hotel operators. Particular niche in banking security.
Company/Commercial/Media: Including a full range of corporate and commercial transactions, with ancillary employment, shareholder and director agreements, flotation, institutional and other funding schemes. Some of the firm's specialist areas include intellectual property, computer contracts, media, entertainment, film and TV funding and production documents.
Litigation: Work handled includes commercial disputes, landlord and tenant litigation and property disputes, employment law, intellectual property, complex personal injury work, professional negligence, insolvency and liquidations.
Environmental Law: The specialist land regeneration unit enjoys high level connections with relevant professionals and government departments. It provides services in a consultancy capacity and as a principal adviser on legal and risk management. Its members are recognised as 'leaders in the field'.
Family Law: As well as usual areas of advice, this team has special expertise in dealing with cohabiting partners and in advising on the financial issues in a practical way.
Employment: The firm provides advice to clients in respect of both contentious and non-contentious work.

CLIENTELE: Clients range from internationally known companies to small businesses and individuals.

INTERNATIONAL: The firm has close links with lawyers in Europe, America, Middle East, Far East and much off-shore and EU compliancy work.

ROSS HARPER

58 West Regent Street, Glasgow, G2 2QZ **Tel:** (0141) 333 6333 **Fax:** (0141) 333 6334 **DX:** 519242 GLW 12 **Email:** westregentstreet@rossharper.com **Website:** www.rossharper.com **Ptnrs:** 9 **Asst solrs:** 16 **Other fee-earners:** 15 • Multi-practice firm specialising in commercial and domestic conveyancing, wills and executries, family law, compensation claims, employment matters, sports and media, white collar and all other crime.

AREAS OF PRACTICE

Criminal	30%
Family	23%
Residential Conveyancing	20%
Litigation & Employment	12%
Claims	8%
Commercial Conveyancing	6%
Sports & Media	1%

ROTHERA DOWSON

2 Kayes Walk, Stoney Street, The Lace Market, Nottingham, NG1 1PZ
Tel: (0115) 9100 600 **Fax:** (0115) 9100 800 **DX:** 10028 Nottingham
Email: enquiries@rotheradowson.co.uk **Website:** www.rotheradowson.co.uk

Managing Partner	Jane George
Senior Partner	Christopher Hodson
Number of partners	14
Assistant solicitors	6
Other fee-earners	11

AREAS OF PRACTICE

Litigation	25%
Probate, Trusts & Tax	20%
Property	20%
Company Commercial & Employment	15%
Family	15%
Other	5%

CONTACTS

Commercial Litigation	Richard Hammond
Company, Commercial & Planning	Christopher Hodson
Crime	Tony Priest
Ecclesiastical/Education	Christopher Hodson
Employment	James Collard
Family & Matrimonial	Clare Bianchina
Financial Advice	Beryl Morgan
Personal Injury	Anton Balkitis
Property	Amanda Redgate
Transport	Ian Rothera
Wills, Trusts, Probate & Tax	Jeremy Allen

SOLICITORS AND NOTARIES

THE FIRM: Rotheras Solicitors was established in 1827 and Dowsons Solicitors in 1824. Rothera Dowson was established following the merger of both firms with effect from 1st January 1999. The new firm has long standing links with the Road Haulage Association and Freight Transport Association. Through its work in connection with the introduction of the Immigration and Asylum Act this year the firm has established an international clientele over the last 12 months. It also has extensive experience in ecclesiastical law. The firm has invested heavily in technology over the last two years. Rothera Dowson serves a wide and varied client base including large institutions and commercial businesses, small companies and individuals. The firm is forward thinking and innovative; this enables clients to achieve their objectives. A number of the partners hold judicial positions including Deputy Coroner, Deputy District Judge, Clerk to the Commissioners of Income Taxes and Southwell Diocesan Registrar.

PRINCIPAL AREAS OF WORK:

Corporate & Commercial: Company formations, share issues, acquisitions, commercial agreements, commercial property employment contracts, intellectual property, commercial property including landlord and tenant, compulsory purchase, leases, town and country planning.

Litigation: Civil litigation of all kinds, including a significant personal injury department with PI Panel members, crime, contentious intellectual property matters, employment disputes, contractual disputes including construction, debt recovery for large companies and also work for housing associations. This department also includes a substantial transport section, with a number of specialist road transport lawyers who advise PCV and road haulage operators in connection with disciplinary and environmental public inquiries, operator licensing, drivers hours and tachograph law, defence of prosecutions, carriage of goods, insurance claims and Immigration Act carriers liability cases. The firm's employment law and commercial property departments also carry out an extensive amount of work for the firm's transport clients.

Private Client: All aspects of personal taxation, trusts, wills, probate and administration. Family and matrimonial solicitors including a qualified SFLA mediator covering all kinds of family work including advice upon divorce, financial disputes, cohabitation, child abduction etc. Panel members available, including members of the Law Society Children Panel and Law Society Family Panel. The firm also undertakes advocacy in mental health law cases and one of its partners is a part time chairman of the Mental Health Review Tribunal. One of its solicitors is a member of the Law Society MHRT Panel.

Independent Financial Advice: In-house independent adviser for all kinds of investment advice. Agency work undertaken. General civil contract for family and mental health.

ROWE COHEN

Quay House, Quay Street, Manchester, M3 3JE **Tel:** 0161 830 4600 **Fax:** 0161 831 7436 **Email:** info@rowecohen.com
Website: www.rowecohen.com **Ptnrs:** 14 **Other fee-earners:** 70

ROWE & MAW

20 Black Friars Lane, London, EC4V 6HD
Tel: (020) 7248 4282 **Fax:** (020) 7248 2009 **DX:** 93
Email: roweandmaw@roweandmaw.com **Website:** www.roweandmaw.com

Canada House, 3 Chepstow Street, Manchester, M1 5FW
Tel: (0161) 236 1612 **Fax:** (0161) 236 9712

Suite 892-894, Lloyds, One Lime Street, London (Lloyd's), EC3M 7QD
Tel: (020) 7327 4144 **Fax:** (020) 7623 7965

Senior Partner	Stuart James
Number of partners	80
Assistant solicitors	148
Other fee-earners	70

AREAS OF PRACTICE

Corporate	31%
Litigation & Dispute Resolution	25%
Property	11%
Intellectual Property	10%
Pensions	8%
Construction	6%
Banking & Projects	5%
Employment	4%

CONTACTS

Banking & Projects	Neil Morrison
Commercial Property	Jeremy Clay
Construction Litigation	Michael Regan
Corporate Finance	Stephen Bottomley
Employment	Julian Roskill
Environment	Cate Sharp
EU/competition Law	Frances Murphy
	Kirin Desai
Insolvency	David Allen

THE FIRM: Rowe & Maw is one of the country's leading commercial law firms, based in the City of London. Founded over 100 years ago, the firm's reputation is based upon delivering pragmatic commercial advice, and it is praised for its professionalism. With over 80 partners and almost 300 lawyers in total, the firm offers its clients a broad range of legal services, both in the UK and internationally. In the past five years the firm has grown rapidly, adding to its traditional strengths in corporate, litigation, pensions and construction with innovative new teams in public law, projects and PFI. Although the firm is classified as a medium-sized firm, its position in the legal market derives from its 'top ten' client base. Industry experience is one factor which differentiates Rowe & Maw. Many of the firm's lawyers have spent time working in industry and therefore have a better understanding of the commercial needs of its client.

Continued overleaf

PRINCIPAL AREAS OF WORK: The firm's main strength has always been in advising companies and businesses, both in day-to-day matters and on special projects. The firm is divided into a number of practice groups, the principal ones of which are listed opposite. The firm also has a number of specialist industry groups, the most notable of which are chemicals and communications (including telecoms, cable TV, broadcasting and satellite).

Corporate: The firm's corporate group is recognised as one of the leading teams in the country. It acts for a number of FTSE 200 companies, as well as a wide range of private and public companies, partnerships, financial institutions and intermediaries. The group advises on all aspects of corporate and commercial law, both in the UK and overseas. Under the corporate umbrella, tax, environment, professions, EU and competition law have established high profile practices in their own right.

Litigation & Dispute Resolution: The group has grown significantly in recent years and, in addition to general commercial litigation and arbitration, has developed a number of specialist litigation based market sectors, most notably in insurance and reinsurance, public law, property and insolvency, all of which are considered to be leaders in their respective fields.

Construction, Pensions & Employment: These groups have long been identified as leaders in their fields. Over the last two years, more recently established groups such as the professions and projects and banking groups have joined them.

Commercial Property: The group continues to expand, both in terms of its client base and through strategic lateral hires in size.

Intellectual Property: The firm's IP/IT group has grown rapidly in recent years, supplementing core IP strengths with a growing reputation in IT matters.

INTERNATIONAL: Rowe & Maw advises clients internationally, either through its EU and competition law office in Brussels or through a well-established network of contacts, particularly in Europe, North America and South East Asia.

CONTACTS

Insurance	Sean Connolly
Intellectual Property	Stephen Gare
Litigation & Dispute Resolution	David Allen
	Sean Connolly
Mergers & Acquisitions	Paul Maher
Partnership	Richard Linsell
Pensions	Stuart James
Public & Administrative	Tony Child
Tax	Peter Steiner

Rowe & Maw

R

ROWLANDS

3 York Street, Manchester, M2 2RW **Tel:** (0161) 835 2020 **Fax:** (0161) 835 2525 **DX:** 14475 Manchester 2
Email: manchester@rowlands-solicitors.co.uk **Website:** www.rowlands-solicitors.co.uk **Ptnrs:** 18 **Asst solrs:** 20 **Other fee-earners:** 14

ROWLEY ASHWORTH

247 The Broadway, Wimbledon, London, SW19 1SE **Tel:** (020) 8543 2277 **Fax:** (020) 8543 0143 **DX:** 300003 Wimbledon South
Email: ra@rowley-ashworth.co.uk **Ptnrs:** 21 **Asst solrs:** 26 **Other fee-earners:** 26

ROYDS TREADWELL

2 Crane Court, Fleet Street, London, EC4A 2BL
Tel: (020) 7583 2222 **Fax:** (020) 7583 2034 **DX:** 102 Chancery Lane
Email: info@royds.com **Website:** www.royds.com

18 Crown Lane, Morden, SM4 5BS
Tel: (020) 8542 1067 **Fax:** (020) 8544 0246

Number of partners	13
Assistant solicitors	10
Other fee-earners	9

AREAS OF PRACTICE

Litigation & Employment	40%
Company	20%
Property	20%
Private Client & Tax	20%

CONTACTS

Company/Commercial	Peter Wootton
Employment	Richard Woodman
Family	Patrick Hart
Litigation	Stewart Wilkinson
Personal Injury	James Millar Craig
Private Client	Christopher Wright
Privy Council	Richard Woodman
Property	Robert Lloyd-Davies
Tax	Arthur Alexander

THE FIRM: Clients include many of the UK's best-known trade unions such as TGWU, AEEU, GMB, MSF and USDAW. In addition, the firm acts for many individuals who have suffered personal injury, including those introduced by major charities in the sector.

PRINCIPAL AREAS OF WORK:

Company/Commercial: The department deals in company formations, disposals, acquisitions, shareholders agreements, joint ventures, MBOs and has particular expertise in intellectual property, insolvency, banking, construction, agency and e-commerce.

Property: The department deals with all aspects of commercial property together with landlord and tenant, and other property related matters. The department also has a wide practice in residential conveyancing.

Litigation: The department deals with the full range of litigation matters. It has experience of all types of litigation for both individuals and corporate clients with expertise in agency, company and partnership disputes, insurance related matters, insolvency, banking, intellectual property construction, and trust and probate disputes. The firm has fully embraced the use of ADR and will do conditional fee work.

Personal Injury: The department has a substantial personal injury unit headed by a member of the personal injury panel, also dealing with fatal accidents and accidents at work as well as specialising in cycle and motorbike accidents.

Family: The department deals with all types of divorce, children and financial provision disputes.

Privy Council: Royds Treadwell is proud to be retained to act for the government of Mauritius in connection with appeals to the Privy Council.

Employment: The firm has a substantial and well regarded employment law practice which is retained by large employers and membership organisations as well as acting for senior executives and employees in a full range of boardroom and workplace disputes.

Private Client & Tax: The firm has a significant private client department acting for substantial high net-worth individuals and trusts. The work of this department includes wills, trusts, probate, pensions, specialist financial services investment advice, estate planning and offshore trusts and tax planning or advice.

INTERNATIONAL: The firm has strong links in France, the Channel Islands, the Far East, Mauritius, Sri Lanka and the USA. Members of the firm are fluent in French and German.

ROY MORGAN & CO

Norfolk House, 57-59 Charles Street, Cardiff, CF1 4ED **Tel:** (029) 20398511 **DX:** 33040 **Ptnrs:** 1 **Asst solrs:** 4

ROYTHORNE & CO

10 Pinchbeck Rd, Spalding, PE11 1PZ **Tel:** (01775) 724141 **Fax:** (01775) 725736 **DX:** 26701 Spalding **Email:** roythorne@roythorne.co.uk **Website:** www.roythorne.co.uk **Ptnrs:** 14 **Asst solrs:** 11 **Other fee-earners:** 20

RUDLINGS & WAKELAM

1 Woolhall Street, Bury St Edmunds, IP33 1LA **Tel:** (01284) 755 771 **Fax:** (01284) 762 436 **DX:** 57202 Bury St Edmunds **Email:** info@rudlings-wakelam.co.uk **Ptnrs:** 6 **Asst solrs:** 5 **Other fee-earners:** 7 **Contact:** Julia Wakelam • Specialists in childcare/family and matrimonial, personal injury and employment (particularly discrimination) law. Also handles agricultural, company/commercial, civil litigation, probate and conveyancing (both commercial and domestic).

R

RUPERT BEAR MURRAY DAVIES

Union Chambers, 11 Weekday Cross, Nottingham, NG1 2GB
Tel: (0115) 924 3333 **Fax:** (0115) 924 2255 **DX:** 10015 Nottingham
Email: rbmdlaw@aol.com

Senior Partner	Murray Davies
Number of partners	3
Assistant solicitors	5

AREAS OF PRACTICE

Matrimonial/Public Child Law	95%
Conveyancing	5%

CONTACTS

Matrimonial	Murray Davies
	Sarah Heathcote
	Isobel England
Mediation	Sarah Heathcote
	Catherine Stevens
Public Child Law	Isobel England
	Russell Tolley

THE FIRM: A specialist family law practice founded in 1992, by Rupert Bear, an established Nottingham family solicitor. The firm encompassed the family law practice of Eversheds, Nottingham and in 1996, was supplemented by the arrival of Murray Davies as partner, bringing with him in excess of 16 years experience in the field. Sarah Heathcote became a partner in the same year, having been with the firm since its inception. Upon Rupert Bear's retirement in 1999, Isobel England, with some 20 years experience, joined the firm, bringing a particular interest in the law relating to children, adoption and matrimonial finance. The firm has established contacts with accountants, pensions advisers, insurance brokers and other professionals, to assist in resolving financial matters resulting from the breakdown of relationships. A Legal Aid franchise for family work is also held by the firm.

PRINCIPAL AREAS OF WORK: Work includes separation and divorce and the financial agreements relating to all aspects of family relationships, the resolution of disputes involving children, their legal status, and adoption. The firm has considerable experience in co-habitation issues and pre-marriage arrangements. Mediation work, conveyancing, wills and the legal requirements of the elderly are also catered for.

RUSSEL & AITKEN

22 & 24 Stirling Street, Denny, FK6 6AZ **Tel:** (01324) 822194 **Fax:** (01324) 824560 **DX:** 1171 **Ptnrs:** 12 **Asst solrs:** 9 **Other fee-earners:** 9

RUSSELL-COOKE

8 Bedford Row, London, WC1R 4BX
Tel: (020) 7405 6566 **Fax:** (020) 7831 2565 **DX:** 112 London
Email: advice@russell-cooke.co.uk

2 Putney Hill, Putney, London, SW15 6AB
Tel: (020) 8789 9111 **Fax:** (020) 8780 1194 **DX:** 59456 Putney
Email: advice@russell-cooke.co.uk

Bishop's Palace House, Kingston Bridge, Kingston-upon-Thames, KT1 1QN
Tel: (020) 8546 6111 **Fax:** (020) 8541 4404 **DX:** 31546 Kingston
Email: advice@russell-cooke.co.uk

Senior Partner	Michael Maskey
Managing Partner	John Gould
Number of partners	24
Assistant solicitors	36
Other fee-earners	23

AREAS OF PRACTICE

Property	30%
Family/Child Care/PI Litigation/other	25%
Probate Wills & Trusts	15%
Criminal Law	10%
Commercial Litigation	10%
Company/Commercial	10%

CONTACTS

Abduction	Fiona Read
Administrative Law/Solicitors	John Gould
Capital Taxes	John Milverton
Child Care	John Hackett

THE FIRM: Russell-Cooke is an energetic, professionally managed firm, which has developed a reputation for specialist expertise in a number of areas without sacrificing its collective breadth of experience. The firm has offices in Bedford Row and Kingston but with the majority of staff based at the Putney office, it manages to keep overheads lower than competing firms based solely in central London and makes substantial reinvest-

Continued overleaf

ment in technology, facilities and human resources. The firm has recently received the Investors in People accreditation. Russell-Cooke's distinctive culture has produced cohesive and committed legal teams who are encouraged to develop and maintain long term relationships with clients.

PRINCIPAL AREAS OF WORK: The areas covered include: commercial property; commercial litigation; company commercial; private client; trusts; wills and probate; family; medical negligence and personal injury; crime; childcare; and conveyancing including French property. Within these areas the firm encourages specialisation. The firm continues to be successful because its cost base is appropriate, it has young partners and staff and it has for many years sub-specialised to match the best competing expertise in the areas in which it operates.

CLIENTELE: The firm has an unusually large client base. The requirements of these clients, who tend to have an ongoing relationship with the firm, mean that the range of services provided by the firm is unusually broad.

CONTACTS CONTINUED

Commercial & Construction Litigation/ADR .... Francesca Kaye
Commercial Property .... Peter Dawson
Company/Commercial ...... Jonathan Thornton
Conveyancing .... Nigel Coates
Criminal Matters .... Ian Ryan
Employment .... Anthony Sakrouge
Family Law .... Camilla Thornton
Family Mediation .... Therese Nichols
French Property & Law .... Dawn Alderson
Insolvency .... Lee Ranford
Medical Negligence & Personal Injury .... Janice Gardner
Probate & Wills .... Richard Frimston
Professional Regulation .... Peter Cadman
Property Litigation .... Jason Hunter
Trusts .... Michael Best

R

RUSSELL JONES & WALKER

Swinton House, 324 Gray's Inn Road, London, WC1X 8DH
Tel: (020) 7837 2808 **Fax:** (020) 7837 2941 **DX:** 202 London Chancery Lane
Email: enquiries@rjw.co.uk **Website:** www.rjw.co.uk

Senior Partner	John Webber
Chief Executive	Mark Feeney
Number of partners	47
Assistant solicitors	88
Other fee-earners	61

THE FIRM: Russell Jones and Walker, founded in London in the 1920s, has grown rapidly in the last 10 years expanding from 100 to nearly 600 staff and partners, and establishing offices in Newcastle, Sheffield, Leeds, Manchester, Birmingham, Bristol, Cardiff and Northampton. In the last year the firm opened an associated office in Edinburgh and so now has a presence across all of mainland Britain. The firm's emphasis on people has enabled it to develop an impressive range of specialist services of particular value to individuals and those who represent them.

PRINCIPAL AREAS OF WORK:

Personal Injury: The firm is one of the leading claimant personal injury practices. A total of over 100 lawyers deal with a wide range of claimant personal injury work including compensation for industrial injury, disasters, chemical poisoning and environmental pollution, road traffic accidents, disease and disablement and criminal assault.

Employment: The firm has a large specialist employment department with a highly respected reputation within the industry. It deals with all aspects of individual and collective claimant employment law, both litigious and non-litigious, including contracts, discrimination, dismissal issues, transfers and pensions and human rights issues.

Criminal Law & Investigations: The firm has a reputation as one of the leading criminal law practices within the UK, advising and representing clients on all aspects of criminal law with a particular focus on white collar crime, tax investigations and commercial fraud.

Litigation: The commercial litigation department advises on all aspects of commercial litigation including professional negligence, defamation, intellectual property and insolvency. The department is particularly well regarded for its libel expertise having successfully acted against all national daily and Sunday newspapers and most radio and TV companies.

Clinical Negligence: The firm has a first class reputation for resolving clinical negligence cases. The department is a rapidly expanding area of the practice with an exceptional success rate. All types of claimant clinical negligence work is undertaken with particular expertise in claims involving young children, representation at inquests and alternative dispute resolution in litigation including mediation.

Other Areas: In addition to the specialist areas of work listed above the firm has expertise in the following areas: commercial and residential conveyancing; landlord and tenant contracts; public and administrative law; public inquiries; family and matrimonial law; and other private client services including wills, probate and trusts and financial services.

AREAS OF PRACTICE

Personal Injury 64%
Crime & Fraud 9%
Defamation 8%
Employment 8%
Clinical Negligence 5%
Professional Negligence, Commercial Litigation, Property & Probate 2%

CONTACTS

Business Services .... Simone Kilka
Clinical Negligence .... Gillian Solly
.... Rosamund Rhodes-Kemp
Crime, Business Investigations & Fraud .... Rod Fletcher
.... Scott Ingram
Defamation .... Jeremy Clarke-Williams
.... Sarah Webb
Employment .... Edward Cooper
Family, Wills, Probate & Trusts Oliver Gravell
Financial Services .... Keith Halford
Personal Injury .... Richard Langton
.... Ian Walker
.... Fraser Whitehead
Professional Negligence, Commercial Litigation & General Commercial
.... Jeremy Clarke-Williams
.... Sarah Webb
Property .... Peter Klim

RUSSELL & RUSSELL

Churchill House, Wood Street, Bolton, BL1 1EE **Tel:** (01204) 399299 **Fax:** (01204) 389223 **DX:** 24146 Bolton 1 **Ptnrs:** 19 **Asst solrs:** 13
Other fee-earners: 28

RUSSELLS

Regency House, 1-4 Warwick St, London, W1R 6LJ
Tel: (020) 7439 8692 **Fax:** (020) 7494 3582 **DX:** 37249 Piccadilly 1
Email: media@russells.co.uk

Managing Partner	R.A.W. Page
Senior Partner	AD Russell
Number of partners	11
Assistant solicitors	3
Other fee-earners	2

THE FIRM: Founded by its present senior partner in 1974, Russells is best known for its experience and reputation in the entertainment industry.

PRINCIPAL AREAS OF WORK: Although recognised as one of the leading firms in the entertainment industry, with eight commercial partners, the firm also advises on general commercial matters. Three litigation partners also handle all types of litigation including breach of copyright, defamation, property disputes and divorce. It is also active in commercial and residential property, wills and probate.

RUSSELLS GIBSON MCCAFFREY

13 Bath Street, Glasgow, G2 1HY **Tel:** (0141) 332 4176 **Fax:** (0141) 332 7908 **Ptnrs:** 4 **Asst solrs:** 2 **Other fee-earners:** 1

S

SACKER & PARTNERS

29 Ludgate Hill, London, EC4M 7NX
Tel: (020) 7329 6699 **Fax:** (020) 7248 0552 **DX:** 63 Ch.Ln.
Email: enquiries@sacker-partners.co.uk **Website:** www.sacker-partners.co.uk

Senior Partner	Jonathan Seres
Number of partners	17
Assistant solicitors	18
Other fee-earners	1

AREAS OF PRACTICE

Pensions 100%

CONTACTS

Pensions ....Ian Pittaway
....Peter Lester
....Chris Close
....Mark Greenlees
....Jonathan Berman
....Monica Coombs

THE FIRM: Sacker & Partners is known as the principal specialist UK law firm practising exclusively in the pensions field. The practice has been known for pensions since its establishment in 1966, and since 1990 has concentrated solely on pensions work and related areas. The firm is well represented in the pensions industry. Its partners serve on the committees of various professional bodies which comment on proposals for changes in pensions law and practice. Several are known through books, specialist articles and speeches to pensions conferences. Clients are employers (including leading public companies), trustees (including independent trustees) and trade unions. Referral work from other law firms (such as pensions advice on transactions) is an important area of the practice. The firm provides an independent trusteeship service through Independent Trustee Ltd, the leading law firm-based independent trustee company in the UK. Sackers attach particular importance to client care through partner supervision. The firm's technical expertise is complemented by its practical approach and its ability to produce innovative solutions when needed.

PRINCIPAL AREAS OF WORK: The workload consists entirely of pensions work and related activities such as employment work, pensions litigation and pensions advice on commercial transactions. Specialist expertise includes the establishment, variation and winding-up of pension schemes (including unapproved arrangements) in the UK and Ireland. The firm sets up stakeholder and personal schemes for insurers and other providers. Other matters handled routinely include acquisitions, disposals, scheme mergers and reorganisations and dispute resolution/litigation on a variety of subjects, such as transfer values and equal treatment claims. Advice is given on international transfers and multinational pension provision. Expertise is also provided concerning privatisations, the contracting-out of central and local government operations (including the impact of TUPE), tax, documentation, powers and duties of employers and trustees, and investment management agreements.

SALANS HERTZFELD & HEILBRONN HRK

Clements House, 14-18 Gresham Street, London, EC2V 7NN
Tel: (020) 7509 6000 **Fax:** (020) 7726 6191 **DX:** 196
Email: london@salans.com **Website:** www.salans.com

Senior Partner	Lionel Rosenblatt
UK	
Number of partners	18
Assistant solicitors	22
Other fee-earners	20
International	
Number of partners	113
Other fee-earners	340

AREAS OF PRACTICE

Banking & Finance/Corporate 35%
Company & Commercial/High-Tech 25%
Litigation 20%
Employment 10%
Commercial Property 10%

THE FIRM: Salans Hertzfeld & Heilbronn (Salans) is an international law firm with substantial offices in London, Paris, New York and Warsaw, together with further full-service offices in St Petersburg, Moscow, Kyiv, Almaty and Baku. The firm currently has approximately 450 fee earners, including about 110 partners. The firm's London office is situated in the City and provides a full range of services to both domestic and international clients. It is particularly well known for its work in the banking/finance sector and the motor vehicle industry. Its employment department enjoys a strong reputation. Founded just over 20 years ago as a general law practice, the firm's growth has been continuous and rapid. On 1 January 1998, Salans merged with London-based Harris Rosenblatt & Kramer and now has a London presence of 65 fee earners, including 18 partners. On 1 January 1999, Salans merged with New York-based Christy & Viener, in the first transatlantic law firm merger. The merged firm is a multinational partnership which includes lawyers of more than a dozen nationalities. The diverse skills, professional qualifications, national backgrounds and linguistic abilities of its lawyers enable the firm to handle matters requiring local expertise as well as skill in cross-border transactions.

Continued overleaf

PRINCIPAL AREAS OF WORK: The London office acts for a wide range of domestic and international businesses, including UK and foreign banks, finance houses, building societies, international financial institutions and investment funds.

Banking: The firm has a well-deserved reputation for its work both in UK and overseas financing (including the emerging markets of Eastern Europe and the former Soviet Union). Its services include advising upon a wide variety of loans (including syndicated loans), lease and security documentation, and terms and conditions for trade, asset-based and project financings and arrangements for development capital and investment funds in the UK and overseas. The department has specialist knowledge of motor vehicle stocking finance, lease and hire-purchase arrangements, consumer credit-related documentation, portfolio securitisations and insolvency-related issues.

Litigation: The firm has extensive expertise in banking and recoveries litigation and professional negligence claims, acting for clearing banks and major institutional lenders. In addition, the firm is experienced in all aspects of general commercial litigation including contractual disputes, insolvency, fraud, asset tracing and breach of trust claims. The firm's work encompasses landlord and tenant disputes, consumer credit claims, LPA receiverships and an expanding domestic and international arbitration practice. The litigators have experience in mediation and ADR.

Corporate: The firm offers a full domestic and international corporate and commercial service and advice on corporate structuring and privatisation in emerging markets. This includes structuring, documenting and negotiating domestic and cross-border mergers and acquisitions, subscription and funding agreements, agency, distribution and franchise arrangements and joint venture agreements.

High-tech & E-commerce: The department represents numerous software, communications and services suppliers, content providers, website designers and users. Its services include: advice, drafting and negotiating on all IT-related transactions, such as licensing, support and maintenance, consultancy; reseller and channels-related contracts; databases and content provision; Internet software and services supply, application service provider master and end-user licences; mobile communications, advice in respect of interception and encryption obligations; outsourcing.

Property: The firm acts for developers, contractors, financiers, operators and investors on projects in the UK and abroad. The work embraces all aspects of acquisitions, disposals, development and financing of commercial properties.

Employment: The firm is widely recognised as a leader in its practice area. It is headed by Barry Mordsley, who sits as a part-time chairman of Employment Tribunals, is a member of the Employment Lawyers' Association and was on the Law Society Employment Law Committee. The department deals with both contentious and non-contentious work, providing advice on such matters as restrictive covenants, employee benefits, unfair dismissals, redundancies and discrimination cases.

Bromley Office: A dedicated out-of-town office in Bromley deals with volume recoveries and title perfection for leading banks, finance houses and building societies.

INTERNATIONAL: The firm has other offices in Paris, New York, Warsaw, Moscow, St Petersburg, Kyiv, Almaty and Baku.

CONTACTS

Banking & Finance	Stephen Finch
	Howard Cohen
Banking Recoveries	Caroline Havers
Commercial Arbitration	Lionel Rosenblatt
Commercial Property	Roger Abrahams
Corporate & Commercial	Philip Enoch
	Richard Thomas
Emerging Markets	Robert Starr
	Philipp Windermuth
	Joel McDonald
Employment	Barry Mordsley
	Michael Bronstein
General Commercial Litigation	Jeffrey Elton
High-Tech & E-commerce	Rachel Burnett
Insolvency	Alison Gaines
International Banking & Finance	
	Stephen Finch
	Philip Prowse
Professional Negligence	Lionel Rosenblatt

SAMUEL PHILLIPS & CO

Gibb Chambers, 52 Westgate Road, Newcastle upon Tyne, NE1 5XU
Tel: (0191) 232 8451 **Fax:** (0191) 232 7664 **DX:** 61028
Email: admin@samuelphillips.co.uk **Website:** www.samuelphillips.co.uk

Managing & Senior Partner	Barry Speker
Number of partners	5
Assistant solicitors	8
Other fee-earners	7

THE FIRM: Samuel Phillips & Co is a long-established firm offering a comprehensive range of legal services to private and business clients. In particular, it has many years' experience in medico-legal matters, and acts for a number of NHS trusts. Members of the firm sit on Law Society panels, which include Clinical Negligence, Personal Injury, Children and Family. It is a Legal Aid franchise, covering areas that include clinical negligence, crime, family, employment, personal injury, and immigration.

PRINCIPAL AREAS OF WORK:

Litigation: Work dealt with includes clinical negligence, employment, commercial disputes, building contract disputes, debt collection, employment and other tribunal representation, crime, immigration and personal injury matters.

Company & Commercial: Work done in this area includes partnerships and joint ventures, acquisitions, formations, reconstructions, commercial contracts, intellectual property, advising on funding, tax and insurance requirements, licensing and services to overseas companies.

Property: The firm covers all aspects of commercial and residential property including investment, funding, planning and residential building estates.

Other Areas: The firm also deals with all family and matrimonial matters, particularly in relation to childcare and adoption, as well as wills, probate and tax planning, and has a large criminal department. It is a specialist in Chinese businesses.

AREAS OF PRACTICE

Clinical Negligence & Related Medico-Legal Work	30%
Crime	20%
Family & Childcare	20%
Property	15%
Civil Litigation	10%
Employment	5%

CONTACTS

Childcare	Robert Gibson
	Barry Speker
Clinical Negligence	Rod Findlay
	Barry Speker
Company/Commercial	Stephen Doberman
Crime	Stuart Grant
Employment	Robert Gibson
	Barry Speker
Family Law	Jenny Goldstein
Immigration	Barry Speker
Personal Injury	Rex Winter
Property	Stephen Doberman

SAUNDERS & CO

71 Kingsway, London, WC2B 6ST
Tel: (020) 7404 2828 **Fax:** (020) 7404 2929 **DX:** 37995 Kingsway
Email: rcp@saunders.co.uk **Website:** www.saunders.co.uk

Managing Senior Partner	James Saunders

AREAS OF PRACTICE

Crime	47%
Civil Litigation	30%
Fraud	23%

CONTACTS

Civil Litigation	Robin Lloyds
Crime	James Saunders
Non-Contentious	Robert Fleischmann

THE FIRM: Established in 1974 by James Saunders, Saunders and Co is a specialist criminal defence firm. It currently holds the Criminal Defence Service contract, and is a member of the Serious Fraud panel. Its civil litigation department deals with business affairs, commercial litigation, employment and licensing. It also handles conveyancing and probate work.

PRINCIPAL AREAS OF WORK: Work includes criminal litigation particularly fraud, heavy traditional crime and asset forfeiture. Privy Council work as well as general civil litigation and non-contentious work are also handled.

CLIENTELE:
Crime: Legally aided and privately funded clients.
Civil & Non contentious: Privately funded work; mixture of business and private clients.

INTERNATIONAL: Privy Council appeals from foreign jurisdictions.

RECRUITMENT: Direct advertising, one to two training vacancies from 2002.

S

SAVAGE CRANGLE

15 High Street, Skipton, BD23 1AJ **Tel:** (01756) 794611 **Fax:** (01756) 791395 **DX:** 21751 **Email:** mail@savagecrangle.co.uk **Website:** www.savagecrangle.co.uk **Ptnrs:** 5 **Other fee-earners:** 5 **Contact:** Peter Crangle • General practice known for private client, agricultural, housing, PFI, PI and commercial work.

AREAS OF PRACTICE

Commercial (including PFI)	40%
Private Client/Agricultural	30%
Housing	20%
Personal Injury	10%

SAVERY PENNINGTON

11, Moira Terrace, Adamsdown, Cardiff, CF24 0EJ **Tel:** 02920 457 222 **Fax:** 02920 452 211 **Email:** solicitors@saverypennington.freeserve.co.uk

SCHILLING & LOM AND PARTNERS

Royalty House, 72-74 Dean St, London, W1D 3TL
Tel: (020) 7453 2500 **Fax:** (020) 7453 2600 **DX:** 89265 (Soho Square 1)
Email: legal@schillingandlom.com **Website:** www.defamationlawyers.com

Senior Partner	Keith Schilling
Number of partners	6
Assistant solicitors	7
Other fee-earners	5

AREAS OF PRACTICE

Libel	40%
Intellectual Property & Sport	20%
Film, Television, New Media & Company/Commercial	20%
Privacy, Confidence & Human Rights	10%
General Commercial Litigation	10%

CONTACTS

Commercial Litigation	Susan Heller
Corporate Media Management	Simon Smith
Film, TV & New Media	Nicholas Lom
Intellectual Property & Sport	Eddie Parladorio
Libel & Privacy	Mark Thomson
Media Advice & Company/ Commercial	Mark Wenborn

THE FIRM: Schilling & Lom and Partners is a leading specialist in libel and privacy that has been involved in a number of successful, ground-breaking cases. Recent successes include libel actions for leading restaurateur Marco Pierre White against the *New York Times* and the *International Herald Tribune*, and the award-winning composer Monty Norman in his action against *The Sunday Times* over composition of the James Bond Theme tune. The firm also acts in substantial commercial litigation, intellectual property and sports related cases, and provides advice on film, television, new media, Internet and company commercial matters. Schilling & Lom and Partners has a flexible approach, and is often able to achieve, through negotiation, highly competitive commercial solutions in a short timescale. It is renowned for its media management and media intervention activities with the press both for individual personalities, corporates and on behalf of its broadcast clients. The firm works with overseas lawyers, talent agents, public relations, advisers, literary agents, managers, business advisers and in-house counsel. Clients range from international media corporations, broadcasters, film producers and distributors, to celebrities and sports personalities. Partners in the firm are involved in the publication of articles as well as legal and industry seminars on topical subjects, most notably of late in relation to the Human Rights Act 1998, copyright issues, the protection of image, and film and television production.

PRINCIPAL AREAS OF WORK:
Litigation: Schilling & Lom and Partners is dedicated to the protection of reputation and brand image. This is achieved through the firm's innovative use of the law of libel, privacy, confidence, copyright, trademark, passing off and domain ownership. Aside from preventing the publication of libels and unwanted invasions of privacy, the firm is effective in obtaining prompt and prominent apologies and corrections from publishers and, in relation to the Internet, quickly identifying offending material through the use of advanced search engines and obtaining its removal within hours of such material being published. The firm is committed to a proper balance between freedom of expression and an individual's right to reputation and privacy.
Media & Commercial: Schilling & Lom and Partners specialises in all aspects of media negotiations, production and distribution including film, TV, video and broadband, finance, licensing, options and merchandising, company documentation and employment advice.
Industry Specialties: The firm is well known for its litigation and its policy of obtaining early settlements where this is in the client's best interests. Its in-depth knowledge and understanding of the various media industries in which it acts enables it to provide legal advice and solutions that further the client's interests.

SCOTT-MONCRIEFF, HARBOUR & SINCLAIR

19 Greenwood Place, London, NW5 1LB **Tel:** (020) 7485 5588 **Fax:** (020) 7485 5577 **DX:** 46465 Kentish Town **Email:** scomo@scomo.com **Ptnrs:** 2 **Other fee-earners:** 12

SCRIVENGER SEABROOK

26 New Street, St Neots, PE19 1XB **Tel:** (01480) 214900 **Fax:** (01480) 474833 **DX:** 100315 St Neots **Email:** email@sslaw.co.uk **Ptnrs:** 3 **Asst solrs:** 1 • The firm deals exclusively in claimant clinical negligence and general healthcare work, with a percentage of personal injury.

SEARLES

The Chapel, 26A Munster Road, London, SW6 4EN **Tel:** (020) 7371 0555 **Fax:** (020) 7371 7722 **Email:** searles@searles-solicitors.co.uk **Ptnrs:** 3 **Asst solrs:** 2 **Other fee-earners:** 1 • Specialising in intellectual property with particular emphasis on entertainment law. Specialist in the music, multimedia and design industries (contentious and non-contentious), merchandising, and literary publishing. Sponsorship advice is also given.

AREAS OF PRACTICE	
Music Industry (both Classical & Popular)	70%
Film & Television	20%
Sponsorship, Merchandising & Advertising	10%

S

SEARS TOOTH

50 Upper Brook Street, London, W1Y 1PG
Tel: (020) 7499 5599 **Fax:** (020) 7495 2970 **DX:** 44643 Mayfair

Senior Partner	R. C. Tooth
Number of partners	5
Assistant solicitors	3
Other fee-earners	3

THE FIRM: Sears Tooth is a specialist matrimonial and family law niche practice, with a commercial and residential property department. The firm is headed by Raymond Tooth, and is supported by three other partners specialising in matrimonial law, namely Elaine Williams, David Lister and Ann Ison. The firm handles all aspects of matrimonial and family law, predominantly dealing with financial issues arising on separation or breakdown of marriage, but also some private child work. The financial issues handled by the firm are usually complex, involving significant assets and frequently have an international aspect. The firm has a reputation for a forthright approach, and the often difficult nature of the cases it routinely tackles is reflected in the quantity of citations the firm enjoys in Family Law Reports, notwithstanding the relatively small size of the practice. Most of the members of the firm are members of the Solicitors Family Law Association. Raymond Tooth is a member of the International Academy of Matrimonial Lawyers.

AREAS OF PRACTICE	
Divorce & Matrimonial	95%
Conveyancing (Commercial & Residential)	5%

CONTACTS	
Conveyancing	JFW Wilson
Matrimonial	R C Tooth

SEDGWICK, DETERT, MORAN & ARNOLD

120 Cannon Street, London, EC4N 6LR
Tel: (020) 7929 1829 **Fax:** (020) 7929 1808
Email: abarker@sdmauk.co.uk **Website:** www.sdma.com

Managing Partner	Adam Barker
Number of partners	4
Assistant solicitors	2
Other fee-earners	3

THE FIRM: Sedgwick, Detert, Moran & Arnold is America's third largest firm specialising in commercial litigation, including insurance and product liability law. Founded in 1933, the firm has a total of 285 attorneys with offices in San Francisco, Los Angeles, Orange County, Chicago, New York, Newark, Dallas, Paris and Zurich. The London office was opened in 1985, and became one of the first multinational partnerships in 1992. Most of the practitioners are dual qualified (US/UK) and one holds a third qualification (Bermuda). With an emphasis on insurance and reinsurance litigation including directors' and officers' liability, fidelity, employment, professional indemnity, entertainment and property claims, as well as international arbitrations, the office acts for a number of major international corporations, insurers and reinsurers and is frequently involved with multijurisdictional disputes.

AREAS OF PRACTICE	
Insurance Litigation	40%
Non-contentious Insurance	20%
Arbitration	20%
Commercial Litigation	20%

SEMPLE FRASER WS

10 Melville Crescent, Edinburgh, EH3 7LU
Tel: (0131) 273 3771 **Fax:** (0131) 273 3776 **DX:** ED 447
Email: info@semplefraser.co.uk

130 St Vincent Street, Glasgow, G2 5HF
Tel: (0141) 221 3771 **Fax:** (0141) 221 3776/3859 **DX:** GW 337
Email: info@semplefraser.co.uk

Managing Partner	Alister Fraser
Number of partners	16
Associate partners	8
Assistant solicitors	20
Consultants	1

AREAS OF PRACTICE

Commercial Property	35%
Company/Commercial	20%
Litigation	15%
Banking	10%
Planning	10%
Construction	10%

CONTACTS

Banking	Angus MacRae
Commercial Property	Elspeth Carson
Company/Commercial	Stuart Russell
Construction	Stuart Macfarlane
Construction Litigation	Stuart Macfarlane
Employment	Alison Gow
Environmental	Margaret McLean
Insolvency	David Ogilvy
IP/IT	Stuart Russell
Landlord & Tenant	Paul Haniford
Leisure	Dolina Caie
Litigation	Alison Gow
PFI	Alister Fraser
Planning	Kenneth Carruthers
	June Gilles
Property Tax	Heather Nisbet
Venture Capital	David Deane

THE FIRM: Established in 1990, Semple Fraser is a specialist commercial law practice with a very strong reputation built on commercialism, innovation and cohesion. A focused practice, the firm believes in doing what it does extremely well, so as to maximise the clients' benefit. With one of the largest commercial property teams in Scotland the firm has developed highly regarded experts in areas such as construction, planning, property tax and property litigation. The firm is also well recognised for its expertise in corporate transactions including MBOs, MBIs and mergers and acquisitions. Semple Fraser's approach is to develop close relationships with clients so as to have a full understanding and appreciation of their individual circumstances and business objectives. The firm is organised on the basis of special sector groups made up of lawyers who share expertise in different and complementary areas of law and industry. These groups keep abreast of business and legal developments in their sector in order to develop optimum and innovative responses to complex commercial transactions. The firm continues to invest heavily in IT, and is committed to maintaining business advantages derived from that investment and enabling the client to receive better value from a faster and better service. The firm believes strongly in the continuous training and development of all its staff. The team spirit at Semple Fraser is the result of this investment and the benefit is recognised by its clients.

PRINCIPAL AREAS OF WORK:

Company & Commercial: Business start-up, acquisition and disposal, take-overs, M&A, corporate finance, MBOs and MBIs, institutional investment, banking, insolvency and reconstruction, taxation, interactive media law, IP, PFI, leisure and recreation matters.
Commercial Property: All matters relating, including property development and investment, leasing, retail, offices, industrial, leisure and recreation and property finance.
Commercial Litigation: A wide range of commercial litigation in both the Court of Session and Sheriff Court with particular strength on property litigation, employment, construction and alternative dispute resolution.
Planning & Environmental Law: Pre-application negotiations, drafting S 75 agreements and planning conditions, representations at planning appeals and other inquiries, statutory challenges in the Court of Session and judicial review.
Construction: Representing a broad cross-section of employers, funders, contractors and design team members; drafting and negotiating building and engineering contracts, professional appointments and warranties; construction related litigation including disputes in the commercial court; arbitration, adjudication and insurance claims.

SEMPLE FRASER W.S.
THE BUSINESS LAW PARTNERSHIP

SENIOR CALVELEY & HARDY

8 Hastings Place, Lytham St Annes, FY8 5NA **Tel:** (01253) 733333 **Fax:** (01253) 794430 **DX:** 28440 Lytham **Email:** lawyers@seniorslaw.co.uk **Contact:** Richard Hardy • Best known for private client work, particularly trust, tax and charity law work. Provides a comprehensive service to elderly clients and deals with commercial, development and agricultural matters.

AREAS OF PRACTICE

Private Client	65%
Commercial	20%
Litigation	15%

SHADBOLT & CO

Chatham Court, Lesbourne Road, Reigate, RH2 7LD
Tel: (01737) 226 277 **Fax:** (01737) 226 165 **DX:** 30402 Reigate 1
Email: mail@shadboltlaw.co.uk **Website:** www.shadboltlaw.co.uk

One Creed Court, 5 Ludgate Court, London, EC4M 7AA
Tel: (020) 7332 5750 **Fax:** (020) 7332 5799 **DX:** 98937 Cheapside 2
Email: mail@shadboltlaw.co.uk

Ibex House, Minories, London, EC3N 1DY
Tel: (020) 7702 1156 **Fax:** (020) 7702 1160 **DX:** 568 London/City
Email: mail@shadboltlaw.co.uk

Managing & Senior Partner	Richard Shadbolt
Number of partners	26
Assistant solicitors	20
Other fee-earners	11

AREAS OF PRACTICE

Disputes	60%
Construction & Engineering (Non-contentious/Major Projects)	20%
Corporate/Other	20%

THE FIRM: Shadbolt & Co is a specialist commercial law practice providing a high quality service to business clients in the United Kingdom and internationally. As well as its office in Reigate, it has two offices in the City

Continued overleaf

of London, one in Hong Kong and an associated office in Paris. The firm originally acquired its outstanding reputation advising clients in the field of major projects and in the construction and engineering industries. It now works in a wide range of practice areas including corporate, property, IT and e-commerce, employment and aviation. The firm offers a cost-effective and imaginative commercial service backed by an unusual degree of experience. The firm's clients range from multinational quoted companies to entrepreneurial family businesses. The firm's clientele has a strong international bias.

PRINCIPAL AREAS OF WORK:

Construction & Engineering: The firm handles a wide range of contentious and non-contentious work relating to the construction, engineering and facilities management industries in the UK and internationally. Recent disputes have been handled in Uganda, China, Hong Kong, Egypt, Ethiopia and Tanzania.

Projects: The firm advises a variety of clients on the commercial and legal aspects of PFI, PPP, concession and BOT schemes and other major projects including reviewing and drafting contract documentation. The firm is used to working in collaboration with financial and other advisers on major projects both in the United Kingdom and elsewhere in the world.

Corporate: The firm has particular expertise in company sales and purchases, corporate finance, reorganisations and joint ventures. The firm also undertakes a wide variety of other high quality commercial work including intellectual property, franchising, European law, competition law and advice on general commercial agreements of all kinds.

Commercial Dispute Resolution: The firm's work includes litigation, arbitration and other forms of dispute resolution in relation to international and domestic business disputes. The firm is experienced in ADR techniques.

Commercial Property: The firm's commercial property practice is able to provide specialist advice on development and commercial property matters of all kinds, particularly in the fields of sales and purchases, property financing and landlord and tenant law.

Employment: The firm acts for many substantial employers as well as for employees. The firm represents clients in the courts and employment tribunals and deals with employment and related matters such as health and safety. Clients are kept up to date with developments under both European and UK law.

IT & E-commerce: The firm provides specialist advice to a growing client base on all aspects of IT, new media and e-commerce law including advice on IT agreements and disputes, software licences and development issues, major IT procurement, web design issues, e-commerce trading terms and the protection of intellectual property rights.

Aviation: The firm's work covers all aspects of international aviation operations including liabilities, insurance, airport planning, air traffic control and environmental and regulatory questions.

RECRUITMENT: The firm has an ongoing recruitment programme for trainee solicitors and for qualified candidates. Considerable importance is attached to in-house training and the continuing education programme for its solicitors.

CONTACTS

Aviation	Tim Unmack
Construction & Engineering	Simon Delves
Corporate	Andrew Trotter
Disputes Resolution/Litigation	Peter Sheridan
Employment	Helen Boddy
IT/E-commerce	John Warchus
Marine	Hugh Bryant
Projects	Joe Bellhouse
	George Rosenberg
Property	Sean Ryan

S

SHAKESPEARES

10 Bennetts Hill, Birmingham, B2 5RS
Tel: (0121) 632 4199 **Fax:** (0121) 643 2257 **DX:** 13015
Email: info@shakespeares.co.uk **Website:** www.shakespeares.co.uk

Managing Partner	Andrew Argyle
Senior Partner	Anthony Jones
Number of partners	22
Assistant solicitors	23
Other fee-earners	34

AREAS OF PRACTICE

Business Services	47%
Insurance Litigation	18%
Private Client	14%
Banking Litigation	11%
Other	10%

CONTACTS

Banking Litigation	Stephen Jones
Business Litigation	Mark Beesley
Charities	Anthony Jones
Company & Commercial	Jill Kennedy
Corporate Finance	Richard Baizley
Crime	Stephen Daly
Debt Collection	Rohit Deepak
Education	Anthony Jones
Employment	Michael Hibbs
Family Law	Nicola Walker
Insurance Litigation	John Buckingham
Investment Management	Graham Englefield
Medical Negligence	Gary Christianson
Private Client	Clare Laird
Professional Indemnity	Diana Wareing
Property	Paul Reading

THE FIRM: As one of Birmingham's larger and broader based firms of solicitors, Shakespeares provides comprehensive legal advice to a wide range of clients including plcs, banks, owner-managed businesses, private individuals, universities, schools and colleges, insurance companies and charities. The firm is recognised for its commitment to the quality of its service, having ISO 9001 accreditation and the Investors in People standard. As one of Birmingham's larger leading law firms, Shakespeares continues to strengthen its position as a key regional player reflected in a number of key long-term strategic decisions. The firm has made some considerable changes in personnel. It has injected young blood into the partnership, through promotions from within the firm and external recruitment of high quality specialists. The firm continues to remain a partner-oriented practice, ensuring access to senior expertise as and when required, and still aims to offer a flexible and personal approach.

PRINCIPAL AREAS OF WORK:

Business Services: Business services offers wide ranging legal services with the aim of providing clients with one pro-active department that can meet all their needs. It includes company and commercial, corporate finance, commercial property, business litigation, employment law, charities and debt recovery work. Business services' client base is varied ranging from large plcs to owner-managed businesses and includes many inward investor organisations from countries such as Germany, USA, Italy, Denmark and the Netherlands.

Company & Commercial: Shakespeares' company and commercial advice extends to a broad range of areas including company structure, corporate finance, general contractual work and other commercial activities, such as licensing and franchising, distribution and agency agreements, insolvency and private finance initiative work. The firm also has a considerable specialism in employment law acting for both employers and

employees. The firm also offers business litigation including alternative dispute resolution. There are three CEDR accredited mediators in business services. The firm also has a large computerised debt recovery department and also handles matters such as intellectual property and construction cases.
Employment: The firm also has a considerable specialism in employment law, acting for both employers and employees.
Property: A comprehensive range of property services are provided for financial institutions, property developers and housing associations, as well as private individuals. Leasing and financing of commercial property are handled as well as joint ventures and taxation matters for a broad range of businesses from owner-managed businesses to plcs.
Charities: Shakespeares has a specialist charity team handling all matters relating to charity law and associated areas such as property, employment and general commercial advice. The firm acts for over 100 charities which include several national ones.
Insurance, Banking & Institutional Litigation, Medical Negligence & Crime: Shakespeares has a substantial litigation department covering a broad range of legal services. The thrust of the work in the department is for businesses, insurance companies, institutional clients, local authorities and banks. Shakespeares also handles litigation matters for individuals including medical negligence, and crime, particularly white collar fraud and professional indemnity claims.
Private Client: The firm offers a broad range of private client services including wills, probate, trusts, enduring power of attorney and tax planning advice. Shakespeares has a specialist family law unit dealing with divorce and ancillary matters, cohabitee disputes, Children's Act matters and childcare provision. Shakespeares have hived their Investment Management Team off to Hathaway Investments but retain controlling interests.

SHARPE PRITCHARD

Elizabeth House, Fulwood Place, London, WC1V 6HG
Tel: (020) 7405 4600 **Fax:** (020) 7242 2210 **DX:** 353
Email: planning@sharpepritchard.co.uk **Website:** www.sharpepritchard.co.uk

Senior Partner	A Badcock
Number of partners	11
Assistant solicitors	12
Other fee-earners	12

AREAS OF PRACTICE

Civil Litigation	41%
Contracts/PPP	22%
Property	15%
Planning	13%
Parliamentary	9%

CONTACTS

Civil Litigation	A Badcock
Contracts	S Millen
Parliamentary	A Lewis
Planning	J Sharland
Property	J Pickering

THE FIRM: A well established practice in the fields of litigation and commercial work mainly for the public sector; with conveyancing, trusts, tax and some company and commercial. Also well known parliamentary agents.

PRINCIPAL AREAS OF WORK:
General Description: A general practice with a strong emphasis on litigation for a wide variety of clients; particularly public and local authorities and professional clients. Undertakes joint ventures, development agreements, public/private partnerships and PFIs for the public authorities. Expanding town and country planning practice.
Litigation: All areas covered particularly construction, environmental and property related litigation, personal injury including medical negligence; local and public authority related litigation – judicial review; commercial and defamation; employment; insolvency and debt collection; Chancery, child care and family.
Parliamentary: A substantial practice for public and local authorities, promotion and opposition of bills for a variety of clients.
Property & Commercial: A wide variety of property-related work, conveyancing and some company/commercial.
Contracts: The firm undertakes drafting and negotiation of contracts for works, services and supplies and advises on EU and UK public procurement, and joint ventures, private finance transactions and public/private partnerships.
Planning: All aspects of town and country planning, mainly for local authorities.
Private Client: Will drafting, probate, tax advice and all types of trust work.
Agency Work: Substantial agency practice in all areas; urgent work. Charges on application.

CLIENTELE: Public and local authorities, professional, private and small corporate, registered social landlords, charities etc.

INTERNATIONAL: Work is handled in Italian and French.

RECRUITMENT: Four trainee solicitors a year are taken on. They should have good academic qualifications and the ability to work as part of a well-knit team. Applications with a CV should be made in September of each year to Ashley Badcock.

SHARRATTS

12 Oxford Street, Whitstable, CT5 1DE **Tel:** (01227) 770888 **Fax:** (01227) 265507 **DX:** 32350 Whitstable **Ptnrs:** 4

SHAW AND CROFT

115 Houndsditch, London, EC3A 7BR
Tel: (020) 7645 9000 **Fax:** (020) 7645 9001 **DX:** 824
Email: shawandcroft@btinternet.com **Website:** shawandcroft.com

Number of partners	11
Assistant solicitors	8
Other fee-earners	11

AREAS OF PRACTICE

Commercial Litigation (& Fraud)	30%
Shipping Litigation	20%
Admiralty	20%
Ship Finance, Corporate & Other Non-contentious	16%
Insurance (Marine & Non-Marine)	9%
Commodities	5%

CONTACTS

Admiralty	Roger Croft
	Hamish Edgar
Commercial Litigation	Nicholas Taylor
Commodities	Robert McCunn
Fraud	Roger Croft
	Robert McCunn
Insurance	Jonathan Kenyon
Personal Injury	Hamish Edgar
Property	Roger Colton
Ship Finance/Corporate	Richard Coles
Shipping Litigation	Mark Aspinall
	Ben Browne
	Roland Jackson

THE FIRM: Established in 1980 as a specialist shipping and commercial law practice, the firm has grown steadily in these fields, while developing expertise in related areas.

PRINCIPAL AREAS OF WORK:

Shipping & Maritime Law: The firm handles every aspect of contentious shipping work, including collisions, salvage, charter parties, bills of lading, cargo damage, pollution, and shipbuilding disputes.
Ship Finance & Corporate: Sale and purchase, finance and registration of ships, yachts and fishing vessels, company acquisitions and disposals, joint ventures, agency and employment law.
Commercial Litigation and Fraud: Work includes commercial fraud, international asset tracings and intellectual property and other commercial disputes.
Commodities: Work handled includes international sale of goods (particularly oil, grain and other commodities), together with other international commercial transactions.
Insurance: Litigation and advice on all aspects of the insurance markets in London and abroad, particularly marine insurance, P&I, Brokers E and O, reinsurance.
Property: Acquisition and disposal of commercial and residential property, landlord and tenant, probate.

CLIENTELE: Shipowners, charterers, P&I clubs and insurers, salvage companies, banks, commodity traders, oil companies, ship managers, shipbuilders, insolvency practitioners, property developers and investors.

INTERNATIONAL: The firm has an office in Greece as well as strong connections with France, Eastern Europe, North Africa and the Middle East. A worldwide network of correspondent lawyers in all major shipping and commercial centres is actively maintained. Work is handled in French, German, Greek, Italian and Spanish.

SHAW PITTMAN

Tower 42, Level 23, 25 Old Broad Street, London, EC2N 1HQ
Tel: (020) 7847 9500 **Fax:** (020) 7847 9501

Managing Partner (US)	Paul Mickey
Managing Partners (UK)	Alistair Maughan
	Andrew Moyle
Number of partners	4
Assistant solicitors	15
Other fee-earners	2

AREAS OF PRACTICE

Technology	95%
Employment	5%

ShawPittman

THE FIRM: Shaw Pittman is an international firm, based in the USA, with a major specialisation in technology law. The London office opened in 1998 to reinforce Shaw Pittman's global reputation for technology law work, and handles significant UK, EU and global technology transactions.

PRINCIPAL AREAS OF WORK: Shaw Pittman's London office focuses exclusively on technology and outsourcing projects, including IT, e-commerce and telecoms. The office also provides employment law advice in the technology sector.

CLIENTELE: UK office clients include government departments, major banks, multinational plcs, e-commerce companies and other users and vendors of technology and services.

SHEAN DICKSON MERRICK

14/16 High Street, Belfast, BT1 2BS
Tel: (028) 9032 6878 **Fax:** (028) 9032 3473 **DX:** 460 Nr Belfast
Email: sdmlegals@dnet.co.uk

Senior Partner	David Moffett
Number of partners	3
Assistant solicitors	2
Other fee-earners	2

CONTACTS

Commercial/Corporate	David Moffett
Liquor Licensing	Maura McKay

THE FIRM: A long established firm providing a full range of services to corporate commercial and private clients. The firm is renowned for its constructive and pragmatic approach to servicing its clients' needs.

PRINCIPAL AREAS OF WORK:

Commercial: All aspects of commercial work are undertaken. The firm has an expanding practice in the area of mergers and acquisitions and has earned an excellent reputation in that field.
Licensing: The firm is highly regarded for its expertise in licensing and acts for major players in the drinks industry in Northern Ireland. It recently obtained (uniquely for Northern Ireland) four new public house licences for the Odyssey Pavilion, a landmark millennium site.

SHEARMAN & STERLING

Broadgate West, 9 Appold Street, London, EC2A 2AP
Tel: (020) 7655 5000 **Fax:** (020) 7655 5500
Email: pgibson@shearman.com **Website:** www.shearman.com

Managing Partner	Pamela Gibson
Number of partners	21

THE FIRM: Shearman & Sterling is one of the world's leading global law firms with expertise in virtually every major area of commercial activity. The London office advises on all areas of international financial transactions, providing both US and English law expertise, and is a recognised market leader in corporate finance and capital markets, mergers and acquisitions, project, banking and leveraged finance, securitisation and international arbitration and litigation. Founded in 1873, Shearman & Sterling has more than 950 lawyers at 15 offices in major financial centres worldwide. Its international expansion has been carefully planned to ensure consistency, depth and quality across borders and in local markets. The London office was established in 1972 and with over 130 lawyers forms a major part of the firm's substantial European practice. Today, over 350 lawyers in Europe serve clients from the firm's London, Paris, Düsseldorf, Frankfurt and Mannheim offices in the major practice areas of the firm: corporate finance/capital markets; mergers and acquisitions; project finance; structured and leveraged finance, banking, securitisation and restructuring, tax; competition law and international trade; and international arbitration and litigation. About half of Shearman and Sterling's lawyers in Europe are admitted to practice locally in France, Germany and the United Kingdom, with the balance qualified in the United States. In 2001, Shearman and Sterling offices will be opened in Brussels, Munich and Rome. The London office work closely with these and other Shearman & Sterling offices worldwide depending on client needs. The strategy of the office is to be the market leader in London in the provision of US/UK legal services while leveraging off the strength of its other European offices. Building on the expansion of its English law practice, Shearman & Sterling will continue to enhance its comprehensive corporate service in all its fields of expertise, combining global coverage with local expertise to its clients.

PRINCIPAL AREAS OF WORK:
Banking & Leveraged Finance: The London office is a focal point of the firm's European banking, leveraged finance and securitisation practices, providing structured senior and subordinated debt, bridge facilities, debt trading and restructuring capability.
Equity Capital Markets: The London office has one of the largest equity capital markets practices in London for US offerings. It specialises in US-registered public offerings, in Rule 144A offerings and private placements of equity, in establishing ADR facilities, and in obtaining US listings. The office has participated in most of the privatisations in the UK and Europe. Together with the firm's French and German offices, Shearman & Sterling has the leading market share for international equity offerings for European issuers.
Debt Capital Markets: The London office has a dedicated team of US and English lawyers specialising in the structuring and execution of high-yield and investment grade debt financing, either US registered or privately placed under Rule 144A in the US and internationally. Shearman & Sterling has a leading market share for high yield debt offerings for European issuers.
M&A: A main strength of the firm is its cross-border mergers and acquisitions and joint ventures practice. The London office handles public and private, intra-European and Europe/US cross-border acquisitions, divestitures, mergers and LBO's. It has the ability to structure and execute M&A transactions under both English and US law, in addition to its strong local M&A practices in France and Germany.
Project Finance: The office has one of the leading project development and finance practices with in-depth expertise advising projects developers and financial institutions on all aspects of structuring, negotiation, development and financing of major projects, particularly in the sectors of power, oil and gas, telecommunications, mining and transport infrastructure.
EU & Competition Law: The firm has now extended its antitrust practice to both London and Brussels. The offices will handle all aspects of competition law, particularly EU, national and multi-jurisdictional mergers, cartel, restrictive practice and abuse of dominance issues, state aid and public procurement, as well as competition matters before the European and national courts. The London practice will also cover utility regulation. The new antitrust practices will complement and work closely with the firm's existing practice in the US, Germany and France.
Tax: The London office provides US and English law tax advice and structuring and works closely with the firm's French and German tax lawyers on European tax products and structuring.
International Arbitration & Litigation: The London office has a dedicated team handling a broad range of international arbitration matters. Shearman & Sterling's international arbitration practice group is one of the few specialist teams operating in this field on a global basis.

CLIENTELE: The London office represents major international companies and investment banks including BG, BT, BOC, Barclays, Corus, Cinven, Citigroup, Deutche Bank, Edison Mission Energy, LM Ericsson, Goldman Sachs, InterGen, Investcorp, Merrill Lynch, Morgan Stanley, Nokia, Novartis, Orange, PowerGen, Rank and Volvo.

SHEPHERD & WEDDERBURN WS

Saltire Court, 20 Castle Terrace, Edinburgh, EH1 2ET
Tel: (0131) 228 9900 **Fax:** (0131) 228 1222 **DX:** 553049 Edinburgh 18
Email: edinburgh@shepwedd.co.uk **Website:** www.shepwedd.co.uk

155 St Vincent Street, Glasgow, G2 5NR
Tel: (0141) 566 9900 **Fax:** (0141) 565 1222 **DX:** GW 409, Glasgow-1
Email: glasgow@shepwedd.co.uk

Bucklersbury House, 83 Cannon Street, London, EC4N 8SW
Tel: (020) 7763 3200 **Fax:** (020) 7763 3250 **DX:** 98945 Cheapside 2
Email: london@shepwedd.co.uk

Chief Executive	Paul Hally
Number of partners	40
Assistant solicitors	81
Other fee-earners	46

CONTACTS

Banking	Shona Sanders
Charities	Andrew Holehouse
Commercial	James Saunders
Commercial Litigation	David Anderson
Competiton & Regulation	Gordon Downie
Construction	Kevin Taylor
Corporate Finance	James Will
Corporate Recovery	Gillian Carty
Debt Recovery	Gillian Carty
Employment	Sheila Gunn
Energy	James Saunders
Funds & Financial Services	Malcolm Gillies
Hotels & Leisure	Hugh Smith
Medical Negligence	Hugh Donald
Parliamentary Consultancy	Kareen Ryden
Pensions	Andrew Holehouse
Personal Injury	Hugh Donald
PFI	David Nash
Planning & Environment	Colin Innes
Property	Nick Ryden
Public Sector	Ian MacLeod
Tax	Malcolm Rust
Technology & IP	Liz McRobb

S

THE FIRM: Shepherd & Wedderburn is one of Scotland's leading law firms, with offices in Edinburgh, Glasgow and London. Its lawyers are able to work from any other location due to the firm's advanced remote access and communications technology. The firm's aim is to be the law firm of choice for clients, intermediaries and both legal and management staff. Its strategy to achieve this goal is to provide a client-focused quality delivery system, supported by the best lawyers, managers and staff. The findings of a recent survey of clients and non-clients by independent researchers confirmed the firm's brand and reputation as very highly regarded, with 95% rating service quality as "very good" or "excellent" and the remaining 5% rating it as "good". The research also revealed that clients perceived the firm's approachability and commercial awareness to be key differentiating factors.

PRINCIPAL AREAS OF WORK: The firm acts for corporate, commercial, public sector and private clients throughout the UK and abroad. Its impressive client base includes not only household name organisations, but also small and medium-sized enterprises, notably in the technology sector, based both in Scotland and increasingly further afield. Client relationship management is an integral part of the firm's approach, with an emphasis on long term, mutually beneficial client relationships. Shepherd & Wedderburn provides a full range of legal services to its clients, including specialisms such as employment, pensions, commercial property, construction, litigation, corporate finance, banking, funds and financial services, insolvency, energy, PFI/PPP, competition and regulation, intellectual property, technology and private client services (tax, trusts and estates). The firm's London office focuses on corporate, technology and projects work. In addition, the firm's parliamentary consultancy division Saltire advises a diverse and growing range of clients on Scottish Parliamentary business and has produced *The Governance of Scotland – A Saltire Guide*, a leading online guide to how a devolved Scotland is governed. The firm's approach is to acquire an in-depth understanding of clients and the legal issues they face and to employ this knowledge in developing solutions-led business advice. All the firm's lawyers understand that delivering an excellent legal service in today's environment demands not only high quality legal advice but also a thorough understanding of the clients' business, its environment and its commercial objectives. It is fully committed to providing high quality, client-focused service, supported by excellent resources in terms of management, training, technology, knowledge management, administration and communications. For further information on Shepherd & Wedderburn and the various services provided, please visit www.shepwedd.co.uk or contact the Chief Executive.

SHEPHERD &
WEDDERBURN WS

SHERIDANS

14 Red Lion Square, London, WC1R 4QL
Tel: (020) 7404 0444 **Fax:** (020) 7831 1982 **DX:** 270
Email: general@sheridans.co.uk

Managing Partner	Howard Jones
Number of partners	14
Assistant solicitors	10
Other fee-earners	6

AREAS OF PRACTICE

Entertainment & Media	40%
Commercial & Other Litigation	35%
Property & Planning	15%
Company/Commercial	10%

CONTACTS

Commercial Litigation	Stephen Taylor
Company/Commercial	Murray Wells
Computers/IT/Internet/E-commerce	Michael Thomas
Entertainment & Media	Howard Jones
Matrimonial & Immigration	Richard Gifford
Property/Planning/Probate	Jay Soneji Gregory Stafford
Residential Conveyancing	Jay Soneji

THE FIRM: This central London firm has notable expertise in the entertainment and media and litigation fields both within the UK and abroad. Related to those activities, the firm specialises in many complementary areas including e-commerce and IT related work, employment, licensing, funding of businesses and sales and purchases. The company/commercial department has a general practice but also specialises in entertainment and media related businesses and their requirements. The firm has substantial property and private client expertise.

PRINCIPAL AREAS OF WORK:
Entertainment & Media: The entertainment and media department spans several departments and includes an e-commerce unit. It offers a comprehensive service covering recording artists, recording and management companies, popular and classical music publishing, contract negotiation and renegotiations and merchandising and sponsorship. Work relating to licensing, franchising, television and video, the theatre, sport, books and magazines, the press, intellectual property, trademarks and domain names is also handled. Other specialisms include royalty audits, computer games, online music delivery and general Internet and e-commerce-related issues and international entertainment law involving European Union law. The department has a substantial employment practice specialising in senior executives in the media and entertainment industry. The department has also been involved in a number of securitizations and other secured lendings, acting in a number of high profile transactions in the last few years.
Litigation: The litigation department handles a wide range of proceedings in many courts and tribunals (often with an international element), including appellate courts and the Privy Council. It is especially strong in commercial litigation and the entertainment and media field, including defamation and the press. Specialisms include audit and copyright, trademark and passing off disputes; banking and insolvency work including asset recovery, securitisations and fraud; IT and Internet disputes including computer hardware and software cases and domain name disputes; employment cases. Immigration and work permits are also dealt with together with non Legal Aid matrimonial and private client disputes, including divorce, maintenance and children. Other areas include restraint of trade and competition law. Some specialist criminal work involving white collar crime, fraud, tax and VAT is also undertaken together with local authority cases and landlord and tenant litigation with particular regard to service charges and dilapidation claims.
Company/Commercial: Company and commercial work undertaken involves mergers, acquisitions and disposals, management buy-outs and buy-ins, corporate finance, joint ventures and corporate re-organisations. General company/commercial work is also undertaken including employment matters, insolvency and winding up, company formations, company taxation and intellectual property rights.
Property & Planning: Services in the property and planning department include sale and purchase of commercial property involving investment, acquisitions and sales, leasehold work, planning matters, granting of leases, secured lending, building and development schemes, property financing and licensing. Domestic conveyancing is also undertaken as are trusts, wills and probate cases.

CLIENTELE: The clientele includes major recording artistes and companies, sports personalities, theatre production companies, classical music composers and publishers, computer software companies, online music distribution companies, book publishers and a bank.

INTERNATIONAL: The work undertaken in the entertainment, media and communications field and the commercial field generally, requires extensive overseas contact, with the result that the firm is well versed in dealing with foreign lawyers and professional advisers.

RECRUITMENT: The firm recruits three trainee solicitors every year. Applications should be made with a CV and an accompanying letter to Cyril Glasser during August 2002 only (for September 2004).

S

SHERRARDS

45 Grosvenor Road, St Albans, AL1 3AW
Tel: (01727) 832830 **Fax:** (01727) 832833 **DX:** 141853 St Albans 17
Email: law@sherrards.co.uk **Website:** www.sherrards.co.uk

Managing Partner	Alasdair McMillin
Number of partners	6
Assistant solicitors	14
Other fee-earners	14

AREAS OF PRACTICE

Commercial Property	26%
Litigation	20%
Direct Conveyancing/Remortgaging	17%
Company Commercial	12%
Residential Conveyancing & Development	12%
Private Client	8%
Employment	5%

CONTACTS

Commercial Litigation	Simon Braun
Commercial Property	Mark Peters
Company/Commercial	Mark Peters
Direct Conveyancing/Remortgaging	John Brian

THE FIRM: Sherrards is one of the major providers of commercial property and corporate advice in the area. The firm acts for a number of major retailers and restaurateurs, both quoted and private. It also acts as preferred commercial property sub-contractor to a major US law firm in London. During the year 2000, Sherrards established an Anglo-German commercial unit, recruiting a former partner from an international law firm. The department deals with all types of inward investment and dispute resolution for clients from Germany and Benelux, and regularly assists UK and US companies establishing a presence in those countries. The firm has a thriving commercial litigation department, with particular expertise in employment law. A further niche area on the litigation side is the firm's unit specialising in anti-social tenant work acting for housing associations and local authorities. Also established in 2000 was a specialist direct conveyancing and remortgaging department, acting principally for a major lender and as a panel member for a nationwide estate agency chain. This expanding part of the business is housed in its own building in a large open plan environment suited to the needs and growth of the operation.

PRINCIPAL AREAS OF WORK: Work includes commercial property; corporate/commercial; commercial litigation; employment; housing association/local authority anti-social tenant work; direct conveyancing.

S

SHERRARDS
Grosvenor Hall, Bolnore Road, Haywards Heath, RH16 4BX **Tel:** 01444 473 344 **Fax:** 01444 473 249 **Email:** advice@harrysherrard.com
Website: www.harrysherrard.com **Ptnrs:** 1 **Asst solrs:** 1 **Other fee-earners:** 3

SHERWIN OLIVER SOLICITORS

New Hampshire Court, St Pauls Road, Portsmouth, PO5 4JT
Tel: (023) 9283 2200 **Fax:** (023) 9286 5884 **DX:** DX 2268 Portsmouth
Email: mail@sherwinoliver.com **Website:** www.sherwinoliver.com

Chairman & Chief Executive	Adrian Davis
Number of partners	12
Assistant solicitors	12
Other fee-earners	10

AREAS OF PRACTICE

Commercial Property	25%
Company Commercial & IP	30%
Commercial Litigation	25%
Corporate Recovery/Insolvency	10%
Employment	5%
General	5%

CONTACTS

Commercial	Nigel Craig
	Geoffrey Sturgess
Commercial Litigation	David Oliver
	Amanda Morris
Commercial Property	Andrew Peck
Corporate	Nigel Craig
Corporate Recovery/Insolvency	Christopher Brockman
	David Oliver
Employment Law	Philip Broom
IP/Franchising	Geoffrey Sturgess
Tax, Trusts & Probate	Clive Saunders

THE FIRM: Sherwin Oliver Solicitors is one of the leading commercial law practices in South Hampshire, providing a wide range of legal services to the business community. The firm is a member of LawNet.

PRINCIPAL AREAS OF WORK:

Company Commercial: The firm advises on acquisitions, mergers, expansion and restructuring of businesses, contracts, conditions of sale and purchase, licensing and all aspects of commercial law.

Commercial Property: This department handles a wide range of property transactions, with a particular specialty in waste management, environmental law and planning, commercial landlord and tenant matters and development.

Corporate Recovery: One of the largest specialist corporate recovery and insolvency departments on the South Coast specialises in all aspects of corporate and personal insolvency, realisation of assets and LPA receiverships and directors disqualification proceedings.

Commercial Litigation: All forms of commercial litigation are handled by this department, including contract disputes, landlord and tenant, construction disputes, insurance claims and debt recovery. The department has acted for two national business organisations in bringing claims against the government in the European Court of Human Rights.

Employment Law: This specialist department advises national and local businesses on all aspects of the law, including trade union negotiations and industrial relations. It also acts for senior employees and members regularly appear in industrial tribunals nationwide.

Intellectual Property: The firm has one of the few specialist IP departments in the region. It deals with IP licensing, litigation, trademarks and franchising. The firm is an affiliate member of the British Franchising Association.

Tax, Trusts & Probate: This department deals with all aspects of wills and probate. It also establishes and administers trusts and advises upon tax planning.

INTERNATIONAL: Sherwin Oliver Solicitors is a member of LawNet Europe and Eurojuris which provide access to a network of 650 associated firms in 19 countries. Work is handled in French, German, Russian and Swedish.

SHOOSMITHS

The Lakes, Bedford Road, Northampton, NN4 7SH
Tel: (01604) 543 000 **Fax:** (01604) 543 543 **DX:** 712280 Northampton-12
Email: northampton@shoosmiths.co.uk **Website:** www.shoosmiths.co.uk

52-54 The Green, Banbury, OX16 9AB
Tel: (01295) 267 971 **Fax:** (01295) 267 751 **DX:** 24204 Banbury-1
Email: banbury@shoosmiths.co.uk

Lock House, Castle Meadow Road, Nottingham, NG2 1AG
Tel: (0115) 906 5000 **Fax:** (0115) 906 5001 **DX:** 10104 Nottingham-1
Email: nottingham@shoosmiths.co.uk

Regents Gate, Crown Street, Reading, RG1 2PQ
Tel: (0118) 965 8765 **Fax:** (0118) 965 8700 **DX:** 4009 Reading-1
Email: reading@shoosmiths.co.uk

Quantum House, Basing View, Basingstoke, RG21 4EX
Tel: (01256) 696 200 **Fax:** (01256) 696 201 **DX:** 98574 BASINGSTOKE
Email: basingstoke@shoosmiths.co.uk

Russell House, 1550 Parkway, Solent Business Park, Whiteley, Fareham, PO15 7AG
Tel: (01489) 881 010 **Fax:** (01489) 881 000 **DX:** 124693 Whiteley
Email: solent@shoosmiths.co.uk

Exchange House, 482 Midsummer Boulevard, Milton Keynes, MK9 2SH
Tel: (01908) 488 300 **Fax:** (01908) 488 488 **DX:** 3140 Central Milton Keynes
Email: milton.keynes@shoosmiths.co.uk

Property Direct, Rushmills, Northampton, NN4 7PD
Tel: (01604) 543 000 **Fax:** (01604) 542 245 **DX:** 712280 Northampton-12
Email: northampton@shoosmiths.co.uk

Managing Partner	Graham New
Number of partners	78
Legal staff	444

AREAS OF PRACTICE

Commercial	49%
Personal Injury	30%
Financial Institutions	21%

CONTACTS

Commercial Property	Nigel Haynes
Construction	Christopher Cox
Corporate/Commercial	Oliver Brookshaw
Dispute Resolution	Claire Rowe
E-commerce	Nicki Martienssen
Employment	Peter Ellis
Environment	Grania Thompson
Financial Institutions/Property Direct	Andrew Tubbs
Food	Ron Reid
Insolvency	Andrew Pickin
Intellectual Property	John Hill
New Media & Technology	Nicki Martienssen
Occupational Safety	Ron Reid
Personal Injury	John Spencer
Planning	Iain Gilbey
Private Capital	Trevor George
Retail	Gary Assim

S

THE FIRM: Shoosmiths is widely regarded as one of the most progressive, innovative and technology driven law firms. Renowned for excellent client service, Shoosmiths delivers City quality advice with relaxed professionalism. Shoosmiths' clients are drawn from most industry sectors, with particular strengths in the consumer goods, financial, food, leisure, new media and IT, property, development and regeneration sectors. Shoosmiths compliments its commercial operations with a thriving private capital practice serving the legal needs of directors, executives and staff of client organisations and other high net worth individuals. Shoosmiths' clients have access to comprehensive national strength and expertise delivered locally and enjoy a fundamental commitment to a partnership relationship founded on an open culture. Fees are discussed at the outset of engagements and reported on as matters progress, enabling complete budgetary control over legal costs. Fixed price, value based, or other bespoke arrangements are available from a flexible pricing menu. Shoosmiths' strongly held ethos of, and investment in, high service standards is underpinned by ISO9001 accreditation and Investors in People status.

PRINCIPAL AREAS OF WORK: Shoosmiths is organised into three divisions: commercial, financial institutions and personal injury. Each has its own management structure, enabling a flexible and responsive approach to the markets they serve.

Commercial Division: The commercial division accounts for almost 50% of turnover. Its business is based on experience and know-how developed through a long tradition of advising listed companies, blue chip private UK companies, rapid growth/emerging technology private companies, European and US owned corporates, financial institutions, developers and public sector organisations throughout the UK and abroad. The quality of the Shoosmiths client list demonstrates an ability to meet the exacting requirements of some of the most successful and demanding global businesses.

Financial Institutions: The financial institutions division acts for many of the UK's top lending institutions. It has a national reputation for its risk management and recoveries arm and is leading the revolution in direct conveyancing with its Property Direct operation – a radical alternative to the traditional conveyancing model. It has developed numerous relationships with corporate estate agency groups and lenders and is pioneering the introduction of electronic conveyancing in a market preparing for sellers information packs.

Personal Injury: The personal injury division represents one of the largest personal injury practices in the country and deals with claimant personal injury work in a new way. Shoosmiths' approach to personal injury litigation is widely recognised to be market leading. A dedicated customer services department receives all new claims instructions over the telephone which are then confirmed to clients in writing to avoid form completion and to ensure comprehensive information from the outset of each case. The division also dedicates units to different specialisations such as road traffic accidents, mixed liability, fast and multi-track and small claims.

Continued overleaf

The personal injury division's principal target market comprises major legal expense insurers and other institutional work providers for whom strict service standards are applied and tailored to their specific requirements.

SHORT RICHARDSON & FORTH

4 Mosley St, Newcastle upon Tyne, NE1 1SR
Tel: (0191) 232 0283 **Fax:** (0191) 261 6956 **DX:** 61037
Email: lawyers@short-richardson-forth.co.uk

Managing Partner	Michael Short
Number of partners	8
Assistant solicitors	4

AREAS OF PRACTICE

Employment Law	42%
Commercial Property	20%
Civil Litigation	18%
Company Commercial	15%
Private Client	5%

CONTACTS

Civil Litigation	David Forth
Commercial Property	David Richardson
Company & Commercial	John Harrison
Employment Law	Michael Short
Tax/Trusts & Probate	Lesley Crinson

THE FIRM: Short Richardson & Forth is a well established commercial firm acting for a wide range of clients, ranging from large plcs to local firms. It is particularly well known for its employment law expertise, but every department provides specialist advice coupled with a very personal service to all clients. All work in the firm is carried out by solicitors; no unqualified executive staff are employed.

PRINCIPAL AREAS OF WORK:

Employment Law: The firm has vast experience covering the full range of employment law matters. All department members are experienced advocates who are able to conduct their own cases before employment tribunals.

Commercial Property: This department handles a wide range of property transactions, but with a particular emphasis on property development, investment purchase and commercial leases.

Commercial Litigation: A full litigation service is provided, including commercial contracts, professional negligence, building disputes, landlord and tenant, arbitrations and common law duty of care.

Company Commercial: Advice is given on a wide range of corporate and commercial matters including mergers, acquisitions, formations, joint ventures, manufacturing and other commercial agreements, as well as advice to directors and shareholders.

SIBLEY & CO

1 Heathcock Court, 415 The Strand, London, WC2R 0NS **Tel:** (020) 7395 9790 **Fax:** (020) 7379 3371 **Ptnrs:** 3 **Other fee-earners:** 1

SIDLEY AUSTIN BROWN & WOOD

1 Threadneedle Street, London, EC2R 8AW
Tel: (020) 7360 3600 **Fax:** (020) 7626 7937 **DX:** 580 LONDON CITY
Email: ukinfo@sidley.com **Website:** www.sidley.com

Princes Court, 7 Princes Street, London, EC2R 8AQ
Tel: (020) 7778 1800 **Fax:** (020) 7796 1807 **DX:** 580 LONDON CITY

Managing Partner	Drew Scott
Resident partners	27
Resident fee earners	91
Total resident staff	175

CONTACTS

Banking Regulation	Sarah Smith
Banking, Export & Project Finance	Robin Parsons
	Howard Waterman
Corporate Securities (US)	Scott Cameron
	Hugh Frame
	Christopher Mead
	Mark Walsh
Corporate Securities (England)	Michael Doran
	John Russell
Corporate/Commercial (England)	Struan Oliver
Corporate/Commercial (US)	Robert Asher
	Tom Thesing
Derivatives & Synthetics	Elizabeth Uwaifo
	Howard Waterman
IP/Technology	Struan Oliver
Property	Julian Goodman
Securitisation & Structured Finance	Margaret Boswell
	Michael Durrer
	Colin Mercer
	Graham Penn
	Sarah Smith
	Marc Wasserman
	Jennifer Williams
Tax (England)	Graeme Harrower
	Drew Scott
Tax (US)	R J Ruble
US Matters	Robert Asher
	Christopher Mead

THE FIRM: Sidley Austin Brown & Wood is the merged firm of Sidley & Austin (founded in Chicago in 1866) and Brown & Wood (founded in New York in 1914). The firm gives advice in all major areas of financial and commercial activity. Its London practice comprises several strong practice areas made up of joint teams of English and US lawyers with particular expertise in securitisation and structured finance, debt/equity capital markets, taxation, property, corporate, banking and investment funds. Clients include many of the world's leading institutions, banks and businesses. The London practice aims to maintain the firm's tradition of furnishing high quality, cross practice, innovative advice in a collegiate environment. The firm has adopted a strategy of matching its clients' requirements with focused advice, emphasising excellence, experience, markets awareness and product knowledge. Its reputation is based on the quality, innovation and client driven focus of its practice. All lawyers in the London office have extensive European practice experience and can assist clients with matters within the European Union and elsewhere. Teams of lawyers are quickly mobilised, and carefully managed, to assist clients wherever their needs arise. The London office liaises with the other offices of the firm and by relationships with leading independent law practices around the world.

PRINCIPAL AREAS OF WORK:

Securitisation & Structured Finance: Securitisation is an area of excellence and work in this field is carried out for originators, underwriters, credit enhancers, liquidity banks and credit rating agencies. The London office works closely with lawyers in the firm's US offices in adapting US financing techniques to European and other non-US assets and markets. The firm's structured finance work covers all aspects of structured derivatives, synthetics and capital markets.

Corporate & Commercial: Advice is given on corporate and commercial matters including mergers, acquisitions and takeovers, joint ventures, flotations, inward investment and company formations. The group's expertise extends to IT/IP and commerce generally and employment law. The group provides expert advice across a broad range of transactions and industries, with an emphasis on the growing e-commerce and internet markets.

Corporate Securities: The firm's corporate securities group regularly represents the principal participants in the European debt and equity capital markets. These include sovereign, agency and private sector issuers and guarantors as well as financial intermediaries such as investment banks, sponsors, financial advisors and trustees. It specialises in structuring and developing new, innovative financial products and execute a broad range of financial transactions in the capital markets.
Banking: The firm's expertise in banking and structured finance covers such areas as banking regulation, domestic and international lending, export and project finance, structured derivatives and synthetics and capital markets.
Taxation: Advice is given on domestic and international transactions, including mergers and acquisitions, corporate structuring, joint ventures, corporate finance, capital markets, banking and structured finance, commercial property, oil and gas, asset finance and tax litigation.
Property & Property Finance: The firm's expertise includes debt and equity based financing, development arrangements, acquisitions and disposals and institutional investment work.
Investment Funds: Offshore investment funds, including umbrella and single fund structures. Advice on hedged, structured and guaranteed products for sale to institutional and retail investors in the US, Europe and Asia, including Japan.

INTERNATIONAL: Other offices are located in Beijing, Chicago, Dallas, Hong Kong, Los Angeles, New York, San Francisco, Seattle, Shanghai, Singapore, Tokyo and Washington DC.

SILKS

Barclays Bank Chambers, 27 Birmingham St, Oldbury, B69 4EZ
Tel: (0121) 511 2233 **Fax:** (0121) 552 6322 **DX:** 20876 Oldbury 2
Email: info@silks-solicitors.co.uk **Website:** www.silks-solicitors.co.uk

Managing Partner	JB Burn
Senior Partner	JG Silk

THE FIRM: This long-established reputable practice offers both its commercial and individual clients a professional, efficient and cost-effective service. The firm has other offices in Netherton and Smethwick.

PRINCIPAL AREAS OF WORK:
Company/Commercial: Work includes small business to plcs, company formations, mergers and acquisitions, partnerships and joint ventures.
Employment: The firm advises on all aspects of employment law.
Licensing: Work handled includes application for or opposition to betting, liquor and entertainment licences.
Other: The firm also handles domestic/commercial property, family, criminal, personal injury and probate and wills work.

SILVER FITZGERALD

15-17 Castle Street, Cambridge, CB3 0AH
Tel: (01223) 562001 **Fax:** (01223) 518310 **DX:** 88009 Cambridge 1

Managing Partner	Suzanne Fitzgerald
Senior Partner	Raphael Silver
Number of partners	3
Assistant solicitors	6
Other fee-earners	2

CONTACTS

Childcare	Raphael Silver
Civil	Victoria Davey
Crime	Jason Coulter
Matrimonial	Karen Anker

THE FIRM: This successful firm offers a specialist range of legal services and is widely recognised as a leading advocacy practice. The firm was one of the first in Cambridge to obtain a Legal Aid Franchise. The firm is a niche litigation practice specialising in family law and childcare, crime, civil litigation and immigration. The family department is one of the largest in Cambridge, having two solicitors on the Children Panel, two solicitors on the Family Law Panel, two solicitors on the SFLA Panel and a trained mediator. The firm is situated close to both the County Court and Magistrates Court and so is ideally located to undertake agency instructions.

THE SIMKINS PARTNERSHIP

45-51 Whitfield St, London, W1T 4HB
Tel: (020) 7907 3000 **Fax:** (020) 7907 3111 **DX:** 7 Ch.Ln
Email: info@simkins.com **Website:** www.simkins.com

Number of partners	19
Assistant solicitors	11
Other fee-earners	8

AREAS OF PRACTICE

Media, Entertainment & Sport	70%
Other	30%

CONTACTS

Advertising/Marketing	Charles Swan
Competition	Stephen Hornsby
Corporate	Jonathan Sellors
Digital Media	Jonathan Sellors
Employment	Roger Billins

THE FIRM: The Simkins Partnership is one of the largest and most broadly-based media law firms in Europe. The firm is a leading adviser in related areas including music, film, theatre, television, advertising and marketing, sport, publishing, digital media and photography. Long term relationships characterise and reflect the success of the firm's approach to its clients. Simkins lawyers are involved in their clients' businesses in a direct way – as business advisers, not just lawyers. While divided into sector groups, music and film lawyers as well as publishing and marketing lawyers frequently work together. With distinct specialisms, the firm is delivering more collaborative advice, as clients' needs develop with digital technology-driven opportunities. A feature

Continued overleaf

of recent years has been the increase in the firm's corporate media clients. The firm is generally known as a media firm and is the sole UK member of Advertising Law International. In addition to its specialist expertise, the firm advises on corporate transactions, competition and employment issues, commercial litigation, private client and family matters. It also has an active property group.

PRINCIPAL AREAS OF WORK: Work includes media, entertainment and sport.

CLIENTELE: The firm advises many of the top advertising agencies and the largest UK below-the-line agency. Unusually, the firm represents both talent and corporates. Music clients include Sony Europe, BMG and EMI International. Artists include Leftfield, James, Underworld, Geri Halliwell and Sir Cliff Richard. Theatre companies include The Really Useful Group. Film and television clients include Film Four, Matrix Securities and Channel Four as well as over 40 production companies. Publishing clients include The Publishing Team, Corbis and Everyman as well as individual writers such as Sebastian Faulks and a number of well-known photographers. The firm publishes e-bulletins on topical issues in the media sector. Registration details can be found on the website.

RECRUITMENT: The firm takes on two trainees a year, and welcomes applications from people with particular experience in the world of media.

CONTACTS

Family	Howard Stacey
Film	Nigel Bennett
Litigation: General	Roger Billins
Litigation: Media	Dominic Free
Music	Julian Turton
Photography	Charles Swan
Private Client	Robert Rutteman
Property	Cyrus Fatemi
Publishing	Julian Turton
Radio	Nigel Bennett
Sport	Stephen Hornsby
Television & Video	Antony Gostyn
Theatre	David Franks

THE SIMKINS PARTNERSHIP

SOLICITORS

S

SIMMONS & SIMMONS

CityPoint, One Ropemaker Street, London, EC2Y 9SS
Tel: (020) 7628 2020 **Fax:** (020) 7628 2070 **DX:** 12
Email: enquiries@simmons-simmons.com **Website:** www.simmons-simmons.com

Managing Partner	David Dickinson
Senior Partner	Janet Gaymer
Number of partners	111
Assistant solicitors	279
Other fee-earners	158

THE FIRM: Simmons & Simmons is a world-class law firm providing advice to financial institutions, corporates, public and international bodies, and private individuals through its international network of offices. Simmons & Simmons has 155 partners, of which 44 are based in its international offices outside the UK, and a total staff worldwide of more than 1,400. It provides a comprehensive range of legal services with strength and depth. The ability to provide technically excellent, commercial and high quality advice is expected of leading law firms. Simmons & Simmons aims to provide an additional dimension by focusing on the way it works with its clients and by shaping its service to fit the clients' needs. It applies considerable expertise to all business sectors but focuses on those key to its clients. They include finance, asset management, energy and utilities, industrial and commercial products, pharmaceuticals and biotechnology, retail and distribution, technology, media and telecommunications (TMT), transport, insurance and reinsurance and public sector. In the past year two independent studies into staff job satisfaction have ranked Simmons & Simmons higher than all its competitors. This is the basis from which Simmons & Simmons is able to recognise and work to its clients' individual needs.

Simmons & Simmons was the first law firm to offer free Internet Service Provider services through its online legal resource, elexica, www.elexica.com. The firm has won two prestigious awards in the legal press for this online resource which offers a current awareness service, legal updates, training modules, know-how documents, a legal discussions forum and an extensive library of web links.

PRINCIPAL AREAS OF WORK: As a leading international law firm, Simmons & Simmons focuses on the needs of its international financial markets and corporate clients. It has particular expertise in mergers and acquisitions, privatisations, venture capital, international securities, corporate finance, financial services, capital markets products, securitisations, repackagings, corporate treasury, bank lending, asset management, major projects, PFI and PPP.

The firm is also able to provide a strength and depth of quality advice in commercial law, EU and competition, intellectual property, communications and media law, development and construction work, property and planning, environmental law, energy, biotechnology, railways, all forms of dispute resolution, employment and pensions advice, and taxation. Other areas of expertise include corporate recovery, unit trusts, insurance, commodities, asset finance and aviation and advice on private capital to individuals.

INTERNATIONAL: Languages spoken in the firm include English, French, German, Spanish, Italian, Swedish, Portuguese, Dutch, Greek, Mandarin, Japanese, Russian, Czech, Slovakian, Polish, Cantonese, Afrikaans, Hungarian, Latvian, Hindi, Arabic and Vietnamese.

AREAS OF PRACTICE

Corporate/Corporate Finance/M&A	41%
Commercial/Intellectual Property/EU	14%
Property	13%
Litigation	12%
Banking & Capital Markets	10%
Tax	6%
Employment	3%
Environmental	1%

CONTACTS

Aviation/Asset Finance	Kim Walkling
Banking	Harvey Chalmers
Capital Markets	Tony Smith
Commercial	Edwin Godfrey, Jeremy Sivyer
Communications	Tom Wheadon
Construction	Robert Bryan
Corporate Finance	Stuart Evans
Corporate Recovery	John Houghton
Corporate/M&A	Jerry Walter, Ken Woffenden
Dispute Resolution	Simon Morgan
Employment	William Dawson, Janet Gaymer
Energy	Jerry Walter
Environmental	Kathy Mylrea
EU/Competition Law	Peter Freeman
Financial Services	Iain Cullen, Richard Slater
Insurance	Christopher Braithwaite
IP	Kevin Mooney, Helen Newman
Pensions	Michael Wyman
Pharmaceuticals/Biotech	Gerry Kamstra
Private Client	Caroline Garnham
Project Finance/PFI	Edwin Godfrey
Property (Commercial)	Alan Butler
Securitisation	James Bresslaw
Tax (Corporate)	Paul Hale
Transport	Charles Mayo
Venture Capital	Alan Karter, Chris Wilkinson

Simmons & Simmons

SIMONS MUIRHEAD & BURTON

50 Broadwick Street, Soho, London, W1V 7AG
Tel: (020) 7734 4499 **Fax:** (020) 7734 3263 **DX:** 144060 Soho Sq 5
Email: rec@smab.co.uk **Website:** www.smab.co.uk

Managing Partner	David Kirk
Senior Partner	Anthony Burton
Number of partners	9
Assistant solicitors	2
Other fee-earners	11

AREAS OF PRACTICE

Criminal Litigation	35%
Civil Litigation	20%
Media Law	20%
Conveyancing	15%
Company & Commercial Law	10%

CONTACTS

Civil Liberties	Anthony Burton
Civil Litigation	Razi Mireskandari
Commercial Fraud	Anthony Burton
	David Kirk
Company & Commercial	Martin Smith
Employment	Martin Smith
General Crime	Anthony Burton
Investigations	David Kirk
Media/Entertainment	Simon Goldberg
Privy Council	Razi Mireskandari
Property & Construction	David Michaels

simons muirhead & burton

THE FIRM: Simons Muirhead & Burton is a media, corporate fraud and commercial practice in the heart of Soho. The firm also has an expanding commercial property and construction department, and an award-winning pro bono human section. All these areas have been strengthened by the recent arrival of the two senior partners of Soho neighbours Offenbachs. Most assignments are undertaken by partners, and the firm aims to provide a high-quality, hands-on service at competitive rates for commercial and private clients.

PRINCIPAL AREAS OF WORK:
Non-Contentious Media & Entertainment: Contract advice for independent film and television production companies, theatre (including Royal Court and Soho Theatre Company) and publishers.
Media Litigation: Defamation, intellectual property and media litigation for broadcasters, book and magazine publishers, national/local newspapers, including Internet-related matters; employment and general litigation.
Commercial Property & Construction: Commercial property transactions, development projects, funding, building contracts, licensing, large-scale development residential conveyancing.
Company/Commercial: Company commercial work, with a particular emphasis on media related companies.
Commercial Fraud: All fraud investigations (SFO, DTI, CPS, Inland Revenue, Customs & Excise, FSA), including commercial fraud, insider dealing, corruption, money laundering, back duty and regulatory proceedings. Advice is provided on international police enquiries and extradition. The firm is a member of the Very High Cost Cases Panel and has a Legal Aid franchise.
Investigations: Investigations carried out, and reports prepared, for commercial clients with fraud and compliance problems.
General Crime: Serious criminal cases are undertaken for private and legally aided clients.
Civil Liberties & Human Rights: The long-established work of the firm in its commitment to providing pro bono advice and representation in death row cases in the Caribbean has won awards and wide media recognition. The firm provides advice on Civil Liberties and Human Rights issues in the UK and Europe.
Privy Council: Private civil and criminal cases undertaken.
Agency work: The firm acts as London agents in all courts and tribunals.

SIMPSON & MARWICK WS

18 Heriot Row, Edinburgh, EH3 6HS
Tel: (0131) 557 1545 **Fax:** (0131) 557 4409 **DX:** 161 Edinburgh
Email: email@simpmar.co.uk **Website:** www.simpmar.co.uk

15 South Tay Street, Dundee, DD1 1NU
Tel: (01382) 200373 **Fax:** (01382) 200370 **DX:** DD52
Email: email@simpmar.co.uk

93 West George Street, Glasgow, G2 1PB
Tel: (0141) 248 2666 **Fax:** (0141) 248 9590 **DX:** GW377
Email: email@simpmar.co.uk

1 Carden Place, Aberdeen, AB10 1UT
Tel: (01224) 624924 **Fax:** (01224) 626590 **DX:** AB6
Email: email@simpmar.co.uk

Senior Partner	John Miller
Chairman	Gordon Keyden
Number of partners	14
Assistant solicitors	28
Other fee-earners	16

AREAS OF PRACTICE

Personal Injury	40%
Professional & Clinical Negligence	35%
Commercial Litigation	15%
Property/Private Client	10%

CONTACTS

Commercial	Peter Anderson
	Charles McGregor
Family	John Thomson
Health & Safety	Robert Leith, Gordon Keyden
Insurance	Gordon Keyden
	Douglas Russell
Local Government	Michael Wood, Kate Shaw
Oil Industry	Douglas Russell, Robert Leith
Personal Injury	Gordon Keyden, Michael Wood
Private Client	John Miller
Professional & Clinical Negligence	Pamela Abernethy, Peter Anderson
Property	Richard Loudon

THE FIRM: Simpson & Marwick is a specialist civil litigation practice with particular expertise in defender reparation work. From offices in Edinburgh, Glasgow, Aberdeen and Dundee, the firm represents clients in courts throughout Scotland. The firm's team of litigators is one of the largest and most experienced in the country.

PRINCIPAL AREAS OF WORK: Personal injury, professional and medical negligence, major accident actions, commercial litigation, public/employers' liability, health and safety, healthcare law, employment law and property.

S

SINCLAIR ROCHE & TEMPERLEY

Royex House, 5 Aldermanbury Square, London, EC2V 7LE
Tel: (020) 7452 4000 **Fax:** (020) 7452 4001
Email: info@srtlaw.com **Website:** www.srtlaw.com

Managing Partner	Jeff Morgan
UK	
Number of partners	29
Assistant solicitors	37
Other fee-earners	25
International	
Number of partners	8
Assistant solicitors	19
Other fee-earners	5

CONTACTS

Aviation	David Relf
Commercial Litigation	Alan Bercow
Commercial Property	Imelda Moffat
Commodities & Trade Finance	Robert Parson
Company/Commercial & Corporate Finance	Kevin Dean
Employment	Alan Bercow
Energy	Gary Campbell
European Union Law	Alfred Merckx
Insolvency	David Middleburgh
Maritime Casualty & Insurance	Joe Atkinson
Ship & Asset Finance	George Hodgkinson
Shipping Litigation	Michael Stockwood
Sport	James Felt
Tax	David Relf

THE FIRM: Sinclair Roche & Temperley is a major commercial international law firm. The firm was founded in the City of London in 1934 and provides high quality, specialised legal advice to the international business community, with a particular focus on shipping, international trade, aviation, energy and finance.

PRINCIPAL AREAS OF WORK: In London and worldwide, Sinclair Roche & Temperley offers clients a broad range of legal expertise, including litigation, arbitration and ADR, corporate and commercial advice, asset, project and trade finance, commercial property, insolvency and corporate restructuring, marine casualty and insurance, oil and gas, commodities and trade finance, new technology and EU law. The firm has developed an active practice in China in shipping, energy and banking and is a leading international maritime law firm in Shanghai. In Hong Kong, the firm primarily focuses on shipping, commodities and corporate work and is becoming increasingly active in telecommunications, media and technology. In Romania, and elsewhere in Europe, the firm is extensively involved in corporate and project finance, particularly energy and water projects, privatisation, investment and property work, with clients ranging from multinational corporations and international financial institutions to Romanian banks and local businesses.

INTERNATIONAL: The firm has offices in London, Hong Kong, Shanghai and Bucharest.

RECRUITMENT: The firm recruits up to eight trainees a year. Candidates should apply by letter and CV to the Director of Human Resources.

SINCLAIRS

Windsor Chambers, Stanwell Road, Penarth, CF64 2AA **Tel:** (0131) 225 8800 **Fax:** (0131) 220 2677 **DX:** 52361
Email: sinclairs.solicitors@bt.internet.com **Ptnrs:** 2 **Asst solrs:** 3 **Other fee-earners:** 2

SINCLAIR TAYLOR & MARTIN

9 Thorpe Close, Portobello Road, London, W10 5XL **Tel:** 0208 969 3667 **Fax:** 0208 969 7044 **DX:** 47601 Ladbroke Grove
Email: enquiries@sinclairtaylor.co.uk **Ptnrs:** 5 **Asst solrs:** 6 **Other fee-earners:** 2

SINGLETONS

The Ridge, South View Road, Pinner, London, HA5 3YD
Tel: (020) 8866 1934 **Fax:** (020) 8429 9212
Email: susan@singlelaw.com **Website:** www.singlelaw.com

Managing Partner	E Susan Singleton
Number of partners	1

AREAS OF PRACTICE

Competition	30%
Commercial	30%
Intellectual Property	25%
Computer/Internet	15%

CONTACTS

All Categories	E Susan Singleton

THE FIRM: Founded in 1994 by well known competition/intellectual property solicitor, Susan Singleton, Singletons provides highly specialised advice on EU/UK competition law, intellectual property, computer/e-commerce and commercial and EU law to over 330 well known public companies and others at £150 per hour. The firm also advises other solicitors' firms and provides in-house training to clients and solicitors. Both contentious and non-contentious work is undertaken. Susan Singleton is author of 20 books including: *Commercial Agency; Competition Act 1998; Data Protection; Business, The Internet & the Law: E-Commerce: A Practical Guide* and edits *IT Law Today, Telecoms Law Today,* and *Comparative Law of Monopolies.*

SINTON & CO

5 Osborne Terrace, Newcastle upon Tyne, NE2 1SQ **Tel:** (0191) 212 7800 **Fax:** (0191) 281 3675 **DX:** 62551 Jesmond **Email:** law@sinton.co.uk **Website:** www.sinton.co.uk **Ptnrs:** 12 **Asst solrs:** 7 **Other fee-earners:** 14 **Contact:** W M Magowan • Sinton & Co is a long established and broad based practice. The firm's recognised pedigrees in litigation and private client are now supplemented by a burgeoning commercial department.

AREAS OF PRACTICE

Litigation	58%
Private Client	31%
Commercial	11%

SKADDEN, ARPS, SLATE, MEAGHER & FLOM LLP

1 Canada Square, Canary Wharf, London, E14 5DS **Tel:** (020) 7519 7000 **Fax:** (020) 7519 7070 **Website:** www.sasmf.com **Ptnrs:** 9 **Asst solrs:** 34 **Other fee-earners:** 8

SKENE EDWARDS WS

5 Albyn Place, Edinburgh, EH2 4NJ **Tel:** (0131) 225 6665 **Fax:** (0131) 220 1015 **DX:** 59 Edinburgh **Email:** reception@skene.co.uk **Asst solrs:** 9 **Other fee-earners:** 4

SLAUGHTER AND MAY

35 Basinghall Street, London, EC2V 5DB
Tel: (020) 7600 1200 **Fax:** (020) 7600 0289 **DX:** LDE and CDE Box No. 11
Email: mail@slaughterandmay.com **Website:** www.slaughterandmay.com

Senior Partner	Tim Clark
Number of partners	121
Number of solicitors	394
Other fee-earners	147

AREAS OF PRACTICE

Corporate, M&A & Financial	69%
Commercial Litigation	9%
Tax (Corporate)	5%
Competition	5%
Property (Commercial)	5%
Pensions & Employment	5%
Intellectual Property	2%

CONTACTS

Competition	Malcolm Nicholson
Corporate/M&A	Nigel Boardman
	Stephen Cooke
Environment	Dermot Rice
Financial Regulation	Ruth Fox
Insurance/Financial Institutions	Glen James
Intellectual Property	Nigel Swycher
Investment Funds	James Cripps
Litigation & Arbitration	Richard Grandison
Pensions & Employment	Eddie Codrington
Property	Graham White
Taxation	Steve Edge
Technology, Media & Telecoms	William Underhill
Financing:	
General	Richard Slater
Acquisition/Leveraged Finance	Andrew Balfour
Asset Finance/Leasing	Tom Kinnersley
Banking	Andrew Balfour
Debt Capital Markets	Sanjev Warna-Kula-Suriya
Derivatives	Sanjev Warna-Kula-Suriya
Insolvency & Restructuring	Jonathan Rushworth
Project Finance	Chris Saunders
Securitisation	Chris Smith
Structured Finance	David Frank

SLAUGHTER AND MAY

THE FIRM: Slaughter and May is one of the pre-eminent law firms in the world. It has a diverse and extensive international practice dealing with a wide range of corporate, commercial and financial work for UK and international clients. Slaughter and May aims to provide a professional service of the highest quality. The firm has a distinctive approach to the practice of law and encourages all its lawyers to gain a wide experience in commercial and financial matters so that they offer not only a depth of legal expertise but also versatility and a breadth of commercial experience. Slaughter and May is noted for its positive approach combining technical excellence, commercial awareness and an ability to provide practical, constructive solutions.

PRINCIPAL AREAS OF WORK: Slaughter and May's practice covers a broad spectrum of corporate, commercial and financial work. Clients include industrial and commercial companies from all business sectors, banks, financial institutions and professional firms as well as governments, public bodies and other organisations. The principal areas of practice comprise:
Corporate & M&A: Securities issues, flotations, mergers and acquisitions and corporate and commercial transactions generally, including privatisation-related work.
Financing: International debt and equities issues and derivatives; international and domestic lending, structured finance and project and asset finance; and insolvency and asset-tracing work.
Financial Regulation: The regulatory aspects of corporate finance, fund management, securities and derivatives as well as supervision and regulation of banks, building societies, insurance companies and the Lloyd's market.
Litigation & Arbitration: A wide range of commercial proceedings and disputes including hearings before the High Court, the House of Lords and the Privy Council, domestic and international arbitrations, formal enquiries, investigations and inter-jurisdictional disputes.
Intellectual Property: All aspects of the creation, acquisition, exploitation and protection of intellectual property rights.
Property: All types of commercial property transactions as well as advice on construction and engineering projects in the UK and overseas.
Environment: Specialist advice on a broad spectrum of environmental issues.
Tax: The tax aspects of corporate transactions and activities, including the development of tax-efficient structures and instruments.
Competition: Advice from London and Brussels on competition law, particularly in relation to acquisitions and mergers and joint ventures.
Pensions & Employment: Employee share benefit schemes, industrial conflicts, sex discrimination and equal pay problems and pensions and employment aspects of company acquisitions, disposals and takeovers.

INTERNATIONAL: International work is fundamental to the firm's practice both in London and in its overseas offices and Slaughter and May's lawyers travel widely. The firm has close working relations with the leading independent law firms in all major jurisdictions so that the best local advice and service is available to each client wherever this is required.

RECRUITMENT: Approximately 85 trainee solicitors are recruited every year. Financial assistance is available for the CPE and LPC in the form of a maintenance grant plus tuition and examination fees. For further information on recruitment, please write to Charlotte Houghton, Personnel Manager, or email grad.recruit@slaughterandmay.com. Please note that at present the firm does not accept applications by email.

AE SMITH & SON

Frome House, London Road, Stroud, GL5 2AF
Tel: (01453) 757444 **Fax:** (01453) 757586 **DX:** 58801 Stroud
Email: stroudenquiries@aesmith.co.uk

Stokescroft, Cossack Square, Nailsworth, GL6 0DZ
Tel: (01453) 832566 **Fax:** (01453) 835441 **DX:** 123329 Nailsworth
Email: nailsworthenquiries@aesmith.co.uk

Number of partners	4
Assistant solicitors	6
Other fee-earners	2

CONTACTS

Nailsworth Office	Caroline James
Stroud Office	John C Bridges

THE FIRM: Founded about 1835, the firm operates from offices in Stroud and Nailsworth. As well as dealing with a very wide range of commercial and private client work, the firm has particular experience in the fields of trusts and probate, property and estate development, advocacy, mental health and education (particularly special educational needs). The firm has Legal Aid franchises in family, mental health, crime, personal injury

Continued overleaf

and education. Members of the firm are on the Law Society Family Law and Mental Health Review Tribunal panels. The firm also has connections with European lawyers.

SMITH LLEWELYN PARTNERSHIP

18 Princess Way, Swansea, SA1 3LW **Tel:** (01792) 464444 **Fax:** (01792) 464726 **DX:** 92051 Swansea 3 **Email:** slp@easynet.co.uk **Ptnrs:** 7 **Asst solrs:** 8 **Other fee-earners:** 9 • Undertakes all work but is also one of the largest plaintiff, personal injury and clinical negligence practices in South Wales.

AREAS OF PRACTICE	
Clinical Negligence	25%
Personal Injury	25%
Matrimonial	15%
Conveyancing	10%
Social Welfare	7%
Other	18%

THE SMITH PARTNERSHIP

25 The Wardwick, Derby, DE1 1HA **Tel:** (01332) 225 300 **Fax:** (01332) 225 303 **DX:** 11539 DERBY **Email:** wardwick@smithpartnership.co.uk **Website:** www.smithpartnership.co.uk **Ptnrs:** 21 **Asst solrs:** 36 **Other fee-earners:** 58

SMITH RODDAM

56 North Bondgate, Bishop Auckland, County Durham, DL14 7PG **Tel:** (01388) 603073 **Fax:** (01388) 450483 **DX:** 60150 Bishop Auckland **Ptnrs:** 3 **Asst solrs:** 3 **Other fee-earners:** 4

S

SPEECHLY BIRCHAM

6 St Andrew Street, London, EC4A 3LX
Tel: (020) 7427 6400 **Fax:** (020) 7427 6600 **DX:** 54 Chancery Lane
Email: speechlys@speechlys.com **Website:** www.speechlybircham.com

Senior Partner	John Avery Jones CBE
Managing Partner	Michael Lingens
Number of partners	36
Assistant solicitors	50
Other fee-earners	23

CONTACTS	
Commercial Dispute Resolution	Stephen Dobson
Construction & Engineering	Tim Raper
Corporate	Michael Lingens
Corporate Tax	John Avery Jones CBE
Employment	Alan Julyan
Financial Institutions	Mervyn Couve
Private Capital	Richard Kirby
Property	Charles Palmer
Property Litigation	Graham Ling
Technology	Tom Shaw

THE FIRM: Speechly Bircham is a medium sized City law firm with an excellent client base that includes a number of well-known corporate and institutional clients. Its strong commercial focus is complemented by a highly regarded private capital practice. The firm handles major transactions as well as commercial disputes, and has a good reputation for several specialist advisory areas, notably personal and corporate tax. There are several discrete practice groups in many of which the firm has an acknowledged reputation and where its performance is competitive with that of larger firms. The structure of the firm and its ability to provide a high level of partner input make it a good alternative to large City firms for many clients. The legal affairs of each client are managed by a single partner, responsible for ensuring that the service is delivered quickly and cost-effectively. Much of the firm's work has an international dimension. It acts for UK clients doing business overseas, supervising and co-ordinating the work of foreign law firms, as well as advising non-UK clients (particularly from the USA and continental Europe) on legal issues and transactions in this country. While the firm has no formal affiliations with non-English law firms, close relationships with other independent law firms mean the firm can offer a seamless service for international projects. The firm is also the first choice for several major US and European law firms wanting UK legal advice for their clients.

PRINCIPAL AREAS OF WORK:

Corporate: Within the corporate practice, merger and acquisitions work ranges from corporate acquisitions and divestments (often cross-border) to buy-outs, joint ventures and the sale of family companies. Finance work includes a full range of debt and equity transactions including private equity financings, banking and capital markets work as well as stock exchange flotations. The financial institutions group advises on an extensive range of transactions in the financial services and insurance sectors (including the recent demutualisation of Scottish Life) as well as regulatory and funds work. The technology practice acts on corporate and commercial IT/IP projects for hi-tech, Internet, media, telecoms and biotech companies.

Corporate Tax: The corporate tax practice is headed by the senior partner, who has an international reputation for tax work and has served on many tax review bodies. Much of the tax work has an international dimension, including advice to major companies on employee benefit and share incentive schemes.

Private Capital: The private capital practice is recognised as a leader in the field of advising individuals and families on wealth management issues. Its members have considerable expertise in planning and implementing tax strategies, including setting up offshore trusts and investment vehicles to protect assets in the UK and abroad.

Employment: The employment practice works closely with the firm's corporate, tax and pensions lawyers to help businesses develop appropriate employment strategies in the face of increasing legislative complexity. It advises on the negotiation of employment contracts and termination packages and handles individual and collective employment disputes.

Dispute Resolution: For clients seeking a cost-effective and commercially satisfactory outcome, the firm advises clients on UK and international dispute resolution methods, including litigation, arbitration, mediation and other forms of Alternative Dispute Resolution (ADR). A particular area of specialisation is handling disputes for financial institutions.

SPEECHLY BIRCHAM

Property: The property practice has an established reputation in advising property investors (including a number of blue chip life companies, property companies, urban estate owners, developers and local authorities) on all aspects of commercial and industrial property. The practice includes a strong property litigation team which advises on management issues, such as possession orders, dilapidation claims, renewals, rent reviews and recovery of arrears. For complex projects the practice draws on a range of internal specialists in tax, corporate structuring, planning and environmental law.
Construction & Engineering: The construction and engineering practice works with investors, developers and contractors to assist them with their development and construction projects (including contractual disputes involving arbitration, mediation or litigation). The practice works with a range of mainly international engineering groups on contractual disputes on major projects in the oil, utility and chemical sectors.

SPIRO GRECH & HARDING-ROBERTS SOLICITORS

Clifton House, 8 Four Elms Road, Roath, Cardiff, CF2 1LE **Tel:** (029) 20222255 **Fax:** (029) 20450162 **Ptnrs:** 3 **Asst solrs:** 1

SPRAGGON STENNETT BRABYN

225 Kensington High Street, London, W8 6SA **Tel:** (020) 7938 2223 **Fax:** (020) 7938 2224 **Email:** legal@ssb.co.uk **Ptnrs:** 3 **Asst solrs:** 2

SPRECHER GRIER HALBERSTAM

Lincoln House, 300 High Holborn, London, WC1V 7JH **Tel:** (020) 7544 5555 **Fax:** (020) 7544 5565 **DX:** 0041 **Email:** info@sprgr.co.uk **Website:** www.sprgr.co.uk **Ptnrs:** 11 **Asst solrs:** 4 **Other fee-earners:** 5

S

SQUIRE & CO

49/50 St. Johns Square, London, EC1V 4RF
Tel: (020) 7490 3444 **Fax:** (020) 7250 4087/4115 **DX:** 46617 Barbican
Email: squire@squireandco.co.uk

Managing Partner	Nicholas Squire
Partners	7
Assistant solicitors	14
Other staff	15
Total	36

THE FIRM: The firm specialises in all types of professional indemnity insurance claims including accountants, solicitors, barristers, insurance brokers, surveyors, independent financial advisers and construction related risks such as engineers, architects, quantity surveyors and project managers. In addition, the firm deals with all classes of liability insurance business, as well as insurance and reinsurance disputes; insurance investigations; construction and civil fraud and is regularly involved in arbitrations and mediations as well as commercial litigation at all levels.

SQUIRE, SANDERS & DEMPSEY LLP

Royex House, Aldermanbury Square, London, EC2V 7HR
Tel: (020) 7776 5200 **Fax:** (020) 7776 5233
Email: ssdinfo_London@ssd.com **Website:** www.ssd.com

UK	
Number of partners	11
Assistant solicitors	21
Other fee earners	2
Worldwide	
Number of partners	287
Counsel/Of Counsel	68
Assistant solicitors	404
Other fee earners	151

CONTACTS

Corporate	Mara Babin
	Cathy Horton
	Paul Lewis
	Stephen Nelson
	James Nimmo
	Richard Sterling Surrey
	Martin Walsh
	Carol Welu
Communications	James Nimmo
	Richard Sterling Surrey
	Mara Babin
	Carol Welu
Dispute Resolution	Carol Welu
Employment	Fiona McLaren
Information Technology/E-Business	Cathy Horton
Property	Daniel Larkin

THE FIRM: Founded in the United States in 1890, Squire Sanders is a full service global law firm with more than 750 attorneys in 28 strategically located offices worldwide. Offices are located throughout the US (fourteen offices), Europe (nine offices) and Asia (five offices). The firm also has an association with a legal firm in Dublin and a "Renaissance" network of 18 law firms in China. The firm's attorneys are fluent in more than 50 languages, have been admitted to practice in more than 60 jurisdictions worldwide and counsel nearly 30,000 clients involved in almost every industry segment.
London Office: An important centre of the firm's international practice, the London office serves the needs of clients with businesses spanning the globe, UK companies and UK operations of companies headquartered in the US, Europe and Asia. Lawyers in the London office take advantage of their position in Europe's largest financial and business market to counsel clients on complex corporate, communications, technology and real estate transactions, as well as employment law matters, international disputes and a host of other issues. Opened in 1992, the London office has grown rapidly to offer a full set of legal services. International transactions frequently require English or US law to govern key contractual relationships. Both legal systems are served from the London office. London is a strategic locale for generating capital and advising, facilitating, negotiating, documenting and executing deals. Most of Squire Sanders' London office lawyers were trained in the UK and are admitted to practice as solicitors in England, Scotland and Wales. In addition, there are a significant number of experienced US educated international transaction lawyers resident in the London office. Collectively, the London lawyers fluently speak nine languages.

PRINCIPAL AREAS OF WORK:
Corporate: Lawyers in the London office advise corporate and investment banking clients on corporate, transactional and commercial matters including cross-border international mergers and acquisitions, joint ventures, project finance, real estate, hospitality and leisure, international capital markets, due diligence, company

Continued overleaf

restructuring and reorganisations, management buyouts and workouts – often in multiple jurisdictions around the UK, Europe and the world.

Communications: Lawyers in the London office have contributed significantly to the firm's communications practice. Frequently operating from the London office, Squire Sanders' telecommunications group provides advice on regulatory and transactional matters to incumbent telephone companies, cable television and telephony companies, satellite service providers, GSM and other wireless operators, data service and network companies, Internet service providers, investors and investment banks, government agencies and multinational development organisations. The London group is particularly active in telecommunications M&A transactions in Europe, having led the acquisition and related equity financings of several large European cable telephony companies, including a controlling interest in the largest-ever leveraged buyout in Germany.

Dispute Resolution: The London office is a hub of Squire Sanders' extensive international dispute resolution practice, managing complex arbitrations, coordinated global trademark litigation and sensitive disputes arising from multi-jurisdictional transactions.

Employment: The London employment group counsels clients on all aspects of UK and European employment law. Areas of particular advancement include domestic and international employment contracts, company handbooks, TUPE issues, secondment arrangements, large-scale redundancy programs, stock options, pensions and other incentives. Squire Sanders plunged into the issues surrounding employee conduct at work, including e-mail and Internet use, and has represented employers in disciplinary matters involving improper computer downloads. The employment team also resolves discrimination and disability matters, handles working time and collective bargaining issues, structures termination arrangements and represents employment clients in tribunal claims.

S

Information Technology/E-Business: The London office has a particular focus on information technology and e-business and represents a number of sophisticated global vendors and purchasers of hardware, software, systems integration services, networking systems and outsourcing and IT services. Squire Sanders has a cutting-edge approach to advising technology clients – an interlocking service platform that combines the firm's leading resources in business, finance and technology consulting. The IT team handles cross-border IT mergers and acquisitions, systems integration, network management and project management contracts, all IT service contracts, software and license agreements and e-commerce contracts.

INTERNATIONAL: Offices abroad: Asia: Almaty, Beijing, Hong Kong, Taipei, Tokyo. Europe: Bratislava, Brussels, Budapest, Kyiv, London, Madrid, Milan, Moscow, Prague. US: Cincinnati, Cleveland, Columbus, Houston, Jacksonville, New York, Los Angeles, Miami, Palo Alto, Phoenix, San Francisco, Tampa, Tysons Corner, Washington DC. The firm also has an association with a legal firm in Dublin.

STAFFORD YOUNG JONES

The Old Rectory, 29 Martin Lane, London, EC4R 0AU
Tel: (020) 7623 9490 **Fax:** (020) 7929 5704 **DX:** 176 London
Email: <recipient>@s-yj.co.uk

Managing Partner	Helen Wenham
Senior Partner	Paul Adams
Number of partners	11
Assistant solicitors	4
Other fee-earners	5

CONTACTS

Company/Commercial	Terry Chandler
Employment	Paul Adams
Family	Paul Adams
Housing Associations	Pamela Yelland
Litigation (General)	Andrew Strong
Property (Commercial)	Martin Gaston
Property (Residential)	Francis Backman
Tax & Personal Planning	Neil Fulton
Wills & Probate	Christopher Munday

THE FIRM: Stafford Young Jones is a long established City of London practice serving the needs of both individual and corporate clients to a high professional standard, using modern methods and technology where appropriate whilst maintaining a friendly and personal service.

PRINCIPAL AREAS OF WORK:

Family Law: The firm is a member of the Relate Quality Partnership Scheme. Advice on all aspects of family law, including: separation and divorce; arrangements for children's residence and education; arrangements for contact with children; separation agreements and financial settlements.

Housing Association Work: The firm acts for a considerable number of registered social landlords in the area of housing and landlord and tenant litigation.

Employment Law: Advice given to both employer and employee on a full range of employment issues.

General Litigation: Experienced in contractual claims, commercial litigation and property litigation, acting for both claimants and defendants. Computerised and cost effective debt recovery for individual and corporate clients.

Wills & Probate: Preparation of wills and living wills; enduring powers of attorney; inheritance tax planning; administration of estates; advice to executors and beneficiaries on probate and succession law; variation of estates and the obtaining of grants of representation in England to the estates of foreign nationals.

Trusts & Personal Tax Planning: Formation, management and administration of trusts; asset management and financial planning; Court of Protection work. The firm offers a Nominee Company service which is a sponsored member of CREST. The firm is authorised by the Law Society to conduct Investment Business.

Residential Property: A fast and efficient service in the purchase and sale of freehold and leasehold property, short term letting and remortgages with specialist advice in the area of insolvency.

Commercial Property: A comprehensive service acting for corporate and individual clients advising buyers and sellers, landlords and tenants and borrowers and lenders in the acquisition, disposal and management of commercial property with specialist advice in the area of insolvency.

Company & Commercial: Advice on the formation, acquisition and disposal of commercial ventures and associated matters. Acting for financial institutions in the areas of lending and borrowing.

INTERNATIONAL: Work can be handled in French, German and Portuguese.

RECRUITMENT: The firm has a maximum number of three trainee solicitors. Prospective trainees should write to Paul Adams enclosing a CV.

STAMP JACKSON AND PROCTER

5 Parliament Street, Hull, HU1 2AZ **Tel:** (01482) 324591 **Fax:** (01482) 224048 **DX:** 11927 HULL 1 **Email:** ail@sjplaw.co.uk **Ptnrs:** 9 **Asst solrs:** 6 **Other fee-earners:** 17

STANLEY TEE

High Street, Bishop's Stortford, CM23 2LU
Tel: (01279) 755 200 **Fax:** (01279) 758 400 **DX:** 50404 Bishop's Stortford
Email: law@stanleytee.co.uk **Website:** www.stanleytee.co.uk

42 High Street, Great Dunmow, CM6 1AH
Tel: (01371) 872 166 **Fax:** (01371) 875 747 **DX:** 89803 Great Dunmow
Email: law@stanleytee.co.uk

Star House, 38 Rayne Road, Braintree, CM7 2QP
Tel: (01376) 552 277 **Fax:** (01376) 551 919 **DX:** 56203 Braintree
Email: law@stanleytee.co.uk

Senior Partner	Rodney Stock
Number of partners	13
Assistant solicitors	13
Other fee-earners	13

AREAS OF PRACTICE

Litigation (incl. Family Law)	40%
Private Client	20%
Residential Property	17%
Commercial Property	12%
Company Commercial	7%
Criminal & Regulatory	4%

CONTACTS

Agricultural & Estates .... Caroline Metcalf, Richard Tee
Commercial Litigation/Personal Injury John Donovan, Caroline Metcalf, David Redfern
Commercial Property .... Govan Bramley, Bob Elms, Jeremy Gillham, Rodney Stock
Company & Commercial .... Govan Bramley, Michael Kirby, Rodney Stock
Employment .... Helena Myska
Family .... David Redfern
Private Client, Personal Tax, Trusts & Probate .... Richard Tee
Residential Property .... Bob Elms

THE FIRM: Stanley Tee provides a broad spectrum of legal services to private and commercial clients, especially agricultural concerns, insurance companies and publicly quoted companies. The main focus of the firm's business is in commercial litigation and defendant personal injury cases, and it is involved in high value, complex and widely publicised cases (e.g. Dowling E-coli, Chechnya Hostages and Queen's Moat). The private client department also accounts for a significant proportion of the firm's activities, with tax and trust advice as an area of specialist expertise. Assets dealt with on behalf of clients have now risen to a figure in the order of £80 million. Founded in 1915, Stanley Tee is a well-established and progressive firm of growing regional and national influence. The year 2000 has been a momentous one for the company, marked by a spirit of dynamism and a substantial expansion of its business. The most tangible evidence of this is the completion and opening of additional premises in Bishop's Stortford, which has increased the area of its existing office complex by more than one third. The modern, open-plan design is purpose built to accommodate new technology and streamlined working methods, which in turn are serving to generate new business. The firm has seen a 16% increase in turnover to May 31st 2000. In addition it has won Lexcel accreditation and has introduced a new management structure. Another recent development has been the launch of a new corporate identity. This reflects the increasing national recognition won by the firm, which benefits from a strategic location close to the City of London and Stansted Airport and fast connections with the M25, the Midlands and East Anglia.

STATHAM GILL DAVIES

55 New Cavendish Street, London, W1G 9TF **Tel:** (020) 7487 5565 **Fax:** (020) 7487 4409 **Email:** sgd@stathamgilldavies.com **Ptnrs:** 12 **Asst solrs:** 1 **Contact:** Philip Loveday • The firm's four core departments – commercial, corporate, employment and litigation – provide legal advice and services to clients in the media, entertainment and sports related industries.

STEEDMAN RAMAGE

6 Alva Street, Edinburgh, EH2 4QQ
Tel: (0131) 260 6600 **Fax:** (0131) 260 6610 **DX:** ED 95
Email: info@steedmanramage.co.uk **Website:** www.steedmanramage.co.uk

Afton House, 26 West Nile Street, Glasgow, G2 1PF
Tel: (0141) 242 6600 **Fax:** (0141) 242 6610 **DX:** GW 14
Email: info@steedmanramage.co.uk

Managing Partner	Iain MacKinnon
Chairman	Sandy Reid
Number of partners	15
Assistant solicitors	16
Other fee-earners	7

AREAS OF PRACTICE

Commercial Property	70%
Litigation	16%
Corporate	14%

THE FIRM: Steedman Ramage is a positive, progressive and proactive law firm. It offers specialist corporate/commercial legal services with independently accredited expertise in commercial property, corporate and commercial litigation. Strategically, the firm continues to pursue its vision of being a dynamic and flexible business with a reputation for excellence and success in the provision of first class specialist legal services.

Continued overleaf

Steedman Ramage's client base ranges from smaller local businesses to large blue chip plcs and other organisations, including financial institutions, property developers, e-commerce companies, retailers, local authorities and central government departments. The firm has recently restructured and brought in new talent to work alongside existing experienced people. Recruitment, investment in IT systems and excellent client care allow the firm to meet the increasing demand for a top quality medium-sized business operating in a competitive market place.

PRINCIPAL AREAS OF WORK:

Property: This remains the firm's area of greatest reputation, derived from the quality and experience of the partners, the teams and its impressive client list. The teams focus on retail and leisure, development and investment and housing associations, taking leading positions in these markets.

Commercial Litigation: The team advises on specialist areas of business including contentious aspects of environmental law, planning, commercial property litigation, human rights and rent review. The team is currently recognised for its expertise in mediation and arbitration and its involvement in one of Scotland's highest profile human rights cases currently before the European Court of Justice.

Planning: Significant instructions, both contentious and non-contentious, ensure that the firm's planning team is at the leading edge. The team is currently involved in the high profile appeal to the Court of Session regarding the proposed development of Princes Street Galleries, Edinburgh and in the personal representation of clients' interests at inquiry without involving counsel.

Construction & Engineering: While targeting the maturing PFI and PPP sector and providing focused advice on capital projects, this team continues to demand attention from construction, construction finance and professional team clients.

Banking & Finance: This team has provided the firm's most impressive area of business growth this year, during which it advised UK clearing banks on corporate banking facilities, handling deals involving helicopters, ships and property.

Insolvency: Led by an accredited insolvency expert, the corporate recovery team acts for the Secretary of State for Trade and Industry handling directors' disqualification work in Scotland. The team also acts for a wide range of clients including major clearing banks, the Accountant in Bankruptcy and Insolvency Practitioners.

Corporate & Commercial: Steedman Ramage's specialist teams include employment and IP and IT (led by an accredited expert), whilst continuing to provide expertise in joint ventures, corporate and business sales/purchases, commercial contracts and corporate finance.

RECRUITMENT: The construction and engineering team has been strengthened by the leadership of Euan Pirie, who has recently been recruited from a highly respected Scottish PFI/PPP legal practice.

CONTACTS

Area	Contact
Alternative Dispute Resolution	Kenny Cumming
Banking & Finance	Alex Innes
	Iain MacKinnon
Commercial Litigation	Victoria Craig
	Kenny Cumming
Commercial Property	Sandy Reid
	Iain McHardy
Construction & Engineering	Euan Pirie
Corporate/Commercial	Scott Kerr
	Alex Innes
Debt Recovery	Rachel Grant
Employment	Scott Kerr
	Victoria Craig
Environment	Kenny Cumming
	David Ratter
EU & Competiton	Scott Kerr
Human Rights	Victoria Craig
Insolvency	Rachel Grant
IP & IT	Scott Kerr
Planning	Kenny Cumming
	Sandy Reid
Retail	Iain McHardy
	Iain McLean
Social Housing	Gregor Mair

steedman ramage
solicitors

STEELE & CO

2 Norwich Business Park, Whiting Rd, Norwich, NR4 6DJ
Tel: (01603) 274 700 **Fax:** (01603) 625 890 **DX:** 5218 Norwich
Email: ca@steele.co.uk **Website:** www.steele.co.uk

10 Park Place, Lawn Lane, London, SW8 1UD
Tel: (020) 7735 9006 **Fax:** (020) 7735 7875 **DX:** 33265 Kennington London
Email: lbc@steele.co.uk

Managing Partner	Philip Hyde
Number of partners	13
Assistant solicitors	18
Other fee-earners	75

AREAS OF PRACTICE

Commercial Property	25%
Commercial Disputes & Debt Recovery	15%
Corporate & Commercial	15%
Local Authority/Planning	13%
Employment	9%
Private Client, Tax, Trusts & Probate	8%
Medical Negligence & Personal Injury	6%
Domestic Conveyancing	5%
Other	4%

THE FIRM: Steele & Co is one of the larger independent commercial law firms. The firm has an increasingly national client base, and is recognised in particular for the strength of its commercial practitioners and for the range and quality of its services to local authorities and the public sector. The firm offers a full range of corporate, commercial, property, litigation and public sector services. The firm is dedicated to delivering high quality value for money services to its clients regardless of location. It was one of the first firms in the country to have fully voice and data networked offices. It was also one of the first and largest firms in the country to be accredited to both ISO 9001 and Investor in People standards. It was recently re-accredited to both standards and was praised by the Assessors. The firm prides itself on its innovative team-based structure. This provides clients with assistance to their legal problems at all levels and ensures appropriate expertise and continuity of service. The firm has been recognised as being truly innovative in the way it has developed its products and services and their delivery to clients. The firm has other offices in Diss and Thetford.

STEELE RAYMOND

Richmond Point, 43 Richmond Hill, Bournemouth, BH2 6LR
Tel: (01202) 294566 **Fax:** (01202) 552285 **DX:** 7643 Bournemouth 1
Email: mail@steeleraymond.co.uk **Website:** www.steeleraymond.co.uk

31 West Street, Wimborne, BH21 1JT
Tel: (01202) 885211 **Fax:** (01202) 887746 **DX:** 45303 Wimborne
Email: mail@steeleraymond.co.uk

Managing Partner	John Raymond
Senior Partner	David Steele
Number of partners	13
Assistant solicitors	8
Other fee-earners	9

AREAS OF PRACTICE

Litigation	30%
Company Commercial	27%
Commercial Property	26%
Private Client	10%
Education	7%

CONTACTS

Aviation/Medical Negligence	John Andrews
Commercial Litigation	Simon Outten
Commercial Property	John Daniels
	Bill Oliver
Company & Commercial	Paul Longland
	David Steele
Education	Peter Rolph
Employment	Simon Outten
Insolvency, Landlord & Tenant	Julian Fenn
Partnership	John Raymond
Personal Injury	John Andrews
Private Client	Paul Causton
Residential Developments	Sue Middleton
Taxation	Paul Causton

THE FIRM: Steele Raymond was formed in 1979 and has expanded rapidly since that date, building up a wide range of business clients both in this country and abroad. The firm advises on all areas of company, commercial and business law, with a niche speciality in education law. It also has a substantial private client practice. Steele Raymond has achieved ISO 9001 accreditation for the complete range of its services. The Wimborne office undertakes all areas of work other than criminal matters.

PRINCIPAL AREAS OF WORK: Company and business sales and purchases, company formations and reorganisations, partnership matters, intellectual property, EC law, competition law, commercial contracts (including computer contracts), aviation, commercial property matters, town and country planning, environmental law, insolvency and commercial litigation, personal injury, professional and medical negligence, education law and high level tax planning and advice. Unusually, the firm has a partner with a particular interest in canine law.
Agency Work: The firm undertakes work, other than criminal work, on an agency basis.

CLIENTELE: The firm advises a wide range of clients including individuals, partnerships, housing associations, higher, further and other educational bodies, insolvency practitioners, private and public companies and insurance companies.

INTERNATIONAL: Increasingly the firm's work involves an overseas element, and it works with legal firms in Europe and the USA.

RECRUITMENT: The firm aims to take on one or two trainee solicitors per year and normally has opportunities for specialist staff in various parts of its practice. Strong emphasis is placed on training at all levels.

STEPHENSON HARWOOD

One, St Paul's Churchyard, London, EC4M 8SH
Tel: (020) 7329 4422 **Fax:** (020) 7606 0822 **DX:** 64 Chancery Lane WC2
Email: info@shlegal.com **Website:** www.shlegal.com

Senior Partner	Tony Scales
Chief Executive	John Pike
UK	
Number of partners	62
Assistant solicitors	103
Other fee-earners	54
International	
Number of partners	13
Assistant solicitors	37
Other fee-earners	31

CONTACTS

Banking & Capital Markets	Tony Stockwell
Business Technology	John Enstone
Commercial Litigation	John Fordham
Commercial Property	Richard Light
Company/Commercial	Andrew Sutch
Construction	Steven Wait
Corporate Finance	Andrew Sutch
Corporate Investigations/ Asset-Tracing	John Fordham
Corporate Tax	Hugo Jenney
Employment	Kate Brearley
	Tom Flanagan
Environment	David Cuckson
EU & Competition	Antony Mair
Family & Matrimonial	Jonathan Walsh
Fraud & Regulation/Business Crime	Tony Woodcock
Funds & Financial Services	Andrew Sutch
Insolvency	Paul Gordon-Saker
Insurance Insolvency	Peter Fidler
Insurance/Reinsurance	Paul Howick
Intellectual Property	James Robertson
International Arbitration	Richard Gwynne
Pensions & Benefits	Michael Cowley
Private Client	Mark Baily

THE FIRM: Stephenson Harwood is a City based, international law firm, with an established position in the financial industry, maritime services and the property market, together with opportunities arising in today's 'growth economy', Stephenson Harwood understand its clients' businesses and the sectors and markets in which they operate. Internationalism and teamwork lies at the heart of its business. The firm has offices in Brussels, Guangzhou, Hong Kong, Madrid, Piraeus and Singapore and about 20% of its worldwide revenue comes from these overseas offices. In London, some 30% of the firm's revenue is earned from clients who are based outside the UK. This contrasts strikingly with other firms of a similar size. Worldwide revenue is over £50m. Stephenson Harwood has over 70 partners and a total of more than 500 staff.

PRINCIPAL AREAS OF WORK:
Corporate: The firm has a well-established corporate department with expertise in flotations, mergers and acquisitions, general corporate and commercial transactions, funds management, E-commerce and technology, and EU/Competition
Employment and pensions: Expertise in all aspects of employment advice including pensions and other employee benefits, for both individuals and large corporate clients.
Banking: The firm conducts a full range of work for both retail and investment banks, not only advising them on commercial lending, syndications, and project finance, but also advice on issues such as managing their property portfolios, employment and pensions advice, e-commerce, IT and IP.
Litigation/Commercial Dispute Resolution: The firm is widely recognised for it's expertise in handling disputes, either through litigation or alternative methods. It has experience in handling complex fraud and asset tracing, insolvency, insurance and reinsurance, regulation and investigation; professional indemnity and international trade.
Finance: The firm provides a comprehensive range of finance services including banking, asset finance, project finance and structured finance for shipping, property and other sectors. Expertise includes tax-based leasing asset finance.
Property: The firm covers all aspects of commercial property (including tax issues), with a particular emphasis in property investment, planning, environment, property finance, office and retail development and PFI transactions.

Continued overleaf

Shipping: The international shipping group is a full service contentious and non contentious practice, advising on finance and commercial issues (eg. P&I, marine insurance, and international trade) and marine accidents (including collision and salvage).
Private Capital: The firm remains one of the few leading City law firms to undertake private client, family and matrimonial work. It has particular experience in advising non-domiciled/non-resident clients and high net-worth individuals.
Tax: Provides wide range of corporate and commercial as well as property and banking advice and shipping/asset finance tax, funds tax and stamp duty. Expertise in international and domestic taxation.
Insurance: The firm's integrated team advises on contentious and non contentious aspects of insurance and reinsurance liability, coverage and recovery issues, for clients ranging from ship owners to finance houses and re/insurers.

INTERNATIONAL: The firm has overseas offices in Brussels, Guangzhou, Hong Kong, Madrid, Piraeus and Singapore. It is also associated with Zuric i Partneri, Croatia; Barbe Carpentier Thibault Groener, France; Elias Sp. Paraskevas Attorneys at Law 1933, Greece; De Berti Jacchia Perno & Associati, Italy; Al Sarraf & Al Ruwayeh, Kuwait; and Routledge-Modise, South Africa.

CONTACTS CONTINUED

Private Finance Initiative	David Cuckson
	Peter Walters
Professional Indemnity	Roland Foord
Property Development	Marcel Haniff
Property Finance	Richard Light
Property Litigation	Ken Duncan
Shipping Admiralty	Robin Slade
Shipping Dry Litigation	Paolo Ghirardani
	Andrew Keates
Shipping Finance	Mark Russell
Town & Country Planning	Barry Jeeps
Trade & Project Finance	Tony Stockwell

S

STEPHENSONS

The Pound, 230 Chapel Street, Salford, M3 5LE **Tel:** (0161) 832 8844 **Fax:** (0161) 832 8912 **DX:** 13747 Salford **Ptnrs:** 22 **Asst solrs:** 26 **Other fee-earners:** 54

STEPHENS & SCOWN

25-28 Southernhay East, Exeter, EX1 1RS **Tel:** (01392) 210700 **Fax:** (01392) 274010 **DX:** 8305 Exeter **Email:** solicitors@stephens-scown.co.uk **Website:** www.stephens-scown.co.uk **Number of partners:** 32 **Assistant solicitors:** 27 **Other fee-earners:** 38

STEPIEN LAKE GILBERT & PALING

4 John Street, London, WC1N 2EH
Tel: (020) 7655 0000 **Fax:** (020) 7655 0055 **DX:** 9 Chancery Lane

Senior Partner	Kaz Stepien
Number of partners	4
Assistant solicitors	1
Other fee-earners	3

THE FIRM: The firm was founded in April 1991. The firm's major activities are in the commercial property field, and this covers all aspects of commercial and residential development, banking, secured lending, investment, property finance and joint ventures.

CLIENTELE: The firm acts for a number of banks, major commercial and residential developers, and a number of UK and overseas investors. It also acts for a number of UK property investment funds and high net worth individuals.

RECRUITMENT: The recruitment partner is MW Thomas.

CONTACTS

Banking/Funding	Kaz Stepien
Development	Tim Lake
	Mark Thomas
Investment	Paul Paling
	Kaz Stepien
Retail/Offices	Paul Paling

STEPTOE & JOHNSON RAKISONS

Clements House, 14/18 Gresham Street, London, EC2V 7JE
Tel: (020) 7367 8000 **Fax:** (020) 7367 8001 **DX:** 206 London
Email: london@steptoe.com **Website:** www.steptoe.com

Senior Partner	Tony Wollenberg
Number of partners	17
Assistant solicitors	22
Other fee-earners	9
Total lawyers worldwide	350

THE FIRM: Steptoe & Johnson Rakisons is a multinational partnership based in the City of London, formed by the merger of premier US-firm Steptoe & Johnson LLP and London's Rakisons. With more than 350 attorneys worldwide, Steptoe & Johnson LLP provides counsel and representation in virtually every area of the law. In more than 50 years of practice, the firm has gained a reputation for vigorous representation of clients before governmental agencies, successful advocacy in litigation and arbitrations, and creative and practical advice in guiding business transactions, especially within the technology, telecommunications and energy sectors. The London office provides large City firm expertise in a smaller environment. The firm has a strong international emphasis and provides a comprehensive range of legal services to market-leading businesses throughout the world.

PRINCIPAL AREAS OF WORK: Steptoe & Johnson Rakisons is a world leader in providing legal services to clients in the telecommunications and technology sectors. It punches above its weight in the more traditional areas of corporate law, commercial litigation and property and has specialist employment and international trade desks, thereby complementing the expertise of Steptoe & Johnson LLP in those fields.
Commercial Litigation: Work handled includes contractual, corporate and partnership disputes, banking, defamation, insurance, professional negligence, cross-border tracing of assets and fraud.
Commercial Property: Industrial and residential development, investment, acquisitions and disposals, property finance, portfolio management, planning and environmental law are handled.

AREAS OF PRACTICE

Corporate/Commercial	35%
Telecommunications/TIM	25%
Commercial Litigation	20%
Commercial Property	13%
Employment	7%

CONTACTS

Commercial Litigation	Franco Barone
Commercial Property	Brendan Patterson
Corporate/Commercial	Jonathan Polin
Employment	Neil Adams
Gaming & Betting	Tony Wollenberg
International Trade/EU Law	Iain MacVay
TIM	David Judah
Telecommunications	Daniel Preiskel

Corporate/Commercial: Work includes takeovers and mergers, joint ventures (UK and cross-border), shareholder agreements and venture capital finance, internet start-ups, EU law and international corporate structures, agency, distribution and franchising.
Employment: The firm handles employee/employer relations, employment documentation, redundancy, termination packages, maternity, discrimination, TUPE and advocacy at tribunals.
EU Law: Work includes anti-dumping and antisubsidy proceedings, EU trade barriers regulation, and EU competition law with representations before the European Commission and the European courts.
Gaming & Betting: The firm handles credit betting, in particular enforcement of contracts for differences worldwide, casino licensing and regulatory law and Internet gaming.
International Trade: Regional and multi-lateral trade negotiations and disputes, US and EU trade policy, customs matters and regulatory requirements are handled.
Technology, Internet & Media: Work handled includes hardware and software licensing, e-commerce, Internet and ISP issues, co-location agreements, domain name disputes, IP law and film and video on demand technology.
Telecommunications: Work includes pan-European regulatory and commercial advice in the fixed and wireless sectors, including satellite work, VOIP, LLU, MVNOs, advising governments on telecoms privatisation and generally negotiating with international telecoms regulators.

CLIENTELE: Clients range in size from the largest international conglomerates to owner-managed businesses.

INTERNATIONAL: Steptoe & Johnson Rakisons is able to provide a seamless flow of legal advice regardless of the location of the client or the nature of the work involved. Several of its partners and staff are fluent in foreign languages and legal services can be provided in French, German, Spanish, Portuguese, Italian, Hebrew, Persian and the Nigerian languages of Ibo and Yoruba. Its partners are frequently invited to lecture on cross-border, technical and commercial issues.

STEPTOE & JOHNSON
RAKISONS

S

STEVENS & BOLTON

The Billings, Walnut Tree Close, Guildford, GU1 4YD
Tel: (01483) 302264 **Fax:** (01483) 302254 **DX:** 2423 Guildford 1
Email: mail@stevens-bolton.co.uk **Website:** www.stevens-bolton.co.uk

Managing Partner	Michael Laver
Number of partners	19
Assistant solicitors	28
Other fee-earners	7

AREAS OF PRACTICE

Company/Commercial	29%
Litigation	23%
Commercial Property	19%
Tax, Trust, Will & Probate	14%
Other Property	6%
Employment	5%
Family/Matrimonial	4%

CONTACTS

Charities & Schools	Richard King
Commercial	Tudor Alexander
Commercial Litigation	Richard King
Commercial Property	James Mitchell
Commercial Recovery Service	Michael Frisby
Competition	Rebecca Homes-Siedle
Corporate	Richard Baxter
E-Commerce, IT & IP	Nick Fieldhouse
Employment	Paul Lambdin
Family/Matrimonial	Caroline Gordon-Smith
Insolvency	Paul Lambdin
Personal Injury	Janet Waine
Personal Tax & Trusts	Nick Acomb
Planning & Environment	Catherine Davey
Residential Property	Andrew Bussy
Sales & Marketing	Beverley Whittakers
Wills & Probate	Michael Hunter

THE FIRM: One of the South East's leading law firms, Stevens & Bolton has grown rapidly in the past five years and is one of the major firms in the region. Located in Guildford, the firm provides a high quality service to commercial and private clients across the UK and further afield. Stevens & Bolton has a long history dating back to 1873, but is very much looking to the future. In 2001, the firm's expertise is being consolidated under one roof, enhancing team co-ordination and management. Stevens & Bolton's main areas of expertise are corporate and commercial (including IT and intellectual property), commercial property (including planning and environment), business litigation, employment and private client services. Commercial clients range from fully listed plcs and major subsidiaries of international groups, to privately owned companies and an increasing number of e-businesses. Private clients are typically medium to high net worth individuals. Particular features of its approach include a high level of specialist skill; the strength in depth and individual discipline to respond swiftly; an emphasis on sound, practical advice aimed at achieving clients' commercial objectives; open, collaborative and friendly relationships with clients and a constructive approach with other lawyers; a continuing investment in technology, know-how and training to enhance the quality, effectiveness and value of its services.

PRINCIPAL AREAS OF WORK:
Company & Commercial: This department, described as 'pre-eminent in Guildford' in *Chambers Guide to the Legal Profession 2000-2001,* is experienced in corporate finance and transactional work, including acquisitions and disposals of companies and businesses, management buy-outs, company restructurings, venture and development capital and other business finance. A broad range of commercial matters is handled and the group has significant expertise in outsourcing, franchising, asset finance (including aviation), competition law and trading agreements. The intellectual property, IT and e-business practice is also flourishing, benefiting from the firm's location in the heart of this hi-tech region.
Commercial Property: Work handled includes acquisitions and disposals of freehold and leasehold properties, landlord and tenant work and the department represents European and overseas property investors, handling associated funding, development and security issues. 'Clearly punching above its weight, with a service which goes down well with clients' was how the department was described in a recent commercial property directory. The firm also enjoys an excellent reputation in the areas of planning and environment.
Commercial Litigation: Work involves predominantly UK and international contract disputes, including complex litigation in the IT and finance and leasing sectors. The commercial litigation department is also experienced in handling professional negligence claims; intellectual property disputes (primarily trademark

STEVENS & BOLTON
SOLICITORS

Continued overleaf

and copyright infringement); insurance matters; construction and civil engineering disputes; shareholder and partnership disputes; property related litigation (including landlord and tenant). The department uses ADR and arbitration to resolve disputes.

Debt Recovery: This is undertaken by the commercial recovery service and a specific cross-departmental team handles insolvency work.

Employment: This dedicated department handles a full range of contentious and non-contentious employment work.

Private Client: As well as advising on wills, probate and personal tax planning, the private client department handles a wide range of trust matters, both UK and offshore. These include employee benefit trusts and work for insurance and trust companies, as well as family trusts. A dedicated team handles family law matters, particularly complex financial cases with an international element. The department also deals with charities work for individuals and commercial organisations.

INTERNATIONAL: Work undertaken often includes an international dimension. Stevens & Bolton is a member of Eurolink, a major global network of associated law firms.

RECRUITMENT: It is now widely accepted by businesses that a visit to London is no longer essential in the search for high quality legal advice. Stevens & Bolton is always seeking to recruit high quality lawyers for varying roles within the firm. If you are interested in finding out about a stimulating career with Stevens & Bolton, please contact the managing partner, contact details above.

STEWARTS

63 Lincoln's Inn Fields, London, WC2A 3LW
Tel: (020) 7242 6462 **Fax:** (020) 7831 6843 **DX:** 369 London
Email: info@stewarts-solicitors.co.uk **Website:** www.stewarts-solicitors.co.uk

Managing Partner	John Cahill
Number of partners	11
Assistant solicitors	8
Other fee-earners	9

AREAS OF PRACTICE

Personal Injury & Clinical Negligence ..70%
Commercial Litigation ..20%
Non-Contentious ..10%

CONTACTS

Commercial Litigation ..Jack Leonard
Non-Contentious ..Chris Horspool
Personal Injury & Clinical Negligence
..John Cahill
..Kevin Grealis

THE FIRM: This medium sized London based firm was founded in 1989. Whilst being well known for its litigation practice (personal injury, clinical negligence, commercial litigation and professional negligence), it is also active in non-contentious matters for a wide range of clients. The firm's philosophy has been to develop focused teams in specialist areas. It provides the quality of service commonly associated with much larger firms at a cost which is highly competitive. All client matters are handled or supervised by a partner with the relevant expertise. The partners seek pragmatic and cost effective solutions to their clients' problems. It is a forward thinking, expanding firm with international contacts delivering a high quality of service to clients.

PRINCIPAL AREAS OF WORK:

Personal Injury/Clinical Negligence: In the past twelve months there has been significant growth in the personal injury and clinical negligence departments, both of which have legal aid franchises and are acknowledged leaders in their fields. The focus on claims of the utmost severity (particularly brain and spinal injuries) continues although further niche areas are developing, including abuse litigation, US travel claims and child injury. Multi-party work is also undertaken by the personal injury department which was awarded a multi-party franchise in March 2000. Claims currently being undertaken include Ladbroke Grove, Kenya Airways, Nwala coach crash, Trilucent breast implants and Firestone Tyres.

Commercial Litigation: The commercial litigation department handles a broad range of work including commercial disputes requiring urgent interim relief. The partners have particular expertise in professional negligence claims, insolvency and regulatory work, banking (including the enforcement of securities) and insurance litigation on behalf of Lloyds syndicates.

Non-Contentious: The firm maintains a significant non-contentious client following acting for individuals, private companies, charities, banks and other financial institutions.

Alternative Dispute Resolution: Stewarts are committed to alternative dispute resolution procedures and four partners are now accredited mediators.

INTERNATIONAL: The firm is a founder member of a worldwide network of lawyers and receives regular instructions from foreign lawyers.

STIBBE

66 Gresham Street, London, EC2V 7PP
Tel: (020) 7600 4400 **Fax:** (020) 7600 4411
Email: info@stibbe.co.uk **Website:** www.stibbe.com

Senior Partner	Jeroen Fleming

AREAS OF PRACTICE

Banking, Finance,& Securities	50%
Mergers & Acquisitions	45%
Miscellaneous	5%

CONTACTS

All Areas	Jeroen Fleming

THE FIRM: The firm operates as a truly multinational partnership of Dutch, Belgian and French lawyers. The history of the constituent parts of the firm goes back to the beginning of the century. The firm has well over 100 partners and 450 fee earners. It is one of the leading law firms in each of its three home jurisdictions.

PRINCIPAL AREAS OF WORK: The firm is a full service law firm with an internationally-oriented general commercial practice, and special emphasis on mergers and acquisitions, banking, securities, corporate and structured finance, project finance, real estate, telecommunications, intellectual and industrial property, environmental law, administrative law, insolvency, litigation and arbitration. The firm distinguishes itself from many other large law firms in Continental Europe because of its specialised tax practice.

INTERNATIONAL: The firm has its principal offices in Amsterdam, Brussels and Paris with a branch office in New York.

S

STIKEMAN ELLIOTT

Regis House, 45 King William Street, London, EC4R 9AN
Tel: (020) 7648 1300 **Fax:** (020) 7648 1400
Email: counsel@lon.stikeman.com **Website:** www.stikeman.com

Managing Partner (London)	Philip Henderson
Number of partners (London)	3
Number of lawyers (London)	10

CONTACTS

London	Philip Henderson

STIKEMAN ELLIOTT

THE FIRM: Stikeman Elliott is a leading international law firm based in Canada with an established and active practice in the City of London. The London office was established in 1969 and currently has over 20 staff, including 10 lawyers of Canadian and English qualification. The firm maintains offices in Montreal, Toronto, Ottawa, Calgary and Vancouver and, outside Canada, in London, New York, Hong Kong and Sydney.

PRINCIPAL AREAS OF WORK: International corporate finance; capital markets; banking and derivative products; mergers and acquisitions; privatisation; infrastructure and project finance; international taxation; political risk planning.

CLIENTELE: Banks; investment banks; multinational corporations; investment managers; pension funds; private equity investors.

STONE KING

13 Queen Square, Bath, BA1 2HJ
Tel: (01225) 337599 **Fax:** (01225) 335437 **DX:** 8001 Bath
Email: admin@stoneking.co.uk

39 Cloth Fair, London, EC1A 7JQ
Tel: (020) 7796 1007 **Fax:** (020) 7796 1017

Senior Partner	Michael King
Number of partners	11
Assistant solicitors	15
Other fee-earners	10

AREAS OF PRACTICE

Commercial & Charities	40%
Private Client Litigation	33%
Private Client	27%

THE FIRM: Established in 1785, Stone King has a substantial commercial and private client practice in the West Country, where its strengths are in the fields of commercial property, employment and commercial litigation, family and matrimonial, crime and trusts. It has a leading national reputation for its charity and education work, and has a London office to service clients in those sectors as well as its London-based commercial clients.

CLIENTELE: The firm's work is divided between private clients and, in the commercial sphere, medium-sized businesses, schools, colleges, other large charities, and landed estates. It also provides specialist assistance in commercial litigation and employment to major national and international companies.

STONES

Linacre House, Southernhay Gardens, Exeter, EX1 1UG
Tel: (01392) 666 777 **Fax:** (01392) 666 770 **DX:** 8306 Exeter
Email: mail@stones-solicitors.co.uk **Website:** www.stones-solicitors.co.uk

21 Fore Street, Okehampton, EX20 1AJ
Tel: (01837) 650 200 **Fax:** (01837) 650 201 **DX:** 82500 Okehampton
Email: mail@stones-solicitors.co.uk

14 South Street, Torrington, EX38 8AF
Tel: (01805) 623 725 **Fax:** (01805) 624 040 **DX:** 140192 Great Torrington
Email: mail@stones-solicitors.co.uk

13 Bampton Street, Tiverton, EX16 6AA
Tel: (01884) 259 660 **Fax:** (01884) 259 661 **DX:** 49015 Tiverton
Email: mail@stones-solicitors.co.uk

Garden Cottage, 12 Middle Street, Taunton, TA1 1SH
Tel: (01823) 323 440 **Fax:** (01823) 335 206
Email: mail@stones-solicitors.co.uk

Senior Partner	Hugh Winterbotham
Managing Partner	Bronwen Courtenay-Stamp
Number of partners	21
Associates	3
Assistant solicitors	14
Other fee-earners	12
Total number of staff in 5 offices	130

AREAS OF PRACTICE

Property	26%
Trusts & Probate	19%
PI	18%
Family (inc. Crime)	14%
Commercial	12%
Commercial Litigation	11%

CONTACTS

Agriculture	Paul Tucker
Charity Law	Helen Honeyball
Childcare	David Howell-Richardson
Commercial Litigation	Paul Keeling
Commercial Property	Christopher Rundle
Company/Commercial	Tony Lloyd
Crime	Peter Seigne
	Zara Svensson
Defence Insurers	Robin Challans
Employment	Kate Gardener
Family	David Howell-Richardson
Housing Association	Nick Dyer
Insolvency	Paul Keeling
Leisure/Timeshare	Tim Bourne
Mental Health (Tiverton & Taunton)	Jim Elliott
Plaintiff Personal Injury	James Browne
Planning & Development	Hugh Winterbotham
Property Landlord/Tenant (Okehampton & Torrington offices)	Philip Bailey
	John Dobie
Residential Property	Mike Giles
	Shirley Parsons
Skiing & Travel Personal Injury	Bronwen Courtenay-Stamp
Wills/Trusts/Probate/Tax	Mike Harris
	Helen Honeyball

THE FIRM: Stones is one of the largest practices in Exeter with a strong presence in Okehampton and an office in Torrington. The firm provides a range of services to both private and corporate clients. The firm was established early in the century and has a progressive outlook, with all offices linked by modern communications systems. It has a community legal service franchise and has been awarded the Law Society's Family Lawyers scheme. On 25 May Stones merged with James Elliott, acquiring offices in Tiverton and Taunton. After nearly 80 years at Northernhay Place, Stones combined the two Exeter offices and moved on 2 June 2001 under one roof to prestigious new modern offices at Linacre House, Southernhay Gardens, Exeter. The new offices comprise 12,500 sq ft on four floors and after an extensive refurbishment programme will provide first class modern premises excellently situated right in the middle of the Exeter business community. Stones was also presented with the Lexcel award in February 2001. Stones are the very first firm in Okehampton and Torrington to be awarded this prestigious accreditation and one of only three firms in Exeter.

PRINCIPAL AREAS OF WORK: The firm has a particularly strong private client and commercial base in the West Country covering private client property development and planning, commercial, commercial litigation, personal injury, employment law, family, trust and probate, criminal, mental health work and marine law. It is known regionally and nationally for its timeshare, housing association, personal injury claims with a speciality in international ski law and holiday claims. The firm's niche areas are:

Housing Associations: The firm has expertise in site acquisition throughout the South and South West and also covers shared ownership schemes; HAMA and Care in the Community schemes with local authorities and health trusts; funding of housing schemes; repossession work.

Personal Injury: With four members on the Personal Injury panel and one also a member of FOIL (the Forum of Insurance Lawyers), the department has longstanding experience of this type of work with particular specialisation in international skiing law, holiday claims and defence litigation for major insurers.

Timeshare: This department acts for some of the leading timeshare development companies, owners' committees and funders, and also advises other countries on compliance with international regulations.

Marine Law: This is a new niche area for Stones. The team leader is a marine specialist who is recognised in the South West as a leading individual for yacht and small craft matters. She has been a solicitor for 21 years, working in the Solent and London areas before relocating to Devon.

Mental Health: A new niche area for Stones. The team leader has been a member of the Law Society Mental Health Review tribunal panel since 1988. This has enabled him to conduct applications to the tribunal and before Parole Board Discretionary Lifer panels. Since the LSC Civil Contracts came into force in the year 2000 his workload has increased to the extent that he dealt with over 90 new cases in the following twelve months. As a rule he will either see or, as a last resort, advise over the telephone, any client within 24 hours of a referral.

Family: The firm has a strong growing family team with representation on the Children panel. It is also a member of the Relate Quality Partnership. The team leader specialises in childcare and the firm is a member of the Law Society's new Family Lawyers scheme.

Development & Planning: This department acts for a number of developers dealing with site acquisition, planning, service agreements and site sales. The team leader acts on a regular basis for landowners looking to co-operate in promoting their land for development. This involves option agreements with development companies, joint venture agreements between the land owners and the schemes involved in both residential and retail development.

INTERNATIONAL: Stones is a member of OTE, with one member of the firm on the committee. Work is handled in French, German, Maltese, Spanish and Tagalog (Philippines).

RECRUITMENT: 2001 saw four new partners added to the list. Mike Giles, a specialist in conveyancing, joined in February 2001 from another local firm. He has been in Exeter for many years and is a very experienced property lawyer. Mrs Shirley Parsons, also a specialist in residential conveyancing, and Zara Svensson, a specialist in criminal defence work and a recognised leader in her field, were both made up to partner from associate in April 2001. Jim Elliott of James Elliott, Tiverton & Taunton joined as a partner, following the merger with James Elliott in May 2001. James specialises in mental health work and has been on the Law Society's Mental Health Review tribunal panel since 1988. New associates in 2001 were Robert Mitchell in the probate department and Clive Williamson in the Okehampton office specialising in litigation work.

STRINGER SAUL

17 Hanover Square, London, W1S 1HU
Tel: (020) 7917 8500 **Fax:** (020) 7917 8555 **DX:** 82984 Mayfair
Email: law@stringersaul.co.uk **Website:** www.stringersaul.co.uk

Managing Partner	Norman Ziman
Number of partners	13
Assistant solicitors	12
Other fee-earners	1

AREAS OF PRACTICE

Company/Commercial	55%
Intellectual Property	13%
General Commercial Litigation	11%
Property	11%
Employment	8%
Tax	2%

CONTACTS

Commercial Property & Planning	Bill Harrup
Company/Commercial	June Paddock
	David Smith
E-Commerce	Allistair Booth
Employment	Ruth Hickling
General Commercial Litigation	Martin Russell
IP & IT	Gary Howes
Mergers & Acquisitions	David Smith
	Nigel Gordon
Pharmaceuticals & Biotechnology	Gary Howes
Property	Bill Harrup
Publishing	Norman Ziman
Reconstruction & Recovery	David Smith
Secured Lending	Martin Ackland
Taxation	Paul Yerbury

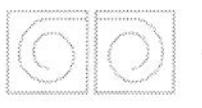
STRINGER SAUL

THE FIRM: Stringer Saul is a general commercial law firm with a number of specialisms. A major focus is advising 'knowledge-based' businesses. As such it acts for many clients involved in intellectual property, for example in the pharma/biotech, publishing and IT sectors. Work conducted for these organisations however, is much broader than IP advice alone; one third of the firm's business is company/commercial work, nearly 20% litigation and 15% property.

PRINCIPAL AREAS OF WORK: The main areas of work are commercial property and planning; corporate advice including insolvency, reconstruction and recovery; corporate finance; mergers and acquisitions; employment; general commercial litigation; e-commerce; intellectual property and information technology (contentious and non-contentious); pharmaceuticals and biotechnology; publishing; secured lending; taxation.

CLIENTELE: The firm's clients range from multinational public companies to small owner managed businesses, including companies in the pharmaceutical and biotechnology sectors, e-commerce, finance, leisure, publishing, the media, property and mining. It currently acts for around 20 plcs across a range of business sectors, including: Celltech Medeva, e-capital investments, The Evolution Group, Nycomed-Amersham, Probus Estates, SmithKline Beecham, SkyePharma and Wolters Kluwer. The firm typically has very long-standing relationships with clients – many reaching back to its very beginnings. Because the firm is committed to its focus on knowledge-based businesses, there is true value to clients in the advice they receive across the full range of commercial legal disciplines – from corporate finance to patents.

INTERNATIONAL: Stringer Saul regularly acts for clients overseas and has long standing relationships with a number of European and US lawyers and accountants with whom the partners work on a regular basis. Work is also handled in German, Russian and Hebrew.

STRONACHS

34 Albyn Place, Aberdeen, AB10 1FW
Tel: (01224) 845845 **Fax:** (01224) 845800 **DX:** Aberdeen AB 41
Email: info@stronachs.co.uk **Website:** www.stronachs.co.uk

Managing Partner	Stephen Park
Managing Partner	David Sheach
Number of partners	19
Assistant solicitors	17
Other fee-earners	18

THE FIRM: Stronachs can trace its roots back to the 1850s in Aberdeen but its main corporate division was formed almost a decade ago and has now grown to include 19 partners (8 of which do company commercial work) and 35 fee earners. Due to the nature of the oil and gas industry, which it heavily represents, a lot of the firm's deals tend to have an international element. For the past few years the firm has held and hosted external annual conferences on current business and legal topics. The firm also have a large private client department which specialises in executories, trust work and an element of personal tax planning as well as a residential division which specialises in the sale and purchase of properties and financial services. The commercial property department is also a growth area for the firm. It is involved in construction projects, licensing, planning and acting for both landlords and tenants in terms of commercial leases.

PRINCIPAL AREAS OF WORK: The main areas of the practice are in corporate commercial work, including corporate finance, commercial, oil and gas, intellectual property and employment and the firm also has an established and growing commercial property unit and court unit. Stronachs has a strong presence acting for entrepeneurs and management teams. It has specialist teams advising third generation upstream oil and gas companies, companies in the oil and gas service sector aside, an employment unit and an intellectual property unit giving a wide range of advice to new technology companies. Stronachs is also active in the food industry which includes fish processors, agricultural merchants and other food processing businesses. Stronachs have Scots, English and Australian qualified lawyers in their team as well as multi-disciplinary personnel including accountants, insurance brokers and financial consultants.

Continued overleaf

S

RECRUITMENT: The firm has an ongoing policy of actively growing their business and recruitment both at a trainee and assistant level. They currently offer 2-3 traineeship a year.

STURTIVANT & CO

17 Bulstrode St, London, W1U 2JH
Tel: (020) 7486 9524 **Fax:** (020) 7224 3164
Email: visas@sturtivant.co.uk

Number of partners	1
Assistant solicitors	1

AREAS OF PRACTICE

UK Immigration, Nationality Law & Work Permits	100%

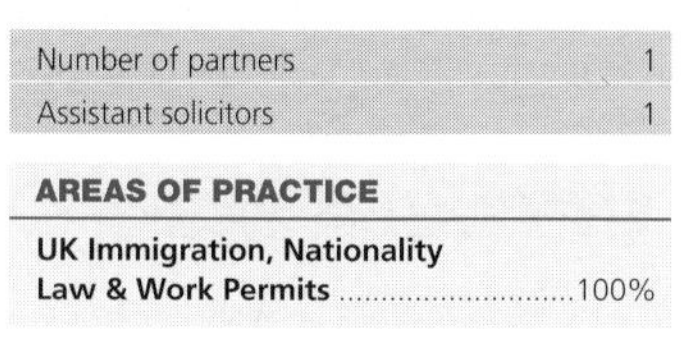

THE FIRM: Established in 1985, and well-known as a specialist practice which is devoted exclusively to UK immigration law. The principal, Karen Sturtivant, is an active member of various professional associations concerned with immigration law and she regularly lectures and gives seminars on this subject.

PRINCIPAL AREAS OF WORK: All types of immigration work undertaken; primarily client representation for work permits, business residence, investor status and other residence categories. Also settlement; extension of stay; visitors, students and temporary stay. Appeals to Adjudicators and Tribunals; Judicial Review and deportation and removal cases.
Additional Areas: Nationality and citizenship problems.

CLIENTELE: Wide corporate and private client base.

INTERNATIONAL: Contacts with immigration lawyers in many other jurisdictions.

S

SUGARÉ & CO

36 Park Square, Leeds, LS1 2NY **Tel:** (0113) 244 6978 **Fax:** (0113) 245 5708 **Ptnrs:** 2 **Asst solrs:** 2 **Other fee-earners:** 6

STUDIO LEGALE SUTTI

19 Princes St, London, W1B 2LW
Tel: (020) 7409 1384 **Fax:** (020) 7409 1384
Email: london@sutti.com **Website:** www.sutti.com

Managing Partner	Stefano Sutti
Office Contact	Livia Oglio
Worldwide	
Number of partners	11
Other fee-earners	48

AREAS OF PRACTICE

Commercial/Company	45%
Intellectual Property/Competition	35%
Employment	20%

THE FIRM: Studio Legale Sutti was established in Milan in 1952 and its activity is organised across three main departments: commercial and company law, intellectual property and competition, and employment law.
London Office: The aim of Studio Legale Sutti's presence in London is that of offering a full range of prompt and efficient on-site legal services regarding Italian and Bulgarian law and jurisdiction. In this respect, the SLS operation in the UK would like to be viewed as a barrister-like practice – fully backed by the combined resources and know-how of its Italian and Bulgarian offices to which it is connected through a high-speed encrypted link – with the purpose of serving British law firms, patent and trademarks agents and corporate counsel for their clients' and employers' needs related to Italy and Bulgaria.

PRINCIPAL AREAS OF WORK: The firm covers the following areas of specialisation: company law; commercial contracts; international contracts; international tax law; M&A; joint ventures; foreign investments; agency and franchise arrangements; EU law; competition law; financial and banking law; debt collection; insolvency; environmental law; construction law; product liability; IT and TLC law; entertainment law; maritime law; commercial litigation and arbitration; white collar crime; administrative law; intellectual property advice and litigation; industrial models and design; licence negotiation; technology transfer; advertising law; pharmaceuticals; patent and trade mark agency service; labour law; employment law; employer's liability; industrial relations and pensions law.

INTERNATIONAL: The firm's main office is situated in Milan. Other offices are located in Rome, Genoa, Sofia and Tokyo.

SWEPSTONE WALSH

9 Lincoln's Inn Fields, London, WC2A 3BP **Tel:** (020) 7404 1499 **Fax:** (020) 7404 1493 **DX:** 142 **Ptnrs:** 4 **Asst solrs:** 4 **Other fee-earners:** 3

TARLO LYONS

Watchmaker Court, 33 St. John's Lane, London, EC1M 4DB
Tel: (020) 7405 2000 **Fax:** (020) 7814 9421 **DX:** 53323 Clerkenwell
Email: info@tarlolyons.com **Website:** www.tarlolyons.com

Managing Partner	Nigel McEwen
Number of partners	24
Assistant solicitors	27
Other fee-earners	13

AREAS OF PRACTICE

Technology & Communications	40%
Dispute Resolution	25%
Property	16%
Commercial	15%
Entertainment	4%

CONTACTS

Commercial	Kevin Barrow
Dispute Resolution	Nick Arnold
Employment	Warren Foot
Entertainment	D Michael Rose
Property	Philip Diamond
Technology & Communications	Lawrence Phillips

tarlo lyons

THE FIRM: Tarlo Lyons is recognised as one of the leading law firms in the country for its expertise in information technology and related areas. The development of Dealmaker, the firm's automated intelligent document generation system, demonstrates its ability to innovate and to embrace change in the legal marketplace. Over the past five years, Tarlo Lyons has transformed itself from a general commercial practice by pursuing a strategy of developing niche areas of expertise and specialist knowledge of particular business sectors. The firm now has one of the largest teams of dedicated technology lawyers in England. With its focus on technology and communications, nearly two-thirds of the firm's turnover now derives from IT, telecommunications and Internet-related clients, including e-commerce. The firm has expanded at 30% per annum over the past three years. Tarlo Lyons has continued to recruit lawyers in all areas of its practice over the past 12 months and, in particular, has attracted senior lawyers from big City firms.

PRINCIPAL AREAS OF WORK:

Technology: The technology and communications practice now numbers more than 25 lawyers including seven partners. Areas of expertise include Internet and e-commerce; global IT procurement and supply arrangements; outsourcing; software and data licensing; intellectual property including designs and trademarks; electronic data interchange; data protection.

Media: Entertainment and media is another strength of the firm, which has among its client list arguably the world's leading theatre producer and a leading film financier. A dedicated team of lawyers provides advice on all aspects of the film, theatre and television industries. Digital technology is taking the entertainment industry into new distribution channels and the firm is well placed to advise clients by combining expertise in entertainment and media with its leading reputation in IT.

Company/Commercial: The firm's company and commercial lawyers are experienced in advising on corporate finance, mergers and acquisitions, business start-ups, company re-organisations and all kinds of commercial agreements. The team has particular expertise in capital-raising and flotations of Internet and IT-related businesses and has an 'equity for fees' scheme for promising hi-tech start-up companies. Advice is also available on EU and UK competition law, intellectual property licensing and for companies in financial difficulties and receivership. Outsourcing of internal functions such as IT or HR, and advising recruitment companies, are significant areas of work.

Commercial Property: The firm's expertise in commercial property encompasses specialised areas including theatres, hotels, retail and business parks, shopping centres, betting and gaming establishments and other leisure premises. Work undertaken includes investment, acquisitions and disposals, landlord and tenant, portfolio acquisitions and sales, finance and funding, site assembly, development and planning, environmental issues and property-related disputes.

ADR: The firm's dispute resolution practice includes a number of specialist areas of expertise in addition to dealing with general commercial disputes. These are: IT/intellectual property, gaming and licensing, tax investigations (mainly defendant), and fraud – including confiscation of assets on behalf of the authorities, insolvencies and corporate recovery.

Employment: Advice on all kinds of employment matters, including disputes, is available and ranges from contracts, service agreements, EU and UK employment law, and collective agreements to all types of discrimination, unfair or constructive dismissals, and tribunals.

CLIENTELE: The firm has a broad and balanced spread of clients, from banks and insurance companies to IT and Internet companies, film financiers and one of the world's largest theatrical producers. Whatever the nature and size of clients' businesses, the firm believes in developing a thorough understanding of clients' commercial priorities in order to provide the right advice. Tarlo Lyons is the co-ordinating member and UK representative of euroITcounsel®, a quality circle of European lawyers that advises on legal issues affecting IT and telecommunications clients in Europe.

TAYLOR JOYNSON GARRETT

Carmelite, 50 Victoria Embankment, Blackfriars, London, EC4Y 0DX
Tel: (020) 7300 7000 **Fax:** (020) 7300 7100 **DX:** 41 London
Email: enquiries@tjg.co.uk **Website:** www.tjg.co.uk

Managing Partner	Declan Tarpey
Senior Partner	Richard Marsh
Number of partners	90
Assistant solicitors	139
Other fee-earners	65

AREAS OF PRACTICE

Corporate	26%
Intellectual Property	21%
Dispute Resolution	17%
Commercial Property	13%
Finance & Projects	9%
Private Client	7%
Employment	7%

CONTACTS

Banking	Rodney Dukes
Central/Eastern Europe	Simon Dayes
Commercial Property	John Whitfield
Construction	Christopher Bourgeois
	Peter Shaw
Corporate Finance	Gordon Jackson
	Tim Stocks
Corporate Tax	Peter Jackson
Corporate/Commercial	Tim Eyles
Dispute Resolution	Neil White
Employment	Andrew Granger
Entertainment/Multimedia	Paul Mitchell
Environment & Planning	Alison Askwith
European Union/Competition	Martin Baker
Insolvency	Michael Frawley
Insurance/Reinsurance	Peter Kempe
Intellectual Property	Charles Lloyd
Inward Investment	David Kent
IT/E-commerce/Internet	Glyn Morgan
Life Sciences	Simon Cohen
	David Kent
London Stock Exchange	Tim Eyles
	Tim Stocks
Pharmaceutical	Mark Hodgson
Professional Indemnity	Clare Ferguson
Projects & PFI	Declan Tarpey
Rail	Jane McKee
Shipping	James Sleightholme
Tax & Personal Planning	Philippa Blake-Roberts
	Michael Stanford-Tuck
Telecommunications/Broadcast	John Edwards
	Edward Mercer

THE FIRM: Taylor Joynson Garrett is a premier, full service law firm based in London and recognised as a market leader in many of its practice areas such as technology, intellectual property, corporate finance for fast growth companies and inward investment from the US. Constructive, commercial advice through a partner-led service with a total, long-term commitment to its clients around the world – these are the firm's hallmarks.

PRINCIPAL AREAS OF WORK:

Corporate: This highly regarded department deals with international and domestic work, with particular expertise in mergers and acquisitions, tax, inward investment, PFI and EU law issues. It acts for a varied client base including public companies, banks and other financial institutions, management teams, private companies and venture capitalists.

Intellectual Property: TJG's IP department is one of the largest in Europe and is recognised as a leader in this field. It deals with contentious and non-contentious work, including patent litigation, trade marks, industrial design, passing off and trade libel. An experienced and respected sector-focused group, forged from the firm's IP and corporate departments, deals with the advances in digital media, e-commerce, Internet, IT and telecoms, advising and protecting inventors, investors, manufacturers, suppliers and users.

Finance & Projects: Lawyers in this department provide an integrated service acting for banks and sponsors in relation to all types of debt financing and in particular international project finance transactions. The department's product range includes all types of debt, security, trade finance and securitisation instruments. Industry specialisations include property, transport, telecoms and energy.

Commercial Property: The firm offers a range of services incorporating specialist planning, property management and environmental teams, meeting the differing needs of trading companies, developers, finance institutions and national and international investors. The firm's dedicated rail practice group adopts a multi-disciplinary approach to meet the needs of businesses active in the rail industry, including development companies.

Dispute Resolution: This department handles a wide variety of commercial litigation and arbitration matters and incorporates particular strengths in construction, banking, fraud, property, insolvency and insurance. In particular the specialised construction and engineering group assists clients to achieve their commercial objectives through drafting of documents to protect their interests, support and assistance in maintaining the smooth running of projects, and if necessary the pursuit or defence of claims in court or arbitration.

Employment: This specialist department handles a wide variety of employment related matters including pensions and employee benefits together with increasingly complex legal relationships both domestically and internationally.

Private Client: The firm's long standing and well respected private client department provides advice on taxation, wills and settlements (including trusts and estates), matrimonial law and residential property.

TAYLOR NICHOL

3 Station Place, London, N4 2DH **Tel:** (020) 7272 8336 **Fax:** (020) 7281 9148 **DX:** 57453 Finsbury Park. **Ptnrs:** 2 **Asst solrs:** 3 **Other fee-earners:** 2

TAYLORS

Rawlings House, Exchange Street, Blackburn, BB1 7JN **Tel:** (01254) 563333 **Fax:** (01254) 682146 **Email:** taylors@taylaw.co.uk **Website:** www.taylaw.co.uk **Ptnrs:** 4 **Asst solrs:** 7 **Other fee-earners:** 2

TAYLOR VINTERS

Merlin Place, Milton Rd, Cambridge, CB4 0DP
Tel: (01223) 423444 **Fax:** (01223) 423486 **DX:** 122892 Cambridge 4
Email: info@taylorvinters.com **Website:** www.taylorvinters.com

Managing Partner	Christine Berry
Number of partners	22
Assistant solicitors	48
Other fee-earners	15

CONTACTS

Bloodstock	Rachel Flynn
Clinical Negligence	Sarah Philbrook
Commercial Litigation	Edward Perrott
Commercial Property	Steven Beach
Company & Commercial	John Short
Corporate Finance	John Short
Family & Matrimonial	Jackie Wells
Personal Injury	Paul Tapner
Planning, Development & Construction	Philip Kratz

THE FIRM: As one of the largest law firms in East Anglia, Taylor Vinters has a reputation for quality legal services to the commercial sector. The University of Cambridge is just one of a number of substantial institutional clients. Taylor Vinters' main strength lies in the firm's extensive experience with high-technology industries.

PRINCIPAL AREAS OF WORK:

Corporate & Commercial: Acquisitions; disposals; MBOs; joint ventures; venture capital funding; construction; employment; insolvency; intellectual property; and commercial litigation.

Commercial Property: Investment sales and purchases; landlord and tenant; large scale sales and purchases; development planning; agricultural and environmental law.

Rural Business Services: Encompasses the wide range of rural-based business activity undertaken for food processors, farmers, estates, institutions and related organisations. The firm has a national reputation for bloodstock and equestrian work.
Other Specialisms: Claimant personal injury, charities and private client.

CONTACTS

Private Client	Jocelyn Fox
Rural Services	Adrian Horwood-Smart

TEACHER STERN SELBY

37-41 Bedford Row, London, WC1R 4JH
Tel: (020) 7242 3191 **Fax:** (020) 7242 1156 **DX:** 177 Ch.Ln.
Email: contact@tsslaw.com **Website:** www.tsslaw.com

Managing Partner	Graham Shear
Number of partners	16
Assistant solicitors	18
Other fee-earners	6

AREAS OF PRACTICE

Commercial Property	37%
Commercial Litigation	30%
Company & Commercial	20%
Secured Lending	8%
Personal Injury/Education/ Judicial Review	3%
Residential Conveyancing/Probate	2%

CONTACTS

Commercial Litigation	Jack Rabinowicz
Commercial Property	Stuart Stern
	Russell Raphael
Corporate/Investment	David Salisbury
Education	Jack Rabinowicz
Entertainment	Graham Shear
General Commercial	David Salisbury
	David Teacher
IT/IP E-Commerce	Martine Nathan
IT/IP Litigation	Colin Richman
Media Companies	David Teacher
Media Litigation	Graham Shear
Medical Negligence	Jack Rabinowicz
Secured Lending	Philip Berry

THE FIRM: A central London-based general commercial firm, with clientele and caseload normally attributed to much larger firms. It has a wide range of contacts overseas.

PRINCIPAL AREAS OF WORK:
Commercial Property: Work includes acquisitions and disposals for developers, investors, landlords and tenants. Secured lending and the drafting of security documentation (acting for banks and building societies) are also handled, as is every aspect of landlord and tenant work.
Company/Commercial: The department is active in the corporate sector, handling takeovers, mergers, joint ventures, MBOs and disposals, demergers, reconstructions and asset sales. The firm also deals with employment law, intellectual property licences and confidentiality agreements. The firm has particular experience in IT, e-commerce and telecommunications contracts, oil exploration agreements and financing, PR and media law, entertainment law (music, film, TV, cable and multimedia), and in the pharmaceutical industry.
Litigation: Primarily in the commercial field, especially banking, insolvency and finance house matters and in particular commodities related litigation and arbitration, together with commercial property litigation. The firm also specialises in medical negligence and personal injury cases, and has a national reputation in the field of education law. The firm has considerable experience in media and entertainment litigation.
Other Areas: The firm gives specialist tax planning advice and has substantial experience in the formation and use of foreign trusts and offshore corporate entities to produce the most efficient tax structure to suit individual circumstances. A full range of private client services from residential conveyancing to wills, trusts, probate and estate administration is also provided.

CLIENTELE: Primarily from the finance, commercial property, IT, corporate and entertainment fields, and also corporate and business clients from Canada, Israel and Eastern Europe. The firm also has excellent links with accountants, banks, financial institutions, and surveyors and has wide-ranging legal contacts overseas.

INTERNATIONAL: Languages spoken include Afrikaans, Arabic, Chinese (Mandarin), French, German, Hebrew, Italian, Russian, Serbo-Croat and Spanish.

THANKI NOVY TAUBE

The Mews, 1A Birkenhead Street, London, WC1H 8NB
Tel: (020) 7833 5800 **Fax:** (020) 7833 5805 **DX:** 37900 Kings Cross
Email: info@tntlaw.co.uk **Website:** www.tntlaw.co.uk

Number of partners	6
Assistant solicitors	8
Other fee-earners	6

CONTACTS

Extraditions/Human Rights	Girish Thanki
General Crime & Appellate	Rod Novy
White Collar Crime	Martin Taube
Civil Actions	Harriet Wistrich
Prison Law	Vicky King

THE FIRM: The firm specialises in the criminal litigation field and the civil liberties area and has considerable experience of handling complex and weighty cases, often with a forensic element.Recent work includes a large number of murder cases (including slow-burn provocation cases); extraditions to the USA, Sweden and Italy; serious frauds; armed robberies; serious assault cases. The firm acts for Manjit Kaur Basuta (the British nanny in California) in the baby battering case. Martin Taube appears regularly on the Jimmy Young show on Radio 2 to advise on legal matters. Girish Thanki is a member of the Law Society's Task Force on implementation of the Human Rights Act 1998. The firm has a strong commitment to excellence and a quality-driven approach. A networked computer system is used for file management, costing and diary systems. The firm provides high quality training to all its staff. It organises conferences in a number of subject areas. Legal Aid rates apply. For private clients charges vary from £150 per hour upwards depending on degree of expertise required.

PRINCIPAL AREAS OF WORK: Work includes criminal litigation; civil liberties; criminal work (comprising white collar crime, murder, child abuse, armed robbery); customs and excise cases; general first division crime. It also has specialist knowledge of extradition law. It has substantial experience of appellate work and it deals routinely with judicial reviews and has specialisation in prison law. It has a specialist department dealing with civil actions against the police and the Home Office. It deals with a large number of inquests. The firm has particular expertise in police station representation and offers 24 hours, seven days service to a detained person. It accepts instructions for advocacy in central London Magistrates' Courts.

CLIENTELE: This is mostly legal aid but with a growing private client base.

THE BERKSON GLOBE PARTNERSHIP

27 Dale Street, 4th Floor, Dale House, Liverpool, L2 2HD **Tel:** (0151) 236 1234 **Fax:** (0151) 236 5678 **Ptnrs:** 3 **Asst solrs:** 1 **Other fee-earners:** 3

THEODORE GODDARD

150 Aldersgate Street, London, EC1A 4EJ
Tel: (020) 7606 8855 **Fax:** (020) 7606 4390 **DX:** 47 London Chancery Lane WC2
Email: info@theodoregoddard.co.uk **Website:** www.theodoregoddard.com

Managing Partner	Peter Cooke
Senior Partner	Paddy Grafton Green
Number of partners	68
Assistant solicitors	95
Other fee-earners	44
Total staff	354

AREAS OF PRACTICE

Corporate/Corporate Finance	32%
Property	20%
Media/IP	18%
Banking & Finance	10%
Litigation	8%
Corporate Tax	6%
Employment	6%

CONTACTS

Advertising	Rupert Earle
Arbitration & ADR	Peter Fitzpatrick
Asset Finance	James Ballingall
Aviation	Rory MacCarthy
Banking & Finance	Nigel West
Collective Investment Schemes	Simon Goodworth
Commercial Litigation	John Kelleher
Commercial Property	Mark Gilbert
Construction	Clive Lovatt
Corporate	Graham Stedman
Corporate Tax	Peter Sayer
EC/Competition	Guy Leigh
E-commerce	Paul Renney
Employment	Peter Cooke
Entertainment	Paddy Grafton Green
Environment	Claire Sheppard
Film/TV	Peter Armstrong
Insolvency	Julian Maples
Insurance	Jennifer Donohue
Intellectual Property	Hamish Porter
IT	Graham Stedman
Media Litigation	Martin Kramer
Music	Paddy Grafton Green
Pensions	Mark Catchpole
PFI	James Ballingall
Planning	Douglas Evans
Private Client	Jo Goldby
Property Finance	Jayesh Patel
Railways	William James
Telecommunications	Edward Pitt
Trade	Dan Horovitz

THE FIRM: Theodore Goddard is a major City law firm serving the business and financial communities, with particular emphasis on the banking and finance and the media and communications sectors. Theodore Goddard's aim is to provide clients with innovative, high quality, practical and speedy advice. Although London-based, Theodore Goddard operates worldwide through an office in Brussels and a network of international associates, including Klein-Goddard in Paris and TG Jersey.

PRINCIPAL AREAS OF WORK:

Banking & Finance: The firm advises on the full range of corporate and finance work, including mergers and acquisitions, management buy-outs and demergers, investment capital and new issues, including Stock Exchange flotations. It has an expanding practice in the field of collective investments, insurance and financial services regulation. The firm acts for a wide range of banks, borrowers, lessors and lessees, arrangers and airlines on general banking and asset finance transactions as well as on more specialist PFI, property, structured and tax driven financings. The firm has a strong record in insolvency and restructuring work. It also has a recognised practice in securities and corporate trust work. Its banking and finance team is led by a banker.

Tax: The firm deals with all tax issues connected with corporate finance work, including the development of tax-related financial instruments and asset finance packages; international tax planning; the tax aspects of takeovers, corporate reconstructions and demergers, management buy-outs and buy-ins; employee share schemes and other employee benefits; personal tax planning including, together with the associated firm in Jersey, the formation and administration of off-shore trusts and companies.

Media & Communications: The firm has a leading practice in the media and communications sector, concentrating on music, film, television, theatre and centred on its expertise in defamation law, newspapers, advertising and publishing; it also advises extensively on the issues relating to new media and information technology including e-commerce, computer games and on-line publishing. The convergence of businesses and technologies in these industries results in the continuous creation of new and complex legal problems, particularly in relation to the creation and exploitation of intellectual property rights and competition and regulatory issues.

Commercial Litigation: The firm has considerable expertise in commercial litigation, particularly in relation to the banking and securities sector; fraud and asset recovery; major contractual disputes; insurance and re-insurance; product liability, especially in the healthcare industry; arbitration and ADR.

Property: In the property field, the emphasis is on commercial and industrial sectors. Specialist groups handle public authority work, environmental law, planning and rating, construction and development, funding and investment, secured lending, property and construction litigation and retail and leisure transactions.

Other Areas: Other groups have excellent reputations in the fields of EC, competition and trade law, employment (both contentious and non-contentious) and pensions. The firm has an established practice in transport law, particularly in relation to aviation and railways.

INTERNATIONAL: Work is handled in Cantonese, French, German, Hebrew, Italian, Japanese and Spanish.

RECRUITMENT: The firm recruits around 20 trainee solicitors a year. A good degree (2:1 plus), which may or may not be in law, is necessary. The firm is looking for trainees with confidence, commitment and sound commercial sense. There is an extensive award-winning training and development programme covering all fee earners, from trainees to partners and including personal skills development, commercial management and business development training alongside legal training. The firm recruits with a view to retaining trainees who after qualification will go on to become partners with the firm. Tuition fees and a maintenance allowance are paid by the firm for both CPE and LPC. The firm runs a summer placement and open day programme. Details of these, along with the firm's brochure for training contracts and application forms, are available from the personnel department. Applications should be made to the recruitment manager

THEODORE GODDARD

THE LAW OFFICES OF RICHARD HEMMINGS LLM SOLICITOR

Sandy Lane, Barham, Ipswich, IP6 0PB **Tel:** 01473 833 844 **Fax:** 01473 833 230 **Email:** hemminga@dial.pipex.com **Website:** hemmings.co.uk

THOMAS A. HIGGINS & CO

Capital Buildings, 10 Seaview Road, Wallasey, L45 4LA **Tel:** (0151) 691 1211 **Fax:** (0151) 630 8007 **DX:** 20063 **Ptnrs:** 1 **Asst solrs:** 1

THOMAS COOPER & STIBBARD

Ibex House, 42-47 Minories, London, EC3N 1HA
Tel: (020) 7481 8851 **Fax:** (020) 7480 6097 **DX:** 548
Email: tcs@tcssol.com **Website:** www.tcssol.com

Managing Partner	Tim Goode
Senior Partner	David Hebden
Number of partners	16
Assistant solicitors	14
Other fee-earners	11

AREAS OF PRACTICE

Shipping (Admiralty, Maritime & Carriage)	60%
Business Finance & Insurance	20%
Commercial Litigation & International Arbitration	10%
Personal Injury	10%

CONTACTS

Banking	Grant Eldred
Commercial Litigation	Nick Green
Company Law	Stephen Swabey
Construction	Tim Goode
Environment	David Hebden
Insurance	Tim Goode
Personal Injury	John Strange
Property	Kate Harrison
Shipping & Maritime Law	David Hebden
	Tim Kelleher

THOMAS COOPER & STIBBARD

THE FIRM: Thomas Cooper & Stibbard was established in 1825 and specialises in commercial law, with a particular emphasis towards shipping and international trade. The firm offers advice to industrial, commercial and financial clients worldwide. Thomas Cooper & Stibbard has built strong, lasting relationships with clients, through a thorough understanding of the demands and developments of their different market places. The firm's client base is broadly international, with many of its multilingual lawyers travelling widely on client business. The firm has a branch office in Singapore which opened in 1996 and covers both admiralty and shipping work. The firm also has a strong presence in Greece, where it opened a branch office in March 1999, undertaking contentious and non-contentious work for clients. The firm is opening an office in Vancouver in the autumn of 2001. Heading it up will be a solicitor who has spent the last five years successfully developing the market in Singapore.

PRINCIPAL AREAS OF WORK:

Maritime: The firm's international reputation in shipping and marine insurance embraces the full range of P&I, FD&D and hull and machinery work covering charter parties, bills of lading, carriage of goods, cargo claims, containers, ship building and repair contracts, terminal and jetty damage, personal injuries, management disputes, multimodal carriage, sale and purchase, electronic shipping and trade documentation. The firm's admiralty specialists also handle casualties, salvage and towage, general average, fires and explosions, pollution, wreck removal and all areas of marine insurance and reinsurance. The firm has been instructed in connection with many of the major casualties of recent years, and the team leader is particularly well known for his work on crisis management. The firm operates a 24 hour emergency response service in respect of maritime related casualties. Thomas Cooper & Stibbard keep close links with specialist maritime lawyers in all major maritime centres worldwide with special emphasis in the Far East, Spain and South America, Scandinavia and Greece.

Personal Injury: The firm is very well known for marine personal injury work, acting in the main for P&I clubs and shipowners.

Company/Commercial: The firm's company and commercial department advises all types of UK and international businesses including public and private companies, partnerships and individuals. Particular areas of expertise include business start-ups, reorganisations, mergers and acquisitions, management buy-outs, corporate recovery, restructuring, Stock Exchange listings, venture capital commercial contracts, employment law, financial services, insolvency, property and commercial litigation.

CLIENTELE: The client base is strongly international and covers a broad spectrum including shipowners, charterers, banks, insurance companies, foreign governments and ministries, major oil companies, commodity traders and manufacturers.

INTERNATIONAL: Many of the firm's lawyers are fluent in several languages including Arabic, Bahasa (Malaysia and Indonesia), French, German, Greek, Italian, Mandarin, Portuguese and Spanish.

THOMAS EGGAR CHURCH ADAMS

76 Shoe Lane, London, EC4A 3JB
Tel: (020) 7842 0000 **Fax:** (020) 7842 3900 **DX:** 183 Chancery Lane
Email: info@teca.co.uk **Website:** www.teca.co.uk

5 East Pallant, Chichester, PO19 1TS
Tel: (01243) 786111 **Fax:** (01243) 775640 **DX:** 30300 Chichester
Email: info@teca.co.uk

Sussex House, North Street, Horsham, RH12 1BJ
Tel: (01403) 214 500 **Fax:** (01403) 241 457 **DX:** 57608 Horsham
Email: info@teca.co.uk

1 Liverpool Gardens, Worthing, BN11 1SL
Tel: (01903) 234 411 **Fax:** (01903) 207 641 **DX:** 3704 Worthing
Email: info@teca.co.uk

Chatham Court, Lesbourne Road, Reigate, RH2 7FN
Tel: (01737) 240 111 **Fax:** (01737) 248 249 **DX:** 30400 Reigate 1
Email: info@teca.co.uk

Managing Partner	John Stapleton
Chairman	Neil Hart
Number of partners	50
Assistant solicitors	37
Other fee-earners	101

CONTACTS

Agriculture	Richard Kyrke
Banking & Finance	Steven Clifford
Commercial Property	Chris Bell
Company & Commercial	Tony Edwards
Construction	Tina Webster
Debt Recovery	Paula Jones
E-Commerce	Philip Krauss
Employment	Peter Stevens
Financial Services	Anthony Wands
Franchising	Michael Crooks
Insolvency	Martin Cross
Intellectual Property	Michael Camps
Litigation	Tom McKeown
Mediation/Family	Jill Goldman
Personal Injury	Stephen Richards
Private Client	Richard Thornely

THE FIRM: Thomas Eggar Church Adams is one of the country's leading regional law firms. It has 188 fee earners with offices in London, Chichester, Horsham, Reigate and Worthing. It is a diversified legal and finan-

Continued overleaf

cial services group that has recently been endorsed as the leading law firm in the South East region by a leading legal magazine. The firm represents a diversified range of clients. It supports some of the largest corporations in the United Kingdom with its leading edge, specialist litigation, commercial property, company commercial, banking and e-commerce expertise. Additionally, the firm has continued to build its pre-eminent private practice, and has the largest solicitor-owned financial services and investment management firm – Thesis Asset Management plc. Recent energies have gone towards building the strength of its commercial practice. The firm offers City-based specialisms through its London office, which last year moved into the prestigious International Press Centre in EC4. Work is sourced across all the offices and conducted in the location offering the best skills and value to the client. The firm has built its business around exceptional customer service and this underpins all its activities. It is the foundation of the firm and assures long-term commitment to its clients. The firm has been accredited with the Law Society's quality mark, Lexcel.

THOMAS EGGAR
CHURCH ADAMS
SOLICITORS

PRINCIPAL AREAS OF WORK: Thomas Eggar Church Adams offers specialist, industry-specific legal expertise that is relied upon by national and international clients.
Commercial Property: Work includes property development and investment, environmental issues, construction law, commercial leases and under-leases and station trading lettings. Within the division there is an unparalleled depth of experience and expertise covering the whole of the spectrum of railway property work.
Company Commercial: The firm handles acquisitions, mergers and disposals, management buy-outs and buy-ins, terms and conditions of trading and company formations.
Financial: The firm handles banking and finance matters. Its specialist financial services and investment management firm, Thesis Asset Management plc, has in excess of £570m of client funds under advisory and discretionary management, offering corporate finance to a range of companies as well as financial planning and investment advice to a large number of private clients.
Litigation: Work includes intellectual property, banking, construction, commercial property, professional negligence and e-commerce.
Private Client: Services focus on taxation and trusts but also cover residential property, family law, pensions and wills.
Other Areas: The firm also has expertise in franchising, insolvency, e-commerce, agriculture, personal injury and employment.

CLIENTELE: Thomas Eggar Church Adams serves a diverse range of clients from local, regional, national and international businesses to well-known personalities and private clients. All clients receive a partner-led, comprehensive service in all areas of legal advice. Major clients include the Alliance and Leicester Group Union Staff, Alliance Unichem plc, Britannia Pharmaceuticals, British Railways Board in property matters, Brighton & Hove Council, LINK Interchange Network Limited, Gleeson, Hamptons Estates Ltd, Maplin plc, Marshall-Tufflex Ltd on the corporate side, Nationwide Building Society, Perfect Pizza, Railtrack plc in property and litigation, as well as Southern Water, The Glanmore Property Fund, West Bromwich Building Society, Wyndeham Press Group plc and Woolwich. The firm is also a leading adviser to the Church of England and various other charities.

INTERNATIONAL: Growth has continued through 2000/2001 and the firm has built up its international links through membership of The Bridge Group, an association of US law firms that enables the firm's clients to have access to advice in the majority of the American states, and AvrioAdvocati, a formal network of European law firms. It is the result of a merger of two organisations. The organisation provides legal advice for its members and their clients in foreign jurisdictions. It has developed significant legal expertise on a group basis in the areas of sports law, international fraud and telecommunications.

THOMPSONS

Congress House, Great Russell Street, London, WC1B 3LW **Tel:** (020) 7290 0000 **Fax:** (020) 7637 0000 **DX:** 35722 Bloomsbury 1
Website: www.thompsons.law.co.uk **Ptnrs:** 56 **Asst solrs:** 128 **Other fee-earners:** 151

THOMPSON SMITH & PUXON

4-5 North Hill, Colchester, CO1 1EB **Tel:** (01206) 574431 **Fax:** (01206) 563174 **DX:** 3617 Colchester
Email: info@tsplegal.com **Website:** www.tsplegal.com **Contact:** Lindsay Brydson • General practice with two offices. Members of Law Society Family panel and Childcare, Clinical Negligence and Personal Injury panels; Legal Aid franchise holders.

THOMSON SNELL & PASSMORE

Stafford House, East Street, Tonbridge, TN9 1HG
Tel: (01732) 771411 **Fax:** (01732) 770445 **DX:** 5502 Tonbridge 1
Email: solicitors@ts-p.co.uk **Website:** www.ts-p.co.uk

3 Lonsdale Gardens, Tunbridge Wells, TN1 1NX
Tel: (01892) 510000 **Fax:** (01892) 549884 **DX:** 3914 Tunbridge Wells 1

Senior Partner	Trevor May
Number of partners	34
Assistant solicitors	21
Other fee-earners	13

CONTACTS

Agriculture	Gilbert Green
Clinical Negligence	Andrew Watson
Commercial Litigation	Peter Radula-Scott
Commercial Property	David White
Company/Commercial	James Partridge
Employment	Jill Kelly
Matrimonial/Family	Barbara Wright
Personal Injury	Julie Reynolds
Probate & Trusts	James Krafft
Professional Negligence	Trevor May
Property Development	Gilbert Green
Residential Property	Michael Sugden
Tax Planning	Jeremy Passmore

THE FIRM: This large regional law firm whose head office is located in Tunbridge Wells is renowned for providing a high quality service, focusing on approachability and friendliness. Thomson Snell & Passmore is an organisation of talented, energetic and efficient lawyers. Founded in 1570 and founder member of The Law South Group, TS&P holds the highly regarded 'Lexcel' award, the Law Society's quality assurance standard. During the last 2 years, the firm has grown substantially in all areas and has a long standing reputation for its expertise, with many of the partners being recognised in the legal press as leaders in their particular area of practice.

PRINCIPAL AREAS OF WORK: The extensive range of legal services offered to commercial and private clients can be viewed at the firm's website.

INTERNATIONAL: The firm is a founder member of INTERLEGAL with associate offices throughout Europe, the USA and Canada.

THOMSON WEBB CORFIELD

94 Regent Street, Cambridge, CB2 1DP **Tel:** (01223) 578070 **Fax:** (01223) 578330 **DX:** 5840 CAMBRIDGE **Ptnrs:** 7 **Asst solrs:** 7 **Other fee-earners:** 8

THORNHILL INCE

Suite 3, Third Floor, Grampian House, 144 Deansgate, Manchester, M3 3ED **Tel:** (0161) 839 2550 **Fax:** (0161) 819 5005 **Ptnrs:** 2 **Asst solrs:** 1

THORNTONS WS

50 Castle Street, Dundee, DD1 3RU **Tel:** (01382) 229111 **Fax:** (01382) 202288 **DX:** LP29 **Email:** enquiries@thorntonsws.co.uk **Website:** www.thorntonsws.co.uk **Ptnrs:** 25 **Asst solrs:** 23 **Other fee-earners:** 35

THRING TOWNSEND

42 Cricklade Street, Swindon, SN1 3HD
Tel: (01793) 410 800 **Fax:** (01793) 539 040 **DX:** 6204 Swindon 1
Email: solicitors@thringtownsend.co.uk **Website:** www.thringtownsend.co.uk

Midland Bridge, Bath, BA1 2HQ
Tel: (01225) 340 000 **Fax:** (01225) 319 735 **DX:** 8002 Bath
Email: solicitors@thringtownsend.co.uk

18 London Road, Newbury, RG14 1JX
Tel: (01635) 31 720 **Fax:** (01635) 32 877 **DX:** 30810 Newbury
Email: solicitors@thringtownsend.co.uk

Senior Partner	Jeremy Thring
Chairman of Management Board	Julian George
Chief Executive	Nigel Cobb
Number of partners	37
Total staff	259

AREAS OF PRACTICE

Litigation	32%
Commercial	28%
Private Client	20%
Conveyancing	19%

CONTACTS

Agriculture	Jonathan Cheal
Banking Law	Brian Jacomb
Building & Construction	David Patterson
Charities	Quentin Elston
Commercial Property	Thomas Sheppard
Commercial/Agricultural Litigation	Peter Cusick
Company Law	Julian George
Employment (Contentious)	
Employment (Non-contentious)	Jonathan Payne
Family	Richard Sharp
Industrial Diseases	Brigitte Chandler
Insolvency	Brian Jacomb
Internet Law	Paul Hardman
Investment Management	Adrian Cantwell
IP/IT	Paul Hardman
Options	Alan Goulding
Personal Injury	Melanie Richens
Private Client	Helen Starkie
Probate	Helen Starkie

THE FIRM: Thring Townsend is one of central southern England's leading law firms, providing a focused range of commercial and private client services. With 259 staff and offices in Swindon, Bath and Newbury, the current practice resulted from the merger of Thrings & Long and Townsends in November 2000. Thring Townsend has already acquired a high profile and reputation for results. The new firm offers greater strength and diversity of legal work and has been appointed legal adviser to the largest provider of post secondary education in the region. The firm's client base is impressive, ranging from local subsidiaries of multinational companies to government bodies, charities and family owned enterprises, through to Internet start-ups and entrepreneurs. Clients are provided with strong, partner led teams that look for innovative solutions and help provide a value added service. Private client services are tailored to meet specific clients' needs and the private client department is renowned for its high level of personal service. Thring Townsend has achieved IIP accreditation, has a Community Legal Service franchise for personal injury and family work and holds the highly regarded 'Lexcel' award. The firm makes considerable investment in both the skills and welfare of its staff and six trainees are recruited annually.

PRINCIPAL AREAS OF WORK:

Company/Commercial: An extensive range of corporate work is handled by one of the largest commercial teams in the region. Services include advice on most aspects of company and commercial matters from start-

Continued overleaf

ups to mergers and acquisitions, MBOs, MBIs, Purple Book work, franchising and partnership agreements.
Commercial Property: The team offers a broad range of expertise covering landlord and tenant work, specialist options, infrastructure agreements, development and associated pensions work. Clients include a national telecommunications company, a major institutional landlord and many of the region's top companies.
Employment: The firm's employment law expertise is well recognised. The team advises on both contentious and non-contentious employment law and handles all employment matters including redundancy, contracts, discrimination, health and safety, equal pay, and employment tribunals.
Agriculture: This is an area of key strength and the firm has won the contract for the provision of legal services to NFU members covering central England.
Commercial Litigation: The team deals with commercial and construction disputes, licensing, debt recovery, defamation, product liability, landlord and tenant and professional negligence.
Family: The renowned family team is one of the largest in central southern England. All lawyers are members of the SFLA and the Law Society's Children and Family Law panels. Two lawyers are also accredited family mediators.
Personal Injury: The reputation of the team is outstanding and the firm has a national reputation in asbestosis, deafness, spinal injuries and serious head injuries for plaintiffs. Sports law is a particular strength and continues to grow in importance.
Private Client: Services include all aspects of wills and probate, estate planning and administration as well as tax planning, wealth management, advice for retirement, private self-assessment and investment management.
Traded Endowment: The firm has a national reputation for dealing with traded endowment work, covering acquisition, gearing and disposal of policies. Clients include market-makers, banks, funds and corporate investors.

CONTACTS

Relocation	William Power
Residential Property	William Power
Sports Law	Stephen Roberts
Tax Planning	Jeremy Thring
Traded Endowment	William Power
Trusts & Tax	Michael Young

Thring Townsend

T

TITE & LEWIS

Alder Castle, 10 Noble St, London, EC2V 7TL
Tel: (020) 7606 2211 **Fax:** (020) 7606 3311

THE FIRM: Tite & Lewis, a fast-growing City-based international law firm, is breaking the boundaries of the legal services marketplace. It regards legal skills as a stepping-off point for achieving clients' commercial ends and it always takes a broad business perspective when advising clients, to ensure this advice is grounded in the real world. To achieve this the firm maintains an unerring focus on clients and the industries they work in. This enables them to provide a purely commercial proposition as an independent full service law firm that can operate – when the client chooses – in close association with Ernst & Young, offering a new tier of choice in the marketplace. Founded in May 2000, Tite & Lewis has grown substantially and anticipates further growth in the coming years. This expansion is driven not by headcount but quality, and reflects a focus on excellence which is embodied both in the firm's client base and its people. The firm's clients succeed because they manage innovation and respond to the speed of today's economy, be they new companies or household name institutions. Tite & Lewis comes from the same mould. It is young, dynamic and founded on a real linkage between ideas and action. There is no red tape to fight through and the staff have a clear line of sight to their clients' business goals.

PRINCIPAL AREAS OF WORK: Tite & Lewis advises national and global clients on the full range of corporate and financial transactions and has all the core competencies clients would expect to find in a City and international law firm. However, what often differentiates Tite & Lewis from its peers is that it puts those skills to use by focusing on clients' needs in the context of their own specific industries. To date, Tite & Lewis has established expertise in seven industry sectors: real estate, industrial products, consumer products, energy, financial services, private equity and the whole nexus of communications, technology and entertainment. Much of the firm's work is focused on enabling major clients to operate commercially and with certainty in the connected economy. To meet the needs of clients in each of these sectors, Tite & Lewis continually draws together expertise from across its legal practice areas, which focus on: corporate, competition, employment, international public affairs, finance, real estate, and IT and e-commerce.

Managing Partner	Christopher Tite
Chairman	Mark Lewis
Number of partners	10
Assistant solicitors	52
Other fee-earners	3

AREAS OF PRACTICE

Corporate	29%
Finance	22%
IT & E-commerce	20%
Real Estate	15%
Employment	6%
Competition	4%
International Public Affairs	4%

CONTACTS

Competition	James Robinson
Corporate	Christopher Tite
Employment	Greg Campbell
Finance	Tamara Box
International Public Affairs	Andrew Silberberg
IT & E-commerce	Mark Lewis
Private Equity	Iain Young
Real Estate	Louise Gowman

Tite & Lewis

TLT SOLICITORS

One Redcliff Street, Bristol, BS99 7JZ
Tel: (0117) 917 7777 **Fax:** (0117) 917 7778 **DX:** 7815 Bristol
Website: www.tltsolicitors.com

Managing Partner	Robert Bourns
Senior Partner	Tim Pyper
Number of partners	33
Assistant solicitors	44
Other fee-earners	62

AREAS OF PRACTICE

Banking & Lender Services	30%
Commercial & Corporate	25%
Property	20%
Dispute Resolution	10%
Employment	9%
Family	6%

CONTACTS

Banking	Judith Brown
Commercial	William Hull
Commercial Dispute Resolution	Philip May
Corporate	David Pester
Employment	Alana Weeks
Family	David Woodward
Insolvency	Philip May
Lender Services	Richard Waller
Planning/Development/Environmental	Edward Cooke
Professional Conduct	Sarah Mumford
Property Dispute Resolution	Julia Lucas
Property Investment	Andrew Glynn
Residential Property	Patrick Rees
Retail	Roger Clothier
Tax & Estate Planning	David Bird

THE FIRM: TLT is one of the leading regional corporate law firms and the UK member of European Law Firm (ELF), which has member firms in over 20 European countries. As a modern and dynamic firm, TLT aims to distinguish itself in the minds of its clients as a powerful business ally. The firm takes the time to understand the requirements and aspirations of its clients and its staff. 140 lawyers provide corporate legal services to a national and increasingly international client base. The firm specialises in corporate finance, banking and lender services, property, employment, insolvency and dispute resolution. It attracts and retains specialist lawyers who understand commercial priorities and have specialist sector knowledge. TLT is active in many sectors, particularly financial services, technology/digital media, leisure, retail, minerals/aggregates, energy/utilities and professional services. The firm's client list includes high net worth individuals whom it advises on both commercial and private issues including family matters, tax and trusts.

PRINCIPAL AREAS OF WORK:

Corporate: Corporate work is handled by one of the largest dedicated corporate teams in the region, including corporate finance, acquisitions, disposals, JVs, stock exchange and a substantial amount of AIM and OFEX work. A specialist team handles tax, pensions, IP, competition and other commercial contracts, and includes dedicated franchising and partnership units. The firm has set up one of the first corporate venturing agencies in the UK, TLT Venturing, operating as a brokerage by facilitating matches between corporate venture investors and developing businesses.

Banking: TLT is one of the few firms in the UK who act for two of the top four banks, as well as for six of the top ten mortgage lenders. The firm provides a comprehensive service to this sector including advising on corporate lending, all types of banking litigation, mortgage documentation and insolvency, in addition to volume recoveries and conveyancing. A new specialist unit handles compliance and regulation issues.

Property: Property is a significant strength with work undertaken nationally including property investment; acquisitions and disposals; property management; development; planning; construction; environmental; landlord and tenant work; dispute resolution.

Litigation & ADR: TLT is renowned for its dispute resolution expertise, handling a wide range of heavy-weight domestic and international litigation, as well as a substantial amount of ADR work, particularly mediation and arbitration.

Employment: Strategic employment work, HR consultancy services and management training are carried out for an impressive national client base.

RECRUITMENT: The firm is always looking for individuals who can contribute to its success. Please see our web site for more information on the firm's activities and its ethos.

TODS MURRAY WS

66 Queen Street, Edinburgh, EH2 4NE
Tel: (0131) 226 4771 **Fax:** (0131) 225 3676 **DX:** ED58
Email: maildesk@todsmurray.com **Website:** www.todsmurray.com

33 Bothwell Street, Glasgow, G2 6NL
Tel: (0141) 275 4771 **Fax:** (0131) 275 4781 **DX:** 512815 Glasgow Central
Email: maildesk@todsmurray.com

Chairman	Charles Abram
Managing Partner	John Biggar
Number of partners	36
Assistant solicitors	49
Other fee-earners	27

AREAS OF PRACTICE

Corporate	38%
Commercial Property	34%
Private Client	20%
Litigation	8%

CONTACTS

Agriculture, Landed Estates & Forestry	John Fulton
	Neil King
Banking	Graham Burnside
	Hamish Patrick
Capital Projects/PFI/PPP	William Simmons
	Ian McPake
Charities	Peter Ryden
Commercial Property	Douglas Moffat
	Sandy McEwen
Construction	Ross Campbell
Corporate & Commercial	David Dunsire
Corporate Finance	Granger Brash

THE FIRM: Tods Murray is one of Scotland's leading commercial law firms with offices in Edinburgh and Glasgow offering a wide range of services to clients throughout the UK. It is a modern, progressive and forward looking firm with a commercial and proactive approach to the changing needs of all its clients. The firm is committed to building strong and broadly based business as well as personal relationships with its clients founded on mutual respect, trust and confidence. Overall Tods Murray's aim is to provide the highest quality of professional advice and expertise combined with an excellent service and demonstrable value for money.

PRINCIPAL AREAS OF WORK:

Banking: The banking team has extensive experience in corporate and public sector lending, project finance, property finance, securitisation and recovery.

Capital Projects: The capital projects team deals with all capital and infrastructure projects including PFI/PPP with particular expertise in healthcare, education, water, waste to energy, social housing and local authority projects.

Corporate: The corporate team is recognised for its experience in corporate finance including public issues, acquisitions, placings, and buy-outs. The team also has significant entertainment, leisure and travel law exper-

Continued overleaf

T

tise including timeshare. In addition, the investment funds and corporate financial services team is recognised as having a leading reputation in these specialist areas.

Commercial Property: The commercial property team, which specialises in major developments and funding agreements, acts for a number of insurers, pension funds and property companies in relation to their property portfolios. The team also offers advice on planning, construction and environmental law.

Litigation: The litigation team handles all types of commercial and civil litigation and employment issues across the firm for both commercial and private clients.

Private Client: The private client team provides services to landowners and farmers, undertaking all the legal work associated with landed estates and farms. The team deals with wills, trusts and executries, charities, tax and estate planning, financial management (on behalf of both individuals and trusts) and the purchase and sale of residential property.

Other Areas: T2M is a specialist service, which offers clients access to an integrated team of experts in the fields of e-commerce, intellectual property, information technology, and media and entertainment.

CLIENTELE: Tods Murray's clients include banks and other financial institutions, listed and private companies, public sector organisations, property investors and developers, large and small businesses, landowners and private individuals.

INTERNATIONAL: On an international level, the firm's membership of Multilaw provides it with a network of associated law firms located in the world's major commercial centres.

RECRUITMENT: The firm is committed to the recruitment and intensive training and development of high quality staff in all areas of work.

CONTACTS CONTINUED

Corporate Financial Services	Chris Athanas
	Martin Thurston Smith
Employment Law	Robert Dobie
	Peter Paterson
Entertainment & Media	Richard Findlay
Hotels & Leisure	Angus McIntyre
Information Technology	Lynn Beaumont
Investment Funds	Chris Athanas
Litigation	Michael Simpson
Pensions	Martin Thurston Smith
Planning & Environment	Ian McPake
Residential Property	Gordon Cunningham
Securitisation	Graham Burnside
	Hamish Patrick
Timeshare	David Anderson
Wills, Tax & Trusts	John Biggar

T

TOLLER BEATTIE

Queens House, Queen Street, Barnstaple, Devon, EX32 8TS **Tel:** (01271) 375 821 **Fax:** (01271) 374 762 **DX:** 34954 **Email:** solicitors@tollerbeattie.co.uk **Ptnrs:** 4 **Asst solrs:** 10 **Other fee-earners:** 5

TOLLER HALES & COLLCUTT

Castilian Chambers, 2 Castilian Street, Northampton, NN1 1JX
Tel: (01604) 258558 **Fax:** (01604) 258500 **DX:** 12422
Email: info@tollers.co.uk **Website:** www.tollers.co.uk

Senior Partner	Anthony Noone
Managing Partner	David Eastwood
Number of partners	22
Assistant solicitors	11
Other fee-earners	24

AREAS OF PRACTICE

Litigation	36%
Private Client	28%
Family	24%
Commercial	12%

THE FIRM: Established in 1877, Toller Hales & Collcutt is a broadly based provincial practice with four offices in Northamptonshire. It offers a full range of legal services to both commercial and private clients. The firm has other offices in Corby, Kettering and Wellingborough.

PRINCIPAL AREAS OF WORK:

Corporate/Commercial: The department undertakes all aspects of company formation, acquisition and disposal, MBOs and MBIs, joint ventures, reconstruction, franchise, agency and distribution agreements, taxation, intellectual property, EC law and insolvency.

Commercial Property: The firm offers a wide-ranging property service covering industrial, retail and offices premises, and acquisition, disposal, leasing, landlord and tenant law, building contracts, joint ventures, property taxation (VAT), investment and development work. A specialist Planning Unit deals with all planning issues.

Litigation: The litigation team handles all aspects of commercial and private client litigation. Specialist areas of practice include employment disputes (contracts, redundancy, wrongful dismissal and discrimination), personal injury (seven PI Panel Solicitors), medical negligence, professional negligence, construction and insurance.

Family/Childcare: The firm has a specialist unit dealing with all aspects of family disputes which is the largest in the County.

Mediation: The firm has a large family mediation unit with 4 trained mediators and this has become an integral part of the family law department.

Private Client: The firm offers a comprehensive service to the private client, including all types of property transfers, wills, trusts, probate.

CLIENTELE: Clients range from insurance companies and Plcs to businesses of all sizes. The firm has a strong private client base and is a member of the Conquest Network.

RECRUITMENT: The firm expects to take on two trainee solicitors every year and applications should be made on the firm's own application form to Mrs C B Scudamore.

TOWNLEYS

7 Devonshire Square, Cutlers Gardens, London, EC2M 4YH
Tel: (020) 7655 1000 **Fax:** 7655 1001 **DX:** 33885 Finsbury Square
Email: townleys@townleys.co.uk **Website:** www.townleys.com

Chief Executive Officer	Ric Martin
Senior Partner	Stephen Townley
Number of partners	4
Assistant solicitors	14
Other fee-earners	5
Total staff	40

AREAS OF PRACTICE

Sport/Media..95%

CONTACTS

Strategic Rights Management ....Stephen Townley
Sports Broadcasting & New Media ....Jonathan Higton
Sports Sponsorship & Event Management ....Andy Korman
Sports Governance ....Jonathan Taylor
Dispute Resolution ....Jonathan Taylor
Sports IP...............................Jeremy Summers
Company Commercial...........Satish Khandke

THE FIRM: Established in 1983, Townleys is widely regarded as being the pre-eminent specialist sports law firm in Europe. As the only dedicated sports law practice operating in this rapidly developing market, Townleys remains at the cutting edge of new legal developments relating to the sports industry both at home and internationally. With specialist fee-earners organised into practice groups, Townleys is large and experienced enough to bring multi-disciplinary skills to bear in relation to any sports property or transaction, whatever the size, yet flexible and entrepreneurial enough to bring a personalised and innovative approach to all its clients' needs. Townleys is now part of Hammond Suddards Edge.

PRINCIPAL AREAS OF WORK:

Strategic Rights Mangement: The firm advises national and international sporting bodies and government bodies on strategic and commercial plans for major sporting events throughout the world.

Sports Broadcasting & New Media: Work includes advising sports bodies and their advisers on domestic broadcasting arrangements, on international exploitation and distribution and on exploitation of related rights. The firm also advises on new media issues including website and multimedia products, the development of interactive rights licensing, revenue-collection and e-commerce models, domain name registration and dispute resolution services relating thereto, and the implementation of programmes for protecting and developing sports rights in digital media.

Sponsorship & Event Management: The firm advises sports rights owners and major sponsors on the structuring and negotiation of substantial sponsorship, sports marketing ventures and event organisation.

Sports Governance: The firm advises governing bodies and other sports organisations on disciplinary regimes, doping programmes, the movement of players, player discipline and participation/eligibility issues, general liability issues and general regulatory frameworks, including manuals of good practice and codes of ethics.

Dispute Resolution: Work includes advising on challenges to the enforceability (under competition law or otherwise) of rules and regulations governing particular sports; advising on the disciplinary and other decisions of governing bodies pursuant to those rules and regulations; acting in a broad range of contractual and non-contractual disputes, generally in the area of sports rights exploitation and particularly in the areas of broadcasting, sponsorship and merchandising; managing the contentious aspects of worldwide sports brand management/ protection programmes.

Sports Intellectual Property: The firm advises sports on intellectual property portfolios and development strategies and related areas. It manages and implements global trademark protection, brand management and enforcement programmes for sports events and properties, utilising its extensive international network of specialist agents. The firm also handles drafting and advising on licensing, merchandising and other sports intellectual property agreements, IP issues in major sports marketing contracts, and undertakes litigation and enforcement actions to protect clients' IP rights.

Company Commercial: The firm provides wide-ranging legal advice in areas such as joint ventures, employment, share structures, shareholder agreements, option schemes, the raising and maintenance of capital, financial services and company/commercial matters relating to the sports industry.

CLIENTELE: Clients include many major international and domestic governing bodies (for example the International Rugby Board and the International Tennis Federation); event organisers (for example Rugby World Cup, Five/Six Nations, Asian PGA, Davis Cup and Fed Cup); corporate sponsors (for example Bacardi-Martini, Nike, Nationwide, Carlsberg-Tetley and npower); sponsorship consultancies; sports television distribution agencies and broadcasters; communications agencies. A great deal of the firm's practice concerns the legal structuring and commercial exploitation of all types of sporting and cultural events and properties. These have included sponsorship of test cricket; Lions Rugby Tour; European Rugby Cup, including the Heineken Cup sponsorship deal; Six Nations broadcasting rights; the Laureus Sports Awards; Davis Cup and Fed Cup; Royal Ascot; acquisition of commercial rights for the Cricket World Cups 2003 and 2007 and many more.

INTERNATIONAL: Fluent French, Italian, Spanish, Polish, Gurjarati, Mandarin, Cantonese, Hokkien, Malay and Afrikaans are spoken by members of the firm.

RECRUITMENT: Trainee applications should be sent to the chief executive.

T

TOZERS

Broadwalk House, Southernhay West, Exeter, EX1 1UA
Tel: (01392) 207020 **Fax:** (01392) 207019 **DX:** 8322
Email: enquiries@tozers.co.uk **Website:** www.tozers.co.uk

2-3 Orchard Gardens, Teignmouth, TQ14 8DR
Tel: (01626) 772376 **Fax:** (01626) 770317 **DX:** 82051 Teignmouth
Email: enquiries@tozers.co.uk

Strand Chambers, Dawlish, EX7 9EZ
Tel: (01626) 862323 **Fax:** (01626) 866851 **DX:** 82100 Dawlish
Email: enquiries@tozers.co.uk

8-10 Paul's Road, Newton Abbot, TQ12 4PR
Tel: (01626) 207020 **Fax:** (01626) 207019 **DX:** 59102 Newton Abbot
Email: enquiries@tozers.co.uk

73 Abbey Road, Torquay, TQ2 5NN
Tel: (01803) 407020 **Fax:** (01803) 407021 **DX:** 59023 Torquay 1
Email: enquiries@tozers.co.uk

9 The Crescent, Plymouth, PL1 3AB
Tel: (01752) 206460 **Fax:** (01752) 301662 **DX:** 118106 Plymouth
Email: enquiries@tozers.co.uk

Managing Partner	Peter Edwards
Chairman	Graham Bond
Number of partners	15
Assistant solicitors	16
Other fee-earners	22

AREAS OF PRACTICE

Litigation	32%
Commercial	30%
Property	21%
Probate	17%

CONTACTS

Charities & Schools	Richard King
Children & Family	Philip Kidd
Clinical Negligence	Tim Dyde
Commercial Lending	Tim Fogarty
Employment	Jill Headford
Leisure, Planning & Mobile Home Law	Tony Beard
Litigation	Jill Headford
Private Client	Vernon Clarke
Property	Michael Brotherton

T

THE FIRM: Tozers has a long and distinguished history of service to clients. Established in Devon over 200 years ago, the firm has adapted and continues to adapt to the rapidly changing environment for legal services.

PRINCIPAL AREAS OF WORK: Specialist teams have been developed to ensure expertise in these niche areas:
Leisure & Environmental Law: The firm's expertise includes licensing and caravan parks and mobile homes law.
Charities & Schools: The team advises religious, educational, health/disability and other charities, as well as schools in both the private and state sector.
Property & Planning: Work is done in both the commercial and residential sectors. The firm has a member on the Law Society's Planning panel.
Litigation: Work includes property disputes and debt recovery. The firm also offers a strong, growing employment law team.
Family & Childcare: This is one of the strongest teams in the South West, dealing with all aspects of family law, including public law childcare and mediation as well as high worth financial disputes. Six of the team's solicitors sit on the Law Society's Children panel, one of whom is an interviewer and assessor for the panel.
Clinical Negligence & Personal Injury: The firm's reputation has grown in the areas of birth injury, gynaecology and cardiac surgery, with members on the AVMA and Law Society's Clinical Negligence and Personal Injury panels.
Private Client: The team covers wills, probate, tax and trusts, including tax planning and investment management for trusts and individuals.
Commercial Lending & Recovery: The team acts on behalf of banks and financial institutions.
Additional Areas: Agency work handled by the firm includes all aspects of civil and criminal litigation, licensing and personal searches.

TRAVERS SMITH BRAITHWAITE

10 Snow Hill, London, EC1A 2AL
Tel: (020) 7295 3000 **Fax:** (020) 7295 3500 **DX:** 79
Email: Travers.Smith@TraversSmith.com **Website:** www.traverssmith.com

Managing Partner	Chris Carroll
Senior Partner	Christopher Bell
UK	
Number of partners	49
Assistant solicitors	105
Other fee-earners	42
International	
Number of partners	1
Assistant solicitors	1

THE FIRM: Travers Smith Braithwaite is a leading corporate, financial and commercial law firm with the expertise and capability to advise on a wide range of business activities. Today's clients include regulatory, financial, trade and industrial organisations throughout the UK and from all over the world. Travers Smith Braithwaite prides itself on not being so large as to have an impersonal atmosphere but enjoys a quality of work and a range of clients normally associated with larger firms. By resisting rapid growth and focusing on quality, the firm has been able to maintain the high standards of service it provides to clients. Closely-knit and consistent teams of lawyers will provide advice to a client year in year out, ensuring a clear understanding of the client's business and an effective working relationship. Central to the firm's approach is the philosophy that partners should be closely involved in most of the matters undertaken and that delegation should not be automatic but considered in every case in the light of both effectiveness and cost.

PRINCIPAL AREAS OF WORK: The firm's business comprises eight main areas:
Corporate Law: Takeovers, mergers and acquisitions, new issues, company law, financial services and regulatory law, capital markets, private equity and venture capital.
Commercial Law: Joint ventures, EU and competition law, intellectual property, information technology, multi-media, privatisations and broadcasting.
Banking/Corporate Recovery: Secured and unsecured lending, finance leasing, acquisition finance, trade and project finance, property finance, banking regulations, rescheduling and insolvency.
Employment: Executive service agreements, restrictive covenants, health and safety, works councils and employee consultation, industrial disputes and employment litigation, employment aspects of mergers, acquisitions and reorganisations (including transfers of undertakings).
Dispute Resolution: Domestic and international, commercial litigation, arbitration and ADR.
Property: Acquisition, disposal and development of industrial, retail and office property, planning and construction law.
Pensions: Establishment, administration and winding up of pension funds and pension litigation.
Tax: Domestic and international corporate tax planning, acquisition and structured finance, employee share (and other) incentive schemes, private client tax planning.

INTERNATIONAL: The firm enjoys a close working relationship with leading law firms in each of the main foreign jurisdictions. The firm believes that its clients' best interests are served by the firm having access to, and the ability to select, established overseas firms which have the necessary expertise and experience. This approach also allows the firm the flexibility to work with a client's existing advisers in different jurisdictions or to select alternative advisers where conflicts of interest arise. Travers Smith Braithwaite opened a Paris liaison office in April 1999. The office sources and manages the provision of French legal services to the firm and its UK and overseas clients. In addition, the office acts as a liaison between French clients (including French law firms) and the London office. Work is handled in French, German, Italian, and Spanish.

RECRUITMENT: Travers Smith Braithwaite continues to develop and is always looking to recruit at both assistant and trainee level, people of academic excellence and sound judgement who are able to take their careers, but not themselves, seriously. The firm's training philosophy is that skill and expertise are best acquired through practical experience complemented by carefully targeted formal instruction. Great emphasis is placed on ensuring that trainees are actively involved in a broad range of work. Applications for traineeships should be made in writing to Jillian Singh (Graduate Recruitment Coordinator) enclosing a full CV together with the names and addresses of academic and personal referees.

AREAS OF PRACTICE	
Corporate	38%
Litigation	15%
Property	15%
Finance	14%
Tax	8%
Pensions	5%
Employment	5%

CONTACTS	
Banking	Neil Murray
Commercial	Margaret Moore
Competition & EU law	Margaret Moore
Construction	Alastair Graham
Corporate	Oliver Barnes
Corporate Recovery	Jeremy Walsh
Dispute Resolution	John Kingston
Employment	Andrew Lilley
Environment	Alison Lea
Financial Services	Margaret Chamberlain
Insurance/Reinsurance	Stephen Paget-Brown
Pensions	Paul Stannard
Planning	Alison Lea
Private Equity	Chris Hale
Property	Robert Harman
Tax	Alasdair Douglas

T

TRETHOWANS

College Chambers, New Street, Salisbury, SP1 2LY
Tel: (02380) 321000 **Fax:** (01722) 411300 **DX:** 58004 Salisbury
Email: Info@treth.co.uk **Website:** www.trethowans.com

The Director General's House, Rockstone Place, Southampton, SO15 2EP
Tel: (023) 8032 1000 **Fax:** (023) 8032 1001 **DX:** 49678 SOUTHAMPTON 2

Managing Partner	Miles Brown
Number of partners	16
Assistant solicitors	15
Other fee-earners	26

AREAS OF PRACTICE	
Licensing	10%
Company/Commercial	20%
Property	25%
Private Client	20%
Litigation	25%

CONTACTS	
Commercial Litigation	Phil Banks-Welsh
Company/Commercial	Catherine MacRae
IP & E-business	Owen Santry
Licensing	Michael Messent
Litigation Services	Neil Elliott
Private Client	Michael Ricketts
Property	John Fletcher

THE FIRM: One of the largest and strongest general law firms in the South of England, this expanding firm provides a complete range of legal services for both commercial and private clients. Genuine expertise and increasing reputations in key areas are a feature of the firm. Its commercial client expertise is increasingly focused on the Southampton office. The private client expertise is spread across the firm but with the Salisbury office at its core. Teams of specialists work as client needs dictate, either individually or, particularly on corporate work and larger litigation cases, in team groups. The firm places an unusually high emphasis in 'knowing its clients' and their objectives. The firm regards its commercial services as providing large London law firm expertise but with more competitive costs structures, and with close direct partner involvement in the work in hand.

PRINCIPAL AREAS OF WORK:
Commercial Client Work
Licensing Services: The firm has an unrivalled reputation in betting, gaming and liquor licensing. Work is undertaken nationwide for Ladbrokes, Pizza Hut, Bacardi Martini and other household names.
Commercial Property Services: A strong client base involving all types of commercial property and significant project work, including insolvency. Again, the firm acts for major national companies in this area.
Commercial & Business Services: An experienced team dealing with major clients shared with other groups within the firm, as well as its own client base. A wide range of corporate work including acquisitions, disposals, management-led transactions, share options and commercial contracts of various kinds. Specialist areas include e-business, insolvency, intellectual property, IT and employment.
Commercial Litigation Services: This includes advisory as well as straightforward representational work in all areas including credit management, general claims and liability cases, and employment. Recent work includes a House of Lords case on directors' personal liabilities in corporate matters.

Continued overleaf

Private Client Work

Litigation Services: This group has a strong reputation for its personal injury and medical negligence work. It acts for both claimants and defendants.

Family Services: A wide range of matrimonial and childcare cases are undertaken for both publicly funded and privately funded clients.

Property Services, Tax Trusts & Agricultural/Estates Services: These areas remain an important part of the practice. The firm has an established and strong client base requiring these services.

CLIENTELE: The firm's clients range from major quoted public companies to start-up businesses, and from private individuals to large landed estates.

TREVOR SMYTH & CO

13 Chichester Street, Belfast, BT1 4JB **Tel:** (028) 90320360 **Fax:** (028) 90325636 **Ptnrs:** 9 **Asst solrs:** 9 **Other fee-earners:** 11

T

TROWERS & HAMLINS

Sceptre Court, 40 Tower Hill, London, EC3N 4DX
Tel: (020) 7423 8000 **Fax:** (020) 7423 8001 **DX:** 774 CDE Lon/City
Email: marketing@trowers.com **Website:** www.trowers.com

Heron House, Albert Square, Manchester, M2 5HD
Tel: (0161) 211 0000 **Fax:** (0161) 211 0001 **DX:** 14323 Manchester 1

Portland House, Longbrook Street, Exeter, EX4 6AB
Tel: (01392) 217466 **Fax:** (01392) 221047 **DX:** 134051 Exeter 15

Managing Partner	David Biggerstaff
Senior Partner	Jonathan Adlington
UK	
Number of partners	55
Assistant solicitors	59
Other fee-earners	40
International	
Number of partners	9
Assistant solicitors	10
Other fee-earners	5

AREAS OF PRACTICE

Property (Housing, Public Sector, Commercial Property)	39%
Company/Commercial & Construction	35%
Litigation	21%
Private Client	5%

CONTACTS

Banking	Ralph Picken
Charities	Jean Dollimore
Commercial Property	Elizabeth McKibbin
Construction	David Mosey
Corporate	Jennifer Gubbins
Corporate Finance	Jennifer Gubbins
Employment	Emma Burrows
Environmental	Ian Doolittle
Health	Joanne Easterbrook
Housing (General)	Jonathan Adlington
	Ian Graham
Housing Finance	Sarah Hayes
International Projects	Martin Amison
Litigation	John Linwood
	Don Moorhouse
Private Client	Michael Williamson
Projects/PFI	Ian Graham
	David Mosey
Public Sector	Ian Doolittle
Tax	Neil Cohen

THE FIRM: City and international law firm Trowers & Hamlins continues to flourish through successful specialisations developed across a broadly-based commercial, property, litigation and private client practice. Particular strengths include housing and housing finance, local government, UK and international projects, company commercial, construction, commercial property and public/private sector initiatives including private finance. Other specialisations include the health sector, environmental law, employment and charities. Trowers & Hamlins provides clear, practical solutions to achieve its clients' objectives. In all matters a client partner will call on appropriate lawyers and resources within the firm to fulfil the particular requirements of the client's brief. The firm's clients include banks, public and private companies, national and local government departments, NHS Trusts, housing bodies, partnerships, charities and individuals.

PRINCIPAL AREAS OF WORK: Through its UK offices and internationally, the firm has developed a dynamic corporate and commercial practice. Particular strengths are recognised in its UK and international finance and project work, including PFI and other DBFO schemes. As leading lawyers to the housing movement, the firm's London, Manchester and Exeter offices advise government bodies, lenders and some 250 housing associations. In addition, the firm has an impressive commercial litigation reputation and a highly regarded private client practice.

Corporate: The department is a substantial team with a growing City profile. It advises public and private companies and individuals operating in the financial, property, industrial and commercial sectors.

Projects & Construction: This department advises UK and international clients in a variety of sectors, spanning innovative PFI/DBFO project structures and joint venture/partnering initiatives.

Property: The department covers commercial, housing, local authority, residential, estate and institutional law. It has a substantial team and has established a reputation for innovation, working in the forefront of changing legislation. It provides a wide range of services to corporate clients, international businesses and individuals. Clients include investment institutions, developers, housing associations and local authorities.

Litigation: This department deals with a wide range of commercial civil litigation, arbitration and ADR both nationally and internationally, with a particular profile in professional and clinical negligence cases. It is also involved in banking, property, insolvency, employment and personal injury work. The department has a high reputation for its construction work, including mediation and adjudication.

Private Client: The department provides legal advice to individuals with industrial or commercial wealth, invested assets or landed estates. It is concerned particularly with tax planning, trusts, wills, probate, charities and the administration of trusts and estates.

TROWERS & HAMLINS

INTERNATIONAL: The firm has a strong international network, particularly in the Middle East, where it has offices in Abu Dhabi, Bahrain, Cairo, Dubai and Oman. It is particularly well known for its energy and infrastructure projects.

RECRUITMENT: The firm is always happy to hear from lawyers interested in working in a commercial environment. It recruits at least 12-15 trainee solicitors each year.

TUCKERS

39 Warren Street, London, W1P 5PD **Tel:** (020) 7388 8333 **Fax:** (020) 7388 7333 **DX:** 123596 Regents Park 3 **Email:** crime@tuckers-law.com **Website:** www.tuckers-law.com **Number of partners :**2 **Assistant solicitors:** 41 **Other fee-earners:** 65

TUGHAN & CO

Marlborough House, 30 Victoria Street, Belfast, BT1 3GS
Tel: (028) 9055 3300 **Fax:** (028) 9055 0096 **DX:** 433Nr Belfast 1
Email: law@tughan.co.uk **Website:** www.tughan.co.uk

Number of partners	13
Assistant solicitors	15
Other fee-earners	4

AREAS OF PRACTICE

Litigation (inc. Insurance & Employment Law) 45%
Company/Commercial/Property (inc. Banking, Finance, M&A & Insolvency) .. 40%
Private Client 10%
Other 5%

CONTACTS

Banking & Finance .... John Mills
Commercial Litigation .... Michael McCord
Commercial Property .... Phyllis Agnew
Conveyancing/Building Estates .... John Mills
Corporate Finance/Commercial .... John-George Willis
Employment & Labour Law .... Grahame Loughlin
Environmental Law .... Deirdre Magill
Litigation & Insurance .. Michael Gibson MBE
M&A .... John-George Willis
Private Client .... John Irwin

THE FIRM: Tughan & Co was established in 1896, and has developed over the years into one of the largest firms of solicitors in Northern Ireland. The firm's main priority is to provide clear, sound advice to its many clients through a personal service which is supported by the latest technological developments. The firm merged with Ronald Rosser and Company in 1999, thereby strengthening the firm's position in respect of defence litigation, commercial property and corporate work. Tughan & Company recently formed an association with Dublin firm William Fry, enabling both firms to offer an all-Ireland service. William Fry is one of Ireland's leading law firms with 110 solicitors. A significant number of new instructions are received on the recommendations of other law firms principally in the City of London and Glasgow/Edinburgh, with whom Tughan & Co has over the years developed strong links. Their knowledge of, and relationship with, these firms enables Tughan & Co to react rapidly upon receipt of instructions, quite often in connection with multijurisdictional transactions, with a Northern Ireland element.

PRINCIPAL AREAS OF WORK:

Litigation: The firm handles a broad range of litigation and arbitration, and is particularly active in insurance defence work and employment disputes.

Commercial Property: The firm acts for a broad range of Irish and UK-based property developers, institutions, investors and national retail chains in connection with developments, town centre regeneration, joint ventures, PFI projects, sales and purchases and leases of commercial and industrial property in Northern Ireland.

Corporate Finance/Commercial: The firm has been involved in a number of high profile corporate transactions in Northern Ireland in recent years, including two privatisations. Principal activities involve acquisitions, mergers, share issues in public and private companies, inward investments, joint ventures and shareholder agreements.

Banking/Financial Services: The banking side of the practice has grown considerably in recent years and the firm now acts for a heavyweight client list of national and international banks and finance institutions requiring assets and securitisation advice. The firm also acts within Northern Ireland for the principal regulators of the UK financial services industry.

TUNNARD CROSFIELD

Cathedral Chambers, 4 Kirkgate, Ripon, HG4 1PA **Tel:** (01765) 600 421 **Fax:** (01765) 690 523 **DX:** 61401 RIPON **Email:** ripondio.reg@connectfree.co.uk **Ptnrs:** 2 **Asst solrs:** 2 **Other fee-earners:** 2

TURBERVILLES WITH NELSON CUFF

122 High Street, Uxbridge, UB8 1JT
Tel: (01895) 201700 **Fax:** (01895) 273519 **DX:** 45116 Uxbridge
Email: solicitors@turbervilles.co.uk **Website:** www.turbervilles.co.uk

Senior Partner	Sess Sigré
Number of partners	11
Assistant solicitors	12
Other fee-earners	13

THE FIRM: The firm was created in April 1998 from the merger of Turbervilles with Nelson Cuff. Its offices are located as follows: two in Uxbridge, one of which is the main office, with branches in Hillingdon and Harrow.

PRINCIPAL AREAS OF WORK: The firm handles a broad spread of work for commercial, company, private and legally-aided clients, covering commercial and domestic property; land acquisition and development; civil, family, employment and personal injury litigation; commercial litigation and debt recovery; wills, probate, estates and trusts; entertainment and liquor licensing; crime; animal welfare; immigration and County court agency.

TURCAN CONNELL

Princes Exchange, 1 Earl Grey Street, Edinburgh, EH3 9EE
Tel: (0131) 228 8111 **Fax:** (0131) 228 8118 **DX:** 723300 Edin 43
Email: enquiries@turcanconnell.com **Website:** www.turcanconnell.com

Joint senior Partners	Robert Turcan, Douglas Connell
Number of partners	14
Assistant solicitors	25
Other fee-earners	45

AREAS OF PRACTICE

Private Client, Tax & Trusts 40%
Agriculture & Estates 35%
Pensions & Investment 15%
Charity 10%

CONTACTS

Agriculture & Estates Robert Turcan, Malcom Strange Steel, Jon Robertson, Adam Gillingham
Charities Robin Fulton, Neil MacLeod, Simon Mackintosh
Heritage Property Douglas Connell
Litigation/Family Alasdair Loudon
Private Client/Trusts Douglas Connell, Simon Mackintosh, Robin Fulton
Tax Ian Clark, Heather Thompson

TURCAN CONNELL
SOLICITORS

THE FIRM: Turcan Connell is a leading Scottish private client practice. It concentrates exclusively on the needs of private clients, trusts, charities and those involved with rural property. As well as a strong team of lawyers, the firm has a large number of other professionals, including an investment management team, a consulting actuary, a life assurance expert, a tax compliance and a trust accounting team. The Guernsey office specialises in the management of offshore trusts and companies, Turcan Connell being the only Scottish firm to offer such a facility, which is a unique and integral part of the service provided to its clients.

PRINCIPAL AREAS OF WORK:

Personal Tax & Financial Planning: The firm acts for a wide range of clients including entrepreneurs, estate owners, expatriates and professionals. The work includes inheritance tax and capital gains tax planning, the handling of large and complex estates, and advice to shareholders on corporate transactions. Tax and financial planning and asset protection involve extensive use of trusts, including their establishment, variation and termination. The firm has one of the largest trust management practices in the UK with over 2000 trusts under management. Offshore trusts are used where appropriate.

Financial Services: This service is seen as integral to the all-round service provided to private clients, trusts and charities, incorporating an investment management team and pensions and life assurance advice.

Agriculture & Estates: The firm advises on all aspects of rural property throughout Scotland, including purchase and sale of estates and their commercial development; farming and agricultural law; fishing and sporting law; and the commercial exploitation of rural property. The firm is active in the residential and small estate market particularly in Edinburgh, Lothian, the Borders, Fife and Perthshire.

Litigation & Family: Advice is given in relation to separation and divorce and the negotiation of financial settlements; and employment and related matters. This area has been strengthened with the recruitment of Alasdair Loudon.

Charity Law & Heritage Property: Charity law is an area of great importance to the firm. The range of charitable clients advised by the firm covers all types of charity from small privately established bodies to major national institutions, and includes grant giving and grant receiving bodies. The firm has a particular expertise in heritage property, acting for the owners of over 150 historic houses.

TURNBULL, SIMSON & STURROCK WS

26 High Street, Jedburgh, TD8 6AE **Tel:** (01835) 862391 **Fax:** (01835) 862017 **DX:** 581223 Jedburgh **Email:** mail@tssjed.co.uk **Ptnrs:** 3 **Other fee-earners:** 3 **Contact:** Mr David Sturrock • Offers a broad range of services. Expertise in relation to agricultural law.

TURNER PARKINSON

Hollins Chambers, 64a Bridge Street, Manchester, M3 3BA
Tel: (0161) 833 1212 **Fax:** (0161) 834 9098 **DX:** 710251 Manchester 3
Email: tp@tp.co.uk **Website:** www.tp.co.uk

Managing Partner	Mark Openshaw-Blower
Senior Partner	Nick Davenport
Number of partners	8
Assistant solicitors	16
Other fee-earners	6

AREAS OF PRACTICE

Company Commercial 40%
Litigation 35%
Property 20%
Private Client 5%

CONTACTS

Company/Commercial Nick Davenport, Richard Parkinson, Mark Openshaw-Blower, Andrew Booth
Litigation Malcolm Hunnisett, Phil Turner, Mark Lund
Private Client Christine Dickinson, Janet Fleming, Colette Johnson
Property David Blackburn, Stephen Daniels, Mike Livesey

THE FIRM: This Manchester-based firm of commercial law specialists has deliberately developed a broad portfolio of services that focuses on the needs of owner-managed businesses, providing them with the very best partner-led legal advice at a highly competitive price. Its results-driven philosophy and highly competitive fee structure is particularly appealing to entrepreneurs, although clients also include larger corporations and institutions.

PRINCIPAL AREAS OF WORK:

Company/Commercial: Work includes company formation, company restructuring, directors' duties, partnership law, joint ventures and shareholders' agreements, franchising, agency and distribution, contract negotiations and drafting, competition law and pensions.

Corporate Finance: The team handles raising finance, venture capital, share, business and asset sales and purchases, joint ventures and shareholders' agreements.

Intellectual Property: Trademarks, passing off, copyright, design right and registered design, patents and confidentiality are handled. Computer contracts and entertainment law are other niche areas of excellence.

Commercial Litigation: The firm handles breach of contract, defective goods, financial claims, construction disputes and defamation. Professional negligence and insolvency are particular specialisms.

Employment: Work includes terms of employment, service agreements, restraint of trade, transfer of undertakings, discrimination, termination of employment, redundancy and unfair or wrongful dismissal.

Commercial Property: Sales, purchases and exchanges, options, auctions and tenders, commercial leases, residential tenancies, mortgages and planning applications are handled.

Private Client: The firm handles divorce and family matters; residential property matters; probate, trusts and wills.

TV EDWARDS
Park House, 29 Mile End Rd, London, E1 4TP **Tel:** 020-7790 7060 **Fax:** (020) 7790 5101 **DX:** 300700 Tower Hamlets
Email: enquiries@tvedwards.com **Ptnrs:** 8 **Asst solrs:** 23 **Other fee-earners:** 10

TWEEDIE & PRIDEAUX (INCORPORATING WOOD, NASH KIMBER)

390 London Road, Mitcham, CR4 4EA
Tel: (020) 8640 5124 **Fax:** (020) 8640 2695 **DX:** 88151 Mitcham South
Email: mitcham@tweedieandprideaux.co.uk

5 Lincoln's Inn Fields, London, WC2A 3BT
Tel: (020) 7405 1234 **Fax:** (020) 7831 1525 **DX:** 6 London/Ch.Ln
Email: enquiry@tweedieandprideaux.co.uk

Number of partners	11
Assistant solicitors	1
Other fee-earners	12

AREAS OF PRACTICE

Probate & Trusts	33%
Residential Conveyancing	17%
Litigation	16%
Commercial Conveyancing	14%
Commercial	12%
Other Private Client Work	4%
Charities	4%

THE FIRM: Tweedie & Prideaux was joined in September 1998 by the firm of Wood Nash Kimber which had previously been in Raymond Buildings, Gray's Inn since 1826, and which brought with it a greater international dimension. Both are long-established practices with Tweedie & Prideaux being at the same address since 1864. The firm undertakes commercial and company work; banking law; foreign and UK commercial and residential property; agricultural property; town and country planning; landlord and tenant; UK and offshore wills, trusts, and probate; business and personal taxation; matrimonial and family; commercial and general civil litigation and work for charities.

INTERNATIONAL: The firm has connections in France, Germany, Zimbabwe and Albania. Work is handled in French, German, and Spanish.

RECRUITMENT: In September 2000, Michael Fowler joined the firm as a consultant from Scott Fowler, and in January 2001 David Eldridge joined as a consultant from Lee & Pembertons.

T

TWITCHEN MUSTERS & KELLY

County Chambers, 25-27 Weston Road, Southend-on-Sea, SS1 1BB
Tel: (01702) 339222 **Fax:** (01702) 331563 **DX:** 2821 Southend
Email: tmk@tmksols.co.uk **Website:** www.tmksols.co.uk

Contact Partner	Patrick Musters
Number of partners	10
Assistant solicitors	12
Other fee-earners	15

AREAS OF PRACTICE

Crime	50%
Family	35%
Civil Litigation	15%

THE FIRM: The largest criminal practice and legal aid firm in Essex, and the first firm in the country to have two Higher Court Advocates conducting criminal work. The firm carries Legal Aid Franchises in ten categories. Partners are Law Society panel members in their respective fields.

PRINCIPAL AREAS OF WORK: Crime, personal injury and civil litigation, family and child care. Agency work welcomed.

TYNDALLWOODS
Windsor House, Temple Row, Birmingham, B2 5TS **Tel:** (0121) 624 1111 **Fax:** (0121) 624 8401 **DX:** 13039 Birmingham 1 **Email:** Mike_Dyer@tyndallwoods.co.uk **Contact:** Mr Mike Dyer • Undertakes a wide range of contracted work within the Community Legal Service and private client work.

AREAS OF PRACTICE

Legal Aid	80%
Private Client	20%

UNDERWOOD & CO (INCORPORATING CORBOULD RIGBY & CO)

40 Welbeck Street, London, W1M 8LN
Tel: (020) 7526 6000 **Fax:** (020) 7486 8974 **DX:** 9074 West End
Email: enquiries@underwoodco.co.uk

Managing Partner	Peter Hughes
Senior Partner	Hilary Guest
Number of partners	8
Assistant solicitors	9
Other fee-earners	4

CONTACTS

Commercial	Peter Hughes, Louise Reid
Commercial Property	Leona Mason
	Justin Roche
Employment	Roger Digby
Litigation	James Baird, Paul Redfern
Private Client	Hilary Guest

THE FIRM: Founded in 1845, Underwood & Co is a forward-looking firm with a broad client base including banks, partnerships, public and private companies and private clients.

PRINCIPAL AREAS OF WORK: All aspects of property, banking and commercial litigation, professional negligence litigation, insolvency, company/commercial, employment law and private client work are handled.

UNDERWOODS

83/85 Marlowes, Hemel Hempstead, HP1 1LF
Tel: (01442) 430900 **Fax:** (01442) 239861
Email: underwoods@compuserve.com

Managing Partner	Robert Males
Number of partners	3
Assistant solicitors	14
Other fee-earners	6

AREAS OF PRACTICE

Employment	35%
Personal Injury	30%
Litigation	15%
Local Governt/Administrative & Public Law	10%
Other	10%

CONTACTS

Administrative/Public Law	Kerry Underwood
Clinical Negligence	Sharon MacArthur
	Joanna McGlew
Employment	Asha Hartnell
	Marc Jones
Human Rights	Kerry Underwood
Litigation	Louise Morgan
Local Government	Kerry Underwood
Personal Injury	Christopher Lavin
Private Client	Robert Males

THE FIRM: Underwoods is a flagship firm and a model for other law firms. It has pioneered contingency and conditional fees, menu pricing and fixed fees and is one of the very few secretary-free law firms. The firm specialises in civil litigation and is particularly well-known for its employment, personal injury and public and administrative law work. It provides a distinctive high-quality service and with its unparalleled standards of client care, Underwoods' glowing reputation is fully deserved. It is one of the best firms of its size. Kerry Underwood leads a team of talented specialist solicitors. Four solicitors are on the Law Society Personal Injury Panel and Marc Jones and Kerry Underwood are members of the Employment Law Advisers Appeal Scheme (formerly the Employment Appeal Tribunal Advice Scheme) and on the Equal Opportunities Commission Panel of Solicitors. The firm undertakes agency advocacy in the Employment Appeal Tribunal as well as Employment Tribunals. The firm has no Legal Aid franchises or contracts and offers a genuinely independent service. The firm's senior partner is a leading authority on conditional fees and author of the best-seller *No Win No Fee No Worries* first published to huge critical acclaim in 1998. He is editor of the Costs Products section of Butterworths *Personal Injury Litigation Service* , on the editorial board of the *Law Society's Litigation Funding* , consultant editor of *Employment Litigation* . Consultant to law firms, local authorities, government departments and Commonwealth Governments, he also conducts seminars for the University of Cambridge, the Law Society and others and contributes to radio, television and to legal journals. He is a former Chairman of Employment Tribunals and a Fellow of the Chartered Institute of Arbitrators.

PRINCIPAL AREAS OF WORK:

Employment: Work includes pensions, transfer of undertakings regulations, sex, race and disability discrimination, maternity law, EU law, Employment Tribunal and Employment Appeal Tribunal advocacy, redundancy and contract, and severance.

Litigation: Work includes personal injury, claimant and defendant (Law Society's Personal Injury Panel), clinical negligence, intellectual property matters, debt recovery and contractual disputes.

Administrative/Public Law: Work includes judicial review, education, civil liberty matters, discrimination, human rights and local authority work.

Local Government Law: Work includes education law, judicial reviews, joint ventures, leasing and funding, transfers of undertakings.

CLIENTELE: Includes local authorities and major companies and employees. Kerry Underwood and Marc Jones are members of the Employment Law Advisers Appeal Scheme (formerly the Employment Appeal Tribunal Advice Scheme), and are both on the Equal Opportunities Commission Panel.

URÍA & MENÉNDEZ

Royex House, Aldermanbury Square, London, EC2V 7NJ
Tel: (020) 7367 0080 **Fax:** (020) 7600 1718
Email: rmn@uria.com **Website:** www.uria.com

Managing Partner	Rodrigo Urla Meruèndano
Number of partners	50
Assistant solicitors	176

AREAS OF PRACTICE

Banking & Securities	35%
Energy & Project Finance	35%
Corporate & M&A	30%

CONTACTS

London Office	Rafael Molina
Madrid Office	Charles Coward
	José Pérez Santos
	Rafael Sebastián
	José María Segovia

THE FIRM: Founded in the 1940s, Uría & Menéndez established itself as a partnership in 1973. Faithful to the tradition begun by Professor Uría, the firm combines the day-to-day practice of law with its scientific and scholarly study. Uría & Menéndez prides itself on the quality of its legal advice, attention to clients, professional objectivity and enduring professional relationships with clients. Currently, the firm comprises 50 partners, 186 associates and over 50 trainee lawyers. A considerable number of Uría & Menéndez's members are actively involved in academic and university life and are authors of numerous legal publications. The London office provides advice on Spanish law to international clients operating from the UK who have interests in Spain or who wish to offer their banking or investment services, make acquisitions or engage in business in Spain. The office also advises Spanish companies already established in the UK or that wish to become established or otherwise engage in business there.

PRINCIPAL AREAS OF WORK: Banking, corporate and commercial, energy law, mergers and acquisitions, foreign investment, project finance and securities.

CLIENTELE: Clients include 54% of the 100 premier companies worldwide and 37% of the 100 premier European companies.

INTERNATIONAL: With its head office in Madrid, Uría & Menéndez also has offices throughout Spain (in Barcelona, Valencia and Bilbao), the rest of Europe (in Brussels, Lisbon and London), the USA (in New York) and in Latin America (in Buenos Aires, Santiago de Chile, Lima, São Paulo and Mexico City). A variety of languages are spoken throughout its various offices including Catalan, English, Finnish, French, German, Italian, Polish, Portuguese, Russian, Spanish and Swedish.

VARLEY HADLEY SIDDALL

3rd Floor, 66-72 Houndsgate, Nottingham, NG1 6BA
Tel: (0115) 958 3737 **Fax:** (0115) 958 3434
Email: post@vhslaw.force9.co.uk

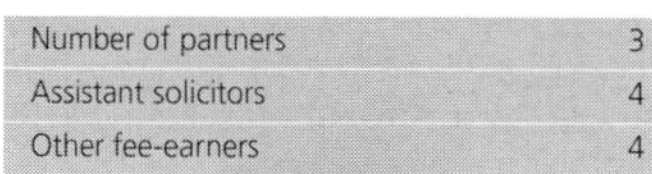

Number of partners	3
Assistant solicitors	4
Other fee-earners	4

THE FIRM: A relatively new practice having previously worked as Berryman & Co crime department. A strong team feeling within the firm means that all clients will receive a high standard of service.

PRINCIPAL AREAS OF WORK: The firm deals almost exclusively with criminal proceedings, with a rapidly developing fraud sector including defending numerous Prescription Pricing Authority matters. The practice has recently prosecuted on behalf of the Health and Safety Executive.

VARLEY HIBBS

Kirby House, Little Park St, Coventry, CV1 2JZ
Tel: (024) 7663 1000 **Fax:** (024) 7663 0808 **DX:** 18892
Email: comm@vhibbs.demon.co.uk
16 Hamilton Terrace, Leamington Spa, CV32 4LY
Tel: (01926) 881251 **Fax:** (01926) 831900 **DX:** 11870

Senior Partner	Edward Bayliss
Number of partners	7
Assistant solicitors	10
Other fee-earners	6

AREAS OF PRACTICE

Company & Commercial	23%
Conveyancing	23%
Civil & Commercial Litigation	18%
Advocacy	17%
Family	10%
Probate & Miscellaneous	9%

THE FIRM: Varley Hibbs is a leading Midlands firm with offices in Coventry and Leamington Spa. Established for over 60 years, the firm offers a wide range of services to a variety of businesses including public and private companies, banks and building societies, along with company directors and private individuals.The practice is committed to being not only a dominant force in commercial law in its own region, but also to providing a real alternative to the major Birmingham practices. The practice is large enough to offer the specialist advice needed by large companies, yet retains the key elements of providing a personal service at competitive rates.

VEALE WASBROUGH

Orchard Court, Orchard Lane, Bristol, BS1 5DS
Tel: (0117) 925 2020 **Fax:** (0117) 925 2025 **DX:** 7831 Bristol
Email: atucker@vwl.co.uk **Website:** www.vwl.co.uk

Managing Partner	Simon Pizzey
Number of partners	23
Assistant solicitors	45
Other fee-earners	55

AREAS OF PRACTICE

Business Non-Contentious	34%
Business Contentious	32%
Personal Legal Services	34%

CONTACTS

Alternative Dispute Resolution	Mike Davies
Central Government	David Worthington
Charities	Gary De'Ath
Clinical Negligence	Gary McFarlane
Commercial Litigation	Simon Heald
Company & Commercial	David Worthington
Construction	Roger Hoyle
Conveyancing	Mike Rendell
Education	Robert Boyd
Employment	Mike Davies
Energy/Environment	Tim Smithers
Estates & Tax Planning	Mary McCartney
Family	Janet Forbes
Insolvency	Simon Heald
International Trade	David Worthington
Local Authorities	Simon Baker
Partnership: Medical Practices	Derek Bellew
Personal Injury	John Webster
Pipeline Projects	Tim Smithers
Planning	Tim Smithers
Property Services	Gary Philpott
Public Sector & Utilities	Simon Baker
Retail	Simon Heald
Sports	Simon Pizzey
Technology & E-Commerce	Paul Sampson
Wastes Management	Tim Smithers

THE FIRM: Veale Wasbrough is a Bristol based firm with a regional and national profile. It is recognised as being a young, dynamic, people-centred firm with a commitment to success and excellence. The team of partners, lawyers and support staff achieve this by providing a professional and personalised service, underpinned by a team culture founded on the principles of partnership and support. The firm is enjoying significant expansion.

PRINCIPAL AREAS OF WORK:

Company & Commercial: The focus of much of the firm's work is in the provision of specialist services to the mid sized business sector in Bristol and the south west. The firm advises its clients on a wide range of issues including MBOs, joint ventures, acquisitions, mergers, sales, company start-ups, partnerships and commercial transactions. Project finance and banking are both growing areas.

Property Services: With one of the biggest and fastest growing property teams in the region, Veale Wasbrough has the breadth of experience and expertise to advise on a whole range of property related matters including property development, property management, property investment and property litigation. Specialist areas include energy and environment, planning, urban regeneration and pipelines.

Education: The nationally recognised education team advises on a whole range of matters affecting schools and colleges around the UK including crisis management.

Construction: The construction team builds on the industry experience of its lawyers and handles all aspects of construction law including contract formation and procurement advice as well as dispute management.

Employment: The full spectrum of issues affecting employment and the workplace is covered: employee benefits and rights, discrimination, grievance procedures, dismissal and transfers of undertakings.

Commercial Litigation: Well known for its strength in commercial litigation, the firm is active in alternative dispute resolution and has a number of qualified mediators.

Technology & E-commerce: The technology and e-commerce team provide advice on all aspects of this growing area, including intellectual property (particularly in the context of technology), computer systems procurement and e-commerce.

Personal Injury: The well-known personal injury team acts for claimants and handles accidents at work, RTAs, sports injuries and clinical negligence claims.

Estates & Tax Planning: Trusts and personal planning requirements are handled by a dedicated team that provides advice and assistance to the business sector as well as to the private investor.

Continued overleaf

INTERNATIONAL: Veale Wasbrough is a founder member of the Association of European Lawyers, which provides a valuable network of lawyers in 27 countries. The firm has a growing client base in Europe, the Far East and the US.

RECRUITMENT: The firm offers seven training contracts each year. Information and an application form are available on the website.

VEITCH PENNY

1 Manor Court, Dix's Field, Exeter, EX1 1UP
Tel: (01392) 278381 **Fax:** (01392) 410247 **DX:** 8309 Exeter 1
Email: credlaw@veitchpenny.co.uk **Website:** www.veitchpenny.co.uk

2 Market Street, Crediton, EX17 2AL
Tel: (01363) 772244 **Fax:** (01363) 775874 **DX:** 54201 Crediton
Email: credlaw@veitchpenny.co.uk

Managing Partner	Simon Young
Number of partners	10
Assistant solicitors	6
Other fee-earners	14

AREAS OF PRACTICE

Defendant Litigation	52%
Plaintiff Litigation	24%
Conveyancing	12%
General Litigation	5%
Commercial	4%
Trust & Probate	3%

CONTACTS

Claimant PI	Andrew Harris
	Alan Crawford
Commercial, Insolvency & Employment	Simon Young
Conveyancing, Probate & Trusts	Charles Dowell
	Ian Penny
Defendant PI	Mark Fowles
	Mark Hammerton
	Michael Penny
	Jessica Ross
	James Ruttledge

V

THE FIRM: Founded over 30 years ago, Veitch Penny was the first firm in the South West to achieve the Law Society's quality award 'Lexcel', in recognition of their commitment to efficiency, quality and client care. The national Investor in People award was also achieved in 1998. Veitch Penny is particularly noted for its expertise in personal injury litigation.

PRINCIPAL AREAS OF WORK: Insurance Department: Veitch Penny is regarded as one of the leading insurance advisors in the South of England, currently acting on behalf of over 24 National Insurers, as well as over 20 Local & Public Authorities. Wide experience is held in motor, employment, public and professional indemnity work, with particular expertise in dyslexia, abuse and stress. The department has its own investigative team, whose services are offered to insurers; advanced IT systems, and a high tech database offering comprehensive statistics to clients.
Claimant Department: Undertakes personal injury and bulk insured/uninsured loss recovery work for legal expense insurers, listing amongst its clients a major motoring organisation. Considered one of the largest claimant practices in the Southwest specialising in accident work, the department handles volume motor RTA claims with fastest growth in 2000-01 in the field of motorcycle accidents.
Other Areas: The firm also works in the areas of company/commercial; insolvency; employment; commercial and residential property; wills, probate, tax and trusts; agricultural litigation; matrimonial. There is a particular expertise in the new field of limited liability partnerships.

VENTERS & CO

1-6 Camberwell Green, London, SE5 7AD
Tel: (020) 7277 0110 **Fax:** (020) 7277 0132 **DX:** 35310 - Camberwell
Email: info@venters.co.uk

Partners	June Venters Alison Todd
Number of partners	2
Assistant solicitors	8
Other fee-earners	11

THE FIRM: Venters & Co. was established in 1991 by June Venters. June Venters is a solicitor/advocate who isPresident (elect) of the London Criminal Courts Solicitors Association. She is an accredited assessor for the children panel and sits as a Recorder of the Crown Court. In 1996 she was the subject of a BBC TV documentary entitled *Law Women.* The firm specialises in crime, family, welfare benefits and mental health. It undertakes both legal aid and privately funded cases. June Venters, as managing partner, heads a strong and committed team which comprises Robin Brown, Practice Director and Alison Todd, salaried partner, along with associate solicitors and support staff. The firm has a recognized and established reputation and is well known for its representation of high profile cases.

VICTOR LISSACK & ROSCOE

8 Bow Street, Covent Garden, London, WC2E 7AJ **Tel:** (020) 7240 2010 **Fax:** (020) 7379 4420 **DX:** 40026 Covent Garden **Email:** law@victorlissack.co.uk **Ptnrs:** 3 **Asst solrs:** 3 **Other fee-earners:** 2 **Contact:** Mr Richard Almond • Specialists in white collar and all other crime including extradition and courts martial.

AREAS OF PRACTICE

Criminal Law	75%
Private Client	25%

VINSON & ELKINS LLP

Regis House, 45 King William Street, London, EC4R 9AN **Tel:** (020) 7618 6000 **Fax:** (020) 7618 6001 **Email:** jlamaster@velaw.com **Ptnrs:** 7 **Asst solrs:** 12 **Other fee-earners:** 1

VIZARD OLDHAM

High Holborn House, 52-4 High Holborn, London, WC1V 6RL
Tel: (020) 7663 2222 **Fax:** (020) 7663 2226 **DX:** 152 London/Chancery Lane
Email: reception@vizold.co.uk **Website:** www.vizold.co.uk

Senior Partner	Richard Foster

AREAS OF PRACTICE

Public Law & Clinical Negligence	30%
Property	20%
Insurance Litigation	20%
Company/Commercial	10%
Commercial Litigation & Employment	10%
Charity Law & Parliamentary	5%
Private Client & Family Law	5%

CONTACTS

Charities & Private Client	Ron Perry
Clinical Negligence	Richard Foster
Commercial & Environmental Litigation	Gary Hay
Company/Commercial	Iain Mitchell
Employment	Gary Hay
Environmental Law (Non-Contentious)	Richard Barber
Family Law	Julia Snow
Local Government/Public Law	John Morrell
Parliamentary	Ron Perry
Personal Injury & Insurance	Mark Whittaker
Professional Negligence	David Hartfield
Property	Richard Barber
Rail & Transport	Justine Lawson

THE FIRM: Founded on 1 May 1999 as a successor firm to Vizards, the new firm of Vizard Oldham prides itself in the pursuit of excellence in the provision of legal services in those specialist areas within which it operates. The firm has doubled in size since its formation and now is undoubtedly a market leader in all of its principal areas of work. Full service standards are in place with accreditation under ISO 9001.

PRINCIPAL AREAS OF WORK:

Public Law & Parliamentary: Vizard Oldham is one of the few firms which is able to handle a wide range of matters on behalf of the public sector, ranging from risk management and liability claims through to judicial review, human rights, education, community care, mental health, planning, immigration, housing and criminal prosecution. The firm is exceptional in having as a partner a Roll 'A' parliamentary agent authorised to promote and oppose private bills in Parliament.

Healthcare & Clinical Negligence: The firm is now undoubtedly one of the leading specialist firms in this area, its capability enhanced by two recent appointments at partnership level. It is one of the small number of firms appointed by the NHS to defend clinical negligence claims. The department also deals with criminal law, commercial work, employment law, charity advice and consent to treatment cases.

Professional Negligence: Led by one of the renowned experts in the field, the department acts for a wide range of insurers defending professional indemnity claims and advising on policy issues. Professions covered include accountants, architects, solicitors, engineers, insurance intermediaries, licensed conveyancers and surveyors.

Property: Vizard Oldham offers a complete property service: commercial and domestic, contentious and non-contentious. In particular it has a specialist online domestic conveyancing service www.perfectlylegal.co.uk

Charity Law: The firm acts for a range of private and public charities, dealing with all aspects of their work including intellectual property rights, property work, formation, variation of Royal Charters and advice in connection with trading subsidiaries.

Private Client & Family Law: This department's work covers the full spectrum of the needs of private clients, including tax planning and trust adminstration. The firm also has a dedicated family law department, covering divorce, separation agreements and the effects of divorce upon the family in terms of both finance and children.

Company Commercial: The company commercial department aims to meet all the day-to-day needs of corporate and business clients, including flotation and issues, terms and conditions of business, partnerships, contracts, share option schemes and takeovers, mergers and buy-outs. The department works closely with the firm's property department and also covers employment law and commercial dispute resolution.

INTERNATIONAL: The firm has a formal association with the French firm Douma, Schofield & Sibenaler in Paris and is represented internationally through the International Grouping of Lawyers.

VIZARDS, STAPLES & BANNISTERS

Asia House, 31-33 Lime Street, London, EC3M 7HT **Tel:** (020) 7400 9999 **Fax:** (020) 7626 7788 **DX:** 165 Chancery Lane **Email:** mrs@vsb.co.uk **Website:** www.vsb.co.uk **Number of partners:**30 **Assistant solicitors:**32 **Total staff:**167

V-LEX LTD.

Ivy House, Gateford Rd, Gateford, Worksop, S81 8AE **Tel:** (01909) 544 000 **Fax:** (01909) 544 001 **Website:** www.v-lex.com **Ptnrs:** 5 **Asst solrs:** 3 **Other fee-earners:** 6

WACE MORGAN

2 Belmont, Shrewsbury, SY1 1TD **Tel:** (01743) 280100 **Fax:** (01743) 280111 **DX:** 19718 **Email:** help@wmlaw.co.uk **Ptnrs:** 8 **Asst solrs:** 11 **Other fee-earners:** 8

W

WACKS CALLER

Steam Packet House, 76 Cross Street, Manchester, M2 4JU
Tel: (0161) 957 8888 **Fax:** (0161) 957 8899 **DX:** 14383 Manchester 1
Email: law@wackscaller.com **Website:** www.wackscaller.com

Managing & senior partner	Martin Caller
Number of partners:	16
Assistant solicitors:	19
Other fee-earners:	2

AREAS OF PRACTICE

Company/Commercial	45%
Litigation	30%
Property	15%
Employment	5%
IT/IP	5%

CONTACTS

Commercial Property	Elizabeth Mackay
Corporate Finance	Kevin Philbin
Employment	Anthony Dempsey
General Company/Commercial	Martin Caller
Information Technology	Simon Wallwork
Litigation	Christopher Sorrell

THE FIRM: Established in 1986, Wacks Caller has grown from its original two partners to be one of the top 10 commercial firms in Manchester with 16 partners in 2001. The firm has continued to strengthen its position as a leading specialist in the realm of corporate finance, company and commercial work. The firm's growth is largely a result of its ethos that the client must come first and aims to provide the very best in expert advice and support to its clients.

PRINCIPAL AREAS OF WORK:
Company/Commercial: The firm provides vigorous expert advice and assistance for the business community on all types of corporate and commercial transactions, including Stock Exchange and Takeover Panel work. It is especially renowned for its skill and pragmatic approach in negotiating merger and acquisition agreements, joint venture agreements and MBOs.
Commercial Litigation: This department has continued to grow rapidly by providing an aggressive yet user-friendly service for the commercial client and institutional client.
Commercial Property: This department handles all commercial property transactions and other property related matters with the emphasis on speed (where required) in addition to skill and experience.
Employment: The firm provides a commercial and practical approach to all employment and related issues for both employers and senior employees.
Information Technology: This department handles a significant amount of work advising clients on start up and finance raising and providing counsel on a variety of internet related issues.
Intellectual Property: This department continues to grow in both contentious and non-contentious fields.

W

WAKE DYNE LAWTON

Worley Bank House, Bolesworth Road, Tattenhall, Chester, CH3 9HL **Tel:** (01829) 773100 **Fax:** (01829) 773109 **Email:** bdw@wdl.co.uk **Website:** www.wdl.co.uk **Ptnrs:** 4 **Asst solrs:** 1 **Other fee-earners:** 5 **Contact:** Mr Brian Wake • Specialist practice dealing on a national basis exclusively with minerals, waste, planning, environmental, road haulage law and health and safety law.

AREAS OF PRACTICE

Minerals	30%
Transport	30%
Planning/Environmental	25%
Waste	15%

WAKE SMITH

68 Clarkehouse Road, Sheffield, S10 2LJ **Tel:** (0114) 266 6660 **Fax:** (0114) 267 1253 **DX:** 10534 Sheffield **Email:** legal@wake-smith.co.uk **Ptnrs:** 14 **Asst solrs:** 5 **Other fee-earners:** 21

WALKER CHARLESWORTH & FOSTER

26 Park Square, Leeds, LS1 2PL **Tel:** (0113) 245 3594 **Fax:** (0113) 244 4312 **DX:** 26415 Leeds Park Square **Email:** mail@walkercharlesworth.co.uk **Ptnrs:** 7 **Asst solrs:** 5 **Other fee-earners:** 7 **Contact:** Colin Birtwistle • A long established practice specialising in registered social landlord and charitable work.

WALKER LAIRD

9 Gilmour Street, Paisley, PA1 1DG **Tel:** (0141) 887 5271 **Fax:** (0141) 889 3268 **DX:** 32 Paisley **Ptnrs:** 6 **Asst solrs:** 6 **Other fee-earners:** 4

WALKER MORRIS

Kings Court, 12 King Street, Leeds, LS1 2HL
Tel: (0113) 283 2500 **Fax:** (0113) 245 9412 **DX:** 12051 LEEDS-1
Email: info@walkermorris.co.uk **Website:** www.walkermorris.co.uk

Managing Partner	Michael Taylor
Number of partners	37
Assistant solicitors	86
Other fee-earners	200

AREAS OF PRACTICE	
Commercial Litigation	30%
Commercial Property	30%
Company & Commercial	20%
Building Societies	16%
Private Clients	2%
Tax	2%

CONTACTS	
Banking & Finance	Michael Taylor
Building Societies	David Duckworth
Commercial Dispute Resolution	Gwendoline Davies
Commercial Property	Paul Walker
Competition	Jeremy Scholes
Construction	Martin Scott
Corporate & Commercial	Peter Smart
Corporate Finance	Ian Gilbert
Corporate Tax	Simon Concannon
Employment	David Smedley
Information Technology/E-commerce	Patrick Cantrill
Insolvency	Philip Mudd
Insurance Litigation	Christopher Caisley
Intellectual Property	Patrick Cantrill
	Alison Murphy
Media & Entertainment	Ralph Coyle
Pensions	Andrew Turnbull
Planning & Environment	Andrew Williamson
Private Client	Richard Manning
Professional Negligence	Andrew Beck
Public Sector & PFI	David Kilduff
Sports Law	Christopher Caisley

THE FIRM: Walker Morris is one of the leading independent law firms in the country. Recent recognition includes the 'Regional Law Firm of the Year' award and the 'Most Successful Regional Law Firm' accolade from leading legal magazines. Walker Morris has achieved its success by always placing clients first. The firm's strong and innovative client service was recognised recently in a weekly legal magazine's marketing awards. Speed, commerciality, value and approachability have been cited by clients as major attributes of the firm. Walker Morris has an extensive and impressive client list including substantial public companies, banks, insurers, venture capitalists, fund managers, multinational corporations and private companies operating in all sectors. The firm's major strength is its ability to recruit, train and motivate top quality lawyers. Walker Morris was the first firm to give clients direct access to its time recording systems to ensure complete transparency on billing and its innovative approach to client service includes sharing its knowhow and providing legal training via its ground-breaking online service *reach...*™

PRINCIPAL AREAS OF WORK:

Corporate: The corporate department acts for corporate clients, institutions and management teams. Its work includes the full range of corporate finance, flotations, acquisitions, disposals, joint ventures and innovative private deals, with specialists dealing with areas such as competition law and pensions advice.

Commercial Property & Planning: The property department is one of the largest outside London, with great strength in depth to deal with transactions involving large portfolios. Clients turn to specialist partners for advice on all aspects of development, including major town centre redevelopments and large-scale residential sites. Its retail team acts for many of the best known national and international high street names and its town and country planning and environmental group includes more nationally ranked partners than any other. The department has a growing institutional client base and its property management service is supported by specialist property litigators.

Commercial Dispute Resolution: Commercial dispute resolution is an important part of Walker Morris' practice. The team deals with a broad range of major dispute work both within the UK and internationally, and has had a number of notable successes in the Court of Appeal during 2000. walkermorriscollect™ is a specialist unit within the group that acts for institutional clients collecting commercial debt, using the latest systems with online access.

Banking & Finance: Banking and finance are particular strengths of the firm. Clients include the major banks, asset based lenders and insolvency practitioners and the team's work includes advising on structured finance, acquisition and project finance, property finance, turnaround and insolvency. Specialist litigators and property lawyers complete the picture to provide a complete service to the finance sector.

Employment & Human Resources: These issues are critical to all large clients and our employment group is held in the highest regard. The group offers a complete service to human resources departments, including helplines and consultancy services.

Construction: The construction sector is well catered for at Walker Morris. It is now one of the strongest groups in the region acting for main contractors, sub-contractors and employers on both contentious and non-contentious matters.

Intellectual Property & Information Technology: Walker Morris has a highly regarded intellectual property and information technology group, which now ranks amongst the largest outside London. Offering a truly one stop practice covering all aspects of contentious and non contentious work, it has achieved a number of successes in patent and other IP/IT actions and been engaged in some high profile licensing, procurement and joint venture projects. In accordance with this full service, the group includes one of the UK's most active and fast growing trade mark management practices. Recently, it has strengthened its new media practice and has carried out some groundbreaking work in the areas of interactive TV and e-commerce.

Public Sector & PFI: The firm's public sector and PFI group provides a full service to public sector clients, including health authorities and trusts, local government, the education sector, utilities and others. Work includes specialist training and support in connection with the Human Rights Act (where the firm was the first to launch a dedicated Human Rights group to advise the sector).

Commercial: Commercial contracting work is a major focus of Walker Morris' development. In both the private and public sectors, the firm provides advice on procurement contracts, joint ventures, agency and distribution agreements, outsourcing and the full range of commercial agreements.

Sports Law: The sports law unit acts for sports personalities, clubs and associations working within this industry and work includes contract negotiations and disputes, personality merchandising and licensing agreements.

Additional Areas: Walker Morris is one of few firms able to provide advocacy and advisory services to directors, corporations and other bodies in connection with commercial fraud, corporate killing, health and safety and other areas where the criminal law touches on corporate or public life. The advocacy group has had

Continued overleaf

W

outstanding successes in coroners' courts, public enquiries and the criminal courts. Walker Morris has developed a service called Walker Morris OnLine which is now a market leader in providing volume mortgage lending services. This has added to the firm's long-standing services to the building society and domestic finance sector which includes mortgage recovery and professional negligence services.

CLIENTELE: Clients are drawn from the whole spectrum of commerce and industry including manufacturing, construction and development, high technology, the financial services industry and the retail and service industries.

INTERNATIONAL: The firm advises on European and EU issues and has a growing international practice and has developed very close and mutually beneficial relationships with law firms in the EU. The consistent element in those relationships is a common philosophy and approach.

RECRUITMENT: The firm's year-on-year expansion has resulted in always having a continuing recruitment policy for motivated young solicitors in all major disciplines. The firm recruits around 10 trainee solicitors every year. Discretionary grants are provided. Career prospects are excellent (most of the partners were articled within the firm). Application forms and recruitment brochures are available from Nick Cannon, Recruitment Partner. A training scheme is available to keep its lawyers up-to-date, consisting of in-house seminars, external conferences, and information updates.

WALKER SMITH & WAY

26 Nicholas Street, Chester, CH1 2PQ **Tel:** (01244) 357 400 **Fax:** (01244) 357 444 **DX:** 19982 Chester 1 **Email:** law.wsw@dial.pipex.com
Ptnrs: 24 **Asst solrs:** 26 **Other fee-earners:** 15

WALLACE & PARTNERS

One Portland Place, London, W1B 1PN
Tel: (020) 7636 4422 **Fax:** (020) 7636 3736 **DX:** 82990 Mayfair
Email: lawyers@wallace.co.uk **Website:** www.wallace.co.uk

Managing Partner	Rex Newman
Number of partners	6
Assistant solicitors	6
Other fee-earners	6

CONTACTS

Company/Commercial	Rex Newman
Employment	Nicholas Yapp
Litigation	Simon Serota
Private Client	Barry Shaw
	Adrian Wallace
Property	Martin Otvos
	Barry Shaw
	Adrian Wallace

THE FIRM: Wallace & Partners is a niche commercial practice based in Portland Place, London. The firm has developed a strong client base and established a reputation for conducting the transactional work more commonly associated with much larger practices. Wallace & Partners prides itself on close team-work generated in a smaller, more collegial environment.

PRINCIPAL AREAS OF WORK:

Company/Commercial: Work includes Stock Exchange advice including public issues, commercial contracts, venture capital, joint ventures, management buy-outs and buy-ins, mergers and acquisitions, loan arrangements, advice on the responsibilities of directors; shareholder agreements; tax planning, franchising and general commercial matters.
Litigation: The firm is strong in property-related litigation as well as professional negligence, shareholder and boardroom disputes, and general commercial litigation. One partner is a Deputy Costs Judge.
Employment: This department deals with all aspects of employment law both contentious and non-contentious.
Property: Work includes development, investment, acquisition and funding, planning and environmental, business leases, rent reviews, estate management and general landlord and tenant work.
Private Client: This department deals with personal financial planning including wills, capital tax advice, trusts and probate, as well as employment-related immigration work.
ADR & Mediation: The firm also handles ADR and mediation work, one partner being a registered mediator.

CLIENTELE: The firm acts for a diverse spread of clients including listed companies, family businesses, entrepreneurs and overseas investors.

INTERNATIONAL: Wallace & Partners has developed a network of contacts throughout Europe and provides advice on many aspects of international commerce. One of the partners is a member of the New York Bar.

RECRUITMENT: Contact Gina Connell for an application form.

WALTONS & MORSE

Birchin Court, 20 Birchin Lane, London, EC3V 9ER
Tel: (020) 7623 4255 **Fax:** (020) 7626 4153 **DX:** City 1065
Email: waltons@wamlaw.co.uk **Website:** www.waltonsandmorse.com

Managing Partner	Ian Charles-Jones
Senior Partner	David Perry
Number of partners	5
Assistant solicitors	5
Other fee-earners	7

AREAS OF PRACTICE

Shipping & Transit......78%
Marine Insurance......10%
International Trade......10%
Reinsurance......2%

CONTACTS

Shipping......David Perry

THE FIRM: Waltons & Morse is a long-established City firm serving the marine insurance market, and with an international reputation in the areas of shipping, transport and international trade.

PRINCIPAL AREAS OF WORK:
General Description: All aspects of marine insurance, shipping and transit law including international trade.

CLIENTELE: Lloyd's, London and overseas insurance companies, ship operators (particularly from the Far East) and salvors.

WARD GETHIN

8-12 Tuesday Market Place, King's Lynn, PE30 1JT **Tel:** (01553) 660033 **Fax:** (01553) 766857 **DX:** 57813 **Email:** enquiries@wardgethin.co.uk
Ptnrs: 14 **Asst solrs:** 9 **Other fee-earners:** 11

W

WARD HADAWAY

Sandgate House, 102 Quayside, Newcastle upon Tyne, NE1 3DX
Tel: (0191) 204 4000 **Fax:** (0191) 204 4001 **DX:** 61265 Newcastle Upon Tyne
Email: legal@wardhadaway.com **Website:** www.wardhadaway.com

Town Hall Chambers, 7 Beach Road, South Shields, NE33 2QR
Tel: (0191) 456 8721 **Fax:** (0191) 456 4125 **DX:** 60755 South Shields

Senior Partner	George Scott
Managing Partner	Jamie Martin
Number of partners	42
Assistant solicitors	43
Other fee-earners	43

AREAS OF PRACTICE

Litigation......38%
Property/Planning......35%
Company/Commercial......20%
Private Client Services......7%

CONTACTS

Agriculture......Christopher Hewitt
Banking......Julie Harrison
Charities......Elizabeth MacRobert
Commercial Litigation......Ian Collinson
Commercial Property......Richard Freeman-Wallace
Company/Commercial......Colin Hewitt
Construction......Paul Reekie
Corporate Finance......Martin Hulls
Corporate Recovery......Jim James
Employment......David Hesselberth
Healthcare......Jeffrey Keeble
IT/IP......Bob Elliott
Licensing......Stephen Graham
Pensions......David Knox
Planning & Development......Neil Robson
Private Client......Susan Craig
Property Litigation......Margaret Lawson
Public Sector......Bob Edgar

wardhadaway

THE FIRM: Ward Hadaway is one of the most progressive commercial law firms in the North of England. Known for its fresh and innovative approach, Ward Hadaway delivers a comprehensive range of legal and town planning services to the highest quality standards. The firm works in partnership with clients to gain a detailed understanding of their business in order to provide clear, appropriate, relevant and commercial advice. With its philosophy of 'clients come first', the firm continues to make significant investments in IT, human resources and marketing in order to further increase efficiency and enhance client focus.

PRINCIPAL AREAS OF WORK: Ward Hadaway is structured around specialist teams which span the four main departments of property, commercial, litigation and private client.
Commercial: Within the commercial department, the corporate finance team advises on acquisitions and disposals, joint ventures, MBOs and MBIs, private equity, business finance, reorganisations, share incentives and Stock Exchange work. Ward Hadaway is increasingly recognised as the leading technology practice in the North East, and the corporate finance team was responsible for floating four technology companies in a six month period last year. The firm's IP/IT team is involved with a wide range of high quality work, both contentious and non contentious, and works closely with incubators in the North East supporting business start-ups in this field. Other commercial areas covered by Ward Hadaway include pensions, competition and charities.
Public Sector: Ward Hadaway's public sector team has acted for more than 50 local government and public sector clients, and work in this area is increasing rapidly. The healthcare team has been appointed to the NHS Litigation Authority panel, and represents NHS trusts and health authorities throughout the north of England. The firm is also a panel solicitor for the United Kingdom Central Council for Nursing, Midwifery and Health Visiting (UKCC) and is the only law firm in the country to sit on both panels.
Litigation: Within the litigation department, the commercial litigation and employment teams both act for clients nationally as well as regionally. The firm's corporate recovery team has invested substantially in IT and human resources to increase debt collection capabilities to service clients throughout the country. Other teams in this department specialise in construction and engineering disputes, property litigation, licensing and family law.
Property: The property department deals with planning and development and commercial property, including landlord and tenant, property investment, residential and estate development, housing associations and town and country planning. The planning team has six chartered town planners and associated staff making it one of the largest planning consultancies in the North East. A specialist agricultural team also advises farmers and landowners on all aspects of farming and environmental law.
Private Client: This department advises on wills, administration of estates, trust planning and administration, capital tax planning, gifts and settlements and charities.

WARNER GOODMAN & STREAT

66 West Street, Fareham, PO16 0JR **Tel:** (01329) 288121 **Fax:** (01329) 822714 **DX:** 40804 **Email:** enquiries@warnergoodman.co.uk **Website:** www.warnergoodman.co.uk **Ptnrs:** 16 **Asst solrs:** 20 **Other fee-earners:** 44

WATERSON HICKS

14-15 Philpot Lane, London, EC3M 8AJ
Tel: (020) 7929 6060 **Fax:** (020) 7929 3748
Email: law@waterson-hicks.com

Managing Partner	Martin Wisdom
Number of partners	4
Assistant solicitors	3
Other fee-earners	2

CONTACTS

Admiralty .... Stuart Parkin
Commodities & Commercial .. Martin Wisdom
.... Subir Karmakar
Insurance .... John Hicks
Shipping .... John Hicks
.... Brian Isola

THE FIRM: Waterson Hicks is a commercial practice specialising in all aspects of maritime law and commodity litigation. The firm's work and clientele are largely international.

PRINCIPAL AREAS OF WORK: Shipping work covers all areas of commercial and admiralty litigation and arbitration including marine insurance.

CLIENTELE: Clients include major ship owners, oil companies, charterers, commodity traders, P&I clubs, insurance companies and shipyards for whom primarily contentious work is carried out.

INTERNATIONAL: The firm has strong overseas connections particularly in Greece, the United States, Spanish-speaking countries and the Indian subcontinent. French, Spanish and Portuguese are spoken within the firm.

W

WATMORES

Chancery House, 53/66 Chancery Lane, London, WC2A 1QU **Tel:** (020) 7430 1512 **Fax:** (020) 7405 7382 **DX:** LDE 246 **Email:** enquiries@watmores.co.uk **Website:** www.watmores.co.uk **Ptnrs:** 8 **Asst solrs:** 2 **Other fee-earners:** 3

WATSON BURTON

20 Collingwood Street, Newcastle upon Tyne, NE99 1YQ **Tel:** (0191) 244 4444 **Fax:** (0191) 244 4500 **DX:** 61009 Newcastle **Email:** WB@dial.pipex.com **Ptnrs:** 19 **Asst solrs:** 22 **Other fee-earners:** 37

WATSON, FARLEY & WILLIAMS

15 Appold Street, London, EC2A 2HB
Tel: (020) 7814 8000 **Fax:** (020) 7814 8141 **DX:** 530 London City EC3
Email: inquiries@wfw.com **Website:** www.wfw.com

Chairman	Christopher Preston
Chief Executive	Michael Reid
Managing Partner	Michael Greville
Number of partners worldwide	55
Number of lawyers worldwide	218

CONTACTS

International Corporate .... Jan Mellmann
International Finance .... Michael Vernell
International Litigation .... David Kavanagh
International Tax .... Stéphane Salou

THE FIRM: Established in 1982, Watson, Farley & Williams is an international corporate and commercial law firm recognised for its excellence in banking and asset financing, particularly ship and aircraft finance. The firm also advises in a number of specialist areas in corporate law, litigation and tax law. Through its spread of international offices and contacts, the firm offers an integrated multijurisdictional service to clients. A key feature is the firm's division into four international practice groups – corporate, finance, litigation and tax. These groups are not divided by location. They work together internationally to serve clients. With its broad base of clients, the international experience of the firm is comprehensive. The firm's international expertise has been acknowledged through a number of awards. In November 2000 the firm was voted by the international shipping industry as the world's leading firm for ship finance. In January 2000, the firm also received international recognition for its asset finance and leasing work.

PRINCIPAL AREAS OF WORK:
International Corporate Group: Public and private company clients have access to a wide range of domestic and international expertise covering all aspects of international corporate law, including acquisitions, disposals and mergers, public offerings of securities, management buy-outs and buy-ins, business and asset sales, debt structuring, equity financings, corporate restructurings, international privatisations, and a wide range of commercial agreements such as distributorship, outsourcing purchase and agency agreements, and joint ventures and partnerships. In addition, the group offers specialist advice on real property, intellectual property, employment, service agreements, share option and incentive schemes, executive immigration, and all aspects of European Union competition law. The group focuses particularly on the provision of advice to clients in the transportation, power, telecommunication and e-commerce sectors.
International Finance Group: Lawyers advise all project participants, covering areas such as general banking finance, structured finance, securities and capital markets, derivatives, trade finance, asset finance, project finance, cross-border tax leverage lending and leasing, and work outs and insolvencies. The group has particular expertise and experience in a number of industry sectors heavily dependent on the financing of large capital assets, including shipping, aviation, telecommunications, power and energy.
International Litigation Group: Large scale litigation, arbitration and dispute resolution matters are handled by the group on a worldwide basis. Lawyers have represented clients involved in international disputes in

the areas of shipping (wet and dry), banking, offshore oil and gas, international trade, and aviation. The group also advises on the enforcement of security over vessels, marine pollution, marine insurance, shipbuilding, charterparties, and offshore oil and gas contracting.

International Tax Group: Lawyers advise on domestic and cross-border tax leasing, non-asset based structured finance, international tax planning, investigations and litigation, and indirect tax. They also give advice generally on all types of transactions. The indirect tax team specialists have considerable VAT experience.

CLIENTELE: The firm's client base spans the world, and includes international banks, financial institutions, quoted and private companies, shipping companies, airlines, off-shore oil and gas companies, and governments and government agencies.

INTERNATIONAL: With offices in Piraeus, Paris, New York, Moscow and Singapore, and a network of correspondent specialist lawyers, the firm's reach is truly international. Lawyers are able to advise on English, French, Russian, New York and US Federal law. All offices have expertise in the laws of the local jurisdiction and an understanding of local business customs and culture. Languages spoken at the firm include Cantonese, Dutch, English, French, Greek, Italian, Mandarin, Malay, Norwegian, Russian, Spanish, Swahili and Swedish.

WEDLAKE BELL

16 Bedford Street, Covent Garden, London, WC2E 9HF
Tel: (020) 7395 3000 **Fax:** (020) 7836 9966 **DX:** 40009 Covent Gdn.
Email: legal@wedlakebell.com **Website:** www.wedlakebell.com

Managing Partner	Julian Cuppage
Senior Partner	Robert Dolman
Number of partners	33
Assistant solicitors	33
Other fee-earners	24

AREAS OF PRACTICE

Property & Construction	30%
Corporate Finance & Banking	25%
Tax & Trusts	20%
Commercial/IP/Internet	15%
Employment, Pensions & Share Schemes	10%

CONTACTS

Banking	Hilary Platt
Commercial	Barry Weatherill
Commercial Property	John Cowlishaw
Construction	Suzanne Reeves
Corporate Finance	Andrew Baker
E-Business/IT	Adrian Heath-Saunders
Employment	Richard Isham
Intellectual Property	Jonathan Cornthwaite
Litigation	Richard Hewitt
Pensions & Share Schemes	Clive Weber
Tax & Trusts	Peter Watts

WEDLAKE BELL

THE FIRM: Wedlake Bell serves business and the owners, managers and inheritors of business and their families. It is recognised as having the transaction experience, skills and back up support of much larger firms from whom it consistently wins business. Its size and approach enable clients to build long-term personal relationships with the individual lawyers of their choice. Its informal, creative culture has resulted in very low staff turnover and has made it an attractive alternative for top class lawyers who wish to escape the big law firm environment. During the last year Wedlake Bell advised clients in the following sectors: banking, computing and software; dot.com start-ups; construction and engineering; consumer goods manufacturing; food manufacturing; healthcare; hotel and catering; information technology; marketing and branding; offshore trusts; oil, gas and mineral extraction; pharmaceuticals; property; publishing and printing; sport and leisure; support services; private wealth planning.

PRINCIPAL AREAS OF WORK:

Corporate Finance & Banking: The corporate finance team advises on mergers and acquisitions, flotations, placings and rights issues, venture capital, asset transactions, joint ventures, inward investment and investment funds. The banking team advises on transaction and project finance, secured, syndicated and bilateral lending for both borrowers and lenders and on asset finance.

Commercial Property & Construction: The commercial property team acts for developers, investors, banks, landlords and tenants in relation to trading, developing, funding, occupying or investing in land. The construction team advises on construction contracts and disputes.

IP/IT, Commercial & Internet: This team advises on e-business issues, intellectual property, data protection, internet law, IT contracts, commercial agreements such as franchises, merchandising and outsourcing and competition law.

Employment, Pensions & Share Schemes: This team advises on both contentious and non-contentious employment law. It acts for the trustees, employers and members of a wide range of occupational pensions schemes, and advise on share schemes and long-term incentive plans.

Private Clients, Tax & Wealth Protection: This team advises on tax planning, trusts, offshore tax jurisdictions, wills and inheritance, asset protection, landed estates, probate, heritage and agricultural properties. It acts for entrepreneurs, business managers and new enterprise investors as well as long established family wealth. The team also provides residential conveyancing and matrimonial dispute services.

Dispute Resolution: Specialists in dispute resolution provide support for all the firm's core practice areas whether by litigation, arbitration, mediation or adjudication (in construction).

INTERNATIONAL: Wedlake Bell has affiliate law firms in most European jurisdictions and in the USA. A significant part of its annual turnover derives from overseas business and clients. The firm has an office in Guernsey, which operates Breams Trustees Limited, a Guernsey trust company and handles UK investment property transactions for offshore investment funds.

RECRUITMENT: The firm recruits up to six trainees each year. It also runs a summer student placement programme every July for three weeks. Trainees consistently report that the quality of training received far exceeds the experiences of those in much larger firms. CVs should be addressed to the HR and Training Manager.

WEDLAKE SAINT

14 John Street, London, WC1N 2EB **Tel:** (020) 7405 9446 **Fax:** (020) 7242 9877 **DX:** 407 Ch.Ln. **Email:** post@wsjs.co.uk **Ptnrs:** 14 **Asst solrs:** 8 **Other fee-earners:** 16

WEIGHTMANS

Richmond House, 1 Rumford Place, Liverpool, L3 9QW
Tel: (0151) 227 2601 **Fax:** (0151) 227 3223 **DX:** 14201 Liverpool
Email: info.liv@weightmans.com **Website:** www.weightmans.com

3rd Floor, 60 Charles Street, Leicester, LE1 1FB
Tel: (0116) 253 9747 **Fax:** (0116) 253 6101 **DX:** 721641 Leicester 18
Email: info.lei@weightmans.com

41 Spring Gardens, Manchester, M2 2BG
Tel: (0161) 833 2601 **Fax:** (0161) 833 1199 **DX:** 14427 Manchester 2
Email: info.mcr@weightmans.com

79-83 Colmore Row, Birmingham, B3 2AP
Tel: (0121) 233 2601 **Fax:** (0121) 233 2600 **DX:** 13035 Birmingham 1
Email: info.bhm@weightmans.com

Senior Partner	Ian Evans
Managing Partner	Mike Radcliffe
Number of partners	58
Assistant solicitors	64
Other fee-earners	57

CONTACTS

Clinical Negligence ..Nigel Dace (Birmingham)
....Patrick Gaul (Liverpool)
Commercial Litigation ....Ian Evans (Liverpool)
Commercial Property
....Lynne McFaul (Liverpool)
....David Morgan (Manchester)
Company Commercial
....Denis Hannon (Liverpool)
Employment ....Michael Ball (Manchester)
Insurance ....Dan Cutts (Leicester)
....Geraint Owen (Manchester)
....Tony Prichard (Liverpool)
....Tim Salthouse (Birmingham)
Large Loss Claims....David Holt (Liverpool)
Licensing ....Anthony Home (Manchester)
....Mark Owen (Liverpool)
Professional Indemnity
....Frank Maher (Liverpool)
....Bill Radcliffe (Manchester)
Public Authorities (including Police)
....Kevin Fletcher (Liverpool)
....Nick Peel (Manchester)
....John Riddell (Leicester)

THE FIRM: Weightmans is the country's largest dedicated insurance-based firm with 58 partners and a complement of more than 120 solicitors and other case handlers. Weightmans is committed to reducing the cost of claims and was the first firm to introduce performance statistics for clients. To ensure that Weightmans remains focused on cost control and technical excellence, the performance of case handlers is measured by criteria which include speed of settlement, accuracy of reserving, savings made on behalf of clients and strike out rates. Transparent billing and alternative charging rates to suit each client's budget demonstrate Weightmans' open approach. Some of the value added services include a free email update service within 24 hours of new legislation or cases; free subscription to Closer LOOK, a quarterly newspaper which reports on initiatives throughout the industry and customised training programmes. Weightmans is committed to harnessing new IT developments to reduce the cost of service delivery. The firm is developing new online business, which will offer its clients full access to all case information, costs to date and other vital case related information. The online service will also offer a number of new value added services aimed at helping insurers drive down the cost of claims. The firm increasingly uses the Internet to keep clients up-to-date on the latest case reports, to provide useful statistical and trend information and for 'live' performance status reports for clients on existing case loads.

PRINCIPAL AREAS OF WORK:

Professional Indemnity: Weightmans has the leading professional indemnity team in the North West with unrivalled experience of solicitors' claims. Statistics produced in the last 12 months show that over 30% of claims were struck out or discontinued while over 90% of mediations were successful.

Public Authorities: This includes the largest police unit in the UK, which handles a range of complex and sensitive issues on behalf of 13 police authorities. The public sector division also acts for numerous local authorities and fire authorities, offering advice on local government law including education, planning and judicial review as well as all aspects of claims handling. Human Rights is a particular speciality.

Insurance: In line with its commitment to the general and specialist insurance industry Weightmans offers its clients dedicated teams that are able to demonstrate a detailed understanding of their needs. A renowned technical motor claims unit handles work on behalf of the MIB. A specialist large loss unit handles technically complex claims valued at over £250,000.

Company/Commercial: A progressive and rapidly expanding department with high profile clients and big ticket work. Work includes mergers and acquisitions; banking ventures; intellectual property; e-commerce; multimedia and sports; telecommunications; IT; commercial property; development and construction; social housing and large-scale stock transfers; public and private finance; pensions and commercial agreements; commercial litigation.

Licensing: Weightmans has formed the Association of Licensing Practitioners (ALP), a government-lobbying group, which has a national voice.

Employment: Weightmans' employment team runs a national practice for a number of blue chip plcs concentrating on the leisure and retail industry. The work is primarily contentious with the emphasis on in-house advocacy together with the full range of support services to HR Managers including telephone help lines.

WEIL, GOTSHAL & MANGES

Head Office – Europe, One South Place, London, EC2M 2WG
Tel: (020) 7903 1000 **Fax:** (020) 7903 0990 **DX:** 124402
Email: weil.london@weil.com **Website:** www.weil.com

UK	
Number of partners	24
Associates	89
Other fee earners	14
Total legal staff	127

THE FIRM: Weil, Gotshal & Manges is a premier international law firm, with over 900 lawyers worldwide and a reputation for leading US and European legal advice that meets the commercial needs of its international corporate and finance clients. Established in New York in 1931, the firm has successfully pursued a strategy of expansion across Europe through organic growth, in response to client demand. The London office, established in 1996, has grown rapidly to become the second largest of the firms' 12 offices and is now the hub of the European practice. With more than 100 corporate and finance lawyers, it is one of the largest US-based international law firms in London, with one of the widest ranging practices. The London office provides its clients with full capability in UK, US and German law.

PRINCIPAL AREAS OF WORK: The firm's practice in London comprises UK and US corporate and finance law, in addition to the resources of a German desk. The London office's international corporate and finance practice encompasses acquisition finance, asset finance and leasing, banking, biotechnology and pharmaceuticals, capital markets, commercial litigation and arbitration, competition, consumer finance, corporate, corporate restructurings and workouts, environmental, financial services, mergers and acquisitions, pensions, private equity, project finance, real estate, securitisation, structured finance, taxation and technology.

Banking: The banking and project finance team has built a practice which is recognised by the London finance market as a serious alternative to the magic circle firms. It has a broad banking client base, representing both major lenders and borrowers in cross border and domestic transactions. The group has been highly recommended in a number of legal publications. Its dual capability with both UK and US law means that it is well placed to advise clients in respect of financing techniques originating in the US such as high yield debt, secondary market trading or asset-backed lending.

Corporate: The firm has an established corporate team, which has built a high profile in London through its work on major public mergers and acquisitions. Its capability in UK, US and German law is a key reason for its appeal to clients seeking advisers on multi-billion pound cross-border deals. Client demand has led to the development of core ancillary areas such as corporate tax, competition, property, pensions, litigation and environmental law. This has complemented the firm's expertise in public and private mergers and acquisitions, joint ventures, private equity, flotations and privatisations.

Capital Markets: Weil, Gotshal & Manges has established a capital markets practice with a track record for innovative and ground-breaking debt and equity offerings, high yield debt issues and structured and derivative capital markets transactions. The strength of the London capital markets practice derives from a commitment to providing UK and US capability, and from the firm's versatile finance lawyers who understand the increasingly sophisticated and interlinked financing techniques required by today's markets. They act for most of the major investment banks as well as representing an extensive list of issuers.

Securitisation: The securitisation team at Weil, Gotshal & Manges has earned a reputation for advising not only on innovative and highly complex transactions but also on transactions involving more mainstream UK consumer assets, such as residential mortgages. The team has extensive CBO/CLO and conduit expertise and is recognised as expert with respect to the establishment of CDOs, structured investment vehicles and ABCP/MTN conduits. The team has been involved in a wide range of transactions in Europe and the US.

Biotechnology & Pharmaceuticals: The firm's pharmaceutical and biotechnology group, based in its London, Silicon Valley and New York offices, comprises lawyers of the highest calibre and technical excellence with a detailed understanding of the pharmaceutical and biotechnology industries across Europe and the US. Their combined European/US experience in these sectors means that they can provide clients and their investors with legal advice on all aspects of their businesses, from mergers and acquisitions and fundraising transactions through to commercial contracts, IPR licensing and regulatory compliance on a worldwide basis.

Technology: The Weil, Gotshal & Manges' technology practice provides integrated UK and US corporate, commercial and finance advice to hi-tech businesses and investors. The firm offers clients the advantage of a significant Silicon Valley presence and lawyers with experience in advising both online companies and investors in relation to venture capital/private equity funding matters and all other aspects of corporate and finance legal issues. Its lawyers are experienced in advising suppliers/vendors and customers on the supply, licensing and exploitation of technology and telecommunications related products and services.

CLIENTELE: The London office represents major corporations and financial institutions including Bank of America, Barclays Capital, Bear Stearns, CeNeS Pharmaceuticals plc, CGU, Credit Suisse First Boston, Deutsche Bank, Dresdner Kleinwort Benson, enba, Estée Lauder, GE Capital, Getty Images, Hicks, Muse, Tate and Furst, Indigo, JP Morgan Chase & Co, Lehman Brothers, Matsushita, Merrill Lynch, Morgan Stanley, Netia, Nomura International, Oxford BioMedica plc, Acambis plc, Pirelli, Schroder Salomon Smith Barney, Sara Lee Corporation, Simply Internet, Telewest, Tokyo Mitsubishi International and Wit Capital.

INTERNATIONAL: The firm also has offices in Brussels, Budapest, Dallas, Frankfurt, Houston, Miami, Prague, New York, Silicon Valley, Warsaw and Washington DC. There are also affiliated offices in Cairo, Paris and Singapore.

Continued overleaf

W

RECRUITMENT: The firm is looking for flexible, highly motivated people who will be expected to take advantage of the wide-ranging legal and business training provided and develop the requisite skills to provide their clients with commercially-driven legal solutions.

WELLMAN & BROWN

23 West Parade, Lincoln, LN1 1NW **Tel:** (01522) 525463 **Fax:** (01522) 513199 **DX:** 11020 Lincoln 1 **Ptnrs:** 3

WENDY HOPKINS & CO

26 Windsor Place, Cardiff, CF1 3BZ **Tel:** (029) 20342233 **Fax:** (029) 20343828 **DX:** 330301 CARDIFF 1 **Email:** whco1@nascr.net **Ptnrs:** 3 **Asst solrs:** 1 **Other fee-earners:** 2

WESLEY GRYK

140 Lower Marsh, London, SE1 7AE **Tel:** (020) 7401 6887 **Fax:** (020) 7261 9985 **DX:** 36517 Lambeth **Email:** wesley@gryklaw.com **Ptnrs:** 1 **Asst solrs:** 5 **Other fee-earners:** 6 • A niche immigration practice.

WHITE & BOWKER

19 St. Peter St, Winchester, SO23 8BU
Tel: (01962) 844440 **Fax:** (01962) 842300 **DX:** 2506 Winchester
Email: wandb@wandb.co.uk **Website:** www.wandb.co.uk

Chief Executive	Gerald Ingram
Chairman	Niall Brook
Number of partners	17
Assistant solicitors	15
Other fee-earners	23

AREAS OF PRACTICE

Private Client	21%
Commercial	6%
Residential Property	12%
Personal Injury/Family	15%
Crime	8%
Commercial Property	21%
Civil Litigation	17%

CONTACTS

Civil Litigation	Laurence Dunn
Commercial	Martin Tomsett
Commercial Property	Graeme Short
Crime	Stephen Piercy
Personal Injury/Family	Simon Burge
Private Client	Martyn Thurston
Residential Property	Lorna Munro

THE FIRM: The firm is well established as a comprehensive provider of both private client and commercial services. It is one of the largest firms in Hampshire, with additional offices in Southampton and Eastleigh. It can trace its roots back to 1750 and partners and staff are active in business and community life as well as holding public appointments. These include the Winchester Diocesan Registrar, the Under Sheriff of Hampshire and HM Coroner for Hampshire (Central).

PRINCIPAL AREAS OF WORK:

Private Client: Comprehensive services for private clients including all aspects of tax and financial planning, wills and probate. Residential conveyancing, personal injury, matrimonial, family and criminal defence work are also undertaken.

Commercial Property: Expertise ranges from small industrial units to major office developments and includes planning applications and appeals, site acquisition, plot sales for developers and work for government departments.

Employment: Includes advice for businesses on sex, race and disability discrimination as well as harassment, maternity rights, dismissal and redundancy contracts.

Agriculture & Environment: Recognised as one of the leading firms in the South. Expertise includes property, tenancy issues, livestock, rights of way, planning appeals, tax and environmental issues.

INTERNATIONAL: Contacts in Europe through its association with Groupe Monassier France, a network of commercial lawyers throughout Europe.

WHITE & CASE

7-11 Moorgate, London, EC2R 6HH
Tel: (020) 7600 7300 **Fax:** (020) 7600 7030
Website: www.whitecase.com

Executive Partner	John Bellhouse
Administrative Partner	Doug Peel
Number of partners	27
Assistant solicitors	72

CONTACTS

Asset Finance	Mark Western
Bank Finance	Maurice Allen
Capital Markets	Francis Fitzherbert-Brockholes
Construction	John Bellhouse
Dispute Resolution	Margaret R. Cole
EU/Competition	Ian Forrester
Insolvency	Margaret R. Cole
Intellectual Property	David Llewelyn
M&A	Greg Hammond
Private Equity	Mats Sacklen
Project Finance	Peter Finlay
Sovereign Debt	Martin Hughes
Structured Finance	Rich Reilly
Taxation	Neil Woodgate
TMT	David Eisenberg

THE FIRM: White & Case is an internationally recognised name in the provision of finance and corporate law with 39 offices in 27 countries and over 1400 lawyers around the world. The London office was founded in 1971 to provide top-flight international legal advice to the world's leading institutions and corporations. White & Case is a full-service law firm, able to advise on all aspects of US, UK and local finance and corporate law transactions including acquisition finance, asset finance and leasing, aviation, bank finance, capital markets, construction, corporate finance, disputes, energy, EU/competition, insolvency, intellectual property, mergers and acquisitions, privatisation, project finance, securitisation, sovereign debt, structured finance, taxation, technology, media and telecoms.

INTERNATIONAL: The firm has other offices in Almaty, Ankara, Bangkok, Bombay/Mumbai, Berlin, Bratislava, Brussels, Budapest, Düsseldorf, Frankfurt, Hamburg, Helsinki, Ho Chi Minh City, Hong Kong, Istanbul, Jakarta, Jeddah, Johannesburg, London, Los Angeles, Mexico City, Miami, Milan, Moscow, New York, Palo Alto, Paris, Prague, Riyadh, Rome, São Paulo, Shanghai, Singapore, Stockholm, Tokyo, Warsaw and Washington.

WHITEHEAD MONCKTON

72 King St, Maidstone, ME14 1BL **Tel:** (01622) 698 000 **Fax:** (01622) 690 050 **DX:** 4807 **Email:** enquiries@whitehead-monckton.co.uk **Website:** www.whitehead-monckton.co.uk **Ptnrs:** 14 **Asst solrs:** 7 **Other fee-earners:** 10 **Contact:** Ron Voden • The firm is best known for its commercial/company, property, private client and investment services, personal injury and family work.

AREAS OF PRACTICE	
Commercial	35%
Private Client	34%
Litigation	18%
Other	13%

WHITELOCK & STORR

5 Bloomsbury Square, London, WC1A 2LX
Tel: (020) 7242 8612 **Fax:** (020) 7404 4131 **DX:** 35739

Senior Partner	Anthony Bloom
Number of partners	4
Assistant solicitors	2
Other fee-earners	4

THE FIRM: Well-established and highly respected firm with specialisation in serious fraud, major crime, extradition, drugs and smuggling cases, revenue and duty matters. Additionally, immigration, civil litigation (including agency work), conveyancing, and landlord and tenant work. Legal Aid franchise holder in crime and extradition, contract holder in immigration and VHCC/ serious fraud panel (Autumn 2000).

PRINCIPAL AREAS OF WORK: The senior criminal litigation partner has 11 years experience and specialises in general crime, serious fraud, substantial drug cases, extradition and immigration. The firm also practices civil litigation, conveyancing, and landlord and tenant.

INTERNATIONAL: The firm has associated offices in Italy, Ireland and USA. Members of the firm speak Italian, French, Turkish, German, Spanish, Hebrew, Arabic and Punjabi.

W

WHITTLES

Pearl Assurance House, 23 Princess Street, Manchester, M2 4ER
Tel: (0161) 228 2061 **Fax:** (0161) 236 1046
Website: www.whittles.com

Suite 9C, Josephs Well, Park Lane, Leeds, LS3 1AB
Tel: (0113) 244 2216 **Fax:** (0113) 242 1214

First Floor, Four Oaks House, Lichfield Road, Birmingham, B74 2TZ
Tel: (0121) 308 1331 **Fax:** (0121) 323 4846

Second Floor, Northumberland House, Princess Square, Newcastle, NE1 8ER
Tel: (0191) 261 4992 **Fax:** (0191) 261 4887

Managing Partner	David Towler
Senior Partner	Charles Hantom
Number of partners	18
Assistant solicitors	21
Other fee-earners	31

AREAS OF PRACTICE	
Personal Injury Litigation	80%
Employment	16%
Private Client	4%

CONTACTS	
Employment	Charles Hantom
	David Towler
	Helen Parkinson
Personal Injury Litigation	David Rogers

THE FIRM: Whittles is a strong and growing trades union and staff association niche practice specialising in plaintiff personal injury work with a growing caseload in wider aspects of employment law. Founded in the 1930s by Preston solicitor John Whittle, the practice's offices currently cover the whole of England and Wales from bases in Manchester, Leeds, the West Midlands and Newcastle upon Tyne. The firm prides itself on its long tradition of working for union members and sees itself as an integral element of the services the unions provide for their members. A high level of client retention and long-term working relationships are borne out of the firm's commitment to plain speaking, openness and listening to their clients needs. Through the adoption of a partnership approach, founded on quality legal advice and built on personal and responsive service, Whittles aims to promote the best interests of union members at all times.

PRINCIPAL AREAS OF WORK:

Personal Injury Litigation: Whittles is committed to using the firm's experience and specialist skills to protect the interests of union members at work. The firm specialises in personal injury litigation. The majority of this work is made up of claims arising from workplace accidents and diseases with an increasingly growing number of high profile, high value and complex claims. In response to this, Whittles has adopted a modern, client led approach to its services. Specialist teams offering expertise on traumatic and fatal accidents through to minor workplace injuries and post-traumatic shock handle accidents in the workplace. Similarly, through the establishment of specialist industrial disease departments at each of its offices, they are able to offer expertise in asbestosis, asthma, dermatitis, vibration white finger, upper limb disorder, repetitive back strain, industrial deafness, stress and industrial cancer cases.

Employment: The firm also has extensive experience in all aspects of employment and labour law including tribunal claims for dismissal, unfair selection for redundancy, sex, race and disability discrimination, equal pay, transfer of undertakings and all aspects of trade union law and human rights.

Other: Additional services for trade union clients and their members include discounted conveyancing and wills services together with free initial legal advice on any aspect of law.

CLIENTELE: Whittles acts mainly for employees and injured claimants, the majority of whom are trade union and staff association members.

WIGGIN & CO

95 The Promenade, Cheltenham, GL50 1WG
Tel: (01242) 224114 **Fax:** (01242) 224223 **DX:** 7427
Email: law@wiggin.co.uk

Senior Partner	Tim Osborne
Managing Partner	Mike Turner
Number of partners	13
Assistant solicitors	13
Other fee-earners	5

AREAS OF PRACTICE

Media, Entertainment & Commercial	50%
Private Client	28%
Litigation	13%
Property	9%

CONTACTS

Media & Entertainment	Tim Osborne
	Sean James
Company/Commercial	Mike Turner
Litigation/Defamation	Caroline Kean
IP/IT	Shaun Lowde
Private Client	Michael Fullerlove
Property	Matthew Bullock

THE FIRM: Founded in 1973, Wiggin & Co has for many years been known for the high quality of its practice and has a national and international reputation for its expertise, with several of the partners being regarded as leaders in their field. Wiggin & Co is recognised as a major player in many areas of the law including private client, broadcast media and entertainment, corporate/commercial and commercial litigation. Based in Cheltenham, the majority of the partners and assistant solicitors have joined the firm from well-known London practices. The firm continues to expand and today many assistant solicitors are retained on qualification. Three trainees are recruited annually. Since the majority of clients are based in London or overseas the firm has a London office as well as a base in Los Angeles. This was set up to advise clients on the west coast of America wishing to do business in the UK and Europe and to assist European clients with US investment and business activities.

W

PRINCIPAL AREAS OF WORK: The principal areas of work are media and private client.
Media, Entertainment & Commercial: The firm handles all aspects of entertainment and media law, including terrestrial, satellite and cable TV, multi-media, publishing, music and defamation, are undertaken. The firm also has particular expertise in intellectual property and the Internet. The firm offers the full range of contentious and non-contentious commercial and corporate services including joint ventures, acquisitions and mergers, buy-outs, reorganisations and financing, insolvency, financial services compliance, employment, immigration and advice in European law.
Private Client, Trusts & Estate Planning: The firm has considerable experience and expertise in tax management and protection of worldwide privately owned wealth, where it continues to be an international leader in the field. Work in this area includes income tax and capital planning work for individuals and for companies, their shareholders and executives. There is a strong international emphasis with particular skills in the establishment and restructuring of UK and overseas trusts. Asset protection, in the UK and internationally, is another area of expertise.
Property: There is a strong commercial property department dealing with development structuring, sales and leaseback funding, secured loan transactions, sale and purchase of agricultural land and private estates in the UK and EU countries.

RECRUITMENT: Due to continuing expansion the firm is always seeking to recruit good quality solicitors. Three trainees are recruited annually. A brochure is available on request.

WIKBORG, REIN & CO

One Knightrider Court, London, EC4V 5JP
Tel: (020) 7236 4598 **Fax:** (020) 7236 4599
Email: wrco@wrco.co.uk **Website:** www.wr.no

London Partner	Morton Lund Mathisen
Associate Lawyers	3

AREAS OF PRACTICE

Shipping/Admiralty	40%
Company/Commercial/Securities	40%
Finance	20%

THE FIRM: Wikborg, Rein & Co is an international law firm founded in 1923 with offices in Oslo, Bergen, London, Singapore and Japan. The two founding partners set the early course of the firm, establishing its reputation as a commercial firm and attracting clients from the world of shipping and other industries. Although one of the largest law firms in Norway with some 135 lawyers, Wikborg, Rein & Co continues to operate on the basis of a close working relationship with each client. The firm is prepared, if required, to take on management responsibility for the detailed handling of transactions. The London office is staffed by four Norwegian lawyers. In addition to providing liaison services for the firm's international clients on Norwegian business and Norwegian clients on international business, the office has particular expertise in the areas of shipping, mergers and acquisitions, finance and securities.

PRINCIPAL AREAS OF WORK:
Company & Corporate: Work includes company formation, corporate acquisitions and disposals, demergers, joint ventures, partnerships, registration services, share issues and voting rights.
Shipping: Work includes agency, arrest, building contracts, broking, cargo claims, charters, collisions, finance, flag changes, insurance, management, mortgages, pollution, protection and indemnity claims, sales, salvage and terminals.
Securities: Work includes private placings, public offers, acquisitions, bonds, capital reorganisations, convertible issues, demergers, investor protection, mergers, registration services, Stock Exchange listings, trading disputes, underwriting agreements and venture capital.
Finance: Work includes ship and other asset finance, project finance, debt rescheduling, guarantees, leases, loan agreements, security documentation, and off-balance sheet instruments.
General Commercial: Including agency and distribution, employment and natural resources.

WILBRAHAM & CO

Minerva House, East Parade, Leeds, LS1 5PS
Tel: (0113) 243 2200 **Fax:** (0113) 244 9777
Email: wilbraham@wilbraham.co.uk **Website:** www.wilbraham.co.uk

Joint Managing Partners	Peter Wilbraham
	Richard Wade-Smith
Number of partners	5
Assistant solicitors	4
Other fee-earners	2

AREAS OF PRACTICE

Planning	85%
Environmental	15%

CONTACTS

Partners .... David Walton
.... Kate Butterfield, Robert Waite

WILBRAHAM & CO
SOLICITORS

THE FIRM: Wilbraham & Co is a niche practice specialising in planning, environmental, highways, compulsory purchase/compensation and administrative law. The firm's philosophy is to provide its commercial clients with the highest quality of advice on planning and environmental matters, and to produce a cost effective service in a commercial context.

PRINCIPAL AREAS OF WORK: The firm handles infrastructure and commercial development projects throughout the UK and has recently advised on a number of high profile residential and employment schemes. In addition to mainstream commercial work it specialises in utility projects for water companies, electricity generators and waste management companies. Further areas of technical expertise include renewable energy, quarrying, waste disposal and regeneration. Public sector work includes advising local authorities, health trusts and educational institutions. The firm increasingly works alongside other legal practices to provide specialist planning advice within property law transactions including the advocacy services of in-house counsel.

W

THE WILKES PARTNERSHIP

41 Church St, Birmingham, B3 2RT
Tel: (0121) 233 4333 **Fax:** (0121) 233 4546 **DX:** 13047
Email: law@wilkes.co.uk **Website:** www.wilkes.co.uk

Managing Partner	Anna Dunford
Senior Partner	Nigel Wood
Number of partners	17
Assistant solicitors	25
Other fee-earners	25

AREAS OF PRACTICE

Litigation (inc. Insolvency)	48%
Corporate & Commercial	18%
Conveyancing	15%
PI	10%
Tax/Trust/Probate	7%
Other	2%

CONTACTS

Building Contracts	Peter Tugwell
Civil Litigation	Nigel Wood
Commercial Conveyancing	Adele McDermott
Corporate/Commercial	Gareth O'Hara
Debt Recovery	David Cleary
Employment	Andrew Yendole
Insolvency	John Cooper
Large Scale Voluntary Transfer	Peter Ewin
Personal Injury	Maxine Kelly
Public Authority & Housing Associations	Adele McDermott
Tax/Trust	Anna Dunford

THE FIRM: Established over 60 years ago, The Wilkes Partnership has developed into a modern commercial practice offering a wide range of legal services to business, industry and private individuals.

PRINCIPAL AREAS OF WORK:
Company & Commercial: The department handles all aspects of company formation, acquisitions and disposal, corporate finance, management buy-outs and corporate restructuring.
Litigation: The firm deals with the full range of commercial litigation services including High Court, County Court and matters arising from EU legislation. It also provides a specialised commercial debt collection service. Other work includes commercial contract disputes, personal injury, employment matters and health and safety at work.
Property: The practice undertakes and advises on domestic and commercial conveyancing, property development, shops, offices, factories, leases, planning matters, joint ventures and landlord and tenant matters.
Private Client: The firm offers advice to individuals regarding wills, settlements, probate, inheritance tax, personal taxation and pensions. The firm also provides a service to private clients on matters of employment, personal injury, consumer legislation, family matters and divorce, criminal work and licensing.

CLIENTELE: Business and industrial clients nationally as well as long-standing private clients.

INTERNATIONAL: The firm has professional links in the major European cities particularly in relation to property buying in Europe. Links with France and Germany are particularly strong. The firm has an associate office in Munich – Messrs Kantenwein von Bechtolsheim.

WILKIN CHAPMAN

PO Box 16, Town Hall Square, Grimsby, DN31 1HE **Tel:** (01472) 358234 **Fax:** (01472) 360198 **DX:** 13511 Grimsby 1
Email: it@wilkinchapman.co.uk **Website:** www.wilkinchapman.co.uk **Ptnrs:** 26 **Asst solrs:** 11 **Other fee-earners:** 30

WILLCOX LANE CLUTTERBUCK

55 Charlotte Street, Birmingham, B3 1PX
Tel: (0121) 236 9441 **Fax:** (0121) 236 4733 **DX:** 717340 Birmingham 44
Email: solicitors@wlc.co.uk **Website:** www.wlc.co.uk

Managing Partner	William Colacicchi
Number of partners	14
Assistant solicitors	8
Other fee-earners	12

AREAS OF PRACTICE

Insurance Litigation	25%
Property	22%
Private Client	22%
Commercial	17%
Criminal/Matrimonial	9%
Employment	5%

CONTACTS

Commercial	Gareth Griffiths
Commercial/Civil Litigation	Mark English
Criminal	John Smitheman
Defendant Personal Injury	Mathu Asokan
Employment	Lorraine Teague
Matrimonial	John Smitheman
Private Client	William Colacicchi
Property/Construction	Susan Stott

THE FIRM: Willcox Lane Clutterbuck is a modern firm with a long pedigree. It has a substantial corporate base, with strength in corporate finance, litigation, property, employment, charities, and tax and trusts in addition to its well known insurance practice.

PRINCIPAL AREAS OF WORK:

Company/Commercial: Work involves corporate finance, acquisitions and sales, flotations, insolvency, management buy ins/outs, intellectual property, computer law, company formations and general commercial advice to businesses, companies and individuals.

Insurance Litigation: The firm handles a wide range of insurance litigation for composite insurers, underwriters and loss adjusters in connection with employers and public liability, personal injury and general liability together with road traffic accidents.

Commercial & Agricultural Property: Work includes the purchase and sale of all types of freehold and leasehold properties for commercial users and investors, property development, employee relocation and planning law.

Employment: The firm offers the full range of contentious and non-contentious employment services provided for employers and employees.

Commercial Litigation: Work includes contract and commercial disputes, intellectual property, building and construction disputes and general litigation. The firm is also able to deal with all aspects of criminal work and matrimonial law. The firm is a member of the Alternative Dispute Resolution Group and has an accredited mediator.

Private Client & Charities: The firm has an acknowledged expertise in this field where clients are advised on all aspects of their financial affairs and investments as well as the handling of all aspects of wills and probate. The firm is also widely involved in the establishment, management and winding up of trusts and charities.

Tax: The firm advises on tax planning and mitigation for individuals, trusts and companies.

CLIENTELE: Clients include public and private companies, insurance companies, public utilities, local authorities, colleges and charities as well as private individuals.

WILLCOX & LEWIS

The Old Coach House, Bergh Apton, Norwich, NR15 1DD
Tel: (01508) 480 100 **Fax:** (01508) 480 001

Lincoln House, 1 Berrycroft, Willingham, Cambridge, CB4 5JX
Tel: (01954) 261 444 **Fax:** (01954) 261 777

Senior Partners	Michael Willcox Ian Lewis
Number of partners	2
Assistant solicitors	2

AREAS OF PRACTICE

Tax Planning	25%
Trust Work	25%
Probate	25%
Charity	20%
Conveyancing	5%

CONTACTS

Cambridge	Ian Lewis
Norwich	Michael Willcox

THE FIRM: Willcox & Lewis is a niche private client law firm, with offices at Cambridge and Norwich, established by two leading specialists in trusts and personal tax. The senior partners are both elected to The International Academy of Estate and Trust Law based in San Francisco, California, and members of the firm belong to the Society of Trust and Estate Practitioners.

PRINCIPAL AREAS OF WORK: The firm advises high net worth individuals, trustees and charities, and specialises in complex trusts and estates containing international and commercial elements. Parallel and complementary to the legal practice, separate corporate structures provide advice on substantial general insurance risk assessment and investment advice. Contentious and commercial work is outsourced, and the firm acts regularly with and for other professionals.

WILLIAMS DAVIES MELTZER

8-10 New Fetter Lane, London, EC4A 1AP **Tel:** (020) 7353 2500 **Fax:** (020) 7353 2552 **DX:** 1026 London
Email: wdm@williamsdaviesmeltzer.co.uk **Website:** www.williamsdaviesmeltzer.co.uk **Ptnrs:** 5 **Asst solrs:** 10 **Other fee-earners:** 8

WILLIAMSON & SODEN

Stanton House, 54 Stratford Road, Shirley, Solihull, B90 3LS
Tel: (0121) 733 8000 **Fax:** (0121) 733 3322 **DX:** 20652
Email: law@williamsonandsoden.co.uk

Citadel, 190 Corporation Street, Birmingham, B4 6QB
Tel: (0121) 212 1155 **Fax:** (0121) 212 4961

Managing Partner	Ian Williamson
Number of partners	9
Assistant solicitors	7
Other fee-earners	10

CONTACTS

Business Clients .... John Soden
.... Scott Withers
Disputes (General & Commercial)
.... Stephen Rowe
.... Kevin Reilly
Family Law .... Clare Fletcher
Motor Racing .... David Munro
.... John Soden
Personal Injury .... Gerard Cusak
Planning Law .... Ian Williamson
Police Matters (inc. Motoring) .... Alan Bryce
.... Fiona Warman
Property .... Lynne Goldsby
Telecommunications .... David Munro
Wills & Inheritance .... Angela Beck

THE FIRM: The practice was founded by Ian Williamson and John Soden in 1979. Williamson & Soden has grown significantly and now operates from its own purpose-built premises at Stanton House, Shirley, Solihull and from offices in the centre of Birmingham, adjacent to the law courts.

PRINCIPAL AREAS OF WORK:

Crime: A large and respected department deals with police matters for clients charged with anything from a motoring offence to a murder. Specialists also deal with Customs & Excise and Inland Revenue Investigations.
Company/Commercial: Work includes company/business sales and purchases, trading agreements, mergers and acquisitions, commercial disputes and insolvencies.
Employment: All aspects, contentious and non-contentious.
Litigation: All types of commercial disputes with particular experience in Directors Disqualification and Landlord and Tenant.
Private Client: A full range of services covers all aspects of family and matrimonial law, personal injury compensation, wills, probate and trusts.
Property: Commercial and residential conveyancing.

W

WILLIAMSONS SOLICITORS

Lowgate, Hull, HU1 1EN **Tel:** 01482 323 697 **Fax:** 01482 328 132 **DX:** 11932 **Website:** www.williamsons.solicitors.co.uk **Ptnrs:** 11 **Asst solrs:** 12 **Other fee-earners:** 18

WILLIAMSONS

Lowgate, Hull, HU1 1EN **Tel:** (01482) 323 697 **Fax:** (01482) 618 147 **Ptnrs:** 11 **Asst solrs:** 12 **Other fee-earners:** 18

LG WILLIAMS & PRICHARD

22 St Andrews Crescent, Cardiff, CF1O 3DD **Tel:** (029) 2022 9716 **Fax:** (029) 2037 7761 **DX:** 50752 Cardiff 2 **Email:** mail@cardiff-law.co.uk **Website:** www.law-wales.co.uk **Ptnrs:** 2 **Asst solrs:** 2 **Other fee-earners:** 1

WILLOUGHBY & PARTNERS

The Isis Building, Thames Quay, 193 Marsh Wall, London, E14 9SG
Tel: (020) 7345 8888 **Fax:** (020) 7345 4555 **DX:** 42677 Isle of Dogs
Email: isis@iprights.com **Website:** www.iprights.com

Pembroke House, Pembroke Street, Oxford, OX1 1BP
Tel: (01865) 791 990 **Fax:** (01865) 791 772
Email: oxford@iprights.com

Managing Partner	Shireen Peermohamed
Senior Partner	Tony Willoughby
Number of partners	10
Assistant solicitors	17
Other fee-earners	14

AREAS OF PRACTICE

Intellectual Property Protection, Enforcement & Exploitation 100%

CONTACTS

Intellectual Property .... Anna Booy
.... Ben Goodger (Oxford)
.... Shireen Peermohamed (London)
.... Rupert Ross-Macdonald
.... Diana Sternfeld
.... Tony Willoughby

THE FIRM: Willoughby & Partners is a specialist firm which practises exclusively in the areas of intellectual property (IP) and information technology (IT). It prides itself on being accessible and responsive and providing high quality and competitively priced legal services that take account of commercial objectives and budgets. It has a well respected and dynamic team of lawyers who are supported by the latest technology and a first rate research capability.

PRINCIPAL AREAS OF WORK: The firm has a proven track record in relation to all aspects of intellectual property litigation. Recent cases include 'Montblanc Simplo Gmbh v Sepia Products Inc'; 'Premier Brands UK Limited v Typhoon Europe Limited & Another'; 'SmithKline Beecham plc & Others v Dowelhurst Limited'. The firm's associated business, Rouse & Co International, provides a full trade mark agency service in the UK and internationally. Willoughby & Partners develops, coordinates and executes enforcement strategies and also advises in relation to the exploitation, acquisition, transfer and financing of IP and IT rights. It can assist in negotiating and structuring deals and drafting agreements – whether as part of a transactional support programme or licensing, distribution or other commercial arrangements. It has developed a strategic IP management service to assist clients in carrying out IP audits and implementing recommendations.The firm offers its services as a 'virtual IP department' for other firms without an IP/IT capability.
Agency Work: The firm acts as London agent for other firms in litigation and has five solicitors with experience of supervising Search Orders on behalf of other firms. It also acts as UK agent for foreign law firms in both contentious and non contentious matters.

Continued overleaf

CLIENTELE: Clients include multinational and domestic companies across a wide range of industries (including pharmaceuticals and consumer healthcare, motor vehicle manufacturing, food and drink, publishing and entertainment, clothing and footwear, IT and the Internet, sports and telecommunications); international and domestic law firms; accountants and financial institutions.

INTERNATIONAL: Willoughby & Partners is associated with the Rouse & Co International Group of companies which provides IP consultancy services throughout the world from offices in Europe, the Middle East, Asia Pacific and the Americas. Investigation services throughout the world are provided by the group's in-house investigation unit. The unit also constantly monitors clients' brands worldwide through its 'spotter' service.

RECRUITMENT: The firm runs regular training programmes for clients as well as staff on a range of IP and IT related issues. Its lawyers also regularly attend and speak at external seminars and industry meetings. The firm also offers a current awareness and research service to clients.

WILMER, CUTLER & PICKERING

4 Carlton Gardens, London, SW1Y 5AA
Tel: (020) 7872 1000 **Fax:** (020) 7839 3537
Email: law@wilmer.com **Website:** www.wilmer.com

Managing Partner	Andrew Parnell
Number of partners	9
Assistant solicitors	14
Other fee-earners	2

AREAS OF PRACTICE

International Arbitration & Litigation	35%
Company & Commercial	30%
Telecommunication	20%
Aviation	15%

CONTACTS

Aviation	Dieter G Lange
	John Kallangher
Company & Commercial	Andrew Parnell
	Michael Holter
International Arbitration & Litigation	
	Gary Born
	Paul Mitchard
Telecommunication	Dieter G Lange
	Michael Holter

THE FIRM: Wilmer, Cutler & Pickering is an international law firm with offices in London, Brussels, Berlin, Washington DC, New York, Baltimore and Northern Virginia. Founded in 1962, WCP has over 300 lawyers engaged in a broadly diversified practice.

PRINCIPAL AREAS OF WORK:
Company & Commercial: International commercial and corporate transactions practice, including: cross-border mergers and acquisitions; venture capital; joint venture and partnership arrangements and international corporate alliances; equity and debt financing; distribution arrangements, technology and licensing matters.
Telecommunications: Specialist advice in multi-jurisdictional, especially internet-related transactions and international joint ventures. Cover all related trade, investment and global information infrastructure issues. Guide clients through regulatory environment of individual European countries, EU and US. Advise telecoms entrants seeking access to liberalised telecoms markets (especially Germany). Particular strengths in the competition law and UK/US – German issues.
Aviation: One of WCP's main practice areas. The aviation team comprises more than 30 lawyers and experts in economic, transport and infrastructure issues involved in multi-jurisdictional transactions. The firm's advice focuses on providing high level strategy, legal and policy guidance. Clients include airlines, airports, governments, and international agencies in the aviation sector.

INTERNATIONAL: The firm has offices in Brussels, Berlin, Washington DC, New York, Baltimore and Northern Virginia. Languages spoken by members of the firm include French, German and Spanish.

WILSON & CO

697 High Road, London, N17 8AD **Tel:** (020) 8808 7535 **Fax:** (020) 8880 3393 **DX:** 52200 Tottenham 2 **Website:** www.wilsonandco.co.uk **Ptnrs:** 5 **Asst solrs:** 15 **Other fee-earners:** 16 • Established Legal Aid firm specialising in immigration and asylum, criminal defence, family/children and mental health. Member of the Serious Fraud Panel.

WILSON, ELSER, MOSKOWITZ, EDELMAN & DICKER

141 Fenchurch Street, London, EC3M 6BQ
Tel: (020) 7623 6723 **Fax:** (020) 7626 9774 **DX:** 858 City
Email: cherryt@wemed.com **Website:** www.wemed.com

Number of partners	1
Assistant solicitors	2
Other fee-earners	1

AREAS OF PRACTICE

US Defence Litigation	50%
Insurance Coverage Disputes	10%
Arbitration	10%
Creditors' Rights	10%
E&O Brokers (US & UK)	10%
D&O	10%

THE FIRM: The firm is one of the largest in the United States, and has been serving clients for more than a quarter of a century. It has grown considerably during this period and now has offices in 14 major cities in the US. The London office of Wilson, Elser, Moskowitz, Edelman & Dicker is a multinational partnership associated with the US firm. The office concentrates on insurance and reinsurance work including product liability, insurance broker errors and omissions and international arbitration. Mr Cherry is both a US lawyer and a solicitor. Mr Cherry is also a Fellow of the Chartered Institute of Arbitrators. The London office conducts litigation in English courts.

PRINCIPAL AREAS OF WORK: Initially, the practice was insurance-related, and the firm maintains a pre-eminent position with regard to all aspects of insurance law and the insurance industry. However, it has broadened its services and expertise to meet the needs of clients in the following areas: corporate organisation, negotiation, rendering business advice for both domestic and international clients on acquisitions, mergers, regulatory matters, financing, real estate and leasing transactions, contract negotiations and drafting, employment law and tax advice. The firm maintains close relationships with insurance specialist law firms in Europe.

INTERNATIONAL: Members of the firm speak French, German, Spanish, Japanese and Korean. There are additional offices in New York, Albany, Baltimore, Boston, Chicago, Dallas, Houston, Los Angeles, Miami, Newark, Paris, Philadelphia, San Diego, San Francisco, Washington DC and White Plains.

WILSON NESBITT

Citylink Business Park, Albert Street, Belfast, BT12 4HB **Tel:** (028) 9032 3864 **Fax:** (028) 9033 3707 **DX:** 484 NR
Email: belfast@wilson-nesbitt.com **Website:** www.wilson-nesbitt.co.uk **Ptnrs:** 8 **Asst solrs:** 22 **Other fee-earners:** 44

WILSONS

Steynings House, Fisherton St, Salisbury, SP2 7RJ
Tel: (01722) 412412 **Fax:** (01722) 411500 **DX:** 58003 Salisbury 1
Email: info@wilsonslaw.co.uk **Website:** www.wilsonslaw.com

Number of partners	18
Assistant solicitors	18
Other fee-earners	25

W

THE FIRM: Wilsons is one of the best-known firms in the South of England, with a nationwide reputation for private client work. Three specialist teams covering trust and tax, landed estates and agriculture offer a full range of quality legal services to UK and overseas clients, both private and commercial. The firm is constantly striving to improve the quality and delivery of its services in order to meet clients' expectations. This requires continuous investment in information technology and training to ensure that it can deliver advice quickly and competitively in a form which is free from jargon and which clients understand. It has acquired both Lexcel and IIP accreditation.

PRINCIPAL AREAS OF WORK:

Private Client: The firm is believed to have one of the highest net worth private client practices outside London. It increasingly acts for financial institutions which have interests in rural land and the agriculture industry. Its extensive expertise in farms and estates law, heritage property, and tax planning is well known. The firm has an exceptionally experienced tax planning team of five partners and three consultants, including Ralph Ray, one of the most eminent solicitors in the field of personal tax, who joined Wilsons as a consultant in 1998.

Family Law: Led by a member of the Family Law Association, who trained at Withers, this department is increasingly rivalling the major London firms for top-drawer High Court family work.

Commercial: Wilsons has substantially increased its commercial practice over the last 18 months, and is recruiting to expand this area further. The firm deals with all types of company-related and business transactions. It has experienced specialist teams advising on employment matters, pensions and commercial property. It also undertakes substantial commercial litigation. Wilsons also provides a company secretarial service to its corporate clients.

Schools: Wilsons acts for a growing number of independent schools. Typical issues dealt with include governors' liabilities, insurance issues, employment problems, charitable appeals, mergers, fee recovery and school/parent contracts.

WINCKWORTH SHERWOOD

35 Great Peter Street, Westminster, London, SW1P 3LR
Tel: (020) 7593 5000 **Fax:** (020) 7593 5099 **DX:** 2312 Victoria
Email: wandp@winckworths.co.uk

Number of partners	20
Assistant solicitors	31
Other fee-earners	26

AREAS OF PRACTICE

Litigation	26%
Parliamentary & Planning	20%
Housing & Local Government	19%
Ecclesiastical, Education & Charities	16%
Private Client	15%
Licensed Property	4%

THE FIRM: Practising in Westminster, the City of London, Chelmsford and Oxford, this firm is known for its excellence in a number of niche areas, including parliamentary work, housing, ecclesiastical law, local government, education, charities, health, licensing and services to the police. The practice was founded in about 1788 in Westminster and acted mainly for private clients. The private client practice remains strong but it is only one part of the firm's core practice. The rest of the firm's core practice centres around institutional clients who are publicly accountable and business-like in their approach but whose raison d'être is the provision of a service for public benefit rather than purely the generation of profit. The partnership which is emerging between private sector investment and public sector know-how provides exciting opportunities for innovative projects in many of these areas. For some time now, the firm has been organised on the basis of client sector groups rather than departments based on work types. Each part of the firm handles the affairs of their client sector and in advising takes into account their clients' objectives, needs, operating environment and administrative and political make-up. This allows the firm's lawyers to work closely with their clients, thereby understanding better their business aims and working practices.

Continued overleaf

PRINCIPAL AREAS OF WORK:

Litigation: Work in this area is conducted on a client-led basis, whenever possible, with a dedicated team following each particular client sector.

Parliamentary: Work handled includes matters relating to legislation and legislative drafting, constitutional law, infrastructure projects (particularly in relation to all forms of transport, ports and other utilities), statutory and other companies, public sector and former public sector bodies, financial institutions, local authorities and professional bodies. Areas of law also include town planning, compulsory purchase and compensation.

Police: Advice to the police covers governance and accountability issues and links between forces. The police lawyers also advise on procurement law, sponsorship schemes, joint ventures and collaboration agreements.

Ecclesiastical, Education & Charity: These are traditional areas of practice and developing client sectors. The firm acts for the Church of England, the Roman Catholic Church and the Archbishop of Canterbury and has acted for charities since its earliest days. Education clients include primary and secondary schools and institutions of further and higher education both with and without church connections.

Housing: The full range of constitutional, property, finance and litigation services are provided to the firm's many housing association clients and to lenders in the housing sector, housebuilders and local authorities. The firm has extensive experience in commercial and licensed property, and licensing generally, including the licensing of petrol stations.

Medical: There is a growing health and medical practice which is being nurtured in the firm's client-led culture.

Employment: This area of law covers all the firm's client sectors.

Costs: The firm provides a specialised costs service to its clients to ensure they maximise their recovery of costs from other parties.This multi-niche public sector practice has led to the firm's involvement in a number of high profile inquiries and investigations. The Bristol Babies inquiry, the Hillsborough scrutiny and the Marchioness investigation represent three recent cases.

INTERNATIONAL: The firm is a founder member of an international network of law firms called Euréseau.

RECRUITMENT: Qualified staff should apply in the first instance to the Partnership Secretary, Mr TF Vesey. The firm recruits three trainee solicitors each year – a 2:2 law or 2:1 non-law degree is usually required and applications should be made by handwritten letter (and typed CV) to Mr RHA MacDougald.

CONTACTS

Charities	Owen Carew-Jones
Commercial Litigation	Jim Rai
Costs	Malcolm Goodwin
Ecclesiastical	Paul Morris
Education	Michael Thatcher
Employment Law	Timothy Watts
Health & Medical	Simon Eastwood
Housebuilders	Roger Fitton
Housing	Andrew Murray
Licensing & Commercial Property	Robert Botkai
Litigation	Peter Williams
Local Government	Andrew Murray
Parliamentary	Alison Gorlov
Police Sector	Nick Owston
Private Client	Hugh MacDougald
Town Planning	Christopher Vine

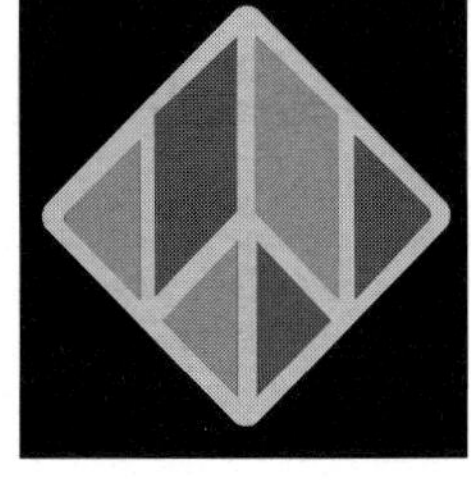

WINSTANLEY-BURGESS

378 City Rd, London, EC1V 2TQ
Tel: (020) 7278 7911 **Fax:** (020) 7833 2135 **DX:** 58253 Islington
Email: law@winstanley-burgess.co.uk **Contact:** Debra Freeman • Established 1975. Handles most areas of general practice including crime, family, housing, personal injury, probate and property. Best known for immigration and public interest law.

AREAS OF PRACTICE

Immigration & Nationality	50%
Crime	10%
Family	10%
Housing	10%
Non-Contentious	10%
Other Civil	10%

WINWARD FEARON

35 Bow St, London, WC2E 7AU
Tel: (020) 7420 2800 **Fax:** (020) 7420 2801 **DX:** 37959 Kingsway
Email: enquiries@winwardfearon.co.uk **Website:** www.winwardfearon.co.uk

Senior Partner	David Cornes
Partnership secretary	Adrian Luto
Number of partners	12
Assistant solicitors	7
Other fee-earners	2

THE FIRM: This central London firm is one of the UK's top construction law practices. It has also established a significant reputation in infrastructure project work. Winward Fearon was founded in 1986. As a matter of policy it concentrates its development around an expanding number of niche areas, rather than professing to expertise across the board. Those niche areas are carefully chosen to facilitate the creation of cross-departmental teams which specialise in industry sectors, rather than technical legal disciplines. In addition to their litigation and arbitration work, the firm's construction and commercial litigation departments increasingly make use of alternative dispute resolution procedures. The firm above all seeks to provide a top-quality and cost-effective service. It has an established and enviable client base, including large plcs, owner-managed businesses, and developers. The firm's international links have been strengthened by its membership of Eurolegal, which is a European Economic Interest Group of law firms in EU jurisdictions.

PRINCIPAL AREAS OF WORK:

Construction: Construction law forms a large part of the firm's practice and is carried out for national and international clients in building, civil engineering, and the professions. Typical issues may concern defective building, formation of contracts, liquidated damages, extension of time, and critical-path analysis, as well as payment. In addition, the department deals with bonds and insurance-related matters, certificates, statutory obligations, variations in construction work, indemnities and warranties, together with product liability. The work of the department is both contentious and non-contentious, including very large cases in the High Court and in ICC, LCIA and UNCITRAL arbitrations. Mediation work is also increasing.

AREAS OF PRACTICE

Construction	58%
Infrastructure Projects, PFI & Corporate Finance	21%
Property	8%
Commercial & Property Litigation	13%

CONTACTS

Commercial & Property Litigation	Clive Levontine
Construction	Richard Winward
Corporate Finance	Edward Gore
Infrastructure Projects, PFI & Corporate Finance	Adrian Luto
Property	Guy Fearon

Commercial & Property Litigation: Winward Fearon's commercial litigation team handles a wide variety of commercial claims, including employment disputes for UK and international clients. Part of the team specialises in property and landlord and tenant litigation, including dilapidation claims, lease renewals, rent review problems, easement and right of way actions, service charge disputes, and franchises. The team often works closely with the firm's property team.
Infrastructure Projects, PFI & Corporate Finance: The infrastructure project, PFI and corporate finance team has handled a number of high profile transactions in the past five years. Adrian Luto has established a reputation in infrastructure projects, particularly in the independent power plant section both in the UK and overseas. Edward Gore focuses on the purchase and sale of private companies and businesses, management buy-outs, other venture capital transactions, joint ventures and partnership agreements.
Property: The property team, headed by Guy Fearon, one of the firm's four founding partners, focuses on commercial property and residential development. Work includes the acquisition and sale of development sites, industrial estates, offices, and other commercial and investment property. The department advises on redevelopment projects, auction contracts, joint ventures, and partnership developments, including taxation, property finance, and landlord and tenant work. The team also provides a service in high quality residential property.

WITHAM WELD

70 St George's Square, London, SW1V 3RD
Tel: (020) 7821 8211 **Fax:** (020) 7630 6484 **DX:** 86164 Victoria 2
Email: postmaster@wwlaw.co.uk

Number of partners	7
Assistant solicitors	2
Other fee-earners	3

THE FIRM: Established for over 200 years, Witham Weld has a long-standing reputation in its work for every kind of client, including religious and civil institutions, charities and trusts, commercial and private clients. Today, the aim remains the same; to provide the highest quality legal services, founded on experience and expertise and supported by innovation and the use of modern working methods.

PRINCIPAL AREAS OF WORK: The firm provides advice and assistance in a wide range of areas including charity law, property, revenue and tax planning, wills and probates, company/commercial, contracts, education, employment, copyright, and all forms of litigation.

WITHERS

16 Old Bailey, London, EC4M 7EG
Tel: (020) 7597 6000 **Fax:** (020) 7597 6543 **DX:** 160/Chancery Lane
Email: claire.o'connor@withers.co.uk **Website:** www.withers.co.uk

Number of partners	50
Assistant solicitors	61
Other fee-earners	46

AREAS OF PRACTICE

Private Client & Charities	42%
Family	15%
Litigation	17%
Corporate, Company & Commercial	13%
Property	13%

CONTACTS

Agricultural Property	Penny Elliott
Banking	David Dannreuther
Charities	Alison Paines
Commercial Litigation & Dispute Resolution	Christopher Coffin
Commercial Property	Claudia D'Ambrosio
Corporate Finance	Hugh Devlin
Employment	Meriel Schindler
Family	Gill Doran
Healthcare, Pharmaceutical & Bioscience	Anthony Indaimo
Information Technology	Riccardo Abbate
Insolvency	Roberto Moruzzi
Intellectual Property	John Maycock
Personal Tax, Trust & Probate	Tony Thompson
Professional Negligence	Christopher Coffin
Residential Property	Henry Stuart
Trust & Probate Litigation	Dawn Goodman

THE FIRM: The firm offers pragmatic and commercial advice, giving all its clients individual attention. Withers has a broad and diverse practice enabling it to offer a comprehensive range of services.

PRINCIPAL AREAS OF WORK:
Private Client: Withers has the largest group of specialists in Europe, which has enabled the firm to respond to clients' needs by forming dedicated teams which service particular types of private clients such as entrepreneurs, families, landed estates and the internationally wealthy. Other professionals use standard textbooks written and edited by the firm's lawyers.
Family: Withers is one of the leading firms in the UK for family law. It is the only firm in the world with five Fellows of the International Academy of Matrimonial Lawyers. Many of its cases have an international dimension and most involve complex financial issues.
Corporate: The firm acts for listed and private companies, financial institutions, partnerships, sole traders and entrepreneurs. Specialist areas of practice include corporate finance (in particular the Alternative Investment Market), intellectual property, banking and employment. Areas of particular industry expertise include healthcare and bioscience, IT, media and fashion.
Litigation: Withers is one of the very few firms that has a specialist practice in litigation relating to trust and probate. It is also well known for its expertise in fraud, employment, insolvency and professional negligence.
Charities: The firm has a business-like approach to charities. Its expanding charities practice acts for over 200 charities and is backed by a range of linked specialisms from other departments.
Property: Withers' property practice encompasses all aspects of commercial, residential and agricultural property. The firm is particularly renowned for its expertise in agricultural law and in handling international property transactions.

INTERNATIONAL: Withers is an international firm with a global practice and a world wide network of contacts particularly in the US and offshore. The firm has more Italian speakers than any other City law firm and has a growing reputation for representing Italian businesses operating in the UK. The firm has a new joint venture with Chantrier & Associés in Paris who are known for their technology practice. Languages spoken include French, German and Italian.

WITHY KING

5 & 6 Northumberland Buildings, Queen Square, Bath, BA1 2JE **Tel:** (01225) 425731 **Fax:** (01225) 315562 **DX:** 8014 Bath
Email: mail@withyking.co.uk **Ptnrs:** 22 **Asst solrs:** 13 **Other fee-earners:** 33

WOLFERSTANS

Deptford Chambers, 60-66 North Hill, Plymouth, PL4 8EP
Tel: (01752) 663295 **Fax:** (01752) 672021 **DX:** 8206 Plymouth -1
Email: info@wolferstans.com **Website:** www.wolferstans.com

Senior Partner	Paul Woods
Chief Executive	Brian Fisher
Number of partners	21
Assistant solicitors	19
Other fee-earners	19

AREAS OF PRACTICE

Personal Injury/Clinical Negligence	45%
Matrimonial & Children	20%
Commercial	10%
Insurance	10%
Litigation	5%
Crime	5%
Private	5%

CONTACTS

Clinical Negligence	Simon Parford
Commercial	Nick Roper
Crime	David Teague
Insurance	Colin Brazier
Litigation	Bill Duncan
Matrimonial/Family	Phil Thorneycroft
Personal Injury	Colin Brazier
Private	John Chapman
Probate	Gill Hollinshead
Sport	Nick Roper

THE FIRM: Wolferstans is a major regional practice with three offices in Plymouth and another in Taunton. Founded in 1812, it is committed to excellence whilst providing a comprehensive personal service. A number of partners are chairmen of various tribunals.

PRINCIPAL AREAS OF WORK:

Company/Commercial: Work handled includes company formations, acquisitions and sales, funding arrangements, management buy-outs, employment matters, licensing, commercial conveyancing and a wide range of commercial litigation. One member of the team is a licensed insolvency practitioner.
Personal Injury: This division of the practice operates from all major offices. The specialist motorcycle division is operated only from the Taunton office. The medical specialist division is headed by an assessor and member of the panel and a referral panel member for AVMA. The firm is involved in a number of group actions. Clinical negligence franchises are held at Plymouth and Taunton.
Crime: The leader of the team is well known for his courts martial work. In addition to defence criminal work, the practice also acts for government agencies in prosecutions and provides advocates for inquests, inquiries, disciplinary hearings and tribunals.
Sport: Clients include Somerset County Cricket Club, Plymouth Argyle Football Club and Plymouth Basketball Club.
Matrimonial & Family: Work handled by this division includes separation and divorce, mediation, custody and access, adoption, child welfare, financial settlements and maintenance agreements. There are three members of the Children's panel and two accredited specialist family lawyers.
Private Client: Work includes wills, probate and trusts and residential conveyancing.
Additional Areas: The firm regularly appears on behalf of accused persons at courts martial and has extensive experience in inquests and inquiries.

INTERNATIONAL: Languages spoken include French, German, Greek and Spanish.

WOLLASTONS

Brierly Place, New London Road, Chelmsford, CM2 0AP
Tel: (01245) 211211 **Fax:** (01245) 354764 **DX:** 89703 Chelmsford 2
Email: enquiries@wollastons.co.uk **Website:** www.wollastons.co.uk

Number of partners	12
Assistant solicitors	11
Other fee-earners	13

AREAS OF PRACTICE

Corporate/Commercial	33%
Litigation	27%
Property/Planning	25%
Employment	9%
Private Client	6%

CONTACTS

Commercial	Nicholas Burnett
Corporate	Richard Wollaston
	Richard Payne
Employment	Kevin Palmer
Family Property & Finance	Charles Brewer
Intellectual Property	Nigel Thompson
Landlord & Tenant	Nicholas Cook
Litigation	Bruce Bowler
Planning	Jim Little
Property Development	Alan Wyatt
Trusts & Tax	Patrick Penny

THE FIRM: Wollastons provides high levels of expertise and service to business clients based mainly in Essex, London and surrounding counties, as well as foreign companies and their UK subsidiaries. It also advises private individuals and families, including some who are resident abroad. The firm is located in Chelmsford, only 35 minutes by train from central London, with easy access to the motorway network and Stansted airport. It is exceptionally well resourced and well organised with first-rate IT and communications.

PRINCIPAL AREAS OF WORK:

Corporate & Commercial: Work includes company sales and acquisitions (especially management buy-outs and buy-ins); insolvency and reconstructions; corporate finance; European law; intellectual property; commercial agreements; business immigration. The firm has considerable international experience.
Employment: The firm handles employment contracts; unfair and wrongful dismissal; redundancy; race and sex discrimination; business transfers; frequent advocacy in the Employment Tribunal.
Property: Work handled includes commercial development, investment and agricultural property; landlord and tenant.
Litigation: The firm handles commercial disputes; professional negligence claims; debt recovery; insolvency; property and inheritance disputes; personal injury.
Private Client: Work includes wills; tax; trusts; estate planning; probate; family property and finance.

INTERNATIONAL: Wollastons is an active member of IAG International, an association of independent professional firms represented throughout Europe and beyond.

RECRUITMENT: Wollastons welcomes enquiries from outgoing candidates with a strong academic record. The firm takes two or three trainees annually, and is prepared to fund LPC course fees in some cases.

WOODFORD-ROBINSON

4 Castilian Terrace, Northampton, NN1 1LE **Tel:** (01604) 624926 / 231444 **Fax:** (01604) 231457 **DX:** 12424 Northampton 1 **Ptnrs:** 5 **Other fee-earners:** 2

WOODROFFES

36 Ebury Street, London, SW1W 0LU
Tel: (020) 7730 0001 **Fax:** (020) 7730 7900 **DX:** 99923 Victoria
Email: enquiries@woodroffes.org.uk

Senior Partner	Peter Woodroffe
Number of partners	3
Assistant solicitors	4

CONTACTS

Banking & Project Finance .... Sarah Taylor
Conveyancing .... Roger Brown
Education & Art .... Peter Woodroffe
Litigation & Other .... Philip Gordon-Smith

THE FIRM: Founded by CG Woodroffe in 1877, it is a general practice with emphasis on individual attention. The office is situated in Belgravia and is close to Victoria Station.

PRINCIPAL AREAS OF WORK: Known for problem solving in the company/commercial field, private client, education, charities and foreign work. A specialist department handles commercial conveyancing including development, hotels, nightclubs and restaurants and licensing for the same. Work also includes the transfer of works of art, residential conveyancing, employment, probate, matrimonial, litigation, European Court, fraud recovery, insurance claims, insolvency and most legal matters.

CLIENTELE: The firm acts for private clients in UK and abroad, public companies, banks and charities.

W

WOOLLCOMBE BEER WATTS

Church House, Queen Street, Newton Abbot, TQ12 2QP **Tel:** (01626) 202404 **Fax:** (01626) 202420 **DX:** 59100 Newton Abbot **Email:** lawyer@wbw.co.uk **Website:** www.wbw.co.uk **Ptnrs:** 24 **Asst solrs:** 11 **Other fee-earners:** 30

WRAGGE & CO

55 Colmore Row, Birmingham, B3 2AS
Tel: (0870) 903 1000 **Fax:** (0870) 214 1000 **DX:** 13036
Email: mail@wragge.com **Website:** www.wragge.com

Managing Partner	Quentin Poole
Senior Partner	John Crabtree
Number of partners	109
Assistant solicitors	290
Other fee-earners	184

CONTACTS

Automotive .... Bob Gilbert
Aviation .... Jane Pittaway
ADR .... Paul Howard
Banking .... Julian Pallett
Biopharmaceuticals .... Patrick Duxbury
Building Societies .... Jonathan Denton
Charities .... Julie Fox
Commercial Litigation .... Paul Howard
Commercial Property .... Mark Dakeyne
Construction .... Simon Baylis
Corporate Finance .... David Vaughan
Employees' Benefit/Share Schemes .... Kevin Poole
Employment .... Andrew Hodge
Energy/Utilities .... David Hamlett
Environmental .... Lee McBride
EU/Competition .... Guy Lougher
Financial Services .... Jonathan Denton
Food .... Richard Haywood
Intellectual Property .... Gordon Harris
International .... Jane Pittaway
Insurance .... Edward Breen
TMT .... Bill Jones
Local Government .... Peter Keith-Lucas
Media & Entertainment .... Conan Chitham-Mosley
Pensions .... Vivien Cockerill
PFI .... Stephen Kenny
Planning .... Dan Hemming
Property Litigation .... Suzanne Lloyd Holt
Retail & Leisure .... Jack Jacovou
Tax .... Kevin Poole
Transport .... Michael Whitehouse
Travel .... Jane Pittaway

THE FIRM: Wragge & Co is a major UK law firm based in Birmingham, with a substantial national and international client base including over 250 UK listed companies and 60 local authorities. As a successful business it is one of the UK's fastest growing law firms – turnover at £76.3 million (end of April 2001) – a 40% increase on the previous year. During the year 2000 staff numbers increased by 19%. Wragge & Co has built its business on four strategic building blocks: clients, quality, people and profits – a focus which has fuelled the firm's national profile and growth rate. There is real strength and depth across a fully comprehensive range of services combined with the development of leading practices. Investment in IT has maximised efficiency while a focus on people culture has secured staff retention and high profile appointments. The firm is committed to providing the highest quality work and client service. In recognition of its progressive personnel policies, the firm was placed 14th in *The Sunday Times'* Best 50 Companies to work for in the UK, and was the highest placed law firm. Other offices are located in Brussels and London.

PRINCIPAL AREAS OF WORK: Wragge & Co is organised into six groups, each comprising several teams and incorporating recognised leading practices.
Corporate: Competes on a national platform. In 2000, the group – which works in client-facing teams for PLC, Private Equity, IT M & A and major corporates – completed 150 transactions worth £7.4 billion. The Thompson league table ranked the firm 15th in a UK league table of law firms, ahead of all national firms and some major City players.
Commercial: Includes a leading UK IP practice, an EU/competition team with a national reputation and the largest TMT team outside London. This group in particular has recruited senior lawyers with specific in-house experience covering financial services, utilities, telecoms and computer sciences.
Dispute Resolution: Includes Wragge & Co's top construction practice and a 32 partner commercial litigation team that is unrivalled outside London. In 2000 this team launched its innovative risk assessment product designed to give early assessment of litigation outcome. The insurance team has invested in new and emerging markets while retaining strength in traditional areas.
Property Development & Retail & Property Services: Represents the UK's third largest property group, providing a full range of services including planning, litigation, environmental and management to landlords and tenants, property developers, contractors, funding institutions, investors and public authorities across the UK. This includes a team dedicated to residential development.
Human Resources: Covers employment, employee benefits, pensions, personal tax, trusts and charities. The group enjoys a reputation for providing workable solutions to business problems.
Finance & Projects: Offers a range of top specialists in the core areas of utilities – now working on an international scale – including banking, financial services, insolvency, PFI and transport.

Continued overleaf

Other: Wragge & Co also operates a number of industry focused teams in aerospace and aviation, automotive, bio-pharmaceuticals, food, media and entertainment and travel. For more information please visit www.wragge.com.

WRIGHT HASSALL

9 Clarendon Place, Leamington Spa, CV32 5QP
Tel: (01926) 886688 **Fax:** (0871) 871 2071 **DX:** 11863 Leamington Spa
Email: email@wrighthassall.co.uk **Website:** www.wrighthassall.co.uk

Managing Partner	Peter Beddoes
Number of partners	21
Assistant solicitors	16
Other fee-earners	28

CONTACTS

Agriculture .... Robin Ogg
Commercial Litigation .... Richard Lane
Commercial Property .... Tim Rowe
Corporate/Commercial .... Peter Beddoes
.... Mark Lewis
Employment .... Ian Besant
Family .... Julia Bunting
Housing .... Carol Matthews
Insurance .... Michael Davis
Intellectual Property .... Laurie Heizler
Private Client .... Charles McKenzie
Residential Property .... Chris Meredith

THE FIRM: Wright Hassall has an enviable portfolio of clients that value the firm's quality of advice, high standard of service and the location. Leamington Spa, located in the heart of the extensive Midlands transport network, is an attractive town with a thriving business community. As a result, the firm continues to attract high quality lawyers from leading firms who enhance the firm's reputation as a major player in the region. 'Regional Firm, City League' sums up Wright Hassall.

PRINCIPAL AREAS OF WORK:

Agriculture: The agricultural team advises local landowners, farmers and major agricultural organisations on all aspects of agricultural law.
Commercial Property: The firm advises a number of blue chip plcs on their property matters as well as advising on leases, the sale and purchase of commercial property and building development work.
Corporate/Commercial: Work includes the sale and purchase of companies and business assets, MBOs and joint ventures. The firm is also strong in employment law, commercial contracts, partnerships and business formations.
Housing Associations: The department, which has doubled in size within the last year, boasts two of the leading practitioners in the country. The team deals with every legal requirement of social housing providers.
Litigation: The department covers a number of disciplines: commercial, property, including landlord and tenant, professional negligence, defendant insurance and personal and corporate insolvency. The firm also has a matrimonial department with a formidable reputation.
Private Client: Work includes advising on trusts, estates and probate as well as residential property transactions.

WRIGHT, JOHNSTON & MACKENZIE

302 St Vincent Street, Glasgow, G2 5RZ **Tel:** (0141) 248 3434 **Fax:** (0141) 221 1226 **DX:** 129 Glasgow **Email:** enquiries@wjm.co.uk
Website: www.wjm.co.uk **Ptnrs:** 12 **Asst solrs:** 20 **Other fee-earners:** 12

WRIGHT SON & PEPPER

9 Gray's Inn Square, London, WC1R 5JF
Tel: (020) 7242 5473 **Fax:** (020) 7831 7454 **DX:** 35
Email: wsp@wrightsonandpepper.co.uk

Number of partners	8
Assistant solicitors	2
Other fee-earners	3

AREAS OF PRACTICE

Regulatory/Disciplinary/Partnership 21%
Company/Commercial 16%
Litigation 16%
Property 16%
Family 16%
Private Client 15%

CONTACTS

Company/Commercial .... Steven Alais
Family .... Paul Butner
Litigation .... Iain Miller
Private Client .... Brian Wates
Property .... Hilary Palmer
Regulatory/Disciplinary/Partnership
.... Iain Miller
.... Nicholas Wright

THE FIRM: Wright Son & Pepper has been established in Gray's Inn Square since 1800. Its clients range from public companies, institutions and regulators through to small businesses and professional and private individuals. The firm is highly regarded for its work in professional and partnership matters.

PRINCIPAL AREAS OF WORK:

Professional Practice & Partnership Matters: The firm advises regulators, professional firms and individuals on all matters relating to the regulation of professional practices. It also advises on the formation and dissolution of partnerships and on disputes in which partnerships or their members are involved as well as on problems which may arise on the admission or retirement of partners.
Litigation: The firm has extensive experience in general commercial and private litigation including professional negligence claims. High Court agency work is also undertaken.
Property: All aspects are covered, with the main emphasis on offices, shop and factory/warehouse leases and developments, planning and funding arrangements.
Company/Commercial: The firm deals with the normal range of company and commercial work and has considerable experience in dealing with all forms of computer-related contracts and restraint of trade covenants.
Family Law: All aspects of matrimonial, family, welfare and childcare law are covered with special emphasis on ancillary relief in matrimonial proceedings.
Private Client & Tax: The firm deals with wills, settlements, trust formation and administration, powers of attorney, Court of Protection, investment advice, personal tax, estate planning, probates and the administration of estates.
Other Areas: The firm also undertakes work in debt recovery, intellectual property, building contract disputes, employment, landlord and tenant, transport, and consumer law.

INTERNATIONAL: The firm has professional connections in Belgium and the USA.

WRIGLEYS

19 Cookridge Street, Leeds, LS2 3AG
Tel: (0113) 244 6100 **Fax:** (0113) 244 6101 **DX:** 12020 Leeds 1
Email: thepartners@wrigleys.co.uk

Managing Partner	Richard Sutton
Senior Partners	Peter Chadwick
	Annabel Duchart
	Matthew Wrigley
Number of partners	11
Assistant solicitors	13
Other fee-earners	7

THE FIRM: Wrigleys was formed as a specialist private client practice in May 1996. It combines the private client departments of DLA, Hammond Suddards and the Leeds and Manchester offices of Eversheds. In August 2000 it was joined by the specialist charities firm of Malcolm Lynch. The department has also seen substantial organic growth and now has 11 partners and a total of 60 staff. The main office is in Leeds and the firm has benefited from the remarkable rise of the city as a professional centre. There is a smaller but thriving office in Sheffield. As a specialist practice with relatively low overheads, the firm presents itself as a logical alternative to London practices.

PRINCIPAL AREAS OF WORK: Wrigleys advises wealthy individuals, charities, foundations, social economy clients and trustees. A great deal of the work is tax and trust based, with a growing property department serving the same clientele. Originally best known for its strength in the heritage and landed areas, the firm now serves a wide spectrum of old and new money. In addition the pensions team advises sponsoring employers, trustees and members of occupational pension schemes and has a particular strength in advising on unapproved and personal pension schemes. Contentious or commercial work is referred elsewhere, and the firm regularly acts with and for other professionals. Recent developments have included the arrival of the specialist charities firm of Malcolm Lynch and the strengthening of the pensions department with the arrival of two experienced pensions lawyers. The department now includes four of the region's best known lawyers.

CLIENTELE: The firm acts for a large number of charities, foundations and well-known families, with most of the individual clients being rich enough to face serious tax problems. Historically, most clients were northern based, but, latterly, the firm has begun to attract clients nationally and internationally, since some offshore clients perceive a cost benefit in using a regional practice for work that has traditionally gone to London. The firm acts for a wide range of charities, particularly in the religious, educational and conservation areas. The firm's pension clients include a number of substantial occupational pension schemes, IFAs and independent trustees.

Y

AE WYETH & CO

Bridge House, High Street, Dartford, DA1 1JR **Tel:** (01322) 297000 **Fax:** (01322) 297001 **DX:** 31904 Dartford **Ptnrs:** 15 **Asst solrs:** 11 **Other fee-earners:** 30

WYNNE BAXTER

Century House, 15-19 Dyke Road, Brighton, BN1 3FE **Tel:** (01273) 775533 **Fax:** (01273) 207744 **DX:** 141292 BRIGHTON 5 **Email:** brighton@wynnebaxter.com **Website:** www.wynnebaxter.com **Ptnrs:** 17 **Asst solrs:** 16 **Other fee-earners:** 25

YOUNG & LEE

No. 6 The Wharf, Bridge Street, Birmingham, B1 2JS **Tel:** (0121) 633 3233 **Fax:** (0121) 632 5292 **DX:** 701255 Edgbaston 4 **Email:** timlee@younglee.co.uk **Website:** www.younglee.co.uk **Ptnrs:** 5 **Asst solrs:** 5 **Other fee-earners:** 5

YOUNG & PEARCE

58 Talbot Street, Nottingham, NG1 5GL **Tel:** (0115) 959 8888 **Fax:** (0115) 947 5572 **DX:** 10025 **Email:** reception@youngandpearce.com **Website:** www.youngandpearce.com **Ptnrs:** 10 **Asst solrs:** 5 **Other fee-earners:** 5

TC YOUNG & SON

30 George Square, Glasgow, G2 1LH
Tel: (0141) 221 5562 **Fax:** (0141) 221 5024 **DX:** GW 78
Email: mail@tcyoung.co.uk

Managing Partner Andrew Cowan

CONTACTS

Charities/Structures ....Mark Ewing
Corporate/Stock Transfers ....Stephen MacGregor
Litigation ....Andrew Cowan
Private Client ....Andrew Robertson
Property ....Isabel Ewing

THE FIRM: TC Young & Son provides a wide range of legal services to housing organisations, lenders, charities, general commercial organisations and private clients. The firm has seen significant growth in the last year, with particular emphasis in the fields of social housing and charities and is now the leading player in the Scottish social housing scene. The firm has been joined, at partnership level, by three of Scotland's leading social housing lawyers, two of whom head up the new Edinburgh Office. TC Young & Son now has strength in depth in all aspects of social housing law.

PRINCIPAL AREAS OF WORK:

Social Housing & Charities: A recognised leader in the field TC Young & Son currently acts for more than 90 social housing organisations. It provides a full range of legal services to its social housing and charity clients, including corporate structures, funding, stock transfers, development services and housing management.

Continued overleaf

Business & Commercial: The firm advises in a wide range of general business and commercial/corporate matters, including corporate structures, funding, commercial property, contracts and employment.
Private Clients: The firm has a significant private client base and offers a full range of personal client legal services.

YUILL & KYLE

79 West Regent Street, Glasgow, G2 2AR **Tel:** 0141 331 2332 **Fax:** 0141 332 4223 **Ptnrs:** 2 **Asst solrs:** 5 **Other fee-earners:** 7

ZERMANSKY & PARTNERS

10 Butts Court, Leeds, LS1 5JS
Tel: (0113) 245 9766 **Fax:** (0113) 246 7465 **DX:** 12061

Managing Partner	David Honeybone
Senior Partner	Russell Graham
Number of partners	11
Assistant solicitors	6
Other fee-earners	6

CONTACTS

Childcare	Lynn McFadyen
Company & Commercial	David Honeybone
Insolvency	Neil Lieberman
Litigation	Richard Lindley
Matrimonial & Family	Norman Taylor
Personal Injury	Gurchan Jandu
Probate	Christopher Dudzinski
Property	Russell Graham
Sports	Richard Lindley

THE FIRM: Zermansky & Partners is an expanding firm combining private client work and a strong commitment to Legal Aid work (franchised in seven areas), with a comprehensive range of services to small to medium sized businesses and not-for-profit organisations.

PRINCIPAL AREAS OF WORK: The firm is particularly known for its large family department, including matrimonial finance, child abduction, emergency and childcare work. The litigation department has specialised employment, housing and personal injury/clinical negligence sections. Insolvency work is a new area of development. It has substantial experience in sports law, particularly with governing bodies.

INTERNATIONAL: Languages spoken include Hindi, Polish and Punjabi.

Z

IN-HOUSE LAWYERS

& COMPANY SECRETARIES

Index of In-house Lawyers & Company Secretaries

For full details see the alphabetical listing of firms on pages 1999-1222

Abdoo, David
Carlton Communications PLC

Adams, Laurie
ABN Amro Equities Holdings (UK) Limited

Ager, Rowley
Tesco Stores PLC

Allen, Paul
Aggreko PLC

Allison, A
TT International

Allnutt, Robert
Nycomed Amersham PLC

Applegarth, Chris
Arriva PLC

Armour, Robert M
British Energy PLC

Arnaouti, Michael
Spirent PLC

Arnott, Derek
Royal Bank of Scotland Group PLC

Ashcroft, Charles P
EMI Group PLC

Ashcroft, Clive
Land Securities PLC

Ashley-Brown, Michael
Canary Wharf Group PLC

Ashton-Jones, Philip
Associated British Foods PLC

Askew, RJA
ED & F Man Holdings Ltd

Aston, Richard
Thomson Travel Group plc

Atkinson, Richard
Merrill Lynch International

Axe, Craig
Christiania Bank of Kreditkasse ASA

Bailey, John PC
Kingston Communications PLC

Baines, Harry
Halifax Group PLC

Baker, Brian
Rolls-Royce PLC

Barratt, Simon
Whitbread Holdings PLC

Bartlett, Stephen
Bear Stearns International Limited

Barton, Heather-Anne
Scottish Football Association

Bates, Deanna
British Sky Broadcasting Group PLC (Sky Digital)

Battle, John
Independent Television News Ltd (ITN)

Baxandall, Cathy
Thistle Hotels PLC

Bellhouse, Rob
Greene King PLC

Bennett, Richard ET
HSBC Holdings PLC

Berman, Darren
Football Association

Berry, John
Iceland Group PLC

Bestmann, Jay
Bank One Corporation

Beswitherick, David P
Manchester United PLC

Bevan, Peter BP
BP plc

Bicheno, Janet
Arab Bank PLC

Bickell, Brian
Shaftesbury PLC

Blacker, Michael
AMEC Capital Projects Ltd

Blake, Tania
Capita Group PLC

Bloom, David
HSBC Holdings PLC

Boad, Robert
BP plc

Bolt, Geoff R
NSB Retail Systems

Bond, Nigel
Trafficmaster PLC

Booth, Sarah
Christian Salvesen PLC

Bowen-Jones, Leigh
Benchmark Group PLC

Bowley, William J
Mersey Docks & Harbour Company

Boyle, Simon
Marconi PLC

Braine, Anthony
British Land Company PLC

Bramwell, Phillip
BT Wireless

Branson, David A
Wolseley PLC

Bratby, Robert
Colt Telecommunications plc

Brett, Alastair
Times Newspapers Ltd

Brierley, Tony
3i Group PLC

Brinley-Codd, Peter
Sir Robert McAlpine (Holdings) Ltd

Britton, Bob
Hiscox PLC

Britton, Rupert J
Civil Aviation Authority (CAA)

Brown, Philip
Elementis PLC

Budd, Geoffrey
Dixons Group PLC

Budge, Duncan
RIT Capital Partners PLC

Burchill, Jeremy
Aberdeen Asset Management PLC

Burge, Patricia
Times Newspapers Ltd

Burke, Jonathan
Wm Morrison Supermarkets PLC

Bush, Daniel
Interserve PLC

Butcher, Ian
Go-Ahead Group PLC

Butler, James
EGG PLC

Butterworth, Siobhain
Guardian Newspapers Limited

Bye, Tim
British Midland Airways Ltd

Byrne, Alison
Independent Insurance Group PLC

Byrne, Stephen G
Bank of Cyprus (London) Limited

Byrne, Stephen G
Lombard Bank Limited / Commercial Services

Cabanagh, Julia
Serco Group PLC

Caller, Mitch
JP Morgan Chase

Calow, David
WPP Group PLC

Cameron, Alex
Barclays Capital

Cameron, Lee
Morse PLC

Campbell, Colin
Channel 5 Broadcasting Limited

Campbell, Stephen
Galen Holdings PLC

Camplin-Smith, Alan
Selfridges PLC

Carfora, Carmelina
Electrocomponents PLC

Carr, Chalmers
Coutts & Co

Chadwick, Peter
Bovis Lendlease Ltd

Chapman, Clare
Reuters Group PLC

Charlton, David
Boots Company (The) PLC

Charnock, Stephen
Hays PLC

Chelsom, Paul
Credit Suisse First Boston

Chester, J Geoffrey
Hilton Group PLC

Churchill-Coleman, Richard
Thomson Travel Group plc

Clarke, James
JD Wetherspoon PLC

Clayton, JRW
Invensys PLC

Clayton, Neil
First Technology PLC

Clifton, Roger C
TBI PLC

Coles, Pamela
Lex Service PLC

Collier-Wright, Charles
Trinity Mirror PLC

Collins, John
ABN Amro Equities Holdings (UK) Limited

Collins, Michael
RMC Group PLC

Cooper, Andy
Airtours UK Leisure Group

Cooper, Nick
Sage Group PLC

Cooper, Richard
Johnston Press PLC

Cormick, Charles
Rank Group PLC

Coventry, JL
IQE PLC

Coward, Nicholas
Football Association

Cowen, Tim
BT Ignite

Cox, Alan
GlaxoSmithKline

Craven, Kate
Merrill Lynch International

Crompton, Andrew
MacMillan Ltd

Crone, Tom
News International PLC

Crown, Giles
TBWA UK Group

Cruddace, Martin
Trinity Mirror PLC

Curran, Sara
Working Title Films Ltd

Curtin, Edmond
Credit Suisse First Boston

Curtis, John E
Intermediate Capital Group

Davidson, Christopher
Bradford & Bingley Building Society

Davidson, Dawn
SMG PLC

Davis, Philip
Bookham Technology PLC

Dawe, Kim
HarperCollins Publishers Ltd

Dawes, Peter G
Vosper Thornycroft Holdings PLC

Dawson, Grant
Centrica PLC

de Laperouse, Marc
Bank of America

Deeley, James
David S Smith (Holdings) PLC

Denison, Graeme
Caledonia Investments plc

Dennis, Will
Lazard Brothers & Co Limited

Dent, Laurence
Barratt Developments PLC

Dhillon, Marla
ING Groep NV

Dixon, Anthony
Pace Micro Technology PLC

Dodds, Simon
Deutsche Bank AG

Doherty, Patrick
Cattles PLC

Doherty, Stephen P
Singer & Friedlander Group PLC

Donnelly, Vincent
Scottish & Southern Energy PLC

Downey, Antonia S
Jim Henson Company Ltd

Dransfield, Graham
Hanson PLC

Dregent, Patricia
Carpetright PLC

Duffield, Stephen
Britax International PLC

Dyball, Jane
Warner Chappell Music Ltd

East, Anna
Britannic PLC

Eastwood, Charlotte
Eidos PLC

Edmunds, MA (Cantab), Paul
Ashtead Group PLC

Edwards, Pamela
Fidelity Investments International

Elliot, William
Goldman Sachs International

Ellis, Gerald
Safeway Stores PLC

Ellis-Rees, James
Scipher PLC

Emery, John
Bovis Homes Group PLC

Enoch, Simon
Baltimore Technologies PLC

Evans, Fiona
Biocompatibles International PLC

Evans, Grenville
BMG Records (UK) Limited

Ezekiel, Ivan
Minerva PLC

Fairhurst, Andrew David
Legal & General UK Select Investment Trust PLC

Farrant, Simon
Johnson Matthey PLC

Featherstone, John
Barclays Bank PLC (Corporate Banking)

Fenwick, John C
AMEC PLC

Fergusson, Peter
Norsk Hydro (UK) Ltd

Field, Roger
The Random House Group Ltd

Firth, Patrick
awg plc

Fisher, Brian
Bank of Scotland

Fitz, J Daniel
Cable & Wireless PLC

FitzHugh, Dirk O
Carillion PLC

Fletcher, Anne
British Telecommuncations PLC

Flinn, David
Viridian Group PLC

Fluker, Louise
De La Rue PLC

Folger, Susan
Liberty International PLC

Foulkes Shaw, Sarah
BBA Group PLC

Foye, Anthony
Taylor & Francis Group PLC

Francis, Neil
Persimmon PLC

Fraser, Jeremy
Lloyds TSB Scotland PLC

Friedrich, William
BG Group PLC

Fulton, Kate
Young & Rubicam Group Ltd

Garner, Margaret
Credit Agricole Indosuez

Garratt-Frost, Stephen
HSBC Holdings PLC

Geen, David
Goldman Sachs International

Geissmar, Svenja
MTV Networks

George, Alastair
Sony Music Entertainment (UK) Ltd

Gibber, Robert
Tate & Lyle PLC

Gibson, David William
Rexam PLC

Gibson, Graham D
John Laing PLC

Gladman, Hugh J
St James's Place Capital PLC

Gledhill, James
Citibank

Goddard, Ian
The Alliance Trust PLC

Goodenough, Adrian
Alliance UniChem

Goulden, Ian S
Exel PLC

Gradon, Michael
Peninsular & Oriental Steam Navigation Co

Graham, Alan
NM Rothschild & Sons

Gray, Andy
Amateur Swimming Association

Grayson, Tim
Goldman Sachs International

Green, Philip E
Meggitt PLC

Green, Ron
London Pacific Group Ltd

Greenwood, David
JJB Sports PLC

Gregory, Janet
GE Capital (Global Equipment Finance) Ltd

Greig, Kenneth
AXA Investment Managers Ltd

Griffiths, Nigel E
Securicor PLC

Grime, John
Bodycote International PLC

Gubbins, William
PowerGen PLC

Guedes, Lawrence
Logica PLC

Guttridge, Ian
Royal & Sun Alliance Insurance Group PLC

Haig, David
Tokai Bank Europe plc

Hall, Jonathan
Rugby Football Union (RFU)

Hamshaw Thomas, Charles
Imperial Tobacco Group PLC

Harding, Iain M
Scottish Investment Trust PLC

Hartrey, Patrick
PizzaExpress PLC

Haydon, Stuart
Hammerson PLC

Heard, Robert
BPB PLC

Heath, Richard
Unilever PLC

Heather, Christopher
Vizzavi Europe Limited

Henderson, Sheila
Reckitt & Benckiser PLC

Herga, Robert
BAA PLC

Heriz-Jones, P Norman
Uniq PLC

Herlihy, Michael HC
Imperial Chemical Industries PLC

Highley, Owen
British Airways PLC

Hildebrand, Andrew
FilmFour

Hodges, Simon
Millennium & Copthorne Hotels PLC

Hogarth-Jones, Bruce
Citigroup Private Bank

Hogwood, Paul
Deutsche Asset Management

Holland, Anthony
Novar plc

Hooper, David
Enodis PLC

Horner, Elizabeth
Rothschild Asset Management Limited

Hosker, David
United Utilities Water plc

Houghton, Ian
WH Smith PLC

House, Richard
Tokyo-Mitsubishi International PLC

Hudson, Dominic
Laird Group PLC

Hughes, Kathrine
Alliance & Leicester PLC

Hui, Carol
Amey PLC

Humphries, Gordon
British Assets Trust PLC

Hunt, Simon
Anite Group PLC

Hurst, Gordon
Capita Group PLC

Hussey, Paul
Bunzl PLC

Ilett, John
Oxford Glycosciences PLC (OGS)

Isaac, Anthony Eric
BOC Group PLC

Isaacs, Robin
Lloyds TSB Leasing Ltd

Jameson, Ian
Lehman Brothers International (Europe)

Jenkins, Mark
Colt Telecomunications plc

Jepson, Susy
Somerfield plc

Jobe, Christopher
Northern Rock PLC

John, Andrew
First Choice Holidays PLC

Johnson, Geoffrey
Lloyds TSB Group PLC

Johnson, Guy
Debenhams PLC

Johnson, Simon
ITV Network Limited

Jones, Clare
Citibank

Jones, Helen
Kingfisher PLC

Jones, Jonathan
Reckitt & Benckiser PLC

Jones, Paul
Polydor Ltd

Joseph, Anne
Reed Elsevier PLC

Jowett, Jonathan D
SSL International PLC

Joy, Larissa
Ogilvy & Mather

Kanter, Andrew
Autonomy Corporation PLC

Kass, Harvey
Daily Mail & General Trust PLC

Keating, Michael
Cadbury Schweppes PLC

Keevil, Tom
Gallaher Group

Keisler, Ben
Anglo American PLC

Kellett, Peter
Environment Agency

Kelley, Russell P
Allied Domecq PLC

Kelloe, Jane
American Express Bank Ltd.

Kembery, Jonathan A
Open Interactive Limited

Kerr, Garth
Intec Telecom Systems PLC

Kilbee, Michael
Lloyds TSB

Kingsley-Daniels, Tracy
Credit Suisse First Boston

Kingston, Mark
Tishman Speyer Properties UK Ltd

Kite, Timothy
Derwent Valley Holdings PLC

Knight, Michael R
Severn Trent Water Ltd

Kyriakides, Evie
Mars Incorporated

Lanaghan, Brian
Mizuho International plc

Lawton, Charles HH
Rio Tinto PLC

Le Marchant, Piers
Lehman Brothers International (Europe)

Lees, Jennifer
Incepta Group PLC

Leff, Clyde M
Pilkington PLC

Lenihan, Martin
Skanska Construction Group Ltd

Lester, Michael
BAE Systems PLC

Levin, Sarah
Universal Music Publishing Group

Lewis, David A
JP Morgan & Co

Lilley, Charles E
Xansa PLC

Lillycrop, David P
Smiths Group PLC

Lizmore, Leonard
Sakura Finance International Limited

Lockie, Victoria
Pearson Education Ltd

Lowes, Robert
Photo-Me International PLC

Lugdon, C N
Hoare Bank

Lush, Paul
BHP Billiton plc

Lynch, Lucy
Morgan Stanley Dean Witter & Co

Lyons, Noel
Signet Group PLC

Ma, Joan
Morgan Stanley Dean Witter & Co

MacDonald, Ian
CGNU PLC

MacKay, David
ARM Holdings plc

Macleod, David
Thus plc

Malkin, Gwyn
Abbey National PLC

Manning, Richard
GWR Group plc

Manson, Ian
Scottish & Southern Energy PLC

Marcus, Robert
IBM UK Ltd

Marshall, Alexander
Goldman Sachs International

Martin, Desna
Great Portland Estates PLC

Martin, Philip
Pillar Property PLC

Index to leading lawyers: p.1647

Martin, Simon
Gartmore Investment Management PLC

Mason, Geoff
Jarvis PLC

Massey, Roger
Daiwa Europe Ltd

Maurice, Emmanuel
European Bank for Reconstruction & Development (EBRD)

May, Robert G
Slough Estates PLC

May, Tatjana
Shire Pharmaceuticals Group PLC

Maynard, Peter
Prudential PLC

McClenan, Michael S
Bank of Scotland

McCormack, Frank
Balfour Beatty PLC

McCracken, Cameron
Pathé Pictures Limited

McDonald, Tony
National Express Group PLC

McElhatton, Jane
Cable & Wireless PLC

McFarlane, Stuart
Kelda Group PLC

McKelvie, Andrew
Energis PLC

McKeown, Mark
William M Mercer Limited

McLean, Suzanne
SkyePharma PLC

McQuoid, Christopher
TTP Communications plc

Mee, David
Nomura International PLC

Mellett, Diane
Cambridge Antibody Tech Group PLC

Mellstrom, Bruce R
Lawn Tennis Association

Milburn, Lucian
Westdeutsche Landesbank Girozentrale (London)

Mileson, Chris
EMI Publishing Ltd

Miller, Cathy
Edinburgh Investment Trust PLC

Miller, Peter
Informa Group

Miller, Therese L
Goldman Sachs International

Mitchelson, Alan
The Weir Group PLC

Moir, Carol
UBS Warburg Group

Monro, Richard
Marshalls PLC

Morley, Ronald
Compass Group PLC

Morris, Philip
Balfour Beatty PLC

Morrison, Angela
Working Title Films Ltd

Mostert, Frederick
Richemont International Limited

Munger, Roger
ABN Amro Equities Holdings (UK) Limited

Murphy, Finbarr
Bank of Ireland

Murray, Martin
Old Mutual plc

Musker, Graeme
AstraZeneca PLC

Nardi, Riccardo
The Association of British Travel Agents (ABTA)

Nealson, Kathleen
Standard Chartered PLC

Neate, Francis W
Schroders PLC

Neylan, Michael
Royal Bank of Canada

Nicholson, Judith
Avis Europe PLC

Nimmo, Mark
Société Générale

Oakes, Andy
Misys PLC

Oakley, Graham
Marks & Spencer PLC

Ogden, Jeremy
Barclays Bank PLC (Wealth Management Legal)

Ogilvie Smals, Rufus
GKN PLC

O'Gorman, Timothy
Carphone Warehouse Limited

O'Hara, Simon
Cookson Group plc

O'Neill, Margaret
Corus Group PLC

Ormond, Jon
Deutsche Bank AG

Osborne, Simon K
Railtrack Group PLC

O'Shea, John
IMI PLC

Owen, Jane
Aon Limited

Page, Ann
Co-Operative Bank PLC

Paget-Brown, Edward
Credit Lyonnais

Pallot, Wendy
GWR Group plc

Pank, Edward
ICAP plc

Parrott, Graham
Granada PLC

Parsliffe, Simon
London Bridge Software Holdings PLC

Parson, Michael G
Smith & Nephew PLC

Partington, Marcus
Trinity Mirror PLC

Patience, John
Lattice Group PLC

Peacock, Helena
The Penguin Group (UK)

Pearce, Michael
Lonmin PLC

Pearce, Simon
P & O Princess Cruises PLC

Pengelly, Faith
Finsbury Trust PLC

Perrot, Robin
Chelsfield PLC

Perry, Tim
Sportsworld Media Group PLC

Phillips, Charles
Wincanton PLC

Pike, Andrew S
Travis Perkins PLC

Pope, John
Cobham PLC

Popper, Andrew
BTG PLC

Porter, Alan
Imperial Tobacco Group PLC

Porter, Leslie
Wolverhampton & Dudley Breweries PLC

Pottinger, Alan
Computacenter PLC

Price, Philip
UBS Warburg Group

Pritchard, Wendy
Berkeley Group PLC

Proctor, Tim
Diageo PLC

Proudfoot, Graeme J
Amvescap PLC - Invesco Global

Pybus, Mark
Company Television

Quinlan, Diane
Kidde PLC

Radice, James
EMI Records Limited

Ramsay, Stephen
International Power PLC

Read, Angela
Orchestream Holdings PLC

Read, Simon
Telewest Communications PLC

Rees, David
Provident Financial PLC

Rees, Hywel
Associated British Ports Holdings plc

Regan, Tim
Regus PLC

Reid, Marijke
Open Interactive Limited

Richards, Allan
ARC International PLC

Rinck, Gary
Pearson PLC

Roberts, Allen CG
Renishaw PLC

Roberts, David
GlaxoSmithKline

Robinson, Deborah
WS Atkins PLC

Robson, Andrew J
RM PLC

Roper Curzon, Holly
Marylebone Cricket Club (MCC)

Rosenthal, Richard
Morgan Stanley Dean Witter & Co

Ross-Stewart, Charles
UBS Warburg Group

Ruppell, Louise
FirstGroup

Sampson, Jeremy
Taylor Woodrow plc

Sanghvi, Rakesh
Sony Music Entertainment (UK) Ltd

Sauerwein, Eleonore
Aegis Group PLC

Schrager von Altishofen, Nicola
Merchants Trust PLC

Schroeder, Anthony
Guardian iT Group

Schwarz, Nathalie
Capital Radio PLC

Scott, Derek
Stagecoach Holdings PLC

Scott, Stephen
Vodafone Group PLC

Scotts, Roger
Goldman Sachs International

Scriven, Jane
Geest PLC

Seabrooke, Mark
Sanwa International plc

Shah, Sheeraz
Working Title Films Ltd

Shaw, THM
Davis Service Group PLC

Shirran, Jane L
Clydesdale Bank PLC

Shirras, James
Film Finances Limited

Slater, John
Celltech Group PLC

Smedley, Christopher
Colt Telecommunications plc

Smethurst, Edward G
Ultraframe PLC

Smith, Fiona
National Grid Company PLC

Smith, Ian A
Matalan PLC

Soley, Martin
Forte Ltd

Solomon, Deryck J
AGA Foodservice Group PLC

Sowerbutts, Kevin
BNP Paribas

Sowerbutts, Kevin
Paribas Principal Investments

Spruzen, David
Axon Group PLC

Stables, Jane
United Business Media plc

Stanley, James
Scottish Power PLC

Stephens, Roger
Spectris plc

Stevinson, Jenny
ABN Amro Equities Holdings (UK) Limited

Stirzaker, Mark
British Vita PLC

Stobart, John
Taylor Nelson Sofres PLC

Stoker, Peter
Bellway PLC

Stride, Andrew
Luminar PLC

Studd, Kevin
Credit Suisse First Boston

Sugrue, Claire
Universal/Island Records Limited

Swift, Angeline
Lattice Property Holdings Limited

Swingland, Charles
Powderject Pharmaceuticals

Switalski, Gillian
Foreign & Colonial Invest Trust PLC (Unit Managers)

Sykes, Stephen
Certa (UK) Ltd

Talbutt, Luke
Bioglan Pharma PLC

Tames, Jane
Scottish Radio Holdings PLC

Tan, Hilary
Innovation Group PLC

Tapp, Richard
Blue Circle Industries PLC

Taylor, Colin
Northern Rock PLC

Taylor, Simon
HIT Entertainment

Thomas, Emma
Nestor Healthcare Group PLC

Thomas, Jonathan
Goldman Sachs International

Thoms, Peter
NXT PLC

Thomson, Hamish
MFI Furniture Group PLC

IN-HOUSE LAWYERS / CO SECS

Thornton, Jane
Gartmore Investment Management PLC

Thurston, David
J Sainsbury PLC

Timms, Geoffrey
Legal & General Group PLC

Tingay, Sarah
Pearson PLC

Todhunter, Barry
DFS Furniture PLC

Tomlinson, Humphrey
Royal & Sun Alliance Insurance Group PLC

Tonkinson, Andrew OC
South African Breweries PLC

Toubkin, Michael
BNP Banque Nationale de Paris PLC

Townsend, Nicolas J
Wilson Bowden PLC

Tredway, Carol
Halma PLC

Trust, Howard B
Barclays PLC

Tubbs, Josephine
Framlington Group Ltd

Tynan, Peter
N Brown Group PLC

Vardy, Val
Towers Perrin

Vaughan, Christopher
Six Continents plc

Vellani, H. Andrew S
Scottish & Newcastle PLC

Ventrella, Tony
FKI PLC

Vickers, Paul
Trinity Mirror PLC

Wade, Vyvienne
Jardine Lloyd Thompson Group PLC

Wailing, Michael
TeleWork Systems PLC

Waldron, Michael
London Merchant Securities PLC (Ord)

Walford, Justin
Express Newspapers Ltd / Express Sunday

Walmsley, Derek
EMAP PLC

Walsh, Stephen
British Airways PLC

Walters, Jayne
Akeler Group of Companies

Ward-Jones, Robert
Rentokil Initial PLC

Waterhouse, Alan
Waste Recycling Group PLC (WRG)

Waters, Antony F
MITIE Group PLC

Watts, Nigel
Brixton PLC

Weaver, Paul
Logica PLC

Webb, Rhic JP
Brockbank Underwriting Group PLC

Webb, Steven
Premier Farnell PLC

Webb QC, Robert
British Airways PLC

Webber, Peter
Next Group PLC

White, Stewart D
Vodafone Group PLC

Whittaker, Andrew
Financial Services Authority - FSA

Williams, Carol
Northern Foods PLC

Williams, Catherine
Channel Four Television Corporation

Williams, Denise
Cordiant Communications Group PLC

Williams, Stephen G
Unilever PLC

Williams, Susan
Chloride Group PLC

Wilson, Andrew
Enterprise Oil PLC

Wilson, Hilary
Skanska Construction Group Ltd

Withington, Neil
British American Tobacco PLC

Witt, David
IBM UK Ltd

Wood, Duncan
Cairn Energy PLC

Woodier, Kenneth D
Pennon Group PLC

Woodward Hill, Sacha
Formula One Management Ltd

Wrangles, Kay
Collins Stewart Holdings PLC

Wynn Davies, Arthur
Telegraph Group Limited

Yapp, Alison
Charter PLC

In-house Lawyers & Company Secretaries

3i Group PLC
91 Waterloo Road London SE1 8XP
Tel: (020) 7928 3131 **Fax:** (020) 7928 3458
Website: www.3i.com
No of lawyers in dept: 32
Work outsourced: Litigation and some corporate and investment work.
Tony Brierley, Company Secretary & Head of Legal
Specialisation: Corporate, venture capital.
Career: 1990 Solicitor, 1981 Barrister-at-Law, Inner Temple.
Other lawyers: UK Investment Legal Services- David Dench; Continental Europe Legal Services- Jane Alexander; Group Legal- David Herbert (Group Solicitor).

Abbey National PLC
Genesis House 301-349 Midsummer Boulevard Milton Keynes MK9 2JE
Tel: (01908) 348070 **Fax:** (01908) 348282
Email: gwyn.malkin@abbeynational.co.uk
Website: www.abbeynational.co.uk
No of lawyers in dept: 26
Gwyn Malkin, Group Legal Services Director
Specialisation: Handles commercial and corporate law matters and management of the legal function. Member of Legal Committee of British Bankers Association.
Career: Qualified 1975. Became Head of Legal Services at Abbey National in July 1992.
Other lawyers: Corporate and Regulatory Law Group: Simon Goldburn, Richenda Kullar, Sally Hopwood, Alan Squires, Jane Stolberger. Commercial Law Group: Desmond Pettit, Carole Jones, Joanna Day, Katie Ward, Ian Wallbank, Jane Hayden, Geoffrey Pope, John Candlish. Consumer Law Group (banking, savings and lending, insurance) : John Thurwell, Gwynedd Miller, John Hamilton, Jacqueline Neblett, John Laing, Pauline Pope, Dawn Adshead. Life Division Law Group: Colin Browning, Janine Pennel, Joanna Morton, John Forsyth. Intellectual & Real Property Law Group: Alison Greene.

Aberdeen Asset Management PLC
One Albyn Place Aberdeen AB10 1TG
Tel: (01224) 631999 **Fax:** (01224) 646651
Website: www.aberdeen-asset.com
No of lawyers in dept: 7
Work outsourced: 50% - Aquisitions: overseas.
Jeremy Burchill, Head of Legal
Specialisation: Financial services, compliance in UK and Europe.
Career: Barrister in Northern Ireland 1979-1984; Financial Services (in-house) since 1984; Educated: Campbell College, Belfast and Queens University, Belfast.
Personal: Married with two children.
Other lawyers: John Brett - Corporate; Paul Campbell - Closed Ended Funds; Elizabeth Moxham - Open Ended Funds.

ABN Amro Equities Holdings (UK) Limited
250 Bishopsgate London EC2M 4AA
Tel: (020) 7678 1240 **Fax:** (020) 7678 6484
Email: jenny.stevinson@uk.abnamro.com
No of lawyers in dept: 4
Work outsourced: 25% - Litigation, IP, property, some company/commercial.
Jenny Stevinson, Head of Legal/Company Secretary
Specialisation: Manages Legal and Secretarial Department providing legal services to London-based equity businesses of ABN AMRO Investment Banking Group. Specific areas include company law, transaction documentation for equity-related products, customer documentation, clearing and banking arrangements, supplies of goods and services, employment, property, intellectual property.
Career: King's College, London University LLB 1975. Called to the Bar, Gray's Inn, 1976. General common law, commercial, EEC, pupillages, 1976-78. Department of Trade and Industry, Solicitor's Department 1978-86: international and EEC trade, telecommunications, company and financial services law. Legal Adviser, Security Pacific Hoare Govett (Holdings) Limited 1987-1990. Group Legal Adviser and Company Secretary, Hoare Govett Limited from 1990, renamed ABV AMNO Equities (UK) Limited 1998.
Other lawyers: Helen Short - product, customer, settlement documentation; Ian Spaxman - contracts for supply of goods and services, employment, IP, property; Gabrielle Ellison - asset management.

250 Bishopsgate London EC2M 4AA
Tel: (020) 7678 3015 **Fax:** (020) 7678 6484
Email: roger.munger@uk.abnamro.com
Roger Munger, Global Head of Fixed Income Legal
Career: BA - Carleton College; JD - University of Colorado; LL.M - University College London.

250 Bishopsgate London EC2M 4AA
Tel: (020) 7678 8000 **Fax:** (020) 7678 6484
Laurie Adams, Global General Counsel

250 Bishopsgate London EC2M 4AA
Tel: (020) 7678 8000 **Fax:** (020) 7678 6484
John Collins, Global Legal Head of Corporate Finance

Aegis Group PLC
43-45 Portman Square London W1H 6LY
Tel: (020) 7070 7700 **Fax:** (020) 7070 7800
Website: www.aegisgroup.co.uk
No of lawyers in dept: 3
Eleonore Sauerwein, Group Legal Director
Other lawyers: Richard Gives, UK; Dan Freedman, US.

AGA Foodservice Group PLC
Headland House New Coventry Road Sheldon Birmingham B26 3AZ
Tel: (0121) 742 2366 **Fax:** (0121) 742 0403
Deryck J Solomon, Company Secretary

Aggreko PLC
Ailsa Court 121 West Regent Street Glasgow G2 2SD
Tel: (0141) 225 5900 **Fax:** (0141) 225 5949
Paul Allen, Company Secretary

Airtours UK Leisure Group
Holiday House Sandbrook Park Sandbrook Way Rochdale OL11 1SA
Tel: (01706) 742500 **Fax:** (01706) 742299
Email: andrew.cooper@airtours.co.uk
Website: www.airtours.co.uk
No of lawyers in dept: 6
Work outsourced: 15% - Overseas litigation, major contractual work, IT contracts, serious personal injury, selected property issues.
Andy Cooper, Head of Legal
Specialisation: Andy is primarily responsible for specific travel law advice, as well as focusing on employment, litigation and procedures to ensure the effective review and implementation of new legislation in so far as it affects a major tour operator. He is responsible for managing a team who provide operational legal advice to all the tour operating and retail businesses within the Airtours UK Leisure Group.
Career: Birmingham University 1978-1981; *Vernon & Shakespeare Solicitors*, Northfield, Birmingham, Articled Clerk 1982-1984; *Smith Fort & Symonds*, Poynton, Cheshire, Assistant Solicitor 1985-1989; Airtours plc / Airtours Holidays Limited, Company Solicitor/Head of Legal 1989 - to date.
Other lawyers: Tamsin Winspear; Alison Charnock; Joanna Edwards; Robin King; Amanda Wilkinson.

Akeler Group of Companies
Akeler 7 Clifford Street London W1S 2UE
Tel: (020) 7864 1826 **Fax:** (020) 7864 1827
Email: info@akeler.com
Website: www.akeler.com
No of lawyers in dept: 1
Work outsourced: 100% - Property development, investment & construction.
Jayne Walters, Commercial Director
Specialisation: Commercial property including development, construction, investments and disposals.
Career: Catherine's College, Cambridge 1980-1983. Articled and qualified (1986) with *Macfarlanes* . Appointed Head of Legal Sevices at Akeler Developments from 1998.

Alliance & Leicester PLC
Group Legal Services Building 3 Floor 2 Carlton Park Narborough LE9 5XX
Tel: (0116) 201 1000 **Fax:** (0116) 200 4995
Kathrine Hughes, Head of Legal

Alliance UniChem
Alliance House 2 Heath Road Weybridge KT13 8AP
Tel: (01932) 870550 **Fax:** (01932) 870555
Adrian Goodenough, Company Secretary

Allied Domecq PLC
The Pavilons Bridgwater Road Bedminster Down Bristol BS13 8AR
Tel: (0117) 978 5000 **Fax:** (0117) 978 5300
Email: firstname.lastname@adsweu.com
Website: www.allieddomecqplc.com
No of lawyers in dept: 30
Work outsourced: 50% - M&A, litigation, conveyancing, employee share schemes.
Russell P Kelley, General Counsel & Company Secretary
Specialisation: Corporate, commercial, compliance, trade controls.
Career: 1998-1999, General Counsel and Company Secretary, Lucas Varity plc; 1977-87, various positions at Schlumberger Ltd.; 1974, Juris Doctor, Boston University School of Law; 1971, Bachelor of Arts, Trinity College (Hartford, USA).
Personal: Member of the bars of Massachusetts, Texas, District of Columbia, California.

Amateur Swimming Association
Harold Fern House Derby Square Loughborough LE11 5AL
Tel: (01509) 221350 **Fax:** (01509) 221351
Email: andy.gray@swimming.org
Andy Gray, Head of Legal Affairs
Specialisation: Full range of legal support for the national governing body of swimming including governance and regulatory issues; media and sponsorship; event staging; doping control and other ethical issues.
Career: University of Keele; College of Law, Chester; *Eking Manning Solicitors* 1986-1996; ASA 1996 - Part Time Senior Lecturer in Business and Sport & Media Law at De Monfort University, Leicester.

AMEC Capital Projects Ltd
AMEC House Heron Drive Langley Slough SL3 8XP
Tel: (01753) 612514 **Fax:** (01753) 612781
Website: www.amec.com
No of lawyers in dept: 9
Work outsourced: Some corporate/commercial work, all commercial property and conveyancing litigation, litigation requiring specialist expertise.
Michael Blacker, Head of Legal Services
Specialisation: Providing legal services to AMEC Capital Projects and AMEC Asia-Pacific, including drafting and negotiating agreements for construction and engineering related projects. Also handles dispute resolution and supervises external solicitors when required.
Career: Attended Nottingham University, BA (Hons) Barrister (1978). Has worked in-house for Taylor Woodrow Group, BP Minerals, George Wimpey Plc (1982-1997) and joined AMEC in 1997.
Personal: Leisure interests include cricket, rugby and gardening.
Other lawyers: AMEC Capital Projects Limited - Michael Blacker (Manager), Kevin Smith (Civil Engineering), John Fenwick (Manager), Andrew Taylor (Offshore Services and

A

Rail) Philip Poxon (Mechanical and Electrical Engineering). AMEC Services Limited - AMEC Project Investments Limited - Tony Rogers (Director of Legal Services), Simon Moore and Alison Sandle (Legal Advisers), AMEC Developments Limited - Sarah-Anne Shankland.

AMEC PLC
Sandiway House Hartford Northwich CW8 2YA
Tel: (01606) 883885 **Fax:** (01606) 883996
Email: john.fenwick@amec.com
Website: www.amec.com
No of lawyers in dept: 9
Work outsourced: Some corporate/commercial work, all commercial property and conveyancing litigation, litigation requiring specialist expertise.
John C Fenwick, Head of Legal Services
Specialisation: Responsible for supervising supply of all legal services to UK members of AMEC group and providing legal services in-house via a de-centralised legal function. Assists in UK and overseas tendering (advice on risk, contract conditions etc.) joint venture agreements, claims and disputes. Management of in-house legal team with lawyers strategically placed within key operating subsidiaries. Also selects and monitors performance of external solicitors where required. Also has particular responsibility for part of group encompassed by AMEC Services Limited.
Career: Qualified 1973. Articled with *Heald Nickinson* and assistant solicitor until 1976. Head of Group Legal Services, John Laing plc 1976-88, then joined AMEC plc.
Other lawyers: AMEC Capital Projects Limited - Michael Blacker (Manager), Kevin Smith (Civil Engineering), John Fenwick (Manager), Andrew Taylor (Offshore Services and Rail) Philip Poxon (Mechanical and Electrical Engineering). AMEC Services Limited - AMEC Project Investments Limited - Tony Rogers (Director of Legal Services), Simon Moore and Alison Sandle (Legal Advisers), AMEC Developments Limited - Sarah-Anne Shankland.

A

American Express Bank Ltd.
60 Buckingham Palace Road London SW1W 0RR
Tel: (020) 7824 6387 **Fax:** (020) 7730 5067
Email: jane.b.kelloe@aexp.com
No of lawyers in dept: 3
Work outsourced: 10% - Complicated transactions/litigation.
Jane Kelloe, Group Counsel
Specialisation: Responsible for legal services for American Express Bank Ltd and its subsidiaries in Europe, Africa and the Middle East. Principal areas of work - banking, regulatory, employment and litigation management.
Career: Solicitor 1976; LLB University of Southampton 1973; *Coward Chance* 1974-1979; American Express Bank Ltd, 1980 to date.
Other lawyers: Lawyers in dept: J Kelloe, M. Semmence, a secondee, vacant - 1.

Amey PLC
24 Hanover Square London W1S 1JD
Tel: (020) 7659 1900 **Fax:**
Carol Hui, Company Secretary

Amvescap PLC - Invesco Global
11 Devonshire Square London EC2M 4YR
Tel: (020) 7626 3434 **Fax:** (020) 7454 3166
Email: graeme_proudfoot@ldn.invesco.com
Website: www.invesco.co.uk
No of lawyers in dept: 8
Work outsourced: 50% - Corporate finance, investment funds (off and on-shore), financial services, litigation, property, tax.
Graeme J Proudfoot, General Counsel, Invesco Global
Specialisation: Corporate, investment funds, financial services. Also Head of Specialist Funds Division.
Career: Education: Royal Grammar School, Newcastle-Upon Tyne. University College, Oxford (1986, Jurisprudence). Articled *Wilde Sapte*, qualified 1989; Legal Manager INVESCO plc 1995. Company Secretary INVESCO plc 1992, Managing Director, Specialist Funds 1999.
Personal: Born 1964. Resides Hertfordshire.
Other lawyers: Rodney Smyth/Ian White - UK; Joe Beashal/Jeremy Crean - Ireland; Anton Allen/Monica Ahweng - Hong Kong; Sander Cohen - Tokyo; Aska Balachandra - Sydney.

Anglo American PLC
20 Carlton House Terrace St James's London SW1Y 5AN
Tel: (020) 7698 8888 **Fax:** (020) 7695 8570
Website: www.angloamerican.co.uk
No of lawyers in dept: 2
Ben Keisler, Executive Vice President, General Counsel
Specialisation: Corporate transactions, commercial, corporate finance, competition/antitrust.
Career: Senior Vice President, General Counsel, Minono, 1997-1999; Vice president and General Counsel, Minono (USA) Inc., 1993-97; Vice President and General Counsel, Terra Industries Inc.
Other lawyers: Paul Roebuck - acquisitions, general corporate, competition.

Anite Group PLC
100 Longwater Avenue Green Park Reading RG2 6GP
Tel: (0118) 945 0121 **Fax:** (0118) 945 0131
Website: www.anite.com
Simon Hunt, Finance Director & Company Secretary

Aon Limited
8 Devonshire Square London EC2M 4PL
Tel: (020) 7623 5500 **Fax:** (020) 7621 1511
Website: www.aon.com
No of lawyers in dept: 9
Work outsourced: 25% - Litigation, major corporate work.
Jane Owen, Senior Lawyer
Specialisation: Responsible for managing the Law Division which provides legal advice and services to all Aon's businesses in the UK and those international offices which report to London, both contentious and non-contentious work.
Career: Howell's School, Denbigh; St Anne's College, Oxford; University of Aix-en-Provence. Called to Bar Middle Temple in 1978. Practised at the Bar from 1978 to 1989 and in 1990 joined Alexander & Alexander Services UK Legal Department. Appointed their Group Legal Adviser in 1991 and on acquisition of A&A by Aon in 1997, appointed Senior Lawyer. In 2000, appointed to the Board with responsibility for legal and compliance.
Personal: Married with 5 children. Lives in London.

Arab Bank PLC
PO Box 138 15 Moorgate London EC2R 6LP
Tel: (020) 7315 8500 **Fax:** (020) 7600 7620
No of lawyers in dept: 1
Work outsourced: 5% - Project finance, some banking, litigation.
Janet Bicheno, Legal Adviser
Specialisation: All aspects of banking law and management of external legal advisers, where necessary.
Career: Felsted School, Dunmow, Essex; LLB (Hons) Leicester University; Guildford Law College.

ARC International PLC
ARC House Waterfront Business Park Elstree Road Elstree WD6 3BS
Tel: (020) 8236 2800 **Fax:** (020) 8236 2801
No of lawyers in dept: 3
Work outsourced: 50% - Corporate, IP, property, employment, litigation.
Allan Richards, General Counsel
Specialisation: Company/commercial, telecommunications & licensing.
Career: Cambridge University 1981-1984; Guildford Law School 19884-1985 (2nd Class Hons); *McKenna & Co* (now *Cameron McKenna*) 1985-1995; Legal & Business Affairs Director - Eurobell (Holdings) PLC - 1995-1996; Head of Legal - Energis Communications Ltd - 1996-1997; Legal & Regulatory Affairs Director - Eurobell (Holdings) PLC - 1997-2000; General Counsel - ARC International PLC - 2001
Other lawyers: Frank Deremer - Contracts Director; Henry Davis - Vice President of Intellectual Property.

ARM Holdings plc
110 Fulbourn Road Cambridge CB1 9NJ
Tel: (01223) 400400 **Fax:** (01223) 400 546
Email: info@arm.com
Website: www.arm.com
No of lawyers in dept: 8
Work outsourced: 1% - Litigation / corporate.
David MacKay, Company Secretary
Other lawyers: Phil David-Trademarks, Hilary Charles-Assistant Company Secretary, Patents.

Arriva PLC
Admiral Way Doxford International Business Park Sunderland SR3 3XP
Tel: (0191) 520 4000 **Fax:** (0191) 520 4001
Website: www.arriva.co.uk
No of lawyers in dept: 6
Work outsourced: 10% - Large transactions, heavy litigation.
Chris Applegarth, Director of Group Legal Services
Specialisation: Principal areas of work are company/commercial matters, banking, employment, consumer credit, equipment leasing, securitisation of receivables and franchising and operation of train services. Other areas of work are matters involving traffic, property, trade and service marks, and business development generally.
Career: Qualified as a Barrister 1975 and practised at the Bar until 1980. Qualified 1983 as a solicitor and took up present position in 1985.
Personal: Educated at Sedbergh School 1966-71 and Inns of Court School of Law 1972-75. Born 1953. Lives in Sunderland.
Other lawyers: Mr J.B. Wainwright.

Ashtead Group PLC
Kings Court 45-51 Kingston Road Leatherhead KT22 7SZ
Tel: (01372) 362300 **Fax:** (01372) 376610
Website: www.ashtead-group.com
No of lawyers in dept: 1
Work outsourced: 10% - Conveyancing Scotland & Eire, large company takeovers, advice on specialist areas, civil litigation.
Paul Edmunds, MA (Cantab), Legal Services Manager
Specialisation: Conveyancing, employment, property administration, contract negotiation. Co-ordination of all legal matters.
Career: 1970-1977 Judd School, Tonbridge, Kent. 1977-1980 St John's College, Cambridge. 1982-1984 *Ingledew Brown Bennison & Garrett* . 1984-1998 *The Reece Jones Partnership* .
Personal: Hobbies: cricket, golf, choral singing, cookery.
Other lawyers: Company/commercial; conveyancing; employment. All apects of legal management of business.

Associated British Foods PLC
Weston Centre Bowater House 68 Knightsbridge London SW1X 7LQ
Tel: (020) 7589 6363 **Fax:** (020) 7584 8560
Philip Ashton-Jones, Head of Legal

Associated British Ports Holdings plc
150 Holborn London EC1N 2LR
Tel: (020) 7430 1177 **Fax:** (020) 7430 1384
Hywel Rees, Company Secretary

The Association of British Travel Agents (ABTA)
68-71 Newman Street London W1P 3AH
Tel: (020) 7637 2444 **Fax:** (020) 7637 0713
Email: rnardi@abta.co.uk
No of lawyers in dept: 3
Work outsourced: 10-15% - Litigation, mergers and acquisitions, competition.
Riccardo Nardi, Head of Legal Services
Specialisation: Travel and tourism/aviation; company and commercial for ABTA and its subsidiaries; company secreterial function for ABTA and its subsidiaries; e-commerce and data protection; lobbying UK government and EU commission/parliament.
Career: Knutsford Highschool; Lancaster University 1985-1988 - LLB (Hons); Inns Court School of Law 1988-1989; Called to the Bar 1989 - Middle Temple.
Personal: Married with 3 children. Lives in Bedfordshire. Interests: skiing, scuba diving.
Other lawyers: Simon Bunce, Paula Macfarlane.

AstraZeneca PLC
15 Stanhope Gate London W1K 1LN
Tel: (020) 7304 5000 **Fax:** (020) 7304 5151
Graeme Musker, Head of Legal & Company Secretary

Autonomy Corporation PLC
Cambridge Business Park Cowley Road Cambridge CB4 0WZ
Tel: (01223) 448 000 **Fax:** (01223) 448 001
Email: andrewk@autonomy.com
Website: www.autonomy.com/
No of lawyers in dept: 3
Andrew Kanter, VP, Legal Affairs
Career: JD, University of Southern California, 1995; BA, Johns Hopkins University, 1991.

Avis Europe PLC
Avis House Park Road Bracknell RG12 2EW
Tel: (01344) 426644 **Fax:** (01344) 485616
Website: www.avis-europe.com
Judith Nicholson, Company Secretary, Director of Legal Services

awg plc
Anglian House Ambury Road Huntingdon PE29 3NZ
Tel: (01480) 323000 **Fax:** (01480) 323288
Email: info@anglianwater.co.uk
Website: www.awg.com
No of lawyers in dept: 13
Work outsourced: 20% - Work where in-house expertise is lacking e.g major corporate transactions.
Patrick Firth, Head of Legal Services
Specialisation: Responsible for providing legal services to the Group using the in-house team wherever possible but outsourcing where specialisations are lacking or volume of work is too great. Personal responsibilities include corporate and commercial work both in the UK and internationally.
Career: Education - Nottingham High School and Sheffield University; Career - Leicestershire and Surrey County Councils before joining Anglian Water (now awg plc) in 1988.
Personal: Leisure interests include Environmental Development, Lepidoptery, Nottingham Forest FC.
Other lawyers: Corporate Commercial - Patrick Firth, Peter Piliounis, Roger Sudbury, Karen Brumpton, Ann Flynn; Litigation - Roger McAdam, Catriona Dunnett, Nita Tinn; Property - Darell Grittenden, Barrie Powell, Peter Thrift; Regulation - Geoffrey Ward, Susan Watkin.

AXA Investment Managers Ltd
7 Newgate Street London EC1A 7NX
Tel: (020) 7003 1000 **Fax:**
Website: www.axa-im.com
No of lawyers in dept: 15
Work outsourced: 15% - Public funds, litigation / contentious.
Kenneth Greig, Head of Legal Services
Specialisation: Asset management and investment funds; corporate and commercial; regulatory.
Career: BA (Jurisprudence) Balliol College, Oxford. Admitted as a solicitor 1986, articled *Norton Rose* (London); Legal Director, Templeton International (Edinburgh); Legal Adviser, Bankers Trust Global Funds Management (London); Head of Legal & Compliance (Europe), Morgan Stanley Asset Management.
Personal: Married, four children. Member Leven Golfing Society, Islam Golf Club, London Scottish Football Club. Interests: rugby, golf, skiing, ornithology, literature.
Other lawyers: Financial services, investment funds, asset management, company, commercial, IT, IP.

Axon Group PLC
Axon Centre Church Road Egham TW20 9QB
Tel: (01784) 480800 **Fax:** (01784) 480900
Website: www.axon.co.uk
No of lawyers in dept: 1
David Spruzen, Chief Finance Officer & Company Secretary

BAA PLC
130 Wilton Road London SW1V 1LQ
Tel: (020) 7932 6763 **Fax:** (020) 7932 6615
Email: Robert_Herga@BAA.CO.UK
Website: www.baa.co.uk
No of lawyers in dept: 6
Work outsourced: 25% - Major projects.
Robert Herga, Group Legal Director
Specialisation: Principal areas of work: company, commercial, funding, property, planning, joint ventures, litigation management, regulation and competition.
Career: LLB (Hons) University of Dundee; MSC (Construction Law and Arbitration) Kings College London; Fellow of the Chartered Institute of Arbitrators.
Other lawyers: Jo Wilkinson: company/commercial; Alison Shropshire: employment; Fiona Hammond: construction; Eddie Biber: property; Sarah Gallagher: property; James Harvey: planning/property.

BAE Systems PLC
Stirling Square 6 Carlton Gardens London SW1Y 5DA
Tel: (01252) 383904 **Fax:** (01252) 383904
Email: michael.lester@baesystems.com
Website: www.baesystems.com
No of lawyers in dept: 50
Work outsourced: Varies - Litigation, conveyancing, major M&A.
Michael Lester, Group Legal Director
Specialisation: Overall responsibility for all legal matters within the BAE Systems Group companies.
Career: Coopers Company's School, New College; Teaching Fellow University of Chicago Law School 1962-64; Articled Solicitor in private practice 1964-80; The General Electric Company plc 1980-99; Director 1983, Vice-chairman, 1994; BAE Systems plc - director, 1999; Premier Farnell plc - non-executive director, 1998.
Personal: Married with one daughter and one son.
Other lawyers: We do not organise by relevance to specialist areas.

Balfour Beatty PLC
130 Wilton Road London SW1V 1LQ
Tel: (020) 7216 6840 **Fax:** (020) 7216 6940
Email: info@balfourbeatty.com
Website: www.balfourbeatty.com
Work outsourced: 90% - Litigation, property, large projects.
Frank McCormack, Head of Legal Services
Specialisation: Corporate law, general counsel.
Career: Finchley Catholic Grammar School 1965-1974, A Levels: English, History, Economics; Liverpool University 1975-1978, BA (Hons), Philosophy; College of Law, London W2, 1978-1980, Common Professional Examination, Solicitors Final Examination; Admitted as solicitor of the Supreme Court April 1983. Articled Clerk 1981-1983, Assistant Solicitor 1983-1984 - *Gregory Rowcliffe & Co*, London; Assistant Solicitor 1984-1985, Partner 1985-1987 - *Bucher, Williams & Harrup*, London; Senior Legal Adviser 1987, Head of Legal Services 1988 to 1999, Company Secretary 1993 to date - Balfour Beatty Group Limited, London; Head of Legal Services 1999 to date - BICC plc, London (now Balfour Beatty plc). Seminar/courses attended: Cranfield 1989; Project finance 1988 (Balfour Beatty); Managing Corporate Legal Services 1992 (Nottingham University). Papers/presentations: Managing Corporate Legal Services; Managing External Lawyers. Associations: Society of Construction Law; Holborn Law Society.
Personal: Rugby (spectator and mini rugby), sailing (RTYC, Bosham SC; Law Society YC). Opera, theatre, film, horse racing and most other sports as spectator. Govenor, St Cuthbert Mayne Catholic Primary School, Cranleigh; Trustee, Surrey Alcohol and Drug Advisory Service.
Philip Morris, Major Projects-Legal
Other lawyers: Company commercial, M&A, banking.

Baltimore Technologies PLC
1310 Waterside Arlington Business Park Theale Reading RG7 4SA
Tel: (0118) 903 8000 **Fax:** (0118) 903 9000
Email: senoch@baltimore.com
Website: www.baltimore.com
Work outsourced: 90% - Corporate, trademarks.
Simon Enoch, Company Secretary
Specialisation: All aspects of company law plus M&A, and major contract negotiations.
Career: Served as the Company Secretary since August 1998. From October 1994 until December 1997 he was Company Secretary and Group Legal Adviser for Central Transport Rental Group plc, a transport company listed on the London Stock Exchange and the New York Stock Exchange. Prior to this, Company Secretary of B&Q from 1992 to 1994 and before then Company Secretary to Chartwell Land pc from 1989 to 1992.
Personal: Married with three children.

Bank of America
PO Box 407 Bank of America House 1 Alie Street London E1 8DE
Tel: (020) 7634 4735 **Fax:** (020) 7809 5662
Email: marc.de_laperouse@bankofamerica.com
Website: www.bankofamerica.com
No of lawyers in dept: 4
Marc de Laperouse, Head of EMEA Legal and Assistant General Counsel
Other lawyers: Banking, securities, financial services regulation, corporate secretarial, litigation.

Bank of Cyprus (London) Limited
87-93 Chaseside Southgate London N14 5BU
Tel: (020) 8267 7330 **Fax:** (020) 8447 8066
Email: sbyrne@bankofcyprus.co.uk
Website: www.bankofcyprus.co.uk
Work outsourced: 35% - Litigation, employment, regulatory advice.
Stephen G Byrne, Legal Adviser & Company Secretary
Specialisation: Banking, compliance, company/commercial, employment, property.
Career: University of Reading - BA (Hons) Modern History and German (1979-1983); College of Law, York (1991-1992); Admitted as a solicitor in July 1994; Worked in Legal Dept, Alliance & Leicester Building Society 1992-1996; Company Solicitor & Company Secretary for Lombard Bank (1996-2001); Bank of Cyprus (London) Ltd (May 2001 to date).
Other lawyers: General banking, banking litigation, compliance, company, commercial, company secretarial, employment, property.

Bank of Ireland
2 College Green Dublin 2
Tel: 00 353 1 677 6801 **Fax:** 00 353 1 670 3602
Finbarr Murphy, Group Legal Adviser

Bank of Scotland
Legal Services 1st Floor Broadstreet House
55 Old Broad Street London EC2P 2HL
Tel: (020) 7601 6666 **Fax:** (020) 7601 6000
Brian Fisher, Head of Legal
Thistle House City Rd Chester CH88 3AN
Tel: (01244) 690000 **Fax:** (01244) 311373
Website: www.bankofscotland.co.uk
Michael S McClenan, In-house Lawyer

Bank One Corporation
Bank One 1 Triton Square London NW1 3FN
Tel: (020) 7903 4359 **Fax:** (020) 7903 4188
Website: www.bankone.com
Jay Bestmann, Senior Vice President & Regional Counsel
Specialisation: Regional Counsel responsible for all legal services, including a small internal group of lawyers as well as supervision of outside lawyers in Europe, the Middle East and Asia Pacific.
Career: Princeton University (BSE, 1969) University of California at Los Angeles (JD, 1975) Qualified California (1975) and Illinois (1976).

Barclays Bank PLC (Corporate Banking)
54 Lombard Street London EC3P 3AH
Tel: (020) 7699 5000 **Fax:** (020) 7699 4474
John Featherstone, Legal Director

Barclays Bank PLC (Wealth Management Legal)
Murray House 5th Floor 1 Royal Mint Court London EC3N 4HH
Tel: (020) 7977 4088 **Fax:** (020) 7977 4648
No of lawyers in dept: 20
Work outsourced: 50% - Litigation, commercial contracts, life and pensions, banking.
Jeremy Ogden, Legal Director

Specialisation: New product development, commercial contracts, litigation and debt recovery, procurement and general advice to Senior Executives in RFS.
Career: *Boodle Hatfield*, 1991-1994; *Wilde Sapte* 1994-1997 (Partner 1997-1998), Admitted January 1983.
Other lawyers: Mark Edwards - Assistant Legal Director; David Pacey - Senior Litigtion Adviser; Henry Firmstone - Senior Commercial Contracts Adviser; Famida Rajah - Barclays Offshore Services.

Barclays Capital
5 The North Colonnade Canary Wharf London E14 4BB
Tel: (020) 7623 2323 **Fax:** (020) 7773 6827
Alex Cameron, Director of Legal for London & Europe

Barclays PLC
54 Lombard Street London EC3P 3AH
Tel: (020) 7699 4034 **Fax:** (020) 7699 3271
Email: GGCO@barclays.co.uk
Website: www.barclays.co.uk
No of lawyers in dept: 200
Work outsourced: 50% - General advisory, commoditised products, business banking, HR, litigation, Barclays Capital Securitisations, structured tax, tax planning/private client, private equity, corporate bank debt recovery, corporate & regulatory.
Howard B Trust, Group General Counsel & Company Secretary
Specialisation: Howard Trust is Group General Counsel and Secretary at Barclays PLC providing advice to the main Board and senior management on legal risk issues as it affects the Barclays Group and its businesses as a whole. As the head of the Barclays Group Legal Function which has some 200 staff world-wide, he chairs the Legal Function Executive and is responsible for the provision of advice on key issues of legal risk affecting the Group including banking and capital markets transactions and dispute resolution. He also lectures regularly to external audiences on a variety of topics. Also secretary to the Group Board and responsible for corporate governance.
Career: Solicitor, *Lovell White & King* 1980-85. Solicitor, *Morgan Grenfell* 1985-87 and Company Secretary 1987-89. Group Legal Director, BZW 1989-95. Group General Counsel and Group Secretary Barclays plc since 1995.
Other lawyers: Howard Trust - Group General Counsel; Jeremy Ogden - Deputy Group General Counsel, General Counsel Wealth Management; John Featherstone - General Counsel Litigation & Disputes and Barclays Africa; Andrew Taylor - Managing Director and General Counsel Barclays Capital (ex Americas); Des O'Connell - Projects and Operations Director; Frances Spencer - General Counsel Human Resources; Joanne Medero - Managing Director and General Counsel BGI; Guy Dempsey - Managing Director and General Counsel Barclays Capital (Americas); Michael Webber - General Counsel RFS Retail; Rachel Harris - General Counsel Barclaycard; Penny Bruce - General Counsel Business Banking; Mark Edwards - General Counsel BB2B and Deputy General Counsel RFS Wealth; Neil Hodges - Deputy General Counsel, Corporate & Commercial.

Barratt Developments PLC
Wingrove House Ponteland Road Newcastle upon Tyne NE5 3DP
Tel: (0191) 286 6811 **Fax:** (0191) 271 2242
Website: www.barratthomes.co.uk
No of lawyers in dept: 1
Laurence Dent, Company Secretary
Specialisation: Company, commercial, employment and pensions.

BBA Group PLC
70 Fleet Street London EC4Y 1EU
Tel: (020) 7842 4900 **Fax:** (020) 7353 5831
Email: sshaw@bbagroup.com
Website: www.bbagroup.com
No of lawyers in dept: 11
Work outsourced: 50% - Corporate, commercial, litigation, property.
Sarah Foulkes Shaw, Group Company Secretary
Specialisation: Corporate, commercial, regulatory, compliance.
Career: Trainee solicitor 1980-82 *Freshfields*, Solicitor 1982-85 *Freshfields*, Corporate Lawyer 1986-89 Cadbury Schweppes plc, Corporate Lawyer 1989-92 Reed International plc, Group Secretary and Legal Advisor 1992-95 Signet Group plc, Group Secretary 1997 to date BBA Group plc.
Personal: Born 1958. Lives in London. Married with 2 daughters.

Bear Stearns International Limited
One Canada Square Canary Wharf London E14 5AD
Tel: (020) 7516 6000 **Fax:** (020) 7516 6621
Email: sbartlett@bear.com
Website: www.bearstearns.com
No of lawyers in dept: 5
Work outsourced: Documentation production.
Stephen Bartlett, Senior Managing Director and Head of Legal
Specialisation: Responsible for all legal matters for firm's investment banking European franchise. Primarily: investment banking, capital markets - new issues; OTC derivatives; structured debt & equity; regulatory; employment litigation.
Career: 19 85-88, BA Jurisprudence (Oxon); LSF 1989; 1989-94 *Slaughter and May*; qualified as solicitor 1991. July 1994 Bear Stearns International Limited.
Other lawyers: Capital markets, investment banking, derivatives, structured products, employment, litigation, regulatory.

Bellway PLC
Seaton Burn House Dudley Lane Seaton Burn Newcastle upon Tyne NE13 6BE
Tel: (0191) 217 0717 **Fax:** (0191) 236 6230
Website: www.bellway.co.uk
No of lawyers in dept: 1
Peter Stoker, Company Secretary

Benchmark Group PLC
25 Sackville Street London W1X 1DA
Tel: (020) 7287 6881 **Fax:** (020) 7287 6883
Work outsourced: 100% - All outsourced.
Leigh Bowen-Jones, Property Manager

Berkeley Group PLC
Berkeley House 19 Portsmouth Road Cobham KT11 1JG
Tel: (01932) 868555 **Fax:** (01932) 860661
Wendy Pritchard, Group Solicitor

BG Group PLC
100 Thames Valley Park Drive Reading RG6 1PT
Tel: (0118) 935 3222 **Fax:** (0118) 935 3484
William Friedrich, Deputy Chief Executive & General Counsel

BHP Billiton plc
1-3 Strand London WC2N 5HA
Tel: (020) 7747 3800 **Fax:** (020) 7747 3900
Paul Lush, Group Legal Counsel

Biocompatibles International PLC
Chapman House Farnham Business Park Weydon Lane Farnham GU9 8QL
Tel: (01252) 732732 **Fax:** (01252) 732777
Fiona Evans, Company Secretary

Bioglan Pharma PLC
Bioglan House 40A Wilbury Way Hitchin SG4 0AP
Tel: (01462) 633286 **Fax:** (01462) 423395
No of lawyers in dept: 1
Work outsourced: 15-20% - Corporate, IP, licensing.
Luke Talbutt, Head of Legal Services
Specialisation: At present, Head of Legal Services and Company Solicitor at Bioglan Pharma Plc where practice focuses on company and commercial, mostly licensing and pharmaceutical matters. Reporting to senior management and with a 25% domestic and 75% international focus, Talbutt characterises the department's role as 'proactive' - Bioglan Pharma is a 'transaction-driven company'. Recent work includes involvement in the acquisition of licensing of dermatology products from Hexal AG and Novartis and the acquisition of an Italian Company. While noting that an overseas network is important when choosing external advisers, cites *Norton Rose* (corporate) and *Roiter Zucker* (IP/licensing) as preferred advisers.
Career: Articled at *Freshfields Bruckhaus Deronger* and qualified in 1992, joined BMI Healthcare in 1994 and then moved to GlaxoWellcome until December 2000.
Other lawyers: Company and commercial.

Blue Circle Industries PLC
84 Eccleston Square London SW1V 1PX
Tel: (020) 7245 8271 **Fax:** (020) 7245 8272
Email: rftapp@bciplc.com
Website: www.bluecircle.co.uk
No of lawyers in dept: 5
Richard Tapp, Company Secretary/Head of Group Legal & Secretariat
Specialisation: Responsible for provision of legal services worldwide, in consultation with overseas subsidiaries, and for company secretarial work in the UK. Principal areas of work are acquisitions and disposals, contract and commercial law, competition law and property. Responsible also for risk management and insurance.
Career: 1981-84 National Coal Board. 1985-86 Imperial Foods Ltd, part of Imperial Group plc. Joined Blue Circle as Commercial Solicitor 1986, Principal Solicitor 1992, Company Secretary and Legal Adviser 1996. LLB (Sheffield), LLM (Leicester) FCIS, MCI Arb. MBA (Nottingham Law School).
Other lawyers: Anne C Ramsay: Senior Commercial Solicitor, Alison Shepley: Senior Property Solicitor; Nigel Millinson: Commercial Solicitor; Karyn Trowbridge: Property Solicitor.

BMG Records (UK) Limited
Elmsdale Media Ltd 60 Charlotte Street London W1P 2AX
Tel: (020) 7462 5621 **Fax:** (020) 7462 5601
Grenville Evans, In-house Lawyer

BNP Banque Nationale de Paris PLC
BNP Paribas London Branch 10 Harewood Avenue London NW1 6AA
Tel: **Fax:** (020) 7929 0310
Michael Toubkin, Head of Legal

BNP Paribas
BNP Paribas 10 Harewood Avenue London NW1 6AA
Tel: (020) 7595 2000 **Fax:** (020) 7595 5025
Kevin Sowerbutts, Head of Legal

BOC Group PLC
Chertsey Road Windlesham GU20 6HJ
Tel: (01276) 477222 **Fax:** (01276) 471333
Anthony Eric Isaac, Chief Executive

Bodycote International PLC
Hulley Road Hurdsfield Macclesfield SK10 2SG
Tel: (01625) 505 300 **Fax:** (01625) 505 313
Email: jgrime@bodycote.co.uk
Website: www.bodycote.com
No of lawyers in dept: 1
Work outsourced: 95% - Corporate finance, M&A, property.
John Grime, Company Secretary
Specialisation: Stock Exchange, regulatory and compliance. Executive share option schemes. Service of board's requirements for meetings. Investor relations, pensions.
Career: 1975-82 & 1996-97 Private practice in Manchester. 1982-95 Principal solicitor (commercial and property) Co-operative Wholesale Society Ltd. 1997-to date Bodycote International plc. London University LLB (external via Trent Polytechnic). Qualified 1977.
Personal: Aged 48, married with 1 daughter. Lives Bramhall, Cheshire. 3 cats. Enjoys golf, walking and entertaining.
Other lawyers: Company law, share option schemes, pensions, corporate governance, stock exchange compliance.

Bookham Technology PLC
90 Milton Park Abingdon OX14 4RY
Tel: (01235) 837781 **Fax:** (01235) 827210
Email: philip.davis@bookham.com
Website: www.bookham.com
No of lawyers in dept: 2
Work outsourced: 75% - Corporate, litigation,

B

property, overflow.
Philip Davis, General Counsel & Company Secretary
Specialisation: Responsible for provision of legal, regulatory and company secretarial services to Bookham Technology Group.
Career: Trinity College, Cambridge 1985-1990; *Rowe & Maw* 1990-1995; *Glannilles* 1995-1996; ICI Paints 1996-1998; ICI Group Asia Pacific 1998-1999; ICI Group HQ 1999-2000.
Other lawyers: Lisa-Jane Neil (commercial contracts).

Boots Company (The) PLC
Legal Services D90E S09 Nottingham NG90 1BS
Tel: (0115) 959 5679 **Fax:** (0115) 959 5650
David Charlton, Solicitor - Legal Services

Bovis Homes Group PLC
Cleeve Hall Cheltenham Road Bishops Cleeve Cheltenham GL52 8GD
Tel: (01242) 662400 **Fax:** (01242) 662997
Website: www.bovishomesgroup.plc.uk/www.bovishomes.co.uk
No of lawyers in dept: 4
Work outsourced: 5% - Litigation, employment, property.
John Emery, Company Secretary/Legal Director

Bovis Lendlease Ltd
142 Northolt Road Harrow HA2 0EE
Tel: (020) 8271 8000 **Fax:** (020) 8271 8018
Peter Chadwick, Company Secretary

BP plc
International Headquarters Britannic House
1 Finsbury Circus London EC2M 7BA
Tel: (020) 7496 4013 **Fax:** (020) 7496 4592
Email: bevanpb@bp.com
Website: www.bp.com
No of lawyers in dept: 330
Work outsourced: 10-20% - Litigation, local employment and land matters.
Peter BP Bevan, Group General Counsel
Career: Peter joined the BP Group in 1970 after qualifying as a solicitor with a City of London firm. He worked initially in the Law Department of BP Chemicals and then of the Parent Company. Subsequently he became Manager of the Legal function within BP Exploration and then Assistant Company Secretary, followed by the Deputy Group Legal Adviser of The British Petroleum Company plc. In September 1992 he became Group General Counsel. His main areas of expertise are corporate and company law, mergers and acquisitions, finance, and cross-jurisdictional and cross-business issues.
Personal: Leisure interests include sailing, walking, cycling, golf, music, local history and travel.
Other lawyers: Associate General Counsel: Robert Moore, Robin Morris and Colin Saunders (UK) Jack Lynch, Robert McGreevey, and Susan Liebson, Steve Winters (USA) Peter Ling (Singapore).

International Headquarters Britannic House
1 Finsbury Circus London EC2M 7BA
Tel: (020) 7496 5510 **Fax:** (020) 7496 5800
Email: boardrw@bp.com
Website: www.bp.com
Robert Boad, Assistant Head of Group Trade Marks
Specialisation: Protection of trade marks for BP Group of companies, together with some work on copyright, design and domain name internet issues. Emphasis recently on retail-related issues including registration of BP's green service station livery as a trade mark and enforcement actions against lookalike service stations.
Career: Formerly Assistant Trade Marks Manager, The Wellcome Foundation Ltd (until July 1983). Registered Trade Mark Attorney (UK) and Professional Representative Before The Office for Harmonisation in the Internal Market. BA (Hons) Business Studies. Diploma in Marketing.
Personal: Keen writer in spare time: co-editor (with Tom Blackett, Interbrand) of 'Co-branding: the science of alliance' (published by Macmillan/Palgrave) and author of numerous articles on brand-related matters.

BPB PLC
Park House 15 Bath Road Slough SL1 3UF
Tel: (01753) 898800 **Fax:** (01753) 898888
Robert Heard, Company Secretary

Bradford & Bingley Building Society
PO Box 88 Crossflatts Bingley BD16 2UA
Tel: (01274) 554186 **Fax:** (01274) 554967
Christopher Davidson, Head of Legal & Compliance

Britannic PLC
1 Wythall Green Way Wythall Birmingham B47 6WG
Tel: (01564) 828888 **Fax:** (01564) 828822
Website: www.britannic.co.uk
No of lawyers in dept: 3
Work outsourced: 40% - Various.
Anna East, Company Secretary & Solicitor
Specialisation: Company Secretarial work including listed and board plc responsibilities, administration of savings related share option scheme and executive schemes. Management of Legal issues and Chairman of Britannic Group Pension Scheme.
Career: Rugby High School. Nottingham University (BA law). Trent Polytechnic (Law Society Finals). *Talbots* (articles), 1982-84. *Eversheds*, 1984-88. Britannic plc 1988 to date.
Personal: Interests: family, tennis, travel.
Other lawyers: Liz Riley - Senior Solicitor, Employment Law; James Bird - Solicitor, Commercial Contracts and IT.

Britax International PLC
Seton House Warwick Technology Park Gallows Hill Warwick CV34 6DE
Tel: (01926) 400040 **Fax:** (01926) 406300
Stephen Duffield, Commercial & Legal Affairs Director

British Airways PLC
Waterside PO Box 365 Harmondsworth West Drayton UB7 0GB
Tel: (020) 8738 6873 **Fax:** (020) 8738 9962
Website: www.britishairways.com
No of lawyers in dept: 19
Work outsourced: Various.
Stephen Walsh, Legal Director
Specialisation: Corporate, alliances, joint ventures.
Career: *Ashurst Morris Crisp* - 1986-1991; Joined British Airways - 1991; Head Legal Adviser - 1996; Legal Director - 1999.
Other lawyers: Jim Blaney (US Law), Caroline Boone (IP, Data Protection), Maria da Cunha (Competition), Julia Harrison (Employment), Chris Haynes (Corporate Commercial), Owen Highley (Air law Commercial), Paul Jasinski (US Law), Claire Large (Employment), Iben McCracken (Commercial), Paul Nichols (IP), Jo Pawley (Employment), Tina Smith (Commercial), Peter Watson (Aircraft Finance), Roger Whipp (Commercial, Litigation).

Waterside PO Box 365 Harmondsworth West Drayton UB7 0GB
Tel: (020) 8738 6878 **Fax:** (020) 8738 9963
Email: owen.highley@britishairways.com
Website: www.britishairways.com
Owen Highley, In-house Solicitor
Specialisation: Aviation Law.

Waterside PO Box 365 Harmondsworth West Drayton UB7 0GB
Tel: (020) 8738 6870 **Fax:** (020) 8738 9964
Website: www.britishairways.com
Robert Webb QC, General Counsel
Specialisation: Government and industry affairs, safety, security, the environment, risk management, legal, compliance.
Career: Wycliffe College 1959-1967; Exeter University 1967-1970; Barrister 1971-1998 (Q.C. 1988. Barrister, Inner Temple 1997).

British American Tobacco PLC
Globe House 4 Temple Place London WC2R 2PG
Tel: (020) 7845 1000 **Fax:** (020) 2400555
Website: www.bat.com
Work outsourced: Specialist advice, property.
Neil Withington, Legal Director & General Counsel
Other lawyers: Aileen McDonald: Company Secretary; Stephen Walzer: Competition and European law; Philip Scourfield: Litigation & Regulation; Robert Casey, Mike Hendershot: Corporate and Treasury.

British Assets Trust PLC
1 Charlotte Square Edinburgh EH2 4DZ
Tel: (0131) 465 1000 **Fax:** (0131) 225 2375
Gordon Humphries, Company Secretary

British Energy PLC
3 Redwood Crescent Peel Park East Kilbride G74 5PR
Tel: (01355) 594020 **Fax:** (01355) 594022
Email: robert.armour@british-energy.com
Website: www.british-energy.com
No of lawyers in dept: 6
Work outsourced: 80+% - Project support, overseas ventures, various specialisms.
Robert M Armour, Director of Corporate Affairs & Company Secretary
Specialisation: Deals with corporate legal issues, corporate governance, regulation and compliance, environmental issues, European Scottish and UK parliamentary matters. Also responsible for planning and estates, facilities, and private shareholder issues.
Career: Assistant solicitor - *Wright Johnston & McKenzie* - Edinburgh 1983-85, and Partner 1986-90. Scottish Nuclear's Company Secretary from 1990-1995. Company Secretary of British Energy plc - 1995 to date. Also Director of Corporate Affairs and General Counsel for British Energy plc.
Other lawyers: Dr Jean MacDonald, John Young, Andrew McMillan, Sue Challenger, Peter McCall.

British Land Company PLC
10 Cornwall Terrace Regent's Park London NW1 4QP
Tel: (020) 7486 4466 **Fax:** (020) 7935 5552
Anthony Braine, Company Secretary/Head of Legal

British Midland Airways Ltd
Donington Hall Castle Donington Derby DE74 2SB
Tel: (01332) 854033 **Fax:** (01332) 850301
Email: tim.bye@flybmi.com
Website: www.iflybritishmidland.co.uk
No of lawyers in dept: 2
Work outsourced: Approx 25% - Property, employment, major corporate transactions, EC.
Tim Bye, Legal Director & Company Secretary
Specialisation: Responsible for all legal issues principally focused on major commercial and corporate transactions. Also Company Secretary and responsible for property, insurance and personnel.
Career: Watford Grammer School; 1971-74 Leicester University (2:1); 1975 College of Law Guildford (Cecil Karuth prize); 1989 London Business School MBA (Distinction). Articles - *Lawrence Messer & Co* 1975-1977; 1977-1983 - John Laing plc Legal Adviser; 1983-1998 - TNT Group Vice President Corporate Affairs.
Personal: Married, 3 children. Lives in Nottingham. Hobbies: golf, skiing and tennis.

British Sky Broadcasting Group PLC (Sky Digital)
6 Centaurs Business Park Grant Way Isleworth TW7 5QD
Tel: (020) 7705 3000 **Fax:** (020) 7705 3030
Email: deanna.bates@bskyb.com
Website: www.sky.co.uk
No of lawyers in dept: 26
Work outsourced: Corporate finance, litigation, specialist competition advice.
Deanna Bates, Head of Legal & Business Affairs
Specialisation: All areas of work relevant to BSkyB Corporate plc and all group companies including broadcasting and new media, telecoms, commercial agreements, joint ventures, rights production and acquisition, consumer issues, regulatory, political and strategic matters.
Career: Educated at Exeter University and Guildford Law College and qualified as a Solicitor in 1987. Completed her training at *Clifford Chance*, and after qualifying joined the *Clifford Chance* commercial department where she stayed for 21/2 years. In 1989 joined Sky Television plc and has been Head of Legal and Business Affairs for Sky (and now BSkyB) since then.

B

British Telecommuncations PLC
BT Centre 81 Newgate Street London EC1A 7AJ
Tel: (020) 7356 5000 **Fax:** (020) 7356 6638
Email: anne.fletcher@bt.com
Website: www.ignite.com
No of lawyers in dept: 135
Anne Fletcher, Group General Counsel
Career: Education: Bolton School Girls Division; Newham College, Cambridge; College of Law, Chester. Career: *Foysters* Manchester (1981-1984); *Freshfields* (1984-1986); BT (1986 to date) - mainly in legal department has also role of Director, Regulatory Compliance.
Personal: Married, two sons.
Other lawyers: Miles Jobling: General Counsel BT Wholesale Legal and Contract Solutions; Christine Moore: General Counsel, Business Services; Tim Cowen: General Counsel, Ignite; Andrew Parker: General Counsel & Head of Business Affairs for BT Openworld; Sarah Betteley: General Counsel, BT Retail; Philip Bramwell: General Counsel & Secretary, BT Wireless; Kevin Purell: Head of Intellectual Property Department; Rupert Orchard: Head of Mergers and Acquisitions and Commercial Team; Rick Tang: Chief Counsel, BT Worldwide; Jeff Fisher: Head of Corporate Law; Tim Jones: Competition Law; Geoffrey Beedham: Legal Counsel, BT exact.

British Vita PLC
Oldham Road Middleton Manchester M24 2DB
Tel: (0161) 643 1133 **Fax:** (0161) 653 5411
No of lawyers in dept: 2
Work outsourced: 30% - Public issues, heavyweight litigation, some M&A.
Mark Stirzaker, Company Solicitor
Specialisation: Principal areas of work are mergers and acquisitions and commercial property. Also provides general commercial advice and deals with intellectual property matters.
Career: Qualified 1980.
Other lawyers: Catherine Parry - Assistant Solicitor.

Brixton PLC
22-24 Ely Place London EC1N 6TQ
Tel: (020) 7400 4404 **Fax:** (020) 7400 4451
Email: nigelwatts@brixton.plc.uk
Website: www.brixton.plc.uk
No of lawyers in dept: 0
Work outsourced: All - Property and corporate.
Nigel Watts, Company Secretary
Specialisation: Company secretarial, employment, share schemes, pension arrangements.
Career: Professionally qualified accountant with extensive UK and International experience in handling complex corporate, secretarial and treasury matters in the context of corporate restructuring and take-overs of leading publicly quoted Groups. Bourner Bullock 1968-1975 - Audit Senior from Junior. Coopers & Lybrand 1975-1976 - Audit Senior. United Kingdom Property Company Ltd (British Land plc) 1976-1980 - Secretary and Group Accountant. John Brown plc (Kvaerner plc Trafalgar House plc) 1980-1984 Group Financial Accountant, 1984-1987 Treasury Manager, 1986-1996 Secretary. Nigel Watts Consultancy Ltd Financial and Secretarial Consultant 1996 to 1999.
Personal: Aged 51, married with 2 sons.
Other lawyers: Company/commercial, employee benefit schemes, pension schemes, employment law.

Brockbank Underwriting Group PLC
XL Brockbank Limited Fitzwilliam House
10 St Mary Axe London EC3A 8NL
Tel: **Fax:**
Rhic JP Webb, Head of Legal

BT Ignite
BT Group Legal Services British Telecom Centre
81 Newgate Street London EC1A 7AJ
Tel: (020) 7356 5897 **Fax:** (020) 7356 8390
Website: www.ignite.com
Tim Cowen, Chief Counsel
Specialisation: Member of the Ignite Executive with Director level responsibility for legal/public policy team and all legal matters affecting BT Ignite. Management of BT's former joint venture legal/commercial/regulatory teams across continental Europe. Wide variety of issues. This had involved litigation, corporate law, commercial trading arrangements, UK listing requirements etc.
Career: 1999-2000: Chief Counsel, Competition Law & Public Policy, BT plc. Managing direct and virtual lobbying on EU and UK legislation. Transactional work and opposition to deals and developments eg. MCI / WorldCom / Sprint, AOL / TimeWarner / EMI, Vodafone / Mannesmann etc. 1994-1999: Head of European Law, BT plc. Responsible for all aspects of EU law and telecommunications regulation affecting the BT Group. Head of the legal and regulatory team dealing with Alliances. 1991-1994: European Lawyer in the Regulatory, Competition & Public Law Division, BT plc. Particular responsibility for competition law/anti-trust and regulatory advice on BT's overseas expansion. 1986-1991: City of London: *Lovell, White, Durrant / Baker & McKenzie* . 1985-1986: Barrister, 1 Brick Court. Gepffreu Vere Scholarship. Inner Temple Award. 1984-1985: Bar School. 1981-1984: Cambridge University. De Somogyi Award for European Law.

BT Wireless
PP.5E209 5 Longwalk Stockley Park Uxbridge
UB11 1TT
Tel: (020) 8606 1140 **Fax:** (020) 7600 8689
Website: www.bt.com
Phillip Bramwell, General Counsel & Secretary
Specialisation: Responsible for legal department, company secretariat, regulatory affairs department, security and risk management.
Career: BA (Hons) Law 1982. Called to Bar 1983, Lincoln's Inn. Secretary and Legal Adviser to Smithkline Beecham Pharmaceuticles International 1985-89, Vice President and General Counsel, Bellsouth Europe 1989-94, Partner DDV Group 1994-98; Chief Counsel, Corporate Development, BT plc 1998-2001.
Personal: Family, reading and old boats.

BTG PLC
10 Fleet Place Limeburner Lane London EC4M 7SB
Tel: (020) 7575 0000 **Fax:** (020) 7575 0010
Website: www.btgplc.com
No of lawyers in dept: 7
Work outsourced: 10% - Litigation.
Andrew Popper, Company Secretary / Head of Group Legal Compliance
Specialisation: Compliance, risk management, ethical guidance, intellectual property, litigation.
Career: Joined BTG 1978; Head of Legal, 1991; Company Secretary, 1999. Educated at St. Paul's School and Oriel College, Oxford.
Other lawyers: R Davison, G Georgiou, Z Ali, A Sekhri, E Simpson, P Mussenden - compliance and corporate, intellectual property, commercial and litigation.

Bunzl PLC
110 Park Street London W1K 6NX
Tel: (020) 7495 4950 **Fax:** (020) 7495 2527
Website: www.bunzl.com
No of lawyers in dept: 2
Work outsourced: 50% - Large corporate transactions, litigation, property.
Paul Hussey, Company Secretary & Group Legal Adviser
Specialisation: Provides legal services and advice on company/commercial and general corporate matters, and a full company secretarial service including compliance.
Career: Qualified 1983 while with *Addleshaw Sons & Latham* . Commercial solicitor, Grand Metropolitan Retailing Division 1985-86 and Senior Solicitor, Contract Services Division 1986-87. Company Secretary and Group Legal Adviser, Compass Group 1987-88. Legal Adviser, Bunzl plc 1988-92 and then took up present position.
Personal: Educated at Woking Grammar School 1970-77, University College, Cardiff 1977-80 and College of Law 1980-81. Leisure pursuits include walking, tennis, music and golf. Born 11 January 1959. Lives in London.

Cable & Wireless PLC
124 Theobalds Road London WC1X 8RX
Tel: (020) 7315 4987 **Fax:** (020) 7315 5093
Email: dan.fitz@cw.com
Website: www.cw.com
No of lawyers in dept: 40
Work outsourced: 20% - Specialist work (IP, technology) some M&A.
J Daniel Fitz, Group General Counsel
Specialisation: Has overall professional and functional responsibility for the provision of legal and regulatory services to the Cable & Wireless Group of companies worldwide. Regular conference speaker on topics concerning in-house lawyers and ethics.
Career: University of North Carolina at Chapel Hill, graduating in 1981 (BA Economics, with Honours) and 1985 (Juris Doctor, with Honours) and The London School of Economics, 1982 (Diploma with Distinction, International and Comparative Politics). *Winthrop Stimson Putnam & Roberts*, 1985-1989 (New York and London), Baring Brothers & Co Ltd, 1989-1991 (London) and Cable & Wireless plc, 1991 to date (Hong Kong and London). General Counsel since March 1999.
Personal: The American Corporate Counsel association - European Chapter (Vice President); The British-American Project; The Law Society of England and Wales (Commerce & Industry Group). Personal Interests: Tennis, swimming, history, Spanish and Portuguese languages.
Other lawyers: Company Commercial: Patty Lee, Jonathan Spencer, Rob Walton, Bertrand Alexis, John Whitehead, Cristine Slight. Corporate Finance: Abby Laurensen, Kingsley Wallman, Louise Marshall, Graeme Akhurst, Patrick McGlinchey, Virginia Porter.

26 Red Lion Square London WC1R 4HQ
Tel: (020) 7315 3493 **Fax:** (020) 7315 6242
Email: jane.meelhatton@cw.com
Website: www.cw.com
Jane McElhatton, Senior Corporate Counsel
Specialisation: Commercial IT, operational transaction support, product development/marketing, outsourcing, legal training.
Career: Barrister (called 1989); Cable & Wireless Group (1989 to date).
Personal: Married, 2 children.

Cadbury Schweppes PLC
PO Box 2138 Legal Department Franklin House
Bourneville Lane Birmingham B30 2NB
Tel: (0121) 625 7000 **Fax:** (0121) 459 0383
Website: www.cadburyshweppes.com
Work outsourced: 20% - Mainly where local overseas input is required
Michael Keating, Legal Director
Specialisation: Manages legal department and provision of legal services including mergers and acquisitions, commercial contracts, licensing and protection of brands all on worldwide basis.
Career: Qualified 1973. Assistant solicitor *Nightingales* 1973-76, member of Group legal department T & N Plc 1977-84. Joined Cadbury Schweppes Plc 1985.
Personal: Educated at De La Salle College and Liverpool University LLB. Leisure pursuits include watching rugby union, good food and wine. Born 5 October 1948. Lives in Solihull.

Cairn Energy PLC
50 Lothian Road Edinburgh EH3 9BY
Tel: (0131) 475 3000 **Fax:** (0131) 475 3030
Email: dwood@cairn-energy.plc.uk
Website: www.cairn-energy.plc.uk
No of lawyers in dept: 3
Work outsourced: 0-20% Depending on type - Potentially from all areas.
Duncan Wood, Company Secretary & Group Legal Adviser
Specialisation: Company/commercial, corporate finance, litigation, pensions, employment.
Career: Aberdeen University 1981-1985; *Blackadder Reid Johnston* 1985-1987; *Linklaters & Paines* 1987-1989; *Bird Semple Fyfe Ireland* 1989-1993; Cairn Energy PLC 1993 - present.
Other lawyers: Pensions, employment.

Caledonia Investments plc
Cayzer House 1 Thomas More Street London
E1W 1YB
Tel: (020) 7481 4343 **Fax:** (020) 7488 0896
Email: enquiries@caledonia.com
Website: www.caledonia.com
Work outsourced: 70% - Company commercial / corporate finance, property.

C

Graeme Denison, Company Secretary
Specialisation: Company commercial, corporate finance.
Career: Tonbridge School, Kent; St. Catharine's College, Cambridge; 1981-1982: Hobsons Press Ltd - sales and marketing; 1982 - 1989: William Sindall plc - Company Secretary; 1989 - present: Caledonia Investments plc - Company Secretary.
Personal: Married, 3 daughters. Interests - sport generally.
Other lawyers: Company commercial, corporate finance.

Cambridge Antibody Tech Group PLC
The Science Park Melbourne SG8 6JJ
Tel: (01763) 263 233 **Fax:** (01763) 263 413
Email: reception@camb-antibody.co.uk
Website: www.cambridgeantibody.com
No of lawyers in dept: 1
Work outsourced: 30% - Property, litigation, corporate finance, tax, IP/commercial contracts.
Diane Mellett, Company Secretary/General Counsel
Specialisation: Intellectual property; commercial agreements.
Career: University of Birmingham LLB (Hons) 1983; Chicago IIT-Kent J.D. 1991; Law Society 1986; Admitted to Illinois Bar, United States & 7th Circuit, 1992.

Canary Wharf Group PLC
One Canada Square Canary Wharf London E14 5AB
Tel: (020) 7418 2000 **Fax:** (020) 7418 2222
Email: webmaster@canary.co.uk
Website: www.canarywharf.com
No of lawyers in dept: 5
Work outsourced: 99% - Litigation / commercial property / IP.
Michael Ashley-Brown, Head of Legal
Specialisation: Commercial property.
Career: Cranleigh School, Surrey; Millbrook School, New York; College of Law.
Personal: Interests: Motorbiking, skiing.
Other lawyers: Commercial property, construction, IP and facilities management.

Capita Group PLC
71 Victoria Street Westminster London SW1H 0XA
Tel: (020) 7799 1525 **Fax:** (020) 7799 1526
Gordon Hurst, Finance Director & Company Secretary
71 Victoria Street Westminster London SW1H 0XA
Tel: (020) 7799 1525 **Fax:** (020) 7799 1526
Tania Blake, Legal Director

Capital Radio PLC
30 Leicester Square London WC2H 7LA
Tel: (020) 7766 6000 **Fax:** (020) 7766 6008
Email: capitalradio.plc.uk
Website: www.capitalradio.co.uk
No of lawyers in dept: 4
Work outsourced: 25% - Corporate finance transactions, property.
Nathalie Schwarz, Company Secretary & Head of Legal Affairs
Specialisation: As Company Secretary and Head of Legal Affairs, provide corporate support to the Plc Board and Sub-Committees. Heads a department of four lawyers and one company secretary assistant. The department advises the group across various pertinent business matters including corporate affairs, joint ventures, acquisitions, disposals, rights clearances, distribution, digital licensing matters and commercial agreements.
Career: The North London Collegiate School; University of Manchester 1988-91; College of Law 1991-92; Degrees/qualifications: Law (LLB, Honours) - 2:1 (1991); Law Society Final Professional Examination - First Class Honours (1992); Articled at *Clifford Chance* . Qualified as a solicitor in the Corporate Department in 1995, specialising in corporate finance, M&A and general corporate/commercial matters. Joined Capital Radio plc as Company Secretary and Head of Legal Affairs in 1998.
Personal: Born 1970, resides in London. Enjoys theatre, cinema, travelling.

Carillion PLC
24 Birch Street Wolverhampton WV1 4HY
Tel: (01902) 316335 **Fax:** (01902) 316340
Email: dfitzhugh@carillion.com
Website: www.carillionplc.com
No of lawyers in dept: 12
Work outsourced:
Dirk O FitzHugh, Company Secretary & Head of Legal Services
Specialisation: Advises Tarmac plc on Group matters, monitors Business Group Legal Departments and supervises major issues including acquisitions and disposals.
Career: Qualified 1968. *Nicholas Williams & Co* 1964-71 becoming partner 1969, John Mowlem & Co Legal Department 1971-73. Joined Tarmac plc 1973; Director/Secretary Tarmac International Ltd 1977-78; Secretary Tarmac Construction Ltd 1984; Group Legal Adviser 1992.
Other lawyers: Building: Alan Foster (Head of Dept of 3); PFI: John Holdenross (Head of Dept of 2); Services: John Perrett (Head of Dept of 2); CHE (Crown House Engineering): Jennifa Charlson; Capital Projects / Infrastructure Management: new appointment; Litigation: Hazel Valarino (Head of Dept.2).

Carlton Communications PLC
25 Knightsbridge London SW1X 7RZ
Tel: (020) 7663 6441 **Fax:** (020) 7663 6370
Website: www.carlton.com
No of lawyers in dept: 2
David Abdoo, Company Secretary
Career: Mill Hill School 1974-1979; Kings College London 1979-1982; *Clifford Chance* (*Clifford Turner*) 1984-1988; Carlton Communications PLC 1988 - to date.
Other lawyers: David Abdoo; Richard Ray.

Carpetright PLC
Amberley House New Road Rainham RM13 8QN
Tel: (01708) 525522 **Fax:** (01708) 559361
Patricia Dregent, Company Secretary

Carphone Warehouse Limited
North Acton Business Park Wales Farm Road London W3 6RS
Tel: (020) 8896 5000 **Fax:** (020) 8896 5005
Timothy O'Gorman, Company Secretary

Cattles PLC
Kingston House Centre 27 Business Park Woodhead Road Birstall Batley WF17 9TD
Tel: (01924) 444466 **Fax:** (01924) 442255
Website: www.cattles.co.uk
No of lawyers in dept: 1
Work outsourced: 50% - Company/commercial, banking, litigation.
Patrick Doherty, Company Secretary
Specialisation: Principal areas of work are consumer credit, employment matters, property, company secretarial and compliance (statutory and Stock Exchange).
Career: Called to the Bar 1976; admitted as a solicitor 1992. With Engineering Employers' Association (Yorkshire and Humberside) 1978-79; Armstrong Equipment plc 1979-85; ASD plc, 1985-90 and joined Cattles plc in 1991.
Personal: Educated at Keble College, Oxford (BA, Jurisprudence 1975). Leisure pursuits include golf. Born 16 October 1952. Lives in Hull.

Celltech Group PLC
208 Bath Road Slough SL1 3WE
Tel: (01753) 534655 **Fax:** (01753) 447859
Website: www.celltech.co.uk
John Slater, Director of Legal Services & Company Secretary
Specialisation: Responsible for the provision of legal and company secretarial services. Main areas of work are general company/commercial matters, intellectual property, licensing, corporate affairs and Yellow Book.
Career: Qualified as a solicitor 1978.

Centrica PLC
Charter Court 50 Windsor Road Slough SL1 2HA
Tel: (01753) 758212 **Fax:** (01753) 758011
Email: Media@centrica.co.uk
Website: www.centrica.co.uk
No of lawyers in dept: 25
Work outsourced: Vast majority undertaken by in-house legal team - Litigation and property.
Grant Dawson, General Counsel & Company Secretary
Specialisation: General Counsel & Company Secretary of Centrica plc. Responsible for the provision of legal, regulatory and company secretarial services to the Centrica Group of Companies.
Career: Educated in Leicester and London. Called to the Bar in 1982. A member of Lincolns Inn. Practised at the Bar for a period of two years before joining the legal department of Racal Electronics plc in 1984. Joined STC plc as Legal Adviser in 1986 until they were taken over in 1991 by Northern Telecom Limited. 1992 appointed Associate General Counsel with Northern Telecom Europe Limited. Appointed General Counsel and Company Secretary of Centrica plc in October 1996.
Personal: Married with three children and lives in Windsor. Enjoys golf, scuba diving, sailing and opera.
Other lawyers: Company commercial; corporate finance; utility regulation; and litigation.

Certa (UK) Ltd
America House 2 America Square London EC3N 2LU
Tel: (020) 7903 6522 **Fax:** (020) 7903 6588
Email: stephen.sykes@certa.com
Website: www.certa.com
No of lawyers in dept: 4
Work outsourced: 2% - Specialist commercial and claims related work.
Stephen Sykes, Legal Director
Specialisation: Legal Director dealing with all legal matters relating to underwriting long term environmental risks for leading global insurers; analysis of liability in property and corporate deals; insurance structures and policy design; negotiating bespoke policies with leading city lawyers for FTSE 100 companies, major property developers, companies in chemical, water and waste, engineering, retail.
Career: Buxton College, Derbyshire; University of Lancaster (1986); University of Oxford (1987-9); De Montfort University (1995-MA). *Addleshaw Sons & Latham* 1990-92; *Booth & Co* 1992-95; *Thomas Miller & Co* Ltd 1995-8; Co-founder of Certa (UK) Ltd, City of London.
Personal: Born 1965. Resides London. Married with one son and one daughter.
Other lawyers: Alan Fieldsend MA - Environmental, Insurance, Property, Commercial. Andrea Muirhead MA - Environmental, Waste Management, Insurance, Commercial.

CGNU PLC
St Helen's 1 Undershaft London EC3P 3DQ
Tel: (020) 7283 2000 **Fax:** (020) 7662 8182
Ian MacDonald

Channel 5 Broadcasting Limited
22 Long Acre London WC2E 9LY
Tel: (020) 7497 5225 **Fax:** (020) 7497 5618
Email: dutyoffice@channel5.co.uk
Website: www.channel5.co.uk
Work outsourced: 10-20% - Corporate finance, employment, some litigation.
Colin Campbell, Director of Legal and Business Affairs
Specialisation: Delivering a high quality legal and business affairs service to Channel 5. Implementing a focussed business affairs strategy. Managing a department of 15 staff. Providing authoritative advice on legal regulatory and commercial issues including programme commissions, programme and rights acquisitions (including sports and films) compliance, arranging for external advice when required.
Career: Educated Royal Russell School and College of Law. 1997 to date - Director of Legal and Business Affairs, Channel 5; 1996-7 Head of Business Affairs, BBC Broadcasting; 1994-6 Head of Rights Group, BBC Network (Television & Radio); 1981-1994 Group Director of Legal and Business Affairs / Company Secretary, Central Independent Television Plc; 1974-1981 Solicitor, Associated Communications Corporation Plc.
Personal: Married with two children. Interests: the Arts generally, most sports, reading, cycling. fine food and wine.
Other lawyers: Company / commercial, media and entertainment, intellectual property.

C

Channel Four Television Corporation
124 Horseferry Road London SW1P 2TX
Tel: (020) 7306 4444 **Fax:** (020) 7306 8366
Catherine Williams, Senior Business Affairs Executive

Charter PLC
7 Hobart Place London SW1W 0HH
Tel: (020) 7838 7000 **Fax:** (020) 7259 5112
No of lawyers in dept: 1
Work outsourced: 50% - M&A, litigation, property and other specialist advice.
Alison Yapp, Group Legal Adviser
Specialisation: Acquisitions, disposals, joint ventures, distribution / agency agreements, competition law, R&D agreements, liscensing agreements, employment issues, management of litigation, property.
Career: Articled *Kenneth Brown*; qualified 1990. Assistant solicitor company/commercial dept. 1990-92. Legal Assistant Johnson Matthey plc 1992-94. Legal Adviser Jonson Matthey plc 1994-95. Sole Legal Adviser Cookson Matthey Ceramics plc 1995-96. Senior Legal Adviser and Company Secretary Cookson Matthey Ceramics plc 1996-98. Group Legal adviser Charter plc 1998 to date.
Personal: Education: St Albans Girls' School. Bristol University (LLB Hons 1987). College of Law, Chancery Lane (Law Society Finals 1988).

C

Chelsfield PLC
67 Brook Street London W1Y 4NJ
Tel: (020) 7493 3977 **Fax:** (020) 7491 9369
Robin Perrot, Company Solicitor

Chloride Group PLC
Abford House 15 Wilton Road London SW1V 1LT
Tel: (020) 7834 5500 **Fax:** (020) 7630 0563
Susan Williams, Company Secretary & Legal Adviser

Christian Salvesen PLC
500 Pavilion Drive Northampton Business Park Brackmills Northampton NN4 7YJ
Tel: (01604) 662600 **Fax:** (01604) 662602
Website: www.salvesen.com
No of lawyers in dept: 3
Work outsourced: 50% - Property, litigation.
Sarah Booth, Legal and Corporate Development Director
Specialisation: Responsible for all legal services throughout the group including mergers and acquisitions.
Career: LLB (Hons) Edinburgh University, *Dickson Minto* 1989-91 (traineeship), Christian Salvesen PLC 1991 to date. Appointed Director of Legal Services September 1997, and Corporate Development Director June 1999.
Other lawyers: Anita Prinjha, Ed Peppiatt, Rachel Brown.

Christiania Bank of Kreditkasse ASA
Lloyds Chambers 1 Portsoken Street London E1 8RU
Tel: (020) 7680 7000 **Fax:** (020) 7481 1860
Craig Axe, Senior Manager - Legal/Documentation

Citibank
1 Canada Square Canary Wharf London E14 5AA
Tel: (020) 7500 5000 **Fax:** (020) 7500 0635
James Gledhill, First Vice President & Co-head of Corporate Finance Legal
1 Canada Square Canary Wharf London E14 5AA
Tel: (020) 7500 5000 **Fax:** (020) 7500 0635
Clare Jones, First Vice President & Co-head of Corporate Finance Legal

Citigroup Private Bank
41 Berkeley Square London W1X 6NA
Tel: (020) 7508 8000 **Fax:** (020) 7508 8472
Email: bruce.hogarth-jones@citicorp.com
Website: www.citigroup.com
No of lawyers in dept: 7
Work outsourced: 5-10% - Litigation.
Bruce Hogarth-Jones, Vice President, Head of Legal
Specialisation: Banking, capital markets/derivatives, corporate finance, IMRO compliance, litigation & anti-money laundering, data protection and bank confidentiality.
Career: MA (Law) Pembroke College, Cambridge 1978-81. Called to Bar 1982. Swiss Bank Corporation 1985-1991. Credit Suisse Financial Products 1991-93. SG Warburg 1993-5. Citibank 1995 to date.
Personal: Married, 2 children. Interests: sailing, computers.

Civil Aviation Authority (CAA)
CAA House 45-59 Kingsway London WC2B 6TE
Tel: (020) 7453 6160 **Fax:** (020) 7453 6163
Website: www.caa.co.uk
Rupert J Britton, Secretary & Legal Adviser
Specialisation: Aviation, litigation, prosecutions, employment, competition, EC and public international.
Career: Bedford School, Bedford; Lincoln College, Oxford.

Clydesdale Bank PLC
European Legal PO Box 43 150 Buchanan Street Glasgow G1 2HL
Tel: (0141) 223 2802 **Fax:** (0141) 223 2887
Jane L Shirran, General Counsel

Cobham PLC
Brook Road Wimborne BH21 2BJ
Tel: (01202) 882020 **Fax:** (01202) 840523
John Pope, Company Secretary

Collins Stewart Holdings PLC
9th Floor 88 Wood Street London EC2V 7QR
Tel: (020) 7283 1133 **Fax:** (020) 7283 8031
Kay Wrangles, Assistant Company Secretary

Colt Telecommunications plc
Beaufort House 15 St Botolph Street London EC3A 7QN
Tel: (020) 7390 3900 **Fax:** (020) 7390 3638
Email: rbratby@colt-telecom.com
Website: www.colt-telecom.com
Robert Bratby, Director of Business Development
Specialisation: Commercial, telecoms.
Career: St. John's College, Cambridge, Nottingham Law School, trained at *Baker & McKenzie*.

Beaufort House 15 St Botolph Street London EC3A 7QN
Tel: (020) 7390 3024 **Fax:** (020) 7390 3750
Email: csmedley@colt-telecom.com
Website: www.colt-telecom.com
Christopher Smedley, Director, Legal & Regulatory
Specialisation: Telecom and internet service and supply agreements; property leases; network agreements; interconnect; competition law; regulation and political.
Career: LLB (Hons) 2:1 (European Law) University of Warwick.
Personal: Golf, rugby, travel.

15 Marylebone Road London NW1 5JD
Tel: (020) 7390 3900 **Fax:** (020) 7390 3701
Email: colt-telecom.com
Website: www.colt-telecom.com
No of lawyers in dept: 1
Work outsourced: 50% - Litigation, property, employment.
Mark Jenkins, Legal Services Director & Company Secretary
Specialisation: Management of all of the legal and secretarial requirements of the group. Corporate/commercial, M&A, employment.
Career: Chelmer. Bar School. M.K. Electric plc/SKF (UK) Ltd/Peek plc.
Personal: Married. 3 children.

Company Television
Suffolk House 1-8 Whitfield Place London W1T 5JU
Tel: (020) 7389 8555
Mark Pybus, Head of Business Affairs

Compass Group PLC
Cowley House Guildford Street Chertsey KT16 9BA
Tel: (01932) 573000 **Fax:** (01932) 569956
Website: www.compass-group.com
Ronald Morley, Company Secretary
Other lawyers: Commercial, investor relations, corporate finance, taxation, litigation, company secretarial.

Computacenter PLC
Head Office Hatfield Avenue Hatfield Hertfordshire AL10 9TW
Tel: (01707) 631 000 **Fax:** (01707) 639 966
Website: www.computacenter.com
No of lawyers in dept: 3
Work outsourced: 30-40% - Corporate, employment, IP, property.
Alan Pottinger, Company Secretary

Cookson Group plc
The Adelphi 1-11 John Adam Street London WC2N 6HJ
Tel: (020) 7766 4500 **Fax:** (020) 7747 6600
Website: www.cooksongroup.co.uk
No of lawyers in dept: 1
Work outsourced: 75% - Various.
Simon O'Hara, General Counsel
Specialisation: Banking and corporate finance, acquisitions and joint ventures, patent and trademark matters. General legal advice and management of external legal advisers. Management of property portfolio.
Career: Qualified in 1992. Previously Solicitor/Team Leader with Lloyd's (1994-2000). Joined Cookson Group in 2000.

Co-Operative Bank PLC
1 Balloon Street PO Box 101 Manchester M60 4EP
Tel: (0161) 832 3456 **Fax:** (0161) 839 8471
Ann Page, Head of Legal Services

Cordiant Communications Group PLC
121-141 Westbourne Terrace London W2 6JR
Tel: (020) 7262 4343 **Fax:** (020) 7262 4300
No of lawyers in dept: 0
Work outsourced: 95% - Litigation, property, banking, corporate, copy clearance.
Denise Williams, Company Secretary

Corus Group PLC
30 Millbank London SW1P 4WY
Tel: (020) 7717 4444 **Fax:** (020) 7717 4455
Website: www.corusgroup.com
No of lawyers in dept: 10
Work outsourced: Variable.
Margaret O'Neill, Director - Corporate Legal Services
Specialisation: Responsible for provision of in-house legal services to Corus Group and managing external advice where required.

Coutts & Co
2 Lower Sloane Street London SW1W 8BJ
Tel: (020) 7753 1000 **Fax:** (020) 7753 1999
Website: www.coutts.com
No of lawyers in dept: 9
Work outsourced: 50% - Litigation, specialist advice, commercial transactions.
Chalmers Carr, Group Legal Counsel
Specialisation: Banking, investment and trusts.
Career: February 1998 to date: Chief Legal Officer, Coutts Group Legal Services; 1989-1997 HSBC Holdings plc, General Manager and Group Legal Adviser; 1983-1989 Central Electricity Generating Board, Head of Legal Services; 1980-1983 Capsticks, helped set up law practice. 1973-1980; Bridon plc, Contracts Director; 1967-1973 Guest Keen & Nettlefolds plc, Assistant Secretary; 1962-1967 Elliott Automation Ltd, Deputy Legal Adviser. 1961-1962 Rolls Royce Ltd, Legal Adviser.
Personal: Married to Julia, 2 sons.
Other lawyers: Sarah Chidgey, Russell Fairbrother, Gloria Glennie, Ian Levene, Julie Teuten, Neil Cave, Merrilie McLeod, Simon Amer.

Credit Agricole Indosuez
Indosuez House 122 Leadenhall Street London EC3V 4QH
Tel: (020) 7971 4000 **Fax:** (020) 7628 4724
Margaret Garner, Head of Group Legal Services (London)

Index to leading lawyers: p.1647

Credit Lyonnais
Broadwalk House 5 Appold Street PO Box 81 London EC2A 2DA
Tel: (020) 7214 7080 **Fax:** (020) 7214 7007
Edward Paget-Brown, General Counsel

Credit Suisse First Boston
One Cabot Square London E14 4QJ
Tel: (020) 7888 8888 **Fax:** (020) 7888 4251
Kevin Studd, General Counsel - Europe
One Cabot Square London E14 4QJ
Tel: (020) 7888 8888 **Fax:** (020) 7888 4251
Website: www.csfb.com
Edmond Curtin, Managing Director and European Deputy General Counsel, Credit Suisse First Boston
Specialisation: Structured finance, embracing credit products, fund-linked products and equity products.
Career: Received the degree of Bachelor of Civil Law from University College Dublin and the degree of Barrister-at-Law from the Honorable Society of Kings Inns in Dublin and was called to the Irish Bar in 1988. Qualified as a Solicitor in England and is admitted as an Attorney in New York.
One Cabot Square London E14 4QJ
Tel: (020) 7888 8888 **Fax:** (020) 7888 4251
Paul Chelsom, Director in Legal & Compliance
One Cabot Square London E14 4QJ
Tel: (020) 7888 8888 **Fax:** (020) 7888 4251
Tracy Kingsley-Daniels, Director of Transaction Management, Credit Suisse First Boston International

Daily Mail & General Trust PLC
Northcliffe House 2 Derry Street Kensington London W8 5TT
Tel: (020) 7938 6000 **Fax:** (020) 7937 3251
Email: webmaster@dmgt.co.uk,
Website: www.dmgt.co.uk
No of lawyers in dept: 5
Harvey Kass, Legal Director
Specialisation: Principal areas of work include libel (pre-publication and litigation), commercial, new media, copyright, competition law, employment and trademarks.
Career: Articled and qualified (1981) with *Webb Syrett*; *Olswang & Co*, associate (1982-84); Legal and Business Adviser to several television and media companies (1984-90) including Goldcrest Films and Television, Albion Films Ltd; Consultant, Beveridge Ross & Prevezers (1988-93); Harvey Kass & Co (1990-93) specialised in libel for national newspapers and commercial law; Associated Newspapers Ltd (1993-94); Legal Director since 1995.ED: Woodhouse Grammar School; BA (Business Law) (1977) City of London Polytechnic, Maxwell Law Prize; LLM (1978) Jesus College, Cambridge.
Personal: Born 1955, resides London. Leisure: family, football, tennis, golf, gardening.

Daiwa Europe Ltd
5 King William Street London EC4N 7AX
Tel: (020) 7548 8080 **Fax:** (020) 7548 8303
Roger Massey, Executive Director of Legal and Transaction Management Department

David S Smith (Holdings) PLC
4-16 Artillery Row London SW1P 1RZ
Tel: (020) 7932 5000 **Fax:** (020) 7932 5003
Email: james.deeley@dssmith.co.uk
Website: www.davidssmith.com
No of lawyers in dept: 4
Work outsourced: 70% - Acquisitions, litigation, conveyancing, employment.
James Deeley, Head of Group Legal
Specialisation: Responsible for managing all legal risks and the provision of legal services throughout the group. Key areas of expertise include cross-boarder M&A, joint ventures and commercial contracts.
Career: Solicitor - *Slaughter and May* - 09/88-10/95; Group Legal Adviser - Charter plc - 10/95-03/98; Director of Legal Services - Regus plc - 03/98-11/99.
Personal: Born 17 June 1963.
Other lawyers: Andrew Miller - M&A/Commercial. Patricia Collins - Company/Commercial (Divisional Adviser). Christophe Gourjon - Company Commercial (Divisional Adviser).

Davis Service Group PLC
4 Grosvenor Place London SW1X 7DL
Tel: (020) 7259 6663 **Fax:** (020) 7259 6948
THM Shaw, General Counsel

De La Rue PLC
De La Rue House Jays Close Viables Basingstoke RG22 4BS
Tel: (01256) 605311 **Fax:** (01256) 605336
Email: louise.fluker@uk.delarue.com
Website: www.delarue.com
No of lawyers in dept: 4
Work outsourced: 30% in UK: Varies according to specialist projects - Conveyancing, litigation, pensions, major transactions, work requiring foreign jurisdiction advice.
Louise Fluker, General Counsel & Company Secretary
Career: MA (Cantab); LLB (Cantab).
Other lawyers: Douglas Denham, Elizabeth Joyce, Hector Martin: Each lawyer concentrates on particular divisions and in addition may have specialist areas across the group.

Debenhams PLC
1 Welbeck Street London W1G 0AA
Tel: (020) 7408 4444 **Fax:** (020) 7408 3765
Guy Johnson, Company Secretary & General Counsel

Derwent Valley Holdings PLC
87 Wimpole Street London W1M 7DB
Tel: (020) 7659 3000 **Fax:** (020) 7465 8198
Timothy Kite, Company Secretary

Deutsche Asset Management
One Appold Street Broadgate London EC2A 2UU
Tel: (020) 7545 6000 **Fax:** (020) 7545 7555
Paul Hogwood, Company Secretary

Deutsche Bank AG
Deutsche Bank AG (London) Winchester House 1 Great Winchester Street London EC2N 2DB
Tel: (020) 7547 4538 **Fax:** (020) 7547 3102
Email: simon.dodds@db.com
Website: www.deutsche-bank.de
No of lawyers in dept: 70
Simon Dodds, General Counsel - UK
Specialisation: Responsible for providing and supervising the provision of legal services to Deutsche Bank in the UK.
Career: 1976-79: MA, Downing College, Cambridge; 1981-84: JD North Western University School of Law, Chicago; 1984-91: Associate, *Cleary Gottlieb Steen and Hamilton*, New York & London; 1991-99: Managing Director, Bankers Trust Company, London.
Personal: Born 27.8.1957.

Deutsche Bank AG (London) Winchester House 1 Great Winchester Street London EC2N 2DB
Tel: (020) 7547 1765 **Fax:** (020) 7545 1481
Email: jon.ormond@db.com
Website: www.deutsche-bank.de
Jon Ormond, Legal Counsel
Specialisation: Derivatives, capital markets - specialising in credit derivatives, emerging markets and commodities.
Career: LL.B (Hons) - Auckland, New Zealand; *Kensington Swan* solicitors, New Zealand (M&A work) 2 years; CSFP - Legal Counsel - 20 months; Deutsche - Legal Counsel - since November 1999.

DFS Furniture PLC
Bentley Moor Lane Adwick-Le-Street Doncaster DN6 7BD
Tel: (01302) 330 365 **Fax:** (01302) 330880
Barry Todhunter, Company Secretary

Diageo PLC
8 Henrietta Place London W1G 0NB
Tel: (020) 7927 5300 **Fax:** (020) 7927 4600
Website: www.diageo.com
No of lawyers in dept: 12
Tim Proctor, Group General Counsel
Other lawyers: The Legal Department at Diageo Plc and Guinness UDV specialise in the following areas: General company/commercial matters including acquisitions, disposals, joint ventures, general commercial contracts and intellectual property. Felicity Moffat (Associate General Counsel - Corporate) Siobhan Moriarty (Associate General Counsel - Europe) Sabine Chalmers (Associate General Counsel - International Markets) Geraldine Downey (Assistant General Counsel - Intellectual Property) David Harlock (Counsel) Adrian Wyn-Griffiths (Counsel) Michael Parsons (Counsel) Sarah Fisher (Counsel) Andrew Donovan (Counsel) Margot Watts (Counsel) James Segal (Counsel).

Dixons Group PLC
Dixons House Maylands Avenue Hemel Hempstead HP2 7TG
Tel: (01442) 353000 **Fax:** (01442) 233218
Geoffrey Budd, Company Secretary

ED & F Man Holdings Ltd
Sugar Quay Lower Thames Street London EC3R 6LA
Tel: (020) 7648 7000 **Fax:** (020) 7648 7067
RJA Askew, Group General Counsel

Edinburgh Investment Trust PLC
Donaldson House 97 Haymarket Terrace Edinburgh EH12 5HD
Tel: (0131) 313 1000 **Fax:** (0131) 313 6300
Cathy Miller, Company Secretary

EGG PLC
1 Waterhouse Square 142 Holborn Bars London EC1N 2ST
Tel: (020) 7526 2500 **Fax:** (020) 7526 2655
Website: www.egg.com
No of lawyers in dept: 7
Work outsourced: Company and commercial, litigation, employment, real property.
James Butler, Legal Director & Company Secretary
Specialisation: Company commercial and corporate finance.
Career: MA (Cantab); *Freshfields* - Assistant Solicitor; *Turner Kenneth Brown* - Partners; Cable & Wireless - Senior Legal Adviser, M&A; Mercury Communications - Director of Legal Services; Lloyds of London - Director of Legal Services.
Other lawyers: All company and commercial matters, corporate finance, litigation, IP, IT and internet.

Eidos PLC
Wimbledon Bridge House 1 Hartfield Road Wimbledon London SW19 3RU
Tel: (020) 8636 3000 **Fax:** (020) 8636 3001
Email: charlotte.eastwood@eidos.co.uk
Website: www.eidos.co.uk
No of lawyers in dept: 2
Work outsourced: Varies from time to time.
Charlotte Eastwood, Company Secretary
Specialisation: Employees share schemes, property work, compliance / corporate governance.
Career: Solicitor and chartered secretary.
Other lawyers: Employees share schemes, property work, compliance / corporate governance.

Electrocomponents PLC
International Management Centre 5000 Oxford Business Park South Oxford OX4 2BH
Tel: (01865) 204000 **Fax:** (01865) 207400
Website: www.electrocomponents.com
No of lawyers in dept: 1
Carmelina Carfora, Company Secretary
Other lawyers: Commercial, intellectual property, employment, property, company, IT, e-commerce, Adam Smith.

Elementis PLC
One Great Tower Street London EC3R 5AH
Tel: (020) 7398 1400 **Fax:** (020) 7398 1401
Philip Brown, Company Secretary

EMAP PLC
1 Lincoln Court Lincoln Road Peterborough PE1 2RF
Tel: (01733) 568900 **Fax:** (01733) 312115
Derek Walmsley, Company Secretary

EMI Group PLC
4 Tenterden Street Hanover Square London W1A 2AY
Tel: (020) 7355 4848 **Fax:** (020) 7495 1308
Charles P Ashcroft, Company Secretary & Group General Counsel

EMI Publishing Ltd
Publishing House 127 Charing Cross Road London WC2H 0QY
Tel: (020) 7434 2151 **Fax:** (020) 7434 3531
Chris Mileson, Director of Legal and Business Affairs

EMI Records Limited
43 Brook Green London W6 7EF
Tel: (020) 7605 5000 **Fax:** (020) 7605 5192
Email: james.radice@emimusic.com
Website: www.emigroup.com
James Radice, Business and Commercial Affairs Director, EMI/Chrysalis Records

Energis PLC
Carmelite 50 Victoria Embankment London EC4Y 0DE
Tel: (020) 7206 5555 **Fax:** (020) 7206 5713
Website: www.energis.net
No of lawyers in dept: 1
Work outsourced: 100% - Corporate, commercial, employment, IP, property.
Andrew McKelvie, Assistant Company Secretary
Specialisation: All aspects of company sectretarial work. Co-ordinates outsourced legal work throughout the group.
Career: Joined Energis in May 1998, previously Asisstant Company Secretary for Henlys Group plc. BA Hons at Leeds for Politics and Sociology, FCIS.
Personal: Born 1964, interests include rugby and golf, married with two children.
Other lawyers: One in-house property lawyer.

E

Enodis PLC
Washington House 40-41 Conduit Street London W1S 2YQ
Tel: (020) 7304 6000 **Fax:** (020) 7304 6001
Email: contact@enodis.com
Website: www.enodis.com
No of lawyers in dept: 1
Work outsourced: 95% - Mostly all.
David Hooper, Company Secretary
Specialisation: Company / commercial, employment.
Career: Qualified solicitor.

Enterprise Oil PLC
Grand Buildings Trafalgar Square London WC2N 5EJ
Tel: (020) 7925 4000 **Fax:** (020) 7925 4321
Andrew Wilson, Head Of Legal Affairs

Environment Agency
5th Floor 10 Albert Embankment London SE1 7TS
Tel: (020) 8305 4024 **Fax:**
Peter Kellett, In-house Lawyer

European Bank for Reconstruction & Development (EBRD)
One Exchange Square London EC2A 2JN
Tel: (020) 7338 6613 **Fax:** (020) 7338 6150
Website: www.ebrd.com
Emmanuel Maurice, General Counsel

Exel PLC
Ocean House The Ring Bracknell RG12 1AN
Tel: (01344) 302000 **Fax:** (01344) 301193
Email: ian.goulden@exel.com
Website: www.exel.com
No of lawyers in dept: 13
Work outsourced: 40% - Major acquisitions and disposals, litigation, property, overseas work, construction, pensions, environmental, competition, IT/IP.
Ian S Goulden, Director of Legal Services, Commercial
Specialisation: Responsible for all commercial matters affecting Exel's operational divisions, with particular emphasis on contractual matters. Manages in-house department comprising thirteen lawyers and seven paralegals worldwide.
Career: Hull University. Partner with *Carter Hodge* (private practice). Joined Ocean Group PLC in 1990. Appointed Head of Legal 1996. Appointed Director of Legal Services, Commercial, on merger of Ocean Group plc and NFC plc in 2000
Other lawyers: By Region: 8 in UK, 3 in US, 1 in Holland and 1 in Singapore.

Express Newspapers Ltd / Express Sunday
Ludgate House 245 Blackfriars Road Blackfriars London SE1 9UX
Tel: (020) 7928 8000 **Fax:** (020) 7620 1654
Justin Walford, Legal Manager

Fidelity Investments International
Kingswood Place Millfield Lane Lower Kingwood Tadworth KT20 6RB
Tel: (01737) 836411 **Fax:** (01737) 836975
Email: pamela.edwards@uk.fid-intl.com
Website: www.fidelity.co.uk
No of lawyers in dept: 17
Work outsourced: 50% approx - Specialist or other jurisdictions.
Pamela Edwards, Executive Director, Legal Services, Europe
Other lawyers: Investment finance lawyers (most); pensions lawyer (one); employment lawyer (one).

Film Finances Limited
14-15 Conduit Street London W1S 2XJ
Tel: (020) 7629 6557 **Fax:** (020) 7491 7530
James Shirras, Head of Legal

FilmFour
76-78 Charlotte Street London W1P 1LY
Tel: (020) 7868 7700 **Fax:** (020) 7868 7773
Website: www.channel4.com
No of lawyers in dept: 4
Andrew Hildebrand, Director of Business Affairs

Financial Services Authority - FSA
25 The North Colonnade Canary Wharf London E14 5HS
Tel: (020) 7676 3310 **Fax:** (020) 7676 9730
Email: andrew.whittaker@fsa.gov.uk
Website: www.fsa.gov.uk
No of lawyers in dept: 35
Andrew Whittaker, General Counsel to the Board
Specialisation: Responsible for legal advice to FSA Board and Senior Management of FSA on UK and European law, overall management and organisation of FSA legal function, quality control of legal advice in FSA, input into proposals for legislative change. Member of FSA Directors Committee; Chairman, FSA Lawyers Consultative Group.
Career: Torquay Boys Grammar School; Balliol College, Oxford, BA 1977, MA 1980, College of Law, Lancaster Gatey 1978. Qualified 1980. DTI 1982-1985. Securities and Investments Board, Deputy Legal Director 1987-1992; Head of Department for International policy and relations; markets policy, supervision of securities markets (1992-1997); Financial Services Authority - Deputy General Counsel 1997-2000, General Counsel 2000 - to date.
Personal: Travel, photography, family.
Other lawyers: Greg Choyce - Banking; Stuart Willey - Investment Business; Robin Ford - Insurance.

Finsbury Trust PLC
12 Appold Street London EC2A 2AW
Tel: (0990) 502017 **Fax:** (020) 7247 4722
Faith Pengelly, Company Secretary

First Choice Holidays PLC
First Choice House London Road Crawley RH10 2GX
Tel: (01293) 560777 **Fax:** (01293) 539039
Andrew John, Group Company Secretary

First Technology PLC
2 Cheapside Buckhurst Road Ascot SL5 7RF
Tel: (01344) 622322 **Fax:** (01344) 622773
Neil Clayton, Company Secretary

FirstGroup
(E Block) 3rd Floor, MacMillan House Paddington Station London W2 1FG
Tel: (020) 7291 0500 **Fax:** (020) 7636 1338
Email: Louise.Howell@Firstgroup.com
Website: www.firstgroup.com
No of lawyers in dept: 1
Work outsourced: 90% - Company/commercial, corporate finance, litigation, property, pensions, employment, regulatory (railways).
Louise Ruppell, Group Legal Adviser & Company Secretary
Specialisation: Company, commercial law, corporate finance.
Career: University of Liverpool (LL.B. First Class Hons) 1985-1988; Guildford College of Law 1988-1989; *Slaughter and May* 1990-1997; Merrill Lynch (UK Counsel) 1997-1998; FirstGroup plc 1998-present.

FKI PLC
Froude Consine Blackpole Road Worcester WR3 8YB
Tel: (01905) 856800 **Fax:** (1905) 856801
Email: tony.ventrella@fkiplc.com
Website: www.fki.co.uk
No of lawyers in dept: 1
Work outsourced: 100% M&A, 90% property, 10% litigation.
Tony Ventrella, Director, Legal Services
Specialisation: All legal matters affecting operational companies, with particular emphasis of all contractual matters. Include supply contracts, purchasing agreements, agency contracts, distributorship and licencing agreements. All but major items of litigation/arbitration and some employment tribunal work. Also responsible for managing external lawyers in the UK and overseas. Provides commercial training of managers.
Career: LL.B. (Hons) Sheffield University 1977. Attended College of Law 1977-1978 and called to the Bar by Lincoln's Inn 1978. MA (Business Law) from City of London Polytechnic 1981. Legal and Commercial Adviser to HVCA 1978-1984, Legal Director and Company Secretary of BEAMA Ltd 1984-1997. Member of the IEE/I. Mech, Conditions of Contract Drafting Panel. Formerly member of a number of CBI Panels.
Personal: Married with three children. Author of 'Contractors Guide to Contract Law'.
Other lawyers: Engineeing contracts and contractual matters generally smaller litigation and arbitration proceedings.

Football Association
25 Soho Square London W1D 4FA
Tel: (020) 7314 5320 **Fax:** (020) 7314 5325
Darren Berman, Company Solicitor

25 Soho Square London W1D 4FA
Tel: (020) 7745 4545 **Fax:** (020) 7745 4546
Website: www.the-fa.olg
Nicholas Coward, Company Secretary
Career: A/C *Freshfields* 1990-92; Assistant Solicitor at *Freshfields* 1992-96; Company Solicitor 1996-98; Company Secretary 1998-.

Foreign & Colonial Invest Trust PLC (Unit Managers)
Exchange House Primrose Street London EC2A 2NY
Tel: (020) 7628 8000 **Fax:** (020) 7825 2346
Website: www.fandc.co.uk
No of lawyers in dept: 2
Work outsourced: 10% - Litigation trust.
Gillian Switalski, Head of Legal
Specialisation: Brokerage and investment management agreements.
Personal: Married with children.

Formula One Management Ltd
6 Princes Gate London SW7 1QJ
Tel: (020) 7584 6668 **Fax:** (020) 7581 1649
Email: swoodwardhill@ukonline.co.uk
Sacha Woodward Hill, In-house Lawyer
Specialisation: Full spectrum of in-house legal work with a broad commercial remit, focusing on event promotion and television work and other sport-related IP issues. Also some regulatory and corporate work.
Career: MA (Cantab) [Corpus Christi College, Cambridge]. Articled at *Taylor Joynson Garrett* (1991-3). Moved to *Allen & Overy* in 1995 and then joined Formula One Group in 1996.
Personal: Born 26 January 1969. Leisure: a discerning collector of accessories, the proud owner of more shoes and handbags than Mrs Imelda Marcos!

Forte Ltd
166 High Holborn London WC1V 6TT
Tel: (020) 7301 2270 **Fax:** (020) 7301 2288
Email: martin.soley@fortehotels.com
Website: www.forte-hotels.com
No of lawyers in dept: 1
Work outsourced: 60% - Employment, property, M&A, litigation.
Martin Soley, Company Solicitor
Specialisation: Commercial - contracts, dispute resolution, sales and marketing (loyalty programme, promotions etc..) joint ventures, franchising, general advice to hotels, construction contract advice. Insurance liaison, secretarial liaison.
Career: Jesus College, Cambridge (M&A in Law); Articled *Herbert Oppenheimer, Nathan & Vandyk*; Assistant Solicitor *Ziman & Co*; Legal Adviser Humphreys & Glasgow Ltd, Vickers plc; Company Solicitor 14 years with Forte Hotel Group.
Personal: Rowed for Jesus College; Chairman of Churchyard Committee (St Marys, N.Mymms, Hertfordshire); Hobbies: Driving MGB Roadster, athletics, reading, travel, gardening.
Other lawyers: Martin Soley - Company/Commercial.

Framlington Group Ltd
155 Bishopsgate London EC2M 3XJ
Tel: (020) 7374 4100 **Fax:** (020) 7330 6406
Josephine Tubbs, Head of Legal & Company Secretariat

Galen Holdings PLC
Seagoe Industrial Estate Craigavon BT63 5UA
Tel: (028) 3833 4974 **Fax:** (028) 3835 0206
Stephen Campbell, Company Secretary

Gallaher Group
Members Hill Brooklands Road Weybridge KT13 0QU
Tel: (01932) 859777 **Fax:** (01932) 832792
Tom Keevil, Corporate Legal Adviser

Gartmore Investment Management PLC
Fenchurch Exchange 8 Fenchurch Place London EC3M 4PH
Tel: (020) 7782 2000 **Fax:** (020) 7782 2075
Email: helpline@gartmore.com
Website: www.gartmore.com
No of lawyers in dept: 6
Work outsourced: 30% - Non UK law; significant corporate transactions; new products.
Jane Thornton, Head of Legal Department & Company Secretary
Specialisation: Strategic support to the Board; corporate transactions; Director of the trustee of the company's pension scheme; Ad hoc significant corporate projects.
Career: 1st class Hons (LL.B) from University of Southampton in 1988; 2nd class Hons in Law Society Final Examinations (1989); Trained at and spent five years past qualification with *Clifford Chance* specialising in financial services and corporate matters (1989-1996), became Head of Legal and Company Secretary later that year.
Other lawyers: Fay Douglas; Sade Kilaso; Simon Martin; Katy Riddell; Rachel Wheeler.

Fenchurch Exchange 8 Fenchurch Place London EC3M 4PH
Tel: (020) 7782 2000 **Fax:** (020) 7374 3075
Simon Martin, Legal Manager

GE Capital (Global Equipment Finance) Ltd
(UK) Capital House Bond Street Bristol BS1 3LA
Tel: (0117) 929 8899 **Fax:** (0117) 946 3539
Janet Gregory, Legal Director

Geest PLC
Midgate House Midgate Peterborough PE1 1TN
Tel: (01775) 763085 **Fax:** (01775) 763086
Jane Scriven, Legal Services Director

GKN PLC
Ipsley House Ipsley Church Lane PO Box 55 Redditch B98 0TL
Tel: (01527) 533253 **Fax:** (01527) 533470
Email: Rufus.OgilvieSmals@gknplc.com
Website: www.gknplc.com
No of lawyers in dept: 5
Work outsourced: Litigation, conveyancing, minor matters, public offers, pensions work, tax, regulatory, employment.
Rufus Ogilvie Smals, Head of Group Legal
Career: Read Law at Emmanuel College, Cambridge University. Attended Inns of Court School of Law. Called to the Bar (Middle Temple) 1973. Studied at Europa Institute, University of Amsterdam. Joined GKN in 1975, from Deputy Head of the Legal Department to Head of the Group Legal Department in 1995. Chairman of CBI Competition Panel.
Personal: Interests include sailing, skiing, military history and current affairs.
Other lawyers: Head of Legal Department: Rufus Ogilvie Smals; Principal Legal Advisers: Sarah Eddowes, David Radford; Legal Advisors: Martin Brostoff, Simon Gardiner.

GlaxoSmithKline
1 New Horizons Court Great West Road Brentford TW8 9EP
Tel: (020) 8975 6339 **Fax:** (020) 8975 6333
Email: Alan.s.cox@gsk.com
Website: www.gsk.com
Alan Cox, Global Head - Trade Marks

1 New Horizons Court Great West Road Brentford TW8 9EP
Tel: (020) 8975 2000 **Fax:** (020) 8975 6344/6177
Email: 975 6345 - Hedda Long/David Roberts
Website: www.gsk.com
David Roberts, Director & Senior Vice-President, Corporate Intellectual Property

Go-Ahead Group PLC
Cale Cross House Level 16 Pilgrim Street Newcastle upon Tyne NE1 6SU
Tel: (0191) 232 3123 **Fax:** (0191) 221 0315
Ian Butcher, Company Secretary

Goldman Sachs International
Peterborough Court 133 Fleet Street London EC4A 2BB
Tel: (020) 7774 1315 **Fax:** (020) 7774 1989
Website: www.gs.com
Therese L Miller, Managing Director & General Counsel

Peterborough Court 133 Fleet Street London EC4A 2BB
Tel: (020) 7774 4815 **Fax:** (020) 7774 4123
Website: www.gs.com
Roger Scotts, Executive Director, Co-Head of Special Execution Group Europe
Specialisation: Equity, M&A, Fixed Income
Career: Bristol University 1981-1984; *Simmons & Simmons* 1986-1989; UBS 1989-1998; Goldman Sachs 1998 to date.

Daniel House 140 Fleet Street London EC4A 2BB
Tel: (020) 7774 1000 **Fax:** (020) 7774 1989
Website: www.gs.com
Jonathan Thomas, Executive Director & Counsel
Specialisation: Funds, financial services regulation, commercial.
Career: 1997-2001: Henderson Global Investors; 1994-1997: *MW Cornish & Co*; 1992-1994: *Stephenson Harwood*; Oxford University.

Daniel House 140 Fleet Street London EC4A 2BB
Tel: (020) 7774 1000 **Fax:** (020) 7774 1989
William Elliot, Executive Legal Director

Peterborough Court 133 Fleet Street London EC4A 2BB
Tel: (020) 7774 1000 **Fax:** (020) 7774 1989
David Geen, Executive Director & Senior Counsel

Peterborough Court 133 Fleet Street London EC4A 2BB
Tel: (020) 7774 1000 **Fax:** (020) 7774 1989
Tim Grayson, Vice President, Capital Markets

Daniel House 140 Fleet Street London EC4A 2BB
Tel: (020) 7774 1000 **Fax:** (020) 7774 1989
Alexander Marshall, Executive Director & Senior Counsel

Granada PLC
The London Television Centre Upper Ground London SE1 9LT
Tel: (020) 7261 8060 **Fax:** (020) 7620 2864
Email: gparrott@granada.co.uk
Website: www.granada.co.uk
No of lawyers in dept: 10
Work outsourced: 90% - All legal work.
Graham Parrott, Commercial Director & Company Secretary
Specialisation: Acquisitions/disposals, pensions, property, insurance, share schemes, legal secretarial and business affairs.
Personal: Born 1949. Lives in London.

Great Portland Estates PLC
Knighton House 56 Mortimer Street London W1N 8BD
Tel: (020) 7580 3040 **Fax:** (020) 7631 5169
Desna Martin, Company Secretary

Greene King PLC
Westgate Brewery Westgate Street Bury St Edmunds IP33 1QT
Tel: (01284) 763222 **Fax:** (01284) 706502
Rob Bellhouse, Company Secretary

Guardian iT Group
Benchmark House St George's Business Centre 203 Brooklands Road Weybridge KT13 0RH
Tel: (01932) 835900 **Fax:** (01932) 835901
Email: anthony.schroeder@guardianit.com
Website: www.guardianit.com
No of lawyers in dept: 3
Anthony Schroeder, Company Secretary & Head of Legal
Other lawyers: Frances Deigh, Michael Brown.

Guardian Newspapers Limited
119 Farringdon Road London EC1R 3ER
Tel: (020) 7278 2332 **Fax:** (020) 7713 4481
Email: siobhain.butterworth@guardian.co.uk
Website: www.guardianunlimited.co.uk
No of lawyers in dept: 4
Work outsourced: 50% - Libel, litigation and contracts.
Siobhain Butterworth, Head of Legal Affairs
Specialisation: Responsible for providing legal services to Guardian Newspapers Ltd, publishers of the Guardian and the Observer newspapers and the Guardian unlimited network of websites. Responsible for all contentious and non-contentious matters; pre-publication, libel and media related litigation, intellectual property and commercial work.
Career: St. Leonards RC Comprehensive School, Durham; Newcastle University 1984. Articled *Stephens Innocent*, Qualified 1991; *Stephens Innocent & Scown* 1992; Solicitor *Stephens Innocent* 1993-1997; Head of Legal Affairs, Guardian Newspaper Ltd 1997-present.
Personal: Born 1963; Resides London.
Other lawyers: Libel and media related litigation, intellectual property, commercial.

GWR Group plc
1 Passage Street Bristol BS2 0JF
Tel: (0117) 900 5316 **Fax:** (0117) 900 5306
Email: richard.manning@musicradio.com
Website: www.gwrgroup.com
No of lawyers in dept: 1
Work outsourced: All types.
Richard Manning, Group Solicitor
Specialisation: All aspects of legal work for GWR Group plc, from corporate/M&A to local radio station issues and everything in between.
Career: Law degree at Leeds University (1983-86) followed by MBA at Bradford Management Centre (1987). After a spell in non-legal roles, articles at *Swainson Son & Reynolds*, Lancaster following 7 years in-house with Burmah Castrol plc. Commenced current head of legal role until GWR Group plc in January 2001.
Personal: Married with 3 children. Interests: music, squash, golf.
Other lawyers: Company/commercial, corporate/M&A, corporate finance, litigation, property, intellectual property.

1 Passage Street Bristol BS2 0JF
Tel: (0117) 900 5316 **Fax:** (0117) 900 5306
Email: richard.manning@musicradio.com
Website: www.gwrgroup.com
No of lawyers in dept: 1
Work outsourced: All types.
Wendy Pallot, Company Secretary
Other lawyers: Company/commercial, corporate/M&A, corporate finance, litigation, property, intellectual property.

Halifax Group PLC
Trinity Road Halifax HX1 2RG
Tel: (01422) 333333 **Fax:** (01422) 333000
Harry Baines, Company Secretary

Halma PLC
Misbourne Court Rectory Way Amersham HP7 0DE
Tel: (01494) 721 111 **Fax:** (01494) 728 032
Carol Tredway, Company Secretary

Hammerson PLC
100 Park Lane London W1Y 4AR
Tel: (020) 7887 1000 **Fax:** (020) 7887 1010/1090
Stuart Haydon, Company Secretary

Hanson PLC
1 Grosvenor Place London SW1X 7JH
Tel: (020) 7245 1245 **Fax:** (020) 7235 3455
Email: graham.dansfield@hansonplc.com
Website: www.hansonplc.com
No of lawyers in dept: 2
Work outsourced: Varies by division - Property, litigation.
Graham Dransfield, Legal Director
Specialisation: Company/commercial, corporate finance. Acting for the UK head office companies and UK subsidiaries in corporate and commercial activities. Property and litigation not dealt with in-house; legal structure operates on decentralised basis.
Career: Colne Valley High School; St Catherine's College, Oxford. Articled *Slaughter and May* 1974-82; Joined Hanson plc 1982, Legal Director since 1992.
Personal: Beckenham Tennis and Squash Club; The Addington Golf Club.
Other lawyers: Steven Hardman: Company, commerical, corporate finance, general.

H

HarperCollins Publishers Ltd
77-85 Fulham Palace Road London W6 8JB
Tel: (020) 8307 4665 **Fax:** (020) 8317 4668
Kim Dawe, Legal Adviser

Hays PLC
Hays House Millmead Guildford GU2 5HJ
Tel: (01483) 302203 **Fax:** (01483) 302226
Email: stephan.charnock@hays.plc.uk
Website: www.hays-plc.co.uk
No of lawyers in dept: 4
Work outsourced: 60% - Acquisitions/disposals of companies/businesses, major commercial contracts, employment, litigation, property, pensions.
Stephen Charnock, Company Secretary & Head of Legal
Specialisation: Acquisitions, joint ventures, major contracts, company secretarial, share options, pensions.
Other lawyers: Paul Dungate - Senior Solicitor. Henry Stevenson - Solicitor. Jon Wellbourne-Green - Solicitor.

Hilton Group PLC
Maple Court Central Park Reeds Crescent Watford WD24 4QQ
Tel: (020) 7850 4000 **Fax:** (020) 7850 4001
Website: www.hiltongroup.com
No of lawyers in dept: 6
Work outsourced: 20% - Various.
J Geoffrey Chester, Solicitor, General Counse & Secretary
Specialisation: Responsible for all legal and company secretarial work for Hilton Group plcs Hotel division including all Hilton International Co's Hotels with particular emphasis in development (new hotels).
Career: Articed *Lloyd Raymond & Co / Edward Thompson & Co*; qualified 1976; company commercial solicitor National Coal Board 1981-1985; head of company / commercial section of the legal department Ladbroke Group plc 1985-1988; transferred in 1988 from Ladbroke to head up Hilton International Co's legal department (solicitor, general counsel and secretary). Univeristy College, Cardiff (1973, BSc); City of London Polytechnic (1977, MA Business Law); City University (1986, MBA).
Personal: Born 1951; resides Kew Gardens.

Hiscox PLC
Hiscox Syndicate 33 1 Great Street Helen's London
Tel: (020) 7448 6000 **Fax:** (020) 7448 6900
Bob Britton, In-house Lawyer

HIT Entertainment
Maple House 5th Floor 149 Tottenham Court Road London W1T 7NF
Tel: (020) 7224 2500 **Fax:** (020) 7388 9744
No of lawyers in dept: 4
Work outsourced: 10% - Corporate finance, trademarks.
Simon Taylor, Director of Legal and Business Affairs
Specialisation: Media and entertainment law, intellectual property, employment, property, company/commercial.
Career: 1994-2000 - BBC Programme Acquisition - Head of Business and Legal Affairs; 1991-1994 - Copyright and Artists Rights - Lawyer; 1989-1991 - *Mishcon de Reya* - Trainee Solicitor.
Personal: Joined HIT in July 2000.
Other lawyers: Intellectual property, media law, employment, property, company/commercial.

Hoare Bank
37 Fleet Street London EC4P 4DQ
Tel: (020) 7353 4522 **Fax:** (020) 7353 4521
C N Lugdon, Company Secretary

HSBC Holdings PLC
10 Lower Thames Street PO Box 506 London EC3R 6AE
Tel: (020) 7260 0500 **Fax:** (020) 7260 0501
Email: richardbennett@hsbc.com
Website: www.hsbc.com
No of lawyers in dept: 46
Work outsourced: 60% - Major transactions, litigation.
Richard ET Bennett, Group General Manager, Legal and Compliance
Specialisation: Responsible for the Legal & Compliance function of the HSBC Holdings Group.
Career: Bristol University (LLB), graduated 1973. Qualified with *Stephenson Harwood*, 1976. Assistant Solicitor with *Harwood* until 1979 (seconded to the East Asiatic Company, Denmark 1977). Appointed Assistant Group Legal Adviser with The Hong Kong and Shanghai Banking Corporation 1979. Deputy Group Legal Adviser 1988. Head of Legal & Compliance of The Hong Kong and Shanghai Banking Corporation Ltd 1993 with responsibility for legal, compliance and secretarial functions in Asia Pacific. Appointed to present position 1 January 1998.
Personal: Born 20th September 1951. Leisure pursuits include; all sports, particularly rugby and golf. Lives in Surrey/London.

Vintners Place 68 Upper Thames Street London EC4V 3BJ
Tel: (020) 7336 3065 **Fax:** (020) 7336 3377
Email: david-bloom@hsbcgroup.com
Website: www.hsbc.com
David Bloom, Senior Legal Adviser

10 Lower Thames Street PO Box 506 London EC3R 6AE
Tel: (020) 7260 0500 **Fax:** (020) 7260 0501
Stephen Garratt-Frost, Head of Legal Services

IBM UK Ltd
South Bank 76 Upper Ground London SE1 9PZ
Tel: (020) 7202 3000 **Fax:** (020) 7202 5935
Email: wittd@uk.ibm.com
Website: www.ibm.com
David Witt, Senior Counsel, Europe Middle East and Africa, Litigation and Intellectual Property
Specialisation: Litigation, intellectual property, competition law.
PO Box 41 North Harbour Portsmouth PO6 3AU
Tel: (01705) 492249 **Fax:** (0990) 426329
Robert Marcus, Senior Counsel

ICAP plc
Park House 16 Finsbury Circus London EC2M 7UR
Tel: (020) 7638 7592 **Fax:** (020) 7463 4365
Website: www.garban-intercapital.com
No of lawyers in dept: 3
Work outsourced: 30% - Property, tax, some corporate finance.
Edward Pank, Company Secretary
Specialisation: Company commercial, share/venture schemes, information technology.
Career: Framlington College 1958-62; Trinity Hall, Cambridge 1963-66; St Thomas's Hospital Medical School 1977-82; *Herbert Smith* 1969-70; Slater Walker Ltd 1970-76; ICAP plc 1986-present.
Other lawyers: Mark Schreiber - General; Peter Hulsich - General.

Iceland Group PLC
Second Avenue Deeside Industrial Park Deeside CH5 2NW
Tel: (01244) 842329 **Fax:** (01244) 814531
Email: customer.care@iceland.co.uk
Website: www.iceland.co.uk
No of lawyers in dept: 3
Work outsourced: 80% - Conveyancing, litigation, corporate tax.
John Berry, Company Secretary
Specialisation: Responsible for Group's legal, company secretarial, licensing, pensions and employee benefits, insurance, fire and health and safety, and car fleet functions. Member of BACFI. Has addressed conference on ESOPs.
Career: Qualified as a Barrister 1976. Assistant company secretary Smith's Industries plc 1973-76. Assistant secretary, The Rank Organisation plc 1976-83. Legal Manager HP Bulmer Holdings plc 1983-85, then joined Iceland Group plc.
Personal: Educated at Glyn Grammar School, Epsom 1963-70 and Coventry Polytechnic (now University) 1970-73 (BA Hons, Business Law). Leisure pursuits include running, skiing, golf, gardening and books. Born 23rd January 1952. Lives in Chester.
Other lawyers: Company/commercial, corporate finance, litigation, employment, property.

IMI PLC
Kynoch Works PO Box 216 Witton Birmingham B6 7BA
Tel: (0121) 356 4848 **Fax:** (0121) 356 3526
Website: www.imi.plc.uk
No of lawyers in dept: 3
Work outsourced: 60% - Corporate, litigation and conveyancing.
John O'Shea, Company Secretary
Other lawyers: Paul Boulton : General Corporate and Commercial; Joanne Bower : General Corporate and Commercial.

Imperial Chemical Industries PLC
Imperial Chemical House 9 Millbank London SW1P 3JF
Tel: (020) 7834 4444 **Fax:** (020) 7834 2042
Email: michael_herlihy@ici.com
Website: www.ici
Work outsourced: Litigation, property and pensions.
Michael HC Herlihy, General Counsel
Specialisation: Oversees the lawyers in the Group and responsible for provision of legal advice to the ICI Board and all members of the ICI Group.
Career: Qualified in 1977. University - St. Catherine's College, Oxford. Joined ICI 1979; 1985-1992 Manager of Legal Affairs Department, ICI Agrochemicals; 1992-1995 Group Taxation Controller; 1996 to date General Counsel.
Other lawyers: RWT Turner, Deputy General Counsel; AR Graham, Corporate Counsel; D Jash, Company Secretary.

Imperial Tobacco Group PLC
PO Box 244 Upton Road Southville Bristol BS99 7UJ
Tel: (0117) 963 6636 **Fax:** (0117) 966 7405
Website: www.imperial-tobacco.com
No of lawyers in dept: 4
Charles Hamshaw Thomas, Corporate Lawyer
Specialisation: M&A, company commercial, general.
Career: Worth School, Downing College, Cambridge. Articled *Slaughter & May;* qualified 1985; assistant solicitor *Clifford Chance 1985-1988;* solicitor Hanson plc 1988-1994; company secretary and legal counsel Beezer Homes 1994-1996; joined Imperial Tobacco Group plc 1996.
Personal: Born 1960; resides Bradford-on-Avon. Married with 3 sons.
Other lawyers: Conrad Tate - company / commercial / litigation / general; Mathew Phillips - M&A / company / commercial / general.

PO Box 244 Upton Road Southville Bristol BS99 7UJ
Tel: (0117) 963 6636 **Fax:** (0117) 966 7405
Website: www.imperial-tobacco.com
No of lawyers in dept: 4
Alan Porter, Legal Manager
Specialisation: Commercial, regulatory, litigation, intellectual property management.
Career: Western-Super-Mare Grammar School; Fellow of the Institute of Legal Executives; Imperial Tabacco Group plc.
Personal: Born 1949, resides Bristol, married with two children. Interests: sport, music and history.
Other lawyers: Conrad Tate - company / commercial / litigation / general; Mathew Phillips - M&A / company / commercial / general.

Incepta Group PLC
3 London Wall Buildings London Wall London EC2M 5SY
Tel: (020) 7282 2800 **Fax:** (020) 7282 8030
Jennifer Lees, In-house Lawyer

Independent Insurance Group PLC
No 2 Minster Court, 5th Floor Mincing Lane London EC3R 7BB
Tel: (020) 7623 8877 **Fax:** (020) 7283 8275
Alison Byrne, Group Solicitor

Independent Television News Ltd (ITN)
200 Grays Inn Road London WC1X 8XZ
Tel: (020) 7833 3000 **Fax:** (020) 7430 4868
Email: contact@itn.co.uk
Website: www.itn.co.uk
John Battle, In-house Lawyer, Head of Compliance ITN
Specialisation: Libel, contempt, copyright and any media law issues. Industry regulatory advice (ITC and BSC codes), data protection.
Career: 2001 Head of Compliance, ITN; 1996-2001 Group Legal Adviser, Associated Newspapers Ltd; 1990-1996 Legal Adviser, News International. Education: Warwick University LLB (Hons) 1984; Kings College, University of London, 2000, Postgraduate Diploma in UK and European Copyright Law and Related Rights; Institute of Chartered Secretaries, Post Qualification Certificate; Advanced Company Secretarial Practice, 1999.

Informa Group
19 Portland Place London W1N 3AF
Tel: (020) 7453 2222 **Fax:** (020) 7453 2450
Peter Miller, Company Secretary

ING Groep NV
Baring Asset Management Holdings 155 Bishopsgate London EC2M 3XY
Tel: (020) 7628 6000 **Fax:** (020) 7638 7928
Marla Dhillon, Group Head of Legal & Compliance, Baring Asset Management Holdings

Innovation Group PLC
Yarmouth House 1300 Parkway Solent Business Park Whiteley PO15 7AE
Tel: (01489) 898 300 **Fax:** (01489) 579 181
Hilary Tan, Company Secretary

Intec Telecom Systems PLC
Wells Court 2 Albert Drive Woking GU21 5UB
Tel: (01483) 745816 **Fax:** (01483) 745891
Email: garth.kerr@intec-telecom-systems.com
Website: www.intec-telecom-systems.com
No of lawyers in dept: 5
Work outsourced: 20% - Litigation and corporate.
Garth Kerr, Group Legal Adviser
Specialisation: Manage the legal department - which provides legal advice to the Intec Group and its associate joint venture companies worldwide. Particular responsibilities for all IT commercial transactions, IT and IP litigation, acquisitions and corporate restructuring and integration, and all company commercial matters. Most significant transactions include advising on the Intec IPO, on the acquisition and integration of Inception to Implementation (M) Sdn Bhd (+£18m), Computer Generation, Inc (£172m), CHA Systems Inc (£11m), Dataphone (UK) Ltd and advising on Intec's numerous multi-million pound global Software Licence and Implementation Agreements.
Career: Qualified 1996; in-house legal counsel for Metso Corporation 1997; in-house legal adviser for Lloyd's Register of Shipping 1998; Group Legal Adviser for Intec Telecom Systems PLC 2000. University of Natal (B.SOC.SC); Howard University College of Law (LLB).
Personal: Reside in Wimbledon; Leisure - golf, rugby, cycling, gym, skiing, scuba diving.

Intermediate Capital Group
62-63 Threadneedle Street London EC2R 8HE
Tel: (020) 7628 9898 **Fax:** (020) 7628 2268
John E Curtis, Company Secretary

International Power PLC
Senator House 85 Queen Victoria Street London EC4V 4DP
Tel: (020) 7615 3000 **Fax:** (020) 7320 8720
Website: www.internationalpowerplc.com
No of lawyers in dept: 7
Work outsourced: International legal advice on projects. Major High Court litigation. Overflow.
Stephen Ramsay, Company Secretary
Other lawyers: Stephen Ramsay - Company Secretary, Rosemary Cook - General Counsel, Roger Simpson, Kian Min Low, Clint Steyn, Graham Methold, David Waldham.

Interserve PLC
Interserve House Ruscombe Park Twyford Reading RG10 9JU
Tel: (01189) 320 123 **Fax:** (01189) 320 206
Daniel Bush, Group Solicitor

Invensys PLC
Carlisle Place London SW1P 1BX
Tel: (020) 7834 3848 **Fax:** (020) 7834 3879
JRW Clayton, Company Secretary

IQE PLC
Pascal Close Cypress Drive St Mellons Cardiff CF3 0EG
Tel: (029) 2083 9400 **Fax:** (029) 2083 9401
JL Coventry, Company Secretary

ITV Network Limited
200 Grays Inn Road London WC1X 8HF
Tel: (020) 7843 8000 **Fax:** (020) 7843 8158
Simon Johnson, Head of Legal

J Sainsbury PLC
Stamford House Stamford Street London SE1 9LL
Tel: (020) 7695 6000 **Fax:** (020) 7695 0011
Email: david.thurston@tao.sainsburys.co.uk
Website: www.j-sainsbury.co.uk
No of lawyers in dept: 8
David Thurston, Head of Group Legal Services
Other lawyers: George Robertson : Deputy Head / Litigation; Nicholas Grant : Commercial and Competition; Su Jenkins : Employment; Sue Redding : Trading and Marketing.

Jardine Lloyd Thompson Group PLC
6 Crutched Friars London EC3N 2PH
Tel: (020) 7528 4444 **Fax:** (020) 7528 4432
No of lawyers in dept: 3
Work outsourced: 10% or less - Litigation only.
Vyvienne Wade, Group Legal Director
Specialisation: Acquisitions, corporate, insurance and reinsurance.
Career: Joined JIB in 1987 and has remained with the group after its merger with Lloyd Thompson Group plc to form Jardine Lloyd Thompson Group plc. Recent announcement of appointment to main board w.e.f. 01/01/2002.
Other lawyers: M&A; Insurance and Reinsurance (contentious and non-contentious), employment, litigation.

Jarvis PLC
Frogmore Park Watton-at-Stone Hertford SG14 3RU
Tel: (01920) 832800 **Fax:** (01920) 832832
Geoff Mason, Company Secretary

JD Wetherspoon PLC
Wetherspoon House Central Park Reeds Crescent PO Box 616 Watford WD1 1YN
Tel: (01923) 477777 **Fax:** (01923) 219810
James Clarke, Finance Director & Company Secretary

Jim Henson Company Ltd
30 Oval Road Camden Town London NW1 7DE
Tel: (020) 7428 4000 **Fax:** (020) 7267 3817
Email: adowney@henson.com
No of lawyers in dept: 2
Work outsourced: 25-30% - Employment, litigation, property.
Antonia S Downey, Vice President, International Business and Legal Affairs
Specialisation: Film and television production, licensing and publishing distribution, TV and video, special effects.
Career: LLB (Hons 2:1) - University College, London; 5 years as trainee and assistant solicitor in media department of Denton Wilde Sapte (formerly Denton Hall).
Personal: Travel, art, films, theatre.

JJB Sports PLC
Martland Park Challenge Way Wigan WN5 0LD
Tel: (01942) 221400 **Fax:** (01942) 629809
Website: www.jjb.co.uk
No of lawyers in dept: 0
Work outsourced: 100% - Lease acquisition/disposal, corporate acquisitions, litigation.
David Greenwood, Company Secretary & Finance Director
Specialisation: Accounting, administration and company secretarial duties. Corporate finance affairs.
Career: FCA.
Other lawyers: JD Greenwood - all except HR/Customer Complaints; K Hollinshead - HR/Customer Complaints.

John Laing PLC
133 Page Street Mill Hill London NW7 2ER
Tel: (020) 8959 3636 **Fax:** (020) 8906 5485
Email: graham.d.gibson@laing.com
Website: www.laing.com
No of lawyers in dept: 4
Work outsourced: Specialist areas and overload.
Graham D Gibson, Manager Group Legal Services
Specialisation: Responsible for the management of legal services and legal advice to group companies. Specialisation in construction law.
Career: Educated City of London School and Exeter University (LL.B Hons). Qualified 1973. Articled and subsequently solicitor at *Speechly Bircham* 1971 to 1979. Joined legal services at John Laing plc 1979 and appointed to present post 1988.
Other lawyers: Ian Smith - Commercial Property; Peter Shell - Commercial/PFI; Andrew Sutherland - Litigation.

Johnson Matthey PLC
2-4 Cockspur Street Trafalgar Square London SW1Y 5BQ
Tel: (020) 7269 8400 **Fax:** (020) 7269 8133
Website: www.matthey.com
Work outsourced: 30% - Major M&A, corporate,

commercial, employment, litigation.
Simon Farrant, Senior Legal Adviser & Company Secretary
Career: Attorney at Law (New York).

Johnston Press PLC
53 Manor Place Edinburgh EH3 7EG
Tel: (0131) 225 3361 **Fax:** (0131) 225 4580
Email: enquiries@johnstonpress.co.uk
Website: www.johnstonpress.co.uk
No of lawyers in dept: 0
Work outsourced: 100% - Corporate, property, pensions and competition.
Richard Cooper, Company Secretary

JP Morgan & Co
60 Victoria Embankment London EC4Y 0JP
Tel: (020) 7325 5708 **Fax:** (020) 7325 8150
Email: lewis_david@jpmorgan.com
Website: www.jpmorgan.com
David A Lewis, Managing Director and Associate General Counsel
Specialisation: Derivatives, structured products, commodities and foreign exchange.
Career: 1990 - present: JP Morgan; 1985 - 1990: Chemical Bank; BA, Politics (1981) - Washington and Lee University; JD, University of Pittsburgh School of Law; LLM, Banking Law - Boston University School of Law.

JP Morgan Chase
125 London Wall London EC2Y 5AJ
Tel: (020) 7777 2000 **Fax:** (020) 7777 3141
Mitch Caller, Senior Vice President & Associate General Counsel

K

Kelda Group PLC
Western House Halifax Road Bradford BD6 2SZ
Tel: (01274) 804159 **Fax:** (01274) 804165
Email: stuart_mcfarlane@keldagroup.com
Website: www.keldagroup.com
No of lawyers in dept: 11
Work outsourced: 15% - Regulatory, commercial, litigation, employment, construction litigation, planning.
Stuart McFarlane, Head of Legal Services
Specialisation: Principal areas of work for the department include conveyancing, company/commercial, litigation (civil and criminal) and environmental.
Career: Articled *Gillis and Co* 1982-84, Solicitor 1984 to date. Joined Yorkshire Water plc 1989, Head of Legal Services since 1994.
Other lawyers: Ann Chapman, Andrew Newton: company/commercial; Peter Cockburn, Matthew Stevens, Julie Graham, Michelle Parlett, Kate Hartland-Westwood: property; Shona Flood, Graeme Stonehouse, Jill Sowden, Deborah Stirling: litigation.

Kidde PLC
Mathisen Way Colnbrook Slough SL3 0HB
Tel: (01753) 766338 **Fax:** (01753) 689309
Email: diane.quinlan@kidde.com
Website: www.kidde.com
No of lawyers in dept: 1
Work outsourced: 50% - Major corporate.
Diane Quinlan, Company Secretary
Other lawyers: Corporate, litigation, company/commercial.

Kingfisher PLC
North West House 119 Marylebone Road London NW1 5PX
Tel: (020) 7724 7749 **Fax:** (020) 7724 1160
Helen Jones, Company Secretary

Kingston Communications PLC
Telephone House 37 Carr Lane Kingston upon Hull HU1 3RE
Tel: (01482) 602576 **Fax:** (01482) 210765
Email: John_Bailey@kingston-comm.co.uk
Website: www.kcom.com
No of lawyers in dept: 4
Work outsourced: 30% - Property matters, litigation, transactions involving foreign law, planning, acquisitions, pensions, some commercial and regulatory work.
John PC Bailey, Company Secretary & Head of Legal Affairs
Specialisation: Company Secretarial and Admin; Commercial Contracts; Competition and Regulatory.
Career: Birmingham University 2.1 LL.B; Liverpool Polytechnic Law Society Finals; *Daniel Ashworth* and *Booth Macclesfield* Articles; Ernest Scragg and Sons Ltd.- Assistant Legal Adviser; Nickerson Plant Breeders Ltd. - Legal Adviser; GEC Telecommunications Ltd - Legal Adviser; Plessy Office Systems Ltd - Legal Adviser.
Personal: Married with four children. Interests include sailing and classic car maintenance.
Other lawyers: John Bailey; Matthew Pearson; Melanie Hall; Stuart North.

Laird Group PLC
3 St James's Square London SW1Y 4JU
Tel: (020) 7468 4040 **Fax:** (020) 7839 2921
Dominic Hudson, Company Secretary

Land Securities PLC
5 Strand London WC2N 5AF
Tel: (020) 7413 9000 **Fax:** (020) 7321 0893
Email: clive.ashcroft@landsecurities.com
Website: www.landsecurities.co.uk
Work outsourced: 80-85% - Some property - all corporate.
Clive Ashcroft, Head of Legal Services Portfolio Management
Specialisation: All areas of property investment development and management.
Career: 1974-1978 University of Kent, Degree in Law [BA]; 1982 - present Land Securities Group, Legal Services Department. Membership of various trade committees and focus groups.
Personal: Lives in Calfont St Peter, wife and two children. Hobbies: travel, walking, camping and reading.
Other lawyers: Keith Weston, Ian Petts: all areas.

Lattice Group PLC
130 Jermyn Street London SW1Y 4UR
Tel: (020) 7389 3219 **Fax:** (020) 7389 3220
John Patience, Company Secretary

Lattice Property Holdings
Aviary Court Wade Road Basingstoke RG24 8GZ
Tel: (01256) 308739 **Fax:** (01256) 308627
Email: angeline.swift@lattice-property.com
Website: www.lattice-property.com
No of lawyers in dept: 1
Work outsourced: 100% - Routine property portfolio transactional work and relates construction, planning and litigation matters.
Angeline Swift, Solicitor & Legal Manager
Specialisation: Property, environment, construction, property project management, management of panel firms, reviewing and updating precedures, intra-group issues and contracts, advising senior management - and on policy issues.
Career: Solicitor; BA Law (Hons); MSc Construction Law and Arbitration.
Personal: Reading, Music, Opera.

Lawn Tennis Association
The Queen's Club Palliser Road West Kensington London W14 9EG
Tel: (020) 7381 7000 **Fax:** (020) 7381 5965
Email: Bruce.Mellstrom@lta.org.uk
Website: www.lta.org.uk
Bruce R Mellstrom, LTA Lawyer
Specialisation: General responsibility for all LTA legal affairs including all LTA rules (including doping), sponsorship and general commercial agreements, events, TV agreements, club loans and other major facility projects, IP, employment matters.
Career: Charterhouse. Nottingham University (LLB), College of Law, Guildford. Previously worked at *Herbert Smith*, British Olympic Association. Qualified November 1989.
Personal: Married. Lives in London. Enjoys watching football (Crystal Palace FC) and tennis and sport generally. Enjoys playing golf, tennis. Member of British Association of Sport and the Law.

Lazard Brothers & Co Limited
21 Moorfields London EC2P 2HT
Tel: (020) 7588 2721 **Fax:** (020) 7920 0670
Website: www.lazard.com
No of lawyers in dept: 4
Will Dennis, Company Secretary & General Counsel
Specialisation: Corporate finance, asset management, capital markets, alternative investment.
Career: Cambridge University 1971-74, MA LLM. Foreign & Commonwealth Office 1977-86. *Cliford Chance* 1987-91. Partner *Denton Hall* 1991-93. Director N M Rothchild & Sons (Hong Kong) Ltd 1993-96. Lazard Brothers since 1996.

Legal & General Group PLC
Temple Court 11 Queen Victoria Street London EC4N 4TP
Tel: (020) 7528 6285 **Fax:** (020) 7528 6222
Email: geoffrey.timms@landg.com
Website: www.landgl.com
No of lawyers in dept: 10
Work outsourced: Large corporate transactions and litigation, and Commercial Property.
Geoffrey Timms, Group Head of Legal
Specialisation: Heads up a small team providing advice and assistance to the Group and its subsidiary components.
Career: BA (Hons): University of Kent 1986; *Clifford Chance*, 1987-89; *Clyde & Co*, 1989-91; Legal & General, 1991 to date.
Other lawyers: Liz Tubb; Sandra Phillips; Andrew Webster; Nigel Spells; Salma Sacranie; David O'Sullivan; Sally Anne Skate; Caroline Richards.

Legal & General UK Select Investment Trust PLC
Temple Court 11 Queen Victoria Street London EC4N 4TB
Tel: (020) 7528 6883 **Fax:** (020) 7528 6830
Andrew David Fairhurst, Company Secretary

Lehman Brothers International (Europe)
One Broadgate London EC2M 7HA
Tel: (020) 7260 2944 **Fax:** (020) 7260 3165
Email: pmarchan@lehman.com
Website: www.lehman.com
No of lawyers in dept: 16
Work outsourced: 20% - Litigation, services of underwriters' counsel, occasional specialist advice.
Piers Le Marchant, European Legal Director
Specialisation: Equity and fixed income capital markets. Derivatives, emerging markets. Some investment banking and litigation. Chairman of the New Products Committee and Transaction Review Group.
Career: Lehman Brothers from Dec 91. Previously Nomura International plc. Qualified as Barrister 1987. Educated London University & Canford School.
One Broadgate London EC2M 7HA
Tel: (020) 7601 0011 **Fax:** (020) 7260 3165
Ian Jameson, European Corporate Counsel

Lex Service PLC
Lex House Boston Drive Bourne End SL8 5YS
Tel: (01628) 843888 **Fax:** (01628) 810294
Website: www.lex.co.uk
No of lawyers in dept: 2
Work outsourced: 90% - Major acquisition-divestments, litigation, property, employment.
Pamela Coles, Company Secretary
Specialisation: Corporate finance, company Law.
Career: BA, FCIS.

Liberty International PLC
40 Broadway London SW1H 0BT
Tel: (020) 7960 1200 **Fax:** (020) 7960 1333
Email: susan-folger@lib-int.com
Website: www.liberty-international.co.uk
Work outsourced: 100% - Commercial contracts, corporate finance, litigation.
Susan Folger, Company Secretary

Lloyds TSB
51 Holdenhurst Road Bournemouth BH8 8EP
Tel: (01202) 522077 **Fax:**
Michael Kilbee, Legal Director, Lloyds TSB Asset Finance Division
Specialisation: Asset finance, banking, consumer finance, company secretarial.

Lloyds TSB Group PLC
71 Lombard Street PO Box 215 London EC3P 3BS
Tel: (020) 7626 1500 **Fax:** (020) 7929 1654
Website: www.lloydstsb.co.uk
Geoffrey Johnson, Group Chief Legal Adviser

Lloyds TSB Leasing Ltd
Great Surrey House 203 Blackfrias Road London SE1 8NH
Tel: (020) 7775 0020 **Fax:** (020) 7922 1800
Robin Isaacs, Head of Legal

Lloyds TSB Scotland PLC
Henry Duncan House 120 George Street PO Box 177 Edinburgh EH2 4TS
Tel: (0131) 225 4555
Email: Jeremy.Fraser@lloydstsb.co.uk
No of lawyers in dept: 2
Work outsourced: 5% - Various.
Jeremy Fraser, Head of Legal Services & Company Secretary
Specialisation: Banking law, contracts, CCA, security, employment, mortgages.
Career: Edinburgh University; Lloyds UDT; Lloyds TSB.
Other lawyers: Banking law, contracts, CCA, security, employment, mortgages.

Logica PLC
Stephenson House 75 Hampstead Road London NW1 2PL
Tel: (020) 7637 9111 **Fax:** (020) 7446 1937
Website: www.logica.com
No of lawyers in dept: 5
Lawrence Guedes, Group Legal Advisor
Specialisation: Merger and acquisition and related commercial work. IT/IP related work. General corporate/commercial matters.
Career: LL.M, LL.B.
Stephenson House 75 Hampstead Road London NW1 2PL
Tel: (020) 7637 9111 **Fax:** (020) 7872 8994
Website: www.logica.com
No of lawyers in dept: 5
Paul Weaver, Company Secretary

Lombard Bank Limited / Commercial Services
Lombard House 339 Southbury Road Enfield EN1 1TW
Tel: (020) 8344 5540 **Fax:** (020) 8344 5546
Stephen G Byrne, Company Solicitor & Deputy Company Secretary

London Bridge Software Holdings PLC
16th Floor New London Bridge House 25 London Bridge Street London SE1 9SG
Tel: (020) 7403 1333 **Fax:** (020) 7403 8981
Simon Parsliffe, Company Secretary

London Merchant Securities PLC (Ord)
Carlton House 33 Robert Adam Street London W1U 3HR
Tel: (020) 7935 3555 **Fax:** (020) 7935 3737
Email: co.secretary@lms-plc.com
Website: www.lms-plc.com
Michael Waldron, Company Secretary/Treasurer

London Pacific Group Ltd
Minden House 6 Minden Place St Helier JE2 4WQ
Tel: (01534) 607 700 **Fax:** (01534) 607 799
Ron Green, Company Secretary

Lonmin PLC
4 Grosvenor Place London SW1X 7YL
Tel: (020) 7201 6000 **Fax:** (020) 7201 6100
Email: contact@lonmin.com
Website: www.lonmin.com
No of lawyers in dept: 0
Work outsourced: Various.
Michael Pearce, Company Secretary

Luminar PLC
41 King Street Luton LU1 2DW
Tel: (01582) 589400 **Fax:** (01582) 589503
Email: mailbox@luminar.co.uk
Website: www.luminar.co.uk
Work outsourced: 75% - All.
Andrew Stride, Company Secretary
Specialisation: Company commercial, property, contracts, litigation, IP.
Career: LLb (Hons) - Qualified ICSA 1998. Qualified as solicitor in 1991, spent five years in Private Practice (*Goodger, Auden, Miles & Cash*) 2 years in house before joining Boots 1997-2000 legal dept. Joined Luminar in May 2000.
Personal: Born 10 November 1967.
Other lawyers: Andrew Stride: Company commercial, property, litigation, IP.

MacMillan Ltd
4-6 Crinan Street London N1 9XW
Tel: (020) 7843 3600 **Fax:** (020) 7843 3648
Website: www.macmillan.com
Andrew Crompton, Business, Legal and Development Director
Specialisation: Legal advice to Macmillan group worldwide.
Career: LL.B Nottingham Trent University; MBA Sheffield University; Qualified in 1993.

Manchester United PLC
Sir Matt Busby Way Old Trafford Manchester M16 0RA
Tel: (0161) 868 8325 **Fax:** (0161) 868 8816
Email: david.beswitherick@manutd.co.uk
Website: www.manutd.com
No of lawyers in dept: 0
David P Beswitherick, Company Secretary

Marconi PLC
1 Bruton Street London W1S 6AQ
Tel: (020) 7493 8484 **Fax:** (020) 7493 1974
Website: www.marconi.com
Simon Boyle, In-house Environmental Lawyer
Specialisation: Coordinator of Marconi Safety and Environment Unit (covers energy, health and safety, environment and product safety). Corporate and property transactions - global but principally UK, USA, Italy and Germany. Marconis EHS policy and strategy.
Career: LL.B - Lancaster University; Solicitors Finals - Guildford College of Law; Admitted Solicitor 1990; MA Environmental Law - De Montford.
Personal: Married with 2 children. Hobbies: climbing, cycling, hill walking, gardening.

Marks & Spencer PLC
Michael House 37-67 Baker Street London W1A 1DN
Tel: (020) 7935 4422 **Fax:** (020) 7487 2670
Graham Oakley, Company Secretary & Group Legal Adviser

Mars Incorporated
c/o Dundee Road Slough SL1 4JX
Tel: (01753) 550055 **Fax:** (01753) 550111
Website: www.mars.com
Evie Kyriakides, Market Property Manager

Marshalls PLC
Birkby Grange 85 Birkby Hall Road Birkby Huddersfield HD2 2YA
Tel: (01422) 306 000 **Fax:** (01422) 306 478
No of lawyers in dept: 0
Work outsourced: 100% - Employment, litigation, company.
Richard Monro, Company Secretary

Marylebone Cricket Club (MCC)
Lord's Cricket Ground London NW8 8QN
Tel: (020) 7289 1611 **Fax:** (020) 7432 1080
Email: holly.roper-curzon@mcc.org.uk
Website: www.lords.org
No of lawyers in dept: 1
Work outsourced: 5-10% - Property transactions; contentious employment matters; specialist on-line matters.
Holly Roper Curzon, Club Solicitor
Specialisation: Entertainment / media, intellectual property, commercial, sports related matters, non-contentious employment.
Career: 1982-85: University of Nottingham - Degree, BA (Hons), Law with French 2:1; 1983-85 & 1986-87: House of Commons Research Assistant; 1986-87: College of Law, Chancery Lane, Law Society finals; 1987-89: *Simmons & Simmons*, articled clerk; 1989-91: Seconded to Copyright Promotions Group e/c; 1992-97: Copyright Promotions Group e/c, Group Legal Director; 1998-2000: The FA Premier League, International Property Director; 2001 to date: Marylebone Cricket Club, Club Solicitor.
Personal: Interests: Sailing, scuba diving, skiing.
Other lawyers: Sport, entertainment / media, intellectual property, IT, employment, property, commercial eg. sponsorship, merchandising, publishing etc.

Matalan PLC
Gillibrands Road Skelmersdale WN8 9TB
Tel: (01695) 552 400 **Fax:** (01695) 552 401
Ian A Smith, Finance Director

Meggitt PLC
Farrs House Cowgrove Wimborne BH21 4EL
Tel: (01202) 847847 **Fax:** (01202) 842478
Website: www.meggitt.com
No of lawyers in dept: 0
Work outsourced: 100% - All.
Philip E Green, Group Corporate Affairs Director
Specialisation: Company secretarial, legal, commercial, pensions, insurance, property, administration.
Career: Fellow: Institute of Chartered Secretaries and Administrators - admitted 1988; B.A. (Law) Durham University, gained 1979.

Merchants Trust PLC
10 Fenchurch Street London EC3M 3LB
Tel: (020) 7475 5617 **Fax:** (020) 7621 1481
Nicola Schrager von Altishofen, Company Secretary

Merrill Lynch International
Ropemaker Place 25 Ropemaker Street London EC2Y 9LY
Tel: (020) 7628 1000 **Fax:** (020) 7867 4040
Email: iweb@exchange.ml.com
iweb@exchange.ml.com>
Website: www.ml.com
Richard Atkinson, Director of Law & Compliance & Senior Counsel
Specialisation: Debt markets, structured drivatives and other financial products.
Career: 74-81 - Kingston GS; 82-85 - Durham University; 87-94 - DKB Financial Products; 97- Merrill Lynch.

Ropemaker Place 25 Ropemaker Street London EC2Y 9LY
Tel: (020) 7628 1000 **Fax:** (020) 7867 4040
Kate Craven, Transactions Management

Mersey Docks & Harbour Company
Maritime Centre Port of Liverpool Liverpool L21 1LA
Tel: (0151) 949 6000 **Fax:** (0151) 949 6338
No of lawyers in dept: 3
Work outsourced: 20% - Litigation, major corporate, joint ventures.
William J Bowley, Director of Legal Services & Company Secretary
Specialisation: Responsible for all the Company's legal affairs and aspects of the company secretarial, insurance, claims and share registration sections. Principal areas of work are general company/commercial matters. Also handles shipping, property and environmental law and advises on litigation. Member of Law Society Commerce and

M

Industry Group.
Career: Articled with *J. Frodsham & Sons*, St. Helens 1971-72 and solicitor 1973-74. Joined The Mersey Docks and Harbour Company in 1974 as an assistant solicitor. Became PA to the MD 1979, Principal assistant solicitor 1981, Company Secretary and Solicitor 1982 and Director of Legal Services 1991.
Personal: Educated at Prescot Grammar School, University of Bristol (LLB) and Guildford Law School. Born 6 October 1947.
Other lawyers: Henry Hrynkiewicz, property; Janet Fallon, litigation, commercial, shipping.

MFI Furniture Group PLC
Southon House 333 The Hyde Edgware Road Colindale London NW9 6TD
Tel: (020) 8200 8000 **Fax:** (020) 8200 8636
Hamish Thomson, Director of Legal Services

Millennium & Copthorne Hotels PLC
Victoria House Victoria Road Horley RH6 7AF
Tel: (01293) 772288 **Fax:** (01293) 772345
Email: simon.hodges@mill-cop.com
Website: www.mill-cop.com
No of lawyers in dept: 0
Work outsourced: 100% - Various - predominantly property, corporate, employment law and licensing.
Simon Hodges, Company Secretary
Specialisation: Corporate mergers and acquisitions, corporate governance, legal services, risk management (Health & safety).
Career: Company Secretary with some 18 years' extensive experience in major international public corporations, non-listed holding companies and in professional practice in the UK and Hong Kong.
Personal: Interests: hockey, tennis, squash, soccer, walking and golf.
Other lawyers: Company/commercial, corporate finance, litigation, health & safety.

M

Minerva PLC
10 Gloucester Place London W1N 3AX
Tel: (020) 7535 1000 **Fax:** (020) 7535 1001
Ivan Ezekiel, Company Secretary

Misys PLC
Burleigh House Chapel Oak Salford Priors WR11 5SH
Tel: (01386) 871373 **Fax:** (01386) 871045
Andy Oakes, Commercial Director

MITIE Group PLC
The Stable Block Barley Wood Wrington Bristol BS40 5SA
Tel: (01934) 862 006 **Fax:** (01934) 862239
Website: www.MITIE.co.uk
No of lawyers in dept: 0
Work outsourced: Various - Acquisitions, property, litigation, employment.
Antony F Waters, Company Secretary

Mizuho International plc
Bracken House One Friday Street London EC4M 9JA
Tel: (020) 7489 6815 **Fax:** (020) 7489 6997
Email: brian.lanaghan@uk.mizuho-sc.com
No of lawyers in dept: 9
Work outsourced: Major transactions and specialist advisory.
Brian Lanaghan, Legal Director
Specialisation: Fixed income and equity new issues, derivatives, funds, custody, investment management, futures, commercial banking, general advisory.
Career: George Watson's College, Edinburgh. The Perse School, Cambridge. (MA) English and Law, Cambridge. Masters in European Community Law, Brussels.
Personal: Tennis, sailing, shooting, garden design, piano, languages; French (fluent), German (reasonable).

Morgan Stanley Dean Witter & Co
Morgan Stanley UK Group 25 Cabot Square Canary Wharf London E14 4QA
Tel: (020) 7425 8000 **Fax:** (020) 7425 8990
Lucy Lynch, Head of Law & Compliance for Europe

Morgan Stanley UK Group 25 Cabot Square Canary Wharf London E14 4QA
Tel: (020) 7425 8000 **Fax:** (020) 7425 8990
Joan Ma, Executive Director

Morgan Stanley UK Group 25 Cabot Square Canary Wharf London E14 4QA
Tel: (020) 7425 8000 **Fax:** (020) 7425 8990
Richard Rosenthal, Head of Legal & European General Counsel

Morse PLC
Brentside Executive Centre Great West Road Brentford TW8 9HE
Tel: (020) 8380 8325 **Fax:** (020) 8560 9900
Email: Lee.cameron@morse.com
Website: www.morse.com
Lee Cameron, Company Secretary & Head of Legal
Specialisation: Corporate, commercial, secretarial.
Career: University of Westminster 1994-1997 LL.B (Hons). Called to the Bar (Middle Temple) 1998.

MTV Networks
180 Oxford Street London W1N 0DS
Tel: (020) 7478 6247 **Fax:** (020) 7284 7788
No of lawyers in dept: 8
Work outsourced: 10-15% - Corporate joint ventures, litigation, distribution contracts, regulatory issues.
Svenja Geissmar, Vice-President of Business Affairs
Specialisation: Advising on all strategic commercial and legal issues across a pan-European television and on-line network including joint ventures, acquisitions, intellectual property rights, regulatory issues, distribution, production, advertising and sponsorship.
Career: Henrietta Barnett School, London; Cambridge University, Sidney Sussex College 1983-1986 (BA Hons MA (CANTAB)); Trained at *Lovells*, qualified 1990; 1990-1995, assistant solicitor at *Lovells* (Competition Law Department); 1995-to date, MTV Networks Europe (appointed General Counsel 1998).
Personal: Born 1964; Resides London; Interests include: Freeing Tibet, Co-founder of me, him & her; a fringe theatre, television & film management company, travel, writing.
Other lawyers: Svenja Geissmar - General Counsel MTVNE; Megan Davis - MTV Nordic / MTV European; Roger James - MTV UK / Seven Pack / VH1 / MTV2; Kathryn David - MTV Holland / MTV France / Broadcast Services / MTV Corporate Services; Giangiacomo Olivi - MTV Italy; Katharina Behrends - MTV Central; Nathalie Andre - MTV Production / Broadcast Standards; Neil Miller - MTVi Group / Ad Sales & Sponsorship.

N Brown Group PLC
53 Dale Street Manchester M60 6ES
Tel: (0161) 236 8256 **Fax:** (0161) 238 2308
Peter Tynan, Company Secretary

National Express Group PLC
75 Davies Street London W1K 5HT
Tel: (020) 7529 2000 **Fax:** (020) 7529 2146
Website: www.nationalexpressgroup.com/
No of lawyers in dept: 2
Work outsourced: 60% - Mergers and acquisitions, commercial, IT, IP.
Tony McDonald, Company Secretary & Group Legal Adviser
Specialisation: Corporate / commercial.
Career: University of Nottingham, 1979-82; *Slaughter and May*, 1983-88; The British Petroleum Company plc, 1988-95; Guardian Royal Exchange plc, 1995 - 2000.
Other lawyers: Tony McDonald - Company Secretary and Group Legal Adviser; Jenny Casson - Deputy Company Secretary; James Meldrum - Legal Adviser.

National Grid Group PLC
National Grid House Kirby Corner Road Coventry CV4 8JY
Tel: (024) 7653 7777 **Fax:** (024) 76423 620
Fiona Smith, Company Secretary

Nestor Healthcare Group PLC
The Colonnades Beaconsfield Close Hatfield AL10 8YD
Tel: (01707) 255635 **Fax:** (01707) 255633
No of lawyers in dept: 2
Emma Thomas, Company Secretary
Specialisation: Cambridge (Law); *Richards Butler* (qualified 1993); Company Secretary, Hazlewood Foods plc 1994-1996; Assistant Company Secretary, Kingfisher plc 1997-1998; Company Secretary, Nestor Healthcare Group plc 1998 -present.
Other lawyers: Corporate, IT, litigation, property.

News International PLC
1 Virginia Street Wapping London E1 9BD
Tel: (020) 7782 4000 **Fax:** (020) 7782 6836
Tom Crone, Head of Legal
Specialisation: Over all responsibility for Legal Affairs on News Internationals for national newspapers.
Career: Leeds University LL.B. Called to Bar 1975; 1975-1980 Practice Barrister; 1980-1985 Mirror Group, Legal Dept; 1985-present, News International plc.

Next Group PLC
Desford Road Enderby Leicester LE9 5AT
Tel: (0116) 286 6411 **Fax:** (0116) 284 8998
Email: peter_webber@next.co.uk
Website: www.next.co.uk
Work outsourced: 20% - Major corporate deals. Specialist litigation areas.
Peter Webber, Head of Legal Department & Company Secretary
Specialisation: Corporate, commercial, secretarial.
Career: Oundle School, Northants. Sheffield University. Head of Legal Dept - Next since 1987.
Other lawyers: Mrs C. Moody - Property Litigation, Employment and trade marks; Ms S Noble - Litigation, Consumer law, IP; M. Davis - Property; J. Tomlinson - Commercial Property.

NM Rothschild & Sons
82 King Street Manchester M2 4WQ
Tel: (0161) 827 3800 **Fax:** (0161) 839 7636
Alan Graham, Company Secretary

Nomura International PLC
Nomura House No 1 St Martins-le-Grand London EC1A 4NP
Tel: (020) 7521 2000 **Fax:** (020) 7521 2121
Website: www.nomura.co.uk
David Mee, General Counsel

Norsk Hydro (UK) Ltd
Bridge House 69 London Road Twickenham TW1 3RH
Tel: (020) 8255 6005 **Fax:** (020) 8892 6872
Email: peter.fergusson@hydro.com
Website: www.hydro.com
No of lawyers in dept: 40
Work outsourced: 50% - Competition, tax, major mergers and acquisitions, litigation, certain major contracts.
Peter Fergusson, Legal Department - UK
Specialisation: M&A, commercial, contract, employment, competition.
Career: BA (Hons) Durham University; Solicitor (England & Wales) 1968; Barrister - Solicitor (New Zealand) 1970; *Norton Rose* 1970-98 (partner 1974-98); Norsk Hydro Legal Department 1998-present.

Northern Foods PLC
Beverley House St Stephen's Square Hull HU1 3XG
Tel: (01482) 325432 **Fax:** (01482) 598355
Email: carol.williams@northern-foods.co.uk
Website: www.northern-foods.co.uk
No of lawyers in dept: 4
Work outsourced: 40% - Commercial conveyancing, corporate finance, litigation, intellectual property.
Carol Williams, Head of Legal
Specialisation: Employment, litigation, commercial.
Career: Qualified, 1985. 1985-87 *Booth & Co* (Leeds). 1987-90 Asda plc. 1990 to date Northern Foods.
Personal: 1998 to date: Chair North East Commerce and Industry Group.

Other lawyers: Jennifer Groves - commercial conveyancing. Andrew Lindley - company commercial. Mark Davis - employment.

Northern Rock PLC

Northern Rock House Gosforth NE3 4PL
Tel: (0191) 285 7191 **Fax:** (0191) 284 8470
Website: www.northernrock.co.uk
No of lawyers in dept: 5
Work outsourced: All mortgage possession, some treasury, commercial litigation and commercial conveyancing.
Christopher Jobe, Company Secretary
Other lawyers: Peter Millican - litigation and employment; Phil Broadhurst - consumer credit, conveyancing and general work; Gwilym Williams - commercial conveyancing and contracts, e-commerce; Colin Greener - conveyancing, consumer credit and general work.

Northern Rock House Gosforth NE3 4PL
Tel: (0191) 285 7191 **Fax:** (0191) 284 8470
Website: www.northernrock.co.uk
No of lawyers in dept: 5
Work outsourced: All mortgage possession, some treasury, commercial litigation and commercial conveyancing.
Colin Taylor, Director Compliance & Legal Services
Other lawyers: Peter Millican - litigation and employment; Phil Broadhurst - consumer credit, conveyancing and general work; Gwilym Williams - commercial conveyancing and contracts, e-commerce; Colin Greener - conveyancing, consumer credit and general work.

Novar plc

Novar House 24 Queens Road Weybridge KT13 9UX
Tel: (01932) 850850 **Fax:** (01932) 823365
Website: www.novar.com
No of lawyers in dept: 2
Anthony Holland, Group Legal Adviser
Other lawyers: Helen Leckey - Legal adviser.

NSB Retail Systems

2650 Kings Court, Birmingham Business Park, B37 7YE
Tel: (0121) 329 8000
Geoff R Bolt, Company Secretary

NXT PLC

37 Ixworth Place London SW3 3QH
Tel: (020) 7343 5050 **Fax:** (020) 7343 5055
Peter Thoms, Company Secretary & Finance Director

Nycomed Amersham PLC

Amersham Place Little Chalfont HP7 9NA
Tel: (01494) 544000 **Fax:** (01494) 542266
Email: robert.allnutt@uk.nycomed-amersham.com
Website: www.nycomed-amersham.com
No of lawyers in dept: 5
Work outsourced: 20% - Property, litigation, corporate acquisitions, employment.
Robert Allnutt, Group Legal Adviser & Company Secretary
Specialisation: Responsible for provision of legal advice on general commercial matters, intellectual property and product liability.
Career: Qualified 1979.
Other lawyers: Kevin Kissane, Tom Kilroy, Sheena Ginnings, Sara Lovick.

Ogilvy & Mather

10 Cabot Square Canary Wharf London E14 4QB
Tel: (020) 7345 3000 **Fax:** (020) 7345 6502
Website: www.ogilvy.com
Larissa Joy, Vice Chairman

Old Mutual plc

3rd Floor Lansdowne House 57 Berkeley Square London W1J 6ER
Tel: (020) 7569 0109 **Fax:** (020) 7569 0209
Email: martin.murray@omg.co.uk
Website: www.oldmutual.com
No of lawyers in dept: 1
Work outsourced: 75% - Corporate finance, property, employment.
Martin Murray, Company Secretary
Specialisation: Responsible for company / commercial matters at plc level and corporate governance.
Career: 1999 to date: Company Secretary, Old Mutual plc; 1997 - 1999: General Counsel and Secretary, The Energy Group plc; 1986 - 1997: Solicitor, Hanson plc. MA, LL.B. (Cantab) , LL.M. (Harvard). Admitted as a solicitor in 1979.

Open Interactive Limited

34-35 Farringdon Street London EC4A 4HL
Tel: (020) 7332 7000 **Fax:** (020) 7332 7100
Email: jonathan.kembery@open-talk.co.uk
No of lawyers in dept: 5
Work outsourced: Specialist areas: litigation, property, employment.
Jonathan A Kembery, Legal & Business Affairs Director
Specialisation: Provision of strategic commercial and regulatory advice to the business and management of all legal services whether provided internally or outsourced.
Career: Oxford University MA, Politics, Philosophy and Economics; Chester Law School. Since qualifying (1993) private practice experience with *Clifford Chance* and *Landwell*.
Personal: Married with two sons, lives in Battersea.
Other lawyers: Sophie Jackson, Emma Garside, Marijke Ried and Andrew Steed - All IT/Commercial law specialists with sector specific regulatory experience.

34-35 Farringdon Street London EC4A 4HL
Tel: (020) 7332 7000 **Fax:** (020) 7332 7100
Email: marijke.reid@open-talk.co.uk
Marijke Reid, Legal/Compliance Manager
Specialisation: Commercial IT/IP work, new media, content acquisition, interactive games, licence development agreements, regulatory work.
Career: BA and LL.B at University of Natal, South Africa. Admitted as attorney in South Africa in 1995. Re-qualified in UK in 1998 and joined British Interactive Broadcast (Holdings) Limited in December 1998 of which open is a subsidiary, moving across to open in May 1999.
Personal: Status: Married. Interests include: Scuba diving, skiing, cooking.

Orchestream Holdings PLC

Avon House Kensington Village Avonmore Road London W14 8TS
Tel: (020) 7348 1500 **Fax:** (020) 7348 1501
Email: aread@orchestream.com
Website: www.orchestream.com
Work outsourced: 40% - Corporate governance, IPK law.
Angela Read, General Counsel
Specialisation: Lead delivery of global legal services to international software companies: corporate, international, M&A, etc.
Career: Phillips Exeter Academy, Columbia University and the London School of Economics and Political Science, the Tulane School of Law, sitting for qualification to be UK Solicitor in December 2001.
Personal: Published in English and French, marathon runner and sailor, avid mountain biker, chess player and world traveller.
Other lawyers: Company/commercial, corporate transactional, international law, mergers and acquisitions.

Oxford Glycosciences PLC (OGS)

The Forum 86 Milton Park Abingdon OX14 4RY
Tel: (01235) 208000 **Fax:** (01235) 208011
Email: info@ogs.co.uk
Website: www.ogs.com
No of lawyers in dept: 1
Work outsourced: 25% - Corporate finance, employment, litigation.
John Ilett, Legal Director & Company Secretary
Specialisation: Responsible for management of The Legal and Company Secretarial function and the provision of legal advice at all levels of OGS, including, intellectual property (contentious and non-contentious); commercial/corporate; corporate finance; mergers and acquisitions; company secretarial.
Career: 2000 to date: Legal Director and Company Secretary, OGS; 1997 to 2000: General Counsel and Company Secretary, British Biotech; 1990 to 1997: Solicitor, *Stringer Saul*; Qualified as a Solicitor in 1992.

P & O Princess Cruises PLC

77 New Oxford Street London WC1A 1PP
Tel: (020) 7805 1200 **Fax:** (020) 7805 1240
Simon Pearce, Company Secretary

Pace Micro Technology PLC

Victoria Road Saltaire Shipley BD18 3LF
Tel: (01274) 532000 **Fax:** (01274) 537127
Website: www.pace.co.uk
No of lawyers in dept: 5
Work outsourced: 30% - Intellectual property, property, litigation.
Anthony Dixon, Director of Legal Services
Specialisation: Corporate/commercial, intellectual property, licensing of digitalmedia software.
Career: St. Peter's School, York; Emmanuel College, Cambridge (M.A. Law); Atricled *Ashurst Morris Crisp* 1986-88; (Corporate Finance) Solicitor 1988-1994; Group Commercial Solicitor - Yorkshire Water plc 1994-1997; Company Secretary / Director of Legal and member of Executive Commitee of Pace 1997 to date.
Personal: Married to Penelope, with two children (Flo and Harry, ages 8 and 6). Member of the Merchant Taylors in the City of York and Hawks Club. Committee member of North East Region of Law Society C&I Group. Member of the GCCA.
Other lawyers: Jane Connor - Legal Counsel; Sandy Bartlett - V.P. Legal and Corporate Affairs - Pace Americas; Jason Irvine-Geddis Legal Counsel; David Gellen - Corporate Counsel, Pace: Americas.

P

Paribas Principal Investments

10 Harewood Avenue London NW1 6AA
Tel: (020) 7595 2000 **Fax:** (020) 7595 5094/2555
Kevin Sowerbutts, Head of International Finance and Legal

Pathé Pictures Limited

Kent House Market Place London W1N 8AR
Tel: (020) 7323 5151 **Fax:** (020) 7462 4417
Email: cameron.mccracken@pathe-uk.com
Website: www.pathe.co.uk
Cameron McCracken, Deputy Managing Director
Specialisation: Film production, finance & distribution.
Career: Balliol College, Oxford.

Pearson Education Ltd

Edinburgh Gate Harlow CM20 2JE
Tel: (01279) 623623 **Fax:** (01279) 431060
Victoria Lockie, Head of Legal Services

Pearson PLC

3 Burlington Gardens London W1S 3EP
Tel: (020) 7411 2000 **Fax:** (020) 7411 2390
Website: www.pearson.com
No of lawyers in dept: 1
Gary Rinck, General Counsel
Specialisation: IP, mergers and aquisitions, substantial litigation.
Other lawyers: Financial Times Group: Sarah Robinson (Company Secretary). Recoletos: Javier Albacar. Pearson Education: Bob Dancy (US) and Vicky Lockie (International). Penguin Putnam Inc. : Alex Gigante (US) and Cecily Engle (Europe). Pearson Television: Sarah Tingay. Paul-Louis Cordier (Les EcLos).

Pearson Television International 1 Stephen Street London W1P 1PJ
Tel: (020) 7691 6000 **Fax:** (020) 7691 6100
Sarah Tingay, Director of Legal & Business Affairs, Pearson Television Ltd

Peninsular & Oriental Steam Navigation Co

79 Pall Mall London SW1Y 5EJ
Tel: (020) 7321 4515 **Fax:** (020) 7930 6042
Email: mlilisons.legal@p-and-o.com
Website: www.p-and-o.com
No of lawyers in dept: 3
Work outsourced: Major corporate and banking.
Michael Gradon, Executive Director, Commercial & Legal Affairs also Company Secretary
Specialisation: Deals with acquisitions, disposals, joint ventures, financing and other major group matters.
Career: Qualified in 1983. With *Slaughter and May* 1981-

86. Became P&O Group Legal Director in 1991 and Company Secretary in 1996. Appointed Board Director in 1998, Appointed Director, Commercial & Legal Affairs in 2001.
Personal: Educated at Haileybury 1972-76 and Downing College, Cambridge 1977-80. Leisure interests include tennis and golf. Born 7th April 1959. Lives in Oxted, Surrey.
Other lawyers: Mark Wandless; Iain Simm.

Pennon Group PLC
Peninsula House Rydon Lane Exeter EX2 7HR
Tel: (01392) 443150 **Fax:** (01392) 443939
Email: kwoodier@pennon-group.co.uk
Website: www.pennon-group.co.uk
No of lawyers in dept: 9
Work outsourced: 10% - Specialist banking and major litigation.
Kenneth D Woodier, Group Company Secretary & Solicitor
Specialisation: Company/commercial, litigation, competition, property, contract/procurement, environmental and employment.
Career: Management (business) prior to qualifying as a solicitor. Articles with Severn Trent Water. Legal Adviser with Investors in Industry plc (3i). Group legal manager with HP Bulmer Holdings plc and Group Legal Adviser with South West Water PLC. 16 years in legal practice.
Other lawyers: Andrew Matthews, John Jelley, Alan Roberts, Alan Podger, Dr Buckingham, Simon Pugsley, James Hyde, Richard Abbot.

P

Persimmon PLC
Persimmon House Fulford York YO19 4FE
Tel: (01904) 642199 **Fax:** (01904) 610014
Website: www.persimmon.plc.co.uk
No of lawyers in dept: 19
Work outsourced: 40% - Corporate, property, litigation.
Neil Francis, Legal Director
Specialisation: Residential housing land development, planning, employment.
Career: Kingston G.S.; College of Law; Partner *Fennemores* Milton Keynes 1983-95.
Personal: Interests: Cricket, hockey, golf, football, skiing.
Other lawyers: N.P. Knight, G.K.E. Hale, J.Baird, P. Bowen, C. Bayerstone, S. McGuinness, C. Cantoni, Ms J. Dempster.

Photo-Me International PLC
Church Road Bookham Leatherhead KT23 3EU
Tel: (01372) 453399 **Fax:** (01372) 459064
Robert Lowes, Company Secretary

Pilkington PLC
Prescot Road St Helens WA10 3TT
Tel: (01744) 28882 **Fax:** (01744) 692660
Website: www.pilkington.com
No of lawyers in dept: 5
Work outsourced: 50% - Major litigation, international, large scale acquisitions and divestments, specialist counsel advice.
Clyde M Leff, Group Legal Adviser / General Counsel
Specialisation: Principal areas of work are antitrust/competition law, acquisitions and disposals, major litigation, senior level service contracts and related matters, and corporate compliance programmes. The majority of work involves international aspects and the necessary management of external legal resources in a number of jurisdictions.
Career: Graduated Law School 1980, University of Chicago, J.D. Numerous U.S. positions, both in private practice (*Mayer, Brown and Platt; Reuben and Proctor*) and Corporate Legal Departments (Ameritech; Owens Corning). Officer level position at Owens Corning before joining Pilkington plc as Group Legal Adviser/General Counsel in 2000.
Personal: Married, two children.
Other lawyers: Miss J. P. Halligan, C. M. Leff, C.R. Bayley, I.J. McKillup, G.M. Chadwick. Specialism: Manages the provision of legal advice to an international Group (80% of turnover overseas).

Pillar Property PLC
Lansdowne House Berkeley Square London W1X 6HQ
Tel: (020) 7915 8000 **Fax:** (020) 7915 8001
Philip Martin, Company Secretary

PizzaExpress PLC
7 McKay Trading Estate Kensal Road London W10 5BN
Tel: (020) 8960 8238 **Fax:** (020) 8969 6913
Patrick Hartrey, Company Secretary

Polydor Ltd
72-80 Black Lion Lane Hammersmith London W6 9BE
Tel: (020) 8910 4844 **Fax:** (020) 8910 4794
No of lawyers in dept: 1
Work outsourced: 10% - Litigation, commercial.
Paul Jones, Director of Legal & Business Affairs

Powderject Pharmaceuticals
Florey House Robert Robinson Avenue Oxford Science Park Oxford OX4 4GA
Tel: (01865) 332600 **Fax:** (01865) 332601
Email: charles_swingland@powderject.com
Website: www.powderject.com
No of lawyers in dept: 4
Work outsourced: 50% - Various.
Charles Swingland, General Counsel & Company Secretary
Other lawyers: Charles Swingland - Head of department; Tom McCracken - Patents; Nicholas Wenban-Smith - Commercial; Zoe Evams - Company / Commercial.

PowerGen PLC
53 New Broad Street London EC2M 1SL
Tel: (020) 7826 2826 **Fax:** (020) 7826 2890
William Gubbins, Head of Legal

Premier Farnell PLC
Armley Road Leeds LS12 2QQ
Tel: (08701) 298608 **Fax:** (08701) 298610
Email: information@premierfarnell.com
Website: www.premierfarnell.com
No of lawyers in dept: 4
Work outsourced: 30% - Broad spectrum, share schemes, employment litigation, major corporate.
Steven Webb, General Counsel/Company Secretary
Specialisation: Corporate/commercial.
Career: King's College, London LLB (Hons); *Norton Rose* 1987-1990; *Walker Morris* 1990-1994; Kalon Group plc 1994-1997, Company Secretary; Kelda Group plc 1997-2000, Company Secretary and General Counsel.

Provident Financial PLC
Colonnade Sunbridge Road Bradford BD1 2LQ
Tel: (01274) 731111 **Fax:** (01274) 727300
Email: david.rees@provident.co.uk
Website: www.providentfinancial.co.uk
No of lawyers in dept: 2
David Rees, Group Legal Advisor
Other lawyers: Rebecca Price, Solicitor.

Prudential PLC
Laurence Pountney Hill London EC4R 0HH
Tel: (020) 7548 3737 **Fax:** (020) 7548 3191
Email: peter.maynard@prudential.co.uk
Website: www.prudential.co.uk
No of lawyers in dept: 4
Work outsourced: 90% - Property, employment, venture capital, corporate financing.
Peter Maynard, Company Secretary & Group Legal Services Director
Specialisation: Heads a small team of commercial lawyers providing legal services to the Corporation and its subsidiaries.
Career: 1971-74 University of Cambridge. 1975-82 *Slaughter and May* . 1982-84 *Clifford-Turner* . 1984-98 Hong Kong Bank Group. (1984-92 Legal Adviser Europe, 1992 Compliance Director, James Capel, 1993-95 President & CEO, James Capel Inc, New York, 1996-98 Deputy Group Legal Adviser, HSBC Group). 1998 Director, Group Legal Services, Prudential Corporation plc.
Other lawyers: D. Higgins: company/commercial.

Railtrack Group PLC
Railtrack House Euston Square London NW1 2EE
Tel: (020) 7557 8000 **Fax:** (020) 7557 9000
Website: www.railtrack.co.uk
Work outsourced: 90% - Corporate, commercial, litigation, conveyancing, EC competition, banking, environmental, construction, employment.
Simon K Osborne, Group Secretary & General Counsel
Specialisation: Company secretarial, corporate governance, corporate and general advisory.
Career: LLB (Lond) 1970; Solicitor June 1973; articled *Goodman Derrick* 1971-73; Solicitor to British Railways Board 1986-93; Company Secretary and Solicitor Railtrack PLC 1993 to present.
Personal: Member of NAPF Committee of Inquiry into UK Vote Execution. Member of Law Society Audit Committee. Member of Railway Heritage Committee. Member of British Transport Police Committee.
Other lawyers: Commercial: Nigel Dewick, Kevin Lynch, Andrew James, Claire Williams; Litigation: Andrew Litherland, Richard Smith, Helen Potton, Alefabi Eubai, Gillian L Johnston (Scotland); Property/Projects: Geoffrey Kitchener, Alison Parkinson, Iain Brown, Brian Spanswick, Anne Galewski, Asheesh Mehta-Hughes, Roberto Mingrino.

The Random House Group Ltd
20 Vauxhall Bridge Road London SW1V 2SA
Tel: (020) 7840 8636 **Fax:** (020) 7840 8830
Website: www.randomhouse.co.uk
No of lawyers in dept: 2
Work outsourced: Varies - Libel reading, litigation.
Roger Field, Group Legal Director
Specialisation: All areas of publishing and commercial law.
Career: Downside School. Bristol University. The Army 1974-83. Qualified 1987. Articles *Farrer & Co, Clyde & Co;* The Daily Telegraph; TV am; Reed Publishing Europe (IPC Magazines, Reed Business Publishing, Reed Regional Newspapers). 1992-1999. 1999 - date, The Random House Group.
Personal: Fly fishing, skiing, sailing, reading, writing.
Other lawyers: Pre publication and post publication work, intellectual property, commercial.

Rank Group PLC
6 Connaught Place London W2 2EZ
Tel: (020) 7706 1111 **Fax:** (020) 7262 9886
Charles Cormick, Company Secretary

Reckitt & Benckiser PLC
67 Alma Road Windsor SL4 3HD
Tel: (01753) 835 835 **Fax:** (01753) 835 830
Jonathan Jones, Senior Vice President, Global Legal Affairs / Company Secretary
67 Alma Road Windsor SL4 3HD
Tel: (01753) 835 835 **Fax:** (01753) 835 830
Sheila Henderson, Trade Marks Director

Reed Elsevier PLC
25 Victoria Street London SW1H 0EX
Tel: (020) 7222 8420 **Fax:** (020) 7227 5799
Anne Joseph, Legal Director

Regus PLC
Chertsey Hillswood Business Park 3000 Hillswood Drive Churtsey KT16 0RS
Tel: (01932) 895000 **Fax:** (01932) 895001
Email: tim.regan@regus.com
Website: www.regus.com
No of lawyers in dept: 3
Work outsourced: 95% - All except customer contracts.
Tim Regan, Legal & Commercial Director
Specialisation: Corporate finance, franchising, key processes, selection and audit of law firms.
Career: 1989-1995 *Ashurst Morris Crisp;* article clerk, solicitor. 1995-1999 ICL plc; Commercial Director, ICL Services. 1999 to date Regus plc. London School of Economics 1985-1988; LLB London College of Law 1988-1989.
Other lawyers: Alex Holland: litigation, treasury, TMT; Margaret Lawrence: All North American Matters.

Renishaw PLC
New Mills Wotton-under-Edge GL12 8JR
Tel: (01453) 524524 **Fax:** (01453) 524001
Allen CG Roberts, Finance Director & Company Secretary

Rentokil Initial PLC
Felcourt East Grinstead RH19 2JY
Tel: (01342) 833022 **Fax:** (01342) 835672
Email: rward-jones@rentokil-initial.co.uk
Website: www.rentokil-initial.com
No of lawyers in dept: 4
Robert Ward-Jones, Company Secretary & Legal Director

Reuters Group PLC
Corporate Headquarters 85 Fleet Street London EC4P 4AJ
Tel: (020) 7250 1122 **Fax:** (020) 7353 3002
Clare Chapman, Area General Counsel - London

Rexam PLC
4 Millbank London SW1P 3XR
Tel: (020) 7227 4100 **Fax:** (020) 7227 4109
Email: david.gibson@rexam.com
Website: www.rexam.co.uk
No of lawyers in dept: 2
Work outsourced: 50% - Large M&A transactions, litigation, conveyancing.
David William Gibson, Company Secretary & Director of Legal Affairs
Specialisation: Company and commercial, company secretarial, intellectual property, insurance, property and Head Office personnel.
Career: Qualified as a Solicitor in 1987. Assistant Solicitor with *Alsop Wilkinson 1987-1989.* Company Solicitor with Rexam PLC (formerly Bowater plc) 1989-1995. Member of the Law Society.

Richemont International Limited
15 Hill Street London W1J 5QT
Tel: (020) 7499 2539 **Fax:** (020) 7493 1018
Email: fred@mr-trademarks.com
Frederick Mostert, Intellectual Property Counsel

Rio Tinto PLC
6 St James's Square London SW1Y 4LD
Tel: (020) 7753 2345 **Fax:** (020) 7753 2197
Email: Charles.Lawton@riotinto.com
Website: www.riotinto.com
No of lawyers in dept: 5
Work outsourced: 15% - Litigation, property, public issues.
Charles HH Lawton, Legal Adviser
Specialisation: Mergers and acquisitions, competition.
Career: Westminster School; Articled Clark then Solicitor, *Slaughter & May*, 1965-1972; *Lovell White Durrant*, 1972; Rio Tinto, 1972- Present.
Other lawyers: M&A, competition, litigation.

RIT Capital Partners PLC
27 St James's Place London SW1A 1NR
Tel: (020) 7493 8111 **Fax:** (020) 7493 5765
Duncan Budge, Chief Operating Officer

RM PLC
New Mill House 183 Milton Park Abingdon OX14 4SE
Tel: (01235) 826000 **Fax:** (01235) 826999
Email: arobson@rm.com
Website: www.rm.com
No of lawyers in dept: 2
Work outsourced: 10% - Litigation and trade marks.
Andrew J Robson, General Counsel & Company Secretary
Specialisation: ICT, Corporate Finance, Internet, PFI.
Career: University of Nottingham. Bar school. PHH. Allied Dunbar. British Aerospace.
Other lawyers: Andy Robson: PFI, Corporate and Finance. Jayne Aspell: Acquisitions and IT.

RMC Group PLC
RMC House Coldharbour Lane Thorpe Egham TW20 8TD
Tel: (01932) 568833 **Fax:** (01932) 568933
Email: michaelcollins@rmc-readymix.co.uk
Website: www.rmc-group.com
No of lawyers in dept: 6
Work outsourced: Work outside specialisms of Department and high volume work.
Michael Collins, Head of UK Legal Department
Specialisation: Conducting advisory and transactional work over a broad spectrum.
Career: LL.B (Birmingham University), Solicitor, Prior to RMC, extensive County Council experience.
Personal: Married.
Other lawyers: Property: Stephen Bottle, Andrew Smith, Martin Hicks; Litigation: Jason Smailey; Environmental / Planning: Stephen Gardiner.

Rolls-Royce PLC
65 Buckingham Gate London SW1E 6AT
Tel: (020) 7222 9020 **Fax:** (020) 7227 9170
Brian Baker, General Counsel

Rothschild Asset Management Limited
Five Arrow House St Swithin's Lane London EC4P 4DU
Tel: (020) 7280 5000 **Fax:** (020) 7634 2814
Elizabeth Horner, In-house Lawyer

Royal & Sun Alliance Insurance Group PLC
67 King Street Manchester M60 8AJ
Tel: (0161) 832 2455 **Fax:** (0161) 828 1925
Ian Guttridge, In-house Lawyer/Head of Legal
Leadenhall Court 1 Leadenhall Street London EC3V 1PP
Tel: (020) 7337 5141/7283 9000 **Fax:** (020) 7337 5133
Humphrey Tomlinson, Legal Director

Royal Bank of Canada
71 Queen Victoria Street London EC4V 4DE
Tel: (020) 7489 1188 **Fax:** (020) 7329 6138
Email: Michael.Neylan@RBCDS.com
Website: www.royalbank.com
No of lawyers in dept: 3
Work outsourced: 30% - Litigation, mergers and acquisitions, structured finance.
Michael Neylan, Group Counsel, Europe
Specialisation: Responsible for all aspects of the activities of the London Law Department of the Royal Bank of Canada and RBC Dominion Securities.
Career: 1984-1988: University of Western Ontario, Canada, B.A. Economics; 1989-1992: Queen's University, Canada LL.B.; 1994: Admitted to Law Society of Upper Canada; 1999: Admitted to Role of Solicitors for England and Wales; 1994-1998: Fraser Beatty, Toronto, Canada, Corporate Litigation; 1998-2000: *Clifford Chance*, London; 2000 - Royal Bank of Canada, London, Group Counsel, Europe.
Other lawyers: Inder Mangat - Global Banking; Gill Driscoll - Specialised Finance.

Royal Bank of Scotland Group PLC
42 St Andrew Square PO Box 31 Edinburgh EH2 2YE
Tel: (0131) 556 8555 **Fax:** (0131) 557 6565
Derek Arnott, Head of Group Legal Services

Rugby Football Union (RFU)
Rugby House 21 Rugby Road Twickenham TW1 1DS
Tel: (020) 8892 2000 **Fax:** (020) 8892 9816
Jonathan Hall, Secretary and Legal Officer
Specialisation: All legal matters associated with sports governing body including: sponsorship, joint ventures, constitutional, general contract and commercial, intellectual property rights.
Career: Haileybury College, St. John's College, Cambridge. Articles ar *Baker and McKenzie*, London; Associate at *Baker and McKenzie*, London; International Management Group - in house lawyer 1995-1999.
Personal: Lives Farnham, Surrey. Married with 2 young children. Born 1968. Regular cricketer.

Safeway Stores PLC
6 Millington Road Hayes UB3 4AY
Tel: (020) 8848 8744 **Fax:** (020) 8756 1069
Gerald Ellis, Deputy Company Secretary/Head of Legal

Sage Group PLC
Sage House Benton Park Road Newcastle upon Tyne NE7 7LZ
Tel: (0191) 255 3000 **Fax:** (0191) 255 0306
Website: www.sage.com
No of lawyers in dept: 8
Work outsourced: 60% - Acquisitions, major litigation.
Nick Cooper, Head of Legal & Group Secretary

Sakura Finance International Limited
8th Floor Temple Court 11 Queen Victoria Street London EC4N 4TA
Tel: (020) 7842 3040 **Fax:** (020) 7842 3185
No of lawyers in dept: 2
Work outsourced: 20% - Capital markets.
Leonard Lizmore, General Manager & Head of Legal
Specialisation: Capital markets, banking, securitisations, derivatives, corporate legal.
Career: Head of Legal at Sakura Finance International since 1998. Previous employments: Nomura; Bank of America; CIBC / Wood Gundy. University of London, LLM (College: London School of Economics & Political Science); University of Windsor, Canada LLB.

Sanwa International plc
City Place House 55 Basinghall Street PO Box 245 London EC2V 5DL
Tel: (020) 7330 5000 **Fax:** (020) 7330 5555
Website: www.sanwaint.com
No of lawyers in dept: 3
Work outsourced: 20% - Documentation for bond and equity issues and securitisations.
Mark Seabrooke, Legal Counsel, Senior Vice President, Head of Legal.
Specialisation: Banking and debt capital markets, derivatives, corporate finance, custody, structured products, corporate and commercial.
Career: 1984-86 Articles, *Stephenson Harwood.* 1986-88 JP Morgan Securites Ltd. 1988 to present, Sanwa International plc. Leeds University (1981 LLB). Magdalene College, Cambridge University (1984 LLM).
Other lawyers: Sorrel Coni V.P., Lourdes Villar Garcia V.P., Pamela SenGupta: banking, debt capital markets, derivatives, corporate finance, custody, structured products, company/commercial.

Schroders PLC
31 Gresham Street London EC2V 7QA
Tel: (020) 7658 6000 **Fax:** (020) 7382 6965
Francis W Neate, Group Legal Director

Scipher PLC
Dawley Road Hayes UB3 1HH
Tel: (020) 8848 6555 **Fax:** (020) 8848 6677
James Ellis-Rees, Head of Legal

Scottish & Newcastle PLC
33 Ellersly Road Edinburgh EH12 6HX
Tel: (0131) 528 2110 **Fax:** (0131) 528 2311
Email: andrew.vellani@scottish-newcastle.co.uk
Website: www.scottish-newcastle.com
No of lawyers in dept: 3
H. Andrew S Vellani, Group Legal Director
Specialisation: The Group Legal Director is responsible for the provision of legal services to the Scottish & Newcastle plc group of companies. Work includes company/commercial, EEC and domestic competition law. International joint ventures; intellectual property; acquisitions and disposals; beer supply agreements; brewing, packaging and distribution agreements; trading law (including food labelling, advertising and promotion).
Career: Kings College, Cardiff; Staffordshire University (LLB Hons); the Inns of Court School of Law, London; called to the Bar (Middle Temple) 1981. Admitted as solicitor 1991. Assistant commercial and legal adviser - Heating and

Ventilating Contractors Association 1982; Assistant Group Secretary/Group Legal Adviser - The Kenneth Wilson Group 1984; Group Legal Adviser - Scottish & Newcastle plc 1986. Other positions held include: Company Secretary and Member of the Board Executive Committee: Scottish Courage Ltd 1986. Secretary: The Fosters European Partnership (an Anglo Australian Joint Venture).
Personal: Born 1957, resides in Edinburgh. Interests include overseas travel, music and reading.

Scottish & Southern Energy PLC
200 Dunkeld Road Perth PH1 3AQ
Tel: (01738) 456000 **Fax:** (01738) 456520
Email: vincent.donelly@scottish-southern.co.uk
Website: www.scottish-southern.co.uk
No of lawyers in dept: 6
Work outsourced: 25% - Litigation, major projects, acquisitions, employment law, competition law.
Vincent Donnelly, Company Secretary
Specialisation: Legal, insurance, company secretarial, property.
Career: LLB-Glasgow University 1976. ACIS-1982. Cranfield Business School-Senior/ Management Programme-1996. FCIS 1999.
Personal: Married, 3 children. Resides Edinburgh.
Other lawyers: Company secretarial, corporate, insurance, property.

S

200 Dunkeld Road Perth PH1 3AQ
Tel: (01738) 456000 **Fax:** (01738) 456520
Email: ian.manson@scottish-southern.co.uk
Website: www.scottish-southern.co.uk
No of lawyers in dept: 6
Work outsourced: 25% - Litigation, major projects, acquisitions, employment law, competition law.
Ian Manson, Director of Legal Services
Specialisation: All legal areas including commercial, litigation, property and projects.
Career: LL.B - 1979.
Personal: Married, 3 children, resides Dundee.
Other lawyers: Company secretarial, corporate, insurance, property.

Scottish Football Association
Hampden Park Glasgow G42 9AY
Tel: (0141) 616 6000 **Fax:** (0141) 616 6001
Email: legal@scottishfa.co.uk
Website: www.scottishfa.co.uk
No of lawyers in dept: 1
Heather-Anne Barton, Head of Legal & Special Projects
Specialisation: Legal Adviser to F.A. and subsidiary associated companies. Company/commercial; company secretarial; intellectual property; admin law; sports law.
Career: LLB Graduate - Dundee University. 1991-1994 - Specialist Litigation, Fist Natinal Bank plc; 1994-1997 - Solicitor, Scottish Media Group plc; 1998-1999 - Company Secretary, Celtic plc; 2000 to date - Scottish F.A.

Scottish Investment Trust PLC
6 Albyn Place Edinburgh EH2 4NL
Tel: (0131) 225 7781 **Fax:** (0131) 226 3663
Iain M Harding, Company Secretary

Scottish Power PLC
1 Atlantic Quay Glasgow G2 8SP
Tel: (0141) 248 8200 **Fax:** (0141) 248 8300
James Stanley, Legal Director

Scottish Radio Holdings PLC
Clydebank Business Park Clydebank Glasgow G81 2RX
Tel: (0141) 565 2200 **Fax:** (0141) 565 2322
Jane Tames, Company Secretary

Securicor PLC
Sutton Park House 15 Carshalton Road Sutton SM1 4LD
Tel: (020) 8770 7000 **Fax:** (020) 8770 1145
Email: nigel.griffiths@plc.securicor.com
Website: www.securicor.co.uk
No of lawyers in dept: 4
Work outsourced: 15% - Litigation, property, major corporate mergers and acquisitions.
Nigel E Griffiths, Group Legal Director & Company Secretary
Specialisation: Contract, insurance, employment, commercial, international, mergers and acquisitons.
Career: Educated at Whitgift School and Liverpool University - LLB (Hons) 1968. Qualified as a solicitor in 1971. Securicor since 1973.
Other lawyers: Peter David: company and commercial; Stephen Lyell: commercial and international; Roger Whetnall: employment; Amanda Wolfe: employment.

Selfridges PLC
400 Oxford Street London W1A 1AB
Tel: (020) 7318 3018 **Fax:** (020) 7491 0569
Email: alan.camplin-smith@selfridges.co.uk
Website: www.selfridges.co.uk
No of lawyers in dept: 0
Work outsourced: 75-80% - Company/commercial.
Alan Camplin-Smith, Company Secretary

Serco Group PLC
Palm Court 4 Heron Square Richmond-upon-Thames TW9 1EW
Tel: (020) 8334 4335 **Fax:** (020) 8334 4320
Julia Cabanagh, Company Secretary

Severn Trent Water Ltd
2297 Coventry Road Birmingham B26 3PU
Tel: (0121) 722 4000 **Fax:** (0121) 722 4228
Email: michael.knight@severntrent.co.uk
Website: www.severn-trent.com
No of lawyers in dept: 4
Work outsourced: 10% - M&A, some conveyancing, litigation.
Michael R Knight, Company Solicitor

Shaftesbury PLC
Pegasus House 37-43 Sackville Street London W1S 3DL
Tel: (020) 7333 8118 **Fax:** (020) 7333 0660
Email: shaftesbury@shaftesbury.co.uk
Website: www.shaftesbury.co.uk
No of lawyers in dept: 0
Work outsourced: 100% - Corporate, property and general matters.
Brian Bickell, Finance Director & Company Secretary
Specialisation: Finance and accounting.
Career: Chartered Accountant (FCA).

Shire Pharmaceuticals Group PLC
Hampshire International Business Park Chineham Basingstoke RG24 8EP
Tel: (01256) 894000 **Fax:** (01256) 894708
Tatjana May, General Counsel & Company Secretary

Signet Group PLC
Hunters Road Hockley Birmingham B19 1DS
Tel: 0870 909 0301 **Fax:** (0121) 697 7915
Noel Lyons, Head of Legal

Singer & Friedlander Group PLC
21 New Street Bishopsgate London EC2M 4HR
Tel: (020) 7623 3000 **Fax:** (020) 7623 2122
Stephen P Doherty, Company Secretary

Sir Robert McAlpine (Holdings) Ltd
Eaton Court Maylands Avenue Hemel Hempstead HP2 7TR
Tel: (01422) 412897 **Fax:** (01422) 248393
Email: p.brinley-codd@sir-robert-mcalpine.com
Website: www.sir-robert-mcalpine.com
Peter Brinley-Codd, Solicitor & Legal Services Manager

Six Continents plc
20 North Audley Street London W1K 6WN
Tel: (020) 7409 1919 **Fax:** (020) 7409 8526
Email: enquiries@sixcontinents.com
Website: www.sixcontinents.com
No of lawyers in dept: 4
Work outsourced: 90% - Commercial, litigation, property.
Christopher Vaughan, Head of Group Legal
Specialisation: General company and commercial matters, with a particular specialisation in M&A transactions. General commercial agreements, joint ventures, employment, IP, anti-trust and management of litigation. Member of CBI Competition Law Panel.
Career: Qualified 1991 with *Freshfields* . Corporate assistant with *Freshfields* until 1994, when moved to *Cameron McKenna* . Joined Bass PLC (now Six Continents PLC) in 1995. Education: Leicester University (LLB Law with French), College of Law (Chester).
Personal: Born 1964. Married with three children. Interests include golf, tennis and skiing.

Skanska Construction Group Ltd
Maple Cross House Denham Way Maples Cross Rickmansworth WD3 9AS
Tel: (01923) 423966 **Fax:** (01923) 423864
Email: martin.Lenihan@skanska.co.uk
Website: www.skanska.co.uk
Martin Lenihan, Legal Adviser
Specialisation: PFI (Private Finance Initiative), major projects, international contracts.
Personal: Manchester United, cycling, good food/wine.

Maple Cross House Denham Way Maples Cross Rickmansworth WD3 9AS
Tel: (01923) 423852 **Fax:** (01923) 423864
Email: hilary.wilson@skanska.co.uk
Website: www.skanska.co.uk
Hilary Wilson, Legal Adviser
Specialisation: Major projects in the UK and overseas. Civil engineering and construction, commercial, PFI. Adviser to civil and engineering and construction companies within the Skanska Construction Group.
Career: Howell's School, Denbigh. Newnham College, Cambridge. Called to bar Gray's Inn 1974. In-house adviser since 1977.

SkyePharma PLC
105 Piccadilly London W1V 9FN
Tel: (020) 7491 1777 **Fax:** (020) 7491 3338
Website: www.skyepharma.com
No of lawyers in dept: 1
Work outsourced: 10-15% - Litigation, corporate mergers and acquisitions.
Suzanne McLean, General Counsel & Company Secretary
Specialisation: Commercial: International licensing, intellectual property.
Career: BA (Hons) Business Law: Guildhall University, 1978; Barrister, Gray's Inn, 1979.

Slough Estates PLC
Slough Estates House 234 Bath Road Slough SL1 4EE
Tel: (01753) 537171 **Fax:** (01753) 820585
Robert G May, Legal Supervisor

SMG PLC
200 Renfield Street Glasgow G2 3PR
Tel: (0141) 300 3300 **Fax:** (0141) 300 3030
Dawn Davidson, Company Secretary

Smith & Nephew PLC
Heron House 15 Adam Street London WC2N 6LA
Tel: (020) 7401 7646 **Fax:** (020) 7930 3353
Email: michael.parson@smith-nephew.com
Website: www.smith-nephew.com
Work outsourced: 100% - Various.
Michael G Parson, Group Company Secretary & Legal Adviser
Career: Qualified in 1965. Legal Department, Cunard/Trafalgar House plc 1970-75. Group Legal Director, Mass Transit Corporation, Hong Kong 1975-85. Group Secretary and Legal Adviser, Bowater plc 1987-91. Has held present position since March 1991.
Personal: Educated at Durham University (LLB) 1958-61. Born 24 October 1940.

Smiths Group PLC
765 Finchley Road Childs Hill London NW11 8DS
Tel: (020) 8458 3232 **Fax:** (020) 8458 4380
David P Lillycrop, General Counsel & Group Company Secretary

Société Générale
SG House 41 Tower Hill London EC3N 4SG
Tel: (020) 7676 6000 **Fax:** (020) 7676 8888
Website: www.socgen.com
No of lawyers in dept: 4
Mark Nimmo, Executive Director and Group Leader

Somerfield plc
Somerfield House Whitchurch Lane Whitchurch Bristol BS14 0TJ
Tel: (0117) 935 7610 **Fax:** (0117) 935 6455
Email: susy.jepson@somerfield.co.uk
Website: www.somerfield.co.uk
No of lawyers in dept: 4
Work outsourced: 75% - Health and safety, property, commercial, corporate, litigation.
Susy Jepson, Head of Group Legal
Specialisation: Company commercial; including IT/IP and advertising and promotional law.
Personal: MA (Cantab).
Other lawyers: Company commercial, employment, property, trading standards, IP/IT, liquor licensing, litigation.

Sony Music Entertainment (UK) Ltd
13 Great Marlborough Street London W1F 7LP
Tel: (020) 7911 8200 **Fax:** (020) 7911 8600
Alastair George, Head of Legal
13 Great Marlborough Street London W1F 7LP
Tel: (020) 7911 8200 **Fax:** (020) 7911 8600
Rakesh Sanghvi, General Manager

South African Breweries PLC
One Stanhope Gate London W1K 1AF
Tel: (020) 7659 0100 **Fax:** (020) 7659 0111
Email: atonkinson@sab.co.za
Website: www.sabplc.com
No of lawyers in dept: 4
Work outsourced: 40% - Conveyancing, registration, opinions, litigation.
Andrew OC Tonkinson, Group Company Secretary
Specialisation: Company Secretarial, remuneration, benefits, corporate law, commercial law, intellectual property law, taxation.
Career: BA (Law and Economics) University of Natal, South Africa - 1996; B. Juris, University of South Africa - 1970 Trust Manager - Syfrets Trust Ltd. - 1968-1975; Company Secretary and Administration Director - The Lion Match Company Ltd. - 1975-1991; Group Company Secretary, South African Breweries, 1991-Present.
Personal: Lecturer part-time in company/commercial and banking law, Natal Technicon, 1970-1973.
Other lawyers: A.O.C. Tonkinson - Company/commercial, corporate finance; J. Romein - Company intellectual property; Ms J. Taylor - General commercial.

Spectris plc
Station Road Egham TW20 9NP
Tel: (01784) 470470 **Fax:** (01784) 470848
Email: headoffice@spectris.com
Website: www.spectris.com
No of lawyers in dept: 1
Work outsourced: 95% - Acquisitions, disposals, litigation, property, employment, pensions.
Roger Stephens, Company Secretary

Spirent PLC
Spirent House Crawley Business Quarter Fleming Way Crawley RH10 9QL
Tel: (01293) 767676 **Fax:** (01293) 767677
Michael Arnaouti, Group Company Secretary

Sportsworld Media Group PLC
6 Henrietta Street Covent Garden London WC2E 8PS
Tel: (020) 7240 9626 **Fax:** (020) 7557 4238
Website: www.sportsworld.co.uk
No of lawyers in dept: 2
Work outsourced: Corporate -100%, litigation - 100%, media, sport, commercial - 15%.
Tim Perry, General Counsel
Specialisation: Sports and media and general commercial. Preliminary litigation work, corporate acquisition/disposal management.
Career: Cambridge University (Jesus College), History. CPE and Law Society Finals, articles and two years PQE at *Simmons & Simmons* then to *Pinsent Curtis*, then *Denton Wilde Sapte*.
Personal: Active sportsman.
Other lawyers: Polly Edwards - Assistant Counsel.

SSL International PLC
Toft Hall Toft Knutsford WA16 9PD
Tel: (01565) 624040 **Fax:** (01565) 624172
Email: Jonathan.Jowett@ssl-International.com
Website: www.ssl-international.com
No of lawyers in dept: 5
Work outsourced: 70% - All.
Jonathan D Jowett, Group Secretary & Legal Director
Specialisation: The provision of legal and administration services to the UK-listed parent company and its subsidiaries. Main legal focus in M&A and general commercial.
Career: LL.B. Business Law 1985; Solicitor 1989; LL.M. European Union Law 1999.

St James's Place Capital PLC
J Rothschild House Dollar Street Cirencester GL7 2AQ
Tel: (01285) 640302 **Fax:** (01285) 653993
Email: hugh.gladman@sjp.co.uk
Website: www.sjpc.co.uk
No of lawyers in dept: 4
Work outsourced: 15-20% - Property, litigation, debt collection, major transactions.
Hugh J Gladman, Legal & Compliance Director
Specialisation: Director in charge of the legal and compliance departments and, in addition, handling the following areas: corporate finance work, large commercial agreements, major litigation, share schemes.
Career: LLB Southampton University. 1986-93 *Herbert Smith* (including articles). 1993-94 *Hammond Suddards* . 1994 Head of Legal Department - J.Rothschild Assurance. 1997 - Legal and Compliance Director for the St James's Place Group.
Personal: Hobbies include tennis, hockey and other sports, film, theatre and family.
Other lawyers: Catherine Thearle, Simon Titterton and Helen Pearne - company/commercial; Carmen Chapple - debt collection.

Stagecoach Holdings PLC
10 Dunkeld Road Perth PH1 5TW
Tel: (01738) 442111 **Fax:** (01738) 643648
Email: dscott@stagecoachholdings.com
Website: www.stagecoachgroup.com
No of lawyers in dept: 0
Work outsourced: 80% - Opinions, drafting, commercial, banking.
Derek Scott, Company Secretary
Specialisation: Company Secretary. Chairman of Group Pension Trustees. Director of Group ESOP Trustee. Director of Railways Pension Scheme Trustee.
Career: University of Glasgow 1971-75. Chartered Accountant 1978. Arthur Andersen 1975-86. Stagecoach Holdings plc 1987 to date. Director of Railways Pension Trustee Company Ltd 1997 to date. Member of NAPF Investment Council 1998 to date.
Other lawyers: Pensions, ESOP's.

Standard Chartered PLC
1 Aldermanbury Square London EC2V 7SB
Tel: (020) 7280 7021 **Fax:** (020) 7280 7112
Website: www.standardchartered.com
No of lawyers in dept: 8
Kathleen Nealson, Group Head of Legal & Compliance
Other lawyers: Gordon Bentley - Deputy Head/Company Secretary; David Brimacombe - litigation, banking, commercial, employment; Susan Adams - litigation, banking commercial, employment; Martin Rowlands - litigation, banking, commercial; Dominic Bacon - M&A, corporate; James Ellington - M&A, corporate; Mark Thomas - IT; Christian Gordon-Pullar - IT.

Tate & Lyle PLC
Sugar Quay Lower Thames Street London EC3R 6DQ
Tel: (020) 7626 6525 **Fax:** (020) 7623 5213
Email: robertgibber@tateandlyle.com
Website: www.tateandlyle.com
No of lawyers in dept: 3
Work outsourced: 20% - Large scale mergers and acquisitions, overseas, significant property and stock exchange issues.
Robert Gibber, Company Secretary & General Counsel
Specialisation: Responsible to the Board for all global legal issues, primarily UK and overseas acquisitions and joint ventures, London Stock Exchange issues, corporate finance and tax, competition law and compliance.pm: Law Society, International Bar Association.
Career: Qualified 1988. Formerly with *Wilde Sapte* as assistant solicitor (1988-90), joined Tate & Lyle plc in 1990 and appointed senior legal adviser in 1992. Appointed General Counsel and joined Tate & Lyle Executive Committee in 1997. Appointed Company Secretary and General Counsel in 2001.
Personal: Born 28 October 1962. Educated at City of London School (1973-79), Wadham College, Oxford (BA Hons, Oriental Studies) (1980-84). Director of Workable, the disabled charity and founder of Legable a scheme providing work experience for disabled law students. Leisure pursuits include cinema, reading, skiing, tennis and being a father.
Other lawyers: Company/commercial, corporate finance, litigation, competition, shipping trading.

Taylor & Francis Group PLC
11 New Fetter Lane London EC4P 4EE
Tel: (020) 7583 9855 **Fax:** (020) 7842 2298
Anthony Foye, Finance Director & Company Secretary

Taylor Nelson Sofres PLC
Westgate London W5 1UA
Tel: (020) 8967 0007 **Fax:** (020) 8967 4060
Email: john.stobart@tnsofres.com
Website: www.tnsofres.com / www.tnagb.com
No of lawyers in dept: 4
Work outsourced: 25% - Excess workload, property, litigation.
John Stobart, Group Company Secretary
Specialisation: Responsible for legal and regulatory affairs of largest European market research company with turnover in excess of £400m. Deals with joint ventures/collaborative arrangements worldwide, product licensing, acquisitions and divestments, yellow book compliance, commercial contracts, data protection registration, property, trade marks, employment, insurance and pensions.
Career: Qualified 1978 while with *Smith Roddam* . Legal adviser 3i plc 1981-86. Partner with *Fennermores* 1986-89 and Director of Legal Services and Company Secretary to Harland Simon Group plc 1989-92. Joined Taylor Nelson Sofres in January 1993.
Other lawyers: John Stobart - Corporate finance; Paul Wright - Licensing; Raj Afghan - Employment; Ellora Ahmed - General; Mike Slotznick - U.S.A.; Jean Guiliani - France; Cornelia Harding - General.

Taylor Woodrow plc
Venture House 42-54 London Road Staines TW18 4HF
Tel: (01784) 428650 **Fax:** (01784) 428750
Website: www.taywood.co.uk
No of lawyers in dept: 9
Work outsourced: 30% - Construction, litigation, property, corporate finance, PFI.
Jeremy Sampson, Group General Counsel
Specialisation: Responsible for the provision of legal services of Taylor Woodrow plc and assists the subsidiary companies and their legal functions where appropriate. Principle area of work is company/commercial work.
Career: Chesham High School - 1980-86; Leicester Polytechnic - 1986-89; College of Law, Chester - 1989-90; Prudential Corporation (Trainee Solicitor) - 1990-91; *Richards Butler* (Trainee Solicitor) - 1991-92; Taylor Woodrow - 1993-present.
Personal: Age 33. Married living in West London. Interests include: Sailing, sport and the theatre.
Other lawyers: Company/commercial.

T

TBI PLC
159 New Bond Street London W1S 2UD
Tel: (020) 7408 7300 **Fax:** (020) 7408 7321
Roger C Clifton, Group Company Secretary

TBWA UK Group
76-80 Whitfield Street London W1T 4EZ
Tel: (020) 7573 6780 **Fax:** (020) 7573 6700
Email: giles.crown@tbwa-london.com
Website: www.tbwa-london.com
Work outsourced: 10% - Significant litigation, specialist and unusually complex matters.
Giles Crown, Head of Legal & Business Affairs
Specialisation: Responsible for providing legal services to eight advertising and marketing companies within the TBWA UK Group, with particular responsibilities for legal and regulatory compliance, commercial and corporate issues and employment.
Career: St Pauls School, Barnes; Jesus College, Cambridge, MA Hons in Law; UCL, LLM; Inns of Court School of Law; Barrister, 1 Brick Court, Chambers of Richard Rampton QC.
Personal: Rowing (Leader Club), adventure racing, triathlons, football, theatre, opera, cinema.
Other lawyers: Advertising, marketing and communications, commercial/company, employment.

Telegraph Group Limited
1 Canada Square Canary Wharf London E14 5DT
Tel: (020) 7538 5000 **Fax:** (020) 7538 7838
Email: corprels@telegraph.co.uk
Website: www.telegraph.co.uk
No of lawyers in dept: 4
Work outsourced: Libel, copyright litigation.
Arthur Wynn Davies, Legal Manager
Specialisation: Publishing, libel, contempt, copyright, contract.
Career: LLB (Hons) Wales (65); Middle Temple - called November 1971; Law lecturer 66-71. Legal Manager, Olhams Newspapers; Legal Manager, Mirror Group 82-87.
Other lawyers: Media law litigation.

Telewest Communications PLC
160 Great Portland Street London W1W 5QA
Tel: (020) 7299 5000 **Fax:** (020) 7299 5640
Email: simon_read@flextech.co.uk
Website: www.telewest.co.uk
No of lawyers in dept: 10
Work outsourced: Corporate finance, banking, mergers and acquisitions, major litigation.
Simon Read, Director of Legal Services
Specialisation: Media and communications, company/commercial, dispute resolution.
Career: Fitzwilliam college, Cambridge 1987-1990; Newcastle Polytechnic Law School 1991-1993; *Denton Wilde Sapte*, 1993-1995; BBC Worldwide Limited, 1996-1998; Telewest Communications plc, 1998-2001.
Other lawyers: Ian Mattingly, Melissa Royale, Marc Sobol, Zach Wilson, Delphine Power, Caroline Ford, Hafiz Wong, Robin McGilligon, Greg Davidson (seconded).

TeleWork Systems PLC
Precedent Drive Rooksley Milton Keynes MK13 8PP
Tel: (01908) 251333 **Fax:** (01908) 251321
Email: enquiries@teleworksystems.com
Website: www.teleworksystems.com
Work outsourced: 100% - All.
Michael Wailing, Chief Financial Officer & Company Secretary
Other lawyers: General legal advice required by commercial IT group.

Tesco Stores PLC
Tesco House PO Box 18 Delamare Road Waltham Cross Cheshunt EN8 9SL
Tel: (01992) 632222 **Fax:** (01992) 630794
Rowley Ager, Company Secretary

The Alliance Trust PLC
Meadow House 64 Reform Street Dundee DD1 1TJ
Tel: (01382) 201700 **Fax:** (01382) 225133
Website: www.alliancetrusts.com
No of lawyers in dept: 1
Ian Goddard, Company Secretary
Specialisation: Company law, corporate governance, contracts.
Career: Rugby School; Brasenose College, Oxford; Bar (Midland & Oxford Circuit) 1974-1984; 3i plc (Manager, Legal Department) 1984-1998; The Alliance Trust (Company Secretary) 1998- to date.

The Penguin Group (UK)
80 Strand London WC2R 0RL
Tel: (020) 7010 3017 **Fax:** (020) 7010 6699
Email: helena.peacock@penguin.co.uk
Helena Peacock, Legal Director & Company Seretary
Specialisation: All aspects of publishing law including copyright and libel. Other main areas are trademarks, litigation, general commercial.
Career: Law degree at St. Annes College Oxford. Qualified as a solicitor in 1978 and as a chartered tax adviser in 1987. Various in-house posts before joining Penguin in 1993.
Personal: Married with one daughter.

Thistle Hotels PLC
2 The Calls Leeds LS2 7JU
Tel: (0113) 243 9111 **Fax:** (0113) 244 5555
Website: www.thistlehotels.com
No of lawyers in dept: 1
Work outsourced: 50% (100% property and litigation) - Property, litigation, certain transactions, foreign jurisdictions.
Cathy Baxandall, Company Secretary
Career: MA (Oxon.) Modern Languages; College of Law; Articled at *Clifford-Turner*, qualified 1985; 1985-90: *Clifford-Turner (later Clifford Chance)* - London and Paris offices; 1990-94: *Simpson Curtis (later Pinsent Curtis)*, partner 1992 (Banking/Corp. Finance); 1994-99: Group Company Secretary, The Spring Ram Corporation plc; 1999-present: Company Secretary, Thistle Hotels plc.
Other lawyers: Compliance/stock exchange, corporate/commercial, property, litigation.

Thomson Travel Group plc
Greater London House Hampstead Road London NW1 7SD
Tel: (020) 7387 9321 **Fax:** (020) 7383 1485
No of lawyers in dept: 6
Work outsourced: 50% - Finance, competition, employment.
Richard Churchill-Coleman, Group General Counsel
Other lawyers: Henry Banks - Commercial / Litigation; Thomas Schmid - Aviation; Nigel Vickery - Property.
Greater London House Hampstead Road London NW1 7SD
Tel: (020) 7387 9321 **Fax:** (020) 7387 8451
Richard Aston, Legal Manager & Company Secretary

Thus plc
Dalmore House 310 St Vincent Street Glasgow G2 5BB
Tel: (0141) 566 3090 **Fax:** (0141) 566 3010
Email: david.macleod@thus.net
Website: www.thus.net
David Macleod, Company Secretary

Times Newspapers Ltd
Times House 1 Pennington Street London E98 1LG
Tel: (020) 7782 5858 **Fax:** (020) 7782 5860
Email: alastair.brett@newsint.co.uk
Website: www.the-times.co.uk / www.sunday-times.co.uk
Alastair Brett, Legal Manager

Times House 1 Pennington Street London E98 1LG
Tel: (020) 7782 5941 **Fax:** (020) 7782 5860
Website: www.the-times.co.uk / www.sunday-times.co.uk
Patricia Burge, Company Solicitor
Specialisation: Libel, defamation, copyright, trademark.

Tishman Speyer Properties UK Ltd
Millbank Tower 21-24 Millbank London SW1P 4QP
Tel: (020) 7333 2405 **Fax:** (020) 7333 2500
Email: mkingsto@tishmanspeyer.co.uk
Website: www.tishmanspeyer.com
Mark Kingston, European General Counsel & Managing Director
Specialisation: Real estate, investment, development, financing, construction, tax structuring, employment.
Career: Attended King David School in Liverpool; Birmingham University 1983-1986 graduating with LL.B Hons. 1987-1989 Articled at *Linklaters*; 1989-March 1999 at *Nabarro Nathanson*, made partner in 1996; 1999 - present Tishman Speyer Properties.
Personal: Keen on Amateur Dramatics, recently played Lord Evelyn Oakleigh in Harrow Light Opera's production of Anything Goes. Keen sportsman, football, golf and tennis. Married with 3 children, 2 girls and a boy.

Tokai Bank Europe plc
1 Exchange Square London EC2A 2JL
Tel: (020) 7638 6030 **Fax:** (020) 7588 5875
Website: www.tbeuk.com
No of lawyers in dept: 4
Work outsourced: 10% - MTN programme updates, repackagings, leases.
David Haig, Head of Legal & Compliance Depts.
Other lawyers: Mary Verghese-Dipple, John White, Elizabeth Hornby.

Tokyo-Mitsubishi International PLC
6 Broadgate London EC2M 2AA
Tel: (020) 7628 5555 **Fax:** (020) 7577 2872
Richard House, Director, Legal

Towers Perrin
Castlewood House 77-91 New Oxford Street London WC1A 1PX
Tel: (020) 7379 4000 **Fax:** (020) 8895 7478
Val Vardy, Principal

Trafficmaster PLC
University Way Cranfield MK43 0TR
Tel: (01234) 759000 **Fax:** (01234) 759317
Nigel Bond, Finance Director & Company Secretary

Travis Perkins PLC
Lodge Way House Lodge Way Harlestone Road Northampton NN5 7UG
Tel: (01604) 683040 **Fax:** (01604) 683160
Email: apike@travisperkins.co.uk
Website: www.travisperkins.co.uk
No of lawyers in dept: 1
Work outsourced: 80% - Property, litigation, major acquisitions, disposals.
Andrew S Pike, Company Secretary & lawyer
Specialisation: General responsibility for groups legal affairs. Also responsible as Company Secretary for pensions, insurance and risk management, and share schemes. General contract and commercial advice, employment law, acquisitions and disposals.
Career: University of Birmingham LL.B 1973; Costain Group 1981-1989; Alfred McAlpine 1989-1994; Ibstock plc 1994-1999; Travis Perkins plc 1999 - date.

Trinity Mirror PLC
Canary Wharf 1 Canada Square London E14 5AP
Tel: (020) 7293 3000 **Fax:** (020) 7293 0435
Website: www.trinity-mirror.co.uk
No of lawyers in dept: 8
Work outsourced: 75% - Property, litigation, corporate finance, pensions, employment.
Paul Vickers, Company Secretary & Group Legal Director
Other lawyers: Commercial contract, employment, IP, property.

Canary Wharf 1 Canada Square London E14 5AP
Tel: (020) 7293 3000 **Fax:** (020) 7293 0435
Charles Collier-Wright, Group Legal Manager

Canary Wharf 1 Canada Square London E14 5AP
Tel: (020) 7293 3000 **Fax:** (020) 7293 0435
Martin Cruddace, Solicitor

Canary Wharf 1 Canada Square London E14 5AP
Tel: (020) 7293 3000 **Fax:** (020) 7293 0435
Marcus Partington, Solicitor

TT International
Martin House 5 Martin Lane London EC4R 0DP
Tel: (020) 7410 3500 **Fax:** (020) 7410 3539
No of lawyers in dept: 2
Work outsourced: 50% - Various.
A Allison, Compliance and Legal Partner
Career: Educated at Liverpool College and Wadham College, Oxford. Called to the Bar 1969. Independent practice at the Bar 1969-1987. Head of Group Compliance, Standard Chartered Bank 1987-1996. Director, Compliance and Legal Affairs, West Merchant 1996-1998, Compliance Director and General Counsel, Westdeutsche Landesbank (London) 1999-2000. Head of Compliance and Legal, TT International since June 2000 (partner from January 2001). Author (with others) 'Banking and the Financial Services Act' (Butterworths, 1993), 'Banking and Financial Services Regulation' (Butterworths 1998).
Personal: Fellow, Chartered Institute of Arbitrators. Chairman, Bar Association for Commerce, Finance & Industry 1995. Memberships - General Council of the Bar 1991-96, Commercial Court Committee 1991- 2000, City Disputes Panel of Arbitrators & Mediators, Securities and Futures Authority's Panel of Arbitrators.

TTP Communications plc
Melbourn Science Park Cambridge Road Melbourn Royston SG8 6EE
Tel: (01763) 266266 **Fax:** (01763) 261216
Website: www.ttpcom.com
Christopher McQuoid, General Counsel

UBS Warburg Group
100 Liverpool Street London EC2M 2RH
Tel: (020) 7568 9102 **Fax:** (020) 7568 7168
Email: philip.price@ubsw.com
Website: www.ubsw.com
No of lawyers in dept: 10
Philip Price, Head of Corporate Legal Services

100 Liverpool Street London EC2M 2RH
Tel: (020) 7567 2308 **Fax:** (020) 7567 2364
Email: carol.moir@ubsw.com
Website: www.ubsw.com
Carol Moir, Executive Director and Head of Transactions Legal
Specialisation: Debt capital markets, equity capital markets (including equity-linked), corporate finance.
Career: BA (Hons) English and French Law - University of Kent at Canterbury; CPE - College of Law, London; admitted as a solicitor; Trainee - *Clifford Chance*; Joined SBC (now UBS Warburg) in 1992.

100 Liverpool Street London EC2M 2RH
Tel: (020) 75687221 **Fax:** (020) 75689247
Email: charles.ross-stewart@ubsw.com
Website: www.ubsw.com
Charles Ross-Stewart, Executive Director
Specialisation: Fixed income, equity and credit derivatives. Structured finance, CDOs, securitisation.
Career: Edinburgh University LL.B (1982-1987); *Dundas & Wilson*, Edinburgh (1987-1989); *Freshfields*, London (1989-1994); Citibank, London (1994-1998); UBS Warburg (1998 to date).

Ultraframe PLC
Enterprise Works Salthill Road Clitheroe BB7 1PE
Tel: (01200) 414622 **Fax:** (01200) 425455
Email: edward.smethurst@ultraframe.com
Website: www.ultraframe.com
No of lawyers in dept: 1
Work outsourced: 100% - Litigation, mergers and acquisitions, corporate.
Edward G Smethurst, Company Secretary & Legal Director
Specialisation: Company Secretary to plc board and all subsidiaries. Responsible for commercial and contract drafting. Major litigation to include IP related litigation, contract litigations. Responsible for pensions and insurance matters. Company Solicitor to the group.
Career: Oulder Hill School, Rochdale; Leeds University LL.B (Hons) 2:1; *Halliwell Landau* 1990-1993; British Nuclear plc 1993-2000 - Senior Legal Advisor; 2000 to date - Ultraframe plc - Company Secretary and Solicitor.
Personal: Chairman Law Society C&I Group Nationally June 1999 to June 2000 and January 2001 to March 2001. Chief Executive of this group June 2000 to date. Chairman Law Society C&I Northwest Group from 1994 to date. European Company Lawyers Association - UK. Director to European Board 2000 to date. Interests: Football, cricket and rugby.

Unilever PLC
Unilever House Blackfriars PO Box 68 London EC4P 4BQ
Tel: (020) 7822 5252 **Fax:** (020) 7822 5951
Email: steve.williams@unilever.com
Website: www.unilever.com
No of lawyers in dept: 20
Stephen G Williams, General Counsel & Joint Secretary
Specialisation: Responsible for all legal, intellectual property and secretarial departments in the head offices in London and Rotterdam and is also responsible for Unilever legal services worldwide.
Career: Educated at Brentwood School, Essex and King's College, University of London where gained Bachelor of Law Degree (LLB) Hons. Following Law School, joined *Slaughter and May* and spent time in their tax planning and commercial departments. In 1975 joined the legal department of Imperial Chemical Industries plc. In 1984 he transferred to ICI's company secretary's department, becoming one of two assistant company secretaries in 1985. Appointed Joint Secretary of Unilever on 1st January 1986 and General Counsel of Unilever in 1993.
Personal: Admitted as a Solicitor and member of the Law Society in April 1972. Member of the Company Law Committee of the Law Society and of the Companies Committee of the CBI. Non-executive director of Bunzl plc.
Other lawyers: Mr R Lock - overseas legal services; Ms T Dougal-Biggs - UK legal services; Mr R Heath - trade mark legal services; Mr L Virelli - patents legal services; Mrs S Franklin - marketing legal services; Mr J Moolenburgh - European legal services (based in Rotterdam); Mrs SBM Andnessen - Netherlands legal services (based in Rotterdam).

Unilever House Blackfriars PO Box 68 London EC4P 4BQ
Tel: (020) 7822 5252 **Fax:** (020) 7822 5951
Richard Heath, Head of Corporate Trade Marks

Uniq PLC
60 Wood Lane London W12 7RP
Tel: (020) 8749 8888 **Fax:** (020) 8576 6071
Website: www.uniqplc.com
No of lawyers in dept: 1
Work outsourced: 40% - M&A, conveyancing.
P Norman Heriz-Jones, Head of Legal
Specialisation: Company/commercial, IP, food legislation, property, franchising, competition law, licensing, agency and distribution.
Career: Cheltenham College

United Business Media plc
Ludgate House 245 Blackfriars Road Blackfriars London SE1 9UY
Tel: (020) 7921 5000 **Fax:** (020) 7921 5047
Email: stablesj@unitedbusinessmedia.com
Website: www.unm.com
No of lawyers in dept: 11
Work outsourced: 60% - Corporate, litigation, employment.
Jane Stables, Group Legal & Personnel Director
Specialisation: M&A, commercial, litigation, employment practices, strategy/development.
Career: Qualified as a lawyer in 1985 and worked in the city firm of *Freshfields* doing mainly mergers and acquisitions but always retaining an employment law specialism. Moved into industry to be company secretary and legal adviser to a retailing plc, prior to joining MAI in 1994. She took over the personnel function at MAI in 1995 and became Legal & Personnel Director on the United/MAI merger. Responsible for the United News & Media plc group legal and personnel issues.

United Utilities Water plc
Dawson House Liverpool Road Great Sankey Warrington WA5 3LW
Tel: (01925) 234000 **Fax:** (01925) 236932
Website: www.unitedutilities.com
No of lawyers in dept: 20
Work outsourced: 50% - Major transactions, litigation, property, employment.
David Hosker, Head of Legal Services, United Utilities Water plc
Other lawyers: Joanne Bream, Group Legal Manager - Company/commercial, corporate finance.

Universal Music Publishing Group
Elsinore House 77 Fulham Palace Road London W6 8JA
Tel: (020) 8752 2600 **Fax:** (020) 8752 2652
Email: sarah.levin@umusic.com
Website: www.umusic.com
Sarah Levin, In-house Lawyer

Universal/Island Records Limited
22 St Peter's Square London W6 9NW
Tel: (020) 8910 3333 **Fax:** (020) 8910 3218
Claire Sugrue, Director of Legal & Business Affairs

Viridian Group PLC
Danesfort House 120 Malone Road Belfast BT9 5HT
Tel: (028) 9066 1100 **Fax:** (028) 9068 9269
Email: legal@nie.co.uk
Website: www.viridiangroup.co.uk
No of lawyers in dept: 2
Work outsourced: Acquisitions, joint venture, commercial.
David Flinn, Group Solicitor
Specialisation: Electricity law, employment law, joint ventures, acquisitions, general commercial.
Career: Educated Rossall School and Queens University Belfast. Qualified Solicitor Northern Ireland 1975. Qualified Solicitor England and Wales 1981. Chairman Belfast Solicitors Association 1993. Chairman Employment Lawyers Group (NI) 1995 to 1999. Chairman Belfast Civic Trust 1999.
Personal: Interests: Skiing and hill walking.
Other lawyers: N Macdougall: Property law, employment, contract, general commercial.

Vizzavi Europe Limited
80 Strand London WC2R 0RJ
Tel: (020) 7212 0271 **Fax:** (020) 7212 0720
Email: chris.heather@corp.vizzavi.net
Website: www.vizzavi.net
No of lawyers in dept: 5
Work outsourced: 20% - Corporate, employment, property.
Christopher Heather, Group Legal Counsel
Specialisation: Non-contentious intellectual property, information technology, corporate and company/commercial.
Career: Articles and 3 years PQE at *Herbert Smith* (IP/IT group), 18 months at *Olswang* (multimedia group), 14 months at *Freshfields* (IP/IT group) and 14 months at boo.com (Group Legal Counsel).
Personal: Current affairs, tennis and reading.

Vodafone Group PLC
The Courtyard 2-4 London Road Newbury RG14 1JX
Tel: (01635) 33251 **Fax:** (01635) 45713
Email: stephen.scott@vf.vodafone.co.uk
Website: www.vodafone.com
Stephen Scott, Company Secretary & Group Legal Director

Fairfax House London Road Newbury RG14 1JX
Tel: (01635) 682802 **Fax:** (01635) 676197
Stewart D White, Good Public Policy Director

Vosper Thornycroft Holdings PLC
Victoria Road Woolston Southampton SO19 9RR
Tel: (023) 8042 6000 **Fax:** (023) 8042 6010
Peter G Dawes, Company Secretary

W

Warner Chappell Music Ltd
Griffin House 161 Hammersmith Road London W6 8BS
Tel: (020) 8563 5800 **Fax:** (020) 8563 5801
Website: www.warnerchappell.com
No of lawyers in dept: 3
Work outsourced: 5% - Litigation, employment.
Jane Dyball, Director of Legal and Business Affairs
Specialisation: Music copyright, contracts, litigation, licencing, employment.
Career: Culford School, Suffolk 1972-1980; Bristol University (LLB Hons) 1984; Virgin Music Publishers Ltd 1986-1992; Warner/Chappell Music Ltd 1992 - current. Music Publishers Association Board Member; MCPS Commercial Committee; Pop Bureau; International Confederation of Music Publishers.

Waste Recycling Group PLC (WRG)
3 Sidings Court White Rose Way Doncaster DN4 5NU
Tel: (01302) 303030 **Fax:** (01302) 303001
Alan Waterhouse, Company Secretary

The Weir Group PLC
149 Newlands Road Cathcart Glasgow G44 4EX
Tel: (0141) 637 7111 **Fax:** (0141) 637 2221
Website: www.weir.co.uk
Alan Mitchelson, Company Secretary & Head of Legal

Westdeutsche Landesbank Girozentrale (London)
Woolgate Exchange 25 Basinghall Street London EC2V 5HA
Tel: (020) 7020 2000 **Fax:** (020) 7020 2420
Email: presse@westlb.de
Website: www.westlb.de
Lucian Milburn, Head of Legal

WH Smith PLC
Nations House 103 Wigmore Street London W1U 1WH
Tel: (020) 7409 3222 **Fax:** (020) 7514 9633
Email: ian.houghton@group-whsmith.co.uk
Website: www.whsmithplc.com
No of lawyers in dept: 2
Ian Houghton, Company Secretary & Director of Legal Services

Whitbread Holdings PLC
The Brewery Chiswell Street London EC1Y 4SD
Tel: (020) 7606 4455 **Fax:** (020) 7806 5456
Email: simon.barratt@whitbread.com
Website: www.whitbread.co.uk
No of lawyers in dept: 3
Work outsourced: 80% - Litigation, property, debt collection, licensing, environmental health and food safety issues.
Simon Barratt, Legal Affairs Director & Company Secretary
Career: Educated at Sevenoaks School; St. Johns College, Oxford (Jurisprudence 1982); Law Society finals 1983). Articled *Slaughter and May*; qualified 1985; assistant solicitor, *Slaughter and May*; solicitor RTZ Legal department, 1987-1989; corporate counsel, Heron Corporation 1989-1991, group legal adviser, Whitbread July 1991-March 1997. Appointed Legal Affairs Director, Company Secretary Whitbread PLC March 1997.
Personal: Born 1959; resides Tunbridge Wells. Leisure pursuits include keeping fit, gardening, keeping the children occupied.
Other lawyers: Russell Fairhurst - Group Legal Advisor (M&A, commercial); Tanya Msimang - Solicitor (commercial).

William M Mercer Limited
1 Grosvenor Place London SW1P 4LZ
Tel: (020) 7488 4949 **Fax:** (020) 7201 0800
Mark McKeown, Litigation Counsel UK & Europe

Wilson Bowden PLC
Wilson Bowden House 207 Leicester Road Ibstock Leicester LE67 6WB
Tel: (01530) 260777 **Fax:** (01530) 262805
Email: ewilson@wilsonbowden.plc.uk
Website: www.wilsonbowden.co.uk
Work outsourced: 80% - Land acquisitions, land sales, plot sales, litigation.
Nicolas J Townsend, Group Legal Director
Specialisation: Responsible for monitoring and supervision of all major contracts for land acquisition/sale, troubleshooting, strategic land acquisition and the provision of external legal services for the group.
Career: Qualified in January 1970. Previously a Partner with *Gardiner & Millhouse* 1976-78, *Marron Townsend* 1978-80, *Nicolas Townsend & Co* 1980-87, *Staunton Townsend* 1987-89 *Edge and & Ellison* 1989-93.
Other lawyers: Owen Hill, Peter Carr, Wendy Satchwell, Verina Wenham, Liz Bailey - planning and property development.

Wincanton PLC
Cale House Station Road Wincanton BA9 9AD
Tel: (01963) 828282 **Fax:** (01963) 828406
No of lawyers in dept: 2
Work outsourced: Principally property/conveyancing and litigation.
Charles Phillips, Company Secretary
Other lawyers: Susan Lomax - Commercial.

Wm Morrison Supermarkets PLC
Hilmore House Thornton Road Bradford BD8 9AX
Tel: (01274) 494166 **Fax:** (01274) 494831
Website: www.morrisons.co.uk
Work outsourced: 100% - All.
Jonathan Burke, Company Secretary

Wolseley PLC
PO Box 18 Vines Lane Droitwich Spa WR9 8ND
Tel: (01905) 777200 **Fax:** (01905) 777201
David A Branson, Group Company Secretary

Wolverhampton & Dudley Breweries PLC
Park Brewery Bath Road PO Box 26 Wolverhampton WV1 4NY
Tel: (01902) 711811 **Fax:** (01902) 429136
Leslie Porter, Company Secretary

Working Title Films Ltd
Oxford House 76 Oxford Street London W1N OHQ
Tel: (020) 7307 3000 **Fax:** (020) 7307 3003
No of lawyers in dept: 3
Sara Curran, Head of Legal and Business Affairs
Specialisation: Management of an in-house legal affairs department which includes negotiating first look agreements, option and writer's agreements, production financing distribution agreements, director, producer, consultancy, main cast and soundtrack album agreements. Recent Films include '40 Days and 40 Nights', 'My Little Eye', 'The Guru', 'About a Boy', and 'Ali G Indahouse'. Previous experience includes negotiating multi-territory acquisition agreements ('Lock Stock and Two Smoking Barrels'), split rights deals with major studios ('The Relic', 'Hard Rain'), 'all rights' licence agreements, artist management and recording agreements (Boyzone), multi million dollar television output deals (Sky, Telemunchen, Canal +), letters of intent and licence agreements in connection with the establishment of the Sundance channel, Section 35/481 arrangements ('Mad About Mambo') and intra group licensing arrangements (PolyGram).
Career: Educated Trinity College, Dublin (Bachelor of Business Studies) and College of Europe, Bruges. Qualified in 1994 with *Mason Hayes and Curran*, Dublin. Joined PolyGram Film International in 1995 as legal adviser, later-promoted to Head of Legal and Business Affairs. Transferred to PolyGram Filmed Entertainment in 1996 and promoted to Vice President Legal and Business Affairs in 1998. Appointed Head of Business Affairs for Canada Film in 1999. Joined Working Title Film in 2000.
Personal: Leisure interests include sailing, snowboarding, travel, yoga, cooking and good wine. Living in Richmond.

Oxford House 76 Oxford Street London W1N OHQ
Tel: (020) 7307 3000 **Fax:** (020) 7307 3003
Sheeraz Shah, Vice President of Legal & Business Affairs

Oxford House 76 Oxford Street London W1N OHQ
Tel: (020) 7307 3000 **Fax:** (020) 7307 3003
Angela Morrison, Chief Operating Officer

WPP Group PLC
27 Farm Street London W1X 6RD
Tel: (020) 7408 2204 **Fax:** (020) 7409 0242
Email: dcalow@wpp.com
Website: www.wpp.com
Work outsourced:
David Calow, Group Chief Counsel
Other lawyers: Company/commercial, corporate finance, corporate governance, employment, international.

WS Atkins PLC
Woodcote Grove Ashley Road Epsom KT18 5BW
Tel: (01372) 726140 **Fax:** (01372) 740055
Email: wsatkinsinfo@wsatkins.com
Website: www.wsatkins.com
No of lawyers in dept: 4
Work outsourced: 5% - Commercial conveyancing, litigation, major acquisition.
Deborah Robinson, Group Legal Adviser
Specialisation: Responsible for legal and commercial issues affecting the WS Atkins Group, both in the UK and overseas.
Career: Articled *Macfarlanes* 1988-90; Assistant Solicitor *Macfarlanes* 1990-94; Assistant Legal Adviser WS Atkins 1994-99; Group Legal Adviser 1999 to date. Sutton High School. University of Bristol (LLB 1986). Kings College London (MSc 1992).
Personal: Born 1964. Resides in Kingston-Upon-Thames.

Xansa PLC
Campus 300 Maylands Avenue Hemel Hempstead HP2 7TQ
Tel: (01442) 434016 **Fax:** (01442) 434242
Email: information@xansa.com
Website: www.xansa.com
No of lawyers in dept: 3
Work outsourced: Mergers and acquisitions, litigation, property, specialist work.
Charles E Lilley, Legal Adviser
Specialisation: M&A, joint ventures, company/commercial.
Career: Newcastle University LL.B. 1985; Qualified 1988 (Articles *Braby & Waller*); *Biddle & Co*; Courtaulds plc; F.I. Group plc, 1999 to date.
Other lawyers: All legal issues.

Young & Rubicam Group Ltd
Greater London House Hampstead Road London NW1 7QP
Tel: (020) 7611 6374 **Fax:** (020) 7611 6743
Email: kathryn_fulton@eu-yr.com
Kate Fulton, Chief Counsel
Specialisation: Advising the Young & Rubicam Group of companies on advertising and related areas (copyright, talent agreements etc.), direct marketing and sales promotion. Company related issues including employment advice.
Career: 1973-83 Manchester High School for Girls; 1983-86 Queen Mary College, University of London; 1987 Bar School; 1988-89 Pupillages.
Personal: Run a legal surgery for a cancer charity. Married with 3 children.

SUPPORT SERVICES

Accountants

ALEXANDERS

Redhill Chambers, High Street, Redhill, RH1 1RJ
Tel: (01737) 779500 **Fax:** (01737) 779548
Email: Alex@Alexanders.uk.co

Contact Partner	J Donoghue

THE FIRM: For a number of years, Alexanders have been helping lawyers and their clients by providing forensic accounting, litigation support and expert witness services whenever financial issues are involved. The firm has worked closely with insurance companies, lawyers, leading counsel and their clients, in such areas as the production of high quality reports, graphs and financial summaries of a clear, concise nature for presentation at court; litigation strategies; the examination and appraisal of documents through Disclosure and assessing the quantum of claims or exposure. Alexanders have a firm grasp of the laws of evidence and understand the necessity of providing reliable evidence. They also have first hand courtroom experience of both the Royal Courts of Justice and the Central Criminal Courts.

LITIGATION SUPPORT PARTNERS: The Litigation Support Partners have all held senior positions within the top ten accountancy firms and have worked in public practice for a number of years. All partners are members of the Academy of Experts and are qualified accountants with a wide range of business experience.

LITIGATION SUPPORT SERVICES: Alexanders have assisted in a wide variety of cases involving loss of earnings; professional negligence; negligence of Investment Managers; fraud; conspiracy to defraud; family and marital disputes; compliance with Investor Protection regulations; insurance claims; breach of contract claims; and offences under the Companies Acts.

BAKER TILLY

2 Bloomsbury Street, London, WC1B 3ST
Tel: (020) 7413 5100 **Fax:** (020) 7413 5101 **DX:** 1040 London/Chancery Ln.
Email: michael.taub@bakertilly.co.uk **Website:** www.bakertilly.co.uk

Contact Partners		
London	Michael Taub	(020) 7413 5100
Birmingham	Charles Fray	(0121) 233 2323
Bradford	Paul Byrne	(01274) 735311
Bromley	John Hudson	(020) 8290 552
Crawley	John Warner	(01293) 565 165
Chester	Alan Tranter	(01925) 265040
Guildford	Jon Cini	(01483) 307000
Manchester	Edward Cobb	(0161) 834 5777
Milton Keynes	Jim Clifford	(01908) 847474
Warrington	Alan Tranter	(01925) 265040
Watford	Jim Clifford	(01923) 816400
Yeovil	Diane Simpson-Price	(01935) 476866
Number of partners		142
Number of staff		1000

THE FIRM: Founded over 125 years ago, Baker Tilly is a top ten firm of chartered accountants and business advisers in the UK. The firm has 139 partners operating nationally, employs some 1,000 staff and is an independent member of Summit International with representatives in over 100 cities worldwide.

LITIGATION SUPPORT SERVICES: Baker Tilly specialists have acted in over 600 litigation cases, providing expert witness and forensic accounting. They are not just experts in court - as practising accountants their evidence is based on practical and commercial experience. For this reason, its litigation support team is active in other specialist fields including corporate finance, information technology, audit, tax and insolvency. It is this mix of experience which makes its specialists effective expert witnesses. Baker Tilly specialists have extensive experience in a wide range of cases that have included IT litigation, breach of contract, security for costs, personal injury, loss of profits, loss of earnings, fatal accidents, share valuations, professional negligence, commercial disputes, divorce, medical negligence, professional indemnity and fraud. The firm has acted for defendants in several high profile cases brought by the SFO and as the DTI Inspector in the Barlow Clowes affair.

A

BDO STOY HAYWARD

8 Baker Street, London, W1U 3LL
Tel: (020) 7486 5888 **Fax:** (020) 7487 3686 **DX:** 0925 West End W1
Email: gervase.macgregor@bdo.co.uk **Website:** www.bdo.co.uk

Contact	Gervase MacGregor
Number of partners	313
Number of staff	2615

THE FIRM: BDO Stoy Hayward has an established national forensic accounting unit in recognition of the need for sophisticated accountancy input into trials and potential proceedings. The unit offers a cost effective approach based on a high level of partner involvement and backed by professional staff familiar with legal concepts and procedures. Through the BDO worldwide network BDO Stoy Hayward are also able to offer forensic services on an international basis.

LITIGATION SUPPORT SERVICES:

Pre-trial: Detailed investigation and analysis of documents including prime accounting records; advice on technical accountancy matters; evaluation of economic loss; tracing of assets.

Trial: Provision of expert witnesses; analysis of opposition's financial evidence; provision of detailed support during cross examination. Available to act as experts in determinations, as arbitrators, mediators and SJES. The firm's partners have considerable witness box experience.

Settlement Support: Assistance with settlement negotiations; evaluation of taxation implications; evaluation of business implications.

IT: Advanced computer software and graphics are used to present complex financial and quantitative data with clarity and precision. The firm is also able to offer sophisticated computer forensic techniques for the purposes of data imaging and retrieval.

PRACTICE AREAS: Types of work undertaken includes breach of warranty; expert determination; fraud; general commercial disputes; loss of profit/earnings including personal injury; mediation; partnership disputes; professional negligence; share purchase agreements; valuations of professional goodwill, wrongful dismissal.

CARTER BACKER WINTER CHARTERED ACCOUNTANTS

C

Hill House, Highgate Hill, London, N19 5UU
Tel: (020) 7263 7111 **Fax:** (020) 7281 2166 **DX:** 54760 Archway
Email: peter_luscombe@cbw.co.uk **Website:** www.cbw.co.uk

Contacts	Peter Luscombe Arthur D. Harverd

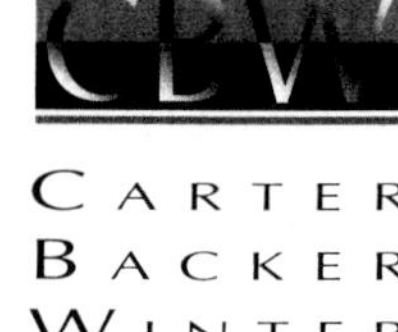

THE FIRM: Carter Backer Winter is a long established, major independent London firm with over 70 personnel. Its litigation specialists have a sound understanding of legal concepts and procedures derived from over 30 years experience of litigation work, including many leading cases. They are able to analyse complex financial data quickly and present their findings in a clear, non-technical manner, both in written form and in oral evidence. The litigation team is led by Peter Luscombe, a CEDR accredited mediator, and Arthur Harverd, a registered arbitrator and a past chairman of The Chartered Institute of Arbitrators. Both are members of the Academy of Experts and have given evidence as expert witnesses on numerous occasions. Their experience covers both civil and criminal cases in the areas of commercial, insurance, fraud, tax, personal injury and matrimonial disputes and professional and medical negligence. Their team also includes experts in the fields of insolvency and banking.

DAVID COLLISON

The Barn, Station Court, Lode, Cambridge, CB5 9HD
Tel: (01223) 813070 **Fax:** (01223) 813147
Email: dc@dcol.co.uk

Contact Partner	David Collison

THE FIRM: A new consultancy practice established 6 April 2000 by David Collison. He was at Peters Elworthy & Moore, Chartered Accountants for 20 years and was the firm's first tax partner.

LITIGATION SUPPORT PARTNERS: David Collison is available as an expert witness on taxation and accountancy matters. He is author of ICAEW Share Valuation Handbook and Tiley & Collison's *UK Tax Guide* (Butterworths). He is executive editor of the ICAEW Practitioner Tax Service.

DELOITTE & TOUCHE

Hill House, 1 Little New Street, London, EC4A 3TR
Tel: (020) 7936 3000 **Fax:** (020) 7936 2638 **DX:** 599
Email: forensic.uk@deloitte.co.uk **Website:** www.deloitte.co.uk

Contact Partners	Mike Barford
	Will Inglis
	Mark Tantam
	George Weldon
	Humphry Hatton
Number of partners	346
Number of staff	7964

THE FIRM: Deloitte & Touche has a dedicated team of forensic specialists in offices throughout the country. The firm's forensic partners have significant experience as expert witnesses, both in the UK and overseas. Where a case requires specific sector or industry expertise the firm is able to provide the appropriate expert from one of its dedicated industry or technical groups. As a leading member of Deloitte Touche Tohmatsu, the firm is also able to call upon the assistance of its 73,000 staff located in some 130 countries throughout the world.

LITIGATION SUPPORT SERVICES:

Commercial Disputes: The firm has extensive experience in general commercial disputes including claims for business interruption and loss of profits, product liability, breach of contract, intellectual property, fidelity and warranty breaches and also valuations. As one of the leading firms providing services to the public sector, Deloitte & Touche has also assisted local authorities and government bodies in a wide range of such disputes.

Determinations, Mediations & Arbitration: The firm has developed considerable expertise in the role of expert in determinations as well as acting for clients during arbitrations and mediations.

Personal Claims: The firm has a significant reputation in personal injury, fatal accident and medical negligence claims, and in the area of structured settlements. They also provide quantum reports in matrimonial disputes and libel actions.

Professional Negligence: The firm provides expert opinion on negligence claims involving accountancy firms as well as quantum reports in claims against other professionals.

Insurance Claims: The firm provides expert accountancy services to insurance companies, loss adjusters and commercial clients and has a significant record in acting for Lloyd's Syndicates involved in disputes.

Fraud & Criminal Work: The firm conducts fraud investigations, traces and recovers assets and carries out reviews to identify the risk of fraud or money laundering in both the public and private sectors. Its investigators have access to the most advanced data recovery and computer investigation tools.

Business Intelligence Service: The firm can undertake detailed research into individuals' backgrounds, connections and other business activities, whether as part of a commercial dispute or fraud investigation or as a prelude to a new business opportunity or joint venture.

Computerised Litigation Systems: The firm's involvement in several major liquidations has led it to develop a computerised database document management and retrieval system for large cases.

E

ERNST & YOUNG LLP

Beckett House, 1 Lambeth Palace Road, London, SE1 7EU
Tel: (020) 7951 2000 **Fax:** (020) 7951 3807 **DX:** 241
Email: forensics@uk.ey.com **Website:** www.eyuk.co.uk

Contacts	
Forensic Services	Sarah Evans
Special Investigations	David Sherwin
Dispute Advisory	Robert Overend
	Nigel Macdonald
Transaction Dispute Managment	Sara Fowler
Manchester	Richard Dyson
Edinburgh	Richard Sweetman
Birmingham	Sara Fowler
Business Valuations	Jim Eales
	Anne Worlledge
Tax Investigations	
Corporate Tax & Income Tax	Bob Brown
	Chris Oates
Customs Duties & Excise Taxes	Mark Perlstrom

THE FIRM: Ernst & Young LLP is one of the leading international firms of business and professional advisers, with offices in twenty cities across the UK and many more throughout the world. Clients include organisations of all types and sizes, from blue chip multinationals and governments to major financial institutions and private individuals.

LITIGATION SUPPORT SERVICES: Ernst & Young's team has extensive experience in all areas of forensic services. The team is organised into three broad areas: special investigations, dispute advisory and transaction dispute management. Each consists of a core of dedicated specialists who can in turn draw on Ernst & Young's global network to ensure the most comprehensive level of industry expertise is brought to a case. Central to Ernst & Young's approach is a thorough understanding of the client's agenda and priorities, ensuring that the areas of real relevance are quickly identified and addressed, and that the end result of any assignment is the delivery of real value. The firm places great emphasis on the quality and clarity of findings and reports and, where legal obligations allow, building a close partnership with clients to continuously improve the solutions it offers.

Special Investigations: The special investigations team focuses on investigating and advising on fraud, money laundering and regulatory issues, forensic IT and asset tracing and recovery. It has developed bespoke software to trace misappropriated funds that have been transferred internationally through various currencies, aiding recovery before the funds are dissipated. In addition to the full range of services for tackling an allegation of fraud, the team can advise on fraud prevention, including risk awareness seminars and the training of key staff in the prevention and detection of fraud, anti–money laundering and regulatory issues.

Dispute Advisory: This area covers services including quantum evaluation, auditor and accountant negligence, the failure of commercial arrangements and the investigation and quantification of insurance claims. The group provides expert witness and related services to lawyers and their clients. The firm's service offering extends to all stages of a case, from development of a statement or claim or defence through to presenting evidence at trial.

Continued overleaf

Transaction Dispute Management: This team provides pre-transaction advice on the accounting aspects of sale and purchase agreements, review of completion accounts, advice on completion account disputes, and expert determinations.
Business Valuations: Ernst & Young has had a dedicated team of full time valuers for over 25 years. The group has unparalleled experience in the field of business and share valuations, typically working on over 300 assignments each year. The group's expertise comprises valuation for almost every business situation including: evaluating acquisition targets, independent valuations under the Companies Act, valuations for taxation purposes and negotiating values with the Inland Revenue; valuing intellectual property and giving evidence as a valuation expert witness in, for example, shareholder disputes, professional negligence claims, and warranty claims.
Tax Investigations: Ernst & Young's Tax Risk Management team efficiently manage Inland Revenue and Customs & Excise enquiries and minimise any consequent disruption to clients. The team comprises: senior ex-Inland Revenue; ex-Customs & Excise investigators; tax and audit professionals, who aim to minimise any risk of exposure to prosecution, achieve a fair and reasonable conclusion to enquiries, and successfully mitigate any penalties. The team has comprehensive experience of approaches from various Inland Revenue and Customs & Excise offices, especially the Inland Revenue's Special Compliance Office and the National Investigation Service of Customs. The team has a national network with a wide understanding of Revenue and Customs tactics and detailed experience of different industry sectors. Members of the team adopt an independent approach based on their knowledge of risk areas and experience of resolving technical disputes. Bob Brown is also a highly regarded expert witness about Revenue prosecutions and investigation work.

FISHER FORENSIC, A DIVISION OF H. W. FISHER & COMPANY, CHARTERED ACCOUNTANTS

Acre House, 11-15 William Road, London, NW1 3ER
Tel: (020) 7388 7000 **Fax:** (020) 7380 4900
Email: forens@hwfisher.co.uk **Website:** www.hwfisher.co.uk

Contact Partner	Stuart Burns
Number of partners	24
Number of staff	320

THE FIRM: Fisher Forensic is the specialist forensic practice within H W Fisher & Company, a medium sized accountancy firm comprising 24 partners and approximately 320 staff. Fisher Forensic offers a level of expertise rarely found outside the ranks of the largest international firms, combined with a commitment to a prompt, effective and personal service. Its effectiveness is enhanced by experience of acting for both plaintiffs and defendants. The firm has in-depth skills in all aspects of litigation support, including professional negligence, breach of contract, business interruption, fraud and criminal investigations, licensing and royalty recovery, matrimonial, share valuations, expert determinations, medical negligence and personal injury.

F

LITIGATION SUPPORT PARTNERS:

Stuart Burns: Stuart heads Fisher Forensic and is a member of the Academy of Experts and of the Association of Certified Fraud Examiners. He has considerable court experience and writes regularly on forensic issues for a range of professional publications. He is an experienced expert witness with a number of single joint expert appointments, and expert determination appointments by the Presidents Appointments Scheme, ICAEW.
David Selwyn: A forensic partner, David is also a former UK Governor of the Association of Certified Fraud Examiners. He has particular expertise in share valuations, a subject on which he has written and lectured widely.

GRANT THORNTON

Grant Thornton House, Melton Street, Euston Square, London, NW1 2EP
Tel: (020) 7383 5100 **Fax:** (020) 7383 4715 **DX:** 2100 Euston
Website: www.grant-thornton.co.uk

Contact Partners	
London	Philip Kabraji
Leeds	Robin Hall
Birmingham	Robert Kerr
Number of partners	229
Number of staff	2999

THE FIRM: Grant Thornton is a leading national and international accounting and consultancy firm providing a comprehensive range of business advisory services to a wide variety of clients from private individuals to major companies. The firm operates from over 40 offices in the UK and has an international network spanning nearly 100 countries. A team of specialist forensic partners and staff offer extensive experience of commercial litigation, complex insurance claims, fraud and personal injury. Investigative financial, accounting and taxation services are provided to assist in the building of a case, obtaining settlement or the giving of expert evidence in court. Forensic services are available from most of the firm's UK offices. The main forensic centres are in the London office (Partner in charge: Philip Kabraji), the Leeds office (Partner in charge: Robin Hall) and the Birmingham office (Partner in charge: Robert Kerr).
LITIGATION SUPPORT SERVICES: The partners in the firm have experience in a wide number of business sectors, including construction, manufacturing, motor dealers, engineering, banking, financial, oil and gas, hotel and leisure, defence and professional services. Partners with appropriate expertise and witness box experience are available to act in contractual and commercial disputes, consequential loss of profit claims, breach of warranty, business and share valuations, fraud, computer disputes, professional negli-

gence claims, trade disputes (including advice on EC and US anti-dumping regulations), directors' disqualification hearings, personal injury, medical negligence and fatal accident claims, structured settlements, royalty disputes, matrimonial disputes and libel claims.

HAYS MACINTYRE

Southampton House, 317 High Holborn, London, WC1V 7NL
Tel: (020) 7969 5500 **Fax:** (020) 7969 5600 **DX:** 1005 Chancery Lane

Contact Partner	Edward Ross-McNairn
Number of partners	28
Number of staff	170

THE FIRM: Hays Allan and Macintyre & Co merged on 1 January 2001to form haysmacintyre, a top 25 Chartered Accountancy. The firm offers a full range of tailored audit, advisory, tax and VAT services, with strong corporate finance capabilities, all complemented by its connection with an international network, MSI.

The Team: The LS and forensic accounting team includes partners and staff who are experts in their field. The firm provides a wide range of services to clients from many different sectors. Edward Ross-McNairn leads the team. He is a member of the Academy of Experts and the Expert Institute, and has wide ranging experience in the field, including considerable experience in giving evidence in court.

LITIGATION SUPPORT SERVICES: Work undertaken includes commercial litigation, personal injury/medical negligence, professional negligence, criminal litigation and fraud, company matters, matrimonial litigation and partnership disputes, forensic accounting and investigations, taxation, insurance, determinations and arbitrations, and mediation.

HORWATH CLARK WHITEHILL

25 New Street Square, London, EC4A 3LN
Tel: (020) 7353 1577 **Fax:** (020) 7353 6435 **DX:** London Chancery Lane 0014
Email: enquiry@horwathcw.co.uk **Website:** www.horwathcw.co.uk

London	Richard Freeman (020) 7353 1577 Humphrey Creed Daniel Djanogly James Gemmell Keith Warner Howard Williams
Thames Valley	Humphrey Creed (01494) 463 200
West Midlands	Chris Bicknell (01922) 725 590
Leeds	Ross MacLaverty (0113) 274 0404 David Baxter
Number of partners	72
Number of staff	532

THE FIRM: Horwath Clark Whitehill is a leading national firm of chartered accountants and business advisers in the UK.

FORENSIC ACCOUNTING: Horwath Clark Whitehill provides forensic accounting services on a national and international basis. Principals act as adviser or expert witness, including single joint expert, in personal and in corporate disputes, supported by a dedicated team of forensic accounting specialists and other experts from within the firm as required. Full use is made of the latest technology including data interrogation software. Dispute resolution services are also provided: arbitration (including London Scheme); mediation; expert determination. The firm is a corporate member of the Academy of Experts and quality control procedures are employed to ensure the high standards of the Code of Practice of the Academy are met. Principals are experienced in giving evidence in court and have undertaken in excess of 1,000 cases, many high profile.0

K

KINGSTON SMITH

Devonshire House, 60 Goswell Road, London, EC1M 7AD
Tel: (020) 7566 4000 **Fax:** (020) 7566 4010
Email: ks@kingstonsmith.co.uk **Website:** www.kingstonsmith.co.uk

Contact Partner	Emile Woolf
Number of partners	40
Number of staff	350

THE FIRM: The Kingston Smith litigation support facility was established in 1980, and all members of the service team have many years' professional and commercial experience to complement their legal and regulatory knowledge and skills. The team undertakes a wide range of specialist assignments for lawyers, insurers, loss adjusters, professional and regulatory bodies and government agencies, acting for either defendants or claimants. Civil and criminal assignments undertaken, including legally aided cases.

LITIGATION SUPPORT PARTNERS:

Emile Woolf: FCA, FCCA, MAE, FInstM, FIIA, has for many years been Chairman of the Professional Indemnity Insurance Panel of the Institute of Chartered Accountants in England and Wales (ICAEW) and represents the Institute on the Joint Advisory Panel of Participating Insurers, of which he is Chairman. He is widely known throughout the profession through his lectures and frequent contributions to the professional press on litigation issues. He is the author of several leading texts including *Professional Liability of Accountants* (ICAEW), *Risk Management for Auditors* (ICAEW), *Preserving Your Right to Audit* (CCH Editions), *Auditing Today* (Prentice Hall), *Emile Woolf on Audit Exemption* (CCH Editions), and *The Legal Liabilities of Practising Accountants* (Butterworths). He is a member of he Academy of Experts and is a CEDR-accredited mediator. He was the founder in 1975 of one of the largest listed accountancy training groups in the UK.

Benjamin Howe: FCA, ATII, MAE is responsible for the consequential and material loss claims assignments arising from, for example medical negligence, personal injury, fire and theft. His background includes advisory appointments and directorships in small companies giving him experience in com-

Continued overleaf

mercial aspects of business management to complement his professional expertise. He is a member of the Academy of Experts.

Martin Muirhead: FCA, MAE undertakes forensic accounting including computer modelling as well as commercial and tax related matters. His extensive business and tax experience includes financial services, investment business and general commercial sectors. Recent matters include acting in relation to liability and quantum in professional negligence disputes, varied commercial litigation including business and share valuations, minority protection, Inland Revenue investigations including Special Compliance Office, PAYE Audit and Benefits compliance and advising on quantum issues. He was appointed by the Charity Commissioners, under the Charities Act 1993, to act as the first Receiver and Manager of a UK registered Charity in dispute resolution of contentious areas including fiduciary duty trustees responsibilities. He is also a Company Director and member of the Academy of Experts.

Adrian Houstoun: FCA, ACIArb is a chartered accountant and a member of the Chartered Institute of Arbitrators. He specialises in matters where knowledge of the law of contract, tort and evidence can be combined with his extensive business experience, including public company acquisitions and VAT services. One of his recent assignments was an appointment by the Secretary of State for Industry, as an inspector under the Financial Services Act, to investigate alleged insider dealing in the securities of a public company. He is on the Institute of Chartered Accountants' panel of arbitrators and also undertakes investigations on their behalf into firms who are unable to obtain insurance cover. He has significant experience with business valuation cases and assisted lawyers in a number of matrimonial cases as well as advising directors following the sale of a business in connection with warranty claims.

LITIGATION SUPPORT SERVICES: Include professional negligence, consequential loss and business interruption including personal injury. Matrimonial, white collar crime, fraud, regulatory and compliance matters including directors' disqualification. Commercial disputes, breach of contract and defamation. Forensic accounting including fraud investigations, asset tracing, modelling in insurance and commercial cases. Inland Revenue and Customs investigations, settlements and related disputes. Business and share valuations. Sectors include financial and investment business. Specialist insolvency division.

KPMG

K

20 Farringdon Street, London, EC4A 4PP
Tel: (020) 7311 1000 **Fax:** (020) 7311 3672
Website: www.kpmg.co.uk

Expert Witness	John Ellison
Fraud Investigations	Alex Plavsic
Fraud Risk Management	David Davies
Regulatory Investigations	Karen Briggs
Birmingham	David Alexander (0121) 232 3000
Edinburgh	Judith Scott (0131) 527 6619
Leeds	Tim Taylor (0113) 231 3000
Manchester	Richard Powell (0161) 838 4000
Reading	Yvonne Craggs (0117) 905 4000

THE FIRM: KPMG Forensic Accounting is a leading member of the KPMG International Forensic Network providing worldwide forensic accounting services. The firm has a global forensic service with over 300 partners and staff, used to working together. KPMG is one of the leading business advisory firms in the world and provides a comprehensive range of accountancy, tax and consulting services. The firm has experience of working with organisations of all sizes from government to individuals, and from multinationals to privately-owned businesses. KPMG has over 100,000 personnel in 159 countries worldwide, and some 10,500 people in 24 offices in the UK.

LITIGATION SUPPORT SERVICES: KPMG Forensic Accounting has a dedicated team of more than 150 partners and professional staff throughout the UK, and a global coordinated forensic accounting service. The provision of these services is enhanced by expert knowledge of various industry sectors including banking; insurance; commodities; information technology; telecommunications; shipping and transportation; construction; manufacturing; oil and gas; infrastructure and government; leasing; retailing; healthcare and pharmaceutical; intellectual property. The firm provides specialist services in seven broad areas:

Commercial Disputes: Loss of profits claims; international and national arbitrations; breach of contract and warranty claims; purchase and sale disputes and agreement vetting; shareholder and partnership disputes; libel and slander actions; intellectual property; e-business disputes; business and share valuations; insurance claims; security for costs applications.

Professional Negligence: Accounting; auditing; corporate finance and IT implementation (liability and quantum); other professions (quantum).

Fraud Investigation: KPMG Forensic Accounting has developed particular expertise in handling investigations into fraud. Numerous assignments for government, police, companies and public bodies bear witness to the firm's reputation in this area. The firm uses a refined investigation methodology which, when combined with advanced technology, allows KPMG Forensic Accounting to investigate suspected frauds of all sizes effectively and efficiently.

Fraud Risk Management: Including fraud risk profiling; procurement diagnostic review; manipulation diagnostic review (including assessing e-business risk); fraud response planning and fraud awareness training.

Personal Disputes: Personal injury claims; fatal accidents; clinical negligence; family and matrimonial disputes; employment; pension disputes.

Regulatory Investigations: Investigations and accounting assistance for regulatory authorities and those under investigation. Also assistance in statutory and disciplinary enquiries.

Determinations & Arbitrations: Expert determinations; arbitrations; mediations; valuations.

LEVY GEE

66 Wigmore Street, London, W1U 2HQ
Tel: (020) 7467 4000
Email: investigations@levygee.com **Website:** www.levygee.com

South Central, 11 Peter Street, Manchester, M2 5LG
Tel: (0161) 833 8300

9 Portland Road, Edgbaston, Birmingham, B16 9HN
Tel: (0121) 456 2828

Contact Partners	
London	David Epstein
	David Stern
	Gail Rifkind
Manchester	David Rabinowitz
Birmingham	Alan Thompson
Number of partners	53
Number of staff	385

THE FIRM: The Levy Gee Forensic Accounting and Dispute Resolution department has dedicated partners and qualified staff in each of its London, Birmingham and Manchester offices. The department assists the legal profession, insurers and regulatory and prosecuting bodies in the pursuance and defence of claims by providing expert opinions on the quantum of loss.

LITIGATION SUPPORT PARTNERS:

David Epstein: (FCA) has thirty years' experience of advising partnerships and owner-managed businesses. David has been instructed on a wide range of disputes including claims for commercial loss and professional negligence. He is a member of The Academy of Experts, a founding member of The Expert Witness Institute, a member of the British Institute of Management, an Associate of The Chartered Institute of Taxation and a member of the Metropolitan Police Liaison Panel at the Institute of Chartered Accountants in England and Wales (ICAEW). He also has a strong financial services background.

David Stern: (FCA) has been instructed on a wide range of both civil and criminal forensic accounting cases. He has also received appointments from the ICAEW to act as an arbitrator and as an expert. In addition, as a CEDR registered mediator, David has acted on a wide range of disputes and is also a mediator on the Sports Dispute Resolution Panel (SDRP). David is also a member of the Academy of Experts, a member of the Chartered Institute of Arbitrators and a member of the Association of Business Recovery Professionals.

Gail Rifkind: (CA - Scotland) specialises in personal injury, clinical negligence and fatal accident work for both claimant and defendant. She has been involved in many headline cases, such as the Kings Cross fire, the Southhall Rail crash, asbestosis claims and pregnancy dismissals at the MOD and has experience of giving evidence in court. Gail is frequently instructed as a single joint expert. Gail is a member of The Academy of Experts and a founding member of The Expert Witness Institute.

Alan Thompson: (FCA) heads up the Birmingham department. He has worked on a wide range of cases such as professional negligence, fraud, breach of contract and matrimonial disputes as well as director disqualification cases. He has also worked with the Crown Prosecution Services in relation to fraud matters. Alan is experienced in dealing with contract and tax disputes in other countries and has given evidence in the USA as well as the UK. Alan is also a member of the Academy of Experts, The Chartered Institute of Taxation and The Society of Practitioners of Insolvency, as well as The Chartered Institute of Arbitrators.

David Rabinowitz: (ACA) has wide ranging experience in all aspects of litigation support, having specialised in this work for the past ten years. His particular areas of specialism are in the commercial litigation and personal injury/clinical negligence fields and he has lectured on these subjects to lawyers and insurance companies. David frequently acts as a single joint expert and has given evidence in court. He has been appointed as expert by the ICAEW and is a CEDR accredited mediator. David is a member of the ICAEW and The Academy of Experts.

LITIGATION SUPPORT SERVICES: Forensic Accounting: Members of the team have significant experience of a range of businesses and industries and provide a partner-led service covering breach of warranty claims; business interruption and consequential loss claims; contractual disputes; due diligence; family and matrimonial disputes; fraud investigations; personal injury and clinical negligence claims; professional negligence claims; shareholder and partnership disputes; share valuations; partners have considerable experience of giving evidence in Court in both civil and criminal proceedings. In addition, partners in the department accept appointments in the areas of arbitration, mediation and expert determination.

LITTLEJOHN FRAZER

1 Park Place, Canary Wharf, London, E14 4HJ
Tel: (020) 7987 5030 **Fax:** (020) 7987 9707 **DX:** 42660
Email: info@littlejohnfrazer.com **Website:** www.littlejohnfrazer.com

Contact Partner	Ian Hobbs
Number of partners	23
Number of staff	150

THE FIRM: Partners at Littlejohn Frazer now have over 15 years' experience of providing litigation support services to the legal profession. Of the firm's 23 partners, 12 have relevant experience and the lead partners (Ian Hobbs and Alastair Campbell) have considerable experience of justifying their expert opinions in the witness box. Ian Hobbs is the co-author of *Expert Accounting Evidence - A Guide for Litigation Support* published by the ICAEW in 1998. Lord Woolf wrote the preface and said: "*I welcome the publication of this book and congratulate the authors on a job well done. I do so, because while I welcome the greater involvement of accountants in the court process, this welcome is conditional. It is conditional on the involvement being constructive. It can only be constructive if the involvement is knowledgeable and proportionate. Unfortunately, sometimes it is not and this is all too often due to ignorance or a lack of professionalism for which this book provides the remedy. The authors rightly stress the need to keep costs under control and echo the messages which are contained in my report in "Access to Justice"..* Partners have experience of investigations for the DTI, and the firm has undertaken a number of assignments for the Serious Fraud Office. Legally aided work is undertaken, in both civil and criminal matters. The firm has extensive experience of the insurance sector and in particular the Lloyd's market.

LITIGATION SUPPORT PARTNERS:
I.C. Hobbs: (FCA) Member of Academy of Experts; CEDR Accredited Mediator. Specialises in accountants' negligence; quantification of loss, particularly consequential loss in construction disputes and fire claims; share valuations; tax as a non-specialist; serious fraud; personal injury; matrimonial.
A.H.F. Campbell: (FCA) Serious fraud, regulatory, Lloyd's, accountants' negligence, breach of financial warranties.
J.G. Ambler: (ACA) Computer consultancy, software contracts.
R.L. Green: (FCCA) Solicitors' Accounts Rules.
D.R.M. Frame: (FCA) Serious fraud, forensic.
M.T. Stenson: (FCA) Serious fraud, regulatory.
D.W. Roberts: (FCA) Regulatory, Lloyd's.

LITIGATION SUPPORT SERVICES:
Civil: Accountants professional negligence; financial consequences of personal injury; consequential loss, particularly in construction and fire-damage claims; insurance and re-insurance disputes; purchase and sales disputes; matrimonial disputes; intellectual property disputes. Experience as single joint expert.
Criminal: Serious fraud; crime with financial motive; Companies Act offences.
Investigations: Computer consultancy; forensic accounting.
Regulatory: ICAEW; FSA; Law Society; RICS; DTI; SFO; Lloyd's.
ADR: Mediations as expert and as mediator.

L

LONDON ECONOMICS

60 Lombard Street, London, EC3V 9EA
Tel: (020) 7446 8400 **Fax:** (020) 7464 8618
Email: competition@londecon.co.uk **Website:** www.londecon.co.uk

Contact	Nils von Hinten-Reed

THE FIRM: LE is Europe's leading independent economics consultancy. Since its foundation in 1986, it has provided comprehensive litigation and arbitration support in cases across the UK, the EU and Australia.

LITIGATION SUPPORT SERVICES: Expertise covers the following areas: interpretation of economic concepts in the context of contract or tort; calculation of damages; competition cases; valuation of intellectual property rights; tax disputes. London Economics' litigation support services are based on a unique combination of skills and resources unavailable from other advisers. As specialist economic consultants, they provide a service that combines the economic expertise of the best independent academics with the professionalism and ability to deliver associated with large accounting firms. Expert witnesses are experienced in giving evidence, appearing in court and reacting to cross-examination. They provide advice on the strengths and weaknesses of the opposition's case and expert opinions, providing ammunition for cross-examination.

MARKS & CLERK

57-60 Lincoln's Inn Fields, London, WC2A 3LS
Tel: (020) 7400 3000 **Fax:** (020) 7404 4910
Email: admin@marks-clerk.com **Website:** www.marks-clerk.com

Contact		
London	John Slater	(020) 7400 3000
Birmingham	Tony Pearce	(0121) 643 5881
Manchester	John Allman	(0161) 233 5800
Glasgow	Bill McCallum	(0141) 221 5767
Cheltenham	Mike Higgins	(01242) 524 520
Oxford	Richard Harding	(01865) 397 900
Leeds	Keith Hodkinson	(0113) 389 5600
Luxembourg	Pierre Weland	+352 400 270
Hong Kong	Simon Speeks	+852 2526 6345
Ottawa	Bob Sterling	+1 613 236 9561
Alicante	Aidan Clarke	+34 96 51 42727
Number of partners		50
Number of staff		200

THE FIRM: Marks & Clerk was founded in 1887. A leader in the field of intellectual property with 50 partners and over 100 fee earners, the firm serves a client base ranging from the private individual to the largest multinational corporations. In addition to preparing and filing patent, trade mark and design applications, Marks & Clerk advises on infringement and its avoidance, reverse engineering and validity issues. It provides technical support to solicitors and barristers in litigation and perform intellectual property audits and due diligence reviews on all aspects of intellectual property transactions. The firm offers expert witnesses for proceedings in the UK and overseas and provides ancillary services such as patent, design and trade mark searching, competitor monitoring and related investigations. It also arranges appropriate documentation for global assignment and licensing transactions and assist in IP portfolio management and training services.

MARKS & CLERK
Intellectual Property

MARTIN GREENE RAVDEN

55 Loudoun Road, St. Johns Wood, London, NW8 0DL
Tel: (020) 7625 4545 **Fax:** (020) 7625 5265
Email: mgr@mgr.co.uk **Website:** www.mgr.co.uk

Contact Partners	
	David Greene
	David Ravden
	Robert Braham

THE FIRM: Martin Greene Ravden is a medium-size firm of chartered accountants with 10 partners and over 70 staff. It represents a broad range of clients and is best known as one of the leading specialists in the media, entertainment and sports industries. The firm has a highly experienced forensic accounting and litigation support group, with an excellent track record in helping solicitors achieve very favourable results in contentious cases.

LITIGATION SUPPORT SERVICES:

Matrimonial Disputes: Valuation of businesses and shares in private companies; investigating the completeness of disclosures; clarifying income and capital positions; assessment of income requirement; tax efficient structuring of settlements.

Commercial Disputes: Entertainment industry and intellectual property disputes; quantification of loss in commercial disputes and claims for damages; shareholder and partnership disputes; claims for consequential loss and loss of earnings; fraud investigations.

M

MAZARS NEVILLE RUSSELL

24 Bevis Marks, London, EC3A 7NR
Tel: (020) 7377 1000 **Fax:** (020) 7377 8931
Website: www.mazars-nr.co.uk

Contact Partners	
	Glyn Williams
	Peter Hyatt
	Paul Smethurst
Number of partners	87
Number of staff	1000

THE FIRM: Mazars Neville Russell is the UK firm of Mazars, the leading international accounting and consultancy group operating in over 50 countries. The growing forensic and investigation services group have advised in, and reported upon, a broad spectrum of cases requiring independent financial analysis. The team is experienced in giving evidence in court and arbitration proceedings. Whilst bringing all the resources that might be expected from an international firm, the emphasis of the service is on ensuring work is undertaken on a timely and efficient basis. This is achieved through the high level of personal involvement at all stages by the reporting expert.

MOORE STEPHENS

St Paul's House, Warwick Lane, London, EC4P 4BN
Tel: (020) 7334 9191 **Fax:** (020) 7248 3408 **DX:** 15 London
Email: postmaster@moorestephens.com **Website:** www.moorestephens.co.uk

Contact Partner	Julian Wilkinson
Number of partners	146
Number of staff	1217

LITIGATION SUPPORT PARTNERS:
Julian Wilkinson FCA, MAE: Shipping related matters including alleged scuttling claims and joint venture disputes. Also loss of profits claims. Has given evidence in Court.
James Smart FCA: London insurance market. Confidential enquiries, loss reviews and investigations for the DTI, PIA, Lloyd's and others and acts as expert in insurance related litigation.
Phillip Sykes ACA: Corporate recovery, insolvency and fraud investigation. Has acted for the Fraud Squad and for defendants. Directors' disqualification proceedings and wrongful and fraudulent trading actions.
Nicholas King FCA: Business planning, project appraisal and the use of computerised accounting models. Salvage and other shipping disputes.

LITIGATION SUPPORT SERVICES:
Loss of Profits: Business interruption; product inadequacy; infringement of intellectual property rights; breach of contract or warranties; personal injury or medical negligence.
Valuations: Business and business assets for settlement of commercial disputes; in separation or divorce cases.
Professional Negligence: Property and information technology matters; due diligence work in business acquisitions and disputes; taxation advice; insolvency; audit and accountancy.
International Trade Claims: Particularly shipping and transport matters.
Fraud & Criminal Work: Forensic accounting; asset tracing; theft/misappropriation; false accounting; fraud investigation; corporate fraud; tax/subsidy fraud; wrongful trading.

MORLEY AND SCOTT

Lynton House, 7-12 Tavistock Square, London, WC1H 9LT
Tel: (020) 7387 5868 **Fax:** (020) 7388 3978 **DX:** 2112 Euston
Email: ms@morley-scott.co.uk **Website:** www.morley-scott.co.uk

Contact Partners	Kay Linnell Simon Howard

THE FIRM: Morley & Scott is a firm of UK chartered accountants with an international perspective and a well-established reputation for a high quality and personal service. The firm services an impressive list of corporate and private clients in the South East of England and has links internationally through the GMN network. The firm combines a forward-looking approach with attention to personal client relationships. Its commitment to its people, the latest technology support systems and its international network of independent practices enables it to deliver a wide-ranging service across many industry sectors.

LITIGATION SUPPORT SERVICES: Morley & Scott has a dedicated litigation support department whose expertise covers the full range of forensic accounting, including assistance for regulatory bodies, civil litigation, investigations of business assets, fraud irregularities, professional negligence, divorce, loss of profits, share valuation, dispute resolution and personal injury. The firm's objective is to provide creative and objective reports and advice giving a constructive and flexible approach to each assignment to encompass the wider implications for either claimants or respondent.

PETER LOBBENBERG & CO

74 Chancery Lane, London, WC2A 1AD
Tel: (020) 7430 9300 **Fax:** (020) 7430 9315 **DX:** 204 London/Chancery Lane

Contact Partner	Peter Lobbenberg
Number of partners	1
Number of staff	2

THE FIRM: A niche practice well known as specialists in matrimonial litigation support throughout the country; its clients include over 80% of the leading London family law firms listed in *Chambers.* The firm also specialises in share valuations, and operates a caring tax service for private clients and trusts. As a member of Horwath Clark Whitehill Associates, the firm has access to a wide range of facilities and specialisms. The contact partner is a fellow of the Academy of Experts.

INTERNATIONAL: Work is handled in German and French.

PINDERS PROFESSIONAL & CONSULTANCY SERVICES LIMITED

Pinder House, Central Milton Keynes, MK9 1DS
Tel: (01908) 350500 **Fax:** (01908) 350501 **DX:** 84752 Milton Keynes 3
Email: pcs@pinders.co.uk **Website:** www.pinders.co.uk

Contact Director	Mark Ellis BSc FRICS MCIArb MAE
Director	Jon Chapman BA Hons QDR
	Simon Bird BSc ARICS MCIArb
Senior Chartered Surveyor	Graham Coulter FRICS
Consultant	Marek Bilecki FRICS
	Justin Cain MRICS
Senior Chartered Building Surveyor	Ray Chamberlain ARICS

THE FIRM: The Pinders name has become synonymous with the appraisal and valuation of businesses since 1969, providing specialist professional services to the legal and banking professions on the health-care, retail, licensed and leisure sectors. Particular areas of expertise include business valuations (both current and retrospective), loss of profits claims, expert witness evidence and professional negligence. Pinders can call upon a database containing detailed trading and valuation information on over 160,000 businesses throughout the United Kingdom, together with continually updated records of sale transactions.

LITIGATION SUPPORT PARTNERS:
Mark Ellis: (BSc FRICS MCIArb MAE), previously a member of The RICS Skills Panel on Trading Related Valuations, heads up the professional services and litigation support team based at the head office in Milton Keynes and a team of regional valuers who combine knowledge of local values, trade sources, legislation and competition with the wider accumulation of centralised information and expertise. The team includes a QDR and Arbitrators.

PKF

New Garden House, 78 Hatton Garden, London, EC1N 8JA
Tel: (020) 7831 7393 **Fax:** (020) 7405 6736 **DX:** 479 Chancery Lane
Email: forename.surname@uk.pkf.com **Website:** www.pkf.co.uk

CONTACTS		
London		(020) 7831 7393
	Richard Bolton	
	Roger Claxton	
	Hugh Mathew-Jones	
	Richard Pearson	
	Nick Whitaker	
Birmingham	David Liddell	(0121) 212 2222
Edinburgh	Jim Riddell	(0131) 225 3688
Glasgow	Frank Paterson	(0141) 429 5900
Gt Yarmouth	Jon Dodge	(01493) 842 281
Guildford	Valerie Martin	(01483) 564 646
Ipswich	Marilyn Martin	(01473) 217 691
Leicester	Tim Aspell	(0116) 250 4400
Leeds	Neill Poole	(0113) 228 0000
Lincoln	Jeff Kirkham	(01522) 531 441
Liverpool	Mark Fairhurst	(0151) 708 8232
Manchester	John Grogan	(0161) 832 5481
Norwich	Roger Walton	(01603) 615 914
Nottingham	Simon Bold	(0115) 960 8171
Sheffield	Jeremy Lai	(0114) 276 7991
Worcester	Mick Maton	(01905) 24 437
Number of partners		113
Number of staff		1414

THE FIRM: PKF is an international grouping with offices in 94 countries. The UK firm of accountants and business advisors was established in 1869 and offers the full range of corporate finance, business advisory, risk management, assurance and taxation skills together with important specialisms such as the international management consultancy and the hotels division. The nationally organised forensic services group provides a partner led service, backed by experienced professional staff with a grounding in commercial and professional life.

LITIGATION SUPPORT SERVICES: The PKF approach to helping clients extends throughout the practice. Multi-disciplinary teams can be assembled to handle the largest corporate actions. Those consulting PKF's forensic accounting section can rely on careful analysis of the issues and clear presentation of the findings by experts in the particular area concerned. PKF gives timely and positive advice whether as advisors or as independent experts.
Forensic Work: Work undertaken includes the quantifying of: breach of contract and warranty claims; commercial business interruption and consequential loss claims; loss of profit from public or product liability issues; reinsurance claims; third party damage and other financial loss claims; professional negligence; personal injury, dependency and clinical negligence claims. Many of these involve valuations of businesses or shares of businesses. PKF forensic accountants are experienced in providing evidence across the spectrum of the Courts, and in various arbitral tribunals. PKF assists clients in their mediation and other ADR endeavours.

REEVES & NEYLAN FORENSIC ACCOUNTING

Victoria House, 20-22 Albion Place, Ramsgate, CT11 8HQ
Tel: (01843) 572300 **Fax:** (01843) 572309 **DX:** 30622 Ramsgate
Email: forensic@reeves-neylan.com **Website:** www.reeves-neylan.com/forensic

Contact Partner	Alan Tinham
Number of partners	20
Number of staff	170

THE FIRM: Reeves & Neylan Forensic Accounting, the dedicated litigation support department of Reeves & Neylan, is a corporate member of the Academy of Experts. Work will usually commence within one to two days of receipt of formal instructions and all reports are CPR compliant. Assistance is available with pre-issue evaluation of quantum and Part 36 offers. Services are provided to claimants and defendants throughout the UK as SJE, party appointed expert or advisor.

LITIGATION SUPPORT SERVICES: Services include calculation of quantum; commercial disputes, product liability claims, environmental pollution; loss of profit claims; personal injury, medical negligence/class actions and fatality claims; divorce; professional negligence; CA S459 investigations and share valuations; theft, fraud and financial irregularities; wrongful and fraudulent trading; S71 confiscation orders; VAT and tax fraud.

OTHER AREAS OF WORK: Reeves & Neylan also provides specialist services in the following areas: VAT consultancy; Solicitors' Accounts Rules audits; tax planning and profit improvement consultancy; design and implementation of practice management information systems; practice finance arrangements; investigations.

P

RGL INTERNATIONAL

17 Devonshire Square, London, EC2M 4SQ
Tel: (020) 7247 4804 **Fax:** (020) 7247 4970
Email: expert@rglinternational.com **Website:** www.rgl.com

Contact Partners	Anthony Levitt Edward Leighton Keith Tuffin Catherine Rawlin James Stanbury

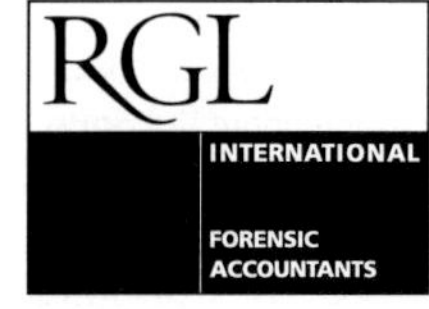

THE FIRM: RGL International is a leading firm of forensic accountants, specialising in the calculation of quantum in claims arising from disputes and disasters. Partners at RGL International assist lawyers in disputes, both in settling them before they go to court, and in providing expert testimony in court. The firm helps with pre-trial conferences, meetings of experts, provides accounting support and frequently gives specialist evidence as expert witnesses. Areas of expertise include business interruption and loss of profits; stock losses; product liability; fatal accident and personal injury; commercial litigation; fraud; breach of contract; third party disputes; insurance claims; reinsurance disputes; subrogation; general quantification of damages. RGL International's UK practitioners are fully conversant with the Rules of Civil Procedure issued by the Lord Chancellor's Department. They are able to identify which documents should be made available for discovery, from both inside and outside any company. The reports provided to instructing solicitors for use in litigation or negotiations highlight the strengths and weaknesses of the claim and draw attention to any errors or omissions within it. Should a claim come to court, RGL International's practitioners can clearly and succinctly explain evidence included in the accounting expert's report under examination-in-chief and cross-examination. As a specialist firm, RGL International very seldom has a conflict of interest; always dedicates a partner and team to every investigation; ensures fees are cost effective and reasonable; utilises experience from forensic accountants throughout its worldwide network of offices.

SAFFERY CHAMPNESS

Lion House, Red Lion Street, London, WC1R 4GB
Tel: (020) 7405 2828 **Fax:** (020) 7405 7887 **DX:** 287-Chancery Lane, London
Email: mail@saffery.com **Website:** www.saffery.com

Saffery Champness
CHARTERED ACCOUNTANTS

THE FIRM: The Saffery Champness litigation team works with lawyers throughout the country on a wide variety of cases. As accountants and business advisors, the firm's expertise in and understanding of the business environment means that it can offer valuable forensic accounting advice. The team includes partners Stewart Garrard, David Macey and Nick Kelsey for general financial issues, Peter Horsman and Mike Beattie for taxation and Michael Cohen for valuations. Saffery Champness is a top twenty accountancy practice with nine offices in the UK and one in Guernsey. The firm has over a century's experience of advising private clients, business owners, their businesses and landed estates and their owners.

S

LITIGATION SUPPORT SERVICES: Areas covered include e-commerce related business and taxation issues; personal injury and fatal accident; matrimonial issues; medical negligence; loss of profits or earnings; professional negligence; valuation of shares and businesses; fraud; Inland Revenue and Customs & Excise investigations.

SMITH & WILLIAMSON

No. 1 Riding House St, London, W1A 3AS
Tel: (020) 7637 5377 **Fax:** (020) 7631 0741
Email: <recipient>@williamson.co.uk **Website:** www.smith.williamson.co

Contact Partners	Douglas J Hall Peter G Mills Iain J Allan Frank A M Akers-Douglas
Number of partners	100
Number of staff	600

THE FIRM: Smith & Williamson combines a firm of chartered accountants and an investment management house. Its full range of accountancy services covers accountancy, auditing, corporate finance, corporate recovery, corporate taxation, investigations, litigation support, management consulting and personal taxation.

LITIGATION SUPPORT SERVICES: Smith & Williamson has a dedicated litigation support team whose expertise covers the full range of forensic accounting, including assistance for regulatory bodies, civil litigation, investigations of fraud and personal injury. The firm has experience in acting for either the claimant or the defendant and its objective is always to understand the wider implications of a case in order to provide a flexible and constructive approach to every assignment.

Consultants

THE ACADEMY OF EXPERTS

2 South Square, Grays Inn, London, WC1R 5HP
Tel: (020) 7637 0333 **Fax:** (020) 7637 1893 **DX:** 283 -London, Chancery Lane
Email: admin@academy-experts.org

Secretary General	Nicola Cohen

THE FIRM: The Academy of Experts is a professional body for Expert Witnesses providing services to its members and the legal profession.

LITIGATION SUPPORT SERVICES: All applicants for practising membership as experts submit to a thorough vetting procedure to ensure the maintenance of standards. Standards are enforced by codes of practice with disciplinary sanctions.

Expert Search: The Academy matches the right accredited expert to a case. This includes speaking to the expert to check suitability, conflict of interests and availability.

Expert Training: The Academy's training programme is designed for all levels of experience from the first time expert to the more experienced. As well as complying with CPR, experts need knowledge, skills and confidence to perform well in conference, meetings of experts and in Court.

Commercial Mediation Training: As one of the longest-running commercial mediation training courses (est.1989) the Academy's course is now under the control of the Faculty of Mediation & ADR. The Academy awards the letters QDR for successful completion and entry onto the Register of Qualified Dispute Resolvers.

Mediation Appointment: Using the same method as in expert search, the Academy appoints the right accredited mediator.

CICERO CONSULTING

56-60 Gresham Street, London, EC2V 7BB
Tel: (020) 7776 6555 **Fax:** (020) 7726 6544
Email: welcome@thinkcicero.com **Website:** www.thinkcicero.com

Litigation PR	Stephen Lock
Political Affairs/PR	Richard Elsen
Corporate Crisis PR	Iain Anderson
Consumer Crisis PR	Melanie Riley

THE FIRM: Cicero Consulting Limited is the 'public interest' issues management consultancy for Europe that specialises in litigation PR; government relations and political affairs; corporate crisis PR management and 'public campaigning'. The firm is named after the inspiring Roman figure of Marcus Tullius Cicero (106-43 BC) who has for centuries been recognised as the 'father of rhetoric'. Cicero is an independent privately owned company whose shareholders include its directors and staff. Cicero is headquartered in London and in Autumn 2001 shall open offices in Paris and Brussels. The firm's Paris office will offer clients litigation PR; French government relations and public affairs and has a particular expertise in crisis PR management. Its Brussels office will be able to assist clients in all the diverse aspects of lobbying 'Brussels DC', as well as offer clients a specialist PR service directed towards the press corps covering the European Parliament and other EU institutions. In addition to these offices, Cicero has carefully selected affiliate consultancies in a number of other European territories, including Austria, Germany, Italy, Poland, Russia, Spain and Turkey. Cicero also has connections with firms outside of Europe, if required.

LITIGATION SUPPORT SERVICES: The Cicero founders include the team that launched litigation PR as a specialist service in Europe. Litigation PR is an area where nimble media relations skills need to be combined with an experience and understanding of the litigation process (including issues related to Contempt of Court avoidance). In the firm's Litigation PR assignments it insists upon working particularly closely with clients' external legal advisers, from whom it usually takes its day-to-day instructions. Cicero has worked on some of the most high profile civil cases of recent years. Those where its work is a matter of public record include Alliance Against the BNRR v Secretary of State, DETR & Midland Expressway*; Diana, Princess of Wales Memorial Fund v Franklin Mint*; Elite* v BBC; Manoukian* v HRH Prince Jefri of Brunei; Nike* v Savacentre (Sainsbury's); Tommy Hilfiger Europe* v Tesco; Trans World v Kazakhstan Mineral Resources Corporation*. The firm has also advised on intense political and media situations involving fatal accidents; product liability; competition issues and medical negligence. Services range from media risk assessment for clients, ahead of legal action, to high profile, high impact media support for injunction actions and at the start of legal proceedings. Services also include (depending on jurisdiction and Bench rulings) through-trial press management and proactive media campaigning.

Other Specialist Services: Outside of the litigation PR practice, the firm has also developed a specialism in witness training for those called to appear before House of Commons Select Committee enquiries, particularly with regard to the political response to a witness's testimony and its likely media impact. The Cicero founders have advised clients in a number of enquiries including (but not limited to) ING Baring/former directors of Baring's (Treasury Select Committee); British Biotech (Science & Technology Select Committee) and the Institute & Faculty of Actuaries (Social Security Select Committee). We have also advised clients involved in fatal accident public enquiries. In its mainstream political practice Cicero

Continued overleaf

seeks to help clients best make their own case: the firm is not a political advocate, nor does it offer a 'black book' of political contacts for hire. Cicero Consulting is a member of the Association of Professional Political Consultants and its UK-based fee-earners are all members or associate members of the Institute of Public Relations. Cicero's litigation PR experience covers many aspects of civil litigation, in many jurisdictions (including UK, USA, Belgium, British Virgin Islands, France, Italy, Spain, Switzerland, Russia and Kazakhstan). Many of its mandates here have been to keep issues out of the public eye. Although most of Cicero's clients are corporates it advises a number of very high net worth individuals and their families. It can, if required, organise discreet personal protection and counter-surveillance services: Cicero has special relationships with corporate intelligence firms in the UK, USA and the CIS.

Internet Campaigning: Cicero has found that the Internet can prove to be a valuable tool in litigation PR campaigns. It has built 'sealed' pressrooms for specific litigation cases, where it has been able to develop an essential media reference point, especially for international press covering cases in hard-to-get-to places, offering journalists real-time news; a 'cast list' for the case; history of, and background to, the litigation; photo-suite and detailed news archive. For a number of clients Cicero has also developed sophisticated Internet monitoring services. These are much faster at picking up new web content (within 12-24 hours rather than the 6-8 weeks of traditional search engines), which operate beyond the usual news sites to which other 'off-the shelf' monitoring services restrict themselves. It has provided these services covering several languages online, including in the Cyrillic alphabet.

* = Client advised by Cicero.

DE VERE & CO.

3 Field Court, Gray's Inn, London, WC1R 5EF
Tel: (020) 7242 1012 **Fax:** (020) 7242 2012 **DX:** 221 Chancery Lane
Email: inv@thedeveregroup.com **Website:** www.thedeveregroup.com

Contact Partners	Simon Kidd Julian Rozario Brian Reeves Tony Kidd Susan Shaw
Number of partners	5
Number of staff	18

THE FIRM: De Vere is a well established, independent firm offering a wide range of specifically tailored services to assist lawyers and their clients with the litigation process in the UK and overseas. Other offices in Birmingham, Bournemouth, Manchester, New York, and Washington DC.

LITIGATION SUPPORT PARTNERS:

Simon Kidd: Fraud, due diligence, asset location, intellectual property.
Brian Reeves: Tracing, staff vetting and investigations.
Julian Rozario: Insurance investigations.

LITIGATION SUPPORT SERVICES:

Fraud: Fraud investigations, forensic studies, asset location, fraud vulnerability studies, fraud prevention techniques, and fraud awareness.
Training: Fraud awareness, fraud prevention, evidence packaging, basic legislation, and money laundering.
Due Dilligence: Companies, directors, and staff vetting.
Insurance: Insurance fraud, surveillance, witness statements.
Intellectual Property: Investigations.

GRANDFIELD

69 Wilson Street, London, EC2A 2BB
Tel: (020) 7417 4170 **Fax:** (020) 7417 9180
Email: paul.jaffa@grandfield.com **Website:** www.grandfield.com

Contact Director	Robert Rice Clare Abbot Paul Jaffa

THE FIRM: Grandfield is an independent corporate communications consultancy and one of the UK's leading public relations specialists advising the professional services sector. It has a specialist team dedicated to advising legal and professional clients, creating communications strategies to manage profile and reputation whilst supporting and adding value to business development activities. The team includes former lawyers, accountants, business managers, journalists, analysts and in house marketing and communications experts. It uses this collective knowledge and experience to produce exceptional results for clients and only recommends communication strategies and programmes which are relevant to clients' business objectives. Grandfield acts for major law firms in the UK, US and Europe as well as leading professional firms in accountancy, surveying, management consultancy, recruitment and insurance. Grandfield's sevices include corporate positioning; crisis and issues management; interview and presentation training; marketing and business development strategies; media relations planning and execution; mergers and acquisitions; communications; opinion research audits; strategic and tactical advice; website and Internet communications analysis. In 1997 Grandfield established a dedicated litigation support unit and we have extensive experience in creating communications strategies to support high profile legal actions in the UK and worldwide.

LITIGATION SUPPORT SERVICES:

Pre Trial Support: Including development of key messages, communictions planning, reputation management and media training.
Trial Support: Including provision of press office services, media monitoring, evaluation, perceptions research and pre-trial review.

LEHMANN COMMUNICATIONS PLC

Lloyds Avenue House, 6 Lloyds Avenue, London, EC3N 3EH
Tel: (020) 7266 3020 **Fax:** (020) 7266 3060
Email: pr@lehmanncommunications.com **Website:** www.lehmanncommunications.com

Chief Executive	Ronel Lehmann MIPR
Corporate & Professional	Adrian Lithgow
	Darshna Patel AMIPR
	Bill Robertson
Financial	Ronel Lehmann MIPR
Consumer	Anthony Poppleton
Business Development	Grenville Burn MIPR
	James Meek

THE FIRM: Lehmann Communications is an international public relations consultancy specialising in the corporate, financial, professional services and consumer sectors. The firm was founded in 1988 and acts for leading solicitors, barristers, accountants, banks, and financial institutions, insurance brokers, management and recruitment consultants and technology businesses. The firm's account directors, managers and executives have well-established, close links with editors, journalists, producers and Internet service providers responsible for news, business and current affairs – people who disseminate information to news sources and build media profiles. Lehmann Communications is a full service consultancy resourced to provide the best people offering the highest levels of service alongside clear, innovative and imaginative thinking across a whole range of communications.

LITIGATION SUPPORT PARTNERS: The firm considers its staff and their expertise to be its greatest asset and its best resource. It has a continuing policy of investing in the recruitment and training of the best people to enable them to provide leading edge thinking and advice. The firm focuses on developing long-term relationships with its clients; most fall into this category even if the firm is instructed on a project basis. It makes a point of investing time and effort in getting to know clients' organisations and their culture. The firm analyses the issues faced by its clients which underline its advice and communications solutions.

LITIGATION SUPPORT SERVICES: The firm's services include public relations advice; public affairs, political and parliamentary consultancy; design and print management; advertising and copywriting; new business presentation; media training; project and event management; sponsorship; crisis management; internal communications; website and e-commerce development. Examples of work undertaken include positioning clients as commentators in breaking news stories; acting for many US law firms in the UK; acting for law firms in mergers; acting for claimants in financial class actions; handling strategic communications during major takeovers. The firm advised the Lincoln's Inn Fields firm of solicitors responsible for for issuing first writs against the junior health minister over the salmonella in-the-eggs row; launched an arbitration scheme for personal injury victims; handled the first ever 'no-win-no-fee' personal injury victim on behalf of a leading regional practice; advised solicitors who made legal history and received indemnity costs on behalf of a client over the incorrect discharge of an Anton Pillar order; worked with a regional firm to launch a Waste and Minerals group; advised in respect of the sleeping drug Halcyon case which, until recently, was one of the longest libel trials since the second world war; launched the first ever City of London law firm's office in Belfast.

INTERNATIONAL: The firm also has an office at 730 Fifth Avenue, New York, NY 10019, USA. Tel: +1 212 333 8780. Fax: +1 212 307 3221.

Investigators

1ST CALL LONDON PRIVATE INVESTIGATIONS

27 Old Gloucester Street, London, WC1N 3XX
Tel: (020) 7531 6666 **Fax:** (020) 7987 1625
Email: sebastiancrispin@yahoo.co.uk **Website:** www.privatedetectiveslondon.co.uk

Contacts	Jonathan Cordrey
	Sebastian Crispin
	Marcus Adams
	Anne Edwards
Number of staff	21

THE FIRM: 1st Call Private Investigations was founded in 1986 and has a vast wealth of experience in dealing with all aspects of surveillance and private investigation throughout the UK and overseas. The firm operates a 24 hour control room and same-day response service for legal firms and provides fast, efficient and effective solutions in all types of investigative/litigation support situations. The firm has four offices with a network of local agents in the UK: please consult www.localdetective.co.uk. Experienced and fully trained staff use the latest digital technology and equipment for hi-tech surveillance/secret filming and also counter surveillance/de-bugging work. All overseas agents and representatives are supervised from our London 24 hour control room, near Canary Wharf.

LITIGATION SUPPORT SERVICES: All types of investigation dealing with criminal and civil cases, matrimonial matters, tracing witnesses and assets/shares/liabilities are undertaken. This includes investigation of property transactions and development projects; acquistions, mergers and takeovers; corporate and professional conflict matters; due diligence, intellectual property, counter surveillance, undercover work and infiltration scenarios; critical path planning and crisis management, security consulting work; electronic sweeps using latest de-bugging equipment; sale and hire of surveillance and monitoring equipment for commercial/domestic cases (room and telephones); same day delivery to central London locations; detailed management schemes, plans and staff-watch assignments prepared and monitored;

Continued overleaf

accident/disability/sickness, compensation and expenses claims verified; employment and health and safety issues, harassment, pilfering, fraud and deception enquiries; staff screening and CV verification; checking of all public record infirmation; medical ethics and company/business enquiries; contract issues, non specific performance/breach of contract/damages; all family, child custody and maintenance matters; domestic violence, blackmail and libel cases; wills, oaths and probate enquiries; property issues, industrial and civil espionage, insurance matters/fraudulent claims verified; tracing of witnesses, beneficiaries, illegal immigrants/asylum seekers, process serving, debt recovery; criminal profiling and DNA analysis; status reports, information gathering/data protection; stalking and personal protection situations; specialist service for VIP/celebrities with secure chauffeur service and video recording of specific events; interim/final reports prepared. Initial consultation 24 hour on (020) 7531 6666 or faxed enquiries on (020) 7987 1625.

INKERMAN (UK) LTD

111a Walton Street, Knightsbridge, London, SW3 2HP
Tel: (020) 7589 5338 **Fax:** (020) 7589 5339
Email: enquiry@inkerman.com **Website:** www.inkerman.com

Inkerman House, 4 Elwick Road, Ashford, TN23 1PF
Tel: (01233) 646940 **Fax:** (01233) 646840 **DX:** 30206 ASHFORD, KENT

Contacts Gerald Moor, William McWilliams, Tony Hall

THE FIRM: The Inkerman Group specialises in offering risk management and investigative services with an international reach to clients in industry, commerce, the legal profession and high net worth individuals.

LITIGATION SUPPORT SERVICES:

Corporate Investigations: Surveillance (overt and covert photography); electronic sweeps and eavesdropping; counter-industrial espionage; fraud (theft and shrinkage), asset tracing; counterfeiting and intellectual property; certificated bailiffs.

Risk Management: Protective security reviews; asset protection; information and IT security; country risk analysis; counter-terrorist surveys; VIP security profiling; VIP protection; crisis counselling; hostage negotiation; individual and corporate training in personal protection (kidnap and ransom prevention).

THE BAR

STARS AT THE BAR

STARS AT THE BAR (ranked in 5 or more sections of this book)

1 RANKED IN 9 AREAS

Gordon Pollock QC *Essex Court Chambers*
Arbitration (International); Banking; Commercial Litigation; Energy & Natural Resources; Fraud: Civil; Insurance; Media & Entertainment; Shipping; Sport.

Jonathan Sumption QC *Brick Court Chambers*
Administrative & Public Law; Banking; Commercial Litigation; Energy & Natural Resources; Financial Services; Fraud: Civil; insurance Media & Entertainment; Professional Negligence.

2 RANKED IN 8 AREAS

Michael Briggs QC *Serle Court*
Commercial Litigation; Commercial Chancery; Company; Financial Services; Fraud: Civil; Insolvency/Corporate Recovery; Partnership; Professional Negligence.

3 RANKED IN 6 AREAS

Christopher Butcher QC *7 King's Bench Walk*
Arbitration (International); Banking; Commercial Litigation; Insurance; Professional Negligence; Shipping.

Elizabeth Gloster QC *One Essex Court*
Commercial Litigation; Commercial Chancery; Company; Energy & Natural Resources; Fraud: Civil; Insolvency/Corporate Recovery.

Bankim Thanki *Fountain Court*
Aviation; Banking; Commercial Litigation; Fraud: Civil; Professional Negligence; Sport.

4 RANKED IN 5 AREAS

Mark Barnes QC *One Essex Court*
Arbitration (International); Commercial Litigation; Energy & Natural Resources; Fraud: Civil; Information Technology.

Anthony Boswood QC *Fountain Court*
Banking; Commercial Litigation; Energy & Natural Resources; Fraud: Civil; Insurance.

Michael Brindle QC *Fountain Court*
Banking; Commercial Litigation; Financial Services; Fraud: Civil; Professional Negligence.

John Brisby QC *4 Stone Buildings*
Commercial Chancery; Company; Financial Services; Fraud: Civil; Insolvency/Corporate Recovery.

Nigel Davis QC *Maitland Chambers*
Commercial Chancery; Company; Insolvency/Corporate Recovery; Media & Entertainment; Partnership.

Robin Dicker QC *3-4 South Square*
Banking; Company; Energy & Natural Resources; Fraud: Civil; Insolvency/Corporate Recovery.

Barbara Dohmann QC *Blackstone Chambers*
Commercial Litigation; Financial Services; Fraud: Civil; Insurance; Media & Entertainment.

Charles Flint QC *Blackstone Chambers*
Administrative & Public Law; Commercial Litigation; Financial Services; Fraud: Civil; Sport.

Ian Glick QC *One Essex Court*
Arbitration (International); Banking; Commercial Litigation; Energy & Natural Resources; Tax: Inland Revenue.

Anthony Grabiner QC *One Essex Court*
Arbitration (International); Banking; Commercial Litigation; Energy & Natural Resources; Fraud: Civil.

Robert Hildyard QC *4 Stone Buildings*
Commercial Chancery; Company; Energy & Natural Resources; Financial Services; Insurance.

Mark Howard QC *Brick Court Chambers*
Banking; Commercial Litigation; Energy & Natural Resources; Insurance; Professional Negligence.

Sydney Kentridge QC *Brick Court Chambers*
Administrative & Public Law; Commercial Litigation; Energy & Natural Resources; Insurance; Media & Entertainment.

Anthony Mann QC *Enterprise Chambers*
Commercial Litigation; Commercial Chancery; Company; Insolvency/Corporate Recovery; Professional Negligence.

Robert Miles *4 Stone Buildings*
Banking; Commercial Chancery; Company; Energy & Natural Resources; Insolvency/Corporate Recovery.

Richard Millett *Essex Court Chambers*
Arbitration (International); Banking; Commercial Litigation; Insolvency/Corporate Recovery; Media & Entertainment.

David Pannick QC *Blackstone Chambers*
Administrative & Public Law; Employment; Human Rights; Immigration; Sport.

Laurence Rabinowitz *One Essex Court*
Banking; Commercial Litigation; Company; Energy & Natural Resources; Fraud: Civil.

Joe Smouha *Essex Court Chambers*
Arbitration (International); Commercial Litigation; Fraud: Civil; Shipping; Tax: VAT.

Alan Steinfeld QC *24 Old Buildings*
Commercial Chancery; Company; Insolvency/Corporate Recovery; Partnerships; Pensions.

Gordon Pollock QC-Essex Court Chambers

Gordon Pollock "adds a dash of brio and flamboyance" to an often monochromatic world. Of imposing physical stature and sporting a luxuriant beard, he cuts an impressive figure in the courtroom. Once in full flow, his "legendary ability at cross-examination" is reinforced by a fine tactical awareness that makes him a natural choice for the weightier cases. Commercial litigation and energy cases are his true forte, reflected by his presence in our starred category for these disciplines.

He is also rated in the first band for banking, arbitration, insurance and media/entertainment, while occasionally dashing off a civil fraud case as if born to it. Oozing talent, he has "a great ability to turn a case in reply" and was described by one commentator as the "finest first instance advocate in the business."

Ever-present on headline cases, his recent CV has included Elton John v PricewaterhouseCoopers and the Star Sea marine insurance affair. Always in demand on the energy front, he also appeared for the appellant in Amoco v Teeside Gas. "One of the few great men at the bar" and an intimidating presence, he is, however, known not to be averse to injecting witty and even idiosyncratic behaviour into his courtroom performances.

Jonathan Sumption QC-Brick Court Chambers

"Profoundly intelligent and capable of lending weight to any case," Jonathan Sumption remains "the man to turn to when chapter and verse of the law is required." His assured demeanour and unswerving conviction in the validity of his arguments unfailingly arrest the attention of the judiciary. Rated in the star category in commercial litigation, energy and financial services, he is further listed in the first band for public law, banking, insurance and professional negligence. His versatility is further apparent from additional ratings in civil fraud and media/entertainment.

"Never one to suffer fools gladly," he is not viewed as one to cosset the client. However, the quality of his "whirlwind submissions" is beyond argument. Regarded in some quarters as "bordering on the genius, with a near photographic memory" he appeared in the Alconbury case, a matter of supreme legal importance in relation to the impact of the Human Rights Act on UK law. Other cases of signal importance have included the competition case of Interbrew v Bass, the Equitable Life v Hyman pensions affair and the Star Sea shipping case. A keen student of, and author on, medieval history, it is widely believed that he would have been Richard III's first choice as defence counsel in any litigation arising from the deaths of the Princes in the Tower.

Michael Briggs QC-Serle Court

Rated highly in eight sections of *Chambers*, Michael Briggs can claim to be something of a Renaissance man. Active in all aspects of commercial, financial and insolvency law, he tackles larger pieces of litigation such as the multi-million pound Sumitomo Finance v Crédit Lyonnais case, and has appeared recently as lead counsel for the banks in Royal Bank of Scotland v Etridge, a matter involving the sale of mortgages.

With many arrows in his quiver, he has further established a reputation in professional negligence and advised on an allegation of negligence against a barrister (Roman Catholic Dioceses of Liverpool v Goldberg). Although far from aggressive in court, he is a match for anyone, being able to "wind up the opposition in a low-key way." Relying on court craft and tactical awareness rather than naked aggression, he is known for "luring the unsuspecting into pits of varying depths and darkness."

Extremely busy, he takes pains to keep himself fresh through regular weekend retreats to the country and trips in his boat. Solicitors stressed, however, his total accessibility, which has been known to extend to conducting conferences by mobile phone whilst out on the high seas.

Christopher Butcher QC-7 King's Bench Walk

Christopher Butcher's elevation to silk has come as no surprise. Always an outstanding junior, he continues to be lauded for his "ferocious intelligence" and "nimble handling of the larger case." The key areas of his practice remain insurance and professional negligence. Still active in the interminable Barings imbroglio, he also continues to be entrenched in film finance litigation, having appeared in HIH Casualty v Chase Manhattan Bank. Casting his net widely, he is also recommended for banking, commercial litigation and shipping. "Trenchant and sparing in his address, his every word has bite," making for "an opponent one can never take lightly."

Elizabeth Gloster QC-One Essex Court

"An infectiously enthusiastic" barrister, Elizabeth Gloster's defining characteristics are "determination and vigour." Content to throw herself in wholeheartedly, she is almost Thatcheresque in her unwearying toil, habitually surviving on four hours sleep a night. "A champion of the commercial arena," she is at her brightest in insolvency work, having spent much of last year in the Isle of Man on the Barlow Clowes litigation. However, she wears a number of different hats, having appeared in the HIH Casualty film finance litigation and on behalf of British Airways in a major pensions case.

Never one to indulge in overwrought histrionics in court, she has a reasoned approach whilst being "capable of presenting a hardened, unyielding façade to evasive witnesses." To add to her formidable workload, she sits as a deputy high court judge in the Chancery Division and is a judge in both the Jersey and Guernsey Courts of Appeal.

Bankim Thanki-Fountain Court

"As smooth as silk," Bankim Thanki is known for his slick handling of clients. "Gliding into the room, he puts the punter at ease immediately with a mixture of sound advice and glossy presentation." Once in court, however, he metamorphoses into "a bullish and persistent advocate" whilst losing none of his "easy charm." Banking is his forte and he has been involved in high-level teams working on such significant matters as the Codelco litigation and the House of Lords case Bank of England v BCCI. He is also rated for aviation, fraud, professional negligence and commercial litigation. Particularly adept at sports law, he has handled a number of FA-related cases through Freshfields Bruckhaus Deringer. "Thoroughly prepared and wholly sophisticated," he is now numerically the leading junior in *Chambers'* ratings.

Mark Barnes QC-One Essex Court

Mark Barnes is "One Essex Court's answer to Jonathan Sumption." "Phenomenally bright, "he seems to work on a different plane," applying his brain to the knottiest problems. At his easiest when totally immersed in a subject, he tends to devote himself fully to one matter at a time, consequently handling the more time-consuming cases. This year, for example, has seen him submerged in Amoco UK Exploration v British American Offshore, a case questioning the fitness for purpose of an oil-rig chartered to drill in the North Sea.

Along with energy, his expertise encompasses fields as diverse as IT and international arbitration. "A lively thinker and tireless worker" he is the first of the new additions to "Stars at the Bar."

Anthony Boswood QC-Fountain Court

Energy, insurance/reinsurance and banking provide the foundations to Anthony Boswood's thriving practice. "A tough operator with a terse style" he is known for "clutching a good point to his breast and running with it." Something of a character, he has a reputation for vigorous prosecution of his cases and expert cross-examination. "He tends to pick up a case as if it were a recalcitrant Victorian child, shaking it until it falls out his way."

Cases that he has cuffed and reproved this year include Strive Shipping (The Grecian Express) and the Morgan Grenfell v SACE litigation where he acted for the Italian Expert Credit Guarantee Agency. Combining knowledge of the old and the new, he is highly computer literate and felt to be one of the "Caesars of the Bar." Fittingly he owns a villa in Tuscany to which he is apt to repair, doubtless clad in purple.

Michael Brindle QC-Fountain Court

For Michael Brindle, financial services, fraud, commercial litigation and professional negligence provide further ballast to a practice focused around banking. "Clever, straightforward and intelligent," he "shoots his cuffs and gets down to business," often on behalf of international banks. His talents in the past year have almost exclusively been confined to the Barings litigation, where he has enjoyed a prominent role in a cast of legal luminaries. His capabilities, however, stretch much wider, allowing him to showcase his "sympathetic client awareness" in a number of different spheres. "Very much in the quiet assassin mould," his "steely cross-examination" allows him to "force the toughest of witnesses to unravel."

John Brisby QC-4 Stone Buildings

More than a few of the headline litigations of the recent past have had John Brisby's fingerprints on them. He has provided input into both the BCCI and Barings sagas and continues to be "a valuable addition to any of the big litigation teams."

Focused around company and insolvency work, his is an eclectic practice, which also takes in fraud and professional negligence. Renowned for his advice on matters relating to financial services, he recently appeared in United Pan Europe v Deutsche Bank, a Court of Appeal case concerning breach of confidence and "Chinese Walls" issues. A "punchy advocate", he is celebrated for his uncompromising cross-examinations and has been described by one observer as "an eloquent bulldog."

Nigel Davis QC-Maitland Chambers

A leading light of the newly constituted Maitland Chambers, and said to possess "a complete mastery of his cases," Nigel Davis excels in the field of general commercial chancery litigation. His work includes company, insolvency, tracing, trusts, professional negligence, property, partnership and media/entertainment matters. His is a "gentlemanly but tough" approach, relying on "cold logic and grit." Respected by the judiciary for his academic pedigree and "considered advocacy," he presents in a "slightly reserved manner" but is recognised as "highly proficient." Consistently in demand, his fame has spread outside these shores, and he now regularly undertakes advisory work in foreign jurisdictions including the Channel Islands, Hong Kong, Singapore and the Cayman Islands. He also sits as a deputy high court judge.

Robin Dicker QC-3-4 South Square

A leading light in an insolvency heavy set, Robin Dicker stretches his practice to cover energy, company banking and partnership matters. He has acted on virtually all the major corporate collapses of recent times including BCCI (for the liquidators), Olympia & York (for the administrators) and the Heron Group (for the company). "Fantastically bright, attentive and knowledgeable," he is "particularly adept at navigating around testing legal problems," and is a frequent visitor to the House of Lords. There, he appeared last year on Three Rivers District Council v Bank of England. Although only a relatively recent appointment to silk, the market indicates a sanguine outlook for this "understated and sedulous performer."

Barbara Dohmann QC-Blackstone Chambers

A commercial litigator of some repute, Barbara Dohmann's practice extends to fraud, financial services, insurance and media/entertainment, many of her cases having an international element.

"Meticulous in her preparation," it is her court work, however, that catches the eye. "Perfect for the client who wants the full twenty shillings for their pound," she "always enters on a war footing." Wheeled on by the banks in those major commercial fraud cases that require detailed cross-examination on assets, she has "the capacity to make hell's foundations quiver." By turns tenacious and forbidding, she has been known to argue her case in court after the judge has given his judgment. Described by one commentator as "a Valkyrie," she has been espied on the battlefield this year on the Kennacot case, a huge insurance dispute.

Charles Flint QC-Blackstone Chambers

Ex SAS man Charles Flint hit the headlines last year for making a citizen's arrest on a fleeing bank robber. His manifold interests include the Territorial Army, climbing, flying stunt planes, and the interface between financial services and public law in the context of commercial litigation.

His is a varied practice that further encompasses fraud, administrative law, and sports law. As his martial background might suggest, he is "a master tactician, capable of outflanking his opponents." Commercially minded, he is "not one to flap around and reaches the kernel of the matter with impressive expedition." His "analytical cast of mind" has been seen on a number of financially complex matters, including the tortuous Prince Jefri litigation. He also appeared for the BAF in Diane Modahl v The British Athletic Federation, successfully defending a claim for damages for breach of contract.

Ian Glick QC-One Essex Court

Feted across a number of disciplines, Ian Glick is especially renowned in energy and tax circles. A favourite with the Inland Revenue and Magic Circle law firms, he has built up "a practice as broad as it is deep." An indication of his rising stock is provided by his recent appointment to one of Peter Goldsmith QC's former cases, Unilever v Mercury Asset Management.

Trusted by regulators, he has acted for the FSA in its enquiry into the Equitable Life affair, and has been involved in litigation regarding the implications of the New Electricity Trading Arrangements legislation. His "grave but by no means humourless" style is widely appreciated, and he often crops up in a straight commercial context such as on the Fruitshippers case, the first where US law firms entrusted litigation solely to their London offices. "Extremely punctilious" when it comes to preparation, he exhibits "a light but skilful touch" once in court.

Anthony Grabiner QC-One Essex Court

Commitments in the Upper House militate against Anthony Grabiner's appearance on lengthier trials, but there is little indication that this "supremely skilful old warhorse" is easing off. Famed for his advisory acumen, he excels in commercial contract, takeovers, mergers and regulatory work and is a "firm fixture in the appellate courts." Years of ceaseless toil have left him with "an instinctive comprehension of the minds of the judiciary," whom he addresses in a "relaxed and mellifluent manner."

The quality of his practice remains high. He has appeared of late in the Goldfish credit card case, and has advised UK Mercedes dealerships on the termination of their contracts by the parent company. Benefiting from increased activity in the energy sphere, he has expanded his practice in this regard and appears in headline cases such as Severn Trent v Dwr Cymru. A concrete commitment to arbitration is underlined by his directorship of the London Court of International Arbitration. He also sits as a deputy high court judge of the Chancery and Queen's Bench Divisions.

Robert Hildyard QC-4 Stone Buildings

The "extremely flexible" Robert Hildyard has built his reputation on company, insolvency and insurance cases. Something of a globetrotter, he is in demand internationally, often negotiating cases in exotic locations such as the Cayman Islands. This peripatetic approach has brought with it "the facility to address tribunals of differing kinds in a language they understand."

Domestically he is a favourite of both insurance companies and regulatory bodies and has acted for the SFA in the AXA Insurance litigation. His "thorough preparation and easy manner" are pleasing to the bench and "highly attractive to clients." Increasingly active in energy cases, his "polished advocacy" has been apparent in a number of contractual disputes in this area.

Mark Howard QC-Brick Court Chambers

Yet to be thoroughly tested in the appellate courts, Mark Howard remains "a doughty opponent at first instance." With "good tactical awareness" and mean cross-examination skills, he has "seriously troubled a number of senior City figures in the witness box." Straight commercial litigation is his natural territory, but he also enjoys high status in banking, insurance, and professional negligence.

Deploying his efforts in the major cases he has appeared in the Solo Industries LC fraud case, the Barings saga, and in Banco Santander v Bayfern, the leading case on documentary credits. Adding the energy sector to his repertoire, he advised on the Cats litigation and on two substantial oil drilling rig/platform disputes in the last year.

Sydney Kentridge QC-Brick Court Chambers

The "measured and modest" Sydney Kentridge, at 78 years of age, continues to be in demand for the most challenging of cases. Now declining three times as much work as he actually undertakes, he is generally only seen in matters of a limited duration. Highly popular amongst his peers, he has an "iconic status" due to his consistent successes in this country and past history as a lawyer in South Africa, where he acted for Nelson Mandela and the family of Steve Biko.

His practice revolves around commercial litigation and public law, with additional specialisms in energy, insurance and the media. His most notable appearances in the last year have been before the Court of Human Rights in Strasbourg. Acting on behalf of the UK government, he appeared in the McGonnell case and also represented the Turkish PKK leader, Abdullah Ocalan on an application concerning Turkey's continued use of the death penalty. In the courtroom, he "radiates a sense of calm and serenity" and is known for his "deliberate, controlled and utterly persuasive style." Exhibiting no sign of impending retirement, it appears he will still be "knocking his opponents cock-eyed" for some time to come.

Anthony Mann QC-Enterprise Chambers

"A big cheese" for insolvency work, Anthony Mann scores well in our tables as a commercial and company lawyer. A great many of his cases have appeared in the law reports, of which a recent example was Re H, a matter concerning the validity of substituted service of statutory demand. Juggling a sizeable practice with commitments as a Recorder and Deputy High Court Judge, he has "a fine insight into the courtroom from both sides of the fence."

In approaching the bench, he is "briskly efficient and not afraid to bite back." Indeed, so fearlessly resolute is his style that on one occasion a member of the judiciary felt compelled to address him thus: "I'd like to ask you a question, Mr Mann, but don't know if I dare." He is, however, "a pleasure to work with," respected by one junior as "not the type of leader to sell you down the river." Effective in a number of fields, his influence now extends into the licensing world, where he has appeared successfully in two substantial cases for London Clubs Management Ltd.

Robert Miles-4 Stone Buildings

Robert Miles is "the type of junior every silk wants to use." An organisational whiz, he possesses "total command of a brief," allowing him to manage the bulkiest of cases. At his best when hacking through mountainous paperwork, he appeared in the Bermuda Fire and Marine insolvency case, impressing observers as "clear-headed and very solid." Insolvency and commercial chancery matters form the prop of his practice, but his tentacles spread into many areas, including banking, where he appeared in United Pan Europe v Deutsche Bank. With a "nicely paced advocacy style," he "has the ear of the judges" and can justly be marked out as "one of the leading juniors at the Bar."

Richard Millett-Essex Court Chambers

Recently appointed to the Treasury Counsel 'A' list, Richard Millett is a " client friendly, bouncy advocate" who "puts the size nines into the opposition with relish." Ranked highest in Chambers for banking and media work, his is "a practice of many shades." He has had involvement in a number of international arbitrations, and is sought after for reinsurance cases, having recently appeared in Arig v Generale and the Merc Skandia litigation. In demand at home and abroad, he also appeared in R v MAFF and Anastasiou Ltd, an international public law ECC case regarding plant health directives.

David Pannick QC-Blackstone Chambers

David Pannick met with virtually unqualified admiration during the research into this year's guide. In the starred category for two sections and in band one in a further three, he is "consistently excellent across the board." His meat and drink are human rights and public law cases. "The leader of the leaders" for judicial review, he successfully represented Camelot over the decision to exclude it from the race to be lottery operator, and appeared for the Secretary of State in the Thompson and Venables affair.

In demand with everybody from the individual applicant to foreign governments, he has appeared for the government of Greece in a claim by former King Constantine and for the UK government in Chapman v United Kingdom, a case concerning the rights of gypsies. Pannick's appeal is his "breathtaking intellect." "His brain races like a dynamo" and his submissions to the court are "a paragon of clarity, precision and logic." Never failing to grip and stir, he "pares the argument down to one or two points and presents the most Byzantine of issues in a comprehensible manner." Not one who is afraid to speak his mind, Pannick is a regular commentator on the law and enters the most contentious of debates, having, for example, recently questioned the process of appointing silks.

Laurence Rabinowitz-One Essex Court

Slack-jawed astonishment greeted the decision once again to deny silk to Laurence Rabinowitz. "One of the top juniors at the Bar, and possibly the finest," he is regularly led by the Pollocks, Sumptions and Boswoods of this world. A Treasury Junior, his standing is such that he has appeared as Amicus Curiae in the House of Lords, and graces many of the major litigation teams.

Commercial litigation and energy law are his mainstays, but he possesses a talent prodigious enough to allow him to tackle areas such as company and banking on an ad hoc basis. Recently he has been led by Anthony Grabiner QC in representing Mercedes dealers over the termination of contracts by the parent company, and has provided a plethora of advice to Railtrack on the legal implications of the Hatfield rail disaster. "A midnight oil burner," his popularity stems from his "nimble navigation of the fattest briefs" and ability to synthesise information into a coherent whole. He gains the respect of those instructing him for his "implacable will and readiness to tell things as they are."

Joe Smouha-Essex Court Chambers

"One of the young chargers," Joe Smouha is recognised as being "in an elite band of the very best juniors." In a profession where juniors rarely conduct their own cases in the House of Lords, his appearance in the VAT case of Eastbourne Cars is testament to the esteem in which he is held.

An expert commercial litigator, he is also rated for his arbitration, tax, and shipping work. The diversity of his practice is illustrated by his recent appearances in copper trading litigation and the Kuwait Airways saga, and he has further carved out a niche in cases relating to the art world. "Confident, clever and effective," solicitors warm to his industry and facility in turning papers around quickly. A boundlessly energetic lawyer, one commentator observed that "he's so bouncy, it's almost as if he's swallowed an industrial spring."

Alan Steinfeld QC-24 Old Buildings

Housed in a set that has a branch in Switzerland, there is something distinctly cosmopolitan about Alan Steinfeld's practice. A Member of the Bar of the Eastern Caribbean, he has variously been sighted litigating in the Bahamas, British Virgin Islands, Bermuda, the Cayman Islands and Hong Kong. Specialising in Chancery, company, insolvency and partnership law, he has "a sizeable following of clients," and has appeared in headline cases. His portfolio includes acting in the Don King Productions v Warren partnership dispute, advising the developers of Wembley Stadium in a claim for rectification, and appearing in National Power & National Grid for the beneficiaries of the pension scheme.

"Communicating at the right level with judge and client alike," he is respected for his "ability to distil complicated matters into a comprehensible form." This keen yachtsman is noted both for his "approachability and tough cross-examination technique."

THE MILLION-A-YEAR CLUB

Our million-a-year club numbers only a tiny proportion of the some ten thousand barristers who are in private practice at the bar, although a number of new names enter the ranks this year. These are some of the best known practitioners, whose legal prowess, reputation and experience are such that they are in huge demand and command the highest fees – in some cases, the 'two-million-a-year club' would be a more accurate description. While the figures charged can seem extraordinary, these are in cases where there are huge amounts are at stake. The continued willingness of clients to pay these charges indicates that those at the top of the game are considered worth the money. Tax lawyers continue to dominate the table, with the rest generally commercial and chancery practitioners.

THE MILLION-A-YEAR CLUB

GRAHAM AARONSON QC	CHARLES ALDOUS QC	REX BRETTEN QC
CHRISTOPHER CARR QC	JEREMY COOKE QC	RODERICK CORDARA QC
IAN CROXFORD QC	MICHAEL CRYSTAL QC	BARBARA DOHMANN QC
JULIAN FLAUX QC	MICHAEL FLESCH QC	JONATHAN GAISMAN QC
JOHN GARDINER QC	ELIZABETH GLOSTER QC	DAVID GOLDBERG QC
ANTHONY GRABINER QC	BRIAN GREEN QC	NICHOLAS GREEN QC
ROBERT HAM QC	MARK HAPGOOD QC	MARK HOWARD QC
GAVIN KEALEY QC	DAVID OLIVER QC	DAVID PANNICK QC
GORDON POLLOCK QC	ROBIN POTTS QC	JULES SHER QC
NICHOLAS STADLEN QC	JONATHAN SUMPTION QC	PETER TREVETT QC
ROBERT VENABLES QC	GEOFFRY VOS QC	

BARRISTERS' CHARGES

These change little from last year, with many sets reporting no great increase in charges. The figures shown are those of receipts, or gross income, and generally reflect the highest and lowest common figures. Fees may vary widely between consultations, advisory and court work, and not all sets charge on an hourly basis. In tax practices, fees may be decided once the paperwork has been inspected on the basis of complexity, liability and clients' circumstances. In the criminal practices a large proportion of both prosecution and defence work is government funded.

HOURLY CHARGE RATES

SENIORITY	Commercial	Tax	Chancery	Common law	Criminal
QC	£250-£850	£300-£1000	£175-£600	£150-£400	£125-£400
10 yrs call	£100-£300	£200-£500	£100-£200	£100-200	£75-£300
4-9 yrs call	£60-£200	£175-£350	£75-£175	£50-£150	£50-£150
1-3 yrs call	£25-£150	£75-150	£30-£100	£40-£100	£25-£75

All figures represent gross earnings before deduction of expenses.

BARRISTERS' REMUNERATION

A representative sample ranging from the lowest to the highest gross receipts, with the higher figures representing the outstanding practitioners, and average earnings tending to be closer to the lower end of the scale. The criminal sector, in particular, reports that the lower rates are far more common. Conversely, those at the very top of sectors such as tax and, to a slightly lesser extent, commercial and chancery, are commanding larger fees than ever. It should be remembered that around 20% of these figures will ordinarily be deducted for expenses at chambers, including rent, with another 20% on average going towards individual expenses. These include costs such as insurance, pensions, travel, hotels, accountancy fees, IT and legal publications. Furthermore, the period between work done and fees received can be anywhere between three months and a year, depending on the type of practice. As a result one year's earnings can vary considerably from the next.

ANNUAL EARNINGS (thousands)

SENIORITY	Commercial	Tax	Chancery	Common law	Criminal
QC	£150-£1 million	£300-£2 million	£150-£1.7 million	£150-£425	£125-£550
10 yrs call	£100-£750	£200-£500	£100-£350	£75-£300	£40-400
4-9 yrs call	£60-£350	£175-£350	£75-£300	£30-£200	£30-£165
1-3 yrs call	£25-£125	£75-£150	£25-£125	£20-£100	£10-£75

All figures represent gross earnings before deduction of expenses.

ADMINISTRATIVE & PUBLIC LAW

RESEARCH: The rankings are based on in-depth interviews with over 5,000 solicitors and barristers in the UK. Chambers research is audited by the British Market Research Bureau (see page 7 for details).

Barristers' profiles 1339-1472

LONDON

ADMINISTRATIVE & PUBLIC LAW • London		QCs	Jnrs
1	**Blackstone Chambers** (Baxendale/Flint)	8	6
2	**4 Breams Buildings** (Christopher Lockhart-Mummery QC)	2	1
	Matrix Chambers (Nicholas Blake QC)	3	4
3	**39 Essex Street** (Nigel Pleming QC)	2	3
	11 King's Bench Walk Chambers (Tabachnik/Goudie)	3	2
4	**Brick Court Chambers** (Christopher Clarke QC)	3	1
	Doughty Street Chambers (Geoffrey Robertson QC)	2	3
	Two Garden Court (Macdonald/Davies)	1	1
	2-3 Gray's Inn Square (Porten/Scrivener)	1	-
	4-5 Gray's Inn Square (Appleby/Mole)	-	1

Numbers show recommended barristers in this practice area

LEADING SILKS • London		
★	**BELOFF Michael**	Blackstone Chambers
	PANNICK David	Blackstone Chambers
1	**DRABBLE Richard**	4 Breams Buildings
	GORDON Richard	Brick Court Chambers
	HOWELL John	Blackstone Chambers
	PLEMING Nigel	39 Essex Street
	SUMPTION Jonathan	Brick Court Chambers
2	**BLAKE Nicholas**	Matrix Chambers
	FLINT Charles	Blackstone Chambers
	GOUDIE James	11 King's Bench Walk Chambers
	KENTRIDGE Sydney	Brick Court Chambers
	LESTER Anthony	Blackstone Chambers
	NICOL Andrew	Doughty Street Chambers
3	**BAXENDALE Presiley**	Blackstone Chambers
	BOOTH Cherie	Matrix Chambers
	FITZGERALD Edward	Doughty Street Chambers
	HAVERS Philip	1 Crown Office Row
	JAY Robert	39 Essex Street
	KATKOWSKI Christopher	4 Breams Buildings
	LOWE Mark	2-3 Gray's Inn Square
	SUPPERSTONE Michael	11 King's Bench Walk Chambers
NEW SILKS		
	CARSS-FRISK Monica	Blackstone Chambers
	GARNHAM Neil	1 Crown Office Row
	KERR Tim	11 King's Bench Walk Chambers
	LANG Beverley	Blackstone Chambers
	LUBA Jan	Two Garden Court
	OWEN Tim	Matrix Chambers

This book is the product of 6,552 1/2-hour interviews. See p.7 for BMRB audit.
For details of these leading barristers see Profiles on p.1339

Blackstone Chambers (see full details p.1481) There exists among our interviewees a feeling that the set is beginning to streak away from its rivals. It houses the two stellar individuals in our tables and a number of established and ascendant leaders. Effective in commercial and public law this set is "big box office" as far as the leading city firms are concerned. To say that praise for **David Pannick QC** (see p.1431) was fulsome would be an understatement. "Supremely efficient and persuasive," he was described by one leading firm as "the best barrister on earth." This year he impressed in the National Lottery affair, successfully representing Camelot after it had initially been excluded from the race to be operator for a second term. He has now been joined in chambers by fellow legal leviathan, **Michael Beloff QC** (see p.1349). Despite reservations as to his availability in the light of his appointment as Master of Trinity College, Oxford, he remains heavily endorsed as "a barrister constantly on the hunt for a creative solution and one who seems to have 36 hours in the day." **Anthony Lester QC** (see p.1410), "appears sporadically but tellingly" in cases such as Turkington v Times Newspapers, the first matter before the Lords following the introduction of the Human Rights Act. Also expert in the human rights area is **John Howell QC** (see p.1398), an "intellectually superior" acquisition from 4 Breams Buildings, who appeared in the Alconbury case as 'amicus' in the Lords. The "sharp and concise" **Charles Flint QC** (see p.1379) practices principally in the commercial and regulatory field. This impressive body of silks is completed by **Presiley Baxendale QC** (see p.1348), **Beverley Lang QC** (see p.1408) and the "diligent, clever and responsive" new silk **Monica Carrs-Frisk QC** (see p.1360). This strength is mirrored in the junior ranks. **Michael Fordham** (see p.1380) "possesses a tremendous knowledge of his subject" which allows him to "swing judges around against their better natures." **Javan Herberg** (see p.1393) is almost as revered and has appeared in cases such as Imperial Tobacco's challenge into a report on passive smoking. He is joined by the "outstandingly quick, bright and pragmatic" **Dinah Rose** (see p.1442), and **Pushpinder Saini** (see p.1445), "a sleek operator who gently eases his opponent into perdition." Equally effective is **Mark Shaw** (see p.1447) "an excellent tactician who is good on straight judicial reviews." Completing a selection of quality performers of all vintages is **Thomas de la Mare** (see p.1370). Although only called in 1995 he is a "vital young player" who is lauded for his advisory work and "brims with positive energy."

4 Breams Buildings (see full details p.1483) The departure of John Howell QC to Blackstone is something of an issue considering his capacity for attracting briefs. However, the set remains respected in planning and local government and for the public law and judicial review work that attends this. A selection of worthy performers includes **Richard Drabble QC** (see p.1372) who "has one of the finest brains at the bar" and "absolutely no side to him." After a distinguished career as a junior **Christopher Katkowski QC** (see p.1404) has consolidated his position as a silk and acts for both treasury solicitors and applicants. The junior highlighted here is **Nathalie Lieven** (see p.1411), "dead straight" she "tells you what she thinks in a quick, practical way." Busy on behalf of government bodies she too regularly turns her hand to applicant work.

Matrix Chambers (see full details p.1538) The much-heralded arrival of Michael Beloff QC has failed to materialise following his decision to move to Blackstone. This has not deflected from the fact that this fledgling chambers still contains some "excellent individuals." **Nicholas Blake QC** is "a composite of many talents" who mirrors the set as a whole via his recognised expertise in human rights issues. **Cherie Booth QC** (see p.1352) is noted for her "solicitude and empathy toward clients" while **Tim Owen QC** (see p.1431) continues to be recommended for his general practice and niche specialism in prison law. Perched atop our junior table is **Rabinder Singh** (see p.1449) who applies his "immeasurable talents" to a diverse range of public law work. Taking the stance of "calm reassurance" he picked up accolades from the vast majority of the leading solicitors for his "intelligence and communication skills." **Helen Mountfield** (see

LEADING JUNIORS • London		
★	FORDHAM Michael	Blackstone Chambers
	SINGH Rabinder	Matrix Chambers
1	GIFFIN Nigel	11 King's Bench Walk Chambers
	GRIFFITHS Alan	One Essex Court
	HERBERG Javan	Blackstone Chambers
	LEWIS Clive	11 King's Bench Walk Chambers
	MOUNTFIELD Helen	Matrix Chambers
	ROSE Dinah	Blackstone Chambers
	SAINI Pushpinder	Blackstone Chambers
	SHAW Mark	Blackstone Chambers
	WOLFE David	Matrix Chambers
2	HARRISON Stephanie	Two Garden Court
	HUNT Murray	Matrix Chambers
	LIEVEN Nathalie	4 Breams Buildings
	RICHARDS Jennifer	39 Essex Street
3	CATCHPOLE Stuart	39 Essex Street
	CLAYTON Richard	Devereux Chambers
	CORNER Timothy	4-5 Gray's Inn Square
	KOVATS Steven	39 Essex Street
	MACLEAN Alan	Brick Court Chambers
	MARKUS Kate	Doughty Street Chambers
	STARMER Keir	Doughty Street Chambers
	TAM Robin	1 Temple Gardens
UP AND COMING		
	CRAGG Stephen	Doughty Street Chambers
	DE LA MARE Thomas	Blackstone Chambers

This book is the product of 6,552 1/2-hour interviews. See p.7 for BMRB audit.
For details of these leading barristers see Profiles on p.1339

p.1425) has a flair for human rights and discrimination cases. She is "not one who lets a case be clouded by her own importance" and is, according to solicitors, "always a key part of the team." Similarly, **David Wolfe** (see p.1469) generated much praise, especially in the provinces, for his "helpful, accessible and thoughtful approach" which allows him to "circumvent the most entrenched positions ." **Murray Hunt** also continues to be recommended in this field as an "impressive speaker."

39 Essex Street (see full details p.1503) This one-time respondent only set has successfully metamorphosed into a broad church which now handles applicant and claimant work alike. **Nigel Pleming QC** (see p.1434) appears in the more prominent public law cases, tackling matters with "trenchancy and quiet efficiency." **Robert Jay QC** (see p.1401) adopts a more expansive style and is noted for his "genuine commitment to the field." The set is blessed with strong representation at the junior level. **Stuart Catchpole** (see p.1360) acts on behalf of the Crown Solicitors and was the main MAFF barrister in the BSE Inquiry. **Jennifer Richards'** (see p.1440) main avenue of interest is community care work, handling children, disability, health and education cases. "Thoroughly grounded in her knowledge of the law" she is highly sought after and known to "turn her papers around quickly." **Steven Kovats** (see p.1407) has built up a healthy practice acting as respondent counsel on behalf of government bodies.

11 King's Bench Walk Chambers (see full details p.1532) A set particularly strong on local authority powers and financing, and judicial review of central and local government. The foremost barrister here is **James Goudie QC** (see p.1388). An "approachable" expert on 'best value' and local authority structuring, he further handles straight public law work, appearing in cases such as R v Lambeth, ex p. Anderson. Similarly "genial," **Michael Supperstone QC** (see p.1455) has a broad practice, which he negotiates with "a fine persuasive manner." These two have now been joined by a brace of barristers from 4-5 Gray's Inn Square. Newly promoted to silk, **Tim Kerr QC** (see p.1405), is judged "a prize catch with a big future" while top junior **Clive Lewis** (see p.1411) is "a pleasure to deal with." **Nigel Giffin** (see p.1384) is of "undeniable quality" being both "fantastically clever and industrious to boot."

Brick Court Chambers (see full details p.1484) This set is seen as increasingly important in a landscape where human rights and EC law issues become ever more pertinent. Its leading light is **Richard Gordon QC** (see p.1387) whose diversity of work leads him into the environment, housing, community care and local authority spheres. "Extremely hard working and with an approach which pleases solicitors" he has had another busy year. Highlights include acting in cases relating to third generation mobile phone licences, London Underground funding and the age of homosexual consent, while representing the Health Secretary in the Shipman Inquiry. **Jonathan Sumption QC** (see p.1455) also makes his mark in this area as in so many others. A "superstar" of the commercial bar, his highlight cases this year include the highly significant Interbrew v Bass case which related to the blocking of a takeover. **Sydney Kentridge QC** (see p.1405) provides "an imposing presence" and has involved himself in landmark cases before the Court of Human Rights in Strasbourg. On the junior front the set does not abound with public law specialists but has in **Alan Maclean** (see p.1414), "a battler with a genuine interest in the subject."

Doughty Street Chambers (see full details p.1492) Attractive to the traditional public law solicitors, this set has an emphasis on civil liberties, human rights, immigration, housing and community care cases. **Andrew Nicol QC** (see p.1428) provides expertise on immigration and media law and is "extremely thorough in both preparation and presentation." He has consistently acted in matters of the highest importance and recently appeared in Farah, a case determining whether the police could be liable for racial discrimination in answering emergency calls. **Edward Fitzgerald QC** (see p.1379) has a vibrant judicial review practice and is well-versed in human rights and prison law. Similarly, **Kate Markus** "shines at prison law" and sits in our junior rankings with the "in tune" **Keir Starmer** (see p.1452), a specialist European human rights lawyer. **Steven Cragg** (see p.1367) enters the lists as up and coming on the back of warm commendation from his peers.

Two Garden Court (see full details p.1509) Now with an associated civil liberties/human rights set called Garden Court North, this set continues to be strong in immigration, housing and crime related public law work. **Jan Luba QC** has been elevated to silk in recognition of his expertise in social housing where he deploys "advocacy skills that make judges listen." The role of leading junior has fallen to **Stephanie Harrison** who handles judicial review especially in asylum and community care matters. She is "driven by a commitment to the justice of the case."

2-3 Gray's Inn Square (see full details p.1513) Mainly specialist in planning and local government, this set draws its work largely from the 200 plus local authority clients it has. The headline performer is **Mark Lowe QC** (see p.1413) who has advised a number of London and regional borough councils in the past year including Cheltenham BC on its dispute with the District Auditor over the externalisation of its debt of £22.5 million. Popular with solicitors across the country, he is "unstuffy, decisive and firmly focused on the client's objectives." Most commented on the speed of his paperwork and his "handy knack of putting the client at ease."

4-5 Gray's Inn Square (see full details p.1515) (Appleby/Mole) Active in public law, judicial review, planning and environmental law, this set has for many years been a worthy player in the field. Concern has been expressed, however, due to a number of defections to rival sets which has led to a consequent reduction in capability. Of those still in situ, **Timothy Corner** (see p.1366) is recommended for his pure public law work.

Other Notable Practitioners **1 Crown Office Row** provides two silks for our tables in the newly appointed **Neil Garnham QC** (see p.1383) and the "modest and mature" **Philip Havers QC** (see p.1392). Other rated juniors are **Alan Griffiths** (see p.1389) of **One Essex Court**, **Richard Clayton** (see p.1363) of **Devereux Chambers** and **Robin Tam** (see p.1457) of **1 Temple Garden.**

AGRICULTURE

RESEARCH: The rankings are based on in-depth interviews with over 5,000 solicitors and barristers in the UK. Chambers research is audited by the British Market Research Bureau (see page 7 for details).

OVERVIEW: By common consent, the last year was a quiet one at the agricultural bar. With the various problems in the industry, the inclination has been more towards settlement than litigation. Falcon Chambers remains by far the dominant force. Nationally praised for its "sensible advice," it remains the only true agricultural chambers.

LONDON

AGRICULTURE • London		QCs	Jnrs
1	**Falcon Chambers** (Gaunt/Lewison)	4	6

Numbers show recommended barristers in this practice area

LEADING SILKS • London		
1	**MORGAN Paul**	Falcon Chambers
	WOOD Derek	Falcon Chambers
2	**BROCK Jonathan**	Falcon Chambers
3	**GAUNT Jonathan**	Falcon Chambers

For details of these leading barristers see Profiles on p.1339

LEADING JUNIORS • London		
1	**MOSS Joanne**	Falcon Chambers
	RODGER Martin	Falcon Chambers
2	**HUTTON Caroline**	Enterprise Chambers
	JOURDAN Stephen	Falcon Chambers
	MCALLISTER Ann	Serle Court
3	**DE FREITAS Anthony**	4 Paper Buildings
	FANCOURT Timothy	Falcon Chambers
	MERCER Hugh	Essex Court Chambers
	THOMAS Nigel	Maitland Chambers
UP AND COMING		
	SHEA Caroline	Falcon Chambers
	WINDSOR Emily	Falcon Chambers

This book is the product of 6,552 1/2-hour interviews. See p.7 for BMRB audit.

For details of these leading barristers see Profiles on p.1339

Falcon Chambers (see full details p.1504) Recognised everywhere as "the strongest chambers in the agricultural world," this set is praised as "the experts." "Offering absolutely first class advice," **Paul Morgan QC** (see p.1423) brings his in-depth knowledge to the table while "genius" **Derek Wood QC** can be called upon for the most complex of issues. "Clearly one of the best," **Jonathan Brock QC** (see p.1355) and respected **Jonathan Gaunt QC** (see p.1383) happily marry practicality with an academic flair. A glittering array of juniors wave the flag for the chambers. **Joanne Moss** and **Martin Rodger** (see p.1441) are the first names uttered by solicitors across the country. Moss is praised for being both "practical and academic" and "dealing with things sensibly and quickly." Rodger "knows his stuff inside out" and is viewed as "head and shoulders above the rest." Respected **Stephen Jourdan** is commended for "getting things right" while the "able and sensible" **Timothy Fancourt** (see p.1377) continues to draw warm recommendations. **Caroline Shea** (see p.1447) and **Emily Windsor** are both seen as important new faces in the field.

Other Notable Practitioners At **Enterprise Chambers Caroline Hutton** (see p.1399) "gives tremendous advice with incredible turn around." Over at **Serle Court Ann McAllister** (see p.1418) is valued for her knowledge of property and for having "good client appeal." **Anthony De Freitas** (see p.1370) of **4 Paper Buildings** is described as "a dark horse, but truly top rate" and is praised for his skills on environmental issues. **Hugh Mercer** (see p.1420) of **Essex Court Chambers** is adjudged "brilliant on anything to do with the common market," while **Nigel Thomas** (see p.1459) of **Maitland Chambers** is best known for knowledge of the Welsh market.

ALTERNATIVE DISPUTE RESOLUTION

RESEARCH: The rankings are based on in-depth interviews with over 5,000 solicitors and barristers in the UK. Chambers research is audited by the British Market Research Bureau (see page 7 for details).

OVERVIEW: Despite the increasing focus displayed by the bar, the mediation market continues to be dominated by solicitors. We refer you to our overview of the solicitors and non-legally trained practitioners in this field in order to complete the picture.

LONDON

LEADING SILKS • London		
★	NAUGHTON Philip	3 Serjeants' Inn
1	RUTTLE Stephen	Brick Court Chambers
2	GAITSKELL Robert	Keating Chambers
	KALLIPETIS Michel	Littleton Chambers
	KERSHEN Lawrence	Tooks Court Chambers

For details of these leading barristers see Profiles on p.1339

LEADING JUNIORS • London		
1	AEBERLI Peter	46 Essex Street
	BRODIE Bruce	39 Essex Street
	ROGERS Beverly-Ann	Serle Court
2	BIRCH Elizabeth	3 Verulam Buildings
	CUNNINGHAM Graham	Littman Chambers
	MANNING Colin	Littleton Chambers

This book is the product of 6,552 1/2-hour interviews. See p.7 for BMRB audit.

For details of these leading barristers see Profiles on p.1339

Philip Naughton QC (see p.1427), **3 Serjeant's Inn** (see full details p.1564) According to clients, "the only barrister who would clearly be top in a list including solicitors," Naughton has conducted a substantial number of mediations in the past year. Seen to have "honed" his skills, he is "clever, tenacious and chameleon-like." Championing a "non-confrontational style" that makes people "confide in him," he specialises in construction and engineering arbitration, commercial and manufacturing contracts and professional negligence cases.

Stephen Ruttle QC (see p.1443), **Brick Court Chambers** (see full details p.1484) An "immensely capable and effective mediator" who combines a "first class forensic ability" with a facility for "capturing the confidence of parties." Has notched up an array of cases in the past year and enjoys "a justifiably impressive reputation" in the field. Has particular expertise in insurance, reinsurance and commercial disputes.

Robert Gaitskell QC (see p.1382), **Keating Chambers** (see full details p.1525) "A silk to watch," Gaitskell boasts much experience of engineering and construction disputes. "Frightfully clever," in addition to his practice at the bar he is a senior engineer, being a Vice-President of the Institution of Electrical Engineers. "Practical and firm" he extends a "quiet but calming influence" which "makes parties think." He gathers a number of referrals through CEDR and from the International Chambers of Commerce.

Michel Kallipetis QC (see p.1403), **Littleton Chambers** (see full details p.1537) Described as "clever, charming and good with people," he is thought "a growing presence" in ADR. Clients vouch that he is "imaginative in his solutions" and that he benefits from his accountancy background. He has mediated disputes concerning pensions rights, solicitors' and valuers' negligence, and commercial contract disputes with claims over £50 million, including referrals from the Commercial Court. Used by CEDR and his chambers' own wholly owned company, Littleton Dispute Resolution Services.

Lawrence Kershen QC, Tooks Court Chambers On the CEDR training faculty and expert in the areas of advocacy, communication, presentation and negotiation, it is little surprise that Kershen is thought to possess a "great track-record as a mediator." Has conducted a large number of general commercial mediations over the last year, and is admired for his "hugely sympathetic and personal style."

Peter Aeberli, Eliciting "favourable reports," former architect Aeberli is "clever, competent and capable." He specialises in construction disputes. Mediates on appointment by CEDR, the Royal Institute of British Architects (London Region) and on direct appointment by parties.

Bruce Brodie (see p.1356), **39 Essex Street** (see full details p.1503) This former solicitor is said to offer "much experience of commercial disputes." A "calm and kind" man, parties "respond well to his gentle but persuasive authority."

Beverly-Ann Rogers (see p.1441), **Serle Court** (see full details p.1565) " The leading junior," according to referral organisations, Rogers is said to be "in a class of her own." In her first full year of mediating she conducted over 15 mediations. Tipped as a "future star," Rogers is described as "quiet and effective" and "always able to see the point."

Elizabeth Birch (see p.1350), **3 Verulam Buildings** (see full details p.1575) A "clever and pleasant" mediator, Birch has a "great amount" of experience in all types of commercial disputes, including banking, insurance, professional negligence, pensions, joint ventures, IT and transportation. Maintains a high success rate. A founder member of the ACI initiative (Arbitration for Commerce and Industry).

Graham Cunningham (see p.1368), **Littman Chambers** (see full details p.1537) "Not one to underestimate." Cunningham's background in IT is thought to make him particularly strong in his mediation work in that area. He also conducts general commercial disputes.

Colin Manning (see p.1416), **Littleton Chambers** (see full details p.1537) Another mediator involved in the Littleton Chambers ADR service, Manning is described by heavy-hitting solicitor mediators as possessing "a real mediation skill." A "clever and witty" individual, he is said to make mediations "rather enjoyable."

ARBITRATION

RESEARCH: The rankings are based on in-depth interviews with over 5,000 solicitors and barristers in the UK. Chambers research is audited by the British Market Research Bureau (see page 7 for details).

OVERVIEW: Our tables include the highly select group of truly specialist international arbitrators, and those whose sector focus (such as maritime or construction) leads them to develop expertise in this field as part of a wider practice.

LONDON

Essex Court Chambers (see full details p.1496) Considered by the majority to be "the foremost set" because of its "outstanding individuals, breadth of arbitration experience and knowledge." Thought to be "uniformly excellent" for general commercial work. **V.V.Veeder QC** (see p.1464) remains "utterly outstanding," roundly praised as an "extraordinarily clever tactician with a fantastic range of experience," and "a spectacular feel for cultural differences between legal systems." **Stewart Boyd QC** (see p.1353) is considered "heavyweight, academic, but user-friendly" and, like his colleague **Ian Hunter QC** (see p.1399), "a powerhouse" for insurance work. As in so many areas, **Gordon Pollock QC** (see p.1434) remains a "tower of strength." **Michael Collins QC** (see p.1365) is "superb both as arbitrator and counsel," while **Michael Thomas QC** (see p.1459) boasts "vast experience and capability." **Jeffrey Gruder QC** (see p.1390) also garners plaudits for his "broad ranging ability." "Extremely talented" new silk **Graham Dunning QC** (see p.1373) is "going to be a force to be reckoned with." Praise is heaped upon "super-confident team-player" **Toby Landau** (see p.1408), who "understands the internationals;" peers consider him "the right man for any job." **Joe Smouha** (see p.1450) is judged a "clear leader" and a "thorough, approachable and excellent advocate." The "admirably tenacious" **Richard Millett** (see p.1421) enters the rankings this year with substantial backing.

Atkin Chambers (see full details p.1475) Voted "a leading set," it is recommended for its expertise in the energy sector, and "pre-eminent for heavy construction." Fields the "vastly respected" **Robert Akenhead QC** (see p.1341) along with the "immensely capable" **John Blackburn QC** (see p.xxx). **Colin Reese QC** (see p.1439) has won many supporters with his "considerable talents," while **Andrew White QC** (see p.1467) is esteemed for his "more rounded practice," and in the construction arena adjudged "on a par with the best."

One Essex Court (see full details p.1497) "Undoubtedly one of the best sets for arbitration," One Essex Court retains its retinue of fans. **Tony Grabiner QC** is described as "astonishingly able with an unbeatably commercial approach," while the "hugely competent" **Ian Glick QC** (see p.1386) maintains his popularity with magic circle firms. "Top-notch advocate" **Mark Barnes QC** (see p.1347) is greatly admired.

20 Essex Street (see full details p.1500) A "favourite" set for many and "recommended for its broad arbitration expertise." **Peter Gross QC** (see p.1390) is adjudged "a cautious and enormously strong advocate" and praised for his "internationalism."

Keating Chambers (see full details p.1525) Considered by some solicitors as "the best set for construction," the set "goes from strength to strength." **Vivian Ramsey QC** (see p.1438) is "highly-rated for international construction and infrastructure" cases and held to be "excellent - whether the case itself is strong or weak." **John Uff QC** (see p.1464) is a "tremendous advocate" while **Richard Fernyhough QC** (see p.1378) is endorsed for his presence in the field. **Timothy Elliott QC** (see p.1375) is "highly-respected," while **Christopher Thomas QC** (see p.1459) and **Paul Darling QC**

Barristers' profiles 1339-1472

ARBITRATION (INTERNATIONAL) • London		QCs	Jnrs
1	**Essex Court Chambers** (Gordon Pollock QC)	8	3
2	**Atkin Chambers** (Robert Akenhead QC)	4	-
	One Essex Court (Anthony Grabiner QC)	3	-
	20 Essex Street (Iain Milligan QC)	1	-
	Keating Chambers (Richard Fernyhough QC)	8	-
3	**Brick Court Chambers** (Christopher Clarke QC)	1	1
	4 Essex Court (Nigel Teare QC)	5	-
	7 King's Bench Walk (Jeremy Cooke QC)	4	-

Numbers show recommended barristers in this practice area

LEADING SILKS • London		
★	**VEEDER V.V.**	Essex Court Chambers
1	**BOYD Stewart**	Essex Court Chambers
	GLICK Ian	One Essex Court
	GRABINER Anthony	One Essex Court
	GROSS Peter	20 Essex Street
	HUNTER Ian	Essex Court Chambers
	POLLOCK Gordon	Essex Court Chambers
	RAMSEY Vivian	Keating Chambers
	UFF John	Keating Chambers
2	**AKENHEAD Robert**	Atkin Chambers
	BLACKBURN John	Atkin Chambers
	COLLINS Michael	Essex Court Chambers
	FERNYHOUGH Richard	Keating Chambers
3	**ELLIOTT Timothy**	Keating Chambers
	FURST Stephen	Keating Chambers
	GEE Steven	4 Field Court
	MALEK Ali	3 Verulam Buildings
	REESE Colin	Atkin Chambers
	TACKABERRY John	Arbitration Chambers
	THOMAS Christopher	Keating Chambers
	THOMAS Michael	Essex Court Chambers
	WHITE Andrew	Atkin Chambers
4	**BARNES Mark**	One Essex Court
	BRENTON Timothy	7 King's Bench Walk
	BUCKNALL Belinda	4 Essex Court
	DARLING Paul	Keating Chambers
	GRUDER Jeffrey	Essex Court Chambers
	HADDON-CAVE Charles	4 Essex Court
	HEILBRON Hilary	Brick Court Chambers
	HOWARD M.N.	4 Essex Court
	JARVIS John	3 Verulam Buildings
	KEALEY Gavin	7 King's Bench Walk
	RUSSELL Jeremy	4 Essex Court
	SCHAFF Alistair	7 King's Bench Walk
	TEARE Nigel	4 Essex Court
NEW SILKS		
	BUTCHER Christopher	7 King's Bench Walk
	DUNNING Graham	Essex Court Chambers
	TAVERNER Marcus	Keating Chambers

For details of these leading barristers see Profiles on p.1339

LEADING JUNIORS • London		
1	**LANDAU Toby**	Essex Court Chambers
2	**SMOUHA Joe**	Essex Court Chambers
3	**MILLETT Richard**	Essex Court Chambers
	PLANTEROSE Rowan	Littman Chambers
4	**DAVIES Helen**	Brick Court Chambers

This book is the product of 6,552 1/2-hour interviews. See p.7 for BMRB audit.

For details of these leading barristers see Profiles on p.1339

(see p.1369) likewise attract their share of commendation. **Marcus Taverner QC** (see p.1458) is a high profile "name" at the chambers and **Stephen Furst QC** (see p.1382), who is "used extensively," is considered "miles better than many."

Brick Court Chambers (see full details p.1484) The "preferred set" with many big-hitters, Brick Court is considered a "heavyweight and safe choice." **Hilary Heilbron QC** (see p.1393) is "highly esteemed," while **Helen Davies** (see p.1369)is an "incredibly bright" junior who provides a "fantastic, thorough, and hard-working service."

4 Essex Court (see full details p.1498) "Trusty" **Charles Haddon-Cave QC** (see p.1390) is described as "redoubtable," while head of chambers **Nigel Teare QC** (see p.1458) remains a perennial favourite alongside **M.N. Howard QC** (see p.1397). **Belinda Bucknall QC** (see p.1357) has her supporters, as does "solid" **Jeremy Russell QC** (see p.1443).

7 King's Bench Walk (see full details p.1530) Deemed a "sensible choice," this set is home to "consistently brilliant" **Alistair Schaff QC** (see p.1444) as well as the the well-liked **Gavin Kealey QC** (see p.1404) and "competent" **Timothy Brenton QC** (see p.1354). New silk **Christopher Butcher** (see p.1358) proves a "popular port of call" with leading solicitors.

Other Notable Practitioners Head of **Arbitration Chambers**, **John Tackaberry QC** continues to garner plaudits. At **3 Verulam Buildings**, **Ali Malek QC** (see p.1415) "knows the subject backwards," while joint head of chambers **John Jarvis QC** (see p.1401) is said to have "distinguished" himself. Over at **4 Field Court**, Head of Chambers **Steven Gee QC** remains "damned useful." **Rowan Planterose** (see p.1434) of **Littman Chambers** wields a "calm, controlled style," and "is easy going with tribunals."

AVIATION

RESEARCH: The rankings are based on in-depth interviews with over 5,000 solicitors and barristers in the UK. Chambers research is audited by the British Market Research Bureau (see page 7 for details).

OVERVIEW: Aviation, essentially not a large field for the bar, lies in the hands of those with the longstanding experience in the sector. The former 5 Bell Yard members still feature as the main players, in their respective new Chambers.

LONDON

	AVIATION • London	QCs	Jnrs
1	**4 Essex Court** (Nigel Teare QC)	1	3
	Fountain Court (Anthony Boswood QC)	1	2
2	**Brick Court Chambers** (Christopher Clarke QC)	1	1
	Essex Court Chambers (Gordon Pollock QC)	1	1

Numbers show recommended barristers in this practice area

	LEADING SILKS • London	
1	CRANE Michael	Fountain Court
2	HADDON-CAVE Charles	4 Essex Court
	HUNTER Ian	Essex Court Chambers
	WOOD William	Brick Court Chambers
3	FOWLER Richard	Monckton Chambers
	MCMANUS Richard	4-5 Gray's Inn Square

For details of these leading barristers see Profiles on p.1339

	LEADING JUNIORS • London	
1	LAWSON Robert	4 Essex Court
	LYDIARD Andrew	Brick Court Chambers
	SHEPHERD Philip	24 Old Buildings
2	SHAH Akhil	Fountain Court
3	KIMBELL John	4 Essex Court
	REEVE Matthew	4 Essex Court
	THANKI Bankim	Fountain Court
4	JOSEPH David	Essex Court Chambers
	OWEN Tudor	9-12 Bell Yard

This book is the product of 6,552 1/2-hour interviews. See p.7 for BMRB audit.
For details of these leading barristers see Profiles on p.1339

4 Essex Court (see full details p.1498) Another set to benefit from the disintegration of 5 Bell Yard, these highly commercial barristers are at the forefront of the aviation field. Leading silk **Charles Haddon-Cave QC** "has built up a defence practice" and is considered "a forceful advocate," having appeared in a cargo case under the Warsaw Convention concerning the theft of a $2 million consignment of Rolex watches from Hong Kong airport. As a junior, **Robert Lawson** (see p.1409) is adjudged "down to earth, a sharp lawyer" and has been involved in a leading case about whether psychiatric injury can be claimed under the Warsaw Convention (Morris v KLM). Displaying an "outstanding intellect" **John Kimbell** (see p.1406)

Barristers' profiles 1339-1472

has been active on cargo cases, as has his colleague **Matthew Reeve** (see p.1440), who was instructed on behalf of the handling agents in the Anglo Belgian Diamonds v Ogden case regarding the theft of diamonds at Heathrow Airport.

Fountain Court (see full details p.1506) Having acquired a fair few of the original 5 Bell Yard barristers, the resident set is considered a strength in the sector. Most predominantly endorsed remains the "fantastic" **Michael Crane QC**, appearing in the high profile Western Digital Corp v British Airways case. Unanimously referred to as the "top silk in the industry" with his "hard working and user friendly" ethics, he "could be working out of a two room shack and still be world class." The market mourns the recent sudden death of Trevor Philipson QC. Of the juniors, the "young and thoughtful" **Akhil Shah** (see p.1446) is "seen a lot" in this field, handling the case for Thomas Cook against British Airways and TAP respectively, concerning the loss of currency during international carriage by air. "Star junior" at the set who continues to tackle aviation cases is **Bankim Thanki** (see p.1459), an all-rounder who successfully acted for the claimant in enforcement proceedings in the Commercial Court and Court of Appeal following a major international arbitration under UNITRAL rules against Air India.

Brick Court Chambers (see full details p.1484) Covering a wide range of commercial cases, this chambers has also established a hold in the aviation field. Active in competition and EU issues as well as disputes over airspace slots. High profile **William Wood QC** (see p.1470) was successfully involved in the Court of Appeal of Tonga on the matter of Polynesian Airlines v Government of Tonga, as was his "accomplished, academic" colleague **Andrew Lydiard** (see p.1414), a "star junior, who undoubtedly commands respect." The pair were also involved in disputes regarding the Concorde crash en route to Nairobi.

Essex Court Chambers (see full details p.1496) Holding onto its standing as a commercial set with aviation expertise, the set is appearing as counsel for Malca Amit in the trial of a second action concerning theft of diamonds en route from Brussels to Heathrow. Leading silk **Ian Hunter QC** (see p.1399) has a "long standing" in the sector, with a well respected aptitude towards mediation. **David Joseph** (see p.1403) received warm recommendation as an advocate growing in stature.

Other Notable Practitioners Heavily involved in competition and regulatory activity, and thereby also seen on the aviation front, **Richard Fowler QC** (see p.1381) of **Monckton Chambers** acts at CAA hearings. Known for his judicial review work, the "lucid and measured" **Richard McManus QC** (see p.1419) at **4-5 Gray's Inn Square** is "often seen on IATA issues." "First choice, brilliant and absolutely dedicated, all-round aviation barrister" **Philip Shepherd** (see p.1448) at **24 Old Buildings** has recently acted for the Secretary of State in a challenge by IATA to the legality of the EC directive removing Warsaw Convention limits for EC carriers. In breaches of regulations and in civil aviation matters, **Tudor Owen** (see p.1431) at **9-12 Bell Yard** (Evans) is considered one of "the best junior advocates around."

BANKING

RESEARCH: The rankings are based on in-depth interviews with over 5,000 solicitors and barristers in the UK. Chambers research is audited by the British Market Research Bureau (see page 7 for details).

OVERVIEW: Despite solicitor advocacy and the high level of advisory expertise on tap at city firms, most commentators see a secure future for the banking bar. Profound operational changes in the sector – e-banking, globalisation and consolidation, together with a predicted economic downturn – are likely to guarantee many years of high profile work. This work may, however, be spread more thinly than it once was as firms become increasingly selective, especially at the junior end. The trend for city firms to do more of their own work has made banking a particularly tough environment in which to become established. Opportunities exist for talented barristers at sets not traditionally known for banking to pick up work. There are almost no specialists – William Blair may well be the closest. At the top of the list, though, are the true heavyweights who do this work regularly, Michael Brindle and Mark Hapgood. The great courtroom stars, Anthony Grabiner, Gordon Pollock and Jonathan Sumption remain the natural choice for many firms on any huge financial sector litigation.

Barristers' profiles 1339-1472

BANKING • London		QCs	Jnrs
1	**Fountain Court** (Anthony Boswood QC)	4	6
	3 Verulam Buildings (Symons/Jarvis)	5	6
2	**Brick Court Chambers** (Christopher Clarke QC)	3	-
3	**One Essex Court** (Lord Grabiner QC)	3	4
4	**Erskine Chambers** (Robin Potts QC)	2	-
	Essex Court Chambers (Gordon Pollock QC)	2	1
	20 Essex Street (Iain Milligan QC)	2	-
	3-4 South Square (Crystal/Alexander)	4	-

Numbers show recommended barristers in this practice area

LEADING SILKS • LONDON		
★	BRINDLE Michael	Fountain Court
	HAPGOOD Mark	Brick Court Chambers
1	GRABINER Anthony	One Essex Court
	POLLOCK Gordon	Essex Court Chambers
	SUMPTION Jonathan	Brick Court Chambers
2	BLAIR William	3 Verulam Buildings
	MALEK Ali	3 Verulam Buildings
	MILLIGAN Iain	20 Essex Street
	POTTS Robin	Erskine Chambers
3	BOSWOOD Anthony	Fountain Court
	HOWARD Mark	Brick Court Chambers
	SALTER Richard	3 Verulam Buildings
	STADLEN Nicholas	Fountain Court
4	DAVIES Rhodri	One Essex Court
	DICKER Robin	3-4 South Square
	GLICK Ian	One Essex Court
	HACKER Richard	3-4 South Square
	JARVIS John	3 Verulam Buildings
	KNOWLES Robin	3-4 South Square
	MALEK Hodge	4-5 Gray's Inn Square
	PHILLIPS Mark	3-4 South Square
	PYMONT Christopher	Maitland Chambers
	RAILTON David	Fountain Court
	RICHARDS David	Erskine Chambers
	THOMAS Neville	3 Verulam Buildings
	WATERS Malcolm	11 Old Square
NEW SILKS		
	ANDREWS Geraldine	Essex Court Chambers
	BUTCHER Christopher	7 King's Bench Walk
	HANCOCK Christopher	20 Essex Street

This book is the product of 6,552 1/2-hour interviews. See p.7 for BMRB audit.
For details of these leading barristers see Profiles on p.1339

LONDON

Fountain Court (see full details p.1506) "A great set" approved of by clients – "nicer and better people to deal with – fair and realistic about fees." Although the loss of Peter Goldsmith QC to the post of attorney general will have an effect, the chambers has such an array of talent that it will undoubtedly weather the setback gracefully. "At the very top" is **Michael Brindle QC** (see p.1355). "Everything you want a heavyweight commercial barrister to be," some sources rate him "clearly the best in banking law." **Anthony Boswood QC** (see p.1352) is "a pleasure to deal with, hard working and he doesn't lose his nerve," while "first rate" **Nicholas Stadlen QC** (see p.1452) is "a bright, hard working advocate." One client judged a recent performance of his in the House of Lords "the best I've ever seen." "Clever, calm and methodical" **David Railton QC** (see p.1438) also has a strong following. The set is blessed with "outstanding juniors." "Clever, funny, hardworking and fantastically good on paper," **Bankim Thanki** (see p.1459) has "the courage of his convictions" and "a knack of giving a clear view." **Timothy Howe** (see p.1398) is "a careful and skilled advocate – extremely hardworking and good on his feet," and **David Waksman** (see p.1465) is "a thorough and reliable all-rounder." Newly ranked **Raymond Cox** (see p.1367) is considered "a sound advocate in the Hapgood style" with a large practice in this area, while **Andrew Mitchell** (see p.1422) also maintains a strong profile. Up and coming **Richard Handyside** (see p.1391) is "excellent – clever, funny, hardworking and a good team player."

3 Verulam Buildings (see full details p.1575) "The specialists in this area," sources agree that "banking is synonymous with 3 Verulam." While it has its share of investment bank work, it is particularly known as "the only set in London with a regular flow of retail banking." Among the silks, **William Blair QC** (see p.1351) is "fantastic on paper" and "about as specialised as you can come across." He is especially recommended for advisory matters without litigation. "Rising star" **Ali Malek QC** (see p.1415) is "flamboyant, entertaining and charming but never over the top." He is regarded as "well liked by judges because he's persuasive but fair" and a match for anyone. "Intellectual, academic" **Richard Salter QC** (see p.1445) may be "the cleverest banking lawyer around" but some consider his advocacy rather dry: "he tends to go for the detail." Newly ranked **John Jarvis QC** (see p.1401), "a big name in banking litigation" and **Neville Thomas QC** (see p.1460), who is less visible now but still recommended for advisory matters, also have followings. The set also stands out for the quality of its juniors. **Ewan McQuater** (see p.1420) "hasn't put a foot wrong – he's persuasive, thoughtful, a good tactician and has sound judgement," while "brilliant" **Adrian Beltrami** (see p.1349) has "a strong following." **Jonathan Nash** (see p.1426) is held to be "a good advocate with a nice manner" and **Stephen Phillips** (see p.1433) "has a significant practice for some of the really big firms." While not quite as high profile this year, **Jonathan Davies-Jones** (see p.1369) is regularly involved in banking cases while "friendly, clever and hardworking" **Sonia Tolaney** (see p.1461) is beginning to carve out a reputation.

LEADING JUNIORS • London		
1	THANKI Bankim	Fountain Court
2	BELTRAMI Adrian	3 Verulam Buildings
	HOWE Timothy	Fountain Court
	MCQUATER Ewan	3 Verulam Buildings
	MILLETT Richard	Essex Court Chambers
	NASH Jonathan	3 Verulam Buildings
	PHILLIPS Stephen	3 Verulam Buildings
	RABINOWITZ Laurence	One Essex Court
	WAKSMAN David	Fountain Court
	WOLFSON David	One Essex Court
3	BROWN Hannah	One Essex Court
	COX Raymond	Fountain Court
	DAVIES-JONES Jonathan	3 Verulam Buildings
	MILES Robert	4 Stone Buildings
	MITCHELL Andrew	Fountain Court
	SULLIVAN Michael	One Essex Court
UP AND COMING		
	HANDYSIDE Richard	Fountain Court
	TOLANEY Sonia	3 Verulam Buildings

This book is the product of 6,552 1/2-hour interviews. See p.7 for BMRB audit.
For details of these leading barristers see Profiles on p.1339

Brick Court Chambers (see full details p.1484) Recommended by major clients "for the higher quality banking disputes" because of its "highly experienced silks," the set still appears top heavy with its juniors yet to make an impression in the sector. At "the pinnacle of banking ability" is **Mark Hapgood QC**. "Seen as the number one and loved by lots of banks" according to peers, he has "not only got a great brain but also huge common sense and is one of the nicest opponents you could want." As an advocate he is "not flamboyant but calm, persuasive and knowledgeable." **Jonathan Sumption QC** (see p.1455) may be "in a class of his own as an advocate." Not perceived to be a banking specialist, "he will occasionally advise on structural, conceptual banking issues," with significant results. Moreover "you can put him in an area he knows nothing about and in no time he's wiping the floor with everyone." The third of the set's trio of high-class silks is **Mark Howard QC** (see p.1398), praised for his "clarity of view and ability to say the right things with clients. He doesn't flap and he doesn't change his mind."

One Essex Court (see full details p.1497) "Clients clearly love" **Anthony Grabiner QC**, the highest profile silk at this heavyweight commercial set. Although not considered a banking specialist, he is "a fighter, tough but engaging, clever and easy to work with," and "a supremely skilful advocate, beautiful to listen to." "Clever" **Rhodri Davies QC** (see p.1369) and **Ian Glick QC** (see p.1386) ("a light touch but very skilful") also have a following in this sector. **Laurence Rabinowitz** (see p.1437) is "one of those unique types – not a specialist in the way that mere mortals are, but still hugely experienced." Solicitors confirm that they would turn to him for really big cases. The set's biggest specialists are **Hannah Brown** (see p.1356), **Michael Sullivan** (see p.1455), who has a strong following amongst retail banks, and **David Wolfson** (see p.1469), considered by some "at the top of the tree – absolutely outstanding with a big practice."

Erskine Chambers (see full details p.1495) Why go to Erskine Chambers? "If you want to browbeat the opposition and you've got an opinion from Erskine you're already ahead of the game." Its renowned corporate expertise spills over into banking, largely due to the efforts and reputation of "brainbox" **Robin Potts QC**, praised by clients as "accessible, practical and reliable with a depth of experience." **David Richards QC** (see p.1440) is also highly regarded by the market and the set as a whole has expertise in highly specialised banking instruments.

Essex Court Chambers (see full details p.1496) Felt to be at its best on large scale international work, this set's commercial expertise ensures it a steady flow of top level banking work. The leading light is "one of the great men of the bar" **Gordon Pollock QC** (see p.1434), "a big name silk who could easily appear on a banking dispute" though he is not considered a banking specialist. "Really outstanding at the junior level," the set includes **Geraldine Andrews QC** (see p.1343) ("bright with a good practice") who took silk this year while "outstandingly clever, user friendly and gifted" **Richard Millett** (see p.1421) carries the torch at the junior end.

20 Essex Street (see full details p.1500) The set has succeeded in developing a banking practice from its shipping roots and leveraging out of commodities work. **Iain Milligan QC** (see p.1421) in particular has "attracted a following." He is said to be "knowledgeable, thorough and good at picking apart a contract word by word." Also active in this sector is "charming and able" **Christopher Hancock QC**.

3-4 South Square (see full details p.1566) "A proactive set spreading its wings into other areas," there is much more to it than insolvency. As a leading solicitor commented "it's our first choice for heavyweight work in all areas of banking." Among a clutch of talented young silks are "terribly nice, clever and precise" **Robin Knowles QC** (see p.1407), "immensely bright" **Robin Dicker QC** (see p.1371), considered "good on a range of banking and commercial matters," and **Mark Phillips QC** (see p.1433) ("bloody good – we like him and use him a lot.") **Richard Hacker QC** (see p.1390) also maintains his high quality reputation, although the set's juniors remain low profile in this field.

Other Notable Practitioners "A future star," **Hodge Malek QC** (see p.1415) of **4-5 Gray's Inn Square** is said share the attributes of brother Ali; "he's got the family charm." Though not considered banking specialists, **Christopher Pymont QC** (see p.1437) of **Maitland Chambers** is "a good barrister, perfectly competent at banking disputes" while new silk **Christopher Butcher QC** (see p.1358) at **7 King's Bench Walk** is "extraordinarily clever" and "good on derivatives and jurisdictional disputes." **Malcolm Waters QC** (see p.1467) at **11 Old Square** is recommended by transactional solicitors as "one of the leading experts on building society law." Amongst juniors, "bright" **Robert Miles** of **4 Stone Buildings** is considered "a skilled draftsman and advocate."

CHANCERY

RESEARCH: The rankings are based on in-depth interviews with over 5,000 solicitors and barristers in the UK. Chambers research is audited by the British Market Research Bureau (see page 7 for details).

Barristers' profiles 1339-1472

LONDON

COMMERCIAL CHANCERY

CHANCERY: COMMERCIAL • London		QCs	Jnrs
1	**Maitland Chambers** (Lyndon-Stanford/Aldous)	7	6
2	**Serle Court** (Lord Neill of Bladen QC)	5	4
	4 Stone Buildings (Philip Heslop QC)	4	3
	Wilberforce Chambers (Edward Nugee QC)	3	3
3	**9 Old Square** (Michael Driscoll QC)	2	2
	3-4 South Square (Crystal/Alexander)	3	2
	11 Stone Buildings (Murray Rosen QC)	2	2
4	**New Square Chambers** (Mowbray/Hamilton)	3	-
	24 Old Buildings (Mann/Steinfeld)	2	-
	3 Stone Buildings (Geoffrey Vos QC)	2	-

Numbers show recommended barristers in this practice area

LEADING SILKS • London		
1	**ALDOUS Charles**	Maitland Chambers
	BRIGGS Michael	Serle Court
	GLOSTER Elizabeth	One Essex Court
	HESLOP Philip	4 Stone Buildings
	SHER Jules	Wilberforce Chambers
	VOS Geoffrey	3 Stone Buildings
2	**BOYLE Alan**	Serle Court
	CRYSTAL Michael	3-4 South Square
	HILDYARD Robert	4 Stone Buildings
	MOSS Gabriel	3-4 South Square
	OLIVER David	Erskine Chambers
	STEINFELD Alan	24 Old Buildings
3	**BOMPAS Anthony**	4 Stone Buildings
	BRISBY John	4 Stone Buildings
	DAVIS Nigel	Maitland Chambers
	MANN Anthony	Enterprise Chambers
	MCDONNELL John	New Square Chambers
	MOWSCHENSON Terence	Wilberforce Chambers
	PURLE Charles	New Square Chambers
	ROSEN Murray	11 Stone Buildings
	TRACE Anthony	Maitland Chambers
4	**BANNISTER Edward**	3 Stone Buildings
	BERRY Simon	9 Old Square
	CROXFORD Ian	Wilberforce Chambers
	DRISCOLL Michael	9 Old Square
	JONES Elizabeth	Serle Court
	KAYE Roger	24 Old Buildings
	NEWMAN Catherine	Maitland Chambers
	PYMONT Christopher	Maitland Chambers
	SMITH Stephen	New Square Chambers
	TALBOT Patrick	Serle Court
NEW SILKS		
	CUNNINGHAM Mark	Maitland Chambers
	GIRET Jane	11 Stone Buildings
	JOFFE Victor	Serle Court
	NEWEY Guy	Maitland Chambers
	TROWER William	3-4 South Square

This book is the product of 6,552 1/2-hour interviews. See p.7 for BMRB audit.
For details of these leading barristers see Profiles on p.1339

Maitland Chambers (see full details p.1538) Born of a merger between 13 Old Square and 7 Stone Buildings this set can claim with some justification to lead the field in terms of strength and depth. Joint head of chambers **Charles Aldous QC** (see p.1342) is a "tower of strength" and has a distinguished "top of the tree practice" which has seen him heavily involved in the Barings litigation. **Anthony Trace QC** (see p.1461) displays "clearness of thinking in all he does" while **Nigel Davis QC** (see p.1370) is noted for his logical approach and "ability to pare an argument down to its essentials." **Catherine Newman QC** (see p.1427) has a "highly confident and assured manner" and has been leading counsel to the DTI inspectors regarding the flotation of the Mirror Group. **Christopher Pymont QC** (see p.1437) is a "young but worthy opponent" who specialises in property related work whereas government and disqualification matters form the backbone of **Mark Cunningham QC**'s (see p.1368) practice. The latter is a new silk this year alongside **Guy Newey QC** (see p.1427) who has "a busy practice" often handling advisory work for government departments. Of the juniors **John Nicholls** leads the way. He is "completely straight" and "however unpalatable the situation, never shys away from telling the client the way it is." Insolvency forms the majority of **Matthew Colling's** (see p.1365) practice while **Paul Girolami** (see p.1385) is a long time treasury counsel of "impeccable credentials." "Serenity and shrewdness" characterise **Alastair Walton**'s approach to a practice which stretches from insolvency to construction. **Lindsey Stewart** (see p.1453), known for her trusts work, and the "promising" **Rebecca Stubbs** (see p.1455) complete a formidable line-up.

Serle Court (see full details p.1565) Enjoying a "fantastic reputation within the inn" **Michael Briggs QC** (see p.1355) "gets on well with both clients and the judiciary." Described as "charming, with no side at all" he is "a man you can have a principled discussion with." Eliciting similarly effusive praise, **Alan Boyle QC** (see p.1353) is "tireless and exceedingly good" but less visible of late due to his continued invovement in the protracted Thyssen case in Bermuda. **Patrick Talbot QC** (see p.1457) is "a decent and thorough performer" who has acted extensively for Lloyds of London while **Elizabeth Jones QC** (see p.1403) impresses in her financial services work. **Victor Joffe QC** (see p.1402) joins the ranks after his recent appointment to silk. Although leading junior **Douglas Close** (see p.1364) has also been tied up on Thyssen, his practice generally impresses solicitors both in trusts and fraud. **Philip Marshall** (see p.1416) was praised by peers for the high quality of the company and insolvency work he receives and his "reassuring manner with clients" while **Philip Jones** (see p.1403) shoulders a remarkably similar workload and is a Junior Counsel to the Crown. Completing the picture is **John Whittaker** (see p.1468) "a reliable senior junior" who is an expert on partnerships.

4 Stone Buildings (see full details p.1568) Chambers head **Philip Heslop QC** is "a star performer, supported by a strong band of fellow silks and juniors" who has a strong banking and company law practice. **Robert Hildyard QC** (see p.1394) maintains support and is seen as "one to watch, due to his shining intelligence." **John Brisby QC** (see p.1355) is "a mercurial performer" whose "forthright and occasionally intimidatory style gets results" while **Anthony Bompas QC** (see p.1352) "delivers with an air of consummate confidence." The juniors include **Robert Miles** who most commentators agreed "has to be at the top." Handling more company law than anything else, **Peter Griffiths** (see p.1389) has "a style all of his own" and is "perfect for the 'last-ditch' type of case" while **Christopher Harrison** is noted for his "dependability."

LEADING JUNIORS • London		
1	MILES Robert	4 Stone Buildings
	NICHOLLS John	Maitland Chambers
2	AYLIFFE James	Wilberforce Chambers
	CLOSE Douglas	Serle Court
	COLLINGS Matthew	Maitland Chambers
	GIROLAMI Paul	Maitland Chambers
	MARSHALL Philip	Serle Court
	WALTON Alastair	Maitland Chambers
3	COHEN Edward	11 Stone Buildings
	GRIFFITHS Peter	4 Stone Buildings
	HOCHBERG Daniel	9 Old Square
	JONES Philip	Serle Court
	LEECH Thomas	9 Old Square
	PASCOE Martin	3-4 South Square
	STEWART Lindsey	Maitland Chambers
4	GOURGEY Alan	11 Stone Buildings
	HARRISON Christopher	4 Stone Buildings
	IFE Linden	Enterprise Chambers
	WHITTAKER John	Serle Court
	ZACAROLI Antony	3-4 South Square
UP AND COMING		
	CAMPBELL Emily	Wilberforce Chambers
	FURZE Caroline	Wilberforce Chambers
	STUBBS Rebecca	Maitland Chambers

This book is the product of 6,552 1/2-hour interviews. See p.7 for BMRB audit.
For details of these leading barristers see Profiles on p.1339

Wilberforce Chambers (see full details p.1576) Another "huge star" resides here in the form of **Jules Sher QC** (see p.1448) who is the possessor of "a brilliant brain" and is "incredibly user friendly." Coming across as "the man in the street's view of a barrister" is **Ian Croxford QC** (see p.1368) who exhibits "flair and gravitas in equal measure." **Terence Mowschenson QC** (see p.1425) is "extremely hard working and straight talking." The consenus was that he is consistently underestimated and accordingly he has risen in the rankings this year. Junior **James Ayliffe** (see p.1345) is "unshakeable and resolute in his self-belief," "ideal for the client who wants to stand firm." Two newcomers to the up and coming ranks present themselves in **Emily Campbell** (see p.1359) and **Caroline Furze** (see p.1382) both of whom received generous praise from a number of their peers.

9 Old Square (see full details p.1550) The two rated silks at this set, **Simon Berry QC** (see p.1350) and **Michael Driscoll QC** (see p.1372) have broadly similar practices covering property litigation and professional negligence to a great extent. Both were praised for their "indefatigable natures" and ability to "navigate through a jungle of papers." Leading junior **Daniel Hochberg** (see p.1396) is an "effective old school practitioner" who appeared in the Jersey end of the Grupo Torras litigation which dealt with offshore trusts and the impact of fraud thereon. **Thomas Leech** (see p.1409) has a respected commercial chancery and related professional negligence practice but, as so many, has been committed to the Thyssen case for some time.

3-4 South Square (see full details p.1566) Performers in insolvency but with a general commercial chancery capability. **Michael Crystal QC** (see p.1368) is "a high-earning big hitter" on call for the heftier matters such as Thyssen. **Gabriel Moss QC** (see p.1424) is a "supremely accomplished insolvency practitioner" who merits inclusion in this table for his "ability to transfer his skills to general chancery work." **William Trower QC** (see p.1463) is also a highly rated silk. Many contemporaries expressed surprise that leading junior **Martin Pascoe** (see p.1432) had not taken silk. He appeared in a major role in the BCCI litigation and is seen as an "extremely talented and capable performer." **Anthony Zacaroli** (see p.1471) has similarly impressed through his efforts on the Sultan of Brunei/Prince Jefri case.

New Square Chambers (see full details p.1546) Three silks of differing vintage impress here. **Charles Purle QC**, is respected for his "analysis and ability to provide unusual solutions" while **John McDonnell QC** "unfailingly gets there in the end." **Stephen Smith QC** (see p.1450), the youngest of the three, has not been a silk for too long but "has a great dry wit" and is tipped to make strides in the future.

24 Old Buildings (see full details p.1548) Particularly effective on tax and companies, **Alan Steinfeld QC** (see p.1453), has a "crunchy, straightforward style" which allows him to "penetrate to the pith of a case." **Roger Kaye QC** (see p.1404) gains approval for being "considered and open-minded."

3 Stone Buildings (see full details p.1568) In **Geoffrey Vos QC** (see p.1465) the set possesses a "barrister near the top of his profession" whose "ethical values are soldered to a modern approach." Fellow silk **Edward Bannister QC** (see p.1346) is "a no frills practitioner" who "won't bump up the costs through wasting time."

Other Notable Practitioners Although perhaps a more straight commercial than commercial chancery barrister, **Elizabeth Gloster QC** (see p.1386) of **One Essex Court** is a "formidable opponent" in this field and has in the past year appeared in the Equitable Life affair. Something of "a maverick," **David Oliver QC** (see p.1429) of **Erskine Chambers** (Potts) is "always good and intermittently capable of periods of sustained brilliance." **Anthony Mann QC** of **Enterprise Chambers** (Mann) is well respected. "No back slapper or glad hander" he "relies on the pure force of his submissions" to earn admiration. **Linden Ife** (see p.1399), a junior at the same set is also recommended. **Murray Rosen QC** (see p.1442) of **11 Stone Buildings** is known as "an arch-ambusher who displays sharp cunning." Always popular with the silks when a junior, **Jane Giret QC** (see p.1385), of the same set, has now advanced to their level and continues to be well thought of. The final juniors in our list area are also housed here. **Edward Cohen** (see p.1364) has "an up front approach" and is "a classically aggressive litigator, typical of his set." **Alan Gourgey** (see p.1388) has one foot in the traditional chancery camp but truly comes into his own on the commercial side.

TRADITIONAL CHANCERY

CHANCERY: TRADITIONAL • London		QCs	Jnrs
1	**Wilberforce Chambers** (Edward Nugee QC)	7	3
2	**5 Stone Buildings** (Henry Harrod)	3	4
3	**Maitland Chambers** (Lyndon-Stanford/Aldous)	2	1
	3 New Square (Lord Goodhart QC)	1	4
	New Square Chambers (Mowbray/Hamilton)	2	3
	10 Old Square (Leolin Price QC)	1	4

This book is the product of 6,552 1/2-hour interviews. See p.7 for BMRB audit.
For details of these leading barristers see Profiles on p.1339

Wilberforce Chambers (see full details p.1576) Clear leaders in this field, with a cluster of eminent names at both silk and junior level. **Brian Green QC** (see p.1388) acts for a number of trustees of major companies and a high proportion of landed estates. "Formidably bright, he consistently cracks the most complicated of problems." **Jules Sher QC** (see p.1448) is particularly adept at pensions and is a name that is "a guarantee of quality." **Robert Ham QC** (see p.1391) is another lost to the Thyssen case but generally recommended for his trusts and tax practice. Chairman of the Chancery Bar, **Nicholas Warren QC** (see p.1466), is similarly blessed with "tremendous brainpower" which he applies to his trusts and pensions practice. **Edward Nugee QC** (see p.1429) has been "a superb authority at the Bar for many years" and although now in his seventies maintains a top notch practice. His son **Christopher Nugee QC** (see p.1429) is no stain on the family escutcheon being "a real star in the making who benefits from

LEADING SILKS • London		
1	GREEN Brian	Wilberforce Chambers
	MCCALL Christopher	Maitland Chambers
	SHER Jules	Wilberforce Chambers
	WARREN Nicholas	Wilberforce Chambers
2	HAM Robert	Wilberforce Chambers
	HERBERT Mark	5 Stone Buildings
	NUGEE Christopher	Wilberforce Chambers
	NUGEE Edward	Wilberforce Chambers
	PROUDMAN Sonia	11 New Square
	TAUBE Simon	10 Old Square
	UNWIN David	Maitland Chambers
3	GOODHART William	3 New Square
	HENDERSON Launcelot	5 Stone Buildings
	LAURENCE George	New Square Chambers
	MARTIN John	Wilberforce Chambers
	MOWBRAY John	New Square Chambers
	SIMMONDS Andrew	5 Stone Buildings
NEW SILKS		
	HINKS Frank	Serle Court

For details of these leading barristers see Profiles on p.1339

LEADING JUNIORS • London		
1	AINGER David	10 Old Square
	BARLOW Francis	10 Old Square
	CHILD John	Wilberforce Chambers
	TUCKER Lynton	New Square Chambers
	WARNOCK-SMITH Shân	5 Stone Buildings
2	CHAPMAN Vivian	9 Stone Buildings
	HARROD Henry	5 Stone Buildings
	MARTEN Hedley	3 New Square
	MASON Alexandra	3 Stone Buildings
	MEADWAY Susannah	10 Old Square
	ROWELL David	3 New Square
	STEWART SMITH Rodney	New Square Chambers
	TIDMARSH Christopher	5 Stone Buildings
3	BRYANT Judith	Wilberforce Chambers
	HAYES Josephine	3 New Square
	LEGGE Henry	5 Stone Buildings
	MULLIS Roger	3 New Square
	ROGERS Beverly-Ann	Serle Court
	RUSSEN Jonathan	Maitland Chambers
	SEMKEN Christopher	New Square Chambers
	TAUSSIG Anthony	Wilberforce Chambers
	TOPHAM Geoffrey	3 Stone Buildings
	WALLINGTON Richard	10 Old Square
UP AND COMING		
	LACEY Sarah	3 Stone Buildings

This book is the product of 6,552 1/2-hour interviews. See p.7 for BMRB audit.
For details of these leading barristers see Profiles on p.1339

the torrent of work within chambers." This formidable array of silks is completed by **John Martin QC** (see p.1417), an ex-Liverpool based barrister who is "huge fun and has a heavyweight probate practice." **John Child** (see p.1362) is "ineluctably a top tier junior" due to his "rarely rivalled prowess as a draftsman." **Anthony Taussig** (see p.1458) and **Judith Bryant** (see p.1357) also received commendation, the latter debuting in the tables as a result of her healthy tax and trusts practice.

5 Stone Buildings (see full details p.1569) "Excellent across the years and a real solid performer", **Mark Herbert QC** (see p.1394) is a leader in trusts and tax work. **Launcelot Henderson QC** (see p.1393) similarly concentrates on revenue work and has acted on a number of treasury matters. **Andrew Simmonds QC** (see p.1449) is a "strong litigator and capable advisor," well regarded in the pensions world. A significant amount of his work is professional negligence – "he'd be the first port of call if a solicitor erred in drawing up a will." Of the juniors **Shân Warnock-Smith** (see p.1392) has one of the bigger practices incorporating a good deal of private client work. "She is confident, open and extremely approachable." **Christopher Tidmarsh** (see p.1461) is standing counsel to the Inland Revenue while **Henry Harrod** (see p.1392) "brings a huge amount of experience to the table." **Henry Legge** (see p.1410) also received support for his "competence in negotiating cases of a complex legal nature."

Maitland Chambers (see full details p.1538) **Christopher McCall QC** (see p.1418) is a "thoroughbred practitioner" engaged on a number of breach of trust cases. He appeared on appeal to the House of Lords in the National Grid/National Power pensions case. **David Unwin QC** has been well used by the Treasury over the years and has had an official role advising charities. "Phenomenally bright," he also appears in many cases with a musical theme. **Jonathan Russen** (see p.1443) also retains a high level of market support among solicitors.

3 New Square (see full details p.1542) Despite being a front bencher for the Liberal Democrats in the House of Lords **William Goodhart QC** (see p.1387) conducts a full practice and remains a "superb tactician." A strong band of juniors includes **Hedley Marten** (see p.1416) who adopts a "traditional approach" to his practice which covers heavy trust work, probate litigation and property law in all its forms. **David Rowell** is a "top backroom boy" whose technical skills as a draftsman were widely commented upon. More on the front line is **Josephine Hayes** (see p.1392) whose "hardboiled, snappy style gets them jumping." New to the tables is **Roger Mullis** (see p.1426) who impresses across a number of fields including landlord and tenant and property.

New Square Chambers (see full details p.1546) **George Laurence QC** has "effectively cornered the market on rights of way" and handles a sizeable amount of parliamentary work. Joint Head of Chambers **John Mowbray QC** (see p.1425) is a "good old stager," pre-eminent over many years and "the cat's whiskers on trusts." Amongst the juniors **Lynton Tucker** is "a clever and circumspect operator" while **Rodney Stewart Smith** is "first rate," applying "ruthless logic" and the fruits of his intensive academic labour to all he does. **Christopher Semken** (see p.1446) also attracted support.

10 Old Square **Simon Taube QC** (see p.1458) concentrates on trusts and tax, largely in an advisory capacity. He "presents well and is confident at all times." At a set blessed with a number of talented juniors, **Francis Barlow** (see p.1347) is universally held to be "senior, eminent and distinguished." **David Ainger** (see p.1341) rarely appears as an advocate, but is conveyancing counsel to the High Court and "highly proficient," according to peers. Solicitors recommend **Susannah Meadway** (see p.1420) for her "user friendly style," while newcomer to the tables **Richard Wallington** (see p.1466) is "highly popular among his peers" and is considered to merit inclusion for his drafting skills.

Other Notable Practitioners At **11 New Square**, **Sonia Proudman QC** (see p.1436) is "meticulous" and "does a superb job without one noticing it." **Frank Hinks QC** (see p.1395) at **Serle Court** has a similarly "low-key but effective" style, "almost imperceptibly achieving results." In a set normally associated with commercial chancery work, he is something of an anomaly, although his colleague, the respected **Beverly-Ann Rogers** (see p.1441) also gains high marks from law firms. **Vivian Chapman** (see p.1361) of **9 Stone Buildings** has an "impressive portfolio of cases, many of which go to the House of Lords." **Geoffrey Topham** (see p.1461) of **3 Stone Buildings** has "enjoyed something of an Indian summer in his career" and impresses on the pensions side. His colleague **Alexandra Mason** (see p.1417) is "a good ferreter who doesn't get bored with the technicalities" and is an expert on the administration of trusts and estates. The set also includes **Sarah Lacey** (see p.1408), who is "able and calmly shinning up the greasy pole."

WESTERN, WALES & CHESTER CIRCUITS

LEADING SILKS • Western, Wales & Chester		
1	DAVIES Stephen	Guildhall Chambers
2	COOKE Nicholas	9 Park Place
NEW SILKS		
	JARMAN Milwyn	9 Park Place
	JONES Geraint	9 Park Place

For details of these leading barristers see Profiles on p.1339

LEADING JUNIORS • Western, Wales & Chester		
1	BAMFORD Jeremy	Guildhall Chambers
	BLOHM Leslie	St John's Chambers
	KEYSER Andrew	9 Park Place
	MAHER Martha	Guildhall Chambers
	SHARPLES John	St John's Chambers

This book is the product of 6,552 1/2-hour interviews. See p.7 for BMRB audit.
For details of these leading barristers see Profiles on p.1339

"Out ahead, especially in insolvency work" is **Stephen Davies QC** of **Guildhall Chambers** (see full details p.1581). At the same set, **Jeremy Bamford**'s "keen intellect allows him to see the wood from the trees," while the "determined and feisty" **Martha Maher** (see p.1415) has "effortlessly picked up the reins" following her return from maternity leave. **Nicholas Cooke QC** (see p.1365) of **9 Park Place** (see full details p.1584) is not a specialist chancery practitioner but has the "industry and analysis" to deliver the goods when he tackles such cases. Servicing the new mercantile court in Cardiff are two new silks from the set, **Milwyn Jarman QC** (see p.1401) and **Geraint Jones QC.** The rated junior here is **Andrew Keyser** (see p.1406), possessor of a "first class brain," and a barrister who "takes great interest in his cases." At **St John's Chambers** (see full details p.1583) **Leslie Blohm** (see p.1352) is a leading commercial property lawyer and probate expert known for "tenacity and technical skill." Colleague **John Sharples** (see p.1446), a one-time practitioner in the USA, is a "serious-minded and able performer."

MIDLANDS CIRCUIT

LEADING SILKS • Midlands		
1	RANDALL John	St Philip's Chambers
2	CORBETT James	St Philip's Chambers

For details of these leading barristers see Profiles on p.1339

LEADING JUNIORS • Midlands		
1	ASHWORTH Lance	St Philip's Chambers
	CHARMAN Andrew	St Philip's Chambers
	STOCKILL David	5 Fountain Court

This book is the product of 6,552 1/2-hour interviews. See p.7 for BMRB audit.
For details of these leading barristers see Profiles on p.1339

St Phillip's Chambers is home to the two silks in our table. **John Randall QC** (see p.1438) practises all aspects of commercial and chancery work and "goes through cases with a fine tooth comb," while **James Corbett QC** (see p.1366) is "small in stature but big in court." Leading juniors at the set include **Lance Ashworth** (see p.1344) and **Andrew Charman** (see p.1361), both "seen on the bigger cases." **David Stockill** of **5 Fountain Court** is also recommended.

NORTHERN & NORTH EASTERN CIRCUITS

LEADING SILKS • Northern & North Eastern		
1	ALLEN James	No.6 Barristers Chambers
	SMITH Peter	40 King St
2	BARTLEY JONES Edward	Exchange Chambers
	BOOTH Michael	40 King St
	ELLERAY Anthony	Exchange Chambers
3	LEEMING Ian	St James's Chambers
NEW SILKS		
	CAWSON Mark	Exchange Chambers
	CHAISTY Paul	40 King St

For details of these leading barristers see Profiles on p.1339

LEADING JUNIORS • Northern & North Eastern		
1	ANDERSON Lesley	40 King St
	BERRAGAN Neil	Merchant Chambers
	DUNN Katherine	40 King St
	HARPER Mark	40 King St
	RIDDLE Nicholas	14 Castle Street
2	CASEMENT David	Exchange Chambers
	JOHNSON Ian	14 Castle Street
	JOHNSON Michael	9 St John Street
	MCCARROLL John	Exchange Chambers
	ORR Nicholas	14 Castle Street
	STERLING Robert	St James's Chambers
	TERRY Jeffrey	8 King St

This book is the product of 6,552 1/2-hour interviews. See p.7 for BMRB audit.
For details of these leading barristers see Profiles on p.1339

At **40 King Street** (see full details p.1604), **Peter Smith QC** (see p.1450) is "a tough negotiator" involved in major litigation of a commercial nature, while **Michael Booth QC** is a "grafter," increasingly moving his broad practice into intellectual property law. Widely tipped as one to watch, **Paul Chaisty QC** (see p.1361) has recently been appointed silk. Recommended juniors at the set are the "switched-on" **Lesley Anderson** (see p.1343), **Mark Harper** (see p.1391), who "rarely takes a bad point," and **Katherine Dunn**. At **Exchange Chambers** (see full details p.1598), **Edward Bartley Jones QC** (see p.1348) "displays profound good sense" while new silk **Mark Cawson QC** (see p.1361) has "earned the trust of all the major solicitors in the area." Senior silk **Anthony Ellerary QC** (see p.1375), formerly at **St James's Chambers** (see full details p.1606), is a new face at the set. Solicitors see him as "fantastic on paper and intellectually on song." **John McCarroll** (see p.1418) is "a bright young man and a lawyer's lawyer" who is joined in the lists by newcomer **David Casement** (see p.1360). **St James's Chambers** (see full details p.1606), despite suffering defections over the past year, has recruited **Ian Leeming QC** (see p.1410), the first practitioner to be appointed silk in Manchester and "a barrister of undoubted pedigree." Head of Chambers **Robert Sterling** (see p.1453) remains in the list for his wide-ranging practice, which takes in property, insolvency and straight chancery work. At **14 Castle Street** (see full details p.1597) **Nicholas Riddle** (see p.1440) is "a busy fellow with real ability" and is recommended alongside **Ian Johnson** (see p.1402) and **Nicholas Orr** (see p.1430). Other leading juniors are **Neil Berragan** of **Merchant Chambers** (see full details p.1605) (Berkley), tax expert **Michael Johnson** (see p.1402) of **9 St John Street** (see full details p.1607), who sits as a Revenue Commissioner, and the "sharp and persuasive" **Jeffrey Terry** (see p.1459) of **8 King St** (see full details p.1604). In Yorkshire, researchers were told by solicitors that **James Allen** of **No. 6 Barristers Chambers** "stands out from the herd."

CHARITIES

RESEARCH: The rankings are based on in-depth interviews with over 5,000 solicitors and barristers in the UK. Chambers research is audited by the British Market Research Bureau (see page 7 for details).

OVERVIEW: A select group of experienced and highly knowledgeable practitioners are featured in this section. Their expertise and profile far overshadow the sets to which they belong, and thus we continue to rank only individuals in this field.

LEADING SILKS • London		
1	MCCALL Christopher	Maitland Chambers
	PICARDA Hubert	3 New Square
2	CRAMPIN Peter	11 New Square
	HERBERT Mark	5 Stone Buildings
	NUGEE Edward	Wilberforce Chambers
	PROUDMAN Sonia	11 New Square
	UNWIN David	Maitland Chambers
	VENABLES Robert	24 Old Buildings
	WATERS Malcolm	11 Old Square
NEW SILKS		
	NEWEY Guy	Maitland Chambers

For details of these leading barristers see Profiles on p.1339

LEADING JUNIORS • London		
1	QUINT Francesca	11 Old Square
2	DUMONT Thomas	11 New Square
	KESSLER James	24 Old Buildings
	WARNOCK-SMITH Shân	5 Stone Buildings

This book is the product of 6,552 1/2-hour interviews. See p.7 for BMRB audit.

For details of these leading barristers see Profiles on p.1339

LONDON

Maitland Chambers (see full details p.1538) "Outstanding practitioner" **Christopher McCall QC** (see p.1418), who is engaged particularly on the tax side, draws praise for his "academic and penetrative mind." The "powerful" **David Unwin QC** displays a "depth of knowledge" and "can cope with anything thrown at him." Counsel to the Charity Commission, **Guy Newey QC** (see p.1427) is widely respected by competitors and solicitors.

3 New Square (see full details p.1541) **Hubert Picarda QC** (see p.1434) is rated for "pushing back the boundaries." Peers consider him a "charities expert" who has "encyclopedic knowledge."

11 New Square (see full details p.1545) One time Counsel to the Attorney General, **Peter Crampin QC** (see p.1367) is "clever" and can be called upon to "put up a fight." "Fearless advocate" **Sonia Proudman QC** (see p.1436) has "a grasp of the issues" and gives "sound, sensible advice." The "entertaining" **Thomas Dumont** (see p.1373) is "enthusiastic about charity law" and has a noted "skill in legacies."

24 Old Buildings (see full details p.1548) **Robert Venables QC** is endorsed as "a charities tax expert" and **James Kessler** (see p.1406) is rated for his "drafting and expertise."

11 Old Square (see full details p.1551) Leading junior **Francesca Quint** is "an authority" of who peers acclaim; "she's not given a wrong answer in five years." "Simply on top of the subject," she is a "sheer genius" who "understands charity law inside out."

11 Old Square (see full details p.1551) "General all-rounder" **Malcolm Waters QC** (see p.1467) garners plaudits for his work in unincorporated associations and friendly societies.

5 Stone Buildings (see full details p.1569) (Harrod) The "top ranking chancery lawyer" **Mark Herbert QC** (see p.1394) draws all-round praise while junior **Shân Warnock-Smith** (see p.1466) received warm recommendation for her strength in trust matters.

Wilberforce Chambers (see full details p.1576) "Eminence gris" **Edward Nugee QC** (see p.1429) is praised as a "heavyweight" on chancery and charitable trust matters.

CHURCH LAW

RESEARCH: The rankings are based on in-depth interviews with over 5,000 solicitors and barristers in the UK. Chambers research is audited by the British Market Research Bureau (see page 7 for details).

OVERVIEW: Few barristers practice in the esoteric area of ecclesiastical and church-related law. Of those that do, many are chancellors of one or more dioceses, and are actively involved with the church with instructions relating to property, employment or organisational matters. Changes are afoot, potentially the most radical of all will be the new clergy discipline measure (rewritten by the General Synod) being put before the House of Lords. If approved it will create a tribunal for dealing with the misconduct of clergymen; a more accessible clerical discipline system than the old consistory court based system. Other changes include the new faculty jurisdiction rules (January 2001) which put greater pressure on parishes to consult outside the church before re-ordering church properties, and the church warden's measure which has now received parliamentary approval and encourages greater accountability.

LONDON

CHURCH: CHURCH OF ENGLAND • London		QCs	Jnrs
1	**2 Harcourt Buildings** (Gerard Ryan QC)	2	2
2	**Pump Court Chambers** (Christopher Harvey Clark QC)	1	1

Numbers show recommended barristers in this practice area

LEADING SILKS • London		
1	**CAMERON Sheila**	2 Harcourt Buildings
2	**GEORGE Charles**	2 Harcourt Buildings
3	**CLARK Christopher**	Pump Court Chambers
	KAYE Roger	24 Old Buildings
	SEED Nigel	3 Paper Buildings

For details of these leading barristers see Profiles on p.1339

LEADING JUNIORS • London		
1	**BRIDEN Timothy**	8 Stone Buildings
2	**HILL Mark**	Pump Court Chambers
3	**BEHRENS James**	Serle Court
	MYNORS Charles	2 Harcourt Buildings
	PETCHEY Philip	2 Harcourt Buildings
	RODGERS June	Harcourt Chambers

This book is the product of 6,552 1/2-hour interviews. See p.7 for BMRB audit.
For details of these leading barristers see Profiles on p.1339

2 Harcourt Buildings (see full details p.1519) "Queen bee" **Sheila Cameron QC** (see p.1429), Master of the Faculties and recently appointed Dean of the Arches, will no longer appear as an advocate although she continues to advise on non judicial matters. Heaped with praises by those within this field, her authority remains undisputed. **Charles George QC** (see p.1384) is consistently rated both for his sharp intellect and for his thoughtful "pastoral" manner. "Practical" **Charles Mynors** (see p.1426) displays specialist knowledge in relation to planning and listed buildings. Chancellor to the Diocese of Worcester, he played a key part in the high profile Pershore Abbey pew case. **Philip Petchey** is noted for the quality of his written work.

Pump Court Chambers (see full details p.1556) **Christopher Clark QC** (see p.1362), a member of the ecclesiastical judges association, is recognised for his specialist knowledge regarding exhumations and remains a highly respected figure. "Learned" **Mark Hill** (see p.1394) has begun his term of appointment to the Legal Advisory Commission of the Church of England. Perceived to combine strength "on the academic side" with an undeniable "panache."

Other Notable Practitioners **Roger Kaye QC** (see p.1404) of **24 Old Buildings** is a "determined opponent." His position as leading silk now firmly established, the "bright" **Nigel Seed** of **3 Paper Buildings** has recently been appointed Chancellor of the Diocese of London and is noted for his criminal practice. "Definitely in the lead," **Timothy Briden** (see p.1355) of **8 Stone Buildings** (see full details p.1569) is "balanced and sensible" and "presents his case with great skill." He acted for the petitioners in the high profile Pershore Abbey case. A dynamic force, **James Behrens** (see p.1349) of **Serle Court** (see full details p.1565) maintains his popularity while "doughty" **June Rodgers** of **Harcourt Chambers** (see full details p.1521) received warm recommendations.

WESTERN, NORTH EASTERN & NORTHERN CIRCUITS

LEADING SILKS • Western, North Eastern & Northern		
1	**COLLIER Peter**	30 Park Square

For details of these leading barristers see Profiles on p.1339

LEADING JUNIORS • Western, North Eastern & Northern		
1	**GARDEN Ian**	Derby Square Chambers
2	**NEWSOM George**	Guildhall Chambers

This book is the product of 6,552 1/2-hour interviews. See p.7 for BMRB audit.
For details of these leading barristers see Profiles on p.1339

"Leading light of the Northern Circuit" **Peter Collier QC** of **30 Park Square** (see full details p.1593) has a strong reputation in this field. **George Newsom** (see p.1427) of **Guildhall Chambers** (see full details p.1581) in Bristol has experience in planning and property law and advises the Church of England and the Church in Wales. **Ian Garden** (see p.1383) of **Derby Square Chambers** in Leeds maintains a high level of involvement in the Archbishops Council and the legal advisory commission of the General Synod.

CLINICAL NEGLIGENCE

RESEARCH: The rankings are based on in-depth interviews with over 5,000 solicitors and barristers in the UK. Chambers research is audited by the British Market Research Bureau (see page 7 for details).

LONDON

CLINICAL NEGLIGENCE • London	QCs	Jnrs
1 **3 Serjeants' Inn** (Francis/Grace)	5	8
2 **1 Crown Office Row** (Robert Seabrook QC)	8	-
3 **6 Pump Court**	1	8
4 **Cloisters** (Laura Cox QC)	2	1
Crown Office Chambers (Spencer/Purchas)	1	2
Doughty Street Chambers (Geoffrey Robertson QC)	1	3
4 Paper Buildings (Jean Ritchie QC)	1	1
No.1 Serjeants' Inn (Edward Faulks QC)	1	1

This book is the product of 6,552 1/2-hour interviews. See p.7 for BMRB audit.

For details of these leading barristers see Profiles on p.1339

3 Serjeants' Inn (see full details p.1564) Remains the pre-eminent set in this area with a good spread of silks and juniors. Each of its six silks and 25 out of 27of its juniors practice in medical law. Members act for claimants and defendants and have blazed a trail in the developing field of treatment decisions. "Always busy" **John Grace QC** is admired by peers for his even-handed, approachable style. He has recently been involved in a persistent vegetative state-related case, NHS Trust A v Mrs M: NHS Trust B v Mrs H. Long-standing practitioner **Adrian Whitfield QC** (see p.1468) is widely respected as "terrifically able in court." **Robert Francis QC** (see p.1381) ("unflappable, dedicated, he consistently fights hard for is clients") is felt to be particularly good on issues of consent. Although this is not the main area of focus for **Nicola Davies QC** (see p.1369) (also operating a respected criminal practice), she draws accolades as "a brilliant advocate" and " a true fighter" when she undertakes clinical negligence work. **James Watson QC** is also respected as a regular player in this field. Amongst a glittering cast of juniors **Adrian Hopkins** (see p.1397) "justifies his top flight position" and was endorsed by several referees. He has been involved in a number of coroner's inquests and is instructed on behalf of the Home Office in respect of deaths in prisons. Well-respected **Angus Moon** (see p.1423) recently appeared in Bhanot v South West London & St George's Mental Health Trust, a case about whether to discipline a doctor for 'personal misconduct'. **Christopher Johnston** (see p.1402) is an "impressive" junior involved in the recent Miles v Redbridge & Waltham Forest Health Authority concerning the misdiagnosis of foetal death. **Fiona Neale** (see p.1427) has "perfectly sound judgment," while the experienced **Mary O'Rourke** "does a huge amount of work" and is "a force to be reckoned with." Pleasant and committed **Michael Horne** has a particular interest in dental negligence and both **Huw Lloyd** and ex-junior surgeon **Richard Partridge** are perceived to have strong practices.

1 Crown Office Row (see full details p.1490) Building on its depth of expertise at both senior and junior level, this set maintains its traditionally strong influence in the clinical negligence market. The success of its juniors in taking silk has left a certain lack of profile at the end of the scale. "Class act" **Philip Havers QC** (see p.1392) moves up into band one this year, felt to deliver "advocacy in another league; excellent and thorough." He acted for the defendants in Warren v Northern General Hospital. **Stephen Miller QC** maintains his top-flight reputation, acclaimed as skilled in court and an "extremely tough advocate," as is his colleague **James Badenoch QC** (see p.1345), although the latter's "loud and flam-

Barristers' profiles 1339-1472

LEADING SILKS • London		
1	**COONAN Kieran**	6 Pump Court
	GRACE John	3 Serjeants' Inn
	HAVERS Philip	1 Crown Office Row
	IRWIN Stephen	Doughty Street Chambers
	MILLER Stephen	1 Crown Office Row
	WHITFIELD Adrian	3 Serjeants' Inn
2	**BADENOCH James**	1 Crown Office Row
	BRENNAN Daniel	Matrix Chambers
	COX Laura	Cloisters
	FAULKS Edward	No. 1 Serjeants' Inn
	FRANCIS Robert	3 Serjeants' Inn
	MASKREY Simeon	7 Bedford Row
	RITCHIE Jean	4 Paper Buildings
	SPENCER Michael	Crown Office Chambers
3	**BROOKE Michael**	Four New Square
	BROWNE Benjamin	2 Temple Gardens
	COGHLAN Terence	1 Crown Office Row
	DAVIES Nicola	3 Serjeants' Inn
	FOSKETT David	1 Crown Office Row
	GIBSON Christopher	Four New Square
	LANGSTAFF Brian	Cloisters
	REES Paul	1 Crown Office Row
	SMITH Sally	1 Crown Office Row
NEW SILKS		
	BOWRON Margaret	1 Crown Office Row
	WATSON James	3 Serjeants' Inn

For details of these leading barristers see Profiles on p.1339

LEADING JUNIORS • London		
1	**HOPKINS Adrian**	3 Serjeants' Inn
	LAMBERT Christina	6 Pump Court
	MOON Angus	3 Serjeants' Inn
	OPPENHEIM Robin	Doughty Street Chambers
	SPINK Andrew	35 Essex Street
	TAYLOR Simon	Cloisters
2	**HOCKTON Andrew**	6 Pump Court
	JOHNSTON Christopher	3 Serjeants' Inn
	JONES Charlotte	Crown Office Chambers
	NEALE Fiona	3 Serjeants' Inn
	O'ROURKE Mary	3 Serjeants' Inn
	SPENCER Martin	4 Paper Buildings
3	**BURDEN Susan**	6 Pump Court
	FOSTER Charles	6 Pump Court
	GARRETT Annalissa	6 Pump Court
	GOODRICH Siobhan	6 Pump Court
	HORNE Michael	3 Serjeants' Inn
	KENNEDY Andrew	6 Pump Court
	LLOYD Huw	3 Serjeants' Inn
	MATTHEWS Dennis	Crown Office Chambers
	PARTRIDGE Richard	3 Serjeants' Inn
	PRATT Duncan	6 Pump Court
	READHEAD Simon	No. 1 Serjeants' Inn
	THOROLD Oliver	Doughty Street Chambers
	TRACY FORSTER Jane	13 King's Bench Walk
UP AND COMING		
	HERMER Richard	Doughty Street Chambers

This book is the product of 6,552 1/2-hour interviews. See p.7 for BMRB audit.

For details of these leading barristers see Profiles on p.1339

boyant" style is not to everyone's taste. **Terence Coghlan QC** (see p.1364) is a "thoughtful and calm advocate" whilst widely regarded **David Foskett QC** (see p.1380) remains a "senior figure, competent with an engaging manner." He has acted in several cases of obstetric mismanagement and appeared for the defendant in Macgranaky Quaye v Guys and Thomas NHS Trust. "Workaholic and dedicated with it," **Paul Rees QC** is judged to be "the new silk most likely to achieve seniority" and described as "fantastic, capable, brilliant with clients." **Sally Smith QC** is described as "good on civil work" and has recently been involved in the Alder Hey Inquiry into organ retention representing the Royal Liverpool Children's Trust. "Able" **Margaret Bowron QC** has taken silk and is rated for her committed, warm approach.

6 Pump Court (see full details p.1559) This respected set has a considerable presence, with its juniors garnering a wealth of accolades. "Extremely busy and highly skilled" **Kieran Coonan QC** flies the flag for silks in this set. Of the juniors, **Christina Lambert** is rated the most highly, perceived to be "a busy and popular silk." **Andrew Hockton** received emphatic recommendations, he is held in high regard by many as "good, a hard-worker and a pleasant guy." **Susan Burden** (see p.1357) is rated particularly for her skills in paper opinions and ex-vet **Charles Foster** (see p.1381) is perceived to be "a strong traditional practitioner." **Annalissa Garrett** (see p.1383) "offers careful advice, she picks out the main issues" and **Siobhan Goodrich** (see p.1387) impresses those she leads. **Andrew Kennedy** was widely recommended for inclusion in this section of the guide; he is particularly active, enjoying "instructions in a lot of big cases." **Duncan Pratt** is rated by peers: "he knows the issues".

Cloisters (see full details p.1487) **Laura Cox QC** (see p.1367) retains her position as a well-respected clinical negligence practitioner and the set's reputation in this field is strengthened by **Brian Langstaff QC** (see p.1408). Recently back in circulation after the Bristol Royal Infirmary inquiry (involving the mysterious deaths of children) he is described as "superb, earnest and thorough." **Simon Taylor** (see p.1458) is lauded by solicitors and barristers alike, he "delivers results" and is described as "one of the leading juniors in this area, excellent in court and a thorough cross-examiner."

Crown Office Chambers (see full details p.1580) **Michael Spencer QC** (see p.1451) is a "respected" silk at this set. He is supported by "experienced and capable" **Dennis Matthews** (see p.1417), well liked by his peers, and the highly praised **Charlotte Jones** (see p.1403). "Cool under fire, she gives sensible and unflappable advice" - what's more she "holds her own in court."

Doughty Street Chambers (see full details p.1492) Houses a respectable number of rated barristers. **Stephen Irwin QC** (see p.1400) garners an excellent reputation among his peers while solicitors would "would use him without hesitation." **Robin Oppenheim** (see p.1430) is "a team player with the ability to talk to others, he works co -operatively and quickly." **Oliver Thorold** (see p.1460) is newly ranked in our table for his "excellent, razor sharp mind." "He's a good all-rounder," agrees one solicitor, while a fellow barrister judged him "occasionally eccentric". "Strong across the board" **Richard Hermer** remains in the up and coming category with respect to this field.

4 Paper Buildings (see full details p.1552) The "excellent" **Jean Ritchie QC** (see p.1440) chaired the Rodney Ledward Inquiry. She is described as "extremely solid and a pleasant person to work with, both for and against." **Martin Spencer** (see p.1451) climbs up the junior ladder after amassing a significant level of recommendations. A "sensible advocate," he is a "decent person to do business with, efficient and level-headed."

No.1 Serjeants' Inn (see full details p.1563) A smaller yet impressive set boasting the presence of "dazzling" **Edward Faulks QC** (see p.1377). He attracts effusive citations: "an absolute dream, one of the best advocates I've ever seen" claims one barrister. Recently involved in Penney & Others v East Kent Health Authority, defending the health authority. At junior level, the "dedicated" **Simon Readhead** (see p.1439) garnered warm recommendations; he acted for the defendant in Marquis v Lewisham Hospital NHS Trust.

Other Notable Practitioners "Outstanding" **Daniel Brennan QC** has moved to Matrix Chambers and is felt to continue his medical negligence work as part of a "broad practice." "Wonderful" **Simeon Maskrey QC** (see p.1417) at 7 Bedford Row is "loved by clients, he's highly analytical." It was widely felt that **Michael Brooke QC** (see p.1356) of 4 New Square should be included in our list of leading silks. He is an experienced practitioner, "a quietly understated, effective advocate" who is "good at longer cases" which perhaps take him out of the public eye. He has been involved in some large blood-related inquiries including HIV Haemophiliac litigation and Hepatitis litigation. His colleague **Christopher Gibson QC** (see p.1384) ("intelligent, down to earth, objective") has been involved in cerebal palsy cases and is held in high esteem amongst peers; he also has a "particular talent with clients." At 2 Temple Gardens, **Benjamin Browne QC** (see p.1356) has acted in several cerebal palsy cases this year and is described by one solicitor as having "been quite exceptional," with "a run of success." **Andrew Spink** (see p.1451) of 35 Essex Street is endorsed by peers and **Jane Tracy Forster** (see p.1462) at 13 Kings Bench Walk is "robust and thorough."

MIDLANDS CIRCUIT

LEADING SILKS • Midlands		
1	LEWIS Ralph	5 Fountain Court

For details of these leading barristers see Profiles on p.1339

LEADING JUNIORS • Midlands		
1	HUNJAN Satinder	5 Fountain Court
2	BRIGHT Christopher	3 Fountain Court
	GREGORY Philip	No.6 Fountain Court

This book is the product of 6,552 1/2-hour interviews. See p.7 for BMRB audit.
For details of these leading barristers see Profiles on p.1339

Ralph Lewis QC (see p.1411) of **5 Fountain Court** (see full details p.1577) is perceived to be a "good, steady chap," trusted by solicitors with clinical negligence work although best known as a personal injury specialist. **Satinder Hunjan** of the same chambers is felt to be "perfectly competent in court," handling complex cases. **Christopher Bright** (see p.1355) at **3 Fountain Court** and **Philip Gregory** of **No. 6 Fountain Court** are described as "the leading juniors in Birmingham."

NORTHERN & NORTH EASTERN CIRCUITS

LEADING SILKS • Northern & North Eastern		
1	REDFERN Michael	28 St John St
	SWIFT Caroline	Byrom Street Chambers
2	ARMITAGE Keith	8 King St
	GOLDREIN Iain	7 Harrington Street Chambers
	GRIME Stephen	Deans Court Chambers
	WINGATE-SAUL Giles	Byrom Street Chambers
NEW SILKS		
	MELTON Christopher	Byron Street Chambers

For details of these leading barristers see Profiles on p.1339

LEADING JUNIORS • Northern & North Eastern		
1	ECCLES David	8 King St
	FREEDMAN Jeremy	Plowden Buildings
	HEATON David	18 St John Street
	ROWLEY James	28 St John St

This book is the product of 6,552 1/2-hour interviews. See p.7 for BMRB audit.
For details of these leading barristers see Profiles on p.1339

"Redfern and Swift predominate up there" claims one solicitor. **Michael Redfern QC** (see p.1439) of **28 St Johns Street** is thought to hold court over the Manchester players, and the respected **Caroline Swift QC** (see p.1456) of **Byrom Street Chambers** is now lead counsel in the Shipman inquiry. "Sharp" **Keith Armitage QC** of **8 King Street** (see full details p.1604) handles mainly defendant work, while **David Eccles** at the same set is thought to be "good to deal with, sensible". **Stephen Grime QC** (see p.1390) of **Deans Court Chambers** (see full details p.1602) (Grime) handles both claimant and defendant work. **Giles Wingate-Saul QC** (see p.1357) of **Byrom Street Chambers** remains respected and **Ian Goldrein QC** (see p.1387) of **7 Harrington Street Chambers** (see full details p.1599) (Steer/Fordham/Goldrein) **Byrom Street Chambers**, a door tenant of 3 Serjeants Inn, has had a strong profile this year. New silk **Christopher Melton QC** (see p.1420) is second leading counsel in the Shipman inquiry. **David Heaton** (see p.1392) at **18 St John Street** (see full details p.1607) remains a leading junior for his efficiency and responsiveness, while **James Rowley** at **28 St Johns Street** "certainly merits his reputation." Of north-eastern junior **Jeremy Freedman** (see p.1382) at **Plowden Buildings** (see full details p.1609) (Lowe) it is claimed: "if anyone is doing the work up there it's him." He was counsel for the Newcastle upon Tyne NHS trust in the highly publicized Re M case over whether a hospital could carry out a heart transplant on a dying patient who had refused consent. He obtained the court order enabling the transplant.

COMMERCIAL (LITIGATION)

RESEARCH: The rankings are based on in-depth interviews with over 5,000 solicitors and barristers in the UK. Chambers research is audited by the British Market Research Bureau (see page 7 for details).

Barristers' profiles 1339-1472

LONDON

COMMERCIAL (LITIGATION) • London		QCs	Jnrs
1	**Brick Court Chambers** (Christopher Clarke QC)	9	8
	Essex Court Chambers (Gordon Pollock QC)	6	10
	One Essex Court (Anthony Grabiner QC)	10	7
	Fountain Court (Anthony Boswood QC)	6	4
2	**Blackstone Chambers** (Baxendale/Flint)	4	2
	3 Verulam Buildings (Symons/Jarvis)	3	6

This book is the product of 6,552 1/2-hour interviews. See p.7 for BMRB audit.
For details of these leading barristers see Profiles on p.1339

Brick Court Chambers (see full details p.1484) "An intellectual colossus," **Jonathan Sumption QC** (see p.1455) is considered by solicitors to be a "tenacious, astute and an outstanding advocate, light on his feet." Much of his profile lies in the most complex of appeals and House of Lords matters. Never one to shy away from an issue, solicitors value his "super judgment" which inspires confidence; "you get his view and that's all you need." **Mark Hapgood QC** is described by one practitioner as "an outstanding talent, most definitely in the Sumption mould." Combining clear communication with a fine bedside manner, "he's brilliant – our first port of call" according to one solicitor. The "tough and unremitting" **Mark Howard QC** (see p.1398) has "excellent mental agility" which enables him to "grasp points of law very quickly indeed." Senior statesman **Sydney Kentridge QC** (see p.1405) is "top drawer for the high profile appeals where a real performance is needed" although these are often shorter appellate matters. **Jonathan Hirst QC** (see p.1395) is considered "highly approachable and good to work with" while one fellow barrister said, "whenever there's a big case he's a favoured leader, a true trial lawyer" who is rated particularly for his appearances in House of Lords matters. Solicitors find **Andrew Popplewell QC** (see p.1435) "excellent to deal with," consistently demonstrating his "astute intelligence," while **Charles Hollander QC** (see p.xxx) is a "talented all-rounder" known for his interest in sports law. Peers acknowledge that he has "written the best book on disclosure and documentary evidence around." **George Leggatt QC** (see p.1410) "never fails to perform well," particularly in professional negligence matters, while **Catharine Otton-Goulder QC** (see p.1430) has a following among the solicitors. Of the juniors, **Michael Swainston** (see p.1456) is said to be "coming along strongly" and is "handy to have on sizeable cases" while **Neil Calver** (see p.1358) has raised his public profile with the recent Elton John case and is known to secure good instructions from Magic Circle firms. With a fine commercial background acquired while a member of an aviation set, **Andrew Lydiard** (see p.1414) is now "making a definite impact in mainstream commercial work." Interviewees praised **Tom Adam** (see p.1341) as "dedicated" and "switched on." **Dominic Chambers** (see p.1361) "gets to the heart of things" and the "frightfully good" **Helen Davies** (see p.1369) is "going places." **Richard Lord** is "attentive and responsive" while **Roger Masefield** (see p.1417) is "especially adept in insurance-related disputes."

Essex Court Chambers (see full details p.1496) "Clearly one of the best," **Gordon Pollock QC** (see p.1434) remains at the forefront of the market. "Single-minded", solicitors feel that he "carries immense gravitas which generally frightens the other side." Many appreciated that "if you're up against Pollock, you know you have a tough nut to crack." **Bernard Eder**

LEADING SILKS • London		
★	**GRABINER Anthony**	One Essex Court
	POLLOCK Gordon	Essex Court Chambers
	SUMPTION Jonathan	Brick Court Chambers
1	**BOSWOOD Anthony**	Fountain Court
	BRINDLE Michael	Fountain Court
	CARR Christopher	One Essex Court
	DOHMANN Barbara	Blackstone Chambers
	GLOSTER Elizabeth	One Essex Court
	HAPGOOD Mark	Brick Court Chambers
	VOS Geoffrey	3 Stone Buildings
2	**BARNES Mark**	One Essex Court
	BRIGGS Michael	Serle Court
	EDER Bernard	Essex Court Chambers
	HOCHHAUSER Andrew	Essex Court Chambers
	HOWARD Mark	Brick Court Chambers
3	**GLASGOW Edwin**	39 Essex Street
	HIRST Jonathan	Brick Court Chambers
	JARVIS John	3 Verulam Buildings
	KENTRIDGE Sydney	Brick Court Chambers
	MILL Ian	Blackstone Chambers
	ONIONS Jeffery	One Essex Court
	POPPLEWELL Andrew	Brick Court Chambers
	ROSEN Murray	11 Stone Buildings
	STADLEN Nicholas	Fountain Court
4	**FIELD Richard**	One Essex Court
	FLINT Charles	Blackstone Chambers
	GROSS Peter	20 Essex Street
	MALEK Ali	3 Verulam Buildings
	MANN Anthony	Enterprise Chambers
	MILLIGAN Iain	20 Essex Street
	MOWSCHENSON Terence	Wilberforce Chambers
	RAILTON David	Fountain Court
	TEMPLE Anthony	4 Pump Court
5	**CRANE Michael**	Fountain Court
	DAVIES Rhodri	One Essex Court
	FLAUX Julian	7 King's Bench Walk
	FREEDMAN Clive	Littleton Chambers
	GEERING Ian	3 Verulam Buildings
	GLICK Ian	One Essex Court
	GRUDER Jeffrey	Essex Court Chambers
	HOLLANDER Charles	Brick Court Chambers
	IVORY Thomas	One Essex Court
	JACOBS Richard	Essex Court Chambers
	KEALEY Gavin	7 King's Bench Walk
	LEAVER Peter	One Essex Court
	LEGGATT George	Brick Court Chambers
	OTTON-GOULDER Catharine	Brick Court Chambers
	TUGENHAT Michael	5 Raymond Buildings
NEW SILKS		
	ANDREWS Geraldine	Essex Court Chambers
	BEAZLEY Thomas	Blackstone Chambers
	BUTCHER Christopher	7 King's Bench Walk
	JONES Elizabeth	Serle Court
	RUBIN Stephen	Fountain Court
	SMITH Stephen	New Square Chambers
	TOZZI Nigel	4 Pump Court

This book is the product of 6,552 1/2-hour interviews. See p.7 for BMRB audit.
For details of these leading barristers see Profiles on p.1339

LEADING JUNIORS • London		
★	RABINOWITZ Laurence	One Essex Court
1	MCCAUGHRAN John	One Essex Court
	ORR Craig	Fountain Court
	SMOUHA Joe	Essex Court Chambers
2	DE GARR ROBINSON Anthony	One Essex Court
	MCQUATER Ewan	3 Verulam Buildings
	PHILIPPS Guy	Fountain Court
	SWAINSTON Michael	Brick Court Chambers
	THANKI Bankim	Fountain Court
3	ANDERSON Robert	Blackstone Chambers
	CALVER Neil	Brick Court Chambers
	HOWE Robert	Blackstone Chambers
	ONSLOW Andrew	3 Verulam Buildings
	WAKSMAN David	Fountain Court
4	BELTRAMI Adrian	3 Verulam Buildings
	CAVENDER David	One Essex Court
	CHAMBERS Dominic	Brick Court Chambers
	DOWLEY Dominic	Serle Court
	FLYNN Vernon	Essex Court Chambers
	JOSEPH David	Essex Court Chambers
	LORD Richard	Brick Court Chambers
	LYDIARD Andrew	Brick Court Chambers
5	ADAM Tom	Brick Court Chambers
	BAKER Andrew	20 Essex Street
	BLANCHARD Claire	Essex Court Chambers
	CHOO CHOY Alain	One Essex Court
	DAVIES Helen	Brick Court Chambers
	EADIE James	Serle Court
	FLETCHER Andrew	3 Verulam Buildings
	FOXTON David	Essex Court Chambers
	GRIFFITHS Martin	Essex Court Chambers
	LOCKEY John	Essex Court Chambers
	MASEFIELD Roger	Brick Court Chambers
	MCGRATH Paul	Essex Court Chambers
	MILLETT Richard	Essex Court Chambers
	PHILLIPS Stephen	3 Verulam Buildings
	TOLEDANO Daniel	One Essex Court
	WEITZMAN Tom	3 Verulam Buildings
	WOLFSON David	One Essex Court
	WYNTER Colin	Devereux Chambers
UP AND COMING		
	STANLEY Paul	Essex Court Chambers

This book is the product of 6,552 1/2-hour interviews. See p.7 for BMRB audit.

For details of these leading barristers see Profiles on p.1339

QC (see p.1374) is "regularly briefed on big cases" particularly for those requiring a "thorough and accomplished orator." "Brilliant advocate" **Andrew Hochhauser QC** (see p.1396) is said to demonstrate a "good combination of intellect and cross-examination skills" while **Jeffrey Gruder QC** (see p.1390) is considered a "formidable advocate." **Richard Jacobs QC** (see p.1400) is recommended for his capability to cross a number of practice areas such as banking and professional negligence, "providing sound and sensible advice." **Geraldine Andrews QC** (see p.1343) "richly deserves" her recent elevation to silk status, with one practitioner commenting that "I've both come up against her and worked with her, and she's never once failed to impress me." Of the juniors, **Joe Smouha** (see p.1450) is, in the eyes of many solicitors, the most outstanding figure at this set. He combines a "wonderful tactical nous with a client-friendly approach," "he's bright and always a pleasure to deal with." **Vernon Flynn** (see p.1380) and **Martin Griffiths** (see p.1389) continue to garner market support, while **Claire Blanchard** (see p.1351) has an "efficient and refreshingly modern approach." The "conscientious" **David Foxton** (see p.1381) "shows acute attention to detail, is thoroughly prepared and gives advice that can be trusted" according to solicitors who instruct him. **John Lockey** (see p.1413) is endorsed for his "common-sense" approach. The "efficient and clever" **David Joseph** (see p.1403) brings his "witty, dry and no-nonsense" manner to each case. As one solicitor claimed, "he's not pompous at all, he's always precise and he chooses his words carefully." **Richard Millett** (see p.1421) is rated for his broad expertise which has recently included insurance and shipping disputes, and "you can rely on him for an early view." **Paul McGrath** (see p.1419) is considered "quite a character and a good scrapper" while **Paul Stanley** (see p.1452) is said to do "an excellent job – he's a bright young thing" who some peers feel is "especially good with US clients."

One Essex Court (see full details p.1497) **Anthony Grabiner QC** has "an uncanny feel for the way the judiciary is going to react," with solicitors commenting that "he's a serious cross-examiner – when you need someone who can be brutal, he's the man." The "fantastic" **Elizabeth Gloster QC** (see p.1386) is a "giant in terms of intellect" who has an "incredibly broad practice." Many peers agree she is a pleasure to work with. "Effective" **Mark Barnes QC** (see p.1347), currently active on the Sumitomo case, is felt to have expertise in technology cases. Solicitors praise his ability to "get his head around technical issues." The "absolutely superb" **Christopher Carr QC** "comes at a high price and is absolutely worth it – he provides excellent quality" and is "a serious player in all respects – such a terrific all-rounder." **Ian Glick QC** (see p.1347) is "bright and persuasive," keeping matters on an "even keel" while **Richard Field QC** (see p.1378) is described by solicitors as being "a team player" and "supportive." **Jeffery Onions QC** (see p.1430) is "at his best in the heat of battle." **Rhodri Davies QC** (see p.1369) and **Peter Leaver QC** are again recommended by the market, while newly ranked **Tom Ivory QC** (see p.1400) received a weight of solicitor commendations, with many describing him as "helpful and constructive." **Laurence Rabinowitz** (see p.1437) is "an exceptionally clever senior junior" who is "inundated with work" and "easy to deal with." The market consensus is best summed up by the comment of one solicitor: "God only knows how they left him off the silks list this year." The "wise and considered" **John McCaughran** (see p.1418) is considered "absolutely first class," while solicitors claim that **Anthony de Garr Robinson** (see p.1370) "manages to make it right every time" with his "client-friendly skills and commercial approach." **David Wolfson** (see p.1469) is "thorough" and **Alain Choo Choy** (see p.1362) is "adaptable and good to work with." **David Cavender** (see p.1361) also received a body of endorsement from barristers and solicitors, while **Daniel Toledano** (see p.1461) has "a capacity for the production of work that is beyond belief."

Fountain Court (see full details p.1506) The "genial, uncomplicated and uncompromising" **Anthony Boswood QC** (see p.1352) is said to be "a master – he can turn his hand to anything and really puts his head down." His style can be "hard-headed" when necessary and many peers agree he is a "tremendous cross-examiner," while solicitors find him "extremely good with clients." **Michael Brindle QC** (see p.1355) is considered "exceptionally bright" and is currently involved in the high profile Barings litigation. Peers believe "he's knocking on the door of the star category in terms of his profile and the work he's getting." **Nicholas Stadlen QC** (see p.1452), known for his involvement in the Bank of England litigation, is said to display "intellectual and analytical ability" in addition to "good advocacy skills, the willingness to work as part of a team and the commitment to deliver first class work on schedule." The "charming" **Michael Crane QC** is a "stunningly good advocate." **David Railton QC** (see p.1438) is "the master of the detail" and is rated as "having an exceptional track record," particularly for banking and insurance litigation matters. Formerly at Farrar's Building, **Stephen Rubin QC** (see p.1443) was another silk to receive market commendation. **Craig Orr** (see p.1430) was described as being "one of the real rising stars of the bar" although he is embroiled in the Barings litigation at the moment. "Super" **Bankim Thanki** (see p.1459) is "incredibly busy with a broad range of instruction." "He's fearsomely bright without making you think you're in the presence of a boffin who doesn't have time for you or your clients – he's able to apply his knowledge practically." "Marvellous draftsman" **Guy Philipps** (see p.1433) is also "ferocious in court," while **David Waksman** (see p.1465) is "punchy, tenacious and terrier-like."

Blackstone Chambers (see full details p.1481) Peers commend **Barbara Dohmann QC** (see p.1371) as a "skilled advocate" who proffers "clear commercial advice." "Good on the detail, she is an incredibly tough opponent." **Charles Flint QC** (see p.1379) is "helpful and supportive," and gives "quality advice in a lucid and user-friendly way." One solicitor praised the "wonderful service given by a man of his eminence, I'm impressed with how he rolls up his sleeves and gets his hands dirty." **Ian Mill QC** (see p.1421) is said to be "great fun to work with and exceptionally good on his feet." He is skilled across a number of commercial spheres including a strong presence in media cases. New silk **Thomas Beazley QC** (see p.1349) has "an excellent manner with clients," with peers valuing his approach as "academically sound." **Robert Howe** (see p.1398) is again endorsed for his "growing presence" in the general commercial arena, bolstered by his media background. **Robert Anderson** (see p.1343) is a "rising star junior," particularly in the competition sphere and is currently supporting a massive workload.

3 Verulam Buildings (see full details p.1575) **Ian Geering QC** (see p.1384) has been described as "forward-thinking and well-organised" while **John Jarvis QC** (see p.1401) is said to be "as good on paper as he is on his feet." **Ali Malek QC** (see p.1415) "works hard and fights hard in court," while **Ewan McQuater** (see p.1420) is considered a "strong operator," particularly rated for his civil fraud matters. He "underplays how bright he actually is," and his "open and approachable style" puts clients and solicitors at ease. Solicitors find **Tom Weitzman** (see p.1467) to be "practical with strong intellect," while the "sensible" **Andrew Onslow** (see p.1430), **Adrian Beltrami** (see p.1349) and **Stephen Phillips** (see p.1433) all retain their share of market support. Newly ranked junior **Andrew Fletcher** (see p.1379) is said to be "quick on the uptake" and "always committed to the task at hand."

Other Notable Practitioners "A perfectly skilled advocate," solicitors see **Geoffrey Vos QC** (see p.1465) of **3 Stone Buildings** as "good for challenging and complicated cases where you need a real heavy hitter." He "exudes confidence" and "dominates the court with his excellent judgment." **Edwin Glasgow QC** (see p.1385) of **39 Essex Street** is a "real workhorse" but is currently locked into the Bloody Sunday inquiry. The "quick-thinking" **Clive Freedman QC** (see p.1381) of **Littleton Chambers** is felt to be "commercial and good with clients." Solicitors agree that **Michael Briggs QC** (see p.1355) of **Serle Court** "gets stuck in" and "gives a good intellectual analysis – he's amazingly clever" while **Elizabeth Jones QC** (see p.1403) is "fast, practical and an excellent advocate." The set also houses junior **Dominic Dowley** (see p.1372), thought to be "more cerebral than some and an exceptionally sharp advocate," while **James Eadie** (see p.1373) also received market commendation. At **20 Essex Street**, the "sharp and incisive" **Peter Gross QC** (see p.1390) is felt to be "client friendly," with particular aptitude for "heavyweight commercial and professional negligence work." **Terence Mowschenson QC** (see p.1425) of **Wilberforce Chambers** has been described as "commercially-minded and approachable." **Murray Rosen QC** (see p.1442) at **11 Stone Buildings** has "a nice all-round mix of skills" and **Anthony Temple QC** (see p.1458) from **4 Pump Court** again receives market endorsement from practitioners. His colleague **Nigel Tozzi QC** (see p.1461) has taken silk. **Stephen Smith QC** (see p.1450) of **New Square Chambers** "knows and understands fraud cases" and is said to have a "laid-back cautiousness about him." Solicitors agree "you can see him thinking through the case and weighing up the options." At **7 King's Bench Walk**, the "methodical and reliable" **Christopher Butcher QC** (see p.1358) is described by one practitioner as "the best of the new silks" in that he "doesn't thump the table and is unshakeable with a particularly thick skin." Peers acknowledge that "some barristers are overawed by judges, but not him." Here also, **Julian Flaux QC** (see p.1379) drew commendation from peers for his "hands-on" and "user-friendly" approach, with one silk noting that "he's been getting high quality work and performing exceptionally well." His colleague **Gavin Kealey QC** (see p.1404) "produces clear, thoroughly researched and detailed opinions" while **Anthony Mann QC** from **Enterprise Chambers** has once more proved to have a following among solicitors. **Michael Tugenhat QC** (see p.1463) at **5 Raymond Buildings** receives commendation for his "calmness under fire," and **Iain Milligan QC** (see p.1421) from **20 Essex Street** is thought to be "careful, thorough and persuasive, both on paper and in court." Also at this set, **Andrew Baker** (see p.1345) is described as "dynamic and likeable" with "no unnecessary airs and graces." **Colin Wynter** (see p.1471) of **Devereux Chambers** remains highly regarded by both peers and solicitors.

WESTERN CIRCUIT

LEADING SILKS • Western		
1	DAVIES Stephen	Guildhall Chambers
2	PALMER Adrian	Guildhall Chambers

For details of these leading barristers see Profiles on p.1339

LEADING JUNIORS • Western		
1	MAHER Martha	Guildhall Chambers
	STEAD Richard	St John's Chambers
	VIRGO John	Guildhall Chambers
2	BAMFORD Jeremy	Guildhall Chambers
	BLOHM Leslie	St John's Chambers
	LEVY Neil	St John's Chambers

This book is the product of 6,552 1/2-hour interviews. See p.7 for BMRB audit.
For details of these leading barristers see Profiles on p.1339

Guildhall Chambers (see full details p.1581) holds its position as market leader for another year. **Stephen Davies QC** (see p.1369) is recommended as a "specialist." Peers say the secret of his success is "his unsurpassable knowledge" mixed with "a thirst for corporate work." **Adrian Palmer QC** has widely-acknowledged "strength across the board" and peers dub him a "pre-eminent silk on commercial matters." Of the leading juniors, **Martha Maher** (see p.1415) is "a technical specialist." **John Virgo** (see p.1465) wins praise again this year while solicitors endorse **Jeremy Bamford** as "competent, thorough and pro-active."

At **St John's Chambers** (see full details p.1583), the "expert" **Richard Stead** (see p.1452) is rated by peers as a "personable chap" and "an excellent researcher, he's thoroughly prepared in court." **Leslie Blohm** (see p.1352) is felt to employ an "assertive approach" and **Neil Levy** is considered "thorough and well-prepared."

MIDLANDS CIRCUIT

LEADING SILKS • Midlands		
1	RANDALL John	St Philip's Chambers
2	CORBETT James	St Philip's Chambers
	COUSINS Jeremy	St Philip's Chambers

For details of these leading barristers see Profiles on p.1339

LEADING JUNIORS • Midlands		
1	KHANGURE Avtar	St Philip's Chambers
	WYVILL Alistair	St Philip's Chambers
2	ANDERSON Mark	3 Fountain Court
	ASHWORTH Lance	St Philip's Chambers
	CAMPBELL Stephen	St Philip's Chambers
	EYRE Stephen	1 Fountain Court

This book is the product of 6,552 1/2-hour interviews. See p.7 for BMRB audit.
For details of these leading barristers see Profiles on p.1339

St Philip's Chambers (see full details p.1578) dominates the region with is array of leading silks. The market consensus of **John Randall QC** (see p.1438) is unanimous: "he's simply brilliant" and "easily takes the crown as best commercial silk in Birmingham." **James Corbett QC** (see p.1366) is another "terrific silk" garnering plaudits for his "meticulous preparation" and "polished performances." The "extremely able" **Jeremy Cousins QC** (see p.1366) is "undoubtedly one of the leading specialist commercial silks." The "astute" **Avtar Khangure** (see p.1406) is "exceptionally pleasant to deal with" and his "broad expertise" makes him "a favourite of the big firms." **Alistair Wyvill** (see p.1471) is commended for his "huge experience in litigation" and "assertive" **Lance Ashworth** (see p.1344) is respected by his peers and solicitors alike. "Charming" **Stephen Campbell** (see p.1359) is "great if you're in a pickle" particularly with his capacity to "win the ear of the court." Over at **3 Fountain Court** the "outstanding" **Mark Anderson** (see p.1343) is said to be "extremely clever" with a "superb courtroom manner." **Stephen Eyre** at **1 Fountain Court** is endorsed for his "robust cross-examining."

NORTH EASTERN CIRCUIT

LEADING SILKS • North Eastern		
1	ALLEN James	No.6 Barristers Chambers

For details of these leading barristers see Profiles on p.1339

LEADING JUNIORS • North Eastern		
1	GROVES Hugo	Enterprise Chambers
	JAMES Michael	Enterprise Chambers
	JORY Hugh	Enterprise Chambers
2	CAMERON Neil	Wilberforce Chambers
	PIPE Gregory	Chancery House Chambers

This book is the product of 6,552 1/2-hour interviews. See p.7 for BMRB audit.
For details of these leading barristers see Profiles on p.1339

There are a number of proven performers in **Enterprise Chambers** (see full details p.1609) with **Hugo Groves** once again attracting the most attention. An insolvency expert but "capable of great versatility," he "fairly rips into his cases, steamrolling all in his path." "Utterly candid and generally jovial" he is known for "telling it like it is." **Michael James** (see p.1401) has a less ostentatious style. "Extremely cerebral," his best arena is that of financial and commercial disputes where he "applies close reasoning to the stickiest of problems." His colleague **Hugh Jory** is a "vastly experienced banking and insolvency expert" who has "provided satisfaction to solicitors over a number of years." His set, although described by one solicitor as "still the best in Leeds", has a rival in **No.6** which houses the prominent commercial silk, **James Allen QC**. **Greg Pipe** (see p.1434) of **Chancery House** is "straight to the point and understands the clients." He enters the tables for the first time this year alongside Hull-based **Neil Cameron** (see p.1359) of **Wilberforce Chambers** (see full details p.1588). "Painstakingly detailed" in his approach, one solicitor confided that "he often knows the case far better than those instructing him."

NORTHERN CIRCUIT

40 King Street (see full details p.1604) "Still the best available option outside London." While the respected Philip Raynor QC has gone to the bench, the set secures its presence with **Peter Smith QC** (see p.1450), "a great first instance advocate." Blunt and forceful, "you either love him or hate him" but there is no denying his talent and "ferocious cross examination skills." Fellow silk **Michael Booth QC** is "immensely hard-working and utterly straight down the line." He negotiates cases of great substance and is hailed as "one of the top drawer trial advocates." He is joined in silk by the "mentally adroit" **Paul Chaisty QC** (see p.1361). Leading junior

LEADING SILKS • Northern		
1	SMITH Peter	40 King St
	WINGATE-SAUL Giles	Byrom Street Chambers
2	BARTLEY JONES Edward	Exchange Chambers
	BOOTH Michael	40 King St
	ELLERAY Anthony	Exchange Chambers
	STEWART Stephen	Byrom Street Chambers
NEW SILKS		
	CAWSON Mark	Exchange Chambers
	CHAISTY Paul	40 King St

For details of these leading barristers see Profiles on p.1339

LEADING JUNIORS • Northern		
1	ANDERSON Lesley	40 King St
	DAVIES Stephen	8 King St
2	BERRAGAN Neil	Merchant Chambers
	COGLEY Stephen	Merchant Chambers
	TERRY Jeffrey	8 King St
3	CASEMENT David	Exchange Chambers
	DOYLE Louis	40 King St

This book is the product of 6,552 1/2-hour interviews. See p.7 for BMRB audit.
For details of these leading barristers see Profiles on p.1339

Lesley Anderson (see p.1343) was praised as being "head and shoulders above the rest." "A real fighter" she is "good on paper, brilliant on her feet and displays all the hallmarks of a QC in waiting." Fellow junior **Louis Doyle** (see p.1372) displays a similar trait of "shooting from the hip." Celebrated particularly for his advocacy, he has a busy general commercial practice, and handles his clients in a "user-friendly" manner.

Byrom Street Chambers **Giles Wingate-Saul QC** (see p.1469) is "one of the grand old men of the commercial bar." Combining "complete mastery of the law" with "a fluent advocacy style that is pleasant on the ear" his practice includes construction, PI, and clinical negligence. His colleague **Stephen Stewart QC** focuses on insurance and commercial negligence. "Tireless" and "highly analytical" he is regarded as "a safe bet for paperwork-heavy, time consuming cases."

Exchange Chambers (see full details p.1598) Adaptable to both chancery and commercial work, **Anthony Elleray QC** (see p.1375) is thought to "sift through voluminous paperwork with celerity and a keen eye." Observers commented upon his "high powers of concentration" which allow him to "unflaggingly handle the meatier cases." **Edward Bartley Jones QC** (see p.1348) manages a practice which covers chancery, insolvency, partnership and professional negligence matters. Regarded as a "sturdy all-rounder," his versatility has proved appealing to a wide range of those solicitors contacted. He has been joined in the set by the well-respected **Mark Cawson QC** (see p.1361). As widely predicted he has been promoted to silk and is recommended for his "thorough dependability" and "quality paperwork." Top junior **David Casement** (see p.1360) is a new addition to our tables. Skilled in property law and professional indemnity as part of a general practice, his "quietly efficient approach to advocacy is pleasing to the court" and has resulted in his retention on a number of quality briefs.

Merchant Chambers (see full details p.1605) Home to two of the better juniors on the circuit. **Stephen Cogley** (see p.1364) has a reputation as "something of a maverick" capable of "intermittent bouts of brilliance." His particular style is felt to be "best suited to big jury trials" where he is "able to turn cases on their heads through powerful advocacy." Similarly, **Neil Berragan** was hailed as "a gifted courtroom manipulator" whose sharp cross-examination "often proves lethal."

8 King Street (see full details p.1604) General commercial litigator **Stephen Davies** "has the ear of the judges" and falls firmly into the "quiet assassin mould of advocacy." **Jeffrey Terry** maintains market support as a "reliable, shrewd and commercial figure" who proffers "attention to detail."

COMPANY

RESEARCH: The rankings are based on in-depth interviews with over 5,000 solicitors and barristers in the UK. Chambers research is audited by the British Market Research Bureau (see page 7 for details).

OVERVIEW: Demand for counsel remains undiminished. According to market leaders, "good silks" are decreasing in number, while US firms liken the bar to a "gold repository," endorsing it as their "legal standard." Erskine Chambers and 4 Stone Buildings are the choice of most for constitutional company law matters, while the other sets feature more on disputes.

LONDON

	COMPANY • London	QCs	Jnrs
1	**Erskine Chambers** (Robin Potts QC)	6	10
2	**4 Stone Buildings** (Philip Heslop QC)	4	4
3	**Maitland Chambers** (Lyndon-Stanford/Aldous)	5	4
4	**Serle Court** (Lord Neill of Bladen QC)	3	1
	3-4 South Square (Crystal/Alexander)	4	-
5	**Enterprise Chambers** (Anthony Mann QC)	1	3
	24 Old Buildings (Mann/Steinfeld)	2	1

Numbers show recommended barristers in this practice area

	LEADING SILKS • London	
★	**POTTS Robin**	Erskine Chambers
1	**RICHARDS David**	Erskine Chambers
2	**ALDOUS Charles**	Maitland Chambers
	BOMPAS Anthony	4 Stone Buildings
	BRIGGS Michael	Serle Court
	DAVIS Nigel	Maitland Chambers
	GLOSTER Elizabeth	One Essex Court
	HESLOP Philip	4 Stone Buildings
	HILDYARD Robert	4 Stone Buildings
	KOSMIN Leslie	Erskine Chambers
	MOWSCHENSON Terence	Wilberforce Chambers
	OLIVER David	Erskine Chambers
	TODD Michael	Erskine Chambers
3	**COHEN Lawrence**	24 Old Buildings
	CRYSTAL Michael	3-4 South Square
	DICKER Robin	3-4 South Square
	HAPGOOD Mark	Brick Court Chambers
	HOLLINGTON Robin	New Square Chambers
	KNOWLES Robin	3-4 South Square
	MANN Anthony	Enterprise Chambers
	PHILLIPS Mark	3-4 South Square
	PURLE Charles	New Square Chambers
	STEINFELD Alan	24 Old Buildings
	VOS Geoffrey	3 Stone Buildings
4	**BANNISTER Edward**	3 Stone Buildings
	BOYLE Alan	Serle Court
	BRISBY John	4 Stone Buildings
	LYNDON-STANFORD Michael	Maitland Chambers
	NEWMAN Catherine	Maitland Chambers
	SMITH Stephen	New Square Chambers
NEW SILKS		
	GIRET Jane	11 Stone Buildings
	JOFFE Victor	Serle Court
	MABB David	Erskine Chambers
	NEWEY Guy	Maitland Chambers

This book is the product of 6,552 1/2-hour interviews. See p.7 for BMRB audit.
For details of these leading barristers see Profiles on p.1339

Erskine Chambers (see full details p.1495) Widely regarded as "the barometer," this "incredibly solid" set is said to be "so far ahead of the others in strength and depth" because it was "for years, the only company law chambers in existence." Many leading firms use it "almost to the exclusion of other sets" for its "uniformly excellent juniors," with the certain knowledge that its silks' expert views represent or even command "the definitive view of the law." The set's continued "recipe for success" is attributed to its regular exposure to "top quality work from all the major firms." Providing "consistently first class advice" in "charming and accommodating" style, clients vouch that "you can never go wrong with them because they know the answers." The set retains cachet for those seeking to "beat a person over the head with an opinion." Having "inherited the style mantle" of the legendary Richard Sykes QC, "doyen on corporate issues" **Robin Potts QC** remains a "favourite" with clients and is "the first choice" for many. Thought to be "extraordinarily sound," he provides the "right mixture of caution and willingness to express a view." Described as "tremendously approachable," he is "an extremely useful safety valve" for many, because of his willingness to "engage in debate and give a robust opinion on what the court's views will be, as opposed to purely what precedent dictates." Highly rated for his expertise in corporate insurance work such as demutualisations and court-sanctioned schemes, **David Richards QC** (see p.1440) is "a man to rely on for the big moment." An "elegant performer," he is said to advise at "the cautious end of the spectrum" and is an "astute, commercial team player." "Good strategist" **Leslie Kosmin QC** provides "direct, straightforward, quick clear analysis," giving clients "confidence that he understands what the issues are, and can rise above the details to see the bigger picture." A "strong performer across the board," he is endorsed as a "clever litigator" and "formidable opponent." Said to have an enormous practice, **David Oliver QC** (see p.1429) "gets straight to the point" and "gives crystal clear commercial advice," while some peers esteem him "a gifted advocate – the best in Lincoln's Inn on his day." "Another of the set's well trained individuals," **Michael Todd QC** (see p.1461) is described as a "neat and tidy advocate." "A barrister who can communicate with clients," he is "not aloof." Said to be "leading" in reconstruction work, new silk **David Mabb QC** is a "good analytical lawyer" who is "reliable and responsive." Acclaimed by peers as "one of the cleverest at the bar," **David Chivers'** (see p.1362) "precise thinking" gets him "to the nub of things quickly." "Extremely knowledgeable about the breadth of the law," he "always comes up with solutions, communicates his opinions well and makes clients feel comfortable." Long-standing "effective transactional" advisor **John Cone** (see p.1365) is "a good lateral thinker" and "can always be relied on to do his stuff" on schemes of arrangement and FSA aspects. Described as "intense but practical," **Richard Snowden** (see p.1450) displays "a good grasp" of financial assistance matters. "Sensible in the advice he gives," he is an "absolute pleasure to work with." An "impressive" specialist on reductions of capital, "affable and able" **Martin Moore** (see p.1423) "explains legal technicalities well and doesn't get bogged down in detail." Thought to be "the brains behind much of the set's product," **Thomas Stockdale** (see p.1454) "wipes the floor with the rest" with his "intelligent, experienced, delightful manner." Possessed of a "fabulous" practice in scheme advisory work, many consider him "in a class of his own in his specialism." **Mary Stokes** (see p.1454) is said to provide "responsive, precise, quick commercial advice at a reasonable cost." Also receiving recommendations are "worthy" **Catherine Roberts**,

	LEADING JUNIORS • London	
1	CHIVERS David	Erskine Chambers
	CONE John	Erskine Chambers
	SNOWDEN Richard	Erskine Chambers
2	MILES Robert	4 Stone Buildings
	MOORE Martin	Erskine Chambers
	STOCKDALE Thomas	Erskine Chambers
	STOKES Mary	Erskine Chambers
3	ARDEN Peter	Enterprise Chambers
	DAVIS-WHITE Malcolm	4 Stone Buildings
	GILLYON Philip	Erskine Chambers
	GREEN Michael	Fountain Court
	GRIFFITHS Peter	4 Stone Buildings
	HARMAN Sarah	4 Stone Buildings
	IFE Linden	Enterprise Chambers
	PRENTICE Dan	Erskine Chambers
	RITCHIE Richard	24 Old Buildings
	ROBERTS Catherine	Erskine Chambers
	SHEKERDEMIAN Marcia	11 Stone Buildings
	STUBBS Rebecca	Maitland Chambers
	ZELIN Geoffrey	Enterprise Chambers
4	COLLINGS Matthew	Maitland Chambers
	GIROLAMI Paul	Maitland Chambers
	MARSHALL Philip	Serle Court
	PARKER Christopher	Maitland Chambers
	RABINOWITZ Laurence	One Essex Court
	THOMPSON Andrew	Erskine Chambers

This book is the product of 6,552 1/2-hour interviews. See p.7 for BMRB audit.
For details of these leading barristers see Profiles on p.1339

who has a mixed advisory practice and "helpful" **Philip Gillyon** (see p.1385) who is known for his insolvency expertise. Both **Dan Prentice** and **Andrew Thompson** (see p.1460) have "excellent" academic reputations.

4 Stone Buildings (see full details p.1568) Typically, researchers were told that this is "the obvious alternative" to Erskine Chambers. "Star" Head of Chambers **Philip Heslop QC** is described by solicitors as "aggressive" and "intellectually outstanding, but always busy." As an advocate, his peers commend him for "an informal, low key but effective presentation." "Clever, considered" **Robert Hildyard QC** (see p.1394) is sought after "for original and difficult points." Teamed with "extremely bright junior" **Robert Miles**, they make "a great combination" because they "really roll up their sleeves and put themselves out" for their clients. **Anthony Bompas QC** (see p.1352) gains approval from clients for his ability to "accept a problem as his own and use his extraordinary analytical powers to bring it towards a solution." An "informative" company and financial services advisor, he gives "clear, succinct advice." **John Brisby QC** (see p.1355) is an "aggressive" litigator - "if it moves, he fights it." **Malcolm Davis-White** (see p.1370) is sought after for his "immense experience" on insurance schemes and reductions of capital. A "difficult and formidable" opponent, **Peter Griffiths** (see p.1389) is "original, conscientious and bright" while **Sarah Harman** is "extremely sound."

Maitland Chambers (see full details p.1538) The new set, formed by the merger between 13 Old Square and 7 Stone Buildings, is strongly associated with contentious work involving insolvency and directors' disqualification issues, with commercial chancery work at the heart of its expertise. Senior figure **Michael Lyndon-Stanford QC** (see p.1414) is respected for his work on commercial and chancery disputes, while researchers found that "grandee in heavy company law disputes," **Charles Aldous QC** (see p.1342) was "typically, the name solicitors look for early on" for his "first-class litigation skills." **Nigel Davis QC** (see p.1370) is "insightful and clear," while communicating "effectively" with clients on general commercial chancery matters. **Catherine Newman QC** (see p.1427) has "a deserved reputation" for SWAPs-related work and constructive trusts. Advisors "have confidence that she will deliver what she says." Known for his expertise in DTI and directors' disqualification matters, new silk **Guy Newey QC** (see p.1427) has a "terrific" reputation with clients for his "immediate, common-sense grasp of the problem" and ability to "present fact, alternative and argument." **Rebecca Stubbs** (see p.1455) is described to researchers as a "rising star" in company and insolvency litigation, while **Matthew Collings** (see p.1365) is active on commercial shareholder disputes. Solicitors also recommend **Paul Girolami** (see p.1385) and **Christopher Parker** (see p.1431) as barristers who "know their stuff."

Serle Court (see full details p.1565) A strong commercial and banking set, with a sound reputation in asset tracing and directors' disqualification work. **Michael Briggs QC** (see p.1355) is hailed by leading peers as "one of the best at the Chancery Bar and an A1 advocate." Specialist in civil fraud work **Alan Boyle QC** (see p.1353) has been working full-time in Bermuda on the Thyssen litigation since 1999. New silk **Victor Joffe QC** (see p.1402) is said to have "a big practice" in company and insolvency work. A specialist and published author on shareholders' disposals matters, he is also admitted to the New York Bar and often practises in the US and Jersey. Commercial litigator **Philip Marshall** (see p.1416) upholds the set's good reputation for insolvency work.

3-4 South Square (see full details p.1566) Excellent for insolvency and corporate reconstruction matters, this is the solicitors' set of choice for commercial contentious work. Typically praised to researchers for his "excellent grasp of the subject," Head of Chambers **Michael Crystal QC** (see p.1368) "gets big cases" such as the long-running Thyssen litigation in Bermuda, which accounts for his decreased profile on domestic matters. Clients find "extremely bright cookie" **Robin Knowles QC** (see p.1407) useful for general commercial issues, while **Mark Phillips QC** (see p.1433) and "solidly reliable" **Robin Dicker QC** (see p.1371) are well regarded for their insolvency expertise.

Enterprise Chambers (see full details p.1494) "Tremendously authoritative" with an "excellent client manner," **Anthony Mann QC** "gets to the issue" and "kills you with reasonableness," admit rivals. Senior junior **Geoffrey Zelin** (see p.1471) is said to be a "formidable" individual. "Tough lady" **Linden Ife** (see p.1399) is "approachable, user-friendly and responsive," while "industrious and intelligent" **Peter Arden** (see p.1344) is a "thoughtful and accurate" company and insolvency specialist.

24 Old Buildings (see full details p.1548) Commended to researchers as "particularly good for company matters with financial or accounts-related aspects," co-head of Chambers **Alan Steinfeld QC** (see p.1453) is "aggressive and clever." Also highly recommended are "bright" **Lawrence Cohen QC** (see p.1364) and **Richard Ritchie** (see p.1440), who is described as "a top notch Treasury devil for insolvency matters."

Other Notable Practitioners "Strong all-rounder" **Elizabeth Gloster QC** (see p.1346) of **One Essex Court** gains "big admirers" for her problem-solving ability in complex work on corporate, city and financial issues, involving drafting legislation or regulatory aspects. Solicitors unanimously agree that she gives "excellent commercial advice" and demonstrates "superb analytical powers." **Laurence Rabinowitz** (see p.1437) "can turn his hand to anything." Sought after for his "wide experience of expertise across lots of different facets of commercial work" **Terence Mowschenson QC** (see p.1425) of **Wilberforce Chambers** is an "aggressive communicator" who provides "good analysis of issues." "Hugely knowledgeable" commercial litigator and banking expert **Mark Hapgood QC** of **Brick Court Chambers** gains top marks from clients for "giving you an answer as opposed to a variety of possibilities." Although better known from its constituent parts (1 New Square and 12 New Square) as a commercial chancery set, **New Square Chambers** boasts several silks who handle significant amounts of company work.

Known as an author on minority shareholder rights and s459 petitions, **Robin Hollington QC** is "as good as anyone" on company scheme work. "Extremely experienced" **Charles Purle QC** is "a real fighter" on Anton Pillar, Mareva and other heavy commercial disputes. Also endorsed for his litigation skills, **Stephen Smith QC** (see p.1450) is "extremely bright." Chairman of the Chancery Bar Association **Geoffrey Vos QC** (see p.1465) of **3 Stone Buildings** is said by peers to be "diligent and effective" on general commercial disputes, while **Edward Bannister QC** (see p.1346) of the same set is "solid and persistent" with "a great sense of humour." **Jane Giret QC** (see p.1385) of **11 Stone Buildings** has taken silk this year, while **Marcia Shekerdemian** (see p.1447) of the same set is generally commended to researchers as "hard-working and good at what she does." **Michael Green** (see p.1388) of **Fountain Court** is a "solid" advisor, while "leading junior."

COMPETITION / ANTI-TRUST

RESEARCH: The rankings are based on in-depth interviews with over 5,000 solicitors and barristers in the UK. Chambers research is audited by the British Market Research Bureau (see page 7 for details).

LONDON

	COMPETITION/ANTI-TRUST • London	QCs	Jnrs
1	Brick Court Chambers (Christopher Clarke QC)	5	5
	Monckton Chambers (John Swift QC)	7	4

Numbers show recommended barristers in this practice area

	LEADING SILKS • London	
1	ANDERSON David	Brick Court Chambers
	FOWLER Richard	Monckton Chambers
	GREEN Nicholas	Brick Court Chambers
	PARKER Kenneth	Monckton Chambers
2	LASOK Paul	Monckton Chambers
	LEVER Jeremy	Monckton Chambers
	SHARPE Thomas	One Essex Court
	SWIFT John	Monckton Chambers
	VAJDA Christopher	Monckton Chambers
3	GRABINER Anthony	One Essex Court
	LLOYD JONES David	Brick Court Chambers
	PLENDER Richard	20 Essex Street
	SHARPSTON Eleanor	4 Paper Buildings
4	BARLING Gerald	Brick Court Chambers
	PAINES Nicholas	Monckton Chambers
	VAUGHAN David	Brick Court Chambers

For details of these leading barristers see Profiles on p.1339

	LEADING JUNIORS • London	
1	ROBERTSON Aidan	Brick Court Chambers
	THOMPSON Rhodri	Matrix Chambers
	TURNER Jon	Monckton Chambers
2	ANDERSON Rupert	Monckton Chambers
	BREALEY Mark	Brick Court Chambers
	FLYNN James	Brick Court Chambers
	HOSKINS Mark	Brick Court Chambers
	MORRIS Stephen	20 Essex Street
	PERETZ George	Monckton Chambers
	RANDOLPH Fergus	Brick Court Chambers
	WATSON Philippa	Essex Court Chambers
UP AND COMING		
	BEARD Daniel	Monckton Chambers

This book is the product of 6,552 1/2-hour interviews. See p.7 for BMRB audit.

For details of these leading barristers see Profiles on p.1339

Brick Court Chambers (see full details p.1484) Playing host to a dazzling array of practitioners, Brick Court retains its reputation as a "competition powerhouse" and is typically described by law firms as "the set for private clients." **David Anderson QC** (see p.1343) was consistently recommended to researchers as "an exceptional advocate," "entirely deserving" of a place in the top tier. Solicitors nationwide are lavish in their praise of "outstanding lawyer and advocate," the "exceptionally intelligent, user-friendly & informal" **Nicholas Green QC** (see p.1389). He conducts a substantial volume of litigation in national courts. Peers profess "the highest admiration" for **David Lloyd Jones QC** (see p.1413), "a tremendously clever, sensible and talented advocate." "Attractive and exuberant thinker" **Gerald Barling QC** is recommended for EC law expertise, while "the most famous EC lawyer in the country," **David Vaughan QC** (see p.1464), is highly regarded by clients for his commercial acumen. Many solicitors believe that **Aidan Robertson** (see p.1441) gives "more consistently sound advice" than any other junior in this area. **Mark Brealey** (see p.1354) is an experienced barrister, who gains high marks from his peers. Ex-solicitor **James Flynn** (see p.1380) impresses clients with "sound advice on a broad range of issues." **Mark Hoskins** (see p.1397) "is essentially an EC lawyer and fantastic at it," whilst "likeable" **Fergus Randolph** (see p.1438) is also principally recognised for EC work.

Monckton Chambers (see full details p.1540) Frequently described to researchers as "a crack team," the firm is said to be "dominant" when it comes to acting for government bodies. **Richard Fowler QC** (see p.1381) "is unquestionably top flight for both competition and EC law" and many solicitors profess themselves to be "huge fans" of his "fast turn-around of instructions and commercial perspective." "Erudite yet never pompous," **Kenneth Parker QC** (see p.1431) is said to have been, "brought up on pure competition law, an area which he knows perfectly." Solicitors find in "understated advocate," **Paul Lasok QC** (see p.1409) "an academic who can sort through the most knotty details." **Jeremy Lever QC** (see p.1410) is thought by some of his peers to possess "the most brilliant mind in this area." **John Swift QC** (see p.1456) is admired as "a flamboyant advocate who gives punchy and commercial advice, sees the big picture and offers lateral solutions." "Particularly good for EU law," **Christopher Vajda QC** (see p.1464) is regularly praised to researchers for his "methodical approach," while **Nicholas Paines QC** (see p.1431) is esteemed for "clear thinking." Among juniors, "experienced competition specialist" **Jon Turner** (see p.1463) "has few equals," according to peers. "Vigorous and logical," **Rupert Anderson** (see p.1343) has his admirers, as does **George Peretz** (see p.1433) who is "ex-OFT and totally up to date." Younger junior **Daniel Beard** (see p.1349) is popular with clients, who find him to be "energetic and focused."

Other Notable Practitioners Thomas Sharpe QC (see p.1446) of **One Essex Court** is "useful and responsive" in the view of leading law firms, while his head of chambers, **Tony Grabiner QC**, "knows the area well and possesses a sound grasp of economics." **Richard Plender QC** (see p.1434) of **20 Essex Street** wins admirers for "his dogged advocacy and knowledge of EC law," while junior at the set, **Stephen Morris** (see p.1424) impresses his peers for his "mastery of his brief." **Eleanor Sharpston QC** (see p.1446) at **4 Paper Buildings** is often recommended to researchers as an "EC lawyer with a government focus." The "brilliant" **Rhodri Thompson** (see p.1460) has established a "super" practice at **Matrix Chambers**, while **Philippa Watson** (see p.1467) of **Essex Court Chambers** maintains her reputation among leading solicitors.

CONSTRUCTION

RESEARCH: The rankings are based on in-depth interviews with over 5,000 solicitors and barristers in the UK. Chambers research is audited by the British Market Research Bureau (see page 7 for details).

Barristers' profiles 1339-1472

LONDON

	CONSTRUCTION • London	QCs	Jnrs
1	**Atkin Chambers** (Robert Akenhead QC)	9	11
	Keating Chambers (Richard Fernyhough QC)	11	9
2	**Crown Office Chambers** (Spencer/Purchas)	3	1
	4 Pump Court (David Friedman QC)	3	3
3	**39 Essex Street** (Nigel Pleming QC)	2	1
	2 Temple Gardens (Dermod O'Brien QC)	2	2
4	**Four New Square** (Justin Fenwick QC)	2	-

Numbers show recommended barristers in this practice area

	LEADING SILKS • LONDON	
★	**RAMSEY Vivian**	Keating Chambers
1	**AKENHEAD Robert**	Atkin Chambers
	BAATZ Nicholas	Atkin Chambers
	BLACKBURN John	Atkin Chambers
	DARLING Paul	Keating Chambers
	FURST Stephen	Keating Chambers
	SLATER John	Crown Office Chambers
	TAVERNER Marcus	Keating Chambers
	WHITE Andrew	Atkin Chambers
2	**DENNYS Nicholas**	Atkin Chambers
	FERNYHOUGH Richard	Keating Chambers
	MARRIN John	Keating Chambers
	TER HAAR Roger	Crown Office Chambers
	UFF John	Keating Chambers
	WILMOT-SMITH Richard	39 Essex Street
3	**ACTON DAVIS Jonathan**	Atkin Chambers
	BARTLETT Andrew	Crown Office Chambers
	BOWDERY Martin	Atkin Chambers
	ELLIOTT Timothy	Keating Chambers
	FRIEDMAN David	4 Pump Court
	GRAY Richard	39 Essex Street
4	**BLACK Michael**	2 Temple Gardens
	BOULDING Philip	Keating Chambers
	FENWICK Justin	Four New Square
	PALMER Howard	2 Temple Gardens
	SPEAIGHT Anthony	4 Pump Court
	THOMAS Christopher	Keating Chambers
NEW SILKS		
	COULSON Peter	Keating Chambers
	DENNISON Stephen	Atkin Chambers
	NICHOLSON Jeremy	4 Pump Court
	STEWART Roger	Four New Square
	STREATFEILD-JAMES David	Atkin Chambers

This book is the product of 6,552 1/2-hour interviews. See p.7 for BMRB audit.
For details of these leading barristers see Profiles on p.1339

Atkin Chambers (see full details p.1475) Continuing to match Keating Chambers stride for stride as the construction set of choice, it fields a devastating array of silks and juniors. The set is perceived to have made substantial progress in its client care programme, with one law firm describing the service as "first-class in every way." **Robert Akenhead QC** (see p.1341) "continues to provide advice of the highest calibre," and demonstrates a winning combination of "commercial awareness" and "an understanding of the client's needs." **John Blackburn QC** (see p.1351) is "at full speed again" and is considered to be "a real favourite, still at the top." "Underrated" **Nicholas Baatz QC** (see p.1345) is held to be "consistently impressive," and earns promotion this year, while **Andrew White QC** (see p.1467) is considered to be a "rising star." He is "a totally reliable all-rounder, good on paper and popular with clients." "Sound" **Nicholas Dennys QC** (see p.1371) is widely recommended by peers, and **Jonathan Acton Davis QC**'s (see p.1341) star has risen this year. He is "excellent with clients, relaxed and friendly," and is commended for his cross-examination skills and his ability to "handle the tribunal." **Martin Bowdery QC** is a "clever new silk," commended for "taking the time to think matters through." The set has two new silks this year. **Stephen Dennison QC** is a "decent, popular lawyer," while **David Streatfeild-James QC** is described as "the best junior of his generation." His "hard-working and intelligent manner" is predicted to take him "right to the top." Among juniors, **Stephanie Barwise** (see p.1348) is a "high calibre junior" who is "great to have on your side." **Chantal-Aimée Doerries** (see p.1371) is held in universally high regard by solicitors, while **Delia Dumaresq** (see p.1373) has made her name in construction-related adjudications. **Peter Fraser** (see p.1381) has impressed peers with "punchy and well-prepared performances," while "user-friendly" **Manus McMullan** (see p.1419) is "a real team player," described by some as "a tip for the top." **Mark Raeside** (see p.1437), "a genuine street-fighter," **Andrew Burr** (see p.1358), who is "enormous fun to work with," and the "classy" **James Howells** (see p.1398) all receive strong market endorsement. **Simon Lofthouse** (see p.1413) and **Fiona Parkin** (see p.1432) also maintain their share of market approval. "Streetwise" **Andrew Goddard** (see p.1386) is said to be "a fine strategist."

Keating Chambers (see full details p.1525) "Phenomenal" depth of talent and experience keeps the set neck and neck with Atkin Chambers, and far ahead of the rest of the construction Bar. **Vivian Ramsey QC** (see p.1438) continues to be the star of the show. "A delight to deal with," he "remains accessible," is "terribly good with clients," and has "an extraordinary appetite for work." **Paul Darling QC** (see p.1369) is a "rambunctious and effective performer," and earns promotion for his "dexterity on his feet." **Stephen Furst QC** (see p.1382) also remains "an obvious target" for industry heavyweights. Although only a silk since 2000, opinion was unanimous that **Marcus Taverner QC**'s (see p.1458) name belongs among the elite. Said to have "added a new dimension to the set's silks," he is "larger than life, aggressive and a great lateral thinker," whose enthusiasm "never fails to impress." Head of chambers **Richard Fernyhough QC** (see p.1378) has been described as "the battleship of the construction bar," while **John Marrin QC** (see p.1416) is praised for being "thorough, hard-working and good at grasping the technical detail." The respected **John Uff QC** (see p.1464) has a "technical background and an academic style." **Tim Elliott QC** (see p.1375) is "extremely bright and lively," **Philip Boulding QC** (see p.1353) is a "bluff performer," who is often active abroad, most notably in Hong Kong, and **Christopher Thomas QC** (see p.1459) also receives commendation from his peers. New silk **Peter Coulson QC** (see p.1366) provides "astute and weighty advice," and has an "aggressive and punchy" manner that is popular with solicitors. **Finola O'Farrell** (see p.1429) combines a "tenacious" courtroom manner with a "conscientious and efficient" attitude to clients. **Adrian Williamson** (see p.1469) "always gives clear advice," and enjoys high standing among leading industry figures. **Nerys Jefford** (see p.1401) is another popular junior, although "oth-

LEADING JUNIORS • London		
1	CATCHPOLE Stuart	39 Essex Street
	O'FARRELL Finola	Keating Chambers
	WILLIAMSON Adrian	Keating Chambers
2	BARWISE Stephanie	Atkin Chambers
	JEFFORD Nerys	Keating Chambers
	NISSEN Alexander	Keating Chambers
3	DAVIES Jane	Crown Office Chambers
	DOERRIES Chantal-Aimée	Atkin Chambers
	DUMARESQ Delia	Atkin Chambers
	FRASER Peter	Atkin Chambers
	HARGREAVES Simon	Keating Chambers
	MCMULLAN Manus	Atkin Chambers
	PLANTEROSE Rowan	Littman Chambers
	RAESIDE Mark	Atkin Chambers
	RANDALL Louise	Keating Chambers
	SEARS David	4 Pump Court
	THOMAS David	2 Temple Gardens
4	BOWSHER Michael	Monckton Chambers
	BRANNIGAN Sean	4 Pump Court
	BURR Andrew	Atkin Chambers
	GODDARD Andrew	Atkin Chambers
	HOWELLS James	Atkin Chambers
	HUGHES Adrian	4 Pump Court
	LOFTHOUSE Simon	Atkin Chambers
	PARKIN Fiona	Atkin Chambers
	PENNICOTT Ian	Keating Chambers
	REED Paul	Hardwicke Building
	ROWLANDS Marc	Keating Chambers
UP AND COMING		
	LEMON Jane	Keating Chambers
	MORT Justin	2 Temple Gardens

This book is the product of 6,552 1/2-hour interviews. See p.7 for BMRB audit.
For details of these leading barristers see Profiles on p.1339

ers can be more concise." "Details man" **Alexander Nissen** (see p.1428), is "an expert at crunching papers." **Simon Hargreaves** (see p.1391) continues to work his way up the rankings, with many commentators describing him as "a star of the future." Fellow barristers appreciate **Louise Randall**'s (see p.1438) understated style, while **Ian Pennicott** (see p.1433) is a "busy and thorough junior." **Marc Rowlands** (see p.1442) has joined from 4 Pump Court and is both "able and user-friendly." Rising name **Jane Lemon** (see p.1410) is a new entry this year, and is praised as "a sound, all-round junior" who is "maturing into a top-notch advocate."

Crown Office Chambers (see full details p.1488) Considered to have improved its position as a challenger to the Big Two, the set boasts three especially respected silks. **John Slater QC** (see p.1449) "really shines" in professional negligence-related construction matters, where he is described as "one of the very best." He is "a good all-round advocate, and a fine communicator." A familiar figure on big cases, **Roger ter Haar QC** (see p.1459) is highly valued by solicitors for his persuasive advocacy. **Andrew Bartlett QC** (see p.1348) is "thorough and knowledgeable" and has a reputation as "a tenacious and difficult" opponent. Of the set's juniors, **Jane Davies** (see p.1369) is a "solid performer" who can "really carve through the papers."

4 Pump Court (see full details p.1557) The set's long-time figurehead Bruce Mauleverer QC has been indisposed much of the year, but it is still frequently commended for its "polished service" and the quality of its younger performers. **David Friedman QC** (see p.1382), who is now head of Chambers, is "a great thinker and a decent man." **Anthony Speaight QC** (see p.1451) has joined the set, and is regarded as "a useful acquisition." Relatively new silk **Jeremy Nicholson QC** (see p.1428) is "thorough and sound" and "ideal for cases with lots of detail." At junior level, **David Sears** (see p.1444) combines a "user-friendly manner" with "intelligence and impressive advocacy skills." **Sean Brannigan** (see p.1354) is "a responsive client man and a fluent advocate." **Adrian Hughes** (see p.1399) is another "competent and user-friendly" practitioner.

39 Essex Street (see full details p.1503) "Hard-working set, without prima donnas," at which **Richard Wilmot-Smith QC** (see p.1469) is highly rated for his "good judgement" and ability to "get his head round complex concepts." **Richard Gray QC** (see p.1388) is "a gentleman of the old school," both "balanced and unflappable." Top-rated junior **Stuart Catchpole** (see p.1360) is a generalist who is "superb in every area."

2 Temple Gardens (see full details p.1572) Despite the untimely death of Patrick Twigg QC, the set remains a popular choice for many solicitors, who are attracted by its reputation for "relaxed accessibility." **Michael Black QC** (see p.1351) is not only "technically sound," but has an "easy charm" which delights clients. They also appreciate that "if he says it will be on your desk at 4 pm on Wednesday, it will be there." **Howard Palmer QC** (see p.1431) joins the rankings this year as a generalist who has the ability to give a "phenomenal performance, even at short notice." **David Thomas** (see p.1459) is a "quick and confident" junior, while **Justin Mort** (see p.1424) joins the rankings for his ability to "roll his sleeves up on the complex technical stuff."

Four New Square (see full details p.1543) **Justin Fenwick QC** (see p.1378) specialises in professional negligence cases, where his "photographic memory" is ideal for "large, complicated cases." New silk **Roger Stewart QC** (see p.1454) has "a sound intellect," is "very sure of himself" and is also particularly good on professional negligence matters.

Other Notable Practitioners Rowan Planterose (see p.1434) at **Littman Chambers** is "a bright and senior player" who is "not averse to settling cases." Michael Bowsher (see p.1353) has left Keating Chambers for **Monckton Chambers**, and is said to have "broad appeal," while **Paul Reed** of **Hardwicke Building** is an "excellent advocate," who is "in particular demand for his mediation skills."

CONSUMER LAW

RESEARCH: The rankings are based on in-depth interviews with over 5,000 solicitors and barristers in the UK. Chambers research is audited by the British Market Research Bureau (see page 7 for details).

OVERVIEW: This section covers the civil and criminal aspects of food, consumer credit, trade descriptions and travel law. In the field of consumer protection, matters such as misleading pricing are covered, whereas for issues relating to compensation for death or injury we refer you to our overview of the product liability bar. Commentators have noted that greater powers have bolstered the confidence of enforcement agencies such as the TSA and the OFT. This more vigorous approach is reflected in the OFT's new guidelines on standards of behaviour expected of consumer credit licence holders and in the new regulations concerning the European 'Injunction Directive' aimed at protecting consumer interests. The latter would enable Trading Standards officers and the DGOF, among others, to seek 'Stop Now' orders to prevent infringements across the range of UK consumer protection laws.

LONDON

CONSUMER LAW • London		QCs	Jnrs
1	Gough Square Chambers (Fred Philpott)	-	5
2	2-3 Gray's Inn Square (Porten/Scrivener)	1	1

Numbers show recommended barristers in this practice area

LEADING SILKS • London		
1	GOODE Roy	Blackstone Chambers
	SCRIVENER Anthony	2-3 Gray's Inn Square
2	DE HAAN Kevin	3 Raymond Buildings
	GOODHART William	3 New Square
3	WATERS Malcolm	11 Old Square

For details of these leading barristers see Profiles on p.1339

LEADING JUNIORS • London		
1	PHILPOTT Fred	Gough Square Chambers
2	ANDREWS Claire	Gough Square Chambers
	HIBBERT William	Gough Square Chambers
	SMITH Julia	Gough Square Chambers
	STEPHENSON Geoffrey	2-3 Gray's Inn Square
	TRAVERS David	6 Pump Court
3	SAYER Peter	Gough Square Chambers
4	SAGGERSON Alan	No.1 Serjeants' Inn

This book is the product of 6,552 1/2-hour interviews. See p.7 for BMRB audit.
For details of these leading barristers see Profiles on p.1339

Gough Square Chambers (see full details p.1510) By far and away the most prevalent and widely acclaimed set for a whole raft of consumer credit, trading standards and food law matters. It is applauded for its "helpful and down-to-earth" approach. "Tactical" **Fred Philpott** is recognised as guru of the field. Over the last year, he represented the First National Bank in an action brought by OFT under the Unfair Contract Terms Act (1995), and has represented a mobile phone retailer prosecuted for misleading pricing. In the food sector he advised on afflatoxin regulations in the importation of nuts and on alleged contamination issues. A "brilliantly prepared" advocate, his style is "understated, with no airs and graces." **Claire Andrews** (see p.1343) is best known for food law, in which she has "a good grasp of the subject and an academic style." She recently acted for manufacturers concerning health and safety and product safety issues. Known for his consumer credit defence work, **William Hibbert** (see p.1394) is acclaimed for his skills "both on paper and in person." He assisted Philpott on the First National Bank unfair contract terms case. **Julia Smith** (see p.1450) has built up a solid reputation, particularly amongst City solicitors and banks for drafting consumer credit agreements and advising on mortgages. **Peter Sayer** received endorsement for his trade descriptions and consumer credit work, and has recently represented a number of department stores on credit and charge card payment schemes.

2-3 Gray's Inn Square (see full details p.1513) "Doyen for this type of work," **Anthony Scrivener QC** (see p.1444) "still has that magic" and continues to command a specialist's knowledge of consumer credit and food law. **Geoffrey Stephenson** (see p.1453) has established a strong profile in public authority prosecution work.

Other Notable Practitioners Respected for his "immense contribution," **Roy Goode QC** (see p.1387) of **Blackstone Chambers** is widely sought for his opinion on matters relating to consumer credit. "Intellectual" **William Goodhart QC** (see p.1387) at **3 New Square** (Goodhart) continues to advise the First National Bank in the OFT unfair contract terms case, now before the House of Lords, and also advised on brochure pricing for a tour operator. "Getting into his silks practice," **Kevin De Haan QC** of **3 Raymond Buildings** is relied upon for his "intimate understanding" of the EU slant, and displays a strength in product safety work. Frequently praised for his "meticulous research," **Malcolm Waters QC** (see p.1467) of **11 Old Square** has made his mark in consumer credit, particularly for issues relating to mortgages. Travel law expert **Alan Saggerson** (see p.1445) at **No. 1 Serjeants' Inn** won warm commendations for his in-depth experience. **David Travers** (see p.1462) of **6 Pump Court** prosecutes and defends in equal measure and reputedly disguises a "sharp intellect" behind an easy-going facade. "Good on his feet and always inventive," he has instructed on health & safety, environmental protection and trading standards matters.

WESTERN CIRCUIT

LEADING JUNIORS • Western		
1	GIBNEY Malcolm	17 Carlton Crescent
	HAGGAN Nicholas	17 Carlton Crescent

This book is the product of 6,552 1/2-hour interviews. See p.7 for BMRB audit.
For details of these leading barristers see Profiles on p.1339

At **17 Carlton Crescent**, **Malcolm Gibney** is best known for product and food safety, whilst **Nicholas Haggan** is rated for his work in trading standards, trade descriptions and consumer safety. He has recently defended an action relating to video classification.

WALES & CHESTER CIRCUIT

LEADING JUNIORS • Wales & Chester	
1 SCHOLZ Karl	Nicholas Street Chambers

This book is the product of 6,552 1/2-hour interviews. See p.7 for BMRB audit.
For details of these leading barristers see Profiles on p.1339

Adjudged a fearsome opponent, **Karl Scholz** of **Nicholas Street Chambers** is consistently "well prepared" and "virtually unbeatable" in consumer protection matters such as misleading pricing.

MIDLANDS CIRCUIT

LEADING SILKS • Midlands	
1 TREACY Colman	3 Fountain Court

For details of these leading barristers see Profiles on p.1339

LEADING JUNIORS • Midlands	
1 BERLIN Barry	St Philip's Chambers

This book is the product of 6,552 1/2-hour interviews. See p.7 for BMRB audit.
For details of these leading barristers see Profiles on p.1339

An established figure, **Colman Treacy QC** (see p.1462) of **3 Fountain Court** is reputed for his criminal and regulatory work, and has recently been involved in a major timeshare case. Senior junior **Barry Berlin** of **St. Philip's Chambers** (see full details p.1578) has a large following. Endorsed for his trade descriptions, food, drugs and weights and measures work, he mostly prosecutes and is reputedly "extremely tough."

CRIME

RESEARCH: The rankings are based on in-depth interviews with over 5,000 solicitors and barristers in the UK. Chambers research is audited by the British Market Research Bureau (see page 7 for details).

LONDON

2 Bedford Row (see full details p.1476) A specialist criminal set headed by **William Clegg QC** (see p.1363), "an accomplished jury advocate and very much the man in the street's idea of what a barrister should be." A host of talented practitioners includes **Philip Hackett QC**, "an intellectually gifted performer with a relaxed manner," "gutsy fighter" **Nigel Lithman QC** (see p.1412) and the "unflappable" **Andrew Munday QC**. The set attracts nationally renowned matters such as the London nail bomber case and the Tony Martin appeal both of which have fallen to **Michael Wolkind QC** (see p.1470). Other respected senior figures include **Howard Godfrey QC** (see p.1386) and new silk **Trevor Burke QC** (see p.1357) "an ace lawyer and a proper advocate." Of the juniors **Jim Sturman** (see p.1455) is "envied for his powers of articulation" while **Brian Altman** (see p.1342) and **Mark Milliken-Smith** (see p.1422) both received commendation.

Doughty Street Chambers (see full details p.1492) "Master of the honeyed word" **Geoffrey Robertson QC** (see p.1441) and the "terrific" **Peter Thornton QC** (see p.1460) both feature high in our rankings. **Edward Fitzgerald QC** (see p.1379) reflects the emphasis of the set as a whole,

Band	CRIME • London	QCs	Jnrs
1	**2 Bedford Row** (William Clegg QC)	8	8
	Doughty Street Chambers (Geoffrey Robertson QC)	9	4
	6 King's Bench Walk (Roy Amlot QC)	10	6
	Hollis Whiteman Chambers (Bevan/Whiteman)	7	4
	3 Raymond Buildings (Clive Nicholls QC)	6	4
	18 Red Lion Court (Anthony Arlidge QC)	9	1
2	**23 Essex Street** (Michael Lawson QC)	5	2
	Two Garden Court (Macdonald/Davies)	3	4
	3 Gray's Inn Square (Rock Tansey QC)	5	5
	2 Hare Court (Stephen Kramer QC)	5	6
3	**7 Bedford Row** (David Farrer QC)	4	-
	Furnival Chambers (Andrew Mitchell QC)	3	3
	2 Harcourt Buildings, Atkinson Bevan Chambers (Atkinson/Bevan)	3	3
	2-4 Tudor Street (Richard Ferguson QC)	2	5
4	**9-12 Bell Yard** (Anthony Evans QC)	3	3
	Matrix Chambers (Nicholas Blake QC)	5	1
	5 Paper Buildings (Carey/Caplan)	3	1
	Tooks Court Chambers (Michael Mansfield QC)	2	4
5	**10 King's Bench Walk** (Georges Khayat QC)	1	2
	1 Middle Temple Lane (Dines/Trollope)	2	2
	3 Temple Gardens (Jonathan Goldberg QC)	2	2

This book is the product of 6,552 1/2-hour interviews. See p.7 for BMRB audit.
For details of these leading barristers see Profiles on p.1339

Band	LEADING SILKS • London			
★	**AMLOT Roy** 6 King's Bench Walk	**ARLIDGE Anthony** 18 Red Lion Court	**BATTEN Stephen** 3 Raymond Buildings	**CLEGG William** 2 Bedford Row
	FULFORD Adrian 14 Tooks Court	**LAWSON Edmund** 9-12 Bell Yard	**MACDONALD Ken** Matrix Chambers	**MANSFIELD Michael** 14 Tooks Court
	MONTGOMERY Clare Matrix Chambers			
1	**BEVAN Julian** Hollis Whiteman Chambers	**BLUNT Oliver** Furnival Chambers	**FERGUSON Richard** 2-4 Tudor Street	**HESLOP Martin** 2 Hare Court
	JONES Alun 3 Raymond Buildings	**PRICE Nicholas** 3 Raymond Buildings	**PURNELL Nicholas** 23 Essex Street	**ROBERTSON Geoffrey** Doughty Street Chambers
	TANSEY Rock 3 Gray's Inn Square	**THORNTON Peter** Doughty Street Chambers	**TROLLOPE Andrew** 1 Middle Temple Lane	
2	**COWARD Stephen** 7 Bedford Row	**FEINBERG Peter** 2-4 Tudor Street	**FITZGERALD Edward** Doughty Street Chambers	**GLASS Anthony** Hollis Whiteman Chambers
	GOLDBERG Jonathan 3 Temple Gardens	**GREENBERG Joanna** 3 Temple Gardens	**LANGDALE Timothy** Hollis Whiteman Chambers	**NICHOLLS Clive** 3 Raymond Buildings
	NUTTING John 3 Raymond Buildings	**RUMFITT Nigel** 7 Bedford Row	**SALLON Christopher** Doughty Street Chambers	**SCRIVENER Anthony** 2-3 Gray's Inn Square
	SEABROOK Robert 1 Crown Office Row	**TEMPLE Victor** 6 King's Bench Walk	**WHITEHOUSE David** 3 Raymond Buildings	**WOLKIND Michael** 2 Bedford Row
3	**ATKINSON Nicholas** 2 Harcourt Buildings	**AUSTIN-SMITH Michael** 23 Essex Street	**BARNES Timothy** 7 Bedford Row	**EVANS Anthony** 9-12 Bell Yard
	FARRER David 7 Bedford Row	**FISHER David** 6 King's Bench Walk	**HILL Michael** 23 Essex Street	**LOVELL-PANK Dorian** 6 King's Bench Walk
	MACDONALD Ian Two Garden Court	**MALLALIEU Ann** 6 King's Bench Walk	**O'CONNOR Patrick** Doughty Street Chambers	**RAGGATT Timothy** 4 King's Bench Walk
	SHAW Antony 18 Red Lion Court			
4	**BATE David** Hollis Whiteman Chambers	**CAPLAN Jonathan** 5 Paper Buildings	**CASSEL Timothy** 5 Paper Buildings	**DE SILVA Desmond** 2 Paper Buildings
	GRIFFITHS Courtenay Two Garden Court	**GRINDROD Helen** 15-19 Devereux Court	**HACKETT Philip** 2 Bedford Row	**KAY Steven** 3 Gray's Inn Square
	KENNEDY Helena Doughty Street Chambers	**LAWSON Michael** 23 Essex Street	**LEDERMAN David** 18 Red Lion Court	**LISSACK Richard** 35 Essex Street
	LITHMAN Nigel 2 Bedford Row	**MUNDAY Andrew** 2 Bedford Row	**REES Edward** Doughty Street Chambers	
5	**BEVAN John** 2 Harcourt Buildings	**CARTER Peter** 18 Red Lion Court	**EDWARDS Susan** 23 Essex Street	**GODFREY Howard** 2 Bedford Row
	GREY Robin Hollis Whiteman Chambers	**GRIEVE Michael** Doughty Street Chambers	**KHAYAT Georges** 10 King's Bench Walk	**KORNER Joanna** 6 King's Bench Walk
	KRAMER Stephen 2 Hare Court	**LESLIE Stephen** Furnival Chambers	**LYNCH Patricia** 18 Red Lion Court	**MYLNE Nigel** 2 Harcourt Buildings
	PERRY John 3 Gray's Inn Square	**SAYERS Michael** 2 King's Bench Walk	**SOLLEY Stephen** Charter Chambers	**STERN Linda** 18 Red Lion Court
	SUTTON Richard 18 Red Lion Court	**WOOD James** Doughty Street Chambers		
6	**BLACK John** 18 Red Lion Court	**CARTER-STEPHENSON George** 3 Gray's Inn Square	**DAVIES Owen** Two Garden Court	**ETHERINGTON David** 18 Red Lion Court
	HIGGS Brian 5 King's Bench Walk	**KELSEY-FRY John** Hollis Whiteman Chambers	**LEONARD Anthony** 6 King's Bench Walk	**MITCHELL Andrew** Furnival Chambers
	WATERS David 2 Hare Court			
NEW SILKS				
	BENSON Jeremy 2 Hare Court	**BORRELLI Michael** 1 Middle Temple Lane	**BOYCE William** Hollis Whiteman Chambers	**BRIGHT Andrew** 9 Bedford Row
	BURKE Trevor 2 Bedford Row	**CHAWLA Mukul** 9-12 Bell Yard	**ELLIS Diana** 3 Gray's Inn Square	**EMMERSON Ben** Matrix Chambers
	JENKINS Edward 5 Paper Buildings	**JENNINGS Anthony** Matrix Chambers	**LODDER Peter** 2 Bedford Row	**LYNCH Jerome** Charter Chambers
	OWEN Tim Matrix Chambers	**RADCLIFFE Andrew** 2 Hare Court	**RYDER John** 6 King's Bench Walk	**SWEENEY Nigel** 6 King's Bench Walk
	WASS Sasha 6 King's Bench Walk			

This book is the product of 6,552 1/2-hour interviews. See p.7 for BMRB audit. *For details of these leading barristers see Profiles on p.1339*

LEADING JUNIORS • London				
★	**DEIN Jeremy** 3 Gray's Inn Square	**DENNIS Mark** 6 King's Bench Walk	**HILLIARD Nicholas** 6 King's Bench Walk	**LAIDLAW Jonathan** 2 Hare Court
	PERRY David 6 King's Bench Walk	**POWNALL Orlando** 2 Hare Court	**STURMAN Jim** 2 Bedford Row	
1	**ALTMAN Brian** 2 Bedford Row	**BLAXLAND Henry** Two Garden Court	**ELLISON Mark** Hollis Whiteman Chambers	**GIBBS Patrick** 2 Harcourt Buildings
	LORAINE-SMITH Nicholas 2 Harcourt Buildings	**MILLIKEN-SMITH Mark** 2 Bedford Row	**TURNER Michael** 14 Tooks Court	**WHITTAM Richard** Furnival Chambers
2	**BARRETT Penelope** 3 Gray's Inn Square	**CONWAY Charles** 2 Bedford Row	**EISSA Adrian** Two Garden Court	**EVANS Jill** Doughty Street Chambers
	FEDER Ami Lamb Building	**GARDINER Nicholas** 1 Middle Temple Lane	**HORWELL Richard** Hollis Whiteman Chambers	**JANNER Daniel** 23 Essex Street
	KHALIL Karim 1 Paper Buildings	**LUCAS Noel** 1 Middle Temple Lane	**MARTIN-SPERRY David** Charter Chambers	**NATHAN David** 10 King's Bench Walk
	PRICE Roderick 14 Tooks Court	**REES Gareth** Hollis Whiteman Chambers	**TURNER Jonathan** 6 King's Bench Walk	
3	**BOURNE Ian** 3 Temple Gardens	**FORTSON Rudi** 3 Gray's Inn Square	**JAFFA Ronald** 3 Gray's Inn Square	**JAFFERJEE Aftab** 2 Harcourt Buildings
	LEWIS James 3 Raymond Buildings	**MILLETT Kenneth** 2 Hare Court	**MOORE Miranda** 5 Paper Buildings	**OWEN Tudor** 9-12 Bell Yard
	TAYLOR Martin 2-4 Tudor Street	**WINBERG Stephen** 2-4 Tudor Street		
4	**ABELL Anthony** 2 Bedford Row	**BANKS Robert** 100E Great Portland Street	**BECK James** 2-4 Tudor Street	**BENNETT-JENKINS Sallie** 2 Hare Court
	CAUDLE John 2 Bedford Row	**FARRELL Simon** 3 Raymond Buildings	**HALL Andrew** Doughty Street Chambers	**JOYCE Michael** 9 Gough Square
	LEIST Ian 2 Hare Court	**LEVY Michael** 2 Bedford Row	**LLOYD-ELEY Andrew** 2 Hare Court	**MALCOLM Helen** 3 Raymond Buildings
	MATTHEWS Richard 2 Bedford Row	**PEART Icah** Two Garden Court	**REILLY John** 14 Tooks Court	**ROWLANDS Peter** 18 Red Lion Court
	SAUNDERS Neil 3 Raymond Buildings			
5	**ARMSTRONG Dean** 6 King's Bench Walk	**BRISCOE Constance** 9-12 Bell Yard	**BRYANT-HERON Mark** 9-12 Bell Yard	**CAUSER John** 23 Essex Street
	CHRISTIE Richard 2 Pump Court	**COOPER John** 3 Gray's Inn Square	**CORRIGAN Peter** 2-4 Tudor Street	**DUNN-SHAW Jason** 6 King's Bench Walk
	EDIE Alastair Two Garden Court	**ENGLAND William** 2-4 Tudor Street	**GOWER Peter** 6 Pump Court	**HENRY Annette** 10 King's Bench Walk
	KAMLISH Stephen 14 Tooks Court	**LANDSBURY Alan** 6 Gray's Inn Square	**MAIDMENT Kieran** Doughty Street Chambers	**OWEN-JONES David Roderic** 3 Temple Gardens
	PEARCE Ivan Furnival Chambers	**REED Piers** 3 Temple Gardens	**RYDER Matthew** Matrix Chambers	**SCOBIE James** Francis Taylor Building
	SHEPHERD Nigel 2 Paper Buildings	**STARMER Keir** Doughty Street Chambers	**STRUDWICK Linda** Hollis Whiteman Chambers	**SWAIN Jon** Furnival Chambers
	VINE James Hardwicke Building			

This book is the product of 6,552 1/2-hour interviews. See p.7 for BMRB audit. *For details of these leading barristers see Profiles on p.1339*

dividing his time between crime and public law and proving himself "one of the leading Court of Appeal silks in the country." **Edward Rees QC** (see p.1439) "gets results through an alliance of fine cross examination skills and very good paperwork." Other well-received silks include **Christopher Sallon QC** (see p.1445) and the "charismatic" **Helena Kennedy QC** (see p.1405). **Jill Evans** remains a highly respected junior.

6 King's Bench Walk (see full details p.1529) This set features a gaggle of quality silks enjoying a pronounced level of representation in the higher courts. **Roy Amlot QC** (see p.1342) is "a quiet, circumspect advocate who tackles cases with surgical precision." **Nigel Sweeney QC** is a senior treasury counsel and "one of the top prosecutors in the country." Boasting strength in depth the set has a fine array of silks including **Victor Temple QC, David Fisher QC** (see p.1379), **Dorian Lovell-Pank QC** (see p.1413), **Ann Mallalieu QC** and **Joanna Korner QC** (see p.1407), who returns to our tables this year. Amongst the juniors is the "thoroughly able" **Nicholas Hilliard** (see p.1395) and **Mark Dennis** (see p.1371); "one of the best treasury counsel, with a wonderful style."

Hollis Whiteman Chambers (see full details p.1524) One of the first criminal megasets encompassing numerous top quality barristers and handled by a sophisticated team of clerks. **Julian Bevan QC** (see p.1350) is "one of the best jury advocates available and has a wonderful presence." **Timothy Langdale QC** (see p.1408) is "eloquent and no pushover" while **John Kelsey-Fry QC** (see p.1405) is "a frighteningly intelligent ex-treasury counsel." **David Bate QC** (see p.1348), **Anthony Glass QC** (see p.1385), **Robin Grey QC** (see p.1389) and new silk **William Boyce QC** (see p.1353) were also highly rated. **Mark Ellison** (see p.1375) and **Richard Horwell** received praise as "juniors on the rise."

3 Raymond Buildings (see full details p.1560) **Stephen Batten QC** (see p.1348) is "bright, industrious and capable of bringing something extra to the table" while **Alun Jones QC** (see p.1403) is an expert on extradition and a "class act." The set as a whole has strength all the way down and includes the respected **Nicholas Price QC** (see p.1436), **Clive Nicholls QC** (see p.1428), **David Whitehouse QC** (see p.1468) and **John Nutting QC** (see p.1429).

18 Red Lion Court (see full details p.1561) An esteemed and senior figure, **Anthony Arlidge QC** (see p.1344) "displays quiet intelligence beneath the cloak of a laconic manner." Fellow silks **David Lederman QC** (see p.1409) and **Antony Shaw QC** (see p.1447) both "regularly appear in the weightier matters" and are part of a distinguished cadre of seasoned practitioners.

Two Garden Court (see full details p.1509) Consolidating following departures to Matrix Chambers, this general common law set is headed by **Ian Macdonald QC,** (see p.1414) "an advocate well-liked by the judges." **Courtenay Griffiths QC** has caught the eye of a number of his peers this year for his "passionate approach to the more sensitive case." Of the juniors **Henry Blaxland** is acclaimed for his miscarriage of justice cases including those of Peter Fell and Carl Bridgwater. **Adrian Eissa** is also recognised for his "wisdom beyond his years."

3 Gray's Inn Square (see full details p.1514) A committed pro-defence set led by the "staunch and persuasive" **Rock Tansey QC** (see p.1457), a practitioner possessed of "great charm and gravitas." Of the other silks **Steven Kay QC** (see p.1404) is best known for his European and international defence work. **Jeremy Dein** (see p.1370) is an "exceptional junior who refuses to lie down" and along with **Penelope Barrett** (see p.1348) was highly praised.

2 Hare Court (see full details p.1522) **Martin Heslop QC** is feted for his tactical acumen, "holding his own against the warmest competition." Standing out amidst a sea of respected juniors are the "skilled senior Treasury Counsel" **Orlando Pownall** and **Jonathan Laidlaw,** a leading junior Treasury Counsel who has been involved with the Dando case.

7 Bedford Row (see full details p.1477) This busy set covers a wide area and has a collection of revered silks involved in cases of the highest profile and gravity. **Stephen Coward QC** (see p.1367) appeared in the case of Winzah, an allegation that a wife had killed her husband through a lethal injection of insulin, while **Timothy Barnes QC** secured the acquittal of former judge Kenneth Bagnall who had been accused of fraudulently obtaining large sums of money. Not to be outdone, fellow silk **Nigel Rumfitt QC** (see p.1443) appeared in the widely publicised Carl Manning case and **David Farrer QC** (see p.1377) prosecuted the Goldfinger time-share fraud.

Furnival Chambers (see full details p.1508) "Adept at the more intricate case," **Oliver Blunt QC** (see p.1352) exhibits an "assured touch". Similarly handling the more complex matters **Stephen Leslie QC** (see p.1410) and **Andrew Mitchell QC** (see p.1422) were both lauded for their "accomplished delivery in court." **Richard Whittam** (see p.1468), Junior Treasury

Counsel at the Old Bailey, is "astute, hardworking and meticulous in his paperwork."

2 Harcourt Buildings, Atkinson Bevan Chambers (see full details p.1518) Active on the South Eastern and Western circuits, this set's joint heads both garnered appreciation. **Nicholas Atkinson QC** (see p.1345) is "a worthy opponent for anybody" while **John Bevan QC** (see p.1350) is hailed as "a fine, dogged prosecutor." **Nicholas Loraine-Smith** (see p.1413), "a Treasury Counsel of some repute," and **Patrick Gibbs** (see p.1384) both received recommendation.

2-4 Tudor Street A predominantly criminally focused set with a noted specialism in prisoners' rights. **Richard Ferguson QC** (see p.1378) is "unflappable and phlegmatic, a candidate for cases of the highest profile and complexity." **Peter Feinberg QC** (see p.1378) "exudes confidence" and is "alive to the smallest detail."

Matrix Chambers (see full details p.1538) A fashionable, new wave set with a pronounced disposition towards human rights. **Ken Macdonald QC** (see p.1414) found favour in all quarters for "his crisp advocacy style and supreme economy of language." He rises to the top band of our table alongside the "brilliant" **Clare Montgomery QC** (see p.1423) who is "a joy to watch, fast on her feet due to a lightning quick mind."

Other Notable Practitioners At **Tooks Court Chambers, Adrian Fulford QC** (see p.1382), many firms' favourite, is celebrated for his "penetrating and deadly cross examination." He shares the limelight with "media darling" **Michael Mansfield QC** "champion of the oppressed and one of a kind." Also nationally known is **Edmund Lawson QC** (see p.1409) of **9-12 Bell Yard**, famed for his work on the Lawrence and Bloody Sunday Inquiries. More of a fraud expert he is nevertheless "the cleverest of the clever" when handling general crime. **Andrew Trollope QC** (see p.1462) of **1 Middle Temple Lane** "infuses his work with his bright personality" and is applauded for his efforts in drug and fraud cases. At the same set **Nicholas Gardiner** is also well-regarded as a senior junior. Two old-stagers who continue to be "the goods" are **Robert Seabrook QC** (see p.1444) of **1 Crown Office Row** and **Anthony Scrivener QC** (see p.1444) of **2-3 Grays Inn Square**, "a natural advocate who expresses his thoughts clearly and attractively." Other praiseworthy silks include **Jonathan Goldberg QC** (see p.1387) and **Joanna Greenberg QC** (see p.1389) of **3 Temple Gardens** and **David Martin-Sperry** (see p.1417) of **Charter Chambers** (Solley) who is often seen in the Court of Appeal and is "clever if a little quixotic."

SOUTH EASTERN & EAST ANGLIAN CIRCUITS

LEADING JUNIORS • South Eastern & East Anglian		
1	AYERS Guy	Octagon House Chambers
	CLARE Michael	Octagon House Chambers
	MOORE Katherine	Octagon House Chambers
2	JAMES Ian	Octagon House Chambers
UP AND COMING		
	MORGANS John	Octagon House Chambers
	OLIVER Andrew	Octagon House Chambers

This book is the product of 6,552 1/2-hour interviews. See p.7 for BMRB audit.
For details of these leading barristers see Profiles on p.1339

At **Octagon House Chambers Guy Ayers** "rolls up his sleeves and wades into the more detailed briefs with gusto." **Michael Clare** has built up a high volume practice through offering "clear, no-nonsense advice" and is known for his "bluff, wholehearted approach." **Katherine Moore** is a firm favourite of local solicitors and is admired as "a keen little terrier with bagfuls of pep." She is a newcomer to our tables this year alongside the "consistent" **Ian James**. **Andrew Oliver**, although junior in call to the others, "has a bright future ahead of him" and **John Morgans** also received recommendations.

WESTERN CIRCUIT

LEADING SILKS • Western		
1	BARTON Charles	Albion Chambers
	ROYCE John	Guildhall Chambers
2	DENYER Roderick	St John's Chambers
	DUNKELS Paul	Walnut House
	GILBERT Francis	Walnut House
	PASCOE Nigel	Pump Court Chambers
	TABOR James	Albion Chambers
3	FORD Neil	Albion Chambers
	GLEN Ian	Guildhall Chambers
	JENKINS Alun	Queen Square Chambers
NEW SILKS		
	MEEKE Martin	Colleton Chambers
	SMITH Richard	Guildhall Chambers

For details of these leading barristers see Profiles on p.1339

LEADING JUNIORS • Western		
1	HORTON Mark	St John's Chambers
	LAMBERT Julian	Albion Chambers
	MERCER Geoffrey	Walnut House
	MORGAN Simon	St John's Chambers
	PICTON Martin	Albion Chambers
2	DIXEY Ian	St John's Chambers
	DUVAL Robert	St John's Chambers
	FITTON Michael	Albion Chambers
	HART William	Albion Chambers
	LANGDON Andrew	Guildhall Chambers
	LETT Brian	South Western Chambers
	LONGMAN Michael	St John's Chambers
	MATHER-LEES Michael	Albion Chambers
	MOONEY Stephen	Albion Chambers
	MUNRO Sarah	Walnut House
	QURESHI Shamim	Queen Square Chambers
3	BURGESS Edward	St John's Chambers
	CULLUM Michael	Albion Chambers
	EVANS Susan	St John's Chambers
	FENNY Ian Charles	Guildhall Chambers
	WHITEHALL Mark	Colleton Chambers

This book is the product of 6,552 1/2-hour interviews. See p.7 for BMRB audit.
For details of these leading barristers see Profiles on p.1339

Life trundles along on the Western Circuit and the usual suspects dominate once again. At **Albion Chambers** (see full details p.1581) **Charles Barton QC** "gets excellent results through pinpoint cross examination" and has been seen in nationally publicised cases. **James Tabor QC** "demonstrates great strength of purpose" and displays "sensitivity and tact with the clients." Respected junior **Martin Picton** (see p.1434) was applauded by solicitors for his "energy and celerity in turning the paperwork around." At **St John's Chambers** (see full details p.1583), **Roderick Denyer QC** "has clearly eaten a lot of fish" but is "never complacent." He is often to be seen in tandem with either "able junior" **Mark Horton** (see p.1397) or **Simon Morgan**, a lawyer "capable of mentally dissecting the most convoluted of cases." **John Royce QC** (see p.1442) of **Guildhall Chambers** (see full details p.1581) is, despite his relative youth, "often seen as the first port of call." In Exeter, **Walnut House** provides **Paul Dunkels QC** "an all rounder with a lambent style" and **Francis Gilbert QC** who deals with "a fat roster of heavyweight offences." The preferred junior here is **Geoffrey Mercer**. **Nigel Pascoe QC** (see p.1432) of **Pump Court Chambers** (see full details p.1617) also received market approval.

WALES & CHESTER CIRCUIT

LEADING SILKS • Wales & Chester		
1	REES John Charles	33 Park Place
2	AUBREY David	Temple Chambers
	ELIAS Gerard	Farrar's Building
	MURPHY Ian	9 Park Place
	THOMAS Roger	9 Park Place
NEW SILKS		
	DAVIES Huw	30 Park Place
	HOPKINS Stephen	Temple Chambers
	LEWIS Paul	30 Park Place
	TAYLOR Gregg	9 Park Place

For details of these leading barristers see Profiles on p.1339

LEADING JUNIORS • Wales & Chester		
1	BULL Gregory	30 Park Place
	DAVIES Trefor	Iscoed Chambers
	THOMAS Keith	9 Park Place
2	EVANS Elwen Mair	Iscoed Chambers
	FERRIER Susan	9 Park Place
	JEARY Stephen	Temple Chambers
	LEWIS Marian	30 Park Place
	MURPHY Peter	30 Park Place
	RIORDAN Kevin	Iscoed Chambers
	THOMAS Paul	Iscoed Chambers
	TREHARNE Jennet	33 Park Place
	TWOMLOW Richard	9 Park Place

This book is the product of 6,552 1/2-hour interviews. See p.7 for BMRB audit.
For details of these leading barristers see Profiles on p.1339

John Charles Rees QC of **33 Park Place** (see full details p.1585) is universally regarded as "the best criminal silk in these parts," "exceptionally gifted and fearless in all he does." At **9 Park Place** (see full details p.1584) **Roger Thomas QC** (see p.1460) "has an eagle eye for the central plank of any case and never lets go" while **Ian Murphy QC** (see p.1426) is in demand for sensitive children related cases. The set possesses in **Keith Thomas** a "resourceful and dedicated" junior. **Gerard Elias QC** (see p.1375) of **Farrar's Building** (see full details p.1505) is well known for his work on a major child abuse inquiry but is equally adept at serious criminal cases and has a "brilliant manner." **Stephen Hopkins QC** of **Temple Chambers** commands a "substantial practice" while debuting in the tables this year is **David Aubrey QC** – a silk with a raft of serious cases behind him who "speaks softly but carries a big stick." In Swansea, **Trefor Davies** (see p.1369) of **Iscoed Chambers** (see full details p.1616) is well thought of and at **30 Park Place** (see full details p.1585), "very competent" **Gregory Bull** is also recommended.

MIDLANDS CIRCUIT

LEADING SILKS • Midlands		
1	BARKER Anthony	5 Fountain Court
	CRIGMAN David	1 Fountain Court
	JOYCE Peter	No.1 High Pavement
	LINEHAN Stephen	5 Fountain Court
	SAUNDERS John	4 Fountain Court
	TREACY Colman	3 Fountain Court
	WAKERLEY Richard	4 Fountain Court
2	ESCOTT-COX Brian	36 Bedford Row
	INMAN Melbourne	1 Fountain Court
	SMITH Roger	No.6 Fountain Court
	TEDD Rex	St Philip's Chambers
NEW SILKS		
	FARRELL David	36 Bedford Row
	MORRISON Howard	36 Bedford Row

For details of these leading barristers see Profiles on p.1339

LEADING JUNIORS • Midlands		
1	DUCK Michael	3 Fountain Court
	EVERARD William	King Charles House Chambers
	JACKSON Andrew	3 Fountain Court
	STOBART John	King Charles House Chambers
	THOMAS Sybil	3 Fountain Court
2	BRAND Simon	Coleridge Chambers
	BURBIDGE James	St Philip's Chambers
	CARR Peter	St. Ive's Chambers
	ELWICK Martin	No.1 High Pavement
	EVANS John	1 Fountain Court
	FARRER Paul	1 Fountain Court
	MANN Paul	No.1 High Pavement
	NAWAZ Amjad	Coleridge Chambers
	REYNOLDS Adrian	No.1 High Pavement
	THOROGOOD Bernard	5 Fountain Court
3	EASTEAL Andrew	No.1 High Pavement
	EVANS Michael	No.1 High Pavement
	HEGARTY Kevin	St Philip's Chambers
	LOCKHART Andrew	St Philip's Chambers
	NICHOLLS Benjamin	1 Fountain Court
	SHANT Nirmal	No.1 High Pavement
	SMITH Shaun	No.1 High Pavement
	STANISTREET Penelope	New Walk Chambers
	WALL Mark	4 Fountain Court

This book is the product of 6,552 1/2-hour interviews. See p.7 for BMRB audit.
For details of these leading barristers see Profiles on p.1339

Little change here as the renowned names continue to receive support. **Anthony Barker QC** (see p.1347) and **Stephen Linehan QC** of **5 Fountain Court** (see full details p.1577) are both seen as "hard-boiled swashbucklers who take no prisoners." At **4 Fountain Court Richard Wakerley QC** "dots the i's and crosses the t's" and shares a reputation for thoroughness with fellow silk **John Saunders QC**. In Nottingham, **Peter Joyce QC** of **No 1 High Pavement** has "chameleon qualities" affording him the opportunity to adapt to differing types of case. **David Crigman QC** of **1 Fountain Court** (see full details p.1577) and **Colman Treacy QC** of **3 Fountain Court** merited the highest approval.

NORTH EASTERN CIRCUIT

LEADING SILKS • North Eastern		
1	HARRISON Michael	Park Court Chambers
	SMITH Robert	Park Court Chambers
	STEWART James	Park Court Chambers
2	BOURNE-ARTON Simon	Park Court Chambers
	MARSON Geoffrey	Sovereign Chambers
	MILFORD John	Trinity Chambers
	SWIFT Malcolm	Park Court Chambers
3	COSGROVE Patrick	Broad Chare Chambers
	HEDWORTH Toby	Trinity Chambers
	HYLAND Graham	Broadway House
	KERSHAW Jennifer	No.6 Barristers Chambers
NEW SILKS		
	MACDONALD Alistair	Park Court Chambers

For details of these leading barristers see Profiles on p.1339

LEADING JUNIORS • North Eastern		
1	BARNETT Jeremy	St. Paul's Chambers
	HARVEY Colin	St. Paul's Chambers
	PALMER Patrick	Sovereign Chambers
2	BATTY Christopher	St. Paul's Chambers
	BUBB Tim	39 Park Square
	JAMESON Rodney	No.6 Barristers Chambers
	LEES Andrew	St. Paul's Chambers
	MYERSON Simon	Park Court Chambers
	PRINCE Christopher	New Court Chambers
	ROSE Jonathan	St. Paul's Chambers
	STUBBS Andrew	St. Paul's Chambers

This book is the product of 6,552 1/2-hour interviews. See p.7 for BMRB audit.
For details of these leading barristers see Profiles on p.1339

Park Court Chambers' dominance in the region persists unabated. **Michael Harrison QC** was unanimously declared by local solicitors to be "very capable" while **Robert Smith QC** can produce "sustained periods of jaw dropping brilliance." **James Stewart QC** is an "exceptionally versatile" silk, "a real name on the circuit and excellent technically." Previously heavily weighted towards Leeds sets the table now reflects the high quality of Newcastle practitioners with the addition of **John Milford QC** and **Toby Hedworth QC** of **Trinity Chambers** both seen widely in murder cases. As regards the juniors, **St Paul's Chambers** wins the battle again providing a myriad of respected names of which **Jeremy Barnett** and **Colin Harvey** are the most highly rated.

NORTHERN CIRCUIT

LEADING SILKS • Northern		
1	GLOBE Henry	Exchange Chambers
	HOLROYDE Tim	Exchange Chambers
	RIORDAN Stephen	25-27 Castle Street
	SHORROCK Michael	Peel Court Chambers
	STEER David	7 Harrington Street Chambers
	TURNER David	Exchange Chambers
2	BIRKETT Peter	18 St John Street
	CARUS Roderick	9 St John Street
	GEE Anthony	28 St John St
	GOLDSTONE Clement	28 St John St
	WRIGHT Peter	Lincoln House Chambers
3	BENTHAM Howard	Peel Court Chambers
	CHRUSZCZ Charles	28 St John St
	EDIS Andrew	14 Castle Street
	GARSIDE Charles	9 St John Street
	MARKS Richard	Peel Court Chambers
	MORRIS Anthony	Peel Court Chambers
	PICKUP James	Lincoln House Chambers
NEW SILKS		
	FISH David	Deans Court Chambers
	REID Paul Campbell	Lincoln House Chambers
	WIGGLESWORTH Raymond	18 St John Street

For details of these leading barristers see Profiles on p.1339

LEADING JUNIORS • Northern		
1	GREGORY James	Lincoln House Chambers
	LLOYD Heather	Chavasse Court Chambers
	MCDERMOTT John	Chavasse Court Chambers
	MCMEEKIN Ian	Kingsgate Chambers
	MEADOWCROFT Stephen	Peel Court Chambers
	STOUT Roger	18 St John Street
	SUMNER David	Lincoln House Chambers
	WILLIAMS David	Chavasse Court Chambers
2	ANDREWS Philip	Young Street Chambers
	BERKSON Simon	Exchange Chambers
	CATTAN Philip	28 St John St
	CLARKE Nicholas	9 St John Street
	DENNEY Stuart	Deans Court Chambers
	FORSYTH Julie	Chavasse Court Chambers
	HARRISON Keith	24A St John Street
	HERMAN Ray	India Buildings Chambers
	MATTISON Andrew	Chavasse Court Chambers
	O'BYRNE Andrew	Peel Court Chambers
3	BLACKWELL Kate	Lincoln House Chambers
	BRENNAND Timothy	Manchester House Chambers
	GOODE Rowena	28 St John St
	LONG Andrew	Peel Court Chambers
	MYERS Benjamin	Young Street Chambers
	ROBERTS Lisa	Lincoln House Chambers
	SAVILL Mark	Deans Court Chambers
	WATSON David	14 Castle Street

This book is the product of 6,552 1/2-hour interviews. See p.7 for BMRB audit.
For details of these leading barristers see Profiles on p.1339

Exchange Chambers boasts a number of talented silks including **Henry Globe QC**, known for prosecuting substantial cases, **Tim Holroyde QC** and **David Turner QC** "one of the best known defenders on the circuit." **Stephen Riordan QC** of **25-27 Castle Street** "lends gravitas and presence in the courtroom" while **David Steer QC** of **7 Harrington Street Chambers** is another "big talent." In common with **Michael Shorrock QC** of **Peel Court Chambers** the latter attains top flight status this year.

DEFAMATION

RESEARCH: The rankings are based on in-depth interviews with over 5,000 solicitors and barristers in the UK. Chambers research is audited by the British Market Research Bureau (see page 7 for details).

OVERVIEW: The defamation bar is still dominated by 1 Brick Court and 5 Raymond Buildings. Each is a breeding ground for barristers whose work is often the subject of public scrutiny and whose clients seek counsel with not only a command of the legal issues and commercial nous, but a jury-friendly delivery. In this respect, the late George Carman QC is missed enormously. Libel actions are thinner on the ground this year, but those at the defamation bar are in prime position to pick up the privacy actions that are expected to become more commonplace.

LONDON

1 Brick Court (see full details p.1484) "Big intellect" and "great strategist" **Andrew Caldecott QC** is acknowledged to be "extremely thorough and hard working." Head of chambers **Richard Rampton QC** (see p.1438) is instructed by those who "like his courtroom manner; he's ruthless, with a smile." When on top form, **Thomas Shields QC** is regarded as an "impressive" performer, while **Patrick Moloney QC** (see p.1423) delights his clients with his "adventurous" style and "ability to think laterally." **Geoffrey Shaw QC** (see p.1447) has a long relationship with the press and is "confident, firm and knows his stuff." As predicted, **Victoria Sharp QC** (see p.1446) took silk this year. Leader on the Sugar case, she is admired for being "great with a jury." Junior **Manuel Barca** (see p.1347) is "just so bright, and sees beyond dry libel debate." "Nothing is too much trouble" for "accomplished street-fighter" **Benjamin Hinchliff** (see p.1395). He is said to be "both responsive and intelligent." For "high quality pleadings," many clients turn to the "extremely thorough" **Stephen Suttle** (see p.1456), while **Caroline Addy** (see p.1341) is "adored" by those who instruct her. New into the rankings this year is the "terrifically personable" **Catrin Evans** (see p.1376), an "accomplished advocate who gives prompt and informed advice." **Rupert Elliott** (see p.1375) is a regular and "solid" choice for many, while **Jane Phillips** (see p.1433) also maintains her share of support among contemporaries and clients. **Harvey Starte** is valued for his good judgement by instructing solicitors: "He looks realistically at the risks." Also newly rated, **Joanne Cash** (see p.1360) is regarded as a "sparky and promising" barrister.

5 Raymond Buildings (see full details p.1561) Reports indicate that **Desmond Browne QC** (see p.1356) just gets "better and better." "He knows everything and is an effective advocate who can batter the opposition." **James Price QC** (see p.1436) has "tremendous energy and is doing superbly at the moment." In the opinion of some, he is the "best all-rounder at the defamation bar." "Intelligent team player" **Patrick Milmo QC** (see p.1422) is "effective and straightforward," and has an enviable rapport with solicitors. "Original thinker" **Adrienne Page QC** (see p.1431) delights clients with her accessibility: "She won't let you down." Newly ranked in *Chambers* this year, **Michael Tugenhat QC** (see p.1463) has an admired mixed practice that encompasses libel and related matters such as injunctions and reporting restrictions. The "rakishly dashing" **Mark Warby** (see p.1466) is hugely admired for his ability to "get on with things." He remains the leading name among a phalanx of top juniors including "star of the future" **Justin Rushbrooke** (see p.1443), commended for his "supportive and encouraging nature." **David Sherborne** (see p.1448) "grasps issues very quickly," and is noted for his ability to charm a jury. **Alexandra Marzec**'s return to full-time practice following maternity leave is "eagerly awaited" by solicitors, while **Matthew Nicklin**'s (see p.1428) fans describe him as "an enthusiastic team man." **Adam Wolanski** is "one of our favourites," according to some newspapers.

Barristers' profiles 1339-1472

DEFAMATION • London		QCs	Jnrs
1	**1 Brick Court** (Richard Rampton QC)	6	9
	5 Raymond Buildings (Patrick Milmo QC)	5	6

Numbers show recommended barristers in this practice area

LEADING SILKS • London		
1	BROWNE Desmond	5 Raymond Buildings
	CALDECOTT Andrew	1 Brick Court
	PRICE James	5 Raymond Buildings
2	RAMPTON Richard	1 Brick Court
3	MILMO Patrick	5 Raymond Buildings
	PAGE Adrienne	5 Raymond Buildings
	SHIELDS Thomas	1 Brick Court
4	MOLONEY Patrick	1 Brick Court
	NICOL Andrew	Doughty Street Chambers
	ROBERTSON Geoffrey	Doughty Street Chambers
	THWAITES Ronald	Ely Place Chambers
5	SHAW Geoffrey	1 Brick Court
	TUGENHAT Michael	5 Raymond Buildings
NEW SILKS		
	SHARP Victoria	1 Brick Court

For details of these leading barristers see Profiles on p.1339

LEADING JUNIORS • London		
★	ROGERS Heather	Matrix Chambers
	WARBY Mark	5 Raymond Buildings
1	BARCA Manuel	1 Brick Court
2	RUSHBROOKE Justin	5 Raymond Buildings
	SHERBORNE David	5 Raymond Buildings
3	HINCHLIFF Benjamin	1 Brick Court
	MARZEC Alexandra	5 Raymond Buildings
	SUTTLE Stephen	1 Brick Court
4	ADDY Caroline	1 Brick Court
	ELLIOTT Rupert	1 Brick Court
	EVANS Catrin	1 Brick Court
	NICKLIN Matthew	5 Raymond Buildings
	PHILLIPS Jane	1 Brick Court
	STARTE Harvey	1 Brick Court
	TOMLINSON Hugh	Matrix Chambers
	WOLANSKI Adam	5 Raymond Buildings
UP AND COMING		
	CASH Joanne	1 Brick Court

This book is the product of 6,552 1/2-hour interviews. See p.7 for BMRB audit.

For details of these leading barristers see Profiles on p.1339

Other Notable Practitioners **Doughty Street Chambers** is home to a pair of leading silks, both seen as "great on freedom to publish cases." **Andrew Nicol QC** (see p.1428) has a "lovely manner and a great intellect," while the "crusading" **Geoffrey Robertson QC** (see p.1441) is "a creative thinker, who knows the law inside out." Since turning his attention to libel cases and, more recently, setting up **Ely Place Chambers**, **Ronald Thwaites QC** (see p.1461) is acknowledged to be making a big impression. "He *reads* the papers, has a voracious appetite for facts and carries the jury brilliantly. He winds up his opponents expertly." **Heather Rogers** (see p.1441) at **Matrix Chambers** impresses everyone with her brainpower. "Extremely bright and hardworking," "she's well out in front." Her colleague **Hugh Tomlinson** makes his debut in the rankings, and is regarded as an "outstanding, erudite" practitioner.

EMPLOYMENT

RESEARCH: The rankings are based on in-depth interviews with over 5,000 solicitors and barristers in the UK. Chambers research is audited by the British Market Research Bureau (see page 7 for details).

OVERVIEW: The employment bar shares much of the Tribunal advocacy with solicitors. Commonly it is the time tribunals take away from the rest of a solicitor's caseload which will prompt the instruction of counsel. Consequently good juniors are of real importance to instructing solicitors. At the top end of the juniors' list is a clutch of truly dedicated barristers, at the lower end a batch of new up and coming names. This year, only 11 Kings Bench Walk takes away the prize of leading set, though the other recommended sets offer superb advocates. London still attracts the meatier instructions, but the regional bars offer up specialists across the country.

Barristers' profiles 1339-1472

EMPLOYMENT • London		QCs	Jnrs
1	**11 King's Bench Walk Chambers** (Tabachnik/Goudie)	7	12
2	**Blackstone Chambers** (Baxendale/Flint)	4	6
	Littleton Chambers (Michel Kallipetis QC)	4	5
	Old Square Chambers (John Hendy QC)	3	11
3	**Cloisters** (Laura Cox QC)	3	2
	Devereux Chambers (Jeffrey Burke QC)	3	4
	Matrix Chambers (Nicholas Blake QC)	2	2

Numbers show recommended barristers in this practice area

LEADING SILKS • London		
1	**COX Laura**	Cloisters
	JEANS Christopher	11 King's Bench Walk Chambers
	LANGSTAFF Brian	Cloisters
	PANNICK David	Blackstone Chambers
2	**BEAN David**	Matrix Chambers
	BOWERS John	Littleton Chambers
	GOULDING Paul	Blackstone Chambers
	HOCHHAUSER Andrew	Essex Court Chambers
	UNDERHILL Nicholas	Fountain Court
3	**ALLEN Robin**	Cloisters
	BELOFF Michael	Blackstone Chambers
	BLOCH Selwyn	Littleton Chambers
	CLARKE Andrew	Littleton Chambers
	MCMULLEN Jeremy	Old Square Chambers
	SLADE Elizabeth	11 King's Bench Walk Chambers
4	**BOOTH Cherie**	Matrix Chambers
	BURKE Jeffrey	Devereux Chambers
	GOUDIE James	11 King's Bench Walk Chambers
	HAND John	Old Square Chambers
	HENDY John	Old Square Chambers
	MCGREGOR Alistair	11 King's Bench Walk Chambers
	TABACHNIK Eldred	11 King's Bench Walk Chambers
NEW SILKS		
	BRENNAN Timothy	Devereux Chambers
	CARSS-FRISK Monica	Blackstone Chambers
	CAVANAGH John	11 King's Bench Walk Chambers
	GRIFFITH-JONES David	Devereux Chambers
	LYNCH Adrian	11 King's Bench Walk Chambers
	STAFFORD Andrew	Littleton Chambers

This book is the product of 6,552 1/2-hour interviews. See p.7 for BMRB audit.
For details of these leading barristers see Profiles on p.1339

LONDON

11 King's Bench Walk Chambers (see full details p.1532) "The darlings of the employment bar and what a good service!" The clerks here have "a good knowledge of the barrister's characteristics," while the barristers themselves "are all good – it's merely a question of seniority." "Top of the tree" **Christopher Jeans QC** (see p.1401) provides "really good depth and analysis." He is "terrific, but he carries his brilliance with a bizarre degree of humility." **Elizabeth Slade QC** (see p.1449) is praised as "diligent and thorough, combined with a calm and reassuring manner." **James Goudie QC** (see p.1388) is recommended "for use in a punch up." **Alistair McGregor QC** (see p.1419) is newly ranked this year and **Eldred Tabachnik QC** (see p.1457) is "excellent on contracts." Instructing solicitors "can't recommend **Adrian Lynch QC** (see p.1414) highly enough – he makes himself accessible." "First class" **John Cavanagh QC** (see p.1361) sits comfortably in the new silks list this year. "Excellent and efficient in his advice," **Séan Jones** (see p.1403) also displays a "good sense of humour." **Jonathan Swift** (see p.1456) has an ability to "grasp quickly and focus on technical and commercial issues." **Charles Béar** (see p.1349) is "prepared to express a practical and robust opinion." Also recommended are **Nigel Giffin** (see p.1384) (also active in public law), **Andrew Hillier**, (see p.1395) **Paul Nicholls** ("good across the board – used for the important cases") and the "intelligent" **Timothy Pitt-Payne**. **Daniel Stilitz** (see p.1454) received a number of commendations, as did newly ranked **Akhlaq Choudhury** (see p.1362). **Simon Devonshire** (see p.1371) has made a move to this set. "He's technically superb and an excellent advocate – the sort of person who'll get on a train to visit clients and sit down with welders." **Peter Wallington** (see p.1466) is endorsed and the up and coming list now includes **Cecilia Ivimy** (see p.1400).

Blackstone Chambers (see full details p.1481) "The clerks are brilliant and will talk you through the details; they are absolutely frank as to availability." Juniors are said to be "bright, efficient, effective and co-operative." Public law guru **David Pannick QC** (see p.1431) holds on to his reputation in the field of employment law. Rapidly making a huge impression, **Paul Goulding QC** (see p.1388) soars up the leading silks table. He is "first class; one of those advocates who can make a case out of not an awful lot. He picks up all the points." The multi-talented **Michael Beloff QC** (see p.1349) oozes "gravitas." **Monica Carss-Frisk QC** (see p.1360) is well endorsed by leading solicitors and has just taken silk. High praise was given to "shining star" **Dinah Rose** (see p.1442) and her "imaginative and creative mind." On a variety of different types of case, **Gerard Clarke** (see p.1363) has impressed with his "charisma" and his client friendly manner – "they understand him." **Thomas Croxford** (see p.1368) is "intellectually sound, an excellent advocate" who builds "good relations with clients." Ranked again, **Gemma White** (see p.1468) has pulled in favourable comment while newly ranked juniors come in the guise of **Kate Gallafent** ("personable, bright and talks the clients language") and **Jane Mulcahy** (see p.1426).

Littleton Chambers (see full details p.1537) A strong choice that some solicitors feel "makes economic sense." Said to have "some really excellent young counsel" and to be "extremely well organised" and good at "working as a team." Heavily endorsed "friendly and approachable" **John Bowers QC** (see p.1353) is noted to be "a good academic and he turns papers around." "Sharp as a button," **Selwyn Bloch QC** (see p.1352) has an "encyclopaedic knowledge and remains user friendly." Leading solicitors hold **Andrew Clarke QC** (see p.1363) in the highest regard while recent silk **Andrew Stafford QC** (see p.1452) continues to impress. At junior level,

LEADING JUNIORS • London		
★	LINDEN Thomas	Matrix Chambers
	ROSE Dinah	Blackstone Chambers
1	CARR Bruce	Devereux Chambers
	EADY Jennifer	Old Square Chambers
	GRIFFITHS Martin	Essex Court Chambers
	JONES Seán	11 King's Bench Walk Chambers
	SWIFT Jonathan	11 King's Bench Walk Chambers
2	BÉAR Charles	11 King's Bench Walk Chambers
	KIBLING Thomas	Cloisters
	MOOR Sarah	Old Square Chambers
	RANDALL Nicholas	Devereux Chambers
	SIMLER Ingrid	Devereux Chambers
	TETHER Melanie	Old Square Chambers
3	BOTHROYD Shirley	Littleton Chambers
	BROWN Damian	Old Square Chambers
	CIUMEI Charles	Essex Court Chambers
	CLARKE Gerard	Blackstone Chambers
	GIFFIN Nigel	11 King's Bench Walk Chambers
	HILLIER Andrew	11 King's Bench Walk Chambers
	NAPIER Brian	Fountain Court
	NICHOLLS Paul	11 King's Bench Walk Chambers
	PITT-PAYNE Timothy	11 King's Bench Walk Chambers
	ROMNEY Daphne	4 Field Court
	SENDALL Antony	Littleton Chambers
	STILITZ Daniel	11 King's Bench Walk Chambers
	TAYLER James	Devereux Chambers
4	CHOUDHURY Akhlaq	11 King's Bench Walk Chambers
	CHUDLEIGH Louise	Old Square Chambers
	CROXFORD Thomas	Blackstone Chambers
	DEVONSHIRE Simon	11 King's Bench Walk Chambers
	DUGGAN Michael	Littleton Chambers
	GATT Ian	Littleton Chambers
	GILL Tess	Old Square Chambers
	KORN Anthony	199 Strand
	MCNEILL Jane	Old Square Chambers
	MOUNTFIELD Helen	Matrix Chambers
	O'DEMPSEY Declan	Coram Chambers
	OMAMBALA Ijeoma	Old Square Chambers
	ROSE Paul	Old Square Chambers
	SCOTT Ian	Old Square Chambers
	SEGAL Oliver	Old Square Chambers
	WALLINGTON Peter	11 King's Bench Walk Chambers
	WHITE Gemma	Blackstone Chambers
UP AND COMING		
	CRASNOW Rachel	Cloisters
	GALLAFENT Kate	Blackstone Chambers
	IVIMY Cecilia	11 King's Bench Walk Chambers
	MULCAHY Jane	Blackstone Chambers
	RITCHIE Stuart	Littleton Chambers
	SMITH Emma	Old Square Chambers

This book is the product of 6,552 1/2-hour interviews. See p.7 for BMRB audit.
For details of these leading barristers see Profiles on p.1339

there is plenty of endorsement for **Shirley Bothroyd** (see p.1352) ("take her along to a hard nosed commercial client and they love her – she talks the right language") and **Anthony Sendall** (see p.1446). Other highly regarded juniors include **Michael Duggan** (see p.1372) and **Ian Gatt** (see p.1383) ("commercial and confident"). Newly ranked **Stuart Ritchie** (see p.1440) is a good young advocate who is "easy to deal with."

Old Square Chambers (see full details p.1549) Valued for the "quality of advice, particularly on discrimination." A host of juniors are especially popular. Three experienced silks are ranked from this chambers: **Jeremy McMullen QC** (see p.1419), who rises up the tables this year, **John Hendy QC** (see p.1393) and **John Hand QC** (see p.1391). At the head of the pack of recommended juniors is "absolute number one favourite" **Jennifer Eady** (see p.1373), not only regarded as "approachable," but simply "excellent" with it. "Punchy advocate" **Sarah Moor** (see p.1423) and ex-Norton Rose partner **Melanie Tether** (see p.1459) ("good knowledge and sense of the lay client – articulate and technically excellent") follow close behind. Displaying "tactical acumen," **Damian Brown** (see p.1356) is "well able to stand his corner." **Louise Chudleigh** (see p.1362) works between London and Bristol, whilst **Tess Gill** (see p.1384), **Jane McNeill** (see p.1420), **Ijeoma Omambala** (see p.1429) and "experienced" **Paul Rose** (see p.1442) all performed well in our research. This year, **Ian Scott** (see p.1444) is newly ranked; he's "excellent on cross examination and witness statement preparation." As **Oliver Segal** (see p.1446) rises out of the up and coming band, **Emma Smith** (see p.1449) enters on the back of heavy endorsement.

Cloisters (see full details p.1487) The set remains recommended for "responsiveness and quality of counsel," especially amongst the seniors. **Laura Cox QC** (see p.1367) is "a star; we keep her for best" claimed one solicitor, while another agreed, "she's absolutely fabulous. On a big discrimination case I'd go to her without hesitation." **Brian Langstaff QC** (see p.1408) and **Robin Allen QC** (see p.1342) also attract praise. Leading junior **Thomas Kibling** (see p.1406) is described as "committed" and "user friendly." He is joined by newly ranked "bright and effective" **Rachel Crasnow** (see p.1367), who has recently returned from Australia.

Devereux Chambers (see full details p.1491) The set offers "good technical expertise and a practical outlook." **Jeffrey Burke QC** comes highly recommended and is joined in the list this year by new silk **David Griffith-Jones QC** (see p.1389) ("highly practical" and a "good all round approach"). This year leading light **Tim Brennan QC** has taken silk. "Robust" junior **Bruce Carr** (see p.1359) "cuts to the chase and inspires confidence." **Nicholas Randall** (see p.1438) is recommended both for his "clear concise advice" and his "robust advocacy" while **Ingrid Simler** (see p.1448) is described as "thorough and effective." Solicitors have found the approach of **James Tayler** (see p.1458) "most helpful."

Matrix Chambers (see full details p.1538) "Incisive" **David Bean QC** (see p.1348) is a "decent advocate and highly personable." **Cherie Booth QC** (see p.1352) is a "good tactician and good at the big picture – her commercial grasp is excellent." **Thomas Linden** (see p.1412) impresses many and is described as an "up-front plain speaking type." The other frequently recommended junior is **Helen Mountfield** (see p.1425).

Other Notable Practitioners At Essex Court Chambers, "excellent advocate" **Andrew Hochhauser QC** (see p.1396) "can really put the boot in." Such is the strength of his reputation that we're told his name has now become a verb. There was widespread support for "first class" **Martin Griffiths** (see p.1389) while "bright" **Charles Ciumei** (see p.1362) has a "realistic approach to litigation." At Fountain Court **Nicholas Underhill QC** (see p.1464) wins the instructions from leading firms and is regarded as a good choice "for a technical case." Here also, **Brian Napier** (see p.1426) doubles up as one of Scotland's top employment barristers. At junior level **Daphne Romney** (see p.1441) of 4 Field Court is "an excellent advocate of the highest possible order." At 199 Strand **Anthony Korn** (see p.1407) is recommended while **Declan O'Dempsey** of Coram Chambers remains popular.

MIDLANDS CIRCUIT

LEADING JUNIORS • Midlands		
1	JONES Jennifer	5 Fountain Court
2	GEORGE Sarah	St Philip's Chambers
	TUCKER Katherine	St Philip's Chambers

This book is the product of 6,552 1/2-hour interviews. See p.7 for BMRB audit.
For details of these leading barristers see Profiles on p.1339

At **5 Fountain Court** (see full details p.1577) in Birmingham **Jennifer Jones** is recommended. Neighbouring set **St Philip's Chambers** (see full details p.1578) offers **Sarah George** ("a safe pair of hands") and **Katherine Tucker** (see p.1463).

WESTERN CIRCUIT

LEADING JUNIORS • Western		
1	KEMPSTER Toby	Old Square Chambers
2	SMITH Nicholas	Queen Square Chambers

This book is the product of 6,552 1/2-hour interviews. See p.7 for BMRB audit.
For details of these leading barristers see Profiles on p.1339

Highly rated **Toby Kempster** (see p.1405) of **Old Square Chambers** (see full details p.1582) practises from the London and Bristol chambers. **Nicholas Smith** of **Queen Square Chambers** "rolls his sleeves up and has a good attitude."

NORTH EASTERN CIRCUIT

LEADING JUNIORS • North Eastern		
1	CAPE Paul	Milburn House Chambers
	SWEENEY James	Milburn House Chambers
2	WOODWARK Jane	Milburn House Chambers
UP AND COMING		
	FALKENSTEIN John	Milburn House Chambers

This book is the product of 6,552 1/2-hour interviews. See p.7 for BMRB audit.
For details of these leading barristers see Profiles on p.1339

At **Milburn House Chambers** (see full details p.1609) four barristers rule the roost. **Paul Cape** (see p.1359) is popular with lawyers across the north of England. **James Sweeney** (see p.1456) is newly ranked this year and, once more, **Jane Woodwark** (see p.1470) has earned favourable comment. Up and coming **John Falkenstein** (see p.1377), is "good with clients and blessed with a large measure of common sense."

NORTHERN CIRCUIT

LEADING SILKS • NORTHERN		
1	MCMULLEN Jeremy	9 St. John Street
2	BENSON John	14 Castle Street
	HAND John	9 St. John Street
NEW SILKS		
	BENSON John	14 Castle Street

For details of these leading barristers see Profiles on p.1339

LEADING JUNIORS • Northern		
1	GILROY Paul	9 St. John Street
2	GRUNDY Nigel	9 St. John Street
3	BRADLEY Richard	Oriel Chambers
	BREEN Carlo	9 St. John Street
	SADIQ Tariq	9 St. John Street
	WEDDERSPOON Rachel	9 St. John Street
UP AND COMING		
	CONNOLLY Joanne	8 King St

This book is the product of 6,552 1/2-hour interviews. See p.7 for BMRB audit.
For details of these leading barristers see Profiles on p.1339

At **9 St John Street** (see full details p.1607) in Manchester, two leading silks dominate the tables: **Jeremy McMullen QC** (see p.1419) and **John Hand QC** (see p.1391). Established junior **Paul Gilroy** (see p.1385) was overwhelmingly popular in our research; he's "a top guy and very client/user friendly." **Nigel Grundy** (see p.1390) is judged to be "practically minded." There is a bumper crop of newly ranked juniors from 9 St. John Street this year; **Carlo Breen** (see p.1354) is "excellent," **Tariq Sadiq** (see p.1443) received warm recommendations while the market feels that **Rachel Wedderspoon** (see p.1467) is "turning into a first rate practitioner." An up and coming name "receiving excellent reports" is **Joanne Connolly** (see p.1365) from **8 King Street** (see full details p.1604) In Liverpool, at **14 Castle Street** (see full details p.1497) **John Benson QC** (see p.1350) ("direct and with common sense. He understands our clients") has recently taken silk. At **Oriel Chambers** (see full details p.1600), **Richard Bradley** (see p.1353) is recommended.

ENERGY & NATURAL RESOURCES

RESEARCH: The rankings are based on in-depth interviews with over 5,000 solicitors and barristers in the UK. Chambers research is audited by the British Market Research Bureau (see page 7 for details).

LONDON

ENERGY & NATURAL RESOURCES • London		QCs	Jnrs
1	**One Essex Court** (Lord Grabiner QC)	6	3
2	**Essex Court Chambers** (Gordon Pollock QC)	4	1
3	**Brick Court Chambers** (Christopher Clarke QC)	3	-
	Fountain Court (Anthony Boswood QC)	1	-
	4 Stone Buildings (Philip Heslop QC)	1	1

Numbers show recommended barristers in this practice area

LEADING SILKS • London		
★	GRABINER Anthony	One Essex Court
	POLLOCK Gordon	Essex Court Chambers
	SUMPTION Jonathan	Brick Court Chambers
1	BOSWOOD Anthony	Fountain Court
	GLICK Ian	One Essex Court
	KENTRIDGE Sydney	Brick Court Chambers
	SHER Jules	Wilberforce Chambers
2	ALDOUS Charles	Maitland Chambers
	CARR Christopher	One Essex Court
	EDER Bernard	Essex Court Chambers
	GLOSTER Elizabeth	One Essex Court
	HILDYARD Robert	4 Stone Buildings
	HOWARD Mark	Brick Court Chambers
3	BARNES Mark	One Essex Court
	CROOKENDEN Simon	Essex Court Chambers
	DICKER Robin	3-4 South Square
	MALES Stephen	20 Essex Street
	ONIONS Jeffery	One Essex Court
	NEW SILKS	
	MILDON David	Essex Court Chambers

For details of these leading barristers see Profiles on p.1339

LEADING JUNIORS • London		
★	RABINOWITZ Laurence	One Essex Court
1	GRIFFITHS Alan	One Essex Court
	MILES Robert	4 Stone Buildings
2	BRYAN Simon	Essex Court Chambers
	MCCAUGHRAN John	One Essex Court

This book is the product of 6,552 1/2-hour interviews. See p.7 for BMRB audit.
For details of these leading barristers see Profiles on p.1339

One Essex Court (see full details p.1497) Acknowledged as the "benchmark" set for oil and gas and electricity matters, it is blessed with "superlative quality" at both silk and junior level. Head of chambers **Anthony Grabiner QC** is "quite obviously the star name here," and appeared on the Severn Trent v Dwr Cymru case. "Fantastically bright" **Ian Glick QC** (see p.1386) is particularly recommended for his experience of utilities regulation. The oil and gas industry particularly admires **Christopher Carr QC** as "a great advocate, a team player and never a prima donna." He acted for British Gas on its case against Phillips Petroleum. "Brilliant but approachable," **Elizabeth Gloster QC** (see p.1386) is also said to be "superb with clients." **Mark Barnes QC** (see p.1347) has had an "outstanding" year, and is commended for his "understanding of industry requirements." He appeared on British American Offshore Ltd v Amoco (UK) Exploration Company. Industry majors have been loud in their acclamation of **Jeffery Onions QC**'s (see p.1430) "down-to-earth style." Still a junior, to universal surprise, **Laurence Rabinowitz** (see p.1437) is considered to be "in a league of his own." An "absolutely superb barrister," he is said to give solicitors "advice whether they like it or not," and to be "the only junior that major companies will use for big-ticket work." **Alan Griffiths** (see p.1389) is "phenomenally intelligent," and is most recognised for his judicial review work, while the respected **John McCaughran** (see p.1418) is an expert on gas supply cases.

Essex Court Chambers (see full details p.1496) Described by one oil company as "a god," and by contemporaries as a "fearsome opponent," **Gordon Pollock QC** (see p.1434) sets the tone for the set, which is the clear number two for this type of work. His reputation is now such that "there's nothing left to say about him." "Unflappable and good on his feet," **Bernard Eder QC** (see p.1374) elicited substantial favourable comment from solicitors, while **Simon Crookenden QC**'s (see p.1368) "quality and expertise" also received widespread endorsement. New silk, **David Mildon QC** (see p.1421) "always does a good job" and was singled out for his work on the British American Offshore Ltd v Amoco (UK) Exploration Company case. Among juniors, **Simon Bryan** (see p.1356) retains his reputation and is saluted for his "exceedingly thorough preparation."

Brick Court Chambers (see full details p.1484) Newly ranked in this sector, the set boasts a formidable line-up of some of the bar's most eminent silks. Still the "cleverest man at the energy bar," **Jonathan Sumption QC** (see p.1455) displays "complete mastery of technical detail." **Sydney Kentridge QC** (see p.1405), although now "a man for shorter cases," is "excellent on contracts, a wonderful advocate and a delight to work with." Peers describe **Mark Howard QC** (see p.1398) as "an outstanding lawyer, well able to master the technical detail and brilliantly tough in court."

Fountain Court (see full details p.1506) Although it is still highly rated as a set for oil, gas and electricity matters, the death of Trevor Philipson QC leaves a gaping hole. Head of chambers **Anthony Boswood QC** (see p.1352) now shoulders an imposing burden, but is considered to be "equal to most tasks." Acclaimed for his work on the Enron litigation, he is said to be "reliable, diligent and superb in court."

4 Stone Buildings (see full details p.1568) Home to a pair of highly regarded barristers, the set maintains its reputation as "a decent alternative" for energy work. **Robert Hildyard QC** (see p.1394) is acclaimed "an attractive advocate," while **Robert Miles** is admired by clients and solicitors alike for his "pragmatic, quick advice."

Other Notable Practitioners "Terrifically bright all-rounder" **Jules Sher QC** (see p.1448) of **Wilberforce Chambers** wins applause for "his incisive analysis of problems and his ability to suggest solutions." Peers describe **Stephen Males QC** (see p.1415) of **20 Essex Street** as "a pretty useful advocate," while **Robin Dicker QC** (see p.1371) of 3-4 **South Square** remains a popular port of call for an opinion. "Versatile" **Charles Aldous QC** (see p.1342) of **Maitland Chambers** is respected for his knowledge of the electricity and oil and gas industries.

ENVIRONMENT

RESEARCH: The rankings are based on in-depth interviews with over 5,000 solicitors and barristers in the UK. Chambers research is audited by the British Market Research Bureau (see page 7 for details).

Barristers' profiles 1339-1472

LONDON

	ENVIRONMENT • London	QCs	Jnrs
1	**Old Square Chambers** (John Hendy QC)	2	4
2	**4 Breams Buildings** (Christopher Lockhart-Mummery QC)	4	-
	2 Harcourt Buildings (Gerard Ryan QC)	2	2
	Eldon Chambers (Lionel Read QC)	2	4
3	**1 Crown Office Row** (Robert Seabrook QC)	1	2
	4-5 Gray's Inn Square (Appleby/Mole)	1	2
	Matrix Chambers (Nicholas Blake QC)	1	3
4	**Blackstone Chambers** (Baxendale/Flint)	1	1
	Brick Court Chambers (Christopher Clarke QC)	1	1

This book is the product of 6,552 1/2-hour interviews. See p.7 for BMRB audit.
For details of these leading barristers see Profiles on p.1339

	LEADING SILKS • London	
1	**BRENNAN Daniel**	Matrix Chambers
	HAND John	Old Square Chambers
	KINGSLAND Christopher	4 Breams Buildings
	RYAN Gerard	2 Harcourt Buildings
2	**ELVIN David**	4 Breams Buildings
	GEORGE Charles	2 Harcourt Buildings
	GORDON Richard	Brick Court Chambers
	HAVERS Philip	1 Crown Office Row
	HOLGATE David	4 Breams Buildings
	HOWELL John	Blackstone Chambers
	KATKOWSKI Christopher	4 Breams Buildings
	READ Lionel	Eldon Chambers
	VALLANCE Philip	4-5 Gray's Inn Square
	WILLIAMS John Melville	Old Square Chambers
	NEW SILKS	
	KING Neil	2 Mitre Court Buildings
	LEWIS Rhodri Price	Eldon Chambers

For details of these leading barristers see Profiles on p.1339

	LEADING JUNIORS • London	
★	**PUGH Charles**	Old Square Chambers
1	**BATES John**	Old Square Chambers
	HART David	1 Crown Office Row
	MCCRACKEN Robert	2 Harcourt Buildings
	TROMANS Stephen	Eldon Chambers
2	**BIRTLES William**	Old Square Chambers
	BYRNE Garrett	4-5 Gray's Inn Square
	FORDHAM Michael	Blackstone Chambers
	JONES Gregory	2 Harcourt Buildings
	SANDS Philippe	Matrix Chambers
3	**CAMERON James**	3 Verulam Buildings
	HARRIS Russell	Eldon Chambers
	HILL Thomas	4-5 Gray's Inn Square
	LEWIS Robert	11 New Square
	MACRORY Richard	Brick Court Chambers
	MEAD Philip	Old Square Chambers
	READ Graham	Devereux Chambers
	UPTON William	Eldon Chambers
	WOLFE David	Matrix Chambers
4	**EDIS William**	1 Crown Office Row
	PUGH-SMITH John	Eldon Chambers
	SHERIDAN Maurice	Matrix Chambers
	WEST Lawrence	2 Harcourt Buildings

For details of these leading barristers see Profiles on p.1339

Old Square Chambers (see full details p.1549) Noted "enthusiasts for the subject," the set retains its top band position for its "genuine interest and commitment to the area." Particularly recommended for toxic tort work, it boasts strength at both silk and junior level. "All-rounder" **John Hand QC** (see p.1391) has shown himself to be a "superb advocate" in contaminated land, emissions and coastal erosion cases. Environmental matters also touch on aspects of his wider employment and personal injury practices. "Dedicated" **John Melville Williams QC** (see p.1469) has a similarly mixed practice in personal injury, environment, and clinical negligence, and received glowing reports for his role in recent toxic tort organophosphate cases. He often works in tandem with water and drainage expert **John Bates** (see p.1348), another "top name in the environmental pantheon." "Urbane and quick-thinking," **Charles Pugh** (see p.1436) is "someone you want in a rough and tumble case." "A rumbustious character," Pugh's practice is a blend of personal injury and environment law, which he applies to carbon monoxide cases and dust nuisance claims. **William Birtles**' (see p.1350) "deceptively mild manner hides a sharp mind." His "balanced" practice embraces statutory nuisance litigation and environmental judicial review. **Philip Mead** (see p.1420) "always pops up" on environmental and health and safety matters. Noted for his "good delivery," he is often used by law firms to settle pleadings in civil cases.

4 Breams Buildings (see full details p.1483) Planning-based set, considered to be "collectively, the best on their feet," which, although lacking recommended juniors, is home to some of the environment sector's most respected silks. "Calm and gentlemanly" **Christopher Kingsland QC** (see p.1406) is an "out and out environment specialist." "Formidably intelligent," he is particularly recommended for his expertise in waste matters, and has recently acted on judicial reviews for public authorities involving airport noise nuisance and the use of waste as fuel in a cement plant in Durham. "Impressive" **David Elvin QC**'s (see p.1375) "technical knowledge and tactical advice is first-class." Solicitors rate him highly for his expertise in judicial review and environmental impact assessment in property-based matters. "Brilliant at the technical detail," **David Holgate QC**'s (see p.1396) "brain works overtime" in relation to environmental aspects of planning inquiries and quarry work. "Unpretentious" **Christopher Katkowski QC** (see p.1404), noted for his willingness to "work as part of a team," "rolls his sleeves up and gets stuck in." He maintains a mixed planning and environmental practice and has recently been seen in a number of environmental assessment cases and judicial reviews relating to waste disposal on protected habitats.

2 Harcourt Buildings (see full details p.1520) Noted for "excellent clerking," the set combines expertise in planning, environment and public law. Waste and minerals expert **Gerard Ryan QC** puts his scientific background to widely commended use, while "superb" **Charles George QC** (see p.1384) is admired for his "thorough and academic approach." "Conspicuously skilled" **Robert McCracken** (see p.1418) is a "terrific fighter," who is especially recommended for his well-drafted submissions. His recent involvement in a number of important environmental impact assessment cases such as R v Durham County Council and others, ex parte Huddleston, and Berkeley v Secretary of State for the Environment has considerably boosted his profile in the area. **Greg Jones** is considered by some to be an "absolute star." Respected for his "holistic understanding of the EU law base that underpins environmental law," he is developing a reputation for advising on third party challenges to planning cases.

Eldon Chambers (see full details p.1493) Head of chambers, the "fantastic" **Lionel Read QC** is renowned for "fighting great battles" in the environment arena. Peers report that "he gives the impression of a pussycat, but to watch him in cross-examination is awe-inspiring." "Personable" **Rhodri Price Lewis QC** (see p.1411) has recently taken silk. Although principally associated with planning, he has received a growing volume of environment instructions, and has a loyal client following for his ability to "get results." A former star of Simmons & Simmons' respected environment department, "shrewd character" **Stephen Tromans** (see p.1462) maintains his strong reputation in his new career. Although "as yet untested as an advocate," he is widely recommended for his written opinions on non-contentious contaminated land questions. Many interviewees asserted that "if I had a tricky point of law, I would go to Stephen." **William Upton** (see p.1464) is reported to have a "good future ahead of him" in environment law. An expert in local government matters and conservation issues, he is considered by some to be "one of the few environmental specialists possessing moral vision." **Russell Harris** brings an "appealing manner" and "good sense of perspective "to environmental prosecutions, while **John Pugh-Smith** (see p.1437) was again recommended for his mixed planning and environment practice.

1 Crown Office Row (see full details p.1490) The "statesmanlike" **Philip Havers QC** (see p.1392) focuses on public law environmental matters. "Fantastically resourceful," he has acted on a number of judicial reviews relating to water pollution. "Bright" **David Hart** (see p.1392) is most frequently seen representing alleged polluters in toxic tort cases. Described as "a man who misses nothing ," his "persuasive manner" is considered to serve him well in the courtroom. A "pungent and pithy advocate," **William Edis** has recently been involved in a hedgerow regulations case.

4-5 Gray's Inn Square (see full details p.1515) This well-known planning set has a number of recommended practitioners with substantial environmental experience. **Philip Vallance QC**'s (see p.1464) reputation for environmental warranties and flooding cases follows him from 1 Crown Office Row. Said to have a "first rate grasp of the science involved," he is a highly rated advocate who is able to "keep the interest of the judges." **Tom Hill** (see p.1395) is reported to have had a particularly busy year. His "attention to detail" shows in his "thorough preparation," and clients particularly appreciate his willingness to "stick his neck out" for them. Formerly 23 Essex Street, the "impressive" **Garrett Byrne** (see p.1358) is an administrative barrister known for his work in environment criminal prosecutions.

Matrix Chambers (see full details p.1538) The set's environmental capacity has been strengthened by the addition of **Dan Brennan QC** from 39 Essex Street. A "weighty presence," he is acknowledged to "command respect in court." His practice is a mix of environmental liability, toxic tort and personal injury litigation. Interviewees report that "when you can get him, he's manna from heaven." Public lawyer **Philippe Sands** (see p.1445) takes an "expansive view of difficult and serious matters." He specialises in international work with EU law components – "if you need an answer on an esoteric environmental treaty in a South Pacific state, he'll give it to you without looking it up." "Client and lawyer friendly" **David Wolfe** (see p.1469) was noted for his "quick turnaround of papers." His "scientific bent" served him well in recent judicial reviews relating to landfill site planning permission and permits for the emission of pollutants within prescribed limits. "Articulate and personable" **Maurice Sheridan** (see p.1448) "always gives 100%" and has advised on a variety of regulatory issues.

Blackstone Chambers (see full details p.1481) A new addition from 4 Breams Buildings, public lawyer **John Howell QC** (see p.1398) was commended for his "concise advice" and "superb legal mind." "Outstandingly good" junior **Michael Fordham** (see p.1380) is reported to have "a real feel for" environmental judicial review cases. The two recently acted together in representing the Environment Agency in R v Environment Agency, ex parte Mayer Parry, relating to the definition of waste.

Brick Court Chambers (see full details p.1484) "Top class" **Richard Gordon QC** (see p.1387) maintains a "huge reputation" for judicial review and public law work, while "formidable academic" **Richard Macrory** (see p.1415) is noted to be "strong on European issues." Particularly recommended for his opinions, "there are few people with such broad familiarity with the people and issues relating to the environment."

Other Notable Practitioners New silk **Neil King QC** (see p.1406) at **2 Mitre Court Buildings** offers "excellent environmental advice" from within a broader planning practice. Recent work includes advising on environment limits for power station emissions. Although also a partner at Baker & McKenzie, **James Cameron** (see p.1462) maintains his environmental practice at **3 Verulam Buildings**. As one of the founders of environmental law group FEILD, he is a prominent figure in environmental debate, with an emphasis on international matters. Peers comment that "we all have to run to catch up with him on the international front." Part of the "first generation of environmental specialists," **Robert Lewis** at **11 New Square** has a "long history as an environment lawyer." His background as a solicitor makes him particularly suited to transactional work. "Consistent" **Graham Read** (see p.1439) of **Devereux Chambers** was commended by interviewees for his willingness to "make himself available" and his "wide experience in the field." "Persuasive" **Lawrence West** (see p.1467) at **2 Harcourt Buildings** is "highly regarded by judges" for his experience in civil claims, particularly those relating to flooding and water pollution. Seen representing defendants, insurers and local authorities in a variety of toxic tort matters, he recently acted for an agrochemical company, following the escape of chemicals onto farmland.

MIDLANDS CIRCUIT

LEADING JUNIORS • Midlands		
1	CAHILL Jeremy	5 Fountain Court
	KIMBLIN Richard	3 Fountain Court
	TRAVERS David	6 Pump Court

For details of these leading barristers see Profiles on p.1339

"Approachable" **Jeremy Cahill** (see p.1358) of **5 Fountain Court** (see full details p.1577) is "user-friendly for corporate clients." Noted for his "practical" approach, he is particularly recommended for waste planning matters. At **3 Fountain Court**, the "analytical" **Richard Kimblin** (see p.1406) is "one of the few barristers who has developed an interest and expertise in the area." His scientific background gives him a "good grasp of the detail." "Down to earth" **David Travers** (see p.1462) has moved from 3 Fountain Court to **6 Pump Court** (see full details p.1559) in London. However, his caseload will still be largely conducted on the Midlands Circuit. He rates highly for his ability to "adapt his approach according to the tribunal." Frequently instructed by the Environment Agency, he has expertise in matters relating to drainage rights and waste management licence appeals.

NORTHERN & NORTH EASTERN CIRCUITS

LEADING SILKS • Northern & North Eastern		
1	PATTERSON Frances	40 King St

For details of these leading barristers see Profiles on p.1339

LEADING JUNIORS • Northern & North Eastern		
1	BARRETT John	40 King St
	CAMERON Neil	Wilberforce Chambers

For details of these leading barristers see Profiles on p.1339

At top Manchester planning set **40 King St** (see full details p.1604), two individuals were recommended for their experience of environmental litigation. **Frances Patterson QC** (see p.1432) stands out for her work in local government matters, while the "switched on" **John Barrett** (see p.1347) is also reputed to be building an impressive reputation. In Hull, "low key" **Neil Cameron** (see p.1347) of **Wilberforce Chambers** (see full details p.1588) is said to "present tight arguments" and to "inspire judges' confidence." "Subtle" in style, he enters this year's rankings for his work on "oodles of environmental regulatory matters."

FAMILY / MATRIMONIAL

RESEARCH: The rankings are based on in-depth interviews with over 5,000 solicitors and barristers in the UK. Chambers research is audited by the British Market Research Bureau (see page 7 for details).

LONDON

FAMILY/MATRIMONIAL • London		QCs	Jnrs
1	**One King's Bench Walk** (Anthony Hacking QC)	12	10
	1 Mitre Court Buildings (Bruce Blair QC)	9	8
	Queen Elizabeth Building (Florence Baron QC)	3	7
2	**29 Bedford Row Chambers** (Peter Ralls QC)	3	9
3	**One Garden Court Family Law Chambers** (Platt/Ball)	3	4
	4 Paper Buildings (Lionel Swift QC)	4	4
4	**14 Gray's Inn Square** (Joanna Dodson QC)	1	4
	Renaissance Chambers (Jubb/Setright)	1	3

This book is the product of 6,552 1/2-hour interviews. See p.7 for BMRB audit.
Numbers show recommended barristers in this practice area

One King's Bench Walk (see full details p.1526) One of the premier sets for children work is also acknowledged to be a strong player on the financial side. Many of the silks and juniors are sought after by provincial firms, as well as those in the metropolis. **Barry Singleton QC** is seen as "something of a mental giant," and is proficient in complex financial matters. **Judith Parker QC** "stands alone" for children cases, and is admired for having "the knack of instilling confidence in clients and solicitors alike." In combination with "outstanding" junior **Deborah Eaton**, she appeared in the conjoined twins case, Re A, acting for Jodie. **James Turner QC** (see p.1463) appeared in the headline case White v White, displaying "boundless intelligence, enormous confidence and an ability to enter into constructive discussion with the court." Appearing in Mubarak v M (another case likely to have a profound effect on the law) was **Charles Howard QC** (see p.1397), a new silk last year, who "has more than found his feet." **Anthony Kirk QC** (see p.1407) has taken silk this year, and is recognised for his "maturity and assurance" in all areas. He appeared with the "phenomenally bright" **Richard Harrison** (see p.1392) as junior in B v B, a case looking at the implications of the Hague Convention for parents' rights of custody. Other recommended silks include "reliable" **Richard Anelay QC** (see p.1343), **Rodger Hayward Smith QC** (see p.1392), "deservedly popular" **Andrew McFarlane QC** (see p.1419) and **Camden Pratt QC** (see p.1435). Among a batch of renowned juniors, **Ian Cook** (see p.1365), the "versatile" **Clive Newton** (see p.1427), "immensely promising" **Christopher Pocock**, **Caroline Budden** (see p.1357), **Susan Maidment** and **Caroline Lister** (see p.1412) were all highly rated by peers and solicitors.

1 Mitre Court Buildings (see full details p.1539) A "well run, full range set" with a marginally higher reputation for financial rather than children cases. Head of Chambers **Bruce Blair QC** (see p.1351) is "wonderfully perceptive" and "always displays great presence of mind." Able to "talk the hind legs off a donkey," **Nicholas Mostyn QC** has "a flamboyant approach." Tackling ancillary relief, **Jeremy Posnansky QC** (see p.1435) is "first class" and is lauded for his "superb attention to detail and negotiation skills." Along with the "meticulous" **Michael Horowitz QC** (see p.1397), he maintains his position in both the children and finance rankings. New to the tables this year is **Martin Pointer QC** (see p.1434), who received support from a number of firms for his "superb advocacy," while new silk **Philip Moor QC** (see p.1423) is "confidently expected" to build on his outstanding junior career. **Mark Everall QC** (see p.1376) was strongly recommended for his talents in handling children cases. Of the

MATRIMONIAL FINANCE: LEADING SILKS • London		
1	**BARON Florence**	Queen Elizabeth Building
	BLAIR Bruce	1 Mitre Court Buildings
	MOSTYN Nicholas	1 Mitre Court Buildings
	SINGLETON Barry	One King's Bench Walk
2	**POINTER Martin**	1 Mitre Court Buildings
	POSNANSKY Jeremy	1 Mitre Court Buildings
	SCOTT Timothy	29 Bedford Row Chambers
	TURNER James	One King's Bench Walk
3	**ANELAY Richard**	One King's Bench Walk
	COHEN Jonathan	4 Paper Buildings
	HAYWARD SMITH Rodger	One King's Bench Walk
	HOROWITZ Michael	1 Mitre Court Buildings
	HOWARD Charles	One King's Bench Walk
	MOYLAN Andrew	Queen Elizabeth Building
	PRATT Camden	One King's Bench Walk
	SEABROOK Robert	1 Crown Office Row
NEW SILKS		
	KIRK Anthony	One King's Bench Walk
	MOOR Philip	1 Mitre Court Buildings
	STONE Lucy	Queen Elizabeth Building
	STOREY Paul	29 Bedford Row Chambers

For details of these leading barristers see Profiles on p.1339

LEADING JUNIORS • London		
1	**AMOS Tim**	Queen Elizabeth Building
	BALCOMBE David	1 Crown Office Row
	DAVIDSON Katharine	1 Mitre Court Buildings
	DYER Nigel	1 Mitre Court Buildings
	FRANCIS Nicholas	29 Bedford Row Chambers
	MARKS Lewis	Queen Elizabeth Building
2	**BANGAY Deborah**	29 Bedford Row Chambers
	CAYFORD Philip	29 Bedford Row Chambers
	CUSWORTH Nicholas	1 Mitre Court Buildings
	EATON Deborah	One King's Bench Walk
	HUSSEY Ann	29 Bedford Row Chambers
	LE GRICE Valentine	1 Mitre Court Buildings
	NATHAN Peter	One Garden Court Family Law Chambers
	NEWTON Clive	One King's Bench Walk
	POCOCK Christopher	One King's Bench Walk
	ROBERTS Jennifer	Queen Elizabeth Building
	SANDERS Neil	29 Bedford Row Chambers
	SHAW Howard	29 Bedford Row Chambers
3	**BRASSE Gillian**	14 Gray's Inn Square
	BRUDENELL Thomas	Queen Elizabeth Building
	CLARKE Elizabeth	Queen Elizabeth Building
	COOK Ian	One King's Bench Walk
	HARRISON Richard	One King's Bench Walk
	MOLYNEUX Brenton	29 Bedford Row Chambers
	MURFITT Catriona	1 Mitre Court Buildings
	PEEL Robert	29 Bedford Row Chambers
	TIDBURY Andrew	Queen Elizabeth Building
	WOOD Christopher	1 Mitre Court Buildings

For details of these leading barristers see Profiles on p.1339

FAMILY: CHILDREN • LEADING SILKS • London		
★	PARKER Judith	One King's Bench Walk
1	EVERALL Mark	1 Mitre Court Buildings
	HOROWITZ Michael	1 Mitre Court Buildings
	LEVY Allan	17 Bedford Row
	MCFARLANE Andrew	One King's Bench Walk
	MURDOCH Gordon	4 Paper Buildings
	PAUFFLEY Anna	4 Paper Buildings
	PLATT Eleanor	One Garden Court Family Law Chambers
	POSNANSKY Jeremy	1 Mitre Court Buildings
	SCOTT Timothy	29 Bedford Row Chambers
	TURNER James	One King's Bench Walk
2	BALL Alison	One Garden Court Family Law Chambers
	DODSON Joanna	14 Gray's Inn Square
	HAYWARD SMITH Rodger	One King's Bench Walk
	JACKSON Peter	4 Paper Buildings
	PEDDIE Ian	One Garden Court Family Law Chambers
NEW SILKS		
	KIRK Anthony	One King's Bench Walk
	SETRIGHT Henry	Renaissance Chambers

For details of these leading barristers see Profiles on p.1339

LEADING JUNIORS • London		
1	COBB Stephen	One Garden Court Family Law Chambers
	EATON Deborah	One King's Bench Walk
2	BRASSE Gillian	14 Gray's Inn Square
	HALL Joanna	14 Gray's Inn Square
	LISTER Caroline	One King's Bench Walk
	NICHOLLS Michael	1 Mitre Court Buildings
	ROWE Judith	One Garden Court Family Law Chambers
	SCOTT-MANDERSON Marcus	4 Paper Buildings
	SLOMNICKA Barbara	14 Gray's Inn Square
	STERNBERG Michael	4 Paper Buildings
	TAYLOR Debbie	Hardwicke Building
3	BARDA Robin	4 Paper Buildings
	BUDDEN Caroline	One King's Bench Walk
	DASHWOOD Robert	Renaissance Chambers
	DREW Jane	Coram Chambers
	HARDING Cherry	Renaissance Chambers
	HORROCKS Peter	One Garden Court Family Law Chambers
	JUBB Brian	Renaissance Chambers
	MAIDMENT Susan	One King's Bench Walk
	MITCHELL Janet	4 Brick Court
	MOLYNEUX Brenton	29 Bedford Row Chambers
	MURFITT Catriona	1 Mitre Court Buildings
	NEWTON Clive	One King's Bench Walk
	ROBERTS Jennifer	Queen Elizabeth Building
	ROSENBLATT Jeremy	4 Paper Buildings

For details of these leading barristers see Profiles on p.1339

more celebrated juniors, **Katharine Davidson** (see p.1369) "impresses in her preparation" and **Nigel Dyer** (see p.1373) "is a permanent fixture on the weightier cases." **Valentine Le Grice** (see p.1409) "is excellent on paper," while **Nicholas Cusworth** (see p.1369) is known for his "effectiveness and ability to jolly along proceedings." Other respected juniors are **Christopher Wood** (see p.1470), **Michael Nicholls** (see p.1428) ("he's getting better and better") and **Catriona Murfitt** (see p.1426).

Queen Elizabeth Building (see full details p.1559) Although it does not possess the numbers of leading silks of its closest rivals, this set has often lost its best and brightest QCs (such as Paul Coleridge QC) to the bench. The quality of practitioner remains undiminished at a set famed for its finance expertise. **Florence Baron QC** (see p.1347) proves extremely popular for her "regular ability to turn losing cases around," while **Andrew Moylan QC** (see p.1425) "invariably grasps the essential facts of a case." New silk **Lucy Stone QC** (see p.1454) "consistently conveys reassurance to the client." The set fields a formidable phalanx of juniors. These include **Timothy Amos** (see p.1342), renowned for "marshalling his facts admirably," and the "assured and reliable" **Lewis Marks** (see p.1416). **Jennifer Roberts** (see p.1441) scores high marks for her work on both children and finance cases, while newly ranked **Elizabeth Clarke** (see p.1363) is seen to be "bright, thorough and on the move." **Andrew Tidbury**'s star is also in the ascendant, and he too makes his debut in the tables for his "unflappable, competent manner." **Thomas Brudenell** (see p.1356) continues to be rated as a "safe pair of hands."

29 Bedford Row Chambers (see full details p.1478) "The best of the rest" is characterised by a preponderance of talent in the finance arena, notably at the junior end. Among silks, though, **Timothy Scott QC** (see p.1444) receives favourable comment both for complex ancillary relief and children matters, and is joined in the rankings by new silk **Paul Storey QC** (see p.1454). At junior level, **Nicholas Francis**' (see p.1381) "reflective, perspicacious" style contrasts with that of the "tigerish and effervescent" **Deborah Bangay** (see p.1346). The respected **Philip Cayford** (see p.1361), **Neil Sanders** (see p.1445) and **Howard Shaw** (see p.1447) are joined in the rankings by newcomer **Ann Hussey**, (see p.1399) who is characterised as a "consummate team player." "Solid" **Robert Peel** (see p.1433) and all-rounder **Brent Molyneux** (see p.1423) ("has a calculating and cool intelligence") complete the line-up.

One Garden Court Family Law Chambers (see full details p.1509) Although a capable set for finance cases, the set really earns its spurs for its children work. **Eleanor Platt QC** (see p.1434) is a "pedigree practitioner" and is joint head of chambers with the "level-headed and sensitive" **Alison Ball QC** (see p.1346). Also highly rated is the "consistent" **Ian Peddie QC** (see p.1432). The set's roll-call at junior level includes **Stephen Cobb** (see p.1364), "a premier league performer" who is "meticulous in his approach." Other noteworthy juniors include the "first-rate" **Judith Rowe** (see p.1442), **Peter Horrocks** (see p.1397) and **Peter Nathan** (see p.1427), who lends his expertise to financial cases.

4 Paper Buildings (see full details p.1553) Active in both financial and children work, this set is regularly instructed by the Official Solicitor. A battery of rated silks includes **Jonathan Cohen QC**, "a dab hand with convoluted finances," leading children experts **Gordon Murdoch QC** (see p.1426) and **Anna Pauffley QC** (see p.1432), and the "eminently reasonable" **Peter Jackson QC** (see p.1400). **Marcus Scott-Manderson** (see p.1444) "has many strings to his bow," excelling in public law and child abduction matters. **Michael Sternberg** (see p.1453) and **Robin Barda** (see p.1347) are also highly respected, as is newcomer to the rankings **Jeremy Rosenblatt** (see p.1442), who received spontaneous acclaim from a number of firms.

14 Gray's Inn Square (see full details p.1517) Particularly noted for its proficiency in children law, the set includes a number of rated practitioners. Head of Chambers, the "straightforward" **Joanna Dodson QC** (see p.1371) continues to receive high praise from peers. Among juniors, **Gillian Brasse**'s (see p.1354) name "crops up more and more" as an obvious port of call for both children and matrimonial matters, and **Barbara Slomnicka** and **Joanna Hall** both maintain their reputations as "reliable performers."

Renaissance Chambers (see full details p.1562) Still a comparatively fledgling set, it has consolidated its name for children law, and possesses in **Henry Setright QC** "a leader in child abduction of great repute." **Robert Dashwood**, **Cherry Harding**, and **Brian Jubb** are the most noted names among a solid assembly of juniors.

Other Notable Practitioners **Allan Levy QC** (see p.1410) of **17 Bedford Row** is commended by many as "an advocate of considerable presence" in children law cases. "Renaissance man" **Robert Seabrook QC** (see p.1444) "appears to fine effect" in financial matters, and operates from **1 Crown Office Row**. Other respected practitioners, noted for their children work, include the "conscientious" **Debbie Taylor** (see p.1458) of **Hardwicke Building** newly ranked **Jane Drew** (see p.1372) of **Coram Chambers** and **Janet Mitchell** (see p.1422) of **4 Brick Court. David Balcombe** of **1 Crown Office Row** also received recommendations for his matrimonial finance work.

SOUTH EASTERN & EAST ANGLIAN CIRCUIT

LEADING SILKS • South Eastern & East Anglian		
NEW SILKS		
	BAKER Jonathan	Harcourt Chambers

For details of these leading barristers see Profiles on p.1339

LEADING JUNIORS • South Eastern & East Anglian		
1	DAVIES Lindsay	Fenners Chambers
	ESPLEY Susan	Fenners Chambers
	KEFFORD Anthony	East Anglian Chambers
	MCLOUGHLIN Timothy	East Anglian Chambers
	TATTERSALL Simon	Fenners Chambers
2	ELLIOTT Margot	Regency Chambers
	MILLER Celia	East Anglian Chambers
	NEWTON Roderick	East Anglian Chambers
	WAIN Peter	East Anglian Chambers
3	JUDD Frances	Harcourt Chambers
	PARNELL Graham	East Anglian Chambers
	RICHARDS Jeremy	Octagon House Chambers

For details of these leading barristers see Profiles on p.1339

East Anglian Chambers (see full details p.1611) houses a sizeable number of recommended barristers who are active across the region. **Anthony Kefford** (see p.1405) exhibits a "steely determination" in financial matters, and is a "hardened cross-examiner." **Timothy McLoughlin** pursues a more "calm and methodical" style in his children and care cases, while **Celia Miller** is praised for her "charm and sensitivity with clients." She has strong links with the local authorities, which are matched by those of the "unflappable" **Peter Wain. Graham Parnell** is admired for his negotiation skills and "trenchant" advice. The head of chambers is the "demonstrative and theatrical" **Roderick Newton.** At **Fenners Chambers** (see full details p.1583), **Lindsay Davies** is "a tireless worker," who is equally effective in ancillary relief and children work. She is applauded for her ability to "unearth creative solutions to knotty problems." **Susan Espley** ploughs a similar furrow, infusing her cases "with an unfailing good humour" and "tackling many a hopeless case with startling results." **Simon Tattersall** brings an analytical approach to cases, and is "terrier-like" in his attitude to complex financial problems. **Regency Chambers** is home to **Margot Elliott**, who gains special mention for efforts in the child care sphere. Here, she is seen as "an indefatigable opponent," who "cheerfully accepts, and succeeds in, cases where others might crumble." The leading name at **Octagon House** continues to be that of **Jeremy Richards**, who is recommended as a child care specialist, often acting for local authorities. **Harcourt Chambers** (see full details p.1613) is considered by many to be the leading choice in Oxford for family law. Here, **Jonathan Baker QC** (see p.1346) is "enthusiastic" and "alive to pertinent issues," while **Frances Judd** (see p.1403) deals with children matters in a "diplomatic and reassuring manner."

WESTERN CIRCUIT

LEADING SILKS • Western		
1	SHARP Christopher	St John's Chambers
	WILDBLOOD Stephen	Albion Chambers
2	EVANS Mark	Queen Square Chambers

For details of these leading barristers see Profiles on p.1339

LEADING JUNIORS • Western		
1	BROMILOW Richard	St John's Chambers
	DIXON Ralph	St John's Chambers
	DUTHIE Catriona	Guildhall Chambers
	HYDE Charles	Albion Chambers
	MILLER Nicholas	Guildhall Chambers
	WILLS-GOLDINGHAM Claire	Albion Chambers
2	ALLARDICE Miranda	Pump Court Chambers
	BOYDELL Edward	Pump Court Chambers
	CAMPBELL Susan	Southernhay Chambers
	CORFIELD Sheelagh	St John's Chambers
	DINAN-HAYWARD Deborah	Albion Chambers
	HORTON Mark	Colleton Chambers
	JACKLIN Susan	St John's Chambers
	KER-REID John	Pump Court Chambers
	MARSTON Nicholas	St John's Chambers
	MEREDITH George	Southernhay Chambers
	NAISH Christopher	Southernhay Chambers
	PINE-COFFIN Margaret	17 Carlton Crescent

For details of these leading barristers see Profiles on p.1339

At **Albion Chambers** (see full details p.1581) the "ferociously hardworking" **Stephen Wildblood QC** gained a recent feather in his cap through his work on the headline case White v White. **Charles Hyde**, said to "have the ear of the judges," is a new entrant to our lists this year, having been warmly praised by local solicitors. **Claire Wills-Goldingham** has carved a niche in child care, and a reputation as a "steel magnolia, eminently reasonable but prepared to dig her heels in." **Deborah Dinan-Hayward** (see p.1371) is also recommended in the field of matrimonial law as "a gifted practitioner with a relaxed manner." **St John's Chambers** (see full details p.1583) is home to a number of the region's most renowned barristers. **Christopher Sharp QC** (see p.1446) is "second to none for tenacity, reliability and attention to detail" in the conduct of high value ancillary relief matters. **Ralph Dixon** is "a superb money case practitioner," while **Richard Bromilow** (see p.1356) attracts praise for his "straightforward and easily intelligible" advice to clients. **Sheelagh Corfield**, a recent arrival to the set from Guildhall Chambers, specialises in the financial implications of divorce and "handles even the most troublesome of clients beautifully." Doing both children and finance work, **Susan Jacklin** (see p.1400) is acknowledged as an authority on child abduction cases, while "client-sensitive" **Nick Marston** (see p.1416) was also commended. **Southernhay Chambers** (see full details p.1588) boasts the services of **Susan Campbell** (see p.1359), who "applies a delicate touch" in her children work, and is said to "tackle clients and judges alike with great tact." Her colleague **George Meredith** (see p.1421) ("as straight as a die") is recognised for his abilities in the child care field, while the "diligent" **Chris Naish** (see p.1426) has strong connections with local authorities. In Winchester, **Pump Court Chambers** (see full details p.1617) provides three new entrants to the tables this year. **John Ker-Reid** (see p.1405) is "an experienced operator in public law," often instructed by guardians. Also active in high value ancillary relief work, he appeared for the wife in White v White. **Edward Boydell** (see p.1353) specialises in complex financial cases, often with an agricultural nature, while the "tenacious" **Miranda Allardice** (see p.1342) is known for her thorough knowledge of Inheritance Act matters. Despite the departure of Sheelagh Corfield, **Guildhall Chambers** (see full details p.1581) retain the services of two of the most highly rated local juniors. **Catriona Duthie** takes a vigorous stance in her ancillary relief cases, and is "guaranteed to provide fireworks." Ex-solicitor **Nicholas Miller** is a "rising presence" in the financial sphere, and was praised for his thoroughness and client handling skills. Highly skilled in high value ancillary relief matters, **Mark Evans QC** of **Queen Square Chambers** is a "seasoned practitioner" who is "the man to go to if you want to pull off a result against the odds." In Southampton, **17 Carlton Crescent** is home to the "studious" **Margaret Pine-Coffin**, who handles both financial and care work "with great efficiency." At **Colleton Chambers**, **Mark Horton** (see p.1397) again received market commendation as a "sound" practitioner, dealing with public law child care cases.

WALES & CHESTER CIRCUIT

LEADING SILKS • Wales & Chester		
1	CROWLEY Jane	30 Park Place
2	BISHOP Malcolm	30 Park Place

For details of these leading barristers see Profiles on p.1339

LEADING JUNIORS • Wales & Chester		
1	FURNESS Jonathan	30 Park Place
	MIFFLIN Helen	30 Park Place
	PARRY Isabel	9 Park Place
	TILLYARD James	30 Park Place
2	ALLEN Mark	30 Park Place
	HENKE Ruth	Iscoed Chambers
	MORGAN Lynne	Temple Chambers
	WALTERS Jill	33 Park Place

For details of these leading barristers see Profiles on p.1339

Generally regarded as "by far the leading set in Wales for this type of work," **30 Park Place** (see full details p.1585) includes a host of recommended practitioners. Prominent among them are **Jane Crowley QC** (see p.1368), a "highly accomplished" expert on children cases, and **Malcolm Bishop QC**, who laces his general practice with a specialism in child care. An impressive array of juniors includes **James Tillyard** and **Jonathan Furness** (see p.1382), both characterised as "excellent with figures," who undertake high value ancillary relief. **Helen Mifflin** is a pure family specialist, known for her care practice, while **Mark Allen** has a "lovely way with the clients," and is recommended for children matters. **9 Park Place** (see full details p.1584) is home to **Isabel Parry**, an all-rounder with "extensive legal knowledge" and "the knack of getting things spot on." At **Iscoed Chambers** (see full details p.1616), **Ruth Henke** is said to be "meticulous in her preparation" of high value ancillary relief and child care cases, while **Lynne Morgan** of **Temple Chambers** received praise for her "sureness of touch in all areas of family law." The star at **33 Park Place** (see full details p.1585) is **Jill Walters**, who handles a substantial proportion of the Official Solicitor's local work.

MIDLANDS CIRCUIT

LEADING SILKS • Midlands		
1	MACUR Julia	St Ive's Chambers
NEW SILKS		
	KEEHAN Michael	St Ive's Chambers

For details of these leading barristers see Profiles on p.1339

LEADING JUNIORS • Midlands		
1	BROWN Stephanie	5 Fountain Court
	HERSHMAN David	St Philip's Chambers
	HODGSON Margaret	St Ive's Chambers
	ROGERS Mark	St Mary's Chambers Family Law Chambers
	ROWLAND Robin	5 Fountain Court
	SMALLWOOD Anne	5 Fountain Court
	THOMAS Sybil	3 Fountain Court
2	BUSH Rosalind	5 Fountain Court
	CASEY Mairin	St Mary's Chambers Family Law Chambers
	FARQUHAR Stuart	St Mary's Chambers Family Law Chambers
	JAMES Christopher	5 Fountain Court
3	BUCHANAN Vivien	St Mary's Chambers Family Law Chambers
	BUTLER Christopher	St Mary's Chambers Family Law Chambers
	GILEAD Beryl	St Mary's Chambers Family Law Chambers
	MEYER Lorna	5 Fountain Court
	PAGE Nigel	St Mary's Chambers Family Law Chambers
	SOMERVILLE Bryce	No.6 Fountain Court

For details of these leading barristers see Profiles on p.1339

St Ive's Chambers can call on the expertise of "the outstanding figure on the circuit," **Julia Macur QC**, renowned for both ancillary relief and child care cases. New silk **Michael Keehan QC** (see p.1405) is similarly active in these areas, and is said to display "conscientiousness and drive." **Margaret Hodgson** (see p.1396) is "a distinguished senior junior," particularly adept at child care cases. Numerically one of the strongest presence in *Chambers'* rankings, **5 Fountain Court** (see full details p.1577) includes a host of top-rated juniors. As ancillary relief practitioners, **Stephanie Brown** "always gives her opponents a run for their money" and **Robin Rowland** can be relied on to take a "vigorous approach." **Anne Smallwood** rises in the rankings for her "excellent financial work," often appearing in cases issued in London. **Rosalind Bush** impresses in child care cases for being "tough and straight-talking," while **Christopher James** and **Lorna Meyer** were also commended for their work in ancillary relief and child care respectively. In the east of the region, **St Mary's Chambers** in Nottingham is felt to lead the way. **Mark Rogers** displays "diligence and industry" in ancillary relief and children matters. **Mairin Casey** is "easy to deal with" in child care matters, while **Stuart Farquhar** "never wastes the court's or the client's time." **Beryl Gilead** and **Nigel Page** are highly rated for children and ancillary relief matters respectively, while newcomer to the rankings **Christopher Butler** is an "old hand on high level cases." **Vivien Buchanan**, a Deputy District Judge, has an established reputation for her mixed public and private law practice. Back in Birmingham, **St Philip's Chambers** (see full details p.1578) houses the "effervescent" **David Hershman** (see p.1394), who boasts one of the region's outstanding reputations for complex child care and abduction cases. At **3 Fountain Court**, **Sybil Thomas** (see p.1460) handles the full spectrum of family work, and is "eagle-eyed and assiduous" in her approach to paperwork. **Bryce Somerville** of **6 Fountain Court** gained recognition for his "affable and sensitive nature" on ancillary relief cases.

NORTH EASTERN CIRCUIT

LEADING SILKS • North Eastern		
1	BRADLEY Sally	York Chambers
	HAMILTON Eleanor	No.6 Barristers Chambers

For details of these leading barristers see Profiles on p.1339

LEADING JUNIORS • North Eastern		
★	ISAACS Paul	Mercury Chambers
1	CAHILL Sally	Park Lane Chambers
	KENNERLEY Ian	Broad Chare Chambers
	KNOX Christopher	Trinity Chambers
2	BICKERDIKE Roger	Zenith Chambers
	COHEN Raphael	Mercury Chambers
	GLOVER Stephen	37 Park Square
3	ARMSTRONG Kester	Broad Chare Chambers
	HAJIMITSIS Anthony	Zenith Chambers
	HUDSON Rachel	Trinity Chambers
	LIGHTWING Stuart	Counsel's Chambers
	PYE Jayne	Sovereign Chambers
	RICHARDSON James	Trinity Chambers
	SHELTON Gordon	Broadway House
	THORNTON Rebecca	Zenith Chambers
	WILSON Adam	No.6 Barristers Chambers
	WOOD Martin	Broadway House

For details of these leading barristers see Profiles on p.1339

At **York Chambers, Sally Bradley QC** is "remarkably accomplished" in public law and child care work, and is seen by some as "the leading silk in Newcastle." At **Broad Chare Chambers** (see full details p.1608), "premier local junior" **Ian Kennerley** (see p.1405) is "thorough and knowledgeable," possessing a "good rapport with both clients and judges." **Kester Armstrong** enters our tables in recognition of his experience in both ancillary relief and child care matters. Also in Newcastle, **Trinity Chambers** (see full details p.1610) continues to strengthen its hand in the sector, a point underlined by the elevation to the rankings of the "studious and tenacious" **James Richardson** (see p.1440), and the sustained progress of the "dynamic" **Rachel Hudson** (see p.1398). Meanwhile, the experienced **Christopher Knox** (see p.1407) is "flamboyant and well-informed," and "inspires confidence in both solicitors and clients." In Leeds, the "tried and tested" **Eleanor Hamilton QC** of **No.6 Barristers Chambers** is "bright, bouncy and knows her way around." She has acted on a number of multi-million pound divorce settlements, often leading the set's respected junior **Adam Wilson**. Jane Shipley has gone to the bench. **Mercury Chambers** can count on the presence of the "combative" **Paul Isaacs** (see p.1400), universally seen as "the top man in the city," as well as the enthusiastically endorsed **Raphael Cohen** (see p.1365). **Zenith Chambers** (see full details p.1596) – the result of a merger between 9 Woodhouse Square and 10 Park Square – can point to **Roger Bickerdike** (see p.1350), "a very strong counsel" specialising in child care, and "definitely one you want on your side." His colleague **Rebecca Thornton** (see p.1460) is "a senior and polished barrister," especially noted for her advocacy skills. From the former 10 Park Square, **Anthony Hajimitsis** (see p.1390) is rated for his work on children cases; he "has a good mind and a dogged nature."At **Park Lane Chambers** (see full details p.1592), **Sally Cahill** is experienced in both financial and children matters and "is someone I would turn to without hesitation." The "formidable intellect" of **Stephen Glover** (see p.1386) at **37 Park Square** (see full details p.1594) remains highly rated by his peers, while at **Sovereign Chambers** (see full details p.1595), **Jayne Pye** (see p.1437) maintains her share of market support. In Middlesbrough, **Stuart Lightwing** (see p.1412) of **Counsel's Chambers** is seen as a "proficient" matrimonial finance practitioner, while **Broadway House** (see full details p.1580) in Bradford numbers **Gordon Shelton** (see p.1447) and newcomer to the ratings **Martin Wood** (see p.1470) among its practitioners. Both received market approval for their general family practices.

NORTHERN CIRCUIT

LEADING SILKS • Northern		
1	RYDER Ernest	Deans Court Chambers
2	DE HAAS Margaret	7 Harrington Street Chambers

For details of these leading barristers see Profiles on p.1339

LEADING JUNIORS • Northern		
1	BOOTH Alan	Deans Court Chambers
2	BANCROFT Louise	Deans Court Chambers
	DODDS Stephen	15 Winckley Square
	GAL Sonia	28 St John St
	HARRISON Sally	28 St John St
	OWEN Gail	India Buildings Chambers
	RODDY Maureen	India Buildings Chambers
3	ASHWORTH Fiona	40 King St
	BENNETT Martyn	Oriel Chambers
	DUGGAN Ross	India Buildings Chambers
	EDGE Timothy	Deans Court Chambers
	GREENWOOD Celestine	Chavasse Court Chambers
	HEATON Frances	Deans Court Chambers
	JOHNSON Christine	14 Castle Street
	KENNEDY Michael	India Buildings Chambers
	SANDER Andrew	Oriel Chambers
	SINGLETON Sarah	28 St John St
	WALKER Jane	28 St John St
	WALLWORK Bernard	28 St John St

For details of these leading barristers see Profiles on p.1339

In Liverpool, **India Buildings Chambers** (see full details p.1599) covers all areas of family law, but has a preponderance of child law experts. The set is briefed by 15 local authorities and has in **Gail Owen** (see p.1430) "a renowned expert," who represented the American mother of the twins in the Kilshaw adoption case. **Maureen Roddy** and **Michael Kennedy** (see p.1405) are regularly briefed by local authorities and guardians, while **Ross Duggan** (see p.1372) also impresses peers, and sits part time as a Recorder. In the same city, **Martyn Bennett** of **Oriel Chambers** (see full details p.1600) "displays a sure touch in high value cases," while his colleague **Andrew Sander** enters the tables this year following consistent peer recommendation. **Christine Johnson** (see p.1402) of **14 Castle Street** (see full details p.1597) is said to be "a solid youngster with a bright future," while **Celestine Greenwood** of **Chavasse Court Chambers** also received strong market support. **Margaret De Haas QC** (see p.1370) at **7 Harrington Street Chambers** (see full details p.1599) maintains an increasingly busy caseload. At Manchester's **Deans Court Chambers** (see full details p.1602), **Ernest Ryder QC** (see p.1443) remains a solicitor's favourite. "Meticulous in everything he does, he is loved to death by clients," and features on high value ancillary relief cases. **Alan Booth** (see p.1352) rises to the top band of juniors due to his "analytical prowess" and "reasoned approach" while the "persistent" **Louise Bancroft** (see p.1346) also improves her standing this year. **Tim Edge** (see p.1374) continues to receive a good press and **Frances Heaton**, "a sensitive but steely child practitioner," maintains her inexorable rise. **28 St John Street** may have lost Lindsey Kushner QC to the bench, but the set preserves its reputation through the strength of its juniors. **Sonia Gal** (see p.1383) handles complex finance matters with "great determination and a quickness of mind" and appeared in Smith v Smith. **Sally Harrison** (see p.1392) "gets better and better," appearing regularly on behalf of CAFCAS. She recently appeared in the high profile money matter N v N. **Sarah Singleton** (see p.1449), **Jane Walker** (see p.1465) and **Bernard Wallwork** (see p.1466) were all consistently praised by solicitors. At **40 King Street** (see full details p.1604) **Fiona Ashworth** (see p.1344) is a "fine junior who hates to lose" while **Stephen Dodds** of **15 Winckley Square** (see full details p.1614) attracts sound reviews from both peers and solicitors.

FINANCIAL SERVICES

RESEARCH: The rankings are based on in-depth interviews with over 5,000 solicitors and barristers in the UK. Chambers research is audited by the British Market Research Bureau (see page 7 for details).

Barristers' profiles 1339-1472

OVERVIEW: Within the confines of the Financial Services Act, financial services work for the Bar continues to narrow in scope. Whereas in 1986 when the FSA came into force, counsel's advice was sought on a broad range of principles, now most City players now rarely go to the bar, seeking either endorsement of opinion or advice on specific matters such as offshore related regulatory issues and new financial services products. It remains to be seen whether the introduction of the Financial Services and Markets Act will generate another upsurge of instruction during the bedding down period. Work on the disciplinary side is more widespread, covering specific regulatory decisions to challenges and disciplinary proceedings. As the table reflects, this is still an area where silks are instructed in preference to juniors.

LONDON

	FINANCIAL SERVICES • London	QCs	Jnrs
1	**Blackstone Chambers** (Baxendale/Flint)	2	-
	Erskine Chambers (Robin Potts QC)	1	1
	Four New Square (Justin Fenwick QC)	1	1
	4 Stone Buildings (Philip Heslop QC)	4	-
	3 Verulam Buildings (Symons/Jarvis)	2	-

Numbers show recommended barristers in this practice area

	LEADING SILKS • London	
★	**POTTS Robin**	Erskine Chambers
	POWELL John	Four New Square
	SUMPTION Jonathan	Brick Court Chambers
1	**BLAIR Michael**	3 Verulam Buildings
	BLAIR William	3 Verulam Buildings
	FLINT Charles	Blackstone Chambers
2	**BRIGGS Michael**	Serle Court
	BRINDLE Michael	Fountain Court
	DOHMANN Barbara	Blackstone Chambers
3	**BOMPAS Anthony**	4 Stone Buildings
	BRISBY John	4 Stone Buildings
	HESLOP Philip	4 Stone Buildings
	HILDYARD Robert	4 Stone Buildings

For details of these leading barristers see Profiles on p.1339

	LEADING JUNIORS • London	
1	**LOMNICKA Eva**	Four New Square
2	**MARQUAND Charles**	4 Stone Buildings
	SNOWDEN Richard	Erskine Chambers

This book is the product of 6,552 1/2-hour interviews. See p.7 for BMRB audit.
For details of these leading barristers see Profiles on p.1339

Blackstone Chambers (see full details p.1481) The set's "first rate" reputation in administrative and public law spills over into its specialist financial services regulatory, advisory and judicial review work on behalf of offshore banks, brokers and regulators. "Astute and perceptive," **Charles Flint QC** (see p.1379) "has more of a slant on financial services than most." He enjoys a profile on advisory matters, as a member of the Financial Services Lawyers Consultative Committee, and equally on contentious matters, in which peers describe him as "a tough, hard fighter." With a primarily contentious practice, advising on serious problems involving the SFA and DTI, "terrific" **Barbara Dohmann QC** (see p.1371) is feared as "quite a rottweiler" and is "a splendid choice for trench warfare defence."

Erskine Chambers (see full details p.1495) "They have the head start over the rest", having grown up within the pioneering tradition set by Richard Sykes QC. Some major players "would go to them for almost anyone" in the set. Its advisory capability on company law aspects of financial services casts a shadow beyond the FSA per se, with notable expertise in banking aspects involving securities and takeovers. A "doughty litigator with an equally good advisory practice" **Robin Potts QC** "really is exceptionally experienced – an outstandingly clever man." Junior counsel **Richard Snowden** (see p.1450) advises on financial services as part of a mixed practice and is said by clients to be "responsive, he drives quite hard" on matters.

Four New Square (see full details p.1543) Equally well known in the field of professional negligence, **John Powell QC** (see p.1435) is nevertheless a name people "immediately think of" as a "true specialist" in the field of financial services. Clients testify as to the depth of his "valuable experience," while peers hail him as "exceptionally able." He edits and co-authors the Financial Services Encyclopaedia with his wife, **Eva Lomnicka** (see p.1413). Specialist in consumer credit law, she has authored several texts on this subject. Clients think she's "simply excellent" because "she has everything at her fingertips – there's no need to lay it out because she's there with you," while peers acknowledge that "there aren't that many who come near her in level of experience."

4 Stone Buildings (see full details p.1568) The set's involvement in advisory and disciplinary matters springs from its roots in company law. Noted for his ability to deal with "superficially unattractive cases," **Philip Heslop QC** can "give advice direct to the client with no holds barred but isn't nasty about it." "Extremely tenacious," **John Brisby QC** (see p.1355) is described by peers as "a tough cross examiner – he will fight a point to the death and spot others you've not begun to think about." **Anthony Bompas QC** (see p.1352) is "more reflective in his approach" but "responsive and practical." Others recommended in the set are "popular" **Robert Hildyard QC** (see p.1394) and "personable" junior counsel **Charles Marquand** (see p.1416).

3 Verulam Buildings (see full details p.1575) Splitting advisory and disciplinary capability equally, this set's major strengths lie in banking and financial services work. "Careful, precise and cautious" **William Blair QC** (see p.1351) is rated by peers and clients alike for his "encyclopaedic knowledge." Matters he has been advising on include the establishment of a major electronic clearing and settlement service, foreign exchange dealing, the investment management services of a new UK bank and regulatory aspects of insurance companies. Returning to the Bar, former General Counsel of the FSA **Michael Blair QC** (see p.1351) gains unstinting approval – "he knows the stuff backwards – he wrote it!"

Other Notable Practitioners Although regarded as "the classic generalist," his "incisive mind, rare analytical powers and judgement" render **Jonathan Sumption QC** (see p.1455) at **Brick Court Chambers** "the first rate choice for a detached view and for a sensitive case." "Star all-rounder" **Michael Briggs QC** (see p.1355) at **Serle Court Chambers** has the "charm and sheer academic ability" which clients seek for "running a point before a judge or in the Court of Appeal." Expert on banking related matters such as money laundering, **Michael Brindle QC** (see p.1355) at **Fountain Court** is "an exceptionally good advocate," and clients are "impressed with his advice."

FRAUD

RESEARCH: The rankings are based on in-depth interviews with over 5,000 solicitors and barristers in the UK. Chambers research is audited by the British Market Research Bureau (see page xx for details).

FRAUD: CRIMINAL

FRAUD: CRIMINAL • London		QCs	Jnrs
1	**Hollis Whiteman Chambers** (Bevan/Whiteman)	9	7
2	**3 Raymond Buildings** (Clive Nicholls QC)	5	5
3	**2 Bedford Row** (William Clegg QC)	3	5
	9-12 Bell Yard (Anthony Evans QC)	2	1
	23 Essex Street (Michael Lawson QC)	5	-
	6 King's Bench Walk (Roy Amlot QC)	2	1
4	**5 Paper Buildings** (Carey/Caplan)	2	-
	18 Red Lion Court (Anthony Arlidge QC)	4	-

This book is the product of 6,552 1/2-hour interviews. See p.7 for BMRB audit.

For details of these leading barristers see Profiles on p.1339

LEADING SILKS • London		
★	BEVAN Julian	Hollis Whiteman Chambers
	LAWSON Edmund	9-12 Bell Yard
	MONTGOMERY Clare	Matrix Chambers
	PURNELL Nicholas	23 Essex Street
1	AMLOT Roy	6 King's Bench Walk
	BATTEN Stephen	3 Raymond Buildings
	EVANS David	Hollis Whiteman Chambers
	GLASS Anthony	Hollis Whiteman Chambers
	JONES Alun	3 Raymond Buildings
	LANGDALE Timothy	Hollis Whiteman Chambers
	MITCHELL Andrew	Furnival Chambers
	NICHOLLS Clive	3 Raymond Buildings
	TROLLOPE Andrew	1 Middle Temple Lane
2	ARLIDGE Anthony	18 Red Lion Court
	CLEGG William	2 Bedford Row
	HILL Michael	23 Essex Street
	KELSEY-FRY John	Hollis Whiteman Chambers
	MACDONALD Ken	Matrix Chambers
	SINGH Kuldip	5 Paper Buildings
3	CAPLAN Jonathan	5 Paper Buildings
	CROXFORD Ian	Wilberforce Chambers
	GODFREY Howard	2 Bedford Row
	GRIEVE Michael	Doughty Street Chambers
	HACKETT Philip	2 Bedford Row
	LAWSON Michael	23 Essex Street
	LISSACK Richard	35 Essex Street
	MISKIN Charles	23 Essex Street
	NICHOLLS Colin	3 Raymond Buildings
	ROBINSON Vivian	Hollis Whiteman Chambers
	ROOK Peter	18 Red Lion Court
	SHAW Antony	18 Red Lion Court
	SOLLEY Stephen	Charter Chambers
	SUCKLING Alan	Hollis Whiteman Chambers
	TEMPLE Victor	6 King's Bench Walk
	WHITEHOUSE David	3 Raymond Buildings
4	ETHERINGTON David	18 Red Lion Court
	GOLDBERG Jonathan	3 Temple Gardens
	KYTE Peter	Hollis Whiteman Chambers
	LYNCH Jerome	Charter Chambers
	PARROY Michael	3 Paper Buildings
	RAWLEY Alan	35 Essex Street
	SCRIVENER Anthony	2-3 Gray's Inn Square
	WOOD Michael	23 Essex Street
NEW SILKS		
	BOWES Michael	2 King's Bench Walk
	BOYCE William	Hollis Whiteman Chambers
	CHAWLA Mukul	9-12 Bell Yard

For details of these leading barristers see Profiles on p.1339

Hollis Whiteman Chambers (see full details p.1524) "An outstanding set with depth," and consistently seen in the plum cases. **Julian Bevan QC** (see p.1350), "the maestro," leads from the front appearing in headline matters such as the Jubilee Line Fraud, and the Andrew Regan Co-op fraud. **David Evans QC** (see p.1376) has had another busy year, which included work on the Daulby whisky and champagne investment fraud. Also eliciting warm commendation, **Timothy Langdale QC** (see p.1408) has been active in the labyrinthine Hinchcliffes case, and **Anthony Glass QC** (see p.1385) is "an able silk who combines thoroughness with flair." Other names involved in the meatier affairs include **Vivian Robinson QC** (see p.1441), **Peter Kyte QC** (see p.1408), "deadly cross-examiner" **Alan Suckling QC** (see p.1455) and **John Kelsey-Fry QC** (see p.1405) who was complimented on his "outstanding paper work and advocacy in the Jubilee Line Case." This distinguished body of silks has now been augmented by the elevation of **William Boyce QC** (see p.1353), whose "deadpan expression mantles a lively mind." A collection of talented juniors waits in attendance. **Mark Ellison** (see p.1375) is "thoroughly excellent" and has just been made a Senior Treasury Council, while **Ian Winter** "wins arguments you wouldn't expect him to and is clearly going straight to the top." **Gareth Rees** (see p.1439) gained credit for his "fantastic relationship with clients" while **Thomas Kark** (see p.1404) is deemed to be "a careful lawyer adept at negotiating the pernickety point." **Peter Finnigan** (see p.1378), **Peter Doyle** and **Ian Stern** (see p.1453) also garnered plaudits.

3 Raymond Buildings (see full details p.1560) "Stuffed to the gills with quality barristers," this set challenges for top honours. **Stephen Batten QC** (see p.1348) has been applying his undoubted talents more to straight crime of late but persists as a leader in fraud and is due to appear in a number of major cases. **Clive Nicholls QC** (see p.1428) maintains his "first class international practice" which has seen him represent 32 sovereign states, while his brother **Colin Nicholls QC** (see p.1428) has a recognised specialism in extradition work. **Alun Jones QC** (see p.1403) runs an orthodox practice with "great diligence and ferociousness" while **David Whitehouse QC** (see p.1468) has been occupied with the long-running John Palmer timeshare trial. Gifted juniors **Alexander Cameron** (see p.1358), **Michael Bromley-Martin** (see p.1356) and **Helen Malcolm** are joined in the rankings by two newcomers this year: the "solid and industrious" **Simon Farrell** (see p.1377) and **Richard Wormald** (see p.1471), who impresses as being "quick on the uptake."

2 Bedford Row (see full details p.1476) Associated primarily with defence work, the set is headed by **William Clegg QC** (see p.1363), a barrister "ever in demand." It houses **Howard Godfrey QC** (see p.1386), "a great one with the juries," and **Philip Hackett QC**, whose "boundless self-belief" has gained him many important briefs. Top of the juniors, **James Sturman** (see p.1455) "gratifies in every respect" courtesy of his "unceasing commitment." He sits alongside the "bright as a button" **Brian Altman** (see p.1342), **Jonathan Ashley-Norman** (see p.1344) and **Nigel Ingram**, who elicits praise for his "equable and unruffled style." New to

LEADING JUNIORS • London		
1	ELLISON Mark	Hollis Whiteman Chambers
	PERRY David	6 King's Bench Walk
	STURMAN Jim	2 Bedford Row
2	CAMERON Alexander	3 Raymond Buildings
	STAFFORD-MICHAEL Simon	4 King's Bench Walk
	WINTER Ian	Hollis Whiteman Chambers
3	DOYLE Peter	Hollis Whiteman Chambers
	EGAN Michael	9-12 Bell Yard
	REES Gareth	Hollis Whiteman Chambers
4	ALTMAN Brian	2 Bedford Row
	ASHLEY-NORMAN Jonathan	2 Bedford Row
	BROMLEY-MARTIN Michael	3 Raymond Buildings
	FARRELL Simon	3 Raymond Buildings
	FINNIGAN Peter	Hollis Whiteman Chambers
	INGRAM Nigel	2 Bedford Row
	KARK Tom	Hollis Whiteman Chambers
	LUCAS Noel	1 Middle Temple Lane
	MALCOLM Helen	3 Raymond Buildings
	MATTHEWS Richard	2 Bedford Row
	STERN Ian	Hollis Whiteman Chambers
	WINBERG Stephen	2-4 Tudor Street
	WORMALD Richard	3 Raymond Buildings

For details of these leading barristers see Profiles on p.1339

the list this year is **Richard Matthews** (see p.1417), a "strident performer, not easily cowed."

9-12 Bell Yard (see full details p.1480) An umbrella criminal set with a highly defined fraud specialism. "A class act by anybody's standards," **Edmund Lawson QC** (see p.1409) is one of the top-flight this field. Although busy with the Bloody Sunday Inquiry of late, he garnered universal approval as a "revered practitioner who commands the respect of the bench." It is no surprise that he now has a fellow silk in **Mukul Chawla QC** (see p.1361), a "silky smooth advocate" whose success has been much trumpeted. Skilled junior **Michael Egan** (see p.1374) merits inclusion for his involvement in the weightier matters.

23 Essex Street (see full details p.1501) Another white-collar crime set, which is home to one of the titans in the area. **Nicholas Purnell QC** (see p.1437) has shone in some of the most eagerly followed cases of recent years including Blue Arrow and the Guinness trial. He has "frightening intelligence" and is "one of the best, if not the best, tactician around." The "debonair" **Michael Hill QC** (see p.1394) and **Michael Lawson QC** (see p.1409) both undertake fraud within the context of glittering general criminal practices while **Charles Miskin QC** (see p.1422) is known for his "sedulous nature." Completing an impressive line-up of silks is **Michael Wood QC** (see p.1470), sometime prosecutor for the SFO.

6 King's Bench Walk (see full details p.1529) **Roy Amlot QC** (see p.1342), a practitioner of national renown, brings to fraud the same "dedication, focus and examination" as his other shades of criminal work. His most distinguished colleague at the set is **Victor Temple QC**, capable of "filleting a fat brief quickly." The set's pride and joy on the junior front is **David Perry** (see p.1433), a Treasury Council and "absolutely outstanding practitioner."

5 Paper Buildings (see full details p.1554) Often retained by the Customs & Excise to handle fraud matters, this set is headed by **Jonathan Caplan QC** who has been "engaged on high kudos work for many years." **Kuldip Singh QC** remains "highly sought after" and a firm favourite of solicitors. "An incisive analyst," he received unanimous support.

18 Red Lion Court (see full details p.1561) A chambers incorporating standing counsel to the Inland Revenue and possessing a clutch of polished performers. **Anthony Arlidge QC** (see p.1344) is hailed as "a fine cross-examiner" with "a wonderful practice and an unsurpassed command of court room procedure." **Peter Rook QC** prosecutes for the Customs and Excise and is "utterly reliable, with an eye like a Swiss watchmaker." His distinguished colleagues include **Antony Shaw QC** (see p.1447) and **David Etherington QC** (see p.1376).

Other Notable Practitioners Matrix Chambers' profile is enhanced by the presence of **Clare Montgomery QC** (see p.1423), praised as a "deluxe advocate with an excellent forensic mind." **Ken Macdonald QC** is seen to "pop up in all the best stuff," having appeared in the Jubilee Line and Hinchcliffe cases. **Andrew Trollope QC** (see p.1462) of **1 Middle Temple Lane** "gets to grips with the papers early on" and is "strong in the courtroom" while colleague **Noel Lucas** is standing counsel to HM Customs & Excise. At **Furnival Chambers**, **Andrew Mitchell QC** (see p.1422) has an international practice, which he conducts with "guile and intelligence." **Ian Croxford QC** (see p.1368) is a "fine fraud practitioner" in the heavily commercial and chancery based **Wilberforce Chambers**. Similarly, **Michael Grieve QC** of **Doughty Street Chambers** operates in a set with a great diversity of work and is acknowledged to be "an all round brilliant advocate." **Charter Chambers** boasts two respected practitioners in **Stephen Solley QC** and **Jerome Lynch QC** (see p.1414) who were noted for their "presence in court." A small but effective presence in the fraud market at **35 Essex Street**, where **Richard Lissack QC** (see p.1412) and **Alan Rawley QC** (see p.1438) are the most admired. **Jonathan Goldberg QC** (see p.1387) of **3 Temple Gardens** "carries himself well in court." **Michael Parroy QC** of **3 Paper Buildings** and new silk **Michael Bowes QC** (see p.1353) of **2 King's Bench Walk** also retained market support, as did "occasional but deadly fraud practitioner" **Anthony Scrivener QC** (see p.1444) of **2-3 Gray's Inn Square**. A talented junior, **Simon Stafford-Michael** of **4 King's Bench Walk** "is capable of flashes of brilliance." He is joined in the lists by **Stephen Winberg** of **2-4 Tudor Street** who "works hard and is highly persuasive."

FRAUD: CIVIL

	FRAUD: CIVIL • London	QCs	Jnrs
1	**Fountain Court** (Anthony Boswood QC)	3	1
2	**One Essex Court** (Lord Grabiner QC)	4	3
3	**Blackstone Chambers** (Baxendale/Flint)	2	-
	Serle Court (Lord Neill of Bladen QC)	2	-
	3 Verulam Buildings (Symons/Jarvis)	3	1
4	**Brick Court Chambers** (Christopher Clarke QC)	2	-

This book is the product of 6,552 1/2-hour interviews. See p.7 for BMRB audit.
For details of these leading barristers see Profiles on p.1339

Fountain Court (see full details p.1506) Whilst many fraud cases are not in the public eye this set handles many of those that are. Better known for straight fraud rather than regulatory matters, it is typified by its head **Anthony Boswood QC** (see p.1352) who has "an acute commercial mind" and appeared in the Grupo Torras affair. **Michael Brindle QC** (see p.1355) stands out for the "exquisite quality of his practice" which has led him to appear in the Brunei/Prince Jefri litigation. Embodying the creative nature of the set as a whole, **Nick Stadlen QC** (see p.1452) was applauded for his "imagination in attacking new methods of fraud." New to the tables, **Bankim Thanki** (see p.1459) is a thoroughly respected junior.

One Essex Court (see full details p.1497) A collection of high profile barristers includes **Anthony Grabiner QC** who is "absolutely top drawer" and juggles a substantial practice with his obligations as a member of the House of Lords. **Mark Barnes QC** (see p.1347) "seems to be involved in everything" and has "a creative and user friendly outlook" while **Christopher Carr QC** is an expert in international financially based work. **Elizabeth Gloster QC** (see p.1386) is a commercial heavyweight who adds fraud to her repertoire, and is adept at asset tracing. She continues to be seen in the

LEADING SILKS • London		
1	BRINDLE Michael	Fountain Court
	FLINT Charles	Blackstone Chambers
2	GEERING Ian	3 Verulam Buildings
	GRABINER Anthony	One Essex Court
	SUMPTION Jonathan	Brick Court Chambers
3	BOSWOOD Anthony	Fountain Court
	BRIGGS Michael	Serle Court
	BROWNE-WILKINSON Simon	Serle Court
	DOHMANN Barbara	Blackstone Chambers
	STADLEN Nicholas	Fountain Court
4	BARNES Mark	One Essex Court
	BRISBY John	4 Stone Buildings
	CARR Christopher	One Essex Court
	CROXFORD Ian	Wilberforce Chambers
	GLOSTER Elizabeth	One Essex Court
	JARVIS John	3 Verulam Buildings
	MALEK Ali	3 Verulam Buildings
	MONTGOMERY Clare	Matrix Chambers
	POLLOCK Gordon	Essex Court Chambers
	POPPLEWELL Andrew	Brick Court Chambers
	PURLE Charles	New Square Chambers
	ROSEN Murray	11 Stone Buildings
NEW SILKS		
	DICKER Robin	3-4 South Square
	SMITH Stephen	New Square Chambers

For details of these leading barristers see Profiles on p.1339

LEADING JUNIORS • London		
1	MCCAUGHRAN John	One Essex Court
	MCQUATER Ewan	3 Verulam Buildings
	RABINOWITZ Laurence	One Essex Court
2	DE GARR ROBINSON Anthony	One Essex Court
	THANKI Bankim	Fountain Court
4	SMOUHA Joe	Essex Court Chambers

For details of these leading barristers see Profiles on p.1339

Barlow Clowes International litigation. **Laurence Rabinowitz** (see p.1437) and **John McCaughran** (see p.1418) are "top notch juniors" who have been joined in the tables by **Anthony de Garr Robinson** (see p.1370), an expert in trans-national fraud.

Blackstone Chambers (see full details p.1481) A set with a healthy contingent of informed practitioners active in the larger cases such as Den Norske Bank and the Prince Jefri saga. **Charles Flint QC** (see p.1379) scales the heights of our table on the back of his regulatory work while **Barbara Dohmann QC** (see p.1371) was congratulated for her "resilience and determination" allied to her skills as "a mean cross-examiner."

Serle Court (see full details p.1565) Now housed in new premises at 6 New Square this set includes **Simon Browne-Wilkinson QC** (see p.1356). He is a "powerful performer with a real talent for court work" and "perfect for a tricky case likely to turn on quality advocacy." He possesses a broad practice in common with his colleague **Michael Briggs QC** (see p.1355) who has appeared in both the Barings and Sumitomo Copper litigation.

3 Verulam Buildings (see full details p.1575) "Bright and possessing tremendous judgment," **Ian Geering QC** (see p.1384) represents both claimants and defendants in complex, cross-border frauds. **Ali Malek QC** (see p.1415) is best known as a banking expert, but remains "highly effective both on paper and in court" when he chooses to turn his hand to it. **John Jarvis QC** (see p.1401) is also "a significant presence" and receives heavy endorsement along with respected junior **Ewan McQuater** (see p.1420).

Brick Court Chambers (see full details p.1484) "Brilliant all-rounder" **Jonathan Sumption QC** (see p.1455) was praised by solicitors and fellow barristers alike for his efforts in this field. "Everything he touches is done well" and his "mega intellect" makes him "a formidable advocate." **Andrew Popplewell QC** (see p.1435) drew favourable comments for his "injection into a case of esprit de corps." A number of solicitors described him as "easy to work with" and he was applauded for his "contribution as regards strategy" in any given action.

Other Notable Practitioners **Essex Court Chambers** provides a new entry to our juniors list in the form of **Joe Smouha** (see p.1450), "an efficient lawyer who is a delight to work with." His Head of Chambers, **Gordon Pollock QC** (see p.1434) is known for his "forceful and resourceful attitude and strong advocacy presence," as seen in the Prince Jefri case. **Murray Rosen QC** (see p.1442) of **11 Stone Buildings** is "a feared opponent, both knowledgeable and inventive." **New Square Chambers** houses two high profile individuals in **Charles Purle QC** and **Stephen Smith QC** (see p.1450), while **Robin Dicker QC** (see p.1371) of **3-4 South Square** continues to attract market support. **Clare Montgomery QC** (see p.1423) of **Matrix Chambers** makes her entry on the civil side for the first time this year. **John Brisby QC** (see p.1355) of **4 Stone Buildings** and **Ian Croxford QC** (see p.1368) of **Wilberforce Chambers** were also highly recommended by our interviewees.

HEALTH & SAFETY

RESEARCH: The rankings are based on in-depth interviews with over 5,000 solicitors and barristers in the UK. Chambers research is audited by the British Market Research Bureau (see page 7 for details).

OVERVIEW: A growing number of prosecutions, and an emphasis on the enforcement of health and safety regulations means that this remains a thriving area for the bar. The main focus recently has been on rail enquiries with several notable barristers involved in lengthy procedures. Several have built up considerable expertise, although few choose to specialise.

LONDON

	HEALTH & SAFETY • London	QCs	Jnrs
1	**1 Temple Gardens** (Hugh Carlisle QC)	3	2
2	**2-3 Gray's Inn Square** (Porten/Scrivener)	1	1
	Old Square Chambers (John Hendy QC)	1	1

Numbers show recommended barristers in this practice area

	LEADING SILKS • London	
1	**BURNETT Ian**	1 Temple Gardens
	CARLISLE Hugh	1 Temple Gardens
2	**HENDY John**	Old Square Chambers
3	**DE NAVARRO Michael**	2 Temple Gardens
	FERGUSON Richard	2-4 Tudor Street
	LISSACK Richard	35 Essex Street
	NICE Geoffrey	1 Temple Gardens
	SCRIVENER Anthony	2-3 Gray's Inn Square
NEW SILKS		
	GARNHAM Neil	1 Crown Office Row

For details of these leading barristers see Profiles on p.1339

	LEADING JUNIORS • London	
1	**MORTON Keith**	1 Temple Gardens
2	**GRIEVE Dominic**	1 Temple Gardens
	KILLALEA Stephen	Devereux Chambers
3	**AGEROS James**	2 Bedford Row
	TREVERTON-JONES Gregory	Farrar's Building
4	**FORD Michael**	Doughty Street Chambers
	FORLIN Gerard	2-3 Gray's Inn Square
	PUGH Charles	Old Square Chambers
	WAITE Jonathan	Crown Office Chambers

This book is the product of 6,552 1/2-hour interviews. See p.7 for BMRB audit.
For details of these leading barristers see Profiles on p.1339

1 Temple Gardens (see full details p.1572) "Absolutely the best," **Hugh Carlisle QC** (see p.1359) remains the top choice among solicitors for substantial HSE prosecutions. **Ian Burnett QC** (see p.1357), widely acknowledged as "first class, clever and pleasant" reinforces the set's reputation in this area. The return of the "effective" **Geoffrey Nice QC** (see p.1428) from The Hague further bolsters the set's standing. "Impressive" **Keith Morton** (see p.1424) is seen to have a keen focus on this area, while **Dominic Grieve** (see p.1389) is considered to have a "polished" courtroom manner.

2-3 Gray's Inn Square (see full details p.1513) "Smooth" **Anthony Scrivener QC** (see p.1444) is an active participant in the market, along with the "ebullient" **Gerard Forlin** (see p.1380). Both were involved in recent major rail enquiries on behalf of ASLEF.

Old Square Chambers (see full details p.1549) "Experienced" **John Hendy QC** (see p.1393) received extensive praise for his "tremendous experience" in this area, and acted as counsel for families in the Southall enquiry. **Charles Pugh** (see p.1436) is a "no-nonsense" junior who "gets his hands dirty."

Other Notable Practitioners **Richard Ferguson QC** (see p.1378) at **2-4 Tudor Street** is regarded as "an excellent jury advocate" and **Michael de Navarro QC** (see p.1465) at **2 Temple Gardens** also maintains his "sound" reputation. "Able performer" **Richard Lissack QC** (see p.1412) at **35 Essex Street** has greatly increased his profile through his work on fatal rail crashes, while new silk **Neil Garnham QC** (see p.1383) of **1 Crown Office Row** is said to display "quiet authority." **James Ageros** (see p.1341) at **2 Bedford Row** is lauded for his prosecution work on behalf of the HSE. **Gregory Treverton-Jones** (see p.1359) at **Farrar's Buildings** has impressed contemporaries with his command of the courtroom, while both **Jonathan Waite** (see p.1380) of **Crown Office Chambers** and **Stephen Killalea** (see p.1397) at **Devereux Chambers** are widely rated by peers. **Michael Ford** (see p.1406) at **Doughty Street Chambers** is commended as "truly excellent."

THE REGIONS

	LEADING SILKS • The Regions	
1	**GLOBE Henry**	Exchange Chambers
	HORLOCK Timothy	9 St. John Street

For details of these leading barristers see Profiles on p.1339

	LEADING JUNIORS • The Regions	
1	**CAMERON Neil**	Wilberforce Chambers
	LAMBERT Julian	Albion Chambers
	TRAVERS David	6 Pump Court

For details of these leading barristers see Profiles on p.1339

Timothy Horlock QC (see p.1397) at **9 St. John Street** (see full details p.1607), Manchester, is described by solicitors and rivals as an intelligent "high flier." **Henry Globe QC** (see p.1412) at **Exchange Chambers** (see full details p.1598), Liverpool is "thorough" and "incisive." **Neil Cameron** (see p.1462) at **Wilberforce Chambers** (see full details p.1588) in Hull is rated for his ability to "get results" while **Julian Lambert** (see p.1465) at **Albion Chambers** (see full details p.1581) in Bristol is said to be a "walking text-book." Newly ranked **David Travers** (see p.1462) has recently left 3 Fountain Court in Birmingham to join **6 Pump Court** (see full details p.1559) in London, and is recommended for his client-friendly approach. He will continue to practice on the Midlands Circuit.

HUMAN RIGHTS

RESEARCH: The rankings are based on in-depth interviews with over 5,000 solicitors and barristers in the UK. Chambers research is audited by the British Market Research Bureau (see page 7 for details).

Barristers' profiles 1339-1472

LONDON

HUMAN RIGHTS • London		QCs	Jnrs
1	**Doughty Street Chambers** (Geoffrey Robertson QC)	6	5
2	**Matrix Chambers** (Nicholas Blake QC)	5	5
3	**Blackstone Chambers** (Baxendale/Flint)	3	1
	Cloisters (Laura Cox QC)	2	-
	Two Garden Court (Macdonald/Davies)	1	2
4	**14 Tooks Court** (Michael Mansfield QC)	1	-

Numbers show recommended barristers in this practice area

LEADING SILKS • London		
★	**FITZGERALD Edward**	Doughty Street Chambers
	PANNICK David	Blackstone Chambers
1	**BLAKE Nicholas**	Matrix Chambers
	LESTER Anthony	Blackstone Chambers
2	**EMMERSON Ben**	Matrix Chambers
	NICOL Andrew	Doughty Street Chambers
	OWEN Tim	Matrix Chambers
3	**ALLEN Robin**	Cloisters
	BELOFF Michael	Blackstone Chambers
	COX Laura	Cloisters
	GORDON Richard	Brick Court Chambers
	MACDONALD Ken	Matrix Chambers
	MANSFIELD Michael	14 Tooks Court
	MONTGOMERY Clare	Matrix Chambers
	O'CONNOR Patrick	Doughty Street Chambers
	ROBERTSON Geoffrey	Doughty Street Chambers
	THORNTON Peter	Doughty Street Chambers
4	**DAVIES Owen**	Two Garden Court
	WOOD James	Doughty Street Chambers

For details of these leading barristers see Profiles on p.1339

LEADING JUNIORS • London		
★	**STARMER Keir**	Doughty Street Chambers
1	**HUNT Murray**	Matrix Chambers
	KAUFMANN Phillippa	Doughty Street Chambers
	SINGH Rabinder	Matrix Chambers
2	**MOUNTFIELD Helen**	Matrix Chambers
	ROSE Dinah	Blackstone Chambers
	THOMAS Leslie	Two Garden Court
3	**BLAXLAND Henry**	Two Garden Court
	FORD Michael	Doughty Street Chambers
	LATHAM Robert	Doughty Street Chambers
4	**HUSAIN Raza**	Matrix Chambers
	KNOWLES Julian	Matrix Chambers
	WILLIAMS Heather	Doughty Street Chambers

This book is the product of 6,552 1/2-hour interviews. See p.7 for BMRB audit.
For details of these leading barristers see Profiles on p.1339

Doughty Street Chambers (see full details p.1492) Admired for its approachability, it is "particularly helpful" when it comes to advice at a senior level. The set's focus remains on the criminal related human rights work, for which it is deeply respected. Highly praised public and administrative law work is also continued. Considered by many to have moved into a league of his own, particularly on prisoners' rights, **Edward Fitzgerald QC** (see p.1379) is "clearly a leader." Showing "phenomenal commitment," he also continues his "excellent international work" on the death penalty. Solicitors claim that **Geoffrey Robertson QC** (see p.1441) is "absolutely pre-eminent and untouchable in every way," particularly in media law and freedom of speech issues. Another "key player" in Doughty's armour, **Andrew Nicol QC** (see p.1428) also has an international dimension to his practice and though known for his immigration work he has an extensive range of rights cases. An "immense talent," **Patrick O'Connor QC** is best known for his track record of actions against the police. The civil liberties work of **James Wood QC** (see p.1470) , including police claims, continues to attract praise. Best known for his criminal advocacy, **Peter Thornton QC** (see p.1460) is respected in the sphere of human rights. **Keir Starmer** (see p.1452) is "so immersed" in his rights work, involving the broad spectrum of public law, that for many he remains the natural choice. He continues to play a leading role in shaping civil liberties. **Phillippa Kaufmann** 's involvement in the Daly case, a landmark case in administrative law this year, and her work on prisoners rights, including voting rights and mandatory life sentences, is winning a volume of plaudits. **Michael Ford** (see p.1380) has this year been absorbed by the Paddington rail crash enquiry, but remains well regarded for his work on privacy. **Robert Latham** (see p.1409) has carved out a profile in housing issues and the tenant rights of refugees and the homeless. "Versatile" **Heather Williams** (see p.1468) is recognised for her work in actions against the police.

Matrix Chambers (see full details p.1538) Undoubtedly playing an active role in shaping the human rights agenda, the set enjoys "greater strength and depth than most, but needs some heavy duty writs in the door." Seen by some solicitors to act as "the hired gun, in an attempt to make human rights mainstream," its real strength lies in the development of its younger silks and juniors. Involved most in the civil aspects of law, "real star" **Nick Blake QC** has created controversy among traditionalists who have questioned his representation of certain foreign governments. There is no question that he remains "a bright advocate," warmly endorsed for his work in the House of Lords. Primarily recognised for covering a breadth of criminal cases, often with an international dimension, **Ken MacDonald QC** (see p.1414) is "highly respected and still covering pure human rights cases." **Ben Emmerson QC**, already "prominent," has quickly established his presence as a silk. He "does the work of two lawyers" and has "a great ability to deal with papers and briefings" while being a "fantastic cross examiner." Although focused on criminal matters, **Clare Montgomery QC** (see p.1423) is still regarded as an indispensable advocate in this sphere. "Surely a candidate for the best first year ever" **Tim Owen QC** (see p.1431) has worked on three consecutive House of Lords cases, all on fundamental issues affecting the application of the Human Rights Act. He advises on prisoners' rights cases as well as a broad spectrum of public law work. Acknowledged for sustaining "a happy marriage between the practical and the academic," **Murray Hunt** is "extremely knowledgeable." The "government's advocate of choice," **Rabinder Singh** (see p.1449) is considered "extremely authoritative." Operating with a "clear and strategic mind" on the one hand and "exceptionally able and sympathetic" on the other, his work is generally on the part of the respondent. **Helen Mountfield** (see p.1425) is "academically hard to beat" with a leading text on human rights to her name. **Raza Husain** (see p.1399) is an "outstanding junior barrister" across public law and immigration issues and has an international dimension to his work, including extradition and confiscation matters. **Julian Knowles** (see p.1407) has also established a strong reputation.

Blackstone Chambers (see full details p.1481) Benefiting from its leading expertise in the area, the set has this year attracted the notable addition of **Michael Beloff QC** (see p.1349) , considered "the best advocate of them all," despite the constraints of his other commitments. Continuing to go from strength to strength, chambers pursues a more commercial focus to human rights issues. Undertaking cases of "extraordinary breadth," **David Pannick QC** (see p.1431) dominates the sector with unanimous approval for his "intellectual calibre." Acknowledged for his long-standing expertise, **Anthony Lester QC** (see p.1410) remains a pre-eminent figure in this field. "A real star," **Dinah Rose** (see p.1442) possesses an extensive range of experience including public law (acting both for and against public authorities) and discrimination. Working at ECHR level, she has also represented individuals on human rights matters.

Cloisters (see full details p.1487) Despite suffering a recent exodus of notable practitioners, the set is felt to have weathered the storm, maintaining its impact with a "strong human rights profile from its broader employment base." A leading discrimination and employment barrister, **Laura Cox QC** (see p.1367) remains "hugely respected" particularly for her work at the International Labour Organisation in Geneva. **Robin Allen QC** (see p.1342) also received recommendations.

Two Garden Court (see full details p.1509) Although it has suffered from losses to Matrix, the set is believed to have "the raw material to provide a sterling service." Well known for immigration and inquest work, where its "commitment to the underdog is clear," chambers is also recommended when informal advice is needed. **Owen Davies QC** has a "strategic mind," particularly when it comes to bringing law and campaigning together. "Talented and hard working," **Henry Blaxland** continues to act at ECHR level, notably working with Courtney Griffiths QC on the appeal of the 'M25 Three,' a case central to determining the application of Article 6 in UK domestic law. **Leslie Thomas** (see p.1459) , a specialist in prisoners' rights, inquests and police actions comes widely recommended.

Tooks Chambers Practitioners in the field consistently recommend the set although its focus lies largely in criminal cases within the sphere of human rights related work. With the Shayler case looming large on the horizon, **Michael Mansfield QC** is not to be dismissed as a pure criminal advocate.

Other Notable Practitioners **Richard Gordon QC** (see p.1387), **Brick Court Chambers**, is a leading domestic judicial review lawyer who is best known for his work on a case regarding rights of prisoners to have access to their children.

IMMIGRATION

RESEARCH: The rankings are based on in-depth interviews with over 5,000 solicitors and barristers in the UK. Chambers research is audited by the British Market Research Bureau (see page 7 for details).

Barristers' profiles 1339-1472

LONDON

IMMIGRATION • London		QCs	Jnrs
1	Two Garden Court (Macdonald/Davies)	2	5
2	Doughty Street Chambers (Geoffrey Robertson QC)	1	3
	Matrix Chambers (Nicholas Blake QC)	1	1
3	39 Essex Street (Nigel Pleming QC)	1	1
4	Blackstone Chambers (Baxendale/Flint)	1	-
	6 King's Bench Walk (Sibghat Kadri QC)	1	1
	Tooks Court Chambers (Michael Mansfield QC)	-	3

Numbers show recommended barristers in this practice area

LEADING SILKS • London		
1	BLAKE Nicholas	Matrix Chambers
	MACDONALD Ian	Two Garden Court
	PANNICK David	Blackstone Chambers
2	FRANSMAN Laurie	Two Garden Court
	NICOL Andrew	Doughty Street Chambers
	PLEMING Nigel	39 Essex Street
	PLENDER Richard	20 Essex Street
3	GILL Manjit	6 King's Bench Walk

Numbers show recommended barristers in this practice area

LEADING JUNIORS • London		
1	SCANNELL Rick	Two Garden Court
2	GILLESPIE James	Renaissance Chambers
	SOORJOO Martin	Tooks Court Chambers
	WEBBER Frances	Two Garden Court
3	COX Simon	Doughty Street Chambers
	DE MELLO Rambert	6 King's Bench Walk
	EICKE Tim	Essex Court Chambers
	FARBEY Judith	Tooks Court Chambers
	FINCH Nadine	Two Garden Court
	HARRISON Stephanie	Two Garden Court
	HUSAIN Raza	Matrix Chambers
	SEDDON Duran	Two Garden Court
	SOUTHEY Hugh	Tooks Court Chambers
	WALSH John	Doughty Street Chambers
UP AND COMING		
	KOVATS Steven	39 Essex Street
	TAGHAVI Shahram	Doughty Street Chambers

This book is the product of 6,552 1/2-hour interviews. See p.7 for BMRB audit.
For details of these leading barristers see Profiles on p.1339

Two Garden Court (see full details p.1509) Pre-eminent in the field of immigration because "it just offers an astoundingly full range," indeed, last year's newsworthy departures from the set have not dented its "sterling reputation." The "brilliant" **Ian Macdonald QC** (see p.1414) is the "first choice" of many firms who are drawn to his "depth of experience." There is still only "one name in nationality" and it is **Laurie Fransman QC** (see p.1381), according to some solicitors. Described as "a one-man walking nationality textbook," his peers agree "there is nothing you can catch him out with." Two Garden Court is still outstanding in its selection of top juniors. **Rick Scannell** is "a leading junior" and "can advise on all aspects of immigration." The "impressive" **Frances Webber** (see p.1467) is thought to "know the law back to front" and consistently "gives an amazingly high service." **Nadine Finch** (see p.1378) is rated for her expertise in family immigration while **Stephanie Harrison** is deemed "user friendly and clever," and **Duran Seddon** (see p.1444) is "great - my first port of call on appeal cases."

Doughty Street Chambers (see full details p.1492) This set retains its fine reputation with its "committed practitioners" and "uniform quality." The "thoughtful" **Andrew Nicol QC** (see p.1428) is judged to be "a committed advocate" with a long-standing reputation for same-sex and political asylum cases. Experienced in immigration and its correlation with cases concerning children, the "knowledgeable" **Simon Cox** (see p.1367) wins praise for his "strength on cases with welfare rights." **John Walsh** (see p.1466) employs a manner that "wins the ear of the court," while up and coming junior **Shahram Taghavi** (see p.1457) remains a respected advocate.

Matrix Chambers (see full details p.1538) A relatively new entrant to the market, the set is proving to be the mainstay of leading immigration law firms. Head of chambers **Nicholas Blake QC** "has been at the top-flight for years." Our interviewees admired his "ability to mould and affect the law." He is said to "build a rapport with judges" and brings a "creative, innovative and brave" approach to every matter. Leading junior **Raza Husain** (see p.1399) has an established strength in applicant cases and EC free movement issues.

39 Essex Street (see full details p.1503) With a long-held reputation for public law, this set continues to be a preferred choice for Treasury solicitors and other government departments. The "street-fighting" **Nigel Pleming QC** (see p.1434) draws praise for his "broad experience" in cutting edge immigration concerns. Up and coming junior **Steven Kovats** (see p.1407) is an advocate respected by peers and solicitors.

Blackstone Chambers (see full details p.1481) This set's immigration profile is still largely considered as part of its expertise in public law and government cases. The "intellectually brilliant" **David Pannick** (see p.1431) **QC** has been busy on a range of immigration cases this year. He represented the Home Secretary on a case to ascertain whether France and Germany are safe third countries for persons claiming asylum from persecution by non-State agents. "A barrister's barrister," he impresses many solicitors although "immigration is just one bow in his quiver."

6 King's Bench Walk (see full details p.1529) Considered to be a progressive set thanks to a "robust reputation" in civil liberties and its crossover with immigration issues. The "excellent all-rounder" **Manjit Gill QC** is "seen all the time on work permit judicial reviews," and garners plaudits for his third country work. At junior level, the set "has some key players." Administration and immigration specialist **Rambert De Mello** is rated for "his imagination" and deemed a "a top advocate - he finds new angles and diligently follows them through."

Tooks Court Chambers It is at junior level that the set's profile is formed. The "wonderful" **Martin Soorjoo** is respected for an immigration practice that is "committed and imaginative." Peers agree "he works incredibly hard" and "you can rely on him for original solutions." **Hugh Southey** (see p.1451) is admired for his "dedicated approach," which "is not secretive, he'll share ideas for the good of immigration law." Another leading junior in the set is "hard worker" **Judith Farbey** (see p.1377) who wins plaudits for her "well prepared and thorough style."

Other Notable Practitioners Leading junior **James Gillespie** from small outer London set **Renaissance Chambers** is said to have "incredible knowledge" and is "completely reliable with a huge level of immigration experience." The "confident and impressive" **Richard Plender QC** (see p.1434) of **20 Essex Street** combines immigration with some arbitration. **Tim Eicke** (see p.1375) at **Essex Court Chambers** draws praise for his "high quality work," particularly in government cases. Peers commend his "knowledge on European immigration issues."

INFORMATION TECHNOLOGY

RESEARCH: The rankings are based on in-depth interviews with over 5,000 solicitors and barristers in the UK. Chambers research is audited by the British Market Research Bureau (see page 7 for details).

OVERVIEW: Following the support of our interviewees, we once again separate the IT Bar's top practitioners from the leading IP players and we refer you also to that section.

Barristers' profiles 1339-1472

INFORMATION TECHNOLOGY • London		QCs	Jnrs
1	8 New Square (Michael Fysh QC)	2	3
	11 South Square (Christopher Floyd QC)	3	2
2	Three New Square (David Young QC)	1	2

Numbers show recommended barristers in this practice area

LEADING SILKS • London		
1	CARR Henry	11 South Square
2	SILVERLEAF Michael	11 South Square
	WILSON Alastair	19 Old Buildings
3	HOBBS Geoffrey	One Essex Court
	HOWE Martin	8 New Square
4	ARNOLD Richard	11 South Square
	BAATZ Nicholas	Atkin Chambers
	BALDWIN John	8 New Square
	BARNES Mark	One Essex Court
	SMITH Andrew	Fountain Court
	STOREY Jeremy	4 Pump Court
	THORLEY Simon	Three New Square
NEW SILKS		
	BLOCH Selwyn	Littleton Chambers
	STREATFEILD-JAMES David	Atkin Chambers

For details of these leading barristers see Profiles on p.1339

LEADING JUNIORS • London		
1	BURKILL Guy	Three New Square
	MEADE Richard	8 New Square
	SPECK Adrian	8 New Square
2	ALEXANDER Daniel	8 New Square
	BIRSS Colin	Three New Square
	CUNNINGHAM Graham	Littman Chambers
3	FREEDMAN Clive	3 Verulam Buildings
4	CHARLTON Alex	4 Pump Court
	FOXTON David	Essex Court Chambers
	LAWRENCE Heather	11 South Square
	MCCALL Duncan	4 Pump Court
	SHIPLEY Graham	19 Old Buildings
	VANHEGAN Mark	11 South Square

This book is the product of 6,552 1/2-hour interviews. See p.7 for BMRB audit.

For details of these leading barristers see Profiles on p.1339

LONDON

8 New Square (see full details p.1544) The general consensus as to this set was summed up by one practitioner's comment that "we have instructed this set many times – we find its efficiency excellent and the range of barristers large enough to undertake any type of problem." **John Baldwin QC** (see p.1346) maintains his reputation with a following among the 'magic circle' firms. **Martin Howe QC** (see p.1398) is felt to be "copyright-oriented" but "equally capable in IT work." Among the impressive line up of juniors, **Adrian Speck** (see p.1451) drew comment that "he will be a major star of the future," while **Richard Meade** (see p.1420) "always strives for a commercial outcome." "Sharp as a tack" **Daniel Alexander** (see p.1342) is rated for his work on large claims.

11 South Square Still a premier IT set, with the "authoritative but approachable" **Henry Carr QC** (see p.1360) widely acknowledged to be "the leading silk on IT-specific disputes." "Enthusiastic" and "easy to work with," many solicitors appreciate "his depth of experience and client-friendly approach". The "consistently superb" **Michael Silverleaf QC** (see p.1448) is seen to be "an extremely talented lawyer" and is "user-friendly," with one practitioner noting that "he can really understand technical experts and they can understand him." **Richard Arnold QC** (see p.1344) has "a lot of scope to him" and is respected as "a listener – he doesn't just sit and pontificate, he responds to your ideas and gives you a straight answer." Newly ranked juniors **Heather Lawrence** (see p.1409) and **Mark Vanhegan** are also highly rated by the market.

Three New Square (see full details p.1542) "One of the traditional IP/IT Chambers," it contains the "quite brilliant" **Simon Thorley QC** (see p.1460) , who is particularly rated for his "thorough" work concerning "copyright in computer systems." **Guy Burkill** (see p.1357) "speaks the language of the industry" while **Colin Birss** is "technically strong."

Other Notable Practitioners Possessing "weighty gravitas, and the respect of his peers," **Geoffrey Hobbs QC** of **One Essex Court** is described by one practitioner as "an enormously clever man," while a client was of the opinion that his "advice comes with a cast iron guarantee." Fellow chamber member **Mark Barnes QC** (see p.1347) is "accessible and gives constructive, commercial advice." **Alastair Wilson QC** of **19 Old Buildings** is considered "an excellent lawyer" who "rolls his sleeves up, gets his hands dirty and becomes part of the team." Also at this set, **Graham Shipley** "has a computer engineering background" which affords him "technical as well as legal ability." **Jeremy Storey QC** (see p.1454) of **4 Pump Court** is recommended for "disputes as to the performance of computers" while colleague **Alex Charlton** (see p.1361) has "commerciality and approachability in equal measures" and provides "prompt, clear and efficient advice." At the same set, **Duncan McCall** (see p.1418) is said to be "good with clients and easy to work with," and solicitors commend him as "a safe pair of hands in a crisis" and "one of the best for contractual interpretation." **Fountain Court**'s **Andrew Smith QC** has "wonderful technical knowledge." **David Foxton** (see p.1381) of **Essex Court Chambers** received warm endorsement. Peers confirmed that **Nicholas Baatz QC** (see p.1345) of **Atkin Chambers** is "expert in the field," while colleague **David Streatfeild-James QC** is described as "highly cognisant of the industry and the issues." **Selwyn Bloch QC** (see p.1352) of **Littleton Chambers** combines IT expertise with a healthy employment practice, while "impressive" **Graham Cunningham** (see p.1368) of **Littman Chambers** has "raised the awareness of issues affecting the industry." "Bright and highly innovative" **Clive Freedman** (see p.1382) of **3 Verulam Buildings** was also recommended for his work in the field.

INSOLVENCY / CORPORATE RECOVERY

RESEARCH: The rankings are based on in-depth interviews with over 5,000 solicitors and barristers in the UK. Chambers research is audited by the British Market Research Bureau (see page 7 for details).

Barristers' profiles 1339-1472

LONDON

INSOLVENCY/CORPORATE RECOVERY • London		QCs	Jnrs
1	**3-4 South Square** (Crystal/Alexander)	11	15
2	**Erskine Chambers** (Robin Potts QC)	4	3
	4 Stone Buildings (Philip Heslop QC)	3	3
3	**24 Old Buildings** (Mann/Steinfeld)	3	2
	Serle Court (Lord Neill of Bladen QC)	3	1
	Maitland Chambers (Lyndon-Stanford / Aldous)	3	2
	11 Stone Buildings (Murray Rosen QC)	1	4

For details of these leading barristers see Profiles on p.1339

LEADING SILKS • London		
★	**MOSS Gabriel**	3-4 South Square
1	**CRYSTAL Michael**	3-4 South Square
	GLOSTER Elizabeth	One Essex Court
	MANN Anthony	Enterprise Chambers
	POTTS Robin	Erskine Chambers
2	**DICKER Robin**	3-4 South Square
	HACKER Richard	3-4 South Square
	MORTIMORE Simon	3-4 South Square
	OLIVER David	Erskine Chambers
	PHILLIPS Mark	3-4 South Square
3	**BROUGHAM Christopher**	3-4 South Square
	KNOWLES Robin	3-4 South Square
	KOSMIN Leslie	Erskine Chambers
	NEWMAN Catherine	Maitland Chambers
	SHELDON Richard	3-4 South Square
4	**ADKINS Richard**	3-4 South Square
	BANNISTER Edward	3 Stone Buildings
	BOMPAS Anthony	4 Stone Buildings
	BOYLE Alan	Serle Court
	BRIGGS Michael	Serle Court
	BRISBY John	4 Stone Buildings
	COHEN Lawrence	24 Old Buildings
	DAVIS Nigel	Maitland Chambers
	DE LACY Richard	3 Verulam Buildings
	HAMILTON Eben	New Square Chambers
	HESLOP Philip	4 Stone Buildings
	HOLLINGTON Robin	New Square Chambers
	KAYE Roger	24 Old Buildings
	PREVEZER Susan	Essex Court Chambers
	RICHARDS David	Erskine Chambers
	STEINFELD Alan	24 Old Buildings
	VOS Geoffrey	3 Stone Buildings
NEW SILKS		
	GIRET Jane	11 Stone Buildings
	JOFFE Victor	Serle Court
	NEWEY Guy	Maitland Chambers
	TROWER William	3-4 South Square

This book is the product of 6,552 1/2-hour interviews. See p.7 for BMRB audit.
For details of these leading barristers see Profiles on p.1339

3-4 South Square (see full details p.1566) Remains the "blue-chip insolvency set" and chambers of choice nationally, with "superb technical skills" and "people who invariably know what they're talking about – true specialists from top to bottom." "Spoiled for choice" with the set's "amazing strength in depth," it leads the field in "creativity and experience." **Gabriel Moss QC** (see p.1424) is the "clear star," with an "excellent brain" suited for advising on "esoteric issues of insolvency law." An "imaginative and powerful advocate," his "household name" is constantly in demand for the "big juicy cases – for anything substantial or complex they don't come much better than Moss." **Michael Crystal QC** (see p.1368) is "a great character" and "one of the best in the field," although he remains tied up with the Thyssen case. **Robin Dicker QC** (see p.1371) is "fantastically bright, attentive and knowledgeable" and "a good man when one needs to make new law – he's an absolute star." Practitioners believe that **Richard Hacker QC** (see p.1390) is "more modest than his contemporaries and thus can be under-rated" while displaying "an extremely commercial, pragmatic and client-friendly approach." He is noted for his work in North Atlantic insurance insolvency cases and "bond issues involving far flung destinations." **Simon Mortimore QC** (see p.1424) is "concise, clear and authoritative on all aspects of insolvency," while **Mark Phillips QC** (see p.1433) has "made his mark quickly as a silk," which is unsurprising given that he is "an excellent all-rounder with good judgement – he's great in court and not afraid to give his opinion." **Christopher Brougham QC** (see p.1356) is a long-standing senior figure while **Robin Knowles QC** (see p.1407) continues to accrue market respect as "a man on his way to the top – he'll replace the Mosses and Crystals one day." The "seriously clever" **Richard Sheldon QC** (see p.1447) is a "fantastic advocate and a real team player," **Richard Adkins QC** (see p.1341) remains respected and new silk **William Trower QC** (see p.1463) is "bright and impressive on shareholder issues." **John Briggs** (see p.1355) receives commendation as "a top bankruptcy guy, good to work with and knowledgeable – it's good to have him holding your hand." The "excellent" **Lexa Hilliard** (see p.1395) ("practical and always on the ball") is rated for her work on administrative exits, while **Martin Pascoe** (see p.1432) has "been around the houses" and is "down to earth and constructive – you get good pragmatic advice from him." **Antony Zacaroli** (see p.1471) is "eminently reasonable – an excellent man for when one needs to appear impartial", while **Stephen Atherton** (see p.1345) is "meticulous in his approach" and a "thoroughly decent scrapper." **Andreas Gledhill** (see p.1385) is "economical with words – he'll give you a short succinct opinion without the padding," and is regarded as "a good cross-examiner" with strength in contested petitions and section 236 examinations. **Adam Goodison** (see p.1387) is described as "down to earth and quick to find the real issues," while **David Marks** (see p.1416) is a "senior junior with extremely practical insight" and is "quick on his feet" with an "extensive knowledge on all aspects of insolvency." **Fidelis Oditah** possesses "an exceptional knowledge of the law" while **Lloyd Tamlyn** (see p.1457) is "an incredibly good speaker and a quick thinker" with "wide-ranging experience." **Felicity Toube** (see p.1461) received an array of plaudits as one of the set's "most impressive younger barristers – efficient, quick on turnaround and approachable" as well as "able to digest what is put in front of her and relay it in a client friendly manner." **Mark Arnold** (see p.1344) is "focused and responsive," while **Hilary Stonefrost** (see p.1454) is "user-friendly and straight to the point." **Glen Davis** (see p.1369) enters the up and coming ranks this year as a "young chap, constructive and diligent, he sees the big picture and gives detailed advice. Plus clients like him." Similarly **Barry Isaacs** (see p.1400) is rated as "hardworking and thorough."

LEADING JUNIORS • London		
★	SNOWDEN Richard	Erskine Chambers
1	AGNELLO Raquel	11 Stone Buildings
	ARDEN Peter	Enterprise Chambers
	BRIGGS John	3-4 South Square
	CHIVERS David	Erskine Chambers
	HILLIARD Lexa	3-4 South Square
	PASCOE Martin	3-4 South Square
	ZACAROLI Antony	3-4 South Square
2	ATHERTON Stephen	3-4 South Square
	COLLINGS Matthew	Maitland Chambers
	DAVIS-WHITE Malcolm	4 Stone Buildings
	GIROLAMI Paul	Maitland Chambers
	GLEDHILL Andreas	3-4 South Square
	GOODISON Adam	3-4 South Square
	MARKS David	3-4 South Square
	MARSHALL Philip	Serle Court
	MCQUATER Ewan	3 Verulam Buildings
	MILES Robert	4 Stone Buildings
	ODITAH Fidelis	3-4 South Square
	SHEKERDEMIAN Marcia	11 Stone Buildings
	TAMLYN Lloyd	3-4 South Square
	TOUBE Felicity	3-4 South Square
3	ARNOLD Mark	3-4 South Square
	DE GARR ROBINSON Anthony	One Essex Court
	GRIFFITHS Peter	4 Stone Buildings
	IFE Linden	Enterprise Chambers
	KYRIAKIDES Tina	11 Stone Buildings
	MILLETT Richard	Essex Court Chambers
	MOVERLEY SMITH Stephen	24 Old Buildings
	RITCHIE Richard	24 Old Buildings
	STOCKDALE Thomas	Erskine Chambers
	STONEFROST Hilary	3-4 South Square
UP AND COMING		
	BOARDMAN Christopher	11 Stone Buildings
	DAVIS Glen	3-4 South Square
	ISAACS Barry	3-4 South Square
	NOURSE Edmund	One Essex Court

For details of these leading barristers see Profiles on p.1339

Erskine Chambers (see full details p.1495) Overwhelming market comment has been that this is an "excellent company set with some good insolvency people" trading on its corporate restructuring strength. **Robin Potts QC** retains his top band rating as an "insolvency guru" who is "as brilliant in court as he is on paper," and is seen to utilise his expertise in straight company law "to devastating effect." The "solid" **Leslie Kosmin QC** is "bright, clear and good with lay clients," while the "top quality" **David Oliver QC** (see p.1429) and the "canny and sensible" **David Richards QC** (see p.1440) continue to attract market support. **Richard Snowden** (see p.1450) remains the "ace junior" with "an understated quality approach – if I ever had a complex matter requiring good commercial skill and good advocacy, I'd go to him." **David Chivers** (see p.1362) and **Thomas Stockdale** (see p.1454) are also well respected by the market for their corporate insolvency expertise.

4 Stone Buildings (see full details p.1568) Widely regarded as having "a big tradition in insolvency and company work." Solicitors rated the barristers as "good technically, flexible in relation to the service they provide and readily available." **Anthony Bompas QC** (see p.1352) is "the consummate technician" and "deceptively understated" while **John Brisby QC** (see p.1355) is "thoroughly tenacious" and "like an eloquent bulldog in court." **Philip Heslop QC** is recommended for his "imaginative approach" on the "higher end corporate insolvency cases." Amongst the juniors, **Malcolm Davis-White** (see p.1370) gives "sound, sensible advice" and is an "exemplary advocate." Although lower profile in this field, **Robert Miles** remains well respected as a "top shelf litigator," while **Peter Griffiths** (see p.1389) is "a force to be reckoned with in court."

24 Old Buildings (see full details p.1548) The market has commented on the "talented individuals" who take on "a lot of large and high profile corporate recovery matters." **Lawrence Cohen QC** (see p.1364) is regarded as "astute and determined," **Roger Kaye QC** (see p.1404) is a "big hitter" who "doesn't mess around in court" and **Alan Steinfeld QC** (see p.1453) is a "quick-thinking and erudite advocate." From the juniors, **Stephen Moverley Smith** (see p.1425) is a "user-friendly and accommodating barrister" noted for his Inland Revenue work, while **Richard Ritchie** (see p.1440) remains "solid and dependable" with DTI work "keeping him busy."

Serle Court (see full details p.1565) Gaining increasing respect for its insolvency expertise, particularly from practitioners in the regions. **Michael Briggs QC** (see p.1355) remains one of the set's "leading lights" for corporate insolvency work while **Alan Boyle QC** (see p.1353) is similarly recommended in spite of his diminished profile due to the Thyssen case. New silk **Victor Joffe QC** (see p.1402) received market plaudits while junior **Philip Marshall** (see p.1416) is "tactically clever" and "capable of getting to the heart of a matter quickly."

Maitland Chambers (see full details p.1538) This merged set is thought to contain "highly capable lawyers" with an "in-depth knowledge of insolvency and commercial law." **Catherine Newman QC** (see p.1427) continues to be heavily briefed while **Nigel Davis QC** (see p.1370) is a "true gentleman" with a "superbly measured court-room manner." New silk **Guy Newey QC** (see p.1427) is "one hell of a litigator" who "thinks of everything and has it covered." Junior **Matthew Collings** (see p.1365) is "a particular favourite – extremely user-friendly and takes more than an academic interest in the instructions he receives." **Paul Girolami** (see p.1385) is "the lawyer's lawyer par excellence" with a "brilliant legal mind."

11 Stone Buildings (see full details p.1570) "Good service – they know insolvency backwards" although the profile lies more with "day to day matters" than the highest profile cases. New silk **Jane Giret QC** (see p.1385) is "the top person there – she's intellectual, extremely easy to deal with in an informal way, practical and down to earth." "Brilliant on her feet in court" and "thorough in her preparation" her recently won silk has bolstered the set in this field. Junior **Raquel Agnello** (see p.1341) is "a good advocate and a fighter, on the ball and straightforward – she gets on and does it" in both bankruptcy and corporate insolvency matters. **Marcia Shekerdemian** (see p.1447) is warmly rated although "because she's so good she's incredibly busy and difficult to get sometimes." **Tina Kyriakides** (see p.1408) maintains a healthy level of market support while newly rated **Chris Boardman** (see p.1352) is "intellectually brilliant – quick and strong in terms of his argument."

Other Notable Practitioners; The list of talented insolvency silks and juniors continues to draw heavily from sets other than those rated above. **Elizabeth Gloster QC** (see p.1386) from **One Essex Court** is widely regarded as "an all-round heavyweight and one of the most talented silks around," with a "thorough, clear, robust and user-friendly approach." Also at that set, "genuine all-rounder" **Anthony de Garr Robinson** (see p.1370) and **Edmund Nourse** (see p.1429) continue to receive high market recommendation. Head of **Enterprise Chambers**, "immensely erudite" **Anthony Mann QC** is "approachable and a team player who rolls up his sleeves and gets stuck in." Amongst the juniors here, **Peter Arden** (see p.1344) is described as "technically sound" with a solicitor noting, "I use Arden a lot, and this is often client-led." **Linden Ife** (see p.1399) is "reliable and good fun to work with" and "one of the all-time favourites." **Richard de Lacy QC** (see p.1370) from **3 Verulam Buildings** "should have been made silk years ago, it's well deserved and well overdue" while junior **Ewan McQuater** (see p.1420) has again been recognised as "the leading insolvency junior at 3 Verulam Buildings." Head of **New Square Chambers Eben Hamilton QC** (see p.1391) and his colleague **Robin Hollington QC**

continue to garner support for their corporate recovery expertise. The "ever-resourceful" **Geoffrey Vos QC** (see p.1465) and **Edward Bannister QC** (see p.1346) from **3 Stone Buildings** again receive a warm share of market recommendation. **Susan Prevezer QC** (see p.1435) from **Essex Court Chambers** is "to the point" and "works very well with clients." Also at this set, "multi-faceted" **Richard Millett** (see p.1421) continues to receive market approval.

WESTERN CIRCUIT

LEADING SILKS • Western		
1	DAVIES Stephen	Guildhall Chambers

For details of these leading barristers see Profiles on p.1339

LEADING JUNIORS • Western		
1	BAMFORD Jeremy	Guildhall Chambers
2	ASCROFT Richard	Guildhall Chambers
	BRIGGS Nicholas	Guildhall Chambers
	FRENCH Paul	Guildhall Chambers
	MAHER Martha	Guildhall Chambers

For details of these leading barristers see Profiles on p.1339

Guildhall Chambers (see full details p.1581) "remains the pre-eminent Chambers in the South West – there is no one else to touch them when it comes to expertise and Guildhall specialisation." "Absolutely exemplary" **Stephen Davies QC** is "still the best in the region by a long haul" with a "truly national reputation" He remains "busy because he's much in demand, but if you can get hold of him you can't go wrong – he's excellent." "Clever" **Jeremy Bamford** is "getting a bigger and better workload" and an accordingly higher profile. Newly ranked juniors **Richard Ascroft** (see p.1344) ("full of potential") and **Nick Briggs** (see p.1355) ("a fine finance background") are "solid performers" with their presence considered a real boost to the insolvency practice. **Paul French** (see p.1382) is someone "going to go places," as he has "developed a maturing successful practice." **Martha Maher** (see p.1415) also gained market approval for her work in the field.

MIDLANDS CIRCUIT

LEADING SILKS • Midlands		
1	RANDALL John	St Philip's Chambers

For details of these leading barristers see Profiles on p.1339

LEADING JUNIORS • Midlands	
ASHWORTH Lance	St Philip's Chambers
KHANGURE Avtar	St Philip's Chambers

For details of these leading barristers see Profiles on p.1339

St Philip's Chambers (see full details p.1578) continues to produce the top insolvency practitioners. **John Randall QC** (see p.1438) is seen to be "far and away the leading silk," while juniors **Lance Ashworth** (see p.1344) and newly joined **Avtar Khangure** (see p.1406) are both seen to have "promising careers ahead of them" in the field.

NORTH EASTERN CIRCUIT

LEADING SILKS • North Eastern		
1	ALLEN James	No.6 Barristers Chambers

For details of these leading barristers see Profiles on p.1339

LEADING JUNIORS • North Eastern		
1	GROVES Hugo	Enterprise Chambers
2	JORY Hugh	Enterprise Chambers
3	COOPER Mark	Chancery House Chambers

For details of these leading barristers see Profiles on p.1339

A variety of sets continue to house the top insolvency barristers in this region, with **James Allen QC** from **No.6 Barristers Chambers** still the "leading silk by a country mile." **Hugo Groves** from **Enterprise Chambers** (see full details p.1590) is widely recognised as having "excellent technical ability" while his colleague **Hugh Jory** ("provides very capable support") has a growing profile. **Mark Cooper** (see p.1366) from **Chancery House Chambers** (see full details p.1590) received favourable market commendation.

NORTHERN CIRCUIT

LEADING SILKS • Northern		
1	BARTLEY JONES Edward	Exchange Chambers
	BOOTH Michael	40 King St
	SMITH Peter	40 King St
NEW SILKS		
	CAWSON Mark	Exchange Chambers
	CHAISTY Paul	40 King St

For details of these leading barristers see Profiles on p.1339

LEADING JUNIORS • Northern		
1	ANDERSON Lesley	40 King St
	DOYLE Louis	40 King St
2	MAYNARD-CONNOR Giles	Exchange Chambers
	STERLING Robert	St James's Chambers

For details of these leading barristers see Profiles on p.1339

40 King Street (see full details p.1604) in Manchester remains the number one insolvency set where **Peter Smith QC** (see p.1450) is rated for his "forceful advocacy" and "formidable grasp of the area." **Michael Booth QC** is also seen as "a top bracket insolvency silk" with a "loyal following locally." The "stalwart" **Paul Chaisty QC** (see p.1361) has recently taken silk while junior **Lesley Anderson** (see p.1343) has "developed a good reputation in the field," rated for property-related insolvency disputes. **Louis Doyle** (see p.1372) is widely regarded as "sensible and client-friendly" with his "winning combination of ability and common sense." **Edward Bartley Jones QC** (see p.1348) from **Exchange Chambers** (see full details p.1598) in Liverpool is seen to be "highly intelligent, a first class advocate." Newly ranked **Robert Sterling** (see p.1453) of **St James Chambers** (see full details p.1606) in Manchester is "starting to make his mark locally," while new silk **Mark Cawson QC** (see p.1361) and colleague **Giles Maynard-Connor** (see p.1418) have both moved from St James' Chambers to **Exchange Chambers** (see full details p.1598). The "well-known" Cawson has an "excellent reputation" as he "always turns papers around quickly – he's good value, easy to work with and judges like him." Giles Maynard-Connor "endeavours to make himself available" and has a "keen focus on insolvency" despite his mixed practice.

INSURANCE

RESEARCH: The rankings are based on in-depth interviews with over 5,000 solicitors and barristers in the UK. Chambers research is audited by the British Market Research Bureau (see page 7 for details).

OVERVIEW: The recent spate of film finance cases has generated many instructions for the bar, as have the PA LMX Spiral, and cases based in Bermuda. Non-contentious scheme documentation advice is included in this section, as well as advocacy, for both general and reinsurance.

Barristers' profiles 1339-1472

LONDON

INSURANCE • London		QCs	Jnrs
1	**Essex Court Chambers** (Gordon Pollock QC)	5	5
	7 King's Bench Walk (Jeremy Cooke QC)	7	2
2	**Brick Court Chambers** (Christopher Clarke QC)	7	1
3	**Fountain Court** (Anthony Boswood QC)	3	2
	4 Pump Court	2	-
4	**3 Verulam Buildings** (Symons/Jarvis)	1	1

This book is the product of 6,552 1/2-hour interviews. See p.7 for BMRB audit.
For details of these leading barristers see Profiles on p.1339

LEADING SILKS • London		
1	**COOKE Jeremy**	7 King's Bench Walk
	CRANE Michael	Fountain Court
	EDELMAN Colin	Devereux Chambers
	FLAUX Julian	7 King's Bench Walk
	KEALEY Gavin	7 King's Bench Walk
	POLLOCK Gordon	Essex Court Chambers
	SUMPTION Jonathan	Brick Court Chambers
	VEEDER V.V.	Essex Court Chambers
2	**BOSWOOD Anthony**	Fountain Court
	EDER Bernard	Essex Court Chambers
	GAISMAN Jonathan	7 King's Bench Walk
	GROSS Peter	20 Essex Street
	HOWARD Mark	Brick Court Chambers
	KENTRIDGE Sydney	Brick Court Chambers
	ROWLAND John	4 Pump Court
	RUTTLE Stephen	Brick Court Chambers
	SCHAFF Alistair	7 King's Bench Walk
	SYMONS Christopher	3 Verulam Buildings
3	**DOHMANN Barbara**	Blackstone Chambers
	HILDYARD Robert	4 Stone Buildings
	HUNTER Ian	Essex Court Chambers
	JACOBS Richard	Essex Court Chambers
	KENDRICK Dominic	7 King's Bench Walk
	LEGGATT George	Brick Court Chambers
	POPPLEWELL Andrew	Brick Court Chambers
	RAILTON David	Fountain Court
	STUART-SMITH Jeremy	2 Temple Gardens
	WOOD William	Brick Court Chambers
NEW SILKS		
	BUTCHER Christopher	7 King's Bench Walk
	TOZZI Nigel	4 Pump Court

For details of these leading barristers see Profiles on p.1339

LEADING JUNIORS • London		
1	**BERRY Steven**	Essex Court Chambers
	EDWARDS David	7 King's Bench Walk
	PHILLIPS Rory	3 Verulam Buildings
2	**FOXTON David**	Essex Court Chambers
	LOCKEY John	Essex Court Chambers
3	**BRYAN Simon**	Essex Court Chambers
	COX Raymond	Fountain Court
	DAVIES Helen	Brick Court Chambers
	EDEY Philip	20 Essex Street
	FENTON Adam	7 King's Bench Walk
	HOWE Timothy	Fountain Court
	TEMPLEMAN Mark	Essex Court Chambers

For details of these leading barristers see Profiles oh p.1339

Essex Court Chambers (see full details p.1496) Highly respected and often the first port of call for solicitors, this set is well stocked with talented silks and juniors who continue to be revered. **Gordon Pollock QC** (see p.1434) is renowned for forcefulness and "although very much a generalist, he is always there in big cases," he is "a fighter; the most forceful advocate at the bar." Widely respected **V.V. Veeder** (see p.1464) **QC** is adjudged "a favourite, extremely skilled on paper and in court," his insurance nous yet to be overshadowed by his greater involvement in arbitration. **Ian Hunter QC** (see p.x1399) is too seen as heavily involved in the arbitration sphere, although this does not preclude him from insurance work. **Bernard Eder QC** (see p.1374) is "attentive and thorough," and **Richard Jacobs QC** (see p.1400) is "careful and trustworthy." Of the juniors, **Steven Berry** (see p.1350) wins the approval of his peers and is felt by solicitors to be "one of the most prominent" in this area. **David Foxton** (see p.1381) is endorsed for his "commonsense approach" and **John Lockey** (see p.1413) is considered "thorough." **Simon Bryan** (see p.1356) is praised for his advocacy in court, while **Mark Templeman** (see p.1458) is thought to have a depth of understanding in this field.

7 King's Bench Walk (see full details p.1530) Maintains its outstanding reputation with its three heavyweights silks going from strength to strength. "Excellent" **Jeremy Cooke QC** (see p.1365) is involved in the Commercial Court trial AXA v AON concerning liability of broker/coverholders. "Extremely effective" **Julian Flaux QC** (see p.1379) not only rakes in a substantial number of recommendations but is also deemed "entertaining to work with." **Gavin Kealey QC** (see p.1404) generates some colourful praise from rivals. Always "fully in control of any given situation," he is applauded for his "intellect and d'Artagnanesque style". **Jonathan Gaisman QC** is a respected member of the set recently involved in Kuwait Airways litigation and "excellent" **Alistair Schaff QC** (see p.1444) has acted in the recent spate of film finance cases. **Dominic Kendrick QC** has a following among solicitors and star new silk **Christopher Butcher QC** (see p.1358) is "bright and sharp" and "good at everything." **David Edwards** (see p.1374) is "first rate" and "maturing into an effective senior junior" while **Adam Fenton** ("thorough") was involved in the Imperio v Heath case.

Brick Court Chambers (see full details p.1484) Fields an outstanding number of high profile silks, but with only one junior receiving the requisite level of endorsement, the top-heaviness of this set persists. **Jonathan Sumption QC** (see p.1455) is a specialist in this, as in many areas. In court he is "an extremely good advocate, he speaks more fluently than one could wish to write." Recently he has been involved in the Star Sea marine insurance case. **Mark Howard QC** (see p.1398) is widely rated for his "specialist knowledge and commercial sense." He has been acting for AIG on film financing reinsurance disputes. **Sydney Kentridge QC** (see p.1405) continues to be respected for his performance in cases before the House of Lords, and **Stephen Ruttle QC** (see p.1443), popular among his peers, is viewed by solicitors as "clever and incisive." He was instructed by Davies Lavery in the HIH Casualty v New Hampshire film finance litigation. **George Leggatt QC** (see p.1410) and "sharp" **Andrew Popplewell QC** (see p.1435) both received warm endorsement. The latter has been involved in various arbitrations against John Hancock arising out of US workers comp spiral. "Decisive and intelligent" **William Wood QC** (see p.1470)is well spoken of by juniors who have seen him in action. **Helen Davies** (see p.1369) has a carved a name for herself in this sphere.

Fountain Court (see full details p.1506) **Michael Crane QC** has a reputation for excellence in this area, and is described as "an elegant advocate." "Intellectually strong and disciplined" **Anthony Boswood QC** (see p.1352) has a particularly strong following amongst solicitors and is respected for his Directors and Officers cases. He is described as "a pleasure to work with." **David Railton QC** (see p.1438) is endorsed as "bright and able" and **Ray Cox** (see p.1367) is a "highly skilled" junior. **Timothy Howe** (see p.1398) received an admirable number of spontaneous recommendations during research, "a great advocate; clever and such a personable barrister."

4 Pump Court (see full details p.1557) **John Rowland QC** (see p.1442) "demonstrates good commercial sense and strikes a good rapport with judges." He is instructed by several major firms to advise on regulatory matters, policy interpretation and policy drafting. New silk **Nigel Tozzi QC** (see p.1461) has a following among solicitors.

3 Verulam Buildings (see full details p.1575) "Favourite" **Christopher Symons QC** (see p.1456) receives strong praise for his insurance work, described as "excellent in every way." As well as a range of advisory work, he has recently been involved in the London Borough of Redbridge v Municipal Mutual Insurance matter. **Rory Philips** (see p.1433) gained a convincing level of commendation from the bar and solicitors and has acted on behalf of the reinsurers in the Charman v GIO case; a dispute concerning the Charman Syndicates' excess of loss reinsurance.

Other Notable Practitioners "Thorough, sensible" **Colin Edelman QC** (see p.1373) of **Devereux Chambers** is described by referees as "extremely good and easy to deal with." He has been involved in activities for Lloyd's Reserving Panel as both advocate and panel member, and his recent cases include General Insurance Ltd and others v Chase Manhattan Bank and others. "Formidable" **Barbara Dohmann QC** (see p.1371) at **Blackstone Chambers** and **Peter Gross QC** (see p.1390) of **20 Essex Street** received heavy endorsement while at the same set, **Philip Edey** (see p.1374) is thought of as "a clever practitioner and approachable." **Robert Hildyard QC** (see p.1394) at **4 Stone Buildings** is judged to be strong on life insurance. **Jeremy Stuart-Smith QC** (see p.1455) of **2 Temple Gardens** is "a strong academic lawyer with good attention to detail and commercial judgement."

INTELLECTUAL PROPERTY

RESEARCH: The rankings are based on in-depth interviews with over 5,000 solicitors and barristers in the UK. Chambers research is audited by the British Market Research Bureau (see page 7 for details).

Barristers' profiles 1339-1472

LONDON

INTELLECTUAL PROPERTY • London		QCs	Jnrs
1	**Three New Square** (David Young QC)	5	6
	8 New Square (Michael Fysh QC)	7	10
2	**11 South Square** (Christopher Floyd QC)	4	6
3	**One Essex Court** (Anthony Grabiner QC)	1	1
	Hogarth Chambers (Morcom/Rayner James)	1	2
	19 Old Buildings (Alastair Wilson QC)	1	1

Numbers show recommended barristers in this practice area

LEADING SILKS • London		
★	**KITCHIN David**	8 New Square
	THORLEY Simon	Three New Square
1	**BALDWIN John**	8 New Square
	CARR Henry	11 South Square
	FLOYD Christopher	11 South Square
	HOBBS Geoffrey	One Essex Court
	PRESCOTT Peter	8 New Square
	WATSON Antony	Three New Square
	WAUGH Andrew	Three New Square
2	**ARNOLD Richard**	11 South Square
	BLOCH Michael	Wilberforce Chambers
	HOWE Martin	8 New Square
	MILLER Richard	Three New Square
	PLATTS-MILLS Mark	8 New Square
	SILVERLEAF Michael	11 South Square
	YOUNG David	Three New Square
3	**FYSH Michael**	8 New Square
	MORCOM Christopher	Hogarth Chambers
	VITORIA Mary	8 New Square
	WILSON Alastair	19 Old Buildings

This book is the product of 6,552 1/2-hour interviews. See p.7 for BMRB audit.
For details of these leading barristers see Profiles on p.1339

Three New Square* (see full details p.1542) Clearly one of the top sets in this area, it is consistently commended for its range of expertise and "intellectual rigour." The "authoritative" **Simon Thorley QC** (see p.1460) remains the flagship here. His "exceptional layering of cases" and "astounding grasp of technical issues" is no less than court mastery: "he makes it look so easy." **Anthony Watson QC** "takes a broad-brush approach" to IP, but is especially highly rated for his patents work. He is said to have "an outstanding nose for a case." **Andrew Waugh QC** (see p.1467) is "technically superb" and wins endorsement for his "thorough preparation," while clients see **Richard Miller QC** (see p.1421) as an "inspiring" figure who "really gets a grip on a case." Noted for his expertise in the chemical industry, the experienced **David Young QC** (see p.1471) belies a "slightly dour" image by "winning more cases than anyone." The set's two most prominent juniors are **Colin Birss** and **Guy Burkill** (see p.1357). The former is a "forceful and popular" advocate, while the latter draws admiration for his "unrivalled scientific excellence." **Douglas Campbell** (see p.1359) is "a good man for the big case," and is said to "work well under pressure," while the "charming" **Denise McFarland** (see p.1419) is "good on her feet" and "a robust fighter." Peers endorse **Justin Turner** for his "bright and obliging manner" and "phenomenal memory," while the "discerning" **Thomas Mitcheson** (see p.1422) "assimilates facts easily," has a "diligent attitude" and has been marked out as a potential star of the future.

8 New Square* (see full details p.1544) Loaded with high profile silks and juniors, the set continues to compete at the top of the IP rankings. Many of our interviewees felt that **David Kitchin QC** (see p.1407) is, quite simply, "the best patent silk around." Clients rave about his "persistence, knowledge, calmness and humour." The "dedicated" **John Baldwin QC** (see p.1346) is especially rated for his expertise in passing off cases and his "razor-sharp judgement." "Logical and ice-cool in his reasoning," **Peter Prescott QC** (see p.1435) moves up the tables, and has emerged as a "genius on new points of law." **Martin Howe QC** (see p.1398) "can always be relied on to deliver a result," while **Mark Platts-Mills QC** (see p.1434) is a "strong cross-examiner," recommended as "one to go to if you need a scrap." **Michael Fysh QC** (see p.1382) is "consistently helpful" and is much admired for his "keen intellect" and international experience. **Mary Vitoria QC** (see p.1465) is another practitioner to be endorsed for her "outstanding academic credentials." Among IP juniors, **Daniel Alexander** (see p.1342) is seen by some as "first amongst equals." He possesses a "phenomenal brain" and "everything he touches seems to turn to gold." **Richard Meade** (see p.1420) vies for top spot, rated as a "perceptive" advocate with a "first-class mind." Peers envy **James Mellor** (see p.1420) his "cleverness and sureness of touch," and **Adrian Speck** (see p.1451) has "sound judgement" and is renowned for his "efficiency on trademark cases." **Michael Tappin**'s (see p.1458) strong suit is in biotechnology cases. Among practitioners at the younger end of the junior bar, **Charlotte May** (see p.1418) is considered by some solicitors to be "in a class of her own." A regular player on major patent cases, she "doesn't posture and point-score; she just gets on charmingly with the business of winning cases." **Fiona Clark** (see p.1362) is "a gutsy advocate," while **George Hamer** (see p.1391), **Thomas Moody-Stuart** (see p.1423) and **Robert Onslow** (see p.1430) all maintain their share of market support.

11 South Square* "Solid as a rock," the set completes the triumvirate of IP leaders. Not considered to be "quite as starry" as its two leading rivals, it nevertheless draws praise for its "ability to get the job done." **Henry Carr QC** (see p.1360) "sees all the issues," "works like a Trojan" and is "a renowned client pleaser." "Utterly reliable, if slightly lugubrious," **Christopher Floyd QC** (see p.1380) scored a huge success this year with his "outstanding work on the Dyson case." Having recently taken silk, **Richard Arnold QC** (see p.1344) shoots up the tables for his "strength at trade marks" and "damned good brain." **Michael Silverleaf QC** (see p.1448) is respected for his "fighting qualities" and "usually getting the right results." Among the set's juniors, **Richard Hacon** is singled out as an "unflappable and persistent" opponent, and **Heather Lawrence** (see p.1409) rises in the tables in recognition of her "sharp and perspicacious judgement." **Iain Purvis** (see p.1437) is a "talented all-rounder," while the "commercial" **Mark Vanhegan** is another whose profile was raised through his work on the famous Dyson case. **Piers Acland** has the ability to "make life uncomfortable for the opposition," and **Henry Whittle** draws praise from solicitors as an "able and experienced" practitioner.

One Essex Court* (see full details p.1497) Renowned commercial set with two well-known experts. "Theatrical" **Geoffrey Hobbs QC** is rated for his "exceptional knowledge," and is generally felt to "have an edge on trade-

LEADING JUNIORS • London		
★	ALEXANDER Daniel	8 New Square
	MEADE Richard	8 New Square
1	BIRSS Colin	Three New Square
	BURKILL Guy	Three New Square
	MELLOR James	8 New Square
2	HACON Richard	11 South Square
	HICKS Michael	19 Old Buildings
	LAWRENCE Heather	11 South Square
	PURVIS Iain	11 South Square
	SPECK Adrian	8 New Square
	TAPPIN Michael	8 New Square
	VANHEGAN Mark	11 South Square
3	ACLAND Piers	11 South Square
	CAMPBELL Douglas	Three New Square
	MAY Charlotte	8 New Square
	MCFARLAND Denise	Three New Square
	MITCHESON Thomas	Three New Square
	TURNER Justin	Three New Square
4	CLARK Fiona	8 New Square
	EDENBOROUGH Michael	Hogarth Chambers
	HAMER George	8 New Square
	HIMSWORTH Emma	One Essex Court
	MOODY-STUART Thomas	8 New Square
	ONSLOW Robert	8 New Square
	TRITTON Guy	Hogarth Chambers
	WHITTLE Henry	11 South Square

This book is the product of 6,552 1/2-hour interviews. See p.7 for BMRB audit.

For details of these leading barristers see Profiles on p.1339

mark cases." **Emma Himsworth** (see p.1395) remains the set's best-known junior.

Hogarth Chambers* (see full details p.1523) Newly constituted set, whose leading figure is **Christopher Morcom QC** (see p.1423) , a trademarks specialist who is said to be "strong on detail." **Michael Edenborough** (see p.1374) also maintains his reputation for trademarks work, while **Guy Tritton** (see p.1462) received solid recommendation from a variety of law firms.

19 Old Buildings* (see full details p.1546) The celebrated **Alastair Wilson QC** is "a good performer" who can be relied on to "get on with things." **Michael Hicks** is "bright, hard-working and charming" and remains a regular choice for leading law firms.

Other Notable Practitioners At **Wilberforce Chambers**, the "approachable" **Michael Bloch QC** (see p.1351) has "a well-honed instinct for what will work best." He is best known for passing off cases.

LICENSING

RESEARCH: The rankings are based on in-depth interviews with over 5,000 solicitors and barristers in the UK. Chambers research is audited by the British Market Research Bureau (see page 7 for details).

Barristers' profiles 1339-1472

OVERVIEW: Liberalising changes to the licensing legislation have led to a reduction in contested hearings. This has been complemented by increased objections launched by residents' groups. Barristers have indicated objections against the move towards using local authority licensing committees rather than the magistrate's court, believing that this will introduce confusion to the proceedings. The changes in betting duty regime have increased the attraction for offshore gambling companies to the UK.

LONDON

LICENSING • London	QCs	Jnrs
1 3 Raymond Buildings (Clive Nicholls QC)	3	5

Numbers show recommended barristers in this practice area

LEADING SILKS • London		
1	BECKETT Richard	3 Raymond Buildings
2	DE HAAN Kevin	3 Raymond Buildings
	FITZGERALD Susanna	One Essex Court
3	GRAY Gilbert	3 Raymond Buildings
	MEHIGAN Simon	5 Paper Buildings
4	MOGER Christopher	4 Pump Court

For details of these leading barristers see Profiles on p.1339

LEADING JUNIORS • London		
1	RANKIN James	3 Raymond Buildings
2	GOURIET Gerald	3 Raymond Buildings
	MUIR Andrew	3 Raymond Buildings
	WALSH Stephen	3 Raymond Buildings
3	BROMLEY-MARTIN Michael	3 Raymond Buildings
	MONKCOM Stephen	Francis Taylor Building

This book is the product of 6,552 1/2-hour interviews. See p.7 for BMRB audit.
For details of these leading barristers see Profiles on p.1339

3 Raymond Buildings (see full details p.1560) Widely recognised to "have the whole thing sewn up," with a "breadth and depth unmatched in any other chambers." With an extensive, glittering register of key silks and juniors, there is no danger of the set loosing its shine. "The leader's leader," **Richard Beckett QC*** (see p.1349) is a "master of advocacy" who sets "the standard by which others should be judged." Universally respected for his ability to "charm the bench," his strength lies in casino work, where he is "top of the tree." Academic and "thorough" **Kevin de Haan QC** is known for his skills in the betting sphere. "Much more committed to his clients than he allows you to think – a deceptively laid back style," he "will always fight, and wins when you don't necessarily expect him to." Respected **Gilbert Gray QC** is sought out for his "excellent opinions." "Pre-eminent" among the juniors, **James Rankin** (see p.1438) has an "excellent legal mind" and is heavily endorsed for his liquor licensing work. His "florid style" is complemented by a "meticulous, commercial" approach to the law. **Gerald Gouriet** (see p.1388) has "re-established himself quickly" after time spent in the States. "Switched on," his "innovative thought processes" and "ingenuous charm" earn him admiration from all quarters. **Andrew Muir** (see p.1425) is clearly "on top of the game," "down to earth" and displays considerable "charm and guile." Peers appreciate **Stephen Walsh** (see p.1466) for his flexible approach. "Good if you want a fight," he is equally highly rated for his "non-aggressive, diplomatic style," while he "handles difficult people well." **Michael Bromley-Martin*** (see p.1356) is "an advocate who uses aggression well – like a terrier, when he gets his teeth in, he doesn't let go."

Other Notable Practitioners **Susanna Fitzgerald QC** (see p.1379) of **One Essex Court** is "extraordinarily positive and assertive," with a "clear and persuasive approach" to betting and gaming matters. Respected for her "understanding of technicalities outside her own field," she is valued as a "tactical choice in difficult cases." **Simon Mehigan QC** (see p.1420) from **5 Paper Buildings** is "good on his feet" and he continues to edit a leading licensing text. **Christopher Moger QC** (see p.1422) of **4 Pump Court** "knows the territory" and impresses with his "excellent judgement." "Cerebral" **Stephen Monkcom** of **Tanfield Chambers** is the "first port of call" for many solicitors.

WESTERN CIRCUIT

LEADING SILKS • Western		
1	GLEN Ian	Guildhall Chambers

For details of these leading barristers see Profiles on p.1339

LEADING JUNIORS • Western		
1	BARKER Kerry	Guildhall Chambers
2	WADSLEY Peter	St John's Chambers

For details of these leading barristers see Profiles on p.1339

The leading silk on the western circuit remains **Ian Glen QC** of **Guildhall Chambers** (see full details p.1581) who consistently offers an "excellent service." Editor of a new licensing report, "affable" **Kerry Barker** (see p.1347) of the same chambers is reputed to be a tough opponent, "you always have a hard fight against him." **Peter Wadsley** (see p.1465) of **St John's Chambers** (see full details p.1583) retains a top ranking in the area, recommended for his advisory skills.

MIDLANDS CIRCUIT

LEADING SILKS • Midlands		
★	SAUNDERS John	4 Fountain Court

For details of these leading barristers see Profiles on p.1339

LEADING JUNIORS • Midlands		
1	GOSLING Jonathan	4 Fountain Court

For details of these leading barristers see Profiles on p.1339

"Probably the strongest liquor licensing lawyer there is," **John Saunders QC** of **4 Fountain Court** draws national recommendations as a leading silk. "Frighteningly knowledgeable," "he fights every little point" and is "marvellous with clients." **Jonathan Gosling**, also of **4 Fountain Court** is adjudged a "senior player" who "inspires confidence."

WALES & CHESTER CIRCUIT

LEADING JUNIORS • Wales & Chester		
1	WALTERS Graham	33 Park Place
	WALTERS Jonathan	33 Park Place

For details of these leading barristers see Profiles on p.1339

"Conscientious," and "good performers" **Graham Walters** (see p.1466) and **Jonathan Walters** of **33 Park Place** (see full details p.1585) continue to hold the lion's share of licensing work on the Welsh circuit.

NORTH EASTERN CIRCUIT

LEADING SILKS • North Eastern		
NEW SILKS		
	SLOAN Paul	Trinity Chambers

For details of these leading barristers see Profiles on p.1339

LEADING JUNIORS • North Eastern		
1	HOLLAND Charles	Trinity Chambers

For details of these leading barristers see Profiles on p.1339

New silk, **Paul Sloan QC** (see p.1449) of **Trinity Chambers** (see full details p.1610) is highly recommended for his advocacy skills while leading junior, **Charles Holland** (see p.1396) is admired for his "meticulous research."

NORTHERN CIRCUIT

LEADING SILKS • Northern		
1	GOLDSTONE Clement	28 St. John St

For details of these leading barristers see Profiles on p.1339

LEADING JUNIORS • Northern		
	WALSH Martin	Peel Court Chambers

For details of these leading barristers see Profiles on p.1339

Clement Goldstone QC (see p.1387) of **28 St John Street** is "persuasive and thorough" and though his reputation is primarily for criminal work, he continues to dominate the region. **Martin Walsh** at **Peel Court Chambers** (see full details p.1606) is "charming" with "tremendous ability – he's good on the detail."

LOCAL GOVERNMENT

RESEARCH: The rankings are based on in-depth interviews with over 5,000 solicitors and barristers in the UK. Chambers research is audited by the British Market Research Bureau (see page 7 for details).

OVERVIEW: After discussions with barristers and lawyers in private practice, we have this year separated the local government and planning sections. Our research illustrated that local government counsel is more than just a variant of planning lawyer. The range of skills required by these practioners is increasing, particularly with regard to human rights and PFI.

LONDON

	LOCAL GOVERNMENT • London	QCs	Jnrs
1	**4 Breams Buildings** (Christopher Lockhart-Mummery QC)	5	1
	4-5 Gray's Inn Square (Appleby/Mole)	3	1
	11 King's Bench Walk Chambers (Tabachnik/Goudie)	6	6
2	**2-3 Gray's Inn Square** (Porten/Scrivener)	2	2
3	**2 Harcourt Buildings** (Gerard Ryan QC)	2	-

Numbers show recommended barristers in this practice area

	LEADING SILKS • London	
1	**GOUDIE James**	11 King's Bench Walk Chambers
	HOWELL John	Blackstone Chambers
2	**ARDEN Andrew**	Arden Chambers
	DRABBLE Richard	4 Breams Buildings
3	**GEORGE Charles**	2 Harcourt Buildings
	KATKOWSKI Christopher	4 Breams Buildings
	LOCKHART-MUMMERY Christopher	4 Breams Buildings
	PURCHAS Robin	2 Harcourt Buildings
	READ Lionel	Eldon Chambers
	STRAKER Timothy	4-5 Gray's Inn Square
4	**HENDERSON Roger**	2 Harcourt Buildings
	LOWE Mark	2-3 Gray's Inn Square
	PORTEN Anthony	2-3 Gray's Inn Square
	STEEL John	4-5 Gray's Inn Square
5	**ELVIN David**	4 Breams Buildings
	HOLGATE David	4 Breams Buildings
	SUPPERSTONE Michael	11 King's Bench Walk Chambers
	TABACHNIK Eldred	11 King's Bench Walk Chambers
NEW SILKS		
	HOBSON John	4-5 Gray's Inn Square

For details of these leading barristers see Profiles on p.1339

	LEADING JUNIORS • London	
1	**BÉAR Charles**	11 King's Bench Walk Chambers
	SINGH Rabinder	Matrix Chambers
2	**BAKER Christopher**	Arden Chambers
	LIEVEN Nathalie	4 Breams Buildings
3	**COOK Mary**	2-3 Gray's Inn Square
	FINDLAY James	2-3 Gray's Inn Square
	GIFFIN Nigel	11 King's Bench Walk Chambers
	HUMPHRIES Michael	2 Mitre Court Buildings
4	**BROWN Paul**	4-5 Gray's Inn Square

This book is the product of 6,552 1/2-hour interviews. See p.7 for BMRB audit.
For details of these leading barristers see Profiles on p.1339

4 Breams Buildings (see full details p.1483) "The strongest team in the book" for many when it comes to local government matters, the set is "more broadly based than some," boasting "serious players" despite the impact of John Howell's departure to Blackstone Chambers. **Richard**

Drabble QC (see p.1372) is commended for his "low key and persuasive approach" with "a bright intellect underneath it all." He has made a "strong impression" with "lots of work over a wide field." **Christopher Katkowski QC** (see p.1404) has had a quieter year on the pure local government front but remains an "effective, leading light." **Christopher Lockhart-Mummery QC** (see p.1413) remains "a leader in the field." It has been an impressive year for **David Elvin QC** (see p.1375), an "intellectually strong, robust advocate" with "an impressive grasp of his fields." Enjoying a broad practice, he is commended as being both "good on paper and skilled on his feet." **David Holgate QC** (see p.1396) retains a notable market presence in both planning and local government, while junior **Nathalie Lieven** (see p.1411) has impressed senior figures as "extremely capable and intelligent."

4-5 Gray's Inn Square (see full details p.1515) A substantial force in the market fielding a number of well-known names. Respected **Timothy Straker QC's** (see p.1455) talents are neatly described by one opponent; "his depth of knowledge in the sector is superb" and he "develops multi-layered arguments seamlessly." Solicitors claim that "he just keeps getting better." **John Steel QC** (see p.1452) is judged "a confident performer" giving strongly commercial opinions. Solicitors describe relative newcomer **John Hobson QC** (see p.1396) as having "a manner which local authorities like," namely "down to earth and not stuffy." Of the juniors, **Paul Brown** (see p.1356) is rated highly by private practice for bringing his "excellent judgement to human rights issues and judicial reviews."

11 King's Bench Walk Chambers (see full details p.1532) Undoubtedly has had a higher profile in local government law this year, most prominently on social services duties, education and schools' PFI advice. Solicitors applaud its "understanding of the impetus behind new changes" and concur that "you're close to the government's ear with them - they have the credibility you're looking for." Central to this success has been **James Goudie QC** (see p.1388) "a strong opponent" thought to be "upfront, practical and knowledgeable." He brings a "first class legal and commercial approach" to the table and solicitors are impressed that he "covers a lot of ground and is prepared to take a decision and express a view." **Michael Supperstone QC** (see p.1455) (a "sound, administrative lawyer,") "tends to be the first choice" of many in private practice. "The elder statesman" **Eldred Tabachnik QC** (see p.1457) is endorsed for his enormous depth of experience. **Charles Béar** (see p.1349) again tops the juniors table with his "authority and confidence" consistently offering "prompt advice – he's a quick thinker." His property regeneration and vires work has caught the eye of leading solicitors, he is "prepared to take a decision and stand by it." "Switched on and practical," **Nigel Giffin** (see p.1384) continues to impress especially for school exclusions and his continued focus on Human Rights issues and their application to public bodies.

2-3 Gray's Inn Square (see full details p.1513) Well-known and long-respected for planning work, the set's local government expertise is also of note, serving many authorities directly. They are driving hard at this area according to a leading rival silk, with particular gains in housing and landlord and tenant cases. Stalwart **Mark Lowe QC** (see p.1413) "really knows and understands how modern PFI deals work" and carries himself "with elegant aplomb." **Anthony Porten QC** (see p.1435) continues to be a respected opponent. Junior **Mary Cook** (see p.1365) has had a successful year in local government issues and is especially endorsed for her regeneration work. **James Findlay's** (see p.1378) public law experience enables him to deal with both planning and pure local government issues.

2 Harcourt Buildings (see full details p.1519) One of the more established sets for local government and property-related areas, has been recommended for its "good service, reasonable fee-rates," and "efficient, friendly clerking." Vires issues and cases involving complaints against ombudsmen have been to the fore in the last twelve months. The "excellent" **Charles George QC** (see p.1384) has "a sound grasp of local government and administrative law" and has moved up the table with the respect shown to him from local government commissions and authorities. He has also driven forward the issues of affordable housing and members of the set have sat as inspectors on behalf of local authorities. Of **Robin Purchas QC** (see p.1437), private practitioners say they "especially use him for urban regeneration" issues, for which he is "absolutely superb" in court and in preparation.

Other Notable Practitioners "Always strong on human rights issues," the new arrival to **Blackstone Chambers** is "phenomenally bright" **John Howell QC** (see p.1398). His "formidable intellect" and "discursive approach" combines with "a clarity of writing and courteousness." Solicitors claim they like to reserve his strong advocacy skills "for the big brain stuff." **Arden Chambers** proffers two names. The "thoughtful and knowledgeable" **Andrew Arden QC** (see p.1343) "can swashbuckle if that's what you need, but he can also be bookish and cerebral." "Always a character" clients like him for his "common sense and powerful mind." Strong on vires issues he is respected for housing and local government finance work. His colleague **Christopher Baker** (see p.1345) "reflects a client-focused, solution-driven approach." Pragmatic and comfortable in court, he is "good with clients, thoughtful, open and bright." **Lionel Read QC**, also known for planning, has had a lower profile at **Eldon Chambers** due to his status as the Head of Gray's Inn. **Roger Henderson QC** (see p.1393) of **2 Harcourt Buildings** has improved his standing "for his expertise on local government vires issues." In deliberations, he remains pragmatic and "plays the role of an impartial and balanced judge." **Rabinder Singh** (see p.1449), an "outstanding public lawyer" and now of **Matrix Chambers** "can turn his hand to most things." Persuasive and committed, he is "marvellous in court, even if he comes over as quite quiet in person." Also well rounded in his approach, **Michael Humphries** (see p.1399) of **2 Mitre Court Buildings** is "good at directing and running a matter, as well as advising on it." Solicitors admire his measured approach.

WALES & CHESTER CIRCUIT

LEADING SILKS • Wales & Chester		
1	COOKE Nicholas	9 Park Place

For details of these leading barristers see Profiles on p.1339

LEADING JUNIORS • Wales & Chester		
1	WALTERS Graham	33 Park Place
	WILLIAMS Rhodri	30 Park Place

For details of these leading barristers see Profiles on p.1339

Nicholas Cooke QC (see p.1365) of **9 Park Place** (see full details p.1584) yet again emerges from our research as the one barrister in Wales with a high standing in this field. Solicitors rate him as "approachable and incisive," while "the clients love him." He "understands the Welsh context," a valuable resource with the work generated by the advent of the Welsh Assembly. Junior **Rhodri Williams** (see p.1469) of **30 Park Place** (see full details p.1585) also received warm endorsements, while new entry to the tables, **Graham Walters** (see p.1466) of **33 Park Place** (see full details p.1585) has honed his "highly conscientious, tenacious" abilities.

MEDIA & ENTERTAINMENT

RESEARCH: The rankings are based on in-depth interviews with over 5,000 solicitors and barristers in the UK. Chambers research is audited by the British Market Research Bureau (see page 7 for details).

OVERVIEW: Music continues to be the most contentious part of the media and entertainment industry with a significant number of management disputes. Most notably, The Shallitt v Church litigation aroused public interest because the defendant was a minor. Barristers featured have been recommended by many senior entertainment litigators and clients within the industry. The table does not include those who are recommended for their expertise in defamation, and we refer you to that section of the Guide.

LONDON

	MEDIA & ENTERTAINMENT • London	QCs	Jnrs
1	**Blackstone Chambers** (Baxendale/Flint)	3	2
2	**Brick Court Chambers** (Christopher Clarke QC)	3	-
	Hogarth Chambers (Morcom/Rayner James)	2	2
	8 New Square (Michael Fysh QC)	3	2
3	**Essex Court Chambers** (Gordon Pollock QC)	1	2
	Maitland Chambers (Lyndon-Stanford Aldous)	2	2
	3 Verulam Buildings (Symons/Jarvis)	2	-

This book is the product of 6,552 1/2-hour interviews. See p.7 for BMRB audit.
For details of these leading barristers see Profiles on p.1339

	LEADING SILKS • London	
1	ENGLEHART Robert	Blackstone Chambers
	MILL Ian	Blackstone Chambers
	POLLOCK Gordon	Essex Court Chambers
2	DAVIS Nigel	Maitland Chambers
	GARNETT Kevin	Hogarth Chambers
	SUMPTION Jonathan	Brick Court Chambers
3	BALDWIN John	8 New Square
	DOHMANN Barbara	Blackstone Chambers
	RAYNER JAMES Jonathan	Hogarth Chambers
4	HIRST Jonathan	Brick Court Chambers
	KENTRIDGE Sydney	Brick Court Chambers
	MERRIMAN Nicholas	3 Verulam Buildings
	PRESCOTT Peter	8 New Square
	PRICE Richard	Littleton Chambers
	SILVERLEAF Michael	11 South Square
	UNWIN David	Maitland Chambers
	VITORIA Mary	8 New Square
NEW SILKS		
	NELSON Vincent	39 Essex Street
	SUTCLIFFE Andrew	3 Verulam Buildings

For details of these leading barristers see Profiles on p.1339

	LEADING JUNIORS • London	
1	SAINI Pushpinder	Blackstone Chambers
	WAKSMAN David	Fountain Court
2	ALEXANDER Daniel	8 New Square
	BATE Stephen	5 Raymond Buildings
	CULLEN Edmund	Maitland Chambers
	HOWE Robert	Blackstone Chambers
	MILLETT Richard	Essex Court Chambers
3	BARKER Simon	Maitland Chambers
	DICKENS Paul	Hogarth Chambers
	FLYNN Vernon	Essex Court Chambers
	MELLOR James	8 New Square
	MICHAELS Amanda	Hogarth Chambers

For details of these leading barristers see Profiles on p.1339

Blackstone Chambers (see full details p.1481) **Robert Englehart QC** (see p.1376) is rated for his "brilliant, enormous intellect" and many of our interviewees saw him as "the first barrister in media." "Liked by entertainment firms," **Ian Mill QC** (see p.1421) is deemed "straightforward and seriously authoritative." Ranked for the second year running, the "formidable" **Barbara Dohmann QC** (see p.1371) is known for her cross examination skills: "she crucifies the other side." Elevated to the top junior ranking is **Pushpinder Saini** (see p.1445), commended for being a "delightfully persuasive advocate." **Robert Howe** (see p.1398) received plaudits for his "smooth" lawyering skills.

Brick Court Chambers (see full details p.1484) The "fabulously clever" **Jonathan Sumption QC** (see p.1455) features for his "high powered intellectual ability." **Jonathan Hirst QC** (see p.1395) was praised by senior entertainment litigators and the "mesmeric" **Sydney Kentridge QC** (see p.1405) is described as an "outstanding advocate."

Hogarth Chambers (see full details p.1523) **Kevin Garnett QC** (see p.1383) is an "authority on copyright law." **Jonathan Rayner James QC** (see p.1439) is well regarded and **Paul Dickens** (see p.1371) is seen as a "competent player." **Amanda Michaels** (see p.1421) is considered a leading junior by many media law firms.

8 New Square (see full details p.1544) **John Baldwin QC** (see p.1346) is seen to be impressive because of his "rare knowledge." The "professional" **Peter Prescott QC** (see p.1435) deserves to be a leader because of his "academic" qualities and the industry considers **Mary Vitoria QC** (see p.1465) a "leading lawyer." Also described as "impressive," **Daniel Alexander** (see p.1342) is known to be "smooth in court." **James Mellor** (see p.1420) is deemed "superlative" for his courtroom tactics.

Essex Court Chambers (see full details p.1496) Widely regarded as a "genius," **Gordon Pollock QC** (see p.1434) is number one for his "incisive mind" and is said to "ooze talent." **Vernon Flynn** (see p.1380) is commended for his knowledge and an ability to "hit the ground running." **Richard Millet** (see p.1421) was rated for "knowing his way around a recording contract."

Maitland Chambers (see full details p.1538) "Conscientious and gritty," these qualities give **Nigel Davis QC** (see p.1370) "complete mastery of the case." **David Unwin QC** is "clever" and recommended for his breadth of experience. "On the rise" is the "silent destroyer" **Edmund Cullen** (see p.1368), who attracts work with his "analytical, ruthless approach." **Simon Barker** (see p.1347) is widely respected by litigators in the field.

3 Verulam Buildings (see full details p.1575) The "patrician" **Nicholas Merriman QC** (see p.1421) is rated as both "an intellectual and charming man." New silk **Andrew Sutcliffe** (see p.1456) is respected for his "strong knowledge of music law."

Other Notable Practitioners **Richard Price QC** (see p.1436) of **Littleton Chambers** garnered plaudits for his practice and **Michael Silverleaf QC** (see p.1448) of **11 South Square** is rated for his "technical knowledge." The warmly commended **Vincent Nelson QC** (see p.1427) at **39 Essex Street** has taken silk this year. Respected for his "enormous clarity," **David Waksman** (see p.1465) at **Fountain Court** has "a relaxed manner that ensures the ear of the court." **Stephen Bate** (see p.1348) of **5 Raymond Buildings** is rated as "a tremendously hard worker" who "solicitors like because he gets results."

PARTNERSHIP

RESEARCH: The rankings are based on in-depth interviews with over 5,000 solicitors and barristers in the UK. Chambers research is audited by the British Market Research Bureau (see page 7 for details).

LONDON

PARTNERSHIP • London		QCs	Jnrs
1	**48 Bedford Row** (Roderick I'Anson Banks)	-	2
	Serle Court (Lord Neill of Bladen QC)	2	2

Numbers show recommended barristers in this practice area

LEADING SILKS • London		
1	**BRIGGS Michael**	Serle Court
2	**DAVIS Nigel**	Maitland Chambers
	STEINFELD Alan	24 Old Buildings
	WILLIAMSON Hazel	Maitland Chambers
NEW SILKS		
	HINKS Frank	Serle Court

For details of these leading barristers see Profiles on p.1339

LEADING JUNIORS • London		
1	**BANKS Roderick I'Anson**	48 Bedford Row
2	**BLACKETT-ORD Mark**	5 Stone Buildings
	MACHELL John	Serle Court
	WHITTAKER John	Serle Court
UP AND COMING		
	JELF Simon	48 Bedford Row

This book is the product of 6,552 1/2-hour interviews. See p.7 for BMRB audit.
For details of these leading barristers see Profiles on p.1339

48 Bedford Row (see full details p.1480) Leading the only chambers solely devoted to partnership, **Roderick I'Anson Banks** (see p.1346) towers over the field. Eliciting an opinion from all, he is considered "so authoritative, the leading light" and "expensive, but deservedly so," although he is occasionally referred to as "aloof." His colleague **Simon Jelf** (see p.1402) has made a name for himself as a promising young junior.

Barristers' profiles 1339-1472

Serle Court (see full details p.1565) Remains a strong set in this field, with the impressive "all-round entertainer," **Michael Briggs QC** (see p.1355) attracting volumes of positive press. **Frank Hinks QC** (see p.1395), who took silk last year, is also carving an "excellent name for himself" in this field. **John Machell** (see p.1414) is "bright and unassuming," and regarded as "a pre-eminent draftsman" while **John Whittaker** (see p.1468) "has a good understanding" of partnership issues.

Other Notable Practitioners The newly formed **Maitland Chambers** (see full details p.1538) appears as a strong set this year. "Traditional leading player" **Nigel Davis QC** (see p.1370) and the "terrific" **Hazel Williamson QC** (see p.1469) continue to generate excellent press. **Alan Steinfeld QC** (see p.1453) of **24 Old Buildings** is "extremely user-friendly." At **5 Stone Buildings, Mark Blackett-Ord** (see p.1351) is seen as "a bit of a maverick with an old-fashioned approach," and "every inch the technician."

NORTHERN CIRCUIT

LEADING SILKS • Northern		
1	**BARTLEY-JONES Edward**	Exchange Chambers

For details of these leading barristers see Profiles on p.1339

Edward-Bartley Jones QC (see p.1348) of **Exchange Chambers** (see full details p.1598), retains his position as the only barrister outside London who receives positive recommendations for partnership law.

PENSIONS

RESEARCH: The rankings are based on in-depth interviews with over 5,000 solicitors and barristers in the UK. Chambers research is audited by the British Market Research Bureau (see page 7 for details).

Barristers' profiles 1339-1472

LONDON

	PENSIONS • London	QCs	Jnrs
1	**Wilberforce Chambers** (Edward Nugee QC)	6	4
2	**35 Essex Street** (Christopher Wilson-Smith QC)	1	5
3	**3 Stone Buildings** (Geoffrey Vos QC)	-	3
	5 Stone Buildings (Henry Harrod)	2	2
4	**Maitland Chambers** (Lyndon-Stanford Aldous)	1	1

Numbers show recommended barristers in this practice area

	LEADING SILKS • London	
★	**WARREN Nicholas**	Wilberforce Chambers
1	**GREEN Brian**	Wilberforce Chambers
	NUGEE Christopher	Wilberforce Chambers
2	**INGLIS-JONES Nigel**	35 Essex Street
	SIMMONDS Andrew	5 Stone Buildings
3	**FURNESS Michael**	Wilberforce Chambers
	NUGEE Edward	Wilberforce Chambers
	SHER Jules	Wilberforce Chambers
	STEINFELD Alan	24 Old Buildings
4	**HERBERT Mark**	5 Stone Buildings
	UNWIN David	Maitland Chambers

For details of these leading barristers see Profiles on p.1339

	LEADING JUNIORS • London	
1	**NEWMAN Paul**	Wilberforce Chambers
	STEPHENS John	35 Essex Street
	TOPHAM Geoffrey	3 Stone Buildings
2	**ASPLIN Sarah**	3 Stone Buildings
	HITCHCOCK Richard	35 Essex Street
3	**CLIFFORD James**	Maitland Chambers
	FURZE Caroline	Wilberforce Chambers
	LACEY Sarah	3 Stone Buildings
	TENNET Michael	Wilberforce Chambers
	TIDMARSH Christopher	5 Stone Buildings
4	**MALDEN Grace**	35 Essex Street
	SPINK Andrew	35 Essex Street
	STALLWORTHY Nicholas	35 Essex Street
UP AND COMING		
	EVANS Jonathan	Wilberforce Chambers
	RICH Barbara	5 Stone Buildings

This book is the product of 6,552 1/2-hour interviews. See p.7 for BMRB audit.
For details of these leading barristers see Profiles on p.1339

Wilberforce Chambers (see full details p.1576) "Still the dominating force" in pensions, "with one or two exceptions it has a complete monopoly on high level expertise." Although praised for its "technical expertise" and "excellent service," some felt that the set's popularity means it is occasionally overworked although it remains "good at providing people at short notice." **Nicholas Warren QC** (see p.1466) is "still talked of as 'the man'" and "the expert's expert – streets ahead of anyone else." "Incredibly responsive" and "able to separate the wood from the trees," his written opinions are highly sought after. **Brian Green QC** (see p.1388) does "an astonishing amount of work" and is "phenomenally bright and totally client focused" and "good on his feet." Rising star **Christopher Nugee QC** (see p.1429) moves up the tables commanding rave reviews. "Absolutely first class," "utterly superb in his style and wit" and "so brilliant it's frightening," he is judged to be "excellent with people," offering "concise advice on complicated problems" and, for many, simply "the first choice if you've got money to spend." **Edward Nugee QC** (see p.1429) can be relied upon to "provide an authoritative opinion." **Michael Furness QC** (see p.1382), relatively new to silk, moves up the table as his profile builds. "Commercial and robust, able to understand the technicalities of pensions law better than most," he is "prepared to roll his sleeves up and get involved." Having a "broad practice" means that **Jules Sher QC** (see p.1448) has been seen less in pensions this year, although he is endorsed as "phenomenally industrious" and "thorough in his clever analysis." Although "charming to work with" his style is seen as a traditional one. Still out of circulation due to his commitments on the Thyssen case, Robert Ham QC is out of the tables this year but retains enormous respect. **Paul Newman** (see p.1427) has "rocketed in the last year" to the "top of any list of juniors." Seen as "forceful, a good man to have on your side" he is "commercial" and "user friendly – clients like him." **Caroline Furze** (see p.1382) is "bright" with "intellectual flair," although her bedside manner is not to everyone's liking. **Michael Tennet** (see p.1458) is "an excellent junior," always "effective and thorough," though some feel he is occasionally "aggressive." **Jonathan Evans** (see p.1376) remains "well regarded" but has had a low profile this year in pensions.

35 Essex Street (see full details p.1502) (Christopher Wilson-Smith QC) The "liveliest opposition to Wilberforce" although it lacks a heavy roster of high profile silks, the set remains bolstered by "a substantial number of up and coming juniors" whom some find "far more approachable." The set remains endorsed for its "technical expertise" and "excellent service." "Incredibly cerebral, extremely intelligent – to see him in action is outstanding," the "mellifluous leader" **Nigel Inglis-Jones QC** (see p.1399) remains "a force to be reckoned with." He has a "unique knowledge of pension schemes," a "wise perspective and client friendliness." As the "grand old man of pensions" solicitors believe that "for certain types of cases he's the silk of first choice." Leading senior figure, "forthright and pragmatic" **John Stephens** (see p.1453) "gives impressive, practical advice" and is often used "on the most complex work." "Sensible" **Richard Hitchcock** (see p.1395) has a "remarkably good grasp of the legal technicalities combined with a pleasant character." Promoted from our up and coming ranks, **Grace Malden** (see p.1415) received warm recommendations. **Andrew Spink** (see p.1451) is "reliable and personable" and is seen to be "establishing himself" at the high end. Raising his profile with work on British Airways and National Grid, **Nicholas Stallworthy** (see p.1452) "combines insight with being approachable;" he "works well as part of a team."

3 Stone Buildings (see full details p.1568) Praised for its individuals, this set has a strong focus on pensions as one of its leading areas. Senior junior **Geoffrey Topham** (see p.1461) is "busy and highly competent," solicitors claim that "clients who have Geoffrey don't need silks." "Straightforward" **Sarah Asplin** (see p.1344) is "not only intelligent but pleasant to work with. "Practical," her "forthright manner" is judged to be a useful asset by solicitors who have worked with her. **Sarah Lacey** (see p.1408) is "thoughtful and fun to work with" and "able to deal with the difficult issues and explain them clearly."

5 Stone Buildings (see full details p.1569) Although praised for the quality of its individuals, this set was felt to lack the volume of pensions work commanded by the leaders. "Bright and extremely client responsive," **Andrew Simmonds QC** (see p.1449) has had a number of high profile cases and is always "thorough and prepared." Standing keenly in the limelight, some have felt he can be "more belligerent than expected." Known for his Ombudsman work, **Mark Herbert QC** (see p.1394) is not perceived to be heavily focused on pure pensions work. Similarly thought of as more involved in tax issues, **Christopher Tidmarsh** (see p.1461) remains active in pensions; he is "thorough and grasps points quickly." **Barbara Rich** (see p.1440) enters the tables this year due to the weight of market recommendation.

Maitland Chambers (see full details p.1538) Now merged with 13 Old Square to form a single commercial Chancery set, the former 7 Stone Buildings is seen to be "beefing up." Although **David Unwin QC** has spent much of the last year on non-pensions work, "what he does, he does well." "Dependable and good on his feet," he is recommended for his "depth of experience." **James Clifford** (see p.1363) is "efficient, knowledgeable and good value for money," praised by clients as "accessible and approachable."

Other Notable Practitioners Leading commercial chancery practitioner **Alan Steinfeld QC** (see p.1453) of **24 Old Buildings** is "a clever lawyer offering excellent judgments," and "a fearsome cross-examiner." He enters the pensions table, having done "a good job in the National Grid Court of Appeal case."

PERSONAL INJURY

RESEARCH: The rankings are based on in-depth interviews with over 5,000 solicitors and barristers in the UK. Chambers research is audited by the British Market Research Bureau (see page 7 for details).

Barristers' profiles 0000-0000

LONDON

PERSONAL INJURY • London		QCs	Jnrs
1	**39 Essex Street** (Nigel Pleming QC)	2	5
	12 King's Bench Walk (Richard Methuen QC)	3	5
	Plowden Buildings (William Lowe QC)	–	3
2	**Crown Office Chambers** (Spencer/Purchas)	3	2
	Devereux Chambers (Jeffrey Burke QC)	2	2
	2 Temple Gardens (Dermod O'Brien QC)	4	2
3	**Farrar's Building** (John Leighton Williams QC)	3	1
	9 Gough Square (John Foy QC)	1	3
	Old Square Chambers (John Hendy QC)	2	1
4	**7 Bedford Row** (David Farrer QC)	1	1
	Cloisters (Laura Cox QC)	1	1
	Doughty Street Chambers (Geoffrey Robertson QC)	1	1

This book is the product of 6,552 1/2-hour interviews. See p.7 for BMRB audit.
Numbers show recommended barristers in this practice area

39 Essex Street (see full details p.1503) Despite the departures of Daniel Brennan to Matrix Chambers and Colin Mackay to the bench, the set's strength in depth keeps it firmly among the leaders for this work. A "doyen" of this type of work, **Edwin Glasgow QC**'s (see p.1385) reputation for "ferocious advocacy" is such that opponents ruefully concede: "You know that you'll get a fight when you face him." **Richard Davies QC**, described by solicitors as "one of the best advocates at the bar," is a regular choice of both claimant and defendant firms. The set is particularly considered to excel in its strength at junior level. Catastrophic injury specialist **Neil Block** (see p.1352) has a huge following among law firms, who consider him to be "obviously first-class." **Christian Du Cann** (see p.1372)is acknowledged to be "a stylish advocate," and peers consider that "on his day," **Charles Brown** (see p.1356)"need tip his hat to nobody." The "fearless" **Charles Cory-Wright** (see p.1366) is "doing bigger and bigger cases," and, according to a typical view expressed to researchers, is "going right to the top." **Geoffrey Brown** (see p.1356) also maintains his share of market support.

12 King's Bench Walk (see full details p.1421) Led by the "excellent" **Richard Methuen QC** (see p.1421), this is regarded by solicitors as a "traditional" personal injury set, which has an enviable balance of highly rated silks and juniors. "Rottweiler" **Ronald Walker QC** was commended to researchers as "the ideal man for a case that involves complex legal points of interpretation," while "exceedingly bright" **Frank Burton QC** (see p.1358) earns special commendation from solicitors for his rapport with clients. "Fighter" **Allan Gore** (see p.1388) is a leading senior junior, hugely popular with Trade Union solicitors, heavily involved with APIL, and described by some as the "last word in asbestos cases." "Star name" **Stephen Worthington** (see p.1471) is "one of our favourites," according to numerous law firms, and is praised for his "indefatigable work rate." **William Featherby** "has had another sound year," while **Susan Rodway** "has the knack of getting to the heart of a case at once." Newly arrived from 2 Temple Gardens, the respected **Stephen Archer**'s (see p.1343) caseload encompasses industrial disease and brain damage cases.

Plowden Buildings (see full details p.1556) Thought by many solicitors to have "a virtual monopoly" on the local PI market, the set includes three ranked juniors. **Catherine Foster** (see p.1381) is best known for her defendant work for British Coal. New entries **Jeremy Freedman** (see p.1382) and **Simon Wood** (see p.1470) came highly recommended, with the latter described as "good on paperwork and solid on his feet."

Crown Office Chambers (see full details p.1580) Said to have a "wonderful personal injury pedigree," solicitors regularly praise the set for its "responsiveness" and the "trouble it takes with clients." "Forensically sharp" **Christopher Purchas QC** (see p.1437) is "a barrister at the top of his game at the moment," while the "larger than life" **Michael Spencer QC** (see p.1451) and "silky smooth" **William Stevenson QC** (see p.1453) are advocates who can "retrieve almost any case by force of personality." Peers acknowledge **Dennis Matthews** (see p.1417) for his mixed clinical negligence/personal injury practice, while **Jonathan Waite** (see p.1465)also comes highly recommended for his "versatility."

Devereux Chambers (see full details p.1491) "Meticulous" **Jeffrey Burke QC** is regarded as "just about the most painstaking practitioner" in the field. "He will never fail through a lack of preparation." "Oasis of calm" **Robert Glancy QC** (see p.1385) retains high standing among clients. **Stephen Killalea** (see p.1406) "always comes up with the goods," in the view of leading solicitors. His recent track record on accident at work cases sees him rise to the top of the juniors' rankings. **Christopher Goddard** (see p.1386) is a frequent port of call for both plaintiff and defendant solicitors, notably in occupational health matters.

2 Temple Gardens (see full details p.1572) Increasingly gaining recognition from peers for its depth of "sound, safe" personal injury practitioners, the set has a strong following among law firms, who value its "personal and friendly style." **Ben Browne QC** (see p.1356) is "a powerful advocate" with "genuine courtroom presence," while "old star" **Dermod O'Brien QC** (see p.1429) "can still be relied on to deliver a first-class performance in big cases." "Urbane and courteous" all-rounder **Jeremy Stuart-Smith QC** (see p.1455) and the respected **Andrew Collender QC** (see p.1365) both gain plaudits from a variety of solicitors. Among juniors, **Tim Lord** was praised to researchers as a "robust, client-friendly and exceptionally thorough" practitioner, while **Martin Porter** "consistently gets the right results."

Farrar's Building (see full details p.1505) "Approachable" head of chambers **John Leighton Williams QC** (see p.1468) is widely commended for his presence in court and "engaging personal manner." **William Norris QC** (see p.1429) is a "sharp cookie," popular with solicitors who appreciate his inclination to "go in hard on key issues." **Alan Jeffreys QC** (see p.1401) continues to receive regular instruction from defendant and claimant solicitors, who profess themselves to be "100% satisfied with him." **Anthony Seys Llewellyn** (see p.1446) retains a solid reputation among his peers, while Edward Southwell has moved to the bench.

9 Gough Square (see full details p.1511) "User friendly" **John Foy QC** (see p.1381) is "just about the tops" for a number of his instructing solicitors, and is acknowledged to be an expert in occupational disease. On the junior front, **Nicolas Hillier** (see p.1395) "is a thorough and impressive student of a case" and **Jacob Levy** (see p.1411)is "quite a character," popular with leading claimant firms. Contemporaries consider **Roger Hiorns** (see p.1395)to be "vastly underrated." John Reddihough has retired.

Old Square Chambers (see full details p.1549) **John Hendy QC** (see p.1393)maintains his reputation among Trade Union law firms, while

PERSONAL INJURY

LEADING SILKS • London		
1	BRENNAN Daniel	Matrix Chambers
	GLASGOW Edwin	39 Essex Street
	PURCHAS Christopher	Crown Office Chambers
2	BURKE Jeffrey	Devereux Chambers
	BURTON Frank	12 King's Bench Walk
	DAVIES Richard	39 Essex Street
	FOY John	9 Gough Square
	GLANCY Robert	Devereux Chambers
	IRWIN Stephen	Doughty Street Chambers
	JEFFREYS Alan	Farrar's Building
	LANGSTAFF Brian	Cloisters
	MASKREY Simeon	7 Bedford Row
	SPENCER Michael	Crown Office Chambers
	WALKER Ronald	12 King's Bench Walk
3	BADENOCH James	1 Crown Office Row
	BROWNE Benjamin	2 Temple Gardens
	BURNETT Ian	1 Temple Gardens
	COLLENDER Andrew	2 Temple Gardens
	FAULKS Edward	No. 1 Serjeants' Inn
	FOSKETT David	1 Crown Office Row
	HENDY John	Old Square Chambers
	KELLY Matthias	Old Square Chambers
	LIVESEY Bernard	Four New Square
	METHUEN Richard	12 King's Bench Walk
	NORRIS William	Farrar's Building
	O'BRIEN Dermod	2 Temple Gardens
	STEVENSON William	Crown Office Chambers
	STUART-SMITH Jeremy	2 Temple Gardens
	WILLIAMS John Leighton	Farrar's Building

For details of these leading barristers see Profiles on p.1339

LEADING JUNIORS • London		
1	BLOCK Neil	39 Essex Street
	FOSTER Catherine	Plowden Buildings
	FREEDMAN Jeremy	Plowden Buildings
	GORE Allan	12 King's Bench Walk
	KILLALEA Stephen	Devereux Chambers
	WOOD Simon	Plowden Buildings
	WORTHINGTON Stephen	12 King's Bench Walk
2	BROWN Charles	39 Essex Street
	CORY-WRIGHT Charles	39 Essex Street
	DU CANN Christian	39 Essex Street
	HILLIER Nicolas	9 Gough Square
	KING Simon	7 Bedford Row
3	ARCHER Stephen	12 King's Bench Walk
	BROWN Geoffrey	39 Essex Street
	BUCHAN Andrew	Cloisters
	COOKSLEY Nigel	Old Square Chambers
	GODDARD Christopher	Devereux Chambers
	MATTHEWS Dennis	Crown Office Chambers
	OPPENHEIM Robin	Doughty Street Chambers
	RODWAY Susan	12 King's Bench Walk
	TUDOR-EVANS Quintin	199 Strand
	WAITE Jonathan	Crown Office Chambers
4	FEATHERBY William	12 King's Bench Walk
	HIORNS Roger	9 Gough Square
	LEVY Jacob	9 Gough Square
	LORD Tim	2 Temple Gardens
	MOAT Frank	Pump Court Chambers
	PORTER Martin	2 Temple Gardens
	SEYS LLEWELLYN Anthony	Farrar's Building

For details of these leading barristers see Profiles on p.1339

Matthias Kelly QC (see p.1405) has a growing profile for his catastrophic injury expertise. A number of claimant law firms expressed a preference for respected junior **Nigel Cooksley** (see p.1365).

7 Bedford Row (see full details p.1477) "Flavour of the month" **Simeon Maskrey QC** (see p.1417) is widely acclaimed as "an amazing talent" with a "forceful style that works." Noted for his strong insurer client base, **Simon King** (see p.1406) is recognised to belong among the leading PI juniors.

Cloisters (see full details p.1487) "Fantastic" **Brian Langstaff QC** (see p.1408) remains hugely popular with solicitors, and has a strong niche in personal injury in the workplace. Newly ranked **Andrew Buchan** (see p.1357) has been involved in a number of high profile stress cases in The House of Lords.

Doughty Street Chambers (see full details p.1492) **Stephen Irwin QC** (see p.1400) is a "notably successful silk" with a particular reputation for multiparty litigation. "Top class" junior **Robin Oppenheim** (see p.1430)was also praised for his "level-headed" approach.

Other Notable Practitioners The arrival of **Dan Brennan QC** at **Matrix Chambers** is considered to be a huge coup for his new set. Formerly at 39 Essex Street, his practice spans a vast swathe of public and common law. Some of his contemporaries have described him as "head and shoulders above the rest of us." **Bernard Livesey QC** (see p.1412) at **Four New Square** has a broad PI practice, and was recently involved on a major stress case. "Scrapper" **James Badenoch QC** (see p.1345) of **1 Crown Office Row** is appreciated for his "never say die" approach to cases, while his colleague **David Foskett QC** (see p.1380) is said to have "his feet firmly on the ground," and receives commendation from solicitors for his "sympathetic way with clients." At **1 Temple Gardens**, **Ian Burnett QC** (see p.1357) maintains a high profile and is said to be "a star in the making." **Edward Faulks QC** (see p.1377) of **No. 1 Serjeants**' Inn has gained a number of accolades for his work on recent child abuse cases. **Frank Moat** (see p.1422) of **Pump Court Chambers** is a well-known name in his industrial disease specialism, while newly ranked junior **Quintin Tudor-Evans** (see p.1463) at **199 The Strand** received frequent recommendation from solicitors.

WALES & CHESTER CIRCUIT

PERSONAL INJURY • Wales & Chester		QCs	Jnrs
1	**9 Park Place** (Ian Murphy QC) Cardiff	1	1
	30 Park Place (John Jenkins QC) Cardiff	-	2
	33 Park Place (John Charles Rees QC) Cardiff	2	-

Numbers show recommended barristers in this practice area

LEADING SILKS • Wales & Chester		
1	BIDDER Neil	33 Park Place
	MURPHY Ian	9 Park Place
2	REES John	33 Park Place

For details of these leading barristers see Profiles on p.1339

LEADING JUNIORS • Wales & Chester		
1	REES Philip	9 Park Place
	VENMORE John	30 Park Place
	WILLIAMS Lloyd	30 Park Place

This book is the product of 6,552 1/2-hour interviews. See p.7 for BMRB audit.
For details of these leading barristers see Profiles on p.1339

9 Park Place (see full details p.1584) **Ian Murphy QC** (see p.1426) is known as a "good all-rounder" with experience in both defendant and claimant work. His colleague **Philip Rees** (see p.1439) is a "very experienced" junior, widely recommended by solicitors in Wales.

30 Park Place (see full details p.1585) **John Venmore** (see p.1464) is a high profile junior in Wales, to the extent that a number of commentators have questioned his absence from the silks lists. **Lloyd Williams** is newly recommended as a "safe pair of hands" for both claimant and defendant work.

33 Park Place (see full details p.1585) Specialising in occupational disease, VWF, asthma, asbestosis and stress, the set has eight barristers working exclusively on PI. Of these, **Neil Bidder QC** and "key figure" **John Rees QC** continue to be specifically recommended by the local market.

WESTERN CIRCUIT

PERSONAL INJURY • Western		QCs	Jnrs
1	**St John's Chambers** (Christopher Sharp QC) Bristol	1	3
2	**Guildhall Chambers** (Adrian Palmer QC) Bristol	-	2

Numbers show recommended barristers in this practice area

LEADING SILKS • Western		
1	**SHARP Christopher**	St John's Chambers

For details of these leading barristers see Profiles on p.1339

LEADING JUNIORS • Western	
BARRIE Peter	Guildhall Chambers
BULLOCK Ian	St John's Chambers
CHIPPINDALL Adam	Guildhall Chambers
COTTER Barry	Old Square Chambers
EDWARDS Glyn	St John's Chambers
STEAD Richard	St John's Chambers

This book is the product of 6,552 1/2-hour interviews. See p.7 for BMRB audit.
For details of these leading barristers see Profiles on p.1339

St John's Chambers (see full details p.1583) Particularly popular with defendant solicitors, the set is led by the "excellent" **Christopher Sharp QC** (see p.1446). A strong hand of juniors includes respected names **Ian Bullock** (see p.1357), **Glyn Edwards** (see p.1374) and **Richard Stead** (see p.1452).

Guildhall Chambers (see full details p.1581) The new inclusion of two juniors highlights the set's increasingly strong reputation for PI. Peers respect **Adam Chippindall** (see p.1362) for his "thoroughness" and the strength of his paperwork, while **Peter Barrie** (see p.1348) is known for his "excellent advocacy."

Other Notable Practitioners **Barry Cotter** (see p.1366) in the Bristol annex of **Old Square Chambers** is a recognised expert in latex allergy.

MIDLANDS CIRCUIT

Ropewalk Chambers (see full details p.1612) "Far and away the strongest set in the region," it appeals to solicitors and clients from all over the country. "Solid performer" **Richard Maxwell QC** (see p.1418) is best known for a range of work relating to occupational disease and child abuse. **Robert Owen QC** (see p.1430) is a respected name in multi-party industrial disease actions. "Extremely good" **Ian McLaren QC** (see p.1419) has established a national reputation for his litigation work, while **William Woodward QC** (see p.1470) is also "visible on the circuit" and a frequent choice of defendant firms. The set monopolises the region's leading juniors. **Jayne Adams** (see p.1341) maintains her status among her peers, as does the "frighteningly capable" **Patrick Limb** (see p.1412). **Dominic Nolan** (see p.1429) continues to impress peers and clients as a "quick, reliable barrister, who pays close attention to technical detail while providing realistic advice." **Rosalind Coe** (see p.1364) and **Douglas Herbert** (see p.1394) are both newly ranked this year, following strong local recommendation.

PERSONAL INJURY • Midlands		QCs	Jnrs
1	**Ropewalk Chambers** (Ian McLaren QC) Nottingham	4	5
2	**5 Fountain Court** (Anthony Barker QC) Birmingham	3	-

Numbers show recommended barristers in this practice area

LEADING SILKS • Midlands		
1	**EVANS Gareth**	5 Fountain Court
	LEWIS Ralph	5 Fountain Court
	MCLAREN Ian	Ropewalk Chambers
	WOODWARD William	Ropewalk Chambers
2	**MAXWELL Richard**	Ropewalk Chambers
	OWEN Robert	Ropewalk Chambers
NEW SILKS		
	BLEASDALE Paul	5 Fountain Court

For details of these leading barristers see Profiles on p.1339

LEADING JUNIORS • Midlands		
1	**LIMB Patrick**	Ropewalk Chambers
	NOLAN Dominic	Ropewalk Chambers
2	**ADAMS Jayne**	Ropewalk Chambers
	ASHWORTH Lance	St Philip's Chambers
	COE Rosalind	Ropewalk Chambers
	HERBERT Douglas	Ropewalk Chambers

This book is the product of 6,552 1/2-hour interviews. See p.7 for BMRB audit.
For details of these leading barristers see Profiles on p.1339

5 Fountain Court (see full details p.1506) **Ralph Lewis QC** (see p.1411) specialises in high value claims, and is viewed by some solicitors as "the region's outstanding name." **Gareth Evans QC** is said to be a "sound advocate," while new silk **Paul Bleasdale QC** (see p.1351) is renowned for his industrial disease expertise. Stephen Oliver-Jones QC has gone to the bench.

Other Notable Practitioners **Lance Ashworth** (see p.1344) of **St Philip's Chambers** continues to receive strong support from local solicitors, although his practice is now much more devoted to chancery work.

NORTH EASTERN CIRCUIT

PERSONAL INJURY • North Eastern		QCs	Jnrs
1	Park Court Chambers (Stewart/Smith) Leeds	-	1
	Park Lane Chambers (Stuart Brown QC) Leeds	-	2

Numbers show recommended barristers in this practice area

LEADING JUNIORS • North Eastern		
1	**ELGOT Howard**	Park Lane Chambers
2	**JACKSON Simon**	Park Court Chambers
	THORPE Simon	Park Lane Chambers

This book is the product of 6,552 1/2-hour interviews. See p.7 for BMRB audit.
For details of these leading barristers see Profiles on p.1339

Park Court Chambers (see full details p.1592) **Simon Jackson** (see p.1400) continues to be highly rated by fellow barristers and local solicitors.

Park Lane Chambers (see full details p.1592) Senior juniors **Howard Elgot** (see p.1375) and **Simon Thorpe** maintain their respected positions in the table this year.

NORTHERN CIRCUIT

Byrom Street Chambers Giles Wingate-Saul QC (see p.1469)"thinks like a judge" and continues to be held in high regard on the Northern circuit. Claimant firm favourite **Caroline Swift QC** (see p.1456) is also held in high regard, and is joined in the table this year by colleague **Geoffrey Tattersall QC**, who attracts endorsement for his "down to earth attitude and excellent rapport with clients." **Winston Hunter QC** (see p.1399) retains his share of market.

Deans Court Chambers (see full details p.1602) Principally acting for defendant firms, **Raymond Machell QC** is "intellectually formidable," and has a reputation among solicitors as "an excellent negotiator." "Sharp" **David Stockdale QC** (see p.1454) is strong on a range of areas in PI, and is recommended for his ability to process cases "with care and speed." Peers recommend **Patrick Field QC** (see p.1378) for his "ability to spot key issues quickly." Newly ranked **Mark Turner QC** (see p.1463) is said to be "super-efficient."

Exchange Chambers (see full details p.1598) The respected **Bill Braithwaite QC** (see p.1354) is known for his specialisation in brain and spinal cord injuries, while relatively new silk **Gerard Martin QC** (see p.1417) also maintains his share of market support.

9 St John Street (see full details p.1607) Solicitors recommend **Nicholas Hinchliffe QC** as a "tenacious and constructive" barrister, while newly rated **Timothy Horlock QC** has a growing reputation for industrial disease cases. At junior level, the "realistic" **Ian Little** gains widespread peer approval.

18 St John Street (see full details p.1607) Leading juniors **David Heaton** (see p.1392) and **Mark Laprell** continue to garner widespread plaudits from solicitors for their "thorough preparation of cases."

28 St John St A newcomer to the rankings **Michael Redfern QC** gains the respect of solicitors for "going the extra mile for us." Leading junior, the "thorough" **James Rowley** (see p.1442), retains his share of market support.

Other Notable Practitioners "Robust and incisive" **Andrew Edis QC** (see p.1374) of **14 Castle Street** is respected for his ability on his feet, yet local solicitors also insist that "he has the technical ability to back it up." **Yaqub Rahman** (see p.1438) at **Oriel Chambers** "really gets to grips with a case," while **Graham Wood** (see p.1470) of **India Buildings Chambers** "seems instinctively to know which line to take to ensure maximum results."

	PERSONAL INJURY • Northern	QCs	Jnrs
1	**Byrom Street Chambers** Manchester	4	-
	Deans Court Chambers (Stephen Grime QC) Manchester	4	-
2	**Exchange Chambers** (Turner/Braithwaite/Globe) Liverpool	2	-
	9 St John Street (John Hand QC) Manchester	2	1
	18 St John Street (Jonathan Foster QC) Manchester	-	2
	28 St John St Manchester	1	1

Numbers show recommended barristers in this practice area

	LEADING SILKS • Northern	
1	**MACHELL Raymond**	Deans Court Chambers
	WINGATE-SAUL Giles	Byrom Street Chambers
2	**STOCKDALE David**	Deans Court Chambers
	SWIFT Caroline	Byrom Street Chambers
	TATTERSALL Geoffrey	Byrom Street Chambers
	TURNER Mark	Deans Court Chambers
3	**BRAITHWAITE Bill**	Exchange Chambers
	EDIS Andrew	14 Castle Street
	FIELD Patrick	Deans Court Chambers
	HINCHLIFFE Nicholas	9 St John Street
	HORLOCK Timothy	9 St John Street
	REDFERN Michael	28 St John St
NEW SILKS		
	HUNTER Winston	Byrom Street Chambers
	MARTIN Gerard	Exchange Chambers

For details of these leading barristers see Profiles on page xxxx

	LEADING JUNIORS • Northern	
1	**HEATON David**	18 St John Street
	ROWLEY James	28 St John St
2	**LAPRELL Mark**	18 St John Street
	LITTLE Ian	9 St John Street
	RAHMAN Yaqub	Oriel Chambers
	WOOD Graham	India Buildings Chambers

This book is the product of 6,552 1/2-hour interviews. See p.7 for BMRB audit.

For details of these leading barristers see Profiles on p.1339

PLANNING

RESEARCH: The rankings are based on in-depth interviews with over 5,000 solicitors and barristers in the UK. Chambers research is audited by the British Market Research Bureau (see page 7 for details).

OVERVIEW: This year sees a reorganisation of our tables following interviews conducted among specialist counsel for planning, local government and parliamentary law. Given the current paucity of private bills and continued predominance of Transport and Works Act bills within the parliamentary sector, this scope of work has been subsumed into the planning bar section. Conversely, many local government specialists confirmed that planning related matters comprised a proportion of their work load, but by no means represented the whole. Accordingly, a separate bar section pertaining to the gamut of local government work has been produced. The resulting shake-up sees a significant overlap of sets ranked in both planning and local government sections, with 2 Mitre Court Buildings and Eldon Chambers (formerly 1 Serjeant's Inn) remaining exclusive to the former and 11 King's Bench Walk falling within the remit of the latter.

Barristers' profiles 1339-1472

PLANNING • London		QCs	Jnrs
1	**4 Breams Buildings** (Christopher Lockhart-Mummery QC)	5	2
	2-3 Gray's Inn Square (Porten/Scrivener)	5	5
	2 Harcourt Buildings (Gerard Ryan QC)	6	5
2	**Eldon Chambers** (Lionel Read QC)	4	5
	4-5 Gray's Inn Square (Appleby/Mole)	5	4
	2 Mitre Court Buildings (Michael FitzGerald QC)	5	3

Numbers show recommended barristers in this practice area

LEADING SILKS • London		
1	**DRABBLE Richard**	4 Breams Buildings
	FITZGERALD Michael	2 Mitre Court Buildings
	HICKS William	Eldon Chambers
	HOWELL John	Blackstone Chambers
	KATKOWSKI Christopher	4 Breams Buildings
	LINDBLOM Keith	2 Harcourt Buildings
	LOCKHART-MUMMERY Christopher	4 Breams Buildings
	PURCHAS Robin	2 Harcourt Buildings
	READ Lionel	Eldon Chambers
2	**ASH Brian**	4-5 Gray's Inn Square
	CLARKSON Patrick	Eldon Chambers
	ELVIN David	4 Breams Buildings
	GEORGE Charles	2 Harcourt Buildings
	PHILLIPS Richard	2 Harcourt Buildings
	PORTEN Anthony	2-3 Gray's Inn Square
	SILSOE David	2 Mitre Court Buildings
3	**DINKIN Anthony**	2-3 Gray's Inn Square
	HOBSON John	4-5 Gray's Inn Square
	KING Neil	2 Mitre Court Buildings
	MOLE David	4-5 Gray's Inn Square
	ROOTS Guy	2 Mitre Court Buildings
	STEEL John	4-5 Gray's Inn Square
	STRAKER Timothy	4-5 Gray's Inn Square
4	**HOLGATE David**	4 Breams Buildings
	HORTON Matthew	2 Mitre Court Buildings
	LOWE Mark	2-3 Gray's Inn Square
	PUGH Vernon	2-3 Gray's Inn Square
	RYAN Gerard	2 Harcourt Buildings
	WOLTON Harry	2-3 Gray's Inn Square
NEW SILKS		
	KELLY Andrew	2 Harcourt Buildings
	LEWIS Rhodri Price	Eldon Chambers

This book is the product of 6,552 1/2-hour interviews. See p.7 for BMRB audit.
For details of these leading barristers see Profiles on p.1339

LONDON

4 Breams Buildings (see full details p.1483) "Rooted in planning as their base," this "broadly-based" set boasts a "well balanced team of serious players." Although viewed as a "grievous loss" to the set's public law capability, John Howell QC's departure to Blackstone Chambers is unlikely to dent the reputation of "the strongest planning law team in the book." Former Treasury Counsel **Richard Drabble QC** (see p.1372) is endorsed for his court and judicial review work. A "charming one-off character" described as "low key and persuasive;" he applies his "commercial brain" "over a wide field." Clients vouch, "you can ring him up, and he's very quick, clear and precise." The "excellent" **Christopher Katkowski QC** (see p.1404) boasts "double strength" in both court work and public inquiries. Described as "diligent and extremely bright," his strong specialisation in retail has seen his involvement in matters such as the Heron Tower proposal in central London and the Dibden Bay Inquiry. "Patrician" **Christopher Lockhart-Mummery QC** (see p.1413) is a "quiet, balanced, concise advocate" who "never gets excited." He is recommended by leading advisors for his "gravitas combined with clear logical advice." "Pleasant, reasonable" **David Elvin QC** (see p.1375) continues to impress on public inquiry work such as the Alconbury case involving human rights issues. "At root a planner," but possessed of a broader practice, he is said to have "an impressive grasp of his fields" and "the ear of the court." Described as an "intellectually strong, robust, focused advocate" who "exudes enormous competence," he "works hard to win a case." With a mixed practice, "aggressive and extremely thorough" **David Holgate QC** (see p.1396) is known as a leader in the fields of both planning and public law. The set's "highly rated" juniors both serve as members of the Attorney General's Panel Counsel for Government work. "Extremely capable and intelligent" **Nathalie Lieven** (see p.1411) is "incisive in court" and "gets on well with clients," while "quiet, charming" **Timothy Mould** (see p.1424) is a "plausible advocate" who "can lay out issues in simple, effective manner" – he is "brief and to the point."

2-3 Gray's Inn Square (see full details p.1513) An "absolutely enormous" set with a "well established" base in planning law. "Well-organised advocate" **Anthony Porten QC** (see p.1435) is considered a "good all-round unpretentious" advisor with a slightly less prominent profile in planning on account of his local government workload. **Anthony Dinkin QC** (see p.1371) is described as "charming and effective" while clients recommend Town and Country planning specialist **Mark Lowe QC** (see p.1413) "without hesitation" because he "really knows and understands how modern PFI deals work." "Everybody speaks well" of **Vernon Pugh QC** (see p.1436) who has a "prominent profile" in planning, environmental and local government matters throughout Wales, including planning and public inquiries and urban regeneration work. **Harry Wolton QC** (see p.1470) has a "strong Midlands following" among in-house solicitors for building and development companies and planning consultants. Among the juniors "tenacious and aggressive" **Mary Cook** (see p.1365) gains strong client recognition for her planning and regeneration work. "Big personality" **Morag Ellis** (see p.1375) is a "thorough advocate" in planning inquiries. Said to be "a rising star" on the planning circuit, **Simon Bird** (see p.1350) is an "extremely thorough, incisive and effective cross examiner" with a busy high court practice. Engaged on the M40 and M25

LEADING JUNIORS • London		
★	CORNER Timothy	4-5 Gray's Inn Square
1	HARRIS Russell	Eldon Chambers
	HILL Thomas	4-5 Gray's Inn Square
	SINGH Rabinder	Matrix Chambers
	WHITE Sasha	Eldon Chambers
2	COOK Mary	2-3 Gray's Inn Square
	DRUCE Michael	2 Mitre Court Buildings
	ELLIS Morag	2-3 Gray's Inn Square
	HOWELL WILLIAMS Craig	2 Harcourt Buildings
	LIEVEN Nathalie	4 Breams Buildings
	MOULD Timothy	4 Breams Buildings
	VILLAGE Peter	4-5 Gray's Inn Square
3	BAKER Christopher	Arden Chambers
	BIRD Simon	2-3 Gray's Inn Square
	CAMERON Neil	Eldon Chambers
	HUMPHREYS Richard	4-5 Gray's Inn Square
	HUMPHRIES Michael	2 Mitre Court Buildings
	MORGAN Stephen	Eldon Chambers
	ORNSBY Suzanne	2 Harcourt Buildings
4	ALBUTT Ian	2-3 Gray's Inn Square
	EDWARDS Douglas	2 Harcourt Buildings
	GLOVER Richard	2 Mitre Court Buildings
	NEWCOMBE Andrew	2 Harcourt Buildings
	STEPHENSON Geoffrey	2-3 Gray's Inn Square
UP AND COMING		
	CLAYTON Joanna	2 Harcourt Buildings
	LYNESS Scott	Eldon Chambers

For details of these leading barristers see Profiles on p.1339

motorway service area development inquiries and Birmingham Bull Ring development CPOs, **Ian Albutt** (see p.1341) has a wide practice in court and inquiries that includes High Court and judicial review work. "Steady old campaigner" **Geoffrey Stephenson** (see p.1453) is better known for his local government work but is equally well rated for his experience in the planning arena.

2 Harcourt Buildings (see full details p.1520) A "strong planning set," rated by long-standing users for its "good service, reasonable fee-rates and efficient, friendly clerking." One of the "new generations of stars" **Keith Lindblom QC** (see p.1412) has been seen on high profile work such as the House of Lords Alconbury case involving human rights issues and an inquiry concerning a railway extension across the New Territories in Hong Kong. A "smooth, highly polished performer" at public inquiries, he is said to be "popular with clients" and "great fun to work with." Endorsed as "absolutely superb" on urban regeneration work, **Robin Purchas QC** (see p.1437) is "extremely thorough on detail" and "cross examines like a demon." He has been heavily involved in the Transport and Works Act proceedings on the West Coast Main Line modernisation programme. "First class intellectual" **Charles George QC** (see p.1384) is seen less on public inquiries but is said to have "an immensely sound grasp" of planning, local government and administrative law. An "effective" advocate with a "traditional" style, he is "great with clients." Known for his ministry work, **Richard Phillips QC** (see p.1433) is said by clients to be an "aggressive performer" with "tremendous presentation skills" on cases such as inquiries into the Broadoaks Business Park and M42 major motorway service area. Experienced practitioner **Gerard Ryan QC** is an "impressive" performer, while new silk **Andrew Kelly QC** (see p.1405) is a "nice smooth operator" who is "well known on planning issues." Among the juniors, "good all-round performer" **Craig Howell Williams** (see p.1398) wins plaudits for his expertise in a range of areas. A "phenomenally bright good lawyer" with "formidable intellect," he can "nit-pick his way through very complicated local government law" and is widely regarded as a "foremost authority on local government finance." Following the Heathrow Terminal 5 case, he has been acting alongside Lindblom QC for the developers in the Alconbury case. Clients use him for "the big brain stuff," rating his "clear writing" ability, "discursive approach" and "incredibly courteous" manner. **Suzanne Ornsby** (see p.1430) and senior junior **Andrew Newcombe** (see p.1427) both have fan clubs of clients that strongly endorse their skills. "Knowledgeable, thorough" **Douglas Edwards** (see p.1374) is "doing well" having had a successful year in the litigation sphere, while supporting Purchas on the West Coast Main Line programme and **Joanna Clayton** is accredited with an "enormously hardworking, competent and mature" approach.

Eldon Chambers (see full details p.1493) "Solid" in planning law, this set (formerly 1 Serjeant's Inn) boasts a broad practice covering environment, local government, administrative, parliamentary and public affairs, health and safety and energy law. Endorsed by clients as "user-friendly, hard-working and commercial," **Bill Hicks QC** (see p.1394) has acted on the UK Waste Management judicial review in the Northern Ireland Court of Appeal and the Brent Cross Retail Inquiry and subsequent human rights challenge. Now heading Eldon Chambers, **Lionel Read QC** is acknowledged as "a great name." A "meticulous, tremendously thorough" advocate, clients still rave about his "old school parliamentary skills combined with enormous common sense." He has acted on several major inquiries, including Southern Water, Medway Cement, Bracknell Town Centre Retail and Canterbury CPO, and most recently, Portsmouth Waste Incinerator. "Solid, calm, reliable performer" **Patrick Clarkson QC** (see p.1363) has promoted a series of major residential schemes for St James Homes as well as retail schemes for Tesco and J Laing. His High Court appearances include R v Cambridge City Council ex p Warner Village (challenge to major leisure scheme) and R v Tower Hamlets ex p Remfrey (quashing of planning approval for £400 million office/retail scheme at Spitalfields). New silk **Rhodri Price Lewis QC's** (see p.1411) recent work includes a LIFFE inquiry into a major road/retail interchange at M25/M4 junction for a government department, Southern Water and Redbourn Motorway Service Area. Highly rated by peers and clients, **Russell Harris** is a "quick and efficient all-round advocate" whose recent cases include the Brent Cross Extension Appeal, the ongoing Aldington Immigration Detention Centre litigation, Fulham Football Stadium and Dibden Bay. "Unpompous, strong advocate" **Sasha White** (see p.1468) has gained a strong market reputation with the Portsmouth Waste Incinerator and Brent Cross Retail inquiries. **Neil Cameron** (see p.1359) receives recommendation for his involvement in Medway Cement and the judicial review of the Swiss Re Tower at the Baltic Exchange site. "Thorough performer" **Stephen Morgan** (see p.1424) has been seen on the Safeway, Wimbledon inquiry and Intergen, a planning inquiry into an underground gas storage facility on the Isle of Man, in addition to the Warner Village leisure scheme challenge. **Scott Lyness** is "well thought of" in relation to his inquiry work, which includes Tesco (Clapham), Trentham Gardens (enabling development in grounds of a listed building) and Southampton International Airport (link road outside airport).

4-5 Gray's Inn Square (see full details p.1515) Thought to have remained "strong in planning" despite the losses of Duncan Ouseley QC and Gregory Stone QC to the Bench. Admired by clients as "one of the most effective advocates in CPO" **Brian Ash QC** (see p.1344) displays a "wonderful, calm grasp of a case," combined with "excellent client skills." He recently acted in Court of Appeal case R v Rochdale MBC ex p Milne. Peers have "great regard" for **John Hobson QC** (see p.1396). Described as "a tough terrier" he has "a manner which local authorities like – he's down to earth, not stuffy." He acted on Thurrock BC v S/S in the Court of Appeal. "Extremely well-respected" in both courtroom and public inquiry work, **David Mole QC** (see p.1422) recently acted in House of Lord case Wildtree Hotels v Harrow BC. "Tough performer" **John Steel QC** (see p.1452) is rated by peers for his "extremely effective public inquiry style." Described as "hugely enthusiastic with inexhaustible energy," he is said to be "incredibly determined on the client's side" and "throws himself into everything one hundred percent of the time." He acted on the Chelsea Stadium/Chelsea Village Development of Stamford Bridge Inquiry. Possessed of a strong local authority client base, **Timothy Straker QC** (see p.1455) receives solid endorsement for his "attractive style in judicial review and courtroom cases. Clients affirm that "his depth and knowledge of the sector is superb – he can develop multi-layered arguments seamlessly, grasp the subtleties and advance them." Recent work includes the House of Lords Birmingham CC v Oakley concerning council's duty to rebuild and Waddell v RB Kensington & Chelsea concerning red bus routes. Among the set's highly rated juniors, **Tim Corner** (see p.1366) has gathered "a lot of work under his belt over the years." He recently appeared in Court of Appeal case Delta v Secretary of State concerning planning conditions and obligations. An "extremely experienced" senior junior, clients love his "thorough attention to detail. "Aristocratic and gentlemanly" **Tom Hill** (see p.1395) "masters all details with utmost thoroughness, combined with old style courtesy." He is said to have the advantage in cross-examination on account of his good rapport with witnesses. "Robust" **Peter Village** (see p.1464) is popular with clients because he "persuades himself of the rightness of their cause." His "pungent and effective advocacy" has been seen in recent cases, which include Copas & Anor v RB Windsor & Maidenhead and R v Bedford B C ex p George Wimpey. Also recommended, **Richard Humphreys** is said to be "doing well with a good following."

2 Mitre Court Buildings (see full details p.1540) A "fantastic planning set" with "fewer of the big stars" due to the some significant retirements, notably Anthony Anderson QC and the "great campaigner" John Taylor QC. With a "tremendous reputation" as a leading planning silk, "wonderfully patrician" **Michael FitzGerald QC** (see p.1379) conducts his work in a "smooth manner." He recently completed a major inquiry into a proposed new racecourse at Fairlop in Essex, in addition to inquiries into a major retail scheme in Liverpool (Chavase Park) and the Westgate Centre development in central Oxford. His recent major redevelopment work includes Middlesborough Cathedral, Gloucester Docks area and Bracknell town centre. With a "history of long cases," **David Silsoe QC** (see p.1448) has applied his "wonderful mind" to substantial inquiries such as the Heathrow Terminal 5 Public Inquiry, on which his leadership has kept him out of the limelight for several years. **Neil King QC** (see p.1406) is liked by peers for his "forceful, robust advocacy" while clients consider him an "excellent team leader." Chairman of the Planning Bar, **Guy Roots QC** (see p.1441) has a lower profile on the circuit on account of his involvement in longer public inquiries, often teamed with Silsoe. An "excellent, established practitioner" with a "gentle, effective style," he is noted for his expertise in compulsory purchase work such as an important central city site for Gloucester City Council, Union Rail and Channel Tunnel Rail Link. He also acted for Harrods in its application to land helicopters on the roof of the store. **Matthew Horton QC** has a "good following" in administrative and planning work. He acted for the major objectors (BT and Midland Electricity) on Gloucester City Council's CPO case. Among the set's juniors, "aggressive" **Michael Druce** (see p.1372) has been busy on the Spitalfields market redevelopment programme, the extension to Metrocentre, the Gateshead Inquiry and Croft Historic Motor Racing Circuit Inquiry. Also taken up in the Heathrow Terminal 5 Inquiry, **Michael Humphries** (see p.1399) has a "charmingly analytical approach." His clients report, he is "very good at directing, running and advising on matters." He acted for Union Rail and Eurotunnel on compensation claims concerned with CTRL, the Chavase Park Inquiry for major retail scheme in Liverpool and the Westgate Centre development in the centre of Oxford. **Richard Glover** (see p.1386) continues to be rated on planning matters such as the Human Genome Campus in Hinxton, Cambridge and inquiries include Wokingham District Local Plan and Oriel Playing Fields.

Other Notable Practitioners Peers recommend **John Howell QC** (see p.1398) of **Blackstone Chambers** as a "highly intellectual" courtroom advocate. **Rabinder Singh** (see p.1449) of **Matrix Chambers** handles planning work as part of a mixed practice, but receives considerable praise as an "outstanding public lawyer who can turn his hand to most things." With an "extremely quick mind and thorough approach," he is described as having a "slightly austere exterior with a quiet sense of humour" but "marvellous in court." Clients endorse **Christopher Baker** (see p.1345) of **Arden Chambers** as a "thoughtful, open, bright" practitioner who "reflects a client-focused, solution-driven approach."

MIDLANDS CIRCUIT

PLANNING • Midlands	QCs	Jnrs
1 **5 Fountain Court** (Anthony Barker QC) Birmingham	1	3

Numbers show recommended barristers in this practice area

LEADING SILKS • Midlands	
★ **KINGSTON Martin**	5 Fountain Court

For details of these leading barristers see Profiles on p.1339

LEADING JUNIORS • Midlands	
1 **DOVE Ian**	5 Fountain Court
2 **CAHILL Jeremy**	5 Fountain Court
UP AND COMING	
CREAN Anthony	5 Fountain Court

This book is the product of 6,552 1/2-hour interviews. See p.7 for BMRB audit.
For details of these leading barristers see Profiles on p.1339

5 Fountain Court (see full details p.1577) This "enormous, specialist" set is recognised as "the only one" catering to the region's planning sector. The "obvious superstar" with "a national profile," **Martin Kingston QC** is "extremely well-regarded within the profession." He retains a "busy strong practice" which includes Dibden Bay in Hampshire, a new settlement proposal in Elstow Bedfordshire and the Alconbury case. "Never flustered," he is "effective with clients and excellent at marshalling detail." "Energetic" **Ian Dove** gains wide respect among peers for his "absolutely superb, robust" court and public inquiry advocacy. Clients endorse his "approachable, friendly and effective" approach. With a lower profile, senior advocate **Jeremy Cahill** (see p.1358) is also recommended. Clients rate newly recommended, **Anthony Crean** as "an extremely good advocate."

NORTHERN CIRCUIT

PLANNING • Northern	QCs	Jnrs
1 **40 King St** Manchester	4	3

Numbers show recommended barristers in this practice area

LEADING SILKS • Northern	
1 **GILBART Andrew**	40 King St
2 **HOGGETT John**	40 King St
PATTERSON Frances	40 King St
SAUVAIN Stephen	40 King St

For details of these leading barristers see Profiles on p.1339

LEADING JUNIORS • Northern	
1 **BARRETT John**	40 King St
2 **MANLEY David**	40 King St
TUCKER Paul	40 King St

This book is the product of 6,552 1/2-hour interviews. See p.7 for BMRB audit.
For details of these leading barristers see Profiles on p.1339

40 King St (see full details p.1604) Endorsed for its "extremely fine people," the set is thought to have "cornered the separate market" while engaging in "some cross-fertilisation" with London. Clients describe its approach as "accessible, convenient and flexible." His "aggressive, robust, extremely dogged style" renders **Andrew Gilbart QC** (see p.1384) among his peers "one of the leading lights at the Manchester Planning bar, while **John**

Hoggett QC has been regaining prominence after a spell of ill health. Possessed of a "keen mind" his style is described as "dry, acerbic and extremely concise." Peers endorse **Frances Patterson QC**'s (see p.1432) "rise to the top." An "effective silk" with a "precise style" she acted on the Manchester Airport second runway inquiry and the Greater Manchester retail circus.

A "quiet and undemonstrative performer," **Stephen Sauvain QC** is "a smooth operator" with a fine brain." Peers rate **John Barrett** (see p.1347) and **David Manley** as "jolly good" juniors, while **Paul Tucker** is seen as "someone to keep an eye on" for his profile in local plans work.

PRODUCT LIABILITY

RESEARCH: The rankings are based on in-depth interviews with over 5,000 solicitors and barristers in the UK. Chambers research is audited by the British Market Research Bureau (see page 7 for details).

OVERVIEW: Amid predictions that group litigation is about to enter a down turn, the number of actual cases has not waned. In light of developments in the Cape Asbestos group action and the recent Hepatitis C decision, the trend seems more hopeful, with foreign claimants able to receive legal aid and the path to proving individual claims under the Consumer Protection Act made a little easier. Unresolved issues remain, most critically concerning funding, with questions raised over solicitors' payment rates and the implications of conditional fee arrangements.

LONDON

PRODUCT LIABILITY • London		QCs	Jnrs
1	2 Harcourt Buildings (Roger Henderson QC)	2	2
2	Crown Office Chambers (Spencer/Purchas)	1	1
	Doughty Street Chambers (Geoffrey Robertson QC)	1	2
	2 Temple Gardens (Dermod O'Brien QC)	1	1

Numbers show recommended barristers in this practice area

LEADING SILKS • London		
1	BRENNAN Daniel	Matrix Chambers
	FENWICK Justin	Four New Square
	SPENCER Michael	Crown Office Chambers
2	IRWIN Stephen	Doughty Street Chambers
	LANGSTAFF Brian	Cloisters
	PRYNNE Andrew	2 Harcourt Buildings
	STUART-SMITH Jeremy	2 Temple Gardens
	UNDERHILL Nicholas	Fountain Court
3	ULLSTEIN Augustus	29 Bedford Row Chambers
NEW SILKS		
	GIBSON Charles	2 Harcourt Buildings

For details of these leading barristers see Profiles on p.1339

LEADING JUNIORS • London		
1	OPPENHEIM Robin	Doughty Street Chambers
	WAITE Jonathan	Crown Office Chambers
2	COTTER Barry	Old Square Chambers
	LYDIARD Andrew	Brick Court Chambers
	POPAT Prashant	2 Harcourt Buildings
3	RILEY-SMITH Toby	2 Harcourt Buildings
	THOROLD Oliver	Doughty Street Chambers
	TURNER David	2 Temple Gardens

This book is the product of 6,552 1/2-hour interviews. See p.7 for BMRB audit.
For details of these leading barristers see Profiles on p.1339

2 Harcourt Buildings (see full details p.1519) Maintains its grip on this area, acting for defendants and claimants in cutting-edge cases including the benzene soft drinks contamination, MMR, Cape asbestos and organophosphates. The "undoubted expert" **Andrew Prynne QC** (see p.1436) possess the knack of "always sounding reasonable." A new defendant silk from whom much is anticipated, **Charles Gibson QC** (see p.1384) is judged to be "absolutely excellent" with a style that is "ever delightful." A new silk, he has already acquired "plenty of gravitas," and is a "great thinker and advocate." "Rising junior" **Prashant Popat's** profile reflects his deep experience in cases which to date include benzodiazepine, Norplant contraceptive implants, silicone breast implants and the MMR litigation. **Toby Riley-Smith**, now an established junior, remains active on the defendant side and is respected for his user-friendly approach and team skills.

Crown Office Chambers (see full details p.1488) A formidable set which boasts some of the best defence lawyers in the field. Work continues on the MMR, organophosphate and oral contraceptive litigation. "Strategic thinker" **Michael Spencer QC** (see p.1451), who is well placed given his medical background, benefits from "a huge experience" and continues to impress with his ability to balance sympathy for individuals with a "tough and aggressive" stance in court. Many have expressed surprise that "extremely bright" **Jonathan Waite** (see p.1465) did not take silk this year. With a proven track record in the area, he has earned plaudits as a redoubtable opponent.

Doughty Street Chambers (see full details p.1492) A leading set for claimant work, in particular for drug-related multi-party actions. Recently active in MMR, the Cape Asbestos and the oral contraceptive pill cases. Favourite of the legal aid board **Stephen Irwin QC** (see p.1400) is perceived to be a "terribly able chap." Established in the pharmaceutical field, he is "maturing into a leading light." Many have noted that **Robin Oppenheim** (see p.1430) has "a superb brain for the medical side and causation." Never appearing to be fazed by large complex cases, he is recognised as "the junior in the tobacco case." "Responsible" **Oliver Thorold** (see p.1460) is an old hand and "very brave as an advocate".

2 Temple Gardens (see full details p.1572) Established on both sides of the market, recent claimant work has revolved around the MMR litigation, while defence work has included LSD, Sodium Valproate and the organophosphate litigation. "Analytical" **Jeremy Stuart-Smith** (see p.1455) is a "lateral thinker" who received warm endorsement. **David Turner** (see p.1463) is continuing to establish his practice in this area.

Other Notable Practitioners It is generally agreed that, given his continued involvement in some of the leading claimant cases, **Daniel Brennan QC** of **Matrix Chambers** is "deserving of the top slot." Constantly praised as "first class," **Justin Fenwick QC** (see p.1378) of **Four New Square** "really pushes the boundaries" employing "excellent legal skills and commercial analysis." His extensive experience includes acting for the Government in the BSE and Hepatitis C litigation, and acting for manufacturers in the tobacco litigation. A contender for best of the claimants, "hardworking" **Brian Langstaff QC** (see p.1408) of **Cloisters** "has presence in court." Although seen more on paper than in court, many rate the effective advocacy of **Nicholas Underhill QC** (see p.1464) at **Fountain Court**. His recent defence work on Hepatitis C has done much to bolster his profile. "A good punchy advocate," **Augustus Ullstein QC** of **29 Bedford Row** remains endorsed for claimant work. Also on the claimant side, **Barry Cotter** (see p.1366) of **Old Square Chambers** is thought to be "intellectually vigorous," while **Andrew Lydiard** (see p.1414) of **Brick Court Chambers** received commendation for his defence work.

PROFESSIONAL NEGLIGENCE

RESEARCH: The rankings are based on in-depth interviews with over 5,000 solicitors and barristers in the UK. Chambers research is audited by the British Market Research Bureau (see page 7 for details).

OVERVIEW: Professional negligence continues to be a significant area of work for the bar, and tends to be split between commercial sets and those with a more common-law bias. The barristers in our tables represent a mixture of these disciplines, and as in our solicitors section, there are those who undertake a relatively small number of big-hitting cases, and those for whom professional negligence forms part of a broader commercial practice those who do a higher volume of cases and who may specialise in certain areas. Expertise in this field relies on a sound understanding of negligence issues and knowledge of the industry in question.

LONDON

	PROFESSIONAL NEGLIGENCE • London	QCs	Jnrs
1	**Four New Square** (Justin Fenwick QC)	5	4
2	**Crown Office Chambers** (Spencer/Purchas)	4	-
	4 Paper Buildings (Jean Ritchie QC)	1	6
	4 Pump Court (Anthony Temple QC)	3	2
3	**Fountain Court** (Anthony Boswood QC)	1	2
	9 Old Square (Michael Driscoll QC)	2	1
	2 Temple Gardens (Dermod O'Brien QC)	2	4

Numbers show recommended barristers in this practice area

	LEADING SILKS • London	
1	**BRINDLE Michael**	Fountain Court
	DAVIDSON Nicholas	Four New Square
	FENWICK Justin	Four New Square
	SUMPTION Jonathan	Brick Court Chambers
2	**EDELMAN Colin**	Devereux Chambers
	HARVEY Michael	Crown Office Chambers
	HUGHES Iain	Four New Square
	POWELL John	Four New Square
	SYMONS Christopher	3 Verulam Buildings
	TER HAAR Roger	Crown Office Chambers
3	**COOKE Jeremy**	7 King's Bench Walk
	HODGE David	9 Old Square
	HOWARD Mark	Brick Court Chambers
	MANN Anthony	Enterprise Chambers
	MOGER Christopher	4 Pump Court
	POOLES Michael	4 Paper Buildings
4	**BARTLETT Andrew**	Crown Office Chambers
	BRIGGS Michael	Serle Court
	DRISCOLL Michael	9 Old Square
	GLASGOW Edwin	39 Essex Street
	MOXON-BROWNE Robert	2 Temple Gardens
	NORRIS Alastair	5 Stone Buildings
	SIMMONDS Andrew	5 Stone Buildings
	STUART-SMITH Jeremy	2 Temple Gardens
	SUSMAN Peter	2 Harcourt Buildings
	TAVERNER Marcus	Keating Chambers
	TEMPLE Anthony	4 Pump Court
NEW SILKS		
	BUTCHER Christopher	7 King's Bench Walk
	GUGGENHEIM Anna	Crown Office Chambers
	STEWART Roger	Four New Square
	TOZZI Nigel	4 Pump Court

For details of these leading barristers see Profiles on p.1339

Four New Square (see full details p.1543) Retains the edge in this field due to the sheer number of high quality silks and juniors it counts as its own. The acquisition of **Nicholas Davidson QC** (see p.1369) from 4 Paper Buildings further strengthens the set's prominence. Described as "frighteningly intelligent and incisive," and a specialist in this area, he has been active in trials such as Bristol & West Building Society v Fancy & Jackson and Nationwide Building Society v Balmer Radmore. **Justin Fenwick QC** (see p.1378) is perceived to be "extremely highly rated and jolly good" while **Iain Hughes QC** (see p.1399) has "tremendous judgement" and is "a tough opponent." The latter is editor of 'Jackson & Powell on Professional Negligence,' the original author of which, **John Powell QC** (see p.1435), is thought to have "a strong practice" and is rated for his innovative work. In recent years his practice has revolved around claims in a commercial and financial context. "Star" new silk **Roger Stewart QC** (see p.1454) is exceptionally well-regarded, described as "outstanding, always gives sensible advice, legal but tinged with commerical." Amongst the juniors fielded, **Sue Carr** (see p.1360) is showered with praise, interviewees describing her as "brilliant, outstanding, and always user friendly." She displays a "sharp intellect and is quick to get to issues." She recently represented Eton college at an inquest into a pupil's death. "Knowledgeable pracitioner" **David Halpern** (see p.1391) is highly recommended and **Mark Cannon** (see p.1359) is an "exceptionally able barrister, a bit of an encyclopedia". **Fiona Sinclair** (see p.1449) is noted for expertise in construction professional negligence.

Crown Office Chambers (see full details p.1580) Houses a number of respected professional negligence barristers including senior **Michael Harvey QC** (see p.1392), who is described by peers as "the doyen of professional negligence." "Persuasive and relaxed" **Roger ter Haar QC** (see p.1459) is used in the more complex, substantial cases and can be called upon to be "tenacious, like a terrier." **Andrew Bartlett QC** (see p.1348) and new silk **Anna Guggenheim QC** (see p.1390) consolidate the set's strength.

4 Paper Buildings (see full details p.1552) In spite of the loss of Nicholas Davidson, this set ups the stakes in professional negligence this year with a particularly impressive array of juniors. **Michael Pooles QC** (see p.1435) is a popular, respected silk. "Charming with a giant brain - he's a real gent," solicitors appreciate that he has a ready, considered answer to any query. Appeared in litigation between Abbey National and SIF. **Derek Holwill** (see p.1397) He is "a pleasure to work with, tenacious and clever," he has been involved in mediations between Halifax and the SIF. **Patrick Lawrence** (see p.1409), who appeared in the Court of Appeal in Cave v Robinson, Jarvis & Rolfe, has "a great court manner" and **Francis Bacon** (see p.1345) ("bright, thorough and good on his feet") elicited warm commendation from solicitors. "Clever chap" **William Flenley** (see p.1379) is newly arrived to our lists on the back of positive recommendations, he co-authored 'Solicitors' Negligence'. **Spike Charlwood** (see p.1361) is felt to be "maturing his skills" as a professional negligence barrister and **Mark Simpson** (see p.1449) is applauded as "dogged and clever."

4 Pump Court (see full details p.1557) A commendable number of barristers at this construction oriented set appear in our tables this year. Of the silks, **Christopher Moger QC** (see p.1422) is a "superb advocate" who represented valuers in connection with their liability to trustees and investors in Royal Bank of Canada v Grimley Eve. **Anthony Temple QC**

LEADING JUNIORS • London		
1	CARR Sue	Four New Square
	EKLUND Graham	2 Temple Gardens
	GATT Ian	Littleton Chambers
	HALPERN David	Four New Square
	HOLWILL Derek	4 Paper Buildings
	LAWRENCE Patrick	4 Paper Buildings
2	BACON Francis	4 Paper Buildings
	LOMAS Mark	Littleton Chambers
	NEISH Andrew	4 Pump Court
	PHILIPPS Guy	Fountain Court
	PHILLIPS Rory	3 Verulam Buildings
	SWAINSTON Michael	Brick Court Chambers
	THANKI Bankim	Fountain Court
3	ALDOUS Grahame	9 Gough Square
	CANNON Mark	Four New Square
	CHARLWOOD Spike	4 Paper Buildings
	CROSS James	4 Pump Court
	FLENLEY William	4 Paper Buildings
	MOODY Neil	2 Temple Gardens
	NEWMAN Paul	Wilberforce Chambers
	PRYOR Michael	9 Old Square
	RAESIDE Mark	Atkin Chambers
	RUSSELL Christopher	2 Temple Gardens
	SIMPSON Mark	4 Paper Buildings
	SINCLAIR Fiona	Four New Square
	TURNER David	2 Temple Gardens
	WEITZMAN Tom	3 Verulam Buildings

For details of these leading barristers see Profiles on p.1339

LEADING SILKS • Northern		
1	EDIS Andrew	14 Castle Street

For details of these leading barristers see Profiles on p.1339

(see p.1458) has "impressed" his peers while **Andrew Neish** (see p.1427) received warm recommendations during research. He acted for brokers sued by the Swedish reinsurers of underwater equipment in LF v Whitsondale. **James Cross** (see p.1368) successfully defended the Secretary of State for Wales and consulting engineers in an action for nuisance concerning an alleged river erosion to property, as a result of the construction of a major road. New silk **Nigel Tozzi QC** (see p.1461) is perceived to be "excellent, his name comes up frequently."

Fountain Court (see full details p.1506) "A serious professional negligence capability," the set has been involved in big commercial cases involving Barings, Unilever and Mercury Asset Management. "Absolutely first rate," **Michael Brindle QC** (see p.1355) was involved in the Barings case and received heavy endorsment. **Guy Philipps** (see p.1433) appeared in the Dubai Aluminum case and has a following among solicitors. **Bankim Thanki** (see p.1459) is a respected junior and has been involved in mortgage advance cases.

9 Old Square (see full details p.1550) "Excellent" **Michael Driscoll QC** (see p.1372) is a leading professional negligence silk at this chambers. Recent cases include Standard Life Assurance v Egan Lawson Ltd. **David Hodge QC** (see p.1396), rated for his "attention to detail and terrific thoroughness," appeared for the successful respondent in Shirley v Caswell. Junior **Michael Pryor** (see p.1436) wins a "double star" from one solicitor while peers describe him as "absolutely superb, up and coming."

2 Temple Gardens (see full details p.1572) Rounded in its expertise and packed with "lovely people to work with." Leading light, **Robert Moxon-Browne QC** (see p.1425) ("rated enormously") was recently in the Court of Appeal defending Ball v Banner & Ors and Western Trust v Acland & Lensam, both surveyors' negligence cases. **Jeremy Stuart-Smith QC** (see p.1455) is "everyone's favourite - absolutely super," and adjudged "bright and thorough." He acted for the successful defendants in Llambias v Baker Tilley. **Graham Eklund** (see p.1375) is a respected junior, "good on policy points and finding original solutions to nitty gritty issues." **David Turner** (see p.1463) has been described by a client as "one of the best juniors I've ever seen." He has expertise in fire cases. **Christopher Russell** (see p.1443) is "bright," and "amenable" **Neil Moody** (see p.1423) is acclaimed "thorough - one for the detailed cases."

Other Notable Practitioners The celebrated **Jonathan Sumption QC** (see p.1455) of **Brick Court Chambers** has a strong commercial slant. It is universally felt that when he takes on professional negligence cases he is "simply the best." Housed at the same set is "top notch" **Michael Swainston** (see p.1456), said to have a "brain like a planet," and **Mark Howard QC** (see p.1398) who is widely perceived to be "leading in the professional negligence field." **Colin Edelman QC** (see p.1373) of **Devereux Chambers** is "strong all round" and continues to be instructed in substantial claims involving solicitors, valuers and brokers. **Christopher Symons QC** (see p.1456) at **3 Verulam Buildings** is "excellent on professional negligence" and has continued to work for the SIF in run-off. Here also is **Tom Weitzman**, (see p.1467) acclaimed "head and shoulders above everyone else" by one solicitor, he was involved in the Bermuda Fire and Marine Insurance Company trial. At the same set, **Rory Phillips** (see p.1433) appeared in the Kepner-Tregoe v Taylor Joynson Garrett case and received many recommendations. A new silk this year from **7 Kings Bench Walk ; Christopher Butcher QC** (see p.1358) is "ferociously bright - someone to look out for." He was involved in the Barings Litigation. Also at the set, **Jeremy Cooke QC** (see p.1365) remains endorsed. **Anthony Mann QC** of **Enterprise Chambers** is " relaxed and easy to deal with." **Edwin Glasgow** (see p.1385) QC at **39 Essex Street** is "a first rate all rounder." **Alastair Norris QC** at **5 Stone Buildings** is "charming and effective" and **Andrew Simmonds QC** (see p.1449) at the same set has expertise in pensions work. **Peter Susman** (see p.1455) QC at **2 Harcourt Buildings** "extremely impressed" a solicitor on a recent complex accountants case. **Marcus Taverner QC** (see p.1458) of **Keating Chambers** is biased towards construction and seen to be "one of the best around." "Star" **Michael Briggs QC** (see p.1355) at **Serle Court** is "a great court room advocate." "Clever chap" **Ian Gatt** (see p.1383) of **Littleton Chambers** is an often commended junior, "good for reliability of advice and prompt turnaround." His colleague **Mark Lom** as (see p.1413) is adjudged "an attractive advocate in court." **Grahame Aldous** (see p.1342) at **9 Gough Square** is newly ranked on the back of wide solicitor endorsement, and **Paul Newman** (see p.1427) of **Wilberforce Chambers** has an expertise in pensions. **Mark Raeside** (see p.1437) of **Atkin Chambers** is recognised as a construction specialist. At **14 Castle Street** in Liverpool, **Andrew Edis QC** (see p.1374) is a notable barrister who does a significant amount of professional negligence work. He appeared for the successful claimants in the House of Lords when advocates immunity was abolished in Hall v Simons.

PROPERTY LITIGATION

RESEARCH: The rankings are based on in-depth interviews with over 5,000 solicitors and barristers in the UK. Chambers research is audited by the British Market Research Bureau (see page 7 for details).

OVERVIEW: Falcon Chambers remains the clear leader for all property litigation matters, and boasts a notably powerful line-up of silks. Wilberforce Chambers and 9 Old Square remain the nearest challengers.

LONDON

	PROPERTY LITIGATION • London	QCs	Jnrs
1	**Falcon Chambers** (Gaunt/Lewison)	6	10
2	**9 Old Square** (Michael Driscoll QC)	4	7
	Wilberforce Chambers (Edward Nugee QC)	4	2
3	**4 Breams Buildings** (Christopher Lockhart-Mummery QC)	2	2
	Enterprise Chambers (Anthony Mann QC)	-	2
	Maitland Chambers (Lyndon-Stanford/Aldous)	1	2

Numbers show recommended barristers in this practice area

Falcon Chambers (see full details p.1504) Top of everybody's list is the "untouchable" **Kim Lewison QC** (see p.1411). He received universal praise for his "dazzling displays of intellect" and "wonderful clarity." Held in equally high esteem is "tenacious terrier" **Paul Morgan QC** (see p.1423). Solicitors consider him "your best bet for a hopeless case," in addition to being "intellectually superb" and "commercially aware." The set also offers the "meticulous" and "charming" **Nicholas Dowding QC** (see p.1372) ("user-friendly, and has a good sense of humour"), and **Jonathan Gaunt QC** (see p.1383), who "has a matter-of-fact yet effective style," provides "excellent service" and "knows how to get what he wants." **Kirk Reynolds QC** (see p.1440)"delves deeply into the detail" and is "loved by his clients." "Aggressive" and "flamboyant" **Jonathan Brock QC** (see p.1355) is also "not to be underestimated." Of the juniors, "concise" **Timothy Fancourt** (see p.1377) has a "quiet, understated style" and is "so good, you are lucky if you can get him." **Stephen Jourdan** is "extremely bright," and rated by solicitors for his "impressive paperwork." **Anthony Radevsky** (see p.1437) was consistently recommended as a "leader in his field - in a league of his own" for leasehold enfranchisement. **Wayne Clark** (see p.1363) is reckoned to have a "fantastically wide understanding of the law" and **Edward Cole** (see p.1365) always adopts a "sensible, commercial and pragmatic" approach. Former surveyor **Barry Denyer-Green** (see p.1371) has an "attractive advocacy style" while **Martin Rodger** (see p.1441) is "approachable" and "easy to work with." **Caroline Shea** (see p.1447) continues to receive market commendation, and two new names join *Chambers'* lists this year. "Excellent" **Guy Fetherstonhaugh** (see p.1378) is "clearly making a name for himself" and **Anthony Tanney** (see p.1457) is "bright" and "technically excellent."

9 Old Square (see full details p.1550) **Simon Berry QC** (see p.1350) is "fantastic with clients" because he "speaks their language," while "just brilliant" **Michael Driscoll QC** (see p.1372) is "persuasive in court." According to competitors, **David Hodge QC** (see p.1396) has an "enormous brain," while **Judith Jackson QC** (see p.1400) also enjoys high approval ratings from clients. Leading junior **John McGhee** (see p.1419) has "a reassuringly calm presence," and "you can rely on him seeing every point that matters." **Timothy Harry** (see p.1392) is "calm" and "user-friendly," **Edwin Johnson** (see p.1402) has a "fantastically diverse property litigation practice," while **John Dagnall** (see p.1369) enters this year's lists through sheer weight of market recommendation. "Clever, practical" **Katharine Holland** (see p.1396) is "coming on fast," **Alan Johns** has an "adaptable" nature and **Andrew Walker** (see p.1465) is a "thorough and reliable grafter."

Wilberforce Chambers (see full details p.1576) "Experienced operator" **Michael Barnes QC** (see p.1347) is a "fiery fighter" who has "been around

Barristers' profiles 1339-1472

	LEADING SILKS • London	
★	LEWISON Kim	Falcon Chambers
	MORGAN Paul	Falcon Chambers
1	DOWDING Nicholas	Falcon Chambers
	GAUNT Jonathan	Falcon Chambers
2	BARNES Michael	Wilberforce Chambers
	BERRY Simon	9 Old Square
	DRISCOLL Michael	9 Old Square
	FURBER John	Wilberforce Chambers
	REYNOLDS Kirk	Falcon Chambers
3	MALE John	4 Breams Buildings
	NUGEE Christopher	Wilberforce Chambers
	WILLIAMSON Hazel	Maitland Chambers
4	BROCK Jonathan	Falcon Chambers
	CHERRYMAN John	4 Breams Buildings
	HODGE David	9 Old Square
	JACKSON Judith	9 Old Square
	MARTIN John	Wilberforce Chambers
	SMITH Peter	11 Old Square

For details of these leading barristers see Profiles on p.1339

	LEADING JUNIORS • London	
1	FANCOURT Timothy	Falcon Chambers
2	BAKER Jacqueline	Enterprise Chambers
	DUTTON Timothy	No. 1 Serjeants' Inn
	JOURDAN Stephen	Falcon Chambers
	KARAS Jonathan	Wilberforce Chambers
	MCGHEE John	9 Old Square
	RADEVSKY Anthony	Falcon Chambers
	SEITLER Jonathan	Wilberforce Chambers
	TAGGART Nicholas	4 Breams Buildings
3	CLARK Wayne	Falcon Chambers
	COLE Edward	Falcon Chambers
	DENYER-GREEN Barry	Falcon Chambers
	HARRY Timothy	9 Old Square
	JOHNSON Edwin	9 Old Square
	RODGER Martin	Falcon Chambers
	SHEA Caroline	Falcon Chambers
	TIPPLES Amanda	Maitland Chambers
4	DAGNALL John	9 Old Square
	FETHERSTONHAUGH Guy	Falcon Chambers
	HOLLAND Katharine	9 Old Square
	HUTTON Caroline	Enterprise Chambers
	JOHNS Alan	9 Old Square
	MCALLISTER Ann	Serle Court
	THOM James	4 Field Court
	WALKER Andrew	9 Old Square
	WONNACOTT Mark	Maitland Chambers
UP AND COMING		
	MORSHEAD Timothy	4 Breams Buildings
	TANNEY Anthony	Falcon Chambers

For details of these leading barristers see Profiles on p.1339

an age." He maintains his reputation as a "fearsome cross-examiner." Solicitors feel that the "hard-working" **John Furber QC** (see p.1382) is "consistently underrated" while the "extremely bright" **Christopher Nugee QC** (see p.1429) is "skilled and capable," and **John Martin QC** (see p.1417) is also rated highly by instructing law firms. **Jonathan Karas** (see p.1404) is a "clever man" with an "unusual, yet effective style," while fellow junior, **Jonathan Seitler** (see p.1446) is "more user-friendly." He adopts a "commercial approach," but is "composed and reasoned" in court, and a "worthy opponent."

4 Breams Buildings (see full details p.1483) "Exceedingly thorough" **John Male QC** (see p.1415) has a burgeoning reputation in this field, and is well regarded both for his "incredible courtesy" and because he "gets it right." "Experienced" **John Cherryman QC** (see p.1362) also continues to display his authority in the area. "Good team player" **Nicholas Taggart** (see p.1457) is a "tenacious" and "commercial" junior, widely appreciated as a "lateral thinker," while **Timothy Morshead** (see p.1424) has increased his profile over the past twelve months.

Enterprise Chambers (see full details p.1494) "Impressive" **Jacqueline Baker** continues to be highly rated for her "careful, analytical and practical style." **Caroline Hutton** (see p.1399) is "imaginative" and adopts "a holistic attitude towards her work."

Maitland Chambers (see full details p.1538) **Hazel Williamson QC** (see p.1469) continues to be "highly thought of," and has a strong reputation for her valuation work. "Energetic and meticulous" **Amanda Tipples** (see p.1461) is "beginning to specialise," in this area, while "knowledgeable" **Mark Wonnacott** is said to "relish an argument."

Other Notable Practitioners **Peter Smith QC** (see p.1450) of **11 Old Square** is "excellent" and has a "delightful sense of humour." **Timothy Dutton** (see p.1373) of **No.1 Serjeants' Inn** (Faulks) is considered a "very able opponent," and continues to have an outstanding name in this area, despite not being at a traditional landlord/tenant set. "Solid and careful" **James Thom** (see p.1459) of **4 Field Court** continues to receive market recommendation and **Ann McAllister** (see p.1418) of **Serle Court** wins "lots of big work."

SHIPPING

RESEARCH: The rankings are based on in-depth interviews with over 5,000 solicitors and barristers in the UK. Chambers research is audited by the British Market Research Bureau (see page 7 for details).

LONDON

SHIPPING • London		QCs	Jnrs
1	Essex Court Chambers (Gordon Pollock QC)	5	7
	4 Essex Court (Nigel Teare QC)	7	9
	20 Essex Street (Iain Milligan QC)	5	4
	7 King's Bench Walk (Jeremy Cooke QC)	8	3
2	4 Field Court (Steven Gee QC)	2	2

This book is the product of 6,552 1/2-hour interviews. See p.7 for BMRB audit.

For details of these leading barristers see Profiles on p.1339

LEADING SILKS • London		
1	GROSS Peter	20 Essex Street
	POLLOCK Gordon	Essex Court Chambers
2	BRENTON Timothy	7 King's Bench Walk
	COOKE Jeremy	7 King's Bench Walk
	HAMBLEN Nicholas	20 Essex Street
	SCHAFF Alistair	7 King's Bench Walk
	TEARE Nigel	4 Essex Court
3	BUCKNALL Belinda	4 Essex Court
	EDER Bernard	Essex Court Chambers
	FLAUX Julian	7 King's Bench Walk
	GAISMAN Jonathan	7 King's Bench Walk
	MILLIGAN Iain	20 Essex Street
	PERSEY Lionel	4 Essex Court
	RAINEY Simon	4 Essex Court
	RUSSELL Jeremy	4 Essex Court
4	GILMAN Jonathan	Essex Court Chambers
	GLENNIE Angus	20 Essex Street
	GRUDER Jeffrey	Essex Court Chambers
	HOWARD M.N.	4 Essex Court
	KAY Jervis	4 Field Court
	KEALEY Gavin	7 King's Bench Walk
	MACDONALD Charles	4 Essex Court
	POPPLEWELL Andrew	Brick Court Chambers
	YOUNG Timothy	20 Essex Street
NEW SILKS		
	BUTCHER Christopher	7 King's Bench Walk
	DUNNING Graham	Essex Court Chambers
	HOFMEYR Stephen	7 King's Bench Walk
	SELVARATNAM Vasanti	4 Field Court

For details of these leading barristers see Profiles on p.1339

LEADING JUNIORS • London		
1	BERRY Steven	Essex Court Chambers
	PARSONS Luke	4 Essex Court
2	BLANCHARD Claire	Essex Court Chambers
	GOLDSTONE David	4 Essex Court
	JACOBS Nigel	4 Essex Court
	LORD Richard	Brick Court Chambers
	PRIDAY Charles	7 King's Bench Walk
	THOMAS Robert	4 Essex Court
3	BAKER Andrew	20 Essex Street
	EDEY Philip	20 Essex Street
	EDWARDS David	7 King's Bench Walk
	FOXTON David	Essex Court Chambers
	HILL Timothy	4 Field Court
	HOPKINS Philippa	Essex Court Chambers
	JOSEPH David	Essex Court Chambers
	KVERNDAL Simon	4 Essex Court
	MATTHEWS Duncan	20 Essex Street
	MEESON Nigel	4 Essex Court
	SOUTHERN Richard	7 King's Bench Walk
	TURNER James	4 Essex Court
4	COBURN Michael	20 Essex Street
	DAVEY Michael	4 Essex Court
	MCGRATH Paul	Essex Court Chambers
	PHILLIPS Nevil	4 Essex Court
	SAUNDERS Nicholas	4 Field Court
	SMOUHA Joe	Essex Court Chambers

For details of these leading barristers see Profiles on p.1339

Essex Court Chambers (see full details p.1496) He made his name as a shipping barrister, but **Gordon Pollock QC** (see p.1434) rarely takes on anything but the largest cases these days. One such was Manifest Shipping Co v Uni-Polaris Shipping Co Ltd, a marine insurance case concerning the ship 'Star C.' "If the case merits it, he's naturally superb." Likewise, **Bernard Eder QC** (see p.1374) enjoys shipping cases but handles fewer of them than in previous years. His generalist profile hasn't affected his standing with shipping solicitors who think he's "streets ahead." For heavy duty cases, "he has this wonderful ability to convert a difficult case into bite-size proportions suited to the right tribunal." **Jonathan Gilman QC** (see p.1385) was labelled "the oracle" by one leading solicitor. The author of the leading textbook on marine insurance, "he is softly spoken, dependable and technically brilliant." **Jeffrey Gruder QC** (see p.1390) is a "tough but conscientious performer," who has acted in a number of offshore cases recently. New silk **Graham Dunning QC** (see p.1373) is a favourite of several leading firms. He "moves quickly into fourth gear" and is "tactically astute." Noted for his ability on his feet, "judges throw things at him, he rocks back on his feet, composes his thoughts and delivers the perfect response." Of a rich crop of juniors, the "outstanding" **Steven Berry** (see p.1350) is rated as one of the leaders of his generation. He specialises in dry matters such as bills of lading, charterparty arbitrations and shipbuilding disputes, and acted for the shipowners in the 'Starsin' case in the Court of Appeal. **Claire Blanchard** (see p.1351) ("extremely prompt") acted for Lloyds Register into the investigation into the loss of the MV Derbyshire. **David Foxton** (see p.1381) "always cuts out the dead wood in a case." He has appeared in the House of Lords in the 'Star Sea' case, considering issues of unseaworthiness and good faith in a hull insurance policy, and in the 'Vergina', a Commercial Court trial involving a claim for salvage expenses under a marine insurance policy. Solicitors speak highly of **Philippa Hopkins** (see p.1397), who is "easy to work with." She appeared successfully on behalf of shipowners in a dispute involving the arrest of a vessel in Fujairah, as a result of the alleged contamination of a cargo of fuel oil, and has advised in several anti-suit injunction applications. **David Joseph** (see p.1403) has a "more flamboyant personality," but he's "hard-working, great with clients and ticks all the right boxes." Although shipping is no longer the main focus of his practice, he still advises on a range of dry shipping matters. **Paul McGrath** (see p.1419) and "class act" **Joe Smouha** (see p.1450) also gained widespread plaudits from the market.

4 Essex Court (see full details p.1498) Although it suffered the loss of high-billing silk Timothy Brenton QC to 7 Kings Bench Walk, the set has comfortably sufficient depth to retain its place in the leading tier, notably after its acquisition of a powerful quartet from 4 Field Court. Versatile **Nigel Teare QC** (see p.1458) "covers both camps well," and has spent much of the last year as leading counsel on the 'Marchioness' Inquiry. He also has expertise in marine insurance, collision actions and bills of lading. **Belinda Bucknall QC** (see p.1357) is "consistently impressive." She is "extremely committed to the client's cause, and her diligence is incredible. She knows every bit of evidence, she reads the papers inside out and remembers every full stop." Her principal areas of activity include marine insurance and salvage. Some leading London solicitors have "virtually lived with" **Simon Rainey QC** (see p.1438), who is "fantastic under pressure and hasn't put a foot wrong." He is rated for both his dry and wet expertise, and was involved in the $130 million 'Maersk Vinlander' dispute, which concerned the bareboat charter of a semi-submersible drilling rig in the North Sea. Other notches on his resumé include the 'Marchioness' inquiry (on behalf of the 'Bowbelle') and the 'Matco Clyde' case, instructed by the Maritime and Coastguard Agency. **Jeremy Russell QC** (see p.1443) is "always very strong," and is valued for his tenacity and his "non-barristerial style." **MN Howard QC** (see p.1397) handles a variety of wet and dry cases. Leading solicitors rate him as a "subtle and clear thinker." **Charles MacDonald QC** (see p.1414) also retains his share of admirers in the City. From 4 Field Court, **Lionel Persey QC** plays it "straight down the middle – he's authoritative but approachable." He has fans from shipping firms around the country, and has an "ability to handle interesting and unusual cases." Top junior **Luke Parsons** (see p.1432) again occupies top spot in the tables. "An exceptional lawyer," he has developed a niche in Eastern European disputes, and acted on a case at the Commercial Court concerning the transport of crude oil into Macedonia. **Nigel Jacobs** (see p.1400) is frequently instructed by some of London's top practices, as is dry, cargo and insurance expert **Robert Thomas** (see p.1460), who is "approachable and popular." The latter has been prominent on the 'Sea Empress' limitation fund case. **Simon Kverndal** (see p.1407) is another "regular choice." He acted in a major salvage case, the 'Msc Rosa M,' while he and Jeremy Russell QC were also instructed on the 'Contship Success' and 'Selat Arjuna' collision cases. **James Turner** (see p.1463) has a practice split between general commercial and shipping work, specialising in charterparty and bills of lading matters. He acted recently on a substantial offshore oil rig arbitration. He "co-ordinates the whole case, is technologically up to speed and really leads you along." **Nevil Phillips** (see p.1433) is a new entrant to the list this year. He is an imposing presence who "fills a court room. He won't go negative on you just as you're about to enter court." Three acclaimed juniors have arrived from 4 Field Court. **David Goldstone** (see p.1387) is a "smart cookie," both "to the point and effective." He has a general dry shipping practice, and is another to have been prominent in the 'Marchioness' inquiry. **Nigel Meeson** (see p.1420) is a "heavyweight litigator" who was counsel to the Attorney General in the 'Derbyshire' public inquiry, represented the families in the 'Marchioness' public inquiry, and acted in the 'Spiros C' Court of Appeal case, concerning liability of shippers under bills of lading for delay at discharge port. **Michael Davey** has family connections to the fishing industry, and is "an interesting, practical guy with a lot of relevant experience."

20 Essex Street (see full details p.1500) An impressive year for the set sees it move into the top band of this year's table. In the big league is **Peter Gross QC** (see p.1390), "without question, a major force," who has "fantastic judgement and experience." He led on the 'Happy Day' case, which dealt with laytime questions. **Nicholas Hamblen QC** (see p.1391) is "wonderfully calm," has a "meticulous, quiet and studious manner" and is "brilliant for heavy duty cases." He was in the Court of Appeal for the 'Fjord Wind' case, which concerned issues of seaworthiness and due diligence. Solicitors admire the input of **Iain Milligan QC** (see p.1421), who "gives a lot of attention and commitment to the case." He featured in the 'Berge Sisar,' an important series of cases relating to the deterioration of cargoes of propane, and in Sinochem International Oil (London) v Mobil Sales & Supply Corp. Scottish silk **Angus Glennie QC** (see p.1386) is said to be "great at guiding you through difficult pieces of litigation." He appeared in Stocznia Gdanska SA v Erik Henriksen (Latreefers), a case concerning interference with contractual relations, and inducing breach of contract. **Tim Young QC** (see p.1471) appeared in the House of Lords on the 'Hill Harmony' case, a leading case on time charters and the scope of charterers' rights to give orders. Among the set's juniors, **Andrew Baker** (see p.1345) is "innovative and always impressive." **Philip Edey** (see p.1374) is another favourite, whose pleasant manner and ability on his feet mean that "judges love him." **Duncan Matthews** (see p.1417) is a "smooth and polished advocate with excellent judgement," who led on the 'Baltic Flame' and 'Havmann' cases. **Michael Coburn** (see p.1364) "really gets to grips with detail and can get his head round the figures."

7 King's Bench Walk (see full details p.1530) "Quality through and through" is seen to be the hallmark of the set, which reinforced its high standing with the arrival of **Timothy Brenton QC** (see p.1354). Rated by leading solicitors for his user friendliness, he has "no airs and graces," and although his delivery can be "a bit mechanical" for some, "he's superb on paper and one of the top choices for a heavy case." A former Royal Navy mariner, "his seafaring background and understanding of navigation is a real bonus." He spent six months on a large oil rig charterparty arbitration, and has handled a clutch of unseaworthiness cases. A well known author of leading shipping texts, **Jeremy Cooke QC** (see p.1365) is a "refreshingly unstuffy heavy hitter." **Alistair Schaff QC** (see p.1444) is "loved by everyone." His "smooth style" and "disarming manner" are much in demand. He "sways the judges by stealth. You think he's being nice, but he's making important points all the time. He's totally committed to his clients' cause." **Julian Flaux QC** (see p.1379) received a number of recommendations for his advocacy, as did **Jonathan Gaisman QC**, who is "stunning on his feet, although he can be aggressive at times." **Gavin Kealey QC** (see p.1404) is "quick, responsive and reasonably priced," say solicitors. "If the case interests him, he's really well prepared." Although new silk **Christopher Butcher QC** (see p.1358) "does everything these days," an appropriately large case "allows him to demonstrate his brilliance." **Stephen Hofmeyr QC** (see p.1396) is still developing his practice as a silk. **Charles Priday** (see p.1436) is the favoured junior for a number of solicitors. "If you give him a case, he does it. He is conscientious, reads the papers, and reduces cases to straightforward analysis." He was involved in the Metro trial on behalf of Texaco, and has handled a series of arbitrations and 'laytime cases.' **David Edwards** (see p.1374) is tipped to go far, and is described as "a likeable up and comer, who will develop substantially." **Richard Southern** (see p.1451) has a "remarkable gift for simplifying complex theories and details." For several solicitors, his "intellectual robustness" sets him apart from his peers.

4 Field Court (see full details p.1506) A tough year for the set became tougher when four leading names, Lionel Persey QC, David Goldstone, Nigel Meeson and Michael Davey departed to 4 Essex Court. Of the remaining shipping specialists at the set, **Jervis Kay QC** (see p.1404) has a particular interest in sailing. He "really understands how yacht problems occur," and "as long as the instructions are clear, he's a great advocate." Recently appointed silk **Vasanti Selvaratnam QC** (see p.1446) received a range of comments for her ability to handle both dry and wet cases. She is said to be "thorough, easy to work with and always on top of a case." At junior level, **Timothy Hill** (see p.1395) has a "flamboyant style, but is a sharp lad." He has acted on a number of oil tanker cases, including one on behalf of a Russian oil shipment company in a dispute over bareboat charters. **Nicholas Saunders** (see p.1445) "doesn't always get the plaudits, but we like him a lot. He always does a good job." His expertise on salvage and total loss cases was highly commended. These include LOF salvage arbitrations and appeals such as 'Leader AII,' 'Emin' and 'Yria,' cargo claims including 'Patraikos II,' and unexplained losses at sea including 'Rema.'

Other Notable Practitioners "Forthright and clever" **Andrew Popplewell QC** (see p.1435) at **Brick Court Chambers** is "brilliant for any insurance and commercial case." Here the talents of **Richard Lord** were widely endorsed "Great at drafting, he's cerebral and articulate."

SPORT

RESEARCH: The rankings are based on in-depth interviews with over 5,000 solicitors and barristers in the UK. Chambers research is audited by the British Market Research Bureau (see page 7 for details).

OVERVIEW: Football remains the primary source of work for the sports bar. However, over the past few years there have been some high profile cases for individuals in athletics, rugby and other disciplines. With the proposed reform of the football transfer system and other changes within sport, there is plenty of scope for development in this sector.

LONDON

SPORT • London	QCs	Jnrs
1 **Blackstone Chambers** (Baxendale/Flint)	5	3
2 **Brick Court Chambers** (Christopher Clarke QC)	2	1

Numbers show recommended barristers in this practice area

	LEADING SILKS • London	
★	**BELOFF Michael**	Blackstone Chambers
1	**FLINT Charles**	Blackstone Chambers
	PANNICK David	Blackstone Chambers
	ROSEN Murray	11 Stone Buildings
2	**GREEN Nicholas**	Brick Court Chambers
	HOLLANDER Charles	Brick Court Chambers
	LEAVER Peter	One Essex Court
	MILL Ian	Blackstone Chambers
	SINGH Kuldip	5 Paper Buildings
3	**GOULDING Paul**	Blackstone Chambers
	POLLOCK Gordon	Essex Court Chambers
	SPEARMAN Richard	4-5 Gray's Inn Square
NEW SILKS		
	GRIFFITH-JONES David	Devereux Chambers
	KERR Tim	11 King's Bench Walk Chambers

For details of these leading barristers see Profiles on p.1339

	LEADING JUNIORS • London	
1	**CRYSTAL Jonathan**	Cloisters
	LEWIS Adam	Blackstone Chambers
2	**FORDHAM Michael**	Blackstone Chambers
	HOSKINS Mark	Brick Court Chambers
	HOWE Robert	Blackstone Chambers
	THANKI Bankim	Fountain Court
3	**BOYD Stephen**	29 Bedford Row Chambers
	STONER Christopher	9 Old Square

This book is the product of 6,552 1/2-hour interviews. See p.7 for BMRB audit.

For details of these leading barristers see Profiles on p.1339

Blackstone Chambers (see full details p.1481) The "pre-eminent" name for sports law, the set is by far the most recognised institution in the market. The recruitment of the "terrific" **Michael Beloff QC** (see p.1349) from 4-5 Gray's Inn Square has strengthened an already strong team immensely. Said to be "at the top of the tree," he is recognised as a "master litigator." "Absolutely superb" **Charles Flint QC** (see p.1379) is a "wonderful resource for an opinion," while the "decisive, heavy-hitting" **David Pannick QC** (see p.1431) is "almost invariably right." **Ian Mill QC** (see p.1421) is "user-friendly and well-informed," while the "outstanding" **Paul Goulding QC** (see p.1388) rises this year, commended as "a strong fighter." Among the set's juniors, **Adam Lewis** (see p.1411) is "highly impressive," and both **Robert Howe** (see p.1398) and **Michael Fordham** (see p.1380) are "popular and versatile choices."

Brick Court Chambers (see full details p.1484) The clear runner-up in this area, the set includes **Charles Hollander QC** , "a redoubtable opponent who knows about every sport under the sun ." Solicitors look to the "expert" **Nicholas Green QC** (see p.1389) "before anyone else," while the set's leading junior is **Mark Hoskins**, (see p.1397) recommended for his work on the EU aspects of sports law.

Other Notable Practitioners At **11 Stone Buildings Murray Rosen QC** (see p.1442) is praised as "a commercial silk with a master niche in sport," while **Peter Leaver QC** (see p.1409) is a "worthy adversary" at **One Essex Court**. At **5 Paper Buildings** the "excellent" **Kuldip Singh QC** "continues to make a strong impression." **Richard Spearman QC** (see p.1451) of **4-5 Gray's Inn Square** is "building up a big name for himself," and **Gordon Pollock QC** (see p.1434) of **Essex Court Chambers** is "a first port of call - if you can get him." Of the new silks, **David Griffith-Jones QC** (see p.1389) of **Devereux Chambers** is praised as a "good man for a scrap," and **Tim Kerr QC** (see p.1405) of **11 King's Bench Walk** is described as "a fine mind, much admired." Among juniors, the "dynamic" **Jonathan Crystal** (see p.1368) of **Cloisters** is praised for his "succinct and to the point analysis." **Bankim Thanki** (see p.1459) of **Fountain Court** wins plaudits for his "commercial acumen." **Stephen Boyd** (see p.1353) of **29 Bedford Row Chambers** is "extraordinarily thorough," while **Christopher Stoner** (see p.1454) of **9 Old Square** also remains respected.

TAX

RESEARCH: The rankings are based on in-depth interviews with over 5,000 solicitors and barristers in the UK. Chambers research is audited by the British Market Research Bureau (see page 7 for details).

Barristers' profiles 1339-1472

LONDON

TAX • Corporate Tax • London		QCs	Jnrs
1	**Gray's Inn Tax Chambers** (Milton Grundy)	3	3
	Pump Court Tax Chambers	4	5
2	**Revenue Law Chambers** (John Gardiner QC)	3	-
3	**One Essex Court** (Lord Grabiner QC)	1	1
	8 Gray's Inn Square (Patrick Soares)	-	2
	24 Old Buildings (Rex Bretten QC)	1	1
	3 Temple Gardens Tax Chambers (Richard Bramwell QC)	1	1

This book is the product of 6,552 1/2-hour interviews. See p.7 for BMRB audit.

For details of these leading barristers see Profiles on p.1339

LEADING SILKS • Corporate Tax • London		
1	**AARONSON Graham**	Pump Court Tax Chambers
	GARDINER John	Revenue Law Chambers
	GOLDBERG David	Gray's Inn Tax Chambers
	MILNE David	Pump Court Tax Chambers
2	**BRETTEN Rex**	24 Old Buildings
	GOY David	Gray's Inn Tax Chambers
	PROSSER Kevin	Pump Court Tax Chambers
	TREVETT Peter	Revenue Law Chambers
3	**BRAMWELL Richard**	3 Temple Gardens Tax Chambers
	FLESCH Michael	Gray's Inn Tax Chambers
	THORNHILL Andrew	Pump Court Tax Chambers
	WHITEMAN Peter	Hollis Whiteman Chambers
NEW SILKS		
	PEACOCK Jonathan	Revenue Law Chambers

For details of these leading barristers see Profiles on p.1339

LEADING JUNIORS • Corporate Tax • London		
1	**GHOSH Julian**	Pump Court Tax Chambers
2	**EWART David**	Pump Court Tax Chambers
	NOCK Reginald	24 Old Buildings
3	**BAKER Philip**	Gray's Inn Tax Chambers
	CULLEN Felicity	Gray's Inn Tax Chambers
	GAMMIE Malcolm	One Essex Court
	JAMES Alun	3 Temple Gardens Tax Chambers
	SHIPWRIGHT Adrian	Pump Court Tax Chambers
	SOARES Patrick	8 Gray's Inn Square
4	**MCKAY Hugh**	Gray's Inn Tax Chambers
	WAY Patrick	8 Gray's Inn Square

For details of these leading barristers see Profiles on p.1339

Gray's Inn Tax Chambers (see full details p.1517) Famed for its expertise in both the corporate and private client spheres, the set is thought to be home to "some pretty juicy work." One port of call for the "trickier issues," **David Goldberg QC** (see p.1386) is heavily endorsed by both peers and leading solicitors. Combining "technical excellence with commercial nous" he is said to be "a real problem solver." Some solicitors feel that **David Goy QC** (see p.1388) is "underrated;" he is "just so hugely experienced and adds real value to the chambers." Much of his profile lies in property tax work but solicitors are increasingly relying on him for the most heavy weight corporate issues. He is judged to "consistently get the best results for his clients," mainly due to the fact that "he is constantly listening and evaluating." "A superb performer who thinks on his feet," **Michael Flesch QC** (see p.1379) received warm commendation for "intensely thorough" advisory work. The set is also blessed with a depth of talented juniors. Amongst these, **Philip Baker** (see p.1346) is "astute and pleasant to work with," heavily endorsed for his international tax advice. Superb advocate **Felicity Cullen** (see p.1368) is "good on her feet" and "user-friendly" according to solicitors. Approachable **Hugh McKay** (see p.1419) also has a following among City solicitors.

Pump Court Tax Chambers (see full details p.1559) One of the "first ports of call" for top tax advice and described by one solicitor as the "perfect set." Skilled in both contentious and advisory work, the set is thought to have a huge volume of instructions. **David Milne QC** (see p.1422) advises on direct and indirect tax issues and is seen as a "real star" for VAT work. Instructing solicitors rate him for his "sound practical advice" which he applies on some of the most complex cases. He has "a good instinct for the course and outcome of litigation" and is felt to win over the court with his clear eloquent distillation of a matter. **Graham Aaronson QC** (see p.1341) has joined the set from One Essex Court and is felt to display "the best combination of technical skills with a feel for where the courts are going." He excels in "technical corporate tax issues." "User-friendly" **Andrew Thornhill QC** (see p.1460) displays an "approachable intelligence" that solicitors admire for his ability to think around an issue. On the VAT side **Kevin Prosser QC** (see p.1436) has a "results driven and commercial outlook." Peers endorse the fact that he "fights hard and never gives up." The set also boasts the presence of **Julian Ghosh** (see p.1384) who must be the best known tax junior around and "punches miles above his weight in financial matters." Solicitors claim he has a "brilliant brain and a great sense of humour," he provides "clear technical advice" on the most complex of issues. Many interviewees commented on **David Ewart**'s (see p.???) skill on matters of direct tax while "strong all-rounder" **Adrian Shipwright** (see p.1448)continues to have a following. Of the VAT juniors, **Andrew Hitchmough** is "on the way up" buoyed by his technical knowledge and sound advocacy skills. **Rupert Baldry** (see p.1346) "has a big brain" and is praised for being "articulate and effective before the VAT tribunal."

Revenue Law Chambers (see full details p.1563) Although smaller than its main rivals, solicitors commend its consistent display of "the collective expertise required." Solicitors judge the set to be "really user-friendly," particularly commenting on its clerk who "puts himself out to fit you in." Heavyweight silk **John Gardiner QC** (see p.1383) is "authoritative and commercial" and has the ability to "grasp a very wide range of transactions." Peers admire that he is "not afraid to roll up his sleeves and get into the nitty gritty of the document," while his gravitas imbues his advice with extra weight. **Peter Trevett QC** (see p.1383) is popular with clients because he is "extremely nice, practical and gets down to the issues without hiding behind a cloud of legalisms." New silk **Jonathan Peacock QC** (see p.1432) is "terribly good" and "technically able and approachable." His clear advice and "fantastic bedside manner" have won him a following among leading solicitors.

One Essex Court (see full details p.1497) Commentators agree that the set has suffered with the loss of Graham Aaronson to Pump Court Tax Chambers, however it is thought to maintain a strong presence in this

LEADING SILKS • Inland Revenue • London		
1	HENDERSON Launcelot	5 Stone Buildings
	MCCALL Christopher	Maitland Chambers
2	FURNESS Michael	Wilberforce Chambers
	GLICK Ian	One Essex Court
NEW SILKS		
	BRENNAN Timothy	Devereux Chambers

For details of these leading barristers see Profiles on page xxxx

LEADING SILKS • VAT • London		
1	MILNE David	Pump Court Tax Chambers
2	CORDARA Roderick	Essex Court Chambers
3	GOY David	Gray's Inn Tax Chambers
	LASOK Paul	Monckton Chambers
	PARKER Kenneth	Monckton Chambers
	PROSSER Kevin	Pump Court Tax Chambers

For details of these leading barristers see Profiles on page xxxx

LEADING JUNIORS • VAT • London		
1	BARLOW Richard	11 King's Bench Walk
	CARGILL-THOMPSON Perdita	Essex Court Chambers
	HITCHMOUGH Andrew	Pump Court Tax Chambers
2	BALDRY Rupert	Pump Court Tax Chambers
	SMOUHA Joe	Essex Court Chambers

This book is the product of 6,552 1/2-hour interviews. See p.7 for BMRB audit.
For details of these leading barristers see Profiles on p.1339

field. **Malcolm Gammie** (see p.1383), who was a solicitor for many years and thus is "much more experienced than most juniors," is a major attraction at the set. His international expertise, client friendly manner and ability to second guess the leanings of a judge continue to draw plaudits. Many interviewees commented on his "technical and pragmatic approach." Although better known as a general commercial litigator, there is no doubt about the skills of **Ian Glick QC** (see p.1386) on Inland Revenue related matters.

8 Gray's Inn Square (see full details p.1516) A small team fielding strong juniors and complementary strengths in the private client and corporate arenas. Commended for his expertise in property related tax issues, **Patrick Soares** (see p.1450) has "lots of ideas and is consistently clear and creative in his advice." **Patrick Way** (see p.1467) can be relied upon to provide "strong commercial advice."

24 Old Buildings (see full details p.1548) Solicitors commend this set, which is known to display its fair share of talent. Although its profile lies more in its private client work, the set has a depth of experience in the corporate sphere. **Rex Bretten QC** (see p.1354) is "sharp and to the point" and provides "clear, clinical and robust" advice. Peers admire **Reginald Nock** who is "excellent on stamp duty."

3 Temple Gardens Tax Chambers (see full details p.1573) A set which has a reputation among our solicitor interviewees as fielding "user-friendly, responsive and able barristers." Of particular note is **Richard Bramwell QC** (see p.1354), who provides tax planning advice for plcs and owner-managed businesses. Of the juniors, **Alun James** (see p.1401) is a "good all-rounder." Deemed to be "hard-working and thorough," he is "strong on corporate tax and share scheme matters."

Other Notable Practitioners **Peter Whiteman QC** (see p.1468) of **Hollis Whiteman Chambers** is considered to display "real strength." Skilled on the VAT side, the "smashing" **Roderick Cordara** (see p.1366) of **Essex Court Chambers** has an "interesting and creative" style making him a favourite with some solicitors. His colleagues **Perdita Cargill-Thompson** (see p.1359) and **Joe Smouha** (see p.1450) are also highly regarded. At **Monckton Chambers Paul Lasok QC** (see p.1409) is "methodical" and **Kenneth Parker QC** (see p.1431) is thought to devote much of his time to acting for the government including much customs slanted work. He is deemed "a good choice when there is a European element to the case." At **11 King's Bench Walk Richard Barlow** (see p.1347), benefiting from an ex-customs perspective, is considered to be "a natural with a fabulous breadth of experience." For Inland Revenue matters, **Launcelot Henderson** (see p.1393) of **5 Stone Buildings** and **Christopher McCall** (see p.1418) of **Maitland Chambers** are "the main stars of in this field," "both conscientious and technically adept." **Michael Furness** (see p.1382) of **Wilberforce Chambers** has a "considerable intellect" while new silk **Tim Brennan QC** at **Devereux Chambers** is judged to be "extremely articulate, good on his feet and accessible."

BARRISTERS PROFILES

LEADERS AT THE BAR

AARONSON, Graham QC
Pump Court Tax Chambers London
(020) 7414 8080
Recommended in Tax

Specialisation: Principal area of practice is commercial taxation, covering all aspects, in particular mergers and acquisitions; structured finance; corporate reorganisations; life insurance taxation; oil taxation, capital allowances and transfer pricing. Acted in Scorer v Olin Energy Systems; Elliss v BP Oil, BMI (No. 3) v Melluish; Unigate v McGregor; Nuclear Electric v Bradley; Prudential v Bibby; Citibank v Griffin, Hoechst v IRC and A-G; HSBC Life v Stubbs. Clients include major companies; the leading city solicitors and the 'Big 5' accountancy firms.
Prof. Memberships: Chairman Revenue Bar Association 1994-98; Chairman, Tax Law Review Committee 1994-98. Bencher of Middle Temple since 1991.
Career: Educated at City of London School and Trinity Hall, Cambridge 1963-66 (Waraker Law Scholar). Called to the Bar 1966 and practised commercial law before joining 4 Pump Court to specialise in taxation, 1968-73. Managing Director of Worldwide Plastics Development Ltd 1973-77. Director Bridgend Group Plc 1973-92. Tenant at Queen Elizabeth Building 1978-91 and 1 Essex Court 1991-00. Took Silk 1982. Rejoined current Chambers in 2000. Advisor on tax reform to Israel Treasury 1986-89 as part of the team brought in to tackle Israel's hyper-inflation.
Personal: Founder, Standford Grange Rehabilitation Centre for Offenders. Born 31st December 1944. Lives in Stanmore, Middlesex.

ABELL, Anthony
2 Bedford Row (William Clegg QC) London
(020) 7440 8888
Recommended in Crime

ACLAND, Piers
11 South Square (Christopher Floyd QC) London
(020) 7405 1222
Recommended in Intellectual Property

ACTON DAVIS, Jonathan QC
Atkin Chambers (Robert Akenhead QC) London
(020) 7404 0102
jadavis@atkinchambers.law.co.uk
Recommended in Construction

Specialisation: Practice covers construction law work and professional negligence, also general common law matters. Clients include most large construction companies, insurers and other commercial bodies.
Prof. Memberships: Tec Bar, Professional Negligence Bar Association, COMBAR, London Common Law Bar Association, Association des Juristes-Franco-Britaniques.
Career: Called the Bar 1977, Member of Bar Council 1993-98, Bencher of Inner Temple 1995; Queens Counsel, 1996. Assistant Recorder 1997, Recorder 2000. Chairman of Professional Conduct Committee of Bar Council 2001; (Vice-Chairman 1999-00).
Personal: Born 15th January 1953. Educated at Harrow School and P.C.L. LLB (Lond.)

ADAM, Tom
Brick Court Chambers (Christopher Clarke QC) London (020) 7379 3550
adam@brickcourt.co.uk
Recommended in Commercial (Litigation)

Specialisation: General commercial law including: commercial fraud & freezing/search orders (eg Merrill Lynch v Raffa Times 14.6.2000); conflicts of interest/Chinese Walls (eg Sea Containers v Denton Hall, settled 1999); dry shipping (eg The Trident Beauty [1994] 1 LLR 365 (HL); Fyffes v MMD Commercial Court June 2000); Insurance and reinsurance (eg the PA LMX spiral litigation; Mander v Commercial Union [1998] LRLR 93). Commercial professional negligence: eg accountants (eg Abbott v Strong [1998] 2 BCLC 420); actuaries (eg NRG v Bacon & Woodrow [1997] LRLR 678); insurance brokers (Mander).
Prof. Memberships: Member of COMBAR.
Career: Cambridge (Trinity) 1983-7; solicitor 1990 (Macfarlanes); called to the Bar 1991.
Publications: Co-author of chapter on negligence of insurance brokers in LLP encyclopaedia 'Professional Negligence and Liability'. 7th edition of 'Documentary Evidence' (with Charles Hollander QC).

ADAMS, Jayne
Ropewalk Chambers (Ian McLaren QC)
Nottingham (0115) 947 2581
clerks@ropewalk.co.uk
Recommended in Personal Injury

Specialisation: Personal injury, industrial disease and clinical negligence. Junior Counsel in both the Leicestershire and North Wales abuse in care multiparty litigation.
Prof. Memberships: Personal Injury Bar Association.
Career: Birmingham University LLB (Hons); called 1982; chairman of the James Stemp inquiry for Leciestershire Health Authority; chairman of the Care Ethics Committee (fertility services); member of the Legal Services Commission Committee.
Personal: Married, three children.

ADDY, Caroline
1 Brick Court (Richard Rampton QC) London
(020) 7353 8845
clerks@1brickcourt.co.uk
Recommended in Defamation

Specialisation: Defamation, confidence, advertising, contempt of court and media related law generally.
Career: LLB (Euro) Exon 1990. Called 1991, joined chambers 1992. Cases include: Upjohn v Oswald, A-G v Limbrick, McPhilemcy v Times Newspapers Limited, Tancic v Times Newspapers Ltd.
Personal: Born 1968. Lives in London. Languages French and German.

ADKINS, Richard QC
3-4 South Square (Michael Crystal QC & Lord Alexander of Weedon QC) London
(020) 7696 9900
clerks@southsquare.com
Recommended in Insolvency/Corporate Recovery

Specialisation: A business and financial law practice, including both domestic and international disputes with particular specialisations in corporate insolvency law and reconstructions, in takeover litigation and professional negligence cases. Advisory work in relation to banking, securities, receivables financing, chattel leasing, debt issues, securitisation and general corporate law issues.
Prof. Memberships: Middle Temple.
Career: MA (Oxon). Called to the Bar 1982; took Silk 1995.
Publications: Contributor, 'Gore Browne on Companies' and a member of the Editorial Board of the 'Insolvency Lawyer' and the 'Company Financial and Insolvency Law Review'.
Personal: Keen tennis player and opera-goer.

AEBERLI, Peter
46 Essex Street (Geoffrey Hawker) London
(020) 7583 8899
Recommended in Alternative Dispute Resolution

AGEROS, James
2 Bedford Row (William Clegg QC) London
(020) 7440 8888
Recommended in Health & Safety

Specialisation: Criminal law specialist with a strong emphasis on health and safety work, both for the Prosecution and Defence. Has appeared in a number of significant health and safety cases in the recent years, including the prosecution of London Underground for dangerous working practices and Imperial College of Science and Technology for propogation of the HIV virus in unsafe conditions. Has also developed a substantial practice within the fields of criminal insolvency and fraud.
Personal: Born 27 June 1965. Called to the Bar in 1990. Lives in London and enjoys sport and good food.

AGNELLO, Raquel
11 Stone Buildings (Murray Rosen QC) London
(020) 7831 6381
agnello@11stonebuildings.com
Recommended in Insolvency/Corporate Recovery

Specialisation: Specialises in corporate and personal insolvency and general company law. Is well known for her involvement in the field of voluntary arrangements, both corporate and individual. It is an area in which she has lectured extensively and has many reported cases. She also practises in commercial litigation, such as contract, banking, guarantees and other securities whilst retaining an interest in private international litigation.

AINGER, David
10 Old Square (Leolin Price CBE QC) London
(020) 7405 0758 / 7242 5002
Recommended in Chancery

Specialisation: Principal area of specialisation is Chancery; he is a general Chancery practitioner with both an advisory and litigation practice. In addition to work in real property, professional negligence, fraud, partnership, trusts (including breach of trust), pensions, probate, banking and insurance, he has experience of public inquiries, local government, water, waterways and highways, ecclesiastical law, commons, village greens and similar matters. He has conducted litigation in Hong Kong and the Isle of Man and advised on Chancery matters in other jurisdictions.
Career: Appointed one of the Conveyancing Counsel of the Supreme Court in November 1991.

AKENHEAD, Robert QC
Atkin Chambers (Robert Akenhead QC) London
(020) 7404 0120
Recommended in Arbitration (International), Construction

Specialisation: Practising Barrister specialising in the field of Construction law – Arbitration and Litigation. Has practised continually and exclusively since 1972 in Construction Law. Practice has been in the English Courts and in British and international arbitrations. International work has involved arbitrations and contracts inter alia in Europe, Africa, Middle East, Asia, Australia, Fiji, W. Indies and USA. Work has frequently included claims relating to final account, defects, delay and disruption and measurement. Has lectured and given seminars on all legal aspects of building and civil engineering. Recent publication: 'Site Investigation and the Law' (Thomas Telford Ltd – 1984). Joint Editor – Building Law Reports.
Career: Called to Bar July 1972; Queen's Counsel 1989; Recorder 1994; Bencher Inner Temple 1997.
Personal: Born 15th September 1949. Educated Exeter University (LL.B. Hons.). Bar Final 1972 (8th out of 700).

ALBUTT, Ian
2-3 Gray's Inn Square (Anthony Porten QC & Anthony Scrivener QC) London (020) 7242 4986
Recommended in Planning

Specialisation: Planning and local government. Practice encompasses all aspects of planning, administrative and local government law. This includes planning inquiries, local plans, CPO, housing and retail development. Extensive recent experience in green belt, conservation and listed building issues including large scale

MSA provision on M4 and M40 including the M25 and M40 reopened inquiries. Court work includes regular appearances for the Treasury Solicitor, s.288 s.289 appeals, judicial review and High Court challenges. Recent planning inquiries include major motorway service area provision on M40 and M25. Birmingham Bull Ring development CPO 2 and 3. Thames Water Utilities v London Borough of Bromley. Leisure Great Britain plc v Isle of Wight Council 2000 PLCR88. Rossington Hall Investments Ltd v Doncaster Metropolitan Borough Council 2000 PLCR 222 (and in CA). Michael Shaneey Group Limited v Secretary of State for the Environment Transport and Regions of Windsor and Maidenhead Royal Borough Council 2000 PLCR 136 CA.
Prof. Memberships: Planning and Environmental Bar Association; Legal Assessor for the RICS; Member of the Bar Disciplinary Tribunal; Bar Council Direct Professional Access Committee member; Regular lecturer on planning topics for RTPI.
Career: Called to the Bar in 1981 by Gray's Inn.

ALDOUS, Charles QC
Maitland Chambers (Michael Lyndon-Stanford QC & Charles Aldous QC) London (020) 7406 1200 caldous@maitlandchambers.com
Recommended in Chancery, Company, Energy & Natural Resources
Specialisation: Specialist in company law, insolvency, and contract and commercial disputes. Practice also covers professional negligence and general Chancery work. Recent notable cases include: Barrings plc v Coopers & Lybrand [2001]; The Society of Lloyds v Sir William Jaffrey & Ors [2000]; Office of Fair Trading v Premier League & Ors [1999], Don King Productions Inc. v Frank Warren & Ors [1998], MCC Proceeds Inc. v Lehman Brothers [1998], Grandmet v William Hill [1997], Amoco (UK) Exploration Company v Teesside Gas and Transportation Ltd. [1997], Macmillan Inc. v Bishopsgate Investment Trust [1995], Macmillan Inc. v Bishopsgate Investment Trust [1996], Mirror Group Newspapers Pension Trustees v Lehman Brothers [1994], Re: Bishopsgate Investment Management Ltd. (No. 2) [1994], GE Capital v Bankers Trusts & Ors [1994], Supreme Travels Ltd. v Little Olympian Each-Ways Ltd. [1994], Macmillan Inc. v Bishopsgate Investment Trust [1993], Re: BSB Holdings (BSkyB) [1993].
Career: Called to the Bar 1967. Took silk 1985. Appointed Junior Counsel to the Department of Trade and Industry.
Personal: Educated at Harrow and University College, London (LL.B). Born 3rd June 1943. Lives in London and Suffolk.

ALDOUS, Grahame
9 Gough Square (John Foy QC) London (020) 7832 0500
Recommended in Professional Negligence
Specialisation: Medical and professional negligence; marine accident (personal injury); property and commercial litigation. Cases include Murray v Lloyd (solicitors negligence); Watson v Lane Fox (estate agents negligence/deceit); Marchioness, Princess Margaret Hovercraft; Hamburg Ferry Marine Disasters; Acori v Algol Maritime (Supreme Court of Gibraltar/ITWF Seaman's Contracts); B&C v Atlantic Computers (Directors' liability); Hall v King (lanlord and tenant).
Career: Called 1979.
Publications: 'Applications for Judicial Review', Butterworths; 'Housing Law for the Elderly', Oyez Longmans.
Personal: Ocean racing, Whitbread Round World Race 1990, DoT yachtmaster. Former lecturer commercial law, City of London University.

ALEXANDER, Daniel
8 New Square (Michael Fysh QC) London (020) 7405 4321 daniel.alexander@8newsquare.co.uk
Recommended in Information Technology, Intellectual Property, Media & Entertainment
Specialisation: Barrister specialising principally in intellectual property, media and entertainment, EC and scientific commercial law. Practice regularly involves cases with international aspects, advocacy and advisory work in a wide variety of cases, many with EC and international aspects. For comprehensive CV and list of recent cases, visit the set's website at www.8newsquare.co.uk.
Prof. Memberships: Intellectual Property Bar Association (IPBA); Bar Council Policy Committee.
Career: Called 1988.
Publications: Joint author of 'Guidebook to Intellectual Property Law'. Author of articles on legal and scientific topics and a regular lecturer and speaker at seminars; joint editor 'Clerk & Lindsell on Torts' (17th edn). 'Encyclopaedia of UK & European Patent Law'; junior counsel to the crown in patent cases (treasury junior).
Personal: Born 1963. Educated at University College Oxford (1985 BA Physics and Philosophy); Central London Polytechnic (1986 Dip Law); Harvard Law School (1987 LLM).

ALLARDICE, Miranda
Pump Court Chambers (Christopher Harvey Clark QC) Winchester (020) 7353 0711
Recommended in Family
Specialisation: Inheritance Act and associated probate issues. Ancillary relief with a particular interest and expertise in pension issues. Cohabitants' property disputes constructive trust/Trust of Land and Appointment of Trustees Act 1996. Professional negligence cases in above area of law. Lectures and contributes articles regularly for outside organisations.
Prof. Memberships: Committee member of Family Law Bar Association; United Kingdom Environmental Law Association.
Career: Called to the Bar 1982. Joined present chambers 1984.
Personal: Educated at Somerville College, Oxford 1978-81 (BA Jurisprudence), Kings College London 1995, LLM Merit. Born 5 March 1959. Lives in London. Chair of IVF Ethics Committee Chelsea and Westminster Hospital.

ALLEN, James H. QC
No.6 Barristers Chambers (Shaun Spencer QC) Leeds (0113) 245 9763
Recommended in Chancery, Commercial (Litigation), Insolvency/Corporate Recovery

ALLEN, Mark
30 Park Place (John Jenkins QC) Cardiff (029) 2039 8421
Recommended in Family

ALLEN, Robin QC
Cloisters (Laura Cox QC) London (020) 7827 4000
Recommended in Employment, Human Rights
Specialisation: Discrimination, European, Human Rights, Employment and Administrative Law.
Prof. Memberships: Chair of the Employment Law Bar Association 1997-99 and committee member of the Discrimination Law Association.
Career: Most important cases include: Bahl v Law Society; Harvest Town Circle v Rutherford (Age Discrimination); London Underground v Edwards (Single Mothers and Shiftwork); Bossa v Ansett (EC Article 48 and Race Relations Act); ex parte Martin (ECHR Article 8 and Access to Medical Records); Balfour v The Foreign and Commonwealth Office (PII and National Security); ex parte Seymour Smith (EC challenge to the unfair dismissal qualifying period); ex parte Gerry Adams (EC challenge exclusion order); Polkey v A E Dayton Services (unfair dismissal); Delaney v Staples (Wages Act); ex parte Puhlhofer (homeless persons in judicial review); ex parte Hammell (interlocutory relief in judicial review); Alexander v Home Office (damages for discrimination); Hampson v Department of Education (Justification for indirect discrimination); ex parte Gallagher (damages for breach of EC law); Jones v Tower Boot (Employer's liability for harassment) ex parte Lightfoot (bankrupt's access to justice); Labour Party v Ahsan (discrimination in selection of political candidates); Kaba v Home Secretary (discrimination against spouses of workers exercising free movement rights); Edmond v Lawson (Minimum Wage and Pupils); Naeem v BCCI (setting aside compromise agreements); Waters v Metropolitan Police (Protection from hostile working environment); R v Kent ex parte Salisbury and Pierre (local authority duties to care leavers); Clark v Novacold (test for disability discrimination); Goodwin v Patent Office (meaning of disabled).Has worked for the European Commision, CRE, EOC and Equity Commission for Northern Ireland. Counsel for the 'Great Ape Trial' on Channel 4 in December 1995. In 1990, acted for PC Singh in the longest ever race discrimination claim, later the subject of a Channel 4 reconstruction. Has co-ordinated the Employment Law Advisers Appeal Scheme at the EAT and is vice chair of the Bar Pro Bono Unit. In 1992 appointed an expert to the European Commission on UK Law and has given evidence to the European Parliament and Select Committees of the UK Parlaiment. Member of Bar Council 1999-01, Bar Council Representative on Home Office Human Rights Act Task Force. 1999-01, Chairman of the Bar Conference 2002. Recorder, writers and lectures widely in his area of law; has contributed chapters to 'A Practitioners Guide to the Human Rights Act' – Hart; 'The Legal Framework and Social Consequences of Free Movement of Persons in the European Union' – Kluwer; 'Women, Work and Inequality' – MacMillan. 'Legal Regulation of the Employment Realation' – Kluwer; 'Anti-Discrimination – The Way Forward' – EC.

ALTMAN, Brian
2 Bedford Row (William Clegg QC) London (020) 7440 8888
Recommended in Crime, Fraud
Specialisation: Crime.
Prof. Memberships: Criminal Bar Association.
Career: Junior Treasury Counsel at CCC from 1997.

AMLOT, Roy QC
6 King's Bench Walk (Roy Amlot QC) London (020) 7583 0410
Recommended in Crime, Fraud
Specialisation: Principal area of practice is criminal law with an emphasis on high profile, serious crime cases and commercial fraud. Defence work includes Barlow Clowes, Blue Arrow, Brent Walker, Fiona Jones MP and Lord Archer and Francis. Prosecution work includes the Brighton bombing, Guildford Four (on appeal) and Clive Ponting cases. Editor, 'Phipson on Evidence' (11th Edition).
Career: Called to the Bar 1963 and became a tenant of King's Bench Walk in 1964. Treasury Counsel 1977-89. Took Silk 1989. Chairman of the Bar, 2001.
Personal: Educated at Dulwich College 1953-60. School Governor, Dulwich College. Leisure pursuits include skiing, music, squash, and windsurfing. Born 22nd September 1942. Lives in London.

AMOS, Tim
Queen Elizabeth Building (Florence Baron QC) London (020) 7797 7837
Recommended in Family
Specialisation: All aspects of family law and related professional negligence, but predominantly family finance, married or unmarried, alive or dead. Specially interested in Anglo-German cases and those with a foreign or international element. Fluent in German (including legal German). Work experience in German Courts and German law firms. Junior Counsel to the Queen's Proctor.
Prof. Memberships: Family Law Bar Association and British German Jurists Association.
Publications: Contributor to 'Essential Family Practice 2000' (Butterworths).

ANDERSON, David QC
Brick Court Chambers (Christopher Clarke QC) London (020) 7379 3550
anderson@brickcourt.co.uk
Recommended in Competition/Anti-trust
Specialisation: European Union law, human rights law, public/administrative law, competition law. Over 70 cases in the European Court of Justice and 25 before the European Commission/Court of Human Rights. Involved at all stages of Factortame and Sunday Trading litigation; ICI v Commission (cartel law); ex p Rees Mogg (Maastricht Treaty); ex p Generics (pharmaceutical licensing); ex p BT (telecoms regulation); Iberian Trading (effect of Commission decision); UK v Commission (BSE); Grant v SW Trains (sexual orientation discrimination); Building Societies v UK (retrospective legislation; human rights); Easyjet v BA (Article 82); Imperial Tobacco (advertising ban); McGonnell v UK (separation of powers); A (conjoined twins); Hatton v UK (night flights); Z v UK (access to court).
Career: Called 1985; Lawyer from Abroad, *Covington & Burling*, Washington DC, 1985-86; Cabinet of Lord Cockfield, EC Commission, 1987-88; Junior Counsel to the Crown, 1995-99; Visiting Professor, King's College London, 1999; QC 1999.
Publications: 'References to the European Court' (1995, 2nd ed 2002).

ANDERSON, Lesley
40 King St Manchester 0161 832 9082
landerson@40kingstreet.co.uk
Recommended in Chancery, Commercial (Litigation), Insolvency/Corporate Recovery
Specialisation: Corporate and personal insolvency including directors' disqualifications; banking; commercial landlord and tenant; professional negligence; commercial litigation.
Prof. Memberships: Chancery Bar Association; Northern Chancery Bar Association; Northern Circuit Commercial Bar Association; On DTI Panel for Directors' Disqualifications.
Career: Lecturer in law at University of Manchester 1984-89; Training Manager, Norton Rose M5 Group of Solicitors 1989-91.
Personal: CEDR Accredited Mediator.

ANDERSON, Mark
3 Fountain Court (Robert Juckes QC) Birmingham (0121) 236 5854
clerks@3fc.co.uk
Recommended in Commercial (Litigation)
Specialisation: Professional negligence and commercial law including banking, employment, restraint of trade and sale of goods. Mortgages and other securities. Personal injury and clinical negligence.
Prof. Memberships: Midland Chancery & Commercial Bar Association. Professional Negligence Bar Association. Personal Injuries Bar Association
Career: Educated at King Edward's School, Birmingham and Exeter College, Oxford.

ANDERSON, Robert
Blackstone Chambers (Presiley Baxendale QC & Charles Flint QC) London (020) 7583 1770
robertanderson@blackstonechambers.com
Recommended in Commercial (Litigation)
Specialisation: Commercial (in particular, commercial fraud), insurance/reinsurance, entertainment and sports law. Instructed in two of the largest fraud trials to have taken place in the last 12 months: Federal Government of Nigeria v ANZB Ltd and Brown v Bennett. Recent reported cases include Pangood v Barclay Brown [1999] Lloyd's Rep IR 405, Brown v Bennett [1999] 1 BCLC 649 and Merrill Lynch v Raffa ('The Times', 14/6/00).
Prof. Memberships: COMBAR, TECBAR, Bar Sports Law Group.
Career: Called 1986 (Gray's Inn & Middle Temple). Teaches advocacy and trains advocacy teachers on behalf of Gray's Inn.
Publications: 'The Impact of Human Rights Act on Sports Tribunals' [2000] ISLR 65.
Personal: Educated at Oundle School and Pembroke College, Cambridge.

ANDERSON, Rupert
Monckton Chambers (John Swift QC) London (020) 7405 7211
randerson@monckton.co.uk
Recommended in Competition/Anti-trust
Specialisation: Practice includes all aspects of EU and domestic competition law including OFT, Competition Commission and EC Commission investigations, EU law generally, VAT and customs and excise, utilities regulation. Recent cases include MMC/competition commission inquiries into BSkyB/Manchester United; Mobile Telephones; Cable & Wireless/NTL; the Supply of Sugar; Ready Mixed Concrete; case T-342/99 Airtours v EC Commission; case T-67/01 JCB v EC Commission; Sinclair Collis v CCE (House of Lords 6 July 2001); F&I Services v CCE (Court of Appeal); Lex v CCE [2000] STC 697; Kingfisher v CCE [2000] STC 992.
Prof. Memberships: Member of the Bar European Group.
Career: Called 1981. MA (CANTAB).
Publications: Weinberg and Blank on Take-Overs and Mergers; Copinger on Copyright; plc Handbook on Competition Law.

ANDREWS, Claire
Gough Square Chambers (Fred Philpott) London (020) 7353 0924
Recommended in Consumer Law
Specialisation: Consumer law – experienced in civil litigation and prosecuting and defending regulatory offences, and advising on interpretation of statutes. Cases include: R v Warwickshire CC [1993] AC 583 (misleading prices); LB Bexley v Gardner Merchant [1991] COD (improvement notices). Clients have included food and other wholesalers and retailers and enforcement authorities. Author 'The Enforcement of Regulatory Offences' and 'Archbold Practical Research Papers on Trade Descriptions'. Other main areas of practice include landlord and tenant, employment and commercial fraud.
Prof. Memberships: Food Law Group, MSOFHT, FCIArb, ALBA, EBA, London Common Law and Commercial Bar Association.

ANDREWS, Geraldine QC
Essex Court Chambers (Gordon Pollock QC) London (020) 7813 8000
gandrews@essexcourt-chambers.co.uk
Recommended in Banking, Commercial (Litigation)
Specialisation: Broad-based commercial practice. In particular shipping, insurance and reinsurance, banking law, asset tracing and preservation, international commodity transactions, company law, insolvency, EC law, entertainment, intellectual property (excluding patents) and general commercial and Chancery matters.
Prof. Memberships: Member of COMBAR; the Chancery Bar Association; the London Common Law and Commercial Bar Association; the Bar European Group; supporting member of the London Maritime Arbitrators' Association.
Career: King's College, University of London: LLB (1st Class Hons), 1980. LLM (1982). Recorder Midland Circuit 2000. Silk 2001.
Publications: Co-author of Andrews and Millett, 'The Law of Guarantees' (3rd edn 2000).
Personal: Born 1959. Languages spoken: French, German, Italian.

ANDREWS, Philip
Young Street Chambers (Lesley Newton) Manchester (0161) 833 0489
Recommended in Crime
Specialisation: Practice encompasses all aspects of criminal law.
Prof. Memberships: Criminal Bar Association.
Career: Called to Bar (Inner Temple) February 1977 thereafter practising on Northern Circuit. Visiting lecturer law, University of Manchester 1979-82.
Personal: Born 24 July 1950. Educated at Blackpool Grammar School and University of Hull (LLB) (Hons).

ANELAY, Richard QC
One King's Bench Walk (Anthony Hacking QC) London (020) 7936 1500
Recommended in Family
Specialisation: All areas of family and criminal law. Has undertaken leading work in matrimonial finance, child care, Inheritance Act provision, international child abduction, serious fraud, murder, manslaughter and rape. Election law: acted in Tower Hamlets Election. Case (1990) – 22 day hearing before Commissioner. In public law children cases has undertaken leading work for local authorities, parents and guardians ad litem in complex medical, Munchausen syndrome by proxy, sexual, physical and emotional abuse cases. Reported cases: Re KDT (Minor) [1994] 2 FCR 721CA; Re G [1994] 2 FCR 216. Re D (care: Natural Parent Presumption) 1999 1 FLR 134 CA.
Career: Called 1970. QC 1993. Recorder 1992. Deputy High Court Judge (Family Division) 1995.
Publications: Consulting editor, 'Encyclopedia of Financial Provision in Family Matters' (General editors Wildblood and Eaton, Sweet & Maxwell, 1998).
Personal: Born 1946. Educated at Queen Elizabeth Grammar School, Darlington and Bristol University (BA Hons Classics and Philosophy). Enjoys golf.

ARCHER, Stephen
12 King's Bench Walk (Richard Methuen QC) London (020) 7583 0811
Recommended in Personal Injury
Specialisation: Industrial disease (with increasing emphasis on multi-party test actions); brain damage, quadriplegia, paraplegia; personal injury work generally with long experience of disputes involving on medical causation; clinical negligence. Recent cases: Abbott and others v Rockware Glass plc (2000 BLC 73); Makepeace v Evans Brothers (2000 BLR 73).
Prof. Memberships: PIBA; ELA.
Career: By 1985 practised almost exclusively in personal injury work. Following Mountenay v Bernard Matthews plc [1994] 5 Med LR 293 has acted increasingly for defendants in a wide range of industrial disease actions including upper limb disorders, asbestos related conditions, vibration white finger, respiratory disease and occupational stress claims.
Personal: Education: Sherborne School; Oxford (Pembroke College); Inner Temple. Leisure/family: cycling; joint research (with wife) into African-American music; large model association.

ARDEN, Andrew QC
Arden Chambers (Andrew Arden QC) London (020) 7242 4244
Recommended in Local Government
Specialisation: Principal areas of practice are housing and landlord and tenant law (including homelessness, right to buy/acquire and enfranchisement, leases and service charges, rents and security of tenure, disrepair and environmental health, business tenancies), housing association law (including finance, disposals, status, powers and procedures, committee membership, mixed-funding arrangements, stock acquisition) local government (including finance, constitution, asset disposals, local authority companies, powers and procedures, best value, access to information, data protection, PFI, public/private partnerships, pensions, waste disposal), and miscellaneous aspects of public and administrative law. Has conducted five local government inquiries/reviews; appeared for the Objectors at the Westminster Audit Hearing (1994). Author/Co-Author: Housing Law, Local Government Constitutional and Administrative Law, Local Government Finance Law, Assured Tenancies (Vol. 3, The Rent Acts, 11th ed.), Manual of Housing Law, Homelessness and Allocation, Annotated Statutes (including Housing Acts 1980, 1985, 1988, 1996, Local Government and Housing Act 1989, Housing Grants,

Construction and Regeneration Act 1996). General Editor: Housing Encyclopaedia, Housing Law Reports, Journal of Housing Law, Arden's Housing Library. Editorial Board Member: Journal of Local Government Law.
Prof. Memberships: Administrative Law Bar Association; Local Government, Planning and Environmental Bar Association; Bar European Group, Property Bar Association, Housing Law Practitioners' Association.
Career: Called to the Bar 1974. Director, Small Heath Community Law Centre 1976-78. Silk 1991. Founded Arden Chambers in 1993.
Publications: 'Local Government Constitutional and Administrative Law'.
Personal: Educated at University College London 1969-72 (LLB). Writes novels and thrillers. Born 20th April 1948. Lives in London.

ARDEN, Peter
Enterprise Chambers (Anthony Mann QC) London (020) 7405 9471
Recommended in Company, Insolvency/ Corporate Recovery
Specialisation: Areas of practice: business and financial law, in particular banking, bank and other securities, insolvency (corporate and individual) and related areas. Regularly instructed by clearing banks, other financial institutions and their appointees. Acted in many of the large insolvencies in recent years.Cases include Re Dallhold Estates (appointment of administrators over foreign companies), Leyland DAF Ltd v Lipe Ltd (interlocutory injunctions against administrative receivers), Re Leyland DAF Ltd (whether administrative receivers bound by exclusive jurisdiction clause), William Gaskell Group Ltd v Highley (whether charge fixed or floating and automatic crystallisation), Re Thomas Christy Ltd (effect of disqualification judgement on proceedings by liquidation), Re Ellis Son & Vidler Ltd (sale of goods and storage contract and equitable interests/remedies), Re WAL Holdings Ltd (contest between debenture holder and finance companies), Walker v Hocking (bankrupt seeking to interfere with exercise of powers by trustee), Re Business City Express Ltd (application for recognition of Eire scheme of arrangement), Re Edennote Ltd (sanction for exercise of powers by liquidator) and Re West Park Gold & Country Club (dismissal of partnership administration petition as an abuse).

ARLIDGE, Anthony QC
18 Red Lion Court (Anthony Arlidge QC) London (020) 7520 6000
anthony.arlidge@18rlc.co.uk
Recommended in Crime, Fraud
Specialisation: Serious fraud from Griffiths and Others in 1965 to Blue Arrow. Author of Arlidge and Parry on Fraud 2nd edn. Revenue cases including Carmel College. Prosecuted Jeremy Bamber and defended Baroness De Stempel. In the past year clients include Michael Allcock defended for corruption in relation to the Revenue, Terence Ramsden, Dr. Crockett (alleged purchase of kidneys for transplant) and Dr Bichan (Butte Mining). Appeared in Graham and Ords, the post-Preddy appeals. Disciplinary tribunals including General Medical Council, Stock Exchange, Lloyds, Fimbra.
Career: Double first class degree in law, Cambridge.

ARMITAGE, Keith QC
8 King St (Keith Armitage QC) Manchester (0161) 834 9560
Recommended in Clinical Negligence

ARMSTRONG, Dean
6 King's Bench Walk (Roy Amlot QC) London (020) 7583 0410
Recommended in Crime
Specialisation: Prosecutes and defends in all forms of crime and commercial fraud.
Career: MA (Cantab).

ARMSTRONG, Kester
Broad Chare Chambers (Patrick Cosgrove QC) Newcastle upon Tyne (0191) 232 0541
Recommended in Family

ARNOLD, Mark
3-4 South Square (Michael Crystal QC & Lord Alexander of Weedon QC) London (020) 7696 9900
markarnold@southsquare.com
Recommended in Insolvency/Corporate Recovery
Specialisation: Business and financial law, including in particular: insolvency (corporate and individual), banking, company, chancery and professional negligence.
Prof. Memberships: COMBAR, Chancery Bar Association, Insolvency Lawyers Association.
Career: MA Cantab. (Downing College, Cambridge).

ARNOLD, Richard QC
11 South Square (Christopher Floyd QC) London (020)7405 1222
Recommended in Information Technology, Intellectual Property
Specialisation: Patents, trade marks, passing off, copyright, design right, registered designs, performers' rights, database right, confidential information, entertainment and media law, computer contract disputes, data protection, restraint of trade, trade libel, trade descriptions, related EU law. Recent cases include Norowzian v Arks[2000] EMLR 67, Glaxo Group v Dowelhurst [2000] FSR 371, Premier Brands v Typhoon Europe [2000] FSR 767 and Fulton v Grant Barnett [2001] RPC 257.
Prof. Memberships: IP Bar Association, Chancery Bar Association, CIPA (Associate).
Career: Called 1985, QC 2000.
Publications: 'Performers' Rights' (2nd ed, Sweet & Maxwell, 1997); 'Computer Software: Legal Protection in the United Kingdom' (2nd edn, Sweet & Maxwell, 1992) (co-author); 'Entertainment and Media Law Reports' (Sweet & Maxwell, 1993-) (editor); articles in 'European Intellectual Property Review', 'Entertainment Law Review', 'Intellectual Property Quarterly' and 'Yearbook of Copyright and Media Law'.

ASCROFT, Richard
Guildhall Chambers (Adrian Palmer QC) Bristol (0117) 927 3366
richard.ascroft@guildhallchambers.co.uk
Recommended in Insolvency/Corporate Recovery
Specialisation: Insolvency: bankruptcy; directors' disqualification; corporate insolvency. Company: shareholders' disputes; directors' duties. Commercial litigation: contractual disputes including sale of goods. Banking: bills of exchange; bank payments; enforcement of securities.
Prof. Memberships: Chancery Bar Association; R3.
Career: Called to Bar 1995. Barrister and Solicitor High Court of NZ 1990.
Personal: Born 9 Aug 1966, Wellington, NZ. Educated NZ (LLB Hons) and Oxford University (BCL).

ASH, Brian QC
4-5 Gray's Inn Square (Elizabeth Appleby QC & David Mole QC) London (020) 7404 5252
Recommended in Planning
Specialisation: Principal area of practice is planning and local government. Work involves public inquiries concerning all forms of development, compulsory purchase and compensation, including references to the Lands Tribunal, and High Court proceedings including statutory appeals and judicial review. Involved in public inquiries concerning expansion of Stansted and Heathrow airports, sub-regional and other major shopping proposals, road development including motorway service areas and large scale commercial, industrial and housing proposals. Clients include Rolls Royce Plc, Safeway Stores Plc, Manchester Ship Canal Company, The Civil Aviation Authority, major insurance companies, local authorities and Metropolitan Borough and District Councils.
Prof. Memberships: Local Government Planning and Environmental Bar Association.
Career: TV Producer, Reporter and Programme Presenter 1967-73. Called to the Bar 1975 and joined current chambers 1977. Took Silk 1990.
Personal: Educated at New Collge, Oxford 1960-64. Leisure pursuits include golf, cricket, sailing and skiing. Born January 31st 1941. Lives in London.

ASHLEY-NORMAN, Jonathan
2 Bedford Row (William Clegg QC) London (020) 7440 8888
Recommended in Fraud
Specialisation: Criminal law specialist in fraud, restraint and confiscation, and drugs related offences. On the approved prosecutors list for Customs and Excise, Department of Trade and Industry, Inland Revenue and DSS. Regularly prosecutes in substantial cases, especially fraud and drugs importation offences. Instructed to defend in major SFO cases including Alpine Windows, concerning the collapse of the double glazing company and Richmond Oil and Gas, concerning a fraudulent company flotation. Undertakes specialist Customs defence work, including anti dumping duty cases and High Court restraint work. Some Company Directors Disqualification Act work undertaken.
Prof. Memberships: Member of Criminal Bar Association.

ASHWORTH, Fiona
40 King St Manchester 0161 832 9082
Recommended in Family
Specialisation: Personal injury (employer's and public liability, disease, road traffic); clinical and PI related professional negligence; family and matrimonial provision.
Prof. Memberships: PIBA; FLBA; Clinical Negligence Association.
Career: Bolton School (Girl's Division). Leeds University.

ASHWORTH, Lance
St Philip's Chambers (John Randall QC) Birmingham (0121) 246 7000
Recommended in Chancery, Commercial (Litigation), Insolvency/Corporate Recovery, Personal Injury
Specialisation: Commercial Law. Group Actions. Insolvency, corporate recovery and directors disqualification – Junior Counsel to the Crown. Personal Injury.
Prof. Memberships: P.I.B.A. Midland Chancery and Commercial Bar Association.
Career: Oundle School. Pembroke College Cambridge. M.A (Cantab).
Personal: Married, three children.

ASPLIN, Sarah J.
3 Stone Buildings (Geoffrey Vos QC) London (020) 7242 4937
sasplin@3sb.law.co.uk
Recommended in Pensions
Specialisation: Principal area of practice: pensions litigation, advice and drafting and actuarial negligence. Acts for principal employers, trustees and beneficiaries in relation to questions of rectification construction, winding up, merger, general administration of pension schemes and appeals from the Pensions Ombudsman. Also general chancery matters including trusts and probate advice and litigation. Cases include Imperial Tobacco, British Coal, Hillsdown Holdings Plc, Spooner & Ors v British Telecommunications plc, Equitable Life v Hyman and Needler v Taber.
Prof. Memberships: Chancery Bar Association, Association of Pension Lawyers.
Career: Called 1984.
Personal: Educated at Fitzwilliam College, Cambridge 1979-82 (MA Law); St Edmund Hall, Oxford 1982-83 (BCL).

ATHERTON, Stephen

3-4 South Square (Michael Crystal QC & Lord Alexander of Weedon QC) London (020) 7696 9900 clerks@southsquare.com

Recommended in Insolvency/Corporate Recovery

Specialisation: Main area of practice: insolvency, general commercial and civil fraud. Major cases: junior counsel to the Brunei Government, junior counsel to majority share holders of BCCI, junior counsel to Mirror Group Pensioners, advising 1986 bond holders in relation to Barings. Highlights of the past year have been a continued involvement in the Barings liquidation and in the programme of recovery of misappropriated public monies in Brunei. In addition, the last twelve months has seen an increase in instructions from law firms in the UK and overseas relating to insolvencies and commercial disputes around the world, in particular in the United States, Hong Kong, Taiwan, Europe and a number of off-shore jurisdictions. On the domestic front: instructed by the administrators of Cammell Laird and other office holders in relation to high profile insolvencies of major retailers and e-commerce companies.

Prof. Memberships: Middle Temple, Gray's Inn, Chancery Bar Association, Commercial Bar Association, Insolvency Lawyers' Association.

Career: LLB (Hons) Lancaster. LLM (Cantab). Secondee to the Fraud Investigation Group (CPS).

Personal: Rugby, cricket. Player/member Old Emanuel RFC and CC. Married 1992 Lucy Atherton (neé Coppock) BBC news correspondent.

ATKINSON, Nicholas QC

2 Harcourt Buildings, Atkinson Bevan Chambers (Nicholas Atkinson QC & John Bevan QC) London (020) 7353 2112 clerks@2hb.co.uk

Recommended in Crime

Specialisation: Criminal law specialist. In last year dealt with cases of murder, rape, child sexual abuse, drugs, corruption and commercial fraud.

Prof. Memberships: Criminal Bar Association and has served on Bar Council on three occasions in 70s, 80s and 90s.

Career: Practice in London and upon Western Circuit. Called to the Bar in 1971. Appointed Assistant Recorder in 1983 and Recorder in 1987. Took Silk in 1991.

Personal: Patron of Road Peace, the national charity for road traffic victims.

AUBREY, David J.M. QC

Temple Chambers (David J.M. Aubrey QC) Cardiff (029) 2039 7364

Recommended in Crime

AUSTIN-SMITH, Michael QC

23 Essex Street (Michael Lawson QC) London (020) 7413 0353 michaelaustin-smith@23essexstreet.co.uk

Recommended in Crime

Specialisation: Fraud, major crime of all types, crime-related civil, including civil jury actions, and police law. Appellate work includes R v Gomez [House of Lords] and Darker v West Midlands Police [House of Lords].

Career: Educated at Hampton Grammar School and Exeter University. Called to the Bar 1969; a Crown Court Recorder since 1986; DTI Inspector 1988 and 1989; Silk 1990. Formerly chairman of the Surrey and South London Bar Mess and member of the South East Area Criminal Justice Consultative Committee.

Personal: Married with two children. Leisure interests include sailing and rugby football.

AYERS, Guy

Octagon House Chambers (Andrew Lindqvist) Norwich (01603) 623186

Recommended in Crime

AYLIFFE, James

Wilberforce Chambers (Edward Nugee QC) London (020) 7306 0102

Recommended in Chancery

Specialisation: Specialises in Commercial/Chancery litigation including asset finance, banking, company, financial services, insolvency, professional negligence, property.

Prof. Memberships: COMBAR, Chancery Bar Association.

Career: BA (Hons) Politics, Philosophy and Economics from New College, Oxford (1985) (First). Diploma in Law from City University, London (1986) (Distinction).

BAATZ, Nicholas QC

Atkin Chambers (Robert Akenhead QC) London (020) 7404 0102

Recommended in Construction, Information Technology

Specialisation: Technology and construction law. Information Technology. Acted in UK and internationally in a wide variety of cases with a scientific and/or technical content. Advised in relation to all the principal standard form building and engineering contracts and upon drafting of standard form contracts. Appointed as arbitrator. Acted in conciliation and mediation proceedings. Editor Current Law 1980-99. Editor Building Law Reports 1986-98. Editor Technology and Construction Law Reports 1999-.

Career: Educated Christ Church, Oxford (MA, BCL). Queen's Counsel, Chartered Arbitrator.

BACON, Francis

4 Paper Buildings (Jean Ritchie QC) London (020) 7353 3366

Recommended in Professional Negligence

Specialisation: All areas of professional negligence with particular emphasis on fraud. Instructed on behalf of the solicitor defendants in the Nationwide Managed Litigation: Nationwide Building Society v Balmer Radmore (1999) Lloyd's Rep PN 241, Nationwide Building Society v Thimbleby (1999) Lloyd's Rep PN 359. Mediation experience includes acting for solicitors in the successful Nat West Loans and Halifax managed mediations. Other main areas of practice are civil fraud (UK and overseas), personal injury and general insurance.

Prof. Memberships: PNBA

Career: Called to the Bar in 1989 (Karmel Scholar – Commercial) Gray's Inn.

Personal: Educated Keele and Loughborough. Married with three children.

BADENOCH, James QC

1 Crown Office Row (Robert Seabrook QC) London (020) 7797 7500 james.badenoch@1cor.com

Recommended in Clinical Negligence, Personal Injury

Specialisation: Principal area of practice is clinical negligence, medical discipline and all medically-related work. Also handles personal injury matters. Major cases include Wilsher v Essex Area Health Authority 1998 AC 1074 (HL); medical negligence, causation principles. The Wendy Savage enquiry, (1986); NHS disciplinary tribunal. Dobbie v Medway Health Authority (1994) 5 Med LR 160 (CA); medical injury limitation, principles. Hossack v General Dental Council (1998), 40 BMLR 97 (PC); appeal to Privy Council, principles. GMC v Rodney Leonard (1999); disciplinary proceedings. Penney & others v East Kent Health Authority (2000) Lloyds Rep Med 41 (CA); applications and limits of 'Bolam Test'. Heil v Rankin (2000) 2 WLR 1173 (CA); Landmark case on general damages. Preiss v General Dental Council 2001 (PC); human rights and professional discipline.

Prof. Memberships: Professional Negligence Bar Association, London Common Law Bar Association.

Career: Called to the Bar in 1968 and joined current chambers in 1968. Appointed Recorder 1987. Took silk 1989. Deputy High Court Judge from 1994 onwards.

Publications: 'Medical Negligence', Powers and Harris, Butterworths (contrib) 1990, 1994, 2000.

Personal: Educated at Dragon School, Rugby School 1959-63 and Magdalen College, Oxford (MA) 1964-67. Born 24th July 1945. Lives in London.

BAKER, Andrew

20 Essex Street (Iain Milligan QC) London (020) 7583 9294 clerks@20essexst.com

Recommended in Commercial (Litigation), Shipping

Specialisation: Main areas of practice are dry shipping, arbitration, banking (principally international trade financing and foreign exchange trading/ derivatives), international trade/ commodities, conflict of laws, insurance and reinsurance (including in particular marine, mortgage indemnity insurance and LMX reinsurance). Experience as arbitrator. Reported cases include Honam Jade [1991] 1 Lloyd's Rep 38 (C/A); PNB v de Boinville [1992] 1 Lloyd's Rep 7 (C/A); Banque Paribas v Cargill [1992] 2 Lloyd's Rep 19 (C/A); Nissho Iwai v Cargill [1993] 1 Lloyd's Rep 80 (Comm Ct); Angelic Grace [1995] 1 Lloyd's Rep 87 (C/A); Orjula [1995] 2 Lloyd's Rep 395 (Comm Ct); Nicholas H [1995] 2 Lloyd's Rep 299 (H/L); Atlas [1996] 1 Lloyd's Rep 642 (Comm Ct); Roar Marine v Bimeh Iran [1998] 1 Lloyd's Rep 423 (Comm Ct); Trade Nomad [1998] 1 Lloyd's Rep 57 (Comm Ct) [1999] 1 Lloyd's Rep 723 (C/A); Morgan Stanley v Puglisi [1998] CLC 481 (Comm Ct); Den Danske Bank v Skipton Building Society [1998] 1 EGLR 155 (Comm Ct); Deepak v ICI [1998] 2 Lloyd's Rep 139 (Comm Ct) [1999] 1 Lloyd's Rep 387 (C/A). CSFB Europe v Seagate [1999] 1 Lloyd's Rep 784 (Comm Ct); Mira Oil v Bocimar [1999] 2 Lloyd's Rep (Comm Ct); Rustal Trading v Gills Duffus [2000] 1Lloyd's Rep 14 (Comm Ct).

Prof. Memberships: Lincoln's Inn, COMBAR.

Career: Born 21 December 1965. Educated at Lenzie Academy, Merton College, Oxford (reading Mathematics 1983-86) and The City University (Diploma in Law, 1987). Called to the Bar 1988. Joined 3 Essex Court (now 20 Essex Street) in 1989.

Personal: Married with three sons. Keen golfer.

BAKER, Christopher

Arden Chambers (Andrew Arden QC) London (020) 7242 4244

Recommended in Local Government, Planning

Specialisation: Principal areas (both contentious and advisory) are all aspects of housing (public, social and private), landlord and tenant, and local government, including human rights.

Prof. Memberships: Administrative Law Bar Association.

Career: Called to the Bar 1984. Founder member of Arden Chambers in 1993. Principal recent cases include Baxter v Camden LBC (No 2), HL (noise nuisance); R v Broadland DC ex p Lashley, CA (local authority standards committee); R v Greenwich LBC ex p Glen International Ltd, CA (renovation grants); Lambeth LBC v Rumbelow, ChD (adverse possession); Lambeth LBC v Henry, CA (possession orders); R v Birmingham City Council ex p Mohammed, QBD (disabled facilities grants); R v Camden LBC ex p Mohammed, QBD (homelessness policy).

Publications: 'Housing and Human Rights Law' (LAG, 2001, co-author); 'Human Rights Act 1998: A Practitioner's Guide' (Sweet & Maxwell, 1998, general editor); Local Government Law Reports (Sweet & Maxwell, editor); 'Encyclopaedia of Local Government Law' (Sweet & Maxwell, editor); 'Housing Law: Pleadings in Practice' (Sweet & Maxwell, 1994, co-author).

BAKER, Jacqueline

Enterprise Chambers (Anthony Mann QC) London (020) 7405 9471

Recommended in Property Litigation

BAKER, Jonathan QC
Harcourt Chambers (June Rodgers) Oxford (020) 7353 6961 (London), (01865) 791559 (Oxford)
jbaker@harcourtchambers.law.co.uk
Recommended in Family
Specialisation: All aspects of family law with particular expertise in children's law.
Prof. Memberships: Midland and Oxford Circuit, Family Law Bar Association, Association of Lawyers for Children.
Career: Called to the Bar in 1978, Middle Temple. Member of Harcourt Chambers since 1979, based in Oxford since 1991. Appointed assistant recorder 1998, recorder 2000.
Personal: Born 6th August 1955. MA in Law St John's College, Cambridge. Married with two children. Chair of Oxfordshire Relate.

BAKER, Philip
Gray's Inn Tax Chambers (Milton Grundy) London (020) 7242 2642
pb@taxbar.com
Recommended in Tax
Specialisation: All forms of revenue law, with particular specialisation in international taxation (issues of residence and domicile, double taxation agreements, foreign tax credit and transfer pricing) also taxation and human rights.
Prof. Memberships: Barrister, Grays Inn (1979); Visiting professorial fellow, Centre for Commercial Law Studies, Queen Mary, London University. Council member, Chartered Institute of Taxation; member, Addington Society; Committee member, International Fiscal Association (UK Branch).
Career: 1979-87, Lecturer in Law, School of Oriental and African Studies, London University. 1987-present, barrister, Grays Inn Tax Chambers.
Publications: 'Double Taxation Conventions and International Tax Law' (3rd edn, 2001).
Personal: Educated: Emmanuel College, Cambridge (MA); Balliol College, Oxford (BCL); University College, London (LLM); SOAS, London (PhD); London Business School (MBA). Married, three children. Awarded OBE, July 1997.

BALCOMBE, David
1 Crown Office Row (Robert Seabrook QC) London (020) 7797 7500
Recommended in Family

BALDRY, Rupert
Pump Court Tax Chambers London (020) 7414 8080
Recommended in Tax
Specialisation: VAT and customs duties; trusts; corporate and EU law. Recent reported cases: CCE v Sinclair Collis; CCE v Continuum; Higher Education Statistics Agency v CCE; R v CCE ex p Bosworth Beverages; CCE v University of Leicester Students Union; R v Dimsey; R v Allen.
Prof. Memberships: Revenue Bar Association; Attorney General's Panel of Junior Counsel, VAT Practitioners' Group.
Career: Specialist tax barrister at Pump Court since 1993.
Publications: Co-author 'Trusts and UK Taxation' (Keyhaven). Editor 'Potter and Monroe's Tax Planning' (Sweet & Maxwell). Editor 'The Use of Offshore Jurisdictions' (Gee). Editor Jacksons 'Matrimonial Finance and Taxation'.
Personal: Marlborough College; London and City Universities.

BALDWIN, John QC
8 New Square (Michael Fysh QC) London (020) 7405 4321
clerks@8newsquare.co.uk
Recommended in Information Technology, Intellectual Property, Media & Entertainment
Specialisation: Barrister specialising in all aspects of intellectual property law, including patents, trade marks, copyrights, confidential information, computer law, passing off, trade libel, EC law, data protection, restrictive covenants and restraint of trade. For comprehensive CV and list of recent cases, visit the set's website at www.8newsquare.co.uk.
Prof. Memberships: Intellectual Property Bar Association (IPBA); The Intellectual Property Lawyers Organisation (TIPLO).
Career: Called 1977, Gray's Inn; QC 1991.
Publications: Co-editor 'Patent Law of Europe & UK'.
Personal: Born 1947. Educated at Nelson Grammar School; University of Leeds (1968 BSc Agricultural Chemistry); St John's College, Oxford (1972 D.Phil 1972 Research Fellowship).

BALL, Alison QC
One Garden Court Family Law Chambers (Eleanor F. Platt QC & Alison Ball QC) London (020) 7797 7900
a.ball@onegardencourt.co.uk
Recommended in Family
Specialisation: All aspects of family law.
Prof. Memberships: Family Law Bar Association, South Eastern Circuit.
Career: Called to the Bar in 1972. Founder member and Head of Chambers of One Garden Court (Family Law Chambers) 1989. Mediator (FMA) 1993. Took silk in 1995. Recorder 1998.
Personal: Educated at Bedales School, 1955-66 and Kings College, London University 1967-71. Lives in London.

BAMFORD, Jeremy
Guildhall Chambers (Adrian Palmer QC) Bristol (0117) 927 3366
Recommended in Chancery, Commercial (Litigation), Insolvency/Corporate Recovery

BANCROFT, Louise
Deans Court Chambers (Stephen Grime QC) Manchester (0161) 214 6000
bancroft@deanscourt.co.uk
Recommended in Family
Specialisation: Practises solely in the field of family law. Particular emphasis on private law including matrimonial finance, residence and contact. Representation on behalf of local authorities, parents and guardians in adoption and care proceedings. International child abduction. Mediation.
Prof. Memberships: Associate Member of the UK College of Family Mediators. Member of the Family Law Bar Association and Child Concern.
Career: MA Hons (Oxon) St Anne's College, Oxford. Diploma in Law, University of Westminster. Called to the Bar in 1985 (Inner Temple).

BANGAY, Deborah
29 Bedford Row Chambers (Peter Ralls QC) London (020) 7404 1044
Recommended in Family
Specialisation: Family law especially matrimonial finance (Re P CA 1991 FLR 1 286 – wordship contempt); private children (GV J CA 1993 FLR 1 1008 – oustev); public law children work (Re H CAA 1994 1 FLR CA 3). H v J MHV (costs: residence proceedings) 2000 IFLR 394.
Prof. Memberships: Family Law Bar Association.
Career: 1972-76, Wycombe High School; 1976-79, Exeter University LLB Hons; 1970-80, Council of Legal Education; 1982-92, 13 Kings Bench Walk/Hardwicke Building; 1992, 29 Bedford Row.
Personal: Football, swimming and cooking.

BANKS, Robert
100E Great Portland Street London (020) 7636 6323
Recommended in Crime

BANKS, Roderick I'Anson
48 Bedford Row (Roderick I'Anson Banks) London (020) 7430 2005
rciab@partnershipcounsel.co.uk
Recommended in Partnership
Specialisation: Exclusively partnership law. Has specialised in this area since 1977. Handles all aspects of partnership law from the drafting and review of agreements to advice and representation in partnership disputes, arbitrations and mediations. Acts for solicitors, doctors, accountants, and other professional firms, as well as various financial and commercial institutions. Acted as a consultant to the Law Commission on its reviews of partnership law and limited partnership law. Has conducted seminars for NIS Group, Lawnet, CLT, National Law Tutors, Jordans and various solicitors' firms and has appeared in two videos for Legal Network TV.
Prof. Memberships: Lincoln's Inn.
Career: Called to the Bar 1974 and joined Stone Buildings, (Chambers of DR Stanford). Set up 48 Bedford Row in 1991, as the only chambers specialising exclusively in partnership law. CEDR Accredited Mediator, 1993. Hon. Associate of British Veterinary Association. Founder member of the Association of Partnership Practitioners.
Publications: Editor of 'Lindley & Banks on Partnership'; author and editor of 'The Encyclopedia of Professional Partnerships'. Contributor of articles to 'Legal Business', 'Solicitors' Journal', 'Commercial Lawyer' and 'The Lawyer'.
Personal: Educated at Westminster School 1965-69 and University College London 1970-73. Leisure pursuits include reading and films. Born 5 December 1951. Lives in Beare Green, Surrey.

BANNISTER, Edward Alexander QC
3 Stone Buildings (Geoffrey Vos QC) London (020) 7242 4937
ebannister@3sb.law.co.uk
Recommended in Chancery, Company, Insolvency/Corporate Recovery
Specialisation: Specialises in company/insolvency and commercial litigation and all related matters, including property and contract; extensive professional negligence litigation practice. Recent cases include Stein v Blake [1996] AC 243 (set off in insolvency); re Duckwari plc [1997] Ch 201 (measure of compensation on breach of 320 Companies Act 1985); Swindle v Harrison [1997] 4 All ER 705 (causation and fiduciary duty claims); Paragon Finance v Thakerar [1999] 1 All ER 400 (limitation and constructive trusts); Worby v Rosser[1999] Lloyd's Rep PN 974 (CA) (whether White v Jones applies to costs of beneficiaries under earlier will); Triffitt Nurseries v Salads Etcetera [2000] 1 All ER Comm 737 (CA) (insolvent agent's right to retain proceeds of sale against principal); re Greenhaven Motors Limited [1999] BCLC 635 (court control over liquidator's discretion); North Holdings Limited v Southern Tropics Limited [1999] 2 BCLC 625 (unfair prejudice petitions and CPR); Garrow v Society of Lloyds [2000] Lloyds Rep IR 38 (effect of sue now pay later clause in bankruptcy proceedings); Jones v Society of Lloyds, Times 2 February 2000 (penalty clauses); Society of Lloyds v Twinn, (2000) 97 (15) LSG 40 (whether acceptance of offer qualified by side letter); Motor Crown Petroleum v SJ Berwin [2000] Lloyd's Rep PN 438 (CA) (whether Allied Maples to be applied in case involving failed planning appeal); Barings Plc v Coopers & Lybrand, [2000] 1 WLR 2352 (CA) (Banking Act 1987 – when exhibits to affidavits available to the public); Mamidoil-Jetoil Greek Petroleum Co SA v OKTA Crude Oil Refinery AD [2000] 1 Lloyd's Rep 554 (Arbitration Act 1996; construction of oil importation contract; Sale of Goods Act 1979); Clef Aquitaine SARL v Laporte Materials (Barrow) [2001] QB 488 (CA) (measure of damages for fraudulent misrepresentation).
Prof. Memberships: Bencher, Honourable Society of Lincoln's Inn; Member Management Committee, Bar Pro Bono Unit.
Career: Called to the Bar 1974, Silk 1991.

BARCA, Manuel
1 Brick Court (Richard Rampton QC) London
(020) 7353 8845
Recommended in Defamation
Specialisation: Media and information law, principally defamation, malicious falsehood, confidence/privacy, contempt of court etc, but also media/literary copyright and passing off.
Career: Graduate trainee, Reuters 1984-5. Called to Bar 1986 (Lincoln's Inn, Levitt Scholar). Joined 1 Brick Court in 1987. Cases include A-G v Associated Newspapers; Cambridge Nutrition v BBC; Pickering v Liverpool Daily Post; Cumming v Scottish Daily Record; Major v New Statesman; Oyston v Blaker; Berkoff v Burchill; Stern v Piper; Watts v Times Newspapers; GMC v BBC; Adams v Associated Newspapers; Godfrey v Demon Internet; Beta Construction v Channel 4; Upjohn v BBC; Walker Wingsail Systems v IPC; Bottomley v Express Newspapers; British Coal v NUM; Barclay Brothers v BBC; Howarth v Guardian Newspapers; Newton v Express Newspapers; Clunes v Express Newspapers; Home Secretary v BBC; Loucas v Channel 4; Dick v Times Newspapers; Marks & Spencer v Granada TV; City of London Police v BBC & Ors; Rondel v BBC; Merciar v BBC; ITN v Living Marxism; Khalili v Associated Newspapers; Trimble v Amazon; Walker v Newcastle Chronicle; R v Shilibier ex p HTV; Multigroup v Oxford Analytica; Rahamim v ITN; Elite Model Management v BBC; Skrine & Co v Euromoney Publications; Austin v Newcastle Chronicle; Steedman v BBC; Green v Times Newspapers; MacIntyre v Chief Constable of Kent.
Personal: Educated at Wimbledon College and Cambridge University (Law Tripos, MA). Bilingual in English and Spanish. Fluent French. Working Italian and Portuguese.

BARDA, Robin
4 Paper Buildings (Lionel Swift QC) London
(020) 7583 0816
rb@4pb.com
Recommended in Family
Specialisation: All aspects of family and matrimonial work, including residence and contact disputes, adoptions, child abductions, public law applications, matrimonial finance, disputes between unmarried couples and Inheritance Act applications. A considerable amount of work for local authorities and guardians, in particular the official solicitor, most in the High Court at the Principal and other district registries, but also in County Courts around London and elsewhere in the Court of Appeal. Cases have involved clients across a broad spectrum of wealth, including well-known personalities, and cases which have received media attention. Recently reported cases include Re I (Adoption: Nationality) [1998] 2 FLR 997, Wilson v Webster [1998] 1 FLR 1097, P v P (Abduction: Acquiescence) [1998] 1 FLR 630, Re R (Adoption: Disclosure) [1999] 2 FLR 1123.
Prof. Memberships: Family Law Bar Association. London Common Law and Commercial Bar Association.
Career: B.A. Oxon. Called to the Bar 1975, Gray's Inn. Joined Chambers of John Byrt QC, 4 Paper Buildings, Temple as a pupil in 1975, taken on as a tenant in 1976.
Personal: Education: Bryanston School 1960-66. Academical Clerk (Choral scholar) Magdalen College, Oxford 1967-70 – BA in Philosophy, Politics and Economics. Hobbies: Freelance musician/singer 1970-74. Chairman of The Sixteen Ltd. Director of Singcircle Ltd. Singing with The Sixteen (occasionally) and the Choir of St Clement Danes, including concerts. Music generally. Squash. Clubs: Savage Club.

BARKER, Anthony QC
5 Fountain Court (Anthony Barker QC)
Birmingham (0121) 606 0500
Recommended in Crime
Specialisation: Criminal law, in particular substantial cases involving expert scientific, accounting and direct expert evidence.
Career: Called 1966, Silk 1985, Bencher 1999.

BARKER, Kerry
Guildhall Chambers (Adrian Palmer QC) Bristol
(0117) 927 3366
Recommended in Licensing
Specialisation: All aspects of licensing law including: liquor licensing, public entertainment and local authority licensing (acting for applicants, objectors, police authorities, licensing justices and local authorities). Has expertise in betting, gaming and lotteries (casinos, bingo, gaming machines, bookmakers and betting, competitions, lotteries and fundraising). Former Justices' Clerk and contributor to Paterson's Licensing Acts.
Publications: Publications include 'Betting Gaming and Lotteries' (Fourmat Publishing 1992). Editor of 'Licensing Law Reforms' [2001] LLR (Jordans Publishing).

BARKER, Simon
Maitland Chambers (Michael Lyndon-Stanford QC & Charles Aldous QC) London (020) 7406 1200
Recommended in Media & Entertainment
Specialisation: Media and entertainment litigation (including copyright, passing off, breach of confidence, format rights); Copyright Tribunal references; commercial litigation and arbitration (including warranty and contract claims on sale of businesses and shares, company law, partnership disputes and professional negligence).
Prof. Memberships: Fellow of Institute of Chartered Accountants. Member of Chartered Institute of Arbitrators.
Career: Qualified as chartered accountant 1976. Called to the Bar 1979 (Lincoln's Inn). Fellow ICAEW 1982. Assistant Recorder 1995. Recorder 2000.

BARLING, Gerald QC
Brick Court Chambers (Christopher Clarke QC)
London (020) 7379 3550
Recommended in Competition/Anti-trust

BARLOW, Francis
10 Old Square (Leolin Price CBE QC) London
(020) 7405 0758 / 7242 5002
Recommended in Chancery
Specialisation: Specialising in the full range of Chancery matters, contentious and non-contentious, with particular emphasis on probate, breach of trust and property and advisory work and drafting relating to UK and foreign trusts and estates with associated tax advice.
Prof. Memberships: STEP, Charity Law Association, Chancery Bar Association.
Career: Dauntsey's School; Christ Church, Oxford; 1962 BA; 1966 MA. Called 1965 Inner Temple; Bencher, Lincoln's Inn; Deputy Social Security Commissioner 1996.
Publications: Joint editor of 'Williams on Wills', 4th, 5th, 6th and 7th editions (1974, 1980, 1987, 1996), Wills title and Executors & Administrators title in Halsbury's Laws 4th ed., vol 50 (reissue) and vol 72 (reissue).

BARLOW, Richard
11 King's Bench Walk (FJ Muller QC) London
(020) 7353 3337
clerks@11kbw.co.uk
Recommended in Tax
Specialisation: Value Added Tax and Customs and Excise.
Prof. Memberships: Revenue Bar Association, Chartered Institute of Arbitrators, Institute of Indirect Tax.
Career: Called to the Bar 1970. Customs and Excise Solicitor's Office 1973-88. Private Practice 1988 to present. Chairman (part-time) Social Security and Disability Appeals Tribunal.
Publications: Contributor to Tax Journals.
Personal: LLB (LSE) 1969. Fellow Chartered Institute of Arbitrators 1999, Accredited Mediator.

BARNES, Mark QC
One Essex Court (Lord Grabiner QC) London
(020) 7583 2000
mbarnes@oeclaw.co.uk
Recommended in Arbitration (International), Commercial (Litigation), Energy & Natural Resources, Fraud, Information Technology
Specialisation: Commercial law and litigation, with experience of company and insolvency law; European Community law and administrative law, where these touch upon commercial disputes. In the commercial field, practice includes banking (and international banking), commodities, gas and electricity supply contracts, IT and telecommunications outsourcing and supply contracts, sale of commercial goods, share sales and professional negligence. Has acted and advised in arbitrations (under ICC and LME rules, and ad hoc) and in or in connection with expert determinations and redeterminations in the gas and construction industries.

BARNES, Michael QC
Wilberforce Chambers (Edward Nugee QC)
London (020) 7306 0102
Recommended in Property Litigation
Specialisation: Property, local government and public law with particular emphasis on landlord and tenant, planning and judicial review. He is an editor (formerly general editor) of Hill and Redman on the 'Law of Landlord and Tenant' and a contributory editor of Halsbury's Law of England, 'Landlord and Tenant'. Sat as Inspector on the Public Inquiry into the Hinkley Point C Nuclear Power Station.
Prof. Memberships: Member of the Hong Kong Bar. Chancery Bar Association. Member of the Planning and Environment Bar Association and a bencher of the Middle Temple.
Career: Called to the Bar in 1965. Took silk in 1981.

BARNES, Timothy QC
7 Bedford Row (David Farrer QC) London
(020) 7242 3555
Recommended in Crime

BARNETT, Jeremy
St. Paul's Chambers (Nigel Sangster QC) Leeds
(0113) 245 5866
Recommended in Crime
Specialisation: Specialist in white collar crime. Fraud: defended in numerous recent high profile SFO and CPSHQ prosecutions. Regulatory breach: wide ranging experience in nursery and toy industries, with emphasis on the defence of due diligence and quality management, also health and safety prosecutions. Director of 'Court 21' project, UK Centre of Courtroom Technology at Leeds University.
Prof. Memberships: Criminal Bar Association and North Eastern Circuit elected member of Bar Council.
Career: Called to Bar 1980. Founder member of St Pauls Chambers in 1982.
Personal: Educated Leeds Grammar School, Liverpool University. Keen interest in computers. Leisure pursuits include golf, football and music.

BARON, Florence QC
Queen Elizabeth Building (Florence Baron QC)
London (020) 7797 7837
Recommended in Family
Specialisation: All aspects of family law and related professional negligence – with a particular emphasis on "Big Money" cases. Appeared in several high profile cases, including F v F 1995 2 FLR 45, Cowan v Cowan (2001) 2 FLR 1999 LG and advised the Prince of Wales in his divorce. Also specialises in cases with an international element.
Prof. Memberships: FLBA.
Career: BA (Oxon). QC (1995). Recorder and Deputy High Court Judge.

BARRETT, John
40 King St Manchester (0161) 832 9082
jbarrett@40kingstreet.co.uk
Recommended in Environment, Planning
Specialisation: Town and country planning; environment; compulsory purchase; highways; local government; judicial review; waste disposal; retail; minerals; housing.
Prof. Memberships: Planning and Environment Bar

Association; member of Northern Circuit and Administrative Law Bar Association.
Career: Called 1982; elected member of Northern Circuit 1983. Occasional lecturer at University of Newcastle-upon-Tyne.
Publications: Former assistant editor of the Encyclopaedia of Environmental Health.
Personal: Married with two children.

BARRETT, Penelope
3 Gray's Inn Square (Rock Tansey QC) London (020) 7520 5600
Recommended in Crime
Specialisation: Criminal defence specialist instructed in leading work. Her range of work includes murder and other violent crime, large scale drugs importations, serious sexual offences and fraud. Lectures on a number of aspects of criminal law/evidence.
Prof. Memberships: Criminal Bar Association, Liberty, British Academy of Forensic Sciences.
Career: Called to the Bar 1982.
Personal: Educated at Haygrove Comprehensive School, Bridgwater College and Trinity Hall, Cambridge (BA Hons 1981). Born 1959. Lives in London.

BARRIE, Peter
Guildhall Chambers (Adrian Palmer QC) Bristol (0117) 927 3366
Recommended in Personal Injury

BARTLETT, Andrew QC
Crown Office Chambers (Michael Spencer QC & Christopher Purchas QC) London (020) 7797 8100 bartlett@crownofficechambers.com
Recommended in Construction, Professional Negligence
Specialisation: Professional negligence, construction, insurance/reinsurance, product liability, commercial contracts. Frequently instructed in major claims and appeals involving complex legal or technical issues. Recent cases include Group Josi Re v Walbrook Insurance Co Ltd [1996], P&O Developments Ltd v Guy's and St Thomas' NHS Trust [1998], Royal Brompton Hospital NHS Trust v Hammond [1999-01], Hammersmith Hospitals NHS Trust v Troup Bywaters & Anders [1999], Albright & Wilson UK v Biachem Ltd [2000], Co-operative Retail Services v Taylor Young Partnership [2000]. Chartered Arbitrator. TECBAR accredited adjudicator. Panel member of Chartered Institute of Arbitrators. Member of London Court of International Arbitration.
Prof. Memberships: COMBAR, PNBA, TECBAR, LCLCBA, Society of Construction Law.
Career: Called 1974, FCI Arb 1988, QC 1993.
Publications: General Editor of 'Emden's Construction Law'.

BARTLEY JONES, Edward QC
Exchange Chambers (David Turner QC & Bill Braithwaite QC & Henry Globe QC) Liverpool (0151) 236 7747/ (0161) 833 2722 jonesqc@exchangechambers.co.uk
Recommended in Chancery, Commercial (Litigation), Insolvency/Corporate Recovery, Partnership
Specialisation: Commercial, professional negligence, insolvency, banking, chancery, companies, commercial property and landlord and tenant, commercial arbitration, intellectual property.
Prof. Memberships: Northern Circuit Chancery Bar Association; Chancery Bar Association; Northern Circuit Commercial Bar Association.
Career: BA (Oxon.) 1973 called 1975. Practised in Liverpool from 1976. Head of Commercial Department, Exchange Chambers, Liverpool and Manchester, since 1994. Formerly part-time tutor in law at Liverpool University. Recorder.QC. (1997).

BARTON, Charles QC
Albion Chambers (Charles Barton QC & Neil Ford QC) Bristol (0117) 927 2144
Recommended in Crime

BARWISE, Stephanie
Atkin Chambers (Robert Akenhead QC) London (020) 7404 0102 clerks@atkinchambers.law.co.uk
Recommended in Construction
Specialisation: General commercial including all aspects of the law relating to the construction and civil engineering industry both in litigation and arbitration. Experience includes major road and tunnel construction (e.g. Conway Crossing), ship refurbishment (Q.E.2), North Sea oil rig construction and Ladbroke Grove Rail Inquiry. Practice also involves professional negligence in general and in particular of architects, engineers and surveyors. A further area of specialisation is rights appurtenant to land and property: party wall disputes, easements including interference with rights of support, e.g. Midland Bank plc v Bardgrove Property Services 60 BLR 1 (Court of Appeal 1992).
Career: Called to the Bar 1988. Joined Atkin Building in 1989.
Personal: Educated at Bolton School and Cambridge University (Downing College). Fluent in French and German.

BATE, David QC
Hollis Whiteman Chambers (QEB) (Julian Bevan QC & Peter Whiteman QC) London (020) 7583 5766
Recommended in Crime
Specialisation: All forms of criminal work. Since 1990 he has concentrated mainly on defence work. Many of his cases involve organised crime; gangland murder, major drug importations, armed robbery, police corruption, blackmail etc. He has appeared in many notorious cases involving members of the Arif, Frazer, Raymond, Reeves, Blundell and Joyce families. Notable cases include R v Doran, R v Johnson (major drug importation), R v McAvoy (Brinks Mat bullion robbery) R v Relton (Brinks Mat money laundering), R v Cuthbert ('Operation Countryman' police corruption). He also specialises in Serious Fraud Office cases representing solicitors, accountants and businessmen charged with 'white collar' fraud of all kinds: corporate, revenue, VAT, etc.
Prof. Memberships: Criminal Bar Association.
Career: Called 1969. Silk 1994. Recorder.
Personal: Hendon Grammar School. Manchester University (LLB). Running, singing and drinking wine.

BATE, Stephen
5 Raymond Buildings (Patrick Milmo QC) London (020) 7242 2902
Recommended in Media & Entertainment
Specialisation: Television, music, film, video, new media and telecommunications, dealing with contractual, intellectual property (including Copyright Tribunal), regulatory, judicial review and competition matters, breach of confidence, privacy and defamation, advisory. Major cases, etc include BBC Enterprises v Hi-Tech Xtravision (rights in encrypted transmissions); Island Records v Tring (election between remedies); A&M records v VCI (copyright in sound recordings); R v ITC ex p TVNI (judicial review of Channel 3 licences); MMC Report on Channel 3 Networking, BBC World Service TV v Star TV (termination of television service); Enigma v Goldcrest (film rights); Nicholl v Ryder (manager/artist dispute); Ludlow v Williams (music publishing), A v B&CS (privacy). Candy Rock v PPL (Copyright Tribunal).
Career: Called 1981.

BATES, John H.
Old Square Chambers (John Hendy QC) London (020) 7269 0300 read@oldsquarechambers.co.uk
Recommended in Environment
Specialisation: An experienced environmental law practitioner in both civil and criminal courts and in statutory inquiries. Has particular expertise in water pollution and waste management cases and has been involved in a number of appeals against noise related abatement notices. In addition has acted in judicial review actions on environmental matters, advised in such areas as nature conservation, contaminated land, trans-frontier shipment of waste, water abstraction licensing, land drainage disputes and fishing rights.
Prof. Memberships: Chairman UK Environment Law Association 1991-93.
Career: Author: 'Water and Drainage Law', 'Marine Environment Law', 'UK Waste Law'.

BATTEN, Stephen QC
3 Raymond Buildings (Clive Nicholls QC) London (020) 7400 6400 chambers@3raymondbuildings.com
Recommended in Crime, Fraud
Specialisation: All forms of Crime: White Collar (First Defendant R v Blackspur Leasing; R Szjraber for SFO; R v Judge Gee); Murder: Kenneth Noye (the M25 Road Rage murder), First Defendant in private prosecution for murder of Stephen Lawrence; Dishonesty (Brinks Matt); Professional Tribunals: Health & Safety (Port Ramsgate Walkway Collapse).
Career: BA (Oxon). Call 1968. QC 1989. Recorder of the Crown Court.

BATTY, Christopher
St. Paul's Chambers (Nigel Sangster QC) Leeds (0113) 245 5866
Recommended in Crime

BAXENDALE, Presiley QC
Blackstone Chambers (Presiley Baxendale QC & Charles Flint QC) London (020) 7583 1770 presileybaxendale@blackstonechambers.com
Recommended in Administrative & Public Law
Specialisation: Principal area of practice is public and administrative law. Also deals with local government, human rights, education, employment, financial services and general commercial law matters. Counsel to the Inquiry into Exports of Defence Equipment and Dual Use of Goods to Iraq.
Prof. Memberships: London Common Law and Commercial Bar Association, Administrative Law Bar Association, Qualified Mediator accredited by CEDR.
Career: Called to the Bar and joined *2 Hare Court* in 1974. Appointed Junior Counsel to Crown (Common Law). Took silk in 1992.
Personal: Educated at Oxford University (MA). Governor of the LSE. Executive Committee: Justice.

BEAN, David QC
Matrix Chambers (Nicholas Blake QC) London (020) 7404 3447
Recommended in Employment
Specialisation: Principal area of practice is employment law. Also deals with commercial and general common law, administrative and education law. Major cases include P v NASUWT (trade dispute); Foley v Post Office (unfair dismissal); Carver v Saudi Arabian Airlines (overseas employment); Re Leyland DAF (employees' rights in insolvency); London Underground v Edwards (indirect discrimination); South Bank University v Anyanwu ('aiding' discrimination); Meade v British Fuels (transfer of undertakings); Chief Constable of West Yorkshire v Khan (victimisation). Clients include major employers and trade unions.
Prof. Memberships: Employment Law Bar Association (Chairman), Employment Lawyers' Association, ALBA.
Career: Called to the Bar 1976. Recorder 1996. QC 1997. Vice-chairman Bar Council 2001.
Publications: Author of 'Enforcement of Injunctions and Undertakings' (Jordans 1991) and 'Injunctions' (FT Law & Tax 7th edn 1997). Editor 'Law Reform for All' (Blackstone 1996).

BÉAR, Charles
11 King's Bench Walk Chambers (Eldred Tabachnik QC & James Goudie QC) London (020) 7632 8500
Recommended in Employment, Local Government
Specialisation: Specialises in commercial, employment and public law. Notable commercial work includes claims arising on business sales, commercial fraud and restitutionary claims. In the employment field, specialises in the protection of business interests after termination of employment, including the enforcement of anti-competition clauses, protection of confidential information and related freezing and search and seizure orders. Other main area of practice is judicial review and public law, with a particular interest in local authority powers and financing.
Prof. Memberships: COMBAR, ALBA.
Career: Called to the Bar in 1986 and joined current chambers in 1988.
Personal: Educated at Oxford University (scholar of Magdalen College) 1982-85 (1st Class Hons). Fluent in French. Born 1963. Lives in London.

BEARD, Daniel
Monckton Chambers (John Swift QC) London (020) 7405 7211
dbeard@monckton.co.uk
Recommended in Competition/Anti-trust
Specialisation: UK and EU competition law – litigation; regulatory and merger advice; also EU state aid and free movement law including parallel importation of goods; particular interests: competition law applied to sport, media and internet. Administrative law and human rights – judicial review of regulators. Recent cases include Interbrew v Competition Commission – judicial review of the Competition Commission report into the acquisition of Bass; Birds Eye Wall's v Coldstream – competition law damages action following Competition Commission report; P&O European Ferries (Vizcaya) v Commission – action to annul state aid recovery order; Competition Commission inquiry into market abuse conditions in power generators' licences – regulatory inquiry on competition matters especially dominance; UFC/Pointing – Competition Commission merger inquiry.
Prof. Memberships: Bar European Group.
Publications: 'Competition Law and the Internet in Laws of the Internet', Gringras 2nd edn (forthcoming); Butterworths 'Competition Law', contributing editor.

BEAZLEY, Thomas QC
Blackstone Chambers (Presiley Baxendale QC & Charles Flint QC) London (020) 7583 1770
clerks@blackstonechambers.com
Recommended in Commercial (Litigation)
Specialisation: Practice encompasses commercial law (including fraud, insurance and reinsurance), private international law and financial services. Commercial fraud work includes acting for and against insurers/ reinsurers, acting in claims relating to takeovers and general international commercial and banking disputes and numerous jurisdictional disputes eg. Government of Brunei v Prince Jefri Bolkiah 2000; Chairman Syndicates v New Cap Re & Others; Kleinwort Benson Ltd v Glasgow City Council [1996] 2 All ER 257 CA 1997 3WLR 923 HOL; Re: Polly Peck International plc [1998] BCLC 185; Marinari v Lloyds Bank [1993] ALL ER (EC) 84; Ansbacher v Binks Stem 141 SJLB 151 CA. Financial services work includes acting for and against regulatory bodies (particularly SFA, IMRO, SIB and now FSA) and for clients under DTI investigations. Has acted for and against a number of foreign states in commercial litigation.
Prof. Memberships: COMBAR.
Career: Called to the Bar 1979 and since 1980 practised as a commercial barrister. Has acted as arbitrator for the London Court of International Arbitration.
Personal: Working knowledge of Dutch, French and German.

BECK, James
2-4 Tudor Street (Richard Ferguson QC) London (020) 7797 7111
Recommended in Crime

BECKETT, Richard QC
3 Raymond Buildings (Clive Nicholls QC) London (020) 7400 6400
chambers@3raymondbuildings.com
Recommended in Licensing
Specialisation: Licensing. Work includes preparation and advice relating to applications and objections in all licensing matters, such as liquor, gaming, betting and amusement centres, representing parties at all levels from local committees to Divisional Court. Advises on lotteries and other related activities. Clients include the Rank Organisation, Ladbrokes and JD Wetherspoon plc.
Career: Called to the Bar 1965 and joined present chambers 1967. Took silk 1988.

BEHRENS, James
Serle Court (Lord Neill of Bladen QC) London (020) 7242 6105
jbehrens@serlecourt.co.uk
Recommended in Church
Specialisation: Chancery and commercial litigation, church law, computer law and Alternative Dispute Resolution. Reported cases include Collings v Lee [2001] 2 All ER 332; Hanbury v Hanbury [1999] 2 FLR 255; TSB Bank plc v Marshall [1998] 3 EGLR. 100; Quinlan v Essex Hinge Co. Ltd [1997] BBC 53.
Prof. Memberships: Chancery Bar Association; Property Bar Association; Association of Contentious Trust and Probate Specialists; Society for Computers and Law (council member); Ecclesiastical Law Society (member of general committee). Associate tenant of Zenith Chambers, Leeds.
Career: Called to the Bar in 1979; member of the Bar Council 1992-94; CEDR accredited mediator 1998; deputy chancery master 2000; chartered arbitrator 2001.
Publications: 'Practical Church Management' (1998); 'Confirmation, Sacrament of Grace' (1995); 'Word Perfect for the Legal Profession' (1991). Contributor to 'Researching the Legal Web' by Nick Holmes and Delia Venables (1999), and 'Case Preparation' by the Inns of Court School of Law (1997).
Personal: Born 22 December 1956, educated Eton College; Trinity College Cambridge (MA); Cardiff University (LLM); married with two children. Lives in Kensington and Yorkshire.

BELOFF, Michael QC
Blackstone Chambers (Presiley Baxendale QC & Charles Flint QC) London (020) 7583 1770
clerks@blackstonechambers.com
Recommended in Administrative & Public Law, Employment, Human Rights, Sport
Specialisation: Extremely wide ranging practice encompasses litigation and arbitration, covering a large number of areas including judicial review, commercial, EU law, employment, libel, insurance, sport, immigration, civil liberties and aviation. Has appeared in more than 350 reported cases in House of Lords, Privy Council, European Court of Justice, European Court of Human Rights and courts in Hong Kong, Singapore, Kuala Lumpur, Kuching, Bermuda,Trinidad, Brunei, Gibraltar and Belfast. In three major public inquiries: Crown Agents 1980-82; Brixton Disorders 1981 (Scarman Inquiry) and Sentosa Collision (Singapore, 1983). Chaired inquiry into academic plagiarism for University of Oxford 1987, and into "The Connection" for Carlton TV 1998. Women's Legal Defence Award 1991. Clients have included governments, local authorities, regulators, unions, national newspapers, television channels, banks, insurance companies, major ports, corporations, universities, statutory bodies, pressure groups, sporting organisations, and leading individuals and personalities from all fields of achievement including The Chief Rabbi, the Aga Khan, L. Ron Hubbard, Robert Maxwell, Ernest Saunders, The Al-Fayeds, Prime Ministers of three countries, Lennox Lewis, George Best, Sebastian Coe, and David Coulthard. Author of numerous articles for legal periodicals. Books include Butterworths 'The Sex Discrimination Act 1976'. Halsbury's Laws 'Time' (1999). Conference addresses include Sweet and Maxwell Conference on Judicial Review (Chairman 1990-91 and 1993-96), ECHR Salzburg (1988). IAAF Monte Carlo (1991) Singapore Law Academy (1992), Hong Kong Bar Association (1994), FCO-arranged 'Human Rights in the UK' (for Mayor of Moscow [1991]). McCarthy – Tetrault – Vancouver (1996) Institute of Human Rights: Moscow (1996), Auckland (1997), Beijing (1997), Berlin (1997), Tokyo, University of Virginia, Tulane University, Commonwealth Law Conference (all 1999). Annual Lectures: ALBA (1994) Statute Law Society (1994) UC Dublin (1997), Lasok Exeter U (1998), Atkin (Reform) 1999. Consultant Editor: 'Judicial Review Bulletin'.
Prof. Memberships: COMBAR, Administrative Law Bar Association (First Chairman, now Emeritus Chairman and Vice-President), Bar European Group. Environmental Law Foundation (Advisory Council). Honorary Fellow, Institute of Advanced Legal Studies.
Career: Called to the Bar 1967. QC 1981. Recorder of the Crown Court 1984-95. Master of the Bench, Grays Inn 1988. Deputy High Court Judge (QBD) 1989. Nominated to sit in Divisional Court of QBD 1992. Joint Head of Chambers at 4-5 Gray's Inn Square from 1992-00. Judge of the Court of Appeal of Guernsey and Jersey 1995. Member Court of Arbitration for Sport (Lausanne) 1995; CAS Ad Hoc Panel Atlanta Olympics 1996; Sydney Olympics 2000; Kuala Lumpa Commonwealth Games 1998. Ad Hoc Legal Advisor to British town, World Atheletics Championship Seville (1990). President Trinity College, Oxford 1996-
Personal: Born 18th April 1942. Educated at Dragon School, Oxford 1950-54, Eton College 1954-60 (King's Scholar and Captain of School 1960) and Magdalen College, Oxford 1960-65 (BA History Class 1, 1963: Jurisprudence 1965, MA 1967). Moved motion which procured admission of women to full membership of the Oxford Union 1964. 5 marathons, including London marathon (twice). Honorary member of International Athletics Club. Member of Gridiron (Oxford), Vincents (Oxford) Achilles Reform Club (on Political Committee), FRSA, FICPD. Lives in London and Oxford. Married to Judith Beloff, Barrister JP, IS, ID.

BELTRAMI, Adrian
3 Verulam Buildings (Christopher Symons QC & John Jarvis QC) London (020) 7831 8441
chambers@3vb.com
Recommended in Banking, Commercial (Litigation)
Specialisation: All aspects of commercial litigation, in particular domestic and international banking, insolvency, commercial fraud and professional negligence. Cases include: BCCI v Price Waterhouse (1996, 1997 & 1998) (Banking Act, auditors' duties and liabilities), Box v Barclays Bank (1998) (banking Act, constructive trusts), Electra v KPMG (1999) (auditors' duty of care), Middle Temple v Lloyds Bank (1999) (cheque collection). Thyssen v Thyssen (undue influence) Principal contributor to Banking Litigation (1999).
Prof. Memberships: COMBAR.
Career: Called to the Bar 1989. Admitted to the Bar of the Cayman Islands on several individual cases.
Personal: Stonyhurst, Downing College, Cambridge and Harvard Law School. MA (1st class) LLM. Born 8 November 1964. Lives in London. Married with one son and one daughter.

BENNETT, M
Oriel Chambers (A Sander) Liverpool (0151) 236 7191/ 236 4321
Recommended in Family

BENNETT-JENKINS, Sallie
2 Hare Court (Stephen Kramer QC) London (020) 7353 5324
Recommended in Crime

BENSON, Jeremy QC

2 Hare Court (Stephen Kramer QC) London
(020) 7353 5324
Recommended in Crime

BENSON, John QC

14 Castle Street (Andrew Edis QC) Liverpool
(0151) 236 4421
101561.623@compuserve.com
Recommended in Employment
Specialisation: Specialist practitioner in all aspects of employment law including interlocutory relief, restrictive covenants, personal injuries, clinical negligence.
Prof. Memberships: Employment Law Bar Association, Personal Injuries Bar Association. Medical Law Association. Northern Circuit.
Career: LL.B (Hons). Called to the Bar in 1978. Northern Circuit. Part-time chairman of employment tribunals 1995. Recorder 1998, Silk 2001.
Personal: Age 46.

BENTHAM, Howard QC

Peel Court Chambers (Michael Shorrock QC) Manchester (0161) 832 3791
Recommended in Crime

BERKSON, Simon

Exchange Chambers (David Turner QC & Bill Braithwaite QC & Henry Globe QC) Liverpool (0151) 236 7747
Recommended in Crime

BERRAGAN, Neil

Merchant Chambers (David Berkley QC) Manchester (0161) 839 7070
Recommended in Chancery, Commercial (Litigation)

BERRY, Simon QC

9 Old Square (Michael Driscoll QC) London
(020) 7405 4682
chembers@9oldsquare.co.uk
Recommended in Chancery, Property Litigation
Specialisation: Property and commercial litigation.
Prof. Memberships: Chancery Bar Association, Professional Negligence Bar Association.
Career: Called to Bar 1977. Silk 1990. Recorder 2000. Deputy High Court Judge 2001.
Publications: Contributor to 'Professional Negligence and Liability'.

BERRY, Steven

Essex Court Chambers (Gordon Pollock QC) London (020) 7813 8000
Recommended in Insurance, Shipping
Specialisation: Broad-based practice, in particular the associated fields of insurance and reinsurance, shipping, international banking, international sale of goods and arbitration.
Career: Exeter College, Oxford BA (Jurisprudence) (1st Class Hons); BCL (1st Class Hons) 1983. Astbury scholar, Middle Temple. Eldon Law scholar. Called to the Bar 1984.
Personal: Born 1961.

BEVAN, John QC

2 Harcourt Buildings, Atkinson Bevan Chambers (Nicholas Atkinson QC & John Bevan QC) London (020) 7353 2112
clerks@2hb.co.uk
Recommended in Crime
Specialisation: General criminal law, emphasis on high-profile serious cases. Prosecutions include child abuse – Jasmine Beckford, Heidi Koseda; terrorism – Sidhu and others (1994: 98 Criminal Appeal Reports 59), Hayes and Taylor (Harrods bombing), Patrick Kelly, McArdle and McKinley (South Quay bombing 1996); murder – Kenneth Erskine (Stockwell Strangler), Morss and Tyler (Child Victim Daniel Handley), Miah and others (Victim, Richard Everitt), Chindamo (Headmaster, Philip Lawrence), Eades and others (Police Sergeant Robertson); Also – McLean (Notting Hill Rapist), Evans, Whitby and Burrell (death of illegal immigrant, Joy Gardner); Ricky Reel inquest.
Prof. Memberships: Criminal Bar Association. South Eastern Circuit.
Career: Called 1970. Treasury Counsel 1983-97. Took Silk 1997.

BEVAN, Julian QC

Hollis Whiteman Chambers (QEB) (Julian Bevan QC & Peter Whiteman QC) London
(020) 7583 5766
Recommended in Crime, Fraud
Specialisation: High profile general crime with emphasis on white collar fraud. Involved in Maxwell case; Gokal; Sanction busting cases. More recently M25 Murder Appeal and advised on corporate manslaughter.
Career: Former 1st Senior Treasury Counsel.

BICKERDIKE, Roger

Zenith Chambers (Andrew Campbell QC & John Collins) Leeds (0113) 245 5438
Recommended in Family
Specialisation: Highly noted junior specialising in family/matrimonial work with particular emphasis on public law children cases and ancillary relief work. Considerable experience in appellate work both in the High Court and in the Court of Appeal. Involved in numerous reported cases, some of them landmark. Busy matrimonial practice, with an emphasis on cases where there are substantial assets.
Prof. Memberships: Member of the Family Bar Association, and Association of Lawyers for Children.
Career: Called to the Bar in 1986.

BIDDER, Neil QC

33 Park Place (John Charles Rees QC) Cardiff
(029) 2023 3313
Recommended in Personal Injury

BIRCH, Elizabeth

3 Verulam Buildings (Christopher Symons QC & John Jarvis QC) London (020) 7831 8441
chambers@3vb.com
Recommended in Alternative Dispute Resolution
Specialisation: Specialist in international and domestic commercial arbitration, mediation, commercial and maritime law including banking and financial services, commodities, conflict of laws and disputes as to jurisdiction, information technology (IT), injunctions (anti-suit, mareva and other), insurance (marine, non-marine and Lloyd's Market), international sale of goods, joint ventures, oil and gas, shipping, transportation and all types of contractual and professional disputes. Tribunal emphasis: Commercial Court, Admiralty Court and Arbitration. Appears as advocate and receives appointments to sit as arbitrator and mediator in general commercial and shipping disputes. Arbitration tribunals include LMAA, LCIA, ICC, ACI and ad hoc. Sat as arbitrator in numerous Lloyd's market disputes determining claims by Names against Members' Agents and Managing Agents. Founder and Director of ACI (Arbitration – a Commercial Initiative), an arbitration group offering lawyer arbitrators to determine business and professional disputes in fields such as banking, insurance and financial services. The group also offers mediation and other forms of ADR. Sits on the Court of Appeal Panel of mediators. Has successfully mediated a substantial number of commercial disputes.
Prof. Memberships: Fellow of the Chartered Institute of Arbitrators (FCIArb), Qualified Mediator (QDR) accredited by the Centre for Dispute Resolution (CEDR) and The Academy of Experts. Appointed to the Panels of the Lloyd's Arbitration Schemes (LAS) Tiers 1 and 2 from 1992 to date. On the ACI Panel of Arbitrators and on the list of supporting members of LMAA available to sit as arbitrator and mediator. Panel member of FEPA Representative Committee (receives appointments to sit as Legal Chairman in appeals against decisions by MAFF in relation to licenses to deposit articles or substances in the sea or under the seabed). Member of the Commercial Court Working Party chaired by Mr Justice Colman which considers ADR and its role in the Commercial Court, leading to the existing Commercial Court Practice Directive on ADR. Member of the Commercial Bar Association (COMBAR) – secretary 1993 to 1996. Member of the London Common Law and Commercial Bar Association (LCLCBA). Supporting member of the London Maritime Arbitrators' Association (LMAA).
Career: Called to Gray's Inn 1978; joined 3 Essex Court in 1980; the Chambers moved in 1994 becoming known as 20 Essex Street; joined 3 Verulam Buildings in 1998.

BIRD, Simon

2-3 Gray's Inn Square (Anthony Porten QC & Anthony Scrivener QC) London (020) 7242 4986
sbird@2-3graysinnsquare.co.uk
Recommended in Planning
Specialisation: A wide range of planning, local government and environmental work. Planning work includes inquiries throughout the country dealing with housing, retail, leisure, waste, industrial, commercial, hospital and other developments. Major inquiry work includes the Cambridge Hinxton Hall and Arbury Park Inquiries and many development plan inquiries, the most recent being the Bedford Borough Local Plan Inquiry. Environmental and local government work includes Court and advisory covering all aspects of the work of public bodies. A particular specialism is waste management licensing.
Prof. Memberships: Planning and Environment Bar Association; South Eastern Circuit; United Kingdom Environmental Law Association.
Career: Called to the Bar in 1987.
Personal: University of Reading.

BIRKETT, Peter QC

18 St John Street (Jonathan Foster QC) Manchester (0161) 278 1800
Recommended in Crime
Specialisation: Criminal law, both prosecution and defence. Has been involved in many high profile and notable trials on circuit over the past 10 years. If he has a specialisation, it is in the field of commercial fraud.
Prof. Memberships: Criminal Bar Association. Leader of the Northern Circuit 1999-.
Career: Called 1972. Q.C. 1989. Recorder of the Crown Court 1989. Acting deemster (Isle of Man). Governing member of the Inns of Court Advocacy Training Committee.
Personal: Married, 2 sons, hobbies include sport, political biography, music (keyboard player in 'The Prestons').Education: Sedbergh School, Yorkshire. University of Leicester LL.B. Master of the Bench (Inner Temple 1996-).

BIRSS, Colin

Three New Square (David Young QC) London (020) 7405 1111
Recommended in Information Technology, Intellectual Property

BIRTLES, William

Old Square Chambers (John Hendy QC) London (020) 7269 0300
birtles@oldsquarechambers.co.uk
Recommended in Environment
Specialisation: Principal areas of practice are environmental, planning and local government law. Has had considerable experience in both civil and criminal aspects of pollution claims including land contamination (arising from oil, toxic waste and industrial waste disposal), water (eg Barry Docks, Cardiff), air (particularly industrial smells and noise). Major inquiries include the Sizewell B Nuclear Power Station Inquiry (1984-86), the second Part I Environmental Protection Act Inquiry (Cumbria 1994), the Westminster Council District Audit Inquiry (1994-95) and various internal inquiries for local authorities.
Prof. Memberships: Planning and Local Government Bar Association; Administrative Law Bar Association;

Environmental Law Foundation. Senior Associate Member St Antony's College Oxford.
Career: Academic lawyer 1968-74. Called to the Bar 1970. Joined Old Square Chambers 1986. Recorder 1993. Frequent speaker at legal conferences.
Publications: Co-author of 'Planning and Environmental Law' (Longman 1994 with Richard Stein); co-author of 'Local Government Finance Law' (Butterworths 2000 with Anna Forge and Tony Child). Numerous articles and chapters in books.
Personal: Married to Patricia Hewitt MP, two children. Opera, classical music and travel.

BISHOP, Malcolm QC
30 Park Place (John Jenkins QC) Cardiff (029) 2039 8421
Recommended in Family

BLACK, John QC
18 Red Lion Court (Anthony Arlidge QC) London (020) 7520 6000
john.black@18rlc.co.uk
Recommended in Crime
Specialisation: Serious crime.
Career: An extensive defence practice that has embraced such notorious trials as Brinks-Mats and Beck.
Personal: Prosecution work embraces fraud, drugs, corruption and serious sexual offences.

BLACK, Michael QC
2 Temple Gardens (Dermod O'Brien QC) London (020) 7822 1200
mblack@2templegardens.co.uk
Recommended in Construction
Specialisation: The resolution of disputes arising out of commercially and technically complex contracts principally concerning building, engineering and other high-technology projects, including those involving the professional liability of parties' advisors. Within the last year he has advised or represented the Liquidators of a Far Eastern development corporation in relation to claims of excess of US$4 billion; Canadian wireless telesystems operators in a US$400 million dispute concerning part of the Brazilian cellular telephone network and parties involved in various forms of private dispute resolution procedures relating to claims each in excess of US$100 million for defective works and cost overruns under EPC and EPCM contracts in the UK, USA and Far East. He has also appeared recently in the following reported cases: Tameside MBC v Barlows [2001] BLR 113, Henry Boot Construction (UK) Limited v Malmaison Hotel (Manchester) Limited, [2000] 2 Lloyds Rep 625 and Al-Naimi v Islamic Press, [2001] 1 Lloyds Rep 522. Regularly acts as an Arbitrator and Mediator.
Prof. Memberships: American Bar Association's forum on the construction industry; Conseil International du batiment pour la Recherche l'Etude et la documentation (CIB) (Rotterdam, The Netherlands); London Court of International Arbitration; Fellow of the Chartered Institute of Arbitrators; Fellow of the Institution of Civil Engineering Surveyors; TECBAR; COMBAR.
Career: Member of the Civil Procedure Rule Committee; Deputy Judge of the Technology and Construction Court; Accredited mediator (Harvard Law School and Chartered Institue of Arbitrators); Visiting Research Fellow, Civil and Construction Engineering Department, UMIST.
Publications: Written and spoken extensively in the UK, Europe and USA. Currently writing chapters on Arbitration and Construction for 5th edition of the 'Law and Practice of Compromise'.

BLACKBURN, John QC
Atkin Chambers (Robert Akenhead QC) London (020) 7404 0102
clerks@atkinchambers.law.co.uk
Recommended in Arbitration (International), Construction
Specialisation: In the fields of building and civil engineering disputes, professional negligence actions involving contractors and engineers and arbitration, including international arbitration. Has conducted several heavy disputes under rules of the International Chamber of Commerce in Paris. Has been appointed Arbitrator in disputes arising out of construction contracts under the International Chamber of Commerce, also acts as arbitrator over disputes arising in England. Has been admitted to the bar in Hong Kong and Singapore to conduct cases arising out of building and civil engineering contracts. Construction Law experience has involved him in advising upon, presenting and defending all kinds of building and civil engineering claims worldwide. Advises and acts for numerous Public Corporations. Advises on and drafts various kinds of building and different types of engineering contracts. Work undertaken generally involves substantial projects involving sophisticated plan, and building and engineering structures including tunnels, dams and hydro-electric schemes.
Career: Called to the Bar 1969. Took silk 1984.

BLACKETT-ORD, Mark
5 Stone Buildings (Henry Harrod) London (020) 7242 6201
Recommended in Partnership
Specialisation: Well-known for his experience in advice and litigation in Chancery matters especially those concerning partnerships and other quasi-corporate bodies, from unincorporated associations to family trusts (Murphy v Murphy [1999] 1 WLR 1P2) and bodies alleged to be carrying on the business of insurance (Re a company No 007816 of 1994) (1997) 2 BCLC 685. Has appeared in cases at all levels to the House of Lords and European Court (Webb v Webb (1994) QB 696). Co-edited the original 4th edition of 'Partnership' in Halsbury Laws of England, and wrote the major new book 'Partnership' (Butterworths, 1997).
Prof. Memberships: ACTAPS; STEP; APP. Chairman of the Chancery Bar Association Working Party on Partnership Law.

BLACKWELL, Kate
Lincoln House Chambers (Mukhtar Hussain QC) Manchester (0161) 832 5701
Recommended in Crime

BLAIR, Bruce QC
1 Mitre Court Buildings (Bruce Blair QC) London (020) 7797 7070
Recommended in Family
Specialisation: All areas of Family Law. Has appeared in many leading cases including A v A (a minor: financial provision); A v A (costs); Baker v Baker (No 2); Browne; Cornick; F v F (ancillary relief: substantial assets); Gojkovic (Nos 1 and 2); Green; Re H (a minor) (blood tests: parental rights); Re Jennings; Omielan; Penrose; Richardson; Van G.
Career: Harrow School and Magdalene College, Cambridge (MA). QC 1989. Deputy High Court Judge Family Division since 1990.
Personal: Born 12 April 1946. Married with 3 daughters, lives in London.

BLAIR, Michael QC
3 Verulam Buildings (Christopher Symons QC & John Jarvis QC) London (020) 7831 8441
mblair@3vb.com
Recommended in Financial Services
Specialisation: Financial services. Advised the Financial Services Authority on content and quality of the FSA Handbook. Also appointed Chairman of the three self-regulating organisations (SFA, IMRO, PIA).
Prof. Memberships: COMBAR. Bencher, Middle Temple.
Career: Under secretary Lord Chancellor's Department 1982-87, general counsel (later Acting Chief Executive) Securities and Investments Board 1987-98, General Counsel, FSA 1998-00. Member, Competition Commission (Appeals Panel) 2000-, Chairman, Review Body on Doctors' and Dentists' Remuneration 2001-.
Publications: Recently, Blackstone's Guides to the Financial Services and Markets Act 2000 (2001) and Bank of England Act 1998 (1998).

BLAIR, William QC
3 Verulam Buildings (Christopher Symons QC & John Jarvis QC) London (020) 7831 8441
chambers@3vb.com
Recommended in Banking, Financial Services
Specialisation: Commercial work, domestic and international banking, arbitration, business law, commercial fraud, company law, financial services, international trade, insolvency, private international law.Cases include: Esal v Oriental Credit 1985; LAFB v Bankers Trust 1988; LAFB v Manufacturers Hanover 1989; IE Contractors v Lloyds Bank 1990; Barclays Bank v O'Brien 1993; Macmillan v Bishopsgate 1994; Polly Peck v Citibank 1994; TSB v Camfield 1995; Macmillan v Bishopsgate 1996; Wahda Bank v Arab Bank 1998; MCC Proceeds v Bishopsgate 1998, Middle Temple v Lloyds 1999. Struggles v Lloyds Bank.
Career: Called to the Bar 1972, Silk 1994. Visiting professor of law (London School of Economics), member of the International Monetary Law committee of the International Law Association, member of FLP working party on Single European Currency, recorder. Co-editor 'Encyclopaedia of Banking Law', co-author 'Banking and Financial Services Regulation' (2nd Ed) 1998, editor 'Banks and Remedies' (2nd Ed) 1999.

BLAKE, Nicholas QC
Matrix Chambers (Nicholas Blake QC) London (020) 7404 3447
Recommended in Administrative & Public Law, Human Rights, Immigration

BLANCHARD, Claire
Essex Court Chambers (Gordon Pollock QC) London (020) 7813 8000
Recommended in Commercial (Litigation), Shipping
Specialisation: Broad-based commercial practice. In particular shipping, insurance, banking, conflicts and employment.
Career: Liverpool Polytechnic LLB (Hons) 1991. Inns of Court School of Law. Called to the Bar 1992.
Personal: Born 1969.

BLAXLAND, Henry
Two Garden Court (Ian Macdonald QC & Owen Davies QC) London (020) 7353 1633
Recommended in Crime, Human Rights

BLEASDALE, Paul QC
5 Fountain Court (Anthony Barker QC) Birmingham (0121) 606 0500
Recommended in Personal Injury
Specialisation: Personal Injury Litigation; Claimants and Defendants. In particular industrial disease claims and also medical negligence. Planning and Environment; Developers and Local Authorities. Appeals and Local Plan, UDP and Compulsory Purchase Inquiries.
Prof. Memberships: Personal Injuries Bar Association, Planning Environment Bar Association.
Career: London University, Recorder of the Crown Court, Deputy Chairman of the Agricultural Lands Tribunal. Queen's Counsel.

BLOCH, Michael QC
Wilberforce Chambers (Edward Nugee QC) London (020) 7306 0102
Recommended in Intellectual Property
Specialisation: Principal areas of practice are general commercial, intellectual property, banking and arbitration. Professional clients include many City law firms.
Prof. Memberships: Chancery Bar Association, Commercial Bar Association
Career: Called to the Bar in 1979. At 1 Brick Court 1979-87. Joined Essex Court in 1987 and Wilberforce Chambers in 2000.
Personal: Educated at Bedales School and the universities of Cambridge (MA) and East Anglia (M Phil). Trustee of Childline and governor of Bedales School. Born 18 October 1951. Lives in London.

BLOCH, Selwyn QC
Littleton Chambers (Michel Kallipetis QC) London (020) 7797 8600
Recommended in Employment, Information Technology
Specialisation: Practice encompasses business law and employment law. Work includes general commercial litigation, restraint of trade, garden leave and other interlocutory injunctions, confidential information, wrongful and unfair dismissal, discrimination, entertainment and sports law. Contributor to conferences on employment law.
Prof. Memberships: ELBA, COMBAR, ELA.
Career: Attorney, South Africa 1976. Called to the Bar 1982 and joined current chambers in the same year.
Publications: Co-author, 'Employment Covenants and Confidential Information' (Butterworths, 2nd edition 1999).
Personal: Educated at Stellenbosch and Witwatersrand Universities, South Africa. (BA, LL.B). Born 23rd February 1952. Lives in London.

BLOCK, Neil
39 Essex Street (Nigel Pleming QC) London (020) 7832 1111
Recommended in Personal Injury
Specialisation: A contract and tort based practice. Insurance (including policy avoidance/fraud and material loss claims eg McGregor v Prudential Assurance Co 1998 Lloyds). Personal injury (including sporting cases eg Smolden v Whitworth & Nolan, O'Neill v Wimbledon & Fashanu, Watson v British Boxing Board of Control), catastrophic injury claims, medical negligence (in particular paediatric brain damage), professional negligence (including solicitors, accountants, surveyors and valuers, architects, stockbrokers and insurance brokers), group actions (Hepatitis C, Supertram, shipyards, organo-phosphates), disaster litigation (eg Selby rail crash) and product liability.
Prof. Memberships: Professional Negligence Bar Association, Personal Injury Bar Association, London Common Law and Commercial Bar Association, Bar Sports Law Group.
Career: Called to the Bar in 1980.
Personal: B.A. (Hons), LLM (Exon).

BLOHM, Leslie
St John's Chambers (Christopher Sharp QC) Bristol (0117) 921 3456 clerks@stjohnschambers.co.uk; chambers@199strand.co.uk
Recommended in Chancery, Commercial (Litigation)
Specialisation: Commercial landlord and tenant; real property; equity and trusts. Counsel for respondent in Bettison v Langton & Penter [2000] Ch.54 (CA) and [2001] 2WLR 1605 (HL) on profits á prendre and rights of common; Brown v Gloucester City Council [1998] 1 EGLR 95 (CA) on construction of rent review clauses.
Prof. Memberships: Chancery Bar Association, Bristol and Cardiff Chancery Bar Association.
Career: Christ's Hospital Horsham & Keble College, Oxford; BA 1981. Lincoln's Inn 1982. Hardwicke & Jenkins scholar of Lincoln's Inn 1981-82. St John's Chambers Bristol 1984. Head of Chancery Department 1992.
Personal: Family, cycling and chess.

BLUNT, Oliver QC
Furnival Chambers (Andrew Mitchell QC) London (020) 7405 3232
Recommended in Crime
Specialisation: Entirely defence-based practice with a substantial emphasis on murder, terrorism, fraud and drugs cases. Murder and violent crime: currently instructed in the Millenium Dome robbery trial. Has represented such clients as John Taft ("Beauty in the Bath" murder trial, Liverpool Crown Court, 1999), Maria Hnautik (murder, Norwich CC, 1996), Ngarimu (female contract killer, CCC, 1995), Syd Owen ('Ricky' of 'Eastenders', wounding, Snaresbrook CC, 1995), Michael Sams (kidnapping, blackmail, murder, Nottingham CC, 1993), also the trial and successful appeal of the 'Chelsea Headhunters' (Regina v Drake and Others). Sexual Crime: including high profile cases such as Richard Baker (DJ Rapist, CCC, 1999). Drugs: represented such clients as Jason Fitzgibbon (Birmingham CC, 2000), Thomas Adams and Others (Woolwich CC, 1998). Successfully defended the first defendant in a £150 million cocaine importation (Regina v Hillier and Others, 1993). Terrorism: has acted on behalf of the Iranian Embassy and represented two members of the Consular Staff in separate terrorist trials at the CCC (Tabari Abcou/Fouladi). Appeared for the second defendant in Regina v Canning and Lamb (IRA trial, CC, 1993). Fraud: including William Casey, acquitted in a multi-million pound arson/insurance fraud, (CCC 1997), and Chananya Gross, acquitted in Hackney electoral fraud trial (Wood Green CC 2001).
Prof. Memberships: SE Circuit. Criminal Bar Association.
Career: Called to Bar 1974. Queen's Counsel 1994. Recorder 1995.
Personal: Born 8/3/51. Married with four children. Member of Roehampton Club, Rosslyn Park Rugby Club and Barnes Cricket Club.

BOARDMAN, Christopher
11 Stone Buildings (Murray Rosen QC) London (020) 7831 6381 boardman@11stonebuildings.com
Recommended in Insolvency/Corporate Recovery
Specialisation: Christopher is a company and insolvency specialist with a practice that extends to partnerships, financial services, asset-tracing and commercial disputes. On the insolvency side, he has particular expertise in voluntary arrangements, administrations, liquidations and directors' disqualification. His company law practice embraces shareholders disputes, claims against directors and security instruments. It also encompasses more technical aspects such as meetings, articles of association and reductions of capital. He has also been involved in several recently reported decisions and is retained by R3 (formerly SPI) to advise on voluntary arrangement terms.

BOMPAS, Anthony George QC
4 Stone Buildings (Philip Heslop QC) London (020) 7242 5524
Recommended in Chancery, Company, Financial Services, Insolvency/Corporate Recovery
Specialisation: Principal area of practice is company law (all aspects, including minority shareholders proceedings and insolvency) and financial services. Other main area of practice is professional negligence work. Has been instructed in many of the major, widely publicised, company matters in recent years, including the Guinness affair, the Blue Arrow, the Barlow Clowes, the Brent Walker and the BCCI affairs. Author of 'Investigations by the DTI' in Tolley's 'Company Law' (3rd Ed.).
Prof. Memberships: Chancery Bar Association, Insolvency Lawyers' Association and Commercial Bar Association (COMBAR). Called to the Bar of the British Virgin Islands and, for specific cases, to the Bar of Trinidad and Tobago.
Career: Called to the Bar 1975 and joined present chambers in 1976. Junior Counsel to the DTI 1989-94. Took Silk in 1994.
Personal: Educated at Merchant Taylors' School, Northwood 1964-69 and Oriel College, Oxford 1970-74. Born 6th November 1951.

BOOTH, Alan
Deans Court Chambers (Stephen Grime QC) Manchester (0161) 214 6000 booth@deanscourt.co.uk
Recommended in Family
Specialisation: Ancillary relief and professional negligence arising out of ancillary relief.
Prof. Memberships: FLBA, PNBA.
Career: Bolton School (Boy's Division). Selwyn College Cambridge.
Personal: Married, two children.

BOOTH, Cherie QC
Matrix Chambers (Nicholas Blake QC) London (020) 7404 3447
Recommended in Administrative & Public Law, Employment
Specialisation: Specialist in all aspects of employment law and administrative and public law. Notable public law cases include E v Dorset County Council and Others [1995]; Phelps v LB of Hillingdon [1998] (dyslexia); White and Others v Ealing LBC (SEN); R v Law Society ex p Dalton [1999]; B v Chief Constable of Avon and Somerset (5/4/2000 Human Rights). Notable employment cases are Grant v SW Trains (sexual orientation discrimination); Preston v Wolverhampton NHS Trusts ECJ 2000; Barry v Midland Bank HL 22/77/99; BCCI v Ali 1999 and Wilson v St Helens Borough Council [1997] IRLR 505; Pearce v Governing Body of Mayfield School (April 2000).

BOOTH, Michael QC
40 King St Manchester (0161) 832 9082
Recommended in Chancery, Commercial (Litigation), Insolvency/Corporate Recovery

BORRELLI, Michael QC
1 Middle Temple Lane (Colin Dines & Andrew Trollope QC) London (020) 7583 0659 (12 lines)
Recommended in Crime

BOSWOOD, Anthony QC
Fountain Court (Anthony Boswood QC) London (020) 7583 3335
Recommended in Banking, Commercial (Litigation), Energy & Natural Resources, Fraud, Insurance
Specialisation: A broad based commercial practice with particular experience in insurance/reinsurance (including Lloyds litigation); mergers and acquisitions (including actions against merchant banks and others arising out of public bids); energy law (including litigation arising out of long term North Sea gas supply and gas transportation contracts); banking and international trade; international civil procedure; professional negligence (solicitors and accountants); computer law; civil fraud; media and entertainment. Notable cases include Outhwaite (Lloyds insurance); SAIL v Farex [1995] LRLR 116 (international property reinsurance); Napier v Hunter [1993] AC 718 and Henderson v Merrett [1995] 2AC 1451 (both Lloyds insurance); Yeoman v Warburgs (breach of duty by merchant bank); GE v Bankers Trust, Arthur Andersen and others (proceedings arising out of an MBO; negligence of lead bank/accountants); Bank Negara v Lariza [1998] AC 583 (letters of credit); Philips Petroleum and Enron Amoco and J Block (oil and gas litigation); EDS v Standard Chartered Bank (computer software; bank message switching system); Dubai Aluminium Company v Salaam & Ors [1999] Lloyds Rep 415 (international fraud); Grupo Torras v Fahad & Ors [1999] (international fraud); Re State of Norway [1990] 1 AC 723 (letters rogatory) Barclays Bank v Broad (film completion guarantees); Arab Bank v Zurich Insurance [1999] 1 Lloyds Rep 262 (construction of composite E&O Policy); Britvic v Messer [2000]: product liability.
Career: Called to Bar 1970; took Silk in 1986. Bencher of Middle Temple. Deputy High Court Judge.
Personal: Italian speaker.

BOTHROYD, Shirley
Littleton Chambers (Michel Kallipetis QC) London (020) 7797 8600
Recommended in Employment
Specialisation: Principal areas of practice:Employment law: appearing in employment tribunals & employment appeal.Tribunal: unfair dismissal, sex & race discimination.High Court: restrictive covenants – all injunctive matters.General commercial & contract, commercial fraud.Cited as a Leading Employment Junior in Chambers & Partners Directory. Frequently instructed in sensitive race & discrimination cases. Has reputation for being a tough litigator, instructed by leading employment solicitors.

Prof. Memberships: COMBAR, ELBAR, South Eastern Circuit, Counsel for Inland Revenue.
Career: Called to the Bar and joined present chambers in 1982.
Personal: Born 23rd July 1958.

BOULDING, Philip QC
Keating Chambers (Richard Fernyhough QC) London (020) 7544 2600
pboulding@keatingchambers.com
Recommended in Construction
Specialisation: Construction and civil engineering law, including arbitration and professional negligence.
Career: Qualified 1979; Gray's Inn; Queen's Counsel 1996. Admitted to Hong Kong Bar 1997.
Personal: Downing College, Cambridge (1976) BA Law 1st class Hons, (1977) postgraduate LLB (now LLM), 1979 MA; 1976 elected to title of Scholar of Downing College, 1976 Harris Scholar, 1976 Pilley Scholar, 1977 Senior Harris Scholar, 1976 Rebecca Flowers Squire Scholar. Gray's Inn Holker Entrance Award (1978) and Gray's Inn Senior Holker Award (1979). Born 1954. Clients in this field include local authorities, major plcs, international joint ventures, governments and professionals from all the construction and engineering disciplines. Current instructions involve many of the largest Hong Kong airport core contracts, as well as nuclear processing plants and infrastructure projects.

BOURNE, Ian
3 Temple Gardens (Jonathan Goldberg QC) London (020) 7583 1155
Recommended in Crime

BOURNE-ARTON, Simon QC
Park Court Chambers (James Stewart QC & Robert Smith QC) Leeds (0113) 243 3277
Recommended in Crime
Specialisation: Fraud: In the last year defended in two cases brought by the SFO. Defended in R v Boid at Hull Crown Court, a case involving supply of unfit meat into the human food chain. Homicide: In particular cases involving joint enterprise. See R v Mitchell & King 163 JP75 CA.Other cases: R v Hedworth 1997 1 Cr.App.R.421; R v Klineberg 1999 1 Cr.App.R.427.
Prof. Memberships: C.B.A
Career: Called 1975; Recorder 1993; Q.C 1994.

BOWDERY, Martin QC
Atkin Chambers (Robert Akenhead QC) London (020) 7404 0102 /Emergency Tel: (020) 7242 4703
Recommended in Construction

BOWERS, John QC
Littleton Chambers (Michel Kallipetis QC) London (020) 7797 8600
franksbower@compuserve.com
Recommended in Employment
Specialisation: Employment law, pensions, judicial review, discrimination. Recent cases have included Associated British Ports v TGWU (injunctions to prevent national dock strike); McLaren v Home Office (role of judicial review in employment); News Group Newspapers Ltd v SOGAT and Others ('the Wapping cases'); Porter & Nanayakkara v Queens Medical Centre (dismissal of Consultant Paediatricians following Allitt murders); Saatchi & Saatchi plc v M. Saatchi and C. Saatchi and Others (garden leave case); Sibson v UK (application to European Court of Human Rights on remedies for disadvantages caused to employees who are not members of trade unions in 'closed shops'); Smith v UK (gay servicemen's case in European Court of Human Rights); Gibson v East Riding of Yorkshire Council (direct effect of Working Time Directive); De Keyser v Wilson (first EAT case on human rights).
Prof. Memberships: Chair of ELBA, member ALBA, ELA. Home Office Task Force on Human Rights; Bar Council Race Relations Committee; Legal adviser, Public Concern at Work; Coordinator of Workplace Mediation Services; member Standards Board of England.
Publications: Author of many publications including 'Bowers on Employment Law', 'Textbook of Labour Law', 'Transfer of Undertakings', 'Employment Tribunal Practice', 'The New Law Employment Law and Human Rights', 'The Employment Law Manual' (chapter on Tribunals) and 'Basic Procedure in Courts and Tribunals'. Atkins Court Form (Employment).

BOWES, Michael QC
2 King's Bench Walk London (020) 7353 1746
Recommended in Fraud
Specialisation: Criminal law, specialising in commercial fraud. Financial services regulatory work.
Prof. Memberships: Criminal Bar Association, Western Circuit.
Career: Called to the Bar in 1980. Joined 2 King's Bench Walk in 1996. Recorder (2000). Queen's Counsel (2001).
Personal: Educated at St George's College, Weybridge (1969-75), Manchester University (LL.B) 1976-79. Born on 22nd December 1956.

BOWRON, Margaret QC
1 Crown Office Row (Robert Seabrook QC) London (020) 7797 7500
Recommended in Clinical Negligence

BOWSHER, Michael
Monckton Chambers (John Swift QC) London (020) 7405 7211
mbowsher@monckton.co.uk
Recommended in Construction
Specialisation: Construction and computer law; international arbitration; European law, especially procurement and competition; environmental law.
Career: Qualified 1985; Middle Temple; tenant Keating Chambers 1986-01; now tenant at Monckton Chambers. Associate, based full-time in offices of *Cleary, Gottlieb, Steen & Hamilton* in Brussels 1988-92; member of editorial team 'Keating on Building Contracts'; Fellow of the Chartered Institute of Arbitrators Member of the Northern Ireland Bar. Involved in numerous procurement disputes, notably as junior counsel for the successful claimant in Harmon v House of Commons. Wide experience of international arbitration involving a variety of foreign laws. Most of his foreign arbitration experience has been for major non-UK contractors. Also active in a broad range of construction and technology matters in court, adjudication and arbitration, including judicial review and environmental disputes. For fuller details see website entry on www.monckton.co.uk.
Personal: Born 1963; Radley College; Brasenose College, Oxford (1984 BA Hons).

BOYCE, William QC
Hollis Whiteman Chambers (QEB) (Julian Bevan QC & Peter Whiteman QC) London (020) 7583 5766
Recommended in Crime, Fraud
Specialisation: Crime and linked regulatory and disciplinary proceedings – especially high profile, grave and complex criminal matters from homicide to serious fraud.
Prof. Memberships: Criminal Bar Association.
Career: Called to the Bar in 1976. Senior Treasury Counsel at the Central Criminal Court. Recorder.

BOYD, Stephen
29 Bedford Row Chambers (Peter Ralls QC) London (020) 7404 1044
sboyd@29bedfordrow.co.uk
Recommended in Sport
Specialisation: Postgraduate Certificate in Sports Law (Kings College, London); commercial, property and personal injury; acted for former world middle weight boxing champion.
Prof. Memberships: Bar Sports Law Group. British Association for Sport and Law. PNBA.
Career: Worked for international trading companies in Hong Kong and South Africa before commencing practice at the Bar.
Personal: Minchenden Grammar School, London N14. BSc (Hons) in Linguistics and International Studies (comprising Russian Swedish and Law), University of Surrey. Kung Fu, Pilates, Films. Married with children aged nine, seven and five.

BOYD, Stewart QC
Essex Court Chambers (Gordon Pollock QC) London (020) 7813 8000
Recommended in Arbitration (International)
Specialisation: Arbitration, banking, commodity contracts, company law and insolvency, competition and restrictive practices, construction, copyright, EEC law, employment, financial services, industrial relations, insurance and reinsurance, oil and gas, private international law, shipping and aviation. Has been appointed an arbitrator in numerous international commercial disputes in many fields, such as advertising, banking, commercial agency, computer software, construction, electricity generation and transmission, insurance and reinsurance, intellectual property, oil and gas, shipping.
Career: Trinity College, Cambridge: MA. Called to the Bar 1967. Queen's Counsel 1981.
Personal: Born 1943.

BOYDELL, Edward
Pump Court Chambers (Christopher Harvey Clark QC) Winchester (020) 73530711
epb@3pumpcourt.com
Recommended in Family
Specialisation: Family: Financial provision, equitable co-ownership, public and private children cases. Civil: Professional negligence concerning solicitors, predominantly as to matrimonial finance matters. Personal injury. Appeared in Hill v Hill [1998] 1 FLR 198, CA; [1997] 1 FLR 730.
Prof. Memberships: FLBA; Western Circuit; PNBA.
Career: Called 1989. Tenant at 3 Pump Court since 1990; Western Circuit London Junior; Qualified Teacher (1987).
Personal: B.Ed. (Hons) (Cantab). DIP. Law (PCL). Married with one son. Leisure interests include sport, theatre, travel.

BOYLE, Alan QC
Serle Court (Lord Neill of Bladen QC) London (020) 7242 6105
clerks@serlecourt.co.uk
Recommended in Chancery, Company, Insolvency/Corporate Recovery
Specialisation: Commercial and chancery litigation, financial services and entertainment. Case during the last year: Thyssen-Bornemisza v Thyssen-Bornemisza Trust-litigation in Bermuda (undue influence).
Prof. Memberships: Chancery Bar Association, Commerical Bar Association. Deputy High Court Judge.
Career: Royal Shrewsbury School, St Catherine's College Oxford (MA). Called to the Bar 1972. Silk 1991.
Publications: Editor and contributor, 'The Practice and Procedure of the Companies Court', Lloyds of London Press.
Personal: Married, two daughters.

BRADLEY, R
Oriel Chambers (A Sander) Liverpool (0151) 236 7191
Recommended in Employment
Specialisation: All aspects of employment law and discrimination. Personal injury. Professional negligence with emphasis on solicitors' and surveyors' negligence. Environmental law. Involved in a wide range of employment matters including Lunt v Merseyside TEC ltd [1999] ICR 17. Involved in both civil and criminal aspects of environmental law including Environmental Agency v Brock plc [1998] Env LR 607 and Environment Agency v Campbell [1999] Env LR 114.
Prof. Memberships: Northern Circuit Commercial Bar Association, Employment Law Bar Association, Tec Bar (northern branch).

Career: Called to the Bar in 1978 and joined present chambers in 1980.
Personal: Educated at King George V Grammar School, Southport and Reading University.

BRAITHWAITE, Bill QC
Exchange Chambers (David Turner QC & Bill Braithwaite QC & Henry Globe QC) Liverpool (0151) 236 7747
Recommended in Personal Injury
Specialisation: Personal injury litigation, including medical negligence, with a particular interest in injury to the brain and spine. The consultant editor of Kemp & Kemp on ' The Quantum of Damages'. Joint editor of 'Medical Aspects of Personal Injury Litigation' (1997).
Prof. Memberships: European Brain Injury Society; International Medical Society of Paraplegia; Spinal Injuries Association; Association of Personal Injury Lawyers; Headway.
Career: Called 1970, QC 1992.
Publications: 'Brain & Spine Injuries – The Fight for Justice'.
Personal: Gordonstoun School, Liverpool University. Class 1 Heavy Goods Vehicle Licence. Motor Racing Competition Licence.

BRAMWELL, Richard QC
3 Temple Gardens Tax Chambers (Richard Bramwell QC) London (020) 7353 7884
clerks@counsel.co.uk
Recommended in Tax
Specialisation: Principal areas of practice are corporate and personal tax planning and tax disputes. Recent litigation: (House of Lords) Redrow Group v Customs (High Court) – tax treatment of pre-payments held by finance lessor on a discontinuance; (Special Commissioners) – application of section 703 to a POS from a pension fund. Recent advisory work: finance leasing of Millennium projects; value-shifting and disposals under section 179(3); corporate film leasing partnerships; investment by means of Relevant Discounted Securities; Sch E consequences of holiday flights in company aircraft; complex private company demergers.
Career: Took Silk in 1989.
Publications: Co-author of 'Taxation of Companies and Company Reconstructions' (7th edn, 1998).

BRAND, Simon
Coleridge Chambers (Simon Brand) Birmingham (0121) 233 8500
Recommended in Crime

BRANNIGAN, Sean
4 Pump Court London (020) 7842 5555
sbrannigan@4pumpcourt.com
Recommended in Construction
Specialisation: Construction and civil engineering: acts for employers, contractors and professionals in a wide variety of disputes, including large international arbitrations. Very significant practice in relation to adjudication (where he has appeared in many of the reported cases) and mediation. Professional negligence: deals especially with cases involving allegations of negligence against valuers, engineers, accountants and solicitors. Instructed by many lending institutions, Professional Indemnity Insurers and the Solicitors Indemnity Fund. Media: acts for artists and management companies in relation to contractual and financial disputes.
Prof. Memberships: COMBAR, Technology and Construction Bar Association, London Common Law and Commercial Bar Association.
Career: BA (Oxon) in Jurisprudence. Called in 1994.

BRASSE, Gillian
14 Gray's Inn Square (Joanna Dodson QC) London (020) 7242 0858
clerks@14graysinnsquare.co.uk
Recommended in Family
Specialisation: Practice covers all aspects of family work including public and private law cases under the Children Act, wardship, adoption and child abduction, as well as ancillary relief matters, and Inheritance Act cases. Reported cases include O v Berkshire CC (Education Procedure) [1992] 2FLR7; Re B Contact [1994] 2FLR1; Re W (arrangements to place for adoption) [1995] 1 FLR 163; Conran v Conran [1997] 2 FLR 615 (Money – wife's contribution); Re J (adoption: appointment of Guardian ad Litem) [1999] 2 FU 86.
Prof. Memberships: Family Law Bar Association, Association of Lawyers for Children, committee member, Bar Benevolent Association.
Career: Called 1977. Appointed Deputy District Judge September 1995.
Personal: Educated at Varndean School for Girls, Brighton, and Liverpool University. Leisure pursuits include: travel, concerts, theatre, eating out, keep fit, my two daughters.

BREALEY, Mark
Brick Court Chambers (Christopher Clarke QC) London (020) 7379 3550
brealey@brickcourt.co.uk
Recommended in Competition/Anti-trust
Specialisation: European Community Law, UK Competition Law. Recently reported cases: Case C-296/95 R v Customs & Excise ex p EMU Tabac [1998] 3 WLR 298 ECJ; Easyjet v British Airways [1998] EuLR 350; Passmore v Morland [1999] 3 AII ER 1005 (CA); Matra Communications v Home Office[1999] 1 WLR 1646 (CA); Courage v Crehan, Times 14 June 1999 (CA); The Inntrepreneur Beer Supply Co v Byrne, Times 14 June 1999; Case T-110/98 RJB Mining v Commission, 9 September 1998. Case C-124/97 Laara, Times 21 September 1999; Plumber v Tibsco, Times 1 December 1999, Glaxo and others v Dowelhurst, [2000] EuLR 493: [2000] UKCLR 278 (Laddie J); Glaxo Group Ltd v Dowelhurst (No 2) [2000] FSR 529: The Times Law Reports 14 March 2000 (Laddie J); Case T-25/95 Blue Circle Industries v Commission 15 March 2000 (CFI); Severn Trent plc v Dwr Cymru (Welsh Water) 10 October 2000 (Lang ley J); R v Secretary of State for Industry ex parte One2One 21 December 2000 (Silber J); Dysan Magnetics v Customs & Excise [2001] EuLR 105 (VAT and Duties Tribunal); Case T-156/98 RJB Mining v Commission 31 January 2001 (CFI); Synstar Computer Service (UK) Ltd v ICL (Sorbus) Ltd The Times Law Reports May 1 2001 (Lightman J).
Prof. Memberships: Bar European Group – Committee.
Career: Called 1984.
Publications: Publications: co-author of 'Remedies in EC Law' (1998 Sweet & Maxwell); co-editor of Butterworths Encyclopedia on Competition Law; co-editor of 'Practitioners' Handbook of EC Law (1998 Bar Council); co-author of 'Civil Procedure The White Book Service' (section on references to the Court of Justice).
Personal: LLB, LLM, DEA.

BREEN, Carlo
9 St. John Street (John Hand QC) Manchester (0161) 955 9000
clerks@9stjohnstreet.co.uk
Recommended in Employment
Specialisation: Practises exclusively in employment law and has very wide experience of Tribunal work including unfair dismissal and breach of contract applications, group redundancy applications and transfer of undertakings. He has extensive experience of advising/drafting work and advocacy. He regularly appears in the Employment Tribunal, the Employment Appeal Tribunal and the High Court and is highly regarded amongst the Judiciary and Chairman of Employment Tribunals. He has a particular interest in disability discrimination, maternity rights and the Working Time Regulations. His specialist interest led to him gaining a Masters Degree from Queensland University in Australia where he completed a thesis on Civil Rights from a European perspective. He has acted for a variety of public institutions including various National Health Trust Hospitals throughout the country and numerous local authorities. He has conducted many multi-party actions involving equal pay cases and has handled cases with as many as 5000 employees involving issues on the Transfer of Undertakings Regulations and the Working Time Regulations. He has also acted for and against the Chief Constable of various constabularies in very serious sex discrimination and race discrimination cases. He is not averse to conducting these cases unassisted by Leading Counsel and frequently appears against eminent Leading Counsel in the employment law field in these and other cases. He is approved by the Commission for Racial Equality and the Equal Opportunities Commission to act in these discrimination cases. In addition, he acted for numerous applicants in the Armed Forces pregnancy dismissal litigation conducted in Industrial Tribunals across the United Kingdom in 1994 and 1995. He is a frequent speaker on employment law and is highly committed to providing the best possible service for his clients whilst still maintaining a personal and professional approach.
Prof. Memberships: Employment Law Bar Association, Employment Lawyers Association, Personal Injury Bar Association, Professional Negligence Bar Association.
Career: LLB Hons, MA, Queensland University. Called to the Bar of Queensland, Australia, 1993. Called to the Bar (Middle Temple), 1987.

BRENNAN, Lord QC
Matrix Chambers (Nicholas Blake QC) London (020) 7404 3447
danbrennan@matrixlaw.co.uk
Recommended in Clinical Negligence, Environment, Personal Injury, Product Liability

BRENNAN, Timothy QC
Devereux Chambers (Jeffrey Burke QC) London (020) 7353 7534
Recommended in Employment, Tax

BRENNAND, Timothy
Manchester House Chambers (J.D.S. Wishart) Manchester (0161) 834 7007
Recommended in Crime

BRENTON, Timothy QC
7 King's Bench Walk (Jeremy Cooke QC) London (020) 7910 8300
clerks@7kbw.law.co.uk
Recommended in Arbitration (International), Shipping
Specialisation: Principal areas of practice are shipping, international trade, commercial contracts, insurance (marine and non-marine) and reinsurance, sale and carriage of goods (international and domestic) and commercial fraud. Appointed QC 1998.
Prof. Memberships: COMBAR, supporting member of London Maritime Arbitration Association.
Career: Royal Navy 1975-79. Lecturer in law at King's College, London 1979-80. Called to the Bar 1981 and joined 4 Essex Court. Moved to 7 King's Bench walk in 2001.
Personal: Educated at King's School, Rochester to 1975; Bristol University 1976-79 (LLB) and Bar School 1980-81. Born 4th November 1957.

BRETTEN, Rex QC
24 Old Buildings (Rex Bretten QC) London (020) 7242 2744
taxchambers@compuserve.com
Recommended in Tax
Specialisation: All aspects of United Kingdom taxation, with special emphasis on multi-national corporate work, the interaction of United Kingdom and foreign taxes, and the operation of double taxation treaties; tax litigation.

Prof. Memberships: Revenue Bar Association.
Career: Commenced practice at the Bar in 1971. Appointed Queen's Counsel in 1980. Appointed a Bencher of Lincoln's Inn in 1989.

BRIDEN, Timothy J
8 Stone Buildings (John M. Cherry QC) London (020) 7831 9881
barristers@8stonebuildings.co.uk
Recommended in Church
Specialisation: Principal area of practice is ecclesiastical law. Editor, 'Macmorran's Handbook for Churchwardens and Parochial Church Councillors' and 'Moore's Introduction to English Canon Law'. Also handles personal injury and health & safety cases.
Prof. Memberships: Inner Temple, Ecclesiastical Law Society.
Career: Called to the Bar 1976; joined 1 Temple Gardens 1977 and moved to 8 Stone Buildings 1996. Appointed Chancellor of the Diocese of Bath and Wells 1993 and Chancellor of the Diocese of Truro 1998. Secretary of Ecclesiastical Judges Association since 1996.
Personal: Educated at Ipswich School 1958-70 and Downing College Cambridge (BA 1974; LL.B 1975; MA 1978). Born 29 October 1951. Lives in South London.

BRIGGS, John
3-4 South Square (Michael Crystal QC & Lord Alexander of Weedon QC) London (020) 7696 9900
clerks@southsquare.com
Recommended in Insolvency/Corporate Recovery
Specialisation: All personal and corporate insolvency related work, including representing insolvency practitioners before Recognised Professional Bodies and Insolvency Practitioners Tribunal.
Prof. Memberships: Insolvency Lawyers' Association. British Italian Law Association (Committee Member). COMBAR. Chancery Bar Association.
Career: LLB (London). Ex Du Doc d'Univ (Nancy, France). 1973: Called to the Bar. 1973-75: Jurist Linguist, European Court of Justice. Deputy Bankruptcy Registrar of the High Court.
Publications: Joint Senior Author, 'Muir Hunter on Personal Insolvency' (Stevens, 1987). Joint Author, 'Asset Protection Trusts' (Keyhaven, 1997). Consultant Editor of 'Bankruptcy and Personal Insolvency Reports' (Jordans, 1996-date).

BRIGGS, Michael QC
Serle Court (Lord Neill of Bladen QC) London (020) 7242 6105
clerks@serlecourt.co.uk
Recommended in Chancery, Commercial (Litigation), Company, Financial Services, Fraud, Insolvency/Corporate Recovery, Partnership, Professional Negligence
Specialisation: Main fields of chancery and commercial litigation including corporate insolvency, property, commercial fraud, professional negligence and regulation and partnership disputes.
Prof. Memberships: Commercial Bar Association; Chancery Bar Association; Association of Partnership Practitioners; Association of Contentious Trust and Probate Specialists.
Career: Called to Bar in 1978, Lincolns Inn. Pupil to Patrick Talbot and John Jarvis. Joined Serle Court in 1979. One of the junior counsel to the Crown, Chancery (1990-94). Took Silk in 1994.
Personal: Married with four children. Leisure activities include sailing, solo and choral singing, member of Bar Yacht Club and Emsworth sailing club.

BRIGGS, Nicholas
Guildhall Chambers (Adrian Palmer QC) Bristol (0117) 927 3366
Recommended in Insolvency/Corporate Recovery
Specialisation: Insolvency: bankruptcy; directors' disqualification; shareholder disputes; corporate insolvency. Commercial litigation: contractual disputes. Banking litigation: enforcement of securities; bank payments. Recent cases: Re Purvis [1997] 3 A11ER 663; Royal Bank of Scotland v Etridge no 2 [1998] 4 A11ER 705 (on appeal to the House of Lords)
Prof. Memberships: Chancery Bar Association; R3.
Career: Former Royal Marine; called to Bar 1994 (Lincoln's Inn); appointed Junior Counsel to the Crown Jan 2000.

BRIGHT, Andrew QC
9 Bedford Row (formerly 4 Brick Court) (Anthony C. Berry QC) London (020) 7489 2727
clerks@9bedford row.co.uk
Recommended in Crime
Specialisation: Specialist Criminal Silk. Regularly appears in cases of murder, child abuse, serious sexual offences, drug trafficking and fraud in London and the Midlands. Notable cases have included R v Grantham, the leading case on fraudulent trading, numerous solicitor, mortgage and VAT frauds lasting 3 months or more and the last two spy cases of the Cold War. Computer literate and likes to produce his own schedules and graphics for use in court.
Prof. Memberships: The Criminal Bar Association (Co-opted to the committee 1993-95).
Career: Called to the Bar 1973. Recorder, South Eastern Circuit.
Personal: Educated at Wells Cathedral School and University College, London. Lives in Hertfordshire with his wife and four children.

BRIGHT, Christopher
3 Fountain Court (Robert Juckes QC) Birmingham (0121) 236 5854
chris.bright@3fc.co.uk
Recommended in Clinical Negligence
Specialisation: All aspects of clinical negligence. Over 80 per cent of Chris Bright's work consists of clinical negligence litigation, handling cases of moderate valuation to severe damage claims in excess of £4 million. An award of £4.55 million in November 1999 was said by the Treasury and NHSLA to be the largest to that date in a clinical negligence claim.
Prof. Memberships: AVMA/APIL. Birmingham Medico-Legal Society.
Career: Durham University BA Hons. Malcolm Hilberry Award, Gray's Inn. Medical Negligence Litigation Pilot Group, Birmingham. Lecturer upon AVMA regional and national courses and to health service professionals/clinicians.
Personal: Interests: Tuscany and Gloucester RFC.

BRINDLE, Michael QC
Fountain Court (Anthony Boswood QC) London (020) 7583 3335
Recommended in Banking, Commercial (Litigation), Financial Services, Fraud, Professional Negligence
Specialisation: Practice encompasses a variety of work in the commercial and corporate sphere as well as employment law. Emphasis is on banking and financial services, company law, professional negligence in financial and commercial matters, insurance and international trade. Experienced in city related matters, including litigation arising out of audits, take-overs and rights issues. Practises in chancery as well as commercial and common law courts. Important cases include Caparo v Dickman [1989] (auditors' negligence); Morgan Crucible v Hill Samuel [1990] (merchant banker's and auditor's negligence and take-over code); G & H Montage v Irvani [1990] (bills of exchange); Deposit Protection Board v Dalia [1993] (depositor compensation); Shah v Bank of England [1994] (banking supervision); Camdex v Bank of Zambia [1997] (liabilities of central banks); BCCI v Price Waterhouse [1997] (Banking Act 1987); Nuova Safim v Sakura Bank [1998] (ISDA standard agreement); Barclays Bank v Boulter [1999] (banking and securities) and Marks & Spencer Plc v Baird [2001] (contractual certainty). Author of journal articles and of 'Law of Bank Payments' [1999] (with Raymond Cox).
Prof. Memberships: Midland & Oxford Circuit.
Career: Called to the Bar in 1975 and joined Fountain Court Chambers in 1976. Took silk in 1992. Recorder since 2000. Chairman of Commercial Bar Association.
Personal: Educated at Westminster School 1965-69 and New College, Oxford (double first in classics and jurisprudence). Chairman of Trustees: Public Concern at Work. Member of Financial Reporting Review Panel. Born 23rd June 1952. Lives in London.

BRISBY, John QC
4 Stone Buildings (Philip Heslop QC) London (020) 7242 5524
clerks@4stonebuildings.law.co.uk
Recommended in Chancery, Company, Financial Services, Fraud, Insolvency/Corporate Recovery
Specialisation: Litigation and advice in the fields of company law, corporate insolvency and financial services. Emphasis on heavy corporate litigation, mainly in the Chancery Division and Court of Appeal. Cases: Instructed in a number of actions resulting out of the Maxwell affair with a view to locating and recovering assets on behalf of the Maxwell pensioners, and in other high profile fraud or asset recovery situations such as DPR Futures, Barlow Clowes and BCCI. Has also acted for and against various regulatory bodies such as SIB, IMRO and LAUTRO. Has appeared in well over 80 reported cases, well-known examples being Re Cloverbay [1991] Ch 90, Re Bishopsgate Investment Management [1993] Ch 1 Re British & Commonwealth Holdings plc [1993] AC 426, Ispahani v Bank Melli Iran [1998] Lloyds Rep 133, Morris v Bank of America National Trust & Others [2000] 1 AER 954, Sasea Finance Ltd v KPMG [2000] 1AER 676, UPC v Deutsche Bank AG, Court of Appeal, 19th May 2000, Re Barings plc, the Vice Chancellor, 18th June 2000.
Prof. Memberships: Member of the Commercial Bar Association (COMBAR) and Chancery Bar Association.
Career: Call 1978. QC 1996.
Publications: Former Contributor: 'Encyclopaedia of Forms and Precedents' (4th edn) Vol 9 Companies.
Personal: Educated at Westminster School 1969-73 and Scholar of Christ Church, Oxford 1974-77. Born 8th May 1956. Lives in London and Northamptonshire.

BRISCOE, Constance
9-12 Bell Yard (D. Anthony Evans QC) London (020) 7400 1800
clerks@bellyard.co.uk
Recommended in Crime
Specialisation: Crime; organised crime, white collar crime. Special interest mental health and juvenile offenders.
Career: Recorder 1996; Arbitrator 2000 crime, civil, family. President MHRT 1994.

BROCK, Jonathan QC
Falcon Chambers (Jonathan Gaunt QC & Kim Lewison QC) London (020) 7353 2484
Recommended in Agriculture, Property Litigation
Specialisation: Commercial property litigation and advice; overseas work particularly in commonwealth jurisdictions; has appeared in Jamaica, Brunei, Jordan, Bermuda etc; agriculture; arbitration; ecclesiastical law. Recent cases include Oliver Ashworth v Ballard [1999] 2 AER 791; Nurdin & Peacock v Ramsden [1999] 1 AER 941; National Grid v M25 Group [1999] 1 EGLR 65; Inntrepreneur v Crehan [1999] The Times 14 June; Sight and Sound v Books Etc [1999] 3 EGLR 45; Chaffe v Kingsley [2000] 1 EGLR 104; Inntrepeneur v Langton [2000] 8 EGLR 34; Amec v Jury's Hotel [2001] 7 EG 163.
Prof. Memberships: Vice-chairman London Common Law and Commercial Bar Association; member Bar Council 1992-98; past chairman Commonwealth Sub-committee; member Court of Appeal Users Committee; Bar permanent representative UK Inter-Professional Group; chairman working party on Bar Joint Arbitration Scheme; Western Circuit; member Chancery Bar Association.
Career: St Pauls School; Corpus Christi College, Cambridge; called 1977; Silk 1997; fellow Chartered Institute

of Arbitrators; Recorder; editor 'Woodfall on Landlord and Tenant'; Blundell Lecturer 1992 and 1998.
Personal: Married with five children. Lives in London and Devon. Captain Snakepit Strollers FC.

BRODIE, Bruce
39 Essex Street (Nigel Pleming QC) London
(020) 7832 1111
bb@39essex.co.uk
Recommended in Alternative Dispute Resolution
Specialisation: Practises as arbitrator and advocate in arbitration with emphasis on international commercial disputes. Also serves as mediator (CEDR accredited mediator). Before transfer to Bar in 1993 was *Frere Cholmeley* senior litigation partner.
Personal: Called 1993.

BROMILOW, Richard
St John's Chambers (Christopher Sharp QC)
Bristol (0117) 921 3456
clerks@stjohnschambers.co.uk
Recommended in Family
Specialisation: Matrimonial finance cases including applications by children under the Children Act 1989.
Prof. Memberships: FLBA, PIBA.
Career: Southampton University, Grays Inn. Recorder.
Personal: Leisure interests include golf, cricket.

BROMLEY-MARTIN, Michael
3 Raymond Buildings (Clive Nicholls QC) London
(020) 7400 6400
chambers@3raymondbuildings.com
Recommended in Fraud, Licensing
Specialisation: Criminal Law, including extradition and mutual assistance. Particularly commercial and investment fraud, both prosecuting and defending. Notable cases include Blue Arrow, BCCI, Norton, Landhurst Leasing, Facia Group, Bhutto/Zardari and advising in Nissan and Maxwell. Police Discipline, Inquests, Food Safety, Health and Safety, Trade Descriptions. All forms of Licensing, including liquor, public entertainment, betting, gaming and lotteries.
Career: Call 1979. Department of Trade and Industry Inspector 1989, 1990. Advisor to the Police Complaints Authority 1996.

BROOKE, Michael QC
Four New Square (Justin Fenwick QC) London
(020) 7822 2000
barristers@4newsquare.com
Recommended in Clinical Negligence
Specialisation: Clinical negligence; product liability; NHS Tribunals; cases with French connections; HIV haemophiliac litigation; Ratcliffe v E Devon HA (1998) 4 Lloyd's Rep Med 162; Roberts v Winbow (1998) 2 Lloyds Rep Med 31; Bristol Royal Infirmary Inquiry; Hepatitis Litigation (2001) 5 Lloyds Rep Med 187.
Prof. Memberships: PNBA, BEG, PIBA, COMBAR, LCCLBA, UIA.
Career: Called 1968. Silk 1994. Assistant Recorder 1997. Recorder 2000. Admitted to Paris Bar 1987. Member SE Circuit.
Personal: Lycée Français de Londres; LLB (Edin).

BROUGHAM, Christopher QC
3-4 South Square (Michael Crystal QC & Lord Alexander of Weedon QC) London
(020) 7696 9900
christopherbrougham@southsquare.com
Recommended in Insolvency/Corporate Recovery
Specialisation: Insolvency, individual and corporate – matrimonial financial provision/insolvency – litigation arising out of insolvencies (security disputes, disqualification of directors, professional negligence etc). Krasner v Dennison [2001] Ch 76, CA.
Prof. Memberships: ILA, ChBA, FLBA, COMBAR.
Career: 1969: called to the Bar (IT). 1984-date: Deputy Bankruptcy Registrar. 1988: Appointed Queen's Counsel. 1990-91: Inspector appointed under Companies Act 1985 s.432(2) to investigate the affairs of BOM Holdings plc.
Publications: Joint senior author of 'Muir Hunter on Personal Insolvency' (Sweet & Maxwell). Author of Personal Insolvency chapter of 'Encyclopedia of Financial Provision in Family Matters' (Sweet & Maxwell)
Personal: BA (Jurisprudence) Worcester College, Oxford. Music; crossword puzzles (solving and setting); theatre. Married with a family.

BROWN, Charles
39 Essex Street (Nigel Pleming QC) London
(020) 7832 1111
Recommended in Personal Injury
Specialisation: Personal injuries, clinical negligence.

BROWN, Damian
Old Square Chambers (John Hendy QC) London
(020) 7269 0300
dbrown@oldsquarechambers.co.uk
Recommended in Employment
Specialisation: Leading cases: UCLH NHS Trust v Unison [1999] 204; Bowden v Tuffnells Parcel Express Ltd [2000] IRLR 560; Greaves v Kwiksave [1998] IRLR 245; PLA v Payne [1994] IRLR9. All employment areas: discrimination, restraint of trade, wrongful dismissal, trade union law and strikes. International labour law (including EU and ILO) and human rights.
Prof. Memberships: Employment Law Bar Association; Industrial Law Society; Employment Lawyers Association; Haldane Society.
Career: Called to Bar 1989.
Publications: Tolleys 'Employment Law' – contributor; 'Employment Tribunal Practice and Procedure' – co-author; 'Employment Law Precedents' – co-author (Gee); numerous pamphlets. Editor 'UK and EU Employee Consultation' (Sweet & Maxwell) 2000.
Personal: Interests include politics, trade union history, Arsenal Football Club and cinema.

BROWN, Geoffrey B.
39 Essex Street (Nigel Pleming QC) London
(020) 7832 1111
Recommended in Personal Injury
Specialisation: Personal injury and related work (including health insurance, clinical negligence and health and safety). Property damage claims (including fire, subsidence, crop and livestock claims, etc). Professional negligence. Insurance and general commercial work.
Career: MA Cantab.

BROWN, Hannah
One Essex Court (Lord Grabiner QC) London
(020) 7583 2000
Recommended in Banking
Specialisation: Principal areas of practice are banking law and general commercial litigation including aviation finance, insurance and reinsurance.

BROWN, Paul
4-5 Gray's Inn Square (Elizabeth Appleby QC & David Mole QC) London (020) 7404 5252
Recommended in Local Government
Specialisation: Town and country planning, environmental law, education law, local government and employment.
Prof. Memberships: PEBA, ALBA, COMBAR, ELBA.
Career: Called to the Bar 1991. LL.B (Hons) (NZ) Ph.D (Cantab). Appointed to the Treasury 'B' Panel (1999).

BROWN, Stephanie
5 Fountain Court (Anthony Barker QC)
Birmingham (0121) 606 0500
Recommended in Family

BROWNE, Benjamin QC
2 Temple Gardens (Dermod O'Brien QC) London
(020) 7822 1200
Recommended in Clinical Negligence, Personal Injury
Specialisation: Personal injury, including many paraplegic, tetraplegic and brain damage claims. Disaster litigation, including Clapham Disaster and M1 air crash, clinical negligence. Professional negligence, especially construction-related (engineers/architects) but also barristers, solicitors, surveyors, valuers, insurance brokers etc. Insurance and insurance related litigation. Product liability.
Career: Christ Church, Oxford. MA Jurisprudence.
Personal: Country and family pursuits, gardening.

BROWNE, Desmond QC
5 Raymond Buildings (Patrick Milmo QC) London
(020) 7242 2902
Recommended in Defamation
Specialisation: Defamation and media law. Recent reported cases Loutchansky v Times Newspapers: CA: 3 April 2001: (ambit of Reynolds qualified privilege); Wagstaff v Health Secretary: DC: (2001) 1 WLR 292: (public inquiry into the Shipman deaths); Ashworth Hospital v MGN: CA: (2001) 1 WLR 515: (journalistic confidentiality); Venables v News Group: (2001) 2 WLR 1038: (privacy injunction in Bulger case); Berezovsky v Michaels: HL: (2000) 1 WLR 1004: (forum conveniens in claim on foreign publication); Hamilton v Fayed: HL: (2000) 2 WLR 609: (libel and parliamentary privilege); Nicholls v BBC: CA: (1999) EMLR 791: (privacy in identity of supergrass); Shah v Standard Chartered Bank: CA: (1999) QB 241: (repetition rule); Watts v Times Newspapers: CA: (1997) QB 650: (qualified privilege for solicitors); Elton John v MGN: CA: (1997) QB 586: (quantum and exemplary damages); Barrymore v News Group: (1997) FSR 600: (kiss and tell injunction). Also acted for successful Defendants in Graham v Rechem (a 15 month toxic nuisance action).
Prof. Memberships: Western Circuit.
Career: Called to the Bar 1969. Legal correspondent for 'British Medical Journal' 1970-79. Silk 1990. Recorder 1994.
Personal: Educated: Eton and New College, Oxford (Scholar). Born 5th April 1947.

BROWNE-WILKINSON, Simon QC
Serle Court (Lord Neill of Bladen QC) London
(020) 7242 6105
clerks@serlecourt.co.uk
Recommended in Fraud
Specialisation: Has a general commercial practice, including shipping, banking, insurance, employment, professional negligence and fraud.
Prof. Memberships: COMBAR
Career: Called to the Bar in 1981. QC 1998
Personal: Educated at Oxford University. Born in August 1957.

BRUDENELL, Thomas
Queen Elizabeth Building (Florence Baron QC)
London (020) 7797 7837
Recommended in Family
Specialisation: Principal areas of practice are family law and equine litigation.
Prof. Memberships: Family Law Bar Association.
Career: Called to the Bar 1977 and joined current chambers in 1978.
Personal: Educated at Eton College 1969-74. Born 12 August 1956. Lives in London.

BRYAN, Simon
Essex Court Chambers (Gordon Pollock QC)
London (020) 7813 8000
clerksroom@essexcourt-chambers.co.uk
Recommended in Energy & Natural Resources, Insurance
Specialisation: Specialist in insurance and reinsurance, shipping, professional negligence litigation, energy and utility litigation, computer litigation and all aspects of commercial law and arbitration. Has experience acting for Lloyd's syndicates, members and managing agents, in the context of litigation and Lloyd's inquiries and disciplinary proceedings.
Prof. Memberships: Commercial Bar Association, supporting member LMAA.

Career: Educated at Arnold School and at Magdalene College, Cambridge (1st Class Hons). Born November 1965.
Publications: Assistant editor, 'Encyclopedia of International Commercial Litigation'.
Personal: Called to the Bar 1988.

BRYANT, Judith
Wilberforce Chambers (Edward Nugee QC) London (020) 7306 0102
Recommended in Chancery
Specialisation: Practice covers a wide range of advisory and litigation work in chancery/commercial matters, with particular emphasis on: trusts and their taxation, including advice on the creation and administration of trusts, the duties of trustees and breaches of trust, contentious trust matters, conflicts of laws, the variation of trusts, and the drafting of trust deeds and related instruments; pension schemes, including advice in relation to the construction of trust deeds and rules of pension schemes, the duties of pension scheme trustees and breaches of those duties, applications to Court in relation to pension schemes, and complaints to the Pensions Ombudsman; wills and probate, including advice on the construction of wills, conflicts of laws, the variation of wills, the administration of estates, the duties of executors, and contentious probate matters; professional negligence relating to trusts and pension schemes.
Prof. Memberships: Society of Trust and Estate Practitioners (STEP) and Chancery Bar Association.
Career: Called to the Bar: 1987. Jesus College, Cambridge 1982-86. BA 1st Class Hons (1985), LLM (1986).

BRYANT-HERON, Mark
9-12 Bell Yard (D. Anthony Evans QC) London (020) 7400 1800
clerks@bellyard.co.uk
Recommended in Crime
Specialisation: Specialist in criminal law. Practice is evenly divided between prosecution and defence work with an emphasis on fraud and Customs & Excise cases. Instructed as leading junior in defence work and in the prosecution of serious drug trafficking and VAT fraud. Specialist in telecommunications fraud.
Prof. Memberships: Criminal Bar Association, South Eastern Circuit.
Career: Called to the Bar in 1986.
Personal: Educated at Cambridge University 1981-84.

BUBB, Tim
39 Park Square (Tim Bubb) Leeds (0113) 245 6633
Recommended in Crime

BUCHAN, Andrew
Cloisters (Laura Cox QC) London (020) 7827 4000
abu@cloisters.com
Recommended in Personal Injury
Specialisation: Serious personal injury cases involving mental health issues. In particular stress and bullying at work. Brain damage. Clinical negligence. Professional negligence work in these fields. Employment law discrimination cases involving psychiatric injury. Has a special interest in mental health law. Recent reported cases include Walker v Northumberland County Council (first successful stress induced breakdown (second) caused by work case); Sheriff v Klyne Tugs Lowestoft Ltd CA (jurisdiction of the employment tribunal for personal injury cases), Waters v Metropolitan Police Commissioner HL (duty of care of police for bullying within the force); Long v Mercury Mobile Communications (successful first breakdown claim for bullying: award of £327, 500).
Prof. Memberships: PIBA; PNBA; ELBA; APIL; AVMA; Inquest; ILSoc; accredited mediator with CEDR.
Career: Called to the Bar 1981.
Publications: 'Personal Injury Practice and Procedure the Guide to Litigation in the County Court and High Court' (2000) Butterworths 3rd edn. Co-author of the chapter on Psychological Injuries for Munkman, 'Employers Liability', 2001 in print, Butterworths. Article, Stress: Forseeability and Breach, 'JPIL', March 2001
Personal: Born 6 December 1956.

BUCHANAN, Vivien
St. Mary's Chambers Family Law Chambers (Christopher M. Butler) Nottingham (0115) 950 3503
Recommended in Family

BUCKNALL, Belinda QC
4 Essex Court (Nigel Teare QC) London (020) 7653 5653
bbucknall@4sx.co.uk
Recommended in Arbitration (International), Shipping
Specialisation: Admiralty practitioner specialising in marine insurance (hull and yacht); collision; salvage; maritime pollution; dry shipping work; PI; fatal accident claims (arising from shipboard incidents). Also land based building and construction disputes and air law (in particular limitation of liability).
Prof. Memberships: Western Circuit; Combar.
Career: Education: The School of St. Helen and St. Katherine (Abingdon); Oxford University (MA). Appointments: QC – 1988; Lloyd's panel of Salvage Arbitrators; Master of Middle Temple – 1996; Recorder – 1997. Deputy High Court Judge. Languages: French and Italian.
Personal: A longstanding interest in the RNLI. Ice skating and canoeing.

BUDDEN, Caroline
One King's Bench Walk (Anthony Hacking QC) London (020) 7936 1500
Recommended in Family
Specialisation: Principal area of practice is family law, including public and private law aspects of the Children Act, adoption, wardship and related social services law, child abduction. South Eastern Circuit. Cases of interest include: Re V (Jurisdiction: Habitual Residence) [2001] 1 FLR 253; Re H (minors) (Care proceedings: Intervenor) [2000] 1 FLR 775; Re G (interim care order) [1992] 2FLR 839 CA; Re H (a minor) (parental responsiblity) [1993] 1FLR 484 CA; Re W (a minor) [1992] 3WLR 758 CA (medical treatment of an anorexic teenager/court's jurisdiction); Re C (adoption by relative) [1989] 1 WLR 61 CA; R v North Yorkshire CC ex p. M [1988] 3WLR 1344 (judicial review of local authority's conduct in care proceedings).
Prof. Memberships: Family Law Bar Association, Professional Negligence Bar Association.
Career: Called to the Bar 1977. Assistant Recorder 1998. Recorder 2000.
Personal: Educated at Alfred Colfox School, Bridport, Dorset, and Bristol University (LL.B 1976). Born 30 July 1954. Lives in London.

BULL, Gregory
30 Park Place (John Jenkins QC) Cardiff (029) 2039 8421
Recommended in Crime

BULLOCK, Ian
St John's Chambers (Christopher Sharp QC) Bristol (0117) 921 3456
clerks@stjohnschambers.co.uk
Recommended in Personal Injury
Specialisation: Employers' liability. General common law. Clinical negligence. Health and safety prosecutions.
Prof. Memberships: PIBA.

BURBIDGE, James
St Philip's Chambers (John Randall QC) Birmingham (0121) 246 7000
Recommended in Crime

BURDEN, Susan
6 Pump Court London (020) 7583 6013
clerks@6pumpcourt.law.co.uk
Recommended in Clinical Negligence
Specialisation: General personal injury work, medical/dental negligence (including high value birth trauma cases) for claimants and defendants; disciplinary hearings. Drafted British Medical Association's green paper response on 'Competition'. Lectures given: IBC/Hempsons' 'Reducing NHS Medical Negligence Liabilities'; Euroforums's 'Claims by Injured Children', 'IBC's Cerebral Palsy Claims', CLT's 'Clinical Negligence Update' (March 2000); chaired Euroforum's 'Spinal Injuries'. Instructed in benzodiazepine litigation. Cases reported Scott v Bloomsbury HA [1990] 1MedLR 214; Walker v Huntingdon HA [1994] 5 MedLR 356, Nawoor v Barking Havering and Brentwood Health Authority [1998] Lloyd's Rep. Med. 313.
Prof. Memberships: Bar Professional Negligence Association.
Career: Guildford County School for Girls, Charterhouse, New College Oxford BA. Hons (Jurisprudence) 1984; MA.
Personal: Born 15 July 1961. Opera, singing.

BURGESS, Edward
St John's Chambers (Christopher Sharp QC) Bristol (0117) 921 3456
Recommended in Crime

BURKE, Jeffrey QC
Devereux Chambers (Jeffrey Burke QC) London (020) 7353 7534
Recommended in Employment, Personal Injury

BURKE, Trevor QC
2 Bedford Row (William Clegg QC) London (020) 7440 8888
Recommended in Crime
Specialisation: Has previously successfully defended John Fashanu in the football corruption trial. Sol Campbell on an alleged assault. Nigel Benn on a serious assault. Terry Marsh on a student grant fraud and The Taylor Sisters. Also defended Gary Glitter. Extensive experience in defending white collar fraud, recently defended Dr Padelis in a large fraud on the NHS. Also undertakes Consumer Protection/Trade description work, particularly experienced representing Solicitors before the OSS.
Prof. Memberships: CBA, Member of South Eastern Circuit.

BURKILL, Guy
Three New Square (David Young QC) London (020) 7405 1111
Recommended in Information Technology, Intellectual Property
Specialisation: All intellectual property aspects, mainly patent with particular interest in computer hardware and software and electronics. Has acted for many leading multinational companies in the computer, electronics, paper, chemical, pharmaceutical, aviation and other fields. Notable cases include Pavel v Sony (Walkman case); Lubrizol v Exxon (oil additives); Hoechst v British Petroleum (chemical manufacture, account of profits); Discovision v Disctronics (compact disc mastering); Texas Instruments v Hyundai (integrated circuitry); Dyson v Hoover (vacuum cleaners, post expiry injunction).
Prof. Memberships: Intellectual Property Bar Association; Chancery Bar Association.
Career: Winchester College; Corpus Christi College Cambridge – MA Degree, 1st Class Hons in Engineering (Electrical Option); called to Bar 1981.
Publications: Co-author of 'Terrell on the Law of Patents' (15th edition)
Personal: Leisure interests include music, opera and travel.

BURNETT, Ian QC
1 Temple Gardens (Hugh Carlisle QC) London (020) 7583 0808
clerks@1templegardens.co.uk
Recommended in Health & Safety, Personal Injury
Specialisation: Public law, coroners, health and safety, professional negligence, personal injury. Public inquiries (King's Cross, Clapham Junction, Guildford Four, Bloody Sunday, Southall Rail). Representative cases: R v Associated Octel (HL) [1996] 1 WLR 1543; Boddington v British Transport Police (HL) [1999] 2 AC 143; R v Home Secre-

tary ex p Daly (HL) [2001] 2 WLR 1622; R v North London Coroner ex p Touche (CA) [2001] 2 ALLER 752; R v Home Secretary ex p Saleem (CA) [2001] IWLR 443.
Prof. Memberships: ALBA, PIBA.
Career: MA (Oxon). Called MT 1980. Junior Counsel to the Crown (Common Law) 1992-98; QC 1998. Recorder.

BURR, Andrew
Atkin Chambers (Robert Akenhead QC) London (020) 7404 0102
clerks@atkinchambers.law.co.uk
Recommended in Construction
Specialisation: Practises primarily in domestic and international construction and technology disputes. Acts as advocate in litigation and arbitration and in an advisory capacity regarding ADR. Experienced in all aspects of construction and technology law and professional negligence, particularly of architects, engineers and surveyors. General and articles editor 'Construction Law Journal' (Sweet and Maxwell).
Prof. Memberships: ACI Arb. (Committee member European Branch), ABA international associate, Swiss Arbitration Association, TECBAR, COMBAR, BILA.
Career: Called November 1981. Joined chambers in 1983. Speaks Italian and French.
Personal: Educated at Barclay School, Stevenage and Trinity Hall, Cambridge. Lives in London.

BURTON, Frank QC
12 King's Bench Walk (Richard Methuen QC) London (020) 7583 0811
Recommended in Personal Injury
Specialisation: Principal area of practice is personal injury work with an emphasis on industrial diseases and medical negligence.
Prof. Memberships: Personal Injury Bar Association, Member of Executive.
Career: University lecturer 1974-83. Called to the Bar and joined present chambers 1982. QC 1998. 1999 Assistant Recorder, Recorder 2000.
Publications: Co-author of 'Medical Negligence Case Law' and 'Personal Injury Limitation Law', both published by Butterworths. Author on medical practitioners chapter in Butterworths Professional Negligence Service.
Personal: BA Hons 1st Class and PhD. Born 19th June 1950. Lives in London.

BUSH, Rosalind
5 Fountain Court (Anthony Barker QC) Birmingham (0121) 606 0500
Recommended in Family

BUTCHER, Christopher QC
7 King's Bench Walk (Jeremy Cooke QC) London (020) 7910 8300
clerks@7kbw.law.co.uk
Recommended in Arbitration (International), Banking, Commercial (Litigation), Insurance, Professional Negligence, Shipping
Specialisation: Insurance and reinsurance, commercial agreements, banking, agency, shipping, international trade, arbitration, and professional negligence.
Career: Called to the Bar 1986. Took Silk 2001. Recent cases include: Vale de Rio v Bao Steel [2000] 2 Lloyd's Rep (arbitration – jurisdiction); HIH Casualty v Chase Manhattan Bank [2001] Lloyd's Rep. IR 191 (insurance, duty of brokers). Barings Plc v Coopers & Lybrand [1997] 1 BCLC 427 (auditors – duty of care), Denby v English and Scottish Maritime Insurance Co. [1998] Lloyd's Rep. IR 343 (reinsurance), Credit Suisse First Boston v MLC [1999] 1 Lloyd's Rep. 767 (practice – anti-suit injunction).
Personal: Born 1962. MA (Oxon), Dip L (City University), Dip Eur Law (King's College, London). Has a working knowledge of French and Italian.

BUTLER, Christopher M.
St. Mary's Chambers Family Law Chambers (Christopher M. Butler) Nottingham (0115) 950 3503
Recommended in Family

BYRNE, Garrett
4-5 Gray's Inn Square (Elizabeth Appleby QC & David Mole QC) London (020) 7404 5252
clerks@4-5graysinnsquare.co.uk
Recommended in Environment
Specialisation: Environmental law and planning. Instructed by major city solicitors to advise and represent substantial industrial concerns and major developers. Regular speaker at conferences.
Prof. Memberships: United Kingdom Environmental Law Association; Environmental Law Foundation, founding member of 'EarthRights', environmental rights charity and public interest law firm.
Career: Called to the Bar in 1986, Masters degree in Environmental Law in 1993.

CAHILL, Jeremy
5 Fountain Court (Anthony Barker QC) Birmingham (0121) 606 0500
Recommended in Environment, Planning
Specialisation: Recent practice examples: British Alcan Aluminium v Secretary of State (1998) 77 P&CR 178 (Quash Local Plan); R v Stratford District Council ex p Lane 1997 NPC 172 (Judicial Review). Chalfont Park 9,000m2 office development, Bucks, Call-in granted consent 1999. Multiplex and leisure centre on Greenwich Peninsula, Consent issued 1999. Areas of practice: housing, retail, leisure, waste, pollution control, minerals, CPO, lands tribunal, statutory nuisance.
Prof. Memberships: Member of PEBA.

CAHILL, Sally
Park Lane Chambers (Stuart Brown QC) Leeds (0113) 228 5000
Recommended in Family

CALDECOTT, Andrew QC
1 Brick Court (Richard Rampton QC) London (020) 7353 8845
Recommended in Defamation

CALVER, Neil
Brick Court Chambers (Christopher Clarke QC) London (020) 7379 3550
Recommended in Commercial (Litigation)
Specialisation: Commercial law, in particular insurance, reinsurance, commercial arbitration, contractual disputes, professional negligence, EC law, sports law. Major cases this year so far include Odyssey Re v OIC Run Off Ltd (Court of Appeal: setting aside judgment on grounds of fraud of witness) and acting for Sir Elton John in professional negligence action against his former accountants. Important previous cases include: Stoke CC v B&Q [1993] AC 900 [HL and ECJ: whether Sunday trading ban contrary to EC law]; Kirklees BC v Wickes [1993] AC 227 [HL: whether public authorities should give cross-undertakings in damages as price of injunctive relief]; Ernst & Young v Butte Mining [1996] 1 LLR 91 and 104 [striking out of accountant's negligence claim]; Wurttembergische v Home Insurance [1999] LRLR 397 [CA: Pool reinsurance dispute]; Junior Counsel for Williams Grand Prix Motor Racing team. Acted for reinsurers in major insurance market arbitration concerning Eastern European shipbuilding losses after collapse of communism.
Prof. Memberships: COMBAR.
Career: LLM, Christ's College, Cambridge University (Double First Class Honours). Elected Life Scholar, Squire Scholar and De Hart Scholar, Christ's College Cambridge University. Gray's Inn Entrance Scholar; David Karmel Scholarship prize winner (Commercial Law, Grays' Inn).
Publications: Contributing author to the Bar Council's 'European Law Handbook' (1998); Contributing author to 'TUPE and the Acquired Rights Directive' (1996).
Personal: Played chess for England at under-18 level; Kent County Chess Champion at under 18, 16 and 14 level. Charlton Athletic FC supporter; Director of the Actors Centre, Covent Garden; Married with baby daughter.

CAMERON, Alexander
3 Raymond Buildings (Clive Nicholls QC) London (020) 7400 6400
chambers@3raymondbuildings.com
Recommended in Fraud
Specialisation: Substantial experience in all areas of criminal law. A specialist in commercial crime/fraud. Has defended solicitors and accountants, businessmen and financiers in matters ranging from conspiracy to defraud, through theft, fraudulent trading, cheating the Revenue, insider dealing and corruption. Recently defended in one of the first prosecutions brought by OPRA. Has advised in money laundering investigations and appeared in the commercial court in relation to criminal and extradition matters. Has prosecuted and defended in many cases of serious crime including murder, attempted murder, robbery, rape and perjury. Has appeared in licensing matters including recently the application to restrict liquor licensing at Twickenham RFC. Notable cases include Jeffrey Archer (perjury); Augusto Pinochet Ugarte (extradition); Jonathan Aitken (perjury); Susan Goddard (extradition); Marquis of Bath (assault); Blackspur Leasing (fraud); Blue Arrow (fraud).
Prof. Memberships: Criminal Bar Association, International Bar Association.
Career: Called 1986. At *3 Raymond Buildings* (formerly QEB) throughout.
Personal: Bristol University (LL.B Hons).

CAMERON, James
3 Verulam Buildings (Christopher Symons QC & John Jarvis QC) London (020) 7831 8441
chambers@3vb.com
Recommended in Environment
Specialisation: International lawyer specialising in environment, trade and human rights questions. Additionally environmental assessments and warranties, "toxic tort" litigation and conflict of laws. In practice is engaged in public law and judicial review of ministerial (and other public) decisions. Important cases include. EU v Korea [1999] WTO Appellate Body (safeguard measures on certain milk products); Ex-parte Pinochet [1998]; Ncobo v Thor Chemicals [1996]; Connelly v RTZ [1996]; R v President of the Board of Trade ex parte Duddridge [1995]; R v Secretary of State for the Environment, ex parte Greenpeace & Lancashire (THORP) [1994]. Involved in several international negotiations, including the UN Climate Change Convention Kyoto Protocol and the Earth Summit [1992]. Editor 'Review of European Community and International Environmental Law' (RECIEL) and 'International Trade Law Reports'. Author of several books including 'Trade and the Environment: Law & Policy', [2000]; 'Reinterpreting the Precautionary Principle', [2000]; 'Dispute Resolution in the WTO' [1998], 'Trade and the Environment, the Search for Balance' [1994].
Prof. Memberships: UK Environmental Law Association, Environmental Law Foundation (Advisory Board), World Trade Law Association (WTLA) Council Member. IUCN Environmental Law Commission. International Law Association (committee on transnational environmental litigation). International Criminal Law Association.
Career: Called to the Bar and joined current chambers 1987.
Personal: Educated at Stowe School, Buckinghamshire. University of Western Australia. University College, London (LL.B, 1985). Queens' College, Cambridge (LL.M, 1986).

CAMERON, Neil
Wilberforce Chambers (Bernard Gateshill) Hull (01482) 323 264
clerks@hullbar.demon.co.uk
Recommended in Commercial (Litigation), Environment, Health & Safety
Specialisation: Civil: cases relating to the conveyancing and use of land (in particular boundaries; restrictive covenants; easements; public rights of way; landlord and tenant and nuisance); commercial litigation. Criminal: health and safety, environmental and local authority prosecutions.
Prof. Memberships: North-Eastern Circuit; Professional Negligence Bar Association; Property Bar Association.
Career: Called 1984, Junior Counsel to the crown (Provincial Panel) 2000.

CAMERON, Neil
Eldon Chambers (Lionel Read QC) London (020) 7583 1355
clerks@eldonchambers.com
Recommended in Planning
Specialisation: Planning and environmental. Recent work includes: UK Nirex RCF appeal, Barnsley MBC CPO Special Parliamentary Procedure, Medway Cement Works Inquiry, Kent & Medway Bills (2000).
Prof. Memberships: Planning and Environment Bar Association, Parliamentary Bar Mess.
Career: Called 1982.
Personal: Educated at Eton College and Durham University.

CAMERON, Sheila QC
2 Harcourt Buildings (Gerard Ryan QC) London (020) 7353 8415
Recommended in Church

CAMPBELL, Douglas James
Three New Square (David Young QC) London (020) 7405 1111
3newsquareip@lineone.net
Recommended in Intellectual Property
Specialisation: All intellectual property matters – chemistry computers. Notable cases: Decon Laboratories v Fred Baker [2001] RPC 293; Raleigh trade mark [2001] RPC 202; Medgen Inc v Passion for Life Products [2001] FSR 496; Thermos v Aladdin [2000] FSR 402; Playhut v Spring Form [2000] FSR 327, TABO trade mark [2000] RPC 360, Demel v Jefferson [1999] FSR 204; Union Carbide v BP [1998] RPC 1, [1999] RPC 409 (CA); Conran (Sir Terence Orby) v Mean Fiddler Holdings [1997] FSR 856; Lubrizol v Exxon [1997] RPC 195, [1998] RPC 727 (CA); Roadtech Computer Systems v Unison Software [1996] FSR 805.
Prof. Memberships: Intellectual Property Bar Assn; Chancery Bar Assn.
Career: Dollar Academy, Scotland 1976-84; (Scholarship to) Hertford College, Oxford 1984 – 1988 1st Class Hons, Chemistry with Distinction in Quantum Chemistry. 1989/90 Employed by Andersen Consulting in Information Technology 1990/91 Teaching English in Kagoshima, Japan. Fluent in Japanese. Called to Bar 1993, Pegasus Scholarship to Melbourne, Australia 1997.
Publications: Contributor to European Patent Litigation Handbook; Terrell on Patents (both Sweet & Maxwell).
Personal: Karate, Equestrian pursuits.

CAMPBELL, Emily
Wilberforce Chambers (Edward Nugee QC) London (020) 7306 0102
Recommended in Chancery
Specialisation: All areas of general chancery work with an emphasis on trust, tax and estate planning and pensions litigation.
Prof. Memberships: Revenue Bar Assoc., Association of Pensions Lawyers, Chancery Bar Assoc.
Career: Lecturer in law of trusts, King's College, London (1994-95). Judicial Assistant to Court of Appeal (1997).
Publications: Halsburys Laws – Settlements title. International Trust Laws (Ed 9 Lassan) – contributor. Various articles: PCB; Sol. J.;Trusts & Estates LJ; Christies Bulletin.
Personal: Classical music

CAMPBELL, Stephen
St Philip's Chambers (John Randall QC) Birmingham (0121) 246 7000
Recommended in Commercial (Litigation)
Specialisation: Commercial law, building, personal injury.
Prof. Memberships: Midland Chancery and Commercial Bar Association; Personal Injury Bar Association; Birmingham Official Referee Users Group; Assistant Deputy Coroner to Birmingham and Solihull. Recorder.
Career: King Edward VI School, Birmingham. Liverpool University.
Personal: Married, three children. Tennis. School Governor.

CAMPBELL, Susan
Southernhay Chambers (Anthony Ward) Exeter (01392) 255777
southernhay.chambers@lineone.net
Recommended in Family
Specialisation: Family law. Practice covers all areas of family law: ancillary relief and all aspects of law relating to children, particularly care proceedings.
Prof. Memberships: Family Law Bar Association.
Career: Called 1986. Spent 7 years as an employed barrister in local government, specialising in care proceedings.
Personal: Born 29 April 1964. Two children. Enjoys swimming and walking.

CANNON, Mark
Four New Square (Justin Fenwick QC) London (020) 7822 2000
barristers@4newsquare.com
Recommended in Professional Negligence
Specialisation: Professional negligence (lawyers, accountants, insurance brokers, Lloyd's members and managing agents, financial advisers, valuers, architects and engineers); general commercial law; building and construction; insurance and reinsurance. Editor, 'Jackson and Powell on Professional Negligence' (3rd ed, 1992: chapter 7, Insurance Brokers; 4th ed, 1997, chapters 7 and 9, 'Insurance Brokers' and 'Members' and Managing Agents at Lloyd's'). Recent interesting cases include ICS v West Bromwich Building Society and Others [1998] 1 WLR 896 and [1999] Lloyd's Rep PN 496.
Prof. Memberships: COMBAR; London Common Law and Commercial Bar Association; Professional Negligence Bar Association.
Career: Educated at Lincoln College, Oxford 1980-83 (BA in Modern History) and Robinson College, Cambridge 1983-84 (Part 1B of Law Tripos). Called to the Bar 1985.

CAPE, Paul
Milburn House Chambers (Paul Cape) Newcastle upon Tyne (0191) 230 5511
Recommended in Employment
Specialisation: Almost exclusively employment and discrimination work, mainly factually complex discrimination, sensitive and/or high value dismissals, restraint of trade and all aspects of the police as an employer. Acts mainly for employers (primarily police and local authorities) as well as employees.
Career: Obtained a 'First' in Law at Newcastle Polytechnic following a career as a trade union official. Co-founder and Head of Chambers, Milburn House Chambers, a set specialising in all aspects of employment and discrimination law. Appointed a part-time Chairman of the Employment Tribunal 2000 and, hence is unable to accept instructions to appear in the Employment Tribunal in the Manchester Region.
Personal: Interests include theatre, reading and watching cricket. Born 5 March 1955.

CAPLAN, Jonathan QC
5 Paper Buildings (Godfrey Carey QC & Jonathan Caplan QC) London (020) 7583 6117
Recommended in Crime, Fraud

CARGILL-THOMPSON, Perdita
Essex Court Chambers (Gordon Pollock QC) London (020) 7813 8000
Recommended in Tax
Specialisation: VAT and Customs & Excise litigation and advisory work; judicial review and human rights; EC litigation and advisory work; Brussels Convention and Rome Convention; UK commercial disputes; broking disputes; banking, guarantee and insolvency work.
Career: Jesus College, Oxford: BA 1984 (Jurisprudence). College of Law: Solicitors' Professional Examinations 1984-85. London School of Economics: Masters in Human Rights and International Law 1991-92. British Academy Scholarship 1991-92. Bar Council: Conversion examinations 1992. Called to the Bar 1993. Treasury Panel (B List).
Personal: Born 1964. Speaks French.

CARLISLE, Hugh QC
1 Temple Gardens (Hugh Carlisle QC) London (020) 7583 1315
clerks@1templegardens.co.uk
Recommended in Health & Safety
Specialisation: Health and safety at work: R v Board of Trustees of Science Museum [1993] IWLR 1171 CA; R v Associated Octel Co Ltd [1996] 4 All ER 846, [1996] 1 WLR 1543 HL; R v British Steel plc [1995] I WLR 1356 CA; R v Nuclear Electric plc [Sept 1995]; R v Coalite Products Ltd [Feb 1996]; HSE v Howletts Zoo [Oct 1995]; R v Port Ramsgate and others [Jan-Feb 1997]; Harris v Evans [1998] 3 All ER 522 CA; R v FH Howe Ltd [1999] 2 All ER 249 CA; R v Balfour Beatty and Geoconsult [Jan-Feb 1999]; Counsel for Department of Health in BSE Inquiry 1999-00; Counsel for HSC/E in the Ladbroke Grove Railway Inquiry 2000, etc. Personal injuries: Fields v Hereford Health Authority [1992] etc.
Career: Called to Bar Middle Temple 1961; Junior Treasury Counsel, personal injuries cases, 1975-78; QC 1978; DTI Inspector into Ramor Investments Ltd 1979-85 and into Milbury plc 1982-85; Bencher, Middle Temple 1985. Recorder of the Crown Court (since 1983).
Personal: Married with two children. Interests include fly fishing, woodworking and croquet.

CARR, Bruce
Devereux Chambers (Jeffrey Burke QC) London (020) 7353 7534
Recommended in Employment
Specialisation: Employment law, commercial law, personal injury. Regularly instructed on behalf of both employers and trade unions, in particular in the EAT. Also frequently appears in interlocutory injunction applications, ranging from restrictive covenants to trade disputes. Substantial practice in descrimination, transfer of undertakings and large scale redundancy matters. Junior Counsel to the Crown (Panel A).
Prof. Memberships: Employment Law Bar Association; Employment Lawyers Association; ILS, Recorder; Member – EAT User Group.
Career: Called 1986. Inner Temple.
Publications: Author 'Emergency procedures', 'Litigation Practice' (Longmans).
Personal: Cambs High School for Boys, Cambridge. Hills Road Sixth Form College, Cambridge. LSE (BSc Economics) 1983, Central London Polytechnic (Dip. Law) 1985

CARR, Christopher QC
One Essex Court (Lord Grabiner QC) London (020) 7583 2000
Recommended in Commercial (Litigation), Energy & Natural Resources, Fraud

CARR, Henry QC

11 South Square (Christopher Floyd QC) London (020) 7405 1222

Recommended in Information Technology, Intellectual Property

Specialisation: Principal areas of practice are patents, copyrights, designs and trade marks. Leading cases include Philips v Remington, Levis v Tesco, Glaxo and others v Dowelhurst and others, all of which were referred to the ECJ and concern the Trade Marks Directive. Also AHP v Novartis (patents); R v Registrar of Designs ex parte Ford Motor Company (House of Lords); R v Licensing Authority ex parte Smith Kline & French (House of Lords) and Scotia v Norgine (European Court). Also has a substantial practice in computer contracts (including negligence claims); and judicial review relating to the grant of product licences. In addition, has appeared in numerous cases in the Data Protection Tribunal on behalf of the registrar.
Career: Called to the Bar 1982. Joined South Square in 1983. Took Silk 1998. Educated at Hertford College, Oxford and the University of British Columbia. Lives in London.
Publications: Computer software: 'Legal Protection in the United Kingdom'.

CARR, Peter

St. Ive's Chambers (Julia Macur QC) Birmingham (0121) 236 0863

Recommended in Crime

CARR, Sue

Four New Square (Justin Fenwick QC) London (020) 7822 2000
s.carr@4newsquare.com

Recommended in Professional Negligence

Specialisation: Principal area of practice is professional negligence: in particular, solicitors, barristers, accountants, clinical, surveyors, architects and engineers. Also handles civil fraud, employment, general contract and insurance work. Important cases include BDG Roof Bond Ltd v Douglas and others [1999] (company/solicitors' negligence); Twinsectra Ltd v Yardley and others [1999] (constructive trusts/accessory liability); Mortgage Express v Newman v SIF [1999] [2001] (solicitors' dishonesty), Broadley v Guy Clapham [1993], Hopkins & MacKenzie [1995] (both concerning limitation); Interde sco S.A v Nullifire Ltd [1992] (registration of foreign judgement) and Morley v Heritage Plc [1993] (employment), Hipwood v Gloucestershire HA [1995] (Disclosure), Halifax plc v Gould & Swayne [1999] (solicitor's duties).
Prof. Memberships: Committee Member Professional Negligence Bar Association, Professional Conduct Committee, Commercial and Common Law Bar Association. Member of New South Wales Bar. The General Editor and contributing author to 'Jackson & Powell: Professional Liability Precedents'.
Career: Called to the Bar 1987 and joined Crown Office Row in 1988.
Personal: Born 1st September 1964. Educated at Wycombe Abbey School 1976-82 and Trinity College, Cambridge 1983-86 (MA). Leisure pursuits include sports, music and acting. Fluent in French and German.

CARSS-FRISK, Monica QC

Blackstone Chambers (Presiley Baxendale QC & Charles Flint QC) London (020) 7583 1770
clerks@blackstonechambers.com

Recommended in Administrative & Public Law, Employment

Specialisation: Judicial review, employment law, with a particular emphasis on discrimination in both domestic and EU law, and the European Convention on Human Rights (particularly in the commercial context). Also handles general commercial contract disputes (including conflict of laws issues) and commercial fraud.
Prof. Memberships: Administrative Law Bar Association, Employment Lawyers Association, COMBAR.
Career: Called to the Bar 1985 and joined current chambers in 1986.
Publications: Contributor to 'Halsbury's Laws on Constitutional Law and Human Rights' and 'Butterworths' Human Rights Law and Practice'.
Personal: Educated at London University (LLB, 1983) and Oxford University (BCL, 1984). Speaks Swedish and has a working knowledge of Finnish. Member of Board of Interights.

CARTER, Peter QC

18 Red Lion Court (Anthony Arlidge QC) London (020) 7520 6000
Peter.Carter@18rlc.co.uk

Recommended in Crime

Specialisation: Principal area of practice is criminal law, both prosecution and defence work. Particular focus on fraud cases, but also handles drugs cases, offences of violence and sexual offences. Acted in BCCI and DPR litigation and has defended in a number of murder cases. Also deals with human rights, local authority and pollution cases. Clients include CPS headquarters, SFO and Customs and Excise. Regular seminar speaker.
Prof. Memberships: Criminal Bar Association, South Eastern Circuit.
Career: Called to the Bar 1974 and joined current chambers in 1975. Secretary of Criminal Bar Association 1987-90. Took Silk 1995. Undertakes pro bono work, especially capital cases.
Publications: 'Offences of Violence' (with Ruth Harrison), Sweet & Maxwell.
Personal: Educated at University College, London 1970-73 (LL.B). Governor of British Institute of Human Rights. Leisure pursuits include poetry, cricket and walking. Born 8th August 1952. Lives in Enfield, Middlesex.

CARTER-STEPHENSON, George QC

3 Gray's Inn Square (Rock Tansey QC) London (020) 7520 5600

Recommended in Crime

Specialisation: Experience in the conduct of the most serious and complex criminal cases including murder, serious fraud, organised crime and drug trafficking. A specialist in the field of criminal defence.
Prof. Memberships: South Eastern Circuit, Criminal Bar Association.
Career: Called to the Bar in 1975 and joined current chambers in 1977.
Personal: Leeds University 1971-74 (LLB Hons).

CARUS, Roderick QC

9 St. John Street (John Hand QC) Manchester (0161) 955 9000

Recommended in Crime

Specialisation: Fraud and related crime involving banking and accountancy disciplines but very experienced in all areas of criminal advocacy from corporate manslaughter to the Trade Marks Act 1994.
Career: 1964: Law degree University College Oxford. 1965: Postgraduate Diploma in Advanced Business Studies (specialising in Finance and Accountancy). 1966-70: Investment Controller for leading merchant bank. 1971: Called to the Bar (Gray's). 1986: Assistant Recorder. 1990: Queen's Counsel and Recorder.

CASEMENT, David

Exchange Chambers (David Turner QC & Bill Braithwaite QC & Henry Globe QC) Liverpool (0151) 236 7747 or (0161) 833 2722
casement@exchangechambers.co.uk

Recommended in Chancery, Commercial (Litigation)

Specialisation: Company and insolvency; commercial landlord and tenant; professional negligence; banking and finance; insurance; technology and construction in particular product liability disputes; sale of goods as well as intellectual property in particular media and entertainment law disputes.
Prof. Memberships: Chancery Bar Association; Northern Circuit Commercial Bar Association; Northern Chancery Bar Association.
Career: BA (Oxon). Called to the Bar by Middle Temple (1992) and King's Inns, Dublin (1997).
Personal: Sports and interests include swimming, tennis, flying light aircraft and playing saxophone. Educated at Methodist College, Belfast and St. Hugh's College, Oxford.

CASEY, Mairin

St. Mary's Chambers Family Law Chambers (Christopher M. Butler) Nottingham (0115) 950 3503

Recommended in Family

CASH, Joanne

1 Brick Court (Richard Rampton QC) London (020) 7353 8845
clerks@1brickcourt.co.uk

Recommended in Defamation

Specialisation: Media law including defamation; confidence and privacy; contempt; reporting restrictions; human rights.
Career: Called 1994. Moved to 1 Brick Court in January 2001.
Personal: Banbridge Academy; Lady Margaret Hall, Oxford.

CASSEL, Timothy QC

5 Paper Buildings (Godfrey Carey QC & Jonathan Caplan QC) London (020) 7583 6117

Recommended in Crime

CATCHPOLE, Stuart

39 Essex Street (Nigel Pleming QC) London (020) 7832 1111

Recommended in Administrative & Public Law, Construction

Specialisation: Construction and civil engineering. Professional negligence. Public law. Commercial law. Cases: Counsel to the Ministry of Agriculture Fisheries and Food at the BSE Inquiry; counsel for Sheffield Wednesday FC at the Hillsborough public inquiry and inquests. Details of reported cases and experience in any of areas of practice can be provided on request.
Prof. Memberships: Tech Bar. Administrative Law Bar Association. Appointed to be Junior Counsel to the Crown ('A' Panel) by the Attorney General in July 1999. Formerly a member of the Supplementary Panel of Treasury Counsel Common Law (appointed May 1992), transferred to the Treasury 'B' Panel on its creation in November 1998.
Career: Durham University 1983-86: First Class Honours Degree in Law (Maxwell Law Prize). Colchester Royal Grammar School 1975-82: A-Level History, English & Classical Civilisation (all Grade A). Judicial appointments: part-time legal member of the Proscribed Organisations Appeal Commission (31st July 2001).
Personal: Married. Three year old son and baby daughter. Speaks French. Enjoys theatre, cinema, wine.

CATTAN, Philip D.

28 St. John St Manchester (0161) 834 8418

Recommended in Crime

CAUDLE, John

2 Bedford Row (William Clegg QC) London (020) 7440 8888

Recommended in Crime

CAUSER, John

23 Essex Street (Michael Lawson QC) London (020) 7413 0353
johncauser@23essexstreet.co.uk

Recommended in Crime

Specialisation: Commercial fraud and related areas of civil and criminal law including disqualification of directors, actions against the police etc. Recent clients include Lord Brocket and Roger Levitt. Legal and other disciplinary proceedings.
Prof. Memberships: Gambian Bar [1982]. Gibraltar Bar [1998].
Career: BA English Literature 1977. Called (Inner Temple) 1979.

Barristers index: p.1619

Personal: Puzzle setting and solving, toy making, bicycling, photography, Babylonic cuneiform.

CAVANAGH, John QC
11 King's Bench Walk Chambers (Eldred Tabachnik QC & James Goudie QC) London (020) 7632 8500
Recommended in Employment
Specialisation: Principal areas of practice are employment law, local government law and judicial review and commercial law. In employment law particular emphasis on discrimination and equal pay, TUPE, the European aspects of employment law, restraint of trade, wrongful dismissal, industrial disputes and large-scale redundancies. Has recently acted in Preston v Wolverhampton Healthcare (part-timers pensions); Gregory v Wallace (breach of contract); Jepson v Labour Party (all-women shortlists); Abbey Life v Tansell (disability discrimination); R v Portsmouth CC, ex p Coles (public procurement); Gregory v Portsmouth CC (malicious prosecution).
Prof. Memberships: Treasurer of Employment Law Bar Association, member of the Employment Lawyers Association, ALBA and COMBAR. Junior Counsel to the Crown – B Panel (1997-01).
Career: Called 1985. Joined 11 King's Bench Walk 1985, QC 2001.
Publications: Contributor to Harvey, Tolley's 'Employment Law', Butterworths 'Local Government Law'.
Personal: Educated: Warwick School; New College, Oxford (MA); Clare College, Cambridge (LLM) and University of Illinois.

CAVENDER, David
One Essex Court (Lord Grabiner QC) London (020) 7583 2000
Recommended in Commercial (Litigation)
Specialisation: Commercial litigation.
Prof. Memberships: COMBAR.
Career: Called to Bar and joined 1 Essex Court in 1993.
Personal: Educated at Kings College, London 1986-89 (LLB 1st class Hons). Born 1964.

CAWSON, Mark QC
Exchange Chambers Manchester (0161) 833 2722 cawsonqc@exchangechambers.co.uk
Recommended in Chancery, Commercial (Litigation), Insolvency/Corporate Recovery
Specialisation: General Chancery/Commercial with emphasis on contentious insolvency and company work, commercial litigation and professional negligence. Recent cases include A.F Budge directors' disqualification, Home Income Scheme litigation, Secretary of State for Trade and Industry v Ashcroft [1998] Ch 71, Barakot v Epiette [1998] 1BCLC 283, Lombard North Central v Brook [1999] BPIR 701.
Prof. Memberships: Northern Circuit, Chancery Bar Association, Northern Chancery Bar Association, Northern Circuit Commercial Bar Association, Professional Negligence Bar Association.
Career: Wrekin College. Liverpool University. Called 1982 (Lincoln's Inn). Junior Counsel to Treasury (Charity/Manchester) 1990-01. Recorder.

CAYFORD, Philip
29 Bedford Row Chambers (Peter Ralls QC) London (020) 7404 1044 pcayford@29bedfordrow.co.uk
Recommended in Family
Specialisation: Family practice, bias towards ancillary relief. Also common law, commercial, entertainment and other family law matters. Court of Appeal decisions on Hague Convention and jurisdiction issues, leave to remove from the jurisdiction (Payne), derivative shareholder action arising from breakdown of family owned company, setting aside consent orders and solicitors' conflict of duty. Other reported decisions on children cases, professional negligence, inquests, etc.
Prof. Memberships: Middle Temple.
Career: Called to the Bar 1975 and joined 29 Bedford Row 1978.

CHAISTY, Paul QC
40 King St Manchester (0161) 832 9082
Recommended in Chancery, Commercial (Litigation), Insolvency/Corporate Recovery
Specialisation: Insolvency; administration; receivership; director disqualification; banking; commercial landlord and tenant; partnership; commercial litigation.
Prof. Memberships: Northern Chancery Bar Association, Chancery Bar.
Career: Recorder 2000, QC 2001. Recent reported cases CIS v Argyle Stores (Holdings) Ltd. [1996] AC 1, Re Sutton Times November 3 1999, Michael Gerson (Leasing) Ltd. v Wilkinson [2000] 3WLR 1645. Lincoln's Inn called 1982 (Hardwicke and Cassell Scholar).

CHAMBERS, Dominic
Brick Court Chambers (Christopher Clarke QC) London (020) 7379 3550 hawes@brickcourt.co.uk
Recommended in Commercial (Litigation)
Specialisation: Principal area of practice is commercial law, including banking, conflicts, negotiable instruments, insurance and reinsurance, guarantees and indemnities. Also handles commercial fraud, partnership and professional negligence. Professional clients predominantly major City and international law firms and law firms in the Channel Islands. Extensive experience of impact of US banking and commercial law in England, and of international commercial arbitrations (as Counsel and as arbitrator).
Prof. Memberships: COMBAR.
Career: Called to the Bar and joined 1 Hare Court in 1987. Joined the Chambers of Christopher Clarke QC in September 1997.
Personal: Educated at Harrow School 1976-81 and King's College, London 1983-86. Born 28th February 1963. Lives in Surrey.

CHAPMAN, Vivian R.
9 Stone Buildings (Michael Ashe QC) London (020) 7404 5055
Recommended in Chancery
Specialisation: Property litigation with particular interest in Law of Commons and Greens. Described as 'a barrister with great experience of this branch of the law' by Lord Hoffmann in R v Oxfordshire CC ex p Sunningwell PC [2000] 1 AC 335 at p. 348g. Recent reported cases: Fitzpatrick v Sterling Housing Association Ltd [2001] 1AC 27 (Landlord and Tenant); R v National Assembly of Wales ex p Robinson [2000] 80 P+CR 348 (rights of way); Bettison v Langton [2001] 2 WLR 1605(Commons); Price Meats Ltd v Barclays Bank plc, The Times 19 January 2000 (forgery of cheques); Fraser v Canterbury Diocesan Board of Finance [2001] 2 WLR 1103 (School Sites Act 1841).
Prof. Memberships: Lincoln's Inn: Middle Temple.

CHARLTON, Alex
4 Pump Court London (020) 7842 5555 acharlton@4pumpcourt.com
Recommended in Information Technology
Specialisation: Predominantly in commercial cases of a technical nature, information technology and computer law, construction and professional negligence. All cases that require cross-examination.
Prof. Memberships: Society for Computers & Law, Professional Negligence Bar Association, London Common Law & Commercial Bar Association, TECBAR, COMBAR.
Career: Called to the Bar 1983.
Publications: Contributing editor to 'Professional Negligence & Liability' published by LLP in 2000; co-author of Chapter 18 'Computer Consultants'.
Personal: Born 13 March 1958. Education: Tonbridge School; University of St Andrews; City University. Leisure interests: sailing, rugby, golf and tennis. Family details: Married with young children.

CHARLWOOD, Spike
4 Paper Buildings (Jean Ritchie QC) London (020) 7353 3366 spike.charlwood@4paperbuildings.com
Recommended in Professional Negligence
Specialisation: Main areas of practice: professional negligence (especially claims against solicitors, barristers, surveyors and valuers) and insurance law (including recovery actions and policy disputes). Reported cases: Brocklesby v Armitage & Guest [2001] 1 All ER 172, CA – solicitors' negligence, Limitation Act 1980, s,32; UCB v Carr [2000] Lloyd's Rep PN 754, QBD – solicitors' negligence, breach of trust, Limitation Act 1980; Abbey National v Sayer Moore [1999] EGCS 114, ChD – solicitors' negligence, lenders' claims, Limitation Act 1980, s.14A; Nationwide Building Society v Various Solicitors [1999] Lloyd's Rep PN 241, ChD – solicitors' negligence, lenders' claims, managed litigation; City Electrical Factors v Hardingham [1996] BPIR 541, ChD – bankruptcy, setting aside statutory demands; Miller v Eyo [1998] NPC 95, CA – landlord & tenant, rights of tenants in multiple occupation. Other interesting cases: Farley v Skinner (2001, HL, judgment awaited) – surveyors' negligence; Abbey National v Various Solicitors (ChD, ongoing) – solicitors' negligence, lenders' claims, managed litigation.
Career: Called to the Bar 1994; supervisor in Tort, Queens' College, Cambridge 1993-5.
Publications: 'Professional Negligence and Liability' (LLP, 2000): assistant editor and joint author of the chapter on barristers' negligence; 'Lloyds Law Reports: Professional Negligence', contributing editor; 'Cordery on Solicitors' (9th edition, looseleaf): contributing editor; 'Property at a Price' (1999) 143 SJ 456 (an article on 'Platform Home Loans v Oyston Shipways' [2000] 2 AC 190).
Personal: Education: Wellingborough School; Queens' College, Cambridge (MA (Hons) 1st Class); Inns of Court School of Law. Leisure interests: hill walking, travel, wine, reading.

CHARMAN, Andrew
St Philip's Chambers (John Randall QC) Birmingham (0121) 246 7000 acharman@st-philips.co.uk
Recommended in Chancery
Specialisation: Company law, commercial law, insolvency, financial services, professional negligence, real property, trusts, wills and probate, litigation, advisory and drafting.
Prof. Memberships: Member of the Chancery Bar Association and the Midland Chancery and Commercial Bar Association. Member of the Chartered Institute of Arbitrators.
Career: Educated at Imberhorne School, East Grinstead and Clare College, Cambridge. Worked as a researcher at The House of Commons then articles with *Freshfields* in London and Tokyo followed by practice as a solicitor in *Freshfields*' corporate department.

CHAWLA, Mukul QC
9-12 Bell Yard (D. Anthony Evans QC) London (020) 7400 1800
Recommended in Crime, Fraud
Specialisation: Defending and prosecuting criminal cases particularly commercial fraud and Customs and Excise cases. Practise also covers general crime and in particular defending Police Officers in criminal and disciplinary proceedings. Currently instructed by Customs and Excise and the Serious Fraud Office in the prosecutions of several high profile individuals and companies. Also instructed to defend the Jubilee line extension corruption trial.
Prof. Memberships: Criminal Bar Association.
Career: Called 1983. 1996-01 Standing counsel to HM Customs and Excise.
Personal: Born 31st May 1961. Educated at Eton College and University College, London.

CHERRYMAN, John QC
4 Breams Buildings (Christopher Lockhart-Mummery QC) London
(020) 7430 1221/7353 5835
Recommended in Property Litigation
Specialisation: Moved from Lincolns Inn to Breams Buildings in 1992 to concentrate on property related litigation and advice, including mining, professional negligence, mortgage securities, contaminated land and rating as well as mainstream landlord and tenant and vendor and purchaser work. A Bencher of Grays Inn and a member of the Chancery Bar and Property Bar Associations. Recent cases include TSB Bank v Camfield 1995 CA and Dunbar Bank v Nadeem 1998 CA (variants of O'Brien); Bentley v Gaisford 1996 CA (solicitors undertaking); Mannai Investment Co. v Eagle Star 1997 HL (validity of break notice); Shimizu (U.K.) v Westminster City Council 1997 HL (listed building: demolition or alteration); Attwell v Michael Perry & Co 1998 V-C (barristers immunity from suit for alleged negligence in property litigation). Sabah Foundation v Dat Syed Kechik 1999 Borneo H Ct and 2001 CA of Malaysia (breaches of fiduciary duty); Prudential Assurance v Eden Restaurants 1999 CA (curative effect of registration) SCB v PNSC 2000 CA (fraud) Morrells of Oxford v Oxford Utd FC 2000 CA (LPA 1925, s 79); Broderick v Alcoa of Jamaica 2000 PC (Leisbosch distinguished); Holding & Barnes plc v Hill House Hammond 2000 ChD, 2001 CA (construction fo repairing obligation).

CHILD, John
Wilberforce Chambers (Edward Nugee QC) London (020) 7306 0102
Recommended in Chancery
Specialisation: Heavy trust work – advice and drafting and some litigation. In part this is private client work dealing with family trusts and landed estates. The remaining part is commercial trust work, mostly relating to the Society of Lloyd's.
Prof. Memberships: Chancery Bar Association; Revenue Bar Association. Books – main contributor vol 19 (Sale of land) Encyclopaedia of Forms and Precedents (4th ed.). Forms of accumulation and maintenance Settlements for Encyclopaedia of Forms and Precedents (5th ed.) Vol 40.
Career: Firsts in Law at University of Southampton and Sidney Sussex College Cambridge. BA Scholar Sidney Sussex College. Droop Scholar and Tancred Common Law Student, Hon Soc of Lincoln's Inn. Supervisor in Law at Sidney Sussex and other Cambridge colleges 1966-78.

CHIPPINDALL, Adam
Guildhall Chambers (Adrian Palmer QC) Bristol (0117) 927 3366
adam.chippindall@guildhallchambers.co.uk
Recommended in Personal Injury
Specialisation: Personal injury: assessment of catastrophic injury cases, WRULD, expert evidence and CPR, together with clinical negligence and some associated professional negligence. Davies v Inman [1999] PIQR Q26; Hale v Guidarch [1999] PNLR 44.
Prof. Memberships: PIBA member.
Career: Clifton College. Southampton University.
Publications: Article on Smith v Manchester 'JPIL'.
Personal: Born 10/10/1953. Interests: rackets, tennis, rugby.

CHIVERS, David
Erskine Chambers (Robin Potts QC) London (020) 7242 5532
Recommended in Company, Insolvency/Corporate Recovery
Specialisation: Principal area of practice is company law, including corporate insolvency. Contributor to 'Gore-Brown on Companies', 'Practice and Procedure in the Companies Court' and 'Co-Operatives That Work'.
Prof. Memberships: Chancery Bar Association, COMBAR, Insolvency Lawyers Association. Member of Chancery Working Group reporting to Lord Woolf.
Career: Called to the Bar 1983 and joined Erskine Chambers 1984.
Personal: Born 1960. Educated at Downing College, Cambridge 1979-82.

CHOO CHOY, Alain
One Essex Court (Lord Grabiner QC) London (020) 7583 2000
achoochoy@oeclaw.co.uk
Recommended in Commercial (Litigation)
Specialisation: Broad range of commercial litigation including banking and financial services. Recent cases include: Sumitomo Corporation v Credit Lyonnais Rouse ltd (first case before the Commercial Court concerning the privileged nature of foreign language translations obtained for litigious purposes in a US$250 million claim); Montrod ltd v Grundkoetter (first case before the Commercial Court regarding whether there is a 'nullity' exception to payment against documents under letters of credit), both of which are due to be heard in the Court of Appeal in the second half of 2001 and also acting for Railtrack in connection with disputes with train companies resulting from the Hatfield crash.
Prof. Memberships: Member of COMBAR.
Career: LLB Hons (Queen Mary College, University of London).
Personal: Married with two children, enjoys classical music, badminton and also table tennis in which he appeared in the 1988 Seoul Olympics.

CHOUDHURY, Akhlaq
11 King's Bench Walk Chambers (Eldred Tabachnik QC & James Goudie QC) London (020) 7632 8500
Recommended in Employment
Specialisation: Employment and public/administrative law including human rights. Recently reported cases: Wincanton v Cranny [2000] IRLR 716, CA (restrictive covenants); Kapfunde v Abbey National [1999] ICR 1, CA (duty of care owed by company doctor).
Prof. Memberships: ELBA, ALBA.
Career: Called 1992.
Publications: Tolley's 'Employment Handbook' (1996 to date), contributor. Butterworths 'Local Government Law', contributor. 'Local Authorities and The Human Rights Act', contributor.
Personal: BSc Hons, Physics (Glasgow); LLB Hons (1st Class) (London). Married with two children. Interests include hill walking, film and cookery. Governor of Tower Hamlets FE College.

CHRISTIE, Richard
2 Pump Court (Philip Singer QC) London (020) 7353 5597
rchristie@2pumpcourt.co.uk
Recommended in Crime
Specialisation: All areas of criminal work but especially fraud and cases requiring substantial client care. Also general common law and family work. (i) R v Johnson (Aldin) [1995] 2 Cr. App. R. I (Albi and severance); (ii) Martin v Watson [1994] Q.B.425 and [1995] A.C.74 (malicious prosecution); (iii) R v Bosson [1999] Crim. L.R. 596 (Handling/theft: Multiple Appropriations); (iv) R v Mian [1997] (£1.5 million cannabis importation by high ranking Pakistani, said to have been framed by Pakistani Regime); (v) R v Parr [1997] (Money laundering following cross-jurisdictional Eurobond fraud); (vi) R v Phipps [1998] (Murder: educationally subnormal defendant, cut-throat defences); (vii) R v Butler [1999] (Leading junior – major local government corruption fraud: stayed for abuse of process); (viii) R v Alkadiki [1999] ($3.5 million international banking fraud: stayed for abuse of process); (ix) R v Robinson [2000] (Paedophile family: allegations of rape etc); R v Rodrigues [2001] (Leading Junior – banking/computer fraud: Stayed for abuse of process). R v Wheeler [2001] (Murder – drugs gang killing). R v Stapleton [2001] (£12 million VAT carousel fraud). R v Smith [2001] (Murder – appeal involving new evidence).
Career: Clifton College; Manchester University; *Touche Ross & Co* (Accountants).
Personal: Cinema and reading. Wife (solicitor) and three children.

CHRUSZCZ, Charles QC
28 St. John St Manchester (0161) 834 8418
Recommended in Crime

CHUDLEIGH, Louise
Old Square Chambers (John Hendy QC) London (020) 7269 0300
chudleigh@oldsquarechambers.co.uk
Recommended in Employment
Specialisation: Principal area of practice is employment law including discrimination, equal pay, internal disciplinary disputes, all post termination difficulties including unfair and wrongful dismissal and injunctive proceedings related to confidential information and restrictive covenants. Also practices in sports law, particularly disciplinary and contractual disputes.
Prof. Memberships: Employment Lawyers Association; Industrial Law Society. Bar Sports Law Group.
Career: Called to the Bar 1987 (England and Wales), 1989 (Bermuda); member of Old Square Chambers since 1988; Honorary lecturer in Labour Law at University of Kent at Canterbury.
Personal: All sports, particularly cycling, swimming and running.

CIUMEI, Charles
Essex Court Chambers (Gordon Pollock QC) London (020) 7813 8000
Recommended in Employment
Specialisation: All areas of employment law including sex, race and disability discrimination, transfers of undertakings (TUPE), industrial relations/strikes, breach of confidence and restrictive covenants. Recent cases include Morse v Wiltshire County Council (disability discrimination); Credit Suisse v Padiachy (restrictive covenants/TUPE); Wandsworth v D'Silva (collective agreements/terms of employment); UCLH v UNISON (strike action); Hall v Woolston Hall Leisure Ltd (discrimination/illegal contracts).

CLARE, Michael
Octagon House Chambers (Andrew Lindqvist) Norwich (01603) 623186
Recommended in Crime

CLARK, Christopher Harvey QC
Pump Court Chambers (Christopher Harvey Clark QC) London (020) 7353 0711
clerks@3pumpcourt.com
Recommended in Church
Specialisation: Western Circuit common law practice in both criminal and civil work. Particular experience in complex fraud cases, and other serious criminal matters.
Prof. Memberships: Chancellor of the Diocese of Winchester since 1993, Deputy Chancellor of the Dioceses of Salisbury, Portsmouth and Chichester. Member of the Ecclesiastical Judges Association Standing Committee.
Career: Called 1969. Recorder of the Crown Court since 1986 QC 1989. Bencher of Gray's Inn.
Personal: Church of England Reader.

CLARK, Fiona
8 New Square (Michael Fysh QC) London (020) 7405 4321
clerks@8newsquare.co.uk
Recommended in Intellectual Property
Specialisation: Barrister specialising in all aspects of intellectual property law including related contractual and EC matters, breach of confidence and trade libel. Has a particular interest in copyright and designs (both registered and unregistered). Trade marks and service marks are a particular speciality with extensive experience of product branding and media and entertainment law. Practice embraces a wide range of cases with technical content covering areas such as mechanical and construction engineering, computer software, architectural design and textiles. For comprehensive CV and list of recent cases, visit our website at www.8newsquare.co.uk.

Prof. Memberships: Chancery Bar Association; Intellectual Property Bar Association (IPBA); The Intellectual Property Lawyers Organisation (TIPLO).
Career: Called 1982. Lecturer Institute of Trade Mark Agents and The Chartered Institute of Patent Agents.
Publications: 'Encyclopedia of United Kingdom and European Patent Law' (senior editor).
Personal: Educated at Trinity College, Cambridge, MA

CLARK, Wayne

Falcon Chambers (Jonathan Gaunt QC & Kim Lewison QC) London (020) 7353 2484
Recommended in Property Litigation
Specialisation: Property litigation, including commercial leases, vendor and purchaser disputes, easements, restrictive covenants, mortgages and property related professional negligence.
Prof. Memberships: Chancery Bar Association, COMBAR.
Career: LLB (Lon), BCL (Oxon), former lecturer in law at QMC, London University. Contributor to Halsbury's Laws of England, Vol 27 (i), 4th edn, 'Landlord and Tenant'. Contributor to Hill and Redman, 'Law of Landlord and Tenant', Standing Counsel (civil) to Attorney General; co-Author, 'Renewal of Business Tenancies Law Practice' (Sweet & Maxwell 1997); co-author 'Tenant's Rights of First Refusal (2001) (Butterworths).
Personal: Keen chess player.

CLARKE, Andrew QC

Littleton Chambers (Michel Kallipetis QC) London (020) 7797 8600
Recommended in Employment
Specialisation: Experienced commercial employment lawyer, having appeared in these areas before all relevant courts and tribunals. Particular specialism in disputes relating to restrictive covenants and confidential information. Also handles company law and sport related matters, both relating to employment (including directors' duties) and generally. Acted for PLA in docks dispute, in relation to industrial action and the two year Industrial Tribunal. Appeared in numerous important cases on individual employment rights, sex and race discrimination, restrictive covenants and "garden leave" injunctions. Clients include major UK companies, solicitors' firms and senior employees, as well as leading sporting bodies, clubs and players.
Prof. Memberships: Employment Law Bar Association; Employment Lawyers Association; COMBAR (Committee Member).
Career: Called to the Bar 1980, QC 1997, joined *Littleton Chambers* in 1981.
Personal: Educated at Crewe County Grammar School, King's College London 1974-77 (LL.B) and Lincoln College, Oxford 1977-79 (BCL). Leisure pursuits include playing and watching cricket and football, and collecting modern prints and porcelain. Lives in Cheshunt. Born 23rd August 1956.

CLARKE, Elizabeth

Queen Elizabeth Building (Florence Baron QC) London (020) 7797 7837
Recommended in Family
Specialisation: Matrimonial finance and private law Children Act proceedings.
Prof. Memberships: Member of Bar Council 1997.
Career: BA (Oxon).

CLARKE, Gerard

Blackstone Chambers (Presiley Baxendale QC & Charles Flint QC) London (020) 7583 1770
clerks@blackstonechambers.com
Recommended in Employment
Specialisation: Public, employment, broadcasting, sports, and media law. Member of the Attorney General's A Panel of Counsel. Interesting cases include R v Two Police Forces ex p A ('Times' October 2000); Allen & Others v AMCO [2000] IRLR; R v North West Lancs; Health Authority ex p A,B,G 1999 TLR, Scully UK v Lee [1998] IRLR, R v Rhonda Cynon Taf DC ex p Evans [1999]; Wallace v Gregory 1998 IRLR, R v Riverside Mental Health NHS Trust ex p London [1999] 3 WLR, Holly v Smyth [1998] IWLR, R v Cobham Hall School ex p G [1998] ELR, Credit Suisse v Armstrong [1996] IRLR 450, Spring v Guardian Assurance plc [1995] 2 AC 296 and Meade Hill v British Council [1995] 1CR 847.
Prof. Memberships: Employment Lawyers' Association, Employment Law Bar Association, Administrative Law Bar Association.
Career: Called to the Bar 1986.
Publications: Author of TUPE section in 'New Law Online Employment Law Service'.
Personal: Born 1962. Educated in Solihull and at Wadham College, Oxford (MA).

CLARKE, Nicholas

9 St. John Street (John Hand QC) Manchester (0161) 955 9000
clerks@9stjohnstreet.co.uk
Recommended in Crime
Specialisation: Defending cases of homicide; drug importation, production and distribution; sexual and physical abuse of children. Particular interest in cases with medical or psychiatric background and has extensive experience cross-examining expert witnesses including pathologists, neuroradiologists and paediatric specialists in various disciplines. Defended the first trial in this country where the Crown relied solely on an earprint identification and also the first murder trial to rely on earprints. Recently defended a consultant orthopaedic surgeon charged with indecently assaulting patients over 25 years.
Prof. Memberships: Criminal Bar Association, Northern Circuit.
Career: Sheffield University, LLB. Called to the Bar, 1981. Assistant Recorder, 1999. Recorder 2000.
Personal: Married, two children. Chairman 3rd Hazel Grove Scout Group. Enjoys snooker, football and cycling.

CLARKSON, Patrick QC

Eldon Chambers (Lionel Read QC) London (020) 7583 1355
Recommended in Planning
Specialisation: Planning, local government, environmental and Parliamentary.
Prof. Memberships: Planning & Environmental Bar Association.
Career: Called 1972, Silk 1991, Recorder 1996.

CLAYTON, Joanna

2 Harcourt Buildings (Gerard Ryan QC) London (020) 7353 8415
Recommended in Planning

CLAYTON, Richard

Devereux Chambers (Jeffrey Burke QC) London (020) 7353 7534
mailbox@devchambers.co.uk
Recommended in Administrative & Public Law
Specialisation: Principal areas of practice are public law and human rights/civil liberties. Public law covers education, health care, prisoners' rights, regulatory and disciplinary matters and local government law. (Visiting Fellow, Centre for Public Law, University of Cambridge). Also handles employment law (both individual and collective), discrimination law, European law and civil actions against the police. Acted in Attorney General v Blake [2001] AC 268 (HL-confiscation of royalties); Greenfield v Secretary of State for Home Department The Times, 6th March 2001 (human rights); R v Wirral ex p B [2001] 1 LGR 1 (special needs); Derby Specialist Engineering v Burton [2001] 2 ALL ER 840; R v CICA ex p Leatherhead, The Times 12 October 2000; RICS v Fryer The Times, 17th May 2000 (CA) R v School Adjudicator ex p Wirral [2000] ELR 620 (school admissions); Saga Oil v Bourgeois EAT June 2000 (discrimination claim worth £1.8 million); R v Swale BC ex p Marchant The Times, November 17th, 1999 (CA-housing benefit); R v Lincolnshire Crown Court ex p Jude [1998] 1 WLR 24; Stewart-Brady v United Kingdom (1998) 27 EHRR CD 284 (European Convention) and R v Press Complaints Commission ex p Stewart-Brady (1997) 9 Admin LR 274 (privacy rights); R v Northamptonshire County Council ex p W [1998] ELR 314 (school expulsion); Bamber v United Kingdom [1998] EHRLR 110 (European Convention); R v Southwestern Magistrates ex p Cfie [1997] 1 WLR 585; Rai v United Kingdom (1995) EHRLR 92 (European Convention); R v Chiief Constable of West Midlands Police ex p Wiley [1995] 1 AC 274 (public interest immunity); Hellenwell v Chief Constable of Derbyshire [1995] 1 WLR 804 (breach of confidence); R v Northern & Yorkshire RHA ex p Trivedi [1995] 1WLR 961 (disciplinary procedure for GPs); R v Home Secretary ex p Hickey No2 [1995] WLR 734 (prisoners' rights); R v Chief Constable of South Wales ex p Merrick [1994] 1 WLR 663 (right to legal advice). Clients include pressure groups like Save Guy's Hospital Campaign, local authorities, plcs and private individuals.
Prof. Memberships: Administrative Law Bar Association (Committee since 1996); Employment Law Bar Association; Liberty; Society of Labour Lawyers.
Career: Called to Bar 1977; *South Islington Law Centre* 1980-82; *Osler Hoskin Harcourt (Toronto)* 1983; Returned to practice 1984; joined Devereux Chambers 1996.
Publications: Author of 'Practice and Procedure at Industrial Tribunals' (LAG) (1986); 'Civil Actions against the Police' (Sweet & Maxwell) (2nd edition 1992); 'Judicial Review Procedure' (Wiley) (2nd edition 1997); 'Law of Human Rights' Oxford University Press (2000).
Personal: Educated New College, Oxford. Leisure pursuits include reading, cinema, theatre and travel. Born 25th May 1954. Lives in London.

CLEGG, William QC

2 Bedford Row (William Clegg QC) London (020) 7440 8888
Recommended in Crime, Fraud
Specialisation: Specialist in defending cases of alleged fraud. Cases include Brent Walker plc; Alliance Resources plc; Bute Mining plc; R v Smith (£100 million bank fraud), R v Khan (income tax fraud); R v Smithson (The Arrows fraud); R v De Vandiere (VAT fraud); R v Alder (international bank fraud); R v Morley (fraudulent trading); R v Hales (solicitors legal aid fraud). Cases of a more general nature include Serafinowicz (war crimes); R v Stone (Chillingden murders); R v Wardell (Nuneaton Building Society murder); R v Stagg (Wimbledon Common murder); R v Varathadasan (Tamil Tigers); R v McMahon (UDA terrorists); R v Sawoniuk (war crimes); Prosecutor v Jelisic (war crimes the Hague); Prosecutor v Tadic (war crimes, The Hague); R v Duckenfield (Hillsborough Disaster). Has also been instructed in a lengthy public enquiry by the Medical Protection Society and many cases in the Court of Appeal Criminal Division and Divisional Court. Was a member of the standing committee of Justice on fraud trials and prepared submissions to the Fraud Trials Committee chaired by Roskill (HMSO 1986).
Prof. Memberships: Criminal Bar Association (committee members); South Eastern Circuit (committee member). Chairman Essex Bar Mess.
Career: Called to the Bar 1972 and joined present chambers in 1973. Took silk 1991. Appointed Recorder 1992. Head of chambers 1995.
Personal: Educated at Bristol University (LLB). Leisure pursuits include squash, cricket and wine. Born 5 September 1949.

CLIFFORD, James

Maitland Chambers (Michael Lyndon-Stanford QC & Charles Aldous QC) London (020) 7406 1200
jclifford@maitlandchambers.com
Recommended in Pensions
Specialisation: Specialises in pensions and trusts and has general commercial chancery litigation practice. Reported cases handled include Barclays Bank v Holmes, ITS v Rowe, Polly Peck v Henry, Re Scientific Investment Pension Plan, Edge v The Pensions Ombudsman, Hood

Sailmakers Ltd v Axford, Miller v Scorey, Process Developments Ltd v Hogg, Coloroll Pension Trustees Limited v Russell, Thrells Ltd v Lomas Nestle v National Westminster Bank, LRT v Hatt, Mettoy Pensions Trustees v Evans. Contributor to Trust Law International, British Pensions Lawyer, and author of Pensions Title, Atkins Court Forms.
Prof. Memberships: Association of Pension Lawyers, Chancery Bar Association.
Career: Called to the Bar in 1984.
Personal: Educated at Oxford University.

CLOSE, Douglas
Serle Court (Lord Neill of Bladen QC) London
(020) 7242 6105
clerks@serlecourt.co.uk
Recommended in Chancery
Specialisation: General commercial chancery litigation, in particular commercial fraud and trust litigation. Cases include: The Thyssen-Bornemisza litigation in Bermuda, Don King Productions Inc v Frank Warren & Ors, the Palumbo litigation and the Wahr-Hansen litigation in the Cayman Islands.
Prof. Memberships: Chancery Bar Association, COMBAR.
Career: Called 1991. Pupil to Michael Briggs QC and Frank Hinks QC
Personal: Born 1966. Educated at Berkhamsted School; Jesus College, Oxford (MA, BCL). Interests include theatre, restaurants, abstract art.

COBB, Stephen
One Garden Court Family Law Chambers (Eleanor F. Platt QC & Alison Ball QC) London
(020) 7797 7900
s.cobb@onegardencourt.co.uk
Recommended in Family
Specialisation: Family law, including public and private law aspects of the Children Act 1989; adoption; child abduction (convention and non-convention) and children cases with an international element including 'leave to remove'; applications with Human Rights Act 1998 element; matrimonial finance, judicial review (mainly family law related); applications/appeals under Part X Children Act 1989.
Prof. Memberships: FLBA; Elected Committee member FLBA
Career: Called to the Bar in 1985.
Publications: General Editor of 'Essential Family Practice 2001' (Butterworths).
Personal: Winchester College. Liverpool University (LLB Hons 1984). Born 12 April 1962. Lives in London. Married, three children.

COBURN, Michael
20 Essex Street (Iain Milligan QC) London
(020) 7583 9294
Recommended in Shipping
Specialisation: Commercial law, including in particular shipping, international sale of goods and insurance and reinsurance.
Career: Called 1990.
Personal: Educated at Charterhouse; Worcester College, Oxford; City University.

COE, Rosalind
Ropewalk Chambers (Ian McLaren QC)
Nottingham (0115) 947 2581
clerks@ropewalk.co.uk
Recommended in Personal Injury
Specialisation: Personal injury; clinical negligence; industrial disease; solicitor's negligence. Currently junior Counsel for Claimants in cases arising from physical and sexual abuse in childrens' homes in the North West of England and Cambridgeshire. Notable cases include Lister v Hesley Hall Limited [2001] UKHL 22 [2001] 2 WLR 1311 (vicarious liability).
Prof. Memberships: Personal Injuries Bar Association; Nottinghamshire Medico-Legal Society.
Career: Called 1983. Circuit Junior (Midland and Oxford Circuit) 1991-92.
Personal: Family, friends and saxaphone.

COGHLAN, Terence QC
1 Crown Office Row (Robert Seabrook QC)
London (020) 7797 7500
terence.coghlan@1cor.com
Recommended in Clinical Negligence
Specialisation: Covers all aspects of medical work including medical negligence. Has appeared for both plaintiffs and defendants in numerous medical negligence actions and arbitrations as well as regularly appearing in the GMC, GDC and other disciplinary bodies. Represented all the health authorities involved in the 'Myodil' litigation and the defendant in Bolitho v City & Hackney HA (House of Lords). Clients have included the Medical Defence Union, Medical Protection Society, MDDUS, the Welsh Office and leading medical negligence solicitors. Has lectured and written on personal injury and medical negligence matters and has appeared on television. Has also acted as mediator. President, Mental Health Review Tribunual.
Prof. Memberships: Professional Negligence Bar Association.
Career: Called in 1968. Recorder of the Crown Court 1989. QC 1993.
Personal: Education: New College, Oxford (BA, MA).

COGLEY, Stephen
Merchant Chambers (David Berkley QC)
Manchester (0161) 839 7070
Recommended in Commercial (Litigation)
Specialisation: Commercial, Banking insolvency. Various reported cases in the fields of insolvency, shareholder disputes, banking, consumer credit/licensing and contract. Instructed frequently in banking and finance leasing cases by banks and finance houses and building societies. Clients include most of the major banks, several major finance houses. Acts in company disputes/shareholder disputes. Has been involved in many high profile cases involving prominent individuals. Has acted on behalf of leading academics, against members of the judiciary, and football clubs (for and against). Lectures solicitors for the Law Society – in commercial matters and directors' duties and director disqualification.
Prof. Memberships: Founder member of Northern Circuit Commercial Bar Association. Member of COMBAR and the Northern Chancery Bar Association.
Career: Called 1984.
Personal: Lives Lancashire and Scotland. Hobbies: fell running, mountaineering, rock climbing, anything with a hint of danger.

COHEN, Edward
11 Stone Buildings (Murray Rosen QC) London
(020) 7831 6381
Recommended in Chancery
Specialisation: He practises in commercial and Chancery litigation and advisory work, including contract, sale of goods, banking, professional negligence, partnership, libel, media & entertainment, real property, company and insolvency, commercial fraud, insurance, arbitration, intellectual property, telecoms and e-commerce. An experienced practitioner and forceful advocate, he has appeared in reported decisions ranging from the House of Lords through the Court of Appeal and courts of first instance involving diverse legal issues. His wide-ranging practice enables him to advise and act in individual cases involving simultaneously different areas of law. He is known for his meticulous approach towards preparation, paperwork and advocacy and for his dedicated support of Newcastle United FC.
Career: Called to the Bar 1972. Member of the chambers of Eric Myers QC, 3 Hare Court 1972-75. Joined present chambers 1975.
Personal: Educated at Clifton College, Bristol 1963-67 and King's College, Cambridge 1968-71. Leisure pursuits include theatre, music and watching football. Born 25 December 1949. Lives in London.

COHEN, Jonathan QC
4 Paper Buildings (Lionel Swift QC) London
(020) 7583 0816
jc@4pb.com
Recommended in Family
Specialisation: Practice encompasses all areas of family law, in particular matrimonial finance, professional negligence arising out of family law matters and childcare. Recent cases include G v G (care proceedings: split trials) [2001] 1 FLR 872 and (Standard of proof [2001] 1 FCR 97, Westbury v Sampson (professional negligence in ancillary relief proceedings) to be reported, Piglowska (House of Lords: ancillary relief (1999) 2FLR 763), N v N (ante nuptial contract: enforceability (1999) 2 FLR 745) and C v C (1997) 2 FLR 26 (financial provision: short marriage).
Prof. Memberships: Family Law Bar Association; Professional Negligence Bar Association.
Career: Called to the Bar 1974. Recorder and Silk 1997. Member, Mental Health Review Tribunal 2000.
Publications: Contributing editor of family law chapters in new edition of 'Foskett on Compromise'.
Personal: School Governor.

COHEN, Lawrence QC
24 Old Buildings (Martin Mann QC & Alan Steinfeld QC) London
(020) 7404 0946; (020) 7419 6226 (Direct)
lcqc@xxiv.co.uk
Recommended in Company, Insolvency/Corporate Recovery
Specialisation: International, corporate, equity and business law matters, including major civil fraud by fiduciaries and professional negligence. Distinguishing features are: (1) large-scale, complex and long-running cases – clients are often investment banks or funds, listed or multinational corporations, foreign governmental organisations or professional litigants such as liquidators; (2) transactional work using extensive experience of financial markets in Europe and the United States and of many aspects of financial accounting and reporting. This requires commercial acumen and sensitivity as well as technical expertise in company and insolvency law and practice; (3) significant cross-border or international cases, requiring private international law expertise (including tracing type claims, conservatory measures, recognition of foreign judgments or awards eg Brussels, Lugano & New York Conventions). Practice often necessitates working closely with lawyers and other professionals (particularly accountants) in different countries (eg Switzerland, Luxembourg, Central and South America), devising creative solutions and overcoming linguistic and cultural barriers. A feature is frequent Court appearances in offshore financial centres including the Cayman Islands, Bermuda and the British Virgin Islands, building wide experience of offshore and cross-border trusts, corporations and other holding structures. A few examples of cases undertaken are: defending Nigerian state claims for alleged "looting" of billions of dollars by its late Head of State (General Sani Abacha); pursuing BCCI litigation for liquidators, which led to damages award of $2.2 billion; recovery of sovereign debt by defaulting states; defending fund managers in 'Maxwell' litigation; claims by the Matthew Harding Estate relating to compulsory acquisition of its shares in Benfield Grieg Plc, with associated professional negligence claims against accountants; hostile takeover litigation in the BAT & ADT bids; large scale trust litigation in Cayman and elsewhere; numerous share warranty claims. Confidential advice is frequently given in relation to mergers, acquisitions and other commercial transactions. Additional expertise includes accountancy and valuation and property law.
Prof. Memberships: Associate Member, Chartered Institute of Arbitrators, Member of the Chancery Bar Association; Member of the Insolvency Lawyers' Association. Also, for specific cases, Attorney-at-law (Cayman, Bermuda and Turks and Caicos Islands) and Barrister – Eastern Caribbean States (BVI).
Career: Queen's Counsel (1993); Assistant Recorder (1995); Recorder (1998).

COHEN, Raphael
Mercury Chambers (Benjamin Nolan QC) Leeds (0113) 234 2265
Recommended in Family
Specialisation: Specialist in matrimonial property work. Involved in cases with substantial assets and with a commercial bias including company accounts and contracts.
Career: Called to the Bar in 1981. A founder member of Mercury Chambers which is a specialist civil and commercial set.

COLE, Edward
Falcon Chambers (Jonathan Gaunt QC & Kim Lewison QC) London (020) 7353 2484 cole@falcon-chambers.com
Recommended in Property Litigation
Specialisation: Real property.
Prof. Memberships: Gray's Inn.
Career: Called to the Bar in 1980.
Personal: Contributor to 'Megarry on the Rents Act', 11th edn; specialist editor Hill & Redman 'Law of Landlord and Tenant'. Contributor Halsbury's Laws, vol 27, title 'Landlord and Tenant'. Atkin's Court Forms: title 'Agriculture'.

COLLENDER, Andrew QC
2 Temple Gardens (Dermod O'Brien QC) London (020) 7822 1200
Recommended in Personal Injury
Specialisation: He specialises in serious personal injury and clinical negligence cases and disaster litigation, appearing for both Claimants and Defendants. He has in depth experience of the conduct of substantial and multi-party actions especially in cases involving recognisable psychiatric injury caused eg by stress or witnessing shocking events, industrially caused diseases, musculo-skeletal disorders, and vicarious liability for sexual abuse. Recent cases include Mughal v Reuters [1993], Frost v South Yorkshire Police [1999] and Lister v Hesley Hall [2001].
Prof. Memberships: London Common Law Bar Association. Professional Negligence Bar Association. Personal Injuries Bar Association.
Career: University of Bristol – LLB (Hons) 1968. Called Lincoln's Inn July 1969. Silk April 1991. Recorder January 1993. Deputy High Court Judge 1998.
Publications: A member of the editorial team for the 13th edition of Munkman on employer's liability and a co-author of the second edition of the Personal Injuries Bar Association Handbook.
Personal: Married, two sons. Interests: violin, sailing.

COLLIER, Peter QC
30 Park Square (J.W. Mellor) Leeds (0113) 243 6388
Recommended in Church

COLLINGS, Matthew
Maitland Chambers (Michael Lyndon-Stanford QC & Charles Aldous QC) London (020) 7406 1200 clerks@maitlandchambers.com
Recommended in Chancery, Company, Insolvency/Corporate Recovery
Specialisation: Company law (litigation and advisory work) including corporate reconstructions, takeovers and mergers, shareholders disputes, directors duties and disqualification; reported cases include British & Commonwealth, Leeds United, Carecraft, Manlon, Barings, UMB v Doherty, Legal Costs Negotiators and Astec. Corporate insolvency; reported cases include Arrows, BCCI, Harris Simons, Wallace Smith, Charnley Davies, Galileo Group, Vanilla Accumulation, Hamlet International and Atlantic Computers. Personal insolvency and bankruptcy; reported cases include Naeem, Murjani and Hadkinson. Regulatory work and financial services including extensive appearances in tribunals, public law and human rights (ex p McCormick and ex p Eastaway), company and insolvency investigations (including Banking Act and criminal), the use of compelled evidence, and competition law. Commercial Chancery including guarantees and securities, banking, share sale warranties and professional negligence; reported cases include The Law Society v KPMG.
Prof. Memberships: Chancery Bar Association. Member, Insolvency Rules Advisory Committee.

COLLINS, Michael QC
Essex Court Chambers (Gordon Pollock QC) London (020) 7813 8000 mcollins@essexcourt-chambers.law.co.uk
Recommended in Arbitration (International)
Specialisation: International and commercial arbitration, insurance, shipping, conflict of laws, commercial and technical contract and tort disputes generally, arbitration.
Prof. Memberships: American Bar Association, International Bar Association, Commercial Bar Association.
Career: University of Exeter LLB (First Class Hons). Called to the Bar 1971. Queen's Counsel 1988. Recorder 1997-00.
Personal: Born 1948.

CONE, John
Erskine Chambers (Robin Potts QC) London (020) 7242 5532 clerks@erskine-chambers.co.uk
Recommended in Company
Specialisation: Corporate reorganisations and reconstructions including reduction of capital and schemes of arrangement. Takeovers and mergers. Schemes of arrangement in insolvencies.
Prof. Memberships: Chancery Bar Association. COMBAR. A Bar Representative on the Law Society Company Law Committee, Member of the Law Reform Committee of the Bar Council.

CONNOLLY, Joanne
8 King St (Keith Armitage QC) Manchester (0161) 834 9560 jconnolly@eightkingstreet.co.uk
Recommended in Employment
Specialisation: All aspects of employment work from simple unfair dismissal and redundancy to the more complex discrimination cases and group actions under the Transfer of Undertakings, Working Time or Minimum Wage legislation both before the Empoyment Tribunal and at appeal. Also Personal Injury, including stress at work and bullying claims. Reported cases include: Mediguard v Thane [1994] 1RLR 504, EAT Staffordshire County Council v Barber [1996] 1LR 379, CA. RCO Support Services and Aintree Hospital Trust v UNISON and others [2000] 1 RLR 624, EAT.
Prof. Memberships: The Employment Law Bar Association, the Employment Lawyers Association and the Professional Negligence Bar Association.
Career: LLB (Nottingham.) Called to the Bar in 1992. Awarded Council of Legal Education Studentship and Jules Thorn scholarship.

CONWAY, Charles
2 Bedford Row (William Clegg QC) London (020) 7440 8888
Recommended in Crime

COOK, Ian
One King's Bench Walk (Anthony Hacking QC) London (020) 7936 1500
Recommended in Family
Specialisation: Main areas of practice: matrimonial finance including recent experience involving UK and overseas based family run businesses and domestic and offshore trusts, public law children cases, child abduction, crime. Reported cases include Re H (Abduction: Acquiescence) [1998] AC 72, Re S (Care Proceedings: Split Hearing) [1996] 2 FLR 773, FD, Re M and R (Child Abuse: Evidence) [1996] 2 FLR 195, CA.
Prof. Memberships: FLBA
Career: BA (Hons) 1st Class Philosophy, King's College London. CPE City of London Polytechnic.

COOK, Mary
2-3 Gray's Inn Square (Anthony Porten QC & Anthony Scrivener QC) London (020) 7242 4986 mcook@2-3graysinnsquare.co.uk
Recommended in Local Government, Planning
Specialisation: Planning and local government work. Wide planning inquiry experience, both promoting and resisting development, called-in applications and Local Plan appearances, the promotion of CPO particularly town centre schemes, footpath and road closures. Court experience includes judicial review and high court challenges involving environmental, planning, property and vires issues.
Prof. Memberships: Planning and Environmental Bar Association.
Career: Called 1982, commenced practice from these chambers in 1985.

COOKE, Jeremy QC
7 King's Bench Walk (Jeremy Cooke QC) London (020) 7910 8300 clerks@7kbw.law.co.uk
Recommended in Insurance, Professional Negligence, Shipping
Specialisation: Specialises in all aspects of commercial law including insurance and reinsurance, shipping, professional negligence, international sale of goods (oil and gas in particular), energy, banking and international arbitration.
Prof. Memberships: Commercial Bar Association; London Maritime Arbitrators Association; LCIA; CEDR accredited mediator, ACI, CBA.
Career: Called to the Bar 1976 and joined present chambers in the same year. Took Silk 1990. Appointed Recorder 1998. Head of chambers 2000.
Personal: (MA Jurisprudence 1st class). Oxford University rugby Blue 1968 and 1969. Harlequins 1970-75. Director of Red Thread, LICC Ltd. Leisure pursuits include golf.Born 28 September 1949. Lives in London.

COOKE, Nicholas QC
9 Park Place (Ian Murphy QC) Cardiff (029) 2038 2731
Recommended in Chancery, Local Government
Prof. Memberships: Wales and Chester circuit; Planning and Environmental Bar Association; Bristol and Cardiff Chancery Bar Association; Wales Public Law and Human Rights Association.
Career: King Edward's School, Birmingham. UCW Aberystwyth (1st Class Hons LLB). Recorder. Appointed Queen's Counsel in 1998. Deputy President Mental Health Review Tribunal for Wales.
Personal: Hockey, theatre.

COOKSLEY, Nigel
Old Square Chambers (John Hendy QC) London (020) 7269 0300 cooksley@oldsquarechambers.co.uk
Recommended in Personal Injury
Specialisation: Principal area of practice for many years has been personal injury litigation and has a widespread practice throughout the country. Other areas of practice include professional negligence, product liability and sporting injuries.
Prof. Memberships: Personal Injury Bar Association, Association of Personal Injury Lawyers, Professional Negligence Bar Association.
Career: Called to the Bar in 1975.
Personal: Educated at Felsted School and Cambridge University. Lives in North Hertfordshire. Outside interests include sport.

COONAN, Kieran QC
6 Pump Court London (020) 7583 6013
Recommended in Clinical Negligence

COOPER, John

3 Gray's Inn Square (Rock Tansey QC) London (020) 7520 5600

Recommended in Crime

Specialisation: Specialist in serious criminal law. Also deals with general common law.

Prof. Memberships: Criminal Bar Association; Essex Bar Mess Committee member; co-opted to Bar Council Public Affairs Committee.

Career: Called to the Bar in 1983. Member New South Wales Bar. Represented the British employees in the BCCI litigation. Butterworths' Law Prizeman. Successfully represented the defendant in the 'Leah Betts' Ecstasy drug trials. Leading authority in Master of the Rolls court on the criminality of wheel clamping (Arthur v Anker) and indictment rules (R v Wrench). Also R v Ward & Baker – 'The Times' (duress) and R v Plummer & Simpkins (juveniles). Instructed for Louise Woodward by campaign committee. Columnist for 'The Times' Legal Section. Advisor to the emerging democracies in Eastern Europe upon criminal law and justice. Judicial commissioner in Lambeth Childcare enquiry. Entry in Debrett's "People of Today" page 414.

Publications: 'Police Interviews' (Sweet & Maxwell); 'Judicial Review from the Magistrates Court' (Sweet & Maxwell); Justis (Context).

Personal: Commended as Barrister of the Year 1998 ('The Lawyer'). Writer: screenplays include 'The Law Lord' (BBC Screen 2), 'The Advocate' (ITV).

COOPER, Mark

Chancery House Chambers (Adrian Dent) Leeds (0113) 244 6691
mark.cooper@chanceryhouse.co.uk

Recommended in Insolvency/Corporate Recovery

Specialisation: Specialises in business, commercial and financial law, in particular banking, corporate restructuring, insolvency (personal and company) and commercial disputes involving contractual, restitutionary and professional negligence claims.

Prof. Memberships: Chancery Bar Association, Insolvency Lawyers Association, Association of Business Recovery Professionals (R3) and Northern Chancery Bar Association.

Career: Investment banking, London and New York 1989-95. Called to the Bar in March 1998 (Middle Temple Harmsworth Exhibitioner). Joined Chancery House Chambers, Leeds as a practising barrister in 1999.

Personal: Educated at Dame Allans Boys School, Newcastle upon Tyne 1979-86 and Exeter College, Oxford 1986-89 (MA in 1995).

CORBETT, James QC

St Philip's Chambers (John Randall QC) Birmingham (0121) 246 7000
jcorbett@st-phillips.co.uk

Recommended in Chancery, Commercial (Litigation)

Specialisation: Also at Serle Court (Lord Neill of Bladen QC) Lincoln's Inn (020) 7242 6105. Practises in commercial, company, insolvency and employment law and particularly cases under Company Director's Disqualification Act.

Prof. Memberships: Fellow of Chartered Institute of Arbitrators; CEDR accredited mediator; member of Chancery Bar Association; Employment Law Bar Association; Professional Negligence Bar Association; COMBAR and PBA.

Career: LLB and LLM (European Legal Studies), University of Exeter. Called in 1975. Irish Bar (1981) and Northern Irish Bar (1994). Joined present chambers in 1983. Lecturer in European and commercial law, 1975-77 (Leicester University). QC, 1999. Recorder, 2000 (Asst Recorder 1996-00).

CORDARA, Roderick QC

Essex Court Chambers (Gordon Pollock QC) London (020) 7813 8000
cordara@aol.com

Recommended in Tax

Specialisation: Indirect tax and duties law and VAT planning; insurance and reinsurance litigation; shipping and shipbuilding work; banking; film industry litigation; oil and gas disputes; general business litigation.

Prof. Memberships: Revenue Bar Association; COMBAR; LMAA.

Career: Trinity Hall, Cambridge: BA (Law) (1st class) 1974. Called to the Bar 1975. Queen's Counsel 1994. Senior Counsel (NSW) 2000.

Publications: Editor, 'Indirect Tax Intelligence'.

Personal: Born 1953.

CORFIELD, Sheelagh

St John's Chambers (Christopher Sharp QC) Bristol (0117) 921 3456

Recommended in Family

CORNER, Timothy

4-5 Gray's Inn Square (Elizabeth Appleby QC & David Mole QC) London (020) 74045252

Recommended in Administrative & Public Law, Planning

Specialisation: Major part of practice is in the fields of town and country planning and compulsory purchase, and public law including education, local government and environmental law. Planning work includes appeals throughout the country relating to housing, retail, employment, minerals, waste, listed buildings and conservation areas. Interesting recent cases include Delta v Secretary of State [2000] 80 P&CR 76, Court of Appeal, planning conditions and obligations, R v North Warwickshire DC (Times 9th March 2001), Court of Appeal, alternative sites as material considerations in planning, W v Special Educational Needs Tribunal (Times, 12th December 2000), Court of Appeal, Special Educational Needs, R v Knowsley Magistrates Court [2001] Env. LR 525, Divisional Court, environmental law, natural justice by magistrates. Recent public enquiries include appearances for Barratt Homes, Land Securities plc, Legal and General, Tesco, B&Q, and Westminster, Leeds and Liverpool City Councils.

Prof. Memberships: Member [and former Committee member] of Planning & Environment Bar Association, Administrative Law Bar Association, United Kingdom Environmental Law Association, and South Eastern Circuit.

Career: Called to the Bar 1981. Appointed Junior Counsel to the Crown, A Panel, 1999. Member, Oxford Joint Planning Law Conference Committee, 2001. Admitted to the Bar of Gibralter 1996.

Publications: Publications include article at [1998] JPL 301 'Planning, Environment and the European Convention on Human Rights.' Frequent speaker at conferences on planning and public law and human rights.

Personal: Educated at Bolton School 1966 to 1976 and Magdalen College, Oxford (Demy, MA Jurisprudence and BCL) 1976 to 1980. Languages include French, Italian and Spanish. Leisure pursuits include singing (studying with Prof. Ian Kennedy at Guildhall School of Music and Drama), walking, gardens and comparative philology. Born 25th July 1958. Lives in London.

CORRIGAN, Peter A.

2-4 Tudor Street (Richard Ferguson QC) London (020) 7797 7111
corrigan@rfqc-law.co.uk

Recommended in Crime

Specialisation: Crime, civil actions against the police.

CORY-WRIGHT, Charles

39 Essex Street (Nigel Pleming QC) London (020) 7832 1111

Recommended in Personal Injury

Specialisation: Main areas of practice: professional negligence, personal injury, insurance, construction. Reported cases: personal injury – Biesheuvel v Birrell (enhanced multiplier for foreign claimant), Nicholls v Rushton (no recovery of damages for shock), Giles v Thompson (CA, HL) (legality of credit hire agreements), Campbell v Mylchreest, Sharp v Pereira (jurisdiction re interim payments), Cutter v Eagle Star (CA, HL) (a car park is not a 'road' for the purpose of the RTA); construction – Barclays v Fairclough (contributory negligence and contract), SAS v John Laing (retention of title clauses); insurance – Banque Financiere v Skandia (insurers duty of utmost good faith).

Prof. Memberships: COMBAR.

COSGROVE, Patrick QC

Broad Chare Chambers (Patrick Cosgrove QC) Newcastle upon Tyne (0191) 232 0541

Recommended in Crime

COTTER, Barry

Old Square Chambers (John Hendy QC) London (0117) 9277 1111
cotter@oldsquarechambers.co.uk
Old Square Chambers (John Hendy QC) Bristol (0117) 9277 1111
cotter@oldsquarechambers.co.uk

Recommended in Personal Injury, Product Liability

Specialisation: All aspects of product liability law, personal injury, health and safety at work, public inquiries and multi-party actions. Appeared in Clapham Junction Rail Inquiry, Strangeways (Woolf) Inquiry, Ashworth Hospital Inquiry, Severn Tunnel Inquiry, Cowden, Southall and Ladbroke Grove Train Crash Inquiries. Cases include Richardson v LRC [2001] PIQR; Williams v BOC 2000 [PIQR] Q 253; MRS Environmental Service Ltd v Marsh [1997] 1 All ER 92; Coventry City Council v Ackerman [1995] Crim. LR 140; P&M Supplies v Walsall [1994] Crim LR 590; Deane v Ealing [1993] ICR 329; R v Secretary of State ex p POA; 'The Times' 28 October 1991. Counsel in the Guards and Shunters multi-party deafness action, larium and organophosphate action.

Prof. Memberships: Personal Injury Bar Association; committee member 1995-99.

Career: LLB; called to Bar in 1985.

Publications: Author 'Defective and Unsafe Products; Law and Practice' (Butterworths 1996).

Personal: LLB University College, Lincoln's Inn, scholarship. Based in London and Bristol.

COULSON, Peter QC

Keating Chambers (Richard Fernyhough QC) London +44 (0) 20 7544 2600
pcoulson@keatingchambers.com

Recommended in Construction

Specialisation: Involved in all types of engineering, construction and related disputes, in the TCC and in arbitration in the UK, Hong Kong, USA and the West Indies; reported cases include: Ashville v Elmer; Ben Barrett v Boot; Barker v Leyden; British Airways v PDP and McAlpine; Copthorne v Bovis; Design 5 v Keniston; Kruger Tissues v Frank Galliers; McAlpine Humbrook v McDermott; Marston v Barnard; Regalian v LDDC; Wates v Bredero; Wessex v HLM; Woodspring v Venn.

Career: Qualified 1982; Gray's Inn; Member of Keating Chambers since 1984; associate of the Chartered Institute of Arbitrators 1990; contributor to 'Construction Law Yearbook'; contributing editor of 'Lloyds Law Reports'; co-author of 'Professional Negligence and Liability' (LLP).

Personal: Lord Wandsworth College; University of Keele (BA Hons Law, English 2.1). Born 1958; resides London. Interests: British art, architecture, music, comedy, cricket. Working knowledge of French.

COUSINS, Jeremy QC

St Philip's Chambers (John Randall QC) Birmingham (0121) 246 7000

Recommended in Commercial (Litigation)

Specialisation: Commercial litigation and professional negligence. AIB v Martin & Gold 2000 2 All ER (Comm) 686 (construction of mortgage deeds). Barry v Ablerex

2001 EWC A Cir 433 (future loss multipliers); Acton v Graham Pearce 1997 3 AII ER 909 (solicitors negligence). Midland Chancery & Commercial Bar Association.
Career: Call 1977; Assistant Recorder 1996; Silk 1999; Recorder 2000.
Personal: Oxford School; Warwick University LIB (Hons); Married with three children; sidesman and PCC member St Anne's, Moseley. Interests include France and Italy; their languages, wine and food.

COWARD, Stephen QC

7 Bedford Row (David Farrer QC) London (020) 7242 3555

Recommended in Crime

Specialisation: Specialist in all aspects of serious crime from murder to fraud. Appeared in the following cases: 1. R v Stanley – assistant bosun Herald of Free Enterprise. 2. R v Nedrick and R v Slack – the liability of secondary parties in murder. 3. R v Ivor Jones and others – the leading authority on section 16 Firearms Act 1968. 4. R v Prime – espionage. 5. R v John Tanner – the murder of Rachel McLean, the Oxford undergraduate. 6. R v Leslie Jones – murder allegation turning on the cooling rate of dead bodies. 7. R v Hayes and others – acted for the SFO. 8. R v Cheung – acted for the SFO. 9. R v Robinson – the 'Yardie' trial. 10. R v Baroness de Stempel – acted for the Defendant.
Career: Educated at King James Grammar School, Huddersfield and University College, London (LL.B). 1962: Lecturer in Law and Constitutional History, University College, London and Bramshill Police College. 1964: Called to the Bar (Inner Temple). 1980: Appointed Recorder. 1984: Took Silk. 1997: High Court Examiner (The State of New York v Don King Boxing Promotions).
Personal: Born 1937, lives in Northampton. Leisure pursuits: gardening, wine, singing.

COX, Laura QC

Cloisters (Laura Cox QC) London (020) 7827 4000 lc@cloisters.com

Recommended in Clinical Negligence, Employment, Human Rights

Specialisation: Practice is divided evenly between employment law, discrimination and professional (principally clinical) negligence with increasing public law and general human rights work. Employment work includes discrimination and equal pay and is predominantly appellate advisory work and representation, with some judicial review. Clinical negligence work involves claims of the utmost severity, including cerebral palsy. Recent cases include: Webb v EMO Air Cargo (pregnancy discrimination), R v MoD ex parte Smith & Others (dismissal of armed forces homosexuals), Burton and Rhule v De Vere Hotels (the 'Bernard Manning' case), Harrods v Elmi (employers' liability for acts of racial discrimination by third parties), FBU v Knowles and Johnson (meaning of 'industrial action'), Crees v Royal London Insurance/Greaves v Kwiksave (maternity – the right to return to work), Smith v Gardner Merchant (homosexual harassment in the workplace), P v S and Somerset County Council (compensation for transsexual discrimination), Sheffield and Horsham v UK (transsexuals birth certificates – amicus submissions to the ECHR on behalf of Liberty), Aydin v Turkey (submissions to the ECHR for Amnesty with Peter Duffy QC on the rape of women prisoners as torture and the requirements, under international standards, for the investigation into allegations of torture of detainees), Davies v Girobank plc, Halfpenny v IGE Medical Systems Ltd (maternity discrimination), Enderby and Others v Frenchay Health Authority (speech therapists – equal pay), D'Souza v London Borough of Lambeth (racial discrimination compensation), R v Secretary of State for Trade and Industry ex parte BECTU (qualifying period under Working Time Regulations, reference to ECJ), K.B v NHS Pensions Agency (transsexuals' pension entitlements), Mahmood v Siggins (GP's negligent treatment of manic depressive), Drury v Grimsby HA (limitation), Bowler v Walker (negligent treatment of psychiatric patient), R v Secretary of State for Social Security ex parte Armstrong (denial of care component of disability living allowance). Pearce v Governors of Mayfield School (homophobic harassment of teacher). Anyanwu & Obuzoen v South Bank University and Students' Union ("aiding" under Race Relations Act) – Bellinger v Bellinger (validity of transexual marriage). Clients include trade unions and individual members, applicants and respondents in employment and discrimination cases, the Equal Opportunities Commission, the Commission for Racial Equality and claimants and defendants in clinical negligence cases. Regular conference and seminar speaker or chair in her fields of practice. Author of discrimination chapter in 'Advising Gay and Lesbian Clients, A Lawyer's Guide' for Butterworths.
Prof. Memberships: Employment Law Bar Association, Professional Negligence Bar Association, Administrative Law Bar Association, Personal Injuries Bar Association, Legal Action Group, Liberty. Member of the Council, Justice. Member of Liberty Human Rights expert counsel panel, and of Human Rights Act Research Project steering group, Kings College. Vice President of the Institute of Employment Rights.
Career: Queens Counsel since 1994. Appointed Recorder 1995 and part-time Judge at Employment Appeal Tribunal 2000. Elected Head of Chambers at *Cloisters* 1995. Chairman of Bar Council Equal Opportunities Committee and member of General Management Committee. United Kingdom representative on the International Labour Organisation Committee of Independent Experts. Elected Bencher of the Inner Temple 1999.
Personal: Educated at Wolverhampton High School for Girls 1963-70 and London University 1970-75 (LL.B and LL.M). Leisure pursuits (work and three children permitting) include music, cooking, theatre, cinema, watching football.

COX, Raymond

Fountain Court (Anthony Boswood QC) London (020) 7583 3335

Recommended in Banking, Insurance

Specialisation: Principal areas of practice are all aspects of reinsurance and insurance, banking (including documentary credits, bills, financial services and credit security) professional negligence (including valuers, accountants, solicitors and banks) and commercial law generally.
Career: Raymond Cox is co-editor of 'Commercial Court Procedure', Cox and Moriarty (Sweet & Maxwell, 1999) and 'Law of Bank Payments', Brindle and Cox (2nd ed, Sweet & Maxwell, 1999) and has lectured on insurance and banking.

COX, Simon

Doughty Street Chambers (Geoffrey Robertson QC) London (020) 7404 1313 s.cox@doughtystreet.co.uk

Recommended in Immigration

Specialisation: Immigration, social security and public law. Particular expertise in welfare support for immigrants. Instructed in test cases by Child Poverty Action Group (CPAG), Joint Council for Welfare of Immigrants and British Union for the Abolition of Vivisection (Home Office interpretation of animal experiments law). Also experience before child support commissioners. Reported cases include: M v Secretary of State, HL [disability benefits for immigrants]; Westminster v Mehanne, HL [housing benefit]; Kadhim v Brent, CA [housing benefit]; Megarry v Secretary of State, CA [disability benefit: IQ tests for autistic child]; ex p Restrepo, CA [child benefit for asylum seeker]; ex p Jeyeanthan, CA [validity of immigration appeal]; Aramide v Secretary of State, CA [deportation]; ex p Akpre, CA [appeal procedure]. Co-author 'Migration and Social Security Handbook,' CPAG, since 1997. Co-author 'Child Support Handbook' 1996-00, CPAG. Regular lecturer to solicitors.
Prof. Memberships: ILPA, ALBA, Bar European Group, Liberty and Justice.
Career: Called to Bar 1992. Social Security and immigration caseworker at Free Representation Unit 1993-95.

CRAGG, Stephen

Doughty Street Chambers (Geoffrey Robertson QC) London (020) 7404 1313 s.cragg@doughtystreet.co.uk

Recommended in Administrative & Public Law

Specialisation: Public law in social welfare and human rights areas, especially community care, mental health, education, travellers' rights, coroners' inquests and policing. Also environmental law cases. Reported cases include Rexworthy v Secretary of State [1998] JPL (section 288 planning appeal – human rights factors to be taken into account in planning decisions involving travelers); R v Gloucestershire County Council ex p Barry [1998] AC 581 (taking resources into account when assessing need for services for disabled people); R v Powys CC ex p Hambidge (1998) 1 CCLR, CA (power to charge for services to disabled persons); R(A) v Lambeth LBC (2001) Times 2 July (nature of duty under section 17 Children Act 1989).
Prof. Memberships: Administrative Law Bar Association; Lawyers for Liberty; Police Actions Lawyers Group.
Career: Called to the Bar 1996. Project solicitor to the Public Law Project (1993-96), developing test case strategy in social welfare law areas. Other area of expertise is in civil actions against the police. Fellow in Public Law Essex University 1997-99; and a member of the Civil Justice Council (1998-00).
Publications: Co- author 'Police Misconduct: Legal Remedies'; consultant editor 'UK Human Rights Reports'; legal update editor for the 'Community Care Law Reports'; co-author of 'An Applicant's Guide to Judicial Review', Sweet and Maxwell (1995).
Personal: LLB (Hons) Kings College, London; MA Sociology and Law (Brunel): Interests: travel; cinema; two young children.

CRAMPIN, Peter QC

11 New Square (Sonia Proudman QC) London (020) 7831 0081

Recommended in Charities

Specialisation: Chancery:- property litigation and advice, trusts, charities, pensions, insolvency, professional negligence, Court of Protection.
Career: Called 1976. 2nd Junior Counsel to the A-G in charity matters 1988-93. Took silk 1993. Recorder.
Personal: Born 7 July 1946.

CRANE, Michael QC

Fountain Court (Anthony Boswood QC) London (020) 7583 3335

Recommended in Aviation, Commercial (Litigation), Insurance

CRASNOW, Rachel

Cloisters (Laura Cox QC) London (020) 7827 4000 rc@cloisters.com

Recommended in Employment

Specialisation: Employment law, with a particular emphasis on discrimination and human rights issues. Practices in all areas of the employment law field from equal pay to individual and collective rights. Also undertakes range of medical law work, public law, civil actions against the police and inquests.
Prof. Memberships: ELBA, ELA, PIBA, DLA, Bar Pro-Bono Unit.
Career: Represents both Applicants and Respondents in wide variety of courts/tribunals. Undertakes casework/research for human rights bodies. Standing counsel for the BPS. Selected for Liberty's specialist Human Rights Litigation Unit panel. Counsel to the 1999-00 Turner Inquiry. Instructed in the 2001 Victoria Climbie Inquiry. Lectures for organsiations like JUSTICE and the Law Society. Appears under the ELAAS scheme at the EAT. Voluntary employment Law Advisor at Camden Law Centre 1996-00. Member of employment panel of Legal Network Television.
Publications: Co-author of 'Employment Law and the Human Rights Act', Blackstone Press, 2001 and an editor of the 'Educational Law Journal's Case Commentaries'. Writes for a range of legal periodicals; has written

responses to many Government Consultation Papers about forthcoming legislation on issues inluding terrorism, the right to work flexible hours and transsexuals' rights.
Personal: Educated at Pembroke College Oxford and City University London. Middle Temple Diplock Scholarship 1993; Pegasus Scholarship 1999 (based at Human Rights and Equal Opportunities Commission, Sydney).

CREAN, Anthony
5 Fountain Court (Anthony Barker QC) Birmingham (0121) 606 0500
Recommended in Planning

CRIGMAN, David QC
1 Fountain Court (David Crigman QC) Birmingham (0121) 236 5721
Recommended in Crime

CROOKENDEN, Simon QC
Essex Court Chambers (Gordon Pollock QC) London (020) 7813 8000 clerksroom@essexcourt-chambers.co.uk
Recommended in Energy & Natural Resources
Specialisation: Shipping. Insurance and Reinsurance: policies; proportional and excess of loss involving both Lloyd's of London and the company market. Building/Engineering. Commodity sales. Arbitration. Energy & Utilities
Prof. Memberships: Fellow of the Chartered Institute of Arbitrators. Panel member, Lloyd's of London Arbitration Panel. Accredited mediator.
Career: Corpus Christi College, Cambridge MA (Mechanical Sciences). Called to the Bar 1975. Queen's Counsel 1996.
Personal: Born 1946.

CROSS, James
4 Pump Court London (020) 7842 5555 chambers@4pumpcourt.com
Recommended in Professional Negligence
Specialisation: A general and varied practice in common law and commercial litigation/arbitration, but with particular emphasis on professional negligence (whether of architects, engineers, the medical profession, solicitors, surveyors or valuers), construction and civil engineering, insurance and reinsurance, banking, product liability, sale of goods and commodities and contractual disputes (both domestic and international).
Prof. Memberships: COMBAR, London Common Law and Commercial Bar Association, TECBAR.
Career: Called to the Bar in 1985 and joined 4 Pump Court in 1986.
Personal: Educated at Shrewsbury and Magdalen College, Oxford.

CROWLEY, Jane QC
30 Park Place (John Jenkins QC) Cardiff (029) 2039 8421
Recommended in Family
Specialisation: Also One Garden Court Family Law Chambers (Miss Eleanor F Platt QC & Miss Alison Ball QC). Child care and other Children Act applications, ancillary relief, public law including education, family related crime eg child abuse, rape etc.
Prof. Memberships: Family Law Bar Association (regional representative).
Career: LL.B (Hons) London. Graduated 1976. Practised 1976-80 at 34 Park Place. 1980 to date at 30 Park Place. Recorder 1996. QC 1998. Director of Education, Wales and Chester Circuit. Deputy Judge of the Family Division (1999). Legal Chair of Mental Health Review Tribunal (1999).
Personal: Married, two children.

CROXFORD, Ian QC
Wilberforce Chambers (Edward Nugee QC) London (020) 7306 0102
Recommended in Chancery, Fraud
Specialisation: Professional negligence (in particular accountants). Administrative law, construction and civil engineering. Crime ('white collar' and consumer protection). Cases include Morgan Crucible v Hill Samuel & Co and Others; Wallace Smith Trust Co v Deloitte Haskins & Sells, 'Bermuda Fire'. Considerable experience in advising in respect of overseas work and has appeared many times in the Cayman Islands and also in Bermuda.
Prof. Memberships: Chancery Bar Association, COMBAR, Criminal Bar Association.
Career: Called to the Bar 1976; QC 1993; First Class Honours degree in law; joined Wilberforce Chambers in 1997.

CROXFORD, Thomas
Blackstone Chambers (Presiley Baxendale QC & Charles Flint QC) London (020) 7583 1770 clerks@blackstonechambers.com
Recommended in Employment
Specialisation: Specialist in employment, financial services and commercial law. Particular interests in employment law-restraint of trade, confidentiality, fiduciary duties and discrimination. Recent cases: GRE v Arnold; DTI v Ward; Devoy v World Duty Free, EAT; British Gas v Clarke-EAT; CMS Dolphin Ltd v Simonet. Others: Blue Circle v MOD [1999] Ch 289 CA; Christmas v Hampshire [1995] 2 AC 633.
Prof. Memberships: ELA, COMBAR
Career: Call: 1992
Personal: Clare College, Cambridge (MA).

CRYSTAL, Jonathan
Cloisters (Laura Cox QC) London (020) 7827 4000 jonathancrystal@cloisters.com
Recommended in Sport
Specialisation: Specialist sports lawyer. Notable cases include: Football League v Chesterfield FC, ISL v Mars Inc, McCord v Cornforth and Swansea City, Watson and Bradford City v Gray and Huddersfield Town, Redman v British Lions, Sarfraz Nawaz v Allan Lamb, Duffy v Newcastle United FC, Margate Town v FA, Bayfield v Eagle Star, and Hinchcliffe v BSMA. Advisory work including Rodney Walker, Prince Naseem Hamed, Brian Lara, Stan Collymore, Audley Harrison, Andy Farrall, Joe Kinnear, Kenny Dalglish, Ellery Hanley, Robbie Fowler, ISL, Leeds United and Liverpool FC, Bristol RFC and WICB. Further specialism in defamation and business law.
Prof. Memberships: Bar Sports Law Group, British Association for Sport and Law, Combar and Sports Steering Group NSPCC.
Career: Called to the Bar 1972. *2* Harcourt Buildings 1973-92. Cloisters 1992- the present. Legal Reader Associated Newspapers until 1985.
Personal: Educated Leeds Grammar School and Queen Mary College, University of London 1968-71. Director, Tottenham Hotspur FC 1991-93, Cardiff city 2000-. Married with young children living in Central London.

CRYSTAL, Michael QC
3-4 South Square (Michael Crystal QC & Lord Alexander of Weedon QC) London (020) 7696 9900 clerks@southsquare.com
Recommended in Chancery, Company, Insolvency/Corporate Recovery
Specialisation: Commercial and financial law.
Career: Called to the Bar, Middle Temple, 1970; Queen's Counsel, 1984; Bencher Middle Temple, 1993; Deputy High Court Judge, since 1995; Admitted to the Bars of the Bahamas, Bermuda, the British Virgin Islands, the Cayman Islands, Gibraltar, Hong Kong and the Isle of Man for specific cases; Senior Visiting Fellow Centre for Commercial Law Studies, University of London since 1987; DTI Inspector 1988-89; Member Insolvency Rules Advisory Committee 1993-97; Member Financial Law Panel since 1996; Member Advisory Council, University of Oxford Law Foundation since 1998; Honorary Fellow, Queen Mary and Westfield College, University of London 1996; Honorary Fellow, Society for Advanced Legal Studies 1997.

CULLEN, Edmund
Maitland Chambers (Michael Lyndon-Stanford QC & Charles Aldous QC) London (020) 7406 1200 ecullen@maitlandchambers.com
Recommended in Media & Entertainment
Specialisation: A broad range of chancery and commercial work including media and entertainment, professional negligence (in particular involving solicitors and accountants), company and insolvency litigation.
Prof. Memberships: Chancery Bar Association and COMBAR.
Career: Called to the Bar 1990.
Personal: Educated at Winchester, University of Bristol.

CULLEN, Felicity
Gray's Inn Tax Chambers (Milton Grundy) London (020) 7242 2642 fe@taxbar.com
Recommended in Tax
Specialisation: All aspects of revenue law including in particular commercial and corporate tax, capital gains tax, stamp duty, taxation of individuals and tax litigation.
Prof. Memberships: Revenue Bar Association. Chancery Bar Association. Called to the Bar 1985. Joined Gray's Inn Tax Chambers 1986.
Career: LLB Birmingham (1st Class Hons), LLM Cantab.

CULLUM, Michael
Albion Chambers (Charles Barton QC & Neil Ford QC) Bristol (0117) 927 2144
Recommended in Crime

CUNNINGHAM, Graham
Littman Chambers (Mark Littman QC) London (020) 7404 4866
Recommended in Alternative Dispute Resolution, Information Technology
Specialisation: Contentious and non-contentious computer, information technology and telecommunications work, including national and international regulatory telecommunications issues; technology transfer; all types of commercial trading relationships, intellectual property law and competition law. Former legal director, company secretary and management team member with computer company Wang, and intellectual property and technology transfer legal adviser with ITT Corporation. Accredited mediator with CEDR for alternative dispute resolution.
Career: Called 1976. Joined Francis Taylor Building in 1994. Littman Chambers (2000).
Personal: Educated at Cranleigh School and Brunel University.

CUNNINGHAM, Mark QC
Maitland Chambers (Michael Lyndon-Stanford QC & Charles Aldous QC) London (020) 7406 1200
Recommended in Chancery
Specialisation: General chancery practitioner, with a bias towards commercially orientated litigation and particular specialisms in the disqualification of directors and company law. He has appeared in reported cases concerning: company law, directors' disqualification, personal insolvency, sale of land, landlord and tenant, rent reviews, easements, land registration, copyright, passing off, entertainment law, the Inheritance Act, subrogation, the Court of Protection, the Copyright Tribunal and betting and gaming. He has also been appointed as a DTI Inspector in relation to insider dealing matters.
Prof. Memberships: Chancery Bar Association, Patent Bar Association.
Career: Called 1980. Appointed Junior Counsel to the Crown (Chancery), February 1992. Appointed Junior Counsel to the Crown 'A
Personal: Educated at Stonyhurst College and Magdalen College Oxford (BA History). Born 6 June 1956. Lives in Buckinghamshire. Four children.

CUSWORTH, Nicholas
1 Mitre Court Buildings (Bruce Blair QC) London (020) 7797 7070
cusworth@imcb.com
Recommended in Family
Specialisation: Ancillary relief. Private law Children Act applications.
Prof. Memberships: Family Law Bar Association. Committee member elected 1998.
Career: MA (Oxon). Called to the Bar 1986. Occasional lecturer for Professional Conferences.
Publications: Contributor to 'Essential Family Practice 2000'.
Personal: Married (to Rachel Platts of Counsel), one daughter.

DAGNALL, John
9 Old Square (Michael Driscoll QC) London (020) 7405 4682
Recommended in Property Litigation
Specialisation: Specialisations are chancery, commercial and property litigation; including banking, trusts, civil fraud, insolvency, property (including mortgages and landlord and tenant) and professional negligence.
Prof. Memberships: Member of Chancery Bar Association, Professional Negligence Bar Association and Parliamentary Bar Mess.
Career: Bristol Grammar School, St John's College, Oxford (BA (Jurisprudence – 1st Class), BCL). Called Nov 1983, tenant Mar 1985.
Personal: Family, church, real tennis, bridge. Further details on application.

DARLING, Paul QC
Keating Chambers (Richard Fernyhough QC) London (020) 7544 2600
Recommended in Arbitration (International), Construction
Specialisation: Building and engineering cases in the UK and abroad. Important cases include: Temloc v Errill; Richard Roberts v Douglas Smith; Wyatt v Gleeson; Yeandle v Wynn Realisations; Vascroft v Seeboard; Mooney v Boot; plc v McAlpine; McAlpine v Unex; Hunt v Paul Sykes; Chatbrown v McAlpine; Barking & Dagenham v Stamford Asphalt; Holbeck Hall Hotel v Scarborough; Flannery v Halifax; BHP v British Steel; Kelston Sparkes v Balfour Beatty.
Career: Qualified 1983. Middle Temple. Queens Counsel 1999. Director Family Pharmaceutical Company; Editor 'Construction Law Newsletter'; member of editorial team ' Keating on Building Contracts'.
Personal: Winchester College; St Edmund Hall, Oxford (1981 BA, 1982 BCL). Horseracing, Newcastle United.

DASHWOOD, Robert
Renaissance Chambers (Brian Jubb & Henry Setright QC) London (020) 7404 1111
Recommended in Family

DAVEY, Michael
4 Essex Court (Nigel Teare QC) London (020) 7653 5653
Recommended in Shipping

DAVIDSON, Katharine
1 Mitre Court Buildings (Bruce Blair QC) London (020) 7797 7070
Recommended in Family
Specialisation: Handles all types of family law, but principally financial relief claims.
Prof. Memberships: Family Law Bar Association.
Career: Educated at Epsom College 1978-80 and the University of Oxford 1981-84. Born 19th June 1962. Called to the Bar in 1987 and joined 1 Mitre Court Buildings in 1988.

DAVIDSON, Nicholas QC
Four New Square (Justin Fenwick QC) London (020) 7822 2000
n.davidson@4newsquare.com
Recommended in Professional Negligence
Specialisation: Solicitors' and financial negligence. Other main areas of work cover general commercial cases, including insurance disputes and computer litigation.
Prof. Memberships: Professional Negligence Bar Association (Chairman 1997-99), Bar European Group, COMBAR, Chancery Bar Association, Society for Computers and Law.
Career: Called 1974; joined present Chambers 1999. Silk 1993.
Personal: Educated at Winchester 1964-69 (Scholar) and Trinity College Cambridge (Exhibitioner in Economics) 1969-72. Certificate of Honour, Bar Finals.

DAVIES, Helen
Brick Court Chambers (Christopher Clarke QC) London (020) 7379 3550
davies@brickcourt.co.uk
Recommended in Arbitration (International), Commercial (Litigation), Insurance
Specialisation: All aspects of Commercial and EU law, including professional negligence, insurance/reinsurance, banking, oil and gas disputes, competition and human rights.
Career: Called November 1991. Brick Court Chambers (1992-present). Stage in European Commission, DGIV (Transport) 1993. Appointed Member of the B Panel to the Crown, 1999.

DAVIES, Huw QC
30 Park Place (John Jenkins QC) Cardiff (029) 2039 8421
Recommended in Crime
Specialisation: Criminal law, particularly Customs and Excise work, environmental protection law, fraud and drug trafficking.
Prof. Memberships: CBA.
Career: LLB. M.Phil. A Recorder. Standing Counsel to HM Customs & Excise.

DAVIES, Jane
Crown Office Chambers (Michael Spencer QC & Christopher Purchas QC) London (020) 7797 8100
davies@crownofficechambers.com
Recommended in Construction
Prof. Memberships: Professional negligence in a building context (architects, engineers, quantity surveyors, project administrators) as well as accountants and solicitors; insurance policy disputes, contract and commercial disputes. Numerous large claims in the building industry, including contractual disputes.
Career: Read English at Lady Margaret Hall, Oxford, entrance scholarship; diploma in Arts Administration, Arts Council of Great Britain, worked as arts administrator and stage designer before coming to the Bar. Jules Thorn Scholar (Middle Temple).
Personal: Second home in France: fluent French.

DAVIES, Lindsay
Fenners Chambers (Lindsay Davies) Cambridge (01223) 368761
Recommended in Family

DAVIES, Nicola QC
3 Serjeants' Inn (Robert Francis QC & John Grace QC) London (020) 7427 5000
Recommended in Clinical Negligence
Specialisation: Medical law including inquiries, professional disciplinary tribunals and crime. Cases include Conjoined Twins, R v Doctor Harold Shipman, BSE Inquiry, GMC – case of Bristol heart surgeons. Chairman of the Committee of Inquiry into the death of Jonathan Newby (Mental Health).
Career: Called to the Bar in 1976. Silk 1992. Recorder 1998.
Personal: Birmingham University (LL.B).

DAVIES, Owen QC
Two Garden Court (Ian Macdonald QC & Owen Davies QC) London (020) 7353 1633
Recommended in Crime, Human Rights

DAVIES, Rhodri QC
One Essex Court (Lord Grabiner QC) London (020) 7583 2000
Recommended in Banking, Commercial (Litigation)
Specialisation: Principal area of practice is banking and professional negligence including disputes over derivatives. Acted in swaps litigation, representing various banks in Hazell v London Borough of Hammersmith & Fulham and in restitution claims in Kleinwort Benson v Birmingham and Kleinworth Benson v Lincoln. Acted for KPMG in Law Society v KPMG and for the liquidator in the litigation against the auditor of Barings Europe. Also handles general commercial work, encompassing contractual disputes, sale of goods, arbitration, insurance and reinsurance.
Prof. Memberships: South Eastern Circuit, LCLCBA.
Career: Called to the Bar in 1979 and joined 1 Essex Court in 1980. QC 1999.
Personal: Educated at Winchester College 1970-74 and Downing College, Cambridge 1975-78. Leisure pursuits include running, walking and sailing. Born 29th January 1957. Lives in Harpenden, Herts.

DAVIES, Richard QC
39 Essex Street (Nigel Pleming QC) London (020) 7832 1111
Recommended in Personal Injury

DAVIES, Stephen
8 King St (Keith Armitage QC) Manchester (0161) 214 4624
sdavies@eightkingstreet.co.uk
Recommended in Commercial (Litigation)
Specialisation: Practice: Commercial litigation of all kinds, construction, professional negligence and banking, predominantly in North West.
Prof. Memberships: Northern Circuit Commercial Bar Association; Tec Bar; Professional Negligence Bar Association.
Career: Educated at Baines' School, Poulton-le-Fylde and Downing College, Cambridge. Called to the Bar in 1985.

DAVIES, Stephen QC
Guildhall Chambers (Adrian Palmer QC) Bristol (0117) 927 3366
Recommended in Chancery, Commercial (Litigation), Insolvency/Corporate Recovery

DAVIES, Trefor
Iscoed Chambers (Trefor Davies) Swansea (01792) 652988/9
Recommended in Crime
Specialisation: Crime

DAVIES-JONES, Jonathan
3 Verulam Buildings (Christopher Symons QC & John Jarvis QC) London (020) 7831 8441
chambers@3vb.com
Recommended in Banking
Specialisation: General commercial work, including banking, insurance and reinsurance, fraud, professional negligence, sale of goods and commercial agency.
Career: MA (Cantab). Worked as an investment banker 1988-92. Called to the Bar in 1994 and joined 3 Verulam Buildings. In 1995 spent six months as a judicial assistant in the Commercial Court.

DAVIS, Glen
3-4 South Square (Michael Crystal QC & Lord Alexander of Weedon QC) London (020) 7696 9900
glendavis@southsquare.com
Recommended in Insolvency/Corporate Recovery
Specialisation: Business, commercial and financial law,

in particular banking, corporate restructuring and insolvency. E-commerce, e-banking and internet law, and related aspects of computer and intellectual property law. Regulatory aspects of UK web-sites and financial restructuring of dot-com companies. Injunctive relief. Fraud, tracing claims and recovery of assets. Duties of directors and insolvency practitioners. Insolvent partnerships and limited partnerships. Company law. Professional negligence and general corporate disputes and advice. Recent cases have included Gwembe Valley Development Co v Koshy (Court of Appeal: construction of debentures); FJL Realisations Ltd (Court of Appeal: priority of payments in Administration); Re Brelec Installations Ltd (Blackburne J: effects of termination on funds in voluntary arrangement); Re Double S Printers (Jonathan Parker J: fixed charge over book debts); advising in connection with provisional liquidations of HIH and Rafidain Bank, and numerous Administrations including Falmers Jeans and AB Airlines.
Prof. Memberships: Member, Insolvency Lawyers Association; associate member, R3; member, Insol Europe; member, International Bar Association; member, International Chamber of Commerce; member, Justice; member, Society for Computers and Law.
Career: Previously television producer/director (BBC, Channel 4, satellite television). Called to Bar 1992, member of Chambers at 3/4 South Square since 1993. Member, Insolvency Courts Users Committee (2001-). Chair, Media Board, Society for Computers and Law (2000-). Panelist, Legal Technology Awards 2001
Publications: Editor, Butterworths 'Insolvency Law Handbook'; consultant editor, Butterworths 'Insolvency Law Manual' (prospective). Co-author, 'Insolvent Partnerships' (Jordans, 1996). Contributing editor, 'Totty & Moss on Insolvency'.
Personal: Educated University College School, Hampstead, and Balliol College, Oxford (Goldsmith Scholar, 1st Class Hons). MA (Oxon), Dip Law (City). Diploma in Investment Management from London Business School. Interests include contemporary art and garden design.

DAVIS, Nigel QC
Maitland Chambers (Michael Lyndon-Stanford QC & Charles Aldous QC) London (020) 7406 1200 clerks@maitlandchambers.com
Recommended in Chancery, Company, Insolvency/Corporate Recovery, Media & Entertainment, Partnership
Specialisation: Principal area of practice is chancery, with emphasis on company, insolvency, banking, property and trust litigation and also general commercial litigation, both domestic and international. Has appeared in numerous reported cases, on subjects extending to: corporate and shareholders disputes; constructive trusts and tracing actions; international banking and fraud litigation; insolvency; and real property. Acted as counsel to the inquiry of the Board of Banking Supervision into the collapse of Barings Bank. Other areas of practice include professional negligence (solicitors); partnership; and media and entertainment.
Personal: Education: University College, Oxford (MA).

DAVIS-WHITE, Malcolm
4 Stone Buildings (Philip Heslop QC) London (020) 7242 5524 clerks@4stonebuildings.law.co.uk
Recommended in Company, Insolvency/Corporate Recovery
Specialisation: Principal area of practice encompasses company, insolvency and financial services law.
Prof. Memberships: Member of the Chancery Bar Association and Commercial Bar Association (COMBAR).
Career: Called to the Bar in 1984 and joined present chambers in 1985. Appointed Junior Counsel to the Crown (Chancery) in 1994.
Publications: Co-author (with Adrian Walters) on 'Directors' Disqualification and Practice'. Contributor to 'Atkin' Vol. 9 (Companies), and Vol. 10 (Companies winding up) and Butterworths' 'Practical Insolvency'.

Personal: Educated at St Edmund's College, Old Hall Green, Ware 1969-78 and Hertford College, Oxford 1979-83. Born 18th September 1960. Lives in Sidlesham, Chichester.

DE FREITAS, Anthony
4 Paper Buildings (Jean Ritchie QC) London (020) 7353 3366
Recommended in Agriculture
Specialisation: Sporting and entertainment contracts, professional negligence. Agricultural holdings. Warren v Mendy 1989 IWLR 853, Featherstone v Staples 1986 IWLR 861, John v George 1996 EGLR 1, Greenbank v Pickles 2001 AELR.
Prof. Memberships: Professional Negligence Bar Association. Agricultural Law Association.
Career: Stonyhurst College, St. John's College Oxford. MA Oxon, Recorder.
Personal: Married, cricket, bridge, horse racing, reading.

DE GARR ROBINSON, Anthony
One Essex Court (Lord Grabiner QC) London (020) 7583 2000
Recommended in Commercial (Litigation), Fraud, Insolvency/Corporate Recovery
Specialisation: Tony de Garr Robinson's practice includes a broad range of substantial commercial litigation, with emphasis on company law, insolvency, banking and transnational fraud. He has considerable experience of international asset tracing, including in the United States, Switzerland, Bermuda, the Channel Islands, the Cayman Islands and the British Virgin Islands. He also has expertise in entertainment and sports disputes.
Prof. Memberships: Commercial Bar Association and Chancery Bar Association.
Career: He was called to the English Bar in 1987. He is also a member of the Bar of the Eastern Caribbean Supreme Court in the Territory of the Virgin Islands.
Personal: He was born in 1963 and was educated at University College and at Harvard University (where he held a Kennedy Scholarship). On coming to the Bar, he was awarded both a Denning Scholarship and a Hardwicke Scholarship.

DE HAAN, Kevin QC
3 Raymond Buildings (Clive Nicholls QC) London (020) 7400 6400
Recommended in Consumer Law, Licensing

DE HAAS, Margaret QC
7 Harrington Street Chambers (David Steer QC & Robert Fordham QC & Iain Goldrein QC) Liverpool (0151) 242 0707 goldhaas@netcom.co.uk
Recommended in Family
Specialisation: Ancillary relief; child care; medical negligence, personal injury.
Prof. Memberships: Family Law Bar Association; Professional Negligence Bar Association.
Career: LL.B (Hons) (Bristol). Author of several books on personal injury litigation and ancillary relief. Recorder: Sits as Deputy High Court Judge, member of Criminal Injuries Compensation Board.
Personal: Theatre; reading; her children.

DE LA MARE, Thomas
Blackstone Chambers (Presiley Baxendale QC & Charles Flint QC) London (020) 7583 1770 tod@blackstonechambers.com
Recommended in Administrative & Public Law
Specialisation: Public law; EC law; human rights; commercial; IP and entertainment; employment.
Prof. Memberships: ALBA (Committee); BEG (Committee); ELA.
Publications: Lester & Pannick (Contributor).

DE LACY, Richard QC
3 Verulam Buildings (Christopher Symons QC & John Jarvis QC) London (020) 7831 8441 rdelacy@3vb.com
Recommended in Insolvency/Corporate Recovery
Specialisation: Principal area of practice is commercial law, particularly banking, finance, financial services, accountants', solicitors' and barristers' professional indemnity, insolvency, company law, property law and arbitration. Acts for clearing banks, major accountancy firms and leading insolvency practitioners.
Prof. Memberships: Fellow of The Chartered Institute of Arbitrators, COMBAR, Chancery Bar Association; Institute of Chartered Accountants Practice Regulation Review Committee; CEDR Accredited Mediator.
Career: Called to the Bar 1976. Bencher, Middle Temple. QC 2000.
Personal: Educated at Hymers College, Hull and Clare College, Cambridge (MA 1979).

DE MELLO, Rambert
6 King's Bench Walk (Sibghat Kadri QC) London (020) 7583 0695 / 7353 4931
Recommended in Immigration

DE NAVARRO, Michael QC
2 Temple Gardens (Dermod O'Brien QC) London (020) 7822 1200
Recommended in Health & Safety
Specialisation: Personal injury, professional and clinical negligence, insurance and health and safety at work. Reported personal injury cases include Adams v SEB [1993] (CA), Green v Building Scene [1994] (CA), O'Shea v Kingston-upon-Thames [1995] (CA), Hunter v Butler [1995] (CA), Jolley v LB of Sutton [1998] (CA). [2001] (HL). Other reported cases include Wentworth v Wiltshire CC [1992] (CA), Nykredit Mortgage Bank v Edward Erdman [1996] (HL), John Monroe (Acrylics) v LFCDA [1997] (CA), Day v Cook [2000].
Prof. Memberships: PIBA (Committee member 1995, Chairman 1997-99). Western Circuit.
Career: Called 1968, QC 1990, Recorder 1990. Bencher Inner Temple 2000.

DE SILVA, Desmond QC
2 Paper Buildings (Desmond de Silva QC) London (020) 7556 5500
Recommended in Crime

DEIN, Jeremy
3 Gray's Inn Square (Rock Tansey QC) London (020) 7520 5600
Recommended in Crime
Specialisation: Specialises in defence crime. Leading junior practice in serious crime of all types, including murder. Particular emphasis on appellate work, having conducted countless appeals for Justice. Recently conducted a chain of successful appeals against conviction which followed from Police Complaints Authority allegations of serious corruption within a branch of the flying squad Metropolitan Police. Also happy to take on pro-bono appellate work. Editor of Police Misconduct Revisited ('Criminal Law Review' October 2000), a detailed analysis of the most recent authorities concerning the Court of Appeal's approach in cases where police officer's face outstanding allegations at the time of a defendant's trial. Has also acted as Legal Adviser to BBC's Rough Justice programme, Channel 4 and other media outlets.
Prof. Memberships: Middle Temple.
Career: 2:1 Hons, University of London. Former lecturer in the Law of Evidence and Criminal Procedure.
Personal: Married with four children. Leisure interests include sport, reading, travel and Latin American dance.

DENNEY, Stuart
Deans Court Chambers (Stephen Grime QC) Manchester (0161) 214 600 denney@deanscourt.co.uk
Recommended in Crime
Specialisation: Crime, including fraud. Actions against the Police.

Prof. Memberships: Criminal Bar Association.
Career: St. Johns School, Leatherhead. Gonville & Caius College Cambridge 77-80. M.A.
Personal: Married, One son. Interests: Rugby Union, Malt Whisky.

DENNIS, Mark
6 King's Bench Walk (Roy Amlot QC) London (0207) 583 0410
clerks@bkbw.com
Recommended in Crime
Specialisation: Crime.
Prof. Memberships: C.B.A.
Career: Call: 1977. Senior Treasury Counsel. (Treasury Counsel since 1993).

DENNISON, Stephen QC
Atkin Chambers (Robert Akenhead QC) London (020) 7404 0102 /Emergency Tel: (020) 7242 4703
Recommended in Construction

DENNYS, Nicholas QC
Atkin Chambers (Robert Akenhead QC) London (020) 7404 0102
Recommended in Construction
Specialisation: Building and Civil Engineering disputes and related matters including Professional Negligence, Insurance, Conflict of Laws, Information Technology, Energy and general commercial work. Extensive arbitration experience as advocate, before both international and domestic tribunals. International disputes usually involving large multi-national corporations or Governmental Agencies in many parts of the world. Appointed to act as sole arbitrator under the Common and Commercial Bar Association Scheme and as Chairman by the London Court of International arbitration.
Career: Admitted to Middle Temple August 1973; Called to the Bar November 1975; Queen's Counsel May 1991.
Personal: Born 14th July 1951. Educated Eton College and Brasenose College, Oxford (P.P.E.).

DENYER, Roderick QC
St John's Chambers (Christopher Sharp QC) Bristol (0117) 921 3456
Recommended in Crime

DENYER-GREEN, Barry
Falcon Chambers (Jonathan Gaunt QC & Kim Lewison QC) London (020) 7353 2484
clerks@falcon-chambers.com
Recommended in Property Litigation
Specialisation: Compulsory purchase and compensation; planning; agricultural tenancies. Member DETR compulsory purchase working party 1998-00.
Prof. Memberships: Fellow, Royal Institution of Chartered Surveyors. Honorary fellow, College of Estate Management.
Career: LLM, PhD (London University).
Publications: Author 'Compulsory Purchase and Compensation' (edn 2000). Joint author 'Development and Planning Law' (3rd edn 1999). Editor 'Estates Gazette Law Reports'. Joint editor 'Planning Law Reports'.

DEVONSHIRE, Simon
11 King's Bench Walk Chambers (Eldred Tabachnik QC & James Goudie QC) London (020) 7632 8500
Recommended in Employment
Specialisation: All aspects of employment and entertainment law, including dismissal, discrimination, restrictive covenants and confidential information, agency, recording, publishing and management disputes, copyright and intellectual property.
Prof. Memberships: Employment Law Bar Association. LCLCBA.
Career: Called 1988.

DICKENS, Paul
Hogarth Chambers (Jonathan Rayner James QC & Christopher Morcom QC) London (020) 7404 0505
paul.dickens@hogarthchambers.com
Recommended in Media & Entertainment
Specialisation: Principal areas are copyright and design rights, moral rights, performers' rights, trade marks, passing off, confidential information, media and entertainment law and computer law. Particular interest in musical copyright infringement, information technology, multimedia and Internet. Clients include leading companies and artistes in the entertainment field, national newspapers, broadcasters and Internet Service Providers. Joint consulting editor, intellectual property, Butterworths' 'Encyclopaedia of Forms and Precedents', entertainment volume. Contributor to new edition of 'Copinger & Skone James on Copyright'.
Prof. Memberships: Intellectual Property Bar Association, Chancery Bar Association.
Career: MA (Cantab), ARCO, former Organ Scholar.
Personal: Recitalist/accompanist at local concerts, school governor, skiing.

DICKER, Robin QC
3-4 South Square (Michael Crystal QC & Lord Alexander of Weedon QC) London (020) 7696 9900
clerks@southsquare.com
Recommended in Banking, Company, Energy & Natural Resources, Fraud, Insolvency/Corporate Recovery
Specialisation: Specialises in business, commercial and financial law and litigation, in particular banking, corporate restructuring and insolvency. He has acted in relation to almost all of the major corporate collapses including BCCI (for the liquidators), MCC (for the administrators) and Olympia & York (for the administrators). Recent reported cases include Three Rivers District Council v Bank of England (No 1) [2000] 3 All ER 1 (House of Lords) and (No 2) [2001] 2 All ER 513 (House of Lords); National Westminster Bank v Utrecht [2001] EWCA CIV 658 (Court of Appeal); Morris v Bank of America [2000] 1 ALL ER 594 (Court of Appeal); Morris v Agrichemicals Ltd [1998] AC 214 (House of Lords).
Prof. Memberships: Commercial Bar Association; Chancery Bar Association; ICC and LCIA.
Career: Exhibitioner at Brasenose College, Oxford (BA and BCL). Called to the Bar (Middle Temple) in 1986 and a Harmsworth Exhibitioner. Appointed Queen's Counsel in 2000. Practises at 3-4 South Square.
Publications: Contributing Editor to 'Totty & Moss on Insolvency' (Sweet & Maxwell). Contributing Editor to 'Professional Negligence and Liability (LLP).

DINAN-HAYWARD, Deborah
Albion Chambers (Charles Barton QC & Neil Ford QC) Bristol (0117) 927 2144
Recommended in Family
Specialisation: Exclusively practicing in matrimonial, child care and family law covering any aspect of this area, especially ancillary relief and care proceedings.
Prof. Memberships: FLBA and Bristol FLBA.
Career: Wykeham House, Fareham. Sheffield University; LLB. Called 1988.
Publications: Contributor to Butterworths' 'Essential Family Practice'.
Personal: Gardening.

DINKIN, Anthony QC
2-3 Gray's Inn Square (Anthony Porten QC & Anthony Scrivener QC) London (020) 7242 4986
chambers@2-3graysinnsquare.co.uk
Recommended in Planning
Specialisation: Specialises in town and country planning, local government, valuation and compensation, landlord & tenant, restrictive covenants. With extensive experience in conducting planning inquiries concerning all aspects of planning including major food & non-food retailing developments, housing, conservation, pollution control and hazardous substances, local plans, CPO's and enforcement. Court experience includes legal challenges/ judicial review of Secretary of State/ Inspector and local government decisions and appearances in the Lands Tribunal.
Career: College of Estate Management (BscEst Management) 1966; Called to the Bar 1968; QC 1991; Recorder 1989; past Lecturer and External Examiner in Law, Reading University. Legal Member of Lands Tribunal 1998-99.

DIXEY, Ian
St John's Chambers (Christopher Sharp QC) Bristol (0117) 921 3456
Recommended in Crime

DIXON, Ralph
St John's Chambers (Christopher Sharp QC) Bristol 0117 921 3456
ralph.dixon@stjohnschambers.co.uk
Recommended in Family
Specialisation: Higher value matrimonial finance cases, in particular business and farming.
Prof. Memberships: Family Law Bar Association.
Career: BA Hons, University of York, Called to the Bar 1980.

DODDS, R. Stephen
15 Winckley Square (R. Stephen Dodds) Preston (01772) 252828
Recommended in Family

DODSON, Joanna QC
14 Gray's Inn Square (Joanna Dodson QC) London (020) 7242 0858
Recommended in Family
Specialisation: Practice encompasses all aspects of family law.
Prof. Memberships: Family Law Bar Association.
Career: Called to the Bar 1971. Joined Gray's Inn Square in 1991 and took Silk in 1993.
Personal: Educated at James Allen's Girls School 1956-63 and Newnham College, Cambridge (BA 1967, MA 1971). Born 5 September 1945. Lives in London.

DOERRIES, Chantal-Aimée
Atkin Chambers (Robert Akenhead QC) London (020) 7404 0102
clerks@atkinchambers.law.co.uk
Recommended in Construction
Specialisation: All stages of disputes from court proceedings, domestic and international arbitration tomediation and adjudication, in respect of construction and engineering, information technology, oil and gas, professional negligence and associated areas of commercial and property law. Recent cases: Floods of Queensferry Ltd. and Anor v Shand Construction Ltd. and Ors (2000) BLR 81, TCC; QPS Consultants Ltd. v Kruger Tissue (Manufacturing) Ltd. (1999) BLR 366, CA; RTZ Pension Trust v ARC and Others (1999) 1 All ER 532, CA; David Flood v Shand Construction Ltd. and Os (1996) 81 BLR 31, CA; Floods of Queensferry Ltd. v Shand Construction Ltd. and Os (1997) 81 BLR 31, TCC.
Prof. Memberships: TECBAR (Bar Council Representative 2000 to date; Secretary 1997-00). Society for Computers and Law. Society of Construction Lawyers.
Career: Called to the Bar 1992. Major Harmsworth Entrance Exhibition and Diplock Scholar, Middle Temple. Gertrude de Gallaix Achievement Award for Study of Law, FAWCO. Editor of the Building Law Reports 1999 to date.
Personal: Educated at Roedean School (1982-86), University of Pennsylvania (1986-87) and New Hall, Cambridge (1987-91). Fluent in German and working knowledge of French.

DOHMANN, Barbara QC
Blackstone Chambers (Presiley Baxendale QC & Charles Flint QC) London (020) 7583 1770
clerks@blackstonechambers.com
Recommended in Commercial (Litigation), Financial Services, Fraud, Insurance, Media & Entertainment

Specialisation: Insurance and reinsurance; financial services; banking; private international law; commercial fraud (civil); commercial arbitration; entertainment and media/intellectual property; disciplinary tribunals; regulatory tribunals.
Prof. Memberships: Chairman of the Commercial Bar Association 1999-01; member London Common Law and Commercial Bar Association, Learned Society for International Civil Procedure Law.
Career: Called to the Bar in 1971; Queen's Counsel 1987; Recorder 1990. Sits as a Deputy High Court Judge.
Personal: Educated in German and American schools, Universities of Erlangen, Mainz and Paris. Languages: German, French, Spanish, Italian.

DOVE, Ian
5 Fountain Court (Anthony Barker QC) Birmingham (0121) 606 0500
Recommended in Planning

DOWDING, Nicholas QC
Falcon Chambers (Jonathan Gaunt QC & Kim Lewison QC) London (020) 7353 2484 dowding@falcon-chambers.com
Recommended in Property Litigation
Specialisation: All aspects of Chancery and real property law, commercial property litigation and arbitration.
Prof. Memberships: Chancery Bar Association; London Common Law and Commercial Bar Association; Property Bar Association.
Career: Called to the Bar 1979. Silk 1997. Corresponding member of Royal Institution of Chartered Surveyors Dilapidations Practice Panel. Member of Falcon Chambers since 1980. Blundell memorial lecturer 1992 and 1997.
Publications: Joint author 'Dilapidations – The Modern Law and Practice'. Joint editor 'Woodfall on Landlord and Tenant'. General editor of 'Landlord and Tenant Reports'.

DOWLEY, Dominic
Serle Court (Lord Neill of Bladen QC) London (020) 7242 6105 clerks@serlecourt.co.uk
Recommended in Commercial (Litigation)
Specialisation: Commercial fraud, insurance/reinsurance, arbitration, banking and financial services/regulation specialist.
Career: Called to the Bar and joined One Hare Court in 1983.
Personal: Educated at Oxford University 1977-80. Bacon Scholar of Gray's Inn: Barstow Law Scholar. Born 25 March 1958.

DOYLE, Louis
40 King St Manchester (0161) 832 9082 ldoyle@40kingstreet.co.uk
Recommended in Commercial (Litigation), Insolvency/Corporate Recovery
Specialisation: Also practices at 5 Park Place (Philip Raynor QC) Leeds (0113) 242 1123. All aspects of corporate and personal insolvency, company law, credit, security, banking and related commercial litigation. Recent reported cases include Lombard v Brook and others [1999] BPIR 701 and Ord v Upton [2000] 1 All ER 163, CA, Cork v Rawlins, The Times, 15th April 2001, Fuller v Cyracuse [2001] 1 BCLC 187 and the administration of Chesterfield Football Club. Appointed to the Treasury Solicitors' Provincial Panel (Civil Litigation), 1999.
Prof. Memberships: Insolvency Lawyers Association, Chancery Bar Association, Northern Chancery Bar Association, Professional Negligence Bar Association.
Career: Educated St. Anselm's College, Birkenhead. LLB (Leeds Polytechnic), LLM (University of Birmingham). Lecturer in Law 1989-92. Admitted as Solicitor 1994. Called to the Bar 1996, Lincolns Inn, 1996.
Publications: Author 'Administrative Receivership: Law and Practice' (1995, 2nd edn forthcoming 2002) and 'Insolvency Litigation' (1998). Also a member of the editorial board of Sweet & Maxwells 'Insolvency Lawyer'.

DOYLE, Peter
Hollis Whiteman Chambers (QEB) (Julian Bevan QC & Peter Whiteman QC) London (020) 7583 5766
Recommended in Fraud

DRABBLE, Richard QC
4 Breams Buildings (Christopher Lockhart-Mummery QC) London (020) 7430 1221/7353 5835
Recommended in Administrative & Public Law, Local Government, Planning
Specialisation: Specialises in public law, planning, local government and social security.
Prof. Memberships: Former Chairman of the Administrative Law Bar Association, member of the Planning and Environmental Bar Association.
Career: Member of the Panel of Junior Counsel to the Crown (Common Law) 1992-95, took Silk 1995, contributor to Goudie and Supperstone Judicial Review.

DREW, Jane
Coram Chambers (Roger McCarthy QC) London (020) 7797 7766
Recommended in Family
Specialisation: Family law. Handles all types of work concerning children with a special emphasis on children in local authority care, care proceedings, adoption, private children law, divorce, matrimonial property, family provision and inheritance. Also deals with cohabitees covering real property disputes, cases under Section 14 of the Trusts of Land and Trustees Act 1996. Has dealt with numerous cases of sexual abuse and non-accidental injury. Regular lecturer and provider of seminars on cohabitees and public law children's work.
Prof. Memberships: Family Law Bar Association.
Career: Called to the Bar 1976. Tenant at Francis Taylor Building 1977-82, then joined current chambers.
Personal: Educated at Stevenage Girls Grammar School 1963-70, Trevelyan College, Durham 1971-74 and Inns of Court School 1974-76. Leisure pursuits include swimming, tennis and badminton. Born 6 June 1952. Lives in Knebworth.

DRISCOLL, Michael QC
9 Old Square (Michael Driscoll QC) London (020) 7405 4682
Recommended in Chancery, Professional Negligence, Property Litigation
Specialisation: General Chancery (advisory and litigation) but in particular property related, partnership and company law matters.
Career: Rugby and Cambridge (BA LLB).

DRUCE, Michael
2 Mitre Court Buildings (Michael FitzGerald QC) London (020) 7583 1380 michael.druce@2mcb.co.uk
Recommended in Planning
Specialisation: Main areas of practice are town and country planning, compulsory purchase and compensation, rating, local government, environmental and administrative law. Recent cases include the major retail proposals for the MetroCentre extension; Croft motor racing circuit; and the proposed development of a registered battlefield site. Has also appeared before the Grand Court of the Cayman Islands.
Prof. Memberships: Planning and Environment Bar Association. Justice.
Career: Called to Bar 1988 and joined current chambers 1990.
Publications: Contributing editor to Butterworths 'Local Government Law'.
Personal: Educated at Repton School and Sidney Sussex College, Cambridge. Born 23rd March 1964. Married with two children. Lives in London.

DU CANN, Christian
39 Essex Street (Nigel Pleming QC) London (020) 7832 1111 cdc@39essex.co.uk
Recommended in Personal Injury
Specialisation: Catastrophic injury. Occupational disease (especially asbestos ULD and stress claims). Disaster claims. Health and safety law (including criminal prosecution). Sports injury claims. Also specialises in medical and professional negligence.
Prof. Memberships: Member of Grays Inn (member of its Continuing Education Committee and Advocacy teacher). Member of PIBA. Member of London Common Law and Commercial Bar Association. Member of Bar Council.
Career: Called to the Bar 1982. Practised at 39 Essex Street since 1991.
Personal: Speaks French and Spanish.

DUCK, Michael
3 Fountain Court (Robert Juckes QC) Birmingham (0121) 236 5854 clerks@3fc.co.uk
Recommended in Crime
Specialisation: Principal areas of practice are crime and police disciplinary matters. R v Sara Thornton, (authority on provocation), R v Christie, Bell, Francis (custody time limits). Grade 4 prosecutor.
Career: Called to the Bar in 1988. Practised at 3 Fountain Court, from April 1989.
Personal: Born 1965. Leisure interests include travel, golf and water-skiing.

DUGGAN, Michael
Littleton Chambers (Michel Kallipetis QC) London 07957 365 302 (Mobile) mdugg@aol.com
Recommended in Employment
Specialisation: The main area of practice is in the field of employment law, covering all areas of discrimination (including disability discrimination), wrongful and unfair dismissal, redundancies and dismissals/variation of employment contracts arising out of re-organisations, restrictive covenants, trade union law including labour disputes and the emerging interface of the European Convention on European Rights with employment issues. Other areas of practice include building and construction law, health and safety and professional negligence and general commercial law including applications for interim injunctions and freezing orders.
Career: Called to the Bar 1984. Regular writer and lecturer on employment and commercial law, human rights law and civil procedure in the light of the Woolf reforms.
Publications: Author: 'The Modern Law of Strikes'; 'Business Re-Organisations and Employment Law (FT Law & Tax)'; 'Termination of Employment of Directors (FT Law & Tax June 1997)'. 'Unfair Dismissal'; 'Law, Practice and Guidance'; 'Wrongful Dismissal'; 'Law Practice and Precedents and Contracts of Employment'; 'Law Practice and Precedents'. Central Law Training. Editor in Chief of the 'Civil Practice Law Reports'.
Personal: BA. BCL. LLM (First Class, Sidney Sussex College, Cambridge University). Holt Scholar of Gray's Inn. Lives in Coton, Cambridgeshire and Gray's Inn. Married with three boys. Interests: music, guitar.

DUGGAN, Ross
India Buildings Chambers (Ray Herman) Liverpool (0151) 243 6000 clerks@indiabuildings.co.uk
Recommended in Family
Specialisation: A specialist in all aspects of family law especially public law children's work for local authorities, parents and guardians ad litem. Also experienced in personal injury work.
Prof. Memberships: FLBA/PIBA.
Career: Called 1978. Recorder 1997.

DUMARESQ, Delia
Atkin Chambers (Robert Akenhead QC) London (020) 7404 0102 /Emergency Tel: (020) 7242 4703
Recommended in Construction
Specialisation: All aspects of construction, building and engineering dispute resolution including international and domestic arbitration, mediation and adjudication. Advocate, mediator, writer and lecturer in ADR. Counsel in leading adjudication cases – Macob v Morrison; Project Consultancy v Gray's Trustees; Bloor Construction; Bridgeway v Tolent; and Cameron v Mowlem.
Prof. Memberships: New South Wales Bar (Australia), TECBAR and CEDR Mediator and panel of adjudicators. Fellow of Chartered Institute of Arbitrators. Inter Mediation and CCMG panel of Mediators.
Career: 1967- BA – Australia. Prior to reading law, worked and travelled extensively in Southeast Asia (as an archaeologist) and Europe. 1973 – MA (Hons) – London (Work and research on disadvantaged groups and communities) 1983 – Dip Law (Hons); 1984 – called; Inner Temple.
Personal: One son. Interests include music, modern art, Italian culture and Language.

DUMONT, Thomas
11 New Square (Sonia Proudman QC) London (020) 7831 0081
Recommended in Charities
Specialisation: Professional negligence principally solicitors and accountants: Paragon Finance v Thakerar & Co (1999); Gibbons v Nelsons (2000). Charity and private client advice and litigation, including trusts, wills and probate, re Ratcliffe (1999). Commercial property: Landlord & tenant. Restrictive covenants and mortgages: Mortgage Corporation v Nationwide Credit Corporation (1994). Rutland House Textiles v Mace (1999)
Prof. Memberships: Charity Law Association; Society of Trust & Estate Practitioners; Professional Negligence Bar Association; ACTAPS.
Career: MA (Cantab) Exhibitioner in Law, Trinity Hall. Called 1979, Gray's Inn. Lecturer in trusts and revenue, University of Westminster 1981-85.
Personal: Married with two children. Fellow of the Zoological Society of London. Plays cricket whenever possible.

DUNKELS, Paul QC
Walnut House (Paul Dunkels QC) Exeter (01392) 279751
Recommended in Crime

DUNN, Katherine
40 King St Manchester (0161) 832 9082
Recommended in Chancery

DUNNING, Graham QC
Essex Court Chambers (Gordon Pollock QC) London (020) 7813 8000
Recommended in Arbitration (International), Shipping
Specialisation: Specialist in all aspects of international and commercial law, particularly arbitration, banking and finance, commodities and trade, insurance and reinsurance, professional negligence and shipping and transport. In the international field practice covers jurisdictional and private international law disputes, arbitrations, injunctions, forum conveniens and applicable law. Commodities and trade work covers cases involving oil, metals, foodstuffs and futures. Practice encompasses all aspects of insurance and reinsurance litigation. Professional negligence experience covers cases involving insurance brokers, actuaries, accountants and solicitors. Shipping and transport practice covers charterparty disputes and bill of lading claims, ship sale and shipbuiding, aviation.
Prof. Memberships: Commercial Bar Association; British Insurance Law Association; British Maritime Law Association; London Maritime Arbitrators Association.
Career: Called to the Bar 1982. QC 2001.
Personal: Educated at Cambridge University (BA Hons 1st Class) 1977-80, and at Harvard Law School (LLM) 1980-81. Scholarships: Emmanuel College Entrance Scholarship (1977); University of Cambridge Squire Law Scholarship (1978 and 1979); Lincoln's Inn Hardwicke Scholarship (1979); Kennedy Scholar, Harvard Law School (1980); Lincoln's Inn Denning Scholarship (1981). Born 13 March 1958. Lives in London.

DUNN-SHAW, Jason
6 King's Bench Walk (Roy Amlot QC) London (020) 7583 0410
jason.dunn-shaw@6kbw.com
Recommended in Crime
Specialisation: Crime, including courts martial and appellate proceedings. Extradition. Available for advisory and regulatory work.
Prof. Memberships: Criminal Bar Association; Committee of the Central London Courts Bar mess; Junior of the Old Bailey Bar mess.
Career: Called to the Bar by Lincoln's Inn in 1992. Wide-ranging practice has included cases of murder, hijack, major drugs importations, sexual offences, money-laundering and fraud.
Personal: Born 18 September 1964. Malvern College; Manchester University; University of Westminster.

DUTHIE, Catriona
Guildhall Chambers (Adrian Palmer QC) Bristol (0117) 927 3366
Recommended in Family

DUTTON, Timothy
No. 1 Serjeants' Inn (Edward Faulks QC) London (020) 7415 6666
clerks@no1serjeantsinn.com
Recommended in Property Litigation
Specialisation: Property-related litigation, with a strong landlord and tenant bias: rent reviews and lease renewals; breaches of covenant and other disputes in respect of commercial property; long leases of residential property (including leasehold enfranchisement); Rent Act and Housing Act tenancies. Recent cases include Forrester v UYCF [2001] EGCS 2 (CA); Wallis Fashions Group Ltd v CGU Life Assurance Ltd [2000] 2 EGLR 49; West Sussex Properties v Chichester DC [2000] NPC 74 (CA); Gilje & Others v Charlegrove Securities Ltd [2000] EG 148 (LT); Hallissey v Petmoor Developments Ltd [2000] NPC 114 (ChD).
Prof. Memberships: Chancery Bar Association.
Career: Called to the Bar in 1985. Employed for several years (post-call) in the property litigation departments of *Speechly Bircham* and *Lovells.*
Personal: Born 1962. Educated at Godalming Grammar School (1972-80) and Durham University (1981-84).

DUVAL, Robert
St John's Chambers (Christopher Sharp QC) Bristol (0117) 921 3456
Recommended in Crime

DYER, Nigel
1 Mitre Court Buildings (Bruce Blair QC) London (020) 7797 7070
Recommended in Family
Specialisation: Family law, principally ancillary relief often involving 'big money cases' where assets are held in companies, trusts and farms in the UK and abroad.
Prof. Memberships: Family Law Bar Association. Co-editor of 'Rayden and Jackson on Divorce and Family Matters'.
Career: Called to the Bar by Inner Temple 1982.
Personal: Married with two children and lives in London.

EADIE, James
Serle Court (Lord Neill of Bladen QC) London (020) 7242 6105
clerks@serlecourt.co.uk
Recommended in Commercial (Litigation)
Specialisation: Junior Counsel to the Crown – Common Law (Member "A" Panel).
Prof. Memberships: COMBAR.

EADY, Jennifer
Old Square Chambers (John Hendy QC) London (020) 7269 0300
JEady@compuserve.com
Recommended in Employment
Specialisation: All aspects employment law (collective and individual), discrimination and restraint of trade. Cases of significance: R v BCC ex p Vardy 1993 (pit-closures JR); R v BCC ex p Price 1993 (collective redundancies); Associated Newspapers v Wilson 1995 HL (trade union); RJB v NUM 1995 CA (strike ballot); MRS v Marsh 1996 CA (TUPE); RMT v Intercity 1996 CA (strike ballot); Smith v BCC 1996 HL (equal pay); BRS v Loughran 1997 NICA (equal pay); NACODS v Gluchowski 1996 EAT (trade union); Halford v UK 1997 ECHR (Human Rights); BBC v Kelly-Phillips 1998 CA (employment contracts); England v Magill (1997) (Westminster 'gerrymandering') Div Ct; Brookes and ors v BCS 1998 EAT (TUPE); Gibson v E Riding Yorks 2000 CA (working time); SoS Trade & Industry v Bottirll 1999 CA (employee status); Cheesman v Brewer 2001 EAT (TUPE). Inquiries: The UCATT Inquiry (1992), the Westminster Audit Hearing (1994/5).
Prof. Memberships: Chair ILS, Committee member ELBA, Bar representative London ET and EAT users' group, ELA, DLA.
Career: 1986 BA Hons PPE (Oxon), 1988 Dip Law. Called 1989, Northern Ireland Bar 1994. Standing junior counsel to NUJ and NUM, appointed to the Treasury A panel.
Publications: 'Discrimination Law: Remedies and Quantum of Damages' (Sweet & Maxwell) (1998); 'Employment Tribunal Procedure' (LAG) (1996); 'Employment Law Review' (IER); contributor: Bullen & Leake, ICSL 'Employment Law Manual' (Blackstone), 'Employment Law Precedents' (Sweet & Maxwell), ILJ.

EASTEAL, Andrew
No.1 High Pavement (John B. Milmo QC) Nottingham (0115) 941 8218
Recommended in Crime
Specialisation: Practising exclusively in crime for the last 11 years (excluding fraud): sexual offences including child abuse; human rights; high profile drugs cases; attempted murder and manslaughter cases (single counsel) involving complex fitness to plead issues.
Personal: Long-suffering Villa fan.

EATON, Deborah
One King's Bench Walk (Anthony Hacking QC) London (020) 7936 1500
Recommended in Family

ECCLES, David
8 King St (Keith Armitage QC) Manchester (0161) 834 9560
Recommended in Clinical Negligence
Specialisation: Clinical negligence, personal injury, civil actions for malicious prosecution and wrongful arrest. Ancillary Relief. Cases include: Smith v West Lanes Health A [1995] PIQP P514; Wagstaffe v Wagstaffe [1992] IWLR 320; Wilding v Chief Constable of Lancashire (March); Hyland v Chief Constable of Lancs – Times 7/2/96.
Prof. Memberships: PIBA, PNBA.
Career: Wilmslow Grammar School and Clare College, Cambridge.
Personal: Theatre, cinema, playing bridge, reading and travel.

EDELMAN, Colin QC
Devereux Chambers (Jeffrey Burke QC) London (020) 7353 7534
Recommended in Insurance, Professional Negligence
Specialisation: Principal areas of practice are insurance and reinsurance, professional negligence and commercial law. Recent reported cases include Killick v Rendall (insurance), Kennecott v Cornhill (insurance/reinsurance), Gan Insurance v Tai Ping (insurance), HIH v Chase Manhattan (insurance).

Prof. Memberships: Commercial Bar Association, member of Middle Temple and Midlands & Oxford Circuit.
Career: Called to the Bar in 1977 and has been a tenant at Devereux Chambers since 1979. Appointed Assistant Recorder in 1993. Took Silk in 1995. Appointed Recorder 1996.
Publications: Has written articles for 'International Insurance Law Review', 'Commercial Liability Law Review' and the 'British Insurance Law Association Journal'. Contributor to "Insurance Disputes" (LLP). Speaker/chairman at conferences on insurance and reinsurance topics.
Personal: Educated at Haberdashers' Aske's School, Elstree 1961-72 and Clare College, Cambridge 1973-76. Leisure pursuits include skiing, walking, badminton. Born 2nd March 1954. Lives in London.

EDENBOROUGH, Michael
Hogarth Chambers (Jonathan Rayner James QC & Christopher Morcom QC) London (020) 7404 0404
michaeledenborough@hogarthchambers.com
Recommended in Intellectual Property
Specialisation: All aspects of intellectual property law, including UK and European competition law, and commercial disputes that involve a technical subject matter. In particular, patents and confidential information; trade marks and passing-off/malicious falsehood; registered designs and design right; internet and data protection issues; copyright; moral rights; performance rights; entertainment law matters and computer litigation.
Prof. Memberships: Member of the Royal Society of Chemistry, ECTA and AIPPI and associate member of CIMA and ITMA.
Career: Tenant since 1st July 1994. Regular lecturer and tutor to CIPA, ITMA, University of Alicante (Spain), solicitors, patent and trade mark attorneys, and at national and international conferences.
Publications: 'Lecture Notes on Intellectual Property Law' (Cavendish Publishing Ltd, May 1995, reprinted 1997); contributor to the CIPA/ITMA handbooks on (a) UK Trade Marks, and (b) Community Trade Marks; 'Organic Reaction Mechanisms: A Step by Step Approach' (Taylor and Francis Ltd, June 1994, reprinted 1996, second edition November 1998).
Personal: MA (Cantab.), MA (Oxon), MSc, DPhil.

EDER, Bernard QC
Essex Court Chambers (Gordon Pollock QC) London (020) 7813 8000
clerksroom@essexcourt-chambers.co.uk
Recommended in Commercial (Litigation), Energy & Natural Resources, Insurance, Shipping
Specialisation: Most work of a litigious nature involving appearances in arbitration and the Commercial Court, Court of Appeal and House of Lords. All aspects of commercial law, including insurance and reinsurance, shipping and banking, international sale of goods, oil and gas.
Career: Downing College, Cambridge BA (Law) (1st Class Hons). Called to the Bar 1975. Queen's Counsel 1990. Visiting professor in the Faculty of Law, University College London.
Personal: Born 1952.

EDEY, Philip
20 Essex Street (Iain Milligan QC) London (020) 7583 9294
clerks@20essexst.com
Recommended in Insurance, Shipping
Specialisation: Commercial litigation including arbitration, commodities, insurance and reinsurance, international sale of goods and shipping. Cases include Shipping – The Laconian Confidence [1997] 1 Lloyd's Rep 139 (NYPE off-hire); Cory Brothers v Baldan [1997] 2 Lloyd's Rep 58 (freight forwarders); The Jalagoruri [1999] 1 Lloyd's Rep 903 and [2000] 1 Lloyd's Rep 515 (CA) (scope of time charterers' obligation to discharge cargo); Insurance/Reinsurance – Wellington names (reinsurance to close; asbestos; professional negligence), Imperio v Heath [1999] LLR I&R 571 and [2001] 1 WLR 112 (CH) (binding authority; time bar for breach of fiduciary duty); Kingscroft v Nissan [1999] LLR I&R 603 (reinsurance; avoidance); HIH v New Hampshire [2001] 1 Lloyd's Rep 378 and unreported decision of CA (21 May 2001) (film finance reinsurance).
Prof. Memberships: COMBAR.
Career: Eton College, Oxford University (BA Hons 1st Class). Gray's Inn Queen Elizabeth Scholar. Called 1994.
Personal: Tennis; squash; real tennis; bridge; opera; theatre.

EDGE, Timothy
Deans Court Chambers (Stephen Grime QC) Manchester (0161) 214 6000
edge@deanscourt.co.uk
Recommended in Family
Specialisation: Matrimonial finance on divorce/separation, including injunctive relief, conflict of laws and disputes following death. Co-habitation and Inheritance Act claims.
Prof. Memberships: FLBA, PNBA.
Career: MA (Oxon)

EDIE, Alastair
Two Garden Court (Ian Macdonald QC & Owen Davies QC) London (020) 7353 1633
Recommended in Crime

EDIS, Andrew QC
14 Castle Street (Andrew Edis QC) Liverpool (0151) 236 4421
Recommended in Crime, Personal Injury, Professional Negligence
Specialisation: Personal injury, including disease and product liability. Professional negligence, in particular legal and clinical negligence. Serious crime including disciplinary tribunals. Police law and human rights. Civil cases involving fraud. Recent cases include: Arthur JS Hall v Simons [2000] 3 WLR 543 House of Lords (abolition of advocates' immunity); LR v Witherspoon & Others [2000] 1 FLR CA; L & B v Reading Borough Council, and the Chief Constable of the Thames Valley Police, 9th March 2001 Unreported CA (striking out negligence claims). Vellino v Chief Constable of Manchester (duty of care owed by police to suspect). Webb v Chief Constable of Merseyside Police [2000] QB 427 CA. Norman v Aziz & Ali [2000] PIQR P72 CA. Nunnerley & Nunnerley v Warrington Health Authority & Liverpool Health Authority [2000] PIQR Q69 (Clinical Negligence). Timmin v Gormley (reported with Locabail v Bayfield Properties Ltd) [2000] QB 451 CA (Judicial Bias). In crime: R v Bruce Grobbelaar; R v Taft (Beauty in the Bath murder); R v Allan (Death on the Nile murder); R v Dietschmann (drink in diminished responsibility); R v Elmore Davies, Bray & Ahearne (Police Corruption).
Prof. Memberships: Northern Circuit; Professional Negligence Bar Association; Bar Sports Law Group, Northern Circuit Commercial Bar Association, Northern Circuit Medical Law Group; Personal Injury Bar Association.
Career: Educated Liverpool College and University College, Oxford. Called 1980. Silk 1997. Assistant Recorder 1994-99, Recorder 1999 to date. Head of Chambers 2000 to date.

EDIS, William
1 Crown Office Row (Robert Seabrook QC) London (020) 7797 7500
Recommended in Environment

EDWARDS, David
7 King's Bench Walk (Jeremy Cooke QC) London (020) 7910 8300
clerks@7kbw.law.co.uk
Recommended in Insurance, Shipping
Specialisation: Commercial law predominantly insurance and reinsurance, international sale of goods, banking and finance, shipping.
Career: Called to the Bar 1989. Recent cases include: The 'Nicholas H' [1996] AC 211 (shipping – duty of care owed by Classification Society); New Hampshire v MGN [1997] RLR 24 (fidelity insurance – joint or composite); Glencore v Portman [1996] 1 Lloyd's Rep. 430 and [1997] 1 Lloyd's Rep. 225 (insurance – non-disclosure); The 'Bergen' [1997] 1 Lloyd's Rep. 380 (Clarke J) (jurisdiction – Brussels Convention); The 'Lendoudis Evangelos II' [1997] 1 Lloyd's Rep. 404 (charterparty – duration expressed 'without guarantee'); The Sumitomo Bank, Limited v Banque Bruxelles Lambert SA [1997] 1 Lloyd's Rep. 487 (syndicated lending – duty owed by arranger to syndicate members); Source v TUV [1997] 3 WLR 364 (jurisdiction – Brussels Convention); HMH v Cecar [2000] 1 Lloyd's Rep 316 (political risks insurance-brokers commission); The 'Seta Maru' [2000] 1 Lloyd's Rep 367 (Shipbuilding exemption clauses); HIH v Chase Manhattan Bank [2001] 1 Lloyd's Rep 30 (insurance-backed film finance).
Personal: Born 1966. King's School, Chester and Peterhouse, Cambridge, M.A. (Cantab). Member of Commercial Bar Association.

EDWARDS, Douglas
2 Harcourt Buildings (Gerard Ryan QC) London (020) 7353 8415
Recommended in Planning
Specialisation: Planning, environmental, administrative, local government, parliamentary, commons and village greens. Appeared in Terminal 5 Inquiry, Heathrow, and for Railtrack in Euston re-modelling inquiry. Recently reported cases include: R v Derbyshire CC ex p Woods (1997) JPL 958; Riordan Communications Ltd v South Buckinghamshire DC (2000) 1 PLR 45; R v St Edmundsbury BC ex p Davidson (2000) JPL 417; House Builders Federation v Sockport MBC (2000) JPL 616; R v South Cambs DC ex p Salek (2000) JPL 748; R v Thanet DC ex p Tapp (0221) plcR 22; R v City of Sunderland ex p Beresford (2001) 1 WLR 1327.
Prof. Memberships: Secretary of Planning and Environment Bar Association (PEBA).

EDWARDS, Glyn
St John's Chambers (Christopher Sharp QC) Bristol (0117) 921 3456
clerks@stjohnschambers.co.uk
Recommended in Personal Injury
Specialisation: Personal Injury. Appointed with effect from July 2000 onto Provincial Panel of Treasury Counsel.
Prof. Memberships: Personal Injury Bar Association.
Career: Formerly lecturer at Oxford Brookes University.
Personal: Married with three children. Welsh-speaking. Education: Penglais Comprehensive and Emmanuel College, Cambridge.

EDWARDS, Susan QC
23 Essex Street (Michael Lawson QC) London (020) 7413 0353
susanedwards@23essexstreet.co.uk
Recommended in Crime
Specialisation: Serious crime including homicide, drugs, robbery, child abuse, vulnerable witnesses etc.
Prof. Memberships: CBA.
Career: Parkstone Grammar School, Poole. Southampton University – LLB (1971). Recorder. QC 1993.
Personal: Tennis, hill walking, travel, gardening.

EGAN, Michael
9-12 Bell Yard (D. Anthony Evans QC) London (020) 7400 1800
Recommended in Fraud
Specialisation: Serious fraud, also representing members of the professions and police officers in crime, internal discipline proceedings, inquests and public inquiries. Notable cases include: The 'Guildford 4' and 'Tottenham 3' officers, DPP v Clegg (in the Hof L only), R v Crawford and others (the European Leisure plc case) R v Falkowsky and others, the Stephen Lawrence inquiry (for all officers under rank of Supt), the operation
Prof. Memberships: Criminal Bar Association.
Career: Five years' articles 1971-76, experience of conveyancing, company and probate. Solicitor 1976-81.

Called to the Bar in 1981. Assistant Recorder 1998, Recorder 2000.

EICKE, Tim

Essex Court Chambers (Gordon Pollock QC) London (020) 7813 8000

Recommended in Immigration

Specialisation: EC law, including EC Association agreements, free movement, equal treatment and EC immigration law (cases: C-75/94 Gallagher [1995] ECR I-4253 (ECJ) and [1996] 2 CMLR 951 (CA); C-416/96 El Yassini [1999] ECR I-1209; Sahota [1999] QB 597; Boukssid [1998] INLR 275; Yiadom [1998] INLR 489, [2000] ECR I – 9265; Kaba [2000] ECR I 2623, Kaba (No.2) (pending before EC)); human rights (cases: R (Alconbury Developments Ltd) v SSETR [2001] 2 WLR 1389, Sepet and Bulbul v SSHD [2001] EWCA Civ 681 (for UNHCR), Shah and Islam [1999] 2 WLR 1015 (HL for UNHCR); Sheffield and Horsham (1999) 27 EHRR 163, A v UK (1999) 27 EHRR 611, Cooke v Austria, (2001) 31 EHRR 11, Laskey et al (1997) 24 EHRR 39; National & Provincial et al (1998) 25 EHRR 127; B v UK (judgment of 24 April 2001); Toguc et al v Turkey (pending); Bosphorus v Ireland (pending); Amicus submissions to the Court Of Human Rights in Chahal (1997) 2; 3 EHRR 413, Akdivar v Turkey (1997) 27 EHRR 143, Ahmed (2000) 29 EHRR 1, McGinley (1999) 27 EHRR 1 Pellegrini v Italy (pending)); judicial review (cases: R v Legal Aid Board ex p. Eccleston, [1998] 1 WLR 1279); employment law; education law (Nabadda v Westminster City Council, [2000] ICR 951); discrimination (race and sex) (KB v NHS Trust Pensions Agency [1999] ICR 1192 (pending before EC)). Private international law; general commercial and civil.
Prof. Memberships: ILPA; Bar European Group; Lawyers for Liberty; Employment Law Bar Association; Administrative Law Bar Association; British German Jurists Association. Member of the Justice Expert Panel on Human Rights in the EU.
Career: Called 1993; LLB (Hons) Dundee University; Junior Councel to the Crown (C Panel) since April 1999.
Publications: Joint editor, 'European Human Rights Reports' (Sweet & Maxwell); contributor Grosz, Beaston and Duffy 'Human Rights – The 1998 Act and the European Convention' (Sweet & Maxwell); co-author of the 'Strasbourg Caselaw: Leading cases from the European Human Rights Reports' (Sweet & Maxwell, 2001); co-author of 'Human Rights Damages' (Sweet & Maxwell, forthcoming).
Personal: Bi-lingual German-English, advanced French.

EISSA, Adrian

Two Garden Court (Ian Macdonald QC & Owen Davies QC) London (020) 7353 1633

Recommended in Crime

EKLUND, Graham

2 Temple Gardens (Dermod O'Brien QC) London (020) 7822 1200

Recommended in Professional Negligence

Specialisation: Professional negligence, particularly surveyors, solicitors, accountants and insurance brokers. Insurance related matters, particularly fraudulent claims, policy construction points, fire and disaster claims, including pollution and contamination claims. Personal injury, particularly serious injuries (including tetraplegic and paraplegic cases). Computer and IT. Reported cases include Jones & Marsh McLennan v Crowley Colosso (1996); Yorkshire Water v Sun Alliance (1996); John Munroe (Acrylics) Limited v London Fire and Civil Defence Authority (1997); Chapman v Christopher (1998); Greatorex v Greatorex (2000); Beckett and others v Midland Electricity plc [2001].
Prof. Memberships: PNBA, PIBA.
Career: Educated at Auckland University (1969-74) BA; LLB (Hons). Barrister and Solicitor of the High Court of New Zealand (1975-78). Solicitor of the Supreme Court of England and Wales (1979-84). Called 1984.
Personal: Married, two children. Interests include music, particularly opera and piano, cricket and wine.

ELGOT, Howard

Park Lane Chambers (Stuart Brown QC) Leeds (0113) 228 5000 helgot@parklanechambers.co.uk

Recommended in Personal Injury

Specialisation: Personal injury (including claims of maximum severity,) industrial disease litigation, clinical and professional negligence, insurance and commercial litigation. Many reported cases at first instance, Court of Appeal and House of Lords. Examples of well-known cases are Clarke v Kato HL (extent of RTA/MIB liability;) Roebuck v Mungovin HL (want of prosecution,) Liddell v Middleton CA (role of expert witnesses) and Dalziel v Donald QC (risk of breakdown of marriage in Total Accident Claim).
Prof. Memberships: PIBA; PNBA
Career: BA BCL New College, Oxford. 3 Paper Buildings, Temple 1974-86, present chambers since 1986. Chairman, Park Lane Chambers Management Committee. Member NE Circuit/Leeds Law Society Liaison Committee. Former Chairman NE Circuit Renumeration and Terms of Work Committee.
Personal: Married, three children. Ski-ing. Italy. Music. Football.

ELIAS, Gerard QC

Farrar's Building (John Leighton Williams QC) London (020) 7583 9241

Recommended in Crime

Specialisation: Crime and public inquiries. Leading counsel to the North Wales Child Abuse Tribunal inquiry, 1996-8; Bloody Sunday inquiry 2000-.
Career: Exeter (LLB); called to the Bar 1968; took silk 1984; Recorder 1984 -; Deputy High Court Judge 1996 -; Master of the Bench, Inner Temple; Former leader of Wales v Chester Circuit (1992-95).
Personal: Chairman of Glamorgan Country Cricket Club; Chairman of Disciplinary Committee England v Wales Cricket Board (ECB).

ELLERAY, Anthony QC

Exchange Chambers Manchester (0161) 833 2722 ellerayqc@exchangechambers.co.uk

Recommended in Chancery, Commercial (Litigation)

Specialisation: Chancery and General Commercial Litigation; Professional Negligence; Landlord and Tenant. Recent cases in C.A. include Walker v Turpin (1994) (payment in); Jervis v Harris (1996) (Landlord and Tenant repairs and 1938 Act); Bass v Latham Crossley and Davies (1996) (partnership/ holding out); Shaikh v Bolton MBC (1996) (statutory interest on compulsory purchase). Pearce Deceased (1998) (Inheritance Act). Lynch [2000] laches. In H.L, Wibberley v Insley (1999).
Prof. Memberships: Chancery Bar Association; Northern Chancery Bar Association; Professional Negligence Bar Association.
Career: Called to the Bar 1977; took Silk 1993.

ELLIOTT, Margot

Regency Chambers Peterborough (01733) 315215

Recommended in Family

ELLIOTT, Rupert

1 Brick Court (Richard Rampton QC) London (020) 7353 8845

Recommended in Defamation

Specialisation: Defamation and media related law; prepublication work; reporting restrictions; contempt; confidence.
Career: Called 1988; joined Chambers 1989.
Personal: Harrow School; Jesus College, Cambridge.

ELLIOTT, Timothy QC

Keating Chambers (Richard Fernyhough QC) London (020) 7544 2600

Recommended in Arbitration (International), Construction

Specialisation: Building and civil engineering; professional negligence; bonds and guarantees. Clients include national and international contractors and developers, professional, national and local government, both in the UK and overseas. Also acts as arbitrator and legal assessor.
Career: Qualified 1975. Middle Temple QC 1992.
Personal: Marlborough College and Trinity College, Oxford (1973 MA Oxon). Born 1950; resides London.

ELLIS, Diana QC

3 Gray's Inn Square (Rock Tansey QC) London (020) 7520 5600

Recommended in Crime

Specialisation: Specialises in defence crime. Wide range of work including murder, fraud, child abuse and sexual abuse, drugs, human rights, appointed counsel at International Criminal Tribunal for Rwanda.
Prof. Memberships: Criminal Bar Association. Liberty. South Eastern Circuit.
Career: LLB Hons London; Diploma in Social Admin, LSE. Called to the Bar in July 1978 – Inner Temple. Worked for several years as a teacher. Recorder, 1998.

ELLIS, Morag

2-3 Gray's Inn Square (Anthony Porten QC & Anthony Scrivener QC) London (020) 7242 4986

Recommended in Planning

Specialisation: Planning and local government. Extensive experience of public inquiries including planning appeals and local plan inquiries, CPO and footpaths, for developers, authorities and other statutory bodies. Recently promoted Bracknell Forest and Wycombe District Local Plan, including major housing, town centre and brown field redevelopment proposals. Town and Village Green inquiries. Court experience includes judicial review and statutory appeals. On editorial panel of Halsbury's laws (Public Health). Regular lecturer on planning topics for RTPI.
Prof. Memberships: Planning and Environment Bar Association (Committee Member and Local Plans Sub-Committee). Ecclesiastical Law Society; Society of Advanced Legal Studies Planning Law Reform Group (Town and Village Greens Sub-Group).
Career: Called to the Bar 1984, (Gray's Inn).
Personal: Educated Penrhos College, Colwyn Bay, and St Catharine's College, Cambridge (MA). Married with three children. Member of Bach Choir and Cambridge Taverner Choir.

ELLISON, Mark

Hollis Whiteman Chambers (QEB) (Julian Bevan QC & Peter Whiteman QC) London (020) 7583 5766

Recommended in Crime, Fraud

Specialisation: Criminal practice specialising in commercial fraud and Treasury Counsel work.
Career: Called 1979. Appointed Junior Treasury Counsel to the Crown at the Central Criminal Court 1994. Senior Treasury Counsel 2000. Recorder.
Personal: Educated at Pocklington School, Skinners School and the University of Wales.

ELVIN, David QC

4 Breams Buildings (Christopher Lockhart-Mummery QC) London (020) 7430 1221/7353 5835 davidelvin@compuserve.com

Recommended in Environment, Local Government, Planning

Specialisation: Real property, landlord and tenant, agriculture, trespass, judicial review, compulsory purchase, compensation, planning, environmental law (including nature conservation), nuisance, highways, local government, education and professional negligence.
Career: Called to the Bar by the Middle Temple in 1983 and is member of the Administrative Law Bar Association, Chancery Bar Association and the Planning and Environmental Bar Association. He took silk in 2000. Educated at the A.J. Dawson Grammar School, Co. Durham and at Hertford College, Oxford obtaining a B.A. (First Class Honours) in Jurisprudence and a B.C.L.

In 1983 he won the Bar Association for Finance Commerce and Industry Prize. He was one of the Junior Counsel to the Crown ('A' Panel) until he took silk, having served as a Supplementary Panellist from 1991 to 1995.
Publications: Co-author of 'Unlawful Interference with Land' (1995) and a number of articles in 'Judicial Review'. Is an Assistant Commissioner with the Boundary Commission.

ELWICK, Martin
No.1 High Pavement (John B. Milmo QC) Nottingham (0115) 941 8218
Recommended in Crime

EMMERSON, Ben QC
Matrix Chambers (Nicholas Blake QC) London (020) 7404 3447
Recommended in Crime, Human Rights

ENGLAND, William
2-4 Tudor Street (Richard Ferguson QC) London (020) 7797 7111
Recommended in Crime

ENGLEHART, Robert QC
Blackstone Chambers (Presiley Baxendale QC & Charles Flint QC) London (020) 7583 1770 robertenglehart@blackstonechambers.com
Recommended in Media & Entertainment
Specialisation: Both commercial and copyright aspects of music business and media, especially broadcasting, disputes; also practices in general commercial law, including commercial judicial review, and intellectual property.
Career: Called 1969, QC 1986, Recorder and Deputy High Court Judge.

ESCOTT-COX, Brian QC
36 Bedford Row (Michael Pert QC) Northampton (01604) 602333
Recommended in Crime
Specialisation: Achieved the first ever murder conviction using 'DNA fingerprinting' and is an acknowledged leading Counsel in this field (R v Pitch fork). Defended Newbury in the civil and criminal action Revill v Newbury which went to the Court of Appeal (elderly man shot burglar to defend allotment shed). Prosecution of Sara Thornton from original murder through the re-trial to manslaughter (1996).
Career: MA Oxford. Called to the Bar 1954. Took Silk 1974. Bencher of Lincoln's Inn. Member of 3 Fountain Court Birmingham (still a door Tenant) now a member of 36 Bedford Row WC1 London.
Personal: Plays in jazz band.

ESPLEY, Susan
Fenners Chambers (Lindsay Davies) Cambridge (01223) 368761
Recommended in Family

ETHERINGTON, David QC
18 Red Lion Court (Anthony Arlidge QC) London (020) 7520 6000 david.etherington@18rlc.co.uk
Recommended in Crime, Fraud
Specialisation: Criminal practitioner. Experienced in wide range of criminal work including commercial fraud, VAT, drugs and serious professional crime. Also experienced in civil jury actions such as malicious prosecution. Adviser to television companies on documentary and dramatic work including 'Kavanagh QC', and 'Judge John Deed'.
Prof. Memberships: Appointed member of the Criminal Bar Association Committee and Vice Chairman of the Professional Conduct Committee. Chambers 18 Red Lion Court (Anthony Arlidge QC).
Career: Call 1979 (Middle Temple), Recorder of the Crown Court 2000, Queen's Counsel 1998.

EVANS, Catrin
1 Brick Court (Richard Rampton QC) London (020) 7353 8845 clerks@1brickcourt.co.uk
Recommended in Defamation
Specialisation: Defamation and trade libel in traditional and electronic media; breach of confidence/privacy and data protection, passing off; media reporting restrictions. European human rights law in media context and media related law generally. Does work for the Treasury Solicitor. Major cases: Libel – Sugar v Associated Newspapers Ltd (2001), £100,000 jury award; Gregson v Channel 4, Times, 11 August 2000, CA; Taylor v SFO [1998] 4 AER 801, HL; McNab v Associated Newspapers Ltd (1996), CA. Breach of confidence – Beckhams v Niblett &Ors (2000), CH.D; British Biotech plc v Millar (1999); Duchess of York v Starkie & Ors.
Career: Called to the Bar 1994.
Publications: Author forthcoming 'Confidence and Data Protection' title, Atkins Court Forms.

EVANS, D. Anthony QC
9-12 Bell Yard (D. Anthony Evans QC) London (020) 7400 1800 clerks@bellyard.co.uk
Recommended in Crime
Specialisation: Principal area of practice is criminal work (both defence and prosecution) encompassing both commercial fraud and general criminal matters. Has acted in DTI inspections, including report on James Neill Holdings plc and other companies. Also handles some licensing work. Appeared for the SFO in part of the BCCI litigation in the Resort Hotels (Feld) case and in the Johnson Matthey litigation; for one of the Guildford 4 policemen and for one of the policemen prosecuted as a result of the Wapping riots. Acting for the SFO in an ongoing matter in respect of the Versailles Group. Defended in the recent horse doping case and for police officers in the South Eastern Regional Crime Squad corruption trials.
Prof. Memberships: Criminal Bar Association. Wales and Chester and South Eastern Circuits.
Career: Called to the Bar 1965. Appointed Recorder 1980. Took silk 1983. Joined current chambers 1990. Head of Chambers.
Personal: Educated Corpus Christi College, Cambridge. Leisure pursuits include rugby football (committee member of Swansea RFC) and horse racing. Lives in Neath, West Glamorgan and London.

EVANS, David QC
Hollis Whiteman Chambers (QEB) (Julian Bevan QC & Peter Whiteman QC) London (020) 7583 5766
Recommended in Fraud
Specialisation: Principal area of specialisation within criminal law is criminal fraud. Before taking silk in 1991 appeared in several high profile cases as Junior. Acted for Ian Posgate in the Howden trial, for Morgan Grenfel in the Guinness enquiry, and for UBS Phillips & Drew in the Blue Arrow trial. Since 1991 has appeared both for the prosecution and defence in a series of major fraud trials including defendants in the BCCI enquiry, the collapse of the Swithland motor group, the Aveling Barford pension fund fraud and several high profile mortgage frauds including acting for the solicitor defendant in the Harrovian case. Has prosecuted for the SFO and the Fraud Investigation Group.
Prof. Memberships: Criminal Bar Association
Career: Educated at the London School of Economics BSc. Econ, MSc 1962-67, Wadham College Oxford B.A. Oxon 1968-70. Q.C. 1991.

EVANS, Elwen Mair
Iscoed Chambers (Trefor Davies) Swansea (01792) 652988/9
Recommended in Crime

EVANS, Gareth QC
5 Fountain Court (Anthony Barker QC) Birmingham (0121) 606 0500
Recommended in Personal Injury

EVANS, Jill
Doughty Street Chambers (Geoffrey Robertson QC) London (020) 7404 1313
Recommended in Crime

EVANS, John
1 Fountain Court (David Crigman QC) Birmingham (0121) 236 5721
Recommended in Crime

EVANS, Jonathan
Wilberforce Chambers (Edward Nugee QC) London (020) 7306 0102
Recommended in Pensions
Specialisation: Chancery and commercial litigation and advice. Pensions including pensions mis-selling, pensions ombudsman complaints. Cases include SWT v Wightman. Oil and gas law, professional negligence (including actuarial negligence). General chancery including property finance, mortgages, landlord and tenant disputes, leasehold enfranchisement, nuisance, rights of common, estates, partnership disputes and insolvency.
Prof. Memberships: Association of Pension Lawyers, Chancery Bar Association, COMBAR.
Career: Called to the Bar 1994. German and Philosophy at Oriel College, Oxford. Contributor to LLP's 'Professional Negligence: Law and Practice', editorial team of LLP's series of 'Professional Negligence Law Reports'.

EVANS, Mark QC
Queen Square Chambers (Anthony Donne QC & T Alun Jenkins QC) Bristol (0117) 921 1966
Recommended in Family

EVANS, Michael
No.1 High Pavement (John B. Milmo QC) Nottingham (0115) 941 8218
Recommended in Crime

EVANS, Susan
St John's Chambers (Christopher Sharp QC) Bristol (0117) 921 3456
Recommended in Crime

EVERALL, Mark QC
1 Mitre Court Buildings (Bruce Blair QC) London (020) 7797 7070 clerks@1mcb.com
Recommended in Family
Specialisation: Work includes matrimonial finance, public and private law children cases, international child abduction, adoption, parentage, surrogacy and assisted conception and cases with an international aspect or involving human rights.
Prof. Memberships: Family Law Bar Association; Bar European Group; International Academy of Matrimonial Lawyers; Administrative Law Bar Association; Inter-country Adoption Lawyers Association.
Career: QC 1994; Recorder 1996; Deputy High Court Judge 1996.
Publications: Editor, Rayden & Jackson on 'Divorce & Family Matters'.

EVERARD, William
King Charles House Chambers (William Everard) Nottingham (0115) 941 8851
Recommended in Crime

EWART, David
Pump Court Tax Chambers London (020) 7414 8080
Recommended in Tax

EYRE, Stephen
1 Fountain Court (David Crigman QC) Birmingham (0121) 236 5721
Recommended in Commercial (Litigation)

FALKENSTEIN, John
Milburn House Chambers (Paul Cape) Newcastle upon Tyne (0191) 230 5511
Recommended in Employment
Specialisation: Employment and discrimination law. Regularly instructed on behalf of employers and employee organisations throughout England and Wales, with a particular interest in police and local government work. Appears frequently in the EAT.
Prof. Memberships: Employment Law Bar Association.
Career: Worked in local government for several years as a policy and employment law advisor before being called to the Bar in 1996.
Publications: Author of 'Disability Discrimination Act 1995' journal of local government law (Sweet and Maxwell).
Personal: Born 4 August 1959.

FANCOURT, Timothy
Falcon Chambers (Jonathan Gaunt QC & Kim Lewison QC) London (020) 7353 2484
fancourt@falcon-chambers.com
Recommended in Agriculture, Property Litigation
Specialisation: Principal area of practice is real property based chancery work (litigation). This includes commercial property, landlord and tenant, surveyors' and solicitors' professional negligence, conveyancing, building contracts, mortgages, easements and restrictive covenants, equity and trusts and insolvency. Other main area is commercial contracts.
Prof. Memberships: Lincoln's Inn; member of Chancery Bar Association and LCLCBA and committee member, Property Bar Association. Member of Bar Council (1996-01).
Career: Called to the Bar in 1987 and joined Falcon Chambers in 1989.
Publications: General editor of Megarry's 'The Rent Acts' and Megarry's 'Assured Tenancies' (1999); author of 'Enforceability of Landlord and Tenant Covenants' (1997).
Personal: Educated at Whitgift School 1974-82 and Gonville & Caius College, Cambridge 1983-86. Born 30 August 1964.

FARBEY, Judith
Tooks Court Chambers (Michael Mansfield QC) London (020) 7405 8828
Judith.Farbey@tooks.law.co.uk
Recommended in Immigration
Specialisation: Immigration; public and administrative law.
Prof. Memberships: Includes ILPA, ALBA; member, JUSTICE Public Law Committee.
Career: Called to the Bar 1992. Selected by HM The Queen as a 'young high achiever' 1998 – Bar Council nominee. Winner, Bar Council Award for Outstanding Commitment to Pro Bono Work 1997. For Joint Council for the Welfare of Immigrants – writing and delivering training programmes for provision of quality legal services to migrants. Tavistock Clinic, London – annual lecture since 1996 on refugee law to providers of social services and healthcare for asylum seekers.
Publications: Include Who is a Refugee? in 'Context' 2001.

FARQUHAR, Stuart A.
St. Mary's Chambers Family Law Chambers (Christopher M. Butler) Nottingham (0115) 950 3503
Recommended in Family

FARRELL, David QC
36 Bedford Row (Michael Pert QC) Northampton (01604) 602333
Recommended in Crime
Specialisation: Fraud and serious crime. Personal injury and clinical/professional negligence. Child cases include R v Neave (murder of a child); Defence Junior counsel. Operations Neath (serious fraud involving motor vehicles, £6 million+); Prosecution counsel (leader). Junior counsel in Revill v Newbery (1996) the leading case on ex turpi causa.
Prof. Memberships: CBA, PNBA, PIBA.
Career: LLB Hons Manchester. Ashby-de-la-Zouch Grammar School. Recorder M&O Circuit, SILK 2000+
Personal: Married, five children. Interests include tennis and sailing.

FARRELL, Simon
3 Raymond Buildings (Clive Nicholls QC) London (020) 7400 6400
chambers@3raymondbuildings.com
Recommended in Crime, Fraud
Specialisation: Serious and complex criminal commercial fraud with particular experience defending in major prosecutions conducted by the SFO and Customs and Excise. Cases undertaken include banking fraud, money laundering, illegal share dealing, illegal deposit taking, conspiracies to cheat the public revenue, VAT and income tax fraud, duty diversion, drawback and smuggling, corruption, companies in debt (Phoenix Trading), fine art forgeries and fakes, advance fee fraud, telephone fraud (cloning, auto dialling, callselling), mortgage fraud (solicitors and brokers), and offences contrary to European law triable in the UK section 71 of the Criminal Justice Act 1993. Other areas of specialisation include the law relating to criminal and civil confiscation, major drugs offences, judicial review, civil actions against the police and the law relating to endangered species. Regularly undertakes work as Leading Junior Counsel. Most notable cases include: R v Maidstone Crown Court ex parte Harrow BC 1999 3ALLER 542; R v Henry Sissen 2001 1 WLR 902 (smuggling endangered species); R v John Drewe 2001 Southwark CC and CA (fake fine art); R v Bimal Pattni and others Southwark CC 2001 (massive alleged VAT fraud involving gold trade); R v Massingham and others Luton CC 2000 (SFO commercial fraud); and R v Brett and others Southwark CC 2000 (Phoenix company fraud).
Career: Gonville and Caius College, Cambridge. B.A (hons), M.A. Diploma Law (City University). Hardwicke Scholar, Lincolns Inn. Call 1983.
Publications: Regular contributor to Legal Action. Article in 'Criminal Law Review on Voluntary Bills', September 1998. Drafted Criminal Bar's response to government proposals for civil seizure of criminal assets in the High Court included in Proceeds of Crime Bill 2001. Drafted Liberty submissions on right of silence to the Royal Commission on Criminal Justice and drafted Liberty's response to government proposals for Community Safety Orders.

FARRER, David QC
7 Bedford Row (David Farrer QC) London (020) 7242 3555
Recommended in Crime
Specialisation: All areas of serious crime including murder and commercial fraud, both prosecution and defence, often with an international dimension. Clients include SFO, DTI, CPS, (HQ and regionally on SE and Midlands and Oxford Circuits), as well as range of large and medium firms. Variety of non-criminal work in QBD and Chancery Divisions involving fraud, undue influence and accounting issues including partnership and insolvency. Civil clients include former England football coach Martin Johnson (England and Lions rugby captain) and boxing promoter Don King. Prosecuted John Packer and others (£40 million timeshare fraud), SFO 'Blackspur' and 'Norton' cases and R v Morgan (Celine Figard murder). Defended first 'DNA profiling' murder (R v Pitchfork). Regularly trains and organises seminars for accountants on investigation, reporting and giving evidence in court. NITA qualified advocacy trainer.
Prof. Memberships: European Bar Group; Criminal Bar Association.
Career: Teaching modern languages 1965-67. Called to Bar in 1967. Appointed Recorder 1983. Took Silk 1986. Member of Bar Council 1987-93. Chairman Bar services committee 1989-92. Edited current Bar action pack (Good practice guide). Educated at Queen Elizabeth's Grammar School, Barnet and Downing College Cambridge. Took LLB in Public and Private International Law.
Personal: Leisure pursuits include tennis, rugby (watching only), local history, after dinner speaking and cabaret, music and cricket (playing and watching). Fluent French & German, working Italian.

FARRER, Paul
1 Fountain Court (David Crigman QC) Birmingham (0121) 236 5721
Recommended in Crime

FAULKS, Edward QC
No. 1 Serjeants' Inn (Edward Faulks QC) London (020) 7415 6666
clerks@no1serjeantsinn.com
Recommended in Clinical Negligence, Personal Injury
Specialisation: Principal areas of practice: clinical negligence disputes for both claimants and defendants; professional negligence; claims against public authorities (he has been involved in many of the leading cases in the last few years concerning the liability in negligence of local authorities); personal injury, including child abuse. He is instructed on behalf of NHS Trusts, local authorities, police authorities, insurance companies and individual claimants. He has been or is involved in group litigation arising out of radiotherapy treatment, cardiac surgery errors, cervical cancer screening errors and child abuse. Recent cases include Johnson v Unisys (HL) [2001]; Phelps v Hillingdon LBC (HL) [2000]; G v Bromley LBC (HL) [2000]; Anderton v Clwyd (HL) [2000]; W v Essex CC (HL) [2000]; Bradford-Smart v West Sussex CC [2000]; Penney v East Kent Health Authority (CA) [1999]; Kent v Griffiths and London Ambulance Service (CA) [1998]; Capital and Counties v Hampshire CC [1997]; X v Bedfordshire CC (HL) [1995].
Prof. Memberships: Fellow of Chartered Institute of Arbitrators, London Common Law & Commercial Bar Association, Professional Negligence Bar Association (vice-chairman).
Career: Called to the Bar 1973. Silk in 1996. Recorder. Head of chambers 1998.
Publications: Contributing editor of 'Local Authority Liabilities' (Jordans).
Personal: Educated at Wellington College and Jesus College, Oxford. Former literary agent. Leisure pursuits include cricket. Lives in London.

FEATHERBY, William
12 King's Bench Walk (Richard Methuen QC) London (020) 7583 0811
Recommended in Personal Injury

FEDER, Ami
Lamb Building (Ami Feder) London (020) 7797 7788
clerks@lambbldg.co.uk
Recommended in Crime
Specialisation: Principal area of practice is fraud work in both the criminal and civil fields and general commercial and international work. Also practices at 9 Malchei Israel Square, Tel-Aviv 64163. Tel: 03-5243381, Fax: 03-5243387, email: mozingel@zahav.net.il
Prof. Memberships: Criminal Bar Association; Common Law and Commercial Bar Association; European Bar Association; European Criminal Bar Association.
Career: Called to the Bar 1965; member of the Israel Bar.
Personal: Educated in Israel (Hebrew University of Jerusalem, the branch in Tel Aviv) and in England (London LSE).

FEINBERG, Peter QC
2-4 Tudor Street (Richard Ferguson QC) London (020) 7797 7111
Recommended in Crime
Specialisation: Criminal law. R v Powell & Daniels – House of Lords; R v Burstow – House of Lords.
Career: Recorder. President, Mental Health Tribunal. Chairman, Liaison Committee.

FENNY, Ian Charles
Guildhall Chambers (Adrian Palmer QC) Bristol (0117) 927 3366
Recommended in Crime
Specialisation: All serious crimes of violence with a particular specialisation in offences against women, children and vulnerable victims. Serious fraud and large-scale conspiracies. Drugs importation and large-scale possession with intent to supply. Category 4 Prosecutor. Lectures to legal practitioners, medical practitioners and police officers on issues involving child abuse both physical and sexual.
Prof. Memberships: Membership Criminal Bar Association. Western Circuit.
Career: LL.B (Reading) 1977. Called to Bar (Gray's Inn) 1978.
Personal: Married to a member of the Bar, three children. Hobbies: motor racing, equestrian sports.

FENTON, Adam
7 King's Bench Walk (Jeremy Cooke QC) London (020) 7910 8300
Recommended in Insurance

FENWICK, Justin QC
Four New Square (Justin Fenwick QC) London (020) 7822 2000
barristers@4newsquare.com
Recommended in Construction, Product Liability, Professional Negligence
Specialisation: Commercial and insurance litigation, professional negligence and construction; product liability.
Prof. Memberships: Combar; PNBA; LCLBA; Tecbar; PGBA.
Career: MA (Cantab) 1971 (Modern Languages and Architectural History). Grenadier Guards 1968-81; called to the Bar November 1980. Lamb Building – July 81 – July 89. 2 Crown Office Row (now 4 New Square) July 1989 – present. (Head of Chambers 2000-) QC 1993. Recorder 1999; Chairman Bar Mutual Indemnity Fund 1999-.

FERGUSON, Richard QC
2-4 Tudor Street (Richard Ferguson QC) London (020) 7797 7111
Recommended in Crime, Health & Safety
Specialisation: All forms of jury advocacy and in particular: commercial fraud; health and safety; criminal defence; libel; food and drugs. Important cases include; Ramsgate Ferry disaster [for Lloyds Register]; Severn Bridge [for consulting engineers]; New Zealand butter importation [for Anchor Butter]; Guiness Trial [for Earnest Saunders]; Hong Kong corruption [for local solicitor]; Solicitor Green form fraud [Liverpool Crown Court]; Cyprus Spy Trial; Terry Marsh; Brighton Bombing; Birmingham 6; Allegation of police perversion of justice [Melvin & Dingle]; Allegation of murder by police shooting [for the officer]; Ronnie Knight; Taylor Sisters; Rosemary West; Branson v Snowden [Libel]; acted in Ireland for Sunday Times and News International; environmental law; [for United Biscuits, food misdescription]; M.O.D. v Green; House of Lords, Brophy [voir dire]; Asiz [good character direction] in re M suit against magustrate; Clegg [shooting by soldier]; Privy Council; judicial review; extradition.
Career: QC [Northern Ireland] 1973; SC [Republic of Ireland] 1982; QC [England and Wales] 1986; practice in Hog Kong, Cayman, Bermuda; Bencher in Gray's Inn; former Chairman, Criminal Bar Association; Bar Council.

FERNYHOUGH, Richard QC
Keating Chambers (Richard Fernyhough QC) London (020) 7544 2600
clerks@keatingchambers.com
Recommended in Arbitration (International), Construction
Specialisation: Construction and engineering law; arbitration both international and domestic; arbitrator, domestic and international including I.C.C.
Career: Qualified 1970; Middle Temple; QC 1986; FCI Arb 1992; Recorder of the Crown Court 1986.
Personal: Merchant Taylors School; University College, London (1966 LLB Hons). Born 1943; resides London. Tennis, flying, opera. Languages: French.

FERRIER, Susan
9 Park Place (Ian Murphy QC) Cardiff (029) 2038 2731
Recommended in Crime

FETHERSTONHAUGH, Guy
Falcon Chambers (Jonathan Gaunt QC & Kim Lewison QC) London (020) 7353 2484
clerks@falcon-chambers.co.uk
Recommended in Property Litigation
Specialisation: Landlord and tenant litigation (commercial and residential) and advisory work particularly in rent review. Other aspects of real property, including easements, restrictive covenants, conveyancing and mortgages. Property-related aspects of professional negligence and insolvency.
Prof. Memberships: Chancery Bar Association; LCLBA; Property Bar Association.
Career: Specialist Standing Counsel to the Rent Assessment Panel; Supplementary Panel of Counsel to do property law work.
Publications: Handbook of 'Rent Review' (co-author); 'The Litigation Practice' (contributing editor).

FIELD, Patrick QC
Deans Court Chambers (Stephen Grime QC) Manchester (0161) 214 6000
field@deanscourt.co.uk
Recommended in Personal Injury
Specialisation: General Common Law particularly personal injury and professional negligence.
Prof. Memberships: Northern Circuit; Personal Injuries Bar Association; Professional Negligence Bar Association.
Career: Called 1981. Educated at Wilmslow Grammar School and Kings College, London.

FIELD, Richard QC
One Essex Court (Lord Grabiner QC) London (020) 7583 2000
rfield@oeclaw.co.uk
Recommended in Commercial (Litigation)
Specialisation: Principal area of practice is commercial law. Has appeared in a wide range of matters in this area including insurance, banking, EC competition law, sale and purchase warranties and distribution agreements. Other areas of practice include professional negligence, especially auditors' negligence, fraud and tracing of assets and judicial review in a commercial context.
Prof. Memberships: COMBAR; London Common Law and Commercial Bar Association, British Insurance Law Association; ALBA.
Career: 1969-77 taught in the law faculties of the Universities of British Columbia; Hong Kong; and McGill; called to the Bar 1977; appointed Queen's Counsel 1987; Deputy High Court Judge (authorised to sit in the Commercial Court) 1998; Master of the Bench of Inner Temple 1998; Recorder 1999.
Personal: Educated: Bristol University (LLB) and London University (LLM).

FINCH, Nadine
Two Garden Court (Ian Macdonald QC & Owen Davies QC) London (020) 7353 1633
Recommended in Immigration
Specialisation: Predominantly civil liberties practice, specialising in all areas of immigration law. Particular experience of cases involving asylum, the interaction between immigration and family law, applications by gay and lesbian appellants, the use of European Convention on Human Rights and European law, and procedures to be employed when an appellant or applicant is suffering from mental illness. She has recently represented a number of appellants who have been detained in prison, pending deportation, at the conclusion of prison sentences, despite conditions in their country having changed since the order was originally made. In June 2001, she was a member of an international workshop in Washington DC, which discussed the situation of refugee children and children, who had been trafficked. Cases include R v Secretary of State for the Home Department ex parte Meftah Zighem [1996] Imm AR 194, R v Secretary of State for the Home Department ex parte Toprak [1996] Imm AR 332, and R v SSHD ex p Lucy Ouma [1997] Imm AR 606. Sepet & Bulbul v Secretary of State for the Home Department (iAT) [2000] Imm AR 445. Sepet & Bulbul v Secretary of State for the Home Department (C of A) The Times 12.7.01.
Prof. Memberships: Executive Member of Immigration Law Practitioners Association, member of Stonewall Immigration Group, Administrative Law Bar Association, Family Law Bar Association. She is a contributor to Macdonald's 'Immigration Law and Practice', 'Human Rights Practice' (Sweet & Maxwell) and 'Cohabitation: Law and Precedents' (Sweet & Maxwell). She is presently working on the revision of 'Halsbury's Laws of England', British Nationality and Immigration section.
Career: Called to the Bar 1991. Joined present chambers in 2000. Previously practiced at Doughty Street Chambers. Prior to 1989 employed in legal research and community work.

FINDLAY, James
2-3 Gray's Inn Square (Anthony Porten QC & Anthony Scrivener QC) London (020) 7242 4986
Recommended in Local Government
Specialisation: Principal area of practice is local government, planning and environment and administrative law. Extensive experience both in Judicial Review (e.g. R v Durham CC & Others, ex parte Huddlestone, R v West Dorset D.C. ex p. Searle, R v Brighton & Hove B.C. ex p. Nacion, Warsame v Hounslow L.B.C, Hughes v Kingston Upon Hull DC, Birmingham CC v Oakley, R v Newell, R v Newcastle Under Lyme Magistrates, ex p. Massey) and Inquiry work (planning and other, both for and against local authorities). Regular lecturer on such matters, including impact of Human Rights Act. On editorial panel of Halsbury's Laws 'Public Health' (waste on land).
Prof. Memberships: PEBA; ALBA.
Career: Called: 1984.
Personal: Born 1961. Educated at Glenalmond and Magdalene College, Cambridge.

FINNIGAN, Peter
Hollis Whiteman Chambers (QEB) (Julian Bevan QC & Peter Whiteman QC) London (020) 7583 5766
Recommended in Fraud
Specialisation: Principal area of practice is criminal law with a particular emphasis on commercial and professional/City fraud cases. Also deals with Revenue offences and V.A.T. frauds. Major cases include Blue Arrow, Iraqi Supergun, Brinks Mat handling (R v Noye and others) and the Guppy case. Clients include the S.F.O., H.M. Customs and Excise and the Fraud Investigation Group of the C.P.S.
Prof. Memberships: Lincoln's Inn.
Career: Called to the Bar 1979 and joined current chambers in 1981. Standing Counsel to H.M. Customs & Excise.
Personal: Educated at Sevenoaks School 1967-74 and University of Newcastle-upon-Tyne 1975-78. Lives in Twickenham, Middlesex.

FISH, David QC

Deans Court Chambers (Stephen Grime QC) Manchester (0161) 214 6000

Recommended in Crime

Specialisation: Fraud, serious drugs cases, licensing.
Prof. Memberships: Criminal Bar Association.
Career: Called 1973, QC 1997, Recorder 1994.
Personal: Ashton-Under-Lyne Grammar School, London School of Economics.

FISHER, David QC

6 King's Bench Walk (Roy Amlot QC) London (020) 7583 0410 clerks@6kbw.com

Recommended in Crime

Specialisation: Criminal law specialist, including drugs, sexual allegations and fraud.
Prof. Memberships: General Council of the Bar 1997 to 1999. Deputy Chairman of the Law Reform Committee 1999 to 2001. Advocacy Studies Board since 1997. Criminal Bar Association. South Eastern Circuit.
Career: Called to the Bar in 1973. Tenant of current chambers since 1974. Recorder since 1991. QC in 1996.

FITTON, Michael

Albion Chambers (Charles Barton QC & Neil Ford QC) Bristol (0117) 927 2144

Recommended in Crime

FITZGERALD, Edward QC

Doughty Street Chambers (Geoffrey Robertson QC) London (020) 7404 1313

Recommended in Administrative & Public Law, Crime, Human Rights

Specialisation: Specialises in public law, criminal law, mental health and European human rights law. Has represented criminal defendants, prisoners, mental patients and extradition in various cases before the Court of Appeal, House of Lords and the European Court. Recent cases include Venables v MGN News (restraining the public from certifying the identity of two juvenile killers), ex parte Hirst (duty to give reasons for the reclassification of prisoners) and Offen (restricted the application of mandatory life sentences), Venables v UK (sentencing of HMP detainees) and U.S. Government v Al-Fawwaz (on jurisdiction in extradition). Less recently he was counsel in Derek Bentley's posthumous appeal and represented Michael Hickey in the Bridgewater Three case. Was counsel for the appellant in numerous constitutional and criminal appeals to the Privy Council from the Commonwealth Caribbean; including Neville Lewis, Hughes, R v Logan and Vasquez and O'Neil. Published work includes articles on psychological defences, and the rights of prisoners and mental patients. Has also lectured on the impact of the Human Rights Act and in both the US and Caribbean on comparative criminal procedure. Advises local authorities on mental health law and has worked for the Official Solicitor in numerous cases involving minors and mental patients.
Career: Called to the Bar 1978. Took silk 1995.
Personal: Education: BA (Hons) (Congratulatory First), M.Phil, criminology. Qualified in both New York and American Law. Languages: French and Italian. Born 1953. Winner of Times/Justice Human Rights Award 1998.

FITZGERALD, Michael QC

2 Mitre Court Buildings (Michael FitzGerald QC) London (020) 7583 1380

Recommended in Planning

Specialisation: All aspects of planning and local government law. Major infastructure cases include channel tunnel; Sizewell nuclear power station; Wynch farm oilfield and pipeline; Maidenhead; Windsor and Eton flood relief scheme; Terminals 4 and 5 Heathrow; Birmingham Northern Relief Road and M20. Major contentious cases include Green Belt – HQ for British Airways; HQ for RMC; HQ and manufacturing for TAG/McLaren; research laboratories for Amersham International; AONB – Holiday villages at Longleat and Sellindge; major land valuation; compensation and rating cases in UK and Hong Kong.
Prof. Memberships: Leader of the Parliamentary Bar; Planning and Environment Bar Association 1993-0; 21 years as a Committee Member of the Joint Oxford Planning Conference; Chairman of the Advisory Panel on Standards for the Planning Inspectorate Executive Agency.
Career: Called to the Bar in 1961. Appointed QC 1980.
Personal: Educated at Downside and Cambridge. Leisure pursuits include opera, music, shooting, fishing.

FITZGERALD, Susanna QC

One Essex Court (Lord Grabiner QC) London (020) 7583 2000

Recommended in Licensing

Specialisation: Specialises in liquor, gaming, betting, internet gambling, and public entertainment licensing and lotteries law. Has represented or advised major leisure and gaming operators, concert promoters, retail liquor companies, breweries and petrol companies. Contributing editor to 'Law of Betting, Gaming and Lotteries' by Smith and Monkcom (2nd ed), author of articles published in 'Licensing Review', 'The Solicitors Journal' and the 'Consumer Policy Review'. Contributor to 'Gambling and Public Policy' (1991). Has drafted submissions to the government on changes in Liquor and Public Entertainment Licensing Law and on amendments to the Gaming Act 1968 for Business in Sport and Leisure. Has lectured at conferences and spoken at seminars in the UK and abroad. Has also appeared on radio and television.
Prof. Memberships: Director of Business in Sport & Leisure, CLCBA, South Eastern Circuit, Commercial Women in Law, Society for the Study of Gambling (Committee Member), Mediator accredited by CEDR.
Career: Called to the Bar in 1973, joined present chambers in 1975 and made QC in 1999.

FLAUX, Julian QC

7 King's Bench Walk (Jeremy Cooke QC) London (020) 7910 8300 clerks@7kbw.law.co.uk

Recommended in Commercial (Litigation), Insurance, Shipping

Specialisation: Specialises in all aspects of commercial law including insurance and reinsurance, shipping, professional negligence, international sale of goods, banking and international arbitration.
Prof. Memberships: Chairman: London Common Law and Commercial Bar Association; Chairman: Supporting Members Liaison Committee of London Maritime Arbitrators Association; Commercial Bar Association; LCIA; ACI.
Career: B.C.L.; M.A. (Oxon: First Class Honours in Jurisprudence); Called to the Bar 1978. Member of present Chambers from 1979; Took silk 1994; Appointed Recorder 2000.
Personal: Born 1955; Married, three sons. Interests: Cricket; opera.

FLENLEY, William

4 Paper Buildings (Jean Ritchie QC) London (020) 7643 5000 William.flenley@dial.pipex.com

Recommended in Professional Negligence

Specialisation: Professional negligence, insurance, real property, freezing orders. Appeared in the Nationwide managed litigation against 400 firms of solicitors (Nationwide v Balmer Radmore (1999) PNLR 606), and was involved in the large-scale mediation between Halifax Plc and the Solicitors' Indemnity Fund. Cases include: Ruparel v Awan (2001) Lloyd's Rep PN 258, solicitors' undertakings; Jenmain v Steed & Steed (2000) PNLR 616, CA, professional negligence – loss of profit; Matlock Green v Potter (2000) Lloyd's Rep PN 935, damages for loss of business tenancy; Mahoney v Purnell (1996) 3 All ER 61, undue influence: solicitors' duties.
Prof. Memberships: PNBA, Society for Computers and Law.
Career: Exeter College, Oxford (BA, BCL); Cornell University, USA (LL M). Called in 1988.
Publications: Flenley & Leech – 'Solicitors' Negligence' (1999); an editor of 'Cordery on Solicitors'; contributor to chapters 1 and 2 (general principles of liability and damages) of ' Professional Negligence and Liability' (2000); Assistant General Editor, Lloyd's law Reports: Professional Negligence; co-author, 'The Mareva Injunction and Anton Piller Order' (1993).

FLESCH, Michael QC

Gray's Inn Tax Chambers (Milton Grundy) London (020) 242 2642

Recommended in Tax

Specialisation: Advises on all aspects of revenue law, and appears before the Commissioners, High Court, Court of Appeal, House of Lords, Privy Council and also in Hong Kong in revenue cases. Regular lecturer on tax-related topics.
Prof. Memberships: Revenue Bar Association, past chairman. Fellow, Charted Institute of Taxation.
Career: Called to the Bar 1963. Teaching Fellow, University of Chicago 1963-64. Part-time lecturer in Revenue law, University College London 1964-82. Joined present chambers 1965. Took Silk 1983. Bencher of Grays Inn 1993.
Personal: Educated at Gordonstoun School 1953-58 and University College, London 1959-62 (LLB Class 1, Hons). Governor of Gordonstoun School 1976-96. Leisure pursuits include all forms of sport. Keen Arsenal and Middlesex supporter, member of MCC, Twickenham and Wimbledon debenture holder. Born 11th March 1940. Lives in London.

FLETCHER, Andrew

3 Verulam Buildings (Christopher Symons QC & John Jarvis QC) London (020) 7831 8441 afletcher@3vb.com

Recommended in Commercial (Litigation)

Specialisation: Particular experience in share purchase agreements (especially misrepresentation and breach of warranty claims); insurance and reinsurance (including involvement in arbitrations relating to the 1993 PA LMX spiral); banking (including disputes as to foreign exchange and margin trading); corporate governance issues; disputes between telecoms carriers and service providers; company and insolvency issues arising out of or inter-relating with commercial disputes; professional negligence, primarily in a financial context; and investigations and inquiries. Recent cases include: Larussa-Chigi v C S First Boston Limited [1998] CLC 227, QBD (Comm Ct) (whether foreign exchange margin trading was subject to SFA Conduct of Business Rules); Thornton Springer v NEM Insurance [2000] 2 All ER 489 (dispute as to policy coverage in respect of the costs of an insured's successful defence of claims brought against it; construction of accontant's minimum wording professional indemnity policy); Rosedale (JW) Investments Ltd and ors v British Steel plc (CA, 15 November 2000) New Law Online 200120603 (construction of provisions in share purchase agreement); Rosedale Investments Ltd and ors v British Steel plc (Comm Ct, 6 December 2000) New Law Online (liability under tax indemnity in share purchase agreement); Elton John and others v Price Waterhouse and anr, ChD (11 April 2001) New Law Online 201047201 (Construction of management agreement; rectification; estoppel by convention; effect of settlement; director's duties; negligence; limitation).

FLINT, Charles QC

Blackstone Chambers (Presiley Baxendale QC & Charles Flint QC) London (020) 7583 1770 clerks@blackstonechambers.com

Recommended in Administrative & Public Law, Commercial (Litigation), Financial Services, Fraud, Sport

Specialisation: Commercial and public law specialist. Practice covers substantial corporate litigation in all divisions of the High Court, financial services litigation, including disciplinary tribunals, and judicial review in a commercial context. Has a particular interest in commer-

cial fraud and sports law. Acted for the plaintiff in Arab Monetary Fund v Hashim litigation, and for the defendant in the action brought by the State of Brunei v HRH Prince Jefri Bolkiah.
Prof. Memberships: Fellow of the Chartered Institute of Arbitrators, Commercial Bar Association, Administrative Law Bar Association, British Association for Sport and Law. CEDR accredited mediator.
Career: Called to the Bar 1975, joining present chambers in the same year. Appointed Junior Counsel to the Crown (Common Law) 1991-95 and took Silk 1995.

FLOYD, Christopher QC
11 South Square (Christopher Floyd QC) London (020) 7405 1222
Recommended in Intellectual Property
Specialisation: Intellectual property including patents, trade marks, copyright and designs, breach of confidence and related EU law. Major cases include Mentor v Hollister [1993] RPC 7 (CA insufficiency principles); Molnlycke v Procter & Gamble [1994] RPC 7 (CA obviousness principles); Gerber v Lectra [1995] RPC 383, [1997] RPC 443 (law damages for patent infringement); Merrell Dow Pharmaceuticals v HN Norton [1996] RPC 76 (HL novelty of a pro-drug); Pearce v Ove Arup [2000] Ch 403 (CA Brussels Convention: infringement of foreign IP rights). Important cases in last year Dyson v Hoover [2001] RPC 473, 544, Rohm & Haas v Collag [2001] FSR 426 (declaration of non-infringement); Texas Iron Works' Patent [2000] RPC 207 (added matter); Cairnstores v Hassle (right to apply for revocation by straw man); Amersham v Amicon (construction, chromatography valves), Asahi v Macopharma (obviousness, blood systems).
Prof. Memberships: IP Bar Association, Chancery Bar Association, Irish Bar.
Career: Called 1975, Inner Temple, QC 1992; Head of IP Chambers at 11 South Square; Deputy Chairman Copyright Tribunal 1995-; Assistant Recorder 1994; Recorder 2000-; Deputy High Court Judge 1998-; Bar Council Professional Conduct Committee 1998-; Chairman IP Bar Association 1999-; Bar Council Member 1999-.
Personal: Educated: Westminster School, Trinity College, Cambridge (BA Natural Sciences and Law 1974). Interests: Austin Sevens, cricket (watching), skiing, walking. Married one son, two daughters.

FLYNN, James
Brick Court Chambers (Christopher Clarke QC) London (020) 7379 3550 flynn@brickcourt.co.uk
Recommended in Competition/Anti-trust
Specialisation: European Community/Competition Law. Reported cases include: (English courts): R v Customs & Excise ex p Lunn Poly (High Court and CA); Sockel GmbH v Body Shop International (High Court); Trent Taverns v Sykes (CA); Welsh Rugby Union and IRB v Campbell (High Court); Whitbread plc v Falla (High Court); (in the European Court of Justice): British Aerospace v Commission; BP Chemicals v Commission No 1; Gencor v Commission; Compagnie Maritime Belge v Commission; BP Chemicals v Commission (No 2).
Prof. Memberships: Competition Law Association (Committee member); UIA EC Section Committee Members; JUSTICE EU Expert Panel; Bar European Group; Law Society; European Group; European Circuit.
Career: Legal Secretary, European Court of Justice (1986-89); Partner, *Linklaters & Paines*, Brussels (1993-96); Tenant Brick Court Chambers, 1996 to date.
Publications: Co-author 'Competition: Understanding the 1998 Act' and many articles and contributions to books on EC and competition law topics.
Personal: Fluent French (written and spoken).

FLYNN, Vernon James Hennessy
Essex Court Chambers (Gordon Pollock QC) London (020) 7813 8000 vflynn@essexcourt-chambers.co.uk
Recommended in Commercial (Litigation), Media & Entertainment
Specialisation: Broad-based practice in international and commercial law. In particular media and entertainment, commercial, banking and finance and shipping.
Career: Trinity College, Cambridge: Law (1st Class Hons). Called to the Bar 1991.

FORD, Michael
Doughty Street Chambers (Geoffrey Robertson QC) London (020) 7404 1313
Recommended in Health & Safety, Human Rights
Specialisation: Principal areas of practice are employment law, public law, civil liberties, tort and health and safety.
Prof. Memberships: Member of the Industrial Law Society, Institute for Employment Rights, Justice, Liberty.
Career: University of Bristol, 1st Class; MA (Distinction). Qualified as solicitor (1989). Lecturer in Law at University of Manchester (1990-92). Called to Bar 1992. Recent cases include Steel, Lush and others v UK (ECHR) (1999) 28 EHRR 603; Vidter v Unison [1999] ICR 746; Allen v AMCO (ECJ) [2000] IRLR 119; Southwark v Whillier [2001] ICR 142; R v Mallet ex p Stunt, 'The Times', 20 March 20001. Counsel for the bereaved and injured at Southall and Ladbroke Grove Railway Accident Public Inquiries (1999-00). Visiting fellow at LSE.
Publications: Co-author of 'Redgrave's Health and Safety' and author of 'Privacy and Surveillance at Work'. Numerous other publications, especially on employment law.
Personal: Keen cyclist.

FORD, Neil QC
Albion Chambers (Charles Barton QC & Neil Ford QC) Bristol (0117) 927 2144
Recommended in Crime

FORDHAM, Michael
Blackstone Chambers (Presiley Baxendale QC & Charles Flint QC) London (020) 75831770 michaelfordham@blackstonechambers.com
Recommended in Administrative & Public Law, Environment, Sport
Specialisation: Specialist in public and administrative law, and particularly judicial review. Member of Attorney-General's Supplementary Panel. Cases include Pinochet [2000] 1AC 61 & 147 (extradition of former head of state), Diane Blood [1999] Fam 151 (posthumous use of sperm), Fayed [1998] 1 All ER 93 (review of Parliamentary Commissioner for Standards), Walker [2000] 1 WLR 806 (UN peacekeeper) and Baby Products [2000] LGR 171. Also environmental law, human rights and sports law. Author of 'Judicial Review Handbook'. Editor of journal 'Judicial Review'. Lectures in administrative law at Hertford College, Oxford. Advisory Board Member, British Institute of International and Comparative Law. Called to the Bar 1990.
Personal: Educated at Spalding Grammar School, Hertford College, Oxford (BA & BCL), and University of Virginia (LL.M). Oxford Hockey Blue (1986). Awarded Karmel, Mould and Prince of Wales Scholarships at Gray's Inn. Lives in St Albans.

FORLIN, Gerard
2-3 Gray's Inn Square (Anthony Porten QC & Anthony Scrivener QC) London (020) 7242 4986 gforlin@2-3graysinnsquare.co.uk
Recommended in Health & Safety
Specialisation: Crime (specialising in health and safety and corporate and gross negligence manslaughter); disaster litigation; aviation; railways; environmental crime; regulatory offences; disciplinary offences; human rights; public inquiries; inquests. Recent major cases: Faversham M2 coach crash; Watford train crash (manslaughter); Southall train crash (manslaughter and public inquiry); Paddington train crash (public inquiry); Mayoress of Croyden (corporate manslaughter); the Belle Tout lighthouse case (manslaughter); Hatfield train crash; D.V.T. and international airline crashes. Numerous other cases involving doctors, nurses, directors, individuals and companies charged with manslaughter and health and safety cases. He also acts for Government Departments in Crown Censure cases. He undertakes numerous inquests including acting recently for the FBU in the Manchester fireman case. He also prosecutes health and safety cases. He chairs and lectures for IBC, CLT, IIR, Lawtel, IATA, TEN, ROSPA, Iosh and numerous universities, law firms and institutions worldwide. He appears regularly on TV and radio as an expert and is a script adviser for various TV companies. He is a lecturer and facilitator for the Bar Council on the HRA.
Prof. Memberships: C.B.A.; Bar pro bono unit; current member of the Attorney General's Panel of Counsel.
Career: Called Lincoln's Inn 1984 – previously Senior Crown Counsel, Hong Kong.
Publications: Numerous articles published, joint author of corporate manslaughter practical research paper (Sweet & Maxwell) – general editor of a major loose-leaf work to be published by Butterworths early in 2002 on corporate manslaughter and a further book on health and safety also due out in early 2002 for Informa.
Personal: Educated London School of Economics LLB (Hons); LLM; Trinity Hall; Cambridge M.Phil; Diploma in Air and Space Law. Leisure – travel, walking, sub-aqua.

FORSYTH, Julie
Chavasse Court Chambers (Theresa Pepper) Liverpool (0151) 707 1191
Recommended in Crime

FORTSON, Rudi
3 Gray's Inn Square (Rock Tansey QC) London (020) 7520 5600
Recommended in Crime
Specialisation: Extensive criminal law experience, with specialist knowledge on law relating to misuse of drugs, drug-trafficking offences, money-laundering and fraud. Author of 'The Criminal Justice Act 1993' and 'Law on the Misuse of Drugs and Drug Trafficking Offences'. Annotator for 'Current Law Statutes' on Criminal Justice Acts 1991 and 1993, Police and Magistrates Courts Act 1994 and Drug Trafficking Act 1994. Member of the Police Foundation Independent Inquiry (2000) into the Misuse of Drugs Act 1971. Former contributing editor of Archbold Criminal Pleading, Evidence and Practice'. Addresses conferences and seminars.
Prof. Memberships: Criminal Bar Association, International Bar Association, American Bar Association, Forensic Science Society.
Career: Called to the Bar 1976 (pupillage at 1 Crown Office Row) and joined current chambers in 1978.
Personal: Educated at University College, London 1972-75 (LLB Hons). Leisure pursuits include yachting, chess and cooking. Born 2 March 1952.

FOSKETT, David QC
1 Crown Office Row (Robert Seabrook QC) London (020) 7797 7500
Recommended in Clinical Negligence, Personal Injury
Specialisation: All fields of common law advocacy and advice including clinical and other professional negligence, personal injury, medical and dental disciplinary tribunals, contract and general domestic commercial work and product liability. He also has experience in judicial review, administrative law and civil and criminal fraud cases. Recent cases include Langford v Hebran, Makepeace v Evans Bros (personal injury); Hunt v NHSLA (clinical negligence); Nwabueze v GMC (appeal to Privy Council in doctor's disciplinary case); Morris v Wentworth-Stanley (commercial); R. v Secretary of State for Health, ex p. Eastside Cheese Co (judicial review).
Prof. Memberships: Fellow of the Chartered Institute of Arbitrators; member London Common Law and Commercial Bar Association; Administrative Law Bar Association; Family Law Bar Association and Midland Circuit; member of the Civil Procedure Rules Committee 1997-.
Career: Called to the Bar (Gray's Inn) 1972. Bencher 1999. Queen's Counsel 1991. Assistant Recorder 1992-95; Recorder 1995 – ; Deputy High Court Judge 1997 -.

Publications: He is the author of 'The Law and Practice of Compromise' (Sweet & Maxwell), the 5th edition of which is to be published during 2001. He has contributed articles to 'The Times' and has lectured extensively on the subject of the settlement of litigation.
Personal: Educated at Warwick School and King's College London (LL.B., President of the Union). Interests include cricket, golf, reading poetry and birdwatching. Lives in London and Gloucestershire.

FOSTER, Catherine
Plowden Buildings (William Lowe QC) London (020) 7583 0808
bar@plowdenbuildings.co.uk
Recommended in Personal Injury
Specialisation: Occupational diseases, medical negligence, general personal injury litigation.
Prof. Memberships: PIBA.

FOSTER, Charles
6 Pump Court London (020) 7583 6013
Recommended in Clinical Negligence
Specialisation: Medical and other professional negligence. Reported cases include Calver v Westwood Group [2001], In re D (mental patient: Habeas Corpus) [2001] 1 FLR 218, Briggs v Pitt-Payne [1999] Lloyd's LR: Med 1, Drake v Pontefract HA [1998] Lloyd's LR: Med 425, Reed v Sunderland HA, The Times, 16 October 1998, Fallows v Randle [1997] 8 Med LR 160, Bancroft v Harrogate HA [1997] 8 Med LR 398, Hind v York HA [1997] 8 Med LR 377, Ogden v Airedale HA [1996] 7 Med LR 153, Kahl v Freistaat Bayern [1995] PIQR P401.
Prof. Memberships: PNBA, Medico-Legal Society.
Career: Educated at Shrewsbury School & St John's College, Cambridge (MA, Vet MB, MRCVS). Research in wild animal anaesthesia in Saudi Arabia and comparative anatomy at RCS, Research Fellow at Hebrew University, Jerusalem. Also a member of the Irish Bar. Numerous publications.

FOWLER, Richard QC
Monckton Chambers (John Swift QC) London (020) 7405 7211
rfowler@monckton.co.uk
Recommended in Aviation, Competition/Anti-trust
Specialisation: EC and UK competition law.
Prof. Memberships: Committee member COMBAR; member Competition Law Association; member Legal Services Committee and Professional Conduct & Complaints Committee of Bar Council.
Career: Specialised since 1973 (including working from 1977 to 1984 on Case No IV/29.479 – IBM) in the preparation, drafting and presentation of submissions on behalf of clients to the European Commission (also OFT and Competition Commission) and in High Court and European Court proceedings, and advising a wide range of national and international clients on competition law matters and in related areas, particularly utility regulation. Recent cases include Re Premier League Football (RP Court); two judicial reviews relating to the mobile phone auction; Synstar v ICL; appearing for the Hong Kong administration in the HK Legislative Council in relation to the HK Telecommunications Bill.

FOXTON, David
Essex Court Chambers (Gordon Pollock QC) London (020) 7813 8000
Recommended in Commercial (Litigation), Information Technology, Insurance, Shipping
Specialisation: Commercial practice, in particular international insurance and reinsurance; shipping and the international carriage of goods; professional negligence; Lloyd's litigation. Banking, sale of goods, company sales, computer supply disputes and professional negligence actions. Has appeared on numerous occasions in commercial arbitration.
Career: Magdalen College, Oxford 1983-86 BA (1st Class Hons) in Jurisprudence, 1986. Bachelor of Civil Law (1st Class Hons). Called to the Bar 1989. PhD (London) 2001.
Publications: Scrutton on Charterparties and Bill of Lading.
Personal: Born 1965.

FOY, John QC
9 Gough Square (John Foy QC) London (020) 7832 0500
clerks@9goughsq.co.uk
Recommended in Personal Injury
Specialisation: Practice encompasses plaintiff and defendant personal injury and clinical negligence work. Appeared in Mountenay v Bernard Matthews [1994]; Mughal v Reuters Ltd [1993]; Hunt v Douglas Roofing [1990] and Arnold v CEGB [1988]; British Coal Respiration Disease Litigation [1998]; Alexander v Midland Bank plc [1999]; Wadey v Surrey County Council [2000]. Clients include all major trade unions. Frequently chairs and addresses conferences and seminars, and has appeared on BBC TV and radio.
Prof. Memberships: Association of Personal Injury Lawyers; Personal Injury Bar Association; Professional Negligence Bar Association.
Career: Called to the Bar and joined 9 Gough Square in 1969; Recorder (2000).
Personal: LL.B (Hons) Birmingham University, 1967. Leisure pursuits include sports. Born 1st June 1946. Lives in Suffolk.

FRANCIS, Nicholas
29 Bedford Row Chambers (Peter Ralls QC) London (020) 7404 1044
nfrancis@29bedfordrow.co.uk
Recommended in Family
Specialisation: Principal area of practice is matrimonial ancillary relief work, with a particular interest in pension issues and foreign asset cases. Other main areas within practice are professional negligence; and residence, contact, education and child abduction cases. Major cases include Re P (A Minor) [1992] (Education); Re D (minors) [1993] (conciliation: Privilege); C v C [1994] (wasted costs order); S v S (reserved costs order) [1995] B v Miller & Co [1996] and H v H [1997]. Several articles on ancillary relief for Family Law with particular emphasis on the issue of costs and discovery. Regular lecturer on costs and discovery and on international aspects of family proceedings; and contributor to Legal Network T.V.
Prof. Memberships: Family Law Bar Association (former committee member). Member for 3 years of Bar Council Professional Conduct and Complaints Committee.
Personal: Educated at Radley College 1971-76 and Downing College, Cambridge 1977-80 (BA Law 1980, MA 1984). Leisure pursuits include racing dinghies. Born 1958. Lives in London.

FRANCIS, Robert QC
3 Serjeants' Inn (Robert Francis QC & John Grace QC) London (020) 7427 5000
Recommended in Clinical Negligence
Specialisation: Principal area of practice is medical law, including medical negligence actions for plaintiffs and defendants, ethical cases concerning treatment of patients (particularly termination of treatment), and disciplinary proceedings (General Medical Council, General Dental Council etc). Leading cases include: Re F (Mental Patient: Sterilization); Airedale NHS Trust v Bland; Roy v Kensington etc FPC; Re T (Wardship: Medical Treatment); Re MB; GMC v Roylance. Other areas of practice include administrative law, employment, crime, public inquiries.
Prof. Memberships: Professional Negligence Bar Association, LCLCBA, CBA.
Career: Called to the Bar 1973; Queen's Counsel 1992. Assistant Recorder 1996.
Personal: Uppingham School, Exeter University. Born 4 April 1950.

FRANSMAN, Laurie QC
Two Garden Court (Ian Macdonald QC & Owen Davies QC) London (020) 7353 1633
Recommended in Immigration
Specialisation: Advice, strategic planning and advocacy in all aspects of immigration and nationality, particularly concerning employment, self-employment and corporate work, the music and entertainment industry, national security and other sensitive cases and complex nationality issues; with an emphasis throughout on European Community law and international and human rights laws.
Prof. Memberships: Administrative Law Bar Association; Bar European Group; Immigration Law Practitioners' Association (co-founder, executive committee member 1993-98, 1999-).
Career: Member of the editorial boards of 'Immigration and Nationality Law and Practice' (Tolleys), and 'Immigration and International Employment Law' (Eclipse). Nationality law consultant to Halsbury's 'Laws of England' (4th ed.). Books: 'British Nationality Law and the 1981 Act' (1982); 'Tribunals Practice and Procedure' (jointly 1985); 'Immigration Emergency Procedures' (jointly, 1986); 'Fransman's British Nationality Law' (1989); 'The Constitution of the United Kingdom' (contrib., 1991); 'Strangers and Citizens' (contrib., 1994); 'Citizenship and Nationality Status in the New Europe' (contrib., 1998); 'Fransman's British Nationality Law' (1998), 2nd ed; 'Immigration, Nationality and Asylum under the Human Rights Act 1998' (contributor and coeditor, 1999)

FRASER, Peter D
Atkin Chambers (Robert Akenhead QC) London (020) 7404 0102
Recommended in Construction
Specialisation: Construction and engineering disputes; multi-party contractual disputes and commercial litigation. Insurance litigation, professional negligence of architects, surveyors and engineers. Arbitration proceedings including international arbitrations. Cases involving following projects: Harbour Exchange, Isle of Dogs; the West Yorkshire Playhouse, Leeds; Bokaa Dam project in Botswana; Euro Disney; Canary Wharf; Copthorne Hotel in Newcastle; New Sadlers Wells Theatre, London; Canary Wharf Riverside Project; Delta Civil Engineering Co. Ltd v LDDC (CA) 81 BLR 19; Copthorne Hotel (Newcastle) Ltd. v Arup Associates (CA) 85 BLR 22.
Career: Called to Bar by Middle Temple 1989. Editor of the Building Law Reports since 1991 to date. Author of 'How to Pass Law Exams' (HLT Publications 1991).
Personal: Born 1963. Educated Harrogate Grammar School and St John's College Cambridge. LLM Cambridge University; MA in Law, Cambridge University. Open exhibitioner and MacMahon Law Scholar of St. John's College, Cambridge. Astbury Scholar of the Middle Temple.

FREEDMAN, Clive QC
Littleton Chambers (Michel Kallipetis QC) London (020) 7797 8600
Recommended in Commercial (Litigation)
Specialisation: Commercial law including franchising, company, partnership, banking, employment, construction, professional negligence, commercial arbitration and professional disciplinary tribunals. Since taking silk in 1997, has appeared in the following representative cases: Arrow v Blackledge C.A. The Times [2000] 2 BCLC 167 CA (striking out section 459 petition), Beeforth v Beeforth CA The Times 17 September 1998 (peremptory orders); Re: Blenheim Restaurants Limited C.A. 26 July 1999 (dissolution of company), Re: Blenheim Restaurants Limited (No.2) (condition regarding restoration) The Times 26 October 1999, Re: Blenheim Restaurants Limited (No.3) (recalling court orders) The Times 7 November 1999, Dubai Aluminium v Al Alawi [1999] 1 All ER 703 (legal professional privilege), Hendry v Chartsearch CA The Times 16 September 1998 (assignment in commercial contract), Hurst v Bryk H.L. [2000] 2 WLR 740 (Solicitors' partnership-repudiatory breach),

Paperlight Ltd v Swinton Insurance [1998] CLR 853 (franchising – reasonable notice); S v S (Supreme Court of Gibraltar) (worldwide Mareva), Stock v London Underground CA The Times 13 August 1999 (payments into Court).
Prof. Memberships: COMBAR, Northern Circuit Commercial Bar Association.
Career: Manchester Grammar School; Pembroke College, Cambridge. Recorder. QC (1997).
Personal: Languages: working knowledge of Hebrew, French and Russian. Married, four children.

FREEDMAN, Clive
3 Verulam Buildings (Christopher Symons QC & John Jarvis QC) London (020) 7831 8441
cfreedman@3vb.com
Recommended in Information Technology
Specialisation: General commercial litigation, including information technology, banking, professional negligence and construction.
Prof. Memberships: COMBAR; TECBAR; Society for Computers and Law; Society for Construction Law; CEDR Accredited Mediator.
Career: Called to the Bar in 1975.
Publications: Contributor to 'Banking Litigation' (1999), Bullen & Leeke's 'Precedents of Pleadings' (section on IT dispute, 2001) and 'Expert Determination' (Kendall, 2001).
Personal: Educated at Harrow School and Trinity College, Cambridge. Interests include computers and bridge.

FREEDMAN, Jeremy
Plowden Buildings (William Lowe QC) Newcastle upon Tyne (020) 7583 0808
jeremy.freedman@btinternet.com
Plowden Buildings (William Lowe QC) London (020) 7583 0808
jeremy.freedman@btinternet.com
Recommended in Clinical Negligence, Personal Injury
Specialisation: Practises exclusively in personal injury work and clinical negligence. Instructed equally on behalf of defendants and claimants, working for NHS trusts, major insurance companies and trade unions. Recent notable cases include Re: M (Child requiring heart transplant) and Ballantine v Newalls Insulation Co Ltd (2000) PIQR, Q57
Prof. Memberships: North Eastern Circuit, Professional Negligence Bar Association and Personal Injury Bar Association. Recorder.
Career: Called to the Bar, 1982. Joined present set of Chambers in 1999.
Personal: Educated at Oundle, Manchester University and City University of London. Born 1959. Married, two children.

FRENCH, Paul
Guildhall Chambers (Adrian Palmer QC) Bristol 0117 927 3366
paul.french@guildhallchambers.co.uk
Recommended in Insolvency/Corporate Recovery
Specialisation: Main areas of practice are insolvency (all aspects of corporate, personal and partnership insolvency, including directors disqualification); bank recovery (including mortgages, receiverships, guarantees and indemnities); company law and partnership (including shareholder and partnership disputes and fiduciary duties); property litigation.
Prof. Memberships: Chancery Bar Association; Bristol and Cardiff Chancery Bar Association; Association of Business Recovery Professionals; Insolvency Lawyer's Association; Bar Sports Law Group; Society for Computers and Law.
Career: Called 1989.

FRIEDMAN, David QC
4 Pump Court London (020) 7842 5555
dfriedman@4pumpcourt.com
Recommended in Construction
Specialisation: Principal area of practice covers all stages and all aspects of construction and engineering litigation and arbitration, both domestic and international. Also deals with professional negligence, particularly in relation to claims relating to professionals in the construction field.
Prof. Memberships: Technology and Construction Bar Association (former chairman).
Career: Called to the Bar 1968. Tenant at 3 Paper Buildings 1970-92. Took Silk 1990. Joined Pump Court 1992. Appointed Recorder 1998. Appointed to act as Deputy Judge of TCC 2000. CEDR Accredited Mediator 1999
Personal: Educated at Tiffin Boys' School, Kingston-upon-Thames and Lincoln College, Oxford 1963-67 (MA, BCL). Born 1 June 1944.

FULFORD, Adrian QC
Tooks Court Chambers (Michael Mansfield QC) London (020) 7405 8828
clerks@tooks.law.co.uk
Recommended in Crime
Specialisation: Crime generally including White Collar fraud and Court of Appeal and Divisional court work.
Prof. Memberships: Criminal Bar Association, South Eastern Circuit, Member Legal Aid Board (Chairman), Member Professional Conduct Committee.
Career: Former contributor Atkins Court Forms. Former Editor of Archibold. Current lecturer in Criminal Law at Middle Temple. Assistant Recorder.
Personal: Keen horseman and motorcyclist. Leisure pursuits also include golf, tennis and scuba diving.

FURBER, John QC
Wilberforce Chambers (Edward Nugee QC) London (020) 7306 0102
jfurber@wilberforce.co.uk
Recommended in Property Litigation
Specialisation: Principally law of landlord and tenant but also covers property litigation, planning and compulsory purchase of land.
Prof. Memberships: Member of Chancery Bar Association and Planning and Environmental Bar Association.
Publications: Contributor to Halsbury's Laws of England, 'Landlord and Tenant' (1981 edn) and 'Compulsory Acquisition'. Contributor to and now general editor of Hill and Redman's law of 'Landlord and Tenant'.
Personal: Called to Bar in 1973, took silk in 1995.

FURNESS, Jonathan
30 Park Place (John Jenkins QC) Cardiff (029) 2039 8421
Recommended in Family
Specialisation: Child care, family work including ancillary relief, residence etc. Reported cases include West Glamorgan v P and R v Cruttenden.
Prof. Memberships: Member of FLBA.
Career: Called 1979. Assistant Recorder 1998. Recorder 2000.

FURNESS, Michael QC
Wilberforce Chambers (Edward Nugee QC) London (020) 7306 0102
Recommended in Pensions, Tax
Specialisation: Trusts, both private and commercial, especially pensions (advisory work, ombudsman appeals and other litigation) and charities (on behalf of HM Attorney General and others, particularly in relation to the making of charitable schemes). Has wide experience of conducting tax litigation at all levels.
Prof. Memberships: Chancery Bar Association, Revenue Bar Association, Association of Pension Lawyers.
Career: Called 1982; Formerly First Standing Junior Counsel to the Inland Revenue in Chancery Matters; QC 2000.
Personal: Secretary, Bar Theatrical Society.

FURST, Stephen QC
Keating Chambers (Richard Fernyhough QC) London +44 (0) 20 7544 2600
sfurst@keatingchambers.com
Recommended in Arbitration (International), Construction
Specialisation: Building and civil engineering; professional negligence including valuation; computers including software; important cases include Darlington v Wiltshire; Bank of East Asia v SDA; Tesco Stores Ltd v Ward Investments; Strachan & Henshaw v Stein Industrial; Macob v Morrison; Henry Boot v Alstom; Bouygues v Dahl-Jensen.
Career: Qualified 1975, Middle Temple; QC 1991; Recorder; editor of 'Construction Law Yearbook' and 'Keating on Building Contracts'; arbitrator; mediator.
Personal: The Edinburgh Academy, St Edmund Hall, Oxford, Leeds University (1972 BA Hons, 1974 LLB Hons). Born 1951; resides London.

FURZE, Caroline
Wilberforce Chambers (Edward Nugee QC) London (020) 7306 0102
Recommended in Chancery, Pensions
Specialisation: Practice covers most aspects of chancery/commercial litigation and advice, including landlord and tenant, professional negligence, insolvency, pension funds, partnership, contentious probate and the administration of estates. Interest in ecclesiastical law and cases under the school sites acts.
Prof. Memberships: Member of Chancery Bar Association.
Career: BA (Cantab): 1st class honours in Natural Sciences (Chemistry). Called to the Bar 1992.
Publications: Contributor to the titles 'Real Property and 'Custom Usage' in Halsburys Laws and to 'Butterworths' Civil Court Precedents' and 'Aikins' Court Forms'.

FYSH, Michael QC
8 New Square (Michael Fysh QC) London (020) 7405 4321
clerks@8newsquare.co.uk
Recommended in Intellectual Property
Specialisation: A specialist in all aspects of intellectual property. Experienced in litigation and advisory work both in the English and Irish courts and in Commonwealth jurisdictions. For comprehensive CV and list of recent cases, visit our website at www.8newsquare.co.uk.
Prof. Memberships: Vice-Chairman, Central Asia and Transcaucasian Law Association; Pakistan/UK Bar Twinning Programme.
Career: Took Silk 1989. Head of chambers since 1993. Calls to overseas Bars: Northern Ireland 1974 (QC 1990), Ireland 1975 (senior counsel 1994), New South Wales 1975, Bombay and Supreme Court of India 1982, Pakistan 1987, Trinidad and Tabago 1990 (senior counsel 1990). Has also practised at the Malaysian, Hong Kong and Singapore Bars and before the European Patent Office, Munich. Lecturer, WIPO, Geneva, Deputy High Court Judge (1998); bencher of the Inner Temple (1999).
Publications: 'Russell-Clarke on Registered Designs'; 'The Industrial Property Citator'; 'The Spycatcher Cases' (Sweet & Maxwell 1989); editor of 'Reports of Patent Cases' and 'Fleet Street Reports' 1974-95.
Personal: Born USA 1940. Educated at Downside School; Grenoble University, France 1958-59; Oxford University (BA Natural Science) 1959-62, MA 1969.

GAISMAN, Jonathan QC
7 King's Bench Walk (Jeremy Cooke QC) London (020) 7910 8300
Recommended in Insurance, Shipping

GAITSKELL, Robert QC
Keating Chambers (Richard Fernyhough QC) London (020) 7544 2600
Recommended in Alternative Dispute Resolution
Specialisation: Construction law, including particularly electrical, mechanical and process engineering; instructed in numerous international and UK major engineering/building disputes, both litigation and arbitration (including frequent appointments as an arbitrator [including as chairman of ICC tribunal] and mediator) concerning, inter alia, complex engineering projects (especially power stations), defence, computer facilities,

chemical processing, food and drink production, oil and gas rigs, hospitals, motorways, bridges, tunnels, dredging, water treatment, airports, abattoirs, nuclear fuel processing and commercial property; cases include University of Glasgow v Whitefield; ICI v Bovis; Lamacrest v Case; Cameron v Mowlem; Surrey Heath v Lovell.
Career: Qualified 1978; Gray's Inn; QC 1994; practising Queen's Counsel; arbitrator, mediator, and adjudicator; Recorder, Vice President of the IEE; Senator of the Engineering Council, practised in UK and abroad as professional electrical engineer, employed by, inter alia, GEC (South Africa); Reyrolle Parsons, Matthew Hall and Rendell Palmer & Tritton, lectures widely in UK and abroad on legal and engineering matters, particularly international construction contracts; lecturer, King's College, London: MSc in Construction Law under Far Eastern Legal Systems; IEE/IMechE Model Form Contracts committee; IEE Arbitration & Adjudication Panel, former member of ORBA Committee and Centre for Dispute Resolution (CEDR) Accredited Mediator; former examiner in contract law, RICS; regular legal columnist 'Engineering Management Journal'; numerous publications on legal and engineering topics, contributor to 'Construction Law Yearbook'.
Personal: BSc Eng, Ph.D. (King's College, London), FIEE, C Eng, FI Mech E, FCI Arb). Born 1948; Worshipful Company of Engineers, Past Chairman IEE Professional Group on Engineering and Law.

GAL, Sonia
28 St. John St Manchester (0161) 834 8418
Recommended in Family
Specialisation: Matrimonial finance, care abduction. Assistant recorder.
Prof. Memberships: FLBA, IBA, ELBA.
Career: French, German, Rumanian, Hungarian, Norwegian. Worked in Eastern Europe on joint ventures.
Personal: Bridge, travel.

GALLAFENT, Kate
Blackstone Chambers (Presiley Baxendale QC & Charles Flint QC) London (020) 7583 1770
kategallafent@blackstonechambers.com
Recommended in Employment
Specialisation: Employment, public, human rights, entertainment/media, sports.
Prof. Memberships: ELA, ALBA, Combar, ELBA, BEG.
Career: Called 1997. Previously worked as a fast-stream civil servant.
Publications: Contributing editor to Lester and Pannick 'Human Rights Law and Practice'.

GAMMIE, Malcolm
One Essex Court (Lord Grabiner QC) London (020) 7583 2000
mgammie@compuserve.com/www.malcolmgammie.com
Recommended in Tax
Specialisation: All commercial taxation and related administrative law, including international and European taxation, corporate and employee taxation, property taxation and value added tax. Director of Research of Tax Law Review Committee; 1998 Unilever Professor of International Business Law at Leiden University, The Netherlands. Visiting professor of tax law, LSE.
Prof. Memberships: Chartered Institute of Taxation (president 1993-94); Association of Taxation Technicians, International Fiscal Association (member, Permanent Scientific Committee), European Bar Group, Revenue Bar Association.
Career: Sidney Sussex College, Cambridge; qualified 1975 as solicitor with *Linklaters & Paines*; subsequently with CBI and as Director of National Tax Services at KMG Thomson McLintock (now KPMG); tax partner at *Linklaters & Paines* 1987-97; called to the Bar 1997.
Publications: 'Land Taxation', 'Tax on Company Reorgansiations', consultant editor of 'Butterworths Tax Handbooks'.
Personal: Married with 4 children. Interests include music and church architecture.

GARDEN, Ian
Derby Square Chambers (Simon Newton) Liverpool (0151) 709 4222
Recommended in Church
Specialisation: Ecclesiastical law; employment; personal injury.
Prof. Memberships: Ecclesiastical Law Society.
Career: Deputy Chancellor, Diocese of Sheffield; member of General Synod for Diocese of Blackburn since 1995; member Crown Appointments Commission since 1996.
Personal: Member Archbishops' Council since 2000; member Legal Advisory Commission since 2001.

GARDINER, John QC
Revenue Law Chambers (John Gardiner QC) London (020) 7242 4017
taxlaw@11newsquare.com
Recommended in Tax
Specialisation: Revenue law. Involved in the two Woolwich cases, Pattison v Marine Midland, Ensign Tankers (Leasing) v Stokes, International Commercial Bank v Willingale, Glaxo Group Ltd v IRC and Nuclear Electric v Bradley.
Prof. Memberships: Revenue Bar Association.
Career: Called to the Bar 1968 and joined New Square in 1970. Took Silk 1982. Treasurer of Senate of Inns of Court and Bar Council, 1985-86; Bencher, Middle Temple.
Personal: Educated at Bancroft's School, Woodford 1957-63 and Fitzwilliam College, Cambridge 1964-68 (MA, LLM) Born 28 February 1946. Lives in London.

GARDINER, Nicholas
1 Middle Temple Lane (Colin Dines & Andrew Trollope QC) London (020) 7583 0659 (12 lines)
Recommended in Crime

GARNETT, Kevin QC
Hogarth Chambers (Jonathan Rayner James QC & Christopher Morcom QC) London (020) 7404 0404
Recommended in Media & Entertainment
Specialisation: Practises extensively in the field of media and entertainment with a particular leaning to music, film, broadcasting and publishing work. Also practises widely in the intellectual property field. Is Senior Editor of 'Copinger and Skone James on Copyright'. Other main area of practice is general Chancery litigation.
Prof. Memberships: Chancery Bar Association; Intellectual Property Bar Association.

GARNHAM, Neil QC
1 Crown Office Row (Robert Seabrook QC) London (020) 7797 7500
neil.garnham@1cor.com
Recommended in Administrative & Public Law, Health & Safety
Specialisation: Principal areas of practice are Administrative and Public Law, Human Rights, Professional Negligence including Medical Negligence, and Personal Injury. Public Law work includes mental health, extradition, education, immigration and asylum. Cases include Thomas v Bunn [1991] (HL – interest in PI cases); Racz v Home Office [1994] (HL – misfeasance in public office); Re K [1994] (CA – adoption of foreign national); ex p McQuillan [1995] (Exclusion orders); Ex parte Onibiyo [1996] (CA – fresh claims for political asylum); T v Home Office [1996] (HL – political offences in asylum law); Gregory v UK [1994] (ECHR – bias in jury trials); D v UK [1997] (ECHR – Article 3); ADT v UK [1999] (ECHR-Articles 6 and 14); TI v UK [2000] (ECHR Articles 2 and 3); R v SSND ex p Salem [1999] (social security benefits and asylum); R v K (a child) [2001] (secure accommodation orders) ADT 5 ECHR; R v W&B [2001] (care order) ADT 688 ECHR.
Prof. Memberships: ALBA, PNBA, PIBA.
Career: Called 1982; Junior Counsel to the Crown 1995-01. Silk 2001. Junior Counsel Ladbroke Grove Road Inquiry (2000); Counsel to Victoria Climbie Inquiry (2001).
Personal: Educated Ipswich School and Peterhouse Cambridge.

GARRETT, Annalissa
6 Pump Court London (020) 7583 6013
Recommended in Clinical Negligence
Specialisation: Specialises in all aspects of medical negligence and medically related work including representing families and Doctors at inquests and disciplinary tribunals. Also handles mental health, physiotherapy negligence, dental negligence and product liability cases. Also serious personal injury and fatal accident cases. Acts for both Plaintiffs and Defendants. Lectures regularly on difficult procedural issues, limitation and the law of costs. Recent cases include: Barr v Dr Matthews (medical negligence case concerning the duties owed by anti-abortion GP's giving advice on abortion); Leighton v North Middlesex Hospital NHS trust (ecstacy induced coma leading to brain damage); Haigh v Pinderfields Hospitals NHS Trust (physiotherapy negligence); Smith v Southampton Health Autority (limitation trial).
Prof. Memberships: PNBA, AVMA, PIBA & APIL.
Career: Called to the Bar in 1991. Joined Chambers in 1992.
Personal: Educated at Durham University (BA (Hons)). Born 21st June 1966. Lives in London.

GARSIDE, Charles QC
9 St. John Street (John Hand QC) Manchester (0161) 955 9000
clerks@9stjohnstreet.co.uk
Recommended in Crime
Specialisation: Also at 9 Bedford Row (Anthony Berry QC) (020) 7489 2727. Specialises in crime, including fraud; employment including discrimination; judicial review; other Crown office work; personal injury.
Prof. Memberships: Employment Law Association.
Career: Called 1971. QC 1993.

GATT, Ian
Littleton Chambers (Michel Kallipetis QC) London (020) 7797 8600
ian@gatt.co.uk
Recommended in Employment, Professional Negligence
Specialisation: Professional negligence (principally solicitors and surveyors). Nationwide managed litigation (1997-99), Birmingham Midshires v David Parry, Nationwide v Thimbleby & Co, Nationwide v Balmer Radmore, Nationwide v Various Solicitors (managed litigation costs). Employment: unfair and wrongful dismissal (Duffield v Jupiter International; Clark v Nomura 2000), sex, race and disability discrimination and restraint of trade. Commercial fraud: Guinness Trial 1990, numerous SFO prosecutions; commercial.
Prof. Memberships: COMBAR; Professional Negligence Bar Association; Employment Law Bar Association; Criminal Bar Association.
Career: Hutton GS, Preston (1974-81); Hertford College, Oxford (1981-84) BA Jurisprudence (1st). Called to the Bar 1985. Joined 2 Crown Office Row (now Littleton Chambers) 1986. CEDR Accredited Mediator. Appointed Recorder, 2000.
Publications: Co-author 'Arlidge and Parry on Fraud' (2nd ed). Bowers and Gatt, 'Procedure in Courts and Tribunals' (2nd ed).
Personal: Married with three children. Interests: rugby, cars, wine. Lives Winchester, Hampshire.

GAUNT, Jonathan QC
Falcon Chambers (Jonathan Gaunt QC & Kim Lewison QC) London (020) 7353 2484
gaunt@falcon-chambers.com
Recommended in Agriculture, Property Litigation
Specialisation: The joint head of Falcon Chambers, the members of which specialise in landlord and tenant and property law. An editor of the landlord and tenant volume of 'Halsbury's Laws', having re-written the chapters on repairing covenants, rent and rent review. Also joint editor of the 1997 edition of 'Gale on Easements'.
Prof. Memberships: Chancery, London Civil and Common Law and Property Bar Associations.
Career: Called to Bar 1972; Silk 1991; Bencher Lincoln's Inn 1998; Deputy High Court Judge 2001.

Publications: 'Halsbury's Laws', Vol 27; 'Gale on Easements' (16th edn).

GEE, Anthony QC
28 St. John St Manchester (0161) 834 8418
Recommended in Crime

GEE, Steven QC
4 Field Court (Steven Gee QC) London (020) 7440 6900
Recommended in Arbitration (International)

GEERING, Ian QC
3 Verulam Buildings (Christopher Symons QC & John Jarvis QC) London (020) 7831 8441
chambers@3vb.com
Recommended in Commercial (Litigation), Fraud
Specialisation: Commercial law, specialising in civil claims based on international and domestic commercial fraud and claims for restitution.
Prof. Memberships: COMBAR, London Common Law and Commercial Association.
Career: Queen's Counsel 1991. Further details are on chambers' web site: www.3vb.com

GEORGE, Charles QC
2 Harcourt Buildings (Gerard Ryan QC) London (020) 7353 8415
clerks@2hb.law.co.uk
Recommended in Church, Environment, Local Government, Planning
Specialisation: Principal area of practice is public law especially planning and environmental law, local government and parliamentary matters. Has advised and represented applicants and local planning authorities in relation to major development schemes, particularly those involving public infrastructure provision, housing, minerals, listed buildings and local government finance. Involved in promoting the King's Cross Railways Bill and Transport and Works Orders for extensions to the Manchester and Leeds Light Rail systems. Counsel in, inter alia, Pioneer Aggregates (UK) Ltd v Secretary of State for the Environment 1985; Save Britain's Heritage v Number 1 Poultry Ltd (1991); R v Parliamentary Commissioner for Administration ex p Balchin Nos 1 and 2 (1996 and 1999); Millington v Secretary of State for the Environment [1999]. Clients include Railtrack; Transco plc; Transport for London; Manchester City Council; Greater Manchester, West Yorkshire and Merseyside Passenger Transport Executives; Laing Homes Ltd. Has frequently represented applicants (many publicly funded) in judicial review proceedings involving public law challenges, particularly in relation to planning and environmental law challenges. Other main area of practice is ecclesiastical law and commons.
Prof. Memberships: Inner Temple; King's Inns, Dublin.
Career: Called to the Bar 1974 and joined 2 Harcourt Buildings in 1975. Conducted independent inquiry into planning decisions in the London Borough of Brent 1991. Took Silk 1992. Called to the Irish Bar 1995. Appointed Recorder 1997. Appointed Chancellor of the Diocese of Southwark 1996
Personal: Educated at Bradfield College 1958-63, Magdalen College, Oxford 1963-66 (1st Class Hons Modern History) and Corpus Christi, Cambridge 1966-67. Author of 'The Stuarts: A Century of Experiment' (1973). Leisure pursuits include tennis, architecture and travel. Born 8 June 1945. Lives in Sevenoaks, Kent.

GEORGE, Sarah
St Philip's Chambers (John Randall QC) Birmingham (0121) 246 7000
Recommended in Employment

GHOSH, Julian
Pump Court Tax Chambers London (020) 7414 8080
clerks@pumptax.com
Recommended in Tax
Specialisation: Mergers and acquisitions, structured finance, loan relationships, foreign exchange, financial instruments EC tax, VAT. Recent cases: Memec v IRC; Trinidad Oilwell Service ltd v Board of Inland Revenue (PC); Nationwide Acess Ltd, PPP Ltd v CEC.
Prof. Memberships: Revenue Bar Association; Bar European Group; Share Scheme Lawyers' Group. Also a member of the Faculty of Advocates, Edinburgh.
Publications: Co-author: 'Taxation of Law Relationships, Financial Instruments and Foreign Exchange' (Butterworths).

GIBBS, Patrick
2 Harcourt Buildings, Atkinson Bevan Chambers (Nicholas Atkinson QC & John Bevan QC) London (020) 7353 2112
clerks@2hb.co.uk
Recommended in Crime
Specialisation: Defence advocacy. Practices in all areas of crime and in regulatory proceedings. Since 1990 has been principally engaged in defending cases involving professional fraud, sex crime and homicide.
Prof. Memberships: Criminal Bar Association.
Career: Called 1986.
Personal: Born 24 April 1962. Educated at Eton College, Christ Church, Oxford and the City University.

GIBNEY, Malcolm T P
17 Carlton Crescent (Jeremy S. Gibbons QC) Southampton (023) 8032 0320/2003
Recommended in Consumer Law

GIBSON, Charles QC
2 Harcourt Buildings (Roger Henderson QC) London (020) 7583 9020
clerks@harcourt.co.uk
Recommended in Product Liability
Specialisation: Common law/commercial with an emphasis on product liability (in particular group actions), professional negligence, personal injury, insurance. Notable cases include Connelly v RTZ; Lubbe v Cape plc; Hodgson v Imperial Tobacco (the tobacco lung cancer litigation); the Opren litigation; the Benzodiazepine litigation; Garland v West Wiltshire District Council; The Norplant litigation; the MMR litigation; involving Prozac, Lariam, Minocin, Shiley heart valve, breast implants, drink contamination; the organo-phosphate litigation; the interest rate swap litigation; asbestos claims, Mine Radiation Injury claims; other product liability cases for various manufacturers including product liability litigation; the King's Cross and Clapham Inquiries for the London Fire Brigade; the Severn Tunnel Inquiry.
Prof. Memberships: PNBA. Common Law and Commercial Bar Association.
Career: Educated Wellington College; BA Hons Durham; Dip Law. Called to the Bar 1984. Author: 'Group Actions – Product Liability Law and Insurance'. CEDR Accredited Mediator. Recorder.
Personal: Born 1960. Married with four children.

GIBSON, Christopher QC
Four New Square (Justin Fenwick QC) London (020) 7822 2000
barristers@4newsquare.com
Recommended in Clinical Negligence
Specialisation: Professional negligence (lawyers, medical practitioners, accountants, valuers and building professionals); general commercial law, insurance, and building and construction. Cases include Mortgage Express v Bowerman, the consolidated appeal in the BBL litigation, Abbey National v Key Surveyors (Court appointed expert), and Thorman v New Hampshire (professional indemnity insurance).
Prof. Memberships: COMBAR, Professional Negligence Bar Association, Fellow of the Chartered Institute of Arbitrators.
Career: Educated at St Paul's School, and Brasenose College, Oxford; called to the Bar Middle Temple 1976; silk in 1995. FCI Arb 1992.
Personal: Married with 2 daughters; interests include Whitstable and motor-cycles.

GIFFIN, Nigel
11 King's Bench Walk Chambers (Eldred Tabachnik QC & James Goudie QC) London (020) 7632 8500
clerksroom@11kbw.com
Recommended in Administrative & Public Law, Employment, Local Government
Specialisation: Specialises principally in public and administrative law including Human Rights Act, commercial judicial review, education, local authority powers, local government finance, environment, housing, social services, travelers, elections, procurement and tendering. Practice also covers employment law and general commercial law. Important cases include Hazell v Hammersmith & Fulham LBC (local authority interest rate swaps); Palmer v A.B.P. (personal contracts and union membership); R v A.B.P. ex parte Plymouth CC (judicial review of animal exports); R v Institute of Chartered Accountants ex parte Brindle (stay of disciplinary proceedings pending litigation); Wandsworth LBC v A (access to school premises); R v Hammersmith & Fulham LBC ex p.M (asylum seeker's rights under National Assistance Act); Hillsdown Holdings plc v Pensions Ombudsman (use of pension fund surplus); London Underground v RMT (industrial action); P v NASUWT (school exclusions).
Prof. Memberships: Administrative Law Bar Association, Education Law Association, Planning and Environmental Bar Association, Employment Law Bar Association, Member of A Panel of Treasury Counsel.
Career: Called to the Bar 1986.
Publications: Contributor of education law chapter to 'Butterworth's Local Government Law'.
Personal: Educated at Worcester College, Oxford (BA Hons 1st class).

GILBART, Andrew QC
40 King St Manchester (0161) 832 9082
Recommended in Planning
Specialisation: Town planning, compulsory purchase, highways, environment law and judicial review. Particularly experienced in major development projects involving airport expansion, roads, incineration, waste disposal, retailing, minerals, housing and motorway services. Contributor of articles to 'Journal of Planning and Environment Law'.
Prof. Memberships: Member of Northern Circuit, Planning and Environment Bar Association, Administrative Law Bar Association, American Bar Association (international associate), UK Environmental Law Association.
Career: Called 1972, elected member of Northern Circuit 1973; Appointed Queens Counsel 1991; Recorder of The Crown Court; Bencher of Middle Temple.
Personal: Read Law at Trinity Hall, Cambridge. Enjoys tramping in the hills of the Peak District when time permits.

GILBERT, Francis QC
Walnut House (Paul Dunkels QC) Exeter (01392) 279751
Recommended in Crime

GILEAD, Beryl
St. Mary's Chambers Family Law Chambers (Christopher M. Butler) Nottingham (0115) 950 3503
Recommended in Family

GILL, Manjit Singh QC
6 King's Bench Walk (Sibghat Kadri QC) London (020) 7583 0695 / 7353 4931
Recommended in Immigration

GILL, Tess
Old Square Chambers (John Hendy QC) London (020)7269 0300
gill@oldsquarechambers.co.uk
Recommended in Employment
Specialisation: Specialises in employment and human rights law, particularly discrimination and equal pay and

industrial and trade union law. She has considerable experience of EC and human rights law and was for many years a member of the EC Network of experts on the equality directives. She has recently appeared in the following significant employment cases: IGE Medical Systems Ltd v Halfpenny, HL [2001] IRLR 96 (maternity and sex discrimination); Allonby v Accrington & Rossendale College, Court of Appeal [2001] IRLR 364, CA (an agency lecturer claiming indirect discrimination, equal pay and access to the teachers pension scheme); Localbail (UK) v Bayfield Properties Ltd [2000] IRLR 96, CA (leading case on what constitutes bias by the court); Coyne v Home Office [2000] ICR 1443, CA (sex discrimination); Carmichael and Leese v National Power [1999] ICR 1226, HL (employment status of casual workers); Banks and Tesco Stores [1999] ICR 1141 (challenge to the exclusion of low paid women from statutory maternity pay); Strathclyde Regional Council v Wallace [1998] ICR 205, HL (the role of the material factor defence in equal pay); Grant v South West Trains [1998] IRLR 188, HC (contractual status of equal opportunities policy in context of discrimination on grounds of sexual orientation); Bennett v Essex County Council EAT, DCLD No 42 (school liable under Race Relations Act 1976 for racial abuse of teacher).
Prof. Memberships: Member of Lawyers for Liberty, Employment Law Bar Association, Personal Injury Bar Association, Industrial Law Society, Discrimination Law Association.
Career: Practised as a solicitor until 1990 when she transferred to the Bar. Has experience in private practice and as the GMB legal officer. She has been a part-time chairman of the employment tribunals since 1995. She is on the advisory panel of the Equal Opportunities Review and a member of the Equal Pay Task Force which made recommendations to reform the Equal Pay Act 1970 in February 2001. She was on the management committee of the Public Law Project until July 2000, and has previously been a management committee member of the National Council of Civil Liberties and Child Poverty Action Group. She is a founder member of Workplace Mediation project, a scheme for mediation of sexual or racial harassment or bullying in the workplace, and is training as a mediator with CEDR in August 2001.
Publications: Author of chapter on discrimination in 'Human Rights at Work' (Institute of Employment Rights, 2000) and the chapter on workers rights in 'Your Rights', the Liberty Guide to Human Rights (Pluto Press, 2000).

GILLESPIE, James
Renaissance Chambers (Brian Jubb & Henry Setright QC) London (020) 7404 1111
Recommended in Immigration

GILLYON, Philip
Erskine Chambers (Robin Potts QC) London (020) 7242 5532
pgillyon@erskine-chambers.co.uk
Recommended in Company
Specialisation: Company law, corporate insolvency, financial services. Cases include Re BSB Holdings Ltd [1996] 1 BCLC 155; Possfund Custodian Trustee Ltd v Diamond [1996] 1 WLR 1351; Re Exchange Travel (Holdings) Ltd [1996] 2 BCLC 524; Guinness Peat Group plc v British Land Company plc [1999] 2 BCLC 243; Banco Nacional de Cuba v Cosmos Trading Corporation [2000] 1 BCLC 813; Jarvis plc v PricewaterhouseCoopers [2000] BCLC 368; Re Layland Daf Ltd [2001] 1 BCLC 419; Banca Carige v Banco Nacional de Cuba (The Times 18.05.01); Winpar Holdings Ltd v Joseph Holt Group plc (The Times 24.05.01). Represents the Secretary of State for Trade and Industry in company director disqualification proceedings in relation to Queens Moat Houses plc.
Prof. Memberships: Commercial Bar Association; Chancery Bar Association; Middle Temple.
Career: Hymers College, (1974-84); Downing College, Cambridge (1984-87). Called 1988. Joined Erskine Chambers 1989.
Personal: Born 1965. Lives in London.

GILMAN, Jonathan QC
Essex Court Chambers (Gordon Pollock QC) London (020) 7813 8000
Recommended in Shipping
Specialisation: Insurance, reinsurance and shipping cases. Appears as counsel in very many London arbitrations. Regularly acts as umpire or arbitrator in London arbitrations. Has been retained as expert witness on English law in foreign proceedings on many occasions (mostly insurance or reinsurance cases).
Career: Called to the Bar 1965. Silk 1990.
Personal: Born 1942.

GILROY, Paul
9 St. John Street (John Hand QC) Manchester (0161) 955 9000
pgilroy@9stjohnstreet.co.uk
Recommended in Employment
Specialisation: Paul Gilroy has extensive experience of all aspects of employment law, ranging from the traditional areas of practice such as non-contentious advisory work, and Employment Tribunal/High Court/County Court litigation, to internal inquiries in the NHS, police and professional sports bodies. He acts for and against local and public authorities, trade unions and plcs. He is approved by the Commission for Racial Equality and the Equal Opportunities Commission to act in discrimination cases. He is a member of the Attorney General's Provincial Panel of Counsel. He has developed a special interest in public inquiries, having acted in the Inquiry into the Personality Unit at Ashworth High Security Hospital, and recently being instructed on behalf of the relatives of the deceased in the Shipman Inquiry. He contributes to professional publications, annotates employment legislation for Current Law Statutes and is a frequent speaker on employment law.
Prof. Memberships: Employment Lawyers Association; Employment Law Bar Association; NCFRAS.
Career: Called 1985 (Gray's Inn). Door Tenant: Farrar's Building, Temple, London EC4Y 7BD. Part-time Chairman of Employment Tribunals (2000).

GIRET, Jane QC
11 Stone Buildings (Murray Rosen QC) London (020) 7831 6381
giret@11stonebuildings.com
Recommended in Chancery, Company, Insolvency/Corporate Recovery
Specialisation: Head of 11 Stone Buildings' company & insolvency group and a specialist in company, corporate and personal insolvency and partnership law. Her practice also includes general Chancery and commercial litigation. Much of her work focuses on company directors and their conduct, including directors' fraud and disqualification proceedings. An experienced and forceful advocate, her expertise includes shareholder disputes, complex receiverships and administrations. She also has a full non-contentious corporate advisory practice encompassing reconstruction, amalgamation and management.

GIROLAMI, Paul
Maitland Chambers (Michael Lyndon-Stanford QC & Charles Aldous QC) London (020) 7406 1200
clerks@maitlandchambers.com
Recommended in Chancery, Company, Insolvency/Corporate Recovery
Specialisation: Practice principally concerns Chancery matters of the commercial type, with an emphasis on litigation, including matters involving company, insolvency (corporate and personal), landlord and tenant, property, equitable remedies and trust questions.
Prof. Memberships: Chancery Bar Association and COMBAR.
Career: Called to the Bar, 1983. Junior Counsel to the Crown (Chancery) 1991-00.
Personal: Born 5th December 1959. Educated St Paul's School London and Corpus Christi College, Cambridge. Lives in London.

GLANCY, Robert QC
Devereux Chambers (Jeffrey Burke QC) London (020) 7353 7534
Recommended in Personal Injury
Specialisation: Principal areas of practice are personal injury and medical negligence cases, professional negligence generally (architects, engineers, surveyors and solicitors), construction law and employment law. Considerable experience of industrial disease cases such as repetitive strain injury, asbestos related conditions and welder's fume cases. Appeared in case of D.F. Estates v Church Commisioners for England on economic loss in tort and whether builder is liable for sub-contractor. Also appeared in a number of medical negligence cases such as Newell v Goldenberg concerned with warnings and sterilisation operations. One of the joint authors of the 'P.I.B.A. Personal Injury Handbook'.
Prof. Memberships: Personal Injury Bar Association.
Career: Called to the Bar 1972. Assistant Recorder 1993. Recorder 1998. Queen's Counsel 1997.
Personal: Educated at Manchester Grammar School and St. John's College, Cambridge. Lives in London.

GLASGOW, Edwin QC
39 Essex Street (Nigel Pleming QC) London (020) 7832 1111
Recommended in Commercial (Litigation), Personal Injury, Professional Negligence
Specialisation: All areas of commercial and common law litigation including insurance, professional negligence and major personal injury cases. Has been involved in most of the public inquiries and litigation associated with disasters over the past ten years. Has extensive experience of litigation, arbitration and human rights work overseas including USA; Australia; Hong Kong; Singapore; France and Africa. Recent cases include: Svenska Bank v Sun Alliance; Trafalgar House v Davy Offshore; Capital and Counties v Planned Maintenance; BBL; Sun Valley Poultry; Kuwait Investment Office; Bloody Sunday Inquiry.
Prof. Memberships: London Common Law and Commercial Bar Association.
Career: LLB (Hons); Called to the Bar 1969; Silk 1987. Chairman Financial Reporting Review Panel 1992-98. CBE 1999.

GLASS, Anthony QC
Hollis Whiteman Chambers (QEB) (Julian Bevan QC & Peter Whiteman QC) London (020) 7583 5766
Recommended in Crime, Fraud
Specialisation: Practice encompasses all aspects of criminal law, with a specialisation in commercial fraud, V.A.T. fraud and drugs importations since taking Silk. Involved in Barlow Clowes; BCCI; Guildford police and O'Brien death in police custody cases. Recently, Reg Ellis arson/fraud and Abbey National Fraud; Sheila Bowler and Excise Duty Diversion Frauds; money laundering; R V Norris and others (price competition).
Prof. Memberships: Criminal Bar Association, South Eastern Circuit.
Career: Called to the Bar 1965 and joined current chambers in 1982. Appointed Recorder 1985. Took Silk 1986. Bencher of Inner Temple.
Personal: Educated at Royal Masonic Schools 1948-58 and Lincoln College, Oxford 1960-63. Born 6 June 1940. Lives in London.

GLASSON, Jonathan
Doughty Street Chambers (Geoffrey Robertson QC) London (020) 7404 1313
Recommended in Clinical Negligence

GLEDHILL, Andreas
3-4 South Square (Michael Crystal QC & Lord Alexander of Weedon QC) London (020) 7696 9900
andreasgledhill@southsquare.com
Recommended in Insolvency/Corporate Recovery
Specialisation: Insolvency, fraud and tracing claims, banking law, company law and related areas of professional negligence.

Prof. Memberships: COMBAR; Chancery Bar Association; Insolvency Lawyers' Association.
Publications: 'Gore-Browne on Companies', 44th edn (contributing chapter 31 on Administrations, Voluntary Arrangements and Administrative Receiverships) and 'Muir Hunter on Personal Insolvency' (junior author).
Personal: Educated Westminster School and Christ's College Cambridge (1st class Hons, 1988).

GLEN, Ian QC
Guildhall Chambers (Adrian Palmer QC) Bristol
(0117) 927 3366
Recommended in Crime, Licensing

GLENNIE, Angus QC
20 Essex Street (Iain Milligan QC) London
(020) 7842 1200
clerks@20essexst.com
Recommended in Shipping
Specialisation: Shipping. Insurance and reinsurance. Arbitration. Recent cases include 'KritiRex', unseaworthiness [1996] 2 W Rep 271Ultisol litigation concerning forum non conveniens, anti-suit injunctions and limitation: reported [1996] 2 Lloyd's Rep 140, [1997] 2 Lloyd's Rep 485, 493, 507, 533; Stocznia Gdanska v Latvian Shipping Co (HL), Shipbuilding, [1998] 1 WLR 574 and subsequently [2001] (1) LLR Rep 537; Baker v Black Sea Baltic General Insurance Co Ltd (HL) re-insurance [1998] 1 WLR 974; Berkling v Tube Developments freight forwarders [1999] 2 4 Rep 55.
Career: MA (Cantab), Trinity Hall. Called 1974, QC 1991. Also practising member of Scots bar (QC 1998). Member of Gibraltar Bar.

GLICK, Ian QC
One Essex Court (Lord Grabiner QC) London
(020) 7583 2000
Recommended in Arbitration (International), Banking, Commercial (Litigation), Energy & Natural Resources, Tax
Specialisation: Principal areas of practice are arbitration (both as arbitrator and counsel), banking, commercial law, energy law, financial services, insurance and revenue litigation. Important cases include PCW litigation; Tin Council litigation; Woolwich BS v CIR (restitution); Smith New Court v Citibank (measure of damages in fraud); Gallagher v Jones (application of accepted principles of commercial accountancy to computation of profits for tax purposes), Shah v Bank of England (banking regulation); Deeny v Gooda Walker (taxability of damages recovered in Lloyds' litigation); R v CIR ex p Warburgs (judicial review of Revenue decisions); Northern Ireland Electricity v Director General of Electricity Supply (electricity price regulation) and Fuji Finance v Aetna (nature of a contract of insurance).
Prof. Memberships: Chairman, Commercial Bar Association, 1997-99; vice-chairman, Education and Training Committee of the Bar Council 1999-00.
Career: Called to the Bar in 1970. At Lamb Building 1970-80. Joined 1 Essex Court in 1980. Junior Counsel to the Crown, Common Law 1985-87. Standing Counsel to the DTI in export credit cases 1985-87. Took Silk in 1987, FCIArb.
Personal: Educated at Bradford Grammar School and Balliol College, Oxford. Born 18 July 1948. Lives in London.

GLOBE, Henry QC
Exchange Chambers (David Turner QC & Bill Braithwaite QC & Henry Globe QC) Liverpool
(0151) 236 7747
Recommended in Crime, Health & Safety

GLOSTER, Elizabeth QC
One Essex Court (Lord Grabiner QC) London
(020) 75832000
egloster@oeclaw.co.uk
Recommended in Chancery, Commercial (Litigation), Company, Energy & Natural Resources, Fraud, Insolvency/Corporate Recovery
Specialisation: Principal areas of expertise are company law, banking, insurance and insolvency. Also covers commercial fraud, financial services, media and telecommunications, energy and professional negligence. Recent major cases include: acting for the Equitable Life in the House of Lords to determine the rights of policyholders (2000); acting for the liquidators of Manhattan Investment Fund (2000); appearing in the House of Lords for defendants in Canada Trust v Stolzenburg (jurisdiction under the Lugano Convention) (2000); acting for BF&M Ltd in the action brought by the liquidators of Bermuda Fire & Marine Insurance Company (1999); acting for the DTI in the disqualification proceedings arising out of the collapse of Barings (1998); acting for EMLICO and its liquidators in the litigation arising out of EMLICO's redomestication to Bermuda (1996-98); acting for Charterhouse Development (France) in its action against Lloyd's underwriters (1996); acting for the administrators of Barings in the action against ING (1996); acting for the banks in the interest rate swaps litigation; representing the liquidators of Barlow Clowes in litigation against various directors and third party professionals (1992-01); acting for banks/administrators of Olympia & York, Canary Wharf (1993-94); acting for the Society of Lloyd's in a case involving the question of priority between the Society and various Names (1993); representing recently-appointed trustees of Maxwell Pension Funds in relation to the Maxwell collapse (1992-95); acting for the D.T.I in the case of Sher v The Policy Holders Protection Board (1993); Hazell v Hammersmith & Fulham Borough Council (1992) (House of Lords); prosecuting in the criminal trials arising out of the Guinness bid for Distillers (1990) and (1991). Called to the Bars of Bermuda, Gibraltar and the Isle of Man for specific cases. Working knowledge of French.
Prof. Memberships: Chancery Bar Association, COMBAR, Insolvency Lawyers' Association, INSOL.
Career: Called to the Bar in 1971. Member of the panel of junior counsel representing the DTI in company matters 1982-89. Took Silk in 1989. Bencher of the Inner Temple and Deputy High Court Judge of the Chancery Division in 1992, Judge of the Courts of Appeal of Jersey & Guernsey (part-time) in 1994 and Recorder 1995.
Personal: Educated at Roedean School 1962-67 and Girton College, Cambridge 1967-70. Born 5th June 1949.

GLOVER, Richard
2 Mitre Court Buildings (Michael FitzGerald QC) London (020) 7583 1380
Recommended in Planning
Specialisation: Specialises in all areas of planning and local government law.
Prof. Memberships: Member of the Planning and Environment Bar Association and The Parliamentary Bar.
Career: Called in 1984. Has acted in a wide range of inquiries including the new HQ for Mclaren Racing near Woking, the Manchester Free Trade Hall, the Genome Campus extension for the Wellcome Trust and the proposals for 2500 houses south of Reading. Parliamentary Bills include Channel Tunnel, Dartford River Crossing and Heathrow Express. Recent rating cases include Mosanto Chemical works, Port Talbot Steelworks, Shall Haven Oil refinery, Anston Properties, Coventry & Solihull Waste Disposal (in the House of Lords) and BT. Editor of 'Ryde on Rating and the Council Tax'.
Personal: Educated at Harrow and Cambridge.

GLOVER, Stephen J
37 Park Square (Stephen J Glover & Paul Kirtley) Leeds (0113) 243 9422
chambers@no37.co.uk
Recommended in Family
Specialisation: Substantial asset matrimonial finance, professional negligence, personal injury, medical law.
Prof. Memberships: PNBA, PIBA. Association of Northern Mediators.
Career: 1978 call.

GODDARD, Andrew
Atkin Chambers (Robert Akenhead QC) London
(020) 7400 8501
clerks@atkinschambers.law.co.uk
Recommended in Construction
Specialisation: Specialises in construction and engineering and the law of commercial obligations. This has involved advocacy and advisory work in respect of major commercial developments, including PFI projects, office and retail accommodation, hospitals, hotels, motorways, stations and railways, power stations, process plants, wet and dry docks as well as off-shore and submarine structures and oil and gas exploration and exploitation. Clients include employers (both public and private), contractors, sub-contractors and professionals. He is familiar with the principal forms of building and engineering contracts including management and development contracts and has advised on amendments to the standard forms as well as drafted bespoke contracts. He has regularly advised and acted in connection with substantial claims for damages, loss and expense and extensions of time (a topic in which he has particular interest) as well as claims in respect of professional negligence including solicitors' negligence. He also has extensive experience of technology disputes involving software development, microelectronics and telecommunications. Although based in London, he has acted on behalf of many international clients, including foreign governments, and has a keen interest in projects with an international element. He has acted in many international arbitrations under the auspices of both the ICC and the LCIA. Related areas of law in which he has detailed experience include sale of goods, performance bonds, guarantees and insurance.
Prof. Memberships: TECBAR.
Career: Called to the Bar 1985.
Personal: Independent Schools Association Whitbread Memorial Trophy; BA Hons. Law (First Class) Sussex 1984; Inner Temple Queen Elizabeth II Scholarship 1985; Poland Prize 1985.

GODDARD, Christopher
Devereux Chambers (Jeffrey Burke QC) London
(020) 7353 7534
goddard@devchambers.co.uk
Recommended in Personal Injury
Specialisation: Principal area of practice is plaintiff and defendant personal injury with a special interest in occupational disease. Also medical and legal professional negligence. Regularly speaks at conferences and seminars in these fields. Co-author 'Health and Safety: The New Legal Framework' Butterworths and contributor to Butterworths 'Personal Injury Handbook'. Executive editor of the 'Personal Injury Handbook', Gee Publishing.
Prof. Memberships: Personal Injury Bar Association.
Career: Manchester University 1969-72. Called to Bar in 1973.

GODFREY, Howard QC
2 Bedford Row (William Clegg QC) London
(020) 7440 8888
Recommended in Crime, Fraud
Specialisation: Serious crime especially fraud, both corporate and personal, including some work overseas. Experienced in VAT and tax frauds, insider dealing, Stock Exchange, banking, accounting, insurance, corruption and extradition. Practice also includes general crime especially drugs cases and civil fraud.
Prof. Memberships: South Eastern Circuit, Criminal Bar Association.
Career: Called 1970. Took Silk in 1991. Recorder 1992.
Personal: Born 17 August 1946. Educated University of London – London School of Economics (LLB). Lives in Berkshire.

GOLDBERG, David QC
Gray's Inn Tax Chambers (Milton Grundy) London
(020) 7242 2642
Recommended in Tax
Specialisation: Practice concentrates on revenue law and commercial litigation with a tax or financial aspect.

Clients include solicitors, accountants and corporations. Co-author of 'Introduction to Company Law' (1971, 3rd edn 1987) and 'The Law of Partnership Taxation' (1976, 2nd edn 1979). Author of various articles and notes for legal periodicals, mainly concerning tax and company law.
Prof. Memberships: Revenue Bar Association; Chancery Bar Association.
Career: Called to the Bar and joined current chambers in 1971. Took Silk 1987. Bencher of Lincoln's Inn 1997.
Personal: Educated at Plymouth College and London School of Economics 1966-70 (LLB, LLM). Chairman of Trustees of the Skills Workshop for Anatomical Techniques. Leisure pursuits include reading, writing letters and thinking. Born 12 August 1947. Lives in London.

GOLDBERG, Jonathan QC

3 Temple Gardens (Jonathan Goldberg QC) London (020) 7583 1155
jongold@talk21.com
Recommended in Crime, Fraud
Specialisation: Has defended in many of the most notable jury trials at the Old Bailey and elsewhere over the past three decades. These include Roger Levitt (white collar fraud); Brinksmat; R v Rosenthal (The Stamford Hill child sex abuse case involving Orthodox Jews); R v Laming (The Sonic Binoculars horse nobbling case); R v Charlie Kray and many others. He is qualified at the New York Bar and has worked in Malaysia, Singapore and Gibraltar. He has had successes in libel and commercial civil and chancery cases requiring strong cross-examination, and is by no means limited to crime. He enjoys battling and winning against seemingly overwhelming odds.
Career: Called in 1971; appointed a QC in 1989; a Recorder in 1992.
Personal: Educated at Manchester Grammar and Trinity Hall Cambridge. A member of the International Presidency of the International Association of Jewish Lawyers and Jurists.

GOLDREIN, Iain QC

7 Harrington Street Chambers (David Steer QC & Robert Fordham QC & Iain Goldrein QC) Liverpool Mobile (0831) 703 156
goldhaas@netcomuk.co.uk
Recommended in Clinical Negligence
Specialisation: Complex Professional (including Medical) Negligence (with particular expertise in brain damage at birth); catastrophic injury claims; general commercial including Insurance coverage; pre-emptive commercial remedies; product liability. Cases of Interest: Rayeware v TGWU; Sion v Hampstead Health Authority.
Prof. Memberships: Professional Negligence Bar Association; Personal Injury Bar Association; London Common Law & Commercial Bar Association. Companion of the Academy of Experts; Fellow of the Royal Society of Arts; Associate of the Chartered Institute of Arbitrators; Nominated Counsel: Environmental Law Foundation; Mediator, registered with the Academy of Experts. Awards: University of Cambridge Squire Scholarship for Law; Exhibitioner and Ziegler Prize, Pembroke College Cambridge; Inner Temple Duke of Edinburgh Scholarship.
Career: Appointments: Queen's Counsel; Assistant Recorder; Visiting Professor (The Sir Jack Jacob Chair in Litigation) Nottingham Law School.
Publications: 'Property Distribution on Divorce' [FT Law and Tax] [1st and 2nd editions with Margaret de Haas QC]; 'Personal Injury Litigation: Practice and Precedents' [Butterworths]; Ship Sale and Purchase, Law and Technique [Lloyds of London Press] with Clifford Chance; 'Commercial Litigation: Pre-emptive Remedies' [Sweet and Maxwell] with Judges Wilkinson and Kershaw QC; 'Butterworths Personal Injury Litigation Service' with Margaret de Haas QC; 'Bullen and Leake and Jacob's Precedents of Pleadings' [Sweet and Maxwell], with Sir Jack Jacob; 'Pleadings, Principles and Practice' [Sweet and Maxwell], with Sir Jack Jacob; 'Structured Settlements' [Butterworths], Editor-in-Chief with Margaret de Haas QC [1st Edition 1993. 2nd Edition May 1997]; 'Medical Negligence: Cost Effective Case Management' [Butterworths] with Margaret de Haas QC, [May, 1997].
Personal: New ideas, classical Hebrew, English legal history and classic motor vehicles. Educated at Merchant Taylors' School, Crosby (Harrison Scholar), Hebrew University, Jerusalem (1971), Pembroke College, Cambridge (1971-74).

GOLDSTONE, David

4 Essex Court (Nigel Teare QC) London (020) 7653 5653
Recommended in Shipping
Specialisation: Shipping (wet and dry), international trade, insurance and reinsurance, banking, commodities, arbitration.
Prof. Memberships: COMBAR, LMAA (supporting member).
Career: Called to the Bar 1986, tenant since 1989, appointed to Treasury A Panel (admiralty junior) 1999.
Personal: Educated at Haberdashers' Aske's School 1973-80; Emmanuel College, Cambridge 1981-84 (BA) (double first in law); 1985-87 New College Oxford (BCL). Married with two daughters. Lives in Islington. Interests include science and technology, chess, skiing, tropical plants.

GOLDSTONE, L Clement QC

28 St. John St Manchester (0161) 834 8418
clerk@28stjohnst.co.uk
Recommended in Crime, Licensing
Specialisation: Crime, licensing. Also at 2-4 Tudor Street London EC4.
Prof. Memberships: Criminal Bar Association.
Career: B.A. (Cantab.) 1970. Called (Middle Temple) 1971. Recorder 1992. Queen's Counsel 1993. Treasurer, Northern Circuit 1998, MHRT (restricted cases), president 1999.

GOODE, Sir Roy QC

Blackstone Chambers (Presiley Baxendale QC & Charles Flint QC) London (020) 75831770
roygoode@blackstonechambers.com
Recommended in Consumer Law
Specialisation: Commercial law; banking; credit and security; international trade law; consumer credit Author of Commercial Law (2nd edn. 1995) and other leading textbooks in the above fields which are widely cited in the courts.
Prof. Memberships: Emeritus Professor of Law in the University of Oxford, Emeritus Fellow of St John's College, Oxford. Former Chairman of Executive Committee of JUSTICE. Panel Chairman of appeal under Consumer Credit Act 1974. Member of Board of London Court of International Arbitration. Former Chairman of the Commission on International Commercial Practice of the International Chamber of Commerce.
Career: Admitted as solicitor 1955; partner, *Victor Mishcon & Co., solicitors*, 1963-71. Appointed Professor of Law, Queen Mary College, University of London 1971, and Crowther Professor of Credit and Commercial Law 1973. Founder and first Director of Centre for Commercial Law Studies, QMC. Transferred to Bar 1988. Took silk 1990. Hon. Bencher, Inner Temple, 1992. Appointed Norton Rose Professor of English Law. University of Oxford, 1990. Member of Department of Trade and Industry Advisory Committee on Arbitration 1985-. Chairman of Pension Law Review Committee 1992-93.LL.B. (Lond.) 1954; LLD (Lond. 1976); OBE 1972, CBE 1994; Hon. DSc Econ (Lond.) 1996; Elected Fellow of the British Academy 1988; Fellow of the Royal Society of Arts 1990. Knighted 2000.

GOODE, Rowena

28 St. John St Manchester (0161) 834 8418
Recommended in Crime

GOODHART, Lord QC

3 New Square (Lord Goodhart QC) London (020) 7405 5577
Recommended in Chancery, Consumer Law
Specialisation: Principal area of practice is Chancery work, encompassing pension funds, trusts and estates, property, consumer credit and personal taxation. Other main area of work is company law and insolvency. Recent cases include Director General of Fair Trading v First National Bank plc [2000] AER 371, Davis v Richards & Wallington Industries [1990] 1WLR 1511 (pensions) and Hambro v Duke of Marlborough [1994] ch. 158 (trusts).
Prof. Memberships: Chancery Bar Association, International Commission of Jurists, Institute for Fiscal Studies, Tax Law Review Committee, Trust Law Committee.
Career: Called to the Bar 1957. In practice at the Chancery Bar since 1960 (QC 1979). Knighted 1989. Member Committee on Standards in Public Life since 1997.
Publications: 'Specific Performance' (with Prof Gareth Jones QC) 2nd edn 1996 (leading modern authority on subject). Section in 'Halsbury's Laws of England', 4th edn re-issue 198, on Corporations.
Personal: Educated at Eton College 1946-51, Trinity College, Cambridge 1953-57 (BA, MA) and Harvard Law School 1957-58 (LL.M). Chairman, Court of Discipline of Cambridge University since 1993. Life Peer, 1997. Born 18 January 1933.

GOODISON, Adam

3-4 South Square (Michael Crystal QC & Lord Alexander of Weedon QC) London (020) 7696 9900
adamgoodison@southsquare.com
Recommended in Insolvency/Corporate Recovery
Specialisation: Commercial law including insolvency, contract, banking, company, directors disqualification. Cases include acting for the liquidators of BCCI (Re Bank of Credit and Commerce International SA (No4) [1995] BCC 453 (Scott V-C); BCCI v Haque (Lightman J & CA); BCCI v Shoaib (Evans Lombe J); BCCI v Makhan Jan (Jonathan Parker J). Also Re Thirty Eight Building Ltd (In Liquidation) [1999] BCC 260 & [2000] BCLC 201 (Hazell Williamson QC) (preferences); Straume v Bradlor Developments, [2000] BCC 333 (leave in administration proceedings); Holder v Supperstone, Independent, December 1999 (costs of proceedings re charging orders).
Prof. Memberships: Chancery Bar Association, Combar, ILA.
Career: Called 1990. Elected member Bar Council 1995-8.
Publications: Chapter on retention of title 'The Law of Receivers', (Lightman & Moss); chapter on company voluntary arrangements 'Insolvency', (Totty & Moss); contributor to 'Rowlatt on Principal and Surety' (5th edn); 'Distress and Distraint' for R3; voluntary arrangements legal update for R3; various solicitor programme lectures (including *Linklaters, Sidley & Austin, Frere Cholmeley, Wragge & Co)*.

GOODRICH, Siobhan

6 Pump Court London (020) 7583 6013
clerks@6pumpcourt.law.co.uk
Recommended in Clinical Negligence
Specialisation: Medical negligence and related work; professional misconduct, disciplinary tribunals, inquests, and inquiries. Acts for plaintiff and defendant. Other areas of practice include professional negligence, personal injury and some crime.
Prof. Memberships: Professional Negligence Bar Association, LCLBA, CBA.
Career: Called to the Bar in 1980. Joined chambers in 1981. Born 15 March 1957.
Personal: Educated at King's College London (LLB).

GORDON, Richard QC

Brick Court Chambers (Christopher Clarke QC) London (020) 7379 3550
gordon@brickcourt.co.uk
Recommended in Administrative & Public Law, Environment, Human Rights

Specialisation: Specialist in public, administrative law and human rights law. Acts for both respondents and applicants in judicial review, especially in the areas of commercial, environmental, local authority, civil liberties and human rights, health and social services. Visiting Professor of Law, University College, London.
Prof. Memberships: Administrative Law Bar Association.
Career: Called to the Bar 1972. Took Silk 1994.
Publications: Author of 'Judicial Review and the Human Rights Act', ' Judicial Review: Law and Procedure', 'Judicial Review and Home Office Practice', 'Local Authority Powers' 'Human Rights in the United Kingdom'; 'The Human Rights Act 1988 and Judicial Review'. Co-editor of 'Local Authority Law'; editor in chief 'Crown Office Digest'. Consultant editor 'Human Rights Law Reports – UK Cases'.
Personal: Educated at Oxford University (Open Scholar).

GORE, Allan
12 King's Bench Walk (Richard Methuen QC) London (020) 7583 0811
Recommended in Personal Injury
Specialisation: Professional negligence, encompassing medical, dental and legal cases both contentious and non-contentious. Personal injury work. Special interest and experience in transport mass accidents and disasters, and industrial disease, particularly concerning asbestos cases.
Prof. Memberships: Executive of Association of Personal Injury Lawyers and Personal Injury Bar Association. Professional Negligence Bar Association, AVMA, ATLA, APLA.
Career: Called1977. Joined current chambers 1991. Recorder 2000.
Publications: Contributing author to 'Butterworths County Court Precedents and Pleadings: Divisions P on Professional Negligence and Q on Personal Injury', 'Cordery on Solicitors: Division J on Negligence', Butterworths 'Personal Injury Litigation Service' Division VIII on Pleadings, 'Personal Injury Handbook' (2nd ed) and 'Curran on Personal Injury Pleadings' (2nd ed). Regular conference and seminar speaker.
Personal: Educated Purley Grammar School, Croydon 1962-69; Trinity Hall, Cambridge 1970-74. Born 25th August 1951. Lives in London.

GOSLING, Jonathan
4 Fountain Court (John Saunders QC) Birmingham (0121) 236 3476
Recommended in Licensing

GOUDIE, James QC
11 King's Bench Walk Chambers (Eldred Tabachnik QC & James Goudie QC) London (020) 7632 8500
clerksroom@11kbw.com
Recommended in Administrative & Public Law, Employment, Local Government
Specialisation: Specialises in all aspects of employment law, with particular emphasis on TUPE, restrictive covenants and European law relating to employment matters. Other main areas of practice include public law (capital finance) and commercial (contractual disputes, insurance).
Career: Solicitor 1966-70. Called to the Bar Inner Temple 1970. Bencher; Recorder; Deputy High Court Judge, Queen's Bench Division; past-chairman Law Reform Committee; General Council of the Bar; past-chairman Administrative Law Bar Association; past-chairman Society of Labour Lawyers.
Personal: Educated at Dean Close School, Cheltenham and LSE (LLB Hons). FCI Arb.

GOULDING, Paul QC
Blackstone Chambers (Presiley Baxendale QC & Charles Flint QC) London (020) 7583 1770
clerks@blackstonechambers.com
Recommended in Employment, Sport
Specialisation: Specialist in employment and sports law. Employment: chairman, Employment Lawyers Association 1998-00. Particular interests – restraint of trade, transfers of undertakings, Europe, discrimination, industrial action. Recent cases – Neary v Dean of Westminster; Biggs v Somerset CC; Reed v Stedman; SoS v Bearman. Sport: recent cases – Modahl v BAF; Korda v ITF; Rudge v Port Vale FC; Formula 1, rugby union and league cases. Member of British Association for Sport and Law. SDRP Arbitrator.
Career: St Edmund Hall, Oxford (MA, BCL, Tutor). Call 1984. Silk 2000.
Publications: 'European Employment Law and the UK' (2001).

GOURGEY, Alan
11 Stone Buildings (Murray Rosen QC) London (020) 7831 6381
Recommended in Chancery
Specialisation: Alan has an established reputation as a leading junior in the field of commercial litigation. His wide ranging practice includes major business disputes, partnership and insolvency. He has acted in many substantial fraud cases ranging from bank to telecommunications fraud. As a media, sports and entertainment lawyer, clients have included pop stars, sportsmen, managers, football clubs and sporting bodies. His expertise extends to intellectual property, e-commerce and IT disputes. He is an experienced trial lawyer and whether as team-leader or part of a team, his particular strengths are in rapid assimilation and analysis of complex material, tactical guidance and forceful advocacy. He is noted in 'The Lawyer' magazine for being a leading commercial junior.
Career: LLB (Bristol). Called 1984.
Personal: Outside Chambers he is the linchpin of his 5-a-side football team.

GOURIET, Gerald
3 Raymond Buildings (Clive Nicholls QC) London (020) 74006400
chambers@3raymondbuildings.com
Recommended in Licensing
Specialisation: Specialist preparation and advice relating to all aspects of liquor, betting and gaming licensing, including advice on all forms of Internet gambling. Advice on lotteries and other related activities. All levels of representation from local committees to Divisional Court and Court of Appeal.
Career: Called to the Bar 1974.

GOWER, Peter
6 Pump Court (Stephen Hockman QC) London (020) 7797 8400
petergower@6pumpcourt.co.uk
Recommended in Crime
Specialisation: Both prosecuting and defending; commercial crime; Customs Excise offences; breaches of health and safety; planning and other regulatory legislation.
Prof. Memberships: Criminal Bar Association.
Career: Educated at Christ Church, Oxford (Classics scholar) (MA Oxon); called Lincoln's Inn 1985; appointed standing counsel for Department of Trade and Industry in 1991.

GOY, David QC
Gray's Inn Tax Chambers (Milton Grundy) London (020) 7242 2642
Recommended in Tax
Specialisation: Specialist in all aspects of revenue law. Has particular expertise in the tax aspects of real property transactions, and in all types of tax litigation. Important cases include Lubbock Fine v HM Customs & Excise [1994] (VAT on the surrender of tenancies); LASMO (TNS) Ltd v IRC [1994] (oil taxation); IRC v Willoughby [1997] (taxation under s739 ICTA); CE v First National Bank of Chicago [1998] (VAT and foreign exchange transactions); Bestway (Holdings) Ltd v Luff [1998] (industrial buildings allowances); United Friendly Insurance plc v IRC [1998] (life assurance taxation); Beneficiary v IRC [1999] (Taxation under S.740); Carr v Fielden & Ashworth Ltd [2000] (relief for ACT). Publications include 'Whiteman on Income Tax', co-editor 3rd edn 1988, 'VAT on Property' (co-author) (Sweet & Maxwell 2nd Edition 1993), and Butterworths 'Tax Planning' (consultant editor). Regular speaker on the subject of revenue law.
Prof. Memberships: Revenue Bar Association.
Career: Called to the Bar 1973. Joined present chambers 1974. Took Silk 1991.
Personal: Educated at Haberdashers' Askes School and King's College, London. Born 11 May 1949. Lives in Guildford.

GRABINER, Lord QC
One Essex Court (Lord Grabiner QC) London (020) 7583 2000
Recommended in Arbitration (International), Banking, Commercial (Litigation), Competition/Anti-trust, Energy & Natural Resources, Fraud

GRACE, John QC
3 Serjeants' Inn (Robert Francis QC & John Grace QC) London (020) 7427 5000
Recommended in Clinical Negligence

GRAY, Gilbert QC
3 Raymond Buildings (Clive Nicholls QC) London (020) 7400 6400
Recommended in Licensing

GRAY, Richard QC
39 Essex Street (Nigel Pleming QC) London (020) 7832 1111
Recommended in Construction
Specialisation: Principal area of practice is construction and engineering litigation or arbitration in UK and abroad. Acts as arbitrator in such disputes, both domestic and international, and as mediator or conciliator.
Prof. Memberships: TecBar (Technology and Construction Bar Association).
Career: Called to the Bar in 1970. Took silk in 1993.

GREEN, Brian QC
Wilberforce Chambers (Edward Nugee QC) London (020) 7306 0102
Recommended in Chancery, Pensions
Specialisation: Pensions and private client specialist having wide ranging experience of contentious and non-contentious general Chancery work. Has acted for the sponsoring companies or the trustees of major pension schemes, and for the trustees and/or the beneficiaries of the largest trusts (private and commercial).
Prof. Memberships: APL, Revenue Bar Association, STEP. Chancery Bar Association.
Career: Called to the Bar 1980. Member of Revenue Law Committee of the Law Society since 1994. (1978-85 tenured lectureship in Law at LSE).
Personal: Educated at Ilford County High School and St Edmund Hall Oxford (BA, BCL: double first).

GREEN, Michael
Fountain Court (Anthony Boswood QC) London (020) 7583 3335
Recommended in Company
Specialisation: Principal areas of work are company, insolvency, civil fraud and professional negligence including large scale commercial actions, having been involved for 3 years in Maxwell litigation (acting for Lehman Brothers), and then Lloyds litigation (acting on behalf of auditors). Noteworthy cases include Derby v Weldon (civil fraud), Macmillan Inc v Bishopsgate Investment Trust Plc (Maxwell recovery actions), numerous public interest winding up petitions acting for the DTI including illegal lotteries and investment schemes; a large number of directors' disqualification cases including Barings, Barlow Clowes, Kaytech International Plc (in Court of Appeal), Secretary of State v Deverell (leading CA authority on shadow directors), Funtime and City Pram and Toy; SIB v FIMBRA (financial services); Cranley

Mansions (Insolvency) Land and Property Trust (corporate insolvency); Wimbledon & Merton Democratic Society (Friendly Societies); Wolverhampton Wanderers v Stones (professional negligence); Shalsan v Russo (civil fraud).
Prof. Memberships: COMBAR, Chancery Bar Association.
Career: Called to the bar in 1987. Joined *7 Stone Buildings* in 1988. Joined present chambers in 1998. Appointed Junior Counsel to the Crown (A Panel) in 1997 and a DTI Inspector in 1997.
Personal: Educated at University College School 1971-82, and Jesus College Cambridge 1983-86.

GREEN, Nicholas QC
Brick Court Chambers (Christopher Clarke QC) London (020) 7379 3550
green@brickcourt.co.uk
Recommended in Competition/Anti-trust, Sport
Specialisation: Litigation, advisory and representational work in relation to the EC and United Kingdom competition law, aspects of mergers and takeovers; intellectual property licensing; sports law; media law and broadcasting; telecommunications; environmental law; public procurement; conflicts of laws; public law. Has been instructed in over fifty cases before the European Court of Justice and Court of First Instance. Recent cases include Factortame, Coloroll, Francovich II, Sunag (shipping conferences), Eurotunnel; matters re the beef ban; acting for pharmaceutical companies in disputes over licenses and consents and use of confidential data; acting for sporting unions in disputes with clubs with regulators and competitors; intellectual property cases involving EU law.
Career: Called to Bar 1986; appointed Queen's Counsel in 1998; Barrister of the Inner Temple, Brick Court Chambers both in London and Brussels. 1981-85: Lecturer in Law, University of Southampton. Visiting professor in law, University of Durham 2000-; Chairman Bar European Group, 1999-; Vice Chairman, International Relations Committee/Bar Council.
Publications: Over sixty articles in publications worldwide and a major textbook in UK and EC competition law. Two principal publications are 'Commercial Agreements and Competition law: Practice and Procedure in the UK and EEC' (1986) (second edition); and 'Legal Foundations of the Single European Market' (1991).
Personal: Born 15 October 1958. LLB (1980), LL.M (1981), PhD (1985).

GREENBERG, Joanna QC
3 Temple Gardens (Jonathan Goldberg QC) London (020) 7583 1155
Recommended in Crime
Specialisation: Defending in all types of serious criminal cases.
Prof. Memberships: Bar Council, Criminal Bar Association, Justice, Liberty.
Career: Called to the Bar 1972, took Silk 1994, Assistant Recorder 1992, Recorder 1995, Chairman of Police Discipline Appeals Tribunals 1997.
Personal: Educated University of London, King's College. Lives in London.

GREENWOOD, Celestine
Chavasse Court Chambers (Theresa Pepper) Liverpool (0151) 707 1191
Recommended in Family

GREGORY, James
Lincoln House Chambers (Mukhtar Hussain QC) Manchester (0161) 832 5701
Recommended in Crime

GREGORY, Philip
No.6 Fountain Court (Roger Smith QC) Birmingham (0121) 233 3282
Recommended in Clinical Negligence

GREY, Robin QC
Hollis Whiteman Chambers (QEB) (Julian Bevan QC & Peter Whiteman QC) London (020) 7583 5766
barristers@holliswhiteman.co.uk
Recommended in Crime
Specialisation: Criminal law. Defends and prosecutes in all areas of criminal law, with a particular emphasis on large-scale fraud in recent years. Has also defended in over thirty high-profile murder cases during the course of his career. Successfully defended in the Richardson Gang case of 1970s, in the 'Nasty Tales' case at the time of the Oz trial, in the 'King Squealer' robberies in the late 1970s, and in the Brinks Matt case in the early 1990s. Fraud trials include a successful defence in the Eagle Trust case (1993). In the past ten years has defended solicitors, accountants and bank managers in relation to white collar offences. Has considerable experience lecturing on professional conduct, jury trials and criminal procedure. Has also written articles for the Centre for Policy Studies and the Criminal Bar Association newsletter. Practice also includes civil matters arising out of criminal cases.
Prof. Memberships: Bar Council, Society of Forensic Medicine, Criminal Bar Association, European Criminal Bar Association, International Bar Association, Eastern Europe Forum and the Council of Russian and UK Cooperation.
Career: Called to the Bar 1957 and worked as Crown Counsel in Aden 1959-63, before joining present chambers in 1963. Took Silk in 1979 and was appointed Recorder in the same year. Chairman of Police Appeals Tribunals 1988. Adviser to the Foreign Office in Russian Federation jury trials in 1993-97. Legal Assessor to General Medical Council, 1995.

GRIEVE, Dominic
1 Temple Gardens (Hugh Carlisle QC) London (020) 7583 1315
Recommended in Health & Safety
Specialisation: Health and safety at work and pollution cases (criminal and civil). Junior prosecution counsel in: R v Nuclear Electric Plc (Mold September 1995 incident at Wylfa Power Station) R v Coalite Ltd (Leicester February 1996 Pollution by Dioxins); R v Port Ramsgate, Old Bailey January – March 1997; R v J Sainsbury Plc, Winchester – November 1998 (operation and maintenance of fork lift trucks). Personal injury. Insurance/negligence work. Local government (enforcement work). Counsel in R v Railcare (derailment of high speed train through wheel failure) Luton Crown Court. London Underground Ltd v HSE (appeal against prohibition notice in relation to the checking of trains before they are reversed in sidings) July 2000. Prosecution counsel R v Homebase (scope of undertaking in relation to accident in service yard) Bristol 2001.
Prof. Memberships: Common Law Bar Association and Criminal Bar Association.
Career: Hon. Degree Modern History Oxford 1978. Called to Bar 1980. 1982-90 Chamber of Anthony Cripps QC: 1, Harcourt Buildings (General Common Law). 1990-date: 1 Temple Gardens.

GRIEVE, Michael QC
Doughty Street Chambers (Geoffrey Robertson QC) London (020) 7404 1313
Recommended in Crime, Fraud

GRIFFITH-JONES, David QC
Devereux Chambers (Jeffrey Burke QC) London (020) 7353 7534
griffith-jones@devchambers.co.uk
Recommended in Employment, Sport
Specialisation: General common lawyer. Specialist in employment (including dismissal, discrimination, TUPE, industrial disputes, restraint of trade and injunctions) and sport (including personal injury, discipline and regulation and the commercial exploitation of sport).
Prof. Memberships: London Common Law and Commercial Bar Association; Employment Lawyers' Association; Employment Law Bar Association; British Association of Sport and the Law; Bar Sports Law Group (Committee Member). Silk 2000.
Career: Called to the Bar 1975. FCIArb 1991. Recorder 1997. Sports Dispute Resolution Panel 2000. Assistant Boundary Commission 2000.
Publications: 'Law and the Business of Sport' (Butterworths, 1997)

GRIFFITHS, Alan
One Essex Court (Lord Grabiner QC) London (020) 7583 2000
Recommended in Administrative & Public Law, Energy & Natural Resources
Specialisation: Administrative and public law (especially commercial judicial review), general commercial law (including insurance, company law, complex contracts', conflict of laws jurisdiction), energy (including oil and gas), utility regulation and environmental law. Most recently: 20 weeks Commercial Court trial on driving services contract. For Milk Marque defeating the JR challenge to the reorganisation of the UK milk industry. For Lloyd's defeating the JR challenge to Lloyd's reconstruction and renewal. For Scottish Power in the successful JR challenge to OFFER's price control decisions. For pharmaceutical, agrochemical, TV and radio, and telecommunications companies in judicial reviews of licensing and planning decisions. For EMLICO (General Electric's main insurer) in insolvency and JR actions in Bermuda. For the ABI in the Policyholders Protection Board litigation (insurance). For Orion in Sphere Drake v Orion (1998) (insurance). Advises major insurance companies on the restructuring of life funds and on legal accounting issues. For the banks in the Hammersmith & Fulham interest rate swaps litigation, and in subsequent restitution cases. In the environmental field, clients include British Nuclear Fuels, National Grid, NORWEB and Powergen. For BNFL defeating the Greenpeace JR challenges to the Sellafield THORP plant.
Prof. Memberships: Administrative Law Bar Association, Commercial Bar Association (Committee).
Career: Called 1981. (Called to Bermuda Bar for EMLICO litigation).
Personal: Born 1953. Educated Jesus College, Oxford (MA, BCL). Formerly Fellow and Tutor in Law, Exeter College, Oxford.

GRIFFITHS, Courtenay QC
Two Garden Court (Ian Macdonald QC & Owen Davies QC) London (020) 7353 1633
Recommended in Crime

GRIFFITHS, Martin
Essex Court Chambers (Gordon Pollock QC) London (020) 7813 8000
Recommended in Commercial (Litigation), Employment
Specialisation: Appears as an advocate in Courts and tribunals including domestic arbitrations, all divisions of the High Court (including Mercantile Courts), the Court of Appeal and the Privy Council. Employment and human rights law practice including domestic disciplinary tribunals, the Employment Tribunal, the Employment Appeal Tribunal, all divisions of the High Court, the Court of Appeal and the Privy Council.
Prof. Memberships: Member of COMBAR; member of ELBA; member of the Bar European Group.
Career: New College, Oxford: BA (1st Class Hons with Distinction) 1984; MA 1988; City University, London: Postgraduate Diploma in Law 1985. Called to the Bar 1986.
Personal: Born 1962.

GRIFFITHS, Peter
4 Stone Buildings (Philip Heslop QC) London (020) 7421 3700
clerks@4stonebuildings.com
Recommended in Chancery, Company, Insolvency/Corporate Recovery
Specialisation: Principal area of practice is company

law, focusing on insolvency and minority shareholder disputes. Other main areas of work include partnership, civil fraud, bankruptcy and professional negligence.
Prof. Memberships: Chancery Bar Association, Insolvency Lawyers' Association and COMBAR.
Career: Called to the Bar in 1977 and joined present chambers in 1978.
Publications: Contributor to 'Atkins Court Forms' Vol 10 (Companies Winding Up) 1988, 'Encyclopaedia of Forms and Precedents' 5th Ed Vol 11 (Companies) 1992, and Butterworths 'Practical Insolvency' 1999.
Personal: Educated at Repton 1966-71 and St Catharine's College, Cambridge, 1972-75.

GRIME, Stephen QC
Deans Court Chambers (Stephen Grime QC) Manchester (0161) 214 6000
grime@deanscourt.co.uk
Recommended in Clinical Negligence
Specialisation: Personal Injury including disease litigation; insurance related litigation; construction; clinical negligence; professional negligence – other than clinical; commercial; arbitration. Significant reported cases: J (a child) v Wilkins [2001] PIQR P 179; JD Williams & Co Ltd v Michael Hyde [2001] BLR 99; Jenkins v Grocott [2000] PIQR Q17; Bence Graphics International v Fasson [1998] QB 87; R v CICB (Ex parte C) [1997] PIQR P128; Thomas v Plaistow [1997] PIQR P540; Wisniewski v Central Manchester HA [1996] 7 Med LR 248; Cruden Construction v Commission for the New Towns [1995] 2 Lloyd's Rep 387; Crocker v British Coal Corporation [1995] 29 BMLR 159; Fairhurst v St Helens & Knowsley HA [1995] PIQR Q1; Khan v Armaguard [1994] 3 All ER 545; Wood v Gahlings [1993] PIQR P76; Family Housing Association (Manchester) Ltd v Michael Hyde [1993] 1 WLR 354; Bradley v Eagle Star Insurance Co Ltd [1989] 1 AC 957; Wilkinson v Ancliff (BLT) Ltd [1986] 3 All ER 427, [1986] 1 WLR 1352; Gandolfo v Gandolfo [1981] QB 359.
Prof. Memberships: Chairman Northern Circuit Medical Law Association; Past Chairman of Northern Arbitration Association; Fellow – Chartered Institute of Arbitrators. Member – Northern Circuit Commercial Bar Association; Society for Computers and Law; United Kingdom Environmental Law Association; Professional Negligence Bar Association; Personal Injury Bar Association.
Career: Trinity College, Oxford (Scholar). Called (Middle Temple) – 1970. Queen's Counsel – 1987. Recorder – 1990. Technology and Construction Recorder – 1996. Fellow – Chartered Institute of Arbitrators – 1996. Bencher of Middle Temple – 1997. Head of Chambers 2000.

GRINDROD, Helen QC
15- Devereux Court (Helen Grindrod QC) London (020) 7583 2792
Recommended in Crime

GROSS, Peter QC
20 Essex Street (Iain Milligan QC) London (020) 7583 9294
clerks@20essexst.com
Recommended in Arbitration (International), Commercial (Litigation), Insurance, Shipping
Specialisation: Arbitration (ICC; LCIA; UNCITRAL; LMAA), aviation, banking, carriage of goods, commodities, conflict, energy, financial services, insurance and reinsurance, shipping (wet and dry).
Prof. Memberships: Director LCIA. Deputy chairman SFA Consumer Arbitration Scheme Panel. Member New South Wales Bar. Chairman LCLCBA, 1996-97. Chairman Bar Council Education & Training Committee 1998-00; International Relations Committee 2001.
Career: Cape Town and Oxford Universities. Rhodes Scholar. Eldon Scholar. Called 1977; Queen's Counsel 1992; Recorder 1995; Deputy High Court Judge 1998.

GROVES, Hugo
Enterprise Chambers (Anthony Mann QC) Leeds (0113) 246 0391
Recommended in Commercial (Litigation), Insolvency/Corporate Recovery

GRUDER, Jeffrey QC
Essex Court Chambers (Gordon Pollock QC) London (020) 7813 8000
Recommended in Arbitration (International), Commercial (Litigation), Shipping
Specialisation: Principal areas of practice are commercial disputes, insurance and reinsurance, banking, oil and gas disputes. Other areas of practice are shipping and transport, financial services and commodity disputes. Recently appeared in Standard Chartered Bank v PNSC; RZB v Five Star; XL v Owens Corning; Czech Ocean v Van Ommeren; Investors Compensation Scheme v West Bromwich Building Society; Vitol Energy v Pisco; Indian Grace (No 2) (1997); Chevron v Total (1996); Autocar v Motemtronic (1996); British Gas v Eastern Electricity (1996). Other important cases have included Sheldon v Outhwaite (1995); Standard Bank v Bank of Tokyo (1995); Indian Grace (1993); Euro-diam v Bathurst (1990); Miss Jay Jay (1987); Nai Genova (1984). Has appeared frequently in arbitrations and acted as arbitrator. Clients include major banks, insurance companies and corporations. Supervisor at Cambridge University 1977-79. Previously part-time lecturer at Central London Polytechnic on International Trade.
Prof. Memberships: COMBAR (secretary).
Career: Called to the Bar in 1977. QC 1997. At 4 Essex Court (now Essex Court Chambers) 1978-93. 1 Essex Court 1993-00. Rejoined Essex Court Chambers February 2000.
Personal: Educated at City of London School 1966-72 and Trinity Hall, Cambridge 1973-76. Born 18 September 1954. Interests include tennis, theatre, cinema and reading. Lives in Radlett.

GRUNDY, Nigel
9 St. John Street (John Hand QC) Manchester (0161) 955 9000
Recommended in Employment
Specialisation: Recent cases: Parkinson v March Consulting Ltd CA 1997 IRLR 519; Boys and Girls Welfare Society v McDonald 1996 IRLR 129; Mennell v Newell and Wright (Transport Contractors) Ltd 1996 ICR 607. Specialises in employment, discrimination and trade union law.
Prof. Memberships: Employment Law Bar Association, Professional Negligence Bar Association, Northern Circuit Commercial Bar Association.
Career: MA (Hons) Oxon Jurisprudence. Recorder.
Personal: Golf, tennis.

GUGGENHEIM, Anna QC
Crown Office Chambers (Michael Spencer QC & Christopher Purchas QC) London (020) 7797 8100
guggenheim@crownofficechambers.com
Recommended in Professional Negligence
Specialisation: Specialises in insurance litigation, construction, product liability, general commercial and common law, personal injury.
Prof. Memberships: London Common Law & Commercial Bar Association; COMBAR; TECBAR.
Career: Called to the Bar 1982. Silk 2001.
Personal: Educated at Somerville College, Oxford (BA Jurisprudence) 1978-81. Born 2nd September 1959. Speaks French. Interests: sailing.

HACKER, Richard QC
3-4 South Square (Michael Crystal QC & Lord Alexander of Weedon QC) London (020) 7696 9900
richardhacker@southsquare.com
Recommended in Banking, Insolvency/Corporate Recovery
Specialisation: A mixed litigation/advisory commercial law practice including contentious and non-contentious insolvency work, banking law, professional negligence, asset tracing and general commercial litigation. Clients have included the major international accountancy firms, major UK banks and a variety of overseas banks and governments. Heavily involved in all major collapses of the last 20 years including Laker, Banco Ambrosiano, Mentor Insurance, Maxwell, BCCI, Rafidain, KWELM, NEMGIA and Barings. Has appeared and given expert evidence in a variety of overseas Courts including New York. Recent significant UK trial appearances include the Grupo Torras litigation in which he appeared for the Kuwait Investment Authority.
Career: Called 1977. QC 1998.

HACKETT, Philip QC
2 Bedford Row (William Clegg QC) London (020) 7440 8888
Recommended in Crime, Fraud

HACON, Richard
11 South Square (Christopher Floyd QC) London (020) 7405 1222
Recommended in Intellectual Property

HADDON-CAVE, Charles QC
4 Essex Court (Nigel Teare QC) London (020) 7653 5653
charles@haddon-cave.com
Recommended in Arbitration (International), Aviation
Specialisation: Has a broad commercial practice which includes a wide variety of cases in the aviation field. He has been instructed in many of the major aviation disasters of recent times including the Knight Air crash at Dunkeswick, the Thai Air crash at Kathmandu, the British Midland crash at Kegworth and the British Airtours disaster at Manchester. He has acted for Virgin Atlantic in CAA routing applications, including London-Shanghai and London-Capetown. He appears regularly as an advocate in the High Court in London, Cayman Islands and Hong Kong and in international arbitrations.
Prof. Memberships: Vice-Chairman of the Royal Aeronautical Society Air Law Committee. Member of COMBAR, the Personal Injury Bar Association and one of the only members of the English Bar called generally to the Hong Kong Bar.

HAGGAN, Nicholas Somerset
17 Carlton Crescent (Jeremy S. Gibbons QC) Southampton (023) 8032 0320/2003
Recommended in Consumer Law

HAJIMITSIS, Anthony
Zenith Chambers (Andrew Campbell QC & John Collins) Leeds 0113 245 5438 / 1986
clerks@10pksq.co.uk
Recommended in Family
Specialisation: Matrimonial Finance, Public Law Children Cases.
Prof. Memberships: FLBA.
Career: Leeds Grammar School; Oxford University; Inner Temple (1984 Call).
Personal: Married. One son.

HALL, Andrew
Doughty Street Chambers (Geoffrey Robertson QC) London (020) 7404 1313
Recommended in Crime
Specialisation: Practice predominantly serious crime, including leading work. Substantial experience of homicide and other serious violence, firearms, explosives, and large drug conspiracies. Growing fraud practice including VAT, mortgage and insolvent trading cases. Has regularly written, lectured and broadcast on a wide range of issues within the criminal justice sphere.
Prof. Memberships: Criminal Bar Association, Bar Overseas Advocacy Committee, South Eastern Circuit.
Career: Educated at Marist College, University of Birmingham (LL.B 1974), University of Sheffield (MA [Criminology] 1976). Admitted as solicitor 1980. Partner and head of criminal law department, *Hodge Jones & Allen*

London before transfer to the Bar in 1991. Former Director of Legal Action Group. Member of Editorial Board of International Journal of Evidence and Proof. Member of General Council of Bar and Human Rights Committee of the Bar of England and Wales.

HALL, Joanna
14 Gray's Inn Square (Joanna Dodson QC) London (020) 7242 0858
Recommended in Family

HALPERN, David
Four New Square (Justin Fenwick QC) London (020) 7822 2000
barristers@4newsquare.com
Recommended in Professional Negligence
Specialisation: Professional negligence and property litigation.
Career: Educated at St Paul's School; won Open Exhibition to Magdalen College, Oxford. Practised from Chancery Chambers for 20 years before moving to 4 New Square in 2000. Practises in professional negligence and in all areas of commercial Chancery work (emphasis on property litigation). Recent cases include Barclays Bank v *Weeks Legg Dean* [1999] QB 309 (solicitor's undertaking to bank), Portman Building Society v *Hamlyn Taylor Neck* [1998] 4 All ER 202 (whether lender may bring restitutionary claim against solicitor reporting on title) and Raja v Rubin [2000] Ch. 274 (power to vary IVA informally). Co-author of chapter on Accountants and Auditors for fifth edition of Jackson & Powell on 'Professional Negligence'.

HAM, Robert QC
Wilberforce Chambers (Edward Nugee QC) London (020) 7306 0102
rham@wilberforce.co.uk
Recommended in Chancery
Specialisation: Practice largely in the fields of trusts and tax law, including offshore trusts and pension schemes, pension schemes, but extends to other areas of property law and associated professional negligence. Special expertise in disputes involving civil law, forced heirship as a result of the Thyspen-Bornemisze case.
Prof. Memberships: Association of Pension Lawyers. Chancery Bar Association, Revenue Bar Association, Society of Trust and Estate Practioners, Wales and Chester Circuit.
Career: BA & BCL (Oxon); Called to the Bar 1973; QC 1994.

HAMBLEN, Nicholas QC
20 Essex Street (Iain Milligan QC) London (020) 7583 9294
clerks@20essexst.com
Recommended in Shipping
Specialisation: Principal areas of practice are shipping, international sale of goods, commodities, insurance and re-insurance, conflicts of laws and arbitration. Acts as arbitrator in maritime, insurance and international commercial arbitrations. ICC, LCIA, LAS and ACI arbitrator.
Career: Called to the Bar 1981. Took Silk 1997. Sits as Recorder.
Personal: Educated at St John's College, Oxford (MA) and Harvard Law School (LL.M). Born 1957.

HAMER, George
8 New Square (Michael Fysh QC) London (020) 7405 4321
george.hamer@8newsquare.co.uk
Recommended in Intellectual Property
Specialisation: Barrister specialising in all aspects of intellectual property and media law, including patents, copyright, passing off, trade marks, service marks and confidential information. Cases include Ordnancey Survey v Automobile Assoc. (copyright); Catnic Components v Hill & Smith (patents); SKM v Wagner Hsiung's Patent (patents); Rolls Royce v Dodd (trade marks/passing off); Neutrogena v Golden (trade marks/passing off); Sillitoe v McGraw Hill (copyright); Goodyear tyre treads (registered designs); Amper S.A ; Estate of Bob Marley (PC); expert witness in Israel (LEGO) and for proceedings in the United States (Apple Computer). For comprehensive CV and list of recent cases, visit our website at www.8newsquare.co.uk.
Prof. Memberships: Intellectual Patent Bar Association (IPBA); The Intellectual Property Lawyers Organisation (TIPLO).
Career: Called to the Bar 1974.
Personal: Born 1949. Educated at Sedbergh School; Imperial College, London University (1971) BSc Chemistry and ARCS.

HAMILTON, Eben QC
New Square Chambers (John Mowbray QC & Eben Hamilton QC) London (020) 7419 8000
clerks@newsquarechambers.co.uk
Recommended in Insolvency/Corporate Recovery
Specialisation: Specialises in company and corporate finance, commercial chancery and insolvency.
Prof. Memberships: Chancery Bar Association, AEPPC, INSOL.
Career: Called to the Bar, 1962. QC 1981. Bencher, Inner Temple 1985. DTI inspector, Atlantic Computers plc 1990-94, Deputy High Court Judge, Chancery division since 1991. Admitted regularly to appear in courts of Hong Kong and Singapore in company and insolvency matters.

HAMILTON, Eleanor QC
No.6 Barristers Chambers (Shaun Spencer QC) Leeds (0113) 245 9763
Recommended in Family

HANCOCK, Christopher QC
20 Essex Street (Iain Milligan QC) London (020) 7583 9294
Recommended in Banking

HAND, John QC
Old Square Chambers (John Hand QC) Manchester (020) 7269 0300
hand@oldsquarechambers.co.uk
Old Square Chambers (John Hendy QC) London (020) 7269 0300
hand@oldsquarechambers.co.uk
Recommended in Employment, Environment
Specialisation: Is experienced in most areas of common law litigation, concentrates on employment law, personal injury and environmental law with emphasis on health and safety litigation and is familiar with EC law principles. In employment law he deals with all aspects of individual and collective disputes including equal opportunity work. Recent cases have been Martin/Bernadone v Pall Mall (TUPE), Khan v West Yorkshire Police (race discrimination) and LUL v RMT (industrial action). In environment/health and safety he has appeared both in the Crown Court and the Magistrates Court in cases of explosions, airborne pollution and radiation. Cases include R v Hickson and Welch (the Castleford explosion), R v Associated Octel (No. 2)(the Ellesmere port Explosion), R v Coalite (Dioxin emissions), R v University of Cambridge (loss of radioactive source) and Clifton v Powergen (Airbourne Pollution).
Prof. Memberships: ELA, ELBA, PIBA, PNBA, UKELA, BEG and Society for Computer and Law.
Career: Called 1972 Bencher 1996 (Gray's Inn); Queen's Counsel (1988); Recorder 1991.

HANDYSIDE, Richard
Fountain Court (Anthony Boswood QC) London (020) 7583 3335
richardhandyside@fountaincourt.co.uk
Recommended in Banking
Specialisation: Commercial litigation, including banking, insurance / reinsurance, civil fraud, conflicts of laws, restitution, international trade and professional negligence. Notable cases include United Pan-Europe Communications v Deutsche Bank (injunction / confidential information / investment bank – customer relationship), Morgan Grenfell v SACE (export credit insurance / due diligence by lending banks), Arab Bank v Zurich Insurance (composite professional indemnity policy / attribution of knowledge), Scottish Equitable Plc v Derby (recovery of payments made by mistake / defences of estoppel and change of position), the Camdex v Bank of Zambia litigation (assignment / champerty; Mareva injunction over unissued bank notes; enforcement of foreign public law), Bates v Robert Barrow (insurance contracts and illegality). Also acted for defendant auditors in the First Tokyo Index Trust litigation (Maxwell related) and in the KWELM litigation.
Prof. Memberships: COMBAR.
Career: Called 1993.
Publications: Contributing Editor to Commercial Court Procedure (Sweet & Maxwell, 2001).
Personal: Educated Marlborough College, Bristol University (LLB Hons 1st Class) and Brasenose College, Oxford (BCL 1st Class). Born 1968.

HAPGOOD, Mark QC
Brick Court Chambers (Christopher Clarke QC) London (020) 7379 3550
Recommended in Banking, Commercial (Litigation), Company

HARDING, Cherry
Renaissance Chambers (Brian Jubb & Henry Setright QC) London (020) 7404 1111
Recommended in Family

HARGREAVES, Simon
Keating Chambers (Richard Fernyhough QC) London +44 (0) 20 7544 2600
shargreaves@keatingchambers.com
Recommended in Construction
Specialisation: All aspects of litigation and arbitration concerning general construction, engineering, power and utilities contracts (both domestic and international). All related negligence and professional negligence claims. ICC Arbitrations. Adjudication and mediation. Cases include: Davies Middleton & Davies Ltd v Toyo engineering Corporation [1997] 85 BLR 59 [CA]; Lobb Partnershipp Ltd v Aintree Racecourse Company Ltd [2000] BLR 65 [QBD, Comm Ct]; Fastrack Contractors v Morrison [2000] BLR 168 [QBD, TCC]; Rainsford House Ltd (in administrative receivership) v Cadogan Ltd [2001] CILL 1709 [QBD, TCC]; JA Payne Ltd v GAJ Construction Ltd (presently unreported) 16 March 2001; Fence Gate Ltd v NEL Construction Ltd (presently unreported) 27 July 2001.
Career: Called to Bar, October 1991 (called to the Bar of Gibraltar, May 1997). Researcher for 'Keating on Building Contracts' (7th Edition)
Personal: Shrewsbury School (scholar), Worcester College, Oxford (1989 BA Law 2(1)). Born 1968. Resides London. Hobbies: Diving.

HARMAN, Sarah
4 Stone Buildings (Philip Heslop QC) London (020) 7242 5524
Recommended in Company

HARPER, Mark
40 King St Manchester (0161) 832 9082
mharper@40kingstreet.co.uk
Recommended in Chancery
Specialisation: Banking and Finance Litigation; Professional Negligence; Directors Disqualification; Personal and Corporate Insolvency, Contracted Disputes.
Prof. Memberships: Chancery Bar Association; Northern Chancery Bar Association.
Career: Called to the Bar by Lincolns Inn in 1993. Pupillage with existing chambers.
Personal: Arnold Hill Comprehensive School, Nottingham. Downing College, Cambridge. Interested in all sports especially football and cricket. Married to Julie. Became a father for the first time in June 2000.

HARRIS, Russell
Eldon Chambers (Lionel Read QC) London (020) 7583 1355
Recommended in Environment, Planning

HARRISON, Christopher
4 Stone Buildings (Philip Heslop QC) London (020) 7242 5524
Recommended in Chancery

HARRISON, Keith
24A St. John Street (Paul Chambers) Manchester (0161) 833 9628
Recommended in Crime

HARRISON, Michael QC
Park Court Chambers (James Stewart QC & Robert Smith QC) Leeds (0113) 243 3277
Recommended in Crime

HARRISON, Richard
One King's Bench Walk (Anthony Hacking QC) London (020) 7936 1500
rharrison@1kbw.co.uk
Recommended in Family
Specialisation: All areas of family law including matrimonial finance, international child abduction, private and public law children, cohabitees' property disputes. Recent cases of interest include: Mubarak [2001] 1 FLR 698 (judgment summons), Murabak [2001] FLR 673 (piercing the corporate veil in ancillary relief), TB v JB [2001] FLR forthcoming (child abduction), Re X and Y [2001] Fam Law 344 [2001] forthcoming (leave to remove), Re M and J (Abduction: International Judicial Collaboration) [2000] 1 FLR 803 (child abduction), Dawson v Wearmouth [1999] 2 AC 308 (change of name), Re C (Abduction: Grave Risk of Physical & Psychological Harm) [1999] 2 FLR 478.
Prof. Memberships: South Eastern Circuit, Family Law Bar Association, Lawyers for Liberty, Criminal Bar Association.
Career: Called to the Bar 1993.
Personal: Educated at Cranleigh School, Emmanuel College Cambridge, City University. Fluent Spanish, proficient French (degree 1991).

HARRISON, Sally
28 St. John St Manchester (0161) 834 8418
clerk@28stjohnst.co.uk
Recommended in Family
Specialisation: Matrimonial property, specialising in big money cases: Junior in NVN [2001] 1 FLR; children's cases both public and private.
Prof. Memberships: FLBA.
Career: Studied for BSc at university, thereafter undertook Diploma of Law at City University. Following Bar Vocational Course took up pupilage at 40 King Street Chambers. Two years ago joined 28 St John's Street chambers as a member of the large and highly specialised family group.

HARRISON, Stephanie
Two Garden Court (Ian Macdonald QC & Owen Davies QC) London (020) 7353 1633
Recommended in Administrative & Public Law, Immigration

HARROD, Henry
5 Stone Buildings (Henry Harrod) London (020) 7242 6201
Recommended in Chancery
Specialisation: Specialises in all areas of Chancery work.
Prof. Memberships: Chancery Bar Association; Society of Trust and Estate Practitioners. Association of Contentious Trust and Probate Specialists.
Career: Called to the Bar 1963. Tenant at 46 Grainger Street, Newcastle-upon-Tyne 1964-68 before joining 4 Paper Buildings in 1968. Member of present chambers since 1969 and head since 1990. Conveyancing Counsel of the Court 1991. Bencher of Lincoln's Inn 1991. Appointed Recorder 1993.

HARRY, Timothy
9 Old Square (Michael Driscoll QC) London (020) 7405 4682
Recommended in Property Litigation
Specialisation: Property litigation, professional negligence and Chancery work.
Prof. Memberships: PNBA, Chancery Bar Association, Property Bar Association.
Career: Called 1983. Lecturer, Hertford College, Oxford, 1983-88. Called to the Bar, 1983, Hong Kong 1992.
Publications: An editor Hill & Redman's 'Landlord & Tenant'. Contributor to 'Lloyds Professional Negligence Law Reports.
Personal: Educated Monmouth School; MA, BCL (Oxford).

HART, David
1 Crown Office Row (Robert Seabrook QC) London (020) 7797 7500
david.hart@1cor.com
Recommended in Environment
Specialisation: Has conducted a wide range of public and private law environmental litigation, including water (Cambridge Water, Bowden on enforceability of EC Directives, Falmouth on abatement notices), particulate emissions (Coalite and Orimulsion), methane (Loscoe), waste (Castle) and claims against consultants arising out of land decontamination surveys and assessment of methane risks. Is also frequently instructed in professional negligence cases, (particularly medical, surveyors and engineers) contract claims, and arbitrations (construction, engineering and general contract), as well as flood and fire claims.
Prof. Memberships: Member of UKELA and ALBA.
Career: Called 1982.
Publications: Articles on environmental issues in JEL, JPEL and NLJ. Chapter on environmental human rights issues in 'Introduction to Human Rights and Common Law' (2000) and Garner bulletin on same subject.

HART, William
Albion Chambers (Charles Barton QC & Neil Ford QC) Bristol (0117) 927 2144
Recommended in Crime

HARVEY, Colin
St. Paul's Chambers (Nigel Sangster QC) Leeds (0113) 245 5866
Recommended in Crime
Specialisation: Criminal specialist with successful practice for both prosecution and defence. R v Geddes (murder); R v Saunders (deception, prison officer); R v Petrie (fraud); R v Elliott tors (drugs importation).
Prof. Memberships: Criminal Bar Association.
Career: Called to Bar 1975. Founder member of St Pauls Chambers in 1982.
Personal: LLB (Hons) (London External).

HARVEY, Michael QC
Crown Office Chambers (Michael Spencer QC & Christopher Purchas QC) London (020) 7797 8100
harvey@crownofficechambers.com
Recommended in Professional Negligence
Specialisation: Predominantly civil and commercial matters, including but not limited to: commercial and contractual disputes, professional negligence, international arbitration, construction and engineering contracts, insurance and reinsurance law, conflict of laws, sale of goods, carriage of goods, agency, product liability. Sits as arbitrator.
Prof. Memberships: Legal Services Committee of Bar Council 1994-99; COMBAR; LCCLBA; TECBAR.
Career: Called 1966. QC 1982. Recorder 1986. Authorised to sit as a Deputy High Court Judge and Deputy Official Referee. Bencher Gray's Inn 1991. Review Board, Council of Legal Education 1993-94; Speaker at conferences; Joint author of title 'Damages' in Halsbury's Laws of England.
Personal: Born 22 May 1943. Educated at St. John's School, Leatherhead and Christ's College, Cambridge. Married with two children.

HAVERS, Philip QC
1 Crown Office Row (Robert Seabrook QC) London (020) 7797 7500
philip.havers@1cor.com
Recommended in Administrative & Public Law, Clinical Negligence, Environment
Specialisation: Principal areas of practice are public and administrative law, clinical negligence, environmental law and human rights law (including cases at the European Court of Human Rights), health law and breach of confidence. Recent reported cases include Hunter v Canary Wharf (1997) (nuisance), R v Falmouth PHA, exp. SWW (watercourse pollution), Thomas v Brighton Health Authority (1998) (multipliers), Findlay v UK (1996) (fair trial), AG v Blake (2000) (fiduciary duties of a spy), R v Collins, ex parte S (rights of a fetus), Heil v Rankin (test cases on level of general damages). Other important cases include Clapham Railway Disaster Inquiry, Southall Rail Inquiry and Ladbroke Grove Rail Inquiry. R v Hull University, ex parte Page (university law), Benzodiazepine litigation and Spycatcher. Regularly addresses seminars on clinical negligence, human rights, contempt of court and freedom of the press.
Prof. Memberships: South Eastern Circuit, Administrative Law Bar Association, Bar European Group, London Common Law and Commercial Bar Association.
Career: Called to the Bar 1974 and joined current chambers 1975. Recorder 1990-00. Took Silk 1995.
Publications: 'An Introduction to Human Rights and the Common Law', Hart, 2000
Personal: Educated at Eton College 1963-68 and Corpus Christi College, Cambridge 1969-73. Leisure pursuits include tennis, music, gardening, wine and travel. Born 16 June 1950. Lives in London.

HAYES, Josephine
3 New Square (Lord Goodhart QC) London (020) 7405 5577
Recommended in Chancery
Specialisation: Pension schemes; property litigation; general chancery. Particular experience in fraud, breach of fiduciary duty and asset recovery. Reported cases include Bank of Scotland v Wright; Springette v Defoe; Penn v Bristol & West BS; Hambros Bank v BHBT; Miller v Stapleton; Miller v Scorey; Seifert v Pensions Ombudsman; Lloyds Bank v Carrick; Buckley v Hudson Forge Ltd; First National Bank v Walker; Steele v Steele.
Prof. Memberships: Chancery Bar Association; Association of Women Barristers (Chairwoman 1996-98; Vice-president 1998-date); Association of Pension Lawyers.
Career: MA (Oxon), 1st Class Hons in Greats. Called 1980. Alumni Fellow, Yale Law School; LLM (Yale).

HAYWARD SMITH, Rodger QC
One King's Bench Walk (Anthony Hacking QC) London (020) 7936 1500
Recommended in Family
Specialisation: Specialises in family law and criminal law.
Prof. Memberships: South Eastern Circuit, Family Law Bar Association, Criminal Bar Association.
Career: Called to the Bar in 1967 and joined 1 King's Bench Walk in 1968. Appointed Recorder in 1986. Took Silk 1988. Deputy High Court Judge Family Division since 1990. Legal Assessor General Medical Council since 2000.
Publications: Co-writer of Jackson's 'Matrimonial Finance and Taxation' (5th and 6th eds) and Child Law Bulletin in Solicitors' Journal.
Personal: Educated at Brentwood School and St. Edmund Hall, Oxford.

HEATON, David
18 St John Street (Jonathan Foster QC) Manchester (0161) 278 1800
dheaton962815025@cs.com
Recommended in Clinical Negligence, Personal Injury
Specialisation: Clinical negligence. Personal injury.
Prof. Memberships: PIBA, PNBA, NCMLA.

Career: Educated at William Hulme's Grammar School, Manchester and Corpus Christi College, Cambridge. MA (Cantab). Avory Studentship.
Personal: Enjoys walking, reading, music, good food and wine. Married, four children.

HEATON, Frances
Deans Court Chambers (Stephen Grime QC) Manchester (0161) 214 6000
Recommended in Family

HEDWORTH, Toby QC
Trinity Chambers (Toby Hedworth QC) Newcastle upon Tyne (0191) 232 1927
info@trinitychambers.co.uk
Recommended in Crime
Specialisation: Crime, particularly homicide and major professional crime (conspiracies to rob, murder and the importation and distribution of controlled drugs), together with white collar crime. In last year, substantial contested caseload including the successful defence of multiple murder (four deaths); murder of husband by abused wife; three other murders (one major gangland enquiry); gangland attempted murder; historical sex abuse; dentist accused of major fraud on NHS; doctor accused of causing death by dangerous driving and successful prosecution of multimillion pound armed robbery. Appreciates importance of early consultation to assist with case preparation.
Prof. Memberships: CBA; Justice.
Career: Called to the Bar 1975. Pupillage then membership of Trinity Chambers since 1976. Head of chambers since 1999. Assistant Recorder 1991. Recorder 1995. QC 1996.
Personal: Born 1952. Educated at Kings School Tynemouth, Royal Grammar School, Newcastle upon Tyne and St Catherine's College, Cambridge. Married with two daughters. Interests away from the Bar: the Lake District, the built environment and Newcastle United.

HEGARTY, Kevin
St Philip's Chambers (John Randall QC) Birmingham (0121) 246 7000
Recommended in Crime

HEILBRON, Hilary QC
Brick Court Chambers (Christopher Clarke QC) London (020) 7379 3550
heilbron@brickcourt.co.uk
Recommended in Arbitration (International)
Specialisation: General commercial law, including financial services; corporate law; insurance; banking; conflict of laws; shipping; international trade and commerce; e-mail and Internet law; sale of goods; mediation; commercial and international arbitration (including sitting as arbitrator); consumer law including consumer credit; administrative law and some common law including professional negligence and defamation law.
Prof. Memberships: Director of The City Disputes Panel Limited. Member of the Advisory Council of CEDR 1996. Member of Civil Justice Council (1998-).
Career: Called to the Bar 1971. Silk 1987. Bencher of Gray's Inn (July 1995). Senior Counsel Bar of NSW, Australia Nov 1997. Deputy High Court Judge. CEDR accredited mediator.
Personal: MA (Oxon).

HENDERSON, Launcelot QC
5 Stone Buildings (Henry Harrod) London (020) 7242 6201
Recommended in Chancery, Tax
Specialisation: General Chancery work, mainly concentrating on trusts, private client work, pensions, charities, Court of Protection, and all aspects of direct taxation. Recent reported cases: Deeny v Gooda Walker (taxation of damages); IRC v Willoughby and McGuckian v IRC (tax avoidance); Bricom Holdings v IRC (controlled foreign companies); Memec Plc v IRC (double tax treaties); LM Tenancies 1 Plc v IRC (stamp duty and the contingency principle); EMI v Coldicott (taxation of payments in lieu of notice); Garner v Pounds (CGT and options); NMB Holdings v Secretary of State for Social Security (national insurance contributions and the Ramsay principle); Harries v Church Commissioners (ethical investment of church funds); Spooner v BT (interaction of BT and Civil Service pension schemes); numerous other cases appearing for the Inland Revenue at all levels. Has acted for the Commissioner of Estate Duty in the Court of Final Appeal in Hong Kong, and appeared in major international trust litigation in the Cayman Islands.
Prof. Memberships: Chancery Bar Association; Revenue Bar Association; STEP.
Career: Called 1977; standing Junior Counsel to the Inland Revenue (Chancery) 1987-91; standing Junior Counsel to the Inland Revenue 1991-95. Took Silk in 1995. Appointed Deputy High Court Judge 2001.
Personal: Born 1951. Educated at Westminster School and Balliol College, Oxford. Fellow of All Souls College, Oxford, 1974-81 and 1982-89. Married with three young children.

HENDERSON, Roger QC
2 Harcourt Buildings (Roger Henderson QC) London (020) 7583 9020
clerks@harcourt.co.uk
Recommended in Local Government
Specialisation: Specialises in local government, common law, public law, public transport and telecommunications. Work covers professional negligence, product liability, contract, personal injuries, judicial review, parliamentary and finance, especially local government finance. Counsel for British Rail at the Clapham Rail Crash Inquiry, counsel to the Kings Cross Fire Inquiry and counsel for Railtrack at the Southall and Ladbroke Grove Rail Crash Inquiries. Has acted for British Rail, Railtrack, GMC, British Telecom, London Regional Transport, Stock Exchange and many local authorities. Promoted numerous Parliamentary Bills. Promoted London Money Bills for GLC. Appeared for International Stock Exchange at numerous Inquiries. Chaired Accountants' Joint Disciplinary Scheme tribunals. Appeared for ABP at Southampton Harbour Inquiry. Involved in three Lloyds' names' actions. Represented the GMC in the 'Turkish Kidneys for Sale' and Bristol Paediatric Heart Surgery cases. Reported cases include Roylance v General Medical Council 1999, The Times 27 January, Privy Council; R v Brent London Borough Council ex p Awua [1996] AC 55; Canterbury City Council v Colley [1993] AC 401; R v International Stock Exchange of the United Kingdom and the Republic of Ireland Limited ex p Else (1982) Limited [1993] QB 534 (CA); R v London Boroughs Transport Committee ex p Freight Transport Association [1991] 1 WLR 828 (HL); R v Secretary of State for the Environment ex p Hammersmith and Fulham London Borough Council and Others [1991] 1 AC 521; R v Secretary of State for Social Services ex p Association of Metropolitan Authorities [1986] 1 WLR 1; R v Secretary of State for Transport ex p GLC [1986] QB 556; In re Westminster City Council [1986] AC 668; Pickwell v Camden London Borough Council [1983] QB 962; R v London Transport Executive ex p GLC [1983] QB 485; R v Secretary of State for the Environment ex p Hackney London Borough Council [1983] 1 WLR 534; R v Secretary of State for the Environment ex p Hackney London Borough Council [1983] 1 WLR 534; R v Secretary of State for the Environment ex p Brent London Borough Council [1982] QB 593.
Prof. Memberships: Bencher of Inner Temple 1985. Member of St Kitts & Nevis Bar.
Career: Called to the bar in 1964. Joined 2 Harcourt Buildings in 1966. Took silk in 1980. Recorder from 1983, Deputy High Court Judge from 1987. Chairman of Civil Service Arbitration Tribunal 1994-date.
Personal: Educated at Radley College 1956-61. 1st Class Hons in Law at St Catharine's College Cambridge. Positions held include Chairman Council of Governors of London Hospital Medical College, former president of British Academy of Forensic Sciences. Leisure pursuits include fly fishing, gardening, shooting and travel. Born 21 April 1943.

HENDY, John QC
Old Square Chambers (John Hendy QC) London (020) 7269 0300
hendyqc@oldsquarechambers.co.uk
Recommended in Employment, Health & Safety, Personal Injury
Specialisation: Primarily trade union and industrial relations law and has appeared in most of the leading cases over the last 20 years. Also deals with employment law more generally. Extensive practice also in PI and clinical negligence. Standing counsel to NUM, NUJ and POA.
Prof. Memberships: ILS; ELA; ELBA, vice-chair 2001-date; APIL; PIBA; ATLA; CLBA; ABA; SE Circuit; W Circuit; Chair Institute of Employment Rights 1989-date. Visiting Professor of Law, King's College London, 1999-date.
Career: Called 1972 Gray's; director Newham Rights Centre 1973-76; practice 1977-date; Silk 1987; bencher of Grays Inn 1995.
Publications: Co-author of: 'Redgrave's Health and Safety', 'Munkman's Employer's Liability' and 'Personal Injury Practice'. Member of editorial board of 'Encyclopaedia of Employment Law'; 'The Litigator'.
Personal: LLB London (external); LLM (Queens, Belfast).

HENKE, Ruth
Iscoed Chambers (Trefor Davies) Swansea (01792) 652988/9
Recommended in Family

HENRY, Annette
10 King's Bench Walk (Georges M Khayat QC) London (020) 7353 2501
annettehenry@10kbw.co.uk
Recommended in Crime
Specialisation: Regularly appears in substantial criminal cases including drugs, fraud and serious sexual and physical assaults. High profile cases include R. v Whittime the largest joint revenue and Customs & Excise prosecution into the illegal activities of the insolvency profession, which resulted in a landmark decision under the European Convention of Human Rights. Defended in R v Murray, the death of an entire family was responsible for the launch of a campaign to combat 'morning after drinking'. Has consistently been recognised as a highly recommended junior at the London Criminal Bar. Special interest in mental health law and has represented many psychiatrically disordered defendants. A Mental Health Act Commissioner and author of the 'Mental Health Law Referencer'. [Sweet and Maxwell]

HERBERG, Javan
Blackstone Chambers (Presiley Baxendale QC & Charles Flint QC) London (020) 7583 1770
javanherberg@blackstonechambers.com
Recommended in Administrative & Public Law
Specialisation: Specialist in commercial law (in particular financial services and civil fraud), public and administrative law and human rights. Interesting cases include (in commercial field) conducting regulatory proceedings for FSA, SIB (including first cases involving use of s.59 disqualification power), PIA and IMRO (Morgan Grenfell / Peter Young unit trusts affair) and against SFA (SBC Warburg disciplinary proceedings over REC derivatives); Btitish Steel v Customs & Excise [1997] 2 All ER 366 (CA) (restitution of overpaid duties); Brunei v Prince Jefri (acting for Prince Jefri in US$30 bn asset recovery claim). In public law field, R v HEFC ex p Institute of Dental Surgery [1994] 1 WLR 242 (right to reasons); Ming Pao Newspapers v AG of Hong Kong [1996] AC 907, PC (freedom of expression); Tan Te Lam v AG of Hong Kong [1997] AC 97, PC (legality of detention); R v Legal Aid Board ex p Eccleston [1998] 1 WLR 1279 (legal expenses); R v Manchester; Legal Stipendiary Magistrate ex parte Granada Television [2000] 2 WLR 1 (HL) (enforceability of Scottish warrant).

Prof. Memberships: Administrative Law Bar Assn (Hon.Sec), COMBAR.
Career: Called 1992.
Publications: Publications include 'Principles of Public Law' (Cavandish, 2000, 2nd edn, co-author); de Smith Woolf and Jowell, 'Judicial Review of Administrative Action' (assistant editor, 5th ed. supplement, 1998); case notes in 'Public Law' and in 'Judicial Review'.
Personal: Educated at University College School, University College London (LL.B), and Merton College, Oxford (BCL).

HERBERT, Douglas
Ropewalk Chambers (Ian McLaren QC) Nottingham (0115) 947 2581 clerks@ropewalk.co.uk
Recommended in Personal Injury
Specialisation: Personal injury and clinical negligence. Professional negligence. Notable cases include Heer v Tutton and Others [1995] 1 W.L.R 1336 C.A (County Court Order 17 rule 11); Whybro v Seymour [1998] P.I.Q.R 130 C.A. (striking out); McCauley v Vine [1999] 1 W.L.R 1977 C.A (Order 14); Shakoor v Situ [2000] 2 A.E.R. 181 (negligence – practitioner of alternative medicine); Darby v The National Trust [2001] CA (duty of care).
Prof. Memberships: Professional Negligence Bar Association.
Career: Called 1973. Assistant Recorder 1996. Recorder 2000.
Personal: Family, golf and rugby.

HERBERT, Mark QC
5 Stone Buildings (Henry Harrod) London (020) 7242 6201 mherbert@5-stonebuildings.law.co.uk
Recommended in Chancery, Charities, Pensions
Specialisation: Principal area of practice is general chancery work including trusts, capital taxation, taxation of trusts, probate, family provision, charities and offshore trusts. Also handles pensions work, both advisory and litigation. Important cases include Mettoy Pension Trustees v Evans [1990]; Re Christy Hunt Pension Fund [1991]; Fitzwilliam v IRC [1993]. Hamar v Pensions Ombudsman, R v Opra ex p Littlewoods (1997); Edge v Pensions Ombudsman (1999); Espinosa v Burke (1999). Co editor of 'Whiteman on Capital Gains Tax'. Other publications include 'The Drafting and Variation of Wills'.
Prof. Memberships: Chancery Bar Association; Revenue Bar Association; Association of Pension Lawyers.
Career: Called to the Bar 1974. Tenant at 17 Old Buildings 1975-77 before joining Queen Elizabeth Building in 1977. At present chambers since 1991. Took Silk 1995.
Personal: Educated at Lancing College 1962-66 and King's College, London 1967-70. Born 12 November 1948. Lives in London.

HERMAN, Ray
India Buildings Chambers (Ray Herman) Liverpool (0151) 243 6000
Recommended in Crime
Specialisation: Deals with substantial criminal cases for both the defence and prosecution in the court at all levels. This includes the most serious offences, such as murder/manslaughter, rape, serious fraud, drugs offences, robbery and crimes of violence.
Prof. Memberships: Criminal Bar Association.
Career: Called 1972.

HERMER, Richard
Doughty Street Chambers (Geoffrey Robertson QC) London (020) 7404 1313
Recommended in Clinical Negligence

HERSHMAN, David
St Philip's Chambers (John Randall QC) Birmingham (0121) 246 7000 hershman@st-philips.co.uk
Recommended in Family
Specialisation: Family Law. Particular expertise in the law relating to children, international child abduction and adoption. Also criminal cases concerning child abuse and Registered Homes Tribunal work.
Prof. Memberships: Family Law Bar Association, The British Agencies for Adoption and Fostering, the Intercountry Adoption Lawyers' Association and the Association of Lawyers for Children. Public and administrative law concerning children.
Career: Called to the Bar in 1981. Appointed part-time chairman of the Registered Homes Tribunal in 1995. Recorder 2001. Lecturer for the Law Society Children Panel and accredited course provider for the Law Society. Lecturer for Judicial Conferences and Justices Family Panel Training.
Publications: Co-author of 'Children: Law and Practice', contributor to 'Family Court Practice and Child Protection Training and Resource Pack' (National Childrens Bureau).
Personal: Educated at The Kings School Worcester, Kings College London. Married with four daughters. Lives near Worcester.

HESLOP, Martin S QC
2 Hare Court (Stephen Kramer QC) London (020) 7353 5324
Recommended in Crime

HESLOP, Philip QC
4 Stone Buildings (Philip Heslop QC) London (020) 7242 5524
Recommended in Chancery, Company, Financial Services, Insolvency/Corporate Recovery

HIBBERT, William
Gough Square Chambers (Fred Philpott) London (020) 7353 0924 william.hibbert@goughsq.co.uk
Recommended in Consumer Law
Specialisation: Consumer law – in particular consumer credit licensing (particulary Minded to Revoke Notices), advising on credit and loan agreements, defending regulatory prosecutions, and acting in civil litigation. Clients include finance houses, product manufacturers, timeshare companies, food producers and multiple retailers. Other main areas of practice include corporate, commercial, insolvency and fraud matters.
Prof. Memberships: Food Law Group and London Common and Commercial Bar Association.
Career: Called to the Bar 1979.
Personal: Charterhouse and Worcester College, Oxford. Lives in London.

HICKS, Michael
19 Old Buildings (Alastair Wilson QC) London (020) 7405 2001
Recommended in Intellectual Property

HICKS, William QC
Eldon Chambers (Lionel Read QC) London (020) 7583 1355
Recommended in Planning
Specialisation: A wide range of planning and related work. Some particular areas of expertise are retail, highways and transportation, energy, environment and listed buildings.
Prof. Memberships: Planning and Environmental Bar Association, Committee Parliamentary Bar Mess, Administrative Law Bar Association, Committee Joint Oxford Planning Conference.
Career: Magdalene College Cambridge MA (Economics). Called to the Bar 1975. Joined present chambers in 1976. Took silk in 1995.

HIGGS, Brian QC
5 King's Bench Walk (Brian Higgs QC) London (020) 7353 5638
Recommended in Crime

HILDYARD, Robert QC
4 Stone Buildings (Philip Heslop QC) London (020) 7242 5524
Recommended in Chancery, Company, Energy & Natural Resources, Financial Services, Insurance
Specialisation: Principally, company law, financial services, company/commercial litigation and corporate insolvency. Specialist in insurance company transfer schemes. Other specialist work areas include insurance/reinsurance litigation and oil and gas litigation. Recent court cases include Macmillan v BIT (Maxwell litigation/conflicts of laws), NRG Victory (insurance company transfer scheme), AXA Sun Life plc (insurance company orphan state), LDDC v Regalian (restitution), Kurz v Stella Musical (choice of jurisdiction clause), Phillips Petroleum v Enron (take or pay gas sales agreement) Market Wizard Systems (UK) Ltd (public interest winding up), Hall v Bank of England (misfeasance in public office; rule in Foss v Harbottle) Charter Re ('pay to be paid' reinsurance clause).
Prof. Memberships: Chancery Bar Association, Insolvency Lawyers' Association, Commercial Bar Association (COMBAR).
Career: Called to the Bar in 1977, Junior Counsel to the Crown (Chancery) 1992-94, appointed Queen's Counsel 1994. Called to the Bar of Bermuda, Cayman Islands, Turks, Caicos Islands, and Hong Kong for specific cases.
Publications: Contributor: Butterworth's 'Encyclopaedia of Forms and Precedents' (company volume); Tolley's 'Company Law'.
Personal: Educated at Eton College; Christ Church Oxford. Languages: Spanish.

HILL, Mark
Pump Court Chambers (Christopher Harvey Clark QC) London (020) 7363 0711 mh@3pumpcourt.com
Recommended in Church
Specialisation: Ecclesiastical law, personal injury, professional and clinical negligence. Leading cases include NEM v Jones [1990] 1 AC 24 (HL); Pacific Associates v Baxter [1990] 1 QB 993 (CA); Tribe v Tribe [1996] Ch 107 (CA); Re St Peter's Oundle [1997] 4 Ecc LJ 163; Re Durrington Cemetery [2001] Fam 33.
Prof. Memberships: PNBA; PIBA; Ecclesiastical Law Society.
Career: Chancellor of the Diocese of Chichester [since 1999]; Deputy Chancellor of the Diocese of Winchester [since 1994]; Case Notes Editor, Ecclesiastical Law Journal [since 1996]; Visiting Fellow, Emmanuel College, Cambridge [1998]. Research Fellow, Centre for Law of Religion, Cardiff [1999-01]; Member of Legal Advisory Commission (General Synod).
Publications: 'English Canon Law' (1998); 'Ecclesiastical Law' (2nd edn, 2001); 'Clergy Discipline in Anglican and Roman Catholic Canon Law' (2001).

HILL, Michael QC
23 Essex Street (Michael Lawson QC) London (020) 7413 0353 michaelhill@23essexstreet.co.uk
Recommended in Crime, Fraud
Specialisation: Principal areas of practice are commercial fraud, international crime, homicide and professional crime.
Prof. Memberships: Criminal Bar Association (Chairman 1982-86); International Society for the Reform of Criminal Law; President (1999-date), Board of Directors (1988-date); Chairman, Management Committee (1992-95); Inns of Court Advocacy Training Committee (Chairman, 1994-00); Bar Mutual Indemnity Fund Ltd (Director 1989-01; Chairman, Investment Committee 1992-01).
Career: Treasury Counsel (Inner London Sessions/Crown Court), 1969-74; Counsel Central Criminal Court 1974-79; Queen's Counsel 1979; Queen's Counsel (NSW) 1991; Recorder 1977-97; called, Gray's Inn, 1958; Bencher, Gray's Inn, 1986.

HILL, Thomas

4-5 Gray's Inn Square (Elizabeth Appleby QC & David Mole QC) London (020) 7404 5252 clerks@4-5graysinnsquare.co.uk

Recommended in Environment, Planning

Specialisation: Principal area of practice is planning and environmental law, in particular public inquiry work involving detailed investigation of environmental and other impacts. Recent instructions have involved proposals for major retail, housing and business development, works to listed buildings, minerals, waste and airport-related development (including successfully promoting Manchester Airport's Second Runway). Also judicial review and advisory work involving the interpretation and application of the Town and Country Planning Act 1990, the Environmental Protection Act 1990 and subordinate legislation; prosecutions under EPA. Has also appeared in parliament for promoters of private legislation with environmental implications.

Prof. Memberships: Planning and Environmental Bar Association (committee member 1990-95); Administrative Law Bar Association.

Career: Called to the Bar 1988.

HILL, Timothy

4 Field Court (Steven Gee QC) London (020) 7440 6900 tim.hill@4fieldcourt.com

Recommended in Shipping

Specialisation: Shipping (charter parties and bills of lading), admiralty, international trade, arbitration (practice and procedure), banking, insurance, commercial property.

Prof. Memberships: COMBAR, Admirality Bar.

Career: 'The Goodpal' [2001] 1 Lloyds Rep 638; The 'Seaflower' [2000] 2 Lloyds Rep 37 (Court of Appeal, unreported as yet); The 'Amber' (unreported as yet); The 'Sea Empress' (unreported as yet); The 'Sea Mass' [1999] 2 Lloyds Rep 281 (Rix J, appeal pending); Bawjem v MC Fabrications ('Hull No. 1029A') 1 All ER (Comm) 377 (CA).

Publications: Contributing to various insurance and law publications such as the 'International Insurance Law Review'.

HILLIARD, Lexa

3-4 South Square (Michael Crystal QC & Lord Alexander of Weedon QC) London (020) 7696 9900 clerks@southsquare.com

Recommended in Insolvency/Corporate Recovery

Specialisation: Insolvency, civil fraud, professional negligence, banking, human rights.

Prof. Memberships: Bar member of Insolvency Law Sub-Committee of Law Society. CEDR Accredited Mediator.

Career: Lecturer in Law, Durham University 1984-87. Lloyds Bank Legal Department 1988. 3-4 South Square 1990 to date.

Publications: Contributor to 'Totty & Moss on Insolvency' (Sweet & Maxwell).

HILLIARD, Nicholas

6 King's Bench Walk (Roy Amlot QC) London (020) 7583 0410

Recommended in Crime

Specialisation: Criminal law.

Career: Senior Treasury Counsel at the Central Criminal Court. Contributing editor to 'Archbold'.

HILLIER, Andrew

11 King's Bench Walk Chambers (Eldred Tabachnik QC & James Goudie QC) London (020) 7632 8500

Recommended in Employment

Specialisation: Principal area of practice is employment law including employer/employee disputes (wrongful/unfair dismissal); protection of confidential information; non-solicitation of customers; board-room disputes; partnership disputes; strikes and collective disputes; trade union law and race and sex discrimination. Particular emphasis on local government and health service law, including employment and public law issues. Other main areas of work are mental health law, including psychiatric damage and medical negligence cases and disciplinary tribunals.

HILLIER, Nicolas

9 Gough Square (John Foy QC) London (020) 7832 0500

Recommended in Personal Injury

Specialisation: Principal areas of practice are personal injury and professional (clinical and legal) negligence litigation. Personal injury work includes both accident claims and occupational disease, particularly asbestos related diseases and noise induced deafness.

Prof. Memberships: Personal Injury Bar Association; Association of Personal Injury Lawyers.

Career: Called to the Bar in 1982. Joined present Chambers in 1983.

Personal: LL.B(Hons) Southampton University, 1977. Leisure pursuits: a young and energetic family. Born 2nd April 1956. Lives in London.

HIMSWORTH, Emma

One Essex Court (Lord Grabiner QC) London (020) 7583 2000

Recommended in Intellectual Property

Specialisation: All aspects of intellectual property law.

Prof. Memberships: The Intellectual Property Lawyers Organisation, The Intellectual Property Bar Association, The Chancery Bar Association and The Commercial Bar Association.

Career: Called 1993.

Personal: BSc in Biological Sciences with Honours in Biochemistry, Dip Law (City), Dip EC Law (Kings).

HINCHLIFF, Benjamin

1 Brick Court (Richard Rampton QC) London (020) 7353 8845

Recommended in Defamation

Specialisation: Defamation, contempt of court, reporting restrictions and media-related law generally.

Career: Called to the Bar 1992.

Personal: Educated Radley College and St John's College Oxford. Lives in London and Yorkshire.

HINCHLIFFE, Nicholas QC

9 St. John Street (John Hand QC) Manchester (0161) 955 9000 clerks@9stjohnstreet.co.uk

Recommended in Personal Injury

Specialisation: Personal injury, industrial disease, catastrophe injury claims, medical negligence.

Prof. Memberships: PIBA. PNBA.

Career: LLB. Manchester, Middle Temple 1980. Assistant Recorder 1998. QC 1999.

Personal: Championship rifle shooting.

HINKS, Frank QC

Serle Court (Lord Neill of Bladen QC) London (020) 7242 6105 clerks@serlecourt.co.uk

Recommended in Chancery, Partnership

Specialisation: Domestic and international trusts including expert evidence in relation to offshore jurisdictions: Re Ojjeh Trusts [1993] (Cayman Islands); Re Hampstead Trusts [1995] (Cayman Islands); Re 18 Aug. 1995 trust [1995] (Jersey); Re 1995 and 1996 Trusts [1998] Washington State; Wight v Olswang [1999] (trustee exemption clauses); Flemmer v HRO [2000] Colorado. Partnership law: Kerr v Morris [1987]. Real property including landlord and tenant and commons: Mid-Glamorgan CC v Ogwr BC [1995] (commons). Dugan – Chapman v Grosvenor Estate Belgravia [1997] (leasehold enfranchisement), National Trust v Ashbrook [1997] (commons). Inspector and counsel in town and village green inquiries. Chancery and commercial litigation: Finers v Miro [1991] (constructive trust); BCCI v Gokal (constructive trust/undue influence); Azaz v Self-realisation Healing Centre (undue influence). Professional negligence and regulation.

Prof. Memberships: Chancery Bar Association, Association of Contentious Trust and Probate Specialists, Association of Partnership Practitioners, Property Bar Association.

Career: Called to Bar in 1973. Joined present chambers in 1974.

Personal: Educated at Bromley Grammar School 1961-67; St Catherine's College,Oxford 1968-72. BA 1st Class Hons; BCL 1st Class Hons.

HIORNS, Roger

9 Gough Square (John Foy QC) London (020) 7832 0500 rhiorns@9goughsq.co.uk

Recommended in Personal Injury

Specialisation: Occupational diseases, particularly work related upper limb disorders. Appeared in Mountenay v Bernard Matthews and Alexander v Midland Bank.

Prof. Memberships: APIL; PIBA.

Career: Has practised for 18 years in all areas of personal injury litigation since completing pupillage in chambers.

Personal: Leisure interests: young family rarely provides time for anything else but keen football supporter.

HIRST, Jonathan QC

Brick Court Chambers (Christopher Clarke QC) London (020) 7379 3550 hirst@brickcourt.co.uk

Recommended in Commercial (Litigation), Media & Entertainment

Specialisation: General commercial law, including shipping, insurance, re-insurance, banking and professional negligence and entertainment. Recent important cases: Heaton v AXA [2001] Ch 173; Groupama Navigation et Transports v Catatumbo CA Seguros (CA) [2001] Lloyd's Rep IR 141; Credit Lyonnais Bank Nederland v ECGD [1999] 1 Lloyd's Reps 563 (HL); JH Rayner v Cafenorte SA Importadara e Exportara SA [1999] 2 Lloyd's Reps 750; Brown v GIO Insurance Ltd (CA) [1998] Lloyd's Reps IR 201; Axa Reinsurance (UK) v Field (HL), [1996] 2 Lloyd's Reps 233; Don King Partnership Inc v Frank Warren; Mother Berta Music [Phil Spector] v Bourne Music Ltd.

Prof. Memberships: QC 1990, Recorder 1997; chairman of the Bar of England and Wales 2000.

Career: Called to Bar 1975, Inner Temple, Bencher 1994.

Publications: Contributor, 'Paget on Banking' (11th edn), chapter on Money Laundering.

Personal: Born 2 July 1953, London. Educated at Eton College and Trinity College, Cambridge (MA Law).

HITCHCOCK, Richard G

35 Essex Street (Christopher Wilson-Smith QC) London (020) 7353 6381

Recommended in Pensions

Specialisation: Specialises in occupational pension schemes (particularly advising on internal trust matters including questions of contruction, scheme amendment and the use of fiduciary powers, and in all aspects of litigation in and around pension schemes, their members, employers, trustees, insurers and advisers, both before the Courts and the Pensions Ombudsman); and employment law (particularly advising on compliance issues deriving from UK and European law, both contentious and non-contentious cases concerning the application of TUPE, actions for wrongful and unfair dismissal, race and sex discrimination and share option schemes. Cases include: McDonald v Horn, CA [1995] (pre-emptive cost orders); Century Life v Christie, ChD [1996] (Administration of multiple schemes with insolvent employer/trustee); Hillsdown Holdings plc v Pensions Ombudsman, ChD [1996] (legality of payment of surplus to employer; Franklin v Sedgwick Noble Lowndes, ChD [1999] (claims against scheme actuaries and administrators); Legal & General v Pensions Ombudsman, ChD [1999] (appeal against and application for judicial review of Ombudsman's preliminary determination.); Lansing Linde v Alber and others, ChD [1999] (rectification of

pension scheme deeds); Norris and 131 others v Brown & Root Ltd. [1999] (outsourcing, TUPE, collective agreements: group action claiming breach of contract, unfair and wrongful dismissal). AMP v Barker and others, ChD [2000] (rectification; application of rule in Hastings-Bass); Stevens and others v Bell and others, ChD [2001] (the British Airways case; construction of powers and an in pension scheme deed; pre-emphasis court order). Has spoken at many conferences and seminars.
Prof. Memberships: Chancery Bar Association, Association of Pensions Lawyers, Employment Lawyers Association, Western Circuit.
Career: Called to the Bar in 1989 and joined chambers at 35 Essex Street in 1990.
Personal: Educated at King Edward's School, Birmingham (1977-84) and Magdalen College Oxford (1985-88). Interests include wine (tasting and consulting), France and Italy, modern European and American painting, theatre and scuba diving.

HITCHMOUGH, Andrew
Pump Court Tax Chambers London (020) 7414 8080
Recommended in Tax

HOBBS, Geoffrey QC
One Essex Court (Lord Grabiner QC) London (020) 7583 2000
Recommended in Information Technology, Intellectual Property

HOBSON, John QC
4-5 Gray's Inn Square (Elizabeth Appleby QC & David Mole QC) London (020) 74045252
Recommended in Local Government, Planning
Specialisation: Public law, local government, planning and environmental law.
Prof. Memberships: Admininstrative Law Bar Association; Planning and Environmental Bar Association.
Career: Former Solicitor, called to Bar 1980. 1995-96 Specialist Adviser to the Northern Ireland Affairs Committee of the House of Commons for its enquiry into the planning system in Northern Ireland. 1992-00: Supplementary Panel of Treasury Counsel. 1997-00: Standing Counsel to the Rent Assessment Panel. Assistant Recorder 1999. Queen's Counsel 2000. Recorder 2000.
Personal: LLM (St John's College, Cambridge).

HOCHBERG, Daniel
9 Old Square (Michael Driscoll QC) London (020) 7405 4682
Recommended in Chancery
Specialisation: "Commercial Chancery" and a wide range of general chancery litigation including offshore trust litigation, real property, business agreements, professional negligence, succession, securities and loans, insolvency and landlord and tenant. Cases include West v Lazards (Jersey breach of trust), Blampied v Ram (Jersey trust; disclosure), Midland Bank v Federated Pension Services (breach of trust and exemption clauses), Co-Operative v Tesco (restrictive covenants), Hammersmith & Fulham v Tops Shop Centre (relief from forfeiture), Wates v Citygate Properties (section 25 notice); Greenhaven Motors Ltd (insolvency); Prestwich v Royal Bank of Canada (Jersey) (offshore trusts, tax indemnities), Corbett v Bond Pearce (solicitors negligence), Abacus (CI) Ltd v Al-Sabah (offshore trusts, fraud).
Prof. Memberships: Chancery Bar Association; Association of Contentious Trust and Probate Specialists; Property Bar Association.

HOCHHAUSER, Andrew QC
Essex Court Chambers (Gordon Pollock QC) London (020) 7813 8000
Recommended in Commercial (Litigation), Employment
Specialisation: Areas of practice include arbitration, banking, breach of contract, company law, commercial fraud, entertainment cases, employment, partnership disputes, professional negligence, takeovers, mergers and share sale disputes.
Prof. Memberships: Fellow of the Chartered Institute of Arbitrators; member of Gibraltan Bar.
Career: University of Bristol (LLB), University of London (LLM). Called to the English Bar 1977. Harmsworth Scholar of Middle Temple. Queen's Counsel 1997.
Personal: Born 1955.

HOCKTON, Andrew
6 Pump Court London (020) 7583 6013
Recommended in Clinical Negligence

HODGE, David QC
9 Old Square (Michael Driscoll QC) London (020) 7405 4682
Recommended in Professional Negligence, Property Litigation
Specialisation: Principal areas of practice are general Chancery and property litigation and related professional negligence, particularly solicitors, barristers and valuers. Notable reported cases include Graham v Philcox [1984] (easements); TCB v Gray [1986-88] (guarantees); Sharma v Knight [1986] (landlord and tenant); Bank of Baroda v Shah [1988] (undue influence); Sen v Headley [1991] (equity); Mortgage Corporation v Nationwide Credit [1994] (registered land); Ridehalgh v Horsefield [1994] (wasted costs); Allied Maples v *Simmons & Simmons* [1995] (professional negligence); Garston v Scottish Widows [1996-98] (landlord and tenant); Railtrack v Gojra [1998] (landlord and tenant); Lemmerbell v Britannia LAS Direct [1998] (landlord and tenant); Bristol & West v Bhadresa [1999] (costs); Shirley v Caswell [2000] (professional negligence).
Prof. Memberships: Chancery Bar Association. Professional Negligence Bar Association. Property Bar Association.
Career: Called to bar in 1979. Joined 9 Old Square in 1980. QC 1997. Assistant Recorder 1998. Recorder 2000. Bencher Lincoln's Inn 2000.
Publications: Contributed chapter on Chancery Matters to the 4th and 5th editions of 'The Law and Practice of Compromise' by David Foskett QC. Author of 'Secret Trusts: The Fraud Theory Revisited' (1980) Conveyancer.
Personal: Born 1956. Educated at University College, Oxford 1974-78 (BA, BCL). Chairman, Lincoln's Inn Bar Representation Committee 1997-98.

HODGSON, Margaret
St. Ive's Chambers (Julia Macur QC) Birmingham 0121 236 0863 stives.chambers@btinternet.com
Recommended in Family
Specialisation: Private matrimonial: residence/contact; financial ancillary relief; adoption. Public family law: child care; freeing; adoption. Representation of parents, local authorities and guardians ad litem. Cases: G and others (minors) and R (A minor) ex parte, R v Birmingham Juvenile Court [1989] CA 2 FLR 454. Re P (Minors) (Breakdown of Adoption Placement) F.D. (1996) 3 FCR 657.
Prof. Memberships: Family Law Bar Association.
Career: Warwick University LL.B. (Hons). Pupil master.

HOFMEYR, Stephen QC
7 King's Bench Walk (Jeremy Cooke QC) London (020) 7910 8300
Recommended in Shipping
Specialisation: Practice encompasses insurance and reinsurance (both marine and non-marine) and shipping and maritime law. Most recent cases include Petrotrade Inc. v Smith (Port agency dispute); Shell UK Ltd. v CLM Engineering (Marine Insurance); the Metro litigation (oil fraud); Raiffeisen Zentralbank Osterreich AG and others v Crosseas Shipping and Others (Bank guarantee); Royal Boskalis v Mountain; Manifest Shipping v Uni-Polaris Insurance (the 'Starsea'), (both marine insurance); Glencore v Bank of China (letters of credit); L'Alsacienne v Unistorebrand (reinsurance); Brown v KMR (Lloyd's litigation). Other specialisations include all aspects of commercial law (arbitration, aviation, banking, oil and gas and professional negligence). His combination of legal and accounting qualifications makes him particularly suited to these areas of the law.
Prof. Memberships: COMBAR.
Career: A Rhodes Scholar from Cape Town, commenced practice at the Bar in 1987, having previously practised as an attorney and conveyancer in South Africa. Also an advocate of the Supreme Court of South Africa.
Personal: Educated at Diocesan College, Rondebosch, Cape Town, University of Cape Town (B. Com 1974-76) and University College, Oxford (MA, Jurisprudence, 1979-81). Leisure pursuits include walking, birdwatching, tennis and skiing. Born 10th February 1956. Lives in Guildford.

HOGGETT, John QC
40 King St Manchester (0161) 832 9082
Recommended in Planning

HOLGATE, David QC
4 Breams Buildings (Christopher Lockhart-Mummery QC) London (020) 7353 5835 clerks@4breams.co.uk
Recommended in Environment, Local Government, Planning
Specialisation: Judicial review, planning, compulsory purchase, rating, local government, environment law and property law. Reported cases covering a wide field include Bushell v Secretary of State, Shimizu v Westminster City Council, Coventry and Solihull Waste Disposal Co v Russell, Surrey Free Inns v Gosport BC, Regina v Hillingdon London Borough ex parte London Regional Transport, R v Secretary of State for Social Services ex p. AMA, R v Somerset CC ex p. Fewings, and Chesterfield Properties v Secretary of State, and, in the Lands Tribunal, Glasshouse Properties v DTp and Fennessy v London City Airport. Has appeared for government bodies, local authorities, developers and local objectors in a broad range of public inquiries including Sizewell B, Canvey Island, Piper Alpha, and Point of Ayr Gas Terminal.
Prof. Memberships: PEBA and ALBA.
Career: Called to Bar in 1978. Formerly a member of the panel of Junior Counsel to the Crown (1986-97) and Junior Counsel to the Inland Revenue in Rating and Valuation matters (1990-97). Queen's Counsel (1997). Called to the Hong Kong Bar (2000) and appeared in the Court of Final Appeal (2001).
Personal: Graduated in Law from Exeter College, Oxford.

HOLLAND, Charles
Trinity Chambers (Toby Hedworth QC) Newcastle upon Tyne (0191) 232 1927 info@trinitychambers.co.uk
Recommended in Licensing
Specialisation: Commercial and licensing. Commercial work includes contracts, company and partnership, landlord and tenant, and professional negligence. Liquor, gaming, public entertainment and taxi licencing matters, advising and representing applicants and objectors at all levels of tribunal.
Prof. Memberships: North Eastern Circuit, Association of Licensing Practitioners.
Career: Called to the Bar in 1994. Practised at Trinity Chambers since 1996. Civil representative, North Eastern Bar Press Office, Newcastle Bar 1999-. Junior Counsel to the Crown (Provincial Panel) 2000-.
Personal: Born in North Yorkshire in 1969. Educated Oundle School, University of Nottingham (LL.B. Law).

HOLLAND, Katharine
9 Old Square (Michael Driscoll QC) London (020) 7405 4682
Recommended in Property Litigation
Specialisation: All aspects of property litigation, including commercial and residential property disputes, surveyors' and solicitors' professional negligence, mortgages, landlord and tenant, leasehold enfranchisement, conveyancing, easements, restrictive covenants, property rights, insolvency and commercial contracts. Reported cases include Wentworth v Wiltshire (highways), Mill-

man v Ellis (easements), Charville v Unipart Group (forfeiture/surrender) Titanic Investments v *Macfarlanes* (solicitors' negligence) Gregory v *Shepherds* (solicitors' negligence) Kaiser v Jones (rectification), Lloyds Bank v *Bond Pearce* (solicitors' negligence), Lloyds Bank v *Parker Bullen* (solicitors' negligence), Carroll v Manek and Bank of India (mortgages/adverse possession), Law Society v Southall (gifts and transactions defrauding creditors).
Prof. Memberships: Chancery Bar Association and Professional Negligence Bar Association.
Career: Called to the Bar in 1989 and joined 9 Old Square in 1990.
Personal: Educated at Lady Manners School, Bakewell and Hertford College, Oxford (BA, BCL).

HOLLANDER, Charles QC
Brick Court Chambers (Christopher Clarke QC) London (020) 7379 3550
Recommended in Commercial (Litigation), Sport

HOLLINGTON, Robin QC
New Square Chambers (John Mowbray QC & Eben Hamilton QC) London (020) 7419 8000
Recommended in Company, Insolvency/Corporate Recovery

HOLROYDE, Tim QC
Exchange Chambers (David Turner QC & Bill Braithwaite QC & Henry Globe QC) Liverpool (0151) 236 7747
Recommended in Crime
Specialisation: Crime. Personal injuries.
Prof. Memberships: Criminal Bar Association. Personal Injuries Bar Association.
Career: Called 1977. QC 1996. Recorder 1997. Educated Bristol GS; Wadham College, Oxford.

HOLWILL, Derek
4 Paper Buildings (Jean Ritchie QC) London (020) 7353 3366
Recommended in Professional Negligence
Specialisation: Principal area of practice is professional negligence including clinical negligence cases. Acts both for defendant insurance companies, Solicitors Indemnity Fund and Health Authorities, and for plaintiffs including mortgage lendors. Also handles commercial litigation, insurance litigation and general common law work, including personal injury cases. Reported cases include Landall v Dennis Faulkner and Alsop; Saddington v Colleys Professional Services; Halifax Plc v Gould & Swayne and others; TSB Plc v Robert Irving and Burns; John A Pike v Independant Insurance Co; Estill v Lowling Swift & Kitchen.
Prof. Memberships: Professional Negligence Bar Association.
Career: Called to the Bar 1982.
Personal: Leisure pursuits include Lindy Hop, scuba diving and travel.

HOPKINS, Adrian
3 Serjeants' Inn (Robert Francis QC & John Grace QC) London (020) 7427 5000
Recommended in Clinical Negligence
Specialisation: Deals with all aspects of medical law, including medical negligence, professional ethics and discipline. Recent cases include Re F (A mental patient – sterilisation); Re C (refusal of medical treatment), Re G and Re S (PVS cases) and Ratcliffe v Plymouth & Torbay Health Authority (res ipsa).
Prof. Memberships: Western Circuit, Professional Negligence Bar Association.
Career: Called to the Bar and joined 3 Serjeants' Inn in 1984. Appointed to supplementary panel of Treasury Counsel, Common Law, in 1995. Appointed to the Attorney General's London B Panel for The Crown's Civil Litigation, in 1999. Contributing editor to Lloyd's 'Medical Law Reports' since 1999.
Personal: Educated at Warwick School and St. Peter's College, Oxford. Leisure interests include travel. Born 16 May 1961. Lives in London.

HOPKINS, Philippa
Essex Court Chambers (Gordon Pollock QC) London (020) 7813 8000
clerksroom@essexcourt-chambers.co.uk
Recommended in Shipping
Specialisation: Commercial practice in line with chambers profile. In particular: aviation; banking; carriage of goods; commercial arbitration; commercial shipping (dry work); commodity and international arbitration; finance of international trade; general commercial and contract (including sale of goods); insurance and reinsurance; international trade; professional negligence; public and private international law.
Career: BA, BCL, Merton College, Oxford. Called to the Bar in 1994.
Personal: Born 1971.

HOPKINS, Stephen QC
Temple Chambers (David J.M. Aubrey QC) Cardiff (029) 2039 7364
Recommended in Crime

HORLOCK, Timothy QC
9 St. John Street (John Hand QC) Manchester (0161) 955 9000
clerks@9stjohnstreet. Co uk
Recommended in Health & Safety, Personal Injury
Specialisation: Personal injury, industrial disease, medical negligence.
Prof. Memberships: PIBA, PNBA, APIL.
Career: Called 1981, Silk 1997. Manchester Grammar School and St John's College, Cambridge. Recorder 1997.
Personal: Football, tennis, cricket. Three sons.

HORNE, Michael
3 Serjeants' Inn (Robert Francis QC & John Grace QC) London (020) 7427 5000
Recommended in Clinical Negligence

HOROWITZ, Michael QC
1 Mitre Court Buildings (Bruce Blair QC) London (020) 7797 7070
horowitz@lmcb.com
Recommended in Family
Specialisation: Family law, including ancillary relief, childcare and child abduction. Contributing Editor Rayden & Jackson on Divorce 17th edition and Butterworths Bulletin 'Human Rights Act 1998 and Family Law'. Essential Family Practice 2001.
Prof. Memberships: Director Bar Mutual Indemnity Fund Ltd.
Personal: Married with one daughter. Lives in London.

HORROCKS, Peter
One Garden Court Family Law Chambers (Eleanor F. Platt QC & Alison Ball QC) London (020) 7797 7900
p.horrocks@onegardencourt.co.uk
Recommended in Family
Specialisation: Principal area of practice is child law, both public and private, including disputes as to residence and contact, care proceedings, wardship, adoption and abduction cases under the Hague and European Conventions. Frequently advises and represents local authorities and children's guardians as well as private clients. Other areas of work include child-related criminal cases, probate, boundaries and easements.
Prof. Memberships: Family Law Bar Association.
Career: Called to the Bar in 1977. Joined present chambers in 1996.
Personal: Educated at Winchester 1968-72; Trinity Hall, Cambridge 1973-76; College of Law 1976-77. Leisure pursuits include real tennis, cricket and opera. Born 31 January 1955. Lives in Surrey.

HORTON, Mark
Colleton Chambers (Martin Meeke QC) Exeter (01392) 274898
Recommended in Family
Specialisation: Public and private law childcare and ancillary relief.
Prof. Memberships: Family Law Bar Association.
Career: Family specialist since 1990.

HORTON, Mark
St John's Chambers (Christopher Sharp QC) Bristol 0117 910 0700
crime@stjohnschambers.co.uk
Recommended in Crime
Specialisation: A balanced practice involving defence and prosecution (principally homicide, commercial fraud, tax and VAT evasion, importation and supply of drugs and car ringing). Has been involved in a number of high profile cases over the past few years.
Prof. Memberships: Criminal Bar Association.
Career: Called to the Bar in 1976 joining St John's Chambers in Bristol in 1983. Appointed a recorder in 1999.

HORTON, Matthew QC
2 Mitre Court Buildings (Michael FitzGerald QC) London (020) 7583 1380
Recommended in Planning

HORWELL, Richard
Hollis Whiteman Chambers (QEB) (Julian Bevan QC & Peter Whiteman QC) London (020) 7583 5766
Recommended in Crime

HOSKINS, Mark
Brick Court Chambers (Christopher Clarke QC) London (020) 7379 3550
hoskins@brickcourt.co.uk
Recommended in Competition/Anti-trust, Sport
Specialisation: Principal areas of practice are EC law, competition law, judicial review, human rights and sports. Has acted in over 40 cases before ECJ/CFI, including Case C-321/95P Greenpeace [1998] ECR I-1651, Case T-85/98 Federation Internationale de l'Automobile, order of 6.12.99, Case C-306/98 Monsanto judgment of 3.5.01, Case C-37/98 First Corporate Shipping The Times 16.11.00. Cases before the domestic courts include ex parte Fayed [2001] Imm AR 134 and ex parte Camelot The Times 12.10.00. Has represented both OFT and private clients in competition proceedings.
Prof. Memberships: Bar European Group, COMBAR.
Career: Called in 1991. Legal Secretary, European Court of Justice, 1994-95. Member of B Panel to the Crown.
Publications: 'Remedies in EC Law' (2nd ed, Sweet & Maxwell).

HOWARD, Charles QC
One King's Bench Walk (Anthony Hacking QC) London (020) 7936 1500
Recommended in Family
Specialisation: Family law. Not only conventional areas but also related matters including Inheritance Act and Probate disputes, constructive trust issues, family-oriented judicial review and solicitor's negligence in relation to family work.
Prof. Memberships: FLBA.
Career: Called to the Bar in 1975. In full-time practice since 1976. QC 1999.
Publications: Wildblood and Eaton 'Encyclopaedia of Family Provision in Family Matters' (contributor); 'Ancillary Relief Applications and Insolvency' (Sweet and Maxwell Practical Research Papers); Speaker at 1999 Expert Witness Institute conference on 'Experts in the New Legal World' which was subsequently published as a booklet for the institute.
Personal: Education: St John's College, Cambridge 1969-72 and St Antony's College, Oxford 1972-73.

HOWARD, M.N. QC
4 Essex Court (Nigel Teare QC) London (020) 7653 5653
mnh@4sx.co.uk
Recommended in Arbitration (International), Shipping
Specialisation: Principal areas of practice are international commercial and shipping law, including insurance,

international trade and sale of goods. Extensive experience of arbitrations both as Counsel and as arbitrator in many international arbitrations connected with international trade, shipping or insurance. Acts for shipowners, charterers, insurers, P&I clubs and salvage companies.
Prof. Memberships: COMBAR, London Common Law and Commercial Bar Association.
Career: Called to the Bar Gray's Inn 1971 (Bencher 1995). Tenant at Queen Elizabeth Building 1972-89. Took Silk 1986. Member of the Panel of Salvage Arbitrators appointed by the Committee of Lloyd's since 1989. Joined 4 Essex Court in 1990. Appointed Recorder 1993. Leader of the Admiralty Bar 2000.
Publications: General editor, 'Phipson on Evidence' (15th Ed 2000), Contributor of 'Frustration and Shipping Law' in 'Frustration and Force Majeure' (ed McKendrick, 2nd edn 1995), 'Foreign Currency Judgments in Contract Claims' in 'Consensus Ad Idem: Essays for Guenter Treitel' (ed Rose, 1996) Halsbury, Laws of England, title, 'Damages' and author of articles in legal periodicals.
Personal: Educated at Clifton College, 1960-64 and Magdalen College, Oxford 1965-70 (MA BCL). Leisure pursuits include books, music and sport. Born 10th June 1947. Lives in London. Other: Visiting Professor of Law, Essex University 1987-92, Visiting Professor of Maritime Law, University College, London 1996-99. Member, Editorial Board, Lloyd's Maritime Commercial Law Quarterly.

HOWARD, Mark QC

Brick Court Chambers (Christopher Clarke QC) London (020) 7379 3550
howard@brickcourt.co.uk

Recommended in Banking, Commercial (Litigation), Energy & Natural Resources, Insurance, Professional Negligence

Specialisation: All areas of commercial law, particularly major contract disputes, City disputes and takeovers, insurance and reinsurance, banking, energy oil and gas, professional negligence, commercial fraud, international disciplinary arbitration, DTI and similar investigations.
Prof. Memberships: Combar, LCLCBA.
Career: Called to Bar in 1980, took Silk in 1996. Recent important cases in which involved include Fyffes Group v Templeman; R v Secretary of State for Department of Health ex parte Source Informatics; Messier Dowty v Sabena; Wurttembergische; Camdex v Bank of Zambia; Banco Santander v Banque Paribas; CATS v TGTL; Sphere Drake v Orion; Deepak v ICI; East European Shipping (Market wide X/L reinsurance dispute); WSTC v Coopers & Lybrand; Axa v Field; CU v Mander; Henderson v Merrett and Ernst & Whinney; Denny v Walker, Willis Corroon and others; CNW v Girozentrale; Kuwait Airways Corporation v Kuwait Insurance Company; B&C v Samuel Montagu v BZW; Sudwestdeutsche Landesbank v Bank of Tokyo; Jones v Sherwood; AMF v Hashim; Channel Tunnel Group v Balfour Beatty. He has advised and acted for various parties in relation to a number of DTI and similar inquiries. Currently retained for auditors in relation to Barings litigation, for brokers in relation to p.a. litigation, for insurers/reinsurers in relation to film finance litigation.
Personal: Born 1st April 1958. Educated at University of London – QMC and LSE (LL.B, 1978; LL.M,1979).

HOWE, Martin QC

8 New Square (Michael Fysh QC) London (020) 7405 4321
clerks@8newsquare.co.uk

Recommended in Information Technology, Intellectual Property

Specialisation: Specialist in all aspects of intellectual property, (patents, trade marks, copyrights, designs, confidential information etc) and European Community law relating both to IP and other fields. Many high technology cases, with particular emphasis on computing, information technology and internet field; also extensive experience in biotechnology/genetic engineering cases. Regular appearances in the ECJ, Luxembourg, and the European Patent Office, Munich. For comprehensive CV and list of recent cases, visit our website at www.8newsquare.co.uk.
Prof. Memberships: Intellectual Property Bar Association (IPBA); The Intellectual Property Lawyers Organisation (TIPLO).
Career: Called 1978. QC 1996. Worked for IBM (UK), computer and engineering contract programmer 1976-78.
Publications: Halsbury's Laws on 'Trade Marks, Trade Names and Designs' (joint editor with Mr Justice Jacob); 'Europe and the Constitution after Maastricht' Nelson & Pollard, Oxford; editor 'Russell-Clarke on Industrial Design' (6th edn).
Personal: Born 1955. Educated at Winchester College; Trinity Hall, Cambridge (1977 BA Engineering and Law, 1979 MA).

HOWE, Robert

Blackstone Chambers (Presiley Baxendale QC & Charles Flint QC) London (020) 7583 1770
roberthowe@blackstonechambers.com

Recommended in Commercial (Litigation), Media & Entertainment, Sport

Specialisation: Principal areas of practice are general domestic and international commercial law; entertainment/media and copyright; sport law; employment /disciplinary law. Handles a range of cases within these fields, including disputes involving conflicts of law, copyright/media, sale of goods and international trade, financial services, commercial fraud. Examples of interesting cases: Re London United Investments [1992] Ch 578 (CA – DTI Inquiry/privilege); Sundt Wrigley v Wrigley (marevas & legal costs/ financial services/ foreign exchange trading/ investment mandates); Baldock v Addison [1995] 1 WLR 158 (copyright/ discovery), 'The Jam' litigation (partnership/ copyright); 'The Smiths' litigation (partnership); Chief Rabbi v Jewish Chronicle (confidentiality/copyright); Edwards v The International Amateur Athletic Federation, The Times, 30th June 1997 (restraint of trade/ EU law – Arts.59/ 60); AG for Gibraltar v May [1999] 1 WLR 598 (CA – discovery & privilege); Memory Corporation v Sidhu, The Times, 3rd November 1999 (freezing orders/cross examination on assets); Virgin Retail Limited v Phonographic Performance Limited [1999] EMLR (Copyright Tribunal); Donahue v Armco Inc [2000] AER (Comm.) 641 (CA – conflicts of laws/anti-suit injunction).
Prof. Memberships: COMBAR, Employment Lawyers Association, Employment Law Bar Association.
Career: Called to the Bar 1988. Joined present chambers 1990.
Personal: Educated at Trinity Hall, Cambridge 1983-86 (MA) and at St. Edmunds Hall, Oxford 1988-89 (BCL). Middle Temple Fox Scholar 1988-89 (one year fellowship in the litigation department of a Canadian commercial law firm, *Frazer & Beatty*, Toronto. Born 10 June 1964.

HOWE, Timothy

Fountain Court (Anthony Boswood QC) London (020) 7583 3335

Recommended in Banking, Insurance

Specialisation: Civil and commercial litigation (domestic and international), including banking and financial services, insurance and reinsurance, international trade, professional negligence, mergers and acquisitions, energy law and commercial arbitration; cases include: Pensions mis-selling PI coverage litigation, film finance insurance litigation; Mannesmann A.G. v Goldman Sachs; Morgan Grenfell v SACE; JP Morgan Securities v MNI; Lloyd's Names Litigation; British and Commonwealth v Atlantic Computers; Polly Peck International v Stoy Hayward; BBL v Eagle Star Insurance and US$2 billion Thyssen litigation in Bermuda. Clients include major investment and merchant banks, leading insurers and reinsurers, FTSE 100 companies and City law and accountancy firms.
Prof. Memberships: Executive Committee Member, COMBAR.
Career: Called 1987. Bermudian Bar 1998. Queen Mother's, Harmsworth and Astbury Scholarships, Middle Temple.
Publications: Co-author, 'Law of Bank Payments' (Longmans). Co-editor 'Commercial Court Procedure' (Sweet & Maxwell).
Personal: St. Paul's School and Magdalen College, Oxford (MA 1st Class Hons 1985).

HOWELL, John QC

Blackstone Chambers (Presiley Baxendale QC & Charles Flint QC) London (020) 7583 1770
johnhowell@blackstonechambers.com

Recommended in Administrative & Public Law, Environment, Local Government, Planning

Specialisation: Public law, human rights, tortious liability and public bodies, local government law including local government powers, decision making and finance, planning highways compulsory purchase and compensation, rating, education, social services, social security, housing, environment law, immigration and asylum, public utilities and procurement and European law.
Prof. Memberships: Committee member of the Administrative Law Bar Association and a member of the Planning and Environment Bar Association.
Career: Queen's College, Oxford. Called 1979, Queen's Counsel (1993).

HOWELL WILLIAMS, Craig

2 Harcourt Buildings (Gerard Ryan QC) London (020) 7353 8415

Recommended in Planning

Specialisation: Town and country planning and environment law.
Prof. Memberships: Planning and Environment Bar Association; Parliamentary Bar.
Career: Called to the Bar in 1983. Junior Counsel to the Crown ('B' Panel) (1993-99); PEBA Secretary (1994-96).
Personal: Chairman of the London Luton Airport Consultative Committee.

HOWELLS, James

Atkin Chambers (Robert Akenhead QC) London (020) 7404 0102
clerks@atkinchambers.law.co.uk

Recommended in Construction

Specialisation: Construction and engineering disputes both domestic and international with experience of litigation, arbitration and other terms of dispute resolution. Experience in engineering disputes has included a number of energy related cases involving, amongst other things, oil and gas production platforms and rigs, FPSO's, gas storage caverns, combined power and desalination plant, power station/dams. Other work includes building and engineering disputes in Hong Kong, Indonesia, Australia and Tanzania. In the past year involved in 7 month commercial court case regarding a North Sea drilling contract.
Prof. Memberships: TECBAR, LCLCBA.
Publications: One time editor of Building Law Reports.
Personal: MA (CANTAB), BCL (Oxon).

HUDSON, Rachel

Trinity Chambers (Toby Hedworth QC) Newcastle upon Tyne (0191) 232 1927
info@trinitychambers.co.uk

Recommended in Family

Specialisation: All aspects of family law, with particular emphasis on care work (acting for local authorities, parents and guardians) and ancillary relief. In recent years has been involved in a large number of significant High Court cases. During the past year these have included issues of consent to medical treatment, fabricated illness and allegations of unlawful killing. Head of the Trinity Chambers family group and the Bar representative on the Newcastle upon Tyne Family Court Business Committee. Trinity Chambers' pupillage and equal opportunities representative.
Prof. Memberships: FLBA, BAAF, North Eastern Circuit.
Career: Called to the Bar in 1985. Practised at Trinity Chambers since 1986.
Personal: Born in 1963. Educated at Newcastle upon

Tyne Church High School and Queen Elizabeth Grammar School, Hexham. London School of Economics (LLB Law). Away from the Bar enjoys spending time with her family, music, sport and eating out.

HUGHES, Adrian
4 Pump Court London (020) 7842 5555
ahughes@4pumpcourt.com
Recommended in Construction
Specialisation: Broad commercial practice which includes insurance and reinsurance, shipping, commodities, construction and engineering and environmental law work. He has a particular interest in international arbitration and public international law.
Prof. Memberships: Recorder; Court Examiner; Lloyd's Arbitrator; CEDR Accredited Mediator; Panel member of the China International Economic and Trade Arbitration Commission; Chairman China Law Council; Bar Council International Relations Committee (Chairman of Far East Sub-Committee), COMBAR, TECBAR.
Career: Royal Naval Officer (1977-84). Called to the Bar 1984; practising from 4 Pump Court.
Personal: Educated at Warwick School and Wadham College, Oxford.

HUGHES, Iain QC
Four New Square (Justin Fenwick QC) London (020) 7822 2000
i.hughes@4newsquare.com
Recommended in Professional Negligence
Specialisation: Principal area of practice is professional negligence and general common law. Work covers all aspects of professional negligence. Editor, 'Jackson and Powell on Professional Negligence'.
Prof. Memberships: Professional Negligence Bar Association.
Career: Called to the Bar 1974 and joined current chambers in 1977. Silk in 1996. Vice-chairman Professional Negligence Bar Association 1998-99; chairman 2000-01.

HUMPHREYS, Richard
4-5 Gray's Inn Square (Elizabeth Appleby QC & David Mole QC) London (020) 7404 5252
Recommended in Planning

HUMPHRIES, Michael
2 Mitre Court Buildings (Michael FitzGerald QC) London (020) 7583 1380
Recommended in Local Government, Planning
Specialisation: Practices principally in the areas of Town and Country Planning and Compulsory Purchase and Compensation. Has acted on behalf of many high profile clients including BAA plc at the Heathrow Terminal 5 public inquiry and Union Rail Property in relation to compulsory purchase and compensation issues arising from the Channel Tunnel Rail Link.
Prof. Memberships: Committee member of the Planning and Environmental Bar Association. Committee member of the Joint Planning Law Conference, Oxford. Member of the Anglo-American Real Property Institute.
Career: Called to the Bar in 1982 and joined current chambers in 1983.
Publications: Senior editor of Butterworths 'Compulsory Purchase and Compensation Service'. Lectured extensively on compulsory purchase and compensation issues.
Personal: Born 1959. Studied law at the University of Leicester. Married with two children. Leisure pursuits include reading, music and travel with family.

HUNJAN, Satinder
5 Fountain Court (Anthony Barker QC) Birmingham (0121) 606 0500
Recommended in Clinical Negligence

HUNT, Murray
Matrix Chambers (Nicholas Blake QC) London (020) 7404 3447
Recommended in Administrative & Public Law, Human Rights

HUNTER, Ian QC
Essex Court Chambers (Gordon Pollock QC) London (020) 7813 8000
Recommended in Arbitration (International), Aviation, Insurance
Specialisation: Broad-based commercial practice. More particularly arbitration, aviation, banking, conflict of laws, European law, financial services, insurance and reinsurance, international commercial fraud, professional negligence and shipping.
Career: Pembroke College, Cambridge MA (Law; double first) 1966; LLB 1967; Harvard Law School, Cambridge, USA LLM 1968. Called to the English Bar 1967. Called to the Bar of New South Wales 1993. Queen's Counsel 1980. Bencher 1986. Recorder 1986. Deputy High Court Judge 1993.
Personal: Born 1944. Fluent French.

HUNTER, Winston QC
Byrom Street Chambers Manchester (0161) 829 2100
Recommended in Personal Injury
Specialisation: Medical negligence, industrial diseases.
Prof. Memberships: PIBA, PNBA.

HUSAIN, Raza
Matrix Chambers (Nicholas Blake QC) London (020) 7404 3447
Recommended in Human Rights, Immigration
Specialisation: Practises mainly in public law with emphasis on immigration and human rights. Co-author with Nicholas Blake QC of 'Immigration and the Human Rights Act 1998', contributor to Jackson, contributor to Simor and Emmerson QC. Important cases include Radiom and Shingara (ECJ), Kaur (ECJ), Adan, (HL), Lamey (PC), Robinson (CA), Chahal (CA), Adimi (QBD), Quaquah (QBD), Cakmak and Uluyol (QBD).
Prof. Memberships: Executive Committee of Immigration Law Practitioners' Association, Council Member of JUSTICE, Liberty Human Rights Panel, Administrative Law Bar Association.
Career: Exeter College, Oxford (1987-90). Called 1993. 2 Garden Court 1994-00; founder member of present chambers.

HUSSEY, Ann
29 Bedford Row Chambers (Peter Ralls QC) London (020) 7404 1044
Recommended in Family
Specialisation: All areas of ancillary relief with extensive experience in both middle income and complex big money cases. Lectures extensively on matrimonial finance.
Prof. Memberships: FLBA.
Career: Middle Temple. Called to the Bar 1981.
Personal: Born 1959. Educated St Albans Girls' Grammar School and University of Kent. Married with four children.

HUTTON, Caroline
Enterprise Chambers (Anthony Mann QC) London (020) 9405 9471
carolinehutton@enterprisechambers.com
Recommended in Agriculture, Property Litigation
Specialisation: Practice covers all aspects of real property law, principally landlord and tenant (commercial, agricultural and residential) and including conveyancing, boundaries, easements, equitable rights and trusts of land, mortgages and professional negligence, insolvency and fraud matters related to major property. Major cases included Saunders v Edwards, Culworth Estates v Licensed Victuallers, Aspen Properties v Ratcliffe, Ponderosa v Pengap and Adams v Michael Batt. Clients include property companies, retailers and banks. Contributed to many commercial conferences on landlord and tenant.
Prof. Memberships: Justice, Association of Women Barristers, Bar European Group, Secretary of Property Bar Association.
Career: Called to the Bar 1979 and joined *Enterprise Chambers* 1981. Chairman Disciplinary and Appeals Tribunal for licensed conveyancing 1988-93. Fellow of Chartered Institute of Arbitrators.
Publications: Co-editor of 'Commercial Property Disputes' (Sweet & Maxwell, 1999).
Personal: Educated at Clare College, Cambridge 1975-78. Leisure pursuits include embroidery, reading, walking, theatre and art history. Born 25th March 1956. Lives in London with MP husband and two sons.

HYDE, Charles
Albion Chambers (Charles Barton QC & Neil Ford QC) Bristol (0117) 927 2144
Recommended in Family

HYLAND, J Graham K QC
Broadway House (J Graham K Hyland QC) Bradford (01274) 722560
Recommended in Crime
Specialisation: Crime.
Prof. Memberships: Criminal Bar Association.
Career: Call 1978 (Inner Temple). Recorder 1992. QC 1998.

IFE, Linden
Enterprise Chambers (Anthony Mann QC) London (020) 7405 9471
Recommended in Chancery, Company, Insolvency/Corporate Recovery
Specialisation: Principal area of practice is commercial chancery, including insolvency, company, commercial agreements, property, professional negligence, banking and securities and financial services. Regularly receives instructions from major clearing banks and other financial institutions, and from insolvency practitioners. Recent cases include Sterling Estates v Pickard [1997] (lease disclaimer by liquidator), TSB v Platts [1997] (cross-claims in bankruptcy), Re Double S Printers Limited [1998] (fixed and floating charges). Member of the Association of Business Recovery Professionals.

INGLIS-JONES, Nigel J QC
35 Essex Street (Christopher Wilson-Smith QC) London (020) 7353 6381
Recommended in Pensions
Specialisation: Specialist with over 40 years experience in occupational pension schemes; also deals with other trusts, contract and tort. During past 15 years he has fought many of the major cases concerning occupational pension schemes. These include RE Imperial Foods' Pension Scheme, Re Courage Group's Pension Scheme (1987), Mettoy Pension Trustees v Evans (1990), LRT Pension Fund Trustee Company v Hatt (1993), British Coal corporation v British Coal Staff Superannuation Scheme (1994), Century Life plc v Pension Ombudsman (1997), Hillsdown Holdings v Pension Ombudsman (1997), Legal and General Assurance Society v Pension Ombudsman (1999), Coloroll Pension Trustees v Sedgwick Noble Lowndes (1999), Re National Grid plc and others v Laws and Mayes (1998, 1999, 2001), Re The National Provident Institute Pension Scheme (2000), The Merchant Navy Ratings Pension scheme (2000), and The British Airways Pension Scheme (2001). Author of 'The Law of Occupational Pension Schemes' (Sweet and Maxwell); has spoken at and chaired many conferences.
Prof. Memberships: Chancery Bar Association, Association of Pensions Lawyers, Western Circuit. Bencher of the Inner Temple since 1982.
Career: National Service with the Grenadier Guards (subaltern) 1953-55. Called to the Bar in 1959 and joined chambers at Essex Street in 1960. Took Silk in 1982. Recorder 1978-93. Deputy Social Security Commissioner since 1993.
Personal: Educated at Eton College 1948-53 and Trinity College, Oxford 1955-58. Leisure pursuits include fishing, collecting English drinking glass and English miniature glass, gardening and travelling. A member of the congregation of St Paul's church, Onslow Square. Born 7th May 1935. Lives in London.

INGRAM, Nigel
2 Bedford Row (William Clegg QC) London (020) 7440 8888
Recommended in Fraud

INMAN, Melbourne QC
1 Fountain Court (David Crigman QC) Birmingham (0121) 236 5721
Recommended in Crime

IRWIN, Stephen QC
Doughty Street Chambers (Geoffrey Robertson QC) London (020) 7404 1313
Recommended in Clinical Negligence, Personal Injury, Product Liability
Specialisation: Principal area of practice is clinical negligence covering a broad range of serious medical accidents including cerebral palsy, surgical and other medical cases. Other main areas of work are major personal injury cases, legal negligence arising out of public law cases with a medical or health content. Major cases include the Human Growth Hormone/ Creutzfeldt – Jacob disease, BSE – linked CJD litigation, PTSD for servicemen and organophosphate sheepdip group action, Gulf War Syndrome, Clunis v Camden & Islington HA Alden Hay body paints case; Birmingham Orthopaedic Hospital Bone Tumour Service; and the Clapham Rail disaster enquiry. Author of 'Practitioner's Guide to Medical Negligence' (Legal Action Group, 1995). Regularly lectures and writes on medico-legal issues. Chairman, Remuneration Committee of Bar Council.
Prof. Memberships: Professional Negligence Bar Association, Association of Personal Injury Lawyers, Action for the Victims of Medical Accidents, Personal Injury Bar Association, Justice.
Career: Called to the Bar 1976 and tenant of No.1 Dr. Johnson's Buildings, founder member of Doughty Street Chambers. Called to the Bar of Northern Ireland 1997. QC 1997.
Personal: Educated at Methodist College, Belfast 1961-71 and Jesus College, Cambridge 1972-75. Leisure pursuits include reading prose and verse, Irish history and hillwalking. Born 5th February 1953. Lives in Radlett, Herts.

ISAACS, Barry
3-4 South Square (Michael Crystal QC & Lord Alexander of Weedon QC) London (020) 7696 9900
barryisaacs@southsquare.com
Recommended in Insolvency/Corporate Recovery
Specialisation: Commercial chancery, insolvency, company, professional negligence. Recent cases: acted for BCCI in Three Rivers v Bank of England [2001] 2 All ER 513; for Equitable Life, a Scheme of Arrangement with its policyholders; for liquidators in Bermuda Fire & Marine litigation.
Prof. Memberships: Associate of the Society of Actuaries.
Career: 1994-present, practising barrister; 1991-93, investment manager, venture capital, Societe Generale; 1987-91, strategy consultant, Bain & Company. MA (Harvard), BA (Oxon).
Personal: Tennis, karate (black belt).

ISAACS, Paul
Mercury Chambers (Benjamin Nolan QC) Leeds (0113) 234 2265
Recommended in Family
Specialisation: Highly regarded specialist in matrimonial property work. The counsel of choice of the leading firms of solicitors in cases involving substantial assets and complex accountancy/ valuation evidence. Recent cases have involved assets of £10-40 million.
Personal: Read Law at Trinity College, Cambridge (Lizette Bentwich prize winner). Called to the Bar in 1974. Recorder of the Crown Court approved to try family cases.

IVIMY, Cecilia
11 King's Bench Walk Chambers (Eldred Tabachnik QC & James Goudie QC) London (020) 7632 8500
ivimy@11kbw.com
Recommended in Employment
Specialisation: Judicial review, human rights, local government, employment and discrimination law.
Prof. Memberships: Employment Law Bar Association; Administrative Law Bar Association.
Career: Called to the Bar 1995.
Publications: Contributor to; Halsbury's Laws 'Administrative Law' (2001 reissue), Tolleys 'Employment Law Handbook', Butterworths 'Local Government Law', 'Local Authorities' and the 'Human Rights Act' (Butterworths).
Personal: Merton College, Oxford BA (1st class); City University Dip Law (distinction).

IVORY, Thomas QC
One Essex Court (Lord Grabiner QC) London (020) 7583 2000
Recommended in Commercial (Litigation)
Specialisation: Principal areas of practice include banking, general commercial disputes, jurisdiction disputes, share sales, oil and gas, telecommunications, professional negligence, pensions.
Prof. Memberships: COMBAR; Chancery Bar Association.

JACKLIN, Susan
St John's Chambers (Christopher Sharp QC) Bristol 0117 921 3456
clerks@stjohnschambers.co.uk
Recommended in Family
Specialisation: Matrimonial finance, cohabitation disputes, Inheritance Act claims, professional negligence in ancillary relief context. Children cases, particularly care applications involving allegations of physical and sexual abuse.
Prof. Memberships: Family Law Bar Associations, Criminal Bar Association.
Career: Durham University (BA). Called to the Bar 1980. Assistant Recorder 1998. Recorder 2000.

JACKSON, Andrew
3 Fountain Court (Robert Juckes QC) Birmingham (0121) 236 5854
clerks@3fc.co.uk
Recommended in Crime
Specialisation: Crime: Prosecution and Defence work.
Prof. Memberships: Criminal Bar Association.
Career: Manchester University: [1981-84] BA (Hons). The City University: (1984-85). Diploma in law.

JACKSON, Judith QC
9 Old Square (Michael Driscoll QC) London (020) 7405 4682
judith.jackson@9oldsquare.co.uk
Recommended in Property Litigation
Specialisation: Commercial property particularly landlord and tenant, chancery and professional negligence. Cases include: Prudential Assurance Co Ltd v Newman Industries Ltd (minority shareholders' rights), Re Bond Worth (retention of title), Abbey National v Moss (trusts for sale), UCB Bank plc v Beasley (s70 (1)(g) Land Registration Act 1925), Scott v National Trust (Judicial Review of Charity), Trustees of the Phillimore Kensington Estate v Jassi Reform – whether house and mews house were together a house), Locabail UK Ltd v Bayfield Properties (conjoined appeals on Judicial bias).
Prof. Memberships: Chancery Bar Association; Professional Negligence Bar Association.
Career: Queen Mary College, London (1970-73) (LLB); (1973-74) (LLM). Called to Bar in 1975. Took Silk in 1994. Bencher of Lincoln's Inn 2001. Director of Bar Mutual Indemnity Fund Ltd (1999-date).
Publications: Contributor to 'Megarry's Rent Acts' (11th edn).

JACKSON, Peter QC
4 Paper Buildings (Lionel Swift QC) London (020) 7583 0816
pj@4pb.com or peterjackson@totalise.co.uk
Recommended in Family
Specialisation: All aspects of child work.
Prof. Memberships: Family Law Bar Association.
Career: Called 1978 and joined present chambers 1979. Assistant Recorder 1998. Recorder 2000. Silk 2000. Reported cases include Re AK (Medical Treatment: Consent) [2001] 1 FLR 129; Re H, Re G (Adoption: consultation of unmarried fathers) [2001]1 FLR 646; Re R (Child of a Teenage Mother) [2000] 2 FLR 660; Re O and J (Paternity: blood tests) [2000] 1 FLR 418; Re A (Adoption: Mother's objections) [2000] 1 FLR 428; Royal Wolverhampton Hospitals NHS Trust v B [2000] 1 FLR 953; Nottingham City Council v October Films Ltd [1999] 2 FLR 347; Re R (Inter-country adoptions: practice) [1999] 1 FLR 1042; Re R (Adoption: Protection from Offenders) [1999] 1 FLR 472; Re K (Adoption and Wardship) [1997] 2 FLR 221; Re C (Refusal of medical treatment 1994] 1 FLR 31.
Personal: Educated at Marlborough College 1969-73 and Brasenose College, Oxford 1974-77. Born 9th December 1955. Lives in London.

JACKSON, Simon
Park Court Chambers (James Stewart QC & Robert Smith QC) Leeds (0113) 243 3277
Recommended in Personal Injury
Specialisation: Personal Injury/Clinical Negligence. Professional Disciplinary Proceedings. Medico-crime/fraud.
Prof. Memberships: PNBA and PIBA.
Career: Leeds University [LL.B (Hons)]. Called 1982. Pupillage in London and Leeds. Practised in specialist field for 10 years plus. Occasional lecturer on medico-legal issues.

JACOBS, Nigel
4 Essex Court (Nigel Teare QC) London (020) 7653 5653
njacobs@4sx.com
Recommended in Shipping
Specialisation: Practice encompasses shipping, insurance, admiralty and general commercial work. Nigel was the successful counsel for the cargo interests in the Starsin (both at first instance and in the Court of Appeal). He was junior counsel to the Marchioness Action Group at the Public Inquiry. Other cases include the Flecha (identity of carrier and jurisdictional dispute, construction of bill of lading), the Markos N (extension of time under s.12 of the Arbitration Act 1996), Citi-March v Neptune Orient Line (the effect of the expiry of a limitation period upon an exclusive jurisdiction clause). He sits as a mediator and maritime arbitrator.
Prof. Memberships: Bar Council, COMBAR.
Career: Called to the Bar 1983 and joined 4 Essex Court in 1986.
Personal: Educated at Pembroke College, Cambridge 1979-82 (MA) and Trinity College, Cambridge 1983-84 (LLM). Leisure pursuits include tennis, cricket, golf and squash. Born 31 May 1960. Lives in London.

JACOBS, Richard QC
Essex Court Chambers (Gordon Pollock QC) London (020) 7813 8000
Recommended in Commercial (Litigation), Insurance
Specialisation: All types of commercial work – shipping, insurance, reinsurance, professional negligence, commodities, banking, Lloyd's disciplinary proceedings, disputes arising from sales of businesses (warranty claims etc).
Career: Pembroke College, Cambridge MA (1st Class Hons), 1978. Called to the Bar, 1979.
Personal: Born 1956.

JAFFA, Ronald

3 Gray's Inn Square (Rock Tansey QC) London (020) 7520 5600

Recommended in Crime

Specialisation: Long-term experience of defending those charged with serious crime including murder, robbery, rape, drugs trafficking, importation and serious assaults. Often instructed in cases where the defendant is difficult, has psychiatric problems or where the allegation revolves around sexual abuse of children. Has conducted many fraud cases involving companies, company VAT, charities, local authority employees, advanced fee and mortgages.
Prof. Memberships: Criminal Bar Association, European Criminal Bar Association.
Career: LLB Nottingham University. One of the founder members who set up the Bar Pro Bono Unit. A member of the management committee solely responsible for considering all applications relating to criminal work.
Personal: Married with two children. An elected trustee of the Rett Syndrome Association UK, a national charity helping families, carers and sufferers of this neurological disorder which only affects females.

JAFFERJEE, Aftab

2 Harcourt Buildings, Atkinson Bevan Chambers (Nicholas Atkinson QC & John Bevan QC) London (020) 7353 2112
clerks@2hb.co.uk

Recommended in Crime

Specialisation: Senior Treasury Counsel to the Crown at the Central Criminal Court since 2001; Junior Treasury Counsel 1997-01. Recent cases include prosecution of The Greek Embassy siege and the Afghan Airlines hijack.
Prof. Memberships: Criminal Bar Association.
Career: Past member of the Committee of the Criminal Bar Association. Past member of the Professional Conduct Committee of the Bar.

JAMES, Alun

3 Temple Gardens Tax Chambers (Richard Bramwell QC) London (020) 7853 7884
clerks@taxcounsel.co.uk

Recommended in Tax

Specialisation: Tax and VAT. Litigation: appeals to the General and Special Commissioners, the VAT and Duties Tribunal and the higher courts, and tax-related professional negligence. Appears both for and against HM Customs & Excise being a member of the Crown's Provincial Panel. Revenue (SCO) enquiries and C&E investigations: advice on handling the enquiry/investigation and representation on appeal. Tax advice generally: particularly corporate tax issues including reorganisations.
Prof. Memberships: Revenue Bar Association.
Career: Called to the Bar 1986 and joined 3 Temple Gardens 1988. Also a member of Exchange Chambers (William Waldron QC), Liverpool.
Publications: Co-author of 'Taxation of Companies and Company Reconstructions' (Sweet & Maxwell, 6th-8th edn).
Personal: Scholar of St John's College, Oxford (BA, Hons 1st Class, Jurisprudence, BCL). Born 13 May 1964.

JAMES, Christopher

5 Fountain Court (Anthony Barker QC) Birmingham (0121) 606 0500

Recommended in Family

JAMES, Ian

Octagon House Chambers (Andrew Lindqvist) Norwich (01603) 623186

Recommended in Crime

JAMES, Michael

Enterprise Chambers (Anthony Mann QC) Leeds (0113) 246 0391

Recommended in Commercial (Litigation)

Specialisation: Commercial and chancery litigation, with particular expertise in disputes with an international aspect. Wide experience of employment law and directors' disqualification cases.
Prof. Memberships: Chancery Bar Association. Chartered Institute of Arbitrators. Association of Northern Mediators.
Career: Open Scholar at Christ Church, Oxford. Solicitor 1983-93.
Personal: Born 17 May 1953. Married, two children.

JAMESON, Rodney

No.6 Barristers Chambers (Shaun Spencer QC) Leeds (0113) 245 9763

Recommended in Crime

JANNER, Daniel

23 Essex Street (Michael Lawson QC) London (020) 7413 0353
danieljanner@23essexstreet.co.uk

Recommended in Crime

Specialisation: Crime (general); police law.
Prof. Memberships: 23 Essex Street.
Career: Called to Bar in 1980 (Jules Thorn Scholar, Middle Temple).
Publications: Editor 'Criminal Appeal Reports' since 1994.
Personal: President Cambridge Union Society (1978).

JARMAN, Milwyn QC

9 Park Place (Ian Murphy QC) Cardiff (029) 2038 2731
milwyn@aol.com

Recommended in Chancery

Specialisation: Chancery, planning and local government, personal injury. Reported cases include BP Properties Ltd v Buckler [1987] 2 EGLR 168 (adverse possession); R v Port Talbot Borough Council ex p Jones [1988] 2 ALL ER 207 (judicial review: housing); R v Dairy Produce Quota Tribunal for England and Wales ex p Davies [1987] 2 EGLR 7 (judicial review: agriculture); R v West Glamorgan County Council ex p Morris and Hood-Williams [1992] JPL 374 (judicial review planning), Huish v Ellis [1995] BCC 462 (professional negligence); Harris v Welsh Development Agency [1999] 3 EGLR 207 (compulsory purchase compensation); Bolwell v Radcliffe Homes Ltd [1999] PIQR P243 (personal injury.)
Prof. Memberships: Chancery Bar Association, Bristol and Cardiff Chancery Bar Association, Wales Commercial Law Association, Wales Public Law and Human Rights Association.
Career: Called 1980.
Personal: Born 1957. LLB (Wales) 1st Class. LLM (Cantab).

JARVIS, John QC

3 Verulam Buildings (Christopher Symons QC & John Jarvis QC) London (020) 7831 8441
chambers@3vb.com

Recommended in Arbitration (International), Banking, Commercial (Litigation), Fraud

Specialisation: Principal areas of practice are banking (both litigation and transactional work) and commercial law. Specialist experience in banking and financing work, insolvency and professional negligence. Practice covers law and practice of international finance, project development and finance, trade disputes, professional liability, insolvency, constructive trusts and arbitration. Has drafted all the major security documentation for a new bank,and appeared in a number of banking cases such as Tai Hing Cotton Ltd v Lin Chong Bank Ltd [1986] AC 80 in the Privy Council and the Etridge appeals in the House of Lords, 2001. Other reported cases include Barclays Bank v O'Brien [1993] (priority in equity of wife's interest against creditor); Deposit Protection Board v Dalia [1993] (validity of equitable assignments to enable claim on fund); Wadha Bank v Arab Bank [1993] (legality of performance bonds and counter guarantees); Re Arrows Ltd Nos 1-4 [1992-93]; Brink Mat Ltd v Noye [1991] (bank as constructive trustee) and Barclays Bank Plc v Taylor, TSB v Taylor [1989] (extent of bank's duty of confidentiality). International Editor of the 'Journal of Banking and Finance Law and Practice'. Author of a number of articles in banking law. Co-author of 'Lender Liability' (1993), and contributing author to 'Banks; Liability and Risk'(1995).
Prof. Memberships: COMBAR, London Common Law and Commercial Bar Association (Chairman 1995/1997).
Career: Called to the Bar and joined present Chambers 1970. Took Silk 1989. Appointed Recorder 1992. Sits as a Deputy High Court Judge.
Personal: Educated at King's College School, Wimbledon 1955-65. Open Exhibitioner and Senior Scholar of Emmanuel College (and Cambridge University Scholar) 1966-69 (MA Hons). Governor of King's College School. Leisure pursuits include riding, tennis, sailing, skiing, cycling, collecting modern British paintings, opera and gardening. Born 20 November 1947.

JAY, Robert QC

39 Essex Street (Nigel Pleming QC) London (020) 7832 1111
rj@39essex.co.uk

Recommended in Administrative & Public Law

Specialisation: Extensive practice in public law, judicial review and general common law, having been Junior Council to the Crown (Common Law) between 1989 and 1998.
Prof. Memberships: Vice-Chairman of the Administrative Law Bar Association.
Career: QC (1998).
Personal: Interests: cooking, classical music and languages.

JEANS, Christopher QC

11 King's Bench Walk Chambers (Eldred Tabachnik QC & James Goudie QC) London (020) 7632 8500

Recommended in Employment

Specialisation: Specialises in employment law.
Prof. Memberships: Employment Lawyers Association, Employment Law Bar Association.
Career: 1974-77: LLB degree at King's College, London. 1977-79: BCL degree at St John's College, Oxford. 1980: called to the Bar (Gray's Inn). Since 1983 has practised full time at the Bar, specialising in employment law, at chambers of Lord Irvine QC (now chambers of Eldred Tabachnik QC and James Goudie QC).
Personal: Main interests: sport (especially football and cricket), travel, theatre, cinema.

JEARY, Stephen

Temple Chambers (David J.M. Aubrey QC) Cardiff (029) 2039 7364

Recommended in Crime

JEFFORD, Nerys

Keating Chambers (Richard Fernyhough QC) London +44 (0) 20 7544 2600
njefford@keatingchambers.com

Recommended in Construction

Specialisation: Construction and civil engineering.
Career: Qualified 1986; Gray's Inn; member of editorial team 'Keating on Building Contracts'.
Personal: Lady Margaret Hall, Oxford (1984, MA); University of Virginia (1985, LLM). Born 1962. London Welsh Chorale.

JEFFREYS, Alan QC

Farrar's Building (John Leighton Williams QC) London (020) 7583 9241

Recommended in Personal Injury

Specialisation: Principal area of practice is personal injury litigation, both claimant and defendant. Work includes motor, employment and public liability claims. Other main areas of practice are clinical and solicitors negligence, general insurance, and health and safety.
Prof. Memberships: P.I.B.A; C.L.C.B.A.
Career: Called to the Bar in 1970 (Gray's Inn) and joined Farrar's Building in 1971. Recorder since 1993. Took Silk April 1996. Member of the C.I.C.A.P. 1999.
Personal: Born 27th September 1947. Lives in London.

JELF, Simon

48 Bedford Row (Roderick I'Anson Banks) London (020) 7430 2005 sjelf@partnershipcounsel.co.uk

Recommended in Partnership

Specialisation: Exclusively partnership law. Deals with a wide variety of partnership matters, including the drafting and construction of agreements, and is known for taking a hands-on commercial approach in providing advice and representation in partnership disputes. Acts for professional and trading partnerships, including accountants, doctors and solicitors.

Prof. Memberships: Association of Partnership Practitioners.

Career: Called to the Bar (Gray's Inn) 1996. Law Commission 1996-98, principally involved with the review of partnership law. Joined 48 Bedford Row (chambers of Roderick I'Anson Banks) in 1999.

Publications: Assists in editing 'Lindley & Banks on Partnership' and the 'Encyclopedia of Professional Partnerships'.

Personal: Educated at John Taylor High School, Burton-upon-Trent, and University of East Anglia. Leisure pursuits include property renovation and golf. Born 21 February 1973. Lives in London.

JENKINS, Edward QC

5 Paper Buildings (Godfrey Carey QC & Jonathan Caplan QC) London (020) 7583 6117

Recommended in Crime

Specialisation: Commercial fraud (tax evasion, corruption, city banking fraud); health and safety, trading standards, control of pollution.

Prof. Memberships: SE Circuit, CBA.

JENKINS, T Alun QC

Queen Square Chambers (Anthony Donne QC & T Alun Jenkins QC) Bristol (01179) 211966 crime@qs-c.co.uk

Recommended in Crime

Specialisation: Criminal and commercial fraud, diversion frauds, money laundering and large scale importation of drugs. Prosecuted: Op Barlow – Customs & Excise diversion fraud; Op Rhythm and Op Jaegar C and E importation of drugs; Op Sirrocco, diversion fraud. Defended: Large scale distribution of drugs, passing-off fraud, long firm fraud, computer frauds, Mareva and Anton Piller injunctions. Defended 'Op Mamba' mobile telephone VAT fraud, [2001].

Career: Recorder.

JENNINGS, Anthony QC

Matrix Chambers (Nicholas Blake QC) London (020) 7404 3447

Recommended in Crime

Specialisation: Involved in major Crown Court criminal cases including terrorism, animal rights, drugs, prison disturbances, armed robbery, murder and fraud. Cases include disturbances at Risley Remand Centre (1990), Dartmoor Prison (1991), Manchester United supporters riot on ferry, dolphin interference case; IRA cases: MacFlhoinn and Hayes and Taylor; Sehan (largest ever police seizure of heroin); Ronnie Lee (animal rights bombing), Whitemoor prison egress, North Wales sex abuse inquiry, Brownbill v M.P.C. (£150,000 damages against the police), Michael Smith v Police (largest damages in W.Midlands), Keith Birchall (murder conviction quashed on appeal). Arms from Serbia/W.Midlands Police Corruption (1999). Condron v UK and the other four right to silence cases.

Prof. Memberships: Criminal Bar Association.

Career: Called to the Bar 1983 and Northern Ireland Bar in 1987, joined current chambers in 1986. CBA lecture November 1999 & 2000 and Human Rights lecturer for Bar Council & CBA 2000.

Publications: Editor of 'Justice under Fire: The Abuse of Civil Liberties in Northern Ireland' (1990). Written articles on criminal justice for The Times, Independent, Guardian, Archbold News and The New Law Journal. Contributing editor of Archbold. Contributor to Simon and Emmerson, 'Human Rights Practice' and Stormer, Strange and Whittaker, 'Criminal Justice, Police Powers & Human Rights'.

Personal: Educated at St Patrick's College, Belfast 1971-78, Warwick University 1978-81 and Inns of Court School of Law 1981-82. Leisure pursuits include theatre, Italy, Liverpool FC and Irish literature. Born 11th May 1960. Lives in London.

JOFFE, Victor QC

Serle Court (Lord Neill of Bladen QC) London (020) 7242 6105 clerks@serlecourt.co.uk

Recommended in Chancery, Company, Insolvency/Corporate Recovery

Specialisation: Main areas of practice are company law (especially shareholders' disputes and minority rights; directors duties and directors' disqualification) and corporate insolvency, with emphasis on litigation. Other areas of practice include commercial chancery and banking (including tracing and proprietary claims). Advises in many litigious matters from overseas, particularly the United States and Jersey.

Prof. Memberships: Chancery Bar Association; Commercial Bar Association; Associate Member of Insolvency Lawyers Association; International Bar Association; American Bar Association.

Career: MA, LL.B (Cantab). Called to the Bar 1975. Attorney, New York State Bar (1998).

Publications: Publications include 'Minority Shareholders – Law Practice and Procedure' and 'Mithani on Disqualification of Directors' (joint editor).

JOHNS, Alan

9 Old Square (Michael Driscoll QC) London (020) 7405 4682

Recommended in Property Litigation

Specialisation: Main expertise is in property litigation, including landlord and tenant, mortgages, real property and professional negligence, but is experienced in a broad range of modern Chancery work. Recent cases include Upton v Taylor & Colley (1999) (Divisional Court) and Inntrepeneur Pub cv (IPC) Ltd v Deans (1999).

Career: Called to the bar in 1994. Part-time tutor at Magdalen College, Oxford during 1996 and 1997.

Personal: Helston School, Cornwall. Magdalen College, Oxford.

JOHNSON, Christine

14 Castle Street (Andrew Edis QC) Liverpool (0151) 236 4421

Recommended in Family

Specialisation: Children and financial relief. Crime.

Prof. Memberships: FBLA. RCN (Royal College of Nursing).

Career: Registerer Nurse, Registerer Sick Childrens Nurse, Registerer Midwife.

JOHNSON, Edwin

9 Old Square (Michael Driscoll QC) London (020) 7405 4682

Recommended in Property Litigation

Specialisation: Property, Chancery and commercial litigation and advisory work. In particular commercial and residential property disputes, professional negligence, mortgages, general landlord and tenant (including leasehold enfranchisement), conveyancing, easements, restrictive covenants, property rights, insolvency and commercial contracts, building and construction work. Recent cases include Church Commissioners v Ibrahim [1997] 1 EGLR 13, (right to indemnity costs in leases); Gardner v Marsh & Parsons (mitigation of damages for professional negligence)[1997] 1 WLR 489; Wallis Fashion Group Ltd v CGU Life Assurance Ltd [2000] 27 EG 145, Rosen v Trustees of the Campden Charities [2001] 2 ALL ER 399, UCB Corporate Services Ltd v Halifax (SW) Ltd [2000] 1 EGLR 87. 14. Rothschild v Bell [1999] 2 WLR 1237.

Prof. Memberships: Chancery Bar Association. Professional Negligence Bar Association.

Career: Called to the Bar in 1987 and joined 9 Old Square in 1988. Educated at Lancing College and Christ Church College, Oxford (BA). Appointed Standing Counsel to the Rent Assessment Panel 2000.

JOHNSON, Ian

14 Castle Street (Andrew Edis QC) Liverpool (0151) 236 6757 I.Johnson@mmu.ac.uk

Recommended in Chancery

Specialisation: General chancery with particular emphasis on: probate and administration of estates, landlord and tenant, conveyancing and real property, trusts, companies and partnerships.

Prof. Memberships: Chancery Bar Association. Northern Chancery Bar Association.

Career: Tenant at 20 North John Street, October 1983 to July 1997. Tenant at 14 Castle Street, August 1997 to date. Senior lecturer in law and Associate Director of the Bar Vocational Course at Manchester Metropolitan University. Continues to practise while holding these appointments.

Personal: Married Elizabeth, eldest daughter Lord and Lady Evans of Claughton (1989). Two daughters (1995 and 1998).

JOHNSON, Michael

9 St. John Street (John Hand QC) Manchester (0161) 955 9000 clerks@9stjohnstreet.co.uk

Recommended in Chancery

Specialisation: General Chancery, with emphasis on traditional chancery fields, and on revenue matters, professional negligence and High Court Litigation.

Prof. Memberships: Chancery Bar Association, Northern Chancery Bar Association (immediate past Chairman) Professional Negligence Bar Association.

Career: Chancery Practitioner since 1972, Recorder (Civil and Crime), part-time Chairman, VAT & Duties Tribunals, part-time Special Commissioner of Taxes.

Personal: Fluent in Spanish, good knowledge of French, educated in North and South America, and at Trinity College, Cambridge University.

JOHNSTON, Christopher

3 Serjeants' Inn (Robert Francis QC & John Grace QC) London (020) 7427 5000

Recommended in Clinical Negligence

Specialisation: Principal areas of practice are medical and dental negligence, medical ethics and police law. Considerable experience acting for both plaintiff and defendant in all aspects of medico-legal work, including high value claims (brain damage, blindness, serious physical injury) and class actions. Experience in medical ethics work (M v a NHS Trust Permanent vegetative state: whether Bland compatible with European Convention on Human Rights; B v Croydon Health Authority: force feeding of mental patient). Joint author of 'Medical Treatment: Decisions and the Law' (Butterworths, 2001). Acting for defendant in first dental negligence class action (Appleton v Garrett – 1996). Professional medical (including HC90(9)), dental and police disciplinary work. Experience acting in police civil actions, police pension and employment cases. Employment experience also comprises unfair dismissal, race and sex discrimination (particularly in health context). Co-presented national seminar on Human Rights Act: Learning from the US experience – 1999.

Prof. Memberships: Professional Negligence Bar Association. LCLCBA.

Career: Called to the Bar in 1990. Joined Serjeants' Inn in 1991. Junior Counsel to the Crown (B Panel)

Personal: School: Ballymena Academy. University: Trinity Hall, Cambridge (Law, 1st class). Interests: cinema and history.

JONES, Alun QC
3 Raymond Buildings (Clive Nicholls QC) London (020) 7400 6400
chambers@3raymondbuildings.com
Recommended in Crime, Fraud
Specialisation: Principal areas of practice are commercial crime and extradition. Acts in cases of serious and complex fraud, both trials and advisory work, primarily for the defence. Undertakes extradition and advisory work for foreign governments and fugitives. Appears frequently on appeal or review in criminal cases and associated matters such as coroners' cases. Notable cases include the Alexander Howden reinsurance trials (appearing for Kenneth Grob in the first SFO trial, 1989-90); the Blue Arrow Trial 1990-91 (defending Stephen Clark); the defence of Andrew Kent in an alleged fraud against The Securities Association (1993) and the Maxwell Criminal Trial (defending Kevin Maxwell, 1995-96); Westminster Council v Dame Shirley Porter & Others 1997; Senator Pinochet 1998-9; Lord Hardwicke 1999; Frank Warren 2000; Private prosecution for the Hillsborough Family Support Group 1996-00. Involved in fourteen full House of Lords appeals in extradition cases, acting in ten of them for foreign governments, including Pinochet in Spain. Author of 'Jones on Extradition' (Sweet & Maxwell 2001); second edition.
Prof. Memberships: Bar Council, Criminal Bar Association.
Career: Called to the Bar in 1972 and joined current chambers in 1973. Took silk 1989. Appointed Recorder 1992.
Personal: Educated at Oldershaw Grammar School, Wallasey 1960-67 and Bristol University 1967-70. Leisure pursuits include bridge, cricket, gardening and writing (currently working on book concerning the law of conspiracy). Born 19th March 1949. Lives in Greenwich, London.

JONES, Charlotte
Crown Office Chambers (Michael Spencer QC & Christopher Purchas QC) London (020) 7797 8100
jones@crownofficechambers.com
Recommended in Clinical Negligence
Specialisation: Specialises in clinical negligence, acting for claimants and defendant health authorities and trusts, in all types of medical cases, in particular brain damaged baby claims, other obstetric, paediatric, gynaecological, anaesthetic, cancer and orthopaedic cases. Other substantial areas of practice are employment, appearing in employment tribunals and the employment appeal tribunal, often for healthcare clients, and personal injuries, particularly in the context of aviation/ mass disasters.
Prof. Memberships: Professional Negligence Bar Association. South Eastern Circuit.
Career: Called to the Bar by Middle Temple (1982).
Personal: Born April 1960. Educated at Queen's School Chester and Trinity Hall Cambridge (BA Hons) 1978-81. Married with 2 children and lives in Kent.

JONES, Elizabeth QC
Serle Court (Lord Neill of Bladen QC) London (020) 7242 6105
clerks@serlecourt.co.uk
Recommended in Chancery, Commercial (Litigation)
Specialisation: Broad range of commercial Chancery and property litigation, with particular emphasis on civil fraud and breach of fiduciary duty (both in commercial and trust contexts), Privy Council appeals and financial services.
Prof. Memberships: Chancery Bar Association, COMBAR, ACTAPS
Career: Called to the Bar 1984. Joined Thirteen Old Square 1985.

JONES, Geraint QC
9 Park Place (Ian Murphy QC) Cardiff (029) 2038 2731
Recommended in Chancery

JONES, Gregory
2 Harcourt Buildings (Gerard Ryan QC) London (020) 7353 8415
clerks@2hb.law.co.uk
Recommended in Environment
Specialisation: Planning, environmental, compulsory purchase, education, local government, administrative, parliamentary, EU, ECHR and immigration. R (on the application of Alconbury Development Ltd) v SSETR (HL) [2001] 2 All ER 929 (compatibility of call-in powers with article 6 ECHR); Berkeley v SSE (HL) [2000] 3 WLR 420 (Directive 85/337EC application of article 10 EC Treaty); R (Lowther) v Durham CC (CA) [2001] Times June 22 (burning of hazardous waste in cement kilns); R (Lichfield Securities) Lichfield DC v Lichfield Securities Ltd (CA) [2001] Times March 30 (fairness and s.106 agreements); R v University of Cambridge ex p Persuad (CA) (diclosure of supervisor's report to PhD student) 10 April 2001; Millington v SSE (CA) [2000] JPL 297 (whether winemaking agriculture); R v Greenwich LBC ex p Glen International (CA) [2000] Times 29 March (housing renovation grants); R v SSETR and Parcelforce ex p Marson (CA) [1999] 1 CMLR 268 (duty to give reasons under EU law); R v Sandhu (CA Criminal Division) [1997] Times January 2 (evidence in strict liability offences).
Prof. Memberships: European Circuit; Panel of approved counsel to appear for the Home Office before special adjudicators; National Council of UKELA; PEBA, ALBA, Bar European Group, Education Law Society; Ecclesiastical Law Society.
Career: Lincoln's Inn (1991); King's Inns, Dublin (1997); joined 2 Harcourt Buildings 1993; Warner Scholar to the European Court of Justice, Luxembourg (1995); head of European law (part-time) South Bank University.
Publications: 'Statutory Nuisance' (2001) (Butterworths). Many articles including 'Judicial Review of Planning Permissions' [2000] JPL 564.
Personal: Colfe's; New College, Oxford (MA); University College, London (LLM) (Euro).

JONES, Jennifer
5 Fountain Court (Anthony Barker QC) Birmingham (0121) 606 0500
Recommended in Employment

JONES, Philip
Serle Court (Lord Neill of Bladen QC) London (020) 7242 6105
clerks@serlecourt.co.uk
Recommended in Chancery
Specialisation: Company and Insolvency; financial sevices; Chancery and Commercial litigation; European law; judicial review and professional negligence in relation to the foregoing.
Prof. Memberships: Chancery Bar Association, COMBAR.
Career: Junior Counsel to the Crown (Chancery) 1994, Junior Counsel to the Crown (A Panel) 1999.
Publications: The Practice and Procedure of the Companies Court (1997).

JONES, Seán
11 King's Bench Walk Chambers (Eldred Tabachnik QC & James Goudie QC) London (020) 7632 8500
sjones@11kbw.com
Recommended in Employment
Specialisation: Principal area of practice is employment law, including discrimination. Acts for both applicants and respondents. Has been instructed by individuals, unions, multi-national businesses, small firms, local authorities and employer's federations. Has lectured/ tutored at Nottingham University, Worcester College, Oxford and King's College, London and given seminars,including addressing the Employment Lawyers' Association.
Prof. Memberships: ELBA (committee member), ELA (committee member), COMBAR, Discrimination Law Association, Industrial Law Society.
Career: Called to the Bar and joined present chambers in 1991.
Personal: Educated at Colchester Royal Grammar School 1977-84 and Worcester College, Oxford 1985-89 (BA Hons in Jurisprudence, BCL). Born 9th July 1966. Lives in London.

JORY, Hugh
Enterprise Chambers (Anthony Mann QC) Leeds (0113) 246 0391
Recommended in Commercial (Litigation), Insolvency/Corporate Recovery

JOSEPH, David
Essex Court Chambers (Gordon Pollock QC) London (020) 7813 8000
Recommended in Aviation, Commercial (Litigation), Shipping
Specialisation: Experienced in arbitration. Advocate in many ad hoc arbitrations in London involving a wide variety of commercial disputes particularly charterparty, aviation, insurance, reinsurance and commodities. Many of these disputes are governed by foreign law. Litigation experience: all types of commercial work including insurance, reinsurance, aviation, shipping, sale of goods, letters of credit, commercial fraud.
Career: Law Society Finals 1983. Called to Bar – 1984; began practice – 1985, in commercial chambers at Essex Court.
Personal: Born 22 April 1961. Educated at Pembroke College, Cambridge, BA Law, 2nd Class Hons. Good working French and basic Italian.

JOURDAN, Stephen
Falcon Chambers (Jonathan Gaunt QC & Kim Lewison QC) London (020) 7353 2484
Recommended in Agriculture, Property Litigation

JOYCE, Michael
9 Gough Square (John Foy QC) London (020) 7832 0500
Recommended in Crime
Specialisation: Criminal practice.
Prof. Memberships: Criminal Bar Association; Midland Circuit.

JOYCE, Peter QC
No.1 High Pavement (John B. Milmo QC) Nottingham (0115) 941 8218
Recommended in Crime

JUBB, Brian
Renaissance Chambers (Brian Jubb & Henry Setright QC) London (020) 7404 1111
Recommended in Family

JUDD, Frances
Harcourt Chambers (June Rodgers) Oxford (01865) 791559 (Oxford), (020) 7353 6961 (London).
fjudd@harcourtchambers.law.co.uk
Recommended in Family
Specialisation: Family law, particulary children's cases – public/private law and adoption. Matrimonial finance. Cases include Re O (Adoption: Witholding Agreement) 1999 1 451, Re M (Adoption or Residence Order) 1998 1 FLR 570, Oxfordshire County Council v L & F 1997 1 235, Oxfordshire County Council v P 1995 1 FLR 552.
Prof. Memberships: FLBA, Association of Lawyers for Children, Midland and Oxford Circuit.
Career: Called to the Bar 1984; Member of Harcourt Chambers since 1985; Based in Oxford since 1993.
Personal: New Hall, Cambridge, 1979-82. Born 1961. Married with two children.

KALLIPETIS, Michel QC
Littleton Chambers (Michel Kallipetis QC) London (020) 7797 8600
michel@kallipetis.com
Recommended in Alternative Dispute Resolution
Specialisation: Professional negligence, employment

law, entertainment and media law, building and construction, general commercial and business law. Other areas of practice include health and safety. Regularly mediates with considerable experience in a variety of Commercial disputes in excess of £30 million, professional negligence, employment, pensions, building and construction and general contractural disputes.
Prof. Memberships: Professional Negligence Bar Association, COMBAR, Employment Law Bar Association, TECBA, accredited CEDR Mediator.
Career: Called 1968 Gray's Inn; QC 1989; Recorder 1989, Deputy High Court Judge, Judge of Technological and Construction Court.
Personal: Cardinal Vaughan School. University College London. Exchequer & Audit Department (now National Audit Office) 1960 to 1968. Languages: German (fluent), French (working knowledge).

KAMLISH, Stephen
Tooks Court Chambers (Michael Mansfield QC) London (020) 7405 8828
Recommended in Crime
Specialisation: Principal area of practice is criminal defence work in particular murder, Prevention of Terrorism Act cases, serious fraud, large scale importation of Class A drugs, armed robbery (flying squad and regional crime squad cases), defence of alleged major 'target' criminals, and extradition in UK and Europe. Acts as leading Junior Counsel in the Central Criminal Court, London Crown Courts, High Court, Court of Appeal and House of Lords. Has made several media appearances.
Prof. Memberships: Criminal Bar Association, Lesbian and Gay Lawyers Association.
Personal: BA (Hons) 1978. Labour Party member. Leisure pursuits include gliding, cookery, badminton and go-karting.

KARAS, Jonathan
Wilberforce Chambers (Edward Nugee QC) London (020) 7306 0102
Recommended in Property Litigation
Specialisation: Practises in the fields of real property and planning (with a particular emphasis on landlord and tenant). Co-author of 'Unlawful Interference with Land' (1996) and a contributing editor to the 'Compulsory Purchase' title of Halsbury's Laws of England (1996) and to Hill and Redman's 'Law of Landlord and Tenant'.
Prof. Memberships: Planning and Environment Bar Association, Chancery Bar Association.
Career: Member of B Panel of Junior Counsel to the Crown.
Publications: Editor of the re-issue of the 'Distress' title of Halsbury's Laws (2000).

KARK, Tom
Hollis Whiteman Chambers (QEB) (Julian Bevan QC & Peter Whiteman QC) London (020) 7583 5766
Recommended in Fraud
Specialisation: Practice principally involves cases of commercial fraud including: fraudulent trading; VAT fraud; duty diversion; mortgage fraud; bankruptcy offences. Has also been involved in cases of alleged insider dealing, prosecuting for the DTI and defending. Also defends and prosecutes cases concerning money laundering, computer misuse and data protection (see DPP v Brown – House of Lords). Landmark cases have included defending as junior several SFO and Special Casework prosecutions (eg. second defendant in the Levitt case; Terry Ramsden; Swithland Motors).Criminal Law (General): Prosecutes and defends in all areas of criminal law. Member of 'Justice'.
Career: Called to the Bar 1982, appointed assistant recorder 1999, Recorder 2000.
Personal: Born 12th December 1960. Educated at Eton, Buckingham University and Ronnie Scotts.

KATKOWSKI, Christopher QC
4 Breams Buildings (Christopher Lockhart-Mummery QC) London (020) 7430 1221/7353 5835
Recommended in Administrative & Public Law, Environment, Local Government, Planning
Specialisation: Planning inquiry experience extends to all fields including (over the last few years, has appeared in at least 20 inquiries each year) acting for all the leading retailers in a large number of shopping inquiries; substantial experience of conservation cases (eg the Mappin & Webb inquiry for English Heritage and obtaining planning permission to develop over an Anglo-Saxon cemetery in Croydon; acting for Heron in the Heron Tower case); promoting a major development for the Army (Otterburn in the Northumberland National Park); Transport & Work Act inquiries (Chester Guided Busway) and conducting Local Plan inquiries. Leading planning court cases include: Tesco Witney (planning gain); Bolton (reasons); Mitchell (affordable housing); Edwards (alternative sites); Walton (implementation of old planning permissions); Porter (issue estoppel); Morris & Perry (old mining permission); Hambleton (PPG 6 and need); Skerritts (listed buildings curtilage, and the Marquee case); ADT (habitats regulations) Burkett (jr six weeks rule). Environmental law experience includes FOE v SSE (quality of drinking water litigation) and Ennerdale Water (abstraction inquiry) and advising in relation to radioactive waste disposal. Leading public law cases include Spycatcher (Contempt of court); Foster (jurisdiction of Social Security commissions); Balfour (national security); Save Our Railways (privatisation); Camden (housing revenue account subsidy); Warren (subpoena of judges). Public affairs experience includes advising various serving and former Cabinet ministers during the Scott inquiry.
Career: Lectured in law at the City of London Polytechnic, 1979-83. Called to the Bar, February 1982. Began practice at the Bar in January 1984. Queens Counsel 1999.
Personal: Born 16 January 1957 in Sussex, Polish parents. Educated at Cardinal Newman School, Hove, Sussex and Fitzwilliam College, Cambridge MA; LLB (1st Class Hons). Elected senior Scholar of College and University prize in law.

KAUFMANN, Phillippa
Doughty Street Chambers (Geoffrey Robertson QC) London (020) 7404 1313
Recommended in Human Rights

KAY, R Jervis QC
4 Field Court (Steven Gee QC) London (020) 7440 0900 JervisKayQC@4fieldcourt.co.uk
Recommended in Shipping
Specialisation: All areas of shipping and commercial law, including international trade, arbitration, marine insurance, carriage of goods, salvage, collision, marine pollution, towage, personal injury and professional negligence. Also sports law particularly related to yachting.
Prof. Memberships: London Maritime Arbitration Association (supporting member), London Common Law and Commercial Bar Association (Committee), COMBAR, British Maritime Law Association, Bar Sports Law Group.
Career: Called to Bar 1972. Called to Bar of New South Wales 1984. Called to Bar of Antigua and Barbuda 1998. Took Silk 1996.
Personal: Educated Wellington College and Nottingham University (LL.B), Editor Atkins Court Forms – vol 3 'Admiralty.'

KAY, Steven QC
3 Gray's Inn Square (Rock Tansey QC) London (020) 7520 5600 goodnightvienna@quista.net
Recommended in Crime
Specialisation: Wide experience in all areas of UK criminal law, with regular appearances in domestic murder, fraud and drug trafficking trials. International Criminal Law now a speciality. Now has an association with Professor Mischa Wladimiroff at Jan Van Nassaustraat 113, 2596 BS Den Haag, Netherlands in joint conduct of international work. Defence counsel for Tadic the first defendant to be tried before the UN War Crimes Tribunal for Yugoslavia and the first International Criminal Trial since the Nuremberg and Tokyo trials. Also representing Musema a defendant before the UN International Criminal Tribunal for Rwanda. First UN Defence Counsel to enter Rwanda. Expertise in European agricultural fraud (in Lomas v The Commission 1992). Lectures at universities and conferences throughout the world on subjects ranging from war crimes to the Financial Services & Markets Act 2000.
Prof. Memberships: Criminal Bar Association, European Criminal Bar Association (founder member and Treasurer), International Bar Association, Forensic Science Society, Society for the Reform of Criminal Law.
Career: Called to the Bar 1977, QC 1997, Secretary CBA 1993-96.
Publications: Contributor to 'Commentary on The Rome Statute of the International Criminal Court', OUP 2001.
Personal: Born 4 August 1954, lives in London.

KAYE, Roger QC
24 Old Buildings (Martin Mann QC & Alan Steinfeld QC) London (020) 7404 0946
Recommended in Chancery, Church, Insolvency/Corporate Recovery
Specialisation: The main areas of Business and Commercial Law including: Insolvency (personal & corporate); Civil Fraud; Company Law; Contract Disputes; Banking and Financial Services; Partnership Law; Professional Negligence; Land and Property Law; Landlord and Tenant; Directors Disqualification and other regulatory work; EU Law.
Prof. Memberships: Member of the Chancery Bar Association, Western Circuit, European Circuit, Ecclesiastical Judges Association.
Career: Birmingham University (LLB); Queen's Counsel 1989; Recorder 1994; Deputy High Court Bankruptcy Registrar 1985; Deputy High Court Judge (Chancery Division) (Queen's Bench Division) 1990; Junior Treasury Counsel (Insolvency) (from 1978-89); Chancellor of the Diocese of Hereford; Deputy Chancellor of the Diocese of St Albans; Judicial Chairman City Disputes Panel 1997; FCIATE (2001).

KEALEY, Gavin QC
7 King's Bench Walk (Jeremy Cooke QC) London (020) 7910 8300 clerks@7kbw.law.co.uk
Recommended in Arbitration (International), Commercial (Litigation), Insurance, Shipping
Specialisation: Specialises in all aspects of commercial law for mainly international clients. Particular emphasis on insurance, reinsurance, arbitration, banking, financial services, professional negligence, conflicts of laws, shipping and contracts of all kinds. Recent reported cases include Kingscroft and Walbrook v Nissan [1999] LRLR 603, (Reinsurance Pool/quota share/ excess of loss/retention/utmost good faith); Rothschild Assurance v Collyear [1999] 1 LRLR Rep 6, (Pensions mis-selling, construction of professional indemnity policy); Denby v Marchant & Yasuda v Lloyds's Underwriters [1998] 1 LRLR 343. CA. (Aggregate Extension Clauses); Den Danske A/S, Normura Bank and others v Kleinwort Benson, Skipton BS and Economic Insurance (Dec. 1997, Thomas J, Loan Portfolio Transfers, lending criteria, insurance construction); Sumitomo Bank Ltd, Sanwa Bank Ltd & Arab Bank Ltd v Banque Bruxelles Lambert [1997] 1 Lloyd's Rep 487 (duties of care owed to syndicate of banks by Agent bank), Tharros Shipping v Bias Shipping [1997] 1 Lloyd's Rep 246 and Pendennis Shipyard v Magrathea [1998] 1 Lloyd's Rep 315 (costs payable by a non-party); Glencore v Portman [1997] 1 Lloyd's Rep 225 (insurance, non-disclosure, waiver); Excess Insurance v Mander [1997] 2

Lloyd's Rep 119 (reinsurance, incorporation, arbitration clause); Also has experience appearing before foreign courts as both advocate and expert. Speaks very good French. Considerable experience of international arbitration in England and abroad eg oil and gas, satellite insurance, company and share valuations.
Career: Called to the Bar 1977; Joined present chambers 1978; Took Silk 1994. Recorder 2000.
Personal: Educated at University College, Oxford (BA Hons Jurisprudence 1st class). Lecturer in law, King's College, London 1976-77.

KEEHAN, Michael QC
St. Ive's Chambers (Julia Macur QC) Birmingham (0121) 236 0863
Recommended in Family
Specialisation: Specialises in family law, dealing with children's cases, both public and private law, ancillary relief and personal injury.
Prof. Memberships: Family Law Bar Association; Personal Injury Bar Association; BAAF.
Career: Birmingham University LLB (Hons); Called to the Bar 1982; QC 2001; Recorder 2001.

KEFFORD, Anthony
East Anglian Chambers (Roderick Newton) Norwich (01603) 617351
Recommended in Family
Specialisation: Divorce, matrimonial finance, all aspects of child law including care proceedings. Local Authority work undertaken.
Prof. Memberships: Family Law Bar Association.
Career: Called to the Bar in 1980.

KELLY, Andrew QC
2 Harcourt Buildings (Gerard Ryan QC) London (020) 7353 8415
clerks@2hb.law.co.uk
Recommended in Planning
Specialisation: Town and country planning, local government, environment, Heathrow Terminal 5 Public Inquiry, (British Airways), retail, housing, minerals, local plan inquiries.
Prof. Memberships: PEBA, ALBA.
Career: Called 1978 (Northern Ireland 1982). Chambers 1981. Silk 2000.
Personal: Education: Bangor Grammar (Northern Ireland), Christ Church, Oxford. MA (Oxon), Lincoln's Inn. Leisure: sport, arts, gardening, travel.

KELLY, Matthias QC
Old Square Chambers (John Hendy QC) London (020) 7269 0300
kelly@oldsquarechambers.co.uk
Recommended in Personal Injury
Specialisation: Personal injuries, health and safety, employment, discrimination and consumer protection. Has dealt with all types of cases for both claimants and defendants. Particular specialisation in catastrophic injuries including brain injuries. Experienced in complicated litigation including radioactive pollution: Merlin v BNFL (1990) 3 WLR 383. Other cases: H v MOD (1991) 2 QB 103; Rastin v British Steel (1994) 1 WLR 732; Wells v Wells, Thomas v Brighton Health Authority; Page v Sheeness Steel (1998) 3WLR 329; Firth v Geo Ackroyd Ltd (2000) Lloyds LR (medical) 312; R v Broxtowe Borough Council, ex p Bradford (2000) IRLR 329; Rozario v Post Office (1997) PIQR P15; R v HM Coroner for Portsmouth, ex p Keane (1989) 153 JP65.
Prof. Memberships: Environmental Law Foundation; vice-chairman, Personal Injury Bar Association.
Career: Called to the Bar 1979. QC 1999. Member Irish Bar (Belfast and Dublin). Member New York State Bar and US Federal Bar. Former consultant to the European Commission on UK health and safety law. Editor, Sweet & Maxwell 'Personal Injuries Manual'. Fellow of Royal Society of Medicine. Member Bar Council 1998-date. Member General Management Committee, Bar Council 1999-date. Chairman Policy Committee, Bar Council 2000-01. member Ogden Tables Working Party (3rd and 4th edns). Chairman Public Affairs Committee Bar Council 2001-date.
Publications: Editor and contributor 'Personal Injury Handbook' (Sweet & Maxwell, 2000). Contributor, Munkman 'Employers' Liability' (13th edn).

KELSEY-FRY, John QC
Hollis Whiteman Chambers (QEB) (Julian Bevan QC & Peter Whiteman QC) London (020) 7583 5766
Recommended in Crime, Fraud
Specialisation: Practice divided between high profile prosecution and defence but now predominantly defence, especially white-collar crime eg Co-op corruption case, Jubilee line extension case etc. Recent cases: Serafinowicz (war crimes); Donald & Cressey (largest police corruption case since 1960s); Charlie Kray, Sawoniuk (war crimes).
Career: Former Senior Treasury Counsel.

KEMPSTER, Toby
Old Square Chambers (John Hendy QC) Bristol (0117) 9277 1111
kempster@oldsquarechambers.co.uk
Recommended in Employment
Specialisation: Concentrates primarily on employment law and personal injury law. His employment practice covers both individual and collective rights, dealing with contractual and statutory remedies. His personal injury practice is mainly work or industry related, but he has been involved in multi-plaintiff product liability, disease and 'disaster' cases. His involvement in both personal injury and employment law has resulted in regular involvement in stress at work claims. Notable cases Alexander v STC; Isle of Scilly v Brintel; Johnson v British Midland Airways.
Prof. Memberships: ILS, ELA and PIBA.
Career: Member of chambers since 1982.
Publications: Contributor to 'EU Employee Consultation 2000', Sweet & Maxwell.
Personal: Sailing, walking, theatre.

KENDRICK, Dominic QC
7 King's Bench Walk (Jeremy Cooke QC) London (020) 7910 8300
Recommended in Insurance

KENNEDY, Andrew
6 Pump Court London (020) 7583 6013
Recommended in Clinical Negligence

KENNEDY, Helena QC
Doughty Street Chambers (Geoffrey Robertson QC) London (020) 7404 1313
Recommended in Crime
Specialisation: Practises predominantly in the criminal law; she also undertakes judicial review, public inquiries and sex discrimination work. She has acted in many prominent cases including the Brighton Bombing Trial and Guilford Four Appeal, the bombing of the Israeli Embassy, the abduction of Baby Abbie Humphries and a number of key domestic violence cases.
Prof. Memberships: British Council (Chair), Human Genetics Commission (Chair), World Bank Institute (Advisory Council). A Labour Peer since 1997 and a Bencher of Gray's Inn.
Publications: 'Eve was Framed' (1992). Seminal report in further education, 'Learning Works' (1997).
Personal: Honorary Doctorates from 15 British Universities. Honorary Fellow of the City and Guilds Institute, the Royal Society of Arts and the Institute for Advanced Legal studies.

KENNEDY, Michael
India Buildings Chambers (Ray Herman) Liverpool (0151) 243 6000
clerks@indiabuildings.co.uk
Recommended in Family
Specialisation: Family law specialist dealing with public law Children Act work, including the representation of Local Authorities, parents and Guardians ad Litem in cases involving, inter alia, issues of physical, sexual and emotional abuse of children.
Prof. Memberships: Family Law Bar Association.
Career: Called 1985.

KENNERLEY, Ian
Broad Chare Chambers (Patrick Cosgrove QC) Newcastle upon Tyne (0191) 232 0541
Recommended in Family

KENTRIDGE, Sir Sydney QC
Brick Court Chambers (Christopher Clarke QC) London (020) 7379 3550
moyler@brickcourt.co.uk
Recommended in Administrative & Public Law, Commercial (Litigation), Energy & Natural Resources, Insurance, Media & Entertainment
Specialisation: General commercial and common law, constitutional law and law relating to newspapers.
Career: Called to Bar 1977, Lincoln's Inn. Practising barrister, England, 1977 to date. Silk 1984. Admitted as Advocate of the Supreme Court of South Africa, 1949. Appointed Senior Counsel, South Africa 1965. Former Judge of the Courts of Appeal of Jersey and Guernsey and Constitutional Court of South Africa.
Personal: Born Johannesburg, South Africa, 1922. Educated University of Witwatersrand (BA 1941) and Oxford University (BA Hons in Jurisprudence, 1948; MA 1955).

KERR, Tim QC
11 King's Bench Walk Chambers (Eldred Tabachnik QC & James Goudie QC) London (020) 7632 8500
kerr@11kbw.com
Recommended in Administrative & Public Law, Sport
Specialisation: Judicial review, sports law, education law, local government, employment law, professional negligence, disciplinary tribunals, defamation, European, human rights and commercial. Sports law clients include Nicholas Anelka, Tottenham Hotspur FC (gaining readmission to FA Cup and six restored points); Chelsea FC; Middlesbrough FC; Ipswich Town FC; Ipswich Town FC; AEK Athens FC (gaining readmission to UEFA Cup); Slavia Prague FC; the Football League (Stevenage FC v Football League, CA, 1996); the Rugby Football League; the Rugby Football Union; the Welsh Rugby Union; Lennox Lewis (Lewis v Bruno and WBC, 1995). Co-author of 'Sports Law' 1999. Judicial reviews include Bart's hospital closure cases (including R v Health Secretary ex p Hackney LBC, CA, 1995); challenges to disciplinary investigations into audits of Maxwell and Polly Peck companies (including R v Chance ex p Smith, DC, 1995); and Camelot's challenge to the "Big Three" bookmakers' competing product (R v DPP ex p Camelot Group plc, DC, 1997). Education cases include X v Bedfordshire CC (HL, 1995), Christmas v Hampshire County Council (1997), Richardson v Solihull MBC (CA, 1998) and R v East Sussex ex p Tandy (1998, HL) and Phelps v Hillingdon LBC / Jarvis v Hampshire CC (2000 HL). Employment cases include Doughty v Rolls-Royce (1992: CA); Duffy v Yeomans & Partners (1995, CA) and Preston v Wolverhampton MBC (HL, 1998 ECJ, 2000).
Prof. Memberships: Administrative Law Bar Association; Employment Law Bar Association; secretary of the Bar Sports Law Group; appointment as part-time chairman of Employment Tribunals from September 2001.
Career: Appointed Silk April 2001.
Personal: Runner of four marathons and keen Chelsea supporter. Married with three children.

KER-REID, John
Pump Court Chambers (Christopher Harvey Clark QC) Winchester (020) 7353 0711
jkr@ker-law.co.uk
Recommended in Family
Specialisation: Family law – ancillary relief. Children – public and private law. Hague and European Convention. Medical issues and the inherent jurisdiction. International and domestic law adoptions. White v White [1999] 2

WLR 1213 [CA]; REL, v, m, h (contact: Domestic violence) 2000 2 FLR 334; REX 1998 2 FER 1124 (adult sterilisations).
Prof. Memberships: FLBA.
Personal: MA (Cantab), Trinity College, Cambridge.

KERSHAW, Jennifer QC
No.6 Barristers Chambers (Shaun Spencer QC) Leeds (0113) 245 9763
Recommended in Crime

KERSHEN, Lawrence QC
Tooks Court Chambers (Michael Mansfield QC) London (020) 7405 8828
Recommended in Alternative Dispute Resolution

KESSLER, James
24 Old Buildings (Rex Bretten QC) London (020) 7242 2744
kessler@kessler.co.uk
Recommended in Charities
Specialisation: Revenue law, more particularly CGT, IHT, and what is loosely described as 'private client' work; offshore trusts; foreign domiciliaries; also taxation of charities and Inland Revenue prosecutions in tax avoidance cases. Has a particular fondness for trust drafting (having written the leading textbook on the subject). Founder of the Trusts Discussion Forum.
Career: Called to the Bar 1984.

KEYSER, Andrew
9 Park Place (Ian Murphy QC) Cardiff (029) 2038 2731
Recommended in Chancery
Specialisation: Contract litigation; banking; professional negligence; partnership; companies.
Prof. Memberships: Chancery Bar Association. Wales Commercial Law Association.
Career: Education: Cardiff High School; Balliol College, Oxford; MA (1st class hons.); Called to Bar 1986. Member of the Attorney General's Panel of Counsel (Provincial). Member of Panel of Counsel (General) for the National Assembly for Wales. Part-time tutor in company law on the Bar Vocational Course, Cardiff Law School, since 1999 (Company Law Course Leader, 2001).

KHALIL, Karim S.
1 Paper Buildings (Roger N. Titheridge QC) London (020) 7353 3728
Recommended in Crime
Specialisation: Defence and prosecution, with particular experience in serious violence (including murder), rape and other sexual offences, Drug Trafficking and Fraud. Represented the principal masochist in R v Brown (consent to assault), and the first Defendant/ Appellant in 'The Cambridge Two' (Misuse of Drugs Act). Criminal and civil litigation relating to company fraud. Represented the Appellant in Hannan v DTI (CA decision on the Company Directors' Disqualification Act). Civil claims against the Police.
Prof. Memberships: S.E Circuit; S.E Circuit Liaison Committee (Sec.); Criminal Bar Association; completed 3 years on the Professional Conduct and Complaints Committee; Bar Disciplinary Tribunal; Cambridge Bar Mess Committee; Norwich Bar Mess.
Career: Cheadle Hulme School (Manchester); Queens' College, Cambridge; call – 1984; Assistant Recorder 1997; Recorder 2000.
Personal: Married with two sons; Member of Hawks Club; lacrosse player, now turned to tennis and golf; alto sax in Soul/Blues band.

KHANGURE, Avtar
St Philip's Chambers (John Randall QC) Birmingham (0121) 246 7000
Recommended in Commercial (Litigation), Insolvency/Corporate Recovery
Specialisation: Company Law; General Commercial Law Insolvency.
Prof. Memberships: Midland Chancery and Commercial Association.
Career: BA, LLM University of Cambridge. Called to the Bar 1985. Recorder.

KHAYAT, Georges M QC
10 King's Bench Walk (Georges M Khayat QC) London (020) 7353 2501
Recommended in Crime
Specialisation: Fraud – white collar cases, banking, mortgage, insurance, VAT etc.
Prof. Memberships: Chairman Surrey and South London Bar Mess 1995-98, Member South Eastern Circuit, Head of Chambers.
Career: Called to the Bar 1967, Lincoln's Inn. Recorder of the Crown Court 1987. Q.C. 1992.
Personal: Reading, music, boating, travel and horse riding.

KIBLING, Thomas
Cloisters (Laura Cox QC) London (020) 7827 4000
thomaskibling@cloisters.org.uk
Recommended in Employment
Specialisation: Employment law with a particular emphasis on discrimination law. In recent years he has been involved in a number of leading appeal cases including Anyanwu and Ebuzoeme v Wouth Bank University (HL); Delaney v Staples HL (unauthorised deductions and notice pay); Jones v Tower Boots CA (liability of employers in respect of discrimination claims); Smith v Gardner Merchant CA (gays bringing claims for unlawful discrimination); Khan v The General Medical Council CA (claims against the GMC for unlawful discrimination); Cowley v Manson Timbers CA (re-employment orders); Aparau v Iceland Frozen Foods CA (scope of employment tribunal powers), Dr Shawkat v Nottingham City Council CA (the definition of redundancy); Jones v The Governors of Burdett Cootes School CA (raising new points of law on appeal); Owusu v London Fire and Civil Defence Authority EAT (continuing acts of discrimination); WA Goold (Pearmak) Ltd v McConnell EAT (implied term concerning the operation of grievance procedures); Coote v Granada Hospitality (victimisation post termination); P v S (transsexuals bringing claims for unlawful discrimination). Sits on the Editorial Board of the Encyclopedia of Employment Law, founder member of the Employment Lawyers Association and is a member of the Employment Bar Association.
Career: Called to the Bar 1990. Joined present chambers 1991.
Publications: Lectures widely on all aspects of employment law and publications include 'The Employment Law Handbook' (LAG).
Personal: Born 19 August 1957.

KILLALEA, Stephen
Devereux Chambers (Jeffrey Burke QC) London (020) 7353 7534
Recommended in Health & Safety, Personal Injury
Specialisation: Principal areas of practice are personal injury and health and safety. Predominantly plaintiff but some defence work. Emphasis on accidents in industry and accidents involving death, brain damage and spinal injury. Also specialised crime, including a substantial health and safety practice.
Prof. Memberships: Personal Injuries Bar Association; Association of Personal Injury Lawyers.
Career: Called to the Bar in 1981.
Personal: Born 25th January 1959. LL.B (Hons) Sheffield. Lives in Sussex.

KIMBELL, John
4 Essex Court (Nigel Teare QC) London (020) 7653 5653
jkimbell@4sx.co.uk
Recommended in Aviation
Specialisation: Aviation, carriage by sea and road.
Prof. Memberships: COMBAR
Career: Called 1995. Inner Temple.
Personal: Education: MA, MPhil Cantab. Single.

KIMBLIN, Richard
3 Fountain Court (Robert Juckes QC) Birmingham (0121) 236 5854
richard.kimblin@3fc.co.uk
Recommended in Environment
Specialisation: Environmental, planning and regulatory criminal law.
Prof. Memberships: The Planning and Environmental Bar Association; United Kingdom Environmental Law Association and Secretary of the West Midlands Group; The Administrative Law Bar Association.
Career: BSc (Dunelm); PhD; Royal Society Western European Fellowship. Prior to his call to the Bar, he was Associate Director of a firm of consultants, advising and negotiating on environmental and planning matters. Waste, water, pollution, minerals and criminal matters involving civil inquiries.
Publications: He has published widely in both academic and practitioner journals, including most recently 'Judicial Review of the Grant of Planning Permission' [22 October 1999]; 'Solicitors Journal', Risk, Jurisprudence and the Environment' [April 2000], JPL 359; 'The New Contaminated Land Regime' [19 May 2000], 'Solicitors Journal'.

KING, Neil QC
2 Mitre Court Buildings (Michael FitzGerald QC) London (020) 7583 1380
neil.king@2mcb.co.uk
Recommended in Environment, Planning
Specialisation: Practice encompasses town and country planning, compulsory purchase and compensation, rating, local government, environmental and public and administrative law.
Prof. Memberships: Planning and Environment Bar Association.
Career: Called to the Bar 1980 and joined current chambers 1982.
Publications: Joint editor 'Ryde on Rating and the Council Tax'.
Personal: Educated at Harrow School 1970-74 and New College, Oxford 1975-78. Married with four children. Leisure pursuits include music, golf and real tennis. Born 14 November 1956. Lives in Whitchurch-on-Thames.

KING, Simon
7 Bedford Row (David Farrer QC) London (020) 7242 3555
Recommended in Personal Injury
Specialisation: Personal injury and professional negligence practice acting for both plaintiffs and defendants but with emphasis on defence work. Regular clients are principally insurers and corporate bodies, including professional indemnity insurers for solicitors, architects and surveyors. Experience includes professional and insurance fraud cases.
Prof. Memberships: Professional Negligence Bar Association, Fellow of the Chartered Institute of Arbitrators (FCIArb).
Career: Called to the Bar in 1987, joined current chambers in 1988. Early practice in crime and general common law; subsequent specialisation as above.

KINGSLAND, The Rt. Hon. Lord QC
4 Breams Buildings (Christopher Lockhart-Mummery QC) London (020) 7430 1221/7353 5835
Recommended in Environment
Specialisation: Waste and waste disposal; contaminated land; integrated pollution control; water resources; pollution and planning; European Community environmental law; judicial review.
Prof. Memberships: PEBA; UKELA; Bar European Group.
Career: Call to the Bar, 1972; Queen's Counsel, 1988; Member of the European Parliament 1979-94; Privy Counsellor 1994; Bencher of the Middle Temple since 1996; Recorder of the Crown Court, since 1997.
Publications: Contributor to Halsbury's Laws on Compulsory Acquisition and on the European Communities

and to the Bar Council's 'Practitioners Handbook of EC Law on Environmental Law'.

KINGSTON, Martin QC
5 Fountain Court (Anthony Barker QC) Birmingham (0121) 606 0500
Recommended in Planning

KIRK, Anthony QC
One King's Bench Walk (Anthony Hacking QC) London (020) 7936 1500
Recommended in Family
Specialisation: Family (including divorce and children), child care, international child abduction.
Prof. Memberships: Committee member of the General Council of the Bar 1996-99. Secretary of the Family Law Bar Association. Member of Family Mediators Association.
Career: Recent cases include: Re B (Wardship: Abortion) 1991 2 FLR 426; Re H (A Minor) (Role of Official Solicitor) 1993 2 FLR 552; Essex County Council v B (Education Supervision Order) 1993 1 FLR 866; Re B (Child Sex Abuse: Standard of Proof) 1995 1 FLR 904; Re C (Adoption: Parties) 1995 2 FLR 483; Re B (Contempt Evidence) 1996 1 FLR 239. Re W (Minor) (Unmarried Father: Child Abduction) Re B (A Minor) (Unmarried father: Child Abduction) 1998 2 FLR 146; Re K (supervision orders) 1999 2 FLR 303. Re C (HIV test) 1999 2 FLR 1004.
Publications: Wrote the chapter in Jackson's 'Matrimonial Finance and Taxation' (6th edition) on 'Enforcement'.
Personal: Ipswich School and King Edward VII School, Lytham; Kings College London (LLB Hons AKC).

KITCHIN, David QC
8 New Square (Michael Fysh QC) London (020) 7405 4321 clerks@8newsquare.co.uk
Recommended in Intellectual Property
Specialisation: All areas of intellectual property including patents, trade marks, passing off, copyright, designs, malicious falsehood, confidential information, media and entertainment law, computer law and EC and other competition law with an intellectual property element. For comprehensive CV and list of recent cases, visit our website at www.8newsquare.co.uk.
Prof. Memberships: Chancery Bar Association; Intellectual Property Bar Association (IPBA); The Intellectual Property Lawyers Organisation (TIPLO).
Career: Called to the Bar 1977 and joined chambers in 1979. Took Silk 1994. Chairman, Code of Practice Committee, National Office of Animal Health (NOAH) 1995. Deputy High Court Judge, 2001. Appointed person to hear Trade Mark Appeals, 2001.
Publications: 'Kerly's Law of Trade Marks and Trade Names' (Sweet & Maxwell); 'The Trade Marks Act 1994' Sweet & Maxwell.
Personal: Educated at Oundle School 1968-72, Cambridge University (Natural Sciences and Law).

KNOWLES, Julian
Matrix Chambers (Nicholas Blake QC) London (020) 7404 3447 julianknowles@matrixlaw.co.uk
Recommended in Human Rights
Specialisation: International human rights, public and constitutional law, extradition, white collar crime including mutual assistance and money laundering. Many reported and unreported cases in these fields. Recent particularly important cases: Ex parte Pinochet Ugarte (Nos 1,2 and 3) (1998-9); Re Ismail (1998) (extradition); Taylor v Director of the SFO (1998) (libel/prosecutorial immunity); R v English (1997) (murder/joint enterprise); Mohammed v State (1998) (evidence/death row); ex parte Fininvest (1996) (mutual assistance); Logan v The Queen (1996) (Privy Council's capital jurisdiction); Thomas v Baptiste (1999) (human rights/death row); Briggs v Baptiste (international law/death row); Lewis v Attorney – General (2000) (judicial review/ prerogative of mercy); Cedeno v Logan (2001)(reasons/due process).
Prof. Memberships: CBA, ALBA
Career: Balliol College, Oxford (BA, 1990). Called 1994.Tenant 3 Raymond Buildings 1996-00. Founder Member, Matrix Chambers, 2000.
Publications: Extradition and Mutual Assistance (2001). Capital Punishment: Strategies for Abolition (2001). Sweet & Maxwell, Human Rights Practice (Contributor)

KNOWLES, Robin QC
3-4 South Square (Michael Crystal QC & Lord Alexander of Weedon QC) London (020) 7696 9900 clerks@southsquare.com
Recommended in Banking, Company, Insolvency/Corporate Recovery
Specialisation: Practice covers a wide aspect of general commercial, business and financial litigation, and legal advice, including banking and financial services, professional negligence, regulation, commercial fraud, corporate insolvency and reconstruction, corporate and partnership disputes, insurance and reinsurance. Reported cases in the last five years include Bermuda International Securities v KPMG [2001] TLR (pre-action disclosure in professional negligence cases); Clark v Nomura International plc [2000] IRLR 766 (proprietary trading and performance bonuses in City-based employment); Hillsbridge Investments Ltd v Moresfield Ltd [2000] 2 BCLC 241 (expert determination clauses; disposals of companies); Grupo Torras SA v Sheikh Fahad Mohammed Al-Sabah [1999] CLC 1469 (commercial fraud and conflict of laws); Moscow Bank v Amadeus Trading [1997] TLR (bills of exchange; company winding up); Re Schuppan [1996] 2 All ER 664 (solicitors and conflicts of interest); Socomex Ltd v Banque Bruxelles Lambert SA [1996] 1 Lloyd's Rep 156 (banking and commodity trading). Alternative Dispute Resolution experience includes mediation advocacy in around 14 mediations.
Prof. Memberships: Commercial Bar Association (Executive, Committee and Chairman, North American Committee); Chancery Bar Association; Solicitors Pro Bono Group (Trustee); Bar Pro Bono Unit (Trustee and Management Committee); Royal Courts of Justice CAB (Management Committee): Member of other Bar Council and Bar committees. Advocacy trainer for Middle Temple, Gray's Inn and South Eastern Circuit. Middle Temple (Hall Committee, co-opted); Education Committee; Gray's Inn; South Eastern Circuit (Committee, co-opted).
Career: Called to the Bar in 1982; Queen's Counsel 1999; Recorder.

KNOX, Christopher John
Trinity Chambers (Toby Hedworth QC) Newcastle upon Tyne (0191) 232 1927 info@trinitychambers.co.uk
Recommended in Family
Specialisation: High value matrimonial property (and cohabitation) cases (not children or public law). Particularly with fiscal, company, pension funds and missing money problems and sometimes trust problems. Keen on resolution of cases without the court system.
Prof. Memberships: FLBA.
Career: Kings School, Tynemouth. Durham University. Recorder 1996.
Personal: Interests include crime and France.

KORN, Anthony
199 Strand (David Phillips QC) London (020) 7520 4000 akorn@chambers2.demon.co.uk
Recommended in Employment
Specialisation: Specialises in all aspects of employment law, including sex, race, and disability discrimination, equal pay, TUPE, contracts of employment, restrictive covenants, unlawful deductions, redundancy and unfair dismissal. Appeared for the Respondent in Kellaway v Thames Valley Police (2000) IRLR 170, Mingo v Kent County Council (2000) IRLR 90 and Rossiter v Pendragon plc (2001) IRLR 256. Sits as an ACAS arbitrator.
Prof. Memberships: Employment Lawyers Association: member of management committee. Member of Employment Law Bar Association.
Career: Magdalen College, Oxford. Called to the Bar 1978. Researcher on 'Industrial Relations Legal Information Bulletin' (1982-90) and editor of 'Intellectual Property in Business' (1989-90). Blackstones 'Compensation for Dismissal'. Columnist for 'Employment Lawyer' and 'Personnel Today'.

KORNER, Joanna QC
6 King's Bench Walk (Roy Amlot QC) London (020) 7583 0410
Recommended in Crime
Specialisation: Practice focuses on all aspects of general criminal law including commercial fraud.
Prof. Memberships: Criminal Bar Association, South Eastern Circuit.
Career: Called to the Bar 1974 and became a tenant of current chambers in 1975. Appointed Recorder 1995. Took Silk 1993. Member Crown Court Rules Committee 1994-00. Elected Master of Bench, Inner Temple 1996. Senior prosecutor War Crimes Tribunal The Hague 1999-date.

KOSMIN, Leslie QC
Erskine Chambers (Robin Potts QC) London (020) 7242 5532
Recommended in Company, Insolvency/Corporate Recovery

KOVATS, Steven
39 Essex Street (Nigel Pleming QC) London (020) 7832 1111
Recommended in Administrative & Public Law, Immigration
Specialisation: Public law, immigration, prisons, social security, mental health, human rights.
Prof. Memberships: ALBA, BEG.
Career: Call 1989.
Publications: Chapters on judicial review and habeas corpus in 'Civil Court Service'; chapters on judicial review and immigration in Bullen and Leake and Jacob.
Personal: Fluent French.

KRAMER, Stephen QC
2 Hare Court (Stephen Kramer QC) London (020) 7353 5324 stephenkramer@2harecourt.com
Recommended in Crime
Specialisation: Criminal law specialist.
Prof. Memberships: Criminal Bar Association: Vice-Chairman 1999-00. Chairman 2000-01.
Career: Called to the Bar in 1970. Joined 1 Hare Court, (now 2 Hare Court), Temple in 1988 from 10 King's Bench Walk. Assistant Recorder 1987-91. Recorder since 1991. Standing Counsel (Criminal Law) to Customs & Excise 1989-95. Appointed QC 1995. Head of Chambers 1996 -. President, Mental Health Review Tribunal.
Personal: Educated at Keble College, Oxford and the University of Nancy (France). Born 12th September 1947.

KVERNDAL, Simon
4 Essex Court (Nigel Teare QC) London (020) 7653 5653 skverndal@4sx.co.uk
Recommended in Shipping
Specialisation: Time and voyage charters; carriage of liquid bulk cargoes; collision; salvage.
Prof. Memberships: LMAA (supporting member), COMBAR, LCLCBA
Career: Called to the Bar in 1982 (Middle Temple, Astbury Scholar).
Personal: Educated at Haileybury; Sidney Sussex College, Cambridge (Open Scholar, MA).

KYRIAKIDES, Tina
11 Stone Buildings (Murray Rosen QC) London (020) 7831 6381 kyriakides@11stonebuildings.com
Recommended in Insolvency/Corporate Recovery
Specialisation: Practises in commercial and Chancery litigation and advisory work, including contract, company law, corporate and personal insolvency, sale of goods, banking, guarantees and other securities, commercial fraud, credit and leasing transactions. Was appointed as an inspector for the Department of Trade and Industry to investigate insider dealing. An extremely effective advocate, she also has an excellent reputation for drafting and advising on company and commercial documentation.
Personal: Interests outside the law include the theatre and enjoying her Scottish art collection.

KYTE, Peter QC
Hollis Whiteman Chambers (QEB) (Julian Bevan QC & Peter Whiteman QC) London (020) 7583 5766
Recommended in Fraud
Specialisation: All aspects of crime, particularly commercial fraud, though recent practice has included murders, robberies and major drugs cases.
Prof. Memberships: Criminal Bar Association.
Career: Five years in mining finance and investment banking before practising at Bar. Called 1970, Recorder 1992, Silk 1996.
Personal: Trinity Hall Cambridge (MA Law). Ex-member NY Stock Exchange and Chicago Board of Trade. Married. Two children.

LACEY, Sarah H.
3 Stone Buildings (Geoffrey Vos QC) London (020) 7242 4937
Recommended in Chancery, Pensions
Specialisation: Pensions litigation and advice, acting for beneficiaries, employers, administrators and trustees, including trustees and administrators of public sector schemes. Also covers other chancery areas including commercial, partnership, trusts, tax and probate.
Prof. Memberships: Chancery Bar Association, Association of Pensions Lawyers, Association of Contentious Trust and Probate Specialists. Sits on the Professional Conduct Committee, Bar Council.
Career: Called to the Bar 1991, and joined 3 Stone Buildings in 1993.
Personal: Educated at Prince William School, Oundle (1982-87) and Downing College, Cambridge (1987-90). Enjoys walking and travelling.

LAIDLAW, Jonathan
2 Hare Court (Stephen Kramer QC) London (020) 7353 5324
Recommended in Crime

LAMBERT, Christina
6 Pump Court London (020) 7583 6013
Recommended in Clinical Negligence

LAMBERT, Julian
Albion Chambers (Charles Barton QC & Neil Ford QC) Bristol (0117) 927 2144 lambert@albionchambers.freeserve.co.uk
Recommended in Crime, Health & Safety
Specialisation: Organised crime, corporate, commercial and regulatory offences, homicide and fraud. Disciplinary tribunals. Notable cases include: R v Canaan (1991) 92 Cr. App. R 16 (joinder with murder); R v Smith (1994) 15 Cr. App. R (S) 106 (contamination of goods); R v Sallis & Others (1994) 15 Cr. App. R (S) 281 (prison riots); R v Hampshire [1995] 2 Cr. App. R 219 (childrens' evidence); Attorney General's Reference No.s 25-27 of 1995 [1996] 2 Cr. App. R (S) 290 (racially aggravated GBH); R v Broad [1997] Crim. LR 666 (conspiracy to produce drugs); R v Sweeting and Thomas [1999] Crim. L.R. 75 (treatment statements section 23 CJA 1988); R v Taylor-Sabori [1999] 1 Cr. App. R 437 (interception of communications); R v GWTC – The Times, 3 July 1999 (corporate manslaughter, health and safety at work).
Prof. Memberships: Criminal Bar Association, Western Circuit.
Career: London School of Economics, call 1983. Recorder.

LANDAU, Toby
Essex Court Chambers (Gordon Pollock QC) London (020) 7813 8000
Recommended in Arbitration (International)
Specialisation: International and commercial arbitration. All aspects of international and commercial litigation.
Prof. Memberships: New York Bar Association; COMBAR; London Court of International Arbitration; Swiss Arbitration Association; Chartered Institute of Arbitrators (MCIArb); Co-Chair of the Young International Arbitration Group (LCIA); Editorial Board of the 'International Arbitration Law Review'.
Career: Merton College, Oxford: BA (Law) – First Class Hons (1990); MA (1994); Bachelor of Civil Law (BCL) – First Class Hons (1991); Eldon Scholarship (1991); Harvard Law School: LL.M (1993); Kennedy Scholarship & Lewis Fellowship; Called to the Bar in 1993 (Middle Temple Queen Mother Scholarship & Harmsworth Exhibition); Admitted as an Attorney-at-Law by the state of New York in 1994; Called to the Bar of Northern Ireland in 2000. Retained by the DTI to advise on and assist in the drafting of the Arbitration Act 1996 (with Lord Saville). Advised on the arbitration provisions of the Contract (Rights of Third Parties) Act 1999 and drafted the ACAS Employment arbitration scheme. Member of the Lord Chancellor's Department Committee on the Hague Judgments Convention. Member of the UK delegation to UNCITRAL (since 2000). Annual visiting lecturer on arbitration law at the Asser Instituut in The Hague. Legal consultant to the Ministry of Justice of Thailand (Arbitration Office): 1993. Director of the London Court of International Arbitration.
Publications: Publications include 'The English Arbitration Act 1996: Text and Notes' (with Martin Hunter), Kluwer 1998.
Personal: Born 1967.

LANDSBURY, Alan
6 Gray's Inn Square (Michael Boardman) London (020) 7242 1052
Recommended in Crime

LANG, Beverley QC
Blackstone Chambers (Presiley Baxendale QC & Charles Flint QC) London (020) 7583 1770
Recommended in Administrative & Public Law
Specialisation: Public law, civil liberties, employment and discrimination law. Interesting cases include DPP v Hutchinson (Greenham Common Byelaws held unlawful by the House of Lords); Lloyd v McMahon (surcharged Liverpool Labour Councillors); Thomas v NUM (right of striking miners to picket); Halford v Sharples (acted for Assistant Chief Constable Alison Halford in her sex discrimination claim against Merseyside Police); Christmas v Hampshire County Council (House of lords held duty of care owed by teachers to children with special education needs); ex parte S (admission to mental hospital and Caesarean section against patient's wishes); R v CCRC ex parte Pearson test case on powers of the Criminal Cases Review Commission. Publications include articles for the Modern Law Review, Industrial Law Journal and Legal Action and co-author of Public Law Project's 'Applicant's Guide to Judicial Review'.
Career: Called to the Bar 1978. Appointed part-time chairman of Industrial Tribunal 1995. Former lecturer in law at the University of East Anglia.
Personal: Born 13 October 1955.

LANGDALE, Timothy QC
Hollis Whiteman Chambers (QEB) (Julian Bevan QC & Peter Whiteman QC) London (020) 7583 5766
Recommended in Crime, Fraud
Specialisation: Principal area of practice is all aspects of criminal law with an emphasis on high profile, serious crime cases and commercial fraud. Has recently been instructed to prosecute the Sarah Payne murder case.
Prof. Memberships: Criminal Bar Association.
Career: Called to the Bar 1966. Treasury Counsel 1979-92. QC 1992.

LANGDON, Andrew
Guildhall Chambers (Adrian Palmer QC) Bristol (0117) 927 3366
Recommended in Crime
Specialisation: Health and safety, serious fraud, confiscation and money laundering, drugs importation.
Prof. Memberships: CBA.
Career: Bristol University, call 1986.

LANGSTAFF, Brian QC
Cloisters (Laura Cox QC) London (020) 7827 4000 bl@cloisters.com
Recommended in Clinical Negligence, Employment, Personal Injury, Product Liability
Specialisation: Principal area of practice is personal injury, collective employment and Trade Union cases. Has been instructed in most major industrial disputes (eg ambulancemen's strike, coal strike, Wapping) since the early 1980s and many important collective employment and Trade Union cases, although majority of practice has been in cases of serious personal injury (usually caused at work). Other area of practice is medical negligence and product liability, including actions against drug producers. Important cases include Page v Hull University (employment); Walker v Northumberland CC (personal injury: stress at work); Reay & Hope v BNFL (The 'Sellafield' case); Peach v Metropolitan Police (Fatal assault by police/discovery issues); Ratcliffe v North Yorkshire CC (Equal Pay); News International v SOGAT (picketing: the 'Wapping' dispute); Clarke & Others v NUM (Miners' strike); Milligan & Securicor (TUPE; employment); R v Employment Secretary ex p Unison (Judicial Review, employment); Adams v Lancs CC (Transfers of Undertaking); Clark v BET (the largest award yet for wrongful dismissal); Carmichael v National Power (contracts of employment); Jesuthasan v Hammersmith (discrimination); MOD v Wheeler (compensation); Barber v RJB Mining (working time); Quinn v MOD (mesothelioma); Jolley v Sutton (personal injury); Humphreys v Oxford (TUPE) and the 'tobacco' cases. Appointed Council to Inquiry into Bristol Heart Babies deaths. Major lay clients include most Trade Unions and their members as well as legally aided victims of accidents (both factory and medical). Professional clients include Trade Union solicitors (in private practice and in-house), law centres, medical and environmental practices and the Medical Defence Union. Former senior lecturer in law. Conference speaker on equal pay and employment issues, and employers' liability for work-related illnesses.
Prof. Memberships: Chairman of PIBA (1999-01); Judge of EAT (2000); LCLCBA; ELBA; ALBA; ILS (Committee Member).
Career: Called to the Bar in 1971. Lecturer in law 1971-75. Joined present chambers in 1977. Appointed Assistant Recorder in 1991, Recorder 1995. Member of Northern Ireland Bar. Took Silk in 1994.
Publications: Consulting editor 'Bullen & Leake' and 'Personal Injury Handbook' (2001); contributor to Munkman; author of 'Health & Safety at Work' in Vol 20 of Halsbury's Laws (4th edn) and of various articles in journals.
Personal: Educated at George Heriot's School, Edinburgh 1953-66 and St. Catharine's College, Cambridge 1967-70. Governor of local primary school. Enjoys sport, theatre and TV, politics, mowing the lawn, his family and travel.

LAPRELL, Mark
18 St John Street (Jonathan Foster QC) Manchester (0161) 278 1800
Recommended in Personal Injury

LASOK, Paul QC

Monckton Chambers (John Swift QC) London (020) 7405 7211

Recommended in Competition/Anti-trust, Tax

Specialisation: Specialist in all aspects of European Community law. Main areas of work include agriculture, competition, trade law and VAT. Cases include R v HM Treasury, ex p British Telecommunications (1996, CA and ECJ: public procurement, interlocutory injunction, state liability); Commission v United Kingdom (1997, ECJ; product liability); United Kingdom v Commission (1998, ECJ; BSE); Philips v Ingman (High Court, 1998, Competition/IPR) Marks & Spencers v CCE (2000, CA: VAT capping); Three Rivers District Council v Bank of England (2000 HL, liability of banking regulator).

Prof. Memberships: Bar European Group.

Career: Called to the Bar 1977. Legal secretary (law clerk) to advocate-general JP Warner and advocate-general Sir Gordon Slynn, Court of Justice of the European Communities 1980-84. Private practice in Brussels, specialising in European Community law 1985-87.

Publications: Publications include 'The European Court of Justice: Practice and Procedure' (Butterworths 2nd edn 1994). European editor of 'Weinberg & Blank on Take-Overs and Mergers' (Sweet & Maxwell). Joint editor of the Common Market Law Reports and CMLR Antitrust Reports.

Personal: Educated at Jesus College, Cambridge 1972-75 (MA) and at Exeter University 1975-77 (LLM). PhD Exeter University 1986.

LATHAM, Robert

Doughty Street Chambers (Geoffrey Robertson QC) London (020) 7404 1313
r.latham@doughtystreet.co.uk

Recommended in Human Rights

Specialisation: Housing, administrative law and civil liberties. Recent human rights challenges have involved the compatibility of the regime of introductory tenancies and the procedures for issuing warrants for possession in the County Court. Judicial review applications have related to unfair and irrational allocation policies, housing duty owed to asylum seekers, assessment of housing need, renewed applications for accommodation, duty to act fairly, interaction between housing and community care duties, abuse of power by councilors. Group actions have involved disrepair, asbestos, infestations, environmental protection and noise nuisance.

Career: Former councillor and health authority member. Currently Chairs Victim Support.

LAURENCE, George QC

New Square Chambers (John Mowbray QC & Eben Hamilton QC) London (020) 7419 8000

Recommended in Chancery

LAWRENCE, Heather

11 South Square (Christopher Floyd QC) London (020) 7405 1222

Recommended in Information Technology, Intellectual Property

Specialisation: All aspects of intellectual property: patents, trade marks, copyright, registered and unregistered design right, passing off and breach of confidence; other matters with a technical content such as computer contract disputes, and data protection.

Prof. Memberships: Intellectual Property Bar Association (formerly Patent Bar Association); (Hon. Sec, 1992-97) Royal Society of Chemistry (Associate Member); Institute of TM Attorneys (Associate Member).

Career: BA Hons (1st Class) Oxon (Chemistry). MA, DPHIL Oxon (Chemistry). Called to the Bar October 1991 (Middle Temple).

LAWRENCE, Patrick

4 Paper Buildings (Jean Ritchie QC) London (020) 7353 3366

Recommended in Professional Negligence

Specialisation: Specialises in professional negligence particularly involving solicitors, barristers, surveyors and accountants. In addition, has extensive experience in general insurance matters. Cases include: Landall v Dennis Faulkner & Alsop [1994] 5 Med LR268 – barristers' and solicitors' immunity: Bristol & West Building Society v May, May & Merrymans [1996] 2 All ER 801, CA – solicitors' liability-causation; Penn v Brill [1997] 1 WLR 1356, CA – breach of warranty of authority by solicitors: Bristol & West Building DSociety v Fancy & Jackson [1997] 4 All ER 582 – solicitors' liabilities to residential lenders: Platform Home Loans Ltd v Oyston Shipways Ltd [1998] 3 WLR 94, CA – lenders claims – deductions for contributory negligence. Cave & Robinson Jarvis & Rolfe [2001] Lloyd's Rep (PN) 290 (solicitor's negligence: deliberate concealment).

Prof. Memberships: PNBA.

Career: B.A. (Oxon). Called 1985.

LAWSON, Edmund QC

9-12 Bell Yard (D. Anthony Evans QC) London (020) 7400 1800

Recommended in Crime, Fraud

Specialisation: Specialist in commercial crime and accounting/auditing negligence. Acts mainly for defendants in large fraud cases as well as advising government departments in relation to insider dealing and regulatory affairs. Has considerable experience in advising on accounting and auditing matters. Practice also covers general crime, particularly the defence of police officers, and judicial review. Interesting cases include 'Blue Arrow' (defended UBS Phillips & Drew); 'Maxwell' (defence of Ian Maxwell); the 'Pan-El' case in Singapore, and the 'Wallace Smith' Chancery case against auditors. Also defended police officers in the prosecutions following the 'Guildford Four' and 'Birmingham Six' cases. 1998: Leading Counsel to Stephen Lawrence Inquiry. 1999-01: representing army personnel in Bloody Sunday Inquiry. 2001: Reading for 1st defendant in Wickes plc SFO prosecution.

Prof. Memberships: Criminal Bar Association.

Career: Called to the Bar 1971. Took silk 1988. Bencher of Gray's Inn (1998); Chairman of Gray's Continuing Education Committee (1999-01).

Personal: Educated at the City of Norwich School and at Trinity Hall, Cambridge 1967-70. Leisure pursuits include music and rugby. Born 17th April 1948. Lives in London.

LAWSON, Michael QC

23 Essex Street (Michael Lawson QC) London (020) 7413 0353
michaellawson@23essexstreet.co.uk

Recommended in Crime, Fraud

Specialisation: Criminal law specialist. Practice covers general crime, serious organized crime, drugs, child sexual abuse, commercial fraud, police related actions. Contributor to the 'Inns of Court School of Law Manual of Professional Conduct' and author of 'Refocus on Child Abuse' (1994). Experience of advocacy teaching. Governing Committee IATC.

Prof. Memberships: Criminal Bar Association.

Career: Called to the Bar in 1969 and joined present chambers in 1971. Appointed Assistant Recorder in 1983 and Recorder in 1987. Took Silk in 1991. Leader of the South Eastern Circuit Nov 1997-00. Boundary Commissioner 2000.

Personal: Educated at Monkton Combe School 1959-64 and London University 1966-69. Born 3 February 1946.

LAWSON, Robert

4 Essex Court (Nigel Teare QC) London (020) 7653 5653
rlawson@4sx.co.uk

Recommended in Aviation

Specialisation: All aspects of aviation litigation, arbitration and advisory work. In particular aviation insurance; liability of carriers; manufacturers; maintainers and tour operators; regulatory issues; aircraft leases and finance; arrest of aircraft.

Prof. Memberships: COMBAR, MRAES.

Career: BA (Oxon). Dip Law (City). Called 1989.

LE GRICE, Valentine

1 Mitre Court Buildings (Bruce Blair QC) London (020) 7797 7070
legrice@lmcb.com

Recommended in Family

Specialisation: Ancillary relief.

Prof. Memberships: FLBA; PNBA.

Career: Called to the Bar in 1977.

Publications: Editor of 'At a Glance'.

Personal: BA (Dunelm).

LEAVER, Peter QC

One Essex Court (Lord Grabiner QC) London (020) 7583 2000

Recommended in Commercial (Litigation), Sport

Specialisation: Main areas of practice are commercial law, insurance, banking and financial services and arbitration. Involved in Tin Council and Mirror Pension Fund litigation, the Ford Europe case in the ECJ and major arbitrations including a large scale arbitration about the validity of the termination of a management contract governed by Middle Eastern law. Contributor to 'Pre-Trial and Pre-Hearing Procedures Worldwide' (Graham & Trotman and IBA, 1990). Deputy High Court Judge. Recently has appeared in a case that was heard in the House of Lords concerning anti-trust injunctions, and in a lengthy international commercial arbitration in Singapore. Has been appointed to the Court of Arbitration for Sport ad hoc division for the winter Olympics at Salt Lake City.

Prof. Memberships: COMBAR, IBA, Bar European Group, Midland & Oxford Circuit, London Common Law & Commercial Bar Association, Society of Commonwealth Lawyers, Society of Public Teachers of Law. Member of the Chartered Institute of Arbitrators. Member of Court of Arbitration of Sport.

Career: Called to the Bar in 1967. At Paper Buildings 1968-72, and joined current chambers in 1973. Took silk in 1987. Member of General Council of the Bar 1987-90 (Chairman of the Bar Committee, 1989). Appointed Recorder and Director of IMRO in 1994. Bencher of Lincoln's Inn 1995.

Personal: Educated at Aldenham School and Trinity College, Dublin. Leisure pursuits include being a football referee, sport, wine, opera and theatre. Born 28th November 1944.

LEDERMAN, David QC

18 Red Lion Court (Anthony Arlidge QC) London (020) 7520 6000
david.lederman@18rlc.co.uk

Recommended in Crime

Specialisation: Crime in all its aspects from fraud to robbery to murder to Brinks Gold Bullion Robbery.

Prof. Memberships: Criminal Bar Association.

Career: Cambridge M.A.

Personal: Eating, drinking, sport, theatre, cinema, opera, history, reading.

LEECH, Thomas

9 Old Square (Michael Driscoll QC) London (020) 7405 4682

Recommended in Chancery

Specialisation: Modern Chancery practitioner with particular experience in commercial Chancery litigation (including equitable remedies, fiduciary duties, financial services, offshore trusts, share disputes, telecommunications and warranty claims), professional negligence (including auditors, barristers, investigating accountants, solicitors, surveyors, valuers and US attorneys) and property litigation (including commercial landlord and tenant, leasehold valuation and real property). Junior counsel for the plaintiff in the Nationwide managed litigation and junior counsel for a number of the defendants in Thyssen-Bornemisa v Thyssen-Bornemisa in Bermuda. Notable cases include Target Holdings Ltd v Redferns (1996) AC 421 (breach of trust), Mannai Investments Ltd v Eagle Star (1997) 1 BCLC 390 (share warranty, rectification), Electra Private Equity Partners v KPMG Peat Mar-

wick (1998) PNLR 137 (auditors' duty of care), Nationwide BS v Balmer Radmore (1999) Lloyd's Rep (PN) 241 (solicitors' negligence, managed litigation).
Prof. Memberships: Chancery Bar Association, Professional Negligence Bar Association.
Career: Educated at Lancaster Royal Grammar School and Wadham College, Oxford (MA, BCL), called in 1988 (Harmsworth Major Scholar of the Middle Temple, winner of the Astbury Prize).
Publications: 'Flenley & Leech, Solicitors' Negligence' (Butterworths, 1999), contributor to the Lloyds's Law Reports (PN).

LEEMING, Ian QC
St. James's Chambers (Robert Sterling & Ian Leeming QC) Manchester (0161) 834 7000
Recommended in Chancery
Specialisation: Chancery and commercial litigation; building and construction work (technology and construction court/arbitrations). Insolvency, contentious company work, banking, professional negligence and civil fraud are emphasised. Reported cases include Williams v Burlington (1977) (Company Charges), Brady v Brady (1988) (Financial assistance for purchase of shares). Re: Abbey Leisure (1990) (Unfair prejudice petitions) P & C & R & T Ltd (1991) (Administrators and Section 11 of Insolvency Act 1986). Sen v Headly (1991) (death-bed gifts of land). Connaught Restaurants (1992) (Indemnity costs in forfeiture proceedings). Morse v Barratt (1993) (exception to Murphy v Brentwood principles). Re Jennings (1994) (Family provisions claims). Kershaw v Whelan (1996) (Discovery and waiver of Professional Privilege). Kershaw v Whelan (No. 2) (1997) (Fiduciary duties). Hurst v Bryk (1999) (solicitors' partnership dispute).
Prof. Memberships: Chancery Bar Association; Northern Chancery Bar Association; TECBAR; Professional Negligence Bar Association; Society of Construction Law.
Career: Called 1970. Silk 1988. Recorder of the Crown Court 1989. Practised at Northern Chancery and Commercial Bar until taking silk. Since has divided time between London and Manchester. Joined Lamb Chambers 1992. Deputy Deemster 1998.
Personal: Born 10 April 1948. Manchester University LL.B (1970). Sometime lecturer in Law Manchester University. Interests: the family; gourmet food; sports cars.

LEES, Andrew
St. Paul's Chambers (Nigel Sangster QC) Leeds (0113) 245 5866
Recommended in Crime

LEGGATT, George QC
Brick Court Chambers (Christopher Clarke QC) London (020) 7379 3550
leggatt@brickcourt.co.uk
Recommended in Commercial (Litigation), Insurance
Specialisation: Commercial Law: including insurance and reinsurance, professional negligence (involving accountants, actuaries, insurance brokers, solicitors and barristers), commercial fraud, computer systems litigation, shipping, company acquisitions, sale of goods and international trade. Other areas of practice include product liability law and media law/defamation.
Career: Called 1983; QC 1997; cases of note: Westdeutsche Landesbank v Islington; NRG v Bacon & Woodrow; Hill v M&G; Guiness Mahon v Kensington & Chelsea; General Union v NRG Victory; Dubai Aluminium v Salaam; South West Water v ICL; Re Medicaments.

LEGGE, Henry
5 Stone Buildings (Henry Harrod) London (020) 7242 6201
Recommended in Chancery
Specialisation: Chancery practitioner with particular emphasis on onshore and offshore trusts with related taxation issues and on pensions and professional negligence. Recent cases include Adam International Trustees v Theodore Goddard (2000) (professional negligence relating to failed export of trust), Meegan v Commercial Vehicle Spares (enforcement of determination of the Pensions Ombudsman) (1998) and Evans v Westcombe (1999) (missing beneficiary indemnity policies and relief from breach of trust). Particular experience of disputes arising out of venture capital acquisitions. Has contributed a number of articles to 'Trusts and Estates Law Journal' and to 'Private Client Business'.
Career: Called in 1993.
Personal: Educated Eton College and Worcester College, Oxford.

LEIST, Ian
2 Hare Court (Stephen Kramer QC) London (020) 7353 5324
Recommended in Crime
Specialisation: Criminal Law and Public Law.
Prof. Memberships: Criminal Bar Association and Administrative Law Bar Association.
Career: Called 1981: currently instructed in the Bloody Sunday Inquiry.
Personal: Film, music, reading, sport and travel.

LEMON, Jane
Keating Chambers (Richard Fernyhough QC) London +44 (0) 20 7544 2600
jlemon@keatingchambers.com
Recommended in Construction
Specialisation: Construction law, professional negligence.
Career: Qualified 1993; Inner Temple.
Publications: 'Professional Negligence and Liability LLP' – Chapter Seven.
Personal: King Edward V1 High School for Girls; Jesus College, Oxford (BA Hons).

LEONARD, Anthony QC
6 King's Bench Walk (Roy Amlot QC) London (020) 7583 0410
worsley@6kbw.freeserve.co.uk
Recommended in Crime
Specialisation: General criminal practice with a concentration on fraud.
Prof. Memberships: Inner Temple, South Eastern Circuit, Criminal Bar Association.
Career: Called to the Bar in 1978 and joined current chambers in 1979. Standing Counsel to the Inland Revenue, South Eastern Circuit 1993-99. Took Silk 1999.
Personal: Leisure interests include music and theatre. Born 21st April 1956. Lives in London.

LESLIE, Stephen QC
Furnival Chambers (Andrew Mitchell QC) London (020) 7405 3232
Recommended in Crime
Specialisation: General and commerical/white collar crime in particular S.F.O Inland Revenue, major custom fraud and other complex fraud (including overseas) criminal taxation appeals. Privy Council Commonwealth Appeals.
Prof. Memberships: Criminal Bar Association. South Eastern practise on other circuits.
Career: Call 1971. Silk 1993.
Publications: Articles in the Times Newspaper Legal Magazine on disclosure in child cases and on legal and criminal taxations.

LESTER OF HERNE HILL, Lord QC
Blackstone Chambers (Presiley Baxendale QC & Charles Flint QC) London (020) 7583 1770
Recommended in Administrative & Public Law, Human Rights
Specialisation: Lord Lester of Herne Hill QC specialises in public law, employment, media and European law. He was called to the English Bar in 1963, appointed QC in 1975 and a Bencher of Lincoln's Inn in 1985. He became a Life Peer in 1993. He is a former Recorder and Deputy High Court Judge. He was Special Adviser to the Home Secretary (Roy Jenkins) 1974-76 on anti-discrimination legislation. He campaigned for thirty years for a Human Rights Act, and is President of INTERIGHTS and a Council and Executive member of JUSTICE. He is co-editor of Butterworths 'Human Rights Law and Practice' (1999), and Honorary Professor of Public Law and University College London. He has argued many leading public law cases in England, in other Commonwealth countries and before both European Courts. He is married to a Special Immigration and Asylum Adjudicator and they have a son and a daughter.

LETT, Brian
South Western Chambers (Brian Lett) Taunton (01823) 331919
lett@SouthWesternChambers_co.uk
Recommended in Crime
Specialisation: H Brian G Lett Born 9 August 1949. Called Inner Temple 1971. Practised exclusively at the London Bar until 1992 when he moved to the West of England and joined the Western Circuit. Now practises mainly in London and the West. Specialises in serious crime and in particular serious fraud. Equally happy prosecuting or defending. Has prosecuted all types of crime as a leading junior, including murders and serious fraud (instructed by the SFO). Led the defence team in many cases involving professional defendants (solicitors, accountants and policemen). Has particular experience in defending United States citizens. Defends regularly before disciplinary tribunals.
Prof. Memberships: Criminal Bar Association. Central Criminal Court Bar Mess.
Personal: Married with four children of school age. RFU youth coach. Chairman, Monte San Martino Trust.

LEVER, Jeremy QC
Monckton Chambers (John Swift QC) London (020) 7405 7211
chambers@monckton.co.uk
Recommended in Competition/Anti-trust
Specialisation: Administrative law, Competition Law, European Community Law, International and Comparative Law, Utilities Regulation. R v Secretary of State for Trade and Industry, ex p Isle of Wight Council, 7 April 2000 (judicial review, EC Law).
Prof. Memberships: Council of Management and Executive Committee, British Institute of International and Comparative Law.
Career: Fellow (1957-) and Senior Dean (1988-), All Souls College, Oxford. Director (non-ex), Dunlop Holdings Ltd. 1973-80; Wellcome plc 1983-94; Member, Arbitral Tribunal, US/UK Arbitration concerning Heathrow Airport User Charges 1989-94. Visiting Fellow Wiessenschaftszentrum Berlin fur Sozialforschung, 1999.
Publications: 'Butterworths Competition Law' (consulting editor); 'Common Law of Europe', 'Tort Law' (comparative casebooks); Bellamy & Child, 'Common Market Law of Competition', 1st-3rd eds. (consulting editor).
Personal: Educated: Bradfield College, Berks; University College Oxford and Nuffield College, Oxford. Interests include classical music and porcelain.

LEVY, Allan QC
17 Bedford Row (Allan Levy QC) London (020) 7831 7314
allanlevyqc@compuserve.com
Recommended in Family
Specialisation: Expertise in child law, medical law and human rights law. Appeared in numerous leading cases in House of Lords, Court of Appeal and European Court of Human Rights including Re F (sterilisation), Re M (Children Act, Re H (Children Act), Barratt v L.B. of Enfield (negligence), W v Essex CC (negligence) and A v UK (Art 3 ECHR). Frequent broadcaster and lecturer. Chairman, Staffordshire Pindown Inquiry 1990-91.
Prof. Memberships: Fellow, Royal Society of Medicine, honorary legal advisor National Children's Bureau; Council of Justice.
Career: Called to the Bar 1969. Silk 1989. Recorder 1993.
Publications: Author and editor of books on child law and child abuse.
Personal: Educated Bury Grammar School 1953-61 and Hull University 1961-64.

LEVY, Jacob
9 Gough Square (John Foy QC) London
(020) 7832 0500
Recommended in Personal Injury
Specialisation: All aspects of clincal negligence and personal injury work, particularly cases involving dental, gynaecological and orthopaedic problems. Has a particular interest in industrial disease work, principally deafness but also work-related upper limb disorders. Bulk of personal injury work comprises slippers, trippers, snippers, lifters, and rear-end shunters.
Career: LLB (Hons) London (LSE) 1984. Called July 1986 and joined 9 Gough Square following pupillage there with John Foy and John Reddihough.
Personal: Young family prevents anything much other than supporting failing football team (as well as playing in one) and watching late night TV whilst eating pizza. Otherwise fanatical film & music buff. Byline! "Eat football, sleep football – practice PI".

LEVY, Michael
2 Bedford Row (William Clegg QC) London
(020) 7440 8888
Recommended in Crime

LEVY, Neil
St John's Chambers (Christopher Sharp QC) Bristol (0117) 921 3456
clerks@stjohnschambers.co.uk
Recommended in Commercial (Litigation)
Specialisation: Banking. Cases of note: Jarrett v Barclays Bank [1999] QB 1; Natwest Bank v Story, The Times 14 May 1999; Woolwich Plc v Gomm, [2000], 79 P and CR 61.
Prof. Memberships: Chancery Bar Association.
Career: Called to the Bar 1986. In-house lawyer, Lloyds Bank 1987. Joined St John's Chambers 1992.
Personal: Contributor to 'Paget's Law of Banking', 11th edn (1996) and to 'Law and Practice of Domestic Banking' (Penn & Wadsley), 2nd edn (2000).

LEWIS, Adam
Blackstone Chambers (Presiley Baxendale QC & Charles Flint QC) London (020) 7583 1770
Recommended in Sport
Specialisation: European Community law within a public, commercial, competition and sports law practice.
Career: Call 1985. Professional experience with *Wilmer Cutler & Pickering* in Washington DC and London and *McCutcheon Doyle Brown & Enersen* in San Francisco between 1985-88, and in the Cabinet of Sir Leon Brittan, European Commissioner responsible for competition and financial institutions, in Brussels in 1991-92.
Personal: Fluent in French and a working knowledge of German and Norwegian.

LEWIS, Clive
11 King's Bench Walk Chambers (Eldred Tabachnik QC & James Goudie QC) London
(020) 7682 8500
lewis@11kbw.com
Recommended in Administrative & Public Law
Specialisation: Main areas of practice are public law and judicial review, EC law, education, local government, discrimination and environmental law. Interesting cases include: R v Secretary for Trade and Industry ex p. BT3G (state aids and mobile phone auction); R v Head Teacher of Alperton Community School ex p. B (Article 6 and school expulsions); R v Secretary of State for the Environment ex p. Eurotunnel (imposition of security measures on Channel Tunnel); Preston v Wolverhampton NHS Trust (1998) (compatibility of time limits for equal pay claims with European law); Barry v Midland Bank plc (1999) (sex discrimination in calculation of redundancy payments); R v Secretary of State ex p. RSPB (1996) (Birds Directive); R v Powys Council ex p. Hambridge (1998) (power to charge for provision of community care services); R v Secretary of State ex p. Lancashire CC (1994) (local government reorganisation). Publications include 'Judicial Remedies in Public Law' (2000, 2nd), and 'Remedies and the Enforcement of European Community Law' (1996). Editor, Civil Procedure (The White Book).
Prof. Memberships: Administrative Law Bar Association; Bar European Group.
Career: Fellow, Selwyn College, Cambridge 1986-1993, Lecturer in Law, University of Cambridge 1989-1993. Called to the Bar 1987. Joined present chambers in 1992.

LEWIS, James
3 Raymond Buildings (Clive Nicholls QC) London
(020) 7400 6400
chambers@3raymondbuildings.com
Recommended in Crime
Specialisation: Extradition; fraud: judicial review of criminal matters and especially review of warrants; case stated; restraint orders; election work. Recent notable cases: R v Bow Street Magistrate ex parte Pinochet (No. 1) [1998] 3 WLR 1456, (No. 2) [1999] 2 WLR 272, (No. 3) [1999] 2 WLR 287; R v Governor of Brixton Prison ex parte Levin [1997] AC 741; R v Secretary of State for the Home Department ex parte Launder HL [1997] 1 WLR 839 (HL); R v Secretary of State for the Home Department ex parte Gilmore [1997] 2 Cr App R 374. R v Bow Street Magistrates Court [1998] 2 WLR 498; R v Staines Magistrates Court ex parte Westfallen [1998] 1 WLR 652; Government of Switzerland v Rey [1998] 3 WLRI (PC). R v Governor of Belmarsh Prison ex parte Gilligan (No 2) [1998] COD 195. Private prosecution for the Hillsborough Family Support Group 1996-00.
Career: B.Sc. (Hons). Call 1987. Recorder of the Crown Court 2000. Attorney General's List 2000.

LEWIS, Marian
30 Park Place (John Jenkins QC) Cardiff
(020) 2939 8421
Recommended in Crime
Specialisation: All forms of serious sexual cases particularly involving the examination and cross-examination of children of all ages and young persons. Serious fraud and serious violence. First language Welsh and able to conduct cases of whatever complexity in that language.
Prof. Memberships: Criminal Bar Association.
Career: Called 1978.
Personal: LLB at University College, London. Married with two children. Involved with advocacy training on Circuit. Outside interests include opera and music, Pembrokeshire. Parent Governor, Ysgol Gyfun Gymraeg Glantaf, Caerdydd.

LEWIS, Paul QC
30 Park Place (John Jenkins QC) Cardiff
(029) 2039 8421
Recommended in Crime

LEWIS, Ralph QC
5 Fountain Court (Anthony Barker QC) Birmingham (0121) 606 0500
Recommended in Clinical Negligence, Personal Injury
Specialisation: Catastrophic Injury Claims; Industrial Diseases; Medical Negligence; Professional Negligence.
Prof. Memberships: Personal Injury Bar Association; Professional Negligence Bar Association.
Career: Jesus College, Oxford MA (Oxon). Called to Bar 1978. Middle Temple. Recorder of the Crown Court. Elected to Bar Council 1999; Silk 1999.
Personal: Born 29 June 1956. Married with 3 children. Wine, antiques, shooting, skiing.

LEWIS, Rhodri Price QC
Eldon Chambers (Lionel Read QC) London
(020) 7583 1355
Recommended in Environment, Planning
Specialisation: Principal area of practice is town and country planning and environmental law including judicial review, public inquiries and statutory appeals to the High Court. Clients include development and waste disposal companies, waste regulation authorities and county and district councils. Author of article on Waste Management in 'Journal of Planning and Environmental Law' 1993. Co-author 'Environmental Law' OUP 2000.
Prof. Memberships: Local Government Planning and Environmental Bar Association, Wales and Chester Circuit, Midland and Oxford Circuit, UK Environmental Law Association 1999.
Career: Called to the Bar 1975. Appointed Recorder 1998. Appointed QC 2001.
Publications: 'Environmental Law' (OUP 2000).

Personal: MA Oxon 1970-73, Dip Crim (Cantab) 1973-74. Born 7 June 1952.

LEWIS, Robert
11 New Square (Sonia Proudman QC) London
(020) 7831 0081
Recommended in Environment

LEWISON, Kim QC
Falcon Chambers (Jonathan Gaunt QC & Kim Lewison QC) London (020) 7353 2484
Recommended in Property Litigation
Specialisation: Specialises in Chancery and real property law. Practice covers landlord and tenant, rent review, interpretation of contracts, agricultural holdings, conveyancing, easements, restrictive covenants, compulsory acquisitions, suretyship and professional negligence in connection with real property. Recent reported cases include Southwark LBC v Mills (quiet enjoyment); Bruton v London and Quadrant (licence or tenancy); Hindcastle v Barbara Attenborough Associates (disclaimer on insolvency); Jervis v Harris (entry to repair); Curtis v London Rent Assessment Committee (fair rent). In 1988 appointed by the Department of the Environment as a member of the Study Team investigating professional negligence and insurance against professional liability. Blundell lecturer three times.
Prof. Memberships: COMBAR; London Common Law & Commercial Bar Association; Chancery Bar Association. Governor of Anglo-American Real Property Institute 1995-97, Chairman elect 2000, Chairman Property Bar Association.
Career: Called to the Bar in 1975. Member of Falcon Chambers since 1976. Took Silk 1991. Appointed Assistant Recorder in 1993. Recorder 1997. Deputy High Court Judge 2000 Bencher Lincoln's Inn.
Publications: Publications include 'Woodfall on Landlord and Tenant' (General Editor since 1990); 'The Interpretation of Contracts' (1997); 'Lease or Licence' (1985); 'Development Land Tax' (1976); 'Drafting Business Leases' (2001). Consultant editor of Property & Compensation Reports since 1990.
Personal: Educated at St Paul's School 1965-70 and Downing College, Cambridge (1st Class Hons in English Tripos) 1970-73. Fluent French speaker. Council member of the Liberal Jewish Synagogue 1989-95; council member Leo Baeck College (1996-01). Trustee Centre for Jewish Education.

LIEVEN, Nathalie
4 Breams Buildings (Christopher Lockhart-Mummery QC) London
(020) 7430 1221/7353 5835
Recommended in Administrative & Public Law, Local Government, Planning
Specialisation: Planning, public and administrative law including local government, social security, education, mental health and community care. Has promoted a number of Parliamentary Bills. Recent cases include Nessa v Chief Adjudication Officer; R v Leominster DC ex p Pothecary; White v Special Educational Needs Tribunal.
Career: Called to the Bar in 1989. Appointed to the Supplementary Panel of Junior Counsel to the Crown (Common Law) in 1995. Member of the Planning and Environmental Bar Association and the Administrative Law Bar Association.
Personal: Educated at Godolphin and Latymer School and Trinity Hall, Cambridge. Awarded Karmel, Reid and Prince of Wales Scholarships at Grays Inn.

LIGHTWING, Stuart
Counsel's Chambers (Stuart Lightwing) Middlesbrough (01642) 315000
Recommended in Family
Specialisation: Family/matrimonial finance, employment, medical and other professional negligence, personal injury and partnership.
Prof. Memberships: Professional Negligence and the Family Law Bar Association.
Career: LL.B, FCIS, FRSA, MIMgt, FCIArb. Called 1972 (M.T). Harmsworth Law Scholar. Also barrister in NSW, Australia. Chairman of Appeal Tribunals.

LIMB, Patrick
Ropewalk Chambers (Ian McLaren QC) Nottingham (0115) 947 2581 clerks@ropewalk.co.uk
Recommended in Personal Injury
Specialisation: Psychiatric harm and industrial diseases litigation: Hicks v Chief Constable of South Yorkshire Police [1992] 2 AER 63; Alcock v Chief Constable of South Yorkshire Police [1992] 1 AC 310; Frost v Chief Constable of South Yorkshire Police [1997] 3 WLR 1195; Bannister v SGB plc [1997] 4 AER 129; VSEL v Cape [1998] PIQR 207; Tranmore v Scudder (CAT April 28, 1998); King v RCO [2001] PIQR 206.
Prof. Memberships: Personal Injuries Bar Association; Nottinghamshire Medico-Legal Society.
Career: The Edinburgh Academy; Pembroke College, Cambridge.

LINDBLOM, Keith QC
2 Harcourt Buildings (Gerard Ryan QC) London (020) 7353 8415
Recommended in Planning
Specialisation: Planning, local government, parliamentary, compulsory purchase and compensation law. Works for both private and public sector clients.
Prof. Memberships: Planning and Environment Bar Association; Parliamentary Bar Mess.
Career: Called to the Bar 1980. Joined 2 Harcourt Buildings (Gerard Ryan QC) in 1981. QC 1996.

LINDEN, Thomas
Matrix Chambers (Nicholas Blake QC) London (020) 7404 3447
Recommended in Employment
Specialisation: Employment law, discrimination law, public law, human rights and sports law. His employment law work tends to be cases which overlap with commercial law (restraint of trade, breach of contract, executive terminations), appellate work, cases with a European dimension (transfer of undertakings, equal pay, working time) and collective labour law (industrial action, recognition, etc). His discrimination law work covers race, sex and disability discrimination in a range of legal contexts. His public sector work is focused mainly on health and education. His sports cases include disputes between sportsmen and clubs or agents, and cases concerning doping in sport.
Prof. Memberships: The Employment Lawyers Association, Administrative Law Bar Association.
Career: BA Jurisprudence (First Class) and BCL at Keble College, Oxford 1984-89; called to the Bar 1989. Awarded Council of Legal Educational Studentship, and Prince of Wales, Atkin and Karmel Scholarships at Gray's Inn. Appointed Junior Counsel to the Crown (B Panel) in 1999.

LINEHAN, Stephen QC
5 Fountain Court (Anthony Barker QC) Birmingham (0121) 606 0500
Recommended in Crime

LISSACK, Richard QC
35 Essex Street (Christopher Wilson-Smith QC) London (020) 7353 6381 www.ralqc.com
Recommended in Crime, Fraud, Health & Safety
Specialisation: Public inquiries; professional negligence including clinical negligence; personal injury; commercial fraud; corporate manslaughter by negligence. He brings to his work his undoubted skill as an advocate, his ability to grasp issues of real difficulty, his appetite for detail and his ability to cross-examine expert and lay witnesses alike. This is all underpinned by the ability to strike up an excellent rapport with all manner of clients – corporate or personal, law enforcement agencies, and claimants and defendants. A team player, Richard Lissack is always open minded and receptive to group preparation whilst not abrogating his position at the head of the legal team. He has recently gained unequalled experience in the field of gross negligence manslaughter, as well as appearing in almost every significant public inquiry of recent times. Each of these areas has embraced health and safety law in all its forms. Recent Inquiries: Shipman Inquiry, Bristol Royal Infirmary Inquiry, Re Ladbroke Grove Rail Inquiry, Southall Rail Inquiry, Burns Inquiry, Royal College of Pathologists Seminar Chair of multi-disciplinary meeting re organ retention, National Seminar on Organ Retention, Royal Brompton Hospital Inquiry. Internal Inquiry, re Lawrence Dallaglio RFU Disciplinary Proceedings, re Coral Cove Internal Inquiry. Recent Criminal Cases: Manslaughter by Gross Negligence – prosecuting: A-G Reference Corporate liability in Crime, CPS Policy Directorate Generic Advice re Manslaughter by gross negligence, re Hatfield Train Crash, re Ladbroke Grove Train Crash, R v Litchfield (Maria Asumpta), R v Great Western Trains Ltd. (Southall Rail Crash), re Imperial War Museum, re Paloma I, re Army Cadet Force, re Exmouth Diving Centre. Manslaughter by Gross Negligence – defending: R v Stoddart and Kite and OLL Ltd, (Lyme Bay Canoe Disaster), R v Ayres O'Connor and Guideday Ltd (Pescado), R v Jessey (Lone Signature), re Imco Plastics Ltd, re Millenium and Copthorne plc, re Norton Serious Fraud for SFO: Maxwell, Operation Holbein Balfron Group, Gidney Securities Serious Fraud for Defence: R v Malik (Pharmaceutical), R v Oza (Pharmaceutical), R v Dean (Millenium Champagne). Recent Civil Cases: Microsoft Europe (Advising on confidential issue), Re Hunting with Dogs (Advising re English and European legal challenge to Hunting Bill), Gregory v Portsmouth City Council (House of Lords/European Court – scope of the tort of malicious prosecution), London Borough of Richmond London Borough of Harrow Manchester City Council and Redcar and Cleveland Council (Court of Appeal and House of Lords test case re cost of care in the community), Nationwide Multi party action re Organ Retention (Multi Claimant series of linked group and representative actions for thousands of claimants), Ratcliff v Harper Adams College (Court of Appeal – Occupiers Liability Act -What is the duty owed to an adult trespasser?), Mirage Inks v Rexam Limited (Court of Appeal/ Mercantile Court case – technical issues re Ink Manufacture), Wyke v Lloyds Bank (Court of Appeal – Extent of duties of Mortgages in possession), Diocese of Honk Kong and Macao v China (High Court, Hong Kong – Change in Education in Hong Kong), Sorsky Defries v C&E (Claim for damages for unlawful C&E raid on firm of accountants – large claim settled), Beverly Allitt litigation (QBD – Clinical Negligence – Including £2m action – infant who survived attack by nurse), re Princess Madawi (Chancery Division – Solicitors negligence Action for Crown Princess and Saudi Arabian Embassy), re Wheelwash Limited (Patents Court), re Hyder plc (Patents Court), Re Home Equity Release Schemes (QBD Multi Claimant series of linked group and representative actions for 11,000+ Claimants).
Career: Called 1978, QC 1994 aged 37, Recorder 1993 onwards.
Publications: For details see www.ralqc.com.

LISTER, Caroline
One King's Bench Walk (Anthony Hacking QC) London (020) 7936 1500
Recommended in Family
Specialisation: Child abduction, public law and private law cases involving children and their families, representing parents, local authorities, guardians and the official solicitor. Ancillary relief and other financial matters.
Prof. Memberships: FLBA.
Career: BSc London University in Comparative Physiology and Microbiology.
Personal: Two children. Endurance riding, renovating ancient cottage.

LITHMAN, Nigel QC
2 Bedford Row (William Clegg QC) London (020) 7440 8888
Recommended in Crime
Specialisation: Serious crime, heavy defence and prosecutions: Cases include high profile and 'sensitive' murders R v Pearce and R v Tien Lai (murder by 16 year olds); R v Ngai (murder by mother of four children); R v Paton (murder by battered wife of husband). Death in custody: R v Linford. Substantial white collar crime: Cases include the Ostrich Farm Fraud and R v Kaye (fraud on Balfour Beatty). R v Messingham (lead defendant in massive SFO case). R v Rasool: £25 million confiscation and restraint. Extradition work: Customs & Excise – briefs in Michael Michael supergrass cases and London city bond diversion frauds. Inland Revenue fraud – R v Litanzios and Edwards. Health and safety: R v Morris (explosion/manslaughter case); R v Wheeler (involuntary manslaughter). Police work: Substantial tribunal and judicial review work. Briefed in public malfeasance trial for high ranking officer involved in zero tolerance policing. Road traffic – for many years specialised in death by dangerous driving cases including private prosecutions and representing the campaign against drunken driving. National television appearances. Has appeared in British Indian Ocean Territories. Recorder of South East circuit; CBA and Essex Bar Mess.

LITTLE, Ian
9 St. John Street (John Hand QC) Manchester (0161) 955 9000
Recommended in Personal Injury

LIVESEY, Bernard QC
Four New Square (Justin Fenwick QC) London (020) 7822 2000 barristers@4newsquare.com
Recommended in Personal Injury
Specialisation: Principal specialisation is litigation in the following fields: general common and commercial law, personal injuries, professional negligence (architects, doctors, engineers, solicitors, surveyors and valuers) and insurance. Leading cases include Rahman v Arearose (contribution between tortfeasors); Pearson v Sanders Witherspoon (damages for loss of a chance); Kapur v JW Francis & Co (liability of insurance broker); Spring v Guardian Assurance (negligent references); Ancell v Chief Constable of Bedfordshire (liability of police); Halford v Brookes (limitation); Kumar v AGF Insurance Ltd (construction of insurance contract); Wood v Bentall Simplex Ltd (Fatal Accidents Act damages).
Prof. Memberships: COMBAR, Bar European Group; Personal Injuries Bar Association, Professional Negligence Bar Association.
Career: Called to the Bar 1969. Recorder 1987. Silk in 1990. Deputy High Court Judge. Bencher of Lincoln's Inn.
Personal: Educated at Peterhouse, Cambridge (MA, LLB).

LLOYD, Heather
Chavasse Court Chambers (Theresa Pepper) Liverpool (0151) 707 1191
Recommended in Crime
Specialisation: Crime, particularly allegations of sexual abuse.
Prof. Memberships: Criminal Bar Association.
Career: Liverpool University 2:1 LLB 1979.
Personal: Married, 2 children.

LLOYD, Huw
3 Serjeants' Inn (Robert Francis QC & John Grace QC) London (020) 7427 5000
Recommended in Clinical Negligence

LLOYD JONES, David QC
Brick Court Chambers (Christopher Clarke QC) London (020) 7379 3550
lloydjones@brickcourt.co.uk
Recommended in Competition/Anti-trust
Specialisation: EU law, public and private international law, public law, commercial law. Recent cases include Al Adsani v UK; Fogarty v UK; McElhinney v UK (State Immunity); Hamilton v Al Fayed (costs); Muvunyi v Secretary of State Lilly v Novo Nordisk; Ex p Pinochet (No 1) & (No 3) (HL); Locabail v Bayfield (CA); R v Lord Saville ex p A; P v P (Diplomatic Immunity) (CA); Philip Brothers v Republic of X (CA); A Ltd v B Bank (Act of State) (CA); Westland Helicopters v Arab Organisation for Industrialisation. Brussels Convention cases in Luxembourg include Webb v Webb; Kleinwort Benson v City of Glasgow; Cinnamond v Von Horn; Mietz v Gesselschaft Yachting; Société Group Josi v UGIC; Connaught Laboratories v SmithKline Beecham. Competition Cases in Luxembourg include LdPE; PVC I; PVC II; TetraPak v Commission; Blue Circle v Commission; British Cement Association v Commission; Banks v British Coal Corporation; Hopkins v National Power; NALOO v Commission I and II; Banks v Coal Authority. EU cases before English Courts include R v MAFF ex p RSPCA; R v Dover Harbour Board ex p Gilder; Richard Cound Ltd v BMW (CA); First County Garages v Fiat Auto; R v Comptroller of Patents ex p Lenzing.
Career: Fellow of Downing College, Cambridge 1975-91. Junior Crown Counsel, Common Law 1997-99; QC 1999.
Personal: Born 7th August 1947. Educated at Stowe School and Trinity College, Cambridge (BA Hons).

LLOYD-ELEY, Andrew
2 Hare Court (Stephen Kramer QC) London (020) 7353 5324
Recommended in Crime

LOCKEY, John
Essex Court Chambers (Gordon Pollock QC) London (020) 7813 8000
clerksroom@essexcourt-chambers.co.uk
Recommended in Commercial (Litigation), Insurance
Specialisation: Insurance and reinsurance. International trade. Shipping law.
Prof. Memberships: Committee member, British Insurance Law Association.
Career: Downing College, Cambridge BA (Law) (starred First) 1985. Harvard Law School LLM 1986. Called to the Bar 1987.
Personal: Born 1963.

LOCKHART, Andrew
St Philip's Chambers (John Randall QC) Birmingham (0121) 246 7000
Recommended in Crime
Specialisation: Experience in all aspects of serious criminal work including PII applications. Specialisation in Trading Standards prosecutions including Trade Marks work.
Prof. Memberships: Criminal Bar Association.
Career: Regular Commissioner in the Army 1984-90.

LOCKHART-MUMMERY, Christopher QC
4 Breams Buildings (Christopher Lockhart-Mummery QC) London (020) 7430 1221/7353 5835
Recommended in Local Government, Planning
Specialisation: Advises and appears for developers and local authorities at public inquiries and in the High Court. Planning inquiries include the Channel Tunnel Terminal (Waterloo), National Gallery Extension, and Mansion House Square Development. Planning cases in the House of Lords include Westminster City Council v British Waterways Board, Westminster City Council v Great Portland Estates, Tesco Stores Ltd v Secretary of State for the Environment.
Career: Called to the Bar July 1971. Took Silk 1986; Bencher Inner Temple 1993; Head of Chambers April 1993; Recorder May 1994; Deputy High Court Judge 1995; Assistant Boundary Commissionary 2000.

LODDER, Peter QC
2 Bedford Row (William Clegg QC) London (020) 7440 8888
Recommended in Crime

LOFTHOUSE, Simon
Atkin Chambers (Robert Akenhead QC) London (020) 7404 0120
Recommended in Construction
Specialisation: Domestic and international construction and civil engineering. Professional negligence (architects, surveyors, engineers and quantity surveyors), energy, oil and gas. Contentious (litigation, arbitration and adjudication), non-contentious mediation and adjudication. Practice includes large engineering projects onshore and offshore, Treasury advisory and litigation, commercial and residential developments, airport terminals, hospitals, computer installations. Cases include Vickery v Modern Securities [1988] 1 BCLC 428 (CA); Cadmus v Amec 51 Con LR 105; Crittal Windows v TJ Evers 54 Con LR 66; Humber Oil Terminals Trustees v Harbour and General 59 BLR 1 (CA); King v McKenna [1991] 2 QB 480. Amec Civil Engineering Ltd and Alfred McAlpine Construction Ltd v Cheshire County Council [1999] BLR 303, ABB v Zedal (2001) BLR 66
Prof. Memberships: TECBAR. Common Law and Commercial Bar Association. TECBAR accredited Adjudicator.
Career: LL.B (Hons) (Lond); Called 1988. Articles Editor for Current Law 1990-95. Member of Bar Council.
Personal: Married. Main leisure interest: squash.

LOMAS, Mark H.
Littleton Chambers (Michel Kallipetis QC) London (020) 7797 8600
Recommended in Professional Negligence
Specialisation: Professional negligence, instructed particularly by insurers of solicitors, barristers and accountants, but also acts for surveyors, engineers, insurance brokers, financial advisers and patent and trade mark agents. Appears regularly for professionals before their professional disciplinary bodies. Particular expertise in wasted costs claims, having conducted numerous cases at first instance for solicitors and barristers and having acted for barristers in two recent cases in the Court of Appeal where indemnity costs were ordered against the claimants – Wall v Lefever and Fryer v RICS. Member of the SIF dishonesty panel, examining solicitors on issues of dishonesty and advising whether cover should be withdrawn. Regularly appointed as arbitrator in disputes between firms of solicitors or between SIF and its insured. Recently successfully defended a firm of solicitors against a claim of racial discrimination brought by a member of the Bar.
Prof. Memberships: Combar; Professional Negligence Bar Association.
Career: Called to the Bar in 1977; 3 years in mixed common law/criminal chambers in 2 Pump Court; joined present chambers in 1982, then situated at 2 Crown Office Row, moving to present address in 1995.
Personal: Educated at Oundle School and Trinity Hall, Cambridge. Lives in London and Rutland.

LOMNICKA, Prof. Eva
Four New Square (Justin Fenwick QC) London (020) 7822 2000
barristers@4newsquare.com
Recommended in Financial Services
Specialisation: Advisory work in consumer credit, securities regulation and financial services, reflecting publications: (1) 'Encyclopedia of Consumer Credit Law'; (2) 'Lomnicka and Powell, Encyclopedia of Financial Services Law'; articles and papers in various national and international publications. (3) 'Palmer's Company Law' (Part 11); (4) 'Ellinger and Lomnicka, Modern Banking Law'. Adviser to UK delegation to UNCITRAL convention on receivables financing (1997- Vienna and New York),
Career: Professor of Law, King's College London. Called to the Bar 1974.
Personal: Born 17 May 1951; 1969-73 Girton College, Cambridge (MA, LLB; Chancellor's Medal). Married with three children.

LONG, Andrew
Peel Court Chambers (Michael Shorrock QC) Manchester (0161) 832 3791
Recommended in Crime

LONGMAN, Michael
St John's Chambers (Christopher Sharp QC) Bristol (0117) 921 3456
Recommended in Crime

LORAINE-SMITH, Nicholas
2 Harcourt Buildings, Atkinson Bevan Chambers (Nicholas Atkinson QC & John Bevan QC) London (020) 7353 2112
Recommended in Crime
Specialisation: Criminal advocacy. Has practised in all areas of crime, including allegations of serious professional and commercial fraud, sexual offences and organised crime. Since 1993, has specialised in allegations of murder, terrorism, police corruption and international drug smuggling.
Career: Called to the Bar in 1977. Appointed Junior Treasury Counsel in 1993 and Senior Treasury Counsel in 1999. Appointed Assistant Recorder in 1994 and Recorder in 2000.

LORD, Richard
Brick Court Chambers (Christopher Clarke QC) London (020) 7379 3550
Recommended in Commercial (Litigation), Shipping

LORD, Tim
2 Temple Gardens (Dermod O'Brien QC) London (020) 7822 1200
Recommended in Personal Injury

LOVELL-PANK, Dorian QC
6 King's Bench Walk (Roy Amlot QC) London (020) 7583 0410
clerks@6kbw.com
Recommended in Crime
Specialisation: General crime including commercial fraud.
Prof. Memberships: Committee Criminal Bar Association 1989-; General Council of the Bar 1989-92 and 1998-; International Bar Association 1993-; Panel of Chairmen Police Discipline Appeals 1991-; Human Rights Institute 1996-. American Bar Association (associate) 1997-.
Career: QC 1993; Recorder since 1989; called 1971.

LOWE, (Nicholas) Mark QC
2-3 Gray's Inn Square (Anthony Porten QC & Anthony Scrivener QC) London (020) 7242 4986
Recommended in Administrative & Public Law, Local Government, Planning
Specialisation: Town and country planning (all areas, with particular experience of shopping; housing; employment; leisure; listed buildings and major energy; waste and incineration projects). Local government and administrative law (particularly local authority powers and finance, including PFI and major projects) environmental and property related litigation and all tribunal work including Lands Tribunal. Judicial Review – both planning and local government.
Prof. Memberships: PEBA, ALBA.
Career: Called to Bar 1972. Same Chambers since 1973. QC 1996.

LUBA, Jan QC
Two Garden Court (Ian Macdonald QC & Owen Davies QC) London (020) 7353 1633
Recommended in Administrative & Public Law

LUCAS, Noel
1 Middle Temple Lane (Colin Dines & Andrew Trollope QC) London (020) 7583 0659 (12 lines)
Recommended in Crime, Fraud

LYDIARD, Andrew
Brick Court Chambers (Christopher Clarke QC) London (020) 7379 3550
lydiard@brickcourt.co.uk
Recommended in Aviation, Commercial (Litigation), Product Liability
Specialisation: Commercial litigation, product liability, insurance, reinsurance and aviation.
Career: BA (Oxon) LLM (Harvard).

LYNCH, Adrian QC
11 King's Bench Walk Chambers (Eldred Tabachnik QC & James Goudie QC) London (020) 7632 8500
Recommended in Employment
Specialisation: Principal area of practice is employment law, covering the full gamut of that specialism such as unfair and wrongful dismissal, sex, race and disability discrimination, trade union law and restrictive covenants. Other areas of practice are commercial and public law.
Prof. Memberships: Gray's Inn.
Career: Called to the Bar in 1983 and joined present chambers in 1984. Took Silk in 2000.
Publications: As an academic teaching at King's College London between 1971-84, Adrian published a number of articles and book reviews, including publications in the 'Law Quarterly Review'.
Personal: Educated at King's College, London. Jelf Medallist 1971.

LYNCH, Jerome QC
Charter Chambers (Stephen Solley QC) London (020) 7832 0300
Recommended in Crime, Fraud
Specialisation: His practice is predominantly crime, includes fraud, corruption, offences under the Companies and Financial Services Acts and other white-collar crime. Recent cases include: R v Lim and Others (the Grobbelaar Trial, alleged match fixing), R v Geoff Knights (Gillian Taylforth's partner) where the case was dismissed on the sole ground of adverse publicity, Football Association v Segers (alleged Bung) and Football Association v Burtenshaw (alleged bung with George Graham). He also practices in other serious crime, which recently included £60 million cocaine importation, money laundering, 'Arms to Iran', 'Arms to Liverpool' and the professional assassination of a 'supergrass'. His pro bono work has ranged far and wide including death row cases from Jamaica and fighting Planning Applications at Public Inquiries.
Prof. Memberships: Criminal Bar Association.
Career: University of Lancashire, BA (Hons). Silk in 2000.
Personal: Television work for Channel 4 – two eight part series of 'Nothing But The Truth' – moral questions set against a court room scene. His latest project is a pilot for a projected series of eight programmes called 'Crime Team' where a team of investigators are set the task of so living a real series of murders in the 19th century.

LYNCH, Patricia QC
18 Red Lion Court (Anthony Arlidge QC) London (020) 7520 6000
Recommended in Crime

LYNDON-STANFORD, Michael QC
Maitland Chambers (Michael Lyndon-Stanford QC & Charles Aldous QC) London (020) 7406 1200
Recommended in Company
Specialisation: Principal fields of practice consist of company and commercial litigation, including minority shareholders proceedings, insolvency, business law, commercial fraud, professional negligence, equity, insurance and reinsurance. Recent cases include Senate Electrical Wholesalers Ltd v Alcatel Submarine Networks Ltd. (Court of Appeal) concerning share purchase agreements and Gruppo Torras SA v At-Sabah (Court of Appeal) concerning commercial fraud.
Prof. Memberships: Chancery Bar Association, Commercial Bar Association, Insolvency Lawyers' Association.
Career: QC 1979. Has practised in foreign jurisdictions and has been called (ad hoc) for cases in Hong Kong, Singapore and the Isle of Man.
Personal: M.A. (Cantab). Bencher of the Inner Temple and Member of Lincoln's Inn.

LYNESS, Scott
Eldon Chambers (Lionel Read QC) London (020) 7583 1355
Recommended in Planning

MABB, David QC
Erskine Chambers (Robin Potts QC) London (020) 7242 5532
Recommended in Company

MACDONALD, Alistair QC
Park Court Chambers (James Stewart QC & Robert Smith QC) Leeds (0113) 243 3277
Recommended in Crime
Specialisation: Principally, drug cases and those in which a scientific or medical element play a large part. These often involve DNA analysis as an important part and forensic pathological evidence is frequently of considerable significance. Commercial fraud is a growing area of practice.
Prof. Memberships: Criminal Bar Association.
Career: Wigan Grammar School followed by an honours degree in biochemistry. He conducted toxicological analyses and immunological research as a student. Once qualified, spent two years as a toxicologist in the Department of Forensic Medicine, Charing Cross Hospital Medical School using sophisticated analytical equipment of the sort used by the Government Forensic Science Service. Has also researched liver transplantation and the development of liver disease in cystic fibrosis patients after which he converted to law.
Personal: Sings second bass with the Leeds Festival Chorus and enjoys music. Also skis, rides, plays tennis and enjoys all sports. Also holds a private pilot's licence.

MACDONALD, Charles QC
4 Essex Court (Nigel Teare QC) London (020) 7653 5653
cmacdonald@4sx.co.uk
Recommended in Shipping
Specialisation: Admiralty and commercial shipping; carriage of goods; international trade; commercial and international arbitration; insurance; private international law; marine/environmental law; transport. Has extensive experience of all types of marine litigation including upwards of 120 salvage arbitration disputes. Among his recent cases concerning road transport, collision, arrest, sovereign immunity, statutory inquiries, carriage by sea and limitation of liability by tonnage are: Spectra v Haye Soak [1997] 1LLR 153, CA; The Giuseppe Di Vittorio [1998] 1LLR 136, CA; Northern Shipping v Deutsche Seereederci and others [2000] 2 LLR 255, CA; The ENIF [1997] 1LLR 643, Admiralty Court; The Sitarem & Spirit 11.4.2001, Admiralty Court; Formal Investigations Derbyshire (2000); Bowbelle/Marchioness (2000); The Zim Piraeus 27.6.2001 CA. Also regularly appears in City of London commercial arbitrations.
Prof. Memberships: Member of the Panel of Lloyds Salvage Arbitrators 2000.
Career: Glasgow Academy, New College Oxford (MA Hons Jurisprudence 1971). Called to Bar, Lincoln's Inn, 1972. Appointments: Queen's Counsel, 1992. Assistant Recorder of the Crown Court, 1996. Recorder of the Crown Court 1999. Lloyd's Salvage Arbitrator 2000.
Publications: Editorial Board, 'International Maritime Law' (Lawtext Publishing Limited).
Personal: DOB 31.8.49, Glasgow. Married with three daughters and lives in East Sussex.

MACDONALD, Ian QC
Two Garden Court (Ian Macdonald QC & Owen Davies QC) London (020) 7353 1633
iamacdonald12@yahoo.co.uk
Recommended in Crime, Immigration
Specialisation: Main specialisations: immigration and criminal law, but also general administrative law, coroners' inquests, employment and trade union law, race and sex discrimination law. Author of 'Macdonald's Immigration Law and Practice', 5th edn 2001. Chaired a number of public and private inquiries including inquiry into racial violence in Manchester schools (1987-88), the report of which is published as 'Murder in the Playground'. Other publications: 'Resale Price Maintenance' (1964); 'The Land Commission Act 1967' (Co-author); 'Race Relations and Immigration Law' (1969); 'Race Relations; The New Law' (1977); 'The New Nationality Law' with Nicholas Blake QC (1984). Is on editorial board of Immigration and Nationality Law and Practice.
Prof. Memberships: Immigration Law Practitioners Association (president since 1984). Criminal Bar Association. Administrative Law Bar Association. Bar European Group.
Career: Called to Bar 1963. QC 1988.
Personal: Fluent French.

MACDONALD, Ken QC
Matrix Chambers (Nicholas Blake QC) London (020) 7404 3447
Recommended in Crime, Fraud, Human Rights
Specialisation: A criminal law specialist. Complex frauds (including SFO work, deposit-taking frauds, advance fee frauds, solicitor frauds etc). Sanctions-busting cases (all aspects, including the illegal export of arms and weapons-making equipment, computers, high technology, pharmaceuticals etc. Clients in this area include major foreign defence corporations). Political violence (Irish, Sikh, Palestinian and Algerian). Bombings, murders and possession of arms and explosives. Major drugs conspiracies (importation, manufacture and supply). Murders (including multiple murders and child killings). Cases include Matrix Churchill; The Ordtech Appeal; R v McKane (an IRA trial involving bombings and multiple murders); R v Kinsella (the Warrington bombing case); R v Sakaria (a Sikh separatist case involving explosives and conspiracies to murder); R v Zekra (the car-bombing of the Israeli Embassy in London).
Prof. Memberships: Deputy Chair, Bar Public Affairs Group; member Treasury Counsel Selection Committee (CCC).

MACHELL, John
Serle Court (Lord Neill of Bladen QC) London (020) 7242 6105
clerks@serlecourt.co.uk
Recommended in Partnership
Specialisation: General commercial/chancery dispute resolution and advisory work, particularly partnership, company, insolvency, property, wills, trusts and probate.
Prof. Memberships: Association of Partnership Practitioners, COMBAR.
Career: University of Southampton 1988-92 LLB (1st Class). Serle Court (formerly 13 Old Square) 1994 to date.
Publications: 'Limited Liability Partnerships', Jordans (forthcoming publication).
Personal: Married with two children.

MACHELL, Raymond QC
Deans Court Chambers (Stephen Grime QC) Manchester (0161) 214 6000
Recommended in Personal Injury

MACLEAN, Alan
Brick Court Chambers (Christopher Clarke QC) London (020) 7379 3550
maclean@brickcourt.co.uk
Recommended in Administrative & Public Law
Specialisation: Administrative and public law specialism within wide-ranging commercial practice. Particular

emphasis on commercial judicial review and related regulatory, EU and human rights issues. Also has experience of administrative law in, among others, the fields of environment, health, funding entitlement, local government and sporting bodies. Has appeared in public law cases in the ECJ, House of Lords and Court of Appeal. Recent cases include BT3G Ltd v Secretary of State (challenge to legality of Third Generation Mobile Phones auction); Hamilton v Al Fayed (resisting costs application against funders of libel action); Heather v Leonard Cheshire (whether private sector body 'public authority' under Human Rights Act). Present work includes Transport for London v London Regional Transport (challenge to PPP tube financing plans). Reported cases include Smith v Bridgend County Borough Council [2000] 1 BCLC 775 CA (powers of company administrator); Legal Aid Board ex p Coe [2000] 1 WLR 1909 CA (circumstances in which the Legal Aid Board could amend a certificate); Gloucestershire ex p Barry [1997] AC 584 (whether local authority entitled to take account of resources when assessing need); Porter v Magill (1997) 96 LGR 157 DC (Westminster 'Homes for Votes' appeal); Cosslett Contractors Ltd [1998] Ch 495 C.A. (equitable charges); Wandsworth ex p Beckwith [1996] 1 WLR 60 (contracting out of local authority services); Secretary of State ex p Richmond [1996] 4 All ER 93 (night flights policy).
Prof. Memberships: Administrative Law Bar Association.
Career: Called 1993. Placed first in year at Bar School. Karmel, Bacon, Prince of Wales and Macaskie Awards from Gray's Inn. Scarman Scholar of Inns of Court School of Law. Appointed to Treasury C Panel 1999. Junior Counsel to the Bristol Royal Infirmary Public Inquiry.
Publications: Contributor to 'Halsbury's Laws of England' (local authority powers, Vol 43(2) reissue), Richard Gordon QC 'Judicial Review Law and Procedure' (2nd ed) (Sweet and Maxwell, 1995). An editor of 'Administrative Court Digest'.
Personal: Educated University College, Oxford (double First in PPE), Harvard University (Kennedy Scholarship) and City University (CPE: distinction).

MACRORY, Richard
Brick Court Chambers (Christopher Clarke QC) London (020) 7379 3550
r.macrory@ucl.ac.uk
Recommended in Environment
Specialisation: Environmental law, EC law.
Prof. Memberships: 2000 – awarded CBE for service to environment and law; UK Environmental Law Association (first chairman).
Career: Called to Bar in 1974. Professor of Environmental Law at Faculty of Laws, University College, London (since 1999). Formerly Professor of Environmental Law at Imperial College, London and University of Oxford. 1997 – specialist advisor House of Commons Select Committee on Environment, Transport and Regions; 1999 – board member, Environment Agency, England and Wales; member Royal Commission on Environmental pollution; chairman, Steering Group, European Environmental Advisory Councils (2000-date).
Publications: Author of 'Bibliography of European Environmental Law' (Oxford University Press 1995). Editor 'Journal of Environmental Law.'
Personal: Hon chairman, Merchant Ivory Publications Ltd.

MACUR, Julia QC
St. Ive's Chambers (Julia Macur QC) Birmingham (0121) 236 0863
Recommended in Family

MAHER, Martha
Guildhall Chambers (Adrian Palmer QC) Bristol (0117) 927 3366
Recommended in Chancery, Commercial (Litigation), Insolvency/Corporate Recovery
Specialisation: Company, especially shareholder actions; insolvency (company and individual); partnership disputes especially involving professional partnerships; banking; director disqualifications; professional negligence involving accountants; vets; commercial contracts and fraud; equestrian work. Recent cases include Bristol and West Building Society v Back and Melinek and Secretary of State for Trade and Industry v Griffiths (RE West Mid Packaging Services Limited) (CA).
Prof. Memberships: Chancery Bar Association, Society of Practitioners in Insolvency.
Career: BCL, LLB (Cork) LLM (Cantab). Call 1987 Inner Temple. Cork Examiner Scholarship, Inner Temple Major Scholarship. Member of Irish Bar and NewSouth Wales Bar.
Personal: Very keen on all equestrian sports, gardening, tennis.

MAIDMENT, Kieran
Doughty Street Chambers (Geoffrey Robertson QC) London (020) 7404 1313
Recommended in Crime

MAIDMENT, Susan R
One King's Bench Walk (Anthony Hacking QC) London (020) 7936 1500
Recommended in Family

MALCOLM, Helen
3 Raymond Buildings (Clive Nicholls QC) London (020) 7400 6400
Recommended in Crime, Fraud

MALDEN, Grace
35 Essex Street (Christopher Wilson-Smith QC) London (020) 7353 6381
Recommended in Pensions
Specialisation: Principal area of specialisation is pensions law, particularly in relation to occupational pension schemes and the mis-selling of personal pension schemes. Acted in Julsarben Ltd (1990) Retirement Benefit Scheme v JHG Norman (appearing for the Trustee in an appeal to the High Court from a decision of the Pensions Ombudsman); HF Pensions Scheme Trustees Ltd v John Gatenby & Others (appearing for the beneficiaries of the Scheme in litigation brought by the Trustees against, inter alia, the solicitors advising the Scheme). In addition, she also covers other areas of general chancery and civil practice including breach of trust cases, professional negligence, and partnership disputes.
Prof. Memberships: Association of Pension Lawyers; Professional Negligence Bar Association; Bar Human Rights Committee.
Career: Called to the Bar in 1993 and joined Essex Street on completing pupillage in 1994.
Personal: Born 21 January 1969; educated Bedales School 1981-86; Trinity Hall Cambridge 1987-90 (BA, Classics); University of Westminster 1992 (Law Diploma).

MALE, John QC
4 Breams Buildings (Christopher Lockhart-Mummery QC) London (020) 7430 1221/7353 5835
Recommended in Property Litigation
Specialisation: Landlord and tenant, town and country planning, compulsory purchase and compensation.
Prof. Memberships: Called to the Bar by Lincolns Inn in 1976 and is a member of the Chancery Bar Association and the Planning and Environment Bar Association.
Career: Educated at Minchenden Grammar School, London and Sidney Sussex College, Cambridge obtaining a BA in law. One of the contributors to Halsbury's Laws on Town and Country Planning. An editor of 'Hill & Redman's Law of Landlord and Tenant'.

MALEK, Ali QC
3 Verulam Buildings (Christopher Symons QC & John Jarvis QC) London (020) 7831 8441
amalek@3vb.com
Recommended in Arbitration (International), Banking, Commercial (Litigation), Fraud
Specialisation: All aspects of commercial law with emphasis on banking. International arbitration and domestic arbitration. Professional negligence, fraud, oil and gas, and conflict of laws. Cases include Cryne v Barclays (1987) (bank's repayment rights); A v B (1993) (Banking Act). Barclays v Khaira (1992) (securities). Re Rafidain (1992) (bank accounts/sovereign immunity). Tudorgrange v Citibank (1992) (releases and UCTA 1977). EDF Mann v Haryanto (1991) (anti-suit injunctions). Natwest v Daniel (1993) (summary judgment). Robertson v CICB (1994) (confidentiality). Glencore v Bank of China (1996) (ICC 500) National Provincial Building Society v Lloyd (1996) (suspended possession orders). Barclays Bank v Thomson (1997) (undue influence). BCCI v PW (1998) (Banking Act). Bank Melli v Ispahani (1998) (illegality/conflict of laws). Box v Barclays (1998) (constructive trusts). Bolkiah v Prince Jefri (1998) (chinese walls). Yorkshire Bank v Lloyds (1999) (collecting bank's duties). Turner v RBS (1999) (confidentiality). Young v Robson Rhodes (1999) (chinese walls). Halewood v Addleshaw Booth & Co (1999) (chinese Walls), Sepoong v Formula One (2000) (contract): Dubai Aluminium v Salaam (2000) (constructive trusts/fraud); Portman v Dussansh (2000) (unconscionable bargain). Alliance and Leicester v Slayford (2000) (mortgagees rights); Montrod v Grundkotter (2000) (letter of credit and fraud); Casson v Ostley (2001) (fire insurance and exclusion clauses). Frequent speaker on these topics at seminars. 'Banks, Fraud and Crime' published in 'Cross-Border Fraudulent Activity' (Pub Lloyd's of London Press, 2nd Edition, 2000). Jack, Malek and Quest; 'Documentary Credits' (3rd edn) (2001).
Prof. Memberships: IBA, COMBAR.
Career: Called to the Bar 1980. QC 1996. Recorder 1998.
Personal: Bedford School, Keble College, Oxford. BA (1978), BCL(OXON) (first class). Leisure pursuits and family life. Born 1956.

MALEK, Hodge M QC
4-5 Gray's Inn Square (Elizabeth Appleby QC & David Mole QC) London (020) 7404 5252
hmalek@4-5graysinnsquare.co.uk
Recommended in Banking
Specialisation: Specialises in commercial law, including accountancy, banking, company, financial services, fraud, insurance, securities, professional negligence and shipping. Instructed in complex commercial litigation in the commercial court and in arbitrations, including Banque Financiere v Westgate [1990] (banking and insurance fraud), Johnson Matthey v Arthur Young (collapse of Johnson Matthey Bank), Ocean v Bimeh Iran Insurance Company [1990] (reinsurance), Trafalgar Tours v Henry (jurisdiction), Gucci v Gucci [1991] (passing-off), Lombard Finance v Brookplain [1991] (banking), Westdeutsche Landesbank v Islington [1994] (interest rate swaps), NPRT v Allen, Allen and Hemsley [1996] (banking), R v Secretary of State ex p Greenpeace [2000] (judicial review), AEI v PPL [1998] (copyright); Richmond Oil [1999 and 2001] (stock exchange/fraud), Baghbadrani v Commercial Union [2000] (insurance). Instructed in fraud cases by Serious Fraud Office. Acted for SRO's in disciplinary proceedings and judicial review. Acts in French proceedings, including Tribunal de Commerce (2001) and investigation into Alma crash [1998]. Counsel for Customs & Excise (European) and on Supplemental Panel for Treasury (1995-99). Lectures on civil procedure.
Prof. Memberships: COMBAR, ALBA, PEBA, Franco-British Lawyers Society, Bar Sports Group. Member, Bar Disciplinary Tribunal (2000-).
Publications: Joint author of 'Disclosure' (Sweet & Maxwell, 2001).
Personal: Educated at Bedford School 1968-77, University of the Sorbonne, 1978 and Keble College, Oxford 1978-82 (MA, BCL).

MALES, Stephen QC
20 Essex Street (Iain Milligan QC) London (020) 7538 9294
clerks@20essexst.com
Recommended in Energy & Natural Resources
Specialisation: International trade and commercial law;

shipping; sale of goods and commodity trading; banking and letters of credit; arbitration; energy law; insurance; conflict of laws; breach of confidence. Acts as arbitrator. Recent cases: The Selda [1999] 1 Lloyd's Rep 729 (GAFTA default clause); Cargill v Bangladesh Sugar [1998] 1 WLR 461 (performance bonds); Scottish Power v Britoil, CA, Nov 1997 (sale of North Sea gas); Czarnikow-Rionda v Standard Bank [1999] 2 Lloyd's Rep. 187 (no injunction to restrain payment under letter of credit); CAI v Muslim Commercial Bank [2000] 1 Lloyd's Rep.275 (documents required by letter of credit); Chailease v CAI [2000] 1 Lloyd's Rep.348 (place of performance of letter of credit); Molins v GD [2000] 1 WLR 1741 (service by fax); The Spiros c [2000] 2 Lloyd's Rep 319 (freight and demurrage under bill of lading); Zenziper v Bulk [2001] 1 All ER (Comm) 385 (free on trucks); Factortame (No 7) [2001] 1 WLR (state liability).
Prof. Memberships: Member of Commercial Court Committee, Combar, LCLCBA, IBA Energy Lawyers Group, supporting member LMAA.
Career: St John's College, Cambridge 1974-77. Called 1978. Queens Counsel 1998. Assistant Recorder 1999. Recorder 2000.
Publications: Confidence in arbitration [1998] LMCLQ 245; Comity and anti-suit injunctions [1998] LMCLQ 543.

MALLALIEU, Ann QC
6 King's Bench Walk (Roy Amlot QC) London (020) 7583 0410
Recommended in Crime

MANLEY, David
40 King St Manchester (0161) 832 9082
Recommended in Planning

MANN, Anthony QC
Enterprise Chambers (Anthony Mann QC) London (020) 7405 9471
Recommended in Chancery, Commercial (Litigation), Company, Insolvency/Corporate Recovery, Professional Negligence

MANN, Paul
No.1 High Pavement (John B. Milmo QC) Nottingham (0115) 941 8218
Recommended in Crime

MANNING, Colin
Littleton Chambers (Michel Kallipetis QC) London (020) 7797 8600
Recommended in Alternative Dispute Resolution
Specialisation: Principal areas of practice are general commercial and business law specialising in commercial contract disputes including computer litigation (involving the supply and implementation of computer systems, networking and associated intellectual property rights) and also professional negligence (primarily solicitors and valuers).
Prof. Memberships: COMBAR London Common Law and Commercial Bar Association. CEDR Accredited Mediator. Fellow of the Chartered Institute of Arbitrators.
Career: Called, Gray's Inn, 1970. Recorder, 2000.
Personal: Educated at University College London.

MANSFIELD, Michael QC
Tooks Court Chambers (Michael Mansfield QC) London (020) 7405 8828
Recommended in Crime, Human Rights

MARKS, David
3-4 South Square (Michael Crystal QC & Lord Alexander of Weedon QC) London (020) 7696 9900
clerks@southsquare.com
Recommended in Insolvency/Corporate Recovery
Specialisation: Insolvency, company, commercial. 1997-01 cases include: John Dee Group v WMH; Re A & C Supplies Ltd; Re Datadeck Ltd; BCCI v Akindele; Winchester Commodities v Black Re Brabon; Ashurst v Pollard; Solomons v Williams; Re Factortame.
Prof. Memberships: Chancery Bar Association. Insolvency Lawyers Association. Society of Practitioners of Insolvency (legal member). Insol. International Bar Association. Justice.
Career: Oxford University: MA, BCL. Member, Illinois and Federal Bars, United States. Deputy Registrar in Bankruptcy. Data Appeal Tribunal, Deputy Chairman.
Publications: Joint Editor: 'Rowlatt on Principal and Surety'. General Editor: 'Tolley's Insolvency Service'. Editor: 'Encyclopaedia of Forms and Precedents' (Guarantees). Contributor to Lightman & Moss: 'Law of Receivers of Companies' and Totty & Moss: 'Insolvency'.
Personal: Bilingual: French.

MARKS, Lewis
Queen Elizabeth Building (Florence Baron QC) London (020) 7797 7837
lewis_marks@msn.com
Recommended in Family
Prof. Memberships: Family Law Bar Association; DPA Accepted.
Career: Recent cases include: White v White [2000] 3 WLR 1571 [2000] 2 FLR 981 H/L; Kellman v Kellman [2000] IFLR 785; F v F (Ancillary Relief: Substantial Assets) [1995] 2 FLR 45. Dart v Dart [1996] 2 FLR 286 C/A; H v H (Child Abduction: Acquiescence) [1997] 1 FLR 872 H/L; S v S (Child Abduction: Non-Convention Country) [1994] 2 FLR 681.
Personal: Born 1961. Called 1984. Educated Oxford University (BA Juris).

MARKS, Richard QC
Peel Court Chambers (Michael Shorrock QC) Manchester (0161) 832 3791
Recommended in Crime

MARKUS, Kate
Doughty Street Chambers (Geoffrey Robertson QC) London (020) 7404 1313
Recommended in Administrative & Public Law

MARQUAND, Charles
4 Stone Buildings (Philip Heslop QC) London (020) 7242 5524
Recommended in Financial Services
Specialisation: Financial services (including insurance and banking) UK and EU, disciplinary tribunals, arbitrations, corporate finance. Also company/commercial. Engaged to advise various ex-Soviet governments on financial services legislation.
Prof. Memberships: Chancery Bar Association; COMBAR; Bar European Group; fellow Chartered Institute of Arbitrators; Member, Bar of Northern Ireland.
Career: Called 1987. Practised at chambers of JJ Rowe QC. 1993-96: legal adviser at HM Treasury dealing with wide range of financial services issues and related areas (company/commercial), drafting legislation (closely involved *inter alia* with Public Offers of Securities Regulations, investment advertisement exemptions, CREST), negotiating EU directives. 1996: returned to the Bar.
Publications: Author of articles on financial services topics; Halsbury's Laws: 'Corporations, Money. Lectures on financial services to universities, solicitors, conferences.
Personal: MA Oxon.

MARRIN, John QC
Keating Chambers (Richard Fernyhough QC) London +44 (0) 20 7544 2600
jmarrin@keatingchambers.com
Recommended in Construction
Specialisation: Barrister practising also as arbitrator, mediator, adjudicator and lecturer in the field of building and civil engineering; professional negligence; contaminated land; bonds and guarantees; computer software disputes; clients include national and international contractors, professionals, and national and local government.
Career: Qualified 1974; Inner Temple; QC 1990; CEDR accredited mediator 1993; recorder 1997; Chartered Arbitrator; FCI Arb 1998.
Personal: Sherborne School and Magdalene College, Cambridge (1973 MA Cantab). Born 1951; resides London.

MARSHALL, Philip
Serle Court (Lord Neill of Bladen QC) London (020) 7242 6105
clerks@serlecourt.co.uk
Recommended in Chancery, Company, Insolvency/Corporate Recovery
Specialisation: Commercial fraud (Cala Cristal v Al-Borno; Canada Trust v Stolzenberg); insolvency (BIM v Maxwell; Re: Murjani; Haig v Aitken; Rooney v Cardona); banking (Wahda Bank v Arab Bank); company (Tech Textiles v Vane); commercial litigation; professional negligence (Brown v GRE; Peach Publishing v Slater; David Lee v Coward Chance; Goose v Wilson Sandford).
Prof. Memberships: Chancery Bar Association, Insolvency Lawyers Association.
Career: Queens' Cambridge; Harvard Law School. Former fellow of Queens' Cambridge.
Publications: Joint editor of 'The Practice and Procedure of the Companies Court'.

MARSON, Geoffrey C. QC
Sovereign Chambers (Geoffrey C. Marson QC) Leeds (0113) 245 1841
Recommended in Crime
Specialisation: After a general common law practice he has specialised in defending and prosecuting criminal cases since 1985. Has spoken at the 1997 Arson Investigation Seminar along with those responsible for the investigation into the channel tunnel fire. Over the years has prosecuted in many fraud cases, including mortgage fraud, VAT evasion, serious drugs cases and the like. He has also defended in a large number of similar cases for both private and legally aided clients. He is a member of Chamber's Fraud Group.
Prof. Memberships: Criminal Bar Association.
Career: Educated Malton Grammar School and King's College London – LLB (Hons). Called to the Bar (Gray's Inn) in 1975. Assistant Recorder 1991, Recorder 1995, Queen's Counsel 1997. Appointed to sit on the Mental Health Review Tribunal–Restricted Patients Panel in January 2000.
Personal: Married to Denise Gresty; two sons. Leisure interests – foreign travel, wine, reading.

MARSTON, Nicholas
St John's Chambers (Christopher Sharp QC) Bristol (0117) 921 3456
clerks@stjohnschambers.co.uk
Recommended in Family
Specialisation: Family law, children, related matters, including prof. leg. in family issues.
Prof. Memberships: FLBA.
Career: Called 1975 (Middle Temple). Assistant Recorder 1998. Recorder 2000. Former National Committee FLBA member.
Personal: LLB (Wales) at Cardiff. Married, two children. Interests include history, theatre, wine, travel, rugby and cricket.

MARTEN, Hedley
3 New Square (Lord Goodhart QC) London (020) 7405 5577
law@threenewsquare.co.uk
Recommended in Chancery
Specialisation: Specialist in a broad area of Chancery work including company law, (particularly minority shareholders' disputes and directors' disqualification proceedings), contract, insolvency, landlord and tenant, trusts and contested probate; judicial review. Also acts for solicitors in proceedings brought by the Law Society under the Solicitors Act 1974. Important cases include Cowan v Department of Health [1991] (landlord and tenant, trusts); Vestey v Clifton-Brown [1991] (Variation of Trusts); Re Packaging Direct Ltd [1993] (Directors'

Disqualification); Re: a Solicitor [1996] (judicial review); Re Bheekun [1999] F.L.379 (domicile); Mander v Evans [2001] WLR (fraud and bankruptcy).
Career: Called to the Bar 1966. Chancery Bar representative on the Bar Council 1989-95. Executive head of chambers since 1995.
Personal: Born 1943. Educated at Winchester College and Magdalene College, Cambridge (MA 1966). Lives in London. Three children.

MARTIN, Gerard QC
Exchange Chambers (David Turner QC & Bill Braithwaite QC & Henry Globe QC) Liverpool (0151) 236 7747
Recommended in Personal Injury
Specialisation: Exclusively personal injury, including clinical negligence; catastrophic injuries including – brain, spine, amputees and cerebral palsy; PI claims against M.O.D.
Prof. Memberships: PIBA, PNBA, APIL.
Career: St Joseph's College Blackpool. Cambridge University. Called 1978. Assistant Recorder 1997. Recorder 2000.

MARTIN, John QC
Wilberforce Chambers (Edward Nugee QC) London (020) 7306 0102
Recommended in Chancery, Property Litigation
Specialisation: Advocate specialising in chancery and commercial Supreme Court litigation. Also advises in contentious matters, covering the wide range of topics comprising modern commercial chancery practice. Since 1993 he has been a Deputy High Court Judge in the Chancery Division. Judicial experience: Deputy High Court Judge.
Career: Called to the Bar in July 1972. Practised at the Chancery Bar in Liverpool joining Wilberforce Chambers in 1981. Took silk in 1991.

MARTIN-SPERRY, David
Charter Chambers (Stephen Solley QC) London (020) 7832 0300
Recommended in Crime
Specialisation: Principal area of practice is criminal defence work across the spectrum of criminal cases. Work includes City fraud cases, international money laundering, drugs, murder, sexual offences including child abuse, professional armed robberies, 'freedom of speech' cases and arson. Also involved in extradition proceedings. Has conducted appeals, or advised pending appeal, to the Court of Appeal in more than 100 criminal cases. Convictions quashed on appeal include 4 murder cases and 19 appeals arising out of the activities of the West Midlands Serious Crime Squad. Appeared on 'Panorama' and acted as adviser to 'Justice', 'Trial and Error' and 'Rough Justice'.
Prof. Memberships: South Eastern Circuit, Criminal Bar Association.
Career: Called to the Bar 1971. Joined Crown Office Row 1979.
Personal: Educated at Harrow School (Headmaster's Scholarship) and Trinity College Cambridge. Captain, Cambridge University Waterski Team, 1967. Speaks French, German and Italian. Leisure pursuits include bridge, cricket and skiing. Born 21st June 1946.

MARZEC, Alexandra
5 Raymond Buildings (Patrick Milmo QC) London (020) 7242 2902
Recommended in Defamation

MASEFIELD, Roger
Brick Court Chambers (Christopher Clarke QC) London (020) 7379 3550 masefield@brickcourt.co.uk
Recommended in Commercial (Litigation)
Specialisation: Commercial law, specialising in insurance and reinsurance; banking (eg Banco Santander v Banque Paribas [2000] 1 All ER (Comm) 776 CA); professional negligence (eg Wallace Smith Trust Co v Deloitte Haskins & Sells 1997); public and private international law (eg State of Qatar v Sheikh Khalifa Al-Thani 1996); restitution and commercial equity (eg Union Eagle v Golden Achievement [1997] 2 WLR 341 PC).
Prof. Memberships: Junior Counsel to the Crown (C Panel); Member of Bar Council Law Reform Committee; COMBAR.
Career: MA (Cantab); BCL (Oxon) – Vinerian Scholar; Called to the Bar 1994; Tenant at Brick Court Chambers 1996.
Publications: Co-author of constructive trusts chapters in latest edition of 'Paget on Banking' (published July 1996); researcher for Lord Alexander's 'Voice of the People' (published September 1997); co-author of Bar Council position paper on 'E-Commerce: Jurisdiction and Applicable Law' (published November 1999).
Personal: Educated at the Dragon School; Marlborough College; Cambridge (St John's); Oxford (Magdalen). Born 24 December 1970.

MASKREY, Simeon QC
7 Bedford Row (David Farrer QC) London (020) 7242 3555
Recommended in Clinical Negligence, Personal Injury
Specialisation: Principal area of practice is professional negligence with an emphasis on clinical negligence. Also involved in disciplinary cases and all forms of litigation with a clinical element (including public law child care proceedings). Past member of the education faculty of the Royal College of Surgeons. Regular contributor to AVMA conferences. Leading counsel in R v Dixon (1995), Poynter v Hillingdon Health Authority (1997), Spargo v Essex Health Authority (1998), Fleming v Lincolnshire Police (1998), In Re D (child assessment) (1999), North Wales child abuse cases (2000), Interlink Mod v Night Trunkers Ltd (2001).
Prof. Memberships: Professional Negligence Bar Association. Member of the Midland and Oxford Circuit. Member of AVMA Bar group.
Career: Called to the Bar in 1977. Appointed Recorder in 1997. Appointed deputy high court judge in 2000. Took silk in 1995.
Personal: Educated at King's School, Grantham and Leicester University. Born 17th May 1955. Married. Lives in London.

MASON, Alexandra
3 Stone Buildings (Geoffrey Vos QC) London (020) 7242 4937
Recommended in Chancery
Specialisation: Private client litigation and advisory work centred on wills and probate, the administration of estates, settlements and the administration of trusts but including related taxation and professional negligence and also Court of Protection matters. Recent litigation has included the construction of wills and trust documents; applications under the Inheritance (Provision for Family and Dependants) Act 1975; contentious probate actions; claims to beneficial interests in property; the rectification of trust documents; the removal of executors and trustees; actions concerning breaches of duty on the part of trustees/executors; applications for statutory wills and settlements for patients; negligence claims in respect of the drafting of wills and trust documents and advice on the administration of estates.
Prof. Memberships: Chancery Bar Association, Revenue Bar Association, STEP.
Career: BA Hons, History, UCL 1979. Diploma in Law, City University 1980. Joint Author of 7th edn 'Spencer Maurice's Family Provision on Death'.

MATHER-LEES, Michael
Albion Chambers (Charles Barton QC & Neil Ford QC) Bristol (0117) 927 2144
Recommended in Crime

MATTHEWS, Dennis
Crown Office Chambers (Michael Spencer QC & Christopher Purchas QC) London (020) 7797 8100
Recommended in Clinical Negligence, Personal Injury
Specialisation: Principal areas of practice are clinical and other professional negligence work, insurance and major personal injury litigation (both group and individual). Clients include health authorities and trusts, medical defence organisations, professional indemnity insurers, corporate insurers and Lloyd's syndicates.
Prof. Memberships: London Common Law and Commercial Bar Association, Professional Negligence Bar Association.
Career: Called to the Bar 1973.
Publications: Sweet & Maxwell 'Practical Research Paper on Structured Settlements'.
Personal: Born 16 March 1950.

MATTHEWS, Duncan
20 Essex Street (Iain Milligan QC) London (020) 7583 9294 clerks@20essexst.com
Recommended in Shipping
Specialisation: Principal areas of work include international and domestic commercial disputes including in particular international trade and carriage of goods, oil and gas, construction, conflict of laws, insurance and reinsurance, banking, financial services, professional negligence. Advocacy: Counsel appearing before the High Court, Court of Appeal and House of Lords in England and a variety of legal and commercial arbitration tribunals both in England and abroad including international bodies such as UNCITRAL and ICC and other domestic organisations such as the LMAA. Have also been appointed and sat as arbitrator and mediator. Major reported cases include House of Lords – 'The Maria D' [1992] 1 AC 21; 'The Naxos' [1990] 1 WLR 1337. Privy Council – 'The Mahkutai' [1996] AC 650. Court of Appeal AIG v Ethniki [2000] W Rep IR 343 'The Berge Sund' [1993] 2 Ll Rep 453; Soules v Intertradex [1991] 1 Ll Rep 378; Dole Dried Fruit v Trustin Kerwood [1990] 1 Ll Rep 309; Medway v Meurer [1990] 2 Ll Rep 112. Ist Instance; KBC Bank v Industrial Steels (UK) Ltd [2001] 1 Ll Rep 370; Sinochem v Fortune oil [2000] 1 W Rep 682; Doce nav v Bosco [2000] 2 4 Rep 1; Minmetals v Ferco Steel; Glencore v Shell [1999] 2 4 Rep 692; 'The Visvliet' [1997] 2 4 Rep 456, 476; Toepfer v Molino Boschi [1996] 1 Ll Rep 510; Aratra v Taylor Joynson Garrett [1995] 4 AER 695; Swiss Bank Corporation v Premier League The Times 9 February 1995; Kaufmann v Credit Lyonnais Bank The Times 1 February 1995; The Sophie J [2001] 1 LLR 763.
Prof. Memberships: COMBAR; LCLCBA. Supporting member LMAA; Franco British Lawyers Society; British Italian Law Association; British German Jurists Association.
Career: Westminster School. Magdalen College, Oxford. BA (Hons) Oxon 1984. MA 1996.

MATTHEWS, Richard
2 Bedford Row (William Clegg QC) London (020) 7440 8888
Recommended in Crime, Fraud
Specialisation: Criminal law specialist including fraud/Health and Safety (Crime)/Trading Standards and Copyright (Crime)/Confiscation and Asset Forfeiture. Cases include: R v Turner & Draghici (Extra-jurisdictional murder/conspiracy to murder trial involving Japanese victim killed in Venezuela). R v Carlton & others (series of kidnaps and armed robberies of bank managers and manager of Tescos). R v Stimson (Alleged supply of police seized drugs to informant and police constable by a serving detective sergeant). R v Trevelyan & others (Corruption trial of senior civil servant in MOD and wife). R v Malcom Walker (Allegation of copyright theft and corruption/theft by consultant retained by Min of Agriculture, MOD and CPS. High Court asset restraint under Criminal Justice Act). R v Morris (Manslaughter

case against gas fitter (CO poisoning)) R v Wheeler (Manslaughter case against landlord following tenant death through CO poisoning). Travel v HM Customs and Excise Commissioners (Divisional Court judicial review of customs powers of seizure under s.141 of the Customs and Excise Management Act 1979). R v Ketchell, Walker et al (Serious Fraud Office prosecution of £22 million fraud – Ostrich Farms). R v Polycarpou & Langley (Inland Revenue/Customs; PAYE, VAT & Corporation tax prosecution concerning 8 years 'phoenix' operation of retail, property holding and manufacturing companies). R v John Palmer & Andrew Palmer (Central CPS unit prosecution of Palmer time-share alleged loss £30 million though alleged mis-selling of timeshare in Tenerife). Health and Safety (Crime) cases: HSE v Edmund Nuttall Ltd: (fatality involving breaches of section 2 & 3 Health and Safety at work etc. Act 1974). HSE v Keltbray Plc [2001] 1 Cr.App.R.(S) 39 (Double fatality of workman on demolition site. Alleged breaches of Health and Safety at work etc. Act 1974 and Construction (Health, Safety and Welfare). Regulations 1996). HSE v Lambeth Borough Council (Massive gas explosion in boiler room of occupied 22-storey tower block. Health and Safety at Work etc. Act 1974 and Gas Safety (Installation and Use) Regulations 1994/8). Environmental Agency v Babtie Group Ltd (Watercourse pollution case alleged against contract supervisors). Environmental Agency/HSE v Pharmacos Ltd and Brown (Prosecution of company and director concerning mercury nitrate processing) HSE v Winieccki (Construction Design and Management) Regulations prosecution of planning supervisor over scaffolding collapse). HSE v Frankham Consultancy (Construction Design and Management). Regulations prosecution of planning supervisor). HSE v Thames Water Products (Criminal case against subsidiary of Thames Water plc concerning accident at water sewage treatment works).
Prof. Memberships: Criminal Bar Association SE Circuit.
Career: Principal Legal Advisor Parliamentary War Crimes Group 1988-89. Called to the Bar 1989. Joined chambers 1989.
Personal: Born 5th April 1966. Educated at Girton College, Cambridge University. (MA Cantab). Lives in London.

MATTISON, Andrew
Chavasse Court Chambers (Theresa Pepper) Liverpool (0151) 707 1191
Recommended in Crime

MAXWELL, Richard QC
Ropewalk Chambers (Ian McLaren QC) Nottingham (0115) 947 2581
clerks@ropewalk.co.uk
Recommended in Personal Injury
Specialisation: Principle areas of practice are personal injury (including insidious disease and health and safety), clinical and professional negligence. Particular emphasis on group and multiparty actions including advising and appearing as Senior Lead Counsel in the Prescription Pricing Authority litigation (repetitive strain injury); Metro-Cammell litigation (asbestosis); British Coal vibration white finger litigation; 'Frank Beck' litigation (physical and sexual abuse in children's homes); North West child abuse cases, Cambridgeshire child abuse cases; Scotforth House litigation (autistic children group action); Hillsborough disaster inquest and inquiry and the leading case regarding vicarious liability – Lister v Hesley Hall Limited [2001] UKHL [2001] 2WLR 1311.
Prof. Memberships: Personal Injuries Bar Association; Nottinghamshire Medico-Legal Society.
Career: Called to the Bar 1968. Queen's Counsel 1988. Recorder and Deputy High Court Judge. Head of Ropewalk Chambers 1994-00.

MAY, Charlotte
8 New Square (Michael Fysh QC) London (020) 7405 4321
clerks@8newsquare.co.uk
Recommended in Intellectual Property
Specialisation: Barrister specialising in all areas of intellectual property law and scientific commercial law, including patents, biotechnology, trade marks, copyrights and database rights, passing off, registered design, design right and confidential information. Cases include Oxford Gene Technology v Affymetrix (biotech patent – revocation- infringement); Monsanto and Others v Merck (biotech patent-infringement-validity); Haberman and Anr v Jackel International Ltd. (patent for drinking vessel – infringement – validity); Unicontinental Holdings Ltd.) and Anr v Eurobond Adhesives Ltd. (patent infringement – industrial copyright – trade mark infringement); Zino Davidoff SA v A & G Imports Ltd (trade mark infringement and passing off). For comprehensive CV and list of recent cases, visit our website at www.8newsquare.co.uk.
Prof. Memberships: Intellectual Property Bar Association (IPBA); The Intellectual Property Lawyers Organisation (TIPLO)
Career: Called 1995.
Personal: Born 1971. Educated at The Abbey School; Brasenose College, Oxford (1993 Biochemistry); City University (1994 Dip Law); Inns of Court School of Law.

MAYNARD-CONNOR, Giles
Exchange Chambers (David Turner QC & Bill Braithwaite QC & Henry Globe QC) Liverpool (0161) 833 2722
maynardconnor@exchangechambers.co.uk
Recommended in Insolvency/Corporate Recovery
Specialisation: General Chancery with emphasis on insolvency (corporate and personal), company, professional negligence and banking. Hull City AFC Ltd and Canell Laird Group (corporate insolvencies).
Prof. Memberships: Chancery Bar Association, Northern Chancery Bar Association, Bar Pro Bono Unit
Career: Called to Bar 24 November 1992.
Personal: University of Lancaster. Leisure interests: football, motor racing, rugby union, travel, film and dining.

MCALLISTER, Ann
Serle Court (Lord Neill of Bladen QC) London (020) 7242 6105
clerks@serlecourt.co.uk
Recommended in Agriculture, Property Litigation
Specialisation: Principal area of practice is landlord and tenant, property law and agricultural tenancies, although practice also includes all aspects of general chancery law (mortgages, partnerships, guarantees, insolvency) and professional negligence work.
Prof. Memberships: Committee member of the Property Bar Association.
Career: Called to the Bar in 1982.
Personal: Read law and languages at Newnham College, Cambridge. After graduating in 1975 went to LSE and gained an LLM in law. Taught law for three years at the University of London (School of Oriental and African Studies).

McCALL, Christopher QC
Maitland Chambers (Michael Lyndon-Stanford QC & Charles Aldous QC) London (020) 7406 1200
Recommended in Chancery, Charities, Tax
Specialisation: Specialises in trust, revenue and charity law. Has appeared in numerous appeals in the House of Lords, Privy Council and Court of Appeal: has regularly addressed specialist associations and seminars and written in legal journals.
Prof. Memberships: Member of Bar Council 1973-76.
Career: Called to Bar Lincolns Inn, November 1966. Took silk, April 1987. Bencher 1993. 2nd Junior Counsel to the Inland Revenue in Chancery Matters 1977-87. Junior Counsel to the Attorney-General in Charity Matters 1981-87. Practised at 7 New Square Lincolns Inn 1967-94, subsequently 13 Old Square.
Personal: Born 3 March 1944. Married 1981, no children. Educated Winchester College (Scholar), Magdalen College, Oxford (Demy): 1st class, Mathematical Moderations 1962 and Finals 1964. Eldon Law Scholarship: 1966. Trustee of British Museum 1999-.

McCALL, Duncan
4 Pump Court London (020) 7842 5555
dmccall@4pumpcourt.com
Recommended in Information Technology
Specialisation: Commercial and technical disputes involving a variety of applications including financial and accounting packages, ERP, logistics software, e-sales and internet. Recent reported cases include Pegler v Wang [2000] BLR 218 and Zockoll Group v Mercury Communications [1998] FSR 354.
Prof. Memberships: TECBAR, Society for Computers & Law.
Personal: BA (Hons) Oxon.

McCARROLL, John J.
Exchange Chambers (David Turner QC & Bill Braithwaite QC & Henry Globe QC) Liverpool (0151) 236 7747
Recommended in Chancery
Specialisation: General chancery, commercial, corporate and personal insolvency, company, professional negligence.
Prof. Memberships: Northern Chancery Bar Association, Northern Circuit Commercial Bar Association, Chancery Bar Association.
Career: Portora Royal School; Trinity College, University of Dublin; Member of the Bar of the Republic of Ireland.

McCAUGHRAN, John
One Essex Court (Lord Grabiner QC) London (020) 7583 2000
Recommended in Commercial (Litigation), Energy & Natural Resources, Fraud
Specialisation: Principal area of practice is commercial litigation.
Prof. Memberships: Commercial Bar Association
Career: Called to the Bar in 1982.
Personal: Educated at Methodist College, Belfast 1969-76 and Trinity Hall, Cambridge 1977-80. Born 24 April 1958. Lives in London.

McCRACKEN, Robert
2 Harcourt Buildings (Gerard Ryan QC) London (020) 7353 8415
clerks@2hb.law.co.uk
Recommended in Environment
Specialisation: Environmental law especially at land use and planning inquiries. Acts for a wide range of clients from multinational corporations and regulatory authorities to small entrepreneurs and groups of active citizens. Promoted Windermere Speed Limit for Lake District NPA, East London Overhead Power Line for National Grid. Represented consortium of oil companies at Heathrow Terminal 5 Inquiry. Acted for successful appellants in Berkeley v SSETR (House of Lords) [2000] 3 WLR 420; R v Durham CC ex p Huddlestone (Court of Appeal) [2000] 1 WLR 1484; R v Flintshire CC ex p Armstong Braun (Court of Appeal) ('Times' 8 March 2001); Hewlings v McLeans (Divisional Court) [2001] Env LR 323; R v St Edmundsbury ex p Walton (High Court) [1999] Env LR 879; R v Cornwall CC ex p hardy (High Court) [2001] ENv LR 473.
Prof. Memberships: Planning and Environmental Bar Association (secretary 1992-94); UK Environmental Law Association (chairman 1995-97).
Career: Called to the Bar 1973. Honorary Standing Counsel to Council for National Parks since 1999.
Publications: Many and various for legal journals. Co-author of Butterworths 'Statutory Nuisance' 2001.
Personal: Worcester College, Oxford, MA 1973. Former educational missionary in East Africa. Leisure pursuits include fell walking, natural science and painting.

McDERMOTT, John
Chavasse Court Chambers (Theresa Pepper) Liverpool (0151) 707 1191
Recommended in Crime

McDONNELL, John QC

New Square Chambers (John Mowbray QC & Eben Hamilton QC) London (020) 7419 8000

Recommended in Chancery

McFARLAND, Denise

Three New Square (David Young QC) London (020) 7405 1111

Recommended in Intellectual Property

Specialisation: All aspects of intellectual property. Recent cases include Shirin Guild v Eskandar Nabavi (Haute Couture, Design Right, "Commonplace"); Ray v Classic FM, (Copyright) Cinpres v Melea (Patents, CA), PLG v Ardon (Patent), Cala v McAlpine (copyright), Norsk Hydro's As Patent, Carflow v Linwood (second trial), Bell (trade marks) Atlantic v Bell, L'Oreal v Johnson & Johnson (meaning of threats), as well as numerous decisions from the European Patent Office, UK Trade Marks and Patents Registry, and Copyright Tribunal.
Prof. Memberships: Hon Fellow Institute of Trade Mark Attorneys; member Chartered Institute of Patent Attorneys Professional Disciplinary Panel; member Royal Institution of Great Britain; British Council member of AIPPI; committee member of T.I.P.L.O; Women's Bar Assn; Intellectual Property Bar Assn; Chancery Bar Assn; former examiner for Chartered Institute of Trade Mark Attorneys professional examination. Appointed expert for settlement of Nominet UK Dispute Resolution Procedures. Nominated as examiner for International IPR disputes deposition hearings.
Career: Cambridge University (MA).
Personal: Riding and all country pursuits, music and theatre.

McFARLANE, Andrew QC

One King's Bench Walk (Anthony Hacking QC) London (020) 7936 1500

Recommended in Family

Specialisation: Principal area of practice is family law. Handles all aspects with particular expertise in the law relating to children (both public and private law), international child abduction and adoption. Has appeared before the House of Lords and before the European Court of Human Rights. Regular lecturer at nationally organised conferences and seminars.
Prof. Memberships: Midlands Circuit, Family Law Bar Association, Association of Lawyers for Children, British Agencies for Adoption and Fostering,.
Career: Called to the Bar in 1977. At Priory Chambers, Birmingham 1978-93 and remains a door tenant at St Philip's Chambers, Birmingham. Joined 1 King's Bench Walk in 1993. Appointed Recorder in 1999. QC 1998. Deputy High Court Judge in 2000.
Publications: Co-author with David Hershman of 'Children: Law & Practice' (Family Law 1991) and contributor to 'Family Court Practice' (Family Law 2001).
Personal: Educated at Shrewsbury School 1968-72, Durham University 1972-76, University of Wales (LLM (Canon Law)) 1994-98. Management Committee member: Young Minds. Leisure interests include theatre, conjuring, walking and his children. Born 20th June 1954. Lives in Malvern.

McGHEE, John

9 Old Square (Michael Driscoll QC) London (020) 7405 4682

Recommended in Property Litigation

Specialisation: John McGhee has wide experience in a broad range of property, Chancery and commercial litigation incuding banking, commercial fraud, landlord and tenant, professional negligence and property disputes. Recent cases include: Escalus Properties v Robinson [1996] QB 231 (forfeiture); Barrett v Morgan [2000] 2 AC 264 (notice to quit); Bankers Trust v Namdar [1997] EGCS 20 (subrogation); Carter v TG Baynes [1998] EGCS 109 (solicitors negligence); Grupo Torras v Al Sabah Litigation [1999] CLC 1469 (civil fraud); Mobil Oil Co Ltd v Birmingham City Council [2000] 97 (18) LSG 38 (rent review; rights of way). Supplemental panel member for Treasury Solicitor.
Career: University College Oxford 1980-83 (MA).
Publications: Editor of Snell's 'Equity' 30th edn.

McGRATH, Paul

Essex Court Chambers (Gordon Pollock QC) London (020) 7813 8000

Recommended in Commercial (Litigation), Shipping

Specialisation: Banking law, (including the Cayman Islands jurisdiction); conflict of laws; equity in a commercial context (eg constructive trusts, bribes, civil fraud); pre-emptive remedies (domestic and world-wide Mareva injunctions, tracing orders, Norwich Pharmacal relief); insolvency (advising liquidators on all aspects thereof, including schemes of arrangement, payment of dividend and the general conduct of liquidations as well as potential claims against directors of insolvent companies); all aspects of restitution, joint ventures, financial services, shipbuilding contracts and general commercial practice involving court and arbitration work.
Career: BA, BCL, University College, Oxford. Called to the Bar in 1994.
Personal: Born 1970.

McGREGOR, Alistair QC

11 King's Bench Walk Chambers (Eldred Tabachnik QC & James Goudie QC) London (020) 7632 8500

Recommended in Employment

Specialisation: Principal area of practice is intellectual property encompassing trade secrets, confidential information (particularly in relation to employment contracts and commercial transactions), restraint of trade (in all areas of application but especially employment law), copyright, trade marks and passing off (especially anti-piracy work). Other main area is commercial law including sale of goods, entertainment contracts, agency, partnership and commercial fraud (especially of directors). Lecturer for London University External LLB (1974-77) and for solicitors and accountant's professional examinations. Has written journal articles.
Prof. Memberships: COMBAR, ELBA.
Career: Called to the Bar in 1974. At Crown Office Row from 1975 until joining present chambers in 1981.
Personal: Educated at Haberdasher's Aske's School, Elstree 1963-70 and Queen Mary College, London University (LLB Hons, 1973). Leisure interests include orchestral music. Professional musician (trombone) and teacher (1970-78). Born 11 March 1950. Lives in Stamford, Lincs.

McKAY, Hugh

Gray's Inn Tax Chambers (Milton Grundy) London (020) 7242 2642
hm@taxbar.com

Recommended in Tax

Specialisation: Revenue law especially tax litigation, commercial/corporate tax issues and VAT.
Prof. Memberships: Secretary, Revenue Bar Association 1996-00, member – Chancery Bar Association, Chartered Institute of Taxation, VAT Practitioners Group, Law Society VAT and Duties Sub-committee (co-opted), 1994-98, Institute of Indirect Taxation, Bar Council 1999-00.
Career: Called to the Bar 1990, joined present chambers 1991. Visiting fellow (tax), London School of Economics 1993 to 1997.
Personal: Born 26 June 1966. Lives in Marylebone. Educated at King's College, London (LLM Tax) and Leeds University (MA), FTII, AIIT.

McLAREN, Ian QC

Ropewalk Chambers (Ian McLaren QC) Nottingham (0115) 947 2581

Recommended in Personal Injury

Specialisation: Personal Injury, common law and local government. Three cases in House of Lords in last three years; Longden v British Coal [1988] A.C. 653; Jameson v CEGB [1999] 2WLR 141; and Dimond v Lovell [2000] 2 WLR 1121.
Prof. Memberships: Personal Injury Bar Association; European Bar Association; Planning and Environment Bar Association.
Career: Called 1962; Bar finals prize, Macaskie Scholar, Gray's Inn plus three other scholarships. Law Tutor, University of Nottingham. Silk 1993; Recorder 1996.
Publications: Various articles in 'New Law Journal'.
Personal: Sandbach School, Blackpool Grammar School, Nottingham University (LLB). Interests: travel, wine and photography. Married, 3 children. President Nottinghamshire Medico-Legal Society 1997-98.

McLOUGHLIN, Timothy

East Anglian Chambers (Roderick Newton) Norwich (01603) 617351

Recommended in Family

McMANUS, Richard QC

4-5 Gray's Inn Square (Elizabeth Appleby QC & David Mole QC) London (020) 7404 5252
clerks@4-5graysinnsquare.co.uk

Recommended in Aviation

Specialisation: Aviation, contempt of court, discrimination, education, employment, European Community law, extradition, Financial Services Act and Social Security. Recent cases: Sirdar v Army Board (combat effectiveness and equal treatment); Coker and Osamor v Lord Chancellor; R v ICS ex p Taylor (financial services and damages); B v Harrow (rights preference and special educational needs); O'Connor v Chief Adjudication Officer (denial of income support to student not an infringement of right to education). Author 'Education and the Courts'.
Prof. Memberships: Administrative Law Bar Association.
Career: Called 1982. Junior Counsel to the Crown (Common Law) 1992 to 1999. Silk 1999
Personal: Educated at Downing College, Cambridge.

McMEEKIN, Ian

Kingsgate Chambers (Beverley Lunt) Manchester (0161) 831 7477

Recommended in Crime

Specialisation: All areas of crime; Junior Counsel in R v Brown (Winston), (House of Lords decision on disclosure) A-G's Counsel for The DTI, i2 Analysts Notebook user for data analysis.
Career: Thirteen years specialising in crime.
Personal: University of Leeds, City University (postgrad).

McMULLAN, Manus

Atkin Chambers (Robert Akenhead QC) London (020) 7404 0102
clerks@atkinchambers.law.co.uk

Recommended in Construction

Specialisation: Construction, arbitration, professional negligence and general commercial litigation. Counsel in Chiltern v Woods Hardwick concerning natural justice in adjudication.
Prof. Memberships: TECBAR
Career: Called 1994
Publications: Editor: Technology and Construction Law Reports (Sweet and Maxwell).
Personal: BA Oxon (1st Class)

McMULLEN, Jeremy QC

Old Square Chambers (John Hendy QC) London (020) 7269 0300
jmcmullenqc@cs.com

Recommended in Employment

Specialisation: Employment, administrative law. Includes discrimination, contracts, restrictive covenants, industrial action, directorships, dismissal, injunctions, inquiries eg Clapham Junction, Ladbroke Grove, Westminster Auditor. Employment Tribunal Chairman. Recorder. Sports arbitrator.
Prof. Memberships: Vice-president ILS and ELBA; former ACAS equal pay expert. Chair, ILO Joint Panel.
Career: Called 1971, worked in New York and for GMB

before practising in 1985. Silk 1994; N Ireland 1996, Cayman Islands 1999.
Publications: 'Employment Tribunal Procedure'; 'Employment Precedents'; 'Labour Law Review'.
Personal: Educated at Oxford and LSE.

McNEILL, Jane
Old Square Chambers (John Hendy QC) London (020) 7269 0300
mcneill@oldsquarechambers.co.uk
Recommended in Employment
Specialisation: Employment including discrimination under domestic and European law; wrongful and unfair dismissal; redundancy; restraint of trade. Cases include Kapur v Barclays; Preston v Wolverhampton Healthcare NHS Trustee; Fletcher v Midland Bank plc; Hallam v Avery; British Airways (European Operations at Gatwick) Ltd v Moore. Also personal injury and medical negligence.
Prof. Memberships: Employment Law Bar Association; PIBA.
Personal: BA Hons (Oxon); Dip Law (City University). Fluent Italian and French. Called 1982.

McQUATER, Ewan
3 Verulam Buildings (Christopher Symons QC & John Jarvis QC) London (020) 7831 8441
chambers@3vb.com
Recommended in Banking, Commercial (Litigation), Fraud, Insolvency/Corporate Recovery
Specialisation: Commercial work specialising in banking, commercial fraud, insolvency and more general finance related work. Also has considerable experince in professional negligence work. Important cases include: the Libyan asset freeze litigation (US freeze on Libyan asset worldwide), the expropriation of the National Bank of Brunei, the collapse of the Maxwell group, the Arrows liquidation (series of important insolvency decisions), BBL (measure of damages in professional negligence cases), the BCCI liquidation, the collapse of the Barings group, Grupo Torras and Prince Jefri of Brunei (defence of claim by State of Brunei and Brunei Investment Agency). Assistant Editor of the 'Encyclopaedia of Banking Law'.
Prof. Memberships: COMBAR.
Career: Called to the Bar 1985 and joined current Chambers 1986. Admitted to the Bar of the Cayman Islands on a series of individual cases.
Personal: Educated at Merchiston Castle School, Edinburgh (1975-80) and Cambridge University 1981-84 (MA Hons in Law, First Class). Born 30th October 1962. Lives in London.

MEAD, Philip
Old Square Chambers (John Hendy QC) London (020) 7269 0300
mead@oldsquarechambers.co.uk
Recommended in Environment
Specialisation: Environmental law (in particular common law and statutory nuisance), personal injury law and health and safety law including toxic torts and product liability, employment and discrimination law. Has particular knowledge of the application of European law and conflicts of law to the above areas. Acts for both claimants/applicants and defendants/respondents, appearing in both the civil and criminal courts. Consultant to the European Commission on Health and Safety.
Prof. Memberships: Association of Personal Injury Lawyers, Personal Injuries Bar Association, Employment Law Bar Association and Bar European Group.
Career: Called to the Bar 1989; member Western Circuit, and practises from chambers' annexe in Bristol.
Publications: Litigation manual for the Environmental Law Foundation on European Environmental Law; co-author of Tort and Product Liability in 'Practitioners' Handbook of EC Law'; co-editor and author of 'Personal Injury Handbook'.

MEADE, Richard
8 New Square (Michael Fysh QC) London (020) 7405 4321
clerks@8newsquare.co.uk
Recommended in Information Technology, Intellectual Property
Specialisation: Barrister specialising in all aspects of intellectual property, with particular experience in biotechnology and electronics patent litigation; trade mark litigation including comparative advertising cases; music copyright; euro defences and jurisdiction under the Brussels Convention. For comprehensive CV and list of recent cases, visit our website at www.8newsquare.co.uk.
Prof. Memberships: Intellectual Property Bar Association (IPBA); The Intellectual Property Lawyers Organisation (TIPLO).
Career: Called 1991.
Publications: Kerly's 'Law of Trade Marks' (co-author).
Personal: Born 1966. Educated at William Ellis School; University College, Oxford (BA Law).

MEADOWCROFT, Stephen
Peel Court Chambers (Michael Shorrock QC) Manchester (0161) 832 3791
Recommended in Crime

MEADWAY, Susannah
10 Old Square (Leolin Price CBE QC) London (020) 7242 5002
susannahmeadway@10oldsquare.ndo.co.uk
Recommended in Chancery
Specialisation: Advisory, drafting and litigation work in the fields of trusts and associated taxation, pensions, wills, probate and the administration of estates, family provision Court of Protection matters and charities and professional negligence in those fields. A contributor to Foster's Inheritance Tax and 'Atkin's Court Forms: Probate & Family Provision', co-editor of 'Williams on Wills', co-editor of 'Halsbury's Laws of England: Wills' and 'Halsbury's Laws of England: Executors & Administrators'. Counsel in Re Segelman [1996] Ch 171.
Prof. Memberships: STEP (Society of Trust and Estate Practitioners). Chancery Bar Association.

MEEKE, Martin QC
Colleton Chambers (Martin Meeke QC) Exeter (01392) 274898
Recommended in Crime
Specialisation: Prosecutes and defends in all serious crime, including murder, manslaughter, drugs, fraud and sexual offences. Prosecutes and defends in environmental consumer and food law cases. Also ancillary relief.
Career: Called 1973. Recorder 1999. Silk 2000
Personal: Born 1950. Bristol University LLB (Hons). Married with two children.

MEESON, Nigel
4 Essex Court (Nigel Teare QC) London (020) 7653 5653
Recommended in Shipping
Specialisation: Practice covers all areas of commercial law and shipping including admiralty, arbitration, aviation, banking, carriage of goods, conflict of laws, insurance and reinsurance, international trade and sale of goods.
Prof. Memberships: LMAA (Supporting Member), COMBAR, BMLA, ABA, Forum on Air and Space Law.
Career: Called 1982. Admitted to California Bar 1990. Accredited Mediator by CEDR 1993. Visiting lecturer University College, London since 1994. Admiralty Court Committee. Supplementary Panel of Treasury Counsel.
Publications: Author of 'Admiralty Jurisdiction & Practice' (1993), 2nd ed (2000), 'Ship & Aircraft Mortgages' (1989), contributor to 'Ship Sale & Purchase' (3rd edition 1998). Various articles and conference papers.
Personal: Magdalen College, Oxford (First Class Hons Jurisprudence).

MEHIGAN, Simon QC
5 Paper Buildings (Godfrey Carey QC & Jonathan Caplan QC) London (020) 7583 6117
Recommended in Licensing
Specialisation: Licensing cases of all types (including casinos) and at every level. Editor (for current and past six editions) of 'Paterson's Licensing Acts'. Also practises in Restraint of Trade, Breach of Confidence, civil and criminal fraud, regulatory and disciplinary fields.
Personal: Called 1980. QC 1998. Door Tenant at Albion Chambers, Bristol.

MELLOR, James
8 New Square (Michael Fysh QC) London (020) 7405 4321
james.mellor@8newsquare.co.uk
Recommended in Intellectual Property, Media & Entertainment
Specialisation: Barrister with wide ranging intellectual property practice in patents (electronic/chemical/mechanical devises/biotech), copyright and designs (engineering drawings/databases/computer software/literary works), trade marks and passing off and confidential information (chemical formulae/business information). Further experience in arbitrations with intellectual property or technical elements and in the Copyright tribunal. For comprehensive CV and list of recent cases, visit our website at www.8newsquare.co.uk.
Prof. Memberships: Intellectual Property Bar Association (IPBA). Member of the Disability panel of the Bar Council. Chancery Bar Association (committee member 1997-79, speaker at two seminars).
Career: Called 1986. Prior work experience in a variety of engineering disciplines in the UK, France, Germany, Somalia, the Congo and Iraq.
Publications: Co-author of 'Kerly on Trade Marks' 13th edn, co-author of 'The Trade Marks Act 1994 – Text and Commentary', editor of 'Patents – Atkin's Court Forms', co-editor of Intellectual Property section of Bullen, Leake & Jacob's 'Precedents of Pleadings' 14th edn, former editor of 'Computers – Atkin's Court Forms'.
Personal: Born 1961. Educated at Rugby School; Kings College, Cambridge (1983 BA, MA Engineering and Production Engineering, 1985 Law (1st Class).

MELTON, Christopher QC
Byrom Street Chambers Manchester (0161) 829 2100
clerks@peelct.co.uk
Recommended in Clinical Negligence
Specialisation: All areas of medical law, including clinical negligence, consent to treatment, criminal cases with medical issues.
Prof. Memberships: PNBA, APIL.

MERCER, Geoffrey
Walnut House (Paul Dunkels QC) Exeter (01392) 279751
Recommended in Crime

MERCER, Hugh
Essex Court Chambers (Gordon Pollock QC) London (020) 7813 8000
Recommended in Agriculture
Specialisation: Specialist in EU and commercial law. Recent practice includes Brussels Convention jurisdictional arguments in the House of Lords; Articles 81/82 in the context of milk distribution and liner shipping; judicial review on EU grounds of decisions to use new food safety legislation, to refuse subsidies to the Isle of Wight, to order a contiguous cull on foot and mouth grounds; right to a hearing for agricultural IACS forms before the European Court of Justice; state aid, competition, public procurement and pharmaceutical product authorisation before the European Commission; proceedings before the High Court and the UK Competition Commission in the context of gas and water regulatory issues.
Prof. Memberships: European Circuit (Circuit Junior); Union Internationale Des Avocats, Agriculture Law Association.

Career: Called to the Bar 1985.
Personal: Downing College, Cambridge 1981-84; Université Libre de Bruxelles 1985-86. Fluent in French, German, and reasonably fluent in Spanish and Italian. Leisure pursuits include squash, mountain walking, and photography.

MEREDITH, George
Southernhay Chambers (Anthony Ward) Exeter (01392) 255777
southernhay.chambers@lineone.net
Recommended in Family
Specialisation: Care proceedings and private law Children Act applications, wardship and inherent jurisdiction cases. Recent cases in court of appeal concerning jurisdiction of county court in family proceedings and power of court to make assessment orders in care cases.
Prof. Memberships: Family Law Bar Association. Christian Mediation and Arbitration Service.
Career: Called to Bar 1969. Wardship and care cases from 1975.
Personal: Married with 3 children. Enjoys walking and computers.

MERRIMAN, Nicholas QC
3 Verulam Buildings (Christopher Symons QC & John Jarvis QC) London (020) 7831 8441
chambers@3vb.com
Recommended in Media & Entertainment
Specialisation: Barrister specialising in commercial work; banking; insurance; international trade, financial services, shipping and related aspects of company and insolvency work. Maritime, commodity and international arbitration. Intellectual property, entertainment law and gaming, and professional negligence. Cases: The Beatles v Lingasong Music 1998; Ritz Casino v Adnan Khashoggi 1998; Creation Records v News Group 1997; Macmillan v Bishopsgate Investment Trust 1995; Re: Paramount Holdings 1993; Barclays Bank v Homan 1993: Baytur v Finagro Holdings 1992; Crockfords v Mehta 1992.
Career: Qualified 1969; QC 1988; recorder; Master of the Bench, Inner Temple

METHUEN, Richard QC
12 King's Bench Walk (Richard Methuen QC) London (020) 7583 0811
methuen@12kbw.co.uk
Recommended in Personal Injury
Specialisation: Personal injury and professional negligence.
Prof. Memberships: PIBA and PNBA.
Career: Called 1972. QC 1997.
Personal: Born 22 August 1950.

MEYER, Lorna
5 Fountain Court (Anthony Barker QC) Birmingham (0121) 606 0500
Recommended in Family

MICHAELS, Amanda
Hogarth Chambers (Jonathan Rayner James QC & Christopher Morcom QC) London (020) 7404 0404
amichaels@hogarthchambers.com
Recommended in Media & Entertainment
Specialisation: Intellectual property, with an emphasis on copyright and design right, trade marks (registration and litigation) and passing off. Entertainment and media law, including music industry, performing rights, publishing, advertising, film and television disputes. Breach of confidence and all other aspects of intellectual property. General Chancery and commercial litigation.
Career: Call: 1981.
Personal: BA in law from Durham, MA in Advanced European Studies from College of Europe, Bruges. Fluent French. Author of 'A Practical Guide to Trade Mark Law' (3rd edn 2001) Sweet & Maxwell.

MIFFLIN, Helen
30 Park Place (John Jenkins QC) Cardiff (029) 2039 8421
Recommended in Family

MILDON, David QC
Essex Court Chambers (Gordon Pollock QC) London (020) 7813 8000
Recommended in Energy & Natural Resources
Specialisation: All types of commercial litigation including oil gas and electricity litigation, insurance, banking, shipping, international sale of goods and international commercial arbitration; also Lloyd's and LIFFE disciplinary proceedings.
Career: Emmanuel College, Cambridge, MA (1st Class Hons); LLB (1st Class Hons). Called to the Bar 1980. Called to Bar of Antigua and Barbuda: 1990. Queen's Council 2000.

MILES, Robert
4 Stone Buildings (Philip Heslop QC) London (020) 7242 5524
Recommended in Banking, Chancery, Company, Energy & Natural Resources, Insolvency/Corporate Recovery

MILFORD, John QC
Trinity Chambers (Toby Hedworth QC) Newcastle upon Tyne (0191) 232 1927
info@trinitychambers.co.uk
Recommended in Crime
Specialisation: Crime – particularly murder with a special interest in cases involving similar fact evidence and serial offenders; also firearms.
Prof. Memberships: NE Circuit; CBA
Career: Called 1969; QC 1989; Recorder 1985; Deputy High Court Judge 1994.
Personal: Educated Hurstpierpoint and Exeter University. Country sports, gardening and collecting. Regional Chairman of Countryside Alliance since 1999 for NE England.

MILL, Ian QC
Blackstone Chambers (Presiley Baxendale QC & Charles Flint QC) London (020) 7583 1770
ianmill@blackstonechambers.com
Recommended in Commercial (Litigation), Media & Entertainment, Sport
Specialisation: Principal areas of practice are commercial law (including financial services and commercial fraud) and intellectual property (copyright, passing off and confidential information) with specialist knowledge and experience in the music industry and other entertainment fields, and in sports law. Major cases include Panayiotou v Sony Music (the George Michael case) and Hadley v Kemp (the Spandau Ballet case). Clients have included all the major record and music publishing companies, film production companies, television and radio broadcasters, recording artists and songwriters, and leading sports organisations and figures.
Prof. Memberships: Recently appointed chairman of UK Athletics Disciplinary Committee, and of the Sports Dispute Resolution Panel.
Career: Called to the Bar 1981 and joined current chambers 1982. Appointed QC in 1999.
Publications: Editorial board member for 'The International Sports Law Review'
Personal: Educated at Epsom College 1971-75 and Trinity Hall, Cambridge 1976-80 (MA in Classics and Law). Leisure pursuits include golf, cricket, theatre and opera. Born 9 April 1958. Lives in London.

MILLER, Celia
East Anglian Chambers (Roderick Newton) Ipswich (01473) 214481
Recommended in Family

MILLER, Nicholas
Guildhall Chambers (Adrian Palmer QC) Bristol (0117) 927 3366
Recommended in Family

MILLER, Richard QC
Three New Square (David Young QC) London (020) 7405 1111
3newsquareip@lineone.net
Recommended in Intellectual Property
Specialisation: Specialist in patents, copyright, design rights, trade marks, passing off, breach of confidence, restrictive covenants and all other aspects of intellectual property, including EU law relating to IP. Also appears at the European Patent Office in Munich on behalf of applicants and opponents for European Patents. Co-editor of 'TERRELL on the Law of Patents'.
Prof. Memberships: Intellectual Property Bar Association, Chancery Bar Association, Bar European Group, International Association for the Protection of Industrial Property (AIPPI).
Career: Called to the Bar 1976 (Middle Temple). Appointed QC 1995.
Personal: Educated: Charterhouse 1966-70; University of Sussex 1971-74, BSc (Chemical Physics).

MILLER, Stephen QC
1 Crown Office Row (Robert Seabrook QC) London (020) 7797 7500
Recommended in Clinical Negligence

MILLETT, Kenneth
2 Hare Court (Stephen Kramer QC) London (020) 7353 5324
Kennerf@lineone.net
Recommended in Crime
Specialisation: Criminal defence; civil liberties; civil actions against the police.

MILLETT, Richard
Essex Court Chambers (Gordon Pollock QC) London (020) 7813 8000
Recommended in Arbitration (International), Banking, Commercial (Litigation), Insolvency/Corporate Recovery, Media & Entertainment
Specialisation: Main areas of practice cover banking, insolvency, commercial litigation, reinsurance, company law, and media and entertainment. Major litigation includes the Maxwell, Polly Peck, Barings, BCCI and Bermuda Fire and Marine cases. Regularly addresses conferences and seminars. Junior Counsel to the Crown, London A Panel.
Prof. Memberships: Commercial Bar Association.
Career: Called to the Bar 1985. Joined present chambers 1990.
Publications: Co-author of 'The Law of Guarantees' (3rd edn, Sweet & Maxwell 2000)

MILLIGAN, Iain QC
20 Essex Street (Iain Milligan QC) London (020) 7583 9294
clerks@20essexst.com
Recommended in Banking, Commercial (Litigation), Shipping
Specialisation: Arbitration, aviation, banking, carriage of goods, commodities, conflict, energy, financial services, insurance and reinsurance, shipping. Recent cases include Glencore Grain Ltd v Agros Trading Co Ltd [1999] 2 Lloyd's Rep 410; Australia New Zealand Banking Group Ltd v Societe Generale [2000] A11 ER (D) 203; Credit Suisse First Boston (Europe) Ltd v MLC (Bermuda) Ltd [1999] 1 Lloyd' Rep 767; Credit Suisse First Boston (Europe) Ltd v Seagate Trading Co Ltd [1999] 1 Lloyd's Rep 784; Shanning International Ltd (in liquidation) v Lloyds TSB Bank plc (formerly Lloyds Bank plc) and others [2000] A11 ER (D) 731; UBS AG v Omni Holding AG (IN liquidation) [2000] 1 WLR 916; Sinochem International Oil (London) Co. Ltd v Mobil Sales and Supply Corporation [1999] 2 Lloyd's Rep 769; Sandvik AB v Pfiffner (UK) Ltd [1999] 1 A11 ER (D) 372; Northern Shipping Co v Deutsche Seereederei GmbH and others [2000] A11 ER (D) 281; Borealis AB v Stargas Ltd [2001] 2 WLR 1118; ACE Insurance SA v Zurich Insurance Co [2001] 1 Lloyd's Rep 618.

Prof. Memberships: Commercial Bar Association London and Common Law Bar Association.
Career: Cambridge (1st) 1972. Queen's Counsel 1991.

MILLIKEN-SMITH, Mark
2 Bedford Row (William Clegg QC) London
(020) 7440 8888
Recommended in Crime
Specialisation: Specialist practitioner in serious crime, with considerable experience of all areas of heavyweight criminal work, from homicide to serious fraud and appellate work, in which he is regularly instructed as a leading junior.
Prof. Memberships: South Eastern Circuit, Criminal Bar Association.
Career: Called to the Bar in 1986.
Personal: Married with two children. Educated at Wellington College and Bristol University. Interests include sport (whenever possible), particularly cricket, rugby and football.

MILMO, Patrick QC
5 Raymond Buildings (Patrick Milmo QC) London
(020) 7242 2902
Recommended in Defamation
Specialisation: Defamation, copyright, breach of confidence and all other areas of law concerned with the media; judicial review; sporting regulations, especially horseracing (acts for the Jockey Club). Recent cases: R v Disciplinary Committee of Jockey Club. Exp Aga Khan [1993] I WLR 909 (judicial review); Time Warner v Channel 4 TV [1994] EMLR 1. [Copyright – film]; McDonald's Corporation v Steel [1995] 3 ALLER 615 [defamation]; Godfrey v Lees [1995] EMLR 307 (copyright – musical work); Broxton v McClelland [1997] EMLR 157; Ramsden v MGN [1998]; Emaco & Electrolux v Dyson TLR 4 Feb 1999 [trade libel and trademark infringement]; Druck v Associated Newspapers [2000] EMLR 284 (defamation by photograph); Alexander v Arts Council of Wales TLR 27 April 2001.
Career: Trinity College, Cambridge. Called 1962. QC 1985. Bencher Middle Temple 1994.
Publications: Publication: joint editor of 'Gatley on Libel & Slander' (9th edn).

MILNE, David QC
Pump Court Tax Chambers London
(020) 7414 8080
clerks@pumptax.com
Recommended in Tax
Specialisation: Specialist in revenue law, especially tax litigation and dispute resolution.
Prof. Memberships: Institute of Chartered Accountants in England and Wales. Currently chairman of the Revenue Bar Association.
Career: Accountant, articled to *Whinney Murray & Co* 1966-69. Called to the Bar 1970 and joined current chambers in 1972. Took Silk 1987. Appointed Recorder 1994. Bencher of Lincoln's Inn.
Personal: Educated at Harrow 1958-63 and Oxford 1963-66. Born 22 September 1945. Lives in London.

MISKIN, Charles QC
23 Essex Street (Michael Lawson QC) London
(020) 7413 0353
charlesmiskin@23essexstreet.co.uk
Recommended in Fraud
Specialisation: (1) Fraud and regulatory cases including those concerning banking, insurance, letters of credit and guarantees, trade, corruption, money laundering, advance fees, loan churning and public revenue. (2) General crime, disciplinary cases and civil cases involving both fraud and police law. (3) Environmental Law.
Prof. Memberships: Criminal Bar Association.
Career: Called to the Bar 1975 (Gray's). Joined what is now Essex Street in 1977. Assistant Recorder of the Crown Court, 1992-98. Recorder 1998. Standing Counsel to the Inland Revenue (Crime), 1993-98. Queen's Counsel 1998.
Personal: Educated at Charterhouse School and Worcester College, Oxford. Lives in London.

MITCHELL, Andrew
Fountain Court (Anthony Boswood QC) London
(020) 7583 3335
Recommended in Banking
Specialisation: Practices in commercial litigation and arbitration, with particular experience of international and domestic banking, civil fraud, professional negligence (particularly solicitors), insurance/reinsurance and employment. Recent cases have included acting for the new Nigerian Government in its claims against the former regime; Bank Leumi v Miloubar (bills of exchange); Ebert v Midland Bank [1999] 3 WLR 670, a leading authority on the power of the Court to control vexatious litigation.
Prof. Memberships: COMBAR.
Career: Called 1992.
Publications: Contributing Editor to 'Commercial Court Procedure' (Sweet & Maxwell, 2000).
Personal: Educated at Cambridge University (1987-90 (MA)) and Oxford University (1990-91), BCL. Harmsworth Scholar of Middle Temple. Born 1968.

MITCHELL, Andrew QC
Furnival Chambers (Andrew Mitchell QC) London
(020) 7405 3232
arm@furnivallaw.co.uk
Recommended in Crime, Fraud
Specialisation: Financial crime: white collar fraud – advance fee, mortgage, computer and letter of credit, handling the transfer of serious and complex fraud, drafting statements of evidence and case statements for both the defence and prosecution. Money laundering – advised on practice and procedures in relation to money laundering regulations and legislation. Acted in both prosecutions and defence of money laundering offences. Asset forfeiture and confiscation – advised, represented prosecuting authorities, defendants, receivers and third parties in House of Lords, Court of Appeal (Civil and Criminal), High Court and Crown Court on all matters affecting the restraint, management receivers and confiscation of property. General crime: defended and represented the prosecution in significant drug cases. Priority interests: asset forfeiture, confiscation, white collar fraud, money laundering, drugs. International work: advised governments of Trinidad and Tobago, Turks and Caicos Islands, Cayman Islands, Canada, USA, Abu Dhabi, Pakistan. Acted in civil and criminal litigation in Trinidad and Tobago, Turks and Caicos Islands and Gibraltar, Cayman Islands.
Career: Called to Bar 1976, Gray's Inn, Ireland, Gibraltar, Trinidad, and the Turks and Caicos Islands. Assistant Recorder 1995. Queens Counsel 1998. Recorder 1999. Has been a principal speaker at training programmes organised by the UN for prosecutors and investigators in the Caribbean as well as at judicial symposiums in Trinidad, Jamaica and the Bahamas. Regular lecturer on matters affecting restraint, confiscation and money laundering for United Nations, National Crime Squad, Criminal Bar Association (England and Wales) and Temple Lectures. Consultant to Caribbean anti money laundering programme.
Publications: Author – 'A Concise Guide to the Criminal Procedure and Investigations Act', 1996. Co-author – 'Confiscation and the Proceeds of Crime', 2nd edn (the leading textbook on asset forfeiture and confiscation, published by Sweet & Maxwell). Articles published in the New Law Journal and the Journal of Criminal Law.
Personal: Born 6 August 1954.

MITCHELL, Janet
4 Brick Court (David Medhurst) London
(020) 7797 8910
Recommended in Family
Specialisation: Child care law, public law cases, family law and litigation. Provided procedure guidelines to local authorities on setting up Care in the Community Programme. Particular areas include: child sexual abuse, child protection issues, female and male paedophiles, public interest immunity. Latest case 5 week representing a local authority in respect of incest, child sexual abuse, sexual abuse by mother, father, stepfather and inter-sibling abuse. Abuse in which question of 13 year old under represented was raised.
Prof. Memberships: Family Law Bar Association. Lawyers for children.
Career: Called to the Bar in 1979. Lecturing on advocacy, litigation and public law cases particularly in the area of child sexual and physical abuse.
Personal: Travel, reading, swimming, tennis, crosswords. Widow – 2 daughters. Husband, also a Barrister, died in 1989.

MITCHESON, Thomas
Three New Square (David Young QC) London
(020) 7405 1111
tom@mitcheson.com
Recommended in Intellectual Property
Specialisation: All aspects of intellectual property law. Recent cases include Norowzian v Arks (Copyright in television advertisement, CA); Kimberly-Clark v Procter & Gamble (Patent Amendment, CA); 3M v ATI Atlas (patent infringement); Collag v Merck (confidential information); Hewlett Packard v Waters (patent infringement); Arsenal v Reed (trademark – ECJ reference).
Career: Internship at Cold Spring Harbor Laboratory, USA 1990-91. Trinity College, Cambridge, 1991-94 – First Class Hons Natural Sciences. City University (DipLaw) 1995 (Distinction). Called to the Bar 1996.
Publications: 'Two Genes in Saccharomyces Cerevisiae Encode a Membrane Bound Form of Casein Kinase-1' Wang, Vancura, Mitcheson & Kuret (1992). Contributor to Terrell on Patents (15th edition).

MOAT, Frank
Pump Court Chambers (Christopher Harvey Clark QC) London (020) 7353 0711
Recommended in Personal Injury
Specialisation: Called 1970. Personal injury specialist, with a particular emphasis on industrial accidents and diseases, including claims for asbestos related conditions. Practice also covers professional negligence and family law.

MOGER, Christopher QC
4 Pump Court London (020) 7842 5555
cmoger@4pumpcourt.com
Recommended in Licensing, Professional Negligence
Specialisation: General commercial and common law, especially insurance, construction matters; professional negligence, and regulatory and disciplinary proceedings.
Prof. Memberships: ORBA; LCLBA; COMBAR; PNBA; Barristers' Overseas Advocacy Committee.
Career: Called 1972; joined 4 Pump Court 1973; Assistant Recorder 1990; Silk 1992; Recorder 1993; FCIA 1997. Deputy Judge of High Court 1999. Trained mediator and member of ADR Chambers, London. Member of Panel of Chairmen of Lloyds Disciplinary Tribunal 2001.
Personal: Educated Sherborne School 1963-68 and Bristol University 1969-71 (LL.B Hons). Born 28th July 1949.

MOLE, David QC
4-5 Gray's Inn Square (Elizabeth Appleby QC & David Mole QC) London (020) 7404 5252
Recommended in Planning
Specialisation: Principal area of practice is local government and administrative law and judicial review, planning, environmental and rating law. Clients include major developers including retailers, housebuilders and other service providers. Also acts for government departments, development corporations and local authorities.
Prof. Memberships: Administrative Law Bar Association, Planning and Environment Bar Association.
Career: Called to the Bar and joined present chambers 1970. Treasury Solicitors Panel 1980. Junior Counsel to Inland Revenue in rating and valuation matters 1984. Took Silk in 1990. Appointed Recorder 1995.
Personal: Educated at Trinity College, Dublin (MA 1966) and London School of Economics (LL.M 1969). Born 1st April 1943. Lives in London and Somerset.

MOLONEY, Patrick QC
1 Brick Court (Richard Rampton QC) London (020) 7353 8845
Recommended in Defamation
Specialisation: Media law, (libel, slander, malicious falsehood, passing off, breach of confidence, contempt of court, reporting restrictions, judicial review).
Prof. Memberships: Northern Irish Bar.
Career: BA BCL (Oxon); Asst. Prof. Univ. of British Columbia (1974-75); 1 Brick Court (1978 to present). QC (1998). Recorder (2000).
Publications: Co-author 'Libel and Slander' Halisbury's Laws of England.

MOLYNEUX, Brenton
29 Bedford Row Chambers (Peter Ralls QC) London (020) 7404 1044
bmolyneux@29bedfordrow.co.uk
Recommended in Family
Specialisation: All aspects of family law but with a particular emphasis on matrimonal finance and private law children work. Recent cases include A v A; B v B [2000] 1 FLR 701 and Roker International Properties Inc and Another v Couvaras and Wolf [2000] 2 FLR 976.
Prof. Memberships: Family Law Bar Association.
Career: Called to the Bar, February 1994.
Personal: Born 31st December 1968. Educated at Birkenhead School, Christ Church, Oxford (BA) and City University (Dip Law). Married. Lives in London.

MONKCOM, Stephen
Tanfield Chambers (Peter Hughes QC) London (020) 7797 7250
Recommended in Licensing

MONTGOMERY, Clare QC
Matrix Chambers (Nicholas Blake QC) London (020) 7404 3447
Recommended in Crime, Fraud, Human Rights
Specialisation: Commercial fraud. Extradition and mutual assistance. Administrative Law. Criminal Law. Counsel in Guinness, Brent Walker and Maxwell trials. Appeared in leading extradition cases, Pinochet and Osman. Represented Bermuda Fire & Marine and Prince Jefri in civil fraud trials. Practitioner Editor Archbold on Commerce, Financial Markets and Insolvency.
Career: Called to the Bar 1980. 1992 – 1996 Supplementary Panel (Common Law). Queen's Counsel 1996. Assistant Recorder 1999. Recorder 2000.

MOODY, Neil
2 Temple Gardens (Dermod O'Brien QC) London (020) 7822 1200
nmoody@2templegardens.co.uk
Recommended in Professional Negligence
Specialisation: Professional Negligence. Widespread experience of claims for and against valuers, surveyors, insurance brokers, accountants and architects. Also specialises in flooding and fire cases, insurance and serious personal injury claims. Recent cases include: Stevens v Gullis [2000] All ER (CA) (architects: duties of experts) and Bybrook Barn v Kent County Council [2001] All ER (CA) (nuisance, flooding).
Prof. Memberships: LCCLBA, PNBA, PIBA.
Career: Tenant 2 Temple Gardens 1990.
Personal: Married: 2 children, sailing.

MOODY-STUART, Thomas
8 New Square (Michael Fysh QC) London (020) 7405 4321
tom.moodystuart@8newsquare.co.uk
Recommended in Intellectual Property
Specialisation: Barrister specialising in all areas of intellectual property including patents, copyright, registered/unregistered design, trade marks, passing off, biotechnology, comparative advertising, broadcasting and breach of confidence. Cases include, Auchincloss v Animal Veterinary Supplies – virucidal disinfectant/chemical composition patent; Horne v Reliance; Quadrant Holdings v Quadrant Bio Resources and Roser; Baby Dan v Brevi – design right; Frayling Furniture Ltd. v Premier Upholstery Ltd. – design right. For comprehensive CV and list of recent cases, visit our website at www.8newsquare.co.uk.
Prof. Memberships: Intellectual Property Bar Association (IPBA); The Intellectual Property Lawyers Organisation.
Career: Called 1995, Middle Temple; conservation research assistant: US Government Captive Breeding Centre 1989.
Personal: Called 1970. Educated at Shrewsbury School; Gonville & Caius College, Cambridge (1993 MA Hons Natural Science); College of Law; Inns of Court School of Law.

MOON, Angus
3 Serjeants' Inn (Robert Francis QC & John Grace QC) London (020) 7427 5000
Recommended in Clinical Negligence
Specialisation: Specialist in medical negligence and medically related litigation. Particular interest in judicial review in the medical context and medical ethical decisions. Instructed by both Plaintiffs and Defendants in medical negligence actions and for parties involved in medical disciplinary tribunals and inquests. Additional areas of practice include commercial contract and employment law. Major reported cases in the medical field include Gregory v Ferro (GB) Ltd and ors [1995] 6 Med LR 321 (Court of Appeal); Mahmood v Siggins [1996] 7 Med LR 76; R v Milling (Medical Referee), ex p West Yorkshire Police Authority [1997] 8 Med LR 392; Re C (A Minor) (Medical Treatment) [1998] 1 Lloyd's Rep Med 1; Palmer v Tees Health Authority [1998] Lloyd's Rep Med 447; Davis v Jacobs & Camden & Islington Health Authority & Novartis [1999] Lloyd's Rep Med 72; Bordin v St Mary's NHS Trust [2000] Lloyd's Rep Med 287; Reynolds v The Health First Medical Group [2000] Lloyd's Rep Med 240. Counsel to Mr James Wisheart, former Medical Director, at the Bristol Royal Infirmary Inquiry. Editor of the Lloyd's Law Reports 'Medical' (formerly the Medical Law Reports.) Member of the Committee of the London Common Law and Commercial Bar Association.
Career: Called to the Bar 1986.
Personal: Christ's College, Cambridge (MA Law).

MOONEY, Stephen
Albion Chambers (Charles Barton QC & Neil Ford QC) Bristol (0117) 927 2144
Recommended in Crime

MOOR, Philip QC
1 Mitre Court Buildings (Bruce Blair QC) London (020) 7797 7070
moor@1mcb.com
Recommended in Family
Specialisation: Family law, with particular emphasis on the financial aspects of marital breakdown. Regular lecturer and contributor (with Nicholas Mostyn QC as co-author) to 'Family Law' magazine.
Prof. Memberships: Family Law Bar Association (Committee member since 1987; head of Education & Training 1993-00; acting treasurer since 2000).
Career: Called to the Bar in 1982 and joined Mitre Court Buildings in 1983. Member of General Council of the Bar 1987-89. Council of Legal Education 1988-91 (Board of Examiners 1989-92). Phillips Committee on Financing Pupillage (1989).
Personal: Educated at Canford School 1972-77 and Pembroke College, Oxford 1978-81. Leisure pursuits include cricket, football and rugby union. Lives in Bromley.

MOOR, Sarah
Old Square Chambers (John Hendy QC) London (020) 7269 0300
moor@oldsquarechambers.co.uk
Recommended in Employment
Specialisation: Principal area of practice is employment law including sex, race and disability discrimination, equal pay, restrictive covenant and industrial action. Recently reported case includes Kenny v Hampshire Constabulary and Edwards v Mid Suffolk District Council.
Prof. Memberships: Employment Law Bar Association, Industrial Law Society and Employment Lawyers Association.
Career: Queen's College, Cambridge BA Law (1989), Kennedy Memorial Scholar at Harvard Law School (1990), Council of Legal Education (1991). Called 1991. Joined Old Square Chambers 1992.
Publications: Contributor to 'Employment Precedents and Company Documents' (FT Law and Tax).

MOORE, Katherine
Octagon House Chambers (Andrew Lindqvist) Norwich (01603) 623186
Recommended in Crime

MOORE, Martin
Erskine Chambers (Robin Potts QC) London (020) 7242 5532
Recommended in Company
Specialisation: Litigation and advice on all aspects of company law, corporate insolvency and corporate reorganisation, including Schemes of Arrangement, and Schemes for transfer of long term insurance business. Recent cases: Re BSB Holdings Ltd (1996) 1 BCLC 155; Possfund Custodian Trustee Ltd v Diamond (1996) 1 WLR 1351, Bermuda Fire and Marine Insurance Company and others v BF&M Limited and others heard in the Supreme Court of Bermuda, during 1999 and Axa Equity 7 Law Life Assurance Security plc and Axa Sun Life plc 2001 1 AER(Comm) 1010.
Career: BA (Oxon). Year Qualified: 1982. Lincoln's Inn.
Personal: Born: 1960.

MOORE, Miranda
5 Paper Buildings (Godfrey Carey QC & Jonathan Caplan QC) London (020) 7583 6117
Recommended in Crime

MORCOM, Christopher QC
Hogarth Chambers (Jonathan Rayner James QC & Christopher Morcom QC) London (020) 7404 0404
cmorcom@hogarthchambers.com
Recommended in Intellectual Property
Specialisation: Intellectual property including in particular trademarks; also copyright; designs; patents; confidential information.
Prof. Memberships: Member of SACIP; council member and vice-president of AIPPI (British Group). Associate member of ITMA, CIPA, INTA, past president of LIDC; honorary president (2000-date); chairman of Competition Law Association (1985-99); director of the Intellectual Property Institute; member of Board of International Trademark Association (INTA) (1998-00).
Career: Called to the Bar 1963 (Middle Temple); Bencher (1996); Certificate of Honour; Astbury Scholarship. Took Silk 1991.
Publications: Author (with Roughton & Graham) of 'The Modern Law of Trade Marks' (Butterworths, 2000).
Personal: Interests include music and walking.

MORGAN, Lynne
Temple Chambers (David J.M. Aubrey QC) Cardiff (029) 2039 7364
Recommended in Family

MORGAN, Paul QC
Falcon Chambers (Jonathan Gaunt QC & Kim Lewison QC) London (020) 7353 2484
morgan@falcon-chambers.com
Recommended in Agriculture, Property Litigation
Specialisation: All aspects of real property, commercial property litigation and agricultural holdings.
Prof. Memberships: Chancery Bar Association, London Commercial and Common Law Bar Association, Professional Negligence Bar Association, Agricultural Law Association.
Career: Called to the Bar in 1975, Silk 1992. Deputy chairman, Agricultural Land Tribunal; assistant boundary commissioner.

Publications: Joint editor 'Woodfall on Landlord and Tenant', looseleaf edition. Joint editor 'Gale on Easements', 16th edn.

MORGAN, Simon
St John's Chambers (Christopher Sharp QC) Bristol (0117) 921 3456
Recommended in Crime

MORGAN, Stephen
Eldon Chambers (Lionel Read QC) London (020) 7583 1355
clerks@eldonchambers.com
Recommended in Planning
Specialisation: Local Government; Town and Country Planning; Environmental Law and Public Law. Compulsory purchase and compensation; highways; advertisements.
Prof. Memberships: PEBA
Career: Law degree, followed by MA in Town and Country Planning. Always been in local government Chambers.
Personal: Family; walking; bird watching; football.

MORGANS, John
Octagon House Chambers (Andrew Lindqvist) Norwich (01603) 623186
Recommended in Crime

MORRIS, Anthony QC
Peel Court Chambers (Michael Shorrock QC) Manchester (0161) 832 3791
Recommended in Crime

MORRIS, Stephen
20 Essex Street (Iain Milligan QC) London (020) 7583 9294
smorris@20essexst.com
Recommended in Competition/Anti-trust
Specialisation: All aspects of EC and UK competition law; other EC law, in particular free movement of goods, intellectual property, air transport, customs, sanctions; commercial and international trade, inparticular conflict of laws, insurance and arbitration. Recent competition/EC cases include Morgan Stanley v Visa (Comm Ct); Shanning v Lloyds TSB (HL); R v Secretary of State for Trade ex parte Thomson Holidays (CA); Sandvik v Pfiffner (CA); Mid Kent Holdings v General Utilities (Ch D); Airtours/First Choice (EC Comm); Mid Kent Holdings (MMC); Foreign Package Holidays (MMC); AIUFFASS v Commission (ECJ); Potato Marketing Board v Hampden Smith (CA); Commercial cases include Maxwell Communication Corportation v New Hampshire Insurance (CA); PASF v Bamberger (CA); Akai v PIC (Comm Ct); Toepfer v Cargill (CA). Further information at www.20essexst.com.
Prof. Memberships: COMBAR, Bar European Group.
Career: Called to the Bar in 1981. At 4 Raymond Buildings, Gray's Inn 1983-91. Joined present chambers in 1992. Junior Counsel to the Crown (A Panel) 1999-. Recorder.
Publications: Bellamy and Child, 'European Community Law of Competition' (5th edn 2001 – chapter on enforcement in member states); contributor to Plender, 'European Courts Practice and Precedent and Bar Council's Practitioners Handbook of EC law'.
Personal: Educated at Bradford Grammar School 1965-75 and Christ's College, Cambridge.

MORRISON, Howard QC
36 Bedford Row (Michael Pert QC) Nottingham (020) 7421 8000
chambers@bedfordrow.co.uk
Recommended in Crime
Specialisation: Criminal law, particularly fraud, serious violence and drugs. International criminal law relating to laws of war, war crimes and command responsibility. Prosecutions for CPS (Grade 4), Customs and Excise 'A', SFO, DTI, firearms cases for Police authorities. Courts Martial defence, UK and overseas. Recent high profile cases include Chalkley [1998] QB 848 CA, the cases of Delalic and Mucic at the International War Crimes Tribunal in The Hague and the case of Mugenzi in the Rwanda genocide trial at the ICTR.
Prof. Memberships: Member of the CBA, the European CBA, Commonwealth Judges and Magistrates Association, Justice, founding member of the ICTY Defence Counsel Association, member of the Race Relations Committee of the Bar Council, member of expert panel of DFID and advisory committee for the UN ICTY, Member of Fijian and Caribbean Bars. Negotiating member of the ICDAA at the ICC New York preparatry commission.
Career: LL.B. (Lond), called to Bar, Grays Inn 1977. Pupil Master and Advocacy Teacher, Grays Inn. Practice on Midland and Oxford Circuit. Former Infantry Officer and experience of voluntary work in Ghana, Zambia and Malawi, former Chief Magistrate of Fiji, Senior Magistrate of Tuvalu and Attorney General of Anguilla. Recorder [Crime, Civil and Family]. OBE (1988). Fellow of Royal Geographical Society.
Personal: Married with one daughter and one son. Qualified yachtsman, scuba diver, private pilot.

MORSHEAD, Timothy
4 Breams Buildings (Christopher Lockhart-Mummery QC) London (020) 7353 5835
tmorshead@4breams.co.uk
Recommended in Property Litigation
Specialisation: All aspects of property law including landlord and tenant law and planning. Also accepts work in certain public law matters. Member of C Panel of Junior Counsel to the Crown.
Prof. Memberships: Chancery Bar Association, Property Bar Association, Planning and Environment Bar Association.

MORT, Justin
2 Temple Gardens (Dermod O'Brien QC) London (020) 7822 1230
jmort@2templegardens.co.uk
Recommended in Construction
Specialisation: Construction disputes. Recent cases have arisen out of a wide range of building and refurbishment projects, as well as process and civil engineering works, both in the UK and in the Far East. He has particular experience of resisting substantial adjudication claims, acting on behalf of the main contractors, private individuals, developers, local authorities and other public bodies. He has also acted in a number of construction related professional negligence disputes, including claims for defective design and negligent contract administration. Represented the employer in David McLean Contractors Ltd v Swansea Housing Association Ltd.
Prof. Memberships: Society of Construction Law, Adjudication Society, King's College Construction Law Association and TECBAR.
Career: Called to the Bar in 1994. Tenant of 2 Temple Gardens since 1995.
Personal: Born 1970. MSc in Construction Law and Arbitration, King's College, London. Dissertation; 'Claims for contribution under the Civil Liability (Contribution) Act 1978'. Jules Thorn Scholar (Middle Temple).

MORTIMORE, Simon QC
3-4 South Square (Michael Crystal QC & Lord Alexander of Weedon QC) London (020) 7696 9900
clerks@southsquare.com
Recommended in Insolvency/Corporate Recovery
Specialisation: Practice covers business and financial law with a particular specialisation in insolvency law. Recent work includes advising and appearing for the liquidators of Barings, the court appointed receivers of Metro Trading International, US investors in $160 million fraud claim. Substantial involvement in most of the major insolvencies of the 1990's : BCCI, Olympia & York, Maxwell, Polly Peck, Ferranti and Facia. More than 50 reported cases including: Triffit v Salads Etc (2000) effect of termination of agency on rights to book debts; Glencore v Metro (1990) forum issues under Brussels Convention; Richbell Information Services (1998); TSB v Platts (1998) effect of cross claims on petition; Cosslett Contractors (1997) effect of charge in building contract; Re BCCI (no10) (1997) cross-border set-off issues; Re Leeds United Holdings (1996) disputed takeover; Macmillan v Bishopsgate (1995) priorities over shares in foreign company.
Prof. Memberships: Chancery Bar Association; COMBAR.
Career: Called to the Bar (Inner Temple) in 1972; QC in 1991. Called to the BVI Bar 1991. Admitted ad hoc to the Bermuda and Cayman Islands Bars. Accredited CEDR mediator.

MORTON, Keith
1 Temple Gardens (Hugh Carlisle QC) London (020) 7583 1315
clerks@1templegardens.co.uk
Recommended in Health & Safety
Specialisation: Health and safety law, in which he regularly advises and represents both prosecution and defendants (eg junior prosecution counsel in R v Balfour Beatty and Geoconsult GmBH – (1999); arising out of collapse of tunnels at Heathrow Airport). Employment law, administrative law, personal injury, coroners (including judicial review) and public inquiries (eg Ladbroke Grove Rail Inquiry).
Prof. Memberships: South Eastern Circuit, Employment Lawyers Association, Justice.
Career: Called to the Bar Lincoln's Inn 1990; Treasury Counsel (common law) B Panel (since 1997).
Personal: University of Hull, City University. Interests include theatre, art, music, architecture, cycling.

MOSS, Gabriel QC
3-4 South Square (Michael Crystal QC & Lord Alexander of Weedon QC) London (020) 7696 9900
clerks@southsquare.com
Recommended in Chancery, Insolvency/Corporate Recovery
Specialisation: Mainly in business and financial law with a special emphasis on insolvency and restructuring. Involved in the two leading Court of Appeal cases on cross border insolvency. Acted as leading counsel for the liquidators in the mammoth trial in Bermuda relating to Bermuda Fire & Marine. Advised on two of the world's largest restructurings, ICO Global and GDE.
Prof. Memberships: Chancery Bar Association, Commercial Bar Association, Insol Europe, Fellow of the Society for Advanced Legal Studies, Bencher of Lincoln's Inn, Honorary Member of the Association of Fellows and Legal Scholars of the Centre for International Legal Studies, Member of Insolvency Lawyers Association.
Career: 1st Class Hons Law Degree at Oxford University (BA), Post Graduate Law Degree from Oxford University (BLC); Lecturer in Law at the University of Connecticut, part-time lecturer/tutor at Oxford University; Eldon Scholar (Oxford); Bar Exams: Appointed QC (1989): Authorised to sit as Deputy High Court Judge (2001).
Publications: Co-editor of Rowlatt on 'Principal and Surety'; Co-author of Lightman & Moss on the 'Law of Receivers of Companies'; Joint Consultant Editor of Totty & Moss on 'Insolvency'.

MOSS, Joanne R.
Falcon Chambers (Jonathan Gaunt QC & Kim Lewison QC) London (020) 7353 2484
Recommended in Agriculture

MOSTYN, Nicholas QC
1 Mitre Court Buildings (Bruce Blair QC) London (020) 7797 7070
Recommended in Family

MOULD, Timothy
4 Breams Buildings (Christopher Lockhart-Mummery QC) London (020) 7430 1221/7353 5835
Recommended in Planning

Specialisation: Specialises in local government and planning law and related areas of public law. Currently on the B Panel of Junior Counsel to the Crown, Junior Counsel to the Inland Revenue on Rating and Valuation matters, and contributor to Halsbury's Laws of England, Town and Country Planning and the Encyclopaedia of Rating and Local Taxation.
Prof. Memberships: Member of the Planning and Environment Bar Association and the Administrative Law Bar Association.

MOUNTFIELD, Helen
Matrix Chambers (Nicholas Blake QC) London (020) 7404 3447
helenmountfield@matrixlaw.co.uk
Recommended in Administrative & Public Law, Employment, Human Rights
Specialisation: Specialises in public law, human rights, discrimination, employment, and EC law. She practices in English, European and Commonwealth courts acting for private individuals, commercial organisations, NGO's and public authorities. She is an editor of the European Human Rights Law Revies and co-author of the Blackstone Guide to the Human Rights Act 1998, and lectures on domestic application of the ECHR and the Human Rights Act for the Judicial Studies Board and elsewhere. Junior Counsel to the Crown (B panel). Notable cases include R v Secretary of State for the Environment ex parte Friends of the Earth (drinking water standards litigation), Meade-Hill v British Council (indirect discrimination), Snares v CAO (free movement of persons, ECJ), R v Secretary of State for Health ex parte Source Informatics (confidentiality and data protection), Faulkner v UK (Article 6 ECHR) and representing the government of Belgium in Pinochet.
Career: Called to the Bar 1991.
Personal: Educated at Magdalen College Oxford (BA (Hons) Modern History (1st Class), City University 1989-90 (Dip Law, King's College London 1994 (Dip European Law).

MOVERLEY SMITH, Stephen
24 Old Buildings (Martin Mann QC & Alan Steinfeld QC) London (020) 7405 1360
stephen.moverlysmith@xxlv.co.uk
Recommended in Insolvency/Corporate Recovery
Specialisation: Specialist areas of practice: international commercial litigation, contentious trust litigation, company, insolvency and arbitration. Stephen Moverly-Smith is expert in high-level litigation relating to commercial, company and business law, both in the UK and overseas. He acted for Robert Maxwell's finance director following the collapse of the Maxwell group of companies and also acted for the liquidators of BCCI in relation to multi-million dollar claims in the Cayman Islands and the UK. He was described as an 'energetic, user-friendly junior' in Chambers 2000-01. Significant areas of his UK practice include financial services (he acted for the Building Societies Commission in relation to the demutualisation of the Halifax and Cheltenham & Gloucester Building Societies), commercial disputes, hostile trust litigation and insolvency (in relation to which he regularly acts for the DTI and the Inland Revenue). Disputes between shareholders of joint venture companies, mutual fund fraud and insolvency have become a regular feature of Stephen's international work. Stephen has participated in contentious trust cases in the British Virgin Islands, the Bahamas and the Isle of Man as well as in England. He is a member of the Bar Council and sits on the Bar Council International Relations Committee with special responsibility for the Commonwealth.
Prof. Memberships: Member of the: Chancery Bar Association, Insolvency Lawyers Association, Bar of the Eastern Caribbean Supreme Court, 'A' Panel of Junior Counsel to the Crown (formerly the Chancery Panel), Bar Council International Relations Committee and European Circuit.
Career: Pembroke College, Oxford (MA). Called to Bar 1985.

MOWBRAY, John QC
New Square Chambers (John Mowbray QC & Eben Hamilton QC) London (020) 7419 8000
clerks@newsquarechambers.co.uk
Recommended in Chancery
Specialisation: Litigation, with some advisory work, mediating and arbitrating, mainly in the following fields: Trusts, including related taxes, pension funds and Caribbean and other offshore trusts; Contract disputes, mainly international; Conflict of laws in connection with the above and generally; Property, including landlord and tenant, mortgages and insolvency aspects. Representative reported cases include: Arlen Bahamas Management v Trust Corporation of Bahamas (1971-6) 1 Law Reports of Bahamas 456 (power of modification of trust instrument); Security Trust v Royal Bank [1976] A.C. 503 P.C. (priority of charges on Bahamian land); Tito v Waddell [1977] Ch. 106 (governmental trusts); Borden U.K. v Scottish Timber Products [1981] Ch. 25 C.A. (retention of title clause); Official Custodian v Parway Estates [1985] Ch. 151 C.A. (insolvency of tenant-equitable relief from forfeiture-mortgagee's rights – and see the next case in the volume); News Group v SOGAT [1986] I.C.R. 716 C.A. (trust of trade union branch funds – sequestration); Basingstoke and Deane BC v Host Group [1988] 1 W.L.R. 348 C.A. (rent review clause); Alghussein v Eton College [1988] 1 W.L.R. 587 H.L. (breach of contract – not profiting from one's own wrong); Australian Commercial Research and Development v ANZ [1989] 3 All E.R. 65 (plaintiff with same action in two jurisdictions); Dubai Bank v Galadari [1990] Ch. 98 C.A. (privilege for copy documents); Imperial Group Pension Trust v Imperial Tobacco [1991] 1 W.L.R. 589 (employment principles applied to pension fund trusts); Lemos v Coutts & Co. (Cayman) 1992-93 CILR 460 Cayman Islands C.A. (cross-border trust litigation – discovery and Mareva orders against trustees); Inverugie Investments v Hackett [1995] 1 W.L.R. 713 P.C. (assessment of damages for trespass in letting property); Re T.C. Pagarani (1998/99) 2 O.F.L.R. 1 British Virgin Islands C.A (incompletely constituted trust); Re Z Trust 1997 CILR 248 (conflicts of interest on amending trusts under a power). Michaels v Harley House (Marylebone) Ltd [2000]Ch. 104 C.A. (enfranchisement of flats – constructive trust arising on the sale of shares); Michaels v Taylor Woodrow [2001] 2 WLR 224 (conspiracy to injure by unlawful means not separately actionable).
Prof. Memberships: Chancery Bar Association; Centre for Dispute Resolution (Accredited Mediator); STEP International Committee; ACTAPS.
Career: Former Chairman Chancery Bar Association, Member of Bar Council and Deputy High Court Judge. A permanent member of the Bars of The Bahamas (1971) and of The Eastern Caribbean (1992) and appears in the Cayman Islands. An Editor of Lewin on Trusts 16th Ed. (17th out in 2000) and of the Chase Journal.

MOWSCHENSON, Terence QC
Wilberforce Chambers (Edward Nugee QC) London (020) 7306 0102
Recommended in Chancery, Commercial (Litigation), Company
Specialisation: Principal areas of practice: company/commercial matters including matters involving the law relating to banking (including bills of exchange, letters of credit, syndicated loan agreements); breach of trust; conflict of laws; contract (including conditions of sale, share and business sale agreements, licensing and franchising, restraint of trade, retention of title, and sale of goods); companies (including shareholder disputes, shareholder agreements, technical aspects of company law, takeovers, Stock Exchange regulations, broking and dealing); equitable remedies; financial services (including matters relating to the various self regulatory organisations); insolvency; insurance; partnership; professional negligence. Reported cases including Derby v Weldon; Sharneyford Supplies v Edge; Elliss v BP Oil Northern Ireland Refinery Ltd; Re Westock Realisations Ltd; Dept of Environment v Bates; Investment and Pensions Services v Gray; Acatos v Watson Crimpfil Ltd v Barclays Bank plc; Eastglen ltd v Grafton; Metalloy (Supplies) Limited v MA (UK) Limited (CA); Wake v Renault (UK) Ltd; BCCI v Prince Fahd Bin Salman Al Saud; Arbuthnot Latham Bank v Trafalgar Holdings; Board of Governors of National Heart and Chest Hospital v Chettle.
Prof. Memberships: Chancery and Commercial Bar and Insolvency Lawyers Associations.
Career: Called to the Bar in 1977. Queen's Counsel 1995. Recorder 2000.
Personal: Educated at Eagle School and Peterhouse. London University, LLB (Hons) and Oxford BCL (Hons). FCIArb 1989.

MOXON-BROWNE, Robert QC
2 Temple Gardens (Dermod O'Brien QC) London (020) 7822 1200
Recommended in Professional Negligence
Specialisation: A well known advocate who heads the professional negligence group at 2 Temple Gardens. His work includes cases involving accountants, solicitors and surveyors as well as construction industry professionals, especially where disputes arise as to allocation of responsibility within multi-disciplinary teams. He is also very experienced in all matters relating to insurance law and practice including subrogated recoveries in cases involving fire, flood and other catastrophic events, policy construction questions and repudiation for fraud. He is a specialist in the law affecting the valuation of loss of change. Recent reported Court of Appeal cases include Sharif v Garrett 2001 CA (solicitors' negligence, loss of a chance); Beckett v Midland Electricity 2001 1 WLR 281 (catasrophic fire, statutory interpretation); Fennelly v Connex SE (vicarious liability); Habib Bank v Abbeypearl CA 2001 (banking fraud); Ball v Banner & Ors CA 2000 L1 L Rep PN 1 (relative responsibility of solicitors and surveyors for investment prospectus); MacAreary v Coal Authority CA 2000 (statutory interpretation); Burns v Shuttleworth (1999) 1 WLR 1449 (insurance law, statutory interpretation); Housing Loan Corporation v Win Browne (1999) L1L Rep PN 185 (relative responsibility of surveyors, solicitors and bankers for loan fraud); Routestone v Minories Finance 1997 BCLC 97 (relative duties of receivers and surveyors to those interested in equity of redemption); Sainsburys v Broadway Malyan 61 Con Law Rep 31 (relative duties of architects and engineers for firewall; loss of chance); Allied Maples v Simmons & Simmons (1995) 1 WLR 1602 (solicitors' duty in takeover negotiations; loss of a chance).
Prof. Memberships: ORBA, Professional Negligence Bar Association, CLBA, COMBAR.
Career: Called to the Bar 1969, QC 1990, Recorder 1992. Deputy Judge of the Technology and Construction Court 1993. Deputy Judge of the High Court 1999.
Personal: Born 1946. Educated Gordonstoun School, University College Oxford (BA).

MOYLAN, Andrew QC
Queen Elizabeth Building (Florence Baron QC) London (020) 7797 7837
Recommended in Family
Specialisation: Ancillary relief; other aspects of family law including child residence/contact; Inheritance Act claims; professional negligence (matrimonial).
Prof. Memberships: Family Law Bar Association.
Career: Junior Counsel to the Queen's Proctor (1997-00).

MUIR, Andrew
3 Raymond Buildings (Clive Nicholls QC) London (020) 7400 6400
chambers@3raymondbuildings.com
Recommended in Licensing
Specialisation: Extensive experience of licensing work encompassing liquor, gaming, betting, lotteries and public entertainment. Represented General Medical Council at disciplinary tribunal hearings. Appointed Department of Trade and Industry Inspector for insider share dealing enquiries. Also practices in Environmental Protection and Health & Safety law.

Prof. Memberships: South Eastern Circuit.
Career: Called to the Bar 1975, and joined 3 Raymond Buildings in 1976. BA (Hons).
Personal: Educated at Stonyhurst College 1965-70, Ealing Technical College 1970-73 and Council of Legal Education 1974-75. Leisure pursuits include horse racing, cricket and rugby. Born 25th December 1951. Lives in Lodsworth.

MULCAHY, Jane
Blackstone Chambers (Presiley Baxendale QC & Charles Flint QC) London (020) 7583 1770
janemulcahy@blackstonechambers.com
Recommended in Employment
Specialisation: Employment, human rights, public, entertainment and media.
Prof. Memberships: Employment Law Association, Administrative Law Bar Association.
Career: Called 1995. Previously worked as a journalist.
Publications: Joint author of chapter in forthcoming book on European Employment Law; contributor to ELA Briefing.

MULLIS, Roger
3 New Square (Lord Goodhart QC) London (020) 7405 5577
law@threenewsquare.co.uk
Recommended in Chancery
Specialisation: Landlord and tenant; real property; probate and administration of estates.
Prof. Memberships: Chancery Bar Association; Professional Negligence Bar Association.
Career: Called 1987.
Personal: Educated at Portsmouth Grammar School and Christ Church, Oxford (BA, BCL). Interests include music, especially singing (lay clerk at St Albans Cathedral). Trustee of Holy Cross Centre Trust.

MUNDAY, Andrew QC
2 Bedford Row (William Clegg QC) London (020) 7440 8888
Recommended in Crime

MUNRO, Sarah
Walnut House (Paul Dunkels QC) Exeter (01392) 279751
Recommended in Crime

MURDOCH, Gordon QC
4 Paper Buildings (Lionel Swift QC) London (020) 7583 0816
gm@4pb.com
Recommended in Family
Specialisation: All types of family litigation, including public and private law Children Act matters; divorce; matrimonial finance; international child abduction; Inheritance Act applications; medico-legal issues; adoption; wardship; disputes between unmarried couples and mental health issues. Reported cases include Re H, Re G (Adoption: Consultation of Unmarried Fathers) [2001] 1 FLR 646 Kelly v BBC [2001] Fam 59; Re X (Injunction Restraining Publication) [2001] 1 FCR 481; Thompson and Venables v News Group Newspapers Ltd [2001] 1 FLR 791; Re C (HIV Test) [1999] 2 FLR 1004; T v T (Abduction: Consent) [1999] 2 FLR 912; Re J (Adoption: Non-Patrial) [1998] 1 FLR 225; Re T (Wardship: Medical Treatment) [1997] 1 FLR 502 (liver transplant case); Conran v Conran [1997] 2 FLR 615 (matrimonial finance).
Prof. Memberships: Family Law Bar Association; London Common Law and Commercial Bar Association.
Career: Called 1970. Recorder and Silk 1995.
Personal: Born 1947. Educated Falkirk High School and Sidney Sussex College, Cambridge (MA, LL.B).

MURFITT, Catriona
1 Mitre Court Buildings (Bruce Blair QC) London (020) 7797 7070
Recommended in Family
Specialisation: Family Law: Child Care (Public and Private Law) and Hague Convention Child Abduction Proceedings; Matrimonial Finance (and financial proceedings under The Children Act and Inheritance Acts)
Prof. Memberships: Family Law Bar Association; Grays Inn. FLBA committee member.
Career: St. Mary's Ascot 1968-76. Leicester Polytechnic School of Law 1977-80. Called to the Bar 1981. From 1981 in Practice at 1 Mitre Court. Assistant recorder 1998, recorder 2000.
Personal: Art and architecture, travel, amateur artist and mosaicist, skiing, gardening and sacred choral music.

MURPHY, Ian QC
9 Park Place (Ian Murphy QC) Cardiff (029) 2038 2731
Recommended in Crime, Personal Injury
Specialisation: Queen's Bench Division work, in particular personal injury litigation. Clinical negligence, criminal law, Children Act, public and private law.
Prof. Memberships: Personal Injury Bar Association.
Career: St.Illtyd's College Cardiff. L.S.E. (LLB), Baltic Exchange. Called 1972. Recorder 1990. QC 1992. Bencher Middle Temple 2001.
Personal: Married Penelope 1974. Two daughters – Anna 3/4/82 and Charlotte 3/12/84. Golf, cricket, skiing.

MURPHY, Peter
30 Park Place (John Jenkins QC) Cardiff (029) 2039 8421
Recommended in Crime

MYERS, Benjamin J.
Young Street Chambers (Lesley Newton) Manchester (0161) 833 0459
Recommended in Crime

MYERSON, Simon
Park Court Chambers (James Stewart QC & Robert Smith QC) Leeds (0113) 243 3277
simon.myerson@netserv.net
Recommended in Crime
Specialisation: All areas of commercial law and regulatory especially corporate fraud (civil and criminal). Working knowledge of Jewish (Talmudic) law. Clinical negligence.
Prof. Memberships: CBA, PIBA.
Career: Downing College, Cambridge (MA).
Personal: Married, four children. Interests – reading, sailing, walking, securing a moment for himself.

MYLNE, Nigel QC
2 Harcourt Buildings, Atkinson Bevan Chambers (Nicholas Atkinson QC & John Bevan QC) London (020) 7353 2112
nmylneswalker@aol.com
Recommended in Crime
Specialisation: Criminal law specialist. In particular, specialises in serious commercial and professional frauds. Prosecutes and defends in all aspects of serious crime, including murder, sexual offences and drugs.
Prof. Memberships: Special adjudicator on asylum appeals and immigration appeals. President in Mental Health Review Tribunals.
Career: Practises in London and on the Western Circuit. Took silk in 1984. Appointed Recorder in 1983.

MYNORS, Charles
2 Harcourt Buildings (Gerard Ryan QC) London (020) 7353 8415
clerks@2hb.law.co.uk
Recommended in Church
Specialisation: Specialises in planning, ecclesiastical and environmental law, compulsory purchase and commons; particular expertise in listed buildings. Appears in the courts and at planning inquiries for and against planning authorities (including a number of significant cases for English Heritage), at consistory court hearings, and in the Lands Tribunal. Member, Society of Advanced Legal Studies Planning and Environment Law Reform Group.
Prof. Memberships: Member of committee, Planning and Environment Bar Association; member of General Committee, Ecclesiastical Law Society; fellow, Royal Town Planning Institute; member, Royal Institution of Chartered Surveyors; member, Institute of Historic Building Conservation.
Career: Local authority planning officer 1977-86; called to the Bar 1988; chancellor, Diocese of Worcester, 1998.
Publications: Author of 'Planning Applications and Appeals', 'Planning Control and the Display of Advertisements' and 'Listed Buildings, Conservation Areas and Monuments' (3rd edn, 1999); member, Editorial Board, 'Journal of Planning and Environment Law'; consultant editor, 'Planning and Environmental Law Bulletin'.
Personal: Degrees in architecture (Cambridge) and town planning (Sheffield). Currently writing next book (on trees and forestry).

NAISH, Christopher
Southernhay Chambers (Anthony Ward) Exeter (01392) 255777
southernhay.chambers@lineone.net
Recommended in Family
Specialisation: Family Law. All aspects of the law relating to children (acting for Local Authorities, guardians and family members); ancillary relief. Family mediator. Personal injuries. Acting mainly for plaintiffs but also for defendants' insurers.
Prof. Memberships: Family Law Bar Association. Personal Injuries Bar Association.
Career: Call 1980. Joined chambers in 1981.
Personal: Born 21st December 1957. Married with three children.

NAPIER, Brian
Fountain Court (Anthony Boswood QC) London (020) 7583 3335
Recommended in Employment
Specialisation: Transfer of Undertakings – Meade and Baxendale v British Fuels [1998] House of Lords; Discrimination (sex, race, disability) and equal pay; General employment law, statutory and common law.
Prof. Memberships: Member, Faculty of Advocates, Edinburgh (Clerk: Susan Hastie); Member ACAS Panel of arbitrators.
Career: Academic lawyer 1975-94. Practising barrister/advocate, 1994-. Joint editor: 1. Harvey on Industrial Relations (chapters on European law, equal opportunities, equal pay); 2. Transfer of Undertakings (Sweet & Maxwell, 1998-). Standing Junior to the Scottish Executive, 2001-.

NASH, Jonathan
3 Verulam Buildings (Christopher Symons QC & John Jarvis QC) London (020) 7831 8441
chambers@3vb.com
Recommended in Banking
Specialisation: Principal areas of work are banking, corporate insolvency, professional negligence (particularly accountants and solicitors), and general commercial work including arbitration. Recent cases include KBC Bank v Industrial Steels (UK) Ltd (non-conforming documents and deceit under letter of credit), Credit Agricole Indosuez v Muslim Commercial Bank (compliance of documents under letter of credit); ANZ Banking v Societe Generale (construction of ISDA Master agreement after close-out of Russian market NDF transaction); Credit Suisse First Boston v MLC (anti-suit injunction in Russian derivatives transaction); J Rothschild v Collyear (notification obligations under professional indemnity insurance in respect of pensions misselling.)
Prof. Memberships: COMBAR; European Society for Banking and Financial Law.
Career: Called to the Bar in 1986 and joined 3 Verulam Buildings in 1987.
Personal: BA (Oxon).

NATHAN, David
10 King's Bench Walk (Georges M Khayat QC) London (020) 7353 2501
clerks@10kbw.co.uk
Recommended in Crime
Specialisation: Criminal defence, acting as a leading

junior in all types of cases. Led in many substantial high profile cases throughout the UK including Regina v Donald & Cressy (police corruption), R v John "Littlelegs" Lloyd (conspiracy) and Regina v Clifford Norris (alleged racist rage). He is instructed in all areas of major criminal law including police corruption, white-collar fraud, and large-scale importation of drugs.

NATHAN, Peter

One Garden Court Family Law Chambers (Eleanor F. Platt QC & Alison Ball QC) London (020) 7797 7900
p.nathan@onegardencourt.co.uk
Recommended in Family
Specialisation: Family.
Prof. Memberships: FLBA.
Career: Called 1973. Spent 15 months as solicitor. Deputy District Judge since 1993. Mediator (trained 1996). Appointed Recorder, 2000.
Personal: Married, three children.

NAUGHTON, Philip QC

3 Serjeants' Inn (Robert Francis QC & John Grace QC) London (020) 7427 5000
Recommended in Alternative Dispute Resolution
Specialisation: Specialist in construction and engineering law, including domestic and international contract disputes, often of a highly technical nature. Commercial and manufacturing contracts. Professional negligence, particularly in relation to surveyors, engineers, architects and lawyers. Also medical law. A recognised expert in the field of Alternative Dispute Resolution. (Experienced and accredited).
Prof. Memberships: Fellow Chartered Institute of Arbitrators, member of LCLCBA, ORBA, ELBA, COMBAR, IBA, LCIA.
Career: Held various positions in the chemical and chemical engineering industry 1964-71. Called to the Bar 1970. Joined present chambers 1973. Took Silk 1988. Bencher Gray's Inn (1997).
Personal: Educated at Nottingham University (LLB) 1961-64.

NAWAZ, Amjad

Coleridge Chambers (Simon Brand) Birmingham (0121) 233 8500
Recommended in Crime

NEALE, Fiona

3 Serjeants' Inn (Robert Francis QC & John Grace QC) London (020) 7427 5000
Recommended in Clinical Negligence
Specialisation: Practice is divided between dental and medical disciplinary work (presenting and defending) and clinical negligence, keeping a balance between claimant and defendant.
Prof. Memberships: PNBA, PIBA, Western Circuit.
Career: Called to the Bar 1981.

NEISH, Andrew

4 Pump Court London (020) 7842 5555
aneish@4pumpcourt.com
Recommended in Professional Negligence
Specialisation: General commercial law. Principal areas of practice are insurance and reinsurance and professional negligence (especially brokers, lawyers and accountants).
Prof. Memberships: COMBAR, London Common Law and Commercial Bar Association.
Career: Called 1988.
Personal: MA (St Andrews), Dip Law (City). Admitted in the BVI.

NELSON, Vincent QC

39 Essex Street (Nigel Pleming QC) London (020) 7832 1111
Recommended in Media & Entertainment
Specialisation: Media and entertainment.
Career: Author of Law of Entertainment & Broadcasting (Publishers: Sweet & Maxwell).

NEWCOMBE, Andrew

2 Harcourt Buildings (Gerard Ryan QC) London (020) 7353 8415
clerks@2hb.law.co.uk
Recommended in Planning
Specialisation: Principal areas of practice are parliamentary and planning work. Also including compulsory purchase, local government, environmental and general public law.
Prof. Memberships: Planning & Environment Bar Association; Parliamentary Bar Mess; Administrative Law Bar Association.
Career: Called to the Bar in 1987; also member of the Irish Bar.
Personal: Born 6 February 1953.

NEWEY, Guy QC

Maitland Chambers (Michael Lyndon-Stanford QC & Charles Aldous QC) London (020) 7406 1200
gnewey@maitlandchambers.com
Recommended in Chancery, Charities, Company, Insolvency/Corporate Recovery
Specialisation: General Chancery practice includes charities, company, financial regulation, insolvency, property, professional negligence and trusts.
Prof. Memberships: Charity Law Association and Insolvency Lawyers' Association.
Career: Called to the Bar 1982. Junior Counsel to the Crown (Chancery) and Junior Counsel to the Crown ('A' Panel) 1990-01. Junior Counsel to the Charity Commissioners 1991-01. DTI Inspector in 1998-99. QC 2001. Recent cases include B&C v BZW [1999] 1 BCLC 86 (company); Prudential v Waterloo [1999] 2 EGLR 85 (land); IRC v Duce [1999] BPIR 189 (IVA); Weth v AG [1999] 1 WLR 686 (charity); Branston & Gothard [1999] 1 All ER (Comm) 289 (trusts/ insolvency/financial services); IRC v Robinson [1999] BPIR 329 (bankruptcy); Swalee v DG of Electricity, Times 28.10.99 (regulation); Britannia, Times 27.6.00 (directors' disqualification); Walker v Stones [2001] 2 WLR 623 (trusts/company); ex parte Baldwin (charity); and IRC v Adam & Partners [2001] 1 BCLC 222 (CVA).
Publications: Contributor to 'Mithani: Directors Disqualification' and to 'Civil Court Service'.
Personal: Educated at Tonbridge School and Queens' College, Cambridge (MA 1st class, LL.M 1st class). Bar Exams 1st class. Born 21st January 1959.

NEWMAN, Catherine QC

Maitland Chambers (Michael Lyndon-Stanford QC & Charles Aldous QC) London (020) 406 1200
cnewman@maitlandchambers.com
Recommended in Chancery, Company, Insolvency/Corporate Recovery
Specialisation: Principal area of work encompasses business and commercial chancery work, including corporate insolvency, business agreements and breach of contract, loans and security, partnership and professional negligence. Involved in large insolvencies: Maxwell, BCCI. Leading Counsel to the DTI Inspectors who investigated the 1991 flotation of Mirror Group Newspapers. Other main area of work is equity and contentious trusts; see for example Satnam Investments v Dunlop Heywood & Co Ltd [1999] 3 All ER652 CA. Acted (for the London Borough of Hammersmith and Fulham) at all stages of the swaps litigation: capacity, restitution and successive claims.
Prof. Memberships: Chancery Bar Association, COMBAR; Bar Sports Law Group.
Career: Called to the Bar 1979 and joined present chambers in 1980. Took Silk in 1995. Assistant Recorder 1998. Recorder 2000. Lieutenant-Bailiff of the Royal Courts of Guernsey 2001. Acts as an arbitrator.
Personal: Educated at Convent of the Sacred Heart High School 1965-72 and University College, London. (LLB 1st Class Hons 1978). Harmsworth Scholar of the Middle Temple 1979-80. Born 7 February 1954. Lives in London.

NEWMAN, Paul

Wilberforce Chambers (Edward Nugee QC) London (020) 7306 0102
Recommended in Pensions, Professional Negligence
Specialisation: Specialises in personal and occupational pension schemes, with a particular interest in the pensions aspects of corporate and personal insolvency. Acts for trustees, beneficiaries and employers across the spectrum of pensions litigation and advisory work and acts both for and against the Pensions Ombudsman in appeals against his determinations. General chancery/ commercial matters (with an emphasis on litigation), disputes relating to the provision of financial services, and professional negligence involving soclicitor, actuaries and accountants. Major pensions cases include Melton Medes; Belling; Simpson Curtis Pension Trustee Ltd v Readson; Cocking v Prudential Insurance, SWT v Wightman and Elliot v Pensions Ombudsman National Grid, British Airways, Kemble v Nicks. Contributor to Ellison on Pensions Law and Practice and to Lightman & Moss, Law of Corporate Receivers.
Prof. Memberships: Association of Pension Lawyers. Member of Chancery Bar Association.
Career: MA (Cantab); LLM (Harvard Law School); Called to the Bar in 1991.

NEWSOM, George

Guildhall Chambers (Adrian Palmer QC) Bristol (0117) 927 3366
GeorgeNewsom@guildhallchambers.co.uk
Recommended in Church
Specialisation: Restrictive Covenants; title; easements; agricultural holdings; farming partnerships; wills; trusts; charities; churches and burial grounds.
Prof. Memberships: Fellow of the Chartered Institute of Arbitrators; Chancery Bar Association; Bristol & Cardiff Chancery Bar Association.
Career: Called to the Bar in 1973, Chairman of the Agricultural Land Tribunal for the South West Area since 1988.
Publications: Current publications: Preston & Newsom's 'Covenants affecting Freehold Land', Newsom's 'Faculty Jurisdiction of the Church of England'.
Personal: Born 1948, MA (Oxon: Eng & Econ), continuing interest in technology and computing.

NEWTON, Clive

One King's Bench Walk (Anthony Hacking QC) London (020) 7936 1500
Recommended in Family
Specialisation: General common law, commercial fraud (civil), family (including divorce and children), child care, matrimonial finance and property.
Career: Recent cases include: Re W (Minors) (sexual abuse, standard of proof) 1994 1 FLR 419 (represented local authority in C.A case as to standard of proof); Re B (Child Sexual abuse; Standard of proof) – 1995 1 FLR 904 (represented local authority in a High Court case involving inter alia the admissibility of expert evidence); Re C (a Minor) Adoption 1994 2 FLR 513 (Represented GAL in adoption case in C.A); Re M and R (Child Abuse: Evidence) 1996 2FLR 195 (represented local authority in important case under the Children Act 1989). Re N (Residence: Hopeless Appeals) 1995 2FLR 230 (represented Official Solicitor) FNCB v Humberts 1995 2 AELR 673 (important CA decision on limitation in professional negligence cases).
Personal: Born 1944. Call 1968 Middle Temple. Oxford University MA (Oxon) Jurisprudence (1st Class Honours), B.C.L. (Oxon); Lecturer in Law, Oriel College, Oxford; Co-Editor of 'Jackson's Matrimonial Finance and Taxation,' 6th edn Co-author of the 'Child Law Bulletin' for the Solicitors' Journal.

NEWTON, Roderick

East Anglian Chambers (Roderick Newton) Ipswich (01473) 214481
Recommended in Family

NICE, Geoffrey QC

1 Temple Gardens (Hugh Carlisle QC) London (020) 7583 1315 gnice@1templegardens.co.uk

Recommended in Health & Safety

Specialisation: Principal areas of practice are general common law, including personal injury, HSE (including Channel Tunnel and Heathrow Express cases), clinical and professional negligence, major crime, commercial and administrative law (eg Ex P: Doody, prisoners rights; Callery v Gray, conditional fees, costs etc).

Prof. Memberships: South Eastern Circuit.

Career: Called to the Bar (Inner Temple) and joined Farrar's Building in 1971. Moved to 1 Temple Gardens in 2001. Appointed Recorder of the Crown Court in 1987. Took Silk in 1990. Member CICB 1995-date. Senior Trial Attorney at ICTY (Yugoslav War Crimes Tribunal) 1998-00.

NICHOLLS, Benjamin

1 Fountain Court (David Crigman QC) Birmingham (0121) 236 5721

Recommended in Crime

NICHOLLS, Clive QC

3 Raymond Buildings (Clive Nicholls QC) London (020) 74006400 chambers@3raymondbuildings.com

Recommended in Crime, Fraud

Specialisation: Principal area of practice is extradition, which he practises worldwide, being a member of the Bar of the Australian Capital Territories and having been specially called and admitted to the Bars of Hong Kong, The Bahamas, Cayman Islands, Malaysia, Ireland and Fiji. The factual complex of his extradition practice includes commercial crime, as well as terrorism and drug trafficking. He is particularly experienced (with teams drawn from his own Chambers) in preparing and presenting extradition requests for foreign governments, both in the UK and abroad. These have included the Bank Bumiputra fraud (the Osman case) in which he represented the Attorney General of Hong Kong in the UK, Hong Kong and Malaysia and the Werner Rey case (corporate fraud) in which he represented the Government of Switzerland in the Bahamas. He has advised and represented many countries and prominent fugitives including Senator Augusto Pinochet Ugarte and appeared in most of the leading extradition cases in England, including 16 in the House of Lords and Privy Council. Much of his practice is outside the UK and includes mutual assistance and human rights.

Prof. Memberships: Member of the International Law Association (British Branch) Committee on Mutual Assistance. Member of the British Institute of International and Comparative Law, Bar European Group, Criminal Bar Association, European Criminal Bar Association, Franco British Lawyers Society. Co-founder and Chairman of the International Criminal Law Association 2000-02.

Career: Educated at Brighton College, Trinity College Dublin, Sidney Sussex College Cambridge, MA LLM. Call 1957. QC 1982. Head of Chambers since 1994.

NICHOLLS, Colin QC

3 Raymond Buildings (Clive Nicholls QC) London (020) 7400 6400 chambers@3raymondbuildings.com

Recommended in Fraud

Specialisation: Principal areas of practice are commercial crime, extradition and civil liberties. Specialises in cases having an international element. Notable trials include 'Guinness' 1990 (defending the stockbroker, Anthony Parnes); 'Brent Walker' 1994 (defending George Walker), and 'BCCI' 1997 (defending the shipping magnate, Abbas Gokal). Significant reported cases include the 'Soering Case', 1989 in the European Court of Human Rights (death row in the US); and R v Horseferry Road Magistrate, ex parte Bennett 1994 (disguised extradition and abuse of power), Gilligan v Governor of HM Prison Belmarsh 1999 (Irish backing of Warrants with the United Kingdom). Advised in the Bhopal, Marcos litigations and in the *mani puliti* trials in Italy.

Prof. Memberships: Admitted ad hoc to the Bar of Hong Kong. Commonwealth Lawyers Association, Vice-President (1985-96), Hon. Treasurer (1997), Secretary (1999), Bar European Group, British Institute of International and Comparative Law, Criminal Bar Association. Fellow of the Society of Advanced Legal Studies.

Career: Called to the Bar 1957, QC in 1981 and elected a Bencher of Gray's Inn in 1990. Recorder of Crown Courts 1983 – 1998.

Personal: M.A., LL.B, Dublin.

NICHOLLS, John

Maitland Chambers (Michael Lyndon-Stanford QC & Charles Aldous QC) London (020) 7406 1200

Recommended in Chancery

NICHOLLS, Michael

1 Mitre Court Buildings (Bruce Blair QC) London (020) 7797 7070 nicholls@1mcb.com

Recommended in Family

Specialisation: International and domestic family law and medical ethics, including jurisdiction, conflicts of laws, child abduction, private children's cases, families and the media (freedom of expression and press injunctions) and disputes about medical treatment. Recent cases include Re TB v JB (abduction: grave risk of harm) CA (19 December 2000); Re N (abduction: habitual residence) [2000] 2 FLR 899; Re W; ReB (child abduction: unmarried father) [1998] 2 FLR 146 (a review of the rights of unmarried fathers under the Hague Child Abduction Convention); Re J (specific issue orders: Muslim upbringing and circumcision) [1999] 2 FLR 678; [2000] 1 FLR 571 (CA) and Nottingham CC v October Films Ltd [1999] 2 FLR 347 (an attempt by a local authority to stop the filming of children living on the streets).

Prof. Memberships: Family Law Bar Association.

Career: Called 1975 (solicitor 1980). Family lawyer in the Official Solicitor's Office and head of Lord Chancellor's Child Abduction Unit 1983-98; consultant to the Council of Europe's Family Law Committee; member of the President's International Family Law Committee; Chairman of Appeals Panels of the Specialist Training Authority of the Medical Royal Colleges 1997-01; member of the BMA's Children's Consent to Medical Treatment Steering Group.

Publications: Recent publications include 'The Human Rights Act 1998 – A Special Bulletin for Family Lawyers' (with Michael Horowitz QC and Geoffrey Kingscote), 'Children and Brussels II', May [2000] Family Law 368 and a contribution to 'Consent, Rights and Choices in Healthcare for Children and Young People', BMA, 2001.

NICHOLLS, Paul

11 King's Bench Walk Chambers (Eldred Tabachnik QC & James Goudie QC) London (020) 7632 8500

Recommended in Employment

NICHOLSON, Jeremy QC

4 Pump Court London (020) 7842 5555 jnicholson@4pumpcourt.com

Recommended in Construction

Specialisation: Construction and professional negligence work, covering all aspects of litigation, arbitration and advisory matters. Also general commercial and contract law work. Clients include insurers, contractors, employers, engineers, architects, surveyors and other professionals. He has acted in a number of international arbitrations, and in mediations. He has given various lectures and seminar papers.

Prof. Memberships: TECBAR, Professional Negligence Bar Association, COMBAR, London Common Law and Commercial Bar Association.

Career: Called to the Bar 1977. Joined 4 Pump Court 1978. Appointed QC 2000. TECBAR Adjudicator.

Personal: Educated at Rugby School 1968-73, Trinity Hall, Cambridge 1973-76 (MA) and College of Law 1976-77 (Harmsworth Scholar). Born 21 March 1955.

NICKLIN, Matthew

5 Raymond Buildings (Patrick Milmo QC) London (020) 7242 2902

Recommended in Defamation

Specialisation: All aspects of media law including defamation, malicious falsehood, confidence, privacy, copyright (and related rights), passing-off, media contempt and reporting restrictions, judicial review and human rights.

Career: LLB (1st class) University of Newcastle upon Tyne. Called to the Bar, 1993 (Lincoln's Inn). Pegasus Scholar to Sydney, Australia, 1998. (*Mallesons Stephen Jaques*).

NICOL, Andrew QC

Doughty Street Chambers (Geoffrey Robertson QC) London (020) 7404 1313 a.nicol@doughtystreet.co.uk

Recommended in Administrative & Public Law, Defamation, Human Rights, Immigration

Specialisation: Media law in all its aspects including defamation, confidence, copyright, contempt, restrictions on court reporting, publicity injunctions and rights of access to information. Administrative law especially immigration and nationality but extending to all situations where decisions of public bodies are subject to judicial review. Civil Liberties especially concerning freedom of expression and privacy. Diverse range of other civil work including (non-medical) professional negligence, race and sex discrimination, contract and tort. Appellate crime including Divisional Court, Court of Appeal and Privy Council.

Prof. Memberships: Chair of Immigration Law Practitioners' Association 1997-00. Member of Council of Europe delegations to advise on media law to Croatia, Albania, Slovakia, Belarus, Moldova, Serbia. Presented papers to international conferences on Media and the Judiciary (Justice, Madrid 1993) and National Security and Freedom of Expression (Article 19, Johannesburg 1995). Libel (LRDC London 1998+2000), security of residence in Europe (Nijmegan 1999). Chaired conference on Family and Immigration (Oxford University Continuing Education 1997) and presented seminars to ILPA, solicitors and university groups.

Career: Called to the Bar in 1978. QC 1995. Asst. Recorder 1998. Recorder 2000. Taught law at London School of Economics for 10 years.

Publications: 'Media Law and Human Rights' (2001), 'Media Law (2001- forthcoming), 'Subjects, Citizens, Aliens and Others' (1990) and contributes an annual survey on Reporting Restrictions to OUP's 'Yearbook of Copyright and Media Law'.

Personal: Born 1951. Degrees: BA 1st Class; LL.B 1st Class, LLM (Harvard), Harkness Fellow 1973-6.

NISSEN, Alexander

Keating Chambers (Richard Fernyhough QC) London (020) 7544 2600 anissen@keatingchambers.com

Recommended in Construction

Specialisation: Construction and civil engineering law including professional negligence, arbitration, mediation and adjudication (both substantive and enforcement). Reported cases include Darlington Borough Council v Wiltshier, Royal Brompton Hospital v Hammond (No 1), Baxall v Sheard Walshaw Partnership, ABB v Northwest Holst and John Mowlem v Hydra-tight.

Career: Qualified 1985; Middle Temple; member of editorial team for 'Keating on Building Contracts' (5th to 7th edition) and 'Construction Law Yearbook'; FCI Arb; TECBAR Adjudicator; member of TECBAR, Society of Construction Law and COMBAR.

Personal: Mill Hill School; Manchester University (1984 LLB Hons). Born 1963; resides London.

NOCK, Reginald
24 Old Buildings (Rex Bretten QC) London
(020) 7242 2744
Recommended in Tax

NOLAN, Dominic
Ropewalk Chambers (Ian McLaren QC)
Nottingham (0115) 947 2581
clerks@ropewalk.co.uk
Recommended in Personal Injury
Specialisation: Large personal injury and medical negligence claims including claims for birth injury and catastrophic injury. Defence of health and safety prosecutions. Recent reported case: Baker v Leicestershire HA (1998) Lloyds Med 93. Advised Grantham Hospital in claims arising from crimes of Beverley Allitt. Chairman of Statutory Inquiry into homicide by a former mental patient.
Prof. Memberships: Professional Negligence Bar Association.
Career: Graduate of Nottingham University; Buchanan Prizeman Lincoln's Inn.
Personal: Family, friends, sport, music.

NORRIS, Alastair QC
5 Stone Buildings (Henry Harrod) London
(020) 7242 6201
Recommended in Professional Negligence

NORRIS, William QC
Farrar's Building (John Leighton Williams QC)
London (020) 7583 9241
Recommended in Personal Injury
Specialisation: Defamation: Morelli & Coyle v Times Newspapers (first conditional fee case in libel). Personal Injury: Allen v BREL (negligent/non-negligent harm); Jefferson v Royal Ordnance (£3.3 million gross award to Mine clearance expert); Scutts v Keyse & Blice (duty of emergency driver); Vossler v Mead (£2.2 million award to tetraplegic); Contract: Albright & Wilson v Biacheim; sports and competition law. Licensing: Jones & Ebbw Vale v WRU (private law challenge to disciplinary process of WRU); Cardiff RFC v WRU (restraint of trade/EU competition law); O'Callaghan v Coral Racing (illegality of gaming contracts/validity of arbitration).
Prof. Memberships: PIBA – Personal Injury Bar Association; Executive Committee.
Career: Benefactors Scholarship, Middle Temple, QC 1997.
Personal: Lecturer to Judicial Studies Board (Damages). Advocacy Teaching UK & USA.

NOURSE, Edmund
One Essex Court (Lord Grabiner QC) London
(020) 7583 2000
Recommended in Insolvency/Corporate Recovery
Specialisation: Insolvency litigation and fraud, directors' disqualification and general commercial. Junior Counsel to The Crown. Recent work includes: Canada Trust v Stolzenberg (HL) [2000] 3 WLR 1555 (for defendants); Re: Barings plc (No 5) [1999] 1 BCLC 433, [2000] 1 BCLC 523 (CA) (for DTI). Currently acting in dishonest assistance claim arising out of the collapse of Barlow Clowes.
Prof. Memberships: Chancery Bar Association, COMBAR.
Career: BA Hons (Oxon) Modern History; Diploma in Law (City University); called 1994 (LI).

NUGEE, Christopher QC
Wilberforce Chambers (Edward Nugee QC)
London (020) 7306 0102
Recommended in Chancery, Pensions, Property Litigation
Specialisation: Practice a broad spread of chancery and commercial litigation including property, landlord and tenant, professional negligence, pensions (including pensions ombudsman appeals) and trusts. Recent cases include Phillips v British Gas (sale of North Sea Gas); Republic of Panama v Noriega (tracing assets); Central London Commercial Estates v Kato Kagaku (adverse possession of registered leasehold land); SWT v Wightman (Railway Pension Scheme); Department of Health v Moss (index linking of public sector pensions).
Prof. Memberships: Member of COMBAR; Association of Pension Lawyers; Chancery Bar Association.
Career: Called 1983. QC 1998.

NUGEE, Edward QC
Wilberforce Chambers (Edward Nugee QC)
London (020) 7306 0102
Recommended in Chancery, Charities, Pensions
Specialisation: Mainstream Chancery practice, with emphasis on trusts, occupational pension schemes, revenue law, landlord and tenant and property law generally. Has appeared in a substantial number of landlord and tenant, revenue and other appeals in the House of Lords, and in many of the leading cases on trusts, land law and pension schemes.
Prof. Memberships: Member of Chancery Bar Association; Association of Pension Lawyers; Trust Law Committee.
Career: Called 1955, Inner Temple (Bencher 1976, Treasurer 1996); Q.C. 1977.
Personal: Educated Radley College; Worcester College, Oxford (Eldon Law Scholar). T.D. 1964. QC Church Commissioner 1990-01. Legal Advisory Commission of the Church of England.

NUTTING, Sir John QC
3 Raymond Buildings (Clive Nicholls QC) London
(020) 7400 6400
chambers@3raymondbuildings.com
Recommended in Crime
Specialisation: Extensive experience in Criminal law: Many IRA trials, Jonathan Aitken (perjury), R v Bailey & Others (child murders), Michael Smith (the GEC Spy) the Taylor Sisters murder trial, Seymon Serafimovich and Anthony Sawoniuk (War Crimes), the Rachel Nickell murder, Donald & Cressey (police corruption), Colin Ireland (multiple murder of homosexuals), Harry Greenway MP (Parliamentary corruption), Lord Blandford (drugs), Sydney Cooke (grave sexual abuse of children).Also specialises in Commercial crime, Disciplinary tribunals, Inquests and Inquiries (the Falkland Islands War Crimes Inquiry).
Prof. Memberships: Member of the Bar Council (1976-80, 1986-87). Chairman of the Young Bar (1978-79). Vice Chairman of the Criminal Bar Association (1995-97). Member of the Lord Chancellor's Advisory Committee on Legal Education and Conduct (1997-).
Career: Called 1968. Recorder of the Crown Court (1986-). Bencher of the Middle Temple (1991-). Treasury Counsel at the Central Criminal (1987-95) (First Junior Treasury Counsel 1987-88; First Senior Treasury Counsel 1993-95) QC 1995-. A Judge of the Courts of Appeal of Jersey and Guernsey (1995-). Deputy High Court Judge attached to the Queen's Bench and Chancery Divisions (1998-).
Personal: Educated at Eton and McGill University BA 1964.

O'BRIEN, Dermod QC
2 Temple Gardens (Dermod O'Brien QC) London
(020) 7822 1200
Recommended in Personal Injury
Specialisation: Insurance claims, policy issues, fires, floods, explosions. Electrical and mechanical engineering. Personal injury. Restitution. Local authority liabilities. Major reported cases include: White v White and MIB [2001] Loans v SSLTR and MIB [2001], Wake and Wylie (SMP Mister White) [2001]. Heil v Rankin [2000], Makepeice v Evans and McAlpine [2000], Mighell v Reading and MIB [1998], Hurst v Hampshire CC [1997], Silverton v Goodall [1997], Evans v MIB [1997], Vernon v Bosley [1997], Hippolyte v Bexley LB [1995], Costellow v Somerset CC [1993], Talbot v Berkshire CC [1993], Lipkin Gorman v Karpnale (Playboy Club) [1991], Legal Aid Board v Russell [1991], Wharf v Eric Cumine Associates [1991 HK], Surtees v Kingston upon Thames BC [1991], Rigby v Chief Constable of Northamptonshire [1985], Russell v Barnet LB [1984], Hobbs v Marlowe [1978], Taylor v Hepworths [1977], Heath v Drown [1972].
Prof. Memberships: London Common Law Bar Association. Western Circuit.
Career: Oxford BA (Law) 1961 MA. Called: Inner Temple 1962. Crown Court Recorder 1978 (and TCC business). QC 1983. Bencher Inner Temple 1993.
Personal: Farming, forestry.

O'BYRNE, Andrew
Peel Court Chambers (Michael Shorrock QC)
Manchester (0161) 832 3791
Recommended in Crime

O'CONNOR, Patrick QC
Doughty Street Chambers (Geoffrey Robertson QC) London (020) 7404 1313
Recommended in Crime, Human Rights

O'DEMPSEY, Declan
Coram Chambers (Roger McCarthy QC) London
(020) 7797 7766
Recommended in Employment

ODITAH, Fidelis
3-4 South Square (Michael Crystal QC & Lord Alexander of Weedon QC) London
(020) 7696 9900
Recommended in Insolvency/Corporate Recovery

O'FARRELL, Finola
Keating Chambers (Richard Fernyhough QC)
London (020) 7544 2600
Recommended in Construction
Specialisation: Construction law in general, including IT disputes, professional negligence insurance, loss and expense claims (lectures regularly on various aspects); energy disputes, shipbuilding and dredging litigation.
Prof. Memberships: Member Bar/IBC Committee; Joint Editor of 'Construction Law Yearbook'; member of Official Referees Bar Association.
Career: Qualified 1983; Inner Temple; Council of Legal Education 1983.
Personal: St Philomena's School; Durham University (1982 BA Hons Dunelm).

OLIVER, Andrew
Octagon House Chambers (Andrew Lindqvist)
Norwich (01603) 623186
Recommended in Crime

OLIVER, David QC
Erskine Chambers (Robin Potts QC) London
(020) 7242 5532
Recommended in Chancery, Company, Insolvency/Corporate Recovery
Specialisation: Principally commercial/Chancery, with some insolvency.
Career: Called to the Bar 1972. Took silk 1986. (Lincoln's Inn: Hardwick Scholar) Standing junior counsel to the director general of fair trading. Acted for Guinness in connection with the aftermath of the distillers takeover, Price Waterhouse in claims arising after the collapse of BCCI, Macmillan Inc. and Swiss Bank with claims arising out of the collapse of Robert Maxwell's corporate empire, Granada plc in connection with the financing of BSB and subsequently BSkyB, and Victor Chandler International in connection with the establishment of off-shore credit betting.
Personal: Born 4 June 1949. Educated Westminster School; Trinity Hall Cambridge; Institut d'Etudes Europeenes, Brussels. BA Cantab (2/1), Licence Special en droit Europeen. Fluent Spanish and working knowledge of French.

OMAMBALA, Ijeoma
Old Square Chambers (John Hendy QC) London
(020) 7269 0300
omambala@oldsquarechambers.co.uk
Recommended in Employment
Specialisation: Ijeoma is a specialist employment

lawyer. Her practice encompasses all aspects of individual and collective employment law together with related contractual work including restraint of trade, restrictive covenant and wrongful dismissal cases. Ijeoma has a particular interest in discrimination law (equal pay, race, gender, orientation and disability) and trade union law. She writes and lectures widely on her chosen areas of expertise. Reported cases include Photostatic Copiers v Okuda [1995] IRLR 11 EAT (TUPE, compensation, admissibility of fresh evidence on appeal; whether where a respondent to an appeal makes an admission to the EAT which is inconsistent with evidence to ET, the EAT may allow the admission of evidence which would by itself have been rejected on grounds of lack of probative value.); Chan v Hackney London Borough Council [1996] ET (race discrimination, constructive dismissal, compensation.); Orlando v Didcott Power Station Sports & Social Club [1996] IRLR 262 EAT (principles applicable to the calculation of compensation for injury to feelings in sex discrimination); Cleveland NHS Trust v Blane [1997] ICR 851 EAT (trade union activities, action short of dismissal, compensation; whether an award for injury to feelings is properly included in an award of compensation); Chief Constable of Lincs & ors v Stubbs [1999] ICR 547 EAT (sex discrimination, employment, vicarious liability; whether incidents at a work related social gathering are in the course of employment).
Prof. Memberships: Justice: Human Rights Steering Group. ELBA, ILS, DLA, APIL.
Career: Called to the Bar in 1989.

ONIONS, Jeffery QC
One Essex Court (Lord Grabiner QC) London (020) 7583 2000
Recommended in Commercial (Litigation), Energy & Natural Resources
Specialisation: Undertakes a wide range of complex commercial work. He has a particular experience in arbitration, banking, insolvency, insurance and reinsurance, oil and gas contracts and media related cases.
Prof. Memberships: London Common Law and Commercial Bar Association, Administrative Law Bar Association.

ONSLOW, Andrew
3 Verulam Buildings (Christopher Symons QC & John Jarvis QC) London (020) 7831 8441 chambers@3vb.com
Recommended in Commercial (Litigation)
Specialisation: Banking and finance; financial services; commercial fraud; solicitors', auditors' and valuers' negligence. Major recent cases include Wallace Smith Trust Co. v Deloittes Haskins and Sells, London Underground Ltd v Kenchington Ford, regulatory proceeding arising from Sumitomo/Hamanaka Affair.
Prof. Memberships: COMBAR.
Career: 1970-74 Lancing College. 1975-79 Corpus Christi College, Oxford. BA Hons Literae Humaniores (1st Class).
Personal: Married. Five children.

ONSLOW, Robert
8 New Square (Michael Fysh QC) London (020) 7405 4321 clerks@8newsquare.co.uk
Recommended in Intellectual Property
Specialisation: A Barrister whose principal areas of practice are intellectual property including trade marks, musical and literary copyright, industrial designs and patents as well as computer law and contract disputes with a technical element; also specialises in advising on legal issues relating to Internet commerce; data protection and commercial uses of data. For comprehensive CV and list of recent cases, visit our website at www.8newsquare.co.uk.
Prof. Memberships: Intellectual Property Bar Association (IPBA); The Intellectual Property Lawyers Organisation (TIPLO).
Career: Called 1991.
Personal: Born 1965. Educated at Eton College and Magdalen College, Oxford (1987 BA Physics). Hobbies include music and entertaining children.

OPPENHEIM, Robin
Doughty Street Chambers (Geoffrey Robertson QC) London (020) 7404 1313
Recommended in Clinical Negligence, Personal Injury, Product Liability
Specialisation: Specialist in the areas of medico-legal work, personal injury and multi-party actions. Personal injury and medico-legal practice includes clinical negligence and serious personal injury (particularly cerebral palsy, spinal and head injuries claims); group actions; medical inquests; mental health law and Human Rights Act 1998/health related public law. He is currently generic counsel in the contraceptive pill litigation, the Alder Hey litigation and a child abuse group action. Recent reported cases: Heil v Rankin (general damages appeal); Warren v Northern General Hospital NHS Trust (multipliers); Rahman v Arearose Ltd (successive torts and several liability); Hope v CC of Greater Manchester (discrimination law); Hutton v East Dyfed HA (clinical negligence); Hodgson v Imperial Tobacco (liability of lawyers under conditional fee arrangements). Regular lecturer to solicitors.
Prof. Memberships: Action for Victims of Medical Accidents; Association of Personal Injury Lawyers; Administrative Law Bar Association; Professional Negligence Bar Association and Personal Injury Bar Association.
Career: Called to the Bar 1988.
Publications: Contributing author of 'Personal Injury Manual' and Bullen and Leake, 'Precedents of Pleadings' (Sweet & Maxwell 2000) and forthcoming books on clinical negligence and quantum.

ORNSBY, Suzanne
2 Harcourt Buildings (Gerard Ryan QC) London (020) 7353 8415
Recommended in Planning
Specialisation: Specialist fields are planning and environmental law (civil and criminal jurisdictions) for both the private and public sector.
Prof. Memberships: Member of the Planning and Environment Bar Association; member of the United Kingdom Environmental Law Association.
Career: Called to the Bar in 1986. Joined present chambers in 1990, previously practised at the Criminal Bar and employed in the electricity supply industry.
Personal: Educated at St Georges College, Weybridge and University College London (LLB Hons 1985).

O'ROURKE, Mary
3 Serjeants' Inn (Robert Francis QC & John Grace QC) London (020) 7427 5000
Recommended in Clinical Negligence

ORR, Craig
Fountain Court (Anthony Boswood QC) London (020) 7583 3335
Recommended in Commercial (Litigation)
Specialisation: Practice covers all areas of commercial law, including city related litigation, especially merchant banking, accountants' negligence, commercial fraud (civil actions) and insurance. Important cases include British & Commonwealth v Quadrex, Caparo v Dickman [1990]; Eagle Trust v Cowan de Groot [1992]; Society of Lloyd's v Mason and Clementson [1995]; AMF v Hashim [1996]; Domicrest v SBC [1998]; Peskin v Anderson [2000] and Barings plc v Coopers & Lybrand [2001].
Prof. Memberships: COMBAR.
Career: Called to the Bar in 1986 and joined Fountain Court in 1988.
Personal: Educated at Cambridge University 1981-84 (MA) and Oxford University (BCL, Vinerian Scholar). Born 8th January 1962.

ORR, Nicholas
14 Castle Street (Andrew Edis QC) Liverpool (0151) 236 6757 nick.orr@14castlestreet.co.uk
Recommended in Chancery
Specialisation: General chancery, particularly property litigation, family provision, landlord and tenant and partnerships. Also commercial litigation and drafting and professional negligence.
Prof. Memberships: Northern Circuit, Chancery Bar Association, Northern Chancery Bar Association, Northern circuit Commercial Bar Association.

OTTON-GOULDER, Catharine QC
Brick Court Chambers (Christopher Clarke QC) London (020) 7379 3550 ottongoulder@brickcourt.co.uk
Recommended in Commercial (Litigation)
Specialisation: General commercial law, restrictive practice and competition law. Cases of note: Tin Litigation; EIL British & Commonwealth v BZW; Barings v LDC; Credit Suisse v Allerdale DC; Arab Monetary Fund v Hashim; Hazell Swaps litigation v London Borough of Hammersmith & Fulham; Director General of Fair Trading v Premier League; Director General of Fair Trading v Pharmacists & Manufacturers.
Career: Called to Bar 22 November 1983, Lincoln's Inn. Pupillages with John Thomas QC (4 Essex Court) and Jonathan Sumption QC (1 Brick Court). At Brick Court Chambers 21 December 1984 to date.
Personal: Born 9 April 1955 in Chester. Educated at King George V School, Hong Kong; King Edward VI High School for Girls and Somerville College, Oxford (1973-77) – Literae Humaniores without Viva Voce Examination, First Class. Qualified as Solicitor of Supreme Court 1980. Gained Seymour Scholarship (on entry to Oxford) and Hardwicke Scholarship at Lincoln's Inn.

OWEN, Gail
India Buildings Chambers (Ray Herman) Liverpool (0151) 243 6000
Recommended in Family
Specialisation: All aspects of public law Children Act work, including the representation of Local Authorities, parents and Guardians ad Litem. This work involves, inter alia, issues of physical, sexual and emotional abuse of children. Also practices in all areas of private law Children Act work, divorce proceedings, adoption proceedings and all aspects of finance and property disputes ancillary relief proceedings and disputes between unmarried couples.
Career: Called 1980.

OWEN, Robert QC
Ropewalk Chambers (Ian McLaren QC) Nottingham 0115 947 2581 clerks@ropewalk.co.uk
Recommended in Personal Injury
Specialisation: Principal areas of practice are personal injury and clinical negligence claims. Insidious disease litigation includes The Metro-Cammell litigation; North East Shipyard Asbestos ligitation (against T & N plc); North West Shipyard Asbestos ligitation (against Cape plc.); Gnitrow v Cape plc. (Isle of Wight asbestos litigation); The Craven Tasker Asbestos litigation; Armstrong & Ors v B.C.C. (V.W.F.); British Steel Deafness ligitation; Parr & Ors v Sunderland Shipbuilders (welders lung); The Tyne Tees Contractors Litigation (V.W.F). Child abuse group actions include the Leicestershire County Council / Beck litigation and the North Wales Childrens' Homes litigation (including Coxon & Others v Flintshire County Council and Rowlands and Others v Bryn Alyn Community Limited).
Prof. Memberships: PNBA, PIBA.
Career: Prestatyn High School. Polytechnic of Central London (University of London Ext.). Called 1977. Queen's Counsel 1996. Assistant Recorder 1997. Recorder 2000.
Publications: New Law Journal, July 2000, 'Causation and Apportionment'.
Personal: Family, friends, sport.

OWEN, Tim QC
Matrix Chambers (Nicholas Blake QC) London (020) 7404 3447
timowen@matrixlaw.co.uk
Recommended in Administrative & Public Law, Crime, Human Rights
Specialisation: Public law (especially criminal, prison, police and inquest law). Criminal law, especially political offences, confiscation, money laundering and mutual assistance, public order and appellate work. Civil actions involving abuse of power (especially police and prison actions) and international human rights law. Commonwealth capital appeals and constitutional motions, extradition and deportation.
Prof. Memberships: ALBA, Criminal Bar Association, INQUEST Lawyers' Group.
Career: Called 1983. Silk 2000.
Publications: Co-author 'Prison Law' (OUP, 2nd edn, 2000), co-editor Halsbury's Laws vol 36(2) 'Prisons and Prisoners', co-author 'Criminal Justice, police powers and human rights', Blackstone 2001.
Personal: Educated at Atlantic College and LSE. Lives in London.

OWEN, Tudor
9-12 Bell Yard (D. Anthony Evans QC) London (020) 7400 1800
clerks@bellyard.co.uk
Recommended in Aviation, Crime
Specialisation: Aviation: All aspects of aviation litigation and advisory work, including insurance, liability of carriers, manufacturers and operators, compliance with ANO. Extensive experience representing AOC holders and pilots prosecuted by the CAA. Qualified pilot (aeroplane and helicopter). Crime: Practice equally divided between prosecution and defence in serious crime, including commercial fraud. Judicial review, especially Abuse of Process. Advises government departments, particularly the DTI, in relation to regulatory matters.
Career: Called 1974. Appointed a Recorder 1990. DTI Inspector 1987. Member of the Bar Council 1988-94.
Personal: King's College, London University (LLB Hons 1973).

OWEN-JONES, David Roderic
3 Temple Gardens (Jonathan Goldberg QC) London (020) 7583 1155
Recommended in Crime
Specialisation: Drugs and fraud cases – prosecution and defence. Environmental Law cases – practice on South Eastern Circuit and Midland Circuit. Recorder of the Crown Court.
Prof. Memberships: CBA.
Career: University of London LLB LLM. Council of Europe, Commission of Human Rights.

PAGE, Adrienne QC
5 Raymond Buildings (Patrick Milmo QC) London (020) 7242 2902
Recommended in Defamation
Specialisation: In practice as a defamation specialist from 5 Raymond Buildings, Gray's Inn 1975. Recently reported cases: Hamilton v Fayed CA The Times 30 March 1999. Hamilton v Fayed (No 2) CA The Times 30 March 1999. Cruise and Kidman v Express Newspapers Plc CA 1999 2 WLR 327. Shah v Standard Chartered Bank CA 1999 QB 241 1998 3 WLR 592. Gladding v Channel 4 Television CA 1999 EMLR 475. Berezovsky v Michaels (Forbes magazine) HL 2000 1 WLR 1004; 2000 EMLR 643. Shrine and Co v Ors v Euromoney Publications 2001 EMLR 434. Recent trials: Trevor Gladding v Channel 4 Television; represented Channel 4 as Junior to George Carman QC in Channel 4's successful defence of David Jessel's 'Trial and Error' against action by a police officer. Bodker, Colver & Eisner v Associated Newspapers Limited; represented Associated Newspapers as Junior to Tom Shields QC. Peter Oates v MGN; represented Mirror Group newspapers in their defence of an action by a former Broadmoor patient over two articles. Mirror Group succeeded in their defence of one article and sustained a jury's award against them of one penny in respect of the second article. Victor Kiam v Mirror Group as leading counsel to Mirror Group. Dr Saad Al Fagin v HH Saudi Research and Marketing as leading counsel for the successful claimant in which defence of justification and 'Reynolds' qualified privilege were defeated (now under appeal).
Prof. Memberships: Fellow of the Society for Advanced Legal Studies.
Career: Called to the Bar, Middle Temple 1974. Appointed to Silk 1999. Appointed Recorder, South Eastern Circuit, 1999.

PAGE, Nigel B.
St. Mary's Chambers Family Law Chambers (Christopher M. Butler) Nottingham (0115) 950 3503
Recommended in Family

PAINES, Nicholas QC
Monckton Chambers (John Swift QC) London (020) 7405 7211
npaines@monckton.co.uk
Recommended in Competition/Anti-trust
Specialisation: Administrative, public, competition and EC law. All areas of administrative and public law, challenges to central and local government and other administrative decision-making, particularly but not exclusively on EC law grounds. Areas of practice include agriculture, anti-dumping duties, competition, customs, employment, free movement of goods, free movement of persons, human rights, public procurement, sex discrimination, social security, state aid, VAT. UK and EC competition law, advice and representation before the Office of Fair Trading, Competition Commission and Competition Commission Appeal tribunals. Has appeared in a number of reported competition cases in the former Restrictive Practices Court and the ECJ, and in monopoly and merger cases before the MMC and Competition Commission. Numerous ECJ appearances include: The Sunday Trading cases; Coloroll and the subsequent cases on pensions; R v Secretary of State for Employment ex p Seymour-Smith; Card Protection Plan v Cmmrs of Customs & Excise (VAT); R v Secretary of State ex p Imperial Tobacco (tobacco advertising directive). Reported cases in English courts include Kirklees MBC v B & Q (Sunday trading injunctions); In re Ready Mixed Concrete Agreements (restrictive trade practices); Iberian v BPB (competition, effect in national court of EC Commission decision); U v W (freedom to provide services and human rights); B v NHS Pensions Agency (sex discrimination and human rights).
Prof. Memberships: Administrative Law Bar Association; Bar European Group (former chairman); Competition Law Association, UK Association for European Law; Bars and Law Societies Joint Working Party on Competition Law.
Career: Called to the Bar 1978. QC 1997.
Publications: Former contributor to Bellamy & Child 'Common Market Law of Competition'; Halsbury's Laws of England; Vaughan 'Law of the European Communities'. Joint editor (with Paul Lasok QC) Common Market Law Reports.
Personal: Educated at Oxford University 1973-76 (MA, jurisprudence) and Université libre de Bruxelles (Licence spéciale en droit Européen).

PALMER, Adrian QC
Guildhall Chambers (Adrian Palmer QC) Bristol (0117) 927 3366
Recommended in Commercial (Litigation)

PALMER, Howard QC
2 Temple Gardens (Dermod O'Brien QC) London (020) 7822 1200
Recommended in Construction
Specialisation: Insurance and Reinsurance: insurance policy disputes; repudiation for fraud/non-disclosure/breach of condition. Personal Injury: local authority and employers' liability. Professional Indemnity: engineers; insurance brokers; surveyors; accountants; architects; solicitors. Construction: contract disputes; building regulations on spread of fire; adjudication and human rights. Commercial Arbitration: international fraud; commercial disputes.
Career: Lecturer at King's College, London 1977-8. Tenant at 2 Temple Gardens 1978 – date. QC 1999.
Personal: Cricket; fieldsports; theatre. Married, four children. Lives in Fulham, London.

PALMER, Patrick J.S.
Sovereign Chambers (Geoffrey C. Marson QC) Leeds (0113) 245 1841
Recommended in Crime
Specialisation: His practice is predominantly heavy crime concerning serious sexual offences and fraud. Civil work of professional negligence, general civil law and legal advice to an inquiry on child sexual abuse complements his criminal practice. He has particular interest in fraud work and is a member of Chamber's Fraud Group and deals with excise, VAT, estate agency, solicitor and patent fraud.
Career: LLB (Hons) London. Called to the Bar (Inner Temple) in 1978. Recorder.

PANNICK, David QC
Blackstone Chambers (Presiley Baxendale QC & Charles Flint QC) London (020) 7583 1770
clerks@blackstonechambers.com
Recommended in Administrative & Public Law, Employment, Human Rights, Immigration, Sport
Specialisation: Practices mainly in the fields of public and administrative law, employment law, immigration law, European law and sports law. He has appeared in more than 40 cases in the House of Lords, over 20 cases in the European Court of Justice, and over a dozen cases in the European Court of Human Rights. He is a Fellow of All Souls College, Oxford, and a member of the Editorial Committee of 'Public Law'. He writes a fortnightly column on the law for 'The Times'. His recent cases include ex p Myra Hindley, Camelot v National Lottery Commission, Lustig-Prean v UK, Thompson and Venables v UK, and R v DPP ex p Kebilene.

PARKER, Christopher
Maitland Chambers (Michael Lyndon-Stanford QC & Charles Aldous QC) London (020) 7406 1200
Recommended in Company
Specialisation: Main areas of practice are company and insolvency law. Also undertakes general Chancery work. Recent reported cases: JJ Harrison Properties Ltd v JP Harrison [2000]; Coutts & Co v Stock [1999]; Solicitor v Carman Construction Co Ltd [1999]; MTI Trading Systems Ltd. v Winter [1997]; Re: A Company (No.002015 of 1996) [1996], Watkins v A.J. Wright (Electrical) Ltd. [1996], R & H Electrical Ltd. and Anor v Haden Bill Electrical Ltd.: Re: Haden Bill Electrical Ltd. [1995].
Career: Called to the Bar 1984.
Personal: Educated at Keble College, Oxford BA Jurisprudence, 1st class, (1977-80) and BCL (1980-81), University of Illinois LL.M (1981-82), Harvard Law School LLM (1982-83). Born 13th October 1958.

PARKER, Judith QC
One King's Bench Walk (Anthony Hacking QC) London (020) 7936 1500
Recommended in Family

PARKER, Kenneth QC
Monckton Chambers (John Swift QC) London (020) 7405 7211
chambers@monckton.co.uk
Recommended in Competition/Anti-trust, Tax
Specialisation: Specialises in EC law, public law and judicial review.Recent reported cases include: R v Secretary of State for the Environment ex p Greenpeace [1994] (challenge to decision to authorise testing at Sellafield), R v Home Secretary ex p Hagan and Croft [1994] (challenge to decision to extradite British women to Oregon), R v MAFF ex p NFFO [1995] ECJ (challenge to fish con-

servation policy), R v Home Secretary ex p Norney [1995] (challenge to policy on referring IRA lifers to Parole Board), R v Secretary of State for Trade and Industry ex p Consumer's Association [1996] (challenge to implementation of Unfair Contract Terms Directive), BRB/SNCF v Commission [1996] ECJ (challenge to decision affecting operation of Channel Tunnel), R v Home Secretary ex p O'Dhuibhir [1997] (challenge to closed visits in high security prisons), MD Foods v Baines [1997] HL (application of RTPA to supply agreements) and R v Home Secretary ex p Launder [1997] CA, and HL (challenge to decision to extradite ex MD of Wardley Merchant Bank to Hong Kong). Also regularly instructed by the Commissioners of Customs and Excise on appeals in VAT cases. Recent cases include Elida Gibbs v CCE [1996] ECJ, Argos v CCE [1996] ECJ and CCE v Wellington Hospital [1997] CA.
Prof. Memberships: Called to the Bar in 1975 and took silk in 1992. Fellow in Law at Exeter College Oxford between 1973 and 1976. He is on the executive of COMBAR.

PARKIN, Fiona
Atkin Chambers (Robert Akenhead QC) London (020) 7404 0102
Recommended in Construction
Specialisation: Construction and Engineering disputes which involves advising and representing employers and contractors on all aspects of disputes arising out of the design, construction and commissioning of large scale construction and engineering projects. Counsel in Whites Properties Ltd v Birse Construction Ltd. Arbitration Adjudication ADR – advising and appearing in domestic and international arbitrations and arbitration appeals. Has been engaged to draft submissions for adjudication proceedings and to advise on the enforcement of adjudicators' decisions. Public Procurement – advising major public bodies on the application of the EU Procurement regulations and remedies for breach. Counsel in Harman v Corporate Officer of the House of Commons. Professional Negligence – advising and acting for and against all professionals connected to the construction industry. Chesham Properties v Bucknell Austin PMC. Technology – advises in connection with disputes concerning bespoke software contractors and telecommunications systems.
Prof. Memberships: Tec bar; London Common Law and Commercial Barristers.
Career: Called 1993.
Personal: LLB (Hons) first class, Exeter; LLM (Hons), Sidney Sussex, Cambridge.

PARNELL, Graham
East Anglian Chambers (Roderick Newton) Ipswich (01473) 214481
Recommended in Family

PARROY, Michael QC
3 Paper Buildings London (020) 7583 8055
Recommended in Fraud

PARRY, Isabel
9 Park Place (Ian Murphy QC) Cardiff (029) 2038 2731
Recommended in Family

PARSONS, Luke
4 Essex Court (Nigel Teare QC) London (020) 7653 5653
iparsons@4sx.co.uk
Recommended in Shipping
Specialisation: Luke Parsons is highly regarded and well known commercial and admiralty junior. His broad practice encompasses insurance/reinsurance, international trade, sale of goods, banking, commercial contracts and shipping. Much of his work combines complex legal and factual analysis, often requiring the co-ordination of a range of expert specialisms. He believes in combining a friendly, down to earth approach with tenacious and well prepared presentation of his clients' case.
Career: LLB (Bristol). Called 1985, Inner Temple.
Publications: Editor of 'Steel & Parsons on Forms & Precedents' (2nd Ed).

PARTRIDGE, Richard
3 Serjeants' Inn (Robert Francis QC & John Grace QC) London (020) 7427 5000
Recommended in Clinical Negligence

PASCOE, Martin
3-4 South Square (Michael Crystal QC & Lord Alexander of Weedon QC) London (020) 7696 9900
clerks@southsquare.com
Recommended in Chancery, Insolvency/Corporate Recovery
Specialisation: Martin Pascoe's practice includes a broad range of commercial and financial law with particular emphasis on corporate insolvency, often with substantial international elements. In the last year he has been lead counsel for the Government of Brunei and the Brunei Investment Agency in worldwide proceedings against HRH Prince Jefri and some 70 other defendants seeking to trace and recover substantial sums of misappropriated public monies. He acted for the English administrators of the Olympia & York group, and has since 1991 acted for the English liquidators of BCCI SA and the Cayman Island liquidators of BCCI Overseas. Some recent reported cases are: Latreefers Inc [1999] BCLC 271 (English court's jurisdiction to wind up foreign companies); Torvale Group [1999] 2 BCLC 591 (scope of ss35A, 322A CA 1985); Re BCCI SA (No11) [1997] 1 BCLC 80 (English ancillary liquidations and cross-border set-off issues); Hughes v Hannover Re [1997] 1 BCLC 497 (the first Court of Appeal case on cross-border cooperation between insolvency courts). He has had substantial experience of insurance insolvencies, including acting for US-based reinsurers of EMLICO in the winding-up proceedings before the Supreme Court of Bermuda and in judicial review proceedings in the Supreme Court, Court of Appeal for Bermuda and Privy Council seeking the quashing of decisions permitting EMLICO's redomestication to Bermuda; Kemper Re v Minister of Finance (Bermuda) [1998] 3 WLR 630 (PC).
Prof. Memberships: Chancery Bar Association, Commercial Bar Association.
Career: BA, BCL (Oxon). Called to the Bar 1977.

PASCOE, Nigel QC
Pump Court Chambers (Christopher Harvey Clark QC) Winchester (01962) 868161
clerks@3pumpcourt.com
Recommended in Crime
Specialisation: Serious crime, including fraud. Also defamation and Courts Martial work.
Prof. Memberships: Former Leader of the Western Circuit.
Career: Called in 1966, joining 3 Pump Court. Recorder: 1979. Silk: 1988. Co-Author of 'Succesful Advocacy' (cassette).
Personal: Presents 'The Trial of Penn & Mead'.

PATTERSON, Frances QC
40 King St Manchester 0161 832 9082
Recommended in Environment, Planning
Specialisation: Specialist in town planning, compulsory purchase, highways, environmental law and judicial review. Experience in projects involving airport expansion, roads, incineration, waste disposal, retailing, minerals and housing.
Prof. Memberships: Member of Planning and Environment Bar Association; member of Administrative Law Bar Association; member of Northern Circuit; committee member Law Reform Working Group on Planning and Environment Law.
Career: Called 1977. Appointed Queen's Counsel 1998. Assistant Boundary Commissioner 2000. Recorder 2000.

PAUFFLEY, Anna QC
4 Paper Buildings (Lionel Swift QC) London (020) 7583 0816
ap@4pb.com
Recommended in Family
Specialisation: Family. Reported cases include Re H, Re G (Adoption: Consultation of Unmarried Fathers) [2001] 1 FLR 646; Re W, Re A, Re B (Change of Name) [1999] 2 FLR 930; Re B (Contact: Stepfather's Opposition) [1997] 2 FLR 579; R v Cambridge District Health Authority [1996] 1 FLR 375; Re G and R (Child Sexual Abuse: Standard of Proof) [1995] 2 FLR 867.
Career: BA (London); called 1979; QC 1995; Recorder 1995.

PEACOCK, Jonathan QC
Revenue Law Chambers (John Gardiner QC) London (020) 7242 4017
taxlaw@11newsquare.com
Recommended in Tax
Specialisation: Revenue law. Work encompasses advice on all aspects of UK tax, including VAT, Customs and Excise duties and EC levies; tax litigation in all tribunals (including tax-related aspects of commercial disputes, judicial review and professional negligence). Recent cases include Amerada Hess v IRC (High Court); Halifax et al v HMCE (VAT Tribunal); Halifax plc v Davidson (SC); NMB Holdings v DSS (High Court).
Prof. Memberships: Revenue Bar Association, Chancery Bar Association, VAT Practitioners Group.
Career: Called to the Bar 1987; joined current chambers 1988.
Publications: 'Taxation for Employment Specialists', Butterworths 2000.
Personal: Educated at King's School, Macclesfield 1975-79, Nunthorpe Grammar School, York 1979-82 and Corpus Christi College, Oxford 1983-86 (1st Class Degree in Jurisprudence). Born 21st April 1964.

PEARCE, Ivan
Furnival Chambers (Andrew Mitchell QC) London (020) 7405 3232
ipearce@furnivallaw.co.uk
Recommended in Crime
Specialisation: Asset forfeiture and confiscation. The appointment of receivers and the general enforcement of confiscation orders in both the High Court and the Magistrates Court.
Prof. Memberships: Criminal Bar Association. Administrative Bar Association.
Career: Priestlands School, Lymington, Merristwood Agricultural College, Exeter University, LLB.
Personal: Rowing, sailing.

PEART, Icah
Two Garden Court (Ian Macdonald QC & Owen Davies QC) London (020) 7353 1633
Recommended in Crime
Specialisation: All major criminal work, including leading work. Areas of particular expertise include public order offences, armed robbery, conspiracy to defraud, terrorism, murder and large-scale drugs conspiracy/importation.
Prof. Memberships: SE Circuit; CBA; LSE Lawyers Group.
Career: 9 Stone Buildings 1978-82; 76B Chancery Lane 1982-87; 2 Garden Court, Temple, 1987-date. Assistant Recorder 1997; Recorder 2000-date.
Personal: Interests include sports, cinema, reading, music and my children (not necessarily in that order!).

PEDDIE, Ian QC
One Garden Court Family Law Chambers (Eleanor F. Platt QC & Alison Ball QC) London (020) 7797 7900
I.Peddie@onegardencourt.co.uk
Recommended in Family
Specialisation: Childcare law: regularly appears in serious Children Act proceedings for parents, local authorities and Guardians ad Litem eg physical and sexual abuse;

Barristers index: p.1619

"Munchhausen" allegations; mental health issues. Many reported cases including recent CA Human Rights case of Wy B, ReW (May 2001). Especially criminal cases where there are children who are victims or witnesses eg murder, attempted murder, (eg R v Owen [Maidstone Crown Court] – revenge attack on lorry driver who caused son's death by dangerous driving and R v Campbell – man who went beserk with a machete in a Wolverhampton Primary School attacking children and nursery teacher, Lisa Potts, who was subsequently given the GC); Munchausen cases, (eg R v Flannery, [Stafford Crown Court] – poisoning son with paracetamol, caffeine and warfarin); paedophile rings, (eg R v Davis and Others – the six month South Wales paedophile case). In addition, has often appeared for the defence in other serious and lengthy criminal cases not involving children eg fraud, drug importation, rape.
Prof. Memberships: Committee Member. FLBA since 1990.
Career: Gordonstoun School, LLB (Hons) University College London. Called to the Bar in 1971; QC in 1991; Assistant Recorder 1993; Recorder of Crown Court 1996.

PEEL, Robert
29 Bedford Row Chambers (Peter Ralls QC) London (020) 7404 1044
rpeel@29bedfordrow.co.uk
Recommended in Family
Specialisation: Principal areas of practice are ancillary relief, child abduction and personal injury.
Prof. Memberships: Member of Bar Council since 1996. Committee member of Family Law Bar Association.
Career: Oxford University (BA Hons). City University (DIP Law). Called to the Bar 1990.
Personal: Fluent in French and Spanish.

PENNICOTT, Ian
Keating Chambers (Richard Fernyhough QC) London +44 (0) 20 7544 2600
ipennicott@keatingchambers.com
Recommended in Construction
Specialisation: Building and engineering contracts.
Career: Qualified 1982; Middle Temple. Member of Hong Kong Bar.
Personal: Born 1958. Leisure, Golf.

PERETZ, George
Monckton Chambers (John Swift QC) London (020) 7405 7211
gperetz@monckton.co.uk
Recommended in Competition/Anti-trust
Specialisation: Competition law: mergers (IMS/PMSI, WJE/Pointing and Icopal/IKO, before Competition Commission; SCA/AMP, BEAP/Keesing and others before OFT); High Court litigation under Competition Act (Claritas v Post Office [2001] UKCLR2, Synstar v ICL); advised OFT on Volvo cars cartel; advice to major companies on UK/EC competition law and telecommunications issues; state aids: Scott v Commission (CFI, Case T-366/00) EC law: Optident v DTI [2000] 2 CMLR 283 (CA), now in House of Lords (meaning of EC directives on cosmetics and medical devices).
Prof. Memberships: Bar European Group, Administrative Law Bar Association.
Career: Legal Adviser, OFT, 1992-97, since then tenant at Monckton Chambers.
Publications: Contributor to: Bellamy and Child, 'Common Market Law of Competition'; Copinger & Skone James on Copyright; plc Competition Manual.

PERRY, David
6 King's Bench Walk (Roy Amlot QC) London (020) 7583 0410
Recommended in Crime, Fraud
Specialisation: Practice focuses on criminal law, particularly commercial fraud. Involved in Blue Arrow, Barlow Clowes, Brent Walker and Polly Peck International litigation.
Prof. Memberships: Criminal Law Bar Association.
Career: Called to the Bar 1980. DTI Inspector and Standing Counsel to the DTI (1991-97). Senior Treasury Counsel to the Crown at the Central Criminal Court.
Personal: Born 7th September 1956. Lives in London.

PERRY, John QC
3 Gray's Inn Square (Rock Tansey QC) London (020) 7520 5600
Recommended in Crime

PERSEY, Lionel QC
4 Essex Court (Nigel Teare QC) London (020) 7653 5653
Recommended in Shipping

PETCHEY, Philip
2 Harcourt Buildings (Gerard Ryan QC) London (020) 7353 8415
Recommended in Church

PHILIPPS, Guy
Fountain Court (Anthony Boswood QC) London (020) 7583 3335
Recommended in Commercial (Litigation), Professional Negligence
Specialisation: All areas of commercial litigation (including arbitration), particularly insurance and reinsurance, banking and financial services, and professional negligence.
Career: Called 1986. Junior Counsel to the Crown (B Panel). Member of California Bar. Admitted to Bahamas and British Virgin Island Bars.
Personal: Born 1961. Educated Magdalen College, Oxford and City University.

PHILLIPS, Jane
1 Brick Court (Richard Rampton QC) London (020) 7353 8845
Recommended in Defamation
Specialisation: Libel & slander, malicious falsehood, contempt, passing-off, breach of confidence, reporting restrictions and all forms of media law, including prepublication advice. Cases include: Walker v Central Television, Adams v Associated Newspapers (CA); Allason v BBC; Ashby v Times Newspapers; C v MGN and others (CA); Lloyd v Express Newspapers (CA); Marks and Spencer plc v Granada; Upjohn v BBC and Professor Oswald; Williamson v Commissioner of Police for the Metropolis (CA); Little v George; Mori v BBC; McCahill v Royal Sun Alliance; Khalili v Associated Newspapers; Blackstone v MGN.
Career: Called to the Bar in July 1989.
Publications: Co-author of the section on 'Libel and Slander, Malicious Falsehood' in Bullen & Leake, 'Precedents & Pleadings'.
Personal: Educated at St. Paul's Girls' School and Worcester College, Oxford.

PHILLIPS, Mark QC
3-4 South Square (Michael Crystal QC & Lord Alexander of Weedon QC) London (020) 7696 9900
clerks@southsquare.com
Recommended in Banking, Company, Insolvency/Corporate Recovery
Specialisation: Area of practice: insolvency – administration, insurance, banking – regulatory work for the Bank of England. Commercial work arising out of insolvencies. Notable cases: Three Rivers District Council + Ors v The Governor and Company of the Bank of England (HL) [2000] 3 WLR 1220; Somji v Cadbury Schweppes plc [2001] 1BCLC 498; Re Galileo Group Ltd, Elles v Hambros bank (Bank of England intervening) (Ch D) [1999] Ch 100; Re Toshoku Finance UK plc [2000] 1 BCLC 683 (CA) 'The Times', 24 March 2000; Barings Plc v Cooper & Lybrand [2000] 3 AER 910.
Career: Education: LLB LLM (commercial) Bristol University. Appointed Assistant Recorder July 1998. Recorder April 2000. QC 1999.
Publications: Butterworths 'Insolvency Law Handbook' (editor); 'Paget's Law of Banking' (contributor); 'Byles on Bills of Exchange' (contributor).
Personal: Motorsport enthusiast.

PHILLIPS, Nevil
4 Essex Court (Nigel Teare QC) London (020) 7653 5653
nphillips@4sx.co.uk
Recommended in Shipping
Specialisation: Commercial and shipping litigation: admiralty; carriage of goods; international sale disputes; commodities; arbitration; insurance, and associated areas. Counsel to the Owners of The Marchioness in the Formal Investigation (2000). Counsel in R v Secretary of State for the Home Office ex parte Balboa (concerning judicial review of the power to impose penalties upon a carrier in respect of the introduction of illegal immigrants) (2001). Counsel to a major ferry operator in a dispute concerning the operation and use of a main UK ferry port (2000).
Prof. Memberships: Supporting member of the London Maritime Arbitration Association; member of Gray's Inn and Middle Temple.
Career: Called to the Bar in 1992.
Publications: 'Merchant Shipping Act 1995 – An Annotated Guide (LLP)', 1st Edition 1996, 2nd Edition 2001.

PHILLIPS, Richard QC
2 Harcourt Buildings (Gerard Ryan QC) London (020) 7353 8415
Recommended in Planning
Specialisation: Principal areas of practice are planning and local government work. Also handles licensing cases.
Prof. Memberships: Planning & Environment Bar Association. Member of South Eastern Circuit.
Career: Called to the Bar 1970 and joined Harcourt Buildings in 1971. Assistant Parliamentary Boundary Commissioner. Took silk in 1990.
Personal: Educated at Kings School, Ely and Sidney Sussex College, Cambridge 1966-69. Born 8 August 1947.

PHILLIPS, Rory
3 Verulam Buildings (Christopher Symons QC & John Jarvis QC) London (020) 7831 8441
chambers@3vb.com
Recommended in Insurance, Professional Negligence
Specialisation: Principal areas of practice are insurance and reinsurance and professional negligence.
Career: Called 1984. Junior Counsel to the Crown (A Panel).

PHILLIPS, Stephen
3 Verulam Buildings (Christopher Symons QC & John Jarvis QC) London (020) 7831 8441
chambers@3vb.com
Recommended in Banking, Commercial (Litigation)
Specialisation: Principal area of practice is commercial and business law. Work includes general contractual disputes, banking and finance, company law and insolvency, international and domestic trade, commercial fraud, professional negligence and gaming contracts. Clients include banks and other financial institutions, insurance companies and funds and casinos.
Prof. Memberships: Wales and Chester Circuit, COMBAR, London Common Law and Commercial Bar Association.
Career: Called to the Bar 1984 and joined present chambers 1985. Recorder.
Personal: Educated at King's School, Chester 1973-80 and University College, Oxford 1980-83. Born 10 October 1961.

PHILPOTT, Fred
Gough Square Chambers (Fred Philpott) London (020) 7353 0924
Recommended in Consumer Law

PICARDA, Hubert QC
3 New Square (Lord Goodhart QC) London
(020) 7405 5577
law@threenewsquare.co.uk
Recommended in Charities

Specialisation: Chancery law generally but particular expertise in all aspects of law relating to charities, banking, corporate insolvency and derivative trading. Recent cases include Wellcome Plc v Glaxo Holdings (disputed take over); Oldham BC v AG (sale of recreation ground); R v Lord President of Council (judicial review of university visitor); Bridge Trust Ld v AG of Caymans; Jyske Bank (Gibraltar) Ltd v Spjeldnaes (banking, fraud and tracing). Clients include: Wellcome Trust, RNLI, British Heart Foundation, Nuffield Homes, Various Oxford Colleges, Great Ormond Street Hospital, Garfield Weston, Wolfson and Clore Foundations, many leading and medium range charities, housing associations, universities and local authorities. Advisory work and appearances in receiverships of Gomba Holdings, BCCI and Royal Masonic Hospital. Advisory work in Singapore, Hong Kong and Caymans.
Prof. Memberships: Chancery Bar Association, Insolvency Lawyers Association, Charity Law Association (President).
Career: Called 1962. QC 1992. Visiting lecturer in banking and derivative trading law 1995-96; 2000-01: Malaysia, Sarawak, Singapore. WA Lee Equity Lecture (2001) Brisbane. Editorial Board: Journal of International Banking and Finance Law, Trust Law International.
Publications: Picarda Law relating to Receivers Managers Administrators (3rd ed 2000), Picarda Law and practice relating to Charities (3rd ed 1999). Halsbury Title on Receivers (1998) and on Charities (2001).

PICKUP, James QC
Lincoln House Chambers (Mukhtar Hussain QC) Manchester (0161) 832 5701
Recommended in Crime

PICTON, Martin
Albion Chambers (Charles Barton QC & Neil Ford QC) Bristol (0117) 927 2144
martin.picton@virgin.net
Recommended in Crime

Specialisation: Fraud (including commercial); organised crime; homicide; computer and Internet crime; health and safety; Customs prosecutions; disciplinary tribunals. Notable cases include defence counsel for Fred West; R v Billington, Locked and Ryder – defending in SFO prosecution; R v Martens, Tuegel and Saia – defence counsel in international banking fraud prosecuted by SFO; defence counsel in both Phase I and II of R v Robinson and Others – legal aid fraud prosecuted by SFO; prosecution counsel in R v Chepstow Plant Hire and Bazley Plant Hire – accident involving multiple deaths prosecuted by CPS under Health and Safety at Work Act; defence counsel in R v Paul Brooks and Others – alleged abuse by carer in South Wales children's home; defence counsel in R v Tully and Others – abuse of mentally disordered adults by carers; prosecution counsel in R v Jones, Jones and Nelson – high profile murder with very sensitive racial overtones.
Prof. Memberships: Criminal Bar Association (Western Circuit Rep.), Western Circuit;
Career: Kings College London, call 1981, Recorder.

PINE-COFFIN, Margaret Ann
17 Carlton Crescent (Jeremy S. Gibbons QC) Southampton (023) 8032 0320/2003
Recommended in Family

PIPE, Gregory
Chancery House Chambers (Adrian Dent) Leeds (0113) 244 6691
gregory.pipe@chanceryhouse.co.uk
Recommended in Commercial (Litigation)

Specialisation: Commercial contract and finance disputes; construction and engineering litigation and associated professional negligence issues; sale and supply of goods; agency; contractual construction; business sales; restraint of trade.
Career: Graduated in 1987 and taught law, latterly at the University of Leeds, until moving to the Bar to undertake commercial and construction work.
Publications: Numerous articles in periodicals on contractual and remedies issues. Some early work on computers and the law.
Personal: MA, Oxford University; LLM Cambridge University; formerly a keen oarsman; now rowing rather less frequently but still playing tennis (badly). Grew up with a strongly scientific/engineering background and entered University with entrance papers in that area; to a greater extent, that has influenced and made accessible the nature of the subject matter of much of the work now undertaken.

PITT-PAYNE, Timothy
11 King's Bench Walk Chambers (Eldred Tabachnik QC & James Goudie QC) London
(020) 7632 8500
Recommended in Employment

PLANTEROSE, Rowan
Littman Chambers (Mark Littman QC) London
(020) 7404 4866
rowanplanterose@littmanchambers.com
Recommended in Arbitration (International), Construction

Specialisation: Principal areas of practice are building and engineering and general commercial litigation. Other areas include more general professional negligence and practice and procedural matters in litigation and arbitration. Engineering related work has ranged widely and included train building, power, computer and telephone technology. Also acts as arbitrator and adjudicator.
Prof. Memberships: TECBAR (Committee Member); COMBAR; Chartered Institute of Arbitrators.
Career: Called to the Bar in 1978.
Personal: Educated at Eastbourne College and Downing College, Cambridge University. Lives in London and Gloucestershire.

PLATT, Eleanor F. QC
One Garden Court Family Law Chambers (Eleanor F. Platt QC & Alison Ball QC) London
(020) 7797 7900
e.plattqc@onegardencourt.co.uk
Recommended in Family

Specialisation: All aspects of family law with particular emphasis upon children and cases involving medical issues. Has been involved in sterilisation/surrogacy matters. Instructed on behalf of the Northern Region in the Cleveland Enquiry. Special interest in Jewish family law.
Prof. Memberships: Family Law Bar Association; SE circuit; deputy chairman National Health Service Tribunal; Legal Assessor General Medical/Dental Councils. Called to the Bar 1960, Recorder 1982, Silk 1982. Deputy Judge, High Court Family Division since 1987.
Personal: LLB London. Married with two children. Many interests including music, travel and skiing.

PLATTS-MILLS, Mark QC
8 New Square (Michael Fysh QC) London
(020) 7405 4321
clerks@8newsquare.co.uk
Recommended in Intellectual Property

Specialisation: Barrister specialising in all aspects of intellectual property, including patents, trade marks, passing off, registered designs, copyright and design right; also handles commercial work with a technical content. For comprehensive CV and list of recent cases, visit our website at www.8newsquare.co.uk.
Prof. Memberships: Intellectual Property Bar Association (IPBA); The Intellectual Property Lawyers Organisation (TIPLO); Chancery Bar Association.
Career: Called 1974; QC 1995.
Personal: Born 1951. Educated at Bryanston School; Balliol College, Oxford (1972 BA Engineering Science and Economics).

PLEMING, Nigel QC
39 Essex Street (Nigel Pleming QC) London
(020) 7832 1111
np@39essex.co.uk
Recommended in Administrative & Public Law, Immigration

Specialisation: Administrative and public law; environmental law and related regulatory work; local government law; and employment/discrimination law.
Career: Called 1971, Junior Counsel to the Crown (Common Law) – 1985 to 1992, Queen's Counsel – 1992. Deputy Judge of the High Court.

PLENDER, Richard QC
20 Essex Street (Iain Milligan QC) London
(020) 7583 9294
Recommended in Competition/Anti-trust, Immigration

Specialisation: European Community, immigration and nationality. Also experienced in public and private international law and administrative law.
Career: Dulwich College, LCC scholar, 1957-64; Queens' College Cambridge, open exhibitioner, BA 1967, LLB 1968 (Rebecca Squire Prize) LLD 1993; University of Illinois, LLM 1970 (summa cum laude), JSD 1971 (College of Law Prize). Called to the Bar 1972 (Berridale Keith Prize); Legal Adviser, UNHCR, 1974-76; Référendaire Court of Justice of the European Communities, 1980-83; QC 1989; Bencher Inner Temple 1996; Recorder 1998; member various WTO panels. Principal publications: 'International Migration Law', 1972, 2nd edn, 1988; 'Cases and Materials on the Law of the European Communities', with JA Usher, 1979, 2nd ed 1988, 3rd edn 1993; 'The European Contracts Convention: The Rome Convention on the Choice of Law for Contracts', 1991, 2nd edn 2001; 'European Courts Practice and Precedents', 1996; loose-leaf edition 'European Courts Procedure' since 2000. Contributions to enyclopaedias, periodicals and books in English, French and German.
Personal: Born 1945.

POCOCK, Christopher
One King's Bench Walk (Anthony Hacking QC) London (020) 7936 1500
Recommended in Family

POINTER, Martin QC
1 Mitre Court Buildings (Bruce Blair QC) London
(020) 7797 7070
Recommended in Family

Specialisation: Handles all types of family law, but principally financial relief claims. Pioneer of pension-splitting in ancillary relief.
Prof. Memberships: Family Law Association, International Academy of Matrimonial Lawyers.
Career: Called to the Bar in 1976 and joined Mitre Court Buildings in 1978. Silk 1996.
Personal: Educated at The King's School, Grantham 1964-71 and the University of Leicester 1972-75. Born 17th July 1953. Lives in London.

POLLOCK, Gordon QC
Essex Court Chambers (Gordon Pollock QC) London (020) 7813 8000
Recommended in Arbitration (International), Banking, Commercial (Litigation), Energy & Natural Resources, Fraud, Insurance, Media & Entertainment, Shipping, Sport

Specialisation: Broad-based commercial lawyer with a substantial court and advisory practice dealing with the major commercial issues of the day. He has been instructed in most of the major commercial litigation of recent years. Areas of practice include arbitration; banking; commodity disputes; conflict of laws; employment law; entertainment and sports law; financial services; insurance and reinsurance; judicial review; monopolies and mergers; oil and gas cases; professional negligence; shipping; takeovers.
Career: Trinity College, Cambridge: MA, LLB. Called to the Bar 1968. Queen's Counsel 1979. Bencher: Gray's Inn.

Sits as Deputy High Court Judge of the Chancery and Queen's Bench Divisions.
Personal: Born 1943.

POOLES, Michael QC
4 Paper Buildings (Jean Ritchie QC) London (020) 7353 3366
Recommended in Professional Negligence
Specialisation: Principal area of practice is professional negligence, particularly concerning solicitors. Also acts for and against members of the Bar, accountants, surveyors, architects, engineers, veterinary surgeons and doctors. Other main areas of practice are personal injury and general insurance matters, on behalf of claimants as well a large number of insurance companies.
Prof. Memberships: Professional Negligence Bar Association.
Career: Called to the Bar 1978 and joined present chambers in 1980. Silk 1999. Recorder 2000.
Personal: Educated at Perse School, Cambridge, 1967-74 and University of London 1974-7. Born 14th December 1955. Lives in Cambridge.

POPAT, Prashant
2 Harcourt Buildings (Roger Henderson QC) London (020) 7583 9020
Recommended in Product Liability

POPPLEWELL, Andrew QC
Brick Court Chambers (Christopher Clarke QC) London (020) 7379 3550
popplewell@brickcourt.co.uk
Recommended in Commercial (Litigation), Fraud, Insurance, Shipping
Specialisation: General commercial, including shipping, banking, insurance and reinsurance, international trade, financial services, arbitration, professional disciplinary, civil fraud and some employment and defamation.
Prof. Memberships: Queens Council 1997. Member of the Bar of the Cayman Islands and Seychelles. Has been appointed as arbitrator in LMAA, ICC and LCIA arbitrations.
Career: Called to Bar of England and Wales 1981. Has been appointed as ICC Arbitrator. Cases of note: Gruppo Torras v Sheikh Fahad, The 'BERGE SISAR', Hill v Mercantile & General, Vitol v Norelf.
Personal: Born 14 January 1959. Educated at Radley College and Downing College, Cambridge (BA Hons (Cantab) in Law, Class: First).

PORTEN, Anthony QC
2-3 Gray's Inn Square (Anthony Porten QC & Anthony Scrivener QC) London (020) 7242 4986
aporten@2-3graysinnsquare.co.uk
Recommended in Local Government, Planning
Specialisation: Planning and local government work, especially public inquiries and High Court; judicial review.
Prof. Memberships: PEBA, ALBA, UKELA.
Career: Called 1969. Silk 1988. Recorder 1993. FSALS 1999.
Personal: Epsom College; Emmanuel College, Cambridge.

PORTER, Martin
2 Temple Gardens (Dermod O'Brien QC) London (020) 7822 1200
Recommended in Personal Injury

POSNANSKY, Jeremy QC
1 Mitre Court Buildings (Bruce Blair QC) London (020) 7797 7070
jeremy@posnansky.net
Recommended in Family
Specialisation: Family Law. Practice covers all areas of family law: ancillary relief and the law relating to children. Appeared in many reported cases, including A v A (interim maintenance to include sums for legal fees) 2001; Re L and others (Court of Appeal guidelines in contact cases involving domestic violence: amicus curiae) 2000; W v W (refusal of decree absolute) 1998; S v S (forum non conveniens) 1997; Baker v Baker (standard of proof in ancillary relief applications) 1995; Cornick v Cornick, Nos. 1 and 2 (leave to appeal out of time and variation of maintenance principles) 1995. Articles in *International Family Law* and *Family Law*. Practice includes advising on and settling pre-nuptial agreements.
Prof. Memberships: Family Law Bar Association; Fellow of International Academy of Matrimonial Lawyers.
Career: Call 1972; Silk 1994. Deputy High Court Judge, 1997. Admitted to the Bar of Antigua.
Personal: Born 8 March 1951. Married with two daughters. Lives in London. Enjoys travel, scuba diving and computers.

POTTS, Robin QC
Erskine Chambers (Robin Potts QC) London (020) 7242 5532
Recommended in Banking, Company, Financial Services, Insolvency/Corporate Recovery

POWELL, John L QC
Four New Square (Justin Fenwick QC) London (020) 7822 2000
barristers@4newsquare.com
Recommended in Financial Services, Professional Negligence
Specialisation: Commercial practice centred on professional liability, financial services and securities regulation (UK, EU and international), fraud recovery, and related insurance (and reinsurance). Practice reflects his publications. Many cases involving accountants, actuaries, investment and pension sellers, banks and other financial institutions (including IPO and M&A claims), regulators, insurers and insurance brokers, valuers, internet providers as well as lawyers and construction industry professionals. Cases in the Gulf, Hong Kong, Jersey, USA and West Indies. Advises extensively on regulatory aspects of financial products and schemes (including collective investment schemes) and internet promotion. Recent reported cases have related to accountants (BCCI v Price Waterhouse (No 2 and No 4)); insolvency practitioners (Mond v DTI); patent agents (Arbiter v Gill Jennings Every); public bodies (Swinney v Chief Constable of Northumbria) and 1999 and a financial regulatory context (Kaufman v Credit Lyonnais). Past cases have related to Barlow Clowes, Maxwell, Lloyd's, lease back transactions and misselling of home income plans, pensions and endowment policies and several in a construction and engineering context. Wide experience of arbitration (as advocate and arbitrator) in the UK and overseas.
Prof. Memberships: COMBAR (Executive Committee 1999-00); PNBA; Bar European Group; Society of Construction Law (President 1991-3); Society for Advanced Legal Studies (Advisory Council member).
Career: Called 1974. Silk 1990. Recorder. Bencher, Middle Temple. Head of Chambers 1997-99. Bar Council member 1999 – (Chairman Bar Law Reform Committee (1997-98)).
Publications: 'Jackson and Powell on Professional Negligence'; 'Encyclopedia of Financial Services Law' (with Prof Eva Lomnicka). 'Palmer's Company Law' (specialist editor 24th ed); 'Issues and Offers of Company Securities'; various papers in national and international legal publications.
Personal: Born 1950. Trinity Hall, Cambridge (MA, LLB); Welsh speaker.

POWNALL, Orlando
2 Hare Court (Stephen Kramer QC) London (020) 7353 5324
Recommended in Crime

PRATT, Camden QC
One King's Bench Walk (Anthony Hacking QC) London (020) 7936 1500
Recommended in Family
Specialisation: Matrimonial finance and property, family (including divorce and children), child care, crime, commercial fraud (criminal), commercial fraud (civil), clinical negligence/disciplinary, medical law, environment, general common law, personal injuries. Interesting cases: Southern Water Authority v Nature Conservancy Council [1992] 3 AER 481, HL (environmental damage/The Wildlife & Countryside Act); Cutter v Eagle Star Insurance 1998 4 AER 417 (HL) (definition of "road": motor insurance); Re C (deceased) [1995] 2 FLR 24 (Inheritance Act – financial provision for illegitimate daughter); Re P [1995] 1 FLR 831 (international child abduction); Wicks v Wicks (C.A) [1998] 1 FLR 470 (matrimonial financial relief: interim lump sum and transfer of property orders); I v I 2001 1 FLR 913 (concurrent habitual residence: divorce); re X and Y 2001 FLR (leave to remove children from the jurisdiction and s1(5) of the Children Act; R v Curtis Howard (the Gatwick Airport 'Body in Boot case'); prosecution counsel case of Regina v Sion Jenkins (the murder of 'Billie Jo') [1998]; R v Ron Brown (case of the MP's mistress's knickers).
Prof. Memberships: South Eastern Circuit (Committee Member); Chairman, Sussex Sessions Bar Mess; Chairman, Sussex Courts Liaison Committee 1993; Member Area Criminal Justice Liaison Committee 16.
Career: Call 1970, Silk 1992. Recorder 1993. Deputy High Court Judge, Family Division.
Personal: Educated at Lincoln College, Oxford (MA Juris).

PRATT, Duncan
6 Pump Court London (020) 7583 6013
Recommended in Clinical Negligence

PRENTICE, Dan
Erskine Chambers (Robin Potts QC) London (020) 7242 5532
Recommended in Company

PRESCOTT, Peter QC
8 New Square (Michael Fysh QC) London (020) 7405 4321
clerks@8newsquare.co.uk
Recommended in Intellectual Property, Media & Entertainment
Specialisation: A specialist in all aspects of intellectual property law; has been involved in numerous reported cases, recent examples include: British Horseracing Board v William Hill; HFC v HSBC; Cantor Fitgerald v Tradition; Biogen v Medeva; Chiron v Murex. For comprehensive CV and list of recent cases, visit our website at www.8newsquare.co.uk.
Prof. Memberships: Intellectual Property Bar Association (IPBA); The Intellectual Property Lawyers Organisation (TIPLO).
Career: Called 1970; QC 1990; deputy high court judge.
Publications: 'Modern Law of Copyright' 2000 and 'Data Processing and the Law' 1984. Contributions to 'European Intellectual Property Review' include Towards a small claims patent court 10 EIPR 246.
Personal: Born 1943. Educated at Dulwich College; University College, London (BSc Physics); Queen Mary College (MSc Nuclear Engineering).

PREVEZER, Susan QC
Essex Court Chambers (Gordon Pollock QC) London (020) 7813 8000
Recommended in Insolvency/Corporate Recovery
Specialisation: Main area of practice covers insolvency, commercial litigation, property law, company law. Major litigation includes BCCI. Millwall FC, Levitt, Emlico, KWELM, contributor to Lightman and Moss on Receivers.
Prof. Memberships: Commercial Bar Association. Chancery Bar Association.
Career: Called to Bar 1983. Seven years at Michael Crystal QC's Chambers. Joined present chambers 1997 (December).

PRICE, James QC

5 Raymond Buildings (Patrick Milmo QC) London (020) 7242 2902

Recommended in Defamation

Specialisation: Defamation, breach of confidence, contempt, media-related human rights, publishing, media copyrights, general commercial and common law. Recent libel cases include Reynolds v Times Newspapers; Aitken v Guardian and Granada; Hamilton v Fayed; Gaddafi v Telegraph Group; Marco Pierre White v Anthony Allan; Monty Norman v Times Newspapers; McPhilemy v Times Newspapers; Branson v Bower. Breach of confidence: John Bryan v Mirror Group (photographs of Duchess of York); Service Corporation International v Channel Four (covert film inside funeral home).
Prof. Memberships: Inner Temple.
Career: Call 1974. QC 1995.
Personal: Born 1948.

PRICE, Nicholas QC

3 Raymond Buildings (Clive Nicholls QC) London (020) 74006400
chambers@3raymondbuilding.com

Recommended in Crime

Specialisation: Criminal law, paricularly murder, corporate manslaughter (Herald of Free Enterprise), rape, blackmail, armed robbery; commercial crime-fraud: corporate, leasing mortgage; public corruption cases; public enquiries (the Guildford and Woolwich Enquiry by Sir John May).
Prof. Memberships: Bencher, Gray's Inn 2000-; Member of the Mental Health Review Tribunal; Member of the Professional Standards Committee.
Career: Called to the Bar in November 1968. Took silk in 1992. Recorder of the Crown Court since 1987. Vice-Chairman of Gray's Inn Continuing Education/ Advocacy Training Committee. Facilitator for the Bar Human Rights Course.

PRICE, Roderick

Tooks Court Chambers (Michael Mansfield QC) London (020) 7405 8828

Recommended in Crime

Specialisation: Specialises in criminal defence work with particular emphasis on fraud, drug trafficking and murder cases. Consistently appeared in leading reported cases which have established important principles in complex areas of the criminal law. More recent cases include R v Ball and Others [1999] (fraudulent trading); R v Cajee [1999] (murder); R v Elias [1998] (conspiracy to defraud); R v Harding [1998] (armed robber received six mandatory life terms – leave to appeal granted specifically to test recommended tariffs in respect of mandatory life sentences); R v Avis [1997] (sentencing guidelines in firearms cases); R v Jones and Barham [1997] (conditional admissability rule in conspiracy and joint enterprise cases); R v Gray and Liggins [1995] (insider dealing); R v Preston [1994] (interception of telecommunications).
Prof. Memberships: Criminal Bar Association.
Career: Called to the Bar 1971, Inner Temple.
Personal: Interests include sailing, badminton and cricket.

PRICE OBE, Richard QC

Littleton Chambers (Michel Kallipetis QC) London (020) 7797 8600
rmp@priceqc.co.uk

Recommended in Media & Entertainment

Specialisation: Principal areas of entertainment and media law experience include film, video and music rights and financing disputes, copyright infringement and piracy, the 'fair dealing' provisions of copyright law (BBC v British Sky Broadcasting Ltd. 1991 re: World Cup Football broadcasts), Anton Piller and Mareva injunctions, and corporate/partnership disputes within the entertainment industry. Clients have included major film and music production and distribution companies and broadcasters, and leading artists, directors and producers. Also specialises in election and administrative law, professional negligence and commercial contract work and mediation.
Prof. Memberships: COMBAR, London Common Law and Commercial Bar Association, PNBA.
Career: Called to the Bar in 1969. Joined present Chambers in 1987, having previously been a member of Chambers of the late Lewis Hawser QC. Appointed QC 1996. Accredited CEDR mediator 1997.
Personal: Educated at King Edward VII School, Sheffield, and King's College London.

PRIDAY, Charles

7 King's Bench Walk (Jeremy Cooke QC) London (020) 7910 8300

Recommended in Shipping

Specialisation: Principal areas of practice are shipping, banking, insurance and general commercial work, acting for shipowners, charterers, oil traders, other commodity traders, banks, insurance companies and brokers. Reported shipping cases of note include: charterparty dispute, the Nour (1999), the Anangel Express (1996), the Ulyanovsk (1990); laytime, the Petr Shmidt (1998), the Agamemnon (1998), the Kyzicos (1989); jurisdiction, the Maciej Rataj (1995), the Deichland (1990).
Prof. Memberships: London Maritime Arbitration Association.
Career: Called to the Bar and joined Seven King's Bench Walk in 1982.

PRINCE, Christopher

New Court Chambers (David Robson QC) Newcastle upon Tyne (0191) 232 1980

Recommended in Crime

PROSSER, Kevin QC

Pump Court Tax Chambers London (020) 7414 8080

Recommended in Tax

Specialisation: Principal area of practice is Revenue law, including litigation. Co-author of Potter and Prosser, 'Tax Appeals' (Sweet & Maxwell).
Career: Called to the Bar 1982 and joined present chambers in 1983. Took Silk in 1996. Became Recorder in 2000.
Personal: Was once expelled from Tanzania for spying.

PROUDMAN, Sonia QC

11 New Square (Sonia Proudman QC) London (020) 7831 0081

Recommended in Chancery, Charities

Specialisation: Area of work: general chancery litigation and advice, with particular emphasis on trusts, charities, bankers' securities and all aspects of property law. Considerable experience in pursuing and in defending breach of trust claims, involving private, charitable and commercial trusts. Also professional negligence.
Prof. Memberships: Chancery Bar Association, STEP, Charity Law Association.
Career: Called to the Bar (Lincoln's Inn) 1972. (Kennedy Scholar, Buchanan Prize). Joined Chambers at 11 New Square in 1974. Took silk in 1994. Bencher 1996. Assistant Recorder 1996. Recorder 2000.
Personal: Born 1949; Married 1987, 1 daughter. Educated at St Paul's Girls' School and Lady Margaret Hall Oxford. BA 1st Class Hons 1971, Eldon Law Scholar 1973, MA 1973. Member Oxford University Law Faculty Advisory Panel 2000.

PRYNNE, Andrew QC

2 Harcourt Buildings (Roger Henderson QC) London (020) 7583 9020
aprynne@harcourt.co.uk

Recommended in Product Liability

Specialisation: General common and commercial law practice with an emphasis on product liability (principally pharmaceuticals), insurance disputes, clinical negligence, personal injury, railway law and employment matters. Notable cases include the MMR litigation for Merck (1999-00); the Benzane litigation for Terra Nitrogen Ltd; the tobacco lung cancer litigation for Imperial Tobacco (1999), the Lariam litigation for Roche Products (1999), the Opren litigation for Eli Lilly from 1986, the Clapham Accident Inquiry for British Railways Board (BRB) (1989), the Benzodiazepine litigation for Roche Products Ltd (1990-92), the Severn Tunnel Accident Enquiry for BRB 1992 and Crizzle v Board of Governors of St. Matthias School (EAT, 1993 – race discrimination). Advised BRB and Railtrack on safety implications and legal duties arising from privatisation. Member of the Lord Chancellor's Working Group on Multi-Party Actions. CEDR Accredited Mediator. Assistant Boundary Commissioner.
Prof. Memberships: South Eastern Circuit.
Career: Called to the Bar 1975 and tenant at King's Bench Walk 1976-78 and then joined current chambers.
Personal: Educated at Marlborough College and Southampton University (LL.B, Hons). Born 28 May 1953. Interests: sailing, shooting and skiing.

PRYOR, Michael

9 Old Square (Michael Driscoll QC) London (020) 7405 4682

Recommended in Professional Negligence

Specialisation: Barrister specialising in property and general commercial Chancery litigation, including real property disputes, landlord and tenant, professional negligence, mortgages and other securities, contentious probate. Cases include the Nationwide Managed Litigation, reported in part as Nationwide v Balmer Radmore [1999] Lloyds Rep PN 241, the Paragon Finance plc Managed Litigation against various solicitors and surveyors during 2000, Edwin Shirley Production Limited v Workspace plc [2001] 23 EG 158, Aubergine Enterprises Ltd v Lakewood International Ltd [2001] EGCS 29.
Career: Qualified 1992.
Personal: University of Newcastle upon Tyne (LLB). Born 1969.

PUGH, Charles

Old Square Chambers (John Hendy QC) London (020) 7269 0300
read@oldsquarechambers.co.uk

Recommended in Environment, Health & Safety

Specialisation: Representing both claimants and defendants, principal areas of practice are pollution/nuisance claims, accident claims (rail, aviation, work place) and statutory crime in health and safety/environmental fields. Recently reported cases include Wadey v Surrey CC, HL, 2000 (interest on damages); Hunter v Canary Wharf, HL, 1998 (leading case on nuisance); Underwood v British Midland, CA, 1996 (injury damages, principles of assessment). Current litigation includes multi-party 'dust nuisance' action (for major plc); statutory appeal against variation of consents (for numerous companies); multi-party toxic occupational exposure; numerous carbon monoxide poisoning claims; advising plc's being prosecuted for health and safety and/or environmental offences; multi-party pharmaceutical product liability. Co-author of 'Toxic Torts' (2nd edn 1995).

PUGH, Vernon QC

2-3 Gray's Inn Square (Anthony Porten QC & Anthony Scrivener QC) London (020) 7242 4986

Recommended in Planning

Specialisation: Town and country planning; local government law; environmental law; common law – professional negligence and personal injury; international law/extradition.
Prof. Memberships: Local Government and Planning Bar.
Career: LL.B (UCW); LLM (Cantab); University Lecturer in Property, Commercial & Planning; Hardwicke Scholar; Sir Thomas Moore Bursary; Bencher Lincoln's Inn; Crown Court Recorder.
Personal: Married, three daughters. Chairman, International Rugby Football Board. Director Rugby World Cup. IOC Federation Member.

PUGH-SMITH, John
Eldon Chambers (Lionel Read QC) London
(020) 7583 1355
clerks@eldonchambers.co.uk
Recommended in Environment

Specialisation: Planning, local government, environmental and parliamentary matters.
Prof. Memberships: Planning and Environment Bar Association (Former Committee Member), United Kingdom Environmental Law Association, Environmental Law Foundation, Fellow, Society of Antiquaries of London.
Career: Called to the Bar 1977. Joined current Chambers 1984.
Publications: Publications for Sweet & Maxwell include 'Neighbours and the Law' (1st to 3rd Editions: 1988 to 2001), 'Archaeology at Law' (1996). Joint Editorial Adviser for 'Property and Compensation Reports' and 'Planning Law Case Reports'. General Editor 'Environmental Law' (Oxford University Press) (2000).
Personal: Born 1954. Lives, mainly, in Norfolk.

PURCHAS, Christopher QC
Crown Office Chambers (Michael Spencer QC & Christopher Purchas QC) London (020) 7797 8600
purchas@crownofficechambers.com
Recommended in Personal Injury

Specialisation: Personal injury, professional and clinical negligence, general insurance law, fire claims, sports injury, highway authority claims, product liability. Recent cases include: Wells v Wells; Page v Sheerness Steel; Heil v Rankin; Griffin v Kingsmill; Doyle v Wallace; Mighell v Reading & MBI; Carroll v Dunlop; Fitzgerald v Ford.
Prof. Memberships: LCLCBA, PIBA.
Career: Called to the Bar 1966. Appointed Recorder 1986. Silk 1990. Deputy High Court Judge 1999.
Personal: Marlborough College 1957-61, Trinity College Cambridge 1962-65. Leisure pursuits golf tennis and shooting. Born 20 June 1943. Lives in Surrey.

PURCHAS, Robin QC
2 Harcourt Buildings (Gerard Ryan QC) London
(020) 7353 8415
Recommended in Local Government, Planning

Specialisation: Principal areas of practice are parliamentary, planning and local government work, compulsory purchase (including Hong Kong and Privy Council), compensation, public and administrative, environmental and human rights law. Recent cases include Prudential Assurance v Waterloo Real Estate 1999 CA; Fletcher v SSE 2000 HL; R v Newbury DC ex p Chieveley PC 1998 CA; English Property Corp v Kingston upon Thames BC 1998 CA; R v SSE ex p Somerfield Stores 1998 DC; Pye v Kingswood DC 1998 CA; Pickering v Kettering BC 1996 CA; Bolton MBC v SSE 1995 HL; Wards v Barclays Bank plc 1994 CA; R v Forbes 2000 HL; Burke v LB Hammersmith 2000 CA; Pepper Street Developments v Staffs CC 2000 CA. Major works promotions include West Coast main Line, Channel Tunnel Rail Link and the Channel Tunnel.
Prof. Memberships: Parliamentary Bar Mess; Bar European Group, Planning and Environment Bar Association; Administrative Law Bar Association; South Eastern and the Bar European Circuit. Chairman, Education and Training Committee 2001.
Career: Called to the Bar in 1968 and joined Harcourt Buildings in 1969. Took silk in 1987. Appointed Recorder in 1989; Deputy High Court Judge 1994; Master of Bench Inner Temple 1996; Bar Council 2000.
Personal: Educated at Marlborough College and Trinity College, Cambridge (Senior Exhibitioner). Born 12 June 1946.

PURLE, Charles QC
New Square Chambers (John Mowbray QC & Eben Hamilton QC) London (020) 7419 8000
Recommended in Chancery, Company, Fraud

PURNELL, Nicholas QC
23 Essex Street (Michael Lawson QC) London
(020) 7413 0353
nicholaspurnell@23essexstreet.co.uk
Recommended in Crime, Fraud

Specialisation: Principal area of practice is criminal law, particularly commercial fraud. Work includes financial regulatory and professional disciplinary tribunals. Member of the Lord Chancellor's Advisory Committee on Legal Education and Conduct 1991-97. Member of the Criminal Committee Judicial Studies Board 1991-96.
Prof. Memberships: South Eastern Circuit. Fellow, Society for Advanced Legal Studies; Fellow, Institute of Continuing Professional Development.
Career: Called to the Bar 1968. Prosecuting Counsel, Inland Revenue 1977-79. Treasury Counsel 1979-85. Took Silk in 1985. Recorder since 1986. Bencher of the Middle Temple since 1990.
Personal: Educated at the Oratory School 1958-62 and King's College, Cambridge 1963-66 (MA). Governor of the Oratory School. Born 29 January 1944.

PURVIS, Iain
11 South Square (Christopher Floyd QC) London
(020) 7405 1222
Recommended in Intellectual Property

Specialisation: All aspects of intellectual property. Reported cases include Gerber v Lectra (patent damages); United Biscuits v ASDA (Penguin/Puffin 'own brand' dispute); Mark Wilkinson v Woodcraft (design right – furniture); Designers Guild v Russell Williams (Copyright – fabric designs); VISX v Nidek (patent infringement – eye surgery); Fylde Microsystems v Key Radio (copyright – computer software).
Prof. Memberships: IPBA member.
Career: MA Cantab; BCL Oxon. 14 years practice in this field, including sitting as arbitrator.
Publications: Co-editor of 'Working with Technology'.
Personal: Married. Three children. Skiing, sailing, watching football and exploring prehistoric monuments.

PYE, M Jayne
Sovereign Chambers (Geoffrey C. Marson QC) Leeds (0113) 245 1841
sovereignchambers@btinternet.com
Recommended in Family

Specialisation: All aspects of family breakdown, particularly financial and children. Much experience in public law matters representing local authority, Guardian ad Litem and parents.
Prof. Memberships: Family Law Bar Association.
Career: Called May 1995. Previously practised as family law solicitor for 10 years when member of Children and Young Persons Act, later Children Act, Law Society Specialist Panel.

PYMONT, Christopher QC
Maitland Chambers (Michael Lyndon-Stanford QC & Charles Aldous QC) London (020) 7406 1200
Recommended in Banking, Chancery

Specialisation: Practice encompasses company, landlord and tenant, banking, commercial chancery and insolvency matters.
Prof. Memberships: Chancery Bar Association.
Career: Called to the Bar 1979 and joined 13 Old Square in 1980 (now merged in Maitland Chambers). Appointed QC 1996.
Personal: Educated at Marlborough College and Christ Church, Oxford (MA). Born 16 March 1956.

QUINT, Francesca
11 Old Square (J. Simeon Thrower) London
(020) 7242 5022
Recommended in Charities

QURESHI, Shamim
Queen Square Chambers (Anthony Donne QC & T Alun Jenkins QC) Bristol (0117) 921 1966
Recommended in Crime

RABINOWITZ, Laurence
One Essex Court (Lord Grabiner QC) London
(020) 7583 2000
Recommended in Banking, Commercial (Litigation), Company, Energy & Natural Resources, Fraud

Specialisation: Regulatory matters, banking, insurance, professional negligence, financial services, oil and gas, computer, and other commercial disputes. Recent cases include: Alcock UK v Phildrew Nominees Ltd & UBS; Shell and Esso v Enterprise; BP and others v Corby Power Limited, Amoco (UK) Exploration Co v Teesside Gas Transportation Limited and Enron Corp; Total Gas Marketing Ltd v ARCO British Ltd & Ors; IBM v Sagem; B & C v Atlantic and others; Evans v Gov. of Brockhill prisons; Marsh & McLennan Companies UK Ltd v Pensions Ombudsman & Anor; Grovit & Ors v Turner. Acting and appearing in major banking and insurance disputes, e.g., Kuwait Shipping v UBS; Alcock & Ors v UBS and Phillips and Drew; Lloyds Bank and Abby National v Lee and Ors. Acting and appearing in major financial services disputes, e.g., AIG International v FirstR and Bank; Decaril and Ors v Prudential Bache International Bank Ltd. Acting in relation to railway industry disputes.
Prof. Memberships: Member of Middle Temple.
Career: One Essex Court 1987. Junior counsel for the crown, Chancery (1995).
Personal: BA LLB (Wits). BA BCL (Oxon). Rhodes Scholar (1983, South Africa).

RADCLIFFE, Andrew QC
2 Hare Court (Stephen Kramer QC) London
(020) 7353 5324
Recommended in Crime

Specialisation: General criminal law, prosecuting and defending, with particular emphasis on commercial fraud. Recent cases include R v Cowan, Gayle, Ricciardi (1996) 1 Cr App R 1; R v Sec State for Home Dept and Director of Serious Fraud Office ex p Fininvest spa (1997) 1 Cr App R 257; R v Graham (H.K.) and others (1997) 1 Cr App R 302, B v DPP (2000) 2 WLR 452 HL.
Prof. Memberships: Criminal Bar Association.
Career: Called 1975. Joined present Chambers 1990. QC 2000.
Personal: Educated St. Edmund Hall, Oxford.

RADEVSKY, Anthony
Falcon Chambers (Jonathan Gaunt QC & Kim Lewison QC) London (020) 7353 2484
radevsky@falcon-chambers.com
Recommended in Property Litigation

Specialisation: Landlord and tenant law relating to commercial and residential property, leasehold enfranchisement, rent review, dilapidations and service charges. Also handles mortgages, specific performance of contracts for the sale of land, restrictive covenants and professional negligence claims against solicitors and surveyors.
Prof. Memberships: Chancery Bar Association, Property Bar Association.
Career: Called to the Bar 1978 and joined Falcon Chambers in 1998.
Publications: 'Service of Documents' (Longman, 2nd edn, 1989); 'Drafting Pleadings' (Tolley, 2nd edn 1995); 'Hague on Leasehold Enfranchisement' (Sweet & Maxwell, 3rd edn 1999); 'Tenants' Right of First Refusal' (Butterworths, 2001).
Personal: Educated at Alleyn's School, Dulwich 1966-73 and Southampton University 1974-77 (LLB, Hons). Born 22 August 1955.

RAESIDE, Mark
Atkin Chambers (Robert Akenhead QC) London
(020) 7404 0102
Recommended in Construction, Professional Negligence

Specialisation: English High Court and both international ICC; LCIA and domestic arbitrations (mediations adjudications); FIDIC, ICE and JCT contracts in most European countries, Africa, Middle and Far East. Cases

including hotels, shipping centres, dams, river and road projects, bridges, power stations, car factory and other developments under English, French, Swiss, Spanish, Swedish, German, Italian, Polish, Egyptian, Turkish, Chinese and Tansanian law. Claims include defects, loss and expense and all related construction issues, professional negligence and fraud together with computer cases.
Career: Called to Middle Temple 1982.
Personal: B.A., M.Phil, (Cantab.).

RAGGATT, Timothy QC
4 King's Bench Walk (Timothy Raggatt QC) London (020) 7353 3581
Recommended in Crime
Specialisation: Undertakes crime and fraud. Regina v Bartlet: defence of the managing director of computer leasing company in £30 million fraud 1995/6. The client was granted bail as the largest surety ever fixed by an English Court. R v Canon (murder of Shirley Banks). Regina v Richards: 54 day bank fraud defence. Dartmoor Prison Riots, "Sleepwalker" murder in Stafford. Prosecuted R v Myles and others: the largest murder trial in the West Midlands since the Birmingham bombings. Prosecuted R v Cotter & Ors: the bogus race conspiracy case surrounding Ashia Hansen and other athletes. R v Trigwell: the 'Black Widow'.
Career: Called to the Bar, 1972. Took silk 1993. Member of 3 Fountain Court Chambers Birmingham until 1994 (still door tenant) now member of 4 King's Bench Walk (Head of Chambers) London EC4. Criminal Bar Association. Midlands and Oxford Circuit. Bencher Inner Temple, 1999.
Personal: Golf. Scuba Diving.

RAHMAN, Y
Oriel Chambers (A Sander) Liverpool (0151) 236 7191/ 236 4321
Recommended in Personal Injury
Specialisation: All aspects of personal injury including clinical negligence and industrial disease. Appeared in Griffin v Mersey Regional Ambulance Service NHS Trust [1998] PIQR p34; Jones and Another v Telford and Wrekin Council, The Times 29 June 1999. Recently involved in occupational rhinitis litigation in Merseyside on behalf of defendants.
Prof. Memberships: Personal Injury Bar Association.
Career: Northgate High School, Ipswich. Trinity College, Oxford BA (Hons) Chemistry, Polytechnic of Central London Diploma in Law. Called Gray's Inn October 1991.

RAILTON, David QC
Fountain Court (Anthony Boswood QC) London (020) 7583 3335
Recommended in Banking, Commercial (Litigation), Insurance
Specialisation: Commercial disputes, in particular banking, insurance and professional negligence. Cases include Banque Bruxelles Lambert v Eagle Star [1995] 1 IRLR 17, Assitalia v Overseas Union Insurance [1995] 1 IRLR 76, Bates v Barrow [1995] 1 LLR 680, O'Brien v Hughes Gibbs [1995] 1 IRLR 90, CTI v Oceanus [1984] 1 LLR 476, RPPC v Bank Leumi [1992] 1 LLR 513, Sumitomo Bank v BBL [1997] 1 LLR 487, Federal Republic of Nigeria v Abacha [2001], Gan v Tai Ping [2001].
Career: Balliol College, Oxford (BA Jurisprudence, first class). Called Gray's Inn 1979; QC, 1996; tenant Fountain Court since 1980. Recorder 2000.
Personal: Born 1957; resides London.

RAINEY, Simon QC
4 Essex Court (Nigel Teare QC) London (020) 7653 5653
strainey@4sx.co.uk
Recommended in Shipping
Specialisation: Simon Rainey's practice centres on shipping and international commerce and he practises almost exclusively in the Commercial and Admiralty Courts as well as in maritime commercial arbitration in London and in commodity trade arbitrations before the major trade associations. He has been consistently singled out over the past five years in the specialist directories as one of the leading shipping practitioners.
Prof. Memberships: Member of COMBAR; supporting member of LMAA.
Career: Called to the Bar in 1982; took silk 2000; appointed Recorder of the Crown Court 2001.

RAMPTON, Richard QC
1 Brick Court (Richard Rampton QC) London (020) 7353 8845
clerks@1brickcourt.co.uk
Recommended in Defamation
Specialisation: Defamation, confidence, contempt of court and media related law generally. Cases include: Lucas-Box v Associated Newspapers; Atkinson v Fitzwalter; Control Risks v New English Library; Telnikoff v Matusevich; Shah v Standard Chartered Bank; Aldington v Tolstoy; McDonald's Corp v Steel and Morris; Irving v Lipstadt and Penguin Books.
Career: Educated at Bryanston and The Queen's College, Oxford. Called to the Bar in 1965, took Silk in 1987.
Publications: 'Duncan & Neill on Defamation' ed, with Sir Brian Neill; 2nd edn (1983); 3rd edn (imminent).
Personal: Speaks French, some Italian and German.

RAMSEY, Vivian QC
Keating Chambers (Richard Fernyhough QC) London (020) 7544 2600
clerks@keatingchambers.com
Recommended in Arbitration (International), Construction
Specialisation: Building and construction law; professional negligence; arbitration, including international arbitration; energy.
Career: Qualified 1979; Middle Temple; QC 1992; Assistant Recorder 1998; Recorder 2000; chartered engineer; member of Institution of Civil Engineers 1976; graduate engineer Ove Arup & Partners, London Middle East 1972-77. Arbitrator (domestic and international, including ICC) 1988 to date; special professor, department of Civil Engineering, University of Nottingham 1990 to date.
Publications: Joint editor 'Construction Law Journal'; joint author 'Keating on Building Contracts' (7th Edition) 2000.
Personal: Harley School, Rochester, USA; Abingdon School; Oriel College Oxford; City University (1972 MA, 1978 Dip Law, C Eng MICE). Born 1950; resides Swanley Village.

RANDALL, John QC
St Philip's Chambers (John Randall QC) Birmingham (0121) 246 7000
clerks@st-philips.co.uk
Recommended in Chancery, Commercial (Litigation), Insolvency/Corporate Recovery
Specialisation: Principal areas of practice are chancery and commercial law, companies, corporate insolvency, judicial review, professional negligence, real property.
Prof. Memberships: Midland and Oxford Circuit; International Bar Association; Chancery Bar Association; Midland Chancery and Commercial Bar Association.
Career: Called Lincoln's Inn 1978; Bar of New South Wales 1979; Silk 1995; Assistant Recorder 1995; Deputy Head of Chambers 1998. Recorder 1999. Deputy High Court Judge 2000. Member, Legal Services Consultative Panel 2000. Head of Chambers 2001. London Chambers: Maitland Chambers Charles Aldous QC and Michael Lindon-Stanford QC/Stone Buildings and Lincolns Inn (020) 7406 1200).
Personal: Born 1956. Educated at Rugby School, Loomis Institute, Conn. USA and Jesus College, Cambridge (MA).

RANDALL, Louise
Keating Chambers (Richard Fernyhough QC) London (020) 7544 2600
lrandall@keatingchambers.com
Recommended in Construction
Specialisation: Construction, engineering and professional negligence.
Career: Qualified 1988; Middle Temple.
Personal: Keele University (BA Hons). Born 1964; resides London.

RANDALL, Nicholas
Devereux Chambers (Jeffrey Burke QC) London (020) 7353 7534
randall@devchambers.co.uk
Recommended in Employment
Specialisation: Broad range of employment and pensions work undertaken for both employers and trade unions. Has appeared at all levels from tribunals up to the House of Lords. Reported cases include Wilson v St. Helens MBC [1998] ICR 114; Credit Suisse v Lister [1998] IRLR 700; Knowles v FBU [1997] ICR 595; TSC v Massey [1999] IRLR 22 and Wild v The Pensions Ombudsman [1996] OPLR 129. Also practices in the fields of VAT and general commercial work.
Prof. Memberships: Employment Law Bar Association. Association of Pension Lawyers.
Career: Part-time lecturer in labour law at LSE (1990-93).
Publications: A contributing editor of Harvey on Industrial Relations and Employment Law and author of Halsbury's Laws Pensions Volume.
Personal: Football, cricket and jazz.

RANDOLPH, Fergus
Brick Court Chambers (Christopher Clarke QC) London (020) 7379 3550
randolph@brickcourt.co.uk
Recommended in Competition/Anti-trust
Specialisation: All aspects of EC law, including trade, competition, commercial agency, shipping and agriculture/ fisheries. Recent reputed case: Chequepoint Sarl v McClelland – security for costs – discrimination on grounds of nationality. [1996] 3 WLR 341; R v SS for Transport ex parte: Factortame [2000] EULR 40; B & I v Sealink [1992] 5CMLR 255.
Career: Harrow School: 1975-79. Buckingham University/ Aix en Provence. Called to the Bar 1985. Stagaire Commission legal service: 1988.

RANKIN, James
3 Raymond Buildings (Clive Nicholls QC) London (020) 7400 6400
chambers@3raymondbuildings.com
Recommended in Licensing
Specialisation: All aspects of licensing law including liquor, public entertainment, betting and gaming and bingo. Regularly appears on behalf of applicants and objectors (including police and local authorities) at Magistrates' Courts, Crown Courts and Town Halls throughout the UK. Advises in lotteries and competitions.
Career: Called to the Bar 1983. Joined Raymond Buildings (Formerly Queen Elizabeth Building) in 1984.
Personal: Educated at Eton and Buckingham University LLB (Hons) 1982.

RAWLEY, Alan D QC
35 Essex Street (Christopher Wilson-Smith QC) London (020) 7353 6381
Recommended in Fraud
Specialisation: Commercial Fraud (Guinness; Blue Arrow et al); Contempt of Court (In Re Lonrho HL (1989); OFT v Norris (1995)); Civil liability of the Police (Hill v Chief Constable of West Yorkshire; Rogers v Chief Constable of Dorset; and many cases involving issues of false imprisonment and malicious prosecution); Medical Negligence (Aboul-Hosn).
Prof. Memberships: Western Circuit; Commercial and Common Law Bar Association; Criminal Bar Association.
Career: Middle Temple; called June 1958; Bencher 1985; Silk 1977; Bar Council and Senate; Deputy Chairman Cornwall Quarter Sessions 1971; A Recorder of the Crown Court 1972 to December 31, 1999; Member CICB; CICAP 2000-; Fellow Commoner, Magdalene Col-

lege, Cambridge, since 1991.
Personal: Educated at Wimbledon College and Brasenose College, Oxford (MA). Served with RTR (Nat Serv) 1956-58.

RAYNER JAMES, Jonathan QC

Hogarth Chambers (Jonathan Rayner James QC & Christopher Morcom QC) London (020) 7404 0404 barristers@hogarthchambers.com

Recommended in Media & Entertainment

Specialisation: Principal areas of practice are media and entertainment law and intellectual property law, in particular contract, licensing, confidence, copyright, design rights, performers' rights, trade marks and passing off. Advisory and litigation. Specialisation in EC aspects.
Prof. Memberships: Member of the Chancery Bar Association, Intellectual Property Bar Association and the International Association of Entertainment Lawyers.
Career: Commenced practice in 1975, having been called to the Bar in 1971. Appointed Silk in 1988. Recorder since 1998.
Publications: Co-editor of 'Copinger and Skone James' on copyright since 1980. Joint Consulting Editor for 'The Encyclopaedia of Forms and Precedents' (entertainment). Member of Editorial Board of 'Entertainment Law Review'.
Personal: Born 26th July 1950. Educated at King's College School, Wimbledon 1961-68, Christ's College, Cambridge 1968-72 (MA, LLM) and Brussels University 1972-73 (Lic. spéc. Droit Européen). Fluent in French. Lives in London.

READ, Graham

Devereux Chambers (Jeffrey Burke QC) London (020) 7353 7534

Recommended in Environment

Specialisation: Commercial, Professional Negligence, Property (including Construction) and Environmental Law. Examples of more recently reported decisions include Reay v BNFL (1994) 1 MLR 1; Agrafax Public Relations v USS Inc Times 22nd May 1995; R v Sec State for Trade and Industry ex p Dudridge Times 26th October 1995; Ngcobo v Thor Times 10th November 1995; R v Greenwich LBC ex p Williams Times 29th December 1995; Sonardyne Limited v Firth (1997) EGCS 84; Connelly v RTZ Times 12th July 1996 (Court of Appeal) and (1998) AC 854; Lubbe v Cape (1998) CLC 155; Sithole v Thor Times 15th Febuary 1999 and Africa v Cape (2000) 1 Lloyds Law Report 139 and (House of Lords) [2000] 1 WCR 1545.
Prof. Memberships: Combar; Professional Negligence Bar Association.
Career: MA Trinity Hall, Cambridge; Arden Scholar Gray's Inn; called 1981.

READ, Lionel QC

Eldon Chambers (Lionel Read QC) London (020) 7583 1355

Recommended in Environment, Local Government, Planning

READHEAD, Simon

No. 1 Serjeants' Inn (Edward Faulks QC) London (020) 7415 6666 clerks@no1serjeantsinn.com

Recommended in Clinical Negligence

Specialisation: Principal areas of practice: clinical negligence (including dental negligence) for both claimants and defendants; professional negligence work (especially solicitors' and barristers' negligence in the areas of clinical negligence and personal injury); a wide range of personal injury work including industrial accidents and occupational diseases; health and safety work; public and administrative law including judicial review. Instructed in the last 12 months on behalf of claimants and defendants in a number of clinical negligence and personal injury cases involving very substantial claims. Expertise of and special interest in catastrophic injury claims including birth trauma, cerebral palsy, head injuries and spinal injuries. Regular speaker at seminars and conferences.
Prof. Memberships: Administrative Law Bar Association; Professional Negligence Bar Association; Personal Injury Bar Association, London Common Law and Commercial Bar Association, AVMA. Trained in mediation by ALARM. Member of the General Council of the Bar's Wasted costs panel.
Career: Called to the Bar in 1979. Appointed Recorder in 1995.
Personal: Educated Lincoln College, Oxford. BCL, MA. Lives in Richmond, Surrey.

REDFERN, Michael QC

28 St. John St Manchester (0161) 834 8418 clerk@28stjohnst.co.uk

Recommended in Clinical Negligence, Personal Injury

Specialisation: Clinical negligence (in particular cerebral palsy), brain injuries, spinal injuries (utmost severity), employers' liability, road traffic accidents.
Prof. Memberships: Personal Injury Bar Association, Northern Circuit Medical Law Association.
Career: Call 1970. Silk 1993. Recorder, Chairman Royal Liverpool Children's Enquiry December 1999 to January 2001.
Publications: Recent cases include: Wisniewski v Central Manchester Health Authority (1998) Lloyds Rep Med 223, (1996) 7 Medical LR 248; Stark v Post Office, (2000) PIQR 105, TLR 29 March 2000; Pickford v ICI (1998) 1 WLR 1189; Brown v Lewisham and North Southwark Health Authority (1999) 4 Lloyds Rep Med 110; Stephens v Doncaster Health Authority, Kemp Vol 3 para A4-107, (1996) 7 Medical LR 357.
Personal: Married to Her Honour Judge Eaglestone. All female household! Active rather than passive sports.

REED, Paul

Hardwicke Building (Nicholas Stewart QC) London (020) 7242 2523

Recommended in Construction

REED, Piers

3 Temple Gardens (John Coffey QC) London (020) 7353 3102

Recommended in Crime

Specialisation: Consumer/Regulatory work (eg) Trading Standards, Food Safety, Health & Safety at Work, defended Birse Construction Re fatal accident prosecution; defended SAPPI (UK) Ltd Re: environmental pollution prosecution; general defence work for MARS (UK) Ltd. Defence work generally from murder to fraud.
Prof. Memberships: Criminal Bar Association. Assistant Junior Herts & Beds Bar Mess. Bar Liason Member St Albans TIG Group.
Career: Called 1974. Member Lincoln's Inn and Northern Ireland Inns of Court. Approved Tutor for Lincoln's Inn continuing education programme.
Personal: Married with two daughters. Fanatic sports follower.

REES, Edward QC

Doughty Street Chambers (Geoffrey Robertson QC) London (020) 7404 1313

Recommended in Crime

Specialisation: Notable cases in which he has appeared include: the trial, appeal, civil litigation and Judicial Review proceedings of Winston Silcott; the M25 prison escape trial; the Whitemoor Prison breakout trial; the Essex "Range Rover" murder trial; the Orgreave Miners trial; the St. Paul's, Bristol riot trial; the 'Bradford Twelve' trial; the trial of Ron Brown M.P.; R v Ben & others – a serious VAT fraud; R v Howes & others – a serious gold fraud; Sharon Roberts (battered woman syndrome).

REES, Gareth

Hollis Whiteman Chambers (QEB) (Julian Bevan QC & Peter Whiteman QC) London (020) 7583 5766 grees@holliswhiteman.co.uk

Recommended in Crime, Fraud

Specialisation: Practice mainly concerned with company and commercial fraud including cases alleging market manipulation, fraudulent trading, mortgage fraud, company director offences (allegations relating to collapse of Johnson Mathey Bank reported as R v Snaresbrook Crown Court ex p Sipra), Customs diversion fraud (R v Hare 1997) and corruption. Frequently in cases prosecuted by the Serious Fraud Office. In 2001 represented three defendants in a prosecution by the Occupational Persons Regulatory Authority. In 2002 will be defending in the Jubilee line extension fraud (corruption fraud). Has continued to defend in murder cases (recently representing a profoundly deaf client) and sexual offences including rape of Austrian tourist at Kings Cross and the allegation of rape by 10 year old boys of a girl in their class. Junior counsel acting for Craig Charles (Red Dwarf) in rape allegations and defended in the Britt Ekland Rolex robbery. Has advised and has presented seminars to accountants, bankers and solicitors on Money Laundering, giving expert evidence and Inland Revenue practice on Search and Seizure prosecutions and on the criminal powers of the FSA. Has spoken and written on deaf people and the court process.
Prof. Memberships: Criminal Bar Association.
Career: Reading University BA. Bar exams 1979. Worked for Canadian Law firm and as journalist before beginning practice in 1981.

REES, John Charles QC

33 Park Place (John Charles Rees QC) Cardiff (029) 2023 3313

Recommended in Crime, Personal Injury

REES, Paul QC

1 Crown Office Row (Robert Seabrook QC) London (020) 7797 7500

Recommended in Clinical Negligence

REES, Philip

9 Park Place (Ian Murphy QC) Cardiff (029) 2038 2731

Recommended in Personal Injury

Specialisation: Personal Injury. Clinical Negligence. Trusts. Commercial. Landlord and Tenant.
Career: LL.B. (Hons) Bristol. Called 1965 (Middle Temple). Recorder of the Crown Court since 1983. Assistant Boundary Commissioner.
Personal: Music, Sport.

REESE, Colin QC

Atkin Chambers (Robert Akenhead QC) London (020) 7404 0120 clerks@atkinchambers.law.co.uk

Recommended in Arbitration (International)

Specialisation: All aspects of arbitration law but mainly concerned with domestic or international building, civil engineering, and associated professional negligence disputes as Counsel and Arbitrator.
Career: Recently engaged in complex employer/main contractor disputes arising from a luxury development in Gibralter – ICC arbitration and associated court proceedings in Gibralter, in employer/professional adviser disputes arising from lottery funded renovations of a theatre and a concert hall; and in enforcement proceedings in the Turks and Caicos Islands successfully upheld in the Privy Council following a Miami arbitration. So far as landmark reported decisions are concerned, can claim his share of the credit for the recognition of "Minter" interest (see: F.G. Minter Ltd. v Welsh Health Mechanical Services Organisation (1980) 13 BLR 1); the development of jurisprudence concerning sub-contractors name-borrowing arbitrations (see: Northern Regional Health Authority v Derek Crouch Construction Co. Ltd. [1984] QB 644 and Gordon Durham & Co. v Haden Young Ltd. (1990) 52 BLR 61); and the availability of Court ordered security for costs in international arbitrations (see Coppée Lavalin v Ken-Ren [1995] 1 AC 38).
Personal: Born 28 March 1950. Called to the Bar 1973. Silk 1987. FCI Arb (Chartered Arbitrator). Recorder/deputy judge of the Technology and Construction Court. Chairman TECBAR 2000.

REEVE, Matthew
4 Essex Court (Nigel Teare QC) London
(020) 7653 5653
mreeve@4sk.co.uk
Recommended in Aviation
Specialisation: Aviation, insurance and reinsurance, professional negligence and employment.
Prof. Memberships: Commercial Bar Association, Professional Negligence Bar Association.
Career: Magdalene College, Cambridge, BA Law 1984; MA 1988; Employed in the Solicitors' Department, Lloyd's of London 1986 and 1987; Called to the Bar 1987 (Inner Temple); Paul Methven, Duke of Edinburgh and Inner Temple Scholarships, Pegasus Scholarship.

REID, Paul Campbell QC
Lincoln House Chambers (Mukhtar Hussain QC) Manchester (0161) 832 5701
paul.reid@lincolnhse.co.uk
Recommended in Crime
Prof. Memberships: Criminal Bar Association.
Career: M.A. (Cantab.) (Engineering). Called to Bar 1973. Recorder 1993. Queen's Counsel 2001.
Personal: Born 27 March 1949. Educated at Merchant Taylors School, Crosby and Christ's College Cambridge (1968-72). Married with 2 children. Leisure interests include tennis, acoustic guitar and amateur dramatics.

REILLY, John
Tooks Court Chambers (Michael Mansfield QC) London (020) 7405 8828
Recommended in Crime

REYNOLDS, Adrian
No.1 High Pavement (John B. Milmo QC) Nottingham (0115) 941 8218
Recommended in Crime
Career: Called 1982. Recorder 2000

REYNOLDS, Kirk QC
Falcon Chambers (Jonathan Gaunt QC & Kim Lewison QC) London (020) 7353 2484
Recommended in Property Litigation
Specialisation: Called to the Bar 1974. Queen's Counsel 1993. Full-time practice as property law specialist at Falcon Chambers since 1975. Co-author 'The Handbook of Rent Review', 'The Renewal of Business Tenancies' and 'Dilapidations: the Modern Law and Practice'. Blundell memorial lecturer 1982, 1987 and 1993. Advisor to Royal Institution of Chartered Surveyors on arbitration practice and course tutor on official RICS training courses for arbitrators.
Prof. Memberships: Member of RICS Committee producing and revising official Guidance Notes for Arbitrators and Independent Experts. Appointed on a number of occasions by president of RICS and president of Law Society as arbitrator, and by arbitrators as legal assessor. Elected an honorary member of RICS in 1997.

RICH, Barbara
5 Stone Buildings (Henry Harrod) London
(020) 7242 6201
brich@5-stonebuildings.law.co.uk
Recommended in Pensions
Specialisation: Pensions, trusts, contentious probate and other succession disputes, administration of estates, Inheritance Act, Court of Protection. Highlights of the last year include Fuller v Strum Times 14 February 2001 (contentious probate – allegation of forgery); Stevens v Bell 2001 PLR 99 (Airways Pensions Scheme litigation); Braymist Ltd v Wise Finance Co Ltd Times 27 March 2001 (pre-incorporation contract for sale of land).
Prof. Memberships: Chancery Bar Association; Association of Pension Lawyers.
Career: 1991-date, practising at 5 Stone Buildings.
Publications: Member of editorial team of forthcoming edition of 'Heywood & Massey: Court of Protection Practice'.
Personal: Education: St Paul's Girls' School, London; Emmanuel College Cambridge (BA, MA); Polytechnic of Central London (Dip Law). Leisure interests include music, history, literature.

RICHARDS, David QC
Erskine Chambers (Robin Potts QC) London
(020) 7242 5532
Recommended in Banking, Company, Insolvency/Corporate Recovery
Specialisation: Company and corporate finance, insolvency and commercial. Recent contentious work includes Re Duckwari plc [1998] 3 WLR 913 (directors' liability), UMB v Doherty [1998] 1 WLR 435 (freezing orders), OR v Vass [1999] BCC 516, DTI v Stephen Hinchliffe and O.R. V. William Stern (directors' disqualification), Re Benfield Greig Group [2000] 2BCLC 488 and Re BAT Industries plc and Re Allied Domecq plc (opposed schemes of arrangement), Re Sedgefield Steeplechase ltd [2000] 2 BCLC 211, Jarvis plc and PcW [2000] 2 BCLC 368, Re Nottingham Forest plc, Queens Moat houses plc v Bairstow, Re AXA Equity and Law. Other recent work includes the demutualisations [2000] 1 BCLC 134 of the AA, Friends Provident and Scottish Life, Granada/Compass merger, Cable & Wireless HKT/Pacific Cyberworks merger (in Hong Kong), Allied Zurich plc reconstruction and Williams plc demerger.
Prof. Memberships: Chancery Bar Association, Commercial Bar Association.
Career: Trinity College, Cambridge (BA 1973, MA 1980).

RICHARDS, Jennifer
39 Essex Street (Nigel Pleming QC) London
(020) 7832 1111
clerks@39essex.co.uk
Recommended in Administrative & Public Law
Specialisation: Specialises in all aspects of public and administrative law, including local government, mental health, community care, health services, education and human rights. Practice also covers general commercial law (general contract, professional negligence and insurance) and discrimination law (with particular emphasis on disability discrimination). Editor of 'Crown Office Digest', co-author of the Social Services title of 'Halsbury's Laws of England' and contributor to R Gordon's 'Judicial Review: Practice and Procedure'. Co-author of forth coming book on 'Health Law and Public Law'.
Prof. Memberships: Administrative Law Bar Association, London Commercial and Common Law Bar Association, Community Care Practitioners Group.
Career: Called to the Bar 1991 and joined present chambers in 1992.
Personal: Educated at Clare College, Cambridge (BA (Hons) Law, 1st class) and at University of Toronto (Masters in Laws, specialist thesis on Canadian Charter of Rights and Freedoms).

RICHARDS, Jeremy
Octagon House Chambers (Andrew Lindqvist) Norwich (01603) 623186
Recommended in Family

RICHARDSON, James
Trinity Chambers (Toby Hedworth QC) Newcastle upon Tyne (0191) 232 1927
info@trinitychambers.co.uk
Recommended in Family
Specialisation: General commercial; ancillary relief; employment.
Career: Called 1982. Appointed Deputy District Judge 2001.

RIDDLE, Nicholas
14 Castle Street (Andrew Edis QC) Liverpool
(0151) 236 8240
nickriddle@14castlestreet.co.uk
Recommended in Chancery
Specialisation: General Chancery, recent cases: Halliwell v Cuozzo (1999, unreported), concerning the duties of a football pools collector; Webb v Chief Constable of Merseyside Police [2000] 2 W.L.R. 546, concerning application of proceeds of drug trafficking; Hardy & Co v Sorrentino (2000, unreported), concerning accountants' negligence. R.v P.I.A.O.B and Goss (judicial review of Ombudsman; decision about construction of policy).
Prof. Memberships: Chancery Bar Association. Northern Chancery Bar Association. Society for Computers and Law.
Career: Educated at The King's School, Canterbury; Gonville and Caius College. Practice in Liverpool Chancery Chambers, from 1972. Head of chambers from 1977, until merger with present chambers in 1996.
Personal: Leisure interests: reading, music, food, wine, travel.

RILEY-SMITH, Toby
2 Harcourt Buildings (Roger Henderson QC) London (020) 7583 9020
Recommended in Product Liability

RIORDAN, Kevin
Iscoed Chambers (Trefor Davies) Swansea (01792) 652988/9
Recommended in Crime

RIORDAN, Stephen QC
25-27 Castle Street (Stephen Riordan QC) Liverpool (0151) 236 5072
Recommended in Crime

RITCHIE, Jean QC
4 Paper Buildings (Jean Ritchie QC) London (020) 7353 3366
Recommended in Clinical Negligence
Specialisation: All aspects of clinical negligence, medical work, and personal injury work. Acts for claimants, trusts and authorities. Cases include Re F [1990]; De Martell v Merton and Sutton Health Authority [1993] and [1995]; Joyce v Merton, Sutton and Wandsworth Health Authority [1995] and [1996]; Corley v North West Hertfordshire Health Authority [1997]. Contributor to 'Safe Practice in Obstetrics and Gynaecology' (Ed. Clements) 1994.
Prof. Memberships: Professional Negligence Bar Association.
Career: Called to the Bar 1970. Silk 1992. Recorder 1993. Member of Supreme Court Rules Committee 1993-97. Chairman of Inquiry into care of Christopher Clunis 1993-94. Member of Judicial Studies Board 1998. Chairman of inquiry into quality and practice in the NHS, arising from actions of Rodney Ledward, 2000.
Personal: Kings College London (LL.B) and McGill University, Montreal (LL.M).

RITCHIE, Richard
24 Old Buildings (Martin Mann QC & Alan Steinfeld QC) London (020) 7404 0946
richard.ritchie@xxiv.co.uk
Recommended in Company, Insolvency/Corporate Recovery
Specialisation: Business and property litigation including insolvency (personal and corporate), directors' disqualification, civil fraud, company law, contract disputes, partnership law, property law and landlord and tenant.
Prof. Memberships: Chancery Bar Association, British Institute of International and Comparative Law.
Career: St. Catherine's College Oxford (BA), Standing Counsel to the DTI, Junior Counsel to the Crown (Chancery).

RITCHIE, Stuart
Littleton Chambers (Michel Kallipetis QC) London (020) 7797 8600
sritchie@littletonchambers.co.uk
Recommended in Employment
Specialisation: Principal areas of practice are employment law and general commercial law. Deals with a wide range of employment disputes, both in court and in tribunals. Principal areas of employment practice are restrictive convenants, garden leave, disputes involving breaches of fiduciary duty and contract and termination of employment generally. Familiar with obligations of

directors under ss212 and 214 of the Insolvency Act 1986. Tribunal work (applicant and respondent) includes unfair dismissal, transfers of undertakings, redundancy. Lectures to solicitors on employment law.
Prof. Memberships: ELBA, COMBAR, PNBA.
Career: Called 1995 (Middle).
Publications: Co-editor with John Bowers QC of Atkins Court Forms, Vol 38 (Trade and Labour); on the Editorial Board of the Civil Practitioner's Case Companion.
Personal: Diploma in Law, Christ Church, Oxford (BA Hons in Modern Languages – French and German). Interests include classical music and sport, in particular golf.

ROBERTS, Catherine
Erskine Chambers (Robin Potts QC) London (020) 7242 5532
Recommended in Company

ROBERTS, Jennifer
Queen Elizabeth Building (Florence Baron QC) London (020) 7797 7837
Recommended in Family
Specialisation: All aspects of family law with an emphasis on financial cases, especially those with an international aspect. Inheritance Act claims. Professional negligence arising out of matrimonial litigation.
Prof. Memberships: Family Law Bar Association. Member of the Western Circuit.
Career: LLB (Hons). Called 1988. Appointed Recorder 1999.

ROBERTS, Lisa
Lincoln House Chambers (Mukhtar Hussain QC) Manchester (0161) 832 5701
Recommended in Crime

ROBERTSON, Aidan
Brick Court Chambers (Christopher Clarke QC) London (020) 7379 3550
robertson@brickcourt.co.uk
Recommended in Competition/Anti-trust
Specialisation: Competition law, European Community law and public and administrative law. Important cases include R v Competition Commission and Secretary of State for Trade and Industry ex p Interbrew, 23 May 2001 High Court; Ordinance Survey v AA [2001] EuLR 80, High Court; C-344/98 Masterfoods [2001] The Times 2 February; C-380/98 R v HM Treasury ex p University of Cambridge [2000] ECR I-8035; Case C-3/99 Cidrerie Ruwet SA v Cidre Stassen SA & HP Bulmer Ltd [2000] ECR I-8749; Case C-27/00 R v Secretary of State ex p Omega Air Ltd [2000] EuLR 254; Supermarket Prices (Competition Commission, October 2000, Cm 4842); New Motor Vehicles (Competition Commission, April 2000, Cm 4660); R v Customs & Excise ex p Lunn Poly [1999] STC 350, Court of Appeal; Crehan v Courage [1999] EuLR 834, Court of Appeal; Passmore v Morland [1999] EuLR 501 Attorney General v Blake [1998] Ch 439, Court of Appeal; R v OFTEL ex p Cellcom [1998] The Times, 7 December, High Court.
Prof. Memberships: Committe Member of the Bar European Group. Also member of Solicitors European Group, Administrative Law Bar Association, COMBAR, the Bar Pro Bono Unit, the Society of Public Teachers of Law (founded SPTL's competition law section) and the Association of Law Teachers.
Career: Called to Bar 1995. Solicitor of the Supreme Court of England and Wales 1988-95. Fellow and Tutor in Law, Wadham College, Oxford 1990-99. University Lecturer at Oxford University 1990-96. 1981-84 BA Hons, Law, Jesus College, Cambridge (1st Class); 1984-85 LLM, Jesus College, Cambridge (1st Class); Member of the Treasury C Panel (1999 -).
Publications: Co-author with Nicholas Green QC of second edition of 'Commercial Agreements and Competition Law' (1997, publisher Kluwer Law International). Co-author with Nicholas Green QC of 'The Europeanisation of UK Competition Law' (1999, publisher Hart Publishing). Numerous articles in academic and professional journals. Member of editorial boards of the European Competition Law Review, European Law Reports and UK Competition Law Reports.

ROBERTSON, Geoffrey QC
Doughty Street Chambers (Geoffrey Robertson QC) London (020) 7404 1313
g.robertson@doughtystreet.co.uk
Recommended in Crime, Defamation, Human Rights
Specialisation: Has appeared in many landmark cases involving public, media and criminal law, both at trial and on appeal, and has argued human rights cases in Commonwealth Courts, the Privy Council and the European Court in Strasbourg. His memoir, 'The Justice Game', was published in 1998, and 'Crimes Against Humanity – The Struggle for Global Justice' was published in 2000.
Career: Called to Bar 1973; Silk 1988. He is a Recorder and Master of the Middle Temple.
Personal: Born 1946. BA, LLB, BCL, Rhodes Scholar. Author of current textbooks, 'Freedom, the Individual and the Law', and 'Media Law'. Visiting Professor in Human Rights at Birkbeck College. His play, 'The Trials of Oz', won a BAFTA 'Best Play' nomination for 1991, and he was the recipient of a 1993 Freedom of Information Award. He has conducted a number of missions on behalf of Amnesty International to South Aftrica and Vietnam, and led the 1992 Bar Council/ Law Society Human Rights Mission to Malawi. In 1990 he served as counsel to the Royal Commission investigating traffick in arms and mercenaries to the Colombian drugs cartels; and in 2000 was counsel to Lord MacKay's Commission on the administration of Justice in Trinidad.

ROBINSON, Vivian QC
Hollis Whiteman Chambers (QEB) (Julian Bevan QC & Peter Whiteman QC) London (020) 7583 5766
Recommended in Fraud
Specialisation: All aspects of crime, particularly commercial fraud. Was involved for the Defence in the Blue Arrow trial and the Blackspur Leasing trial and has prosecuted cases on behalf of the Serious Fraud Office. In 1998 defended in a substantial fraud trial in Hong Kong.
Prof. Memberships: Criminal Bar Association.
Career: Educated at Queen Elizabeth Grammar School, Wakefield. The Leys School, Cambridge and Sidney Sussex College, Cambridge. Called to the Bar in 1967. Took Silk 1986. A Recorder of the Crown Court since 1986.
Personal: Married with three children. Lives in Oxfordshire.

RODDY, Maureen
India Buildings Chambers (Ray Herman) Liverpool (0151) 243 6000
Recommended in Family

RODGER, Martin
Falcon Chambers (Jonathan Gaunt QC & Kim Lewison QC) London (020) 7353 2484
Recommended in Agriculture, Property Litigation
Specialisation: Handles all aspects of commercial and agricultural property litigation, including landlord and tenant, rent review, milk quota, agricultural holdings, licensed premises and real property. Important cases include Courage v Crehan (Court of Appeal, 1999 – beer tie litigation), Attwood v Bovis (Chancery Division, 2000 – easements) and Zubaida v Hargreaves (Court of Appeal, 1995 – negligence of expert).
Prof. Memberships: Chancery Bar Association, Agricultural Law Association, Professional Negligence Bar Association.
Career: Called to the Bar and joined Falcon Chambers in 1986.
Publications: Editor of 'Woodfall on Landlord & Tenant'.
Personal: Educated at St Aloysius College, Glasgow 1973-79 and University College, Oxford 1979-83. Born 1962. Lives in Kent.

RODGERS, June
Harcourt Chambers (June Rodgers) London (020) 7353 6961
Recommended in Church

RODWAY, Susan
12 King's Bench Walk (Richard Methuen QC) London (020) 7583 0811
Recommended in Personal Injury

ROGERS, Beverly-Ann
Serle Court (Lord Neill of Bladen QC) London (020) 7242 6105
clerks@serlecourt.co.uk
Recommended in Alternative Dispute Resolution, Chancery
Specialisation: Chancery and commercial litigation and advice. All aspects of property litigation and advice. Professional negligence. Contentious trusts and probate, charities, partnerships.
Prof. Memberships: Chancery Bar. Association of Contentious Trust and Probate Specialists.
Career: Called to Bar in 1978. Joined Serle Court in 1980. CEDR registered mediator.

ROGERS, Heather
Matrix Chambers (Nicholas Blake QC) London (020) 7404 3447
heatherrogers@matrixlaw.co.uk
Recommended in Defamation
Specialisation: Media law, including defamation, malicious falsehood, breach of confidence/privacy, contempt of court, judicial review. Cases include Irving v Penguin Books (CA July 2001, Gray J April 2000); Patrick v Department of Health (2001) AER (D) 198 (summary judgment); Hamilton v Al Fayed [2000] 2 WLR 609 (Parliamentary privilege); Loveless v Earl [1999] EMLR 530 (malice); Hinduja v Asia TV [1998] EMLR 530 (meaning); Elton John v MGN [1997] QB 586 (damages); R v BBC ex parte BBC [1995] EMLR 241 (judicial review). Contributor to OUP Yearbook of Media and Entertainment Law (1995 – 2000). Further information at www.matrixlaw.co.uk.

ROGERS, Mark N.
St. Mary's Chambers Family Law Chambers (Christopher M. Butler) Nottingham (0115) 950 3503
Recommended in Family

ROMNEY, Daphne
4 Field Court (Steven Gee QC) London (020) 7440 6900
Recommended in Employment
Specialisation: Employment law, particularly in the fields of wrongful and unfair dismissal, restrictive covenants and discrimination. Clients include insurance companies, plcs, merchant banks, health authorities and NHS trusts. Also practises in the field of defamation and media law.
Prof. Memberships: Employment Law Bar Association.
Career: Called to the Bar in 1979. Libel reader for 'The Observer' since 1982.
Personal: Born 29 July 1955. BA (Cantab).

ROOK, Peter QC
18 Red Lion Court (Anthony Arlidge QC) London (020) 7520 6000
Recommended in Fraud

ROOTS, Guy QC
2 Mitre Court Buildings (Michael FitzGerald QC) London (020) 7583 1380
Recommended in Planning
Specialisation: Main areas of practice are town and country planning, environmental law, compulsory purchase and compensation, rating, local government, parliamentary and administrative law. Has been involved in many leading cases acting for a wide cross section of clients in the public and private sectors. Has spoken at and chaired numerous conferences and seminars. Gener-

al Editor of 'Ryde on Rating and the Council Tax'. General Editor of 'Butterworths Compulsory Purchase Law Service'.
Prof. Memberships: Chairman Planning and Environment Bar Association, Administrative Law Bar Association.
Career: Called to the Bar in 1969. Joined 2 Mitre Court Buildings in 1972. Took Silk in 1989.
Personal: Educated at Winchester College and Brasenose College, Oxford (MA in Jurisprudence).

ROSE, Dinah
Blackstone Chambers (Presiley Baxendale QC & Charles Flint QC) London (020) 7583 1770
clerks@blackstonechambers.com
Recommended in Administrative & Public Law, Employment, Human Rights
Specialisation: Administrative and public law, human rights, discrimination, employment, European law, sports law. Particular interests include equal pay, maternity rights, financial services, City regulation and the Human Rights Act 1998, European social policy, pharmaceuticals, telecommunications, broadcasting, prisoners rights.
Prof. Memberships: ALBA, ELBA, member Council of JUSTICE.
Career: Called to Bar 1989. Member of Treasury A Panel.
Publications: Co-editor Halsbury's Laws 4th edn re-issue, 'Race Relations'; contributor to Halsbury's Laws 4th edn re-issue, 'Constitutional Law and Human Rights'; contributor to Lester & Pannick 'Human Rights Law and Practice' (Butterworths 1999).

ROSE, Jonathan
St. Paul's Chambers (Nigel Sangster QC) Leeds (0113) 245 5866
Recommended in Crime

ROSE, Paul
Old Square Chambers (John Hendy QC) London (020) 7269 0300
rose@oldsquarechambers.co.uk
Recommended in Employment
Specialisation: Discrimination, unfair dismissal, wrongful dismissal and restraint of trade. Personal injury/medical negligence.
Prof. Memberships: ELA, Employment Law Bar Association, Personal Injury Bar Association, APIL.
Career: Called to Bar 1981. In employment law acted in leading cases in discrimination, unfair dismissal, Transfer of Undertakings regulations. Undertaken injunctive work in field of restraint of trade and wrongful dismissal litigation, also instructed regularly in collective redundancy litigation. In personal injury acted on behalf of the plaintiffs in Opren litigation, Benzodiazepine litigation, British Midland air crash, Camelford Water Pollution, Mull of Kyntyre helicopter crash. Acted in a substantial number of catastrophic injury claims particularly involving servicemen in claims against Ministry of Defence.

ROSEN, Murray QC
11 Stone Buildings (Murray Rosen QC) London (020) 7831 6381
rosen@11stonebuildings.com
Recommended in Chancery, Commercial (Litigation), Fraud, Sport
Specialisation: Head of Chambers at 11 Stone Buildings. An incisive and creative tactitian and advocate. Is experienced as a leader or team-member in a wide range of international commercial cases, especially involving asset tracing, and in sports, media and entertainment disputes. Has guided and executed many cases in the fields of fraud and insolvency and lawyers' and accountants' negligence, whether acting for banks, insurers and enforcement agencies, or for corporate, professional and individual defendants. Consistently features in Chambers Directory as a leading silk in the areas of sport and commercial law and was founding chairman of the Bar Sports Law Group. He is also a Fellow of the Chartered Institute of Arbitrators.

ROSENBLATT, Jeremy
4 Paper Buildings (Lionel Swift QC) London (020) 7583 0816
jr@4pb.com
Recommended in Family
Specialisation: Children, international child law and matrimonial finance. Reported cases include Glaser v UK [European Court of Human Rights] [2001] 1 FLR 153; B v UK [European Court of Human Rights] [2000] 1 FLR 1; Re L (Abduction: European Convention: Access) [1999] 2 FLR 1089. Represented the American father in the Internet twins case.
Prof. Memberships: FLBA; IBA; chair: Bar Committee on the rights of the child.
Career: Barrister, called 1985, LLB, Therapist (systemic and psychodynamic).
Publications: 'International Child Abduction' (Sweet & Maxwell); 'International Adoption' (Sweet & Maxwell); 'International Conventions Affecting Children' (Jordan); 'Children and Immigration' (Cavendish).
Personal: Representative of the people of inner London National Lottery Charity Board; TV, radio and newspaper contributor. Education: London School of Economics, Asser Institute of International Law, the Hague, London Centre for Psychotherapy.

ROWE, Judith
One Garden Court Family Law Chambers (Eleanor F. Platt QC & Alison Ball QC) London (020) 7797 7900
jrowe@onegardencourt.co.uk
Recommended in Family
Specialisation: All aspects of family law including public and private law aspects of the Children Act, adoption, child abduction and children cases with an international element; matrimonial finance judicial review and professional negligence (family law related).
Prof. Memberships: FLBA.
Career: Called to the Bar in 1979. Moved to One Garden Court in 1996 to specialise wholly in family law. Appointed Assistant Recorder, 1999. Recorder 2000.
Personal: Born 7 August 1957. Educated at Rednock School, Gloucestershire. University College London (LLB Hons 1978). Lives in London. Married with two young children.

ROWELL, David
3 New Square (Lord Goodhart QC) London (020) 7405 5577
Recommended in Chancery

ROWLAND, John QC
4 Pump Court London (020) 7842 5555
jrowland@4pumpcourt.com
Recommended in Insurance
Specialisation: Principal areas of practice are insurance and reinsurance disputes, professional negligence and general advisory work related to the insurance industry. Recent work has included close involvement in Lloyd's names litigation, policy disputes, broker's negligence and regulatory work. Other areas of practice include general commercial disputes including complex engineering projects and a number of major ICC Arbitrations, inter alia, for Total Oil Company in relation to worldwide uranium sales, for Sogex Construction Group and numerous mining and chemical plants operators; professional negligence involving claims against lawyers, accountants and brokers; gaming and casino licensing work and the provision of commercial law advice direct to overseas lawyers.
Prof. Memberships: COMBAR.
Career: Called to the Bar in 1979 and joined 4 Pump Court in 1980. Took Silk in 1996.
Personal: Educated at Aquinas College, Perth, Western Australia; University of Western Australia (B.Econs, Hons) and King's College, University of London LLB (Hons).

ROWLAND, Robin
5 Fountain Court (Anthony Barker QC) Birmingham (0121) 606 0500
Recommended in Family

ROWLANDS, Marc
Keating Chambers (Richard Fernyhough QC) London (020) 7842 5555
mrowlands@keatingchambers.com
Recommended in Construction
Specialisation: Technology and Construction cases, arbitration law & practice.
Prof. Memberships: ORBA, COMBAR.
Career: Magdalen, Oxford (Law).

ROWLANDS, Peter
18 Red Lion Court (Anthony Arlidge QC) London (020) 7520 6000
peter.rowlands@18rlc.co.uk
Recommended in Crime
Specialisation: Major drugs and fraud cases, murder and serious crime. Specialises in criminal defence work.
Prof. Memberships: CBA, Justice.
Career: Solicitor 1984-89. Barrister 1990 to date. Moved to 18 Red Lion Court in 1999.

ROWLEY, James
28 St. John St Manchester (0161) 834 8418
clerk@28stjohnst.co.uk
Recommended in Clinical Negligence, Personal Injury
Specialisation: Personal injuries and clinical negligence together with inquiries involving a medical content. Cases of maximum severity: Brain injury (Jebson v MOD [2000] 1 WLR 2055; Cargill v PR Excavations, apil vol 10 issue two, May 2000, QBD). Spinal injury (Craven v John Riches et al and Knockhill Racing Circuit, CA Transcript and Lawtel 5 March 2001). Amputee cases at all levels (McFarlane v Clifford Smith and Buchanan, current law May 2000 189, QBD). Psychiatric injury including PTSD (Monk Wearmouth mining disaster; British Airways wind shield blow-out; Veterans' groups one and two v MOD – ongoing). Obstetric and neo-natal surgery (Swift v South Manchester Health Authority – QBD 9.2000 unrep.) Experienced in cases involving: Delay in diagnosis of cancers (especially breast and colon), meningitis, subarachnoid haemorrhage, aortic aneurysm, ectopic pregnancy and slipped femoral epiphysis. Cardiac disease. Minimally-invasive surgery; ERCP including torn oesophagus. Gastro-enterological and colo-rectal disease; acute pancreatitis; hepato-biliary tract disease. Radiation enteritis.
Prof. Memberships: Co-opted member of Bar Council CFA Panel and Personal Injuries' Bar Association Executive Committee.
Career: MA (Classics) Cantab; Dip. Law. Stonyhurst and Emmanuel. Hardwicke Scholar of Lincoln's Inn. Called 1987. Regional Treasury Counsel. Counsel to the Royal Liverpool Children's Inquiry (Redfern Report into organ retention at Alder Hey Hospital). Lectured widely in PI.
Personal: Married with three children. Armchair sportsman, gardener and cook.

ROYCE, John QC
Guildhall Chambers (Adrian Palmer QC) Bristol (0117) 927 3366
Recommended in Crime
Specialisation: Serious crime; commercial fraud; personal injuries. Cryptosporidiosis litigation against Thames Water and Yorkshire Water. Lead contaminated cattle feed group action for NFU. Public inquiries. Counsel to inquiry into Ashworth High Security Hospital.
Prof. Memberships: Criminal Bar Association; Personal Injury Bar Association; Sports Law Bar Association.
Career: QC 1987; Recorder 1986; Deputy High Court Judge QBD 1993.
Personal: Austrian qualified ski instructor.

RUBIN, Stephen QC
Fountain Court (Anthony Boswood QC) London
(020) 7583 3335
sr@fountaincourt.co.uk
Recommended in Commercial (Litigation)
Specialisation: General commercial litigation particularly civil fraud, banker/customer disputes, foreign exchange, business disputes and professional negligence. Recent reported cases: First American v Sheihk Zayad Al Nahayan [1999] 1 WLR 1154, Den Norske Bank v Antonatos [1999] QB 271, Pharaon v BCCI [1998] 4 All ER 455, BOC plc v Centeon Inc [1991] 1 All ER (Comm) 970, Finance for Mortgage v Farley & Co [1998] 2 PNLR 145. IPC v Middlesborough F.C. [2000]; Sequin v UBS A.G. [2000].
Prof. Memberships: London Common Law and Commercial Bar Association; Professional Negligence Bar Association.
Career: Called to Bar 1977; QC 2000; Professional Conduct and Complaints Committee of Bar 1995-99.
Personal: Merchant Taylor's School, Northwood; Exhibition Brasenose College, Oxford – MA Jurisprudence; Married with four children.

RUMFITT, Nigel QC
7 Bedford Row (David Farrer QC) London
(020) 7242 3555
Recommended in Crime
Specialisation: Crime of all types, prosecuting and defending. Extensive experience of medical issues (Junior, Beverley Allitt case). Since taking Silk has done a number of high profile cases. Successfully defended Ruth Neave, helped expose police/Home Office malpractice in R v Robinson & Ors at Leceister (Yardie case). Prosecuted Bedford Hotel murder and Celia Beckett (child poisoner).
Career: Educated at Leeds Modern School; Pembroke College, Oxford; Northwestern University School of Law, Chicago Illinois. MA (Oxon) in Jurisprudence; BCL (Oxon); 2:2 in Bar Finals; Harmsworth Law Scholar (Middle Temple). Called to Bar (Middle Temple) 1974. Assistant Recorder 1991, Recorder 1995. Chambers of D. Draycott QC, *1 Essex Court* 1975-88. Present chambers 1988 to date. QC 1994.
Personal: Born 6.3.1950, Leeds. Married. Interests include skiing, windsurfing and sailing. Speaks fluent French and has studied French law, holds consultations in French without interpreter.

RUSHBROOKE, Justin
5 Raymond Buildings (Patrick Milmo QC) London
(020) 7242 2902
Recommended in Defamation
Specialisation: Defamation including Internet libel; entertainment and media law, including copyright, passing off, trademarks, privacy and confidence, contempt; general chancery and commercial litigation. Recent cases include: Burstein v Times Newspapers Ltd. [2001] 1WLR 579 (CA); Berezovsky v Forbes [200\ 1WLR 1004 (HL; Takanaka v Frankl Oct. 2000 (QB) – first ever 'anonymous' email libel trial; Beckham v Niblett etc 2000/2001 (Ch.D.) – privacy claim for Beckhams against former bodyguard; Godfrey v Demon [2001] 1Q8 201; Loveless v Earl [1999] EMLR 53; Aitken v Pressdram [1997] EMLR 415 (CA); Botham v Khan, The Times, 15 July 1996 (CA); Attorney General v Newspaper Publishing [1997] 1 WLR 926 (CCA); Re:Austintel [1997] 1WLR 616 (CA).
Career: MA (Oxon). Worked for Morgan Grenfell & Co Ltd, 1986-88.

RUSSELL, Christopher
2 Temple Gardens (Dermod O'Brien QC) London
(020) 7822 1200
crussell@2templegardens.co.uk
Recommended in Professional Negligence
Specialisation: Professional negligence with an emphasis on valuers', surveyors' and clinical negligence. Personal injury, in particular industrial diseases and stress and other claims for psychiatric injury. Health and safety. General insurance, common law and procedural matters. Cases include Wentworth v Wiltshire CC [1993], BBL v Eagle Star [1993], Lancashire CC v Municipal Mutual [1997], Burns v General Accident [1999], Farrell v Avon HA [2001].
Career: LLB (Exeter). Called 1982. PNBA; LCLCBA; PIBA.

RUSSELL, Jeremy QC
4 Essex Court (Nigel Teare QC) London
(020) 7653 5653
jjr@4sx.co.uk
Recommended in Arbitration (International), Shipping
Specialisation: Specialist in shipping law and international trade. Practice covers shipping, admiralty, insurance (marine and non-marine), sale and carriage of goods (domestic and international). Also handles commercial arbitrations both as advocate and occasionally as arbitrator. Has addressed a number of conferences in London and Singapore on shipping matters.
Prof. Memberships: COMBAR; London Common Law and Commercial Bar Association; London Maritime Arbitrators Association (supporting member); LCIA (member); FSALS.
Career: Called to the Bar 1975. Joined present chambers 1977. Took Silk 1994. Appointed to panel of Lloyd's Salvage Arbitrators 2000. CEDR accredited mediator.

RUSSEN, Jonathan
Maitland Chambers (Michael Lyndon-Stanford QC & Charles Aldous QC) London (020) 7406 1200
jrussen@maitlandchambers.com
Recommended in Chancery
Specialisation: Commercial litigation: contractual disputes. Insolvency: bankruptcy; directors' disqualification; shareholders' disputes; corporate insolvency; insolvent partnerships. Property and Traditional Chancery. Recent cases: candare v Welsh Development Agency; Rolls Royce v Heavylift Volga-Dnieper [2000] 1 All ER (Comm) 796; Re Bayoil [1999] 1 WLR 147; Re Philip Alexander Securities [1998] BPIR 383; Scott v Church Scientology [1997] BPIR 4. Contributor to Butterworth's 'Practical Insolvency'.
Prof. Memberships: Chancery Bar Association. COMBAR.
Career: University of Wales LLB (1st Class Hons.) 1984. University of Cambridge LLM 1985. Called to Bar (Lincoln's Inn) 1986.
Personal: Married 2 children.

RUTTLE, Stephen QC
Brick Court Chambers (Christopher Clarke QC) London (020) 7379 3550
ruttle@brickcourt.co.uk
Recommended in Alternative Dispute Resolution, Insurance
Specialisation: (i) Reinsurance, insurance and Lloyds. Also shipping, commodities, general commercial and professional negligence. Co-author of Insurance Brokers section in 'Professional Negligence and Liability', LLP 12/2000 publication date. (ii) ADR. CEDR accredited and registered mediator 1998. Has acted as mediator in over 60 disputes since Feb 1999, with about 35 in the 12 month period from April 2000. Most disputes from fields in (i) above. Member of CEDR, Mediation UK (Community mediation); on the mediation panels of various mediation service providers; involved in insurance and reinsurance market initiatives.
Prof. Memberships: Member: British Insurance Law Association: LMAA; Lloyds Arbitrator Tier 1 and Tier 2.
Career: Called to Bar 1976, Gray's Inn. Pupillage with Sir Nicholas Lyell QC MP. Practised at Brick Court Chambers since 1976. Queen's Counsel 1997.
Personal: Educated Westminster School (Queen's Scholar) and Queens' College, Cambridge (Exhibitioner). BA Honours Degree in English/Law. Lecturer at numerous insurance and reinsurance seminars.

RYAN, Gerard QC
2 Harcourt Buildings (Gerard Ryan QC) London
(020) 7353 8415
Recommended in Environment, Planning

RYDER, John QC
6 King's Bench Walk (Roy Amlot QC) London
(020) 7583 0410
Recommended in Crime

RYDER, Matthew
Matrix Chambers (Nicholas Blake QC) London
(020) 7404 3447
Recommended in Crime
Specialisation: Specialising in all areas of serious criminal work including fraud and the interface between civil and criminal work such as judicial review, civil actions against the police, human rights, inquests, regulatory work, forfeiture and confiscation. Editor of several publications including police and the law. Notable cases include Abraham v Commissioners of Police for the Metropolis (acceptance of a police caution is not a bar to civil proceedings; R v Muhammad (highly publicised disturbance outside the Stephen Lawrence Inquiry); R v During (conceptual challenge to 'image analysis' identification); DPP v Todd (judicial review of prosecution of roads protestors); R v CPS ex p Hitchins (judicial review of decision not to prosecute after inquest); R v Haringey Justices ex p Spencer (judicial review of costs awarded by magistrates).
Career: Called to Bar 1992. Recently conducted extensive research into human rights at Columbia University, New York. Called to New York Bar 1999.
Personal: Graduated from Emmanuel College, Cambridge in 1989.

RYDER TD, Ernest QC
Deans Court Chambers (Stephen Grime QC) Manchester (0161) 214 6000
ryder@deanscourt.co.uk
Recommended in Family
Specialisation: Family, public and administrative law; providing a specialist service in matrimonial finance and all disputes relating to children, public authorities, health care, professional negligence and ethics. Private and public tribunal work.
Prof. Memberships: Chairman: Manchester region. FLBA. PIBA. Child Concern. NYAS (Professional Advisory Group). ALC.
Career: MA (Cantab). Call 1981 Gray's Inn. Assistant Recorder 1996. QC 1997. Counsel to the Tribunal (North Wales) 1996-98. Recorder 2000. Deputy High Court Judge 2001.
Publications: Editor: Clarke Hall and Morrison on Children (Butterworths).
Personal: TA Commission 1982. TD 1996.

SADIQ, Tariq
9 St. John Street (John Hand QC) Manchester
(0161) 955 9000
clerks@9stjohnstreet.co.uk
Recommended in Employment
Specialisation: Employment law, discrimination law and human rights law. Recently appointed by the Attorney General as Junior Counsel to the Crown (Provincial Panel) and regularly instructed in cases for Ministry of Defence, the Lord Chancellor's Department and the Prison Service. In addition, he is approved by the Commission for Racial Equality, the Equal Opportunities Commission and the Disability Rights Commission to act in discrimination cases. His employment law work includes unfair dismissal, redundancy (individual and collective), transfer of undertakings and restraint of trade. He has a substantial practice in all areas of discrimination law, with particular expertise in complex discrimination cases. As well as appearing regularly in the Employment Tribunal and the EAT, he has appeared before internal police disciplinary inquiries. He also advises police forces and local authorities on human rights issues.

SAYER, Peter
Gough Square Chambers (Fred Philpott) London (020) 7353 0924
Recommended in Consumer Law

SAYERS, Michael QC
2 King's Bench Walk London (020) 7353 1746
Recommended in Crime

SCANNELL, Rick
Two Garden Court (Ian Macdonald QC & Owen Davies QC) London (020) 7353 1633
Recommended in Immigration

SCHAFF, Alistair QC
7 King's Bench Walk (Jeremy Cooke QC) London (020) 7910 8300
clerks@7kbw.law.co.uk
Recommended in Arbitration (International), Insurance, Shipping

Specialisation: All aspects of international commercial law: specifically, conflict of laws/ jurisdiction disputes, shipping, insurance (marine and non-marine), reinsurance, banking, international sale of goods, oil disputes, professional and commercial negligence. Leading cases: "The Maciej Rataj" [1999] 2 WLR 181 (ECJ; Art.21&22 of Brussels Convention); Effort v Linden [1998] AC 605 (HL; dangerous goods); Royal Boskalis v Mountain [1999] QB. 674 (CA; illegality and marine insurance); MacFarlane / Hegarty v Caledonia [1994] 1 LLR 16; [1997] 2 LLR 259 (CA; Piper Alpha/negligence); Huyton v Peter Cremer [1999] 1 LLR 620 (sale of goods/economic duress); Kingscroft v Nissan [1999] LRLR 603 (reinsurance); Glencore v Metro [2001] 1 LLR 283 (conflicts of laws and title to oil in M East); Jan de Nul v Royale Belge [2000] 2 LLR 700 (liability insurance).
Career: Called to the Bar 1983; Queen's Counsel 1999.
Personal: Born 1959. MA (Cantab).

SCHOLZ, Karl
Nicholas Street Chambers (Robert Trevor-Jones) Chester (01244) 323886
Recommended in Consumer Law

SCOBIE, James
Francis Taylor Building (Nicholas Valios QC) London (020) 7353 7768
Recommended in Crime

Specialisation: Specialist in all areas of criminal law. Exclusively defence work. Acted in high profile cases including offences of murder, attempted murder, sexual offences and cases involving the supplying and/ or importation of drugs on a large scale. Leading Junior in large scale armed robbery conspiracies, multi-million diversion fraud, VAT fraud involving "outsourcing", multi-handed conspiracy to supply class A drugs and a trial involving the systematic torture of a mentally vulnerable family by a number of youths in a tower block flat.
Career: Educated at Eton College 1974-78. Exeter University 1979-81. Dip Law City Universtiy 1982. Called 1984.
Personal: Secretary Old Etonian Football Club. Interested in playing and watching all sports, especially football and cricket. MCC member since 1979.

SCOTT, Ian
Old Square Chambers (John Hendy QC) London (020) 7269 0329
scott@oldsquarechambers.co.uk
Recommended in Employment

Specialisation: Discrimination, in particular disability discrimination and whistleblowing. Also specialising in labour law including recognition. Further interest in local government employment issues. Recent cases: Post Office v Howell [2000] IRLR 224; [2000] ICR 913 Employment Appeal Tribunal; Care First Partnership Ltd v Roffey [2001] IRLR 65; [2001 ICR 87 Court of Appeal (November 2000).
Prof. Memberships: Employment Law Bar Association; Industrial Law Society; Employment Lawyers Association.
Career: Prior to being called to the Bar in October 1991, had been employed by a major trade union as a research and press officer and negotiator. Also held position of elected councillor in a London Borough.
Personal: BA Hons Economics, Newcastle-upon-Tyne University; MSC Industrial Relations, London School of Economics. Enjoys sport. Member of Wimbledon Squash Club.

SCOTT, Timothy QC
29 Bedford Row Chambers (Peter Ralls QC) London (020) 7404 1044
Recommended in Family

Specialisation: Principal area of practice is family law. Works in all areas, including ancillary relief, child abduction, private and public law children's cases. Involved in a large amount of international work including jurisdictional disputes, recognition of foreign decrees and transnational enforcement. Other main area of practice is solicitors' negligence, both arising out of family law matters and generally. Clients include leading Family Law solicitors firms in and outside London. Contributor of articles to Family Law magazine and of chapter on matrimonial law in 'International Tracing of Assets' (FT Law & Tax 1997). Regular speaker at seminars on various family law topics.
Prof. Memberships: Family Law Bar Association; Professional Negligence Bar Association.
Career: Called to the Bar in 1975 and joined present Chambers in 1976. Appointed Q.C. and Assistant Recorder in 1995. Appointed recorder in 1999.
Personal: Queen's Scholar, Westminster School 1962-66, Open Exhibitioner New College, Oxford 1967-70. Born 19th July 1949. Lives in London.

SCOTT-MANDERSON, Marcus
4 Paper Buildings (Lionel Swift QC) London (020) 7583 0816
clerks@4pb.com
Recommended in Family

Specialisation: International child abduction, International child law, human rights – child cases. Important cases: Venables v News Group Newspapers Ltd [2001] 1 WLR 1038; Re M&J (abduction: International Judicial Collaboration) [2000] FLR 803; Re P (a child) (mirror orders) [2000] 1 FLR 350; Re JS (Private International Adoption) [2000] 2 FLR 638; Re H (abduction: acquiescence) [1998] AC 72 (HL).
Prof. Memberships: Trustee for REUNITE, International Child Abduction Centre, member of its Legal Working Group; member of British Academy of Forensic Sciences; Family Law Bar Association
Career: Harrow School (1969-74); Christ Church Oxford (1975-79), Boulter Exhibition in Law, BCL, MA; Hague Academy of International Law in the Netherlands, Dana Fellowship (1980); Glasgow University (Dept of Forensic Medicine); Inns of Court School of Law; Ver Heyden de Lancey Prize in Forensic Medicine; called Lincoln's Inn 1980, Hardwicke Scholarship, Droop Scholarship.
Publications: Contributor to Butterworths 'Essential Family Practice' 2001.
Personal: Year of birth: 1956. Town of residence: London. Clubs: Lansdowne Club.

SCRIVENER, Anthony QC
2-3 Gray's Inn Square (Anthony Porten QC & Anthony Scrivener QC) London (020) 7242 4986
chambers@2-3graysinnsquare.co.uk
Recommended in Consumer Law, Crime, Fraud, Health & Safety

Specialisation: Administrative and public law, consumer law, health and safety, crime, serious fraud, civil liberties, environmental law, personal injury, local government and City regulatory, monopolies work and food law. Also specialises in appeal work (over 30 appearances in house of Lords). Has appeared in courts Hong Kong, Malaysia, Singapore, Australia, Trinidad, Jamaica, British Virgin Islands as well as European Court of Justice. Also called to Bar in Jamaica and Tasmania.
Career: Practice 1961. Took Silk 1975. Chairman of the Bar 1991. Bencher of Lincoln's Inn.
Personal: Leisure: walking, opera, chess.

SEABROOK, Robert QC
1 Crown Office Row (Robert Seabrook QC) London (020) 7797 7500
robert.seabrook@1cor.com
Recommended in Crime, Family

Specialisation: Extensive experience includes notably professional negligence (clinical, solicitors, surveyors, accountants), civil jury actions, matrimonial finance and property, commercial fraud and major crimes. Cases include Al Kandari v Brown [1987]; Smith v Bush [1990]; Baker v Kaye (1997); Kapkunde v Abbey National Building Society (1998); Professor Nicolaides (GMC) (1998) John Studd (GMC) 1996; Rodney Ledward (GMC) 1999; Lady Foster v H M Customs and Excise [1993]; Silcott v Metropolitan Police Commissioner [1996]; Waters v Metropolitan Police Commissioner (2000); Farah v Metropolitan Police Commissioner (1998); Henderson v Chief Constable of Cleveland (2001); HRH The Prince of Wales (Royal Divorce) (1996); Tombolis [1991]; Flick [re-appeal 1995]; the Charing Cross Lynn Rogers murder case [1992].
Career: Called to Bar in 1964. Took silk in 1983. Recorder since 1985. Deputy High Court Judge since 1991. Leader of the South Eastern Circuit 1989-92. Chairman of the Bar, 1994. Member of the Investigatory Powers Tribunal since 2000.
Personal: Educated at St Georges's College, Harare, Zimbabwe and University College, London (LL.B). Member of the court of the University of Sussex 1988-93. Chairman of the Governors of Brighton College since 1998. Interests include travel, listening to music and wine. Lives in London and Brighton.

SEARS, David
4 Pump Court London (020) 7842 5555
dsears@4pumpcourt.com
Recommended in Construction

Specialisation: Building/civil engineering disputes and professional negligence – the latter including not only building professionals (engineers, quantity surveyors and architects) but also solicitors, accountants and surveyors.
Prof. Memberships: TECBAR, Professional Negligence Bar Association, London Common Law and Commercial Bar Association, COMBAR.
Career: 1979-83: Civil Servant – Ministry of Defence; 1984 to date in practice at Bar.
Personal: Education: Trinity College, Oxford (MA Oxon). Leisure interests: sailing, flying, motorcycling, travelling and being at home in the country. Family: married with two children.

SEDDON, Duran
Two Garden Court (Ian Macdonald QC & Owen Davies QC) London (020) 7415 6300
duran@2gardenct.law.co.uk
Recommended in Immigration

Specialisation: All aspects of immigration law including asylum, enforcement, human rights, family reunion and support. Also specializes in social welfare law. Notable cases Onibiyo [1996] QB 768 CA (junior), Radiom & Shingara [1997] 3 CMLR 703 (junior), Mersin (junior), Holub [2001] 1 WLR 1359 (junior), Singh & Singh -v- SSHD (2000) SIAC, R -v- HBRB South Tyneside ex parte Tooley [1996] COD 143.
Prof. Memberships: Immigration Law Practitioners Association.
Career: Member of editorial board of 'Immigration Nationality Law and Practice' (Tolleys), Member of Management Committee of Islington Law Centre. Publications: Migration and Social Security Handbook (CPAG) 2nd and 3rd Editions (1997)(2001), contributor to Macdonald's Immigration Law and Practice 5th Ed (2001), contributor to Blake & Fransman Immigration Nationality and Asylum under the Human Rights Act 1998, course designer and tutor for College of Law BVC (1998-99).

Prof. Memberships: Employment Lawyers Association, Employment Law Bar Association (Committee Member), Race Relations Committee of the Bar Council (Committee Member), Industrial Law Society, NCFRAS.
Career: Called to the Bar in 1993 (Gray's Inn). Awarded Gray's In Scholarship. Appointed Junior Counsel to the Crown (Provincial Panel) in 1999.
Personal: Enjoys cricket, football and walking.

SAGGERSON, Alan

No. 1 Serjeants' Inn (Edward Faulks QC) London (020) 7415 6666
clerks@no1serjeantsinn.com
Recommended in Consumer Law
Specialisation: Main areas of practice: all aspects of travel and personal injury litigation – with particular emphasis on the package travel industry, foreign accidents (including health and food safety) and international travel conventions. Highlights of the last year include several group actions arising out of travel and natural disasters, food poisoning; swimming pool and leisure facility safety. Significant cases in the last year have included: Hulse v Chambers and Hamill v Hamill [Private International Law Act 1995]; Watson v Aparta Hotels Caledonia SA [CA – Brussels Convention on Jurisdiction]; Hone v Going Places Leisure Travel [QBD], and Logue v First Choice Holidays Ltd [Package Travel Regulations 1992]. Other important cases include: Codd v Thomson Tour Operations Ltd [CA – Package Travel Regulations 1992]; Brannan v Airtours Holidays Limited and Williams v Travel Promotions [CA – Tour operators' contractual liability for compliance with local standards]. Regular speaker on travel law to consumers and the industry and various accredited training providers.
Prof. Memberships: Chairman of the Travel and Tourism Lawyers Association. Member of PIBA and PNBA. Lincoln's Inn continuing education teams in advocacy and ethics.
Career: Called to the Bar in 1981.
Publications: Author: Travel Law & Litigation (2nd Edition 2000 CLT Professional Publishing). Editor: 'Personal Injury Quarterly' (1996 to date).
Personal: Educated: Hertford College, Oxford (MA Jurisprudence; BCL). Born 1956. Resides, London.

SAINI, Pushpinder

Blackstone Chambers (Presiley Baxendale QC & Charles Flint QC) London (020) 7583 1770
clerks@blackstonechambers.com
Recommended in Administrative & Public Law, Media & Entertainment
Specialisation: Commercial law (including copyright and entertainment law) public law (including human rights). Cases include George Michael v Sony; A&M Records v VCI Ltd; ZYX Music v King; Wailer v Island Records; R v Radio Authority ex p Guardian Media Group; Tony Bland, Banks v CBS; R v Secretary of State ex p O'Dhiuibir; A-G v Blake; Lisa Stansfield v Sovereign; R v Secretary of State ex p RP Scherer; R v Secretary of State ex p Monsanto; Reynolds v Times newspapers; Walmsley v Acid Jazz; R v DG Telecoms ex p Mercury; Ludlow Music v Robbie Williams; Charlotte Church v Shalit.
Prof. Memberships: JUSTICE, ELA, ALBA, BEG
Career: Called to the Bar 1991.
Publications: Co-author, 'Halsbury's Laws, European Convention on Human Rights' and Lester & Pannick, 'Human Rights Law and Practice'.
Personal: Educated at Corpus Christi College, Oxford (BA and BCL, both 1st Class) Atkin Scholar of Gray's Inn. Languages: Punjabi, Hindi, French, Urdu.

SALLON, Christopher QC

Doughty Street Chambers (Geoffrey Robertson QC) London (020) 7404 1313
Recommended in Crime
Specialisation: Criminal law. Defends in commercial fraud, revenue and customs, VAT and duty evasion prosecutions, also in murders. Member of the Bar Working Party on the Guildford and Woolwich Bombings and the Seabrook Working Party on the Efficient Disposal of Business in the Crown Court. Has lectured extensively at US universities, including Yale and Stamford, on civil liberties issues. Member of the board of Counsel magazine. Fellow – American Board of Criminal Lawyers.
Prof. Memberships: Bar Council, Chairman – Public Affairs Committee.
Career: Called to the Bar 1973 and helped to found current chambers 1990. Appointed Recorder 1996. Took Silk 1994. Called to Bar of Eastern Caribbean 1994.

SALTER, Richard QC

3 Verulam Buildings (Christopher Symons QC & John Jarvis QC) London (020) 7831 8441
chambers@3vb.com
Recommended in Banking
Specialisation: Principal areas of practice are banking, commercial law, financial services, insolvency, insurance, professional negligence and building. Clients include most major UK and international banks.
Prof. Memberships: London Common Law and Commercial Bar Association, COMBAR, TECBAR, Chartered Institute of Arbitrators.
Career: Called to the Bar 1975. Tenant at Hare Court, 1977-82, then joined current chambers. Bencher of the Inner Temple 1991. Member of the Council of Legal Education 1990-96. Chairman of the Board of Examiners, Bar Vocational Course, 1992-93. Governor of the Inns of Court School of Law 1996-. Took Silk in 1995. Recorder 2000- (Assistant Recorder 1997-00).
Publications: Contributor to 'Banks – Liability and Risk' (3rd ed 2001) and 'Banks and Remedies' (2nd ed 1999) for Lloyd's of London Press; and to Vol. 20 'Halsbury's Laws' (4th ed 1993 – Re-issue 'Guarantees'). Consulting editor, All England Commercial Cases 1999-. Legislation editor, Encyclopedia of Insurance Law 1999-. Editor, 'Legal Decisions Affecting Bankers', vols 12-4 (2001). Lectures frequently on banking and other commercial law topics.
Personal: Educated at Harrow County School for Boys 1963-70, Balliol College, Oxford 1970-73 and Inns of Court School of Law 1973-75. Chairman, Shoscombe Village Cricket Club.

SANDER, A

Oriel Chambers (A Sander) Liverpool (0151) 236 7191/ 236 4321
Recommended in Family

SANDERS, Neil

29 Bedford Row Chambers (Peter Ralls QC) London (020) 7404 1044
Recommended in Family
Specialisation: Principal area of practice encompasses all areas of matrimonial finance and the law relating to children including child abduction cases. Other main areas of practice cover work relating to the Inheritance (Provision for Family and Dependents) Act 1975.
Prof. Memberships: Family Law Bar Association.
Career: Called to the Bar 1975 and joined present chambers in 1976.
Personal: Educated at Fettes College, Edinburgh 1966-71, Pembroke College, Cambridge 1971-74 and the College of Law 1974-75. Leisure pursuits include tennis, sailing, skiing, music and theatre. Born 17th April 1953. Lives in London.

SANDS, Philippe

Matrix Chambers (Nicholas Blake QC) London (020) 7404 3447
Recommended in Environment
Specialisation: Barrister specialising in litigation and advisory work for governments, international organisations, corporations and individuals on public international law (including ICJ and Arbitration), EU and public law, environmental law. Cases include R v Secretary of State ex p (High Court) Hungary/Slovakia (International Court of Justice); Greenpeace and others v European Commission (ECJ); Tradex v Republic of Albania (International Centre for the Settlement of Investment Disputes – arbitration); St Vincent v Guinea (International Tribunal for the Law of the Sea); Swissbourgh Diamond Mines v World Bank (World Bank Inspection Panel); numerous intergovernmental negotiations and consultancies (EC, World Bank, Asia Development Bank).
Career: Qualified 1985, Professor of international law at the University of London (SOAS); global professor of law. New York University.
Publications: 'Manual of International Courts and Tribunals' (Butterworths 1999); 'Principles of International Environmental Law', 1995; 'Bowett's Law of International Institutions' (Sweet & Maxwell 2001).

SAUNDERS, John QC

4 Fountain Court (John Saunders QC) Birmingham (0121) 236 3476
Recommended in Crime, Licensing

SAUNDERS, Neil

3 Raymond Buildings (Clive Nicholls QC) London (020) 7400 6400
chambers@3raymondbuildings.com
Recommended in Crime
Specialisation: General crime – prosecuting and defending in all criminal courts. Leading and junior work includes murder, manslaughter (R v Hardy – defence for rugby player), robbery, serious assault, sexual offences including children and video evidence, drugs cases and confiscation hearings, police corruption (Donald & Cressey). Appeared in Divisional Court in cases involving drink driving legislation and custody time limits. Serious fraud and commercial crime (including defence of His Honour Judge Gee). Instructed by defence in SFO case involving directors of Wickes. Police Disciplinary Tribunals. Licensing appearances involving liquor, public entertainment, betting and gaming at first instance and on appeal.
Prof. Memberships: Bar Council, Criminal Bar Association.
Career: BA (Hons) Law 1982; called to the Bar 1983. Govenor ICSL 1999-.

SAUNDERS, Nicholas

4 Field Court (Steven Gee QC) London (020) 7440 6900
nicholasjsaunders@hotmail.com
Recommended in Shipping
Specialisation: Shipping law: practice covers all aspects of wet and dry work. Aviation law: practice covers all aspects, including air accidents, pilot/aircrew negligence, aviation insurance, carriage of goods by air, and licensing. General commercial work also undertaken, including international trade and insurance.
Prof. Memberships: COMBAR.
Career: Former RAF pilot. Joined present Chambers 1990.
Personal: Educated at Radley College 1967-72, Hull University LL.B (1987) and Cambridge University LL.M (1988). Governor of Woodleigh Preparatory School, Malton, N.Yorks. Leisure pursuits include shooting, fly fishing and golf. Born 20th July 1954. Lives in Cambridgeshire.

SAUVAIN, Stephen QC

40 King St Manchester (0161) 832 9082
Recommended in Planning

SAVILL, Mark

Deans Court Chambers (Stephen Grime QC) Manchester (0161) 214 6000
savill@deanscourt.co.uk
Recommended in Crime
Specialisation: Specialises in all areas of criminal law.
Prof. Memberships: Criminal Bar Association.
Career: Called to the Bar – November 1993 (Inner Temple).
Personal: Born 17 May 1969. Educated at Eton College and Durham University BA (Hons). Interests include sport and cooking.

SEED, Nigel QC
3 Paper Buildings London (020) 7583 8055
Recommended in Church

SEGAL, Oliver
Old Square Chambers (John Hendy QC) London (020) 7269 0300
segal@oldsquarechambers.co.uk
Recommended in Employment
Specialisation: Employment; commercial agency; commercial sale of goods. Cases: RMT v LUL [1998] 1RLR 636, CA; BBC v Farnworth [1998] ICR 1116 EAT; Moore v Piretta PTA Ltd [1999] 1 ALL ER 174, H Ct; Newbold & Smith v Leicester City Council; [1999] ICR 1182, CA; Barrett McKenzie v Escada UK Ltd, 'The Times', May 15, 2001, H Ct.
Prof. Memberships: ELBA.
Career: Corpus Christi College, Oxford (1981-85). School Oriental & African Studies, University. London (1985-86). Called 1992, Middle Temple.
Personal: Expert bridge player and writer.

SEITLER, Jonathan
Wilberforce Chambers (Edward Nugee QC) London (020) 7306 0102
Recommended in Property Litigation
Specialisation: Property litigation and associated professional negligence including: landlord and tenant, bank securitisation and negligence claims against solicitors and valuers. Acts for both landlords and tenants, banks and their customers and, in professional negligence actions, plaintiffs and insurers.
Prof. Memberships: Professional Negligence Bar Association, COMBAR.
Career: Called to the Bar 1985
Publications: Co-author of 'Property Finance Negligence: Claims Against Solicitors and Valuers' (Sweet & Maxwell) and the new looseleaf 'Commercial Property Disputes' (Sweet & Maxwell). Lectures widely both at conferences and in-house.
Personal: Educated Pembroke College, Oxford, City University (Dip. Law).

SELVARATNAM, Vasanti QC
4 Field Court (Steven Gee QC) London (020) 7440 6900
vasanti.selvaratnam@4fieldcourt.co.uk
Recommended in Shipping
Specialisation: All aspects of international commercial and shipping law, including admiralty. Clients include the major P & I clubs, shipowners, charterers and salvors.
Prof. Memberships: COMBAR; European Bar Association; LMAA; BMLA.
Career: Called to the Bar 1983: joined current chambers (formerly located at Queen Elizabeth Building) in 1985. Recorder 2000. Queen's Counsel 2001.
Personal: Born 9.4.61. Educated at St. Augustine's Priory, Ealing and King's College, London LL.B (Hons.) 1982, LL.M (1st) 1984.

SEMKEN, Christopher
New Square Chambers (John Mowbray QC & Eben Hamilton QC) London (020) 7419 8000
Recommended in Chancery
Specialisation: General Chancery, especially property including landlord and tenant, partnership, wills and trusts, professional negligence in such areas, both for and against solicitors, barristers, and surveyors.
Prof. Memberships: Chancery Bar Association, Professional Negligence Bar Association.
Personal: MA Oxon 1976, called to the Bar 1977, in practice at New Square Chambers, Lincoln's Inn 1978 to date.

SENDALL, Antony
Littleton Chambers (Michel Kallipetis QC) London (020) 7797 8600
antony@sendall.co.uk
Recommended in Employment
Specialisation: Principal areas of practice are employment, all areas including wrongful/unfair dismissal, redundancy, transfer of undertakings, discrimination, equal pay, working time, restraint of trade, industrial disputes; sports law, mostly employment and disciplinary issues; professional indemnity; mostly solicitors and surveyors; commercial; all forms of commercial disputes, including interim injunctions and arbitrations.
Prof. Memberships: Employment Law Bar Association, Employment Lawyers Association, Industrial Law Society, Bar Sports Law Group, Professional Negligence Bar Association, London Commercial and Common Law Bar Association, chambers member of COMBAR.
Career: Called to the Bar 1984.
Personal: Born 1 July 1961. Educated: Cambridge University (Law: 1st Class Hons). Interests: photography, cooking, amateur dramatics, running.

SETRIGHT, Henry QC
Renaissance Chambers (Brian Jubb & Henry Setright QC) London (020) 7404 1111
Recommended in Family

SEYS LLEWELLYN, Anthony
Farrar's Building (John Leighton Williams QC) London (020) 7583 9241
Recommended in Personal Injury
Specialisation: Practice in personal injury, clinical and professional negligence and inquiries. Also general common law and insurance. Not restricted to but predominantly engaged in heavy cases of severe injury or disability, for both claimants and insurers/authorities. Recent cases include Heil v Rankin 2000 (CA general increase in damages for personal injuries) and Ladbroke Grove Rail Inquiry 2000 (leading counsel for Thames Trains a principal party).
Prof. Memberships: PIBA; APIL; LCLCB.
Career: Called 1972. Joined chambers 1974. Appointed Recorder 1990.
Personal: King's School, Chester 1957-67; Jesus College, Oxford 1967-71 (MA and BCL). Fluent in French; working knowledge of German. Assistant Boundary Commissioner. Leisure pursuits include music, sport and art. Born 24th April 1949. Lives in Buckinghamshire.

SHAH, Akhil
Fountain Court (Anthony Boswood QC) London (020) 7583 3335
Recommended in Aviation
Specialisation: General commercial work specialising in: carriage by air of goods and passengers; aircraft insurance disputes; air disasters – product liability; aviation finance and operating lease disputes; conditions of carriage; jurisdiction; regulatory work – operators' licences. Counsel in Airbus Industrie G.I.E v Patel [1999] 1 AC 119: (Product liability; Jurisdiction; anti-suit injunction) House of Lords. Counsel in Western Digital v British Airways [1999] 2 Lloyds 380; (Warsaw Convention : Article 18 : right of owner to sue for loss of goods). Councel in First Security National Bank v Air Gabon [1999] 2 Lloyds 380 (Aircraft lease, delivery of aircraft); Counsel in Messier Dowty Ltd v Airbus Industrie G.I.E and another [2000] 1 All ER (comm) 101 (stay of proceedings; product design)
Prof. Memberships: COMBAR.

SHANT, Nirmal K.
No.1 High Pavement (John B. Milmo QC) Nottingham (0115) 941 8218
Recommended in Crime

SHARP, Christopher QC
St John's Chambers (Christopher Sharp QC) Bristol (0117) 921 3456
clerks@stjohnschambers.co.uk
Recommended in Family, Personal Injury
Specialisation: Matrimonial Finance. Personal Injury. Professional negligence in these fields.
Prof. Memberships: FLBA. PIBA.
Career: MA Oxon. Called to the Bar 1975; Silk 1999. Head of Chambers.
Publications: Articles in 'Legal Press'.

SHARP, Victoria QC
1 Brick Court (Richard Rampton QC) London (020) 7353 8845
clerks@1brickcourt.co.uk
Recommended in Defamation
Specialisation: Defamation, confidence, contempt of court and media related law generally. Cases include David Irving v Guardian Newspapers Ltd, Marks & Spencer v Granada, Branson v Snowden and GTECH, Bennett v Guardian Newspapers Ltd, Sugar v Venables, Hamilton/Greer v Guardian Newspapers Ltd, Souness v MGN, HRH Princess of Wales v MGN, Angelsea v HTV, Rt Hon Michael Foot v Times Newspapers, Maxwell v Bower, Lord Aldington v Tolstoy, Marco Pierre White v Anthony Allan.
Prof. Memberships: London Commercial and Common Bar Association.
Career: North London Collegiate School, University of Bristol (1978). Called to the Bar 1979. Member of the Supreme Court Committee on Defamation (the Neill Committee). Recorder (South Eastern Circuit).

SHARPE, Thomas QC
One Essex Court (Lord Grabiner QC) London (020) 7583 2000
Recommended in Competition/Anti-trust
Specialisation: Principal areas of practice are European Community and UK competition law (Competition Commission/ OFT, EC Commission and European Court). Cases representing British Gas, British Telecom, British Sugar, Eurostar. Extensive telecommunications practice in UK and Hong Kong. Wide range of Art 81, 82 in High Court and general EC law cases in the European Court of Justice. Also judicial review. Leading cases include Eurostar (in European Court), Clear Communications Ltd v New Zealand Telecommunications (in Privy Council) on interconnection; Shearson Lehman v Maclaine Watson; An Bord Bainne v Milk Marketing Board; R v MAFF exp. Fedesa; Hopkins v National Power; Contributor to Halsbury (European Community Law) and author of monographs and articles on UK and EEC competition law and utility regulation in Law Quarterly Review, European Law Review etc. Formerly Fellow in Law, Nuffield College, Oxford.
Career: Called to the Bar in 1976. Of counsel to *Gibson, Dunn & Crutcher* (US law firm) 1984-88; on board of NERA, 1982-88 and executive director, Institute for Fiscal Studies, 1981-87. Commenced practise in 1987. Took silk in 1994.
Personal: Educated at Trinity Hall, Cambridge. Degrees in Economics and in Law.

SHARPLES, John
St John's Chambers (Christopher Sharp QC) Bristol (0117) 921 3456
clerks@stjohnschambers.co.uk
Recommended in Chancery
Specialisation: Commercial landlord and tenant; real property; equity and trusts; residential landlord and tenant.
Prof. Memberships: Property Bar Association; Chancery Bar Association; Bristol and Cardiff Chancery Bar Association.
Career: Oxford University BA (1st class) 1986; Cambridge University LLM 1987; University of Pennsylvania LLM 1988; Thouron Scholar 1987-88; Attorney-at-Law New York 1991; Associate, Davis Polk and Wardwell, New York 1989-91; Middle Temple 1991; Queen Mother's Fund Scholar (Middle Temple) 1991; Sachs Prize and Campbell Foster Prize (Middle Temple) 1992; St John's Chambers Bristol 1993.
Personal: Rugby league, sailing and raising daughter.

SHARPSTON, Eleanor QC
4 Paper Buildings (Jean Ritchie QC) London (020) 7353 3366
Recommended in Competition/Anti-trust
Specialisation: All areas of EU law, from competition, equal treatment and immigration to agriculture, free movement of goods and intellectual property; also ECHR

work. Major recent cases include Kalanke (positive discrimination), Atlanta (interim relief), the UK challenge to the Working Time Directive, Fantask (time limits after Emmott), Factortame (damages action) and Laskey, Brown and Jaggard v UK (Spanner: ECtHR).
Prof. Memberships: UKAEL, BEG, COMBAR; member of Irish Bar; member of Bar of Gibraltar; fellow, King's College Cambridge; senior fellow, Centre for European Legal Studies (CELS), Cambridge.
Career: Undergraduate degree at King's College, Cambridge (economics and law); research at Corpus Christi College, Oxford. Private practice in Brussels chambers 1981-87. Référendaire (legal secretary) at Court of Justice of the EC 1987-90. Since 1990, in practice at the Bar concurrently with academic appointments at UCL (1990-92) and Cambridge (1992-).
Publications: 'Interim and Substantive Relief in Claims under Community Law'; 'Practitioners' Handbook of EC Law' (1998-contributor).
Personal: Main off-duty interests: classical music, theatre and European literature; rowing, scuba diving and sailing square-riggers.

SHAW, Antony QC
18 Red Lion Court (Anthony Arlidge QC) London (020) 7520 6000
antony.shaw@18rlc.co.uk
Recommended in Crime, Fraud
Specialisation: General crime and fraud, including SFO, VAT, corporate, mortgage, ECGD, tax, charity and other frauds. Major SFO cases include Guinness, Polly Peck, Eagle Trust, BCCI, Butte Mining, Alpine, Alliance.
Prof. Memberships: Criminal Bar Association.
Career: Major History Scholar, Trinity College, Oxford: 1967-70. Astbury Scholar, Middle Temple: 1976. QC: 1994. Assistant Recorder: 1998; Recorder, 2000.
Publications: Co-editor, Archbold, 'Criminal Pleadings and Practice': 1991 to date.
Personal: Governor, International Students House.

SHAW, Geoffrey QC
1 Brick Court (Richard Rampton QC) London (020) 7353 8845
Recommended in Defamation
Specialisation: Defamation.
Prof. Memberships: Gray's Inn.
Career: BA, BCL (Oxon). Called to the Bar 1968. Took Silk, 1991. Trials include: unification church case, Gee v BBC, Archer v Star, Rantzen v People, Upjohn v Oswald; Ashby v Sunday Times. Reported cases include: Lucas-Box 1986 1 WLR 147; Khashoggi 1986 1 WLR 1412; Bobolas 1987 1 WLR 1101; AL-Fayed 1988 1 WLR 1412; Tebbitt 1989 1 WLR 640; Sutcliffe 1991 1 QB 153; Kingshott 1991 1 QB 88; Rantzen 1994 QB 670; Condliffe 1996 1 WLR 753; Evans 1996 EMLR 429; Geenty 1998 EMLR 524; S v Newham 1998 EMLR 583; Awwad v Geraghty and Co, 2000 1 AER 608.

SHAW, Howard
29 Bedford Row Chambers (Peter Ralls QC) London (020) 7404 1044
hshaw@29bedfordrow.co.uk
Recommended in Family
Specialisation: All aspects of family law. Professional negligence (particularly clinical negligence). Major cases include: C v C (Financial Provision: Personal Damages) (1995), Pereira v Keleman (1995), R v R (Divorce: Stay of Proceedings) (1994), London Borough of Sutton v Davis (Costs) (No 2) (1994) C v C (Wasted Costs Order) (1994), London Borough of Sutton v Davies (1994), L v L (Minors) (Separate Representation), Edmonds v Edmonds (1990), Newton v Newton (1990), B v B (Financial Provision) (1987), Barder v Barder (Caluori Intervening) (1987), RE M (Minors) (confidential documents), (1987), Singer (Formerly Sharegin) v Sharegin (1984), Norman v Norman (1983). Brava v Spring (1994) 5MR120. Duties of a G.P. Dobbie v Medway Health Auth. (1992). Rawlinson v North Essex Health Authority (1999). 2001 achieved highest award (including IHT provision) under Schedule One Children Act 1989.
Prof. Memberships: Professional Negligence Bar Association, Personal Injury Bar Association, Family Law Bar Association.
Career: Head of chambers 3 Dr Johnsons Buildings 1989. Joined present chambers 1995. Member Irish Bar 1998.
Personal: Married with two children. Lives in London. Leisure pursuits: Sport and walking the dogs. Theatre.

SHAW, Mark
Blackstone Chambers (Presiley Baxendale QC & Charles Flint QC) London (020) 7583 1770
markshaw@blackstonechambers.com
Recommended in Administrative & Public Law
Specialisation: Principal area of practice is administrative/public law, with an emphasis on judicial review, human rights, immigration and nationality, local government, regulatory/disciplinary proceedings, environment, prisons, social security, health, social services and EU law. Publications include 'Halsbury's Laws of England' (4th Edn) volume on Immigration and Nationality (Butterworths, 1992), 'The Primary Purpose Rule: A Rule With No Purpose', co-author, (Justice, 1993) and 'Human Rights Law and Practice', contributor, (Butterworths, 1999). Member of the Advisory Board of, and contributor to, 'JR'.Notable Cases include: R v SSHD ex parte Thompson and Venables [1998] AC 407 (HL) and T and V v UK 16th December 1999 (ECtHR); R v SSHD ex parte Myra Hindley [2000] 2 WLR 730 (HL); R v SSHD, ex parte Al-Fayed [1998] 1 WLR 763 (CA); Reeves v Metropolitan Police Commissioner [1999] 3 WLR 363 (HL); R v DPP, ex parte Duckenfield [2000] 1 WLR 55 (DC); SSSS v Harmon, Carter and Cocks [1998] 2 FLR 598 (CA); R v SSHD, ex parte Robinson [1998] QB 929 (CA); R v SSHD, ex parte Rahman [1998] QB 136 (CA); R v SSHD, ex parte Mbanja [1999] Imm AR 63 (QBD) and 508 (CA); R v SSSS, ex parte W [1999] 2 FLR 604 (QBD); Adan v SSHD [1999] 1 AC 293 (HL); Laskey, Jaggard and Brown v UK [1997] 24 EHRR 39 (ECtHR); A v UK (1999) 27 EHRR 611 (ECtHR); Condron v UK [2000] 8 BHRC 290 (ECtHR) R v DETR, ex parte First Corporate Shipping 7th November 2000 (QBD and ECJ); Pyrah & Lichniak v SSHD, Times, 16th May 2001 (DC); R (Anderson & Taylor v SSHD, 22nd February 2001 (DC); B v SSHD [2000] Imm AR 478 (CA); Jain v SSHD [2000] Imm AR 76 (CA); Mark Wilkinson Furniture Ltd v CITB, Times, 10th October 2000 (QBD); R v GMC, ex parte Richards, Times, 9th January 2000 (QBD); Kingsley v UK, Times, 9th January 2001 (ECtHR); R (Bulger v Lord Chief Justice & SSHD 16th February 2001 (DC); V & T v News Group Newspapers Ltd [2001] 2 WLR 1038 (Fam Div).
Prof. Memberships: Administrative Law Bar Association, Immigration Law Practitioners' Association, Justice, Bar Golfing Society (Honorary Secretary).
Career: Member of Borough Solicitor's Department, Bournemouth Borough Council 1985-87. Stagiaire at the European Parliament (Human Rights Unit) 1986. Called to the Bar 1987 and joined current chambers in 1988. Pegasus scholarship to Melbourne law firm 1991. Junior Counsel to the Crown (Common Law) (the 'A' list) since 1995. Member of the Attorney General's panel of counsel appointed to act for the Government and as a Special Advocate for immigrants before the Special Immigration Appeals Commission (dealing with national security immigration cases)
Personal: Educated at Durham University (BA) and Cambridge University (LL.M). Born 6th June 1962.

SHEA, Caroline
Falcon Chambers (Jonathan Gaunt QC & Kim Lewison QC) London (020) 7353 2484
shea@falcon-chambers.com
Recommended in Agriculture, Property Litigation
Specialisation: Landlord and tenant, commercial, residential, agricultural, property litigation.
Prof. Memberships: Chancery Bar Association. LCLCBA. Property Bar Association.
Career: MA Cantab. Diploma in Law (City University). Called to Bar 1994. Joined Falcon Chambers 1995. Previously a management consultant. Diplock Scholar.
Publications: Editor of 'plc Property Service'.
Personal: Born 1961. Lives in London. Married with three children.

SHEKERDEMIAN, Marcia
11 Stone Buildings (Murray Rosen QC) London (020) 7831 6381
shekerdemian@11stonebuildings.com
Recommended in Company, Insolvency/Corporate Recovery
Specialisation: Specialises in company law and all aspects of personal and corporate insolvency, including administrations, receiverships, voluntary arrangements, shareholders' disputes, wrongful trading, misfeasance and disqualification of directors. Was one of the counsel instructed in the Carecraft case. Her practice also includes other areas of commercial litigation, including contractual disputes, partnerships and banking.

SHELDON, Richard QC
3-4 South Square (Michael Crystal QC & Lord Alexander of Weedon QC) London (020) 7696 9900
clerks@southsquare.com
Recommended in Insolvency/Corporate Recovery
Specialisation: Banking, bank securities, bankruptcy and insolvency. Corporate insolvency, general commercial and fraud (civil), company law, mergers, acquisitions and disposal of companies, financial services, international trade, finance of international trade, mortgages, partnership, solicitors' negligence, accountants' negligence. Recent cases: Three Rivers DC v Bank of England (HL) [2001] 2 All ER 513; Re BCCI, Banque Arabe Internationale d'Investissement SA v Morris [2001] 1 BCLC 263; Banco Nacional de Cuba v Cosmos Trading Corp (CA) [2000] 1 BCLC 813; Morris v Bank of America National Trust (CA) [2000] 1 All ER 954; Bank of Credit and Commerce International (overseas) Ltd v Akindele (CA) [2000] 3 WLR 1423.
Prof. Memberships: Chancery Bar Association, Commercial Bar Association.
Career: Called to the Bar 1979. Queen's Counsel 1996. Cambridge MA.
Publications: Contributed to Halsbury's Laws (4th ed vol 7).

SHELTON, Gordon
Broadway House (J Graham K Hyland QC) Bradford (01274) 722560
Recommended in Family
Specialisation: Principal area of practice family law.
Prof. Memberships: Family Law Bar Association.
Career: Called 1981.
Personal: Educated Ashville College, Harrogate. Leicester University.

SHEPHERD, Nigel
2 Paper Buildings (Desmond de Silva QC) London (020) 7556 5500
shepherd@dial.pipex.com
Recommended in Crime
Specialisation: Crime; commercial fraud; money-laundering; drugs; VAT fraud; mortgage fraud; bond laundering; advance fee fraud; computer fraud. R-v- Edwards CA 11/5/99; Drug Trafficking hearing period cannot be extended retrospectively. R-v- Deroda CA 24/5/99; Archbold News. S.23 unavailable witness requirements clarified. R-v- Tomas Honz [1998] 2 Cr.App.R(S) 283 – importation: sentence 24 years reduced to 16.
Prof. Memberships: Criminal Bar Association; NE Circuit.
Career: Inner Temple, Lincolns Inn; called 1973. Receiving leading briefs since 1991.
Publications: 1973 Criminal Law Review: 'When is a Court not a Court?'
Personal: Two sons. Leisure interests: high altitude sport, leasehold reform, comparative penology, annoying normative people.

SHEPHERD, Philip
24 Old Buildings (Martin Mann QC & Alan Steinfeld QC) London (020) 7404 0946
philip.shephard@xxiv.co.uk
Recommended in Aviation
Specialisation: Specialise in aviation law since 1985. Practice includes aviation insurance, product liability, finance and leasing, EC competition and regulation, air accidents, carriage by air, arrest of aircraft, CAA prosecutions. Advises in aircraft sales and purchase transactions. Acted as counsel in most of the significant aviation cases in the UK in recent years. The most recent include: The Secretary of State For The Environment, Transport & The Regions v The International Air Transport Association [2000] 1 Lloyd's Law Reports 242; Acting for the Secretary of State in challenge by IATA to legality of EC directive removing limits of Warsaw Convention for EC carriers, including possible referral to European Court – Messier Dowty v Sabana SA [2000] 1 Lloyd's Law Reports 428 – Court of Appeal; Declatory Judgement – forum shopping conflict laws – Article 6 of the Brussels Convention. Product liability claim for $75 million following collapse of Airbus A340 undercarriage; Association of British Travel Agents v British Airways, Virgin and Lufthansa – [2000] 2 Lloyd's Law Reports 209. Acting on behalf of the UK's travel agents, Passenger service charge, construction of standard IATA contracts. Attempt by airlines to change agents' commission agreements declared unlawful; Estate of Mathew Harding v Michael Goss Aviation [2000] 2 Lloyd's Law Reports 222 – Court of Appeal. Helicopter crash. In which Mathew Harding director of Chelsea FC was killed – claim for £59 million – carriers liability. Leading case on Article 25 of the Warsaw Convention – willful misconduct action struck out and liability limited to £80,000; Western Digital Corporation v British Airways – [2000] 2 Lloyd's Law Reports 142 – Court of Appeal. Whether carrier liable only to names on air waybill. Claim for loss or damage to cargo under article 18 of the Warsaw Convention. Leading case on who can sue the carrier; Applied Implant Technology v Lufthansa [2000] 2 Lloyd's Reports 46 – 1 All ER (comm) 95B Warsaw Convention – compulation of liability limit – whether weight of all packages to be taken into account under article 22(2) (b); Dance Air Transport v Air Canada [2000] Weekly Law Reports 395. Court of Appeal. Dispute between airline and general sales agent for breach of GSAcontract governed by Greek Law; H5 Air Service Norway v CAA [1998] Lloyd's Law Reports 364 – Court of Appeal EC regulation 2407/92 access for community carrier to community air routes: Licensing of air carriers. Led to amendment to Air Navigation Order. Acts as Counsel and arbitrator in commercial arbitrations and mediations. Has extensive experience in international arbitration under ICC and UNCITRAIL rules.
Prof. Memberships: European Air Law Association, Lawyers Flying Association, Royal Aeronautical Society, Air Law Group, Grays Inn, COMBAR.
Career: St George's College, London School of Economics, Monash University Melbourne (Aus). Inns of Court Law School. Assistant Recorder 1998, Recorder 2000.
Personal: Flying light aircraft. Fluent in Italian and French.

SHER, Jules QC
Wilberforce Chambers (Edward Nugee QC) London (020) 7306 0102
Recommended in Chancery, Energy & Natural Resources, Pensions
Specialisation: Chancery and commercial litigation and advice. Covers the wide range of work comprised in a modern commercial chancery practice including Lloyd's litigation and advice; North Sea Oil and Gas tract participation disputes (acting for British Gas and major oil companies in litigation in the Commercial Court and Chancery Division); trust litigation in the UK and abroad (Singapore, Cayman Islands, Bahamas, Hong Kong); trust aspects of takeovers (acted in Glaxo takeover of Wellcome and Granada takeover of Forte and Wolverhampton and Dudley take over of Mansfield Brewery); professional negligence (accountants, solicitors); pensions litigation (Imperial Group v Imperial Tobacco, London Regional Transport Pension Fund Trustee Co Ltd v Hatt, MacDonald v Horn and the BT Pension Schemes Trust).
Career: B Comm, LLB (Rand), BCL (Oxon). Called to the Bar of England and Wales in 1968. Took silk 1981. Recorder. Advocate of the Supreme Court of South Africa; Deputy High Court Judge (Commercial Court and Chancery Division); member of the Commercial Bar Association and Chancery Bar Association.

SHERBORNE, David
5 Raymond Buildings (Patrick Milmo QC) London (020) 7242 2902
davidsherborne@5rb.co.uk
Recommended in Defamation
Specialisation: Defamation, privacy and confidentiality (including data protection); human rights; freedom of the press and contempt of court; intellectual property; entertainment and sports law. Recent cases: Douglas, Zeta-Jones & OK v Hello! [2001] 2 WLR 992 (landmark case establishing actionable right to privacy); Schellenberg v BBC [2000] EMLR 296 (relitigation abuse and first 'summary judgment' in libel); Adams & ors v Attridge 'Times', 25 July 1998 (committal and confidence proceedings by Spice Girls against former chauffeur); Jarvis v BBC, 'Times' 17 March 1998 (test case on privacy over fly-on-the-wall documentary); McDonald's Corp v Steel & Morris (1995) 3 All ER 615 (principles of pleading justification and use of witness statements); Elite Model Management v BBC (acted for claimants in libel action; mode of trial and reference); Albert Reynolds v Times (acted for newspaper in defence of former Irish PMs action); Davies & anor v Newman & anor (acted for claimants in copyright/partnership action establishing rights in early Spice Girl's footage); Western Provident Association v Norwich Union (acted for defendant in first email action); in the matter of Mike Tyson and British Boxing Board of Control (acted for boxer in disciplinary hearing).
Career: Called to the Bar 1992. Senior Scholar, Gray's Inn.
Personal: Educated at University College School, London and New College, Oxford.

SHERIDAN, Maurice
Matrix Chambers (Nicholas Blake QC) London (020) 7404 3447
Recommended in Environment
Specialisation: EC environmental, especially regarding direct effect of Directives; domestic environmental, including nuisance and negligence, waste management, water legislation and utilities regulatory active professional negligence and commercial.
Prof. Memberships: Bar European Group; British Italian Law Association; British Bulgarian Law Association; COMBAR.
Career: Sorbonne 1980; Stage with EC Commission 1985; LLB Bristol 1983; LLM (International law) Cantab 1985-96; assisting in approximation programmes regarding EC environmental Acquis in Central and Eastern Europe – 1992 to 1999.
Personal: Travelling, theatre, cinema, contemporary dance.

SHIELDS, Thomas QC
1 Brick Court (Richard Rampton QC) London (020) 7353 8845
Recommended in Defamation

SHIPLEY, Graham
19 Old Buildings (Alastair Wilson QC) London (020) 7405 2001
Recommended in Information Technology

SHIPWRIGHT, Adrian J.
Pump Court Tax Chambers London (020) 7414 8080
Recommended in Tax
Specialisation: All tax related matters including dispute resolution and litigation particularly corporate matters such as reorganisations, financings and share purchases and sales including takeovers, trust matters, land development, indirect taxation and the taxation of intellectual property.
Prof. Memberships: Lincoln's Inn; Chartered Institute of Taxation; Institute of Indirect Taxation; VAT Practitioners Group; STEP [FRSA]. Member of the Trust Law Committee chaired by Sir John Vinelott.
Career: Admitted as a solicitor 1976, called to the Bar 1993. Visiting Professor, King's College London 1996-. Professor of Business Law and director of the Tax Research Unit, King's College, London 1992-96. Tax partner *SJ Berwin & Co* 1987-92 (consultant till 1993). Tax partner *Denton Hall* 1982-87. Official student (fellow) and tutor in Law, Christ Church, Oxford and lecturer in law (CUF), Oxford University 1977-82. Member of the tax department and articles *Linklaters & Paines* 1974-77.
Publications: Publications include 'Trusts and UK Tax' (Key Haven); 'UK Taxation Intellectual Property' (Sweet & Maxwell); 'Tax Avoidance and the Law' (editor for SPTL); 'Tax Planning and UK Land Development' (Key Haven); textbook on Revenue Law. Member of the editorial boards of 'The Tax Journal' and Tolley 'Trust Law International'.
Personal: Education: BA (1972), BCL (1973), MA (1977), Christ Church, Oxford. King Edward VI School, Southampton (governor till 1995).

SHORROCK, Michael QC
Peel Court Chambers (Michael Shorrock QC) Manchester (0161) 832 3791
Recommended in Crime

SILSOE, Lord QC
2 Mitre Court Buildings (Michael FitzGerald QC) London (020) 7583 1380
Recommended in Planning
Specialisation: Main areas of practice include town and country planning; environmental law; compulsory purchase and compensation; rating and the council tax; utilities and infrastructure; local government; public and administrative law; Transport and Works Act orders.
Prof. Memberships: Planning and Environment Bar Association.
Career: Called to the Bar in 1955. Joined current chambers in 1956. Appointed QC in 1972.
Publications: Editor of Ryde 11th, 12th and 13th Editions.
Personal: Educated at Winchester College, Christ Church, Oxford and Columbia University (New York).

SILVERLEAF, Michael QC
11 South Square (Christopher Floyd QC) London (020) 7405 1222
clerks@11southsquare.com
Recommended in Information Technology, Intellectual Property, Media & Entertainment
Specialisation: Intellectual property, computer law, entertainment and media, disputes with high technical content and related EC and domestic competition law.
Prof. Memberships: IP Association, Chancery Bar Association.
Career: Member of Gray's Inn. Called 1980. Junior Counsel to the Treasury in Patent Matters 1991-96. QC 1996.
Personal: Publications: 'Passing off Law and Practice' (Butterworths), 'Butterworths Patent Litigation' (contributor). Attended King's College School, Wimbledon, Imperial College (BSc, Physics).

SIMLER, Ingrid
Devereux Chambers (Jeffrey Burke QC) London (020) 7353 7534
simler@devchambers.co.uk
Recommended in Employment
Specialisation: Principal area of practice is employment, encompassing all areas of individual and collective employment law, including discrimination, restraint of

trade and business transfers. Also handles general commercial work, professional negligence and personal injury work. Member of B Panel – Junior Counsel to the Crown.
Prof. Memberships: Secretary of Employment Law Bar Association, member of Employment Lawyers Association, Commercial Law Bar Association, Administrative Law Bar Association.
Career: Called to the Bar 1987.
Publications: Contributor to 'Tolleys' Employment Law'. Co-author of Butterworths 'Discrimination Law' (published Autumn 1999).
Personal: Educated at Cambridge University 1982-85 (MA) and University of Amsterdam 1985-86 (Diploma in European law).

SIMMONDS, Andrew QC
5 Stone Buildings (Henry Harrod) London (020) 7242 6201
Recommended in Chancery, Pensions, Professional Negligence
Specialisation: Specialises in professional negligence litigation (other than medical) and contentious pensions work. In the former field, has particular experience of claims against solicitors, barristers and accountants but has also acted in claims against actuaries, insurance brokers, fund managers and others. Pensions experience covers all manner of disputes involving employers, trustees and members, claims against pensions professionals and complaints to the Pensions Ombudsman. Recent cases include various aspects of the Maxwell litigation; National Power v Feldon [1997] PLR 157; ITN v Ward [1997] PLR 131; MMI v Harrop [1998] PLR 149; Wakelin v Read [1998] PLR 337; University of Nottingham v Eyett (Nos 1 and 2) [1999] 2 AER 437, 445; Spooner v BT [2000] PLR 65; Barclays Bank v Holmes [2000] PLR 339; Walker v Stones [2000] 4 AER 412; Liverpool v Goldberg [2001] 1 AER 182.
Prof. Memberships: Member of the Association of Pension Lawyers, the Professional Negligence Bar Association and the Pension Litigation Court Users' committee chaired by Lloyd J.
Career: Called 1980. Silk 1999.

SIMPSON, Mark
4 Paper Buildings (Jean Ritchie QC) London (020) 7353 3366
Recommended in Professional Negligence
Specialisation: General Editor of Professional Negligence and Liability (LLP 2000, 2 vols). General Editor of Lloyd's Law Reports: Professional Negligence. Associate Editor of Tolley's Professional Negligence. Regular contributor to Solicitors Journal on professional negligence topics. Specialises in all aspects of professional negligence acting for and against solicitors, barristers, surveyors, valuers, estate agents, architects, insurance brokers, financial advisers, accountants, auditors, IT professionals, pension fund and other trustees. Also general insurance, including professional indemnity insurance, and general commercial work. Recent reported cases include Green v Hancocks (2001) Lloyd's Rep PN 212 (CA); Ruiss v Palmano (2001) Lloyd's Rep PN 341 (QBD); Hall v Simons (2000) 3 WLR 543 (HL): Farley v Skinner (2000) PNLR 441; (2000) Lloyd's Rep PN 516 (CA); UCB Corporate Services Ltd v Halifax (SW) Ltd – Times, 23 December 1999 (CA); Brick v Colleys Professional Services [1999] Lloyd's Rep PN 309 (CA); Mortgage Corporation v Halifax (SW) Ltd (1999) Lloyd's Rep PN 159 (QBD); Brophy v Dunphys (1998) EGCS 37 (CA); S v M (1998) 3 PCR 665 (ChD). Lectured widely on professional negligence and evidence.
Prof. Memberships: Professional Negligence Bar Association. London Common Law and Commercial Bar Association. Bar European Group.
Career: Called to Bar 1992. Educated at King's School Canterbury, Oriel College Oxford (MA Classics 1986), Hughes Hall Cambridge (PCGE 1987), City University (Dip Law 1991), ICSL (Bar Finals 1992), King's College London (Dip European Law 1994). Taught classics at St Paul's School, Barnes (1987-90).
Personal: Born 5 January 1963. Lives in London. Working knowledge of French.

SINCLAIR, Fiona
Four New Square (Justin Fenwick QC) London (020) 7822 2000 f.sinclair@4newsquare.com
Recommended in Professional Negligence
Specialisation: Practice: professional negligence in relation to construction (architects, engineers, quantity surveyors), finance (accountants, solicitors, insurance brokers, financial advisers) and property (solicitors and surveyors); insurance and reinsurance contracts; construction law; financial services law. Editor of 'Jackson and Powell on Professional Negligence' (Chapter 2, Architects and Engineers).
Prof. Memberships: Professional Negligence Bar Association, Official Referees' Bar Association, Society of Construction Law.
Career: Called 1989.
Personal: Born 1963. Educated at Jesus College, Cambridge (B.A. in Philosophy and Law, 1983-87; LL.M, 1987-88). Interests: mountaineering, skiing, flying.

SINGH, Kuldip QC
5 Paper Buildings (Godfrey Carey QC & Jonathan Caplan QC) London (020) 7583 6117
Recommended in Fraud, Sport

SINGH, Rabinder
Matrix Chambers (Nicholas Blake QC) London (020) 7404 3447
Recommended in Administrative & Public Law, Human Rights, Local Government, Planning
Specialisation: All aspects of public law, employment law and European Community and human rights law.
Prof. Memberships: Administrative Law Bar Association (Treasurer), Planning and Environment Bar Association, Employment Law Bar Association; Bar European Group.
Career: Called:1989. Appointed to A panel of junior counsel to the Crown: 2000. Additional Junior Counsel to the Inland Revenue: 1997.
Personal: B.A. (Law) 1985: Trinity College, Cambridge LL.M. 1986: University of California, Berkeley. Visiting fellow, Queen Mary and Westfield College, London since 1995.

SINGLETON, Barry QC
One King's Bench Walk (Anthony Hacking QC) London (020) 7936 1500
Recommended in Family

SINGLETON, Sarah
28 St. John St Manchester (0161) 834 8418 clerk@28stjohnst.co.uk
Recommended in Family
Specialisation: Family law, money and children (public and private law).
Prof. Memberships: FLBA.
Career: Called 1983. Recorder.

SLADE, Elizabeth QC
11 King's Bench Walk Chambers (Eldred Tabachnik QC & James Goudie QC) London (020) 7632 8500
Recommended in Employment
Specialisation: Specialises in all aspects of employment law with particular emphasis on European aspects of employment law, transfer of undertakings, sex and race discrimination, equal pay, employment aspects of pensions. Leading cases include Westminster City Council v Pensions Ombudsman and Haywood, Halfpenny v IGE Medical Systems Ltd, London Regional Transport v Nagarajan, Foster & Others v British Gas, Reed Executive plc v Sommers, Newns v British Airways plc.
Prof. Memberships: Employment Law Bar Association; Employment Lawyers Association; ALBA; Bar European Group.
Career: Called to the Bar in 1972; Recorder 1998; Deputy High Court Judge 1998-; part-time judge of the Employment Appeal Tribunal 2000-; 1990 bencher of the Inner Temple; 1992 Appointed QC; 1994-98 Master of the Staff, Inner Temple; chair of Employment Law Bar Association 1995-97; Hon Vice-President 1998-; Chairman Sex Discrimination Committee, Bar Council 2000-; trustee, Free Representation Unit; member of the Administrative Tribunal of the Bank for International Settlements.
Publications: Original author of 'Tolleys Employment Handbook' and editor or co-editor of 2nd to 7th edns.
Personal: Education: Lady Margaret Hall, Oxford. Exhibitioner, 1971 BA.

SLATER, John QC
Crown Office Chambers (Michael Spencer QC & Christopher Purchas QC) London (020) 7797 8100 jslaterqc@crownofficechambers.com
Recommended in Construction
Specialisation: Construction and civil engineering; professional negligence (architects, engineers, surveyors, accountants, solicitors and trade mark agents); insurance/reinsurance; product liability. Recent cases include Arab Bank v John D Wooz; Capital & Counties v Hampshire County Council (first leader for claimants); Alzal v Ford, Wessex Regional Health Authority v HLM; Alliance & Leicester v Edgestop; Team Services v Kier Management; Kier Construction v Royal Insurance. Mainly briefed by insurers and major corporations. Much used for lengthy complex trials with large volumes of paper. Reputation as an effective cross examiner. Previously used in interrelated insurance policy and project disputes eg in fire, flood, building collapse, product failure cases. Enjoys Court and arbitration work of all types.
Career: Called to the Bar 1969, QC 1987 (Aged 40), sits as domestic and international arbitrator (LCIA, ICC UNCITRAL).
Personal: Born 1946. Educated Sedbergh School, University College, Oxford. Lives in Highgate with wife and three offspring.

SLOAN, Paul QC
Trinity Chambers (Toby Hedworth QC) Newcastle upon Tyne (0191) 232 1927 info@trinitychambers.co.uk
Recommended in Licensing
Specialisation: Crime (prosecution and defence), licensing (liquor and public entertainment), firearms and shotguns (all aspects), police disciplinary tribunals (presenting cases for and against police officers and acting as legal advisor to Chief Constables).
Prof. Memberships: Inner Temple. North Eastern Circuit. Criminal Bar Association. Bar representative on Area Criminal Justice Strategy Committee. North Eastern Bar Press Office spokesman.
Career: LL.B (Lond.) Call 1981. Recorder 2000. Queens Counsel 2001.

SLOMNICKA, Barbara
14 Gray's Inn Square (Joanna Dodson QC) London (020) 7242 0858
Recommended in Family

SMALLWOOD, Anne
5 Fountain Court (Anthony Barker QC) Birmingham (0121) 606 0500
Recommended in Family

SMITH, Andrew QC
Fountain Court (Anthony Boswood QC) London (020) 7583 3335
Recommended in Information Technology

SMITH, Emma
Old Square Chambers (John Hendy QC) London (020) 7269 0300 smith@oldsquarechambers.co.uk
Recommended in Employment
Specialisation: Employment law, including unfair and wrongful dismissal, discrimination, equal pay, redundancy and collective disputes. Personal injury and clinical negligence.

Prof. Memberships: Industrial Law Society; Employment Law Bar Association; Employment Lawyers' Association; Personal Injury Bar Association; Association of Personal Injury Lawyers.
Career: LLB (Hons), University of Leicester (1993); MA Medical Ethics and Law, Kings College, London (1994); called to the Bar 1995.
Publications: Co-author 'Discrimination: Remedies and Quantum' (Sweet & Maxwell); contributor 'UK and EU Employee Consultation' (Sweet & Maxwell).
Personal: Born 1971.

SMITH, Julia

Gough Square Chambers (Fred Philpott) London (020) 7353 0924
Recommended in Consumer Law
Specialisation: Consumer Law – in particular consumer credit and mortgage actions (eg First National Bank v Syed [1991] 2 All ER 250, Jarrett v Barclays Bank [1997] 2 All ER 484 and Kenyon-Brown v Desmond Banks [2000] Lloyd's Rep. Banks) including consumer credit drafting, extortionate credit bargains, and licensing. Clients include banks, finance houses, leasing companies and retailers.
Prof. Memberships: London Common Law and Commercial Bar Association.
Career: Called to the Bar 1988
Personal: Cheltenham Ladies College and Liverpool University.

SMITH, Nicholas G

Queen Square Chambers (Anthony Donne QC & T Alun Jenkins QC) Bristol (0117) 921 1966
Recommended in Employment

SMITH, Peter QC

40 King St Manchester (020) 7430 0341
clerks@11oldsquare.co.uk
11 Old Square (Grant Crawford & Jonathan Simpkiss) London (020) 7430 0341
clerks@11oldsquare.co.uk
Recommended in Chancery, Commercial (Litigation), Insolvency/Corporate Recovery, Property Litigation
Specialisation: Insolvency, landlord and tenant, professional negligence. Recent cases: Re: Exchange Travel (1996) BCLC 524; Norglen v Reeds Rains (1998) HL 1 AER 218; CIS v Argyll Stores, HL (1997); Medforth v Blake (1999) 3 All ER 97 CA; Allen v Rochdale BC (1999) 3 All ER 443 CA; Re RSM Engineering (1999) 3 WLR 697 CA.
Prof. Memberships: Professional Negligence Bar Association, Northern Chancery Bar Association, Chancery Bar Association.
Career: Called to Bar in 1975. Lecturer at Manchester University 1977-83. Northern Circuit 1979-96. Took Silk in 1992. Assistant Recorder 1994. Deputy High Court Judge 1996.
Publications: 'Barnsley Conveyancing Law & Practice' 2nd edn 1982 Butterworths. 'Distribution on Intestacy' 1987 Oyez and Longman.
Personal: Born 1952; resides Wilmslow.

SMITH, Richard QC

Guildhall Chambers (Adrian Palmer QC) Bristol (0117) 927 3366
Recommended in Crime

SMITH, Robert QC

Park Court Chambers (James Stewart QC & Robert Smith QC) Leeds (0113) 203 5501
robert.smithqc@btinternet.com
Recommended in Crime
Specialisation: A balanced practice involving prosecution and defence work (principally homicide, commercial fraud and specialist issues such as corporate manslaughter, data protection, etc). Defence instructions include a large proportion of professional defendants such as medical practitioners, accountants and police officers. Has a particular interest in medico-legal matters and scientific evidence. Recent cases of importance: Attorney General's Reference (No 3 of 1994): Criminal Liability for pre-natal injuries, House of Lords [1998] AC 245; R v Beedie, Court of Appeal Criminal Division: The Double Jeopardy Rule in Criminal Proceedings [1997] 2 Cr.App.R. 167; R v Woolin: Foresight of consequences as proof of intent in murder, House of Lords [1999] AC 82.
Prof. Memberships: Member of the International Bar Association, Personal Injuries Bar Association, Bar European Group and Criminal Bar Association.
Career: Common Law Practitioner specialising in criminal and civil litigation (principally personal injury and medical and professional negligence) from commencing practice in Leeds in 1971. Appointed Queen's Counsel and a Recorder in 1986. Served for three years as a Member of the Criminal Injuries Compensation Board. Joined London chambers at 3 Serjeants' Inn [Adrian Whitfield QC] as a door tenant in 1994.

SMITH, Roger QC

No.6 Fountain Court (Roger Smith QC) Birmingham (0121) 233 3282
Recommended in Crime

SMITH, Sally QC

1 Crown Office Row (Robert Seabrook QC) London (020) 7797 7500
Recommended in Clinical Negligence

SMITH, Shaun

No.1 High Pavement (John B. Milmo QC) Nottingham (0115) 941 8218
Recommended in Crime

SMITH, Stephen QC

New Square Chambers (John Mowbray QC & Eben Hamilton QC) London (020) 7419 8000
stephen.smith@newsquarechambers.co.uk
Recommended in Chancery, Commercial (Litigation), Company, Fraud
Specialisation: Complex and heavy commercial litigation, often with a Chancery or jurisdictional element (especially issues arising under the Brussels/ Lugano Convention) and involving restraints on disposals of assets; also professional negligence, civil fraud, insurance, property disputes and insolvency. Conducted numerous witness examinations, including several in the USA and in New Zealand. Called to the Bar of the Eastern Caribbean States Supreme Court and conducted several hearings on Tortola BVI at first instance (including at trial) and on appeal to the Court of Appeal of the Eastern Caribbean, and appeared on a further appeal to the Privy Council. Previous cases: Derby v Weldon (acted for Salomon Inc); DSQ Property Company (formerly DeLorean Motor Company) v Lotus Cars (acted for John Z. DeLorean); Morris v Mahfouz BCCI (acted for Khalid Bin Mahfouz and others); FTIT Ltd v Morgan Stanley and Coopers & Lybrand (acted for liquidators (Deloitte Touche) appointed by Swiss Bank Corporation); Senate Electrical Wholesalers v Alcatel Submarines Networks (acted for Northern Telecom); Village Cay Marina v Acland (Privy Council decision about share registration and receivership in the BVI); Trustor v Moyne, Trustor v Smallbone; Trustor v Barclays (acted for Trustor); Pagarani v T Choithram International SA (Privy Council decision); W v H (restraint orders in the Family Division).
Prof. Memberships: Middle Temple (Jules Thorn Scholar).
Career: Scholar, University College Oxford 1979-82. First Class Hons. degree in Jurisprudence, Oxford University 1982 (Wronker and Jurisprudence Prizes winner). Called to the Bar in England and Wales, August 1983. QC 2000.
Personal: Married to Lorraine, five children. Principal leisure interests: family, alpaca farming.

SMOUHA, Joe

Essex Court Chambers (Gordon Pollock QC) London (020) 7813 8000
Recommended in Arbitration (International), Commercial (Litigation), Fraud, Shipping, Tax
Specialisation: Litigation involving appearances in arbitration, the Commercial Court, Court of Appeal, the House of Lords and other courts hearing civil claims. All aspects of commercial law including shipping, banking, insurance and reinsurance, international sale of goods, oil and gas, public international law and other related areas. Art litigation including title, dealer commission, purchasing syndicate disputes. VAT: includes both substantial High Court and tribunal work and general advisory work on non-contentious matters, schemes etc.
Career: Magdalene College, Cambridge, BA Law (Hons) 1984. MA 1988. New York University School of Law, 1984-85: LLM in International Trade Law. Called to the Bar 1986 (Middle Temple).
Personal: Born 1963.

SNOWDEN, Richard

Erskine Chambers (Robin Potts QC) London (020) 242 5532
rsnowden@erskine-chambers.co.uk
Recommended in Company, Financial Services, Insolvency/Corporate Recovery
Specialisation: Company law, corporate insolvency, financial services and related commercial litigation. Currently, about 75% of cases are contentious matters, with the remainder being non-contentious advisory work. Notable cases include acting for the successful employees in Paramount Airways (Powdrill v Watson) in all courts up to and including the House of Lords; for the bondholders in the hearings to approve the sale of Barings to ING; for Lloyds of London in litigation in Bermuda relating to the insolvency of EMLICO; for the English and Luxembourg liquidators of BCCI in various cases in England including BCCI no 10 and Mahomed v Morris; for the SPI in relation to multiple searches of court records; for the successful majority shareholder in Re Astec (BSR) plc; for the company in Re Osiris Insurance Limited; for the successful majority shareholders in Arrow Nominees v Blackledge; for the administrative receivers of Transtec plc in a dispute with various motor manufacturers; for the OFT in judicial review proceedings concerning estate agents; and for the liquidators of Leyland Daf Limited concerning the priority of liquidation expenses.
Prof. Memberships: Chancery Bar Association, COMBAR, R3, The Financial Law Panel working groups on directors' duties, The British Association for Sport and Law.
Career: Called to the Bar in 1986; appointed Junior Counsel to the Crown (A Panel) in 1999.
Publications: Joint Editor of Lightman and Moss, 'The Law of Receivers and Administrators of Companies' and 'Company Directors: Law and Liability' (both Sweet and Maxwell). Regularly speaks and lectures at conferences.
Personal: Educated at Downing College, Cambridge 1981-84 (MA, 1st Class Hons; Harvard Law School 1984-85 (LLM). Leisure pursuits include golf, cricket rugby and music. Born 22nd March 1962. Lives in East Sussex.

SOARES, Patrick C.

8 Gray's Inn Square (Patrick C. Soares) London (020) 7242 3529
clerics.8graysinn@btconnect.com
Recommended in Tax
Specialisation: Specialist in all aspects of revenue law, including structuring land transactions for the optimum tax position, value added tax and stamp duty on land transactions, taxation of overseas trusts and international estate and trust planning. Also conducts tax appeals at all levels. Publications include 'Vat Planning for Property Transactions', 'Land and Tax Planning', 'Trusts and Tax Planning', 'Taxation of Non-Resident Trusts', 'Taxation of Land Development', 'Offshore Investment in UK Property' and 'Tax Strategy for Conveyancing Transactions'. Tax editor of the 'Property Law Bulletin' and co-editor of 'Trusts for Europe'.

Prof. Memberships: Fellow of the Institute of Taxation.
Career: Called to the Bar 1983. Previously a tax partner in a leading firm of London solicitors, having been admitted a solicitor in 1972.
Personal: Educated at University College, London (MA Taxation).

SOLLEY, Stephen QC
Charter Chambers (Stephen Solley QC) London (020) 7832 0300
Recommended in Crime, Fraud

SOMERVILLE, Bryce
No.6 Fountain Court (Roger Smith QC) Birmingham (0121) 233 3282
Recommended in Family

SOORJOO, Martin
Tooks Court Chambers (Michael Mansfield QC) London (020) 7405 8828
Recommended in Immigration

SOUTHERN, Richard
7 King's Bench Walk (Jeremy Cooke QC) London (020) 7910 8300
Recommended in Shipping
Specialisation: Main areas of practice are shipping and maritime, insurance and reinsurance, professional negligence, and commercial fraud, as well as general commercial litigation and arbitration. Recent cases include Aneco Reinsurance Underwriting v Johnson & Higgins [2000] P.N.L.R 152, Jordan Grand Prix Ltd v Baltic Insurance Group [1999] 2 AC 127, Glencore International v Metro Trading [1999] 2 Lloyd's Rep 632, Dubai Aluminium Co Ltd v Salaam [1999] 1 Lloyd's Rep 415.
Prof. Memberships: The Commercial Bar Association.
Career: Called 1987.

SOUTHEY, David Hugh
Tooks Court Chambers (Michael Mansfield QC) London (020) 7405 8828
Recommended in Immigration
Specialisation: Immigration and asylum, Human Rights Act 1998, crime, prisoners rights, mental health, privacy, education and other public law. Cases include R (P and Q) v SSHD (2001) The Times, 1 June; R (Akhtar) v SSHD (2001) The Times; 23 February; Gomez v SSHD (2000) INLR 549; Zaitz v SSHD (2000) INLR 346; R v IAT ex p Aziz [1999] INLR 355; Darbiye v SSHD [1998] Imm AR 64; In re H, in re D [1999] The Times, 13 August; R v York Mags ex p Grimes [1997] The Times, 27 June.
Prof. Memberships: ILPA, Prisoners Legal Rights Group.
Publications: Joint editor of 'United Kingdom Human Rights Reports' and ' Human Rights' and joint author of 'A Criminal Practitioners Guide to Judicial Review and Case Stated'.

SPEAIGHT, Anthony QC
4 Pump Court London (020) 7842 5555
aspeaight@4pumpcourt.com
Recommended in Construction
Specialisation: Construction contracts, professional negligence (especially architects, surveyors and engineers), other commercial contracts and financial services, other property-related work, public law. Cases include Linden Gardens v Lenesta Sludge [1994] 1 AC 85 (assignment of cause of action between successive owners of property); Gable House Estates v Halpern [1995] CILL 1072 (architects' negligence); Kelly v Norwich Union [1990] 1 WLR 139 (subsidence claim); R v Wicks [1998] AC 92 (planning enforcement); Thornton Springer v NEM Insurance [2000] 2 All ER 489 (meaning of professional indemnity insurance policy wording); R (Fleurose) v Securities and Futures Authority 'The Times' 15 May 2001 (European Convention of Human Rights and financial services regulation).
Prof. Memberships: Technology and Construction Bar Association, Professional Negligence Bar Association, London Common Law and Commercial Bar Association, Personal Injury Bar Association, Administrative Law Bar Association.
Career: Barrister in practice in the Temple since 1973. Silk 1995.
Publications: Co-editor of 'Butterworths Professional Negligence Service'; co-author of 'The Law of Defective Premises' (1982).
Personal: Married with three children. Chairman of Bar Council working party on Modernising Civil Justice (2001).

SPEARMAN, Richard QC
4-5 Gray's Inn Square (Elizabeth Appleby QC & David Mole QC) London (020) 74045252
Recommended in Sport
Specialisation: Wide range of practice in all divisions of High Court, and Copyright Tribunal. Including commercial fraud, media and entertainment, sports law, professional negligence, defamation, confidence and privacy, insurance, reinsurance, sale of goods, restraint of trade. Reported cases concerning restraint of trade/boxing, Mareva injunctions, letters of credit, copyright Euro-defences, as well as Istel v Tully (privilege against self-incrimination); R v Jockey Club ex p Aga Khan (Jockey Club/judicial review); AIRC v PPL (Copyright Tribunal/licensing scheme); Formica v ECGD (discovery/privilege/ECGD guarantee); Brinks v Abu Saleh (tracing); Hyde Park Residence v Yelland and Ashdown v Telegraph (copyright/ public interest/fair dealing); Kazakstan Wool Processors v NCM (insurance/ construction of contract); Grobbelaar v News Group (defamation / qualified privilege / perverse jury verdict).
Career: Called 1977, silk 1996.
Personal: Educated Bedales; King's College, Cambridge. Born 19.1.53.

SPECK, Adrian
8 New Square (Michael Fysh QC) London (020) 7405 4321
clerks@8newsquare.co.uk
Recommended in Information Technology, Intellectual Property
Specialisation: Barrister specialising in all aspects of intellectual property, including patents trade marks and passing off, confidential information, designs, copyright and performers' rights; also specialises in jurisdiction disputes under the CJJA 1982/Brussels Convention and entertainment litigation. For comprehensive CV and list of recent cases, visit our website at www.8newsquare.co.uk.
Prof. Memberships: Patent Bar Association (PBA); Chancery Bar Association; The Intellectual Property Lawyers Organisation (TIPLO).
Career: Called 1993.
Publications: 'Modern Law of Copyright', 3rd edn.
Personal: Born 1969. Educated at Seaford Head Comprehensive; Kings College, Cambridge (1992 BA Physics and Theoretical Physics – 1st Class); College of Law 1991 (Common Professional Exam with distinction); ICSL 1993 (Bar Vocational Course).

SPENCER, Martin
4 Paper Buildings (Jean Ritchie QC) London (020) 7353 3366
Recommended in Clinical Negligence
Specialisation: Clinical negligence, professional negligence and personal injury. Recent cases include Farley v Skinner (HL), Daniels v Walker, Swain v LAS, Forbes v Wandsworth HA.
Prof. Memberships: Professional Negligence Bar Association (Executive Committee member), Personal Injury Bar Association.
Career: MA (Oxon), BCL (Oxon), called to Bar 1979. Danish Government Scholar in 1979/80. Pupil at Fountain Court 1980-81, Recorder 2001. Director, Bar Services Company Limited.
Publications: 'The Civil Procedure Rules in Action' (2000) with Ian Grainger and Michael Feeley; 'The Danish Criminal Code' (1999) with Gitte Hoyer and Vagn Greve; 'The Danish System of Criminal Justice with Vagn Greve and others.
Personal: Married with three children. Languages: Danish. Interests: music, sport and bridge. School Governor.

SPENCER, Michael QC
Crown Office Chambers (Michael Spencer QC & Christopher Purchas QC) London (020) 7797 8100
Recommended in Clinical Negligence, Personal Injury, Product Liability
Specialisation: Disaster Litigation, most particularly pharmaceutical claims. Has represented manufacturers in claims involving Eraldin, Opren, Whooping cough vaccine, Benzodiazepines sex hormones including pregnancy tests, OC's and HRT, and many other products. Other specialist areas are general consumer PI claims, such as tobacco related disease, medical negligence and more general professional negligence and personal injury.
Prof. Memberships: Midland and Oxford circuit, London Common Law and Commercial Bar Association, Professional Negligence Bar Association and Medico-Legal Society.
Career: Called to Bar 1970; Recorder 1987; QC 1989; Bencher Inner Temple 1996.
Personal: Born 1 December 1947. Educated Ampleforth College and Hertford College, Oxford (MA).

SPINK, Andrew JM
35 Essex Street (Christopher Wilson-Smith QC) London (020) 7353 6381
andrewspink@mac35.demon.co.uk
Recommended in Clinical Negligence, Pensions
Specialisation: Specialises in clinical negligence (individual and group actions, particularly in the areas of perinatal brain or brachial plexus injury and cancer), pensions, personal injury (particularly spinal and brain injury and conditions caused by exposure to asbestos and other toxic substances; individual and group actions) and professional negligence (particularly cases involving allegations of negligence, breach of fiduciary duty or breach of trust against actuaries and other pension scheme advisers or trustees, commercial property valuers and surveyors, solicitors and barristers). Clinical negligence and personal injury cases include – The Shipman Inquiry (public inquiry into the activities of Harold Shipman; 2001 ongoing); 'Afrika' group action (claims by in excess of 7,000 South African sufferers of asbestos related disease for damages from Cape plc, a British holding company allegedly controlling the mines and mills in South Africa in which claimants were exposed; QBD 2000 ongoing); North Staffordshire Hospital cases (proposed civil claims arising out of CNEP ventilator trials on premature infants, 2000 ongoing); Devon Breast Screening Service cases (proposed claims by group of women for negligence delay in diagnosing breast cancer; 1999-01); S v Birmingham Health Authority (joint instruction of single experts on liability in clinical negligence claims; QBD 1999); Hatcher v Plymouth Hospitals NHS Trust (application of legal professional privilege to NHS Complaints file; QBD 1999); O'Toole v Irish Rail & J.W. Roberts (duty of care owed by sub-contractor; QBD 1999); Ward v Newalls Insulation (law relating to loss of earnings from partnership by injured dominant partner, asbestosis; CA 1998); Poynter v Harefield Hospital (informed consent to paediatric heart transplant; QBD 1997); Margereson & Hancock v J.W. Roberts (liability for environmental exposure to asbestos; CA 1996). Pensions and professional negligence cases include: Hogg Robinson Trustees Ltd v Scott Lang (claim by trustees of pension scheme against investment advisers for negligent investment strategy; ChD 2001 ongoing); AMP (UK) plc v Barker & others (rectification of pension scheme trustees' resolution to amend scheme benefits; setting aside trustees' decision and employers' consent; ChD 2000); Hogg Robinson Trustees Ltd v Buck & Willis Healthcare Limited (claim by trustees of pension scheme against former actuaries and administrators for breach of contract, negligence and breach of fiduciary duty in and about the preparation and content of successive actuarial valuations of the scheme; ChD 1996-00); PLT Ltd v Smith Melzack (action

by bank against commercial property surveyor for negligent valuation; TCC 1999); Coloroll Carpets Works Pension Scheme (Beddoe action relating to claim against pension scheme actuary and administrator; ChD 1994-98); Hopkins v MacKenzie (accrual of clause of action in solicitor's negligence action; CA 1995).
Prof. Memberships: Professional Negligence Bar Association, Association of Pension Lawyers, Personal Injury Bar Association, Association of Personal Injury Lawyers, London Common Law & Commercial Bar Association, Association for Victims of Medical Accidents.
Career: Called to the Bar in 1985. Joined present set of chambers (then situated at Lamb Building, Temple) in 1986.
Personal: Born 21st April 1962. Educated at Sherborne School, Dorset 1975-80 and Queens' College, Cambridge 1981-84. Lives in Dorset.

STADLEN, Nicholas QC
Fountain Court (Anthony Boswood QC) London (020) 7583 3335
Recommended in Banking, Commercial (Litigation), Fraud
Specialisation: 1) General commercial law including banking, insurance, city takeovers and professional negligence and 2) libel. In last two years acted for Bank of England on BCCI in House of Lords (twice), for British Commonwealth against Atlantic Computers, BZW, NM Rothschild and Spicer and Oppenheim, in ADR leading to £150 million settlement, for Milk Marketing Board in EU law dispute, for the Guardian, Sunday Times and BBC in libel actions brought by Keith Schellenberg, for Daily Mail and News International in libel actions brought by Sir Alan Sugar, for Glaxo Wellcome against Inland Revenue and for Belling Pension Fund in professional negligence action against Hereward Phillips. Previously acted for British Airways against Virgin, British & Commonwealth against Samuel Montagu & Quadrex, ACLI against M&R, Savoy against THF, CE Heath against Gooda Walker Syndicates. Pro Bono: Privy Council Capital Punishment Appeal from Jamaica; successful appeal by President of Oxford Union against dismissal from office.
Prof. Memberships: Former member: Combar North American Committee; Bar Council Public Affairs Committee. Recorder, South Eastern Circuit.
Career: Classical Scholar at St. Paul's and Trinity College, Cambridge. English Speaking Union Scholar, Hackley School, New York. President Cambridge Union Society. Winner Observer Mace Debating Championship. 1st in Order of Merit, Part 1 Bar Exams.

STAFFORD, Andrew QC
Littleton Chambers (Michel Kallipetis QC) London (020) 7797 8600
Recommended in Employment
Specialisation: Employment law: garden leave, restraint of trade, breach of confidence, discrimination, whistleblowing, wrongful & unfair dismissal, share options, directors duties, pension rights, TUPE, human rights, European law, strikes etc. Recent cases: Symbian v Christensen; Whitewater Leisure Management Ltd v Barnes; SBJ Stephenson v Mandy; University of Nottingham v Eyett; Malik v BCCI; Rock Refrigeration v Jones. General commercial: guarantees, share warranty claims, share option schemes, fraud, breach of confidence, debt collection, company law, sale of goods. Professional negligence & discipline: solicitors, barristers, accountants, stockbrokers, insurance brokers, financial advisers, architects, engineers, surveyors.
Career: Called 1980.

STAFFORD-MICHAEL, Simon
4 King's Bench Walk (Robert Rhodes QC) London (020) 7822 8822
Recommended in Fraud

STALLWORTHY, Nicolas
35 Essex Street (Christopher Wilson-Smith QC) London (020) 7353 6381
Recommended in Pensions
Specialisation: Specialises in pensions law (particularly in relation to occupational pension schemes). Acted in Stevens v Bell (for pensioners and deferred pensioners re: the proper construction of a British Airways pension schemes; ChD, 2001; appeal pending); Abbey National Independent Trustee Ltd v Woodhead & Lewis (for trustee alleging willful default by previous trustees; ChD and oral hearing before Pensions Ombudsman, 2000); Southernhay Pension Trustees Ltd v Orris & Neep (for beneficiaries resisting hostile Beddoes application; ChD, 2000); In re: Alan Charles Wrigley, a bankrupt (for trustees in insolvency proceedings re: vesting of pension entitlements in trustee in bankruptcy; ChD, 2000) and In re: the Thomas Christy Ltd Pension Fund (court approval of distribution of surplus on winding up of scheme; ChD, 1999). Involved in National Grid Co Plc v Laws; HL, 2000. Cases have concerned maladministration and breaches of trust/fiduciary duty by trustees; tracing/restitution of trust property; the distribution of surpluses; applications for Beddoes relief; pensions mis-selling; appeals from and complaints to the Pensions Ombudsman; submissions to OPRA re: civil and criminal proceedings against former trustees; and submissions to the PIA Ombudsman re: pensions mis-selling. Direct professional access work from, eg, Norwich Union and Hogg Robinson Trustees Ltd. Also practices in general chancery work (contractual/property litigation) and professional negligence (particularly relating to solicitors).
Prof. Memberships: Association Pension Lawers; Chancery Bar Association; Professional Negligence Bar Association.
Career: Called to the Bar in 1993; completed pupillage 1994; post-graduate degree 1995; joined 35 Essex Street in 1996.
Personal: Born 10 June 1970; educated Radley College 1983-88; Christ Church, Oxford 1989-92 (BA, Jurisprudence) & 1994-95 (Bachelor of Civil Law).

STANISTREET, Penelope
New Walk Chambers (John Snell) Leicester (0115) 255 9144 clerks@newwalkchambers.law.co.uk
Recommended in Crime
Specialisation: Crime, prosecuting and defending. Youth specialist in Youth Court and Crown Court, often dealing with young and vulnerable witnesses and defendants. Also recently involved in a number of high profile fatal road traffic accidents.
Prof. Memberships: Criminal Bar Association, FLBA.
Career: Having graduated in Classical Civilisation from Nottingham University, undertook the CPE at City University, then ICSL, being called in 1993 by Lincoln's Inn. Took a career break to have son returning to Nottingham for pupillage and has been practising at the Bar in Leicester for the last three years.
Personal: Interested in classical history, fine art and photography, also keeping fit and keeping one step ahead of young family.

STANLEY, Paul
Essex Court Chambers (Gordon Pollock QC) London (020) 7813 8000
Recommended in Commercial (Litigation)
Specialisation: Commercial litigation and advisory work (especially international commercial litigation and arbitration, insurance and reinsurance, commercial fraud); EC litigation and advisory work.
Prof. Memberships: COMBAR; British Maritime Law Association European Committee.
Career: Downing College, Cambridge: BA 1991 (Law); Harvard Law School: LLM 1992. Called to Bar 1993. Treasury Panel (C List).
Publications: Current Law Statutes annotations to Human Rights Act 1998 (with Peter Duffy QC).
Personal: Born 1970.

STARMER, Keir
Doughty Street Chambers (Geoffrey Robertson QC) London (020) 7404 1313
Recommended in Administrative & Public Law, Crime, Human Rights
Specialisation: Expert in European human rights law, public law and crime. Extensive experience of litigation before the European Court of Human Rights. Winner of the Justice/Liberty Human Rights Lawyers of the Year award, 2000.
Career: Called to the Bar 1987.
Publications: Author of 'European Human Rights Law' CLAG, 1999, Blackstone's Human Rights Digest (Blackstone Press, 2001), 'Criminal Justice, Police Powers and Human Rights' (Blackstone Press 2001), 'Human Rights and Directors'. Disqualification (in Mitham's 'Directors' Disqualification Proceedings; Butterworths), 'Disciplinary Proceedings' (in Human Rights and Civil Practice' (Sweet & Maxwell, 2001)).
Personal: Education: LLB (Hons) 1st class, BCL. Former legal officer at the National Council of Civil Liberties (now Liberty). Born 1962.

STARTE, Harvey
1 Brick Court (Richard Rampton QC) London (020) 7353 8845
Recommended in Defamation

STEAD, Richard
St John's Chambers (Christopher Sharp QC) Bristol (0117) 921 3456 clerks@stjohnschambers.co.uk
Recommended in Commercial (Litigation), Personal Injury
Specialisation: Specialist in construction law, personal injury and professional negligence.
Prof. Memberships: Personal Injury Bar Association – Sol and Construction Law.
Career: Called to the Bar in 1979. Recorder 1996.

STEEL, John QC
4-5 Gray's Inn Square (Elizabeth Appleby QC & David Mole QC) London (020)74045252 clerks@4-5graysinnsquare.co.uk
Recommended in Local Government, Planning
Specialisation: Has worked for many national and international clients in both the public and private sectors at the highest level in public, administrative, planning and environmental law. Practices in judicial review and public inquiry work. Specialities include retail, leisure, sports (especially football stadia), housing, minerals, waste disposal, highways, aviation, compulsory purchase and licensing. Particularly experienced in cases involving scientific, engineering and technically complex issues.
Prof. Memberships: Planning and Environment Bar Association; Administrative Law Bar Association. Fellow Royal Geographical Society.
Career: Called to the Bar 1978. Silk 1993. Appointed Assistant Recorder 1998; Former Junior Counsel member of Attorney General's Supplementary Panel (Common Law); Vice Chairman of The Durham University Research Institute of Durham University Business School; Member of Junior Barrister's Committee of Bar 1979; Sitting as Recorder on Midland and Oxford Circuit Crown and County Courts (Crime and Civil); Honorary Legal Adviser to Local Authorities World Heritage Forum; Honorary Legal Adviser to The Air League and Greener by Design Parliamentary Committee; Legal Adviser on Planning and local government matters to Telford and Wrekin Council; Legal Adviser on planning and local government to West Oxfordshire District Council.
Personal: Educated: Harrow School 1967-72; Durham University (BSc Hons chemistry) 1973-76; President Durham University Athletic Union 1975; Gray's Inn Moots Prize 1978, Member Attorney General's panel (planning etc) 1979-93; PPL (Helicopters and Fixed Wing); Director; Kandahar Ski Club. Director, The Busoga Trust (water relief in Uganda). Member of Durham University Institute of Change.

STEER, David QC

7 Harrington Street Chambers (David Steer QC & Robert Fordham QC & Iain Goldrein QC) Liverpool (0151) 242 0707

Recommended in Crime

Specialisation: Crime.
Prof. Memberships: BA Hons Law.
Career: Recorder.
Personal: Gardening, carriage driving, rugby league.

STEINFELD, Alan QC

24 Old Buildings (Martin Mann QC & Alan Steinfeld QC) London (020) 7404 0946

Recommended in Chancery, Company, Insolvency/Corporate Recovery, Partnership, Pensions

Specialisation: The main areas of business law including: insolvency (personal and corporate), civil fraud, company law, contract disputes, financial services, partnership law, professional negligence, property law, landlord and tenant, pensions, hostile trust litigation.
Prof. Memberships: Chancery Bar Association, Insolvency Lawyers Association.
Career: Downing College, Cambridge (BA Hons, LLB). Year of Call 1968. Year of Silk 1987. Deputy High Court Judge 1994 (Chancery Division).

STEPHENS, John L

35 Essex Street (Christopher Wilson-Smith QC) London (020) 7353 6381

Recommended in Pensions

Specialisation: Principal area of practice is pensions, covering all aspects of UK and international occupational pension schemes and claims associated therewith (eg professional negligence, executive severance etc). Subsidiary areas of practice include offshore trusts, shipping, finance and claims to ownership of antiquities (ie claims by nations, museums, temples, etc to ownership of ancient works of art). Frequently addresses both commercial and legal conferences.
Prof. Memberships: Association of Pensions Lawyers, Chancery Bar Association, IPEBLA.
Career: Called to the Bar in 1975. Joined present chambers in 1977.
Personal: Educated at Oxford University (BA, 1974). Born 30th March 1953. Leisure pursuits include travel. Lives in London.

STEPHENSON, Geoffrey

2-3 Gray's Inn Square (Anthony Porten QC & Anthony Scrivener QC) London (020) 7242 4986

Recommended in Consumer Law, Planning

Specialisation: Local government and public law with particular emphasis on planning local government finance and administration, housing and consumer and environmental law.
Prof. Memberships: Planning and Environment Bar Association. Administrative Law Bar Association. Parliamentary Bar Association. Fellow of the Chartered Insurance Institute. Member of the Bar of Texas.

STERLING, Robert

St. James's Chambers (Robert Sterling & Ian Leeming QC) Manchester (0161) 834 7000

Recommended in Chancery, Insolvency/Corporate Recovery

Specialisation: Chancery with emphasis on commercial litigation, corporate and personal insolvency and professional negligence. Recently reported cases: White v Richards (1993) 68 P & CR 105; Griffiths v Yorkshire Bank plc (1994) 2W.L.R. 1427; Alsop Wilkinson v Neary (1996) 1W.L.R. 1220; Ross v Telford (1998) 1 BCLC 82; Provincial North West plc v Bennett, 'The Times' February 12 1999 CA; Naidoo v Naidu and Brown Turner Crompton Carr ('The Times' November 1st 2000); Transco plc (British Gas plc) v Stockport MBC 2001 EGCS27CA.
Prof. Memberships: Chancery Bar Association, Northern Chancery Bar Association, Professional Negligence Bar Association, Northern Circuit Commercial Bar Association.
Career: Head of chambers, chairman of Northern Chancery Bar Association 1994-97. Acts as arbitrator in commercial disputes.

STERN, Ian

Hollis Whiteman Chambers (QEB) (Julian Bevan QC & Peter Whiteman QC) London (020) 7583 5766

Recommended in Fraud

Specialisation: Fraud: involved in a number of large fraud cases. Disciplinary Tribunals: appeared at a number of professional bodies – most regularly at the General Medical Council and the General Optical Council. Serious Crime: Murder; attempted murder; rape, drugs and firearms offences.
Prof. Memberships: Member of the Criminal Bar Association, South East Circuit and a number of local Bar Messes. Called to the New South Wales Bar, Australia in 1989.
Personal: Married to a G.P. and has three daughters. Runs on a fairly regular basis and completed the London Marathon in 1992 and 2000.

STERN, Linda QC

18 Red Lion Court (Anthony Arlidge QC) London (020) 7520 6000

Recommended in Crime

STERNBERG, Michael

4 Paper Buildings (Lionel Swift QC) London (020) 7583 0816
mvs@4pb.com

Recommended in Family

Specialisation: All aspects of family and family-related law including matrimonial, finance, wardship, disputes. Reported cases include Re: S (Removal from between unmarried persons, Inheritance Act claims, and child law with specific reference to sexual abuse and contested adoptions. Matrimonial finance work includes investigation of overseas trusts and companies. Recent cases include Re: M (Sexual abuse allegations Interviewing Techniques) 1999 2FLR G2. Re: AMR (Adoption procedure) 1999 2FLR 801. Re J (adoption procedure Isle of Man) 2000 2FLR 633. Re: AGN (Adoption: Foreign adoption) 2000 2FLR 431 and B v P (adoption of one natural parent to exclusion of another) 2001 1FLR 589 CA – on appeal to HL now. Re: M (Petition to European Commission of Human Rights) [1997] IFLR 755. Description: Wardship – Court ordering ward to be returned to natural parents in South Africa. Woman caring for ward in England seeking to petition ECHR on rights of ward and herself.; S v S [1997] 1WLR 1621, financial relief – inference of tax evasion by husband, Inland Revenue receiving copy of judgement – confidential information – breach of confidence, public interest. Re: F (a minor: paternity test) [1993] 3 WLR 369 (C.A.). Description: evidence – blood test -application blood test for DNA profiling by claimant for paternity; H v H (financial provision: capital allowance) [1993] 2FLR 335. Financial provision – divorce – capital adjustment – availability of "Besterman cushion" and if court should apply it; R v Plymouth Justices ex parte w, [1993] 2FLR 777. Family proceedings – judicial review – rules of natural justice – cross-examination on previous convictions; H v H (Residence order leave to remove from jurisdiction) [1995] 1FLR 529 (C.A.). Applicability of Children Act 1989 to applications to take child permanently overseas; Re: M (child's upbringing) [1996] 2FLR 441 (C.A.). Zulu parents contesting adoption by white woman of Zulu boy resident with her in England – importance of cultural heritage. DI v UK government admissible complaint in ECHR on rights of post/operative gender reassigned individuals (case pending).
Prof. Memberships: Family Law Bar Association. Assistant Secretary Family Law Bar Association 1986-88.
Career: Called to the Bar 1975 and joined 3 Dr. Johnson's Buildings. Moved to 4 Paper Buildings EC4 in 1994.
Personal: Educated at Carmel College, Wallingford 1962-70, Queens College, Cambridge 1970-74. (MA, LL.M). Governor of North London Collegiate School, Trustee of Sternberg Charitable Settlement. Freeman of the City of London and Member of the Worshipful Company of Horners. Member of Reform Club and City Livery Club. Born 12th September 1951. Decoration: Medaglia D'Argento di Benemerenza of sacred military Constantinian Order of St. George (1990).

STEVENSON, William QC

Crown Office Chambers (Michael Spencer QC & Christopher Purchas QC) London (020) 7797 8100
wsqc@crownofficechambers.com

Recommended in Personal Injury

Specialisation: Principal area of practice involves health and safety; product public and employers' liability; occupation-related diseases and disorders including legionella pneumophilia, asthmas, asbestos-related diseases and disorders, cancers and noise induced hearing loss. Has acted in WRULD claims by ceramic, banking and electronics industry employees and toxic shock syndrome claims against sanitary protection manufacturers. Has chaired and addressed conferences and seminars on occupational diseases. Other reported personal injury cases include Cox v HCB Angus [1991] ICR 687 (construction of s. 29 Factories Act 1961); Kenning v Eve Construction [1989] 1 WLR 118 (disclosure of expert report); Gaskill v Preston [1981] 3 All ER 427 (deductibility of Family Income Supplement from claim for loss of earnings); Hunter v Butler (1995) Kemp Vol 1 25-008/1 (black economy earnings in Fatal Accidents claims); Cox v Hockenhull [2000] 1 WLR 750 (dependency on state benefits). Other major cases encompass air handling and ventilation problems and product liability claims including Aswan Engineering v Lupdine [1987] WLR 1 (CA) (plastic containers).
Prof. Memberships: London Common Law and Commercial Bar Association.
Career: Called to the Bar 1968 and joined present chambers in 1969. Appointed Recorder in 1992.
Personal: Educated at Marlborough College 1957-61. Evan Williams Exhibitioner at Trinity College Oxford 1962-65 (MA 1969). Admitted Lincoln's Inn 1962 – Hardwicke and Droop Scholarships, Bencher 2001. Honourable Artillery Company 1965-81 (TD 1980). Leisure pursuits include country sports, skiing and sailing. Born 17 October 1943. Lives in London.

STEWART, James QC

Park Court Chambers (James Stewart QC & Robert Smith QC) Leeds (0113) 243 3277
clerks@parkcourtchambers.co.uk

Recommended in Crime

Specialisation: Crime, commercial fraud. Representative cases; R v Francom (2000) CLR 1018 (adverse inference from silence), R v Cheshire 93 CV App R 251 (causation in murder). R v Tandy 87 Cr. App. R 45 (alcoholism as a basis of diminished responsibility). R v Ali 1993 2 ALLER 409 (bugged cell confessions) R v Camplin 1978 AC 705 (provocation).
Career: Call 1966; QC 1982: Bencher Inner Temple 1993. Head of Chambers 1997. Appointments – Recorder 1982. Deputy High Court Judge 1993. Approved to sit at Central Criminal Court 1990.

STEWART, Lindsey

Maitland Chambers (Michael Lyndon-Stanford QC & Charles Aldous QC) London (020) 7406 1200
lstewart@maitlandchambers.com

Recommended in Chancery

Specialisation: Specialises in Chancery and commercial litigation. Practice covers company law, corporate and personal insolvency, banking, civil fraud, credit and security, professional negligence and trusts. Cases include: Butigan v Negus-Fancey & Ors [2000]; Ministry of Sound Holdings Ltd & Ors v Cosgrave [1999]; Dubai Aluminium Co Ltd v Salaam & Ors [1996]; Alsop Wilkinson & Ors v Neary & Ors [1995]; Fuji Finance Inc v Aetna Insurance Co Ltd & Anor [1995]; Re: SN Group plc [1993]; Dubai Bank Ltd v Galadari [1992]; Derby & Co Ltd & Ors v Weldon & Ors [1991].
Prof. Memberships: Chancery Bar Association, Insol-

vency Lawyers Association, Association of Contentious Trusts and Probate Specialists, Faculty of Advocates.
Career: Called to the Bar 1983. Tenant at Queen Elizabeth Building 1985-90. Called to the Scottish Bar 1990. Joined present chambers 1991.
Personal: Educated at Harris Academy, Dundee 1973-79 and University College, Oxford 1979-82. Born 24th April 1961.

STEWART, Roger QC
Four New Square (Justin Fenwick QC) London (020) 7822 2000 barristers@4newsquare.com
Recommended in Construction, Professional Negligence
Specialisation: Sorting wheat from chaff.
Prof. Memberships: TECBAR, PNBA, COMBAR, LCLCBA.
Career: MA LLM, General Editor 'Jackson and Powell on Professional Negligence'.

STEWART, Stephen QC
Byrom Street Chambers Manchester (0161) 829 2100
Recommended in Commercial (Litigation)

STEWART SMITH, Rodney
New Square Chambers (John Mowbray QC & Eben Hamilton QC) London (020) 7419 8000 rodneystewartsmith@newsquarechambers.co.uk
Recommended in Chancery
Specialisation: General chancery, especially commercial and residential property, easements, partnership, wills, trusts and court of protection matters, professional negligence.
Prof. Memberships: Chancery Bar Association.
Career: Called to the Bar 1964. Practised since then at *1 New Square, Lincoln's Inn.* Assistant Recorder 1990-94. Recorder 1994 to date. Member of Land Registration Rules Committee since 1991. General Tax Commissioner since 1991.
Publications: 'Butterworths Land Development Encyclopaedia' (1976).
Personal: Winchester College and Trinity Hall, Cambridge (B.A. 1963, LL.B 1964). Leisure Interests: watching cricket and hill walking.

STILITZ, Daniel
11 King's Bench Walk Chambers (Eldred Tabachnik QC & James Goudie QC) London (020) 7632 8500 stilitz@11kbw.com
Recommended in Employment
Specialisation: Employment law, public law and commercial law.
Prof. Memberships: Employment Law Bar Association; Administrative Law Bar Association; COMBAR; CEDR accredited mediator (1997).
Career: Called to the Bar in 1992. Junior Counsel to the Crown (Panel B).
Personal: New College Oxford, BA (1st Class Hons). City University, MA. Born 1 August 1968.

STOBART, John
King Charles House Chambers (William Everard) Nottingham (0115) 941 8851
Recommended in Crime
Specialisation: Crime including complex frauds eg Britannia Park, R v Charlton & Ors, R v Hancock, HSE and Local Authority prosecutions (for defence), and Junior for defence in R v Martin. Practice also has a preponderance of sexual/violence cases.

STOCKDALE, David QC
Deans Court Chambers (Stephen Grime QC) Manchester (0161) 214 6000
Recommended in Personal Injury
Specialisation: All aspects of personal injury work, including accident, industrial disease and multi-claimant litigation; employer's liability; health and safety; professional negligence (in particular, medical and solicitors). Also associated with 7 Bedford Row, London WC1R 4BU Tel: (020) 7242 3555 and Chancery House Chambers, 7 Lisbon Square, Leeds LS1 4LY Tel: (0113) 244 6691.
Prof. Memberships: Northern Circuit, Personal Injuries Bar Association, Professional Negligence Bar Association.
Career: Called 1975. Assistant Recorder 1990. Recorder 1993. Queen's Counsel 1995.
Personal: Educated at Giggleswick School and Pembroke College, Oxford.

STOCKDALE BT, Thomas
Erskine Chambers (Robin Potts QC) London (020) 7242 5532
Recommended in Company, Insolvency/Corporate Recovery
Specialisation: Corporate reorganisation and reconstructions including reduction of capital and schemes of arrangement. Takeovers and mergers. Schemes of arrangement in insolvency, including insolvent insurance companies.
Prof. Memberships: COMBAR. Chancery Bar Association. Law Society's Company Law Committee.
Career: Worcester College, Oxford MA. Bencher, Lincoln's Inn.
Publications: Contributor to 'Buckley on the Companies Act' (15th edition).

STOCKILL, David
5 Fountain Court (Anthony Barker QC) Birmingham (0121) 606 0500
Recommended in Chancery

STOKES, Mary
Erskine Chambers (Robin Potts QC) London (020) 7242 5532
Recommended in Company
Specialisation: Principal area of practice is company law including corporate insolvency, commercial law with a company element and financial services both advisory and litigation. Recent cases include British Commonwealth Holdings plc v Atlantic Computers plc & ors; North Holdings Ltd. v Southern Tropics Ltd [1999] 2 BCLC 625; New Hampshire Insurance v Rush & Tompkins [1998] 2 BCLC 47.
Prof. Memberships: Chancery Bar Association, COMBAR.
Career: BA, BCL (Oxon), LL.M (Harvard). Former fellow and Tutor in Law, Brasenose College. Called to the Bar in 1989, in practice at Erskine Chambers since 1990.
Publications: Consultant editor of 'Butterworths Company Law Cases'. Contributed chapter on Reductions of Capital to 'Butterworths Corporate Law Service'.

STONE, Lucy QC
Queen Elizabeth Building (Florence Baron QC) London (020) 7797 7837 l.stone@qeb.co.uk
Recommended in Family
Specialisation: Specialises in family law, principally 'big money' ancillary relief cases. Has acted on behalf of numerous high-profile media clients.
Prof. Memberships: Member of Bar Council Law Reform committee 1994 -97; Family Law Bar Association committee 1998-96; F v F [1996] 1 FLR 833; Clark v Clark [1999] 2 FLR 498.
Career: MA Cantab; called to the Bar in 1983; Silk 2001.
Personal: Born 1959. Married with one child. Lives in London.

STONEFROST, Hilary
3-4 South Square (Michael Crystal QC & Lord Alexander of Weedon QC) London (020) 7696 9900 hilarystonefrost@southsquare.com
Recommended in Insolvency/Corporate Recovery
Specialisation: Insolvency, company law and banking law. General commercial work arising out of insolvencies. Minority shareholders' petitions. Directors' disqualifications.
Career: Called to the Bar (Middle Temple) in 1991. Economist, Bank of England 1979-89.
Publications: Contributor to the 'Law of Receivers of Companies,' Lightman and Moss.
Personal: MSc London School of Economics 1978. Diploma in law, City University 1990.

STONER, Christopher
9 Old Square (Michael Driscoll QC) London (020) 7405 4682
Recommended in Sport
Specialisation: All aspects of sports law with a particular emphasis on litigation, drafting and enforcement of rules and regulations. Member of editorial board: 'Sports Law Administration and Practice'. Recent cases include: Wilander & Anor v Tobin & Anor; Korda v ITF Limited. Bingham v British Boxing Board of Control; Clients include The International Tennis Federation; The International Cricket Council; The British Boxing Board of Control, The FA Premier League and The Football Association. All aspects of property litigation, particularly landlord and tenant. Recent cases include McDonalds Property Co Ltd v HSBC plc; Ipswich Borough Council v Duke & Moore.
Prof. Memberships: Chancery Bar Association. Bar Sports Law Group (committee member).
Career: Called to the Bar in 1991. Tenant at 9 Old Square since 1992.
Personal: Educated at Shoreham College and the University of East Anglia.

STOREY, Jeremy QC
4 Pump Court London (020) 7842 5555 jstorey@4pumpcourt.com
Recommended in Information Technology
Specialisation: Practice encompasses commercial work, professional negligence, construction, information technology, personal injury and general common law. Conducted advocacy courses in Kuala Lumpur, Trinidad, Hong Kong and Mauritius.
Prof. Memberships: COMBAR, London Common Law and Commercial Bar Association (Committee), TECBAR, Barristers Overseas Advocacy Committee (Chairman), Professional Negligence Bar Association, Personal Injuries Bar Association, Society for Computers and Law.
Career: Called to the Bar 1974. Appointed Assistant Recorder (Western Circuit) 1990. Took Silk 1994. Appointed Recorder, and Deputy Judge of the TCC in 1995 and Acting Deemster of the Isle of Man Courts in 1999. Arbitrator and Mediator.
Personal: Educated at Uppingham School 1966-70 and Downing College, Cambridge (Scholar, BA Law 1st Class) 1970-73. Leisure pursuits include cricket, travel and theatre. Born 21 October 1952.

STOREY, Paul QC
29 Bedford Row Chambers (Peter Ralls QC) London (020) 7404 1044
Recommended in Family
Specialisation: Family law: public law/adoption (eg 1999 – appeared for applicants for adoption in Re Jade & Hannah Bennett); private law (re B [1998] 1 FLR 368, Re W [1999] 1 FLR 869); cases with a European element (eg U v W [1997] 2 FLR 282); matrimonial and cohabitee finance (eg Roy v Roy [1996] 1 FLR 541).
Prof. Memberships: FLBA
Career: Called Lincoln's Inn Trinity 1982. Chambers: 7 Stone Buildings 1983-85; Goldsmith Building 1985-91; 29 Bedford Row 1992-. Tutor professional ethics at CLE 1989-97. Chairman Nagalro annual conference 1996. Appears in legal network tv training videos. Articles in Family Law (12/95, 4/96, 10/96, 3/97). Speaker at Law Society Local Government Child Care Group annual conference 1998. Regular speaker at national and local conferences/training days. Recorder.
Personal: Married, four children. Cycling, rugby, football, motor racing, golf.

STOUT, Roger
18 St John Street (Jonathan Foster QC) Manchester (0161) 278 1800
Recommended in Crime

STRAKER, Timothy QC
4-5 Gray's Inn Square (Elizabeth Appleby QC & David Mole QC) London (020) 7404 5252
tstraker@4-5graysinnsquare.co.uk
Recommended in Local Government, Planning
Specialisation: Principal areas of practice are local government, public law and town and country planning. Has acted in many leading public law cases concerning, inter alia, environmental assesments, compulsory purchase, planning, housing and housing benefits, Sunday trading, caravan sites and 'new age travellers', free speech, professional advertising, discrimination and professional conduct. Appeared in many Privy Council Appeals. Represented the returning officers in the first challenge to a European election result and in the first challenge to a Parliamentary result for 70 years. Acts for many local authorities and regulatory bodies. Consultant editor of the Registration of Political Parties Act 1998, contributor to the Rights of Way Law Review and to Judicial Review. Advisory editor Public Health and Environmental Protection (Halsbury's Laws of England) and Local Government (Halsbury's Laws of England). Editor Civil Court Practice.
Prof. Memberships: Administrative Law Bar Association, Planning Bar Association, Administrative Court Users' Committee.
Career: Called to the Bar 1977. Silk 1996. Assistant Recorder 1998, Recorder 2000.
Personal: Educated at Malvern College and Downing College, Cambridge (1st Class Hons). Senior Harris Scholar, Downing College Prize for Law, Holt Scholar of Gray's Inn, awarded Lord Justice Holker Senior Award. Admitted (2001), for the purposes of planning and election cases, to the Bars of Northern Ireland and Trinidad and Tobago.

STREATFEILD-JAMES, David QC
Atkin Chambers (Robert Akenhead QC) London (020) 7404 0102 /Emergency Tel: (020) 7242 4703
Recommended in Construction, Information Technology

STRUDWICK, Linda
Hollis Whiteman Chambers (QEB) (Julian Bevan QC & Peter Whiteman QC) London (020) 7583 5766
Recommended in Crime
Specialisation: Specialises in defence work but also handles prosecution. 25 years covering all areas of serious crime including murder, manslaughter, fraud, sexual offences, drug offences and disciplinary tribunal work.
Career: Called 1973.
Personal: Educated Manchester University.

STUART-SMITH, Jeremy QC
2 Temple Gardens (Dermod O'Brien QC) London (020) 7822 1253
jstuart-smith@2templegardens.co.uk
Recommended in Insurance, Personal Injury, Product Liability, Professional Negligence
Specialisation: Insurance and insurance related disputes; product liability; professional negligence; general commercial and common law.
Prof. Memberships: LCLCBA, PIBA.
Career: MA Cantab. QC 1997, Recorder 1999.
Publications: 'Recovery of Damages After Misrepresentation', 2000 MLJ 865.
Personal: Playing the french horn, skiing, history, keeping sheep.

STUBBS, Andrew
St. Paul's Chambers (Nigel Sangster QC) Leeds (0113) 245 5866
Recommended in Crime

STUBBS, Rebecca
Maitland Chambers (Michael Lyndon-Stanford QC & Charles Aldous QC) London (020) 7406 1200
rstubbs@maitlandchambers.com
Recommended in Chancery, Company
Specialisation: Company and commercial chancery litigation with particular emphasis on insolvency, civil fraud, restitution and conflicts of law. Reported cases include Grand Metropolitan plc v The William Hill Group Ltd [1997] (rectification); Jordan Grand Prix Limited v Baltic Insurance Group [1999] (Brussels Convention), Piccadilly Property Management Limited v Commissioners of Inland Revenue [1999] (corporate insolvency), Gehe v NBTY Inc [1999] (corporation tax, rectification) and Re Cedarwood Productions Ltd [2001] (directors disqualification).
Prof. Memberships: Chancery Bar Association, COMBAR, Insolvency Court Users' Committee.
Career: Called to the Bar 1994. Appointed Junior Counsel to the Crown (B Panel) 2001.
Publications: Contributor to Butterworths 'Practical Insolvency'.
Personal: Educated at Darton High School and Downing College Cambridge (1st class hons 1993). Former Queen Mother Scholar of the Middle Temple.

STURMAN, Jim
2 Bedford Row (William Clegg QC) London (020) 7440 8888
jsturman@2bedfordrow.co.uk
Recommended in Crime, Fraud
Specialisation: Specialist criminal defence advocate involved in many major cases. Particular expertise in fraud, regulatory work and advisory work to banks on criminal matters and in 'quasi criminal' tribunals. Regularly instructed in asset confiscation and DTA work. Extensive experience in The Court of Appeal Criminal Division, particularly in cases where he did not act in the lower court. Example, R v Lummes 17 December 2000, convictions for murder quashed and no evidence offered at retrial. Also FA Disciplinary tribunal work, acted for Chelsea FC, Dennis Wise, Graeme Le Saux and Celestine Babayaro. Major cases include R v Stagg (Wimbledon common murder). Sivalingham, Tamil Tigers. Vanduvall, financial insturment fraud. Richardson, fraud on the revenue of another EU state. Villiers-diversion fraud. R v Bonner 'Hare Wines'. R v Gould and Charles Kray. R v Machin-'sex on an aeroplane' case. R v Ian Kay 'Woolworths' murder. R v Kelly-first appeal on the 'two strikes' life sentence, currently awaiting a further appeal both in England and before the European Court. Reilly-disclosure. Callan-DTA. Woodward-effect of drink in reckless driving. McGovern-section 76 PACE. Griffiths-abuse of process. Coswell-timeshare fraud. Extensive experience in all serious crime, including mortgage, VAT and diversion frauds.
Prof. Memberships: Member of Gibraltar Bar, CBA, IBA, BAFS.
Career: Called 1982, joined chambers 1983.
Personal: Cricket, football, chasing his two young children around the house.

SUCKLING, Alan QC
Hollis Whiteman Chambers (QEB) (Julian Bevan QC & Peter Whiteman QC) London (020) 7583 5766
Recommended in Fraud
Specialisation: Crime and Fraud. Clowes. Maxwell. Warren. Shivpuri 1987 AC 1, Howe & Others 1987 AC 417.
Prof. Memberships: Middle Temple, Bencher. CBA.
Career: Queens' College, Cambridge MA LL.M. Harmsworth Law Scholar, Middle Temple.
Personal: b. Hong Kong 1938.

SULLIVAN, Michael
One Essex Court (Lord Grabiner QC) London (020) 7583 2000
Recommended in Banking
Specialisation: Banking, aviation finance and commercial litigation. Also professional negligence.

SUMNER, David
Lincoln House Chambers (Mukhtar Hussain QC) Manchester (0161) 832 5701
Recommended in Crime

SUMPTION, Jonathan QC
Brick Court Chambers (Christopher Clarke QC) London (020) 7379 3550
sumption@brickcourt.co.uk
Recommended in Administrative & Public Law, Banking, Commercial (Litigation), Energy & Natural Resources, Financial Services, Fraud, Insurance, Media & Entertainment, Professional Negligence
Specialisation: Specialist in all areas of commercial law, including banking, corporate finance, financial services, insolvency, oil and gas, insurance and sale of goods. Practice also covers administrative law and intellectual property. Recent cases included: Smith New Court v Scirmgeour Vickers; South Australia Asset Management v York Montague Ltd (House of Lords only); Westdeutsche Landesmark Girozentrale v Islington BC; Investors' Compensation Scheme v West Bromwich Building Society (House of Lords only); DGFT v FA Premier League & BSkyB; R v Home Secretary ex parte Belgium; Equitable Life Assurance Society v Hyman; Sphere Drake v Orion; Alconbury Developments Ltd v Secretary of State (House of Lords only).
Career: Called to the Bar 1975. Joined chambers 1977. Took silk 1986. Recorder 1994-01. Judge of the Courts of Appeal of Jersey and Guernsey, 1996-.
Personal: Educated at Eton 1961-66 and Magdalen College, Oxford 1967-70. Fellow, Magdalen College, Oxford 1971-75. Interests include history and music.

SUPPERSTONE, Michael QC
11 King's Bench Walk Chambers (Eldred Tabachnik QC & James Goudie QC) London (020) 7632 8500
clerksroom@11kbw.com
Recommended in Administrative & Public Law, Local Government
Specialisation: All aspects of administrative and public law. Other main areas of practice include employment law.
Career: Called to the Bar in 1973. Bencher, Middle Temple. Appointed Queen's Counsel 1991. Recorder 1996; Deputy High Court Judge 1998; past Chairman of Administrative Law Bar Association; Principal editor of latest edition of the Administrative Law title of 'Halsbury's Laws of England'; contributor to the latest edition of the Extradition Law title of 'Halsbury's Laws of England'; co-editor of 'Supperstone and Goudie on Judicial Review'; co-author of Supperstone, Goudie and Coppel on 'Local Authorities and the Human Rights Act 1998'; contributor to Butterworth's 'Local Government Law'; consulting editor of 'Supperstone and O'Dempsey on Immigration and Asylum'. Member of editorial committee of 'Public Law'.
Personal: Educated at St. Paul's School and Lincoln College, Oxford (MA; BCL).

SUSMAN, Peter QC
2 Harcourt Buildings (Roger Henderson QC) London (020) 7583 9020
clerks@harcourt.co.uk
Recommended in Professional Negligence
Specialisation: Complex contract litigation, with particular experience of acting for suppliers and users in contractual disputes arising from the supply of computer software; construction and engineering project litigation; and property finance claims and professional negligence.
Prof. Memberships: Professional Negligence Bar Asso-

ciation. London Common Law Bar Association, Society for Computers and Law.
Career: Called 1966, took silk 1997. Associate with Debevoise & Plimpton, Attorneys, New York City, USA 1970-72. Appointed Recorder 1993. Deputy Judge of TCC 1998.
Personal: Educated Dulwich College 1953-61, Lincoln College, Oxford 1961-64 (Oldfield Scholar and BA 1964, MA 1969) and University of Chicago Law School, 1964-65 (British Commonwealth Fellow and Fulbright Scholar, JD 1965). Leisure pursuits include clarinet, windsurfing and skiing. Born 20 February 1943.

SUTCLIFFE, Andrew QC
3 Verulam Buildings (Christopher Symons QC & John Jarvis QC) London (020) 7831 8441
asutcliffe@3vb.com
Recommended in Media & Entertainment
Specialisation: Principal area of practice is commercial and business law, with emphasis on entertainment law, intellectual property (copyright, breach of confidence), banking and finance, professional negligence (especially in commercial transactions), fraud, company law/insolvency and conflict of laws. Cases include: Elton John v Dick James (1991); Holly Johnson v ZTT Records (1993); Gabrielle v Trim (1996); MCA Records v Charly Records (2001); Hadley v Kemp (1999); Spice Girls v Aprilia (2000); Dexter Ltd v Harley (2001); Saab v Saudi American Bank (1998); Wallace v RBS (1999); Chapman v Barclays Bank (1997); Barclays Bank v Sumner (1996); Investors Compensation Scheme v Various Solicitors (Home Income Plan litigation) (1999); West Bromwich BS v Manor Hadley (1998). Acts as arbitrator in commercial and IP matters; CEDR mediator.
Prof. Memberships: COMBAR, LCLCBA; PNBA.
Career: Call 1983; Recorder 2000; QC 2001.
Personal: Born September 1960. Educated at Winchester College and Worcester College Oxford. Lives in London and Yorkshire.

SUTTLE, Stephen
1 Brick Court (Richard Rampton QC) London (020) 7353 8845
ss@1brickcourt.co.uk
Recommended in Defamation
Specialisation: Defamation, malicious falsehood, contempt of court, reporting restrictions, confidence and media related law generally. Cases include Jameson v BBC, Bobolas v Economist, Papandreou v Time, Bookbinder v Tebbitt, Skuse v Granada, Taylforth v News Group and Police, Bottomley v Express, Botham v Imran Khan, Bennett v Guardian, Al Fayed v Conde Nast, Bleakley v Granada, Frost Group v RMIF, Venables & Thompson v News Group (identification ban).
Personal: Chorister Westminster Abbey, Westminster School, Christ Church Oxford (graduated in Classics 1972), taught Classics 1973-8, City University (Law Diploma 1979). Called to Bar 1980). Interests include music, cricket, Greece.

SUTTON, Richard QC
18 Red Lion Court (Anthony Arlidge QC) London (020) 7520 6000
Recommended in Crime

SWAIN, Jon
Furnival Chambers (Andrew Mitchell QC) London (020) 7405 3232
clerks@furnivallaw.co.uk
Recommended in Crime
Specialisation: SPE General crime drugs: led for defendant in a major drug trial, and defended in many high profile cases. Murder: defended in a number of murder trials including special verdicts of insanity. Fraud: prosecuted high profile mortgage fraud and in a variety of other trials. Sexual crime: defended in number of high profile cases. Firearms: defended in number of high profile cases. Large-scale dishonesty: defended in number of high profile cases. Cases involving child witnesses: successfully defended in every case in which instructed. Experienced in use of TV and video links. Financial crime asset forfeiture and confiscation. Advised and represented prosecuting authorities and defendants in High Court and Crown Court. Priority interests cases with scientific evidence which engage background in biochemistry and biology.

SWAINSTON, Michael
Brick Court Chambers (Christopher Clarke QC) London (020) 7379 3550
Swainston@Brickcourt.co.uk
Recommended in Commercial (Litigation), Professional Negligence
Specialisation: Michael Swainston is a commercial litigator and adviser with a broad practice covering insurance and reinsurance, banking, financial services (litigation and disciplinary tribunals), commercial fraud, professional negligence, international trade, shipping, energy and competition law. His cases of note generally include the Lloyd's litigation (Cox v Bankside, Napier and Ettrick v Kershaw, Axa v Field, Brown v GIO), the Maxwell litigation and the defence of claims by Qatar against the former Emir. In the past year they include: Peregrine Fixed Income Limited v Robinson Department Store plc on the ISDA master swaps agreement, the Solitaire arbitration and related hearings in the Commercial Court, Guild (Claims) Ltd v Eversheds (a firm) (successful defence of claims arising from the takeover of Sunsail plc), a record FSA prosecution and related human rights proceedings, Mann and another v Lexington Insurance Co, (CA) [2001] Lloyd's Rep 1 (reinsurance dispute in relation to Indonesian riots), Shaker v MBC (claims arising out of acquisition of US TV and radio enterprise).
Prof. Memberships: Called in 1985. Called to the California Bar in 1988. Executive Committee of the Commercial Bar Association (COMBAR), North American Committee of COMBAR, Law Reform Committee of the Bar Council, International Relations Committee of the Bar Council (responsible for North America), Insurance Litigation Sub-Committee of the American Bar Association.
Publications: 'Commercial Regulation and Judicial Review (Court Procedures and Remedies)' Hart 1998; 'White Book, European Jurisdiction'; 'Retrospectivity of the Human Rights Act: New Law Journal.

SWEENEY, Nigel QC
6 King's Bench Walk (Roy Amlot QC) London (020) 7583 0410
Recommended in Crime

SWEENEY, Seamus
Milburn House Chambers (Paul Cape) Newcastle upon Tyne (0191) 230 5511
Recommended in Employment
Specialisation: Specialises exclusively in all aspects of employment law acting for private individuals, commercial organisations and local authorities.
Career: Called to the Bar in 1989 and practised in London until 1996. In 1996 he joined the Newcastle office of *Eversheds* and their specialist employment team. He returned to private practice at the Bar in September 1999 when he joined Milburn House Chambers.
Personal: Born 14 February 1966 in Derry City. Main interests are his family, reading and football. He is also known as James.

SWIFT, Caroline QC
Byrom Street Chambers Manchester (0161) 829 2100
cs@byromstreet.com
Recommended in Clinical Negligence, Personal Injury
Specialisation: Personal injury; clinical negligence; industrial disease.
Prof. Memberships: PIBA.
Career: Called to the Bar 1977. Appointed Silk 1993. Assistant Recorder 1992-95. Recorder 1995-date. Deputy High Court Judge 2000 – date. Governing Bencher of the Temple, 1997-date.

SWIFT, John QC
Monckton Chambers (John Swift QC) London (020) 7405 7211
jswift@monckton.co.uk
Recommended in Competition/Anti-trust
Specialisation: John Swift QC returned to the Bar as head of Monckton Chambers in January 1999, having completed a five year appointment as the first Rail Regulator, a public office established under the Railways Act 1993. Since his return he has been engaged on a series of major cases in the area of UK and European Communities competition law, including the British Airways/City Flyer, IMS/PMSI, Universal Foods Corporation/Pointing, NTL/Cable & Wireless merger references, the reference of supermarkets before the Competition Commission, the Director General of Fair Trading's reference of the supply of medicaments to the Restrictive Practices Court, the Airtours/First Choice merger on appeal to the CFI, Luxembourg and the reference of the supply of banking services to SMEs, before the Competition Commission.
Prof. Memberships: Member of the Competition Law Association and fellow of the Chartered Institute of Transport.

SWIFT, Jonathan
11 King's Bench Walk Chambers (Eldred Tabachnik QC & James Goudie QC) London (020) 7632 8500
swift@11kbw.com
Recommended in Employment
Specialisation: Specialises in all aspects of employment and trade union law including dismissal, discrimination, collective disputes and European law advising and appearing for both employees and employers. Employment practice also includes restraint of trade, protection of confidential information and interim injunctions. Other practice areas include public and administrative law and all aspects of local government law and the law of education. Appointed to the Attorney General's B Panel in July 1999.
Prof. Memberships: Employment Law Bar Association, Employment Lawyers Association; Industrial Law Society; Discrimination Law Association; COMBAR; Administrative Law Bar Association.
Career: Called to the Bar in 1989; joined present chambers in the same year.
Publications: Contributor to 'Judicial Review' (eds Supperstone & Goudie) Butterworths 1997; contributing editor Butterworths 'Local Government Law' 1999; contributor to Halsbury's Laws of England: 'Administrative Law' 2001.
Personal: Educated at New College, Oxford (BA (Hons) Jurisprudence) and Emmanuel College, Cambridge (LLM). Born 11 September 1964. Lives in London.

SWIFT, Malcolm QC
Park Court Chambers (James Stewart QC & Robert Smith QC) Leeds (0113) 243 3277
malswiftqc@aol.com or clerks@parkcourtchambers.co.uk
Recommended in Crime
Prof. Memberships: Leader of the North Eastern Circuit (January 1998-); member of the Bar Council (January 1997-); Criminal Bar Association; American Bar Association.
Career: LLB; AKC (Kings College London). Called to the Bar Trinity 1970 – Grays Inn. Recorder of the Crown Court (1987-). Queens Counsel (1988).

SYMONS, Christopher QC
3 Verulam Buildings (Christopher Symons QC & John Jarvis QC) London (020) 7831 8441
chambers@3vb.com
Recommended in Insurance, Professional Negligence
Specialisation: Commercial work particularly insurance/reinsurance and professional negligence. Appeared in many commercial court cases and arbitrations for and against insurance companies, reinsurers, Lloyd's syndicates, brokers and other professionals. Recent cases

include acting for J Rothschild in claim against insurers arising from pension mis-selling; acting regularly for Solicitors Indemnity Fund; acting for Willis Corroon in successful defence of action brought by Kuwait Airways; acting for Spicer and Pegler in the British and Commonwealth litigation; acting for Ernst and Young in successful defence of action brought by NRG concerning acquisition of Victory Re; acting for John D Wood in BBL. Environmental law, particularly environmental warranty claims and landfill problems. Town and country planning. Construction particularly engineers and architects. Aviation. Acted in two leading rugby accident cases successfully defending Bedford School in the Van Oppen case and successfully defending front row prop in the Smoldon case. Arbitration: sits regularly as an arbitrator and appears in arbitrations as counsel. Mediation: has experience acting as mediator and for parties at mediation.
Career: Called to the Bar in 1972; Junior Counsel to the Crown (Common Law) 1985-89; Silk 1989; Recorder 1993; Deputy High Court Judge 1998; Bencher Middle Temple 1998.

TABACHNIK, Eldred QC
11 King's Bench Walk Chambers (Eldred Tabachnik QC & James Goudie QC) London (020) 7632 8500
Recommended in Employment, Local Government
Specialisation: Principal area of practice is employment law. Has appeared in numerous matters for individuals, trade unions, multi-national businesses, local authorities and employer's federations in the areas of unfair dismissal, wrongful dismissal, discrimination, collective disputes, restraint of trade and European law relating to employment.
Prof. Memberships: ALBA; London Common Law and Commercial Bar Association.
Career: Called to the Bar 1970; appointed Queen's Counsel 1982; Assistant Recorder 1995; Master of the Bench, Inner Temple 1988; Recorder 2000.
Publications: 'Anticipatory Breach of Contract' (Current Legal Problems 1971).
Personal: Educated at University of Cape Town (BA, LLB) and London University (LLM).

TABOR, James QC
Albion Chambers (Charles Barton QC & Neil Ford QC) Bristol (0117) 927 2144
Recommended in Crime

TACKABERRY, John QC
Arbitration Chambers (John Tackaberry QC) London (020) 7267 2137
Recommended in Arbitration (International)

TAGGART, Nicholas
4 Breams Buildings (Christopher Lockhart-Mummery QC) London (020) 7450 1221
clarks@4breams.co.uk
Recommended in Property Litigation
Specialisation: All aspects of property law, including landlord and tenant, conveyancing and property related professional negligence matters.
Prof. Memberships: Member of Chancery Bar Association, Property Bar Association.
Career: Called to the Bar 1991.
Publications: Specialist Editor of Hill and Redman's 'Law of Landlord and Tenant'.

TAGHAVI, Shahram
Doughty Street Chambers (Geoffrey Robertson QC) London (020) 7404 1313
s.taghavi@doughtystreet.co.uk
Recommended in Immigration
Specialisation: Specialises in Administrative, Immigration and Nationality, Human Rights, European Union and Education Law, with experience at all levels including the House of Lords, European Court of Human Rights and European Court of Justice. Recently reported cases include: Milan Horvath v Secretary of State for the Home Department [2000] 3 WLR 379, HL (definition of 'persecution' and the relevance of State protection); R v Secretary of State for the Home Department, ex parte S [1998] Imm AR 252, QBD (vires of subordinate legislation denying oral hearings in asylum appeals); R v Secretary of Sate for the Home Department, ex parte Manjit Kaur [2001] ECR I – 1237, ECJ (European Union citizenship and British nationality).
Prof. Memberships: Member of Administrative Law Bar Association, Bar European Group, Education Law Association, Immigration Law Practitioners Association and International Bar Association (Human Rights Section) and a Executive Committee member of the Joint Council for the Welfare of Immigrants.
Career: Called to the Bar in 1994 (*Gray's Inn*). Teaches Administrative and Constitutional law at the School of Oriental and African Studies, University of London.
Publications: Immigration and Nationality Law Reports (joint editor), The Human Rights Act 1998 (contributing author).

TALBOT, Patrick QC
Serle Court (Lord Neill of Bladen QC) London (020) 7242 6105
clerks@serlecourt.co.uk
Recommended in Chancery
Specialisation: Chancery/ Commercial Litigation and advice, including commercial fraud, commercial and agricultural property, banking and credit, professional negligence, sports law, charities, computer law, insolvency, trusts and probate.
Prof. Memberships: Chancery Bar Association, British Association for Sport and Law, COMBAR.
Career: Joined Serle Court 1970, QC 1990. Recorder, Judicial chairman of The City Disputes Panel.

TAM, Robin B-K
1 Temple Gardens (Hugh Carlisle QC) London (020) 7583 1315
clerks@1templegardens.co.uk
Recommended in Administrative & Public Law
Specialisation: Administrative and public law/judicial review, immigration/asylum, nationality, human rights. Personal injuries. General common law. Major reported cases: Bugg v DPP [1993] QB 473, M v Home Secretary [1996] 1 WLR 507, Percy v Hall [1997] QB 924, ex parte Flood [1998] 1 WLR 156, Harris v Evans [1998] 1 WLR 1285, Defence Secretary v Percy [1999] 1 AII ER 732, ex parte Jeyeanthan [2000] 1 WLR 354, Horvath v Home Secretary [2000] 3 WLR 379, Home Secretary v Rehman [2000] 3 WLR 1240, R (Montana) v Home Secretary [2001] 1 WLR 552.
Prof. Memberships: Administrative Law Bar Association. Personal Injuries Bar Association. South Eastern Circuit. Hong Kong Bar. New South Wales Bar.
Career: Called 1986. Junior counsel to the Crown (A Panel). Standing Prosecuting Junior counsel to Inland Revenue (South Eastern Circuit).

TAMLYN, Lloyd
3-4 South Square (Michael Crystal QC & Lord Alexander of Weedon QC) London (020) 7696 9900
lloydtamlyn@compuserve.com
Recommended in Insolvency/Corporate Recovery
Specialisation: Insolvency; company; professional negligence; instructed in Re Leigh Estates (UK) Limited [1994] BCC 292 (Disputed winding-up petition based on liability order for unpaid rates); Re Kingscroft Insurance Company Limited [1994] 2 BCLC 80 (Continuation of orders under section 236 of IA 1986 when provisional liquidators discharged from office); Re Dollar Land (Feltham) Limited [1995] 2 BCLC 370 (Court's power to review winding-up orders); Mytre Investments Limited v Reynolds & Others (No 2) [1996] BPIR 464 (Time limits for IVAs); Tam Wing Chuen & Anor v Bank of Credit and Commerce Hong Kong Limited [1996] 2 BCLC 69 (Privy Council: Charge backs); Mutual Reinsurance Co Limited v Peat Marwick Mitchell & Co [1997] 1 BCLC 1 (Court of Appeal: entitlement of auditors to rely on indemnity granted in Articles of Association of a Bermudian company); Aspinalls Club Limited v Halabi [1998] BPIR 322 (Jurisdiction to amend bankruptcy petition); Re Structures and Computers Limited [1998] 1 BCLC 283 (Exercise of Court's discretion to make an administration order where major creditor is opposed); Kempe v Ambassador Insurance Company [1998] 1 WLR 271 (Privy Council: power of Court to extend time limits under Scheme of Arrangement); Alf Vaughan & Co Limited v Royscot Trust Plc [1999] 1 All ER (Commercial) 856 (Hire purchase agreements with 'equity' at date of receivership; extent of remedy for relief from forfeiture); Commissioners of Inland Revenue v Robinson [1999] BPIR 329 (Extent of Court's jurisdiction to review the making of a bankrupcy order); Re J N Taylor Finance Pty Limited [1999] 2 BCLC 256 (Extent of Court's jurisdiction under section 426 of IA 1986 re letters of request from foreign courts); Morgans (A Firm) v Needham (Court of Appeal: The Times, 5th November 1999) (Power to strike out for failure to comply with ambiguous unless orders); Re Bank of Credit and Commerce International SA & Anor; Morris & Ors v State Bank of India [1999] BCC 943 (transaction defrauding creditors); Re Deadduck Limited [2000] 1BCLC 148 (disqualification of director); Smith v UIC Insurance Co limited (19 January 2000 unreported, Commercial Court)(Status of provisional liquidators of insolvent insurance company; power to award security for costs against company in provisional liquidation).
Publications: Contributor to 'Halsbury's Laws of England' (4th edn 1996 reissue) volumes 7(2) and 7(3); 'The Law of Receivers of Companies' (2nd and 3rd edn) Sir Gavin Lightman and Gabriel Moss QC, Chapters 11 (Receivers and Winding-up) and 17 (Receivers and Unsecured Creditors: Execution, Distress, Marevas and Trusts); 'Insolvency of Banks: Managing the Risks (ed Oditah) (1996) Chapter 4 ' Choice and Initiation of Insolvency Procedure, with Mark Phillips QC.

TANNEY, Anthony
Falcon Chambers (Jonathan Gaunt QC & Kim Lewison QC) London (020) 7353 2484
tanney@falcon-chambers.com
Recommended in Property Litigation
Specialisation: All aspects of the law of real property including litigation and advisory work, with an emphasis on landlord and tenant.
Prof. Memberships: Chancery Bar Association; Property Bar Association.
Career: Called 1994; (Lincoln's Inn); member Falcon Chambers 1995-date.
Publications: 'Distress for Rent', A Tanney & I Travers (Jordans 2000).

TANSEY, Rock QC
3 Gray's Inn Square (Rock Tansey QC) London (020) 7520 5600
Recommended in Crime
Specialisation: Specialist Criminal Defence Silk with considerable expertise and experience in the conduct of the gravest cases in particular human rights, terrorism, espionage, murder, serious fraud, drug trafficking and organised crime. Most notable cases include the attempted assassination of the Israeli Ambassador; the Tottenham Riots which concerned the murder of PC Blakelock; the Blackmail of Heinz Plc; a conspiracy to post incendiary devices; numerous terrorist cases including the bombing of the Israeli Embassy (also the Brighton and Warrington 'Bombings'); uniquely the trading of State Secrets by a KGB Spy. Accomplishments in the sphere of human rights comprise inter alia; the representation of the Directorate of Human Rights of the Council of Europe at a conference in St Petersburg, Russia 1994; the formation, chairmanship and organisation of conferences in Europe for the European Criminal Bar Association in order to advance major legal issues of mutual concern among European Defence Lawyers.
Prof. Memberships: South Eastern Circuit, Criminal Bar Association (Committee member 1990-96, 2000),

IBA, Chairman of the European Criminal Bar Association 1997-01.
Career: Called to the Bar 1966 and head of chambers 1988.
Personal: Educated at Bristol University – LLB and Diploma in Social Studies

TAPPIN, Michael

8 New Square (Michael Fysh QC) London (020) 7405 4321 michael.tappin@8newsquare.co.uk
Recommended in Intellectual Property
Specialisation: Barrister specialising in all aspects of intellectual property law, but with a particular interest in chemical, pharmaceutical and biotechnological work. For comprehensive CV and list of recent cases, visit our website at www.8newsquare.co.uk.
Prof. Memberships: Intellectual Property Bar Association (IPBA)
Career: Called 1991.
Personal: Born 1964. Educated at Cheltenham Grammar School; St John's College, Oxford (1986 BA Hons Chemistry); Merton College, Oxford (1989 DPhil Biochemistry).

TATTERSALL, Geoffrey QC

Byrom Street Chambers Manchester (0161) 829 2100
Recommended in Personal Injury

TATTERSALL, Simon

Fenners Chambers (Lindsay Davies) Cambridge (01223) 368761
Recommended in Family

TAUBE, Simon QC

10 Old Square (Leolin Price CBE QC) London (020) 7405 0758 / 7242 5002
Recommended in Chancery
Specialisation: Specialising in Chancery work (both litigation and advisory work) with special expertise in the fields of trusts, estates and tax, professional negligence, charity, real property, Inheritance Act claims; important cases include Berill v IRC (1981), Moore v IRC (1985), Re: Bunning (1984), Sinclair v Lee (1993), Re: Hobley (1997), Re: Ingram (1998), Re: Hoicrest (1999) X v A (1999), Public Trustee v Cooper
Prof. Memberships: Member Chancery Bar Association, STEP and Working Party Trust Law Committee.
Career: Westminster School; Merton College, Oxford (1978 Modern History 1st class), Called 1980, Middle Temple and Lincoln's Inn, QC 2000.
Personal: Singing, tennis.

TAUSSIG, Anthony

Wilberforce Chambers (Edward Nugee QC) London (020) 7306 0102
Recommended in Chancery
Specialisation: Equity and trusts, land/conveyancing, revenue, pensions, financial services, charities, housing associations.
Career: Called to the Bar 1966. Conveyancing Counsel of the Court since 1991. Publication: 'Housing associations and their committees'. A guide to the legal framework. 1992.
Personal: Educated at Winchester College and Magdalen College, Oxford.

TAVERNER, Marcus QC

Keating Chambers (Richard Fernyhough QC) London (020) 7544 2600 mtaverner@leatingchambers.com
Recommended in Arbitration (International), Construction, Professional Negligence
Specialisation: Construction and engineering; professional negligence: Arbitrator in domestic and international disputes.
Career: Qualified 1981; Gray's Inn.
Personal: Monmouth School; Leicester University; King's College, London (1979 LLB Hons, 1980 LLM). Interests, music, drama, literature, sport, trees. Born 1958; resides Benington, Herts.

TAYLER, James

Devereux Chambers (Jeffrey Burke QC) London (020) 7353 7534 tayler@devchambers.co.uk
Recommended in Employment
Specialisation: Employment; Discrimination; Administrative and Local Government. Cases of interest include Hayes v Security and Facilities Executive [2001] IRLR 81 CA. ECM v Cox; [1999] ICR 1162, CA (transfer of undertakings); Noorani v Merseyside Tec [1999] IRLR 184 CA (procedure); Thompson v Walon and BRS Automotive [1997] IRLR 343 EAT; BSG Property Services v Tuck [1996] IRLR 134 EAT (transfers of undertakings) and Allen v Redbridge LBC [1994] 1 WLR 139 DC (Trading Standards).
Prof. Memberships: ELBA (Committee member); ILS; ELA; ALBA.
Career: Wadham College Oxford; BA (Hons) Biology (1983-86): PCL (1987-88); CPE: ICSL Bar Finals (1988-89). [Queen Mother Scholarship; CLE Studentship]. Editor 'Butterworths Discrimination Law'. Contributor Halsbury's Laws (Equal Pay)'.
Publications: PCL contributor to Dix on Contracts of Employment (Butterworths 1997). Regular journal articles and conference appearances.

TAYLOR, Debbie

Hardwicke Building (Nicholas Stewart QC) London (020) 7242 2523
Recommended in Family
Specialisation: International family law disputes including child abduction, divorce and the cross-jurisdiction enforcement of financial orders. Expert evidence in Australian family law matters, particular interest and experience in Indian and Middle Eastern family law cases. Mental health related private and public law applications and child protection.
Career: Called 1984. Solicitor and Barrister Western Australia 1990. Legal member, Mental Health Review Tribunals 1994.

TAYLOR, Gregg QC

9 Park Place (Ian Murphy QC) Cardiff (029) 2038 2731
Recommended in Crime
Specialisation: All aspects of criminal law.
Prof. Memberships: CBA.
Career: Called 1974 (Middle Temple). Keele University.
Personal: Rock and roll. Fluent in Welsh.

TAYLOR, Martin

2-4 Tudor Street (Richard Ferguson QC) London (020) 7797 7111
Recommended in Crime

TAYLOR, Simon W.

Cloisters (Laura Cox QC) London (020) 7827 4000 simontaylor@cloisters.com
Recommended in Clinical Negligence
Specialisation: Specialises in medical law, including clinical negligence, medical disciplinary cases, mental health cases, health service administrative law, inquests and defamation and criminal cases involving medical disputes. Interesting cases include R (Touche) v Inner North London Coroner [2001] 3 WLR 148 (duty to hold inquest), Re A (children) (Conjoined Twins: Surgical Separation) [2001] 2 WLR 480 (case of Jodie and Mary), Hooper v Young (CA) [1998] Lloyd's Rep Med 61 (hysterectomy – ureteric damage – res ipsa locquitur), Williamson v East London Health Authority [1998] Lloyd's Rep Med 6 (silicone breast implants – mastectomy), Crouchman v Burke and Others 40 BMLR 163, (sterilisation – existing pregnancy – warnings), Taylor v West Kent Health Authority [1997] 8 Med LR 251, (breast cancer – effect of delay in diagnosis), GMC v Dr Eagles and Others (October 1995), (confidentiality – case reports in medical literature), R v Canterbury & Thanet DHA, ex parte F & W [1994] 5 Med LR 132 (complaints procedure where litigation is pending), Silverman v Singer & Others (1992 and ff) (bowel damage at laparoscopic operation).
Prof. Memberships: Professional Negligence Bar Association; British Academy of Forensic Sciences; Society of Doctors In Law; British Medical Association.
Career: Qualified doctor. Called to the Bar 1984. Joined present chambers 1998.
Personal: Educated at Cambridge (BA Hons) 1983. MB BChir 1987. Born 4th July 1962.

TEARE, Nigel QC

4 Essex Court (Nigel Teare QC) London (020) 7653 5653 nteare@4sx.co.uk
Recommended in Arbitration (International), Shipping
Specialisation: General commercial work with particular emphasis on carriage of goods, sale of goods, ship finance and all aspects of shipping law.
Prof. Memberships: COMBAR.
Career: Junior Counsel to Treasury in Admiralty Matters 1987-91. Queen's Counsel 1991. Recorder (Crown Court) 1997. Lloyd's Salvage Arbitrator 1995. Lloyd's Salvage Appeal Arbitrator 2000. Acting Deemster Isle of Man High Court 1998.
Personal: Educated: King William's College, Isle of Man. St. Peter's College, Oxford.

TEDD, Rex QC

St Philip's Chambers (John Randall QC) Birmingham (0121) 246 7000
Recommended in Crime

TEMPLE, Anthony QC

4 Pump Court London (020) 7842 5555
Recommended in Commercial (Litigation), Professional Negligence
Specialisation: Principal areas of practice are insurance and reinsurance, commercial fraud, stock exchange and Lloyd's disciplinary enquiries, banking, gaming lotteries and licensing. Also, common law cases of all kinds particularly professional negligence and construction.
Prof. Memberships: COMBAR, London Common Law and Commercial Bar Association, TECBA, Professional Negligence Bar Association.
Career: Called to the Bar in 1968; took silk in 1986. Recorder 1986. Deputy High Court Judge 1994.
Personal: MA (Oxon) Jurisprudence.

TEMPLE, Victor QC

6 King's Bench Walk (Roy Amlot QC) London (020) 7583 0410
Recommended in Crime, Fraud

TEMPLEMAN, Mark

Essex Court Chambers (Gordon Pollock QC) London (020) 7813 8000
Recommended in Insurance
Specialisation: Insurance and reinsurance, shipping, international sale of goods and international trade finance, in the context of both domestic and international litigation and arbitration. Also general commercial litigation of all types.
Career: Keble College, Oxford MA (Jurisprudence); BCL (1980). Inns of Court, 1979. Called to the Bar 1981.
Personal: Born 1958.

TENNET, Michael

Wilberforce Chambers (Edward Nugee QC) London (020) 7306 0102
Recommended in Pensions
Specialisation: Undertakes a broad range of commercial / chancery litigation specialising in the areas of occupational pension schemes, financial services and professional negligence. Has appeared in a number of important cases concerning the rights of members of occupation pension schemes, including SWT v Wightman (1998) PLR 114, Lansing Linde v Albe & Others [2000] PLR 15; AMP v Baker [2000] PLR 77 and BEST v Harrod [1999] 2 ALL ER 993. Contributions to Ellison on Pensions Law and Practice in the area of professional negligence work centres around the work of solicitors, actuaries and accountants. Considerable experience in general chancery / commercial litigation (other reported

cases include Ashley Guarantee v Zacaria (CA) (1993) 1 ALL ER 254 (principle and surety / mortgages). Yale v Newman (1990) FSR 320 (competition law). Is also a contributor to International Trust Laws (Jordan).
Career: Called to the Bar 1985. Law at New College, Oxford. Contributor to Ellison on Pensions Law and Practice and LLP's Professional Negligence Law and Practice.

TER HAAR, Roger QC
Crown Office Chambers (Michael Spencer QC & Christopher Purchas QC) London (020) 7797 8100
terhaar@crownofficechambers.com
Recommended in Construction, Professional Negligence
Specialisation: Practice encompasses professional negligence, construction law and insurance and reinsurance work.
Prof. Memberships: Official Referee's Bar Association, Administrative Law Bar Association, London and Commercial Bar Association, COMBAR.
Career: Called to the Bar and joined Crown Office Row 1974. Took Silk 1992. Bencher of the Inner Temple.
Personal: Educated at Magdalen College, Oxford 1970-73. Born 14th June 1952.

TERRY, Jeffrey
8 King St (Keith Armitage QC) Manchester (0161) 834 9560
jeffreyterry@genie.co.uk
Recommended in Chancery, Commercial (Litigation)
Specialisation: Commercial and Chancery. Recent reported cases include Universities Superannuation Scheme v Royal Insurance (2000) 1 All ER (Comm) 266; Unchained Growth v Granby Village (2000) 1 WLR 739; Re Hancock (1998) 2 FLR 346; Co-Operative Bank plc v Tipper (1996) 4 All ER 366; Transthene v Royal Insurance (1996) LRLR 32; Bank of Baroda v Reyarel (1995) 2 FLR 376; Jones v Roberts (1995) 2 FLR 422.
Prof. Memberships: Northern Circuit Commercial Bar Association; COMBAR; Northern Arbitration Association; Northern Chancery Bar Association; American Bar Association; Professional Negligence Bar Association; Union Internationale des Avocats; Bar European Group.
Career: LLB (Lond) 1975. Called 1976. MA (Business Law) with Distinction 1981. Fellow of the Chartered Institute of Arbitrators, President's Prize, 1996. CEDR Accredited Mediator 1999.
Publications: Various papers and publications in England, USA and Canada.
Personal: Married, two children (born 1983, 1987). Interests: theology and church affairs. Smallholding husbandry.

TETHER, Melanie
Old Square Chambers (John Hendy QC) London (020) 7269 0300
tether@oldsquarechambers.co.uk
Recommended in Employment
Specialisation: Formerly a partner in *Norton Rose*, transferred to the Bar in 1995. Deals with all aspects of employment law, including unfair and wrongful dismissal, transfer of undertakings, collective disputes, restraint of trade and all areas of discrimination law. Leading cases in which she has been involved include Kerry Foods Ltd v Creder and others [2000] IRLR 10; Unicorn Consultancy Services Ltd v Westbrook and others [2000] IRLR 80; Everson and another v Secretary of State for Trade and Industry and Bell Lines Limited (in liquidation) Case C – 198/98 [2000] IRLR 202; Chief Constable of West Yorkshire Police v Khan [2000] IRLR 324; Preston and others v Wolverhampton NHS Trust and others Case C – 78/98 [2000] IRLR 236 and Jones v Post Office [2001] IRLR 384.
Prof. Memberships: Former Chair and current Vice-President of the Industrial Law Society.
Publications: Writes the Equal Pay section of 'Tolley's Employment Law'.

THANKI, Bankim
Fountain Court (Anthony Boswood QC) London (020) 7583 3335
Recommended in Aviation, Banking, Commercial (Litigation), Fraud, Professional Negligence, Sport
Specialisation: Commercial and civil including general commercial litigation, banking, aviation, professional negligence, arbitration, insurance, and sports law. Noteworthy cases include acting for Barclays Bank in Deposit Protection Board v Barclays Bank and Dalia (banking), for the Bank of England in Three Rivers DC v Bank of England (BCCI) (banking), for Swiss Bank Corporation in NRG v Bacon & Woodrow & others (reinsurance/professional negligence), disciplinary proceedings for the Football Association against Leicester City players over the 1999 Worthington Cup Final and against Tottenham Hotspur FC over players' contractual terms (sport), Nuova Safim v Sakura Bank (banking/swap agreements),Nat West v Utrecht America Finance (conflicts) Federal Republic of Germany v Sotheby's (conflicts), Dowles Manor Properties v Bank of Namibia (unless orders), Hall v Bank of England (banking) Gurtner v Beaton (aviation/agency), Conchita Martinez v Ellesse International (sport), Gotha City v Sotheby's (privilege), Paragon Finance v *Freshfields* (privilege), Minories Finance v Afribank Nigeria (documentary credits/bills & exchange), Leeds Rugby League Club v Craig Innes (sport), BCCI v Price Waterhouse (discovery, Banking Act 1987, auditor's negligence), Southampton CC v Academy Cleaning (local authority/contract tenders), Re a firm of solicitors (solicitors/conflicts), British Coal v Smith (employment/equal pay), Kecskemeti v Rubens Rabin (solicitors' negligence/wills), HIV haemophilia litigation, Shannon v Country Casuals (Subpoena). Involved in civil and disciplinary aspects of Barlow Clowes and Polly Peck affairs. Joint editor of 'Commercial Court Procedure' (Sweet & Maxwell) and co-author of Fountain Court on 'Carriage by Air' (Butterworths).
Prof. Memberships: Commercial Bar Association, London Common Law & Commercial Bar Association.
Career: Called to the Bar 1988.
Personal: Educated at Balliol College, Oxford (MA, 1st Class Hons 1986). Harmsworth Scholar, Middle Temple 1988.

THOM, James
4 Field Court (Steven Gee QC) London (020) 7440 6900
chambers@4fieldcourt.com
Recommended in Property Litigation
Specialisation: Principal area of work is commercial property litigation, including disputes arising out of commercial conveyancing transactions, dilapidations cases, service charge disputes, rent reviews and lease renewals. Other main areas of work are professional negligence (for both claimants and defendants) in claims against solicitors, surveyors and valuers, often in cases with a commercial property aspect and also in claims against architects, engineers and others (not medical); commercial law (with emphasis on commercial contracts, banking and commercial lending). Regular speaker at conferences and seminars on the law of landlord and tenant.
Prof. Memberships: Professional Negligence Bar Association, COMBAR, Bar Sports Law Group.
Career: Called to the Bar 1974. Called to the Bar of St. Vincent and the Grenadines 1997.
Publications: Joint author of 'Handbook of Dilapidations' (Sweet & Maxwell, 1992).
Personal: Educated at Felsted School 1965-68 and Corpus Christi College, Oxford 1969-73 (BA 1972, BCL 1973). Born 19th October 1951. Lives in Highgate, London.

THOMAS, Christopher QC
Keating Chambers (Richard Fernyhough QC) London (020) 7544 2600
clerks@keatingchambers.com
Recommended in Arbitration (International), Construction
Specialisation: Construction and engineering; professional negligence; bonds and guarantees; oil, power and transport projects in UK and overseas; arbitration and mediation – domestic and international; Arbitrator under ICC and other rules; cases include Croudace Ltd v Lambeth BC; Int'l Press Centre v Norwich Union Life Insurance Society; McAlpine Humberoak v McDermott Int'l.
Career: Qualified 1973; Lincoln's Inn, Queen's Counsel 1989, admitted to the Bar of Gibraltar 1990; Recorder; lecturer; Fellow of the Chartered Institute of Arbitrators.
Personal: University of Kent, Canterbury (BA Law 1st class); Faculté International de Droit Compare (Diplôme de Droit Comparé avec merite); King's College, London (PhD. Law). CEDR accredited mediator. Born 1950; resides London.

THOMAS, David
2 Temple Gardens (Dermod O'Brien QC) London (020) 7822 1200
Recommended in Construction
Specialisation: Construction, engineering and other technical contracts. Associated professional liability, litigation and UK and international arbitration. Recent reported cases: Davy Offshore v Emerald Field Contracting, GPT Realisations v Panatown. Soundcraft v Padmanor, Balfour Beatty v DLR, Chesham Properties v Bucknall Austin, Cook v Shimizu, Weldon v CNT.
Prof. Memberships: ORBA, BEG.
Career: Oxford: 1st Class Honours in Law 1981. Called to Bar 1982; Called to Bar of Gibraltar 1996.

THOMAS, Keith
9 Park Place (Ian Murphy QC) Cardiff (029) 2038 2731
Recommended in Crime

THOMAS, Leslie
Two Garden Court (Ian Macdonald QC & Owen Davies QC) London (020) 7353 1633
leslie@global.force9.net
Recommended in Human Rights
Specialisation: Civil actions against the police and prisons. Inquests (deaths in custody and fatal shootings). Judicial review of Police Complaints Authority, Coroners, Magistrates. Human Rights specialist.
Prof. Memberships: Lawyers for liberty; Inquest Lawyers; Member of Civil Liberties Trustees; APIL.
Publications: Numerous articles and case notes on Inquests for various legal journals and media.

THOMAS, Michael QC
Essex Court Chambers (Gordon Pollock QC) London (020) 7813 8000
Recommended in Arbitration (International)
Specialisation: Maritime, International Trade, Construction, Sale and Purchase. Recent arbitrations: Oil Rig Charterparty dispute, sale of high speed vessel, shipbuilding dispute.
Prof. Memberships: Member of Hong Kong Bar.
Career: Practice at the English Bar since 1959, Treasury Junior (MOD) 1966, Queen's Counsel 1973.
Publications: Temperley: 'Merchant Shipping Act'.

THOMAS, Nigel
Maitland Chambers (Michael Lyndon-Stanford QC & Charles Aldous QC) London (020) 7406 1200
Recommended in Agriculture
Specialisation: Agricultural Law: Davies v H & R Eckroyd Ltd (1996) EGCS 77; Law of Commons and Village Green: R v Suffolk CC ex Parte Steed (1995) 2EGLR 232, Lord Dynevor v Richardson [1995] ChD 173.
Prof. Memberships: Chancery Bar Association, Bristol and Cardiff Chancery Bar Association Wales and Chester Circuit.

Career: Called to the Bar 1976 (Gray's Inn). Sometime lecturer in Agricultural Law, Central Law Training. Chairman Agricultural Lands Tribunal (Midland Area).

THOMAS, Paul Huw

Iscoed Chambers (Trefor Davies) Swansea (01792) 652988/9

Recommended in Crime

Specialisation: Prosecuted and defended all major categories. Junior Counsel in Pembrokeshire paedophile case (1993-94) for Crown.
Prof. Memberships: Criminal Bar Association.
Career: MA (Cantab). Recorder.
Personal: Theatre, reading, travel. Sport especially Rugby (Committee member Swansea R.F.C.). Married with two children. Passably proficient in Welsh.

THOMAS, R. Neville QC

3 Verulam Buildings (Christopher Symons QC & John Jarvis QC) London (020) 7831 8441 chambers@3vb.com

Recommended in Banking

Specialisation: Principal area of practice encompasses all aspects of commercial contracts, especially for banks, shipping companies, trading companies, commodity dealers and property companies.
Prof. Memberships: Commercial Bar Association, London Common Law Bar Association.
Career: Called to the Bar and joined present chambers 1962. Took Silk 1975. Recorder 1975-81. Master of the Bench, Inner Temple 1985.
Personal: Educated at Oxford University (MA 1960, BCL 1961). Born 31 March 1936. Lives in London and Wales.

THOMAS, Robert

4 Essex Court (Nigel Teare QC) London (020) 7653 5653 rthomas@4sx.co.uk

Recommended in Shipping

Specialisation: All aspects of shipping and related areas, including insurance, international sale of goods, jurisdiction disputes, etc and salvage and collisions.
Prof. Memberships: Commercial Bar Association, LCIA and supporting member of LMAA.
Career: M.A. (Hons), Trinity College, Cambridge. Licence Spéciale en Droit Européen, Université Libre de Bruxelles. BCL, St Catherine's College, Oxford. Fluent French, working knowledge of German.

THOMAS, Roger QC

9 Park Place (Ian Murphy QC) Cardiff (029) 2038 2731

Recommended in Crime

Specialisation: Criminal law of all types including Revenue and Excise fraud.
Prof. Memberships: CBA.
Career: Recorder 1987, Silk 1994.
Personal: LLB (Wales.)

THOMAS, Sybil

3 Fountain Court (Robert Juckes QC) Birmingham (0121) 236 5854 clerks@3fc.co.uk

Recommended in Crime, Family

Specialisation: All aspects of criminal and family law, with a particular interest in cases involving the disabled and mentally ill.
Prof. Memberships: Midland Circuit, Family Law Bar Association (Chairman, Birmingham branch), Criminal Bar Association.
Career: LLB (Hons) (Bristol) Called to the Bar 1976. Recorder.

THOMPSON, Andrew

Erskine Chambers (Robin Potts QC) London (020) 7242 5532

Recommended in Company

Specialisation: Specialist in commercial litigation, particularly involving issues of company law, corporate insolvency, partnership disputes and professional negligence; advisory work in the same fields; cases include Re BSB Holdings Ltd (No 2) (1996 1 BCLC 155), Re H & K (Medway) Ltd (1997 1 WLR 1422), Re Sentinel Securities plc (1996 1 WLR 316), Re SH & Co (Realizations) 1990 Ltd (1993 BCC 60), Re CSTC Ltd (1995 BCC 173), Banque Financière de la Cité v Parc (Battersea) Ltd (1999 1 AC 221), New Hampshire Insurance v Rush & Tompkins (1998 2 BCLC 471), Re Holiday Promotions (1996 BCC 671), Re Lummus Agricultural Services (1999 BCC 953), Re Kaytech (1999) 2 BCLC 351, Gwembe Valley Development Company v Koshy (No 2) [2000] 2 BCLC 705, Re Sedgefield Staplechase Co [2000] 2 BCLC 211.
Career: Merchant Taylors' School; St Catharine's College, Cambridge (1989 BA; 1990 LLM; 1992 MA); Called to Inner Temple 1991.
Personal: Leisure: gardening, hill walking, birding.

THOMPSON, Rhodri

Matrix Chambers (Nicholas Blake QC) London (020) 7404 3447 rhodrithompson@matrixlaw.co.uk

Recommended in Competition/Anti-trust

Specialisation: European Community law including administrative law and competition. Treasury Panel. Cases include BCCI et al v Bank of England (misfeasance in public office); R v Chief Constable of Sussex ex p ITF (exports of livestock); R v Secretary of State for the Home Department ex p Hoverspeed (carriers liability); acted for BBC in RPC reference of Premier League TV contract. Contributor to 'Bellamy & Child, Common Market Law of Competition', (5th edn); Vaughan Law of the European Communities Service, 'Rights of Establishment and Freedom to Provide Services' (looseleaf); 'Human Rights Practice', ed Emerson and Simor (looseleaf) (freedom of assembly); author of 'The Single Market for Pharmaceuticals' (1994). Regular speaker at conferences/in house seminars on EC law.

THORLEY, Simon QC

Three New Square (David Young QC) London (020) 7405 1111 3newsquareip@lineone.net

Recommended in Information Technology, Intellectual Property

Specialisation: Extensive intellectual property practice particularly in field of Chemical and Biotechnical Patents and expanding to passing off, trade marks, copyright, designs and breach of confidence. Advises on EC law relating to IP. Experience in arbitrations. Recent Cases: Biogen v Medeva, Biotech Patents, House of Lords; Canon v Green Cartridge, patent/copyright, Hong Kong Privy Council; Harrods v Harrodian School – passing off; Phillips v Remington – trade marks; Lubrizol v Exxon and Union Carbide v BP – patents. Arsenal v Reed (trademark – ECJ Reference).
Prof. Memberships: Chairman Intellectual Property Bar Assn (1995-99); Member Chancery Bar Assn; AIPPI; Member of Bar Council (1995-99).
Career: Rugby School, 1963-67. Keble College, Oxford, MA Jurisprudence, 1968-71. Called to Bar 1972. Q.C.1989. Appointed person to hear Trade Mark Appeals, 1996. Deputy High Court Judge, 1998. Deputy Chairman Copyright Tribunal, 1998.

THORNHILL, Andrew QC

Pump Court Tax Chambers London (020) 7414 8080

Recommended in Tax

Specialisation: Principal area of practice is revenue law, both advisory and litigation. Specialisations include Schedule E, share schemes and private companies.
Prof. Memberships: Revenue Bar Association.
Career: Called to the Bar 1969. Took Silk 1985. Currently Head of Chambers.
Personal: Born 4 August 1943.

THORNTON, Peter QC

Doughty Street Chambers (Geoffrey Robertson QC) London (020) 7404 1313

Recommended in Crime, Human Rights

Specialisation: Principal area of practice is criminal defence work including commercial fraud; appellate work, notably Privy Council appeals (Caribbean, Mauritius, New Zealand) often in capital cases; and all forms of serious crime including murder, terrorism, Official Secrets Act, corruption and drugs cases. Other main area of work is civil rights cases including actions against the police or government, suspects' and prisoners' rights and international human rights. Recent reported cases include R v Christou [1992] (undercover police); Walker v R [1994] (Privy Council jurisdiction: appeal against death sentence); R v Basford and Lawless (witness too ill to continue); R v Aroyewumi [1994] (sentencing in Class A drugs cases); Freemantle v R [1994] (the proviso in identification cases), Re W [1994] (rights of children), Lobban [1995] (editing co-defendant's statement) and R v Kelly and Lindsay [1998] (stealing body parts), R v Smith (Morgan) [1999] (provocation and the reasonable man). Author of 'Public Order Law' (Blackstone Press 1987) and 'Decade of Decline: Civil Liberties in the Thatcher Years' (Liberty 1989). Editor of the Penguin Civil Liberty Guide (1989); currently contributing editor to Archbold and member of editorial board of the Criminal Law Review. Regular broadcaster on legal and civil liberty topics. Teaches human rights, advocacy and criminal evidence to solicitors and barristers. Has lectured and chaired seminars, on trial by jury, PACE, police powers, the CPS, evidence, white collar crime, emergency powers, miscarriages of justice, and the right of silence.
Prof. Memberships: Midland and Oxford Circuit, Criminal Bar Association, Administrative Law Bar Association, formerly chairman of the National Council for Civil Liberties and of the Civil Liberties Trust.
Career: Called to the Bar 1969. Also called to the Bars of Trinidad, Northern Ireland, Isle of Man. Tenant at 1 King's Bench Walk 1971-78 and at 1 Dr Johnson's Buildings 1978-90. Founder member of Doughty Street Chambers in 1990 and currently deputy head of chambers. Took Silk 1992. Recorder of the Crown Court 1997.

THORNTON, Rebecca

Zenith Chambers (Andrew Campbell QC & John Collins) Leeds (0113) 245 5438

Recommended in Family

Specialisation: A well thought of specialist in every aspect of family work. Called to the Bar in 1976. Combines a successful practice with a family. Work undertaken at every level of Court and for private, professional and local authority clients. Instructed in the 'Cleveland' litigation. Active Member of the Family Bar Association.

THOROGOOD, Bernard

5 Fountain Court (Anthony Barker QC) Birmingham (0121) 606 0500

Recommended in Crime

Specialisation: Criminal Law – all areas covered but very extensive experience of the most serious categories of offences, including commercial fraud. Very significant experience of Video-Link and Appellate work. Particular interest in matters involving claims of public interest immunity and matters involving expert evidence. Trading Standards, Health and Safety, Road Traffic, Customs Work.
Prof. Memberships: Criminal Bar Association. Forensic Science Society.
Career: 1981-85 Short Service Commission (Army). 1986 Called to the Bar.
Personal: Married, three children.

THOROLD, Oliver

Doughty Street Chambers (Geoffrey Robertson QC) London (020) 7404 1313

Recommended in Clinical Negligence, Product Liability

THORPE, Simon
Park Lane Chambers (Stuart Brown QC) Leeds (0113) 228 5000
Recommended in Personal Injury

THWAITES, Ronald QC
Ely Place Chambers (Ronald Thwaites QC) London (020) 7400 9600
Recommended in Defamation
Specialisation: Principal area of practice is high-profile criminal trials. Recent examples, R v Tracie Andrews (1997) and R v Pearce (1999) (Mardi Gras Bombing). Some civil actions (mainly involving the police) and professional disciplinary work also undertaken. Expanding area of work is in defamation acting for both claimants and defendants: Cooper v Roger Cook & Central television (1993 trial); Dr Osagie v Doncaster Health Authority and Others (1995 trial); Kevin McKenzie v Business Magazines (UK) Ltd & Others (1996 reported); Basham v Martyn Gregory & Little Brown (1996 trial and reported); Morgan v MGN (1997); Harris v Three Valleys Water Board (1997); Mickey Duff v MGN (1999 trial); Bridle v MGN (2000); Blackstone v MGN (2000); Arobieke v MGN (2000); Frank Warren v BBC and Naseem Hamed (2000); Foulds v MGN (2000); Rahamin v Channel 4 TV (2001).
Prof. Memberships: South Eastern Circuit: Criminal Bar Association: British Association of Sport and Law.
Career: Educated at Grangefield Grammar School (Stockton-on-Tees) and Kingston College of Technology (now university) LLB (Lon). Called to the Bar in 1970: Appointed Queen's Counsel 1987. Developed mixed common law practice until crime took over, making a return in recent years to more varied work. Occasional lectures on advocacy and professional ethics.

TIDBURY, Andrew
Queen Elizabeth Building (Florence Baron QC) London (020) 7797 7837
Recommended in Family

TIDMARSH, Christopher
5 Stone Buildings (Henry Harrod) London (020) 7242 6201
Recommended in Chancery, Pensions
Specialisation: Chancery practitioner, with a particular emphasis on trusts and probate, pension schemes and professional negligence, principally solicitors and accountants. Standing junior counsel to the Inland Revenue (Chancery). Important cases include AG of Cayman Islands v Wahr Hansen (charities) [2001]; British Coal v British Coal Staff Superannuation Scheme Trustees [1994]; Stannard v Fisons [1991]; Electricity Supply Nominees litigation, Royal Masonic Hospital v PO [2001] (all pensions); The Pointwest litigation (solicitors negligence); Re a Debtor (415 of 1993) [1994] (bankruptcy); IRC v Lloyds Private Banking, IRC v Botner (1999), Cooper v Billingham (2001) (all tax).
Prof. Memberships: Chancery Bar Association, STEP.
Career: Called 1985.
Personal: Educated at Merton College, Oxford (BA) 1980-83.

TILLYARD, James
30 Park Place (John Jenkins QC) Cardiff (029) 2039 8421
Recommended in Family

TIPPLES, Amanda
Maitland Chambers (Michael Lyndon-Stanford QC & Charles Aldous QC) London (020) 7406 1200 atipples@maitlandchambers.com
Recommended in Property Litigation
Specialisation: Practice covers business and commercial chancery work, (litigation emphasis), including corporate and personal insolvency, partnership, landlord and tenant and property law generally.
Prof. Memberships: Chancery Bar Association, COMBAR, Property Bar Association.
Career: Called to the Bar in 1991 and joined *13 Old Square* in 1992.
Personal: Educated at Roedean School and Gonville and Caius College, Cambridge (1986-90). Lives in London.

TODD, Michael QC
Erskine Chambers (Robin Potts QC) London (020) 7242 5532
Recommended in Company
Specialisation: Company law, corporate finance and corporate insolvency; work involves all advisory and litigation aspects with an emphasis on litigation both in the UK and abroad and covers areas such as mergers, acquisitions and disposals of companies, shareholder disputes, board meetings, bank securities, financial services and related commercial and professional negligence (accountants and solicitors). Recent reported cases include North Holdings Ltd. v Southern Tropics Ltd. [1999] BCLC 625; Re Rotadata Ltd. [2000] 1 BCLC 122; Re: Allied Domecq plc [2000] BCLC 134; Re Sedgefield Steeplechase Co (1927) Ltd. [2000] 2 BCLC 211.
Prof. Memberships: COMBAR, Chancery Bar Association, Insolvency Lawyers Association.
Career: Called to the Bar in 1977 and joined Erskine Chambers. QC year 1997.
Personal: Educated at Keele University (BA). Born 16th February 1953.

TOLANEY, Sonia
3 Verulam Buildings (Christopher Symons QC & John Jarvis QC) London (020) 7831 8441 chambers@3vb.com
Recommended in Banking
Specialisation: Commercial litigation, arbitration and mediation. Advisory work. Specialist areas: domestic and international banking (including bills of exchange, letters of credit, bonds, guarantees, standbys and flawed asset arrangements); domestic and international commercial fraud and asset tracing; corporate and personal insolvency, insurance and reinsurance, contractual disputes, professional negligence. Recent cases include Smith v Lloyds CA (2000) (conversion, fraudulent alteration of a cheque, s64 Bills of Exchange Act); Lloyds Bank v Voller, CA (2000) (Bank's right to charge interest on unauthorised overdraft); Casson & anr v Ostley PJ Ltd & Ors, CA (2001) (construction of an exclusion clause in an insurance policy); Anglian Water Services v Crawshaw Robbins (2000) (contract, construction of an indemnity clause, nuisance, negligence, breach of statutory duty); Crest Holmes (South East) v Browne (1999) (application of s284, Insolvency Act 1986 to trust property).
Prof. Memberships: COMBAR.
Career: MA (Oxon), Jurisprudence. Called to the Bar in 1995, Middle Temple. Tenant at 3 Verulam Buildings from October 1996 to date. CEDR Accredited Mediator (2000).
Publications: Chapter on Financing International Sales (emphasis on letters of credit, bonds and standbys) in 'McKendrick on Sale of Goods' (Dec 2000)
Personal: Education: Bolton School, Girls' Division. Lady Margaret Hall, Oxford.

TOLEDANO, Daniel
One Essex Court (Lord Grabiner QC) London (020) 7583 2000
Recommended in Commercial (Litigation)
Specialisation: Broad commercial practice including energy and utilities, financial services, insurance, sale of goods, company/insolvency and arbitration. Recent work includes BP Amoco v British American Offshore (oil and gas), Armco v Donohue (jurisdiction/anti-suit injunctions) and Sumitomo Corporation v Credit Lyonnais Rouse (options and futures trading).
Prof. Memberships: COMBAR.
Career: Called to the Bar 1993 (Inner Temple). Junior Counsel to the Crown (C Panel).
Personal: Born 1969. MA, Jesus College, Cambridge.

TOMLINSON, Hugh
Matrix Chambers (Nicholas Blake QC) London (020) 7404 3447
Recommended in Defamation

TOPHAM, Geoffrey J.
3 Stone Buildings (Geoffrey Vos QC) London (020) 7242 4937
Recommended in Chancery, Pensions
Specialisation: Main field of practice is occupational pension schemes, acting both in Litigation and Advisory work for members, pensioners, trustees and employers (cases include Imperial Tobacco, Courage, Brooks v Brooks, Lloyds Bank, National Grid). Other main areas are trusts and estates, and capital taxes.
Prof. Memberships: Chancery Bar Association, Association of Pensions Lawyers, Associate of Pensions Management Institute, Revenue Bar Association.
Career: Called June, 1964. Member of Lincoln's Inn. Joined Stone Buildings in 1965.
Personal: Educated at Haileybury and Trinity Hall, Cambridge.

TOUBE, Felicity
3-4 South Square (Michael Crystal QC & Lord Alexander of Weedon QC) London (020) 7969 9900 felicitytoube@southsquare.com
Recommended in Insolvency/Corporate Recovery
Specialisation: Insolvency, company, general commercial, banking, restitution. Cases: Secretary of State v Anderson [1999] BCC 121; Continental Assurance [1999] 1 BCLC 751; BCCI v Bank of America; Douai School [2000] 1 WLR 502; Toshoku Finance UK [2000] 1 WLR 2478; Ross [2000] BPIR 636; Horne v Dacorum BC [2000] 4 All ER 550; UCT (UK) Limited [2001] 1 WLR 436; Hawk Insurance Co; Liberty Mutual v HSBC.
Prof. Memberships: COMBAR, Chancery Bar Association.
Publications: Rose (ed) 'Failure of Contracts' and 'Restitution and Banking Law'; 'Insolvency Intelligence' board member; cases editor (Totty & Moss, Sweet & Maxwell Complete Insolvency Service CD ROM); Lightman & Moss on Receivers, Rowlatt, Halsbury's Laws, Totty & Moss; 'Recovery' case summaries.

TOZZI, Nigel QC
4 Pump Court London (020) 7842 5555
Recommended in Commercial (Litigation), Insurance, Professional Negligence
Specialisation: General commercial and common law practice, specialising in commercial litigation, professional negligence (especially solicitors, accountants, financial advisers, surveyors, valuers, brokers and barristers), insurance and reinsurance, fire claims, media and entertainment, financial and banking disputes and gaming. He also has experience in aviation, employment, agency, advertising, construction work and professional disciplinary hearings.
Prof. Memberships: COMBAR, Professional Negligence Bar Association, London Common Law and Commercial Bar Association.
Career: Called to the Bar 1980, took Silk 2001.
Personal: Educated at Exeter University (LL.B Hons first class) 1976-79. Bar Finals 1980 (first class). Leisure pursuits include sport (especially hockey), theatre and cinema. Born 31st August 1957.

TRACE, Anthony QC
Maitland Chambers (Michael Lyndon-Stanford QC & Charles Aldous QC) London (020) 7406 1200 clerks@maitlandchambers.com
Recommended in Chancery
Specialisation: Principal area of practice encompasses insolvency, property, trusts, chancery and general commercial work, including a number of cases outside the UK. Recent cases include: Re Jeffrey S. Levitt Ltd [1992] (privilege against self-incrimination); Re Mirror Group (Holdings) Ltd [1993] (liability of assignees on liquidation); Gomba Holdings (UK) Ltd v Minories Finance Ltd

(No.2) [1993] (mortgagee's costs); Lotteryking Ltd v AMEC Properties Ltd [1995] (set – off against assignees); Re BCCI SA (No.10) [1996] (insolvency set – off); Slough Estates Plc v Welwyn Hatfield DC [1996] (measure of damages for fraudulent misrepresentation); Grand Metropolitan plc v The William Hill Group Ltd [1997] (rectification); Bogg v Raper [1998] (will drafting and exclusion clauses); Plant v Plant [1998] (individual voluntary arrangements); Jordan Grand Prix Ltd v Baltic Insurance Group [1999] (Brussels Convention); Landare Investments Ltd v Welsh Development Agency [2000] (misfeasance in public office); Shalson v Russo [2001] (committal). Has sat as an Arbitrator. Vice-Chairman, Chancery Bar Association.
Prof. Memberships: Chancery Bar Association; COMBAR; Bar Sports Law Group; ACTAPS (Association of Contentious Trust and Probate Specialists).
Career: Called to the Bar 1981.
Publications: Contributor to 'Butterworths European Law Service' (company law) and 'Butterworths Practical Insolvency'. Deputy Managing Editor: 'Receivers, Administrators and Liquidators Quarterly'. Member, International Editorial Board, Briefings in Real Estate Finance.
Personal: Educated at Magdalene College, Cambridge (MA, 1st Class Honours).

TRACY FORSTER, Jane
13 King's Bench Walk (Roger Ellis QC) London (020) 7353 7204
clerks@13kbw.co.uk
Recommended in Clinical Negligence
Specialisation: Clinical Negligence of all descriptions. Recent Cases: Miles v West Kent Health Authority 1997 Med LR 191; Smith v Leicester Health Authority 1998 Lloyds Rep. (Med) 77; Thurman v Bath and Wiltshire Health Authority 1997 P.I.Q.R. Q115.
Prof. Memberships: Professional Negligence Bar Association; Personal Injury Bar Association; Employment Law Bar Association.
Career: LLB (Hons) Liverpool University 1974; Called July 1975 (Inner Temple); Sept 1975 – May 1986 Peel House Chambers, Liverpool. From May 1986 – 13 King's Bench Walk.
Personal: Married with one son. Lives in London.

TRAVERS, David
6 Pump Court (Stephen Hockman QC) London (020) 7797 8400
clerks@6pumpcourt.co.uk
Recommended in Consumer Law, Environment, Health & Safety
Specialisation: Practice made up of all aspects of regulatory work; including trading standards, consumer protection and health and safety as well as environmental protection, waste management and planning, and public law. Experienced in appellate work and cases with a strong technical or scientific component. Clients include well known high street names (as well as small traders), local authorities and regulatory bodies. Cases include: R v Coffey [1987] Crim LR 498, CA; A v Wigan MBC [1986] FLR 608, DC; Birmingham CC v H [1994] 2 WLR 31, HL; Farrand v Tse (1992) Times 10 December, DC (meaning of "application" for emergency prohibition order – Food Safety Act); Dudley MBC v Firman BTCL (1992) Independent 26 October DC ("due diligence" – sufficiency of sampling); Janbo Trading v Dudley MBC [1993] 157 JPN 256, DC ("due diligence"); Gale v Dixons Stores Group (1994) 158 JPN 256, DC (extent of trade description); T&S Stores Ltd v Hereford & Worcester CC [1995] Tr LR 337 (under age sales – "due diligence"); Edwards v CPS [1881] 155 JP 746, DC (licensing); Lazarus v Coventry CC 91995) Sol J Vol 139, No 32 826 (consumer credit advertisement -meaning of "information" – "due diligence"); North Yorkshire CC v Entergold Guardian 8.2.95 (breach of site licence and planning control at waste transfer station); Meston Technical Services v Warwickshire CC [1995] Env LR D36 (breach of site licence – meaning of "waste"); Taw & Torridge Fisheries Byelaw Inquiry, Daily Telegraph 31.1.97; Hilliers Ltd v Sefton MBC [1997] 3CL 424 (delegation of powers within Food authority); R v Snaresbrook Crown Court, ex parte Input Management [1999] Times 29 April (duty to give reasons). HSE Harvestime Bakeries and others new item Times 12 June 2001 (double fatality in commercial bakery oven), waste management licensing appeals and numerous public inquiries, particularly involving waste management facilities.
Prof. Memberships: Food Law Group, Planning and Environment Bar Association, Administrative Law Bar Association, UKELA. Midland and Oxford Circuit.
Career: Called Middle Temple 1981, Kings College London 1975-80 (LLB, LLM, AKC). Editor 'Kings Counsel' the KCL Law Journal 1978. President Kings College London Union of Students 1979, elected Honorary Life Member 1981. Harmsworth Scholar 1982. Member of the Bar Council 1995 – Member of Law Reform and IT Committees 1996-98. Sometime Occasional Lecturer School of Management Sciences University of Manchester Institute of Science and Technology. Sometime Royal Institution Australian Science Scholar. Accredited mediator. Also at 3 Fountain Court Birmingham.
Personal: Married with children. Interests language, music, running and family life.

TREACY, Colman QC
3 Fountain Court (Robert Juckes QC) Birmingham (0121) 236 5854
clerks@3fc.co.uk
Recommended in Consumer Law, Crime
Specialisation: Criminal Law. All types of serious crime cases including commercial fraud and miscarriage of justice cases. Equal split between prosecution and defence work. Recent reported cases: Fellows (computer pornography); Callender (res gestae); Kendrick & Hopkins (theft and gifts inter vivos); Ryan James (successful vet murder appeal); Jeremy Bamber appeal (forthcoming). Regulatory law of all types, representing businesses and local authorities; Popelcy (Timeshare Act), Nottinghamshire CC v BT (Streetworks Act).
Career: Jesus College Cambridge (open scholar): Call 1971: Silk 1990: Recorder. Bencher Middle Temple. Mental Health Review Tribunal. Assistant Boundary Commissioner.

TREHARNE, Jennet
33 Park Place (John Charles Rees QC) Cardiff (029) 2023 3313
Recommended in Crime

TREVERTON-JONES, Gregory
Farrar's Building (John Leighton Williams QC) London (020) 7583 9241
Recommended in Health & Safety
Specialisation: Wide-ranging common law practice, particularly judicial review and public inquiries, personal injury, employment and civil liberties. Junior Counsel to the North Wales Child Abuse Tribunal of Inquiry, 1996-8; represented First Great Western at the Southall Rail Crash Inquiry 1999 and the Association of Train Operating Companies at the Ladbroke Grove Rail Crash Inquiry 2000.
Career: MA (Oxon). Called 1977. Recorder.
Publications: 'Imprisonment: The Legal Status and Rights of Prisoners' (1989).
Personal: Married, three children. Interests include most sports, particularly cricket, skiing, mountaineering, tennis and golf.

TREVETT, Peter QC
Revenue Law Chambers (John Gardiner QC) London (020) 7242 4017
taxlaw@11newsquare.com
Recommended in Tax
Specialisation: Revenue Law. Practice covers all aspects of commercial, private client and trust taxation in the UK, including stamp duty, VAT, unit trusts, insurance company taxation and offshore trusts. Hong Kong profits tax, stamp duty and estate duty planning. Regular lecturer on revenue law.
Prof. Memberships: Revenue Bar Association, Society of Trust and Estate Practitioners. Fellow of the Society for Advanced Legal Studies.
Career: Called to Bar 1971. Joined present chambers 1973. Took Silk 1992.
Personal: Educated Kingston Grammar School. Queens' College, Cambridge (1966-71) (MA LLM). Born 25 November 1947.

TRITTON, Guy
Hogarth Chambers (Jonathan Rayner James QC & Christopher Morcom QC) London (020) 7404 0404
guytritton@hogarthchambers.com
Recommended in Intellectual Property
Specialisation: Intellectual property. Experienced in both soft IP (trade marks, copyright and passing off) and hard IP (patents and technical design). A number of reported cases including Springsteen v Flute and Ors (big media copyright dispute); WILD CHILD TM (leading trade mark case); Fylde Microsystems v Key Radio (joint authorship in computer programmes); Hodgkinson & Corby v Wards (passing off in functional items); Hazelgrove Superleague v Business Machines (right to modify patented articles); Chiron v Organon (biotechnological patent infringement action). Also substantial practices in franchise and IT disputes; Dyno Rod v Reeve (enforceability of post-termination restraint of trade covenants in franchise).
Prof. Memberships: Intellectual Property Bar Association, Bar European Group, Chancery Bar Association, Institute of Trade Mark Agents.
Career: Eton College; Durham University BSc Natural Sciences (applied physics, computing, psychology and mathematics). Inner Temple Pegasus scholar. Author of a number of computer programmes including a chambers fee billing package, a legal discovery programme and a designer and programmer of chambers own website.
Publications: Author of 'Intellectual Property in Europe', Sweet & Maxwell, 800 pp 1996. This has become a university text book in several universities including University of Maastricht. Second edition to be released in 2002.
Personal: Married. Two children. Piano, computers and windsurfing.

TROLLOPE, Andrew QC
1 Middle Temple Lane (Colin Dines & Andrew Trollope QC) London (020) 7583 0659 (12 lines)
Recommended in Crime, Fraud
Specialisation: Co-head of chambers specialising in criminal law with wide experience of fraud cases. Own practice has predominantly consisted of City, commercial and other fraud cases for more than 15 years. Cases include R v Thomas Ward (Guinness), R v Cohen (Blue Arrow), R v Masterson (Caird plc), R v Michael Ward (European Leisure plc), R v Johnston (Harrovian Properties/Leisure).
Prof. Memberships: Criminal Bar Association Committee member. International Relations Committee Bar Council; Council of Management British Institute of International and Comparative Law; fellow of the Society of Advanced Legal Studies; International Relations Committee Bar Council; Council of Management British Institute of International and Comparative Law; fellow of the Society of Advanced Legal Studies.
Career: A Recorder of the Crown Court since 1989.

TROMANS, Stephen
Eldon Chambers (Lionel Read QC) London (020) 7583 1355
Recommended in Environment
Specialisation: Environmental law, planning law, public law. R v Durham County Council, ex p Huddleston (Court of Appeal); R (Vetterlesh) v Hampshire County Council.
Prof. Memberships: PEBA, ALBA, UKELA, Chartered Institute of Water & Environmental Management.
Career: Former University Lecturer (Cambridge 1981-87) Former solicitor.
Publications: Textbooks: 'The Encyclopedia of Environ-

mental Law', 'Planning Law, Practice & Precedents', 'Commercial Leases', 'Nuclear Installations & Radioactive Substances', 'Contaminated Land: The New Regime'.
Personal: Council member, English Nature.

TROWER, William QC
3-4 South Square (Michael Crystal QC & Lord Alexander of Weedon QC) London
(020) 7696 9900
williamtrower@southsquare.com
Recommended in Chancery, Insolvency/Corporate Recovery
Specialisation: Business law especially corporate and international insolvency banking, company law and professional negligence.
Prof. Memberships: COMBAR, Chancery Bar Association, CEDR accredited mediator.
Career: Called 1983. Acted in many of the major insolvencies of the 1990s (BCCI, Polly Peck, Maxwell and Barings). Litigation in Bermuda throughout 1999 (Bermuda Fire and Marine). Particular interest in insurance insolvency.
Publications: Fletcher Higham and Trower: 'Law and Practice of Corporate Administrations' (1994)

TUCKER, Katherine
St Philip's Chambers (John Randall QC) Birmingham (0121) 246 7000
Recommended in Employment
Specialisation: Employment law, European law and commercial law.
Prof. Memberships: Employment Lawyers Association; Bar European Group; Employment Law Bar Association; Midland Chancery and Commercial Bar Association.
Career: Hardwicke, Mansfield and J.P. Warner Scholar, Lincoln's Inn. Sometime Stagière to Advocate General Jacobs, European Court of Justice. Visiting lecturer at Birmingham University. Particular interest in discrimination law. Speaks fluent French.
Publications: Author of the contractual restraints section for online CCH/New Law Employment Law Service and regular contributor to CCH 'Employment Lawyer'.

TUCKER, Lynton
New Square Chambers (John Mowbray QC & Eben Hamilton QC) London (020) 7419 8000
Recommended in Chancery

TUCKER, Paul
40 King St Manchester (0161) 832 9082
Recommended in Planning

TUDOR-EVANS, Quintin
199 Strand (David Phillips QC) London
(020) 7379 9779
Recommended in Personal Injury
Specialisation: Specialises in personal injury litigation. Undertakes work for claimants and for insurers, handling cases arising from accidents at work including Factory Act claims, public liability claims and serious road traffic accidents. Has a particular interest in cases involving technical expert evidence and a detailed knowledge of the road transport industry. Has extensive experience of cases for local authorities and has previously lectured to local authority insurance officers. In addition to personal injury litigation he deals with non-accident insurance cases, for example, fire damage claims and product liability matters and is also instructed by the NHSLA, principally in respect of issues of quantum.
Career: Called 1977.

TUGENHAT, Michael QC
5 Raymond Buildings (Patrick Milmo QC) London
(020) 7242 2902
Recommended in Commercial (Litigation), Defamation
Specialisation: Defamation, media law and contempt of court. Wide range of domestic and international commercial law -including experience as an arbitrator.
Prof. Memberships: Member of the Bar Council 1992-94. Member of Commercial Bar Association – member of Executive 1992-94. Member of the London Court of International Arbitration. Fellow of the Institute of Advanced Legal Studies.
Career: Born 21 October 1944. 1963-67 Gonville & Caius College Cambridge, Scholar and MA; 1967-68 Yale University, Henry Fellowship; 1969 called to the Bar, Inner Temple; 1986 Queen's Counsel; 1988 Master of the Bench of the Inner Temple. Judge of the Courts of Appeal of Jersey and Guernsey. Recorder of the Crown Court, Deputy Judge of the High Court, trained as a mediator with World Intellectual Property Organisation, Geneva. Publications: contributions to 'Yearbook of Copyright and Media Law 2000', 'Restitution and Banking Law' ed Francis Rose Mansfield Press 1998 and to various legal journals.

TURNER, David
2 Temple Gardens (Dermod O'Brien QC) London
(020) 7822 1200
dturner@2templegardens.co.uk
Recommended in Product Liability, Professional Negligence
Specialisation: Professional negligence, (engineers/architects/barristers/solicitors/accountants). Non-marine commercial insurance (interpretation/repudiation) Commercial product liability (including IT). Recorded cases include GNER v Avon Insurance (2001), Flynn v Robin Thompson & Partners (2000).

TURNER, David QC
Exchange Chambers (David Turner QC & Bill Braithwaite QC & Henry Globe QC) Liverpool
(0151) 236 7747
Recommended in Crime

TURNER, James
4 Essex Court (Nigel Teare QC) London
(020) 7653 5653
jturner@4sx.co.uk
Recommended in Shipping
Specialisation: Shipping, commercial and related private international law. Cases include Red Sea Insurance v Bouygues [1995] 1AC 190; Citi-March v Neptune Orient Lines [1997] 1 Lloyd's Rep. 72; Colonia Versicherug AG v Amoco [1997] 1 Lloyd's Rep. 261; Netherlands v Youell [1998] 1 Lloyd's Rep 236; "Giuseppe di Vittorio" [1998] 1 Lloyd's Rep. 136 & 661; Mata K [1998] 2 Lloyd's Rep. 614; Glencore v MTI [1999] 2 Lloyds Rep. 632; 'Chitral' [2000] 1 Lloyd's Rep. 529.
Prof. Memberships: COMBAR; Institute of Linguists; LCLCBA; British-German Jurists; CEDR.
Career: B.A. (Dunelm), LL.M (Tübingen). Call 1990. CEDR accredited mediator.
Personal: Married, three children. Fluent German and Dutch.

TURNER, James QC
One King's Bench Walk (Anthony Hacking QC) London (020) 7936 1500
jturner@1kbw.co.uk
Recommended in Family
Specialisation: Principal areas of practice encompass all areas of criminal law, family law and administrative law. Many reported cases in each of these fields. Criminal work includes both prosecution and defence and regular instructions to represent medical practitioners in connection with both criminal and disciplinary matters. Considerable knowledge and experience of technical and procedural points of law. Within family law, has particular expertise in financial matters and international child abduction work and has appeared in finance cases in the Grand Court of the Cayman Islands. Speaker at criminal and family law conferences. Administrative law includes work for the Treasury Solicitor and extradition work in England and abroad.
Prof. Memberships: Criminal Bar Association, Family Law Bar Association and Administrative Law Bar Association.
Career: Called to the Bar and joined current Chambers, 1976. Appointed Queen's counsel 1998.
Publications: Archibold, 'Criminal Pleading, Evidence and Practice'.
Personal: Educated at Robertsbridge Secondary Modern School, Bexhill Grammar School and the University of Hull (LLB (Hons) 1975). Born 23rd November 1952. Lives in London.

TURNER, Jon
Monckton Chambers (John Swift QC) London
(020) 7405 7211
jturner@monckton.co.uk
Recommended in Competition/Anti-trust
Specialisation: Specialisms include European Community law, competition law at both national and EC levels, public law (especially environmental law) and judicial review. Practice also includes utility regulation work in the water, electricity and telecommunications sectors (nine months working as legal adviser to the Telecommunications and Posts division of the DTI) and commercial litigation. Competition law litigation includes the ready mixed concrete contempt case [1996], the Net Book Agreement review [1997], the reference of the agreement relating to freight forwarding services [1997], the reference of arrangements for televising Premier League football [1999] and the review of resale price maintenance of medicaments [2000-01] (all in the Restrictive Practices Court); Clover Leaf Cars v BMW (CA and High Court); Philips v Ingman [1998]. Environmental/ judicial review cases include R v Secretary of State for the Environment ex p Greenpeace [1994] (the "THORP" nuclear reprocessing plant litigation); R v Secretary of State for the Environment ex p Standley [1997] (concerning the EC Nitrates Directive and nitrate levels in certain East Anglian rivers), R v Environment Agency ex p Leam [1997] (concerning the use of substitute liquid fuel in lime and cement kilns), Bowden v South West water (pollution of shellfish by sewage). Acted in numerous MMC inquiries, including Plasterboard, National Newspapers, Carlsberg-Tetley, South West Water and Number Portability.
Prof. Memberships: Member of the New York Bar.
Career: Standing Counsel to the Director General of Fair Trading since August 1997. Member of the Treasury B Panel.
Publications: Contributor to Bellamy & Child, 'The Common Market Law of Competition', 5th edn.
Personal: LLM (Harvard).

TURNER, Jonathan
6 King's Bench Walk (Roy Amlot QC) London
(020) 7583 0410
jonathan.turner@6kbw.com
Recommended in Crime
Specialisation: All and any criminal matters.
Prof. Memberships: CBA.
Career: Hindley & Abram Grammar School. University College, London.
Personal: Golf, cricket, rugby league.

TURNER, Justin
Three New Square (David Young QC) London
(020) 7405 1111
Recommended in Intellectual Property

TURNER, Mark QC
Deans Court Chambers (Stephen Grime QC) Manchester (0161) 214 6000
Recommended in Personal Injury
Specialisation: Industrial disease litigation; Group actions; Insurance law; Professional negligence.
Prof. Memberships: Personal Injury Bar Association; Northern Commercial Bar Association.
Career: Sedbergh School 1972-77. The Queen's College, Oxford 1977-80. Dean's Court Chambers 1981. Assistant Recorder 1997-. Queens Counsel 1998. Recorder 2000.

TURNER, Michael
Tooks Court Chambers (Michael Mansfield QC) London (020) 7405 8828
Recommended in Crime

TWOMLOW, Richard
9 Park Place (Ian Murphy QC) Cardiff (029) 2038 2731
Recommended in Crime
Specialisation: Criminal work of all types, prosecution and defence.
Prof. Memberships: Criminal Bar Association.
Career: Called *(Gray's)* 1976; Recorder (1997).
Personal: BA (Cantab). Married. Sport, literature, music, languages, travel.

UFF, John QC
Keating Chambers (Richard Fernyhough QC) London (020) 7544 2600 juff@keatingchambers.com
Recommended in Arbitration (International), Construction
Specialisation: Construction and engineering; international arbitration; appointed arbitrator in many substantial disputes in most parts of the world.
Career: Qualified 1970. Gray's Inn; assistant engineer 1966-70; barrister in construction chambers 1970; arbitrator in various disputes 1977; QC 1983; Recorder 1998; Professor of Engineering Law, King's College, London 1991; chairman of Commission of Inquiry into Yorkshire Water 1996; Chairman of Public Enquiry into rail accident at Southall (1997); FICE, FCI Arb, Fellow Royal Academy of Engineering; publications of note: 'Construction Law'; Construction Industry Model Arbitration Rules; contributor to 'Keating on Building Contracts'.
Personal: King's College, London (BSc Engineering PhD).

ULLSTEIN, Augustus QC
29 Bedford Row Chambers (Peter Ralls QC) London (020) 7404 1044
Recommended in Product Liability

UNDERHILL, Nicholas QC
Fountain Court (Anthony Boswood QC) London (020) 7583 3335 nunderhill@fountaincourt.co.uk
Recommended in Employment, Product Liability
Specialisation: Specialist in commercial, employment and medical/pharmaceutical product liability. Recent cases include Kleinwort Benson v Lincoln (HL: restitution/mistake of law); Barber v RJB Mining (working time regs); Meade v British Fuels (HL: TUPE); Grant v South West Trains (ECJ: sexual orientation discrimination); Associated Newspapers v Wilson (HL: Union derecognition); A v National Blood Authority (product liability – hepatitis C); also haemophilia/HIV and other multi-party actions; experience both as Chairman and as advocate in HC (90)9 cases.
Prof. Memberships: COMBAR; Employment Lawyers Association; Employment Law Bar Association; Industrial Law Society.
Career: Called to the Bar 1976. Joined present chambers 1977. Took silk 1992. Recorder 1994. Deputy High Court Judge 1998. Appointed Attorney-General to Prince of Wales 1998. Judge (part-time) of Employment Appeal Tribunal 2000.
Personal: Born 12 May 1952.

UNWIN, David QC
Maitland Chambers (Michael Lyndon-Stanford QC & Charles Aldous QC) London (020) 7406 1200
Recommended in Chancery, Charities, Media & Entertainment, Pensions

UPTON, William
Eldon Chambers (Lionel Read QC) London (020) 7583 1355 clerks@eldonchambers.com
Recommended in Environment
Specialisation: Main area of practice is environmental, planning and local government law. Clients include local authorities, developers and local amenity groups. Experienced lecturer.
Prof. Memberships: Planning and Environment Bar Association.
Career: Called to the Bar in 1990.
Publications: General Editor, Environmental Law (OUP 2000); contributing editor, 'Encyclopaedia of Forms and Precedents' (Butterworths Environment Volume 2000 Reissue); 'Contaminated Land' (CLT; 2001).
Personal: Educated at Trinity College, Cambridge 1985-89 (MA & LLM). Fellow of the Royal Society of Arts. UKELA council member.

VAJDA, Christopher QC
Monckton Chambers (John Swift QC) London (020) 7405 7211 cvajda@monckton.co.uk
Recommended in Competition/Anti-trust
Specialisation: All aspects of EC law, competition law and judicial review.
Career: Has appeared in over 50 cases before the Court of Justice of the European Communities and Court of First Instance acting for companies, private individuals and the UK government. Cases include Ford v Commission (1982 and 1984), Bulk Oil (1986), Sharp v Council (1988), the Factortame cases, Saeger v Dennemeyer (1991), Air France v Commission (1994), Alpine Investments (1995), the Ladbroke cases, Cartonboard (1998) and ICI (1998). Domestic EC reported cases include Garden Cottage Foods v Milk Marketing Board, (HL), Factortame (HL), Thorn (HL), Mann (HL), ABTA (RPC), Bourgoin v MAFF (CA), Optident (CA) Shearson Lehman Hutton v Maclaine Watson & Co (Commercial Ct), Apple Corps Ltd v Apple Computer (Ch. D). R v OFTEL ex parte BT (QBD) and R v Secretary of State for Health ex p Imperial Tobacco (CA). Numerous publications including the state aid chapter in Bellamy & Child, 'Common Market Law of Competition' 5th edn.

VALLANCE, Philip QC
4-5 Gray's Inn Square (Elizabeth Appleby QC & David Mole QC) London (020) 7404 5252 clerks@4-5graysinnsquare.co.uk
Recommended in Environment
Specialisation: Principal area of practice is professional negligence and indemnity/liability insurance, especially in the construction and environmental context. Cases range from Anns v Merton (1978) to Cambridge Water v E Counties Leather (1994). Also advises extensively on environmental law (contaminated land, "waste", pollution exclusion clauses, nuisance etc), where clients include major insurance companies, water companies, local authorities and waste disposal/landfill operators.
Prof. Memberships: Official Referees' Bar Association, London Common Law and Commercial Bar Association.
Career: Called to the Bar 1968 and joined 1 Crown Office Row. Took Silk in 1989.
Personal: Educated at Bryanston School and New College, Oxford (Scholar; BA Modern History). Born 20 December 1943. Lives in London.

VANHEGAN, Mark
11 South Square (Christopher Floyd QC) London (020) 7405 1222
Recommended in Information Technology, Intellectual Property

VAUGHAN, David QC
Brick Court Chambers (Christopher Clarke QC) London (020) 7379 3550 vaughan@brickcourt.co.uk
Recommended in Competition/Anti-trust
Specialisation: EC law generally, EC-related public law cases and competition law.
Prof. Memberships: Honorary vice-president of the Bar European Group.
Career: QC (1981) QC (NI) 1981. Judge of the County Appeals of Jersey and Guernsey, Deputy High Court Judge. Leader of the European Circuit. Appeared in over 90 cases in the European Court of Justice since 1975 in a wide range of cases and in major EC related public law cases, in particular Factortame I, II, III, IV; Stoke City Council v B&Q; Woodpulp, Volvo v Veng, Magill, Daily Mail; Crehan v Courage; Anastasiou I and II; Kesko; the Petrochemical Cartel cases (PP, PVC I and II, LDPE); the Soda Ash cases; the Coal Cases (Bank I and II, Hopkins. NALOO I and II)

VEEDER, V.V. QC
Essex Court Chambers (Gordon Pollock QC) London (020) 7813 8000
Recommended in Arbitration (International), Insurance
Specialisation: Practised at the Commercial Bar to date, principally as advocate and arbitrator in the field of international trade.
Prof. Memberships: Chairman of ARIAS (UK). Member of the United Kingdom's Department of Trade and Industry Advisory Committee on the Law of Arbitration 1990-96.
Career: Jesus College, Cambridge MA 1970 (Modern Languages & Law). Called to the English Bar 1971. Queen's Counsel 1986.
Personal: Born 1948.

VENABLES, Robert QC
24 Old Buildings (Rex Bretten QC) London (020) 7242 2744
Recommended in Charities

VENMORE, John
30 Park Place (John Jenkins QC) Cardiff (029) 2039 8421
Recommended in Personal Injury
Specialisation: Personal injury including industrial disease litigation. Some clinical negligence. Professional negligence claims arising out of the conduct of personal injury and clinical accident litigation.
Prof. Memberships: Wales and Chester Circuit. PIBA.
Career: Called 1971.

VILLAGE, Peter
4-5 Gray's Inn Square (Elizabeth Appleby QC & David Mole QC) London (020) 7404 5252
Recommended in Planning
Specialisation: All aspects of planning, compulsory purchase and environmental law, including High Court challenges to the grant of planning permission (statutory and judicial review) and local plans. Recent cases include acting for Guinness in its Lands Tribunal litigation against Railtrack (instructed by *Herbert Smith*), for Hammerson and Birmingham City Council in promoting the Bull Ring CPO (*Herbert Smith*), for Wereldahave in promoting the Folkestone Town Centre CPO (*Masons*), for University College Hospital NHS Trust in promoting the new UCL/Middlesex Hospital CPO (*Herbert Smith & Linklaters*). Currently instructed by Peel Investments in promoting the new Doncaster Finningley Airport (*Berwin Leighton Paisner*). Undertakes a substantial amount of planning inquiry work for national volume housebuilders, most notably George Wimpey plc. Recently promoted the proposed new Canterbury College (*Stephenson Harwood*). Notable cases include: The Rose Theatre case [1990] 2 WLR 186 (*Theodore Goddard*); Ex parte Sister Frost [1997] 73 P&CR 186 on behalf of the owners of Canary Wharf (*Clifford Chance*); the Costco litigation (for Safeway, instructed by *Clifford Chance*) [1993] 3 PLR 114; British Railways Board v Slough BC [1993] 2 PLR 42 (quashing a planning permission).
Prof. Memberships: Planning and Environmental Bar Association; Administrative Bar Association.
Career: Educated: Repton, Leeds University. Called 1983. Called to Bar of Northern Ireland 1997.
Personal: Lives in Wimbledon; married with 3 children; Governor Repton School since 1998; Leisure pursuits: fly fishing.

VINE, James
Hardwicke Building (Nicholas Stewart QC) London (020) 7242 2523 james.vine@hardwicke.co.uk
Recommended in Crime
Specialisation: Both prosecution and defence of: drugs importation, VAT and Inland Revenue fraud, confiscation proceedings and computer fraud. Customs & Excise list 'A' and Inland Revenue approved list. Extensive experience of P.I.I. proceedings. Appears regularly as a leading junior. Recently successfully prosecuted a 20 defendant excise fraud. Current practice includes Inland Revenue Phoenix fraud, Railtrack fraud, World Wide American Express fraud and an ongoing SFO investigation. Successful prosecution and defence of large scale VAT frauds.
Prof. Memberships: SE Circuit. CBA Kent & Inner London Bar Messes.
Career: He has developed and used a computer database program which has been used successfully in the preparation and presentation of numerous cases.
Personal: Travels when possible, and speaks a few foreign languages badly.

VIRGO, John
Guildhall Chambers (Adrian Palmer QC) Bristol (0117) 927 3366
Recommended in Commercial (Litigation)
Specialisation: Professional negligence of surveyors, solicitors, and financial advisers; lead Counsel in mis-sold pensions litigation, Bristol Mercantile Court.
Prof. Memberships: Bristol and Cardiff Chancery Bar Association; Professional Negligence Bar Association.
Career: Reported cases include Bell v McCubbin 1990 1 A11 ER.54 (CA); Rhone v Stevens 1994 2 WLR 429 (HL); Cocking v Prudential 1996 CCH 692; May v Woollcombe Beer Watts 1999 PNLR 283; Hayle v Guildarch 1999 PNLR 44; Searles v Cann & Hallett 1999 PNLR 494; Truk (UK) Ltd. v Tokmakidis GmbH 2000 1 Lloyds Law Rep.543; Loosemore v Financial Concepts 2001 Lloyds Law Rep. PN 235; Devine v Jefferies 2001 Lloyds Law Rep. PN301.
Publications: 'Surveyors' Liability, Law and Practice' (Jordans 1998); 'Financial Advice and Financial Products' (Oxford University Press 2001).
Personal: Regularly lectures and contributes articles to leading law journals on all aspects of professional negligence.

VITORIA, Mary QC
8 New Square (Michael Fysh QC) London (020) 7405 4321 clerks@8newsquare.co.uk
Recommended in Intellectual Property, Media & Entertainment
Specialisation: Barrister specialising in intellectual property law and media law, covering patents, copyright, trade marks, passing off, performers' rights, design rights, confidential information and contracts relating to the above. Recent cases include Pensher Security v Sunderland City Council (Court of Appeal); French Connection Ltd v Sutton (Chancery Division, passing- off, internet domain names; copyright – design drawings); Jones v London Borough of Tower Hamlets (Chancery Division, copyright – architect's drawings). For comprehensive CV and list of recent cases, visit our website at www.8newsquare.co.uk.
Prof. Memberships: Intellectual Property Bar Association (IPBA).
Career: Called 1975; QC 1997; patent examiner – chemical patents; lecturer in law – Polytechnic of North London and Queen Mary College, University of London (1975 – 1978);
Publications: Co-author 'Modern Law of Copyright & Designs'; co-editor 'European Intellectual Property Review'; editor 'Fleet Street Reports' and 'Reports of Patent Design & Trade Mark Cases'. Author of sections on copyright and patents in 'Halsbury's Laws.'
Personal: Educated at Bedford College, University of London (Paterson Scholarship, Amy-Lady Tate Scholarship), BSc Chemistry, PhD Chemistry, LLB.

VOS, Geoffrey QC
3 Stone Buildings (Geoffrey Vos QC) London (020) 7242 4937
Recommended in Chancery, Commercial (Litigation), Company, Insolvency/Corporate Recovery
Specialisation: Principal area of practice is chancery and commercial litigation, including particularly company, insurance and reinsurance, financial services, media and pensions. Acted in Estate of Francis Bacon; Bermuda Fire & Marine Insurance Co Ltd; Director General of Fair Trading v Premier League; Investors Compensation Scheme v West Bromwich Building Society; Deeny v Gooda Walker; Global Container Lines v Bonyal Shipping Co; Cox v Bankside; LDC Trustees Ltd v Barings plc; MGN Pension Trustees Limited v Credit Suisse; Scher v Policyholder Protection Board; Re MC Bacon Limited amongst others.
Prof. Memberships: Chancery Bar Association. Bencher of Lincoln's Inn.
Career: Called to the Bar 1977 and joined current chambers in 1979. Took Silk in 1993.
Personal: Educated at University College School, and Gonville and Caius College, Cambridge.

WADSLEY, Peter
St John's Chambers (Christopher Sharp QC) Bristol (0117) 921 3456 clerks@stjohnschambers.co.uk
Recommended in Licensing
Specialisation: Town & Country Planning; Environmental Law; Practice covers advice and public inquiries; judicial review. Also deals with solicitors' negligence. Planning: Extensive experience at appeals and local Plan Inquiries. Major appeals include MSA Inquiries; minerals and wind turbine inquiries; major housing sites and commercial developments; Two Rivers inquiry. Licensing: Liquor, gaming and public entertainment licensing for public bodies (including local authorities) as well as private and commercial clients.
Prof. Memberships: Planning & Environment Bar Association.
Career: MA., LL.M (Cantab.); Post-Graduate certificate in environmental law (Bristol University); formerly a solicitor.

WAIN, Peter
East Anglian Chambers (Roderick Newton) Ipswich (01473) 214481
Recommended in Family

WAITE, Jonathan
Crown Office Chambers (Michael Spencer QC & Christopher Purchas QC) London (020) 7797 8100
Recommended in Health & Safety, Personal Injury, Product Liability
Specialisation: Product liability, personal injury, health and safety, professional negligence. Important cases: Bourne v Colodense [1987] ICR 291 (costs in relation to Trade Union backed plaintiff); McFarlane v EE Caledonia (No 2) [1995] IWLR 366 (costs – maintenance/ champerty); Hegarty v EE Caledonia [1996] 1 LIR 413 (Piper Alpha – psychiatric injury); R v Trustees of Science Museum [1993] 3 AER 853 (legionnaires disease – s.3 Health & Safety at Work Act 1974); Carroll v Fearon & Dunlop Limited [1998] PIQR P416 (manufacture of defective tyre). Instructed in Organophosphate Sheep Dip litigation, MMR/MR litigation and oral contraceptive litigation: all group actions.
Prof. Memberships: Personal Injury Bar Association; London Common Law and Commercial Bar Association.
Career: Sherborne, Trinity College, Cambridge. Called to the Bar 1978.
Personal: Golf, skiing, bridge.

WAKERLEY, Richard QC
4 Fountain Court (John Saunders QC) Birmingham (0121) 236 3476
Recommended in Crime

WAKSMAN, David
Fountain Court (Anthony Boswood QC) London (020) 7583 3335 dwaksmon@fountaincourt.co.uk
Recommended in Banking, Commercial (Litigation), Media & Entertainment
Specialisation: Commercial Litigation. Main areas of practice are banking, civil fraud, commercial litigation, copyright, entertainment law (advisory and contentious) and professional negligence. Clients include clearing and international banks, and other financial institutions and substantial corporations. Also major record and publishing companies, artistes, managers and producers. Recent cases: Murray v YFM (CA) [1998] 1 WLR 951 (confidential information in management buy-out context), Morgan v Lloyds Bank (CA) [1998] Lloyd's Rep. Banking 73 (duties of bank concerning sale of mortgaged property), Girobank v Clarke (CA) [1998] 1 WLR 942 (tax treatment of Girobank data-processing centre), News International v Clinger (Chd) 1998 (major international commercial fraud), Next Room v FX Music (Chd) Times 8 July 1999 (trust claim relating to recording royalties). He has lectured extensively on commercial law topics and is a contributor to 'The Law of Bank Payments' (Sweet & Maxwell), 'Banks and Remedies' (Lloyd's of London Press) 'Commercial Court Procedure' (Sweet & Maxwell) and Bullen & Leake & Jacobs (Professional Negligence) (Sweet & Maxwell).
Prof. Memberships: Commercial Bar Association. Chancery Bar Association.
Career: Called to the Bar 1982. Recorder of the Crown Court.
Personal: Born 28.8.57 LLB (Manchester) BCL (Oxon). Leisure pursuits include running, fell walking, music, sailing. Married. Lives in London.

WALKER, Andrew P.D.
9 Old Square (Michael Driscoll QC) London (020) 7405 4682
Recommended in Property Litigation
Specialisation: Property and commercial Chancery litigation, with the main emphasis on landlord and tenant, commercial and residential property and development disputes, mortgages, commercial disputes, professional negligence (solicitors, surveyors, accountants, actuaries), trust litigation, partnerships, company and insolvency. Most recent reported cases include BHP Petroleum GB Ltd v Chesterfield Properties Ltd [2001] 2 All ER 914 (ChD); Melbury Road Properties 1995 Ltd v Kreidi [1999] 43 EG 157 (CC); Courage Ltd v Crehan, Walker Cain Ltd v McCaughey [1999] 2 EGLR 145 (CA); Platform Home Loans Ltd v Oyston Shipways Ltd [2000] 2 AC 190 (HL); Electricity Supply Nominees Ltd v The National Magazine Company Ltd [1999] 1 EGLR 130 (TCC).
Prof. Memberships: Chancery Bar Association, Professional Negligence Bar Association.
Career: Haberdashers' Aske's School, Elstree; Trinity College, Cambridge (MA); Called Lincoln's Inn (1991).
Personal: Born Chester.

WALKER, Jane
28 St. John St Manchester (0161) 834 8418
Recommended in Family
Specialisation: Specialises exclusively in family law, particularly in children's cases, regularly representing local authorities and guardians as well as parents.
Prof. Memberships: Family Law Bar Association, Child Concern (former chair).
Career: Called to the Bar 1987 and joined current chambers in 1998.
Personal: Born 21st May 1965. Educated at Failsworth School and Balliol College, Oxford. Leisure pursuits include football, travel, photography and reading.

WALKER, Ronald QC
12 King's Bench Walk (Richard Methuen QC) London (020) 7583 0811
Recommended in Personal Injury

WALL, Mark
4 Fountain Court (John Saunders QC) Birmingham (0121) 236 3476
Recommended in Crime
Specialisation: All types of criminal work undertaken, mostly on the Midland and Oxford Circuit. In particular much of his time has been spent recently dealing with murder and fraud work including defending in complicated and lengthy frauds. Prosecutes for the CPS and the DSS for whom he is their chief crown court prosecutor in Birmingham. Prosecutes and defends in equal measure. Undertakes health and safety, and similar criminal litigation.
Career: Former Junior of the Midland and Oxford Circuit.

WALLINGTON, Peter
11 King's Bench Walk Chambers (Eldred Tabachnik QC & James Goudie QC) London (020) 7632 8500
Recommended in Employment
Specialisation: Principal area of practice is employment law. Deals with all types of work in Employment Tribunals and Employment Appeal Tribunal, High Court and County Court litigation on all aspects of employment disputes including injunctions, wrongful dismissal, discrimination, and European social legislation. Advises and lectures on all these areas. Also has extensive industrial consultancy experience. Other main area of practice is public law, especially in relation to local authorities and education.
Prof. Memberships: Employment Lawyers Association, Employment Law Bar Association, Industrial Law Society.
Career: Fellow of Trinity Hall, Cambridge, and University Lecturer in Law 1973-79. Professor of Law, Lancaster University 1979-88, Brunel University 1988-91. Called to the Bar in 1987 and joined present chambers in 1990.
Publications: Editor 'Butterworths Employment Law Handbook'; advisory editor, 'Harvey on Industrial Relations and Employment Law'; contributor to 'Supperstone and Goudie on Judicial Review'; 'Tolley's Employment Law Handbook'.
Personal: Educated Hemel Hempstead Grammar School 1957-64 and Trinity Hall, Cambridge 1965-69 (MA and LLM, both 1st Class Hons). Past area chairman NACAB. Enjoys hill walking, music and reading. Born 25 March 1947. Lives in Wadhurst, E Sussex.

WALLINGTON, Richard
10 Old Square (Leolin Price CBE QC) London (020) 7405 0758
richard.wallington@virgin.net
Recommended in Chancery
Specialisation: Wills, trusts, probate, inheritance tax, capital gains tax.
Prof. Memberships: Chancery Bar Association; Revenue Bar Association; STEP.
Career: Called to the Bar 1972. In practice at the Chancery Bar from 1974.
Publications: Williams on Wills (co-editor); Halsbury's Laws of England, 'Wills' and 'Executors and Administrators' titles (co-editor); Foster's Inheritance Tax (general editor).
Personal: Educated at Dulwich College and Gonville and Caius College, Cambridge.

WALLWORK, Bernard
28 St. John St Manchester (0161) 834 8418
clerk@stjohnst.co.uk
Recommended in Family
Specialisation: Family law: Ancillary relief, public law children.
Prof. Memberships: FLBA Manchester Regional Representative.
Career: Called 1976. Recorder
Personal: Pembroke College, Oxford. Interests are people and places.

WALSH, John
Doughty Street Chambers (Geoffrey Robertson QC) London (020) 7404 1313
Recommended in Immigration
Specialisation: Specialist in immigration and education law, having appeared before numerous adjudicators and tribunals. Particular interest in European and Human Rights Law. Reported cases include: ex parte Yennin [1995] Imm AR 93; M v SSHD [1996] 1 ALL ER 870; ex parte Granavarathan [1995] Imm AR 64; Munchula v SSHD [1996] Imm AR 344; ex parte Kurmoorthy [1998] Imm AR 410; ex parte Savas [2000] INLR 398 (ECJ case on standstill clause in Turkish-EC Association Agreement); case C-60/00 Carpenter (ECJ case on right to free movement within the European Union and provision of services); Pardeepan v SSHD [2000] INLR 447 (leading case of the retrospective effect of the HRA 1998 in immigration appeals).
Prof. Memberships: Member of ILPA, ALBA, Education Law Association and Bar European Group.
Career: BA, MA, LLB. A former fellow of Trinity College, Dublin.

WALSH, Martin
Peel Court Chambers (Michael Shorrock QC) Manchester (0161) 832 3791
Recommended in Licensing

WALSH, Stephen
3 Raymond Buildings (Clive Nicholls QC) London (020) 7400 6400
chambers@threeraymond.demon.co.uk
Recommended in Licensing
Specialisation: All aspects of licensing. Advising on liquor and public entertainment licensing issues affecting a wide range of clients and establishments, from small independent operators seeking to maintain or expand existing licensed outlets to major new leisure developments by public companies. Appearing on behalf of applicants and objectors before local authorities and courts including case stated and judicial review hearings in the High Court. Representing and advising clients on criminal prosecutions and health and safety matters affecting the licensed trade. Advising on betting, gaming and lotteries.

WALTERS, Graham
33 Park Place (John Charles Rees QC) Cardiff (029) 2023 3313
clerks@33parkplace.co.uk
Recommended in Licensing, Local Government
Specialisation: Most aspects of local government work, in particular highways, compulsory purchase and planning. Property and housing disputes. Judicial review of public authority functions generally, for example, education, police powers/procedures. Liquor licensing.
Prof. Memberships: Wales Commercial Law Association (Committee Member).
Career: Called to the Bar 1986. Appointed to the panel of Counsel to the National Assembly for Wales for planning and judicial review.
Personal: Queen Mary's Grammar School, Walsall. Wadham College, Oxford MA (Jurisprudence).Former solicitor and clerk to licensing committee.

WALTERS, Jill Mary
33 Park Place (John Charles Rees QC) Cardiff (029) 2023 3313
Recommended in Family

WALTERS, Jonathan
33 Park Place (John Charles Rees QC) Cardiff (029) 2023 3313
Recommended in Licensing

WALTON, Alastair
Maitland Chambers (Michael Lyndon-Stanford QC & Charles Aldous QC) London (020) 7406 1200
Recommended in Chancery

WARBY, Mark
5 Raymond Buildings (Patrick Milmo QC) London (020) 7242 2902
markwarby@5rb.co.uk
Recommended in Defamation
Specialisation: Media and entertainment, principally defamation, privacy, breach of confidence and contempt of court. Also contractual disputes, literary and artistic copyright, sports disciplinary and related matters. Libel cases include Frank Warren v Terry Marsh [1992], Jonathan Aitken v Guardian & Granada [1997], Jessye Norman v Classic CD [1998] Mickey Duff v MGN [1999], Michael Ashcroft v Times [1999], Monty Norman v Times [2001] (James Bond Theme dispute) and O'Shea v Mirror Group [2001] (Article 10 ECHR overriding common law). Privacy/breach of confidence: Paddy Ashdown v News Group [1992], John Bryan v Mirror Group [1993] (photographs of Duchess of York), Michael Barrymore v MGN [1995], Bunn v BBC [1998] (Robert Maxwell finance director's police statements), Imutran v Uncaged Campaigns [2001] (internet publication of animal research data. Newspaper night lawyer 1981-86. Legal Correspondent 'Small Business Outlook' 1984-85.
Prof. Memberships: Gray's Inn.
Career: Called to the Bar 1981 and joined current chambers 1983.
Publications: 'Life after Reynolds' (privilege in defamation), Farrers Media Bulletin, Autumn 2000; 'Confidentiality and the Media' CLT conferences 1999 and 2000.
Personal: Educated at Bristol Grammar School and St John's College, Oxford. Born 1958.

WARNOCK-SMITH, Sh,n
5 Stone Buildings (Henry Harrod) London (020) 7242 6201
Recommended in Chancery, Charities
Specialisation: Practice encompasses all aspects of trusts, estates, charities and associated taxation. Handles both advisory and contentious work in the UK and offshore in connection with trusts and estates, variations of trusts, construction and rectification of settlements and wills; probate actions; Court of Protection applications; professional negligence in those areas. Lecturer, writer and broadcaster on trust and estate matters.
Prof. Memberships: Society of Trust and Estate Practitioners, Charity Law Association, Chancery Bar Association and the Association of Contentious Trust and Probate Specialists.
Career: Called to the Bar 1971. Joined 10 Old Square in 1979 following an academic career. Moved to 5 Stone Buildings in January 1996.

WARREN, Nicholas QC
Wilberforce Chambers (Edward Nugee QC) London (020) 7306 0102
Recommended in Chancery, Pensions
Specialisation: Main areas of practice are in the fields of pensions and private client business, both advisory and litigation. Has appeared in many of the leading pensions cases including Imperial Foods, Courage, Thrells, LRT, Coloroll, Chloride, National Grid/ National Power and South West Trains. Also has wide experience of revenue litigation having formerly been standing junior counsel to the Inland Revenue in Chancery matters.
Prof. Memberships: Association of Pensions Lawyers; STEP; Revenue Bar Association; Chancery Bar Association (Chairman)
Career: BA (Oxon) 1970. Called to the Bar in 1972; QC 1993. Recorder; Deputy High Court Judge.
Personal: Chairman, London Musici.

WASS, Sasha QC
6 King's Bench Walk (Roy Amlot QC) London (020) 7583 0410
Recommended in Crime
Specialisation: Criminal Law. Defence and Prosecution practice. Serious fraud: professional (e.g. lawyer's), commercial (e.g. gambling industry), and financial cases (City, eg. defence of Roger Levitt). Environmental Law: specialist expertise on criminal aspects of oil spillage etc (eg. Sea Empress 1996). Serious Crime: murder, rape, police corruption, drug importation, money laundering, sexual abuse of children and specialist expertise in complex medical, scientific and identification cases (eg. Rosemary West, Popat I & II) and criminal misconduct of the medical profession.
Prof. Memberships: Elected member of the Committee of the Criminal Bar Association: 1992-95; 1995-98; 2000- and the South Eastern Circuit Committee: 1989-92; 1993-96; Treasurer of the CBA 1997-99.
Career: Called 1981; Assistant Recorder 1997; Recorder 2000; Queen's Counsel 2000.

WATERS, David QC
2 Hare Court (Stephen Kramer QC) London (020) 7353 5324
Recommended in Crime

WATERS, Malcolm QC
11 Old Square (Grant Crawford & Jonathan Simpkiss) London (020) 7430 0341 clerks@11oldsquare.co.uk
Recommended in Banking, Charities, Consumer Law
Specialisation: Principal specialist areas are mortgage lending, savings products, building societies and charities. Also covers other areas of general chancery practice, including land law, trusts and professional negligence. Acted in C.&G. v B.S.C. and B.S.C. v Halifax B.S. and Leeds P.B.S. (building society conversions), C.&G. v Norgan and Woolwich v Gomm (mortgages), Harwood-Smart v Caws (pensions) and Peggs v Lamb (charities). Drafts standard form mortgage, investment and consumer credit documentation for banks and building societies. Regularly advises on constitutional issues affecting mutual organisations and charities. Member of working parties involved in drafting Standard Conditions of Sale and the Standard Commercial Property Conditions.
Prof. Memberships: Chancery Bar Association, Charity Law Association, Professional Negligence Bar Association.
Career: Called to Bar 1977. Joined 11 Old Square 1978. Took silk 1997.
Publications: Joint editor of 'Wurtzburg & Mills – Building Society Law', and 'Current Law Commentary on the Building Societies Act 1986'.
Personal: Educated at Whitgift School 1963-71 and St. Catherine's College Oxford 1972-76 (B.A. and B.C.L.).

WATSON, Antony QC
Three New Square (David Young QC) London (020) 7405 1111
Recommended in Intellectual Property

WATSON, David
14 Castle Street (Andrew Edis QC) Liverpool (0151) 236 4421
Recommended in Crime

WATSON, James QC
3 Serjeants' Inn (Robert Francis QC & John Grace QC) London (020) 7427 5000
Recommended in Clinical Negligence

WATSON, Philippa
Essex Court Chambers (Gordon Pollock QC) London (020) 7813 8000
Recommended in Competition/Anti-trust
Specialisation: EU law, in particular competition law, agricultural law, energy law, social law of an advisory and litigious nature. Litigation involves appearance before the EC Commission, Court if First Instance, Court of Justice and UK and Irish specialist courts and tribunals. UK Competition law. UK social security law. Butterworth Tolley Chair in Competition Law and Practice Nottingham Law School.
Career: Trinity College, Dublin: MA (Legal Science) 1973. King's Inn, Dublin. Called to Bar of Ireland 1973. University of Cambridge, LLB 1974, PhD in Law 1977. Called to the Bar of England and Wales 1988.
Personal: Born 1951.

WAUGH, Andrew QC
Three New Square (David Young QC) London (020) 7405 1111 3newsquareip@lineone.net
Recommended in Intellectual Property
Specialisation: All aspects of intellectual property with particular emphasis on chemical, pharmaceutical and biotechnical/generic engineering matters. Appears regularly at European Patent Office in Munich for clients which have included Eli Lilly, Amgen and Biogen.Notable UK cases have included: 3M v Rennicks – patents (thermoformed laminates); Bonzel v Intervention (cardiac catheters); Optical Recording v Hayden Labs (compact discs); Biogen v Medeva (recombinant Hepatitis B vaccine); Amgen v Boehringher Mannheim (erythropoietin); SKB v Norton (augmentin); Merrell Dow v Norton (terfenadine); Optical Sciences v Aspect Vision Care (contact lenses); Hoechst v B.P (purification of acetic acid); UCC v BP (polyethylene production); Palmaz v Boston Scientific (cardiac stents); HFC Bank plc v Midland Bank plc (trade name); Lilly Icos v Pfizer (Viagra).
Prof. Memberships: Intellectual Property Bar Assn; Chancery Bar Assn; AIPPI.
Career: City University First Class Hons in Chemical and Administrative Studies; 1981 Dip-Law; 1982 Called to the Bar. QC 1998, 6 Month Pupillage at Chambers of Kenneth Rokison QC. 1983 joined Chambers of William Aldous QC at 6 Pump Court (now headed by David Young QC at 3 New Square).
Personal: Tennis, rugby, Association Football, cycling.

WAY, Patrick
8 Gray's Inn Square (Patrick C. Soares) London (020) 7242 3529 clerks8graysinn@btconnect.com
Recommended in Tax
Specialisation: All forms of taxation both as an adviser and an advocate. Publications include 'Tax advice for company transactions' (Gee); 'The Enterprise Investment Scheme: A Practical Guide' (Longman); co-author 'Death and Taxes' (Longman); contributor Tolley's 'Tax Planning 2001-02' ('The Enterprise Investment Scheme' and 'Stamp Duty in Property Transactions'). Recent High Court cases: Wannell v Rothwell (share dealing); Barnett v Brabyn (SchD/Sch E); 'Continental Shipping' (judicial review and s20 TMA); Templeton v Jacobs (benefits in kind); 'Archon Shipping' (judicial review and s20 TMA).
Prof. Memberships: Revenue Bar Association and VAT Practitioners' Group.
Career: Admitted as a solicitor (1979). Head of tax at *Gouldens* (1987-94). Called to the Bar 1994.

WEBBER, Frances
Two Garden Court (Ian Macdonald QC & Owen Davies QC) London (020) 7415 6265 fran.webber@mcr1.poptel.org.uk
Recommended in Immigration
Specialisation: All aspects of immigration, particularly refugee law, human rights, family and same sex cases, European Community law, deportation, work, detention. Judicial review, habeas corpus, statutory appeals. Criminal work with immigration angle. Recent reported cases include: R v Uxbridge MC ex Adimi; R v SSHD ex p Popatia; R v SSHD ex p Khatib; R (Mahmood) v SSHD.
Prof. Memberships: ILPA.
Career: BSc (social science), has written extensively on immigration and refugee issues for lay audience (eg. Crimes of Arrival 1996; Inside Racist Europe 1994), regular contributor to 'Race & Class', 'Statewatch'. Teaches courses for ILPA, LAG/ and Liberty.
Publications: Co-editor of MacDonald's 'Immigration Law and Practice' (5th edition, July 2001).

WEDDERSPOON, Rachel
9 St. John Street (John Hand QC) Manchester (0161) 455 4000 clerks@9stjohnstreet.co.uk
Recommended in Employment
Specialisation: Principal area of practice is employment law. She specialises in race, disability and sex discrimination, unfair and wrongful dismissal before the Employment Tribunal and at appeal.
Prof. Memberships: The Employment Lawyers Association and the Professional Negligence Bar Association.
Career: LLB (Manchester). Called to the Bar in 1993.

WEITZMAN, Tom
3 Verulam Buildings (Christopher Symons QC & John Jarvis QC) London (020) 7831 8441 chambers@3vb.com
Recommended in Commercial (Litigation), Professional Negligence
Specialisation: General commercial practice specialising in insurance and reinsurance work. He also does a substantial amount of professional negligence work. In recent years, his practice has also included some product liability work. He has experience of both commercial arbitration and ADR. Clients have included major UK insurers, various Lloyd's syndicates, major UK brokers, major UK plcs, the trustees of the Maxwell Pension Funds, international accountancy firms (professional negligence claims) and a major UK tobacco manufacturer (product liability claims).
Prof. Memberships: COMBAR.
Career: BA (Oxon), 1984 Call, Gray's Inn.
Publications: Bullen & Leake & Jacob's 'Precedents and Pleadings' (insurance section).

WEST, Lawrence
2 Harcourt Buildings (Roger Henderson QC) London (020) 7583 9020 clerks@harcourt.co.uk
Recommended in Environment
Specialisation: Regularly instructed in environmental cases on behalf of the chemical, petrochemical and agrochemical industries, local authorities, statutory water undertakers, general industry and private individuals. Other areas of practice: personal injury, including clinical negligence; product liability; commercial; local authority and governmental agency law; professional negligence of all kinds and insurance.
Career: Called to Bar in Ontario in 1973. Practised in Toronto as an advocate with the leading Canadian law firm, McCarthy, Tetrault, where he was involved with a substantial amount of commercial and medical negligence litigation. Called to Bar by Gray's Inn 1979. Since then has practised from 2 Harcourt Buildings. Reported cases include Cambridge Water Co v Eastern Counties Leather Plc (1994 – environmental pollution), Stubbings v Webb (1993 – limitation in personal injury action) and Thake v Maurice (1985 – public policy aspects of claims for damages following conception after vasectomy). Also, junior counsel for Paul McKenna in the hypnotherapy/schizophrenia case brought against him.
Personal: Toronto, 1946. LLM (London); LLB, BA (Toronto).

WHITE, Andrew QC
Atkin Chambers (Robert Akenhead QC) London (020) 7404 0102
Recommended in Arbitration (International), Construction
Specialisation: Domestic and international civil engineering, building, shipbuilding and ship repair disputes. Major projects include the Channel Tunnel: Counsel for TML in main and sub-contract disputes; Harbour City Hong Kong: Counsel for the contractors in disputes with the employer; Oil Rigs: Counsel for contractors in connection with several oil rig construction projects (High Court). Accountants' negligence actions. Solicitors' negli-

gence actions. Publication: 'Contributor Forms & Precedents: Building Contracts'.
Career: Called to the Bar Lincoln's Inn 1980. Queen's Counsel (1997). Megarry Scholar and Hardwicke Scholar.
Personal: Born 25th January 1958. LL.B. (Hons.) Wales (1979) 2:1. Interests include music, farming and gardening.

WHITE, Gemma

Blackstone Chambers (Presiley Baxendale QC & Charles Flint QC) London (020) 7583 1770 clerks@blackstonechambers.com
Recommended in Employment
Specialisation: Specialises in employment law and public law (including human rights). Particular interests in the employment field include discrimination, confidential information, data protection, Regulation of Investigatory Powers Act 2000 and Article 8 ECHR.
Prof. Memberships: ELA, ALBA.
Career: Educated at King's College London and the University of Paris I (Pantheon-Sorbonne) (LLB and Maitrise en Droit Francais 1992); University of Oxford (BCL 1993). Called to the Bar in 1994. Junior Counsel to the Crown (C Panel) since 1999.

WHITE, Sasha

Eldon Chambers (Lionel Read QC) London (020) 7583 1355
Recommended in Planning
Specialisation: Principal areas of practice is planning, environmental and local government law.
Prof. Memberships: Planning and Environmental Bar Association.
Career: Called to Bar in 1991. Pupil to William Hicks Q.C. Joined Chambers as tenant 1993.
Personal: Educated Bedales and Trinity College, Cambridge. Born 1967. Author of 'Planning Law Appeals' (Central Law Publishing) March 1997.

WHITEHALL, Mark

Colleton Chambers (Martin Meeke QC) Exeter (01392) 274898
Recommended in Crime

WHITEHOUSE, David QC

3 Raymond Buildings (Clive Nicholls QC) London (020) 74006400 chambers@3raymondbuildings.com
Recommended in Crime, Fraud
Specialisation: Principal specialist areas are crime, including Victoria Aitken (attempting to pervert the course of justice), Mafia and Colombian cartel drugs importing trials and the murder of Lennie 'The Gov'ner' McLean; fraud including Timeshare Fraud (R v John 'Goldfinger' Palmer), City fraud (Barlow Clowes – Investment fraud, Landhurst Leasing Plc – leasing fraud and corruption, Abbey National plc – corruption and Norton Plc – rights issue); local authority fraud (West Wiltshire privatisation case, Brent housing); mortgage fraud (R v Annen and others), Insolvency fraud (Baron Group of Companies), Legal Aid fraud (O'Malley), licensing – liquor, casino and bingo. Also specialises in disciplinary tribunals and has appeared before the Institute of Chartered Accountants, Securities and Futures Authority, LIFFE, General Medical Council, Institute of Chartered Engineers, British Boxing Board of Control.
Prof. Memberships: Criminal Bar Association, International Bar Association.
Career: Called to the Bar 1969 and joined current chambers in 1970 after pupilage in defamation Chambers. Libel read The Sun 1969-75. Appointed Recorder 1987. Took silk 1990.
Personal: Educated at Trinity College, Cambridge 1964-67 (MA).

WHITEMAN, Peter QC

Hollis Whiteman Chambers (QEB) (Julian Bevan QC & Peter Whiteman QC) London (020) 7583 5766 petergwhiteman@hotmail.com
Recommended in Tax
Specialisation: All areas of corporate and commercial taxation with special emphasis on mergers and acquisitions, structured financing arrangements, oil company taxation, insurance company taxation, international corporate taxation, cross-border transactions, transfer pricing and capital allowances. Appeared in BP Oil Development Ltd v IRC, Esso Petroleum Ltd v IRC, Girobank plc v Clarke, ICI plc v Colmer, Bradley v London Electricity plc, Padmore v IRC, Post Office Counters Ltd v Customs & Excise, Johnson v Prudential Assurance Co Ltd, J. Sainsbury plc v O'Connor. Also appeared in Exxon Corporation v Internal Revenue Commissioner in the US Tax Court as the UK tax expert witness. Clients include major international companies, solicitors and accountancy firms.
Prof. Memberships: Revenue Bar Association; Honorary Adviser to the Unitary Tax Campaign 1982.
Career: Lecturer London School of Economics 1965-70. Called to the Bar 1967; Queen's Counsel 1977. Founded Chambers of Peter Whiteman QC in 1977, becoming joint head of Hollis Whiteman Chambers on merger in 1991. Bencher of Lincoln's Inn 1985. Professor of International Tax Law, University of Florida and University of Virginia 1980. Attorney-at-Law, State of New York 1982. Recorder 1986; Deputy High Court Judge 1994.
Publications: Author 'Whiteman on Income Tax', 'Whiteman on Capital Gains Tax', 'British Tax Encyclopedia'.
Personal: Educated Leyton County High School and London School of Economics (LLB Hons; LLM Distinction).

WHITFIELD, Adrian QC

3 Serjeants' Inn (Robert Francis QC & John Grace QC) London (020) 7427 5000
Recommended in Clinical Negligence
Specialisation: Principal area of practice is medical negligence and other medical law, including treatment decisions. Cases include Sidaway, Hotson, in Re F (sterilisation) and de Martell. Has extensive G.M.C and other tribunal experience. Acts for claimants and defendants. Writes and lectures regularly on medico-legal subjects.
Prof. Memberships: London Common Law and Commercial Bar Association, Professional Negligence Bar Association, Medico-Legal Society.
Career: Call 1964: Queen's Counsel 1983: Chairman of NHS Tribunal 1993.
Personal: Educated Ampleforth College and Magdalen College Oxford: Demy (Open Scholar). Lives in London.

WHITTAKER, John

Serle Court (Lord Neill of Bladen QC) London (020) 7242 6105 clerks@serlecourt.co.uk
Recommended in Chancery, Partnership
Specialisation: Principal area of practice is chancery including related commerce and property. A specialist area of practice is partnership law.
Prof. Memberships: Association of Partnership Practitioners, COMBAR
Career: Called 1969, joined Serle Court in 1970.
Publications: Co-author of 'Limited Liability Partnerships The New Law', Jordans 2001.
Personal: Magdalen College, Oxford (MA, BCL).

WHITTAM, Richard

Furnival Chambers (Andrew Mitchell QC) London (020) 7405 3232
Recommended in Crime
Specialisation: Junior Treasury Counsel to the Crown at the Central Criminal Court. Specialist Criminal practitioner with considerable experience in complex cases. Serious fraud experience in advance fee, leasing, Certificate of Deposit, mortgage and DSS frauds. Defended in substantial Customs and Excise cases. Public Interest Immunity. Information Technology.
Prof. Memberships: Criminal Bar Association; S E Circuit.
Personal: Educated at Marple Hall School and University College London. Formerly active in sport, now golf and occasional cricket.

WHITTLE, C.D. (Henry)

11 South Square (Christopher Floyd QC) London (020) 7405 1222
Recommended in Intellectual Property

WIGGLESWORTH, Raymond QC

18 St John Street (Jonathan Foster QC) Manchester (0161) 278 1800
Recommended in Crime

WILDBLOOD, Stephen QC

Albion Chambers (Charles Barton QC & Neil Ford QC) Bristol (0117) 927 2144
Recommended in Family

WILLIAMS, David H.

Chavasse Court Chambers (Theresa Pepper) Liverpool (0151) 707 1191
Recommended in Crime
Specialisation: General crime. Junior Counsel James Bulger murder trial. Counsel in North Wales Tribunal of Inquiry into Child Abuse.
Prof. Memberships: Criminal Bar Association.
Career: BA (Hons) University of Lancaster Queen's Scholar in History. Liverpool Polytechnic Part I & II solicitors examinations. Solicitor 1975-90. Called Feb 1990. Assistant Recorder 1996. Recorder 2000.
Personal: Married. Foreign travel, reading history, hill walking, gardening.

WILLIAMS, Heather

Doughty Street Chambers (Geoffrey Robertson QC) London (020) 7404 1313 h.williams@doughtystreet.co.uk
Recommended in Human Rights
Specialisation: Civil liberties and human rights, particularly actions against the police and related judicial review work and all aspects of discrimination law. Recent reported cases include: Farah v Commr. of Metropolitan Police [1998] QB 65 C.A. (liability of police – Race Relations Act), Percy v A.S. Hall [1997] QB 924 C.A. (false imprisonment), N v Agrawal (1999) PNLR 939 C.A. (duty of care – F.M.E.), Rovenska v G.M.C. [1998] ICR 85 C.A. (race discrimination), Cast v Croydon College [1998] ICR 500 C.A. (sex discrimination), Derby Specialist Fabrications Ltd. v Burton [2001] 2 All ER 840 EAT (race discrimination).
Prof. Memberships: Discrimination Law Association, Police Actions Lawyers Group, ALBA & Liberty.
Career: Called to Bar in 1985; in practice since 1987.
Publications: Contributor to ;Making Rights Real (Using the Human Rights Act to Challenge Racism & Race Discrimination)'; various articles and lectures on areas of specialisation.
Personal: Married with two children. Born 1963. LLB – Kings's College London 1981 – 1984; Scarman Scholarship for Bar Finals 1985.

WILLIAMS, John Leighton QC

Farrar's Building (John Leighton Williams QC) London (020) 7583 9241
Recommended in Personal Injury
Specialisation: General common law, with emphasis on personal injuries and medical negligence work.
Prof. Memberships: LCBA; PIBA; SE Circuit.
Career: Called to the Bar 1964. Appointed Recorder 1985. Took silk 1986. Member of the Criminal Injuries Compensation Board since 1987. Master of the Bench, Grays Inn 1994.

WILLIAMS, John Melville QC
Old Square Chambers (John Hendy QC) London (020) 7269 0300
jmwq@dial.pipex.com
Recommended in Environment
Specialisation: Environmental toxic torts; agricultural environmental damages claims; waste-incineration; environmental insurance; some planning; particular interest in scientific aspects of environmental issues; Y2K millennium bug issues. Notable cases: Graham v Rechem; Camelford Water Claims, organophosphate sheep dip cases.
Prof. Memberships: Environmental Law Foundation – member of Advisory Council; Association of Personal Injury Lawyers (1st president 1990-94); Association of Trial Lawyers of America (chair International Practice Section 1992); Personal Injury Bar Association.
Career: Called 1955; QC 1977; Recorder 1985-93; legal assessor to the General Medical Council and General Dental Council 1984-date. Member CICB 1998-00; member of CICAP 2000-date. Chairman Y2K Lawyers Association. Member of editorial board SPIL.
Publications: Various articles.
Personal: Hill walking.

WILLIAMS, Lloyd
30 Park Place (John Jenkins QC) Cardiff (029) 2039 8421
Recommended in Personal Injury

WILLIAMS, Rhodri
30 Park Place (John Jenkins QC) Cardiff (029) 2039 8421
rjw@30parkplace.law.co.uk
Recommended in Local Government
Specialisation: Local Government and administrative law; E.C. law. Cases include: R v HM Treasury ex parte University of Cambridge (2000) AER(EC) 920 ECJ; Ealing Community Transport Ltd v Ealing LBC (2000) 1 PPLR CS27 Cof A.
Prof. Memberships: Bar European group;\~Association for Regulated Procurement; Wales Public Law & Human Rights Association.
Career: Qualified 1987; Gray's Inn; tenant 30 Park Place since 1997; tenant *2 Harcourt Buildings* since 1999; appointed to Attorney General's list of approved Counsel (provincial panel) 2000; appointed to list of Counsel General to the National Assemby for Wales 2000.
Publications: Public Procurement Law Review, Butterworths Expert Guide to the European Union (Internal Market).
Personal: Educated Cardiff High School and Exeter College, Oxford. BA Modern Languages 1985; Dip Law 1986.

WILLIAMSON, Adrian
Keating Chambers (Richard Fernyhough QC) London (020) 7544 2600
awilliamson@keatingchambers.com
Recommended in Construction
Specialisation: Construction and engineering law; professional negligence; disputes concerning substantial commercial and technical projects; international commercial arbitration; cases include Aughton v Kent; Damond Lock v Laing Investments; Barclays Bank v Fairclough Building Ltd; West Faulkner Associates v LB Newham; Birse v Haiste; Hytec v Coventry CC; Bernhards Rugby Landscapes Ltd v Stockley Park; Royal Brompton Hospital v Hammond & Others.
Career: Qualified 1983; Middle Temple; tenant in chambers of John Loyd QC 2 Crown Office Row 1985-89; tenant at Keating Chambers 1989 to date; wrote chapters on JCT and NSC Forms of Contract for 'Keating on Building Contracts'. (5th 1991, 6th 1995 and 7th 2001editions).
Personal: Highgate School, Trinity Hall, Cambridge (1982 BA 1st Class Hons 1985 MA). Born 1959. Married with 3 children.

WILLIAMSON, Hazel QC
Maitland Chambers (Michael Lyndon-Stanford QC & Charles Aldous QC) London (020) 7406 1200
hwilliamson@maitlandchambers.com
Recommended in Partnership, Property Litigation
Specialisation: Chancery litigation including property, company and insolvency, commercial contract, partnership and related negligence aspects. Particular emphasis on commercial property including acquisition, financing and development and landlord and tenant aspects. Also, leasehold enfranchisement, markets and fairs, Court of Protection. Cases include National Westminster Bank v Arthur Young (1986-93) series of cases on rent review, arbitration procedure and appeals; BCCI v Aboody (1988); Banco Exterior v Thomas (1997); Barclays Bank v Coleman (1999) undue influence and bank mortgages; Crown Estate Commissioners v Signet Ltd (1997); Moss Bros Group v CSC Properties (1999): refusal of consent to leasehold assignment; Lumsden Ltd v Holdswarth (Isle of Man 1998 and 1999 on appeal): failed timeshare, dishonest assistance in breach of trust, partnership, solicitors' negligence; Re: Forester & Lamego Ltd (1997) public interest winding up; Re Brian D Pierson (Contractors) Ltd 1999; decision on wrongful trading and misfeasance, Re: Thirty Eight Building Ltd 1999: decision on undue preferences; Locabail (UK) Ltd v Bayfield Properties Ltd and anor (1999): judicial bias/proprietary estoppel, undue influence, overriding interests in land registration, scope of bank mortgagee's right or subrogation; Coventry and Solihull Waste Disposal v Russell (VO) (1999) HL: rating: Re C (2000): Enduring Powers of Attorney.
Career: Qualified 1972, Gray's and Lincoln's Inn. Silk 1988. Recorder 1996. Deputy High Court Judge 1994. Chairman of the Chancery Bar Association 1994-97. Member of the DETR, Property Advisory Group. Publications: 'Law and Valuation of Leisure Property' (Estates Gazette), joint editor and contributor. Mediator (ADR chambers) 2000.
Personal: Educated Wimbledon High School and St Hilda's College, Oxford. BA 1969, MA 1982, FCIArb 1992.

WILLS-GOLDINGHAM, Claire
Albion Chambers (Charles Barton QC & Neil Ford QC) Bristol (0117) 927 2144
Recommended in Family

WILMOT-SMITH, Richard QC
39 Essex Street (Nigel Pleming QC) London (020) 7832 1111
Recommended in Construction
Specialisation: A specialist in all aspects of construction and engineering, process engineering, oil and gas, mining and other energy litigation and arbitration. His experience includes disputes involving performance bonds, guarantees, insolvency and related professional negligence claims against architects, engineers and surveyors and insolvency. He has acted in litigation and arbitration concerned with major projects in the United Kingdom, the United States, Tanzania, Egypt, India, Singapore, Hong Kong, Canada, Iran, Iraq, Dubai, Qatar, Pakistan, Bangladesh, Malaysia and Saudi Arabia. These projects include major tunnels, roads, bridges and other structures including ports and drylocks, housing estates and universities, factories, power stations and other energy systems, food processing plants, oil platforms and refineries. John Mowlem & Co plc v Eagle Star Insurance Co Ltd and others 44 Con LR 134 (CA); Trafalgar House v General Surety [1996] AC 119 (HL); In re Cosslett (Contractors) Ltd [1998] 2 WLR 131 (CA); Scottish Power plc v Britoil (Exploration) Ltd and Others, 141 SJ LB 246 (CA); Bedford County Council v Fitzpatrick (1998) CILL 1440 (QB); Pozzolanic Lytag Ltd v Bryan Hobson Associates (1998) CILL 1450 (QB); Deepak Fertilizers and Petrochemicals Ltd v Davy McKee (London) Limited [1999] 1 ALL ER (COMM) 69 (CA).
Prof. Memberships: ORBA, London Common Law and Commercial Bar Association.
Career: Called to Bar in 1978, took silk 1994.

WILSON, Adam
No.6 Barristers Chambers (Shaun Spencer QC) Leeds (0113) 245 9763
Recommended in Family

WILSON, Alastair QC
19 Old Buildings (Alastair Wilson QC) London (020) 7405 2001
Recommended in Information Technology, Intellectual Property

WINBERG, Stephen
2-4 Tudor Street (Richard Ferguson QC) London (020) 7797 7111
Recommended in Crime, Fraud

WINDSOR, Emily
Falcon Chambers (Jonathan Gaunt QC & Kim Lewison QC) London (020) 7353 2484
Recommended in Agriculture

WINGATE-SAUL, Giles QC
Byrom Street Chambers Manchester (0161) 829 2100
gws@byromstreet.com
Recommended in Clinical Negligence, Commercial (Litigation), Personal Injury
Specialisation: Catastrophic injury, mercantile/commercial law, contract, tort, insurance, building and construction.
Prof. Memberships: Northern Circuit Commercial Bar Association, Society of Construction Law, Technology and Construction Court Bar Association, Professional Negligence Bar Association, Personal Injury Bar Association, Bar European Group.
Career: Winchester College, Southampton University (LLB Hons). Called to the Bar 1967. QC 1983. Deputy High Court Judge, Deputy Judge of Technology & Construction Court, Governing Bencher of Inner Temple, Chairman Northern Circuit Commercial Bar Association.
Personal: Church affairs and sport.

WINTER, Ian
Hollis Whiteman Chambers (QEB) (Julian Bevan QC & Peter Whiteman QC) London (020) 7583 5766
Recommended in Fraud

WOLANSKI, Adam
5 Raymond Buildings (Patrick Milmo QC) London (020) 7242 2902
Recommended in Defamation

WOLFE, David
Matrix Chambers (Nicholas Blake QC) London (020) 7404 3447
davidwolfe@matrixlaw.co.uk
Recommended in Administrative & Public Law, Environment
Specialisation: Public law including judicial review, local government, town and country planning and environmental law (including cases involving substantial scientific and technical evidence), discrimination, education, community care, social security.
Prof. Memberships: Administrative Law Bar Association; Planning and Environmental Bar Association; UK Environmental Law Association; Discrimination Law Association.
Career: BSc MEng (Manchester) 1987, PhD (Engineering, Cambridge) 1991. Called to the Bar 1992.

WOLFSON, David
One Essex Court (Lord Grabiner QC) London (020) 7583 2000
dwolfson@oeclaw.co.uk
Recommended in Banking, Commercial (Litigation)
Specialisation: Practice encompasses all areas of commercial law (particularly banking, insolvency and domestic and international sale of goods), professional negligence and entertainment law. Appears regularly in

both domestic courts and in arbitrations, domestic and international. Recent cases include Ghana Commercial Bank v C&L (Times 3 March 1997) (tracing proceeds of fraud); Barclays Bank v Zaroovabli [1997] Ch 321 (mortgages and registrable interests); Re Schuppan (a bankrupt) [1996] 2 AER 664 (conflict of interest in insolvency); Art Corporation v Schuppan (Times 21 January 1994) (duty of disclosure on Mareva injunctions), Art Corporation v Schuppan (international sale of goods), Blackspur Leasing (negligent audit claim), Investors Compensation Scheme v West Bromwich Building Society [1999] Lloyds Rep PN 496 (acted for solicitor third parties in major action re home income plans); Royal Bank of Scotland v Etridge [1999] 4 AER 705 (the current leading authority on the O'Brien jurisdiction); Harvey Jones v Woolwich [2000] 3 WLR 1725 (bills of exchange); Barclays Bank v Ellis ('Times' 24 October 2000) (banking and Human Rights Act); AIB v Hennelly ('Times' 7 June 2000) (mortgages in escrow). Advised about the recovery of gold and other assets from Second World War. Clients include banks and other lenders, insurers and professional indemnity insurers, Solicitors' Indemnity Fund, liquidators and insolvency practitioners, general commercial clients. Lecturer at legal seminars and conferences.
Prof. Memberships: COMBAR
Career: MA (Cantab) (Oriental Studies and Law). Exhibitioner and Scholar of Selwyn College. Stuart of Rannoch award. Squire scholarship. Inner Temple Major scholarship. Council of Legal Education scholarship. Called to the Bar in 1992.
Publications: Contributing author to 'Bank Liability and Risk', (2nd edn); 'Banking Litigation'(1999); several articles in various legal journals including 'New Law Journal', 'Commercial Lawyer' and 'International Insurance Law Review'. Articles for in-house magazines of various firms of solicitors. Contributor to 'Law Commission Consultation Paper on the Third Party (Rights against Insurers) Act 1930'.

WOLKIND, Michael QC
2 Bedford Row (William Clegg QC) London (020) 7440 8888
Recommended in Crime
Specialisation: Michael Wolkind has led in more than 120 murder cases, with specialities of psychiatric and medical causation defences. He regularly acts for the very top target criminals and has appeared in many notorious gangland trials. He has also acted in the largest drug matters and in substantial frauds. Cases include a dismemberment 'nagging wife' provocation (Boyce); paedophile killing of six year old (Morss); killing of a brother where the jury refused to convict even after a change of plea (Jennings); ten year old girl accused of three murders (Lynch); killing of four family members (Aderdour); middle aged professional man accused of road rage killing (Janjirker); teenager charged with murder of abusive stepfather (Keaveney); the London Nailbomber (David Copeland); the Appeal of the Norfolk farmer convicted of murdering a burglar (Tony Martin). He has acted in Turkish and Libyan terrorist cases and he advised in the Lockerbie Bombing. He has appeared in Privy Council Capital cases and in fraud has acted for lawyers, accountants and bankers. He has been described in the independent Chambers Directory as 'the distilled essence of the great Jury advocate'.

WOLTON, Harry QC
2-3 Gray's Inn Square (Anthony Porten QC & Anthony Scrivener QC) London (020) 7242 4986 harry@wolton.com
Recommended in Planning
Specialisation: Town & Country Planning in all respects.
Prof. Memberships: Planning & Environment Bar Association.
Career: Called 1969. Silk 1982. Recorder 1985. Authorised to sit as Deputy High Court Judge 1990.
Personal: Director, Bar Mutual Insurance Fund. Cattle breeding & dendrology.

WONNACOTT, Mark
Maitland Chambers (Michael Lyndon-Stanford QC & Charles Aldous QC) London (020) 7406 1200
Recommended in Property Litigation

WOOD, Christopher
1 Mitre Court Buildings (Bruce Blair QC) London (020) 7797 7070 wood@lmcb.com
Recommended in Family
Specialisation: Principally ancillary relief.
Prof. Memberships: FLBA.
Career: Oxford University (MA). Université d'Aix-Marseilles III (Diplôme d'Etudes Supérieures d'Université). Called 1986; occasional lecturer.
Personal: Married with a daughter. Interests: history, politics, Norway, France.

WOOD, Derek QC
Falcon Chambers (Jonathan Gaunt QC & Kim Lewison QC) London (020) 7353 2484
Recommended in Agriculture

WOOD, Graham
India Buildings Chambers (Ray Herman) Liverpool (0151) 243 6000 gnwood@rapid.co.uk
Recommended in Personal Injury
Specialisation: Personal injury, including health and safety and industrial disease, medical and other professional negligence. Commercial and construction disputes. Administrative law, especially education and local government cases. Employment, including race and sex discrimination. Recent work has involved test litigation for 85 dBA liability against Fords and other major industrial deafness cases and solicitor negligence in handling large scale scheme settlements for industrial disease. Particular interest in catastrophic injury.
Prof. Memberships: PIBA PNBA
Career: Recorder 2000. Co-founder Northern Circuit Free Representation and Advice Scheme.
Publications: 'Binghams Negligence Cases'.
Personal: Sailing. Married with three children.

WOOD, James QC
Doughty Street Chambers (Geoffrey Robertson QC) London (020) 7404 1313
Recommended in Crime, Human Rights
Specialisation: Specialist in human rights and criminal appellate work including the Bridgewater and Birmingham Six appeals. Practice include all forms of serious crime, including homicide, fraud and particularly cases raising political, policing and public order issues. Civil work includes actions against the police, inquests and prisoners' rights. Author of 'The Right to Silence: The Case for Retention' (1991).
Prof. Memberships: Liberty, and of Sweet and Maxwell Practical research Papers on 'Stop and Search' and 'Compensation for Miscarriages of Justice'.
Career: Silk 1999, Recorder 1999.

WOOD, Martin
Broadway House (J Graham K Hyland QC) Bradford (01274) 722560
Recommended in Family
Specialisation: Family law, specialising in high value ancillary relief cases.
Prof. Memberships: F.L.B.A
Career: King James' Grammar School, Almondbury; Christ's College, CANTAB; call 1973.

WOOD, Michael QC
23 Essex Street (Michael Lawson QC) London (020) 7413 0353 michaelwood@23essexstreet.co.uk
Recommended in Fraud
Specialisation: All aspects of criminal work both prosecuting and defending, with an emphasis on commercial fraud, including advising those concerned or interested in fraud litigation such as solicitors and accountants.
Prof. Memberships: Criminal Bar Association; Bar Human Rights Committee.
Career: Called to the Bar 1976; QC 1999; Recorder 1999.
Personal: Born 22nd October 1953. Attended Rugby School and Southampton University.

WOOD, Simon
Plowden Buildings (William Lowe QC) London (020) 7583 0808 bar@plowdenbuildings.co.uk
Recommended in Personal Injury
Specialisation: All aspects of personal injury law acting for claimants and defendants alike, including clinical negligence. Professional negligence claims involving solicitors arising out of personal injury claims. Stark v The Post Office [2000] PIQR P105, CA.
Career: Called in 1981, Harmsworth Scholar. Practised continuously in North of England, from Plowden Buildings since 1999. Recorder 2000.
Publications: Member editorial team, 'Charlesworth & Percy on Negligence' (10th edn, published Autumn 2001).
Personal: Born 1958. Choristers' School, Durham; Royal Grammar School, Newcastle upon Tyne (governor, 1999); University of Newcastle upon Tyne. Married with four sons. Music.

WOOD, William QC
Brick Court Chambers (Christopher Clarke QC) London (020) 7379 3550 wood@brickcourt.co.uk
Recommended in Aviation, Insurance
Specialisation: Aviation, insurance and reinsurance, commercial, competition and mediation.
Prof. Memberships: Member of Combar, Bar European Group and Competition Law Association.
Career: BA (1st class) Oxford, BCL (1st class) Oxford, LLM (Harvard Law School). Called 1980, silk 1998, CEDR accredited mediator 1999, member of the Bar of Tonga, 2000.

WOODWARD, William QC
Ropewalk Chambers (Ian McLaren QC) Nottingham (0115) 947 2581 clerks@ropewalk.co.uk
Recommended in Personal Injury
Specialisation: Embraces common law; personal injury; employer's liability; insurance; disaster; insidious disease; poisoning; clinical, professional and other negligence throughout the land. Involvement in consequences of Markham mine; Flixborough; Hillsborough disasters and in asbestos; noise induced hearing loss; white finger; bladder and other cancer; mucous membrane; fire and explosion litigation for example.
Prof. Memberships: Bar European Group. Founder member Nottinghamshire Medico-Legal Society and East Midlands Business and Property Bar Association. Special Professor Nottingham University Law Department.
Career: St. John's College Oxford. Called 1964, Inner Temple. Queen's Counsel 1985. Head of Ropewalk Chambers 1985-94. Recorder. Deputy High Court Judge. President Mental Health Review Tribunal.
Personal: Married, three children. Ponds. Fungi. Serendipity.

WOODWARK, Jane
Milburn House Chambers (Paul Cape) Newcastle upon Tyne (0191) 230 5511
Recommended in Employment
Specialisation: Almost exclusively employment and discrimination law, acting for both employers and employees. Background in local government.
Prof. Memberships: Employment Law Bar Association; Industrial Law Society.
Career: Master's degree in Industrial Relations, London School of Economics 1983. Called 1995. Prior to the Bar, worked for a national employers' organisation advising on employment law, particularly equalities issues and transfers of undertakings. Advised employers during three national industrial disputes in 1986, 1989 and 1992. Co-founder Milburn House Chambers.

WORMALD, Richard

3 Raymond Buildings (Clive Nicholls QC) London (020) 7400 6400
chambers@3raymondbuildings.com

Recommended in Fraud

Specialisation: A criminal practitioner with experience of commercial law. Increasingly a specialist in fraud and business crime. Crime includes murder, attempted murder, rape, serious assault, blackmail, robbery and arson. Notable fraud cases include SFO v Massingham & others (SFO fraud), HM Customs & Excise v Knight (£60 million fraud), DTI v Mahady (serious and complex fraud). Particular knowledge of restraint and confiscation proceedings, appearing in the High Court on behalf of companies and individuals. Regularly appears on behalf of the Police Federation and the Royal College of Nurses. Civil law includes contempt proceedings and defamation law (worked as a libel lawyer at the Daily Mail), VAT disputes and tribunals, judicial review, civil actions against the police, licensing and extradition.
Career: BA (Joint Hons) University of York. Call 1993.

WORTHINGTON, Stephen

12 King's Bench Walk (Richard Methuen QC) London (020) 7581 0811
worthington@12kbw.co.uk

Recommended in Personal Injury

Specialisation: Professional negligence, personal injury, environmental law. Blue Circle v Ministry of Defence, Nuclear Pollution, [1998] 3 All ER 385. Meil v Rankin (2001) QB 272.
Prof. Memberships: PIBA, LCLCBA, TECBAR, PNBA.
Career: Trinity College, Cambridge.
Publications: Contributor to Butterworths 'Professional Negligence' and 'Structured Settlements: A Practical Guide'.

WRIGHT, Peter QC

Lincoln House Chambers (Mukhtar Hussain QC) Manchester (0161) 832 5701

Recommended in Crime

WYNTER, Colin

Devereux Chambers (Jeffrey Burke QC) London (020) 7353 7534

Recommended in Commercial (Litigation)

Specialisation: Insurance and reinsurance, general commercial, professional negligence.
Prof. Memberships: COMBAR.
Career: All aspects of insurance and reinsurance: Cases include: Gan Insurance Co. Ltd v Tai Ping Insurance Co Ltd (No.1) [1999] LRIR, 229, and (CA) [1999] LRIR 472, (No.2) [2001] LRIR, 291 and (No.3) (2001, to be reported) and (CA) (2001, to be reported), Mabey & Johnson v Ecclesiastical & Ors [2001] LRIR 369, Baker & Ors v McCall International [2001] LRIR 149, Trygg Hansa v Equitas [1998] 2 Lloyd's Rep 439, Pacific & General Insurance v Baltica Insurance [1996] LRIR 8, Equitas v Sirius (1999, Commercial Court), Home Insurance Co. v ME Rutty [1996] LRIR 415, Colonial v Chung, (Privy Council) (to be reported 2001 Lloyd's Rep), Pride Valley v The Independent Insurance Co. (1997) and (CA) (1999), Caudle v Sharp (arbitration only). Also various Lloyd's Names Insurance actions: Stockwell v Outhwaite (1990-92), Agnew v Wellington (1994-96). Other Commercial: Sale and carriage of goods, and general commercial disputes: Cases include Stephenson v Rogers (CA) [1999] 2 WLR 1064, [1999] 1 All ER 613, Cicatiello v Anglo European [1994] 1 LLR 678, Governor of Bank of Scotland v Butcher (CA) (1998), Barnard Marcus v Ashraf (CA) [1988] 1 EGLR 7, Lambert v West Devon Borough Council, [1997] JPL 735. Employment: Unfair and wrongful dismissals, race and sex discrimination (not equal pay, equal value or part time workers), Injunctive relief. Cases include Schultz v Esso Petroleum (CA) [1999] 3 All ER 338, [1999] ICR 1202, and Virdee v National Grid Co. Plc [1992] IRLR 555.
Publications: Author of Insurance Chapter in 'Law and the Business of Sport', by Griffith-Jones (Butterworths, 1997). Has appeared on legal education videos to discuss certain of the above and other cases. Lectures frequently on insurance and reinsurance matters.
Personal: LLB (1st Class) (London), M.Phil (Cantab); fluent in French.

WYVILL, Alistair

St Philip's Chambers (John Randall QC) Birmingham (0121) 246 7000
awyvill@st-philips.co.uk

Recommended in Commercial (Litigation)

Specialisation: General commercial litigation, including intellectual property (particularly in information technology), insolvency, commercial fraud, construction law and human rights in commercial law.
Prof. Memberships: Chancery Bar Association, Midland Chancery and Commercial Bar Association.
Career: B.Econ.; LLB (Hons) (Qld), LLM (Distinction)(Lond.) Admitted as a solicitor in Australia in 1984. Called to the Bar in Australia in 1986. Practiced in Australia as a barrister in commercial and company law for 12 years. Also admitted in Papua New Guinea. Called to the Bar in England and Wales in 1998.
Publications: 'Enrichment, Restitution and the Collapsed Negotiations Cases' (1993-94)' 11 Aust Bar Review 93. With D Fitzpatrick, 'Business Bankruptcy Law Reform in Vietnam' (1996) 5 Asia Pacific Law Review 37. 'The Law of Fraudulent Conveyances as the Basis of Mareva Jurisdiction' (1998) 73, Australian Law Journal 672.

YOUNG, David QC

Three New Square (David Young QC) London (020) 7405 1111
3newsquareip@lineone.net

Recommended in Intellectual Property

Specialisation: All aspects of intellectual property, patent (especially chemical patent cases), and passing off, trade marks, copyright, franchising, restrictive practices, designs, breach of confidence and computer law. Appears in Hong Kong and Singapore. Notable cases include: American Cyanamid v Ethicon (interloc. injunction); 3M v Rennicks (patent); Windsurfing International v Tabur Marine (GB) Ltd (patent); Willemijn v Madge Networks (patent/computers); Germinal Holdings (plant variety); Allied Signal v Sundstrand (Patent County Court – electronics); Glaverbel v British Coal; Hoechst v BP (patent, account of profits) Improver Corpn. v Remington Consumer Products (patent, infringement) Lubrizol Corpn. v Exxon; Monsanto v Merck (patent infringement, pharmaceuticals); Scandecor Development v Scandecor Marketing (passing off and trade mark); Collag Corpn. v Merck & Co. (confidential information).
Prof. Memberships: Intellectual Property Bar Association; Chancery Bar Association.
Career: Monckton Combe School, Hertford College Oxford – MA. Called to Bar 1966, appointed QC 1980. Bencher of Lincolns Inn; Recorder of Crown Court (1987 – 2000); Chairman Plant Seeds and Varieties Tribunal (1987-); Deputy High Court Judge Chancery Division (1993-); Deputy Judge of Patent County Court (1993-).
Publications: Co-author 'Terrell on Law of Patents' (12th – 14th ed); 'Young on Passing Off', 1985; 1994.
Personal: Tennis, skiing, country pursuits.

YOUNG, Timothy QC

20 Essex Street (Iain Milligan QC) London (020) 7583 9294
clerks@20essexst.com

Recommended in Shipping

Specialisation: Main areas of practice are commercial law and international trade and related areas including arbitration and judicial review. Author of 'Voyage Charters' (1993, LLP). Sometime lecturer in law at St. Edmund Hall, Oxford. Significant recent reported cases: Glencore Grain Rotterdam v Lorico [1997] 2 Lloyd's Rep 386 (FOB Sale Letter of credit waiver) CA; The Kriti Rex [1996] 2 Lloyd's Rep 171 (COA, unseaworthiness, damages); AG of New Zealand v Anderson [1995] 2 Lloyd's Rep 264 (due diligence); Gill & Duffus v Rionda Futures [1994] 2 Lloyd's Rep 67 (sale of goods, demurrage, counter guarantee); The Island Archon [1994] 2 Lloyd's Rep 227 (implied indemnities); Standard Chartered Bank v PNSC/Mehra [2000] 1 LLR 218/[2000] 2 LLR 511; Hill Harmony 2001 [AC] 638.
Prof. Memberships: COMBAR, London Common Law & Commercial Bar Association.
Career: Called to the Bar in 1977 and joined present chambers in 1978. Took Silk 1996.
Publications: Voyage Charters (LLP).
Personal: Supporting member of the London Maritime Arbitrators Association and panel member of Securities and Futures Authority arbitrators. Educated at Malvern College 1967-71 and Magdalen College, Oxford 1972-76 (BA, BCL). Born 1 December 1953. Lives in London.

ZACAROLI, Antony

3-4 South Square (Michael Crystal QC & Lord Alexander of Weedon QC) London (020) 7696 9900
clerks@southsquare.com

Recommended in Chancery, Insolvency/Corporate Recovery

Specialisation: Practice covers a wide area of business and commercial law, including all aspects of corporate and personal insolvency, litigation relating to property, commercial fraud, constructive trusts, banking, securities, insurance, pensions and professional negligence. Recent reported cases include Re CE King [2000] 2 BCLC 297; Grupo Torras SA v Al Sabah [1999] CLC 1469; Don King Productions v Warren [1998] 2 All ER 607; Re Cosslett (Contractors) Limited [1998] Ch 495.
Career: Called to the Bar (Middle Temple) November 1987. Lecturer in Law at Pembroke College, Oxford, from 1987-91.
Publications: Contributor to Lightman & Moss: 'The Law of Receivers of Companies'; Totty & Moss: 'Insolvency'; Gore-Browne on Companies.

ZELIN, Geoffrey

Enterprise Chambers (Anthony Mann QC) London (020) 7405 9471

Recommended in Company

Specialisation: London (020) 7405 9471 Newcastle (0191) 222 3344 Leeds (0113) 246 0391. Practises in all areas of company and partnership law including shareholder and partnership disputes, insolvency, enforcement of directors' duties and disqualification. Apart from company law his practice encompasses all areas of commercial Chancery work including property disputes and professional negligence.
Prof. Memberships: Chancery Bar Association, Property Bar Association.
Career: Called to the Bar 1984. Practising in these Chambers since December 1986.
Personal: Interests include skiing, cricket.

THE BAR

A-Z

Set No.
1 **ARBITRATION CHAMBERS** (John Tackaberry QC)

22 Willes Road, London, NW5 3DS **Tel:** (020) 7267 2137 **Fax:** (020) 7482 1018 **DX:** 46454 LDN/Kentish Town **Email:** jatqc@atack.demon.co.uk

Set No.
2

ATKIN CHAMBERS (Robert Akenhead QC)

1 Atkin Building, Gray's Inn, London, WC1R 5AT
Tel: (020) 7404 0102 **Emergency Tel:** (020) 7242 4703 **Fax:** (020) 7405 7456 **DX:** 1033
Email: clerks@atkinchambers.law.co.uk **Website:** www.atkinchambers.law.co.uk

Head of Chambers	Robert Akenhead QC
Senior Clerks	Stuart Goldsmith
	David Barnes
Tenants	30

Members:

Ian N D Wallace QC (1948) (QC-1973)
John Blackburn QC (1969) (QC-1984)
Colin Reese QC (1973) (QC-1987)
Robert Akenhead QC (1972) (QC-1989)
Nicholas Dennys QC (1975) (QC-1991)
Jonathan Acton Davis QC (1977) (QC-1996)
Andrew White QC (1980) (QC-1997)
Nicholas Baatz QC (1978) (QC-1998)
Martin Bowdery QC (1980) (QC-2000)
Stephen Dennison QC (1985) (QC-2001)
David Streatfeild-James QC (1986) (QC-2001)
Donald Valentine (1956)
Darryl Royce (1976)
Andrew Burr (1981)
Mark Raeside (1982)
Delia Dumaresq (1984)
Andrew Goddard (1985)
Stephanie Barwise (1988)
Simon Lofthouse (1988)
Robert Clay (1989)
Peter D. Fraser (1989)
Dominique Rawley (1991)
Chantal-Aimèe Doerries (1992)
Steven Walker (1993)
Fiona Parkin (1993)
Manus McMullan (1994)
James Howells (1995)
Nicholas Collings (1997)
Patrick Clarke (1997)
Christopher Lewis (1998)

The Chambers: Atkin Chambers is known particularly for its expertise in litigation and advice on the law relating to domestic and international construction and engineering projects. Within this wide area of practice chambers has developed particular experience in the following areas: arbitration, insurance, energy, professional negligence and information technology. The set was the first to specialise in the law relating to domestic and international construction and engineering projects. Chambers have steadily expanded in size and have developed their expertise in the many aspects of construction and engineering projects and also in the area of information technology. There are now 30 members including 11 QCs. Members have wide experience of courts and tribunals ranging from the House of Lords, Privy Council, international and domestic arbitrations, public enquiries, adjudications and all forms of ADR. Members also have experience dealing with litigation and advice in many offshore jurisdictions including China, Australia, Hong Kong, Singapore, Malaysia, Indonesia, Jersey and Greece. Some members are qualified as mediators, some sit as arbitrators both in domestic and in offshore jurisdictions and as adjudicators. All members undertake direct professional access instructions. Since 1959 the leading standard textbook, *Hudson's Building and Engineering Contracts*, has been edited in chambers. The editors of both the *Building Law Reports* and the *Technology and Construction Law Reports* are also members of chambers. Members are available to act as mediators, adjudicators and arbitrators.
Specialist Areas: Alternative Dispute Resolution; arbitration (international); construction; energy and natural resources; information technology; professional negligence; shipping – dry shipping.

Work Undertaken:

Construction & Engineering: This is the core specialism of chambers. Within this very broad area members provide representation and advice on a wide range of legal issues in a domestic and an international context. Projects in relation to which members services are sought include house construction, road building, power plants, tunnels, bridges, office construction, airports, telecommunication projects, railway construction and rolling stock disputes, hydrocarbon and chemical pipelines, offshore and submarine structures, shipbuilding and ship repair projects. The legal aspects of such projects are varied and so are the legal services which members are called upon to provide. These services range from advice in connection with the drafting of contracts for their procurement, advice on claims and representation in court or in domestic or international arbitrations and representation in mediations and adjudications.
Energy: Members act in connection with large scale national and international projects for the exploration and exploitation of oil and gas, often involving joint ventures. Advice is given on differing aspects of the oil and gas world including long-term natural gas contracts, tariff agreements, oil and gas transportation, pipeline installation and the design and construction of off-shore structures including platforms and FPSOs. Members frequently act in connection with contracts and disputes concerning the design, construction and commissioning of power stations (coal, gas, combined cycle and nuclear) and related funding and development agreements.
Information Technology: In 1998 the Official Referee's Court was replaced by the Technology and Construction Court. This was a recognition of the close similarity between the legal and technical skills which are required for construction and engineering disputes and those which are required in the field of infor-

Continued overleaf

mation technology disputes. Members offer advice on hardware and software agreements, including IT procurement, management and internet contracts and they represent parties involved in related disputes.
Professional Negligence: Members provide advice and representation in the field of professional negligence concerning architects, engineers, surveyors, quantity surveyors, project managers, valuers and solicitors.
Commercial Law: Members have developed expertise on a wide range of commercial matters both as an adjunct to construction, energy and IT matters but also independently of them. Services are provided in connection with banking, performance bonds and guarantees, insurance, PFI matters and the financing and structuring of large multi-party commercial projects.

Set No. 3

2 BEDFORD ROW (William Clegg QC)

2 Bedford Row, London, WC1R 4BU
Tel: (020) 7440 8888 **Fax:** (020) 7242 1738 **DX:** 17
Email: (initialsurname)@2bedfordrow.co.uk **Website:** www.2bedfordrow.co.uk

Head of Chambers	William Clegg QC
Senior Clerk	John Grimmer
Tenants	50

Members:

William Clegg QC (1972) (QC-1991) +
The Rt Hon Lord Morris of Aberavon QC (1954) (QC-1973) +
Michael Lewis QC (1956) (QC-1975) +
Howard Godfrey QC (1970) (QC-1991) +
Peter Griffiths QC (1970) (QC-1995) +
Andrew Munday QC (1973) (QC-1996) +
T Alun Jenkins QC (1972) (QC-1996) * +
Nigel Lithman QC (1976) (QC-1997) +
Michael Wolkind QC (1976) (QC-1999)
Philip Hackett QC (1978) (QC-1999)
Maura McGowan QC (1980) (QC-2001) +
Trevor Burke QC (1981) (QC-2001)
Peter Lodder QC (1981) (QC-2001) +
David Thomas QC (1992) (QC-1996) *
Robert Flach (1950)
Charles Conway (1969)
Deborah Champion (1970) +
Nigel Ingram (1974) †
Mark Halsey (1974)
Robert Neill (1975)
Margaret Barnes (1976)
John Caudle (1976) +
Anthony Abell (1977)
Barry Gilbert (1978)
John Dodd (1979) +
Margaret Dodd (1979) *
Michael Levy (1979)
John Livingston (1980)
Brian Altman (1981) ‡
Keith Mitchell (1981)
Jim Sturman (1982)
Gelaga King (1985) +
Timothy Kendal (1985)
Mark Milliken-Smith (1986)
Christopher Campbell-Clyne (1988)
Richard Matthews (1989)
Jonathan Ashley-Norman (1989)
Tayo Adebayo (1989)
Thomas Derbyshire (1989)
Craig Rush (1989)
James Ageros (1990)
Christine Agnew (1992)
Adam Budworth (1992)
Michael Epstein (1992)
Valerie Charbit (1992)
John Hurlock (1993)
Alison Pople (1993)
Christine Henson (1994)
Kieran Galvin (1996)
Maria Dineen (1997)
Navaz Daruwalla (1997)
Andrew McGee (1999)
Emma King (1999)

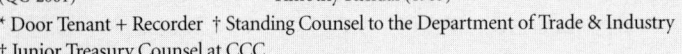

* Door Tenant + Recorder † Standing Counsel to the Department of Trade & Industry
‡ Junior Treasury Counsel at CCC

The Chambers: 2 Bedford Row is well established as a leading Chambers specialising in criminal law and related areas of practice. After many years in the Temple, the set moved to its own freehold premises at 2 Bedford Row in January 2000. Chambers have continued the tradition of both defending and prosecuting in all types of criminal work, and have developed to meet the demands of modern practice by providing a complete range of experience in general criminal matters as well as in a number of specialist areas (see below). Chambers presently consist of 14 Queen's Counsel and 39 juniors. Members include the former Attorney-General, Treasury Counsel at the Central Criminal Court and Standing Counsel to the Department of Trade and Industry. Additionally, a number of members of chambers hold office as Recorders and as Deputy District Judges. For further information please visit the chambers website which includes profiles for individual members.

Work Undertaken: In general criminal practice, the size and varied experience of chambers enables them to offer practitioners at all levels and for all types of cases. Members of chambers appear before all tribunals from the Magistrates' Court to the House of Lords and also before foreign courts and the International War Crimes Tribunal at The Hague. Specialist areas include fraud (including computer fraud), money laundering, restraint and confiscation proceedings, health and safety, environmental law and trading standards. Individual members of chambers are experienced in judicial review, extradition and immigration. Human rights law and practice now plays a major part in the work of chambers. There is particular experience in investigations and prosecutions brought by the Serious Fraud Office and in advising parties from the commencement of the investigation, including issues arising from international judicial assistance. A growth area relates to regulatory and disciplinary work, especially in con-

nection with financial services and the disciplinary tribunals of professional and professional sporting bodies. Members have also represented both Premiership clubs and players before the Football Association. Members of chambers have appeared in many leading cases including:
Serious Crime: R v Colin Stagg; R v Fashanu, Grobbelaar and Ors; R v David Copeland; R v Colin Ireland; R v Michael Stone; R v Corporal Lee Clegg; R v Sawoniuk; R v Duffy & Mulcahy.
Fraud: R v Mawell & Ors, BCCI, Polly Peck; R v Levitt and Ors, Resort Hotels, Bute Mining, Richmond Oil and Gas, Alliance Resources; R v Leslie Cairns and Ors; R v Leckie & Ors and Alpine Double Glazing.

International: Work is handled in Arabic, Dutch, French, German, Hebrew, Italian, Kiro (Sierra Leone) and Serbo-Croat.

Set No. 4

7 BEDFORD ROW (David Farrer QC)

7 Bedford Row, London, WC1R 4BU
Tel: (020) 7242 3555 **Fax:** (020) 7242 2511 **DX:** 347 (Ch.Ln.)
Email: clerks@7br.co.uk **Website:** www.7br.co.uk

Head of Chambers	David Farrer QC
Senior Clerk	Christopher Owen
Tenants	56

Members:

David Farrer QC (1967) (QC-1986)
Martin Wilson QC (1963) (QC-1982)
Stephen Coward QC (1964) (QC-1984)
Timothy Barnes QC (1968) (QC-1986)
Nigel Baker QC (1969) (QC-1988)
Richard Latham QC (1971) (QC-1991)
Christopher Hotten QC (1972) (QC-1994)
William Coker QC (1973) (QC-1994)
Nigel Rumfitt QC (1974) (QC-1994)
Simeon Maskrey QC (1977) (QC-1995)
Philip P. Shears QC (1972) (QC-1996)
Collingwood Thompson QC (1975) (QC-1998)
Joan Butler QC (1977) (QC-1998)
Kate Thirlwall QC (1982) (QC-1999)
Yvonne A. Coen QC (1982) (QC-2000)
Nigel G. Godsmark QC (1979) (QC-2001)
Timothy Spencer QC (1982) (QC-2001)
Derek Sweeting QC (1983) (QC-2001)
Witold Pawlak (1970)
David H. Christie (1973)
J. Philip T. Head (1976)
Julian D. Matthews (1979)
Simon Wheatley (1979)
Jeremy Pendlebury (1980)
John Pini (1981)
Nicholas Dean (1982)
Ebraham Mooncey (1983)
Farooq Ahmed (1983)
Susan C. Reed (1984)
Maureen Baker (1984)
Barbara Connolly (1986)
Louise Varty (1986)
David Matthew (1987)
Rupert Mayo (1987)
Simon King (1987)
Andrew Wheeler (1988)
Gordon Aspden (1988)
Brendan Roche (1989)
Rachel Langdale (1990)
Cathryn McGahey (1990)
Steven Ford (1992)
Adam Korn (1992)
Maryam Syed (1993)
Adam Weitzman (1993)
Vanessa Marshall (1994)
Hugh Preston (1994)
Matthew Jowitt (1994)
Bilal Rawat (1995)
William Redgrave (1995)
Anwar Nashashibi (1995)
Susannah Johnson (1996)
Simon Thomas (1995)
David Allan (1998)
Louise Bass (1999)
Jenny Carter-Manning (1999)
Gareth Weetman (1999)

The Chambers: The chambers at 7 Bedford Row are a long-established set of chambers, whose members have a wide experience of advocacy and advisory work in a number of specialised fields. Instructions are accepted from lawyers and professional clients in the United Kingdom and from abroad. In early 1995 chambers moved from 2 Crown Office Row and acquired the freehold of two buildings at 9 Bedford Row and 9 Jockey's Fields. In May 2000 chambers moved to a much larger freehold complex at 7 Bedford Row.

Work Undertaken:
Civil Litigation: Members have experience and can advise upon and present cases in the following areas: building and construction work; commercial contracts; consumer law; employment; environmental pollution (including waste disposal); financial services; information technology; insurance and reinsurance law; licensing; partnership disputes; personal injury; product liability; professional negligence and clinical negligence.
Criminal Law: Members have a great deal of experience in the provision of legal advice and advocacy in the criminal field. Chambers can provide representation at all levels of seniority and all members both prosecute and defend. There is a particular emphasis on commercial and international fraud.
Family Law: Members conduct all aspects of family and matrimonial work, with particular emphasis on children's work. In public law members act for parents, Guardian ad litem, the Official Solicitor and local authorities. In private law, members advise and appear on child abduction, international disputes, residence and contact issues.

Continued overleaf

Tribunals: Chambers appear and advise in Disciplinary Tribunals of professional and other bodies, Industrial Tribunals, the Employment Appeal Tribunal, the Criminal Injuries Compensation Board, Public Inquiries, and hearings before the Traffic Commissioner. Chambers are also able to provide trained members in Alternative Dispute Resolution. For any further information concerning individual members of chambers and areas of practice, as well as the current level of fees and charging rates, please contact the Senior Clerk.

International: Instructions are welcomed from overseas lawyers directly. Several members of chambers speak one or more foreign languages fluently; and several members have taught and lectured on legal matters in the United States. There are practising door tenants in Hong Kong, Jersey, and Greece.

Set No. 5

17 BEDFORD ROW (Allan Levy QC)

17 Bedford Row, London, WC1R 4EB
Tel: (020) 7831 7314 **Fax:** (020) 7831 0061 **DX:** 370 Ldn/Ch
Email: IBoard7314@aol.com

Head of Chambers	Allan Levy QC
Senior Clerk	Ian Boardman
Tenants	23

Members:

Allan Levy QC (1969) (QC-1989)
Michael Gettleson (1952)
Nigel Jennings (1967)
Jane Gill (1973)
Susan Garnett (1973)
John McLinden (1991)
Dennis Sharpe (1976)
Brian Huyton (1977)
Graham Campbell
Hashim Reza (1981)
Richard Anthony Southall (1983)
John Critchley (1985)
Miles Croally (1987)
Julian Date (1988)
Mark Twomey
Bernard Lo (1991)
Barry McAlinden (1993)
Christopher Stirling
Christina Michalos (1994)
John Crosfil (1995)
Max Thorowgood
Carolyn Hamilton (1996)
Michael Joy (1997)
Neville Maryon Green (1963) *
James Chapman (1987) *
Hugh Bevan (1959) *

* Door Tenant

The Chambers: Members are instructed by solicitors' firms throughout the country and by or on behalf of government departments, local authorities and financial institutions. Chambers were founded in the Temple over 50 years ago by Leonard Caplan QC. Former members include Lord Justice Farquharson and Sir Laurence Verney, the Recorder of London. Mobile telephone number is (0831) 234 861.

Work Undertaken: Particular areas of work in which individuals specialise are asset recovery and preservation, including tracing; banking; building society and insurance law; criminal law; commercial work; entertainment and media, including defamation; music business; copyright and other intellectual property; medical law; human rights; family, children and divorce; landlord and tenant and property law; personal injury; professional negligence; direct professional access work.

International: Work is handled in French, German and Italian. For overseas bars in New Zealand, contact John McLinden. France: strong connections with foreign jurisdictions, contact Neville Maryon Green (Paris). Western Australia: Allan Levy QC.

Set No. 6

29 BEDFORD ROW CHAMBERS (Peter Ralls QC)

29 Bedford Row Chambers, London, WC1R 4HE
Tel: (020) 7404 1044 **Fax:** (020) 7831 0626 **DX:** 1044
Email: chambers@29bedfordrow.co.uk **Website:** www.29bedfordrow.org.uk

Head of Chambers	Peter Ralls QC
Senior Clerk	Robert Segal
Tenants	47

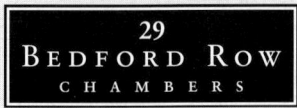

29 BEDFORD ROW CHAMBERS

Members:

Peter Ralls QC (1972) (QC-1997)
Evan Stone QC (1954) (QC-1979)
Augustus Ullstein QC (1970) (QC-1992)
Timothy Scott QC (1975) (QC-1995)
Ajmalul Hossain QC (1976) (QC-1998)
Peter Duckworth (1971)
John Zieger (1962)
Clare Renton (1972)
Howard Shaw (1973)
John Tonna (1974)
Mark Warwick (1974)
Neil Sanders (1975)
Philip Cayford (1975)
Charles Atkins (1975)
Geoffrey Ames (1976)
Simon Gill (1977)
Stephen Boyd (1977)
Simon Edwards (1978)
Michael Keane (1979)
Jonathan Ferris (1979)
Deborah Bangay (1981)
Ann Hussey (1981)
Nicholas Francis (1981)
John Wilson (1981)
Paul Storey QC (1982) (QC-2001)
Timothy Walker (1984)
Nicholas Bowen (1984)
David Holland (1986)
Stephen Reynolds (1987)
Rupert Butler (1988)
Nicholas Chapman (1990)
Robert Peel (1990)
Nichola Gray (1990)
Jonathan Southgate (1992)
Stuart Hornett (1992)

Members continued:

Craig Barlow (1992)
Patrick Chamberlayne (1992)
Victoria Domenge (1993)
Brenton Molyneux (1994)
Duncan Kynoch (1994)
Nicholas Tse (1995)
Nicholas Allen (1995)
Peter Mitchell (1996)
Gary Pryce (1997)
Laura Heaton (1998)
Robert Upex *
Galina Ward (1999)
Emma Summer (1999)

* Door Tenant

The Chambers: Bedford Row Chambers is a progressive and growing set committed to providing its clients with an effective and efficient legal service. It operates from one of the Bar's largest and contemporary offices, having added a further 50% to its office space by taking over its neighbouring premises. Bedford Row Chambers resides in two Grade II listed buildings, completely modernised and wired for the latest technology and with room to expand.

Work Undertaken: The work of chambers is primarily in commercial, property, family, personal injury and general common law, and extends to a wide range of litigation, advisory and drafting work.
Chancery: Breach of trust, Court of Protection, partnership, trusts, wills and probate.
Commercial: Arbitration, building and construction, commercial, companies, consumer credit, contract, economic torts, guarantees, licensing, misrepresentation, and sale of goods.
Common Law: Injunctions, employment, libel and slander, nuisance and property-related torts, personal injuries, tort, professional negligence.
Family: Family law and family provision.
Intellectual Property: Confidential information, intellectual property, copyright and passing off, trade marks and trade names.
Insolvency: Bankruptcy, insolvency, liquidations and administrations and receivership.
Property: Conveyancing, housing, land law, landlord and tenant, mortgages and securities, planning, rent reviews.
Public & Administrative Law: Judicial review, statutory appeals and tribunal work, particularly education, special educational needs, community care and mental health work.

Set No. 7

33 BEDFORD ROW (David Barnard)

33 Bedford Row, London, WC1R 4JH
Tel: (020) 7242 6476 **Fax:** (020) 7831 6065 **DX:** 75
Email: clerks@33bedfordrow.co.uk **Website:** www.33bedfordrow.co.uk

Head of Chambers	David Barnard
Senior Clerk	Michael Lieberman
Tenants	29

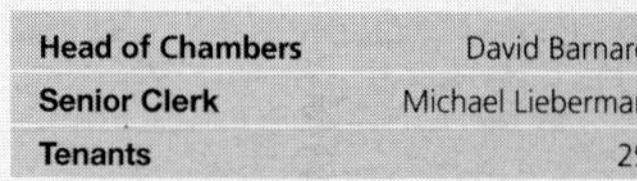

Members:

David Barnard (1967) +
Barry Kogan (1973) +
Nigel May (1974) +
Constance Whippman (1978)
Richard Bendall (1979)
Marc Galberg (1982)
Michael Burke (1985)
Christopher Spratt (1986)
Susan Castle (1986)
Timothy Thorne (1987)
Joanne Oxlade (1988)
David Lonsdale (1988)
Jean-Paul Sinclair (1989)
Rhys Jones (1990)
Mukhtiar Otwal (1991)
Philip Brown (1991)
Thomas Cleeve (1993)
Ronnie Bergenthal (1993)
Mark Kendal (1993)
Tom Boyd (1995)
Stuart Armstrong (1995)
Frida Hussain (1995)
John Law (1996)
Piers Harrison (1997)
Daniel Dovar (1997)
Mark Stanger (1998)

+ Recorder

The Chambers: Chambers undertake work in property, criminal law, family law and commercial and civil litigation. Members regularly publish and lecture. David Barnard is Standing Counsel to HM Customs and Excise, and Nigel May and Timothy Thorne are part-time Judge Advocates.

Publications: These include *Residential Possession Proceedings* (Webber), *Possession of Business Premises* (Webber), and *The Woolf Reforms: A Practitioner's Guide* (Barnard, Galberg & Lonsdale).

Set No.
8

48 BEDFORD ROW (Roderick I'Anson Banks)

48 Bedford Row, London, WC1R 4LR
Tel: (020) 7430 2005 **Fax:** (020) 7831 4885 **DX:** 284 LDE
Email: pm@partnershipcounsel.co.uk **Website:** www.partnershipcounsel.co.uk

Head of Chambers	Roderick I'Anson Banks
Practice Manager	Kim Pangratis
Tenants	2

Members:

Roderick I'Anson Banks (1974)LLB (London)

Simon Jelf (1996)LLB (Eur)

The Chambers: Specialise exclusively in partnership law and provide solicitors and other professional and trading partnerships with a full range of legal services, from the drafting of new agreements and the review of existing agreements to advice and representation in partnership disputes, arbitrations and mediations. Chambers' aim, where possible, is to assist clients with the process of resolving disputes, without recourse to litigation and provide ongoing support from the embryonic stages of a developing dispute, right through to the conclusion of any litigation or until a negotiated settlement is reached. Direct Professional Access work is undertaken. Mobile number (0775) 102 2914.

Publications: Roderick I'Anson Banks is the editor of *Lindley & Banks on Partnership* , the authoritative guide to partnership law, and the author and editor of the *Encyclopedia of Professional Partnerships.*

Set No.
9

9 BEDFORD ROW (FORMERLY 4 BRICK COURT) (Anthony C. Berry QC)
9 Bedford Row, London, WC1R 4AZ **Tel:** (020) 7489 2727 **Fax:** (020) 7489 2828 **DX:** 453 **Email:** clerks@9bedfordrow.co.uk

Set No.
10

9-12 BELL YARD (D. Anthony Evans QC)

9-12 Bell Yard, London, WC2A 2JR
Tel: (020) 7400 1800 **Fax:** (020) 7404 1405 **DX:** 390
Email: clerks@bellyard.co.uk

Head of Chambers	D. Anthony Evans QC
Senior Clerk	Gary Reed
Tenants	61

Members:

D. Anthony Evans QC (1965) (QC-1983)BA (Cantab)
Edmund Lawson QC (1971) (QC-1988)BA (Cantab)
Lord Carlile of Berriew QC (1970) (QC-1984)LLB (AKC)
Michael Birnbaum QC (1969) (QC-1992)BA (Oxon)
Jeremy Carter-Manning QC (1975) (QC-1993)
Patrick Curran QC (1972) (QC-1995)MA (Oxon)
Sonia Woodley QC (1968) (QC-1996)
Peter Christopher Rouch QC (1972) (QC-1996)LLB (Wales)
Robin Spencer QC (1978) (QC-1999)MA (Cantab)
Philip Katz QC (1976) (QC-2000)MA (Oxon)
John McGuinness QC (1980) (QC-2001)BA (Lond)
Mukul Chawla QC (1983) (QC-2001)LLB (Lond)
Herbert Kerrigan QC (1970) (QC-1992)
Edward Grayson (1948)MA (Oxon)
Richard Cherrill (1967)MA (Cantab) LLB
Martin Field (1966)
Bernard Phelvin (1971)BA (Cantab)
Richard Merz (1972)LLB (Soton)
Alison Barker (1973)LLB (Hons), Harmsworth Law Scholar 1973
John Greaves (1973)LLB (Lond)
Anthony Heaton-Armstrong (1973)LLB
Tudor Owen (1974)LLB (Lond)
Alexander Cranbrook (1975)BA (Hons)
Stephen John (1975)MA (Oxon)
John Harwood-Stevenson (1975)MA (Oxon)
Timothy Spencer (1976)
Peter Moss (1976)
Keith Hadrill (1977)
Simon Wild (1977)BA (Lond)
Michael Orsulik (1978)BA, LLM (Lond)
Dianne Chan (1979)LLB (Bris)
John Alban Williams (1979)
Michael Egan (1981)
Jonathan Davies (1981)LLB (Lond)
Sean Enright (1982)LLB (Nott)
Graham Brown (1982)BA
Constance Briscoe (1983)LLB (Newcastle)
Christine Laing (1984)LLB
Mohammed Khamisa (1985)BA (Hons) (Lond)
Philippa McAtasney (1986)LLB (Lond)
Mark Bryant-Heron (1986)MA (Cantab)
William Hughes (1989)BSc (Leic)
Sarah Ellis (1989)LLB (Wales)
Adrian Chaplin (1990)BA (Cantab)
Alexandra Healy (1992)MA (Cantab)
Mark Seymour (1992)MA (Hons)
Richard Jory (1993)BA (Hons) (Reading)
Suzanne Reeve (1993)BA (Hons) (Oxon)
Warwick Tatford (1993)BA (Hons) (Oxon)
Tina Davey (1993)LLB (Hons) (Cardiff)
Jonathan S Kinnear (1994)LLB
Christina Russell (1994)MA (Cantab)
Jessica Gavron (1995)BA (Cantab)
Michelle Denton (1996)LLB (Soton)
Neil Griffin (1996)LLB (Hons) (Lond)

Members continued:

Anita Saran (1996)LLB (Lond)
Michael Goodwin (1996)BSc (Hons)
Kristian Mills (1998)LLB (Hons) (Wales)
Neerja Sharma (1998)BA (Hons)
Ryan Richter (1998)BA (Hons)
Stuart Biggs (1999)BA (Hons) (Cantab)

The Chambers: A leading criminal set which can also provide general common law expertise. Members of chambers regularly appear in notable public enquiries such as the Stephen Lawrence and 'Bloody Sunday' enquiry. Tribunal work and judicial review are well established areas of practice.

Work Undertaken: From the largest of City firms to the smallest of High Street practices, advocacy and advisory work is undertaken at all levels across a wide spectrum of criminal cases. Chambers' professional clients include in-house lawyers from legal departments of major companies, government departments and local authorities. Direct professional instructions are accepted. Members deal with every aspect of criminal litigation. Defence experience is broadly based, ranging from serious and complex commercial fraud cases to the more common offences against person and property. Established expertise includes drugs offences and related confiscation hearings, money laundering, sexual offences and judicial review. Prosecution work of all kinds and at all levels is undertaken, not only for the Crown Prosecution Services, Customs & Excise, the Serious Fraud Office and the Department of Trade and Industry, but also for British Telecom, the Post Office and many local authorities. Appeals are conducted at all court levels, with senior members presenting appeals from Commonwealth countries to the Privy Council. Members have been involved in some of the most widely-reported cases, involving such well-known names as Blue Arrow, Maxwell, BCCI, the Marchioness disaster, the Stephen Lawrence and 'Bloody Sunday' public enquiries. Some leading and junior members of chambers undertake civil litigation work. This includes aviation, banking, building, company, consumer credit, contract, employment, insurance, landlord and tenant, partnership, personal injury, professional negligence and sports law. Work is undertaken in London, throughout the country and overseas. A number of members of chambers have been recognised by their appointments to a variety of judicial and other legal positions, such as standing counsel to Customs & Excise and the Department of Trade and Industry.

Additional Specialisations: Other areas of practice include arbitration, criminal injuries compensation, inquests, licensing, planning, professional disciplinary, public inquiries, self-regulatory tribunals and trading standards.

Set No.

1 BLACKSTONE CHAMBERS (Presiley Baxendale QC & Charles Flint QC)

Blackstone House, Temple, London, EC4Y 9BW
Tel: (020) 7583 1770 **Fax:** (020) 7822 7350 **DX:** 281
Email: clerks@blackstonechambers.com **Website:** www.blackstonechambers.com

Head of Chambers	Presiley Baxendale QC Charles Flint QC
Senior Clerk	Martin Smith
Practice Manager	Julia Hornor
Tenants	63

Members:

Colin Ross-Munro QC (1951) (QC-1972)
Stanley Brodie QC (1954) (QC-1975)
Lord Lester of Herne Hill QC (1963) (QC-1975)
Sir Ian Sinclair QC (1952) (QC-1979)
Ian Brownlie QC (1958) (QC-1979)
Michael Beloff QC (1967) (QC-1981)
David Donaldson QC (1968) (QC-1984)
Robert Englehart QC (1969) (QC-1986)
David Hunt QC (1969) (QC-1987)
Barbara Dohmann QC (1971) (QC-1987)
Andrew Pugh QC (1961) (QC-1988)
Ian Forrester QC (1972) (QC-1988)
Sir Roy Goode QC (1988) (QC-1990)
Maurice Mendelson QC (1965) (QC-1992)
Jonathan Harvie QC (1973) (QC-1992)
Presiley Baxendale QC (1974) (QC-1992)
David Pannick QC (1979) (QC-1992)
Jeffrey Jowell QC (1965) (QC-1993)
Stephen Nathan QC (1969) (QC-1993)
John Howell QC (1979) (QC-1993)
Charles Flint QC (1975) (QC-1995)
Bob Hepple QC (1966) (QC-1996)
Ian Mill QC (1981) (QC-1999)
Beverley Lang QC (1978) (QC-2000)
Paul Goulding QC (1984) (QC-2000)
Thomas Beazley QC (1979) (QC-2001)
Monica Carss-Frisk QC (1985) (QC-2001)
Gerald Levy (1964)
Dawn Oliver (1965)
Guy Goodwin-Gill (1971)
Alastair Sutton (1972)
Hugo Page (1977)
Judith Beale (1978)
Nicholas Khan (1983)
Anthony Peto (1985)
Gerard Clarke (1986)
Adam Lewis (1985)
Robert Anderson (1986)
Mark Shaw (1987)
Andrew Green (1988)
Robert Howe (1988)
Adrian Briggs (1989)
Dinah Rose (1989)
Michael Fordham (1990)
Pushpinder Saini (1991)
Thomas Croxford (1992)

Continued overleaf

Members continued:

Javan Herberg (1992)
Joanna Pollard (1993)
Andrew Hunter (1993)
Gemma White (1994)
Jane Collier (1994)
Emma Dixon (1994)
Thomas de la Mare (1995)
Tom Weisselberg (1995)
Jane Mulcahy (1995)
Julia Ellins (1994)
Andrew George (1997)
Kate Gallafent (1997)
Claire Weir (1998)
Ben Jaffey (1999)
Brian Kennelly (1999)
Catherine Callaghan (1999)
Stephanie Palmer (2000)

The Chambers: Blackstone Chambers is a long established set, combining formidable strengths in commercial, public and employment law, with state of the art facilities and a friendly and open approach to client service.

Work Undertaken: Chambers' practice breaks down into the following practice areas:
Commercial: Within this area, members' established skills and specialisations include international trade; banking; insurance and reinsurance; carriage of goods; conflict of laws; corporate fraud; financial services; regulatory tribunals; shipping; defamation; intellectual property; media, entertainment and sports law.
Public Law & Human Rights: Work includes judicial review, both for and against public bodies and regulatory authorities, arising from decisions and areas such as freedom of expression; equality of treatment; immigration; education; social security; housing; planning; local government. The combined expertise of members of chambers in commercial and public law proves particularly valuable in City regulation and financial services cases. Advice in the human rights arena is also available, with particular reference to the impact of the Human Rights Act 1998 in all its aspects.
Employment Law: Within this area, members of chambers have extensive expertise in all aspects of employment law, ranging from pure contract work, to sex, race and disability discrimination.

Publications: These are many in number and include: *Legal Problems of Credit and Security*; *Hire Purchase Law and Practice*; *Principles of Corporate and Insolvency Law*; *Consumer Credit Legislation*; *Halsbury on Arbitration and Dicey & Morris (13th ed)*; *Principles of Public International Law*; *The Vienna Convention on the Law of Treaties and International Law Commission*; *De Smith Woolf and Jowell: Judicial Review of Administrative Action*; *Judicial Review Handbook*; *Halsbury on Aliens*; *Halsbury on the European Convention of Human Rights*; *Butterworths Human Rights – Law and Practice*; *Constitutional Law & Human Rights.*

International: European law with its ever growing impact on national law is an integral part of chambers' practice in all areas of specialism. One member of chambers is a former member of the Legal Service of the European Commission and two other members of chambers practise full-time in European Community law from offices in Brussels. Chambers also has a strong tradition of practice in the specialised field of public international law. Several members of chambers are highly experienced in advising in litigation in public international law disputes arising before national and international courts and tribunals. A current member was formerly the legal adviser to the Foreign and Commonwealth Office. Members of chambers have a wide-ranging experience of advocacy before English, European and Commonwealth courts and tribunals, and frequently appear before the European Courts of Justice and the European Court of Human Rights. Work is handled in Finnish, French, German, Hindi, Italian, Japanese, Punjabi, Spanish, Swedish and Urdu.

Recruitment: Chambers is a member of OLPAS. A first or upper second class degree is usually required, although not necessarily in law. Pupillage awards of up to £30,000 are available. Mini-pupillages for a week in the year preceding pupillage are strongly encouraged for potential pupils of chambers. Further information, either about chambers generally or about pupillage in particular, is available from chambers' web site www.blackstonechambers.co.uk.

Set No.
12

4 BREAMS BUILDINGS (Christopher Lockhart-Mummery QC)

4 Breams Buildings, London, EC4A 1AQ
Tel: (020) 7430 1221/7353 5835 **Fax:** (020) 7421 1399 **DX:** 1042
Email: clerks@4breams.co.uk **Website:** www.4breams.co.uk

Head of Chambers	Christopher Lockhart-Mummery QC
Senior Clerk	Stephen Graham
Junior Clerk	Jay Fullilove
Director of Marketing & Administration	Vicky Thompson
Tenants	37

Members:

Christopher Lockhart-Mummery QC (1971) (QC-1986)
Nigel Macleod QC (1961) (QC-1979)
John Cherryman QC (1955) (QC-1982)
Michael Howard QC (1964) (QC-1982)
The Rt. Hon. Lord Kingsland QC (1972) (QC-1988)
Joseph Harper QC (1970) (QC-1992)
Richard Drabble QC (1975) (QC-1995)
David Holgate QC (1978) (QC-1997)
Christopher Katkowski QC (1982) (QC-1999)
John Male QC (1976) (QC-2000)
David Elvin QC (1983) (QC-2000)
Colin Sydenham (1963)
Stephen Bickford-Smith (1972)
Eian Caws (1974)
Robert Bailey-King (1975)
Anne Seifert (1975)
Christopher Lewsley (1976)
Viscount Dilhorne (1979)
David Smith (1980)
Anne Williams (1980)
Thomas Jefferies (1981)
Alice Robinson (1983)
Timothy Mould (1987)
Nathalie Lieven (1989)
John Litton (1989)
Nicholas Taggart (1991)
Karen McHugh (1992)
David Forsdick (1993)
Timothy Morshead (1995)
Graeme Keen (1995)
Camilla Lamont (1995)
James Maurici (1996)
Alison Oakes (1996)
David Abrahams (1998)
Daniel Kolinsky (1998)
Katherine Olley (1999)
Carine Patry (1999)

The Chambers: 4 Breams Buildings is a well established leading set of chambers in public law, local government, planning, environmental law and property. Chambers advise, and appear regularly for all types of client, including individuals, pressure groups, landlords (including institutional landlords), developers, regulators, local authorities and central government. Chambers offers a high quality, efficient and friendly service which meets their clients' requirements. Direct Professional Access is welcomed.

Work Undertaken:
Public & Administrative Law Including Human Rights: Members have considerable experience in judicial review and statutory applications and appeals. They frequently advise and appear both for public bodies and those who wish to challenge their decisions. Several junior members are on a Treasury Panel. Particular subject areas in which chambers specialise include local government, education, health, housing, mental health, community care and social services, social security, utility and other regulators, public procurement and the tortious liability of public authorities.
Planning & Environmental Law: All aspects. Chambers include 24 members of the Planning and Environmental Bar Association. Their clients include individuals; pressure groups; amenity and local residents groups; developers (such as large retailers, housebuilders and mineral undertakers); a large number of local authorities; the Environment Agency and the Secretary of State for the Environment Transport and the Regions. Members of chambers have been involved, for example, in recent cases on the impact of European law in this area.
Other: All aspects of landlord and tenant and property (including vendor and purchaser, covenants, easements, mortgages and party walls). There are related specialisms in mining, rating, property related torts (including trespass and nuisance) and professional negligence. Around these main areas of work chambers also offer a specialist service in European law, compulsory purchase and compensation (the volume on which for Halsbury's Laws was edited entirely by members of chambers), Parliamentary work and Transport and Works Act inquiries, and building contracts.

Publications: Chambers' publications include *Hill's Law of Town and Country Planning (4th edn); Town Planning Law Handbook and Case Book; Atkins Court Forms – Town and Country Planning; Hill and Redmond's Law of Landlord and Tenant; Halsbury's Laws – Town and Country Planning; Halsbury's Laws – Compulsory Acquisition; Atkin's Court Forms – Rating and Community Charge; Journal of Planning Law; Judicial Review; Corfield and Carnwath's Compulsory Acquisition and Compensation; Emden's Building Contracts and Practice; Unlawful Interference with Land; Party Walls – the New Law.*

Recruitment: Pupillage applications are accepted via the OLPAS scheme. Up to three funded pupillages are awarded annually each of £19,000 for 12 months. Applications for mini-pupillages are encouraged and should be made in writing with full CV. All pupillage enquiries to be addressed to Nathalie Lieve. All mini-pupillage applications to be addressed to the Administrator Ann Day.

Set No.
13

BRICK COURT CHAMBERS (Christopher Clarke QC)

7-8 Essex Street, London, WC2R 3LD
Tel: (020) 7379 3550 **Fax:** (020) 7379 3558 **DX:** 302
Email: [surname]@brickcourt.co.uk **Website:** www.brickcourt.co.uk

Head of Chambers	Christopher Clarke QC
Senior Clerks	Julian Hawes
	Ian Moyler
Tenants	61

Members:

Christopher Clarke QC (1969) (QC-1984)
Sir Sydney Kentridge QC (1977) (QC-1984)
David Vaughan QC (1962) (QC-1981)
Jonathan Sumption QC (1975) (QC-1986)
Hilary Heilbron QC (1971) (QC-1987)
Mark Cran QC (1973) (QC-1988)
Jonathan Hirst QC (1975) (QC-1990)
Gerald Barling QC (1972) (QC-1991)
Peregrine Simon QC (1973) (QC-1991)
Timothy Charlton QC (1974) (QC-1993)
Richard Gordon QC (1972) (QC-1994)
Mark Hapgood QC (1979) (QC-1994)
Mark Howard QC (1980) (QC-1996)
Stephen Ruttle QC (1976) (QC-1997)
Andrew Popplewell QC (1981) (QC-1997)
George Leggatt QC (1983) (QC-1997)
William Wood QC (1980) (QC-1998)
Nicholas Green QC (1986) (QC-1998)
David Lloyd Jones QC (1975) (QC-1999)
Charles Hollander QC (1978) (QC-1999)
Paul Walker QC (1979) (QC-1999)
David Anderson QC (1985) (QC-1999)
Catharine Otton-Goulder QC (1983) (QC-2000)
Peter Irvin (1972)
Peter Brunner (1971)
James Flynn (1978)
Andrew Lydiard (1980)
Richard Lord (1981)
Mark Brealey (1984)
Michael Swainston (1985)
Fergus Randolph (1985)
Conor Quigley (1985)
David Garland (1986)
Neil Calver (1987)
Dominic Chambers (1987)
Richard Slade (1987)
Harry Matovu (1988)
Cyril Kinsky (1988)
Paul Wright (1990)
Sarah Lee (1990)
Helen Davies (1990)
Tom Adam (1991)
Mark Hoskins (1991)
Michael Rollason (1992)
Alan Roxburgh (1992)
Alan Maclean (1993)
Jemima Stratford (1993)
Alec Haydon (1993)
Michael Bools (1991)
Roger Masefield (1994)
Aidan Robertson (1995)
Simon Salzedo (1995)
Marie Demetriou (1995)
Jasbir Dhillon (1996)
Andrew Thomas (1996)
Martin Chamberlain (1997)
Margaret Gray (1998)
Simon Birt (1998)
Kelyn Bacon (1998)
Colin West (1999)
Andrew Henshaw (2000)
Derrick Wyatt QC (1972) (QC-1993) *
Richard Macrory (1974) *
Andrew Le Sueur (1987) *
Jan Woloniecki (1983) *

* Door Tenant

The Chambers: A leading set in the fields of commercial, European and public law. The core of its work includes all aspects of international trade, finance and commerce. For further information on chambers' expertise please visit the website www.brickcourt.co.uk

Set No.
14

1 BRICK COURT (Richard Rampton QC)

1 Brick Court, Temple, London, EC4Y 9BY
Tel: (020) 7353 8845 **Fax:** (020) 7583 9144 **DX:** 468
Email: clerks@1brickcourt.co.uk

Head of Chambers	Richard Rampton QC
Senior Clerk	David Mace
Tenants	21

Members:

Richard Rampton QC (1965) (QC-1987)
Richard Hartley QC (1956) (QC-1976)
Geoffrey Shaw QC (1968) (QC-1991)
Harry Boggis-Rolfe (1969)
Thomas Shields QC (1973) (QC-1993)
Andrew Caldecott QC (1975) (QC-1994)
Edward Garnier QC (1976) (QC-1995)
Patrick Moloney QC (1976) (QC-1998)
Stephen Suttle (1980)
Victoria Sharp QC (1979) (QC-2001)
Harvey Starte (1985)
Manuel Barca (1986)
Timothy Atkinson (1988)
Rupert Elliott (1988)
Jane Phillips (1989)
Caroline Addy (1991)
Benjamin Hinchliff (1992)
Catrin Evans (1994)
Joanne Cash (1994)
Lorna Skinner (1997)
Sarah Palin (1999)

The Chambers: The Chambers of Richard Rampton QC (formerly Richard Hartley QC) are a long-established set which has specialised in the law of libel and slander for at least 85 years. Chambers' expertise covers all claims based on the publication of false or damaging material, and encompasses breach of confidence, contempt of court, malicious falsehood, reporting restrictions, data protection, cases concerning the Internet and human rights and judicial reviews concerning this area of practice. Members of chambers are experienced in the pre-publication review of newspapers, books, radio and television programmes, and have written or contributed to many of the leading works on defamation including *Duncan & Neill of Defamation*, *Halsburys Laws of England*, Bullen & Leake & Jacobs *Precedents of Pleadings* and Atkin's *Court Forms and Precedents.*

International: The set frequently receive instructions from solicitors worldwide including Malaysia, Hong Kong and Singapore (acting for Prime Ministers, MPs, Royalty and large corporations) and often conduct cases in these jurisdictions.

5 4 BRICK COURT (David Medhurst)

4 Brick Court, Temple, London, EC4Y 9AD
Tel: (020) 7797 8910 **Fax:** (020) 7797 8929 **DX:** 491
Email: clerks@4bc.co.uk

Head of Chambers	David Medhurst
Senior Clerk	Michael Corrigan
Tenants	36

Members:

David Medhurst (1969)
Mira Chatterjee (1973)
David Burgess (1975)
Robert Colover (1975)
Marianna Hildyard (1977)
Janet Mitchell (1979)
Michael Haynes (1979)
Roma Whelan (1981)
Richard St Clair-Gainer (1983)
Susan Quinn (1983)
Roderick Jones (1983)
Marc Roberts (1984)
Peter Lynch (1985)
Anthony Bell (1985)
Simon Molyneux (1986)
Alexa Storey-Rea (1990)
Abigail Sheppard (1990)
Annabel Wentworth (1990)
Peter Marshall (1991)
Isabelle Watson (1991)
Edward Knapp (1992)
Jacqui Gilliatt (1992)
Gwynneth Knowles (1993)
Levi Peter (1993)
Caroline Sumeray (1993)
Sue Piyadasa (1994)
Teresa Pritchard (1994)
Lisa Smith (1994)
Sarah Morris (1996)
Sarah Elliott (1996)
Ian Griffin (1997)
Jonathan Goldring (1997)
Maria Gallagher (1997)
Hannah Rought-Brooks (1999)
Nairn Purss (1999)
Laura Bayley (1999)

The Chambers: A progressive set of chambers consisting of 36 barristers who provide a comprehensive service to solicitors and local government authorities.

6 BRIDEWELL CHAMBERS (Colin Challenger)

Bridewell Chambers, 2 Bridewell Place, London, EC4V 6AP
Tel: (020) 7797 8800 **Fax:** (020) 7797 8801 **DX:** 383
Email: HughesGage@bridewell.law.co.uk **Website:** www.bridewell.law.co.uk

Head of Chambers	Colin Challenger
Senior Clerk	Lee Hughes-Gage
Tenants	34

Members:

Colin Challenger (1970)
Baroness Scotland of Asthal QC (1977) (QC-1991) †
Jo Boothby (1972)
Gordon Pringle (1973)
Juliet Oliver (1974)
Ernest James (1977)
Roger Davey (1978)
Adrienne Knight (1981)
Elizabeth Goodchild (1981)
Peter Gray (1983)
Ian Lawrie (1985)
† Associate member
David Josse (1985)
Adam Clemens (1985)
James Doyle (1985)
Pieter Briegel (1986)
Simon Walsh (1987)
Sally Atherton (1987)
Alan Walmsley (1991)
Brian Cummins (1992)
Andrew Slaughter (1993)
Lloyd Sefton-Smith (1993)
Paul Walker (1993)
Stuart Nicol (1994)
Maria Scotland (1995)
Christopher Pearson (1995)
Jason Bartfeld (1995)
Victoria Maude (1995)
Stephen Morley (1996)
Elaine Banton (1996)
Karen Dempsey (1996)
Parosha Chandran (1997)
Charles Woodhouse (1997)
Guy Coleman (1998)
Polly Higgins (1998)

The Chambers: Chambers cover most significant areas of criminal, civil and family law. Specialist teams deal with serious crime, housing, landlord and tenant, family and children, personal injury and cases for and against police forces. Individual tenants specialise in commercial law, judicial review, licensing, wills and probate, professional negligence, Official Referee work, marine accidents and family law. A detailed guide to the full services provided, including the Bridewell Conditional Fee Agreement, can be found on the chambers' website at www.bridewell.law.co.uk or by contacting the clerks.

International: Work is handled in French and German.

Recruitment: Pupillage applications to OLPAS. Tenancy applications may be sent to Ian Lawrie.

Set No.
17

CHARTER CHAMBERS (Stephen Solley QC)

Two Dr Johnson's Buildings, Temple, London, EC4Y 7AY
Tel: (020) 7832 0300 **Fax:** (020) 7334 0242 **DX:** 429 Ch.Ln
Email: clerks@charterchambers.com

Head of Chambers	Stephen Solley QC
Senior Clerk	Patrick Duane
Consultant	Michael Martin
Clerks	Kevin Crawley
	Rod McGurk
	Claire Wright
	Ashley Balm
	Paul Martin
	Jonathan Spanjar
Administration	Nick Pickels
	Chris Blake
	Jean Brown
Tenants	59

Members:

Stephen Solley QC (1969) (QC-1989) +
Jerome Lynch QC (1983) (QC-2000)
Brian Forster QC (1977) (QC-1999) +
Peter Kelson QC (1981) (QC-2001) +
David Batcup (1974) +
Alan Bayliss (1968) +
Anthony Fogg (1970)
Graham Davies (1971)
David Martin-Sperry (1971)
Richard Bruce (1968)
David Wurtzel (1974)
Peter Higginson (1975)
Robert Sherman (1977)
Ian Wheatly (1977)
Ivor Frank (1979)
Stephen Mejzner (1978)
Susan Williams (1978)
Mark Paltenghi (1979)
Nicholas Rhodes (1981)
Mark Tomassi (1981)
Timothy Horgan (1982)
Thomas Buxton (1983)
Tyrone Belger (1984)
Bernard Tetlow (1984)
David Taylor (1986)
Jonathan Rose (1986)
Anna Hamilton-Shield (1989)
Neil Hawes (1989)
Alan Fraser (1990)
Michael Lavers (1990)
Paul Phillips (1991)
Mary Teresa Deignan (1991)
Claire Robinson (1991)
Jennifer Edwards (1992)
Robert Benzynie (1992)
Julia Flanagan (1993)
Gary Morton (1993)
Siobhan Grey (1994)
Daniel Jones (1994)
Tarquin McCalla (1994)
Zafar Ali (1994)
Paul Raudnitz (1994)
Andrew Bodnar (1995)
Philip Norman (1995)
Dominic Alexander (1995)
Martin Goudie (1996)
Adam Morgan (1996)
Alison Slater (1996)
Jonathan Lennon (1997)
Lucy Murray (1997)
Rachel Darby (1997)
Juliet Bewyer (1997)
Stephen Bentley (1997)
Dominic Thomas (1998)
Susan Doris (1998)
Roshnee Shah (1998)
Roddy James (1999)
Alex Dos Santos (1999)
Mellisa Tollman (1999)

\+ Recorder

The Chambers: Charter Chambers is a busy criminal and common law set of chambers offering practitioners in a variety of fields at all levels of seniority.

Work Undertaken:

Criminal Law: Criminal practitioners accept instructions in both prosecution and defence work. A number of members of chambers have been involved in substantial fraud and drugs cases as well as cases involving serious sexual offences.

Civil Litigation: In particular chambers provide civil practitioners who specialise in the areas of personal injury, landlord and tenant and other property work, general commercial and contractual litigation, actions against the police and employment law.

Family Law: Chambers can offer practitioners who are experienced in all aspects of family law, including divorce, ancillary relief, Children Act work and domestic violence cases, specialising in Social Security Law and Child Support Agency matters.

International: French, German, Italian and Spanish are spoken.

Set No.
18

CLARENDON CHAMBERS

7 Stone Buildings, Lincoln's Inn, London, WC2A 3SZ
Tel: (020) 7681 7681 **Fax:** (020) 7681 7684 **DX:** LDE 0022 Chancery Lane
Email: clerks@clarendonchambers.com

Senior Clerk	Russell Burton
Tenants	40

Members:

Gay Martin (1970)
John Bishop (1970)
Julian Lynch (1976)
Robert Anthony (1979)
Simon Birks (1981)
Stephen Crouch (1982)
Adrian Jenkala (1984)
Juliann Manson (1985)
Susan Pyle (1985)
Geoffrey Porter (1988)
Adam Swirsky (1989)
Stuart Yeung (1989)
Mark Gordon (1990)
Terry Burns (1990)
Simon Livingstone (1990)
Stephen Murch (1991)
Andrew Bullock (1992)
Lucinda Benner (1992)
Richard Carron (1992)
Simon Gerrish (1993)
Michael Ellis (1993)
Richard Holloway (1993)
Catherine Le Quesne (1993)
Anna Mathias (1994)
Mary Abbott (1994)
Peter Linstead (1994)
Nicola Smith (1994)
Ben Gow (1994)
Cliona Papazian (1994)
Matthew Rudd (1994)
Jonathan Ellis (1995)
Richard Harris (1997)
David Willans (1995)

Members continued:

Mugni Islam-Choudhury (1996)
Alexander McGregor (1996)
Sarah Porter (1996)
Laureen Husain (1997)
Steven Evans (1997)
Penny Van Spall (1998)
Joanne Wardale (1998)

The Chambers: Clarendon Chambers is a busy and highly regarded common law set with 40 barristers. The members of chambers practise in specialist teams in the fields of crime, family, civil and commercial, landlord and tenant, personal injury, employment, licensing, immigration and town and country planning. Chambers have a very strong client base in London and the South East and particularly so in the East Midlands where chambers have an annexe in Northampton. All enquiries in respect of the services chambers offer should be referred to the Senior Clerk. Business Hours: 8.30am-6.30pm Out of Hours Tel: (07971) 285796. Annexe at: Clarendon Chambers, 5 St Giles Terrace, Northampton, NN1 2BN Tel: (01604) 637245 Fax: (01604) 633167 DX: 12404 Northampton.

t No.
9

CLOISTERS (Laura Cox QC)

Cloisters, 1 Pump Court, Temple, London, EC4Y 7AA
Tel: (020) 7827 4000 **Fax:** (020) 7827 4100 **DX:** LDE 452
Email: clerks@cloisters.com **Website:** www.cloisters.com

Head of Chambers	Laura Cox QC
Senior Clerk	Glenn Hudson
Clerks	Michelle Hughton
	Kaye Brooks
Senior Fees Clerk	Stephen Herbert
Junior Fees Clerk	Alberta Sharpe
Chambers Administrator	Christine Brown
Tenants	40

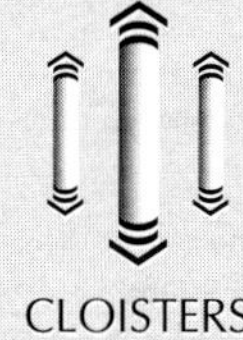

Members:

Laura Cox QC (1975) (QC-1994)
John Platts-Mills QC (1932) (QC-1964)
Brian Langstaff QC (1971) (QC-1994)
Arthur Davidson QC (1953) (QC-1976)
Robin Allen QC (1974) (QC-1995)
Jonathan Crystal (1972)
Philip Engelman (1979)
Jacques Algazy (1980)
Martin Kurrein (1981)
Andrew Buchan (1981)
Simon W. Taylor (1984)
Pauline Hendy (1985)
Simon Dyer (1987)
Declan O'Dempsey (1987)
Patricia Hitchcock (1988)
Paul Epstein (1988)
Paul Spencer (1988)
Anthony Bradley (1989)
Thomas Kibling (1990)
Paul Michell (1991)
Jason Galbraith-Marten (1991)
Joĭl Donovan (1991)
Yvette Genn (1991)
Christopher Quinn (1992)
Caspar Glyn (1992)
John Horan (1993)
Louise Brooks (1994)
Damian McCarthy (1994)
Rachel Crasnow (1994)
Sally Robertson (1995)
James Laddie (1995)
William Latimer-Sayer (1995)
Thomas Coghlin (1998)
Adam Solomon (1998)
Jonathan Cohen (1999)
Schona Jolly (1999)
David Massarella (1999)
Akua Reindorf (1999)
Peter J. Pimm (1991) †
John Whitmore (1976) †

† Associate member

Work Undertaken: Administrative, public, and local government law; alternative dispute resolution and mediation; civil liberties and human rights law; contract and commercial law; EU law; employment, industrial and discrimination law; personal injury and clinical negligence; family law; fraud (civil); media and defamation; sports law; international law.

Recruitment: Cloisters expects to offer three 12 month pupillages each year. Awards of £15,500, plus reasonable travelling costs, are made to each pupil. Chambers have a strong track record of recruiting from their pupils. Applications may only be made via OLPAS.

Set No. 20

CORAM CHAMBERS (Roger McCarthy QC)

4 Brick Court, Temple, London, EC4Y 9AD
Tel: (020) 7797 7766 **Fax:** (020) 7797 7700 **DX:** 404 (Chancery Lane)
Email: mail@coramchambers.co.uk **Website:** www.coramchambers.co.uk

Head of Chambers	Roger McCarthy QC
Senior Clerk	Paul Sampson
Chambers Manager	Martin Dyke
Tenants	50

coram

Members:

Roger McCarthy QC (1975) (QC-1996)
Shelagh Farror (1970)
Jane Drew (1976)
Catherine Nicholes (1977)
Aditya Kumar Sen (1977)
Laura Harris (1977)
David Boyd (1977)
Vera Mayer (1978)
Martha Cover (1979)
Anne Spratling (1980)
Melanie Lewis (1980)
Kate Hudson (1981)
Meena Gill (1982)
Nicola Simpson (1982)
Fiona Gibb (1983)
Christina Morris (1983)
Carol Atkinson (1985)
Nicholas O'Brien (1985)
Anne Gibberd (1985)
Divya Bhatia (1986)
Debora Price (1987)
Michelle Corbett (1987)
Jane Probyn (1988)
Kate Purkiss (1988)
Mark Mullins (1988)
Elpha LeCointe (1988)
Jennifer Driscoll (1989)
Neil Bullock (1989)
Frances Orchover (1989)
Andrew Short (1990)
Anthea Parker (1990)
Jillian Brown (1991)
Anthony Ross (1991)
Neil Fry (1992)
Sharon Sawyerr (1992)
David Vavrecka (1992)
Sima Kothari (1992)
Michel Horton (1993)
Rajeev Thacker (1993)
Susan Gore (1993)
Dermot Casey (1994)
Alison Easton (1994)
Andrew Allen (1995)
Emma Furley (1995)
Gerald Browne (1995)
Timothy Parker (1995)
Sarah Marley (1995)
Jerry Fitzpatrick (1996)
Mai-Ling Savage (1998)
Daisy Hughes (1999)

The Chambers: Chambers undertake a wide range of work which falls into two main fields: family and civil.

Work Undertaken:

Family: Including divorce; matrimonial finance; public and private Children Act proceedings; child abduction; domestic violence; adoption; wardship; inheritance and cohabitees.

Civil: Employment (including trade union law), discrimination, landlord and tenant, local government, social services, community care, mental health, education, judicial review, human rights, housing and residential homes.

International: Work is handled in Bengali, French, Hebrew, Hindi, Italian, Punjabi and Spanish.

Set No. 21

CROWN OFFICE CHAMBERS (Michael Spencer QC & Christopher Purchas QC)

1 Paper Buildings, Temple, London, EC4Y 7EP
Tel: (020) 7797 8100 **Fax:** (020) 7797 8101 **DX:** 80 LONDON/CHANCERY LANE
Email: mail@crownofficechambers.com **Website:** www.crownofficechambers.com

Head of Chambers	Michael Spencer QC
	Christopher Purchas QC
Senior Clerk	Julian Campbell
	David Newcomb
Tenants	71

CROWN OFFICE CHAMBERS

Members:

Michael Spencer QC (1970) (QC-1989)
Christopher Purchas QC (1966) (QC-1990)
John Crowley QC (1962) (QC-1982)
Michael Harvey QC (1966) (QC-1982)
John Slater QC (1969) (QC-1987)
Nigel Wilkinson QC (1972) (QC-1990)
Antony Edwards-Stuart QC (1976) (QC-1991)
Roger ter Haar QC (1974) (QC-1992)
Andrew Bartlett QC (1974) (QC-1993)
Simon Brown QC (1976) (QC-1995)
William Stevenson QC (1968) (QC-1996)
Richard Lynagh QC (1975) (QC-1996)
Michael Kent QC (1975) (QC-1996)
Richard Hone QC (1970) (QC-1997)
Anna Guggenheim QC (1982) (QC-2001)
Jonathan Woods (1965)
Martyn Berkin (1966)
Margaret Bickford-Smith (1973)
Colin Nixon (1973)
David Tucker (1973)
Dennis Matthews (1973)
Thomas Saunt (1974)
John Powles (1975)
John Stevenson (1975)
Nicholas Davies (1975)
James Holdsworth (1977)
Jonathan Waite (1978)
Andrew Phillips (1978)
John Greenbourne (1978)
Gordon Catford (1980)
Julian Field (1980)
Jane Davies (1981)
Michael Curtis (1982)
Paul Dean (1982)
Charlotte Jones (1982)
Deborah Taylor (1983)
Steven Coles (1983)
Kim Franklin (1984)
James Medd (1985)
Ian Swan (1985)
Shaun Ferris (1985)
David Platt (1987)

Members continued:

Jane DeCamp (1987)
Raymond Ng (1987)
William Vandyck (1988)
Marion Egan (1988)
Steven Snowden (1989)
Ian Wright (1989)
Erica Power (1990)
Jason Evans-Tovey (1990)
Benedict Newman (1991)
Simon Howarth (1991)
Toby Gee (1992)
Andrew Rigney (1992)
Clive Weston (1993)
Patrick Blakesley (1993)
Alexander Antelme (1993)
Claire Toogood (1995)
James Maxwell-Scott (1995)
Robert Stokell (1995)
Suzanne Chalmers (1995)
Andrew O'Connor (1996)
Andrew Davis (1996)
Muhammed Haque (1997)
Susan Lindsey (1997)
Ben Quiney (1998)
Victoria Woodbridge (1998)
Jack Ferro (1998)
Julian Horne (1998)
Sarah McNally (1999)
Daniel Shapiro (1999)

The Chambers: Crown Office Chambers was founded in 2000 and brought together the two long-established common law sets of chambers, One Paper Buildings and Two Crown Office Row. It is the largest civil common law set in London and has currently 71 members of chambers. Operating from both buildings, it has its administrative and reception facilities at 1 Paper Buildings. Chambers offer a modern, flexible and friendly service. They operate block agreements and protocols for the return of paperwork and for court appearances. They are able to provide first class reception and conference facilities. The size of the merged chambers has also permitted the development of a new centre for alternative dispute resolution, and Crown Office Chambers offers a fully administered ADR service.

Work Undertaken: Crown Office Chambers specialises in professional and clinical negligence, product liability, personal injury, insurance and reinsurance, commercial, contract and construction work. Within these areas it is able to offer depth and breadth of experience at all levels of call, and is widely recognised as a market leader.

Professional Negligence: Chambers undertake all forms of professional negligence, and in particular clinical negligence. They also specialise in construction-related claims (architects, engineers, valuers, residential, commercial and quantity surveyors); legal negligence (barristers and solicitors); claims against other professionals (accountants and insurance brokers).

Product Liability: Product liability is a leading component of chambers' work. They have participated in most of the major multi-party claims which have so far been brought, including the tobacco, benzodiazepine, organo-phosphate, MMR and the oral contraceptive litigation.

Personal Injury/Health & Safety: Personal Injury and Health and Safety are an important part of Crown Office Chambers. Industrial accident, occupational disease, disaster claims, road traffic litigation, aviation/marine claims and local authority based disputes are all undertaken. Chambers act for both claimants and defendants, although they are widely acknowledged for their established connections with insurance-funded litigation.

Insurance & Reinsurance: Insurance and reinsurance work is a major element of chambers' business. Crown Office Chambers has strong links with the insurance market, and many of its clients are major insurers, underwriting syndicates and brokers. All forms of contentious and advisory work are undertaken, including work in the Commercial Court and in arbitration.

Commercial Contract: Members conduct general commercial litigation and arbitration including ICC arbitrations. These involve contractual claims of all kinds.

Construction: Construction and engineering disputes form a significant part of the workload of chambers. Members have substantial experience in the Technology and Construction Courts, acting for employers, contractors, construction professionals, insurers and developers.

Other: Members of chambers have particular expertise in other areas of law. Such specialities include administrative law and judicial review, public enquiries, planning and environmental work, employment law, commercial fraud and banking. Chambers also undertake all forms of residual negligence and nuisance claims. Direct access, conditional fee work and instructions in all forms of alternative dispute resolution are accepted.

Publications: Members of chambers contribute to *Medical Negligence* and *Emden's Construction Law* (general editor, Andrew Bartlett QC).

Set No.
22

1 CROWN OFFICE ROW (Robert Seabrook QC)

Temple, London, EC4Y 7HH
Tel: (020) 7797 7500 **Fax:** (020) 7797 7550 **DX:** LDE1020
Email: mail@1cor.com **Website:** www.1cor.com

Head of Chambers	Robert Seabrook QC
Chambers Director	Bob Wilson
Senior Clerk	Matthew Phipps
Tenants	43

ONE CROWN OFFICE ROW

Members:

Robert Seabrook QC (1964) (QC-1983)
James Badenoch QC (1968) (QC-1989)
Stephen Miller QC (1971) (QC-1990)
David Foskett QC (1972) (QC-1991)
Terence Coghlan QC (1968) (QC-1993)
Guy Mansfield QC (1972) (QC-1994)
Philip Havers QC (1974) (QC-1995)
Sally Smith QC (1977) (QC-1997)
Paul Rees QC (1980) (QC-2000)
Margaret Bowron QC (1978) (QC-2001)
Neil Garnham QC (1982) (QC-2001)
Gregory Chambers (1973)
Anthony Niblett (1976) †
David Balcombe (1980)
James King-Smith (1980) †
David Hart (1982)
Martin Forde (1984)
William Edis (1985)
John Gimlette (1986)
David Evans (1988)
Amanda Grant (1988)
Paul Rogers (1989) †
Angus McCullough (1990)
Keeley Bishop (1990) †
John Whitting (1991)
Martin Downs (1990) †
Jeremy Cave (1992) †
Richard Booth (1993)
Philippa Whipple (1994)
Giles Colin (1994)
Sydney Chawatama (1994)
Sarah Lambert (1994)
Owain Thomas (1995)
Jeremy Hyam (1995)
Ben Collins (1996)
Shaheen Rahman (1996)
Zoe Taylor (1998)
Neil Sheldon (1998)
Caroline Neenan (1998)
Richard Smith (1999)
Christopher Mellor (1999)
Jennifer Johnston (1999)
Robert Kellar (1999)

† Mainly practises from Brighton

The Chambers: Long established as a leading civil set providing the full range of advisory and advocacy services, with an emphasis on professional negligence, public law, and human rights. With a modern and friendly commitment to client service, chambers welcome direct instructions from fellow professionals such as accountants, architects and engineers. A number of members (†) practise mainly from its Brighton Annexe at the recently expanded and modernised premises at Blenheim House, 120 Church Street, Brighton BN1 1WH, Tel: (01273) 625625, which is available for local conferences. To celebrate nearly 50 years at 1 Crown Office Row, chambers have now acquired and refurbished all five floors at this lovely building, providing four conference rooms and the latest IT systems.

Work Undertaken: Professional negligence, in particular clinical and solicitors' negligence; multi-party actions and group litigation; personal injury; health law; domestic commercial contract; administrative law and judicial review; technology; construction and environmental law; planning and local government; representation at public inquiries and before professional disciplinary tribunals; human rights and civil liberties; employment and discrimination; matrimonial finance; sports law, immigration and VAT. Chambers are informally grouped into teams in these specialist areas in which they have in depth expertise at both senior and junior level. Criminal work is also undertaken, in particular fraud and other serious crime. Full details of chambers' services are available at www.1cor.com or in the chambers brochure on request. Building on the set's recognised expertise on the Human Rights Act, on which members regularly lecture and write, chambers provide all the professional support for the Internet services on the Act provided by Lawtel and the College of Law.

Publications: Members are authors of or contributors to a number of textbooks including *The Law and Practice of Compromise* and *Settlement under the Civil Procedure Rules* (both by David Foskett QC); four contributors to *Clinical Negligence* (Editors Powers & Harris); five contributors to *Personal Injury Handbook* (Editors Brennan & Curran); four contributors to *Professional Negligence and Liability*; 14 contributors to *Human Rights and the Common Law* (edited by Rosalind English and Philip Havers QC).

Recruitment: Up to three pupils are taken annually for 12 months. There are generous awards for the first six months with a guaranteed level of earnings for the second six. A first or upper second class degree is required. The set is a member of the OLPAS scheme. Applications for a third six month pupillage are invited from July for selection in September. In 2001 we launched a £10,000 scholarship in Lord Woolf's name to support a deserving student through the Bar Vocational Course (details at www.1cor.com).

Set No.
23

15-19 DEVEREUX COURT (Helen Grindrod QC)

15-19 Devereux Court, 4th Floor, London, WC2R 3JJ **Tel:** (020) 7583 2792 **Fax:** (020) 7353 0608 **DX:** 425 LDE

Set No.
24

DEVEREUX CHAMBERS (Jeffrey Burke QC)

Devereux Chambers, Devereux Court, London, WC2R 3JH
Tel: (020) 7353 7534 **Fax:** (020) 7353 1724 **DX:** 349 (Ch.Ln.)
Email: mailbox@devchambers.co.uk **Website:** www.devchambers.co.uk

Head of Chambers	Jeffrey Burke QC
Senior Clerk	Elton Maryon
Practice Managers	Clifford Holland
	Andrew Frankland
Practice Development Manager	
	Angela Griffiths
Tenants	44

Members:

Jeffrey Burke QC (1964) (QC-1984)
Diana Cotton QC (1964) (QC-1983)
Alan Pardoe QC (1971) (QC-1988)
Colin Edelman QC (1977) (QC-1995)
Robert Glancy QC (1972) (QC-1997)
David Griffith-Jones QC (1975) (QC-2000)
Timothy Brennan QC (1981) (QC-2001)
Roy Lemon (1970)
Peter Wulwik (1972)
Ian Smith (1972)
Gerald Rabie (1973)
Christopher Goddard (1973)
Ian Lee (1973)
Elizabeth Andrew (1974)
Richard Greening (1975)
Richard Clayton (1977)
Ruth Downing (1978)
Nicholas Bard (1979)
Stephen Killalea (1981)
Graham Read (1981)
Bruce Silvester (1983)
Colin Mendoza (1983)
Colin Wynter (1984)
Bruce Carr (1986)
Ingrid Simler (1987)
Joanna Heal (1988)
Philip Thornton (1988)
James Tayler (1989)
Nicholas Randall (1990)
Keith Bryant (1991)
Richard Harrison (1991)
Natasha Joffe (1992)
Alison Padfield (1992)
Robert Weir (1992)
Andrew Burns (1993)
Suzanne McKie (1991)
Peter Edwards (1992)
Katharine Gollop (1993)
Dijen Basu (1994)
Anna Thomas (1995)
David Craig (1997)
Lydia Seymour (1997)
Ben Adamson (1999)
Akash Nawbatt (1999)

The Chambers: Devereux Chambers offers a comprehensive interdisciplinary service to its clients. Areas of special expertise include administrative and local government law; commercial litigation; employment law; insurance and reinsurance; professional negligence; personal injury and clinical negligence. There is a strong emphasis on advocacy. Devereux Chambers is a thriving and well-established set of chambers with a wide client base, ranging from public companies, underwriters and brokers to local authorities, government departments, trades unions and individual litigants. A number of senior members of chambers are deputy High Court Judges, and Recorders. Members of chambers sit on the Criminal Injuries Compensation Appeals Panel, Mental Health Independent Review Tribunal, Rent Assessment Panel and Boundary Commission. They also chair tribunals and inquiries. Members of chambers hold or have held various government appointments including Junior counsel to the Inland Revenue, Common Law and membership of the A&B Panels of Treasury Counsel, Common Law. Members of chambers play a prominent role in the Bar's professional bodies and associations and chambers includes members of the Bar Council Professional Conduct Committee. Members of chambers are available to give lectures and seminars in their specialist fields both externally and part of chambers' own Law Society accredited seminar programme.

Work Undertaken: The major areas of practice are commercial and common law, especially administrative and local government; commercial; construction; consumer and business credit; discrimination; education; employment; environment; Europe; health and safety; human rights; industrial injury and disease; insurance and reinsurance; judicial review; landlord and tenant; pensions; personal injury and clinical negligence; police complaints and civil liberties; product liability; professional negligence; property; public interest immunity; sport; revenue; telecommunications; tribunals and inquiries; VAT/Customs & Excise. In addition, individual members of chambers offer expertise in the following areas of law: community care; contempt; crime (including white-collar crime); defamation; electoral and parliamentary; family; and housing.

Publications: Members of chambers regularly appear in leading cases and have written or co-written prominent text and practitioner's books in their specialist fields. Professor Ian Smith co-wrote *Smith and Wood on Industrial Law* and is the author of the Employment Law and Social Security titles in *Halsbury's Laws*. He and Nicholas Randall are editors of *Harvey on Industrial Relations and Employment Law* of which Timothy Brennan QC is also a co-editor. Richard Clayton is the co-author of *Civil Actions against the Police* (Sweet & Maxwell 2nd ed. 1992), *Judicial Review Procedure* (Wiley 2nd ed. 1997) and co-author of *The Bill of Rights in English Law* (Oxford University Press 2000), *Judicial Review of Local Government Decisions* (Wiley) and *Commercial Judicial Review* (Wiley). David Griffith-Jones is the author of *Law & the Business of Sport* (Butterworths 1998) to which Timothy Brennan QC and Colin Wynter are also contributors. Bruce Carr is a contributing author to *FT Law & Tax, Litigation Practice (Emergency Procedures)*. Ingrid Simler is a contributing author to *Tolley's Employment Law* (1994). James Tayler is a contributor to *Dix on Employment Law* (Butterworths), and Nicholas Randall is the author of the *Pensions* title in *Halsbury's Laws* and a contributor to *Butterworths Employment Law Guide*. Alison

Continued overleaf

Padfield is the co-author of the *Contempt of Court* title in *Halsbury's Laws.* Nicholas Randall and Ian Smith are co-authors of *Butterworth's Guide to Employment Relations Act 1999.* James Tayler, Ingrid Simler, Natasha Joffe and Andrew Burns co-wrote *Butterworths Discrimination Law 1999* (with assistance from Lydia Seymour, David Craig and Richard Greening). James Tayler is the co-author of the Equal Pay section of *Halsbury's Laws* and he, Andrew Burns, Ingrid Simler, Keith Byrant and Natasha Joffe co-wrote the Discrimination section of *Halsbury's Laws.* Three members of chambers, Professor Ian Smith, Christopher Goddard and Nicholas Randall, co-wrote *Health and Safety – The New Legal Framework* published by Butterworths. Stephen Killalea is a co-author of the 2001 edition. Members of chambers are also contributors to *Personal Injury Factbook* (Sweet & Maxwell).

Recruitment: Great emphasis is placed on the calibre of pupils received to ensure that the high standards are maintained and generous pupillage awards are offered.

Set No.
25

DOUGHTY STREET CHAMBERS (Geoffrey Robertson QC)

Doughty Street Chambers, 10-11 Doughty Street, London, WC1N 2PL
Tel: (020) 7404 1313 **Fax:** (020) 7404 2283 **DX:** 223 Chancery Lane
Email: enquiries@doughtystreet.co.uk **Website:** www.doughtystreet.co.uk

Head of Chambers	Geoffrey Robertson QC
Practice Manager	Christine Kings
Senior Clerk	Michelle Simpson
Tenants	70

Members:

Geoffrey Robertson QC (1973) (QC-1988)
Louis Blom-Cooper QC (1952) (QC-1970)
Richard Maxwell QC (1968) (QC-1988)
Peter Thornton QC (1969) (QC-1992)
Patrick O'Connor QC (1970) (QC-1993)
Helena Kennedy QC (1972) (QC-1991)
Christopher Sallon QC (1973) (QC-1994)
Andrew Nicol QC (1978) (QC-1995)
Edward Fitzgerald QC (1978) (QC-1995)
Stephen Irwin QC (1976) (QC-1997)
Edward Rees QC (1973) (QC-1998)
Michael Grieve QC (1975) (QC-1998)
Frank Panford QC (1972) (QC-1999)
James Wood QC (1975) (QC-1999)
Gavin Millar QC (1981) (QC-2000)
Oliver Thorold (1971)
Robert Latham (1976)
David Hislop (1989)(1979 NZ)
Nicolas Paul (1980)
Jill Evans (1986) †
Andrew Hall (1991) †
Kate Markus (1981)
Christopher Hough (1981)
Isabella Forshall (1982)
Jeannie Mackie (1995) †
Paul Bogan (1983)
David Bentley (1984)
Tracey Bloom (1984)
Heather Williams (1985)
Martin Westgate (1985)
Aswini Weereratne (1986)
Gerwyn Samuel (1986)
Francis FitzGibbon (1986)
Anthony Metzer (1987)
Keir Starmer (1987)
Sally Hatfield (1989)
Robin Oppenheim (1988)
Michelle Strange (1989)
Kieran Maidment (1989)
Paul Taylor (1989)
Hugh Barton (1989)
Paul Brooks (1989)
Sadakat Kadri (1989)
Phillippa Kaufmann (1991)
Quincy Whitaker (1991)
Stephen Reeder (1991)
Michael Ford (1992)
Ian Wise (1992)
Simon Cox (1992)
Lucy Moorman (1992)
Richard Hermer (1993)
Paul Bowen (1993)
John Walsh (1993)
Mark Henderson (1994)
Paula Sparks (1994)
Siza Agha (1994)
Shahram Taghavi (1994)
Althea Brown (1995)
Rebecca Trowler (1995)
Jonathan Glasson (1996)
Anthony Hudson (1996)
Stephen Cragg (1996)
Joseph Middleton (1997)
Ulele Burnham (1997)
Henrietta Hill (1997)
Steven Powles (1997)
Peter Lownds (1998)
Neil McInnes (1999)
Jamie Burton (1999)
Guy Ollivry QC (1957) (QC-1987) ‡
Fenton Ramsahoye (1953) ‡
Adrian Hardiman (1988)(1974 Ireland) ‡
Prof. Kevin Boyle (1992)(1971 N. Ireland) ‡
Christine Booker (1977) ‡
Julian Fulbrook (1977) ‡
Geraldine Van Bueren (1980) ‡
Gilbert Marcus (1999) ‡
Jill Peay (1991) ‡
Jonathan Cooper (1992) ‡

† Qualified Solicitor ‡ Associate Tenant

The Chambers: Emphasis is on civil liberties and human rights with specialists in criminal law; media law and defamation; public law; prisoners' rights and cases involving issues of mental health; discrimination; immigration; employment; housing; personal injury and clinical negligence. Chambers of the Year, 1995 and 1996. Silver Award, 1998. Bronze Award, 1999. Bronze winners, Law Firm Management Award, 1997. Bar Pro Bono Award, 1999. Investor in People, 2000.

Set No.
26

2 DYERS BUILDINGS (Nadine Radford QC)

2 Dyers Buildings, Holborn, London, EC1N 2JT
Tel: (020) 7404 1881 **Fax:** (020) 7404 1991 **DX:** 175 London Chancery Lane
Email: admin@2dyersbuildings.com **Website:** www.2dyersbuildings.com

Head of Chambers	Nadine Radford QC
Clerks	Graham Islin (07956) 985 929
	David Scothern (07931) 776 630
	Ryan Bartlett (07870) 866 048
Administration	Lisa Young
Tenants	28

2 DYERS BUILDINGS

Members:

Nadine Radford QC (1974) (QC-1995) +
Michael Gledhill QC (1976) (QC-2001) +
Raymond Lewis (1971)
Andrew Campbell-Tiech (1978) +
Sanderson Munro (1981)
Ian Jobling (1982)
Daniel Flahive (1982)
Julia Postill (1982)
Charles Burton (1983)
Adam Davis (1985)
Terence Boulter (1986)
Harriette Black (1986)
Lauren Soertsz (1987)
Michael Magarian (1988)
Simon Kitchen (1988)
Sam Stein (1988)
Tobias Long (1988)
Andrew Jefferies (1990)
Dominic Bell (1992)
Robert Tolhurst (1992)
Timothy Forte (1994)
Ibtihal Bsis (1994)
Peter Caldwell (1995)
Gavin Irwin (1996)
Gregory Fishwick (1996)
Trilby Millet (1996)
Zarif Khan (1996)
Ben Cooper (1999)
Ian Way (1988) *

* Door Tenant + Recorder

The Chambers: Chambers specialise in criminal law and associated matters. Members of chambers regularly represent clients charged with the most serious of offences, from fraud, money laundering and drugs to computer crime and murder. In addition chambers has a particular specialisation in High Court restraint and confiscation matters. Chambers' service includes the provision of counsel for overnight, weekend and bank holiday cases. Clerks may be contacted anytime.
Continuing Education: Chambers see continuing education as vital to their ongoing expansion. Lectures are held on a regular basis – both in house and for professional clients.

Work Undertaken: Members of chambers are increasingly instructed in other niche areas, including extradition, mental health tribunals, environmental law and matters relating to health and safety at work. In addition, members of chambers appear before coroner's inquests and a variety of regulatory and disciplinary tribunals.
Human Rights: Pro bono work is undertaken for the Free Representation Unit and Bar Pro Bono Unit. Members of chambers have advised Amnesty International and a number of foreign bar associations with regards to the incorporation of human rights legalisation in foreign jurisdictions. Chambers regularly undertakes Privy Council 'death row' cases.

International: Languages spoken include Arabic, French, German, Italian, Punjabi and Urdu.

Recruitment: Pupillage contact: Gavin Irwin. Training and Lectures: Andrew Jefferies.

Set No.
27

ELDON CHAMBERS (Lionel Read QC)

Falcon Court, 30-32 Fleet Street, London, EC4Y 1AA
Tel: (020) 7583 1355 **Fax:** (020) 7583 1672 **DX:** 440 LDE
Email: clerks@eldonchambers.com

Head of Chambers	Lionel Read QC
Senior Clerk	William King
Tenants	26

Members:

Lionel Read QC (1954) (QC-1973)MA (Cantab)
David Woolley QC (1962) (QC-1980)MA (Cantab)
Anthony Rumbelow QC (1967) (QC-1990)
Patrick Clarkson QC (1972) (QC-1991)
Christopher Whybrow QC (1965) (QC-1992)LLB (London)
William Hicks QC (1975) (QC-1995)MA (Cantab)
Rhodri Price Lewis QC (1975) (QC-2001)MA (Oxon) DipCrim (Cantab)
Roy Martin (1990) (QC-Scotland), LLB (Glasgow)
Martin Wood (1972)LLB (London)
John Pugh-Smith (1977)MA (Oxon)
Simon Pickles (1978)MA (Cantab)
John Dagg (1980)BSc, LLB MRTPI
Neil Cameron (1982)BA (Dunelm)
Stephen Morgan (1983)LLB (Warw), MA (Nott)
Richard Langham (1986)BA (Oxon)
Russell Harris (1986)MA (Cantab)
Megan Thomas (1987)BA (Sheff)
William Upton (1990)MA, LLM (Cantab)
Sasha White (1991)MA (Cantab)
Richard Harwood (1993)MA, LLM (Cantab)
Martin Edwards (1995)BA, MA LMRTPI

Continued overleaf

Members continued:

Matthew Reed (1995)MA (Cantab) MA (City)
Scott Lyness (1996)LLB (Hull)
Christiaan Zwart (1997)BA BArch(Newcastle) RIBA
Edmund Robb (1998)MA (Oxon)
Stephen Tromans (1999)MA (Cantab)

The Chambers: A specialist planning, local government, environmental and public law set. Members undertake both advocacy and advisory work and accept Direct Professional Access.

Work Undertaken: Town and country planning; environment; integrated pollution control; waste disposal; contaminated land; compulsory purchase and compensation; highways; public health; local government; statutory undertakers; administrative law and judicial review; parliamentary work; landlord and tenant; rating; related human rights.

International: Members of chambers also practise in Scotland, Northern Ireland and the Isle of Man.

Recruitment: Pupillage applications to chambers. Chambers offer up to two first six-months' and up to two second six-months' pupillages each year. Chambers may offer a 12-months' pupillage. Awards of up to £9,000 are available.

Set No. 28

ELY PLACE CHAMBERS (Ronald Thwaites QC)

30 Ely Place, London, EC1N 6TD
Tel: (020) 7400 9600 **Fax:** (020) 7400 9630 **DX:** 291 Chancery Lane
Email: admin@elyplace.com

Head of Chambers	Ronald Thwaites QC
Senior Clerk	Christopher Drury
Administration	Richard Sheehan
Tenants	10

Members:

Ronald Thwaites QC (1970) (QC-1987)
William McCormick (1985)
Simon Cheetham (1991)
Russell Stone (1992)
Iain Daniels (1992)
Hefin Rees (1992)
Garry Herbert (1996)
Charles Barker (1997)
Simon Butler (1996)
Scott Pearman (1999)

The Chambers: Ely Place Chambers was established in July 2000 within modernised accommodation, including a purpose-built seminar/conference suite from which a continuous programme of Law Society accredited lectures is provided. Members accept instructions both to advise and represent clients across a wide spectrum of civil work including personal injuries, clinical negligence, contracts, employment, housing, landlord and tenant, actions involving police forces, defamation, sports related disputes, environmental law and public enquiries. Chambers are fully computerised, enabling a speedy response from both members and the clerking team, who can assist in the choice of counsel on request.

Set No. 29

ENTERPRISE CHAMBERS (Anthony Mann QC)

9 Old Square, Lincoln's Inn, London, WC2A 3SR
Tel: (020) 7405 9471 **Fax:** (020) 7242 1447 **DX:** LDE 301
Email: enterprise.london@dial.pipex.com **Website:** www.enterprisechambers.com

Head of Chambers	Anthony Mann QC
Senior Clerk	Antony Armstrong
Practice Development Clerk	Barry Clayton
Clerks	Dylan Wendleken
	Mark Belford
	Robert McGill
Tenants	26

Members:

Anthony Mann QC (1974) (QC-1992)
Bernard Weatherill QC (1974) (QC-1996)
Charles Morgan (1978)
Caroline Hutton (1979)
Michael James (1976) †
Linden Ife (1982)
Peter Arden (1983)
Geoffrey Zelin (1984)
Jacqueline Baker (1985)
Nigel Gerald (1985)
Jonathan Holmes (1985)
James Barker (1984)
Adrian Jack (1986)
Hugo Groves (1980) †
Zia Bhaloo (1990)
James Pickering (1991)
Soraya McKinnell (1991)
Hugh Jory (1992)
Bridget Williamson (1993) †
Jonathan Klein (1992)
Sarah Richardson (1993)
Edward Francis (1995)
Shanti Mauger (1996)
Shaiba Ilyas (1998)
Timothy Calland (1999)
Jonathan Rodger (1999)
Niall McCulloch (2000)

† Practised as a solicitor before joining chambers.

The Chambers: Enterprise Chambers is a leading commercial Chancery set, specialising in company and commercial law, insolvency, landlord and tenant and property, professional negligence and general Chancery work. Chambers have qualified arbitrators and members use alternative dispute resolution procedures in appropriate cases. Chambers have branches in Leeds and Newcastle that affords them the unique advantage of providing a high quality service to clients from two major legal centres in the North East as well as from London. As part of their service, chambers offer cost-effective video conferencing facilities to clients with the ability of linking all chambers sites with each other. Enterprise Chambers aims to combine an excellent quality of service and to anticipate clients' needs with a progressive and flexible approach to practice at the Bar. Members of chambers recognise the importance of working as a team and being approachable and accessible to solicitors and clients. Chambers know that clients often find it useful to be given fee estimates and their clerks are happy to provide hourly rates or give overall estimates for items of work. Members regularly speak at seminars and chambers are authorised by the Law Society as a course provider.

Set No.
30

ERSKINE CHAMBERS (Robin Potts QC)

Erskine Chambers, 30 Lincoln's Inn Fields, London, WC2A 3PD
Tel: (020) 7242 5532 **Fax:** (020) 7831 0125 **DX:** 308 Lon Ch'ry Lane
Email: clerks@erskine-chambers.co.uk

Head of Chambers	Robin Potts QC
Senior Clerk	Mike Hannibal
Tenants	22

Members:

Robin Potts QC (1968) (QC-1982)BA, BCL (Oxon)
Thomas Stockdale Bt (1966)MA (Oxon)
David Oliver QC (1972) (QC-1986)BA (Cantab)
David Richards QC (1974) (QC-1992)MA (Cantab)
John Cone (1975)LLB
Leslie Kosmin QC (1976) (QC-1994)MA, LLM (Cantab), LLM (Harvard)
Michael Todd QC (1977) (QC-1997)BA (Keele)
David Mabb QC (1979) (QC-2001)MA (Cantab)
Martin Moore (1982)BA (Oxon)
David Chivers (1983)BA (Cantab)
Ceri Bryant (1984)MA, LLM (Cantab)
Richard Snowden (1986)MA (Cantab), LLM (Harvard)
Catherine Roberts (1986)MA, LLM (Cantab)
Philip Gillyon (1988)BA (Cantab)
Mary Stokes (1989)MA (Oxon), LLM (Harvard)
Andrew Thompson (1991)MA, LLM (Cantab)
Dan Prentice (1982)LLB (Belfast) JD (Chicago), MA (Oxon)
Nigel Dougherty (1993)BA, LLM (Cantab)
Leon Kuschke (1993)BCOM, LLB
James Potts (1994)BA (Oxon)
Andrew Thornton (1994)LLB (Hull)
Edward Davies (1998)BA (Cantab), BCh (Oxon)
Richard Nolan (1999)BA, MA (Cantab) *

* Door Tenant

The Chambers: Erskine Chambers has a long-established reputation as a company law set. It covers all aspects of company law; corporate finance; corporate insolvency; financial services and related commercial and professional negligence matters. Alongside its reputation in company law, the set is known for its commercial litigation experience over a range of practice areas and business sectors. There are 23 members of chambers including six QCs. The practices of the majority of the individual members of chambers are litigation-based, although they also continue to maintain their strength in advisory and drafting matters. It is chambers' aim to provide a professional service in a personal and approachable manner and the clerks are always available to discuss the practices of individual members. The office is open Monday to Friday 8.30am to 7.00pm and at other times an answerphone message provides numbers to contact.

Work Undertaken: In the company law field, chambers cover a full range of litigation, advisory work and drafting. Members of chambers deal with all areas where company law issues may arise, including directors' duties; shareholders' disputes; takeovers; mergers and acquisitions; corporate reconstructions; loan capital and banking securities; schemes of arrangement; reductions of capital; insurance schemes. Erskine Chambers' standing in the corporate insolvency field is demonstrated by their involvement in the largest and most high-profile insolvencies of recent years. The set has traditionally attracted substantial litigation work and members advise on, and appear in, a considerable number of general commercial and professional negligence disputes. Direct Professional Access is accepted from members of recognised professional institutions.

International: There is a strong international dimension to Erskine Chambers' work – the type of business on which the set advises and the clients for whom they act inevitably raise issues or involve disputes in other parts of the world. Members of chambers are frequently engaged as experts, or advocates, in other jurisdictions.

Recruitment: All applications for pupillage in 2002/3 should be made directly using Chambers' application form.

Set No.
31

ESSEX COURT CHAMBERS (Gordon Pollock QC)

24 Lincoln's Inn Fields, London, WC2A 3EG
Tel: (020) 7813 8000 **Fax:** (020) 7813 8080 **DX:** 320
Email: clerksroom@essexcourt-chambers.co.uk
Website: www.essexcourt-chambers.co.uk

Head of Chambers	Gordon Pollock QC
Senior Clerk	David Grief
Clerks	Joe Ferrigno
	Nigel Jones
	Sam Biggerstaff
Office Manager	Jean Muircroft
Tenants	65

Members:

Gordon Pollock QC (1968) (QC-1979)
Michael Thomas QC (1955) (QC-1973)
Ian Hunter QC (1967) (QC-1980)
Stewart Boyd QC (1967) (QC-1981)
V.V. Veeder QC (1971) (QC-1986)
Michael Collins QC (1971) (QC-1988)
Richard Siberry QC (1974) (QC-1989)
Jonathan Gilman QC (1965) (QC-1990)
Bernard Eder QC (1975) (QC-1990)
Roderick Cordara QC (1975) (QC-1994)
Simon Crookenden QC (1975) (QC-1996)
Jeffrey Gruder QC (1977) (QC-1997)
Andrew Hochhauser QC (1977) (QC-1997)
Jack Beatson QC (1973) (QC-1998)
Richard Jacobs QC (1979) (QC-1998)
Christopher Greenwood QC (1978) (QC-1999)
David Mildon QC (1980) (QC-2000)
Susan Prevezer QC (1983) (QC-2000)
Anthony Dicks QC (1961) (QC-1994)
Franklin Berman QC (1966) (QC-1992)
Geraldine Andrews QC (1981) (QC-2001)
Graham Dunning QC (1982) (QC-2001)
Victor Lyon (1980)
Mark Smith (1981)
Mark Templeman (1981)
Steven Berry (1984)
David Joseph (1984)
Richard Millett (1985)
Huw Davies (1985)
Joe Smouha (1986)
Philippa Watson (1988)
Hugh Mercer (1985)
Martin Griffiths (1986)
Karen Troy-Davies (1981)
John Lockey (1987)
Simon Bryan (1988)
David Foxton (1989)
Christopher Smith (1989)
Malcolm Shaw (1988)
Sara Cockerill (1990)
John Snider (1982)
Vernon James Hennessy Flynn (1991)
Brian Dye (1991)
Nigel Eaton (1991)
Charles Ciumei (1991)
Claire Blanchard (1992)
Perdita Cargill-Thompson (1993)
Vaughan Lowe (1993)
Toby Landau (1993)
Paul Stanley (1993)
Martin Hunter (1994)
Philippa Hopkins (1994)
Paul McGrath (1994)
James Collins (1995)
Tim Eicke (1993)
Stephen Houseman (1995)
Paul Key (1997)
Martin Lau (1996)
David Scorey (1997)
Sam Wordsworth (1997)
Nathan Pillow (1997)
Salim Moollan (1998)
Ricky Diwan (1998)
Neil Hart (1998)
Edmund King (1999)

The Chambers: A full-service commercial set, acting for clients ranging from institutions and multinational corporations to private companies and individuals. Members advise across the whole spectrum of international, commercial and European law, and act as advocates in litigation and commercial arbitration worldwide. Essex Court Chambers has a particularly strong reputation in international commercial arbitration; insurance and reinsurance; wet and dry shipping; banking; international trade; energy and utilities; media and entertainment; commodities; public international law; professional negligence; tax and VAT; aviation and employment. Essex Court Chambers (formerly known as Four Essex Court) was established as a separate chambers in 1961, when the set at Three Essex Court split into two sets. The founding members were Michael Kerr (later Lord Justice Kerr), Robert MacCrindle, Michael Mustill (now Lord Mustill), Anthony Evans (now Lord Justice Evans), and Anthony Diamond (later Judge Diamond). Chambers grew rapidly, developing a strong reputation as a leading commercial set and attracting a number of prominent legal figures: Mark Saville (now Lord Saville), Johan Steyn (now Lord Steyn), Anthony Colman (now Mr Justice Colman) and John Thomas (now Mr Justice Thomas). Now under the leadership of Gordon Pollock the set comprises 65 members and has recently acquired the two adjacent buildings to 24 – 26 Lincoln's Inn Fields, the location the set moved to in 1994. Chambers is not a 'firm' or a 'partnership' but a collection of individuals. Individual barristers have been recognised as leaders in their fields of specialisation and David Grief and his clerks have acquired a reputation for responsiveness and integrity. Focus is always on client requirements. Care and attention is given to matching the most appropriate barrister to the case and the client's individual needs. This is achievable because of the close working relationship between tenants and clerks within chambers. Office Hours: 7.45am – 7.00pm

Work Undertaken: The fields of work for which chambers are best known are arbitration; banking and financial services; European law; insurance and reinsurance; international trade and transport; maritime law; professional negligence. Other areas of work covered include: administrative law and judicial review; agriculture and farming; Australian trade practices law; aviation; Chinese law; commodity transaction; computer law; construction and engineering; customs duty; employment law; energy and utilities; entertainment and sports law; European law; Hong Kong law; human rights; immigration and nationality law; industrial relations; injunctions and arrests; insolvency law; insurance and re-insurance; intellectual property; international commercial fraud; Irish law; oil and gas; public law; public international law; rail disputes; sale of goods and product liability; South Asian law; tribunals and inquiries; VAT law. Also, members act as arbitrators in both domestic and international arbitrations. Some members also act as mediators.

International: The international nature of chambers sets it apart from other practices. Not only does the set have members with language skills in all the major European tongues and Chinese but it also has barristers qualified to practise in non-UK jurisdictions. Members have appeared as advocates in the European Commission; European Court of Justice; European Court of Human Rights and International Court of Justice; in the courts of Hong Kong, Malaysia, Australia, Belfast, Dublin, Gibraltar, St Vincent, Brunei, Kenya and the Cayman Islands; in arbitrations in places such as Paris, Geneva, Singapore, New Orleans and Beijing.

Recruitment: Up to four funded 12 month pupillages are offered each year for an October start. Chambers welcome applications through OLPAS in 2002 for pupillage in October 2003 and for deferred pupillage in October 2004. Chambers offer up to 30 mini-pupillages during the months of June and July. Applicants who have completed at least one year of a law degree or have passed, or are in the course of studying for the Common Professional Examination, should contact Miss Lucy Paterson, the secretary to the Pupillage committee, by letter, fax or email (lpaterson@essexcourt-chambers.co.uk).

Set No. 32

ONE ESSEX COURT (Lord Grabiner QC)

One Essex Court, Temple, London, EC4Y 9AR
Tel: (020) 7583 2000 **Fax:** (020) 7583 0118 **DX:** 430 (Ch.Ln.)
Email: clerks@oeclaw.co.uk **Website:** www.oeclaw.co.uk

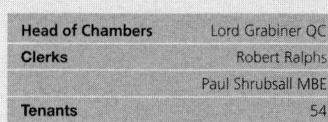

Head of Chambers	Lord Grabiner QC
Clerks	Robert Ralphs
	Paul Shrubsall MBE
Tenants	54

Members:

Lord Grabiner QC (1968) (QC-1981)
Gerald Butler QC (1955) (QC-1975)
Christopher Carr QC (1968) (QC-1983)
Nicholas Strauss QC (1965) (QC-1984)
Roydon Thomas QC (1960) (QC-1985)
Peter Leaver QC (1967) (QC-1987)
Ian Glick QC (1970) (QC-1987)
Richard Field QC (1977) (QC-1987)
Elizabeth Gloster QC (1971) (QC-1989)
Geoffrey Hobbs QC (1977) (QC-1991)
Mark Barnes QC (1974) (QC-1992)
Alastair MacGregor QC (1974) (QC-1994)
Thomas Sharpe QC (1976) (QC-1994)
Thomas Ivory QC (1978) (QC-1998)
Jeffery Onions QC (1981) (QC-1998)
Susanna FitzGerald QC (1973) (QC-1999)
Stephen Auld QC (1979) (QC-1999)
Rhodri Davies QC (1979) (QC-1999)
Alan Redfern (1995)
Malcolm Gammie (1997)
Michael Malone (1975)
Ian Grainger (1978)
Alan Griffiths (1981)
Clare Reffin (1981)
John McCaughran (1982)
Richard Gillis (1982)
Andrew Lenon (1982)
Michael Sullivan (1983)
Siobhan Ward (1984)
Kenneth MacLean (1985)
Charles Graham (1986)
Anthony de Garr Robinson (1987)
Laurence Rabinowitz (1987)
Neil Kitchener (1991)
Alain Choo Choy (1991)
Hannah Brown (1992)
David Wolfson (1992)
David Cavender (1993)
Daniel Toledano (1993)
Zoe O'Sullivan (1993)
Emma Himsworth (1993)
Jacob Grierson (1993)
Lisa Lake (1994)
Edmund Nourse (1994)
Graeme Halkerston (1994)
Sa'ad Hossain (1995)
Daniel Jowell (1995)
Camilla Bingham (1996)
Philip Roberts (1996)
Michael Fealy (1997)
Anushka Rosen (1997)
Orlando Gledhill (1998)
Simon Colton (1999)
Piu Das Gupta (1999)

Work Undertaken: The range of work carried out embraces every aspect of domestic and international commerce and finance. The principal areas of practice are arbitration; commercial law; company and insolvency; European Union law; intellectual property and revenue law.

Continued overleaf

Recruitment: Chambers offer four 12 month pupillages each year. Chambers operate an award scheme which offers to each pupil the sum of £35,000 in his or her year of pupillage. Part of the award may, at the discretion of chambers, be advanced during a prospective pupil's year of vocational training. Applicants for pupillage should (save in exceptional circumstances) have at least an upper second class degree. Chambers participate in OLPAS, and all applications for pupillage should be made through OLPAS.

Set No. 33

4 ESSEX COURT (Nigel Teare QC)

4 Essex Court, Temple, London, EC4Y 9AJ
Tel: (020) 7653 5653 **Fax:** (020) 7653 5654 **DX:** 292 London (Chancery Lane)
Email: clerks@4sx.co.uk **Website:** www.4sx.co.uk

Head of Chambers	Nigel Teare QC
Senior Clerk	Gordon Armstrong
Tenants	40

Members:

Nigel Teare QC (1974) (QC-1991)
M.N. Howard QC (1971) (QC-1986)
Belinda Bucknall QC (1974) (QC-1988)
Charles Macdonald QC (1972) (QC-1992)
Jeremy Russell QC (1975) (QC-1994)
Lionel Persey QC (1981) (QC-1997)
Charles Haddon-Cave QC (1978) (QC-1999)
Simon Rainey QC (1982) (QC-2000)
John Suttner SC (1979)
George Economou (1965)
Simon Gault (1970)
Michael Nolan (1981)
Marion Smith (1981)
Simon Kverndal (1982)
Nigel Meeson (1982)
Nigel Jacobs (1983)
Michael McParland (1983)
Luke Parsons (1985)
Simon Croall (1986)
David Goldstone (1986)
Nigel Cooper (1987)
Matthew Reeve (1987)
Chirag V. Karia (1988)
Poonam Melwani (1989)
Robert Lawson (1989)
James Turner (1990)
Michael Davey (1990)
Robert Thomas (1992)
Nevil Phillips (1992)
John Russell (1993)
Thomas Macey-Dare (1994)
John Kimbell (1995)
Nichola Warrender (1995)
Jonathan Chambers (1996)
Stewart Buckingham (1996)
Guy Blackwood (1997)
Peter Ferrer (1998)
Nicholas Craig (1998)
Nathan Tamblyn (1999)
Christopher M Smith (1999)
His Honour Harvey Crush *
Nicholas Gaskell (1976) *
Paul Griffin (1979) *
Francis D. Rose (1983) *
Richard Gardiner (1969) *
Harold Caplan (1955) *
Asif Qureshi (1978) *

* Door Tenant

The Chambers: Members of chambers at 4 Essex Court (formerly situated at 2 Essex Court) are available to give specialist advice (including direct advice to foreign lawyers and members of certain other professional bodies) and to undertake advocacy work in their respective fields. They conduct all types of commercial litigation in London and abroad, together with arbitrations and marine, aviation and other inquiries. Information on the specialist fields of practice of particular members can be obtained from chambers' staff.

Work Undertaken: Members of chambers specialise in a wide spectrum of commercial law, with a particular emphasis on aviation and maritime law, international trade and insurance.
Commercial Law, Shipping & International Trade: Including banking; carriage of goods by sea, land and air; marine and non-marine casualties; marine and general insurance and reinsurance; salvage; collision and oil-pollution; domestic and international sale of goods; ship and civil construction and financing.
Business Law & Financial Services: Including insurance and reinsurance; banking; securities and commodities trading; company law and insolvency.
EU Law: Including competition law; intellectual property; public procurement; mergers and acquisitions; the business law aspects of 1992 and the Single European Market.
Other: Disaster and multi-party litigation; air law; entertainment and media law; sports law; employment law; Judicial Review in related areas.

International: There are members of the French, Spanish, Greek, Cypriot, New South Wales, Hong Kong and New York Bars in chambers. There is a close association with Temple Chambers in Hong Kong.

Set No.
34

5 ESSEX COURT (Christopher Moss QC)

5 Essex Court, Temple, London, EC4Y 9AH
Tel: (020) 7410 2000 **Fax:** (020) 7410 2010 **DX:** 1048
Email: barristers@5essexcourt.co.uk **Website:** www.5essexcourt.co.uk

Head of Chambers	Christopher Moss QC
Senior Clerk	Michael Dean
Tenants	33

Members:

Christopher Moss QC (1972) (QC-1994)
Jeremy Gompertz QC (1962) (QC-1988)
Marie Catterson (1972)
Nicholas Ainley (1973)
John Bassett (1975)
Simon Freeland (1978)
Nicholas Wilcox (1977)
Gerard Pounder (1980)
Charles Apthorp (1983)
John Butcher (1984)
Gareth Hughes (1985)
Fiona Barton (1986)
Andrew Waters (1987)
Stephanie Farrimond (1987)
Anne Studd (1988)
Christopher Kerr (1988)
Kate Davey (1988)
Georgina Kent (1989)
Giles Powell (1990)
Lyn Hayhow (1990)
Sarah Buckingham (1991)
Jason Beer (1992)
Samantha Leek (1993)
Stephen Akinsanya (1993)
Jeremy Johnson (1994)
Prabjot Virdi (1995)
Stephen Rose (1995)
Nadeem Ahmad (1996)
Mandy McLean (1996)
Lawrence Selby (1997)
Mathew Holdcroft (1998)
Barnabas Branston (1999)
Paul Llewellyn (1999)

The Chambers: Founded in 1954 at its present address by the late Mr Justice Michael Eastham, 5 Essex Court is a thriving and well-established set of chambers with a wide client base. It offers up-to-date facilities including the latest information technology and dedicated conference rooms together with a strong emphasis on client care. Several senior members of chambers sit as recorders in the Crown Court (including the Central Criminal Court) and the County Court. Additionally, one of its Queen's Counsel sits as chairman of the Mental Health Independent Review Tribunal. A number of members of chambers have been appointed to the panel of Treasury Counsel, Common Law. Others are approved by the Attorney General to prosecute on behalf of Her Majesty's Customs and Excise and the Department of Trade and Industry. Work is also undertaken for the Serious Fraud Office.

Work Undertaken: Members of chambers are concerned in all aspects of police and civil liberties law. They act predominantly for police authorities in actions for damages arising out of allegations of trespass, false imprisonment and malicious prosecution. Members of the set appear in inquests, disciplinary tribunals, applications for judicial review and public inquiries. They are also regularly asked to advise upon sensitive issues of police policy. The criminal team is experienced in all aspects and levels of criminal work, both for prosecution and defence. The strength and depth of the criminal team, throughout the set, is such that a true service can be offered to its professional clients. No matter is so small nor is any case so complicated or of such high profile that chambers cannot provide the necessary level of seniority and expertise, from the most junior tenent to highly experienced Queen's Counsel. The personal injury team undertakes work both for claimants and for defendants, including public authorities. It accepts instructions, and offers a swift screening service, in matters subject to conditional fee agreements. Aside from the three main practice groups individual members are able to advise on other areas. The clerking team will be able to advise as required.

Recruitment: Chambers have accreditation by Law Society and the Institute of Legal Executives. Members of chambers regularly assist with either in-house training in conjunction with solicitors or in organising conference and lectures specific to client needs. Tenancy applications should be sent to the Head of Chambers. All applications from established practitioners will be treated in confidence. Applications for pupillage should be made via the OLPAS scheme. Up to two pupillage awards are offered of £12,000 for 12 months commencing in October.

Set No.
35

20 ESSEX STREET (Iain Milligan QC)

20 Essex Street, London, WC2R 3AL
Tel: (020) 7583 9294 **Fax:** (020) 7583 1341 **DX:** 0009 (Ch.Ln.)
Email: clerks@20essexst.com **Website:** www.20essexst.com

Head of Chambers	Iain Milligan QC
Chambers Manager	
	Janet Newton (020) 8533 3789
	Mobile (07374) 274841
Clerks	Neil Palmer (020) 8660 2633
	Mobile (07775) 713925
	Brian Lee (020) 8642 5865
	Mobile (0797) 759 0229
Tenants	45

20 Essex Street

Members:

Iain Milligan QC (1973) (QC-1991)
Sir Elihu Lauterpacht QC (1950) (QC-1970)
Sir Arthur Watts QC (1957) (QC-1988)
David Johnson QC (1967) (QC-1978)
Murray Pickering QC (1963) (QC-1985)
Nicholas Legh-Jones QC (1968) (QC-1987)
Richard Plender QC (1972) (QC-1989)
Angus Glennie QC (1974) (QC-1991)
Peter Gross QC (1977) (QC-1992)
Alexander Layton QC (1976) (QC-1995)
Timothy Young QC (1977) (QC-1996)
Nicholas Hamblen QC (1981) (QC-1997)
Stephen Males QC (1978) (QC-1998)
Christopher Hancock QC (1983) (QC-2000)
Julian Cooke (1965)
Richard Wood (1975)
Michael Tselentis SC (1995) (SC – South Africa – 1989)
Edmund Broadbent (1980)
Stephen Morris (1981)
David Owen (1983)
Duncan Matthews (1986)
William Godwin (1986)
Andrew Baker (1988)
Daniel Bethlehem (1988)
Michael Coburn (1990)
Lawrence Akka (1991)
Clare Ambrose (1992)
Karen Maxwell (1992)
Graham Charkham (1993)(CEDR Accredited)
Guy Morpuss (1991)
Sara Masters (1993)
Philip Edey (1994)
Charles Kimmins (1994)
Michael Collett (1995)
Michael Ashcroft (1997)
Sudhanshu Swaroop (1997)
Julian Kenny (1997)
Malcolm Jarvis (1998)
David Lewis (1999)
Susannah Jones (1999)
Thomas Raphael (1999)
Sean Snook (2000)
Henry Byam-Cook (2000)
Michael Lee (2001)
David St John Sutton (2001)

The Chambers: This long established, progressive set of chambers is one of the leading sets in commercial law. Members advise on all aspects of international trade, commerce and finance with specialist expertise in banking, shipping, insurance, public international law and European Community law. Although much of chambers' work is in the Commercial Court, the practice and clientele are international. Chambers aim to combine an outstanding standard of work with a friendly and approachable attitude to clients, lay and professional. Notable recent events include the continuing expansion of chambers' distinguished panel of senior arbitrators with the addition of Sir Philip Otton (from the Court of Appeal), Sir Peter North CBE QC (practising barrister and Principal of Jesus College, Oxford), Malcolm Holmes QC (Australia), The Honorable Charles N Brower (formerly *White & Case*, Washington), Michael Lee (formerly *Norton Rose*) and David St John Sutton (formerly *Allen & Overy*). Office Hours: 8.15am-6.45pm.

Work Undertaken:

Commercial: Members advise on a range of commercial matters including the following: admiralty; agency; arbitration; aviation; bailment; banking and financial services; carriage by land, sea and air; commodities and futures; company law and partnership; conflicts of laws; construction; disciplinary proceedings; entertainment law; insurance and reinsurance; international sales and commodity trading; IT; oil and gas; professional negligence; sale of goods; shipping; all types of domestic and international commercial agreements.

European Union: A number of members are specialists in European Community law and are regularly engaged to provide advice and representation to Community institutions, member states and other litigants on such issues as agriculture, the free movement of goods, those relating to individuals, services and capital, competition and state aids.

Domestic & International Arbitration & Mediation: All senior members, together with Lord Donaldson, Lord Bridge, Lord Griffiths (CEDR accredited), Sir Brian Neill (CEDR registered), Sir Christopher Staughton and Kenneth Rokison QC (CEDR accredited) accept appointment as arbitrators under a variety of auspices, including, ICC, LCIA, Stockholm Chamber of Commerce and ICSID, as well as in accordance with LMAA terms or UNCITRAL rules. Mediations and inquiries are conducted through recognised appropriate bodies as well as ad hoc.

Publications: A number of members are authors and editors of leading publications and journals, full details of which are available on chambers' website, address given above.

International: Work is handled in French, German, Italian, Spanish, Dutch and Hindi. Members of chambers engaged in this field appear before the International Court of Justice and other international tribunals. Some members specialise in public international law, dealing with such matters as boundaries, interpretation of treaties, state immunity, international investment and human rights. Those practising in these areas appear as advocates in the International Court of Justice; the European Court of Human Rights; Dispute Settlement Panels of the World Trade Organisation; the International Tribunal on the Law of the Sea and comparable tribunals. Members also practise in private international law, including the Brussels and Lugano Conventions on Jurisdiction and the Enforcement of Judgements and the Rome Convention on the Law Applicable to Contractual Obligations. Some have experience of conducting litigation before the Court of Justice of the European Communities on the Brussels Convention. Members will accept instructions to appear in courts abroad including Hong Kong, Singapore, Malaysia and other jurisdictions subject to admission rules, whilst some members have been called to the local bars of Australia, Gibraltar and South Africa.

Set No. 36

23 ESSEX STREET (Michael Lawson QC)

23 Essex Street, London, WC2R 3AS
Tel: (020) 7413 0353 **Fax:** (020) 7413 0374 **DX:** 148 (LDE) Chancery Lane
Email: clerks@23essexstreet.co.uk **Website:** www.23essexstreet.co.uk

Head of Chambers	Michael Lawson QC
Practice Manager	Nicholas Hopgood
Deputy Practice Manager	Daren Milton
Tenants	60

Members:

Michael Lawson QC (1969) (QC-1991) +
Michael Hill QC (1958) (QC-1979)
Nicholas Purnell QC (1968) (QC-1985) +
Michael Austin-Smith QC (1969) (QC-1990) +
Susan Edwards QC (1972) (QC-1993) +
Stuart Lawson Rogers QC (1969) (QC-1994) +
Charles Miskin QC (1975) (QC-1998) +
Nigel Sangster QC (1976) (QC-1998) †
Michael Wood QC (1976) (QC-1999) +
Christopher Kinch QC (1976) (QC-1999) +
P. James Richardson (1975)
Brendan Finucane (1976)
Simon Davis (1978) +
John Causer (1979)
Robin Johnson (1979)
Daniel Janner (1980)
Simon Russell Flint (1980) +
John Price (1982)
Oscar Del Fabbro (1982)
Graham Cooke (1983)
Joanna Glynn (1983) +
Sally Howes (1983)
Elroy Claxton (1983) +
Rupert Pardoe (1984)
James Lloyd (1985)
Philip St. John-Stevens (1985)
Dafydd Enoch (1985)
Alan Kent (1986)
Johannah Cutts (1986)
Wayne Cranston-Morris (1986)
Paul Ozin (1987)
Karen Holt (1987)
Cairns Nelson (1987)
Heather Norton (1988)
Iain Morley (1988)
William Carter (1989)
Hugh Forgan (1989)
Keith Hotten (1990)
Isobel Ascherson (1990)
Lynn Griffin (1991)
Ian Acheson (1992)
Mark Fenhalls (1992)
Andrew Hurst (1992)
Richard Milne (1992)
Fiona Horlick (1992)
Giles Curtis-Raleigh (1992)
Andrew Rodger (1993)
Eloise Marshall (1994)
Hannah Swain (1994)
Rufus Stilgoe (1994)
Alexia Durran (1995)
Clare Strickland (1995)
Alan May (1995)
Ian Hope (1996)
Marcus Thompson (1996)
Gareth Branston (1996)
Emily Belson (1997)
Sarah Campbell (1997)
Kathrine Hunter (1997)
Tetteh Turkson (1998)
Alison Jones (1988) *
Simon Medland (1991) *

* Door Tenant + Recorder † Practising principally in Leeds

Work Undertaken:

Criminal: Mainstream crime, both defending and prosecuting. A number of silks and juniors specialise in commercial fraud/white collar crime on a national and international level. Expertise is available in third party disclosure, mutual assistance and ECHR implications. Teams available. Advice and representation available for regulatory hearings, disciplinary proceedings (Lloyd's of London, police, GMC and GDC), inquests, extradition hearings, DTI investigations and director disqualification proceedings. Individuals also specialise in public and administrative, employment, licensing, planning, defamation and environmental law.

Civil: Members are instructed in areas of common law, particularly where they are crime related: civil fraud, actions against the police for malicious prosecution, false imprisonment etc.

Publications: James Richardson is editor of *Archbold and Criminal Law Week*. Joanna Glynn and William Carter are contributing editors for *Archbold*. Daniel Janner is one of the two editors of the *Criminal Appeal Reports*.

Recruitment: Tenancy applications to Michael Wood.

Pupillage: Chambers offer three 12 month (funded) pupillages. Travel allowances are available. Sponsored pupils are accepted additionally. Chambers is a member of OLPAS. Full details are published in the Bar Council's Chambers' Pupillages and Awards Handbook. Applications to Simon Russell Flint.

Mini-pupillages: A limited number are available. Applications to Cairns Nelson on or after 1st April 2001.

Training: Chambers have an internal continuing education programme for members and pupils. Members of chambers devise and conduct external programmes.

Set No.
37

35 ESSEX STREET (Christopher Wilson-Smith QC)

35 Essex Street, Temple, London, WC2R 3AR
Tel: (020) 7353 6381 **Fax:** (020) 7583 1786 **DX:** 351 London
Email: derekjenkins@35-essex-street.com **Website:** www.35essexstreet.com

Head of Chambers	Christopher Wilson-Smith QC
Senior Clerk	Derek Jenkins
Chambers' Administrator	Daniel Clark
Tenants	35

Members:

Christopher Wilson-Smith QC (1965) (QC-1986)
Nigel J Inglis-Jones QC (1959) (QC-1982)
David C Calcutt QC (1955) (QC-1972)
Alan D Rawley QC (1958) (QC-1977)
Philip C Mott QC (1970) (QC-1991)
Linda E Sullivan QC (1973) (QC-1994)
Richard Lissack QC (1978) (QC-1994)
Paul Garlick QC (1974) (QC-1996)
Robin S Tolson QC (1980) (QC-2001)
Hywel I Jenkins (1974)
John L Stephens (1975)
Richard M Mawhinney (1977)
William L Coley (1980)
Stephen Climie (1982)
David G Westcott (1982)
Christopher M Kemp (1984)
Harry Trusted (1985)
Andrew JM Spink (1985)
Alison McCormick (1988)
Susan C Freeborn (1989)
Richard G Hitchcock (1989)
Jonathan ES Hand (1990)
Thomas RG Leeper (1991)
Nathan W Tavares (1992)
Grace Malden (1993)
Matthew J Phillips (1993)
Nicolas Stallworthy (1993)
Abhijeet Mukherjee (1995)
Robert-Jan Temmink (1996)
Clare Vines (1997)
Peter Skelton (1997)
Harriet Jerram (1998)
David Grant (1999)
Cara Guthrie (2000)
Samantha Presland (2001)

The Chambers: 35 Essex Street is a thriving, well-established and progressive set which successfully combines the levels of expertise and specialisations expected of the leading sets with an accessible and open approach to all. Chambers have developed strongly over the years to meet successfully the demands of both lay and professional clients across all their common and commercial law practices. With proven high quality barristers, strength in depth and experience at all levels of call, chambers are renowned for providing a genuinely first-class service tailored specifically to the needs of each individual client. Approachable, receptive and flexible in its handling of casework, the set has shown itself adept at responding to the fast changing requirements of the legal world. The set is acknowledged to be among the leading chambers in the fields of pensions, clinical negligence, personal injury and corporate crime, and members of chambers also undertake work relating to child care, professional negligence, employment and extradition. Members of 35 Essex Street have considerable experience of arbitration and are also increasingly recognized for their expanding involvement in Public Inquiry work, having been involved in almost every major inquiry in the last 5 years.

Work Undertaken: Members of 35 Essex Street appear regularly in high profile cases covering the complete spectrum of work undertaken in chambers. In addition to appearing as advocates in the English Appellant Courts, the High Court, the County Courts and a wide variety of tribunals and arbitration work, chambers place particular emphasis on providing focused and practical advice both on paper and in conference on litigious and non-litigious matters. Work is also undertaken in foreign jurisdictions. Members of chambers regularly work for the Bar pro-bono unit and have also conducted litigation on a pro bono basis until funding has been made available. Chambers also have wide experience and a successful record of undertaking work on a conditional fee basis in many of their areas of specialisation, and of assisting solicitors in the initial risk assessment process.

Pensions & Employment: Chambers are among the leading sets in respect of occupational pension schemes and trusts. Nigel Inglis-Jones QC is the author of a leading pensions text book and is recognised as one of the experts in this field of law. Several of the leading juniors in this field are members of chambers. The pension team has been involved in all the recent major cases, including British Airways, National Grid, NPI and Merchant Navy.

Personal Injury & Clinical Negligence: A large group within chambers has extensive experience in both these fields, acting on behalf of both claimants and defendants in cases covering the full spectrum of work within these specialisations, including major group actions (Cape Litigation, Nationwide Organ Retention, Corby Limb Disorders and Devon Breast Screening) and related Public Inquiry work (Bristol Royal Infirmary and Shipman).

Professional Negligence: Members of chambers specialise in most areas of professional negligence, including surveyors', actuaries', accountants' and lawyers' negligence. 35 Essex Street is also among the leading sets covering all areas in which corporations and their directors are called to account, including cases relating to corporate killing, directors' responsibilities, regulatory provisions, governance, civil liability and professional negligence.

Corporate Crime, Commercial Fraud & Criminal Negligence: Chambers' considerable experience in this area of law extends to involvement in the Maxwell, Blue Arrow and Guinness fraud cases. Members of chambers are instructed in a number of large case for the SFO. Chambers are established at the forefront of criminal negligence work, having been involved in major prosecutions arising out of sea-borne disasters of Lyme Bay, Pescado, Maria Asumpta and Lone Signature, as well as the three recent rail crashes at Southall, Ladbroke Grove and Hatfield. In addition, chambers are involved in dozens of similar, if less high profile, cases.

Child Care & Child Abuse Litigation: An experienced team of barristers within chambers specialises in child care law, acting in particular for local authorities, guardians and the Official Solicitor (now CAFCASS). It instructed in the recent case of Re: W & B and Re: W, which will effect substantial changes in practice required for all professionals in this field. Chambers are instructed on civil actions on behalf of children arising out of abuse sustained in care and/or inadequate educational provision.

Extradition: Chambers are steadily building a reputation for successful advocacy in this specialised area of law, including for example The Government of India v Saifi.

Public Inquiries: Increasingly, members of chambers are being instructed in major public inquiry work including the Southall and Ladbroke Grove train inquiries, the BRI Inquiry, Alder Hey Inquiry, The Organ Retention Commission and the Shipman Inquiry.

International: Languages spoken include: French, German, Russian, Italian, Bengal, Hindi. Chambers have one Italian affiliate practising in Milan, Avv Mauro Rubino-Sammartano.

Set No. 38

39 ESSEX STREET (Nigel Pleming QC)

39 Essex Street, London, WC2R 3AT
Tel: (020) 7832 1111 **Fax:** (020) 7353 3978 **DX:** 298
Email: clerks@39essex.co.uk **Website:** www.39essex.co.uk

Head of Chambers	Nigel Pleming QC
Chambers Director	Michael Meeson
Tenants	46

39 ESSEX STREET
LONDON WC2R 3AT

Members:

Nigel Pleming QC (1971) (QC-1992)
Simon Goldblatt QC (1953) (QC-1972)
Edwin Glasgow QC (1969) (QC-1987)
Wyn Lewis Williams QC (1974) (QC-1992)
Richard Gray QC (1970) (QC-1993)
Richard Davies QC (1973) (QC-1994)
Richard Wilmot-Smith QC (1978) (QC-1994)
Michael Tillett QC (1965) (QC-1996)
Robert Jay QC (1981) (QC-1998)
Frances Patterson QC (1977) (QC-1998)
Vincent Nelson QC (1980) (QC-2001)
Alan Cooper (1969)
David Melville (1975)
Charles Brown (1976)
Roderick Noble (1977)
Colin McCaul (1978)
Neil Block (1980)
Geoffrey B. Brown (1981)
Christian Du Cann (1982)
Charles Cory-Wright (1984)
Alison Foster (1984)
Jonathan Bellamy (1986)
Stuart Catchpole (1987)
David Bradly (1987)
Steven Kovats (1989)
Jeremy Morgan (1989)FCI Arb
Eleanor Grey (1990)
Bernard Doherty (1990)
Fenella Morris (1990)
Jennifer Richards (1991)
Sean Wilken (1991)
Rohan Pershad (1991)
Daniel Oudkerk (1992)
Bruce Brodie (1993)
Matthew Seligman (1994)
Adam Robb (1995)
Gordon Nardell (1995)
Sam Grodzinski (1996)
Parishil Patel (1996)
Kristina Stern (1996)
Judith Ayling (1998)
Kate Grange (1998)
Caroline Trustcott (1998)
Nicola Greaney (1999)
Katie Scott (1999)
Colin Thomann (1999)
Sharise Weiner (1978) (SC (South Africa)-1998) *

* Door Tenant

The Chambers: 39 Essex Street is a long established set whose barristers have widespread expertise and experience in almost every aspect of commercial, public and common law. Members of chambers have wide experience of all courts and tribunals from the House of Lords, Privy Council, Court of Appeal and International and Domestic Arbitrations, through to Public Inquiries, Industrial and VAT tribunals. They have also participated in significant investigations before Parliamentary Select Committees. Several members of chambers are on the Main and Supplementary Treasury Panels of Counsel instructed on behalf of the Crown. Members also undertake pro bono work for public interest organisations.

Work Undertaken: Chambers' particular expertise lies in the fields of commercial law, administrative and public law, employment, personal injury and clinical negligence, construction and engineering, entertainment and sports law and European law. Within this broad range, members of chambers have developed specialisms in the following areas:

Commercial: Insurance and reinsurance, commodities and derivatives, funding disputes, banking, mergers and acquisitions, sale and carriage of goods, insolvency, company law, financial services law, professional negligence and professional indemnity work for auditors and legal advisers and international commercial arbitration.

Continued overleaf

Administrative & Public Law: All aspects of judicial review and public law, including civil liberties and human rights, commercial and environmental law, planning, education, local authorities, health trusts, mental health, community care, housing and housing associations, immigration, VAT and Customs & Excise.
Employment: All aspects of employment work for employers and employees, local authorities and central government. Particular emphasis is on public law related work, discrimination, restrictive covenants, wrongful dismissal and breach of fiduciary duties.
Personal Injury & Clinical Negligence: The full range of personal injury litigation, especially sea, air and crowd disasters, group actions, industrial disease, sports injuries, injuries of maximum severity, pharmaceuticals, product liability and high-profile and complex matters, ranging from sensitive consent-to-treatment cases to those involving serious disability and death.
Construction & Engineering: All categories of construction and engineering litigation and related claims, including professional negligence and indemnity work; from major international ventures to smaller domestic contracts, acting for employers, contractors, subcontractors and professional advisers. Members act as advocates, mediators and arbitrators in the United Kingdom, the EU and worldwide.
Entertainment & Sports Law: All entertainment and media-related work including performers' contracts, passing-off, breach of confidence, film and management agreements and broadcasting regulation. Sports-related work includes public liability of sports clubs for acts of their players, employer's liability, disciplinary tribunals, disputes concerning control of clubs, transfer fee disputes, EU free movement and other employment issues.
European Law: All areas of EU law before domestic and EU courts, including competition, discrimination and equality law, public procurement, free movement, state aids and milk quotas.
Public Inquiries: Members of chambers have been instructed in most of the major public inquiries over the past 10 years, including Hillsborough, BSE, the King's Cross fire and most recently, the Bristol Royal Infirmary Inquiry and the Saville Inquiry.

Publications: Numerous publications including *Waiver, Variation and Estoppel* (Wilken); *The Law of Entertainment and Broadcasting* (Nelson).

International: Languages spoken include French, German, Italian, Spanish and Gujarati. Many members of chambers also act as advocates in overseas jurisdictions including Hong Kong, Singapore, India, Malaysia, Australia, Bermuda and the USA.

Recruitment: Chambers are a member of OLPAS. They offer up to three pupillages each year, with scholarship awards of £25,000. The decision as to offers of pupillage depends in particular upon: academic record (a first or upper second class degree is usually required), performance at interview, performance in any mini-pupillages and references.

Set No. 39

46 ESSEX STREET (Geoffrey Hawker)

46 Essex Street, London, WC2R 3GH **Tel:** (020) 7583 8899 **Fax:** (020) 7583 8800 **DX:** 1014 London/Chancery Lane **Email:** clerks@46essexst.co.uk

Set No. 40

FALCON CHAMBERS (Jonathan Gaunt QC & Kim Lewison QC)

Falcon Court, London, EC4Y 1AA
Tel: (020) 7353 2484 **Fax:** (020) 7353 1261 **DX:** 408
Email: clerks@falcon-chambers.com **Website:** www.falcon-chambers.com

Head of Chambers	Jonathan Gaunt QC
	Kim Lewison QC
Chambers Director	Edith A. Robertson
Senior Clerk	Steven Francis
Tenants	29

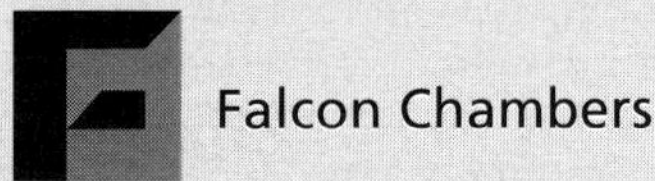

Members:

Derek Wood QC (1964) (QC-1978)MA, BCL
Jonathan Gaunt QC (1972) (QC-1991)BA
Kim Lewison QC (1975) (QC-1991)MA
Paul Morgan QC (1975) (QC-1992)MA
Kirk Reynolds QC (1974) (QC-1993)MA
Jonathan Brock QC (1977) (QC-1997)MA
Nicholas Dowding QC (1979) (QC-1997)MA
Edwin Prince (1955)BA
Paul de la Piquerie (1966)LLB
Joanne R Moss (1976)MA LLM (EC Law)
Anthony Radevsky (1978)LLB
Edward Cole (1980)MA
Wayne Clark (1982)LLB, BCL
Guy Fetherstonhaugh (1983)BSc
Martin Rodger (1986)BA
Timothy Fancourt (1987)MA
Barry Denyer-Green (1972)LLM, PhD
Stephen Jourdan (1989)MA
Gary Cowen (1990)LLB
Jonathan Small (1990)BA
Janet Bignell (1992)MA, BCL
Martin Dray (1992)LLB
Caroline Shea (1994)MA
Anthony Tanney (1994)BA MJur
Catherine Taskis (1995)BA BCL
Emily Windsor (1995)BA DSU (EC Law)
Edward Peters (1998)BA
Katherine Astill (1998)BA MPhil
Adam Rosenthal (1999)BA

The Chambers: A set of 29 barristers, including seven QCs, all of whom specialise in litigation and property law. Members are the authors or editors of leading textbooks such as Woodfall, Megarry, Gale, Muir Watt and Moss, Bernstein and Reynolds and Hague. Chambers enjoy strong links with the RICS and the CIArb, and organise the annual Blundell Memorial Lectures. All are members of the Chancery Bar Association and LCLCBA.

Work Undertaken: Falcon Chambers is generally recognised as the leading set for landlord and tenant (commercial, residential and agricultural); property litigation, including all aspects of general property law (easements, restrictive covenants, mortgages, options); property-related areas, such as insolvency and solicitors' and surveyors' professional negligence. Chambers have particular expertise in contract and arbitration law. Some members specialise in agricultural production controls, competition law, compulsory purchase, planning and building disputes. Litigation is the core of chambers' work, but much advisory and drafting work is also carried out. Direct Professional Access is welcomed, and members often sit as arbitrators, experts and legal assessors.

Set No.
41 **FARRAR'S BUILDING** (John Leighton Williams QC)

Farrar's Building, Temple, London, EC4Y 7BD
Tel: (020) 7583 9241 **Fax:** (020) 7583 0090 **DX:** 406
Email: chambers@farrarsbuilding.co.uk **Website:** www.farrarsbuilding.co.uk

Head of Chambers	John Leighton Williams QC
Senior Clerk/Practice Manager	Alan Kilbey
Chambers Manager	Janet Eades
Tenants	34

Members:

John Leighton Williams QC (1964) (QC-1986) +
Gerard Elias QC (1968) (QC-1984) +
Douglas Day QC (1967) (QC-1989) +
Patrick Harrington QC (1973) (QC-1993) +
Leighton Davies QC (1975) (QC-1994) +
Alan Jeffreys QC (1970) (QC-1996) +
William Norris QC (1974) (QC-1997)
Stephen Hopkins QC (1973) (QC-2000) +
Christopher Vosper QC (1977) (QC-2000) +
Richard Nussey (1971)
Anthony Seys Llewellyn (1972) +
Ian Ridd (1975)
Gregory Treverton-Jones (1977) +
Stephen Jones (1978)
Tom McDermott (1980)
Gillian Keene (1980)
Simon Peter Buchanan Browne (1982)
Tracy Ayling (1983)
Daniel Matovu (1985)
Nigel Spencer Ley (1985)
Jonathan Watt-Pringle (1987)
Andrew Peebles (1987)
David Wicks (1989)
Georgina Middleton (1989)
Shabbir Lakha (1989)
James Todd (1990)
Helen Hobhouse (1990)
Peter Freeman (1992)
Melissa Pack (1995)
Lee Evans (1996)
Huw Davies (1998)
James Pretsell (1998)
Sarah Tozzi (1998)
Senay Rodgers (1999)

+ Recorder

The Chambers: Farrar's Building is a long established set of common law chambers with an excellent reputation built up over many years.

Work Undertaken: Areas of practice fall under general common law but members of chambers have particular specialities in administrative and public law; contract and commercial litigation; criminal law; defamation and media law; disciplinary tribunals; employment; environmental and agricultural law; health and safety; insurance litigation; landlord and tenant; licensing; medical law; personal injury; police actions and civil liberties; product liability; public inquiries and tribunals; professional negligence; solicitors' costs and taxation; sports law; competition law.

Set No.
42 **FIELD COURT CHAMBERS** (Melanie Spencer)

Field Court Chambers, 2nd Floor, 3 Field Court, Grays Inn, London, WC1R 5EP
Tel: (020) 7404 7474 **Fax:** (020) 7404 7475 **DX:** 136 (Ch.Ln.)
Email: enquiries@fieldcourtchambers.com **Website:** www.fieldcourtchambers.com

Head of Chambers:	Melanie Spencer
Senior Clerk:	Paul Mellor
Tenants:	6

A civil set practising in the following areas: commercial, employment, environmental, family, immigration, landlord and tenant, local authority, personal injury and professional negligence.

Set No. 43

4 FIELD COURT (Steven Gee QC)

Gray's Inn, London, WC1R 5EF
Tel: (020) 7440 6900 **Fax:** (020) 7242 0197 **DX:** 483 London/Chancery Lane
Email: Chambers@4FieldCourt.com **Website:** www.4FieldCourt.com

Head of Chambers	Steven Gee QC
Clerks	Paul Coveney
	Jean-Pierre Schulz
Tenants	28

Members:

Steven Gee QC (1975) (QC-1993)
Richard Stone QC (1952) (QC-1968)
John Reeder QC (1971) (QC-1989)
R Jervis Kay QC (1972) (QC-1996)
Elizabeth Blackburn QC (1978) (QC-1998)
Allan Myers (1988)(QC Aus)
Vasanti Selvaratnam QC (1983) (QC-2001)
Sarah Miller (1971)
Lloyd Lloyd (1973)
Alison Green (1974)
James Thom (1974)
William Whitehouse-Vaux (1977)
Robert Bourne (1978)
Daphne Romney (1979)
Jonathan D C Turner (1982)
Colin Wright (1987)
David Brook (1988)
Nicholas Saunders (1989)
Stephen Wilson (1990)
Timothy Hill (1990)
Arshad Ghaffar (1991)
Nicholas Dugdale (1992)
Charles Davies (1995)
Madeleine Heal (1996)
Eoin O'Shea (1996)
Rachel Toney (1998)
Ishfaq Ahmed (1999)
Mary Gibbons (1999)

The Chambers: 4 Field Court – a dynamic, friendly and innovative commercial set – combines a long-standing, leading expertise in shipping and maritime law with expanding practices in insurance, banking, oil and gas, employment, property, intellectual property and computer law, among others.

Work Undertaken: 4 Field Court provides a comprehensive and client-focused service, from interim applications (such as freezing and searching orders) through to trial. Several members are or have been Treasury Counsel in admiralty matters, including the current first standing counsel, David Goldstone. Members are all specialist advocates and appear in all courts and tribunals in England and Wales. Members often act or sit in public inquiries, including most recently The Derbyshire and The Marchioness. Senior members also act as arbitrators.

International: Much of the work of chambers is international. Members appear in courts and tribunals overseas, and the European Court of Justice. 4 Field Court has particularly strong Australian and US connections, with members belonging to the bars of several states and of a number of jurisdictions in the West Indies. Languages spoken by members include French, German, Italian, Spanish, Urdu, Hindi, Arabic, Greek and Welsh.

Set No. 44

FOUNTAIN COURT (Anthony Boswood QC)

Fountain Court, Temple, London, EC4Y 9DH
Tel: (020) 7583 3335 **Fax:** (020) 7353 0329 **DX:** LDE 5
Email: chambers@fountaincourt.co.uk **Website:** www.fountaincourt.co.uk

Head of Chambers	Anthony Boswood QC
Senior Clerks	Mark Watson
	Michael Couling
Chambers Administrator	Prue Woodbridge
Tenants	52

Members:

Conrad Dehn QC (1952) (QC-1968)
Christopher Bathurst QC (1959) (QC-1978)
Anthony Boswood QC (1970) (QC-1986)
Lord Goldsmith QC (1972) (QC-1987) •
Michael Lerego QC (1972) (QC-1995)
Michael Brindle QC (1975) (QC-1992)
Michael Crane QC (1975) (QC-1994)
Nicholas Underhill QC (1976) (QC-1992)
Nicholas Stadlen QC (1976) (QC-1991)
David Railton QC (1979) (QC-1996)
Timothy Dutton QC (1979) (QC-1998)
Brian Doctor QC (1991) (QC-1999)
Stephen Moriarty QC (1986) (QC-1999)
Stephen Rubin QC (1977) (QC-2000)
Timothy Wormington (1977)
Michael McLaren (1981)
Philip Brook Smith (1982)
Raymond Cox (1982)
David Waksman (1982)
Anthony Martino (1982)
Thomas Keith (1983)
Guy Philipps (1986)
Craig Orr (1986)
Michael Green (1987)
Timothy Howe (1987)
Bankim Thanki (1988)
Patricia Robertson (1988)
Jeffrey Chapman (1989)
Bridget Lucas (1989)
Brian Napier (1990)
Derrick Dale (1990)
Akhil Shah (1990)
Marcus Smith (1991)
Paul Gott (1991)
Veronique Buehrlen (1991)
Andrew Mitchell (1992)
Richard Handyside (1993)
John Taylor (1993)
Richard Coleman (1994)
Adam Tolley (1994)
Louise Merrett (1995)
Philippa Hamilton (1996)
Paul Sinclair (1997)

Members continued:

Patrick Goodall (1998)
Deepak Nambisan (1998)
Giles Wheeler (1998)
Henry King (1998)
Rosalind Phelps (1998)
Edward Levey (1999)
Natalie Stopps (2000)
James Cutress (2000)
Nik Yeo (2000)

Neil Andrews *(1981) (Fellow, Clare College Cambridge); Peter Carter QC *†(1947) (QC-1990) (Emeritus Fellow, Wadham College, Oxford); Gladys Li * (SC) (Resides in Hong Kong); Peter Scott QC *† (1960) (QC-1978) (Accepts appointments through chambers as an arbitrator); Izzet Sinan * (Resident in Brussels); Andrew Burrows ‡ (Norton Rose Professor, Commercial and Financial Law, Oxford); William Swadling ‡ (Fellow and Tutor in law at Brasenose College, Oxford and Lecturer at University of Oxford).

* Door Tenant † Non-practising ‡ Academic Associate • Attorney General

The Chambers: Fountain Court is a leading commercial set of chambers with 52 barristers, of whom 14 are silks. The core of its work is commercial, and members advise and represent clients over the entire range of business problems. The set offers a high quality and efficient service which meets the practical requirements of commercial clients. Members of chambers appear in courts and tribunals of all levels from complex high-value commercial disputes to more straightforward County Court and tribunal work. The size of chambers, and the range of experience of its members, enables Fountain Court to assemble balanced teams of counsel to suit the requirements of individual cases. Prominent former members include Lord Bingham of Cornhill and many other current and former Lords of Appeal and High Court Judges. Hours: 8.00am to 9.00pm Monday to Friday and from 9.00am to 1.00pm on Saturdays. After hours (0786) 780 3335.

Work Undertaken: Members of Fountain Court are recognised leaders in the fields of commercial litigation, banking, financial services, insurance and reinsurance, professional negligence, aviation and employment. Fountain Court also retains a strong 'generalist' tradition and is notable for the wide range of other civil work undertaken, including oil and gas, entertainment and media, intellectual property, company, insolvency, product liability, human rights, administrative, civil fraud, sports, international trade, shipping and telecommunications law. Several members of chambers have experience of sitting as arbitrators in commercial and other disputes, and of mediation and alternative dispute resolution.

Publications: Many members of chambers have written or contributed to legal textbooks and other articles. *Carriage By Air*, an aviation textbook by a number of members of chambers was published by Butterworths in January 2001. A second edition of *The Law of Bank Payments* by Michael Brindle QC and Raymond Cox, with contributions by other members of Chambers, was published in 1999. Brian Napier is an editor of *Harvey on Employment and Industrial Relations Law* and has published widely on employment law. Chambers provides the editorial team under Stephen Moriarty QC and Raymond Cox as general editor of the *Commercial Court Procedure* published by Sweet & Maxwell as a part of the White Book series.

International: There are members of chambers who are fluent in Afrikaans, French, German and Italian; others have a working knowledge of Greek and Russian. Members regularly work abroad, not only in international arbitrations but also as advocates in overseas jurisdictions, including Hong Kong and Singapore and in the European Court of Justice. Members of chambers are also members of the bars of California, New York and Gibraltar and of the Faculty of Advocates in Scotland.

et No.

45 FRANCIS TAYLOR BUILDING (D A Pears)

Francis Taylor Building (2nd Floor), Temple, London, EC4Y 7BY
Tel: (020) 7353 9942 **Fax:** (020) 7353 9924 **DX:** LDE 211 London/Chancery Lane
Email: clerks@ftblaw.co.uk

Head of Chambers	D A Pears
Senior Clerk	Kevin Moore
Tenants	31

Members:

D A Pears (1975)
Nemone Lethbridge (1956)
Gavin Merrylees (1964)
Dennis Naish (1966)
Philip Conrath (1972)
Paul Staddon (1976)
Mark Dencer (1978)
Mark Hoyle (1978)
Kerstin Boyd (1979)
Simon Cheves (1980)
Henrietta Manners (1981)
William Holland (1982)
Sebastian Reid (1982)
Jane Carpenter (1984)
Philip Dixon (1986)
Michael Buckpitt (1988)
Clare Roberts (1988)
Gerald Wilson (1989)
Carole Murray (1989)
Philip Rainey (1990)
Stephen Heath (1992)
Catriona MacLaren (1993)
Jonathan Green (1993)
Andrew Butler (1993)
Alexander Bastin (1995)
Christopher Heather (1995)
Robert Bowker (1995)
David Holloway (1996)
James Fieldsend (1997)
Matthew Line (1997)
Charlotte Jewell (1999)
Richard Selwyn-Sharpe (1985) *
Gilbert Chirimuuta (1990) *

* Door Tenant

Continued overleaf

Work Undertaken:

Administrative & Public Law: Including local government and judicial review.
Commercial: Including international sale of goods, franchise agreements and partnership disputes, arbitration, joint ventures and conflict of laws.
Consumer Law: Including credit, sale and supply of goods and services.
Crime: All areas and aspects of criminal law undertaken, both defending and prosecuting.
Employment: Including restraint of trade, transfer of undertakings and restrictive covenants.
Family Law: Both children and property.
Professional Negligence: All areas undertaken but particularly medical, surveyors, solicitors and architects.
Property: Particularly landlord and tenant (both commercial and residential), rent review, leasehold enfranchisement and insolvency.
Personal Injuries: Direct Private Access and Conditional Fee work accepted. Refer to clerks for advice on relevant expertise and availability. Fee estimates can be given in advance. Mortgages and security and product liability are also undertaken.

Set No.
46 **FRANCIS TAYLOR BUILDING** (Nicholas Valios QC)
Francis Taylor Building, Temple, London, EC4Y 7BY **Tel:** (020) 7353 7768 **Fax:** (020) 7353 0659 **DX:** 441 London/Chancery Lane

Set No.
47 **FURNIVAL CHAMBERS** (Andrew Mitchell QC)

32 Furnival Street, London, EC4A 1JQ
Tel: (020) 7405 3232 **Fax:** (020) 7405 3322 **DX:** 72
Email: clerks@furnivallaw.co.uk **Website:** www.furnivallaw.co.uk

Head of Chambers	Andrew Mitchell QC
Clerks	John Gutteridge
	Joanne Thomas
Tenants	50

Members:

Andrew Mitchell QC (1976) (QC-1998)
Oliver Blunt QC (1974) (QC-1994)
Stephen Leslie QC (1971) (QC-1993)
Sally O'Neill QC (1976) (QC-1997)
Michel G.A. Massih QC (1979) (QC-1999)
Hugh Griffiths (1972)
Christopher Baur (1972)
Gino Connor (1974)
Lisa Matthews (1974)
Michael Latham (1975)
Stephen Holt (1978)
Kim Hollis (1979)
Vincent Coughlin (1980)
Francis Sheridan (1980)
Paul Mytton (1982)
Richard Whittam (1983)
Nicola Merrick (1983)
Jon Swain (1983)
Sherrie Caddle (1983)
Roy Headlam (1983)
John Carmichael (1984)
Kennedy Talbot (1984)
Carolyn Blore (1985)
Charles Sherrard (1986)
Allison Hunter (1986)
Philip Romans (1982)
Kathryn Hirst (1986)
Barry Gregory (1987)
Patricia Lees (1988)
Nicolas Gerasimidis (1988)
Stephen Earnshaw (1990)
Tim Forster (1990)
Tanya Woolls (1991)
Sandip Patel (1991)
Andrew Henley (1992)
Alexia Power (1992)
Mark Giuliani (1993)
Fiona Henderson (1993)
Ivan Pearce (1994)
John Kearney (1994)
Julian Winship (1995)
Giles Cockings (1996)
Christopher Convey (1994)
Mark Summers (1996)
Laban Leake (1996)
Fer Chinner (1998)
Fiona Jackson (1998)
Sally Fudge (1998)
Linda Candler (1977) *
Elizabeth Coughlin (1989) *
Leon de Costa (1992)
Kate Mulkerrins (1998) *
Simon Reevell (1990) *
Graham Henson (1976) *
Gerard McEvilly (1994) *
Lefi Panayioti (1992)

* Door Tenant

The Chambers: A set of specialist criminal practitioners, housed in fully computerised modern offices with dedicated conference facilities and a comprehensively equipped library.

Work Undertaken:

Criminal Law Service: Furnival Chambers was formed in 1985 as a specialist criminal set and has continued to provide both a comprehensive and specialist criminal law service to professional and lay clients. Chambers comprise leading and junior counsel of considerable and varied experience enabling them to deal expertly with the entire range of criminal cases from the most serious and complicated cases down to the relatively straightforward. There is particular expertise throughout chambers in white collar fraud and cases involving very serious violence and abuse. Chambers are well-placed to deal competently with the rapidly increasing use of technology to both investigate cases and present the evidence in court. Chambers are particularly concerned to ensure that high standards are maintained by their pupils and junior tenants and have their own advocacy training scheme.
Asset Forfeiture & Money Laundering: Furnival Chambers has a specialist team which deals with confiscation, asset forfeiture and money laundering. Members of the team have appeared in most of the lead-

ing cases in the High Court, Court of Appeal and House of Lords as well as both advising and appearing in cases in Trinidad, the Turks and Caicos Islands and Cayman Islands and advising in Pakistan and Antigua.

International: French, German, Arabic, Hindi, Russian and Spanish are spoken.

Recruitment: Furnival Chambers takes four 12 month pupillages, terminable at the end of the first six months by either Chambers or the pupil. Selection is made from OLPAS applications by two-stage interviews. Financial assistance is available for the first six months. Contact chambers for further detail.

Set No. 48

ONE GARDEN COURT FAMILY LAW CHAMBERS (Eleanor F. Platt QC & Alison Ball QC)

One Garden Court, Temple, London, EC4Y 9BJ
Tel: (020) 7797 7900 **Fax:** (020) 7797 7929 **DX:** 1034 (Ch.Ln.)
Email: clerks@onegardencourt.co.uk **Website:** www.onegardencourt.co.uk

Head of Chambers	Eleanor F. Platt QC
	Alison Ball QC
Chief Executive	Claire Wilford-Smith
Senior Clerk	Howard Rayner
First Junior Clerk	Chris Ferrison
Fees Clerk	Dennis Davies
Tenants	44

Members:

Eleanor F. Platt QC (1960) (QC-1982)
Alison Ball QC (1972) (QC-1995)
Ian Peddie QC (1971) (QC-1992)
Jane Crowley QC (1976) (QC-1998) †
Caroline Willbourne (1970)
Bruce Coleman (1972)
Peter Nathan (1973)
Suzanne H. Shenton (1973)
Elizabeth Szwed (1974)
Peter Horrocks (1977)
Martin O'Dwyer (1978)
Ann Marie Wicherek (1978)
Richard Scarratt (1979)
Judith Rowe (1979)
Kay Halkyard (1980)
Janet Bazley (1980)
Susan Shackleford (1980)
Kay Firth-Butterfield (1980)
Susannah Walker (1985)
Stephen Cobb (1985)
John Stocker (1985)
Charles Geekie (1985)
Gary Crawley (1988)
Gillian Cleave (1988)
Sarah Morgan (1988)
Alan Inglis (1989)
Andrew Bagchi (1989)
Michael Liebrecht (1989)
David Burles (1985)
Malcolm Chisholm (1989)
Catherine Jenkins (1990)
Ariff Rozhan (1990)
Claire Heppenstall (1990)
Ian Robbins (1991)
Doushka Krish (1991)
Andrew Norton (1992)
Emma Hudson (1995)
Gillian C. Downham (1993)
Susan Budaly (1994)
Sally Stone (1994)
Alexander Chandler (1995)
Nicola Fox (1996)
Sassa-Ann Amaouche (1996)
Marcus Lazarides (1999)

† Practices mainly from 30 Park Place, Cardiff

The Chambers: One Garden Court is the largest chambers where all members specialise in family law. Work includes ancillary relief, local authorities, human rights, child abduction, care and adoption, mediation and ADR service.

Set No. 49

TWO GARDEN COURT (Ian Macdonald QC & Owen Davies QC)

1st Floor, 2 Garden Court, Temple, London, EC4Y 9BL
Tel: (020) 7353 1633 **Fax:** (020) 7353 4621 **DX:** 34 Chancery Lane
Email: barristers@2gardenct.law.co.uk **Website:** www.2gardenct.law.co.uk

Head of Chambers	Ian Macdonald QC
	Owen Davies QC
Senior Clerk	Colin Cook
Clerks	Matthew Jones
	Lesley Perrott
	Bob Archer
	Amanda Boylen
	Caroline Mitchell
	Danielle Morriss
	Emma McCreight
Tenants	68

Members:

Ian Macdonald QC (1963) (QC-1988)
Owen Davies QC (1973) (QC-1999)
Courtenay Griffiths QC (1980) (QC-1998)
Laurie Fransman QC (1979) (QC-2000)
Jan Luba QC (1980) (QC-2000)
David Watkinson (1972)
Marguerite Russell (1972)
Michael House (1972)
Terry Munyard (1972)
Mark George (1976)
Frances Webber (1978)
Henry Blaxland (1978)
Icah Peart (1978)
Lalith De Kauwe (1978)
Kathryn Cronin (1980)
Anne Jessup (1981)
Celia Graves (1981)
Markanza Cudby (1983)
Michael Hall (1983)
Ravinder Rahal (1983)
Nerida Harford-Bell (1984)
Stephen Cottle (1984)
Beatrice Prevatt (1985)
Debra Gold (1985)
Peter Jorro (1986)
Mary McKeone (1986)
Rick Scannell (1986)
Elizabeth Veats (1986)
Stephen Knafler (1993)
Dexter Dias (1988)
Adrian Eissa (1988)
Leslie Thomas (1988)
Judy Khan (1989)
Alexander Taylor-Camara (1989)
Alison Grief (1990)
Bethan Harris (1990)
Colin Hutchinson (1990)
Liz Davies (1994)
Maggie Jones (1990)

Continued overleaf

Members continued:

Michael Baker (1990)
Joanne Harris (1991)
Jon Holbrook (1991)
Stephanie Harrison (1991)
Malek Wan Daud (1991)
Sonali Naik (1991)
Nadine Finch (1991)
Catrin Lewis (1991)
Stephen Simblet (1991)
Alastair Edie (1992)
Helen Curtis (1992)
Peter Weatherby (1992)
Valerie Easty (1992)
Julia Krish (1992)
Rajiv Menon (1993)
Robert Littlewood (1993)
Kieran Vaughan (1993)
David Jones (1994)
Duran Seddon (1994)
Sam Momtaz (1995)
Shereener Browne (1996)
Anya Lewis (1997)
Maya Sikand (1997)
Patrick Lewis (1997)
Louise Hooper (1997)
Adrian Marshall Williams (1998)
Josephene Uzuegbunam (1998)
Emma Favata (1999)
Ronan Toal (1999)

The Chambers: The set's work reflects the progressive aspirations it has to develop the law to make a difference to people's lives and enhance the causes of social justice and human rights for which the set has always stood. Chambers' historical commitment to fostering a multidisciplinary set continues to produce cases on the cutting edge of the 'law'. Chambers' motto continues to be 'Do Right, Fear No-one'.

Work Undertaken: Criminal; family; housing; immigration; public law and judicial review; extradition; actions against the police; discrimination and employment; environmental law; community care; mental health; personal injury; education.

Set No. 50

GOUGH SQUARE CHAMBERS (Fred Philpott)

6-7 Gough Square, London, EC4A 3DE
Tel: (020) 7353 0924 **Fax:** (020) 7353 2221 **DX:** 476
Email: gsc@goughsq.co.uk **Website:** www.goughsq.co.uk

Head of Chambers	Fred Philpott
Senior Clerk	Bob Weekes
Chambers Administrator	Elizabeth Owen-Ward
Tenants	12

Members:

Fred Philpott (1974)
Peter Sayer (1975)
Claire Andrews (1979)
William Hibbert (1979)
Barry Stancombe (1983)
Jonathan Goulding (1984)
Stephen Neville (1986)
Julia Smith (1988)
Julian Gun Cuninghame (1989)
Anthony Vines (1993)
Iain MacDonald (1996)
Sandra McCalla (1999)

The Chambers: Gough Square Chambers is a commercial set with a particular specialisation in both the civil and criminal aspects of consumer law. Chambers aim to provide an efficient, friendly and flexible service at competitive rates. Outside normal working hours, the Senior Clerk can be contacted on 07860 219162.

Work Undertaken:

Consumer Law: Consumer credit (agreements, licensing and advertising); trade descriptions and trademarks; food safety; pricing; weights and measures; consumer contracts; mortgages; trading schemes; timeshare; sale and supply contracts; product safety; package travel. Chambers are instructed in this specialist area by in-house lawyers and solicitors acting for high street lenders, manufacturers, food producers, distributors and retailers. Members of chambers also prosecute on behalf of the consumer protection departments of local authorities.

Business & Commercial Law: Banking; secured lending; company and partnership; insolvency; employment; commercial contracts; professional negligence; criminal and civil fraud.

Publications: Chambers publish a free quarterly *Trading Law Bulletin* which charts the recent developments in this area of law. Please visit chambers' website or contact the Senior Clerk to join the mailing list.

Set No. 51

9 GOUGH SQUARE (John Foy QC)

9 Gough Square, London, EC4A 3DG
Tel: (020) 7832 0500 **Fax:** (020) 7353 1344 **DX:** 439
Email: clerks@9goughsq.co.uk **Website:** www.9goughsq.co.uk

Head of Chambers	John Foy QC
Chief Executive	Joanna Poulton MBA LLB
Tenants	44

Members:

John Foy QC (1969) (QC-1998) +
Gary Burrell QC (1977) (QC-1996) +
Andrew Baillie QC (1970) (QC-2001) +
Giles Eyre (1974)
David Gerrey (1975) +
Michael Joyce (1976)
Trevor Davies (1978)
Frederick Ferguson (1978)
Grahame Aldous (1979) +
Philip I Henry (1979)
Duncan Macleod (1980)
Christopher Wilson (1980)
Graham Robinson (1981)
Nicolas Hillier (1982)
Roger Hiorns (1983)
Simon Carr (1984)
Gaurang Naik (1985)
Andrew Ritchie (1985)
Vincent Williams (1985)
Jacob Levy (1986)
Jonathan Loades (1986)
Alexander Verdan (1987)
Edwin Buckett (1988)
James Shaw (1988)
Susan Baldock (1988)
Mark Whalan (1988)
Rosina Cottage (1988)
Leslie Keegan (1989)
Sally Bradley (1989)
Stephen Glynn (1990)
Jane Sinclair (1990)
Philip Jones (1990)
Clare Padley (1991)
John Tughan (1991)
Jeremy Crowther (1991)
Aileen Downey (1991)
Laura Begley (1993)
Christopher Stephenson (1994)
Daniel Lawson (1994)
Rajeev Shetty (1996)
Tara Vindis (1996)
Laura Elfield (1996)
Tom Little (1997)
Perrin Gibbons (1998)

+ Recorder

The Chambers: A well-established common law set specialising in personal injury; clinical negligence; professional negligence; serious fraud; crime; family; employment. Chambers pride themselves on their friendly yet commercial approach which they believe enhances their ability to provide realistic advice to their clients. Focused around specialist teams, Chambers draw upon their considerable depth of knowledge and expertise through regular team meetings. Facilities are modern and up-to-date including disabled facilities, large dedicated conference rooms and full computerisation. They are professionally managed by a qualified Chief Executive who is happy to discuss any aspect of their service and in particular to recommend suitable counsel. A brochure is available on request.

Work Undertaken:

Personal Injury: Representing either claimants or defendants, chambers can offer experts on complex multi-party actions; industrial disease; RSI; deafness; lifting; marine accidents; PTSD; RTA; accidents at work, etc. Special payment terms are negotiable for union or insurance-backed claims. All members of chambers have agreed to accept conditional fee work and where appropriate single agreements covering individual firms can be negotiated.

Clinical Negligence: Chambers can offer experts who are sensitive to the issues in these cases, while remaining tenacious advocates and negotiators. Areas of experience, for both claimants and defendants, includes brain injuries; birth defects; failed sterilisations; surgical and non-surgical maltreatment.

Professional Negligence: Members of chambers' professional negligence team regularly advise on, and appear in, cases involving all aspects of professional negligence, but particularly actions involving solicitors, accountants, insurance brokers, surveyors etc.

Serious Fraud: Chambers have some of the country's leading fraud practitioners. Members of chambers regularly prosecute for the SFO and for CPS HQ. They have also defended some of the most complex fraud cases, such as Blue Arrow and Nissan. Chambers can provide experts in all areas of fraud but particularly on advance fee frauds, city frauds, pension frauds, mortgage frauds, etc.

General Crime: The crime team has established a reputation for both prosecuting and defending general crime on the Midlands and Oxford Circuit, particularly at Northampton, Luton, St Albans, Aylesbury, Birmingham Crown Courts. In addition members of chambers regularly appear in the major London Crown Courts.

Family: Chambers' specialist family team undertakes a full range of family law work but is particularly known for its experience in care proceedings, adoption, residence and contact applications and ancillary relief.

Employment: The employment group is able to provide advice and representation both before and once litigation has commenced. Members of chambers regularly undertake cases involving claims for sexual, race and disability discrimination, equal pay, restraint of trade, TUPE, national minimum wage, unfair dismissal and redundancy etc. The group can provide expert advice swiftly on the telephone to minimise unnecessary litigation.

Set No. 52

2 GRAY'S INN SQUARE CHAMBERS

2 Gray's Inn Square, London, WC1R 5AA
Tel: (020) 7440 8450 **Fax:** (020) 7440 8452 **DX:** 43 London Chancery Lane
Email: clerks@2gis.co.uk **Website:** www.2gis.co.uk

Senior Clerk	Perry Allen
First Junior Clerk	Sue Reding
Second Junior Clerk	Ian Kitchen
Tenants	34

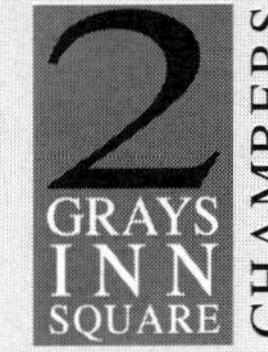

Members:

Keith Knight (1969)
Edward Cross (1975)
John Parker (1975)
Richard Robinson (1977)
Peter Fortune (1978)
Christopher McConnell (1979)
David Hughes (1980)
Nergis-Anne Matthew (1981) †
Milan Dulovic (1982)
Jane Rayson (1982)
Jacqueline Marks (1984)
Gabrielle Jan Posner (1984)
John Church (1984)
Fawzia King (1985)
Francis Collaco Moraes (1985)
Surinder Bhakar (1986)
Sorrel Dixon (1987)
Adrian Roberts (1988)
Terence Woods (1989)
James Holmes-Milner (1989)
Myles Watkins (1990) †
Christopher Rice (1991)
Chima Umezuruike (1991)
Delyth Evans (1991)
Christopher Wagstaffe (1992)
Henry Drayton (1993)
Daniel Barnett (1993)
Neelima Mehendale (1993)
Paul Hepher (1994)
Philip McCormack (1994)
Tony Badenoch (1996)
Piers Martin (1997)
Elizabeth Conaghan (2000)
Justin Slater (1999)

† Associate Member

The Chambers: Chambers provide an efficient service in all areas of common law practice. Specialisation is achieved through the use of practice groups, which enable members to pool their specialist knowledge and expertise. Comprehensive details of chambers' fee structures are available from the Senior Clerk. Chambers also operate a Law Society accredited seminar programme offering CPD credit.

Work Undertaken:

Family: Matters covered encompass child law including public and private Children Act proceedings, care work (including representing guardians ad litem), adoption, wardship and child abduction, matrimonial and related proceedings (including property and financial disputes and disputes between cohabitees.

Criminal: Members practise in all areas of crime, receiving instructions on behalf of the defence. Members have particular experience in areas of fraud, child abuse, drug trafficking, sexual offences, public order, licensing and actions against the police.

Personal Injury & Clinical Negligence: Members act for individuals, trade unions and insurance company clients, for both plaintiff and defendant, in claims arising from accidents at work, clinical negligence, road traffic accidents, occupiers' liability and defective products. Conditional Fee Agreements are undertaken.

Employment: Chambers undertake advisory and advocacy work in Employment Tribunals, EAT, High Court and internal disciplinary hearings. Specific areas of expertise are unfair dismissal, redundancy, discrimination and the provision of advice to employers prior to the dismissal of employees and directors.

Property: Chambers offer representation and advice on all property matters including public and private sector housing, business tenancies and all aspects of landlord and tenant law, trusts, claims to possession of land, easement and mortgage disputes, conveyancing and disputes involving joint owners and cohabitees.

Contract & Commercial: Areas of law covered include contract and tort, partnership disputes, professional negligence, sale of goods, agency, bills of exchange, banking, insolvency, building and engineering contracts, consumer credit, insurance, guarantee and suretyship and disqualification of directors.

Publications: Gabrielle Jan Posner is author of *The Teenager's Guide to The Law* (Cavendish 1995). Jane Rayson is co-author of *How to Make Applications in the Family Proceeding Court* and Blackstone's *Guide to the Family Law Act 1996.* Jane Rayson and Gabrielle Jan Posner are contributors to the Sweet & Maxwell *Practical Research Papers* and are respectively the authors of *Defending Divorce* and *The Welfare Officer.* Daniel Barnett is the author of *Avoiding Unfair Dismissal Claims*, a guide for employers and advisors on how to dismiss employees (John Wiley 1999).

International: French, Serbo-Croat, Malay and Punjabi are spoken.

Recruitment: Pupillage applications through OLPAS. Mini-pupillages are available.

53 ## 2-3 GRAY'S INN SQUARE (Anthony Porten QC & Anthony Scrivener QC)

2-3 Gray's Inn Square, Gray's Inn, London, WC1R 5JH
Tel: (020) 7242 4986 **Fax:** (020) 7405 1166 **DX:** 316 (Ch.Ln.)
Email: chambers@2-3graysinnsquare.co.uk **Website:** www.2-3graysinnsquare.co.uk

Head of Chambers	Anthony Porten QC Anthony Scrivener QC
Chambers Director	Douglas Lewis
Senior Clerk	Martin Hart
Tenants	41

2-3
GRAY'S INN
SQUARE

Members:

Anthony Porten QC (1969) (QC-1988)
Anthony Scrivener QC (1958) (QC-1975)
Malcolm Spence QC (1958) (QC-1979)
Patrick Ground QC (1960) (QC-1981)
Harry Wolton QC (1969) (QC-1982)
Christopher Cochrane QC (1965) (QC-1988)
Anthony Dinkin QC (1968) (QC-1991)
Vernon Pugh QC (1969) (QC-1986)
(Nicholas) Mark Lowe QC (1972) (QC-1996)
John Haines (1967)
Geoffrey Stephenson (1971)
David Lamming (1972)
Adrian Trevelyan Thomas (1974)
Nicholas Nardecchia (1974)
Tobias Davey (1977)
Graham Stoker (1977)
David Matthias (1980)
Ian Albutt (1981)
Steven Gasztowicz (1981)
Mary Cook (1982)
Morag Ellis (1984)
James Findlay (1984)
Gerard Forlin (1984)
Katie Astaniotis (1985)
Michael Bedford (1985)
Philip Kolvin (1985)
Simon Bird (1987)
Ranjit Bhose (1989)
Jonathan Clay (1990)
Celina Colquhoun (1990)
Robin Green (1992)
Harriet Murray (1992)
Peter Miller (1993)
Thomas Cosgrove (1994)
Richard Ground (1994)
David Lintott (1995)
Jonathon Easton (1995)
Wayne Beglan (1995)
Rory Clarke (1996)
Katy Skerrett (1999)
Johanna Boyd (1999)

The Chambers: Established in the late 19th century, 2-3 Gray's Inn Square is recognised as one of the leading local government sets with highly rated expertise in nine specialist areas. Former members of chambers include Sir Edward Marshall Hall KC, Lord Birkett, Lord Chief Justice Widgery, Lord Bridge of Harwich, Mr Justice Hidden, and Mr Justice Penry-Davey. Current members of chambers include Anthony Scrivener QC, a former chairman of the Bar, and Malcolm Spence QC, the erstwhile chairman of the Planning and Environment Bar Association. Over the last 40 years, and with increasing size, chambers have widened their original common law base to develop substantial practices in administrative law, local government law and town and country planning law. They have, however, retained a strong common law practice, covering both general and large commercial disputes, and they continue to enjoy a solid criminal practice.

Work Undertaken: First-class representation is provided in all the principal areas of work undertaken by chambers, and details of the specialities of each member are available on request from the senior clerk. Counsel are available at any level of experience required. The junior tenants are available at short notice for all Magistrates' Court, County Court and tribunal hearings as well as for any procedural applications. Members of chambers will work in any part of England, Wales, Scotland (planning matters only) and Ireland. Chambers' administration has been upgraded to meet the demands of a modern business environment.
Town & Country Planning, Administrative & Local Government Law: Including judicial review, housing law, public and local government finance, compulsory purchase, rating, highways and environmental law.
Common Law: Including personal injuries; professional negligence including medical, accountants and solicitors; employment law, including industrial tribunal work.
Consumer Law: Including sale of goods, trade descriptions, trading law, food safety and data protection.
Criminal Law: Including white collar crime, serious fraud and capital cases.
Property Law: Including landlord and tenant, mortgages and housing associations.

International: French, German, Greek and Italian are spoken. Various members also practice or are admitted in other jurisdictions including Hong Kong, Singapore, Malaysia, Jamaica, Trinidad, the Cayman Islands, the British Virgin Islands and certain Australian jurisdictions.

Recruitment: Pupils are received each year; pupillage funds are available.

Set No.
54

3 GRAY'S INN SQUARE (Rock Tansey QC)

3 Gray's Inn Square, Gray's Inn, London, WC1R 5AH
Tel: (020) 7520 5600 **Fax:** (020) 7520 5607 **DX:** 1043 (Ch.Ln.)
Email: clerks@3gis.co.uk **Website:** www.3gis.co.uk

Head of Chambers	Rock Tansey QC
Senior Clerk	Guy Williams
Clerks	Marc King
	Stephen Lucas
Tenants	44

Members:

Rock Tansey QC (1966) (QC-1990)
John Perry QC (1975) (QC-1989)
Steven Kay QC (1977) (QC-1997)
George Carter-Stephenson QC (1975) (QC-1998)
William Taylor QC (1990) (QC-1998)
Diana Ellis QC (1978) (QC-2001)
David Hooper (1971)
Colin Allan (1971)
David Farrington (1972)
Ronald Jaffa (1974)
Brendan Keany (1974)
Jonathan Mitchell (1974)
Philip Statman (1975)
Rudi Fortson (1976)
Roger Offenbach (1978)
Chester Beyts (1978)
Charles Bott (1979)
Paul Keleher (1980)
Paul Mendelle (1981)
Penelope Barrett (1982)
Jeremy Dein (1982)
Simon Pentol (1982)
Bill Maley (1982)
Leroy Redhead (1982)
John Cooper (1983)
Colin Wells (1987)
Paul Hynes (1987)
Alison Levitt (1988)
Adrian Kayne (1989)
Jonathan Mann (1989)
Helen Valley (1990)
Arlette Piercy (1990)
Emma Akuwudike (1992)
Sylvia de Bertodano (1993)
Ali Naseem Bajwa (1993)
Harry Potter (1993)
Naujot Sidhu (1993)
Richard Furlong (1994)
Tyrone Smith (1994)
Aisling Byrnes (1994)
Nicola Howard (1995)
Sebastian Gardiner (1997)
Lindsey Rose (1996)
Gillian Higgins (1997)

The Chambers: Established in 1975, 3 Gray's Inn Square is a specialist criminal defence set which aims to ensure that everyone has equal access to the best representation. The set has earned a reputation as a leader in its field by maintaining the highest standards of professionalism, integrity, commitment and both accessibility and approachability. Services for the set include: conference rooms, video conferences, e-mail, disks accepted, voice mail for all members of chambers. A 24-hour clerking service for emergencies and overnight cases is provided. Chambers are fully computerised as is their Crown Court list checking system. In December 1999, the set became the first chambers to be awarded the Bar Mark, the Bar Council's kite mark for quality assurance.

Work Undertaken: First-class representation is provided at every level of seniority by practitioners who appear regularly in high-profile cases and who offer experience in the conduct of all categories of criminal case including European human rights, international criminal tribunal, (international) terrorism and war crimes, murder, serious fraud, organised crime, international drugs trafficking/allied money laundering and offences of extreme/sexual violence. Within this framework there is a positive commitment to legally-aided clients and, where appropriate, pro bono work is undertaken. Particular expertise is provided in all aspects of appellate work, including judicial review and Privy Council. Further, there is experience in the conduct of civil cases, especially actions against the police and allied issues and mental health review tribunals. Chambers present lectures to solicitors and practitioners generally, concerning the effect of significant changes in criminal legislation. Some members also lecture nationally and internationally to and on behalf of legal/human rights organisations on drug trafficking and international war crimes.

Publications: Rudi Fortson: *Law on the Misuse of Drugs.* Several members are regular contributors to legal publications, including *The Solicitors Journal* and *The Lawyer.*

International: Rock Tansey QC & Steven Kay QC founded the European Criminal Bar Association in order to advance issues of mutual concern for European criminal defence lawyers. Rock Tansey QC is the first chairman of the ECBA and organised its inaugural conference at the European Commission for Human Rights. Steven Kay QC, Defence Counsel in the first International Criminal tribunal for the former Yugoslavia undertakes European Human Rights cases. John Perry QC also practises in Bermuda and is a member of the West Indian Bar.

Set No. 55

4-5 GRAY'S INN SQUARE (Elizabeth Appleby QC & David Mole QC)

4-5 Gray's Inn Square, Gray's Inn, London, WC1R 5JP
Tel: (020) 7404 5252 **Fax:** (020) 7242 7803 **DX:** 1029
Email: clerks@4-5graysinnsquare.co.uk **Website:** www.4-5graysinnsquare.co.uk

Head of Chambers	Elizabeth Appleby QC
	David Mole QC
Head Clerk	Michael Kaplan
Clerks	Mark Regan
	Daniel Perry
	Pavel Milsom
Chambers Manager	Tracey Jones
Tenants	47

Members:

Elizabeth Appleby QC (1965) (QC-1979)
David Mole QC (1970) (QC-1990)
William Wade QC (1946) (QC-1968)
Gary Flather QC (1962) (QC-1984)
Philip Vallance QC (1968) (QC-1989)
Reg Weir QC (1970) (QC-1985)QC (NI)
Brian Ash QC (1975) (QC-1990)
W Robert Griffiths QC (1974) (QC-1993)
John Steel QC (1978) (QC-1993)
Lady Hazel Fox QC (1950) (QC-1993)
Richard Spearman QC (1977) (QC-1996)
Timothy Straker QC (1977) (QC-1996)
Richard McManus QC (1982) (QC-1999)
Hodge M Malek QC (1983) (QC-1999)
John Hobson QC (1980) (QC-2000)
Sam Aaron (1986)SC(SA)
Robin Campbell (1969)
Nicholas Huskinson (1971)
Prof Ingrid Detter (1977)
Julian Chichester (1977)
Timothy Corner (1981)
Peter Village (1983)
Andrew Carnes (1984)
Murray Shanks (1984)
Paul Stinchcombe (1985)MP
Richard Humphreys (1986)
Garrett Byrne (1986)
James Ramsden (1987)
Philip Coppel (1994)
Thomas Hill (1988)
Geraldine Clark (1988)
Gillian Carrington (1990)
Paul Brown (1991)
Andrew Tabachnik (1991)
Andrew Fraser-Urquhart (1993)
Robert White (1993)
Dr Ami Barav (1993)
Sarah-Jane Davies (1996)
Jonathan Moffett (1996)
Andrew Sharland (1996)
James Strachan (1996)
Robert Palmer (1998)
Deok-Joo Rhee (1998)
Prof Malcolm Grant (1998)
Clare Lockhart (1999)
Paul Greatorex (1999)
Jonathan Auburn (1999)

The Chambers: 4-5 Gray's Inn Square is regarded as one of the leading chambers in London, and its pre-eminence has been recognised for many years in various independent legal publications. Members of chambers possess expertise and experience of the highest quality in the fields of public law and judicial review, planning and environmental law, commercial law, EU law, human rights, employment law and sports law. The intersection of these specialisations within chambers allows collaboration between members on complex litigation. Many members hold part time judicial appointments in England, as well as overseas. The joint Head of Chambers Elizabeth Appleby QC was the first woman to head a leading set of chambers. Several of the present juniors are on the Treasury Panels of Counsel instructed on behalf of the Crown.The chambers have been the first set to appoint an academic panel as a research and advisory facility. Its members are Professor Craig (administrative), Professor M Grant (local government and planning), Professor P Davies (Employment), Professor J Usher (EU), Professor E Barendt (media, human rights, welfare), Professor A Arnull (Birmingham), Professor D Harris (Nottingham – international law and human rights).

Former Members: The Right Honourable Lord Justice Schiemann; The Right Honourable Lord Justice Keene; The Honourable Mr Justice Collins; The Honourable Mr Justice Moses; The Honourable Mr Justice Sullivan; The Honourable Mr Justice Ouseley; Sir Douglas Frank QC, former President of the Lands Tribunal; His Honour Judge Marder QC, former President of the Lands Tribunal; His Honour Judge Barratt QC, Victor Wellings QC, former President of the Lands Tribunal, His Honour Judge Gregory Stone QC.

Door Tenants: Professor G H Treitel QC; Professor E P Ellinger; Lord Borrie QC; Sir John Freeland QC (1952)(QC-1987); Professor Sir D G T Williams; Patrick Patelin (Juriste d'Enterprise, Paris); Narinder Hargun (Bermuda); Brian Harris QC; Jeremy Gauntlett (SC) (South Africa); John Sacker QC (NSW); Mansoor Jamal Malik (Oman); Professor M Grant (Cantab); William Orbinson.

Work Undertaken:

Public Law/Judicial Review: Members of chambers have considerable experience in the fields of public law and judicial review. Members appear frequently in court on behalf of individual applicants and companies whose rights may be affected by the decisions of public bodies and on behalf of local authorities, central government departments and other public bodies such as regulatory authorities. Chambers are especially well placed to advise on all matters relating to the Human Rights Act 1998 which will inevitably impact on all areas of UK law.

Planning & Environmental Law: 4-5 Gray's Inn Square is one of the leading sets in both planning and environmental law, providing advice or advocacy to developers, government departments, local authorities and objectors in all aspects of these and related fields. Members of chambers regularly appear in public

Continued overleaf

inquiries held under planning and related legislation and in the High Court in statutory appeals and applications for judicial review.

Commercial Law: The core of the set's commercial work relates to domestic and international banking (including securities), insurance and reinsurance and the sale of goods and international trade. A wide range of other contract-related work is also done. There is considerable experience in dealing with conflict of law problems and jurisdictional disputes, including under the Brussels Convention and its successors, and in financial regulation work which intersects with judicial review.

European Law: This is one of the leading sets in both European Union Law and the European Convention on Human Rights. Members of chambers have appeared in Luxembourg and in Strasbourg. Chambers is in pole position to advise clients on the implications of the Human Rights Act 1998.

Employment Law: The work includes commercial (restraint of trade; wrongful dismissal), European (transfer of undertakings; equal pay), collective (trade unions; industrial action) and individual (sex, race and disability discrimination; unfair dismissal).

Other Areas: Defamation, media law, sports law, breach of confidence, professional negligence.

Publications: All members of chambers have either written or contributed to leading legal publications, ranging from Halsbury's *Laws of England* to text books on human rights and the *Encyclopedia of Planning.*

International: Members of chambers have appeared in the Privy Council, the European Court of Justice and of Human Rights, international arbitration tribunals and other courts worldwide, including the Far East, the Carribean, Gibraltar, Belfast, Bermuda, Anguilla and Trinidad. One member is a former Judge of the Court of Appeal in Swaziland and a current Judge of the Court of Appeal in Lesotho.

Set No.
56 **6 GRAY'S INN SQUARE** (Michael Boardman)

6 Gray's Inn Square, Gray's Inn, London, WC1R 5AZ **Tel:** (020) 7242 1052 **Fax:** (020) 7405 4934 **DX:** 224 **Email:** 6graysinn@clara.co.uk
Website: www.6gis.co.uk

Set No.
57 **8 GRAY'S INN SQUARE** (Patrick C. Soares)

8 Gray's Inn Square, Gray's Inn, London, WC1R 5AZ
Tel: (020) 7242 3529 **Fax:** (020) 7404 0395 **DX:** 411 (Ch.Ln.)

Head of Chambers	Patrick C. Soares
Senior Clerk	Jane Fullbrook
Tenants	8

Members:

Patrick C. Soares (1983)LLB, LLM, FTII
Barry McCutcheon (1975)BA, LLM, FTII
David J. Brownbill (1989)LLB
Patrick Way (1994)
Christopher Whitehouse (1997)
Emma J.M. Chamberlain (1998)
Ian Ferrier (1976)MA (Oxon)
Denzil Davies (1965)

The Chambers: 8 Gray's Inn Square is a leading set of tax chambers. The primary work of chambers is to advise on all aspects of taxation, with additional specialisations offered in respect of trusts, wills, company law, international estate and tax planning and related chancery matters. A major distinguishing feature of the set is that all members have previous professional or commercial experience before commencing practice at the Bar.

Work Undertaken: UK tax planning, international tax and estate planning, Chancery.

Publications: *The Property Law Bulletin; Trusts for Europe; VAT Planning for Property Transactions; Land and Tax Planning; Trusts and Tax Planning; Taxation of Overseas Trusts; Taxation of Land development; Tax Strategy for Conveyancing; McCutcheon on Inheritance Tax; Planning for Executive Share Schemes; Private Client Business; Journal of International Trust and Corporate Planning; British Tax Encylopedia; Conveyancer and Property Lawyer; Tolley's UK Taxation of Trusts; Value Added Tax – The British System Explained.*

8 14 GRAY'S INN SQUARE (Joanna Dodson QC)

14 Gray's Inn Square, Gray's Inn, London, WC1R 5JP
Tel: (020) 7242 0858 **Fax:** (020) 7242 5434 **DX:** 399 (Ch.Ln.)
Email: clerks@14graysinnsquare.co.uk

Head of Chambers	Joanna Dodson QC
Senior Clerk	Geoffrey Carr
Tenants	28

Members:

Joanna Dodson QC (1970) (QC-1993)
Louise S. Godfrey QC (1972) (QC-1991) *
David G P Turner QC (1976) (QC-2000)
Joanna Hall (1973)
Mhairi McNab (1974)
Barbara Slomnicka (1976)
Sarah Forster (1976)
Gillian Brasse (1977)
Brenda Morris (1978)
Gillian Marks (1981)
Karen McLaughlin (1982)
Caroline Reid (1982)
Monica Ford (1984)
Mark Emanuel (1985)
Pamela Warner (1985)
Richard Buswell (1985)
Karoline Sutton (1986)
Patricia Roberts (1987)
Rebecca Brown (1989)
Mark Jarman (1989)
Richard Alomo (1990)
Samantha King (1990)
Jonathan Tod (1990)
David Bedingfield (1991)
Dominic Brazil (1995)
Samantha Whittam (1995)
Ronan O'Donovan (1995)
Michael Glaser (1998)
Christopher Miller (1998)

* Door Tenant

The Chambers: A family and civil set with particular expertise in children's cases and financial matters, with a strong general common law side. Members of chambers belong to the Family Law Bar Association. Chambers are both Barmark and ISO 9002 accredited.

Work Undertaken: Family and matrimonial, including wardship, adoption, care, children and ancillary relief; personal injury, including running-down accidents; employment and labour law; landlord and tenant; housing; licensing work; building and construction; contract cases.
Additional Areas of Work: Civil liberties; crime; company; discrimination; ecclesiastical; judicial review; police cases; product liability; professional negligence; sale of goods; welfare; immigration/asylum.

Clientele: Individuals, companies, local authorities, guardians ad litem, the Official Solicitor.

International: One member is a member of the Georgia Bar.

Recruitment: Tenancy applications should be sent to Joanna Dodson QC; pupillage applications to Ronan O'Donovan. Two first six and one second six months pupils are taken each year. Awards of £4,000 are offered for the first six months of pupillage and minimum earnings are guaranteed at that level for the second six. Mini-pupillages are available.

9 GRAY'S INN TAX CHAMBERS (Milton Grundy)

Third Floor, Gray's Inn Chambers, Gray's Inn, London, WC1R 5JA
Tel: (020) 7242 2642 **Fax:** (020) 7831 9017 **DX:** 352 London Chancery Lane
Email: clerks@taxbar.com **Website:** www.taxbar.com

Head of Chambers	Milton Grundy
Senior Clerk	Chris Broom
Tenants	14

Members:

Milton Grundy (1954)
Michael Flesch QC (1963) (QC-1983)
David Goldberg QC (1971) (QC-1987)
David Goy QC (1973) (QC-1991)
John Walters QC (1977) (QC-1997)
Felicity Cullen (1985)
Philip Baker (1979)
Barrie Akin (1976)
Hugh McKay (1990)
Aparna Nathan (1994)
Conrad McDonnell (1994)
Nicola Shaw (1995)
Claire Simpson (1999)
Michael Thomas (2001)
Graham Wilson (1975) *
Brian Cleave QC (1999) (QC-1999) *

* Door Tenant

The Chambers: Gray's Inn Tax Chambers is a leading set of specialist tax practitioners. Its members deal with all aspects of UK revenue law and cover all areas of work dealt with by tax practitioners, from accumulation and maintenance settlements to zero-coupon bonds. They have established expertise in litigation before the Special Commissioners, General Commissioners, the VAT and Duties Tribunals, the Supreme Court, the House of Lords, the Privy Council, the European Court of Justice and the courts of certain colonies, Commonwealth and foreign jurisdictions. Chambers are fully computerised and maintain a popular website, which offers a rapid reporting of tax cases. The address is www.taxbar.com.
Appointments & Memberships: All members of chambers belong to the Revenue Bar Association of which Michael Flesch is a former chairman and Hugh McKay is a former secretary. Milton Grundy is president of the International Tax Planning Association and a fellow of the Chartered Institute of Taxa-

Continued overleaf

tion; he is the draftsman of the Trusts Law of the Cayman Islands and (with Philip Baker) of the IBC Act and the Trusts Act of Belize. John Walters QC and Barrie Akin are chartered accountants. Philip Baker is a visiting professor, and Aparna Nathan a visiting lecturer, at London University. Hugh McKay is on the Customs and Excise VAT Tribunal advocates list.

Work Undertaken: Members give advice to taxpayers who are in dispute with the Inland Revenue or Customs and advise clients on the planning of their business and personal affairs. They advise on corporate tax planning including acquisitions, mergers, takeovers and methods of financing, property transactions, international business, cross-border transactions, offshore and domestic trusts estate planning and all the direct and indirect taxes, including VAT. Work is accepted from (amongst others) local authorities, companies, charities and private clients. Direct Professional Access is accepted from members of the appropriate professional bodies.

Publications: Members have written, contributed to, or edited: *Whiteman on Income Tax*; *VAT and Property*; *British Tax Review*; *Asset Protection Trusts*; *Double Taxation Conventions and International Tax Law*; *Value Added Tax Encyclopedia*; *Offshore Business Centres*; *The Law of Partnership Taxation*; *Copinger and Skone James on Copyright*; *The Laws of the Internet*; *The International Trust and Estate Law Reports and International Law Reports*; various articles on domestic and international tax developments.

International: Languages spoken include Chinese (Mandarin and some Cantonese), French, German, Hebrew, Hindi, Italian and Tamil. Members of chambers advise clients from Hong Kong, Singapore, Australia, New Zealand, the USA and Mauritius. Chambers also advise the revenue departments of Commonwealth countries and ex-colonies on the interpretation and drafting of their statutes.

Set No. 60

100E GREAT PORTLAND STREET

100E Great Portland Street, London, W1N 5PD **Tel:** (020) 7636 6323 **Fax:** (020) 7436 3544 **DX:** 94252 Marylebone

Set No. 61

2 HARCOURT BUILDINGS, ATKINSON BEVAN CHAMBERS

(Nicholas Atkinson QC & John Bevan QC)

2 Harcourt Buildings, Temple, London, EC4Y 9DB
Tel: (020) 7353 2112 **Fax:** (020) 7353 8339 **DX:** 489 Chancery Lane
Email: clerks@2hb.co.uk **Website:** www.2hb.co.uk

Head of Chambers	Nicholas Atkinson QC John Bevan QC
Senior Clerk	Hadyn Robson
Tenants	33

Members:

Nigel Mylne QC (1963) (QC-1984)
John Bevan QC (1970) (QC-1997)MA (Cantab)
Nicholas Atkinson QC (1971) (QC-1991)
John Williams (1973)LLB
Stephen Smyth (1974)
Stephen Clayton (1973)
Nicholas Loraine-Smith (1977)BA (Oxon)
William Adlard (1978) *
Philip Shorrock (1978)BA (Cantab)
Robin Leach (1979)MA (St Andrews)
Mark Gadsden (1980)BA (Oxon)
Aftab Jafferjee (1980)BA (Dunelm)
Timothy Probert-Wood (1983)LLB (Hull)
Rhyddian Willis (1984)LLB (Nottingham)
Ian Darling (1985)LLB (London)
Lucia Whittle-Martin (1985)BSc (London)
Patrick Gibbs (1986)BA (Oxon)
Jonathan Rees (1987)BA (Oxon)
Matthew Farmer (1987)BA (London)
Peter Clement (1988)LLM LLB (London)
Laura Cobbs (1989)LLB (Buckingham) *
Stewart Hamblin (1990)BA (Leicester)
Toby Fitzgerald (1993)BSc (Bristol)
Thomas Wilkins (1993)BSc (Bristol)
James Dawes (1993)BSc (Dunelm)
Lisa Wilding (1993)MA (Cantab)
Peter Coombe (1994)BA (Oxon)
Sally Halkerston (1994)BA (Kingston)
Sally Thompson (1994)AGSM
Benedict Kelleher (1994)LLB MSc (Bristol)
William Emlyn Jones (1996)(Soton) LLB
Jennifer Knight (1996)LLB (Exeter)
Kevin Baumber (1998)LLB (Essex & Nijmegen) BCL (Oxon)
Marina Churchill (1989)LLB (Buckingham) *
Quinn Hawkins (1999)LLB (Westminster)
Christopher Stimpson (1999)MA (Edinburgh)

* Door Tenant

The Chambers: With three QCs and two Senior Treasury Counsel, Atkinson Bevan Chambers is a specialist criminal set practising predominantly in London and on the South Eastern and Western Circuits. The set has been continuously represented on the Treasury Counsel team since 1953.

Work Undertaken: Members of chambers both defend and prosecute the full spectrum of criminal cases, ranging from high profile and sensitive matters requiring specialist expertise such as terrorism, murder, corruption and serious fraud, to the more routine offences found everyday in the Magistrates and Crown

Courts. Chambers also undertake work in other practice areas including confiscation, sports law, regulatory work, health and safety, food and drugs, trades descriptions, police and medical disciplinary tribunals, coroners' inquests, extradition, data protection, courts martial and ecclesiastical matters.

Clientele: Chambers receive instructions from individual private and public clients including government departments (SFO, CPS), local authorities, corporate bodies and sporting clients.

Recruitment: Applications to Lisa Wilding or Sue Watt. The set is a member of OLPAS/PACH. Chambers take four to five pupils completing six and 12 month pupillages at any one time. Discretionary funding is available.

No. 2

2 HARCOURT BUILDINGS (Roger Henderson QC)

2 Harcourt Buildings (Ground Floor), Temple, London, EC4Y 9DB
Tel: (020) 7583 9020 **Fax:** (020) 7583 2686 **DX:** LDE 1039
Email: clerks@harcourt.co.uk **Website:** www.harcourt.co.uk

Head of Chambers	Roger Henderson QC
Senior Clerk	John White
Tenants	43

Members:

Roger Henderson QC (1964) (QC-1980) +
Piers Ashworth QC (1956) (QC-1973) +
Richard Mawrey QC (1964) (QC-1986) +
Adrian Brunner QC (1968) (QC-1994) +
Stephen Powles QC (1972) (QC-1995) +
Andrew Prynne QC (1975) (QC-1995)
Peter Susman QC (1966) (QC-1997)
Alan Dashwood (1969)
Adrian Cooper (1970) +
Bernard O'Sullivan (1971)
Gavin Gore-Andrews (1972)
Andrew Jordan (1974)
Jonathan Harvey (1974)
Kenneth Hamer (1975) +
Lawrence West (1979) +
Mark Piercy (1976)
Roger Eastman (1978)
Barbara Cameron (1979)
James Palmer (1983)
Charles Gibson QC (1984) (QC-2001)
George Alliott (1981)
Terence Bergin (1985)
Conrad Griffiths (1986)
Jonathan Steinert (1986)
Benjamin Battcock (1987)
Marina Wheeler (1987)
Rhodri Williams (1987)
Andrew Davies (1988)
Wendy Outhwaite (1990)
Patrick Green (1990)
Charles Bourne (1991)
Prashant Popat (1992)
Oliver Campbell (1992)
Isabella Zornoza (1993)
Malcolm Sheehan (1993)
Felicia Fenston (1994)
Geraint Webb (1995)
Toby Riley-Smith (1995)
Julianna Mitchell (1994)
Andrew Kinnier (1996)
James Martin-Jenkins (1997)
Andrew Henderson (1999)
Tamara Trefusis (1999)
Adam Heppinstall (1999)
Adrian Garner (1985) *
Lance Ashworth (1987) *
Frank Schoneveld (1992) *
Debra Holland (1996) *
Heather Tibbo (1989) *
Melissa Cacciutti (1997) *

* Door Tenant + Recorder

Work Undertaken: Commercial and common law, particularly product liability; personal injury; medical and other professional negligence; insurance; local government; public procurement; public law; judicial review; environmental law; health and safety; railways; telecommunications; information technology; intellectual property; education; food; sport; employment and discrimination; human rights: construction and engineering; consumer credit; financial services; EU law; competition; property litigation; land; housing; landlord and tenant; family and inheritance.

International: Members of chambers also practise at the above address in association with the English barristers of the firm of Stanbrook & Hooper, 2 Rue de Taciturne, B-1000 Brussels under the name Stanbrook and Henderson.

Set No. 63

2 HARCOURT BUILDINGS (Gerard Ryan QC)

2 Harcourt Buildings, Temple, London, EC4Y 9DB
Tel: (020) 7353 8415 **Fax:** (020) 7353 7622 **DX:** 402 LDE
Email: clerks@2hb.law.co.uk

Head of Chambers	Gerard Ryan QC
Senior Clerk	Allen Collier
First Junior Clerk	Paul Munday
Second Junior Clerk	Andrew Briton
Tenants	24

Members:

Gerard Ryan QC (1955) (QC-1981)
Sheila Cameron QC (1957) (QC-1983)
Robin Purchas QC (1968) (QC-1987)
Richard Phillips QC (1970) (QC-1990)
Charles George QC (1974) (QC-1992)
Clive Newberry QC (1978) (QC-1993)
Keith Lindblom QC (1980) (QC-1996)
Andrew Kelly QC (1978) (QC-2000)
Robert McCracken (1973)
Philip Petchey (1976)
Jonathan Milner (1977)
Timothy Comyn (1980)
Andrew Tait (1981)
Craig Howell Williams (1983)
Suzanne Ornsby (1986)
Meyric Lewis (1986)
Andrew Newcombe (1987)
Charles Mynors (1988)
Gregory Jones (1991)
Douglas Edwards (1992)
Paul Hardy (1992)
Joanna Clayton (1995)
James Pereira (1996)
Hereward Phillpot (1997)

The Chambers: A specialist chambers for more than half a century with particular expertise in planning, environmental, property, and administrative law. Disabled conference facilities are available by prior arrangement. Members accept instructions via Direct Professional Access. A chambers' brochure is available on request. All members of chambers belong to the Planning and Environment Bar Association, of which Robin Purchas QC is Vice Chairman and Douglas Edwards is Secretary. Members of chambers also belong to the Administrative Law Bar Association, the Bar European Group, the Association for Regulated Procurement, the United Kingdom Environmental Law Association, the Ecclesiastical Law Society, The Education Law Society and the Parliamentary Bar. Robin Purchas QC is a Deputy High Court Judge, three members of chambers are Recorders of the Crown Court and two are Diocesan Chancellors. Meyric Lewis is a member of the Supplementary Panel of Junior Counsel to the Crown. Gerard Ryan QC chaired the Tribunal of Inquiry into the gas explosion at Loscoe, Derbyshire. Charles George QC conducted the Independent Inquiry into Planning Decisions in the London Borough of Brent. Robert McCracken was Chairman of the United Kingdom Environmental Law Association. Sheila Cameron QC is Dean of the Arches and Auditor, Vicar General of the Province of Canterbury and was a Parliamentary Boundary Commissioner for England. Four members of chambers are Assistant Parliamentary Boundary Commissioners for England.

Former Members: Roy Vandermeer QC, the Inspector at the Heathrow Terminal Five inquiry; Peter Boydell QC, former Leader of the Parliamentary Bar and first Chairman of what is now the Planning and Environment Bar Association; Michael Harrison QC, now Mr Justice Harrison; Michael Mann QC, later Lord Justice Mann; Sir John Drinkwater QC.

Work Undertaken: Public law, planning, environmental (including regulatory offences), contaminated land, compulsory purchase, administrative, local government, public procurement, parliamentary, transport and works, energy, utilities, education, highways, licensing, housing, human rights (European Convention) and EU Law.

Additional Areas: Ecclesiastical law; landlord and tenant; the law of commons and that relating to easements, agricultural tenancies, rating and restrictive covenants.

Publications: *Education Case Reports* (editor-in-chief), *Journal of Planning and Environment Law* (editorial board), *Journal of Architectural Conservation* (editorial board), *Planning Appeal Decisions* (joint editor), *Planning and Environmental Law Bulletin* (joint editor), *Yearbook of European Law* (co-editor), *The Company Lawyer* (editorial board) and *European Financial Services Law* (advisory board). Charles Mynors is the author of *Planning Applications and Appeals* (1987), *Planning Control and the Display of Advertisements* (1992) and *Listed Buildings and Conservation Areas* (1995). Robert McCracken, Gregory Jones and James Pereira are co-authors of *Statutory Nuisance – Law and Practice* (2001).

International: Chambers include members called to the Dublin and Northern Ireland Bars.

Set No. 64

HARCOURT CHAMBERS (June Rodgers)

2 Harcourt Buildings, Temple, London, EC4Y 9DB
Tel: (020) 7353 6961 **Fax:** (020) 7353 6968 **DX:** 373
Email: clerks@harcourtchambers.law.co.uk **Website:** www.harcourtchambers.law.co.uk

Head of Chambers	June Rodgers
Senior Clerk	Brian Wheeler
Tenants	24

Members:

June Rodgers (1971)MA (Dublin), MA(Oxon), Chancellor Diocese of Gloucester
Roger Evans (1970)MA (Cantab)
Benedict Sefi (1972)BA (Oxon)
John Dixon (1975)MA (Oxon)
Gavyn Arthur (1975)MA (Oxon)
Stephen Barstow (1976)MA (Cantab)
Jonathan Baker QC (1978) (QC-2001)MA (Cantab)
Alicia Collinson (1982)MA, MPhil (Oxon)
Christopher Frazer (1983)MA, LLM (Cantab)
Frances Judd (1984)BA (Cantab)
Edward Hess (1985)MA (Cantab)
Matthew Brett (1987)BA (Oxon)
Piers Pressdee (1991)BA (Cantab)
Sara Granshaw (1991)BA (Oxon)
Sally Max (1991)BA (Cantab)
Rohan Auld (1992)BA (Cantab)
Louise Potter (1993)MA (Oxon)
John Vater (1995)BA (Oxon)
Nicholas Goodwin (1995)BA (Oxon)
Aidan Vine (1995)BA (Oxon) MA (Cornell)
Jonathan Sampson (1997)BA (Cantab)
Oliver Wright (1998)BA (Cantab)
Andrew Leong (1998)LLB (Bristol)
Edward Kirkwood (1999)LLB (Exeter)
Peter Clarke (1970) *
Bernard Lever (1975) *

* Door Tenant

The Chambers: Based in London and Oxford, Harcourt Chambers provides a friendly and efficient advisory and advocacy service within five specialist practice groups: family, business, property, local government and personal injury. Individual members of chambers have additional areas of personal specialisation, particularly in election law, judicial review, planning, media, criminal and ecclesiastical law.

Set No. 65

HARDWICKE BUILDING (Nicholas Stewart QC)

Hardwicke Building, New Square, Lincoln's Inn, London, WC2A 3SB
Tel: (020) 7242 2523 **Fax:** (020) 7691 1234 **DX:** LDE393
Email: clerks@hardwicke.co.uk **Website:** www.hardwicke.co.uk

Head of Chambers	Nicholas Stewart QC
Clerks	Kevin Mitchell
	Greg Piner
	Gary Brown
	Lloyd Smith
Tenants	85

Members:

Nicholas Stewart QC (1971) (QC-1987)
Walter Aylen QC (1962) (QC-1983)
George F. Pulman QC (1971) (QC-1989)
Romie Tager QC (1970) (QC-1995)
Patrick Upward QC (1972) (QC-1996)
Nigel Jones QC (1976) (QC-1999)
Robert Willer (1970)
Frederic Coford (1971)
Kenneth Aylett (1972)
Lindsay Burn (1972)
Michael Hopmeier (1974)
James Pavry (1974)
Kenneth Craig (1975)
Philip Kremen (1975)
Stephen Lennard (1976)
Stephen Warner (1976)
Michael Oliver (1977)
James Vine (1977)
Steven Weddle (1977)
Philip Wakeham (1978)
Peter Walsh (1978)
Nicholas Baker (1980)
Rory Field (1980)
Indira Ramsahoye (1980)
David Aaronberg (1981)
Hugh Jackson (1981)
Alan Smith (1981)
Neil Mendoza (1982)
William Bojczuk (1983)
Ian Brook (1983)
Timothy Banks (1983)
John Greenan (1984)
Debbie Taylor (1984)
Charles Briefel (1984)
Lindsey MacDonald (1985)
Jonathan Whitfield (1985)
Karl King (1985)
Montague Palfrey (1985)
Christopher Baylis (1986)
Michelle Stevens-Hoare (1986)
Tom Nicholson Pratt (1986)
James Mulholland (1986)
Francis Lloyd (1987)
Judith Spooner (1987)
Stephen Lyon (1987)
Paul Reed (1988)
Peter Kirby (1989)
Ann Mulligan (1989)
Steven Woolf (1989)
Caroline Hallissey (1990)
Eithne Ryan (1990)
Ian Clarke (1990)
Alexis Campbell (1990)
Sara Benbow (1990)
Kyriakos Argyropoulos (1991)
Kevin McCartney (1991)
Ingrid Newman (1992)
Colm Nugent (1992)
Richard Bates (1992)
Kerry Bretherton (1992)
Arthur Moore (1992)
Roshi Amiraftabi (1993)
Sabuhi Chaudhry (1993)
Emily Formby (1993)

Continued overleaf

Members continued:

David Preston (1993)
Niki Langridge (1993)
Brian St. Louis (1994)
Alexander Goold (1994)
Deanna Heer (1994)
Bart Casella (1995)
Lynn Freeston (1996)
Sarah Wood (1996)
Philip Grey (1996)
Edward Rowntree (1996)
David Pliener (1996)
Charles Bagot (1997)
Tianne Bell (1998)
Nicola Muir (1998)
Peter Roberts (1998)
Stephen Coyle (1998)
Rommilly Cummerson (1998)
Simon Calhaem (1999)
Andrew Lane (1999)
Charlotte Hadfield (1999)
Sophie Shotton (1999)
Sa'id Mosteshar *
Stephen Joelson *
Pauline Gray *

* Door Tenant

The Chambers: This modern, progressive set is large enough to contain strong teams specialising in civil and commercial law, crime and family law. Above all, it is dedicated to providing a high quality client-focused service to all its solicitors. For the latest and fullest information about Hardwicke Building, its teams and individual barristers, you are invited to visit their website.

Set No. 66

2 HARE COURT (Stephen Kramer QC)

2 Hare Court, Temple, London, EC4Y 7BH
Tel: (020) 7353 5324 **Fax:** (020) 7353 0667 **DX:** 444 (Ch.Ln.)
Email: clerks@2harecourt.com **Website:** www.2harecourt.com

Head of Chambers	Stephen Kramer QC
Senior Clerk	Deryk Butler
First Junior Clerk	Ian Fitzgerald
Chambers Administrator	Stephen Wall
Tenants	43

2 HARE COURT

Members:

Stephen Kramer QC (1970) (QC-1995)
Sir Allan Green QC (1959) (QC-1987)
Paul Worsley QC (1970) (QC-1990)
Anthony Morris QC (1970) (QC-1991)
Martin S Heslop QC (1972) (QC-1995)
Charles Salmon QC (1972) (QC-1996)
David Waters QC (1973) (QC-1999)
Andrew Radcliffe QC (1975) (QC-2000)
Jeremy Benson QC (1978) (QC-2001)
Brian Warner (1969)
Jacqueline Samuel (1971)
John Jones (1972)
Louise Kamill (1974)
Orlando Pownall (1975)
Martin Hicks (1977)
Andrew Lloyd-Eley (1979)
Andrew Colman (1980)
Ian Leist (1981)
David Howker (1982)
Jonathan Laidlaw (1982)
James Dawson (1984)
Sallie Bennett-Jenkins (1984)
David Brock (1984)
Michael Holland (1984)
Shani Barnes (1986)
Brian O'Neill (1987)
Kenneth Millett (1988)
Michael Logsdon (1988)
Brendan Kelly (1988)
Parmjit-Kaur Cheema (1989)
Marios P. Lambis (1989)
Christopher Hehir (1990)
Alex Lewis (1990)
Craig Ferguson (1992)
Kate Bex (1992)
Karim Khan (1992)
Nina Grahame (1993)
Christopher Foulkes (1994)
Stephen Brassington (1994)
Oliver Glasgow (1995)
Riel Karmy-Jones (1995)
Emma Lowe (1996)
Christopher Coltart (1998)

The Chambers: Chambers specialise in criminal law. Prosecution and defence work is undertaken at all levels of seriousness in London and throughout England and Wales. Chambers offer particular expertise, both prosecution and defence, in cases involving serious fraud and corruption. Other specialisations include extradition work (on behalf of both individuals and foreign governments), courts martial, coroners inquests, licensing and cases involving trades description and food and drugs legislation. Members of chambers include three Treasury Counsel at the Central Criminal Court, Standing Counsel to HM Customs and Excise, and many Recorders of the Crown Court. More information can be found on chambers' website and a brochure is available on request.

Set No.
67

3 HARE COURT (Mark Strachan QC)

3 Hare Court, Temple, London, EC4Y 7BJ
Tel: (020) 7415 7800 **Fax:** (020) 7415 7811 **DX:** 212 London
Email: clerks@3harecourt.com **Website:** www.3harecourt.com

Head of Chambers	Mark Strachan QC
Senior Clerk	James Donovan (07956) 498 217
Tenants	23

Members:

Mark Strachan QC (1969) (QC-1987)
Sir Godfray Le Quesne QC (1947) (QC-1962)
James Guthrie QC (1975) (QC-1993)
Richard Jones QC (1972) (QC-1996)
Michael Irvine (1964)
Iain McLeod (1969)
Terence Walker (1973)
Sebastian Neville-Clarke (1973)
Andrew Young (1977)
Pierre Janusz (1979)
Peter Knox (1983)
James Dingemans (1987)
Simon Davenport (1987)
Joseph O'Neill (1987)
Howard Stevens (1990)
Paul Marshall (1991)
Aidan Casey (1992)
Marcus Dignum (1994)
Thomas Roe (1995)
Ian Rogers (1995)
Katherine Deal (1997)
Katherine Awadalla (1998)
Sarah Crowther (1999)

The Chambers: A long-established set which offers a comprehensive service in all areas of law, with the exception of the well-recognised specialist fields, such as revenue. It has always had a strong connection with the work of the Privy Council. The chambers moved last year to 3 Hare Court from 1 Crown Office Row. The new accomodation will enable chambers to continue to provide a friendly, efficient and high quality service. The set has numerous connections abroad through its work in the Privy Council. A brochure is available from the senior clerk. Alternatively, up-to-date information can be found on chambers' website.

Work Undertaken: Members of chambers offer expertise in commercial and common law, although individual practices differ significantly.
General Commercial: Both domestic and international (including ICC and other arbitrations), banking, negotiable instruments, agency, insurance, sale and carriage of goods, building and engineering disputes, employment and industrial relations and professional negligence.
Appellate Work: In the Privy Council from overseas, covering most fields of law and in particular commercial and general common law work, cases dealing with the written constitutions of Commonwealth countries and criminal law.
Human Rights: Chambers already has considerable experience of the application of the Human Rights Act in English litigation.
Common Law: Most forms of civil litigation including personal injury and landlord and tenant work. Fields of practice of individual members of chambers include public and administrative law, family law and clinical negligence.

International: Languages spoken include Dutch, French, German, Italian and Spanish.

Recruitment: Chambers are a member of the OLPAS Scheme.

Set No.
68

HOGARTH CHAMBERS (Jonathan Rayner James QC & Christopher Morcom QC)

5 New Square, Lincoln's Inn, London, WC2A 3RJ
Tel: (020) 7404 0404 **Fax:** (020) 7404 0505 **DX:** 16 London
Email: barristers@hogarthchambers.com **Website:** www.hogarthchambers.com

Head of Chambers	Jonathan Rayner James QC Christopher Morcom QC
Chambers Director	Ian Duggan
Senior Clerk	Susan Harding
Assistant Clerk	Clive Nicholls
Clerks	Spencer Davis Matthew Morley
Tenants	27

Members:

Jonathan Rayner James QC (1971) (QC-1988)
Christopher Morcom QC (1963) (QC-1991)MA (Cantab)
Kevin Garnett QC (1975) (QC-1991)
Roger Wyand QC (1973) (QC-1997)MA (Cantab)
James Sunnucks (1950)DL
Ernest Scamell (1949)
Patrick Sinclair (1961)
John Ross Martyn (1969)FCIArb
David Micklethwait (1970)MA (Cantab)
Alexander Stewart (1975)
Edward Bragiel (1977)
Paul Dickens (1978)ARCO
Amanda Michaels (1981)
Julia Clark (1984)
John Adams (1984)LLB (Dunelm)
Nicholas Caddick (1986)
Guy Tritton (1987)BSc (Dunelm)
Gwilym Harbottle (1987)
Jessica Jones (1991)BSc (Soton)
Ashley Roughton (1992)BSc (Lond) PhD (Cantab)
Michael Edenborough (1992)MA (Cantab) DPhil (Oxon)
Richard Davis (1992)
James Graham (1994)MSc (Bristol)
Andrew Norris (1995)
Alistair Abbott (1996)
Simon Malynicz (1997)
George Hayman (1998)

Continued overleaf

The Chambers: This 27 member set was formed in April 2001 with the merger of 5 New Square (Jonathan Rayner James QC) and One Raymond Buildings (Christopher Morcom QC). Members specialise particularly in Intellectual Property and Media and Entertainment. They are responsible for several of the leading texts and have appeared in a number of important cases in the field.

Work Undertaken:

Intellectual Property: All aspects including patents (UK and European); trade marks (UK and CTM); passing off; registered designs; unregistered design right; plant varieties; rights in databases; copyright; copyright tribunal and related EC aspects.

Media & Entertainment: Including publising agreements; recording contracts; management agreements; merchandising rights; performers' rights; moral rights; confidential information and privacy; criminal remedies and related EC aspects.

Chancery/Commercial & Insolvency: General Commercial including e-commerce, general company law, including directors' duties, partnership and professional negligence. Property including landlord and tenant, boundaries and covenants. Succession. Insolvency both personal and corporate.

Set No. 69

HOLLIS WHITEMAN CHAMBERS (QEB) (Julian Bevan QC & Peter Whiteman QC)

Queen Elizabeth Building, Temple, London, EC4Y 9BS
Tel: (020) 7583 5766 **Fax:** (020) 7353 0339 **DX:** 482 London/Chancery Lane
Email: barristers@holliswhiteman.co.uk **Website:** www.holliswhiteman.co.uk

Head of Chambers	Julian Bevan QC Peter Whiteman QC
Senior Clerk	Will Whitford
Tenants	53

Queen Elizabeth Building | *Hollis Whiteman Chambers*

Members:

Julian Bevan QC (1962) (QC-1991)
Peter Whiteman QC (1967) (QC-1977)
Lord Carlisle QC (1954) (QC-1971)
Robin Grey QC (1957) (QC-1979)
Alan Suckling QC (1963) (QC-1983)
Anthony Glass QC (1965) (QC-1986)
Vivian Robinson QC (1967) (QC-1986)
John Hilton QC (1964) (QC-1990)
David Evans QC (1972) (QC-1991)
Timothy Langdale QC (1966) (QC-1992)
David Bate QC (1969) (QC-1994)
Rebecca Poulet QC (1975) (QC-1995)
Peter Kyte QC (1970) (QC-1996)
Peter Clarke QC (1973) (QC-1997)
John Kelsey-Fry QC (1978) (QC-2000)
William Boyce QC (1976) (QC-2001)
Anthony Wilcken (1966)
Christopher Mitchell (1968)
Linda Strudwick (1973)
Ian Paton (1975)
Peter Doyle (1975)
Richard Horwell (1976)
David Jeremy (1977)
Jeremy Donne (1978)
Mark Ellison (1979)
Peter Finnigan (1979)
Nick Wood (1980)
Gareth Rees (1981)
Tom Kark (1982)
Edward Brown (1983)
Ian Stern (1983)
Jane Sullivan (1984)
Phillip Bennetts (1986)
Sean Larkin (1987)
Jocelyn Sparks (1987)
Edward Henry (1988)
Sarah Plaschkes (1988)
Ian Winter (1988)
Zoe Johnson (1990)
Emma Lowry (1991)
Lydia Barnfather (1992)
Victoria Coward (1992)
Peter Warne (1993)
Selva Ramasamy (1992)
Adrian Darbishire (1993)
Benjamin Summers (1994)
Mark Aldred (1996)
Jonathan Barnard (1997)
Julian Evans (1997)
Rebecca Harris (1997)
Clare Sibson (1997)
Natasha Tahta (1998)
Jocelyn Ledward (1999)

The Chambers: Hollis Whiteman Chambers (QEB) is a long-established specialist criminal set, providing advocacy and advice of the highest quality. Chambers are dedicated to giving an effective and individual service whenever needed, and at short notice. The 53 members have expertise at all levels of seniority: 16 QCs and three Treasury Counsel are matched with a strong middle order and 20 tenants of less than 15 years' call. 23 tenants sit as Recorders in the Crown Court. Chambers defend and prosecute from the Magistrates' Court to the House of Lords. Members of chambers are regularly involved in complex, high profile and grave cases. There is also daily representation in courts of all levels, at every stage of

proceedings. In addition to 'pure crime' the set specialises in confiscation proceedings, judicial review regarding criminal and disciplinary matters, food law, Health and Safety Act, environmental law, trading standards cases, licensing, extradition and public inquiries. It has prepared for, and is already experienced in, the impact of human rights law upon all areas of practice. The set's expertise and excellence has led to increased demand for services in areas other than crime. As a result, it now enjoys an established reputation for advice and advocacy of the highest quality before professional tribunals including the General Medical Council, General Optical Council, General Dental Council, Courts-Martial and Police Disciplinary Boards. Peter Whiteman QC, a deputy High Court judge, provides specialist advice, particularly on corporate and international tax law, and representation at both national and international levels.

Set No.
70

KEATING CHAMBERS (Richard Fernyhough QC)

10 Essex Street, Outer Temple, London, WC2R 3AA
Tel: (020) 7544 2600 **Fax:** (020) 7240 7722 **DX:** 1045
Email: clerks@keatingchambers.com

Head of Chambers	Richard Fernyhough QC
Senior Clerk	Barry Bridgman
Tenants	36

KEATING 10 ESSEX STREET CHAMBERS

Members:

Richard Fernyhough QC (1970) (QC-1986)
John Uff QC (1970) (QC-1983)
Martin Collins QC (1952) (QC-1972)
Christopher Thomas QC (1973) (QC-1989)
John Marrin QC (1974) (QC-1990)
Stephen Furst QC (1975) (QC-1991)
Timothy Elliott QC (1975) (QC-1992)
Vivian Ramsey QC (1979) (QC-1992)
Robert Gaitskell QC (1978) (QC-1994)
Philip Boulding QC (1979) (QC-1996)
Paul Darling QC (1983) (QC-1999)
Marcus Taverner QC (1981) (QC-2000)
Peter Coulson QC (1982) (QC-2001)
Alan Steynor (1975)
Rosemary Jackson (1981)
Ian Pennicott (1982)
Finola O'Farrell (1983)
Adrian Williamson (1983)
Alexander Nissen (1985)
Nerys Jefford (1986)
Louise Randall (1988)
Robert Evans (1989)
Sarah Hannaford (1989)
Marc Rowlands (1991)
Simon Hargreaves (1990)
Vincent Moran (1991)
Richard Harding (1992)
Jane Lemon (1993)
Piers Stansfield (1993)
Jonathan Lee (1993)
Simon Hughes (1995)
Abdul-Lateef Jinadu (1995)
Richard Coplin (1997)
Gaynor Chambers (1998)
Gideon Scott-Holland (1999)
Samuel Townend (1999)

The Chambers: Keating Chambers specialises in all aspects of construction and engineering matters in the UK and abroad, and in the associated areas of professional negligence, IT and other property-related matters.

Work Undertaken: Chambers' work covers the whole spectrum of disputes and advisory work from the very small to the exceptionally large. Members of chambers undertake advisory work and act in litigation and arbitration both in the UK and abroad. Senior members of chambers are also often appointed as arbitrators and legal assessors. Members of chambers are active in all forms of alternative dispute resolution (some being accredited mediators) and in all aspects of adjudication, both acting for the parties and as adjudicators.

Main Areas: Construction and all kinds of engineering matters (including civil, mechanical, electrical and chemical engineering projects, major infrastucture projects, process plants, power plants, oil, coal and gas recovery); development contracts; contractual claims; claims in respect of defective buildings and other structures; the professional negligence of architects, surveyors, valuers, engineers and other consultants concerned with buildings and engineering projects; local authority work (including building control work); IT; European law, particularly public procurement and competition law as it affects building, engineering and IT projects.

Additional Areas: Performance bonds and warranties; most types of commercial and insurance contracts; freezing and other types of injunctions. Some members of chambers also have experience in environmental law, aviation law, landlord and tenant and other property-related areas.

Clientele: Building contractors (both main and sub-contractors); property owners and developers; government departments and agencies; local authorities; architects; engineers; quantity surveyors; surveyors; insurance companies; and professional indemnity insurers. Members of chambers accept work by Direct Professional Access.

International: Many members of chambers advise or act in international litigation or arbitration, whether based on the UK or abroad. Members of chambers act in and are appointed as arbitrators particularly in ICC, LCIA, FIDIC and Hong Kong arbitrations.

Recruitment: Both six- and twelve-month pupillages are offered. Awards of up to £27,500 over a 12 month period are available to pupils, with an additional £7,500 to cover the BVC year available.

Set No.
71

ONE KING'S BENCH WALK (Anthony Hacking QC)

1 King's Bench Walk, Temple, London, EC4Y 7DB
Tel: (020) 7936 1500 **Fax:** (020) 7936 1590 **DX:** LDE 20
Email: ddear@1kbw.co.uk **Website:** www.1kbw.co.uk

Head of Chambers	Anthony Hacking QC
Senior Clerk	David Dear
Practice Manager	Lisa Pavlovsky
Tenants	46

One King's Bench Walk
THE CHAMBERS OF ANTHONY HACKING QC

Members:

Anthony Hacking QC (1965) (QC-1983)
Rodger Hayward Smith QC (1967) (QC-1988)
James Townend QC (1962) (QC-1978)
Barry Singleton QC (1968) (QC-1989)
Judith Parker QC (1973) (QC-1991)
Camden Pratt QC (1970) (QC-1992)
Pamela Scriven QC (1970) (QC-1992)
Richard Anelay QC (1970) (QC-1993)
Roderic Wood QC (1974) (QC-1993)
Stephen Bellamy QC (1974) (QC-1996)
Michael Gale QC (1957) (QC-1979)
James Turner QC (1976) (QC-1998)
Andrew McFarlane QC (1977) (QC-1998)
Charles Howard QC (1975) (QC-1999)
Anthony Kirk QC (1981) (QC-2001)
Clive Newton (1968)
Michael Warren (1971)
John Reddish (1973)
Gordon Jackson (1989)(1979 QC 1990 Scot.)
Caroline Budden (1977)
Sarah Staite (1979)
Caroline Lister (1980)
Susan R Maidment (1968) *
Julian Woodbridge (1981)
Christopher Pocock (1984)
Stephen Shay (1984)
Deborah Eaton (1985)
Janet Waddicor (1985)
Sarah O'Connor (1986)
Deiniol Cellan-Jones (1988)
Neil Mercer (1988)
Philip Marshall (1989)
Elizabeth Selman (1989)
Richard Barton (1990)
Marcus Fletcher (1990)
Caroline Gibson (1990)
Joanna Grice (1991)
James Roberts (1993)
Richard Harrison (1993)
Ian Cook (1994)
Graham Crosthwaite (1995)
Benedick Rayment (1996)
Shaun Esprit (1996)
Alan Gardner (1997)
Nicholas Anderson (1995)
Richard Castle (1998)
Harry Oliver (1999)
Stephen Wildblood QC (1981) (QC-1999) *
Heather Swindells QC (1974) (QC-1995) *

* Door Tenant

The Chambers: This chambers is a large, long established set, specialising in family, criminal and civil law. It has strength at all levels of seniority and teams of counsel can be provided for more protracted and complex cases. The work of chambers is principally in London and on the South Eastern Circuit but work is also undertaken throughout the country. Also at One King's Bench Walk at Lewes, 174 High Street, Lewes, BN7 1YE. Tel: (01273) 402600; Fax: (01273) 402609

Work Undertaken: Chambers has specialist groups of members for the three main areas of work who meet regularly holding internal and external lectures and drawing upon their members' expertise and experience.
Family: Chambers has considerable depth of expertise in all aspects of family law including the related areas of probate and trusts, Inheritance Act, Human Rights Act, judicial review and solicitors negligence work. The family law group is subdivided into child law and matrimonial finance in order to allow for greater emphasis to be placed upon each of these distinct areas.
Criminal: Chambers has an established criminal law practice in London and the South East representing both prosecution and defence and including serious fraud work.
Civil: Members of chambers have expertise in personal injury, professional and clinical negligence, medical disciplinary, employment, judicial review, landlord and tenant, contracts (including sale of goods), police cases, and cases for the European Court of Human Rights. Individual members of chambers are willing to accept Conditional Fee and Direct Professional Access instructions.

Publications: R. Hayward Smith QC & Clive Newton are the editors of Jackson's *Matrimonial Finance & Taxation.* James Turner QC and Stephen Shay are editors of *Archbold: Criminal Pleading Evidence & Practice.* Andrew McFarlane QC is co-author of *Hershman and McFarlane: Children Law and Practice.* Stephen Wildblood QC and Deborah Eaton are authors of *The Encyclopaedia of Family Provision in Family Matters,* Deborah Eaton is an author of *Essential Family Practice.*

Set No.
72

2 KING'S BENCH WALK

2 King's Bench Walk, Temple, London, EC4Y 7DE **Tel:** (020) 7353 1746 **Fax:** (020) 7583 2051 **DX:** 1032

73 2 KING'S BENCH WALK (James Cartwright)

2 King's Bench Walk, Temple, London, EC4Y 7DE
Tel: (020) 7353 9276 **Fax:** (020) 7353 9949 **DX:** 477 Chancery Lane
Email: chambers@2kbw.co.uk

Head of Chambers	James Cartwright
Titular Head of Chambers	Lord Campbell of Alloway ERD
Senior Administrator	Brenda Anderson
Practice Manager	Robert Ruegg
Clerks	Alex Mark
	Brian Newton
Tenants	35

2
Kings Bench Walk Chambers
(Lord Campbell of Alloway)
Temple
London EC4Y 7DE

Members:

Lord Campbell of Alloway ERD QC (1939) (QC-1965)
David Owen Thomas QC (1952) (QC-1972)
Peter Shier (1952)
James Cartwright (1968)
Philip Rueff (1969)
Arnold Cooper (1969)
Anthony Dalgleish (1971)
Alun Evans (1971)
René Yee Lock Wong (1973)
Ian Slack (1974)
David Mendes da Costa (1976)
Robert Gifford (1977)
Patricia Lloyd (1979)
George Papageorgis (1981)
James Shrimpton (1981)
Sheila Gaylord (1983)
Deepak Kapur (1984)
Steven Perian (1987)
Anthony Montgomery (1987)
Nan Alban-Lloyd (1988)
Claudia Lorenzo (1991)
Brian Kennedy (1992)
Tanya Callman (1993)
David Sandeman (1993)
Janice Johnson (1994)
Anne Donelon (1995)
Andrew Frymann (1995)
Philippa Daniels (1995)
Carolina Guiloff (1996)
Robin Halstead (1996)
Sukhwant Sidhu (1996)
Michael Hall (1996)
Richard Miles (1997)
Hugh Blake-James (1998)
Shardi Shameli (1998)
Mark Stephens (1998)
Julia Livesay *
Robert Baker *
Osmond Lam *
Keith Oderberg *
Zahid Yaqub *
Simon Watters (1992) *
Karen Phillips *
Stephen Owen-Conway QC *

* Door Tenant

The Chambers: These chambers are located on the first and second floors of one of the oldest buildings in the Temple, built by Christopher Wren. A wide range of work is undertaken in the field of general common law as well as criminal law, family law, administrative law, work before tribunals, education law, employment law and human rights. Constant review is kept on the changing needs of solicitors and the public, while at the same time the Bar's traditional values are maintained and fostered by members who present a welcoming attitude to lay and professional clients.

74 4 KING'S BENCH WALK (Timothy Raggatt QC)

2nd floor, 4 King's Bench Walk, Temple, London, EC4Y 7DL
Tel: (020) 7353 3581 **Fax:** (020) 7583 2257 **DX:** 1050 London (Chancery Lane)
Email: clerks@4kbw.co.uk **Website:** www.4kbw.co.uk

Head of Chambers	Timothy Raggatt QC
Clerks	Lee Cook
	Philip Burnell
	Graeme Logan
Tenants	32

Members:

Timothy Raggatt QC (1972) (QC-1993)
Stephen Williamson QC (1964) (QC-1981)
Nicholas Jarman QC (1965) (QC-1985)
Basil Hillman (1968)
Robert Spencer Bernard (1969)
Christopher Cousins (1969)
John Denniss (1974)
Moira Pooley (1974)
Kate Mallison (1974)
Barnaby Evans (1978)
John Riley (1983)
Reginald Arkhurst (1984)
Jane Alt (1984)
Philip Goddard (1985)
Peter Nightingale (1986)
Andrew Granville Stafford (1987)
Claire Jacobs (1989)
John Metcalf (1990)
Paul Wakerley (1990)
Michael Skelley (1991)
Kim Preston (1991)
Timothy Ashmole (1992)
Jillian Hurworth (1993)
Brendan Davis (1994)
Benn Maguire (1994)
Sarah Phillimore (1994)
Tamala McGee (1995)
Amanda Millmore (1996)
Nadia Chbat (1996)
Alan Blake (1997)
Cameron Brown (1998)
Kirsten Allan (1998)

The Chambers: Areas of practice include contract, crime, education, employment, family, immigration, landlord and tenant, personal injury, planning, probate, professional negligence and tort.

Set No.
75

4 KING'S BENCH WALK (Robert Rhodes QC)

4 King's Bench Walk, Temple, London, EC4Y 7DL
Tel: (020) 7822 8822 **Fax:** (020) 7822 8844 **DX:** 422
Email: 4kbw@barristersatlaw.com **Website:** www.barristersatlaw.com

Head of Chambers	Robert Rhodes QC
Consultant	Ian Lee
Tenants	35

Members:

Robert Rhodes QC (1968) (QC-1989)
Raymond Walker QC (1966) (QC-1988)
John Toogood (1957)
Malcolm Knott (1968)
Anthony Clover (1971)
Greville Davis (1976)
Clive Anderson (1976)
Bruce Stuart (1977)
Graham Hulme (1977)
David Mayall (1979)
Chris Van Hagen (1980)
Justin Shale (1982)
John Evan Jones (1982)
Simon Stafford-Michael (1982)
David Harounoff (1984)
Martin Hurst (1985)
Samuel Jarman (1989)
Graham Huston (1991)
Michael Nelson (1992)
Nigel Hood (1993)
Emma Edhem (1993)
Katherine Dunn (1993)
Adrian Maxwell (1993)
Oliver Mishcon (1993)
Simon Taylor (1993)
Derek Kerr (1994)
Nicola Murphy (1995)
Lawrence Power (1995)
Lisa Hatch (1995)
Clare Evans (1995)
Samantha Riggs (1996)
Kimberly Farmer (1997)
Francesca Levett (1997)
Adam Cannon (1997)
Christopher Rodwell (1997)
HHJ Heppel QC *
David Cattle (1975) *
Anika Khan (1988) *
Walter Rudeloff (1990) *
Jim Wilson (1994) *
Kathleen Anderson (1997) *
Michel Horton (1993) *

* Door Tenant

The Chambers: Common law set specialising in commercial and criminal fraud, financial services, heavy crime, commercial litigation, environmental law and insurance and reinsurance. In association with King's Bench Chambers, 175 Holdenhurst Road, Bournemouth, BN8 8DQ.

Set No.
76

5 KING'S BENCH WALK (Brian Higgs QC)

5 King's Bench Walk, London, EC4Y 7DN
Tel: (020) 7353 5638 **Fax:** (020) 7353 6166 **DX:** 367 Chancery Lane
Email: clerks@5kbw.co.uk **Website:** www.5kbw.co.uk

Head of Chambers	Brian Higgs QC
Senior Clerk	Russell Ayles
First Junior Clerk	Michael Bazeley
Practice Manager	Chris Eadie
Tenants	43

Members:

Brian Higgs QC (1955) (QC-1974)
Richard Sones (1969)
Michael O'Sullivan (1970) +
Martin Joy (1971) +
Graeme Ford (1972)
James O'Mahony (1973) +
John Hillen (1976) +
David Tomlinson (1977) +
Robert Ward (1977)
John Fairhead (1978)
John Burton (1979)
Simon Sandford (1979)
Peter Hofford (1979)
Gillian Frost (1979)
Alexander Laban (1980)
Bartholomew O'Toole (1980)
Sappho Dias (1982)
Mark Heywood (1986)
Mark Dacey (1985)
Dominic Webber (1985)
Fiona Moore-Graham (1986)
Sarah Forshaw (1987)
Jonathan Higgs (1987)
Andrew Collings (1987)
Stephen Chippeck (1988)
Andrew Forsyth (1989)
Christopher Blake (1990)
Carl Hackman (1990)
Edmund Fowler (1992)
Danny Robinson (1993)
Andrew Espley (1993)
Jonathan Hall (1994)
Danny Moore (1994)
Timothy Crosland (1994)
Charlotte Newell (1994)
Paul Cavin (1995)
Kimberley Aiken (1995)
Robert Ellison (1996)
Felicity Mileham (1996)
Catherine Donnelly (1997)
Benjamin Temple (1997)
Zillah Williams (1997)
Xenia Stavrou (1998)

\+ Recorder

The Chambers: A specialist criminal set, this year increased to 43 tenants having been joined by members of the chambers of John Burton, Mitre Court Chambers, 199 Strand. This enables chambers to now offer even more strength in depth in criminal cases as well as the following areas: Chancery, matrimonial, Children Act, personal injury, licensing, local authority, public law and human rights. Chambers also have on average at least eight working pupils at any one time able to undertake work in the lower courts if required.

Set No.
77

6 KING'S BENCH WALK (Roy Amlot QC)

6 King's Bench Walk, Temple, London, EC4Y 7DR
Tel: (020) 7583 0410 **Fax:** (020) 7353 8791 **DX:** 26 (Ch.Ln.)
Email: clerks@6kbw.co.uk

Head of Chambers	Roy Amlot QC
Senior Clerk	David Garstang
Tenants	45

Members:

Michael Worsley QC (1955) (QC-1985)
Ann Curnow QC (1957) (QC-1985)
Roy Amlot QC (1963) (QC-1989)
Ann Mallalieu QC (1970) (QC-1988)
James Curtis QC (1970) (QC-1993)
Victor Temple QC (1971) (QC-1993)
Dorian Lovell-Pank QC (1971) (QC-1993)
Joanna Korner QC (1974) (QC-1993)
Bruce Houlder QC (1969) (QC-1994)
David Spens QC (1973) (QC-1995)
David Fisher QC (1973) (QC-1996)
Wendy Joseph QC (1975) (QC-1998)
Anthony Leonard QC (1978) (QC-1999)
Nigel Sweeney QC (1976) (QC-2000)
John Ryder QC (1980) (QC-2000)
Sasha Wass QC (1981) (QC-2001)
Howard Vagg (1974)
Jonathan Turner (1974)
Mark Dennis (1977)
Philippa Jessel (1978)
Marks Moore (1979)
David Perry (1980)
Nicholas Hilliard (1981)
Martyn Bowyer (1984)
Simon Denison (1984)
Emma Broadbent (1986)
Irena Ray-Crosby (1990)
Dean Armstrong (1985)
Peter Grieves-Smith (1989)
Timothy Cray (1989)
Duncan Penny (1992)
Jason Dunn-Shaw (1992)
Isabel Dakyns (1992)
Annabel Darlow (1993)
Sarah Whitehouse (1993)
Gareth Patterson (1995)
Duncan Atkinson (1995)
Annabel Pilling (1996)
Jacob Hallam (1996)
Adina Ezekiel (1997)
Alison Foulkes (1997)
Louis Mably (1997)
Kate Wilkinson (1999)
Miranda Hill (1999)
Mark Weekes (1999)
Prof Di Birch *
David Turner QC (1971) (QC-1991) *
Andrew Oldland (1990) *
Simon Laws (1991) *

* Door Tenant

The Chambers: A specialist criminal set with 16 QCs, three Senior and one Junior Treasury Counsel. Chambers have particular experience in advocacy in the higher courts. Members also handle civil work with individual specialisations. 20 members of chambers are recorders and one is a DTI Inspector. Additionally, members of chambers belong to the committees of the Bar Council and the Criminal Bar Association. Roy Amlot QC is the Chairman of the Bar Council and Bruce Houlder QC is Chairman of the Criminal Bar Association.

Work Undertaken:

Criminal: For both prosecution and defence, mainly in London and the South Eastern Circuit, specialising in: commercial crime, fraud, VAT cases and regulatory work.

Other: Individual members also appear in defamation, libel, licensing and trades descriptions cases. Members appear at Mental Health Tribunals, City Tribunals, Employment Tribunals, Police Disciplinary Tribunals, before Coroners' Courts and for defendants in Courts Martial. Members also undertake all aspects of human rights cases.

International: Languages spoken include French, German, Italian and Spanish.

Recruitment: Applications for tenancy should be sent to the head of chambers, those for pupillage to Sarah Whitehouse. There are 10 pupils in chambers at any one time. Awards and mini-pupillages are available.

Set No.
78

6 KING'S BENCH WALK (Sibghat Kadri QC)

6 King's Bench Walk, Temple, London, EC4Y 7DR **Tel:** (020) 7583 0695 / 7353 4931 **Fax:** (020) 7353 1726 **DX:** 471 (Ch.Ln.) **Email:** clerks@6kbw.co.uk **Website:** www.6kbw.co.uk

Set No.
79

7 KING'S BENCH WALK (Jeremy Cooke QC)

7 King's Bench Walk, Temple, London, EC4Y 7DS
Tel: (020) 7910 8300 **Fax:** (020) 7583 0950 **DX:** LDE 239
Email: clerks@7kbw.law.co.uk

Head of Chambers	Jeremy Cooke QC
Senior Clerk	Bernie Hyatt
Clerks	Greg Leyden
	Eddie Johns
	Gary Rose
Arbitrators	Lord Goff
	Adrian Hamilton QC
	John Willmer QC
Tenants	35

Members:

Jeremy Cooke QC (1976) (QC-1990) ¶ †
Timothy Saloman QC (1975) (QC-1993)
Francis Reynolds (Hon) QC (1960) (QC-1993)
Gavin Kealey QC (1977) (QC-1994)
Julian Flaux QC (1978) (QC-1994)
Jonathan Gaisman QC (1979) (QC-1995)
Dominic Kendrick QC (1981) (QC-1997)
Timothy Brenton QC (1981) (QC-1998)
Alistair Schaff QC (1983) (QC-1999)
Stephen Hofmeyr QC (1982) (QC-2000)
Christopher Butcher QC (1986) (QC-2001)
Charles Priday (1982)
Adam Fenton (1984)
Stephen Kenny (1987)
Richard Southern (1987)
Robert Bright (1987)
Gavin Geary (1989)
David Bailey (1989)
David Edwards (1989)
Simon Picken (1989)
David Allen (1990)
Andrew Wales (1992)
Siob·n Healy (1993)
S.J. Phillips (1993)
Rebecca Sabben-Clare (1993)
Jawdat Khurshid (1994)
Richard Waller (1994)
Timothy Kenefick (1996)
John Bignall (1996)
Charles Holroyd (1997)
Simon Kerr (1997)
James Drake (1998)
Peter MacDonald Eggers (1999)
James Brocklebank (1999)
Michael Holmes (1999)

¶ Accredited Mediator † Arbitrator

The Chambers: The core areas of work undertaken by this major commercial set are commercial litigation; international and domestic arbitration; insurance and reinsurance; shipping; banking; professional negligence; conflicts of law and private international law; energy; oil and gas; City work. The set was founded in 1883 and its experience in commercial matters is well established and respected. The many distinguished former members include Lord Denning, Lord Brandon, Lord Goff, Lord Hobhouse, Lord Justice Mance and Lord Justice Longmore and most recently Mr Justice Tomlinson. 7 KBW is recognised for its strength at all levels. Its members provide legal advice and litigation expertise of the highest quality. Their commitment to their clients and to those who instruct them is widely acknowledged. This is reflected not only in the quality of their work but also in the promptness of their assistance. The clerks do not accept second bookings for court, arbitration or tribunal fixtures unless specifically requested by instructing solicitors to do so. The members of chambers appear principally in the higher courts (Commercial Court, Court of Appeal and House of Lords) in London and before arbitration tribunals within and outside the UK. They are instructed also to appear in the European Court of Justice and the Privy Council, as well as in other jurisdictions such as Hong Kong, Singapore, Bermuda and the Cayman Islands. Members of chambers are regularly appointed as arbitrators under various terms of reference, including LCIA, ICC, LMAA and Lloyd's. Lord Goff, Adrian Hamilton QC and John Wilmer QC accept appointments as arbitrator and mediator through the clerks. The chambers include fully accredited mediators (CEDR). Under its head, Jeremy Cooke, QC, 7KBW confidently expects to grow whilst maintaining its recognised qualities and strengths in its core areas of work. There is a duty clerk available 24 hours a day, seven days a week.

Publications: Several members are authors and editorial team members who have cooperated in legal publications in the areas of contract, agency, shipping, insurance/reinsurance law and professional negligence.

Recruitment: Chambers attract pupils of only the highest quality, and pursues a policy of only taking new tenants of such quality either from those starting their careers in law or from those in mid-career who have elected to change from another part of the profession. This emphasis on quality has meant a steady but selective growth in the overall number of tenants over the past years.

Set No.
80

9 KING'S BENCH WALK (Ali Mohammed Azhar)

9 King's Bench Walk, Temple, London, EC4Y 7DX
Tel: (020) 7353 9564 **Fax:** (020) 7353 7943 **DX:** 118 Chancery Lane

Head of Chambers:	Ali Mohammed Azhar
Senior Clerk:	Barry Henderson
Tenants:	14

The range of work covers crime, family law, landlord and tenant, personal injury, immigration, clinical and professional negligence, arbitration, commercial and construction law, employment, banking law, corporate insolvency and individual bankruptcy. Experts in Islamic and Hindu law. Languages: Urdu, Punjabi, Bengali, and Sinhalese.

31 10 KING'S BENCH WALK (Claudius Algar)

10 King's Bench Walk, Temple, London, EC4Y 7EB
Tel: (020) 7353 7742 **Fax:** (020) 7583 0579 **DX:** 24 London/Chancery Lane
Email: 10kbw@lineone.net **Website:** www.10kingsbenchwalk.co.uk

Head of Chambers	Claudius Algar
Senior Clerk	Alan Curtis
Civil Clerk	Colin Middleton
Criminal Clerk	Matthew Harper
Fees Clark/Administrator	Terry Lee
Junior Clerk	Kevin Morrow
Tenants	30

10
KING'S BENCH
WALK

Members:

Claudius Algar (1972)
Rosina Hare QC (1956) (QC-1976)
Colin Hart (1966)
Charles Vaudin (1971)
Susan Tapping (1975)
Carlton Christensen (1977)
Leonard Hedworth (1979)
Reid Pearce
Bernard Limbrey (1980)
Peter Herrity (1982)
Orlando Gibbons (1982)
Leslie Wise (1985)
Carlo Talacci (1986)
Simon Thompson (1988)
Patrick Lynch (1988)
Sukhjinder Johal (1991)
James Bogle (1991)
Andrew Noble (1992)
Michael Harris (1993)
Jonathan Martin (1994)
Patricia Harding (1994)
Rosana Bailey (1994)
Alastair Panton (1996)
Dominic Bevis (1996)
Sherry Nabijou (1996)
Nicholas O'Brien (1996)
Simon Perhar (1997)
Sharan Bhachu (1998)
Rhiannon Crimmins (1999)
Sabina Khan (1999)

The Chambers: A common-law set offering particular strength in all aspects of criminal, civil and family work (public and private). DPA accepted.

32 10 KING'S BENCH WALK (Georges M Khayat QC)

10 King's Bench Walk, Temple, London, EC4Y 7EB
Tel: (020) 7353 2501 **Fax:** (020) 7353 0658 **DX:** 294 Chancery Lane
Email: clerks@10kbw.co.uk **Website:** www.10kbw.co.uk

Head of Chambers	Georges M Khayat QC
Senior Clerk	Michael Price
Tenants	41

Members:

Georges M Khayat QC (1967) (QC-1992)
Alper Riza QC (1973) (QC-1991)
Richard Akinjide (1956)
David Nathan (1971)
Jonathan Lurie (1972)
Peter Prideaux-Brune (1972)
Sheilagh Davies (1974)
Timothy Sewell (1976)
Laura Brickman (1976)
Robin Miric (1978)
Jonathan Woodcock (1981)
Jollyon Robertson (1983)
Nicholas Doherty (1983)
Julie O'Malley (1983)
Annette Henry (1984)
Helen McCormack (1986)
Bibiana Ihuomah (1986)
Najma Khatoon (1986)
Michael Lee (1987)
Andrew Jackson (1987)
Trevor Berriman (1988)
Nigel Daniel (1988)
Dina Karallis (1989)
Susan Rodham (1989)
Bosmath Sheffi (1991)
M. Ayaz Qazi (1993)
Sanjay Lal (1993)
Mary Ruck (1993)
Glenn Harris (1994)
James Kirby (1994)
Phillip Lucas (1995)
Mark A Balysz (1995)
Francesca Wiley (1996)
Melanie Winter (1996)
Martin Lewis (1997)
Pauline Thompson (1997)
Christopher Surtees-Jones (1997)
Busola Johnson (1998)
Paul Richmond (1999)
Harriet Butterfield (1999)
Robert Garson (1999)

The Chambers: A powerful, long-established leading set which has offered strong representation in common law matters over many years. Members of chambers appear in criminal courts at every level. Chambers have an acknowledged reputation in commercial 'white collar' fraud. Chambers offer spacious conference rooms and a computerised administration centre. Practitioners are able to offer written work in a wide variety of formats for the convenience of clients.

Work Undertaken:
Criminal: Work embraces all aspects of crime, especially commercial crime, serious fraud, drugs and DTOA confiscation orders, money laundering, computer crime, licensing and firearms. Many members defend in major trials and undertake cases on behalf of the prosecuting authorities.
Family: All aspects of matrimonial law, including wardship and local authority work. Immigration work

Recruitment: Chambers are a member of the OLPAS pupillage scheme administered by the Bar Council. Awards are available. No third six-month pupils or squatters are taken. 10 King's Bench Walk is an equal opportunities organisation.

Set No.
83

11 KING'S BENCH WALK (FJ Muller QC)

11 King's Bench Walk, Temple, London, EC4Y 7EQ
Tel: (020) 7353 3337 **Fax:** (020) 7583 2190 **DX:** DX 389 CHANCERY LANE
Email: clerks@11kbw.co.uk **Website:** www.11kbw.co.uk

Head of Chambers	FJ Muller QC
Senior Clerk	Jo Pickersgill
Clerks	Jayne Turner
	Deborah Pain
	Chris Gittins
Administration/Fees	Amanda Kershaw
Tenants	27

Members:

FJ Muller QC (1961) (QC-1978)
Andrew Robertson QC (1975) (QC-1996)
Roger Thorn QC (1970) (QC-1990)
Nicholas Campbell QC (1979) (QC-2000)
Jeremy Richardson QC (1980) (QC-2000)
Matthew Caswell (1968)
Francis Radcliffe (1962)
Richard Barlow (1970)
Michael O'Neill (1979)
Christopher Attwooll (1980)
Mio Sylvester (1980)
Toby Wynn (1982)
Rebecca Caswell (1983)
Fiona P. Swain (1983)
Graham Reeds (1984)
Simon Mallett (1987)
Peter Johnson (1986)
Adrian Waterman (1988)
Sarah Mallett (1988)
David Brooke (1990)
Robert Toone (1993)
Ian Skelt (1994)
Tom Mitchell (1995)
Sarah Margree (1996)
Tina Dempster (1997)
Matthew Bean (1997)
Shabbir Merali (1998)

The Chambers: 11 King's Bench Walk is a long-established common-law London set with a distinguished history.

Set No.
84

11 KING'S BENCH WALK CHAMBERS (Eldred Tabachnik QC & James Goudie QC)

11 King's Bench Walk, Temple, London, EC4Y 7EQ
Tel: (020) 7632 8500 **Fax:** (020) 7583 9123 **DX:** 368 (Ch.Ln.)
Email: clerksroom@11kbw.com **Website:** www.11kbw.com

Head of Chambers	Eldred Tabachnik QC
	James Goudie QC
Senior Clerk	Philip Monham
Tenants	37

Members:

Eldred Tabachnik QC (1970) (QC-1982)
James Goudie QC (1970) (QC-1984)
Michael Supperstone QC (1973) (QC-1991)
Elizabeth Slade QC (1972) (QC-1992)
Alistair McGregor QC (1974) (QC-1997)
Christopher Jeans QC (1980) (QC-1997)
Adrian Lynch QC (1983) (QC-2000)
Tim Kerr QC (1983) (QC-2001)
John Cavanagh QC (1985) (QC-2001)
Philip Sales (1985) First Junior Counsel to the Treasury, Common Law
Andrew Hillier (1972)
Elisabeth Laing (1980)
Jane Oldham (1985)
Nigel Giffin (1986)
Charles Béar (1986)
Peter Wallington (1987)
Clive Lewis (1987)
Simon Devonshire (1988)
Jonathan Swift (1989)
Timothy Pitt-Payne (1989)
Peter Oldham (1990)
Sarah Moore (1990)
Seán Jones (1991)
Akhlaq Choudhury (1992)
Paul Nicholls (1992)
Daniel Stilitz (1992)
Clive Sheldon (1991)
Nigel Porter (1994)
Jason Coppel (1994)
Cecilia Ivimy (1995)
Tom Restrick (1995)
Karen Steyn (1995)
Richard Leiper (1996)
Julian Wilson (1997)
Anya Proops (1998)
Jane McCafferty (1998)
Harini Iyengar (1999)

Work Undertaken: The 37 members of these chambers (nine of whom are Queen's Counsel) provide specialist legal advisory and advocacy services covering the following three principal areas:

Employment Law: Company directors; share options; incentive bonuses and pension rights; wrongful and unfair dismissal; the protection of confidential information; restrictive covenants; transfers of undertakings; sex and race discrimination and equal pay; strikes and other trade disputes; trade union membership; EU employment law.

Public and Administrative Law: Local authorities, especially their powers and financing; judicial review of central and local government and other public bodies, including financial services institutions; competitive tendering and public authority contracts; education; sex and race discrimination; elections; civil liberties; immigration; EU public law; housing and housing associations; environmental law.

Commercial Law/International Trade: Arbitration (domestic and international); agency; competition; confidential information; copyright; economic torts, financial regulation; professional negligence; share options; technology – software licensing; trade secrets; unlawful competition; search and freezing orders.

Other Details: Full brochure available upon request. Office hours: Monday – Friday 8:00am – 7:00pm. Out of office hours: (07831) 304714 (mobile).

Publications: Members of chambers have written or contributed to *Halsbury's Laws (Administrative Law and Extradition Titles)*; *Supperstone & Goudie on Judicial Review*; *Harvey on Industrial Relations and*

Employment Law; Butterworths *Employment Law Handbook*; Tolley's *Employment Handbook*; *Immigration Law and Practice*; Butterworths *Local Government Law*; Supperstone, Goudie & Coppel *Local Authorities and the Human Rights Act*; Butterworths *Local Government Reports*; Supperstone & O'Dempsey on *Immigration and Asylum*; Brownlie's *Law of Public Order and National Security*; *Sports Law*; Tolley's *Employment Law*; Butterworths *Education Law Manual*; *The Human Rights Act 1998: Enforcing the European Convention in the Domestic Courts*; *Judicial Remedies in Public Law*; *Supreme Court Practice*.

Set No.
85

12 KING'S BENCH WALK (Richard Methuen QC)

12 King's Bench Walk, Temple, London, EC4Y 7EL
Tel: (020) 7583 0811 **Fax:** (020) 7583 7228 **DX:** 1037 (Ch.Ln.)
Email: chambers@12kbw.co.uk **Website:** www.12kbw.co.uk

Head of Chambers	Richard Methuen QC
Senior Clerk	John Cooper
Practice Manager	Roderick Marshall
Tenants	40

Members:

Richard Methuen QC (1972) (QC-1997)
Charles Whitby QC (1952) (QC-1970)
Ronald Walker QC (1962) (QC-1983)
Anthony Goldstaub QC (1972) (QC-1992)
Frank Burton QC (1982) (QC-1998)
Toby Hooper QC (1973) (QC-2000)
Neville Spencer-Lewis (1970)
John King (1973)
Andrew Hogarth (1974)
Brian Gallagher (1975)
Stephen Worthington (1976)
Nicholas Heathcote Williams (1976)
Allan Gore (1977)
Lincoln Crawford (1977) OBE
Alexander Hill-Smith (1978)
William Featherby (1978)
Stephen Archer (1979)
Susan Rodway (1981)
Paul Russell (1984)
David Sanderson (1985)
Nigel Lewers (1986)
Freya Newbery (1986)
Andrew Pickering (1987)
Hugh Hamill (1988)
Adam Chambers (1989)
Catherine Brown (1990)
Kate Chandler (1990)
Patrick Vincent (1992)
Willliam Audland (1992)
Stephanie Jackson (1992)
Joel Kendall (1993)
Richard Viney (1994)
Carolyn D'Souza (1994)
Catherine Peck (1995)
Timothy Petts (1996)
Harry Steinberg (1997)
Joanna Droop (1998)
Kweku Aggrey-Orleans (1998)
David White (1999)
Lisa Stephenson (1999)

The Chambers: 12 King's Bench Walk is widely recognised as being one of the three leading sets specialising in personal injury. Chambers are also known for the particular expertise of their specialist groups of barristers in clinical negligence, professional negligence, construction, insurance and employment law. One of the longest established sets in the Temple, chambers have the reputation of being friendly and approachable. Considerable expansion during the past ten years has enabled chambers to invest in staff development and the latest computer technology, ensuring that work is dealt with quickly and efficiently. Members are fully conversant with the requirements of recent human rights legislation and its implications for the work undertaken by chambers. Video conferencing: (020) 7583 4190.

Work Undertaken:

Personal Injury: Includes all industrial disease claims, particularly asbestos, RSI and VWF; brain damage; spinal injuries; all other employers', public and product liability claims; all road traffic related work.

Clinical Negligence: Includes injuries at birth; catastrophic brain damage; injuries from pharmaceutical products; all other cases involving complex medical and scientific issues.

Professional Negligence: Includes solicitors' and barristers' negligence; architects', engineers', surveyors' and valuers' negligence; accountants' and bankers' negligence; insurance brokers' and IFAs' negligence; auctioneers' negligence; veterinary negligence; IT professionals' negligence.

Construction & Technology: Includes contractual claims arising out of the JCT, ICE and other standard forms of construction contract and subcontracts; engineering and mining contracts; computer contracts.

Insurance & Reinsurance: Includes policy wording issues and drafting of policy wording amendments; acting for insurance clients in professional indemnity, employers' liability, motor policy and public liability claims.

Employment: Includes race relations; equal opportunity; trade union work; restrictive covenants; transfers of undertakings; wrongful and unfair dismissal; equal pay; bonus and pension schemes; expertise in all aspects of EU employment law. In addition to the above work undertaken by chambers' specialist teams, individual members can offer expertise in the following areas:

Property Law: Includes commercial and residential landlord and tenant; Housing Association; local authority disrepair work.

Enviromental: Includes pollution of land by chemicals and nuclear matter; pollution related criminal charges; advising clients on obtaining site licences.

Equine Law: Includes insurance policy disputes; contractual disputes; misrepresentation and misdescription; disputes concerning membership and rules of riding and racing organisations; disciplinary proceedings; riding accidents.

Continued overleaf

Other Information: Chambers are fully computer networked and all members have email facilities. Meetings, conferences and interviews can be arranged through chambers' video conferencing facilities. Brochures and individual member details are available on request. Details of chambers' seminar and lecture programme can be found on the website. Chambers accept Direct Professional Access instructions and Conditional Fee work, by prior arrangement with the clerks. They also offer qualified and experienced mediators and arbitration services.

Publications: Up-to-date details of publications which members of chambers have written, edited or contributed to can be found on the 12 King's Bench Walk website at www.12kbw.co.uk. The website also gives details and analysis of important cases involving members of chambers.

Recruitment: Chambers are a member of PACH to which all applications for pupillage should be made. Pupils are offered 12 month pupillage with a comprehensive training package and a guaranteed income of £18,000.

Set No. 86

13 KING'S BENCH WALK (Roger Ellis QC)

13 King's Bench Walk, Temple, London, EC4Y 7EN
Tel: (020) 7353 7204 **Fax:** (020) 7583 0252 **DX:** 359 London
Email: clerks@13kbw.co.uk **Website:** www.13kbw.co.uk

Head of Chambers	Roger Ellis QC
Senior Clerks	Stephen Buckingham Kevin Kelly
Chambers Director	Stephen Rogers
Chambers Administrator	Penny Macfall
Tenants	43

Members:

Roger Ellis QC (1962) (QC-1996)LLB BSc (Lond)
Graeme Williams QC (1959) (QC-1983)MA (Oxon)
Julian Baughan QC (1967) (QC-1990)BA (Oxon)
David Ashton (1962)MA (Oxon)
Alexander Dawson (1969)MA (Oxon)
Anthony McGeorge (1969)MA (Cantab)
Robert Lamb (1973)MA (Cantab)
Deirdre Goodwin (1974)LLB (Lond)
Jane Tracy Forster (1975)LLB (Liverpool)
Paul W. Reid (1975)MA (Cantab)
David Bright (1976)
Simon Hughes M.P. (1974)BA (Cantab)
Simon Draycott (1977)
Alasdair Brough (1979)MA (Cantab)
Nigel Daly (1979)LLB (London)
Nicholas Syfret (1979)MA (Cantab)
Andrew Glennie (1982)MA (Oxon)
A. John Williams (1983)MA (Cantab)
Jonathan Coode (1984)BA (East Anglia)
Neil Vickery (1985)MA (Cantab)
Neil Moore (1986)LLB (Nottingham)
Sarah Gibbons (1987)BA (Birmingham)
Arthur Blake (1988)LLB (Lond)
Sinclair Cramsie (1988)LLB (Leeds)
Fiona Hay (1989)BSc BA (Exeter)
Andrew Pote (1983)LLB (East Anglia)
Adrian Higgins (1990)MA (Oxon)
Edmund Walters (1991)BA (Bristol)
Heather Wenlock (1991)MPhil DPhil (Oxon)
Vivian Walters (1991)BA (Leic)
Deshpal Singh Panesar (1993)LLB (Lond)
Susan Chan (1994)BA (Oxon)
Patrick Wainwright (1994)MA (Oxon)
Paul Mitchell (1994)BA (York)
Rachel Drake (1995)LLB (Hons) (Brunel)
Lucy Owens (1997)LLB (Hons) (Kingston)
James Cox (1997)LLB (Wales)
Thómas Payne (1998)BA (Oxon) LLM (research) (Birmingham)
Christopher Mann (1998)BA (Oxon)
Clare Harrington (1998)LLB (Oxon)
Julie Hopkins (1999)BA (Oxon)
John Simmons (2000)LLB (Oxon)
Peter Ross (2000)PhB (Pontifical Gregorian University)

The Chambers: These are an established chambers with some 40 members in premises in the Inner Temple in London and Beaumont Street in Oxford. They cover a wide spectrum of common law and chancery matters, have an expanding family practice, and provide a comprehensive service in criminal law on the Midland and Oxford circuit. Chambers have recently upgraded telecommunications, moved to Meridian specialist software and installed a new email system. They like to take a commercial approach by combining prompt action with practical advice. Chambers are proud of their client service, and are now preparing for Barmark Quality assessment.

Work Undertaken: Chambers have nine practice areas as follows: Administrative and public law, which includes immigration and civil liberties, environmental and consumer law; clinical negligence; company and commercial, including banking, commercial litigation, insolvency, insurance, partnerships and professional negligence; construction; crime, including criminal fraud; employment; family; personal injury; property and chancery, which includes real property, landlord and tenant, chancery remedies and other related matters.

Set No. 87

LAMB BUILDING (Ami Feder)

Lamb Building, Ground Floor, Temple, London, EC4Y 7AS
Tel: (020) 7797 7788 **Fax:** (020) 7353 0535/7797 7453 **DX:** 1038 (Ch.Ln.)
Email: clerks@lambbldg.co.uk **Website:** www.lambbldg.co.uk

Head of Chambers	Ami Feder
Senior Clerk	Gary Goodger Mobile (07721) 339232
Tenants	35

Members:

Ami Feder (1965)LLB
Anna Worrall QC (1959) (QC-1989) +
Ivan Krolick (1966)LLB (Dunhelm)
David Edlin (1971)MA (Oxon)
John Fox (1973)LLB, BDS, LDSRCS
Anthony Edie (1974)LLB
Jeremy Gordon (1974)LLB (Lond)
John Waters (1974)
Alan Barton (1975)LLM (Lond)
Spenser Hilliard (1975)LLB (Lond)
Jaqueline Perry (1975)MA (Oxon)
Angela Hodes (1979)BA (Lond)
Michael Phillips (1980)LLB (Lond)
J David Cook (1982)BA (Keele)
Richard Roberts (1983)BA (Cantab)
Julie O'Malley (1983)LLB (Sheffield)
Deborah Sawhney (1987)BA (Keele)
Susannah Cotterill (1988)
Bernard Richmond (1988) +
M Jane Terry (1988)
Maureen O'Connor (1988)
Jonathan de Rohan (1989)
Jeremy Haughty (1989) *
David Brounger (1990)
JM Seamus Kearney (1992)
Lindsay Weinstein (1992)
Paul Crampin (1992)
Anita Geser (1992)
Pippa Alderson (1993)
Dafna Spiro (1994)
Joy Dykers (1995)
Anne Faul (1996)
Geri Peterson (1997) *
Andreas Pretzell (1997)
Nicola Shannon (1997)
A Mark Tempest (1997)
Andrew Alexander (1999)

* Door Tenant + Recorder

Work Undertaken: The work of chambers covers all aspects of English common law and some general Chancery, predominantly on the South Eastern and Western Circuits. The principal areas of practice are civil and criminal commercial fraud; professional and particularly medical negligence; personal injury; family and childcare including wardship and property; landlord and tenant and housing law; insolvency and bankruptcy; contractual disputes including partnership and sale of goods; all criminal law; disciplinary hearings and the armed forces; consumer credit, hiring, and leasing transaction; building law; licensing; employment, immigration specialists.
Additional Specialisations: Individual members offer expertise in actions against the police, prisoners' rights, food and drugs, mental health, fine arts, computer law, and Israeli law (Ami Feder is qualified as an advocate in Israel). One member belongs to the Chartered Institute of Arbitrators. A brochure is available on request.

Set No. 88

LAMB CHAMBERS (Christopher Gardner QC)

Lamb Building, Temple, London, EC4Y 7AS
Tel: (020) 7797 8300 **Fax:** (020) 7797 8308 **DX:** 418 London
Email: info@lambchambers.co.uk **Website:** www.lambchambers.co.uk

Head of Chambers	Christopher Gardner QC
Senior Clerk	John Kelly
Tenants	38

Members:

Christopher Gardner QC (1968) (QC-1994)
Julian Priest QC (1954) (QC-1974)
Ian Leeming QC (1970) (QC-1988)
Christopher Lau (1972)SC (Singapore)(SC-1999)
J A L Sterling (1953) †
Alastair Sharp (1968)
Anthony McNeile (1970)
Mark West (1973)
David di Mambro (1973)
Jeremy Carey (1974)
Anthony Connerty (1974)
Stephen Shaw (1975)
Anthony Allston (1975)
Paul Stewart (1975)
Simon Brilliant (1976)
Lawrence Caun (1977)
Paul M. Emerson (1984)
Simon Williams (1984)
Richard Ough (1985)
Clive Blackwood (1986)
Timothy Meakin (1989)
Napier Miles (1989)
James Stuart (1990)
Daniel Gatty (1990)
Shantanu Majumdar (1992)
Elizabeth F. Haggerty (1994)
Dominic Happé (1993)
Rhiannon Jones (1993)
Gary Blaker (1993)
Richard Hayes (1995)
Jonathan Richards (1996)
Timothy Frith (1996)
Annette Prand (1995)
Alexandra Stagi (1997)
Howard Daley (1997)
Andrew Wille (1998)
Peter Ellis (1997)
Guy Watkins (1999)

† Consultant

The Chambers: Lamb Chambers is a long-established set which specialises in mainstream civil litigation and is structured in three specialist groups: commercial, personal injury and clinical negligence and property.

Continued overleaf

Work Undertaken:

Commercial Group: This group specialises in all commercial litigation including: commercial contracts; sale and carriage of goods; supply of goods and services; companies, partnerships, corporate and personal insolvency; service contracts; guarantees; credit and security; banking; bills of exchange; passing off; intellectual property and confidentiality; competition; franchising; insurance, economic and other commercial torts; professional negligence connected with the above areas. Members undertake commercial arbitrations, both LCIA and ICC, Alternative Dispute Resolution and Direct Professional Access work.

Personal Injury & Clinical Negligence Group: This group specialises in tortious litigation including personal injury, fatal accidents, clinical negligence and associated professional negligence claims; all matters relating to assessment of damages; structured and infant settlements and insurance; product liability; claims relating to toxins, infectious diseases; factory, construction and road traffic and other transport accidents; claims for damages arising out of criminal injuries. Three of the members of the group are medical doctors.

Property Group: This group specialises in all property-related work and construction litigation including all aspects of landlord and tenant law (commercial, residential and agricultural); leasehold enfranchisement; construction disputes before the Technology and Construction Court and in arbitration; professional negligence of architects and engineers and professional negligence relating to all property issues; mortgages; housing options; easements and restrictive covenants; torts relating to land; the drafting, construction and enforcement of contracts. Members of the group also undertake arbitrations, Alternative Dispute Resolution and Direct Professional Access work.

Publications: 21 members of chambers are the contributing editors to Butterworths' *Law of Limitation*. David di Mambro is a member of the editorial board of the *Civil Court Practice* (The Green Book), is the general editor of Butterworths' *Manual of Civil Appeals* and is a contributing editor to *Atkin's Court Forms* (CPR volumes). Dr Richard Ough is the author of *The Mareva Injunction and Anton Piller Order* (Butterworths 1st edn, 1987; 2nd edn, 1993; 3rd edn, in preparation). Timothy Meakin is assistant editor of *Powers and Harris Clinical Negligence* (3rd edn) and is assistant editor of Butterworths' *Personal Injury Litigation Service*. Professor Adrian Sterling (Professorial Fellow, Queen Mary and Westfield College, and visiting Professor, King's College, University of London) is author of *The Data Protection Act 1984* (2nd edn, 1985), *Copyright Law in the United Kingdom and the Rights of Performers, Authors and Composers in Europe* (1986, supplement 1987) (with M C L Carpenter), *Intellectual Property Rights in Sound Recordings, Film and Video* (1992, supplement 1994) and *World Copyright Law* (1998).

Other Information: Lamb Chambers is accredited by the Law Society for CPD. A list of seminars which chambers is willing to undertake and a list of articles and publications produced by chambers is available at the Lamb Chambers website. Enquiries in respect of seminars on any other subjects in which Lamb Chambers practises are welcome. Chambers' brochure, containing detailed individual CVs, is available on request.

Set No. 89

LION COURT (David Wolchover)

7 Bell Yard, London, WC2A 2JR
Tel: (020) 7831 0636 **Fax:** (020) 7831 0719 **DX:** 98 London Chancery Lane
Email: LionCrtChambers@aol.com **Website:** www.lioncourt.co.uk

Head of Chambers	David Wolchover
Senior Clerk	Kevin Tarrant
Tenants	27

Members:

David Wolchover (1971)
Tariq Rafique (1961)
Gerard Boyd (1967)
Laraine Kaye (1971)
Shini Cooksley (1975)
Georgina Nicholas (1983)
Steve Hosking (1988)
Paula Bignall (1989)
Paul Brinkworth (1990)
John Honey (1990)
David Newberry (1990)
Stephen Bailey (1991)
Louise McCullough (1991)
Philippa Mendel (1992)
David Robinson (1992)
Alex Balancy (1992)
Gregory Hopewell (1992)
Paul Kaffel (1993)
Maureen Flaherty (1995)
Alexander Krikler (1995)
Adrian Langdale (1996)
Claire Davenport (1996)
Jessica Walker (1996)
Joshua Dubin (1997)
Daniel Murray (1997)
Gary Grimshaw (1998)
Paul Costello (1998)

The Chambers: A well established common law set, with an emphasis on crime. Lion Court has developed and grown in recent years to meet the changing demands expected of the Bar. Chambers seek to provide a fast and friendly service, providing expertise at each level of call, with fee structures and response times adaptable to clients' needs, supported by an experienced and flexible clerking team.

Work Undertaken: Chambers undertake all types of general common law – civil, criminal (both prosecution and defence) and family

Publications: Members have written, contributed to or edited: *The Exclusion of Improperly Obtained Evidence, Wolchover and Heaton-Armstrong on Confession Evidence, Analysing Witness Testimony, Silence and Guilt, Bail in Criminal Proceedings, Current Law Week*, and *FHM!*

Set No.

90 LITTLETON CHAMBERS (Michel Kallipetis QC)

3 King's Bench Walk North, Temple, London, EC4Y 7HR
Tel: (020) 7797 8600 **Fax:** (020) 7797 8699/8697 **DX:** 1047
Email: clerks@littletonchambers.co.uk

Head of Chambers	Michel Kallipetis QC
Chief Executive	David Douglas
Clerks	Alistair Coyne
	Tim Tarring
	Jason Drakeford
A/Cs Receivable Manager	Nita Johnston
Tenants	37

Members:

Michel Kallipetis QC (1968) (QC-1989)
Julian Malins QC (1972) (QC-1991)
Ian Mayes QC (1974) (QC-1993)
Richard Price OBE QC (1969) (QC-1996)
Clive Freedman QC (1978) (QC-1997)
Andrew Clarke QC (1980) (QC-1997)
John Bowers QC (1979) (QC-1998)
Andrew Stafford QC (1980) (QC-2000)
Selwyn Bloch QC (1982) (QC-2000)
Colin Manning (1970)
Richard Perkoff (1971)
Philip Bartle (1976)
Mark Lomas (1977)
Timothy Higginson (1977)
Caroline Harry Thomas (1981)
John Davies (1981)
Shirley Bothroyd (1982)
David Reade (1983)
Antony Sendall (1984)
Ian Gatt (1985)
Michael Duggan (1984)
Peter Trepte (1987)
Raoul Downey (1988)
Sam Neaman (1988)
Martyn Barklem (1989)
Charles Samek (1989)
Jeffrey Bacon (1989)
Jeremy Lewis (1992)
Naomi Ellenbogen (1992)
Gavin Mansfield (1992)
Daniel Tatton-Brown (1994)
Stuart Ritchie (1995)
Carol Davis (1996)
Dale Martin (1997)
Niran de Silva (1997)
Lucy Bone (1999)
Matthew Sheridan (2000)
Donald Harris (1958) *
David Hacking (1963) *
Neil MacCormick (1971) *
Klaus Reichert *
Jean Yves de Cara *

* Door Tenant

Work Undertaken: A set practising in all areas of civil and commercial law with a wide spread of work including all aspects of business, contract and employment law, professional negligence and human rights. Chambers are members of COMBAR. Chambers have formed a Ltd company providing mediation and arbitration services.

Main Areas: There are four main specialities in chambers: employment law; professional negligence, including medical negligence; ADR and arbitration; commercial law incorporating banking, financial services and insurance, entertainment and media, construction, commercial fraud, public and European and insolvency.

Additional Areas: Carriage of goods; company law; consumer credit law; corporate finance; insolvency; international trade; letters of request; competition law; computer law; EU; environment; family; pharmaceuticals; telecommunications; transport; sale of goods; administrative law; civil liberties; charities; discrimination; education; election law; housing; judicial review; landlord and tenant; local government; mental health; parliamentary; planning; construction; sports and entertainment law; matrimonial finance and children; and pensions. Members of chambers provide lectures on a wide range of subjects and chambers are accredited by the Law Society and Bar Council.

International: Languages spoken include Cantonese, French, German and Italian.

Recruitment: Members of chambers fund two pupils per year. Chambers are not members of OLPAS.

Set No.

91 LITTMAN CHAMBERS (Mark Littman QC)

12 Gray's Inn Square, Gray's Inn, London, WC1R 5JP
Tel: (020) 7404 4866 **Fax:** (020) 7404 4812 **DX:** 0055 (Ch.Ln.)
Email: admin@littmanchambers.com **Website:** www.littmanchambers.com

Head of Chambers	Mark Littman QC
Senior Clerk	Lee Cutler
Junior Clerk	Andrew Moore
Tenants	22

LITTMAN CHAMBERS
BARRISTERS
12
GRAY'S INN SQUARE
GRAY'S INN
LONDON WC1R 5JP

Members:

Mark Littman QC (1947) (QC-1961)
John Tackaberry QC (1967) (QC-1982) †
Michael Stimpson (1969)
Robert Kirk (1972)
Brian McClure (1976)
Graham Cunningham (1976)
Rowan Planterose (1978)
Andrzej Kolodziej (1978)
Jonathan Tecks (1978)
Barbara Hewson (1985)
Monique Allan (1986)
Se·n Naidoo (1990)
Martin Gibson (1990)
Rupert Higgins (1991)
Niamh McCarthy (1991)
Julie Anderson (1993) †
Damian Falkowski (1994)
James Roberts (1996)
Richard Holden (1996)
Richard Clegg (1999)
Philip Lewis (1958)
John Finnis (1970)

† Standing Counsel to the Crown.

The Chambers: Members of chambers offer specialist advocacy, advisory, drafting, arbitration and mediation services to solicitors and to those with direct access to the Bar.

Set No.
92

MAITLAND CHAMBERS (Michael Lyndon-Stanford QC & Charles Aldous QC)

7 Stone Buildings, Lincoln's Inn, London, WC2A 3SZ
Tel: (020) 7406 1200 **Fax:** (020) 7406 1300 **DX:** LDE 326
Email: clerks@maitlandchambers.com **Website:** www.maitlandchambers.com

Head of Chambers	Michael Lyndon-Stanford QC
	Charles Aldous QC
Chief Executive	Peter Bennett FCCA MCIM
Clerks	Tony Marsh
	Jim Bisland
	Martin Colley
	Andy Flanagan
Fees Clerk	John Rugg
Tenants	42

maitland
CHAMBERS

Members:

Michael Lyndon-Stanford QC (1962) (QC-1979)
Charles Aldous QC (1967) (QC-1985)
Christopher McCall QC (1966) (QC-1987)
Hazel Williamson QC (1972) (QC-1988)
Nigel Davis QC (1975) (QC-1992)
David Unwin QC (1971) (QC-1995)
Catherine Newman QC (1979) (QC-1995)
Christopher Pymont QC (1979) (QC-1996)
Anthony Trace QC (1981) (QC-1998)
Mark Cunningham QC (1980) (QC-2001)
Guy Newey QC (1982) (QC-2001)
Michael Nield (1969)
Nigel Thomas (1976)
Alastair Walton (1977)
Timothy Evans (1979)
Simon Barker (1979)
Paul Girolami (1983)
Lindsey Stewart (1983)
Christopher Parker (1984)
James Clifford (1984)
Matthew Collings (1985)
John Nicholls (1986)
Carolyn Walton (1980)
Jonathan Russen (1986)
Richard Morgan (1988)
Nicholas Peacock (1989)
Gregory Banner (1989)
Mark Wonnacott (1989)
David Brownbill (1989)
Edmund Cullen (1991)
Amanda Tipples (1991)
Patricia Carswell (1993)
Michael Gibbon (1993)
Rebecca Stubbs (1994)
James Aldridge (1994)
Andrew Westwood (1994)
Siward Atkins (1995)
Andrew Ayres (1996)
Catherine Addy (1998)
Louise Hutton (1998)
Oliver Mitchell (1999)
David Mumford (2000)

The Chambers: Maitland Chambers was formed in January 2001 by the merger of two long established chancery sets – 13 Old Square (Michael Lyndon-Stanford QC) and 7 Stone Buildings (Charles Aldous QC). It is pre-eminent in the field of commercial chancery litigation. All barristers are members of the Chancery Bar Association and the Commercial Bar Association. All members can receive instructions by email to their desks.

Work Undertaken: Chambers and Partners recommended members of Maitland as leaders in their field in the following areas – commercial chancery, company, charities, insolvency, media and entertainment, traditional chancery, property litigation, partnership, pensions, banking, energy, tax, agriculture and professional negligence. Expertise is available in all areas of chancery and commercial law.

Clientele: Instructions are received from most of the top 100 solicitors in the UK, and also from a very wide range of firms, whose instructions are very valued. Many members are or have been junior counsel to the Crown. Chambers welcome instructions under Direct Professional Access and Bar Direct rules and regularly receive them from accountants, local authorities and others. Members are regularly instructed by international firms for work in the UK and in many offshore jurisdictions.

Recruitment: Three, £30,000, 12 month pupillages are offered each year. Full details are available on the website. Chambers does not currently participate in OLPAS. Mini-pupillages are encouraged.

Set No.
93

MATRIX CHAMBERS (Nicholas Blake QC)

Griffin Building, Gray's Inn, London, WC1R 5LN
Tel: (020) 7404 3447 **Fax:** (020) 7404 3448 **DX:** 400 Chancery Lane
Email: matrix@matrixlaw.co.uk **Website:** www.matrixlaw.co.uk

Head of Chambers	Nicholas Blake QC
Chief Executive	Nicholas Martin
Practice Managers	Amanda Campbell
	Paul Robinson
Administrator	Kevin Hooper
Practice Assistants	Andy Hall
	Carla Owen
	Zoe Osmotherly
Legal Information Manager	Anna Edmundson
Tenants	35

Members:

Lord Brennan QC (1967) (QC-1985)
Nicholas Blake QC (1974) (QC-1994)
David Bean QC (1976) (QC-1997)
Cherie Booth QC (1976) (QC-1995)
Andrew Clapham (1985)
James Crawford SC (1999) (NSW-1987) (SC-1997)
Ben Emmerson QC (1986) (QC-2000)
Daniel Friedman (1996)
Conor Gearty (1995)
Murray Hunt (1992)
Raza Husain (1993)
Anthony Jennings QC (1983) (QC-2001)
Julian Knowles (1994)
Thomas Linden (1990)
Kenneth Macdonald QC (1978) (QC-1997)
Jonathan Marks (1992)
Clare Montgomery QC (1980) (QC-1996)
Helen Mountfield (1991)
Tim Owen QC (1983) (QC-2000)
Heather Rogers (1983)LLB
Matthew Ryder (1992)

Members continued:

Philippe Sands (1985)
Maurice Sheridan (1984)
Jessica Simor (1992)
Rabinder Singh (1989)
Dan Squires (1998)
Rhodri Thompson (1989)
Hugh Tomlinson (1983)
Antony White QC (1983) (QC-2001)
David Wolfe (1992)
Mark Afeeva (1997)
Kate Cook (1991)
Janet Kentridge (1999)
Karon Monaghan (1991)
Gillian Morris (1997)

The Chambers: Matrix is a new legal practice set up in anticipation of the complex challenges facing the law in the new century. The lawyers who set up Matrix aim to innovate in the way legal services are delivered and to move beyond the traditional divisions – between practitioners and academics, private and public law, and domestic and international law. They are also committed to collaborative ventures that will break down traditional divisions within the legal profession itself. The members of Matrix practice in a wide range of disciplines including UK public, private and criminal law, as well as European Union law, human rights law and public international law. These diverse areas will be linked through common principles of human rights, international and constitutional law and Matrix will lead the way in providing advice and representation that draws on the emerging synergies of its many practice specialities. Matrix will also innovate through the provision of teams of lawyers and the full integration of leading academics into its practice. Matrix is committed to quality of service and to delivering the highest levels of value to its clients. It will seek feedback from clients on an active basis and is committed to continuous improvement.

Set No. 94 **1 MIDDLE TEMPLE LANE** (Colin Dines & Andrew Trollope QC)

1 Middle Temple Lane, Temple, London, EC4Y 9AA **Tel:** (020) 7583 0659 (12 lines) **Fax:** (020) 7353 0652 **DX:** 464 **Email:** chambers@lmtl.co.uk

Set No. 95 **1 MITRE COURT BUILDINGS** (Bruce Blair QC)

1 Mitre Court Buildings, Temple, London, EC4Y 7BS
Tel: (020) 7797 7070 **Fax:** (020) 7797 7435 **DX:** LDE 342 Chancery Lane
Email: clerks@1mcb.com **Website:** www.1mcb.com

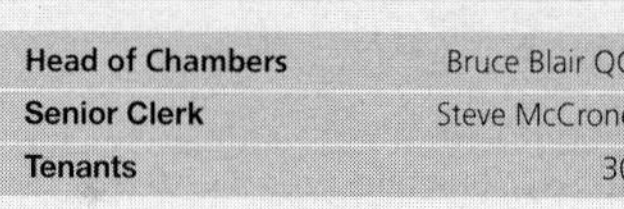

Head of Chambers	Bruce Blair QC
Senior Clerk	Steve McCrone
Tenants	30

Members:

Bruce Blair QC (1969) (QC-1989)
Michael Horowitz QC (1968) (QC-1990)
Jeremy Posnansky QC (1972) (QC-1994)
Mark Everall QC (1975) (QC-1994)
Martin Pointer QC (1976) (QC-1996)
Nicholas Mostyn QC (1980) (QC-1997)
John Elvidge (1968)
Michael Nicholls (1975)
Robin Spon-Smith (1976)
Valentine Le Grice (1977)
Heather Pope (1977)
Nicholas Carden (1981)
Catriona Murfitt (1981)
Gavin Smith (1981)
Nigel Dyer (1982)
Philip Moor QC (1982) (QC-2001)
Charles Todd (1983)
Christopher Wood (1986)
Nicholas Cusworth (1986)
Katharine Davidson (1987)
Richard Todd (1988)
Rachel Platts (1989)
Elisabeth Todd (1990)
Timothy Bishop (1991)
Geoffrey Kingscote (1993)
Stephen Trowell (1995)
Justin Warshaw (1995)
Nicholas Yates (1996)
Simon Webster (1997)
Rebecca Wood (1999)

The Chambers: 1 Mitre Court Buildings is the longest established set practising exclusively in the area of family law. The set offers advocacy, advisory and drafting expertise over the entire range of family and matrimonial law, whether child or finance oriented, and undertakes work at all levels of court. Together with its service to privately paying clients, 1 Mitre Court Buildings has a strong commitment to and involvement in publicly funded family work. The set is instructed by CAFCASS and local authorities, as well as on behalf of individual clients. 1 Mitre Court Buildings frequently handles cases with an international dimension. All members of chambers belong to the Family Law Bar Association.

Set No.
96 ## 2 MITRE COURT BUILDINGS (Michael FitzGerald QC)

2 Mitre Court Buildings, Temple, London, EC4Y 7BX
Tel: (020) 7583 1380 **Fax:** (020) 7353 7772 **DX:** 0032 Chancery Lane
Email: clerks@2mcb.co.uk

Head of Chambers	Michael FitzGerald QC
Senior Clerk	Robert Woods
Clerks	Frances Kaliszewska
	Kirstie Durrant
	John Keegan
Clerk (Administrator)	Joan Matthewson
Tenants	20

2MCB

Members:

Michael FitzGerald QC (1961) (QC-1980)
David Widdicombe QC (1950) (QC-1965)
Lord Silsoe QC (1951) (QC-1972)
Gerald Moriarty QC (1951) (QC-1974)
Anthony Anderson QC (1964) (QC-1982)
Matthew Horton QC (1969) (QC-1989)
Guy Roots QC (1969) (QC-1989)
Neil King QC (1980) (QC-2000)
Alun Alesbury (1974)
Robert Fookes (1975)
Michael Humphries (1982)
Richard Glover (1984)
Mary Macpherson (1984)
Paul Shadarevian (1984)
Michael Druce (1988)
Reuben Taylor (1990)
Rupert Warren (1994)
Christopher Boyle (1994)
Richard Wald (1997)
Robert Walton (1999)

The Chambers: A long-established and well known set currently comprising 20 members of whom eight are QCs. All members specialise in planning and local government law.

Work Undertaken: The main specialist area practised by all members comprises planning and local government which includes town and country planning, environmental law, compulsory purchase and compensation, rating and council tax, utilities and infrastructure, local government, public and administrative law, parliamentary bills and transport and works act orders. All members appear at public inquiries, the Lands Tribunal and the courts.

Clientele: A wide range including companies, corporations, public and private utilities, local authorities, government departments and foreign governments, individuals and residents associations. Instructions are accepted under the Direct Access Scheme.

International: Members have appeared or advised in relation to a number of jurisdictions including Hong Kong, Jersey and Bermuda.

Recruitment: Applications for tenancy should be addressed to the chair of the executive committee. Applications for pupillage should be addressed to the administrator. Chambers have two to three pupils at any one time and substantial awards are available for pupils; details will be provided on application. Mini-pupillages are also available.

Set No.
97 ## MONCKTON CHAMBERS (John Swift QC)

4 Raymond Buildings, Gray's Inn, London, WC1R 5BP
Tel: (020) 7405 7211 **Fax:** (020) 7405 2084 **DX:** 257
Email: chambers@monckton.co.uk **Website:** www.monckton.co.uk

Head of Chambers	John Swift QC
Senior Clerk	Graham Lister
Tenants	27

Members:

John Swift QC (1965) (QC-1981)
Jeremy Lever QC (1957) (QC-1972)
Nicholas Lyell QC (1965) (QC-1980)
Richard Fowler QC (1969) (QC-1989)
Kenneth Parker QC (1975) (QC-1992)
Paul Lasok QC (1977) (QC-1994)
Peter M. Roth QC (1976) (QC-1997)
Nicholas Paines QC (1978) (QC-1997)
Christopher Vajda QC (1979) (QC-1997)
Rupert Anderson (1981)
Michael Patchett-Joyce (1981)
Melanie Hall (1982)
Michael Bowsher (1985)
Andrew Macnab (1986)
Jon Turner (1988)
Peter Mantle (1989)
George Peretz (1990)
Jennifer Skilbeck (1991)
Raymond Hill (1992)
Paul Harris (1994)
Rebecca Haynes (1994)
Tim Ward (1994)
Kassie Smith (1995)
Daniel Beard (1996)
Ian Hutton (1998)
Meredith Pickford (1999)
Piers Gardner (2000)

The Chambers: Monckton Chambers provides specialised advocacy and advice in European and competition law, commercial litigation, construction and judicial review. Members of chambers regard client care as paramount. They are committed to providing the best legal advice and advocacy, responding promptly and efficiently to all instructions, offering specialist services as part of an integrated professional team and remaining accessible and approachable at all times.

Work Undertaken:

European Law: Members of chambers appear regularly before the ECJ on cases involving agriculture, competition, employment, human rights, media and telecommunications, pharmaceuticals, state aids, utilities, VAT and customs. Recent cases before the European courts include Levez v T H Jennings [1999]; Mann v Sec of State for Employment [1999]; R v Sec of State for Transport ex p Factortame [1999]; Arnhem v BFI Holdings BV [1998]; Blue Circle v Commission [1998]; Ladbroke Racing v Commission [1998]; Partridge v Adjudication Officer [1998]; McLeod v United Kingdom [1998] (ECHR). Members of chambers have also been involved in numerous high profile European cases in the UK courts including R v Sec of State for Health ex p Imperial Tobacco [1999]; R v CCE ex p Lunn Poly [1999] (CA); Three Rivers District Council v Bank of England [1999] (CA) Factortame case; Redrow v CCE [1999] HL; Optident Ltd v Sec of State [1999]; Preston & Others v Wolverhampton Healthcare NHS Trust and Fletcher v Midland Bank PLC [1998] HL; Philips v Ingman [1998]; R v MAFF ex p Anastasiou (No 2) [1998] HL; R v CCE ex p Institute of Chartered Accountants [1998] HL; Midland Bank v CCE [1998], Case C – 180/96 UK v Commission [1998].

Competition: Chambers extensive experience in competition law matters includes Competition Commission ("CC") references, OFT inquiries, appeals to the new Competition Commission Appeal Tribunal, European Commission and ECJ cases. High profile competition cases in which members of chambers have appeared include the CC inquiry into the IMS/PMSI merger (pharmaceutical services), the BA/CityFlyer merger and the UFC/Pointing merger, the Airtours/First Choice merger proceedings before the European Commission, the CC inquiry into Mobile Telephones, Gencor v Commission [1999], European Night Services v Commission [1998], the Scancem/Skanska/Aker merger proceedings, the RPC reference in relation to the resale price maintenance of medicaments, the CC reference on supermarkets and the RPC reference in relation to the televising of Premier League football. Members of chambers are also extensively involved in competition and related regulatory matters concerning the utilities; acting both for the regulators (including Oftel, Ofwat and Offer) and the regulated companies. See R v Director General of Telecommunications ex p Cellcom [1999] and R v OFWAT ex p Oldham MBC & Ors [1998].

Judicial Review: Recent major cases include R v Sec of State ex p Imperial Tobacco [1999]; R v CCE ex p Marks & Spencer [1999]; Evans v MIB [1999]; R v ITC ex p Flextech [1999]; R v Governor of Gibraltar ex p Ouzza [1999]; R v Secretary of State for Home Department ex p Hoverspeed [1999]; R v Chief Constable of Sussex ex p ITF [1999] (HL); R v Home Office ex p McAvoy [1998] CA; R v Secretary of State for Employment ex p Seymour-Smith [1997] HL; R v Home Office ex p Camden City Council [1997] HL. Members of chambers also appear regularly before the VAT Tribunal and Higher Courts in relation to VAT and EC Customs legislation. Recent cases include Eastbourne Town Radio Cars Association v CCE [2000] HL; Marks & Spencer v CCE [1999]; Redrow v CCE [1999] HL; Institute of Chartered Accountants v CCE [1998] HL; McNicholas v CCE [1998]; Thorn Materials v CCE [1998] HL.

Commercial Law: Expertise includes international and domestic arbitration, banking, international and domestic commercial fraud recovery and tracing, construction law, insurance and reinsurance and professional negligence. Members of chambers have appeared in international arbitrations in the Middle East, Africa and Europe as well as in London.

Set No. 98

3 NEW SQUARE (Lord Goodhart QC)

3 New Square, Lincoln's Inn, London, WC2A 3RS
Tel: (020) 7405 5577 **Fax:** (020) 7404 5032 **DX:** 384 (L.D.E)
Email: law@threenewsquare.co.uk **Website:** www.threenewsquare.co.uk

Head of Chambers	Lord Goodhart QC
Senior Clerk	Richard Bayliss
Tenants	13

Members:

Lord Goodhart QC (1957) (QC-1979)
Hubert Picarda QC (1962) (QC-1992)
Hedley Marten (1966)
David Rowell (1972)
Andrew G. Walker (1975)
Michael Heywood (1975)
Josephine Hayes (1980)
Roger Mullis (1987)
Adam Deacock (1991)
Justin Holmes (1994)
Dov Ohrenstein (1995)
Camilla Lamont (1995)
Adrian Carr (1999)

The Chambers: 3 New Square is a specialist Chancery and commercial set, undertaking a wide range of work relating mainly to property, commerce and corporate activities.

Work Undertaken:

Commercial: Banking; credit and security; competition; conflict of laws; contracts; consumer credit; economic torts; finance; franchising; fraud; forgery and misrepresentation; guarantees; partnerships; title retention; restitution; tracing.

Company: Companies Court; changes in capital; charges; directors' disqualification; directors' duties; liquidation; receiverships; securities; shareholder disputes.

Insolvency: Corporate and personal; including international.

Continued overleaf

Pension Schemes: All aspects of occupational and personal pension schemes; fraud and insolvency.
Professional Negligence: Lawyers; accountants and other financial advisors; surveyors, land agents and valuers.
Property: Commercial, agricultural and residential; constructive trusts; conveyancing; easements; highways; landlord and tenant; Lands Tribunal; licences; mortgages and securities; planning; property-related torts; restrictive covenants.
Traditional Chancery: Charities; court of protection; equitable remedies; fiduciary duties; probate; tax and tax planning (including VAT); trusts and settlements; wills.
Alternative Dispute Resolution: Members include qualified arbitrators who undertake arbitrations and mediations both as arbitrators/mediators and as advocates.
Direct Professional Access: Work is accepted from members of the qualifying professions.

Publications: *Specific Performance* (2nd edn 1996) by Lord Goodhart QC (with Prof Gareth Jones QC); *The Law & Practice Relating to Charities* (3rd edn 1999) by Hubert Picarda QC; *The Law Relating to Receivers, Managers & Administrators* by Hubert Picarda QC (3rd edn 2000); *Halsbury's Laws of England* (4th edn): titles on corporations by Lord Goodhart QC; on money by Dov Ohrenstein; on mortgages by Camilla Lamont; specific performance by Lord Goodhart QC; receivers by Hubert Picarda QC; charities by Hubert Picarda QC.

International: Members are regularly instructed and appear in overseas jurisdictions.

Set No.
99

THREE NEW SQUARE (David Young QC)

3 New Square, Lincoln's Inn, London, WC2A 3RS
Tel: (020) 7405 1111 **Fax:** (020) 7405 7800 **DX:** 454
Email: 3newsquareip@lineone.net **Website:** www.3newsquare.co.uk

Head of Chambers	David Young QC
Senior Clerk	Ian Bowie
Tenants	14

Members:

David Young QC (1966) (QC-1980)
Antony Watson QC (1968) (QC-1986)
Simon Thorley QC (1972) (QC-1989)
Richard Miller QC (1976) (QC-1995)
Guy Burkill (1981)
Andrew Waugh QC (1982) (QC-1998)
Denise McFarland (1987)
Colin Birss (1990)
Justin Turner (1992)
Douglas James Campbell (1993)
Thomas Mitcheson (1996)
Thomas Hinchliffe (1997)
Geoffrey Pritchard (1998)
Helyn Mensah (1998)

The Chambers: A specialist intellectual property set. Members belong to the Intellectual Property and Chancery Bar Associations. David Young is the author of *Passing Off*, chairman of the Plant Seeds Varieties tribunal and Deputy Judge of the Patent County Court. David Young and Simon Thorley are Deputy High Court Judges in Chancery and Queens' Bench Division. Simon Thorley is a part-time chairman of the Copyright tribunal and is also an appointed person to hear appeals from the Trade Mark Registry. In addition, for many years, members have edited *Terrell on the Law of Patents.*

Work Undertaken:
Intellectual Property: Particularly science, technology, biotechnology, entertainment and media. Including patents (UK and European), copyright, designs (registered and unregistered), service marks, plant-breeders rights, trade marks (registered and unregistered), passing off, trade libel and malicious falsehood, confidential information, franchising and licensing (including licences of right and product licensing) and IT. Members also handle related aspects of competition law and general litigation with a significant technical content. Direct Professional Access is accepted.
Additional Areas: Arbitration and professional negligence.

International: Languages include French, German and Japanese. Chambers' QCs have appeared in Singapore and Hong Kong.

Recruitment: Tenancy and pupillage applications should be made via the OLPAS scheme. Awards of £9,000 per six months are available. Mini-pupillages are offered throughout the year. A science degree is preferred.

Set No.
100

FOUR NEW SQUARE (Justin Fenwick QC)

4 New Square, Lincoln's Inn, London, WC2A 3RJ
Tel: (020) 7822 2000 **Fax:** (020) 7822 2001 **DX:** 1041 L.D.E.
Email: barristers@4newsquare.com **Website:** www.4newsquare.com

Head of Chambers	Justin Fenwick QC
Senior Clerk	Lizzy Wiseman
Tenants	45

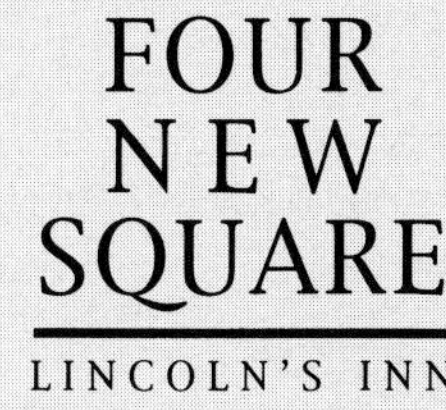

Members:

Justin Fenwick QC (1980) (QC-1993)
John L Powell QC (1974) (QC-1990)
Bernard Livesey QC (1969) (QC-1990)
Nicholas Davidson QC (1974) (QC-1993)
Michael Brooke QC (1969) (QC-1994)
Christopher Gibson QC (1976) (QC-1995)
Iain Hughes QC (1974) (QC-1996)
Roger Stewart QC (1986) (QC-2001)
Prof. Eva Lomnicka (1974)
Simon Russen (1976)
Charles Douthwaite (1977)
Glen Tyrell (1977)
Michael Soole (1977)
David Halpern (1978)
Gavin Hamilton (1979)
Simon Monty (1982)
Graeme Mew (1982)
Martin Fodder (1983)
Mark Cannon (1985)
Ian Holtum (1985)
Paul Parker (1986)
Ben Patten (1986)
Sue Carr (1987)
Hugh Evans (1987)
Jalil Asif (1988)
Fiona Sinclair (1989)
Nicholas Brown (1989)
Andrew R Nicol (1991)
Ben Hubble (1992)
Charles Phipps (1992)
Paul Sutherland (1992)
Graeme McPherson (1993)
Leigh-Ann Mulcahy (1993)
Aisha Bijlani (1993)
Nicola Shaldon (1994)
Jamie Smith (1995)
Anneliese Day (1996)
Ben Elkington (1996)
Seánin Gilmore (1996)
Siân Mirchandani (1997)
Graham Chapman (1998)
Richard Liddell (1999)
Amanda Savage (1999)
Stephen Innes (2000) From October 2001
Scott Allen (2000) From October 2001

The Chambers: Four New Square is a commercial and civil set with a particular reputation for claims involving professionals and other service providers. It also has a strong construction, financial services, insurance, commercial and employment practice. Based for over 50 years in the Temple (most recently at 2 Crown Office Row), the set moved to new, larger premises in 1999 in Lincoln's Inn. This has allowed chambers to introduce a modern IT network and to acquire enlarged conference facilities (including video-conferencing) as part of its continuing commitment to providing all its clients with the highest level of service, both as advocates and as advisers.

Work Undertaken: Chambers have particular expertise in the field of professional liability and cover the full range of claims against professionals, including claims for fraud, breach of fiduciary duty and trust, negligence and breach of contract and regulatory and disciplinary proceedings. The main professions covered are accountants and auditors, architects and engineers, solicitors and barristers, bankers, financial intermediaries and institutions, insurance intermediaries, Lloyd's agents, surveyors and valuers and medical practitioners. *Jackson & Powell on Professional Negligence* is edited by current members of chambers. Other major areas of practice include construction and engineering; commercial litigation; banking and financial services (including UK, EU and international securities regulation); consumer credit; insurance and reinsurance; employment; IT and computer contracts; product liability and personal injury. Chambers have considerable experience of multi-party litigation in the context of product liability, professional negligence, fraud recovery and disaster claims.

Publications: Apart from *Jackson & Powell on Professional Negligence* (General editors John L Powell QC and Roger Stewart QC; specialist editors Christopher Gibson QC, David Halpern, Mark Cannon, Hugh Evans, Fiona Sinclair, Paul Sutherland, Graeme McPherson, Ben Elkington, Graham Chapman and Sian Merchandani), publications include *Lawyer's Liabilities* (Hugh Evans), *Confidentiality* (Charles Phipps with Toulson J.), and *The Encyclopedia of Financial Services Law* (Professor Eva Lomnicka and John L Powell QC). Last year also saw the arrival of the companion work to *Jackson & Powell*, *Professional Liability Precedents*, (General editor Sue Carr, contributors Simon Russen, Simon Monty, Paul Parker, Jalil Asif, Ben Hubble, Charles Phipps, Paul Sutherland and Ben Elkington). *Encyclopedia of Consumer Credit and Modern Banking Law* (Professor Eva Lomnicka). Leigh-Ann Mulcahy is one of the co-authors of *Human Rights and Civil Practise* which is due to be published in September 2001. Professor Andrew Tettenborn, a door tenant, is an editor of *Clerk & Lindsell on Torts.*

International: Members of chambers appear in court and arbitration proceedings in Hong Kong, Singapore, Paris and the West Indies. Michael Brooke QC is an Avocat á la Cour d'Appel de Paris.

Set No.
101 **7 NEW SQUARE** (Bernard Pearl)

7 New Square, Lincoln's Inn, London, WC2A 3QS
Tel: (020) 7430 1660 **Fax:** (020) 7430 1531 **DX:** 106 (Ch.Ln.)
Website: www.sevennewsquare.com

Head of Chambers	Bernard Pearl
Senior Clerk	John A Harwood IBC MTTS
Tenants	16

Members:

Bernard Pearl (1970)
Margaret Puxon QC (1954) (QC-1982)
Philip Proghoulis (1963)
Andrew Gifford (1988)
Simon Airey (1989)
Linda Goldman (1990)
John Scott Price (1990)
Andrew Baker (1990)
Lisa Sinclair (1993)
Dr Catherine MacKenzie (1995)
Marianne Perkins (1997)
Melvyn Harris (1997)
Alastair B Hodge (1997)
Leon Taylor (1997)
Cecilia Hulse (1998)
Sarah Malik (1999)

WORK UNDERTAKEN: Civil/commercial, especially professional negligence (members include two former solicitors, two dentists, a doctor and a pharmacist); commercial and residential property; insolvency; employment; local authority; judicial review. Seminars and lectures are available.

INTERNATIONAL: Languages spoken include Bengali, French, German and Italian.

Set No.
102 **8 NEW SQUARE** (Michael Fysh QC)

8 New Square, Lincoln's Inn, London, WC2A 3QP
Tel: (020) 7405 4321 **Fax:** (020) 7405 9955 **DX:** 379 (Ch.Ln)
Email: clerks@8newsquare.co.uk **Website:** www.8newsquare.co.uk

Head of Chambers	Michael Fysh QC
Senior Clerk	John Call
Deputy Senior Clerk	Tony Liddon
Principal Clerks	Nicholas Wise
	Martin Williams
Assistant Clerks	Martin Kilbey
	Andrew Clayton
Tenants	23

Members:

Michael Fysh QC (1965) (QC-1989)
Peter Prescott QC (1970) (QC-1990)
John Baldwin QC (1977) (QC-1991)
David Kitchin QC (1977) (QC-1994)
Mark Platts-Mills QC (1974) (QC-1995)
Martin Howe QC (1978) (QC-1996)
Mary Vitoria QC (1975) (QC-1997)
George Hamer (1974)
Fiona Clark (1982)
James Mellor (1986)
Daniel Alexander (1988)
Robert Onslow (1991)
Michael Tappin (1991)
Richard Meade (1991)
Adrian Speck (1993)
James St. Ville (1995)
Charlotte May (1995)
Thomas Moody-Stuart (1995)
Lindsay Lane (1996)
James Abrahams (1997)
Iona Berkeley (1999)
Mark Chacksfield (1999)
Henery Ward (2000)

The Chambers: The set specialises in intellectual property law of all kinds, and is the largest set in the country practising in this area. Many members of chambers are authors of, or contributors to, the leading books and encyclopaedias on intellectual property law. All are members of the Intellectual Property Bar and Chancery Bar Associations. A brochure giving further information and individual biographies of all members of chambers is available upon request. Biographies may also be viewed on 8 New Square's website along with current news. The senior clerks have been with chambers for over 20 years and have considerable experience of the work undertaken by chambers. They will be happy to assist in choice of Counsel.

Work Undertaken: Intellectual property, including patents; copyright; passing off; trade and service marks; designs and registered designs; counterfeiting; data protection; franchising; publishing; telecommunications; internet domain names; trade libel; trade descriptions; trade secrets and confidential information; hallmarks; plant breeders' rights. Members also specialise in European law, competition and restrictive trade practices, entertainment and media law, advertising law, computer law, licensing and administrative law (principally where these are ancillary to intellectual property cases). Commercial, environmental and other work with a significant scientific or technical content are also handled.

International: French, German, Spanish and Italian. Several members of chambers conduct cases in the Far East, Australia, India and Ireland.

Recruitment: Up to two pupillages are offered each year, usually for twelve months. Pupils with scientific or technical backgrounds are strongly encouraged, although others will be considered in exceptional circumstances. Awards of £20,000 are offered. Chambers are members of OLPAS (Online Pupillage Application System).

Set No.
103

11 NEW SQUARE (Sonia Proudman QC)

11 New Square, Lincoln's Inn, London, WC2A 3QB
Tel: (020) 7831 0081 **Fax:** (020) 7405 0798/2560 **DX:** 319
Email: clerks@11newsquare.co.uk

Head of Chambers	Sonia Proudman QC
Practice Director	John Lister
Senior Clerk	Mike Gibbs
Tenants	23

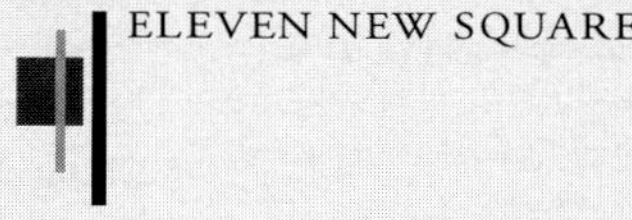

Members:

Sonia Proudman QC (1972) (QC-1994)
Peter Crampin QC (1976) (QC-1993)
Miles Shillingford (1964)
Roger Horne (1967)
Peter Castle (1970)
Stephen Lloyd (1971)
Jill Gibson (1972)
Michael Jefferis (1976)
Mark Studer (1976)
Robert Lewis (1996)Admitted as a solicitor (1977)
Robert Pearce (1977)
Andrew Francis (1977)
Thomas Dumont (1979)
Simon Randle (1982)
Alistair Craig (1983)
Ulick Staunton (1984)
Piers Feltham (1985)
Howard Smith (1986)
Clive Moys (1998)Admitted as a solicitor (1988)
Peter Smith (1993)
Marie-Claire Bleasdale (1993)
Siri Cope (1997)
Catherine Finely (1999)

The Chambers: 11 New Square is a leading and progressive set of chambers in chancery, commercial and planning and public law work. Its members, two silks and 21 juniors, have specialist expertise in both the traditional and evolving areas of chambers' practice. The aims of the chambers are to provide first class advocacy, advice and drafting in the areas of members' expertise; to develop constructive, innovative and lasting working relationships with clients; to represent clients' interests both in litigation and in other situations; to be approachable and responsive to the needs of clients.

Work Undertaken:

Charities & Pensions: Chambers contain groups of members with particular expertise in both these areas.

Commercial Law: Particularly in areas such as banking and security, partnerships and joint ventures.

Company, Corporate & Individual Insolvency: In the corporate field, members have particular experience in areas such as minority shareholders' rights and directors' conduct, winding up, administration and receivership.

Planning & Public Law: Chambers have an experienced team dealing with all aspects of planning and public law, including judicial review, Human Rights legislation, local authority powers and duties and those of other governmental and quasi-governmental bodies.

Professional Negligence: Members of chambers at all levels have wide experience in the conduct and defence of claims for professional negligence, particularly of solicitors, accountants and surveyors.

Property: All aspects of land law and conveyancing, as well as landlord and tenant work. Chambers contain specialists in restrictive covenants; easements (including rights of light); mines and minerals.

Trusts & Estates: All aspects of the administration of trusts and estates, including probate and family provision litigation. Members offer specialist expertise in the field of the taxation of trusts.

Other: Individual members of chambers have developed particular expertise in a wide variety of other fields such as ADR (commercial arbitration and mediation), cross-border cases, environmental law, intellectual property, court of protection work and detailed cost assessment. They give expert opinion on English law in foreign courts and also receive instructions and appear as advocate in various foreign and overseas courts, including recently the courts of Hong Kong, Cayman Islands and Cyprus. Members of chambers are members of the Chancery Bar Association, the Professional Negligence Bar Association, COMBAR, INSOL, IBA (creditors' right and ADR committees), American Bar Association, American Bankruptcy Institute, PEBA, STEP, the Charity Law Association and ACTAPS.

Set No.
104
NEW SQUARE CHAMBERS (John Mowbray QC & Eben Hamilton QC)

12 New Square, Lincoln's Inn, London, WC2A 3SW
Tel: (020) 7419 8000 **Fax:** (020) 7419 8050 **DX:** 1056 London/Chancery Lane
Email: clerks@newsquarechambers.co.uk **Website:** www.newsquarechambers.co.uk

Head of Chambers	John Mowbray QC Eben Hamilton QC
Senior Clerk	Clive Petchey
Tenants	43

NEW SQUARE CHAMBERS

Members:

John Mowbray QC (1953) (QC-1974)
Eben Hamilton QC (1962) (QC-1981)
John Macdonald QC (1955) (QC-1976)
John McDonnell QC (1968) (QC-1984)
Charles Purle QC (1970) (QC-1989)
George Laurence QC (1972) (QC-1991)
Robin Mathew QC (1974) (QC-1992)
Robin Hollington QC (1979) (QC-1999)
Stephen Smith QC (1983) (QC-2000)
Rodney Stewart Smith (1964)
Michael Kennedy (1967)
Lynton Tucker (1971)
Colin Braham (1971)
Christopher Russell (1971)
Kenneth Munro (1973)
Gordon Bennett (1974)
Nicholas Le Poidevin (1975)
Malcolm Chapple (1975)
Christopher Semken (1977)
Michael Roberts (1978)
Stuart Barber (1979)
Clive Jones (1981)
Leigh Sagar (1983)
David Eaton Turner (1984)
Kathryn Lampard (1984)
Claire Staddon (1985)
Thomas Graham (1985)
Ross Crail (1986)
Sandra Corbett (1988)
Stephen Schaw Miller (1988)
Colette Wilkins (1989)
Ian Peacock (1990)
Gerard van Tonder (1990)
Edwin Simpson (1990)
Mark Hubbard (1991)
Simon Adamyk (1991)
John Eidinow (1992)
Jane Evans-Gordon (1992)
Sebastian Prentis (1996)
David Warner (1996)
Adrian Pay (1999)
James Bailey (1999)
Professor Richard Buckley (1969)

The Chambers: New Square Chambers was formed in October 2000 by the merger of two leading chancery sets, 1 New Square and 12 New Square.

Work Undertaken: New Square Chambers undertakes litigation and advisory work both in the UK and internationally, including Direct Professional Access and Legal Aid. The work done by members of chambers covers three broad areas: company and commercial (including individual and corporate insolvency, receivership, partnership, freezing injunctions, search orders and fraud); property (including landlord and tenant, mortgages, intellectual property, construction and conveyancing); taxes, trusts and wills (including probate, pension schemes and both revenue and capital taxation. Members also cover public/administrative law including parliamentary law, public inquiries, local government and planning law, judicial review and constitutional law. Members cover professional negligence related to the above fields. A brochure, containing a more detailed profile of chambers, is available on request, or via chambers website.

International: Languages spoken include French and German. Members are regularly instructed to appear in overseas jurisdictions, including Antigua, the Bahamas, Bermuda, the British Virgin Islands, the Caymans, the Channel Islands, Gibraltar, Hong Kong and Singapore and before the Privy Council.

Recruitment: Applications for pupillage via OLPAS.

Set No.
105
19 OLD BUILDINGS (Alastair Wilson QC)

19 Old Buildings, Lincoln's Inn, London, WC2A 3UP
Tel: (020) 7405 2001 **Fax:** (020) 7405 0001 **DX:** 397 (Ch.Ln.)
Email: clerks@19oldbuildings.com **Website:** www.19oldbuildings.com

Head of Chambers	Alastair Wilson QC
Senior Clerk	Barbara Harris
Tenants	7

Members:

Alastair Wilson QC (1968) (QC-1987)MA (Cantab)
Brian Reid (1971)MA (Cantab), LLM (Lond)
Graham Shipley (1973)MA (Cantab), Dip Comp Sci (Cantab)
Michael Hicks (1976)BA (Cantab)
Peter McLean Colley (1989)BSc (Lond), PhD (Lond), LLB (Lond)
Cedric Puckrin (1990)BA, LLB (Cape Town)
Jeremy Reed (1997)MA (Cantab)

The Chambers: This set, founded by Sir Duncan Kerly, has specialised for over a century in intellectual property law. Chambers also offer expertise in cases relating to computers (and other technical subject-matter), competition, media and entertainment. Direct Professional Access work is undertaken. A chambers brochure is available on request.

Work Undertaken:
Intellectual Property: Patents; copyright; designs; trade marks; passing off; plant varieties; confidential information (including ex-employee cases).
Science & Technology: Work requiring understanding of scientific and technical issues.
Computers & IT: All aspects of litigation involving computers and information technology including data protection and internet disputes.
Media & Entertainment: Public performance, film, recording and performers' rights; merchandising; broadcasting; cable and satellite distribution.
Competition Law: UK and EU monopolies and restrictive practices law, in particular relating to R&D, licensing, distribution and franchising.
Additional Areas: Pharmaceutical registration.

Publications: Publications written, or contributed to, by members of chambers include: *European Patent Office Reports*, *The Future of Legal Protection for Industrial Design*, *The CIPA Black Book*, *Melville's Forms and Agreements on Intellectual Property and International Licensing.*

International: Work is handled in French.

et No.
06 ## 22 OLD BUILDINGS (Benet Hytner QC)

22 Old Buildings, Lincoln's Inn, London, WC2A 3UP
Tel: (020) 7831 0222 **Fax:** (020) 7831 2239 **DX:** 201 London Chancery Lane
Email: clerks@22oldbuildings.law.co.uk

Head of Chambers	Benet Hytner QC
Senior Clerk	Alan Brewer

Members:

Benet Hytner QC (1952) (QC-1970)
John Price QC (1961) (QC-1980)
John Rowe QC (1960) (QC-1982)
Giles Wingate-Saul QC (1967) (QC-1983)
Rodney Scholes QC (1968) (QC-1987)
Timothy King QC (1973) (QC-1991)
Geoffrey Tattersall QC (1970) (QC-1992)
Caroline Swift QC (1977) (QC-1993)
Andrew G. Moran QC (1976) (QC-1994)
David Allan QC (1974) (QC-1995)
Stephen Stewart QC (1975) (QC-1996)
Winston Hunter QC (1985) (QC-2000)
Christopher Melton QC (1982) (QC-2001)
Patrick Hamlin (1970)
Mark Batchelor (1971)
Susan Cooper (1976)
Michael Daiches (1977)
Philip Newman (1977)
Charles Utley (1979)
Jane Hill (1980)
Howard Lederman (1982)
Rehna Azim (1984)
Jonathan Bennett (1985)
Garfield Braithwaite (1987)
Tina Cook (1988)
Frank Feehan (1988)
Gemma Taylor (1988)
Nicholas Berry (1988)
Ronald Coster (1989)
Anthony Jerman (1989)
Desmond Kilcoyne (1990)
Lee Arnot (1990)
Richard Furniss (1991)
Mary Lazarus (1991)
Paul Lonergan (1991)
Carolyn Rothwell (1991)
Marcia Hyde (1992)
Benjamin Uduje (1992)
Christopher McCourt (1993)
Matthew Hutchings (1993)
Naomi Hawkes (1994)
Stefano Nuvoloni (1994)
Anna McKenna (1994)
Tina Villarosa (1995)
Damian Woodward-Carlton (1995)
Angus Withington (1995)
Henry Pitchers (1996)
Scott Matthewson (1996)
Gareth Compton (1997)
Toby Watkin (1996)
Eilidh Gardner (1997)
William Thomas (1998)
Rebecca Thomas (1999)
Jude Shepherd (1996)

22
OB
22 Old Buildings

The Chambers: Also at Byrom Street Chambers, 12 Byrom Street, Manchester M3 4PP. Telephone: (0161) 829 2100.

et No.
07 **24 OLD BUILDINGS** (Rex Bretten QC)
24 Old Buildings (First Floor), Lincoln's Inn, London, WC2A 3UP **Tel:** (020) 7242 2744 **Fax:** (020) 7831 8095 **DX:** 386 **Email:** taxchambers@compuserve.com **Website:** www.taxchambers.com

Set No.
108 **24 OLD BUILDINGS** (Martin Mann QC & Alan Steinfeld QC)

24 Old Buildings, Lincoln's Inn, London, WC2A 3UP
Tel: (020) 7404 0946 **Fax:** (020) 7405 1360 **DX:** LDE 307
Email: clerks@xxiv.co.uk **Website:** www.xxiv.co.uk

Head of Chambers	Martin Mann QC
	Alan Steinfeld QC
Senior Clerk	Nicholas Luckman
Clerks	Jeremy Hopkins
	Daniel Wilson
	Chris Lane
Administrator	Marshall Thomson
Tenants	29

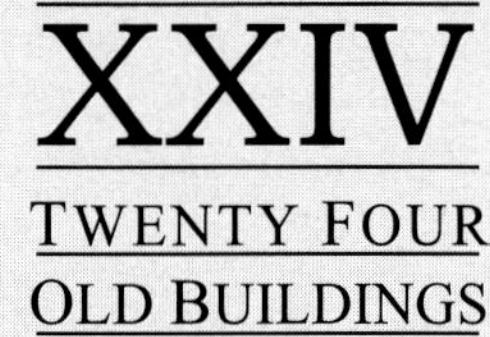

Members:

Martin Mann QC (1968) (QC-1983)
Alan Steinfeld QC (1968) (QC-1987)
Roger Kaye QC (1970) (QC-1989)
Lawrence Cohen QC (1974) (QC-1993)
Thomas Baxendale (1962)
Michael King (1971)
Philip Shepherd (1975)
Paul Teverson (1976)
Richard Ritchie (1978)
Francis Tregear (1980)
Daniel Gerrans (1981)
Michael Gadd (1981)
Elizabeth Weaver (1982)
Stephen Moverley Smith (1985)
Helen Galley (1987)
Adrian Francis (1988)
Christopher Young (1988)
Amanda Harington (1989)
Elspeth Talbot Rice (1990)
Nicholas Cherryman (1991)
Clare Stanley (1994)
Marcus Staff (1994)Geneva
Stuart Adair (1995)
Alexander Pelling (1995)
Bajul Shah (1996)
Steven Thompson (1996)
Jessica Chappell (1997)
Lyndsey Mein (1999)
Edward Knight (1999)
Graham Virgo *

* Door Tenant

The Chambers: 24 Old Buildings is a leading London barristers' chambers which has continuously adapted to meet the changing needs of modern business. Chambers' experience and reputation is in business litigation and international trust law. Instructions are taken from UK firms, in-house legal departments, recognised institutions under Direct Professional Access and Bar Direct, international law firms and foreign clients. Barristers and staff are well known for their friendly, efficient and practical approach, and their commitment to the highest standards of professional service. Cases in recent years have included Atlantic Computers, Gruppo Torras Litigation, Maxwell, Baring and BCCI; Pan Am in the Lockerbie air disaster, and ABTA on passenger service charges. 24 Old Buildings' strength lies in its ability to handle complex cases involving more than one aspect of the law, offering both breadth and depth of expertise.
Office Hours: 8am to 7pm, Monday to Friday. Please call the Clerks or visit the website for further information. Chambers provides 24-hour cover for urgent cases – Nicholas Luckman at (07774) 240112.

Work Undertaken: Key areas of expertise are company law; insolvency and corporate rescue, bankruptcy; civil fraud; asset tracing and recovery; international trusts; insurance; property; partnership; professional negligence. Growth areas are arbitration and mediation, e-commerce and IT litigation. Some members have niche specialisms in banking; aviation and travel; pensions; financial services; probate; EU law; charities and church law.

Clientele: Multi-national corporations, private companies and partnerships, financial institutions, trustees and trust companies, insolvency practitioners, accountants, overseas lawyers, property developers, government departments, industry associations, and private individuals.

International: Chambers have a permanent officce in Geneva. Members regularly advise and appear as advocates in other jurisdictions including the Isle of Man and Channel Islands; Bahamas, Bermuda, British Virgin Islands; Cayman; the Far East and Europe. Chambers have particular expertise in multi-jurisdictional disputes, ICC and UNCITRAL arbitrations, and the European Convention on Human Rights. Chambers have a strong association with a leading Swiss law firm.

Set No.

109 OLD SQUARE CHAMBERS (John Hendy QC)

1 Verulam Buildings, Gray's Inn, London, WC1R 5LQ
Tel: (020) 7269 0300 **Fax:** (020) 7405 1387 **DX:** 1046 Chancery Lane/London
Email: clerks@oldsquarechambers.co.uk **Website:** www.oldsquarechambers.co.uk

Head of Chambers	John Hendy QC
Senior Clerk	John Taylor
Tenants	47

Members:

John Hendy QC (1972) (QC-1987)
John Melville Williams QC (1955) (QC-1977)
Frederic Reynold QC (1960) (QC-1982)
John Hand QC (1972) (QC-1988)
Lord Wedderburn QC (1953) (QC-1990)
Jeremy McMullen QC (1971) (QC-1994)
Ian Truscott QC (1995) (QC-1997)
David Wilby QC (1974) (QC-1998)
Matthias Kelly QC (1979) (QC-1999)
Charles Lewis (1963)
Christopher Carling (1969)
William Birtles (1970)
Diana Brahams (1972)
John H. Bates (1973)
Christopher Makey (1975)
Nigel Cooksley (1975)
Charles Pugh (1975)
Toby Kempster (1980)
Paul Rose (1981)
Jane McNeill (1982)
Mark Sutton (1982)
Barry Cotter (1985)
Louise Chudleigh (1987)
Ijeoma Omambala (1989)
Jennifer Eady (1989)
Philip Mead (1989)
Damian Brown (1989)
Tess Gill (1990)
Jonathan Clarke (1990)
Christopher Walker (1990)
Nicholas Booth (1991)
Sarah Moor (1991)
Ian Scott (1991)
Oliver Segal (1992)
Helen Gower (1992)
Roy Lewis (1992)
Mark Whitcombe (1994)
Elizabeth Melville (1994)
Melanie Tether (1995)
Emma Smith (1995)
Rohan Pirani (1995)
Rebecca Tuck (1998)
Hilary Winstone (1998)
Steven Langton (1998)
Stuart Brittenden (1999)
Anya Palmer (1999)
Daniel Bennett (2000)

The Chambers: Chambers have an annexe at Hanover House, 47 Corn Street, Bristol, BS1 1HT. DX: 78229. Tel: (0117) 927 7111. Fax: (0117) 927 3478.

Work Undertaken:

Employment Law: Chambers boast several of the UK's leading specialists at the Bar. Seven members of the six QCs and 28 junior team are part-time Employment Tribunal chairmen. Members constantly appear in landmark cases in this interesting and developing area of law.

Personal Injury: Dealt with from the head of chambers down to the junior tenant, chambers cover the entire range of claims including Package Holiday Regulations and Forum Non Conveniens. Disaster litigation is an area where chambers have particular expertise, as well as complex multi-party actions. Members are active in all relevant associations and they regularly write and speak on topical cases and developments.

Clinical Negligence: The group covers not only traditional clinical negligence work but – perhaps uniquely – is able to offer representation at both professional body and internal NHS disciplinary proceedings, as well as expertise in the handling of waste material from hospitals and public inquiries arising out of accidents in hospitals. As part of chambers' strategy for attempting to anticipate clients' demands, they have also strengthened the group by recruiting David Wilby QC, who joined them in January 2001 and who will be spearheading the launch of the new Clinical Law Group later in 2001.

Environmental: Chambers' expertise incorporates major toxic tort litigation, work on behalf of regulatory bodies and a wide variety of prosecutions for statutory nuisance. The highly respected group has been instructed in some of the most notable cases.

Product Liability & Regulatory Compliance Group: The product liability work has expanded to incorporate health and safety compliance. Chambers are former consultants to the EC on the implementation of European Health and Safety Directives in the UK. Members have appeared in the Southall and the Ladbroke Grove Train Inquiries. Chambers expertise in product liability lies in advising and appearing for companies, local authorities, individuals and specialist associations with regard to all aspects of civil and criminal liability in respect of defective and unsafe products.

Sports Law: Members have represented various clubs and individual sporting personalities in breaches of contract, injuries and appeals to governing bodies.

Public Inquiries: Chambers have been instructed in the majority of inquiries over the last decade, ranging from rail, fire, prisons, hospitals and children's homes.

Set No. 110

9 OLD SQUARE (Michael Driscoll QC)

9 Old Square, Lincoln's Inn, London, WC2A 3SR
Tel: (020) 7405 4682 **Fax:** (020) 7831 7107 **DX:** 305 LONDON/CAHMCERY LANE
Email: chambers@9oldsquare.co.uk **Website:** www.9oldsquare.co.uk

Head of Chambers	Michael Driscoll QC
Tenants	21

Members:

Michael Driscoll QC (1970) (QC-1992)
Judith Jackson QC (1975) (QC-1994)
Simon Berry QC (1977) (QC-1990)
David Hodge QC (1979) (QC-1997)
Daniel Hochberg (1982)
John Dagnall (1983)
John McGhee (1984)
Timothy Harry (1983)
Edwin Johnson (1987)
Thomas Leech (1988)
Katharine Holland (1989)
Christopher Stoner (1991)
Andrew P.D. Walker (1991)
Simon Burrell (1988)
Michael Pryor (1992)
Thomas Grant (1993)
Alan Johns (1994)
Daniel Margolin (1995)
Stephanie Tozer (1996)
William V.W Norris (1997)
Paul Clarke (1997)
Charles Courtenay (1999)

9 OLD SQUARE

The Chambers: 9 Old Square is a long-established and leading set of commercial chancery chambers. It has an established reputation for all aspects of property and modern chancery litigation. Particular fields of expertise for all members include landlord and tenant, conveyancing, contract, professional negligence, trusts, banking, company, and partnership law and for some members, also, the fields of insolvency, mining, judicial review, and sports law. Former members include Sir Robert Megarry and Lord Hoffmann. There are presently four QCs and 18 junior members of chambers. Many members of chambers are listed in professional publications (such as this one) as leaders in their fields and such is the breadth of experience and years of call within the members of chambers that all cases from the largest to the smallest can be catered for. Members of chambers sit as arbitrators and as legal assessors. Direct Professional Access is available. The rates charged by members are intended to be competitive and flexible, and the aim of chambers is to provide clients with a professional and efficient but approachable service. A brochure is available on request and the Senior Clerk, Christopher McSweeney, can be contacted for further information on the experience of and rates charged by individual members.

Work Undertaken:

Real Property & Landlord & Tenant: Members advise on, and appear as advocates in disputes relating to, all aspects of landlord and tenant law, all types of land and buildings, and all manner of dispute viz claims for possession, rent reviews, 1954 Act renewals, leasehold enfranchisement claims, dilapidations claims, breaches of alienation and other covenants, service charge disputes, environmental protection etc. Also in relation to all other real property work viz contracts and conveyancing, development agreements and options, restrictive covenants, easements, overriding interests, mortgages, subrogation, liens, removal of cautions etc.

Professional Negligence: Members have appeared in many of the leading cases against solicitors, valuers, barristers and accountants in relation to all types of claim from property finance to company acquisitions, flotations to domestic conveyancing. Members from 9 Old Square have already appeared in Platform Home Loans v Oyston Shipways in the House of Lords and Nationwide BS v Balmer Radmore (the Nationwide managed litigation), perhaps the two leading decisions on professional negligence claims against solicitors and valuers in 1999.

Other Commercial & Chancery Areas of Work: Chambers regularly undertake not only the modern commercial chancery work based upon contractual interpretation and litigation but also the more traditional work of the Chancery Bar, trusts and wills, though nowadays this latter work involves more often than not disputes relating to off-shore trusts, constructive trusts and tracing remedies. Some members also practise in the fields of company and partnership law, particularly in relation to share valuations, and disputes between shareholders and partners.

Publications: 9 Old Square has continued the tradition of contributing to leading textbooks and publications within its members' fields of expertise. Publications in which present members of chambers have participated and papers which they have presented include: Michael Driscoll QC, *Halsbury's Laws: Law of Family Arrangement*; Nicholas Patten QC, *1998 Blundell Memorial Lecture*; Judith Jackson QC, contributor to *Megarry's Rent Acts* (Sweet & Maxwell); consultant editor on *Enforcement of Money Judgments* (Butterworths); Simon Berry QC, *1995 Blundell Memorial Lecture*; David Hodge QC, *Foskett on Compromise (Chancery Matters)*; *Secret Trusts: The Fraud Theory Revisited*; Daniel Hochberg, *Phipson on Evidence: Encyclopaedia of Forms & Precedents*; Tim Harry, *Hill and Redman's Law of Landlord and Tenant*, and case editor of LLP *Professional Negligence Law Reports*; John McGhee, editor of *Snell on Equity*; Tom Leech, co-author *Solicitor's Negligence* (Butterworths), case editor of LLP *Professional Negligence Law Reports*; Christopher Stoner, contributor to *Sports Law Administration and Practice*. Members are also invited regularly to give lectures and seminars for the Bar, solicitors and other professionals.

International: Members appear as advocates in all courts and tribunals in England & Wales, and in Jersey, Hong Kong, Bermuda, the Far East, the Bahamas, and Brunei. They also act as arbitrators, legal assessors, legal experts and advocates in arbitrations and expert determinations.

Set No.
111 **10 OLD SQUARE** (Leolin Price CBE QC)

10 Old Square, Lincoln's Inn, London, WC2A 3SU **Tel:** (020) 7405 0758 / 7242 5002 **Fax:** (020) 7831 8237 / 7831 9188 **DX:** 306 **Email:** clerks@tenoldsquare.com **Website:** www.tenoldsquare.com

Set No.
112 **11 OLD SQUARE** (Grant Crawford & Jonathan Simpkiss)

11 Old Square, Lincoln's Inn, London, WC2A 3TS
Tel: (020) 7430 0341 **Fax:** (020) 7831 2469 **DX:** 1031
Email: clerks@11oldsquare.co.uk **Website:** www.11oldsquare.co.uk

Head of Chambers	Grant Crawford Jonathan Simpkiss
Senior Clerk	Keith Nagle
Tenants	24

11 OLD SQUARE

Members:

Edward Davidson QC (1966) (QC-1994)
Gordon Nurse (1973)
Grant Crawford (1974)
Jonathan Simpkiss (1975)FCI Arb
Peter Smith QC (1975) (QC-1992)
Reziya Harrison (1975)FCI Arb ¶
Malcolm Waters QC (1977) (QC-1997)
Stephen Acton (1977)
Elizabeth Ovey (1978)
Keith Rowley QC (1979) (QC-2001)
Siân Thomas (1981)
Glenn Campbell (1985)
Mark West (1987)
Katherine McQuail (1989)
Nigel Burroughs (1991)
Peter Dodge (1992)
Tony Oakley (1994)
Nicole Sandells (1994)
Kate Selway (1995)
Alex Hall Taylor (1996)
Michael Bowmer (1997)
Myriam Stacey (1998)
Iqbal Moollan (1998) (Mauritius Bar)
William Moffett (2000)

¶ Accredited Mediator

The Chambers: IT: Chambers word processing system is Microsoft Word, IBM compatible and floppy disks. Please speak to the clerks if you wish to deliver or receive text on disk or by electronic communication.

Work Undertaken: The work undertaken by members of chambers is primarily in the chancery and commercial fields, and extends to a wide range of litigation, advisory and drafting work.
Business: Agency, commercial litigation, consumer credit, intellectual property, freezing and other injunctions, partnerships, sale of goods, supply of services, securities and guarantees.
Charities & Associations: Charities, clubs, friendly societies, industrial and provident societies and unincorporated associations.
Company & Insolvency: Acquisition; amalgamation; dissolution and disposal of companies; corporate governance; directors' duties and disqualification; shareholder and boardroom disputes; tracing and recovery of corporate assets; company insolvency; administrations; liquidations; receiverships and voluntary arrangements; insolvent partnerships and all aspects of personal insolvency.
Financial: Banking; building societies; consumer credit; financial services and regulation; insurance; mortgages; pensions; securities and guarantees; standard form documentation for commercial and residential lending transactions; trustee and fiduciary duties; unfair terms in consumer contracts.
Private Client: Administration of estates, Court of Protection, family provision, probate, taxation, trusts and trustees and wills.
Professional Negligence: Includes accountants; barristers; financial advisors; solicitors; surveyors and valuers; disciplinary proceedings.
Property: Agricultural holdings, commercial property, conveyancing, landlord and tenant, mineral rights, mortgages and property litigation.

Publications: 'Swaps and Local Authorities: A Mistake?' in *Swaps and Off-Exchange Derivatives Trading: Law and Regulation*, Mark West (co-author); *Good Faith in Sales*, Reziya Harrison; *Wurtzburg and Mills on Building Society Law*, eds. Malcolm Waters QC, Elizabeth Ovey, Kate Selway; *Barnsley, Conveyancing Law and Practice*, Peter Smith QC; *Constructive Trusts, and Parker & Mellows, The Modern Law of Trusts*, Tony Oakley; pending, *Lifetime Gifts*, Nicole Sandells (co-author).

Clientele: Chambers operate the Direct Professional Access scheme. Instructions are also accepted from lawyers abroad, in particular the Far East, but also from jurisdictions in Europe and elsewhere.

International: Languages spoken include French, German and Spanish.

Set No.
113 **11 OLD SQUARE** (J. Simeon Thrower)

11 Old Square, Lincoln's Inn, London, WC2A 3TS **Tel:** (020) 7242 5022 **Fax:** (020) 7404 0445 **DX:** 164 London Chancery Lane **Email:** clerks@11oldsquare.com **Website:** www.11oldsquare.com

Set No.
114 **1 PAPER BUILDINGS** (Roger N. Titheridge QC)
1 Paper Buildings (1st Floor), Temple, London, EC4Y 7EP **Tel:** (020) 7353 3728 **Fax:** (020) 7353 2911 **DX:** 332 **Email:** clerks@onepaperbuildings.com

Set No.
115 **2 PAPER BUILDINGS** (Mark Love)

2 Paper Buildings, Temple, London, EC4Y 7ET
Tel: (020) 7936 2613 **Fax:** (020) 7353 9439 **DX:** 210 (Ch.Ln.)
Email: post@2paper.co.uk **Website:** www.2paper.co.uk

Head of Chambers	Mark Love
Senior Clerk	Stephen Lavell
First Junior	Marc Newson
Second Junior	Jamie Thornton
Tenants	27

Members:

Mark Love (1979)
Robin Griffiths (1970)
Charlotte Buckhaven (1969)
Richard Hayden (1964)
Peta Gee (1973)
Wendy Fisher-Gordon (1983)
Neil Petersen (1983)
Andrew Evans (1984)
James Dennison (1986)
Mark Stern (1988)
Sandra Briggs-Watson (1985)
Jamal Sapsard (1987)
Alison Robins (1987)
Polly-Anne Comfort (1988)
John Talbot-Bagnall (1988)
Kevin Dent (1991)
Simon Tolkien (1994)
Sandra Folkes (1989)
Pankaj Pathak (1992)
Jane Keysall (1992)
Jason Elliott (1993)
Caroline Whysall (1993)
Fay Baker (1994)
Silas Reid (1995)
Peter Dahlsen (1996)
Simone Start (1994)
Michael McAlinden (1996)
David Jones
Mark Braid
Ben Smitten
Jason Reed
Robert English
Richard Craven
Nanta Bahra
Poonam Bhairi

The Chambers: An established common law set offering a wide range of services with particular emphasis upon all aspects of criminal law and family law.

Work Undertaken: Criminal law; family law; personal injury; judicial review; landlord and tenant; courts martial; mental health; licensing; immigration; education.

International: Certain members of chambers are fluent in foreign languages such as French, German, Hindi, Punjabi and Urdu.

Recruitment: Four pupillages will be offered: two first six pupillages (to commence in October 2001) and two second six pupillages to commence in April 2002. Two of these will be funded.

Set No.
116 **2 PAPER BUILDINGS** (Desmond de Silva QC & Ivan Lawrence QC)
First and Second Floors, 2 Paper Buildings, London, EC4Y 7ET **Tel:** (020) 7556 5500 **Fax:** (020) 7583 3423 **DX:** LDE 494 **Email:** clerks@2pbbarristers.co.uk **Website:** www.2pbbarristers.co.uk

Set No.
117 **3 PAPER BUILDINGS**
3 Paper Buildings, Temple, London, EC4Y 7EU **Tel:** (020) 7583 8055 **Fax:** (020) 7353 6271 (Two lines) **DX:** 1024 **Email:** london@3paper.co.uk

Set No.
118 **4 PAPER BUILDINGS** (Jean Ritchie QC)

4 Paper Buildings (Ground Floor), Temple, London, EC4Y 7EX
Tel: (020) 7353 3366 **Fax:** (020) 7353 5778 **DX:** 1036 London/Chancery Lane
Email: clerks@4paperbuildings.com **Website:** www.4paperbuildings.com

Head of Chambers	Jean Ritchie QC
Senior Clerk	Stephen Smith
Tenants	38

4 Paper Buildings

Members:

Jean Ritchie QC (1970) (QC-1992)
Harvey McGregor QC (1955) (QC-1978)
Harold Burnett QC (1962) (QC-1982)
Antonio Bueno QC (1964) (QC-1989)
Douglas Hogg QC (1968) (QC-1990)
Michael J Powers QC (1979) (QC-1995)
Michael Pooles QC (1978) (QC-1999)
Eleanor Sharpston QC (1980) (QC-1999)
LJ West-Knights QC (1977) (QC-2000)
Christina Gorna (1960)
Michael Keane (1963)
Anthony De Freitas (1971)
Jane Mishcon (1979)
Martin Spencer (1979)
Derek Holwill (1982)
Prof Peter Kunzlik (1983)
Patrick Lawrence (1985)
Matthew Jackson (1986)
Julian Picton (1988)
Francis Bacon (1988)
William Flenley (1988)
Clare Price (1988)
Alison Gulliver (1989)
Evelyn Pollock (1991)
Mark Simpson (1992)
Philip Moser (1992)
Graham Reid (1993)
Simon Wilton (1993)

Members continued:

Sarah Christie-Brown (1994)
Spike Charlwood (1994)
Kieron Beal (1995)
Catherine Ewins (1995)
Katrine Sawyer (1996)
Simon Young (1998)
Eva Ferguson (1999)
Paul Mitchell (1999)
Eleni Mitrophanous (1999)
Prof Takis Tridimas (2000)

The Chambers: This is a long-established set whose members practise civil and commercial law, principally in professional and clinical negligence. Chambers aim to provide a service of excellence, adopting a flexible, practical and commercial approach to litigation which is driven by the needs and convenience of its clients.

Work Undertaken: The set specialises in professional negligence and clinical negligence, commercial contract matters, European and human rights law and personal injury claims. Members of chambers act for both claimants and defendants. In the field of professional negligence they appear in cases concerning all the various professions, but particularly solicitors, barristers, accountants, surveyors and insurance brokers. In the area of clinical negligence members represent patients, NHS trusts and doctors. The European and human rights group undertake judicial review and civil actions involving European Union law, the Brussels Convention and the Human Rights Act.

Additional Areas: Chambers also have considerable expertise in IT law, civil litigation relating to commercial fraud and money laundering, landlord and tenant, and professional disciplinary work.

Publications: Significant legal publications produced or contributed to by members of chambers include *McGregor on Damages; Cordery on Solicitors, Powers and Harris – Clinical Negligence; Simpson – Professional Negligence and liability; Flenley and Leech – Solicitors' Negligence; Lloyd's Reports: Professional Negligence; A Practitioner's Handbook of EC Law; General Principles of EC Law; Jordan's Civil Procedure; Butterworths' Personal Injury Litigation Service.*

Set No. 119

4 PAPER BUILDINGS (Lionel Swift QC)

4 Paper Buildings, Temple, London, EC4Y 7EX
Tel: (020) 7583 0816 **Fax:** (020) 7353 4979 **DX:** 1035
Email: clerks@4pb.com **Website:** www.4pb.com

Head of Chambers	Lionel Swift QC
Senior Clerk	Michael Reeves
Chambers Manager	Kay May
Tenants	35

Members:

Lionel Swift QC (1959) (QC-1975)
Gordon Murdoch QC (1970) (QC-1995)
Anna Pauffley QC (1979) (QC-1995)
Jonathan Cohen QC (1974) (QC-1997)
Peter Jackson QC (1978) (QC-2000)
Harry Turcan (1965)
Roger Smith (1968)
Amanda Barrington-Smyth (1972)
Rozanna Malcolm (1974)
Robin Barda (1975)
Michael Sternberg (1975)
Christopher Coney (1979)
Marcus Scott-Manderson (1980)
Charles Joseph (1980)
Michael Stern (1983)
Mark Johnstone (1984)
Elizabeth Coleman (1985)
Catherine Wood (1985)
Jeremy Rosenblatt (1985)
Christopher Hames (1987)
Adrienne Morgan (1988)
Barbara Mills (1990)
Christopher Cope (1990)
Joy Brereton (1990)
David Williams (1990)
Cyrus Larizadeh (1992)
William Hansen (1992)
Charles Hale (1992)
Michael Simon (1992)
Justin Ageros (1993)
Judith Murray (1994)
Sarah Lowe (1995)
Justine Johnston (1997)
James Copley (1997)
Darren Maw (1999)

The Chambers: A leading family law set with a strong civil side.

Work Undertaken:

Family Law: Adoption; care proceedings (for local authorities, families and children's guardians); child abduction; Children Act cases; cohabitees; divorce; inheritance and family provision; judicial review; matrimonial finance and wardship.

Civil: Arbitration; banking and securities; construction; contract (commercial and general); employment and industrial tribunals; judicial review; landlord and tenant; personal injury; professional negligence; sale of goods; consumer credit; tort.

Recruitment: Chambers is a member of OLPAS.

Set No.
120 **5 PAPER BUILDINGS** (Godfrey Carey QC & Jonathan Caplan QC)

5 Paper Buildings, Temple, London, EC4Y 7HB
Tel: (020) 7583 6117 **Fax:** (020) 7353 0075 **DX:** 365
Email: clerks@5-paperbuildings.law.co.uk Null

Head of Chambers	Godfrey Carey QC Jonathan Caplan QC
Senior Clerk	Stuart Bryant
Tenants	37

Members:

John Mathew QC (1949) (QC-1977)
Michael Corkery QC (1949) (QC-1981)
Timothy Cassel QC (1965) (QC-1988)
Godfrey Carey QC (1969) (QC-1991)
Jonathan Caplan QC (1973) (QC-1991)
Kuldip Singh QC (1975) (QC-1993)
Oliver Sells QC (1972) (QC-1995)
Simon Mehigan QC (1980) (QC-1998)
Edward Jenkins QC (1977) (QC-2000)
Stanley Hughes (1971)
Michael Brompton (1973)
Ian Wade (1977)
Graham Trembath (1978)
Nicholas Fooks (1978)
Penelope Rector (1980)
Charles Judge (1981)
Maurice Aston (1982)
Miranda Moore (1983)
Mark Wyeth (1983)
Amanda Pinto (1983)
Miles Bennett (1986)
David Groome (1987)
Robert O'Sullivan (1988)
Julian Christopher (1988)
Martin Evans (1989)
Anuja Dhir (1989)
Justin Cole (1991)
Nicholas Griffin (1992)
Emma Deacon (1993)
Janet Weeks (1993)
Tom Allen (1994)
Michael Hick (1995)
Alex Bailin (1995)
Denis Barry (1996)
Tom Quinton (1997)
Gaby Bonham Carter (1997)
Catherine Purnell (1999)

The Chambers: For more than a century these chambers have been recognised as one of the leading sets of criminal advocates. Chambers expertise has led in recent years to a broadening of their areas of practice extending to environmental and trading law, media law, disciplinary tribunals of all kinds, and specialist areas of civil law.

Work Undertaken:
Criminal Law: This set deals with all aspects of criminal law, including commercial fraud (members of these chambers have been involved in almost every major fraud case in the past decade) and members regularly appear in all levels of criminal courts, including capital appeals in the Privy Council. Work is regularly undertaken in Singapore, Hong Kong and the West Indies. Chambers both prosecute and defend.
Licensing: Considerable experience in both liquor and gaming licensing.
Consumer Protection & Trading Law: Including environmental law, food and drugs, health and safety, trade descriptions and copyright theft.
Tribunals: Disciplinary and Regulatory proceedings (e.g. IMRO/GMC/DTI), Coroner's Inquests, Employment Tribunals and Courts Martial.
Civil Law: Commercial litigation (including fraud), defamation, contempt, sports law.

Publications: Simon Mehigan QC is an editor of *Patersons Licensing Acts* and *Mehigan and Griffiths on Restraint of Trade.* Forthcoming publications: *Martin Evans and Amand Pinto on Corporate Criminal Liability.*

Set No.
121 **5 PAPER BUILDINGS** (Richard King)

5 Paper Buildings, Temple, London, EC4Y 7HB
Tel: (020) 7815 3200 **Fax:** (020) 7815 3201 **DX:** 415
Email: clerks@5paper.com **Website:** www.5paper.com

Head of Chambers	Richard King
Senior Clerk	Alan Stammers
Tenants	36

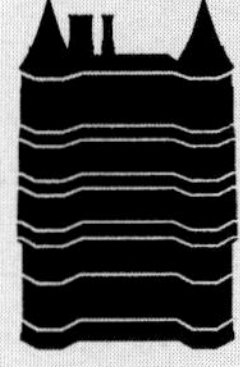

5 PAPER BUILDINGS

Members:

Richard King (1978)
Paul Norris (1963)
Angus Nicol (1963)
Steven Walsh (1965)
Robert Denman (1970)
Nicholas Wood (1970)
Graham Platford (1970)
Donald Broatch (1971)
Robert Percival (1971)
Roger Bull (1974)
Adrian Iles (1980)
Paul Infield (1980)
Mark Lyne (1981)
Norman Joss (1982)
Ian Wright (1983)
Lawrence Jacobson (1985)
Alison Rowley (1987)
Oliver Hyams (1989)
Jonathan Rich (1989)
Peter John (1989)
Stuart Nichols (1989)
Satinder Gill (1991)
Julian Benson (1991)
Nicholas Grundy (1993)
Nicola Rushton (1993)
Richard Evans (1993)
Paul Pavlou (1993)
Simon Mills (1994)
Cyril Adjei (1995)
Rachel Sleeman (1996)
Joanna Brownhill (1997)
Jake Davies (1997)
Robert Harrap (1997)
Adam Rooney (1997)
Ben Maltz (1998)
Sara Beecham (1999)

The Chambers: 5 Paper Buildings is committed to exceptional standards of expertise and service. It aims to provide true expertise through a range of specialist practice teams. Each team maintains a continuing programme of development through meetings, writing and seminars, designed to ensure that members are at the forefront of the specialist Bar. Individual members are able to offer specific expertise within the teams in which they practise. Chambers are Barmark accredited. The set's commitment to excellence is underwritten in the guide: *Standards of Professional Service.* Chambers' facilities include conference rooms, E-mail, voicemail, lectures and seminars. Chambers' opening times are 8.00am to 6.30pm. Out of hours telephone number: (07930) 463737.

Work Undertaken: Specialisations include commercial, property, ancillary relief, employment, personal injury, public law and any inclusionary issues of human rights and professional negligence.
Commercial: All aspects of domestic and international commercial litigation, arbitration and mediation, including freezing and search orders, tracing and asset-recovery, sale of goods, partnership, agency and factoring. Domestic and international banking, including syndicated lending, lender's liability, documentary credits, negotiable instruments, guarantees and other securities. Personal and corporate insolvency, including liquidation, voluntary arrangements, administration, receivership and related property matters. Construction and consumer credit.
Property: Commercial and residential landlord and tenant, including renewal of business tenancies, rent review, service charge disputes and leasehold enfranchisement. Recovery of possession, disrepair, right to buy, succession and management and similar orders. Easements, restrictive covenants, boundary disputes and adverse possession, mortgages, options and rights of pre-emption, and conveyancing. Construction and validity of wills, administration of estates and claims under the Inheritance (Provision for Family and Dependants) Act 1975.
Ancillary Relief: Dispositions of property and finance on domestic and foreign divorce, disputes between cohabitees, and protective and pre-emptive remedies.
Employment: Contracts of employment, wrongful and unfair dismissal, redundancy, discrimination and equal opportunities, industrial disputes, restrictive covenants, trade secrets and confidential information.
Personal Injury: Claims for fatalities and injuries of all degrees of severity arising out of all types of accident and clinical negligence.
Public Law: Health and safety, food safety, trading standards and similar regulatory matters. Admissions and exclusions in educational matters. Special educational needs, further and higher education. Local Authority allocations in housing matters, homelessness. Business, asylum and family rights in immigration matters.
Recent Cases: Barry v Heathcote Ball [2001] 1 All ER 94; Cohort Construction Ltd v Julius Melchior [2001] CP Rep 23; D v D [2001]1FLR 633; Evans v Secretary of State for the Environment and Transport [2001] PIQR 33; Levy v Legal Aid Board [2001] 1 All ER 895; Print Concept GmbH v GEW (EC) Ltd [2001] All ER; Re B and T (Care Proceedings: Legal representation) [2001] 1 FLR 485; Southwark London Borough Council v Mills [2001] 1 AC 1; Standard Chartered Bank v Pakistan National Shipping Corporation (No 4) [2001] QB 167; Standard Chartered Bank v Pakistan National Shipping Corporation (No 2) [2000] 1 Lloyd's Rep 218; Jacobs v Coster [2000] CLL Rev 3(Sep); R v Stockton-on-Tees Borough Council, ex parte W [2000] ELR 93; R v London Borough of Brent and Vassie, ex parte F [2000] ELR 550; Alex Lawrie Factors v Morgan [1999] The Times 18 August; Burrells Wharf Freeholds Ltd v Galliards (1999) 65 Con LR 1; Honourable Society of the Middle Temple v Lloyds Bank plc [1999] Lloyd's Rep 50; Lilly v Davidson [1999] BPIR 81; R v Brent London Borough Council, ex parte F [1999] ELR 32; R v Wakefield Diocesan Board of Education and the Governors of Holy Trinity School, ex parte J [1999] EdCR 566; Re Bremner [1999] BPIR 185; and Standard Chartered Bank v Pakistan National Shipping Corporation (No 3) [1999] 1 Lloyd's Reports 749.

Publications: These include *Employment in Schools – A Legal Guide*, 2000, Jordans, Oliver Hyams; *Law of Education*, Sweet & Maxwell, 1998, Oliver Hyams; *The Law of Harassment & Stalking*, Butterworths, 2000, Graham Platford and Paul Infield; Gulteridge & Megrah's *Law of Bankers' Commercial Credits*, 8th edn, 2001, editor Richard King.

International: Work is handled in English, French, German, Italian, Punjabi and Spanish.

Recruitment: Pupillage applications forms available from Mr Stuart Nichols. Awards are available of £17,500 per pupil per year. Mini-pupillage applications to Mr Robert Harrap. Chambers operate an equal opportunities policy.

Set No.
122

PLOWDEN BUILDINGS (William Lowe QC)

2 Plowden Buildings, Temple, London, EC4Y 9BU
Tel: (020) 7583 0808 **Fax:** (020) 7583 5106 **DX:** 0020 (Ch.Ln.)
Email: bar@plowdenbuildings.co.uk

Head of Chambers	William Lowe QC
Senior Clerk	Paul Hurst
Tenants	24

Members:

William Lowe QC (1972) (QC-1997) +
Catherine MacKenzie Smith (1968)
Christopher Williams (1981) + †
Simon Wood (1981) + †
Jeremy Freedman (1982) †
Philip Kramer (1982) ‡
Lawrence McNulty (1985)
Catherine Foster (1986)
David Lyons (1987)
Peter Morton (1988)
Arnold Cooper (1969)
Michael James (1989)
Martin Haukeland (1988)
Mark Watson-Gandy (1990) †
Andrew Crouch (1990)
Kerry Cox (1990)
Claire Lindsay (1991)
Frances Zammit (1993)
Jayne Atkinson (1994)
Jamie Clarke (1995)
Edward Broome (1996)
Stephen Vullo (1997)
Dominic Bayne (1997)
Holly Pelham (1999)

+ Recorder † Junior Counsel to the Crown ‡ Junior Counsel to the Crown/Deputy District Judge

The Chambers: Plowden Buildings is an established London chambers with a strong North-eastern presence and a long record of quality service which has resulted in it being consistently rated as a leading common law set. Five tenants are treasury counsel, one is a prosecuting counsel to the DTI and four tenants sit part-time as Recorders and one as a Deputy District Judge. Tenants sit as arbitrators for the Institute of Chartered Accountants, the London Court of International Arbitration, ARDS and the World Intellectual Property Organisation.

Work Undertaken: The set is highly regarded for its work, in the North, for personal injury and clinical negligence and, in London, for its commercial and insolvency work. Chambers have fielded counsel for many recent high profile cases such as Thompson v Sheffield Fertility Clinic (the 'unwanted third baby' case), Landhurst Leasing, ReM, Stark v The Post Office, the Vibration White Finger litigation and the Lloyds Names litigation.

Publications: Members of chambers include editors of *European Current Law*, the *Thomson Tax Guide*, *Charlesworth & Percy on Negligence*, and the author of *Watson-Gandy on The Law of Accountants.*

Set No.
123

PUMP COURT CHAMBERS (Christopher Harvey Clark QC)

3 Pump Court, Temple, London, EC4Y 7AJ
Tel: (020) 7353 0711 **Fax:** (020) 7353 3319 **DX:** 362
Email: clerks@3pumpcourt.com **Website:** www.3pumpcourt.com

Head of Chambers	Christopher Harvey Clark QC
Senior Clerk	David Barber
Deputy Senior Clerk	Danny Fantham
Tenants	57

Members:

Christopher Harvey Clark QC (1969) (QC-1984)
Nigel Pascoe QC (1966) (QC-1988)
Guy Boney QC (1968) (QC-1990)
Peter Birts QC (1968) (QC-1990)
Jane Miller QC (1979) (QC-2000)
Geoffrey Still (1966)
Stewart Patterson (1967)
Adam Pearson (1969)
Frank Moat (1970)
Giles Harrap (1971)
Frank Abbott (1972)
Charles Parry (1973)
Michael Butt (1974)
John Ker-Reid (1974)
Charles Gabb (1975)
Andrew Barnett (1977)
Michael Dineen (1977)
Jonathan Swift (1977)
Julie MacKenzie (1978)
Timothy O'Flynn (1979)
Robert Hill (1980)
Miranda Allardice (1982)
Damien Lochrane (1983)
Sandra Stanfield (1984)
Oba Nsugbe (1985)
Matthew Scott (1985)
Desmond Bloom-Davies (1986)
Mark Hill (1987)
Anne Waddington (1988)
Hugh Travers (1988)
Philip Warren (1988)
Leslie Samuels (1989)
Edward Boydell (1989)
Justin Gau (1989)
Anthony Akiwumi (1989)
Helen Khan (1990)
Penelope Howe (1991)
Geoffrey Kelly (1992)
James Newton-Price (1992)
Patricia Poyer-Sleeman (1992)
Mark Ruffell (1992)
Elizabeth Gunther (1993)
Oliver Peirson (1993)
Marcus Tregilgas-Davey (1993)
Helen Fields (1993)
Luke Blackburn (1993)
Mark Ashley (1993)
Roderick Moore (1993)
Jonathan Simpson (1993)
Richard Ferry-Swainson (1994)
Robert Pawson (1994)
Mark Dubbery (1996)
Ruth Arlow (1997)
Andrew Grime (1997)
Anne Ward (1997)
Lorna Sproston (1998)
Louise de Rozarieux (1999)

The Chambers: An established set undertaking a wide variety of work, with members working in specialist teams. DPA and Bar Direct work accepted.
Associated Chambers: 31 Southgate Street, Winchester; Temple Street, Swindon.

Work Undertaken:
Main Areas: Family, employment, inheritance, property, PI, crime.
Specialisations: Childcare; matrimonial finance; all areas of crime; professional and clinical negligence; contract; ecclesiastical law; Inheritance Act; courts martial; environment; landlord and tenant; taxation appeals.

International: Oba Nsugbe is also a barrister and solicitor of the Supreme Court of Nigeria.

Recruitment: Tenancy applications should be sent to Head of the Tenancy Committee. Pupillage applications should be made via OLPAS.

Set No. 124 **2 PUMP COURT** (Philip Singer QC)
2 Pump Court, Temple, London, EC4Y 7AH **Tel:** (020) 7353 5597 **Fax:** (020) 7583 2122 **DX:** 290 (Ch.Ln.) **Email:** clerks@2pumpcourt.co.uk

Set No. 125
4 PUMP COURT

4 Pump Court, Temple, London, EC4Y 7AN
Tel: (020) 7842 5555 **Fax:** (020) 7583 2036 **DX:** 303 LDE
Email: chambers@4pumpcourt.com **Website:** www.4pumpcourt.com

Senior Clerk	Carolyn McCombe
Tenants	42

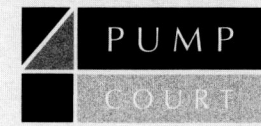

Members:

Anthony Temple QC (1968) (QC-1986)
Bruce Mauleverer QC (1969) (QC-1985)
David Friedman QC (1968) (QC-1990)
David Blunt QC (1967) (QC-1991)
Christopher Moger QC (1972) (QC-1992)
Jeremy Storey QC (1974) (QC-1994)
Jonathan Marks QC (1975) (QC-1995)
Anthony Speaight QC (1973) (QC-1995)
John Rowland QC (1979) (QC-1996)
Michael Douglas QC (1974) (QC-1997)
Lindsay Boswell QC (1982) (QC-1997)
Jeremy Nicholson QC (1977) (QC-2000)
Laurence Marsh (1975)
Allen Dyer (1976)
Oliver Ticciati (1979)
Nigel Tozzi QC (1980) (QC-2001)
Peter Hamilton (1968)
Alex Charlton (1983)
David Sears (1984)
Adrian Hughes (1984)
James Cross (1985)
Duncan McCall (1988)
Aidan Christie (1988)
Andrew Neish (1988)
Nicholas Vineall (1988)
Kirsten Houghton (1989)
Simon Henderson (1993)
Michael Davie (1993)
Alexander Gunning (1994)
Sean Brannigan (1994)
Kate Vaughan-Neil (1994)
Richard Cartwright (1994)
Rachel Ansell (1995)
Alexander Hickey (1995)
Claire Packman (1996)
Sean O'Sullivan (1997)
Benjamin Pilling (1997)
Lynne McCafferty (1997)
Michael Taylor (1996)
Yash Kulkarni (1998)
James Purchas (1997)
James Leabeater (1999)

The Chambers: 4 Pump Court's main focus is on litigation. It aims to provide, at every level, experienced advisors and strong and effective advocates. It is an expanding set which welcomes the opportunities that the relaxation of the ways in which the Bar can offer its services has provided. It is always ready, in the interests of clients, to consider new ideas for improving the way business is done.

Work Undertaken: The work of chambers covers a wide spectrum of commercial and common law with the following specialist areas:
Professional Negligence: Members of chambers have expertise acting for both plaintiffs and insurers and dealing with a wide range of claims against all professionals, including solicitors and barristers, architects, engineers, surveyors and valuers, accountants, auditors and actuaries, brokers, consultants, agents and IT professionals, bankers and financial intermediaries and advisers, doctors and other medical practitioners. Members of chambers regularly advise on policy interpretation and indemnity questions.
Construction: A substantial number of silks and juniors specialise in construction and civil engineering work and are recognised as leading practitioners in the field. They have acted in numerous major disputes arising out of onshore and offshore projects both in the UK and overseas, acting variously for employers, contractors and sub-contractors, and professional advisers. Adjudication, mediation and arbitration are other areas in which the team is similarly skilled and expert.
Insurance & Reinsurance: Members of chambers have been involved in most of the significant events in the London insurance market over the last decade, including the Longtail claims in the USA arising from problems such as asbestosis, pollution and more recently with pensions and other investment product

Continued overleaf

compensation claims against life insurers and claims arising from US workers' compensation rules. Work with Lloyd's and other insurance markets includes litigation and arbitration of both insurance and reinsurance disputes between syndicates and with outside insurers, litigation between names and agents, disciplinary hearings and regulatory control.

Commercial: Members of chambers deal with a range of matters including commercial fraud, insurance and reinsurance, banking, sale and carriage of goods, aviation, shipping, the purchase and sale of commodities, the construction and performance of mercantile contracts and media and entertainment.

Information Technology: Members of chambers include experts in computer law (including in law relating to the internet and e-commerce) and disputes arising out of computer contracts and consultancy. Such expertise involves a detailed understanding of complex technical matters as well as the legal and commercial issues. Members of chambers were retained in the early landmark case of Salvage Association v CAP Financial Services Limited and have been instructed in a large number of high-profile cases since that decision.

Licensing, Gaming & Lotteries: Expertise in this field has been built up over many years of acting for and advising the regulator of the gaming industry and many of its major operators.

Financial Services: The work of members of chambers spans investment business, including life assurance and personal pensions and the rules of various regulatory bodies.

Additional Areas: Members of chambers undertake mainstream common law work of all types, including personal injury, contractual disputes and property and employment law. Some members of chambers have particular expertise in matrimonial finance.

Set No.
126 ## 5 PUMP COURT (Rex Bryan)

5 Pump Court, Temple, London, EC4Y 7AP
Tel: (020) 7353 2532 **Fax:** (020) 7353 5321 **DX:** 497 LDE
Email: FivePump@netcomuk.co.uk

Head of Chambers	Rex Bryan
Senior Clerk	Tim Markham
First Junior	Jayne Goodrham
Tenants	33

Members:

Anthony Russell QC (1974) (QC-1999) *
Rex Bryan (1971)
Norman Primost (1954)
Anthony Hunter (1962)
Simeon Hopkins (1968)
Kenneth Dow (1970)
Helen Christodoulou (1972)
John Evison (1974)
Alistair Keith (1974)
Crispian Cartwright (1976)
Tristan Chaize (1977)
Hugo Charlton (1978)
Anne Ratcliffe (1981)
Tristram Hodgkinson (1982)
Roger Gray (1984)
Simon O'Toole (1984)
Michael Collard (1986)
Mark James (1987)
Tazeen Hasan (1988)
Deborah Toussaint (1988)
Sebastian Gooch (1989)
Derek O'Sullivan (1990) *
Jack Nicholls (1991)
Stephen Ellis-Jones (1992)
Bradley Say (1993)
Mary Poku (1993)
Mo Taylor (1993)
Emma Smith (1994)
Matthew Roberts (1994)
Annabel Maxwell Scott (1996)
Sarah Prager (1997)
Elizabeth Darlington (1998)
Hannah Markham (1998)
Nicholas Mather (1998)
Kambiz Larizadeh (1999)

* Door Tenant

The Chambers: Fees for paperwork can be agreed in advance upon sight of the papers, or guidance can be given as to the appropriate hourly rates. Direct Professional Access and Conditional Fee work is undertaken. Chambers have dedicated conference rooms with video facilities, and free parking can be arranged. Chambers are open from 8.30 am to 7.00 pm and the clerks can be contacted in the evenings or at weekends. For further information please contact the Senior Clerk.

Work Undertaken: Five Pump Court Chambers is a long established common law set of 33 members in three specialised practice groups focusing on civil, criminal and family law. A guide to their practices is available upon request.

Civil: Landlord and tenant; real property; contract/commercial; professional negligence; personal injury; construction; partnership; trusts; trade description, industrial deafness; insolvency; judicial review; employment; arbitration; consumer credit and licensing; education.

Criminal: Fraud; sexual offences; DTI; serious violence; car ringing; importation of drugs.

Family: Financial provision and children; private and public law; Inheritance Act claims; trusts.

International: Members of chambers speak French, German, Greek, Hindi, Italian, Urdu

Set No.
127 ## 6 PUMP COURT

6 Pump Court, Ground and Lower Ground, London, EC4Y 7AR **Tel:** (020) 7583 6013 **Fax:** (020) 7353 0464 **DX:** 409 **Email:** clerks@6pumpcourt.law.co.uk **Website:** www.6pumpcourt.law.co.uk

Set No. 128

6 PUMP COURT (Stephen Hockman QC)

6 Pump Court, Temple, London, EC4Y 7AR
Tel: (020) 7797 8400 **Fax:** (020) 7797 8401 **DX:** 293 Chancery Lane, London
Email: clerks@6pumpcourt.co.uk **Website:** www.6pumpcourt.co.uk

Head of Chambers	Stephen Hockman QC
Senior Clerk	Richard Constable
Tenants	28

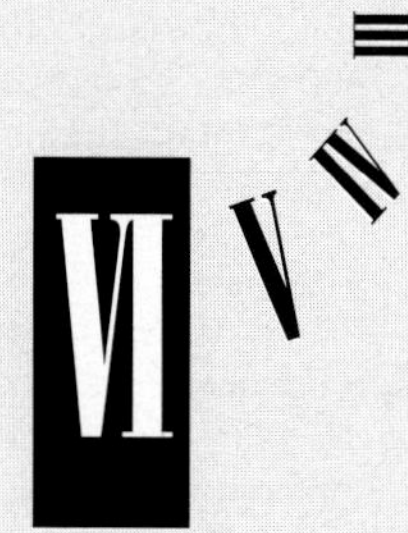

Members:

Stephen Hockman QC (1970) (QC-1990)
David Mitchell (1972)
Neville Willard (1976)
Grant Armstrong (1978)
Richard Barraclough (1980)
David Travers (1981)
Nicholas Baldock (1983)
Caroline Topping (1984)
David Walden-Smith (1985)
Peter Gower (1985)
Kevin Leigh (1986)
Peter Harrison (1987)
Eleanor Laws (1990)
Peter Forbes (1990)
Oliver Saxby (1992)
Paul Mee (1992)
Judith Butler (1993)
Mark Watson (1994)
Edward Grant (1994)
Nina Ellin (1994)
Clare Wright (1995)
Peter Alcock (1995)
Mark Beard (1996)
Deborah Charles (1996)
Tanya Robinson (1997)
Richard Banwell (1998)
Gordon Menzies (1998)
Lee Bennett (1998)

Work Undertaken: The work of chambers includes a wide range of common law work in London and on the South Eastern Circuit. The set has specialists in criminal law; personal injury; planning; environmental; local government and administrative law and family law.

Set No. 129

PUMP COURT TAX CHAMBERS

16 Bedford Row, London, WC1R 4EB
Tel: (020) 7414 8080 **Fax:** (020) 7414 8099 **DX:** London 312
Email: clerks@pumptax.com **Website:** www.pumptax.com

Senior Clerk	Geraldine O'Sullivan
Tenants	24

Members:

Donald Potter QC (1948) (QC-1972)
Andrew Thornhill QC (1969) (QC-1985)
Graham Aaronson QC (1966) (QC-1982)
David Milne QC (1970) (QC-1987)
William Massey QC (1977) (QC-1996)
Kevin Prosser QC (1982) (QC-1996)
John Tallon QC (1975) (QC-2000)
Ian Richards (1971)
Janek Matthews (1972)
Roger Thomas (1979)
Penelope Hamilton (1972)
Michael Conlon (1974)
Jeremy White (1976)
Giles W.J. Goodfellow (1983)
David Ewart (1987)
Jeremy Woolf (1986)
Andrew Hitchmough (1991)
Adrian J. Shipwright (1993)
Rupert Baldry (1987)
Julian Ghosh (1993)
Elizabeth Wilson (1995)
Richard Vallat (1997)
James Henderson (1997)
Sarah Dunn (1998)

Work Undertaken: Pump Court Tax Chambers is the largest specialist tax set. Chambers undertake litigation and advisory work on all aspects of tax law, corporate and personal.

Set No. 130

QUEEN ELIZABETH BUILDING (Florence Baron QC)

Queen Elizabeth Building, Temple, London, EC4Y 9BS
Tel: (020) 7797 7837 **Fax:** (020) 7353 5422 **DX:** London 339
Email: clerks@qeb.co.uk **Website:** www.qeb.co.uk

Head of Chambers	Florence Baron QC
Senior Clerk	Ivor Treherne
Tenants	26

Members:

Florence Baron QC (1976) (QC-1995)
Andrew Moylan QC (1978) (QC-2000)
Lucy Stone QC (1983) (QC-2001)
Lord Phillimore (1972)
Peter Wright (1974)
Michael Hosford-Tanner (1974)
Andrew Tidbury (1976)
Thomas Brudenell (1977)
Roderick Blyth (1981)
Oliver Wise (1981)
Lewis Marks (1984)
Rowena Corbett (1984)
Tim Amos (1987)
Jennifer Roberts (1988)
Sarah Edwards (1990)
Matthew Firth (1991)
Elizabeth Clarke (1991)
Camilla Henderson (1992)
Stewart Leech (1992)
Alexander Thorpe (1995)
Catherine Cowton (1995)
James Ewins (1996)
Antonia Lyon (1997)
Sarah Phipps (1997)
Rachael Young (1997)
Mark Saunders (1999)

Continued overleaf

Work Undertaken: A set specialising in family law and undertaking general and common law work including disciplinary tribunals; employment law; equine and animal law; judicial review; landlord and tenant; medical negligence; personal injury; professional negligence; and sports law.

International: Members are fluent in French, German and Italian.

Set No. 131

3 RAYMOND BUILDINGS (Clive Nicholls QC)

3 Raymond Buildings, Gray's Inn, London, WC1R 5BH
Tel: (020) 7400 6400 **Fax:** (020) 7242 4221 **DX:** 237 London
Email: chambers@3raymondbuildings.com **Website:** www.3raymondbuildings.com

Head of Chambers	Clive Nicholls QC
Senior Clerk	Ian Collins
Tenants	39

Members:

Clive Nicholls QC (1957) (QC-1982)
Colin Nicholls QC (1957) (QC-1981)
Gilbert Gray QC (1953) (QC-1971)
Richard Beckett QC (1965) (QC-1987)
Sir John Nutting QC (1968) (QC-1995)
Stephen Batten QC (1968) (QC-1989)
Alan Newman QC (1968) (QC-1989)
Alun Jones QC (1972) (QC-1989)
David Whitehouse QC (1969) (QC-1990)
Nicholas Price QC (1968) (QC-1992)
Montague Sherborne QC (1960) (QC-1993)
Kevin de Haan QC (1976) (QC-2000)
John Blair-Gould (1970)
Gerald Gouriet (1974)
Andrew Muir (1975)
Richard Atchley (1977)
Michael Bromley-Martin (1979)
Mark Harris (1980)
James Hines (1982)
James Rankin (1983)
Jane Humphryes (1983)
Neil Saunders (1983)
Stephen Walsh (1983)
Simon Farrell (1983)
Crispin Aylett (1985)
Alexander Cameron (1986)
Helen Malcolm (1986)
James Lewis (1987)
John Hardy (1988)
Hugo Keith (1989)
Hugh Davies (1990)
Campaspe Lloyd-Jacob (1990)
Tania Bromley-Martin (1983)
Richard Wormald (1993)
Alisdair Williamson (1994)
Saba Naqshbandi (1996)
Edmund Gritt (1997)
Ailsa Williamson (1997)
Clair Dobbin (1999)

The Chambers:A multi-disciplined set with a national and international reputation.

Work Undertaken:

Criminal Law: All types of cases at all levels, prosecuting and defending before judges, juries and magistrates in England and Wales. Members also appear before international courts as well as the national courts of foreign jurisdictions.

Commercial Crime: Serious and complex frauds and financial regulatory offences, again with expertise in international aspects. Major criminal and fraud cases include Palmer and Ketley (timeshare fraud), Lord Archer (perjury), Kenneth Noye (road rage murder), Frank Warren (VAT fraud), Sawoniuk (war crimes), Jonathan Aitken (perjury), Lord Hardwicke (drugs offences), Judge Gee (mortgage fraud), Donald & Cressey (police corruption), Kevin Maxwell (pension fraud), BCCI (bank fraud). Members advise on custom duties and appear before the VAT and Duties Tribunal.

Extradition: Involvement worldwide and includes commercial crime as well as terrorism and drug trafficking. Members have appeared in almost every extradition case in England over the past 25 years including Senator Pinochet. Members advise on international mutual assistance and have considerable experience in bringing judicial review proceedings in connection with them. Particular expertise includes warrants, restraint orders and financial aspects of mutual assistance.

Licensing: A major area of expertise, notably betting, gaming and lotteries, liquor and public entertainment and Internet gaming. Chambers have the only team of barristers specialising exclusively in licensing.

Public & Administrative Law: Representing public bodies and private clients in judicial review proceedings. One member of chambers is appointed to the Common Law Treasury Panel A List.

European & Human Rights Law: Conducting cases before the European Court of Human Rights, the UN Human Rights Committee and the Inter-American Commission on Human Rights.

Environmental & Health & Safety Law: Expertise includes advising the Environment Agency on such matters as licensing of atomic power stations, waste management, the BSE Enquiry and water pollution. Members have acted in many HSE prosecutions involving major construction companies, supermarket chains and waste management.

Professional Regulation & Tribunals: Appearing at coroners' inquests and before regulatory and disciplinary tribunals. One member is chairman of the UK Athletics Drug Advisory Committee. Other regulatory matters include insurance cases, firearms work and criminal aspects of copyrights, designs and patents/trademarks.

Other Areas: Individual members have expertise in computer crime and actions against the police.

Set No.
132

5 RAYMOND BUILDINGS (Patrick Milmo QC)

5 Raymond Buildings, Gray's Inn, London, WC1R 5BP
Tel: (020) 7242 2902 **Fax:** (020) 7831 2686 **DX:** 1054 LDE
Email: clerks@5rb.co.uk **Website:** www.5rb.co.uk

Head of Chambers	Patrick Milmo QC
Senior Clerk	Kim Janes
Tenants	24

Members:

Patrick Milmo QC (1962) (QC-1985)MA (Cantab)
Gordon Bishop (1968)MA (Cantab)
Michael Tugenhat QC (1969) (QC-1986)MA (Cantab)
Desmond Browne QC (1969) (QC-1990)BA (Oxon)
Adrienne Page QC (1974) (QC-1999)BA (Kent)
James Price QC (1974) (QC-1995)BA (Oxon)
Richard Parkes (1977)MA (Cantab)
Mark Warby (1981)MA (Oxon)
Stephen Bate (1981)MA (Cantab) Dip Law
Andrew Monson (1983)BA (Oxon)
Iain Christie (1989)BA (Dunelm)
Alexandra Marzec (1990)LLB (Warw)
David Sherborne (1992)BA(Oxon)
Justin Rushbrooke (1992)MA(Oxon)
Matthew Nicklin (1993)LLB (Newcastle)
Jonathan Barnes (1999)BA (Hons) (Oxon) †
Godwin Busuttil (1994)MA, MPhil(Cantab)
Adam Wolanski (1995)MA(Cantab)
William Bennett (1994)BA (Liverpool)
Jacob Dean (1995)BA (Oxon)
Anna Coppola (1996)BA (London) Dip Law
Sara Mansoori (1997)LLB (Leeds)
Adam Speker (1999)BA (Bristol)
Sapna Jethani (1999)BA (Oxon)

† Formerly a solicitor (admitted 1993)

The Chambers: An established set specialising in all areas of the law that effect the media and world of entertainment, with particular emphasis on defamation and intellectual property, privacy and freedom of expression, as well as undertaking work in a broad range of commercial matters. Though chiefly practising in the High Court, members represent clients before professional and sporting tribunals and in arbitrations, conduct cases before the ECHR, and advise on, and appear in, overseas litigation.

Work Undertaken: All matters concerning all forms of publishing (including pre-publication advice), news dissemination, broadcasting and IT communication or arising from disputes in the entertainment world. The areas of law particularly engaged in these fields include defamation, trade libel, passing off, contempt, statutory restrictions on reporting and PACE applications, breach of confidence, the rights and restrictions on publication arising under Human Rights legislation, copyright and contractual disputes of all kinds (in relation to books, music, film, video and television), Copyright Tribunal applications; restraint of trade disputes (in sport and pop), data protection and freedom of information.

Set No.
133

18 RED LION COURT (Anthony Arlidge QC)

18 Red Lion Court, London, EC4A 3EB
Tel: (020) 7520 6000 **Fax:** (020) 7520 6248/9 **DX:** 478 LDE
Email: stephen.requena@18rlc.co.uk

Head of Chambers	Anthony Arlidge QC
Senior Clerk	Kenneth Darvill
First Junior	Mark Bennett
Tenants	69

Members:

Anthony Arlidge QC (1962) (QC-1981)
Derek Spencer QC (1961) (QC-1980)
David Cocks QC (1961) (QC-1982)
James Stewart QC (1966) (QC-1982)
Henry Green QC (1962) (QC-1988)
David Lederman QC (1966) (QC-1990)
Graham Parkins QC (1972) (QC-1990)
Linda Stern QC (1971) (QC-1991)
Peter Rook QC (1973) (QC-1991)
Richard Sutton QC (1969) (QC-1993)
Antony Shaw QC (1975) (QC-1994)
Peter Carter QC (1947) (QC-1990)
Rosamund Horwood-Smart QC (1974) (QC-1996)
James Goss QC (1975) (QC-1997)
Nigel Peters QC (1976) (QC-1997)
John Black QC (1975) (QC-1998)
Patricia Lynch QC (1979) (QC-1998)
David Etherington QC (1979) (QC-1998)
Linda Dobbs QC (1981) (QC-1998)
David Green QC (1979) (QC-2000)
David Radcliffe (1966)
Carey Johnston (1977)
Peter Fenn (1979)
Stephen Harvey (1979)
Jonathan Fisher (1980)
Alexander Milne (1981)
Kim Jenkins (1982)
Janine Sheff (1983)
Richard Kovalevsky (1983)
Mark Lucraft (1984)
Angela Morris (1984)
Rupert Overbury (1984)
David Marshall (1985)

Continued overleaf

Members continued:

Brendan Morris (1985)
Simon Spence (1985)
Robert Boyle (1985)
Robin du Preez (1985)
Jane Bewsey (1986)
John Lyons (1986)
Max Hill (1987)
David Walbank (1987)
Shane Collery (1988)
Sally-Ann Hales (1988)
David Huw Williams (1988)
John Anderson (1989)
Peter Rowlands (1990)
Candida Hill (1990)
Sara Lawson (1990)
David Holborn (1991)
Sean Hammond (1991)
Allison Clare (1992)
Matthew Gowen (1992)
Rufus D'Cruz (1993)
Tom Forster (1993)
Barnaby Jameson (1993)
Jennifer Dempster (1993)
Claudia Mortimore (1994)
Michelle Nelson (1994)
Jacqueline Hall (1994)
Adam Wiseman (1994)
Noel Casey (1995)
Samantha Leigh (1995)
Elizabeth Webster (1995)
Gillian Jones (1996)
Stephen Requena (1997)
Nicholas Medcroft (1998)
Louis-Peter Moll (1998)
Rebecca Chalkley (1999)
Ella Schulster (1999)

The Chambers: With 20 QCs, the set specialises in criminal law dealing with serious crimes in particular. Some members offer general common law. Members practise in London and on the South East Circuit, which is served by our annexe in Chelmsford. Chambers have standing counsel to the Inland Revenue, DTI Inspectors, and recorders.

Work Undertaken:

Criminal: Commercial fraud; Inland Revenue and Customs & Excise offences; drugs and problems arising from the Drug Trafficking Offences Act; money laundering; extradition; child abuse; obscene publications; road traffic; licensing; judicial review; privy council; health and safety at work; personal injury; medical negligence; professional negligence; disciplinary and tribunal work; immigration; civil liberties; human rights; family.

Publications: Arlidge and Parry on *Fraud*; Arlidge and Eady on *Contempt; Journal of International Banking Law* (UK Correspondent); Dobbs and Lucraft, *Road Traffic Law and Practice* (Sweet & Maxwell 1994); Rook and Ward, *Sexual Offences* (Waterlows 1990); Carter and Harrison *Offences of Violence* (Waterlows 1991); Fisher and Merrills *Pharmacy Law and Practices* (Blackwells 1995); Fisher and Bewsey, *The Law of Investor Protection, Mortimore on Immigration and Adoption* (Hammicks 1994).

Clientele: Individuals, public and private companies, HM Customs and Excise, local authorities, Serious Fraud Office and CPS government departments.

International: Nigel Peters is a member of the Northern Ireland Bar and Barbados Bar. David Marshall is a member of the Hong Kong Bar and the New York Bar.

Recruitment: Applications for tenancy should be sent to the Head of Chambers; pupillage applications to Stephen Requena. Chambers have up to seven pupils at any one time, four of whom are guaranteed £10,000 for the year. Mini-pupillages are available.

Set No. 134

RENAISSANCE CHAMBERS (Brian Jubb & Henry Setright QC)

5th Floor, Gray's Inn Chambers, Gray's Inn, London, WC1R 5JA
Tel: (020) 7404 1111 **Fax:** (020) 7430 1522/1050 **DX:** 0074 (Ch.Ln.)
Email: clerks@renaissancechambers.co.uk

Head of Chambers	Brian Jubb
	Henry Setright QC
Principal Clerks	Mark Darvell
	Mark Venables
Tenants	40

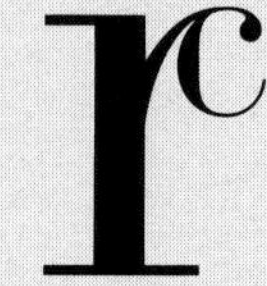

renaissance chambers

Members:

Brian Jubb (1971)
Henry Setright QC (1979) (QC-2001)
Caroline Rodger (1968)
Elisabeth Brann (1970)
Richard Guy (1970)
Noah Weiniger (1984)
Richard Clough (1971)
David Houston (1976)
Janette Haywood (1977)
Dermot Main Thompson (1977)
Cherry Harding (1978)
Simon Lillington (1980) *
Kharin Cox (1982)
Heather MacGregor (1982)
Geoffrey Mott (1982)
Jonathan Cowen (1983)
Timothy Compton (1984)
Melanie Nazareth (1984)
Alistair Perkins (1986)
Nigel Cox (1986)
Ian Lewis (1989) *
James Gillespie (1991)
Teertha Gupta (1990)
Shiva Ancliffe (1991)
Navita Atreya (1999)
Shivani Jegarajah (1993)
Helen Morgan (1993)
Sandra Fisher (1993)
Justin Gray (1993)
Margaret Phelan (1993)
Buster Cox (1993)
Gregor Ferguson (1995)
Amina Ahmed (1996)
Tublu Mukherjee (1996)
William Metaxa (1997)
Charlotte Bayati (1997)
Christopher Archer (1996)
Sarah Orriss (1999)
Anita Guha (1999)
Arlene Small (1999)
Nick Horsley (1999)
Doreen Hinchliffe (1953) *
Diane Redgrave (1977) *
Melanie Den Brinker (1984) *
Marilyn Freeman (1986) *
Nicholas Stonor (1993) *
Gillian Higson Smith *

* Door Tenant

Set No.
135 **REVENUE LAW CHAMBERS** (John Gardiner QC)

11 New Square, Lincoln's Inn, London, WC2A 3QB
Tel: (020) 7242 4017 **Fax:** (020) 7831 2391 **DX:** 315
Email: taxlaw@11newsquare.com **Website:** www.11newsquare.com

Head of Chambers	John Gardiner QC
Senior Clerk	John Moore
Tenants	8

Members:

John Gardiner QC (1968) (QC-1982)
Barry Pinson QC (1949) (QC-1973)
Peter Rees QC (1953) (QC-1969)
Peter Trevett QC (1971) (QC-1992)
Jonathan Peacock QC (1987) (QC-2001)
Francis Fitzpatrick (1990)
Grania Lyster (1992)
Jolyon Maugham (1997)

The Chambers: This is the oldest established set to specialise exclusively in revenue law. Members advise in the UK and abroad on all aspects of tax law including all personal and corporate taxes, VAT, customs & excise and stamp duties. Tax planning and advocacy services are provided for clients ranging from large multinational corporations to private individuals, including those of modest means. The set also advises in relation to professional negligence actions. Chambers offer a considerable range of experience in litigation before tribunals of first instance including the Commissioners of Inland Revenue and VAT Tribunals, through the High Court to the House of Lords, the European Court of Human Rights and the Courts of certain colonies and Commonwealth jurisdictions. Chambers can accommodate electronic file transfer with or without secure encryption. Worldwide video conferences can be arranged. Chambers have a website displaying information about chambers, including tax law articles.

International: Languages spoken include French and Luxembourgeoise.

Set No.
136 **NO. 1 SERJEANTS' INN** (Edward Faulks QC)

No.1 Serjeants' Inn, Fleet Street, London, EC4Y 1LH
Tel: (020) 7415 6666 **Fax:** (020) 7583 2033 **DX:** 364 London
Email: clerks@no1serjeantsinn.com **Website:** www.no1serjeantsinn.co.uk

Head of Chambers	Edward Faulks QC
Senior Clerk	Clark Chessis
Practice Development Manager	Rosemary Thorpe
Tenants	32

NO.1 SERJEANTS' INN

Members:

Edward Faulks QC (1973) (QC-1996) +
Adrian Redgrave QC (1968) (QC-1992) +
David Pittaway QC (1977) (QC-2000) +
John Ross QC (1971) (QC-2001) +
William Andreae-Jones QC (1965) (QC-1984) + †
Jonathan Foster QC (1970) (QC-1989) + †
Brian Leech (1967) +
William Hunter (1972)
John Bryant (1976)
Veronica Hammerton (1977) +
Simon Readhead (1979) +
Nicholas Yell (1979)
John Norman (1979)
Alan Saggerson (1981)
Alastair Hammerton (1983)
Timothy Dutton (1985)
Edward Bishop (1985)
Sarah Paneth (1985) +
Julian Waters (1986)
Marc Rivalland (1987)
Justin Althaus (1988)
Angus Piper (1991)
Andrew Warnock (1993)
Paul Stagg (1994)
David Thomson (1994)
Matthew Chapman (1994)
Ivor Collett (1995)
Sophie Mortimer (1996)
Zachary Bredemear (1996)
Mohinderpal Sethi (1996)
David Bridgman (1997)
Ian Miller (1999)

+ Recorder † Associate member

The Chambers: No. 1 Serjeants' Inn is an established common law set which is known particularly for its handling of professional and clinical negligence claims, property litigation, insurance disputes, claims against public authorities and personal injury litigation.

Work Undertaken:

Professional Negligence: Members of chambers represent claimants and defendants in all aspects of professional negligence litigation, but particularly in actions involving surveyors, accountants, solicitors, financial advisors and insurance brokers.

Clinical Negligence: Members of chambers represent the NHSLA and have been involved in many highly publicised clinical negligence cases, including ongoing litigation concerning cervical cancer screening errors. Chambers also represents claimants and has particular expertise in handling cerebral palsy cases.

Property Litigation: The property team is well known for its landlord and tenant and commercial property work. It also deals with real property matters, including land registration, as well as matters relating to agricultural holdings and housing.

Insurance Disputes: As a leading professional negligence set, much of the work undertaken by members of chambers has a significant insurance content. Members are also instructed in the widest range of non-marine insurance and reinsurance claims, including fire actions, recovery actions and policy disputes.

Continued overleaf

Public Authorities: The team undertaking this area of work has been involved in many of the leading cases concerning the liabilities in negligence of public authorities, particularly in matters of education. Members of chambers also appear on behalf of the police in the defence of civil claims.

Personal Injury: Members of chambers represent claimants and defendants in claims involving catastrophic injuries and complex issues on the assessment of damages and the implementation of structured settlements. They have been instructed in class actions, have particular expertise in disaster litigation including rail disasters, and claims involving child abuse, industrial injuries, road traffic accidents and sport injuries.

Travel Litigation: A specialist team handling claims involving the travel industry represents claimants and defendants in a whole range of actions including personal injury, foreign accidents, conflicts and all issues arising from travel and tourism.

Set No. 137

3 SERJEANTS' INN (Robert Francis QC & John Grace QC)

3 Serjeants' Inn, London, EC4Y 1BQ
Tel: (020) 7427 5000 **Fax:** (020) 7353 0425 **DX:** 421
Email: clerks@3serjeantsinn.com

Head of Chambers	Robert Francis QC
	John Grace QC
Senior Clerk	Nick Salt
Junior Clerks	Lee Johnson
	Tracy Barker
Administrator	Helen Barton-Smith
Tenants	34

Members:

Robert Francis QC (1973) (QC-1992)
John Grace QC (1973) (QC-1994)
Adrian Whitfield QC (1964) (QC-1983)
Philip Naughton QC (1970) (QC-1988)
Nicola Davies QC (1976) (QC-1992)
James Watson QC (1979) (QC-2000)
Philip Gaisford (1969)
Malcolm Fortune (1972)
Geoffrey D Conlin (1973)
Huw Lloyd (1975)
Andrew Grubb (1980)
Fiona Neale (1981)
Mary O'Rourke (1981)
George Hugh-Jones (1983)
Adrian Hopkins (1984)
Angus Moon (1986)
John Beggs (1989)
Michael Mylonas (1988)
Jonathan Holl-Allen (1990)
Christopher Johnston (1990)
Michael Horne (1992)
Fionnuala McCredie (1992)
Gerard Boyle (1992)
Richard Partridge (1994)
Mark Ley-Morgan (1994)
Anthony Jackson (1995)
Debra Powell (1995)
George Thomas (1995)
Clodagh Bradley (1996)
Ranald Davidson (1996)
Bridget Dolan (1997)
Sharon Flockhart (1997)
Abigail Johnson (1998)
Simon Cridland (1999)

The Chambers: Three Serjeants' Inn is consistently recognised as one of the leading chambers specialising in all aspects of law relating to medicine, and is renowned also for its strong civil police team and its expertise in commercial construction and engineering law. Chambers occupy recently modernised and extended accommodation, and have a modern IT infrastructure, including video conferencing facilities. The set has facilities for ADR, in which a number of its members are trained. It has full disabled access and facilities, including parking (by prior arrangement) for the disabled. It has air-conditioned conference rooms, but members are willing to attend conferences elsewhere if convenient. The clerking team is efficient, friendly and helpful. Chambers are happy to carry out work on a BarDIRECT, as well as Direct Professional Access basis. Clients' needs are the chambers' priority.

Work Undertaken:

Medical & Related Areas of Law: Members of chambers act in clinical negligence cases for claimants, NHS bodies, private hospitals and their insurers, and all the medical defence organisations. They have appeared in many of the leading cases such as Sidaway, Hotson and Kent v London Ambulance Service, multi-party cases such as the breast radiation litigation, and in cases of maximum damage; members of all levels of seniority do this work. Members also use their extensive scientific and medical expertise in pharmaceutical product liability claims. They have unrivalled experience in medical ethics cases, having appeared in most of the leading cases in this sensitive and often urgent area of work, for example Bland, Re F (sterilisation), B v Croydon HA, Re MB (caesarean section, and the first PVS cases since the coming into affect of the Human Rights Act (NHS Trust A v Mrs M). Members also have particular expertise and experience in mental health cases, and judicial review and human rights related to medical issues, for example Bournewood, Clunis and ex p Fisher. They regularly appear in professional disciplinary tribunals and inquiries, such as the General Medical Council, General Dental Council and the UKCC, as well as internal hospital disciplinary proceedings. Examples are the Bristol paediatric cardiac surgery inquiry and GMC proceedings. Members are also instructed in criminal cases related to medicine, most significantly in the recent case of Dr Harold Shipman.

Civil Police Law: Three Serjeants' Inn is one of the leading police law chambers, and acts for some 30 police forces, including three metropolitan forces. 12 members of chambers of all levels of seniority are part of the police team and cover the entire spectrum of police work, including civil jury trials, human rights, police discipline, police pensions, employment, public enquiries, judicial review, and operational advice. Recent noted cases conducted by members include ex p Harman (s. 40 PACE reviews), Lamothe

v MPS (PII), and Yates and Stewart (pensions), and the Marchioness inquiry. The police team has a strong reputation for providing risk management and training seminars for police forces.

Building & Engineering: Members of the construction team advise and act for employers, local authorities, contractors, insurers, and construction professionals in a wide variety of construction, engineering and other technical disputes. Areas covered include building and engineering, industrial processes and nuclear plants, mechanical and electrical engineering, dredging, temporary works, and cases concerning the liability of construction professionals and health and safety matters. Both domestic and overseas matters are dealt with, in the context of court-based litigation, arbitrations and ADR.

Additional areas of work:

Employment: Members act for both employers and employees, particularly in the specialist areas of the health and police services, in employment and internal tribunals, with a particular emphasis on discrimination cases.

Professional Negligence: Architects, surveyors, engineers, valuers, accountants and lawyers.

Personal Injuries: A wide range of cases, from major brain damage cases to road traffic and factory accidents, is undertaken.

Commercial Contract & Sale of Goods

Recruitment: Chambers offer two or three funded (£17,500 p.a.) pupillages starting each October. A chambers brochure and profiles of individual members are available from the senior clerk, Nick Salt.

Set No.

138 SERLE COURT (Lord Neill of Bladen QC)

6 New Square, Lincoln's Inn, London, WC2A 3QS
Tel: (020) 7242 6105 **Fax:** (020) 7405 4004 **DX:** LDE 1025
Email: clerks@serlecourt.co.uk **Website:** www.serlecourt.co.uk

Head of Chambers	Lord Neill of Bladen QC
Senior Clerks	Terry Buck
	Steven Whitaker
	Barry Ellis
	Paul Ballard
Chief Executive	Helena Miles
Tenants	44

serle court

Members:

Lord Neill of Bladen QC (1951) (QC-1966)
Richard Southwell QC (1959) (QC-1977)
Howard Page QC (1967) (QC-1987)
Patrick Talbot QC (1969) (QC-1990)
Alan Boyle QC (1972) (QC-1991)
Nicholas Padfield QC (1972) (QC-1991)
Frank Hinks QC (1973) (QC-2000)
Victor Joffe QC (1975) (QC-2001)
Michael Briggs QC (1978) (QC-1994)
Simon Browne-Wilkinson QC (1981) (QC-1998)
Elizabeth Jones QC (1984) (QC-2000)
Nicholas Asprey (1969)
John Whittaker (1969)
William Ballantyne (1977)
Beverly-Ann Rogers (1978)
William Henderson (1978)
James Behrens (1979)
Peter McMaster (1981)
Ann McAllister (1982)
Dominic Dowley (1983)
James Eadie (1984)
Richard Walford (1984)
Philip Jones (1985)
Philip Marshall (1987)
Nicholas Harrison (1988)
Andrew Moran (1989)
Nicholas Lavender (1989)
Khawar Qureshi (1990)
Clare Hoffmann (1990)
Kathryn Purkis (1991)
Douglas Close (1991)
David Blayney (1992)
Andrew Bruce (1992)
John Machell (1993)
David Drake (1994)
Justin Higgo (1995)
Daniel Lightman (1995)
Hugh Norbury (1995)
Timothy Collingwood (1996)
Jonathan Adkin (1997)
Giles Richardson (1997)
Thomas Braithwaite (1998)
SinÈad Agnew (1998)
Simon Hattan (1999)

The Chambers: The merger in February 2000 of One Hare Court and Serle Court Chambers was the first between leading sets from the Temple and Lincoln's Inn. The merger is a tangible manifestation of Serle Court's forward-looking approach to business and commitment to excellence. The merger has provided a unique product: a set of chambers which transcends the outmoded division between 'commercial' and 'Chancery commercial' work. The full range of business law expertise is now available under one roof. Serle Court contains individuals at all levels who are recognised in the principal directories as leading practitioners in their fields. Chambers' commitment is to intellectual and forensic excellence delivered in an approachable and efficient way. Chambers is housed in extensive and newly refurbished premises in Lincoln's Inn. It prides itself on high standards of administration and is backed by an experienced clerking team, which its clients can rely on and trust.

Work Undertaken: Chambers covers a broad range of business-related litigation, arbitration and legal advice, both in the UK and internationally. The main areas of work are administration and public law, arbitration, banking, civil fraud, commercial litigation, company, financial services, human rights, insolvency, partnership, professional negligence, property, regulatory and disciplinary matters, trusts and probate. Chambers can provide a first-class team at all levels of call in each of these areas. Members are equally happy working as part of a team with those who instruct it. Individual members of chambers have particular expertise in the following additional areas: Arab laws, charities, public international law, sports law and telecoms law. *Continued overleaf*

International: A significant proportion of Chambers' work originates overseas. Members of chambers appear in proceedings in Europe, the British Virgin Islands, Cayman Islands, Bermuda, the Channel Islands, the United States of America, Hong Kong and Singapore.

Set No. 139

SETTLEMENTCOUNSEL.COM

The Lloyd's Building, 12 Leadenhall Street, London, EC3V 1LP
Tel: (020) 7816 3600 **Fax:** (020) 7816 7130
Email: thecounsel@settlementcounsel.com **Website:** www.settlementcounsel.com

Practice Manager	Nicholas Brand
Tenants	5

Members:

Gerald Godfrey QC (1954) (QC-1971) †
David Stern (1989)
Michael Beckman QC (1954) (QC-1976) †
Margaret Howard (1977)
Anthony van Hagen (1974)
Stephen Mason †

† Associate Member

The Chambers: SettlementCounsel.com is an international commercial practice with significant experience in the resolution of major national and international disputes. Members provide an advisory and dispute resolution service, specialising in areas affecting global commerce and industry. Members are instructed by solicitors, international companies and foreign law firms under the IPR. Chambers have associate offices in Paris and New York.

Work Undertaken: Members specialise primarily in the fields of insurance, environmental protection, maritime law, corporate financial services and fraud, European Community law and in the resolution of other cross-border disputes.

Set No. 140

3-4 SOUTH SQUARE (Michael Crystal QC & Lord Alexander of Weedon QC)

3-4 South Square, Gray's Inn, London, WC1R 5HP
Tel: (020) 7696 9900 **Fax:** (020) 7696 9911 **DX:** 338 (Ch.Ln.)
Email: clerks@southsquare.com **Website:** www.southsquare.com

Head of Chambers	Michael Crystal QC
	Lord Alexander of Weedon QC
Senior Practice Manager	Paul Cooklin
Practice Managers	Michael Killick
	Jim Costa
	Dylan Playfoot
	Nicola Skinner
Administrator	Lesley Mortimer
Tenants	40

Members:

Michael Crystal QC (1970) (QC-1984)LLB (Lond), BCL (Oxon)
Lord Alexander of Weedon QC (1961) (QC-1973)MA (Cantab)
Christopher Brougham QC (1969) (QC-1988)BA (Oxon)
Gabriel Moss QC (1974) (QC-1989)MA, BCL (Oxon)
Simon Mortimore QC (1972) (QC-1991)LLB (Exon)
Stuart Isaccs QC (1975) (QC-1991)MA (Cantab) Lic Sp Dr Eur (Bruxelles)
Marion Simmons QC (1970) (QC-1994)LLB, LLM (Lond)
Richard Adkins QC (1982) (QC-1995)MA (Oxon)
Richard Sheldon QC (1979) (QC-1996)MA (Cantab)
Richard Hacker QC (1977) (QC-1998)MA (Cantab) Lic sp Dr Eur (Bruxelles)
Robin Knowles QC (1982) (QC-1999)MA (Cantab)
Mark Phillips QC (1984) (QC-1999)LLB, LLM (Bristol)
Robin Dicker QC (1986) (QC-2000)BA, BCL (Oxon)
William Trower QC (1983) (QC-2001)MA (Oxon)
Prof. Ian Fletcher (1971) MA, LLM, Phd, LLD, (Cantab), MCL (Tulane)
John Briggs (1973) LLB, (Lond) Ex, Du D d'U (Nancy)
David Marks (1974) MA, BCL (Oxon)
Martin Pascoe (1977) BA, BCL (Oxon)
David Alexander (1987) MA (Cantab)
Antony Zacaroli (1987) BA, BCL (Oxon)
Mark Arnold (1988) MA (Cantab)
Lexa Hilliard (1987) LLB, (Lond)
Stephen Atherton (1989) LLB, (Lancaster) LLM (Cantab)
Sandra Bristoll (1989) MA (Cantab)
Adam Goodison (1990) BA (Dunelm)
Hilary Stonefrost (1991) MSC (Lond)
Lloyd Tamlyn (1991) BA (Cantab)
Glen Davis (1992) MA (Oxon)
Andreas Gledhill (1992) MA (Cantab)
Fidelis Oditah (1992) MA BCL D Phil (Oxon)
Roxanne Ismail (1993) LLB (Lond)
Barry Isaacs (1994) BA (Oxon) MA (HARV) ASA
Ben Valentin (1995) BA BCL (Oxon) LLM (Cornell)
Felicity Toube (1995) BA BCL (Oxon)
Jeremy Goldring (1996) BA (Oxon) MA (Yale)
Samantha Knights (1996) BA (Oxon)
Lucy Frazer (1996) MA (Cantab)
David Allison (1998) BA (Cantab)
Daniel Bayfield (1998) BA (Cantab)
Thomas Smith (1999) BA LLM (Cantab)
Muir Hunter QC (1938) (QC-1965) MA (Oxon) †
Clive Cohen (1989) (SC 1975) BA, LLB (Witwatersrand) †
Prof. Marc Dassesse Doctor of Law (ULB) †
Prof. Peter Ellinger M.Jur (Jerusalem) D.Phil (Oxon) †
Andrew Martin (1983) LLB †

† Associate Member

The Chambers: A set with a pre-eminent reputation in insolvency and reconstruction law and specialist expertise in banking; financial services; company law; professional negligence; domestic and international arbitration; European Union law; insurance, reinsurance and general commercial litigation. 3-4 South Square has 40 practising barristers, including 14 Queen's Counsel. Chambers aims to provide the most effective professional services to clients and has developed a modern administration system which is supported by advanced information technology. Members of chambers adopt a commercial and business-like approach to their practice and are capable of reacting swiftly (individually or as members of a team) to urgent problems as the need may arise. 3-4 South Square is accustomed to dealing with matters at all levels of complexity often at very short notice. In the course of their work, members see similar problems from many different angles and keep abreast of recent developments in business, financial and commercial law. The Practice Managers are available 24 hours per day, seven days a week to deal with all enquiries.

Work Undertaken:

Insolvency: 3-4 South Square is well-known for its insolvency work. Work undertaken includes contentious and non-contentious problems arising out of domestic and international corporate and personal insolvencies. This work is not just limited to the technical issues that arise in receiverships, administrations, liquidations and personal bankruptcies. It also includes analysis and problem-solving in the diverse areas that arise in the rescue and reconstruction of failed and failing businesses. Many important issues of banking and business law only ever arise for determination in the context of an insolvency. It follows that members of 3-4 South Square have considerable experience of those issues. They arise in the many different types of litigation in which officeholders are seeking to recover assets on behalf of an insolvent estate.

Other: 3-4 South Square's expertise is by no means limited to work related to or arising out of insolvency. Members of chambers are frequently instructed in banking, insurance and other commercial disputes, dealing with every kind of contentious problem such as the civil aspects of commercial fraud and the obtaining of evidence for foreign proceedings. These problems can arise in many different situations in which a good general understanding of commercial law is required. Members of chambers also have much experience of professional negligence proceedings (primarily in cases against accountants and solicitors) and in disciplinary proceedings.

Publications: The members of 3-4 South Square have written, edited and contributed to numerous books and articles on corporate and personal insolvency, company law and banking.

International: Several members of chambers are fluent in or have a good working knowledge of foreign languages including French, German, Italian, Spanish, Russian, Hungarian and Chinese (Mandarin). The barristers at 3-4 South Square are regularly instructed to appear in courts and tribunals overseas. These jurisdictions include Bermuda, the Cayman Islands, the British Virgin Islands, Channel Islands, Singapore, Hong Kong and the USA. They are also retained as expert witnesses to appear before both arbitrators and courts in these and other overseas jurisdictions.

Set No.
141 **11 SOUTH SQUARE** (Christopher Floyd QC)

11 South Square (2nd Floor), Gray's Inn, London, WC1R 5EY **Tel:** (020) 7405 1222 **Fax:** (020) 7242 4282 **DX:** 433 **Email:** clerks@11southsquare.com **Website:** www.11southsquare.com

Set No.
142 **STANBROOK & HENDERSON** (Clive Stanbrook QC & Roger Henderson QC)

2 Harcourt Buildings, Temple, London, EC4Y 9DB
Tel: (020) 7353 0101 **Fax:** (020) 7583 2686 **DX:** LDE 1039
Email: clerks@harcourt.co.uk **Website:** www.harcourt.co.uk

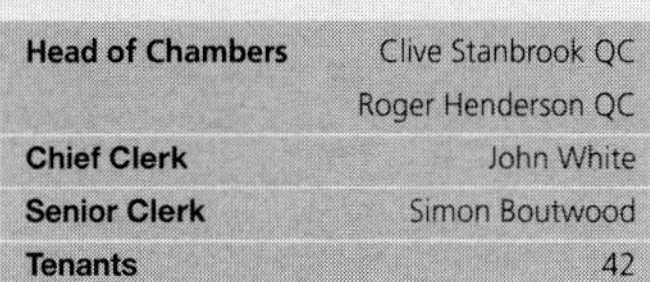

Head of Chambers	Clive Stanbrook QC Roger Henderson QC
Chief Clerk	John White
Senior Clerk	Simon Boutwood
Tenants	42

The Chambers: Stanbrook & Henderson is an association between the chambers of Roger Henderson QC at 2 Harcourt Buildings (see other reference for a full list) and the members of the European law firm of Stanbrook & Hooper in Brussels who are also members of the English bar, namely Clive Stanbrook OBE QC (1972) (QC-1989), Philip Bentley QC (1970) (QC-1991), and Debra Holland (1996). The association was initiated in 1991 to satisfy clients' growing requirement for combined expertise in European and domestic law by providing a single port of call for solicitors and other professionals requiring advice and advocacy and by taking advantage of Stanbrook & Hooper's link with legal practices throughout mainland Europe. The work undertaken reflects chambers' detailed knowledge of EU institutions and the way in which they work, knowledge which is essential for anyone affected by EU action or legislation. The Brussels-based barristers have a close link with daily developments in the European Commission, the Council and the Parliament Secretariat, with the result that a complete legal monitoring and information service can be offered.

Work Undertaken: Areas covered include the law relating to competition; merger control; trade; financial services; insurance; offshore investment; fiscal policy; local government and the public sector; the environment; product liability; agriculture and food; health and safety; employment and discrimination; human rights; immigration and freedom of movement; intellectual property; sport; and general EU regulatory policy.

Set No. 143 **3 STONE BUILDINGS** (Geoffrey Vos QC)

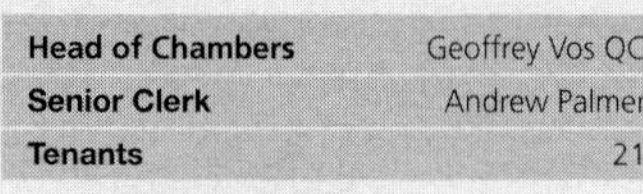

Head of Chambers	Geoffrey Vos QC
Senior Clerk	Andrew Palmer
Tenants	21

3 Stone Buildings, Lincoln's Inn, London, WC2A 3XL
Tel: (020) 7242 4937 **Fax:** (020) 7405 3896 **DX:** 317
Email: clerks@3sb.law.co.uk

Members:

Geoffrey Vos QC (1977) (QC-1993)MA (Cantab)
Edward Alexander Bannister QC (1974) (QC-1991)BA (Oxon)
David R. Stanford (1951)LLB, MA (Cantab)
Geoffrey J. Topham (1964)MA (Cantab)
Andrew J. Cosedge (1972)LLB (Exon)
James Gibbons (1974)
Alan M. Tunkel (1976)BA (Oxon)
David da Silva (1978)MA (Oxon)
Alexandra Mason (1981)BA (Hons) (London)
Robert A. Hantusch (1982)MA (Cantab)
Teresa Rosen Peacock (1982)MA BA (Mich)
Gilead Cooper (1983)MA (Oxon) Dip Law
Sarah J. Asplin (1984)MA (Cantab), BCL (Oxon)
David W. Lord (1987)LLB (Bristol)
Carlos Pimentel (1990)LLB, LLM(Exon)
Asaf Kayani (1991)LLB (Leeds), BCL (Oxon)
Sarah H. Lacey (1991)MA (Cantab)
Andrew M. Twigger (1994)BA (Oxon)
Fenner Moeran (1996)BSc (Bristol)
Andrew J. Child (1997)BA (Cantab)
Kerry Bornman (1999)LLB (Reading)

The Chambers: 3 Stone Buildings is a thriving set of Chancery and commercial chambers. Its main practice areas are commercial and Chancery litigation, pensions, company and insolvency, property and trusts, and insurance and reinsurance. In addition, 3 Stone Buildings offers specialists in media entertainment and sports, partnership, professional negligence and banking and financial services. Members of chambers undertake litigation drafting and advice in all these areas. Direct instructions are accepted from accountants, and other professionals, and under the BarDirect scheme.

Set No. 144 **4 STONE BUILDINGS** (Philip Heslop QC)

4 Stone Buildings, Lincoln's Inn, London, WC2A 3XT
Tel: (020) 7242 5524 **Fax:** (020) 7831 7907 **DX:** 385
Email: clerks@4stonebuildings.law.co.uk **Website:** www.4stonebuildings.com

Head of Chambers	Philip Heslop QC
Senior Clerk	David Goddard
Tenants	25

Members:

Philip Heslop QC (1970) (QC-1985)
Peter Curry QC (1953) (QC-1973)
Stephen Hunt (1968)
Anthony George Bompas QC (1975) (QC-1994)
Robert Hildyard QC (1977) (QC-1994)
Peter Griffiths (1977)
John Brisby QC (1978) (QC-1996)
Jonathan Crow (1981)
John Scott (1982)(QC Hong Kong 1996)
Malcolm Davis-White (1984)
Robert Miles (1987)
Rosalind Nicholson (1987)
Sarah Harman (1987)
Christopher Harrison (1988)
Jonathan Brettler (1988)
Paul Greenwood (1991)
Andrew Clutterbuck (1992)
Nicholas Cox (1992)
Richard. G Hill (1993)
Orlando Fraser (1994)
Charles Marquand (1987)
Anna Markham (1996)
Hermann Boeddinghaus (1996)
Andrew de Mestre (1998)
Vina Shukla (1992)

The Chambers: There are 25 members of chambers, including five silks and one Hong Kong QC. One of the juniors in chambers is the first Junior Counsel to the Treasury in Chancery (the 'Treasury Devil'), and another is on the main Chancery 'A' Panel. Six other members are on the Treasury 'B' Panel. Chambers belong to the Commercial Bar Association, the Chancery Bar Association and the Insolvency Lawyers Association. 4 Stone Buildings specialises in company/commercial law, covering all aspects of company law, commercial and general business law, corporate insolvency, as well as financial services and regulatory work, with a particular emphasis on litigation.

Work Undertaken: Company law, corporate fraud and asset recovery, financial services and regulatory work; shareholder disputes, commercial litigation, banking and public law.

Publications: Members of chambers are contributing editors to *Tolly's Company Law, Atkins Court Forms on Winding-up, the Encyclopaedia of Forms & Precedents on Companies, Halsbury's Laws of Hong Kong, Directors' Disqualification: Law & Practice, Butterworths Practical Insolvency, Table A-Articles of Association* and several other legal publications.

International: Members of chambers travel regularly to America, the Far East and Europe, as well as the Bahamas and Gibraltar. They have particularly strong connections with Hong Kong, Bermuda, Turks & Caicos Islands, Trinidad and the Cayman Islands.

Recruitment: Applicants are expected to have good degrees, but a successful candidate will also be expected to have the common sense to recognise the advice that a client really needs, and the confidence and ambition to succeed. A mini-pupillage in chambers is strongly encouraged.

Set No. 145

5 STONE BUILDINGS (Henry Harrod)

5 Stone Buildings, Lincoln's Inn, London, WC2A 3XT
Tel: (020) 7242 6201 **Fax:** (020) 7831 8102 **DX:** 304 London/Chancery Lane
Email: clerks@5-stonebuildings.law.co.uk **Website:** www.5-stonebuildings.law.co.uk

Head of Chambers	Henry Harrod
Senior Clerk	Paul Jennings
Tenants	21

5 STONE BUILDINGS

Members:

Henry Harrod (1963) +
Shân Warnock-Smith (1971)
Alastair Norris QC (1973) (QC-1997) +
Richard Fawls (1973)
Mark Herbert QC (1974) (QC-1995)
Mark Blackett-Ord (1974)
Martin Farber (1976)
Launcelot Henderson QC (1977) (QC-1995)
Andrew Simmonds QC (1980) (QC-1999)
Penelope Reed (1983)
Christopher Tidmarsh (1985)
Michael O'Sullivan (1986)
Patrick Rolfe (1987)
Barbara Rich (1990)
Karen Walden-Smith (1990)
Tracey Angus (1991)
Henry Legge (1993)
David Rees (1994)
Anna Clarke (1994)
Leon Sartin (1997)
Sarah Haren (1999)

+ Recorder

The Chambers: 5 Stone Buildings is a chancery set known for specialist expertise in the fields of private client, estate planning, partnership, property litigation, professional negligence, occupational pensions and commercial litigation. Two former members are now in the Court of Appeal, and a third has recently been appointed to the chancery bench. Members act both for and against the Revenue and appear in the leading cases on tax avoidance, undue influence, right to buy, ethical investment, pension surplus and duties of pension trustees. All members advise on trusts, wills, administration of estates and land law. A fast, efficient modern service of the highest standard is provided.

Set No. 146

8 STONE BUILDINGS (John M. Cherry QC)

8 Stone Buildings, Lincoln's Inn, London, WC2A 3TA
Tel: (020) 7831 9881 **Fax:** (020) 7831 9392 **DX:** 216 Chancery Lane
Email: alanl@8stonebuildings.law.co.uk

Head of Chambers	John M. Cherry QC
Senior Clerk	Alan Luff
	Mobile (0802) 411348
Junior Clerk	Paul Eeles
Tenants	11

Members:

John M. Cherry QC (1961) (QC-1988)
Timothy J Briden (1976)
Kieran May (1971)
Martin Seaward (1978)
Nigel Waddington (1992)
Richard Menzies (1993)
Marcus Baldwin (1994)
Peregrine Hill (1995)
Martyn McLeish (1997)
Mark King (1997)
Camilla Church (1998)

Work Undertaken: Members of chambers practise principally in the areas of personal injury and professional negligence. Individual specialisations include ecclesiastical law; health and safety; Inheritance Act claims; insurance; asbestos related diseases; industrial deafness; employment law; clinical negligence; occupational pensions; administrative law.

Set No.
147

9 STONE BUILDINGS (Michael Ashe QC, SC)

9 Stone Buildings, Lincoln's Inn, London, WC2A 3NN
Tel: (020) 7404 5055 **Fax:** (020) 7405 1551 **DX:** 314 Chancery Lane
Email: clerks@9stonebuildings.com

Head of Chambers	Michael Ashe QC, SC
Senior Clerk	Alan Austin
Tenants	21

9 STONE BUILDINGS

Members:

Michael Ashe QC (1971) (QC-1994)(QC N I 1998) (SC Ireland 2000) +
Isaac Jacob (1963) +
Cenydd I. Howells (1964) +
Vivian R. Chapman (1970) +
Christopher I. Cant (1973)
Edward Denehan (1981)
Martin Young (1984)
Araba Taylor (1984)
Lynne M. Counsell (1986)
Robert S. Levy (1988)
Sheila Foley (1988)
Timothy Sisley (1989)
John Smart (1989)
Philip Flower (1979)
Helene Pines Richman (1992)
Lana Wood (1993)
Peter Shaw (1995)
Jonathan Lewis (1996)
James Hanham (1996)
Daniel Bromilow (1996)
Richard Wilson (1996)
Graeme C. Wood (1968) *
Peter Clayton (1977)(Hong Kong Bar) *
N. Critelli (1991)(Iowa and New York Bar USA) *
James Levy (Gibraltar) *
Anthony Provasoli (Gibraltar) *

* Door Tenant + Recorder

The Chambers: A general Chancery set undertaking litigation, advisory work and drafting over a wide range of subjects including wills and trusts; landlord and tenant; business agreements; companies and insolvency; tax and tax planning (including stamp duties); financial services and securities regulations; charities; commons registration; employment law; and professional negligence. Some members are practitioners in US and Ireland. Full details and information can be obtained from the chambers' information booklet, which is available on request.

Set No.
148

11 STONE BUILDINGS (Murray Rosen QC)

11 Stone Buildings, Lincoln's Inn, London, WC2A 3TG
Tel: (020) 7831 6381 **Fax:** (020) 7831 2575 **DX:** 1022 Chancery Lane WC2
Email: clerks@11stonebuildings.com **Website:** www.11stonebuildings.com

Head of Chambers	Murray Rosen QC
Senior Clerk	Christopher Berry
Clerks	Gareth Davies
	Caron Levy
	Matthew Curness
Listing	Will Shrubsall
Marketing & Client Care	Sarah Longden
Tenants	41

Members:

Murray Rosen QC (1976) (QC-1993)
Gerald Godfrey QC (1954) (QC-1971)
Michael Beckman QC (1954) (QC-1976)
Peter Sheridan QC (1956) (QC-1977)
Jane Giret QC (1981) (QC-2001)
Edward Cousins (1971)
Edward Cohen (1972)
Alan Bishop (1973)
Adrian Salter (1973)
Donald McCue (1974)
John Phillips (1975)
Nigel Meares (1975)
Robert Deacon (1976)
Jonathan Arkush (1977)
Sidney Ross (1983)
Roland Higgs (1984)
Marc Dight (1984)
Alan Gourgey (1984)
Tina Kyriakides (1984)
Raquel Agnello (1986)
Marcia Shekerdemian (1987)
Charles Holbech (1988)
Tim Penny (1988)
Sally Barber (1988)
Marilyn Kennedy-McGregor (1989)
David Stern (1989) †
Jonathan Middleburgh (1990)
Birgitta Meyer (1992)
Christopher Wilkins (1993)
Max Mallin (1993)
James Barnard (1993)
Nick Parfitt (1993)
Timothy Cowen (1993)
Jonathan Lopian (1994)
Denis Daly (1995)
Christopher Boardman (1995)
Tom Weekes (1995)
Jamie Riley (1995)
Alaric Watson (1997)
Douglas Keel (1997) ‡
Stephen Tudway (1998)

† Associate Member ‡ Associate Members

The Chambers: The barristers at 11 Stone Buildings practise in commercial litigation with specialist groups for all types of contract, company, insolvency and property disputes. The set has won awards for Barristers' Chambers of the year and has been praised in the press for its responsiveness, flexibility in working practices and approach to fee levels. There are 41 barristers working for law firms across the country and internationally as well as with in-house legal departments and direct access clients. They are particularly well known for their expertise in the specialist bar categories listed below.
Emergency Overnight & Weekend Service: Contact Christopher Berry on (020) 8241 7903 (home) or (07836) 566 251 (mobile), or Gareth Davies on (020) 8542 1211 (home) or (07767) 445 519 (mobile), or Matthew Curness on (020) 8300 9634.

Work Undertaken:
Commercial Chancery: Highly regarded as a set with Murray Rosen QC profiled as a leading silk.
Contract & Commercial: The largest group dealing with all aspects of business and banking litigation and commercial drafting.

Company: Jane Giret QC and Marcia Sherkerdemian are profiled as leaders in the company field.
Insolvency: A leading set with Jane Giret QC, Tina Kyriakides, Raquel Agnello, Marcia Sherkerdemian and Chris Boardman particularly recommended. Recent cases of interest include Re Lomax Leisure Ltd, Re Floor Fourteen Ltd (Lewis v HM Inland Revenue), Re Levey v Legal Services Commission.
Fraud: The specialist groups deal in all aspects of civil fraud such as commercial fraud; fraudulent trading; property fraud; professional misconduct and VAT fraud. Michael Beckman QC deals with both civil and criminal fraud and all aspects of serious crime.
Intellectual Property: A major area of work for the set, their experience includes a wide variety of copyright, trademark, design rights and non-technical patent work, internet and e-commerce disputes.
Media & Entertainment: Chambers deal with a significant amount of work in the media and music industry including defamation, press freedom, publishing and film and music contracts.
Sports Law: Chambers has a well developed sports law practice with a history of representing high profile clubs, organisations and individuals in a variety of sports. Murray Rosen QC is highly recommended as a leading silk in this area of law. He was the founding chairman of the Bar Sports Law Group.
Property & Land: Jonathan Arkush is recommended as a leading junior. Tribunals: The work in this area relates mainly to disciplinary, employment, regulatory, sports and VAT.
Succession & Trusts: Members of this group are specialists in trust drafting and advisory work and are experienced in friendly and hostile litigation. They offer expertise in the Court of Protection.
Professional Negligence: Using the experience of all the specialist groups, chambers deal with a substantial amount of lawyers', accountants', architects' and surveyors' negligence.
Alternative Disputes Resolution: 11 Stone Buildings has a fully equipped ADR/Arbitration facility available for commercial use and each of the chambers specialist groups has accredited barristers available for dispute resolution.
Fees: Levels are carefully monitored and a flexible approach is maintained, as chambers believe that each case has its own special requirements. This flexibility includes fixed fees and package fees, which allows lay clients greater access to experienced lawyers. However, hourly rates can be quoted to assist the client in budgeting for services. Conditional fee work is being continually developed and the chambers will respond to government and other initiatives such as Thai Trading as they arise. As an aid to efficient and cost effective legal services chambers has a team of lawyers for multi-track cases available on a fixed fee basis. For a copy of the chambers' specialist brochures or legal bulletins contact Sarah Longden or alternatively visit their website www.11stonebuildings.com.

Publications: John Phillips is author of the *Modern Contract of Guarantee and Protecting Designs: Law and Litigation;* Edward Cousins is the author of *Cousins on Mortgages and Pease and Chitty's Law of Markets and Fairs*'; Sidney Ross is the author of *Inheritance Act Claims, Law and Practice.*

et No. 49

199 STRAND (David Phillips QC)

199 Strand, London, WC2R 1DR
Tel: (020) 7379 9779 **Fax:** (020) 7379 9481 **DX:** 322 Ch.Ln.
Email: chambers@199strand.co.uk **Website:** www.199strand.co.uk

Head of Chambers	David Phillips QC
Chief Executive	Nick Quarrelle
Business Development Director	Martin Griffiths
Senior Clerk	Graham Johnson
Tenants	43

199 strand

Members:

David Phillips QC (1976) (QC-1997) +
Peter Andrews QC (1970) (QC-1991) +
Robin de Wilde QC (1971) (QC-1993) +
Elizabeth-Anne Gumbel QC (1974) (QC-1999)
Neville Sarony (1964)QC Hong Kong 1992
Malcolm Stitcher (1971)
Keith Walmsley (1973)
Steven Whitaker (1973)
Simon Levene (1977) +
Quintin Tudor-Evans (1977)
Andrew Goodman (1978)
Anthony Korn (1978)
Sara Hargreaves (1979)
Francis Treasure (1980)
Jacqueline Beech (1981)
Leslie Blohm (1982)
Kevin Haven (1982)
Patrick Sadd (1984)
David Fisher (1985)
Philomena Harrison (1985)
Martin Hutchings (1986)
Michael Harrison (1986)
Henry Charles (1987)
James Aldridge (1987)
Richard Selin (1987)
Henry Witcomb (1989)
Sophie Garner (1990)
Timothy Nesbitt (1991)
Amanda Eilledge (1991)
Rachel Vickers (1992)
Anthony Cheshire (1992)
Robert Dudderidge (1992)
Eliot Woolf (1993)
Nick Isaac (1993)
Louise Thomson (1996)
Mark Sefton (1996)
Jeremy Ford (1996)
Toby Vanhegan (1996)
Stuart McKechnie (1997)
Simon Brindle (1998)
Sarah Nielsen (1999)
Farrah Mauladad (1999)
Prof Stephen Guest (1980) †

+ Recorder † Associate Tenant

The Chambers: 199 Strand is a long-established set specialising in civil work and undertakes instructions for clients in London, throughout the country and abroad.

Continued overleaf

Work Undertaken: The principal areas of work undertaken, in which specialist groups are offered, are personal injury, clinical negligence, property, professional negligence and general commercial litigation. Smaller teams within chambers specialise in employment law and in road transport law. Their web site at www.199strand.co.uk provides full details of the areas of work undertaken by chambers as well as detailed profiles of the members. A comprehensive brochure is also available on request from the clerks. Chambers accept instructions under the Direct Professional Access and the Bar DIRECT rules and also accept cases under Conditional Fee Agreements.

International: Members are fluent in French, German, Hebrew, Japanese, Mandarin, Chinese.

Set No.
150 **TANFIELD CHAMBERS** (Andrew Thompson & David Guy)
Francis Taylor Building (3rd Floor), Temple, London, EC4Y 7BY **Tel:** (020) 7797 7250 **Fax:** (020) 7797 7299 **DX:** 46 London Chancery Lane
Email: clerks@tanfieldchambers.co.uk **Website:** www.tanfieldchambers.co.uk

Set No.
151 1 TEMPLE GARDENS (Hugh Carlisle QC)

1 Temple Gardens, Temple, London, EC4Y 9BB
Tel: (020) 7583 1315 **Fax:** (020) 7353 3969 **DX:** 382 London
Email: clerks@1templegardens.co.uk **Website:** www.1templegardens.co.uk

Head of Chambers	Hugh Carlisle QC
Senior Clerk	Dean Norton
Tenants	41

Members:

Hugh Carlisle QC (1961) (QC-1978)
Lord Mayhew of Twysden QC (1955) (QC-1972)
Norman Miscampbell QC (1952) (QC-1974)
Geoffrey Nice QC (1971) (QC-1990)
Ian Burnett QC (1980) (QC-1998)
John Bate-Williams (1976)
Ian Ashford-Thom (1977)
Angus Macpherson (1977)
William Hoskins (1980)
Dominic Grieve (1980)
Mark Bishop (1981)
Alison Hewitt (1984)
Alastair McFarlane (1985)
Robin B-K Tam (1986)
Paul Kilcoyne (1985)
James Bell (1987)
Simon Brown (1988)
Jane Llewelyn (1989)
Philip Astor (1989)
Keith Morton (1990)
James Laughland (1991)
Charles Curtis (1992)
Richard Wilkinson (1992)
Nicholas Bacon (1992)
James Arney (1992)
Marcus Grant (1993)
David Barr (1993)
Alexandra Issa (1993)
Benjamin Williams (1994)
Robert Marven (1994)
Alexander Glassbrook (1995)
Nicholas Moss (1995)
Timothy Kevan (1996)
Emma-Jane Hobbs (1996)
Jonathan Hough (1997)
Paul McGrath (1997)
Dominic Adamson (1997)
Anna Kotzeva (1998)
Sacha Ackland (1998)
Stephen Cottrell (1998)
Angus Edwards (1999)

Work Undertaken: General common law, including personal injury, professional negligence and product liability claims and claims in nuisance and other torts; insurance and other contractual disputes; consumer credit; public and administrative law and judicial review; immigration law; employment law; public inquiries and inquests; health and safety; fraud both civil and criminal.

International: Members are fluent in Bulgarian, French, German, Russian and Spanish.

Set No.
152 2 TEMPLE GARDENS (Dermod O'Brien QC)

2 Temple Gardens, London, EC4Y 9AY
Tel: (020) 7822 1200 **Fax:** (020) 7822 1300 **DX:** 134 (Ch.Ln.)
Email: clerks@2templegardens.co.uk **Website:** www.2templegardens.co.uk

Head of Chambers	Dermod O'Brien QC
Senior Clerk	Christopher Willans
Tenants	47

Members:

Dermod O'Brien QC (1962) (QC-1983)
Timothy Preston QC (1964) (QC-1982)
Michael de Navarro QC (1968) (QC-1990)
Robert Moxon-Browne QC (1969) (QC-1990)
Andrew Collender QC (1969) (QC-1991)
Benjamin Browne QC (1976) (QC-1996)
Jeremy Stuart-Smith QC (1978) (QC-1997)
Michael Black QC (1978) (QC-1995)
Daniel Pearce-Higgins QC (1973) (QC-1998)
Howard Palmer QC (1977) (QC-1999)
Henry de Lotbiniere (1968)
Rosalind Foster (1969)
Roger Hetherington (1973)
Monya Anyadike-Danes (1980)
John McDonald (1981)
David Thomas (1982)
Christopher Russell (1982)
Sarah Vaughan-Jones (1983)
Graham Eklund (1984)
Martin Porter (1986)
Katharine Gordon (1988)
Andrew Miller (1989)
Neil Moody (1989)
Bradley Martin (1990)
Timothy Otty (1990)

Members continued:

Daniel Crowley (1990)
John Snell (1991)
Paul Downes (1991)
Tim Lord (1992)
Rupert Reece (1993)
David Turner (1993)
Clare Brown (1993)
Dore Green (1994)
Lucy Wyles (1994)
Justin Mort (1994)
Bruce Gardiner (1994)
Nina Goolamali (1995)
Adam Constable (1995)
Neil Hext (1995)
Roger Harris (1996)
Krista Lee (1996)
Charles Dougherty (1997)
Peter de Verneuil Smith (1998)
Niazi Fetto (1999)
Darren Eales (2000)
Brent McDonald (2000)
Leona Powell (2000)

Work Undertaken: The major areas of practice are general common and commercial law including personal injuries (including employers' liability, health and safety and occupational diseases); building construction and engineering cases; accountancy and banking; employment law; commercial and civil fraud; insurance and reinsurance; all areas of professional negligence including medical negligence; disaster litigation; product liability (including pharmaceutical products and cases concerning fire, flood, electricity, gas, water, highways). Disputes involving conflicts of law, jurisdiction and EU problems are regularly handled. In the area of alternative dispute resolution (ADR), members are accredited mediators and qualified arbitrators. Chambers are happy to accept instructions under the Bar Council's direct access rules.

International: Members are fluent in French, German, Italian, Spanish and Swedish. Many members work extensively overseas.

Recruitment: Pupillages and mini-pupillages by arrangement. Apply to the Secretary of the Pupillage Committee. Applications are also welcomed from experienced practitioners: please write in confidence to the chambers director.

Set No.

153 **3 TEMPLE GARDENS TAX CHAMBERS** (Richard Bramwell QC)

3 Temple Gardens, Temple, London, EC4Y 9AU
Tel: (020) 7353 7884 **Fax:** (020) 7583 2044
Email: clerks@taxcounsel.co.uk **Website:** www.taxcounsel.co.uk

Head of Chambers	Richard Bramwell QC
Senior Clerk	Anne de Rose
Tenants	8

Members:

Richard Bramwell QC (1967) (QC-1989)
John Dick (1974)
Michael Sherry (1978)
Alun James (1986)
Eamon McNicholas (1994)
David Southern (1982)
Jonathan Schwarz (1998)(SA 1977, Can 1981)
Peter Harris (1980)

Work Undertaken: Specialist tax practitioners offering comprehensive tax planning. Advice on domestic and international tax investigations, disputes and appeals before all Courts. Professional liability involving tax. Current positions held by members of chambers include Chairman of the Tax Faculty of the ICAEW; Secretary of the Revenue Bar Association; visiting Professor at Queen Mary & Westfield College, London University; memberships of the CIOT Corporation Tax Technical Sub-committee, the International Tax Sub-Committee, the Working Party on Reform of Intellectual Property Taxation, the Inland Revenue E-commerce Forum; Editorial Board Taxation. Details on individual members are to be found at www.taxcounsel.co.uk

Publications: Members have written, contributed to or edited: *Taxation of Companies and Company Reconstructions; Whiteman on Income Tax; Tolley's Taxation of Corporate Debt and Financial Instruments; Simon's Taxes; De Voil on VAT; Taxation; the Tax Journal; British Tax Review; Bulletin for International Fiscal Documentation; the Financial Times; CCH British International Tax Agreements.*

International: Members have specific experience in relation to Canada, France, South Africa, the United States, Germany and Latvia. Members are fluent in French and German.

Set No.
154 **3 TEMPLE GARDENS** (John Coffey QC)

3 Temple Gardens, Temple, London, EC4Y 9AU
Tel: (020) 7353 3102 **Fax:** (020) 7353 0960 **DX:** 485
Email: clerks@3tg.co.uk

Head of Chambers	John Coffey QC
Senior Clerk	Kevin Aldridge
Tenants	38

Members:

John Coffey QC (1970) (QC-1996)
Jeffrey Pegden QC (1973) (QC-1996)
Ann Cotcher QC (1979) (QC-2000)
Geoffrey Birch (1972)
Richard Crabtree (1974)
Piers Reed (1974)
Jayne Gilbert (1976)
Robert Whittaker (1977)
David Stanton (1979)
William Saunders (1980)
Simon Connolly (1981)
Simon Smith (1981)
Alasdair Smith (1981)
Brian Stork (1981)
David Barnes (1981)
Kim Halsall (1982)
Dee Connolly (1982)
Stella Reynolds (1983)
Martin Lahiffe (1984)
Wayne Cleaver (1986)
Gordon Ross (1986)
Catherine Popert (1987)
Benjamin Aina (1987)
Nicholas Bleaney (1988)
Frances McKeever (1988)
Martin Rutherford (1990)
Sibby Salter (1991)
Clemency Firth (1992)
Evan Nuttall (1993)
Nicholas Corsellis (1993)
Alexander Williams (1995)
Amanda Hamilton (1995)
Caroline Carberry (1995)
Matthew Lawson (1995)
Nicola Cafferkey (1998)
Ruby Selva (1998)
Simon Shannon (1999)
Graham Smith (1999)

The Chambers: Chambers of John Coffey are a well-established set providing a high level of advocacy and advice to an extensive range of clients. Chambers have widespread expertise and experience at every level and advise across the whole spectrum of criminal law. In addition, some members practice in the field of family law. Accreditation to Barmark in October 2000 ensures that Chambers are committed to providing an excellent quality of service and meeting clients' needs in a rapidly changing profession. Members appear in the Magistrates Court, Crown Court, High Court, Queen's Bench, Divisional Court, the Court of Appeal and the House of Lords. Other tribunals include Professional tribunals, Mental Health tribunals, Industrial tribunals, inquests and other judicial inquiries. Some members are able to provide qualified training, accredited by Inner Temple and Lincoln's Inn, under the criminal advocacy module of the Professional Skills Course.

Recruitment: Training and pupillage applications should be sent to Ruby Selva, including a detailed CV and references. Chambers currently offer pupillage awards.

Set No.
155 **3 TEMPLE GARDENS** (Jonathan Goldberg QC)

Three Temple Gardens, Temple, London, EC4Y 9AU **Tel:** (020) 7583 1155 **Fax:** (020) 7353 5446 **DX:** 0064 **Email:** clerks@3templegardens.co.uk

Set No.
156 **TOOKS COURT CHAMBERS** (Michael Mansfield QC)

14 Tooks Court, Cursitor St, London, EC4A 1LB **Tel:** (020) 7405 8828 **Fax:** (020) 7405 6680 **DX:** 68 (Ch.Ln.) **Email:** clerks@tooks.law.co.uk

Set No.
157 **2-4 TUDOR STREET** (Richard Ferguson QC)

2-4 Tudor Street, London, EC4Y 0AA **Tel:** (020) 7797 7111 **Fax:** (020) 7797 7120 **DX:** 226 **Email:** clerks@rfqc-law.co.uk **Website:** www.rfqc.co.uk

Set No.
158 **3 VERULAM BUILDINGS** (Christopher Symons QC & John Jarvis QC)

3 Verulam Buildings, Gray's Inn, London, WC1R 5NT
Tel: (020) 7831 8441 **Fax:** (020) 7831 8479 **DX:** LDE 331
Email: chambers@3vb.com **Website:** www.3vb.com

Head of Chambers	Christopher Symons QC
	John Jarvis QC
Senior Practice Managers	
	Roger Merry-Price
	Nicholas Hill
Tenants	51

Members:

Christopher Symons QC (1972) (QC-1989)
John Jarvis QC (1970) (QC-1989)
R. Neville Thomas QC (1962) (QC-1975)
Nicholas Merriman QC (1969) (QC-1988)
Ian Geering QC (1974) (QC-1991)
William Blair QC (1972) (QC-1994)
Nicholas Elliott QC (1972) (QC-1995)
Richard Salter QC (1975) (QC-1995)
Ali Malek QC (1980) (QC-1996)
Gregory Mitchell QC (1979) (QC-1997)
Ross Cranston QC (1976) (QC-1998)
Richard de Lacy QC (1976) (QC-2000)
Andrew Sutcliffe QC (1983) (QC-2001)
Michael Blair QC (1965) (QC-1996)(Hon Causa)
Clive Freedman (1975)
Elizabeth Birch (1978)
Mark Pelling (1979)
Andrew Fletcher (1980)
Andrew Onslow (1982)
Peter Cranfield (1982)
Stephen Phillips (1984)
Rory Phillips (1984)
Tom Weitzman (1984)
Ewan McQuater (1985)
Jonathan Nash (1986)
James Cameron (1987)
Michael Lazarus (1987)
Juliet May (1988)
Angharad Start (1988)
Paul Lowenstein (1988)
Adrian Beltrami (1989)
Amanda Green (1990)
Annie Hockaday (1990)
John Odgers (1990)
Jonathan Mark Phillips (1991)
James Evans (1991)
David Quest (1993)
Richard Edwards (1993)
Jonathan Davies-Jones (1994)
Matthew Hardwick (1994)
Richard Brent (1995)
Sonia Tolaney (1995)
Ian Wilson (1995)
Natalie Baylis (1996)
Catherine Gibaud (1996)
Matthew Parker (1997)
David Head (1997)
Ewan McKendrick (1998)
Christopher Hare (1998)
Peter Ratcliffe (1998)
Sophie Mallinckrodt (1999)

The Chambers: 3 Verulam Buildings is a leading set of chambers specialising in commercial work. Members accept instructions and briefs to advise and represent clients in court, arbitration and other tribunals in England, Wales and internationally.

Work Undertaken: All members of chambers are specialist advocates in various aspects of commercial work. Among them are acknowledged experts in the fields of banking; insurance and reinsurance; professional negligence; insolvency; entertainment and media; commercial fraud; public international and environmental law. The set also has an established reputation in international and domestic arbitration. Chambers include a number of individuals who have been involved in EU cases in the national courts and the European Court of Justice. Expertise is also offered in an extremely wide range of other matters, including agency, agriculture, building and construction, commodities trading, all aspects of company law, competition law, IT, telecoms and computer legislation, employment, financial services, gaming, intellectual property, judicial review, landlord and tenant matters, pensions, restraint of trade, and sale of goods. The diversity of experience available enables 3 Verulam Buildings to offer advice and representation to clients in the huge variety of business contexts in which legal issues arise. Barristers work individually or in teams to carry out all the preparatory and interlocutory work necessary to bring a case to trial or to settle a case by way of ADR. They also undertake non-contentious legal work, for example, drafting standard terms and conditions in contracts both for financial institutions and commercial clients. Additionally, members advise clients on the effects of new law. Chambers are managed by a friendly and efficient team of practice managers and support staff. In appropriate circumstances, chambers will carry out work on a conditional fee basis. The practice managers would be pleased to discuss this further and a draft agreement is available on request.

Recruitment: Chambers offer three or four pupillages of 12 months, each with an award of not less than £27,000. Candidates should have a first class or 2.1 degree (which need not be in law). Applications must be made through the OLPAS scheme operated by the Bar Council.

Set No.
159 **WILBERFORCE CHAMBERS** (Edward Nugee QC)

8 New Square, Lincoln's Inn, London, WC2A 3QP
Tel: (020) 7306 0102 **Fax:** (020) 7306 0095 **DX:** 311 London Chancery Lane
Email: chambers@wilberforce.co.uk **Website:** www.wilberforce.co.uk

Head of Chambers	Edward Nugee QC
Senior Clerk	Declan Redmond
Chambers Director	Gareth Mason
Clerks	Danny Smillie
	Tanya Tong
Tenants	35

Members:

Edward Nugee QC (1955) (QC-1977)
Jules Sher QC (1968) (QC-1981)
Michael Barnes QC (1965) (QC-1981)
David Lowe QC (1965) (QC-1984)
John Martin QC (1972) (QC-1991)
Nicholas Warren QC (1972) (QC-1993)
Ian Croxford QC (1976) (QC-1993)
Robert Ham QC (1973) (QC-1994)
John Furber QC (1973) (QC-1995)
Terence Mowschenson QC (1977) (QC-1995)
Brian Green QC (1980) (QC-1997)
Michael Bloch QC (1979) (QC-1998)
Christopher Nugee QC (1983) (QC-1998)
Michael Furness QC (1982) (QC-2000)
Anthony Taussig (1966)
John Child (1966)
Thomas Seymour (1975)
Gabriel Hughes (1978)
John Wardell (1979)
Michael Tennet (1985)
Jonathan Seitler (1985)
Thomas Lowe (1985)
Jonathan Karas (1986)
James Ayliffe (1987)
Judith Bryant (1987)
Joanna Smith (1990)
Joanne Wicks (1990)
Paul Newman (1991)
Gabriel Fadipe (1991)
Caroline Furze (1992)
Jonathan Evans (1994)
Emily Campbell (1995)
Rupert Reed (1996)
Julian Greenhill (1997)
Tiffany Scott (1998)

The Chambers: Wilberforce Chambers is a set of 35 barristers including 14 QCs, based in Lincoln's Inn, London. Chambers are able to offer specialist barristers at all levels of seniority and across the broad range of the commercial and Chancery fields. Members of chambers are forward thinking and responsive to the rapidly changing environment of the Bar.

Other Information: Details of each member's practice can be obtained from Gareth Mason, Chambers' Director, and Declan Redmond, Senior Clerk, or by visiting chamber's website.

Work Undertaken: The work of chambers includes litigation, advice and drafting in the following areas:

Commercial & Other Contracts (both domestic and international): Banking, insurance loans and security, guarantees, financial services, Lloyds' drafting and litigation, economic torts, breach of confidence, oil and gas law.

Occupational & Personal Pension Schemes

Property: Including all matters relating to land, commercial property transactions, landlord and tenant, property finance, negligence, fraud, mortgages and other securities.

Tax: Including personal tax and estate planning, including offshore tax planning, and a wide range of tax litigation.

Trusts: Drafting, advice on administration and construction and contentious and non-contentious litigation.

Professional Negligence: Of accountants, actuaries, auditors, barristers, solicitors, surveyors, trustees and construction-related professional negligence.

Equitable Remedies: Injunctions, tracing, constructive trusts and proprietary estoppel.

Company Law: Including shareholders' disputes; directors' disqualification proceedings, mergers and acquisitions, partnerships, and joint ventures.

Wills: Probate (both contentious and non-contentious), administration of estates, intestacy and family provision.

Insolvency: Both corporate and individual.

Charities: Housing Associations, partnerships, clubs, societies, and the law as it relates to other associations.

Sports & Media Law

Additional Areas: Individual members have particular expertise in local government and administrative law; employment law; heritage property; school sites; commons registration; highways; town and country planning and compulsory purchase; white-collar crime, eg breaches of health and safety legislation and intellectual property.

Publications: Members write for and/or edit a number of well-known publications. In the last two years chambers has written and published books covering the impact of the new CPR Rules (published March 1999) and the Human Rights Act 1998 (published March 2000). A book on the new Financial Services Act is being written for publication in 2001.

International: Members frequently appear in jurisdictions outside the UK, including Bahamas, Bermuda, the Cayman Islands, Hong Kong, Singapore and Gibraltar.

Birmingham

Set No.
160 **COLERIDGE CHAMBERS** (Simon Brand)
Coleridge Chambers, 190 Corporation Street, Birmingham, B4 6QD **Tel:** (0121) 233 8500 **Fax:** (0121) 233 8501 **DX:** 23503

Set No.
161 **1 FOUNTAIN COURT** (David Crigman QC)

1 Fountain Court, Steelhouse Lane, Birmingham, B4 6DR
Tel: (0121) 236 5721 **Fax:** (0121) 236 3639 **DX:** 16077
Email: clerks@fountaincourt.com **Website:** www.fountaincourt.com

Head of Chambers	David Crigman QC
Senior Clerk	CT Hayfield
Tenants	38

Members:

David Crigman QC (1969) (QC-1989)
Melbourne Inman QC (1979) (QC-1998)
Malcolm Morse (1967)
Robert Hodgkinson (1968)
Michael Dudley (1972)
Thomas Busby (1975)
Christopher Millington QC (1976) (QC-2001)
Giles Harrison-Hall (1977)
Benjamin Nicholls (1978)
Michael Conry (1979)
Stephen Eyre (1981)
Thomas Dillon (1983)
John Evans (1983)
Neal Williams (1984)
Simon Ward (1986)
Blondelle Thompson (1987)
Jonathan Salmon (1987)
Sarah Buxton (1988)
Paul Farrer (1988)
Gerard Quirke (1988)
Richard Atkins (1989)
James Puzey (1990)
Gary Thornett (1991)
Alison Scott-Jones (1991)
William Baker (1991)
Paul Considine (1992)
Anthony Johnston (1993)
Mark Garside (1993)
Nicholas Smith (1994)
Thomas Williams (1995)
Stuart Baker (1995)
Carolyn Jones (1995)
Simon Phillips (1996)
Andrew Smith (1997)
Emma Kelly (1997)
Elizabeth Muir (1998)
Leisha Bond (1999)
Lucianne Allen (1999)

The Chambers: Broadly based chambers practising in all aspects of criminal, civil, commercial and family law.

Set No.
162 **3 FOUNTAIN COURT** (Robert Juckes QC)
3 Fountain Court, Steelhouse Lane, Birmingham, B4 6DR **Tel:** (0121) 236 5854 **Fax:** (0121) 236 7008 **DX:** 16079 **Email:** clerks@3fc.co.uk

Set No.
163 **4 FOUNTAIN COURT** (John Saunders QC)
4 Fountain Court, Steelhouse Lane, Birmingham, B4 6DR **Tel:** (0121) 236 3476 **Fax:** (0121) 200 1214 **DX:** 16074
Email: clerks@4fountaincourt.law.co.uk

Set No.
164 **5 FOUNTAIN COURT** (Anthony Barker QC)

5 Fountain Court, Steelhouse Lane, Birmingham, B4 6DR
Tel: (0121) 606 0500 **Fax:** (0121) 606 1501 **DX:** 16075 Fountain Ct. Birmingham
Email: info@5fountaincourt.law.co.uk **Website:** www.5fountaincourt.law.co.uk

Head of Chambers	Anthony Barker QC
Deputy Head of Chambers	Gareth Evans QC
Senior Clerk	Tony McDaid
Tenants	107

Members:

Anthony Barker QC (1966) (QC-1985)
Gareth Evans QC (1973) (QC-1994)
Ian Alexander QC (1964) (QC-1989)
David Stembridge QC (1955) (QC-1990)
Martin Kingston QC (1972) (QC-1992)
Stephen Linehan QC (1970) (QC-1993)
William Wood QC (1970) (QC-1997)
Ralph Lewis QC (1978) (QC-1999)
Paul Bleasdale QC (1978) (QC-2001)
John West (1965)
Stephen Whitaker (1970)
Allan Dooley (1991)
Michael Elsom (1972)
John Harvey (1973)
Jeremy Cahill (1975)
Roger Giles (1976)
Walter Bealby (1976)
Graham Henson (1976)
Anne Smallwood (1977)
Robin Rowland (1977)
Christopher James (1977)
David Iles (1977)
Kevin O'Donovan (1978)
Rosalind Bush (1978)
Simon Michael (1978)
Alasdair Brough (1979)
Jean Draycott (1980)
Timothy Newman (1981)
Stephanie Brown (1982)
Neil Thompson (1982)
Michael Stephens (1983)
Andrew McGrath (1983)
Satinder Hunjan (1984)
David Stockill (1985)
Richard Lee (1985)
Richard Moat (1985)

Continued overleaf

Members continued:

Ian Dove (1986)
Lorna Meyer (1986)
Bernard Thorogood (1986)
Mark Heywood (1986)
Simon Drew (1987)
Anthony Crean (1987)
Eugene Hickey (1988)
Caroline Baker (1988)
Joanna Chadwick (1988)
Ekwall Singh Tiwana (1988)
Ian Bridge (1988)
Sara Williams (1989)
Malcolm Duthie (1989)
Martin Liddiard (1989)
Becket Bedford (1989)
Gary Bell (1989)
Douglas Armstrong (1990)
Michael Anning (1990)
Melanie McDonald (1990)
Ashley Wynne (1990)
Mary Bennett (1990)
Andrew Baker (1990)
Mark Radburn (1991)
Michele Friel (1991)
Jennifer Jones (1991)
Marion Wilson (1991)
Howard Reid (1991)
Hugh O'Brien-Quinn (1992)
David Park (1992)
Peter Goatley (1992)
Nicholas Xydias (1992)
Marc Wilkinson (1992)
Nicola Preston (1992)
Hugh Richards (1992)
Isabel Hitching (1992)
David Taylor (1993)
Sarah Clover (1993)
Nageena Khalique (1994)
Rachael Price (1994)
Robert Smallwood (1994)
Rachel Cotter (1994)
Joanne Duffy (1994)
Anthony Potter (1994)
Victoria Green (1994)
Peter Collie (1994)
Satnam Choongh (1994)
Anna Diamond (1995)
David Mitchell (1995)
Naomi Gilchrist (1996)
Jeremy Wright (1996)
Emma Hogan (1996)
Michael Walsh (1996)
Talbir Singh (1997)
Sally Hancox (1996)
Tim Mayer (1997)
Karl Hirst (1997)
Christopher Young (1997)
Richard Hadley (1997)
Joanne Wallbanks (1997)
Harbinder Lally (1997)
Tarlowchan Dubb (1997)
Matthew Brunning (1997)
Beth Coll (1997)
Moira Phillips (1989)
Alexander Stein (1998)
Jamie Gamble (1999)
Louisa Denning (1999)
Tessa Hargreaves (1999)
Charles Crow (1999)
Jonathan Barclay (1999)
Raza Mithani (2000)

The Chambers: Chambers have six specialist practice groups, each with its own membership, group identity and Head of Group. This enables them to offer genuine expertise in all main areas of work. The younger tenants usually gain experience from several disciplines until their particular field of expertise is ascertained, at which point they will join one of the established specialist groups. The six specialist groups are: personal injury and clinical negligence; crime and licensing; commercial and chancery; planning and environment; family; and employment. 5 Fountain Court offers unrivalled facilities for its clients, including 11 purpose-built dedicated conference rooms; a video-conference studio capable of providing both national and international video conference links; a large arbitration room; and a seminar suite, capable of seating 40 delegates.

Set No.
165 **NO.6 FOUNTAIN COURT** (Roger Smith QC)

6 Fountain Court, Steelhouse Lane, Birmingham, B4 6DR **Tel:** (0121) 233 3282 **Fax:** (0121) 236 3600 **DX:** 16076 **Email:** clerks@sixfountain.co.uk

Set No.
166 **ST. IVE'S CHAMBERS** (Julia Macur QC)

St. Ive's Chambers, Whittall Street, Birmingham, B4 6DH **Tel:** (0121) 236 0863 **Fax:** (0121) 236 6961 **DX:** 16072 Birmingham **Email:** stives.chambers@btinternet.com **Website:** www.stiveschambers.co.uk

Set No.
167 **ST PHILIP'S CHAMBERS** (John Randall QC)

55 Temple Row, Birmingham, B2 5LS
Tel: (0121) 246 7000 **Fax:** (0121) 246 7001 **DX:** 723240 BIRMINGHAM 56
Email: clerks@st-philips.co.uk **Website:** www.st-philips.co.uk

Head of Chambers	John Randall QC
Deputy Head of Chambers	William Davis
Chief Executive	Paul Wilson
Clerks	Matthew Fleming
	Clive Witcomb
	Richard Fowler
	David Partridge
	Jenny Culligan
	Su Gilbert
	Marguerite Lawrence
	Claire Meyrick
	Joe Wilson
Administrator	Linda Taylor
Tenants	91

Members:

Rex Tedd QC (1970) (QC-1993) + †
John Randall QC (1978) (QC-1995) +
Heather Swindells QC (1974) (QC-1995) + †
William Davis QC (1975) (QC-1998) +
James Corbett QC (1975) (QC-1999) +
Jeremy Cousins QC (1977) (QC-1999) +
Michael Garrett (1967)
Brian Healy (1967)
John Price (1969) +
Peter Clarke (1970)
Douglas Readings (1972) +
Graham Cliff (1973) +
James Quirke (1974)
Timothy Jones (1975)
Guy Spollon (1976)
Andrew Neaves (1977)
William Pusey (1977)
Morris Cooper (1979)
James Burbidge (1979) +
Simon Clegg (1980)
Martine Kushner (1980)
Stephen Thomas (1980)
Roger Dyer (1980)
David Worster (1980)

Members continued:

Makhan Shoker (1981)
David Hershman (1981)
Nergis-Anne Matthew (1981)
Stephen Campbell (1982)
Kevin Hegarty (1982)
John Edwards (1983)
Peter Haynes (1983)
Lawrence Messling (1983) ‡
Petar Starcevic (1983)
Thomas Rochford (1984)
Avtar Khangure (1985) +
Samantha Powis (1985)
Mohammed Zaman (1985)
Christopher Adams (1986)
Nicolas Cartwright (1986)
Gareth Walters (1986)
Lorna Findlay (1987)
Lance Ashworth (1987) *
Elizabeth McGrath (1987)
Alastair Smail (1987)
Conrad Rumney (1988)
Lawrence Watts (1988)
Alison Cook (1989)
Ailsa Cox (1989)
Mark Knowles (1989)
Edward Pepperall (1989)
Amarjit Rai (1989)
Simon Davis (1990)
John Robotham (1990)
Edmund Beever (1990)
Philip Capon (1990)
Vanessa Meachin (1990)
Andrew Lockhart (1991)
Lisa Evans (1991)
Sarah George (1991)
Robert Grierson (1991)
Robin Lewis (1991)
Glyn Samuel (1991)
Claire Starkie (1991)
Hugh Williams (1992) ‡
John de Waal (1992)
Julie Moseley (1992)
Katherine Tucker (1993)
Anthony Verduyn (1993)
Simon Fox (1994)
David Maxwell (1994)
Jane Owens (1994) ‡
Elizabeth Walker (1994)
Angus Burden (1994)
Rosalyn Carter (1994)
Andrew Charman (1994) ‡
Darron Whitehead (1995)
Brian Dean (1994)
David Tyack (1994)
Alistair MacDonald (1995)
Louise McCabe (1996)
James Morgan (1996)
Claire Cunningham (1996)
Huw Jones (1997)
Alastair Young (1997)
Tracey Lloyd-Nesling (1998)
Alistair Wyvill (1998)
Elizabeth Hodgetts (1998)
Barbara Caulfield (1999)
Shakhil Najib (1999)
Jane Sarginson (2000)
Andrew McFarlane QC (1977) (QC-1998) *
Anna-Rose Landes (1986)
Aubrey Craig (1987) *
Philip Le Cornu (1992)
Karen Leason (1997) *
Jennifer Josephs ¶
Jonathan Nosworthy ¶
Edmund Williams ¶

* Door Tenant + Recorder † Deputy High Court Judge ‡ Formerly a practising solicitor ¶ Pupil

The Chambers: The client's professional needs are always met by individually tailored service, which is rooted in traditional practices and wedded to modern approaches. This results in a highly successful set which is one of the largest and most progressive in the country. Chambers are housed in wholly refurbished premises, providing the best of modern facilities: well-appointed conference rooms, a large arbitration room, a first class library and full IT capabilities. Innovation geared towards an effective and professional client service lies at the heart of St Philip's Chambers' ethos.

Work Undertaken: Specialist groups are established in chancery and commercial; criminal law; employment and discrimination law; family law; personal injury and clinical negligence; property planning and public law. St Philip's also provides expertise in a very wide range of other subjects including licensing and general common law.

Set No. 68

VICTORIA CHAMBERS (Lee Masters)

Victoria Chambers, 177 Corporation St, Birmingham, B4 6RG
Tel: (0121) 236 9900 or 236 7863 **Fax:** (0121) 233 0675 **DX:** 23520 Birmingham 3
Email: clerks@victoriachambers.co.uk **Website:** www.victoriachambers.co.uk

Head of Chambers	Lee Masters
Senior Clerk	Lisa Clarke
Assistant Clerk	Patricia Venables
Tenants	20

Members:

Lee Masters (1984)
Stephen Migdal (1974)
David Pearson (1983)
Andrew Dickens (1983)
Julie Slater (1988)
Gary Cook (1989)
John Smart (1989)
Dorothy Thomas (1991)
Pauline Bennet (1991)
Catherine Rowlands (1992)
Tracy Lakin (1993)
Kate Thomas (1994)
Patricia Hawthorne (1995)
Oliver Woolhouse (1996)
Sara Pratt (1996)
Andrew Willetts (1999)
Nicola Beese (1998)
Harjinder Johal (1998)
Gurbinder Dosanjh (1998)
Simon Perkins (1999)

The Chambers: An established common law set handling all areas of criminal and civil litigation. Specialist teams deal with family; crime; personal injury; employment/immigration; civil litigation and housing law before all tribunals. Chambers promise a 14 day turnaround for paperwork. Chambers have new premises available for conferences, lectures and training. Members of chambers are always willing to travel to meet lay or professional clients.

Work Undertaken: Crime; family; civil litigation; housing; judicial review; personal injury and professional negligence; chancery.

Bradford

Set No.
169 **BROADWAY HOUSE** (J Graham K Hyland QC)

Broadway House, 9 Bank St, Bradford, BD1 1TW
Tel: (01274) 722560 **Fax:** (01274) 370708 **DX:** 11746
Email: clerks@broadwayhouse.co.uk **Website:** www.broadwayhouse.co.uk

Head of Chambers	J Graham K Hyland QC
Practice Manager	Matthew Clarke
Tenants	30

Members:

J Graham K Hyland QC (1978) (QC-1998)
Martin Wood (1973)
John Topham (1970)
Roger Thomas QC (1976) (QC-2000)
Ian Newbon (1977)
David Kelly (1980)
Gordon Shelton (1981)
Jonathan Gibson (1982)
DA McGonigal (1982)
David Jones (1985)
Peter Birkby (1987)
Ian Howard (1987)
Simon Myers (1987)
Nicholas Askins (1989)
Sophie Drake (1990)
Mark Fletton (1990)
Stephen Wood (1991)
Tahir. Khan (1986)
J Ben Crosland (1992)
Gerald Hendron (1992)
Michelle Colborne (1993)
Julia Nelson (1993)
Jayne Chaplain (1995)
Nicola Peers (1996)
Camille Morland (1996)
Robert Blantern (1996)
Simon Anderson (1997)
Ian Brown (1971)
Tasaddat Hussain (1998)
Ian Miller (1999)
David Mitchell (1972) *
Jonathan Cannan (1989) *
Aisha Jamil (1995) *

* Door Tenant

The Chambers: Broadway House Chambers is a long established set within 200 yards of the city's Combined Court Centre. In April 1999, chambers also opened further fully staffed premises at 31 Park Square, Leeds.

Work Undertaken: General common law; commercial; Chancery; family and crime. Civil work includes contract, commercial, personal injuries, professional negligence, matrimonial property and finance, employment, immigration, landlord and tenant, real property and income and capital taxation. Criminal work includes all aspects of prosecution and defence work mostly in the North East Circuit.

International: French, German, Hindi, Punjabi, and Urdu.

Brighton

Set No.
170 **CROWN OFFICE ROW CHAMBERS** (Robert Seabrook QC)

Blenheim House, 119-120 Church Street, Brighton, BN1 1WH
Tel: (01273) 625625 **Fax:** (01273) 698888 **DX:** 36670 Brighton 2
Email: clerks@1cor.com **Website:** www.1cor.com

Head of Chambers	Robert Seabrook QC
Chambers Director	Bob Wilson
Senior Clerk	Matthew Phipps
Clerks (Brighton)	Jenny Lewis
	Matthew Archer
Tenants	21

Members:

Robert Seabrook QC (1964) (QC-1983)
Anthony Niblett (1976)
James King-Smith (1980)
Paul Ashwell (1977)
Christopher Smyth (1972)
Jacqueline Ross (1985)
Adam Smith (1987)
Timothy Bergin (1987)
Paul Rogers (1989)
Keeley Bishop (1990)
Martin Downs (1990)
Jeremy Cave (1992)
Ian Bugg (1992)
Darren Howe (1992)
Simon Sinnatt (1993)
Rachael Claridge (1996)
Richard Balchin (1997)
William Cloherty (1997)
Robert Hall (1997)
Pegah Sharghy (1998)
Jane Peckham (1999)

The Chambers: Chambers have been in Brighton for nearly 30 years as an Annexe of 1 Crown Office Row, a long-established common law set in the Temple which has maintained strong Sussex connections for nearly half a century. Members practise from centrally located modern premises which doubled in size in 2001 to accommodate the set's rapid growth. Chambers are equipped with modern computer technology and direct telephone and computer links to 1 Crown Office Row. Conference and seminar facilities are excellent. The Brighton County and Magistrates' Courts are a few minutes walk away.

Work Undertaken: Chambers undertake all types of general common law work - civil, criminal and family. Particular expertise can be offered in the areas of professional negligence, personal injury, landlord and tenant, building, employment, licensing and all types of family proceedings.

Recruitment: Please apply to Miss Keeley Bishop for pupillages in Brighton.

Bristol

Set No.
171 **ALBION CHAMBERS** (Charles Barton QC & Neil Ford QC)

Albion Chambers, Broad St, Bristol, BS1 1DR
Tel: (0117) 927 2144 **Fax:** (0117) 926 2569 **DX:** 7822

Head of Chambers	Charles Barton QC
	Neil Ford QC
Director of Client Services	D.H. Milsom
Senior Clerk (Criminal)	Bonnie Colbeck
Senior Clerk (Civil/Family)	Michael Harding
Junior Clerk (Criminal)	Nicholas Jeanes
Junior Clerk (Civil/Family)	Paul Taylor
Fees Clerks	Lesley Carpenter
	Rosemarie Blanshard
Tenants	45

Members:

Charles Barton QC (1969) (QC-1989)
James Tabor QC (1974) (QC-1995)
Neil Ford QC (1976) (QC-1997)
Stephen Wildblood QC (1981) (QC-1999)
Christopher Jervis (1966)
Timothy Hills (1968)
Nicholas O'Brien (1968)
David Spens (1972)
Nicholas Fridd (1975)
Martin Steen (1976)
William Hart (1979)
John Geraint Norris (1980)
Michael Mather-Lees (1981)
Martin Picton (1981)
Tacey Cronin (1982)
Julian Lambert (1983)
Caroline Wright (1983)
Ignatius Hughes (1986)
Stephen Mooney (1987)
Charles Hyde (1988)
Deborah Dinan-Hayward (1988)
Claire Wills-Goldingham (1988)
Myles Watkins (1990)
John Livesey (1990)
Caroline Ralph (1990)
Alexander Ralton (1990)
Virginia Cornwall (1990)
Nkumbe Ekaney (1990)
Claire Rowsell (1991)
Michael Cullum (1991)
Michael Fitton (1991)
Fiona Elder (1991)
Nicholas Sproull (1992)
Simon Burns (1992)
Paul Cook (1992)
Allan Fuller (1993)
Jason Taylor (1995)
Richard English (1996)
Daniel Leafe (1996)
Kirsty Real (1996)
Archna Dawar (1996)
James Wilson-Smith (1999)
Charlotte Pitts (1999)
Samuel Butterfield (1999)
Jon Holmes (1999)
Christopher Wilson-Smith QC (1965) (QC-1986) *
Paul Dunkels QC (1972) (QC-1993) *

* Door Tenant

The Chambers: A large and still expanding set, the members of which handle a wide variety of specialist legal areas.

Set No.
172 **ASSIZE COURT CHAMBERS** (John Isherwood)
Assize Court Chambers, 14 Small St, Bristol, BS1 1DE **Tel:** (0117) 926 4587 **Fax:** (0117) 922 6835 **DX:** 78134 **Email:** chambers@assize-court-chambers.co.uk **Website:** www.assize-court-chambers.co.uk

Set No.
173 **GUILDHALL CHAMBERS** (Adrian Palmer QC)

Guildhall Chambers, Broad Street, Bristol, BS1 2HG
Tel: (0117) 927 3366 **Fax:** (0117) 930 3800 **DX:** 7823
Email: info@guildhallchambers.co.uk

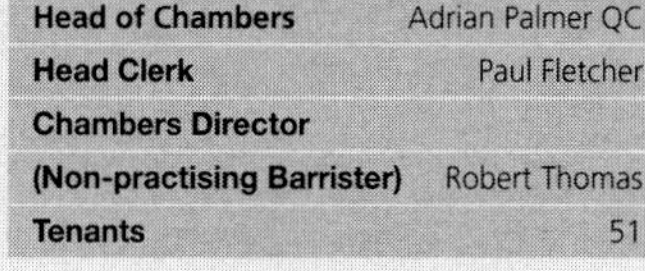

Head of Chambers	Adrian Palmer QC
Head Clerk	Paul Fletcher
Chambers Director	
(Non-practising Barrister)	Robert Thomas
Tenants	51

Members:

John Royce QC (1970) (QC-1987)
Adrian Palmer QC (1972) (QC-1992)
Ian Glen QC (1973) (QC-1996)
Stephen Davies QC (1983) (QC-2000)
Richard Smith QC (1986) (QC-2001)
Christopher Gosland (1966)
George Newsom (1973)
Adam Chippindall (1975)
Peter Barrie (1976)
Ian Charles Fenny (1978)
Brian Watson (1978)
Ian Pringle (1979)
Malcolm Warner (1979)
James Townsend (1980)
Catriona Duthie (1981)
Ralph Wynne-Griffiths (1981)
John Virgo (1983)
Peter Blair (1983)
Andrew Langdon (1986)
Raj Sahonte (1986)
Martha Maher (1987)
Ray Tully (1988)
James Patrick (1989)
Jeremy Bamford (1989)
Paul French (1989)
Robert Davies (1990)
Stephen Dent (1991)
Kerry Barker (1972)
Anthony Reddiford (1991)
Louise Price (1972)
Euan Ambrose (1992)
Christopher Quinlan (1992)
Gerard McMeel (1993) †
Nicholas Miller (1994)
Mark Worsley (1994)
Matthew Wales (1994)
Gabriel Farmer (1994)
Victoria Hufford (1994)
Nicholas Briggs (1994)
Andrew Macfarlane (1995)
Richard Ascroft (1995)
James Hassall (1995)
Rosaleen Collins (1996)
Anna Vigars (1996)
Ramin Pakrooh (1996)

Continued overleaf

Members continued:

Rhys Taylor (1996)
Ewan Paton (1997)
Zira Hussain (1998)
Hugh Sims (1999)
Matthew Porter-Bryant (1999)
Katherine Gibb (1999)

† Associate member

The Chambers: An established set with a modern outlook. Work undertaken includes insolvency/company; professional negligence; commercial/bank recovery; personal injury; property; crime and family.

Set No.
174 **OLD SQUARE CHAMBERS** (John Hendy QC)

Hanover House, 47 Corn Street, Bristol, BS1 1HT
Tel: (0117) 927 7111 **Fax:** (0117) 927 3478 **DX:** 78229 Bristol
Email: clerks@oldsquarechambers.co.uk **Website:** www.oldsquarechambers.co.uk

Head of Chambers	John Hendy QC
Senior Clerk	John Taylor
Tenants	47

OLD SQUARE CHAMBERS

Members:

John Hendy QC (1972) (QC-1987)
John Melville Williams QC (1955) (QC-1977)
Frederic Reynold QC (1960) (QC-1982)
John Hand QC (1972) (QC-1988)
Lord Wedderburn QC (1953) (QC-1990)
Jeremy McMullen QC (1971) (QC-1994)
Ian Truscott QC (1995) (QC-1997)
David Wilby QC (1974) (QC-1998)
Matthias Kelly QC (1979) (QC-1999)
Charles Lewis (1963)
Christopher Carling (1969)
William Birtles (1970)
Diana Brahams (1972)
John H. Bates (1973)
Christopher Makey (1975)
Nigel Cooksley (1975)
Charles Pugh (1975)
Toby Kempster (1980)
Paul Rose (1981)
Jane McNeill (1982)
Mark Sutton (1982)
Barry Cotter (1985)
Louise Chudleigh (1987)
Ijeoma Omambala (1989)
Jennifer Eady (1989)
Philip Mead (1989)
Damian Brown (1989)
Tess Gill (1990)
Jonathan Clarke (1990)
Christopher Walker (1990)
Nicholas Booth (1991)
Sarah Moor (1991)
Ian Scott (1991)
Oliver Segal (1992)
Helen Gower (1992)
Roy Lewis (1992)
Mark Whitcombe (1994)
Elizabeth Melville (1994)
Melanie Tether (1995)
Emma Smith (1995)
Rohan Pirani (1995)
Rebecca Tuck (1998)
Hilary Winstone (1998)
Steven Langton (1998)
Stuart Brittenden (1999)
Anya Palmer (1999)
Daniel Bennett (2000)

The Chambers: Also at: 1 Verulam Buildings, Gray's Inn, London WC1R 5LQ DX: 1046 Chancery Lane/London. Tel: (020) 7269 0300 Fax: (020) 7405 1387.

Work Undertaken: Employment law, personal injury, clinical negligence, product liability and health and safety compliance law, environmental law and sports law (see London entry for more details).

International: Work is handled in French, German, Ibo, Italian and Spanish. There are door tenants practising at the Hong Kong, Bermuda and Jersey Bars. Tenants are also members of the Scottish and Northern Irish Bars. John Hendy QC is a member of the NSW and Australian High Court.

Set No.
175 **QUEEN SQUARE CHAMBERS** (Anthony Donne QC & T Alun Jenkins QC)
Queen Square Chambers, 56 Queen Square, Bristol, BS1 4PR **Tel:** (0117) 921 1966 **Fax:** (0117) 927 6493 **DX:** 7870 Bristol
Email: civil@qs-c.co.uk/crime@qs-c.co.uk

Set No.
176

ST JOHN'S CHAMBERS (Christopher Sharp QC)

Civil Department, St John's Chambers, Small St, Bristol, BS1 1DW
Tel: (0117) 921 3456 **Fax:** (0117) 929 4821 **DX:** 78138
Email: clerks@stjohnschambers.co.uk **Website:** www.stjohnschambers.co.uk

Head of Chambers	Christopher Sharp QC
Chief Executive	Kate Blackburn
Senior Clerk (Civil)	Dick Hyde
Senior Clerk (Family/Civil)	Maureen Rowe
Senior Clerk (Crime)	Annette Moles
Tenants	57

Members:

Christopher Sharp QC (1975) (QC-1999)
Nigel Hamilton QC (1965) (QC-1981)
Martin Mann QC (1968) (QC-1983)
Roger Kaye QC (1970) (QC-1989)
Roderick Denyer QC (1970) (QC-1990)
David Fletcher (1971)
George Threlfall (1972)
Paul Grumbar (1974)
Ian Bullock (1975)
Nicholas Marston (1975)
Timothy Grice (1975)
Sheelagh Corfield (1975)
Mark Horton (1976)
John Blackmore (1983)
Michael Longman (1978)
Richard Stead (1979)
Robert Duval (1979)
Ralph Dixon (1980)
Susan Jacklin (1980)
Charles Auld (1980)
Peter Wadsley (1984)
Ian Dixey (1984)
Richard Bromilow (1977)
Leslie Blohm (1982)
Susan Hunter (1985)
Glyn Edwards (1987)
Graham Howard (1987)
Lynne Matthews (1987)
Simon Morgan (1988)
Louise O'Neill (1989)
Jean Corston (1991)
Neil Levy (1986)
Guy Adams (1989)
Susan Evans (1989)
Andrew Marsden (1994)
Kamala Das (1975)
Derek O'Sullivan (1990)
John Sharples (1992)
Dianne Martin (1992)
Roy Light (1992)
Christine Bateman (1992)
Edward Burgess (1993)
Kathryn Skellorn (1993)
David Maunder (1993)
Andrew McLaughlin (1993)
Jacqueline Humphreys (1994)
David Regan (1994)
John Dickinson (1995)
Giles Nelson (1995)
Judi Evans (1996)
Simon Goodman (1996)
Matthew White (1997)
Rupert Lowe (1998)
Kambiz Moradifar (1998)
Emma Zeb (1998)
Alex Troup (1998)
Nigel Lowe (1972) †

† Associate Member

The Chambers: Chambers offer a specialised and expert service on a departmental basis: chancery and commercial, personal injury, family and criminal law, with particular expertise in commercial, insolvency, revenue law, banking, local government work, professional negligence, construction, planning, licensing, environmental and employment matters. Chambers' criminal department is located at St John's Chambers, St Bartholomew's Court, Bristol BS1 5BT, Tel: (0117) 910 0700 Fax: (0117) 910 0701.

Cambridge

Set No.
177

FENNERS CHAMBERS (Lindsay Davies)

Fenners Chambers, 3 Madingley Road, Cambridge, CB3 0EE
Tel: (01223) 368761 **Fax:** (01223) 313007 **DX:** 5809 Cambridge 1
Email: clerks@fennerschambers.co.uk **Website:** www.fennerschambers.co.uk

Head of Chambers	Lindsay Davies
Tenants	30

Members:

Lindsay Davies (1975) +
Kenneth Wheeler (1956) *
Geraint Jones (1972)
Oliver Sells QC (1972) (QC-1995) * +
Andrew Gore (1973)
Stephen Franklin (1974)
Susan Espley (1976)
Caroline Pointon (1976)
Oliver Heald (1977)
Simon Tattersall (1977)
Paul Leigh-Morgan (1978)
Tim Brown (1980)
Paul Hollow (1981)
Andrew Gordon-Saker (1981)
Stuart Bridge (1981) *
Martin Collier (1982)
Liza Gordon-Saker (1982)
Meryl Hughes (1987)
George Foxwell (1987)
Alasdair Wilson (1988)
Clive Pithers (1989)
Jeffrey Deegan (1989)
Andrew Taylor (1989)
Sally Hobson (1991)
Caroline Horton (1993)
Katharine Ferguson (1995)
William Josling (1995)
Daniel Pitt (1995)
Mike Magee (1997)
Roderick Spinks (1997)
George Keightley (1997)
Giles Surman (1997) *
Alasdair Foster (1998)
Martin Kingerley (1999)

* Door Tenant + Recorder

The Chambers: An established East of England set, occupying extensive premises with on-site parking and full disabled access. See also Chambers entry for Peterborough.

Work Undertaken: Chambers operate through six specialist teams: business; crime; employment; family; personal injury; property, planning, local government and environment.

Canterbury

Set No. 178

BECKET CHAMBERS

17 New Dover Road, Canterbury, CT1 3AS
Tel: (01227) 786331 **Fax:** (01227) 786329 **DX:** 5330 Canterbury
Email: clerks@becket-chambers.co.uk **Website:** www.becket-chambers.co.uk

Senior Clerk	Julie Lewis-MacKay
Tenants	10

Members:

Philip Newton (1984)
Ronald Edginton (1984)
Kevin Jackson (1984)
Christopher Wall (1987)
Corey Mills (1987)
Jeremy Hall (1988)
Clive Styles (1990)
Paul Tapsell (1991)
Louisa Adamson (1994)
Nicholas Fairbank (1996)
Lionel Swift QC (1959) (QC-1975) *
John Bishop (1970) *

* Door Tenant

The Chambers: Becket Chambers are located only a few minutes drive from the local courts and the city centre. There is a dedicated conference facility, and a large private car park.

Work Undertaken: Chambers undertake all aspects of general common law and criminal work. Members specialise in the following areas: children and family proceedings; matrimonial finance and family provision; medical and professional negligence; personal injury; bankruptcy and insolvency; employment; sale of goods; consumer credit; housing; landlord and tenant; local government; and crime. The senior clerk will be happy to provide further details on any aspect upon request.

International: Work is also handled in French.

Cardiff

Set No. 179

9 PARK PLACE (Ian Murphy QC)

9 Park Place, Cardiff, CF1 3DP
Tel: (029) 2038 2731 **Fax:** (029) 2022 2542 **DX:** 50751 Cardiff 2
Website: www.9parkplace.co.uk

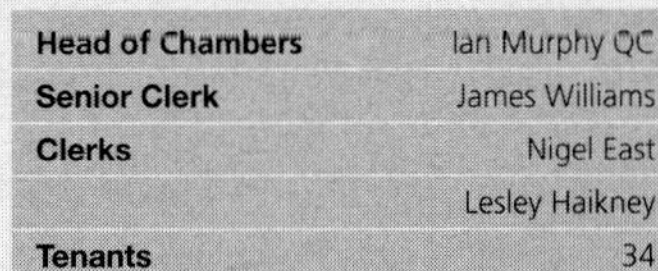

Head of Chambers	Ian Murphy QC
Senior Clerk	James Williams
Clerks	Nigel East
	Lesley Haikney
Tenants	34

Members:

Ian Murphy QC (1972) (QC-1992)
Roger Thomas QC (1969) (QC-1994)
Nicholas Cooke QC (1977) (QC-1998)
Philip Rees (1965)
Martyn Kelly (1972)
Gregg Taylor QC (1974) (QC-2001)
Richard Francis (1974)
David Essex Williams (1975)
Geraint Jones QC (1976) (QC-2001)
Richard Twomlow (1976)
Keith Thomas (1977)
Isabel Parry (1979)
Ieuan Morris (1979)
Milwyn Jarman QC (1980) (QC-2001)
Karl Williams (1982)
Janet McDonald (1985)
Paul Hopkins (1985)
Owen Prys Lewis (1985)
Susan Ferrier (1985)
Andrew Keyser (1986)
Peter Brooks (1986)
Emily Davies (1989)
Julian Reed (1991)
Steven Donoghue (1992)
Hugh Wallace (1993)
David Elias (1994)
Owen Thomas (1994)
Gwydion Hughes (1994)
Peter Davies (1996)
Heath Edwards (1996)
Lisa Thomas (1998)
Matthew Cobbe (1998)
Emyr Jones (1999)
Elizabeth Pearson (1999)

The Chambers: A long established set of chambers, offering varied legal services. Several members of chambers also practise from Farrar's Building, Temple. Members undertake a broad range of work, although each has particular areas of specialisation. Former members of chambers include a Lord Justice of Appeal and several circuit judges. Several members of chambers are fluent in Welsh.

Work Undertaken: Specialisations include criminal, personal injury, professional negligence, chancery, planning, commercial, family and employment.

Set No.
180

30 PARK PLACE (David Phillips QC & John Jenkins QC)

30 Park Place, Cardiff, CF1 3BA
Tel: (029) 2039 8421 **Fax:** (029) 2039 8725 **DX:** 50756 Cardiff 2
Email: clerk@30parkplace.law.co.uk

Head of Chambers	David Phillips QC
	John Jenkins QC
Senior Clerk	Huw Davies
Practice Manager	Gwyn Lloyd
Tenants	44

Members:

John Jenkins QC (1970) (QC-1990)
Malcolm Bishop QC (1968) (QC-1993)
Peter Griffiths QC (1970) (QC-1995)
John Venmore (1971)
Andrew Green (1974)
Gregory Bull (1976)
Jane Crowley QC (1976) (QC-1998)
Paul Hartley-Davies (1977)
Marian Lewis (1977)
James Tillyard (1978)
Huw Davies QC (1978) (QC-2001)
Jonathan Furness (1979)
Peter Murphy (1980)
Lloyd Williams (1981)
Paul Lewis QC (1981) (QC-2001)
Mark Allen (1981)
Helen Mifflin (1982)
Ieuan Rees (1982)
Rhodri Williams (1987)
Ruth Henke (1987)
Robert Harrison (1988)
Mair Coombes-Davies (1988)
Peter Heywood (1988)
Joanne Barnett (1989)
Jonathan Austin (1992)
Robert Buckland (1991)
Catherine Louise Heyworth (1991)
Catrin John (1992)
Kate Hughes (1992)
Harry Baker (1992)
Eugene Egan (1993)
Elizabeth McGahey (1994)
Caroline Rees (1994)
Michael Jones (1995)
Hywel Hughes (1995)
Andrew Jones (1996)
Thomas Williams (1996)
Harriet Edmondson (1997)
Ben Davies (1999)
Sarah Waters (1999)
Rachel Knight (2000)
Matthew Lewis (2000)
Stuart McLeese (2000)
Natalie Sandercock (2000)
Patrick Harrington QC (1973) (QC-1993) *
Patrick Curran QC (1972) (QC-1995) *
David Phillips QC (1976) (QC-1997) *
William Rees (1973) *
Simon Picken (1989) *
Richard Hermer (1993) *
Shamini Jayanathan (1996) *
Vivienne Harpwood (1969) †

* Door Tenant † Academic Member

The Chambers: 30 Park Place is committed to continuing development and aims to provide a skilled and professional service whilst remaining approachable, flexible and accessible. It has full disabled access and facilities.

Work Undertaken: A wide variety of work is undertaken with members working in teams. Direct Professional Access work is accepted. The specialist areas are administrative and public law (including public procurements); childcare; commercial law; employment law; planning, building and environment; crime; family law; personal injury (including clinical negligence).

Recruitment: Chambers operate an award scheme.

Set No.
181

33 PARK PLACE (John Charles Rees QC)

33 Park Place, Cardiff, CF10 3TN
Tel: (029) 2023 3313 **Fax:** (029) 2022 8294 **DX:** 50755 Cardiff 2
Email: clerks@33parkplace.co.uk **Website:** www.33parkplace.co.uk

Head of Chambers	John Charles Rees QC
Senior Clerk	Graham Barrett
Clerks	Stephen Price
	Sandra Williams
Tenants	33

Members:

John Charles Rees QC (1972) (QC-1991)
Neil Bidder QC (1976) (QC-1998)
Mary Parry Evans (1953)
Roger Garfield (1965)
Charles Cook (1966)
Richard Jones (196[illegible]
Nicholas G Jones (1970)
Charles Parsley (1973)
Colin Davies (1973)
Bryan Thomas (1979)
Jill Mary Walters (1979)
Jonathan Walters (1984)
Timothy Evans (1984)
Jeremy Jenkins (1984)
Andrew Taylor (1984)
Theodore Huckle (1985)
Graham Walters (1986)
Nicholas D Jones (1987)
Ieuan Bennett (1989)
Robert O'Leary (1990)
Alan Troy (1990)
Michael Brace (1991)
Gareth Jones (1991)
Lucy Higginson (1992)
Nicola Harris (1992)
Daniel Williams (1992)
Nigel Osborne (1993)
Helen Edwards (1995)
Andrew Arentsen (1995)
Christopher L Rees (1996)
Joan Campbell (1996)
Simon John (1998)
David Callow (1998)
Heather Pope (1977) †

† Associate Member

Continued overleaf

The Chambers: A leading set of many years' standing. Accommodation is substantial and well furbished and includes a well stocked library, conference rooms (including a disabled conference room) and all other necessary facilities. It is fully equipped with the most up-to-date technology. A chambers brochure is available on request. Several members of chambers are fluent in Welsh.

Work Undertaken: Members of chambers practise across a broad range of legal areas including commercial and company law; criminal law, employment law, family law; judicial review; landlord and tenant; local government; Official Referee's business; personal injury, planning; professional negligence; property; tribunal work; trusts, wills and probate. Particular expertise can be offered in the following areas:
Crime: All areas of criminal work including fraud.
Personal Injury (inc. Clinical Negligence): A well deserved reputation has been acquired over many years. A dedicated Conditional Fees team has been set up.
Family: The family team has recently been strengthened by the addition of established practitioners.
Public Law: A team has been put in place to deal with this rapidly growing area of work.

Set No.
182 **TEMPLE CHAMBERS** (David J.M. Aubrey QC)
32 Park Place, Cardiff, CF1 3BA **Tel:** (029) 2039 7364 **Fax:** (029) 2023 8423 **DX:** 50769 Cardiff 2

Chester

Set No.
183 **NICHOLAS STREET CHAMBERS** (Robert Trevor-Jones)
22 Nicholas Street, Chester, CH1 2NX **Tel:** (01244) 323886 **Fax:** (01244) 347732 **DX:** 22154

Set No.
184 **SEDAN HOUSE** (Meirion Lewis-Jones)
Sedan House, Stanley Place, Chester, CH1 2LU
Tel: (01244) 348282 **Fax:** (01244) 342336 **DX:** 19984

Head of Chambers	Meirion Lewis-Jones
Senior Clerk	Gavin James Reeves
Practice Manager	Angela Malcolmson
Tenants	25

Common law and criminal chambers with some members specialising in planning, chancery, landlord and tenant, agricultural holdings, trade descriptions, local government, licensing, matrimonial, employment, personal injury, commercial contract and civil.

Chichester

Set No.
185 **CHICHESTER CHAMBERS** (Michael Beckman QC)
12 North Pallant, Chichester, PO19 1TQ
Tel: (01243) 784538 **Fax:** (01243) 780861 **DX:** 30303 Chichester
Email: clerks@chichesterchambers.law.co.uk

Head of Chambers	Michael Beckman QC
Senior Clerk	Alister Williams
Tenants	24

Members:
Michael Beckman QC (1954) (QC-1976)
Bernard Weatherill QC (1974) (QC-1996) †
Charles Taylor (1974)LLB Hons
Lucinda Davis (1981)LLB Hons
Wendy Rowlinson (1981)BA Hons
Orlando Gibbons (1982) †
Roger Mullis (1987)BA (Oxon) †
Clifford Darton (1988)BA (Oxon)
Colin Morgan (1989)BA (Oxon)
Adam Deacock (1991)BA (Oxon) †
Mary Loosemore (1992)BSc Hons ‡
William Emerson (1992)LLB (Hons)
Portia Spears (1992)BA (Oxon)
Simon Hamilton (1992)BA (Oxon)
Rosein Magee (1994)BA Hons
Emma Burgess (1995)LLB Hons
Fraser Mogridge (1995)LLB Hons
Beverley Cherrill (1996)LLB Hons
Raj Kothari (1996)BA Hons
Charles Barker (1997)BA Hons †
Nerys Wyn Rees (1997)LLB Hons
Andrew Selby (1997)BA Hons
Claire Sparrow (1997)MA Hons
Sarah Earley (1998)LLB Hons

† Associate Tenant ‡ Former Solicitor

The Chambers: Chichester Chambers continues to expand its provision of specialist advocates to the south of England in its three core areas of family, civil and crime.

Work Undertaken:

Family: The set's seven specialist practitioners cover all aspects of family law, particularly care proceedings and ancillary relief. Chambers is regularly instructed by local authorities and guardian ad litems in both High Court and County Court cases.

Civil: Employment, personal injury, chancery and probate, property, landlord and tenant, insolvency, company, building and contractual disputes.

Crime: Defence and prosecution work undertaken, with specialists in trading standards, health and safety and environment law.

Colchester

Set No.

186 **EAST ANGLIAN CHAMBERS** (Roderick Newton)

52 North Hill, Colchester, CO1 1PY

Tel: (01206) 572756 **Fax:** (01206) 562447 **DX:** 3611

Email: colchesterchambers@dial.pipex.com **Website:** www.ealaw.co.uk

Head of Chambers	Roderick Newton
Senior Clerk	Fraser McLaren
Administrator	Carol Bull (01473) 254559
Tenants	53

Members:

Roderick Newton (1982)
John Akast (1968)
John Wardlow (1971)
Peter Wain (1972)
Andrew Marsden (1975)
Caroline Bryant (1976)
Celia Miller (1978)
David Pugh (1978)
Martyn Levett (1978)
Timothy McLoughlin (1978)
Graham Sinclair (1979)
John Hamey (1979)
Anthony Kefford (1980)
John Brooke-Smith (1981)
Simon Redmayne (1982)
Graham Parnell (1982)
Michael Lane (1983)
Hugh Vass (1983)
Jane Davies (1983)
Lindsay Cox (1984)
Janet Bettle (1985)
Steven Dyble (1986)
Anthony Bate (1987)
Nicholas Elcombe (1987)
Rebecca Degel (1987)
Jonathan Seely (1987)
Rosalyne Mandil-Wade (1988)
David Richards (1989)
Andrew Jackson (1990)
Ray Smith (1991)
Katharine Bundell (1991)
Marika Bell (1991)
Jeremy Dugdale (1992)
Carole Parry-Jones (1992)
Dominic Barratt (1992)
Helen Gilbertson (1993)
Amanda Rippon (1993)
Patricia Walsh (1993)
Jacqui Hanlon (1994)
Richard Kelly (1994)
Jude Durr (1995)
Sally Freeman (1995)
Alan Wheetman (1995)
David Wilson (1996)
Fiona Baruah (1996)
Ashley Thain (1996)
Saqib Rauf (1996)
Marc Cannatella (1997)
David Sunman (1997)
Stephen Goodfellow (1997)
Andrew Shaw (1998)
Joanne Bradbury (1999)
Ian Hugh Dyble (2000)

The Chambers: For further information, please see full entry under East Anglian Chambers, Ipswich.

Exeter

Set No.

187 **COLLETON CHAMBERS** (Martin Meeke QC)

Colleton Crescent, Exeter, EX2 4DG **Tel:** (01392) 274898 **Fax:** (01392) 412368 **DX:** 8330 Exeter

Set No.
188 **WALNUT HOUSE** (Paul Dunkels QC)

Walnut House, 63 St. David's Hill, Exeter, EX4 4DW
Tel: (01392) 279751 **Fax:** (01392) 412080 **DX:** 115582 Exeter St. Davids
Email: 106627.2451@compuserve.com

Head of Chambers	Paul Dunkels QC
Senior Clerk	Chris Doe
Tenants	20

Members:

Paul Dunkels QC (1972) (QC-1993)
Jonathan Barnes (1970)
Geoffrey Mercer (1975)
Iain Leadbetter (1975)
Shane Lyon (1976)
Corinne Searle (1982)
Sarah Munro (1984)
Martin Edmunds (1983)
Michael Melville-Shreeve (1986)
Mark Treneer (1987)
Andrew Eaton Hart (1989)
Elizabeth Ingham (1989)
Robert MacRae (1990)
Andrew Oldland (1990)
Sean Brunton (1990)
Simon Laws (1991)
Mary McCarthy (1994)
David Evans (1996)
Adam Vaitilingam (1987)
Hannah Marshall (1998)

The Chambers: Established in 1972, the chambers now have 20 members, including five who sit as recorders. The work of chambers covers the full range of civil and criminal matters in the South West. Brochures are available on request detailing the areas of expertise of members in chambers.

Work Undertaken: Includes construction; courts martial; criminal law; discrimination; employment; family; children; general common law; general Chancery; housing; judicial review; landlord and tenant; licensing; matrimonial; mental health; personal injury; planning; police cases; professional negligence; sale of goods; trusts and wills.

Set No.
189 **SOUTHERNHAY CHAMBERS** (Anthony Ward)

33 Southernhay East, Exeter, EX1 1NX
Tel: (01392) 255777 **Fax:** (01392) 412021 **DX:** 8353 Exeter
Email: southernhay.chambers@lineone.net

Head of Chambers	Anthony Ward
Senior Clerk	Joy Daniell
Tenants	15

Members:

Anthony Ward (1971)
Jeremy Posnansky QC (1972) (QC-1994) *
Alastair Norris QC (1973) (QC-1997) *
George Meredith (1969)
Hugh Lewis (1970)
Robert Alford (1970)
Michael Templeman (1973)
Valentine Le Grice (1977) *
Christopher Naish (1980)
Susan Campbell (1986)
Nicholas Berry (1988)
Rebecca Ogle (1989)
Jacqueline Ahmed (1988)
Deborah Archer (1989)
Emma Crawforth (1992)
Benjamin Winzer (1997)
Heather Burwin (1983)
Stephen Ball (1995)

* Door Tenant

The Chambers: Established in 1975, chambers have 18 members. Its strategy has been one of carefully planned expansion, and it has grown to become one of the leading specialist family/civil sets on the Western Circuit. Brochure and further information on request.

Work Undertaken: Family/Civil. Children Act (public and private law); matrimonial finance; family provision; chancery; equity trusts and wills; landlord & tenant; personal injury; professional negligence; commercial. Conditional Fee Agreements accepted in all civil cases.

Grimsby

Set No.
190 **WILBERFORCE CHAMBERS** (Bernard Gateshill)

2 Abbey Walk, Grimsby, DN31 1NQ
Tel: (01472) 355567

Head of Chambers:	Bernard Gateshill
Tenants:	19

Annexe and conference rooms. See entry for Wilberforce Chambers, Hull.

Hull

Set No. 191

WILBERFORCE CHAMBERS (Bernard Gateshill)

Wilberforce Chambers, 7 Bishop Lane, Hull, HU1 1PA
Tel: (01482) 323264 **Fax:** (01482) 325533 **DX:** 11940
Email: clerks@hullbar.demon.co.uk **Website:** www.hullbar.demon.co.uk

Head of Chambers	Bernard Gateshill
Senior Clerk	Frances Sheard
Practice Manager	Phillip Paxton
Tenants	19

Members:

Bernard Gateshill (1972)
Lorna Cole (1950)
Tony Stevenson (1972)
Paul Miller (1974)
Paul Genney (1976)
John Godfrey (1985) †
James Sampson (1985)
David Tremberg (1985)
Mark Bury (1986)
Neil Cameron (1984)
Anil Murray (1989)
Elizabeth Shaw (1986)
Andrew Comaish (1989)
Carol Trimmer (1993) ‡
Simon Hirst (1993)
John Thackray (1994)
Simon Pickering (1996)
Stephen Robinson (1999)
Nigel Clive (1998)

† Former solicitor (admitted 1976) ‡ Former solicitor (admitted 1979)

The Chambers: Established in Hull in 1957 and now occupying modern premises within the Old Town conservation area together with an annexe in Grimsby.

Work Undertaken: Members practise from specialist groups in crime; family; personal injury; property, commercial and employment; licensing; immigration.

Ipswich

Set No. 192

EAST ANGLIAN CHAMBERS (Roderick Newton)

5 Museum St, Ipswich, IP1 1HQ
Tel: (01473) 214481 **Fax:** (01473) 218466 **DX:** 3227
Email: ipswichchambers@dial.pipex.com **Website:** www.ealaw.co.uk

Head of Chambers	Roderick Newton
Senior Clerk	Peter Hall
Administrator	Carol Bull (01473) 254559
Tenants	53

Members:

Roderick Newton (1982)
John Akast (1968)
John Wardlow (1971)
Peter Wain (1972)
Andrew Marsden (1975)
Caroline Bryant (1976)
Celia Miller (1978)
David Pugh (1978)
Martyn Levett (1978)
Timothy McLoughlin (1978)
Graham Sinclair (1979)
John Hamey (1979)
Anthony Kefford (1980)
John Brooke-Smith (1981)
Simon Redmayne (1982)
Graham Parnell (1982)
Michael Lane (1983)
Hugh Vass (1983)
Jane Davies (1983)
Lindsay Cox (1984)
Janet Bettle (1985)
Steven Dyble (1986)
Anthony Bate (1987)
Nicholas Elcombe (1987)
Rebecca Degel (1987)
Jonathan Seely (1987)
Rosalyne Mandil-Wade (1988)
David Richards (1989)
Andrew Jackson (1990)
Ray Smith (1991)
Katharine Bundell (1991)
Marika Bell (1991)
Jeremy Dugdale (1992)
Carole Parry-Jones (1992)
Dominic Barratt (1992)
Helen Gilbertson (1993)
Amanda Rippon (1993)
Patricia Walsh (1993)
Jacqui Hanlon (1994)
Richard Kelly (1994)
Jude Durr (1995)
Sally Freeman (1995)
Alan Wheetman (1995)
David Wilson (1996)
Fiona Baruah (1996)
Ashley Thain (1996)
Saqib Rauf (1996)
Marc Cannatella (1997)
David Sunman (1997)
Stephen Goodfellow (1997)
Andrew Shaw (1998)
Joanne Bradbury (1999)
Ian Hugh Dyble (2000)

The Chambers: East Anglian Chambers was founded in 1947 as a provincial common law set of chambers, and has developed over the years, retaining its broad common law base. It is now able to offer teams of specialists in commercial, Chancery, construction, crime, family, land, personal injury and planning. Many members of East Anglian Chambers are active members of professional groups and associations within their field of practice, have contributed to, edited and written textbooks, and sit as Recorders, Stipendiary Magistrates and Deputy District Judges. East Anglian Chambers is instructed by most firms

Continued overleaf

of solicitors in East Anglia, as well as many from further afield. In addition, it receives work in all fields of practice from local authorities, and does an increasing amount of DPA work. Chambers is actively involved in the Community Legal Services in East Anglia. It prosecutes for the CPS, HM Customs & Excise and Government Departments throughout the region.

Recruitment: East Anglian Chambers operates from three centres in Norwich, Ipswich and Colchester. 12 month pupillages are offered each year, with pupils being expected to divide their time between the three centres. In addition, from time to time, working pupillages are offered. Procedures and timetables for applications can be obtained by contacting the Chambers Administrator.

Leeds

Set No.
193 CHANCERY HOUSE CHAMBERS (Adrian Dent)

7 Lisbon Square, Leeds, LS1 4LY
Tel: (0113) 244 6691 **Fax:** (0113) 244 6766 **DX:** 26421 Leeds
Email: colin.hedley@chanceryhouse.co.uk **Website:** www.chanceryhouse.co.uk

Head of Chambers	Adrian Dent
Senior Clerk	Colin Hedley
Tenants	13

Members:

Adrian Dent (1974)
Harry Wolton QC (1969) (QC-1982) *
David Stockdale QC (1975) (QC-1995) *
Richard Carpenter (1981)
Mark Walker (1986)
David Partington (1987)
Aubrey Craig (1987) †
Stephen Howd (1989)
Paul Creaner (1990)
Bruce Walker (1994)
Gregory Pipe (1995)
Lisa Linklater (1995)
Jonathan French (1997)
Mark Cooper (1998)
Richard Wilson (1996) *
Paul Lakin (2000)

* Door Tenant † Member of the New York Bar

The Chambers: Chancery House Chambers is a specialist not generalist set and offers relaxed and informal access to specialist barristers with ready access to and candour from a specialist and experienced senior clerk. Chambers do not try to do everything but do try to be the best at what they do and are committed to quality and manageability of service, with papers back on or before the date promised.

Work Undertaken: Commercial litigation; commercial property; construction; company and commercial; chancery; banking; bankruptcy; insolvency; intellectual property; trademarks; planning/environmental; competition law; insurance/re-insurance; consumer credit; sale and carriage of goods; international trade; professional negligence; partnership; equity, wills and trusts; employment/discrimination.

Set No.
194 ENTERPRISE CHAMBERS (Anthony Mann QC)

38 Park Square, Leeds, LS1 2PA
Tel: (0113) 246 0391 **Fax:** (0113) 242 4802 **DX:** 26448 (Leeds Park Square)
Email: enterprise.leeds@dial.pipex.com **Website:** www.enterprisechambers.com

Head of Chambers	Anthony Mann QC
Senior Clerk (London)	Antony Armstrong
Practice Development Clerk	Barry Clayton
Clerk	Joanne Glew
Tenants	26

For a full list of members please see the London entry. For further information about the set please visit the chambers' website.

Set No.
195 11 KING'S BENCH WALK (FJ Muller QC)

3 Park Court, Park Cross Street, Leeds, LS1 2QH
Tel: (0113) 297 1200 **Fax:** (0113) 297 1201 **DX:** 26433

Head of Chambers	FJ Muller QC
Senior Clerk	Jo Pickersgill
Clerks	Jayne Turner
	Deborah Pain
	Chris Gittins
Administration/Fees	Amanda Kershaw
Tenants	27

London common law set with extensive North East Circuit practice. 3 Park Court is the Leeds annexe for 11 King's Bench Walk, London. See London entry for details of practice and members.

Set No.
196 **5 PARK PLACE**

5 Park Place, Leeds, LS1 2RU
Tel: (0113) 242 1123 **Fax:** (0113) 242 1124 **DX:** 713113 (LEEDS PKSQ)
Email: clerks@40kingstreet.co.uk **Website:** www.40kingstreet.co.uk

Senior Clerk	William Brown
Bar Management Service	William Brown, Colin Griffin, Michael Stubbs
Assistant Clerks	Lisa Williams, Paul Clarke
Tenants	49

40 KING STREET
MANCHESTER

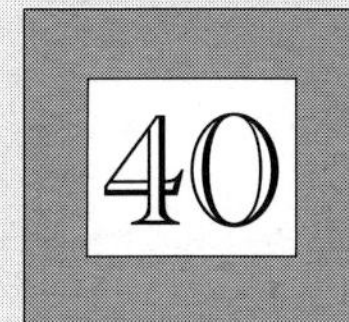

5 PARK PLACE
LEEDS

Members:

Andrew Gilbart QC (1972) (QC-1991)
Peter Smith QC (1975) (QC-1992)
John Hoggett QC (1969) (QC-1986)
Stephen Sauvain QC (1977) (QC-1995)
Frances Patterson QC (1977) (QC-1998) †
Michael Booth QC (1981) (QC-1999)
Nicholas Braslavsky QC (1983) (QC-1999)
Vincent Fraser QC (1981) (QC-2001)
Paul Chaisty QC (1982) (QC-2001)
Eric Owen (1969)
Harold Halliday (1972)
Shokat Khan (1979)
David Manley (1981)
John Barrett (1982)
Alan Evans (1978)
Mark Halliwell (1985)
John Cooper (1985)
Simon Hilton (1987)
Katherine Dunn (1987)
Ruth Stockley (1988)
Fiona Ashworth (1988)
Paul Tucker (1990)
Geoffrey Pass (1975)
Andrew Singer (1990)
Stephen Pritchett (1990)
Lesley Anderson (1989)
Matthew Smith (1991)
Martin Carter (1992)
Wilson Horne (1992)
Lucy Powis (1992)
Mark Harper (1993)
Sarah Pritchard (1993)
Richard Lander (1993)
Ian Ponter (1993)
Simon Antrobus (1995)
Andrew Latimer (1995)
Louis Doyle (1996)
Elizabeth Berridge (1996)
Katie Nowell (1996)
Colin Crawford (1997)
Nicholas Siddall (1997)
Giles Cannock (1998)
Andrew McGee (1998)
Matthew Hall (1999)
Helen Mulholland (1999)
Catherine Brown (1999)
John Tackaberry QC (1967) (QC-1982) †
John Campbell (1981)(QC Scotland 1999) †
Julian Ghosh (1993) †

† Associate Member

The Chambers: A large and well-established set, the members of which appear before the full range of courts and statutory tribunals. Counsel is available at all ranks of seniority, including seven silks, and the breadth of individual specialities and aptitudes available in chambers means that they offer a wide range of specialist advisory and advocacy services. Members have written, edited or contributed to a large number of legal journals, most notably in the fields of planning, local government and highway law. Iain Glidewell is the arbitrator for the set.

Work Undertaken: Town and country planning; local government law and finance; administrative law; parliamentary law; compulsory purchase and compensation; highways law; environmental protection; public health; commercial chancery litigation; landlord and tenant law; law of trusts; partnerships; intellectual property; insolvency (corporate and individual); banking; wills and intestacy; civil liability; personal injury; professional liability; employment and industrial law; building disputes; consumer credit; sale of goods; family and matrimonial law; hire purchase; licensing; criminal law.
Additional Areas: Markets and fairs; trading standards; EC law; housing; data protection; company law; immigration; defamation. Members accept Direct Professional Access from the approved professions.

International: Languages spoken include French, German, Punjabi, Urdu, Spanish and Russian.

Set No.
197 **MERCURY CHAMBERS** (Benjamin Nolan QC)

Mercury House, 33-35 Clarendon Road, Leeds, LS2 9NZ **Tel:** (0113) 234 2265 **Fax:** (0113) 244 4243 **DX:** 713115 LEEDS PARK SQUARE **Email:** cdexter@mercurychambers.co.uk

Set No.
198 **NO.6 BARRISTERS CHAMBERS** (Shaun Spencer QC)

6 Park Square, Leeds, LS1 2LW **Tel:** (0113) 245 9763 **Fax:** (0113) 242 4395 **DX:** 26402 **Email:** chambers@no6.co.uk **Website:** www.no6.co.uk

Set No.
199 **PARK COURT CHAMBERS** (James Stewart QC & Robert Smith QC)

16 Park Place, Leeds, LS1 2SJ
Tel: (0113) 243 3277 **Fax:** (0113) 242 1285 **DX:** 26401
Email: clerks@parkcourtchambers.co.uk **Website:** www.parkcourtchambers.co.uk

Head of Chambers	James Stewart QC
	Robert Smith QC
Senior Clerk	Terry Creathorn
Tenants	43

Members:

James Stewart QC (1966) (QC-1982)
Robert Smith QC (1971) (QC-1986)
Michael Harrison QC (1969) (QC-1987)
Malcolm Swift QC (1970) (QC-1988)
Anton Lodge QC (1966) (QC-1989)
Paul Worsley QC (1970) (QC-1990)
Louise S. Godfrey QC (1972) (QC-1991)
Simon Bourne-Arton QC (1975) (QC-1994)
David Hatton QC (1976) (QC-1996)
Alistair MacDonald QC (1983) (QC-2000)
Henry Prosser (1969)
John Muir (1969)
Timothy Hartley (1970)
Tom Bayliss (1977)
Jonathan Devlin (1978)
Bryan Cox (1979)
Adrian Robinson (1981)
John Lodge (1980)
Michael Taylor (1980)
Simon Jackson (1982)
Caroline Wigin (1984)
Simon Phillips (1985)
Sharon Beattie (1986)
Simon Myerson (1986)
Nadim Bashir (1988)
Taryn Turner (1990)
Maria Davies (1988)
Chistopher Tehrani (1990)
Elyas Patel (1991)
Ashley Tucker (1990)
Joanna Cross (1992)
Paul Greaney (1993)
Nicholas Johnson (1994)
Jenny Kent (1993)
Jason Pitter (1994)
Ceri Widdett (1994)
Uthra Rajgopal (1998)
Valerie Sterling (1981)
Alan Taylor (1986)
Samuel Green (1998)
Alexander Offer (1998)
Franklyn Zakers (1999)
Nicola Twine (1999)
Gilbert Gray QC (1953) (QC-1971) *
James Chadwin QC (1958) (QC-1976) *
Andrew Thornhill QC (1969) (QC-1985) *
Peter Feinberg QC (1972) (QC-1992) *
Joanna Dodson QC (1970) (QC-1993) *
Roger Thomas (1979) *
Jeremy Woolf (1986) *

* Door Tenant

The Chambers: Park Court Chambers is one of the largest sets of chambers outside London. It is a long-established but modern and expanding set based in the thriving commercial centre of Leeds. It offers a wide range of services.

Work Undertaken: Crime, corporate fraud, personal injury, general commercial, family, landlord and tenant, licensing, medical negligence and tax are undertaken.

Set No.
200 **PARK LANE CHAMBERS** (Stuart Brown QC)

Park Lane House, 19 Westgate, Leeds, LS1 2RD
Tel: (0113) 228 5000 **Fax:** (0113) 228 1500 **DX:** 26404 Leeds Park Square
Email: clerks@parklanechambers.co.uk **Website:** www.parklanechambers.co.uk

Head of Chambers	Stuart Brown QC
Chambers Director	Mike Sayers
Senior Team Clerks	John Payne
	Andy Gray
Tenants	31

Members:

Martin Bethel QC (1965) (QC-1983)
Stuart Brown QC (1974) (QC-1991)
Christopher Storey QC (1979) (QC-1995)
David Wilby QC (1974) (QC-1998)
Alaric Dalziel (1967)
Tim Hirst (1970)
Howard Elgot (1974)
Sally Cahill (1978)
Elizabeth O'Hare (1980)
Lindy Armitage (1985)
William Hanbury (1985)
Simon Thorpe (1988)
Joanne Astbury (1989)
Craig Moore (1989)
Richard Copnall (1990)
Alexander Foster (1990)
Kaiser Nazir (1991)
Guy Swiffen (1991)
Andrew Axon (1992)
James Murphy (1993)
Corin Furness (1994)
Steven Turner (1993)
Dornier Whittaker (1994)
Sara Anning (1995)
Stephen Friday (1996)
Alan Weir (1996)
Simon Plaut (1997)
Helen Waddington (1998)
Simon Stevenson (1999)
Tom Nossiter (1999)
Heather Anderson (2000) †

† Former solicitor

The Chambers: This set of chambers has a strong reputation in civil litigation with particular emphasis on personal injury, clinical and professional negligence and commercial work. Members of chambers belong to specialist bodies including the Personal Injuries Bar Association, the Association of Personal Injury Lawyers, Action for Victims of Medical Negligence (AVMA), the Professional Negligence Bar Association, the Family Bar Association, the Chancery Bar Association and the Criminal Bar Association. Martin Bethel QC and Stuart Brown QC are both Deputy High Court judges.

Work Undertaken:

Personal Injury: There is a long history of clinical negligence and employers' liability work within chambers. Major litigation cases have involved industrial deafness; pharmaceuticals; British Coal respiratory disease. 'Credit hire' litigation has expanded following the reported case of Dimond v Lovell (HL). Members have long-standing relationships with major institutional clients, unions and insurers. Other specialisms include sports injuries, holiday claims, RSI and stress at work.

Family: The team has extensive experience in public law childcare and adoption, private proceedings involving children, divorce and ancillary relief (including high value claims), cohabitees' property disputes, trusts and inheritance disputes and applications for committal and injunctions.

Chancery & Commercial: A growing team deals with construction; landlord and tenant; general Chancery; insolvency; company and partnership law; insurance law; direct and indirect taxation including VAT.

Crime: Members, and in particular the four silks, undertake criminal work including fraud, health and safety prosecutions for claimants and defendants and trading standards prosecutions.

Set No.

201 30 PARK SQUARE (J.W. Mellor)

30 Park Square, Leeds, LS1 2PF
Tel: (0113) 243 6388 **Fax:** (0113) 242 3510 **DX:** 26411
Email: clerks@30parksquare.co.uk **Website:** www.30parksquare.co.uk

Head of Chambers	J.W. Mellor
Senior Clerk	Jennifer Thompson
Tenants	27

Members:

J.W. Mellor (1953)
Peter Collier QC (1970) (QC-1992) +
A. Kershaw (1975) +
M. Haigh (1970) †
S.N. Haring (1982)
M.S. Rodger (1983)
R.M.L. Hallam (1984) +
K. Buckingham (1986)
C.L. Hill (1988)
M. Pearson (1984)
A. Granville-Fall (1990)
J. Hargan (1990)
R. Cole (1991)
N. Frith (1992)
M. Teeman (1993) †
Joanna Geddes (1992)
T. White (1993)
I. Shiels (1992)
N. Barker (1994)
P. Williams (1994)
Jonathan Edwards (1994)
E. Auckland (1995)
W. Tyler (1996)
A. Stewart (1997)
A. Rhys-Davies (1998)
Claire Hurden (1999)
Karamjit Singh (2000)

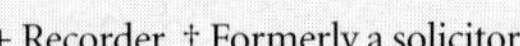
+ Recorder † Formerly a solicitor

The Chambers: Specialists in criminal and family law. Also undertake work (including non-contentious and advisory) in a wide range of common law subjects. Advocates with experience in all courts, tribunals and inquiries.

Work Undertaken: All aspects of family law; divorce; child care; injunctions; criminal defence and prosecution. Common law expertise in personal injury; contract; property disputes; professional negligence; licensing; insolvency; planning; employment law.

Set No.
202 **37 PARK SQUARE** (Stephen J Glover & Paul Kirtley)

37 Park Square, Leeds, LS1 2NY
Tel: (0113) 243 9422 **Fax:** (0113) 242 4229 **DX:** 26405 Leeds
Email: chambers@no37.co.uk **Website:** www.no37.co.uk

Head of Chambers	Stephen J Glover Paul Kirtley
Senior Clerk	Ann Fothergill
Criminal Clerk	Ian Spencer
Civil Clerk	Donna Mullen
Tenants	27

Members:

Stephen J Glover (1978)
Paul Kirtley (1982)
Douglas Hogg QC (1968) (QC-1990)
Robert Marshall-Andrews QC (1967) (QC-1989)
John Sleightholme (1982)
Rodney Ferm (1972)
John Dunning (1973)
Paul Fleming (1983)
Freddy Apfel (1986)
Jeremy Lindsay (1986)
Amanda Ginsburg (1985)
Dawn Tighe (1989)
Linda Cains (1990)
Steven Crossley (1992)
Piers Hill (1987)
Caroline Ford (1993)
Mark Gore (1994)
David Taylor (1995)
Joanne Holroyd (1994)
Stuart Roberts (1994)
Taryn Lee (1992)
Michael Burdon (1993)
Kama Melly (1997)
Michael Collins (1998)
Claire Thompson (1998)
Amanda Howard (1994)
Hugh Milburn (1997)

Work Undertaken: General common law including criminal law, licensing, family law, personal injury, contract, employment law, company and commercial, landlord and tenant, real property disputes, planning and local government law.

Set No.
203 **39 PARK SQUARE** (Tim Bubb)

39 Park Square, Leeds, LS1 2NU **Tel:** (0113) 245 6633 **Fax:** (0113) 242 1567 **DX:** 26407 **Email:** seniorclerk@39parksquarechambers.co.uk
Website: www.39parksquarechambers.co.uk

Set No.
204 **ST. PAUL'S CHAMBERS** (Nigel Sangster QC)

5th Floor, St. Paul's House, 23 Park Square South, Leeds, LS1 2ND
Tel: (0113) 245 5866 **Fax:** (0113) 245 5807 **DX:** 26410 Leeds (Park Square)
Email: catherinegrimshaw@stpauls-chambers.demon.co.uk
Website: www.stpauls-chambers.co.uk

Head of Chambers	Nigel Sangster QC
Senior Clerk	Catherine Grimshaw
Tenants	33

Members:

Nigel Sangster QC (1976) (QC-1998) +
Peter Benson (1975) +
Colin Harvey (1975)
Jeremy Barnett (1980) +
Philip Standfast (1980)
Jonathan Rose (1981) +
Guy Kearl (1982) +
Andrew Lees (1984) +
Derek Duffy (1997)
Alison Hunt (1986)
Fiona Dix-Dyer (1986)
Howard Crowson (1987)
David De Jehan (1988)
Andrew Stubbs (1988)
Simon Bickler (1988)
Christopher Batty (1989)
Jonathan Godfrey (1990)
Robin Mairs (1992)
Jonathan Sandiford (1992)
Nicola Saxton (1992)
Sukhbir Bassra (1993)
Sarah Barlow (1993)
Scott Wilson (1993)
Alex Bates (1994)
John Harrison (1994)
Kirstie Watson (1995)
Nigel Edwards (1995)
Ann Marie Gregory (1994)
Nick Dry (1996)
Rukhshanda Hussain (1998)
Natasha Wood (1997)
Oliver Longstaff (1999)
Gavin Pope (1999)

+ Recorder

The Chambers: Founded in 1982, St. Paul's Chambers has expanded to 33 practitioners. Members have complementary areas of expertise, with the specific intention of providing a service in most areas of legal work. Nigel Sangster QC and Jeremy Barnett are elected members of the Bar Council. Members of Chambers belong to the Family Law Bar Association and the Criminal Bar Association.

Work Undertaken:
Criminal: Work includes the traditional areas of crime, with members acting for both prosecution and defence. In addition, there are specialists in fraud and corporate crime, serious crime (including violence and sexual offences), breathalyser cases, licensing, Courts Martial, Firearms Act offences and asset seizure work.
Civil: Chambers have particular expertise in personal injury claims; employment; landlord and tenant; Trading Standards cases; Directors' Disqualification cases; family and childcare work; matrimonial; professional negligence; police disciplinary cases; immigration work.

ST. PAULS CHAMBERS

Set No.
205 **SOVEREIGN CHAMBERS** (Geoffrey C. Marson QC)

25 Park Square, Leeds, LS1 2PW
Tel: (0113) 245 1841 **Fax:** (0113) 242 0194 **DX:** 26408 Leeds Park Square
Email: sovereignchambers@btinternet.com **Website:** www.sovereignchambers.co.uk

Head of Chambers	Geoffrey C. Marson QC
Practice & Finance Manager	Paul Slater
Chambers Administrator	Chris Dixon
Tenants	34

Members:

Geoffrey C. Marson QC (1975) (QC-1997)
Richard L. Newbury (1976)
Patrick J.S. Palmer (1978)
Charles W. Ekins (1980)
Felicity A. Davies (1980)
Mushtaq A. Khokhar (1982)
Steven D. Garth (1983)
David M. Gordon (1984)
Andrew W. Lewis (1985)
Mark D. McKone (1988)
Stephen Bedeau (1980)
Denise L. Gresty (1990)
Jason MacAdam (1990)
Andrew P. Haslam (1991)
Roger A. Birch (1979)
David S. Dixon (1992)
Nicholas J H Lumley (1992)
Richard I Woolfal (1992)
Charity E. Rigby (1993)
Andrew B. Semple (1993)
M Jayne Pye (1995) †
Darren Finlay (1994)
Emma L.V. Burden (1994)
Anne Munday (1994)
Matthew R. Smith (1996)
Christopher Dunn (1996)
James F. Keeley (1993)
Peter J. Wilson (1995)
William McCarthy (1996)
Diana Maudslay (1997)
Richard Paige (1997)
Craig Hassall (1999)
Sally Clayden (1999)
Patrizia Doherty (2000) †
Lynton Tucker (1971) *
Colin Braham (1971) *
Christopher Russell (1971) *
Nicholas Le Poidevin (1975) *
Stuart Barber (1979) *
Sara Hargreaves (1979) *
Margaret McCabe (1981) *
Leigh Sagar (1983) *
Claire Staddon (1985) *
Ian Peacock (1990) *
Jane Evans-Gordon (1992) *
John Mowbray QC (1953) *
John MacDonald QC (1955) *
Charles Purle QC (1970) *
George S Laurence QC (1972) *
Stephen J Smith (1983) *
Ross Crail (1986) *
Louise Davis (1995) *

* Door Tenant † Formerly a solicitor

The Chambers: Sovereign Chambers is a modern, forward thinking set providing a specialist service focusing on its core practice groups. Members of chambers act for a wide range of clients, from multinational public companies to private individuals. One of the leading chambers in the commercial city of Leeds, the set has been established for more than 75 years.

Work Undertaken: Teams of members forming specialist practice groups, combined with a first class administration, aim to provide an excellent service in the following areas: commercial/Chancery; intellectual property; environmental/planning; personal injury; employment; family/matrimonial; crime; fraud.

Commercial/Chancery: In the commercial field, members handle contractual cases, both domestic and international, sale of goods, consumer credit, banking, franchising, international trade and documentary credits as well as building disputes involving defects in designs and workmanship and performance obligations. Chancery members deal with company and insolvency, both corporate and personal, inheritance, land law, conveyancing and trusts.

Intellectual Property: All intellectual property rights, including patents, design rights (both registered and unregistered), trademarks, copyright and passing off. Also the related areas of information technology law (including internet-related disputes), media law, moral rights and franchising.

Personal Injury/Clinical Negligence: One of the leading chambers in the area in personal injury and clinical negligence work, the set acts for both defendants and claimants and clients include major insurers, legal expenses insurers, trade unions, private individuals and medical defence societies. Work in this area is regularly undertaken both on and off circuit, and members regularly litigate in the field of professional negligence.

Employment: The employment team is led by a part-time chairman of the Employment tribunals and is particularly active in the emerging areas of stress and disability discrimination.

Family/Matrimonial: Some of the group are recognised as 'leaders in their field', regularly appearing for local authorities, parents or guardians ad litem. Their work includes substantial private client - probate, wills and family provision for which members have particular expertise.

Criminal/Fraud: The group is led by the Head of Chambers who is acknowledged as a 'leader in his field'. The team undertakes serious crime for both prosecution and defence. One of the members of the complimentary specialist fraud group has completed one of the largest prosecutions ever undertaken by the Department of Trade and Industry.

Set No. 206

ZENITH CHAMBERS (Andrew Campbell QC & John Collins)

10 Park Square, Leeds, LS1 2LH
Tel: (0113) 245 5438 **Fax:** (0113) 242 3515 **DX:** 26412
Email: clerks@10pksq.co.uk

Head of Chambers	Andrew Campbell QC
	John Collins
Practice Director	Robin Butchard
Assistant Practice Director	
	Samantha Ashford
Clerks	Helen Dring
	Clive Taylor
	Martin Finn
	Rebecca Hartley
Fees Administrators	Erica Newby
	Angela Rushby
	Veronica Cliff
Tenants	60

Members:

Andrew Campbell QC (1972) (QC-1994)
John Collins (1956)
Heather Swindells QC (1974) (QC-1995) †
David Hodge QC (1979) (QC-1997) †
James Corbett QC (1975) (QC-1999) †
Brian Kealy (1965)
Charles Sinclair-Morris (1966)
Gerald Lumley (1972)
Andrew Woolman (1973)
Simon Jack (1974)
David Bradshaw (1975)
Rebecca Thornton (1976)
Robert Collins (1978)
Jeffrey Lewis (1978)
James Behrens (1979) †
David Hall (1980)
James Clappison MP (1981)
Julian Goose (1984)
John Worrall (1984)
Christopher Dodd (1984)
Anthony Hajimitsis (1984)
Simon Hickey (1985)
Paul Brook (1986)
Sarah Greenan (1987)
Austin Newman (1987)
Roger Bickerdike (1986)
Simon Waley (1988)
John Holroyd (1989)
Simon Read (1989)
Mavis Pilkington (1990)
Simon Reevell (1990)
Aelred Hookway (1990)
Simon Kealey (1991)
Steven Lunt (1991)
Gordon Exall (1991)
Clive Heaton (1992)
John Hayes (1992)
Elmear McAllister (1992) †
Tom Storey (1993)
Edward Bindloss (1993)
Justin Crossley (1993)
Elaine McLaughlin (1993)
Abdul Ibqal (1994)
Anesh Pema (1994)
Jonathan Carroll (1994)
Mark Henley (1994)
Philippa Wordsworth (1995)
Andrew Wilson (1995)
Heather Humpage (1996)
Geraldine Kelly (1996)
Sean Yates (1996)
George Branchflower (1997)
Pankaj Madan (1997)
Helen Greatorex (1997)
John Brodwell (1998)
Nicholas Worsley (1998)
Louise McCallum (1999)
Nicola Phillipson (1999)
Jillian Bell (2000)
Rosemary Exall (2000)

† Associate Tenants

The Chambers: Founded in 2001 as the result of a merger between 9 Woodhouse Square and 10 Park Square, chambers are committed to providing a comprehensive, flexible and user friendly service comprising advocacy and advisory work. The latest information technology has been installed to enable effective communication and the clerks are always available to discuss solicitors' particular requirements. In anticipation of Legal Aid changes, chambers already operate a successful block contracting system with efficient administration and a speedy return of papers. This is achieved by the distribution of work within agreed teams, all with relevant experience. Chambers additionally offer six specialist groups, each with their own head, who meet regularly to ensure that a cohesive service is provided with the required expertise. Members of the teams regularly lecture at national and local levels. Chambers hold seminars on a regular basis, all of which are accredited by the Law Society. For further information about the set's seminar programme, please contact Samantha Ashford. Out of hours telephone number is (07000) 781 576.

Work Undertaken: Administrative; ancillary relief; arbitration; aviation; bankruptcy; boundaries; building; care proceedings; chancery; charities; children; civil actions involving the police; civil liberties; commercial litigation; contract; construction; crime; disciplinary tribunals; ecclesiastical; employment; environment; equity wills and trust; family; housing; immigration; intellectual property; landlord and tenant; licensing; medical negligence; mediation; mental health; partnership; personal injury; probate and administration; planning; professional negligence; road traffic; sale and carriage of goods; tax - capital and income; town and country planning. Specialist departments: crime, family, business and property, personal injury/clinical negligence, housing and employment.

International: Languages spoken include French, German, Spanish, Punjabi and Urdu.

Leicester

Set No.
207 **NEW WALK CHAMBERS** (John Snell)

27 New Walk, Leicester, LE1 6TE
Tel: (0116) 255 9144 **Fax:** (0116) 255 9084 **DX:** 10872 Leicester 1
Email: clerks@newwalkchambers.law.co.uk **Website:** www.newwalkchambers.co.uk

Head of Chambers	John Snell
Practice Manager	Michael Ryan
Tenants	27

Members:

John Snell (1973)
Jonathan Durham-Hall QC (1975) (QC-1995)
Patrick Thomas QC (1973) (QC-1999) *
John Ginns (1977)
Paul Atkinson (1978)
Robert Rees (1978)
Peter Bates (1978)
Simon Liddy (1979)
Rebecca Fitton Brown (1981)
Nicholas George (1983)
Nala Lawrence (1987)
Robin Chaudhuri (1988)
Sean McGovern (1990)
Timothy Cockrill (1991)
Steven Taylor (1992)
Phillipa Eade (1992)
Mark Hurd (1993)
Penelope Stanistreet (1993)
Simon Parsons (1993)
Craig Lowe (1994)
Richard Nicholls (1994)
Janet Ruscoe (1995)
Harinder Kaur (1995)
John Ryan (1997)
Semon Piper (1997)
Emma Cutts (1998)
Sasha Watkinson (1998)
Simon Reed (1998)

* Door Tenant

The Chambers: New Walk Chambers is a long established set situated in a large Georgian property close to the Crown Court, County Court and Industrial Tribunal building.

Liverpool

Set No.
208 **14 CASTLE STREET** (Andrew Edis QC)

14 Castle Street, Liverpool, L2 0NE
Tel: (0151) 236 4421 **Fax:** (0151) 236 1559 **DX:** 14176
Email: clerks@14castlestreet.co.uk

Head of Chambers	Andrew Edis QC
Clerks	Stuart Jones
	Gary Quinn
	Neil Grisdale
	David Blunsden
Tenants	44

Members:

Andrew Edis QC (1980) (QC-1997)
John Benson QC (1978) (QC-2001)
Eric Goldrein (1961)
Nicholas Riddle (1970)
Nicholas Orr (1970)
Ian Haselhurst (1976)
Robert Warnock (1977)
Thomas Eaton (1976)
Nigel Ginniff (1978)
David Dennis (1979)
Michael Sellars (1980)
Arthur Gibson (1980)
Ian Johnson (1982)
John Corless (1984)
Ivan Woolfenden (1985)
Nicholas Ryan (1984)
Simon Booth (1985)
Andrew Pickering (1987)
Stuart Driver (1988)
Simon Gorton (1988)
Celia Lund (1988)
Malcolm Sharpe (1988)
Robert Golinski (1990)
Graham Sellers (1990)
David Watson (1990)
Christine Johnson (1991)
Richard Hall (1991)
Nicholas Jackson (1992)
Timothy Grace (1993)
Anne Whyte (1993)
David Green (1993)
Michelle Davey (1993)
Rachael Banks (1993)
Gwynneth Knowles (1993)
Andrew Williams (1994)
Andrew Banks (1994)
Liam Grundy (1995)
Charles Prior (1995)
Kenderik Horne (1996)
Mark Rawcliffe (1996)
Neil Downey (1997)
Sophie Smith (1999)
Alison Miller (1999)
Lee Bonner (2000)

The Chambers: The result of two mergers involving three sets, two specialist Chancery sets and one common law. Now divided into departments offering specialist advice and advocacy in 5 broad areas. A Conditional Fee scheme is in place which covers all areas of work where this is permitted. The departments are as follows:

Crime: Prosecuting and defending at all levels from the Magistrates' Court upwards. Serious fraud, murder, sexual offences are covered by experienced practitioners, but less serious work is given equal attention. The availability of commercial expertise in chambers and the library and IT facilities which they have means that they are particularly capable of dealing with large and complex cases involving fraud or other similar offences.

Continued overleaf

Chancery & Commercial: A large group (16) offering all levels of experience and considerable specialist expertise. The group includes a specialist tax and pensions lawyer, and covers probate, property, tax and trust work as well as contractual and professional negligence disputes. Contentious and non-contentious work is covered.
Civil Litigation: This includes clinical negligence, personal injury, police and human rights law, and other professional negligence cases. Chambers cover Judicial Review cases, and other local authority work. They have lawyers who deal with civil litigation who also have experience in areas such as child care and education law for cases which may require dual experience. Chambers act for claimants and defendants.
Family: A highly experienced group dealing with public and private law child care work and financial aspects of divorce. The group acts for individuals and local authorities. The presence of the Chancery group enables chambers to deal with all aspects of family finance and property under one roof.
Employment: This is a specialism of these chambers. John Benson QC is an employment expert and leads a substantial group of experienced employment lawyers who act for claimants and respondents. The respondents include local authorities, police forces, and major national companies. The claimants are treated with equal respect.

Recruitment: Chambers recruit throughout OLPAS. Chambers will seek and fund pupils who will be able to choose which areas of work they wish to pursue and will train appropriately.

Set No.
209 25-27 CASTLE STREET (Stephen Riordan QC)
25-27 Castle Street, 1st Floor, Liverpool, L2 4TA **Tel:** (0151) 236 5072 **Fax:** (0151) 236 4054 **DX:** 14224

Set No.
210 CHAVASSE COURT CHAMBERS (Theresa Pepper)
2nd Floor, Chavasse Court, 24 Lord Street, Liverpool, L2 1TA **Tel:** (0151) 707 1191 **Fax:** (0151) 707 1189 **DX:** 14223 Liverpool

Set No.
211 DERBY SQUARE CHAMBERS (Simon Newton)
Merchants Court, Derby Square, Liverpool, L2 1TS **Tel:** (0151) 709 4222 **Fax:** (0151) 708 6311 **DX:** 14213 Liverpool 1
Email: clerks@derbysquare.co.uk

Set No.
212 EXCHANGE CHAMBERS (David Turner QC & Bill Braithwaite QC & Henry Globe QC)

Pearl Assurance House, Derby Square, Liverpool, L2 9XX
Tel: (0151) 236 7747 **Fax:** (0151) 236 3433 **DX:** 14207 Liverpool
Email: info@exchangechambers.co.uk **Website:** www.exchangechambers.co.uk

Head of Chambers	David Turner QC Bill Braithwaite QC Henry Globe QC
Practice Manager	Tom Handley
Senior Clerk	Roy Finney
Tenants	60

Members:

William Waldron QC (1970) (QC-1982)
David Turner QC (1971) (QC-1991)
Bill Braithwaite QC (1970) (QC-1992)
Charles Chruszcz QC (1973) (QC-1992)
Anthony Elleray QC (1977) (QC-1993)
Henry Globe QC (1972) (QC-1994)
Graham Morrow QC (1974) (QC-1996)
Tim Holroyde QC (1977) (QC-1996)
Edward Bartley Jones QC (1975) (QC-1997)
Gerard Martin QC (1978) (QC-2000)
Mark Cawson QC (1982) (QC-2001)
Bernard Weatherill QC (1974) (QC-1996)
Francis Nance (1970)
Simon Earlam (1975)
Christopher Cornwall (1975)
Eric Lamb (1975)
James Rae (1976)
Judith Fordham (1991)
Gordon Cole (1979)
Tania Griffiths (1982)
Roger Hillman (1983)
Neil Cadwallader (1984)
Karen Gregory (1985)
Dennis Talbot (1985)
Paul Clark (1994)
Simon Berkson (1986)
Alun James (1986)
William F Waldron (1986)
Mark Mulrooney (1988)
Brian Cummings (1988)
John J. McCarroll (1988)
Louis Browne (1988)
Ian Foster (1988)
Rebecca Clark (1989)
Catherine Howells (1989)
Michael Wood (1989)
Jonathan Cannan (1989)
Christopher Stables (1990)
Julie Case (1990)
John Philpotts (1990)
Christopher Cook (1990)
Amanda Yip (1991)
Paul Timothy Evans (1992)
David Casement (1992)
Ian Unsworth (1992)
Giles Maynard-Connor (1992)
Charlotte Kenny (1993)
Robert Dudley (1993)
Simon Fox (1994)
Kelly Pennifer (1994)
Rachel Silverbeck (1996)
Kevin Slack (1997)
Claire Gourley (1996)
Louise Metcalf (1997)
Nancy Dooher (1997)
Paul Burns (1998)
Sarah O'Brien (1999)
Jonathan Clarke (1999)
Daniel Travers (1999)
David Mohyuddin (1999)

The Chambers: The set has an annexe at: 4 Ralli Courts, West Riverside, Manchester, M3 5FI Tel: (0161) 833 2722 Fax: (0161) 833 2789 DX: 14330 Manchester.

Set No. 213

7 HARRINGTON STREET CHAMBERS (David Steer QC & Robert Fordham QC & Iain Goldrein QC)

7 Harrington Street, Liverpool, L2 9YH
Tel: (0151) 242 0707 **Fax:** (0151) 236 2800 **DX:** 14221 Liverpool 1

Head of Chambers	David Steer QC
	Robert Fordham QC
	Iain Goldrein QC
Practice Director	John Kilgallon
Tenants	65

Members:

David Steer QC (1974) (QC-1993)
Robert Fordham QC (1967) (QC-1993)
Iain Goldrein QC (1975) (QC-1997)
David Aubrey QC (1974) (QC-1998)
Margaret de Haas QC (1977) (QC-1998)
David Geey (1970)
David Kerr (1971)
Andrew McDonald (1971)
Jack Cowan (1971)
Gordon Bellis (1972)
Antonis Georges (1972)
Rodney Halligan (1972)
Mary Compton-Rickett (1972)
Michael J. Pickavance (1974)
Kevin Grice (1977)
Michael Davies (1979)
Richard Pratt (1980)
Neil Flewitt (1981)
Henry Riding (1981)
Grant Lazarus (1981)
Andrew Menary (1982)
Peter Gregory (1982)
James McKeon (1982)
Kevin Reade (1983)
Mark Chatterton (1983)
Deirdre McGuire (1983)
Andrew Loveridge (1983)
Philip J. O'Neill (1983)
Donal McGuire (1983)
Simon J. Killeen (1984)
Sarah Leigh (1984)
Stephen Knapp (1986)
Jamil Khan (1986)
Peter Davies (1986)
David Knifton (1986)
Peter Kidd (1987)
Janet Reaney (1987)
Steven Parker (1987)
Nigel Lawrence (1988)
Keith Sutton (1988)
Andrew Downie (1990)
Kate Symms (1990)
Timothy Grover (1991)
Stephen Seed (1991)
Jonathan Dale (1991)
Christine Bispham (1991)
Deborah Shield (1991)
Trevor Parry-Jones (1992)
Robert Altham (1993)
David Edwards (1994)
Helen Wrenn (1994)
Malcolm Dutchman-Smith (1995)
Gregory Hoare (1992)
Andrew Carney (1995)
Jeremy Greenfield (1995)
Brendon Burke (1995)
Clive Baker (1995)
Daniel Rogers (1997)
Stuart Clare (1997)
Mark Beesley (1998)
Martin Knight (1998)
Lloyd Morgan (1999)
Nicola Miles (1999)
Rachel Spearing (2001)
William Ralston (2001)
Nicola Shaw (1992) *

* Door Tenant

The Chambers: These chambers have their work base in the North but have established contacts in Cheshire and North Wales. The size of chambers has enabled a broad base of specializations to be developed particularly in the following fields: crime, family law, personal injuries, professional negligence (in particular clinical, legal and surveyors), all forms of local government work and general common law work. In addition there are specialists available in the following fields: employment, mental health, commercial work, licensing, housing and welfare law. Some members of chambers write for legal publications and lecture whilst several retain working links with London chambers.

Set No. 214

INDIA BUILDINGS CHAMBERS (Ray Herman)

India Buildings, Water Street, Liverpool, L2 0XG
Tel: (0151) 243 6000 **Fax:** (0151) 243 6040 **DX:** 14227
Email: clerks@indiabuildings.co.uk

Head of Chambers	Ray Herman
Practice Manager / Senior Clerk	
	J Robert Moss
Clerks	Helen Southworth
	Alastair Webster, Gail Curran
	Greg Brooker, Claire Labio
	Elisa Roberts
Tenants	38

Members:

Ray Herman (1972) +
Michael Wolff (1964)
Michael Byrne (1971) +
Stephen Bedford (1974) +
Geoffrey Lowe (1975) +
Maureen Roddy (1977) +
Ross Duggan (1978) +
Graham Wood (1979) +
Gail Owen (1980) +
Gareth Jones (1984)
Michael Kennedy (1985)
Jacqueline Wall (1986)
Jean France-Hayhurst (1987)
Charles Davey (1989)
Damian Sanders (1988)
Simon Holder (1989)
Rachel Andrews (1989)
Deborah Gould (1990)
Zia Chaudhry (1991)
Jonathan Taylor (1991)
Patricia Pratt (1991)
Steven Swift (1991)
Jonathan Butler (1992)
John Gibson (1993)
Ben Jones (1993)
David Flood (1993)
Leona Harrison (1993)
David Polglase (1993)
Sara Mann (1994)
Michael Scholes (1996)
John Dixon (1995)
John Chukwuemeka (1994)
Emma Barron-Eaves (1998)

Continued overleaf

Members continued:

Katharine Titchmarsh (1998)
Kate Burnell (1998)
Helen Conway (1999)
David Watson (1963)(Deputy District Judge)
Matthew Stockwell (1998)

+ Recorder

The Chambers: There are currently 38 members of chambers.

Work Undertaken:

Main Areas: Chambers practise in the following fields: crime, both prosecution and defence, including fraud work; all aspects of family work, including disputes about children and ancillary relief claims; personal injury litigation; commercial disputes; professional negligence claims; employment law; general common law.

Additional Areas: Certain members of chambers have experience in building disputes; administrative law; insurance disputes; landlord and tenant; licensing; financial services; company law; partnership disputes; contract law.

Recruitment: Normally one pupillage each year. Financial support on merit and subject to negotiation. All pupils stand a good chance of tenancy.

Set No.
215 ORIEL CHAMBERS (Andrew Sander)

Oriel Chambers, 14 Water Street, Liverpool, L2 8TD
Tel: (0151) 236 7191/236 4321 **Fax:** (0151) 227 5909/236 3332 **DX:** 14106 Liverpool
Email: clerks@oriel-chambers.co.uk **Website:** www.oriel-chambers.co.uk

Head of Chambers	Andrew Sander
Chambers Director	Sarah Cavanagh
Chambers Manager	Paul Thompson
Clerks	Michael Gray, Andrew Hampton
	Ian Pitt, John Newsham
Accounts	Wendy O'Donnell, Jenny Connor
Tenants	41

Members:

A Sander (1970) +
M Bennett (1969)
C Alldis (1970) +
A Edwards (1972) +
W Rankin (1972)
A Murray (1974) +
NA Wright (1974) +
R Bradley (1978)
T Somerville (1979)
P Cowan (1980) +
T Gibson (1981)
P Fogarty (1982)
G Bundred (1982)
S Evans (1985)
A Fox (1986)
P Goodbody (1986)
J Nicholls (1989)
J Baldwin (1990)
J Lewthwaite (1990)
Y Rahman (1991)
J Gruffydd (1992) †
H Belbin (1992)
RS Mills (1992)
P Foster (1992)
P Brant (1993)
H Brandon (1993)
J Dawson (1994)
F Somerset-Jones (1994)
WK Rankin (1994)
IJ Whitehurst (1994)
L Whaites (1994)
S Kemp (1995)
R Hughes (1995)
M Cottrell (1996)
AM Frodsham (1996)
J Sawyer (1978) ‡
S Clarke (1996)
J Close (1997)
M Stephenson (1997)
L Morgan (1999) †
L Clarke (1999)

+ Recorder † Former Solicitor ‡ Previously CPS

Maidstone

Set No.
216 EARL STREET CHAMBERS (Kevin Sparks)

47 Earl Street, Maidstone, ME14 1PD
Tel: (01622) 671222 **Fax:** 01622 671776 **DX:** 4844 Maidstone 1
Email: earlstreetchambers@legalisp.net

Head of Chambers	Kevin Sparks
Senior Clerk	Mary Gunner
Tenants	7

Members:

Kevin Sparks (1983)
Paul Hogben (1993)
Thomas Halpin (1994)
Alexander Scott-Phillips (1995)
Shona Gardiner (1998)
Evelyn Hawkins (1998)
Joanne Barker (1998)

The Chambers: Established in 1996, Earl Street Chambers is a friendly and approachable set, which aims to provide a professional efficient service to its clients throughout London and Kent. Chambers are predominately a common law set, where a wide range of civil and criminal law work is undertaken. Members specialise in criminal law (both prosecution and defence), all aspects of family law, contract, tort, personal injury and licensing. Conferences can be arranged either at chambers or at the solicitors offices.

Set No.
217 **MAIDSTONE CHAMBERS** (Alison Ginn & Richard Travers)

33 Earl St, Maidstone, ME14 1PF
Tel: (01622) 688592 **Fax:** (01622) 683305 **DX:** 51982 Maidstone 2
Email: clerks@maidstonechambers.co.uk

Head of Chambers	Alison Ginn Richard Travers
Senior Clerk	Neil Calver
Tenants	11

Members:

Alison Ginn (1980)
Richard Travers (1985)
Aviva Le Prevost (1990)
Mary Jacobson (1992)
Paul Greene (1994)
Thomas Stern (1995)
Philip Sinclair (1995)
Richard Samuel (1996)
Simon Wickens (1998)
Thomas Allen (1995)
Alex Wilson (1998)

The Chambers: Maidstone Chambers are a general common law set established in 1994, prior to which it was the annexe to a London chambers from 1987. A broad range of civil and criminal work is undertaken at all levels in London, Kent and throughout the South East circuit. Individual members also specialise in various areas of law including crime, family (including childcare), ancilliary relief, licensing, planning, contract, tort (including professional negligence and personal injury), commercial and general civil work. Conferences can be held in chambers or at the instructing solicitor's office.

Manchester

Set No.
218 **BYROM STREET CHAMBERS**
12 Byrom St, Manchester, M3 4PP **Tel:** (0161) 829 2100 **Fax:** (0161) 829 2101 **DX:** 718156 **Email:** clerks@byronstreet.com **Website:** www.byronstreet.com

Set No.
219 **CENTRAL CHAMBERS**

89 Princess Street, Manchester, M1 4HT
Tel: (0161) 236 1133 **Fax:** (0161) 236 1177 **DX:** 14467 Manchester 2

Senior Clerk	Jayne Lever
Clerk	Neil Vickers
Tenants	11

Members:

Stella Massey (1990)
Vincent Deane (1976)
Anthony J Morris (1986)
Tonia Grace (1992)
Nazmun Nisha Ismail (1992)
Steven Wild (1994)
Tony Thorndike (1994)
Bob Sastry (1996)
James Collins (1997)
Wayne Goldstein (1999)(New South Wales 1992)
Prof Rebecca Wallace (1999)

The Chambers: A modern, approachable, progressive set of chambers with a particular emphasis on civil liberties and human rights. Individual practitioners specialise in administrative law, criminal law, housing, family law, welfare rights, human rights, personal injury, clinical negligence, immigration, judicial review, mental health, care in the community law, employment, prison law and civil actions against the police. Chambers specialise in serving the disadvantaged and putting at the forefront the interests of clients in a manner consistent with the very high duty owed to them. At the same time chambers pride themselves in being professional, realistic, frank yet friendly and approachable. Established in 1996. Out of hours emergency contact: (07973) 744906.

Set No.
220 **COBDEN HOUSE CHAMBERS** (Howard Baisden)

19 Quay Street, Manchester, M3 3HN
Tel: (0161) 833 6000 **Fax:** (0161) 833 6001 **DX:** 14327 Manchester 3
Email: clerks@cobden.co.uk **Website:** www.cobden.co.uk

Head of Chambers	Howard Baisden
Senior Clerk	Trevor Doyle
Junior Clerk	David Hewitt
Assistant Clerks	Daniel Monaghan
	Gary Douglas
Administrator	Jackie Morton
Tenants	43

Members:

Roger Farley QC (1974) (QC-1993)
Howard Baisden (1972)
Peter Keenan (1962)
Harry Narayan (1970)
John Broadley (1973)
Charles Machin (1973)
Carolyn Johnson (1974)
Nigel Fieldhouse (1976)
Stuart Neale (1976)
Michael Goldwater (1977)
Richard Oughton (1978)
Paula Fallows (1981)
Colin Green (1982)
Louise Blackwell (1985)
Ian Metcalfe (1985)
Richard Hartley (1985)
Mark Monaghan (1987)
Deanna Hymanson (1988)
Joanne Woodward (1989)
Robin Kitching (1989)
Timothy Willitts (1989)
Martin Littler (1989)
Sarah Harrison (1989)
Jonathan Gregg (1990)
Sean Kelly (1990)
Marc Willems (1990)
Yasmin Wright (1990)
Alison Kilpatrick (1991)
Rajen Dalal (1991)
Jonathan Smith (1991)
Simon Nichol (1994)
Richard Littler (1994)
Susan Gilmour (1994)
David Maddison (1995)
Julian Orr (1995)
Chris Oakes (1996)
Hilary Manley (1996)
Martin Callery (1997)
Adrian Farrow (1997)
Michael Jones (1998)
Richard Goddard (1999)
Rebecca Pearson (1999)
Michael J Knowles (2000)
John Duncan (1971) *
Michael Heywood (1975) *
James Morris *
Matthew Kime (1988) *
Richard Gee (1993) *

* Door Tenant

The Chambers: Cobden House Chambers is able to offer a wide range of expertise by means of specialist departments in the area of Chancery, commercial law, crime, employment law, family, housing and personal injury. Individual members are able to offer additional specialisms and full details can be obtained from the clerk. Chambers provide a fast and efficient service and a timetable for the completion of instructions can be given on delivery. In addition, chambers provide services for alternative dispute resolution and mediation and video conferences. The senior clerk will be happy to discuss fee levels and tailor quotations to meet most budgets. Further details can be found on the website and in chambers' brochure which can be obtained on request.

Set No.
221 **DEANS COURT CHAMBERS** (Stephen Grime QC)

Deans Court Chambers, 24 St John Street, Manchester, M3 4DF
Tel: (0161) 214 6000 **Fax:** (0161) 214 6001 **DX:** 718155 Manchester 3
Email: clerks@deanscourt.co.uk **Website:** www.deanscourt.co.uk

Head of Chambers	Stephen Grime QC
Acting Senior Clerk	Matthew Gibbons
Tenants	47

Members:

Stephen Grime QC (1970) (QC-1987)
Keith Goddard QC (1959) (QC-1979)
Raymond Machell QC (1973) (QC-1988)
David Stockdale QC (1975) (QC-1995)
David Fish QC (1973) (QC-1997)
Ernest Ryder TD QC (1981) (QC-1997)
Mark Turner QC (1981) (QC-1998)
Patrick Field QC (1981) (QC-2000)
Craig Sephton QC (1981) (QC-2001)
Kevin Talbot (1970)
John Bromley-Davenport (1972)
John Gregory (1972)
Peter Atherton (1975)
Alan Booth (1978)
Ruth Trippier (1978)
Philip Butler (1979)
Peter Main (1981)
Stuart Denney (1982)
Timothy Smith (1982)
Timothy Trotman (1983)
Russell Davies (1983)
Louise Bancroft (1985)
Frances Heaton (1985)
Paul Humphries (1986)
Karen Brody (1986)
Christopher Hudson (1987)
Jonathan Grace (1989)
Nicholas Grimshaw (1989)
Julia Cheetham (1990)
Andrew Grantham (1991)
Seamus Andrew (1991)
Janet Ironfield (1992)
Timothy Edge (1992)
Andrew Alty (1992)
Alison Woodward (1992)
Peter Burns (1993)
Hannah Spencer (1993)
Mark Savill (1993)
Michael Hayton (1993)
Lisa Judge (1993)
Sebastian Clegg (1994)
David Boyle (1996)
Simon McCann (1996)
Richard Whitehall (1999)
Sophie Cartwright (1999)
Ross Olson (1999)
Howard Cohen (1999)

The Chambers: Deans Court Chambers is a progressive set with a reputation for the highest standards of professionalism, service and response to clients' needs. It offers specialist advocacy and drafting expertise at every level of seniority. Chambers' purpose-designed premises at 24 St John Street provide a wide range of services to clients. A new seminar suite enables them to deliver lectures and seminars on current topics of interest; video-conferencing has been installed; facilities for arbitration, mediation and alternative dispute resolution are also available.

Work Undertaken:

Civil Litigation: Personal injury (including injuries of the utmost severity, class actions, industrial disease, factory accidents, road traffic and credit hire); professional negligence, particularly clinical, lawyers, architects and surveyors; insurance (including coverage, Road Traffic Act and Motor Insurers' Bureau); contractual disputes; sale of goods; consumer credit; product liability; technology and construction; human rights; false imprisonment.

Commercial & Chancery: Including arbitration; banking; carriage of goods; civil fraud and tracing of assets; corporate and personal insolvency; company law; credit and leasing; financial services; injunctions and equitable remedies; insurance and reinsurance; intellectual property; landlord and tenant; 'old' Chancery; partnerships; pensions; sale of goods.

Family: Including matrimonial finance; children; incapacity and competence; public and administration; education and special educational needs; Inheritance Act claims; professional negligence; mediation.

Criminal: Including prosecution and defence work in all fields at every level, including homicide; offences of serious violence and sexual offences; commercial fraud; conspiracy; drug importation and supply; excise and revenue offences; health and safety.

Set No.
222 **EXCHANGE CHAMBERS**

4 Ralli Courts, West Riverside, Manchester, M3 5FT **Tel:** (0161) 833 2722 **Fax:** (0161) 833 2789 **Email:** info@exchangechambers.co.uk

Set No.
223 **KENWORTHY'S CHAMBERS** (Frank Burns)

Kenworthy's Chambers, 83 Bridge St, Manchester, M3 2RF
Tel: (0161) 832 4036 **Fax:** (0161) 832 0370 **DX:** 718200
Email: clerks@kenworthys.co.uk

Head of Chambers	Frank Burns
Practice Manager	Maria Rushworth
Clerk	Joan Walter
Listing Clerk	Paul Mander
Fees Clerk	Nicola Davies
Administrator	Sue Barlow
Tenants	17

Members:

Frank Burns (1971)
Richard Heap (1963)
Deborah Lambert (1977)
Barry Grennan (1977)
Patrick Cassidy (1982)
Gita Patel (1988)
Kathryn Korol (1996)
Andrew Marrs (1995)
Mark Smith (1997)
Janet Ruscoe (1995)
Imran Shafi (1996)
Geoff Whelan (1996)
Louise Kitchin (1998)
Vanessa Thomson (1998)
Sharon Amesu (1998)
Erica Carleton (2000)
Alison Mather (1997)

KENWORTHY'S CHAMBERS

The Chambers: The hallmark of Kenworthy's Chambers is its approachability, blended with a commitment to the highest professional standards.

Work Undertaken: The strengths of chambers lie in criminal law, family law and immigration matters. The criminal team divides into a defence team and a prosecution team of varying experience. A particular strength is the quality of chambers' defence work, which regularly involves cases of murder, gang violence, fraud and drug trafficking. The family team is hugely experienced in representing children's cases, working with guardians and local authorities including matters of the utmost gravity with links to criminal proceedings. Complex ancillary relief matters are a particular forte of the team. Chambers offer a comprehensive nationwide service on all apsects of immigration law and judicial review. Members of chambers also undertake personal injury work on a conditional fee and contract arrangements.

International: Languages spoken include Gujarati, Hindi, Punjabi and Urdu.

Recruitment: Chambers have an established training programme and are accredited by the Law Society, ILEX and the Bar Council as a training provider.

Set No.
224 **KINGSGATE CHAMBERS** (Beverley Lunt)

First Floor, Kingsgate House, 51-53 South King St, Manchester, M2 6DE **Tel:** (0161) 831 7477 **Fax:** (0161) 832 5645 **DX:** 710297 Manchester 3
Email: clerks@kingsgatechambers.co.uk

Set No. 225

8 KING ST (Keith Armitage QC)

8 King St, Manchester, M2 6AQ
Tel: (0161) 834 9560 **Fax:** (0161) 834 2733 **DX:** 14354 Manchester 1
Email: clerks@eightkingstreet.co.uk **Website:** www.8kingstreet.co.uk

Head of Chambers	Keith Armitage QC
Senior Clerk	Peter Whitman
Practice Manager & Clerk	David Lea
Clerks	David Haslam
	Martin Leech
Research & Marketing Manager	Catherine Healy LLM
Academic Consultant	Geraint Howells
Tenants	38

Members:

Keith Armitage QC (1970) (QC-1994)LLB
Clive Freedman QC (1978) (QC-1997)MA
Gerard McDermott QC (1978) (QC-1999)LLB
Elizabeth Rylands (1973)LLB
David Eccles (1976)MA (Cantab)
Jeffrey Terry (1976)LLB, MA, FCIArb
Digby C Jess (1978)PhD BSc , LLM, FCIArb
Philip Holmes (1980)MA (Cantab)
Glyn Williams (1981)BA
Kim Frances Foudy (1982)LLB
Farooq Ahmed (1983)LLB
Stephen Davies (1985)MA
Michael Smith (1989)MA, BCL
Mark Forte (1989)LLB
Simon Vaughan (1989)LLB, LLM
Ian Wood (1990)BA
Jonathan Thompson (1990)LLM, MA
Christopher Scorah (1991)BA
Timothy Hodgson (1991)BA, D.Phil
Alistair Bower (1986)LLB
Joanne Connolly (1992)LLB
Kevin Naylor (1992)MB,CH.B, MRCGP, LLB, LLM
Karim Sabry (1992)BA
Kirsten Barry (1993)LLB
John Parr (1989)LLB
Rachael Hamilton-Hague (1993)BA
Graham Bailey (1993)LLB
James Boyd (1994)LLB, LLM
Andrew Clark (1994)MA
David Sandiford (1995)BA
Paul Higgins (1996)BA
David Hoffman (1997)BA
Anna Short (1997)MA
Lee Nowland (1997)LLB
Nigel Edwards (1998)BA
Jane Bresnahan (1998)LLB
Zoe Allen (1999)LLB
Matthew Haisley (1999)LLB

The Chambers: A leading Manchester set offering high quality advice and advocacy services across a broad range of specialisations.

Work Undertaken: General common law; commercial and chancery; criminal law; personal injury; clinical and professional negligence; employment (including race and sex discrimination); commercial fraud; matrimonial and childcare law; landlord and tenant; contract (including building); administrative law; Anglo-American disputes; insurance law; arbitration; environmental law; company law; licensing; construction; sale of goods; consumer credit. Video-conferencing is available within chambers.

Set No. 226

40 KING ST

40 King St, Manchester, M2 6BA
Tel: (0161) 832 9082 **Fax:** (0161) 835 2139 **DX:** 718188 Mch 3
Email: clerks@40kingstreet.co.uk **Website:** www.40kingstreet.co.uk

Senior Clerk	William Brown
Bar Management Services	William Brown
	Colin Griffin, Michael Stubbs
Assistant Clerks	Lisa Williams, Paul Clarke
Tenants	49

Members:

Andrew Gilbart QC (1972) (QC-1991)
John Hoggett QC (1969) (QC-1986)
Peter Smith QC (1975) (QC-1992)
Stephen Sauvain QC (1977) (QC-1995)
Frances Patterson QC (1977) (QC-1998) †
Michael Booth QC (1981) (QC-1999)
Nicholas Braslavsky QC (1983) (QC-1999)
Vincent Fraser QC (1981) (QC-2001)
Paul Chaisty QC (1982) (QC-2001)
Eric Owen (1969)
Harold Halliday (1972)
Shokat Khan (1979)
David Manley (1981)
John Barrett (1982)
Alan Evans (1978)
Mark Halliwell (1985)
John Cooper (1985)
Simon Hilton (1987)
Katherine Dunn (1987)
Ruth Stockley (1988)
Fiona Ashworth (1988)
Paul Tucker (1990)
Geoffrey Pass (1975)
Andrew Singer (1990)
Stephen Pritchett (1990)
Lesley Anderson (1989)
Matthew Smith (1991)
Martin Carter (1992)
Wilson Horne (1992)
Lucy Powis (1992)
Mark Harper (1993)
Sarah Pritchard (1993)
Richard Lander (1993)
Ian Ponter (1993)
Simon Antrobus (1995)
Andrew Latimer (1995)
Louis Doyle (1996)
Elizabeth Berridge (1996)
Katie Nowell (1996)
Colin Crawford (1997)
Nicholas Siddall (1997)
Giles Cannock (1998)
Andrew McGee (1998)
Matthew Hall (1999)
Helen Mulholland (1999)
Catherine Brown (1999)
John Tackaberry QC (1967) (QC-1982) †
John Campbell (1981)(QC Scotland 1999) †
Julian Ghosh (1993) †

† Associate Member

The Chambers: A large and well-established set, the members of which appear before the full range of courts and statutory tribunals. Counsel are available at all ranks of seniority, including seven silks, and the breadth of individual specialities and aptitudes available in chambers mean that they offer a wide range of specialist advisory and advocacy services. Members have written, edited or contributed to a large number of legal journals, most notably in the fields of planning, local government and highway law.

Work Undertaken: Town and country planning; local government law and finance; administrative law; parliamentary law; compulsory purchase and compensation; highways law; environmental protection; public health; commercial chancery litigation; landlord and tenant law; law of trusts; partnerships; intellectual property; insolvency (corporate and individual); banking; wills and intestacy; civil liability; personal injury; professional liability; employment and industrial law; building disputes; consumer credit; sale of goods; family and matrimonial law; hire purchase; licensing; criminal law.

Additional Areas: Markets and fairs; trading standards; EU law; housing; data protection; company law; immigration and defamation. Members accept Direct Professional Access from the approved professions.

International: Languages include French, German, Punjabi, Urdu, Russian and Spanish.

Set No.
227 **LINCOLN HOUSE CHAMBERS** (Mukhtar Hussain QC)

5th Floor Lincoln House, 1 Brazennose Street, Manchester, M2 5EL **Tel:** (0161) 832 5701 **Fax:** (0161) 832 0839 **DX:** 14338 Manches 1 **Email:** info@lincolnhse.co.uk **Website:** www.lincolnhse.co.uk

Set No.
228 **MANCHESTER HOUSE CHAMBERS** (J.D.S. Wishart)

Manchester House Chambers, 18-22 Bridge St, Manchester, M3 3BZ **Tel:** (0161) 834 7007 **Fax:** (0161) 834 3462 **DX:** 718153 Manchester 3

Set No.
229 **MERCHANT CHAMBERS** (David Berkley QC)

Number One, North Parade, Parsonage Gardens, Manchester, M3 2NH
Tel: (0161) 839 7070 **Fax:** (0161) 839 7111 **DX:** 710280 Manchester 3
Email: inquiries@merchantchambers.com **Website:** www.merchantchambers.com

Head of Chambers	David Berkley QC
Senior Clerk	Alastair Campbell
Tenants	10

Members:

David Berkley QC (1979) (QC-1999)
David Uff (1981)
Neil Berragan (1982)
Stephen Cogley (1984)
Catherine Fisher (1990)
Andrew Noble (1992)FRICS FCIArb
Jonathan Rule (1993)
Stefan Brochwicz-Lewinski (1995)
Ghazan Mahmood (1997)
Susanne Muth (1998)

The Chambers: Merchant Chambers were founded in 1996 by established practitioners in order to provide a high quality service to the banking and business community in the north west region and beyond. Since its launch the chambers have attracted other specialists to become a leading commercial set on the Northern Circuit. The approach of the set is to offer effective advocacy at all levels and efficient and cost effective return of papers and advice. The set prides itself on delivering its services in a relaxed, unstuffy and down to earth manner. The work of chambers includes banking, insolvency, partnership and general commercial work. Full details can be found in the chambers information booklet available on request. In addition to its core services, Merchant Chambers provides training and offers seminars to solicitors.

Set No. 230

PEEL COURT CHAMBERS (Michael Shorrock QC)

Peel Court Chambers, 45 Hardman Street, Manchester, M3 3PL
Tel: (0161) 832 3791 **Fax:** (0161) 835 3054 **DX:** 14320
Email: clerks@peelct.co.uk

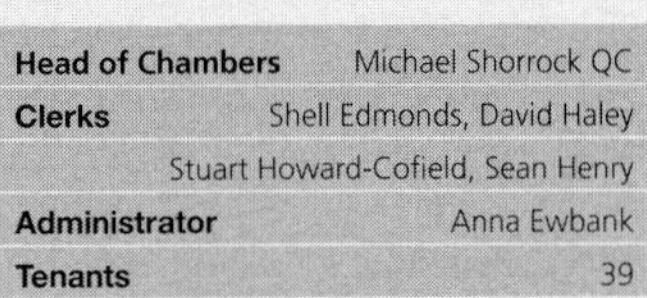

Head of Chambers	Michael Shorrock QC
Clerks	Shell Edmonds, David Haley
	Stuart Howard-Cofield, Sean Henry
Administrator	Anna Ewbank
Tenants	39

Members:

Michael Shorrock QC (1966) (QC-1988)
Anthony Morris QC (1970) (QC-1991)
David Lane QC (1968) (QC-1991)
Howard Bentham QC (1970) (QC-1996)
Paul Richardson (1972)
Stephen Meadowcroft (1973)
Anthony Russell QC (1974) (QC-1999)
Richard Marks QC (1975) (QC-1999)
Andrew O'Byrne (1978)
Andrew Long (1981)
Fiorella Brereton (1979)
David Pickup (1984)
Steven Johnson (1984)
Paul Sheridan (1984)
Richard Pearce (1985)
Julian Taylor (1986)
Jeremy Grout-Smith (1986)
Tina Landale (1988)
Neil Fryman (1989)
Mark Rhind (1989)
Martin Walsh (1990)
Rachel Smith (1990)
Graham Knowles (1990)
Simon Burrows (1990)
David Toal (1990)
Michael Lavery (1990)
William Baker (1991)
Mark Ainsworth (1992)
Henry Blackshaw (1993)
Richard Orme (1993)
Claire Evans (1994)
Rebecca Lloyd-Smith (1994)
June Morris (1995)
Mary Ruck (1993)
Darryl Allen (1995)
Gavin McBride (1996)
Anthony Mazzag (1996)
Alexandra Simmonds (1998)
Maisie Burke (1999)

The Chambers: A large general common law set including six QCs.

Work Undertaken: A wide range of common law work is covered, with particular emphasis on crime; clinical negligence and medical law; licensing (gaming and liquor); commercial fraud; personal injury; professional negligence; family law including childcare and matrimonial finance. Chambers also provide expertise in consumer credit and commercial law; landlord and tenant; health and safety law; EC and revenue law.

International: Languages spoken include French, German and Mandarin.

Set No. 231

ST. JAMES'S CHAMBERS (Robert Sterling & Ian Leeming QC)

St. James's Chambers, 68 Quay St, Manchester, M3 3EJ
Tel: (0161) 834 7000 **Fax:** (0161) 834 2341 **DX:** 14350 M1
Email: clerks@stjameschambers.co.uk

Head of Chambers	Robert Sterling
	Ian Leeming QC
Senior Clerk	Stephen J. Diggles
Tenants	18

Members:

Ian Leeming QC (1970) (QC-1988) +
Robert Sterling (1970)
Percy Wood (1961)
Barrie Searle (1975) +
David Porter (1980)
Timothy Lyons (1980)
Michael Mulholland (1976)
David Binns (1983)
Lucy Wilson-Barnes (1989)
Sarah Wheeldon (1990)
Ruth Tankel (1990)
James Hurd (1994)
David Calvert (1995)
James Fryer-Spedding (1994)
Richard Moore (1992)
Christopher Taft (1997)
Fayaz Hammond (1999)
Paul Tindall (1999)
Anthony Rubin (1960) *
Joseph Jaconelli (1972) *

* Door Tenant + Recorder

The Chambers: A Chancery and general common law set of chambers.

Work Undertaken:

Chancery: All aspects of property law, including land law; mortgages; nuisance and trespass; rights of way; landlord and tenant; joint property; agricultural holdings work; trusts; settlements and wills; pension schemes; charities; personal property; intellectual property; business and commercial law, including business agreements and breach of contract; injunctions and other equitable remedies; fraud; professional negligence and indemnity insurance; loans and securities; companies and partnerships; associations; receivers; bankruptcy and insolvency; confidential information; taxation; tribunals.

Common Law: Including building and construction law; sale of goods; contract law; consumer and consumer credit law; crime; employment law; employers' liability and health and safety at work; environmental law; family (divorce, children, matrimonial finance and property); licensing; personal injuries; professional and clinical negligence; police disciplinary hearings; road traffic cases; tribunals.

Publications: Timothy Lyons has written works on inheritance tax and insolvency, and sits on the editorial board of the *Law and Tax Review.*

International: French, German, Hebrew, Russian and Spanish are spoken.

Set No.
232

9 ST. JOHN STREET (John Hand QC)

9 St. John Street, Manchester, M3 4DN
Tel: (0161) 955 9000 **Fax:** (0161) 955 9001 **DX:** 14326
Email: clerks@9stjohnstreet.co.uk **Website:** www.9stjohnstreet.co.uk

Head of Chambers	John Hand QC
Chambers Administrator	Jo Kelly
Senior Clerk (Crime)	Graham Livesey
Senior Clerk (Civil)	Tony Morrissey
Senior Clerk (Family)	Paul Morecroft
Assistant Civil Clerk	Jane Slingsby
Assistant Criminal Clerk	Susan Lea
Tenants	43

Members:

John Hand QC (1972) (QC-1988)
Ian Leeming QC (1970) (QC-1988)
Roderick Carus QC (1971) (QC-1990)
Charles Garside QC (1971) (QC-1993)
Jeremy McMullen QC (1971) (QC-1994)
Timothy Horlock QC (1981) (QC-1997)
Matthias Kelly QC (1979) (QC-1999)
Nicholas Hinchliffe QC (1980) (QC-1999)
Terence Rigby (1971)
Michael Johnson (1972)
Leslie Hull (1972)
John Dowse (1973)
Peter Cadwallader (1973)
Christine Riley (1974)
Simon Temple (1977)
Michael Murray (1979)
Nicholas Clarke (1981)
Nigel Grundy (1983)
Michael Leeming (1983)
Gillian Irving (1984)
Paul Gilroy (1985)
Carlo Breen (1987)
David Gilchrist (1987)
Nicola Gatto (1987)
Simon James (1988)
David Friesner (1988)
Thomas Fitzpatrick (1988)
Ian Little (1989)
Christopher L.P. Kennedy (1989)
Nigel Bird (1991)
Anthony Howard (1992)
Rachel Wedderspoon (1993)
Jaime Hamilton (1993)
Alaric Bassano (1993)
Tariq Sadiq (1993)
Robert Darbyshire (1995)
Brian McCluggage (1995)
Gary Woodhall (1997)
Kate Hollyoak (1997)
Rachael Heppenstall (1997)
Helen Redmond (1999)
Sophie Buckley (1999)
Lucinda Leeming (1999)

The Chambers: In order to meet the increasing demand for specialisation, members of chambers have formed themselves into the following five special interest groups: employment, criminal, commercial and property, personal injury and family. They are therefore able to offer specialised advice and advocacy in the following areas: employment; industrial relations and discrimination; human/civil rights; personal injury; clinical negligence; environmental law; commercial and property with general chancery; crime; trading standards work; family and mental health. Chambers also has an association with chambers at 42 Castle Street, Liverpool.

Set No.
233

18 ST JOHN STREET (Jonathan Foster QC)

18 St. John Street, Manchester, M3 4EA
Tel: (0161) 278 1800 **Fax:** (0161) 835 2051 **DX:** 728854 Manchester 4
Email: clerks@eighteen-stjohn.co.uk **Website:** www.eighteen-stjohn.co.uk

Head of Chambers	Jonathan Foster QC
Senior Clerks	John Hammond
	William Sheldon
Chambers Administrator	Pippa Jessop
Tenants	37

Members:

Jonathan Foster QC (1970) (QC-1989)
Peter Birkett QC (1972) (QC-1989)
Martin Steiger QC (1969) (QC-1994)
Raymond Wigglesworth QC (1974) (QC-1999)
Roger Hedgeland (1972)
Alastair Forrest (1972)
Paul Dockery (1973)
Jennifer Caldwell (1973)
Paul O'Brien (1974)
Christopher Diamond (1975)
Roger Stout (1976)
Malcolm McEwan (1976)
Nicholas Fewtrell (1977)
Mark Laprell (1979)
David Heaton (1983)
Richard Vardon (1985)
Brian Williams (1986)
Yvonne Healing (1988)
Toby Sasse (1988)
Samantha Birtles (1989)
Nigel Poole (1989)
Elisabeth Tythcott (1989)
Edward Morgan (1989)
Mark Benson (1992)
Susan Harrison (1993)
Raquel Simpson (1990)
Simon Csoka (1991)
Rachel Shenton (1993)
Chris Daw (1993)
Sarah Williams (1995)
Simon Kilvington (1995)
Andrew Moore (1996)
Saul Brody (1996)
Rachel Faux (1997)
Richard Chapman (1998)
N Jonathan Grierson (1999)
Darren Dunn (1999)

The Chambers: A general common law chambers with distinct civil, family and criminal departments, together with four chancery practitioners and expertise at all levels.

Set No.
234 **24A ST. JOHN STREET** (Paul Chambers)
24A St. John Street, Manchester, M3 4DF **Tel:** (0161) 833 9628 **Fax:** (0161) 834 0243 **DX:** 710301 (Manchester 3) **Email:** clerks@24aStJohnStreet.co.uk

Set No.
235 **28 ST. JOHN ST**
28 St. John St, Manchester, M3 4DJ **Tel:** (0161) 834 8418 **Fax:** (0161) 835 3929 **DX:** 728861 Manchester 4 **Email:** clerk@28stjohn.co.uk

Set No.
236 **YOUNG STREET CHAMBERS** (Lesley Newton)
38 Young Street, Manchester, M3 3FT **Tel:** (0161) 833 0489 **Fax:** (0161) 835 3938 **DX:** 25583 M5 **Email:** clerks@young-st-chambers.com **Website:** www.clerks

Middlesbrough

Set No.
237 **COUNSEL'S CHAMBERS** (Stuart Lightwing)
Tudor House, Church Lane, Nunthorpe, Middlesbrough, TS7 0PD **Tel:** (01642) 315000 **Fax:** (01642) 315500 **DX:** 60524 (Middlesbrough)

Newcastle upon Tyne

Set No.
238 **BROAD CHARE CHAMBERS** (Patrick Cosgrove QC)

Broad Chare Chambers, 33 Broad Chare, Newcastle upon Tyne, NE1 3DQ
Tel: (0191) 232 0541 **Fax:** (0191) 261 0043 **DX:** 61001
Email: clerks@broadchasechambers.law.co.uk
Website: www.broadchasechambers.law.co.uk

Head of Chambers	Patrick Cosgrove QC
Senior Clerk	Brian Bell
Tenants	39

Members:

Patrick Cosgrove QC (1976) (QC-1994)
James Chadwin QC (1958) (QC-1976)
Paul Batty QC (1975) (QC-1995)
James Harper (1957)
Giles Bavidge (1968)
Ian Dawson (1971)
Euan Duff (1973)
Christine Harmer (1973)
J Ronald Mitchell (1973)
Robin Horner (1975)
Roger Elsey (1977)
Christopher Dorman O'Gowan (1979)
Thomas Finch (1981)
Brian Mark (1981)
Kester Armstrong (1982)
Lesley McKenzie (1983)
Ian Kennerley (1983)
Pauline Moulder (1983)
John O'Sullivan (1984)
Richard Selwyn-Sharpe (1985)
Anne Richardson (1986)
Anthony Davis (1986)
David Rowlands (1988)
Mark Styles (1988)
Joseph O'Brien (1989)
James Brown (1990)
Stephanie Jarron (1990)
Julie Clemitson (1991)
Claire Middleton (1991)
Michelle Temple (1992)
Rachel Smith (1992)
S Anderson (1993)
Elizabeth Lugg (1994)
Sara Robinson (1994)
Nicholas Peacock (1996)
Jodie James-Stadden (1996)
Sam Faulks (1997)
Kirti Jeram (1997)
Andrew Walker (1998)

The Chambers: A large and long-established set, with an increasing range of specialists. Four members of chambers are Recorders.

Work Undertaken:
Criminal Work: All aspects.
Family Law: Including all aspects of child law, financial disputes, divorce, Inheritance Act cases and emergency protection.
Civil Work: Including personal injury, professional negligence, general contract, building disputes, employment law, licensing, planning and some commercial.
Chancery Work: Most aspects.

Set No.
239 **ENTERPRISE CHAMBERS** (Anthony Mann QC)

65 Quayside, Newcastle upon Tyne, NE1 3DS
Tel: (0191) 222 3344 **Fax:** (0191) 222 3340 **DX:** 61134 Newcastle upon Tyne 1
Email: enterprise.newcastle@dial.pipex.com
Website: www.enterprisechambers.com

Head of Chambers:	Anthony Mann QC
Senior Clerk:	Antony Armstrong (London)
Practice Development Clerk:	Barry Clayton
Clerk:	Dylan Wendleken
Tenants:	26

For a full list of members please see the London entry. For further information about the set please visit the chambers' website.

Set No.
240 **MILBURN HOUSE CHAMBERS** (Paul Cape)

E Floor, Milburn House, Dean Street, Newcastle upon Tyne, NE1 1LE
Tel: (0191) 230 5511 **Fax:** (0191) 230 5544 **DX:** 716640 Newcastle 20
Email: admin@milburnhousechambers.co.uk
Website: www.milburnhousechambers.co.uk

Head of Chambers	Paul Cape
Practice Manager/Senior Clerk	Norma McKellar
Clerk/Admin	Muriel Hurst
Tenants	5

Members:

Paul Cape (1990)	John Falkenstein (1996)	David Mason (1984)
Jane Woodwark (1995)	Seamus Sweeney (1989)	Robert Monks *

* Door Tenant

The Chambers: Chambers was founded in 1998 with two members and currently has five members and one door tenant.

Work Undertaken: Four members of chambers practise almost exclusively in the fields of employment and discrimination. Chambers has a strong following amongst public sector employers. One member specialises in traditional and commercial chancery matters.

Recruitment: Consideration will be given to written applications for tenancy and pupillage from those with excellent academic qualifications and practical experience of industrial relations. Applications to Head of Chambers.

Set No.
241 **NEW COURT CHAMBERS** (David Robson QC)

3 Broad Chare, Newcastle upon Tyne, NE1 3DQ **Tel:** (0191) 232 1980 **Fax:** (0191) 232 3730 **DX:** 61012

Set No.
242 **PLOWDEN BUILDINGS** (William Lowe QC)

Lombard House, Lombard Street, Newcastle upon Tyne, NE1 1AE
Tel: (0191) 245 4647 **Fax:** (0191) 245 4650 **DX:** 61062 Newcastle-upon-Tyne

Head of Chambers:	William Lowe QC

See the entry under Plowden Buildings, London for more information.

Set No.
243

TRINITY CHAMBERS (Toby Hedworth QC)

Trinity Chambers, 9-12 Trinity Chare, Quayside, Newcastle upon Tyne, NE1 3DF
Tel: (0191) 232 1927 **Fax:** (0191) 232 7975 **DX:** 61185 (Newcastle)
Email: info@trinitychambers.co.uk **Website:** www.trinitychambers.co.uk

Head of Chambers	Toby Hedworth QC
Practice Director	Simon Stewart
Criminal Clerks	Sharon Robson
	Alisa Charlton
Civil & Family Clerks	Chris Swann
	Clare Thomas
Tenants	37

Members:

Toby Hedworth QC (1975) (QC-1996)
John Milford QC (1969) (QC-1989)
Brian Forster QC (1977) (QC-1999)
Paul Sloan QC (1981) (QC-2001)
Charles Kelly (1965)
Stephen Duffield (1969)
Christopher John Knox (1974)
Graham Duff (1976)
Christopher Vane (1976)
John Lowe (1976)
David Callan (1979)
John Wilkinson (1979)
Jacqueline Smart (1981)
James Richardson (1982)
Peter Walsh (1982)
Tim Spain (1983)
Rachel Hudson (1985)
Fiona McCrae (1987)
Paul Richardson (1986)
Caroline Goodwin (1988)
Shaun Routledge (1988)
Tim Gittins (1990)
Crispin Oliver (1990)
Robert Adams (1993)
Michael Ditchfield (1993)
Rosalind Scott Bell (1993)
Nicholas Stonor (1993)
Jane Gilbert (1994)
Charles Holland (1994)
Sarah Woolrich (1994)
Gavin Doig (1995)
Paul Caulfield (1996)
Fiona Parkin (1998)
Michael Graham (1999)
Simon Goldberg (1999)
Rachel Hedworth (1999)
Angela Nelson (2000)

INVESTOR IN PEOPLE

The Chambers: Trinity Chambers is a leading and progressive common law set in the north of England that has completed a major review of its services, procedures and client care standards. This determination to modernise has resulted in the award of the Bar Mark in April 2000, the Bar Council's kitemark of quality assurance. Trinity Chambers was the first set north of London and the fourth in the country to receive this acknowledgement of quality assurance and attention to client care. All members and staff of chambers believe in the importance of the Bar Mark accreditation and welcome feedback from clients as well as guidance on how services may be improved. Trinity Chambers was also awarded the Investors in People in 2000 which, for a profession that deals with people, is singularly appropriate. The barristers of Trinity Chambers are members of one or more of the six practice groups: criminal law (four QCs and 17 Juniors); common law (one QC and 10 Juniors); family law (one QC and 11 Juniors); chancery and commercial (six Juniors); employment law (six Juniors); licensing law (two QCs and 4 Juniors). As well as having the silks' clerk, chambers have two specialist clerking teams (criminal law and civil and family law). Each practice group has a member who is prepared to discuss areas of work, specialisations and notable abilities. Fees are negotiated through the clerks from the outset. Chambers have an open charging policy. Urgent work receives special handling. As part of the determination to provide a high quality service, Trinity Chambers has made a significant investment in the provision of support facilities.
Chambers have disabled access, video and audio conferencing facilities and the on-going seminar programme. Practice groups regularly give seminars, with the Law Society's CPD accreditation, that are free to clients; in 2000 they gave seminars in Newcastle and Middlesbrough at which over 400 solicitors attended. The set has its own Equality Policy, copies of which are available on request.Trinity Chambers understands the importance of being approachable and so welcomes inquiries, of a general nature to the Practice Director, or of aspects of the barristers' work through the appropriate specialist clerks. Chambers' brochure is also available on request. (Can you spot the ghost?)

Northampton

Set No.
244

CHARTLANDS CHAMBERS (Jane Page & Joy Pinkham)

3 St Giles Terrace, Northampton, NN1 2BN
Tel: (01604) 603322 **Fax:** (01604) 603388 **DX:** 12408 Northampton

Head of Chambers:	Jane Page
	Joy Pinkham
Senior Clerk:	Andrew Davies
Tenants:	12

Family and general common law service including matrimonial finance; cohabitation disputes; children; domestic violence; personal injury; employment; tort; contract; criminal law.

Set No.
245

CLARENDON CHAMBERS

5 St. Giles Terrace, Northampton, NN1 2BN
Tel: (01604) 637245 **Fax:** (01604) 633167 **DX:** 12404 Northampton

Senior Clerk: Russell Burton (020) 7681 7681

Annexe of Clarendon Chambers, 7 Stone Buildings, Lincoln's Inn, LondonWC2A 3SZ Tel: (020) 7681 7681

Norwich

Set No.
246 **EAST ANGLIAN CHAMBERS** (Roderick Newton)

East Anglian Chambers, 15 The Close, Norwich, NR1 4DZ
Tel: (01603) 617351 **Fax:** (01603) 751400 **DX:** 5213
Email: norwichchambers@dial.pipex.com **Website:** www.ealaw.co.uk

Head of Chambers	Roderick Newton
Senior Clerk	Stephen Collis
Administrator	Carol Bull (01473) 254559
Tenants	53

Members:

Roderick Newton (1982)
John Akast (1968)
John Wardlow (1971)
Peter Wain (1972)
Andrew Marsden (1975)
Caroline Bryant (1976)
Celia Miller (1978)
David Pugh (1978)
Martyn Levett (1978)
Timothy McLoughlin (1978)
Graham Sinclair (1979)
John Hamey (1979)
Anthony Kefford (1980)
John Brooke-Smith (1981)
Simon Redmayne (1982)
Graham Parnell (1982)
Michael Lane (1983)
Hugh Vass (1983)
Jane Davies (1983)
Lindsay Cox (1984)
Janet Bettle (1985)
Steven Dyble (1986)
Anthony Bate (1987)
Nicholas Elcombe (1987)
Rebecca Degel (1987)
Jonathan Seely (1987)
Rosalyne Mandil-Wade (1988)
David Richards (1989)
Andrew Jackson (1990)
Ray Smith (1991)
Katharine Bundell (1991)
Marika Bell (1991)
Jeremy Dugdale (1992)
Carole Parry-Jones (1992)
Dominic Barratt (1992)
Helen Gilbertson (1993)
Amanda Rippon (1993)
Patricia Walsh (1993)
Jacqui Hanlon (1994)
Richard Kelly (1994)
Jude Durr (1995)
Sally Freeman (1995)
Alan Wheetman (1995)
David Wilson (1996)
Fiona Baruah (1996)
Ashley Thain (1996)
Saqib Rauf (1996)
Marc Cannatella (1997)
David Sunman (1997)
Stephen Goodfellow (1997)
Andrew Shaw (1998)
Joanne Bradbury (1999)
Ian Hugh Dyble (2000)

The Chambers: For further information, please see full entry under East Anglian Chambers, Ipswich.

Set No.
247 **OCTAGON HOUSE CHAMBERS** (Andrew Lindqvist)
Octagon House Chambers, 19 Colegate, Norwich, NR3 1AT **Tel:** (01603) 623186 **Fax:** (01603) 760519 **DX:** 5249 Norwich-1
Email: admin@octagon-chambers.co.uk

Nottingham

Set No.
248 **NO.1 HIGH PAVEMENT** (John B. Milmo QC)
No.1 High Pavement, Nottingham, NG1 1HF **Tel:** (0115) 941 8218 **Fax:** (0115) 941 8240 **DX:** 10168 Nottingham

Set No.
249 **KING CHARLES HOUSE CHAMBERS** (William Everard)
King Charles House, Standard Hill, Nottingham, NG1 6FX **Tel:** (0115) 941 8851 **Fax:** (0115) 941 4169 **DX:** 10042 **Email:** clerks@kch.co.uk
Website: www.kch.co.uk

Set No.
250 **ROPEWALK CHAMBERS** (Ian McLaren QC)

24 The Ropewalk, Nottingham, NG1 5EF
Tel: (0115) 947 2581 **Fax:** (0115) 947 6532 **DX:** 10060 Nottingham 17
Email: clerks@ropewalk.co.uk **Website:** www.ropewalk.co.uk

Head of Chambers	Ian McLaren QC
Senior Clerk	David Austin
Clerk	Tony Hill
Tenants	37

Members:

Ian McLaren QC (1962) (QC-1993)
William Woodward QC (1964) (QC-1985)
Richard Maxwell QC (1968) (QC-1988)
Anthony Goldstaub QC (1972) (QC-1992)
Robert Owen QC (1977) (QC-1996)
G M Jarand (1965)
Graham Machin (1965)
Richard Burns (1967)
Richard Swain (1969)
Antony Berrisford (1972)
Douglas Herbert (1973)
Stephen Beresford (1976)
Simon Gash (1977)
Alison Hampton (1977)
Simon Beard (1980)
Jayne Adams (1982)
Rosalind Coe (1983)
Richard Hedley (1983)
Soofi Din (1984)
Dominic Nolan (1985)
Bryony Clark (1985)
Andrew Prestwich (1986)
Patrick Limb (1987)
Richard Seabrook (1987)
Philip Turton (1989)
Toby Stewart (1989)
Jinder Boora (1990)
Jonathan Mitchell (1992)
Jason Cox (1992)
Deborah Davies (1993)
Elizabeth Hodgson (1993)
Richard Gregory (1993)
Andrew Hogan (1996)
Mark Diggle (1996)
Judith Butler (1997)
Nick Blake (1997)
Michael Bridge (1994)

The Chambers: A long established set which has grown to become one of the largest purely civil sets outside London. Chambers undertake a broad range of general common law, commercial, planning and environmental, employment and human rights cases. Enhanced by a competitive pricing policy, punctual return of paperwork and the utilisation of current information technology, members of chambers offer a specialist independent advisory and advocacy referral service. Chambers are strategically positioned, both regionally and nationally, to offer the services of individuals or teams with expertise of the highest calibre.

Work Undertaken:
Personal Injury & Clinical Negligence: The personal injury and clinical negligence specialist group covers all areas including industrial and insidious disease (asbestos-induced, asthma, cancer, dermatitis, poisoning, radiation, repetitive strain injury, stress at work, vibration white finger amongst others); every aspect of clinical negligence litigation; disaster; employers' liability; product liability; road traffic; sports injuries; health and safety at work.
Business & Property: Work undertaken by the business and property group includes commercial (banking, competition, consumer credit and protection, corporate finance and sale of goods); professional negligence (legal, financial and negligence within the building, engineering and surveying professions); chancery (boundaries, conveyancing, easements, inheritance, probate, wills and trusts); building and construction; company; engineering; intellectual property; landlord and tenant (commercial, residential, agricultural and housing); partnership.
Planning & Environment: The planning and environment group offers advice and representation in the following areas : administrative; compulsory purchase; heritage; judicial review; lands tribunal; local government; nature conservation; pollution; rating and planning enquiries.
Employment: The work of the employment practice group covers cases involving wrongful and unfair dismissal; D.D.A.; discrimination; European related matters; human rights; restrictive covenants; trade secrets; trade unions and TUPE.
Additional Specialisations: Full arbitration, including alternative dispute resolution (ADR).

Clientele: All clients, without discrimination: insurer; trade union; corporate; local government; privately funded or otherwise. Direct Professional Access is available.

Set No.
251 **ST. MARY'S CHAMBERS FAMILY LAW CHAMBERS** (Christopher M. Butler)

50 High Pavement, Nottingham, NG1 1HW **Tel:** (0115) 950 3503 **Fax:** (0115) 958 3060 **DX:** 10036 **Email:** clerks@smc.law.co.uk
Website: www.barristersnottingham.co.uk

Oxford

Set No.
252 HARCOURT CHAMBERS (June Rodgers)

Churchill House, 3 St. Aldates Courtyard, St. Aldates, Oxford, OX1 1BA
Tel: (01865) 791559 **Fax:** (01865) 791585 **DX:** 96453 Oxford 4
Email: clerks@harcourtchambers.law.co.uk **Website:** www.harcourtchambers.law.co.uk

Head of Chambers:	June Rodgers
Senior Clerk:	Brian Wheeler
Tenants:	24

Annexe of Harcourt Chambers (June Rodgers QC), Temple, London. See under entry in London.

Set No.
253 KING'S BENCH CHAMBERS (Roger Ellis QC)

King's Bench Chambers, 32 Beaumont St., Oxford, OX1 2NP
Tel: (01865) 311066 **Fax:** (01865) 311077 **DX:** 4318 Oxford
Email: clerks@13kbw.co.uk **Website:** www.13kbw.co.uk

Head of Chambers	Roger Ellis QC
Senior Clerk	Stephen Buckingham
Chambers Director	Stephen Rogers (020) 7353 7204
Chambers Adminstrator	Penny McFall
Tenants	38

13
KBW

Members:

Roger Ellis QC (1962) (QC-1996)
Graeme Williams QC (1959) (QC-1983)
Julian Baughan QC (1967) (QC-1990)
David Ashton (1962)
Alexander Dawson (1969)
Anthony McGeorge (1969)
Robert Lamb (1973)
David Richardson (1973)
Deirdre Goodwin (1974)
Jane Tracy Forster (1975)
Paul W. Reid (1975)
David Bright (1976)
Simon Hughes M.P. (1974)
Simon Draycott (1977)
Nigel Daly (1979)
Nicholas Syfret (1979)
Andrew Glennie (1982)
A. John Williams (1983)
Andrew Pote (1983)
Jonathan Coode (1984)
Neil Vickery (1985)
Neil Moore (1986)
Sarah Gibbons (1987)
Arthur Blake (1988)
Sinclair Cramsie (1988)
Fiona Hay (1989)
Adrian Higgins (1990)
Edmund Walters (1991)
Heather Wenlock (1991)
Vivian Walters (1991)
Deshpal Singh Panesar (1993)
Paul Mitchell (1994)
Susan Chan (1994)
Patrick Wainwright (1994)
Rachel Drake (1995)
Lucy Owens (1997)
Matthew White (1997)
Thomas Payne (1998)

Peterborough

Set No.
254 FENNERS CHAMBERS (Lindsay Davies)

Fenners Chambers, 8-12 Priestgate, Peterborough, PE1 1JA
Tel: (01733) 562030 **Fax:** (01733) 343660 **DX:** 12314 Peterborough 1
Email: clerks@fennerschambers.co.uk **Website:** www.fennerschambers.co.uk

Head of Chambers	Lindsay Davies
Tenants	30

Members:

Lindsay Davies (1975) +
Kenneth Wheeler (1956) *
Geraint Jones (1972)
Andrew Gore (1973)
Stephen Franklin (1974)
Susan Espley (1976)
Caroline Pointon (1976)
Oliver Heald (1977)
Simon Tattersall (1977)
Paul Leigh-Morgan (1978)
Tim Brown (1980)
Paul Hollow (1981)
Andrew Gordon-Saker (1981)
Stuart Bridge (1981) *
Martin Collier (1982)
Liza Gordon-Saker (1982)
Meryl Hughes (1987)
George Foxwell (1987)
Alasdair Wilson (1988)
Clive Pithers (1989)
Jeffrey Deegan (1989)
Andrew Taylor (1989)
Sally Hobson (1991)
Caroline Horton (1993)
Katharine Ferguson (1995)
William Josling (1995)
Daniel Pitt (1995)
Mike Magee (1997)
Roderick Spinks (1997)
George Keightley (1997)
Giles Surman (1997) *
Alasdair Foster (1998)
Martin Kingerley (1999)

* Door Tenant + Recorder

The Chambers: Please refer to the main entry under Cambridge.

et No.
255 REGENCY CHAMBERS

Cathedral Square, Peterborough, PE1 1XW **Tel:** (01733) 315215 **Fax:** (01733) 315851 **DX:** 12349 Peterborough 1
Email: clerks@regencychambers.law.co.uk

Portsmouth

Set No. 256

GUILDHALL CHAMBERS PORTSMOUTH (Lee Young)

Prudential Buildings, 16 Guildhall Walk, Portsmouth, PO1 2DE
Tel: (023) 9275 2400 **Fax:** (023) 9275 3100 **DX:** 2225 Portsmouth 1

Head of Chambers	Lee Young
Senior Clerk	Tristan Thwaites
Junior Clerk	Jodi McGuire
Tenants	17

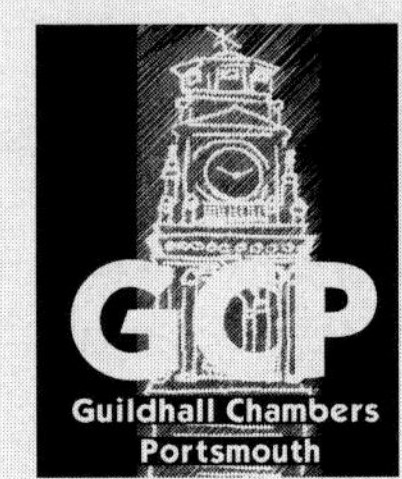

Members:

Lee Young (1991)
Peter Griffith (1964)
Peter Fortune (1978)
John Sabine (1979)
Richard Colbey (1984)
Stuart Ellacott (1989)
Sheila Taurah (1991)
Lisa England (1992)
Lincoln Brookes (1992)
Yasmin Hall (1993)
Tim Concannon (1993)
Martyn Booth (1996)
James Britton (1996)
Richard Withey (1996)
Robyn Day (1997)
John Atwill (1997)
Roderick Jones (1983) *
Edo de Vries (Ret.) (1969) †

* Door Tenant † Associate Member

The Chambers: An established common law set of chambers handling a wide range of law including landlord and tenant, personal injury, professional negligence, family and crime.

Set No. 257

PORTSMOUTH BARRISTERS' CHAMBERS (Andrew Parsons)

Victory House, 7 Bellevue Terrace, Portsmouth, PO5 3AT
Tel: (023) 9283 1292 **Fax:** (023) 9229 1262 **DX:** 2239 Portsmouth
Email: clerks@portsmouthbar.com **Website:** www.portsmouthbar.com

Head of Chambers:	Andrew Parsons
Senior Clerk:	Jackie Morrison
Tenants:	5

Chambers undertakes predominantly civil work and aims to provide a modern, high quality, fast, friendly and efficient service. A brochure is available on request.
Business & Commerce: Arbitration, carriage of goods, contract, company, construction and partnership.
Family & Matrimonial: Ancillary relief.
Negligence: Especially professional negligence.
Property & Finance: Banking, consumer credit, financial services, insolvency, land law, mortgages, pensions and trusts.

Preston

Set No. 258

15 WINCKLEY SQUARE (R. Stephen Dodds)

15 Winckley Square, Preston, PR1 3JJ
Tel: (01772) 252828 **Fax:** (01772) 258520 **DX:** 17110 Preston 1
Email: clerks@15winckleysq.co.uk **Website:** www.15winckleysq.co.uk

Head of Chambers	R. Stephen Dodds
Senior Clerk	Michael Jones
Tenants	34

Members:

R. Stephen Dodds (1976)
Roger M. Baldwin (1969)
Simon Newell (1973)
Kenneth Hind (1973)
Robert Crawford (1976)
P. Nicholas D. Kennedy (1977)
Timothy G. White (1978)
Richard A. Haworth (1978)
David J. Kenny (1982)
Jane E. Cross (1982)
Anthony Cross (1982)
Paul Hart (1982)
Paul Hague (1983)
John Woodward (1984)
Richard M. Hunt (1985)
D. Mark Stuart (1985)
Richard J. Bennett (1986)
Bruce Henry (1988)
Peter J. Anderson (1988)
Kathryn Johnson (1989)
Samantha Bowcock (1990)
Michael Whyatt (1992)
Louise Harvey (1991)
Julie Taylor (1992)
Fraser Livesey (1992)
Jonathan Buchan (1994)
Martin Hackett (1994)
Lee Blakey (1995)
Paul Davis (1996)
Jacob Dyer (1995)
Paul Gillott (1996)
Zabeda Maqsood (1996)
Prudence Beever (2000)
Saima Bhat (1999)

The Chambers: A medium sized set, seeking to provide a comprehensive service to solicitor clients both in private and institutional practice throughout the town, the county and beyond into Cumbria, Manchester and Merseyside. Several tenants are members of the Family Law Bar Association.

Work Undertaken: All common law work, with particular emphasis and experience in all areas of family work; crime; contract; personal and industrial injury; licensing; planning; landlord and tenant; employment law. Work on a Direct Access basis is accepted. Expanding Chancery and associated case types.

Southampton

Set No.
259 **17 CARLTON CRESCENT** (Jeremy S. Gibbons QC)

17 Carlton Crescent, Southampton, SO15 2XR **Tel:** (023) 8032 0320/2003 **Fax:** (023) 8032 0321 **DX:** 96875 Southampton 10
Email: sue@jg17cc.co.uk **Website:** www.jeremygibbonsqc.co.uk

Set No.
260 **EIGHTEEN CARLTON CRESCENT** (Martin Blount)

Eighteen Carlton Crescent, Southampton, SO15 2ET
Tel: (023) 8063 9001 **Fax:** (023) 8033 9625 **DX:** 96877 Southampton
Email: clerks@18carltoncrescent.co.uk **Website:** www.18carltoncrescent.co.uk

Head of Chambers	Martin Blount
Senior Clerk	Lynda Knight
	Paul Cooke
Tenants	19

Members:

Andrew Massey (1969)
Ashley Ailes (1975)
Gary Fawcett (1975)
Charles Cochand (1978)
Angus Robertson (1978)
Simon Lillington (1980)
Richard Egleton (1981)
Martin Blount (1982)
Elizabeth Manuel (1987)
Andrew Houston (1989)
Omar Malik (1990)
Christine Munks (1991)
Imogen Robins (1991)
Peter Glenser (1993)
Sally Carter (1994)
Richard Hall (1995)
Peter Asteris (1996)
Timothy Dracass (1998)
Rachel Robertson (1998)
Guy Boney QC (1968) (QC-1990) *
Helene Pines Richman (1992) *

* Door Tenant

Work Undertaken: General common law, including personal injury; criminal law; family and matrimonial law, including child care law, wardship and matrimonial property; landlord and tenant; planning; employment; commercial law; licensing; professional negligence; Chancery.

Set No.
261 **COLLEGE CHAMBERS** (Robin Belben)

College Chambers, 19 Carlton Crescent, Southampton, SO1 2ET
Tel: (023) 8023 0338 **Fax:** (023) 8023 0376 **DX:** 38533 (Southampton 3)

Head of Chambers	Robin Belben
Senior Clerk	Wayne Effeny
Tenants	19

Members:

Robin Belben (1969)
Kenneth Pain (1969)
Derek Marshall (1980)
Douglas Taylor (1981)
Mark Courtney Stewart (1989)
Anthony Hand (1989)
Jessica Habel (1991)
Gary Self (1991)
Catherine Breslin (1990)
Andrew Kinghorn (1991)
Daniel Nother (1994)
Arabella Grundy (1995)
Andrew Lorie (1996)
Baljinder Bath (1996)
Graeme Harrison (1997)
Amanda Gillett (1998)
Anil Patil (1999)
Andrew Bond (1999)
Katherine Huyton (1999)

Work Undertaken: General common law including family and matrimonial, childcare law, wardship, matrimonial property and cohabitee disputes; personal injury; contract; tort; landlord and tenant; employment; licensing; professional and medical negligence; commercial law; chancery; land law (including boundary disputes); criminal law. Instructing solicitors are always welcome to have an informal discussion with the clerks.

Swansea

Set No.
262 **ISCOED CHAMBERS** (Trefor Davies)

Iscoed Chambers, 86 St Helen's Rd, Swansea, SA1 4BQ
Tel: (01792) 652988/9 **Fax:** (01792) 458089 **DX:** 39554 Swansea
Email: iscoed@iscoedchambers.co.uk

Head of Chambers	Trefor Davies
Senior Clerk	Wally Rainbird
First Junior	Jeff Evans
Second Junior	Kris Thorne
Tenants	29

Members:

Trefor Davies (1972)
Peter Christopher Rouch QC (1972) (QC-1996)
Kevin Riordan (1972)
Frank Phillips (1972)
Patrick Thomas John Griffiths (1973)
James John Jenkins (1974)
Philip Derek Marshall (1975)
Paul Huw Thomas (1979)
Robert Michael Craven (1979)
Stephen Robert Tristram Rees (1979)
Elwen Mair Evans (1980)
Stewart Karl Anthony Sandbrook-Hughes (1980)
Francis Jones (1980)
Owen Huw Rees (1983)
Mark Spackman (1986)
Ruth Henke (1987)
John Hipkin (1989)
David Andrew Harris (1990)
Catherine Louise Heyworth (1991)
William Peters (1992)
Kate Hughes (1992)
Dean Pulling (1993)
Ian Wright (1994)
Peter Maddox (1994)
Iwan Davies (1995)
Elizabeth Gow (1995)
Mathew Rees (1996)
Simon Hoffman (1997)
Robin Rouch (1999)

Work Undertaken: This well-established set of chambers offers an all-round service to solicitors and others with the right of Direct Professional Access. The principal fields of work are civil, criminal and family law, but with specialised expertise in a variety of areas, including personal injury; planning; local government; environment; highways; fraud; trade descriptions; licensing; family; child law; Chancery; housing.

00Set No.
263 **PENDRAGON CHAMBERS** (Laraine Roblin)

124 Walter Road, Swansea, SA1 5RG
Tel: (01792) 411188 **Fax:** (01792) 411189 **DX:** 39572 Swansea
Email: clerks@pendragonchambers.fsnet.co.uk

Head of Chambers	Laraine Roblin
Senior Clerk	Gwyn Davies
Junior Clerk	Julie Wintersgill
Tenants	13

Members:

Laraine Roblin (1981)
Desmond Keane QC (1964)
Robert Walters (1974)
Huw Rees Davies (1982)
Andrew David (1986)
John Brooks (1990)
Wayne Beard (1991)
Catherine Jones (1992)
Sara Rudman (1992)
Gareth Thomas (1993)
Rebecca Mann (1995)
Kathryn McConnochie (1997)
Susan Jenkins (1998)
Nicholas Bourne *
Donald Anderson MP *

* Door Tenant

The Chambers: Progressive set established in 1996. Predominantly civil and family chambers.

Work Undertaken: Personal injury, medical negligence, landlord and tenant, local authority, agricultural holdings, general chancery, revenue, family and crime.

Publications: Members have published articles for various periodicals including *Taxation,* the *Tax Journal,* and *Financial Advisor.* Kathryn McConnochie is extensively published in medical journals and other medical publications.

Recruitment: Tenancy and pupillage applications to Head of Chambers with detailed CV.

Swindon

Set No.
264 **PUMP COURT CHAMBERS** (Christopher Harvey Clark QC)

5 Temple Chambers, Temple Street, Swindon, SN1 1SQ
Tel: (01793) 539899 **Fax:** (01793) 539866 **DX:** 38639 Swindon 2
Email: clerks@3pumpcourt.com **Website:** www.3pumpcourt.com

Head of Chambers	Christopher Harvey Clark QC
Senior Clerk	David Barber
Swindon Clerk	Dot Hewitt
Tenants	57

An established set undertaking a wide variety of work. Members practise within specialist teams, for civil, family and all aspects of criminal law. Chambers are also at London and Winchester.

Taunton

Set No.
265 **SOUTH WESTERN CHAMBERS** (Brian Lett)

12 Middle Street, Taunton, TA1 1SH **Tel:** (01823) 331919 **Fax:** (01823) 330553 **DX:** 32146 (Taunton) **Email:** barclerk@clara.net
Website: www.southwesternchambers.co.uk

Winchester

Set No.
266 **PUMP COURT CHAMBERS** (Christopher Harvey Clark QC)

31 Southgate Street, Winchester, SO23 9EB
Tel: (01962) 868161 **Fax:** (01962) 867645 **DX:** 2514
Email: clerks@3pumpcourt.com **Website:** www.3pumpcourt.com

Head of Chambers	Christopher Harvey Clark QC
Senior Clerk	David Barber
Tenants	57

Members:

Christopher Harvey Clark QC (1969) (QC-1984)
Nigel Pascoe QC (1966) (QC-1988)
Guy Boney QC (1968) (QC-1990)
Peter Birts QC (1968) (QC-1990)
Jane Miller QC (1979) (QC-2000)
Geoffrey Still (1966)
Stewart Patterson (1967)
Adam Pearson (1969)
Frank Moat (1970)
Giles Harrap (1971)
Frank Abbott (1972)
Charles Parry (1973)
Michael Butt (1974)
John Ker-Reid (1974)
Charles Gabb (1975)
Andrew Barnett (1977)
Michael Dineen (1977)
Jonathan Swift (1977)
Julie MacKenzie (1978)
Timothy O'Flynn (1979)
Robert Hill (1980)
Miranda Allardice (1982)
Damien Lochrane (1983)
Sandra Stanfield (1984)
Oba Nsugbe (1985)
Matthew Scott (1985)
Desmond Bloom-Davies (1986)
Mark Hill (1987)
Anne Waddington (1988)
Hugh Travers (1988)
Philip Warren (1988)
Leslie Samuels (1989)
Edward Boydell (1989)
Justin Gau (1989)
Anthony Akiwumi (1989)
Helen Khan (1990)
Penelope Howe (1991)
Geoffrey Kelly (1992)
James Newton-Price (1992)
Patricia Poyer-Sleeman (1992)
Mark Ruffell (1992)
Elizabeth Gunther (1993)
Oliver Peirson (1993)
Marcus Tregilgas-Davey (1993)
Helen Fields (1993)
Luke Blackburn (1993)
Mark Ashley (1993)
Roderick Moore (1993)
Jonathan Simpson (1993)
Richard Ferry-Swainson (1994)
Robert Pawson (1994)
Mark Dubbery (1996)
Ruth Arlow (1997)
Andrew Grime (1997)
Anne Ward (1997)
Lorna Sproston (1998)
Louise de Rozarieux (1999)

The Chambers: An established set undertaking a wide variety of work, with members working in specialist teams. DPA and Bar Direct work accepted.
Associated Chambers: 3 Pump Court, London; Temple Street, Swindon.

Work Undertaken:
Main Areas: Family; employment; inheritance; property; PI; crime.
Specialisations: Childcare; matrimonial finance; all areas of crime; professional and clinical negligence; contract; ecclesiastical law; Inheritance Act; courts martial; environment; landlord and tenant; taxation appeals.

Recruitment: Tenancy applications should be sent to Head of the Tenancy Committee. Pupillage applications should be made via OLPAS.

INDEX OF

PRACTISING BARRISTERS

INDEX TO THE BAR

Aaron, Sam (1986) Set 55
Aaronberg, David (1981) Set 65
Aaronson, Graham (1966) (QC-1982) Set 129 Profile p.1341
Abberton, David (1994) Set 183
Abbott, Alistair (1996) Set 68
Abbott, Frank (1972) Sets 123, 264, 266
Abbott, Mary (1994) Set 18
Abell, Anthony (1977) Set 3 Profile p.1341
Aberavon, The Rt Hon Lord Morris of (1954) (QC-1973) Set 3
Abrahams, David (1998) Set 12
Abrahams, James (1997) Set 102
Ace, Richard (1993) Set 163
Acheson, Ian (1992) Set 36
Achurch, Mark (1996) Set 248
Ackland, Sacha (1998) Set 151
Acland, Piers (1993) Set 141 Profile p.1341
Acton, J (1995) Set 224
Acton, Stephen (1977) Set 112
Acton Davis, Jonathan (1977) (QC-1996) Set 2 Profile p.1341
Adair, Stuart (1995) Set 108
Adam, Tom (1991) Set 13 Profile p.1341
Adams, Christopher (1986) Set 167
Adams, Guy (1989) Set 176
Adams, Jamie (1978) Set 241
Adams, Jayne (1982) Set 250 Profile p.1341
Adams, John (1984) Set 68
Adams, Robert (1993) Set 243
Adamson, Ben (1999) Set 24
Adamson, Dominic (1997) Set 151
Adamson, Louisa (1994) Set 178
Adamyk, Simon (1991) Set 104
Addezio, Mario (1971) Set 56
Addison, Paul (1987) Set 155
Addy, Caroline (1991) Set 14 Profile p.1341
Addy, Catherine (1998) Set 92
Adebayo, Tayo (1989) Set 3
Adedeji, Yinka (1997) Set 78
Adewale, R.A.S. (1996) Set 80
Adjei, Cyril (1995) Set 121
Adkin, James (1992) Set 241
Adkin, Jonathan (1997) Set 138
Adkin, Tana (1992) Set 23
Adkins, Richard (1982) (QC-1995) Set 140 Profile p.1341
Adlard, William (1978) Set 61
Aeberli, Peter (1990) Set 39 Profile p.1341
Afeeva, Mark (1997) Set 93
Agbamu, Alexander (1988) Set 124
Ageros, James (1990) Set 3 Profile p.1341
Ageros, Justin (1993) Set 119
Aggrey-Orleans, Kweku (1998) Set 85
Agha, Siza (1994) Set 25
Agnello, Raquel (1986) Set 148 Profile p.1341
Agnew, Christine (1992) Set 3
Agnew, SinÈad (1998) Set 138
Aherne, Catherine (1997) Set 150
Ahmad, Nadeem (1996) Set 34
Ahmad, Zubair (1995) Set 114
Ahmed, Amina (1996) Set 134
Ahmed, Farooq (1983) Sets 4, 225
Ahmed, Ishfaq (1999) Set 43
Ahmed, Jacqueline (1988) Set 189
Ahya, Sonal (1995) Set 248
Aiken, Kimberley (1995) Set 76
Ailes, Ashley (1975) Set 260
Aina, Benjamin (1987) Set 154
Ainger, David (1961) Set 111 Profile p.1341
Ainley, Nicholas (1973) Set 34
Ainsworth, Mark (1992) Set 230
Airey, Simon (1989) Set 101
Aitken, John Russell (1984) Set 241
Akast, John (1968) Sets 186, 192, 246
Akenhead, Robert (1972) (QC-1989) Set 2 Profile p.1341
Akin, Barrie (1976) Set 59
Akinjide, Richard (1956) Set 82
Akinsanya, Jonathan (1993) Set 9
Akinsanya, Stephen (1993) Set 34
Akiwumi, Anthony (1989) Sets 123, 264, 266
Akka, Lawrence (1991) Set 35
Akuwudike, Emma (1992) Set 54
Alban-Lloyd, Nan (1988) Set 73
Albutt, Ian (1981) Set 53 Profile p.1341
Alcock, Peter (1995) Set 128
Alderson, Pippa (1993) Set 87
Aldous, Charles (1967) (QC-1985) Set 92 Profile p.1342
Aldous, Grahame (1979) Set 51 Profile p.1342
Aldous, Robert (1985) Set 247
Aldred, Mark (1996) Set 69
Aldridge, James (1987) Set 149
Aldridge, James (1994) Set 92
Aleeson, Warwick (1994) Set 94
Alesbury, Alun (1974) Set 96
Alexander, Andrew (1999) Set 87
Alexander, Daniel (1988) Set 102 Profile p.1342
Alexander, David (1987) Set 140
Alexander, Dominic (1995) Set 17
Alexander, Ian (1964) (QC-1989) Set 164
Alford, Robert (1970) Set 189
Algar, Claudius (1972) Set 81
Algazy, Jacques (1980) Set 19
Al'Hassan, Khadim (1993) Set 198
Ali, Huma (1997) Set 211
Ali, Ishtiyaq (1996) Set 244
Ali, Zafar (1994) Set 17
Aliker, Phillip (1990) Set 124
Allan, Colin (1971) Set 54
Allan, David (1974) (QC-1995) Sets 106, 218
Allan, David (1998) Set 4
Allan, Kirsten (1998) Set 74
Allan, Monique (1986) Set 91
Allardice, Miranda (1982) Sets 123, 264, 266 Profile p.1342
Alldis, C (1970) Set 215
Allen, Andrew (1995) Set 20
Allen, Darryl (1995) Set 230
Allen, David (1990) Set 79
Allen, James H. (1973) (QC-1995) Set 198 Profile p.1342
Allen, Lucianne (1999) Set 161
Allen, Mark (1981) Set 180 Profile p.1342
Allen, Nicholas (1995) Set 6
Allen, Robin (1974) (QC-1995) Set 19 Profile p.1342
Allen, Scott (2000) Set 100
Allen, Thomas (1995) Set 217
Allen, Tom (1994) Set 120
Allen, Zoe (1999) Set 225
Allfrey, Richard (1974) Set 25
Alliott, George (1981) Sets 62, 142
Allison, David (1998) Set 140
Allman, Marisa (1998) Set 198
Alloway ERD, Lord Campbell of (1939) (QC-1965) Set 73
Allston, Anthony (1975) Set 88
Alomo, Richard (1990) Set 58
Al-Qasem, Anis (1959) Set 116
Alt, Jane (1984) Set 74
Altham, Robert (1993) Set 213
Althaus, Justin (1988) Set 136
Altman, Brian (1981) Set 3 Profile p.1342
Alty, Andrew (1992) Set 221
Al-Yunusi, Abdullah (1994) Set 46
Amakye, Grace (1983) Set 155
Amaouche, Sassa-Ann (1996) Set 48
Ambrose, Clare (1992) Set 35
Ambrose, Euan (1992) Set 173
Ames, Geoffrey (1976) Set 6
Amesu, Sharon (1998) Set 223
Amiraftabi, Roshi (1993) Set 65
Amis, Christopher (1991) Set 72
Amlot, Roy (1963) (QC-1989) Set 77 Profile p.1342
Amor, Christopher (1984) Set 94
Amos, Tim (1987) Set 130 Profile p.1342
Ancliffe, Shiva (1991) Set 134
Anders, Jon (1990) Set 23
Anderson, Anthony (1964) (QC-1982) Set 96
Anderson, Brendan (1985) Set 183
Anderson, Clive (1976) Set 75
Anderson, David (1985) (QC-1999) Set 13 Profile p.1343
Anderson, Heather (2000) Set 200
Anderson, John (1989) Set 133
Anderson, Julie (1993) Set 91
Anderson, Kathleen (1997) Set 75
Anderson, Lesley (1989) Sets 196, 226 Profile p.1343
Anderson, Mark (1983) Set 162 Profile p.1343
Anderson, Nicholas (1995) Set 71
Anderson, Peter J. (1988) Set 258
Anderson, Robert (1986) Set 11 Profile p.1343
Anderson, Rupert (1981) Set 97 Profile p.1343
Anderson, S (1993) Set 238
Anderson, Simon (1997) Set 169
Andreae-Jones, William (1965) (QC-1984) Sets 136, 160
Andrew, Elizabeth (1974) Set 24
Andrew, Seamus (1991) Set 221
Andrews, Claire (1979) Set 50 Profile p.1343
Andrews, Geraldine (1981) (QC-2001) Set 31 Profile p.1343
Andrews, Peter (1970) (QC-1991) Sets 149, 162
Andrews, Philip (1977) Set 236 Profile p.1343
Andrews, Rachel (1989) Set 214
Andrews, Samuel (1991) Set 203
Anelay, Richard (1970) (QC-1993) Set 71 Profile p.1343
Angus, Tracey (1991) Set 145
Anning, Michael (1990) Set 164
Anning, Sara (1995) Set 200
Ansell, Rachel (1995) Set 125
Antelme, Alexander (1993) Set 21
Anthony, Peter (1981) Set 166
Anthony, Robert (1979) Set 18
Antrobus, Simon (1995) Sets 195, 196, 226
Anyadike-Danes, Monya (1980) Set 152
Apfel, Freddy (1986) Set 202
Appleby, Elizabeth (1965) (QC-1979) Set 55
Apsion, Gordon (1977) Set 113
Apthorp, Charles (1983) Set 34
Arbuthnot M.P, James (1975) Set 111
Archer, Christopher (1996) Set 134
Archer, Deborah (1989) Set 189
Archer, Stephen (1979) Set 85 Profile p.1343
Arden, Peter (1983) Sets 29, 194, 239 Profile p.1344
Arentsen, Andrew (1995) Set 181
Argles, Robert (1965) Set 107
Argyle, Brian (1972) Set 94
Argyropoulos, Kyriakos (1991) Set 65
Aris, Jason (1998) Set 163
Arkhurst, Reginald (1984) Set 74
Arkush, Jonathan (1977) Set 148
Arlidge, Anthony (1962) (QC-1981) Set 133 Profile p.1344
Arlow, Ruth (1997) Sets 123, 264, 266
Armitage, Keith (1970) (QC-1994) Set 225 Profile p.1344
Armitage, Lindy (1985) Set 200
Armstrong, Dean (1985) Set 77 Profile p.1344
Armstrong, Douglas (1990) Set 164
Armstrong, Grant (1978) Set 128
Armstrong, Kester (1982) Set 238 Profile p.1344
Armstrong, Stuart (1995) Set 7
Arney, James (1992) Set 151
Arnfield, Robert (1996) Set 111
Arnold, Mark (1988) Set 140 Profile p.1344
Arnold, Peter (1972) Set 162
Arnold, Richard (1985) (QC-2000) Set 141 Profile p.1344
Arnot, Lee (1990) Set 106
Arora, Anita (1994) Set 9
Arran, Graham (1969) Set 94
Arthur, Gavyn (1975) Sets 64, 252
Ascherson, Isobel (1990) Set 36
Ascroft, Richard (1995) Set 173 Profile p.1344
Ash, Brian (1975) (QC-1990) Set 55 Profile p.1344
Ashcroft, Michael (1997) Set 35
Ashe, Michael (1971) (QC-1994) Set 147
Ashford-Thom, Ian (1977) Set 151
Ashley, Mark (1993) Sets 123, 264, 266
Ashley-Norman, Jonathan (1989) Set 3 Profile p.1344
Ashman, Peter M. (1985) Set 187
Ashmole, Timothy (1992) Set 74
Ashton, David (1962) Sets 86, 253
Ashwell, Paul (1977) Set 170
Ashworth, Fiona (1988) Sets 196, 226 Profile p.1344
Ashworth, Lance (1987) Sets 62, 167 Profile p.1344
Ashworth, Piers (1956) (QC-1973) Sets 62, 142
Asif, Jalil (1988) Set 100
Askham, Nigel (1973) Set 265
Askins, Nicholas (1989) Set 169
Aspden, Gordon (1988) Set 4
Aspinall, John (1975) (QC-1995) Set 117
Asplin, Sarah J. (1984) Set 143 Profile p.1344
Asprey, Nicholas (1969) Set 138
Astaniotis, Katie (1985) Set 53
Astbury, Joanne (1989) Set 200
Asteris, Peter (1996) Set 260
Astill, Katherine (1998) Set 40
Aston, Maurice (1982) Set 120
Astor, Philip (1989) Set 151
Atchley, Richard (1977) Set 131
Atherton, Peter (1975) Set 221
Atherton, Sally (1987) Set 16
Atherton, Stephen (1989) Set 140 Profile p.1345
Atkins, Charles (1975) Set 6
Atkins, Richard (1989) Set 161
Atkins, Siward (1995) Set 92
Atkinson, Carol (1985) Set 20
Atkinson, Duncan (1995) Set 77
Atkinson, Jayne (1994) Set 122
Atkinson, Nicholas (1971) (QC-1991) Set 61 Profile p.1345
Atkinson, Paul (1978) Set 207
Atkinson, Timothy (1988) Set 14
Atreya, Navita (1999) Set 134
Attwood, John (1989) Set 165
Attwooll, Christopher (1980) Sets 83, 195
Atwill, John (1997) Sets 256, 257
Aubrey, David (1974) (QC-1998) Set 213
Aubrey, David J.M. (1976) (QC-1996) Set 182 Profile p.1345
Auburn, Jonathan (1999) Set 55
Auckland, E. (1995) Set 201
Audland, William (1992) Set 85
Auld, Charles (1980) Set 176
Auld, Rohan (1992) Sets 64, 252
Auld, Stephen (1979) (QC-1999) Set 32
Austin, Jonathan (1992) Set 180
Austins, Christopher (1988) Set 172
Austin-Smith, James (1999) Set 72
Austin-Smith, Michael (1969) (QC-1990) Set 36 Profile p.1345
Auty, Michael (1990) Set 248
Awadalla, Katherine (1998) Set 67
Axon, Andrew (1992) Set 200
Ayers, Guy (1979) Set 247 Profile p.1345
Aylen, Walter (1962) (QC-1983) Set 65
Aylett, Crispin (1985) Set 131
Aylett, Kenneth (1972) Set 65
Ayliffe, James (1987) Set 159 Profile p.1345
Ayling, Judith (1998) Set 38
Ayling, Tracy (1983) Set 41
Aylwin, Christopher (1970) Set 117
Ayres, Andrew (1996) Set 92
Azhar, Ali Mohammed (1962) Set 80
Azhar, S. (1995) Set 80
Azim, Rehna (1984) Set 106
Aziz, Shahzad (1996) Set 166
Baatz, Nicholas (1978) (QC-1998) Set 2 Profile p.1345
Backhouse, Roger (1965) (QC-1984) Set 94
Bacon, Francis (1988) Set 118 Profile p.1345
Bacon, Jane (1999) Set 244
Bacon, Jeffrey (1989) Set 90
Bacon, Kelyn (1998) Set 13
Bacon, Nicholas (1992) Set 151
Badenoch, James (1968) (QC-1989) Set 22 Profile p.1345
Badenoch, Tony (1996) Set 52
Badley, Pamela (1974) Set 209
Bagchi, Andrew (1989) Set 48
Bagley, Michael (1984) Set 210
Bagnall, Mathew (1993) Set 39
Bagot, Charles (1997) Set 65
Bailey, Anthony R. (1972) Set 72
Bailey, David (1989) Set 79
Bailey, Edward (1990) Set 72
Bailey, Graham (1993) Sets 225, 228
Bailey, James (1999) Set 104
Bailey, Michael (1986) Set 150
Bailey, Rosana (1994) Set 81
Bailey, Russell (1985) Set 117
Bailey, Stephen (1991) Set 89
Bailey, Steven (1992) Set 162
Bailey, Thomas (1984) Set 151
Bailey-King, Robert (1975) Set 12
Bailin, Alex (1995) Set 120

de Silva, Desmond (1964) (QC-1984) Set 116 Profile p.1370
de Silva, Harendra (1970) (QC-1995) Set 116
de Silva, Niran (1997) Set 90
De Sousa Turner, Camilla (1989) Set 252
de Verneuil Smith, Peter (1998) Set 152
de Vries (Ret.), Edo (1969) Set 256
de Waal, John (1992) Set 167
de Wilde, Robin (1971) (QC-1993) Set 149
Deacock, Adam (1991) Set 98
Deacock, Adam (1991) Set 185
Deacon, Emma (1993) Set 120
Deacon, Robert (1976) Set 148
Deal, Katherine (1997) Set 67
Dean, Brian (1994) Set 167
Dean, Jacob (1995) Set 132
Dean, Nicholas (1982) Set 4
Dean, Paul (1982) Set 21
Deane, Vincent (1976) Set 219
Deans, Jacqueline (1998) Set 210
DeCamp, Jane (1987) Set 21
Dedezade, Sibel (1994) Set 151
Dee, Jonathon (1989) Set 249
Deegan, Jeffrey (1989) Sets 177, 254
Degel, Rebecca (1987) Sets 186, 192, 246
Dehn, Conrad (1952) (QC-1968) Set 44
Deignan, Mary Teresa (1991) Set 17
Dein, Jeremy (1982) Set 54 Profile p.1370
Del Fabbro, Oscar (1982) Set 36
Del Mese, Francesca (1998) Set 78
Delahunty, Jo (1986) Set 156
Delaney, Kenneth (1996) Set 211
Demetriou, Marie (1995) Set 13
Dempsey, Karen (1996) Set 16
Dempster, Jennifer (1993) Set 133
Dempster, Tina (1997) Sets 83, 195
Den Brinker, Melanie (1984) Set 134
Dencer, Mark (1978) Set 45
Denehan, Edward (1981) Set 147
Denison, Simon (1984) Set 77
Denman, Robert (1970) Set 121
Dennett, Angelina (1980) Set 234
Denney, Stuart (1982) Set 221 Profile p.1370
Denning, Louisa (1999) Set 164
Dennis, David (1979) Set 208
Dennis, Mark (1977) Set 77 Profile p.1371
Dennis, Rebecca (1994) Set 175
Dennison, James (1986) Set 115
Dennison, Stephen (1985) (QC-2001) Set 2 Profile p.1371
Denniss, John (1974) Set 74
Denny, R.H.A. (1969) Set 203
Dennys, Nicholas (1975) (QC-1991) Set 2 Profile p.1371
Dent, Adrian (1974) Set 193
Dent, Kevin (1991) Set 115
Dent, Stephen (1991) Set 173
Denton, Michelle (1996) Set 10
Denyer, Roderick (1970) (QC-1990) Set 176 Profile p.1371
Denyer-Green, Barry (1972) Set 40 Profile p.1371
Derbyshire, Thomas (1989) Set 3
Desmond, Denis (1974) Set 165
Detter, Prof Ingrid (1977) Set 55
Devlin, Jonathan (1978) Set 199
Devlin, Tim (1985) Set 124
Devonshire, Simon (1988) Set 84 Profile p.1371
Dew, Richard (1999) Set 111
Dewsbery, Richard (1992) Set 166
Dhadli, Pami (1984) Set 249
Dhillon, Jasbir (1996) Set 13
Dhir, Anuja (1989) Set 120
di Mambro, David (1973) Set 88
Diamond, Anna (1995) Set 164
Diamond, Christopher (1975) Set 233
Dias, Dexter (1988) Set 49
Dias, Sappho (1982) Set 76
Dick, John (1974) Set 153
Dick, Julia (1988) Set 156
Dickens, Andrew (1983) Set 168
Dickens, Paul (1978) Set 68 Profile p.1371
Dicker, Robin (1986) (QC-2000) Set 140 Profile p.1371
Dickinson, Gregory (1981) Set 248
Dickinson, J.D. (1986) Set 224
Dickinson, John (1995) Set 176
Dicks, Anthony (1961) Set 31
Digby, Charles (1982) Set 124
Diggle, Mark (1996) Set 250
Dight, Marc (1984) Set 148
Dignum, Marcus (1994) Set 67
Dilhorne, Viscount (1979) Set 12
Dillon, Thomas (1983) Set 161
Din, Soofi (1984) Set 250
Dinan-Hayward, Deborah (1988) Set 171 Profile p.1371
Dineen, Maria (1997) Set 3
Dineen, Michael (1977) Sets 123, 175, 264, 266
Dines, Colin (1970) Set 94
Dines, Sarah (1988) Set 150
Dingemans, James (1987) Set 67
Dinkin, Anthony (1968) (QC-1991) Set 53 Profile p.1371
Dismorr, Edward (1983) Set 166
Ditchfield, Michael (1993) Set 243
Diwan, Ricky (1998) Set 31
Dix-Dyer, Fiona (1986) Set 204
Dixey, Ian (1984) Set 176 Profile p.1371
Dixon, David S. (1992) Set 205
Dixon, Emma (1994) Set 11
Dixon, John (1975) Sets 64, 252
Dixon, John (1995) Set 214
Dixon, Philip (1986) Set 45
Dixon, Ralph (1980) Set 176 Profile p.1371
Dixon, Sorrel (1987) Set 52
Dobbin, Clair (1999) Set 131
Dobbs, Linda (1981) (QC-1998) Set 133
Dockery, Paul (1973) Set 233
Docking, Tony (1969) Set 94
Doctor, Brian (1991) (QC-1999) Set 44
Dodd, Christopher (1984) Set 206
Dodd, John (1979) Set 3
Dodd, Margaret (1979) Set 3
Dodd, S. (1987) Set 224
Dodds, R. Stephen (1976) Set 258 Profile p.1371
Dodge, Peter (1992) Set 112
Dodson, Joanna (1970) (QC-1993) Sets 58, 199 Profile p.1371
Doerries, Chantal-AimÈe (1992) Set 2 Profile p.1371
Doherty, Bernard (1990) Set 38
Doherty, Nicholas (1983) Set 82
Doherty, Patrizia (2000) Set 205
Dohmann, Barbara (1971) (QC-1987) Set 11 Profile p.1371
Doig, Gavin (1995) Set 243
Dolan, Bridget (1997) Set 137
Domenge, Victoria (1993) Set 6
Donaldson, David (1968) (QC-1984) Set 11
Donelon, Anne (1995) Set 73
Donne, Anthony (1973) (QC-1988) Sets 72, 175
Donne, Jeremy (1978) Set 69
Donnelly, Catherine (1997) Set 76
Donnelly, Kevin (1991) Set 227
Donoghue, Steven (1992) Set 179
Donovan, JoÎl (1991) Set 19
Donovan, Scott (1975) Set 211
Dooher, Nancy (1997) Set 212
Dooley, Allan (1991) Set 164
Dooley, Christine (1980) Set 124
Doran, Gerard (1993) Set 157
Doris, Susan (1998) Set 17
Dorman O'Gowan, Christopher (1979) Set 238
Dos Santos, Alex (1999) Set 17
Dosanjh, Gurbinder (1998) Set 168
Dougherty, Charles (1997) Set 152
Dougherty, Nigel (1993) Set 30
Doughty, Peter (1988) Set 259
Douglas, Colin (1998) Set 182
Douglas, Michael (1974) (QC-1997) Set 125
Douglas, Stephen (1994) Set 234
Douthwaite, Charles (1977) Set 100
Dovar, Daniel (1997) Set 7
Dove, Ian (1986) Set 164 Profile p.1372
Dow, Kenneth (1970) Set 126
Dowding, Nicholas (1979) (QC-1997) Set 40 Profile p.1372
Dowley, Dominic (1983) Set 138 Profile p.1372
Down, Jonathan (1993) Set 163
Downes, Paul (1991) Set 152
Downey, Aileen (1991) Set 51
Downey, Neil (1997) Set 208
Downey, Raoul (1988) Set 90
Downham, Gillian C. (1993) Set 48
Downie, Andrew (1990) Set 213
Downing, Ruth (1978) Set 24
Downs, Martin (1990) Sets 22, 170
Dowse, John (1973) Set 232
Doyle, James (1985) Set 16
Doyle, Louis (1996) Sets 196, 226 Profile p.1372
Doyle, Peter (1975) Set 69 Profile p.1372
Drabble, Richard (1975) (QC-1995) Set 12 Profile p.1372
Dracass, Timothy (1998) Set 260
Drake, David (1994) Set 138
Drake, James (1998) Set 79
Drake, Rachel (1995) Sets 86, 253
Drake, Sophie (1990) Set 169
Dray, Martin (1992) Set 40
Draycott, Jean (1980) Set 164
Draycott, Simon (1977) Sets 86, 253
Drayton, Henry (1993) Set 52
Drew, Jane (1976) Set 20 Profile p.1372
Drew, Sandhya (1993) Set 156
Drew, Simon (1987) Set 164
Drinkwater, Philip (1995) Set 187
Driscoll, Jennifer (1989) Set 20
Driscoll, Lynn (1981) Set 198
Driscoll, Michael (1970) (QC-1992) Set 110 Profile p.1372
Driver, Emily (1988) Set 78
Driver, Simon (1991) Set 209
Driver, Stuart (1988) Set 208
Droop, Joanna (1998) Set 85
Druce, Michael (1988) Set 96 Profile p.1372
Drummond, Bruce (1992) Set 183
Dry, Nick (1996) Set 204
D'Souza, Carolyn (1994) Set 85
D'Souza, Dominic (1993) Set 116
Du Cann, Christian (1982) Set 38 Profile p.1372
du Preez, Robin (1985) Set 133
Dubb, Tarlowchan (1997) Set 164
Dubbery, Mark (1996) Sets 123, 264, 266
Dubin, Joshua (1997) Set 89
Duck, Michael (1988) Set 162 Profile p.1372
Duckworth, Peter (1971) Set 6
Dudderidge, Robert (1992) Set 149
Dudley, Michael (1972) Set 161
Dudley, Robert (1993) Set 212
Duff, Euan (1973) Set 238
Duff, Graham (1976) Set 243
Duffield, Stephen (1969) Set 243
Duffy, Derek (1997) Set 204
Duffy, Joanne (1994) Set 164
Dugdale, Jeremy (1992) Sets 186, 192, 246
Dugdale, Nicholas (1992) Set 43
Dugdale, Paul (1990) Set 72
Duggan, Michael (1984) Set 90 Profile p.1372
Duggan, Ross (1978) Set 214 Profile p.1372
Dulovic, Milan (1982) Set 52
Dumaresq, Delia (1984) Set 2 Profile p.1373
Dumont, Thomas (1979) Set 103 Profile p.1373
Duncan, John (1971) Set 220
Dunford, Matthew (1992) Set 183
Dunkels, Paul (1972) (QC-1993) Sets 171, 188 Profile p.1373
Dunn, Christopher (1996) Set 205
Dunn, Darren (1999) Set 233
Dunn, Katherine (1987) Sets 196, 226 Profile p.1373
Dunn, Katherine (1993) Set 75
Dunn, Sarah (1998) Set 129
Dunne, Jonathan (1986) Set 155
Dunning, Graham (1982) (QC-2001) Set 31 Profile p.1373
Dunning, John (1973) Set 202
Dunn-Shaw, Jason (1992) Set 77 Profile p.1373
Dunstan, James (1995) Set 165
Durham-Hall, Jonathan (1975) (QC-1995) Set 207
Durose, David W. (1996) Set 116
Durr, Jude (1995) Sets 186, 192, 246
Durran, Alexia (1995) Set 36
Dutchman-Smith, Malcolm (1995) Set 213
Duthie, Catriona (1981) Set 173 Profile p.1373
Duthie, Malcolm (1989) Set 164
Dutton, Timothy (1979) (QC-1998) Set 44
Dutton, Timothy (1985) Set 136 Profile p.1373
Duval, Robert (1979) Set 176 Profile p.1373
Dyble, Ian Hugh (2000) Sets 186, 192, 246
Dyble, Steven (1986) Sets 186, 192, 246
Dye, Brian (1991) Set 31
Dyer, Allen (1976) Set 125
Dyer, Jacob (1995) Set 258
Dyer, Nigel (1982) Set 95 Profile p.1373
Dyer, Roger (1980) Set 167
Dyer, Simon (1987) Set 19
Dykers, Joy (1995) Set 87
Eade, Phillipa (1992) Set 207
Eadie, James (1984) Set 138 Profile p.1373
Eady, Jennifer (1989) Sets 109, 174 Profile p.1373
Eales, Darren (2000) Set 152
Earlam, Simon (1975) Set 212
Earle, Judy (1994) Set 117
Earley, Sarah (1998) Set 185
Earnshaw, Stephen (1990) Set 47
Easteal, Andrew (1990) Set 248 Profile p.1373
Eastman, Roger (1978) Sets 62, 142
Easton, Alison (1994) Set 20
Easton, Jonathon (1995) Set 53
Eastwood, Charles (1988) Set 235
Easty, Valerie (1992) Set 49
Eaton, Bernard (1978) Set 94
Eaton, Deborah (1985) Set 71 Profile p.1373
Eaton, Nigel (1991) Set 31
Eaton, Thomas (1976) Set 208
Eaton Hart, Andrew (1989) Set 188
Eaton Turner, David (1984) Set 104
Eccles, David (1976) Set 225 Profile p.1373
Eccles, Patrick (1968) (QC-1990) Set 252
Eckersley, Simon (1995) Set 249
Economou, George (1965) Set 33
Edelman, Colin (1977) (QC-1995) Set 24 Profile p.1373
Edenborough, Michael (1992) Set 68 Profile p.1374
Eder, Bernard (1975) (QC-1990) Set 31 Profile p.1374
Edey, Philip (1994) Set 35 Profile p.1374
Edge, Ian (1981) Set 117
Edge, Timothy (1992) Set 221 Profile p.1374
Edginton, Ronald (1984) Set 178
Edhem, Emma (1993) Set 75
Edie, Alastair (1992) Set 49 Profile p.1374
Edie, Anthony (1974) Set 87
Edis, Andrew (1980) (QC-1997) Set 208 Profile p.1374
Edis, William (1985) Set 22 Profile p.1374
Edlin, David (1971) Set 87
Edmondson, Harriet (1997) Set 180
Edmunds, Martin (1983) Set 188
Edwards, A (1972) Set 215
Edwards, Angus (1999) Set 151
Edwards, David (1989) Set 79 Profile p.1374
Edwards, David (1994) Set 213
Edwards, Douglas (1992) Set 63 Profile p.1374
Edwards, Glyn (1987) Set 176 Profile p.1374
Edwards, Heath (1996) Set 179
Edwards, Helen (1995) Set 181
Edwards, Jennifer (1992) Set 17
Edwards, John (1983) Set 167
Edwards, Jonathan (1994) Set 201
Edwards, Martin (1995) Set 27
Edwards, Nigel (1995) Set 204
Edwards, Nigel (1998) Set 225
Edwards, Owen (1992) Set 184
Edwards, Peter (1992) Set 24
Edwards, Richard (1993) Set 158
Edwards, Sarah (1990) Set 130
Edwards, Simon (1978) Set 6
Edwards, Simon (1987) Set 114
Edwards, Susan (1972) (QC-1993) Set 36 Profile p.1374
Edwards, Susan (1998) Set 211
Edwards-Stuart, Antony (1976) (QC-1991) Set 21
Egan, Caroline (1993) Set 165
Egan, Eugene (1993) Set 180
Egan, Marion (1988) Set 21
Egan, Michael (1981) Set 10 Profile p.1374
Egbuna, Robert (1988) Set 248
Egerton, C. (1992) Set 203
Egleton, Richard (1981) Set 260
Eicke, Tim (1993) Set 31 Profile p.1375
Eidinow, John (1992) Set 104
Eilledge, Amanda (1991) Set 149
Eissa, Adrian (1988) Set 49 Profile p.1375
Ekaney, Nkumbe (1990) Set 171
Ekins, Charles W. (1980) Set 205
Eklund, Graham (1984) Set 152 Profile p.1375
Elcombe, Nicholas (1987) Sets 186, 192, 246
Elder, Fiona (1991) Sets 171, 175
Elfield, Laura (1996) Set 51
Elgot, Howard (1974) Set 200 Profile p.1375
Elias, David (1994) Set 179

CHAMBERS INDEX TO THE LEADING LAWYERS

INDEX TO LEADING LAWYERS

A

KEY TO RANKINGS: ★ = Star Individual **U & C** = Up and coming

INDEX TO LEADING LAWYERS

KEY TO RANKINGS: ★ = Star Individual **U & C** = Up and coming

KEY TO RANKINGS: ★ = Star Individual **U & C** = Up and coming

KEY TO RANKINGS: ★ = Star Individual **U & C** = Up and coming

INDEX TO LEADING LAWYERS

KEY TO RANKINGS: ☆ = Star Individual **U & C** = Up and coming

KEY TO RANKINGS: ★ = Star Individual **U & C** = Up and coming

E

KEY TO RANKINGS: ★ = Star Individual **U & C** = Up and coming

F

KEY TO RANKINGS: ★ = Star Individual **U & C** = Up and coming

INDEX TO LEADING LAWYERS

KEY TO RANKINGS: ★ = Star Individual **U & C** = Up and coming

KEY TO RANKINGS: ★ = Star Individual **U & C** = Up and coming

H

KEY TO RANKINGS: ★ = Star Individual **U & C** = Up and coming

KEY TO RANKINGS: ★ = Star Individual **U & C** = Up and coming

INDEX TO LEADING LAWYERS

KEY TO RANKINGS: ★ = Star Individual **U & C** = Up and coming

J

K

INDEX TO LEADING LAWYERS

L

KEY TO RANKINGS: ★ = Star Individual **U & C** = Up and coming

N

KEY TO RANKINGS: ★ = Star Individual **U & C** = Up and coming

O

P

KEY TO RANKINGS: ★ = Star Individual **U & C** = Up and coming

S

KEY TO RANKINGS: ★ = Star Individual **U & C** = Up and coming

INDEX TO LEADING LAWYERS

KEY TO RANKINGS: ★ = Star Individual **U & C** = Up and coming

T

KEY TO RANKINGS: ★ = Star Individual **U & C** = Up and coming

INDEX TO LEADING LAWYERS

INDEX TO LEADING LAWYERS

KEY TO RANKINGS: ★ = Star Individual **U & C** = Up and coming

Y

Z